Car Sections

Notices

CHILTON TIME

CHILTON TIME for each operation indicated in this Manual is based on the independent judgment of Chilton automotive editors who have extensive automotive service experience. Among the factors they consider in determining CHILTON TIME are:

1) Timing the performance of operations.
2) Surveys of the experience of professional mechanics and automotive repair shops with respect to the time required to perform the operations.
3) The time allowed by the respective car manufacturer for its authorized dealers to perform specific operations on cars under warranty conditions (suggested warranty time, listed in this manual as FACTORY TIME).
4) The consideration that the operations will be performed upon a car in used condition and in a shop with standard equipment.

Not all of the factors enumerated above are considered in each year with respect to each operation.

This Manual is published in an attempt to provide meaningful data to the auto service profession and its customers. CHILTON TIME is not intended for use as an indication of the actual time required to perform any of the operations indicated in any particular instance. Actual times to perform an operation will, of course, vary according to such factors as the skill and motivation of the mechanic, the working conditions and tools available, and the condition of the vehicle.

The dollar amount appearing under the column "Parts" (as well as all other parts prices shown in the manual) reflect the manufacturers' suggested retail price with respect to the parts utilized in the operation. These prices are not intended to imply that they are actual prices in particular transactions. Actual prices will, of course, be determined by the parties to any such transaction.

Care must be taken to avoid any misunderstanding of the information published. This may be done by reading carefully the indications of which operations are and are not included in a particular CHILTON TIME figure.

Chilton Company is not responsible for any errors, car manufacturer product changes, or omissions that may occur during the preparation or publication of this Manual.

FOR YOUR SAFETY

Proper service and repair procedures are vital to the safe, reliable operation of all motor vehicles, as well as the personal safety of those performing repairs. This manual outlines procedures for servicing and repairing vehicles using safe effective methods. The procedures contain many NOTES, CAUTIONS and WARNINGS which should be followed along with standard safety procedures to eliminate the possibility of personal injury or improper service which could damage the vehicle or compromise its safety.

It is important to note that repair procedures and techniques, tools and parts for servicing motor vehicles, as well as the skill and experience of the individual performing the work vary widely. It is not possible to anticipate all of the conceivable ways or conditions under which vehicles may be serviced, or to provide cautions as to all of the possible hazards that may result. Standard and accepted safety precautions and equipment should be used when handling toxic or flammable fluids, and safety goggles or other protection should be used during cutting, grinding, chiseling, prying, or any other process that can cause material removal or projectiles.

Some procedures require the use of tools specially designed for a specific purpose. Before substituting another tool or procedure, you must be completely satisfied that neither your personal safety, nor the performance of the vehicle will be endangered.

While striving for total accuracy, Chilton Book Company cannot assume responsibility for any errors, changes, or omissions that may occur in the compilation of this data. Although information in this manual is based on industry sources and is as complete as possible at the time of publication, the possibility exists that some car manufacturers made later changes which could not be included here.

CHILTON'S

1987

LABOR GUIDE
and
PARTS MANUAL

Managing Editor John H. Weise, S.A.E. □ **Assistant Managing Editor** David H. Lee, A.S.E., S.A.E.

Service Editors Lawrence C. Braun, S.A.E., A.S.C., Dennis Carroll, Nick D'Andrea,
Jack T. Kaufmann, Robert McAnally, Ron Webb
Editorial Consultants Edward K. Shea, S.A.E., Stan Stephenson

Production Manager John J. Cantwell
Manager Editing & Design Dean F. Morgantini S.A.E.
Art & Production Coordinator Robin S. Miller
Supervisor Mechanical Paste-up Margaret A. Stoner
Mechanical Artists Cynthia Fiore, William Gaskins

National Sales Manager Albert M. Kushnerick □ **Assistant** Jacquelyn T. Powers
Regional Sales Managers Joseph Andrews, David Flaherty, James O. Callahan

OFFICERS
President Lawrence A. Fornasieri
Vice President & General Manager John P. Kushnerick

CHILTON BOOK COMPANY Chilton Way, Radnor, Pa. 19089
Manufactured in USA ISBN 0-8019-7691-X
ISSN 0749-5579 Library of Congress Catalog Card No. 82-72943
1234567890 5432109876

SKILL LEVEL CODES

Each labor operation is preceded by a skill level code for that operation. It is suggested assignment of mechanics be made on the basis of the skill listed for that operation. Definitions of the code shown for each operation are as follows.

(P) PRECISION

A really skilled man is needed. An operation where precision measuring devices are used for repair (micrometer, dial indicator, etc.). The mechanic must be highly skilled and have a thorough technical understanding of the function of complex components.

EXAMPLES

Automatic transmission overhaul
Engine overhaul
Valve reface
Axle overhaul

(G) GENERAL

A normally skilled man. An operation where a simpler measuring device, such as a feeler gauge or tach-dwell meter, is needed to obtain proper fit or adjustment. The mechanic is required to have a thorough working knowledge of the component.

EXAMPLES

Automatic transmission linkage adjustment
Fuel/ignition system adjustments
Axle shaft replacement
Brake overhaul
Door opening area body adjustments
Front end alignment
Air conditioning airflow adjustments

(M) MAINTENANCE

A semi-skilled man. An operation to replace parts generally not requiring any adjustment; or operations frequently performed as listed in the labor groups.

EXAMPLES

Oil/filter change
Belt check
Body or chassis lubrication

Parts interchangeability is indicated for parts manufactured and sold by American Motors, AMC/Jeep, General Motors Corporation, Chrysler Corporation and Ford Motor Company. The part numbers indicated show that a part may be purchased at any of the dealerships listed below. Knowing that a part may be purchased close by, could save the user much valuable time. The numbers indicated are the car manufacturers part numbers.

AMERICAN MOTORS & AMC/JEEP VEHICLES

A bullet (●) preceding the part number indicates that this part is interchangeable. The part numbers indicated are used on both **American Motors** cars and **AMC/Jeep** vehicles.

CHRYSLER CORPORATION

A black square (■) preceding a part number indicates that this part is interchangeable between two or more divisions of Chrysler Corporation cars. A numerical list of Chrysler Corporation part numbers and their interchangeability is given in this manual (see "Contents" page).

The letters following the part numbers in this list show the Chrysler Corporation Divisions that use the part.

Codes are as follows:

C—**Chrysler**
I—**Imperial**
D—**Dodge**
P—**Plymouth.**

FORD MOTOR COMPANY

A triangle (▲) preceding the part number indicates that this part is interchangeable between the Ford Motor Company cars. A triangle preceding a **Ford** part number indicates that this part may be purchased at a **Lincoln-Mercury** dealer. A triangle preceding a **Lincoln-Mercury** part number indicates that this part may be purchased at a **Ford** dealer.

GENERAL MOTORS CORPORATION

A diamond (♦) preceding a part number indicates that this part is interchangeable between two or more divisions of General Motors Corporation cars. A numerical list of General Motors Corporation part numbers and their interchangeability is given in this manual (See "Contents" page).

The digits following the part numbers in this list show the General Motors Divisions that use the part.

Codes are as follows:

1 Indicates that this part is used by **Buick.**
2 Indicates that this part is used by **Oldsmobile.**
3 Indicates that this part is used by **Pontiac.**
5 Indicates that this part is used by **Chevrolet.**
9 Indicates that this part is used by **Cadillac.**

PART NUMBERS

Part numbers listed in this reference are not recommendations by Chilton for any product by brand name. They are references that can be used with interchange manuals and aftermarket supplier catalogs to locate each brand supplier's discrete part number.

GROUP INDEX

ALPHABETICAL INDEX

American Motors

AMX • CONCORD • EAGLE • SX4 • SPIRIT

YEAR IDENTIFICATION

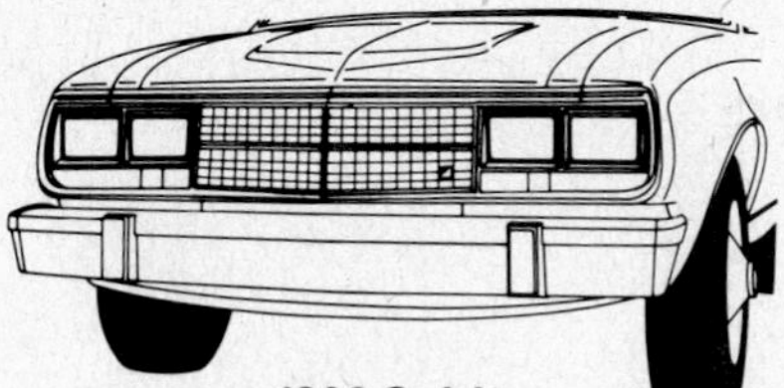

1983 Spirit

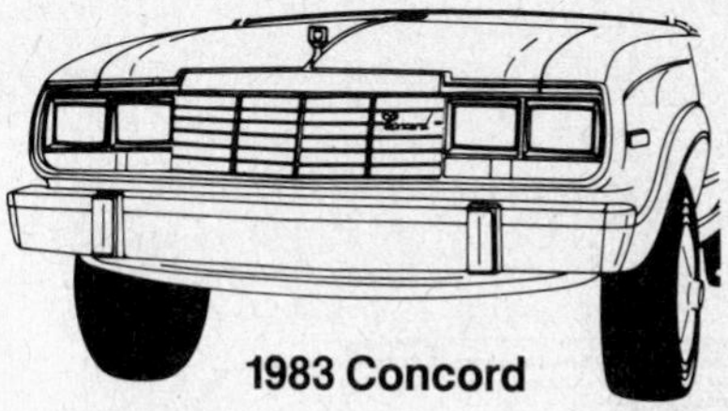

1983 Concord

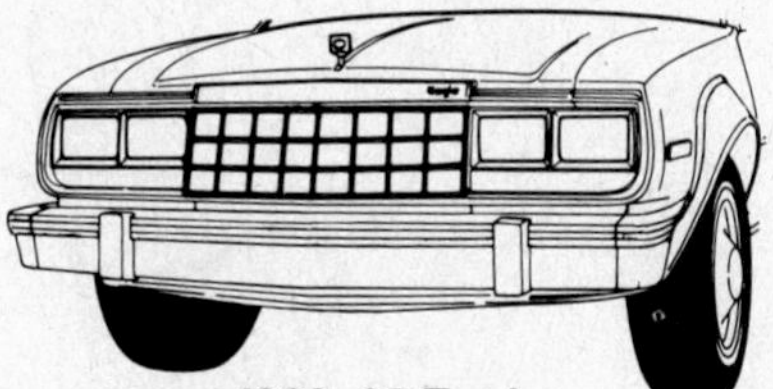

1983–87 Eagle

1983 Eagle SX-4

VEHICLE IDENTIFICATION NUMBER (VIN)

It is important for servicing and ordering parts to be certain of the vehicle and engine identification. The VIN (vehicle identification number) is a 13 or 17 digit number visible through the windshield on the driver's side of the dash and contains the vehicle and engine identification codes. It can be interpreted as follows:

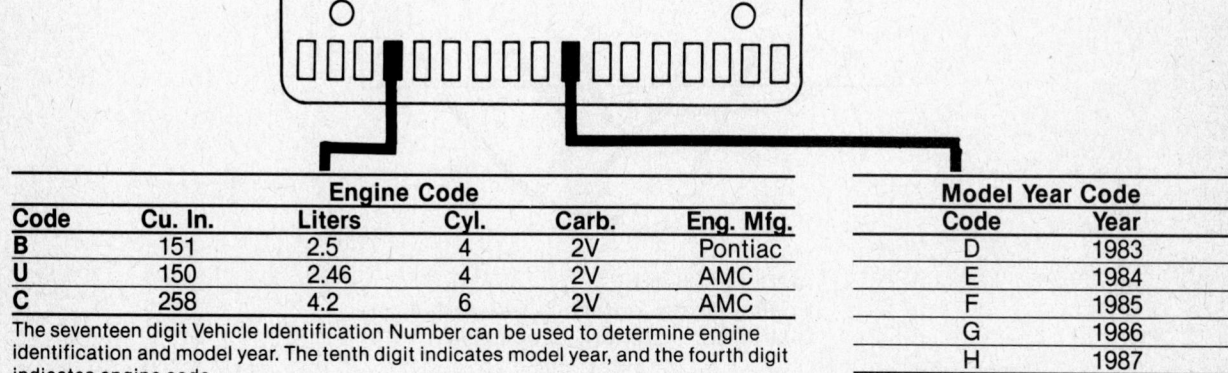

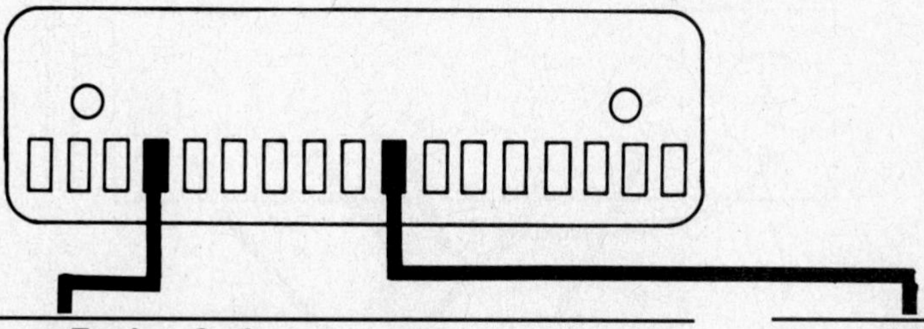

Engine Code

Code	Cu. In.	Liters	Cyl.	Carb.	Eng. Mfg.
B	151	2.5	4	2V	Pontiac
U	150	2.46	4	2V	AMC
C	258	4.2	6	2V	AMC

The seventeen digit Vehicle Identification Number can be used to determine engine identification and model year. The tenth digit indicates model year, and the fourth digit indicates engine code.

Model Year Code

Code	Year
D	1983
E	1984
F	1985
G	1986
H	1987

TUNE-UP SPECIFICATIONS

(When analyzing compression test results, look for uniformity among cylinders rather than specific pressures.)

Year	Engine No. Cyl. Displacement (cu. in.)	Eng. VIN Code	HP	Eng. Mfg.	Spark Plugs Orig. Type	Spark Plugs Gap (in.)	Distributor Point Dwell (deg.)	Distributor Point Gap (in.)	Ignition Timing (deg.)▲ Man. Trans.	Ignition Timing (deg.)▲ Auto. Trans.	Valves Intake Opens ▪(deg.)	Fuel Pump Pressure (psi)	Idle Speed (rpm)▲ Man Trans.	Idle Speed (rpm)▲ Auto Trans.*
'83	4-151	B	2 bbl	Pontiac	R44TSX	.060	Electronic		10B ②	12B ①	25	6½-8	900	700
	6-258	C	2 bbl	AMC	RFN14LY	.033	Electronic		③	④	9	5-6½	680	600
'84	4-150	U	1 bbl	AMC	RFN14LY	.035	Electronic		12B ⑤	12B ⑤	27B	6½-8	750 ⑥	700 ⑥
	6-258	C	2 bbl	AMC	RFN14LY	.033	Electronic		③	④	9	5-6½	680	600
'85-'87	6-258	C	2 bbl	AMC	RFN14LY	.033	Electronic		③	④	9	5-6½	680	600

▲If underhood emissions decal differs, always use the specifications on the decal.
*With transmission in Drive.
▪All figures before Top Dead Center
B Before Top Dead Center
TDC Top Dead Center (zero degrees)
① 8B—Eagle for Calif.
Not used
② Eagle except for Calif.—11B
③ Concord, Spirit—6B
Eagle except Calif.—8B
Eagle Calif.—4B High Alt.—15B
④ Concord, Spirit—6B
Eagle except Calif.—8B
Eagle Calif.—6B High Alt.—15B
⑤ High Alt.—19° ± 1°
⑥ ± 50 RPM

FIRING ORDERS

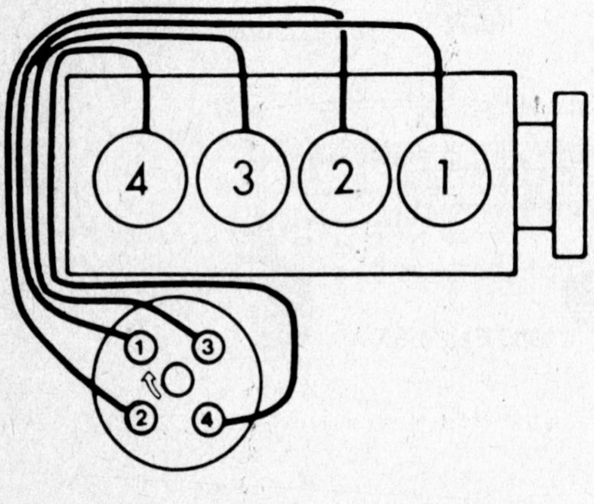

AMC 151 4-cyl
Engine firing order: 1–3–4–2
Distributor rotation: clockwise

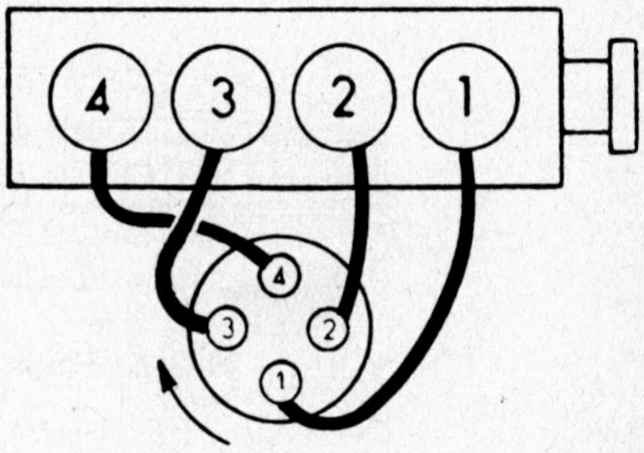

AMC 150 4-cyl
Engine firing order: 1–3–4–2
Distributor rotation: clockwise

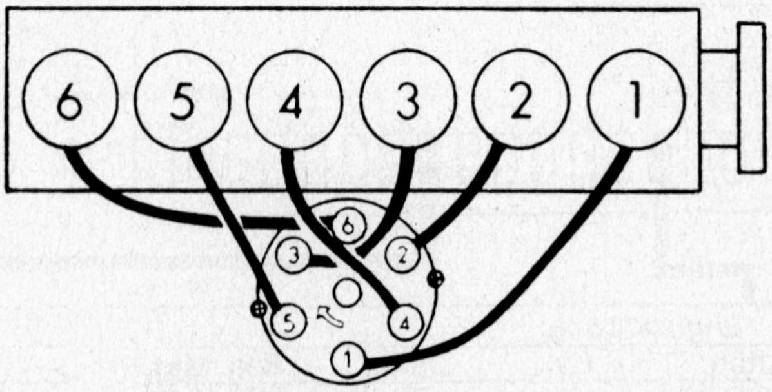

AMC 258 6-cyl
Engine firing order: 1–5–3–6–2–4
Distributor rotation: clockwise

WHEEL ALIGNMENT SPECIFICATIONS

Year	Model	Caster Range (deg.)	Caster Pref. Setting (deg.)	Camber Range (deg.)	Camber Pref. Setting (deg.)	Toe-in (in.)	Steering Axis Inclin. (deg.)	Wheel Pivot Ratio Inner Wheel (deg.)	Wheel Pivot Ratio Outer Wheel (deg.)
'83	Spirit, Concord	3½P-5P	4½P	①	②	1/16 to 3/16	7¾	38	N.A.
'83-'87	Eagle	3P-5P	4P	1/8N-5/8P	3/8P	1/16 to 3/16	11½	38	N.A.

N Negative
P Positive
N.A. Not Available
① Left: 3/4P to 1/8P; Right: 1/2P to 1/8N
② Left: 3/8P; Right: 1/8P

LABOR SERVICE BAY OPERATIONS LABOR

(Factory Time) Chilton Time

COOLING

(M) Winterize Cooling System

Includes: Run engine to check for leaks, tighten all hose connections. Test radiator and pressure cap, drain radiator and engine block. Add anti-freeze and refill system.

All models 5

(M) Thermostat, Renew

1983-87 (.5) 6

(M) Fan Belt, Renew

Four–1983-87 (.3) 3
Six–1983-87 (.3) 3
Serpentine (.5) 6
w/P.S., A.C. or Air guard add (.2) 2

FUEL

(M) Carburetor Air Cleaner, Service

1983-87 (.2) 3

(G) Carburetor, Adjust (On Car)

1983-87 (.5) 6

BRAKES

(G) Brakes, Adjust (Minor)

Includes: Adjust brakes at four wheels, fill master cylinder.

All models (.3) 3

(M) Parking Brake, Adjust

1983-87 (.3) 4

LUBRICATION SERVICE

(M) Lubricate Chassis, Change Oil & Filter

Includes: Inspect and correct all fluid levels.

All models 6
Install grease fittings add 1

(M) Lubricate Chassis

Includes: Inspect and correct all fluid levels.

All models 4
Install grease fittings add 1

CHILTON'S 10 POINT SAFETY CHECK

CHECK OPERATION & CONDITION OF THE FOLLOWING ITEMS:

1. Legal Registration (serial no.)
2. Tires & Wheels
3. Brake System (R&R all wheels)
4. Light Systems & Signals
5. Accelerator Linkage, Neutral Safety Switch, Shift Indicator Pointer & Seat Position Locks
6. Glass, Mirrors, Door Locks, Seat Belts & Harness
7. Wipers, Washers & Defrosters
8. Frame, Steering, Shocks, Front & Rear Suspension
9. Fuel & Exhaust Systems
10. Road Test Vehicle

All models 1.0
Exhaust Smog Analysis, add 4

(Factory Time) Chilton Time

(M) Engine Oil & Filter, Change

Includes: Inspect and correct all fluid levels.

All models 4

WHEELS

(M) Wheel, Renew

one (.4) 5

(Factory Time) Chilton Time

(G) Wheels, Balance

one 3
each adtnl 2

(G) Front Wheel Bearings, Clean and Repack (Both Wheels)

w/Disc brakes (1.0) 1.2
w/4 whl drive (1.9) 2.3

(M) Front Wheel Bearings, Adjust

All models (.3) 4

ELECTRICAL

(G) Headlamp Switch, Renew

1983-87 (.4) 5
w/Pkg tray add (.1) 1

(G) Headlamp Dimmer Switch, Renew

1983-87 (.3) 4

(G) Stoplight Switch, Renew

1983-87 (.4) 5

(G) Neutral Safety (w/Back-Up Lamp) Switch, Renew

1983-87
Concord-Spirit (.4) 5
Eagle (.7) 1.0

(G) Back-Up Lamp Switch, Renew

1983-87 (.3) 4

(G) Turn Signal Switch Assy., Renew

1983-87 (.6) 1.0

(M) Turn Signal or Hazard Warning Flasher, Renew

1983-87 (.2) 3

(G) Horns, Renew

1983-87–one (.2) 3
both (.3) 5

(G) Horn Relay, Renew

1983-87 (.3) 3

LABOR 1 TUNE UP 1 LABOR

(Factory Time) Chilton Time

(G) Compression Test

Four(.3) 6
Six(.4) 7

(G) Engine Tune Up, (Electronic Ignition)

Includes: Test battery and clean connections. Tighten manifold and carburetor mounting bolts. Check engine compression, clean and adjust or renew spark plugs. Test resistance of spark plug cables. Inspect distributor cap and rotor. Adjust air gap. Check vacuum advance operation. Reset ignition timing. Adjust idle mixture and idle speed. Service air cleaner. Inspect crankcase ventilation system. Inspect and adjust drive belts. Inspect choke operation and adjust or free up. Check operation of EGR valve.

(Factory Time) Chilton Time

Four–1983-87 .... 1.6
Six–1983-87 .... 2.0
w/A.C. add 6

LABOR 2 IGNITION SYSTEM 2 LABOR

	(Factory Time)	Chilton Time
(G) Spark Plugs, Clean and Reset or Renew		
Four	(.3)	.5
Six	(.4)	.6
(G) Ignition Timing, Reset		
1983-87-Four	(.5)	.7
Six	(.2)	.3
(G) Distributor Cap and/or Rotor, Renew		
1983-87		
Four		
150 eng.	(.2)	.4
151 eng.	(.4)	.5
Six	(.3)	.4
(G) Vacuum Control Unit, Renew		
Includes: Check dwell and reset timing.		
1983-87-Four	(.9)	1.1
Six	(.4)	.5
(G) Ignition Coil, Renew		
1983-87	(.3)	.5
(G) Ignition Cables, Renew		
Four & Six	(.4)	.5
(G) Ignition Switch, Renew		
1983-87	(.4)	.5
w/Pkg tray add	(.1)	.2
(G) Ignition Lock (Column Lock), Renew		
1983-87	(.6)	.9
(G) Control Unit or Module, Renew		
Includes: Reset ignition timing.		
1983-87-Four	(.4)	.5
Six	(.3)	.4
(G) Distributor, Renew		
Includes: Reset ignition timing.		
1983-87		
Four		
150 eng.	(.3)	.6
151 eng.	(.8)	1.1
Six	(.4)	.6
Renew driven gear add		1.0
(G) Distributor, R&R and Recondition		
Includes: Reset ignition timing.		
1983-87		
Four		
150 eng.	(1.3)	1.8
151 eng.	(1.8)	2.3
Six	(1.4)	1.9
(G) Sensor, Renew		
Includes: Reset ignition timing.		
1983-87	(.5)	.7
(G) Electronic Ignition Trigger, Renew		
Includes: R&R distributor and reset timing.		
1983-87	(.4)	.6
(G) Distributor Pick-Up Coil, Renew		
Includes: R&R distributor and reset timing.		
Four-1983-87	(.8)	1.1
Six-1983-87	(.3)	.6
(G) Spark Knock Sensor, Renew		
1983-87	(.3)	.4

PARTS 2 IGNITION SYSTEM 2 PARTS

	Part No.	Price
SIX-258		
(1) Distributor Assy. (wo/Cap & Rotor)		
1983-87	●3242409	110.00
(2) Vacuum Control		
1983-87	●8134678	32.75
(3) Washer		
1983-87	●8128465	.75
(4) Distributor Gear		
1983-87	●8133652	18.25
(5) Distributor Cap		
1983-87	●3230457	15.50
(6) Rotor		
1983-87	●3230821	2.75
(7) Trigger Wheel		
1983-87	●8128422	5.25
(8) Washer (Wave)		
1983-87	●8128468	.25
(9) Sensor Assy. (Stator Complete)		
1983-87	●8128445	29.25
(10) Plate (Sensor Mounting)		
Not Used		
Module		
1983-87	●3230451	97.00
Ignition Coil		
1983-87	●3230427	27.50

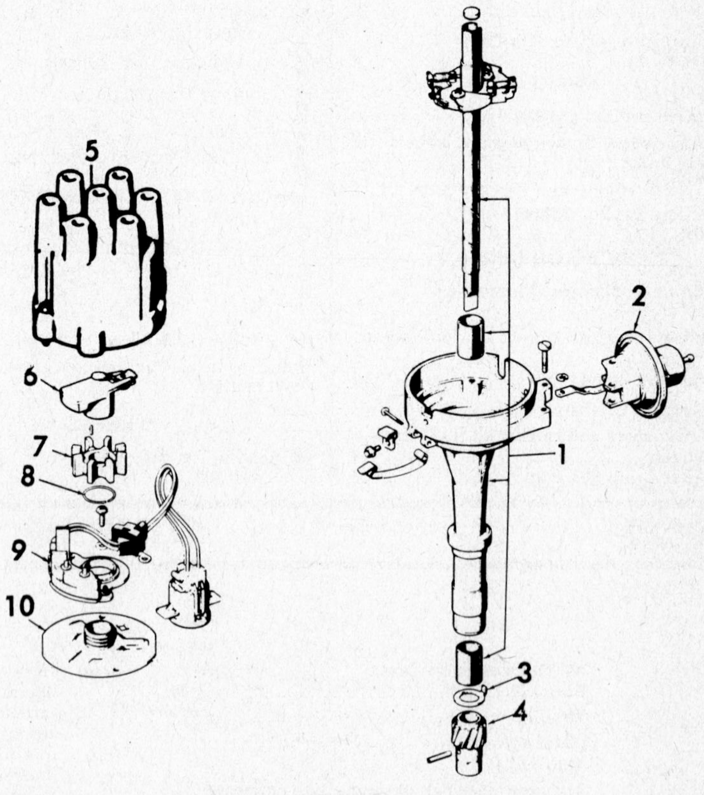

PARTS 2 ELECTRONIC IGNITION 2 PARTS

	Part No.	Price
FOUR–151		
Distributor Assy		
1983–exc. Calif.	●8134001	352.75
Calif.	●8134799	345.75
(1) Distributor Cap		
1983	●8134006	20.75
(2) Rotor		
1983	●8134113	10.75
(3) Main Shaft Assy. (Complete)		
1983–exc. below	●8134195	91.25
Calif	8134210	91.25
(4) Pole Piece & Plate Assy.		
1983	●8134119	51.00
(5) Vacuum Control		
1983 (stand. trans.)		
exc. Calif	8134115	33.50
Calif	8134114	33.50
auto. trans	8134116	33.50
(6) Module		
1983	●8134117	69.00
(7) Terminal Block Assy.		
1983	●8134118	15.25

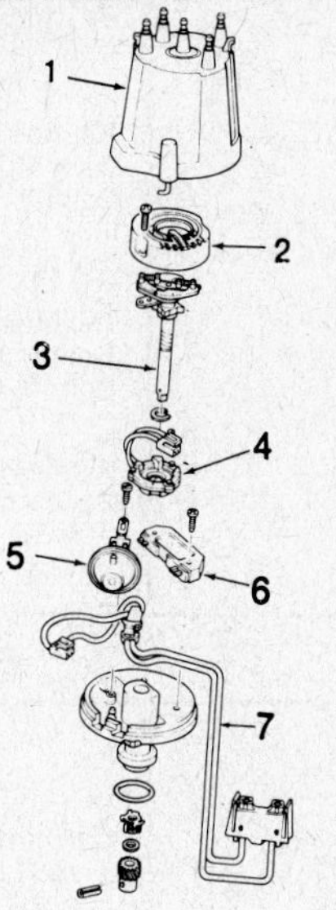

PARTS 2 ELECTRONIC IGNITION 2 PARTS

	Part No.	Price
FOUR–150		
(1) Distributor Assy.		
1983-87	●3242700	110.00
(2) Distributor Cap		
1983-87	●3234451	8.00
(3) Rotor		
1983-87	●3234452	6.50
(4) Trigger Wheel		
1983-87	●8983500412	10.50
(5) Sensor Assy. (Complete)		
1983-87	●8983500409	18.75
(6) Plate		
1983-87	●8983500410	7.00
(7) Vacuum Control		
1983-87	●8983500413	19.25
(8) Distributor Gear		
1983-87	●8133652	18.25
Module		
1983-87	8230451	N.L.
Ignition Coil		
1983-87	●3230427	27.50

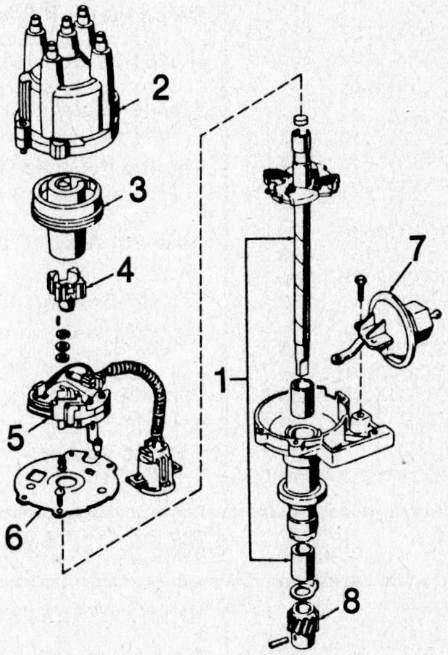

LABOR 3 FUEL SYSTEM 3 LABOR

(Factory Time)	Chilton Time
(G) Fuel Pump, Test	
Includes: Disconnect line at carburetor, attach pressure gauge.	
All models	.3
(M) Carburetor Air Cleaner, Service	
1983-87 (.2)	.3
(G) Carburetor, Adjust (On Car)	
1983-87 (.5)	.6
(G) Carburetor Choke Cover, Renew	
Four–151 eng. (.7)	1.0
Six–(.8)	1.1
(G) Carburetor Float Level, Adjust	
Four–151 eng. (.6)	.8
(M) Fuel Filter, Renew	
1983-87 (.3)	.4
(G) Carburetor, Renew	
Includes: Necessary adjustments.	
Four–1983-87	
150 eng. (.9)	1.3
151 eng. (.5)	.8
Six–1983-87 (.8)	1.2
(G) Carburetor, R&R and Clean or Recondition	
Includes: Necessary adjustments.	
Four–1983-87	
150 eng. (1.6)	2.3
151 eng. (1.7)	2.4
Six–1983-87	
1 bbl (1.0)	1.3
2 bbl (1.6)	2.3
(G) Dash Pot or Idle Solenoid, Renew	
Includes: Adjust.	
1983-87 (.2)	.3

LABOR 3 FUEL SYSTEM 3 LABOR

	(Factory Time)	Chilton Time
(G) Float or Needle Valve & Seat, Renew		
1 bbl	(.4)	.7
2 bbl	(.5)	.8
(G) Carburetor Bowl Cooling Timer, Renew		
1983-87	(.2)	.5
(G) Fuel Pump, Renew		
Four–1983-87-exc below	(.5)	.8
Eagle-SX-4-1983-87	(1.5)	1.9
Six–1983-87	(.5)	.8
Add pump test if performed.		
(G) Fuel Tank, Renew		
Concord-Eagle-1983-87	(1.0)	1.4
Spirit-SX-4-1983-87	(.8)	1.1
(G) Fuel Gauge (Tank), Renew		
Includes: Drain and refill tank.		
Concord-Eagle-1983-87	(.9)	1.5
Spirit-SX-4-1983-87	(.6)	1.2
(G) Fuel Gauge (Dash), Renew		
Concord-Spirit-AMX-Eagle' 1983-87	(.6)	.9
(G) Intake Manifold or Gasket, Renew		
Four–1983-87		
150 eng.	(1.9)	2.7
151 eng.	(1.4)	2.0
Renew manif add	(.2)	.4
Six–1983-87	(1.7)	2.5
Renew manif add	(.4)	.5
w/P.S. add	(.3)	.3
(G) Intake and Exhaust Manifold or Gaskets, Renew		
Six–1983-87	(2.4)	3.0
w/Air guard and/or P.S. add	(.3)	.3

PARTS 3 FUEL SYSTEM 3 PARTS

	Part No.	Price
Air Cleaner Element		
1983-87-Four	●8991386	5.50
1983-87-Six	●8991386	5.50
Carburetor Assy. Carter (New)		
1983-Six (w/2 bbl)		
8362	●8933000482	326.50
8364	●8933000469	326.50
8367	8933000483	326.50
1984-87 (w/2 bbl.)		
8383	●8933001707	284.25
8384	●8933001708	303.25
Carburetor Assy. Rochester (New)		
1983-Eagle & SX4 (w/2 bbl)		
2380	●3241118	434.25
3384	8933000475	1036.50
3385	●8933000601	1036.50
1983-Eagle & SX4 (w/1 bbl)		
7452	8953000650	493.00
7453	●8953000651	493.00
7454	●8933002116	339.75
7455	●8933002117	339.75
1984-87-Eagle (w/1 bbl)		
7701	●8933002114	339.75
7700	●8933002115	339.75
7703	●8933002116	339.75
7702	●8933002117	339.75
Carburetor Repair Kit (Carter)		
1983-87	●8134232	12.00
Carburetor Overhaul Kit (Rochester)		
1983		
M.T.	●8134332	40.50
A.T.	8133488	34.50
1984-87	●8983500453	21.25
Carb. Needle & Seat (Carter)		
1983-87-Six	8127326	6.75
Carb. Needle & Seat (Rochester)		
1983	8132728	6.75
1984-87	8983500932	7.50
Stepper Motor (Carter)		
1984-87	8132632	80.75
Throttle Solenoid (Carter)		
1984-87	8983500171	N.L.
Dash Pot Assy. (Carter)		
1983	8127729	10.25
Throttle Solenoid (Rochester)		
1983	8133480	31.75
1984-87	8983500466	108.00
Pulse Solenoid (Rochester)		
1984-87	8983500919	50.50
Throttle Sensor		
1984-87	8983500922	58.50
Fuel Pump Assy. (New)		
Four		
1983-151	●8132364	36.00
1983-87-150	●3240172	44.25
Six		
1983-87	●3228191	34.25
Fuel Tank		
1983		
Spirit & SX4	8127669	179.25
1983-87-Eagle & Concord (83)	8131654	189.75
Fuel Gauge (Tank)		
1983-Concord	3230700	32.25
1983-SX4	3230701	32.25
1983-Spirit		
exc 151 (2 dr) sdn	3230701	32.25
151 (2 dr) sdn	3233287	31.50
1983-87-Eagle	3230700	32.25
Fuel Gauge (Dash)		
1983-87	8128863	26.25
Intake Manifold Gasket		
Four		
1983-151	●8134694	7.75
1983-87-150	●3242854	5.25
Six		
1983-87	3242855	7.25

LABOR 3A EMISSION CONTROLS 3A LABOR

	(Factory Time)	Chilton Time
EVAPORATIVE EMISSION TYPE		
(M) Charcoal Canister, Renew		
1983-87	(.3)	.4
(M) Charcoal Canister Filter, Renew		
1983-87	(.2)	.3
(M) Charcoal Canister Hoses, Renew		
1983-87-each	(.2)	.2
(M) Crankcase Ventilation Valve, Renew		
1983-87	(.3)	.3
EXHAUST GAS RECIRCULATION SYSTEM		
(G) Emission Maintenance Switch, Renew		
Concord-Spirit 1983	(.3)	.5

CHILTON'S EMISSION CONTROL TUNE-UP

1. Clean or renew P.C.V. valve, hoses and filter.
2. Check fuel tank cap for sealing ability.
3. Check fuel tank and fuel lines for leakage.
4. Check evaporation canister and filter. Replace if necessary.
5. Check engine compression to determine leakage of unburned gases. (Add time for items of interference).
6. Test and clean or renew spark plugs.
7. Check engine oil dipstick for sealing ability.
8. Test exhaust system with analyzer and check system for leakage.
9. Check exhaust manifold heat valve for operation.
10. Adjust ignition timing and carburetor idle speed and mixture.
11. Check automatic choke mechanism for free operation.
12. Inspect air cleaner and element.
13. On models so equipped, test distributor vacuum control switch and transmission control switch.

Four **1.3**
Six **1.5**
V-8 .... **1.8**

For repairs made, charge accordingly.

LABOR 3A EMISSION CONTROLS 3A LABOR

(Factory Time) Chilton Time

(M) E.G.R. Valve, Renew
1983-87 (.5) 7

(G) E.G.R. Coolant Temperature Override Switch, Renew
1983-87 (.4) 7

(G) Thermal Vacuum Switch, Renew
1983-87 (.2) 5

(G) Air Control Valve, Renew
1983-87-Six (.2) 3

(G) Exhaust Check Valve, Renew
1983-87 (.4) 5

(G) Pulsair Valve, Renew
1983-87-Four (.4) 6

(G) Deceleration Valve, Renew
1983-87 (.2) 3

THERMOSTATIC CONTROLLED AIR CLEANER

(G) Air Cleaner Temperature Sensor, Renew
1983-87 (.3) 6

(G) Thermal Vacuum Switch, Renew
1983-87 (.2) 4

(G) Air Cleaner Vacuum Motor, Renew
1983-87 (.3) 5

TRANSMISSION CONTROLLED SPARK

(G) TCS Vacuum Solenoid, Renew
1983-87 (.2) 4

(G) TCS Coolant Temperature Override Switch, Renew
1983-87 (.4) 6

(G) TCS Solenoid Control Switch, Renew
1983-87-w/M.T. (.2) 4
1983-87-w/A.T. (.2) 4

ELECTRONIC EMISSION CONTROLS

(G) Stepper Motor Actuator, Renew
1983-87-Six (.4) 5

(G) Idle Speed Controller, Renew
1983-87 (.3) 4

(G) Microprocessor Assembly, Renew
1983-87 (.3) 5

(G) Sole-Vac Throttle Positioner, Renew
1983-87 (.3) 4

(G) Mixture Control Solenoid, Renew
1983-87-Four (.3) 4

(G) Oxygen Sensor, Renew
Includes: Renew or reset timer.
1983-87 (.3) 7

PARTS 3A EMISSION CONTROLS 3A PARTS

AIR GUARD SYSTEM

	Part No.	Price
Crankcase Ventilation Valve		
1983-151	●8132309	4.00
1983-87-150	●8933001239	N.L.
1983-87-Six	●8933000887	3.25
Pulse Air Valve		
1983-87	●8933000355	18.75
Pulse Air Check Valve		
1983-87	●8933000354	14.50

EVAPORATIVE EMISSION TYPE

	Part No.	Price
Vapor Canister		
1983-151	●3237477	71.50
1983-87	●3239479	36.75

EXHAUST GAS RECIRCULATION SYSTEM

	Part No.	Price
E.G.R. Valve		
Four-151		
1983-87-exc Calif	8953001090	70.75
Calif A.T.	8933001516	111.50
Calif M.T.	8933001944	56.00
H. Alt. A.T.	8933001517	70.75
H. Alt. M.T.	8953001089	70.75
Canada A.T.	8953001090	70.75
Canada M.T.	8953001089	70.75
Six		
1983-87-exc Calif.		
M.T.	3241729	69.00
A.T.	8933000956	71.00
1983-87-Calif.		
M.T.	3239371	N.L.
A.T.	8953000828	N.L.
Exhaust Check Valve		
1983-Four	3239802	10.00
Decel Valve		
1983-87-Four M.T.	8933001010	23.50
1983-87-Six M.T.	3237284	22.00

ELECTRONIC EMISSION CONTROL

	Part No.	Price
MicroProcessor Assy.		
1983-Four (Calif.)		
Code H4	●8933000495	112.00
1983-Six (exc. Calif.)		
Code S1	●8933001078	147.00
Code S2	●8933001079	147.00
Code S4	●8933001081	147.00
Code 1S	●8933001078	147.00
Code 2S	●8933001079	147.00
Code 4S	●8933001081	147.00
Code 7S	●8933001083	147.00
Code R3	8933001287	147.00
Code R4	8933001288	147.00
1983-87-Six (Calif.)		
Code S3	●8933001080	147.00
Code S5	●8933000494	154.50
Code 3S	●8933001080	147.00
Code 5S	●8933001082	147.00
1984-87-Four (exc. Calif.)		
stand. trans.	8933001736	147.00
auto. trans.	8933001737	147.00
1984-87-Four (Calif.)		
stand. trans.	8933001738	147.00
auto. trans.	8933001739	147.00
1984-87-Six (exc. Calif.)		
stand. trans.	8933001732	147.00
auto. trans.	●8933001080	147.00
1984-87-Six (Calif.)		
stand. trans.	8933001734	147.00
auto. trans.	8933001733	147.00
Thermal Electric Switch		
1983-87	3240825	13.25
Heat Relay (Manifold)		
1983-87	8936000400	9.00

LABOR 4 ALTERNATOR AND REGULATOR 4 LABOR

(Factory Time) Chilton Time

(G) Alternator Circuits, Test
Includes: Test battery, regulator and alternator output.
All models 6

(M) Alternator Drive-Belt, Renew
1983-87 5

(G) Alternator, Renew
Four-1983-87 (.4) 7
Six-1983-87 (.3) 7
w/A.C. add (.1) 1
Add circuit test if performed.

(G) Alternator, R&R and Recondition
Four-1983-87 (1.0) 1.5
Six-1983-87 (.8) 1.4
w/A.C. add (.1) 1
Add circuit test if performed.

(G) Alternator Regulator, Renew
Four-1983-87 (.6) .... *.9
Six-1983-87 (.5) .... *.9
*Includes: R&R alternator.

PARTS 4 ALTERNATOR AND REGULATOR 4 PARTS

	Part No.	Price
DELCO REMY		
Alternator Assy–(New)		
1983-87-42 amp	8134663	243.25
56, 66, 78 amp	●8134664	264.00
(1) Bearing		
1983-87	●8134644	7.00
(2) Housing (Rear)		
1983-87-42 amp	8132555	33.75
56, 66, 78 amp	●8134651	48.50
(3) Diode Trio Assembly		
1983-87	●8133268	7.75
(4) Regulator Assembly		
1983-87	●8125176	31.25
(5) Brush Holder		
1983-87	●8134652	9.50
(6) Capacitor		
1983-87	●8125183	5.75
(7) Stator		
1983-87-42 amp	8134674	46.00
56, 66, 78 amp		
I.D 5044	●8134648	51.75
I.D 5045	8134649	42.00
(8) Rotor		
1983-87-42 amp	●8134645	63.50
56, 66, 78 amp		
I.D. 5044	●8134645	63.50
I.D. 5045	8134646	74.00
(9) Bearing		
1983-87	8126709	11.00
(10) Housing (Front)		
1983-87-42 amp	8134654	23.00
56, 66, 78 amp.	●8134655	28.25

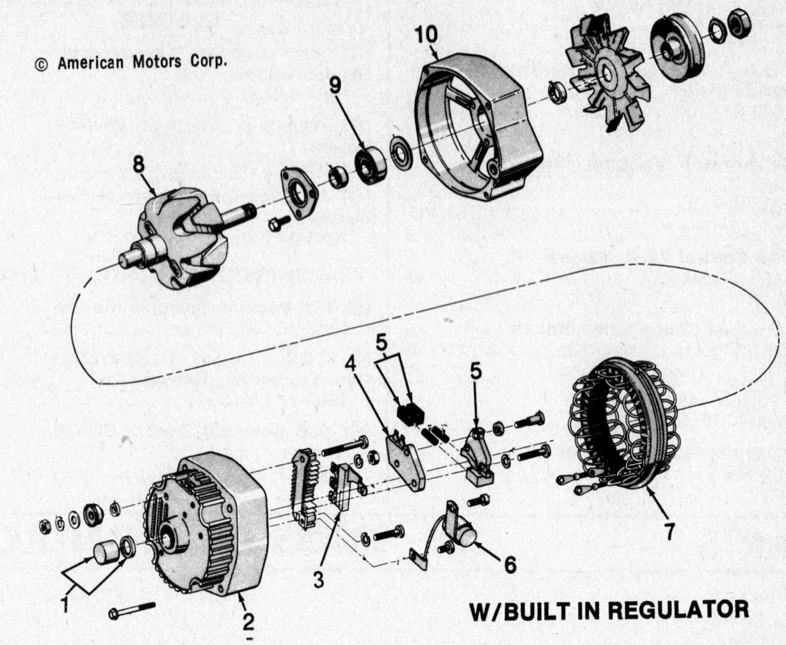

W/BUILT IN REGULATOR

LABOR 5 STARTING SYSTEM 5 LABOR

	(Factory Time)	Chilton Time
(G) Starter Draw Test (On Car)		
All models	(.2)	.4
(G) Starter, Renew		
1983-87-exc. below	(.4)	.7
150 eng.	(.2)	.5
Add draw test if performed.		
(G) Starter, R&R and Recondition		
Includes: Turn down armature.		
1983-87-exc. below	(1.1)	2.3
150 eng.	(.7)	2.0
Renew field coils add	(.3)	.5
Add draw test if performed.		
(G) Starter Drive, Renew		
Includes: R&R starter.		
1983-87-exc. below	(.6)	1.0
150 eng.	(.4)	.8
(G) Neutral Start and Back-Up Lamp Switch, Renew		
1983-87		
Concord-Spirit	(.4)	.5
Eagle	(.7)	1.0
(G) Starter Solenoid, Renew		
1983-87-exc. below	(.9)	1.2
150 eng.	(.7)	1.0
(G) Starter Relay, Renew (On Wheelhouse)		
1983-87	(.3)	.3
(G) Ignition Switch, Renew		
1983-87	(.4)	.5
w/Pkg tray add	(.1)	.2
(G) Ignition Lock (Column Lock Assy.), Renew		
1983-87	(.6)	.9
Renew ignition switch actuator and/or rack add	(.6)	.6
(M) Battery Cables, Renew		
1983-87-one	(.2)	.3
all	(.3)	.5
SEAT BELT INTERLOCK		
(G) Seat Belt Buckle Switch, Renew		
1983-87	(.2)	.4
(G) Warning Buzzer, Renew		
1983-87	(.2)	.5

PARTS 5 STARTING SYSTEM 5 PARTS

	Part No.	Price
(1) Starter Assembly		
1983-87-Four		
151	●8134193	198.50
150	●3242283	140.25
1983-87-Six	●5752791	177.00
(2) Starter Drive Assy.		
1983-87-Four		
151	●8130940	24.25
150	●8983500399	22.00
1983-87-Six	●8120193	21.00
(3) Starter Brushes		
1983-87-Four		
151	●8130934	.75
150		
neg.	●8983500402	1.00
pos.	●8983500401	1.75
1983-87-Six	●8128434	5.75
(4) Drive End Bushing		
1983-87-exc 151	●8120030	1.50
151	●8130953	.50
(5) Commutator End Plate		
1983-87-Four		
151	●8133922	7.50
150	●8983500397	7.75
1983-87-Six	●8128440	5.75
(6) Armature		
1983-87-Four		
151	●8134198	94.00
150	●8983500396	44.00
1983-87-Six	●8120028	72.25

PARTS 5 STARTING SYSTEM 5 PARTS

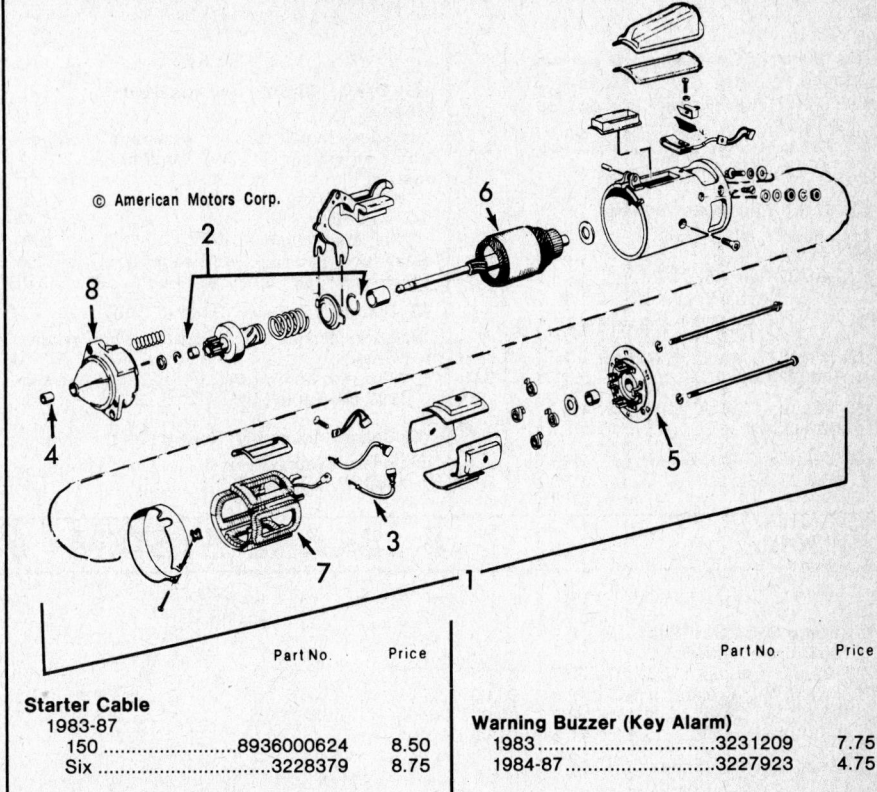

	Part No.	Price
(7) Field Coils		
1983-87		
150	●8983500392	36.00
Six	●8128438	66.75
Frame & Field Assy.		
1983-151	●8134196	83.50
(8) Drive End Housing		
1983-87-Four		
151	●8133923	29.00
150	●8983500396	44.00
1983-87-Six	●8133036	20.00
Ignition Switch		
1983-87 (w/Column dimmer switch)		
wo/Adjust whl	●3250576	17.00
w/Adjust whl	3250575	17.00
Starter Neutral Switch		
1983-87	●3232844	9.25
Starter Motor Relay		
1983-87-exc 151		
M.T.	●3235898	11.25
A.T.	3235897	11.25
1983-151	3236793	13.50
Starter Relay Fusible Link		
1983-87-Six	8134201	3.50
Battery Ground Cable		
1983-87-Six	3240721	7.50
Four	3242507	N.L.
Battery Positive Cable		
1983-87-Six	3240719	5.75
1983-87-Four		
151	3240713	20.75
150	8956000299	4.25

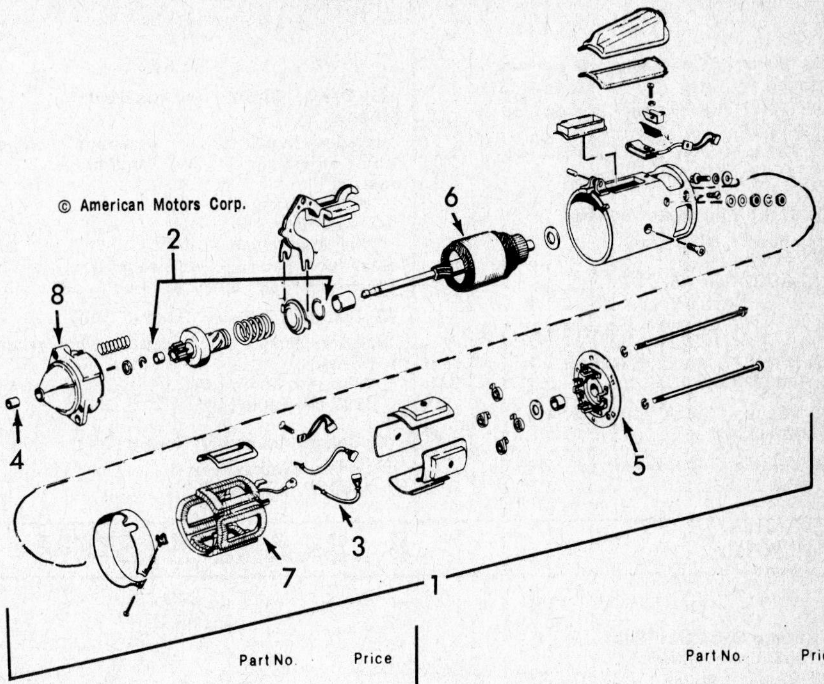

	Part No.	Price
Starter Cable		
1983-87		
150	8936000624	8.50
Six	3228379	8.75

	Part No.	Price
Warning Buzzer (Key Alarm)		
1983	3231209	7.75
1984-87	3227923	4.75

LABOR 6 BRAKE SYSTEM 6 LABOR

	(Factory Time)	Chilton Time
(G) Brake Pedal Free Play, Adjust		
1983-87		.3
(G) Bleed Brakes (Four Wheels)		
Includes: Add fluid.		
1983-87	(.4)	.6
(G) Brake Shoes and/or Pads, Renew		
Includes: Install new or exchange shoes or pads, adjust service and hand brake. Bleed system.		
1983-87-front-disc	(.7)	1.2
rear-drum	(.9)	1.4
all four wheels	(1.5)	2.5
Resurface disc rotor, add-each		.9
Resurface brake drum, add-each		.5
(G) Brake Drum, Renew (One)		
1983-87-rear	(.3)	.5
(G) Brake Pressure Differential Warning Valve Assy., Renew		
Includes: Bleed system.		
1983-87	(.8)	1.0

COMBINATIONS

Add to Brakes, Renew

See Machine Shop Operations

(G) RENEW WHEEL CYLINDER		
Each	(.2)	.2
(G) REBUILD WHEEL CYLINDER		
Each	(.3)	.3
(G) REBUILD CALIPER ASSEMBLY		
Each		.5
(G) RENEW CALIPER ASSEMBLY		
Each	(.1)	.3
(G) RENEW MASTER CYLINDER		
All models	(.5)	.8
(G) REBUILD MASTER CYLINDER		
All models	(1.0)	1.3
(G) RENEW BRAKE HOSE		
Each	(.3)	.3
(G) RENEW REAR WHEEL GREASE SEALS		
Right	(1.0)	1.0
Left	(.7)	.8
Both	(1.3)	1.5
(G) REPACK FRONT WHEEL BEARINGS (BOTH WHEELS)		
Drum brakes	(.2)	.4
Disc brakes	(.6)	.6
(G) RENEW BRAKE DRUM & HUB		
Front	(.1)	.2
Rear	(.4)	.4
(G) RENEW DISC BRAKE ROTOR		
Each	(.3)	.3

BRAKE HYDRAULIC SYSTEM

	(Factory Time)	Chilton Time
(G) Wheel Cylinders, Renew		
Includes: Bleed system.		
1983-87-one	(.7)	1.0
each adtnl	(.3)	.5
(G) Wheel Cylinder, R&R and Recondition		
Includes: Hone cyl. and bleed system.		
1983-87-one	(.7)	1.2
each adtnl	(.3)	.5
(G) Master Cylinder, Renew		
Includes: Bleed system.		
1983-87		
std brks	(.9)	1.2
pwr brks	(.6)	.9

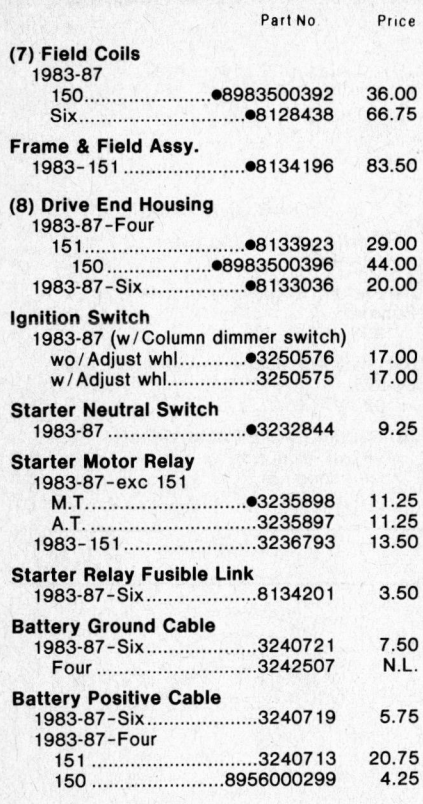

LABOR — 6 BRAKE SYSTEM 6 — LABOR

(Factory Time) — Chilton Time

(G) Master Cylinder, R&R and Rebuild
Includes: Hone cyl. and bleed system.

1983-87	
std brks (1.4)	1.7
pwr brks (1.1)	1.4

(G) Brake Flex Hose, Renew
Includes: Bleed system.

Eagle	
1983-87-one (.6)	.8

POWER BRAKES

(G) Brake Power Unit, Renew

1983-87 (.6)	1.0

(G) Vacuum Check Valve, Renew

1983-87 (.2)	.3

(G) Vacuum Hose, Renew

1983-87 (.3)	.4

DISC BRAKES

(G) Brake Shoes and/or Pads, Renew
Includes: Install new or exchange shoes or pads, adjust service and hand brake. Bleed system.

1983-87-front-disc (.7)	1.2
rear-drum (.9)	1.4
all four wheels (1.5)	2.5
Resurface disc rotor, add-each	.9
Resurface brake drum, add-each	.5

(G) Disc Brake Rotor, Renew (One)
Includes: Repack and adjust bearings, where required.

1983-exc below (.6)	1.0
1983-87-Eagle (.3)	.5

(G) Caliper Assembly, Renew (One)
Includes: Bleed system.

1983-87 (.8)	1.1

(G) Caliper Assy., R&R and Recondition (One)
Includes: Bleed system.

1983-87 (.9)	1.5

PARKING BRAKE

(M) Parking Brake, Adjust

1983-87 (.3)	.4

(G) Parking Brake Indicator Switch, Renew

1983-87 (.3)	.4

(G) Parking Brake Lever Assy., Renew

1983-87 (.9)	1.3

(G) Parking Brake Cable, Renew

1983-87-front (.8)	1.0
rear-one (.8)	1.0
both (1.3)	1.7

PARTS — 6 BRAKE SYSTEM 6 — PARTS

	Part No.	Price
(1) Brake Shoe Set (Rear)		
1983-Concord, Spirit		
9″ x 2″ brakes	8133817	69.00
10″ x 1¾″ brakes	●8133818	69.00
1983-SX4	●8133818	69.00
1983-87-Eagle	●8133818	69.00
(2) Rear Wheel Cylinder (R.H.)		
1983-Concord, Spirit		
9″ x 2″ brakes	3229063	25.25
10″ x 1¾″ brakes	3225198	25.75
1983-SX4	3225198	25.75
1983-87-Eagle	3225198	25.75
Wheel Cylinder Repair Kit (Rear)		
1983-Concord, Spirit		
9″ x 2″ brakes	8136664	4.25
10″ x 1¾″ brakes	8125880	5.75
1983-SX4	8125880	5.75
1983-87-Eagle	8125880	5.75
Rear Brake Hose		
1983-Concord, Spirit		
14⅞″ long	3236906	12.25
15⅝″ long	3237961	13.00
1983-SX4	3237005	14.25
1983-87-Eagle	3237005	14.25
Master Cylinder Assy.		
1983-87	●3241807	94.50
Power Brake Unit		
1983-87	8133906	183.00

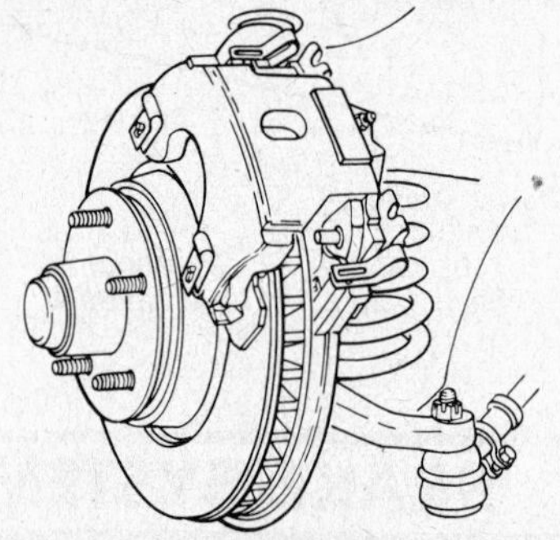

FRONT BRAKE

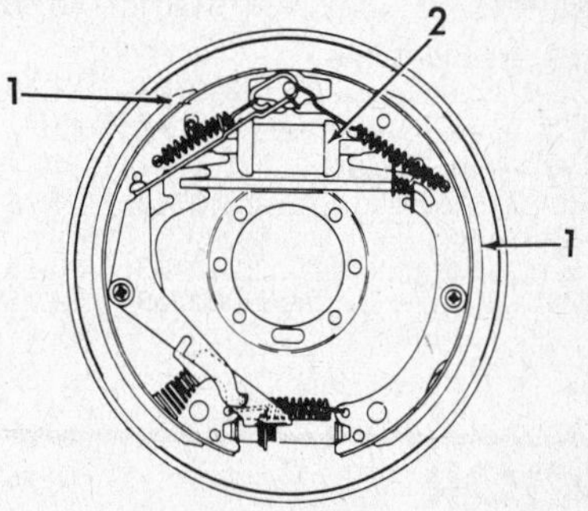

REAR BRAKE

	Part No.	Price
Master Cylinder Repair Kit		
1983-87	8133913	23.25
Rear Hub & Drum		
1983-Concord, Spirit		
9″ x 2″ brakes	3225884	109.00
10″ x 1¾″ brakes	3237948	106.50
1983-SX4	3237948	106.50
1983-84-Eagle	3237948	106.50
Drum (only)		
1983-87-Eagle	8132615	107.25

PARKING BRAKE

	Part No.	Price
Parking Brake Lever		
1983-87	3229104	38.25
Parking Brake Front Cable		
1983-87-exc Spirit	3236915	27.50
Spirit	3236916	27.50
SX4	3236916	27.50
Parking Brake Rear Cables		
1983	3230014	27.50
1984-87-left	3237936	23.50
right	3230014	27.50

PARTS — 6 DISC BRAKES 6 — PARTS

CONCORD & SPIRIT

	Part No.	Price
(1) Caliper Assy.		
1983		
right	●8133846	102.00
left	●8133847	102.00
(2) Repair Kit		
1983		
wo/piston	●8133852	6.75
w/piston	●8133845	19.00
(3) Brake Pad Set		
1983	●8133853	53.00
(4) Brake Hose		
1983	3240887	10.50

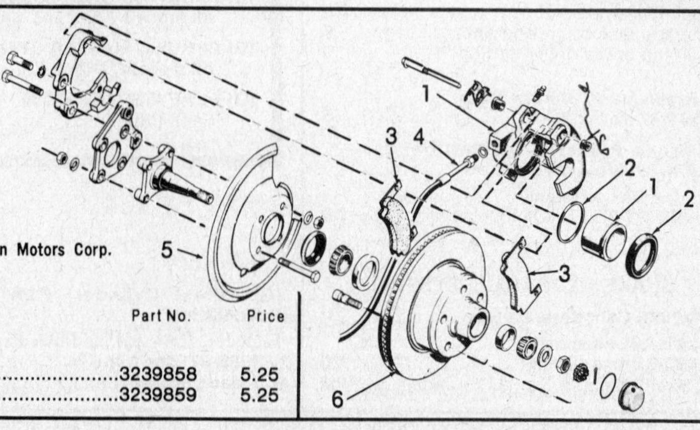

© American Motors Corp.

	Part No.	Price
(5) Shield		
1983		
right	3239858	5.25
left	3239859	5.25

PARTS — 6 DISC BRAKES 6 — PARTS

	Part No.	Price
(6) Rotor		
1983	3250578	100.50
Master Cylinder Assy. (Power)		
1983	●3241807	94.50
Repair Kit (Master Cylinder)		
1983	8133913	23.25

PARTS — 6 DISC BRAKES 6 — PARTS

EAGLE & SX4

	Part No.	Price
(1) Anchor Plate (R.H.)		
1983-87	3240026	42.25
(2) Splash Shield (R.H.)		
1983-87	8952000114	5.25
(3) Hub Assy. (w/Bearings & Seals)		
1983-87	3238527	173.00
(4) Rotor		
1983-87	●3251156	117.00
(5) Brake Pad Set		
1983-87	●8133853	53.00
(6) Caliper Repair Kit		
1983-87	●8133845	19.00
Note: Includes Boot, Piston and Seal.		
(7) Caliper Assembly (R.H.)		
1983-87	●8133846	102.00
(8) Front Brake Hose (R.H.)		
1983-87	3240888	18.25
(9) Support Pin		
1983-87	3239866	8.00
Bushing (Inner)		
1983-84	3239867	3.25
1985-87	8952001700	2.00
Bushing (Outer)		
1983-84	3240890	N.L.
1985-87	8952001701	3.00
Note: Component parts for front hub follow.		
(10) Hub		
1983-87	3238525	68.50
(11) Inner Bearing		
1983-87	3238136	27.00

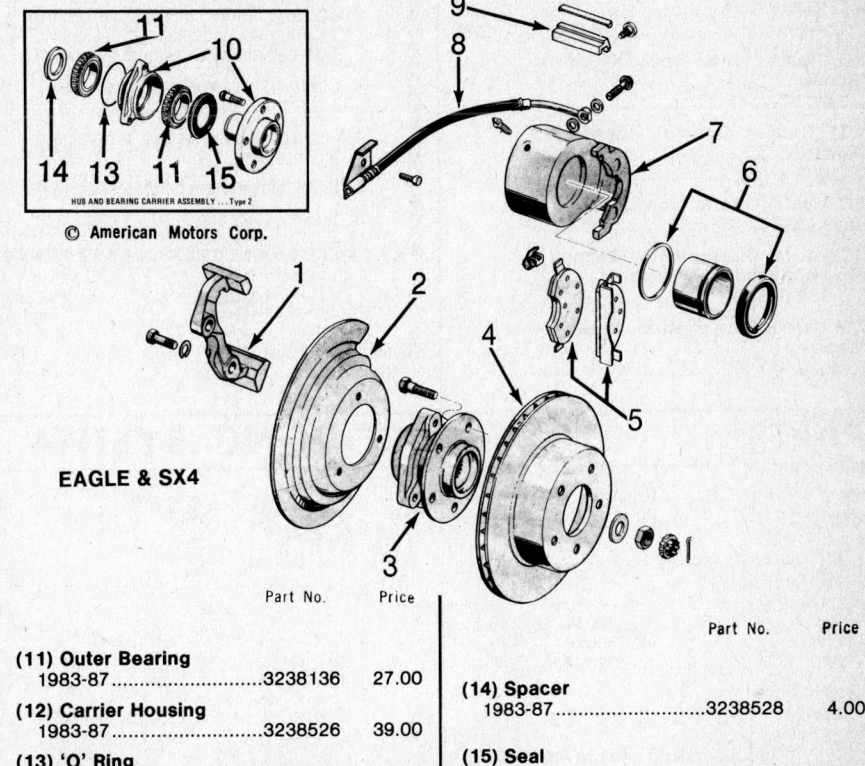

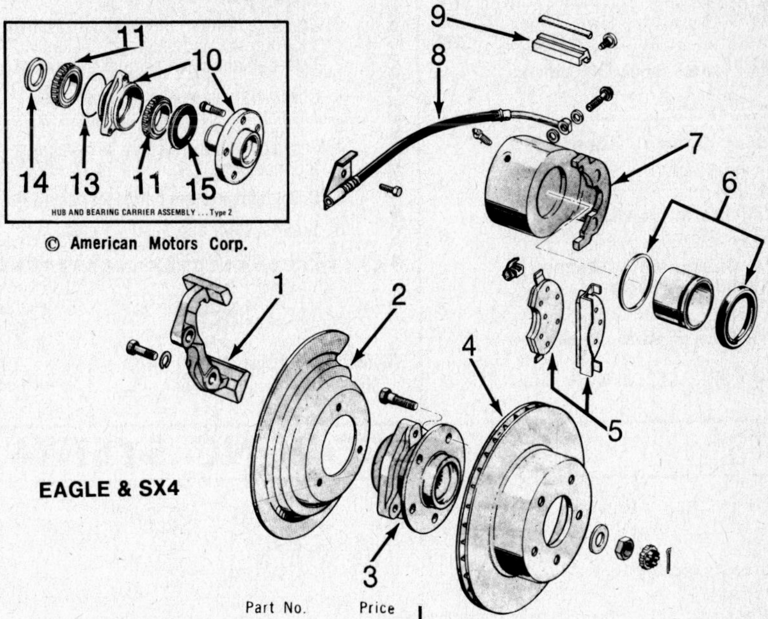

© American Motors Corp.

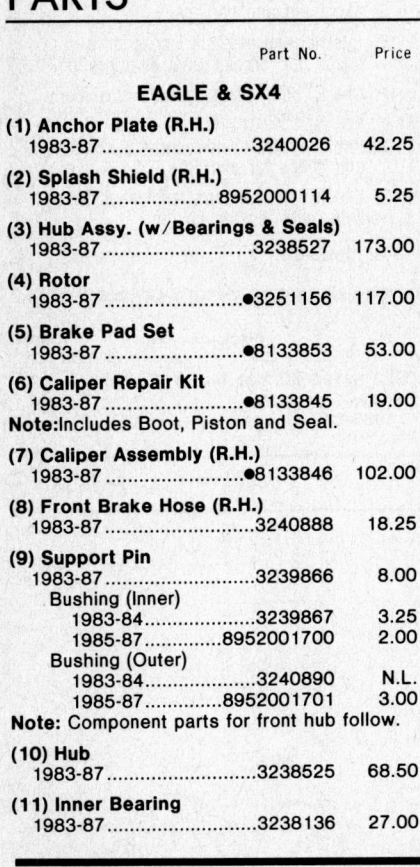

	Part No.	Price
(11) Outer Bearing		
1983-87	3238136	27.00
(12) Carrier Housing		
1983-87	3238526	39.00
(13) 'O' Ring		
1983-87	3238141	.75
(14) Spacer		
1983-87	3238528	4.00
(15) Seal		
1983-87	●3238137	2.00

LABOR — 7 COOLING SYSTEM 7 — LABOR

(Factory Time)	Chilton Time
(G) Winterize Cooling System	
Includes: Run engine to check for leaks, tighten all hose connections. Test radiator and pressure cap, drain radiator and engine block. Add anti-freeze and refill system.	
All models	.5
(M) Thermostat, Renew	
1983-87 (.5)	.6
(G) Radiator Assembly, R&R or Renew	
1983-87 (.6)	1.0
w/A.C. add (.1)	.1
w/A.T. add (.1)	.1
ADD THESE OPERATIONS TO RADIATOR R&R	
(G) Boil & Repair	1.5
(G) Rod Clean	1.9
(G) Repair Core	1.3
(G) Renew Tank	1.6
(G) Renew Trans. Oil Cooler	1.9
(G) Recore Radiator	1.7
(M) Radiator Hoses, Renew	
1983-87-upper (.4)	.4
lower (.7)	.8
(G) Water Pump, Renew	
Four–1983-87	
150 eng. (1.0)	1.5
151 eng. (.7)	1.2
w/P.S. add (.1)	.1
Six–1983-87 (1.0)	1.5
w/P.S. add (.1)	.1
w/Air guard add (.1)	.1
w/A.C. add (.3)	.3
(M) Fan Blades, Renew	
Four–1983-87 (.2)	.3
w/P.S. add (.1)	.1
Six–1983-87 (.5)	.6
w/P.S. add (.1)	.1
w/A.C. add (.1)	.1
w/Air guard add (.1)	.1
(M) Fan Belt, Renew	
Four–1983-87 (.3)	.3
Six–1983-87 (.3)	.3
Serpentine (.5)	.6
w/P.S., A.C. or Air guard add (.2)	.2
(G) Viscous Fan Assembly, Renew	
1983-87 (.5)	.7
(G) Temperature Gauge (Engine Unit), Renew	
1983-87 (.3)	.4
(G) Temperature Gauge (Dash Unit), Renew	
Concord-Spirit-AMX	
1983 (.6)	1.0
Eagle	
1983-87 (.6)	1.0
(G) Water Jacket Expansion Plugs, Renew (Engine Block)	
Four–1983-87	
right side-front (.8)	1.3
right side-center (.7)	1.3
right side-rear (.6)	1.2
left side-front (.5)	1.1
left side-center (.7)	1.3
left side-rear (.5)	1.1
Six–1983-87	
left side-front (.4)	.9
left side-rear (.4)	.9
left side-center (1.7)	2.4
(M) Heater Hoses, Renew	
1983-87-one (.3)	.5
two (.4)	.6

LABOR 7 COOLING SYSTEM 7 LABOR

(Factory Time)	Chilton Time
(G) Heater Core, R&R or Renew	
Concord-Spirit-AMX-Eagle	
1983-87 (1.1)	1.7
ADD THESE OPERATIONS TO HEATER CORE R&R	
(G) Boil & Repair	1.2
(G) Repair Core	.9
(G) Recore	1.2
(G) Heater Water Shut Off Valve, Renew	
1983-87 (.4)	.6
(G) Heater Control Assembly, Renew	
1983-87 (.6)	.9
(G) Heater Control Valve, Renew	
Six–1983-87 (.3)	.6
(G) Heater Blower Motor, Renew	
Concord-Spirit-AMX-Eagle	
1983-87 (.5)	.7
(G) Heater Blower Motor Resistor, Renew	
1983-87 (.3)	.4

COOLING SYSTEM TUNE-UP

An Annual Cooling System Tune-Up Suggestion List should include (with some exceptions):

1. A visual check of the cooling system for indications of leaks or excessive oil content.
2. Pressure check the cooling system for internal and external leaks with filler cap and neck adapter and tester.
3. Check crankcase and automatic transmission oil for water content.
4. Test coolant thermostat with radiator thermometer.
5. Check temperature gauge for accuracy.
6. Drain system and flush till clean.
7. Clean foreign matter from radiator fins.
8. Test radiator pressure cap with cap tester.
9. Check fan blades and pulleys for alignment and damage.
10. Internal and external inspection of all hoses for cracks and deterioration.
11. Check core plugs (where possible) for seepage.
12. Refill system with correct coolant and check for air locks.
13. Check condition and tension of drive belts with tension gauge.

All models 1.5

(Factory Time)	Chilton Time
(G) Blower Motor Relay, Renew	
1983-87 (.3)	.4
(G) Heater Blower Motor Switch, Renew	
1983-87 (.5)	.6

PARTS 7 COOLING SYSTEM 7 PARTS

	Part No.	Price
(1) Radiator Assembly		
1984-87-Eagle		
Four-150		
Std.	8933001071	149.50
H.D.	8933001072	149.50
Six	3235286	378.25
(2) Thermostat		
1983-87		
(Four)		
151	●8134146	10.25
150	●8983501426	8.50
Six	3983500360	N.L.
(3) Radiator Hoses		
Order by year and model.		
(4) Water Pump Assembly		
Four		
1983-151	●8126699	47.50
1983-87-150		
w/ or wo/Serpentine belt		
wo/belt	8134320	112.00
w/belt	8134321	112.00
Six		
w/or wo/Serpentine belt		
wo/belt	8134320	112.00
w/belt	8134321	112.00
(5) Fan Belt		
Note: Order by model & description.		
Heat Sending Unit (Engine)		
1983-87-exc. 151	3233831	7.25
151	3236655	9.00
Eng. Temperature Indicator (Dash)		
1983-87	8128861	27.50

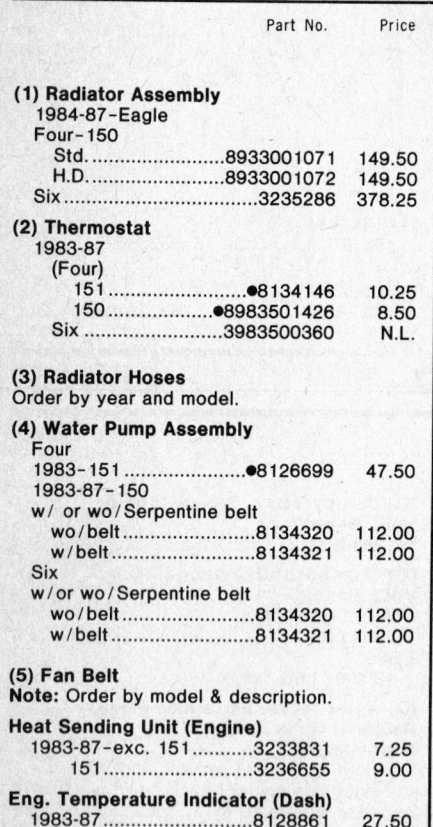

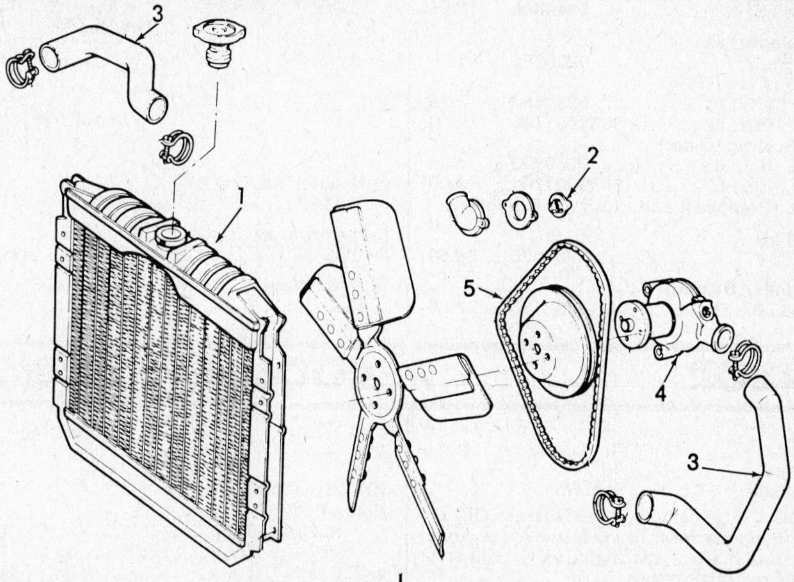

	Part No.	Price
Heater Core		
1983-87	3728196	99.75
Blower Motor (wo/Dealer Installed American Air)		
1983-87-w/A.C.	3741261	38.25
1984-87-wo/A.C.	3238874	38.25
Blower Motor (w/Dealer Installed American Air)		
1983	8128125	62.75

	Part No.	Price
Heater Switch		
1983-Concord, Spirit & SX4		
wo/A.C.	3692961	4.50
w/A.C.	3693111	9.75
1983-87-Eagle		
wo/A.C.	3692961	4.50
w/A.C.	3693111	9.75
Temperature Control Valve		
1983-151 eng	3728027	33.00
1983-87	3728148	33.25

LABOR 8 EXHAUST SYSTEM 8 LABOR

(Factory Time)	Chilton Time
(G) Muffler, Renew	
1983-87-one (.6)	.9
(G) Tail Pipe, Renew	
1983-87-one (.4)	.6
(G) Catalytic Converter, Renew	
1983-87-one (.7)	1.0

LABOR 8 EXHAUST SYSTEM 8 LABOR

	(Factory Time)	Chilton Time
(G) Catalytic Beads, Replace (On Car)		
1983-87-one	(.6)	.9
both	(.9)	1.3
(G) Exhaust Pipe Flange Gasket, Renew		
1983-87-each	(.3)	.6
(G) Exhaust Pipe, Renew		
1983-87		
front	(.5)	.8
rear	(.4)	.8
intermediate	(.5)	.9
(G) Oxygen Sensor, Renew		
Includes: Renew or reset timer.		
Six-1983-87	(.3)	.7
(G) Exhaust Manifold or Gaskets, Renew		
Four-1983-87		
150 eng.	(2.1)	3.0
151 eng.	(1.5)	2.2
Six-1983-87	(2.0)	3.0
(G) Intake and Exhaust Manifold or Gaskets, Renew		
Six-1983-87	(2.0)	3.0
w/Air guard and/or P.S. add	(.3)	.3
COMBINATIONS		
(G) Muffler, Exhaust and Tail Pipe, Renew		
All models		1.2
(G) Muffler and Tail Pipe, Renew		
All models		.8

PARTS 8 EXHAUST SYSTEM 8 PARTS

	Part No.	Price
Muffler Assy.		
Muffler Assembly		
1983		
Concord	8133944	60.75
Spirit	8133944	60.75
SX4		
151	8133168	75.75
151-Calif.	8134671	N.L.
150	8983500423	78.00
Six	8133944	60.75
Eagle		
151	8133168	75.75
151-Calif.	8134671	N.L.
150	8983500423	78.00
Six	8133944	60.75
1984-Eagle		
Four	8983500423	78.00
Six	8133944	60.75
1985-87-Eagle	8133944	60.75
Tail Pipe		
1983		
Concord	3237830	29.75
Spirit	3237832	26.50
SX4		
Four	3237829	19.50
Six	3237832	26.50
Eagle		
Four	3237831	37.75
Six	3237830	29.75
1984-87-Eagle	3237830	29.75
Exhaust Pipe		
1983-Front pipe		
Concord, Spirit	8933000970	275.00
SX4 & Eagle		
151-A.T.	8933000939	40.25
151-M.T.	8933000940	42.50
150	8933001142	45.00
Six	8933000970	275.00
1983-Rear pipe		
Concord	8133167	21.50
Spirit	8133170	14.50
SX4		
151	8133108	17.50
150	8133109	28.75
Six	8133109	28.75
Eagle	8133106	35.00
1984-Eagle		
Front pipe		
Four	893301142	N.L.
Six-M.T.	8933000652	38.00
Six-A.T.	8933000650	47.00
Rear pipe	8133106	35.00
1985-87-Eagle		
Front pipe		
M.T.	8933000652	38.00
A.T.	8933000650	47.00
Rear pipe	8133106	35.00
Catalytic Converter		
1983		
Concord, Spirit	8933000622	410.50
SX4 & Eagle		
151	3239096	398.75
151-Calif.	3240171	355.00
Six	8933000626	402.00
1984-87-Eagle	8933000626	402.00
Exhaust Manifold		
1983		
Four-151	8134697	116.50
Four-150	3242625	N.L.
Six	3237427	179.25
1984-87		
Four	3242625	N.L.
Six	3237427	179.25
Oxygen Sensor		
1983-87	●8933002455	35.00

LABOR 9 FRONT SUSPENSION 9 LABOR

Note: On all front suspension operations alignment charges must be added if performed. Time given does not include alignment.

	(Factory Time)	Chilton Time
(M) Wheel, Renew		
one	(.4)	.5
(G) Wheels, Balance		
one		.3
each adtnl.		.2
(G) Check Alignment of Front End		
All models	(.4)	.5
Note: Deduct if alignment is performed.		
(G) Toe-In, Adjust		
All models	(.4)	.6
(G) Align Front End		
Includes: Adjust front wheel bearings.		
All models	(1.2)	1.5
w/A.C. interference add		.5
(G) Front Wheel Bearings, Clean and Repack (Both Wheels)		
w/Disc brakes	(.9)	1.2
w/4 whl drive	(1.9)	2.3
(G) Front Wheel Bearings and Cups, Renew		
Includes: Repack bearings.		
With Disc Brakes		
one wheel	(.6)	.8
both wheels	(1.1)	1.4
With 4 Whl Drive		
one wheel	(1.1)	1.3
both wheels	(2.0)	2.5
(G) Front Wheel Grease Seals, Renew		
Includes: Repack bearings.		
With Disc Brakes		
one wheel	(.5)	.7
both wheels	(.9)	1.2
(G) Upper Ball Joint, Renew		
Add alignment charges.		
1983-87-one	(.6)	.9
both	(.9)	1.5
(G) Lower Control Arm, Renew (One)		
Add alignment charges.		
1983-87	(.9)	1.2
(G) Upper Control Arm, Renew (One)		
Add alignment charges.		
1983-87	(1.3)	1.6
(G) Lower Control Arm Bushings, Renew (One)		
Add alignment charges.		
1983-87	(.8)	1.1
(G) Upper Control Arm Bushings, Renew (One Side)		
Add alignment charges.		
1983-87	(1.5)	1.9
(G) Steering Knuckle Pin, Renew (One) (With Disc Brakes)		
Add alignment charges.		
Except Eagle		
1983	(1.1)	1.4
Eagle		
1983-87	(.8)	1.1
(G) Strut Rod, Renew		
Add alignment charges.		
1983-87-one	(.6)	.7

LABOR 9 FRONT SUSPENSION 9 LABOR

(Factory Time) — Chilton Time

both (.8) ... 1.1

(G) Strut Rod Bushings, Renew (One Side)
Add alignment charges.
1983-87 (.7) ... 1.0

(G) Stabilizer Bar Link Bushings, Renew
1983-87 (.4) 6

(G) Steering Knuckle Spindle, Renew
Add alignment charges.
1983-87 (.8) ... 1.2

(G) Front Coil Spring, Renew (One)
1983-87 (.8) ... 1.2

(G) Front Stabilizer Bar, Renew
1983-87 (.7) 9

(G) Control Arm Rubber Bumpers, Renew
1983-87-each (.2) 4

(G) Front Suspension Cross Member, Renew
Add alignment charges.
Except Eagle
1983 (1.1) ... 2.4
Eagle
1983-87 (2.3) ... 4.0

(G) Front Shock Absorbers, Renew
1983-87-one (.4) 5
both (.5) 8

(G) Rebuild Front Suspension
Includes: Disassemble, renew necessary parts, reassemble, lubricate and align front end.
1983-87
w/Disc brakes
one side (5.8) ... 6.8
both sides (8.9) ... 10.5

(G) Steering Knuckle, Renew
Add alignment charges.
1983-one side (1.2) ... 1.5
both sides (2.1) ... 2.7

(G) Lower Ball Joint, Renew
Add alignment charges.
1983-87-one (1.1) ... 1.4
both (1.8) ... 2.5

4 WHEEL DRIVE FRONT AXLE

(M) Front Differential, Drain & Refill
All models 8

(M) Front Axle Housing Cover and/or Gasket, Renew
1983-87 (1.1) ... 1.4

(G) Front Axle Half-Shaft, Renew
Eagle
1983-87-one (.5) 7
both (.8) ... 1.3

(G) Front Axle Half-Shaft U-Joint, Renew
Includes: R&R half-shaft.
Eagle
1983-87-one (.8) ... 1.3
both (1.5) ... 2.5

(G) Front Axle Outer Drive Shaft, R&R or Renew (w/Select Drive)
Eagle
1983-87-one (.8) ... 1.2
Renew shaft add (.2) 3
Renew brg add (.2) 3
Renew gear add (.2) 3
Renew seal add (.2) 3

(G) Axle Shifter Vacuum Motor Assy., R&R or Renew
Eagle
1983-87 (.6) 8
Renew motor add (.1) 2
Renew cover/gasket add (.2) 3
Renew shift fork add (.2) 3

(G) Mode Selector Vacuum Harness, Renew
Eagle
1983-87 (.6) 8

(G) Vacuum Check Valve, Renew
Eagle
1983-87 (.2) 3

(G) Steering Knuckle Oil Seal, Renew
Includes: R&R half-shaft.
1983-87-one (1.0) ... 1.4
both (1.8) ... 2.6

(G) Pinion Shaft Oil Seal and/or Yoke, Renew
Eagle
1983-87 (.9) ... 1.2

(G) Front Axle Shaft Inner Oil Seal, Renew
Includes: R&R differential case assy.
Eagle
1983-87 (3.8) ... 5.0

(P) Front Axle Differential Case Assy., Renew
Eagle
1983-87 (3.6) ... 4.8

(P) Front Differential Assy., R&R and Recondition
Includes: Disassemble, clean and inspect all parts. Check case run out, adjust side bearing preload, backlash, drive pinion depth and preload. Replace pinion oil seal, cover gasket and axle shaft inner oil seals. Road test.
Eagle
1983-87 (4.8) ... 7.2

(G) Front Axle Assembly, Renew
(As Supplied For Service)
Eagle
1983-87 (1.2) ... 2.0
Renew axle shaft brgs or seals, add (.3) 6

(G) Front Drive Shaft, Renew
Eagle
1983-87 (.4) 6

(G) Front Universal Joints, Renew
Includes: R&R driveshaft.
Eagle
1983-87-one (.6) 9
both (.7) ... 1.2

(G) Steering Knuckle Arm, Renew
Add alignment charges.
Eagle
1983-87-one (.6) 8
both (.9) ... 1.5
Renew knuckle pin add-each 2

(G) Front Hub and Bearing Assy., Renew
Eagle-Type II
1983-87-one (.8) ... 1.0
both (1.4) ... 2.0
Renew brgs and seals, add each side (.4) 5

PARTS 9 FRONT SUSPENSION 9 PARTS

	Part No.	Price
EAGLE		
(1) Knuckle Pin		
1983-87	3240900	168.50
(2) Seal Assy. (Inner)		
1983-87	3250733	1.75
(3) Steering Knuckle Arm (R.H.)		
1983-87	3235692	59.75
(4) Ball Joint (Lower Arm)		
Note: Included in Lower Arm Assembly.		
(5) Lower Control Arm (R.H.)		
1983-87	3238006	106.75
(6) Bushing (Lower)		
1983-87	3235246	4.25
(7) Skid Plate		
1983-87	3236927	51.25
(8) Lower Control Arm (L.H.)		
1983-87	3238007	106.75

EAGLE

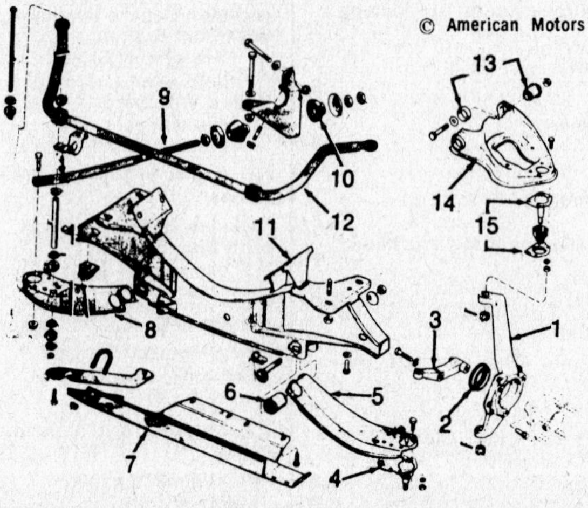

PARTS 9 FRONT SUSPENSION 9 PARTS

	Part No.	Price
(9) Strut Rod		
1983-87	3235664	20.00
(10) Bushing Kit (Strut Rod)		
1983-87	3234707	12.50
(11) Crossmember		
1983-87-exc. Four	3235515	248.75
Four		
151	3239263	248.75
150	3242710	152.00
(12) Stabilizer		
1983-87	3237045	46.00
(13) Bushing Kit (Upper)		
1983-87	8123074	16.75
(14) Upper Control Arm (R.H.)		
1983-87	3251320	103.25
(15) Ball Joint (Upper)		
1983-87	8130792	28.75

PARTS 9 FRONT SUSPENSION 9 PARTS

SPIRIT & CONCORD

	Part No.	Price
Front Wheel Bearing		
1983 (exc Bendix)		
inner	3141139	8.25
outer	3141140	6.75
Front Wheel Seal		
1983	3173532	5.50
Steering Knuckle		
1983	3233630	85.00
(1) Coil Spring Seat (Lower)		
1983	3234610	30.75
(2) Upper Control Arm (R.H.)		
1983	3251320	103.25
(3) Ball Joint Kit (Upper)		
1983	8130792	28.75
(4) Upper Bushing Kit		
1983	8123074	16.75
(5) Retainer		
1983	3197845	.75
(6) Knuckle Pin		
1983	3213951	59.75
(7) Shock Absorber		
1983	8133028	27.25
(8) Coil Spring		
Note: Order by model & description.		
(9) Coil Spring Cushion (Upper)		
1983	3210133	2.75
(10) Lower Control Arm		
1983	3222626	87.75
(11) Bumper		
1983-exc below	3196498	4.25
AMX	3229311	4.25
Four cyl	3229311	4.25
(12) Bushing		
1983	3227823	11.75
(13) Crossmember		
1983	3235057	115.00
1983-Six	8131803	108.50
(14) Ball Joint Kit (Lower)		
1983	8121427	28.75

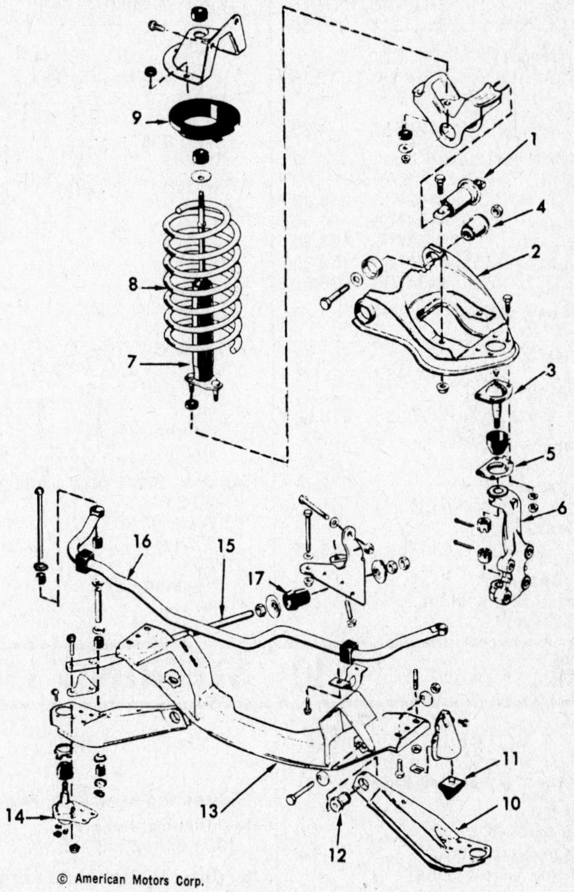

© American Motors Corp.

	Part No.	Price
(15) Strut Rod		
1983-right	3241838	35.00
left	3241839	20.00
(16) Stabilizer		
1983	3234612	47.50
Bushing Kit (Strut)		
1983	3234707	12.50
(17) Stabilizer Bushing		
1983	3163485	.25

PARTS 9 FRONT DRIVE AXLE 9 PARTS

4 WHEEL DRIVE FRONT AXLE

	Part No.	Price
(1) Yoke (Propeller Shaft)		
1983-87-exc below	8133525	74.00
Six cyl.	●8133241	33.50
(2) Oil Seal		
1983-87	●998092	2.25
(3) Oil Slinger (Outer)		
1983-87	●636566	.75
(4) Bearing Kit (Outer)		
1983-87	●8124052	29.50
(5) Shim Set		
1983-87	8130759	11.25
(6) Oil Baffle		
1983-87	934937	1.00
(7) Shim Set		
1983-87	8130759	11.25
(8) Bearing Kit (Inner)		
1983-87	●3156066	18.50
(9) Oil Slinger (Inner)		
1983-87	●916372	1.00
(10) Bearing (Side)		
1983-87	●8126500	33.50
(11) Pinion & Ring Gear Set		
1983-87		
3.54:1 ratio	●8126518	379.75

PARTS 9 FRONT AXLE (4 WHEEL DRIVE) 9 PARTS

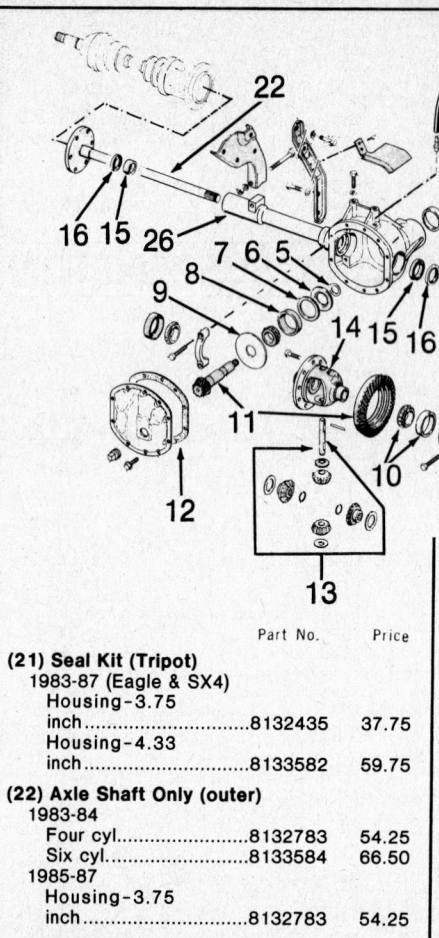

	Part No.	Price
3.07:1 ratio	8130754	409.00
2.73:1 ratio	●8133063	393.00
2.35:1 ratio	8134029	383.25
(12) Cover Gasket		
1983-87	8120360	N.L.
(13) Gear Set (Side & Pinion)		
1983-87	8133721	105.00
(14) Carrier Case Assy.		
1983-87		
2.35:1 ratio	8133720	234.75
exc 2.35:1 ratio	8134324	230.50
(15) Bearing (Needle)		
1983-87	8134586	16.75
(16) Oil Seal		
1983-87	8134587	4.25
(17) Axle Shaft (Inner)		
1983-84		
Right Kit	8133610	214.25
Left hub	8134585	96.50
Left Kit	8133606	169.75
1984-87-right	8130751	152.25
left	8134585	96.50
(18) Housing Assy. (Tripot)		
1983-87		
Housing-3.75 inch	8132437	136.75
Housing-4.33 inch	8133583	213.50
(19) Spider Assy.		
1983-87		
Housing-3.75 inch	8132434	67.00
Housing-4.33 inch	8133581	95.25
(20) Retainer (Seal Kit)		
1983-87-part of (21) seal kit		

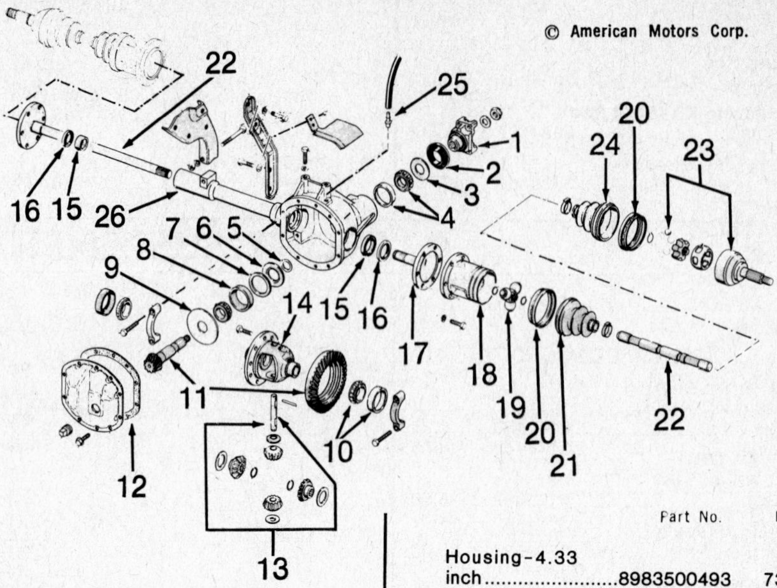

	Part No.	Price
(21) Seal Kit (Tripot)		
1983-87 (Eagle & SX4)		
Housing-3.75 inch	8132435	37.75
Housing-4.33 inch	8133582	59.75
(22) Axle Shaft Only (outer)		
1983-84		
Four cyl	8132783	54.25
Six cyl	8133584	66.50
1985-87		
Housing-3.75 inch	8132783	54.25

	Part No.	Price
Housing-4.33 inch	8983500493	73.50
CV housing-3.375	8983500494	70.25
(23) Joint Assy. (Constant Velocity)		
1983	8132441	209.50
1984-87	8983500497	215.50
(24) Seal Kit (Constant Velocity)		
Housing-3.75 inch	8983500976	19.76
Housing-4.35 inch	8983500495	18.00
(25) Vent Fitting		
1983-87	5353495	5.75
(26) Axle Housing (w/Tube)		
1983-84	8134566	577.50
1985-87	8983501545	N.L.

LABOR 10 STEERING LINKAGE 10 LABOR

(Factory Time)	Chilton Time
(G) Tie Rod or Tie Rod Ends, Renew	
Includes: Reset toe-in.	
1983-87-one side (.8)	1.0
both sides (1.1)	1.8
(G) Steering Arm, Renew (One)	
Add alignment charges.	
1983-87 (1.1)	1.6
(G) Steering Idler Arm, Renew	
Add alignment charges.	
1983-87 (.4)	.7
(G) Center Cross Link, Renew	
Includes: Reset toe-in.	
1983-87 (.7)	1.3
(G) Pitman Arm, Renew	
1983-87 (.7)	1.0
(G) Steering Damper, Renew	
1983-87 (.3)	.5

PARTS 10 STEERING LINKAGE 10 PARTS

	Part No.	Price
SPIRIT & CONCORD		
(1) Idler Arm Assy.		
1983	3241837	46.50
(2) Steering Knuckle Arm (R)		
1983	3240906	36.25
(3) Tie Rod		
1983	3209636	26.25
(4) Tie Rod End		
1983	3215775	18.75
(5) Pitman Arm		
1983-wo/P.S.	3231636	50.00
w/P.S.	3231635	37.25

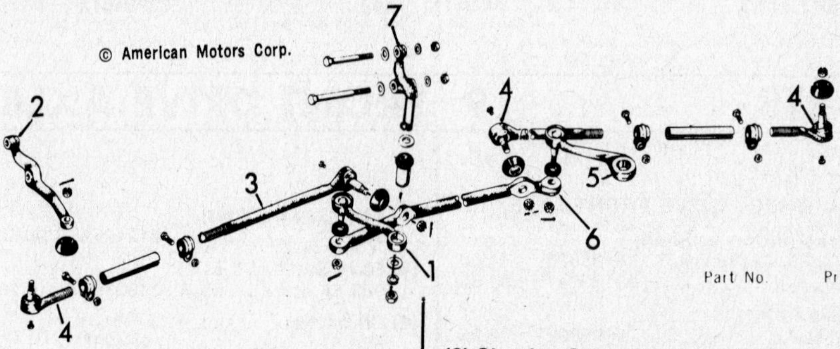

	Part No.	Price
(6) Steering Cross Tube		
1983-exc below	3204739	53.75
Four	3229266	53.75

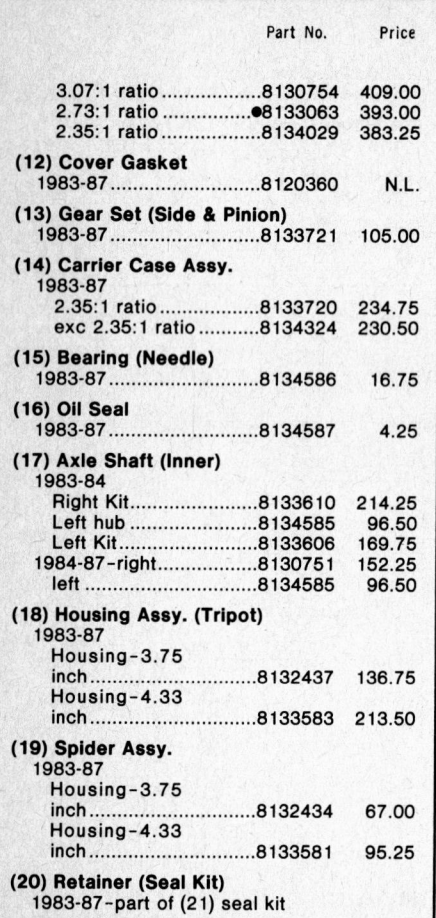

PARTS 10 STEERING LINKAGE 10 PARTS

	Part No.	Price
EAGLE		
(1) Spacer (Idler Arm)		
1983-87-exc. Four	3235505	22.50
Four		
150	3242721	22.50
151	3235505	22.50
(2) Idler Arm		
1983-87	3241837	46.50
(3) Seal		
1983-87	3204741	2.25
(4) Dust Cover (Tie Rod End)		
1983-87	3204742	3.75
(5) Inner Tie Rod End Assy.		
1983-87	3235507	34.50
(6) Tube Assy. (Adjusting)		
1983-87	3204745	15.00
(7) Outer Tie Rod End Assy.		
1983-87	3235661	34.50
(8) Center Cross Link		
1983-87	3235024	98.00

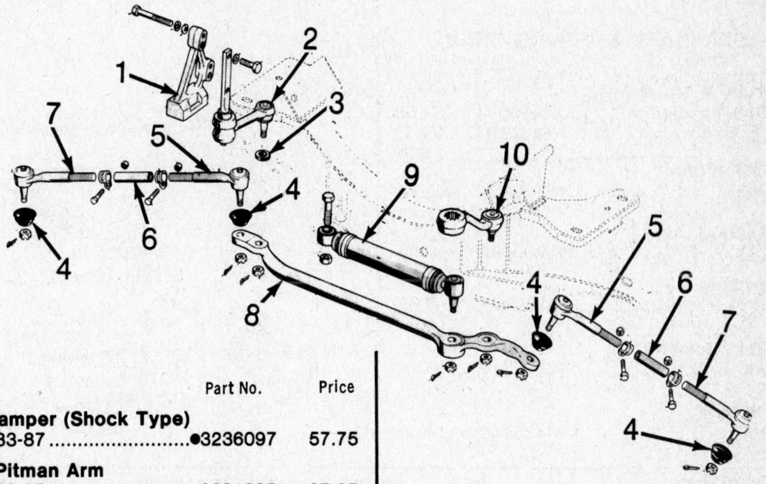

	Part No.	Price
(9) Damper (Shock Type)		
1983-87	●3236097	57.75
(10) Pitman Arm		
1983-87	3231635	37.25

LABOR 11 STEERING GEAR 11 LABOR

	(Factory Time)	Chilton Time
STANDARD STEERING		
(G) Horn Contact, Renew		
1983-87		
center horn	(.2)	.4
spoke horn	(.3)	.5
(G) Steering Wheel, Renew		
1983-87		
w/Center horn	(.5)	.7
w/Spoke contact	(.3)	.6
(G) Steering Gear, Adjust (On Car)		
1983-87	(.3)	.5
(G) Steering Gear Assembly, Renew		
Concord-Spirit-AMX		
1983	(1.1)	1.6
Eagle		
1983-87	(.9)	1.5
(G) Steering Gear Assy., R&R and Recondition		
Includes: Disassembly, renew necessary parts, reassemble and adjust.		
Concord-Spirit-AMX		
1983	(1.7)	2.5
Eagle		
1983-87	(2.1)	3.0
(G) Pitman Shaft Seal, Renew		
1983-87	(1.0)	1.5
(G) Steering Column, Renew		
1983-87	(1.0)	1.7
(G) Steering Column, R&R and Recondition		
1983-87		
w/Trans lock	(1.6)	2.3
less trans lock	(1.1)	2.0
(G) Shift Tube, Renew		
Includes: R&R steering column.		
1983-87	(1.0)	1.6
(G) Shift Bowl or Housing, Renew		
Includes: R&R steering column.		
1983-87		
w/Trans lock	(1.4)	2.0
less trans lock	(1.1)	1.7
(G) Steering Jacket Tube, Renew		
1983-87		
w/Trans lock	(1.3)	1.9
less trans lock	(1.0)	1.6
POWER STEERING		
(G) Power Steering Oil Pressure Check and Diagnosis		
1983-87	(.2)	.5
(G) Power Steering Gear, Adjust		
Includes: R&R pitman arm, perform pitman shaft overcenter adjustment.		
1983-87	(.4)	.8
(M) Power Steering Pump Drive Belt, Renew		
1983-87	(.3)	.4
w/Air guard or A.C. add	(.1)	.1
(G) Power Steering Gear, Renew		
Concord-Spirit-AMX-Eagle		
1983-87	(.9)	1.6
(P) Power Steering Gear, R&R and Recondition		
Includes: Complete disassembly and assembly, perform all adjustments.		
Concord-Spirit-AMX-Eagle		
1983-87	(2.1)	3.0
(G) Adjustor Plug, Renew		
Includes: R&R gear assy.		
Concord-Spirit-AMX-Eagle		
1983-87	(1.2)	1.9
(G) Valve Body Assembly, Renew		
Includes: R&R gear assy.		
Concord-Spirit-AMX-Eagle		
1983-87	(1.4)	2.2
(G) Power Steering Pump, Renew		
1983-87	(.9)	1.4
(G) Power Steering Pump, R&R and Recondition		
1983-87	(1.6)	1.9
(G) Pump Driveshaft Oil Seal, Renew		
Includes: R&R pump.		
1983-87	(1.0)	1.5
(G) Pump Reservoir and/or 'O' Rings, Renew		
Includes: R&R pump.		
1983-87	(1.1)	1.6
(G) Pump Flow Control Valve, Renew		
1983-87	(.4)	.7
(M) Power Steering Hoses, Renew		
1983-87-one	(.3)	.5
both	(.5)	.7
TILT STEERING COLUMN		
(G) Tilt Steering Column, Renew		
1983-87	(1.0)	1.8
(G) Tilt Column, R&R and Recondition		
1983-87	(2.0)	2.7
(G) Steering Shaft, Renew		
Includes: R&R column.		
1983-87	(1.3)	1.7
(G) Shift Tube, Renew		
Includes: R&R column.		
1983-87	(.7)	2.0
(G) Shift Bowl or Housing, Renew		
Includes: R&R column.		
1983-87	(1.5)	2.4
(G) Steering Jacket Tube, Renew		
Includes: R&R column.		
1983-87	(1.6)	2.2

PARTS 11 STEERING GEAR - (STANDARD) 11 PARTS

	Part No.	Price
STANDARD STEERING GEAR		
(1) Tube & Worm Assy.		
1983-exc below	4489094	94.50
Four cyl	4487881	94.50
(2) Pinion Shaft		
1983	●8120221	55.75
(3) Bearing Cup		
1983	●3200492	9.00
(4) Bearing		
1983	●3200491	6.25
(5) Gear Housing		
1983	●8130319	123.75
(6) Oil Seal		
1983	4486140	4.00

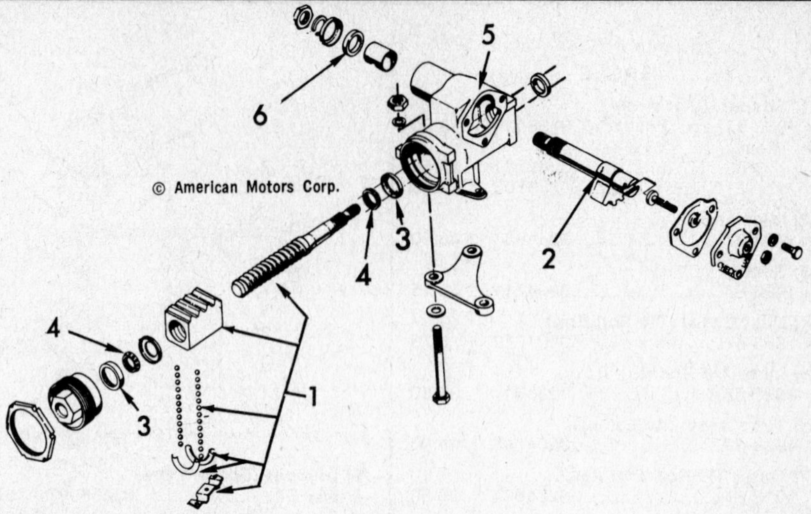

PARTS 11 POWER STEERING GEAR 11 PARTS

	Part No.	Price
Seal and Ring Kit (Gear Valve)		
1983-87	●3204833	13.00
Check Valve Kit		
1983-87	8132538	4.00
Adjuster Seal Kit (Upper Thrust Bearing)		
1983-87	●8130157	8.50
(1) Pitman Shaft		
1983-87	8122819	72.75
(2) Guide		
1983-87	●4487887	2.25
(3) Ball Kit		
1983-87	●3204836	13.50
(4) Retaining Ring		
Refer to Seal and Ring Kit.		
(5) Seal Kit (Piston)		
1983-87	8125039	12.65
(6) Rack Piston Assy.		
1983-87	8130156	130.25
(7) Shaft Bearing		
1983-87	●4487154	16.75
(8) Pitman Shaft Seal Kit		
1983-87	●8134568	15.25
(9) Housing Assy.		
1983-87-exc. Eagle	●8132540	196.50
Eagle & SX4	8134567	194.50

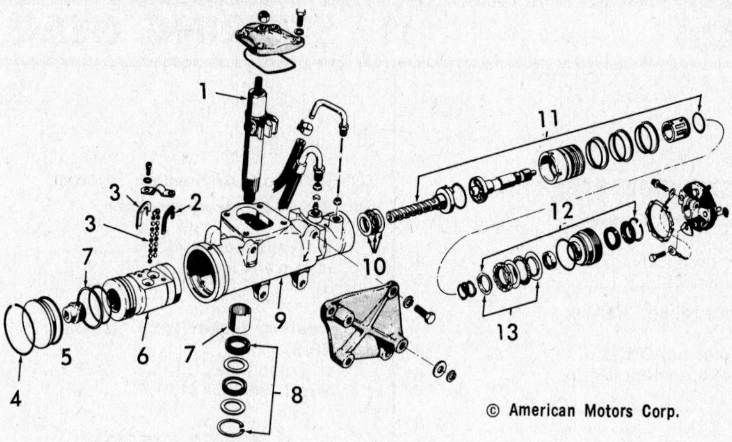

	Part No.	Price
(10) Bearing Kit		
1983-87	●8127645	11.50
(11) Valve Assy.		
1983-87-exc Rally susp	8130144	172.75
Rally susp	●8130146	172.75

	Part No.	Price
(12) Adjuster Assy.		
1983-87	●8130155	54.00
(13) Bearing Kit (Adjuster)		
1983-87	●8130152	11.75

PARTS 11 POWER STEERING PUMP 11 PARTS

	Part No.	Price
Pump Assembly		
Four		
1983-87-exc Eagle & SX4	●3251017	217.50
Eagle & SX4		
151	●3237193	225.25
150	●8953000092	124.00
Six		
1983-87-exc Eagle & SX4	●3251017	217.50
Eagle & SX4	●3237193	225.25
(1) Power Steering Hose (Pressure)		
Four		
1983-87		
151	3236918	24.50
150	3242726	22.50

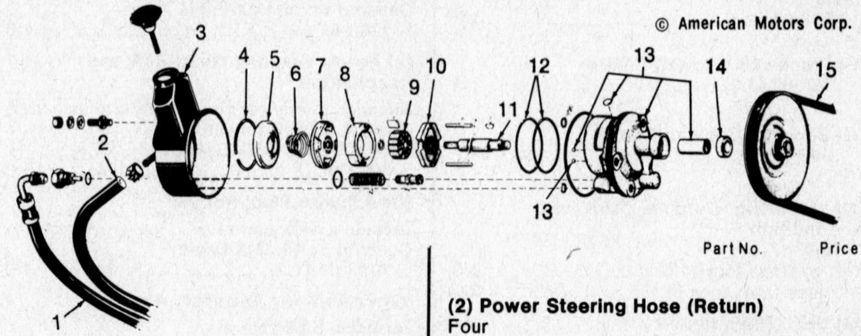

	Part No.	Price
Six		
1983-87	3251236	21.75

	Part No.	Price
(2) Power Steering Hose (Return)		
Four		
151	3236919	6.75
150	3242725	6.50

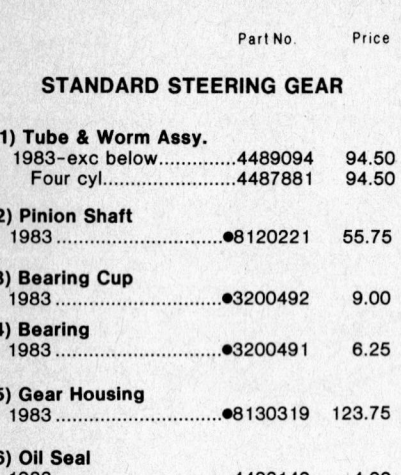

PARTS 11 POWER STEERING PUMP 11 PARTS

	Part No.	Price
Six		
1983	3236919	6.75
1984-87	3251242	6.50
(3) Reservoir Assy.		
1983-87-exc. 150	●8127369	60.00
150	●8983500244	92.75
(4) Retaining Ring (End Plate)		
1983-87	3209664	1.50
(5) End Plate		
1983-87	●3209661	3.50
(6) Spring (Pressure Plate)		
1983-87	●8133958	.75
(7) Plate Pressure		
1983-87	●8133957	16.25
(8) Ring		
1983-87	●8127365	31.25
(9) Rotor, Vane Kit		
1983-87	●8133829	98.75
(10) Plate (Thrust)		
1983-87	8121412	14.75
(11) Drive Shaft Kit		
1983-87	●8133828	39.00
(12) Seal Kit		
1983-87	●3209678	12.50
(13) Pump Body		
1983-87	●8132473	66.25
(14) Seal (Drive Shaft)		
1983-87	●4488330	4.50

(15) Power Steering Belt
Order by model and description.

LABOR 12 CYLINDER HEAD & VALVE SYSTEM 12 LABOR

(Factory Time)	Chilton Time
(G) Compression Test	
Four-1983-87 (.3)	.6
Six-1983-87 (.4)	.7
(G) Cylinder Head Gasket, Renew	
Includes: Clean carbon.	
Four-1983-87	
150 eng. (3.8)	5.5
151 eng. (2.4)	3.3
Six	
1983-87 (3.9)	*5.6
w/P.S. add (.3)	.3
w/A.C. add (.6)	.6
w/Air guard add (1.0)	1.0

*Lower front crossmember add appropriate time.

(Factory Time)	Chilton Time
(G) Cylinder Head, Renew	
Includes: Transfer parts not supplied with replacement head. Clean carbon from cylinder block.	
Four-1983-87	
150 eng. (4.2)	6.0
151 eng. (2.8)	4.0
Six	
1983-87 (4.2)	*6.0
w/P.S. add (.3)	.3
w/A.C. add (.6)	.6
w/Air guard add (1.0)	1.0

*Lower front crossmember add appropriate time.

(Factory Time)	Chilton Time
(P) Clean Carbon and Grind Valves	
Includes: R&R cylinder head(s), recondition seats, reface valves, replace valve stem oil seals. Minor engine tune-up.	
Four-1983-87	
150 eng. (4.9)	6.8
151 eng. (4.4)	6.4
Six	
1983-87 (5.2)	*9.5
w/P.S. add (.3)	.3
w/A.C. add (.6)	.6

COMBINATIONS

Add to Valve Job

See Machine Shop Operations

(Factory Time)	Chilton Time
(G) DRAIN, EVACUATE & RECHARGE AIR CONDITIONING SYSTEM	
All models (.9)	1.0
(G) ROCKER ARMS, PUSH RODS AND/OR PIVOTS, CLEAN OR RENEW	
Four (.1)	.4
Six (.6)	.8
(G) HYDRAULIC VALVE LIFTERS, DISASSEMBLE AND CLEAN	
Each	.2
(G) DISTRIBUTOR, RECONDITION	
All models (.8)	1.2
(G) CARBURETOR, RECONDITION	
1 BBL (1.3)	1.3
2 BBL (1.5)	1.5
(P) VALVE GUIDES, REAM OVERSIZE	
Each (.1)	.2
(P) RECONDITION CYL. HEAD (HEAD REMOVED)	
Four	
151 eng	2.0
Six	3.0

(Factory Time)	Chilton Time
w/Air guard add (1.0)	1.0

*Lower front crossmember add appropriate time.

(Factory Time)	Chilton Time
(G) Valve Springs or Valve Stem Oil Seals, Renew (Head on Car)	
Four-1983-87-151 eng.	
one cyl (.9)	1.0
all cyls (1.5)	1.9
150 eng.	
one cyl. (1.2)	1.7
all cyls. (1.8)	2.6
Six	
1983-87-one cyl (1.7)	*2.2
all cyls (2.5)	*3.7

*Lower front crossmember add appropriate time.

(Factory Time)	Chilton Time
(G) Cylinder Head Cover Gasket, Renew or Reseal	
Four-1983-87	
150 eng. (1.0)	1.4
151 eng. (.7)	1.0
(G) Rocker Arm Cover Gaskets, Renew or Reseal	
Six	
1983-87 (1.5)	*1.8

*Lower front crossmember add appropriate time.

(Factory Time)	Chilton Time
(G) Valve Tappets, Renew (All)	
Includes: R&R cylinder head on 6 cylinder models.	
Four-1983-87	
150 eng. (1.2)	1.8
151 eng. (1.9)	2.7
Six	
1983-87 (3.8)	*5.5
w/A.C. add (.3)	.3
w/P.S. add (.4)	.4
w/Air guard add (.2)	.2

*Lower front crossmember add appropriate time.

(Factory Time)	Chilton Time
(G) Rocker Arm, Push Rod and/or Pivot, Renew	
Four-1983-87-all (1.9)	2.5
Six	
1983-87-one cyl (1.5)	*2.0
each adtnl cyl	.1

*Lower front crossmember add appropriate time.

PARTS 12 CYLINDER HEAD & VALVE SYSTEM 12 PARTS

FOUR-151

	Part No.	Price
Valve Grind Gasket Set		
1983	●8134689	57.75
(1) Cylinder Head		
1983	●8133706	401.00
(2) Cylinder Head Gasket		
1983	●8133701	12.25
(3) Valve Cover Gasket		
1983	●8132811	7.50
sealant	●8993317	4.75

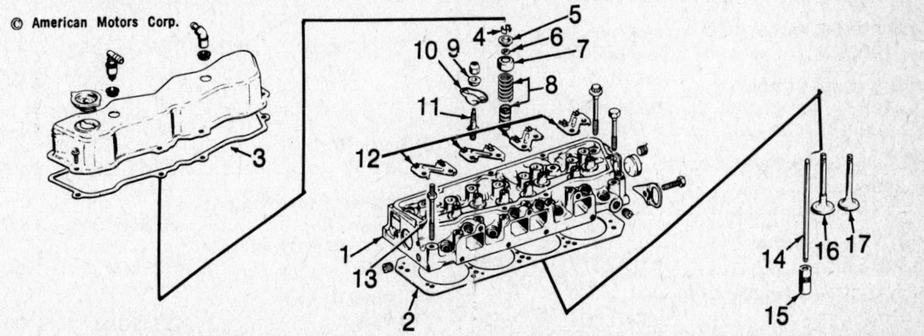

PARTS 12 CYLINDER HEAD & VALVE SYSTEM 12 PARTS

	Part No.	Price
(4) Valve Lock		
1983	●8132931	1.00
(5) Spring Retainer (Valve)		
1983	●8132231	1.00
(6) Seal (Valve Stem)		
1983	8132233	.75
(7) Shield (Valve Stem Oil)		
1983	8132234	.75
(8) Spring (Valve)		
1983	●8132232	3.75
(9) Ball (Rocker Arm)		
1983	8132771	.75
(10) Rocker Arm		
1983	●8132770	8.25
(11) Stud (Rocker Arm)		
1983	8132240	2.65
(12) Guide (Valve Push Rod)		
1983		
No. 1	8132773	1.00
No. 2	8132774	1.00
No. 3	8132775	1.00
No. 4	8132776	1.00
(13) Bolt (Cylinder Block)		
1983 (exc Calif.)		
M11 x 1.5 x 70	8132209	2.00
M11 x 1.5 x 100	8133671	3.25
1983 (California)		
M11 x 1.5 x 72	8132208	2.00
(14) Push Rod		
1983	●8134133	3.00
(15) Tappet (Valve)		
1983	8136656	7.75
(16) Intake Valve		
1983	●8134389	17.50
(17) Exhaust Valve		
1983	●8134392	30.00

PARTS 12 CYLINDER HEAD & VALVE SYSTEM 12 PARTS

SIX-258

	Part No.	Price
Valve Grind Gasket Set		
1983-85	●8133352	35.50
1986-87	●8983502384	15.00
(1) Cylinder Head (less valves)		
1983-85	8983501395	376.25
1986-87	●8983502372	267.50

Order head by description-number and type of rocker cover attachments.

	Part No.	Price
(2) Cylinder Head Gasket		
1983-85	●3237756	10.00
1986-87	●3228469	14.50
(3) Rocker Arm Cover Gasket		
1983-87-sealant	●8993317	4.75
(4) Intake Valve		
1983-87	3240768	10.25
(5) Exhaust Valve		
1983-87	3240767	11.75
(6) Valve Spring		
1983-87	●3228192	6.00
(7) Valve Keys		
1983-87	●3180458	.75
(8) Rocker Arm		
1983-87	●3242393	2.00
(9) Valve Push Rods		
1983-87	●3242395	2.75

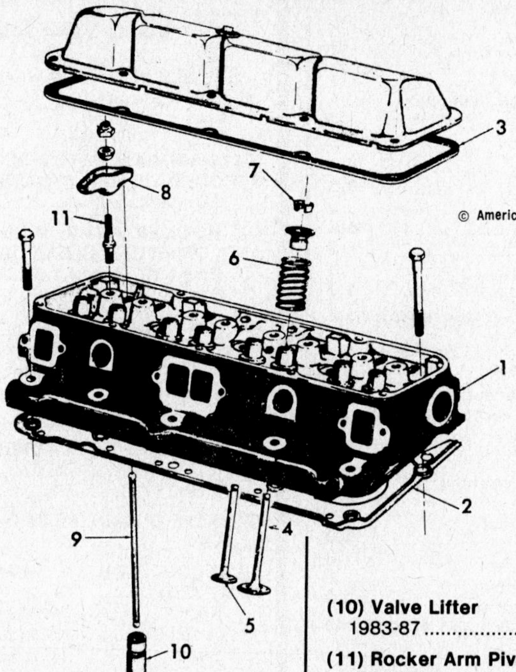

© American Motors Corp.

	Part No.	Price
(10) Valve Lifter		
1983-87	●3189883	9.00
(11) Rocker Arm Pivot		
1983-87	●3235090	1.50

PARTS 12 CYLINDER HEAD & VALVE SYSTEM 12 PARTS

	Part No.	Price
Valve Grind Gasket Set		
1983-87	●8983500255	16.75
(1) Cylinder Head		
1983	●8983500254	258.75
1984-87	●8983500675	265.75
(2) Cylinder Head Gasket		
1983-87	●3241649	3.25
(3) Intake Valve		
1983-87	●3242659	7.75
(4) Exhaust Valve		
1983	●3242660	17.50
1984-87	●3242896	15.50
(5) Oil Deflector (Exhaust)		
1983	3242864	.75
1984-87	3242864	.75
(6) Valve Spring		
1983-87	●3242678	3.75
(7) Retainer (Valve Spring)		
1983-87	●3242661	1.50

FOUR-150

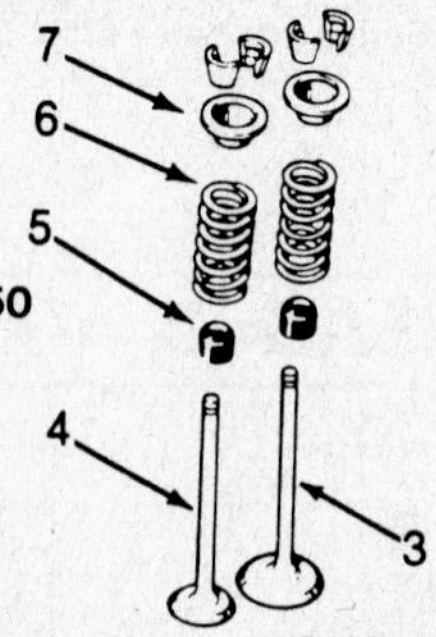

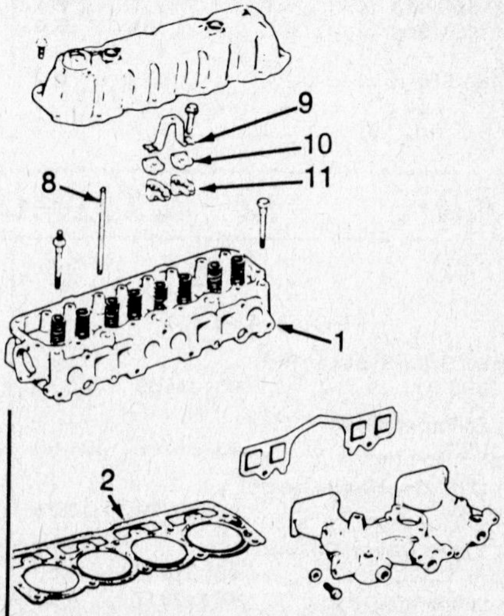

	Part No.	Price
(8) Push Rod		
1983-87	●3241709	3.25
(9) Rocker Arm Bridge		
1983-87	3236513	1.50
(10) Rocker Arm Pivot		
1983-87	●3235090	1.50
(11) Rocker Arm		
1983-87	●3242393	2.00

LABOR 13 ENGINE ASSEMBLY & MOUNTS 13 LABOR

(Factory Time) Chilton Time

(G) Engine Assembly, Remove and Install

Does not include transfer of any parts of equipment.

Four–1983-87	
Concord-Spirit (2.7)	5.0
Eagle	
150 eng. (5.9)	8.5
151 eng. (3.4)	5.7
Six–except Eagle	
1983 (3.3)	6.3
Eagle	
1983-87 (3.7)	5.8
w/A.C. add (.6)	.6
w/P.S. add (.4)	.4
w/Air guard add (.6)	.6

(P) Short Engine Assembly, Renew

Consists of: Cylinder block, pistons and rod assemblies, crankshaft, camshaft, timing gear and chain. Does not include cylinder heads.

Includes: R&R engine, transfer of component parts, clean carbon, grind valves. Minor engine tune-up.

Four–1983-87	
150 eng. (9.6)	14.4
151 eng. (10.0)	15.0
Six–except Eagle	
1983 (10.2)	15.5
Eagle	
1983-87 (10.2)	15.5
w/A.C. add (.6)	.6
w/P.S. add (.4)	.4
w/Air guard add (.6)	.6

(P) Engine Assy., R&R and Recondition

Includes: Rebore block, install new pistons, rings, pins, rod and main bearings. Clean carbon, grind valves. Tune engine.

Four–1983-87	
150 eng. (15.0)	21.7
151 eng. (17.6)	23.5
Six–except Eagle	
1983 (20.0)	32.5
Eagle	
1983-87 (23.3)	33.0
w/A.C. add (.6)	.6
w/P.S. add (.4)	.4
w/Air guard add (.6)	.6

(P) Engine Assembly, Recondition (In Car)

Includes: Renew pistons, rings, rod and main bearings. Clean carbon, grind valves. Tune engine.

Four–1983-87	
150 eng. (11.0)	17.0
151 eng. (9.4)	16.0
Six–except Eagle	
1983 (17.8)	25.5
Eagle	
1983-87 (16.2)	26.0
w/A.C. add (.3)	.3
w/P.S. add (.4)	.4
w/Air guard add (1.0)	1.0

(G) Engine Mounts, Renew

Front	
Four–1983-87–exc below (.2)	.5
Concord-Spirit	
1983–one (.4)	.6
both (.7)	1.0
Eagle	
1983-87–one (.8)	1.0
both (1.3)	1.8
Six	
1983-87–one (.5)	.7
both (.7)	1.1
Rear	
Four–1983-87	
one (.4)	.6
both (.5)	.9
Six	
1983-87 (.4)	.6

(G) Crankshaft, R&R or Renew (Engine Out)

Four–1983-87 (2.1)	3.0
Six–1983-87 (2.2)	3.0

PARTS 13 ENGINE ASSEMBLY & MOUNTS 13 PARTS

Short Block Assy.

Fitted Pistons, Pins, Rings, Rods, Crankshaft & Bearings. Camshaft & Bearings, Timing Gears & Chain. Valve Lifters on Six OHV.

	Part No.	Price
Four		
1983		
151	●8133990	1541.25
150	●8983500245	1407.50
1984-87		
150	●8983500245	1407.50
Six		
1983-85	●8134599	1575.50
1986-87	●8983502299	1551.25

Cylinder Block (Less Pistons, Rings & Bearings)

	Part No.	Price
1983		
151	●8133991	1089.50
150	●8983500246	726.50
1984-87		
150	●8983500246	726.50
1983-85–Six	●8133837	857.75
1986-87–Six	8983502298	570.75

Gasket Set (Engine Lower)

	Part No.	Price
1983-87–Six	●8133353	41.75
1983-87–Four		
151	●8134688	25.50
150	●8983500256	21.25

Eng. Supt. Cushion (Front)

	Part No.	Price
Four		
1983–151		
exc Eagle	3251154	18.75
Eagle & SX4	3236980	18.75
1983-87–150		
right	●3242711	17.25
left	3242728	18.75
Six		
1983-87–exc Eagle	●8128488	18.25
Eagle & SX4	3236865	18.75

Eng. Supt. Cushion (Rear)

	Part No.	Price
Four		
1983-87	3239286	38.75
Six		
1983-87–exc Eagle	3224935	23.50
1983-87–Eagle & SX4		
M.T.	●3238013	25.25
A.T.	3236067	18.25

LABOR 14 PISTONS, RINGS & BEARINGS 14 LABOR

(Factory Time) Chilton Time

(P) Rings, Renew (See Engine Combinations)

Includes: Remove cylinder top ridge, deglaze cylinder walls, clean carbon. Minor tune-up.

Four–1983-87	
150 eng. (6.9)	10.0
151 eng. (6.2)	8.1
Six–except Eagle	
1983 (6.4)	9.9
Eagle	
1983-87 (7.2)	10.7
w/P.S. add (.3)	.3
w/A.C. add (.6)	.6
w/Air guard add (1.0)	1.0

(P) Piston or Connecting Rod, Renew

Includes: Remove cylinder top ridge, deglaze cylinder walls, replace connecting rod bearings, install new rings. Minor tune-up.

Four–1983-87	
150 eng.–one (6.4)	9.2
all (8.6)	12.0
151 eng.–one (5.5)	6.9
all (5.9)	9.0
Six–except Eagle	
1983–one (4.9)	7.1
all (6.0)	9.6
Eagle	
1983-87–one (6.6)	10.0
all (7.3)	12.5
w/P.S. add (.3)	.3
w/A.C. add (.6)	.6
w/Air guard add (1.0)	1.0

(P) Connecting Rod Bearings, Renew

Includes: Plastigauge all bearings.

Four	
Concord-Spirit	
1983 (2.4)	3.2
Eagle	
1983-87	
150 eng. (3.0)	4.4
151 eng. (2.7)	4.0
Six–except Eagle	
1983 (3.1)	5.4
Eagle	
1983-87 (5.3)	7.2

LABOR 14 PISTONS, RINGS & BEARINGS 14 LABOR

COMBINATIONS

Add to Engine Work

See Machine Shop Operations

(Factory Time)	Chilton Time
(G) DRAIN, EVACUATE & RECHARGE AIR CONDITIONING SYSTEM	
All models (.9)	1.0
(G) ROCKER ARM, PUSH ROD AND/OR PIVOT, CLEAN OR RENEW	
Four (.1)	.4
Six (.6)	.8
(G) HYDRAULIC VALVE LIFTERS, DISASSEMBLE & CLEAN	
Each	.2
(G) DISTRIBUTOR, RECONDITION	
All models (.8)	1.2
(G) CARBURETOR, RECONDITION	
1 BBL (1.3)	1.3
2 BBL (1.5)	1.5
(G) DEGLAZE CYLINDER WALLS	
Four (.2)	.4
Six (.9)	1.3
(G) REMOVE CYLINDER TOP RIDGE	
Each (.1)	.1
(G) TIMING CHAIN, RENEW (COVER REMOVED)	
All models (.4)	.5
(G) MAIN BEARINGS, RENEW (PAN REMOVED)	
Four (.7)	1.2
Six (.9)	1.5
(G) PLASTIGAUGE BEARINGS	
Each (.1)	.1
(G) OIL PUMP, RECONDITION	
Four (1.0)	1.4
Six (.2)	.4
(M) OIL FILTER ELEMENT, RENEW	
All models (.3)	.3

PARTS 14 PISTONS, RINGS & BEARINGS 14 PARTS

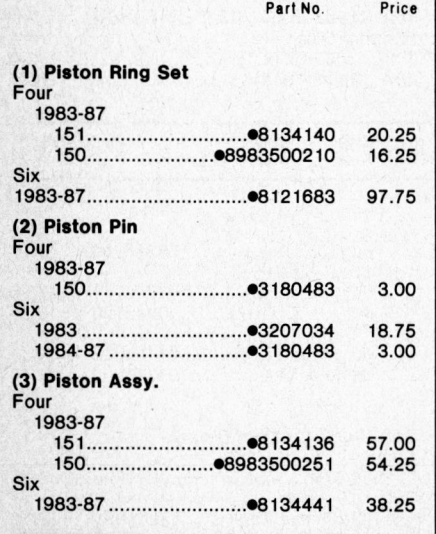

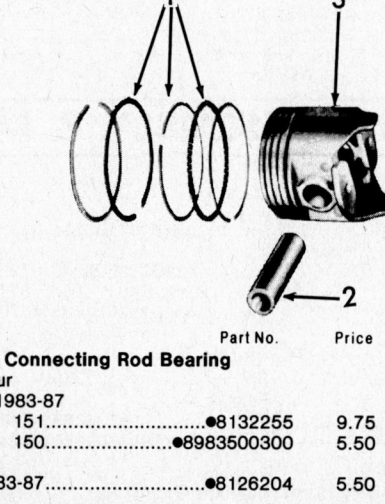

	Part No.	Price
(1) Piston Ring Set		
Four		
1983-87		
151	●8134140	20.25
150	●8983500210	16.25
Six		
1983-87	●8121683	97.75
(2) Piston Pin		
Four		
1983-87		
150	●3180483	3.00
Six		
1983	●3207034	18.75
1984-87	●3180483	3.00
(3) Piston Assy.		
Four		
1983-87		
151	●8134136	57.00
150	●8983500251	54.25
Six		
1983-87	●8134441	38.25

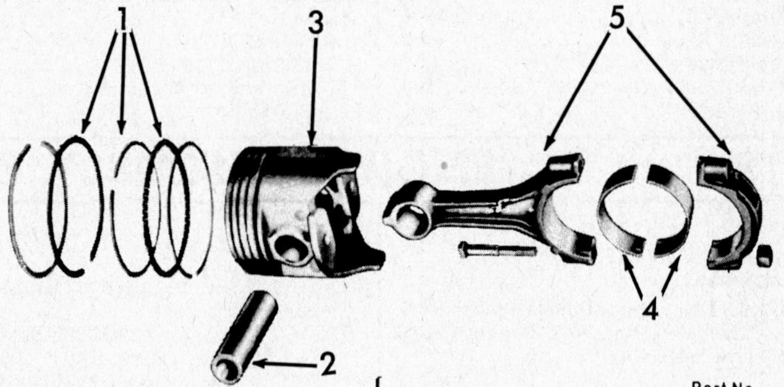

	Part No.	Price
(4) Connecting Rod Bearing		
Four		
1983-87		
151	●8132255	9.75
150	●8983500300	5.50
Six		
1983-87	●8126204	5.50
(5) Connecting Rod Assy.		
Four		
1983-87		
151	●8132253	55.75
150	●3237816	37.25
Six		
1983	3180444	36.50
1984-87	●3237812	43.25

LABOR 15 CRANKSHAFT & DAMPER 15 LABOR

(Factory Time)	Chilton Time
(P) Crankshaft and Main Bearings, Renew	
Includes: R&R engine, replace rear main bearing oil seal.	
Four–1983-87	
Concord-Spirit (4.8)	9.0
Eagle	
150 eng. (7.9)	11.5
151 eng. (5.5)	9.7
Six–except Eagle	
1983 (5.9)	10.0
Eagle	
1983-87 (6.3)	11.5
w/P.S. add (.4)	.4
w/A.C. add (.6)	.6
w/Air guard add (.6)	.6
(P) Main and Rod Bearings, Renew	
Includes: Replace pan gasket and seals, rear main bearing oil seal and plastigauge all bearings.	
Four	
Concord-Spirit	
1983 (2.7)	4.7
Eagle	
1983-87 (3.3)	5.5
Six–except Eagle	
1983 (5.3)	7.7
Eagle	
1983-87 (4.5)	7.5
(P) Main Bearings, Renew	
Includes: Renew pan gasket and seals, rear main bearing oil seal and plastigauge all bearings.	
Four	
Concord-Spirit	
1983 (2.1)	3.5
Eagle	
1983-87 (2.7)	4.3
Six–except Eagle	
1983 (3.7)	7.0
Eagle	
1983-87 (3.5)	5.7
(G) Rear Main Bearing Oil Seals, Renew (Upper & Lower)	
Four	
Concord-Spirit	
1983 (2.1)	3.0
Eagle	
1983-87 w/M.T. (2.6)	3.8
w/A.T. (3.4)	4.9
Six–except Eagle	
1983 (1.8)	3.0
Eagle	
1983-87 (3.4)	4.5
(G) Vibration Damper or Pulley, Renew	
Four–1983-87 (.4)	.7
Six–1983-87 (.5)	.8
w/A.C. add (.2)	.2
w/P.S. add (.2)	.2

PARTS 15 CRANKSHAFT & DAMPER 15 PARTS

	Part No.	Price
(1) Crankshaft Kit (w/bearings)		
Four		
1983-87		
151	●8131280	363.25
150	●8983500242	420.75
Six		
1983	8133741	515.75
1984-87	●8133008	437.50
(2) Main Bearing Set		
Four cylinder		
1983-151		
exc. thrust brg.	●8132210	11.50
Thrust brg.	●8132214	21.00
1983-87-150		
exc. thrust brg.	●8133252	6.50
Thrust brg.	●8133253	14.50
Six		
1983-87-exc. thrust brg.	●8133252	6.50
Thrust brg.	●8133253	14.50
(3) Rear Main Bearing Oil Seal		
Four		
1983-87		
151	●8132218	6.50
150	●3241669	6.75
Six		
1983-87	●3205331	7.50

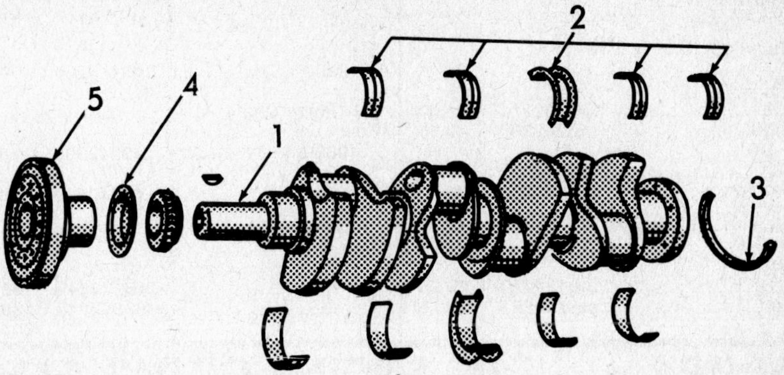

	Part No.	Price
(4) Timing Case Oil Seal		
Four		
1983-87		
151	8132221	4.25
150	●3224704	6.25
Six		
1983-87	●3224704	6.25
(5) Vibration Damper		
Four		
1983-151	●8134144	42.50

	Part No.	Price
1983-150 (w/ or wo/serpent. belt)		
wo/belt	●3242856	60.75
w/belt	●3242857	51.75
1984-87-150 (w/ or wo/serpent. belt)		
wo/belt	●3242885	60.75
w/belt	●3242886	51.75
Six		
1983-87		
exc. serpentine belt	●3237196	75.50
serpentine belt	3237723°	

LABOR 16 CAMSHAFT & TIMING GEARS 16 LABOR

(Factory Time)	Chilton Time
FOUR CYLINDER ENGINE	
(G) Timing Gear Cover, R&R or Renew	
1983-87	
150 eng. (1.2)	**1.7**
151 eng. (1.0)	**1.4**
w/P.S. add (.1)	**.1**
w/Air guard add (.6)	**.6**
(G) Timing Chain and/or Sprocket, Renew	
1983-87	
150 eng. (1.6)	**2.3**
151 eng. (1.4)	**2.0**
w/P.S. add (.1)	**.1**
(G) Timing Gear Cover Seal, Renew	
1983-87 (.6)	**.9**

(Factory Time)	Chilton Time
(G) Camshaft, Renew	
1983-87	
150 eng. (3.4)	**4.9**
151 eng. (3.2)	**4.6**
w/P.S. add (.2)	**.2**
w/Air guard add (.6)	**.6**
Renew dist drive gear add (.1)	**.2**
(G) Camshaft Rear Bearing Plug, Renew or Reseal	
Concord-Spirit	
1983-w/M.T. (1.2)	**1.8**
w/A.T. (1.7)	**2.4**
Eagle	
1983-87 (2.0)	**2.9**
SIX CYLINDER ENGINE	
(G) Timing Chain Cover and/or Gasket, Renew	
Six-1983-87 (1.4)	**2.2**

(Factory Time)	Chilton Time
w/A.C. add (.6)	**.6**
w/P.S. add (.3)	**.3**
(G) Timing Chain and/or Sprocket, Renew	
Six-1983-87 (1.8)	**2.8**
(G) Timing Chain Cover Seal, Renew	
Six-1983-87 (.9)	**1.5**
w/A.C. add (.6)	**.6**
w/P.S. add (.3)	**.3**
(G) Camshaft, Renew	
Six-1983-87 (5.6)	**8.4**
w/A.C. add (.6)	**.6**
w/P.S. add (.3)	**.3**
(G) Camshaft Rear Bearing Plug, Renew	
Six-1983-87	
w/M.T. (2.4)	**3.5**
w/A.T. (3.5)	**5.0**

PARTS 16 CAMSHAFT & TIMING GEARS 16 PARTS

	Part No.	Price
(1) Timing Cover Gasket		
Four		
1983-87		
151	8132220	3.00
150	●3225187	1.50
Six		
1983-87	●3225187	1.50
(2) Timing Case Oil Seal		
Four		
1983-87		
151	8132221	4.25
150	●3224704	6.25
Six		
1983-87	●3224704	6.25

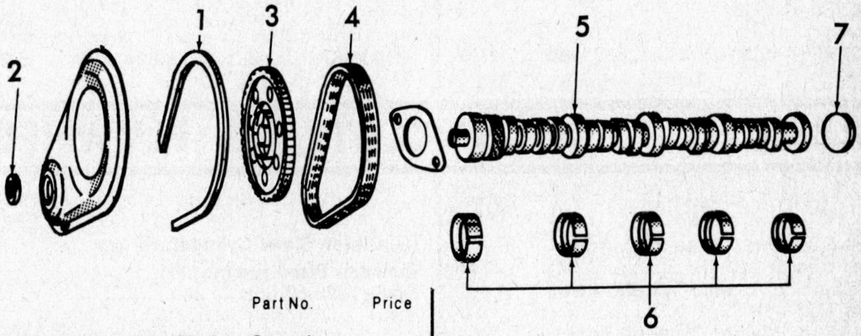

	Part No.	Price
Gasket & Seal Kit (Timing Cover)		
Four & Six		
1984-87	8129097	6.75

PARTS 16 CAMSHAFT & TIMING GEARS 16 PARTS

	Part No.	Price
(3) Camshaft Timing Gear		
Four		
1983-87		
151	●8132271	61.00
150	●3242280	42.75
Six		
1983	●3206693	38.00
1984-87	3172306	35.50
Crankshaft Timing Gear		
Four		
1983-87		
151	●8132270	29.25
150	●3242281	38.75
Six		
1983-87	●3173205	34.50
(4) Timing Chain		
Four		
1983-87	●3242300	18.50
Six		
1983-87	●3240502	34.00
(5) Camshaft		
Four		
1983-87		
151	●8132249	138.50
150	●8983500249	138.50
Six		
1983-87	●8133009	178.50
(6) Camshaft Brgs. (Set)		
Four		
1983-151		
exc. Thrust	8132251	16.75
Thrust	●8132250	6.75
1983-150	3208985	75.75
1984-87	●3205711	25.75
Six		
1983-87	●3205711	25.75
(7) Camshaft Welsh Plug		
1983-87	3172313	.75

LABOR 17 ENGINE OILING SYSTEM 17 LABOR

(Factory Time)	Chilton Time
(G) Oil Pan and/or Gasket, Renew	
Four	
Concord-Spirit	
1983 (1.4)	2.0
Eagle	
1983-87	
150 eng. (2.3)	3.3
151 eng. (2.0)	2.8
Six–except Eagle	
1983 (1.9)	2.7
Eagle	
1983-87 (2.7)	4.2
(P) Pressure Test Engine Bearings (Pan Off)	
All models	1.0
(G) Oil Pump, Renew	
Four	
Concord-Spirit	
1983 (1.6)	2.3
Eagle	
1983-87	
150 eng. (2.4)	3.5
151 eng. (2.2)	3.1
Six–except Eagle	
1983 (2.2)	3.1
Eagle	
1983-87 (2.8)	4.4
(G) Oil Pump, R&R and Recondition	
Four–1983-87	
150 eng. (2.8)	4.0
151 eng. (2.6)	3.5
Six–except Eagle	
1983 (2.6)	3.7
Eagle	
1983-87 (3.3)	5.0
(M) Oil Filter Element, Renew	
1983-87 (.3)	.3

PARTS 17 ENGINE OILING SYSTEM 17 PARTS

	Part No.	Price
Oil Pan Gasket		
Four		
1983-87		
151	●8133754	10.00
150	●8983500270	6.00
Front seal	3172848	2.25
Rear seal	3241609	1.25
Six		
1983-87	●4488770	8.00
Oil Pump		
Four		
1983-151	●8132303	77.00
1983-87-150	●3241602	93.00
Six		
1983-87-exc. Eagle	3242139	90.25
Eagle & SX4	3242138	90.25
Idler Gear		
Four		
1983-87-150	3196843	3.50
Six		
1983-87	3196843	3.50
Idler Shaft		
Four		
1983-87-150	3171956	1.75
Six		
1983-87	3171956	1.75
Pump Drive Shaft (w/Gear)		
Four		
1983-87-150	●3172334	13.25
Six		
1983-87	●3172334	13.25
Oil Pump Drive Shaft		
Four		
1983-151	●8132854	11.00
Oil Pump Drive Gear		
Four		
1983-151	8132855	13.00
Pump Cover		
Four		
1983-151	8132305	3.00
1983-87-150	3241733	5.25
Six		
1983-87	3241733	5.25
Inlet Tube (w/Screen)		
Four		
1983-87-150	3241617	8.25
Six		
1983-87-exc. Eagle	3242137	8.00
Eagle & SX4	3242144	8.25
Release Valve Plunger		
Six		
1983-87	3188661	1.50
Four		
151	8132299	1.50
150	3188661	1.50
Oil Pressure Switch (Engine)		
1983-87 (with dash gauge)		
single terminal	●3212004	15.50
1983-87 (with light)		
3 terminals	3231347	6.25
Oil Filter Element		
Four		
1983-87	8132313	5.75
Six		
1983-87	3242397	N.L.

LABOR 18 CLUTCH & FLYWHEEL 18 LABOR

(Factory Time)	Chilton Time
(G) Clutch Pedal Free Play, Adjust	
All models (.2)	.3
(G) Clutch Hydraulic System, Bleed	
Four–1983-87	.3
(G) Clutch Master Cylinder, Renew	
Includes: Bleed system .	
Four–1983-87 (.8)	1.2
(G) Clutch Slave Cylinder, Renew	
Includes: Bleed system.	
Four–1983-87 (.5)	.9
(G) Clutch Release Cable, Renew	
1983-87 (.3)	.6
(G) Clutch Assembly, Renew	
Includes: R&R transmission, R&R clutch housing, adjust clutch pedal free play.	
Four–1983-87	
Concord-Spirit (1.9)	2.7
Eagle (2.3)	3.3

LABOR 18 CLUTCH & FLYWHEEL 18 LABOR

(Factory Time) Chilton Time

Six–1983-87
Concord-Spirit (1.9) 2.7
Eagle (2.3) 3.3
Renew T.O. brg add 2

(G) Clutch Release Bearing, Renew
Includes: R&R transmission and adjust clutch pedal free play.
Four–1983-87
Concord-Spirit (1.5) 2.1
Eagle (2.1) 3.0
Six–1983-87
Concord-Spirit (1.5) 2.1
Eagle (2.1) 3.0

(G) Flywheel, Renew
Includes: R&R transmission and clutch assembly.
Four–1983-87
Concord-Spirit (1.9) 3.0
Eagle (2.5) 3.6

Six–1983-87
Concord-Spirit (1.9) 3.0
Eagle (2.5) 3.6
Renew ring gear add (.3) 5

PARTS 18 CLUTCH & FLYWHEEL 18 PARTS

	Part No.	Price
Clutch Disc		
Four		
1983-151	●8132577	78.25
1983-87-150	8953001420	86.00
Six		
1983-87-exc. Eagle	3241492	97.50
Eagle & SX4	3240549	89.25
Cover Assembly		
Four		
1983-151	●8132576	157.25
1983-87-150	●8953000167	121.25
Six		
1983-87-exc. Eagle	3241493	144.25
Eagle & SX4	3240548	139.75
Throwout Bearing		
Four		
1983-151	3241263	35.00
1983-87-150	●8953000175	35.50
Six		
1983-87-exc. Eagle	●3236561	32.00
Eagle & SX4	3237553	N.L.
Pilot Bearing		
1983-87-exc Four	●3236726	2.00
Four-150	●3250005	6.00
Flywheel		
Four		
1983-151	●8132267	174.25
1983-87-150	●3242667	170.00
Six		
1983-87	3236257	153.00
Ring Gear (Flywheel)		
1983-87-exc. Four	●3179741	29.50
Four-150	●3241718	24.75
Clutch Master Cylinder		
Six		
1983-87	3238951	99.75
Four		
1983-87		
151	3236757	93.75
150	3238493	79.25
Clutch Master Cylinder Repair Kit		
1983-87-Four-150	8983500677	14.50
Six	8132911	15.00
Clutch Slave Cylinder		
Four		
1983-151	3241867	58.25
1983-87-150	●8952000070	79.25
Six		
1983-87	3241868	58.75
Clutch Slave Cylinder Repair Kit		
Six		
1983	8132782	11.75
1984-87	●8983500678	33.75
Four		
1983-87	●8983500670	18.25

LABOR 21 SHIFT LINKAGE 21 LABOR

(Factory Time) Chilton Time

MANUAL

(G) Shift Linkage, Adjust
1983-87
4 spd. (.4) 5
5 spd. (.5) 6

(G) Gear Shift Lever, Renew
1983-87 (.6) 8

(G) Steering Column Gear Shift Tube, Renew
Includes: R&R steering column and adjust linkage.
Standard Column
1983-87 (1.0) 1.6
Tilt Column
1983-87 (1.4) 2.0

(G) Steering Column Shift Bowl or Housing, Renew
Includes: R&R steering column.
1983-87
w/Trans lock (1.4) 2.0
less trans lock (1.1) 1.7
w/Tilt column (1.8) 2.4

AUTOMATIC

(G) Shift Linkage, Adjust
1983-87 (.3) 4

(G) Gear Shift Lever, Renew
1983-87
column mount (.3) 4
floor mount (.5) 6

(G) Gear Shift Rod, Renew
Includes: Adjust linkage.
1983-87-one (.3) 5

(G) Shift Lever Dial, Renew
1983-87
on column (.3) 7
in console (.3) 7
in inst cluster (.6) 1.2

(G) Steering Column Gear Shift Tube, Renew
Includes: R&R steering column and adjust linkage.
Standard Column
1983-87 (1.0) 1.6
Tilt Column
1983-87 (1.4) 2.0

(G) Steering Column Shift Bowl or Housing, Renew
Includes: R&R steering column.
1983-87
w/Trans lock (1.4) 2.0
less trans lock (1.1) 1.7
w/Tilt column (1.8) 2.4

LABOR 25 U-JOINTS & DRIVESHAFT 25 LABOR

(Factory Time) Chilton Time

(G) Universal Joints, Recondition
Includes: R&R drive shaft.
1983-87-front (.7) 1.1
rear (.6) 1.0

(G) Drive Shaft, Renew
1983-87 (.4) 6

PARTS 25 UNIVERSAL JOINTS & DRIVE SHAFT 25 PARTS

	Part No.	Price
Universal Joint Repair Kit (Rear)		
1983-87	●8126614	22.75
Universal Joint Repair Kit (Front)		
1983-87	●8126614	22.75

LABOR 26 REAR AXLE 26 LABOR

(Factory Time)	Chilton Time
(M) Differential, Drain and Refill	
All models (.4)	.6
(M) Inspection Cover Gasket, Renew	
1983-87 (.5)	.6
(G) Axle Shaft Oil Seal, Renew	
Inner and outer	
1983-87-left side (1.4)	2.1
right side (1.8)	2.3
both sides (2.0)	3.0
Outer only-one	
1983-87-9″ brake (1.0)	1.4
10″ brake (.7)	.9
(G) Axle Shaft and/or Bearing, Renew	
1983-87-left side (1.4)	2.2
right side (1.8)	2.4
both sides (2.0)	3.1
(G) Pinion Shaft Oil Seal, Renew	
1983-87 (1.0)	1.2
(G) Rear Axle Assy., (Exchange Unit), Renew	
1983-87 (3.1)	4.5
(P) Ring Gear and Pinion Set, Renew	
1983-87	
7⁹⁄₁₆ axle (4.4)	6.5
8⁷⁄₈ axle (5.2)	7.3
(P) Differential Side Bearings, Renew	
1983-87	
7⁹⁄₁₆ axle (4.3)	6.0
8⁷⁄₈ axle (5.1)	6.8
(P) Differential Case, R&R and Renew or Recondition	
1983-87	
7⁹⁄₁₆ axle (2.8)	4.0
8⁷⁄₈ axle (2.7)	*4.0
*w/Twin grip add (.2)	.4

PARTS 26 REAR AXLE 26 PARTS

	Part No.	Price
(1) Pinion Seal		
1983	●3208474	8.00
1984-87	●8953002642	8.00
(2) Front Pinion Bearing		
1983-87	●3156063	11.75
(3) Front Bearing Cup		
1983-87	●3156062	5.25
(4) Axle Housing		
Concord & Spirit		
1983	8133864	393.00
Eagle & SX4		
1983-87	8133865	446.75
(5) Axle Oil Seal (Inner)		
1983-87	3170699	4.00
(6) Axle Oil Seal (Outer)		
1983-87	3230430	9.00
(7) Axle Bearing Cup		
1983-87	3143329	4.75
(8) Axle Bearing		
1983-87	3141139	8.25
(9) Axle Shaft		
Concord & Spirit		
1983	8131697	67.25
Eagle & SX4		
1983-87	8131696	67.25
(10) Shim		
Various sizes.		
(11) Rear Pinion Bearing Cup		
1983-87	3156065	7.50
(12) Rear Pinion Bearing		
1983-87	●3170947	15.50
(13) Ring Gear & Pinion Set		
1983-87		
2.35 ratio	8133863	263.50
2.73 ratio	4487812	278.50
3.08 ratio	4487813	278.50
3.54 ratio	●8130782	278.50
(14) Differential Case Assy.		
1983-87		
2.35 ratio	8933001578	151.25
2.73 ratio	8933001579	151.25
3.08 ratio	8933001927	151.25
3.54 ratio	8933001927	151.25

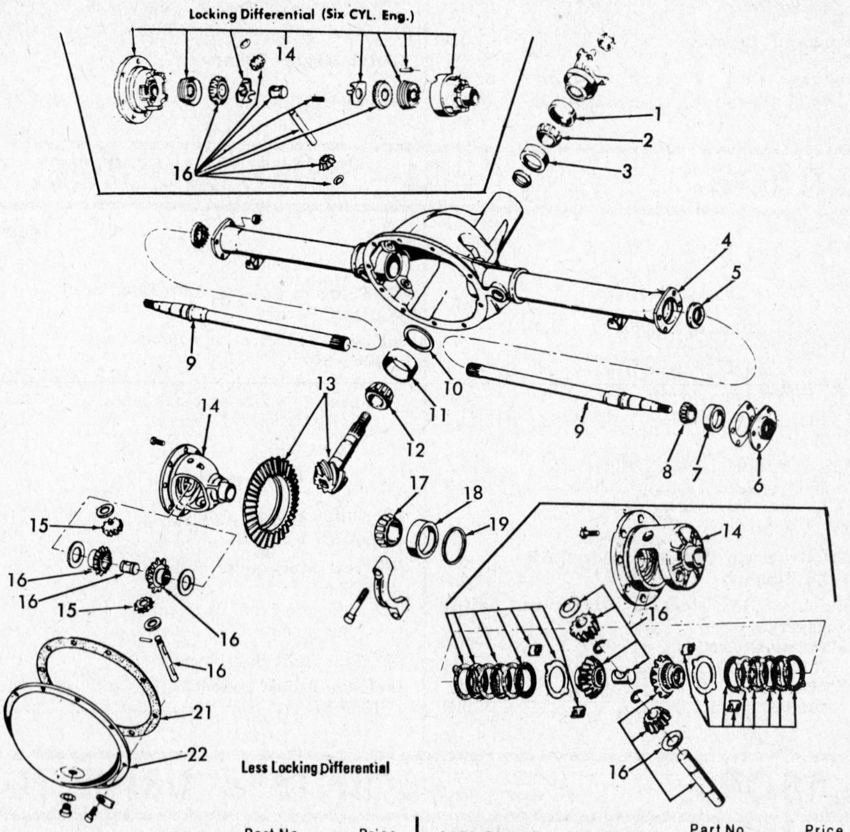

	Part No.	Price
(15 & 16) Gear Set (Side)		
1983-87	●8983500138	58.75
Gear set includes side gears, pinion gears, thrust washers, block and pinion shaft.		
(17) Side Bearing		
1983-87	●3156052	11.50
(18) Side Bearing Cup		
1983-87	●3171166	5.75
(19) Shim		
Various sizes.		
(21) Cover Gasket		
1983-87	●3229429	2.00
(22) Cover		
1983-87	●3223375	8.25

LABOR 27 REAR SUSPENSION 27 LABOR

(Factory Time) Chilton Time

(G) Rear Spring, Renew (One)
1983-87 (.8) 1.1

(G) Rear Spring Front Eye Bushing, Renew
1983-87-one side (.7) 1.0
both sides (1.1) 1.8
Renew bushing add (.3) 3
w/Sway bar add (.1) 2

(G) Rear Stabilizer Links, Renew
1983-87 (.3) 5

(G) Rear Spring Shackle and/or Bushing, Renew
All models
1983-87-one side (.7) 1.0
both sides (1.1) 1.8

(G) Rear Shock Absorber, Renew
All models
1983-87-one (.4) 5
both (.5) 8

(G) Rear Axle Stabilizer Bar, Renew
1983-87 (.3) 7

AUTOMATIC LEVEL CONTROL

(G) Air Compressor Relay, Renew
1983-87 (.4) 5

(G) Height Sensor, Renew
1983-87 (.3) 4

(G) Air Shock Compressor, Renew
1983-87 (.6) 9

(G) Air Shock Switch, Renew
1983-87 (.3) 4

PARTS 27 REAR SUSPENSION 27 PARTS

	Part No.	Price
Rear Spring		
Order by model & description.		
Front Bushing		
1983-87	3232169	12.00
Shackle Kit		
1983-87	8123359	8.50
Shock Absorber		
1983-exc Eagle & SX4	8130217	23.50
Eagle, SX4	8133426	21.25
1984-87	8131910	29.25

LABOR 28 AIR CONDITIONING 28 LABOR

(Factory Time) Chilton Time

Note: If more than one item requires replacement where evacuation and discharging the system is already included in the operation, deduct 1.0 hour for each additional item to the times listed.

(G) Discharge, Evacuate, Leak Test and Charge System
All models (.9) 1.0

(G) Partial Charge
Includes: Leak test.
All models (.4) 6

(G) Compressor Belt, Renew
1983-87 (.3) 4

COMPRESSOR–SD-5

(G) Compressor Assembly, Renew
Includes: Transfer parts as required. Evacuate and charge system.
1983-87 (1.6) 2.5

(G) Compressor Front Seal, Renew
Includes: R&R compressor. Evacuate and charge system.
1983-87 (1.4) 2.4

(G) Compressor Cyl. Head and/or Valve Plate Gasket, Renew
Includes: R&R compressor. Evacuate and charge system.
1983-87 (1.3) 2.2

(G) Compressor Service Valve, Renew
Includes: Evacuate and charge system.
1983-87 (.9) 1.5

TWO CYLINDER COMP.

(G) Compressor Assembly, Renew
Includes: Evacuate, leak test and charge system.
Four & Six (1.3) 2.4
R&R mounting bracket add (.2) 2

(G) Compressor Front Seal, Renew (On Car)
Includes: Evacuate, leak test and charge system.
1983-87 (1.1) 2.0

AIR CONDITIONER TUNE-UP

For efficient operation and satisfactory performance in hot weather. The following air conditioner tune-up is suggested:

1. Clean intake filter
2. Clean condenser fins
3. Pressure test system
4. Adjust drive belt tension
5. Check antifreeze/coolant
6. Tighten compressor mounts
7. Tighten condenser and evaporator mounts
8. Inspect system for leaks (hoses, couplings, valves, etc.)
9. Partial charge system

All models 1.0
If necessary to evacuate and charge system, add 1.0

(Factory Time) Chilton Time

(G) Compressor Clutch Pulley, Renew
1983-87 (.4) 6
Renew coil add (.1) 2

(G) Compressor Valve Plate and/or Gasket, Renew (On Car)
Includes: Evacuate, leak test and charge system.
1983-87 (1.1) 1.9

(G) Condenser and/or Receiver Drier, Renew
Includes: Evacuate, leak test and charge system.
Concord-Spirit-AMX-Eagle
1983-87 (1.4) 2.4
Renew pressure relief valve add (.2) 3

(G) Evaporator Assembly, Renew
Includes: Evacuate, leak test and charge system.
Concord-Spirit-AMX-Eagle
1983-87 (2.5) 3.8

(G) Expansion Valve, Renew
Includes: Evacuate, leak test and charge system.
Concord-Spirit-AMX-Eagle
1983-87 (1.3) 2.1

(G) Low Pressure Switch, Renew
Includes: Evacuate, leak test and charge system, where required.
1983-87 (.3) 4

(G) Temperature Control Thermostat, Renew
Concord-Spirit-AMX-Eagle
1983-87 (.8) 1.2

(G) Temperature Control Assembly, Renew
Concord-Spirit-AMX-Eagle
1983-87 (.6) 9

(G) Blower Motor, Renew
Concord-Spirit-AMX-Eagle
1983-87 (.5) 8

(G) Blower Motor Resistor, Renew
1983-87 (.3) 4

(G) Blower Motor Relay, Renew
1983-87 (.3) 4

(G) Blower Motor Switch, Renew
1983-87 (.5) 9

(G) Vacuum Storage Tank, Renew
1983-87 (.2) 5

(G) Temperature Override Switch, Renew
1983-87 (.3) 5

(G) Air Conditioning Hoses, Renew
Includes: Evacuate, leak test and charge system.
Compressor to condenser
Concord-Spirit-AMX-Eagle
1983-87 (.9) 1.6
Receiver to evaporator
Concord-Spirit-AMX-Eagle
1983-87 (1.3) 2.0

PARTS 28 AIR CONDITIONING 28 PARTS

	Part No.	Price
Compressor Belt		
Order by model & description.		
Compressor Assembly		
(wo/American air)		
1983-87-exc. 151	●8133449	270.75
151	8134182	270.75
(w/American air)		
1983-87	●8133196	270.75
Compressor Seal Kit		
1983-87	8133183	13.25
Compressor Clutch		
wo/Serpentine belt drive		
1983 (wo/American air)		
Four	8134181	150.50
Six	●8134178	150.50
1984-87 (wo/American air)		
Four & Six	●8983510033	139.50
1983-87 (w/American air)		
Four & Six	●8133195	152.75
w/Serpentine belt drive		
1983 (wo/American air)		
Four & Six	●8133448	139.50
1984-87 (wo/American air)		
Four & Six	●8983510034	139.50
Compressor Pulley & Bearing		
wo/Serpentine belt drive		
1983-87-exc. Four		
(1983)	8134177	95.75
Four (1983)	8134180	109.00
w/Serpentine belt drive		
1983-87	8133446	124.25
Compressor Coil		
wo/American air		
1983	8133447	66.00
1984-87	8983510032	66.00
w/American air		
1984-87	8133194	71.25
Condenser Core		
1983-87-exc Amer.		
Air	3229447	235.75
w/Amer. Air	8121846	235.75
Evaporator Core		
1983-87-exc.		
Amer. Air	3728052	189.75
w/Amer. Air	8132638	130.75
Receiver Pressure Relief Valve		
1983-87	3692994	10.75
Expansion Valve		
1983-87-exc.		
Amer. Air	3728053	67.75
Amer. Air	3126897	N.L.
Receiver/Drier		
1983-87-exc.		
Amer. Air	3229446	70.50
Amer. Air	8132643	51.25
Temp. Control Thermostat		
1983-87	3728088	41.00
Blower Motor		
1983-87	3741261	38.25
Blower Control Switch		
1983-87-wo/A.C.	3692961	4.50
w/A.C.	3693111	9.75
Air Condition Hoses		
Order by model and description.		
Vacuum Storage Tank		
1983-87	3741279	4.00
Low Pressure Switch (Cut Out)		
1983-87	3741260	16.50
Suction Valve		
Four-150	●5459857	18.00
Six	3228592	18.75

LABOR 29 LOCKS, HINGES & WIND. REGULATORS 29 LABOR

(Factory Time)	Chilton Time
(G) Hood Lock, Renew	
1983-87 (.3)	.5
(G) Hood Hinge, Renew	
1983-87-one (.3)	.5
both (.5)	.8
(G) Door Lock, Renew (Front or Rear)	
Includes: Renew lock cylinder.	
1983-87 (.5)	.9
Recode cylinder add (.2)	.2
(G) Lock Cylinder and Key, Renew	
Includes: Code cylinder to key.	
1983-87 (.7)	1.1
(G) Door Lock Remote Control, Renew (Front or Rear)	
1983-87 (.3)	.7
(G) Door Handle (Outside), Renew (Front or Rear)	
1983-87 (.4)	.7
(G) Lock Striker Plate, Renew	
1983-87 (.2)	.3
(G) Door Window Regulator (Manual), Renew	
Front	
Concord-Spirit-AMX-Eagle	
1983-87 (.5)	.9
Rear	
1983-87 (.4)	.8
(G) Door Window Regulator (Electric), Renew	
1983-87 (.8)	1.0
Renew motor add (.1)	.2
Renew gear pinion add (.2)	.2
(G) Trunk Lock, Renew	
1983-87 (.3)	.5
(G) Trunk Lock Cylinder and Key, Renew	
Includes: Code cylinder to key.	
1983-87 (.5)	.7
(G) Trunk Hinge Assembly, Renew (One)	
1983-87 (.9)	1.3

PARTS 29 LOCKS, HINGES & WIND. REGULATORS 29 PARTS

	Part No.	Price
Hood Lock (Inside Release)		
1983-87	3714202	25.00
Release Cable		
1983-87	3697380	5.25
Hood Hinge		
1983-87-right	3697284	30.25
left	3697285	30.25
Front Door Lock		
1983-87-Manual		
left	3661539	N.L.
right	3661538	38.25
1983-87-Electric		
left	3719479	47.50
right	3719478	47.50
Rear Door Lock		
1983-87-Manual		
right	3661546	47.25
left	3661547	N.L.
1983-87-Electric		
right	3719760	47.25
left	3719761	47.25
Door Lock Cylinder Assy.		
1983-87	●8122874	7.25
Door Outer Handle (L.H.)		
1983-87	3631163	20.50
Trunk Lock		
1983-87-exc Spirit	3731626	13.50
1983-Spirit		
2 dr lift gate	3719492	13.75
wag.	3616091	13.75
Trunk Lock Cylinder & Key		
1983-87	●8122874	7.25
Front Door Window Regulator		
1983-87-manual		
(L.H.)	3740995	64.00
electric (L.H.)	8132929	63.75
Rear Door Window Regulator		
1983-87-manual		
(L.H.)	3719319	54.75
electric (L.H.)	8132581	86.50
Window Motor		
1983-87		
front (L.H.)	8132880	114.50
rear (L.H.)	3743079	131.00
Window Drive Cable		
1983-87	8132881	19.25

LABOR 30 HEAD AND PARKING LAMPS 30 LABOR

	(Factory Time)	Chilton Time
(G) Aim Headlamps		
two		.4
four		.6
(M) Headlamp Sealed Beam Bulb, Renew		
1983-87	(.3)	.3
(G) Headlamp Warning Buzzer, Renew		
1983-87	(.2)	.3
(M) Parking Lamp Lens, Renew		
1983-87	(.3)	.4
(M) Tail and Stop Lamp Lens, Renew		
Concord-Spirit-AMX-Eagle		
1983-87-2 door	(.6)	.8
4 door	(.3)	.4
Station wagons	(.2)	.3

PARTS 30 HEAD AND PARKING LAMPS 30 PARTS

	Part No.	Price
Headlamp Bulb		
1983-87-Inner		
Beam	8129671	14.75
Halogen	8130367	29.50
1983-87-Outer		
Beam	8129670	14.75
Halogen	8133703	28.75
Parking Lamp Lens		
Serviced with Lamp Assy on Concord & Spirit models.		
1983-87-Eagle & SX4		
left	3237311	25.00
right	3237310	25.00
Parking Lamp Assy.		
1983 Concord & Spirit		
right	3719418	25.00
left	3719419	25.00
Tail Lamp Lens		
1983-Spirit (2 door sedan)		
right	3684276	16.75
left	3684277	16.75
1983-Spirit (2 door liftback)		
right	3721150	38.00
left	3721151	38.00
1983-Concord		
right	3242510	45.75
left	3242511	45.75
1983-87-Eagle (silver)		
right	3242510	45.75
left	3242511	45.75
1983-87-Eagle (black)		
right	3242514	41.50
left	3242515	41.50
1983-SX4		
right	3736316	38.00
left	3736317	38.00
Head Lamp Warning Buzzer		
1983-87	3229545	5.00

LABOR 31 WINDSHIELD WIPER & SPEEDOMETER 31 LABOR

	(Factory Time)	Chilton Time
(G) Windshield Wiper Motor, Renew		
1983-87	(.4)	.5
(G) Wiper Linkage, Renew		
1983-87	(.5)	.9
(G) Wiper Switch, Renew		
Concord-Spirit-AMX-Eagle		
1983-87	(.3)	.5
(G) Intermittent Windshield Wiper Governor Control, Renew		
Concord-Spirit-AMX-Eagle		
1983-87	(.3)	.4
w/Pkg tray add	(.2)	.2
(G) Washer Motor and/or Reservoir, Renew (Front or Rear)		
1983-87	(.4)	.5
(G) Speedometer Head, R&R or Renew		
Includes: R&R instrument cluster.		
1983-87	(.7)	1.3
w/Pkg tray add	(.2)	.2
Reset odometer add		.2
(G) Speedometer Cable and Core, Renew		
1983-87	(.4)	.8
(G) Speedometer Cable (Inner), Renew or Lubricate		
1983-87	(.5)	.7
(G) Radio, R&R		
1983-87	(.4)	.7
(G) Rear Window Wiper Motor, Renew		
1983-87	(.4)	.6

PARTS 31 WINDSHIELD WIPER & SPEEDOMETER 31 PARTS

	Part No.	Price
Wiper Motor		
1983-87-Front	3665760	72.25
rear	3735274	82.00
Wiper Pivot Shaft		
1983-87	3731385	58.00
Wiper Control		
1983-87		
wo/Intermittent	3665126	21.50
w/Intermittent	3741268	29.75
Windshield Washer Pump		
1983-87	8132903	26.75
Speedometer Head		
1983-87		
w/Indicator	8133841	73.00
wo/Indicator	8133842	73.00
Speedo. Cable and Housing		
Order by year and model.		

LABOR 32 LIGHT SWITCHES & WIRING 32 LABOR

	(Factory Time)	Chilton Time
(G) Headlamp Switch, Renew		
1983-87	(.4)	.5
w/Pkg tray add	(.1)	.1
(G) Headlamp Dimmer Switch, Renew		
1983-87	(.3)	.4
(G) Stoplight Switch, Renew		
1983-87	(.4)	.5
(G) Neutral Safety (w/Back-Up Lamp) Switch, Renew		
1983-87		
Concord-Spirit	(.4)	.5
Eagle	(.7)	1.0
(G) Back-Up Lamp Switch, Renew		
1983-87	(.3)	.4
(G) Turn Signal Switch Assy., Renew		
1983-87	(.6)	1.0
(M) Turn Signal or Hazard Warning Flasher, Renew		
1983-87	(.2)	.3
(G) Horns, Renew		
1983-87-one	(.2)	.3
both	(.3)	.5
w/A.C. add	(.3)	.3
(G) Horn Relay, Renew		
1983-87	(.3)	.4
(G) Body Wiring Harness, Renew		
Consists of wiring from connection with chassis to trunk.		
1983-87		
Sedan models	(2.9)	4.9
Station wagons	(2.9)	4.9
(G) Instrument Panel Wiring Harness, Renew		
Concord-Spirit-AMX-Eagle		
1983-87	(1.6)	2.9
w/A.C. add	(.4)	.6

PARTS 32 LIGHT SWITCHES & WIRING 32 PARTS

	Part No.	Price
Headlamp Switch		
1983-87	3240717	14.75
Headlamp Dimmer Switch		
1983-87		
on floor	3160926	5.25
on column	●3239703	21.50
Stop Light Switch		
1983-87 (wo/speed control)		
wo/Power brks	3215939	9.00
w/Power brks	●3215938	9.00
1983-87 (w/speed control)		
wo/Power brks	3225788	8.50
w/Power brks	●3225787	8.50
Turn Signal & Warning Switch		
1983-87	●3229970	35.50
Turn Signal Flasher		
1983-87	3212067	2.50
Back-Up Light Switch		
1983-87		
4 spd trans	●3229472	9.25
auto trans	●3232844	9.25
Horns		
1983-87-Low tone	3741254	22.50
1983-87-High tone	3229530	23.25
Horn Relay		
1983-87	3242520	7.25
Wiring Harness		
Order by model and description.		

LABOR 33 GLASS 33 LABOR

(Factory Time)	Chilton Time
(G) Windshield Glass, Renew	
1983-87 (2.2)	3.0
(G) Front Door Glass, Renew	
Concord-Spirit-AMX-Eagle	
1983-87 (.6)	1.0
(G) Rear Door Window Glass, Renew	
AMX-Concord-Eagle	
1983-87 (.4)	.8
(G) Tailgate or Liftgate Glass, Renew	
Concord-AMX-Eagle	
1983-87 (1.1)	1.6
Spirit	
1983 (.5)	1.0
w/Elec heated glass add (.1)	.2
(G) Back Window Glass, Renew	
1983-87 (1.1)	2.2
w/Grid defogger add (.5)	.5
(G) Rear Quarter Window Glass, Renew	
1983-87	
Spirit-Eagle	
2 DR Sdn (.4)	.7
Concord-Eagle	
4 DR Sdn-one (1.6)	2.3
both (2.7)	4.0
Concord-Eagle	
2 DR Sdn-one (1.4)	2.1
both (2.1)	3.4
Concord-Eagle	
Sta Wagon-one (1.3)	2.0
both (2.2)	3.5

LABOR 34 CRUISE CONTROL 34 LABOR

(Factory Time)	Chilton Time
(G) Speed Control Regulator, Renew	
1983-87 (.4)	.7
(G) Speed Control Wiring Harness, Renew	
1983-87 (.5)	.9
w/A.C. add (.2)	.2
w/Pkg tray add (.1)	.1
(G) Speed Control Brake Release Switch, Renew	
1983-87 (.4)	.5
(G) Speed Control Switch, Renew	
1983-87 (.4)	.6
(G) Speed Control Cable and Core, Renew	
Speed control to trans	
1983-87 (.3)	.6
Speed control to speedo	
1983-87 (.3)	.6
w/A.C. add (.3)	.3
(G) Speed Control Throttle or Servo Cable, Renew	
1983-87 (.4)	.6
(G) Speed Control Vacuum Reservoir, Renew	
1983-87 (.2)	.4
(G) Speed Control Speed Sensor, Renew	
1983-87 (.3)	.5
(G) Speed Control Servo, Renew	
1983-87 (.7)	1.0
w/Pkg tray add (.1)	.1
(G) Speed Control Vacuum Bleed Switch, Renew	
1983-87 (.3)	.4
(G) Tach Generator, Renew	
1983-87 (.4)	.6

PARTS 34 CRUISE CONTROL 34 PARTS

	Part No.	Price
ELECTRONIC SPEED CONTROL		
Speed Control Regulator		
1983-87	●3237117	167.00
Valve (Control Vacuum)		
1983-87	●3232970	3.75
Tach Generator (Spd. Cont.)		
1983-87	●3242195	21.00
Wiring Harness (Spd. Cont.)		
1983	3242915	31.50
Servo (Throttle Cont.)		
1983-87	●3240500	93.75
Cable (Servo to Throttle Chain)		
1983-87		
150	8933001323	12.75
151	3237091	17.25
Six	●3242185	6.25
Chain & Clevis Assy. (Spd. Cont.)		
1983-87-Four	3237229	2.00
Six	3234025	2.00
Vacuum Storage Tank		
1983-87-Six	3232992	7.75
1983-87-Four	●3232991	7.75
Vacuum Hose (Tank to Servo)		
1983-87-exc below	3233113	1.50
Four	3237209	1.50
Vacuum Hose (Tank to Manifold)		
1983-87	4487656	1.50
Vacuum Hose (Servo to Bleed Switch)		
1983-87	●8125823	1.75

GROUP INDEX

ALPHABETICAL INDEX

AMC/Jeep

CJ SERIES • WAGONEER • CHEROKEE • COMMANCHE

YEAR IDENTIFICATION

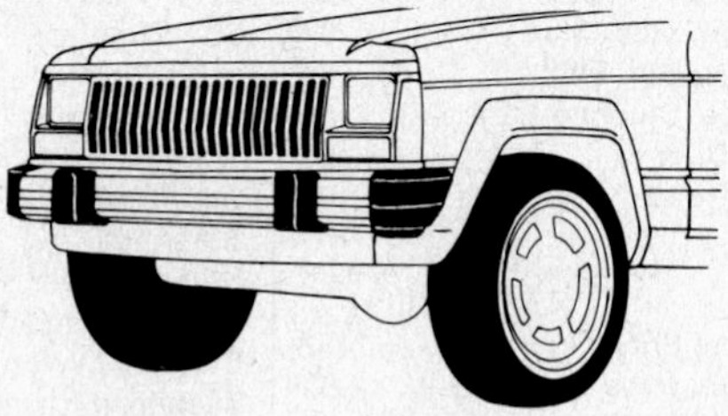

Cherokee Chief

Wagoneer Limited

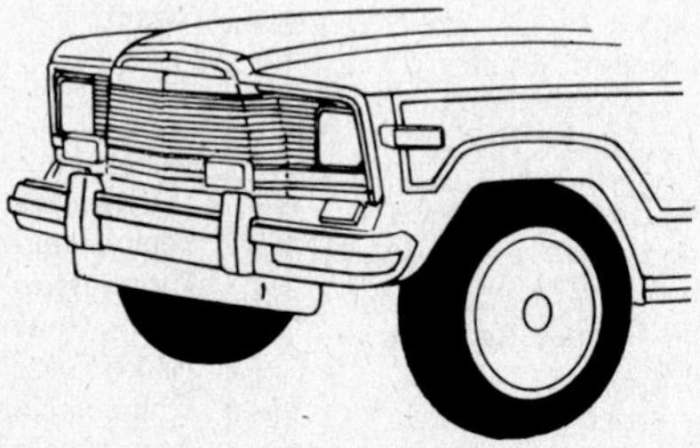

Grand Wagoneer

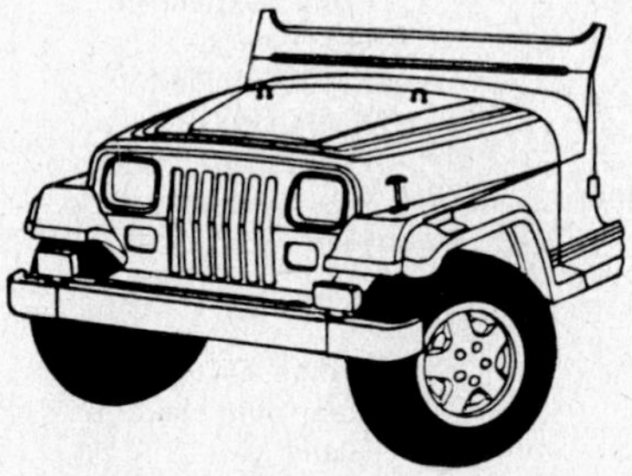

CJ7

TUNE-UP SPECIFICATIONS

Year	Engine No. Cyl Displacement (cu. in.)	hp	Spark Plugs Type	Spark Plugs Gap (in.)	Distributor Point Dwell (deg)	Ignition Timing (deg) ②	Valves Intake Opens ③ (deg)	Fuel Pump Pressure (psi)	Idle Speed Man Trans	Idle Speed Auto Trans
'83	4-150	—	RFN14LY	.035	Electronic	12B	27	6½–8	750	750
	4-151	87	R44T5X	.060	Electronic	10B ⑤	33	6½–8	900	750
	6-173	110	RUT2YC	.041	Electronic	10B	21	5–7	750	750
	6-258	110	RFN14LY	.035	Electronic	8B ⑥	14½	4–5	700	600
	8-360	175	RN12Y	.035	Electronic	8B	14¾	5–6	800	600

TUNE-UP SPECIFICATIONS

Year	Engine No. Cyl Displacement (cu. in.)	hp	Spark Plugs Type	Spark Plugs Gap (in.)	Distributor Point Dwell (deg)	Ignition Timing (deg) ②	Valves Intake Opens ③ (deg)	Fuel Pump Pressure (psi)	Idle Speed Man Trans	Idle Speed Auto Trans
'84	4-150	—	RFN14LY	.035	Electronic	12B	27	6½-8	750	750
	6-173	110	RUT2YC	.041	Electronic	10B	21	5-7	750	750
	6-258	110	RFN14LY	.035	Electronic	8B ⑥	14½	4-5	700	600
	8-360	175	RN12Y	.035	Electronic	8B	14¾	5-6	800	600
'85-'87	4-126	—	NONE		NONE	—	—	N/A	750-850	750-800
	4-150	—	RFN14LY	.035	Electronic	12B	27	6½-8	750	750
	6-173	110	RUT2YC	.041	Electronic	10B	21	5-7	750	750
	6-258	110	RFN14LY	.035	Electronic	8B ⑥	14½	4-5	700	600
	8-360	175	RN12Y	.035	Electronic	8B	14¾	5-6	800	600

NOTE: If the information given in this chart disagrees with the information on the engine tune-up decal, use the specifications on the decal.
NOTE: Figures in parentheses are for California engines
B—Before top dead center (BTDC)
① w/manual trans.—5B, CJ model only
② With vacuum advance disconnected
③ All figures before TDC
④ Both manual and automatic transmissions
⑤ w/auto. trans; 12B
⑥ Calif. CJ w/man. trans; 6B

FIRING ORDER

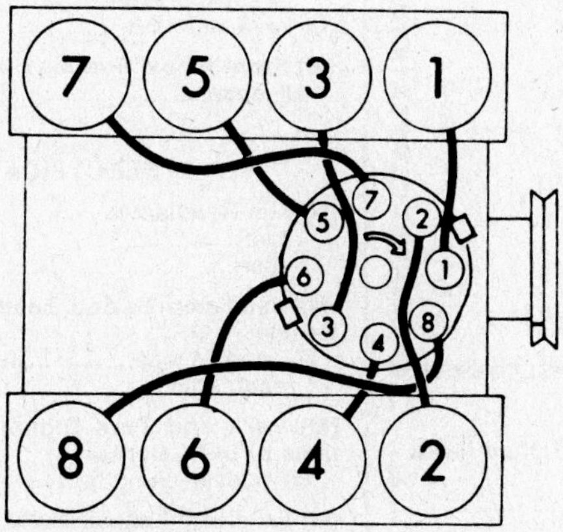

V8 Engine firing order 1-8-4-3-6-5-7-2

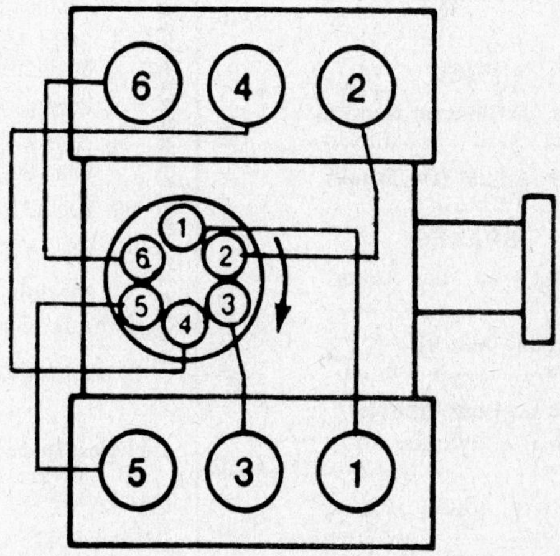

V6-173 CID Engine firing order 1-2-3-4-5-6

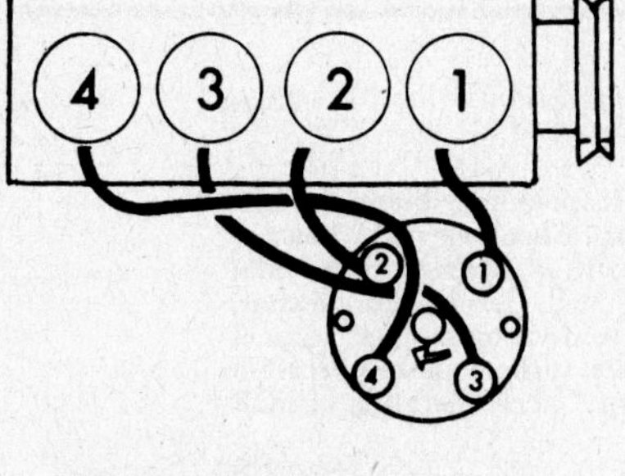

AMC 151 CID 4-cyl.
Engine firing order: 1-3-4-2
Distributor rotation: clockwise

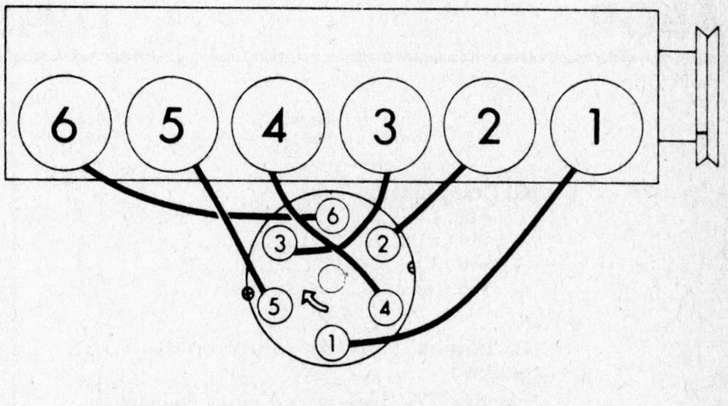

6-258 CID Engine firing order 1-5-3-6-2-4

WHEEL ALIGNMENT SPECIFICATIONS

Model	Caster Pref. Setting (deg.)	Camber Pref. Setting (deg.)	Toe-In (in.)	Steering Axis Inclination (deg.)	Turning Angle (deg.)
CJ-5, CJ-6, CJ-7 DJ-5, DJ-6, CJ-5A, CJ-6A, Scrambler	6°	0°	3/64–3/32	8½°	31°–32°
Wagoneer, Cherokee	4°	0°	3/64–3/32	8½°	37°–38°

LABOR — SERVICE BAY OPERATIONS — LABOR

(Factory Time) — Chilton Time

COOLING

(M) Winterize Cooling System

Includes: Run engine to check for leaks, tighten all hose connections. Test radiator and pressure cap, drain radiator and engine block. Add anti-freeze and refill system.

All models 5

(M) Thermostat, Renew

All models (.5) 6

(M) Radiator Hoses, Renew

All models
- upper (.4) 5
- lower (.5) 6

FUEL

(M) Carburetor Air Cleaner, Service

All models 3

(M) Carburetor, Adjust (On Truck)

All models 4

BRAKES

(G) Brake Pedal Free Play, Adjust

All models 4

(G) Brakes, Adjust (Minor)

two wheels 4

(G) Bleed Brakes (Four Wheels)

Includes: Fill master cylinder.

All models (.4) 5

(M) Parking Brake, Adjust

All models (.3) 4

LUBRICATION SERVICE

(M) Lubricate Chassis, Change Oil & Filter

Includes: Inspect and correct all fluid levels.

All models 6

Install grease fittings add 1

(M) Lubricate Chassis

Includes: Inspect and correct all fluid levels.

All models 4

Install grease fittings add 1

CHILTON'S 10 POINT SAFETY CHECK

CHECK OPERATION & CONDITION OF THE FOLLOWING ITEMS:

1. Legal Registration (serial no.)
2. Tires & Wheels
3. Brake System (R&R all wheels)
4. Light Systems & Signals
5. Accelerator Linkage, Neutral Safety Switch, Shift Indicator Pointer & Seat Position Locks
6. Glass, Mirrors, Door Locks, Seat Belts & Harness
7. Wipers, Washers & Defrosters
8. Frame, Steering, Shocks, Front & Rear Suspension
9. Fuel & Exhaust Systems
10. Road Test Vehicle

All models 1.0

Exhaust Smog Analysis, add 4

(Factory Time) — Chilton Time

(M) Engine Oil & Filter, Change

Includes: Inspect and correct all fluid levels.

All models 4

WHEELS

(M) Wheel, Renew

one 5

(G) Wheel, Balance

one 3

each adtnl 2

(G) Front Wheel Bearings, Clean and Repack (Both Wheels)

w/Disc brakes 1.2

w/4 whl drive 2.3

(M) Front Wheel Bearings, Adjust

All models 4

ELECTRICAL

(G) Aim Headlamps

two 4

four 6

(M) Headlamp Sealed Beam Bulb, Renew

All models-one 3

each adtnl 2

(M) Park and Turn Signal Lamp Lens or Bulb, Renew

All models-one (.3) 4

(M) Tail Lamp Lens or Bulb, Renew

All models-one (.3) 4

(M) License Lamp Assembly, Renew

All models-one (.3) 4

LABOR — 1 TUNE UP 1 — LABOR

(Factory Time) — Chilton Time

(G) Compression Test

- Four (.4) 5
- Six (.4) 6
- V-6 (.6) 7
- V-8 (.7) 9

(G) Engine Tune Up (Electronic Ignition)

Includes: Test battery and clean connections. Tighten manifold and carburetor mounting bolts. Check engine compression, clean and adjust or renew spark plugs. Test resistance of spark plug cables. Inspect distributor cap and rotor. Adjust air gap. Check vacuum advance operation. Reset ignition timing. Adjust idle mixture and idle speed. Service air cleaner. Inspect crankcase ventilation system. Inspect and adjust drive belts. Inspect choke operation and adjust or free up. Check operation of EGR valve.

- **Four**–1983-87 (2.0) 2.8
- **Six**–1983-87 (1.4) 2.0
- **V-6**–1984-87 (2.1) 3.0
- **V-8**–1983-87 (1.9) 2.5
- w/A.C. add 6

LABOR 2 IGNITION SYSTEM 2 LABOR

(Factory Time)	Chilton Time
(G) Spark Plugs, Clean & Reset or Renew	
Four (.3)	.4
Six (.3)	.5
V-6 (.5)	.6
V-8 (.6)	.8
(G) Ignition Timing, Reset	
CJ/Scrambler	
Four (.5)	.6
Six (.2)	.3
All other models (.3)	.4
(G) Distributor Assy., R&R or Renew	
Includes: Reset ignition timing.	
All models (.5)	.7
Renew driven gear add (1.0)	1.0
(G) Distributor, R&R and Recondition	
Includes: Reset ignition timing.	
All models (.9)	1.3
(G) Distributor Sensor, Renew	
All models (.5)	.7
(G) Distributor Trigger Wheel, Renew	
All models (.4)	.6
(G) Ignition Pick-Up Coil, Renew	
CJ/Scrambler	
Four (.8)	1.1
Six (.3)	.5
Cherokee/Grand Wagoneer/Truck	
Six (.3)	.5
Che/Wag/Comanche	
Four (.3)	.5
V-6 (.8)	1.1
(G) Vacuum Control Unit, Renew	
Includes: R&R distributor and reset ignition timing.	
CJ/Scrambler	
Four (.9)	1.2
Six (.4)	.6
Cherokee/Grand Wagoneer/Truck	
Six (.4)	.6
Che/Wag/Comanche	
Four (.4)	.6
V-6 (.9)	1.2
(G) Ignition Cables, Renew	
All models (.4)	.7
(G) Ignition Coil, Renew	
All models (.3)	.5
(G) Ignition Control Unit, Renew	
All models (.5)	.7
(G) Spark Knock Sensor, Renew	
All models (.3)	.5
(G) Distributor Cap and/or Rotor, Renew	
All models (.3)	.5
(G) Ignition Switch, Renew	
All models (.4)	.7

PARTS 2 ELECTRONIC IGNITION 2 PARTS

FOUR-151 ENG
V-6-173 ENG

	Part No.	Price
Distributor Assy.		
1983-Four		
Exc Calif.	●8134001	363.25
Calif.	●8134799	345.75
1984-V-6		
Exc Calif.		
M.T.	8983500947	293.00
A.T.	8983500948	293.00
Calif.	8983500949	284.50
1985-87-V-6		
Exc Calif.		
M.T.	8983501493	237.25
A.T.	8983501494	237.25
Calif.	8983501870	230.25
(1) Distributor Cap		
1983-Four	●8134006	20.75
1984-87-V-6	8983500934	19.00
(2) Rotor		
1983-Four	●8134113	10.75
1984-87-V-6	8983501085	8.00
(3) Trigger Wheel		
1983	N.L.	n.l.

The following component part numbers are representative: Always order by distributor I.D. number.

	Part No.	Price
(4) Main Shaft Assy (Complete)		
1983-Four	●8134195	91.25
1984-V-6		
Exc Calif.		
M.T.	8983501083	89.00
A.T.	8983501084	67.00
Calif.	8983501082	59.00
1985-87-V-6		
Exc Calif.	8983501491	65.25
Calif.	8983501081	59.00
(5) Pole Piece & Plate Assy. (Sensor)		
1983-Four	●8134119	51.00
1984-87-V-6		
Exc Calif.	8983501089	28.50
Calif.	8983500935	30.50

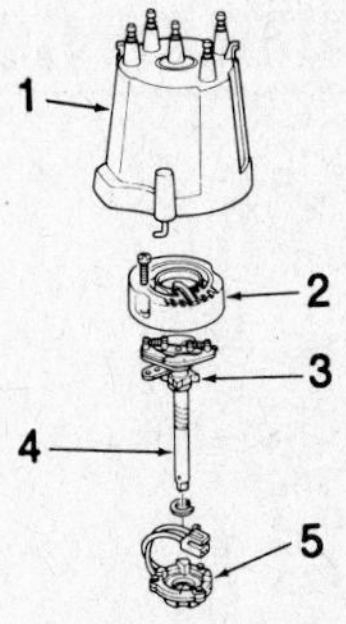

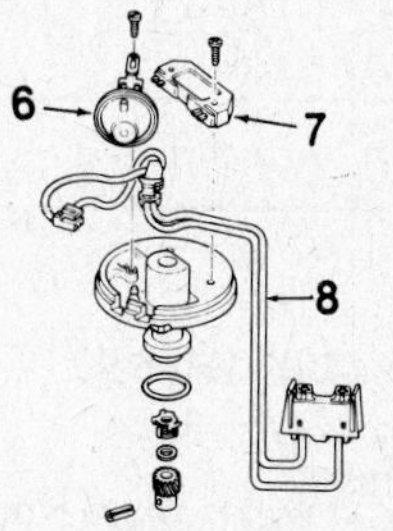

	Part No.	Price
(7) Module		
1984-87-Exc Calif.	●8134117	69.00
1984-87-Calif.	8983500087	32.00
(8) Terminal Block Assy.		
1983	●8134118	15.25
1984-Exc. Calif.	8983501090	35.50
Calif.	8983501337	37.75
1985-87-Exc Calif.	8983501492	12.00
Calif.	8983501496	29.50
Wire Set		
1983-87-V-6	8983500946	46.25
Ignition Coil		
1984-V-6	8134003	79.00
1985-87-V-6	8983501871	40.25

PARTS 2 ELECTRONIC IGNITION 2 PARTS

SIX-258 ENG
V-8-360 ENG

	Part No.	Price
(1) Distributor Assy.		
1983-87-Six	●3242409	110.00
1983-87-V-8	3233174	110.00

Distributor numbers shown are representative: Order by I.D. number on the side of housing.

	Part No.	Price
(2) Vacuum Control		
1983-87-Six	●8134678	32.75
1983-87-V-8	8129470	35.00

Part numbers shown are representative: Order by distributor I.D. number.

	Part No.	Price
(3) Washer		
1983-87	●8128465	.75
(4) Distributor Gear		
1983-87-Six	3231391	17.00
V-8	3208615	31.50
(5) Distributor Cap		
1983-87-Six	●3230457	15.50
V-8	3230757	15.50

PARTS 2 ELECTRONIC IGNITION 2 PARTS

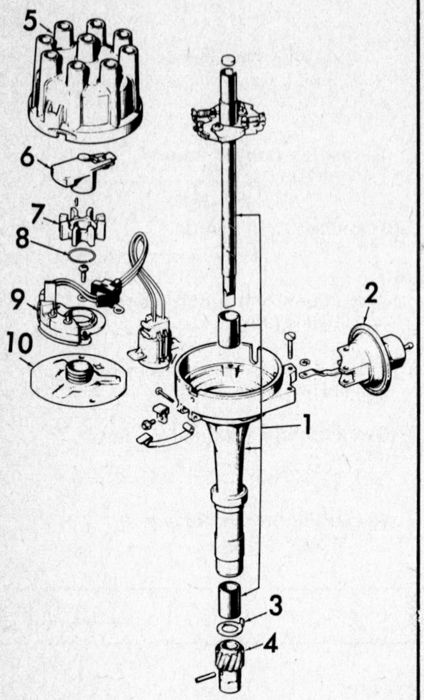

	Part No.	Price
(6) Rotor		
1983-87-Six	●3230821	2.75
V-8	3230765	2.50
(7) Trigger Wheel		
1983-87-Six	●8128422	5.25
V-8	8128899	6.25
(8) Washer (Wave)		
1983-87-V-8	●8128468	.25
(9) Sensor Assy. (Stator Complete)		
1983-87-Six	●8128445	29.25
V-8	8128900	27.25
(10) Plate (Sensor Mounting)		
1983-87-V-8	8128957	3.75

	Part No.	Price
Module		
1983-87	●3230451	119.25
Ignition Coil		
1983-87	●3230427	27.50
Ignition Cable Set		
1983-87		
Six	8134371	13.75
V-8	8129048	20.50
Ignition Switch		
1983-87		
wo/Tilt whl	8128889	16.00
w/Tilt whl	8128890	14.00

PARTS 2 ELECTRONIC IGNITION 2 PARTS

FOUR-150 ENG

	Part No.	Price
(1) Distributor Assy.		
1983-86-w/carb.		
Tag-2700	●3242700	110.00
Tag-3066	3243066	105.75
1986-87-injected	8953002107	34.50
(2) Distributor Cap		
1983-87	●3234451	8.00
(3) Rotor		
1983-87	●3234452	6.50
(4) Trigger Wheel		
1983-87	●8983500412	10.50
(5) Sensor Assy. (Stator Complete)		
1983-87	●8983500409	18.75
(6) Plate		
1983-87	●8983500410	7.00

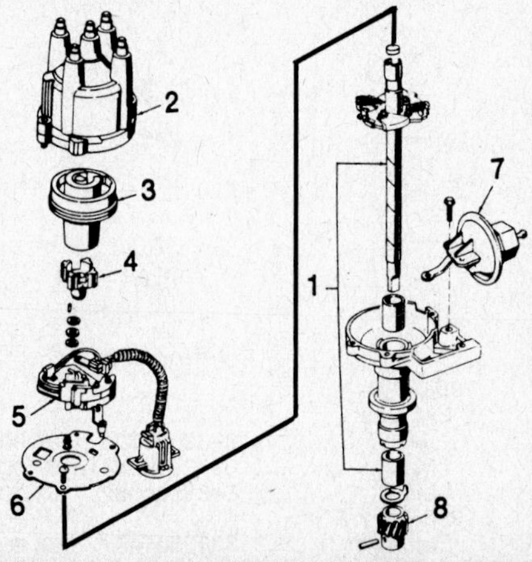

	Part No.	Price
(7) Vacuum Control		
1983-87		
Tag-2700	●8983500413	19.25
Tag-3066	8132802	12.50
Injected	8132802	12.50
(8) Distributor Gear		
1983-87	●8133652	18.25
Ignition Wires		
1983-87	8983502400	11.00
Ignition Coil		
1983-87		
Carb	●3230427	27.50
Injected	7701031135	77.75
Module		
1983-87		
Carb	●3230451	97.00
Injected	8933002299	57.25

LABOR 3 FUEL SYSTEM 3 LABOR

(Factory Time)	Chilton Time
(G) Fuel Pump, Test	
Includes: Disconnect line at carburetor, attach pressure gauge.	
All models	.3
(G) Carburetor Air Cleaner, Service	
All models	.3
(G) Carburetor, Adjust (On Truck)	
All models	.4
(G) Carburetor Assembly, Renew	
Includes: All necessary adjustments.	
Four	
150 eng (.5)	.8
151 eng (.9)	1.3
Six (.8)	1.2
V-6 (.7)	1.1
V-8 (.9)	1.3
(G) Carburetor, R&R and Clean or Recondition	
Includes: All necessary adjustments.	
Four	
150 eng (1.7)	2.5
151 eng (1.6)	2.4
Six (1.6)	2.4
V-6 (1.5)	2.3
V-8 (1.6)	2.4

(Factory Time)	Chilton Time
(G) Idle Speed Solenoid, Renew	
All models (.4)	.5
(G) Carburetor Float Level, Adjust	
Includes: Renew needle valve and seat if required.	
Four-150 eng (.6)	.8
(G) Choke Vacuum Diaphragm, Renew	
All models (.4)	.6
(G) Vacuum Delay Valve, Renew	
All models (.2)	.3

PARTS 3 FUEL SYSTEM 3 PARTS

	Part No.	Price
(G) Electric Choke Relay, Renew		
All models (.3)		.4
(G) Fuel Pump, Renew		
Four (.5)		.7
Six (.5)		.7
V-6 (.5)		.7
V-8 (.7)		.9
(G) Fuel Filter, Renew		
All models (.3)		.4
(G) Fuel Tank, Renew		
CJ/Scrambler (1.0)		1.3
Cherokee/Grand Wagoneer/ Truck (1.4)		1.7
Cke/Wag/Comanche (.8)		1.1
(G) Fuel Gauge (Tank Unit), Renew		
CJ/Scrambler (1.3)		1.6
Cherokee/Grand Wagoneer/ Truck (1.2)		1.5
Cke/Wag/Comanche (.7)		1.0
(G) Fuel Gauge (Dash Unit), Renew		
CJ/Scrambler (1.3)		1.7
Cherokee/Grand Wagoneer/ Truck (.9)		1.2
Cke/Wag/Comanche (.6)		1.0
(G) Intake Manifold and/or Gaskets, Renew		
Four		
150 eng (2.5)		3.6
151 eng (1.4)		2.0
Six (1.5)		2.0
V-6 (3.4)		4.9
V-8 (1.5)		2.2
Renew manif add		.5

THROTTLE BODY INJECTION

	Part No.	Price
(G) Injection System Electrical Test		
All models (.3)		.5
(G) Throttle Plate Assy., Renew		
Includes: System test.		
All models (.7)		1.1
(G) Fuel Injectors, Renew		
Includes: System test.		
All models-one (.7)		1.0
each adtnl		.3
(G) Throttle Body Assy., R&R or Renew		
All models (.4)		1.0
(G) Fuel Meter Assembly, Renew		
All models (.5)		.7
(G) Fuel Pressure Regulator, Renew		
All models (.7)		.9
(G) Fuel Pressure Regulator, Adjust		
All models (.4)		.6
(G) Manifold Pressure Sensor, Renew		
All models (.3)		.4
(G) Wide Open Throttle Switch, Renew		
All models (.4)		.5
(G) Idle Speed Control Motor, Renew		
All models (.4)		.6
(G) Manifold Air Temperature Sensor, Renew		
All models (.3)		.4
(G) Coolant Temperature Sensor, Renew		
All models (.4)		.7
(G) Throttle Position Sensor, Renew		
All models (.5)		.8
(G) Electronic Control Module (ECU), Renew		
All models (.3)		.4
(G) Oxygen Sensor, Renew		
All models (.3)		.5

DIESEL ENGINE

	Part No.	Price
(G) Turbocharger Assy., R&R or Renew		
All models (1.6)		2.5
(G) Intercooler, Renew		
All models (.8)		1.2
(G) Fuel Injector, Renew		
All models-one (.4)		.6
all (1.1)		1.5
(G) Fuel Injection Pump, Renew		
All models (3.7)		5.4
(G) Glow Plug Timer, Renew		
All models (.2)		.4
(G) Glow Plugs, Renew		
All models-one (.4)		.6
all (.7)		1.1
(G) Injection Timing, Adjust		
All models (1.2)		1.5
(G) Intake Manifold and/or Gasket, Renew		
All models (.6)		1.1
Renew manif add (.2)		.5

PARTS 3 FUEL SYSTEM 3 PARTS

	Part No.	Price
Carburetor Assy. (Carter)		
Six-258		
1983-87		
BBD-8338	3241121	322.75
BBD-8339	3241122	335.75
BBD-8340	3241127	323.00
BBD-8341	3241128	336.00
BBD-8349	3241125	317.25
BBD-8351	3241129	262.25
BBD-8360	8933000468	326.50
BBD-8362	●8933000482	326.50
BBD-8364	●8933000469	326.50
BBD-8367	8933000468	326.50
BBD-8383	●8933001707	284.25
BBD-8384	●8933001708	303.25
Carburetor Assy. (Motorcraft)		
V-8-360		
1983-87		
1RHA2	3238411	.75
1RHM2	3238412	255.00
2RHA2A	3241630	246.00
4RHA2	8933001726	209.50
5RHA2	8953002537	209.75
Carburetor Assy. (Rochester)		
Four-150		
1983-87		
7453	●8953000651	493.00
7455	8953000653	N.L.
7700	●8933002115	339.75
7701	●8933002114	339.75
7702	●8933002117	339.75
7703	●8933002116	339.75
7704	8953002637	329.75
7705	8953002638	329.75
7706	8953002639	329.75
7707	8953002640	329.75
7708	8953002641	415.25
Four-151		
1983		
2380	●3241118	434.25
3385	●8933000601	1036.50
V-6-173		
1984-87		
4584	8933001893	698.75
5006	8953002751	735.00
5380	8953002230	544.75
5381	8953002229	544.75
5382	8953002226	544.75
5383	8953002225	551.00
5388	8953002231	696.00
6081	8953004303	574.75
Carburetor Repair Kit (Carter)		
Six-258		
1983-87	●8134232	12.00
Carburetor Repair Kit (Motorcraft)		
1983-87-V-8-360		
exc 5RHA2	8133822	29.00
5RHA2	8983502174	29.50
Carburetor Repair Kit (Rochester)		
Four		
1983	●8134332	40.50
1984-87	●8983500453	21.25
V-6-173		
1984-85-exc. Calif.	8983501011	34.55
1984-Calif.	8983500924	27.50
1985-Calif.	8983501938	33.75
Fuel Pump Assembly (New)		
Four Cyl.		
1983-151	●8132364	36.00
1983-87-150 (w/Carb.)		
CJ	●3228191	34.25
exc CJ	8933002652	35.75
1986-87-150 (wo/Carb) Injected	8983502751	81.50
Six-258		
1983-87		
exc CJ	●3240172	44.25
CJ	●3228191	34.25
V-6-173		
1984-85	8983500873	60.75
1986-87	8983502715	68.50
V-8-360		
1983-87	3227884	34.25
Fuel Flex Line		
1983-87		
1/4″ I.D.	8125843	1.50
5/16″ I.D.	●8125823	1.75

Fuel Tank

Tank and gauge numbers shown are representative: Order by model, year and capacity, in some cases, additional parts are needed.

	Part No.	Price
Wagoneer & Cherokee-10 Series		
1983-87	5362496	130.50
Wagoneer & Cherokee-70 Series		
1984-87-20 gal.	8983500267	204.25
CJ-Series		
1983-87		
15 gal. tank	8128585	191.75
20 gal. tank	5361825	127.75
Fuel Gauge (Tank)		
CJ-Series		
1983-87		
15 gal. tank	5357373	32.25
20 gal. tank	5362090	32.25

PARTS 3 FUEL SYSTEM 3 PARTS

	Part No.	Price
Wagoneer & Cherokee-10 Series		
1983	5363490	21.00
1984-87	5363490	21.00
Wagoneer & Cherokee-70 Series		
1984-87-gas eng.		
13.5 gal.	8953001251	43.75
20 gal.	8953001249	43.75
1984-87-diesel eng.		
13.5 gal.	8953001834	35.25
20 gal.	8953001673	35.25

	Part No.	Price
Fuel Gauge (Dash)		
CJ-Series		
1983-87	8126919	29.75
Wagoneer & Cherokee-10 Series		
1983-84	8126927	22.00
1985-87	8983501434	19.75
Wagoneer & Cherokee-70 Series		
1984-87	8983500298	20.50

	Part No.	Price
Intake Manifold Gasket		
Four		
1983-87		
150 eng.	●3242854	5.25
151 eng.	●8134694	7.75
diesel	7701348923	12.75
Six cyl.		
1983-87-w/258	3237775	6.75
1984-87-w/V-6	8983500828	16.75
V-8-360		
1983-87	8125869	18.25

PARTS 3 ELECTRONIC FUEL INJECTION 3 PARTS

THROTTLE BODY INJECTION

FOUR CYLINDER-150 ENG

	Part No.	Price
Throttle Body Assy.		
1986-87		
M.T.	8953002153	243.75
A.T.	8953002152	243.75
Fuel Body		
1986-87	8983502747	191.75
Pressure Regulator Kit		
1986-87	8983501829	39.75
Fuel Injector		
1986-87	8983502748	134.00
Mounting Kit (Injector)		
1986-87	8983500064	6.75
Gasket Kit (Flare)		
1986-87	8983500065	5.25
O-Ring Kit (Injector)		
1986-87	8983500067	5.25

	Part No.	Price
Idle Speed Actuator Kit		
1986-87	8983502375	64.00
Throttle Position Sensor Kit		
1986-87	8933000169	50.25
Mounting Gasket		
1986-87	8953002154	.50
Switch (Wide Open Throttle)		
1986-87	8983502749	22.75
Fuel Pump		
1986-87	8983502751	81.50

FOUR CYL DIESEL

	Part No.	Price
Injection Pump (New)		
1984-87	7700726944	N.L.
Solenoid Idle Speed		
1984-86	8983502349	197.25

	Part No.	Price
Idler Assy		
1984-87	7946003828	102.75
Solenoid Fuel Shut-Off		
1984-86	8983502331	89.75
Injector Nozzle Assy		
1984-87	7700679943	N.L.
Injector Gasket		
1984-87	7700663363	2.50
Injector O-Ring		
1984-87	7700690542	1.50
Fuel Tube Assy.		
1984-87	7700696528	17.50
Fuel Return Line Assy.		
1984-87	7700695743	30.75
Turbocharger		
1984-87	7701463600	565.25
Vacuum Pump		
1984-87	7700679259	100.25

LABOR 3A EMISSION CONTROLS 3A LABOR

AIR INJECTION SYSTEM

(Factory Time)	Chilton Time
(G) Air Pump, Renew	
CJ/Scrambler	
Four (.9)	1.2
Cke/Wag/Comanche	
V-6 (.5)	.8
All other models	
wo/Serpentine belt (.6)	1.0
w/Serpentine belt (.7)	1.1
(G) Exhaust Check Valve, Renew	
All models (.4)	.5
(G) Air Injection Manifold, Renew	
Four (.5)	.9
Six	
w/V-belt (1.0)	1.6
w/Serpentine belt (1.2)	1.8
V-6-each (.3)	.6
V-8-each (.5)	.9
(G) Diverter Valve, Renew	
Cke/Wag/Comanche	
V-6 (.5)	.7
All other models (.4)	.6
(G) Deceleration Valve, Renew	
Cke/Wag/Comanche	
Four (.4)	.5
All other models (.2)	.3

CHILTON'S EMISSION CONTROL TUNE-UP

1. Clean or renew P.C.V. valve, hoses and filter.
2. Check fuel tank cap for sealing ability.
3. Check fuel tank and fuel lines for leakage.
4. Check evaporation canister and filter. Replace if necessary.
5. Check engine compression to determine leakage of unburned gases. (Add time for items of interference).
6. Test and clean or renew spark plugs.
7. Check engine oil dipstick for sealing ability.
8. Test exhaust system with analyzer and check system for leakage.
9. Check exhaust manifold heat valve for operation.
10. Adjust ignition timing and carburetor idle speed and mixture.
11. Check automatic choke mechanism for free operation.
12. Inspect air cleaner and element.
13. On models so equipped, test distributor vacuum control switch and transmission control switch.

Four	**1.3**
Six	**1.5**
V-6	**1.7**
V-8	**1.8**

For repairs made, charge accordingly.

(Factory Time)	Chilton Time
(G) Air Control Valve, Renew	
All models (.4)	.5

EXHAUST GAS RECIRCULATION

(Factory Time)	Chilton Time
(G) E.G.R. Valve, Renew	
All models (.5)	.6

LABOR 3A EMISSION CONTROLS 3A LABOR

(Factory Time) Chilton Time

FUEL VAPOR RECIRCULATION

(M) P.C.V. Valve, Renew
All models (.3) 3

(M) Charcoal Canister, Renew
Cke/Wag/Comanche (.5) 6
All other models (.3) 4

ELECTRONIC EMISSION CONTROLS

(G) Microprocessor (MCU), Renew
All models (.3) 4

(G) Enrichment Actuator, Renew
All models
stepper motor (.4) 6
duty cycle solenoid (.4) 6

(G) Electric Choke Relay, Renew
All models (.3) 4

(G) Idle Cut-Off Solenoid, Renew
All models (.3) 4

(G) Oxygen Sensor, Renew
All models (.3) 5

PARTS 3A EMISSION CONTROLS 3A PARTS

	Part No.	Price
AIR GUARD SYSTEM		
Air Injection Pump		
1984-87-V-6	8953001371	149.50
1983-87-V-8	8134211	153.75
Diverter Valve		
1984-87		
V-6-exc Calif.	8953000956	36.75
Calif.	8933001322	66.50
(CJ-7 w/Auto trans)		
1983-87-V-8	3230822	41.00
Air Management Valve		
1984-85	8933001682	37.00
1986-87	8953002380	35.00
PULSE AIR		
Pulse Air Control Valve		
1983-87	●8933000355	18.75
Check Valve		
1983-87	●8933000354	14.50
EVAPORATIVE EMISSION TYPE		
Vapor Canister		
1983-87-Four cylinder		
150 eng.	●3239479	36.75
151 eng.	●3237477	71.50
1983-87-6-258	●3239479	36.75
V-8	3232956	43.25
V-6	●3239479	36.75
Filter (Vapor Canister)		
1983-87	3227279	2.75
Crankcase Ventilator Valve (PCV)		
1983-87		
150	●8933001239	N.L.
151	●8132309	4.00
1983-87-Six-258	●8933000887	3.25
1984-87-V-6	8953000960	N.L.
1983-87-V-8	3234216	2.25
PCV Shut-Off Solenoid		
1983-87		
Four-150	8933000722	15.25
Six	8933000722	15.25
TAC SYSTEM		
Air Cleaner Vacuum Motor		
1983	8129407	12.00
Temperature Sensor Kit		
1983-87	8128338	9.50
Thermal Vacuum Switch		
1983-87-exc. V-6	3235329	7.75
1984-87-V-6	8953000714	17.75
Thermal Electric Switch		
1986-87-Injected	8953002951	10.25
1983-87-Six (258)	3240149	13.25
1984-87-V-6	8933001974	11.75

	Part No.	Price
Air Cleaner Element		
1983-87		
exc V-8	●8991386	N.L.
V-8	8992661	N.L.
Injected	8953002184	7.25
Diesel	8953501843	N.L.

EXHAUST GAS RECIRCULATION SYSTEM

E.G.R. Valve

Replacement E.G.R. valves must be ordered according to the stamping number on the original valve.

	Part No.	Price
TRANSMISSION CONTROLLED SPARK		
Solenoid (Vacuum Control)		
1983-87	3218737	33.25
Thermostatic Vacuum Switch		
1983-87 (Number molded on switch)		
switch No.	3216448	23.00
Switch No.	3228894	21.25
Switch No.	3229450	19.50
1983-87 (Number molded on switch)		
Switch No.	3216448	23.00
Switch No.	3228894	21.25
Switch No.	3229450	19.50
Temperature Switch (Override)		
(w/Dual function ported)		
exc. Six	3241784	19.50
Six-258	3238932	19.50
1983	3238932	19.50
1984-87-exc. V-8	3238932	19.50
V-8	8933001669	18.25
T.C.S. Switch		
1983-87	3211322	7.00
ELECTRONIC EMISSION CONTROLS		
MicroProcessor		
Calif.		
M.T.	3240802	147.00
A.T.	3240801	147.00
1983-Four (Calif.)		
Code H4	●8933000495	112.00
1983-Six (CJ Series)		
M.T.		
Code S5	●8933000494	154.50
Code 2S	●8933001079	147.00
Code 5S	●8933001082	147.00
Code S2	●8933001079	147.00
A.T.		
Code S3	●8933001080	147.00
Code 1S	●8933001078	147.00
Code 3S	●8933001080	147.00
Code S1	●8933001078	147.00

	Part No.	Price
1983-Six (Wagoneer & Cherokee)		
M.T.		
Code 2S	●8933001079	147.00
Code S7	8953000523	154.50
Code S2	●8933001079	147.00
Code 7S	●8933001083	147.00
A.T.		
Code 1S	●8933001078	147.00
Code S4	●8933001081	147.00
Code S1	●8933001078	147.00
Code 4S	●8933001081	147.00
1984-87-Four (CJ-Series)		
Code RJ	8933001757	147.00
Code RL	8933001759	147.00
Code RM	8933001760	147.00
1984-87-Six (CJ-Series)		
Code SE	8933001748	147.00
Code SF	8933001749	147.00
Code SG	8933001750	147.00
Code SH	8933001751	147.00
1984-87-Six-Wagoneer & Cherokee-10-Series		
M.T.	8933001744	147.00
A.T.	8933001743	147.00
1984-87-Wagoneer & Cherokee-70-Series		
Code RJ	8933001757	147.00
Code B2	8933001347	147.00
Code RK	8933001758	147.00
Code RN	8953001948	147.00
Code RR	8953001950	145.50
Code RL	8933001759	147.00
Code RM	8933001760	147.00
Code RP	8953001949	145.50
Code RS	8953001951	145.50
Idle Speed Controller		
1983-87	3240762	127.50
Oxygen Sensor		
1983-87-exc. below	8933000598	52.00
1985-Four	●8933002455	34.00
1984-87-V-6	8953000886	36.75
Emission Maintenance Switch		
1983-87-Four		
Calif.	3235649	60.50
Electric Choke Relay		
1983-87	8953000919	11.00
Sol-Vac Throttle Positioner		
1983-87	8983500342	49.25

LABOR 4 ALTERNATOR AND REGULATOR 4 LABOR

	(Factory Time)	Chilton Time
(G) Alternator Circuits, Test		
Includes: Test battery, regulator and alternator output.		
All models		.6
(G) Alternator Assy., Renew		
Cke/Wag/Comanche		
Four	(.4)	.6
V-6	(.3)	.5
Diesel	(1.1)	1.6
All other models	(.4)	.6
Add circuit test if performed.		
(G) Alternator, R&R and Recondition		
Cke/Wag/Comanche		
Four	(1.0)	1.7
V-6	(.8)	1.5
Diesel	(2.0)	3.0
All other models	(.9)	1.6
Add circuit test if performed.		
(G) Alternator Regulator, Renew		
Cke/Wag/Comanche		
Four	(.6)	1.0
V-6	(.7)	1.1
Diesel	(1.3)	2.0
All other models	(.6)	1.0
Add circuit test if performed.		
(G) Voltmeter, Renew		
CJ/Scrambler	(.5)	.9
(G) Ammeter, Renew		
Cherokee/Grand Wagoneer/Truck	(.8)	1.3

PARTS 4 ALTERNATOR AND REGULATOR 4 PARTS

DELCO REMY

Heavy Duty (78) alternator used for service: (78 Amp) (Remanufactured No. 8982775005).

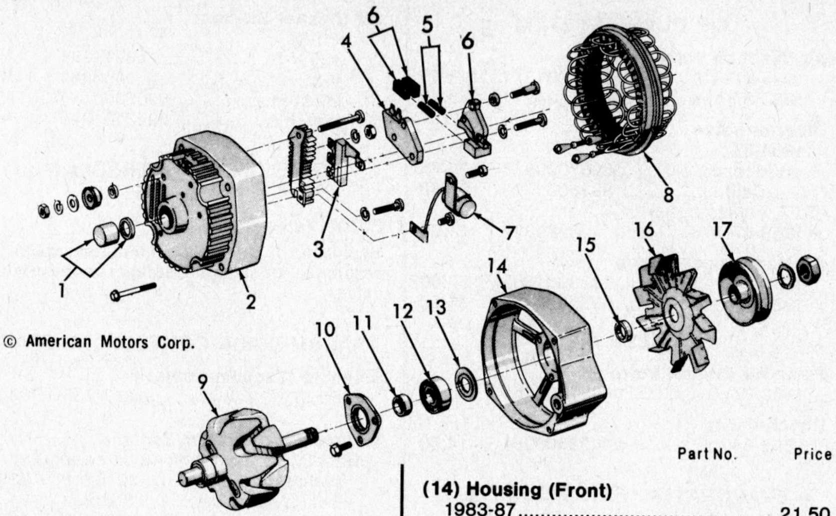

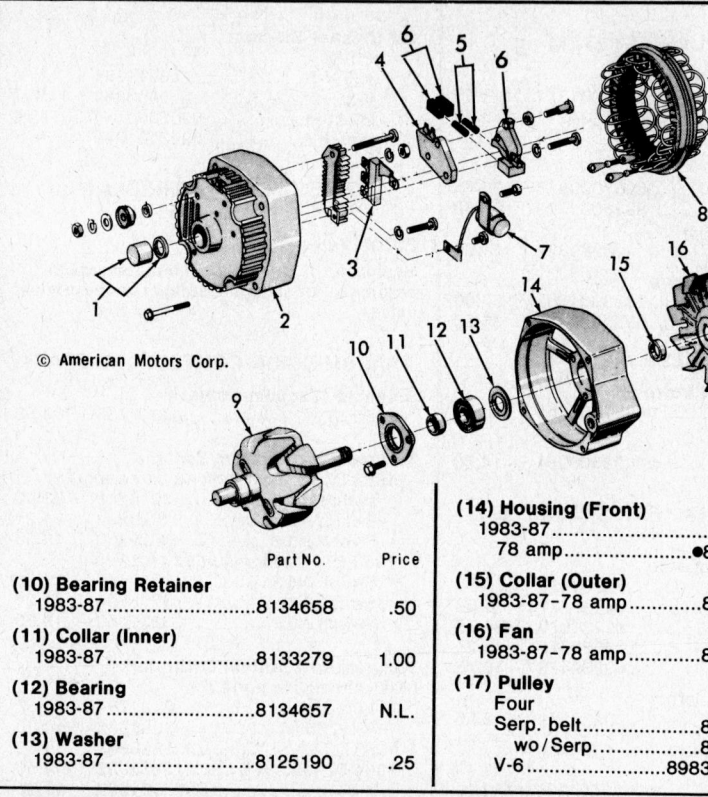

© American Motors Corp.

	Part No.	Price
Alternator Assy.		
1983-87-exc. Diesel		
78 amp	●8134664	264.00
(1) Bearing		
1983-87	●8134644	7.00
(2) Housing (Rear)		
1983-87-exc. Diesel		
78 amp	●8134651	48.50
(3) Diode Trio Assembly		
1983-87	●8133268	7.75
Rectifier, Diode		
1983-87	8134650	33.75
(4) Regulator Assembly		
1983-87	●8125176	31.25
(5) Spring		
1983-87	8133272	.50
(6) Brush Holder		
1983-87	●8134652	9.50
(7) Capacitor		
1983-87	●8125183	5.75
(8) Stator		
1983-87		
78 amp	●8134648	51.75
(9) Rotor		
1983-87	●8134645	63.50
(10) Bearing Retainer		
1983-87	8134658	.50
(11) Collar (Inner)		
1983-87	8133279	1.00
(12) Bearing		
1983-87	8134657	N.L.
(13) Washer		
1983-87	8125190	.25
(14) Housing (Front)		
1983-87		21.50
78 amp	●8134655	28.25
(15) Collar (Outer)		
1983-87-78 amp	8134659	3.50
(16) Fan		
1983-87-78 amp	8134662	10.00
(17) Pulley		
Four		
Serp. belt	8134194	8.75
wo/Serp.	8132698	11.50
V-6	8983500433	22.50

PARTS 4 ALTERNATOR AND REGULATOR 4 PARTS

PARIS-RHONE (DIESEL)

	Part No.	Price
Alternator Assy.		
1984-87		
60 amp	8982775028	134.00
70 amp	8982775029	141.50
(1) Housing (Front)		
1984-87	8983502018	42.00
(2) Rotor		
1984-87		
60 amp	8983502028	89.75
70 amp	8983502015	89.75
(3) Stator		
1984-87		
60 amp	8983501991	71.00
70 amp	8983502016	90.50
(4) Bearing		
1984-87	8983501998	17.75
(5) Bearing Cap		
1984-87	8983501997	2.50
(6) Housing		
1984-87	8983502019	42.00
(7) Rectifier		
1984-87		
60 amp	8983502029	59.75
70 amp	8983502020	94.50
(8) Cover		
1984-87	8983502002	4.75
(9) Regulator		
1984-87		
60 amp	8983502031	75.00
70 amp	8983502023	52.25
Brush Kit		
1984-87		
60 amp	8983502030	39.50
70 amp	8983502021	6.00

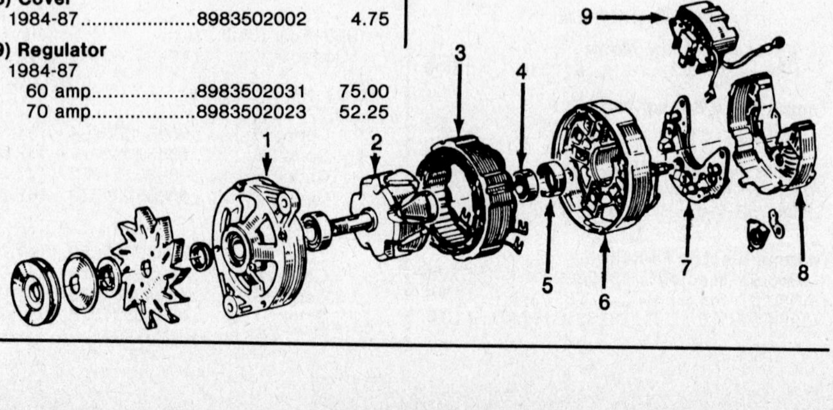

LABOR 5 STARTING SYSTEM 5 LABOR

(Factory Time)	Chilton Time
(G) Starter Draw Test (On Truck)	
All models	.3
(G) Starter Assy., Renew	
All models	
Gas (.4)	.6
Diesel (2.0)	2.9
Add draw test if performed.	
(G) Starter, R&R and Recondition	
Includes: Turn down armature.	
All models	
Gas (1.0)	2.0
Diesel (2.6)	4.0
Renew field coils add	.5
Add draw test if performed.	
(G) Starter Drive, Renew	
Includes: R&R starter.	
All models	
Gas (.6)	.9
Diesel (2.2)	3.2
(G) Starter Solenoid, Renew	
Includes: R&R starter.	
All models	
Gas (.9)	1.2
Diesel (2.5)	3.5
(G) Starter Relay, Renew	
All models (.3)	.4
(M) Battery Cables, Renew	
All models	
positive	.3
negative	.3
(M) Battery Terminals, Clean	
All models	.3

PARTS 5 STARTING SYSTEM 5 PARTS

	Part No.	Price
Starter Motor (Exc. V-6 & Diesel)		
1983-87-exc. Four	●5752791	177.00
Four cylinder		
150 eng.	●3242283	140.25
151 eng.	●8134193	198.50
(1) Seal (Cup)		
1983-87	8120029	.25
(2) Bushing		
1983-87-exc Four	●8120030	1.50
Four	●8130953	.50
(3) Drive End		
1983-87-exc. Four	●8133036	20.00
Four cylinder		
150	8983500398	16.00
151	●8133923	29.00
(4) Spring		
1983-87-exc. Four	3207426	1.00
Four	8133928	2.00
(5) Drive Assy.		
1983-87-exc Four	●8120193	21.00
Four cylinder		
150	●8983500399	22.00
151	●8130940	24.25
(6) Spacer or Bearing		
1983-87	8121196	1.25
(7) Armature (New)		
1983-87-exc. Four	●8120028	72.25
Four		
150	8133926	100.00
151 eng.	●8983500396	44.00
(8) Point Kit		
1983-87-exc. 150	8128446	9.00
150 eng.	8983510190	12.00
(9) Field Coil Set		
1983-87-exc. 150	●8128438	66.75
150 eng.	●8983500392	36.00
Frame & Field Assy.		
1983-87-Four	8133924	74.00
(10) Brush Set		
1983-87-exc. Four	●8128434	5.75

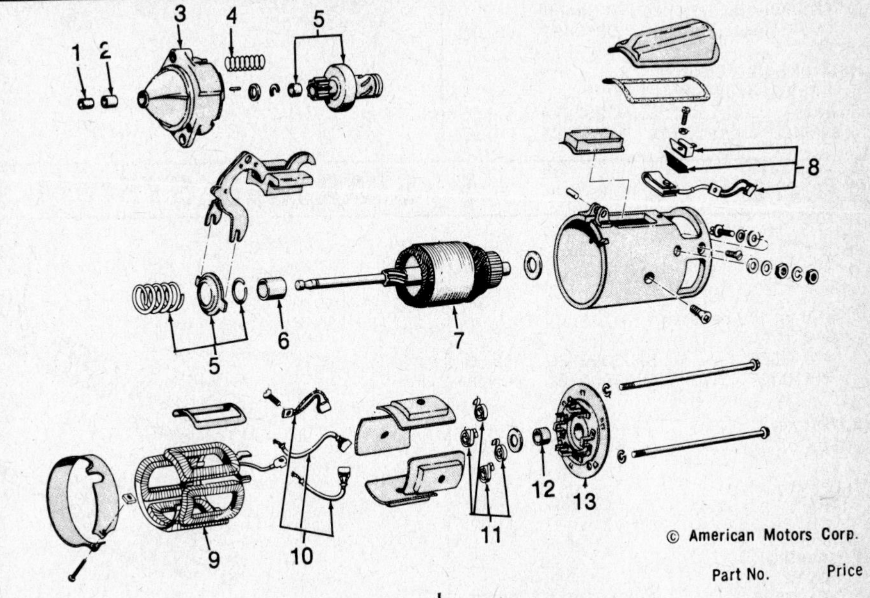

	Part No.	Price
Four		
150 (Pos.)	●8983500401	1.75
150 (Neg.)	●8983500402	1.00
151	●8130934	.75
Brush Holder Assy.		
1983-87-exc. Four	●8134652	9.50
Four		
150	8983500403	1.75
151	8130935	1.75
(11) Springs		
1983-87-exc. Four	8128441	1.75
Four		
150	8983500395	1.00
151	8133928	2.00

	Part No.	Price
(12) Bushing		
1983-87-exc. 151	8121196	1.25
151	●8130953	.50
(13) Commutator End		
1983-87-exc. Four	●8128440	5.75
Four		
150	●8983500397	7.75
151	●8133922	7.50
Starter Motor Relay		
1983-87-exc Four		
M.T.	3230406	11.25
A.T.	5752125	13.75
1983-87-Four		
150	●3235898	11.25
151	5758600	15.25

PARTS 5 STARTING SYSTEM 5 PARTS

DIESEL

	Part No.	Price
Starter Motor Assy.		
1985-87	8982775042	136.50
(1) Solenoid		
1985-87	N.L.	
(2) Bushing		
1985-87	8983502044	3.25
(3) Lever Assy.		
1985-87	8983502045	29.50
(4) Plate		
1985-87	8983502051	65.50
(5) Bushing		
1985-87	8983502052	4.75
(6) Bushing		
1985-87	8983502054	6.50
(7) Cover (Rear)		
1985-87	8983502053	98.75
(8) Drive Assy.		
1985-87	8983502041	84.50
(9) Armature		
1985-87	8983502039	214.25
(10) Starter Field (Coil Kit)		
1985-87	8983502049	114.50

PARTS 5 STARTING SYSTEM 5 PARTS

	Part No.	Price
Brush Kit		
1985-87	8983502055	23.00
Ignition & Starter Switch (Dash)		
1983-87		
wo/Tilt whl	●3250576	17.00
w/Tilt whl	8128890	14.50
Battery Cable (Ground)		
1983-87-exc. Four	5465067	14.75
Four		
150	5764178	9.75
151	5752037	13.50
Battery Cable to Starter Relay		
(Exc. 70 Series)		
1983-87-Four	5752038	11.50
1983-87-Six	5350457	10.00
1983-87-V-8-exc below	5465069	9.25
Wagoneer & Cherokee (70 Series)		
CJ-Series	5350457	10.00
Neutral Safety Switch		
1983-87-exc.		
Diesel	●3232844	9.25
1985-87-Diesel	●3232844	9.25

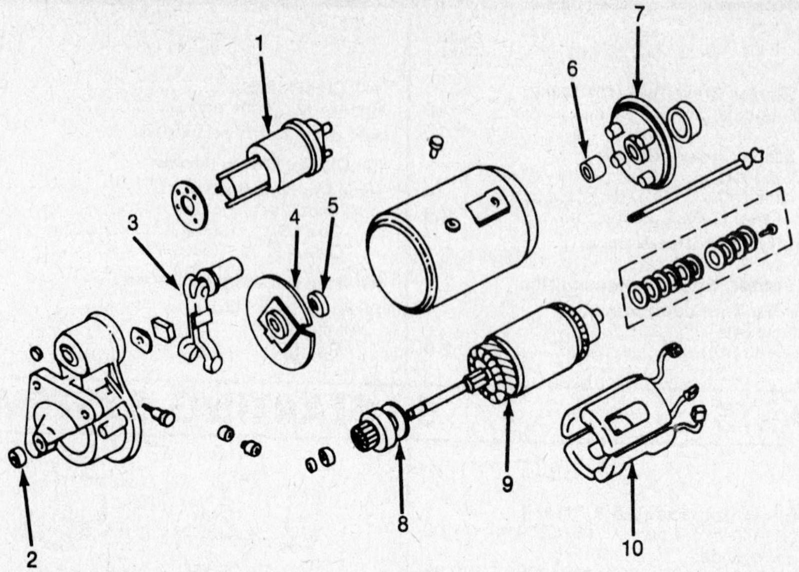

PARTS 5 STARTING SYSTEM 5 PARTS

V-6-173

	Part No.	Price
(1) Starter Motor Assy.		
1984-87		
No. 9535	8953000760	169.50
No. 8427	8953002124	N.L.
(2) Plunger		
1984-87	8133927	11.50
(3) Lever		
1984-87	8130942	7.00
(4) Housing		
1984-87		
No. 9535	8983500939	26.50
No. 8427	8983501385	27.50
(5) Drive Assy.		
1984-87		
No. 9535	●8130940	24.25
No. 8427	8983501388	24.75
(6) Armature		
1984-87		
No. 9535	●8134198	94.00
No. 8427	8983501382	97.00
(7) Rear Cover		
1984-87	●8133922	7.50

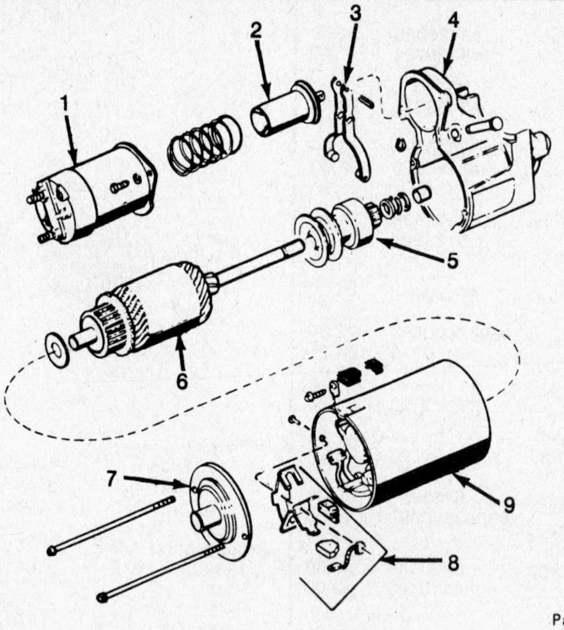

	Part No.	Price
(8) Brush and Holder (Kit)		
1984-87	8130933	14.50
(9) Housing		
1984-87		
No. 9535	●8134196	83.50
No. 8427	8983501383	86.00

LABOR 6 BRAKE SYSTEM 6 LABOR

	(Factory Time)	Chilton Time
(G) Brake Pedal Free Play, Adjust		
All models		.4
(G) Bleed Brakes (Four Wheels)		
Includes: Fill master cylinder.		
All models	(.4)	.5
(G) Brake Shoes and/or Pads, Renew		
Includes: Install new or exchange brake shoes or pads. Adjust service and hand brake. Bleed system.		
front-disc	(.7)	1.1
rear		
semi-float axle	(.9)	1.5
full float axle	(1.2)	1.9
Resurface disc rotor, add-each		.9
Resurface brake drum, add-each		.5
(G) Rear Brake Drum, Renew		
All models-one	(.3)	.5
(G) Pressure Limiting Valve, Renew		
Includes: Bleed system.		
All models	(1.0)	1.4

LABOR 6 BRAKE SYSTEM 6 LABOR

	(Factory Time)	Chilton Time

BRAKE HYDRAULIC SYSTEM

(G) Wheel Cylinders, Renew
Includes: Bleed system.

All models-one (.9)	1.3
both (1.5)	2.3

(G) Wheel Cylinders, R&R and Recondition
Includes: Bleed system.

All models-one (.9)	1.6
both (1.5)	2.9

(G) Master Cylinder, Renew
Includes: Bleed system.

CJ/Scrambler (.9)	1.4
All other models (.7)	1.2

(G) Master Cylinder, R&R and Rebuild
Includes: Bleed system.

CJ/Scrambler (1.4)	2.0
All other models (1.2)	1.8

(G) Brake Hose, Renew (Flex)
Includes: Bleed system.

All models-one (.6)	.9

(G) Brake System, Flush and Refill

All models	1.2

DISC BRAKES

(G) Disc Brake Pads, Renew
Includes: Install new disc brake pads only.

All models (.7)	1.1

COMBINATIONS

Add to Brakes, Renew

See Machine Shop Operations

(G) RENEW WHEEL CYLINDER	
Each	.2
(G) REBUILD WHEEL CYLINDER	
Each	.3
(G) RENEW MASTER CYLINDER	
All models	1.0
(G) REBUILD MASTER CYLINDER	
All models	1.5
(G) RENEW BRAKE HOSE	
Each	.3
(G) RENEW REAR WHEEL GREASE SEALS	
Semi-floating axle	1.4
Full floating axle	.6
(G) REPACK FRONT WHEEL BEARINGS (BOTH WHEELS)	
Drum brake	.6
Disc brake	.8
(G) RENEW BRAKE DRUMS	
Each	.2
(G) RENEW DISC BRAKE ROTOR	
Each	.3
(G) CALIPER ASSEMBLY, RENEW	
Each	.3
(G) CALIPER ASSEMBLY, REBUILD	
Each	.5

	(Factory Time)	Chilton Time

(G) Disc Brake Rotor, Renew

Cke/Wag/Comanche	
one (.3)	.5
both (.6)	.9
All other models	
one (.6)	1.0
both (1.2)	1.8

(G) Caliper Assembly, Renew
Includes: Bleed system.

All models-one (.6)	1.0
both (1.0)	1.8

(G) Caliper Assy., R&R and Recondition
Includes: Bleed system.

All models-one (.9)	1.5
both (1.5)	2.8

POWER BRAKES

(G) Power Brake Booster, Renew

All models (.6)	1.0

(G) Vacuum Check Valve, Renew

All models (.2)	.3

PARKING BRAKE

(G) Parking Brake, Adjust

All models (.3)	.4

(G) Parking Brake Lever, Renew

All models (.5)	.7

(G) Parking Brake Cables, Renew

All models	
primary (.7)	1.0
secondary	
semi-float axle (.7)	1.0
full float axle (1.2)	1.5

PARTS 6 BRAKE SYSTEM 6 PARTS

REAR BRAKES

	Part No.	Price
(1) Brake Shoe Set (Rear)		
CJ-Series		
1983-87	8128616	58.50
Wagoneer & Cherokee		
1983-87-10 Series	8127782	46.75
1984-87-70 Series	●8133818	69.00
(2) Brake Wheel Cylinder (Rear)		
CJ-Series		
1983-87-right	3225196	24.82
left	3225197	24.82
Wagoneer & Cherokee		
1983-87-10 Series	8126742	27.75
1984-87-70 Series		
right	8952000848	23.00
left	8952000849	23.00
Rear Wheel Cyl. Repair Kit		
CJ-Series		
1983-87	8125878	3.75
Wagoneer & Cherokee		
1983-87-10 Series	8124566	4.75
1984-87-70 Series	8983500987	7.25
Brake Hose (Front)		
CJ-Series		
1983-87-exc. below	5363917	12.00
CJ 7 & 8		
right	5363756	18.75
left	5363908	18.75

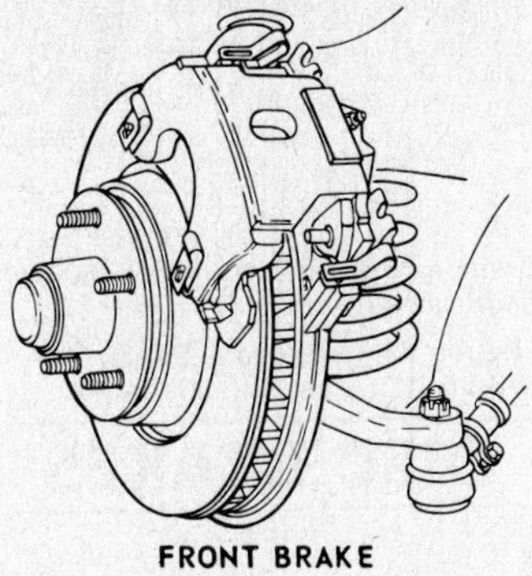

FRONT BRAKE

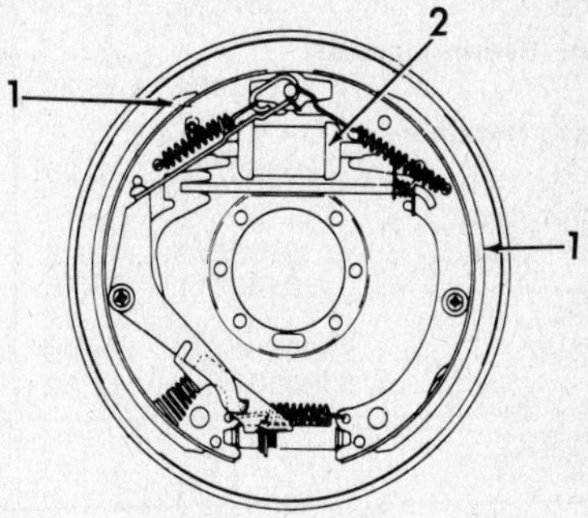

REAR BRAKE

	Part No.	Price
Wagoneer & Cherokee		
1983-87-10 Series	5359323	18.75
1984-85-70 Series		
right	8952000160	10.00
left	8952000161	10.00
1986-87-70 Series		
right	8952001404	10.25
left	8952001405	10.25
Brake Hose (Rear)		
CJ-Series		
1983-87	5362842	18.75
Wagoneer & Cherokee		
1983-87-10 Series	5355076	14.75
1984-87-70 Series	8952000162	8.50

	Part No.	Price
Master Cylinder Assy. (Manual)		
CJ-Series		
1983-87	5364779	105.00
Master Cylinder Repair Kit (Manual)		
CJ-Series		
1983-87	8983500896	27.50
Brake Drum (Rear)		
CJ-Series		
1983-87	5359028	74.50
Wagoneer & Cherokee		
1983-87-10 Series	5359281	74.00
1984-87-70 Series	8952001151	74.00

PARTS 6 BRAKE SYSTEM 6 PARTS

	Part No.	Price
Grease Retainer (Front)		
1983-exc CJ	5359703	6.25
CJ-Series	5365082	6.00
1984-87-exc. below	5359703	6.25
CJ-Series	5365082	6.00
70 Series	●3238137	2.00
Rear Oil Seal		
CJ-Series		
1983-87	3170700	4.25
Wagoneer & Cherokee		
1983-87-10 Series	3235929	6.00
1984-87-70 Series	8953000476	1.00

PARKING BRAKE

	Part No.	Price
Parking Brake Lever (Foot Operated)		
1983-87-exc below	5362139	29.00
CJ-Series	5355477	28.50
Parking Brake Lever (Hand Operated)		
1984-87-70 Series	7700086078	N.L.
Brake Cable (Front)		
CJ-Series		
1983-87-CJ-5	5355287	18.25
CJ-8	5355286	23.00
CJ-7	5353238	20.00
Wagoneer & Cherokee		
1983-87-exc 70 Series		
4 Spd	5370041	13.75
5 Spd	5370042	13.50
(auto trans)		
Six	5370042	13.50
V-8	5370041	13.75
Brake Cable (Rear)		
CJ-Series		
1983-87-right	3239949	15.50
left-CJ-7, CJ-8	3242203	15.25
left-CJ-5	3233903	15.25
Wagoneer & Cherokee		
1983-87-10 Series	5362132	21.50
1984-87-70 series	8952001153	11.00

POWER BRAKES

	Part No.	Price
Master Cylinder Assy. (Power)		
CJ-Series		
1983-87	8983500995	104.75
Wagoneer & Cherokee		
1983-87-10 Series	8133316	136.25
1984-87-70 Series		
w/Sensor	8952000657	129.00
wo/Sensor	●3241807	94.50
Repair Kit (Master Cylinder)		
10 Series	8133317	69.00
CJ-Series	8134247	39.75
70 Series	8983510015	25.75
Power Section (Power Unit)		
1983-87-exc. below	8983500986	208.50
CJ-Series	8133909	218.50
1984-87-70 Series		
Gas eng.	8983501196	225.00
Diesel eng.	8983501534	127.00
Vacuum Hose (Power Unit)		
1983-87 (One foot)	8125883	2.50
1984-87-Wagoneer & Cherokee-70 Series		
Four-150	3242729	3.00
Vacuum Check Valve (Power Unit)		
1983-87-exc. below	8125991	8.25
CJ-Series	4487455	8.25
1984-87-70 Series		
Gas eng.	4487455	8.25
Diesel eng.	8983501532	5.50

PARTS 6 DISC BRAKES 6 PARTS

GRAND WAGONEER & CHEROKEE (10 SERIES)

	Part No.	Price
(1) Drive Flange		
1983-87	5358494	24.50
(2) Cup (Spring)		
1983-87	5352650	3.00
(3) Wheel Bearing (Outer)		
1983-87	●3156052	11.50
(4) Bearing Cup (Outer)		
1983-87	925447	5.25
(5) Disc Assy. (w/Hub)		
1983-87	5357391	157.00
(6) Bearing Cup (Inner)		
1983-87	5357394	116.25
(7) Wheel Bearing (Inner)		
1983-87	5357401	15.75
(8) Grease Retainer		
1983-87	5359703	6.25
(9) Caliper Assy.		
1983-85-right	8133312	170.25
left	8133311	170.25
1985-87		
right	8983501980	175.25
left	8983501981	175.25

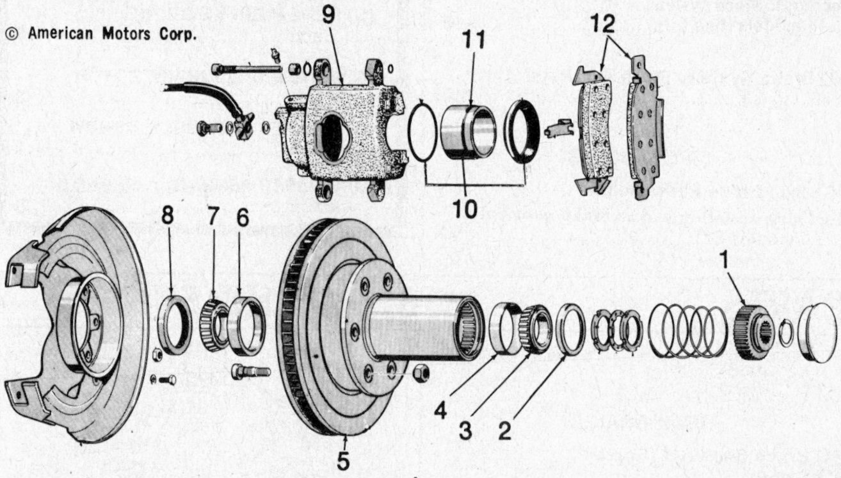

Used with caliper casting number 18007117 (on outboard surface).

	Part No.	Price
(10) Repair Kit (w/Boot & Seals)		
1983-87	8124574	9.75
(11) Piston		
1983-87	8124571	17.75
(12) Pad Set		
1983-87	8983501356	61.00

PARTS 6 DISC BRAKES 6 PARTS

WAGONEER & CHEROKEE-70 SERIES

	Part No.	Price
(1) Rotor		
1984-87	●3251156	117.00
(2) Hub		
1984-87	8953000234	61.00
Hub Assembly		
Contains hub, carrier and all bearings and seals.		
1984-87	8953000228	167.75
(3) Seal		
1984-87	●3238137	2.00

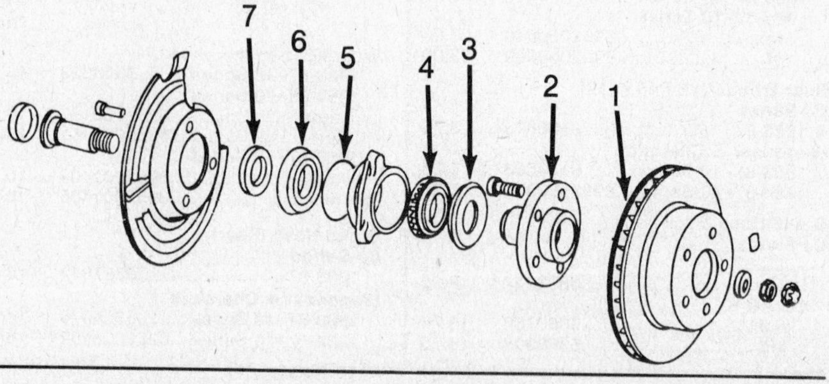

PARTS 6 DISC BRAKES 6 PARTS

	Part No.	Price
(4) Bearing		
1984-87	8953000238	23.75
(5) Carrier (Hub)		
1984-87	8953000228	167.75
(6) Bearing		
1984-87	8953000238	23.75
(7) Seal		
1984-87	8953000239	1.75
(8) Pad Kit		
1984-85	8983500414	58.00
1986-87	8983501167	59.25
(9) Caliper Assy.		
1984-87-left	●8133847	102.00
right	●8133846	102.00
(10) Piston Kit		
1984-87	●8133845	19.00
(11) Seal Kit		
1984-87	●8133852	6.75

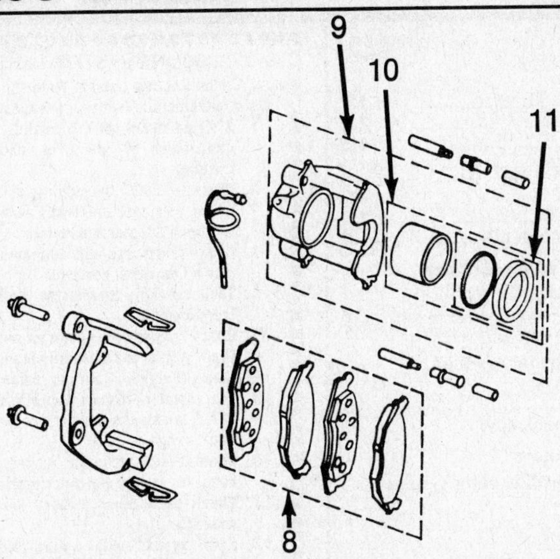

PARTS 6 DISC BRAKES 6 PARTS

	Part No.	Price
(1) Flange & Gasket		
1983-87	5362000	31.50
(2) Wheel Bearing Assy.		
1983-87-outer	●3156052	11.50
inner	5356661	10.50
(3) Bearing Cup		
1983-87-outer	925447	5.25
inner	8127630	5.50
(4) Pad Set		
1983-87	●8133853	53.00
(5) Rotor Assy. (w/Hubs)		
1983-87	5363421	149.50
(6) Grease Retainer (Inner)		
1983-87	5365082	6.00
(7) Front Brake Hose		
1983-87-exc.		
below	5363917	12.00
CJ-7 & CJ-8		
right	5363756	18.75
left	5363908	18.75

FRONT DISC BRAKES

© American Motors Corp.

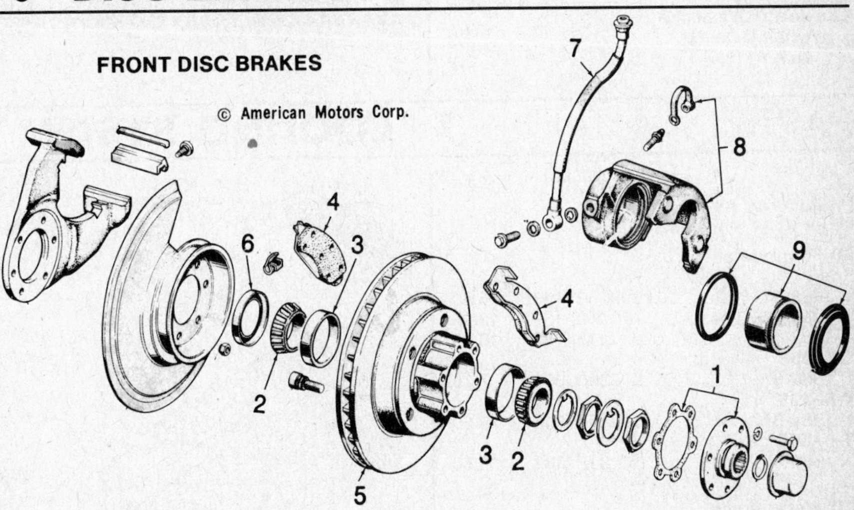

	Part No.	Price
(8) Caliper Assy.		
1983-87-right	●8133846	102.00
left	●8133847	102.00

	Part No.	Price
(9) Repair Kit (w/Boot & Seals)		
1983-87		
wo/Piston	●8133852	6.75
w/Piston	●8133845	19.00

LABOR 7 COOLING SYSTEM 7 LABOR

(Factory Time)	Chilton Time
(M) Winterize Cooling System	
Includes: Run engine to check for leaks, tighten all hose connections. Test radiator and pressure cap, drain radiator and engine block. Add anti-freeze and refill cooling system.	
All models	.5
(M) Thermostat, Renew	
All models (.5)	.6
(M) Radiator Assy., R&R or Renew	
Includes: Drain and refill cooling system.	
Cke/Wag/Comanche	
wo/A.C. (.8)	1.2
w/A.C. (1.5)	2.2
All other models (.5)	.9
ADD THESE OPERATIONS TO RADIATOR R&R	
(G) Boil & Repair	1.5
(G) Rod Clean	1.9
(G) Repair Core	1.3
(G) Renew Tank	1.6
(G) Renew Trans. Oil Cooler	1.9
(G) Recore Radiator	1.7
(M) Radiator Hoses, Renew	
All models	
upper (.4)	.5
lower (.5)	.6
(M) Viscous Fan Assembly, Renew	
All models (.5)	.7
(G) Water Pump, Renew	
CJ/Scrambler	
Four	
150 eng (1.1)	1.7
151 eng (.7)	1.2
Six (1.0)	1.5
Cherokee/Grand Wagoneer/Truck	
Six (1.0)	1.5
V-8	
wo/A.C. (1.3)	2.0
w/A.C. (1.9)	2.8

LABOR 7 COOLING SYSTEM 7 LABOR

(Factory Time)	Chilton Time
Cke/Wag/Comanche	
Four (1.1)	1.7
V-6 (1.3)	2.0
Diesel (3.0)	4.5
(G) Temperature Gauge (Dash Unit), Renew	
CJ/Scrambler (1.3)	1.6
Cke/Wag/Comanche (.6)	1.0
(G) Temperature Gauge (Engine Unit), Renew	
All models (.3)	.4
w/Diesel eng add	.1
(G) Water Jacket Expansion Plugs, Renew	
each	.5
Add time to gain accessibility.	
(G) Heater Hoses, Renew	
Includes: Drain and refill cooling system.	
All models	
one or all (.5)	.7
(G) Heater Core, R&R or Renew	
CJ/Scrambler (1.2)	2.3
Cherokee/Grand Wagoneer/Truck (.8)	1.5
Cke/Wag/Comanche	
wo/A.C. (1.7)	3.3
w/A.C. (2.0)	3.9

COOLING SYSTEM TUNE-UP

An Annual Cooling System Tune-Up Suggestion List should include (with some exceptions):

1. A visual check of the cooling system for indications of leaks or excessive oil content.
2. Pressure check the cooling system for internal and external leaks with filler cap and neck adapter and tester.
3. Check crankcase and automatic transmission oil for water content.
4. Test coolant thermostat with radiator thermometer.
5. Check temperature gauge for accuracy.
6. Drain system and flush till clean.
7. Clean foreign matter from radiator fins.
8. Test radiator pressure cap with cap tester.
9. Check fan blades and pulleys for alignment and damage.
10. Internal and external inspection of all hoses for cracks and deterioration.
11. Check core plugs (where possible) for seepage.
12. Refill system with correct coolant and check for air locks.
13. Check condition and tension of drive belts with tension gauge.

All models 1.5

(Factory Time)	Chilton Time
ADD THESE OPERATIONS TO HEATER CORE R&R	
(G) Boil & Repair	1.2
(G) Repair Core	.9
(G) Recore	1.2
(G) Heater Water Control Valve, Renew	
All models (.4)	.5
(G) Temperature Control Head, Renew	
Cke/Wag/Comanche (.4)	.7
Cherokee/Grand Wagoneer/Truck	
1985 & later (.3)	.6
1984 & earlier (.7)	1.1
All other models (.7)	1.1
(G) Heater Blower Motor, Renew	
CJ/Scrambler (1.0)	1.6
All other models (.4)	.7
(G) Blower Motor Switch, Renew	
CJ/Scrambler	
Heater (.3)	.5
A.C. (.6)	1.1
Cherokee/Grand Wagoneer/Truck	
Heater (.7)	1.2
A.C. (.6)	1.1
Cke/Wag/Comanche (.4)	.7

PARTS 7 COOLING SYSTEM 7 PARTS

	Part No.	Price
(1) Radiator Assy.		
Order by year and model.		
(2) Thermostat		
Four		
1983-87-150	●8983501426	8.50
1985-87-Diesel	7700697157	12.25
1983-151	●8134146	10.25
Six-258		
1983-87	8983500360	7.75
V-6-173		
1984-87	8983500813	9.00
V-8-360		
1983-87	8127383	8.50
(3) Water Pump		
Four		
1985-87-Diesel	8982775056	38.75
1983-87-150		
w/Serp. belt	8982775047	24.75
wo/Serp. belt	8982775046	24.75
1983-151	●8126699	47.50
Six cyl.-258		
1983-87		
w/Serp. belt	8982775047	24.75
wo/Serp. belt	8982775046	24.75
V-6-173		
1984-87	8982775049	29.00
V-8-360		
1983-87	3234427	64.75
(4) Fan Belt		
Order by model & description.		
Heat Indicator Sending Unit		
1983-87-exc 151 eng.	3177594	7.50
151 eng.	5751811	8.25
1984-85-70 Series		
Light	3230408	7.25
Gauge	3242662	10.50
V-6 eng.		
Light	8933001542	8.75
Gauge	8933001543	17.50

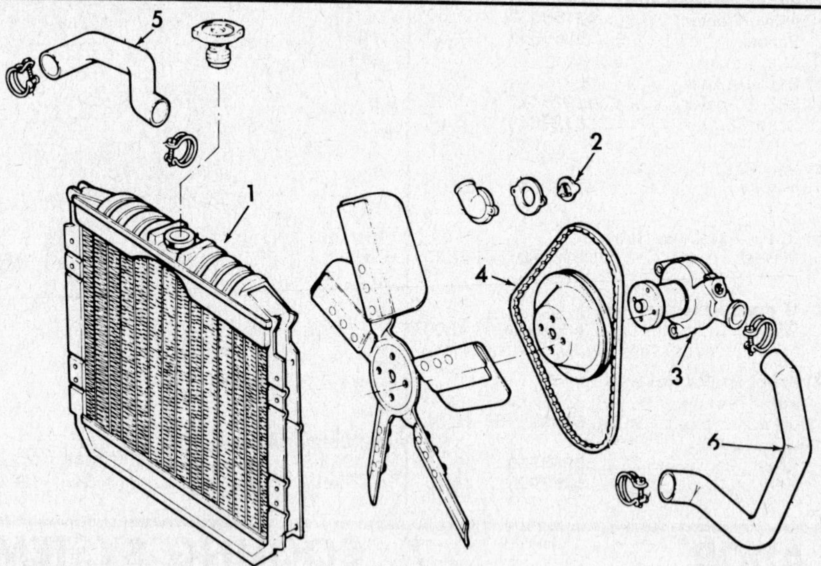

	Part No.	Price
Heat Indicator (Dash)		
CJ-Series		
1983-87	8126920	27.50
Wagoneer & Cherokee		
1983-84-10 Series	8126928	27.50
1985-87		
10 Series	8983501428	19.75
1984-87-70 Series		
Gas eng.	8983500311	19.75
Diesel eng	8983501560	21.25
w/Light	8983510028	5.00
bezel	8983501592	8.00
(5) Radiator Hose (Upper)		
CJ-Series		
1983-87-150	5364659	9.75
151	5360950	12.75

	Part No.	Price
258	5362697	9.75
360	999632	11.25
Wagoneer & Cherokee		
1983-87-258	5362698	9.75
360	5354528	8.50
1984-87		
w/Diesel	8953001175	8.75
150		
w/A.C.	8983001439	N.L.
wo/A.C.	8953001471	N.L.
V-6		
w/A.C.	8953000013	9.75
wo/A.C.	8953000509	9.75
(6) Radiator Hose (Lower)		
CJ-Series		
1983-87-150	5364660	9.75
151	5360951	16.25

PARTS 7 COOLING SYSTEM 7 PARTS

	Part No.	Price
258	5354380	8.50
360	5354528	8.50
Wagoneer & Cherokee		
1983-87-258	5354405	9.75
360	5354528	8.50
1984-87-150	8953000012	9.75
Diesel eng	8953001176	8.75
V-6	8953000014	9.75
Heater Core		
1983-87-10 Series	8128784	103.25
CJ-Series	5469877	104.00
1984-87-70 Series		
gas engs	8956000049	116.75
diesel eng	8956001321	89.50
Heater Blower Motor Switch		
1983-87-10 Series	3631605	10.25
Control Valve		
Four	8956000414	27.50
V-6	3222290	31.75
CJ-Series	5462784	7.25
70 Series	8983502184	7.25
Heater Blower Motor		
1983-87-exc. below	8128778	57.50
70 Series	8956000173	53.63
CJ-Series	5751827	46.00
Heater Blower Motor Resistor		
1983-87-exc. 70 Series	961042	1.75
70-Series		
w/Air	8956000177	8.25
wo/Air	8956000522	8.25

LABOR 8 EXHAUST SYSTEM 8 LABOR

(Factory Time)	Chilton Time
(G) Exhaust Pipe Seal, Renew	
Cke/Wag/Comanche (.7)	1.2
All other models (.4)	.7
(G) Front Exhaust Pipe, Renew	
Cke/Wag/Comanche (.9)	1.3
All other models (.7)	1.1
(G) Rear Exhaust Pipe, Renew	
All models (.4)	.5
(G) Muffler, Renew	
Cke/Wag/Comanche (.9)	*1.4
All other models (.6)	.9
*Includes R&R tail pipe and converter.	
(G) Tail Pipe, Renew	
Cke/Wag/Comanche (.9)	*1.4
All other models (.6)	.8
*Includes R&R tail pipe and converter.	
(G) Catalytic Converter, Renew	
Cke/Wag/Comanche (.8)	1.2
CJ/Scrambler (.8)	1.2
All other models (.7)	1.1
(G) Manifold Heat Valve (Heat Riser), Renew	
All models	
V-8 (1.0)	1.5
(G) Exhaust Manifold, Renew	
Four	
150 eng (2.8)	3.9
151 eng (1.5)	2.1
Six (1.7)	2.4
V-6-each (.9)	1.4
V-8-each (.9)	1.4
Diesel (2.3)	*3.5
*Includes R&R turbo.	

PARTS 8 EXHAUST SYSTEM 8 PARTS

	Part No.	Price
Muffler		
Order by year and model.		
Tail Pipe		
CJ-Series		
Tail pipes not listed included with Muffler.		
Wagoneer & Cherokee-10 Series		
1983-V-8	5360080	55.00
1983-87-Six	5363115	34.50
1984-87-V-8	5364858	38.50
Wagoneer & Cherokee-70 Series		
1984-87		
Gas engs.	8983501931	31.50
Diesel engs	8983501069	31.75
Exhaust Pipe		
CJ-Series		
Four-151		
1983-CJ-5	5364523	21.50
CJ-7	5364524	21.50
CJ-8	5364525	24.50
Four-150		
1983-87		
CJ-7 & CJ-8	5364648	31.25
Six-258		
1983-87-CJ-5	5364311	28.00
CJ-7	5364312	35.25
CJ-8	5364312	35.25
Wagoneer & Cherokee		
Four-150		
1984-87		
Gas eng.	8953000067	45.50
Diesel eng	8952001819	24.25
Six		
1983-87-w/258 eng.	5364317	32.00
1984-87-70 Series		
V-6	8953001392	56.50
V-8		
1983-87		
M.T.	5362534	52.75
A.T.	5362536	63.50
Exhaust Pipe (Between Converter and Muffler)		
1983-87-C-8	5364441	10.00
Catalytic Converter		
1983-87-V-8	5370051	380.00
Four-150		
1983-exc. Calif.	5370129	473.25
Calif.	5370129	473.25
1984-87		
10 Series	5370129	473.25
70 Series	8953001627	367.50
Four-151		
1983-exc. Calif.	5370049	417.25
Calif.	5370048	398.75
Six-258		
1983-87-Wag., Cher.	5370123	417.25
1983-87-CJ	5370129	473.25
V-6		
1984-87	8953001268	325.50
Exhaust Manifold		
Order by model and description.		
Exhaust Manifold Damper		
1983-87	3238998	42.75
Exhaust Pipe Seal (To Manifold)		
1983-87-Four	8933001058	4.25
1983-87-Six	8983300053	4.50
1983-87-V-8	8983300051	4.50
1984-87-V-6	8953000692	5.00

LABOR 9 FRONT SUSPENSION 9 LABOR

Note: On all front suspension operations alignment charges must be added if performed. Time given does not include alignment.

(Factory Time)	Chilton Time
(M) Wheel, Renew	
one	.5
(G) Wheels, Balance	
one	.3
each adtnl	.2
(G) Check Alignment of Front End	
All models	.5
Note: Deduct if alignment is performed.	
(G) Toe-In, Adjust	
All models (.3)	.4
(G) Align Front End	
Includes: Adjust front wheel bearings.	
All models (1.0)	1.4
(G) Lower Control Arm, Renew	
Add alignment charges.	
Cke/Wag/Comanche	
one side (.4)	.7

LABOR 9 FRONT SUSPENSION 9 LABOR

	(Factory Time)	Chilton Time
(G) Upper and Lower Ball Joints, Renew		
Add alignment charges.		
Cke/Wag/Comanche		
one side	(.8)	1.2
both sides	(1.4)	2.2
(G) Upper Control Arm Bushings, Renew		
Add alignment charges.		
Cke/Wag/Comanche		
in axle housing	(.6)	1.0
(G) Front Spring, Renew		
CJ/Scrambler		
one	(.7)	1.0
both	(.9)	1.5
Cherokee/Grand Wagoneer/Truck		
one	(.9)	1.3
both	(1.2)	1.9
Cke/Wag/Comanche		
one or both	(1.3)	2.0
(G) Front Spring Center Bolt, Renew		
All models-one	(.7)	1.1
(G) Front Spring Shackle Bracket, Renew		
All models-one	(.5)	.8
(G) Front Spring Eye Bushing, Renew		
Includes: Renew shackle and bolt.		
All models-one	(.7)	1.2
(G) Front Spring, R&R and Recondition		
CJ/Scrambler		
one side	(1.8)	2.5
both sides	(3.0)	4.4
All other models		
one side	(1.2)	1.8
both sides	(1.8)	2.9
(G) Front Shock Absorbers, Renew		
Cke/Wag/Comanche		
one	(.2)	.4
both	(.3)	.5
All other models		
one	(.4)	.5
both	(.5)	.7
(G) Front Stabilizer Bar, Renew		
All models	(.5)	.7
(G) Front Stabilizer Bar Bushings, Renew		
Cke/Wag/Comanche	(.4)	.6
All other models	(.7)	1.0

4 WHEEL DRIVE FRONT AXLE

	(Factory Time)	Chilton Time
(G) Front Differential Cover, Renew or Reseal		
All models		.6
(G) Front Axle Shaft, R&R or Renew		
Cke/Wag/Comanche	(.5)	.9
All other models	(.7)	1.2
Renew shaft joint add-		
U-Joint, each	(.3)	.3
C/V Joint, each	(.6)	.6
Renew outer oil seal add,		
each	(.2)	.2
Renew C/V Joint boot add	(.4)	.4
(G) Front Axle Outer Shaft Oil Seals, Renew		
All models		
w/Select-Trac	(1.0)	1.7
Renew outer brg add	(.1)	.1
(G) Front Axle Bearing and Hub Assy., Renew		
Cke/Wag/Comanche		
one side	(.5)	.8
Renew roller brg and/or seal add	(.4)	.4
(G) Pinion Shaft Oil Seal, Renew		
All models	(.9)	1.2
(G) Steering Knuckle, Renew		
All models		
one side	(1.1)	1.7
Renew oil seal add	(.2)	.2
(G) Steering Spindle and/or Bearing, Renew		
All models-one side	(.6)	.9
(G) Front Axle Assy., R&R or Renew		
Cke/Wag/Comanche		
2 WD	(1.7)	2.5
4 WD	(1.9)	2.7
All other models	(2.5)	3.4
(G) Front Axle Assy., R&R and Recondition		
All models	(5.6)	7.8
Renew axle brgs and seals add	(.3)	.5

PARTS 9 FRONT SUSPENSION 9 PARTS

CJ-SERIES

	Part No.	Price
(1) Shackle (Side Plates)		
1983-87	5364404	2.25
(2) Bracket (Spring Shackle)		
1983-87	5355689	16.25
(3) Bushing (Spring Shackle)		
1983-87	5355966	1.00
(4) Bushing (Front Spring)		
1983-87	5353851	10.00
(5) U-Bolt		
1983-87	8130369	10.75
(6) Spring Assy.		
Note: Order by model & description.		
(7) Bracket (Spring Pivot)		
1983-87	8127712	22.25
(8) Bushing (Front Spring)		
1983-87	5353851	10.00
(9) Leaf, No. 1 (Front Spring)		
Note: Leaf No. 1 is serviced with front spring assembly.		
(10) Plate (U-Bolt Tie)		
1983-87-right	5364022	14.75
left	5364021	14.75
(11) Shock Absorber		
1983-87	8134101	27.25

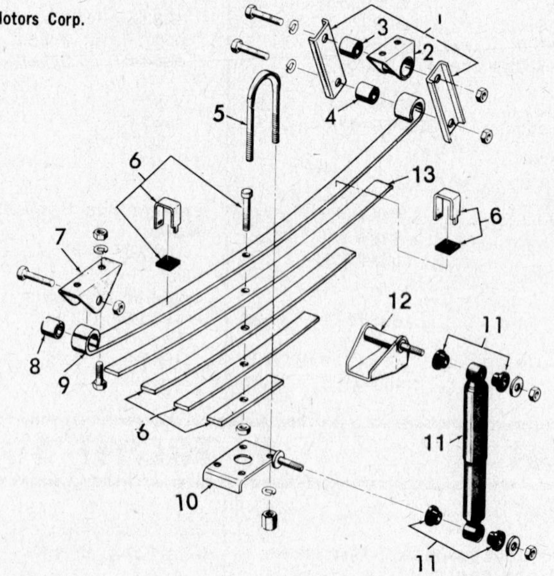

	Part No.	Price
(12) Bracket (To Frame)		
1983-87-right	5364228	24.50
left	5364229	24.50
(13) Leaf, No. 2 (Front Spring)		
Note: Leaf, No. 2 is serviced with front spring assembly.		

PARTS 9 FRONT SUSPENSION 9 PARTS

Part No. Price

WAGONEER & CHEROKEE-10 SERIES

(1) Spring Assy.
Note: Order by model & description.

(2) Plate (U-Bolt Tie)
1983-87-right.................5359583 14.75
left 5359582 14.75

(3) Bushing (Front Spring)
1983-87...........................944870 10.00

(4) Shock Absorber (Front)
1983-87-exc below.........8129467 33.75
soft ride......................8129467 33.75

(5) Washer
1983-87 ....G131016 1.00

(6) Bushing (Shock Absorber)
1983-87............................637936 .75

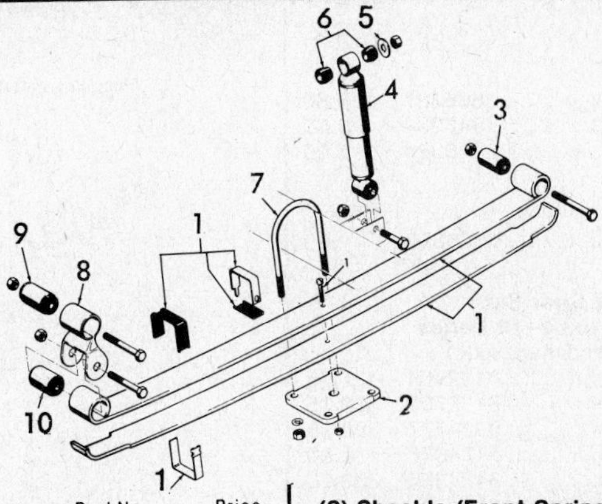

Part No. Price

(7) U-Bolt
1983-87
$5\frac{1}{2}$" long......................8129475 9.75
6" long.........................8129476 9.75
$6\frac{3}{4}$" long......................8129474 9.75

Part No. Price

(8) Shackle (Front Spring)
1983-87..........................5352863 16.00

(9) Bushing (Spring Shackle)
1983-87..........................5352079 7.50

(10) Bushing (Front Spring)
1983-87...........................944870 10.00

PARTS 9 FRONT SUSPENSION 9 PARTS

Part No. Price

WAGONEER & CHEROKEE-70 SERIES

Upper Control Arm
1984-87....................8952000213 14.25

Lower Control Arm
1984-87....................8952001162 28.00

Control Arm Bushings
upper........................8952000211 3.75
lower 8952001161 5.50

Ball Stud Kit (2WD)
1984-87....................8983500202 97.75

Part No. Price

Steering Knuckles (2WD)
1984-87-left.............8953000625 103.00

Coil Spring
Note: Order by letter code on spring. Example (EC, ED etc.)

Upper Spring Cushion
1984-87....................8952000230 5.25

Upper Spring Isolator
1984-87....................8952000229 4.00

Part No. Price

Shock Absorber
1984-87....................8983500312 20.00

Upper Shock Grommets
1984-87..........................3216638 .75

Front Stabilizer Bar
1984-87....................8952001128 45.00

Front Stabilizer Link
1984-87....................8952001130 12.75

Track Bar
1984-87....................8952000609 62.25

PARTS 9 FRONT AXLE (4 WHEEL DRIVE) 9 PARTS

Part No. Price

(1) Spindle Assembly
Wagoneer & Cherokee
1983-87-exc.
below.............................8128767 130.75
(w/Disconnect axle)
right 8128767 130.75
left 8134218 119.75
CJ-Series
1983-87..........................8128147 118.25

(2) Bearing Assy. (Spindle)
1983-87..........................8121402 7.50

(4) Oil Seal (Spindle)
1983-87..........................8127350 4.00

(5) Spacer (Spindle)
1983-87..........................8127348 4.25

(6) Ball Stud (Upper)
1983-87..........................8122495 45.75

(7) Steering Knuckle
Wagoneer & Cherokee
1983-87-10 Series
right 8128610 145.25
left 8128611 145.25
1984-87-70 Series
right 8953000626 118.50
left 8953000625 103.00
CJ-Series
1983-87 (knuckle with 2 bolts)
right 8129654 170.75
left 8129655 162.75

Part No. Price

(8) Snap Ring (Ball Stud)
1983-87-exc.
below.............................8124362 1.00
70 Series..............8983500203 6.25

(9) Ball Stud (Lower)
1983-87-exc.
below.............................8122496 45.75
70 Series..............8983500202 97.75

(10) Axle Shaft Oil Seal (Inner)
1983-87-exc. 10
Ser.................................8121781 6.25
Wagoneer & Cherokee-10 Series
wo/Discon. axle 8129096 5.50
w/Discon. axle 8134216 6.75

(11) Side Gear Set
1983-87-exc.
below.............................8126497 102.25
Wagoneer & Cherokee-10 Series
wo/Discon. axle 8129228 125.75
w/Discon. axle 8134225 123.25
1984-87-Wagoneer & Cherokee
70 Series..............8983500190 109.00

(12) Thrust Washer (Pinion Gear)
1983-87-exc below..........645790 .50
CJ-Series.....................8120831 .50
70 Series......................8933724 2.75

Part No. Price

(13) Thrust Washer (Side Gear)
1983-87-exc below...........645789 2.00
CJ-Series....................8120832 1.00
70 Series.....................8120831 .50

(14) Shim Set
1983-87-exc below.........8125924 15.25
CJ-Series.....................8126502 14.75

(15) Bearing (Side)
1983-87-exc below.........8124071 60.25
CJ-Series..................•8126500 33.50
70 Series.......................•8126500 33.50

(16) Shim Set
1983-87-exc below.........8129222 28.00
CJ-Series.....................8126506 7.75

(17) Carrier Case Assy.
Wagoneer & Cherokee-10 Series
1983-87 (w/or wo/Disconnect axle)
wo/Discon. axle 8124038 280.00
w/Discon. axle 8134224 288.00
w/4.88 ratio.................8124077 269.75
CJ-Series
1983-87-exc below.........8126513 223.00
3.73 to 1 ratio.............8126495 220.00

Wagoneer & Cherokee-70 Series
1984-87
3.31 & 3.54............8983500168 243.25
4.10 ....8983500169 253.00

	Part No.	Price
(18) Pinion Shaft		
1983-87-exc below	805327	8.50
CJ-Series	946384	8.00
70 Series	946384	8.00
(19) Shaft Pin		
1983-87	636360	.50
(20) Pinion & Ring Gear Set		
Wagoneer & Cherokee-10 Series		
1983-87 (wo/Disconnect axle)		
2.73 to 1 ratio	8132704	427.75
3.31 to 1 ratio	8132703	372.75
3.73 to 1 ratio	8124777	388.25
4.09 to 1 ratio	8124076	418.50
4.88 to 1 ratio	8124386	388.25
1983-87 (w/Disconnect axle)		
2.73 to 1 ratio	8134222	396.50
3.31 to 1 ratio	8134219	416.00
Wagoneer & Cherokee-70 Series		
1984-87		
3.31 to 1	8983500188	349.00
3.54 to 1	8983502355	295.25
3.73 to 1	8983500189	349.00
4.10 to 1	8983502353	293.00
CJ-Series		
1983-87		
2.73 to 1 ratio	●8133063	393.00
3.31 to 1 ratio	945344	370.50
3.73 to 1 ratio	945345	363.00
3.54 to 1 ratio	●8126518	379.75
4.09 to 1 ratio	8126494	356.50
(21) Housing Cover		
1983-87-exc below	8124352	25.25
CJ-Series	8126498	23.50
1983-87-10 Series w/Discon. axle	8983500435	41.00
1984-87-70 Series (Kit)	8983500194	41.50
(22) Cover Gasket (In-a-Tube)		
1983-87	●8993317	4.75
(23) Oil Slinger (Inner)		
1983-87	●916372	1.00
(24) Bearing & Cup (Inner)		
1983-87-Wagoneer & Cherokee-10 Series		
bearing	807266	20.25
cup	52877	11.00
Pinion Bearing Kit (Inner)		
1983-87-exc below	8124051	32.50
1983-87 CJ-Series	●3156066	18.50
1984-87 70 Series	8126499	7.50

Note: Bearing kit contains 1 bearing cone and 1 cup.

	Part No.	Price
(25) Shim Set		
1983-87-exc. below	8125924	15.25
CJ-Series	8126502	14.75
70 Series	8983500192	26.00
(26) Bearing & Cup (Outer)		
1983-87		
bearing	52878	20.50
cup	52879	8.75
Pinion Bearing Kit (Outer)		
1983-87	●8124052	29.50

Note: Bearing kit contains 1 bearing cone and 1 cup.

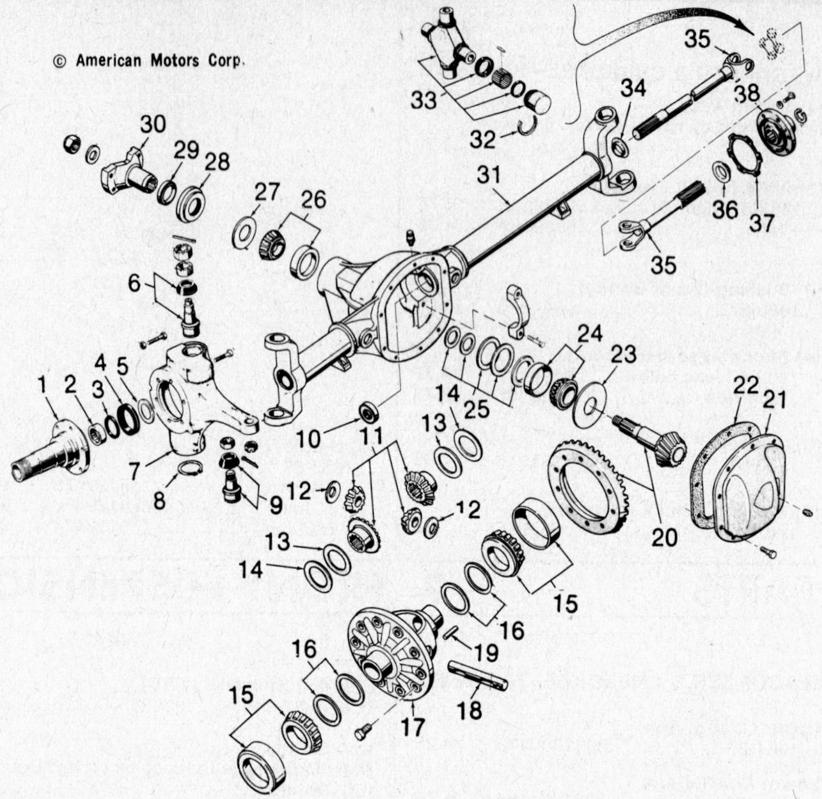

	Part No.	Price
(27) Oil Slinger (Outer)		
1983-87	●636566	.75
(28) Oil Seal		
1983-87	●998092	2.25
(29) Dust Shield (Yoke)		
1983-87	636568	1.50
(30) Yoke (Propeller Shaft)		
1983-87	●8133241	33.50
(31) Axle Housing (w/Tubes)		
Wagoneer & Cherokee-10 Series		
1983-87 (wo/Disconnect axle)		
exc. below	8132705	994.75
2 door	8132706	1107.50
1983-87 (w/Disconnect axle)		
exc. below	8134223	826.75
2 door	8134220	965.50
Wagoneer & Cherokee-70 Series		
1984-87	8983500193	1055.25
CJ-Series		
1983-87-exc. below	8133868	766.25
CJ-5	8133897	766.25
(32) Snap Ring (Spider Assy.)		
1983-87	909453	.50
(33) Spider Assembly		
1983-87-exc below	8126638	27.50
CJ-Series	8126637	23.00
70 Series	8126637	23.00
(34) Retainer (Inner)		
1983-87		
CJ-Series	8126232	1.25

	Part No.	Price
(35) Axle Shaft Assy.		
Wagoneer & Cherokee-10 Series		
1983-87 (exc Cherokee 2 dr wide track)		
right	8132912	272.25
left	8132913	244.00
1983-87 (Cherokee 2 dr wide track)		
right	8132915	274.75
left	8132916	247.00
1983-87 (w/Disconnect axle)		
Exc. 2 door Cherokee		
right	8132912	272.25
left	8134226	307.75
2 door Cherokee		
right	8132915	274.75
left	8134217	307.75
Wagoneer & Cherokee-70 Series		
1984-87-left	8953000684	213.75
right	8953000224	228.50
CJ-Series		
1983-87-CJ-7 & CJ-8		
right	8134294	255.50
left	8134293	276.75
1983-87-CJ-5		
right	8127598	226.75
left	8127599	258.50
(36) Retainer (Outer)		
1983-87	8128285	2.25
(37) Flange Gasket (Drive Shaft)		
1983-87-exc below	992273	.75
CJ-Series		
w/5 holes	5362001	.25
w/6 holes	649784	1.25
(38) Flange (Drive Shaft)		
1983-87-exc below	5358494	24.25
CJ-Series		
w/5 holes	5362000	31.50

LABOR 10 STEERING LINKAGE 10 LABOR

	(Factory Time)	Chilton Time
(G) Steering Damper, Renew		
All models	(.3)	.5
(G) Tie Rod Assy., Renew		
Does not include reset toe-in.		
All models-one	(.7)	.9
(G) Pitman Arm, Renew		
Does not include reset toe-in.		
All models	(.5)	.7
(G) Steering Center Link, Renew		
Does not include reset toe-in.		
Cke/Wag/Comanche	(.5)	.8

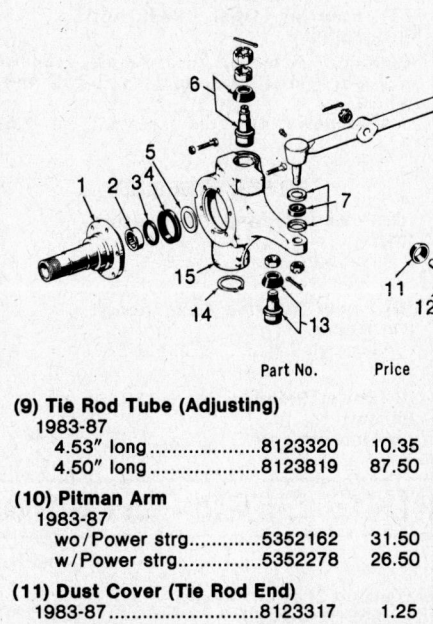

PARTS 10 STEERING LINKAGE 10 PARTS

WAGONEER & CHEROKEE - 10 SERIES

	Part No.	Price
(1) Spindle Assembly		
1983-87		
wo/Discon. axle	8128767	130.75
(w/Disconnect axle)		
right	8128767	130.75
left	8134218	119.75
(2) Bearing Assy. (Spindle)		
1983-87	8127356	12.00
(4) Oil Seal (Spindle)		
1983-87	8127350	4.00
(5) Spacer		
1983-87	8127348	4.25
(6) Ball Stud (Upper)		
1983-87	8122495	45.75
(7) Washer		
1983-87	8124820	1.25
(8) End Assy. (Strg. Arm to Strg. Arm)		
1983-87		
46½" long	8124816	68.25
50½" long	8124823	74.00
short	8124817	26.50

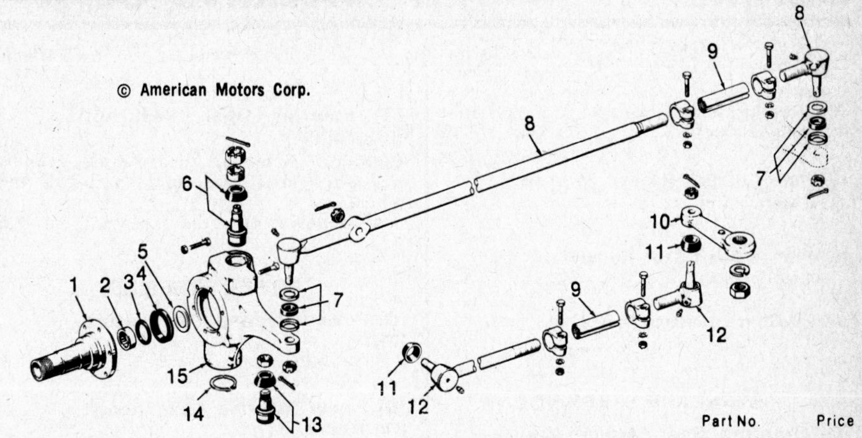

	Part No.	Price
(9) Tie Rod Tube (Adjusting)		
1983-87		
4.53" long	8123320	10.35
4.50" long	8123819	87.50
(10) Pitman Arm		
1983-87		
wo/Power strg	5352162	31.50
w/Power strg	5352278	26.50
(11) Dust Cover (Tie Rod End)		
1983-87	8123317	1.25
(12) End Assy. (Pitman Arm To Strg. Arm)		
1983-87		
3.75" long	8123319	25.75
21.88" long	8123315	39.00
(13) Ball Stud (Lower)		
1983-87	8122496	45.75
(14) Snap Ring		
1983-87	8124362	1.00
(15) Knuckle (Steering)		
1983-87		
right	8128610	145.25
left	8128611	145.25

PARTS 10 STEERING LINKAGE 10 PARTS

CJ-SERIES

	Part No.	Price
(1) Spindle Assembly		
1983-87	8128147	118.25
(2) Bearing Assy. (Spindle)		
1983-87	8127356	12.00
(5) Oil Seal (Spindle)		
1983-87	8127350	4.00
(7) Ball Stud (Upper)		
1983-87	8122495	45.75
(8) Knuckle (Steering)		
1983-87-right	8129654	170.75
left	8129655	162.75
(9) Dust Cover (Arm to Steering)		
1983-87	645134	1.75
(10) Dust Cover (Pitman Arm to Steering)		
1983-87	645134	1.75
(11) Ball Stud (Lower)		
1983-87	8122496	45.75
(12) End Assy. (Strg. Arm to Strg. Arm)		
1983-87-right	8136674	17.00
left	8136600	33.50
(13) Rod Assy. (w/Ends)		
1983-87-exc.		
below	8134295	90.25
CJ-5	5350586	58.00

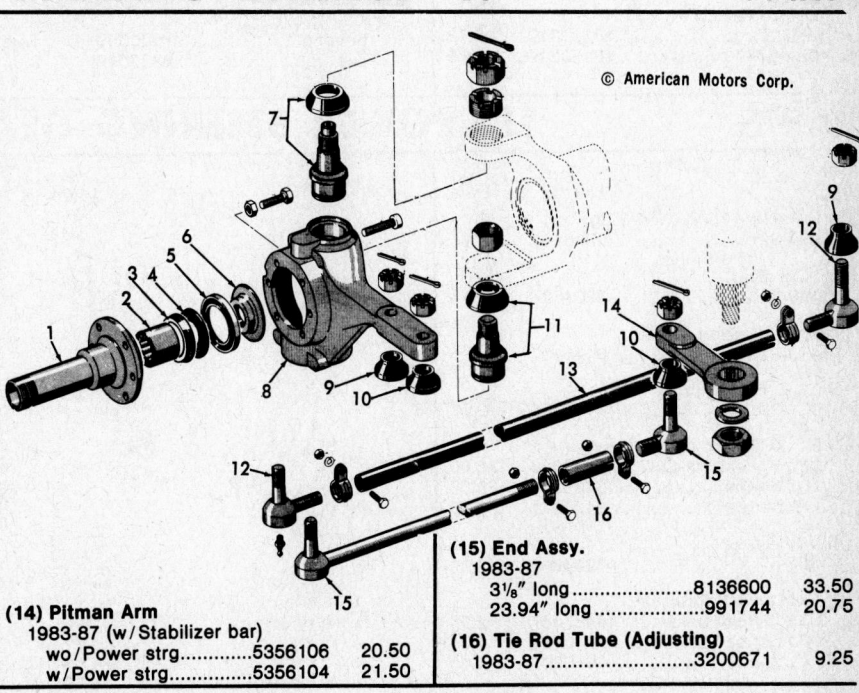

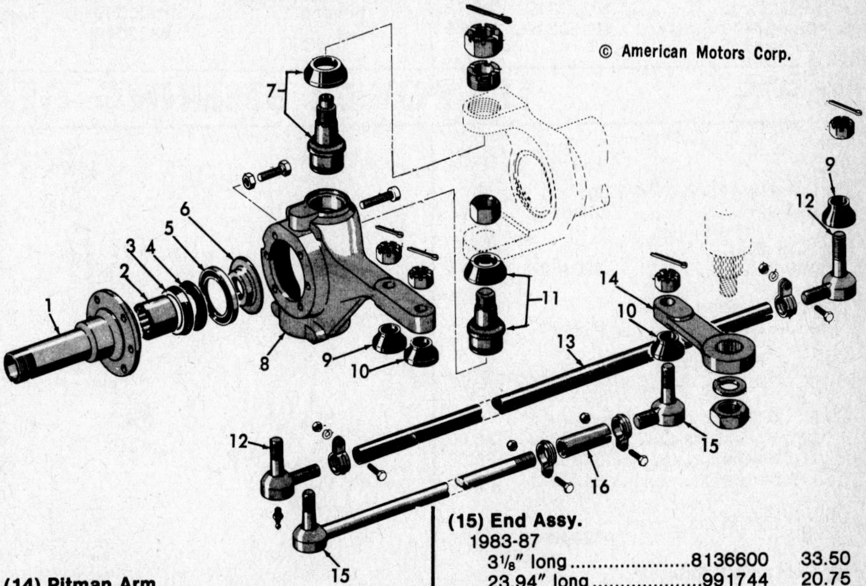

	Part No.	Price
(14) Pitman Arm		
1983-87 (w/Stabilizer bar)		
wo/Power strg	5356106	20.50
w/Power strg	5356104	21.50
(15) End Assy.		
1983-87		
3⅛" long	8136600	33.50
23.94" long	991744	20.75
(16) Tie Rod Tube (Adjusting)		
1983-87	3200671	9.25

PARTS 10 STEERING LINKAGE 10 PARTS

	Part No.	Price
WAGONEER & CHEROKEE - 70 SERIES		
Tie Rod End		
1984-87		
Left outer	8952000598	18.00
Pit. arm	8952000608	18.00
Rt. long	8952000601	60.50
Rt. short	8952000599	18.00
Adjusting Tube		
1984-87		
Short	8952000604	8.50
Long	8952000596	40.50
Pitman Arm		
1984-87		
w/P.Str.	8952000615	19.75
wo/P.Str.	8952000616	19.75
Dampner (Shock Absorber)		
1984-87	●3236097	57.75

LABOR 11 STEERING GEAR 11 LABOR

(Factory Time) — Chilton Time

(G) Steering Wheel, Renew
All models (.4) .... **.5**

(G) Horn Contact, Renew
All models (.3) .... **.4**

(G) Pitman Shaft Seal, Renew
All models (.8) **1.2**

(G) Flexible Coupling, Renew
All models (.7) **1.0**

STANDARD STEERING

(G) Steering Gear, Adjust (On Truck)
All models (.4) .... **.5**

(G) Steering Gear, R&R or Renew
All models (.8) **1.2**

(G) Steering Gear, R&R and Recondition
Includes: Remove, disassemble, renew necessary parts, reassemble, reinstall and adjust.
All models (1.4) **2.5**

POWER STEERING

(G) Power Steering Oil Pressure Check
All models .... **.5**

(G) Power Steering Gear, Adjust (On Truck)
All models (.4) .... **.6**

(G) Power Steering Gear, R&R or Renew
All models (1.0) **1.7**

(P) Power Steering Gear, R&R and Recondition
Includes: Remove, disassemble, renew necessary parts, reassemble, reinstall and adjust.
All models (2.2) **3.5**

(G) Power Steering Pump, Renew
Cke/Wag/Comanche
Four (1.1) **1.6**
V-6 (.6) **1.0**
Diesel (.7) **1.2**
All other models (1.0) **1.5**
Recond pump add (.9) **1.0**

(G) Pump Flow Control Valve, Renew
All models (.4) .... **.7**

(G) Pump Reservoir, Renew
All models (1.3) **1.8**

(M) Power Steering Hoses, Renew
All models-one (.8) **1.1**

PARTS 11 STEERING GEAR-(STANDARD) 11 PARTS

	Part No.	Price
Steering Gear Assy.		
1983-87-exc. 70 Ser.	994509	350.25
1984-87-70 Series	8952000089	131.75
Housing		
1983-87-exc. 70 Ser.	●8130319	123.75
1984-87-70 Series	●8130319	123.75
Steering Shaft (w/Worm)		
1983-87-exc. 70 Ser.	998504	130.50
1984-87-70 Series	8983500948	293.00
Cam Bearing		
1983-87-exc. 70 Ser.		
bearing	●3200491	6.25
cup	●3200492	9.00
Cam Seal		
1983-87-exc. 70 Ser.	4486141	3.50
Shaft (Steering Gear Cross)		
1983-87-exc. 70 Ser.	●8120221	55.75
1984-87-70 Series	●8120221	55.75

PARTS 11 POWER STEERING GEAR 11 PARTS

	Part No.	Price
(1) Retaining Ring (End Plug)		
1983-87	940703	.75
(2) Plug (End)		
1983-87	3204820	8.75
(3) 'O' Ring (End Plug)		
1983-87	8125037	6.25
(4) Plug (Piston End)		
1983-87	8127965	2.75
(7) Rack, Piston & Nut Assy.		
1983-87-exc below	8125036	136.00
CJ-Series	8134372	136.00
70 Series	8125471	135.50
(8) Ball Kit		
1983-87	●3204836	13.50
(9) Guide (Ball Return)		
1983-87-exc below	●4487887	2.25
CJ-Series	940707	1.00
70 Series	940707	1.00

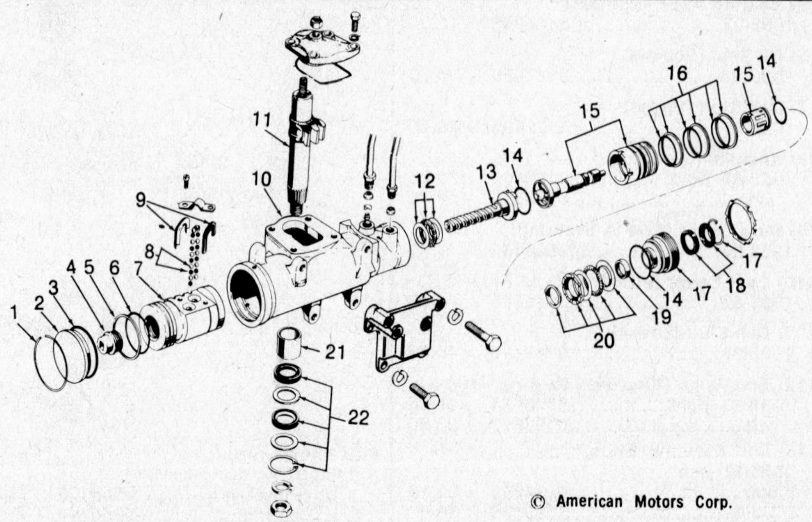

PARTS 11 POWER STEERING GEAR 11 PARTS

	Part No.	Price
(10) Housing Assy.		
1983-87-exc. 70 Ser.	8132537	196.50
70 Series	●8132540	196.50
(11) Shaft Assy. (Pitman)		
1983-87	8122958	95.75
(12) Bearing Kit		
1983-87	●8127645	11.50
(13) Piston		
Note: Serviced in No. 7.		
(14) 'O' Ring Kit		
Note: Serviced in No. 7.		
(15) Valve Assy.		
1983-84-exc below	8130409	174.50
1985-87-exc. below	●8130146	172.75
CJ-Series	8121746	157.00
70 Series	8983500250	172.75
(16) Ring & Seal Kit		
1983-87	●3204833	13.00
(17) Adjuster Assy.		
1983-87-exc CJ	●8130155	54.00
CJ-Series	8125035	44.50
(18) Seal		
1983-87-exc CJ	●8130157	8.50
CJ-Series	8983500369	10.25
(19) Bearing		
1983-87-exc CJ	8130142	4.25
CJ-Series	3204803	6.00
(20) Bearing Kit		
1983-87-exc CJ	●8130152	11.75
CJ-Series	8127644	13.75
(21) Bearing (Pitman Shaft)		
1983-87	●4487154	16.75
(22) Seal Kit (Pitman Shaft)		
1983-87-exc. below	●8134568	15.25
70 Series	8125038	10.00
Gear Assembly		
1983-84-10 Series	5369003	N.L.
1985-87-10 Series	8952002085	213.75
1983-87-CJ	5363231	486.75
1984-87-70 Series		
EK	8952000088	244.63
38	8983502253	411.25
ES	8952002737	257.50

PARTS 11 POWER STEERING PUMP 11 PARTS

GASOLINE ENGINES

	Part No.	Price
Pump Assembly		
CJ-Series		
1983-87-exc. 150	●3251017	217.50
150	8933001907	104.75
Wagoneer & Cherokee–10 Series		
1983-84	●3237193	225.25
1985-87	8953002714	84.00
Wagoneer & Cherokee–70 Series		
1984-85-Four	●8953000092	124.00
V-6	8953000719	108.50
1986-87-4 cyl.	8953003903	92.00
V-6	8953003904	104.00
(1) Power Steering Hose (Pressure)		
CJ-Series		
1983-Six	5363661	26.50
1983-84-Four		
150	5364672	27.00
151	5363659	23.75
Wagoneer & Cherokee–10 Series		
1983-87-Six	5370024	23.00
V-8	5370022	23.50
Wagoneer & Cherokee–70 Series		
1984-87	8952001141	21.25
(2) Power Steering Hose (Return)		
CJ-Series		
1983-87-Four	5363660	11.25
Six	5363662	11.50

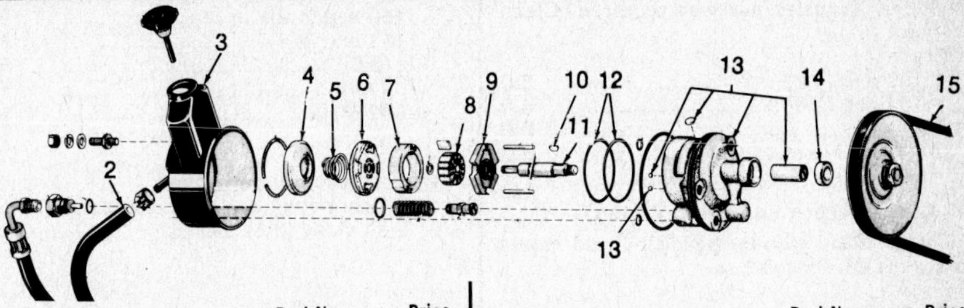

	Part No.	Price
Wagoneer & Cherokee–10 Series		
1983-87-Six	5370025	10.00
V-8	5370023	10.00
Wagoneer & Cherokee–70 Series		
1984-87	8952001140	4.50
(3) Reservoir		
1983-87-exc. below	●8127369	60.00
150	●8983500244	92.75
V-6	8983500331	88.00
(4) End Plate		
1983-87	●3209661	3.50
(5) Spring (Pressure Plate)		
1983-87	●8133958	.75
(6) Plate (Pressure)		
1983-87	●8133957	16.25
(7) Ring		
1983-87	●8127365	31.25
(8) Rotor, Vane & Ring Kit		
1983-87	●8133829	98.75
(9) Plate (Thrust)		
1983-87	8983500071	14.75
(10) Key (Drive Shaft)		
Note: No longer used.		
(11) Drive Shaft Kit		
1983-87	●8133828	39.00
(12) Seal Kit		
1983-87	●3209678	12.50
(13) Pump Body		
1983-87	●8132473	66.25
(14) Seal (Drive Shaft)		
1983-87	●4488330	4.50
(15) Power Steering Belt		
Note: Order by model & description.		

PARTS 11 POWER STEERING PUMP 11 PARTS

DIESEL ENGINES

	Part No.	Price
Pump Assembly		
1985-87	8953001765	95.75
Housing		
1985-87	8983500265	80.50
Seal Kit		
1985-87	8983500074	6.00
Valve		
1985-87	8125923	10.75
Shaft Kit		
1985-87	●8133828	39.00
Ring Kit		
1985-87	●8133829	98.75
Power Steering Hose (Pressure)		
1985-87	8952001604	22.00
Power Steering Hose (Return)		
1985-87	8952001606	5.75

LABOR 12 CYLINDER HEAD & VALVE SYSTEM 12 LABOR

(Factory Time)	Chilton Time

GASOLINE ENGINES

(G) Compression Test

Four (.4)	.5
Six (.4)	.6
V-6 (.6)	.7
V-8 (.7)	.9

(G) Cylinder Head Gasket, Renew

Includes: Clean carbon.

Four	
150 eng (3.8)	5.5
151 eng (2.4)	3.3
Six (3.9)	5.6
V-6-right side (4.1)	5.8
left side (3.8)	5.4
both sides (4.4)	6.3
V-8-right side (2.8)	4.0
left side (3.7)	5.3
both sides (4.4)	6.3

(G) Cylinder Head, Renew

Includes: Transfer parts as required. Clean carbon.

Four	
150 eng (4.2)	6.0
151 eng (2.8)	4.0
Six (4.2)	6.0
V-8-one side (3.7)	5.3
both sides (5.4)	7.7

(P) Clean Carbon and Grind Valves

Includes: R&R cylinder head(s). Grind valves and seats. Minor tune up.

Four	
150 eng (4.9)	6.8
151 eng (4.4)	6.4
Six (5.2)	9.5
V-6 (5.0)	9.0
V-8 (7.1)	10.0

(G) Rocker Arm Cover Gasket, Renew or Reseal

Four	
150 eng (1.0)	1.4
151 eng (.7)	1.0
Six (1.5)	1.8
V-6-one side (1.0)	1.4
both sides (2.0)	2.8
V-8-one side (.7)	1.0
both sides (1.0)	1.4

COMBINATIONS

Add to Valve Job

See Machine Shop Operations

(G) DRAIN, EVACUATE & RECHARGE AIR CONDITIONING SYSTEM

All models (.9)	1.0

(G) ROCKER ARMS, PUSH RODS AND/OR PIVOTS, CLEAN OR RENEW

Six (.6)	.8
V-8 (.5)	.8

(G) HYDRAULIC VALVE LIFTERS DISASSEMBLE AND CLEAN

Each	.2

(G) DISTRIBUTOR, RECONDITION

All models (1.0)	1.4

(G) CARBURETOR, RECONDITION

1 bbl (1.3)	1.6
2 bbl (1.5)	2.1
4 bbl (1.5)	2.1

(P) VALVE GUIDES, REAM OVERSIZE

Each (.1)	.2

(Factory Time)	Chilton Time

(G) Valve Tappets (Lifters), Renew (All)

Four	
150 eng (1.2)	1.8
151 eng (2.1)	2.7
Six (3.6)	5.5
V-6 (4.1)	5.8
V-8 (2.6)	3.7

(G) Valve Clearance, Adjust

V-6-one side (1.3)	1.8
both sides (2.6)	3.6

(G) Valve Springs and/or Valve Stem Oil Seals, Renew (Head on Truck)

Includes: Renew valve push rods, rocker arms and pivots if required.

Four	
one or all cyls (1.7)	2.6
Six	
one cyl (1.7)	2.2
all cyls (2.6)	3.7
V-6	
all cyls (3.2)	4.6
V-8	
one cyl (.7)	1.2
all cyls (2.1)	3.7

(Factory Time)	Chilton Time

DIESEL ENGINE

(G) Compression Test

All models (1.3)	1.8

(G) Cylinder Head Gasket, Renew

Includes: Clean carbon and make all necessary adjustments.

All models (7.4)	10.5

(G) Cylinder Head, Renew

Includes: Transfer parts as required. Make all necessary adjustments.

All models (9.2)	13.0

(P) Clean Carbon and Grind Valves

Includes: R&R cylinder head, grind valves and seats. Make all necessary adjustments.

All models (8.8)	12.5

(G) Valve Cover and/or Gasket, Renew

All models (.6)	1.0

(G) Valve Clearance, Adjust

All models (.8)	1.4

PARTS 12 CYLINDER HEAD & VALVE SYSTEM 12 PARTS

	Part No.	Price
Valve Grinding Gasket Set		
Four		
1983-151	●8134689	57.75
1983-150	●8983500255	16.75
1984-87-exc. 70 Series		
7/16″ bolts	●8983500255	17.25
1/2″ bolts	8983502501	15.75
1984-85-70 Ser.	●8983500255	17.25
1986-87-70 Ser.	8983502501	15.75
1984-87-Diesel	7701461765	49.50
Six-258		
1983-85-7/16″ blts.	●8133352	35.50
1986-87-1/2″ blts.	●8983502384	15.00
V-6-173		
1984-85	8983500847	72.75
1986-87	8983502133	64.75
V-8-360		
1983-87	8128192	83.00
(1) Cylinder Head Assembly		
Four		
1983-151	●8133706	401.00
1983-150	●8983500254	N.L.

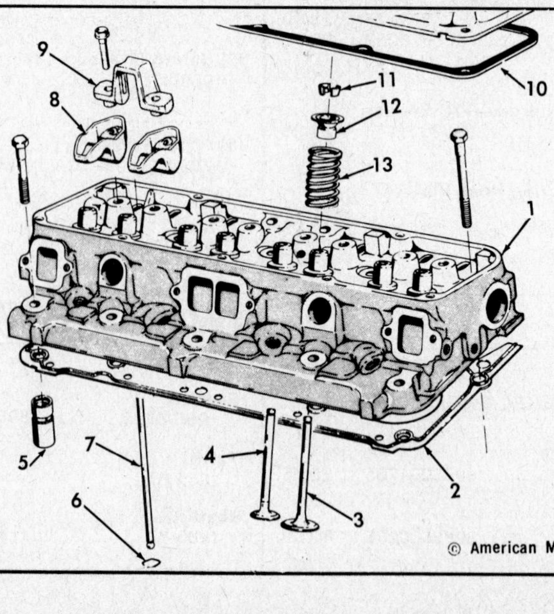

	Part No.	Price
1984-87-exc. 70 Series		
7/16″ bolts	●8983500675	265.75
1/2″ bolts	8983502487	213.00
1984-85-70 Series		
No. 2893	●8983500675	265.75
No. 2684	8983501411	301.75
1986-87-70 Series		
No. 2403	8983502487	213.00
No. 2405	8983502488	289.75
1984-87-Diesel	7701463380	512.00
Six-258		

1984 models used two types of Valve Cover mounting: 2 bolt or 5 bolt. Head mounting bolts also changed from 7/16″ to 1/2″.

	Part No.	Price
1983-85		
2 blt. & 7/16″	8134764	N.L.
5 blt. & 7/16″	8983501495	N.L.
1986-87	●8983502372	267.50
V-6-173		
1984-87	8983500730	250.00
V-8-360		
1983-87	8130366	395.00

(2) Cylinder Head Gasket

	Part No.	Price
Four		
1983-151	●8133701	12.25
1983-150	●3241649	3.25
1984-87-exc. 70 Series		
7/16″ bolts	●3241649	3.25
1/2″ bolts	8933002419	4.75
1984-85-70 Ser.	●3241649	3.25
1986-87-70 Ser.	8933002419	4.75
Diesel (by thickness)		
1.6mm	7701028289	66.50
1.7mm	7700711666	63.50
1.8mm	7701028290	68.50
Six-258		
1983-87-7/16″ blts.	●3237756	10.00
1/2″ blts.	●3228469	14.50
V-6-173		
1984	8933500731	N.L.
1985-87	8983502172	7.00
V-8-360		
1983-87	3227352	12.00

(3) Valve (Intake)

	Part No.	Price
Four		
1983-87-151	●8134389	17.50
150	●3242659	7.75
Diesel	7701462232	116.00
Six-258		
1983-87	3237465	N.L.
V-6-173		
1984-87	8983500739	15.00
V-8-360		
1983-87	3229657	13.50

(4) Valve (Exhaust)

	Part No.	Price
Four		
1983-151	●8134392	30.00
150	●3242660	17.50
1985-87		
Diesel	7701461339	101.00
1984-87-150	●3242896	15.50
1986-87-70 Ser.	8933002429	14.75
Six-258		
1983-87	3237464	N.L.
V-6-173		
1984-87	8983500743	23.25
V-8-360		
1983-87	3224598	17.50

(5) Valve Tappet

	Part No.	Price
1983-87-exc below	●3189883	9.00
151	8132248	8.25
V-6	8983500766	20.00

(6) Snap Ring

	Part No.	Price
1983-87	6440614	.25

(7) Push Rod (Valve)

	Part No.	Price
Four		
1983-87-151 eng.	●8134133	3.00
150	●3241709	3.25
Six-258		
1983-87	●3242395	2.75
(V-6-173)		
1984-87	8983500762	6.00
V-8-360		
1983-87	3214014	4.25

(8) Rocker Arm (Valve)

	Part No.	Price
Four		
1983-87-exc. below	●8132770	8.25
Diesel eng.	7946009641	30.00
150	●3242393	2.00
Six-258		
1983-87	●3242393	2.00
V-6-173		
1984-87	8983500756	6.25
V-8-360		
1983-87	3223539	6.50

Pivot (Valve Rocker Arm)

	Part No.	Price
1983-87-Four	●3235090	1.50

(10) Valve Cover Gasket

	Part No.	Price
Four		
1983-87		
150 exc. 70 Ser.	3241731	9.25
70 Ser.	●8993317	N.L.

RTV sealant used.

	Part No.	Price
Diesel	7700665229	6.00
151	●8132811	7.50
Six-258 & V-8		
1983-87-Sealant	●8993317	4.75
V-6-173		
1984-87	8983500854	7.75

(11) Lock (Valve Spring)

	Part No.	Price
Four		
1983-87		
150	3242664	.75
Diesel	7701394125	---
151	●8132931	1.00
Six-258		
1983-87	●3180458	.75
V-8-360		
1983-87	3156157	.75
V-6-173		
1984-87	8983500755	.50

(12) Retainer (Valve Spring)

	Part No.	Price
Four		
1983-87		
150	●3242661	1.50
Diesel	7700268948	3.00
151	●8132231	1.00
Six-258		
1983-87	3231483	1.00
V-8-360		
1983-87	3231483	1.00
V-6-173		
1984-87	8983500754	1.00

(13) Valve Spring

	Part No.	Price
Four		
1983-87		
150	●3242678	3.75
Diesel	7700673343	1.75
151	●8132232	3.75
Six-258 & V-8		
1983-87	●3228192	6.00
V-6-173		
1984-87	8983500747	4.75

LABOR 13 ENGINE ASSEMBLY & MOUNTS 13 LABOR

GASOLINE ENGINES

(G) Engine Assembly, Remove and Install

Does not include transfer of any parts or equipment.

(Factory Time)	Chilton Time
Four	
CJ/Scrambler	
150 eng (3.8)	**5.4**
151 eng (2.6)	**3.7**
Cke/Wag/Comanche (5.7)	**8.0**
Six	
w/M.T. (3.5)	**5.0**
w/A.T. (3.9)	**5.5**
V-6 (5.7)	**8.1**
V-8	
w/M.T. (3.7)	**5.3**
w/A.T. (3.9)	**5.5**
w/A.C. add (.7)	**.7**

(G) Engine Assembly, Renew (Less Head)

Includes: R&R engine assy. Transfer all component parts not supplied with replacement engine. Minor tune up.

(Factory Time)	Chilton Time
Four	
CJ/Scrambler	
150 eng (6.5)	**9.2**
151 eng (5.3)	**7.5**
Cke/Wag/Comanche (8.4)	**11.9**
Six	
w/M.T. (7.8)	**11.1**
w/A.T. (8.2)	**11.6**
V-6 (9.3)	**13.2**
V-8	
w/M.T. (8.9)	**12.6**
w/A.T. (9.1)	**12.9**
w/A.C. add (.7)	**.7**

(P) Engine Assembly, R&R and Recondition (Complete)

Includes: Rebore block, remove cylinder top ridge, deglaze cylinder walls, replace pistons, rings, rod and main bearings. Clean carbon, grind valves. Tune engine.

(Factory Time)	Chilton Time
Four	
CJ/Scrambler	
150 eng (17.5)	**24.8**
151 eng (16.3)	**23.1**
Cke/Wag/Comanche (19.4)	**27.5**
Six	
w/M.T. (18.2)	**25.8**
w/A.T. (18.6)	**26.4**
V-6 (19.9)	**28.3**
V-8	
w/M.T. (20.8)	**29.5**
w/A.T. (21.0)	**29.8**
w/A.C. add (.7)	**.7**

LABOR 13 ENGINE ASSEMBLY & MOUNTS 13 LABOR

	(Factory Time)	Chilton Time
(G) Engine Mounts, Renew		
Cke/Wag/Comanche		
right side	(.9)	1.2
left side	(.5)	.8
All other models		
one side	(.5)	.8

DIESEL ENGINE

(G) Engine Assembly, Remove & Install

Does not include transfer of any parts or equipment.

	(Factory Time)	Chilton Time
All models	(6.1)	8.7
w/A.C. add	(.7)	.7

(P) Cylinder Block, Renew

Includes: R&R engine assy. Transfer all component parts not supplied with replacement engine. Make all necessary adjustments.

	(Factory Time)	Chilton Time
All models	(19.5)	27.6
Renew cyl head add	(1.8)	2.4
w/A.C. add	(.7)	.7

(P) Engine Assy., R&R and Recondition

Includes: Renew cylinder liners, pistons and rings. Renew main and rod bearings. Clean carbon and grind valves. Make all necessary adjustments.

	(Factory Time)	Chilton Time
All models	(22.6)	32.0
w/A.C. add	(.7)	.7
(G) Engine Mounts, Renew		
All models		
right side	(.9)	1.2
left side	(.5)	.8

PARTS 13 ENGINE ASSEMBLY & MOUNTS 13 PARTS

Engine Assembly (Short)

Included: All internal moving parts, less cylinder head, oil pan, valve cover and manifold.

	Part No.	Price
Four–Diesel		
1985-87-Complete		
M.T.	7701463606	2508.25
A.T.	7701463972	4352.00
Four–151		
1983	●8133990	1541.25
Four–150		
1983-85	●8983500245	1407.50
1986-87	8983502499	1055.75
Six–258		
1983-85	●8134599	1575.50
1986-87	●8983502299	1551.25
V-6–173		
1984	8983500706	1260.25
1985-87	8983501875	1262.25
V-8–360		
1983-87	8133592	1876.25

Cylinder Block (Only)

	Part No.	Price
Four		
1983-151	●8133991	1089.50
1984-85-150	●8983500246	726.50
1986-87	8983502498	485.25
Diesel		
No. 3799	7701463298	719.75
No. 3800	7701463647	888.75
Six–258		
1983-87	●8133837	857.75
V-6–173		
1984	8983500707	942.25
1985-87	8983502057	911.25
V-8–360		
1983-87	4487212	1092.00

Engine Gasket Set (Lower)

	Part No.	Price
Four		
1983-151	●8134688	25.50
1983-87-150	●8983500256	21.25
Diesel	7701461334	42.00
Six–258		
1983-87	●8133353	41.75
V-6–173		

Refer to Group 15 for separate gasket and seal numbers.

	Part No.	Price
V-8–360		
1983-87	8125727	25.75

Note: Also order valve grind gasket set to complete overhaul gasket set.

Engine Mount (Front)

	Part No.	Price
4 cyl.–150		
1983-87-exc. 70 Ser.	5361829	18.75
70 Series (left)	8952000074	17.75
70 Series (right)	●3242711	17.25
4 cyl.–151		
1983	5361829	18.75
4 cyl.–Diesel		
1985-87	8952000957	16.25
Six–258		
1983-87	●8128488	18.25
V-6–173		
1984-87	8952000141	15.25
V-8–360		
1983-87	●8128488	18.25

Engine Shock Absorber Kit

	Part No.	Price
1984-87-70 Series 150 eng.	8983500358	47.50

Engine Mount (Rear)

	Part No.	Price
1983-87 (w/Auto. trans.)		
exc. below	1370910	19.75
CJ-7 & CJ-8	●3238013	25.25
1984-87-Wagoneer & Cherokee 70 Series	8952001180	23.75

LABOR 14 PISTONS, RINGS & BEARINGS 14 LABOR

GASOLINE ENGINES

(P) Rings, Renew (See Engine Combinations)

Includes: Remove cylinder top ridge, deglaze cylinder walls, replace rod bearings, clean carbon. Minor tune up.

	(Factory Time)	Chilton Time
Four		
CJ/Scrambler		
150 eng	(7.4)	10.0
151 eng	(5.6)	8.1
Cke/Wag/Comanche	(7.8)	11.0
Six	(6.4)	9.9
V-6	(8.6)	12.2
V-8	(8.5)	12.0
w/A.C. add	(.3)	.3

(P) Piston or Connecting Rod, Renew (One)

Includes: Remove cylinder top ridge, deglaze cylinder wall, replace rod bearing, clean carbon. Minor tune up.

	(Factory Time)	Chilton Time
Four		
CJ/Scrambler		
150 eng	(6.7)	9.5
151 eng	(4.8)	6.9

COMBINATIONS

Add to Engine Work

See Machine Shop Operations

(G) DRAIN, EVACUATE & RECHARGE AIR CONDITIONING SYSTEM		
All models	(.9)	1.0
(G) ROCKER ARMS, PUSH RODS AND/OR PIVOTS, CLEAN OR RENEW		
Four	(.4)	.7
Six	(.6)	.8
V-8	(.5)	.8
(G) HYDRAULIC VALVE LIFTERS, DISASSEMBLE & CLEAN		
Each		.2
(G) DISTRIBUTOR, RECONDITION		
All models	(1.0)	1.4
(G) CARBURETOR, RECONDITION		
1 bbl	(1.3)	1.6
2 bbl	(1.5)	2.1
4 bbl	(1.5)	2.1
(G) DEGLAZE CYLINDER WALLS		
Four	(.7)	1.0
Six	(.9)	1.3
V-8	(1.2)	1.5
(G) REMOVE CYLINDER TOP RIDGE		
Each	(.1)	.1
(G) TIMING CHAIN, RENEW (COVER REMOVED)		
All models	(.4)	.6
(G) MAIN BEARINGS, RENEW (PAN REMOVED)		
Four	(.7)	1.2
Six	(.9)	1.5
V-8	(.7)	1.2
(G) PLASTIGAUGE BEARINGS		
Each	(.1)	.1
(G) OIL PUMP RECONDITION		
Six	(.2)	.4
(M) OIL FILTER ELEMENT, RENEW		
All models	(.3)	.3

LABOR 14 PISTONS, RINGS & BEARINGS 14 LABOR

(Factory Time)	Chilton Time
Cke/Wag/Comanche (7.0)	9.9
Six (5.8)	8.2
V-6 (6.6)	9.4
V-8 (6.0)	8.5

(P) Connecting Rod Bearings, Renew

(Factory Time)	Chilton Time
Four	
CJ/Scrambler	
150 eng (2.2)	3.2
151 eng (1.8)	2.8
Cke/Wag/Comanche (3.0)	4.3
Six (2.2)	3.1
V-6 (3.4)	4.8
V-8 (2.5)	3.6

DIESEL ENGINE

(P) Pistons and Liners, Renew

Includes: R&R cylinder head and oil pan. Renew pistons, rings and cylinder liners. Make all necessary adjustments.

(Factory Time)	Chilton Time
All models (12.5)	17.7
w/A.C. add (.3)	.3

(P) Connecting Rod Bearings, Renew

(Factory Time)	Chilton Time
All models (2.9)	4.1

PARTS 14 PISTONS, RINGS & BEARINGS 14 PARTS

	Part No.	Price
(1) Piston Ring Set		
Four		
1983-151	●8134140	20.25
1983-87		
Diesel	7701462255	32.50
150	●8983500210	16.25
Six-258		
1983-87	●8121683	97.75
V-6-173		
1984	8983500782	16.00
1985-87	8983501893	17.50
V-8-360		
1983-87	3208065	158.50
(2) Piston Pin (Standard)		
Four-150		
1983-87-exc. 150	8132258	6.75
150	●3180483	3.00
Six-258		
1983-87	●3207034	18.75
V-8-360		
1983-87	3206582	24.25
V-6-173		
Note: Included with piston.		
(3) Piston Assy. (Standard)		
Four		
1983-87		
150	●8983500251	54.25
Diesel	7701462222	883.50
151	●8134136	57.00
Six-258		
1983-87	●8134441	38.25

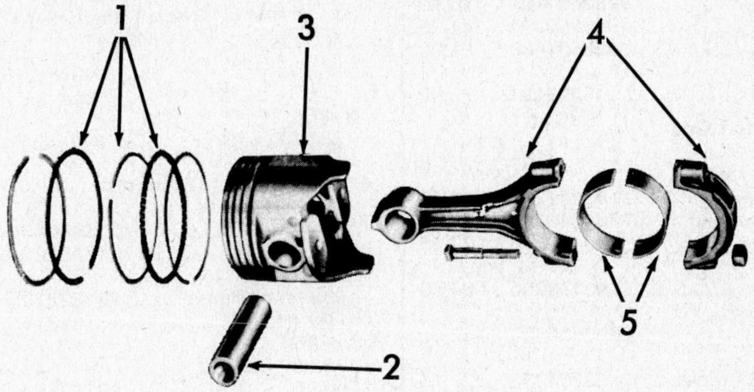

	Part No.	Price
V-6-173		
1984	8983500778	55.25
1985-87	8983501889	45.75
V-8-360		
1983-87	8133807	62.50
(4) Connecting Rod Assy.		
Four-Diesel		
1985-87	7701462223	241.50
Four-151		
1983	●8132253	55.75
Four-150		
1983-87	●3237816	37.25
Six-258		
1983-87	●3237812	43.25
V-6-173		
1984-87	8983500773	55.75
V-8-360		
1983-87	3237814	44.50
(5) Connecting Rod Bearing (Std.)		
Four		
1983-87		
150	●8983500300	5.50
Diesel	7701462227	16.50
151	●8132255	9.75
Six-258 & V-8		
1983-87	●8126204	5.50
V-6-173		
1984-87	8983500774	17.75

LABOR 15 CRANKSHAFT & DAMPER 15 LABOR

GASOLINE ENGINES

(P) Crankshaft and Main Bearings, Renew

Includes: R&R engine assembly.

(Factory Time)	Chilton Time
Four	
CJ/Scrambler	
150 eng (5.6)	8.0
151 eng (4.7)	6.7
Cke/Wag/Comanche (7.1)	10.0
Six	
w/M.T. (6.0)	8.5
w/A.T. (6.4)	9.0
V-6 (7.2)	10.2
V-8	
w/M.T. (6.6)	9.4
w/A.T. (6.8)	9.6
w/A.C. add (.7)	.7

(G) Rear Main Bearing Oil Seals, Renew

(Factory Time)	Chilton Time
Four (2.9)	4.1
Six (1.6)	2.5
V-6	
split lip	
May '84 & earlier (2.9)	4.3
full circle	
May '84 & later (8.5)	*12.0
wide 1 piece seal	
1985 & later (3.0)	4.5
V-8 (1.6)	2.5
*w/A.C. add (.7)	.7

DIESEL ENGINE

(P) Crankshaft and Main Bearings, Renew

Includes: R&R engine assembly.

(Factory Time)	Chilton Time
All models (14.8)	21.0
w/A.C. add (.7)	.7

(G) Rear Main Bearing Oil Seal, Renew

(Factory Time)	Chilton Time
All models (2.9)	4.2

(G) Crankshaft Front Oil Seal, Renew

(Factory Time)	Chilton Time
All models (2.0)	2.9

PARTS 15 CRANKSHAFT & DAMPER 15 PARTS

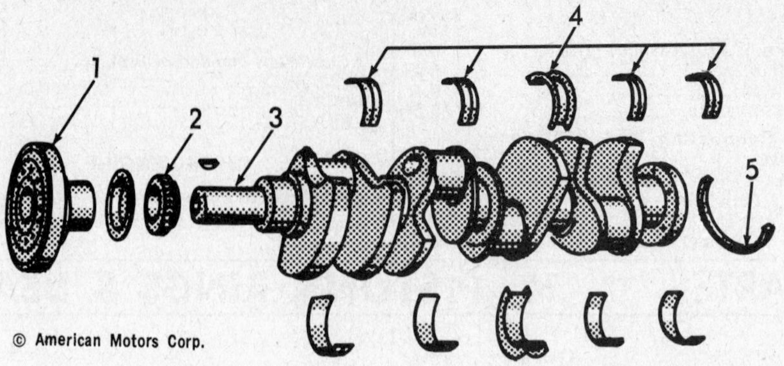

© American Motors Corp.

	Part No.	Price
(1) Vibration Damper		
Four		
1983-151	●8134144	42.50
1983-150 (w/ or wo/Serpentine Belt)		
wo/Belt	●3242856	60.75
w/Belt	●3242857	51.75
1984-87-150 (w/ or wo/Serpentine Belt)		
wo/Belt	●3242885	60.75
w/Belt	●3242886	51.75
Six-258		
1983-87-exc Calif.	●3237196	75.50
Calif	3237723	88.75
V-6-173		
1984-85-M.T.	8983500787	46.50
A.T.	8983500844	44.25
1986-87	8983501488	51.00
V-8-360		
1983-87	3230131	75.50
(2) Crankshaft Gear		
Four		
1983-87		
150	●3242281	38.75
Diesel	7701349583	11.00
151	●8132270	29.25
Six-258		
1983-87	●3173205	34.50
V-6-173		
1986-87	8983500800	42.00
V-8-360		
1983-1/2" wide	3234235	27.75
1984-87-5/8" wide	3223199	N.L.
(3) Crankshaft		
Four-Diesel		
1985-87	7700701165	614.25
Four-150		
1983-87-w/Brgs.	●8983500242	420.75
Four-151		
1983	●8131280	363.25
Six-258		
1983-87-w/Brgs.	●8133008	N.L.
V-6-173		
1984	8983502056	299.25
1985-87	8983501896	321.25

	Part No.	Price
V-8-360		
1983-87-w/Brgs.	8125451	N.L.
(4) Main Bearing (Standard)		
Four-128 (Diesel)		
1985-87	7701348543	54.25
Thrust kit	7701348320	10.25
Four-151		
1983-exc. Thrust	●8132210	11.50
Thrust	●8132214	21.00
Four-150		
1983-87-exc. Thrust	●8133252	6.50
Thrust	●8133253	14.50
Six-258		
1983-87-exc Thrust	●8133252	6.50
Thrust	●8133253	14.50
V-6-173		
1984-No. 1	8983500715	20.75
No. 2	8983500717	20.75
No. 3	8983500719	28.25
No. 4	8983500721	26.75
1985-87-No. 1	8983501962	26.75
No. 2	8983501963	26.75
No. 3	8983501968	25.50
No. 4	8983501962	26.75

	Part No.	Price
V-8-360		
1983-87-exc Thrust	8125928	9.50
Thrust	8125933	20.50
(5) Rear Main Bearing Seal (Kit)		
Four		
1983-87-151	●8132218	6.50
Diesel	7701349596	12.50
150	●3241669	6.75
Six cyl.-258		
1983-87	●3205331	7.50
V-6-173		
1984-87		
2 piece	8983501452	N.L.
5.5mm tk.	8983500723	11.75
11.0mm tk.	8983501888	31.75
V-8-360		
1983-87	3206691	7.50
Intermediate Shaft		
Four-diesel		
1985-87	7700590867	43.50
Intermediate Shaft Sprocket		
Four-diesel		
1985-87	7701349584	11.50

LABOR 16 CAMSHAFT & TIMING GEARS 16 LABOR

(Factory Time)	Chilton Time
GASOLINE ENGINES	
(G) Timing Cover Oil Seal, Renew	
Four	
150 eng (.9)	1.5
151 eng (.6)	1.0
Six (.9)	1.5
V-6 (.8)	1.4
V-8 (.9)	1.5
w/A.C. add (.3)	.3
(G) Timing Cover and/or Gasket, Renew	
Four	
150 eng (1.2)	1.7
151 eng (.9)	1.3
Six (1.4)	2.0
V-6 (1.9)	2.7
V-8 (3.2)	4.5
w/A.C. add (.3)	.3
(G) Timing Chain, Renew	
Four	
150 eng (1.5)	2.0
151 eng (1.3)	1.8
Six (1.7)	2.5
V-6 (2.2)	3.2
V-8 (3.5)	5.0
w/A.C. add (.3)	.3
(G) Camshaft, Renew	
Four (3.4)	4.8
Six (6.0)	8.5
V-6 (5.4)	7.7
V-8 (4.9)	7.1
w/A.C. add (.3)	.3
DIESEL ENGINE	
(G) Timing Belt Cover, R&R or Renew	
All models (1.6)	2.3
(G) Timing Belt, Renew	
All models (1.9)	2.7
Renew tensioner add (.1)	.1
(G) Camshaft Front Oil Seal, Renew	
All models (2.2)	3.1
(G) Camshaft, Renew	
All models (2.5)	3.5

PARTS 16 CAMSHAFT & TIMING GEARS 16 PARTS

	Part No.	Price
Timing Case Oil Seal (Front)		
Four		
1983-87-151	8133748	7.00
150	●3224704	6.25
Six-258		
1983-87	●3224704	6.25
V-6-173		
1984	8983500729	7.00
1985-87	8983501487	7.00
V-8-360		
1983-87	3193613	6.75

	Part No.	Price
Timing Case Gasket		
Four		
1983-87-151	8133747	3.00
150	●3225187	1.50
Six-258		
1983-87	●3225187	1.50

PARTS 16 CAMSHAFT & TIMING GEARS 16 PARTS

	Part No.	Price
V-6-173		
1984-87	8983500843	3.00
V-8-360		
1983-87	3180216	1.50
Camshaft Gear		
Four		
1983-87		
150	●3242280	42.75
Diesel	7701349586	22.00
151	●8132271	61.00
Six-258		
1983-87	●3206693	38.00
V-6-173		
1984-87	8983500801	43.75
V-8-360		
1983-87-1/2" tk.	3234234	27.25
5/8" tk	3197138	N.L.
Timing Chain		
1983-87-Four-150	●3242300	18.50
1983-87-Six-258	●3240502	34.00
1984-87-V-6	8983500799	32.75
1983-87-V-8-1/2"	3234433	29.75
5/8" tk	8134343	34.50
Timing Belt		
1985-87		
Diesel	7700663544	41.25
Camshaft		
Four		
1983-87		
150	●8983500249	138.50
Diesel	7700699231	140.50
151	●8132249	138.50
Six-258		
1983-87	●8133009	178.50
V-6-173		
1984-87	8983500767	119.25
V-8-360		
1983-87	4486476	172.50
Camshaft Bearings		
1983-87-exc.		
below	●3205711	25.75
151	●8132250	6.75
V-8	4486286	32.00
1984-87-V-6		
Frt.	8983500768	15.25
Int.-(2)	8983500769	15.25
Rear	8983500770	15.25

LABOR 17 ENGINE OILING SYSTEM 17 LABOR

(Factory Time)	Chilton Time
(G) Oil Pan and/or Gasket, Renew	
Cke/Wag/Comanche	
All engs (2.3)	3.3
All other models	
All engs (1.2)	1.7
(P) Pressure Test Engine Bearings (Pan Off)	
All models	1.0
(G) Oil Pump, Renew	
Cke/Wag/Comanche	
All engs (2.4)	3.4
All other models	
All engs (1.4)	1.9
(G) Oil Pump, R&R and Recondition	
Cke/Wag/Comanche	
All engs (2.7)	3.8
All other models	
All engs (1.8)	2.6
(G) Oil Pressure Gauge (Dash), Renew	
CJ/Scrambler (1.3)	1.7
Cherokee/Grand Wagoneer/ Truck (.8)	1.2
Cke/Wag/Comanche (.6)	1.0
(G) Oil Pressure Gauge (Engine), Renew	
All models (.3)	.4
(M) Oil Filter Element, Renew	
All models (.2)	.3
DIESEL ENGINE	
(G) Oil Pan and/or Gasket, Renew	
All models (2.5)	3.5
(P) Pressure Test Engine Bearings (Pan Off)	
All models	1.0
(G) Oil Pump, Renew	
All models (2.7)	3.8
(G) Oil Pump, R&R and Recondition	
All models (3.2)	4.5
(M) Oil Filter Element, Renew	
All models (.2)	.3

PARTS 17 ENGINE OILING SYSTEM 17 PARTS

	Part No.	Price
Oil Pan Gasket Set		
1983-87		
Diesel	7700695923	10.75
150	●8983500270	6.00
151	●8133754	10.00
258	●4488770	8.00
V-8-360	3206690	9.25
V-6	8983500853	7.25
Oil Pump Assembly		
1983-87		
Diesel	7946004404	93.50
150	●3241602	93.00
151	●8132303	77.00
258	3242141	93.00
1984-V-6	8983500826	90.25
1985-87-V-6	8983501486	80.25
Oil Pump Drive Shaft (w/Gear)		
1983-87-exc.		
below	●3172334	13.25
151	●8132854	11.00
Diesel	7700724211	4.00
V-8-360	3182698	13.25
V-6	8983500823	1.75
Oil Pressure Sending Unit (Eng.) Except 70 Series		
1983-87-exc.		
below	●3212004	15.50
151	3241716	14.75
70 Series		
1984-87-exc.		
diesel	8953000834	12.00
Diesel	8933002472	32.00
Oil Gauge (Dash Unit)		
1983-87-exc below	8126929	20.25
1983-87-CJ-Series		
(w/Gauge depth)		
1"	5750279	20.25
2"	5460640	29.25
1984-87-70 Series		
Gas eng.	8983500307	19.00

LABOR 18 CLUTCH & FLYWHEEL 18 LABOR

(Factory Time)	Chilton Time
(G) Clutch Pedal Free Play, Adjust	
All models (.3)	.4
(G) Clutch Master Cylinder, Renew	
Includes: Bleed system.	
All models (1.0)	1.4
(G) Clutch Slave Cylinder, Renew	
Includes: Bleed system.	
All models (.7)	1.1
(G) Clutch Reservoir, Renew	
All models (.3)	.5
(G) Clutch Assembly, Renew	
Includes: R&R trans. Renew T.O. brg, clutch plate and disc. Make all necessary adjustments.	
CJ/Scrambler (2.7)	3.7
Cherokee/Grand Wagoneer/ Truck (3.4)	4.7
Cke/Wag/Comanche	
2 WD (1.9)	2.6
4 WD (2.9)	4.0
Diesel (3.0)	4.2
Renew f/wheel add (.3)	.3
Renew ring gear add (.3)	.3
Renew pilot bush add (.2)	.2

PARTS 18 CLUTCH & FLYWHEEL 18 PARTS

	Part No.	Price
Clutch Disc		
1983-87		
150	8953000168	80.50
151	●8132577	78.25
Diesel	7700729376	154.25
V-6	8983500806	91.75
258	3240278	93.75
360	3184867	106.50
Pressure Plate Assy.		
1983-87		
150	●8953000167	121.25
151	●8132576	157.25
Diesel	7700723977	128.50
258	3240278	93.75
360	3184955	193.50
V-6	8983500804	157.00
Release Bearing		
1983-87-exc.		
below	●3236561	32.00
150	●8953000175	35.50
151	5361614	33.00
Clutch Pilot Bearing		
1983-87-exc.		
below	●3236726	2.00
150	●3250005	6.00
151	3752487	5.00
Flywheel		
1983-87		
Diesel	7701596861	162.00
150	●3242667	170.00
151	●8132267	174.25
258	3240094	146.75
360	3236524	151.00
1984-V-6	8983500792	153.50
1985-87-V-6	8983501897	152.00
Flywheel Ring Gear		
1983-87-exc.		
below	●3179741	29.50
150	●3241718	24.75
Diesel	7700664055	38.00
V-6	8983500795	29.50
Clutch Master Cylinder		
1983-87-exc.		
below	5359822	103.75
1984-85-70 Series		
Gas	8952000068	115.00
Diesel eng.	8953001163	112.00
1986-87	8953001163	112.00
Repair Kit (Clutch Master Cylinder)		
1983-87-exc.		
below	8132781	20.25
1984-85		
70 Series	8983500669	16.25
1986-87		
70 Series	8983501531	17.00
Clutch Slave Cylinder		
1983-87-exc.		
below	3237886	71.50
150 and V-6	●8952000070	79.25
Diesel	8953001324	77.25
Repair Kit (Slave Cylinder)		
1983-87-exc.		
below	●8983500678	33.75
150, V-6, Diesel	●8983500670	18.25

LABOR 21 SHIFT LINKAGE 21 LABOR

	(Factory Time)	Chilton Time
(G) Gearshift Lever, Renew		
Cke/Wag/Comanche		
w/M.T.	(.6)	.8
w/A.T.	(.7)	.9
All other models		
w/M.T.	(.6)	.8
w/A.T.	(.4)	.6
(G) Transfer Case Shifter Assy., R&R or Renew		
CJ/Scrambler	(1.1)	1.6
All other models		
w/M.T.	(1.1)	1.6
w/A.T.	(.4)	.8

LABOR 25 U-JOINTS & DRIVESHAFT 25 LABOR

	(Factory Time)	Chilton Time
(G) Propeller Shaft, R&R or Renew		
CJ/Scrambler		
front	(.5)	.7
rear	(.6)	.8
Cke/Wag/Comanche		
front	(.6)	.8
rear	(.4)	.6
All other models		
front	(.7)	.9
rear	(.6)	.8
Recond U-joint add		
single carden	(.4)	.5
double joint	(1.1)	1.5

PARTS 25 UNIVERSAL JOINTS & DRIVE SHAFT 25 PARTS

	Part No.	Price
Universal Joint Repair Kit (Front Shaft)		
Wagoneer & Cherokee		
1983-87-10 Series		
front	●8126614	22.75
center	8130750	30.75
rear	8130750	30.75
1984-87-70 Series		
L.D. (F&R)	●8126614	22.75
H.D. double	8130750	30.75
1983-87-CJ-Series		
front & rear	●8126614	22.75
Universal Joint Repair Kit (Rear Shaft)		
1983-87 (All)		
front & rear	●8126614	22.75

LABOR 26 REAR AXLE 26 LABOR

	(Factory Time)	Chilton Time
(M) Differential, Drain & Refill		
All models		.6
(G) Inspection Cover Gasket, Renew or Reseal		
All models		.6
(G) Pinion Shaft Oil Seal, Renew		
All models	(1.0)	1.2
(G) Axle Shaft Bearings, Renew		
CJ/Scrambler		
right side	(1.8)	2.4
left side	(1.4)	1.8
both sides	(2.0)	2.7
All other models		
semi-float axle		
one side	(1.0)	1.3
both sides	(1.7)	2.3

LABOR 26 REAR AXLE 26 LABOR

	(Factory Time)	Chilton Time
full float axle		
each side	(.4)	.6
(G) Axle Shaft Oil Seal, Renew (Outer)		
semi-float axle		
one side	(.7)	.9
both sides	(1.1)	1.5
full float axle		
each side	(.4)	.6
(G) Axle Shaft Oil Seal, Renew (Inner & Outer)		
CJ/Scrambler		
right side	(1.8)	2.4
left side	(1.4)	1.8
both sides	(2.0)	2.7
(G) Axle Shaft, Renew		
CJ/Scrambler		
right side	(1.6)	2.2
left side	(1.2)	1.6
both sides	(1.7)	2.3
All other models		
semi-float axle		
one side	(.5)	.8
both sides	(.8)	1.2
full float axle		
one side	(.3)	.5
both sides	(.4)	.7
(G) Rear Axle Assy., R&R or Renew		
Cherokee/Grand Wagoneer/ Truck	(2.3)	3.2
All other models	(3.1)	4.3
(P) Rear Axle Assembly, R&R and Recondition (Complete)		
All models	(4.0)	5.5
(P) Differential Case, R&R and Recondition		
Includes: Renew side bearings, gears and thrust washers.		
All models	(2.8)	3.9
(G) Rear Axle Housing Assy., Renew		
CJ/Scrambler	(6.3)	8.7
All other models	(5.7)	7.9

PARTS 26 REAR AXLE 26 PARTS

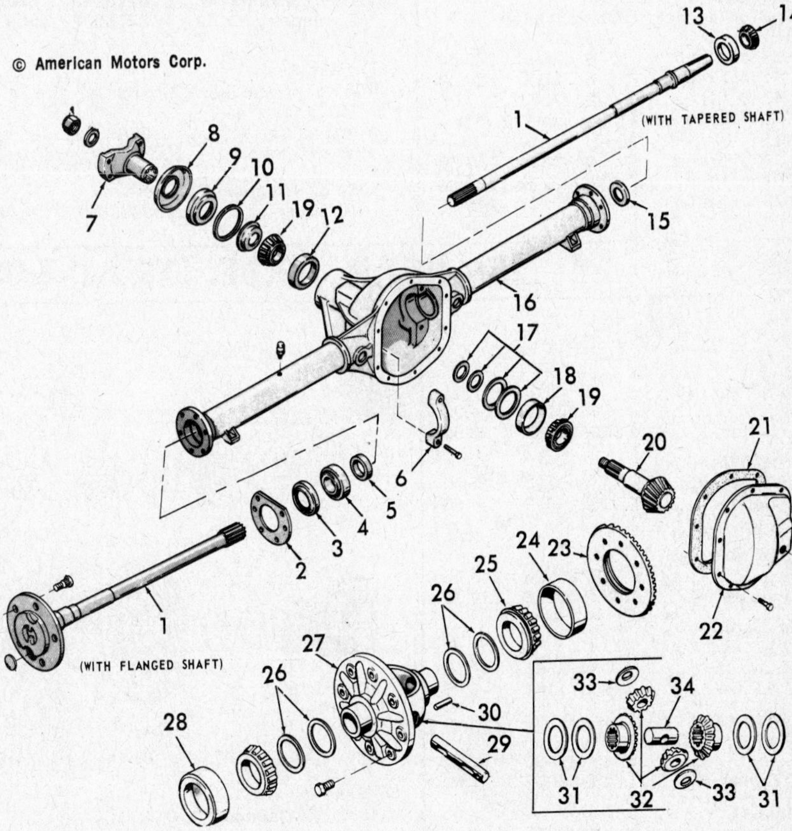

	Part No.	Price
(1) Axle Shaft		
1983-87-Wagoneer & Cherokee-10 Series		
right	3235806	176.00
left	3235807	190.50
1983-87-Cherokee 2 dr wide track-10 Series		
right	3235810	180.00
left	3235811	187.25
1984-87-Wagoneer & Cherokee-70 Series		
right	8953000404	133.00
left	8953000403	133.00
1983-87-CJ-7 & CJ-8		
right	8133886	78.50
left	8133885	79.50
1983-87-CJ-5		
right	8127071	86.00
left	8127070	86.00
(2) Bearing Retainer		
Note: 1983-87, included with bearing.		
(3) Seal (Bearing)		
Note: 1983-87, included with bearing.		
(4) Bearing (Kit)		
1983-87-exc CJ	3230115	21.00
CJ-Series	3150046	9.50
1984-87-Wagoneer & Cherokee 70 Series	8983500141	55.00
Note: Retainer and seal also included with bearing.		
(5) Ring (Flanged Axle)		
1983-87	3239074	3.25
(6) Cap		
1983-87-Part or Housing		
(7) Yoke (Pinion)		
1983-87-exc. 70 Ser.	8132702	40.00
1984-87-Wagoneer & Cherokee 70 Series	8983500140	26.00
(8) Seal (Yoke)		
1983-87	925869	1.00
(9) Oil Seal (Bearing)		
1983-87-exc below	●3208474	8.00
Model 60	8134810	8.25
1984-87-Wagoneer & Cherokee 70 Series	●8953002642	8.00
(11) Oil Slinger		
1983-87	●636566	.75
(12) Cup (Front)		
1983-87-exc. 70 Ser.	3172134	6.00
1984-87-Wagoneer & Cherokee 70 Series	●3156062	5.25
(13) Cup (Tapered Axle)		
1983-87	5360955	4.75
(14) Bearing (Tapered Axle)		
1983-87-exc. below	3230115	21.00
CJ-Series	3150046	9.50
(15) Seal (Inner)		
1983-87-exc below	3235929	6.00
CJ-Series	3170700	4.25
(16) Axle Housing		
1983-87-Wagoneer & Cherokee-10 Series		
exc below	8130993	537.25
wide track	8130991	537.25
1984-87-Wagoneer & Cherokee 70 Series	8983500139	535.25
1983-87-CJ-Series		
exc. below	8133887	535.25
CJ-5	8130994	588.25
(17) Shim Set		
1983-87-exc. 70 Ser.	3205533	4.00
1984-87-Wagoneer & Cherokee 70 Series	8122677	3.75
(18) Cup (Rear)		
1983-87-exc. 70 Ser.	3172564	8.00
1984-87-Wagoneer & Cherokee 70 Series	●3156062	5.25
(19) Bearing		
1983-87-exc. below		
outer	3172135	11.75

PARTS — 26 REAR AXLE 26 — PARTS

	Part No.	Price
inner	3172563	17.00
1984-87-Wagoneer & Cherokee-70 Series		
outer	●3156063	11.75
inner	●3170947	15.50
(20) Pinion		
1983-87-sold only in set		
(21) Gasket (Cover)		
1983-87-exc. 70 Ser.	3172122	2.50
1984-87-Wagoneer & Cherokee 70 Series	●3229429	2.00
(22) Cover		
1983-87-exc. below	3215943	9.00
1984-87-Wagoneer & Cherokee 70 Series	●3223375	8.25
(23) Ring Gear & Pinion Set		
1983-87-Wagoneer & Cherokee-10 Series		
2.73 to 1 ratio	8132699	280.00
3.31 to 1 ratio	8132700	288.00
4.10 to 1 ratio	8127072	294.00
1984-87-Wagoneer & Cherokee-70 Series		
3.31 to 1 ratio	4487814	278.50
3.54 to 1 ratio	●8130782	278.50
3.73 to 1 ratio	8983500257	246.50

	Part No.	Price
4.11 to 1 ratio	8983502486	224.75
1983-87-CJ-Series		
3.54 to 1 ratio	4486825	285.75
3.73 to 1 ratio	8133179	354.25
4.10 to 1 ratio	8127072	294.00
(24) Cup (Side)		
1983-87-exc. 70 Ser.	3172566	7.50
1984-87-Wagoneer & Cherokee 70 Series	●3171166	5.75
(25) Bearing (Side)		
1983-87-exc. below	3172565	12.50
1984-87-Wagoneer & Cherokee 70 Series	●3156052	11.50
(26) Shim Set (Side)		
1983-87-exc below	8129243	36.00
CJ-Series	3205532	50.00
(27) Case Assy.		
1983-87-Wagoneer & Cherokee 10 Series		
exc below	3235502	165.00
w/2.73 ratio	3235503	169.50
1984-87-Wagoneer & Cherokee 70 Series	8953000561	138.00

	Part No.	Price
1983-87-CJ-Series		
exc below	3228921	159.00
w/2.73 ratio	3236220	164.00
(28) Cup (Side)		
1983-87-exc. 70 Ser.	3172566	7.50
1984-87-Wagoneer & Cherokee 70 Series	●3171166	5.75
(29) Shaft		
1983-87-exc. 70 Ser.	3218195	9.00
70 Series	3224231	5.75
(30) Pin		
1983-87	G455313	1.00
(31) Washer		
1983-87-exc. 70 Ser.	3220250	1.00
70 Series	3237817	1.00
(32) Gear Set (Side)		
1983-87-exc. below	8127092	100.75
70 Series	●8983500138	58.75
(33) Thrust Washer		
1983-87	3222999	.50
(34) Block		
1983-87	3162323	5.50

PARTS — 26 REAR AXLE (TRAC-LOK) 26 — PARTS

	Part No.	Price
(1) Disc Kit		
1983-87-exc. 70 Ser.	8120325	104.00
70 Series	8983500263	83.50
(2) Thrust Washer		
1983-87-exc CJ	645790	.50
CJ-Series	3222999	.50
(3) Gear Set (Side)		
1983-87-exc. 70 Ser.	8120326	243.75
70 Series	8983500262	232.00
(4) Cup (Side)		
1983-87-exc. 70 Ser.	3172566	7.50
70 Series	●3171166	5.75
(5) Bearing Assy.		
1983-87-exc. 70 Ser.	3172565	12.50
70 Series	●3156052	11.50
(6) Shim Set		
1983-87-exc below	8129243	36.00
CJ-Series	3205512	4.50
70 Series	3202344	70.50

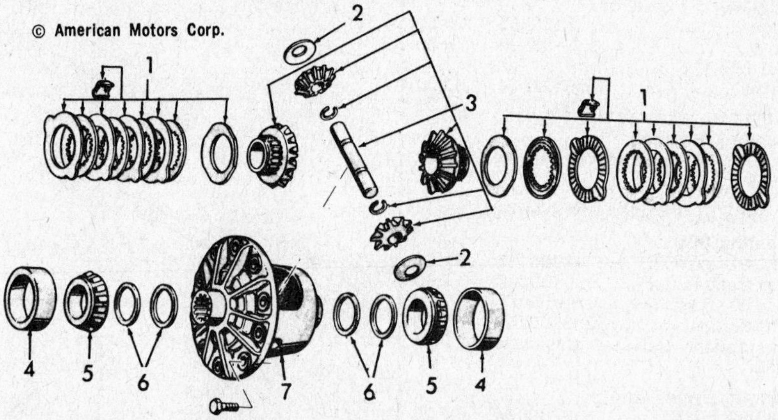

	Part No.	Price
(7) Case		
1983-87-Wagoneer & Cherokee-10 Series		
2.73 ratio	3239844	425.00
3.31 ratio	3230153	382.75

	Part No.	Price
1984-87-Wagoneer & Cherokee 70 Series	8953000986	380.50
1983-87-CJ-Series		
exc. below	3212192	519.50
2.73 ratio	3239844	425.00

LABOR — 27 REAR SUSPENSION 27 — LABOR

	(Factory Time)	Chilton Time
(G) Rear Springs, Renew		
Cke/Wag/Comanche		
one	(.9)	1.3
both	(1.5)	2.3
All other models		
one	(.9)	1.3
both	(1.8)	2.6

	(Factory Time)	Chilton Time
(G) Rear Spring Shackle, Renew (One)		
Cke/Wag/Comanche	(.7)	1.0
(G) Rear Springs, R&R and Recondition		
CJ/Scrambler		
one	(1.8)	2.4
both	(3.1)	4.2

	(Factory Time)	Chilton Time
All other models		
one	(1.3)	1.8
both	(1.9)	2.6
(G) Rear Spring Center Bolt, Renew		
All models-one	(.7)	1.0

LABOR 27 REAR SUSPENSION 27 LABOR

(Factory Time) Chilton Time

(G) Rear Spring Eye Bushing, Renew
Includes: Renew shackle and pivot bolt.
All models-one side (.6)................ .9
both sides (.7)............................ 1.2

(G) Rear Shock Absorbers, Renew
Cke/Wag/Comanche
one (.2)................................ .4
both (.3)................................ .5

All other models
one (.4)................................ .5
both (.5)................................ .7

(G) Rear Stabilizer Bar, Renew
Cke/Wag/Comanche (.5).......... .8

PARTS 27 REAR SUSPENSION 27 PARTS

	Part No.	Price
(1) Rear Spring Assy.		
Note: Order by model & description.		
(2) Bushing		
1983-87-exc below	5355369	10.00
Wagoneer & Cherokee-10 Series		
1½" O.D.	5355369	10.00
2" O.D.	5358985	12.50
70 Series	8952000504	7.25
(3) Shackle (Rear Spring)		
CJ-Series		
1983-87	5357499	4.50
Wagoneer & Cherokee		
1983-87-10 Series	5352863	16.00
70 Series	8952000507	11.00
(4) Shackle Bushing (Spring)		
1983-87-exc below	5352079	7.50
CJ-Series	5355841	1.50
70 Series	8952000503	7.25
(5) Bracket (Shock Absorber)		
1983-87-10 Series	8126859	25.00
CJ-Series	8127713	25.00
(6) Shock Absorber (Rear)		
CJ-Series		
1983-87	8133838	15.00
Wagoneer & Cherokee		
1983-87-10 Series	8133733	25.50
70 Series	8983500315	29.25
(7) Plate (U-Bolt Tie)		
CJ-Series		
1983-87-right	5363440	12.25
left	5363439	12.25
Wagoneer & Cherokee		
1983-87-10 Series	5352087	14.75
70 Series	8952000508	5.75

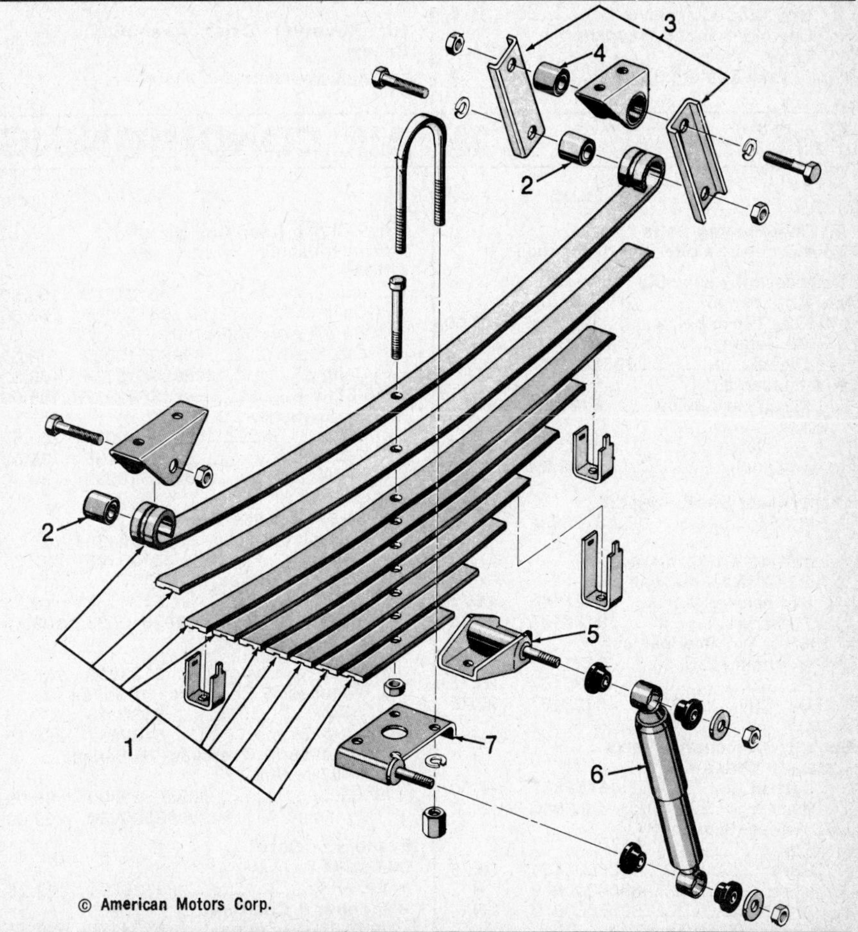

© American Motors Corp.

LABOR 28 AIR CONDITIONING 28 LABOR

(Factory Time) Chilton Time

Note: If more than one item requires replacement where evacuation and discharging the system is already included in the operation, deduct 1.0 hour for each additional item to the time listed.

(G) Drain, Evacuate and Recharge System
All models (.8)............................... 1.0

(G) Refrigerant, Add (Partial Charge)
All models (.5)............................... .6

(G) Compressor Drive Belt, Renew
All models
V-Belt (.3).................................. .4
Serpentine (.5)............................ .6

(G) Compressor Assembly, Renew
Includes: Transfer parts as required. Evacuate and charge system.

AIR CONDITIONER TUNE-UP

For efficient operation and satisfactory performance in hot weather. The following Air Conditioner Tune-Up is suggested:

1. Clean intake filter
2. Clean condenser fins
3. Pressure test system
4. Adjust drive belt tension
5. Check anti freeze/coolant
6. Tighten compressor mounts
7. Tighten condenser and evaporator mounts
8. Inspect system for leaks (hoses, couplings, valves, etc.)
9. Partial charge system

All models.. 1.0
If necessary to evacuate and charge system, add 1.0

(Factory Time) Chilton Time

V-8 engs (2.0)............................ 3.0
All other engs (1.0)...................... 2.0
Recond comp add (1.8).................. 2.5

(G) Compressor Clutch and/or Pulley, Renew
Does not include R&R compressor.
All models (.4)............................ .6

(G) Condenser Assembly, Renew
Includes: Evacuate and charge system.
Cke/Wag/Comanche (1.8)........ 2.5
All other models (1.4).................... 2.0

(G) Expansion Valve, Renew
Includes: Evacuate and charge system.
All models (1.1)............................ 1.7

(G) Evaporator Core, Renew
Includes: Evacuate and charge system.
CJ/Scrambler (1.6).................... 2.9

LABOR 28 AIR CONDITIONING 28 LABOR

(Factory Time) — Chilton Time

Cherokee/Grand Wagoneer/
Truck (1.5) 2.7
Cke/Wag/Comanche (2.1) 3.9

(G) A.C. Control Module, Renew
Cherokee/Grand Wagoneer/
Truck (.2) 4

(G) A.C. Control Assembly, Renew
Cke/Wag/Comanche (.4) 6
Cherokee/Grand Wagoneer/
Truck
1985 & later (.3) 6
1984 & earlier (.7) 1.1
Renew potentiometer add (.1) 2

(G) Evaporator Fan Motor, Renew
Does not include evacuate and charge A.C. system.
CJ/Scrambler (.6) 1.0
All other models (.4) 6

(G) Receiver Drier Assembly, Renew
Includes: Evacuate and charge system.
CJ/Scrambler (1.2) 1.7
Cherokee/Grand Wagoneer/
Truck (1.4) 2.0
Cke/Wag/Comanche (1.8) 2.5

(G) A.C. Low Pressure Switch, Renew
All models (.3) 5

(G) Air Conditioning Hoses, Renew
Includes: Evacuate and charge system.
All models-one 1.7
each adtnl 3

PARTS 28 AIR CONDITIONING 28 PARTS

	Part No.	Price
Air Conditioning Belts		
Note: Order by model and description.		
Compressor Assembly		
wo/American air		
1983-87-exc below	3228826	260.00
70 Series	●8133449	270.75
Diesel	8983501450	262.75
w/American air		
1983-87-exc below	8121817	260.00
Four		
wo/clutch	●8133196	270.75
w/clutch	8132866	343.75
Compressor Shaft Seal Kit		
1983-87	3133183	15.75
Valve Plate Kit (Compressor)		
1983-87 (wo/American air)		
exc below	8127440	44.75
70 Series	8133187	29.75
1983-87 (w/American air)		
exc below	8121821	51.50
Four	8133187	29.75
Six-Calif.	8133187	29.75
Suction & Discharge Valve		
exc. 70 Series		
suction	●5459857	18.00
discharge	5459856	18.00
70 Series-Suction		
Four		
Carb	8936000454	23.25
Inject	8956000679	N.L.
V-6	8956000679	N.L.
70 Series-Discharge		
Four	8932000262	29.50
V-6	8953000573	18.00
Valve Kit-V-6	8983502083	16.50
Drive Clutch (Incl. Coil & Pulley)		
wo/American air		
1983		
exc. Calif.	●8134178	150.50
Calif.	●8133448	139.50
1984-87-exc. Series 70		
exc. Calif.	●8983510033	139.50
Calif.	●8983510034	139.50
1983-87-V-8	3692973	156.00
1984-87-Series 70		
150	●8983510034	139.50
V-6	8983510035	139.50
w/diesel	●8983510033	139.50
w/American air		
1983-87-exc. 70 Series		
exc below	8126139	126.50
Four	●8133195	152.75
1984-87-70 Series		
150	3134181	140.25
V-6	8983510035	139.50
Condenser Core		
1983-87-exc below	8133893	263.50
Wagoneer & Cherokee-10 Series		
Six	8130313	235.75
V-8	8130312	235.75
Wagoneer & Cherokee-70 Series		
1984-87-w/Amer.		
Air	8983501909	109.00
wo/Amer. Air	8956000230	229.00
Evaporator Core		
CJ-Series		
1983-87	8128124	112.75
Wagoneer & Cherokee		
1983-87-10 Series	8134176	217.75
1984-87-70 Series		
w/Amer. Air	8956000210	210.25
wo/Amer. Air	8983501906	78.50
Thermostat (Temp. Cont.)		
1983-87-exc below	5464350	51.75
CJ-Series	8121840	29.00
Receiver/Drier		
1983-87-exc below	8128141	61.50
Wagoneer & Cherokee-10 Series		
Six	8130315	61.50
V-8	8130314	61.50
1984-87-Wagoneer & Cherokee		
70 Series	8956000687	91.25
Expansion Valve		
CJ-Series		
1983-87	8121823	46.75
Wagoneer & Cherokee		
1983-87-10 Series	5464379	53.25
1984-87-70 Series		
w/Amer. Air	8956000212	48.75
wo/Amer. Air	8983501907	22.75
Air Condition Hoses		
Note: Order by model and description.		
Blower Motor Assy.		
CJ-Series		
1983-87	8126691	65.00
Wagoneer & Cherokee		
1983-87-10 Series	5752943	54.50
1984-87-70 Series	8956000173	52.25
Blower Motor Switch		
CJ-Series		
1983-87	8129018	7.25
Wagoneer & Cherokee		
1983-87-10 Series	5763546	6.75
1984-87-70 Series	8983502184	7.25

LABOR 29 LOCKS, HINGES & WIND. REGULATORS 29 LABOR

(Factory Time) — Chilton Time

(G) Hood Lock, Renew
All models (.2) 4

(G) Hood Release Cable, Renew
All models (.3) 6

(G) Hood Hinge, Renew
All models-one (.4) 5
both (.6) 7

(G) Door Lock Cylinder, Renew (Front or Rear)
All models (.6) 8
Recode cyl add (.3) 3

(G) Door Handle (Outside), Renew (Front or Rear)
CJ/Scrambler (.4) 7
Cherokee/Grand Wagoneer/
Truck (.6) 9
Cke/Wag/Comanche (.4) 7

(G) Front Door Window Regulator (Manual), Renew
Cke/Wag/Comanche (.9) 1.5
All other models (.6) 1.0

(G) Front Door Window Regulator (Electric), Renew
Cke/Wag/Comanche (1.1) 1.7
All other models (.7) 1.2

(G) Lock Striker Plate, Renew
All models (.2) 2

(G) Rear Door Window Regulator, Renew
Cherokee/Grand Wagoneer
manual (.7) 1.2
power (.9) 1.5
Cke/Wag/Comanche
manual (.9) 1.5
power (1.1) 1.7

(G) Rear Compartment Lid Lock Cylinder, Renew
All models (.3) 4
Recode cyl add (.3) 3

PARTS 29 LOCKS, HINGES & WIND. REGULATORS 29 PARTS

	Part No.	Price
Hood Lock		
1983-87-exc below	5752530	17.75
Wagoneer & Cherokee-10 Series		
upper	5758026	38.00
lower	956418	16.50
Wagoneer & Cherokee-70 Series		
upper	8955000735	3.00
lower	8955000731	5.75
Hood Hinge		
1983-87-CJ-Series		
right	5459516	13.50
left	5459516	13.50
1983-87-Wagoneer & Cherokee-10 Series		
right	956964	32.00
left	956963	32.00
1984-87-Wagoneer & Cherokee-70 Series		
right	8955000738	8.25
left	8955000739	8.25
Front Door Lock		
1983-87-CJ-7		
right	5461866	77.00
left	5461867	77.00
1983-87-Wagoneer & Cherokee-10 Series		
right	5750018	40.50
left	5750017	40.50
1984-87-Wagoneer & Cherokee-70 Series		
right	8955000766	17.25
left	8955000767	17.25
1983-87-Scrambler		
right	5758176	56.50
left	5758177	56.50

	Part No.	Price
Door Lock Cylinder & Key		
1983-87-exc below	8128289	11.25
CJ-7 & Scrambler	●8122874	7.25
Series 70	●8122874	7.25
Door Handle (Outside)		
1983-87-Wagoneer & Cherokee-10 Series		
right	956856	20.50
left	956855	20.50
1984-87-Wagoneer & Cherokee-70 Series		
right	8955007466	10.00
left	8955000467	N.L.
1983-87-CJ-7	8128461	17.75
1983-87-CJ-8		
right	5758172	25.75
left	5758173	25.75
Door Window Regulator (Manual)		
1983-87-Wagoneer & Cherokee-Series 10 (Front)		
right	5456004	53.50
left	5456005	53.50
1984-87-Wagoneer & Cherokee-Series 70 (Front)		
right	8955000586	22.75
left	8955000587	22.75
1983-87-CJ-7 & CJ-8 (Front)		
right	5454146	53.50
left	5454145	53.50
1983-87-Wagoneer & Cherokee-Series 10 (Rear)		
right	5456002	63.75
left	5456003	63.75
1984-87-Wagoneer & Cherokee-Series 70 (Rear)		
right	8955000594	22.75
left	8955000595	22.75

	Part No.	Price
Door Window Regulator (Electric)		
1983-87-Wagoneer & Cherokee-Series 10 (Front & rear) (T-Track type)		
right	8134242	12.00
left	8134243	12.00
1984-87-Wagoneer & Cherokee-Series 70 (Front)		
right	8955000660	100.50
left	8955000661	100.50
1984-87-Wagoneer & Cherokee-Series 70 (Rear)		
right	8955000558	100.50
left	8955000559	100.50
Electric Window Regulator Motor		
1983-87-Wagoneer & Cherokee (Front & Rear) (w/Flex drive)		
right	8134244	185.75
left	8134245	185.75
Tail Gate Lock		
1983-87-exc below	663195	1.25
body half	663112	3.25
CJ-7 & CJ-8	5454030	2.50
1984-87 Series 70	8955000632	18.00
Tail Gate Handle		
All models	956374	3.25
Tail Gate Hinge		
1983-87-CJ-Series		
CJ-5 & CJ-6	663669	11.75
CJ-7 & CJ-8	5462416	14.50
1983-87-Wagoneer & Cherokee w/Alum.	5751937	32.75

LABOR 30 HEAD AND PARKING LAMPS 30 LABOR

	(Factory Time)	Chilton Time
(G) Aim Headlamps		
two		.4
four		.6
(M) Headlamp Sealed Beam Bulb, Renew		
All models-one		.3
each adtnl		.2
(M) Park and Turn Signal Lamp Lens or Bulb, Renew		
All models-one	(.3)	.4

	(Factory Time)	Chilton Time
(M) Park and Turn Signal Lamp Assy., Renew		
All models-one	(.4)	.5
(M) Tail Lamp Lens or Bulb, Renew		
All models-one	(.3)	.4

	(Factory Time)	Chilton Time
(M) Tail Lamp Assembly, Renew		
Cherokee/Grand Wagoneer/Truck-one	(.5)	.6
All other models-one	(.4)	.5
(M) License Lamp Assembly, Renew		
All models-one	(.3)	.4
(M) Side Marker Lamp Assembly, Renew		
All models-one	(.3)	.4

PARTS 30 HEAD AND PARKING LAMPS 30 PARTS

	Part No.	Price
Headlight		
1983-87-CJ-Series		
exc below	8124687	7.75
Halogen	8983500341	48.50
1983-87-Wagoneer & Cherokee-10 Series		
exc below	8128683	21.25
Halogen	8134319	50.00
1984-87-Wagoneer & Cherokee-70 Series		
Single	8134319	50.00
Upper	8936001059	19.50
Lower	8936001058	19.50
Halogen	3242537	N.L.

	Part No.	Price
Parking Lamp Lens		
1983-87-CJ-Series		
two screws	8127449	5.75
three screws	991402	6.00
1983-87-Wagoneer & Cherokee-10 Series		
right	5460102	8.00
left	5460103	8.00
Parking Lamp Assy.		
1984-87-Wagoneer & Cherokee-70 Series		
right	8956000852	11.75
left	8956000853	11.75
Tail Lamp Lens		
1983 CJ-Series	5457724	14.00

	Part No.	Price
1983-Wagoneer		
inner	5459550	5.50
outer (R.H.)	5459552	14.75
outer (L.H.)	5459551	14.75
1983-Cherokee	8134111	18.50
1984-87-exc. below	8134111	18.50
CJ-Series	5457724	14.00
Tail Lamp Assy.		
1984-87-Wagoneer-70 Series		
right	8956000116	50.50
left	8956000117	50.50
1984-87-Cherokee-70 Series		
right	8956000316	50.50
left	8956000317	50.50

LABOR 31 WINDSHIELD WIPER & SPEEDOMETER 31 LABOR

(Factory Time)	Chilton Time
(G) Windshield Wiper Motor, Renew	
Cke/Wag/Comanche (.4)	.6
All other models (.6)	.9
(G) Wiper Timer/Governor, Renew	
All models (.3)	.5
(G) Rear Window Wiper Motor, Renew	
Cke/Wag/Comanche (.3)	.5
(G) Wiper Linkage, Renew	
Cherokee/Grand Wagoneer/Truck (1.1)	1.7
CJ/Scrambler (.6)	.9
Cke/Wag/Comanche (.4)	.7
(G) Windshield Washer Pump, Renew	
Cke/Wag/Comanche (.2)	.3
All other models (.4)	.5
(G) Rear Window Washer Pump, Renew	
Cke/Wag/Comanche (.2)	.3
(G) Wiper Switch, Renew (Front or Rear)	
Cke/Wag/Comanche (.7)	1.1
All other models (.4)	.7
(G) Speedometer Head, R&R or Renew	
CJ/Scrambler (1.2)	1.8
Cherokee/Grand Wagoneer/Truck (.8)	1.2
Cke/Wag/Comanche (.6)	1.0
Reset odometer add	.2
(G) Speedometer Cable, Renew	
All models	
one or two piece cable and core (.4)	.7
one piece cable and core (.6)	1.0
(G) Radio, R&R	
All models (.7)	1.0
(G) Rear Window Defogger Switch, Renew	
All models (.4)	.6
(G) Liftgate Wiper Switch, Renew	
Cke/Wag/Comanche (.4)	.6

PARTS 31 WINDSHIELD WIPER & SPEEDOMETER 31 PARTS

	Part No.	Price
Wiper Motor (Front)		
CJ-Series		
1983-87	5763696	57.00
Wagoneer & Cherokee		
1983-87-10 Series	5758467	94.00
70 Series	8956000899	110.50
Wiper Motor (Rear)		
1984-87-Wagoneer & Cherokee Series 70	8956000701	68.50
Wiper Linkage		
1983-87-CJ-Series		
right	5453958	44.25
left	5453957	31.75
1983-87-Wagoneer & Cherokee		
10 Series	5758474	57.00
70 Series	8983500660	90.00
Wiper Control		
Wagoneer & Cherokee-10 Series		
1983-87 (wo/intermittent wiper)		
1/4"-20 threads	5750036	43.75
3/8"-24 threads	5758687	18.50
1983-87 (w/intermittent wiper)		
1/4"-20 threads	5750035	41.75
3/8"-24 threads	5758687	18.50
Wagoneer & Cherokee-70 Series		
wo/Intermittent	8956000431	48.00
w/Intermittent	8956000033	61.25
CJ-Series		
1983-87		
wo/interm.	5758687	18.50
w/interm.	5758904	27.00
Windshield Washer Pump (Two Speed)		
1983-87-exc CJ	5454940	36.50
CJ-Series	8121404	24.75
1984-87-Wagoneer & Cherokee 70 Series	8936001132	18.00
Speedometer Cable & Casing		
Order by year and model.		
Speedometer Head Assy.		
CJ-Series		
1983-87		
85 m.p.h.	8134184	82.75
Wagoneer & Cherokee		
1983-87-10 Series		
85 m.p.h.	8134124	82.75
1984-87-70 Series	8983500293	72.75

LABOR 32 LIGHT SWITCHES & WIRING 32 LABOR

(Factory Time)	Chilton Time
(G) Turn Signal Switch, Renew	
Cke/Wag/Comanche (.6)	1.0
All other models (.8)	1.1
(M) Turn Signal or Hazard Warning Flasher, Renew	
All models (.2)	.3
(G) Hazard Warning Switch, Renew	
All models (.8)	1.1
(G) Headlamp Dimmer Switch, Renew	
All models (.3)	.4
(G) Headlamp Switch, Renew	
All models (.4)	.6
(G) Stoplight Switch, Renew	
All models (.3)	.4
(G) Back-Up Lamp or Neutral Switch, Renew	
All models	
w/M.T. (.5)	.6
w/A.T. (.4)	.5
(G) Parking Brake Switch, Renew	
All models (.3)	.4
(G) Horn, Renew	
All models-one (.4)	.4
each adtnl	.2
(G) Horn Relay, Renew	
All models (.3)	.4

PARTS 32 LIGHT SWITCHES & WIRING 32 PARTS

	Part No.	Price
Headlamp Switch		
1983-87-exc. below	5751098	15.50
1986-87-10 Ser.	8956001861	14.50
1984-87-70 Series	8956001197	11.50
Headlamp Dimmer Switch		
1983-87-exc. 70 Ser.	5461816	6.75
1984-87-70 Series	●3239703	21.50
Stop Light Switch		
1983-87-exc. 70 Ser.	5352620	4.50
1984-87-70 Series		
w/sp. cont.	●3225787	8.50
wo/sp. cont.	●3215938	9.00
Turn Signal Switch		
1983-87	●3229970	35.50
Back-Up Lamp Switch		
1983-87-exc. 70 Ser.	5751207	8.75
1984-87-70 Series	●3229472	9.25
Horns		
1983-87-Wagoneer & Cherokee-10 Series (single)		
low pitch	5758484	23.25
1983-87-Wagoneer & Cherokee-10 Series (dual)		
low pitch	5758484	23.25
high pitch	5758485	23.25
1984-87-Wagoneer & Cherokee-70 Series		
low pitch	8956000912	15.25
high pitch	8956001134	15.25
1983-87-CJ-Series		
single	5758484	23.25
Horn Relay		
1983-87-exc. below	5764039	6.50
Series 70	8956001111	6.50

LABOR 33 GLASS 33 LABOR

	(Factory Time)	Chilton Time
(G) Windshield Glass, Renew		
CJ/Scrambler	(.9)	1.4
All other models	(1.4)	1.9
(G) Rear Window Glass, Renew		
Truck	(.8)	1.3
CJ/Scrambler	(.6)	1.1
(G) Front Door Glass, Renew		
CJ/Scrambler	(.4)	.7
Cherokee/Grand Wagoneer/Truck	(.8)	1.2
Cke/Wag/Comanche	(.6)	1.0
(G) Front Door Stationary Glass, Renew		
Cke/Wag/Comanche	(.8)	1.2
(G) Rear Door Glass, Renew		
Cherokee/Grand Wagoneer	(.8)	1.2
All other models	(.6)	1.0
(G) Tailgate Glass, Renew		
Cherokee/Grand Wagoneer	(.6)	.9
Cke/Wag/Comanche	(.9)	1.2
(G) Rear Quarter Window, Renew		
All models	(.6)	1.0
(G) Rear Quarter Window (Movable), Renew		
Cke-Wag/Comanche 2 dr model	(.3)	.6
(G) Side Stationary Window, Renew		
CJ/Scrambler H/Top	(.6)	1.0

LABOR 34 CRUISE CONTROL 34 LABOR

	(Factory Time)	Chilton Time
(G) Cruise Control Switch, Renew		
Cke/Wag/Comanche	(.7)	1.1
All other models	(.5)	.9
(G) Cruise Control Speed Sensor, Renew		
All models	(.4)	.6
(G) Cruise Control Regulator, Renew		
Cke/Wag/Comanche	(.3)	.4
All other models	(.5)	.7
(G) Cruise Control Chain/Cable, Renew		
All models	(.4)	.5
(G) Cruise Control Vacuum Bleed Switch, Renew		
All models	(.3)	.5
(G) Cruise Control Servo, Renew		
All models	(.5)	.7
(G) Cruise Control Brake Release Switch, Renew (Vacuum Dump)		
All models	(.4)	.6
(G) Cruise Control Wiring Harness, Renew		
All models	(.5)	.9

PARTS 34 CRUISE CONTROL 34 PARTS

	Part No.	Price
ELECTRONIC SPEED CONTROL		
Speed Control Regulator		
1983-87-Six	●3237117	167.00
V-8	●3237117	167.00
Series 70	8953000320	95.25
Valve (Vacuum Bleed Switch)		
1983-87	●3232970	3.75
Tach Generator (Spd. Cont.)		
1983-87-exc. 70 Ser.	●3242195	21.00
1984-87-70 Series 7/8"	8933000044	26.50
5/8"	8933002448	16.25
Wiring Harness (Spd. Cont.)		
1983-87-exc. below	5757442	21.00
Wagoneer & Cherokee-10 Series		
M.T.	5762580	25.50
A.T.	5762560	14.25
Wagoneer & Cherokee-70 Series		
Gas	8956000758	32.75
Diesel	8956001333	25.50
Servo (Throttle Cont.)		
1983-87-exc. 70 Ser.	5761988	124.50
70 Series	●3240500	93.75
Cable (Servo To Throttle Chain)		
1983-87-Six	●3242185	6.25
V-8	3240422	18.25
1984-87-Wagoneer & Cherokee 70 Series	8953001734	11.50
Chain & Clevis Assy. (Spd. Cont.)		
1983-87-Six	3240407	2.00
V-8	3234026	2.00
Vacuum Storage Tank		
1983-87-exc. below	8953001068	5.75
1984-87-Wagoneer & Cherokee 70 Series	●3232991	7.75
Vacuum Hose		
1983-87-1/8" I.D.	8125810	.75
1/4" I.D.	8125815	138.50

Note: Hose only serviced from bulk roll order by feet.

GROUP INDEX

ALPHABETICAL INDEX

Chrysler Corporation
Front Wheel Drive Cars

ARIES • RELIANT • LeBARON • DODGE 400 • 400LS • LANCER

YEAR IDENTIFICATION

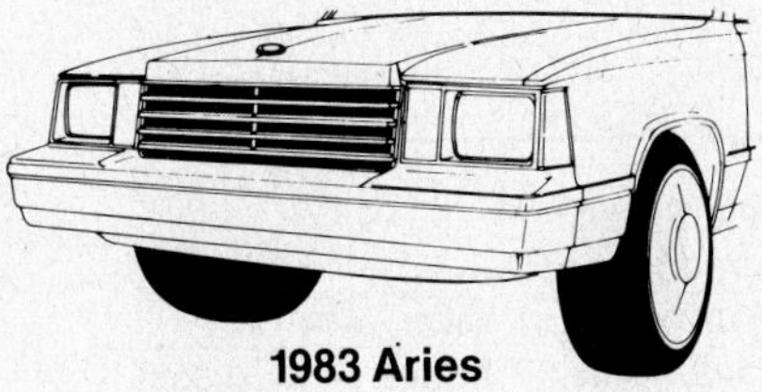

1983 Aries

1984 Aries

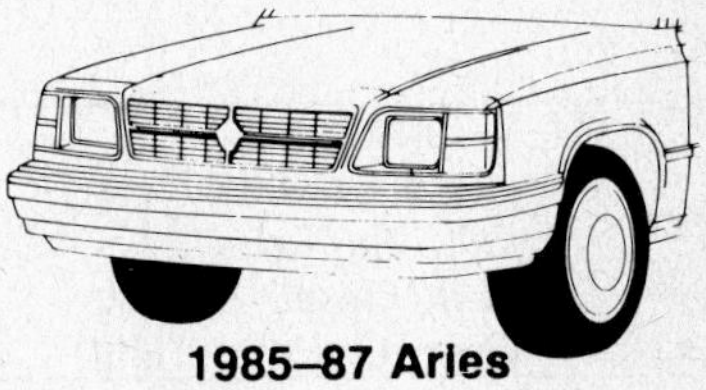

1985–87 Aries

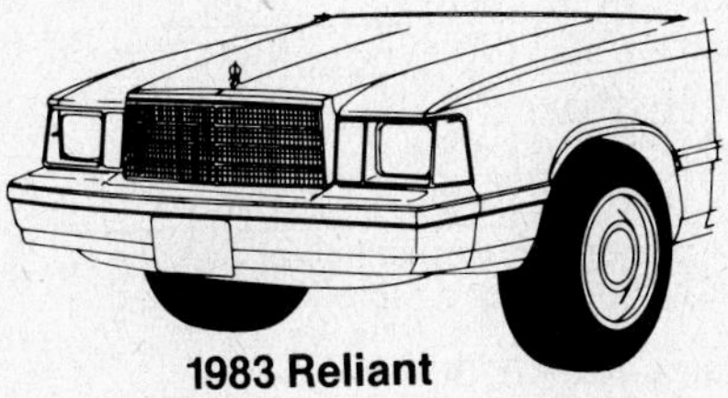

1983 Reliant

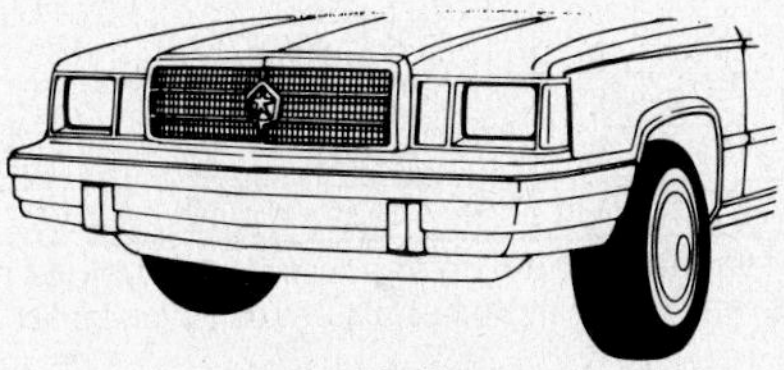

1984 Reliant

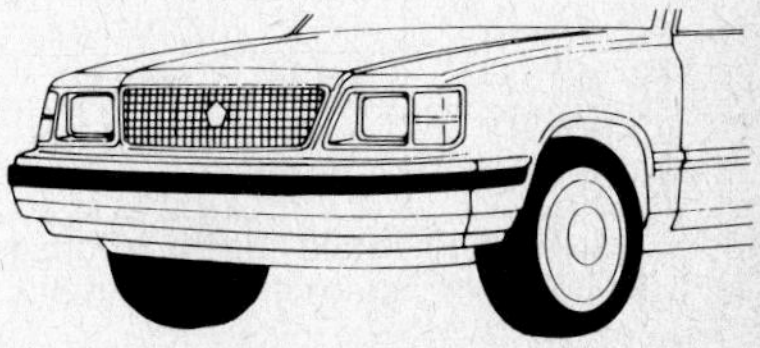

1985–87 Reliant

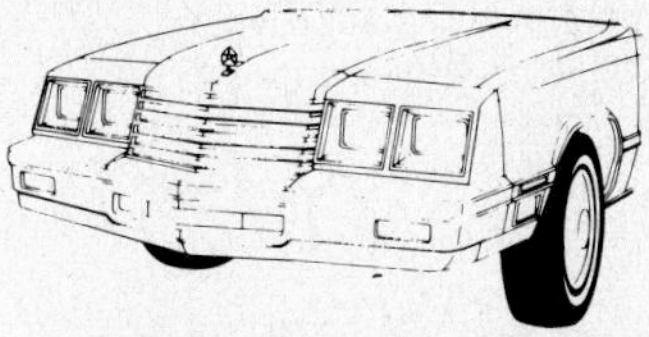

1983–87 Dodge 400, 600

1985–87 Lancer

1987 LeBaron, E-Class

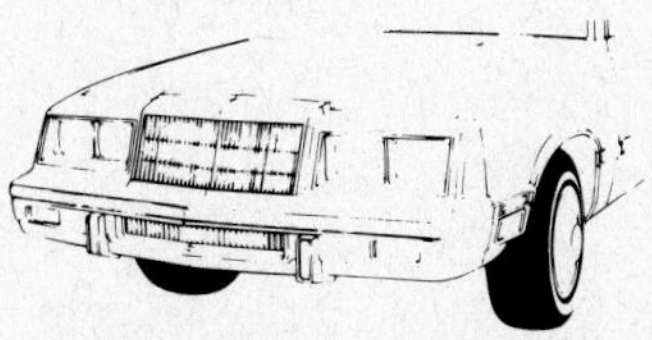

1984 LeBaron, E Class

1984–87 LeBaron, GTS

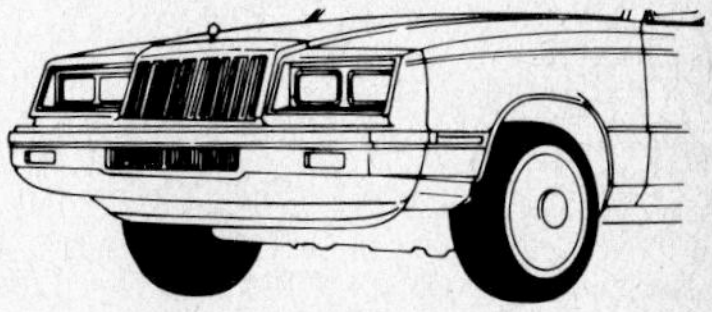

1985–87 LeBaron

VEHICLE IDENTIFICATION NUMBER (VIN)

It is important for servicing and ordering parts to be certain of the vehicle and engine identification. The VIN (vehicle identification number) is a 13 or 17 digit number visible through the windshield on the driver's side of the dash, and contains the vehicle and engine identification codes. It can be interpreted as follows:

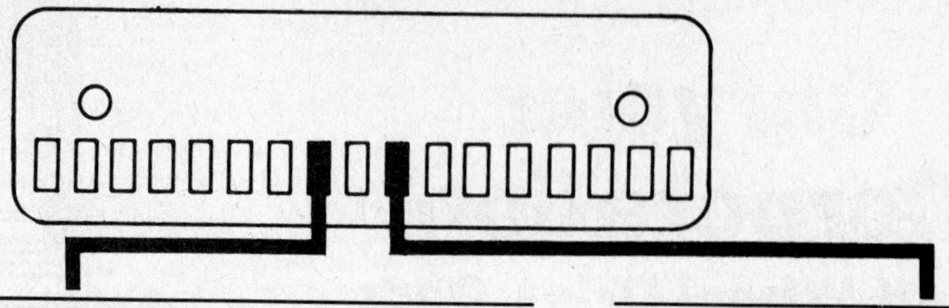

ENGINE CODE

Code	Cu. In.	Liters	Cyl	Carb. bbl	Eng. Mfg.
A (84-85)	98	1.6	4	2	Peugeot
B (83)	105	1.7	4	2	VW
C (83-87)	135	2.2	4	2	Chrysler
D (83-87)	135	2.2	4	EFI	Chrysler
E (84-87)	135	2.2	4	Turbo	Chrysler
G (83-85)	156	2.6	4	2	Mitsubishi
K (86-87)	153	2.5	4	EFI	Chrysler

MODEL YEAR CODE

Code	Year
C	82
D	83
E	84
F	85
G	86
H	87

The seventeen digit Vehicle Identification Number can be used to determine engine application and model year. The tenth indicates the model year, and the eighth digit identifies engine displacement.

TUNE-UP SPECIFICATIONS

Year	Eng. V.I.N. Code	No. Cyl. Displ. Cu. In.	Eng. Mfg.	h.p.	Spark Plugs Orig. Type	Spark Plugs Gap (in.)	Ignition Timing (deg.) Man. Trans.	Ignition Timing (deg.) Auto Trans.	Intake Valve Opens (deg.)■	Fuel Pump Pressure (psi)	Idle Speed (rpm) Man. Trans.	Idle Speed (rpm) Auto Trans.	Valve Lash (in.) Intake	Valve Lash (in.) Exhaust
'84-'86	A	4-98	Peugeot	64	RN12YC	.035	12B	12B	16.5	4.5-6.0	850	1000	.012H	.014H
'83	A	4-105	VW	63	65PR	.035	20B	12B	14	4.4-5.8	900	900	.008-.012H	.016-.020H
'83-'86	C	4-135	Chrysler	All	RN12YC	.035	10B	10B	16 ⑤	4.5-6.0	900	900	Hyd.	Hyd.
'86-'87	D ⑦	4-135	Chrysler	99	RN12YC	.035	12B	12B	10.5	36	850	750	Hyd.	Hyd.
'86-'87	E ⑥	4-135	Chrysler	146	RN12YC	.035	12B	12B	10	53	950	950	Hyd.	Hyd.
'83-'85	G	4-156	Mitsubishi	92	RN11YC4	③	7B	7B	25	4.5-6.0	800 ①	800 ①	.006H ⑧	.010H
'86-'87	K	4-153	Chrysler	100	RN12YC	.035	⑨	⑨	12	14.5 ⑩	⑨	⑨	Hyd.	Hyd.

NOTE: The underhood specifications sticker often reflects tune-up specification changes made in production. Sticker figures must be used if they disagree with those in this chart. Part numbers in this chart are not recommendations by Chilton for any product by brand name.

■ Before top dead center
Hyd.—Hydraulic
H—Hot
C—Cold
① 750 rpm-Canada
③ .035-.040 RN11Y—.030 in For Canada
⑤ Shelby and Hi Performance—10.5° BTDC
Turbocharged—10° BTDC
⑥ Turbo with multipoint fuel injection
⑦ EFI with single point fuel injection
⑧ Jet valve clearance—.010 in.
⑨ Refer to underhood emission control information label
⑩ '86-'87 with multipoint fuel injection—55 lbs

FIRING ORDERS

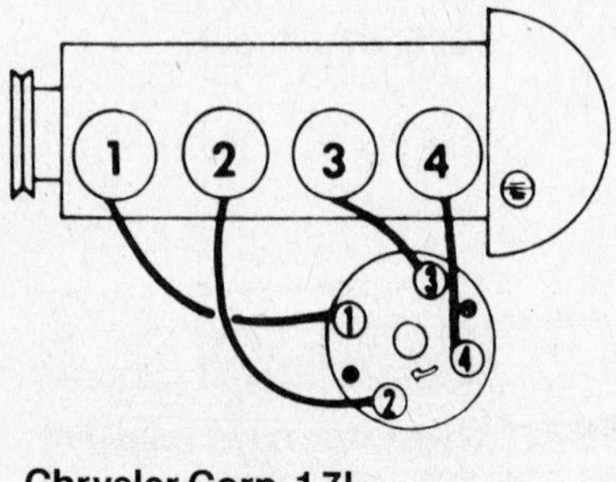

Chrysler Corp. 1.7L
Engine Firing Order: 1-3-4-2
Distributor Rotation: Clockwise

FIRING ORDERS

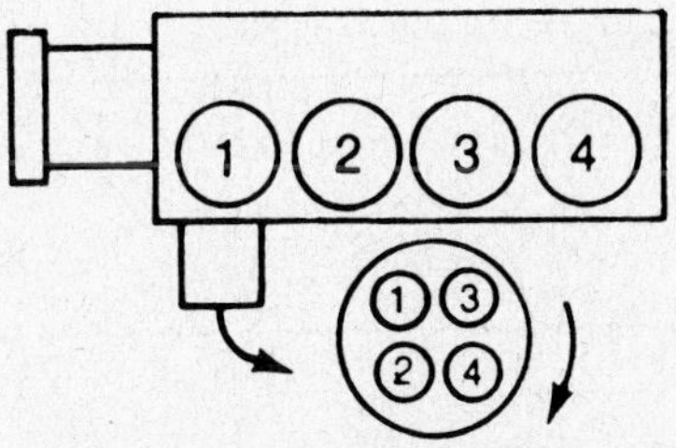

Chrysler Corp. (Mitsubishi) 2.6L
Engine firing order: 1–3–4–2
Distributor rotation: clockwise

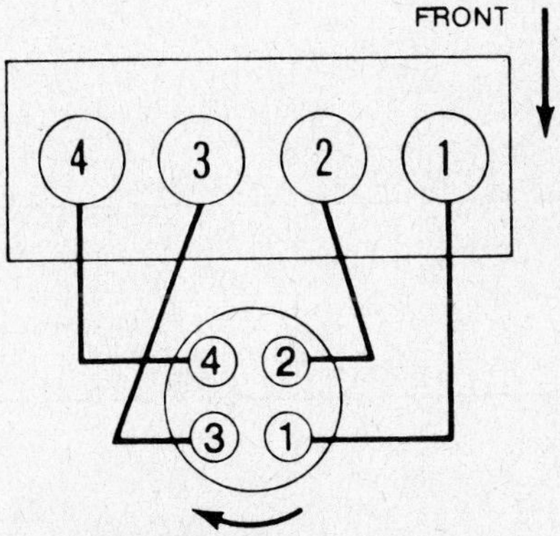

Chrysler Corp: 1.6L
Engine firing order: 1–3–4–2
Distributor rotation: clockwise

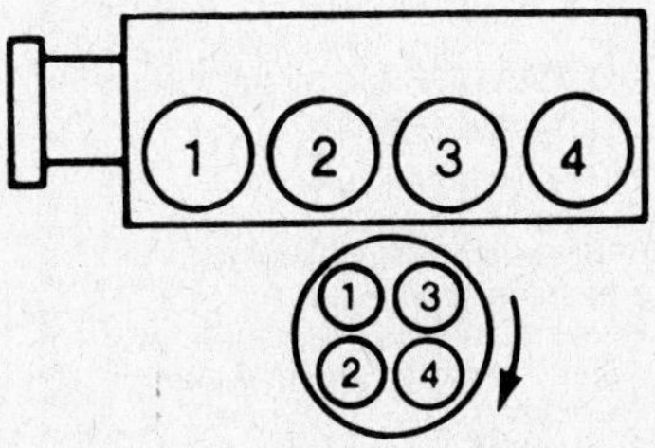

Chrysler Corp. 2.2L/2.5L
Engine Firing Order: 1-3-4-2
Distributor Rotation: Clockwise

WHEEL ALIGNMENT SPECIFICATIONS

Caster is not adjustable

Year and Model	Caster	Front Camber Range (deg.)	Front Camber Preferred	Rear Camber Range (deg.)	Rear Camber Preferred	Toe-In (inches) Front	Toe-In (inches) Rear
CHRYSLER '83–'85 LeBaron, GTS, E. Class, New Yorker, Laser	1 3/16P ①	1/4N–3/4P	5/16P	1N–0	1/2N	1/16	0
'86–'87 LeBaron GTS, New Yorker Laser	1 3/16P ①	1/4N–3/4P	5/16P	1 1/4N–1/4P	1/2P	1/16	0

WHEEL ALIGNMENT SPECIFICATIONS

Caster is not adjustable

Year and Model	Caster	Front Camber Range (deg.)	Front Camber Preferred	Rear Camber Range (deg.)	Rear Camber Preferred	Toe-In (inches) Front	Toe-In (inches) Rear
DODGE '83–'85 Aries, 400, 600, 600 ES Daytona, Lancer	1 3/16P ①	1/4N–3/4P	5/16P	1N–0	1/2N	1/16	0
'86–'87 Aries, 400, 600, Daytona, Lancer, Shadow	1 3/16P ①	1/4N–3/4P	5/16P	1 1/4N–1/4P	1/2P	1/16	0

① Wagon—7/8P°
② 4 door—1 3/8P°
③ Rampage, Scamp—Rear Camber
Min.—1 1/8N°
Max.—1/8N°
Pref—5/8N°

LABOR — SERVICE BAY OPERATIONS — LABOR

(Factory Time) — Chilton Time

COOLING

(M) Winterize Cooling System
Includes: Run engine to check for leaks, tighten all hose connections. Test radiator and pressure cap, drain radiator and engine block. Add anti-freeze and refill system.
All models 5

(M) Thermostat, Renew
1983-87 (.4) 6

(M) Drive Belts, Adjust
All models-one 2
each adtnl 1

(M) Drive Belts, Renew
1983-87
Water pump-2.6L eng (.3) 5
Fan & alter (.2) 3
Air pump (.3) 4
Pwr str (.4) 6
w/A.C. add (.1) 2

(M) Radiator Hoses, Renew
1983-87-upper (.3) 4
lower (.4) 6

FUEL

(M) Carburetor Air Cleaner, Service
1983-87 (.3) 3

(M) Carburetor, Adjust (On Car)
Includes: Adjust idle mixture and idle speed. Check and reset ignition timing.
1983-87
Holly-2 bbl 6
All others 5

(G) Automatic Choke, Renew
1983-87
Holly (.7) 1.0
All others (1.2) 1.5

(G) Carburetor Choke Vacuum Kick, Adjust
1983-87
Holly (.2) 3

BRAKES

(G) Brake Pedal Free Play, Adjust
All models 3

CHILTON'S 10 POINT SAFETY CHECK

CHECK OPERATION & CONDITION OF THE FOLLOWING ITEMS:
1. Legal Registration (serial no.)
2. Tire & Wheels
3. Brake System (R&R all wheels)
4. Light Systems & Signals
5. Accelerator Linkage, Neutral Safety Switch, Shift Indicator Pointer & Seat Position Locks
6. Glass, Mirrrors, Door Locks, Seat Belts & Harness
7. Wipers, Washers & Defrosters
8. Frame, Steering, Shocks, Front & Rear Suspension
9. Fuel & Exhaust Systems
10. Road Test Vehicle

All models 1.0
Exhaust Smog Analysis, add 4

(Factory Time) — Chilton Time

(G) Brakes, Adjust (Minor)
Includes: Adjust brake shoes, fill master cylinder.
two wheels 4

(G) Bleed Brakes (Four Wheels)
Includes: Add fluid.
All models (.4) 6

(M) Parking Brake, Adjust
1983-87 (.3) 4

LUBRICATION SERVICE

(M) Lubricate Chassis, Change Oil & Filter
Includes: Inspect and correct all fluid levels.
All models 6
Install grease fittings add 1

(M) Engine Oil & Filter, Change
Includes: Inspect and correct all fluid levels.
All models 4

(M) Lubricate Chassis
Includes: Inspect and correct all fluid levels.
All models 4
Install grease fittings add 1

(Factory Time) — Chilton Time

WHEELS

(G) Wheels, Balance
one 3
each adtnl 2

(M) Wheel, Renew
one (.3) 5

(M) Wheels, Rotate (All)
All models 5

ELECTRICAL

(G) Aim Headlamps
two 4
four 6

(M) Headlamp Sealed Beam Bulb, Renew
Does not include aim headlamps.
All models-each (.2) 3

(M) License Lamp Lens, Renew
All models (.2) 2

(M) License Lamp Assembly, Renew
All models (.2) 3

(M) Turn Signal and Parking Lamp Assy., Renew
All models (.3) 4

(M) Tail Lamp Assembly, Renew
All models (.3) 4

(M) Side Marker Lamp Assy., Renew
All models-each (.2) 3

(M) Turn Signal or Hazard Warning Flasher, Renew
All models (.2) 3

(G) Horn Relay, Renew
All models (.2) 3

(G) Horn, Renew
All models-one (.2) 4

(M) Battery Cables, Renew
All models
positive (.5) 6
negative (.2) 2

LABOR 1 TUNE UP 1 LABOR

	(Factory Time)	Chilton Time
(G) Compression Test		
Four–1983-87		.6

(G) Engine Tune Up, (Electronic Ignition)

Includes: Test battery and clean connections. Tighten manifold bolts and carburetor mounting bolts. Check engine compression, clean and adjust or renew spark plugs. Test resistance of spark plug cables. Inspect distributor cap, rotor, reluctor and pick up plate. Adjust air gap. Check vacuum advance operation. Reset ignition timing. Adjust idle mixture and idle speed. Service air cleaner. Inspect crankcase ventilation system. Inspect and adjust drive belts. Inspect choke operation and adjust or free up. Check operation of EGR valve.

	(Factory Time)	Chilton Time
Four–1983-87		1.5
w/Turbo add		.5

LABOR 2 IGNITION SYSTEM 2 LABOR

	(Factory Time)	Chilton Time
(G) Spark Plugs, Clean and Reset or Renew		
1983-87	(.5)	.6
(G) Ignition Timing, Reset		
1983-87	(.3)	.4
(G) Spark Control Computer, Renew (SCC)		
1983	(.7)	1.0
1984-87	(.3)	1.0
(G) Distributor Assembly, Renew		
Includes: Reset ignition timing.		
1983-87	(.4)	.6
(G) Distributor, R&R and Recondition		
Includes: Reset ignition timing.		
1983-87	(.9)	1.5
(G) Electronic Control Unit, Renew		
1983-87		
2.6L eng	(.3)	.5
(G) Distributor Pick-Up Plate and Coil Assy., Renew (Hall Effect)		
Does not require R&R of distributor.		
1983-87		
2.2L & 2.5L engs	(.3)	.6
(G) Distributor Pick-Up Set, Renew		
Does not require R&R of distributor.		
1983-87		
2.6L eng	(.5)	.7
(G) Distributor Ignitor Set, Renew		
Does not require R&R of distributor.		
1983-87		
2.6L eng	(.4)	.6
(G) Distributor Breaker Assy., Renew		
Does not require R&R of distributor.		
1983-87		
2.6L eng	(.4)	.6
(G) Distributor Reluctor and Governor Assy., Renew		
Does not require R&R of distributor.		
1983-87		
2.6L eng	(.3)	.5
(G) Distributor Vacuum Advance Control Unit, Renew		
Does not require R&R of distributor.		
1983-87		
2.6L eng	(.6)	.9
(G) Distributor Cap and/or Rotor, Renew		
1983-87	(.2)	.4
(G) Ignition Coil, Renew		
1983-87	(.2)	.4
(G) Ignition Cables, Renew		
1983-87	(.2)	.4
(G) Ignition Switch, Renew		
1983-87		
std column	(.4)	.8
tilt column	(.4)	.9
(G) Ignition Key Warning Buzzer, Renew		
1983-87	(.2)	.4
(G) Ignition Switch Time Delay Relay, Renew		
1983-87	(.2)	.3
(G) Ignition Key Buzzer/Chime Switch, Renew		
1983-87		
std column	(.6)	1.2
tilt column	(.5)	1.0
(G) Ignition Lock Housing, Renew		
Does not include painting.		
1983-87-std column	(.8)	1.3
Tilt column		
console shift	(1.1)	1.7
column shift	(.8)	1.3

PARTS 2 IGNITION SYSTEM 2 PARTS

	Part No.	Price
(1) Distributor Assy. (2.2L & 2.5L)		
1983	4240470	66.25
1984-85-exc. Turbo	4240470	66.25
Turbo	5213525	79.75
1986-87-exc. Turbo	5226575	N.L.
Turbo	5213525	79.75
(2) Distributor Cap		
1983-85	4240446	8.25
1986-87	5226527	N.L.
(3) Rotor Assy.		
1983-85	5213728	8.25
1986-87	5226535	8.25
(4) Switch		
1983	4240471	30.50
1984-85-exc. Turbo	5213522	32.00
Turbo	5213524	44.50
1986-87-exc. Turbo	5226616	26.50
Turbo	5226617	N.L.
1986-87-2.5L	5226616	26.50
Ballast Resistor		
1983-84	4106140	4.00

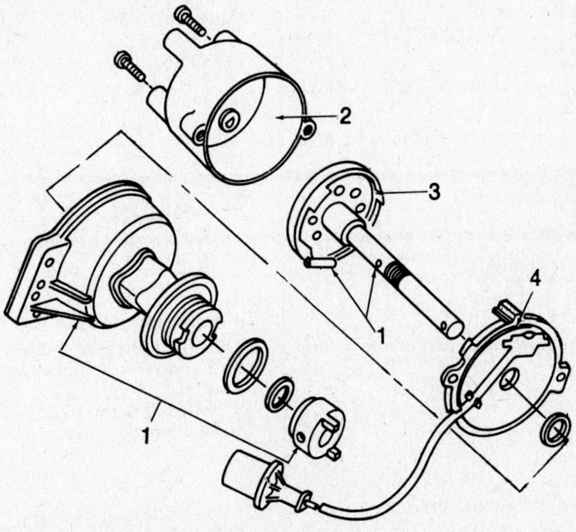

PARTS 2 IGNITION SYSTEM 2 PARTS

	Part No.	Price
Coil		
1983-87	4176009	26.75
Ignition Wire Set		
1983-87	4240435	19.75
Ignition Switch		
1983-87		
wo/Tilt whl	3747882	14.50
w/Tilt whl	4221201	23.00
Ignition Warning Buzzer		
1983-87		
wo/Tilt whl	4221303	7.00
w/Tilt whl	3488432	7.50

	Part No.	Price
Power Module		
1983	5213980	140.00
1984-w/Turbo	5213574	140.00
E.F.I.	5213581	105.00
1985-86-w/Turbo	5226766	105.00
E.F.I.		
exc. Calif.	5226765	105.00
Calif.	5226648	140.00
Control (Electronic Advance)		
1983-M.T.		
exc. Calif.	5213834	N.L.
Calif.	5213838	110.00
1983-A.T. (exc. Calif.)		
to 10-8-82	5213852	N.L.
after 10-8-82	5213854	110.00

	Part No.	Price
(Calif.)		
to 11-1-82	5213836	110.00
after 11-1-82	5213858	110.00
High Alt.	5213840	N.L.
1984-M.T.		
exc. Calif.	5226284	110.00
Calif.	5213838	110.00
1984-A.T.		
exc. Calif.	5226286	110.00
Calif.	5213858	110.00
High Alt.	5213840	N.L.
1985-86-M.T.		
exc. Calif.	5226439	110.00
Calif.	5226455	110.00
1986-87-A.T.		
exc. Calif.	5226505	N.L.
Calif.	5226451	110.00
Canada	5226527	N.L.

PARTS 2 IGNITION SYSTEM 2 PARTS

	Part No.	Price
Distributor Assy. (2.6L)		
1983-84-exc. Calif.	MD013791	288.75
Calif.	MD013793	288.75
1985	MD067134	288.75
(1) Distributor Cap		
1983-85	MD607466	14.50
(2) Rotor Assy.		
1983-85	MD607734	9.00
(3) Governor Set		
1983-84	MD607474	59.75
1985	MD607886	40.00
(4) Pick Up Set		
1983-85	MD607770	16.75
(5) Igniter Set		
1983-85	MD607478	157.50
(6) Breaker Assy.		
1983-85	MD607470	31.75
(7) Plate		
1983-85	MD607359	1.25
(8) Vacuum Set		
1983-84-exc. Calif.	MD607475	19.00
Calif.	MD607477	21.00
1985	MD607885	17.25
(9) "O" Ring		
1983-85	MD602412	1.25
(10) Drive Gear & Pin		
1983-85	MD607226	15.50
(11) Shaft Assy		
1983-85	MD607468	42.75
(12) Oil Seal		
1983-85	MD607405	5.75

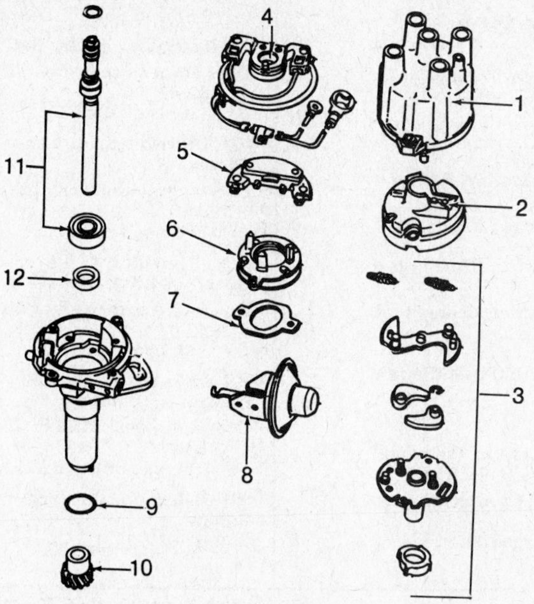

	Part No.	Price
Ignition Wire Set		
1983-84	MD027766	27.50
1985-85	MD085766	29.00
Coil Assy.		
1983-84	MD025703	37.00
1985-85	MD013789	25.75

	Part No.	Price
High Tension Cable		
1983-85	MD027723	5.25
Ignition Switch		
1983-85-wo/tilt whl	3747882	14.50
w/tilt whl.	4221201	23.00

LABOR 3 FUEL SYSTEM 3 LABOR

(Factory Time)	Chilton Time
(G) Fuel Pump, Test	
Includes: Disconnect line at carburetor, attach pressure gauge.	
All models	
mechanical	.3
electric	.4
(M) Carburetor Air Cleaner, Service	
1983-87 (.3)	.3

(Factory Time)	Chilton Time
(G) Carburetor, Adjust (On Car)	
Includes: Adjust idle mixture and idle speed. Check and reset ignition timing.	
1983-87	
Holly-2 bbl	.6
All others	.5
(G) Idle Solenoid, Renew	
1983-87 (.4)	.6

(Factory Time)	Chilton Time
(G) Coolant Temperature Sensor/Switch, Renew	
1983-87 (.2)	.4
(G) Accelerator Pump, Renew	
1983-87	
Holly (.4)	.8
All others (.8)	1.1
(G) Automatic Choke, Renew	
1983-87	
Holly (.7)	1.0
All others (1.2)	1.5

LABOR 3 FUEL SYSTEM 3 LABOR

(Factory Time)	Chilton Time
(G) Choke Vacuum Kick Diaphragm, Renew	
1983-87	
Holly (.2)	.4
(G) Choke Vacuum Kick, Adjust	
1983-87 (.2)	.3
(G) Heated Air Door Sensor, Renew	
1983-87-one (.2)	.4
(G) Carburetor Assembly, Renew	
Includes: All necessary adjustments.	
1983-87	
Holly (.8)	1.3
All others (.7)	1.2
(G) Carburetor, R&R and Clean or Recondition	
Includes: All necessary adjustments.	
1983-87	
Holly (1.6)	2.4
All others (2.5)	3.5
(G) Carburetor Needle and Seat, Renew	
Includes: Adjust float level, idle speed and mixture.	
1983-87	
Holly (.7)	1.1
All others (1.1)	1.5
(M) Fuel Filter, Renew	
1983-87	
in line (.2)	.3
in tank (.5)	.8
(G) Fuel Pump, Renew	
1983-87	
mechanical (.5)	.7
electric (.6)	1.0
Add pump test if performed.	

(Factory Time)	Chilton Time
(G) Fuel Tank, Renew	
1983-87 (1.2)	1.6
(G) Fuel Gauge (Tank), Renew	
1983-87 (.7)	1.0
(G) Fuel Gauge (Dash), Renew	
1983-87 (.4)	.8
(G) Intake Manifold or Gasket, Renew	
1983-87	
2.2L & 2.5L engs (2.0)	3.7
w/Turbo add (.6)	.6
2.6L eng (1.9)	3.0
Renew manif add (.2)	.5
(G) Intake and Exhaust Manifold Gaskets, Renew	
1983-87	
2.2L & 2.5L engs (1.9)	3.5
w/Turbo add (.6)	.6
TURBOCHARGER	
(G) Turbocharger Assy., Renew	
Includes: Renew gaskets.	
1984-87 (2.7)	3.5
(G) Fuel Pressure Regulator, Renew	
1984-87 (.3)	.5
(G) Vehicle Speed Sensor, Renew	
1984-87 (.3)	.6
(G) Detonation Sensor, Renew	
1984-87 (.2)	.4
(G) Change Temperature Sensor, Renew	
1984-87 (.2)	.4
(G) Fuel Pump, Renew (In Tank)	
1984-87 (1.0)	1.6

(Factory Time)	Chilton Time
ELECTRONIC FUEL INJECTION	
(G) Throttle Body, Renew	
1984-87 (.5)	.9
(G) Fuel Pressure Regulator, Renew	
1984-87 (.2)	.4
w/Turbo add (.1)	.1
(G) Fuel Pump, Renew	
1984-87 (.6)	.9
(G) Fuel Inlet Chamber, Renew	
1984-87 (.4)	.7
(G) Automatic Idle Speed Assy., Renew	
1984-87	
motor (.3)	.5
adapter (.3)	.5
(G) Fuel Injector Rail, Renew	
1984-87 (.6)	1.0
(G) Fuel Injector, Renew	
1984-87	
wo/Turbo (.3)	.5
w/Turbo	
one (.4)	.6
each adtnl (.1)	.2
(G) Logic Module, Renew	
1984-87 (.2)	.3
(G) Power Module, Renew	
1984-87 (.3)	.4
(G) M.A.P. Sensor, Renew	
1984-87 (.4)	.6
(G) Throttle Position Sensor (Potentiometer), Renew	
1984-87 (.2)	.3

PARTS 3 FUEL SYSTEM 3 PARTS

	Part No.	Price
Carburetor Assy. (Holley New)		
1983-2.2L (carb. 5220)		
(M.T.)		
R-40023-1	4227382	325.75
R-40024-1	4227383	325.75
(A.T.)		
R-40025-1	4227384	325.75
R-40026-1	4227385	325.75
1983-2.2L (carb. 6520)		
(M.T.)		
R-40003-1	4227365	325.75
R-40005-1	4227374	325.75
(A.T.)		
R-40004-1	4287087	325.75
R-40006-1	4293879	326.00
R-40008-1	4287093	325.75
R-40010-1	4287087	325.75
R-40012-1	4227372	325.75
R-40014-1	4227375	325.75
1984-2.2L (carb. 5220)		
(M.T.)		
R-40076	4288425	Disc.
R-40170	4288482	Disc.
(A.T.)		
R-40078	4288428	Disc.
R-40171	4288483	Disc.
1984-2.2L (carb. 6520)		
(M.T.)		
R-40064-1	4288440	325.75
R-40061-1	4288444	325.75
(A.T.)		
R-40065-1	4288441	325.75
R-40062-1	4288445	325.75

	Part No.	Price
1985-2.2L		
R-40135	4342890	325.75
R-40139-1	4342890	325.75
R-40134-1	4342890	325.75
Carburetor Assy. 2.6L		
1983		
wo/Calif. em.	MD073978	521.50
w/Calif. em.	MD017066	536.50
w/Hi alt.	MD017307	521.50
1984		
wo/Calif. em.	MD068740	521.50
w/Calif. em.	MD068743	536.50
w/Hi alt.	MD017307	521.50
1985 (up to eng. no. DW6223)		
exc. Calif.	MD081509	521.50
Calif.	MD084289	536.50
1985 (from eng. no. EA2116)		
exc. Calif.	MD088137	521.50
Calif.	MD082758	521.50
Carburetor Repair Kit		
1983 (carb. 5220)		
2.2L	4273725	N.L.
1983-2.2L (carb. 6520)		
(M.T.)		
exc. Hi Alt.	4240199	27.00
Hi Alt.	4293776	31.00
(A.T.)		
exc. below	4293773	22.25
Calif.	4267177	31.00
Hi alt.	4293776	31.00

	Part No.	Price
1984-2.2L		
5220 carb.	4293854	26.25
6520 carb.	4293856	31.00
1985-2.2L		
5220 carb.	4342876	38.75
6520 carb.	4342882	31.00
Carburetor Gasket Kit		
1983-2.2L		
5220 carb.	4271875	6.75
6520 carb.	4267174	6.75
1983-2.6L	MD608571	35.75
1984-2.2L		
5220 carb.	4293850	7.25
6520 carb.	4293838	7.25
1984-2.6L		
exc. Calif.	MD608643	35.75
Calif.	MD608571	35.75
1985-87-2.2L		
5220 carb.	4342872	7.00
6520 carb.	4293838	7.25
1985-2.6L		
up to eng. no. DW6223	MD608797	36.75
from eng. no. EA2116	MD612215	36.75
Carburetor Needle and Seat		
1983-85-2.2L	4131116	6.50

PARTS 3 FUEL SYSTEM 3 PARTS

	Part No.	Price
Float and Needle Valve Kit		
1983-84-2.6L	MD606946	23.50
1985-2.6L		
up to eng. no. DW6223	MD606946	23.50
from eng. no. EA2116	MD612217	10.75
Solenoid (Anti-Diesel)		
1983-85-2.2L	4271882	61.50
Carburetor Pump Diaphragm		
1983-85		
2.2L	4131121	17.25
2.6L	MD606849	21.50
Fuel Pump Assy.		
1984-exc below	4293802	36.00
Turbo	4279296	217.00
2.6L	MD026591	50.50
1985-exc below	4293802	36.00
E.F.I.	4279951	225.25
Turbo	4279917	217.00
2.6L	MD026591	50.50
1986-87		
E.F.I.	4075445	36.00
Turbo	4279917	217.00

	Part No.	Price
Fuel Tank		
1983	4279485	140.00
1984	4279605	141.50
1985-exc. below	4279653	141.50
T.B.I.	4279657	141.75
Turbo	4279911	141.50
1986-87	4279603	140.00
Fuel Gauge (Tank)		
1983		
wo/Warn. signal	4051682	30.25
w/warn. signal	4051684	30.25
1984	4051867	30.50
1985-exc. below	4051849	30.50
T.B.I.	4279950	32.50
Turbo	4051895	30.50
1986-87	4051663	30.25
Fuel Gauge (Dash)		
1983 (Aries & Reliant)		
Unleaded	4051541	19.75
Leaded	4051542	19.00
1983 (Le Baron & Dodge 400)		
Unleaded	4051565	24.25
1984-exc. below	4051772	30.75

	Part No.	Price
Le Baron	4051565	24.25
1985-exc. below	4051565	24.25
Combination	4051772	30.75
Lancer, GTS	4051869	45.00
1986-87-exc. below	4375010	35.50
Lancer, GTS	4375085	45.25
Fuel Filter		
1983-87		
2.2L (Carb)	4240102	5.75
2.6L	MD026581	13.51
1984-E.F.I.	4279599	23.50
1985-87-E.F.I.	4279987	23.25
Manifold Gasket (Intake & Exh.)		
2.2L		
1983-87	4105745	6.75
2.5L		
1986-87	4105745	6.75
2.6L		
1983-intake	MD024628	5.00
exhaust	MD025534	131.75
1984-85-intake	MD024628	5.00
exhaust	MD025684	11.25

PARTS 3 ELECTRONIC FUEL INJECTION 3 PARTS

	Part No.	Price
Throttle Body (exc. Turbo)		
1984	4275617	735.50
1985	4342948	N.L.
1986-87-2.2L	4300265	290.00
2.5L	4300266	290.00
Throttle Body (Turbo)		
1984	4268801	325.00
1985	4288276	325.00
1986-87	4307255	325.00
(1) Fitting Kit (Hose)		
1984-85	4287316	11.00
1986-87	4300252	6.75
(2) Injector Kit		
1984-85	4275985	160.00
1986-87 (Seals)	4300254	6.50
Injector (w/O-rings)		
1986-87	4300257	53.55
(3) Hose & Seal Kit (Pressure Regulator)		
1984-85	4287324	5.25
(4) Gasket (Intake Manifold)		
1984-85	4275531	1.75
(5) Potentiometer Kit		
exc Turbo		
1984	4287743	32.00
1985	4179848	32.00
Turbo		
1984	4221396	N.L.
1985-87	4179849	32.00
Throttle Position Sensor		
exc Turbo		
1986-87	5226509	29.00
(6) Housing Kit (A.I.S. Motor)		
1984-85	4287730	17.75
(7) Regulator Kit		
1984-85	4287320	53.25
1986-87	4300263	60.00
(8) Motor Kit (A.I.S.)		
1984-85	4287712	64.00
(9) "O" Ring Kit (A.I.S. Motor)		
1984-85	4287714	3.50
Motor (w/O-ring)		
1986-87	4300264	N.L.

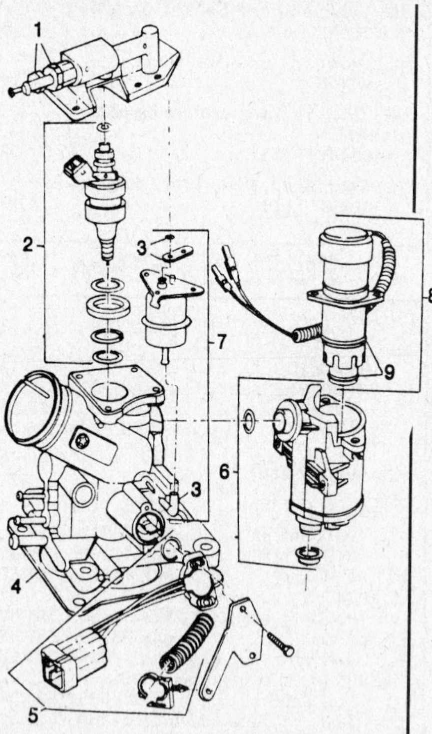

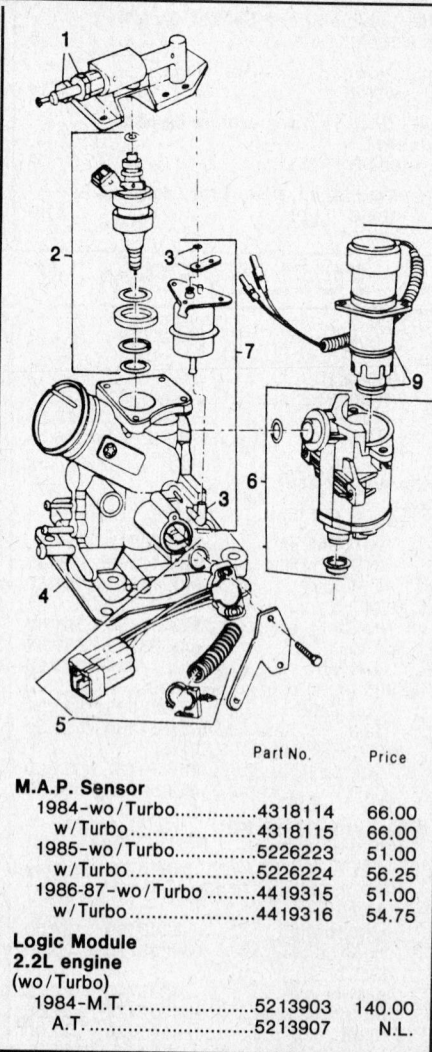

	Part No.	Price
M.A.P. Sensor		
1984-wo/Turbo	4318114	66.00
w/Turbo	4318115	66.00
1985-wo/Turbo	5226223	51.00
w/Turbo	5226224	56.25
1986-87-wo/Turbo	4419315	51.00
w/Turbo	4419316	54.75
Logic Module		
2.2L engine		
(wo/Turbo)		
1984-M.T.	5213903	140.00
A.T.	5213907	N.L.

	Part No.	Price
1985-M.T.	5226272	140.00
A.T.-exc Cal.	5226741	140.00
A.T.-Calif.	5226648	140.00
1986-87-M.T. (exc Cal.)		
to 10/20/85	5227309	N.L.
from 10/20/85	5227400	140.00
1986-87-M.T. (Cal.)		
to 10/20/85	5227315	140.00
from 10/20/85	5227449	140.00
1986-87-A.T.		
exc Cal.	5227160	N.L.
Calif.	5227306	140.00

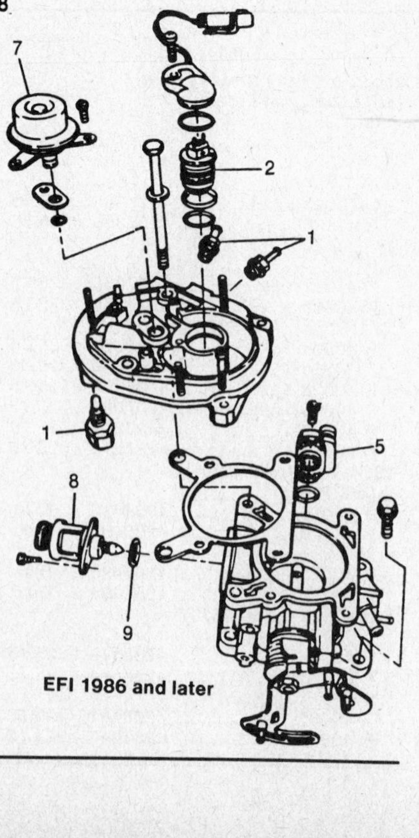

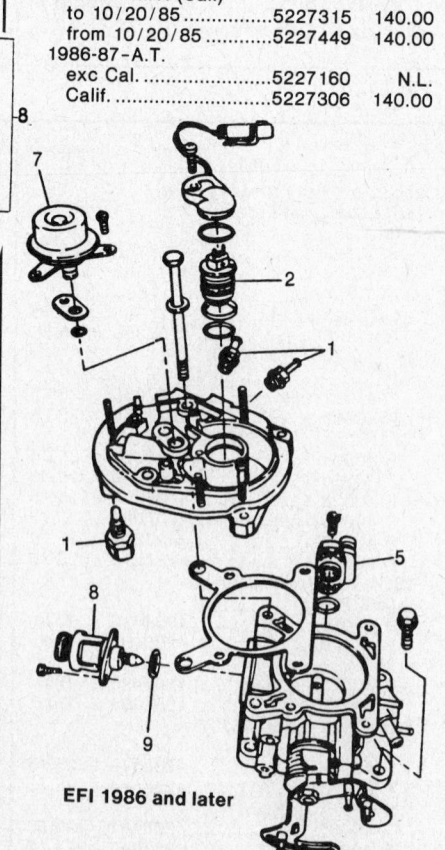

EFI 1986 and later

PARTS 3 ELECTRONIC FUEL INJECTION 3 PARTS

	Part No.	Price
(w/Turbo)		
1984-M.T.	5213898	N.L.
A.T.	5213921	N.L.
1985-M.T.	5226794	140.00
A.T.	5226611	140.00
1986-87-M.T.	5227371	140.00
A.T.	5227255	140.00
2.5L engine		
1986-87		
exc Lancer & GTS		
to 10/25/85		
A.T.-exc Cal.	5227318	140.00
Calif.	5227321	140.00
after 10/25/85		
A.T. exc Cal.	5227452	140.00
Calif.	5227455	140.00
Lancer & GTS		
to 10/25/85		
M.T.-exc Cal.	5227328	140.00
Calif.	5227331	140.00
after 10/25/85		
M.T.-exc Cal.	5227458	140.00
Calif.	5227461	140.00
Fuel Injectors (Turbo)		
1984	4275312	56.75
1985-87	4306024	53.75
Regulator (Fuel Pressure-Turbo)		
1984-87	4275313	53.75
Fuel Rail (Turbo)		
1984	4275301	3.25
1985-87	4275555	39.25
2.6L engine		
1984	MD072035	230.75
1985	MD082058	230.75
Auto. Shutdown Relay		
1984-87	4221279	13.75
Detonation Sensor		
1985-87-wo/turbo	5213629	23.75
w/turbo	4318118	23.75
Temperature Sensor		
1986-87	4330251	52.50

PARTS 3 TURBOCHARGER SYSTEM 3 PARTS

	Part No.	Price
(1) E.G.R. Valve		
Replacement E.G.R. valve must be ordered according to the stamping number on the original valve.		
(2) Elbow (Compressor Inlet)		
1984-87	4105461	30.50
(3) Gasket (Inlet Elbow)		
1984-87	4227973	.50
(4) Turbocharger Assy.		
1984	4105794	566.25
1985-87	4105800	567.00
(5) Oxygen Sensor		
1984-87	4301346	36.75
(6) Hose Connector		
1984-87-up to 2-1-84	5214609	6.00
from 2-1-84	4323444	6.00
(7) Strap (Vane Hose)		
1984-87	4105719	2.00
(8) Vane (Air Flow)		
1984-87	4105465	3.00

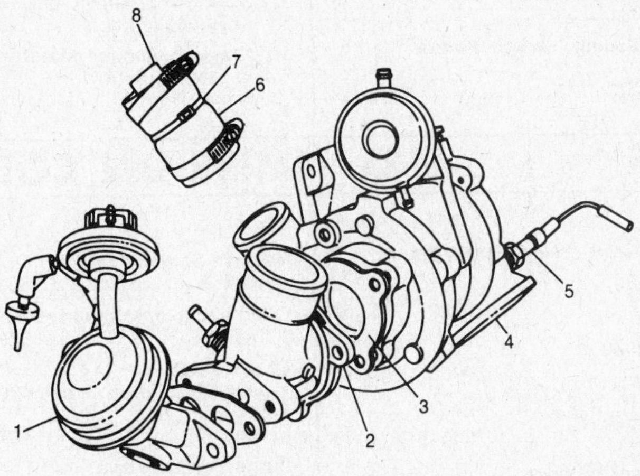

LABOR 3A EMISSION CONTROLS 3A LABOR

	(Factory Time)	Chilton Time
CRANKCASE EMISSION		
(M) Crankcase Vent Valve, Renew		
1983-87	(.2)	.3
(M) Crankcase Vent Hose, Renew		
1983-87-one	(.2)	.2
AIR INJECTION SYSTEM		
(G) Air Pump, Renew		
1983-87		
2.2L eng	(.4)	.7
(G) Injection Tube and Aspirator Valve Assy., Renew		
1983-87-2.2L eng		
exh manif mount	(.5)	.8
to conv		
one or both	(.4)	.6
EFI engs		
to conv	(.5)	.8
(G) Air Pump Diverter/Switching Valve, Renew		
1983-87		
2.2L eng	(.3)	.6

CHILTON'S EMISSION CONTROL TUNE-UP

1. Clean or renew P.C.V. valve, hoses and filter
2. Check fuel tank cap for sealing ability
3. Check fuel tank and fuel lines for leakage
4. Check evaporation canister and filter. Replace if necessary
5. Check engine compression to determine leakage of unburned gases. (Add time for items of interference
6. Test and clean or renew spark plugs
7. Check engine oil dipstick for sealing ability
8. Test exhaust system with analyzer and check system for leakage
9. Check exhaust manifold heat valve for operation
10. Adjust ignition timing and carburetor idle speed and mixture
11. Check automatic choke mechanism for free operation
12. Inspect air cleaner and element
13. On models so equipped test distributor vacuum control switch and transmission control switch

All models
Four 1.2
For repairs made charge accordingly

	(Factory Time)	Chilton Time
(G) Aspirator Valve, Renew		
1984-87	(.2)	.4
w/E.F.I. add	(.1)	.1
(G) Enrichment Solenoid Valve, Renew		
1984-87		
2.6L eng	(.3)	.4
(G) Jet Mixture Solenoid Valve, Renew		
1984-87		
2.6L eng	(.4)	.6
(G) Deceleration Solenoid Valve, Renew		
1984-87	(.3)	.6

LABOR 3A EMISSION CONTROLS 3A LABOR

	(Factory Time)	Chilton Time
(G) Distributor/Air Switching Valve Solenoid Assy., Renew		
1984-87	(.2)	.3
(G) Change Temperature Sensor, Renew		
1984-87	(.2)	.4
(G) Intake Air Temperature Sensor, Renew		
1984-87	(.2)	.3

EVAPORATIVE EMISSION

	(Factory Time)	Chilton Time
(M) Vapor Canister, Renew		
1983-87	(.3)	.4
(M) Vapor Canister Filter, Renew		
1983-87	(.2)	.3
(M) Vapor Canister Valve, Renew		
1985-87	(.2)	.3

E.G.R. SYSTEM

	(Factory Time)	Chilton Time
(G) Jet Air Control Valve, Renew		
1984-87	(.5)	.7
(G) Coolant Vacuum Switch, Renew (CCEVS)		
1983-87	(.3)	.4
(G) E.G.R. Back Pressure Valve, Renew		
1984-87	(.2)	.3
(G) E.G.R. and Purge Control Solenoid Bank, Renew		
1984-87	(.2)	.3
(G) Exhaust Gas Recirculation Control Valve, Renew		
1983-87		
2.2L & 2.5L engs	(.6)	.8
w/Turbo add	(.2)	.2
2.6L eng	(.3)	.5
(G) Coolant Control Vacuum Valve (CCEGR), Renew		
1983-87-one	(.3)	.5
both	(.4)	.6

EFE SYSTEM

	(Factory Time)	Chilton Time
(G) Oxygen Sensor, Renew		
1983-87		
2.2L & 2.5L engs	(.2)	.4
2.6L eng	(.5)	.7
(G) Oxygen Sensor Maintenance Lamp Switch, Renew		
All models	(.2)	.4
(G) High Altitude Compensator, Renew		
1983-87	(.3)	.5
(G) Detonation Sensor, Renew		
1984-87	(.2)	.4

HEATED INLET AIR SYSTEM

	(Factory Time)	Chilton Time
(M) Carburetor Air Cleaner, Service		
1983-87	(.3)	.3
(G) Heated Air Door Delay Valve, Renew		
1983-87-one	(.2)	.3
(G) Heated Air Door Sensor, Renew		
1984-87		
2.6L eng	(.2)	.3

PULSE AIR SYSTEM

	(Factory Time)	Chilton Time
(G) Pulse Air Feeder, Renew		
1983-87	(.6)	.9
(G) Pulse Air Feeder Tube, Renew		
1983-87	(.7)	1.1

PARTS 3A EMISSION CONTROLS 3A PARTS

AIR INJECTION SYSTEM

	Part No.	Price
Air Pump Assy.		
1983-85	4267227	162.50
Air Pump Pulley		
1983-85	5203585	4.75
Air Pump Drive Pulley		
1983-85	5214518	7.75
Air Pump Diverter Valve		
1983-85	4179719	30.50
Switch & Relief Valve		
1983-85	4275053	30.00

ASPIRATOR SYSTEM (E.F.I.)

	Part No.	Price
Aspirator Valve		
1984-85	4041966	10.75
1986-87	4300376	19.50
Silencer		
1984-85	4287704	3.50
1986-87	4300382	4.50
Aspirator Valve (2.6L)		
1984	4041966	10.75
1985	4300376	19.50

EVAPORATIVE EMISSION SYSTEM

	Part No.	Price
Vapor Canister		
2.2L		
1983	4241836	47.25
1984-85-3 port	4271982	49.25
4 port	4241838	52.75
1986-87	4241838	52.75
Vacuum Solenoid (E.F.I.)		
1986-87	5227169	20.50
Quad Vacuum Solenoid (Turbo)		
1986-87	5226352	57.00
Check Valve		
1986-87-E.F.I.	4306923	1.50
2.6L		
1983-85	4241837	48.75
Purge Control Valve		
1983-85		
2.6L	4241831	16.00

EXHAUST GAS RECIRCULATION SYSTEM

E.G.R. Valve
Replacement E.G.R. valves must be ordered according to the stamping number on the original valve. Transducer valve is serviced with the EGR valve.

	Part No.	Price
Coolant Control Switch (C.C.E.G.R.)		
1983-85-98°	4049277	17.50
125°	3879736	17.50
Engine Coolant Control Switch (C.C.E.V.)		
1983-85		
orange	4049208	17.50
natural	3879707	17.50
green	4049276	17.50
Oxygen Sensor		
1983	4301175	34.00
1984-85-2.2L eng.	4301346	36.75
2.6L eng.	MD082058	230.75
1986-87-exc. Turbo	4301375	40.00
Turbo	4301346	36.75
Crankcase Vent Valve		
2.2L & 2.5L		
1983-84	3671076	4.25
1985-exc. Turbo	4273145	4.00
Turbo	3671076	4.25
1986-87-exc. Turbo	4343766	7.00
Turbo	3671076	4.25
2.6L		
1983-85	MD026613	9.75
Vacuum Idle Speed Solenoid		
1983-85-2.6L	5213348	16.00
Vacuum Valve Solenoid (A/C)		
1984	4240417	16.00
1985	5226347	28.75
Solenoid Valve		
1984-85-2.6L		
exc. Calif.	MD071769	48.75
Calif.	MD025274	66.75
Sensor (Eng. Speed)		
1984-85-2.6L	MD025273	128.25
Thermo. Valve		
1984-85-2.6L		
exc. Calif.	MD073096	27.50
Calif.	MD025263	32.75
High Altitude Compensator		
2.2L		
1985	4306202	62.00
2.6L		
1983-87-exc. Calif.	MD026725	96.00
Calif.	MD026708	96.00
Carburetor Control Unit (2.6L)		
1984	MD072033	N.L.
1985	MD080152	230.75

LABOR 4 ALTERNATOR AND REGULATOR 4 LABOR

	(Factory Time)	Chilton Time
(G) Alternator Circuits, Test		
Includes: Test battery, regulator and alternator output.		
All models		.6
(M) Alternator Drive Belt, Renew		
1983-87	(.2)	.3
w/A.C. add	(.1)	.1
(G) Alternator Assembly, Renew		
Includes: Transfer pulley if required.		
1983-87	(.8)	1.2
w/A.C. add	(.3)	.3
Add circuit test if performed.		
(G) Alternator, R&R and Recondition		
Includes: Test and disassemble.		
1983-87	(1.5)	2.1
w/A.C. add	(.3)	.3
(G) Alternator Front Bearing or Retainer, Renew		
Includes: R&R alternator.		
1983-87	(.8)	1.1
Renew rear brg add		.2
w/A.C. add	(.3)	.3
(G) Voltage Regulator, Test and Renew		
1983-87		
external type	(.2)	.4
internal type	(1.0)	*1.6
*w/A.C. add	(.3)	.3
(G) Instrument Cluster Voltage Limiter, Renew		
1983	(.4)	.6
(G) Electronic Voltage Monitor, Renew		
1983-87	(.4)	.6
(G) Alternator Gauge, Renew		
1985-87		
Lancer-LeBaron GTS	(.3)	.6
(G) Gauge Alert Module, Renew		
1985-87		
Lancer-LeBaron GTS	(.7)	1.1

PARTS 4 ALTERNATOR AND REGULATOR 4 PARTS

	Part No.	Price
Alternator Assembly–2.6L		
1983	MD025215	334.00
1984-85	MD062007	334.00
(1) Pulley		
1983	MD607426	14.00
1984-85	MD607779	27.50
(2) Fan		
(3) Bearing (Front)		
1983-85	MM502264	10.00
(4) Rotor Assy.		
1983-85	MD607425	122.00
(5) Bearing (Rear)		
1983-85	MD602789	8.00
(6) Stator Assy.		
1983-85	MD607428	101.50
(7) Rectifier Set		
1983-85	MD607430	64.00

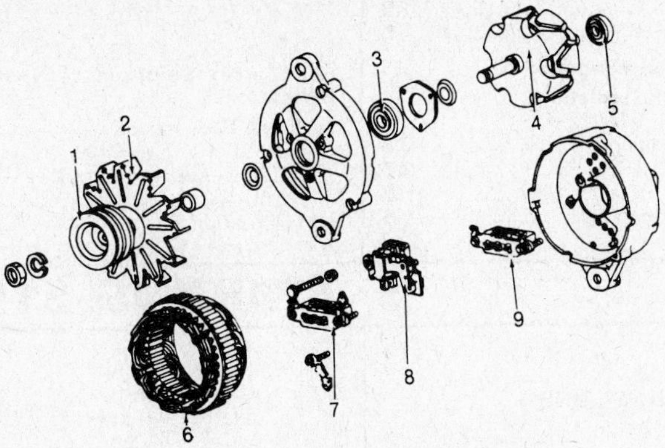

	Part No.	Price
(8) Regulator Assy.		
1983-85	MD607372	71.75
(9) Rectifier Assy.		
1983-85	MD607429	69.50

PARTS 4 ALTERNATOR AND REGULATOR 4 PARTS

	Part No.	Price
Alternator Assembly (exc. 2.6L)		
1983-84-exc. E.F.I.		
60 amp	5213079	129.00
65 & 78 amp	5213053	129.00
1984-w/E.F.I.		
60 amp	5213540	129.00
78 amp	5213541	129.00
1985-87-60 amp	5213762	129.00
78 amp	5213763	129.00
90 amp	4339440	154.50
100 amp ('85)	5213847	161.50
100 amp ('86)	5226432	129.00
(1) Drive End Shield		
1983-87-60 amp	5206421	20.00
65 & 78 amp	5206422	20.25
90 amp	5226840	39.50
(2) Drive End Shield Bearing		
1983-87	3656444	8.75
(3) Rotor Assy.		
1983-87-60 amp	4240413	62.00
65 & 78 amp	4240414	62.00
90 amp	5226841	102.25

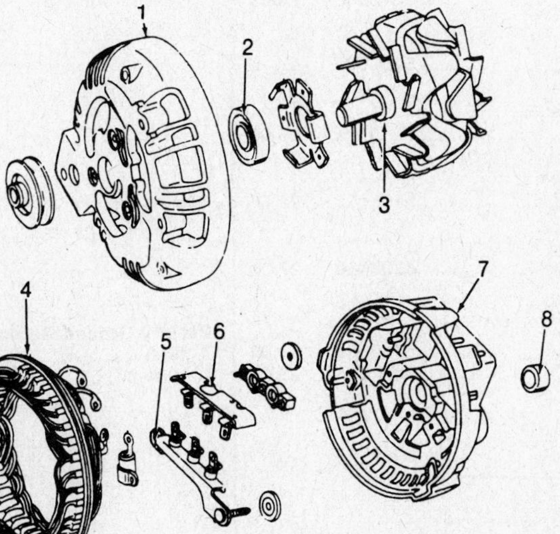

PARTS 4 ALTERNATOR AND REGULATOR 4 PARTS

	Part No.	Price
(4) Stator		
1983-87-60 amp.	4091515	36.75
65 & 78 amp.	4091517	36.75
90 amp.	5226315	151.00
(5) Battery Terminal & Positive Heat Sink Pkg.		
1983-87-60 amp.	4026082	17.50
65 & 78 amp.	4240488	17.50
(6) Heat Sink (Negative)		
1983-87-60 amp.	3438721	17.75
65 & 78 amp.	3755114	17.75
(7) Rectifier End Shield		
1983-87-60 amp.	5213092	57.00
65 & 78 amp.	4240405	58.75
(8) End Shield Bearing (Rectifier)		
1983-87	3755184	3.25
Brush & Washer Pkg.		
1984-87-exc. 90 amp	5211772	4.50
90 amp.	5266572	5.50
Voltage Regulator		
1983-85	4111990	29.00
1986-87	4379100	29.00

LABOR 5 STARTING SYSTEM 5 LABOR

(Factory Time)	Chilton Time
(G) Starter Draw Test (On Car)	
All models	.3
(G) Starter Assy., Renew	
Includes: Test starter relay, starter solenoid and amperage draw.	
1983-87	
2.2L & 2.5L engs (1.0)	1.3
2.6L eng (.7)	1.0
w/Turbo add (.5)	.5
(G) Starter, R&R and Recondition	
Includes: Turn down armature.	
1983-87	
2.2L & 2.5L engs	2.8
2.6L eng	2.5
w/Turbo add (.5)	.5
Renew field coils add (.5)	.5
(G) Starter Drive, Renew	
Includes: R&R starter.	
1983-87	
2.2L & 2.5L engs (1.4)	1.8
2.6L eng (.8)	1.1
w/Turbo add (.5)	.5
(G) Starter Solenoid or Switch, Renew	
Includes: R&R starter.	
1983-87	
2.2L & 2.5L engs (1.0)	1.4
2.6L eng (1.0)	1.4
w/Turbo add (.5)	.5
(G) Starter Relay, Renew	
1983-87 (.2)	3
(G) Neutral Safety Switch, Renew	
1983-87 (.3)	.4
(G) Ignition Switch, Renew	
1983-87	
std column (.4)	.8
tilt column (.4)	.9
(M) Battery Cables, Renew	
1983-87	
positive (.5)	.6
ground (.2)	.2

PARTS 5 STARTING SYSTEM 5 PARTS

	Part No.	Price
2.2L ENGINE		
Starter Assy.		
1983-85-exc. Turbo	5213045	105.50
Turbo	5213450	147.00
1986-87	4339472	148.75
(1) Drive End Housing		
1984-87	5213382	42.75
(2) Clutch Starter Drive		
1984-87	5213384	35.25
(3) Armature		
1983-87	5213383	78.50
(4) Solenoid		
1984-87	5206607	57.25
(5) Field Frame		
1983-87	5213385	69.00
(6) Brush Holder		
1983-87	5206605	21.75
(7) Head End		
1983-87	5206606	27.00
Ignition Switch		
1983-87-wo/tilt whl.	3747882	14.50
w/tilt whl.	4221201	23.00

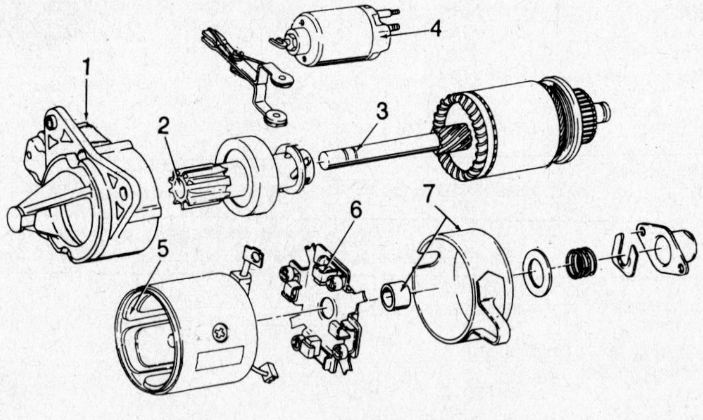

	Part No.	Price
Neutral Safety Switch		
1983-87	4057750	8.75
Battery Ground Cable		
1983	4274887	8.00
1984-87	4274273	8.00
Battery Positive Cable		
1983-M.T.	4274975	23.00
A.T.	4274272	29.50
1984-M.T.	4304473	29.50
A.T.	4304555	29.50
1985-M.T.	4331482	26.75
A.T.	4331481	20.75
1986-87-M.T.	4368367	26.75
A.T.	4368366	20.75

PARTS 5 STARTING SYSTEM 5 PARTS

2.5L ENGINE

	Part No.	Price
Starter Assembly		
1986-87	5226444	105.50
Gear Train		
1986-87	5227114	102.50
Clutch Starter Drive		
1986-87	5227115	27.25

	Part No.	Price
Armature		
1986-87	5227125	158.25
Solenoid		
1986-87	5227607	N.L.

	Part No.	Price
Brush Holder		
1986-87	5227131	75.00
Fork Lever		
1986-87	5227119	5.00

PARTS 5 STARTING SYSTEM 5 PARTS

2.6L ENGINE

	Part No.	Price
Starter Assembly		
1983-85	MD025235	272.75
(1) Housing Sub. Assy.		
1983-85	MD604320	38.25
(2) Clutch Sub. Assy.		
1983-85	MD604319	96.00
(3) Retainer		
1983-85	MD604332	2.50
(4) Pinion		
1983-85	MD604324	10.50
(5) Magnetic Switch Assy.		
1983-85	MD604321	102.50
(6) Armature Assy.		
1983-85	MD604318	115.50
(7) Yoke Assy.		
1983-85	MD604317	74.00
(8) Holder Assy.		
1983-85	MD604322	19.25
Battery Ground Cable		
1983	4274887	8.00
1984-85	4274273	8.00

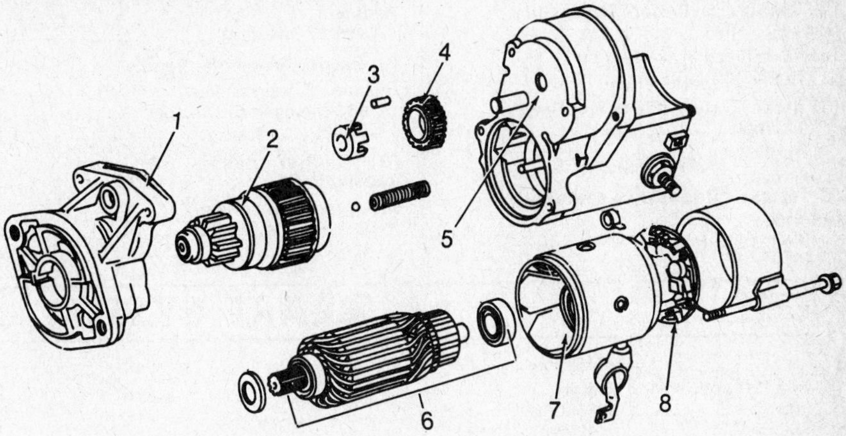

	Part No.	Price
Battery Positive Cable		
1983	4274272	29.50
1984	4274886	24.75
1985	4331519	28.25

	Part No.	Price
Ignition Switch		
1983-87-wo/tilt whl.	3747882	14.50
w/tilt whl.	4221201	23.00

LABOR 6 BRAKE SYSTEM 6 LABOR

(Factory Time) — Chilton Time

(G) Brake Pedal Free Play, Adjust
All models 3

(G) Brakes, Adjust (Minor)
Includes: Adjust brake shoes, fill master cylinder.
two wheels 4

(G) Bleed Brakes (Four Wheels)
Includes: Add fluid.
All models (.4) 6

(G) Brake Shoes and/or Pads, Renew
Includes: Install new or exchange brake shoes or pads. Adjust service and hand brake. Bleed system.
1983-87-front-disc (.5) 8
rear-drum (.8) 1.5
all four wheels (1.3) 2.2
Resurface disc rotor, add-each 9
Resurface brake drum, add-each 5

(G) Rear Brake Drum, Renew (One)
1983-87 (.5) 6

BRAKE HYDRAULIC SYSTEM

(G) Wheel Cylinder, Renew
Includes: Bleed system.
1983-87-one (.7) 1.1
both (1.3) 2.1

COMBINATIONS

Add To Brakes, Renew

See Machine Shop Operations

(G) RENEW WHEEL CYLINDER
Each 3

(G) REBUILD WHEEL CYLINDER
Each 4

(G) REBUILD CALIPER ASSEMBLY
Each 5

(G) RENEW MASTER CLYINDER
All models 6

(G) REBUILD MASTER CYLINDER
All models 8

(G) RENEW BRAKE HOSE
Each (.3) 3

(G) RENEW REAR WHEEL GREASE SEALS
One side 3

(G) RENEW DISC BRAKE ROTOR
Each 2

(G) RENEW BRAKE DRUM
Each (.3) 3

(G) DISC BRAKE ROTOR STUDS, RENEW
Each 1

(Factory Time) — Chilton Time

(G) Wheel Cylinder, R&R and Rebuild
Includes: Hone cylinder and bleed system.
1983-87-one 1.2
both 2.3

(Factory Time) — Chilton Time

(G) Brake Hose, Renew (Flex)
Includes: Bleed system.
1983-87-front-one (.4) 8
rear-one (.5) 8

LABOR — 6 BRAKE SYSTEM 6 — LABOR

	(Factory Time)	Chilton Time
(G) Master Cylinder, Renew		
Includes: Bleed complete system.		
1983-87		
w/Manual brks	(.7)	1.1
w/Pwr brks	(.5)	.9
(G) Master Cylinder, R&R and Rebuild		
Includes: Bleed complete system.		
1983-87		
w/Manual brks		1.9
w/Pwr brks		1.6
(G) Master Cylinder Reservoir, Renew		
Includes: Bleed brake system.		
1983-87	(.6)	1.0
(G) Brake System, Flush and Refill		
All models		1.2
POWER BRAKES		
(G) Brake Booster Assembly, Renew		
1983-87	(1.3)	1.6
(G) Brake Booster Check Valve, Renew		
1983-87	(.2)	.2
DISC BRAKES		
(G) Disc Brake Pads, Renew		
Includes: Install new disc brake pads only.		
1983-87	(.5)	.8
(G) Disc Brake Rotor, Renew		
1983-87-one	(.3)	.6
(G) Disc Brake Rotor and Hub, Renew		
1983-87-one	(1.0)	1.4
(G) Caliper Assembly, Renew		
Includes: Bleed system.		
1983-87-one	(.5)	.9
both		1.7
(G) Caliper Assy., R&R and Recondition		
Includes: Bleed system.		
1983-87-one	(.8)	1.4
both		2.7
(G) Brake System Combination Valve, Renew		
Includes: Bleed complete system.		
1983-87	(1.2)	1.5
PARKING BRAKE		
(M) Parking Brake, Adjust		
1983-87	(.3)	.4
(G) Parking Brake Warning Lamp Switch, Renew		
1983-87	(.2)	.3
(G) Parking Brake Control, Renew		
1983-87	(.5)	.7
(G) Parking Brake Cables, Renew		
Includes: Adjust parking brake.		
1983-87-front	(.5)	.7
intermediate	(.3)	.5
rear-each	(.6)	.8

PARTS — 6 BRAKE SYSTEM 6 — PARTS

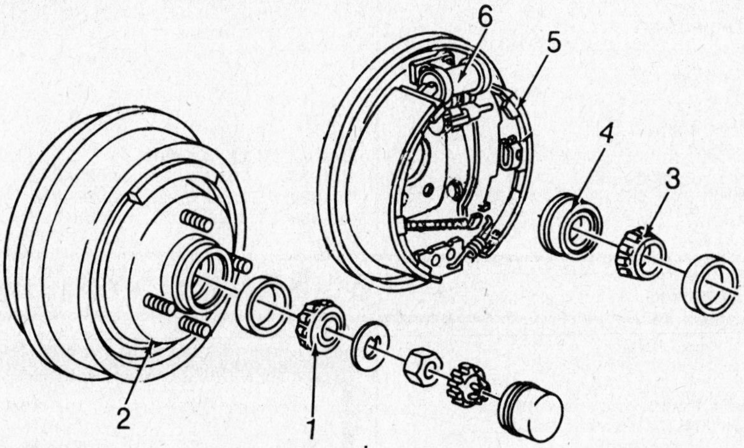

	Part No.	Price
(1) Rear Wheel Bearing (Outer)		
1983	3580888	9.25
1984-87	4293196	9.25
(2) Hub and Drum (Rear)		
1983	4238538	100.50
1984	4238531	89.75
1985-87 (4 stud)		
exc. H.D.	4238531	89.75
H.D.	4238538	100.50
1985-87 (5 stud)		
exc. below	4313635	100.50
Le Baron GTS, Lancer	4313634	100.50
(3) Rear Wheel Bearing (Inner)		
1983-87	4238567	14.75
(4) Dust Seal		
1983-87	4238570	3.50
(5) Brake Shoes & Lining Set (Rear)		
1983-87-exc. H.D.	4238827	36.25
H.D.	4238826	39.75
(6) Wheel Cylinder (Rear)		
1983-87-exc. H.D.	4238701	22.50
H.D.	4238706	22.50
Master Cylinder Assy.		
1983-84	4271388	70.50
1985-87	4294268	80.00
Reservoir (Master Cylinder)		
1983-85	3766498	5.00
1983-87	5204149	1.00
Proportioning Valve		
1983	4205995	35.75
1984-85-exc. H.D.	4238588	35.75
H.D.	4313054	28.50
Lancer & GTS	4313029	36.75
Power Brake Booster		
1983-84-M.T.	3880277	192.50
A.T.	4294212	198.00
1985-87-M.T.	4364773	169.00
A.T.	4342709	218.25
Booster Check Valve		
1983-87	4271382	8.50
PARKING BRAKE		
Parking Brake Control		
1983-87-exc. below	3880426	40.00
Lancer & GTS	4294136	40.00
Front Cable		
1983-87	3766435	14.75
Intermediate & Rear Cable		
1983		
200mm-Std.	3880408	8.00
220mm-H.D.	3880409	8.00
1984-85		
200mm-Std.	4318708	24.75
220mm-H.D.	4318709	24.75
200mm-Std.	4294445	9.50
220mm-H.D.	4294515	9.50

PARTS — 6 DISC BRAKES 6 — PARTS

	Part No.	Price
(1) Disc Rotor		
1983 (Aries & Reliant)		
Std.	4126947	56.00
H.D.	4238551	56.00
1983 (Le Baron & 400)		
Std.	4238551	56.00
1984 (Aries & Reliant)		
Std.	4313592	56.00
H.D.	4313593	56.00
1984 (Le Baron & Town/Country)		
Std.	4313593	56.00
1985 (Aries & Reliant)		
Std.	4313592	56.00
H.D. (4 stud)	4313593	56.00
H.D. (5 stud)	4313633	56.00
1985 (Le Baron & Town/Country)		
4 stud	4313593	56.00
5 stud	4313633	56.00

PARTS 6 BRAKE SYSTEM 6 PARTS

	Part No.	Price
1986-87 (Aries & Reliant)		
Std.	4313758	56.00
H.D. (4 stud)	4313593	56.00
H.D. (5 stud)	4313633	56.00
1986-87 (Le Baron, GTS & Lancer)		
4 stud	4313593	56.00
5 stud	4313633	56.00

(2) Splash Shield

(3) Brake Pads

	Part No.	Price
1983 (Aries & Reliant)		
Std.	4238698	46.50
H.D.	4238788	55.25
1983 (Le Baron & 400)		
Std.	4238788	55.25
1984 (Aries & Reliant)		
Std.	4293200	51.25
H.D.	4238788	55.25
1984 (Le Baron & Town/Country)		
Std.	4313238	72.25
1985 (Aries & Reliant)		
Std.	4293200	51.25
H.D.	4313429	72.25
1985 (Le Baron & Town/Country)		
Std.	4313238	72.25
H.D.	4313429	72.25
1985 (Lancer & GTS)		
w/Sensors	4313642	N.L.
1986-87 (Aries & Reliant)		
Std.	4293200	51.25
H.D.	4313429	72.25
1986-87 (Le Baron, GTS & Lancer)		
Sdn. & Wag.	4313429	72.25
GTS & Lancer	4313642	N.L.

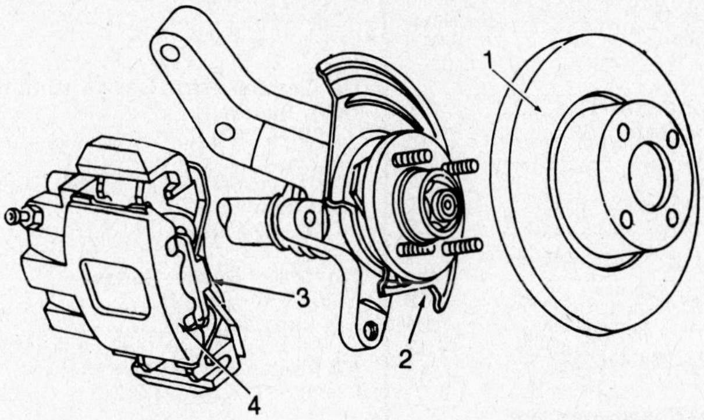

	Part No.	Price
Piston Seal & Boot Pkg.		
1983-87-exc. below	4205984	19.00
GTS, Lancer, Convert.	4364778	22.00
Boot & Seal Pkg.		
1983-87-exc. below	4205985	3.75
GTS, Lancer, Convert.	4364779	5.50
Bushing Pkg.		
1983-87-exc. below	4205982	1.75
GTS, Lancer, Convert.	4267331	3.00
Adapter		
1983	4126737	36.25
1984-87 (Aries & Reliant)		
Std.	4238683	36.25
H.D.	4238712	36.25
1984-87 (Le Baron)		
Std.	4238712	36.25
1985-87 (GTS, Lancer, Convert.)		
right	4313962	36.25
left	4313963	36.25
Brake Pad Sensors		
1984-87	4313040	7.50

LABOR 7 COOLING SYSTEM 7 LABOR

(Factory Time) — Chilton Time

(M) Winterize Cooling System

Includes: Run engine to check for leaks, tighten all hose connections. Test radiator and pressure cap, drain radiator and engine block. Add anti-freeze and refill system.

	Chilton Time
All models	.5

(M) Thermostat, Renew

1983-87 (.4)	.6

(M) Radiator Assembly, R&R or Renew

1983-87 (.5)	.9
w/A.T. add (.1)	.1

ADD THESE OPERATIONS TO RADIATOR R&R

(G) Boil & Repair	1.5
(G) Rod Clean	1.9
(G) Repair Core	1.3
(G) Renew Tank	1.6
(G) Renew Trans. Oil Cooler	1.9
(G) Recore Radiator	1.7

(M) Fan Blades, Renew

1983-87 (.2)	.5

(M) Drive Belts, Adjust

All models-one	.2
each adtnl	.1

(M) Drive Belts, Renew

1983-87	
Water pump-2.6L eng (.3)	.5
Fan & alter (.2)	.3
Pwr str (.4)	.6
Air pump (.3)	.4
w/A.C. add (.1)	.2

COOLING SYSTEM TUNE-UP

An Annual Cooling System Tune-up Suggestion List should include (with some exceptions):
1. A visual check of the cooling system for indications of leaks or excessive oil content
2. Pressure check the cooling system for internal and external leaks with filler cap and neck adapter and tester
3. Check crankcase and automatic transmission oil for water content
4. Test coolant thermostat with radiator thermometer
5. Check temperature gauge for accuracy
6. Drain system and flush till clean
7. Clean foreign matter from radiator fins
8. Test radiator pressure cap with cap tester
9. Check fan blades and pulleys for alignment and damage
10. Internal and external inspection of all hoses for cracks and deterioration
11. Check core plugs (where possible) for seepage
12. Refill system with correct coolant and check for air locks
13. Check condition and tension of drive belts with tension gauge

All models 1.5

(Factory Time) — Chilton Time

(M) Radiator Hoses, Renew

1983-87-upper (.3)	.4
lower (.4)	.6

(G) Water Pump, Renew

1983-87	
2.2L & 2.5L engs (1.1)	1.6
2.6L eng (.7)	1.2
w/A.C. add (.5)	.5

(G) Radiator Fan Coolant Sensor, Renew

1983-87 (.2)	.3

(G) Radiator Fan Motor, Renew

1983-87-wo/A.C. (.4)	.5
w/A.C. (.4)	.5

(G) Radiator Fan Switch, Renew

1983-87 (.3)	.6

(Factory Time) — Chilton Time

(G) Radiator Fan Motor Relay, Renew

1983-87 (.2)	.3

(G) Transaxle Auxiliary Oil Cooler, Renew

1983-87 (.3)	.6

(G) Water Jacket Expansion Plugs, Renew (Cylinder Block)

1983-87	
2.6L eng	
right side	
front (.7)	1.0
center or rear (1.1)	1.5

LABOR 7 COOLING SYSTEM 7 LABOR

(Factory Time)	Chilton Time
left side	
upper front or center (2.1)	3.0
lower front or center (.3)	.5
rear (1.0)	1.4
2.2L & 2.5L engs	
left side	
front (.7)	1.0
rear (.4)	.6
right side	
front or center (.6)	.9
rear (1.0)	1.4
w/P.S. add (.3)	.3
w/Pulse air add (.6)	.6

(G) Water Jacket Expansion Plugs, Renew (Cylinder Head)

1983-87	
2.2L & 2.5L engs	
front (.6)	.9
rear (.8)	1.1
2.6L eng	
rear (.5)	.7

(Factory Time)	Chilton Time
(G) Temperature Gauge (Engine Unit), Renew	
1983-87 (.3)	.4
(G) Temperature Gauge (Dash Unit), Renew	
1985-87 (.3)	.6
(G) Heater Hoses, Renew	
1983-87-one (.4)	.4
each adtnl (.1)	.2
(G) Heater Water Valve, Renew	
1983-87-w/A.C. (.3)	.5
(G) Heater Control Assembly, Renew	
1983-87-wo/A.C. (.4)	.7
w/A.C. (.4)	.7
(G) Vacuum Switch (Push Button), Renew	
1983-87-w/A.C. (.5)	.9

(Factory Time)	Chilton Time
(G) Blower Motor Switch, Renew	
1983-87-wo/A.C. (.4)	.8
w/A.C. (.4)	.8
(G) Heater Core, R&R or Renew	
1983-87-wo/A.C. (1.0)	1.7
w/A.C. (2.4)	*5.5

*Includes recharge A.C. system.

ADD THESE OPERATIONS TO HEATER CORE R&R

(G) Boil & Repair	1.2
(G) Repair Core	.9
(G) Recore	1.2
(G) Heater Blower Motor, Renew	
1983-87-wo/A.C. (.4)	.6
w/A.C. (.6)	1.2
(G) Blower Motor Resistor, Renew	
1983-87-wo/A.C. (.2)	.3
w/A.C. (.3)	.4

PARTS 7 COOLING SYSTEM 7 PARTS

	Part No.	Price
(1) Radiator Assy.		
Order by year and model.		
(2) Radiator Hose (Upper)		
2.2L & 2.5L		
1983	4140574	10.25
1984-85	4266721	6.25
1986-87-exc. below	4266696	6.25
Silicone	4266692	N.L.
2.6L		
1983-85-exc. below	4140576	6.00
Silicone	4266138	35.25
(3) Radiator Hose (Lower)		
2.2L & 2.5L		
1983	4266260	14.75
1984-85-right	4266762	14.25
left (85)	4266763	5.50
1986-87-exc. below	4266697	13.75
Silicone	4266954	38.75
2.6L		
1983	4266255	10.25
1984-85-exc. below	4266348	12.50
Silicone	4266349	44.25
(4) Radiator Fan		
(wo/air cond.)		
1983-87	4266069	16.75
(w/air cond.)		
1983-2.2L	4266282	17.75
2.6L	4266074	17.75
1984-87 (rad. stamping no.)		
4266374	4266282	17.75
4266291	4266293	27.50
4266375	4266282	17.75
(5) Motor (Radiator Fan)		
1983	5211115	83.00
1984-87-wo/A.C.	4240493	83.00
w/A.C.	4240494	83.00
Water Pump		
2.2L & 2.5L		
1983	5203432	N.L.
1984	4293898	48.00
1985-87	4293898	48.00
2.6L		
1983-85	MD025190	59.25

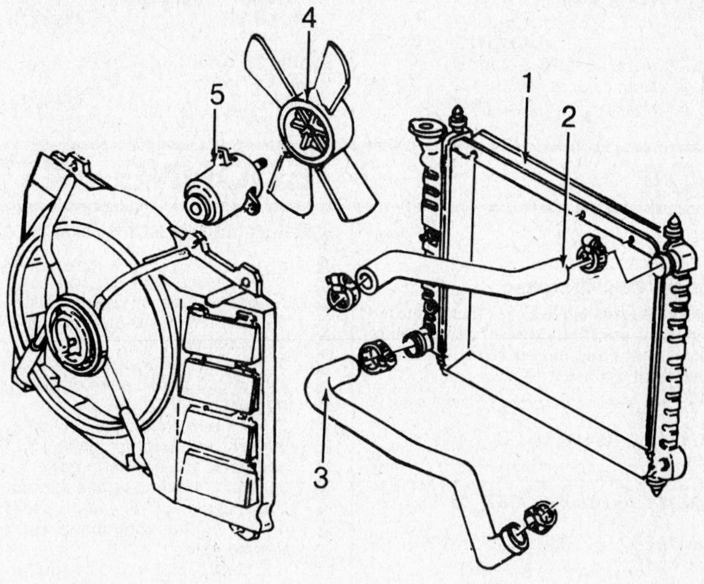

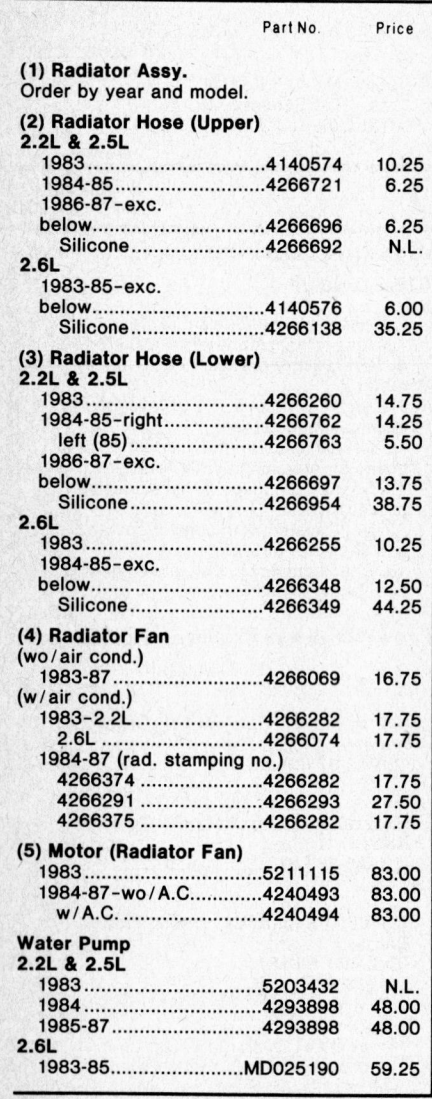

	Part No.	Price
Bypass Hose (Water Pump)		
2.2L & 2.5L		
1983-84	4273486	4.75
1985-87	4273488	1.75
2.6L		
1983-85	MD025199	8.00
Thermostat		
2.2L & 2.5L		
1983-84-185°	4105442	6.50
195°	4105768	.75
1985-87	4105768	.75
2.6L		
1983	MD005131	6.50
1984-85	MD075460	9.75
Heater Core		
1983-85	4205838	91.50
1986-87	3847943	90.75

	Part No.	Price
Blower Motor		
1983	4240472	68.75
1984	4318117	68.75
1985-wo/A.C.	4339432	70.50
w/A.C.	3849032	59.00
1986-87	3849266	59.00
Resistor (Blower Motor)		
1983	3848236	5.50
1984	3848689	4.50
1985	3849075	N.L.
1986-87	3849235	8.50
Blower Motor Switch		
1983-84	3847940	10.25
1985-87	3849160	8.00

PARTS 7 COOLING SYSTEM 7 PARTS

	Part No.	Price
Heat Sending Unit (Engine)		
1983-2.2L		
A.T.	4091471	16.25
M.T.	4145716	6.75
1983-2.6L	4221071	6.75
1984-exc. below	4051687	10.25
w/T.B.I., turbo	4267281	16.25
1985-87-exc. below	4267281	16.25
w/T.B.I., turbo	5226374	16.75
Auxiliary Oil Cooler (Air Cooled)		
1983-85-2.6L eng.	4266196	76.25
Transmission Oil Cooler (Radiator)		
2.2L & 2.5L		
1983	4140569	52.50
1984-87	4266729	52.25
2.6L		
1983	4266482	76.25
1984-85	4266482	76.25

LABOR 8 EXHAUST SYSTEM 8 LABOR

	(Factory Time)	Chilton Time
(G) Muffler, Renew		
1983-87	(.4)	.7
Cut exhaust pipe add	(.2)	.2
(G) Exhaust Pipe, Renew		
1983-87	(.7)	1.1
Cut at muffler add	(.2)	.2
(G) Exhaust Pipe Extension, Renew (Intermediate Pipe)		
1983-87	(.6)	1.0
(G) Tail Pipe, Renew		
1983	(.4)	.6
Cut at muffler add	(.2)	.2
(G) Catalytic Converter, Renew		
1983-87		
floor mount	(.7)	.9
exh pipe mount	(.7)	.9
manif mount	(.9)	1.3
(G) Exhaust Manifold or Gasket, Renew		
1983-87		
2.2L & 2.5L engs	(2.7)	3.7
2.6L eng	(.7)	1.2
w/Turbo add	(.6)	.6

COMBINATIONS

	(Factory Time)	Chilton Time
(G) Exhaust System, Renew (Complete)		
1983-87		1.5

PARTS 8 EXHAUST SYSTEM 8 PARTS

System numbers shown are for pricing reference only. Order parts with complete year, model and engine information.

	Part No.	Price
Converter–Front (w/pipes)		
2.2L		
1983	4150796	307.25
1984-exc. Calif.	4301266	256.75
Calif.	4301263	285.50
1985-exc. Canada	4301473	280.00
Canada	4301426	N.L.
1986-87-exc. Calif.		
M.T.	4301659	255.75
A.T.	4301661	255.75
1986-87-Calif.		
M.T.	4301666	255.75
A.T.	4301660	255.75
2.5L		
1986-87-exc. Calif.	4301663	255.75
Calif.	4301662	255.75
Canada	4301583	N.L.
2.6L		
1983-84	MD015531	262.50
1985	MD069867	251.75
Converter–Rear (w/Pipes)		
2.2L		
1984-85-exc. below	4301231	256.75
Lancer, GTS	4301232	256.75
1986-87-exc. Limo	4301502	244.50
Limo	4301630	244.50
Exhaust Pipe (w/Resonator)		
2.2L		
1983-84	4150847	45.50
2.6L		
1983-84	4301315	N.L.
Exhaust Pipe (wo/Resonator)		
2.2L		
1983-85	4301037	14.50
2.6L		
1985-Limo	4342154	118.75
Extension Pipe (w/Resonator)		
2.2L		
1983-85	4301227	47.00
1986-87	4301538	47.00
2.5L		
1986-87	4301538	47.00
2.6L		
1983-85	4301227	47.00
Extension Pipe (wo/Resonator)		
2.2L		
1985	4301428	36.75
1986-87	4301494	36.25
Muffler & Tailpipe		
2.2L		
1983-exc. Can.	4150783	50.00
Canada	4301070	48.50
1984-exc. below	4150783	50.00
Canada	4301303	N.L.
Le Baron	4301240	59.00
Turbo (exc Coupe)	4301247	N.L.
Turbo coupe	4301254	N.L.
1985-2bbl	4301429	50.00
1985-E.F.I.		
Exc. Coupe	4150783	50.00
Canada	4301429	50.00
Lancer, GTS (Can)	4301448	N.L.
Lancer, GTS	4301576	56.50
1985-Turbo		
4 dr & wag	4301547	115.50
Coupe & Conv	4301530	115.50
Lancer, GTS	4301578	115.50
1986-87-E.F.I.		
Aries, Reliant	4301572	50.00
Le Baron, Town & Country	4301506	50.00
Turbo	4301507	115.50
2.5L		
1986-87	4301506	50.00
2.6L		
1983-85	4150784	48.50

LABOR 9 FRONT SUSPENSION 9 LABOR

Note: On all front suspension operations alignment charges must be added if performed. Time given does not include alignment.

	(Factory Time)	Chilton Time
(M) Wheel, Renew		
one		.5
(M) Wheels, Rotate (All)		
All models		.5
(G) Wheels, Balance		
one		.3
each adtnl		.2
(G) Check Front End Alignment		
All models		.5

Note: Deduct if alignment is performed.

	(Factory Time)	Chilton Time
(G) Toe-Out, Adjust		
All models		.6
(G) Align Front End		

Includes: Adjust camber, toe, car height and center steering wheel.

	(Factory Time)	Chilton Time
All models	(.8)	1.4
(G) Steering Knuckle Bearing, Renew (Wheel Bearing)		

Add alignment charges.

	(Factory Time)	Chilton Time
1983-87-one side	(1.2)	1.6
both sides	(2.3)	3.0

LABOR 9 FRONT SUSPENSION 9 LABOR

(Factory Time) — Chilton Time

(G) Steering Knuckle, Renew (One)
Add alignment charges.
1983-87 (1.0) 1.6

(G) Front Strut Assy., R&R or Renew
Add alignment charges
1983-87-one (.8) 1.4
both (1.5) 2.7

(G) Front Suspension Strut (Dual Path) Mount Assy., Renew
Includes: Renew bearing.
1984-87 (.8) 1.5

(G) Lower Control Arm Assy., Renew
Includes: Reset toe-in.
1983-87-one (1.1) 1.6

(G) Lower Control Arm Strut Bushings, Renew
Add alignment charges.
1984-87-one side (.6) 9

(G) Lower Ball Joint, Renew (One)
Add alignment charges.
1983-87 (.8) 1.2

(G) Front Coil Spring or Strut Bearing, Renew
Includes: R&R front strut.
Add alignment charges.
1983-87-one (.8) 1.5
both (1.5) 2.8

(G) Front Sway Bar, Renew
1983-87 (.4) 7

(G) Sway Bar Bracket and Bushings, Renew
1983-87-both (.5) 9

(P) K-Frame Assembly, Renew
Add alignment charges.
All models (2.5) 4.0

(G) Drive Shaft Boot, Renew
Includes: Clean and lubricate C/V joint.
All models
1983-87
one-inner or outer (.7) 1.0
both-one side (1.0) 1.4
Renew shaft seal, add
right side (.1) 1
left side (.3) 3

(G) Drive Shaft C/V Joint, Renew
All models
1983-87
one-inner or outer (.7) 1.0
both-one side (1.0) 1.4
inter shaft U-joint (.6) 1.0
Renew shaft seal, add
right side (.1) 1
left side (.3) 3

(G) Front Wheel Drive Shaft Assy., Renew
All models
1983-87
inter spline yoke (.6) 1.0
inter stub shaft (.6) 1.0
all others-each (1.0) 1.4
Renew shaft seal, add
right side (.1) 1
left side (.3) 3

(G) Intermediate Shaft Support Bearing, Renew
1984-87-each (.6) 1.0

(G) Drive Shaft Oil Seal, Renew
All models
1983-87
right side (.5) 8
left side (.7) 1.1

PARTS 9 FRONT SUSPENSION 9 PARTS

	Part No.	Price
Front Wheel Bearing		
1983	4271389	44.50
Front Wheel Bearing Retainer		
1983	5212547	3.00
(1) Steering Knuckle		
1983-right	4052580	89.75
left	4052581	89.75
(2) Shock Absorber Pkg.		
1983	4052544	40.00
(3) Coil Spring		
Note: Order by model and description.		
(4) Bushing (Strut Arm Rear)		
1983	5204538	1.25
(5) Upper Mounting (Front Shock)		
1983	4052684	15.25
(6) Ball Bearing		
1983	5204595	4.50
(7) Retainer (Shock Upper)		
1983	4014469	6.00
(8) Bumper (Jounce)		
1983	5204608	3.25
(9) Dust Shield		
1983	5204610	1.75
(10) Bushing (Arm Pivot Shaft)		
1983	5204622	8.00
(11) Lower Control Arm		
1983-right	4052634	92.75
left	4052635	92.75
(12) Lower Ball Joint		
1983	4014323	37.25
(13) Sway Bar		
1983-2 door & 4 door (w/Belted tires)		
Glass type	4052541	75.00
Steel type	4318721	84.00

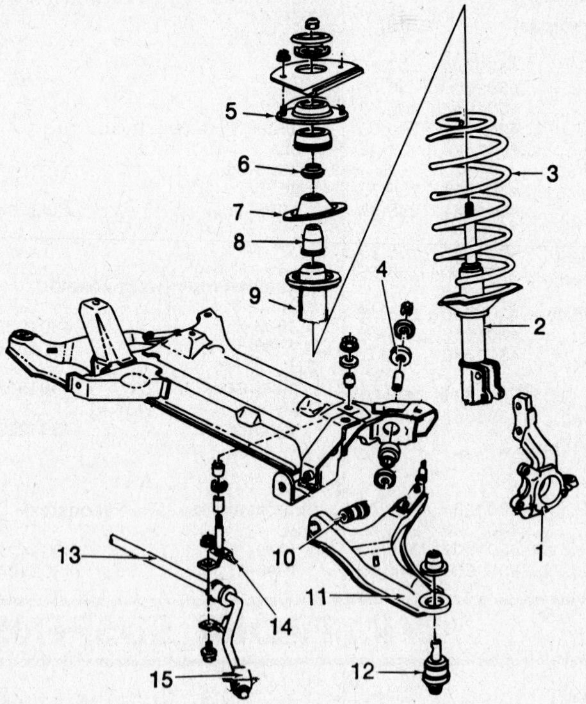

	Part No.	Price
1983		
Convertible	4014436	76.00
Sta. wagon	4318721	84.00
(14) Retainer Shaft		
1983	4014330	10.00

	Part No.	Price
(15) Cushion (w/Clamp)		
1983	4014362	8.50
Crossmember (Complete)		
1983	4322249	455.50

	Part No.	Price

This parts list is for vehicles built up to 1-2-86. Refer to next section for vehicles built after 1-2-86.

	Part No.	Price
(1) Retainer (Shock Stop)		
1984-86	4052822	1.75
(2) Front Shock Mount (Upper)		
1984	4052850	19.00
1985-86	4322298	19.00
(3) Shock Seat (Upper)		
1984	4052819	6.25
1985-86	4322701	6.25
(4) Bumper (Jounce)		
1984-85	4052824	2.75
1986	4322705	2.75
(5) Front Isolator (Upper)		
1984-86	4322046	2.25
(6) Dust Shield		
1984-85	4052825	1.50
1986	4322704	1.50
(7) Strut Spring Assy.		
Order by model and description.		
(8) Strut (Shock Absorber) (Std.)		
1984	4322059	50.00
1985-86-exc. below	4052861	40.00
Lancer, Le Baron GTS	4322059	50.00
(9) Steering Knuckle		
1984-86-right	4052838	89.75
left	4052839	89.75
(10) Seal (Ball Joint)		
1984-86	4052509	1.25
(11) Ball Joint		
1984-85	4052583	32.75
1986	4364782	37.25
(12) Control Arm Assy.		
1984-86-right	4322158	92.75
left	4322159	92.75
(13) Control Arm Bushing		
1984-86	5204622	8.00
(14) Bolt (Pivot Shaft)		
1984-86	4014239	4.00
(15) Retainer (Strut Bushing)		
1984-86	5204534	1.50
(16) Strut Bushing (Front)		
1984	4052671	2.00
1985-86	4322285	2.00
(17) Sleeve (Strut Bushing)		
1984-86	5204535	1.50
(18) Strut Bushing (Rear)		
1984	4052672	2.00
(19) Retainer (Strut Bushing)		
1984-86	5204534	1.50
(20) Front Sway Shaft Assy.		
1984-86	4322014	81.25
(21) Front Cushion (Sway Shaft)		
1984-86	4322017	3.25
(22) Lower Clamp (Shaft Bushing)		
1984-86	4052522	3.00
(23) Retainer (Shaft Arm)		
1984-86	4014418	3.00
Crossmember (Complete) exc. Lancer, Le Baron GTS		
1984-M.T.	4322250	455.50

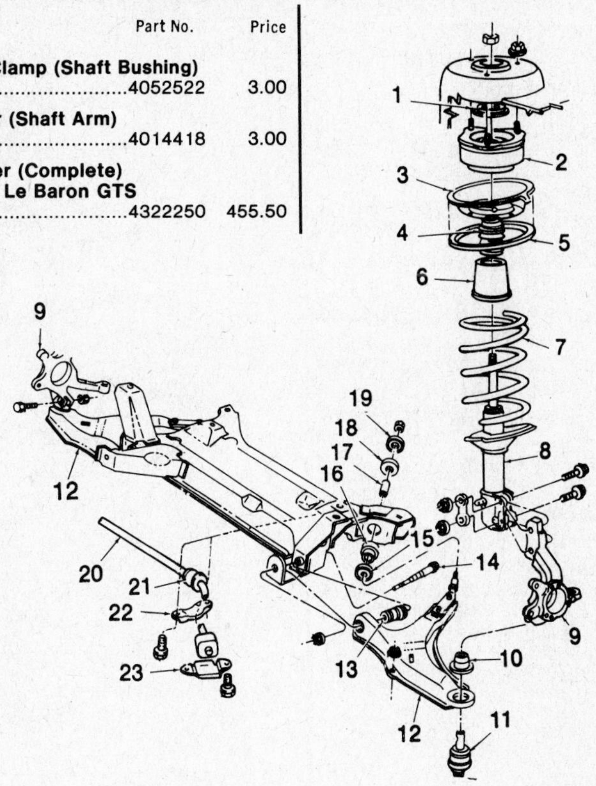

	Part No.	Price
(A.T.)		
to 10-24-83	4322249	455.50
from 10-24-83	4322249	455.50
1985-86	4322249	455.50
Lancer, Le Baron GTS		
1985-86-A.T.	4322733	455.50
(M.T.)		
wo/turbo	4322734	455.50
w/turbo	4322735	455.50

Part numbers shown are for pricing reference only. Order by year model and type.

	Part No.	Price
Driveshaft		
1.6L		
1983-Right	5212676	137.50
Left	5212677	76.00
1984-87-Right	5212862	137.50
Left	5212863	76.00
1.7L		
1983-Right	5212646	137.50
Left	5212647	72.50
2.2L, 2.5L & 2.6L		
Horizon, Omni, 024, TC3, Turismo, Charger		
(G.K.N.)		
1983-Right	5212660	137.50
Left	5212661	76.00
1984-87-Right	5212862	137.50
Left	5212863	76.00
1986-87-H/P		
Right	5212862	137.50
Left	5212933	76.00
(Citroen)		
1985-wo/Turbo		
Right	5212766	85.00
Left	5212765	52.25
Turbo	5212765	52.25
1986-87-Right	5212766	85.00
Left	5212935	52.25
Turbo	5212935	52.25
Exc. Horizon, Omni, TC3, 024, Turismo, Charger		
(G.K.N.)		
1983-Right	5212662	137.50
Left	5212663	76.00
1984-87-Right	5212872	123.00
Left	5212913	76.00
(Citroen)		
1983-Right	5212744	85.00
Left	5212745	52.50
1984-wo/Turbo		
right	5212798	85.00
left	5212799	N.L.
Turbo	5212799	N.L.
1985-87-wo/Turbo		
Right	5212798	85.00
Left	5212763	52.25
Turbo	5212763	52.25
(A.C.I.)		
1984-87-Right	5212826	123.00
Left	5212827	76.00

PARTS 9 FRONT SUSPENSION 9 PARTS

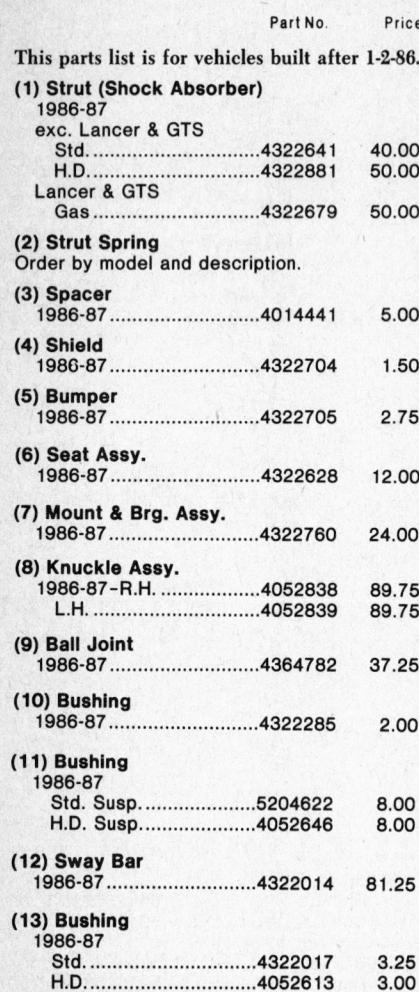

	Part No.	Price
This parts list is for vehicles built after 1-2-86.		
(1) Strut (Shock Absorber)		
1986-87		
exc. Lancer & GTS		
Std.	4322641	40.00
H.D.	4322881	50.00
Lancer & GTS		
Gas	4322679	50.00
(2) Strut Spring		
Order by model and description.		
(3) Spacer		
1986-87	4014441	5.00
(4) Shield		
1986-87	4322704	1.50
(5) Bumper		
1986-87	4322705	2.75
(6) Seat Assy.		
1986-87	4322628	12.00
(7) Mount & Brg. Assy.		
1986-87	4322760	24.00
(8) Knuckle Assy.		
1986-87-R.H.	4052838	89.75
L.H.	4052839	89.75
(9) Ball Joint		
1986-87	4364782	37.25
(10) Bushing		
1986-87	4322285	2.00
(11) Bushing		
1986-87		
Std. Susp.	5204622	8.00
H.D. Susp.	4052646	8.00
(12) Sway Bar		
1986-87	4322014	81.25
(13) Bushing		
1986-87		
Std.	4322017	3.25
H.D.	4052613	3.00

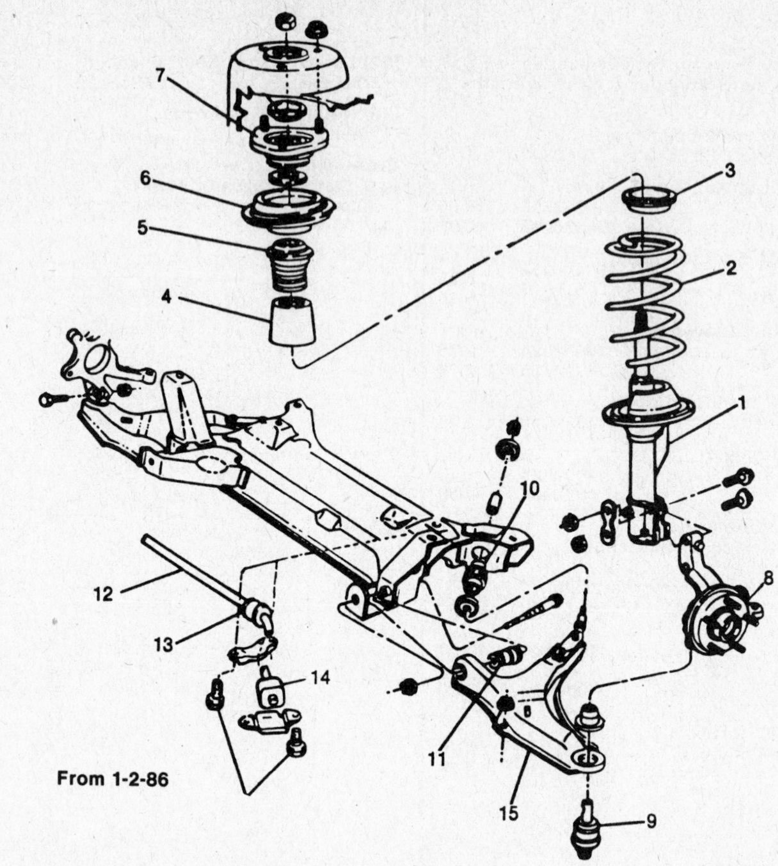

From 1-2-86

	Part No.	Price
(14) Bushing		
1986-87	4322751	3.75

	Part No.	Price
(15) Lower Control Arm Assy.		
1986-87-R.H.	4322154	92.75
L.H.	4322155	92.75

LABOR 11 STEERING GEAR 11 LABOR

	(Factory Time)	Chilton Time
(G) Tie Rods or Tie Rod Ends, Renew		
Includes: Reset toe-out.		
1983-87		
outer-one	(.9)	1.2
inner & outer-w/P.S. one side	(1.9)	2.5
STANDARD STEERING		
(G) Horn Contact Cable and Ring, Renew		
1983-87	(.2)	.3
(G) Horn Switch, Renew		
1983-87	(.2)	.3
(G) Steering Wheel, Renew		
1983-87	(.2)	.4
(G) Steering Column Jacket, Renew		
Does not include painting.		
1983-87		
Std Column		
console shift	(1.1)	1.8
column shift	(1.5)	2.3
Tilt Column		
console shift	(1.5)	2.6
column shift	(1.6)	2.8
(G) Upper Mast Jacket Bearing, Renew		
Includes: Replace insulators if necessary.		
1983-87		
std column	(.4)	.9
tilt column	(1.2)	2.0
(G) Steering Column Gear Shift Tube, Renew		
1983-87		
std column	(1.3)	2.1
tilt column	(1.8)	2.6
(G) Steering Column Lower Shaft Bearing, Renew		
Includes: Replace support if necessary.		
1983-87		
Std Column		
console shift	(.8)	1.6
column shift	(.9)	1.7
Tilt Column		
console shift	(.6)	1.0
column shift	(.6)	1.0
(G) Steering Gear Assy., R&R or Renew		
1983-87	(1.6)	3.0
POWER STEERING		
(G) Power Steering Pump Pressure Check		
All models		.5
(M) Power Steering Pump Belt, Renew		
1983-87	(.4)	.6
w/A.C. add	(.1)	.1
w/Air inj add	(.1)	.1
(G) Power Steering Gear Assy., R&R or Renew		
Includes: Reset toe-in.		
1983-87	(1.1)	2.4
Renew gear add	(.6)	1.0
(G) Upper and Lower Valve Pinion Seals, Renew		
1983-87	(1.4)	2.0
Renew brgs add	(.3)	.5

LABOR 11 STEERING GEAR 11 LABOR

	(Factory Time)	Chilton Time
(G) Steering Gear Oil Seals, Renew (All)		
Includes: R&R gear assy. and reset toe-in.		
1983-87	(2.9)	5.1
(G) Power Steering Pump, Renew		
Includes: Test pump and transfer pulley.		
1983-87		
2.2L & 2.5L engs	(1.0)	1.4
2.6L eng	(.8)	1.2
(G) Power Steering Pump, R&R and Recondition		
1983-87		
2.2L & 2.5L engs	(1.5)	2.3
2.6L eng	(1.3)	2.0
(G) Pump Flow Control Valve, Test and Clean or Renew		
1983-87		
2.2L & 2.5L engs	(.6)	1.0
2.6L eng	(.7)	1.1
(G) Power Steering Reservoir or Seals, Renew		
1983-87	(.7)	1.1
(G) Pump Drive Shaft Oil Seal, Renew		
1983-87		
2.2L & 2.5L engs	(.9)	1.4
2.6L eng	(.7)	1.1
(M) Power Steering Hoses, Renew		
1983-87-each	(.4)	.5

PARTS 11 STEERING GEAR-(STANDARD) 11 PARTS

	Part No.	Price
(1) Steering Gear (Manual)		
1983	3643360	242.75
1984	4147231	242.75
1985-87	4147415	242.75
(2) Clamp (Boot To Tube)		
1983-84-right	3815816	1.50
left	3815811	1.50
1985-87-right	4147140	N.L.
left	4147139	N.L.
(3) Boot Kit		
1983-87-right	4131348	13.50
left	4131349	13.50
(4) Clamp (Boot To Tie Rod)		
1983-87	5205313	1.25
(5) Tie Rod (Outer)		
1983-87	4106180	39.75
(6) Bracket (Outer)		
1983-87	5205225	4.00
(7) Bushing		
1983-87	5205227	2.00
(8) Bracket (Inner)		
1983-87	5205226	1.00

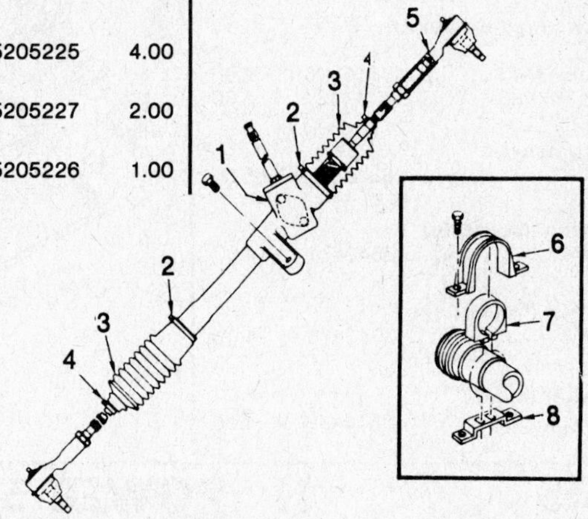

PARTS 11 POWER STEERING GEAR 11 PARTS

TRW TYPE

	Part No.	Price
(1) Tie Rod End (Outer)		
1983-87	4106180	39.75
(2) Boot Service Kit		
1983-87		
up to 9-30-83	3815880	14.25
after 9-30-83	4147303	14.75
(3) Breather Tube		
1983-87	3815871	2.00
(4) Horizontal Socket Assy.		
1983-84-to 9-30-83	3815879	50.00
1984-from 9-30-83	4147353	N.L.
1985	4147356	
1986-87	4333450	50.00
(5) Service Ring Kits		
1983-87	3815874	2.75
(6) Lock Ring Bushing		
1983-87	3815883	2.50
(7) Bushing Rack Service Kit		
1983-87	3815881	6.00
(8) Rack Assy.		
1983-85	3815861	103.00
1986-87		
Std.	4333451	103.00
H.D.	4333449	103.00
(9) Rack Seal Service Kit		
1983-87	3815878	2.75
Also serviced in rack assembly number 8.		

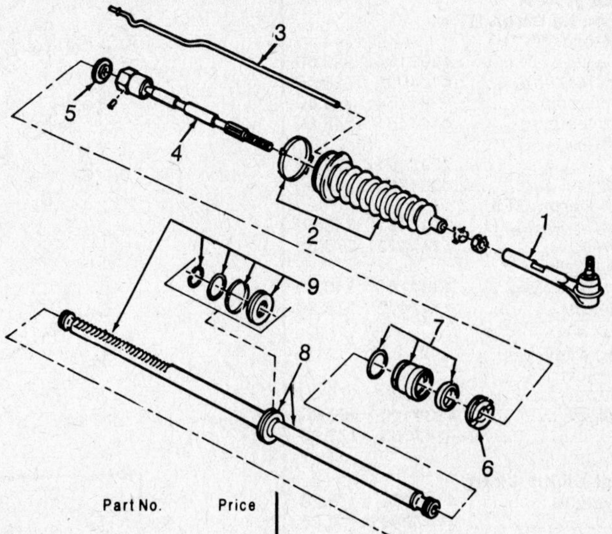

	Part No.	Price
(10) Retaining Wire		
1983-87	3815884	.50
(11) Housing (Rack & Pinion)		
1983-85		
up to 9-30-83	3815862	125.75
after 9-30-83	4147307	125.75
1986-87		
Std.	4333275	125.75
H.D.	4333148	275.50

	Part No.	Price
(12) Bearing Assy.		
1983-87	3815868	4.75

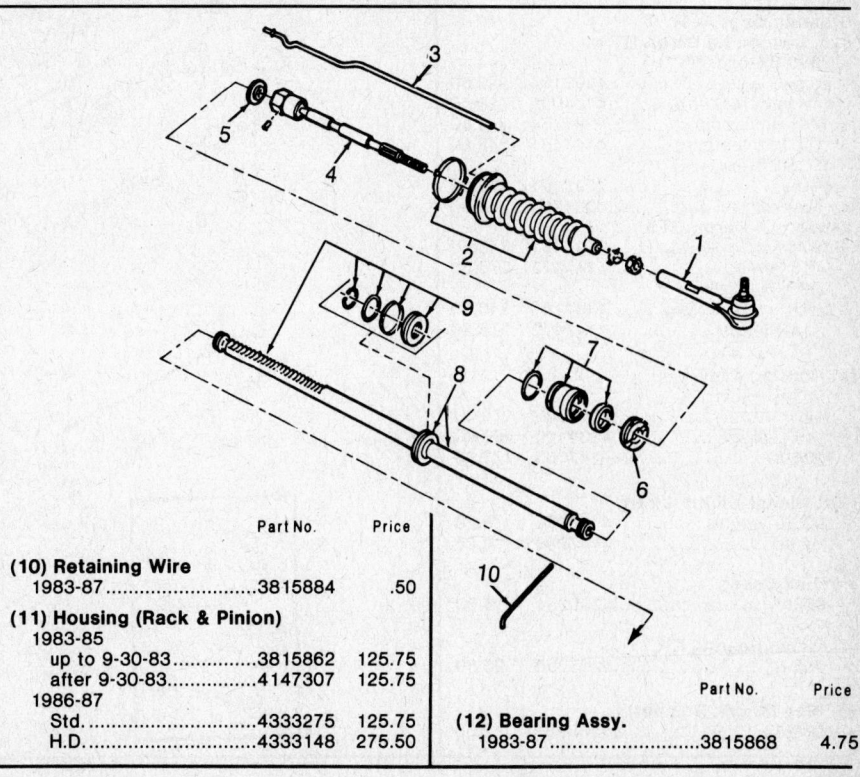

PARTS 11 POWER STEERING GEAR 11 PARTS

	Part No.	Price
(13) Plug (Pinion)		
1983-84	3815870	7.50
1985-87	4147306	3.75
(14) Cylinder Line Assy.		
1983-87-right	3815873	3.75
left	3815872	3.75
(15) Plug (Yoke)		
1983-87	3815866	6.75
(16) Bearing & Spring Yoke		
1983-87	3815865	4.75
(17) Pinion Shaft Bearing Kit		
1983-87		
up to 9-30-83	3815882	15.00
after 9-30-83	4147420	15.00
(18) Valve Rings & Seal Kit		
1983-87		
up to 9-30-83	3815876	2.00
after 9-30-83	4147421	5.50
(19) Valve Assy.		
1983-87	3815875	85.50
(20) Bushing (Mounting)		
1983-87	3643471	4.00
(21) Bracket (Outer)		
1983-87	3643470	4.00
(22) Bracket (Inner)		
1983-87	3643469	1.00

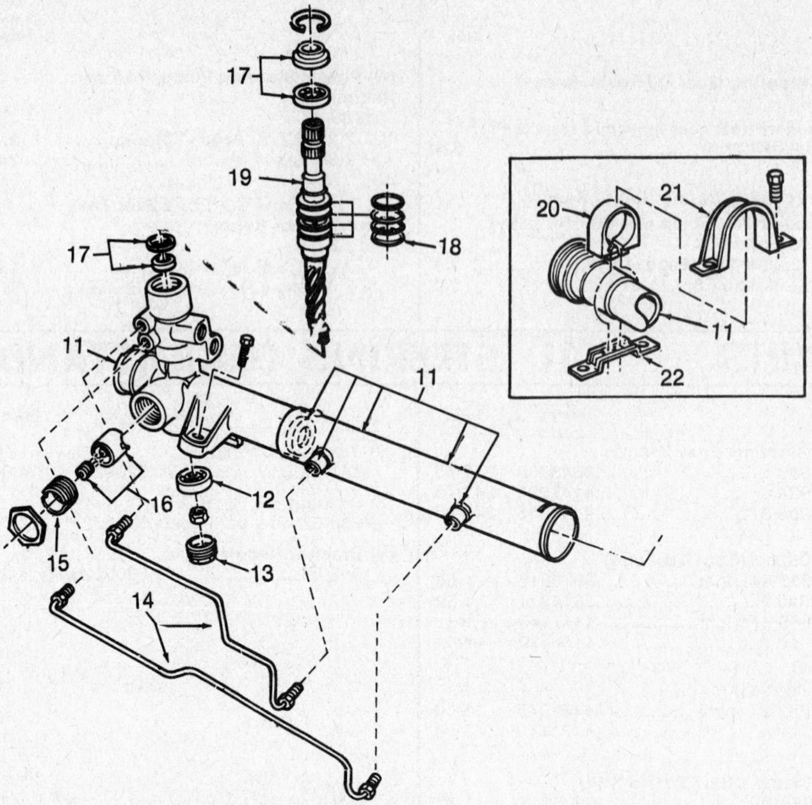

PARTS 11 POWER STEERING GEAR 11 PARTS

	Part No.	Price
SAGINAW		
Steering Gear Assy.		
exc. Lancer, Le Baron GTS		
1983-84-exc. below	4293164	343.50
w/firm feel strg	4174009	28.50
1985-exc. below	4293164	343.50
w/firm feel strg	4147451	343.50
1986-87-exc. below	4293164	343.50
w/firm feel strg	4364785	343.50
Lancer, Le Baron GTS		
1985-exc. below	4147451	343.50
15" tires	4147472	275.50
1986-87-exc. below	4364785	343.50
15" tires	4147472	275.50
(1) Housing Assy.		
1983-85-exc. below	4147083	178.00
15" tires	4333100	200.00
1986-87	4147083	178.00
(2) Cylinder Oil Kit (Lines)		
1983-87-right	4147089	8.25
left	4147090	8.25
(3) Dust Cover		
1983-87	5205284	3.50
(4) Pinion Bearing Kit		
1983-87	5205295	25.50
(5) Ring (Shock Damper)		
1983-87	5205287	2.50

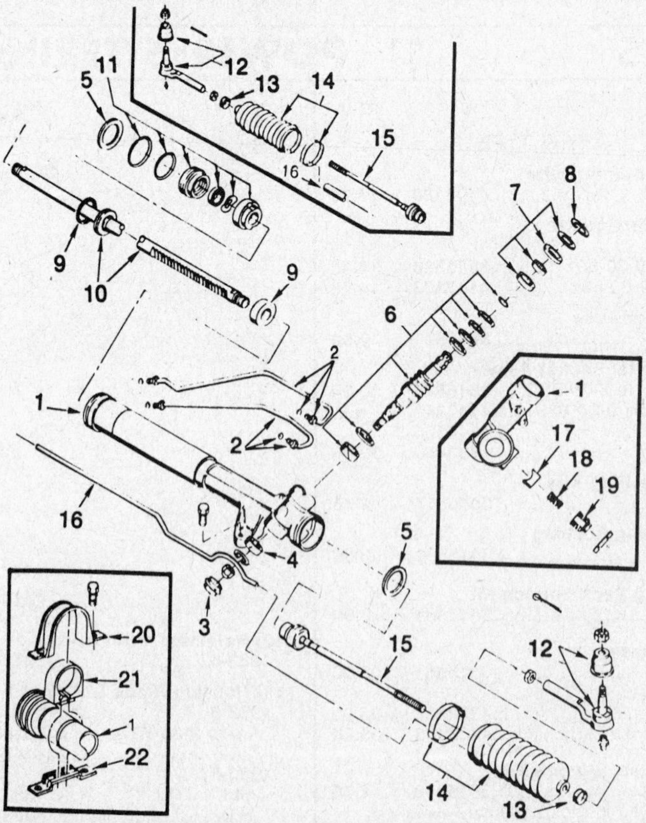

PARTS 11 POWER STEERING GEAR 11 PARTS

	Part No.	Price
(6) Valve Kit (Pinion Assy.)		
1983-Std.	5205328	150.50
Firm	5205336	150.50
1984-Std.	5205328	150.50
Firm	4147091	150.50
1985-Std.	3815947	150.50
Firm	4333098	150.50
1986-87-Std.	3815947	150.50
Firm	4333434	150.50
(7) Spool Shaft Bearing Kit		
1983-87	5205299	19.25
(8) Retainer Ring		
1983-87	5205278	1.75
(9) Seal (Inner Rack)		
1983	5205293	15.00
1984-87 (Kit)	4147098	33.75
(10) Rack Assy. (w/Piston)		
1983-87-Std.	4147080	128.75
Firm	4147081	128.75
(11) Bulkhead Assy. Kit		
exc. Lancer, Le Baron GTS		
1983-87-Std.	4147096	41.50
Firm	4333147	41.50
Lancer, Le Baron GTS		
1985-87-exc. below	4333147	41.50
15″ tires	4333103	41.50
(12) Tie Rod Assy. (Outer)		
1983-87	4106180	39.75
(13) Clamp (Tie Rod End)		
1983-87	4147085	5.00
(14) Boot Service Kit		
1983-87-right	4147092	30.75
left	4147093	28.75
(15) Tie Rod Assy. (Inner)		
wo/15″ tires		
1983-84-right	4147095	48.50
left	4147136	47.50
1985-87-right	4147095	48.50
left	4333104	46.25
w/15″ tires		
1985-87-right	4333123	47.25
left	4333122	46.25
(16) Breather Tube		
1983-87	4147087	9.00
(17) Rack Bearing		
1983-87	5205282	5.25
(18) Spring (Adjuster)		
1983-87	5205280	2.00
(19) Plug (Adjuster)		
1983-87	5205286	7.75
(20) Bracket (Outer)		
1983-87-right	3643470	4.00
left	3643424	4.00
(21) Bushing		
1983-87-right	3643471	4.00
left	3643425	4.00
(22) Bracket (Inner)		
1983-87-right	3643469	1.00
left	3643423	1.00

PARTS 11 POWER STEERING PUMP 11 PARTS

	Part No.	Price
Power Steering Pump		
1983-87-Std.	3815956	170.25
H.D.	4188832	170.25
Oil Pressure Hose		
1983-85	4147280	25.25
1986-87	4333130	25.25
Oil Return Hose		
1983-87	3879925	77.75

Serviced from 50 ft. roll must cut to required size.

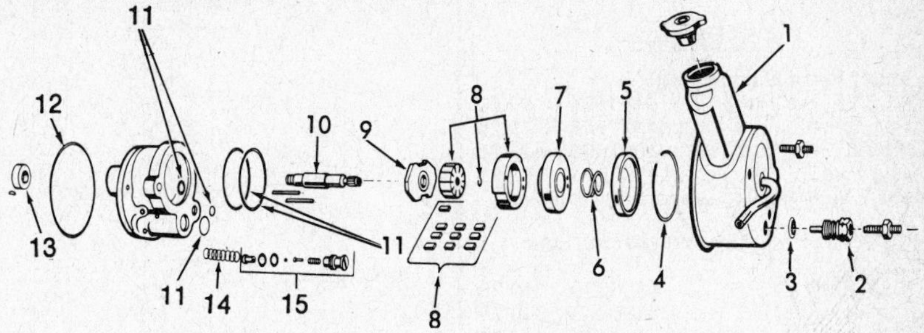

	Part No.	Price
(1) Reservoir		
1983-87	3643453	60.75
(2) Union Assy. (Fitting)		
1983-87-Std.	5205267	7.00
Firm	3815983	6.00
(3) Seal		
1983-87	2537838	11.00
(4) Retaining Ring (End Plate)		
1983-87	2537823	1.00
(5) End Plate		
1983-87	2537820	3.50
(6) Spring (Pressure Plate)		
1983-87	3815966	1.00
(7) Plate (Pressure)		
1983-87	3815967	13.75
(8) Rotor Repair Kit		
1983-87	3815964	89.00
(9) Plate (Thrust)		
1983-87	3815914	12.25
(10) Shaft (Rotor)		
1983-87	3815961	39.00
(11) Seal Kit		
1983-87	2537838	11.00
(12) "O" Ring		
1983-87	2537828	3.25
(13) Seal (Drive Shaft)		
1983-87	2537899	4.50
(14) Spring (Control Valve)		
1983-87	2537833	1.50
(15) Control Valve		
1983-87-Std.	3815965	12.50
Firm	2891695	13.00

LABOR 12 CYLINDER HEAD & VALVE SYSTEM 12 LABOR

(Factory Time)	Chilton Time
(G) Compression Test	
1983-87	.6
(G) Cylinder Head Gasket, Renew	
Includes: Clean carbon.	
1983-87	
2.2L & 2.5L engs (3.4)	4.8
2.6L eng (2.8)	4.5
w/P.S. add (.2)	.2
w/Air inj add (.2)	.2
w/Turbo add (.5)	.5
(G) Cylinder Head, Renew	
Includes: Transfer parts as required. Clean carbon, make all necessary adjustments.	
1983-87	
2.2L & 2.5L engs (5.3)	8.0
2.6L eng (4.7)	7.4
w/P.S. add (.2)	.2
w/Air inj add (.2)	.2
w/Turbo add (.5)	.5
(P) Clean Carbon and Grind Valves	
Includes: R&R cylinder head. Reface valves and seats. Minor tune up.	
1983-87	
2.2L & 2.5L engs (4.8)	6.8
2.6L eng (5.4)	8.0
w/P.S. add (.2)	.2
w/Air inj add (.2)	.2
w/Turbo add (.5)	.5
(G) Cylinder Head Cover Gasket, Renew or Reseal	
1983-87	
2.2L & 2.5L engs (.8)	1.1
2.6L eng (.4)	.6
(G) Valve Rocker Arms or Shafts, Renew	
1983-87	
2.2L & 2.5L engs all arms (1.2)	1.6
2.6L eng-one shaft (1.0)	1.4
both shafts (1.1)	1.7

LABOR 12 CYLINDER HEAD & VALVE SYSTEM 12 LABOR

(Factory Time)	Chilton Time
(G) Valve Tappets, Renew	
1983-87	
2.2L & 2.5L engs	
one (1.0)	1.4
each adtnl (.1)	.1
(G) Valve Tappets, Adjust	
1983-87	
2.6L eng (.9)	1.5
(G) Jet Valves, Renew	
1983-87	
2.6L eng-one or all (.9)	1.1
(G) Valve Springs and/or Valve Stem Oil Seals, Renew	
1983-87	
2.2L & 2.5L engs	
one (1.2)	1.5
all (1.9)	2.9
2.6L eng (4.7)	*6.0
*w/Head on car	3.5
w/P.S. add (.2)	.2

COMBINATIONS

Add To Valve Job
See Machine Shop Operations

(G) DRAIN, EVACUATE & RECHARGE AIR CONDITIONING SYSTEM	
All models	1.0
(G) DISTRIBUTOR, RECONDITION	
All models (.7)	.7
(G) RECONDITION CYL. HEAD (HEAD REMOVED)	
All models (1.4)	2.0
(G) CAMSHAFT, RENEW (HEAD DISASSEMBLED)	
OHC engs (.1)	.2
(G) CARBURETOR, RECONDITION	
Holly (.5)	.9
(G) REMOVE CYLINDER TOP RIDGE	
Each (.1)	.1
(G) RENEW OIL PUMP	
All engs (.2)	.3
(G) ROD BEARINGS, RENEW (PAN REMOVED)	
All engs (.7)	1.2
(G) DEGLAZE CYLINDER WALLS	
Each (.1)	.1
(G) PLASTIGAUGE BEARINGS	
Each (.1)	.1
(M) OIL FILTER ELEMENT, RENEW	
All models (.3)	.3

PARTS 12 CYLINDER HEAD & VALVE SYSTEM 12 PARTS

2.2L ENGINE

	Part No.	Price
Cylinder Head Gasket Pkg.		
1983-85-wo/Turbo	4271994	30.50
w/Turbo	4271926	29.25
1986-87-wo/Turbo	4397680	28.25
w/Turbo	4397681	28.25
Use R.T.V. sealer for gaskets not supplied.		
(1) Cylinder Head (wo/Valves, Springs, etc.)		
1983-Early	4105399	340.25
Late	4105443	340.25
1984	4105443	340.25
1985	4323288	340.25
1986-87-wo/Turbo	4105783	340.25
Turbo	4343627	340.25
(2) Cylinder Head Gasket		
1983	5203780	N.L.
1984-85	4105468	11.50
1986-87	4387319	11.50
(3) End Seal (Head Cover)		
1983-87-wo/Turbo	5214479	2.25
w/Turbo	4105475	2.25
(4) Valve Spring		
1983-84-wo/Turbo	4105755	2.25
w/Turbo	4105793	2.25
1985-87-wo/Turbo	4323225	2.25
w/Turbo	4105793	2.25
(5) Valve Guide		
1983-87-Exhaust	4105715	7.75
Intake	4105716	7.75
(6) Exhaust Valve (Std.)		
1983-85-wo/Turbo	5214866	9.00
w/Turbo	5214959	21.00
1986-87-wo/Turbo	4298142	9.00
w/Turbo	4323249	21.00
(7) Intake Valve (Std)		
1983-85-wo/Turbo	5214861	8.25
w/Turbo	5214895	8.75
1986-87-wo/Turbo	4298137	8.25
w/Turbo	4323244	8.75

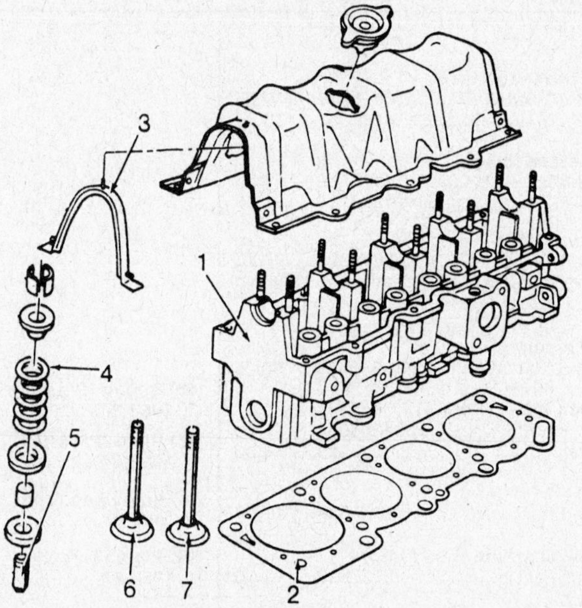

2.5L ENGINE

	Part No.	Price
Cylinder Head Gasket Pkg.		
1986-87	4397680	28.25
Use R.T.V. sealer for gaskets not supplied.		
(1) Cylinder Head (Bare)		
1986-87	4343627	340.25
(2) Cylinder Head Gasket		
1986-87	4387319	11.50
(3) End Seal (Head Cover)		
1986-87	5214479	2.25
(4) Valve Spring		
1986-87	4323225	2.25
(5) Valve Guide		
1986-87-Exhaust	4105715	7.75
Intake	4105716	7.75
(6) Exhaust Valve (Std.)		
1986-87	4298142	9.00
(7) Intake Valve (Std.)		
1986-87	4298137	8.25

PARTS 12 CYLINDER HEAD & VALVE SYSTEM 12 PARTS

2.6L ENGINE

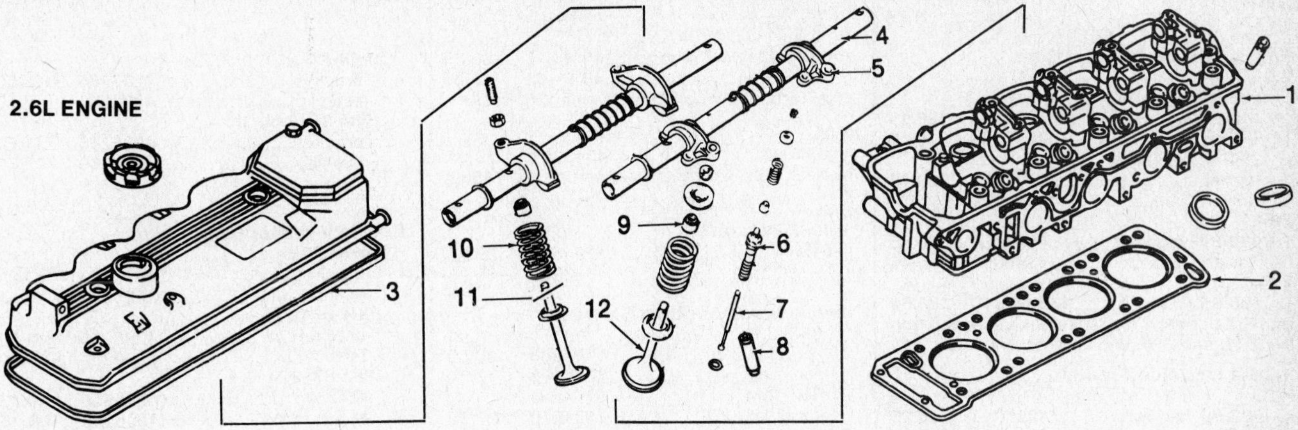

	Part No.	Price
2.6L ENGINE		
Cylinder Head Gasket Pkg.		
1983-85	MD997021	54.25
(1) Cylinder Head		
1983-85	MD026510	550.00
(2) Cylinder Head Gasket		
1983-85	MD026654	16.00
(3) Valve Cover Gasket		
1983-85	MD024682	6.75
(4) Rocker Arm Shaft		
1983-85-right	MD023198	27.00
left	MD023196	27.00
(5) Rocker Arm		
1983-85	MD023226	12.00
(6) Jet Valve Assy.		
1983-85	MD009440	20.50
(7) Jet Valve Rod		
(8) Valve Guide (Std.)		
1983-85-Exhaust	MD020561	2.50
Inlet	MD020551	2.50
(9) Valve Stem Seal		
1983-85	MD000508	2.50
(10) Valve Spring		
1983-85		
up to 5-84	MD022591	3.50
from 5-84	MD073398	3.50
(11) Exhaust Valve		
1983	MD024519	15.25
1984-85		
up to 5-84	MD024548	5.00
from 5-84	MD083851	15.25
(12) Intake Valve		
1983-85		
up to 5-84	MD024518	8.50
from 5-84	MD083848	8.50

LABOR 13 ENGINE ASSEMBLY & MOUNTS 13 LABOR

	(Factory Time)	Chilton Time
(G) Engine Assembly, Remove & Install		
Includes: R&R engine and transmission as a unit.		
1983-87		
2.2L & 2.5L engs		**6.0**
2.6L eng		**5.2**
w/A.C. add	(.5)	**.5**
w/P.S. add	(.2)	**.2**
w/Air inj add	(.3)	**.3**
(P) Short Engine Assembly, Renew (w/All Internal Parts Less Cyl. Head and Oil Pan)		
Includes: R&R engine and transmission as a unit. Transfer all necessary parts not supplied with replacement engine. Clean carbon, grind valves. Minor tune up.		
1983-87		
2.2L & 2.5L engs	(9.1)	**15.0**
2.6L eng	(9.4)	**15.5**
w/A.C. add	(.5)	**.5**
w/P.S. add	(.2)	**.2**
w/Air inj add	(.3)	**.3**
(P) Engine Assy., R&R and Recondition (Complete)		
Includes: Rebore block, install new pistons, rings, rod and main bearings. Clean carbon, grind valves. Replace valve stem oil seals. Tune engine.		
1983-87		
2.2L & 2.5L engs	(17.8)	**25.2**
2.6L eng	(17.0)	**23.4**
w/A.C. add	(.5)	**.5**
w/P.S. add	(.2)	**.2**
w/Air inj add	(.3)	**.3**
(P) Engine Assembly, Recondition (In Car)		
Includes: Expand or renew pistons, install rings, pins, rod and main bearings. Clean carbon, grind valves. Tune engine.		
1983-87		
2.2L & 2.5L engs	(15.2)	**20.8**
2.6L eng	(14.4)	**19.0**
w/P.S. add	(.2)	**.2**
(G) Engine Support, Renew		
1983-87-right side	(.3)	**.5**
left side	(.3)	**.5**
center	(.4)	**.6**
Trans/Axle		
Roll rod	(.2)	**.5**

PARTS 13 ENGINE ASSEMBLY & MOUNTS 13 PARTS

	Part No.	Price
Engine Assy.		
Consists of block, pistons, rings, connecting rods, crankshaft, bearings & caps.		
2.2L		
1983-84-wo/Turbo	5214968	1200.50
w/Turbo	5214969	1200.50
1985-wo/Turbo	4387201	1200.50
w/Turbo	4387202	1200.50
1986-87-wo/Turbo	4343590	1200.50
w/Turbo	4343871	1200.50
2.5L		
1986-87	4343588	1287.50
2.6L		
1983-87		
up to 4-83	MD025787	1946.00
after 4-83	MD076310	1946.00
Cylinder Block		
2.6L		
1983	MD024505	1077.75
1984-85		
up to 4-83	MD026200	1077.75
after 4-83	MD076312	1077.75

The 2.2L and 2.5L are serviced in short engine assy.

PARTS 13 ENGINE ASSEMBLY & MOUNTS 13 PARTS

	Part No.	Price
Engine Overhaul Gasket Set		
2.2L		
1983-87 (exc. Turbo)		
upper	4271994	30.50
lower	4240098	5.75
1984-87 (w/Turbo)		
upper	4271926	29.25
lower	4240098	5.75
2.5L		
1986-87-upper	4397680	28.25
lower	4240098	5.75
2.6L		
1983-85	MD997050	106.50

Use R.T.V. sealer for gaskets not supplied with the 2.2L and 2.5L engine sets.

	Part No.	Price
Engine Insulator (Front)		
2.2L		
1983-85-wo/Turbo	4295018	25.25
w/Turbo	4329588	28.25
1986-87-wo/Turbo	4295018	25.25
w/Turbo	4377458	25.25

Use Turbo mount on models with H.D. brakes.

	Part No.	Price
2.5L		
1986-87	4348327	25.25

Models with Fleet H.D. brakes use 4377458.

	Part No.	Price
2.6L		
1983-87-exc.		
below	4191891	25.25
H.D. brks	4340035	25.25
Engine Insulator (Right Side)		
1983-2.2L		
bracket	4191988	20.50
bushing	4295198	12.50
1983-2.6L		
bracket	4191970	20.75
bushing	4295198	12.50
1984-87-2.2L & 2.5L		
bracket	4295265	11.50
bushing	4295260	12.50
1984-85-2.6L		
bracket	4295266	11.50
bushing	4295260	12.50
Engine Insulater (Left Side)		
1983-2.2L		
bracket	4267209	18.25
bushing	4295198	12.50
1984-87-2.2L		
bracket	4295255	9.75
bushing	4295237	9.00
1986-87-2.5L		
A.T.	4295255	9.75
M.T.	4295257	9.75
bushing	4295237	9.00

LABOR 14 PISTONS, RINGS & BEARINGS 14 LABOR

COMBINATIONS

(G) DRAIN, EVACUATE & RECHARGE AIR CONDITIONING SYSTEM
All models 1.0

(G) DISTRIBUTOR, RECONDITION
All models (.7) 7

(G) RECONDITION CYL. HEAD (HEAD REMOVED)
All models (1.4) 2.0

(G) CAMSHAFT, RENEW (HEAD DISASSEMBLED)
OHC engs (.1) 2

Add To Engine Work

See Machine Shop Operations

(G) R&R CYLINDER HEAD (ENGINE REMOVED)
All models 1.5

(G) CONNECTING ROD, RENEW (ENGINE DISASSEMBLED)
Each 4

(G) CARBURETOR, RECONDITION
Holly (.5) 9

(G) REMOVE CYLINDER TOP RIDGE
Each (.1) 1

(G) RENEW OIL PUMP
All engs (.2) 3

(G) ROD BEARINGS, RENEW (PAN REMOVED)
All engs (.7) 1.2

(G) MAIN BEARINGS, RENEW (PAN REMOVED)
All models (.9) 1.4

(G) DEGLAZE CYLINDER WALLS
Each (.1) 1

(G) PLASTIGAUGE BEARINGS
Each (.1) 1

(M) OIL FILTER ELEMENT, RENEW
All models (.3) 3

(Factory Time) — Chilton Time

(P) Rings, Renew (See Engine Combinations)

Includes: Replace connecting rod bearings, deglaze cylinder walls, clean carbon. Minor tune up.

	Chilton Time
1983-87	
2.2L & 2.5L engs	
one cyl (4.6)	6.9
all cyls (5.9)	8.1
2.6L eng-one cyl (4.1)	6.3
all cyls (5.7)	8.0
w/P.S. add (.2)	.2
w/Air inj add (.2)	.2
w/Turbo add (.5)	.5

(P) Piston or Connecting Rod, Renew

Includes: Replace connecting rod bearings and piston rings, deglaze cylinder walls. Clean carbon from cylinder head.

	Chilton Time
1983-87	
2.2L & 2.5L engs	
one cyl (4.9)	7.2
all cyls (6.1)	9.3
2.6L eng-one cyl (4.7)	6.6
all cyls (7.2)	9.2
w/P.S. add (.2)	.2
w/Air inj add (.2)	.2
w/Turbo add (.5)	.5

(P) Connecting Rod Bearings, Renew

	Chilton Time
1983-87	
2.2L & 2.5L engs (2.1)	3.0
2.6L eng (1.2)	2.2

PARTS 14 PISTONS, RINGS & BEARINGS 14 PARTS

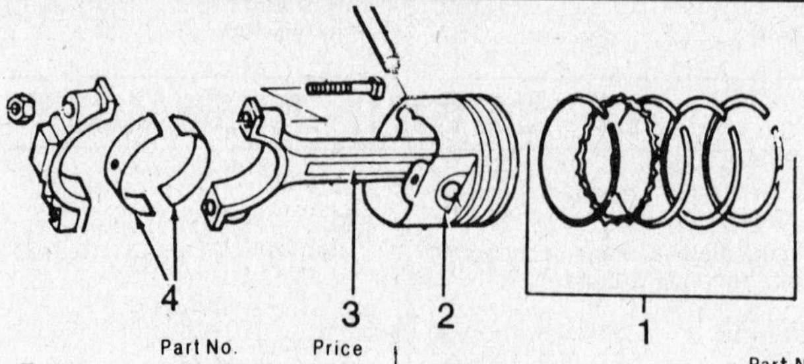

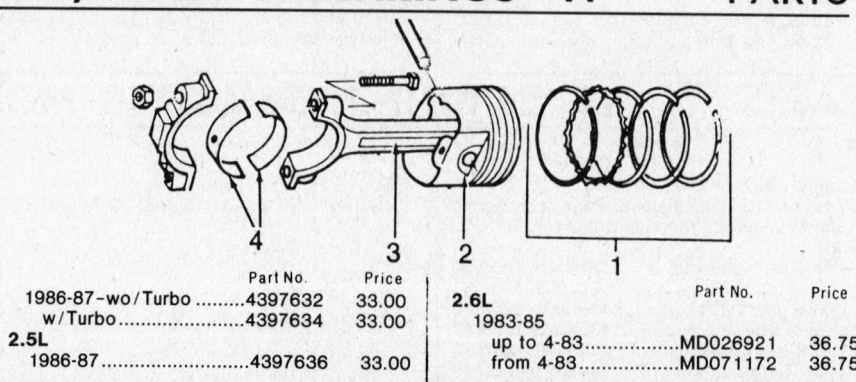

	Part No.	Price
(1) Piston Ring Set (Std.)		
2.2L		
1983-87-wo/Turbo	4240137	54.00
w/Turbo	4293799	54.00
2.5L		
1986-87	4240137	54.00
2.6L		
1983-85		
up to 4-83	MD026835	65.75
from 4-83	MD061258	69.50
(2) Piston Assy. (Std.)		
2.2L		
1983-85-wo/Turbo	4271929	33.00
w/Turbo	4271927	33.00
1986-87-wo/Turbo	4397632	33.00
w/Turbo	4397634	33.00
2.5L		
1986-87	4397636	33.00
2.6L		
1983-85		
up to 4-83	MD026921	36.75
from 4-83	MD071172	36.75

PARTS 14 PISTONS, RINGS & BEARINGS 14 PARTS

	Part No.	Price
(3) Connecting Rod		
2.2L		
1983-85-wo/Turbo	5203384	35.00
w/Turbo	4105486	35.00
1986-87	4343725	35.00
2.5L		
1986-87	4343436	35.00
2.6L		
1983-85	MD020855	62.25
(4) Connecting Rod Bearings		
2.2L		
1983-87-wo/Turbo	4240025	4.00
w/Turbo	4342751	4.00
2.5L		
1986-87	4240025	4.00
2.6L		
1983-85	MD026430	40.25

LABOR 15 CRANKSHAFT & DAMPER 15 LABOR

(Factory Time)	Chilton Time
(P) Crankshaft and Main Bearings, Renew	
Includes: R&R engine assembly.	
1983-87	
2.2L & 2.5L engs (6.7)	**11.2**
2.6L eng (7.6)	**12.1**
w/A.C. add (.5)	**.5**
w/P.S. add (.2)	**.2**
w/Air inj add (.3)	**.3**
(P) Main Bearings, Renew	
1983-87	
2.2L & 2.5L engs	
No 2-3 or 4 (1.8)	**2.8**
No 1 (3.0)	**4.0**
No 5 (5.6)	**8.8**
all (7.0)	**11.0**
2.6L eng (2.2)	**3.0**
(P) Main and Rod Bearings, Renew	
1983-87	
2.6L eng (2.9)	**4.2**
(G) Rear Main Bearing Oil Seals, Renew (Complete)	
1983-87	
2.2L & 2.5L engs (3.0)	**5.4**
2.6L eng-w/A.T. (3.2)	**5.5**
(G) Crankshaft Pulley, Renew	
1983-87	
2.2L & 2.5L engs (.5)	**.7**
2.6L eng (.4)	**.6**
w/A.C. add (.1)	**.1**
w/P.S. add (.1)	**.1**
(G) Crankshaft Front Oil Seal, Renew	
1983-87	
2.2L & 2.5L engs (1.3)	**2.0**
w/A.C. add (.2)	**.2**
w/P.S. add (.2)	**.2**

PARTS 15 CRANKSHAFT & DAMPER 15 PARTS

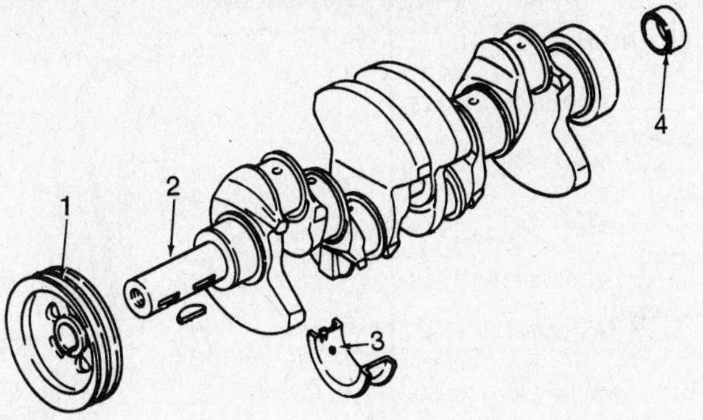

	Part No.	Price
(1) Pulley		
2.2L		
1983-w/A.C.	4201464	19.00
wo/A.C.	4201459	19.00
1984-87-w/A.C.	4298125	19.00
wo/A.C.	4273184	14.25
2.5L		
1986-87-w/A.C.	4323099	19.00
wo/A.C.	4323100	14.75
2.6L		
1983-85		
up to 4-83	MD062006	36.25
from 4-83	MD074096	36.25
(2) Crankshaft		
2.2L		
1983-84-wo/Turbo	5214737	317.50
w/Turbo	4105498	317.50
1985-wo/Turbo	5214737	317.50
w/Turbo	4105498	317.50
1986-87	4343407	317.50
2.5L		
1986-87	4343405	335.00
2.6L		
1983-87	MD026408	386.25
(3) Crankshaft Bearing Pkg. (Upper & Lower)		
2.2L & 2.5L		
1983-87-wo/Turbo		
No. 1, 2, 4, 5	4240013	6.00
No. 3	4240019	6.00
1984-87-w/Turbo		
No. 1, 2, 4, 5	4293824	6.00
No. 3	4293830	12.75
2.6L		
1983-87-complete set	MD026815	67.75
(4) Crankshaft Bushing		
2.6L		
1983-87	MD024893	3.50
Crankshaft Oil Seal (Front)		
1983-87-2.2L & 2.5L	4105395	2.75
2.6L	MD020308	4.50
Crankshaft Oil Seal (Rear)		
1983-87-2.2L & 2.5L	5203590	6.50
2.6L	MD050604	14.50

LABOR 16 CAMSHAFT & TIMING GEARS 16 LABOR

(Factory Time)	Chilton Time
(G) Timing Chain or Belt Case/Cover, Renew	
Includes: Renew gasket.	
1983-87	
2.2L & 2.5L engs	
upper cover (.2)	**.4**
lower cover (.6)	**1.0**
2.6L eng (3.2)	**4.5**
w/A.C. add (.5)	**.5**
w/P.S. add (.1)	**.1**
(G) Timing Belt, Renew	
1983-87	
2.2L & 2.5L engs (1.6)	**2.2**
w/A.C. add (.5)	**.5**
w/P.S. add (.2)	**.2**
(G) Timing Chain, Adjust	
1983-87	
2.6L eng (.4)	**.8**

LABOR 16 CAMSHAFT & TIMING GEARS 16 LABOR

(Factory Time) — Chilton Time

(G) Timing Chain, Renew
Includes: Renew cover oil seal.

	Chilton Time
1983-87	
2.6L eng	
cam drive (3.6)	5.0
shaft drive (3.4)	4.8
w/A.C. add (.2)	.2
w/P.S. add (.1)	.1

(G) Timing Chain Guide, Renew

	Chilton Time
1983-87	
2.6L eng-cam drive	
right or left (3.2)	4.6
silent shaft-upper (3.2)	4.6
lower (3.2)	4.6
w/A.C. add (.2)	.2
w/P.S. add (.1)	.1

(G) Timing Chain Tensioner, Renew

	Chilton Time
1983-87	
2.6L eng (3.5)	4.9
w/A.C. add (.2)	.2
w/P.S. add (.1)	.1

(G) Timing Belt Tensioner, Renew

	Chilton Time
1983-87	
2.2L & 2.5L engs (.9)	1.5
w/A.C. add (.6)	.6

(G) Timing Chain Cover Oil Seal, Renew

	Chilton Time
1983-87	
2.6L eng (.5)	.9
w/P.S. add (.1)	.1

(G) Camshaft Sprocket, Renew
Includes: Renew cover oil seal, timing chain and crankshaft sprocket.

	Chilton Time
1983-87	
2.2L & 2.5L engs (1.7)	2.4
2.6L eng (3.6)	5.0
w/A.C. add (.2)	.2
w/P.S. add (.2)	.2

(G) Camshaft Oil Seal, Renew

	Chilton Time
1983-87	
2.2L & 2.5L engs (.7)	1.1
2.2-2.6L engs-rear (.4)	.8

(G) Camshaft, Renew

	Chilton Time
1983-87	
2.2L & 2.5L engs (1.7)	*2.8
2.6L eng (1.6)	2.2
*Renew valve springs add (1.1)	1.1

(G) Camshaft Distributor Drive Gear, Renew

	Chilton Time
1983-87	
2.6L eng (.7)	1.1

(G) Intermediate Shaft, Renew

	Chilton Time
1983-87	
2.2L & 2.5L engs (1.3)	2.5
w/A.C. add (.2)	.2

(G) Silent Shaft Sprocket, Renew

	Chilton Time
1983-87	
2.6L eng-one or both (3.4)	4.7
w/A.C. add (.2)	.2
w/P.S. add (.1)	.1

(G) Intermediate Shaft Sprocket, Renew

	Chilton Time
1983-87	
2.2L & 2.5L engs (1.7)	2.7
w/A.C. add (.2)	.2
w/P.S. add (.2)	.2

(G) Silent Shaft, Renew

	Chilton Time
1983-87	
2.6L eng-right (4.0)	5.6
left (5.0)	7.0
both (5.3)	7.5
w/A.C. add (.4)	.4
w/P.S. add (.1)	.1

PARTS 16 CAMSHAFT & TIMING GEARS 16 PARTS

2.6L ENGINE

	Part No.	Price
(1) Camshaft		
1983-85	MD026730	163.25
(2) Sprocket (Camshaft)		
1983-85	MD021246	21.75
(3) Gear (Distributor)		
1983-85	MD021247	13.75
(4) Sleeve (Complete)		
1983-85	MD021233	11.75
(5) Sprocket (Crankshaft)		
1983-85	MD020843	14.00
(6) Timing Chain		
1983-85	MD021230	43.50
(7) Chain (B)		
1983-85	MD021155	49.75
(8) Sprocket (Crankshaft)		
1983-85	MD021170	22.75
(9) Sprocket Assy.		
1983-85	MD021172	20.50
(10) Thrust Plate Assy.		
1983-85	MD020897	22.50

2.6L ENGINE

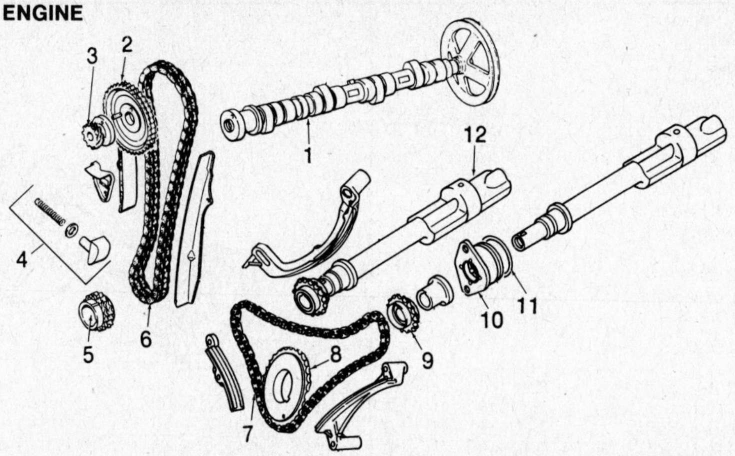

	Part No.	Price
(11) "O" Ring		
1983-85	MD021045	1.00
(12) Counterbalance Shaft		
1983-85-right	MD024845	66.50
left	MD024846	66.50

PARTS 16 CAMSHAFT & TIMING GEARS 16 PARTS

2.2L ENGINE

	Part No.	Price
(1) Timing Belt Cover (Upper)		
1983-87	4105714	10.00
(2) Pulley (Tension)		
1983-87	5203469	41.75
(3) Sprocket (Crankshaft)		
1983-87	5203575	14.00
(4) Timing Belt Cover (Lower)		
1983-84	4105293	10.00
1985-87	4343639	10.50
(5) Sprocket (Interm. Shaft)		
1983	5214870	16.25
1984-87-exc.		
below	4201974	16.50
w/Turbo	4201992	22.50
(6) Timing Belt		
1983-85	5203401	22.75
1986-87	4343946	22.75
(7) Retainer Assy. (Interm. Shaft)		
1983-87	5203325	8.50
(8) Intermediate Shaft		
1983-85	4293815	95.75
1986-87-exc. Carb	4343428	86.75
Carb	4293815	95.75
(9) Seal (Interm. Shaft)		
1983-87	4105395	2.75
(10) Camshaft		
1983	4271910	154.00
1984-87-wo/Turbo	4293817	161.50
w/Turbo	4293819	161.50

PARTS 16 CAMSHAFT & TIMING GEARS 16 PARTS

	Part No.	Price
(11) Adjuster (Valve Lash)		
1983-87	4240007	12.50
(12) Rocker (Valve)		
1983-84	5203491	5.00
1985-87	4173390	7.00
(13) Sprocket (Camshaft)		
1983	5214870	16.25
1984-87-wo/Turbo	4201974	16.50
w/Turbo	4201992	22.50
2.5L ENGINE		
(1) Timing Belt Cover (Upper)		
1986-87	4343820	10.75
(2) Pulley (Tension)		
1986-87	4273241	14.00
(3) Sprocket (Crankshaft)		
1986-87	4273269	10.25
(4) Timing Belt Cover (Lower)		
1986-87	4343821	10.00
(5) Sprocket (Interm. Shaft)		
1986-87	4273238	16.50
(6) Timing Belt		
1986-87	4343824	22.75
(7) Retainer Assy. (Interm. Shaft)		
1986-87	5203325	8.50
(8) Intermediate Shaft		
1986-87	4343428	86.75
(9) Seal (Interm. Shaft)		
1986-87	4105395	2.75
(10) Camshaft		
1986-87	4293817	161.50

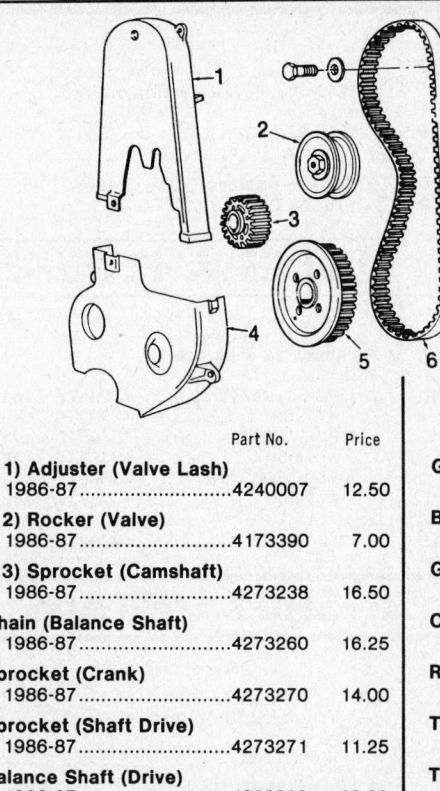

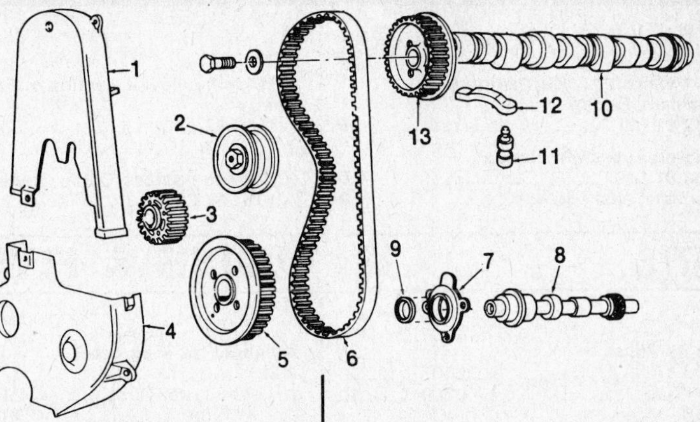

	Part No.	Price
(11) Adjuster (Valve Lash)		
1986-87	4240007	12.50
(12) Rocker (Valve)		
1986-87	4173390	7.00
(13) Sprocket (Camshaft)		
1986-87	4273238	16.50
Chain (Balance Shaft)		
1986-87	4273260	16.25
Sprocket (Crank)		
1986-87	4273270	14.00
Sprocket (Shaft Drive)		
1986-87	4273271	11.25
Balance Shaft (Drive)		
1986-87	4323026	23.00

	Part No.	Price
Gear (Shaft Drive)		
1986-87	4343783	26.50
Balance Shaft (Driven)		
1986-87	4323028	23.00
Gear (Shaft Driven)		
1986-87	4343785	26.50
Carrier & Bearings		
1986-87	4323038	70.50
Rear Cover		
1986-87	4323043	1.50
Trough (Carrier Gear Cover)		
1986-87	4323041	1.25
Trough Front Cover (Chain)		
1986-87	4323039	5.75

LABOR 17 ENGINE OILING SYSTEM 17 LABOR

(Factory Time)	Chilton Time
(G) Oil Pan or Gasket, Renew or Reseal	
1983-87	
2.2L & 2.5L engs (1.0)	1.4
2.6L eng (.6)	1.0
(P) Pressure Test Engine Bearings (Pan Off)	
All models	1.0
(G) Oil Pump, Renew	
1983-87	
2.2L & 2.5L engs (1.3)	1.7
2.6L eng (3.8)	5.2
w/A.C. add (.2)	.2
(G) Oil Pump, R&R and Recondition	
1983-87	
2.2L & 2.5L engs (1.7)	2.2
(G) Oil Pressure Relief Valve Spring, Renew	
1983-87	
2.2L & 2.5L engs (1.6)	2.2
2.6L eng (3.4)	4.7
(G) Oil Pressure Gauge (Engine Unit), Renew	
1983-87 (.3)	.4
(G) Oil Pressure Gauge (Dash), Renew	
1985-87 (.3)	.6
(M) Oil Filter Element, Renew	
1983-87 (.2)	.3

PARTS 17 ENGINE OILING SYSTEM 17 PARTS

	Part No.	Price
Oil Pump Assy.		
2.2L		
1983	5203415	N.L.
1984	4323327	58.50
1985	4293888	N.L.
1986-87	4397827	66.00
2.5L		
1986-87	4397827	66.00
2.6L		
1983-85	MD060517	143.50
Drive Shaft & Rotor Pkg.		
2.2L		
1983-85	4240008	24.25
1986-87	4342940	24.50
2.5L		
1986-87	4342940	24.50

	Part No.	Price
Oil Pump Driven Gear		
2.6L		
1983	MD022558	32.50
1984-85	MD061314	29.75
Oil Pump Drive Gear		
2.6L		
1983	MD022557	33.25
1984-85	MD061313	34.50
Gasket Oil Pan		
2.2L		
1983-87-use RTV sealer		
2.6L		
1983-85	MD024777	7.25

	Part No.	Price
Seal (Front & Rear) Oil Pan		
1983-87-2.2L	5203778	1.75
1986-87-2.5L		
Front	4273243	1.75
Rear	5203778	1.75
Oil Filter Assy.		
1983-87-2.2L & 2.5L	4105409	5.50
2.6L	MD031805	5.75
Screen Assy. (Oil)		
1983-85-2.2L	5203324	7.75
1986-87	4343198	7.65
1986-87-2.5L	4343521	4.50
2.6L	MD025223	13.25

LABOR 18 CLUTCH & FLYWHEEL 18 LABOR

(Factory Time)	Chilton Time
(G) Clutch Self-Adjusting Mechanism, Renew	
1983-87 (.3)	.6
(G) Clutch Assembly, Renew	
1983-87 (2.9)	4.0
Renew input seal add (.2)	.2
(G) Clutch Release Bearing or Fork, Renew	
1983-87 (2.8)	3.8
(G) Clutch Release Cable, Renew	
1983-87 (.3)	.5
(G) Flywheel, Renew	
1983-87	
2.2L & 2.5L engs (3.0)	4.2
(G) Clutch Release Lever and/or Seal, Renew	
1983-87 (.5)	.8

PARTS 18 CLUTCH & FLYWHEEL 18 PARTS

	Part No.	Price
Pressure Plate		
1983-87-wo/Turbo	4295007	122.50
w/Turbo	4269309	122.50
Clutch Disc		
1983-87-wo/Turbo	4295006	66.50
w/Turbo	4269308	68.25
Flywheel (w/Ring gear)		
2.2L		
1983-84-wo/Turbo	4329177	142.75
w/Turbo	4348314	142.75
1985-wo/turbo	4348312	142.50
w/Turbo	4348314	142.75
1986-87-wo/Turbo	4338874	142.75
w/Turbo	4338872	142.75
2.5L		
1986-87	4338872	142.75
Clutch Release Bearing		
1983-87	4202378	44.00
Clutch Control Cable		
1983	4019750	N.L.
1984-wo/Turbo	4295584	21.00
w/Turbo	4295596	N.L.
1985-87	4377769	18.50

LABOR 21 SHIFT LINKAGE 21 LABOR

(Factory Time)	Chilton Time
MANUAL	
(G) Gearshift Linkage, Adjust	
1983-87 (.2)	.4
(G) Gearshift Lever, Renew	
1983-87 (.4)	.6
(G) Gearshift Control Rod and/or Swivel, Renew	
1983-87 (.3)	.4
(G) Gearshift Mechanism, Renew	
1983-87	
linkage shift (.7)	1.1
cable shift (.7)	1.1
w/Console add (.4)	.4
(G) Selector Shaft Seal, Renew	
1983-87 (.8)	1.1
(G) Trans/Axle Selector Shaft, Renew	
1983-87 (1.3)	1.7
(G) Gearshift Selector Cable, Renew	
1983-87 (.9)	1.4
Lancer-LeBaron GTS (1.7)	2.5
(G) Gearshift Crossover Cable, Renew	
1983-87 (.8)	1.3
Lancer-LeBaron GTS (1.7)	2.5
AUTOMATIC	
(G) Throttle Linkage, Adjust	
1983-87 (.2)	.4
(G) Selector Lever, Renew	
1983-87 (.3)	.4
(G) Gearshift Mechanism, Renew	
1983-87 (.4)	.8
(G) Gearshift Control Cable, Renew	
1983-87 (.5)	.8
(G) Throttle Lever Control Cable, Renew	
Includes: Adjust cable.	
1983-87 (.3)	.6
(G) Gear Selector Dial, Renew	
1983-87 (.7)	1.1

LABOR 26 REAR AXLE 26 LABOR

(Factory Time)	Chilton Time
(G) Rear Wheel Bearings, Renew or Repack	
1983-87-one side (.6)	.9
both sides (1.1)	1.7
(G) Rear Wheel Grease Seal, Renew	
1983-87-one side (.4)	.7
(G) Rear Shock Absorbers, Renew	
1983-87-one (.3)	.5
both (.4)	.7
(G) Rear Springs, Renew	
1983-87-one (.3)	.6
both (.5)	.8
(G) Lower Control Arm Bushing, Renew	
1983-87-one side (.6)	1.0
(G) Stub Axle Spindle, Renew	
1983-87-each (.5)	.7
(G) Rear Sway Bar, Renew	
1983-87 (.4)	.7
(G) Rear Wheel Mounting Studs, Renew	
1983-87-one (.5)	.8
each adtnl	.1
AIR SUSPENSION	
(G) Air Suspension Lines, Renew	
1986-87-one (.3)	.4
all	.5
(G) Height Sensor, Renew	
1986-87 (.4)	.5
(G) Compressor Assembly, Renew	
1986-87 (.5)	.7
(G) Compressor Relay, Renew	
1986-87 (.6)	.9

PARTS 26 REAR AXLE AND SUSPENSION 26 PARTS

	Part No.	Price
(1) Rear Spindle		
1983-84	4228123	62.75
1985-87	4228117	50.50
(2) Shim (Whl. Alignment)		
1983-87	5205114	2.25
(3) Shock Absorber		
1983-87 (Aries & Reliant)		
standard	4147848	15.00
heavy duty	4228260	21.50
extra duty	4228261	20.00
1983-87 (Le Baron & Dodge 400)		
standard	4147849	16.25
heavy duty	4228260	21.50
1985-87 (Lancer, Le Baron GTS)		
w/firm susp.	4228336	30.00

PARTS 26 REAR AXLE AND SUSPENSION 26 PARTS

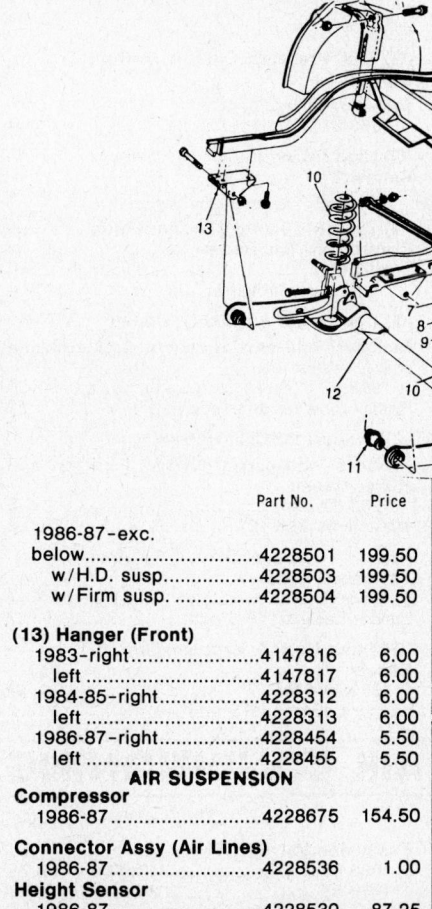

	Part No.	Price
(4) Track Bar Pkg.		
1983-84	4271370	58.00
1985	4318723	63.25
1986-87	4228256	63.25
(5) Brace (Track Bar Mtg.)		
1983-84	4147852	17.75
1985-87	4228251	17.75
(6) Pivot Bolt		
1983-87	6500415	1.25
(7) Cup (Jounce Bumper)		
1983-w/13" whls	4147747	6.25
w/14" whls.	4147813	6.75
1984-exc. below	4147752	7.00
SBR tires	4147813	6.75
1985	4228096	7.00
1986-87		
one notch	4228096	7.00
three notch	4228440	7.00
(8) Isolator (Spring Upper)		
1983-87	4147759	2.75
(9) Bumper (Jounce)		
1983-84	4147708	7.50
1985-87	4228159	6.50
(10) Coil Spring		
Order by model and description.		
(11) Bushing (Cont. Arm)		
1983-87-Std.	4147857	9.25
H.D.	4147951	9.00
(12) Control Arm (w/Axle Channel)		
1983-84-exc.		
below	4147814	199.50
w/Firm susp.	4147903	199.50
1985-exc. below	4147814	199.50
w/H.D. susp	4147903	199.50
w/Firm susp.	4147904	199.50

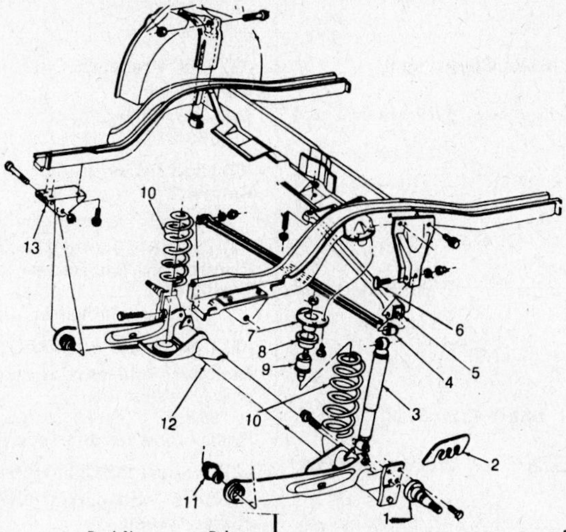

	Part No.	Price
1986-87-exc.		
below	4228501	199.50
w/H.D. susp	4228503	199.50
w/Firm susp.	4228504	199.50
(13) Hanger (Front)		
1983-right	4147816	6.00
left	4147817	6.00
1984-85-right	4228312	6.00
left	4228313	6.00
1986-87-right	4228454	5.50
left	4228455	5.50
AIR SUSPENSION		
Compressor		
1986-87	4228675	154.50
Connector Assy (Air Lines)		
1986-87	4228536	1.00
Height Sensor		
1986-87	4228530	87.25

	Part No.	Price
Shock Absorber		
1986-87		
Normal	4228540	41.50
H.D.	4228541	45.50
Track Bar		
1986-87	4228256	63.25
Relay		
1986-87	4228673	15.50
Link (Height Sensor)		
1986-87	4228672	4.25
Air Line		
1986-87		
Right	4228537	3.50
Left	4228538	4.50
Compressor	4228539	4.50
Filter		
1986-87	4228671	3.25

LABOR 28 AIR CONDITIONING 28 LABOR

	(Factory Time)	Chilton Time
Note: If more than one item requires replacement where evacuation and discharging the system is already included in the operation, deduct 1.0 hour for each additional item to the times listed.		
(G) Drain, Evacuate, Leak Test and Charge System		
All models		1.0
(G) Partial Charge		
Includes: Leak test.		
All models	(.4)	.6
(G) Performance Test		
All models		.8
(G) Vacuum Leak Test		
All models		.8
(G) Compressor Drive Belt, Renew		
1983-87	(.2)	.3

AIR CONDITIONER TUNE-UP

For efficient operation and satisfactory performance in hot weather. The following air conditioner tune-up is suggested:

1. Clean intake filter
2. Clean condenser fins
3. Pressure test system
4. Adjust drive belt tension
5. Check antifreeze/coolant
6. Tighten compressor mounts
7. Tighten condenser and evaporator mounts
8. Inspect system for leaks (hoses, couplings, valves, etc.)
9. Partial charge system

All models 1.0

If necessary to evacuate and charge system, add 1.0

C-171 COMPRESSOR

	(Factory Time)	Chilton Time
(G) Compressor Assembly, Renew		
Includes: Transfer parts as required. Pressure test and charge system.		
1983-87		
2.2L & 2.5L engs	(1.4)	2.5
2.6L eng	(1.9)	3.0
(G) Compressor Clutch Field Coil, Renew		
1983-87		
2.2L & 2.5L engs	(.6)	.9
2.6L eng	(.9)	1.4
(G) Compressor Clutch Pulley, Renew (w/Hub)		
1983-87		
2.2L & 2.5L engs	(.4)	.5
2.6L eng	(.7)	1.0
(G) Compressor Clutch Assembly, Renew		
1983-87		
2.2L & 2.5L engs	(.6)	.8
2.6L eng	(.9)	1.3
(G) Compressor Front Cover Seal, Renew		
Includes: R&R compressor. Pressure test and charge system.		
1983-87		
2.2L & 2.5L engs	(1.8)	3.1
2.6L eng	(2.3)	3.6

LABOR 28 AIR CONDITIONING 28 LABOR

(Factory Time) Chilton Time

(G) Compressor Rear Cover Seal, Renew
Includes: R&R compressor. Pressure test and charge system.
1983-87
2.2L & 2.5L engs (1.7)............... 3.0
2.6L eng (2.2)............... 3.5

(G) Compressor Center Seal, Renew
Includes: R&R compressor. Pressure test and charge system.
1983-87
2.2L & 2.5L engs (1.9)............... 3.2
2.6L eng (2.4)............... 3.7

(G) Compressor Shaft Gas Seal, Renew
Includes: R&R compressor. Pressure test and charge system.
1983-87
2.2L & 2.5L engs (1.8)............... 3.1
2.6L eng (2.3)............... 3.6

(G) Expansion Valve, Renew
Includes: Pressure test and charge system.
1983-87 (1.0)............... 1.7

(G) Receiver Drier, Renew
Includes: Add partial charge, leak test and charge system.
1983-87 (.9)............... 1.6

(G) Low Pressure Cut Off Switch, Renew
Includes: Charge system.
1983-87 (.9)............... 1.4

(G) High Pressure Cut Off Switch, Renew
1983-87 (.3)............... .5

(G) Clutch Cycling (Thermostatic Control) Switch, Renew
1983-87 (.3)............... .6
pressure activated (.2)............... .4

(G) Condenser Assembly, Renew
Includes: Add partial charge, leak test and charge system.
1983-87 (1.5)............... 2.5
Renew receiver drier add............... .2

(G) Evaporator Coil, Renew
Includes: Add partial charge, leak test and charge system.
1983-87 (2.6)............... 4.5
w/Console add (.2)............... .2

(G) Temperature Control Assembly, Renew
1983-87 (.4)............... .7
Lancer-LeBaron GTS add 2

(G) Push Button Vacuum Switch, Renew
1983-87 (.5)............... .9
Lancer-LeBaron GTS add 2

(G) Blower Motor Switch, Renew
1983-87 (.4)............... .8
Lancer-LeBaron GTS add 2

(G) Temperature Control Cable, Renew
1983-87 (.3)............... .6
Lancer-LeBaron GTS add 2

(G) Blower Motor, Renew
1983-87 (.6)............... .9

(G) Blower Motor Resistor, Renew
1983-87 (.3)............... .4

(G) A.C. On-Off Switch, Renew
1985-87 (.6)............... .8

(G) Vacuum Actuators, Renew
1983-87
outside air door (.2)............... .4
heater/defroster door (.3)............... .6
A/C mode door (.8)............... 1.5

(G) Air Conditioning Hoses, Renew
Includes: Add partial charge, leak test and charge system.
1983-87
Suction hose
2.2L eng (1.1)............... 1.5
2.6L eng (1.3)............... 1.7
Discharge hose
2.2L eng (1.1)............... 1.5
2.6L eng (1.7)............... 2.1
Renew receiver drier add............... .2

PARTS 28 AIR CONDITIONING 28 PARTS

	Part No.	Price
Compressor Assy.		
1983-84	4176059	275.00
1985-87-2.2L	4339456	275.00
2.6L	4339455	275.00
Compressor Shaft Seal Pkg.		
1983-87	3847916	7.75
Pulley & Armature (Drive Clutch)		
2.2L		
1983-84	5210384	101.50
1985-87	3848982	101.75
2.6L		
1983-84	3847764	101.50
1985	3848983	86.25
Field Coil (Drive Clutch)		
1983	3846845	60.75
1984	3848673	60.75
1985-87	3848969	29.50
Check Valve (A.C. Discharge Line)		
1983-87	3847576	1.75
Expansion Valve (H Type)		
1983-85	4176999	59.75
1986-87	3849240	59.75
Receiver Drier		
1983-87	3848217	37.25
Low Pressure Cut Off Switch		
1983-87	5210377	17.25
High Pressure Cutoff Switch		
1983-85	3848674	45.50
1986-87	3849335	45.50
Condenser Assy.		
1983-84	3848015	219.75
1985-87	3848530	219.75
Evaporator Coil		
1983	3848195	341.75
1984	3848840	29.50
1985-87	4339423	317.25
Heater Core		
1983-87	3847943	90.75
Blower Motor		
1983-84	4240426	66.25
1985	3849032	59.00
1986-87	8349266	N.L.
Blower Motor Resistor		
1983-84	3848807	7.75
1985	3849075	N.L.
1986-87	3849235	8.50
Blower Motor Switch		
1983-84	3847940	10.25
1985-87	3849139	10.25
Push Button Vacuum Switch		
1983-84	3847742	27.50
1985-87	3849140	28.50
Water Control Valve		
1983-85-2.2L	3848307	27.75
2.6L	4240422	29.25
1986-87-wo/Turbo	3849199	27.75
w/Turbo	3848460	27.75

LABOR 29 LOCKS, HINGES & WIND. REGULATORS 29 LABOR

(Factory Time) Chilton Time

(G) Hood Hinge, Renew (One)
Does not include painting.
1983-87 (.3)............... .4

(G) Hood Latch, Renew
1983-87 (.2)............... .4

(G) Hood Release Cable, Renew
1983-87 (.3)............... .6

(G) Door Latch, Renew
1983-87
2 dr models (.5)............... .7
4 dr & wagon models (.5)............... .7

(G) Lock Striker Plate, Renew
1983-87 (.2)............... .3

(G) Door Lock Remote Control, Renew
1983-87
All models-one (.5)............... .8

(G) Front Door Window Regulator, Renew
1983-87
2 dr models
manual (.8)............... 1.4
electric (.8)............... 1.5
4 dr & wagon models
manual (.8)............... 1.4
electric (.9)............... 1.5

LABOR 29 LOCKS, HINGES & WIND. REGULATORS 29 LABOR

(Factory Time)	Chilton Time
(G) Rear Door Window Regulator, Renew	
1983-87-manual (.7)	1.3
electric (.9)	1.5
(G) Door Handle (Outside), Renew	
1983-87	
Front-2 dr models (.5)	.7
4 dr & wagon models (.4)	.6
Rear-All models (.4)	.6
Lancer-LeBaron GTS	
Front door (.6)	.9
Rear door (.5)	.7
(G) Trunk Hinge, Renew (One)	
1983-87 (.3)	.5
(G) Liftgate Hinge, Renew	
1983-87-each (.3)	.5

PARTS 29 LOCKS, HINGES & WIND. REGULATORS 29 PARTS

	Part No.	Price
Hood Lock		
1983-87	4103194	6.50
Hood Latch (Inside Release)		
1983-87	5232057	13.00
Hood Hinges		
1983-87-right	4103760	22.25
left	4103761	22.25
Front Door Latch		
1983-right	4184620	35.25
left	4184623	35.25
1984-right	4310018	N.L.
left	4310017	N.L.
1985-87-right	4336378	35.25
left	4336377	35.25
Rear Door Latch		
1983-right	4184624	35.25
left	4184625	35.25
1984-right	4310014	35.25
left	4310015	N.L.
1985-right	4336380	35.25
left	4336381	35.25
1986-87-exc Lancer & GTS		
right	4336380	35.25
left	4336381	35.25
1986-87-Lancer & GTS		
right	4365928	23.75
left	4365929	23.75
Electric Motor (Power Lock)		
1983-84	4184156	60.00
1985-exc. below	4184156	60.00
Lancer, GTS	4310739	60.00
1986-87-exc. below	4396015	60.00
Lancer, GTS	4396016	60.00
Door Handle (Outside)		
1983-87	4184228	11.25
Lock Cylinder & Key (Pkg.)		
1983-87		
wo/Tilt whl	4054805	20.50
w/Tilt whl	3548955	18.25
Window Regulator (Manual)		
Front		
1983-87 (2 door)		
right	4184018	52.00
left	4184019	52.00
1983-87 (4 door & sta. wag.)		
right	4184060	52.00
left	4184061	52.00
Rear		
1983-84-right	4184566	52.00
left	4184567	52.00
1985-right	4310688	51.75
left	4310689	51.75
(exc. Lancer & GTS)		
1986-87-right	4365464	51.75
left	4365465	51.75
(Lancer & GTS)		
1986-87	4310206	51.75
Window Regulator (Power)		
Front		
1983-87 (2 door)		
right	4280436	67.50
left	4280437	67.50
1983-87 (4 door & sta. wag.)		
right	4280432	67.50
left	4280433	67.50
Rear		
1983-84-right	4184616	67.50
left	4184617	67.50
1985-right	4336544	65.50
left	4336545	67.50
(exc. Lancer & GTS)		
1986-87-right	4365474	67.50
left	4365475	67.50
(Lancer & GTS)		
1985-87-right	4336542	67.50
left	4336543	67.50
Power Window Motor		
Front		
1983-right	4280640	N.L.
left	4280641	N.L.
1984-85-right	4184316	173.25
left	4184317	173.25
Rear		
1983-84-right	4184548	173.25
left	4184549	173.25
1985-87-right (exc. below)	4310938	173.25
left	4310939	173.25
1985-87		
Lancer, GTS-right	4310642	173.25
left	4310643	173.25
Limo-right	4339704	153.25
left	4339705	153.25
Lift Gate Latch		
exc. Lancer, Le Baron GTS		
1983-87-man.	4246597	32.00
elec.	4246596	33.25
Lancer, Le Baron GTS		
1985-87	4317001	22.25
Lift Gate Hinges		
exc. Lancer, Le Baron GTS		
1983	4246360	11.00
1984-87	4246837	11.75
Lancer, Le Baron GTS		
1985-87-right	4317030	11.75
left	4317031	11.75
Lift Gate Cylinder & Key		
1983-87	5207386	21.25

LABOR 30 HEAD AND PARKING LAMPS 30 LABOR

(Factory Time)	Chilton Time
(G) Aim Headlamps	
two	.4
four	.6
(M) Headlamp Sealed Beam Bulb, Renew	
Does not include aim headlamps.	
All models-each (.2)	.3
(M) License Lamp Lens, Renew	
All models (.2)	.2
(M) License Lamp Assembly, Renew	
All models (.2)	.3
(M) Turn Signal and Parking Lamp Assy., Renew	
All models (.3)	.4
(M) Turn Signal and Parking Lamp Lens, Renew	
1983-87-each (.2)	.3
(M) Tail Lamp Assembly, Renew	
All models (.3)	.4
(M) Side Marker Lamp Assy., Renew	
All models-each (.2)	.3

PARTS 30 HEAD AND PARKING LAMPS 30 PARTS

	Part No.	Price
Sealed Beam Unit		
(Reliant, Aries)		
1983-87-exc.		
below	153199	16.00
Halogen	153590	31.00
(exc. Reliant, Aries)		
(High & Low Beams)		
1983-84-exc.		
below	153201	11.00
Halogen	153481	16.00
1985-87	153784	16.00
(High Beams)		
1983-84-exc.		
below	153200	11.00
Halogen	153440	16.00
1985-87	153775	16.00
Parking & Turn Signal Lamp Assy.		
(Reliant, Aries)		
1983-84-right	4174002	9.25
left	4174003	9.25
1985-87-right	4321740	9.50
left	4321741	9.50
(Le Baron, Dodge 400)		
1983-85-right	4174200	20.25
left	4174201	20.25
1986-87-right	4321578	21.25
left	4321579	21.25
(Le Baron GTS, Lancer)		
1985-87-right	4321716	11.75
left	4321717	11.75
Tail, Stop & Back-up Lamp Assy.		
(Aries)		
(2 dr. & 4 dr.)		
1983-right	4174422	34.00
left	4174423	34.00
1984 (low cost)		
right	4174804	34.00
left	4174805	34.00
1984 (high cost)		
right	4174808	42.00
left	4174809	42.00
1985-87-right	4321068	64.00
left	4321069	64.00
(sta. wagon)		
1983-87-right	4174096	27.75
left	4174097	27.75
(Reliant)		
(2 dr. & 4 dr.)		
1983-right	4174046	32.25
left	4174047	32.25
1984 (low cost)		
right	4174790	34.00
left	4174791	34.00
1984 (high cost)		
right	4174796	42.00
left	4174797	42.00
1985-87-right	4321062	63.00
left	4321063	63.00
(sta. wagon)		
1983-87-right	4174080	27.75
left	4174081	27.75
(Le Baron, Dodge 400)		
(2 dr. & 4 dr.)		
1983-right	4174214	62.75
left	4174215	62.75
1984-87-right	4174744	90.25
left	4174745	90.25
(sta. wagon)		
1983-87-right	4174080	27.75
left	4174081	27.75
(Lancer, Le Baron GTS)		
1985-87-right	4318794	39.25
left	4318795	39.25
High Mount Stoplight		
1986-87	4364485	16.75
License Lamp Assy.		
1983-87	4176560	30.75
Side Marker Lamp Assy.		
(Reliant & Aries)		
1983-84-right	4174118	6.25
left	4174119	6.25
1985-87-w/Bezel	4321072	10.00
wo/Bezel	4321074	6.25
(Le Baron & Dodge 400)		
1983-87-front	4174224	11.25
rear	4174311	11.25

LABOR 31 WINDSHIELD WIPER & SPEEDOMETER 31 LABOR

(Factory Time)	Chilton Time
(G) Windshield Wiper Motor, Test and Renew	
1983-87 (.4)	.7
(G) Wiper/Washer Switch Assy., Renew	
1983-87	
std column (.8)	1.2
tilt column (1.1)	1.5
(G) Rear Window Wiper/Washer Switch, Renew	
1983-87 (.3)	.5
(G) Rear Window Wiper Motor, Renew	
1983-87 (.3)	.5
Lancer-LeBaron GTS (.5)	.7
(G) Washer Pump, Renew	
1983-87	
front (.3)	.4
rear (.7)	1.0
(G) Wiper Link Assembly, Renew	
1983-87 (.5)	.7
(G) Windshield Wiper Pivot, Renew	
1983-87-one (.5)	.8
(G) Intermittent Wiper Control Module, Renew	
1983-87 (.2)	.4
(G) Speedometer Head, R&R or Renew	
Does not include reset odometer.	
1983-87 (.5)	.8
Reset odometer add	.2
(G) Speedometer Cable and Casing, Renew	
1983	
speed control to trans (.2)	.4
speed control to speedo (.4)	.8
trans to speedo (.5)	.9
1984-87	
upper (.3)	.6
lower (.5)	.9
one piece (.6)	1.0
(G) Speedometer Cable (Inner), Renew or Lubricate	
1983	
speed control to trans (.2)	.4
speed control to speedo (.3)	.5
trans to speedo (.3)	.5
1984-87	
upper (.3)	.5
lower (.4)	.8
one piece (.4)	.8
(G) Electronic Instrument Cluster Assy., Renew	
1984-87 (.4)	.6
(G) Odometer Memory Chip, Renew Electronic Cluster	
1984-87 (.4)	.6
(G) Speedometer Drive Pinion, Renew	
Includes: Renew oil seal.	
1983-87 (.3)	.4
(G) Radio, R&R	
1983-87 (.3)	.7

PARTS 31 WINDSHIELD WIPER & SPEEDOMETER 31 PARTS

	Part No.	Price
Wiper Motor (Windshield)		
1983-84	4205951	106.75
1985-87	4339449	106.75
(Lancer & GTS)		
1985-87	4339450	107.00
Wiper Pivot		
(exc. Lancer, Le Baron GTS)		
1983-87-right	4240511	17.00
left	4240512	17.00
(Lancer, Le Baron GTS)		
1985-87-right	4334132	17.00
left	4334131	17.00
Link w/Bushing (Winshield Wiper)		
(exc. Lancer, Le Baron GTS)		
1983-87-right	3799595	6.50
left	3799600	6.50
(Lancer, Le Baron GTS)		
1985-87-right	4270980	6.50
left	4270976	6.50
Armature Pkg. (Wiper Motor)		
1983-84	3799087	27.75
Crank w/Pin (Windshield Wiper)		
(exc. Lancer, Le Baron GTS)		
1983-87	3799597	4.50
(Lancer, Le Baron GTS)		
1985-87	4270978	2.50

PARTS 31 WINDSHIELD WIPER & SPEEDOMETERS 31 PARTS

	Part No.	Price
Wiper Motor (Lift Gate)		
(exc. Lancer, Le Baron GTS)		
1983-87	4240484	106.75
(Lancer, Le Baron GTS)		
1985-87	4270773	120.25
Washer Pump & Seal Pkg.		
(exc. Lancer, Le Baron GTS)		
1983-85	3799090	21.50
1986-87-snap-in	4334569	21.25
(Lancer, Le Baron GTS)		
1985-87	3799462	21.25
Washer Reservoir (Front)		
(exc. Lancer, Le Baron GTS)		
1983-84	3799713	7.00
1985	3799858	7.00
1986-87-w/Hole	4334564	11.00
wo/Hole	4334562	11.00
(Lancer, Le Baron GTS)		
1985-87	4270997	18.25
Washer, Reservoir (Rear)		
1983-87-exc. below	3799684	14.25
Lancer, Le Baron GTS	3799795	14.00
Washer Pump Filter		
1983-87	3799324	4.25
Wiper & Washer Switch		
1983-87-2 sp.	3747914	34.25
Interm.-wo/Tilt whl.		
1983-84	4221125	36.00
1985	4221232	36.00
1986-87	4221899	36.25
Interm.-w/Tilt whl.		
1983-85	4221233	60.25
1986-87	4221902	60.50
Rear Wiper Switch		
1983-87	4221080	25.75
Speedometer Cable & Casing		
1983		
41″ long (upper)	4220748	13.25
25″ long (lower)	4220742	14.75
1984		
44″ long (upper)	4312332	13.25
23″ long (lower)	4312334	12.75
1985-87		
44″ long (upper)	4312332	13.25
22″ long (lower)	4312816	12.75
Speedometer Cable to Speed Control		
1983	4220745	13.25
1984-87	4312332	13.25
Speedometer Assy.		
Reliant, Aries, Le Baron, Town & Country		
1983-85 m.p.h.	4051479	56.75
125 m.p.h.	4051480	78.00
1984-87-85 m.p.h.	4051786	56.75
125 m.p.h.	4051793	78.00
Lancer & GTS		
1985	4051831	79.25
1986-87	4375081	80.25

LABOR 32 LIGHT SWITCHES & WIRING 32 LABOR

(Factory Time)	Chilton Time
(G) Headlamp Switch, Renew	
1983-87 (.3)	.4
(G) Headlamp Dimmer Switch, Renew	
1983-87 (.3)	.6
(G) Back-Up Lamp Switch, Renew	
(w/Manual Trans)	
1983-87 (.2)	.4
(G) Stop Light Switch, Renew	
1983-87 (.3)	.4
w/Cruise control add (.1)	.1
(G) Neutral Safety Switch, Renew	
1983-87 (.3)	.4
(G) Parking Brake Warning Lamp Switch, Renew	
1983-87 (.2)	.3
(G) Turn Signal Switch, Renew	
1983-87	
std column (.5)	1.0
tilt column (.8)	1.5
(M) Turn Signal or Hazard Warning Flasher, Renew	
1983-87 (.2)	.3
(G) Horn Switch, Renew	
1983-87 (.2)	.3
(G) Horn Relay, Renew	
1983-87 (.2)	.3
(G) Horn, Renew	
1983-87-one (.2)	.4
(G) Wiring Harness, Renew	
1983-87	
Main Harness to Dash (1.2)	3.0
Body Harness	
2 & 4 dr models (.7)	1.3
sta wag models (1.3)	2.5

PARTS 32 LIGHT SWITCHES & WIRING 32 PARTS

	Part No.	Price
Headlamp Switch		
1983	4221248	16.00
1984-87-exc. below	4221405	17.25
Lancer, GTS	4221407	17.25
Stoplight Switch		
1983-84-exc. below	3747993	8.00
w/spd. cont.	3747995	11.00
1985-87	4221651	15.50
Headlamp Beam Selector Switch		
1983-87-wo/tilt whl.	4221198	11.75
w/tilt whl.	4221200	13.25
Turn Signal & Hazard Warning Switch		
(wo/cornering lamp)		
1983-84-wo/tilt whl.	4221337	38.50
w/tilt whl.	4221304	47.00
1985-87-wo/tilt whl.	4221680	38.00
w/tilt whl.	4221304	47.00
(w/cornering lamp)		
1983-84-wo/tilt whl.	4221338	40.75
w/tilt whl.	4221305	53.50
1985-87-wo/tilt whl.	4221681	52.00
w/tilt whl.	4221305	53.50
Turn Signal Flasher		
1983-87-w/2 lamp	3837161	4.25
w/3 lamp	3837162	4.25
Hazard Warning Flasher		
1983-87	2932877	4.50
Backup Switch		
1983-84-M.T.	2258404	9.50
A.T.	4057750	8.75
1985-87-M.T.	4221587	10.00
A.T.	4057750	8.75
Horn Assy.		
1983-87-High note	2808869	24.00
Low note	4222288	18.25
Horn Relay		
1983-87-exc. below	3747298	6.25
Le Baron	4221670	8.75
Wiring Harness		
Order by model and description.		

LABOR 33 GLASS 33 LABOR

(Factory Time)	Chilton Time
(G) Windshield Glass, Renew	
Includes: Replace weatherstrip if necessary, where applicable.	
1983-87 (1.8)	2.8
w/Cabriolet conv roof add (.6)	.6
(G) Front Door Glass, Renew	
1983-87	
2 dr models (.6)	.9
4 dr models (.7)	1.0
2 dr-folding top (.7)	1.0
(G) Rear Door Glass, Renew	
1983-87	
fixed (.5)	.8
movable (.7)	1.2

LABOR 33 GLASS 33 LABOR

(Factory Time)	Chilton Time
(G) Quarter Window Glass, Renew	
1983-87	
2 dr-rear-movable (1.0)	1.4
2 dr-front-fixed (1.0)	1.4
4 dr	
Aries-Reliant (.8)	1.2
Lancer-LeBaron GTS (1.4)	2.0
(G) Rear Door Fixed Vent Glass, Renew	
1983-87	
Lancer-LeBaron GTS (.6)	1.0
All other models (.8)	1.2
(G) Liftgate Glass, Renew	
1983-87 (1.1)	1.5
(G) Rear Window Glass, Renew	
1983-87 (1.6)	3.0
w/Padded roof add (2.9)	4.0
Cabriolet conv roof equip add (1.3)	2.0

LABOR 34 CRUISE CONTROL 34 LABOR

(Factory Time)	Chilton Time
(G) Speed Control Servo Assy., Renew	
1983-87 (.4)	.6
w/Turbo add (.1)	.1
(G) Speed Control Cable, Renew	
1983-87 (.4)	.7
(G) Speed Control Turn Signal Lever Switch, Renew	
1983-87	
std column (.5)	.9
tilt column (1.0)	1.5
(G) Speed Control Wiring Harness, Renew	
1983-87 (.3)	.6
(G) Speed Control Safety (Cut-Out) Switch, Renew	
1983-87 (.3)	.5
(G) Electronic Speed Control Module, Renew	
1985-87 (.2)	.4

PARTS 34 CRUISE CONTROL 34 PARTS

	Part No.	Price
Cruise Control Servo		
1983-87	4179306	129.75
1986-87	4307221	130.00
Cruise Control Switch & Lever		
(wo/tilt whl.)		
1983	3747895	41.75
1984	4221455	41.75
1985-87	4221482	41.75
(w/tilt whl.)		
1983	3747881	41.75
1984	4221482	41.75
1985-87	3747881	41.75
Electronic Cruise Control Switch		
1985-87	4342207	41.75
Module (ECC)		
1985-87	4318829	116.50
Vacuum Motor (ECC)		
1985-87	4318819	27.50
Valve Body (ECC)		
1985-87	4318818	103.75
Cruise Control Switch (Clutch)		
1983-84	4221677	13.50
1985-87	4221697	21.75
Cruise Control Switch (on Brake)		
1983-84	3747995	11.00
1985-87	4221651	15.50
Cruise Control Cable		
1983-2.2L	4241773	22.00
2.6L	4241774	22.00
1984-87-2.2L	4288055	24.25
2.6L	4288059	24.25

GROUP INDEX

ALPHABETICAL INDEX

Chrysler Corporation
Front Wheel Drive Cars

DODGE DAYTONA • PLYMOUTH LASER

YEAR IDENTIFICATION

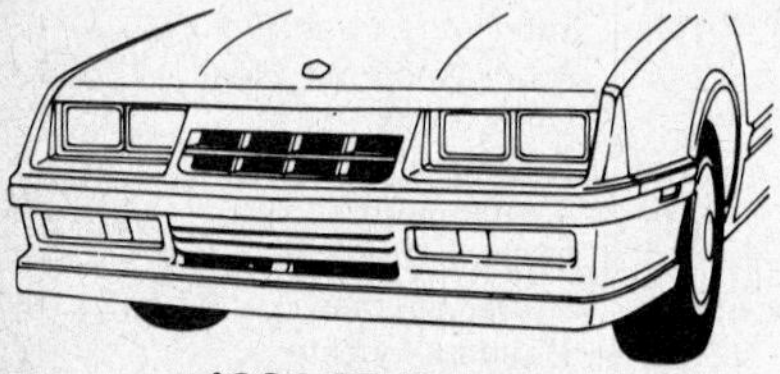

1984-87 Daytona

1984-87 Daytona Turbo

1984-87 Laser

1984-87 Laser XE

VEHICLE IDENTIFICATION NUMBER (VIN)

It is important for servicing and ordering parts to be certain of the vehicle and engine identification. The VIN (vehicle identification number) is a 13 or 17 digit number visible through the windshield on the driver's side of the dash, and contains the vehicle and engine identification codes. It can be interpreted as follows:

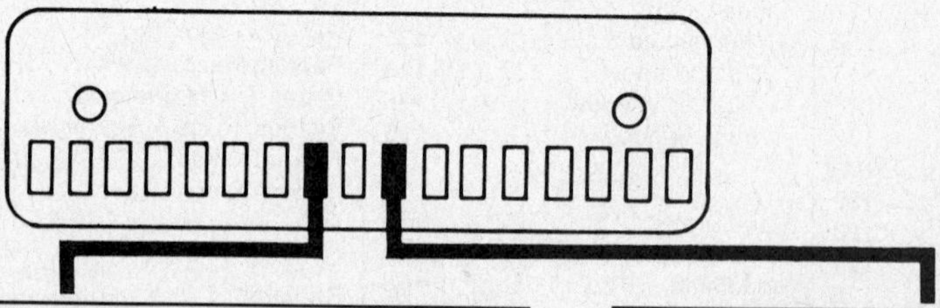

ENGINE CODE

Code	Cu. In.	Liters	Cyl	Carb. bbl	Eng. Mfg.
A (84-85)	98	1.6	4	2	Peugeot
B (83)	105	1.7	4	2	VW
C (83-87)	135	2.2	4	2	Chrysler
D (83-87)	135	2.2	4	EFI	Chrysler
E (84-87)	135	2.2	4	Turbo	Chrysler
G (83-85)	156	2.6	4	2	Mitsubishi
K (86-87)	153	2.5	4	EFI	Chrysler

MODEL YEAR CODE

Code	Year
C	82
D	83
E	84
F	85
G	86
H	87

The seventeen digit Vehicle Identification Number can be used to determine engine application and model year. The tenth indicates the model year, and the eighth digit identifies engine displacement.

TUNE-UP SPECIFICATIONS

Year	Eng. V.I.N. Code	No. Cyl. Displ. Cu. In.	Eng. Mfg.	h.p.	Spark Plugs Orig. Type	Spark Plugs Gap (in.)	Ignition Timing (deg.) Man. Trans.	Ignition Timing (deg.) Auto Trans.	Intake Valve Opens (deg.)▪	Fuel Pump Pressure (psi)	Idle Speed (rpm) Man. Trans.	Idle Speed (rpm) Auto Trans.	Valve Lash (in.) Intake	Valve Lash (in.) Exhaust
'84-'86	A	4-98	Peugeot	64	RN12YC	.035	12B	12B	16.5	4.5-6.0	850	1000	.012H	.014H
'83	A	4-105	VW	63	65PR	.035	20B	12B	14	4.4-5.8	900	900	.008-.012H	.016-.020H
'83-'86	C	4-135	Chrysler	All	RN12YC	.035	10B	10B	16 ⑤	4.5-6.0	900	900	Hyd.	Hyd.
'84-'86	D ⑦	4-135	Chrysler	99	RN12YC	.035	12B	12B	10.5	36	850	750	Hyd.	Hyd.
'84-'86	E ⑥	4-135	Chrysler	146	RN12YC	.035	12B	12B	10	53	950	950	Hyd.	Hyd.
'83-'85	G	4-156	Mitsubishi	92	RN11YC4	③	7B	7B	25	4.5-6.0	800 ①	800 ①	.006H ⑧	.010H
'86-'87	K	4-153	Chrysler	100	RN12YC	.035	⑨	⑨	12	14.5 ⑩	⑨	⑨	Hyd.	Hyd.

NOTE: The underhood specifications sticker often reflects tune-up specification changes made in production. Sticker figures must be used if they disagree with those in this chart. Part numbers in this chart are not recommendations by Chilton for any product by brand name.

▪ Before top dead center
Hyd.—Hydraulic
H—Hot
C—Cold
① 750 rpm-Canada
③ .035-.040 RN11Y—.030 in For Canada
⑤ Shelby and Hi Performance—10.5° BTDC
Turbocharged—10° BTDC
⑥ Turbo with multipoint fuel injection
⑦ EFI with single point fuel injection
⑧ Jet valve clearance—.010 in.
⑨ Refer to underhood emission control information label
⑩ '86-'87 with multipoint fuel injection—55 lbs

FIRING ORDERS

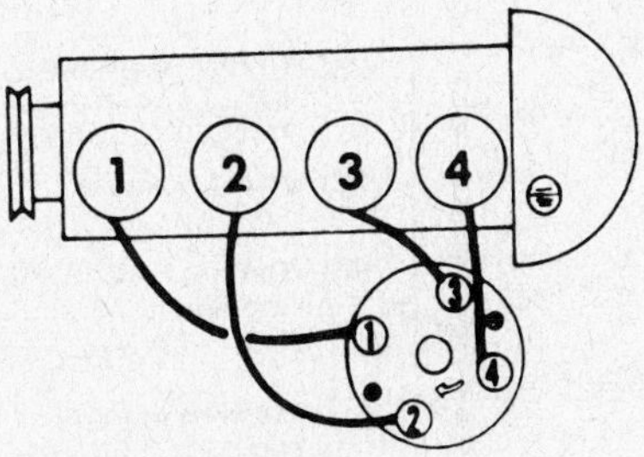

Chrysler Corp. 1.7L
Engine Firing Order: 1-3-4-2
Distributor Rotation: Clockwise

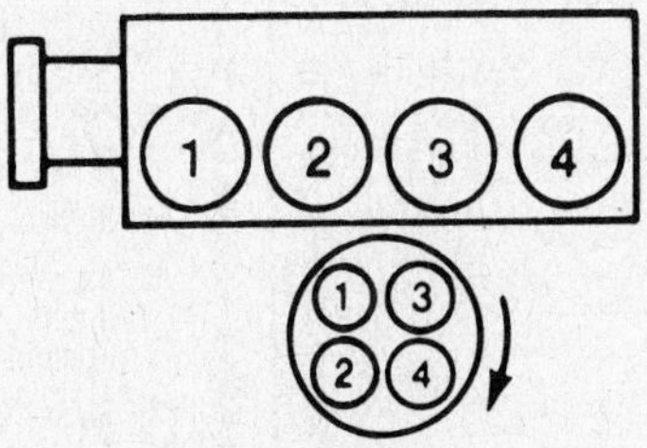

Chrysler Corp. 2.2L/2.5L
Engine Firing Order: 1-3-4-2
Distributor Rotation: Clockwise

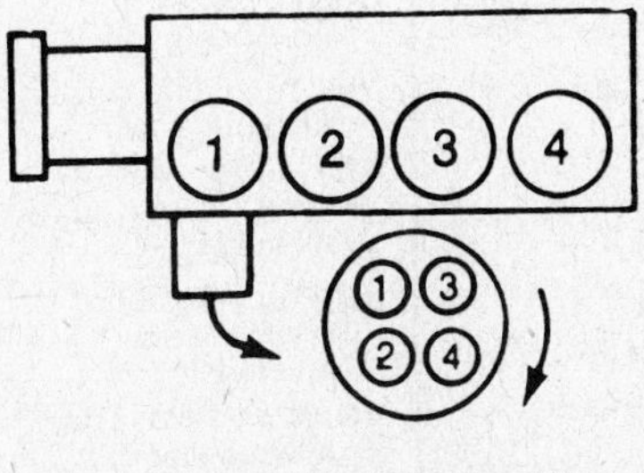

Chrysler Corp. (Mitsubishi) 2.6L
Engine firing order: 1–3–4–2
Distributor rotation: clockwise

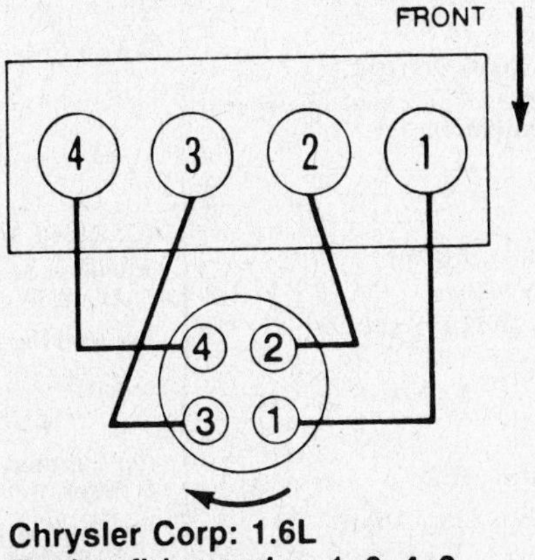

Chrysler Corp: 1.6L
Engine firing order: 1–3–4–2
Distributor rotation: clockwise

WHEEL ALIGNMENT SPECIFICATIONS

Caster is not adjustable

Year and Model	Caster	Front Camber Range (deg.)	Front Camber Preferred	Rear Camber Range (deg.)	Rear Camber Preferred	Toe-In (inches) Front	Toe-In (inches) Rear
'86–'87 LeBaron GTS, New Yorker Laser	1 3/16P ①	1/4N–3/4P	5/16P	1 1/4N–1/4P	1/2P	1/16	0
DODGE '83–'85 Aries, 400, 600, 600 ES Daytona, Lancer	1 3/16P ①	1/4N–3/4P	5/16P	1N–0	1/2N	1/16	0
'86–'87 Aries, 400, 600, Daytona, Lancer, Shadow	1 3/16P ①	1/4N–3/4P	5/16P	1 1/4N–1/4P	1/2P	1/16	0

LABOR — SERVICE BAY OPERATIONS — LABOR

(Factory Time) — Chilton Time

COOLING

(M) Winterize Cooling System
Includes: Run engine to check for leaks, tighten all hose connections. Test radiator and pressure cap, drain radiator and engine block. Add anti-freeze and refill system.
All models 5

(M) Thermostat, Renew
1984-87 (.4) 6

(M) Drive Belts, Adjust
All models-one 2
each adtnl 1

(M) Drive Belts, Renew
1984-87
Fan & alter (.2) 3
Air pump (.3) 4
Pow str (.4) 6
w/A.C. add (.1) 1

(M) Radiator Hoses, Renew
1984-87-upper (.3) 4
lower (.4) 6

FUEL

(M) Carburetor Air Cleaner, Service
All models 3

(M) Carburetor, Adjust (On Car)
Includes: Adjust idle mixture and idle speed. Check and reset ignition timing.
All models
Holly 2 bbl 6
All others 5

(G) Automatic Choke, Renew
1984 (.7) 1.0

(G) Carburetor Choke Vacuum Kick, Adjust
1984
Holly (.2) 3

BRAKES

(G) Brake Pedal Free Play, Adjust
All models 3

(G) Brakes, Adjust (Minor)
Includes: Adjust brake shoes, fill master cylinder.
two wheels 4

CHILTON'S 10 POINT SAFETY CHECK

CHECK OPERATION & CONDITION OF THE FOLLOWING ITEMS:

1. Legal Registration (serial no.)
2. Tires & Wheels
3. Brake System (R&R all wheels)
4. Light Systems & Signals
5. Accelerator Linkage, Neutral Safety Switch, Shift Indicator Pointer & Seat Position Locks
6. Glass, Mirrors, Door Locks, Seat Belts & Harness
7. Wipers, Washers & Defrosters
8. Frame, Steering, Shocks, Front & Rear Suspension
9. Fuel & Exhaust Systems
10. Road Test Vehicle

All models 1.0
Exhaust Smog Analysis, add 4

(Factory Time) — Chilton Time

(G) Bleed Brakes (Four Wheels)
Includes: Add fluid.
All models (.4) 6

(M) Parking Brake, Adjust
All models 4

LUBRICATION SERVICE

(M) Lubricate Chassis, Change Oil & Filter
Includes: Inspect and correct all fluid levels.
All models 6
Install grease fittings add 1

(M) Engine Oil & Filter, Change
Includes: Inspect and correct all fluid levels.
All models 4

(Factory Time) — Chilton Time

(M) Lubricate Chassis
Includes: Inspect and correct all fluid levels.
All models 4
Install grease fittings add 1

WHEELS

(G) Wheels, Balance
one 3
each adtnl 2

(M) Wheel, Renew
one 5

(M) Wheels, Rotate (All)
All models 5

ELECTRICAL

(G) Aim Headlamps
two 4
four 6

(M) Headlamp Sealed Beam Bulb, Renew
Does not include aim headlamps.
All models-each (.2) 3

(M) License Lamp Lens, Renew
All models (.2) 2

(M) License Lamp Assembly, Renew
All models (.2) 3

(M) Turn Signal and Parking Lamp Assy., Renew
All models (.3) 4

(M) Tail Lamp Assembly, Renew
All models (.5) 7

(M) Side Marker Lamp Assy., Renew
All models-each (.2) 3

(M) Turn Signal or Hazard Warning Flasher, Renew
All models (.2) 3

(G) Horn Relay, Renew
All models (.2) 3

(G) Horn, Renew
All models-one (.2) 4

(M) Battery Cables, Renew
All models
positive (.5) 6
negative (.2) 2

LABOR 1 TUNE UP 1 LABOR

	(Factory Time)	Chilton Time
(G) Compression Test		
Four-1984-87		.6

(G) Engine Tune Up, (Electronic Ignition)

Includes: Test battery and clean connections. Tighten manifold and carburetor mounting bolts. Check engine compression, clean and adjust or renew spark plugs. Test resistance of spark plug cables. Inspect distributor cap and rotor, reluctor and pick up plate. Check vacuum advance operation. Reset ignition timing. Adjust idle mixture and idle speed. Service air cleaner. Inspect crankcase ventilation system. Inspect and adjust drive belts. Inspect choke operation and adjust or free up. Check operation of EGR valve.

	(Factory Time)	Chilton Time
Four-1984-87		1.5
w/Turbo add		.5

LABOR 2 IGNITION SYSTEM 2 LABOR

	(Factory Time)	Chilton Time
(G) Spark Plugs, Clean and Reset or Renew		
1984-87	(.5)	.6
(G) Ignition Timing, Reset		
1984-87	(.3)	.4
(G) Spark Control Computer, Renew (SCC)		
1984-87	(.3)	1.0
(G) Distributor Assembly, Renew		
Includes: Reset ignition timing.		
1984-87	(.4)	.6
(G) Distributor, R&R and Recondition		
Includes: Reset ignition timing.		
1984-87	(.9)	1.5
(G) Distributor Pick-Up Plate and Coil Assy., Renew (Hall Effect)		
Does not require R&R of distributor.		
1984-87		
2.2L eng	(.3)	.6
(G) Distributor Cap and/or Rotor, Renew		
1984-87	(.2)	.4
(G) Ignition Coil, Renew		
1984-87	(.2)	.4
(G) Ignition Cables, Renew		
1984-87	(.2)	.4
(G) Ignition Switch, Renew		
1984-87		
std column	(.4)	.8
tilt column	(.4)	.9
(G) Ignition Key Warning Buzzer, Renew		
1984-87	(.2)	.4
(G) Ignition Switch Time Delay Relay, Renew		
1984-87	(.2)	.3
(G) Ignition Key Buzzer/Chime Switch, Renew		
1984-87		
std column	(.6)	1.2
tilt column	(.5)	1.0
(G) Ignition Lock Housing, Renew		
1984-87-std colm	(.8)	1.3
Tilt Column		
console shift	(1.1)	1.7

PARTS 2 IGNITION SYSTEM 2 PARTS

	Part No.	Price
(1) Distributor Assy.		
1984-85-exc. Turbo	4240470	66.25
Turbo	5213525	79.75
1986-87-exc. Turbo	5226575	N.L.
Turbo	5213525	79.75
(2) Distributor Cap		
1984-85	4240446	8.25
1986-87	5226527	N.L.
(3) Rotor Assy.		
1984-85	5213728	8.25
1986-87	5226535	8.25
(4) Switch (w/Plate)		
1984-85-exc. Turbo	5213522	32.00
Turbo	5213524	44.50
1986-87-exc. Turbo	5226616	26.50
Turbo	5226617	N.L.
1986-87-2.5L	5226616	26.50
Ballast Resistor		
1984	4106140	4.00
Coil		
1984-87	4176009	26.75
Ignition Switch		
1984-87-w/tilt whl.	4221218	23.00
wo/tilt whl.	3747882	14.50
Ignition Key Buzzer Switch		
1984-87-w/tilt whl.	3488432	7.50
wo/tilt whl.	4221497	7.00
wo/floor shf.	4221954	10.25

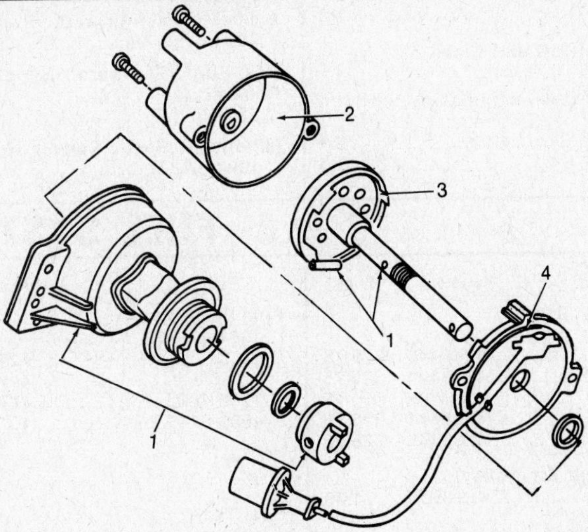

	Part No.	Price
Ignition Wire Set		
1984-87	4240435	19.75
Power Module		
(wo/Turbo)		
1984	5213581	105.00
1985-87-exc. Calif.	5226765	105.00
Calif.	5226648	140.00
(w/Turbo)		
1984	5213574	140.00
1985-87	5226766	105.00

LABOR 3 FUEL SYSTEM 3 LABOR

(Factory Time) — Chilton Time

(G) Fuel Pump, Test
All models
- mechanical 3
- electric 4

(M) Carburetor Air Cleaner, Service
All models 3

(G) Carburetor Idle Speed and Mixture, Adjust
Includes: Check and reset ignition timing.
All models
- Holly-2 bbl 6
- All others 5

(G) Idle Solenoid, Renew
1984 (.4) 6

(G) Coolant Temperature Sensor/Switch, Renew
1984-87 (.2) 4

(G) Throttle Position Sensor, Renew
1984-87
- 2.2L Turbo (.2) 4

(G) Accelerator Pump, Renew
1984
- Holly (.4) 8
- All others (.8) 1.1

(G) Air Cleaner Vacuum Sensor, Renew
1984-one (.2) 3

(G) Carburetor Assembly, Renew
Includes: All necessary adjustments.
1984
- Holly (.8) 1.3
- All others (.7) 1.2

(G) Carburetor, R&R and Clean or Recondition
Includes: All necessary adjustments.
1984
- Holly (1.6) 2.4
- All others (2.5) 3.5

(G) Carburetor Needle and Seat, Renew
Includes: Adjust float level, idle speed and mixture.
1984
- Holly (.7) 1.1
- All others (1.1) 1.5

(G) Fuel Filter, Renew
1984-87
- in line (.2) 3
- in tank (.5) 8

(G) Fuel Pump, Renew
1984-87
- mechanical (.5) 7
- electric (.6) 1.0

Add pump test if performed.

(G) Fuel Tank, Renew
1984-87 (1.2) 1.6

(G) Fuel Gauge (Tank Unit), Renew
1984-87 (.7) 1.0

(G) Fuel Gauge (Dash Unit), Renew
1984-87 (.4) 8

(G) Intake Manifold, Renew
1984-87
- 2.2L eng (2.0) 3.7

w/Turbo add (.6) 6

(G) Intake and Exhaust Manifold Gaskets, Renew
1984-87
- 2.2L eng (1.9) 3.5

w/Turbo add (.6) 6

TURBOCHARGER

(G) Turbocharger Assy., Renew
Includes: Renew gaskets.
1984-87 (2.7) 3.5

(G) Fuel Pressure Regulator, Renew
1984-87 (.3) 5

(G) Vehicle Speed Sensor, Renew
1984-87 (.3) 6

(G) Detonation Sensor, Renew
1984-87 (.2) 4

(G) Change Temperature Sensor, Renew
1984-87 (.2) 4

(G) Fuel Pump, Renew (In Tank)
1984-87 (1.0) 1.6

ELECTRONIC FUEL INJECTION

(G) Throttle Body, Renew
1984-87 (.5) 9

(G) Fuel Pressure Regulator, Renew
1984-87 (.2) 4
w/Turbo add (.1) 1

(G) Fuel Pump, Renew
1984-87 (.6) 9

(G) Fuel Inlet Chamber, Renew
1984-87 (.4) 7

(G) Automatic Idle Speed Assy., Renew
1984-87
- motor (.3) 5
- adapter (.3) 5

(G) Fuel Injector Rail, Renew
1984-87 (.6) 1.0

(G) Fuel Injector, Renew
1984-87
- wo/Turbo (.3) 5
- w/Turbo
  - one (.4) 6
  - each adtnl (.1) 2

(G) Logic Module, Renew
1984-87 (.2) 3

(G) Power Module, Renew
1984-87 (.3) 4

(G) M.A.P. Sensor, Renew
1984-87 (.4) 6

(G) Throttle Position Sensor (Potentiometer), Renew
1984-87 (.2) 3

PARTS 3 FUEL SYSTEM 3 PARTS

	Part No.	Price
Carburetor Assy. (Holley)		
1984-M.T.		
R-40064-1	4288440	325.75
R-40061-1	4288444	325.75
A.T.		
R-40065-1	4288441	325.75
R-40062-1	4288445	325.75
Carburetor Repair Kit (Holley)		
1984	4293856	31.00
Carburetor Needle & Seat		
1984	4131116	6.50
Carburetor Pump Diaphragm		
1984	4131121	17.25
Fuel Pump Assy.		
1984-87-exc. below	4293802	36.00
Turbo	4279917	217.00
1985-E.F.I.	4279951	225.25
1986-87-E.F.I.	4075445	36.00
Fuel Tank		
1984-exc. below	4279605	141.50
E.F.I., Turbo	4279603	140.00
1985-w/E.F.I.	4279657	141.75
Turbo	4279603	140.00
1986-87	4279603	140.00
Fuel Gauge (Tank Unit)		
1984-85-exc. below	4051867	30.50
E.F.I.	4279950	32.50
Turbo	4051895	30.50
1986-87	4051663	30.25
Fuel Gauge (Dash)		
1984-85	4051805	45.25
1986-87	4375130	45.25
Fuel Filter		
1984	4213582	9.25
1985-87	4279987	23.25
Manifold Gasket (Intake & Exhaust)		
1984-87	4105745	6.75

PARTS 3 ELECTRONIC FUEL INJECTION 3 PARTS

	Part No.	Price
Throttle Body (exc. Turbo)		
1984	4275617	735.50
1985	4342948	N.L.
1986-87-2.2L	4300265	290.00
2.5L	4300266	290.00
Throttle Body (Turbo)		
1984	4268801	325.00
1985	4288276	325.00
1986-87	4307255	325.00
(1) Fitting Kit (Hose)		
1984-85	4287316	11.00
1986-87	4300252	6.75

PARTS 3 ELECTRONIC FUEL INJECTION 3 PARTS

	Part No.	Price
(2) Injector Kit		
1984-85	4275985	160.00
1986-87 (seals)	4300254	6.50
Injector (w/O-rings)		
1986-87	4300257	53.55
(3) Hose & Seal Kit (Pressure Regulator)		
1984-85	4287324	5.25
(4) Gasket (Intake Manifold)		
1984-85	4275531	1.75
(5) Potentiometer (Kit)		
exc. Turbo		
1984	4287743	32.00
1985	4179848	32.00
Turbo		
1984	4221396	N.L.
1985-87	4179849	32.00
Throttle Position Sensor		
exc. Turbo		
1986-87	5226509	29.00
(6) Housing Kit (AIS)		
1984-85	4287730	17.75
(7) Regulator Kit		
1984-85	4287320	53.25
1986-87	4300263	60.00
(8) Motor Kit (AIS)		
1984-85	4287712	64.00
(9) "O" Ring Kit (AIS Motor)		
1984-85	4287714	3.50
Motor (w/O-ring)		
1986-87	4300264	N.L.
Detonation Sensor		
1984-87-wo/Turbo	5213629	23.75
w/Turbo	4318118	23.75
Temperature Sensor		
1986-87	4330251	52.50
M.A.P. Sensor		
1984-wo/Turbo	4318114	66.00
Turbo	4318115	66.00
1985-wo/Turbo	5226223	51.00
Turbo	5226224	56.25
1986-87-wo/Turbo	4419315	51.00
w/Turbo	4419316	54.75

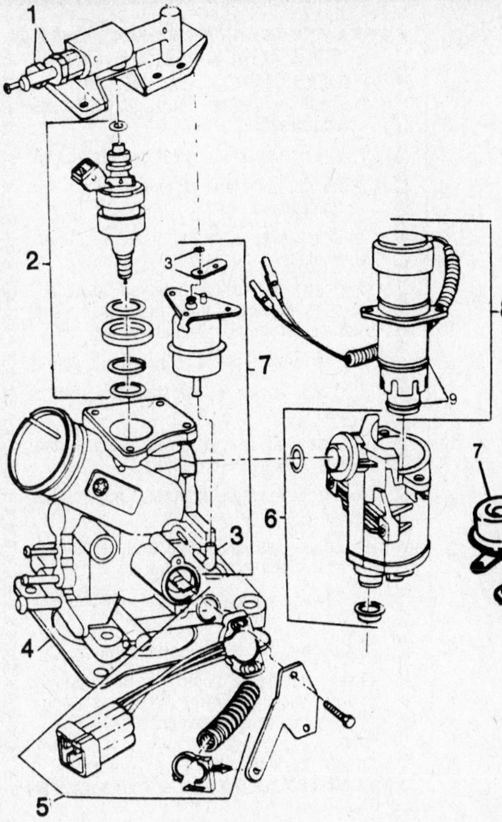

	Part No.	Price
Fuel Injectors (Turbo)		
1984	4275312	56.75
1985-87	4306024	53.75
Regulator (Fuel Pressure-Turbo)		
1984-87	4275313	53.75
Fuel Rail (Turbo)		
1984	4275301	3.25
1985-87	4275555	39.25

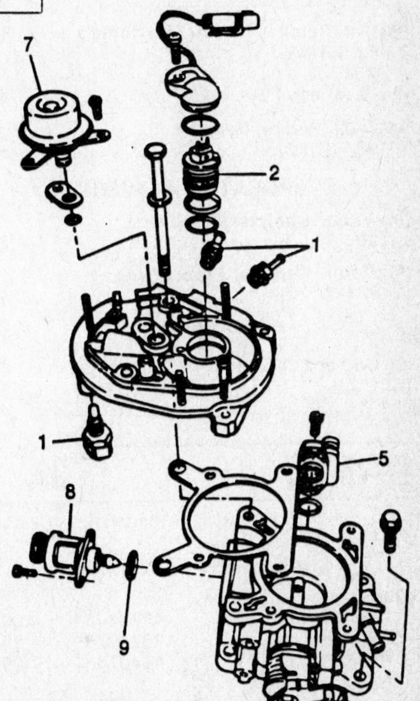

EFI 1986 and later

PARTS 3 TURBOCHARGER SYSTEM 3 PARTS

	Part No.	Price
(1) E.G.R. Valve		
Replacement E.G.R. valve must be ordered according to the stamping number on the original valve.		
(2) Elbow (Compressor Inlet)		
1984-87	4105461	30.50
(3) Gasket (Inlet Elbow)		
1984-87	4227973	.50
(4) Turbocharger Assy.		
1984	4105794	566.25
1985-87	4105800	567.00
(5) Oxygen Sensor		
1984-87	4301346	36.75
(6) Hose Connector		
1984-87		
up to 5-84	5214609	6.00
from 5-84	4323444	6.00
(7) Strap (Vane Hose)		
1984-87	4105719	2.00

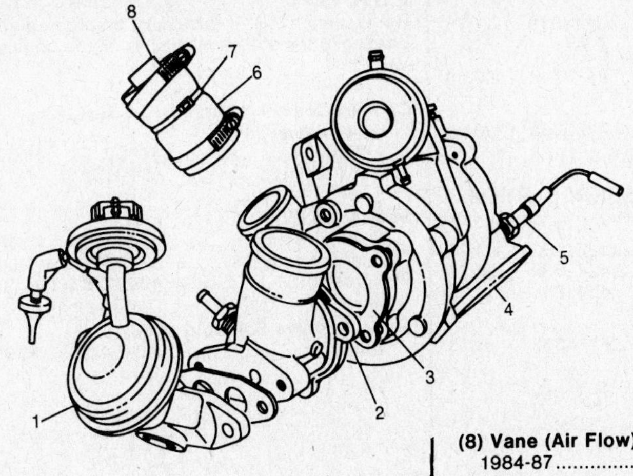

	Part No.	Price
(8) Vane (Air Flow)		
1984-87	4105465	3.00

LABOR 3A EMISSION CONTROLS 3A LABOR

(Factory Time) Chilton Time

CRANKCASE EMISSION

(M) Crankcase Vent Valve, Renew
1984-87 (.2) 3

AIR INJECTION SYSTEM

(G) Air Pump, Renew
1984
2.2L eng (.4) 7

(G) Injection Tube and Aspirator Valve Assy., Renew
1984-2.2L eng
ex manif mount (.5) 8
to conv
one or both (.4) 6
EFI engs
to conv (.5) 8

(G) Air Pump Diverter/Switching Valve, Renew
1984
2.2L eng (.3) 5

Aspirator Valve, Renew
1984-87 (.3) 5

EVAPORATIVE EMISSION

(M) Vapor Canister, Renew
1984-87 (.3) 4

(M) Vapor Canister Filter, Renew
1984-87 (.2) 3

E.G.R. SYSTEM

(G) Coolant Vacuum Switch, Renew (CCEVS)
1984 (.3) 4

CHILTON'S EMISSION CONTROL TUNE-UP

1. Clean or renew P.C.V. valve, hoses and filter.
2. Check fuel tank cap for sealing ability.
3. Check fuel tank and fuel lines for leakage.
4. Check evaporation canister and filter. Replace if necessary.
5. Check engine compression to determine leakage of unburned gases. (Add time for items of interference).
6. Test and clean or renew spark plugs.
7. Check engine oil dipstick for sealing ability.
8. Test exhaust system with analyzer and check system for leakage.
9. Check exhaust manifold heat valve for operation.
10. Adjust ignition timing and carburetor idle speed and mixture.
11. Check automatic choke mechanism for free operation.
12. Inspect air cleaner and element.
13. On models so equipped, test distributor vacuum control switch and transmission control switch.

Four **1.3**
For repairs made, charge accordingly.

(Factory Time) Chilton Time

(G) Exhaust Gas Recirculation Control Valve, Renew
1984-87
2.2L eng (.6) 8
w/Turbo add (.2) 2

(G) E.G.R. Back Pressure Valve, Renew
1984-87 (.2) 3

(G) E.G.R. and Purge Control Solenoid Bank, Renew
1984-87 (.2) 3

(G) Coolant Control Vacuum Valve, Renew (CCEGR)
1984-87-one (.3) 4
both (.4) 6

EFE SYSTEM

(G) Oxygen Sensor, Renew
1984-87
2.2L eng (.2) 4

(G) Detonation Sensor, Renew
1984-87 (.2) 4

HEATED INLET AIR SYSTEM

(M) Carburetor Air Cleaner, Service
1984 3

(G) Air Cleaner Vacuum Sensor, Renew
1984-one (.2) 3

PARTS 3A EMISSION CONTROLS 3A PARTS

CRANKCASE EMISSION

	Part No.	Price
Crankcase Vent Valve		
1984-87-wo/Turbo	4273145	4.00
Turbo	3671076	4.25
E.F.I.	4343766	7.00

AIR INJECTION SYSTEM

	Part No.	Price
Air Pump Assy.		
1984-85	4267227	162.50
Air Pump Pulley		
1984-85	5203585	4.75
Air Pump Drive Pulley		
1984-85	5214518	7.75
Air Pump Diverter Valve		
1984-85	4179719	30.50
Switch and Relief Valve		
1984-85	4275053	30.00

EVAPORATIVE EMISSION SYSTEM

	Part No.	Price
Vapor Canister		
1984-85-3 ported	4271982	49.25
4 ported	4241838	52.75
1986-87	4241838	52.75
Valve (Bowl Vent)		
1984	5214336	4.75
By Pass Valve (Tank Vent)		
1984-87	4185414	15.50
Vacuum Solenoid (E.F.I.)		
1986-87	5227169	20.50
Quad Vacuum Solenoid (Turbo)		
1986-87	5226352	57.00
Check Valve		
1986-87-E.F.I.	4306923	1.50

EXHAUST GAS RECIRCULATION SYSTEM

E.G.R. Valve
Replacement E.G.R. valve must be ordered according to the stamping number on the original valve.

	Part No.	Price
Coolant Control Switch (C.C.E.G.R.)		
1984-85 (stamped)		
4030351	4049277	17.50
3870549	3079736	N.L.
Switch (CCEV)		
1984-85-orange	4049208	17.50
natural	3879707	17.50
green	4049276	17.50
Vacuum Valve Solenoid (A/C)		
1984	4240417	16.00
Dual Vacuum Solenoid (w/EFI)		
1984-85	5213957	28.50
Vacuum Solenoid Valve (A/C Speed Up)		
1984	5213348	16.00
Vacuum Solenoid Valve		
1985-E.F.I.	5226359	20.50

EFE SYSTEM

	Part No.	Price
Oxygen Sensor		
1984-85	4301346	36.75
1986-87-exc. Turbo	4301375	40.00
Turbo	4301346	36.75
Charge Temperature Switch		
1984-87	4111482	7.00

HEATED INLET AIR SYSTEM

	Part No.	Price
Air Cleaner Filter		
1984-87-exc. below	4213582	9.25
E.F.I.	4342801	9.00
Turbo	4342800	11.75
Air Cleaner Vacuum Sensor		
1984-87	4131147	7.00
Heated Air Delay Valve		
1984-87	4201385	4.25

LABOR 4 ALTERNATOR AND REGULATOR 4 LABOR

(Factory Time)	Chilton Time
(G) Alternator Circuits, Test	
Includes: Test battery, regulator and alternator output.	
All models	.6
(M) Alternator Drive Belt, Renew	
1984-87 (.2)	.3
w/A.C. add (.1)	.1
(G) Alternator Assembly, Renew	
Includes: Transfer pulley if required.	
1984-87 (.8)	1.2
w/A.C. add (.3)	.3
Add circuit test if performed.	
(G) Alternator, R&R and Recondition	
Includes: Test and disassemble.	
1984-87 (1.5)	2.1
w/A.C. add (.3)	.3
(G) Alternator Front Bearing or Retainer, Renew	
1984-87 (.8)	1.1
w/A.C. add (.3)	.3
Renew rear brg add	.2
(G) Voltage Regulator, Test and Renew	
1984-87	
external type (.2)	.4
internal type (1.0)	*1.6
*w/A.C. add (.3)	.3
(G) Alternator Gauge, Renew	
1984-87 (.3)	.6
(G) Gauge Alert Module, Renew	
1984-87 (.7)	1.1

PARTS 4 ALTERNATOR AND REGULATOR 4 PARTS

	Part No.	Price
Alternator Assy.		
1984 (w/EFI)		
60 amp	5213540	129.00
78 amp	5213053	129.00
1984 (wo/EFI)		
60 amp	5213079	129.00
78 amp	5213053	129.00
1985-87-60 amp	5213762	129.00
78 amp	5213763	129.00
90 amp	4339440	154.50
100 amp	5213847	161.50
(1) Drive End Shield		
1984-87-60 amp	5206421	20.00
78 amp	5206422	20.25
90 amp	5226840	39.50
(2) Drive End Shield Bearing		
1984-87	3656444	8.75
(3) Rotor Assy.		
1984-87-60 amp	4240413	62.00
78 amp	4240414	62.00
90 amp	5226841	102.25
(4) Stator		
1984-87-60 amp	4091515	36.75
78 amp	4091517	36.75
90 amp	5226315	151.00
(5) Battery Terminal & Positive Heat Sink		
1984-87-60 amp	4026082	17.50
78 amp	4026083	17.50
(6) Heat Sink (Negative)		
1984-87-60 amp	3438721	17.75
78 amp	3755114	17.75
(7) Rectifier End Shield		
1984-87-60 amp	5213092	57.00
78 amp	4240405	58.75
90 amp	5226845	57.50
(8) End Shield Bearing (Rectifier)		
1984-87	3755184	3.25

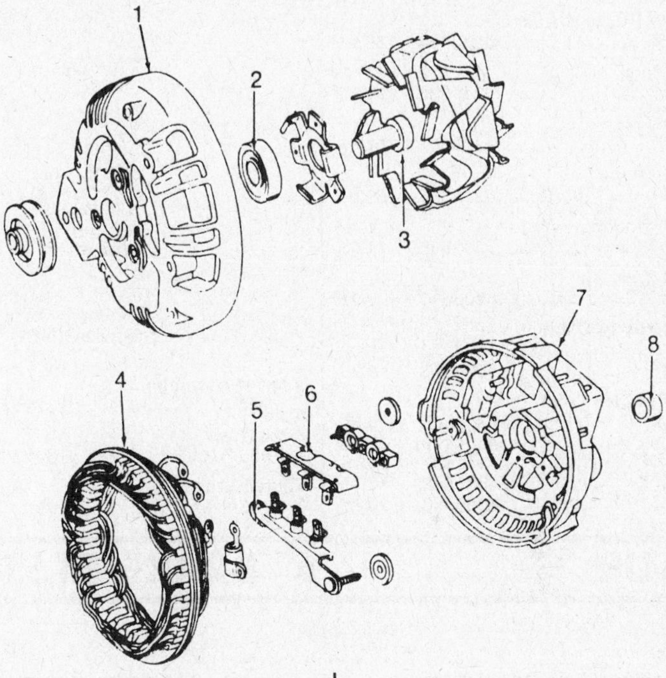

	Part No.	Price
Brush & Washer Pkg.		
1984-87-exc. 90 amp	5211772	4.50
90 amp	5266572	5.50

	Part No.	Price
Voltage Regulator		
1984-85	4111990	29.00
1986-87	4379100	29.00

LABOR 5 STARTING SYSTEM 5 LABOR

(Factory Time)	Chilton Time
(G) Starter Draw Test (On Car)	
All models	.3
(G) Starter Assy., Renew	
Includes: Test starter relay, starter solenoid and amperage draw.	
1984-87 (1.0)	1.3
w/Turbo add (.5)	.5
(G) Starter, R&R and Recondition	
Includes: Turn down armature.	
1984-87	2.8
w/Turbo add (.5)	.5
Renew field coils add (.5)	.5
(G) Starter Drive, Renew	
Includes: R&R starter.	
1984-87 (1.4)	1.8
w/Turbo add (.5)	.5
(G) Starter Solenoid, Renew	
Includes: R&R starter.	
1984-87 (1.0)	1.4
w/Turbo add (.5)	.5
(G) Starter Relay, Renew	
1984-87 (.2)	.3
(G) Neutral Start and Back-Up Lamp Switch, Renew	
1984-87 (.3)	.4

LABOR 5 STARTING SYSTEM 5 LABOR

	(Factory Time)	Chilton Time
(G) Ignition Switch, Renew		
1984-87		
std column	(.4)	.8
tilt column	(.4)	.9

	(Factory Time)	Chilton Time
(M) Battery Cables, Renew		
1984-87		
positive	(.5)	.6
negative	(.2)	.2

PARTS 5 STARTING SYSTEM 5 PARTS

2.2L ENGINE

	Part No.	Price
Starter Assy.		
1984-85-exc. Turbo	5213045	105.50
Turbo	5213450	147.00
1986-87	4339472	148.75
(1) Drive End Housing		
1984-87	5213382	42.75
(2) Clutch Starter Drive		
1984-87	5213384	35.25
(3) Armature		
1984-87	5213383	78.50
(4) Solenoid		
1984-87	5206607	57.25
(5) Field Frame		
1984-87	5213385	69.00
(6) Brush Holder		
1984-87	5206605	21.75
(7) Head End		
1984-87	5206610	2.25
Battery Ground Cable		
1984	4274273	8.00
1985-87	4304678	10.75
Battery Positive Cable		
1984-A.T.	4304555	29.50
M.T.	4304473	29.50
1985-A.T.	4331481	20.75
M.T.	4331482	26.75
1986-87-A.T.	4368366	20.75

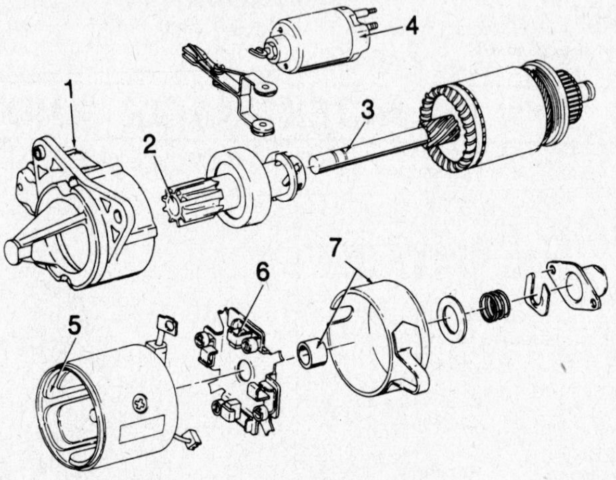

2.5L ENGINE

	Part No.	Price
Starter Assembly		
1986-87	5226444	105.50
Gear Train		
1986-87	5227114	102.50
Clutch Starter Drive		
1986-87	5227115	27.25
Armature		
1986-87	5227125	158.25
Solenoid		
1986-87	5227607	N.L.
Brush Holder		
1986-87	5227131	75.00
Fork Lever		
1986-87	5227119	5.00

LABOR 6 BRAKE SYSTEM 6 LABOR

	(Factory Time)	Chilton Time
(G) Brake Pedal Free Play, Adjust		
All models		.3
(G) Brakes, Adjust (Minor)		
Includes: Adjust brake shoes, fill master cylinder.		
two wheels		.4
(G) Bleed Brakes (Four Wheels)		
Includes: Add fluid.		
All models	(.4)	.6
(G) Brake Shoes and/or Pads, Renew		
Includes: Install new or exchange brake shoes or pads. Adjust service and hand brake. Bleed system.		
1984-87-front-disc	(.5)	.8
rear-drum	(.8)	1.5
all four wheels	(1.3)	2.2
Resurface disc rotor, add-each		.9
Resurface brake drum, add-each		.5
(G) Rear Brake Drum, Renew (One)		
1984-87	(.5)	.6

BRAKE HYDRAULIC SYSTEM

	(Factory Time)	Chilton Time
(G) Wheel Cylinder, Renew		
Includes: Bleed system.		
1984-87-one	(.7)	1.1
both	(1.3)	2.1
(G) Wheel Cylinder, R&R and Rebuild		
Includes: Hone cylinder and bleed system.		
1984-87-one		1.2
both		2.3
(G) Brake Hose, Renew (Flex)		
Includes: Bleed system.		
1984-87-front-one	(.4)	.8
rear-one	(.4)	.8
(G) Master Cylinder, Renew		
Includes: Bleed complete system.		
1984-87	(.5)	.9
(G) Master Cylinder, R&R and Rebuild		
Includes: Bleed complete system.		
1984-87		1.6
(G) Master Cylinder Reservoir, Renew		
Includes: Bleed complete system.		
1984-87	(.6)	1.0
(G) Brake System, Flush and Refill		
All models		1.2

POWER BRAKES

	(Factory Time)	Chilton Time
(G) Brake Booster Assembly, Renew		
1984-87	(1.3)	1.6
(G) Brake Booster Check Valve, Renew		
1984-87	(.2)	.2

DISC BRAKES

	(Factory Time)	Chilton Time
(G) Disc Brake Pads, Renew		
Includes: Install new disc brake pads only.		
1984-87	(.5)	.8
(G) Disc Brake Rotor, Renew		
1984-87-one	(.3)	.6
(G) Disc Brake Rotor and Hub, Renew		
1984-87-one	(1.0)	1.4

LABOR — 6 BRAKE SYSTEM 6 — LABOR

	(Factory Time)	Chilton Time
(G) Caliper Assembly, Renew		
Includes: Bleed system.		
1984-87-one	(.5)	.9
both		1.7
(G) Caliper Assy., R&R and Recondition		
Includes: Bleed system.		
1984-87-one	(.8)	1.4
both		2.7
(G) Brake System Combination Valve, Renew		
Includes: Bleed complete system.		
1984-87	(1.2)	1.5

PARKING BRAKE

	(Factory Time)	Chilton Time
(G) Parking Brake, Adjust		
1984-87	(.3)	.4
(G) Parking Brake Warning Lamp Switch, Renew		
1984-87	(.2)	.3
(G) Parking Brake Control, Renew		
1984-87	(.5)	.7

COMBINATIONS

Add To Brakes, Renew

See Machine Shop Operations

	(Factory Time)	Chilton Time
(G) RENEW WHEEL CYLINDER		
Each		.3
(G) REBUILD WHEEL CYLINDER		
Each		.4
(G) REBUILD CALIPER ASSEMBLY		
Each		.5
(G) RENEW MASTER CYLINDER		
All models		.6
(G) REBUILD MASTER CYLINDER		
All models		.8
(G) RENEW BRAKE HOSE		
Each		3
(G) RENEW REAR WHEEL GREASE SEALS		
One side		.3
(G) RENEW DISC BRAKE ROTOR		
Each		.2
(G) RENEW BRAKE DRUM		
Each		.3
(G) DISC BRAKE ROTOR STUDS, RENEW		
Each		.1

	(Factory Time)	Chilton Time
(G) Parking Brake Cables, Renew		
Includes: Adjust parking brake.		
1984-87-front	(.5)	.7
intermediate	(.3)	.5
rear-each	(.6)	.8

PARTS — 6 BRAKE SYSTEM 6 — PARTS

	Part No.	Price
(1) Rear Wheel Bearing (Outer)		
1984-87	4293196	9.25
(2) Hub and Drum (Rear)		
1984	4293195	87.00
1985-87-4 stud	4238538	100.50
5 stud	4313635	100.50
(3) Rear Wheel Bearing (Inner)		
1984-87	4238567	14.75
(4) Dust Seal		
1984-87	4238570	3.50
(5) Brake Shoes & Lining Set (Rear)		
1984-87	4238826	39.75
(6) Wheel Cylinder (Rear)		
1984-87	4238706	22.50
Master Cylinder Assy.		
1984	4271388	70.50
1985-87	4294268	80.00
Reservoir (Master Cylinder)		
1984-85	3766498	5.00
1986-87	4294495	N.L.
Mounting Grommets (Reservoir)		
1984-87	5204149	1.00
Brake Warning Switch		
1984	3747993	8.00
1985-87	4221651	15.50
Proportioning Valve		
1984-87	4238588	35.75

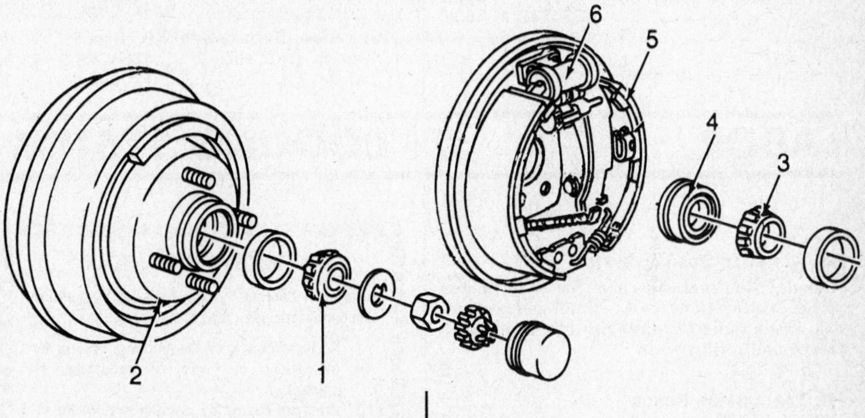

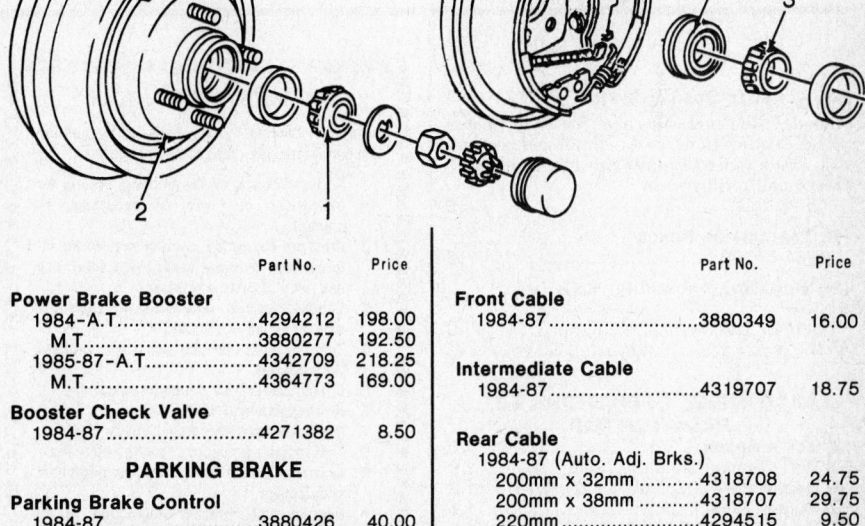

	Part No.	Price
Power Brake Booster		
1984-A.T.	4294212	198.00
M.T.	3880277	192.50
1985-87-A.T.	4342709	218.25
M.T.	4364773	169.00
Booster Check Valve		
1984-87	4271382	8.50

PARKING BRAKE

	Part No.	Price
Parking Brake Control		
1984-87	3880426	40.00
Front Cable		
1984-87	3880349	16.00
Intermediate Cable		
1984-87	4319707	18.75
Rear Cable		
1984-87 (Auto. Adj. Brks.)		
200mm x 32mm	4318708	24.75
200mm x 38mm	4318707	29.75
220mm	4294515	9.50

PARTS — 6 DISC BRAKES 6 — PARTS

	Part No.	Price
(1) Pin Pkg.		
1984-87-exc. H.D.	4267330	9.00
H.D.	4267329	12.25
(2) Bushing Pkg.		
1984-87-exc. H.D.	4267331	3.00
H.D.	4205982	1.75
(3) Brake Pads (Inner w/Sensor)		
refer to (10) Brake Pad Set		

PARTS — 6 DISC BRAKES 6 — PARTS

	Part No.	Price
(4) Rotor		
1984	4238551	56.00
1985-87-4 stud	4313593	56.00
5 stud	4313633	56.00
(5) Hub		
1984	5212521	60.00
1985-87-4 stud	5212545	60.00
5 stud	5212770	60.00
(6) Retainer (Bearing)		
1984-87	5212980	3.00
(7) Gasket		
1984-87	5212559	.50
(8) Bearing		
1984-85	4293185	42.25
1986-87	4397498	42.25
(9) Seal		
1984-87	5212535	3.50
(10) Brake Pad Set		
1984 (w/clips)		
wo/sensor	4313238	72.25
w/sensor	4313239	79.75
1985-87-exc. H.D.		
wo/sensor	4313238	72.25
w/sensor	4313642	N.L.
1985-87-H.D.	4313429	72.25
(11) Sensor (outer pads)		
included with pad		
(12) Adapter		
1984-right	4313236	36.25
left	4313237	36.25
1985-87-exc. H.D.		
right	4313962	36.25
left	4313963	36.25
H.D.	4238712	36.25
(13) Seal		
see (13 & 14) for kits		

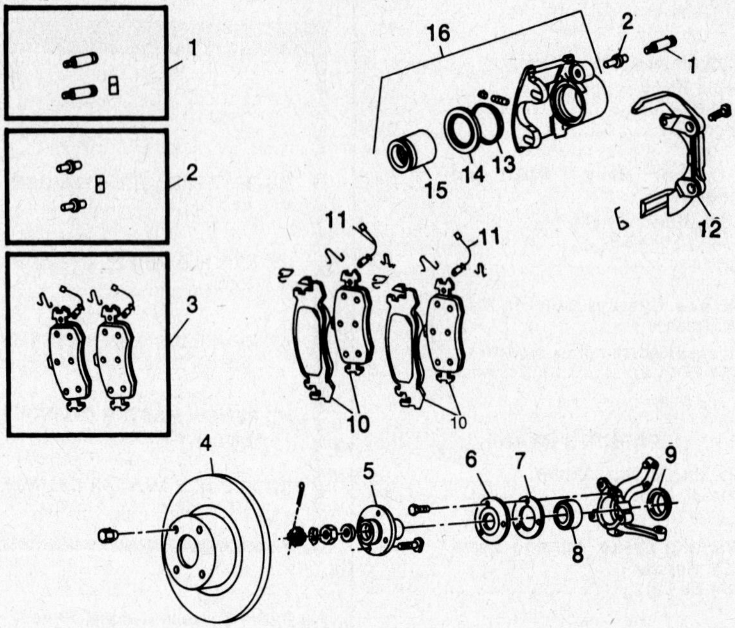

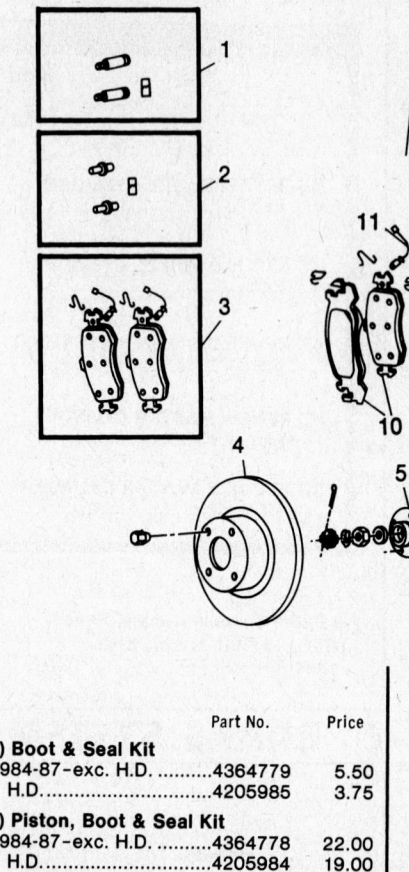

	Part No.	Price
(14) Boot & Seal Kit		
1984-87-exc. H.D.	4364779	5.50
H.D.	4205985	3.75
(15) Piston, Boot & Seal Kit		
1984-87-exc. H.D.	4364778	22.00
H.D.	4205984	19.00

	Part No.	Price
(16) Caliper Housing (Partial)		
1984-87-exc. H.D.		
right	4238692	114.75
left	4238693	114.75
1985-87-H.D.		
right	4238710	114.75
left	4238711	114.75

LABOR — 7 COOLING SYSTEM 7 — LABOR

(Factory Time)	Chilton Time
(M) Winterize Cooling System	
Includes: Run engine to check for leaks, tighten all hose connections. Test radiator and pressure cap. Drain radiator and engine block. Add anti-freeze and refill system.	
All models	.5
(M) Thermostat, Renew	
1984-87 (.4)	.6
(M) Radiator Assembly, R&R or Renew	
1984-87 (.5)	.9
w/A.T. add (.1)	.1

ADD THESE OPERATIONS TO RADIATOR R&R

(G) Boil & Repair	1.5
(G) Rod Clean	1.9
(G) Repair Core	1.3
(G) Renew Tank	1.6
(G) Renew Trans. Oil Cooler	1.9
(G) Recore Radiator	1.7
(M) Fan Blades, Renew	
1984-87 (.2)	.5
(M) Drive Belts, Renew	
1984-87	
Fan & alter (.2)	.3
Pow str (.4)	.6
Air pump (.3)	.4
w/A.C. add (.1)	.1

COOLING SYSTEM TUNE-UP

An Annual Cooling System Tune-Up Suggestion List should include (with some exceptions):

1. A visual check of the cooling system for indications of leaks or excessive oil content.
2. Pressure check the cooling system for internal and external leaks with filler cap and neck adapter and tester.
3. Check crankcase and automatic transmission oil for water content.
4. Test coolant thermostat with radiator thermometer.
5. Check temperature gauge for accuracy.
6. Drain system and flush till clean.
7. Clean foreign matter from radiator fins.
8. Test radiator pressure cap with cap tester.
9. Check fan blades and pulleys for alignment and damage.
10. Internal and external inspection of all hoses for cracks and deterioration.
11. Check core plugs (where possible) for seepage.
12. Refill system with correct coolant and check for air locks.
13. Check condition and tension of drive belts with tension gauge.

All models 1.5

(Factory Time)	Chilton Time
(M) Drive Belts, Adjust	
All models-one	.2
each adtnl	.1
(M) Radiator Hoses, Renew	
1984-87-upper (.3)	.4
lower (.4)	.6
(G) Water Pump, Renew	
1984-87 (1.1)	1.6
w/A.C. add	.5
(G) Radiator Fan Motor, Renew	
1984-87-wo/A.C. (.4)	.5
w/A.C. (.4)	.5
(G) Radiator Fan Switch, Renew	
1984-87 (.3)	.6
(G) Radiator Fan Motor Relay, Renew	
1984-87 (.2)	.3
(G) Water Jacket Expansion Plugs, Renew (Cylinder Block)	
1984-87	
2.2L eng	
left side	
front (.7)	1.0
rear (.4)	.6
right side	
front or center (.6)	.9
rear (1.0)	1.4
w/P.S. add (.3)	.3

LABOR 7 COOLING SYSTEM 7 LABOR

	(Factory Time)	Chilton Time
(G) Water Jacket Expansion Plugs, Renew (Cylinder Head)		
1984-87		
2.2L eng		
front	(.6)	.9
rear	(.8)	1.1
(G) Temperature Gauge (Engine Unit), Renew		
1984-87		
sending unit	(.3)	.4
light switch	(.3)	.4
(G) Heater Hoses, Renew		
1984-87-one	(.4)	.4
each adtnl	(.1)	.2
(G) Heater Water Valve, Renew		
1984-87-w/A.C.	(.3)	.5
(G) Heater Control Assembly, Renew		
1984-87-wo/A.C.	(.4)	.7
w/A.C.	(.4)	.7
(G) Vacuum Switch (Push Button), Renew		
1984-87-w/A.C.	(.5)	.9
(G) Blower Motor Switch, Renew		
1984-87-wo/A.C.	(.4)	.8
w/A.C.	(.4)	.8
(G) Heater Core, R&R or Renew		
1984-87-wo/A.C.	(1.0)	1.7
w/A.C.	(2.4)	*5.5

*Includes recharge A.C. system.

ADD THESE OPERATIONS TO HEATER CORE R&R

	(Factory Time)	Chilton Time
(G) Boil & Repair		1.2
(G) Repair Core		.9
(G) Recore		1.2
(G) Heater Blower Motor, Renew		
1984-87-wo/A.C.	(.4)	.6
w/A.C.	(.6)	1.2
(G) Blower Motor Resistor, Renew		
1984-87-wo/A.C.	(.2)	.3
w/A.C.	(.3)	.4

PARTS 7 COOLING SYSTEM 7 PARTS

	Part No.	Price
Radiator Assy.		
Order by year and model.		
Radiator Hose (Upper)		
1984-85	4266721	6.25
1986-87	4266696	6.25
Silicone	4266952	35.25
Radiator Hose (Lower)		
1984-85-right	4266762	14.25
left	4266763	5.50
1986-87	4266697	13.75
Silicone	4266954	38.75
Radiator Fan		
Part numbers for price reference only. Order by number stamped on part assembly.		
1984-87-wo/A.C.	4266069	16.75
w/A.C.	4266282	17.75
Motor (Radiator Fan)		
Part number for price reference only. Order by number stamped on part assembly.		
1984-87-wo/A.C	4240493	83.00
w/A.C.	4240494	83.00
Thermostat		
1984-87-185°	4105442	6.50
195°	4105768	.75
By Pass Hose		
1984	4273486	4.75
1985-87	4273488	1.75
Water Pump		
1984	4293898	48.00
1985-87	4293898	48.00
Heater Core		
1984-85	4205838	91.50
1986-87	3847943	90.75
Blower Motor Assy.		
1984	4318117	68.75
1985	3849032	59.00
1986-87	3849266	59.00
Resistor (Blower Motor)		
1984	3848999	4.25
1985	3849075	N.L.
1986-87	3849235	8.50
Blower Motor Switch		
1984	3848645	10.25
1985-87	3849160	8.00
Heat Sending Unit (Engine)		
1984-87	4051687	10.25
Heat Indicator (Dash)		
1984-87	4051804	38.75
Transmission Auxiliary Oil Cooler		
1984-87-wo/Turbo	4266196	76.25
Turbo	4266378	76.25
Transmission Oil Cooler (Water Cooled)		
1984-87	4266729	52.25

LABOR 8 EXHAUST SYSTEM 8 LABOR

	(Factory Time)	Chilton Time
(G) Muffler, Renew		
1984-87	(.4)	.7
Cut exhaust pipe add	(.2)	.2
(G) Exhaust Pipe, Renew		
1984-87	(.7)	1.1
Cut at muffler add	(.2)	.2
(G) Exhaust Pipe Extension, Renew		
1984-87	(.6)	1.0
(G) Catalytic Converter, Renew		
1984-87		
floor mount	(.7)	.9
exh pipe mount	(.7)	.9
manif mount	(.9)	1.3
(G) Exhaust Manifold or Gasket, Renew		
1984-87		
2.2L eng	(2.7)	3.7
w/Turbo add	(.6)	.6

COMBINATIONS

	(Factory Time)	Chilton Time
(G) Exhaust System, Renew (Complete)		
1984-87		1.5

PARTS 8 EXHAUST SYSTEM 8 PARTS

System numbers shown are for pricing reference only. Order parts with complete year and engine information.

	Part No.	Price
Muffler (w/Tail Pipe)		
wo/Turbo		
1984	4301240	59.00
1985	4301438	56.50
1986-87	4301467	56.50
Turbo		
1984	4301242	110.00
1985	4301406	115.50
1986-87	4301468	115.50
Exhaust Pipe Extension (wo/Resonator)		
1984	4301037	14.50
1985	4301229	26.25
1986-87	4301453	36.25
Exhaust Pipe Extension (w/Resonator)		
1984	4301291	51.75
1985	4301591	N.S.S.
1986-87	4301558	N.L.
Exhaust Pipe		
1984-87-Turbo	4301037	14.50

PARTS 8 EXHAUST SYSTEM 8 PARTS

	Part No.	Price
Catalytic Converter (w/Pipes)		
Front		
1984	4301265	256.75
1985	4301441	244.75
1986-87-2.2L	4301518	N.L.
1986-87-2.5L		
exc. Calif.	4301664	255.75
Calif.	4301665	255.75
Rear		
1984	4301230	256.75
1986-87	4301460	244.50

LABOR 9 FRONT SUSPENSION 9 LABOR

	(Factory Time)	Chilton Time
Note: On all front suspension operations alignment charges must be added if performed. Time given does not include alignment.		
(M) Wheel, Renew		
one		.5
(M) Wheels, Rotate (All)		
All models		.5
(G) Wheels, Balance		
one		.3
each adtnl		.2
(G) Check Alignment of Front End		
All models		.5
Note: Deduct if alignment is performed.		
(G) Toe-Out, Adjust		
All models		.6
(G) Align Front End		
Includes: Adjust camber, toe, car height and center steering wheel.		
All models	(.8)	1.4
(G) Steering Knuckle Bearing, Renew (Wheel Bearing)		
Add alignment charges.		
1984-87-one	(1.2)	1.6
both	(2.3)	3.0
(G) Steering Knuckle, Renew (One)		
Add alignment charges.		
1984-87	(1.0)	1.6
(G) Front Strut Assy., R&R or Renew		
Add alignment charges.		
1984-87-one	(.8)	1.4
both	(1.5)	2.7
(G) Front Suspension Strut (Dual Path) Mount Assy., Renew		
Includes: Renew bearing.		
1984-87	(.8)	1.5
(G) Lower Control Arm Assy., Renew		
Includes: Reset toe-in.		
1984-87-one	(1.1)	1.6
(G) Lower Control Arm Strut Bushings, Renew		
Add alignment charges.		
1984-87-one side	(.6)	.9
(G) Lower Ball Joint, Renew (One)		
Add alignment charges.		
1984-87	(.8)	1.2
(G) Front Coil Spring or Strut Bearing, Renew		
Includes: R&R front strut.		
Add alignment charges.		
1984-87-one	(.8)	1.5
both	(1.5)	2.8
(G) Front Sway Bar, Renew		
1984-87	(.4)	.7
(G) Sway Bar Bracket and Bushings, Renew		
1984-87-both	(.5)	.9
(P) K-Frame Assembly, Renew		
Add alignment charges.		
All models	(2.5)	4.0
(G) Drive Shaft Boot, Renew		
Includes: Clean and lubricate C/V joint.		
All models		
1984-87		
one-inner or outer	(.7)	1.0
both-one side	(1.0)	1.4
Renew shaft seal, add		
right side	(.1)	.1
left side	(.3)	.3
(G) Drive Shaft C/V Joint, Renew		
All models		
1984-87		
one-inner or outer	(.7)	1.0
both-one side	(1.0)	1.4
inter shaft U-joint	(.6)	1.0
Renew shaft seal, add		
right side	(.1)	.1
left side	(.3)	.3
(G) Front Wheel Drive Shaft Assy., Renew		
All models		
1984-87		
inter spline yoke	(.6)	1.0
inter stub shaft	(.6)	1.0
all others-each	(1.0)	1.4
Renew shaft seal, add		
right side	(.1)	.1
left side	(.3)	.3
(G) Intermediate Shaft Support Bearing, Renew		
1984-87-each	(.6)	1.0
(G) Drive Shaft Oil Seal, Renew		
All models		
1984-87		
right side	(.5)	.8
left side	(.7)	1.1

PARTS 9 FRONT SUSPENSION 9 PARTS

This parts list is for vehicles built up to 1-2-86. Refer to next section for vehicles built after 1-2-86.

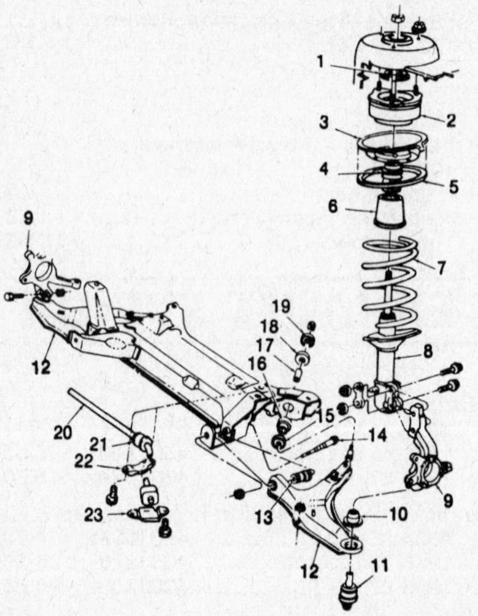

	Part No.	Price
(1) Retainer (Shock Stop)		
1984-86	4052822	1.75
(2) Front Shock Mount (Upper)		
1984	4052850	19.00
1985-86	4322298	19.00
(3) Shock Seat (Upper)		
1984	4052819	6.25
1985-86	4322701	6.25
(4) Bumper (Jounce)		
1984-85	4052824	2.75
1986	4322705	2.75
(5) Front Isolator (Upper)		
1984-86	4322046	2.25
(6) Dust Shield		
1984-85	4052825	1.50
1986	4322704	1.50
(7) Strut Spring Assy.		
Order by model and description.		
(8) Strut (Shock Absorber) (Std.)		
1984	4322059	50.00
1985-86-exc.		
below	4052862	45.50
gas press.	4322059	50.00
(9) Steering Knuckle		
1984-86-right	4052838	89.75
left	4052839	89.75
(10) Seal (Ball Joint)		
1984-86	4052509	1.25
(11) Ball Joint		
1984-85	4052583	32.75
1986	4364782	37.25
(12) Control Arm Assy.		
1984-86-right	4322158	92.75
left	4322159	92.75
(13) Control Arm Bushing		
1984	5204622	8.00
1985-86	4052646	8.00
(14) Bolt (Pivot Shaft)		
1984-86	4014239	4.00

PARTS 9 FRONT SUSPENSION 9 PARTS

	Part No.	Price
(15) Retainer (Strut Bushing)		
1984-86	5204534	1.50
(16) Strut Bushing (Front)		
1984	4052671	2.00
1985-86	4322285	2.00
(17) Sleeve (Strut Bushing)		
1984-86	5204535	1.50
(18) Strut Bushing (Rear)		
1984-86	4052672	2.00
(19) Retainer (Strut Bushing)		
1984-86	5204534	1.50
(20) Front Sway Shaft Assy.		
1984-86	4322014	81.25
(21) Front Cushion (Sway Shaft)		
1984-85	4052613	3.00
1986	4322745	81.25
(22) Lower Clamp (Shaft Bushing)		
1984-86	4052522	3.00
(23) Retainer (Shaft Arm)		
1984-86	4014418	3.00
Crossmember (Complete)		
1984-wo/turbo	4322249	455.50
w/turbo	4322250	455.50

Part numbers shown are for pricing reference only. Order by year model and type.

	Part No.	Price
Driveshaft		
1.6L		
1983-Right	5212676	137.50
Left	5212677	76.00
1984-87-Right	5212862	137.50
Left	5212863	76.00
1.7L		
1983-Right	5212646	137.50
Left	5212647	72.50
2.2L, 2.5L & 2.6L		
Horizon, Omni, 024, TC3, Turismo, Charger		
(G.K.N.)		
1983-Right	5212660	137.50
Left	5212661	76.00
1984-87-Right	5212862	137.50
Left	5212863	76.00
1986-87-H/P		
Right	5212862	137.50
Left	5212933	76.00
(Citroen)		
1985-wo/Turbo		
Right	5212766	85.00
Left	5212765	52.25
Turbo	5212765	52.25
1986-87-Right	5212766	85.00
Left	5212935	52.25
Turbo	5212935	52.25
Exc. Horizon, Omni, TC3, 024, Turismo, Charger		
(G.K.N.)		
1983-Right	5212662	137.50
Left	5212663	76.00
1984-87-Right	5212872	123.00
Left	5212913	76.00
(Citroen)		
1983-Right	5212744	85.00
Left	5212745	52.50
1984-wo/Turbo		
right	5212798	85.00
left	5212799	N.L.
Turbo	5212799	N.L.
1985-87-wo/Turbo		
Right	5212798	85.00
Left	5212763	52.25
Turbo	5212763	52.25
(A.C.I.)		
1984-87-Right	5212826	123.00
Left	5212827	76.00

PARTS 9 FRONT SUSPENSION 9 PARTS

This parts list is for vehicles built after 1-2-86.

	Part No.	Price
(1) Strut (Shock Absorber‡		
1986-87-Std.	4322736	40.00
H.D. (gas)	4322679	50.00
(2) Strut Spring		
Order by model and description.		
(3) Spacer		
1986-87	4014441	5.00
(4) Shield		
1986-87	4322704	1.50
(5) Bumper		
1986-87	4322705	2.75
(6) Seat Assembly		
1986-87	4322628°	
(7) Mount & Brg. Assy.		
1986-87	4322760	24.00
(8) Knuckle Assy.		
1986-87-R.H.	4052838	89.75
L.H.	4052839	89.75
(9) Ball Joint		
1986-87	4364782	37.25
(10) Bushing		
1986-87	4322285	2.00
(11) Bushing		
1986-87-Std.	5204622	8.00
H.D.	4052646	8.00
(12) Sway Bar		
1986-87-Std.	4322014	81.25
H.D.	4322745	81.25
(13) Bushing		
1986-87-Std.	4052613	3.00
H.D.	4322820	6.00
(14) Bushing		
1986-87	4322751	3.75
(15) Lower Control Arm Assy.		
1986-87		
R.H.-Std.	4322154	92.75
L.H.-Std.	4322155	92.75
R.H.-H.D.	4322158	92.75
L.H.-H.D.	4322159	92.75

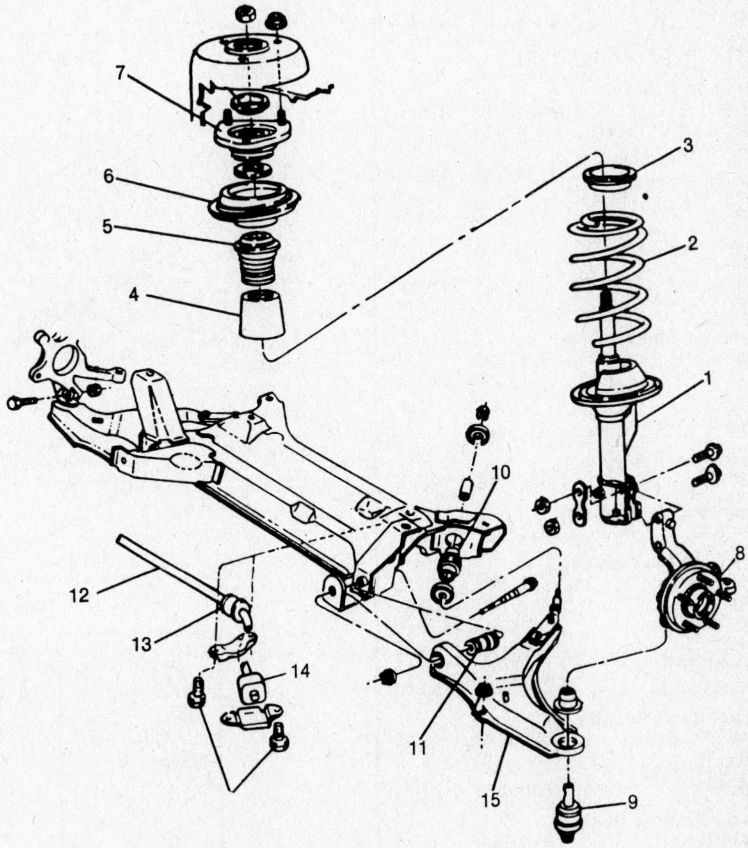

From 1-2-86

LABOR 11 STEERING GEAR 11 LABOR

	(Factory Time)	Chilton Time
(G) Tie Rods or Tie Rod Ends, Renew		
Includes: Reset toe-out.		
1984-87		
outer-one	(.9)	1.2
inner and outer-w/P.S. one side	(1.9)	2.5
(G) Horn Contact Cable and Ring, Renew		
1984-87	(.2)	.4
(G) Horn Switch, Renew		
1983-87	(.2)	.3
(G) Steering Wheel, Renew		
1984-87	(.2)	.3
(G) Steering Column Jacket, Renew		
Does not include painting.		
1984-87		
Std Column		
console shift	(1.1)	1.8
Tilt Column		
console shift	(1.5)	2.6
(G) Upper Mast Jacket Bearing, Renew		
Includes: Replace insulators if necessary.		
1984-87		
std column	(.4)	.9
tilt column	(1.2)	2.0
(G) Steering Column Lower Shaft Bearing, Renew		
Includes: Replace support if necessary.		
1984-87		
Std Column		
console shift	(.8)	1.6
Tilt Column		
console shift	(.6)	1.0
POWER STEERING		
(G) Power Steering Pump Pressure Check		
All models		.5
(M) Power Steering Pump Belt, Renew		
1984-87	(.4)	.6
w/A.C. add	(.1)	.1
w/Air inj add	(.1)	.1
(G) Power Steering Gear, R&R or Renew		
Includes: Reset toe-in.		
1984-87	(1.1)	2.4
Renew gear add	(.6)	1.0
(G) Steering Gear Oil Seals, Renew (All)		
Includes: R&R gear assy. and reset toe-in.		
1984-87	(2.9)	5.1
(G) Upper and Lower Valve Pinion Seals, Renew		
1984-87	(1.4)	2.0
Renew brgs add	(.3)	.5
(G) Power Steering Pump, Renew		
1984-87	(1.0)	1.4
(G) Power Steering Pump, R&R and Recondition		
1984-87	(1.5)	2.3
(G) Pump Flow Control Valve, Test and Clean or Renew		
1984-87	(.6)	1.0
(G) Power Steering Reservoir or Seals, Renew		
1984-87	(.7)	1.1
(G) Pump-Drive Shaft Oil Seal, Renew		
1984-87	(.9)	1.4
(M) Power Steering Hoses, Renew		
1984-87-each	(.4)	.5

PARTS 11 POWER STEERING GEAR 11 PARTS

SAGINAW TYPE

	Part No.	Price
Steering Gear Assy.		
1984	4147009	275.50
1985-wo/15" tires	4147451	343.50
1986-87-wo/15" tires	4364785	343.50
1985-87-w/15" tires	4147289	275.50
(1) Housing Assy.		
1984-87-wo/15" tires	4147083	178.00
w/15" tires	4333100	200.00
(2) Cylinder Oil Kit (Lines)		
1984-87-right	4147089	8.25
left	4147090	8.25
(3) Dust Cover		
1984-87	5205284	3.50
(4) Pinion Bearing Kit		
1984-87	5205295	25.50
(5) Ring (Shock Damper)		
1984-87	5205287	2.50
(6) Valve Kit (Pinion Assy.)		
1984-Std.	5205328	150.50
Firm	4147091	150.50
1985-Std.	3815947	150.50
Firm	4333098	150.50
1986-87-Std.	3815947	150.50
Firm	4333434	150.50
(7) Spool Shaft Bearing Kit		
1984-87	5205299	19.25
(8) Retainer Ring		
1984-87	5205278	1.75
(9) Seal Kit (Inner Rack)		
1984-87	4147098	33.75
(10) Rack Assy. (w/Piston)		
1984-87-Std.	4147080	128.75
Firm	4147081	128.75

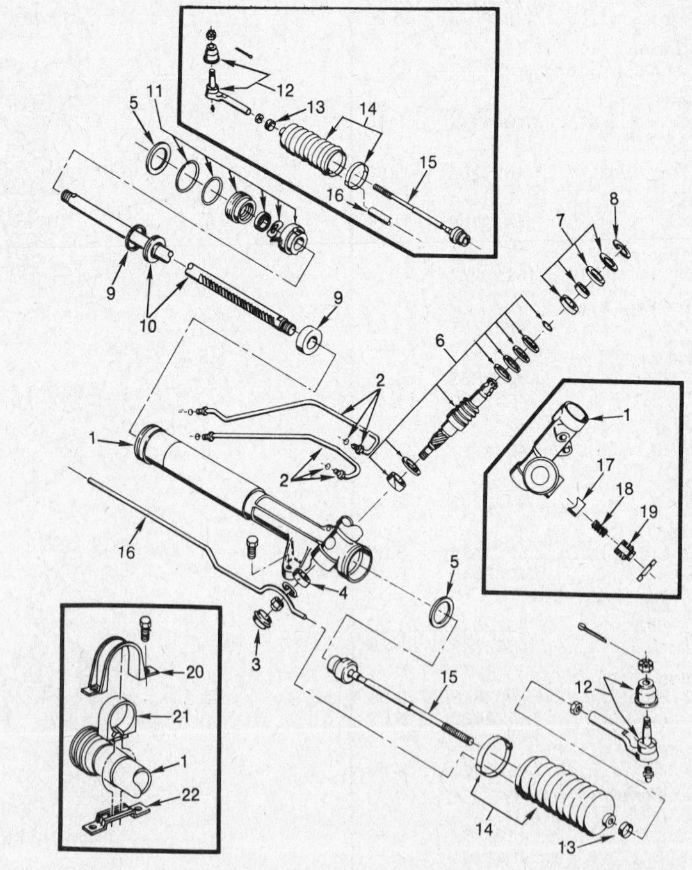

PARTS 11 POWER STEERING GEAR 11 PARTS

	Part No.	Price
(11) Bulkhead Assy. Kit		
1984-87-Std.	4147096	41.50
Firm (15″ tires)	4333103	41.50
(12) Tie Rod Assy. (Outer)		
1984-87	4106180	39.75
(13) Clamp (Tie Rod End)		
1984-87	4147085	5.00
(14) Boot Service Kit		
1984-87-right	4147092	30.75
left	4147093	28.75
(15) Tie Rod Assy. (Inner)		
wo/15″ tires		
1984-87-right	4147095	48.50
left	4333104	46.25
w/15″ tires		
1985-87-right	4333123	47.25
left	4333122	46.25
(16) Breather Tube		
1984-87	4147087	9.00
(17) Rack Bearing		
1984-87	5205282	5.25
(18) Spring (Adjuster)		
1984-87	5205280	2.00
(19) Plug (Adjuster)		
1984-87	5205286	7.75
(20) Bracket (Outer)		
1984-87-right	3643470	4.00
left	3643424	4.00
(21) Bushing		
1984-87-right	3643471	4.00
left	3643425	4.00
(22) Bracket (Inner)		
1984-87-right	3643469	1.00
left	3643423	1.00

PARTS 11 POWER STEERING GEAR 11 PARTS

TRW Type

	Part No.	Price
(1) Tie Rod End (Outer)		
1985-87	4106180	39.75
(2) Boot Service Kit		
1985-87	4147303	14.75
(3) Breather Tube		
1985-87	3815871	2.00
(4) Horizontal Socket Assy.		
1985	4147356	
1986-87-right	4333450	50.00
(5) Service Ring Kits		
1985-87	3815874	2.75
(6) Lock Ring Bushing		
1985-87	3815883	2.50
(7) Bushing Rack Service Kit		
1985-87	3815881	6.00
(8) Rack Assy.		
1985	3815861	103.00
1986-87	4333449	103.00
(9) Rack Seal Service Kit		
1985-87	3815878	2.75
(10) Retaining Wire		
1985-87	3815884	.50
(11) Housing (Rack & Pinion)		
1985	4147307	125.75
1986-87	4333148	275.50
(12) Bearing Assy.		
1985-87	3815868	4.75
(13) Plug (Pinion)		
1985-87	4147306	3.75
(14) Cylinder Line Assy.		
1985-87-left	3815872	3.75
right	3815873	3.75
(15) Plug (Yoke)		
1985-87	3815866	6.75
(16) Bearing & Spring Yoke		
1985-87	3815865	4.75
(17) Pinion Shaft Bearing Kit		
1985-87	4147420	15.00
(18) Valve Rings & Seal Kit		
1985-87	4147421	5.50
(19) Valve Assy.		
1985-87	3815875	85.50
(20) Bushing (Mounting)		
1985-87	3643471	4.00
(21) Bracket (Outer)		
1985-87	3643470	4.00
(22) Bracket (Inner)		
1985-87	3643469	1.00

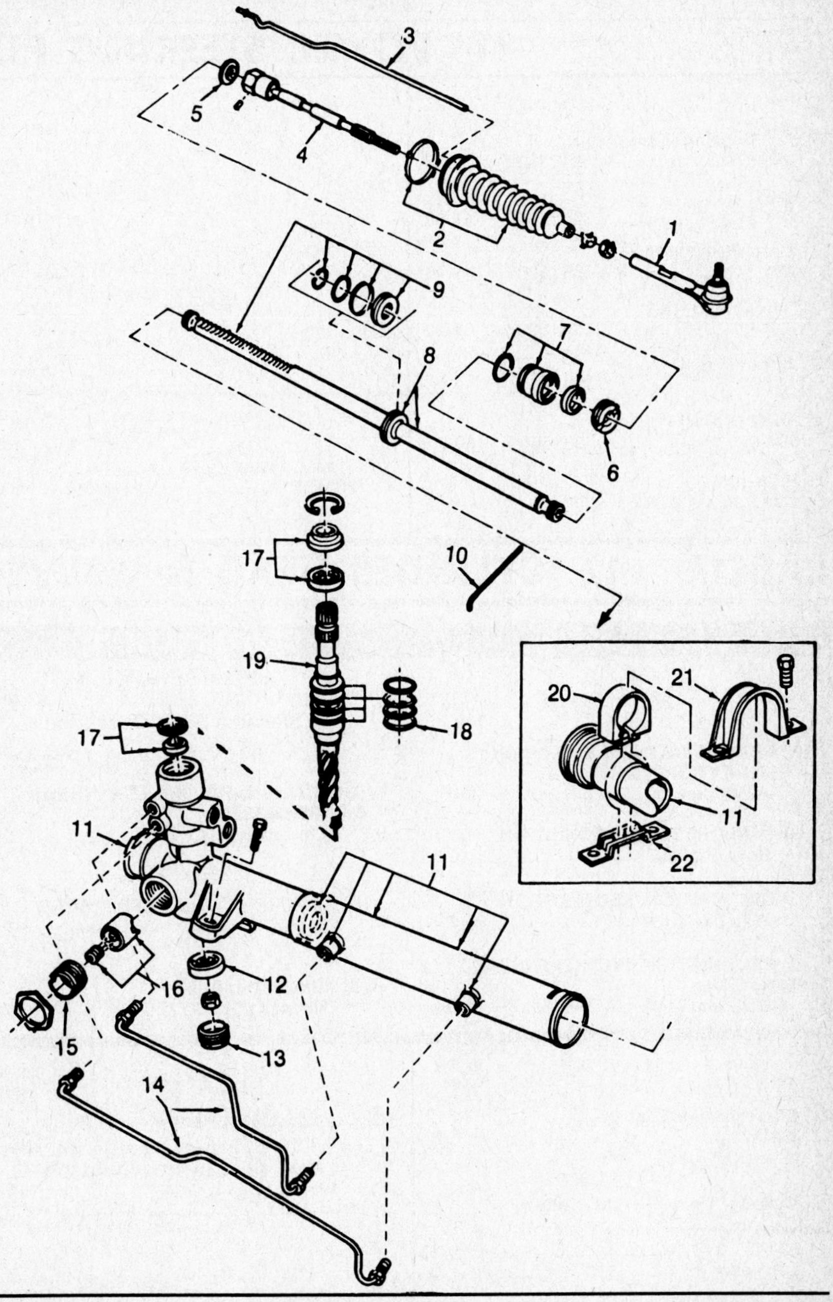

PARTS 11 STEERING GEAR-(STANDARD) 11 PARTS

	Part No.	Price
(1) Steering Gear (Manual)		
1984	4147231	242.75
1985	4147415	242.75
(2) Clamp (Boot to Tube)		
1984-85-right	4147140	N.L.
left	4147139	N.L.
(3) Boot Kit		
1984-85-right	4131348	13.50
left	4131349	13.50
(4) Clamp (Boot to Tie Rod)		
1984-85	5205313	1.25
(5) Tie Rod (Outer)		
1984-85	4106180	39.75
(6) Bracket (Outer)		
1984-85	5205225	4.00

	Part No.	Price
(7) Bushing		
1984-85	5205227	2.00
(8) Bracket (Inner)		
1984-85	5205226	1.00

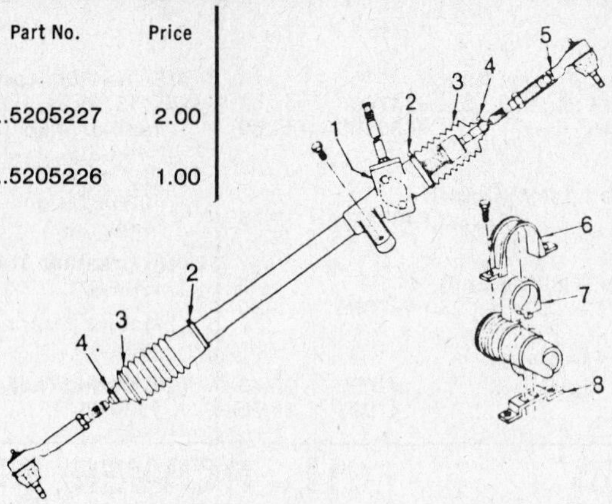

PARTS 11 POWER STEERING PUMP 11 PARTS

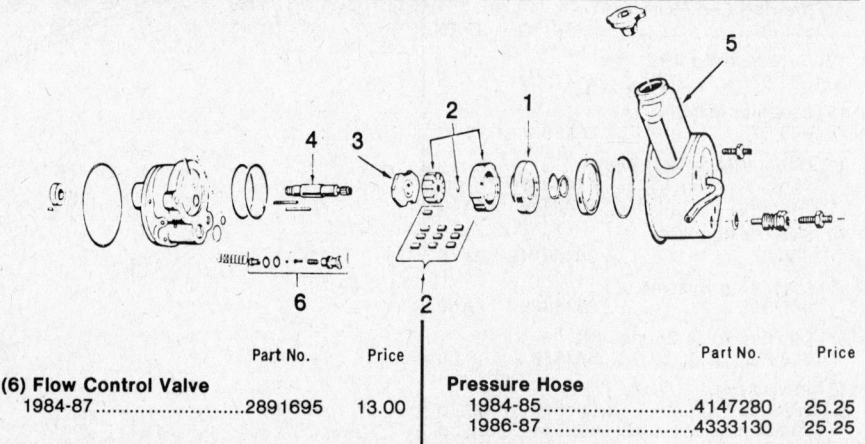

	Part No.	Price
Power Steering Pump Assy.		
1984-87	4188832	170.25
Seal Kit		
1984-87	2537838	11.00
(1) Plate (Pressure)		
1984-87	3815967	13.75
(2) Rotor Repair Kit		
1984-87	3815964	89.00
(3) Plate (Thrust)		
1984-87	3815914	12.25
(4) Shaft (Rotor)		
1984-87	3815961	39.00

(5) Housing
Serviced only in pump assembly.

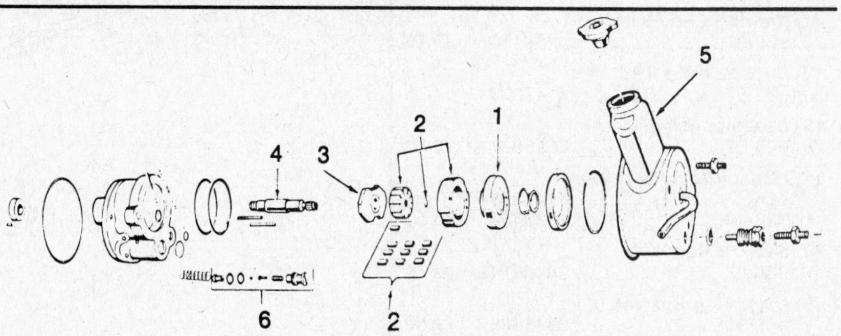

	Part No.	Price
(6) Flow Control Valve		
1984-87	2891695	13.00

	Part No.	Price
Pressure Hose		
1984-85	4147280	25.25
1986-87	4333130	25.25

LABOR 12 CYLINDER HEAD & VALVE SYSTEM 12 LABOR

COMBINATIONS

Add to Valve Job

See Machine Shop Operations

(Factory Time)	Chilton Time
(G) DRAIN, EVACUATE & RECHARGE AIR CONDITIONING SYSTEM	
All models	1.0
(G) CARBURETOR, RECONDITION	
Holly (.5)	.9
(G) DISTRIBUTOR, RECONDITION	
All models (.7)	.7
(G) RECONDITION CYL. HEAD (HEAD REMOVED)	
2.2L eng (1.4)	2.0
(G) CAMSHAFT, RENEW (HEAD DISASSEMBLED)	
OHC engs (.1)	.2
(G) REMOVE CYLINDER TOP RIDGE	
Each (.1)	.1
(G) RENEW OIL PUMP	
All engs (.2)	.3
(G) ROD BEARINGS, RENEW (PAN REMOVED)	
All engs (.7)	1.2
(G) DEGLAZE CYLINDER WALLS	
Each (.1)	.1
(G) PLASTIGAUGE BEARINGS	
Each (.1)	.1
(G) OIL FILTER ELEMENT, RENEW	
All models (.3)	.3

(Factory Time)	Chilton Time
(G) Compression Test	
1984-87	.6
(G) Cylinder Head Gasket, Renew	
Includes: Clean carbon.	
1984-87 (3.4)	4.8
w/Turbo add (.5)	.5
(G) Cylinder Head, Renew	
Includes: Transfer parts as required. Clean carbon, make all necessary adjustments.	
1984-87 (5.3)	8.0
w/Turbo add (.5)	.5
(P) Clean Carbon and Grind Valves	
Includes: R&R cylinder head. Reface valves and seats. Minor tune up.	
1984-87 (4.8)	6.8
w/Turbo add (.5)	.5
(G) Cylinder Head Cover Gasket, Renew or Reseal	
1984-87 (.8)	1.1

LABOR 12 CYLINDER HEAD & VALVE SYSTEM 12 LABOR

(Factory Time) Chilton Time

(G) Valve Rocker Arms or Shafts, Renew
1984-87-all arms (1.2) 1.6

(G) Valve Tappets, Renew
1984-87-one (1.0) 1.4
each adtnl (.1) 1

(G) Valve Springs and/or Valve Stem Oil Seals, Renew
1984-87-one (1.2) 1.5
all (1.9) 2.9

PARTS 12 CYLINDER HEAD & VALVE SYSTEM 12 PARTS

2.2L ENGINE

	Part No.	Price
Cylinder Head Gasket Pkg.		
1984-85-wo/Turbo	4271994	30.50
w/Turbo	4271926	29.25
1986-87-wo/Turbo	4397680	28.25
w/Turbo	4397681	28.25
Use R.T.V. sealer for gasket not supplied.		
(1) Cylinder Head (Partial)		
1984	4105443	340.25
1985	4323288	340.25
1986-87-wo/Turbo	4105783	340.25
w/Turbo	4343627	340.25
(2) Cylinder Head Gasket		
1984-85	4105468	11.50
1986-87	4387319	11.50
(3) End Seal (Head Cover)		
1984-87-wo/Turbo	5214479	2.25
w/Turbo	4105475	2.25
(4) Valve Spring		
1984-87-wo/Turbo	4323225	2.25
w/Turbo	4105793	2.25
(5) Valve Guide		
1984-87-Exhaust	4105715	7.75
Intake	4105716	7.75
(6) Exhaust Valve (Std.)		
1984-85-wo/Turbo	5214866	9.00
w/Turbo	5214959	21.00
1986-87-wo/Turbo	4298142	9.00
w/Turbo	4323249	21.00

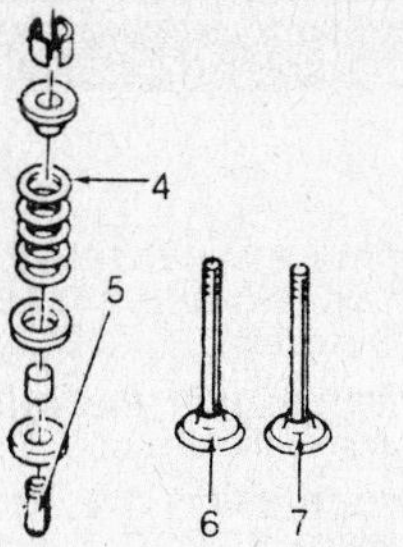

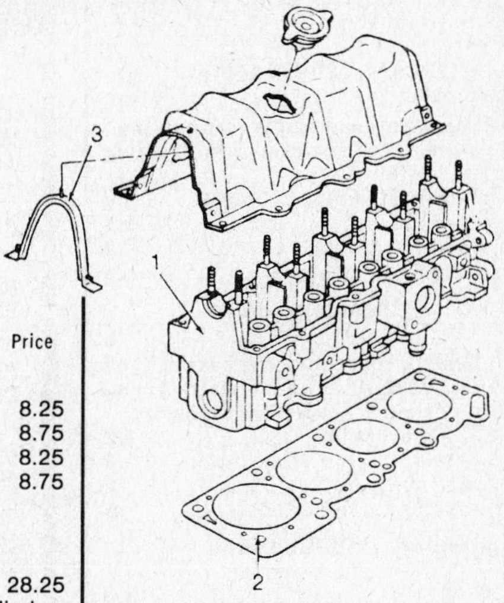

	Part No.	Price
(7) Intake Valve (Std.)		
1984-85-wo/Turbo	5214861	8.25
w/Turbo	5214895	8.75
1986-87-wo/Turbo	4298137	8.25
w/Turbo	4323244	8.75

2.5L ENGINE

	Part No.	Price
Cylinder Head Gasket Pkg.		
1986-87	4397680	28.25
Use R.T.V. sealer for gaskets not supplied.		
(1) Cylinder Head (Bare)		
1986-87	4343627	340.25
(2) Cylinder Head Gasket		
1986-87	4387319	11.50
(3) End Seal (Head Cover)		
1986-87	5214479	2.25
(4) Valve Spring		
1986-87	4323225	2.25
(5) Valve Guide		
1986-87-Exhaust	4105715	7.75
Intake	4105716	7.75
(6) Exhaust Valve (Std.)		
1986-87	4298142	9.00
(7) Intake Valve (Std.)		
1986-87	4298137	8.25

LABOR 13 ENGINE ASSEMBLY & MOUNTS 13 LABOR

(Factory Time) Chilton Time

(G) Engine Assembly, Remove & Install
Includes: R&R engine and transmission as a unit. Does not include transfer of any parts or equipment.
1984-87 .... 6.0
w/A.C. add 5
w/P.S. add 2

(P) Short Engine Assembly, Renew (w/All Internal Parts Less Cyl. Head and Oil Pan)
Includes: R&R engine and transmission as a unit. Transfer all necessary parts not supplied with replacement engine. Clean carbon, grind valves. Minor tune up.
1984-87 (9.1) 15.0
w/A.C. add (.5) 5
w/P.S. add (.2) 2

(P) Engine Assy., R&R and Recondition (Complete)
Includes: Rebore block, install new pistons, rings, rod and main bearings. Clean carbon, grind valves. Replace valve stem oil seals. Tune engine.
1984-87 (17.8) 25.2
w/A.C. add (.5) 5
w/P.S. add (.2) 2

(P) Engine Assembly, Recondition (In Car)
Includes: Expand or renew pistons, install rings, pins, rod and main bearings. Clean carbon, grind valves. Tune engine.
1984-87 (15.2) 20.8
w/P.S. add (.2) 2

(G) Engine Support, Renew
1984-87-right side (.3) 5
left side (.3) 5
center (.4) 6
Trans/Axle
Roll rod (.2) 5

PARTS 13 ENGINE ASSEMBLY & MOUNTS 13 PARTS

	Part No.	Price
Lower Engine Gasket Kit		
1984-87-2.2L	4240098	5.75
1986-87-2.5L	4240098	5.75
Use R.T.V. sealer for gaskets not supplied.		
Engine Assy.		
Consists of block, pistons, rings, connecting rods, crankshaft, bearings and caps.		
2.2L		
1984-wo/Turbo	5214968	1200.50
w/Turbo	5214969	1200.50
1985-wo/Turbo	4387201	1200.50
w/Turbo	4387202	1200.50
1986-87-wo/Turbo	4343590	1200.50
w/Turbo	4343871	1200.50
2.5L		
1986-87	4343588	1287.50

PARTS 13 ENGINE ASSEMBLY & MOUNTS 13 PARTS

	Part No.	Price
Engine Insulator (Front)		
1984-85-wo/Turbo	4295018	25.25
w/Turbo	4329588	28.25
1986-87-wo/Turbo	4295018	25.25
w/Turbo	4377458	25.25
1986-87-2.5L	4348327	25.25
Engine Insulator (Right Side)		
1984-87-bracket	4295265	11.50
bushing	4295260	12.50
Engine Insulator (Left Side)		
1984-87-bushing	4295237	9.00
bracket		
A.T.	4295255	9.75
M.T.	4295257	9.75

LABOR 14 PISTONS, RINGS & BEARINGS 14 LABOR

(Factory Time)	Chilton Time
(P) Rings, Renew (See Engine Combinations)	
Includes: Replace connecting rod bearings, deglaze cylinder walls, clean carbon. Minor tune up.	
1984-87-one cyl (4.6)	6.9
all cyls (5.9)	8.1
w/Air inj add (.2)	.2
w/Turbo add (.5)	.5
(P) Pistons or Connecting Rods, Renew	
Includes: Replace connecting rod bearings and piston rings, deglaze cylinder walls. Clean carbon from cylinder head. Minor tune up.	
1984-87-one cyl (4.9)	7.2
all cyls (6.1)	9.3
w/Air inj add (.2)	2
w/Turbo add (.5)	.5
(P) Connecting Rod Bearings, Renew	
1984-87 (2.1)	3.0

COMBINATIONS

Add To Engine Work
See Machine Shop Operations

(G) DRAIN, EVACUATE & RECHARGE AIR CONDITIONING SYSTEM	
All models	1.0
(G) DISTRIBUTOR, RECONDITION	
All models (.7)	.7
(G) RECONDITION CYL. HEAD (HEAD REMOVED)	
2.2L eng (1.4)	2.0
(G) R&R CYLINDER HEAD (ENGINE REMOVED)	
All models	1.5
(G) CONNECTING ROD, RENEW (ENGINE DISASSEMBLED)	
Each	.4
(G) CAMSHAFT, RENEW (HEAD DISASSEMBLED)	
OHC engs (.1)	.2
(G) CARBURETOR, RECONDITION	
Holly (.5)	.9
(G) REMOVE CYLINDER TOP RIDGE	
Each (.1)	.1
(G) RENEW OIL PUMP	
All engs (.2)	.3
(G) ROD BEARINGS, RENEW (PAN REMOVED)	
All engs (.7)	1.2
(G) DEGLAZE CYLINDER WALLS	
Each (.1)	.1
(G) PLASTIGAUGE BEARINGS	
Each (.1)	.1
(G) OIL FILTER ELEMENT, RENEW	
All models (.3)	.3

PARTS 14 PISTONS, RINGS & BEARINGS 14 PARTS

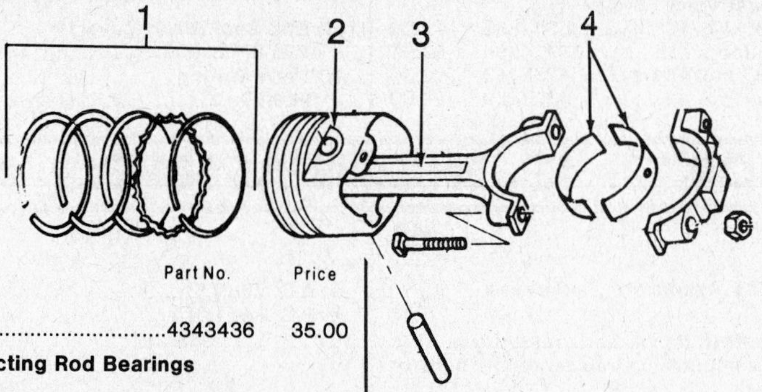

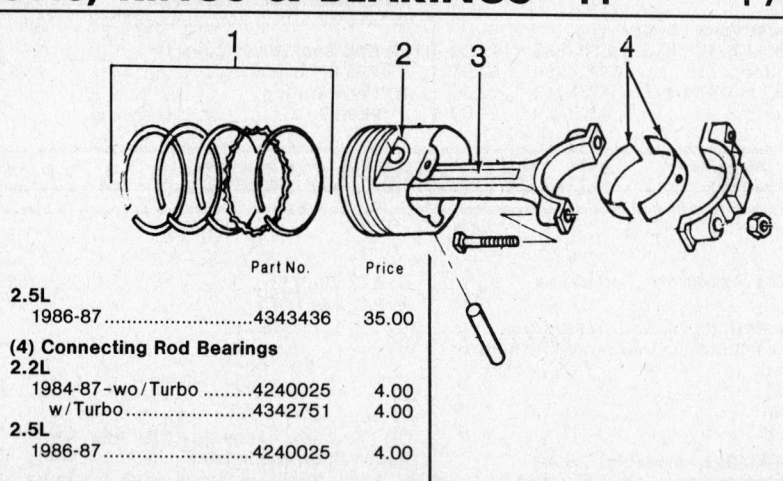

	Part No.	Price
(1) Piston Ring Set (Std.)		
2.2L		
1984-87-wo/Turbo	4240137	54.00
w/Turbo	4293799	54.00
2.5L		
1986-87	4240137	54.00
(2) Piston Assy. (Std.)		
2.2L		
1984-85-wo/Turbo	4271929	33.00
w/Turbo	4271927	33.00
1986-87-wo/Turbo	4397632	33.00
w/Turbo	4397634	33.00
2.5L		
1986-87	4397636	33.00
(3) Connecting Rod		
2.2L		
1984-85-wo/Turbo	5203384	35.00
w/Turbo	4105486	35.00
1986-87	4343725	35.00
2.5L		
1986-87	4343436	35.00
(4) Connecting Rod Bearings		
2.2L		
1984-87-wo/Turbo	4240025	4.00
w/Turbo	4342751	4.00
2.5L		
1986-87	4240025	4.00

LABOR 15 CRANKSHAFT & DAMPER 15 LABOR

(Factory Time)	Chilton Time
(P) Crankshaft and Main Bearings, Renew	
Includes: R&R engine assembly.	
1984-87 (6.7)	11.2
w/A.C. add (.5)	.5
w/P.S. add (.2)	.2
(P) Main Bearings, Renew	
1984-87	
No 2-3 or 4 (1.8)	2.8
No 1 (3.0)	4.0
No 5 (5.6)	8.8
all (7.0)	11.0
(G) Rear Main Bearing Oil Seals, Renew (Complete)	
1984-87 (3.0)	5.4
(G) Crankshaft Pulley, Renew	
1984-87 (.5)	.7
w/A.C. add (.1)	.1
w/P.S. add (.1)	.1
(G) Crankshaft Front Oil Seal, Renew	
1984-87 (1.3)	2.0
w/A.C. add (.2)	.2
w/P.S. add (.2)	.2

PARTS 15 CRANKSHAFT & DAMPER 15 PARTS

	Part No.	Price
(1) Crankshaft		
2.2L		
1984-85-wo/Turbo	5214737	317.50
w/Turbo	4105498	317.50
1986-87	4343407	317.50
2.5L		
1986-87	4343405	335.00
(2) Crankshaft Bearing Pkg. (Upper & Lower)		
2.2L & 2.5L		
1984-87-wo/Turbo		
No. 1, 2, 4, 5	4240013	6.00
No. 3	4240019	6.00
1984-87-w/Turbo		
No. 1, 2, 4, 5	4293824	6.00
No. 3	4293830	12.75
Crankshaft Oil Seal (Front)		
1984-87	4105395	2.75
Crankshaft Oil Seal (Rear)		
1984-87	5203590	6.50

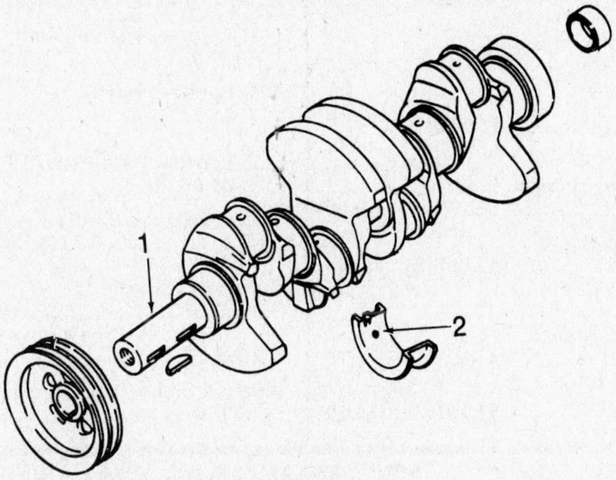

LABOR 16 CAMSHAFT & TIMING GEARS 16 LABOR

(Factory Time)	Chilton Time
(G) Timing Belt Case/Cover, Renew	
Includes: Renew gasket.	
1984-87	
upper cover (.2)	.4
lower cover (.6)	1.0
w/A.C. add (.2)	.2
w/P.S. add (.1)	.1
(G) Timing Belt, Renew	
1984-87 (1.6)	2.2
w/A.C. add (.2)	.2
w/P.S. add (.1)	.1
(G) Timing Belt Tensioner, Renew	
1984-87 (.9)	1.5
w/A.C. add (.2)	.2
w/P.S. add (.2)	.2
(G) Camshaft Sprocket, Renew	
1984-87 (1.7)	2.4
w/A.C. add (.2)	.2
w/P.S. add (.2)	.2
(G) Camshaft Oil Seal, Renew	
1984-87-front (.7)	1.1
rear (.4)	.8
(G) Camshaft, Renew	
1984-87 (1.7)	2.8
Renew valve springs add (1.1)	1.1
(G) Intermediate Shaft, Renew	
1984-87 (1.3)	2.5
w/A.C. add (.2)	.2
w/P.S. add (.1)	.1
(G) Intermediate Shaft Sprocket, Renew	
1984-87 (1.7)	2.7
w/A.C. add (.2)	.2
w/P.S. add (.2)	.2

PARTS 16 CAMSHAFT & TIMING GEARS 16 PARTS

	Part No.	Price
2.2L ENGINE		
(1) Timing Belt Cover (Upper)		
1984-87	4105714	10.00
(2) Pulley (Tension)		
1984-87	5203469	41.75
(3) Sprocket (Crankshaft)		
1984-87	5203575	14.00
(4) Timing Belt Cover (Lower)		
1984	4105293	10.00
1985-87	4343639	10.50
(5) Sprocket (Interm. Shaft)		
1984-87	4201974	16.50
(6) Timing Belt		
1984-85	5203401	22.75
1986-87	4343946	22.75
(7) Retainer Assy. (Interm. Shaft)		
1984-87	5203325	8.50
(8) Intermediate Shaft		
1984-85	4293815	95.75
1986-87	4343428	86.75
(9) Seal (Interm. Shaft)		
1984-87	4105395	2.75
(10) Camshaft		
1984-87-wo/turbo	4293817	161.50
w/turbo	4293819	161.50

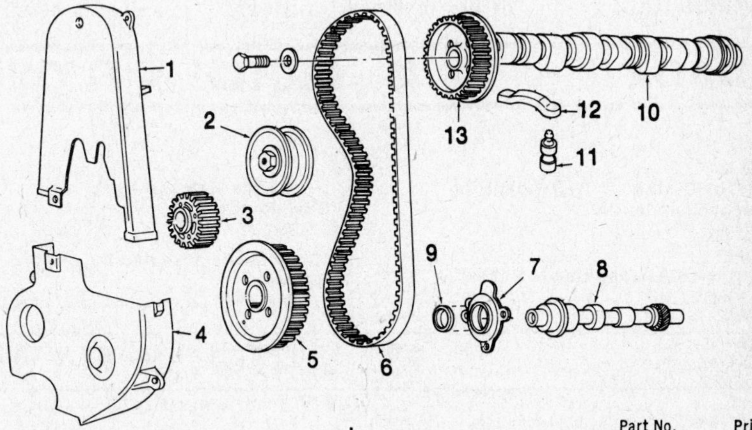

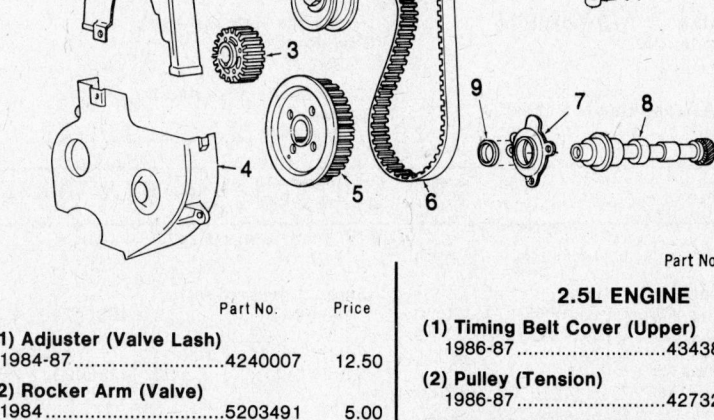

	Part No.	Price
(11) Adjuster (Valve Lash)		
1984-87	4240007	12.50
(12) Rocker Arm (Valve)		
1984	5203491	5.00
1985-87	4173390	7.00
(13) Sprocket (Camshaft)		
1984-87-wo/Turbo	4201974	16.50
w/Turbo	4201992	22.50

	Part No.	Price
2.5L ENGINE		
(1) Timing Belt Cover (Upper)		
1986-87	4343820	10.75
(2) Pulley (Tension)		
1986-87	4273241	14.00
(3) Sprocket (Crankshaft)		
1986-87	4273269	10.25
(4) Timing Belt Cover (Lower)		
1986-87	4343821	10.00

PARTS 16 CAMSHAFT & TIMING GEARS 16 PARTS

	Part No.	Price
(5) Sprocket (Interm. Shaft)		
1986-87	4273238	16.50
(6) Timing Belt		
1986-87	4343824	22.75
(7) Retainer Assy (Interm. Shaft)		
1986-87	5203325	8.50
(8) Intermediate Shaft		
1986-87	4343428	86.75
(9) Seal (Interm. Shaft)		
1986-87	4105395	2.75
(10) Camshaft		
1986-87	4293817	161.50
(11) Adjuster (Valve Lash)		
1986-87	4240007	12.50
(12) Rocker (Valve)		
1986-87	4173390	7.00
(13) Sprocket (Camshaft)		
1986-87	4273238	16.50
Chain (Balance Shaft)		
1986-87	4273260	16.25
Sprocket (Crank)		
1986-87	4273270	14.00
Sprocket (Shaft Drive)		
1986-87	4273271	11.25
Balance Shaft (Drive)		
1986-87	4323026	23.00
Gear (Shaft Drive)		
1986-87	4343783	26.50
Balance Shaft (Driven)		
1986-87	4323028	23.00
Gear (Shaft Driven)		
1986-87	4343785	26.50
Carrier & Bearings		
1986-87	4323038	70.50
Rear Cover		
1986-87	4323043	1.50
Trough (Carrier Gear Cover)		
1986-87	4323041	1.25
Trough Front Cover (Chain)		
1986-87	4323039	5.75

LABOR 17 ENGINE OILING SYSTEM 17 LABOR

(Factory Time)	Chilton Time
(G) Oil Pan or Gasket, Renew or Reseal	
1984-87 (1.0)	1.4
(P) Pressure Test Engine Bearings (Pan Off)	
All models	1.0
(G) Oil Pump, Renew	
1984-87 (1.3)	1.7
(G) Oil Pump, R&R and Recondition	
1984-87 (1.7)	2.2
(G) Oil Pressure Relief Valve Spring, Renew	
1984-87 (1.6)	2.2
(G) Oil Pressure Gauge (Engine Unit), Renew	
1984-87 (.2)	.4
(G) Oil Pressure Gauge (Dash), Renew	
1984-87 (.3)	.6
(M) Oil Filter Element, Renew	
1984-87 (.2)	.3

PARTS 17 ENGINE OILING SYSTEM 17 PARTS

	Part No.	Price
Oil Pump Assy.		
2.2L		
1984	4323327	58.50
1985	4293888	N.L.
1986-87	4397827	66.00
2.5L		
1986-87	4397827	66.00
Drive Shaft & Rotor Pkg.		
2.2L		
1984-85	4240008	24.25
1986-87	4342940	24.50
2.5L		
1986-87	4342940	24.50
Oil Filter Assy.		
1984-87	4105409	5.50
Screen Assy. (Oil)		
2.2L		
1984-85	5203324	7.75
1986-87	4343198	7.65
2.5L	4343521	4.50
Oil Pan Seal		
1984-87	5203778	1.75

LABOR 18 CLUTCH & FLYWHEEL 18 LABOR

(Factory Time)	Chilton Time
(G) Clutch Self-Adjusting Mechanism, Renew	
1984-87 (.3)	.6
(G) Clutch Release Cable, Renew	
1984-87 (.3)	.5
(G) Clutch Release Lever and/or Seal, Renew	
1984-87 (.5)	.8
(G) Clutch Release Bearing or Fork, Renew	
1984-87 (2.8)	3.8
(G) Clutch Assembly, Renew	
1984-87 (2.9)	4.0
Renew input seal add (.2)	.2
(G) Flywheel, Renew	
1984-87 (3.0)	4.2
w/Cruise control add (.2)	.2

PARTS 18 CLUTCH & FLYWHEEL 18 PARTS

	Part No.	Price
Pressure Plate		
1984-87-wo/Turbo	4295007	122.50
w/Turbo	4269309	122.50
Clutch Disc		
1984-87-wo/Turbo	4295006	66.50
w/Turbo	4269308	68.25
Clutch Release Bearing		
1984-87	4202378	44.00
Clutch Release Shaft		
1984-87	4295426	31.25
Clutch Release Fork		
1984-87	4295428	18.00
Clutch Control Cable		
1984-wo/Turbo	4295584	21.00
w/Turbo	4295596	N.L.
1985-87	4377769	18.50
Flywheel Assy.		
2.2L		
1984-wo/Turbo	4329177	142.75
w/Turbo	4348314	142.75
1985-wo/Turbo	4348312	142.50
w/Turbo	4348314	142.75
1986-87-wo/Turbo	4338874	142.75
w/Turbo	4338872	142.75
2.5L		
1986-87	4338872	142.75

LABOR 21 SHIFT LINKAGE 21 LABOR

	(Factory Time)	Chilton Time
MANUAL		
(G) Gearshift Linkage, Adjust		
1984-87	(.2)	.4
w/Console add	(.7)	.7
(G) Gearshift Lever, Renew		
1984-87	(.4)	.6
(G) Gearshift Control Rod and/or Swivel, Renew		
1984-87	(.3)	.4
(G) Gearshift Mechanism, Renew		
1984-87		
cable shift	(.9)	1.5
w/Console add	(.1)	.1
(G) Selector Shaft Seal, Renew		
1984-87	(.8)	1.1
(G) Trans/Axle Selector Shaft, Renew		
1984-87	(1.3)	1.7
(G) Gearshift Selector Cable, Renew		
1984-87	(.9)	1.4
w/Console add	(.7)	.7
(G) Gearshift Crossover Cable, Renew		
1984-87	(.8)	1.3
w/Console add	(.7)	.7
AUTOMATIC		
(G) Throttle Linkage, Adjust		
1984-87	(.2)	.4
(G) Selector Lever, Renew		
1984-87	(.3)	.4
(G) Gearshift Mechanism, Renew		
1984-87	(.4)	.8
(G) Gearshift Control Cable, Renew		
1984-87	(.5)	.8
(G) Throttle Lever Control Cable, Renew		
1984-87	(.3)	.6
(G) Gear Selector Dial, Renew		
1984-87	(.7)	1.1

LABOR 26 REAR AXLE 26 LABOR

	(Factory Time)	Chilton Time
(G) Rear Wheel Bearings, Renew or Repack		
1984-87-one side	(.6)	.9
both sides	(1.1)	1.7
(G) Rear Wheel Grease Seal, Renew		
1984-87-one side	(.4)	.7
(G) Rear Shock Absorbers, Renew		
1984-87-one	(.3	.5
both	(.4)	.7
(G) Rear Springs, Renew		
1984-87-one	(.3)	.6
both	(.5)	.8
(G) Lower Control Arm Bushings, Renew		
1984-87-one side	(.6)	1.0
(G) Stub Axle Spindle, Renew		
1984-87-each	(.5)	.7
(G) Rear Sway Bar, Renew		
1984-87	(.4)	.7
(G) Rear Wheel Mounting Studs, Renew		
1984-87-one	(.5)	.8
each adtnl		.1

PARTS 26 REAR AXLE 26 PARTS

	Part No.	Price
(1) Rear Spindle		
1984	4228123	62.75
1985-87	4228117	50.50
(2) Shim (Whl. Alignment)		
1984-87	5205114	2.25
(3) Shock Absorber		
1984-87-std.	4228334	30.00
firm	4228333	30.00
sport	4228337	30.00
(4) Track Bar Pkg.		
1984-85	4318723	63.25
1986-87	4228256	63.25
(5) Brace (Track Bar Mtg.)		
1984	4147852	17.75
1985-87	4228251	17.75
(6) Pivot Bolt		
1984-87	6500415	1.25
(7) Cup (Jounce Bumper)		
1984	4147752	7.00
1985	4228096	7.00
1986-87		
one notch	4228096	7.00
three notch	4228440	7.00
(8) Isolator (Spring Upper)		
1984-87	4147759	2.75
(9) Bumper (Jounce)		
1984	4147708	7.50
1985-87	4228159	6.50
(10) Coil Spring		
Order by model and description.		
(11) Bushing (Control Arm)		
1984-87-Std.	4147857	9.25
H.D.	4147951	9.00

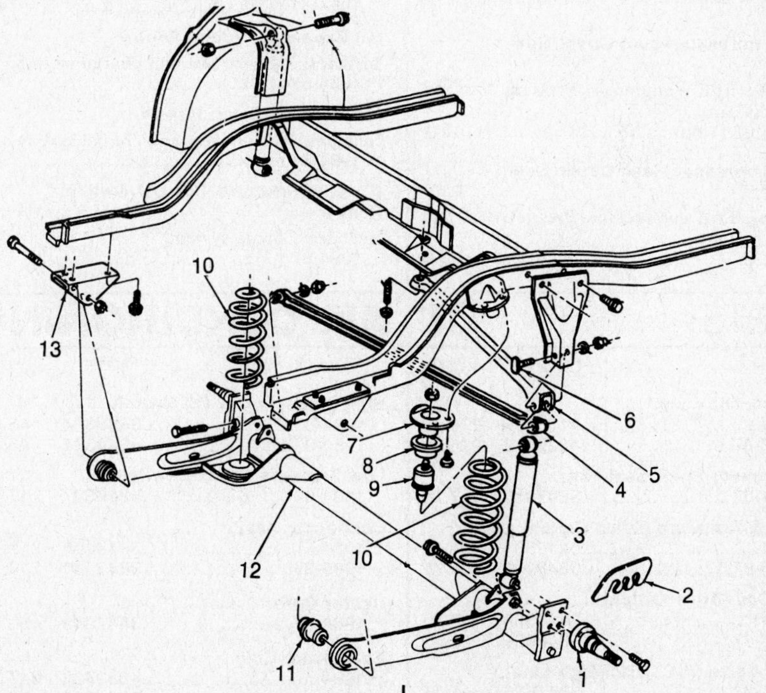

	Part No.	Price
(12) Control Arm (w/Axle Channel)		
1984	4147903	199.50
1985	4147912	193.75
1986-87-exc. Sport	4228505	N.L.
Sport	4228516	199.50
(13) Hanger (Front)		
1984-85-right	4228098	6.00
left	4228099	6.00
1986-87-right	4228452	N.L.
left	4228453	N.L.

LABOR 28 AIR CONDITIONING 28 LABOR

(Factory Time) Chilton Time

Note: If more than one item requires replacement where evacuation and discharging the system is already included in the operation, deduct 1.0 hour for each additional item to the times listed.

(G) Drain, Evacuate, Leak Test and Charge System
All models.......... 1.0

(G) Partial Charge
Includes: Leak Test.
All models (.5).......... .6

(G) Performance Test
All models.......... .8

(G) Vacuum Leak Test
All models.......... .8

(G) Compressor Drive Belt, Renew
1984-87 (.2).......... .3

C-171 COMPRESSOR

(G) Compressor Assembly, Renew
Includes: Transfer parts as required. Pressure test and charge system.
1984-87 (1.4).......... 2.5

(G) Compressor Clutch Field Coil, Renew
1984-87 (.6).......... .9

(G) Compressor Clutch Pulley (w/Hub), Renew
1984-87 (.4).......... .5

(G) Compressor Clutch Assembly, Renew
1984-87 (.6).......... .8

(G) Compressor Front Cover Seal, Renew
Includes: R&R compressor. Pressure test and charge system.
1984-87 (1.8).......... 3.1

(G) Compressor Rear Cover Seal, Renew
Includes: R&R compressor. Pressure test and charge system.
1984-87 (1.7).......... 3.0

AIR CONDITIONER TUNE-UP

For efficient operation and satisfactory performance in hot weather. The following air conditioner tune-up is suggested:

1. Clean intake filter
2. Clean condenser fins
3. Pressure test system
4. Adjust drive belt tension
5. Check antifreeze/coolant
6. Tighten compressor mounts
7. Tighten condenser and evaporator mounts
8. Inspect system for leaks (hoses, couplings, valves, etc.)
9. Partial charge system

All models.......... 1.0
If necessary to evacuate and charge system, add.......... 1.0

(Factory Time) Chilton Time

(G) Compressor Center Seal, Renew
Includes: R&R compressor. Pressure test and charge system.
1984-87 (1.9).......... 3.2

(G) Compressor Shaft Gas Seal, Renew
Includes: R&R compressor. Pressure test and charge system.
1984-87 (1.8).......... 3.1

(G) Expansion Valve, Renew
Includes: Pressure test and charge system.
1984-87 (1.0).......... 1.7

(G) Receiver Drier, Renew
Includes: Pressure test and charge system.
1984-87 (.9).......... 1.6

(G) Low Pressure Cut Off Switch, Renew
Includes: Charge system.
1984-87 (.9).......... 1.4

(Factory Time) Chilton Time

(G) High Pressure Cut Off Switch, Renew
1984-87 (.3).......... .5

(C) Clutch Cycling (Thermostatic Control) Switch, Renew
1984-87 (.3).......... .6
pressure activated (.2).......... .4

(G) Condenser Assembly, Renew
Includes: Add partial charge, leak test and charge system.
1984-87 (1.5).......... 2.5
Renew receiver drier add.......... .2

(G) Evaporator Coil, Renew
Includes: Add partial charge, leak test and charge system.
1984-87 (2.6).......... 4.5
w/Console add (.2).......... .2

(G) Temperature Control Assembly, Renew
1984-87 (.4).......... .7

(G) Push Button Vacuum Switch, Renew
1984-87 (.5).......... .9

(G) Blower Motor Switch, Renew
1984-87 (.4).......... .8

(G) Temperature Control Cable, Renew
1984-87 (.3).......... .6

(G) Blower Motor, Renew
1984-87 (.6).......... .9

(G) Blower Motor Resistor, Renew
1984-87 (.3).......... .4

(G) A.C. On-Off Switch, Renew
1985-87 (.6).......... .8

(G) Vacuum Actuators, Renew
1984-87
outside air door (.2).......... .4
heater/defroster door (.3).......... .6
A/C mode door (.8).......... 1.5

(G) Air Conditioning Hoses, Renew
Includes: Add partial charge, leak test and charge system.
1984-87-one (1.1).......... 1.6
each adtnl (.3).......... .5
Renew receiver drier add.......... .2

PARTS 28 AIR CONDITIONING 28 PARTS

	Part No.	Price
Compressor Assy.		
1984	4176059	275.00
1985-87	4339456	275.00
Compressor Shaft Seal Pkg.		
1984-87	3847916	7.75
Pulley & Armature (Drive Clutch)		
1984	5210384	101.50
1985-87	3848982	101.75
Field Coil (Drive Clutch)		
1984	3848673	60.75
1985-87	3848969	29.50
Check Valve (A.C. Discharge Line)		
1984-87	3847576	1.75
Expansion Valve (H Type)		
1984-85	4176999	59.75
1986-87	3849240	59.75
Receiver Drier		
1984-87	3848217	37.25

	Part No.	Price
High Pressure Cut Off Switch		
1984-85	3848674	45.50
1986-87	3849335	45.50
Low Pressure Cut Off Switch		
1984-87	5210377	17.25
Condenser Assy.		
1984	3848015	219.75
1985-87	3848530	219.75
Heater Core		
1984-87	3847943	90.75
Evaporator Coil		
1984	4339423	317.25
1985	3848840	29.50
1986-87	4339423	317.25
Blower Motor		
1984	4240426	66.25
1985	3849032	59.00
1986-87	3849266	59.00

	Part No.	Price
Blower Motor Switch		
1984	3848645	10.25
1985-87	3849139	10.25
Control Switch (Vacuum)		
1984	3848654	25.50
1985-87	3849140	28.50
Blower Motor Resistor		
1984	3848807	7.75
1985	3849075	N.L.
1986-87	3849235	8.50
Relay (A.C. Cut Out)		
1984	4221549	59.50
1985-87	4221576	14.00
Water Control Valve		
1984-85	3848307	27.75
1986-87-wo/Turbo	3849199	27.75
w/Turbo	3848460	27.75

LABOR 29 LOCKS, HINGES & WIND. REGULATORS 29 LABOR

(Factory Time)	Chilton Time
(G) Hood Hinge, Renew	
Does not include painting.	
1984-87 (.3)	.4
(G) Hood Latch, Renew	
1984-87 (.2)	.4
(G) Hood Release Cable, Renew	
1984-87 (.3)	.6
(G) Door Latch, Renew	
1984-87 (.5)	.7
(G) Lock Striker Plate, Renew	
1984-87 (.2)	.3
(G) Door Lock Remote Control, Renew	
1984-87 (.3)	.7
(G) Front Door Window Regulator, Renew	
1984-87	
manual (.8)	1.4
electric (.8)	1.5
(G) Door Handle (Outside), Renew	
1984-87 (.7)	1.0
(G) Liftgate Latch, Renew	
1984-87-one (.3)	.5
(G) Liftgate Hinge, Renew	
1984-87-one (.3)	.5

PARTS 29 LOCKS, HINGES & WIND. REGULATORS 29 PARTS

	Part No.	Price
Hood Lock		
1984	4270091	10.00
1985	4296593	10.00
1986-87	4341952	9.50
Hood Hinges		
1984-86-right	4296976	25.25
left	4296977	25.25
1986-87-after 10/1/85		
right	4386384	N.L.
left	4386385	N.L.
Front Door Lock		
1984		
wo/override (R.H.)	4336150	35.25
w/override (L.H.)	4336149	35.25
1985-87		
wo/override (R.H.)	4336378	35.25
w/override (L.H.)	4336377	35.25
Solenoid (Electric Door Lock)		
1984-85	4184156	60.00
1986-87	4396015	60.00
Switch (Door Lock)		
1984-87	4221135	14.00
Front Door Handle (Outside)		
1984-87 (wo/Illuminated entry)		
right	4336196	29.00
left	4336197	29.00
1984-87 (w/Illuminated entry)		
right	4336192	28.00
left	4336193	28.00
Lock Cylinder & Key Package		
(wo/Illum. entry)		
1984-wo/Tilt whl.	4246296	53.25
w/Tilt whl.	4246517	46.25
1985-87-wo/Tilt whl.	4246801	46.25
w/Tilt whl.	4246800	46.25
(w/Illum. entry)		
1984-wo/Tilt whl.	4246328	47.75
w/Tilt whl.	4246798	46.25
1985-87-wo/Tilt whl.	4246799	46.25
w/Tilt whl.	4246798	46.25
Window Regulator (Manual)		
1984-87-right	4336394	52.00
left	4336395	52.00
Window Regulator (Power)		
1984-87-right	4336444	67.50
left	4336445	67.50
Regulator Motor (Power)		
1984-right	4310940	173.25
left	4310941	173.25
1985-87-right	4365062	178.50
left	4365063	178.50
Lift Gate Latch		
1984	4246701	22.00
1985-87	4246827	19.00
Lift Gate Hinge		
1984-87	4246782	12.75
Lift Gate Electric Release Solenoid		
1984-87	4246500	41.00

LABOR 30 HEAD AND PARKING LAMPS 30 LABOR

(Factory Time)	Chilton Time
(G) Aim Headlamps	
two	.4
four	.6
(M) Headlamp Sealed Beam Bulb, Renew	
Does not include aim headlamps.	
All models-each (.2)	.3
(M) License Lamp Lens, Renew	
All models (.2)	.2
(M) License Lamp Assembly, Renew	
All models (.2)	.3
(M) Turn Signal and Parking Lamp Assy., Renew	
All models (.3)	.4
(M) Turn Signal and Parking Lamp Lens, Renew	
All models-each (.2)	.3
(M) Tail Lamp Assembly, Renew	
All models (.5)	.7
(M) Side Marker Lamp Assy., Renew	
All models-each (.2)	.3

PARTS 30 HEAD AND PARKING LAMPS 30 PARTS

	Part No.	Price
Seal Beam Unit		
(High Beam)		
1984-exc. below	153200	11.00
Halogen	153440	16.00
1985-87	153775	16.00
(High & Low Beam)		
1984-exc. below	153201	11.00
Halogen	153481	16.00
1985-87	153784	16.00
Parking and Turn Signal Lamp Assy.		
1984-87-right	4174510	14.50
left	4174511	14.50
High Mount Stop Light		
1986-87	4321643	8.00
Tail, Stop & Back-Up Lamp Assy.		
1984-87 (Laser)		
right	4174842	87.50
left	4174843	87.50
1984-87 (Daytona)		
right	4174814	94.00
left	4174815	94.00
Turbo Z		
right (lens)	4321116	50.25
left (lens)	4321117	50.25
Tail Lamp Outage Sensor		
1985-87	4312035	44.50
Side Marker Lamp Assy.		
1984-87	4174837	7.25
License Lamp Assy.		
1984-87	4174560	5.75

LABOR 31 WINDSHIELD WIPER & SPEEDOMETER 31 LABOR

(Factory Time)	Chilton Time
(G) Windshield Wiper Motor, Test and Renew	
1984-87 (.4)	.7
(G) Wiper/Washer Switch Assy., Renew	
1984-87	
std column (.8)	1.2
tilt column (1.1)	1.5
(G) Rear Window Wiper/Washer Switch, Renew	
1984-87 (.3)	.5
(G) Rear Window Wiper Motor, Renew	
1984-87 (.3)	.5
(G) Washer Pump, Renew	
1984-87	
front (.3)	.4
rear (.7)	1.0
(G) Wiper Link Assembly, Renew	
1984-87 (.5)	.7
(G) Windshield Wiper Pivot, Renew	
1984-87-one (.5)	.8
(G) Intermittent Wiper Control Module, Renew	
1984-87 (.2)	.4
(G) Speedometer Head, R&R or Renew	
Does not include reset odometer.	
1984-87 (.5)	.8
Reset odometer add	.2
(G) Speedometer Cable and Casing, Renew	
1984-87	
upper (.3)	.6
lower (.5)	.9
one piece (.6)	1.0
(G) Speedometer Cable (Inner), Renew or Lubricate	
1984-87	
upper (.3)	.5
lower (.4)	.8
one piece (.4)	.8
(G) Speedometer Drive Pinion, Renew	
Includes: Renew oil seal.	
1984-87 (.3)	.4
(G) Radio, R&R	
1984-87 (.3)	.7

PARTS 31 WINDSHIELD WIPER & SPEEDOMETER 31 PARTS

	Part No.	Price
Wiper Motor (Front)		
1984	4205951	106.75
1985-87	4339449	106.75
Wiper Pivot		
1984-87-right	4240511	17.00
left	4240512	17.00
Link w/Bushing (Windshield Wiper)		
1984-87-right	3799595	6.50
left	3799600	6.50
Armature Pkg. (Wiper Motor)		
1984	3799087	27.75
Crank w/Pin (Windshield Wiper)		
1984-87	3799597	4.50
Wiper Motor (Rear)		
1984-87	3799837	106.75
Washer Pump & Seal Pkg.		
1984-87-front	3799090	21.50
rear	3799462	21.25
Reservoir & Cap		
(Front)		
1984	3799713	7.00
1985-87	3799858	7.00
(Rear)		
1984-87	3799795	14.00
Sensor (Washer Fluid Level)		
1984-87-front	3799814	21.75
rear	3746813	22.75
Washer Pump Filter		
1984-87	3799324	4.25
Wiper & Washer Switch		
(Front)		
1984-87-wo/Tilt whl.	4221232	36.00
w/Tilt whl.	4221233	60.25
(Rear)		
1984-87	4221180	16.25
Speedometer Cable		
1984-87-upper	4312332	13.25
lower	4312816	12.75
Speedometer Assy.		
1984-85	4051602	79.25
1986-87	4375099	N.L.
Tachometer Assy.		
1984	4051614	43.25
1985-87	4051882	56.50

LABOR 32 LIGHT SWITCHES & WIRING 32 LABOR

(Factory Time)	Chilton Time
(G) Headlamp Switch, Renew	
1984-87 (.3)	.4
(G) Headlamp Dimmer Switch, Renew	
1984-87 (.3)	.6
(G) Back-Up Lamp Switch, Renew	
(w/Manual Trans)	
1984-87 (.2)	.4
(G) Stop Lamp Switch, Renew	
1984-87 (.3)	.4
w/Cruise control add (.1)	.1
(G) Neutral Safety Switch, Renew	
1984-87 (.3)	.4
(G) Parking Brake Warning Lamp Switch, Renew	
1984-87 (.2)	.3
(G) Turn Signal Switch, Renew	
1984-87	
std column (.5)	1.0
tilt column (.8)	1.5
(M) Turn Signal or Hazard Warning Flasher, Renew	
1984-87 (.2)	.3
(G) Horn, Renew	
1984-87-one	
electric (.2)	.4
air (.3)	.5
(G) Horn Relay, Renew	
1984-87 (.2)	.3
(G) Horn Switch, Renew	
1984-87 (.2)	.3
(G) Wiring Harness, Renew	
1984-87	
Main harness to dash (1.2)	3.0
Body harness (.7)	1.3
Intermediate harness (.9)	1.7
(G) Air Horn Pump Assy., Renew	
1985-87 (.2)	.4

PARTS 32 LIGHT SWITCHES & WIRING 32 PARTS

	Part No.	Price
Headlamp Switch		
1984-87	4221407	17.25
Stoplight Switch		
1984-exc. below	2926275	5.25
w/Spd. cont.	3747995	11.00
1985-87	4221651	15.50
Head Lamp Beam Selector Switch		
1984-87-wo/Tilt whl.	4221198	11.75
w/Tilt whl.	4221200	13.25
Turn Signal & Hazard Warning Switch		
1984-87-wo/Tilt whl.	4221498	36.75
w/Tilt whl.	4221304	47.00
1985-87	4221680	38.00

PARTS 32 LIGHT SWITCHES & WIRING 32 PARTS

	Part No.	Price
Backup Switch		
(A.T.)		
1984-87	4057750	8.75
(M.T.)		
1984	4221462	10.00
1985-87	4221587	10.00
Turn Signal Flasher		
1984-87-2 lamps	3837161	4.25
3 lamps	3837162	4.25
Hazard Warning Flasher		
1984-87	2932877	4.50
Horn Assy.		
1984-87-high note	2808869	24.00
low note	2808868	24.00
Horn (Air)		
1984-87	4372065	44.00
Compressor (Air Horn)		
1984-87	4372064	50.75
Wiring Harness		
Order by model and description.		

LABOR 33 GLASS 33 LABOR

	(Factory Time)	Chilton Time
(G) Windshield Glass, Renew		
Includes: Replace weatherstrip if necessary, where applicable.		
1984-87	(1.8)	2.8
(G) Front Door Glass, Renew		
1984-87	(.8)	1.1
(G) Quarter Window Glass, Renew		
1984-87	(1.0)	1.5
(G) Liftgate Glass, Renew		
1984-87	(1.1)	1.5

LABOR 34 CRUISE CONTROL 34 LABOR

	(Factory Time)	Chilton Time
(G) Speed Control Servo Assy., Renew		
1984-87	(.4)	.6
w/Turbo add	(.1)	.1
(G) Speed Control Cable, Renew		
1984-87	(.4)	.7
(G) Speed Control Turn Signal Lever Switch, Renew		
1984-87		
std column	(.5)	.9
tilt column	(1.0)	1.5
(G) Speed Control Wiring Harness, Renew		
1984-87	(.3)	.6
(G) Speed Control Safety (Cut-Out) Switch, Renew		
1984-87	(.3)	.5
(G) Electronic Speed Control Module, Renew		
1986-87	(.2)	.4

PARTS 34 CRUISE CONTROL 34 PARTS

	Part No.	Price
Cruise Control Servo.		
1984-85-exc.		
below	4179306	129.75
Turbo	4241575	129.75
Fuel inj.	4241575	129.75
1986-87-EFI	4307221	130.00
Cruise Control Switch & Lever		
1984-87-wo/Tilt		
whl.	4221455	41.75
w/Tilt whl.	4221456	41.75
Cruise Control Switch (Clutch)		
1984-87	4221697	21.75
Cruise Control Switch (On Brake)		
1984-87	4221651	15.50
Cruise Control Cable		
1984-87-exc.		
below	4288055	24.25
Turbo	4288058	24.25
Fuel inj.	4288057	24.75
Electronic Speed Control Switch		
1986-87	4342207	41.75
Module (ESC)		
1986-87	4318829	116.50
Stoplight Switch (ESC)		
1986-87	4221976	15.50
Vacuum Motor (ESC)		
1986-87	4318819	27.50
Clutch Switch (ESC)		
1986-87	4221697	21.75
Cable (ESC)		
1986-87-w/Turbo	4288057	24.75
EFI	4307565	24.75

Dodge 600 • 600ES • New Yorker • Caravelle

GROUP INDEX

ALPHABETICAL INDEX

Chrysler Corporation

Front Wheel Drive Cars

DODGE 600 • 600ES • NEW YORKER • CARAVELLE

YEAR IDENTIFICATION

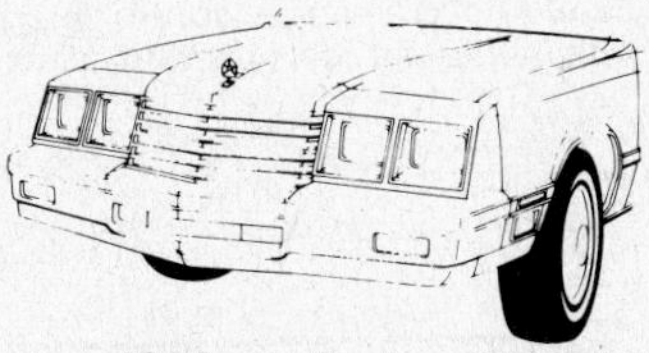

1983–87 Dodge 400, 600

1983–87 New Yorker

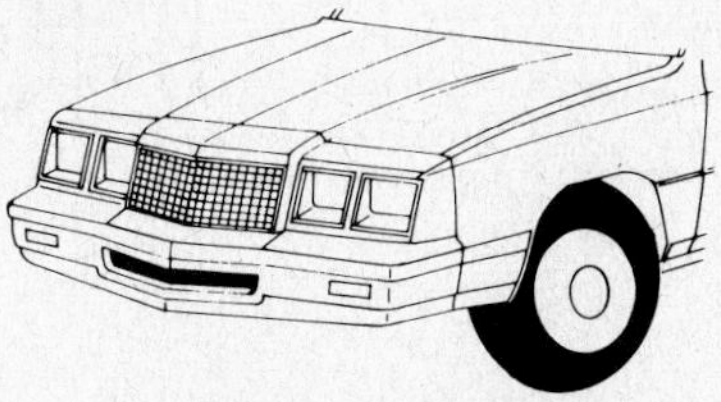

1985–87 Caravelle

VEHICLE IDENTIFICATION NUMBER (VIN)

It is important for servicing and ordering parts to be certain of the vehicle and engine identification. The VIN (vehicle identification number) is a 13 or 17 digit number visible through the windshield on the driver's side of the dash, and contains the vehicle and engine identification codes. It can be interpreted as follows:

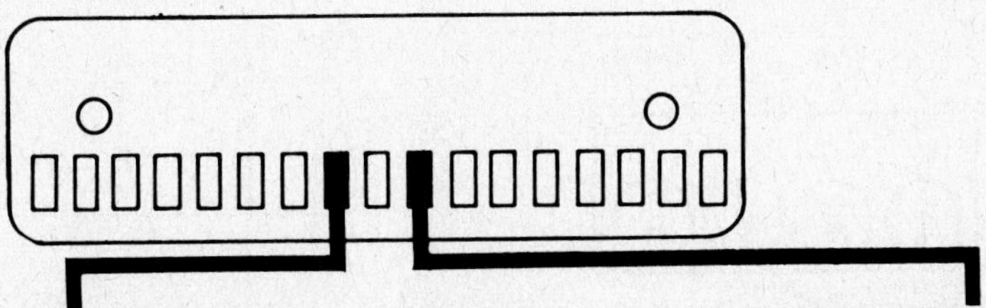

ENGINE CODE					
Code	**Cu. In.**	**Liters**	**Cyl**	**Carb. bbl**	**Eng. Mfg.**
A (84-85)	98	1.6	4	2	Peugeot
B (83)	105	1.7	4	2	VW
C (83-87)	135	2.2	4	2	Chrysler
D (83-87)	135	2.2	4	EFI	Chrysler
E (84-87)	135	2.2	4	Turbo	Chrysler
G (83-85)	156	2.6	4	2	Mitsubishi
K (86-87)	153	2.5	4	EFI	Chrysler

MODEL YEAR CODE	
Code	**Year**
C	82
D	83
E	84
F	85
G	86
H	87

The seventeen digit Vehicle Identification Number can be used to determine engine application and model year. The tenth indicates the model year, and the eighth digit identifies engine displacement.

TUNE-UP SPECIFICATIONS

Year	Eng. V.I.N. Code	No. Cyl. Displ. Cu. In.	Eng. Mfg.	h.p.	Spark Plugs Orig. Type	Spark Plugs Gap (in.)	Ignition Timing (deg.) Man. Trans.	Ignition Timing (deg.) Auto Trans.	Intake Valve Opens (deg.)■	Fuel Pump Pressure (psi)	Idle Speed (rpm) Man. Trans.	Idle Speed (rpm) Auto Trans.	Valve Lash (in.) Intake	Valve Lash (in.) Exhaust
'84-'86	A	4-98	Peugeot	64	RN12YC	.035	12B	12B	16.5	4.5-6.0	850	1000	.012H	.014H
'83	A	4-105	VW	63	65PR	.035	20B	12B	14	4.4-5.8	900	900	.008-.012H	.016-.020H
'83-'86	C	4-135	Chrysler	All	RN12YC	.035	10B	10B	16 ⑤	4.5-6.0	900	900	Hyd.	Hyd.
'84-'86	D ⑦	4-135	Chrysler	99	RN12YC	.035	12B	12B	10.5	36	850	750	Hyd.	Hyd.
'84-'86	E ⑥	4-135	Chrysler	146	RN12YC	.035	12B	12B	10	53	950	950	Hyd.	Hyd.
'83-'85	G	4-156	Mitsubishi	92	RN11YC4	③	7B	7B	25	4.5-6.0	800 ①	800 ①	.006H ⑧	.010H
'86-'87	K	4-153	Chrysler	100	RN12YC	.035	⑨	⑨	12	14.5 ⑩	⑨	⑨	Hyd.	Hyd.

NOTE: The underhood specifications sticker often reflects tune-up specification changes made in production. Sticker figures must be used if they disagree with those in this chart. Part numbers in this chart are not recommendations by Chilton for any product by brand name.

■ Before top dead center
Hyd.—Hydraulic
H—Hot
C—Cold
① 750 rpm-Canada
③ .035-.040 RN11Y—.030 in For Canada
⑤ Shelby and Hi Performance—10.5° BTDC
Turbocharged—10° BTDC
⑥ Turbo with multipoint fuel injection
⑦ EFI with single point fuel injection
⑧ Jet valve clearance—.010 in.
⑨ Refer to underhood emission control information label
⑩ '86-'87 with multipoint fuel injection—55 lbs

FIRING ORDERS

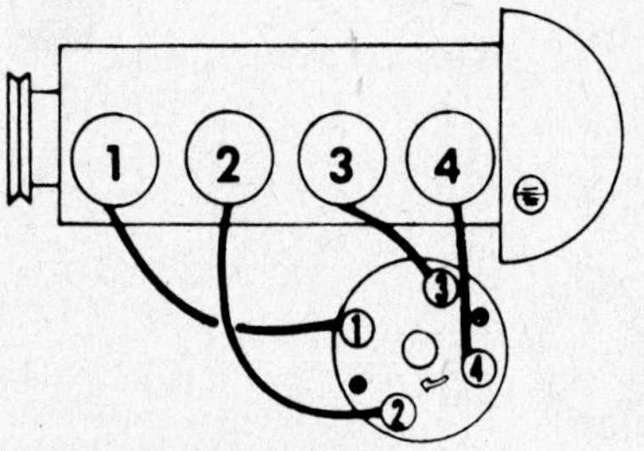

Chrysler Corp. 1.7L
Engine Firing Order: 1-3-4-2
Distributor Rotation: Clockwise

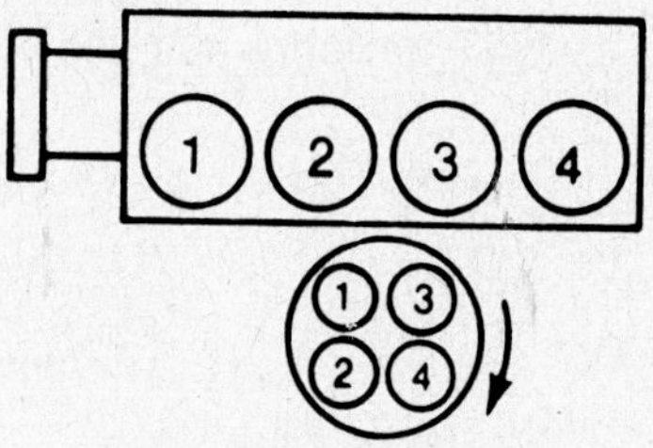

Chrysler Corp. 2.2L/2.5L
Engine Firing Order: 1-3-4-2
Distributor Rotation: Clockwise

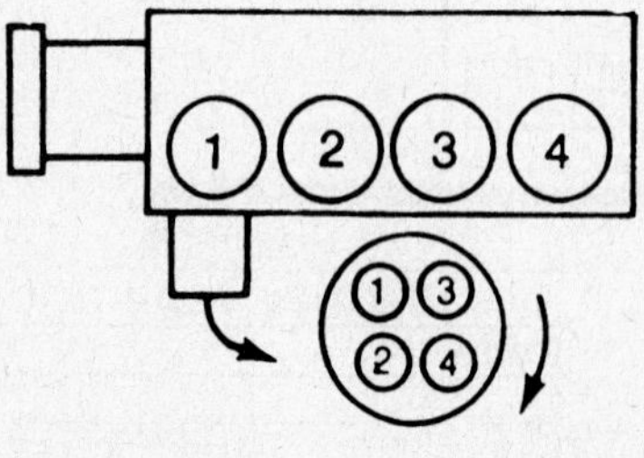

Chrysler Corp. (Mitsubishi) 2.6L
Engine firing order: 1–3–4–2
Distributor rotation: clockwise

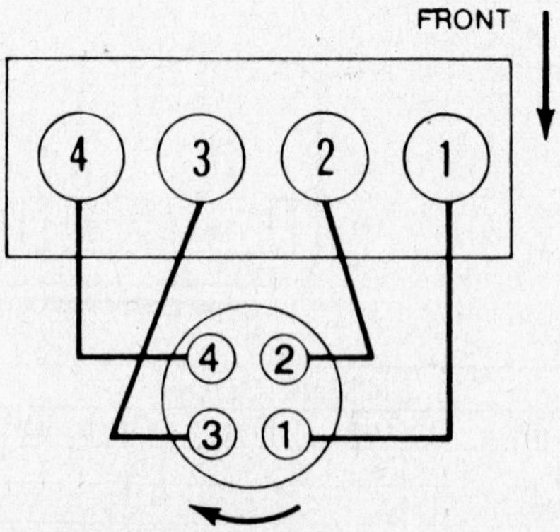

Chrysler Corp: 1.6L
Engine firing order: 1–3–4–2
Distributor rotation: clockwise

WHEEL ALIGNMENT SPECIFICATIONS

Caster is not adjustable

Year and Model	Caster	Front Camber Range (deg.)	Front Camber Preferred	Rear Camber Range (deg.)	Rear Camber Preferred	Toe-In (inches) Front	Toe-In (inches) Rear
CHRYSLER '83-'85 LeBaron, GTS, E. Class, New Yorker, Laser	1 3/16P ①	1/4N-3/4P	5/16P	1N-0	1/2N	1/16	0
'86-'87 Aries, 400, 600, Daytona, Lancer, Shadow	1 3/16P ①	1/4N-3/4P	5/16P	1 1/4N-1/4P	1/2P	1/16	0
PLYMOUTH '83-'85 Reliant, Caravelle	1 3/16P	1/4N-3/4P	5/16P	1N-0	1/2N	1/16	0
'86-'87 Reliant, Caravelle, Sundance	1 3/16P	1/4N-3/4P	5/16P	1 1/4N-1/4P	1/2P	1/16	0

① Wagon—7/8P°
② 4 door—1 3/8P°
③ Rampage, Scamp—Rear Camber
Min.—1 1/8N°
Max.—1/8N°
Pref—5/8N°

LABOR — SERVICE BAY OPERATIONS — LABOR

(Factory Time) Chilton Time

COOLING

(M) Winterize Cooling System
Includes: Run engine to check for leaks, tighten all hose connections. Test radiator and pressure cap, drain radiator and engine block. Add anti-freeze and refill system.
All models 5

(M) Thermostat, Renew
1983-87 (.4) 6

(M) Drive Belts, Renew
1983-87
Water pump-2.6L eng (.3) 5
Fan & alter (.2) 3
Air pump (.3) 4
w/A.C. add (.1) 2

(M) Radiator Hoses, Renew
1983-87-upper (.3) 4
lower (.4) 6

FUEL

(M) Carburetor Air Cleaner, Service
1983-87 (.3) 3

(M) Carburetor, Adjust (On Car)
Includes: Adjust idle mixture and idle speed.
1983-87
Holly 6
All others 5

(G) Automatic Choke, Renew
1983-87
Holly (.7) 1.0
All others (1.2) 1.5

(G) Carburetor Choke Vacuum Kick, Adjust
1983-87
Holly (.2) 3

CHILTON'S 10 POINT SAFETY CHECK

CHECK OPERATION & CONDITION OF THE FOLLOWING ITEMS:
1. Legal Registration (serial no.)
2. Tire & Wheels
3. Brake System (R&R all wheels)
4. Light Systems & Signals
5. Accelerator Linkage, Neutral Safety Switch, Shift Indicator Pointer & Seat Position Locks
6. Glass, Mirrrors, Door Locks, Seat Belts & Harness
7. Wipers, Washers & Defrosters
8. Frame, Steering, Shocks, Front & Rear Suspension
9. Fuel & Exhaust Systems
10. Road Test Vehicle

All models 1.0
Exhaust Smog Analysis, add 4

(Factory Time) Chilton Time

BRAKES

(G) Brake Pedal Free Play, Adjust
All models 3

(G) Brakes, Adjust (Minor)
Includes: Adjust brake shoes, fill master cylinder.
two wheels 4

(G) Bleed Brakes (Four Wheels)
Includes: Add fluid.
All models (.4) 6

(M) Parking Brake, Adjust
1983-87 (.3) 4

(Factory Time) Chilton Time

LUBRICATION SERVICE

(M) Lubricate Chassis, Change Oil & Filter
Includes: Inspect and correct all fluid levels.
All models 6
Install grease fittings add 1

(M) Engine Oil & Filter, Change
Includes: Inspect and correct all fluid levels.
All models 4

(M) Lubricate Chassis
Includes: Inspect and correct all fluid levels.
All models 4
Install grease fittings add 1

WHEELS

(G) Wheels, Balance
one 3
each adtnl 2

(M) Wheel, Renew
one (.3) 5

(M) Wheels, Rotate (All)
All models 5

ELECTRICAL

(G) Aim Headlamps
two 4
four 6

(M) Headlamp Sealed Beam Bulb, Renew
Does not include aim headlamps.
All models-each (.2) 3

(M) License Lamp Lens, Renew
All models (.2) 2

LABOR — SERVICE BAY OPERATIONS — LABOR

(Factory Time)	Chilton Time
(M) License Lamp Assembly, Renew	
All models (.2)	.3
(M) Turn Signal and Parking Lamp Assy., Renew	
All models (.3)	.4
(M) Tail Lamp Assembly, Renew	
All models (.3)	.4
(M) Side Marker Lamp Assy., Renew	
All models-each (.2)	.3
(M) Turn Signal or Hazard Warning Flasher, Renew	
All models (.2)	.3
(G) Horn Relay, Renew	
All models (.2)	.3
(G) Horn, Renew	
All models-one (.2)	.4
(M) Battery Cables, Renew	
All models	
positive (.5)	.6
negative (.2)	.2

LABOR — 1 TUNE UP 1 — LABOR

(Factory Time)	Chilton Time
(G) Compression Test	
Four–1983-87	.6

(G) Engine Tune Up, (Electronic Ignition)

Includes: Test battery and clean connections. Tighten manifold bolts and carburetor mounting bolts. Check engine compression, clean and adjust or renew spark plugs. Test resistance of spark plug cables. Inspect distributor cap, rotor, reluctor and pick up plate. Adjust air gap. Check vacuum advance operation. Reset ignition timing. Adjust idle mixture and idle speed. Service air cleaner. Inspect crankcase ventilation system. Inspect and adjust drive belts. Inspect choke operation and adjust or free up. Check operation of EGR valve.

(Factory Time)	Chilton Time
Four–1983-87	1.5
w/Turbo add	.5

LABOR — 2 IGNITION SYSTEM 2 — LABOR

(Factory Time)	Chilton Time
(G) Spark Plugs, Clean and Reset or Renew	
1983-87 (.5)	.6
(G) Ignition Timing, Reset	
1983-87 (.3)	.4
(G) Spark Control Computer, Renew (SCC)	
1983 (.3)	1.0
(G) Distributor Assembly, Renew	
Includes: Reset ignition timing.	
1983-87 (.4)	.6
(G) Distributor, R&R and Recondition	
Includes: Reset ignition timing.	
1983-87 (.9)	1.5
(G) Electronic Control Unit, Renew	
1983-87	
2.6L eng (.3)	.5
(G) Distributor Pick-Up Plate and Coil Assy., Renew (Hall Effect)	
Does not require R&R of distributor.	
1983-87	
2.2L & 2.5L engs (.3)	.6
(G) Distributor Pick-Up Set, Renew	
Does not require R&R of distributor.	
1983-87	
2.6L eng (.5)	.7
(G) Distributor Ignitor Set, Renew	
Does not require R&R of distributor.	
1983-87	
2.6L eng (.4)	.6
(G) Distributor Breaker Assy., Renew	
Does not require R&R of distributor.	
1983-87	
2.6L eng (.4)	.6
(G) Distributor Reluctor and Governor Assy., Renew	
Does not require R&R of distributor.	
1983-87	
2.6L eng (.3)	.5
(G) Distributor Vacuum Advance Control Unit, Renew	
Does not require R&R of distributor.	
1983-87	
2.6L eng (.6)	.9
(G) Distributor Cap and/or Rotor, Renew	
1983-87 (.2)	.4
(G) Ignition Coil, Renew	
1983-87 (.2)	.4
(G) Ignition Cables, Renew	
1983-87 (.2)	.4
(G) Ignition Switch, Renew	
1983-87	
std column (.4)	.8
tilt column (.4)	.9
(G) Ignition Key Warning Buzzer, Renew	
1983-87 (.2)	.4
(G) Ignition Switch Time Delay Relay, Renew	
1983-87 (.2)	.3
(G) Ignition Key Buzzer/Chime Switch, Renew	
1983-87	
std column (.6)	1.2
tilt column (.5)	1.0
(G) Ignition Lock Housing, Renew	
Does not include painting.	
1983-87-std column (.8)	1.3
Tilt column	
console shift (1.1)	1.7
column shift (.8)	1.3

PARTS — 2 ELECTRONIC IGNITION 2 — PARTS

2.2 & 2.5 LITER ENGINE

	Part No.	Price
(1) Distributor Assy.		
1983-85-exc. Turbo	4240470	66.25
Turbo	5213525	79.75
1986-87-exc. Turbo	5226575	N.L.
Turbo	5213525	79.75
(2) Distributor Cap		
1983-85	4240446	8.25
1986-87	5226527	N.L.
(3) Rotor Assy.		
1983-85	5213728	8.25
1986-87	5226535	8.25
(4) Switch		
1983	4240471	30.50
1984-85-exc. Turbo	5213522	32.00
Turbo	5213524	44.50
1986-87-exc. Turbo	5226616	26.50
Turbo	5226617	N.L.
1986-87-2.5L	5226616	26.50
Coil		
1983-87	4176009	26.75
Ignition Switch Assy.		
1983-87-w/Tilt whl.	4221201	23.00
wo/Tilt whl.	3747882	14.50

PARTS 2 ELECTRONIC IGNITION 2 PARTS

	Part No.	Price
Power Module		
1983	5213980	140.00
1984-w/Turbo	5213574	140.00
E.F.I.	5213581	105.00
1985-87-w/Turbo	5226766	105.00
E.F.I.		
exc. Calif.	5226765	105.00
Calif.	5226648	140.00
Control (Electronic Advance)		
1983-M.T.		
exc. Calif.	5213834	N.L.
Calif.	5213838	110.00
1983-A.T. (exc. Calif.)		
to 10-8-82	5213852	N.L.
after 10-8-82	5213854	110.00
(Calif.)		
to 11-1-82	5213836	110.00
after 11-1-82	5213858	110.00
High Alt	5213840	N.L.
1984-M.T.		
exc. Calif.	5226284	110.00
Calif.	5213838	110.00
1984-A.T.		
exc. Calif.	5226286	110.00
Calif.	5213858	110.00
High Alt	5213840	N.L.
1985-87-M.T.		
exc. Calif.	5226439	110.00
Calif.	5226455	110.00
1985-87-A.T.		
exc. Calif.	5226505	N.L.
Calif.	5226451	110.00
Canada	5226527	N.L.

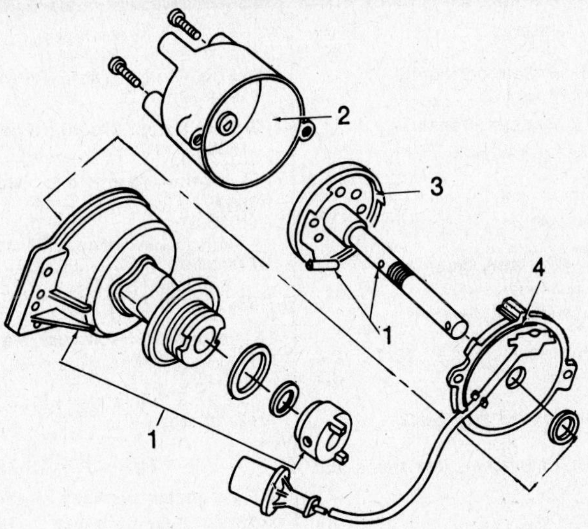

PARTS 2 ELECTRONIC IGNITION 2 PARTS

2.6 LITER ENGINE

	Part No.	Price
Distributor Assy.		
1983-84-exc.		
below	MD013791	288.75
w/Calif. em.	MD013793	288.75
1985	MD067134	288.75
(1) Distributor Cap		
1983-85	MD607466	14.50
(2) Rotor Assy.		
1983-85	MD607734	9.00
(3) Governor Set		
1983-85	MD607886	40.00
(4) Pick Up Set		
1983-85	MD607770	16.75
(5) Igniter Set		
1983-85	MD607478	157.50
(6) Breaker Assy.		
1983-85	MD607470	31.75
(7) Plate		
1983-85	MD607359	1.25

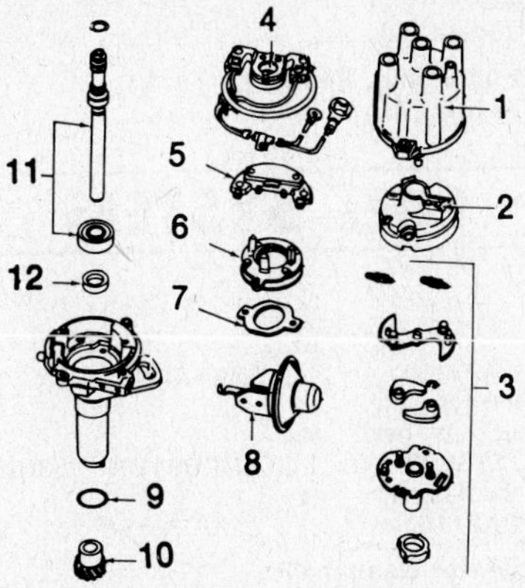

	Part No.	Price
(8) Vacuum Control		
1983-84-exc.		
below	MD607475	19.00
w/Calif. em.	MD607477	21.00
1985	MD607885	17.25
(9) "O" Ring		
1983-85	MD602412	1.25
(10) Drive Gear & Pin		
1983-85	MD607226	15.50
(11) Shaft Assy.		
1983-85	MD607468	42.75
(12) Oil Seal		
1983-85	MD607405	5.75
Ignition Wire Set		
1983-84	MD027766	27.50
1985	MD085766	29.00
Coil Assy.		
1983-84	MD025703	37.00
1985	MD013789	25.75
High Tension Cable		
1983-84	MD027723	5.25
1985	MD088537	8.00
Ignition Switch		
1983-85-w/Tilt whl	4221201	23.00
wo/Tilt whl.	3747882	14.50

LABOR 3 FUEL SYSTEM 3 LABOR

(Factory Time)	Chilton Time
(G) Fuel Pump, Test	
All models	
mechanical	.3
electric	.4
(M) Carburetor Air Cleaner, Service	
1983-87 (.3)	.3
(G) Carburetor, Adjust (On Car)	
Includes: Adjust idle mixture and idle speed. Reset ignition timing.	
1983-87	
Holly	.6
All others	.5
(G) Idle Solenoid, Renew	
1983-87 (.4)	.6
(G) Coolant Temperature Sensor/Switch, Renew	
1983-87 (.2)	.4
(G) Accelerator Pump, Renew	
1983-87	
Holly (.4)	.8
All others (.8)	1.1
(G) Automatic Choke, Renew	
1983-87	
Holly (.7)	1.0
All others (1.2)	1.5
(G) Choke Vacuum Kick Diaphragm, Renew	
1983	
Holly (.2)	.4
(G) Throttle Position Sensor, Renew	
1984-87 (.2)	.4

LABOR 3 FUEL SYSTEM 3 LABOR

	Factory Time	Chilton Time
(G) Heated Air Door Sensor, Renew		
1983-87-one	(.2)	.3
(G) Carburetor Assembly, Renew		
Includes: All necessary adjustments.		
1983-87		
Holly	(.8)	1.3
All others	(.7)	1.2
(G) Carburetor, R&R and Clean or Recondition		
Includes: All necessary adjustments.		
1983-87		
Holly	(1.6)	2.4
All others	(2.5)	3.5
(G) Carburetor Needle and Seat, Renew		
Includes: Adjust float level, idle speed and mixture.		
1983-87		
Holly	(.7)	1.1
All others	(1.1)	1.5
(M) Fuel Filter, Renew		
1983-87		
in line	(.2)	.3
in tank	(.5)	.8
(G) Fuel Pump, Renew		
1983-87		
mechanical	(.4)	.7
electric	(.6)	1.0
Add pump test if performed.		
(G) Fuel Tank, Renew		
1983-87	(1.2)	1.6
(G) Fuel Gauge (Tank), Renew		
1983-87	(.7)	1.0
(G) Fuel Gauge (Dash), Renew		
1983-87	(.3)	.6
(G) Intake Manifold or Gasket, Renew		
1983-87		
2.2L & 2.5L engs	(2.0)	3.7
w/Turbo add	(.6)	.6
2.6L eng	(1.9)	3.0
Renew manif add	(.2)	.5
(G) Intake and Exhaust Manifold Gaskets, Renew		
1983-87		
2.2L & 2.5L engs	(1.9)	3.5
w/Turbo add	(.6)	.6
TURBOCHARGER		
(G) Turbocharger Assy., Renew		
Includes: Renew gaskets.		
1984-87	(2.7)	3.5
(G) Fuel Pressure Regulator, Renew		
1984-87	(.3)	.5
(G) Vehicle Speed Sensor, Renew		
1984-87	(.3)	.6
(G) Detonation Sensor, Renew		
1984-87	(.2)	.4
(G) Change Temperature Sensor, Renew		
1984-87	(.2)	.4
(G) Fuel Pump, Renew (In Tank)		
1984-87	(1.0)	1.6
ELECTRONIC FUEL INJECTION		
(G) Throttle Body, Renew		
1984-87	(.5)	.9
(G) Fuel Pressure Regulator, Renew		
1984-87	(.2)	.4
w/Turbo add	(.1)	.1
(G) Fuel Pump, Renew		
1984-87	(.6)	.9
(G) Fuel Inlet Chamber, Renew		
1984-87	(.4)	.7
(G) Automatic Idle Speed Assy., Renew		
1984-87		
motor	(.3)	.5
adapter	(.3)	.5
(G) Fuel Injector Rail, Renew		
1984-87	(.6)	1.0
(G) Fuel Injector, Renew		
1984-87		
wo/Turbo	(.3)	.5
w/Turbo		
one	(.4)	.6
each adtnl	(.1)	.2,
(G) Logic Module, Renew		
1984-87	(.2)	.3
(G) Power Module, Renew		
1984-87	(.3)	.4
(G) M.A.P. Sensor, Renew		
1984-87	(.4)	.6
(G) Throttle Position Sensor (Potentiometer), Renew		
1984-87	(.2)	.3

PARTS 3 FUEL SYSTEM 3 PARTS

	Part No.	Price
Carburetor Assy. (Holley, New)		
1983-2.2L (Model 5220)		
R40023	4227382	325.75
R40024	4227383	325.75
R40025	4227384	325.75
R40026	4227385	325.75
1984-2.2L (Model 5220)		
R40076	4288425	Disc.
R40078	4288428	Disc.
1983-2.2L (Model 6520)		
R40003	4227365	325.75
R40010	4287087	325.75
R40004	4287087	325.75
R40012	4227372	325.75
R40008	4287093	325.75
R40005	4227374	325.75
R40014	4227375	325.75
R40006	4293879	326.00
Carburetor Assy. (2.6L)		
1983-exc. below	MD073978	521.50
Calif. & Hi alt.	MD017066	536.50
Hi alt.	MD017307	521.50
1984-exc. below	MD068740	521.50
Calif.	MD068743	536.50
Hi alt.	MD017307	521.50
1985 (exc. Calif.)		
to eng. no. DW6223	MD081509	521.50
from eng. no. EA2116	MD088137	521.50
1985 (w/Calif.)		
up to eng. no. DW6223	MD084289	536.50
from eng. no. EA2116	MD082758	521.50
Carburetor Gasket Kit		
2.2L		
1983-Model 5220	4271875	6.75
Model 6520	4267174	6.75
1984-Model 5220	4293850	7.25
2.6L		
1983	MD608571	35.75
1984-exc. Calif.	MD608643	35.75
Calif.	MD608571	35.75
1985-exc. Calif.	MD608797	36.75
Calif.	MD612215	36.75
Carburetor Repair Kit		
2.2L		
1983-Model 5220	4293725	41.25
1984-Model 5220	4293854	26.25
With model 6520 order by carburetor tag number.		
Fuel Pump Assy.		
2.2L		
1983	4271892	35.00
1984-wo/Turbo	4293802	36.00
Turbo	4279296	217.00
1985-exc. below	4293802	36.00
E.F.I.	4279951	225.25
Turbo	4279917	217.00
1986-87-E.F.I.	4075445	36.00
Turbo	4279917	217.00
2.6L		
1983-87	MD026591	50.50
Fuel Gauge (Tank)		
1983-exc. below	4051682	30.25
w/warn. signal	4051684	30.25
1984-exc. below	4051867	30.50
E.F.I. & Turbo	4051866	30.25
1985-exc. below	4051849	30.50
E.F.I.	4279950	32.50
Turbo	4051895	30.50
1986-87-E.F.I.	4051663	30.25
Turbo	4051663	30.25
Fuel Gauge (Dash)		
1983-85	4051565	24.25
1986-87	4375010	35.50
Manifold Gasket (Intake & Exhaust)		
2.2L		
1983-87	4105745	6.75
2.6L		
1983-85-intake	MD024628	5.00
exhaust	MD025684	11.25

PARTS 3 ELECTRONIC FUEL INJECTION 3 PARTS

	Part No.	Price
Throttle Body Assy. (Exc. Turbo)		
1984	4275617	735.50
1985	4342948	N.L.
1986-87-2.2L	4300265	290.00
2.5L	4300266	290.00
Throttle Body Assy. (Turbo)		
1984	4268801	325.00
1985	4288276	325.00

PARTS 3 ELECTRONIC FUEL INJECTION 3 PARTS

	Part No.	Price
1986-87	4307255	325.00
(1) Fitting Kit (Hose)		
1984-87	4287316	11.00
(2) Injector Kit		
1984-85	4275985	160.00
1986-87 (Seals)	4300254	6.50
Injector (w/O-rings)		
1986-87	4300257	53.55
(3) Hose & Seal Kit (Pressure Regulator)		
1984-87	4287324	5.25
(4) Gasket (Intake Manifold)		
1984-87	4275531	1.75
(5) Potentiometer (Kit)		
exc Turbo		
1984	4287743	32.00
1985	4179848	32.00
Turbo		
1984	4221396	N.L.
1985-87	4179849	32.00
Throttle Position Sensor		
exc Turbo		
1986-87	5226509	29.00
(6) Housing Kit (AIS)		
1984-85	4287730	17.75
(7) Regulator Kit		
1984-85	4287320	53.25
1986-87	4300263	60.00
(8) Motor Kit (AIS)		
1984-85	4287712	64.00
(9) "O" Ring Kit (AIS)		
1984-85	4287714	3.50
Motor (w/O-ring)		
1986-87	4300264	N.L.
M.A.P. Sensor		
1984-wo/Turbo	4318114	66.00
Turbo	4318115	66.00
1985-wo/Turbo	5226223	51.00
Turbo	5226224	56.25

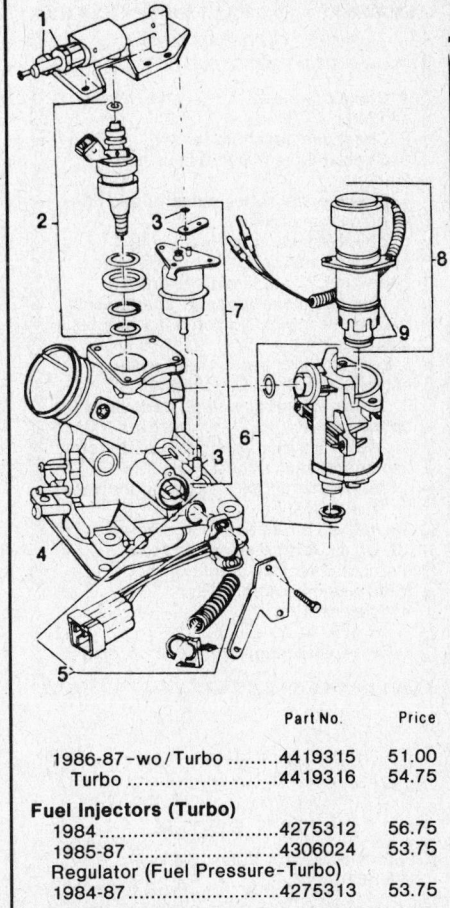

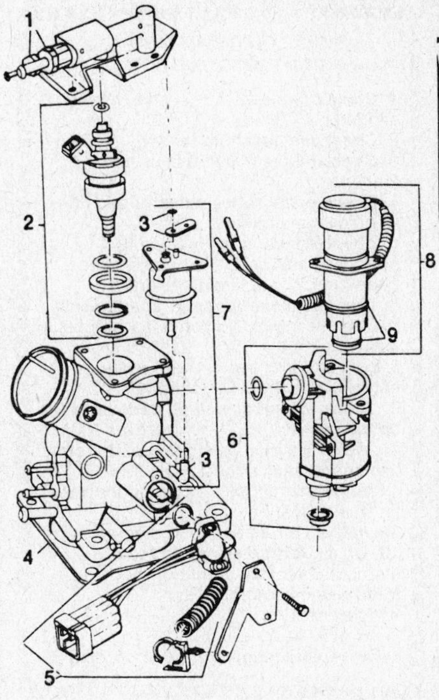

	Part No.	Price
1986-87-wo/Turbo	4419315	51.00
Turbo	4419316	54.75
Fuel Injectors (Turbo)		
1984	4275312	56.75
1985-87	4306024	53.75
Regulator (Fuel Pressure-Turbo)		
1984-87	4275313	53.75
Fuel Rail (Turbo)		
1984	4275301	3.25

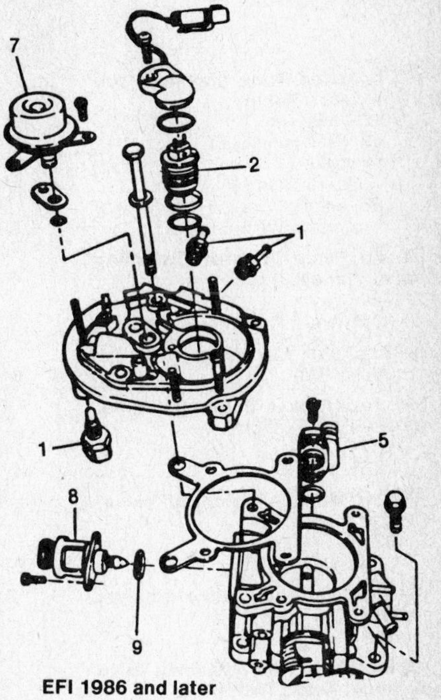

EFI 1986 and later

	Part No.	Price
1985-87	4275555	39.25
Auto. Shutdown Relay		
1984-87	4221279	13.75
Charge Temp. Sensor		
1984	5213463	15.00
1985-87	5226355	15.00
Detonation Sensor		
1985-87-wo/Turbo	5213629	23.75
Turbo	4318118	23.75

PARTS 3 TURBOCHARGER SYSTEM 3 PARTS

	Part No.	Price
(1) E.G.R. Valve		

Replacement E.G.R. valve must be ordered according to the stamping number on the original valve.

	Part No.	Price
(2) Elbow (Compresser Inlet)		
1984-87	4105461	30.50
(3) Gasket (Inlet Elbow)		
1984-87	4227973	.50
(4) Turbocharger Assy.		
1984	4105794	566.25
1985-87	4105800	567.00
(5) Oxygen Sensor		
1984-87	4301346	36.75
(6) Hose Connector		
1984	5214609	6.00
1985-87	4323444	6.00

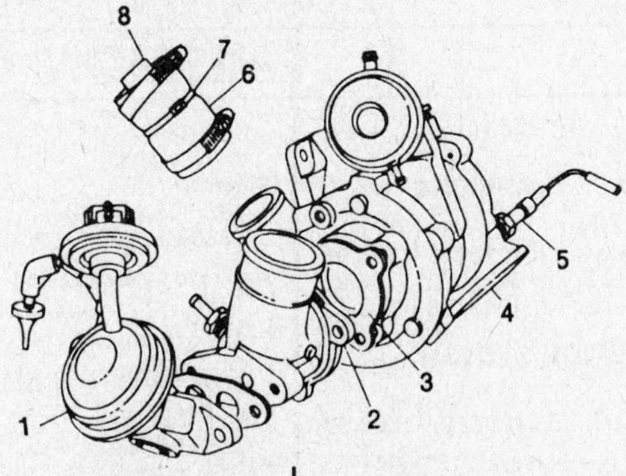

	Part No.	Price
(7) Strap (Vane Hose)		
1984-87	4105719	2.00
(8) Vane (Air Flow)		
1984-87	4105465	3.00

LABOR 3A EMISSION CONTROLS 3A LABOR

CRANKCASE EMISSION

(Factory Time)		Chilton Time
(M) Crankcase Vent Valve, Renew		
1983-87	(.2)	.3
(M) Crankcase Vent Hose, Renew		
1983-87-one	(.2)	.2

AIR INJECTION SYSTEM

(Factory Time)		Chilton Time
(G) Air Pump, Renew		
1983		
2.2L eng	(.4)	.7

LABOR 3A EMISSION CONTROLS 3A LABOR

(Factory Time) Chilton Time

(G) Injection Tube and Aspirator Valve Assy., Renew
1983-2.2L eng.
ex manif mount (.5) 8
to conv
one or both (.4).......... .6
EFI engs
to conv (.5).......... .8

(G) Air Pump Diverter/Switching Valve, Renew
1983
2.2L eng (.3).......... .5

(G) Aspirator Valve, Renew
1984-87 (.3).......... .5

(G) Enrichment Solenoid Valve, Renew
1984-87
2.6L eng (.3).......... .4

(G) Jet Mixture Solenoid Valve, Renew
1984-87
2.6L eng (.4).......... .6

(G) Deceleration Solenoid Valve, Renew
1984-87 (.3).......... .6

(G) Distributor/Air Switching Valve Solenoid Assy., Renew
1984-87 (.2).......... .3

(G) Change Temperature Sensor, Renew
1984-87 (.2).......... .4

(G) Intake Air Temperature Sensor, Renew
1984-87 (.2).......... .3

EVAPORATIVE EMISSION

(M) Vapor Canister, Renew
1983-87 (.3).......... .4

(M) Vapor Canister Filter, Renew
1983-87 (.2).......... .3

(M) Vapor Canister Valve, Renew
1985-87 (.2).......... .3

CHILTON'S EMISSION CONTROL TUNE-UP

1. Clean or renew P.C.V. valve, hoses and filter
2. Check fuel tank cap for sealing ability
3. Check fuel tank and fuel lines for leakage
4. Check evaporation canister and filter. Replace if necessary
5. Check engine compression to determine leakage of unburned gases. (Add time for items of interference
6. Test and clean or renew spark plugs
7. Check engine oil dipstick for sealing ability
8. Test exhaust system with analyzer and check system for leakage
9. Check exhaust manifold heat valve for operation
10. Adjust ignition timing and carburetor idle speed and mixture
11. Check automatic choke mechanism for free operation
12. Inspect air cleaner and element
13. On models so equipped test distributor vacuum control switch and transmission control switch

All models
Four 1.2
For repairs made charge accordingly

(Factory Time) Chilton Time

E.G.R. SYSTEM

(G) Jet Air Control Valve, Renew
1984-87 (.5).......... .7

(G) Coolant Vacuum Switch, Renew (CCEVS)
1983-87 (.3).......... .4

(G) E.G.R. Back Pressure Valve, Renew
1984-87 (.2).......... .3

(Factory Time) Chilton Time

(G) E.G.R. and Purge Control Solenoid Bank, Renew
1984-87 (.2).......... .3

(G) Exhaust Gas Recirculation Control Valve, Renew
1983-87
2.2L & 2.5L engs (.6).......... .8
w/Turbo add (.2).......... .2
2.6L eng (.3).......... .5

(G) Coolant Control Vacuum Valve (CCEGR), Renew
1983-87-one (.3).......... .4
both (.4).......... .6

EFE SYSTEM

(G) Oxygen Sensor, Renew
1983-87
2.2L & 2.5L engs (.2).......... .4
2.6L eng (.5).......... .7

(G) High Altitude Compensator, Renew
1983-87 (.3).......... .5

(G) Detonation Sensor, Renew
1984-87 (.2).......... .4

HEATED INLET AIR SYSTEM

(M) Carburetor Air Cleaner, Service
1983-87 (.3).......... .3

(G) Heated Air Door Delay Valve, Renew
1983-87-one (.2).......... .3

(G) Heated Air Door Sensor, Renew
1984-87
2.6L eng (.2).......... .3

PULSE AIR SYSTEM

(G) Pulse Air Feeder, Renew
1983-87 (.6).......... .9

(G) Pulse Air Feeder Tube, Renew
1983-87 (.7).......... 1.1

PARTS 3A EMISSION CONTROLS 3A PARTS

CRANKCASE EMISSIONS

	Part No.	Price
Crankcase Vent Valve		
1984-87-wo/Turbo	4273145	4.00
Turbo	3671076	4.25
E.F.I.	4343766	7.00

AIR INJECTION SYSTEM

	Part No.	Price
Air Pump Assy.		
1983-85	4267227	162.50
Air Pump Pulley		
1983-85	5203585	4.75
Air Pump Drive Pulley		
1983-85	5214518	7.75
Air Pump Diverter Valve		
1983-85	4179719	30.50
Air Switch & Relief Valve		
1983-85	4275053	30.00

ASPIRATOR SYSTEM

	Part No.	Price
Aspirator Valve		
1984-85	4041966	10.75
1986-87	4300376	19.50
Silencer		
1984-85	4287704	3.50
1986-87	4300382	4.50
Aspirator Valve (2.6L)		
1984	4041966	10.75
1985	4300376	19.50

EVAPORATIVE EMISSION SYSTEM

	Part No.	Price
Vapor Canister		
1983-85-2.2L		
3ported	4271982	49.25
4ported	4241838	52.75
1986-87	4241838	52.75
1983-85-2.6L	4241837	48.75

EXHAUST GAS RECIRCULATION SYSTEM

E.G.R. Valve
Replacement E.G.R. valve must be ordered according to the stamping number on the original valve.

	Part No.	Price
Coolant Control Switch (C.C.E.G.R.)		
1983-85-Black	4049277	17.50
Yellow	3879736	17.50
Engine Coolant Control Switch (C.C.E.V.)		
1983-85-Orange	4049208	17.50
Natural	3879707	17.50
Green	4049276	17.50
Vacuum Idle Speed Solenoid		
1983-85	5213348	16.00
E.G.R. Time Delay Control		
1983-Blue	4145202	45.25
Red	4111481	43.00
Charge Temperature Switch		
1983-87	4111482	7.00
Crankcase Vent Valve (P.C.V.)		
1983-87-2.2L	4111482	7.00
2.6L	MD026613	9.75
Solenoid Valve		
1984-87 (2.6L)		
exc. Calif.	MD071769	48.75
Calif.	MD025274	66.75
Solenoid Vacuum Valve (A/C)		
1984	4240417	16.00
1985-87-exc. below	5226361	20.50
E.F.I.	5226359	20.50

PARTS 3A EMISSION CONTROLS 3A PARTS

	Part No.	Price
Solenoid Vacuum Valve (A/C Speed Up)		
1984-87	5213348	16.00
Dual Vacuum Solenoid (w/TBI)		
1984-87	5213957	28.50
Quad Vacuum Solenoid		
1985-87-Turbo	5226352	57.00
Sensor (Eng. Speed)		
1984-85-2.6L	MD025273	128.25
Thermo Valve		
2.6L		
(exc. Calif.)		
1984	MD025264	40.25
1985	MD073096	27.50
(Calif.)		
1984-85	MD073500	40.25
Control Unit (Carburetor)		
2.6L		
1984	MD076139	387.00
1985	MD080152	230.75

EFE SYSTEM

	Part No.	Price
Oxygen Sensor		
2.2L		
1983-84	4301346	36.75
1985-87	4301346	36.75
2.6L		
1983-84	MD073036	132.50
1985	MD082058	230.75
High Altitude Compensator		
2.2L		
1983-87	4306202	62.00
2.6L		
1983-84-exc. Calif.	MD026725	96.00
Calif.	MD026706	98.50
1985	MD026708	96.00

PULSE AIR SYSTEM

	Part No.	Price
Pulse Air Feeder		
1983-85	MD025587	139.75
Valve Assy. (Reed)		
1983-85	MD071430	41.75
Pulse Air Feeder Tube		
1983-85	MD070897	31.50

LABOR 4 ALTERNATOR & REGULATOR 4 LABOR

(Factory Time)	Chilton Time
(G) Alternator Circuits, Test	
Includes: Test battery, regulator and alternator output.	
All models	.6
(M) Alternator Drive Belt, Renew	
1983-87 (.2)	.3
w/A.C. add (.1)	.1
(G) Alternator Assembly, Renew	
Includes: Transfer pulley if required.	
1983-87 (.8)	1.2
w/A.C. add (.3)	.3
Add circuit test if performed.	
(G) Alternator, R&R and Recondition	
Includes: Test and disassemble.	
1983-87 (1.5)	2.1
w/A.C. add (.3)	.3
(G) Alternator Front Bearing or Retainer, Renew	
Includes: R&R alternator.	
1983-87 (.8)	1.1
w/A.C. add (.3)	.3
Renew rear brg add	.2
(G) Voltage Regulator, Test and Renew	
1983-87	
external type (.2)	.4
internal type (1.0)	*1.6
*w/A.C. add (.3)	.3
(G) Electronic Voltage Monitor, Renew	
1983-87 (.4)	.6

PARTS 4 ALTERNATOR & REGULATOR 4 PARTS

2.2L & 2.5L ENGINE

	Part No.	Price
Alternator Assy.		
1983-84 (wo/EFI)		
60 amp	5213079	129.00
78 amp	5213053	129.00
1984 (EFI)		
60 amp	5213540	129.00
78 amp	5213541	129.00
1985-87-60 amp	5213762	129.00
78 amp	5213763	129.00
90 amp	4339440	154.50
100 amp	5213847	161.50
(1) Drive End Shield		
1983-87-60 amp	5206421	20.00
78 amp	5206422	20.25
90 amp	5226840	39.50
(2) Drive End Shield Bearing		
1983-87	3656444	8.75
(3) Rotor Assy.		
1983-87-60 amp	4240413	62.00
78 amp	4240414	62.00
90 amp	5226841	102.25
(4) Stator		
1983-87-60 amp	4091515	36.75
78 amp	4091517	36.75
90 amp	5226315	151.00
(5) Battery Terminal & Positive Heat Sink Pkg.		
1983-87-60 amp	4026082	17.50
78 amp	4026083	17.50
(6) Heat Sink (Negative)		
1983-87-60 amp	3438721	17.75
78 amp	3755114	17.75

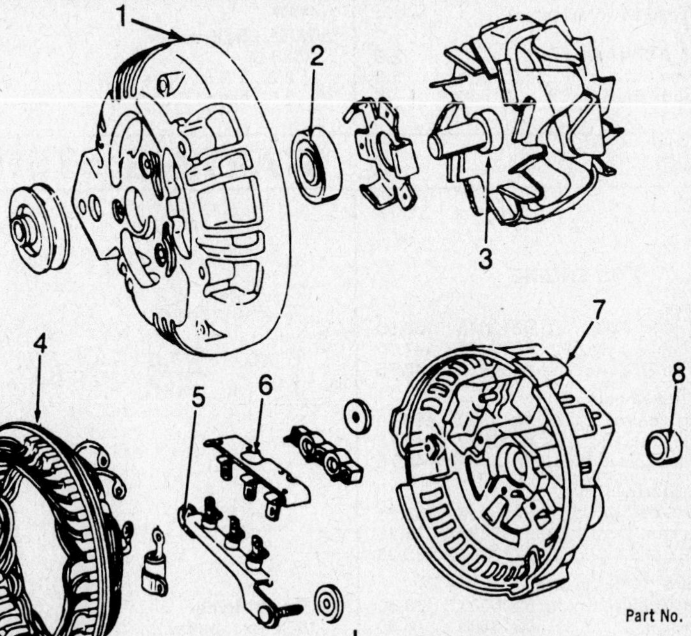

	Part No.	Price
(7) Rectifier End Shield		
1983-87-60 amp	5213092	57.00
78 amp	4240405	58.75
90 amp	5226845	57.50
(8) End Shield Bearing (Rectifier)		
1983-87	3755184	3.25
Brush & Washer Pkg.		
1984-87-exc. 90 amp	5211772	4.50
90 amp	5266572	5.50
Instrument Voltage Regulator		
1983-87	2258413	8.25
Voltage Regulator		
1983-87	4111990	29.00
1986-87	4379100	29.00

PARTS 4 ALTERNATOR AND REGULATOR 4 PARTS

	Part No.	Price
2.6 LITER ENGINE		
Alternator Assy.		
1983	MD025215	334.00
1984-85	MD062007	334.00
(1) Pulley		
1983	MD607426	14.00
1984-85	MD607779	27.50
(2) Fan		
(3) Bearing (Front)		
1983-85	MM502264	10.00
(4) Rotor Assy.		
1983-85	MD607425	122.00
(5) Bearing (Rear)		
1983-85	MD602789	8.00
(6) Stator Assy.		
1983-85	MD607428	101.50
(7) Rectifier Set		
1983-85	MD607430	64.00

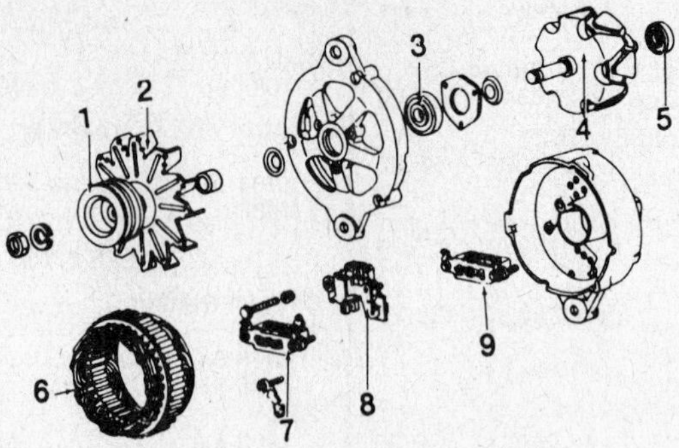

	Part No.	Price
(8) Regulator Assy.		
1983-85	MD607372	71.75

	Part No.	Price
(9) Rectifier Assy.		
1983-85	MD607429	69.50

LABOR 5 STARTING SYSTEM 5 LABOR

(Factory Time)	Chilton Time
(G) Starter Draw Test (On Car)	
All models	.3
(G) Starter Assy., Renew	
Includes: Test starter relay, starter solenoid and amperage draw.	
1983-87	
2.2L & 2.5L engs (1.0)	1.3
2.6L eng (.7)	1.0
w/Turbo add (.5)	.5
(G) Starter, R&R and Recondition	
Includes: Turn down armature.	
1983-87	
2.2L & 2.5L engs	2.8
2.6L eng	2.5
w/Turbo add (.5)	.5
Renew field coils add (.5)	.5
(G) Starter Drive, Renew	
Includes: R&R starter.	
1983-87	
2.2L & 2.5L engs (1.4)	1.8
2.6L eng (.8)	1.1
w/Turbo add (.5)	.5
(G) Starter Solenoid or Switch, Renew	
Includes: R&R starter.	
1983-87	
2.2L & 2.5L engs (1.0)	1.4
2.6L eng (1.0)	1.4
w/Turbo add (.5)	.5
(G) Starter Relay, Renew	
1983-87 (.2)	.3
(G) Neutral Safety Switch, Renew	
1983-87 (.3)	.4
(G) Ignition Switch, Renew	
1983-87	
std column (.4)	.8
tilt column (.4)	.9
(M) Battery Cables, Renew	
1983-87	
positive (.5)	.6
ground (.2)	.2

PARTS 5 STARTING SYSTEM 5 PARTS

	Part No.	Price
2.2L ENGINE		
Starter Assy.		
1983-85-exc. Turbo	5213045	105.50
Turbo	5213450	147.00
1986-87	4339472	148.75
(1) Drive End Housing		
1983-exc. below	5213309	28.50
Bosch	5213382	42.75
1984-87	5213382	42.75
(2) Clutch Starter Drive		
1983-exc. below	5213310	35.25
Bosch	5213384	35.25
1984-87	5213384	35.25
(3) Armature		
1983-exc. below	5206631	78.50
Bosch	5213383	78.50
1984-87	5213383	78.50
(4) Solenoid		
1983-exc. below	5213313	48.75
Bosch	5206607	57.25
1984-87	5206607	57.25
(5) Field Frame		
1983-exc. below	5213311	56.75
Bosch	5213385	69.00
1984-87	5213385	69.00

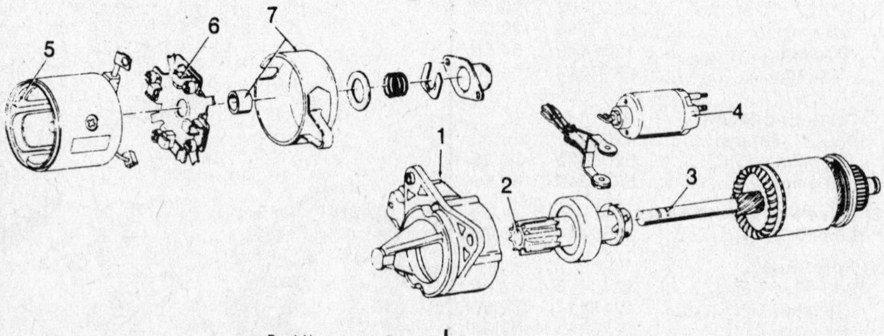

	Part No.	Price
(6) Brush Holder		
1983-exc. below	5206634	10.75
Bosch	5206605	21.75
1984-87	5206605	21.75
(7) Head End (w/Bearing)		
1983-exc. below	5213312	16.25
Bosch	5206606	27.00
1984-87	5206606	27.00
Battery Ground Cable		
1983	4274887	8.00
1984-87	4274273	8.00

	Part No.	Price
Battery Positive Cable		
1983-A.T.	4274272	29.50
M.T.	4274975	23.00
1984-A.T.	4304555	29.50
M.T.	4304473	29.50
1985-A.T.	4331481	20.75
M.T.	4331482	26.75
1986-87		
A.T.	4368366	20.75
M.T.	4368367	26.75

PARTS 5 STARTING SYSTEM 5 PARTS

	Part No.	Price
2.5L ENGINE		
Starter Assembly		
1986-87	5226444	105.50
Gear Train		
1986-87	5227114	102.50
Clutch Starter Drive		
1986-87	5227115	27.25
Armature		
1986-87	5227125	158.25
Solenoid		
1986-87	5227607	N.L.
Brush Holder		
1986-87	5227131	75.00
Fork Lever		
1986-87	5227119	5.00

PARTS 5 STARTING SYSTEM 5 PARTS

	Part No.	Price
2.6L ENGINE		
Starter Assy.		
1983-85	MD025235	272.75
(1) Housing Sub. Assy.		
1983-85	MD604320	38.25
(2) Clutch Sub. Assy.		
1983-85	MD604319	96.00
(3) Retainer		
1983-85	MD604332	2.50
(4) Pinion		
1983-85	MD604324	10.50
(5) Magnetic Switch Assy.		
1983-85	MD604321	102.50
(6) Armature Assy.		
1983-85	MD604318	115.50
(7) Yoke Assy.		
1983-85	MD604317	74.00
(8) Holder Assy.		
1983-85	MD604322	19.25
Battery Ground Cable		
1983	4274887	8.00
1984-85	4274273	8.00

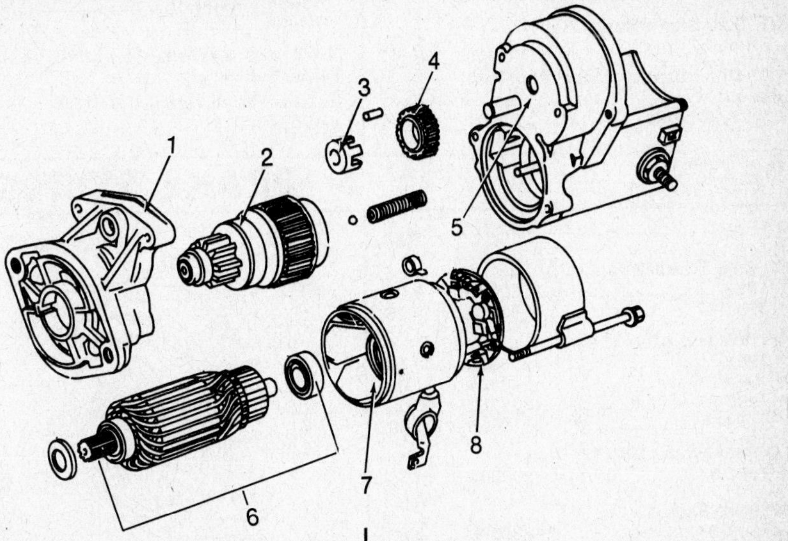

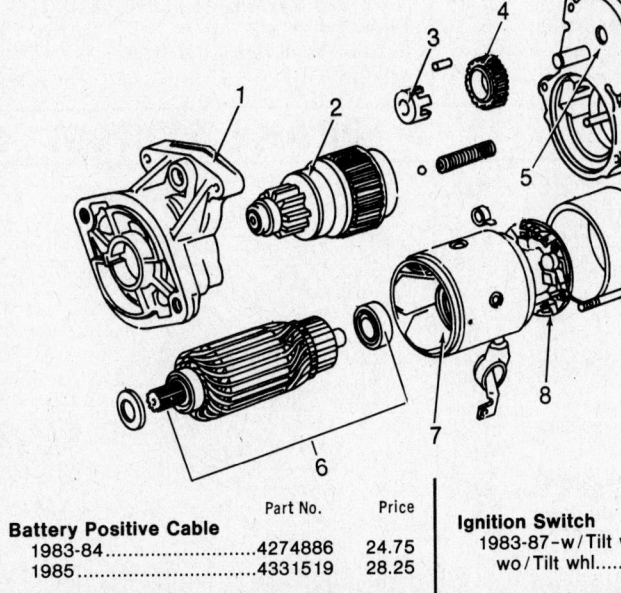

	Part No.	Price
Battery Positive Cable		
1983-84	4274886	24.75
1985	4331519	28.25
Ignition Switch		
1983-87-w/Tilt whl.	4221201	23.00
wo/Tilt whl.	3747882	14.50

LABOR 6 BRAKE SYSTEM 6 LABOR

	(Factory Time)	Chilton Time
(G) Brake Pedal Free Play, Adjust		
All models		.3
(G) Brakes, Adjust (Minor)		
Includes: Adjust brake shoes, fill master cylinder.		
two wheels		.4
(G) Bleed Brakes (Four Wheels)		
Includes: Add fluid.		
All models	(.4)	.6
(G) Brake Shoes and/or Pads, Renew		
Includes: Install new or exchange brake shoes or pads. Adjust service and hand brake. Bleed system.		
1983-87-front-disc	(.5)	.8
rear-drum	(.8)	1.5
all four wheels	(1.3)	2.2
Resurface disc rotor, add-each		.9
Resurface brake drum, add-each		.5
(G) Rear Brake Drum, Renew (One)		
1983-87	(.5)	.6

BRAKE HYDRAULIC SYSTEM

	(Factory Time)	Chilton Time
(G) Wheel Cylinder, Renew		
Includes: Bleed system.		
1983-87-one	(.7)	1.1
both	(1.3)	2.1

COMBINATIONS

Add To Brakes, Renew

See Machine Shop Operations

	(Factory Time)	Chilton Time
(G) RENEW WHEEL CYLINDER		
Each		.3
(G) REBUILD WHEEL CYLINDER		
Each		.4
(G) REBUILD CALIPER ASSEMBLY		
Each		.5
(G) RENEW MASTER CYLINDER		
All models		.6
(G) REBUILD MASTER CYLINDER		
All models		.8
(G) RENEW BRAKE HOSE		
Each	(.3)	.3
(G) RENEW REAR WHEEL GREASE SEALS		
One side		.3
(G) RENEW DISC BRAKE ROTOR		
Each		.2
(G) RENEW BRAKE DRUM		
Each	(.3)	.3
(G) DISC BRAKE ROTOR STUDS, RENEW		
Each		.1

	(Factory Time)	Chilton Time
(G) Wheel Cylinder, R&R and Rebuild		
Includes: Hone cylinder and bleed system.		
1983-87-one		1.2
both		2.3
(G) Brake Hose, Renew (Flex)		
Includes: Bleed system.		
1983-87-front-one	(.4)	.8
rear-one	(.4)	.8
(G) Master Cylinder, Renew		
Includes: Bleed complete system.		
1983-87	(.5)	.9
(G) Master Cylinder, R&R and Rebuild		
Includes: Bleed complete system.		
1983-87		1.6
(G) Master Cylinder Reservoir, Renew		
Includes: Bleed brake system.		
1983-87	(.6)	1.0
(G) Brake System, Flush and Refill		
All models		1.2

POWER BRAKES

	(Factory Time)	Chilton Time
(G) Brake Booster Assembly, Renew		
1983-87	(1.3)	1.6

LABOR — 6 BRAKE SYSTEM 6 — LABOR

(Factory Time) Chilton Time

(G) Brake Booster Check Valve, Renew
1983-87 (.2) 2

DISC BRAKES

(G) Disc Brake Pads, Renew
Includes: Install new disc brake pads only.
1983-87 (.5) 8

(G) Disc Brake Rotor, Renew
1983-87-one (.3) 6

(G) Disc Brake Rotor and Hub, Renew
1983-87-one (1.0) 1.4

(G) Caliper Assembly, Renew
Includes: Bleed system.
1983-87-one (.5) 9
both 1.7

(G) Caliper Assy., R&R and Recondition
Includes: Bleed system.
1983-87-one (.8) 1.4
both 2.7

(G) Brake System Combination Valve, Renew
Includes: Bleed complete system.
1983-87 (1.2) 1.5

PARKING BRAKE

(M) Parking Brake, Adjust
1983-87 (.3) 4

(G) Parking Brake Warning Lamp Switch, Renew
1983-87 (.2) 3

(G) Parking Brake Control, Renew
1983-87 (.5) 7

(G) Parking Brake Cables, Renew
Includes: Adjust parking brake.
1983-87-front (.5) 7
intermediate (.3) 5
rear-each (.6) 8

PARTS — 6 BRAKE SYSTEM 6 — PARTS

	Part No.	Price
(1) Rear Wheel Bearing (Outer)		
1983	3580888	9.25
1984-87	4293196	9.25
(2) Hub and Drum (Rear)		
1983	4238538	100.50
1984	4293195	87.00
1985-87-4 stud	4238538	100.50
5 stud	4313635	100.50
(3) Rear Wheel Bearing (Inner)		
1983-87	4238567	14.75
(4) Dust Seal		
1983-87	4238570	3.50
(5) Brake Shoes & Lining Set (Rear)		
1983-87	4238826	39.75
(6) Wheel Cylinder (Rear)		
1983-87	4238706	22.50
Master Cylinder Assy.		
1983-84	4271388	70.50
1985-87	4294268	80.00
Reservoir (Master Cylinder)		
1983-85	3766498	5.00
1986-87	4294495	N.L.
Mounting Grommets (Reservoir)		
1983-87	5204149	1.00

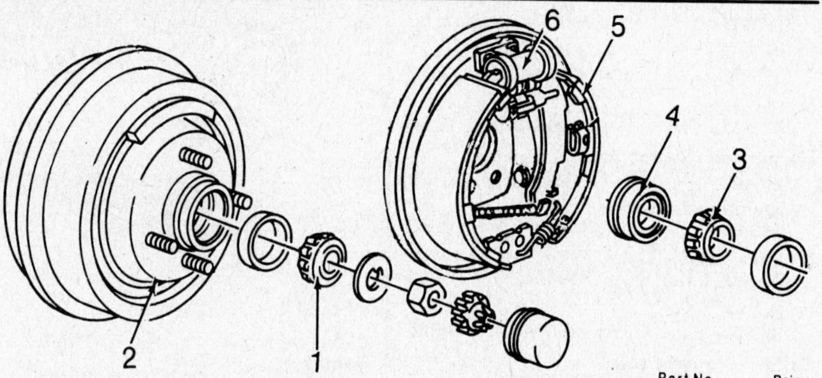

	Part No.	Price
Brake Warning Switch		
1983-84	3747993	8.00
1985-87	4221651	15.50
Power Brake Booster		
1983-84-exc. below	4294212	198.00
2.2L (M.T.)	3880277	192.50
1985-87-A.T.	4342709	218.25
M.T.	4364773	169.00

PARKING BRAKE

	Part No.	Price
Parking Brake Control		
1983-87	3880426	40.00
Front Cable		
1983-87	3766435	14.75
Intermediate Cable		
1983	3880410	8.00
1984-87	4294139	8.00
Rear Cable		
1983-84	4294069	8.50

PARTS — 6 DISC BRAKES 6 — PARTS

	Part No.	Price
(1) Rotor		
1983	4238551	56.00
1984-87-4 stud	4313593	56.00
5 stud	4313633	56.00
(2) Splash Shield		
(3) Brake Pad Set		
1983	4238786	55.25
1984	4238788	55.25
1985-87	4313429	72.25
(4) Caliper Housing (Partial)		
1983-87-right	4238710	114.75

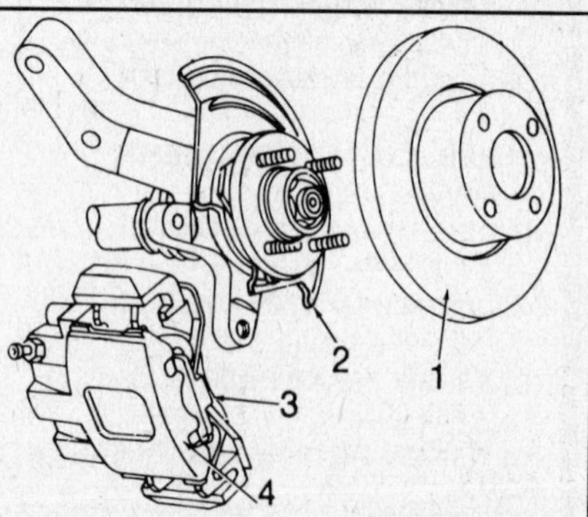

	Part No.	Price
left	4238711	114.75
Piston Seal & Boot Pkg.		
1983-87	4205984	19.00
Boot & Seal Pkg.		
1983-87	4205985	3.75
Bushing Pkg.		
1983-87	4205982	1.75
Adapter		
1983-87	4238712	36.25

LABOR — 7 COOLING SYSTEM 7 — LABOR

(Factory Time) Chilton Time

(M) Winterize Cooling System
Includes: Run engine to check for leaks, tighten all hose connections. Test radiator and pressure cap. Drain radiator and engine block. Add anti-freeze and refill system.
All models 5

(M) Thermostat, Renew
1983-87 (.4) 6

LABOR 7 COOLING SYSTEM 7 LABOR

(Factory Time)	Chilton Time
(M) Radiator Assembly, R&R or Renew	
1983-87 (.5)	.9
w/A.T. add (.1)	.1
ADD THESE OPERATIONS TO RADIATOR R&R	
(G) Boil & Repair	1.5
(G) Rod Clean	1.9
(G) Repair Core	1.3
(G) Renew Tank	1.6
(G) Renew Trans. Oil Cooler	1.9
(G) Recore Radiator	1.7
(M) Fan Blades, Renew	
1983-87 (.2)	.5
(M) Drive Belts, Adjust	
All models-one	.2
each adtnl	.1
(M) Drive Belts, Renew	
1983-87	
Water pump-2.6L eng (.3)	.5
Fan & alter (.2)	.3
Pow str (.4)	.6
Air pump (.3)	.4
w/A.C. add (.1)	.2
(M) Radiator Hoses, Renew	
1983-87-upper (.3)	.4
lower (.4)	.6
(G) Water Pump, Renew	
1983-87	
2.2L & 2.5L engs (1.1)	1.6
2.6L eng (.7)	1.2
w/A.C. add (.5)	.5
(G) Radiator Fan Coolant Sensor, Renew	
1983-87 (.2)	.3
(G) Radiator Fan Motor, Renew	
1983-87-wo/A.C. (.4)	.5
w/A.C. (.4)	.5
(G) Radiator Fan Switch, Renew	
1983-87 (.3)	.6
(G) Radiator Fan Motor Relay, Renew	
1983-87 (.2)	.3
(G) Transaxle Auxiliary Oil Cooler, Renew	
1983-87 (.3)	.6

COOLING SYSTEM TUNE-UP

An Annual Cooling System Tune-up Suggestion List should include (with some exceptions):

1. A visual check of the cooling system for indications of leaks or excessive oil content
2. Pressure check the cooling system for internal and external leaks with filler cap and neck adapter and tester
3. Check crankcase and automatic transmission oil for water content
4. Test coolant thermostat with radiator thermometer
5. Check temperature gauge for accuracy
6. Drain system and flush till clean
7. Clean foreign matter from radiator fins
8. Test radiator pressure cap with cap tester
9. Check fan blades and pulleys for alignment and damage
10. Internal and external inspection of all hoses for cracks and deterioration
11. Check core plugs (where possible) for seepage
12. Refill system with correct coolant and check for air locks
13. Check condition and tension of drive belts with tension gauge

All models 1.5

(Factory Time)	Chilton Time
(G) Water Jacket Expansion Plugs, Renew (Cylinder Block)	
1983-87	
2.6L eng	
right side	
front (.7)	1.0
center or rear (1.1)	1.5
left side	
upper front or center (2.1)	3.0
lower front or center (.3)	.5
rear (1.0)	1.4
2.2L & 2.5L engs	
left side	
front (.7)	1.0
rear (.4)	.6
right side	
front or center (.6)	.9
rear (1.0)	1.4
w/P.S. add (.3)	.3
w/Pulse air add (.6)	.6
(G) Water Jacket Expansion Plugs, Renew (Cylinder Head)	
1983-87	
2.2L & 2.5L engs	
front (.6)	.9
rear (.8)	1.1
2.6L eng	
rear (.5)	.7
(G) Temperature Gauge (Engine Unit), Renew	
1983-87 (.3)	.4
(G) Heater Hoses, Renew	
1983-87-one (.4)	.4
each adtnl (.1)	.2
(G) Heater Water Valve, Renew	
1983-87-w/A.C. (.3)	.5
(G) Heater Control Assembly, Renew	
1983-87-wo/A.C. (.4)	.7
w/A.C. (.4)	.7
(G) Vacuum Switch (Push Button), Renew	
1983-87-w/A.C. (.5)	.9
(G) Blower Motor Switch, Renew	
1983-87-wo/A.C. (.4)	.8
w/A.C. (.4)	.8
(G) Heater Core, R&R or Renew	
1983-87-wo/A.C. (1.0)	1.7
w/A.C. (2.4)	*5.5

*Includes recharge A.C. system.

ADD THESE OPERATIONS TO HEATER CORE R&R	
(G) Boil & Repair	1.2
(G) Repair Core	.9
(G) Recore	1.2
(G) Heater Blower Motor, Renew	
1983-87-wo/A.C. (.4)	.6
w/A.C. (.6)	1.2
(G) Blower Motor Resistor, Renew	
1983-87-wo/A.C. (.2)	.3
w/A.C. (.3)	.4

PARTS 7 COOLING SYSTEM 7 PARTS

	Part No.	Price
(1) Radiator Assy.		
Order by year and model.		
(2) Radiator Hose (Upper)		
2.2L & 2.5L		
1983	4140574	10.25
1984-85	4266721	6.25
1986-87	4266696	6.25
Silicone	4266952	35.25
2.6L		
1983-85	4140576	6.00
Silicone	4266138	35.25
(3) Radiator Hose (Lower)		
2.2L & 2.5L		
1983	4266260	14.75
1984-85-right	4266762	14.25
left	4266763	5.50
1986-87	4266697	13.75
Silicone	4266954	38.75
2.6L		
1983	4266255	10.25
1984-85-exc.		
below	4266348	12.50
Silicone	4266349	44.25
(4) Radiator Fan		
1983-2.2L	4266069	16.75
2.6L	4266074	17.75
1984-87 (wo/Air cond.)		
rad. stamping no.		
4266007	4266069	16.75
1984-87 (w/Air cond.)		
Rad. stamping no.		
4266374	4266282	17.75
4266291	4266293	27.50
4266375	4266282	17.75

Part numbers are for price reference only. Order by number stamped on part assembly.

	Part No.	Price
(5) Motor (Radiator Fan)		
1983	5211115	83.00
wo/A.C.	5211115	83.00
1984-87 (wo/Air cond.)		
Rad. stamping no.		
4266007	4240493	83.00
1984-87 (w/Air cond.)		
Rad. stamping no.		
4266374	4240494	83.00
4266291	4240495	95.00
4266375	4240494	83.00

Part numbers are for price reference only. Order by number stamped on part assembly.

	Part No.	Price
Water Pump		
2.2L & 2.5L		
1983	5203432	N.L.
1984-87	4293898	48.00
2.6L		
1983-85	MD025190	59.25
Bypass Hose (Water Pump)		
1983-85-2.2L	4273486	4.75
1986-87	4273488	1.75
2.6L	MD025199	8.00

PARTS 7 COOLING SYSTEM 7 PARTS

	Part No.	Price
Thermostat		
2.2L		
1983-87-185 deg.	4105442	6.50
195 deg.	4105768	.75
2.6L		
1983-85	MD005371	N.L.
Heater Core		
1983-85	4205838	91.50
1986-87	3847943	90.75
Blower Motor		
1983	4240472	68.75
1984	4318117	68.75
1985	3849032	59.00
1986-87	3849266	59.00
Resistor (Blower Motor)		
1983	3848236	5.50
1984	3848689	4.50
1985	3849075	N.L.
1986-87	3849235	8.50
Blower Motor Switch		
1983-84	3847940	10.25
1985-87	3849160	8.00
Temperature Sending Unit (Engine)		
1983-exc. below	4221071	6.75
125° (blue)	4145716	6.75
150° (silver)	4091719	6.75
1984-87	4051687	10.25
Transmission Oil Cooler (Radiator)		
1983-2.2L	4140569	52.50
1984-exc. below	4266729	52.25
2.6L	4266482	76.25
1985-87	4266482	76.25

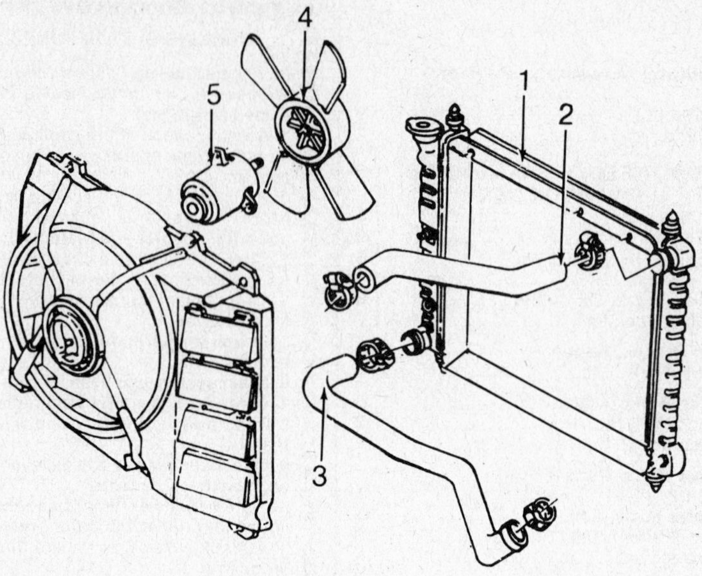

	Part No.	Price
Transmission Auxilliary Oil Cooler		
1983-87	4266196	76.25

LABOR 8 EXHAUST SYSTEM 8 LABOR

(Factory Time)	Chilton Time
(G) Muffler, Renew	
1983-87 (.4)	.7
Cut exhaust pipe add (.2)	.2
(G) Exhaust Pipe, Renew	
1983-87 (.7)	1.1
Cut at muffler add (.2)	.2
(G) Exhaust Pipe Extension, Renew (Intermediate Pipe)	
1983-87 (.6)	1.0
(G) Catalytic Converter, Renew	
1983-87	
floor mount (.7)	.9
exh pipe mount (.7)	.9
manif mount (.9)	1.3
(G) Exhaust Manifold or Gasket, Renew	
1983-87	
2.2L & 2.5L engs (2.7)	3.7
2.6L eng (.7)	1.2
w/Turbo add (.6)	.6

COMBINATIONS

(G) Exhaust System, Renew (Complete)	
1983-87	1.5

PARTS 8 EXHAUST SYSTEM 8 PARTS

System numbers shown are for pricing reference only. Order part with complete year and engine information.

	Part No.	Price
Muffler & Tailpipe		
2.2L		
1983-84-wo/Turbo	4150772	48.50
Turbo	4301305	48.50
1985-wo/Turbo	4301193	48.50
Turbo.	4301551	120.75
1986-87-wo/Turbo	4301512	48.50
Turbo	4301513	115.50
2.5L		
1986-87	4301512	48.50
2.6L		
1983-85	4301193	48.50
Exhaust Pipe Extension (w/Resonator)		
2.2L & 2.5L		
1983-85	4301225	47.00
1986-87	4301539	47.00
2.6L		
1983	4150809	71.00
1984-exc. Calif.	4301294	N.L.
Calif.	4301226	54.25
1985	4301225	47.00
Catalytic Converter (w/Pipes)		
2.2L		
(front)		
1983-exc. below	4150796	307.25
E.F.I.	4301233	256.75
1984	4301266	256.75
1985	4301427	244.75
1986-87-wo/Turbo	4301660	255.75
2.5L		
1986-87-exc Calif.	4301663	255.75
Calif.	4301662	255.75
(rear)		
1983-87	4301232	256.75
1986-87-Turbo	4301503	244.50
2.6L		
1983-84	MD015531	262.50
1985	MD069867	251.75
Exhaust Pipe		
1983-85-Turbo	4301037	14.50
2.6L	4301037	14.50

LABOR 9 FRONT SUSPENSION 9 LABOR

Note: On all front suspension operations alignment charges must be added if performed. Time given does not include alignment.

(Factory Time)	Chilton Time
(M) Wheel, Renew	
one	.5
(M) Wheels, Rotate (All)	
All models	.5

LABOR 9 FRONT SUSPENSION 9 LABOR

(Factory Time)	Chilton Time
(G) Wheels, Balance	
one	.3
each adtnl	.2
(G) Check Front End Alignment	
All models	.5
Note: Deduct if alignment is performed.	
(G) Toe-Out, Adjust	
All models	.6
(G) Align Front End	
Includes: Adjust camber, toe, car height and center steering wheel.	
All models (.8)	1.4
(G) Steering Knuckle Bearing, Renew (Wheel Bearing)	
Add alignment charges.	
1983-87-one side (1.2)	1.6
both sides (2.3)	3.0
(G) Steering Knuckle, Renew (One)	
Add alignment charges.	
1983-87 (1.0)	1.6
(G) Front Strut Assy., R&R or Renew	
Add alignment charges.	
1983-87-one (.8)	1.4
both (1.5)	2.7
(G) Front Suspension Strut (Dual Path) Mount Assy., Renew	
Includes: Renew bearing.	
1984-87 (.8)	1.5
(G) Lower Control Arm Assy., Renew	
Includes: Reset toe-in.	
1983-87-one (1.1)	1.6
(G) Lower Control Arm Strut Bushings, Renew	
Add alignment charges.	
1984-87-one side (.6)	.9
(G) Lower Ball Joint, Renew (One)	
Add alignment charges.	
1983-87 (.8)	1.2
(G) Front Coil Spring or Strut Bearing, Renew	
Includes: R&R front strut.	
Add alignment charges.	
1983-87-one (.8)	1.5
both (1.5)	2.8
(G) Front Sway Bar, Renew	
1983-87 (.4)	.7
(G) Sway Bar Bracket and Bushings, Renew	
1983-87-both (.5)	.9
(P) K-Frame Assembly, Renew	
Add alignment charges.	
All models (2.5)	4.0
(G) Drive Shaft Boot, Renew	
Includes: Clean and lubricate C/V joint.	
All models	
1983-87	
one-inner or outer (.7)	1.0
both-one side (1.0)	1.4
Renew shaft seal, add	
right side (.1)	.1
left side (.3)	.3
(G) Drive Shaft C/V Joint, Renew	
All models	
1983-87	
one-inner or outer (.7)	1.0
both-one side (1.0)	1.4
inter shaft U-joint (.6)	1.0
Renew shaft seal, add	
right side (.1)	.1
left side (.3)	.3
(G) Front Wheel Drive Shaft Assy., Renew	
All models	
1983-87	
inter spline yoke (.6)	1.0
inter stub shaft (.6)	1.0
all others-each (1.0)	1.4
Renew shaft seal, add	
right side (.1)	.1
left side (.3)	.3
(G) Intermediate Shaft Support Bearing, Renew	
1984-87-each (.6)	1.0
(G) Drive Shaft Oil Seal, Renew	
All models	
1983-87	
right side (.5)	.8
left side (.7)	1.1

PARTS 9 FRONT SUSPENSION 9 PARTS

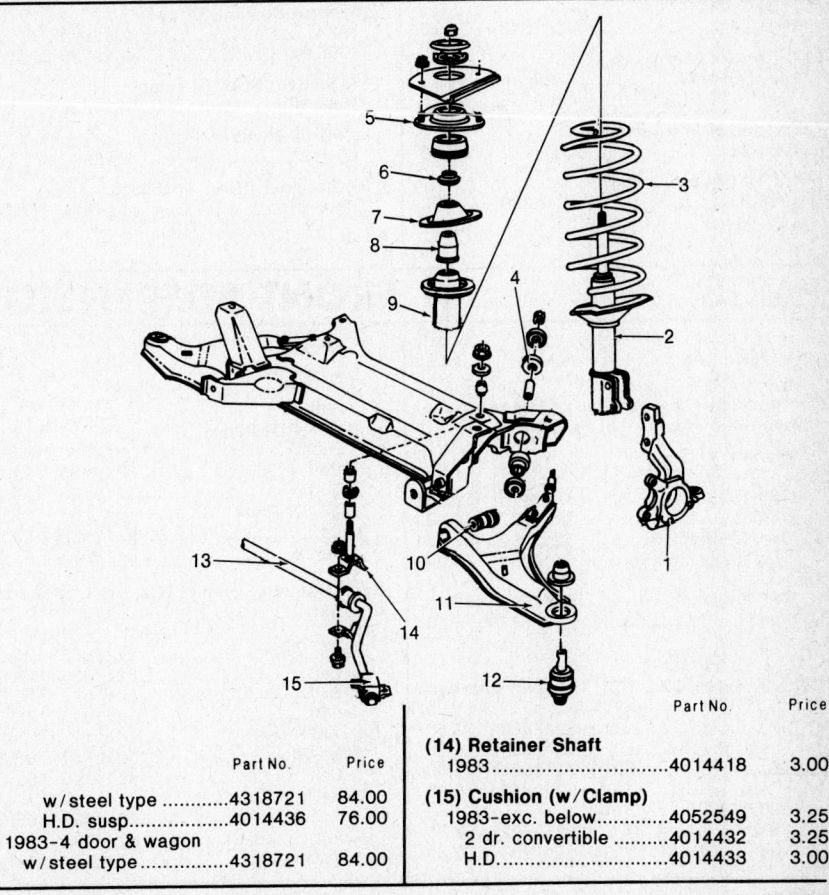

	Part No.	Price
Front Wheel Bearing		
1983	4271389	44.50
(1) Steering Knuckle		
1983-right	4052580	89.75
left	4052581	89.75
(2) Shock Absorber Pkg.		
1983-Std	4052544	40.00
H.D.	4052545	43.25
(3) Coil Spring		
Order by model and description.		
(4) Bushing (Strut Arm Rear)		
1983	5204538	1.25
(5) Plate Shock Tower		
1983-right	4296448	59.50
left	4296449	59.50
(6) Ball Bearing		
1983	5204595	4.50
(7) Retainer (Shock Upper)		
1983	4014469	6.00
(8) Bumper (Jounce)		
1983	5204608	3.25
(9) Dust Shield		
1983	5204610	1.75
(10) Bushing (Arm Pivot Shaft)		
1983	5204622	8.00
(11) Lower Control Arm		
1983-right	4052634	92.75
left	4052635	92.75
(12) Lower Ball Joint		
1983	4014323	37.25
(13) Sway Bar		
1983-exc. 4 door & wagon (type tires)		
w/glass type	4052541	75.00
w/steel type	4318721	84.00
H.D. susp	4014436	76.00
1983-4 door & wagon		
w/steel type	4318721	84.00
(14) Retainer Shaft		
1983	4014418	3.00
(15) Cushion (w/Clamp)		
1983-exc. below	4052549	3.25
2 dr. convertible	4014432	3.25
H.D.	4014433	3.00

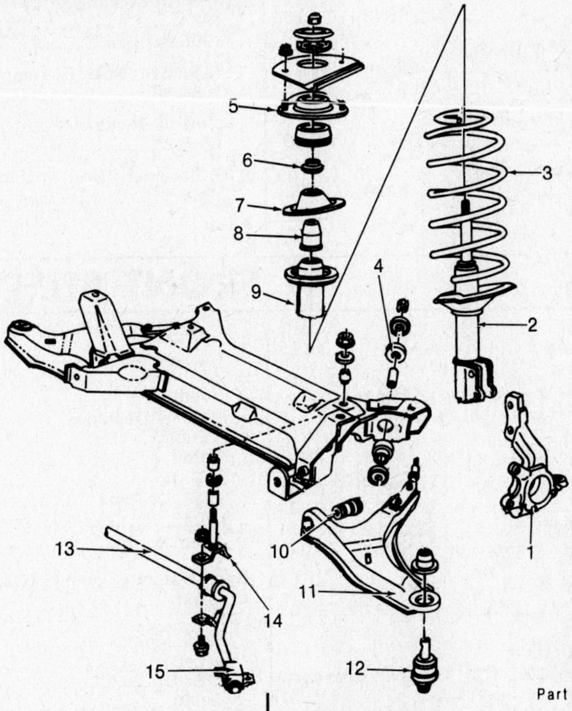

This parts list is for vehicles built up to 1-2-86. Refer to next section for vehicles built after 1-2-86.

	Part No.	Price
(1) Retainer (Shock Stop)		
1984-86	4052822	1.75
(2) Front Shock Mount (Upper)		
1984	4052850	19.00
1985-86	4322298	19.00
(3) Shock Seat (Upper)		
1984	4052819	6.25
1985-86	4322701	6.25
(4) Bumper (Jounce)		
1984-86	4052824	2.75
(5) Front Isolator (Upper)		
1984-86	4322046	2.25
(6) Dust Shield		
1984-86	4052825	1.50
(7) Spring Assy.		
Order by model and description.		
(8) Shock Absorber (Std.)		
1984-exc. below	4052861	40.00
H.D.	4052862	45.50
1985-86-exc. below	4052861	40.00
New Yorker	4322277	50.00
Gas	4322276	50.00
(9) Steering Knuckle		
1984-86-right	4052838	89.75
left	4052839	89.75
(10) Seal (Ball Joint)		
1984-86	4052509	1.25
(11) Ball Joint		
1984-86	4052583	32.75
(12) Control Arm Assy.		
1984-86-right	4322154	92.75
left	4322155	92.75
(13) Control Arm Bushing		
1984-86	5204622	8.00
(14) Bolt (Pivot Shaft)		
1984-86	4014239	4.00

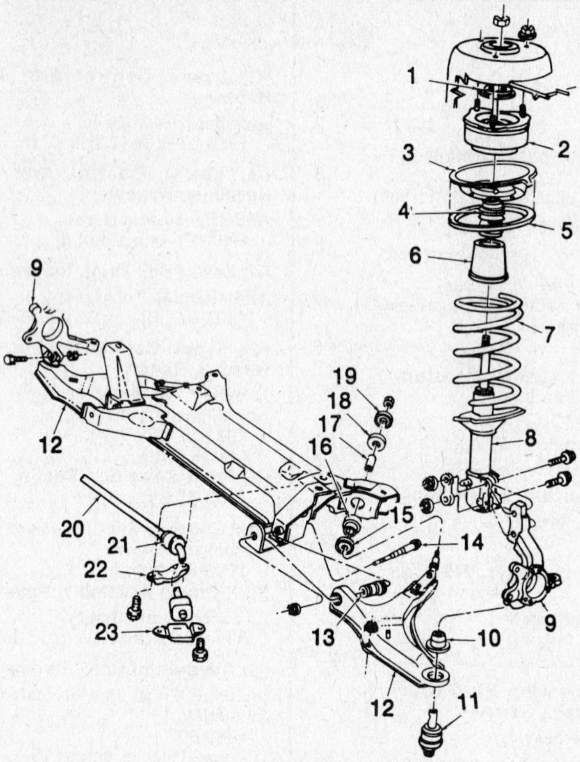

	Part No.	Price
(15) Retainer (Strut Bushing)		
1984-86	5204534	1.50
(16) Strut Bushing (Front)		
1984	4052671	2.00
1985-86	4322285	2.00
(17) Sleeve (Strut Bushing)		
1984-86	5204535	1.50
(18) Strut Bushing (Rear)		
1984-86	4052672	2.00
(19) Retainer (Strut Bushing)		
1984-86	5204534	1.50

	Part No.	Price
(20) Front Sway Shaft Assy.		
1984-86-exc. below	4322028	78.25
Firm susp.	4322014	81.25
(21) Front Cushion (Sway Shaft)		
1984-86	4322017	3.25
(22) Lower Clamp (Shaft Bushing)		
1984-86	4052522	3.00
(23) Retainer (Shaft Arm)		
1984-86	4014418	3.00

Part numbers shown are for pricing reference only. Order by year model and type.

	Part No.	Price
Driveshaft		
1.6L		
1983-Right	5212676	137.50
Left	5212677	76.00
1984-87-Right	5212862	137.50
Left	5212863	76.00
1.7L		
1983-Right	5212646	137.50
Left	5212647	72.50
2.2L, 2.5L & 2.6L		
Horizon, Omni, 024, TC3, Turismo, Charger		
(G.K.N.)		
1983-Right	5212660	137.50
Left	5212661	76.00
1984-87-Right	5212862	137.50
Left	5212863	76.00
1986-87-H/P		
Right	5212862	137.50
Left	5212933	76.00

	Part No.	Price
(Citroen)		
1985-wo/Turbo		
Right	5212766	85.00
Left	5212765	52.25
Turbo	5212765	52.25
1986-87-Right	5212766	85.00
Left	5212935	52.25
Turbo	5212935	52.25
Exc. Horizon, Omni, TC3, 024, Turismo, Charger		
(G.K.N.)		
1983-Right	5212662	137.50
Left	5212663	76.00
1984-87-Right	5212872	123.00
Left	5212913	76.00
(Citroen)		
1983-Right	5212744	85.00
Left	5212745	52.50
1984-wo/Turbo		
right	5212798	85.00
left	5212799	N.L.
Turbo	5212799	N.L.

	Part No.	Price
1985-87-wo/Turbo		
Right	5212798	85.00
Left	5212763	52.25
Turbo	5212763	52.25
(A.C.I.)		
1984-87-Right	5212826	123.00
Left	5212827	76.00

This parts list is for vehicles built after 1-2-86.

	Part No.	Price
(1) Strut (Shock Absorber)		
1986-87-Std.	4322641	40.00
Gas (H.D.)	4322679	50.00
(2) Strut Spring		
Order by model and description.		
(3) Spacer		
1986-87	4014441	5.00
(4) Shield		
1986-87	4322704	1.50
(5) Bumper		
1986-87	4322705	2.75

PARTS 9 FRONT SUSPENSION 9 PARTS

	Part No.	Price
(6) Seat Assembly		
1986-87	4322628	12.00
(7) Mount & Brg. Assy.		
1986-87	4322760	24.00
(8) Knuckle Assy.		
1986-87-R.H.	4052838	89.75
L.H.	4052839	89.75
(9) Ball Joint		
1986-87	4364782	37.25
(10) Bushing		
1986-87	4322285	2.00
(11) Bushing		
1986-87	5204622	8.00
(12) Sway Bar		
1986-87	4322014	81.25
(13) Bushing		
1986-87-Std.	4322017	3.25
H.D.	4052613	3.00
(14) Bushing		
1986-87	4322099	3.75
(15) Lower Control Arm Assy.		
1986-87-R.H.	4322154	92.75
L.H.	4322155	92.75

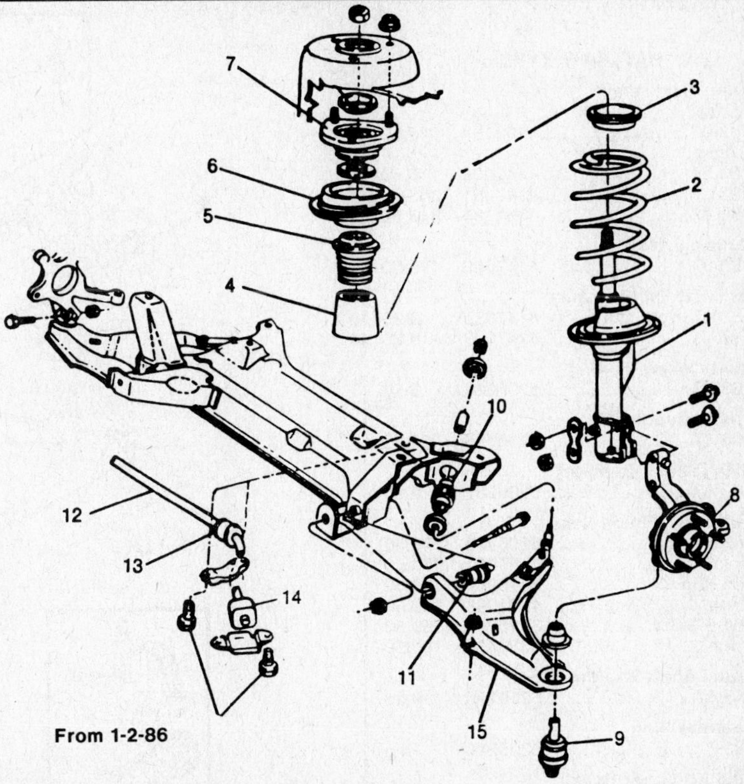

LABOR 11 STEERING GEAR 11 LABOR

	(Factory Time)	Chilton Time
(G) Tie Rods or Tie Rod Ends, Renew		
Includes: Reset toe-out.		
1983-87		
outer-one	(.9)	1.2
inner & outer-w/P.S. one side	(1.9)	2.5
(G) Horn Contact Cable and Ring, Renew		
1983-87	(.2)	.4
(G) Horn Switch, Renew		
1983-87	(.2)	.3
(G) Steering Wheel, Renew		
1983-87	(.2)	.3
(G) Steering Column Jacket, Renew		
Does not include painting.		
1983-87		
Std Column		
console shift	(1.1)	1.8
column shift	(1.5)	2.3
Tilt Column		
console shift	(1.5)	2.6
column shift	(1.6)	2.8
(G) Upper Mast Jacket Bearing, Renew		
Includes: Replace insulators if necessary.		
1983-87		
std column	(.4)	.9
tilt column	(1.2)	2.0
(G) Steering Column Gear Shift Tube, Renew		
1983-87		
std column	(1.3)	2.1
tilt column	(1.8)	2.6
(G) Steering Column Lower Shaft Bearing, Renew		
Includes: Replace support if necessary.		
1983-87		
Std Column		
console shift	(.8)	1.6
column shift	(.9)	1.7
Tilt Column		
console shift	(.6)	1.0
column shift	(.6)	1.0
POWER STEERING		
(G) Power Steering Pump Pressure Check		
All models		.5
(M) Power Steering Pump Belt, Renew		
1983-87	(.4)	.6
w/A.C. add	(.1)	.1
w/Air inj add	(.1)	.1
(G) Power Steering Gear Assy., R&R or Renew		
Includes: Reset toe-in.		
1983-87	(1.1)	2.4
Renew gear add	(.6)	1.0
(G) Upper and Lower Valve Pinion Seals, Renew		
1983-87	(1.4)	2.0
Renew brgs add	(.3)	.5
(G) Steering Gear Oil Seals, Renew (All)		
Includes: R&R gear assy. and reset toe-in.		
1983-87	(2.9)	5.1
(G) Power Steering Pump, Renew		
Includes: Test pump and transfer pulley.		
1983-87		
2.2L & 2.5L engs	(1.0)	1.4
2.6L eng	(.8)	1.2
(G) Power Steering Pump, R&R and Recondition		
1983-87		
2.2L & 2.5L engs	(1.5)	2.3
2.6L eng	(1.3)	2.0
(G) Pump Flow Control Valve, Test and Clean or Renew		
1983-87		
2.2L & 2.5L engs	(.6)	1.0
2.6L eng	(.7)	1.1
(G) Power Steering Reservoir or Seals, Renew		
1983-87	(.7)	1.1
(G) Pump Drive Shaft Oil Seal, Renew		
1983-87		
2.2L & 2.5L engs	(.9)	1.4
2.6L eng	(.7)	1.1
(M) Power Steering Hoses, Renew		
1983-87-each	(.4)	.5

PARTS 11 POWER STEERING GEAR 11 PARTS

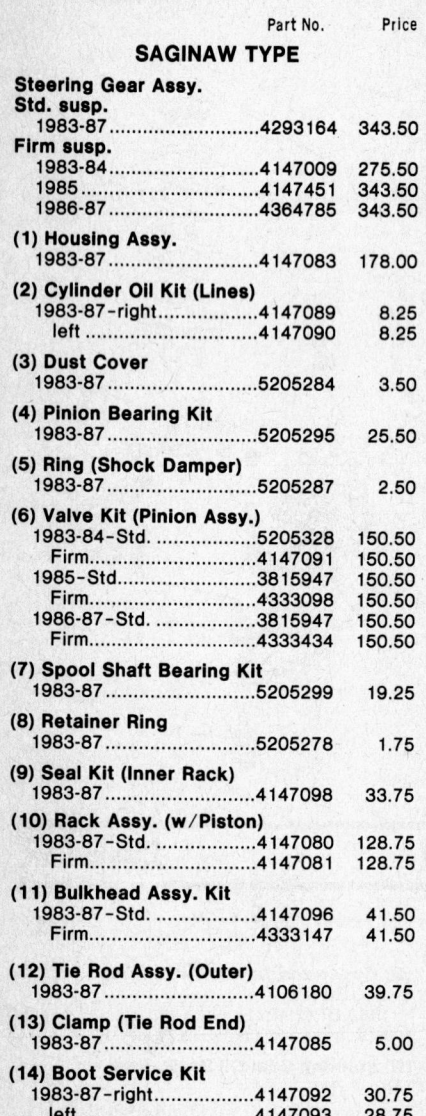

	Part No.	Price
SAGINAW TYPE		
Steering Gear Assy.		
Std. susp.		
1983-87	4293164	343.50
Firm susp.		
1983-84	4147009	275.50
1985	4147451	343.50
1986-87	4364785	343.50
(1) Housing Assy.		
1983-87	4147083	178.00
(2) Cylinder Oil Kit (Lines)		
1983-87-right	4147089	8.25
left	4147090	8.25
(3) Dust Cover		
1983-87	5205284	3.50
(4) Pinion Bearing Kit		
1983-87	5205295	25.50
(5) Ring (Shock Damper)		
1983-87	5205287	2.50
(6) Valve Kit (Pinion Assy.)		
1983-84-Std.	5205328	150.50
Firm	4147091	150.50
1985-Std.	3815947	150.50
Firm	4333098	150.50
1986-87-Std.	3815947	150.50
Firm	4333434	150.50
(7) Spool Shaft Bearing Kit		
1983-87	5205299	19.25
(8) Retainer Ring		
1983-87	5205278	1.75
(9) Seal Kit (Inner Rack)		
1983-87	4147098	33.75
(10) Rack Assy. (w/Piston)		
1983-87-Std.	4147080	128.75
Firm	4147081	128.75
(11) Bulkhead Assy. Kit		
1983-87-Std.	4147096	41.50
Firm	4333147	41.50
(12) Tie Rod Assy. (Outer)		
1983-87	4106180	39.75
(13) Clamp (Tie Rod End)		
1983-87	4147085	5.00
(14) Boot Service Kit		
1983-87-right	4147092	30.75
left	4147093	28.75

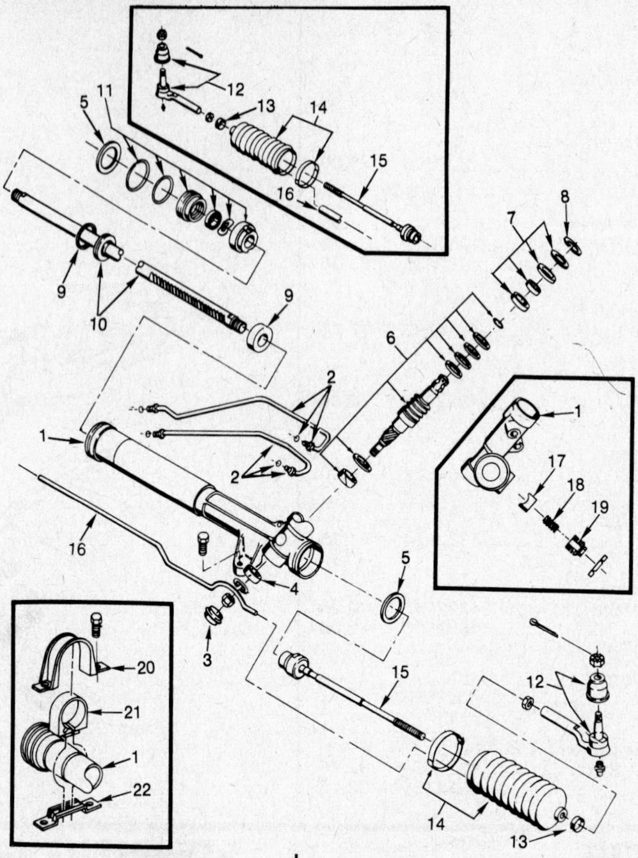

	Part No.	Price
(15) Tie Rod Assy. (Inner)		
1983-87-right	4147095	48.50
left	4333104	46.25
(16) Breather Tube		
1983-87	4147087	9.00
(17) Rack Bearing		
1983-87	5205282	5.25
(18) Spring (Adjuster)		
1983-87	5205280	2.00

	Part No.	Price
(19) Plug (Adjuster)		
1983-87	5205286	7.75
(20) Bracket (Outer)		
1983-87-right	3643470	4.00
left	3643424	4.00
(21) Bushing		
1983-87-right	3643471	4.00
left	3643425	4.00
(22) Bracket (Inner)		
1983-87-right	3643469	1.00
left	3643423	1.00

PARTS 11 POWER STEERING PUMP 11 PARTS

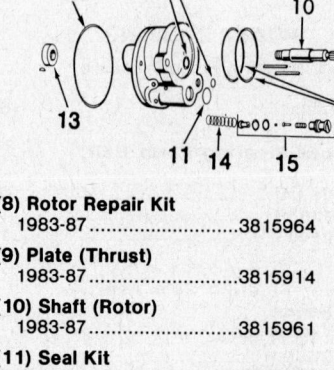

	Part No.	Price
Power Steering Pump		
1983-87-Std. susp.	3815956	170.25
H.D. susp.	4188832	170.25
Oil Pressure Hose		
1983	3815840	30.25
1984-85	4147280	25.25
1986-87	4333130	25.25
(1) Reservoir		
1983-87	3643453	60.75
(2) Union Assy. (Fitting)		
1983-87-Std. susp.	5205267	7.00
H.D. susp.	3815983	6.00
(3) Seal		
1983-87	2537838	11.00
(4) Retaining Ring (End Plate)		
1983-87	2537823	1.00
(5) End Plate		
1983-87	2537820	3.50
(6) Spring (Pressure Plate)		
1983-87	3815966	1.00
(7) Plate (Pressure)		
1983-87	3815967	13.75

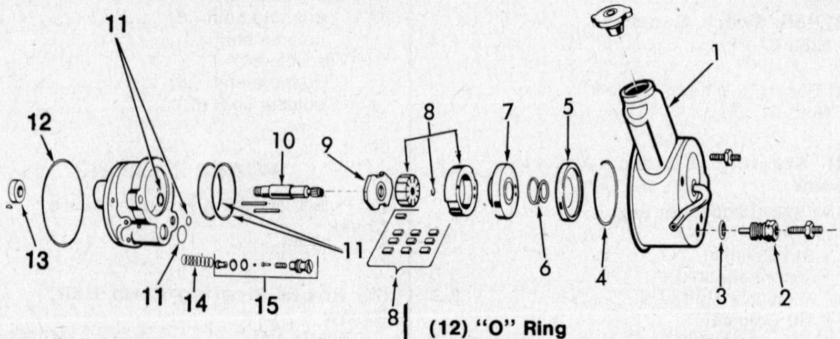

	Part No.	Price
(8) Rotor Repair Kit		
1983-87	3815964	89.00
(9) Plate (Thrust)		
1983-87	3815914	12.25
(10) Shaft (Rotor)		
1983-87	3815961	39.00
(11) Seal Kit		
1983-87	2537838	11.00

	Part No.	Price
(12) "O" Ring		
1983-87	2537828	3.25
(13) Seal (Drive Shaft)		
1983-87	2537899	4.50
(14) Spring (Control Valve)		
1983-87	2537833	1.50
(15) Control Valve		
1983-87-Std. susp.	3815965	12.50
H.D. susp.	2891695	13.00

PARTS 11 POWER STEERING GEAR 11 PARTS

TRW TYPE

	Part No.	Price
Steering Gear Assy.		
1983-87	4293164	343.50
(1) Tie Rod End (Outer)		
1983-87	4106180	39.75
(2) Boot Service Kit		
1983-87		
up to 9-30-83	3815880	14.25
after 9-30-83	4147303	14.75
(3) Breather Tube		
1983-87	3815871	2.00
(4) Horizontal Socket Assy.		
1983-84	3815879	50.00
1985-87	4333450	50.00
(5) Service Ring Kit		
1983-87	3815874	2.75
(6) Lock Ring Bushing		
1983-87	3815883	2.50
(7) Bushing Rack Service Kit		
1983-87	3815881	6.00
(8) Rack Assy.		
1983-87	3815861	103.00
(9) Rack Seal Service Kit		
1983-87	3815878	2.75
(10) Retaining Wire		
1983-87	3815884	.50
(11) Housing (Rack & Pinion)		
1983-87		
up to 9-30-83	3815862	125.75
after 9-30-83	4147307	125.75
1986-87	4333148	275.50
(12) Bearing Assy.		
1983-87	3815868	4.75
(13) Plug (Pinion)		
1983-84	3815870	7.50
1985-87	4147306	3.75
(14) Cylinder Line Assy.		
1983-87-right	3815873	3.75
left	3815872	3.75
(15) Plug (Yoke)		
1983-87	3815866	6.75
(16) Bearing & Spring Yoke		
1983-87	3815865	4.75
(17) Pinion Shaft Bearing Kit		
1983-84	3815882	15.00
1985-87	4147420	15.00

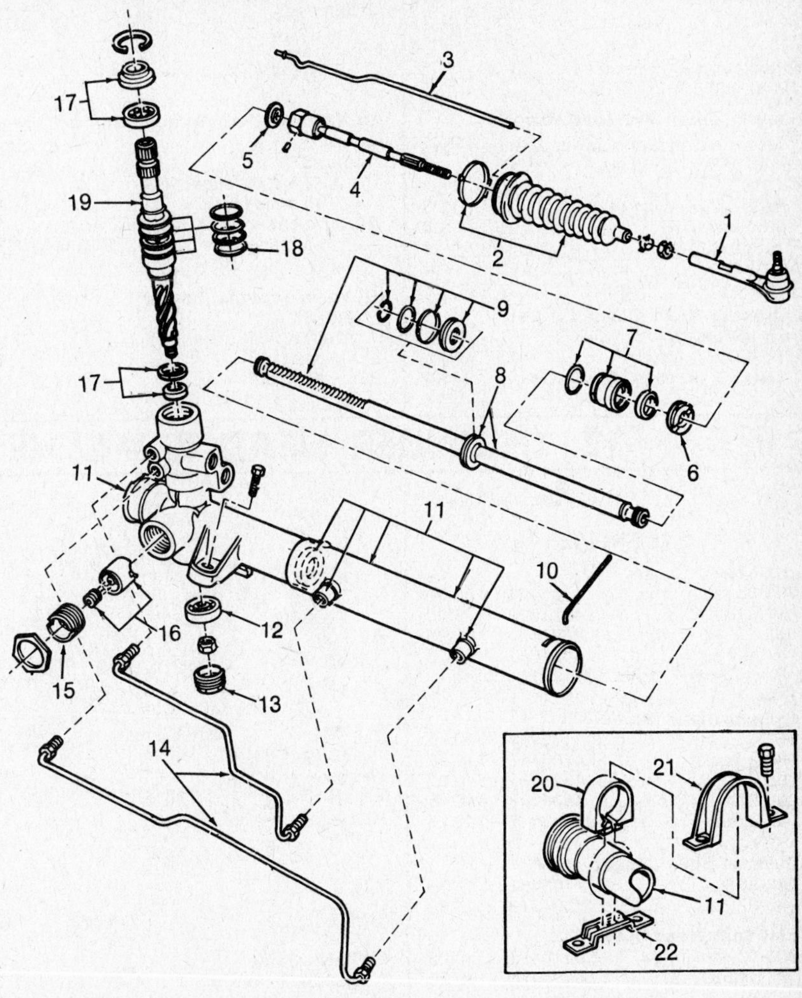

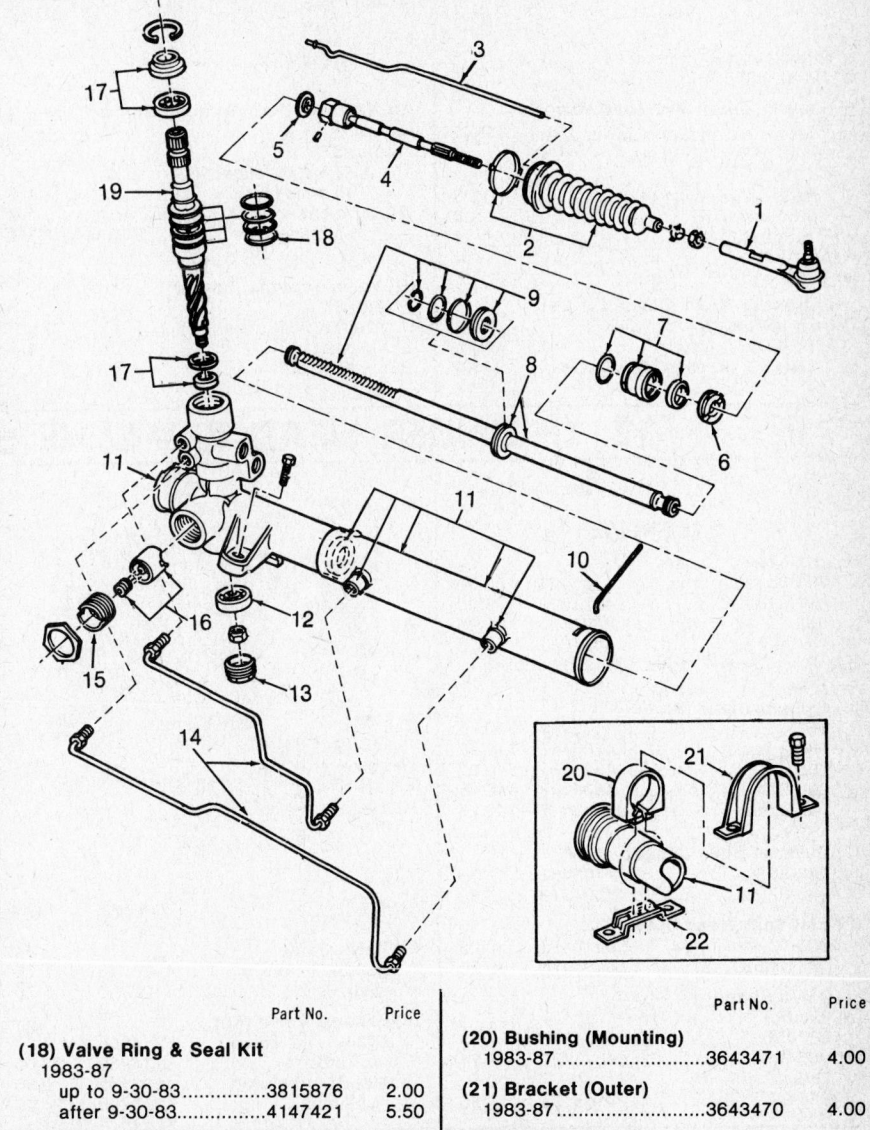

	Part No.	Price
(18) Valve Ring & Seal Kit		
1983-87		
up to 9-30-83	3815876	2.00
after 9-30-83	4147421	5.50
(19) Valve Assy.		
1983-87	3815875	85.50

	Part No.	Price
(20) Bushing (Mounting)		
1983-87	3643471	4.00
(21) Bracket (Outer)		
1983-87	3643470	4.00
(22) Bracket (Inner)		
1983-87	3643469	1.00

LABOR 12 CYLINDER HEAD & VALVE SYSTEM 12 LABOR

(Factory Time)	Chilton Time
(G) Compression Test	
1983-87	.6
(G) Cylinder Head Gasket, Renew	
Includes: Clean carbon.	
1983-87	
2.2L & 2.5L engs (3.4)	4.8
2.6L eng (2.8)	4.5
w/P.S. add (.2)	.2
w/Air inj add (.2)	.2
w/Turbo add (.5)	.5
(G) Cylinder Head, Renew	
Includes: Transfer parts as required. Clean carbon, make all necessary adjustments.	
1983-87	
2.2L & 2.5L engs (5.3)	8.0
2.6L eng (4.7)	7.4
w/P.S. add (.2)	.2

COMBINATIONS

Add To Valve Job
See Machine Shop Operations

(G) DRAIN, EVACUATE & RECHARGE AIR CONDITIONING SYSTEM	
All models	1.0
(G) DISTRIBUTOR, RECONDITION	
All models (.7)	.7
(G) RECONDITION CYL. HEAD (HEAD REMOVED)	
2.2L eng (1.4)	2.0
(G) CAMSHAFT, RENEW (HEAD DISASSEMBLED)	
OHC engs (.1)	.2
(G) CARBURETOR, RECONDITION	
Holly (.5)	.9
(G) REMOVE CYLINDER TOP RIDGE	
Each (.1)	.1
(G) RENEW OIL PUMP	
All engs (.2)	.3
(G) ROD BEARINGS, RENEW (PAN REMOVED)	
All engs (.7)	1.2
(G) DEGLAZE CYLINDER WALLS	
Each (.1)	.1
(G) PLASTIGAUGE BEARINGS	
Each (.1)	.1
(M) OIL FILTER ELEMENT, RENEW	
All models (.3)	.3

LABOR 12 CYLINDER HEAD & VALVE SYSTEM 12 LABOR

(Factory Time)	Chilton Time
w/Air inj add (.2)	.2
w/Turbo add (.5)	.5

(P) Clean Carbon and Grind Valves

Includes: R&R cylinder head. Reface valves and seats. Minor tune up.

(Factory Time)	Chilton Time
1983-87	
2.2L & 2.5L engs (4.8)	6.8
2.6L eng (5.4)	8.0
w/P.S. add (.2)	.2
w/Air inj add (.2)	.2
w/Turbo add (.5)	.5

(G) Cylinder Head Cover Gasket, Renew or Reseal

(Factory Time)	Chilton Time
1983-87	
2.2L & 2.5L engs (.8)	1.1
2.6L eng (.4)	.6

(G) Valve Rocker Arms or Shafts, Renew

(Factory Time)	Chilton Time
1983-87	
2.2L & 2.5L engs	
all arms (1.2)	1.6
2.6L eng-one shaft (1.0)	1.4
both shafts (1.1)	1.7

(G) Valve Tappets, Renew

(Factory Time)	Chilton Time
1983-87	
2.2L & 2.5L engs	
one (1.0)	1.4
each adtnl (.1)	.1

(G) Valve Tappets, Adjust

(Factory Time)	Chilton Time
1983-87	
2.6L eng (.9)	1.5

(G) Jet Valves, Renew

(Factory Time)	Chilton Time
1983-87	
2.6L eng-one or all (.9)	1.1

(G) Valve Springs and/or Valve Stem Oil Seals, Renew

(Factory Time)	Chilton Time
1983-87	
2.2L & 2.5L engs	
one (1.2)	1.5
all (1.9)	2.9
2.6L eng (4.7)	*6.0
*w/Head on car	3.5
w/P.S. add (.2)	.2

PARTS 12 CYLINDER HEAD & VALVE SYSTEM 12 PARTS

2.2L ENGINE

	Part No.	Price
Cylinder Head Gasket Pkg.		
1983-85-wo/Turbo	4271994	30.50
w/Turbo	4271926	29.25
1986-87-wo/Turbo	4397680	28.25
w/Turbo	4397681	28.25

Use R.T.V. sealer for gaskets not supplied.

	Part No.	Price
(1) Cylinder Head (Partial)		
1983	4105399	340.25
1984	4105443	340.25
1985	4323288	340.25
1986-87-wo/Turbo	4105783	340.25
w/Turbo	4343627	340.25
(2) Cylinder Head Gasket		
1983-85	4105468	11.50
1986-87	4387319	11.50
(3) End Seal (Head Cover)		
1983-87-wo/Turbo	5214479	2.25
w/Turbo	4105475	2.25
(4) Valve Spring		
(wo/Turbo)		
1983-84	4105755	2.25
1985-87	4323225	2.25
(w/Turbo)		
1984-87	4105793	2.25

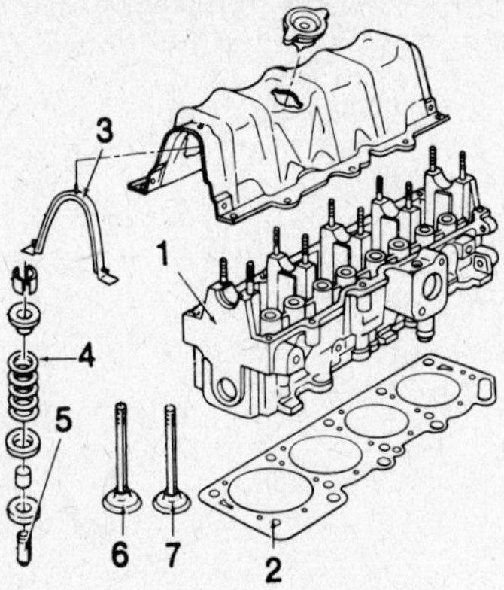

	Part No.	Price
(5) Valve Guide		
1983-87-Intake	4105716	7.75
Exhaust	4105715	7.75
(6) Exhaust Valve (Std.)		
1983-85-wo/Turbo	5214866	9.00
w/Turbo	5214959	21.00
1986-87-wo/Turbo	4298142	9.00
w/Turbo	4323249	21.00
(7) Intake Valve (Std.)		
1983-85-wo/Turbo	5214861	8.25
w/Turbo	5214895	8.75
1986-87-wo/Turbo	4298137	8.25
w/Turbo	432344	N.L.

2.5L ENGINE

	Part No.	Price
Cylinder Head Gasket Pkg.		
1986-87	4397680	28.25

Use R.T.V. sealer for gaskets not supplied.

	Part No.	Price
(1) Cylinder Head (Bare)		
1986-87	4343627	340.25
(2) Cylinder Head Gasket		
1986-87	4387319	11.50
(3) End Seal (Head Cover)		
1986-87	5214479	2.25
(4) Valve Spring		
1986-87	4323225	2.25
(5) Valve Guide		
1986-87-Exhaust	4105715	7.75
Intake	4105716	7.75
(6) Exhaust Valve (Std.)		
1986-87	4298142	9.00
(7) Intake Valve (Std.)		
1986-87	4298137	8.25

PARTS 12 CYLINDER HEAD & VALVE SYSTEM 12 PARTS

2.6L ENGINE

	Part No.	Price
Upper Engine Gasket Kit		
1983-85	MD997021	54.25
(1) Cylinder Head		
1983-85	MD026510	550.00
(2) Cylinder Head Gasket		
1983-85	MD026654	16.00
(3) Valve Cover Gasket		
1983-85	MD024682	6.75
(4) Rocker Arm Shaft		
1983-85-right	MD023198	27.00
left	MD023196	27.00
(5) Rocker Arm		
1983-85-right	MD023226	12.00
left	MD023225	12.00
(6) Jet Valve Assy.		
1983-85	MD009440	20.50

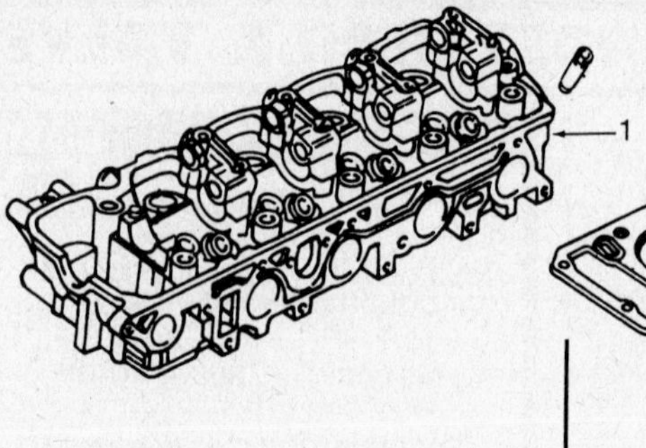

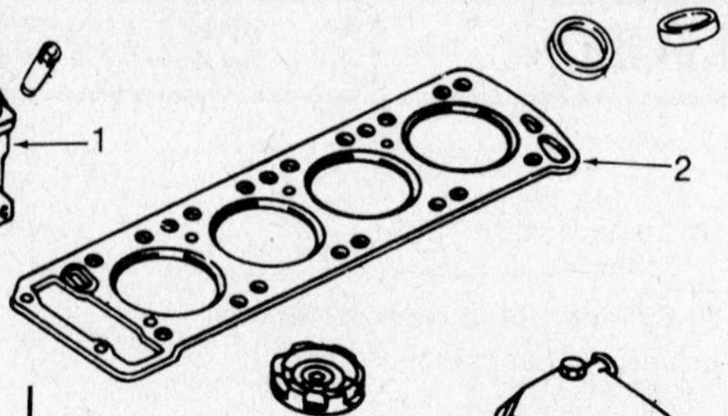

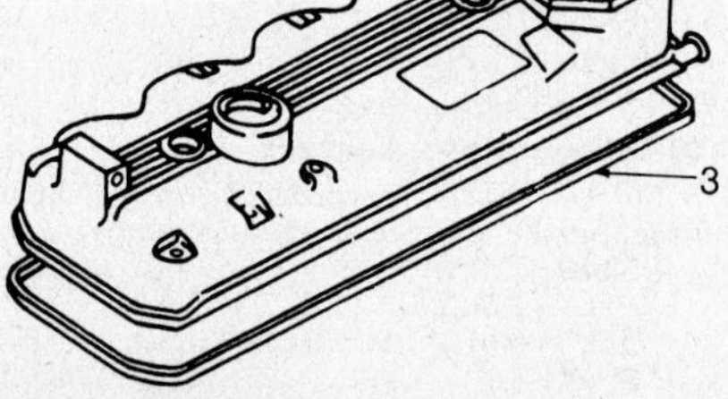

	Part No.	Price
(7) Jet Valve Rod		
1983-85-included with no. 6		
(8) Valve Guide (.20 OS.)		
1983-85-Intake	MD020551	2.50
Exhaust	MD020561	2.50

PARTS 12 CYLINDER HEAD & VALVE SYSTEM 12 PARTS

	Part No.	Price
(9) Valve Stem Seal		
1983-85	MD000508	2.50
(10) Valve Spring		
1983-85		
up to 4-84	MD022591	3.50
from 4-84	MD073398	3.50
(11) Exhaust Valve		
1983-84	MD024519	15.25
1985		
up to 5-84	MD024548	5.00
from 5-84	MD083851	15.25
(12) Intake Valve		
1983-85		
up to 5-84	MD024518	8.50
from 5-84	MD083848	8.50

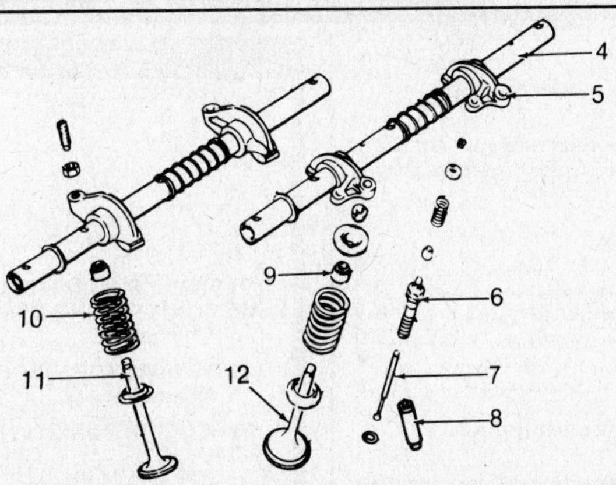

LABOR 13 ENGINE ASSEMBLY & MOUNTS 13 LABOR

	(Factory Time)	Chilton Time
(G) Engine Assembly, Remove & Install		
Includes: R&R engine and transmission as a unit.		
1983-87		
2.2L & 2.5L engs		6.0
2.6L eng		5.2
w/A.C. add	(.5)	.5
w/P.S. add	(.2)	.2
w/Air inj add	(.3)	.3
(P) Short Engine Assembly, Renew (w/All Internal Parts Less Cyl. Head and Oil Pan)		
Includes: R&R engine and transmission as a unit. Transfer all necessary parts not supplied with replacement engine. Clean carbon, grind valves. Minor tune up.		
1983-87		
2.2L & 2.5L engs	(9.1)	15.0
2.6L eng	(9.4)	15.5
w/A.C. add	(.5)	.5
w/P.S. add	(.2)	.2
w/Air inj add	(.3)	.3
(P) Engine Assy., R&R and Recondition (Complete)		
Includes: Rebore block, install new pistons, rings, rod and main bearings. Clean carbon, grind valves. Replace valve stem oil seals. Tune engine.		
1983-87		
2.2L & 2.5L engs	(17.8)	25.2
2.6L eng	(17.0)	23.4
w/A.C. add	(.5)	.5
w/P.S. add	(.2)	.2
w/Air inj add	(.3)	.3
(P) Engine Assembly, Recondition (In Car)		
Includes: Expand or renew pistons, install rings, pins, rod and main bearings. Clean carbon, grind valves. Tune engine.		
1983-87		
2.2L & 2.5L engs	(15.2)	20.8
2.6L eng	(14.4)	19.0
w/P.S. add	(.2)	.2
(G) Engine Support, Renew		
1983-87-right side	(.3)	.5
left side	(.3)	.5
center	(.4)	.6
Trans/Axle		
Roll rod	(.2)	.5

PARTS 13 ENGINE ASSEMBLY & MOUNTS 13 PARTS

	Part No.	Price
Short Engine Assy.		
Consists of block, pistons, rings, connecting rods, crankshaft, bearings and caps.		
2.2L		
1983-84-wo/Turbo	5214968	1200.50
w/Turbo	5214969	1200.50
1985-wo/Turbo	4387201	1200.50
w/Turbo	4387202	1200.50
1986-87-wo/Turbo	4343590	1200.50
w/Turbo	4343871	1200.50
2.5L		
1986-87	4343588	1287.50
2.6L		
1983-85		
up to 4-83	MD025787	1946.00
(from 4-83)		
exc. Calif.	MD076310	1946.00
Calif.	MD076311	1946.00
Cylinder Block		
2.6L		
1983	MD024505	1077.75
1984-85 (exc. Calif.)		
up to 4-83	MD026200	1077.75
after 4-83	MD076312	1077.75
(Calif.)	MD024505	1077.75
The 2.2L engine is serviced only in short engine assy.		
Engine Overhaul Gasket Set (2.2L)		
1983-85-wo/Turbo		
upper	4271994	30.50
lower	4240098	5.75
1986-87-wo/Turbo		
upper	4397680	28.25
lower	4240098	5.75
1984-85-w/Turbo		
upper	4271926	29.25
lower	4240098	5.75
1986-87-w/Turbo	4297681	N.L.
upper	4240098	5.75
2.5L		
1986-87-upper	4397680	28.25
lower	4240098	5.75
2.6L		
1983-85	MD997050	106.50
Use R.T.V. sealer for gaskets not supplied with the engine set.		
Engine Insulator (Front)		
2.2L		
1983-85-wo/Turbo	4295018	25.25
w/Turbo	4329588	28.25
1986-87-wo/Turbo	4295018	25.25
w/Turbo	4377458	25.25
2.5L		
1986-87	4348327	25.25
2.6L		
1983-85	4191891	25.25
Engine Mounting Brackets		
2.2L		
1983-right	4191988	20.50
(left side)		
M.T.	4267206	12.50
A.T.	4267205	12.50
1984-87-right	4295265	11.50
(left side)		
M.T.	4295257	9.75
A.T.	4295255	9.75
2.6L		
1983-right	4191970	20.75
left	4267205	12.50
1984-85-right	4295266	11.50
left	4295255	9.75
Mounting Bracket Bushings		
1983	4295198	12.50
1984-87-right	4295260	12.50
left	4295237	9.00

LABOR 14 PISTONS, RINGS & BEARINGS 14 LABOR

(Factory Time) Chilton Time

(P) Rings, Renew (See Engine Combinations)

Includes: Replace connecting rod bearings, deglaze cylinder walls, clean carbon. Minor tune up.

1983-87	
2.2L & 2.5L engs	
one cyl (4.6)	6.9
all cyls (5.9)	8.1
2.6L eng-one cyl (4.1)	6.3
all cyls (5.7)	8.0
w/P.S. add (.2)	.2
w/Air inj add (.2)	.2
w/Turbo add (.5)	.5

(P) Piston or Connecting Rod, Renew

Includes: Replace connecting rod bearings and piston rings, deglaze cylinder walls. Clean carbon from cylinder head.

1983-87	
2.2L & 2.5L engs	
one cyl (4.9)	7.2
all cyls (6.1)	9.3
2.6L eng-one cyl (4.7)	6.6
all cyls (7.2)	9.2
w/P.S. add (.2)	.2
w/Air inj add (.2)	.2
w/Turbo add (.5)	.5

(P) Connecting Rod Bearings, Renew

1983-87	
2.2L & 2.5L engs (2.1)	3.0
2.6L eng (1.2)	2.2

COMBINATIONS

Add To Engine Work

See Machine Shop Operations

(Factory Time) Chilton Time

(G) DRAIN, EVACUATE & RECHARGE AIR CONDITIONING SYSTEM	
All models	1.0
(G) DISTRIBUTOR, RECONDITION	
All models (.7)	.7
(G) RECONDITION CYL. HEAD (HEAD REMOVED)	
2.2L eng (1.4)	2.0
(G) CAMSHAFT, RENEW (HEAD DISASSEMBLED)	
OHC engs (.1)	.2
(G) R&R CYLINDER HEAD (ENGINE REMOVED)	
All models	1.5
(G) CONNECTING ROD, RENEW (ENGINE DISASSEMBLED)	
Each	.4
(G) CARBURETOR, RECONDITION	
Holly (.5)	.9
(G) REMOVE CYLINDER TOP RIDGE	
Each (.1)	.1
(G) RENEW OIL PUMP	
All engs (.2)	.3
(G) ROD BEARINGS, RENEW (PAN REMOVED)	
All engs (.7)	1.2
(G) MAIN BEARINGS, RENEW (PAN REMOVED)	
All models (.9)	1.4
(G) DEGLAZE CYLINDER WALLS	
Each (.1)	.1
(G) PLASTIGAUGE BEARINGS	
Each (.1)	.1
(M) OIL FILTER ELEMENT, RENEW	
All models (.3)	.3

PARTS 14 PISTONS, RINGS & BEARINGS 14 PARTS

	Part No.	Price
(1) Pistons Ring Set (Std.)		
2.2L engine		
1983-87-wo/Turbo	4240137	54.00
w/Turbo	4293799	54.00
2.5L		
1986-87	4240137	54.00
2.6L		
1983-85		
up to 4-83	MD026835	65.75
from 4-83	MD061258	69.50
(2) Piston Assy. (Std.)		
2.2L		
1983-85-wo/Turbo	4271929	33.00
w/Turbo	4271927	33.00
1986-87-wo/Turbo	4397632	33.00
w/Turbo	4397634	33.00
2.5L		
1986-87	4397636	33.00

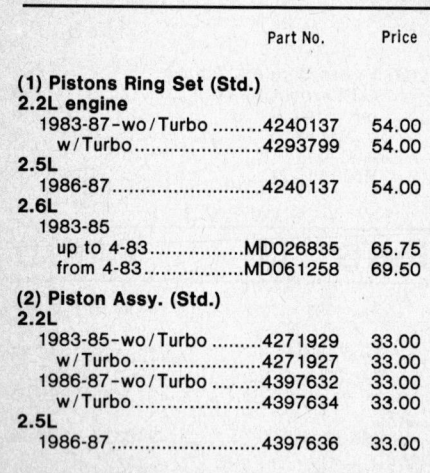

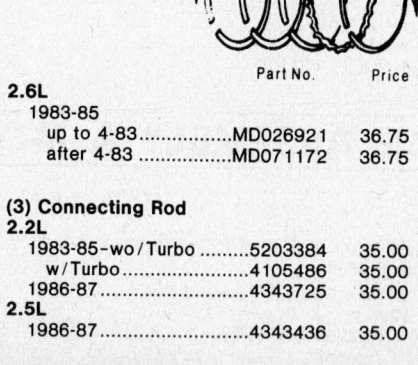

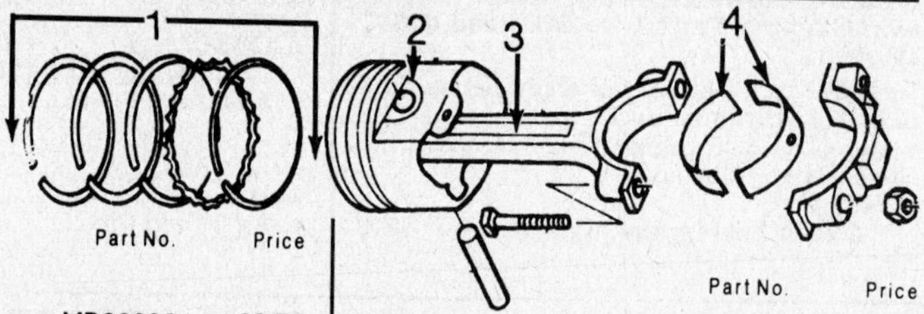

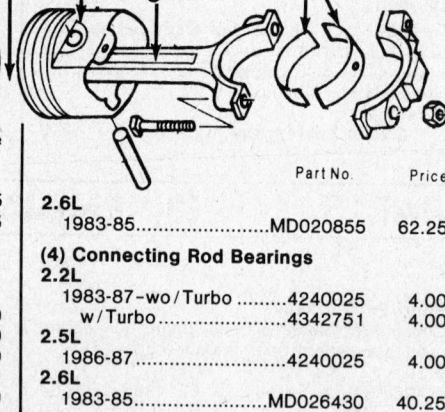

	Part No.	Price
2.6L		
1983-85		
up to 4-83	MD026921	36.75
after 4-83	MD071172	36.75
(3) Connecting Rod		
2.2L		
1983-85-wo/Turbo	5203384	35.00
w/Turbo	4105486	35.00
1986-87	4343725	35.00
2.5L		
1986-87	4343436	35.00

	Part No.	Price
2.6L		
1983-85	MD020855	62.25
(4) Connecting Rod Bearings		
2.2L		
1983-87-wo/Turbo	4240025	4.00
w/Turbo	4342751	4.00
2.5L		
1986-87	4240025	4.00
2.6L		
1983-85	MD026430	40.25

LABOR 15 CRANKSHAFT & DAMPER 15 LABOR

(Factory Time) Chilton Time

(P) Crankshaft and Main Bearings, Renew

Includes: R&R engine assembly.

1983-87	
2.2L & 2.5L engs (6.7)	11.2
2.6L eng (7.6)	12.1
w/A.C. add (.5)	.5
w/P.S. add (.2)	.2
w/Air inj add (.3)	.3

(P) Main Bearings, Renew

1983-87	
2.2L & 2.5L engs	
No 2-3 or 4 (1.8)	2.8
No 1 (3.0)	4.0
No 5 (5.6)	8.8
all (7.0)	11.0
2.6L eng (2.2)	3.0

(P) Main and Rod Bearings, Renew

1983-87	
2.6L eng (2.9)	4.2

(G) Rear Main Bearing Oil Seals, Renew (Complete)

2.2L & 2.5L engs (3.0)	5.4
2.6L eng-w/A.T. (3.2)	5.5

(G) Crankshaft Pulley, Renew

1983-87	
2.2L & 2.5L engs (.5)	.7
2.6L eng (.4)	.6
w/A.C. add (.1)	.1
w/P.S. add (.1)	.1

(G) Crankshaft Front Oil Seal, Renew

1983-87	
2.2L & 2.5L engs (1.3)	2.0
w/A.C. add (.2)	.2
w/P.S. add (.2)	.2

PARTS 15 CRANKSHAFT & DAMPER 15 PARTS

	Part No.	Price
(1) Pulley		
2.6L		
1983-84	MD062006	36.25
1985	MD074096	36.25
(2) Crankshaft		
2.2L		
1983-85-wo/Turbo	5214737	317.50
w/Turbo	4105498	317.50
1986-87	4343407	317.50
2.5L		
1986-87	4343405	335.00
2.6L		
1983-85	MD026408	386.25
(3) Crankshaft Bearing Pkg. (Upper & Lower)		
2.2L & 2.5L		
1983-87 (wo/Turbo)		
No. 1, 2, 4, 5	4240013	6.00
No. 3	4240019	6.00
1984-87 (w/Turbo)		
No. 1, 2, 4, 5	4293824	6.00
No. 3	4293830	12.75
2.6L		
1983-85-pkg	MD026815	67.75

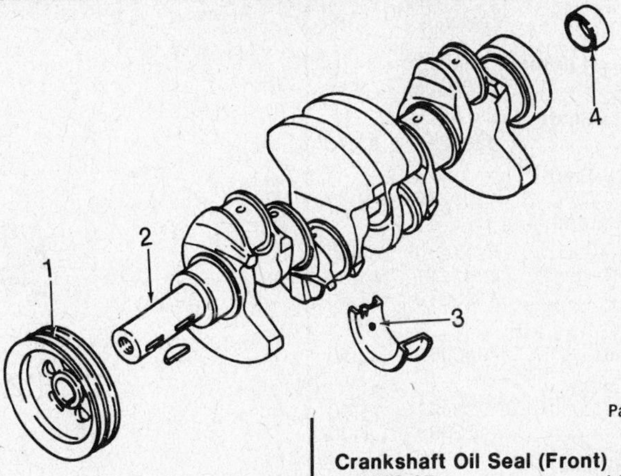

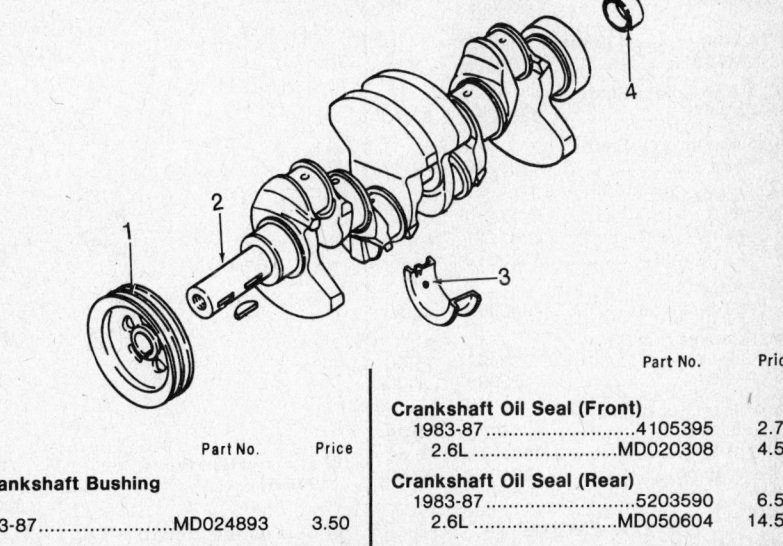

	Part No.	Price
(4) Crankshaft Bushing		
2.6L		
1983-87	MD024893	3.50

	Part No.	Price
Crankshaft Oil Seal (Front)		
1983-87	4105395	2.75
2.6L	MD020308	4.50
Crankshaft Oil Seal (Rear)		
1983-87	5203590	6.50
2.6L	MD050604	14.50

LABOR 16 CAMSHAFT & TIMING GEARS 16 LABOR

(Factory Time)	Chilton Time
(G) Timing Chain or Belt Case/Cover, Renew	
Includes: Renew gasket.	
1983-87	
2.2L & 2.5L engs	
upper cover (.2)	.4
lower cover (.6)	1.0
2.6L eng (3.2)	4.5
w/A.C. add (.5)	.5
w/P.S. add (.1)	.1
(G) Timing Belt, Renew	
1983-87	
2.2L & 2.5L engs (1.6)	2.2
w/A.C. add (.5)	.5
w/P.S. add (.2)	.2
(G) Timing Chain, Adjust	
1983-87	
2.6L eng (.4)	.8
(G) Timing Chain, Renew	
Includes: Renew cover oil seal.	
1983-87	
2.6L eng	
cam drive (3.6)	5.0
shaft drive (3.4)	4.8
w/A.C. add (.2)	.2
w/P.S. add (.1)	.1
(G) Timing Chain Guide, Renew	
1983-87	
2.6L eng-cam drive	
right or left (3.2)	4.6

(Factory Time)	Chilton Time
silent shaft-upper (3.2)	4.6
lower (3.2)	4.6
w/A.C. add (.2)	.2
w/P.S. add (.1)	.1
(G) Timing Chain Tensioner, Renew	
1983-87	
2.6L eng (3.5)	4.9
w/A.C. add (.2)	.2
w/P.S. add (.1)	.1
(G) Timing Belt Tensioner, Renew	
1983-87	
2.2L & 2.5L engs (.9)	1.5
w/A.C. add (.6)	.6
(G) Timing Chain Cover Oil Seal, Renew	
1983-87	
2.6L eng (.5)	.9
w/P.S. add (.1)	.1
(G) Camshaft Sprocket, Renew	
Includes: Renew cover oil seal, timing chain and crankshaft sprocket.	
1983-87	
2.2L & 2.5L engs (1.7)	2.4
2.6L eng (3.6)	5.0
w/A.C. add (.2)	.2
w/P.S. add (.2)	.2
(G) Camshaft Oil Seal, Renew	
1983-87	
2.2L & 2.5L engs (.7)	1.1
2.2-2.6L engs-rear (.4)	.8

(Factory Time)	Chilton Time
(G) Camshaft, Renew	
1983-87	
2.2L & 2.5L engs (1.7)	*2.8
2.6L eng (1.6)	2.2
*Renew valve springs add (1.1)	1.1
(G) Camshaft Distributor Drive Gear, Renew	
1983-87	
2.6L eng (.7)	1.1
(G) Intermediate Shaft, Renew	
1983-87	
2.2L & 2.5L engs (1.3)	2.5
w/A.C. add (.2)	.2
(G) Silent Shaft Sprocket, Renew	
1983-87	
2.6L eng-one or both (3.4)	4.7
w/A.C. add (.2)	.2
w/P.S. add (.1)	.1
(G) Intermediate Shaft Sprocket, Renew	
1983-87	
2.2L & 2.5L engs (1.7)	2.7
w/A.C. add (.2)	.2
w/P.S. add (.2)	.2
(G) Silent Shaft, Renew	
1983-87	
2.6L eng-right (4.0)	5.6
left (5.0)	7.0
both (5.3)	7.5
w/A.C. add (.4)	.4
w/P.S. add (.1)	.1

PARTS 16 CAMSHAFT & TIMING GEARS 16 PARTS

	Part No.	Price
2.2L ENGINE		
(1) Timing Belt Cover (Upper)		
1983-87	4105714	10.00
(2) Pulley (Tension)		
1983-87	5203469	41.75

	Part No.	Price
(3) Sprocket (Crankshaft)		
1983-87	5203575	14.00
(4) Timing Belt Cover (Lower)		
1983-84	4105293	10.00
1985-87	4343639	10.50

	Part No.	Price
(5) Sprocket (Interm. Shaft)		
1983	5214870	16.25
1984-87	4201974	16.50
(6) Timing Belt		
1983-85	5203401	22.75
1986-87	4343946	22.75

PARTS 16 CAMSHAFT & TIMING GEARS 16 PARTS

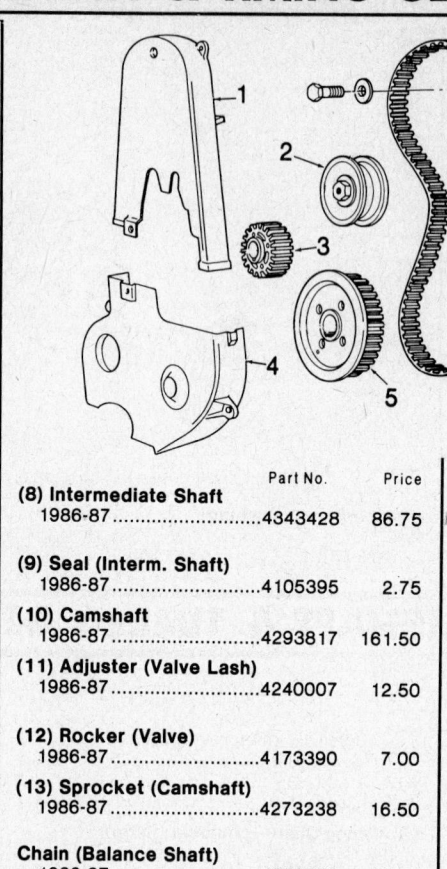

	Part No.	Price
(7) Retainer Assy. (Interm. Shaft)		
1983-87	5203325	8.50
(8) Intermediate Shaft		
1983-87	4293815	95.75
(9) Seal (Interm. Shaft)		
1983-87	4105395	2.75
(10) Camshaft		
1983	4271910	154.00
1984-87-wo/Turbo	4293817	161.50
w/Turbo	4293819	161.50
(11) Adjuster (Valve Lash)		
1983-87	4240007	12.50
(12) Rocker (Valve)		
1983-84	5203491	5.00
1985-87	4173390	7.00
(13) Sprocket (Camshaft)		
1983	5214870	16.25
1984-87-wo/Turbo	4201974	16.50
w/Turbo	4201992	22.50

2.5L ENGINE

	Part No.	Price
(1) Timing Belt Cover (Upper)		
1986-87	4343820	10.75
(2) Pulley (Tension)		
1986-87	4273241	14.00
(3) Sprocket (Crankshaft)		
1986-87	4273269	10.25
(4) Timing Belt Cover (Lower)		
1986-87	4343821	10.00
(5) Sprocket (Interm. Shaft)		
1986-87	4273238	16.50
(6) Timing Belt		
1986-87	4343824	22.75
(7) Retainer Assy (Interm. Shaft)		
1986-87	5203325	8.50

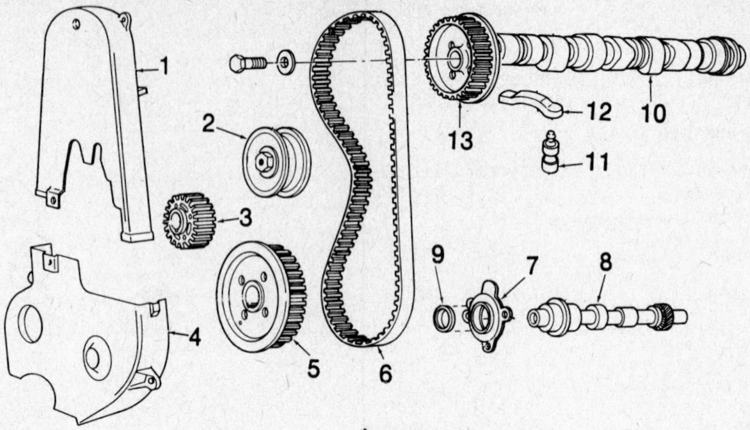

	Part No.	Price
(8) Intermediate Shaft		
1986-87	4343428	86.75
(9) Seal (Interm. Shaft)		
1986-87	4105395	2.75
(10) Camshaft		
1986-87	4293817	161.50
(11) Adjuster (Valve Lash)		
1986-87	4240007	12.50
(12) Rocker (Valve)		
1986-87	4173390	7.00
(13) Sprocket (Camshaft)		
1986-87	4273238	16.50
Chain (Balance Shaft)		
1986-87	4273260	16.25
Sprocket (Crank)		
1986-87	4273270	14.00

	Part No.	Price
Sprocket (Shaft Drive)		
1986-87	4273271	11.25
Balance Shaft (Drive)		
1986-87	4323026	23.00
Gear (Shaft Drive)		
1986-87	4343783	26.50
Balance Shaft (Driven)		
1986-87	4323028	23.00
Gear (Shaft Driven)		
1986-87	4343785	26.50
Carrier & Bearings		
1986-87	4323038	70.50
Rear Cover		
1986-87	4323043	1.50
Trough (Carrier Gear Cover)		
1986-87	4323041	1.25
Trough Front Cover (Chain)		
1986-87	4323039	5.75

PARTS 16 CAMSHAFT & TIMING GEARS 16 PARTS

2.6L ENGINE

	Part No.	Price
(1) Camshaft		
1983-85	MD026730	163.25
(2) Sprocket (Camshaft)		
1983-85	MD021246	21.75
(3) Gear (Distributor)		
1983-85	MD021247	13.75
(4) Sleeve (Complete)		
1983-85	MD021233	11.75
(5) Sprocket (Crankshaft)		
1983-85	MD020843	14.00
(6) Timing Chain		
1983-85	MD021230	43.50
(7) Chain		
1983-85	MD021155	49.75
(8) Sprocket (Crankshaft)		
1983-85	MD021170	22.75
(9) Sprocket Assy.		
1983-85	MD021172	20.50
(10) Thrust Plate Assy.		
1983-85	MD020897	22.50

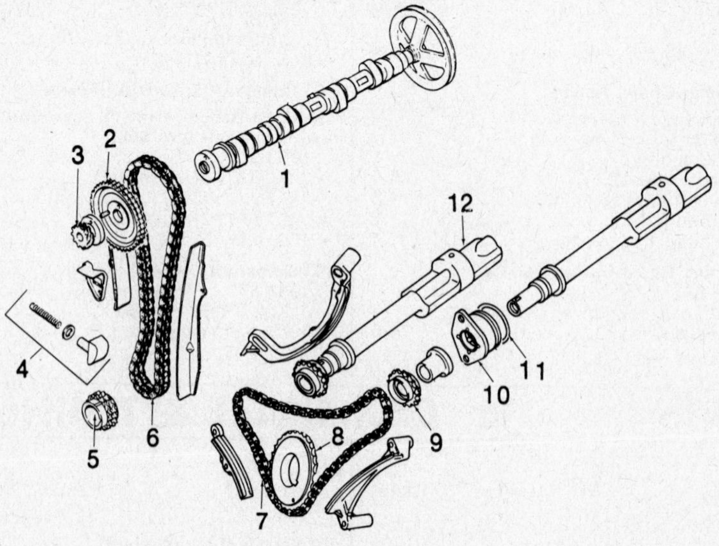

	Part No.	Price
(11) "O" Ring		
1983-85	MD021045	1.00

	Part No.	Price
(12) Counterbalance Shaft		
1983-85-right	MD024845	66.50
left	MD024846	66.50

LABOR 17 ENGINE OILING SYSTEM 17 LABOR

	(Factory Time)	Chilton Time
(G) Oil Pan or Gasket, Renew or Reseal		
1983-87		
2.2L & 2.5L engs	(1.0)	1.4
2.6L eng	(.6)	1.0
(P) Pressure Test Engine Bearings (Pan Off)		
All models		1.0
(G) Oil Pump, Renew		
1983-87		
2.2L & 2.5L engs	(1.3)	1.7
2.6L eng	(3.8)	5.2
w/A.C. add	(.2)	.2
(G) Oil Pump, R&R and Recondition		
1983-87		
2.2L & 2.5L engs	(1.7)	2.2
(G) Oil Pressure Relief Valve Spring, Renew		
1983-87		
2.2L & 2.5L engs	(1.6)	2.2
2.6L eng	(3.4)	4.7
(G) Oil Pressure Gauge (Engine Unit), Renew		
1983-87	(.3)	.4
(M) Oil Filter Element, Renew		
1983-87	(.2)	.3

PARTS 17 ENGINE OILING SYSTEM 17 PARTS

	Part No.	Price
Oil Pump Assy.		
2.2L		
1983	5203415	N.L.
1984	4323327	58.50
1985	4293888	N.L.
1986-87	4397827	66.00
2.5L		
1986-87	4397827	66.00
2.6L		
1983-85	MD060517	143.50
Drive Shaft & Rotor Pkg.		
2.2L		
1983-85	4240008	24.25
1986-87	4342940	24.50
2.5L		
1986-87	4342940	24.50
Oil Pump Driven Gear		
2.6L		
1983	MD022558	32.50
1984-85	MD061314	29.75
Oil Pump Drive Gear		
2.6L		
1983	MD022557	33.25
1984-85	MD061313	34.50
Gasket Oil Pan		
2.2L		
1983-87-seal	5203778	1.75
2.6L		
1983-85	MD024777	7.25
Oil Filter Assy.		
1983-87-w/2.2L eng.	4105409	5.50
w/2.6L eng.	MD031805	5.75
Screen Assy. (Oil)		
1983-85-2.2L	5203324	7.75
2.6L	MD025223	13.25
1986-87-2.2L	4343198	7.65
1986-87-2.5L	4343521	4.50

LABOR 18 CLUTCH & FLYWHEEL 18 LABOR

	(Factory Time)	Chilton Time
(G) Clutch Self-Adjusting Mechanism, Renew		
1983-87	(.3)	.6
(G) Clutch Assembly, Renew		
1983-87	(2.9)	4.0
Renew input seal add	(.2)	.2
(G) Clutch Release Bearing or Fork, Renew		
1983-87	(2.8)	3.8
(G) Clutch Release Cable, Renew		
1983-87	(.3)	.5
(G) Flywheel, Renew		
1983-87		
2.2L & 2.5L engs	(3.0)	4.2
(G) Clutch Release Lever and/or Seal, Renew		
1983-87	(.5)	.8

PARTS 18 CLUTCH & FLYWHEEL 18 PARTS

	Part No.	Price
Pressure Plate		
1983-87-wo/Turbo	4295007	122.50
w/Turbo	4269309	122.50
Clutch Disc		
1983-87-wo/Turbo	4295006	66.50
w/Turbo	4269308	68.25
Flywheel (w/Ring Gear)		
2.2L		
1983-84-wo/Turbo	4329177	142.75
w/Turbo	4348314	142.75
1985-wo/Turbo	4348312	142.50
w/Turbo	4348314	142.75
1986-87-wo/Turbo	4338874	142.75
w/Turbo	4338872	142.75
2.5L		
1986-87	4338872	142.75
Clutch Release Bearing		
1983-87	4202378	44.00
Clutch Control Cable		
1983	4019750	N.L.
1984-wo/Turbo	4295584	21.00
w/Turbo	4295596	N.L.
1985-87	4377769	18.50
Clutch Release Fork		
1983	5222707	18.00
1984-85	4295428	18.00
Clutch Release Shaft		
1983	5222708	31.25
1984-85	4295426	31.25

LABOR 21 SHIFT LINKAGE 21 LABOR

	(Factory Time)	Chilton Time
MANUAL		
(G) Gearshift Linkage, Adjust		
1983-87	(.2)	.4
(G) Gearshift Lever, Renew		
1983-87	(.4)	.6
(G) Gearshift Control Rod and/or Swivel, Renew		
1983-87	(.3)	.4
(G) Gearshift Mechanism, Renew		
1983-87		
linkage shift	(.6)	.9
cable shift	(.7)	1.1
(G) Selector Shaft Seal, Renew		
1983-87	(.8)	1.1
(G) Trans/Axle Selector Shaft, Renew		
1983-87	(1.3)	1.7
(G) Gearshift Selector Cable, Renew		
1983-87	(.9)	1.4

LABOR 21 SHIFT LINKAGE 21 LABOR

(Factory Time)	Chilton Time
(G) Gearshift Crossover Cable, Renew	
1983-87 (.8)	1.3
AUTOMATIC	
(G) Throttle Linkage, Adjust	
1983-87 (.2)	.4
(G) Selector Lever, Renew	
1983-87 (.3)	.4
(G) Gearshift Mechanism, Renew	
1983-87 (.4)	.8
(G) Gearshift Control Cable, Renew	
1983-87 (.5)	.8
(G) Throttle Lever Control Cable, Renew	
Includes: Adjust cable.	
1983-87 (.3)	.6
(G) Gear Selector Dial, Renew	
1983-87 (.7)	1.1

LABOR 26 REAR AXLE & SUSPENSION 26 LABOR

(Factory Time)	Chilton Time
(G) Rear Wheel Bearings, Renew or Repack	
1983-87-one side (.6)	.9
both sides (1.1)	1.7
(G) Rear Wheel Grease Seal, Renew	
1983-87-one side (.4)	.7
(G) Rear Shock Absorbers, Renew	
1983-87-one (.3)	.5
both (.4)	.7
(G) Rear Springs, Renew	
1983-87-one (.3)	.6
both (.5)	.8
(G) Lower Control Arm Bushings, Renew	
1983-87-one side (.6)	1.0
(G) Stub Axle Spindle, Renew	
1983-87-each (.5)	.7
(G) Rear Sway Bar, Renew	
1983-87 (.4)	.7
(G) Rear Wheel Mounting Studs, Renew	
1983-87-one (.5)	.8
each adtnl	.1
AIR SUSPENSION	
(G) Air Suspension Lines, Renew	
1986-87-one (.3)	.4
all	.5
(G) Height Sensor, Renew	
1986-87 (.4)	.5
(G) Compressor Assembly, Renew	
1986-87 (.5)	.7
(G) Compressor Relay, Renew	
1986-87 (.6)	.9

PARTS 26 REAR AXLE AND SUSPENSION 26 PARTS

	Part No.	Price
(1) Rear Spindle		
1983-84	4228123	62.75
1985-87	4228117	50.50
(2) Shim (Whl. Alignment)		
1983-87	5205114	2.25
(3) Shock Absorber		
1983-84-Std.	4147849	16.25
H.D.	4228260	21.50
1985-87-Std.	4228377	30.00
H.D.	4228335	30.00
(4) Track Bar		
1983	4271370	58.00
1984-85	4318723	63.25
1986-87	4228256	63.25
(5) Brace (Trac Bar Mtg.)		
1983-84	4147852	17.75
1985-87	4228251	17.75
(6) Pivot Bolt		
1983-87	6500415	1.25
(7) Cup (Jounce Bumper)		
1983-w/13" whl.	4147747	6.25
w/14" whl.	4147813	6.75
1984-exc. below	4147752	7.00
S.B.R. tires	4147813	6.75
1985	4228096	7.00
1986-87		
one notch	4228096	7.00
three notch	4228440	7.00
(8) Isolator (Spring Upper)		
1983-87	4147759	2.75
(9) Bumper (Jounce)		
1983-84	4147708	7.50
1985-87	4228159	6.50
(10) Coil Spring		
Order by model and description.		
(11) Bushing (Control Arm)		
1983-87-Std.	4147857	9.25
H.D.	4147951	9.00

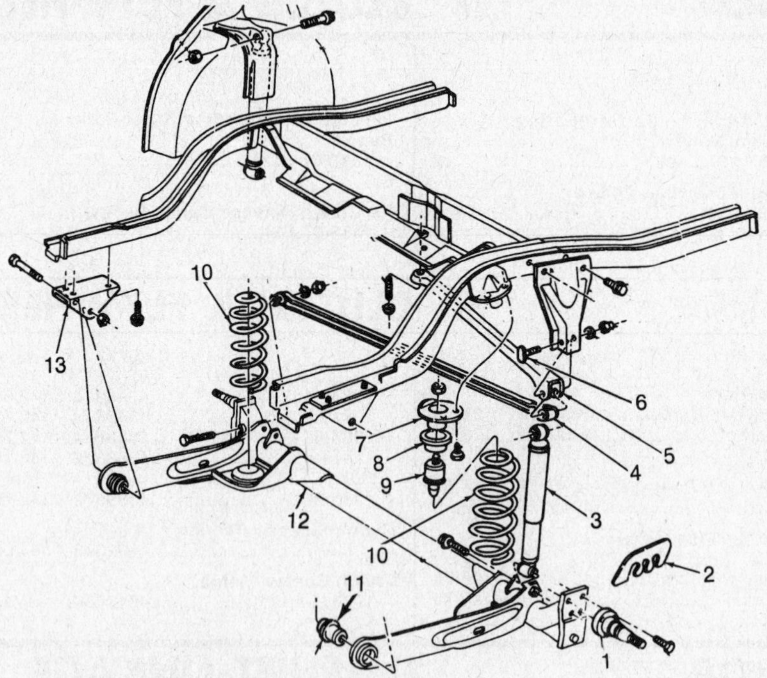

	Part No.	Price
(12) Control Arm (w/Axle Channel)		
1983-84-Std.	4147814	199.50
H.D.	4147903	199.50
1985-Std.	4147814	199.50
H.D.	4147903	199.50
Firm	4147904	199.50
1986-87-Std.	4228501	199.50
H.D.	4228503	199.50
Firm	4228504	199.50

	Part No.	Price
(13) Hanger (Front)		
1983-right	4147816	6.00
left	4147817	6.00
1984-85-right	4228312	6.00
left	4228313	6.00
1986-87-right	4228454	5.50
left	4228455	5.50

PARTS 26 REAR AXLE AND SUSPENSION 26 PARTS

	Part No.	Price
AIR SUSPENSION		
Compressor		
1986-87	4228675	154.50
Air Line Connector Assy.		
1986-87	4228536	1.00
Height Sensor		
1986-87	4228530	87.25
Ball Stud Connector		
1986-87-link	6501297	.75
Shock Absorber		
1986-87-Std.	4228540	41.50
H.D.	4228541	45.50
Relay (w/Bracket)		
1986-87	4228673	15.50
Link (Height Sensor)		
1986-87	4228673	15.50
Filter		
1986-87	4228671	3.25
Air Line		
1986-87-right	4228537	3.50
left	4228538	4.50

LABOR 28 AIR CONDITIONING 28 LABOR

(Factory Time) Chilton Time

Note: If more than one item requires replacement where evacuation and discharging the system is already included in the operation, deduct 1.0 hour for each additional item to the times listed.

(G) Drain, Evacuate, Leak Test and Charge System
All models.......... 1.0

(G) Partial Charge
Includes: Leak test.
All models (.5) 6

(G) Performance Test
All models.......... .8

(G) Vacuum Leak Test
All models.......... .8

(G) Compressor Drive Belt, Renew
1983-87 (.2).......... .3

C-171 COMPRESSOR

(G) Compressor Assembly, Renew
Includes: Transfer parts as required. Pressure test and charge system.
1983-87
2.2L eng (1.4).......... 2.5
2.6L eng (1.9).......... 3.0

(G) Compressor Clutch Field Coil, Renew
1983-87
2.2L eng (.6).......... .9
2.6L eng (.9).......... 1.4

(G) Compressor Clutch Pulley, Renew (w/Hub)
1983-87
2.2L eng (.4).......... .5
2.6L eng (.7).......... 1.0

(G) Compressor Clutch Assembly, Renew
1983-87
2.2L eng (.6).......... .8
2.6L eng (.9).......... 1.3

(G) Compressor Front Cover Seal, Renew
Includes: R&R compressor. Pressure test and charge system.
1983-87
2.2L eng (1.8).......... 3.1
2.6L eng (2.3).......... 3.6

(G) Compressor Rear Cover Seal, Renew
Includes: R&R compressor. Pressure test and charge system.
1983-87
2.2L eng (1.7).......... 3.0

AIR CONDITIONER TUNE-UP

For efficient operation and satisfactory performance in hot weather. The following air conditioner tune-up is suggested:

1. Clean intake filter
2. Clean condenser fins
3. Pressure test system
4. Adjust drive belt tension
5. Check antifreeze/coolant
6. Tighten compressor mounts
7. Tighten condenser and evaporator mounts
8. Inspect system for leaks (hoses, couplings, valves, etc.)
9. Partial charge system

All models 1.0
If necessary to evacuate and charge system, add 1.0

(Factory Time) Chilton Time

2.6L eng (2.2).......... 3.5

(G) Compressor Center Seal, Renew
Includes: R&R compressor. Pressure test and charge system.
1983-87
2.2L eng (1.9).......... 3.2
2.6L eng (2.4).......... 3.7

(G) Compressor Shaft Gas Seal, Renew
Includes: R&R compressor. Pressure test and charge system.
1983-87
2.2L eng (1.8).......... 3.1
2.6L eng (2.3).......... 3.6

(G) Expansion Valve, Renew
Includes: Pressure test and charge system.
1983-87 (1.0).......... 1.7

(G) Receiver Drier, Renew
Includes: Add partial charge, leak test and charge system.
1983-87 (.9).......... 1.6

(G) Low Pressure Cut Off Switch, Renew
Includes: Charge system.
1983-87 (.9).......... 1.4

(Factory Time) Chilton Time

(G) High Pressure Cut Off Switch, Renew
1983-87 (.3).......... .5

(G) Clutch Cycling (Thermostatic Control) Switch, Renew
1983-87 (.3).......... .6
pressure activated (.2).......... .4

(G) Condenser Assembly, Renew
Includes: Add partial charge, leak test and charge system.
1983-87 (1.5).......... 2.5
Renew receiver drier add.......... .2

(G) Evaporator Coil, Renew
Includes: Add partial charge, leak test and charge system.
1983-87 (2.6).......... 4.5
w/Console add (.2).......... .2

(G) Temperature Control Assembly, Renew
1983-87 (.4).......... .7

(G) Push Button Vacuum Switch, Renew
1983-87 (.5).......... .9

(G) Blower Motor Switch, Renew
1983-87 (.4).......... .8

(G) Temperature Control Cable, Renew
1983-87 (.3).......... .6

(G) Blower Motor, Renew
1983-87 (.6).......... .9

(G) Blower Motor Resistor, Renew
1983-87 (.3).......... .4

(G) A.C. On-Off Switch, Renew
1985-87 (.6).......... .8

(G) Vacuum Actuators, Renew
1983-87
outside air door (.2).......... .4
heater/defroster door (.3).......... .6
A/C mode door (.8).......... 1.5

(G) Air Conditioning Hoses, Renew
Includes: Add partial charge, leak test and charge system.
1983-87
Suction hose
2.2L eng (1.1).......... 1.5
2.6L eng (1.3).......... 1.7
Discharge hose
2.2L eng (1.1).......... 1.5
2.6L eng (1.7).......... 2.1
Renew receiver drier add.......... .2

PARTS 28 AIR CONDITIONING 28 PARTS

	Part No.	Price
Compressor Assy.		
1983-84	4176059	275.00
1985-87-2.2L	4339456	275.00
2.6L	4339455	275.00
Compressor Shaft Seal Pkg.		
1983-87	3847916	7.75
Pulley & Armature (Drive Clutch)		
1983-84-2.2L	5210384	101.50
2.6L	3847764	101.50
1985-87-2.2L	3848982	101.75
2.6L	3848983	86.25
Field Coil (Drive Clutch)		
1983	3846845	60.75
1984	3848673	60.75
1985-87	3848969	29.50
Check Valve (Discharge Line)		
1983-87	3847576	1.75
Expansion Valve (H-Type)		
1983-85	4176999	59.75
1986-87	3849240	59.75
Drier Filter		
1983-87	3848217	37.25
Low Pressure Cut Off Switch		
1983-87	5210377	17.25
Condenser Assy.		
1983-84	3848015	219.75
1985-87	3848530	219.75
Heater Core		
1984-87	3847943	90.75
Evaporator Coil		
1983	3848195	341.75
1984	4339423	317.25
1985	3848840	29.50
1986-87	4339423	317.25
Blower Motor		
1983-84	4240426	66.25
1985	3849032	59.00
1986-87	3849235	8.50
Blower Motor Resistor		
1983-84	3848807	7.75
1985	3849075	N.L.
1986-87	3849266	59.00
Blower Motor Switch		
1983-84	3847940	10.25
1985-87	3849139	10.25
A.C. Control Switch		
1985-87-bright	3849150	13.75
black	3849142	26.75
Sensor ATC (Ambient)		
1986-87	3848789	12.25
Module Power ATC		
1986-87	3848563	86.00
Module Vacuum ATC		
1986-87	3848564	115.50
In Car Sensor ATC		
1986-87	3848859	37.75
Water Control Valve		
1984-85		
1986-87-wo/Turbo	3849199	27.75
w/Turbo	3848460	27.75

LABOR 29 LOCKS, HINGES & WIND. REGULATORS 29 LABOR

(Factory Time)	Chilton Time
(G) Hood Hinge, Renew (One)	
Does not include painting.	
1983-87 (.3)	.4
(G) Hood Latch, Renew	
1983-87 (.2)	.4
(G) Hood Release Cable, Renew	
1983-87 (.3)	.6
(G) Door Latch, Renew	
1983-87	
2 dr models (.5)	.7
4 dr & wagon models (.5)	.7
(G) Lock Striker Plate, Renew	
1983-87 (.2)	.3
(G) Door Lock Remote Control, Renew	
1983-87	
All models-one (.5)	.8
(G) Front Door Window Regulator, Renew	
1983-87	
2 dr models	
manual (.8)	1.4
electric (.8)	1.5
4 dr & wagon models	
manual (.8)	1.4
electric (.9)	1.5
(G) Rear Door Window Regulator, Renew	
1983-87-manual (.7)	1.3
electric (.9)	1.5
(G) Door Handle (Outside), Renew	
1983-87	
Front-2 dr models (.5)	.7
4 dr & wagon models (.4)	.6
Rear-all models (.4)	.6
(G) Trunk Hinge, Renew (One)	
1983-87 (.3)	.5

PARTS 29 LOCKS, HINGES & WIND. REGULATORS 29 PARTS

	Part No.	Price
Hood Lock		
1983-87	4103194	6.50
Hood Latch (Inside Release)		
1984-87	5232057	13.00
Hood Hinges		
1983-87-right	4103760	22.25
left	4103761	22.25
Front Door Lock (Power)		
1983-right	4184620	35.25
left	4184623	35.25
1984-right	4336150	35.25
left	4336149	35.25
1985-87-right	4336378	35.25
left	4336377	35.25
Rear Door Lock (Power)		
1983-right	4184624	35.25
left	4184625	35.25
1984-right	4310014	35.25
left	4310015	N.L.
1985-87-right	4336380	35.25
left	4336381	35.25
Electric Solenoid (Power Lock)		
1983-85	4184156	60.00
1986-87	4396015	60.00
Door Lock Cylinder & Key		
(wo/Illum. entry)		
1983-84-wo/Tilt whl.	4246564	20.75
w/Tilt whl.	4246563	35.25
1985-wo/Tilt whl.	4054805	20.50
w/Tilt whl.	3548955	18.25
1986-87	4378171	10.50
(w/Illum. entry)		
1983-84-wo/Tilt whl.	4246611	47.75
w/Tilt whl.	4246610	47.75
1985-wo/Tilt whl.	4246628	36.50
w/Tilt whl.	4246627	47.75
1986-87	4378172	29.50
Window Regulator (Manual)		
Front		
(2-door)		
1983-87-right	4184018	52.00
left	4184019	52.00
(4-door)		
1983-87-right	4184060	52.00
left	4184061	52.00
Rear		
1983-84-right	4184566	52.00
left	4184567	52.00
1985-right	4310688	51.75
left	4310689	51.75
1986-87-right	4365464	51.75
left	4365465	51.75
Window Regulator (Power)		
Front		
(2-door)		
1983-87-right	4280436	67.50
left	4280437	67.50
(4-door)		
1983-84-right	4280432	67.50
left	4280433	67.50
1985-right	4336604	65.50
left	4336605	65.50
1986-87-right	4280432	67.50
left	4280433	67.50
Rear		
1983-84-right	4184616	67.50
left	4184617	67.50
1985-right	4336544	65.50
left	4336545	67.50
1986-87-right	4365474	67.50
left	4365475	67.50
Power Window Motor		
Front		
1983-right	4280640	N.L.
left	4280641	N.L.
1984-85-right	4184316	173.25
left	4184317	173.25

PARTS 29 LOCKS, HINGES & WIND. REGULATORS 29 PARTS

	Part No.	Price
1986-87-right		
up to 10-7-85	4336600	173.25
from 10-7-85	4396402	173.25
1986-87-left		
up to 10-7-85	4336601	173.25
from 10-7-85	4396403	173.25
Rear		
1983-84-right	4184548	173.25
left	4184549	173.25
1985-87-right	4310938	173.25
left	4310939	173.25
Deck Lid Latch		
Manual		
1983-84	4054825	29.00
1985-87	4378053	17.50
Deck Lid Hinges		
1983-84-right	4314194	14.50
left	4314195	14.50
1985-right	4337402	16.25
left	4337403	16.25
1986-87-right	4371930	16.00
left	4371931	16.00
Deck Lid Cylinder & Key		
1983	4054081	16.25
1984	4246299	12.25
1985	4246984	8.50

LABOR 30 HEAD & PARKING LAMPS 30 LABOR

	(Factory Time)	Chilton Time
(G) Aim Headlamps		
two		.4
four		.6
(M) Headlamp Sealed Beam Bulb, Renew		
Does not include aim headlamps.		
All models-each	(.2)	.3
(M) License Lamp Lens, Renew		
All models	(.2)	.2
(M) License Lamp Assembly, Renew		
All models	(.2)	.3
(M) Turn Signal and Parking Lamp Assy., Renew		
All models	(.3)	.4
(M) Tail Lamp Assembly, Renew		
All models	(.2)	.4
(M) Side Marker Lamp Assy., Renew		
All models-each	(.2)	.3

PARTS 30 HEAD & PARKING LAMPS 30 PARTS

	Part No.	Price
Sealed Beam Unit		
(High & Low Beams)		
1983-84-exc.		
below	153201	11.00
Halogen	153481	16.00
1985-87	153784	16.00
(High Beams)		
1983-84-exc.		
below	153200	11.00
Halogen	153440	16.00
1985-87	153775	16.00
Parking & Turn Signal Lamp Assy.		
1983-right	4174206	28.25
left	4174207	28.25
1984-85-right	4174200	20.25
left	4174201	20.25
1986-87-right	4321578	21.25
left	4321579	21.25
Tail, Stop & Backup Lamp Assy.		
Dodge 600		
1983-right	4174500	70.75
left	4174501	70.75
E Class-New Yorker		
1983-right	4174502	77.75
left	4174503	77.75
Caravelle		
1985-right	4174832	87.25
left	4174833	87.25
1986-87-right	4321526	87.50
left	4321527	87.50
Tail, Stop & Turn Signal		
E Class New Yorker		
1984-85-right	4174768	80.75
left	4174769	80.75
1986-87-right	4321530	92.50
left	4321531	92.50
Dodge 600		
1984-85-right	4174762	75.00
left	4174763	75.00
1986-87-right	4321528	89.25
left	4321529	89.25
License Lamp Assy.		
1983-87	4176560	30.75
Side Marker Lamp Assy.		
1983-87-front	4174224	11.25
rear	4174311	11.25
High Mount Stoplight		
1986-87		
lens & housing	4321992	9.75
adapter	4321649	7.75
New Yorker	4321650	7.75
Cornering Lamp Assy.		
1983-87-right	4174206	28.25
left	4174207	28.25

LABOR 31 WINDSHIELD WIPER & SPEEDOMETER 31 LABOR

	(Factory Time)	Chilton Time
(G) Windshield Wiper Motor, Test and Renew		
1983-87	(.4)	.7
(G) Wiper/Washer Switch Assy., Renew		
1983-87		
std column	(.8)	1.2
tilt column	(1.1)	1.5
(G) Washer Pump, Renew		
1983-87	(.3)	.4
(G) Wiper Link Assembly, Renew		
1983-87	(.5)	.7
(G) Windshield Wiper Pivot, Renew		
1983-87-one	(.5)	.8
(G) Intermittent Wiper Control Module, Renew		
1983-87	(.2)	.4
(G) Odometer Memory Chip, Renew Electronic Cluster		
1984-87	(.4)	.6
(G) Speedometer Head, R&R or Renew		
Does not include reset odometer.		
1983-87	(.4)	.8
Reset odometer add		.2
(G) Speedometer Cable and Casing, Renew		
1983		
speed control to trans	(.2)	.4
speed control to speedo	(.4)	.8
trans to speedo	(.5)	.9
1984-87		
upper	(.3)	.6
lower	(.5)	.9
one piece	(.6)	1.0
(G) Speedometer Cable (Inner), Renew or Lubricate		
1983		
speed control to trans	(.2)	.4
speed control to speedo	(.3)	.5
trans to speedo	(.3)	.5
1984-87		
upper	(.3)	.5
lower	(.4)	.8
one piece	(.4)	.8
(G) Speedometer Drive Pinion, Renew		
Includes: Renew oil seal.		
1983-87	(.3)	.4
(G) Radio, R&R		
1983-87	(.3)	.7
(G) Electronic Instrument Cluster Assy., Renew		
1984-87	(.4)	.6

PARTS 31 WINDSHIELD WIPER & SPEEDOMETER 31 PARTS

	Part No.	Price
Wiper Motor (Windshield)		
1983-84	4205951	106.75
1985-87	4339449	106.75
Wiper Pivot		
1983-87-right	4240511	17.00
left	4240512	17.00
Link w/Bushing (Windshield Wiper)		
1983-87-right	3799595	6.50
left	3799600	6.50
Armature Pkg. (Wiper Motor)		
1983-87	3799087	27.75
Crank w/Pin (Windshield Wiper)		
1983-87	3799597	4.50
Wiper & Washer Switch		
(wo/Intermittent wipers)		
1983-84	4221231	25.25
1985-87	3747914	34.25
(w/Intermittent Wipers)		
1983-87-wo/tilt whl.	4221232	36.00
w/tilt whl.	4221233	60.25
Intermittent Wiper Control		
1983	4222060	28.25
1984-85	4312002	28.25
Pump & Seal Package		
1983-85	3799090	21.50
Speedometer Cable & Casing		
(Manual Trans.)		
1983		
25″ Long (lower)	4220742	14.75
41″ Long (upper)	4220748	13.25
1984-87	4312331	14.00
(Auto. Trans.)		
1983	4220744	14.00
1984-87	4312331	14.00
Speedometer Cable to Speed Control		
1983-M.T.	4240747	35.25
A.T.	4240746	35.25
1984-87	4312332	13.25
Speedometer Assy.		
1983-85	4051640	56.75
1986-87	4051786	56.75

LABOR 32 LIGHT SWITCHES & WIRING 32 LABOR

	(Factory Time)	Chilton Time
(G) Headlamp Switch, Renew		
1983-87	(.3)	.4
(G) Headlamp Dimmer Switch, Renew		
1983-87	(.3)	.6
(G) Back-up Lamp Switch, Renew		
(w/Manual Trans)		
1983-87	(.2)	.4
(G) Stop Light Switch, Renew		
1983-87	(.3)	.4
w/Cruise control add	(.1)	.1
(G) Neutral Safety Switch, Renew		
1983-87	(.3)	.4
(G) Parking Brake Warning Lamp Switch, Renew		
1983-87	(.2)	.3
(G) Turn Signal Switch, Renew		
1983-87		
std column	(.5)	1.0
tilt column	(.8)	1.5
(M) Turn Signal or Hazard Warning Flasher, Renew		
1983-87	(.2)	.3
(G) Horn Switch, Renew		
1983-87	(.2)	.3
(G) Horn Relay, Renew		
1983-87	(.2)	.3
(G) Horn, Renew		
1983-87-one	(.2)	.4
(G) Wiring Harness, Renew		
1983-87		
Main harness to dash	(1.2)	3.0
Body harness		
2 & 4 dr models	(.7)	1.3

PARTS 32 LIGHT SWITCHES & WIRING 32 PARTS

	Part No.	Price
Head Lamp Switch		
1983-wo/Tilt whl.	4221198	11.75
w/Tilt whl.	4221200	13.25
1984-87	4221407	17.25
Stop Light Switch		
1983-84-wo/Speed cont.	3747993	8.00
w/Speed Cont.	3747995	11.00
1985-87	4221651	15.50
Turn Signal & Hazard Warning Switch		
(wo/Cornering lamp)		
1983-84-wo/Tilt whl.	4221337	38.50
w/Tilt whl.	4221304	47.00
1985-wo/Tilt whl.	4221337	38.50
w/Tilt whl.	4221205	47.00
1986-87-wo/Tilt whl.	4221680	38.00
w/Tilt whl.	4221304	47.00
(w/Cornering lamp)		
1983-84-wo/Tilt whl.	4221338	40.75
w/Tilt whl.	4221305	53.50
1985-wo/Tilt whl.	4221338	40.75
w/Tilt whl.	4221206	53.50
Turn Signal Flasher		
1983-87-2 lamp	3837161	4.25
3 lamp	3837162	4.25
Hazard Warning Flasher		
1983-87	2932877	4.50
Back Up Switch		
(A.T.)		
1983-87	4057750	8.75
(M.T.)		
1983	2258404	9.50
1984	4221462	10.00
1985-87	4221587	10.00
Horn Assy.		
1983-87-low	4222288	18.25
high	2808869	24.00
Horn Relay		
1983-87	4221670	8.75
Wiring Harness		
Order by model and description.		

LABOR 33 GLASS 33 LABOR

	(Factory Time)	Chilton Time
(G) Windshield Glass, Renew		
Includes: Replace weatherstrip if necessary, where applicable.		
1983-87	(1.8)	2.8
Conv add	(.3)	.3
(G) Front Door Glass, Renew		
1983-87		
2 dr models	(.6)	.9
4 dr models	(.7)	1.0
(G) Rear Door Glass, Renew		
1983-87	(.7)	1.0
(G) Rear Door Fixed Vent Glass, Renew		
1983-87	(.8)	1.2
(G) Center or Quarter Glass, Renew		
1983-87		
2 dr-rear		
movable	(1.0)	1.4
2 dr-front		
fixed	(1.0)	1.4
4 dr Sdn	(.7)	1.1
(G) Rear Window Glass, Renew		
1983-87	(1.6)	3.0
w/Padded full roof add	(2.9)	4.0
w/Padded Landau roof add		
4 dr	(.4)	.4
conv	(2.9)	4.0

LABOR 34 CRUISE CONTROL 34 LABOR

	(Factory Time)	Chilton Time
(G) Speed Control Servo Assy., Renew		
1983-87	(.4)	.6
w/Turbo add	(.1)	.1
(G) Speed Control Cable, Renew		
1983-87	(.4)	.7
(G) Speed Control Turn Signal Lever Switch, Renew		
1983-87		
std column	(.5)	.9
tilt column	(1.0)	1.5
(G) Speed Control Wiring Harness, Renew		
1983-87	(.3)	.6
(G) Speed Control Safety (Cut-Out) Switch, Renew		
1983-87	(.3)	.5
(G) Electronic Speed Control Module, Renew		
1985-87	(.2)	.4

PARTS 34 CRUISE CONTROL 34 PARTS

	Part No.	Price
Cruise Control Servo		
1983-85	4179306	129.75
1986-87	4307221	130.00
Cruise Control Switch & Lever		
(wo/Tilt wheel)		
1983-84	3747895	41.75
1985	4221482	41.75
(w/Tilt wheel)		
1983-85	3747881	41.75
1986-87	4342209	41.75
Cruise Control Cable		
1983-2.2L	4241773	22.00
2.6L	4241774	22.00
1984-87-2.2L	4288055	24.25
2.6L	4288059	24.25
Cruise Control Switch (On Brake)		
1983-84	3747995	11.00
1985-87	4221651	15.50
Cruise Control Switch (Clutch)		
1983-84	4221677	13.50
1985-87	4221697	21.75
Electronic Speed Control Switch		
1986-87	4342207	41.75
Module (ESC)		
1986-87	4318829	116.50
Stoplight Switch (ESC)		
1986-87	4221976	15.50
Vacuum Motor (ESC)		
1986-87	4318819	27.50
Clutch Switch (ESC)		
1986-87	4221697	21.75
Cable (ESC)		
1986-87-w/Turbo	4288057	24.75
EFI	4307565	24.75

GROUP INDEX

ALPHABETICAL INDEX

Chrysler Corporation
Front Wheel Drive Cars

HORIZON • OMNI • TC3 • 024

YEAR IDENTIFICATION

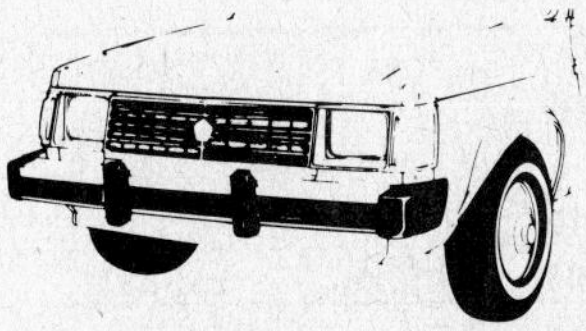

1983 Omni

1984 Omni

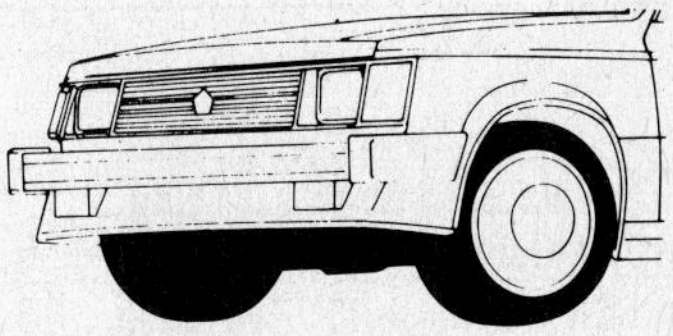

1985 and later Omni GLH

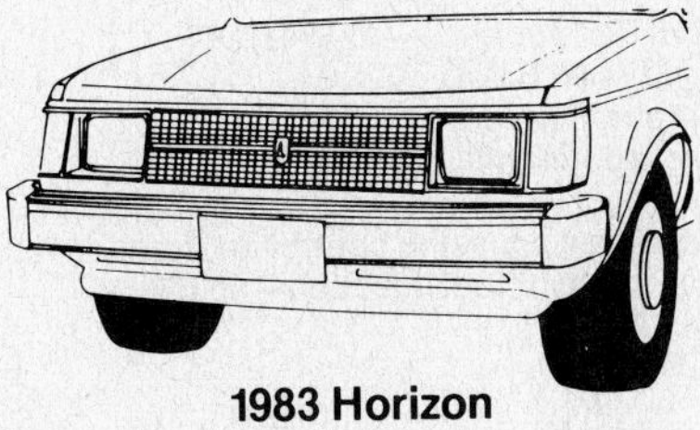

1983 Horizon

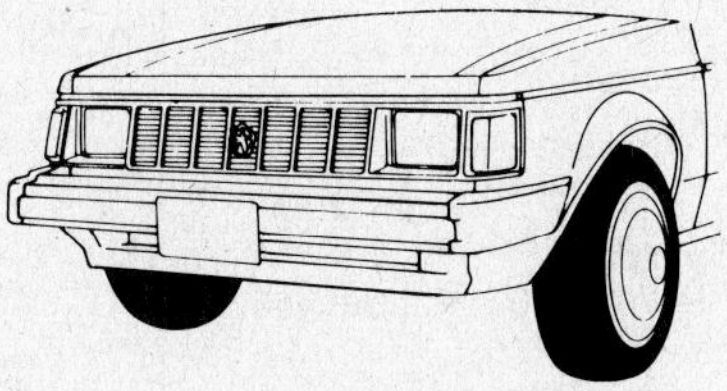

1984–87 Horizon

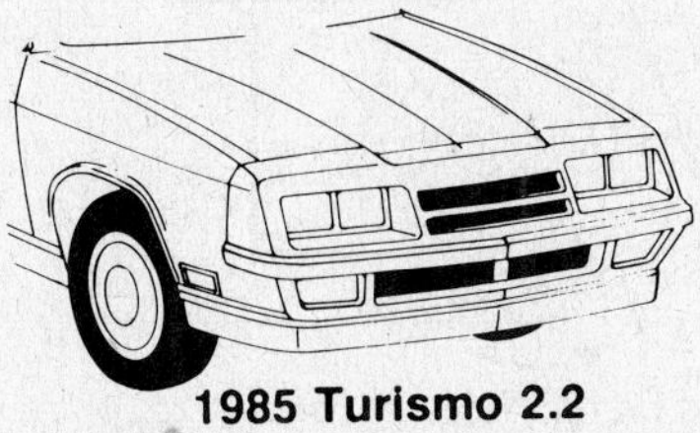

1985 Turismo 2.2

1985–87 Turismo Duster

VEHICLE IDENTIFICATION NUMBER (VIN)

It is important for servicing and ordering parts to be certain of the vehicle and engine identification. The VIN (vehicle identification number) is a 13 or 17 digit number visible through the windshield on the driver's side of the dash, and contains the vehicle and engine identification codes. It can be interpreted as follows:

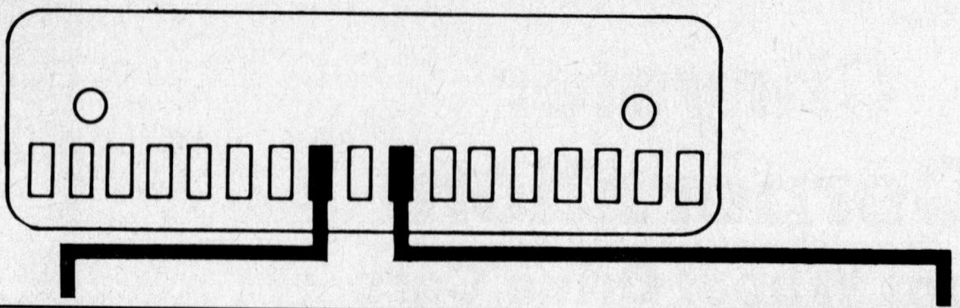

ENGINE CODE					
Code	Cu. In.	Liters	Cyl	Carb. bbl	Eng. Mfg.
A (84-85)	98	1.6	4	2	Peugeot
B (83)	105	1.7	4	2	VW
C (83-87)	135	2.2	4	2	Chrysler
D (83-87)	135	2.2	4	EFI	Chrysler
E (84-87)	135	2.2	4	Turbo	Chrysler
G (83-85)	156	2.6	4	2	Mitsubishi
K (86-87)	153	2.5	4	EFI	Chrysler

MODEL YEAR CODE	
Code	Year
C	82
D	83
E	84
F	85
G	86
H	87

The seventeen digit Vehicle Identification Number can be used to determine engine application and model year. The tenth indicates the model year, and the eighth digit identifies engine displacement.

TUNE-UP SPECIFICATIONS

Year	Eng. V.I.N. Code	No. Cyl. Displ. Cu. In.	Eng. Mfg.	h.p.	Spark Plugs Orig. Type	Spark Plugs Gap (in.)	Ignition Timing (deg.) Man. Trans.	Ignition Timing (deg.) Auto Trans.	Intake Valve Opens (deg.)▪	Fuel Pump Pressure (psi)	Idle Speed (rpm) Man. Trans.	Idle Speed (rpm) Auto Trans.	Valve Lash (in.) Intake	Valve Lash (in.) Exhaust
'84-'86	A	4-98	Peugeot	64	RN12YC	.035	12B	12B	16.5	4.5-6.0	850	1000	.012H	.014H
'83	A	4-105	VW	63	65PR	.035	20B	12B	14	4.4-5.8	900	900	.008-.012H	.016-.020H
'83-'86	C	4-135	Chrysler	All	RN12YC	.035	10B	10B	16 ⑤	4.5-6.0	900	900	Hyd.	Hyd.
'84-'86	D ⑦	4-135	Chrysler	99	RN12YC	.035	12B	12B	10.5	36	850	750	Hyd.	Hyd.
'84-'86	E ⑥	4-135	Chrysler	146	RN12YC	.035	12B	12B	10	53	950	950	Hyd.	Hyd.
'83-'85	G	4-156	Mitsubishi	92	RN11YC4	③	7B	7B	25	4.5-6.0	800 ①	800 ①	.006H ⑧	.010H
'86-'87	K	4-153	Chrysler	100	RN12YC	.035	⑨	⑨	12	14.5 ⑩	⑨	⑨	Hyd.	Hyd.

NOTE: The underhood specifications sticker often reflects tune-up specification changes made in production. Sticker figures must be used if they disagree with those in this chart. Part numbers in this chart are not recommendations by Chilton for any product by brand name.

▪ Before top dead center
Hyd.—Hydraulic
H—Hot
C—Cold
① 750 rpm-Canada
③ .035-.040 RN11Y—.030 in For Canada
⑤ Shelby and Hi Performance—10.5° BTDC
Turbocharged—10° BTDC
⑥ Turbo with multipoint fuel injection
⑦ EFI with single point fuel injection
⑧ Jet valve clearance—.010 in.
⑨ Refer to underhood emission control information label
⑩ '86-'87 with multipoint fuel injection—55 lbs

FIRING ORDERS

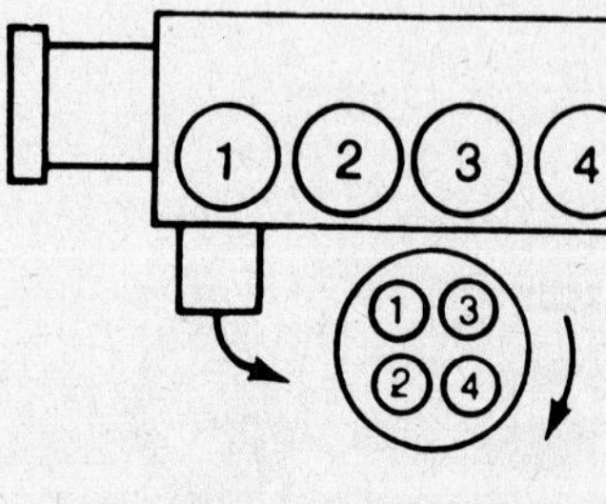

Chrysler Corp. (Mitsubishi) 2.6L
Engine firing order: 1–3–4–2
Distributor rotation: clockwise

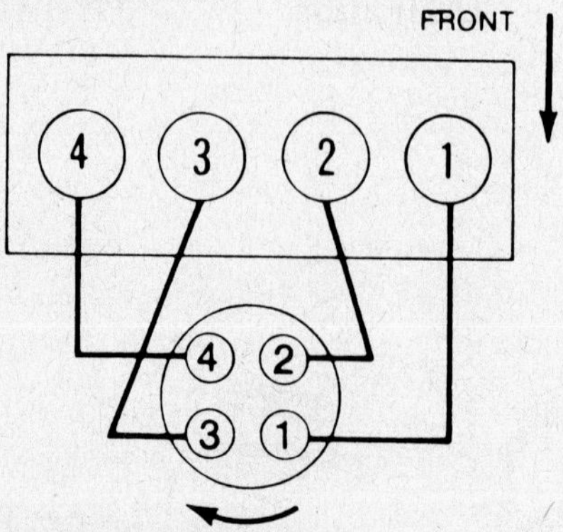

Chrysler Corp: 1.6L
Engine firing order: 1–3–4–2
Distributor rotation: clockwise

FIRING ORDERS

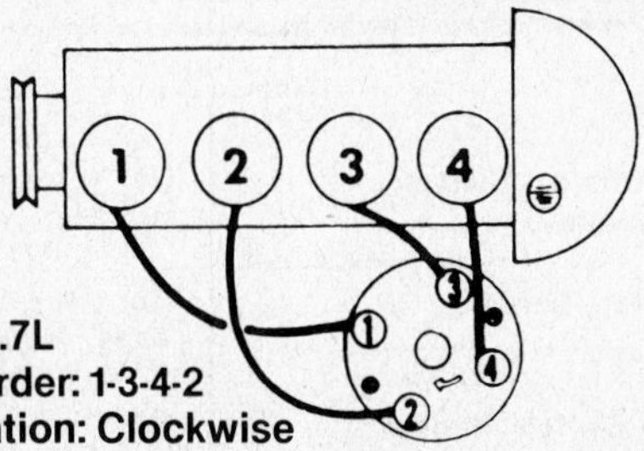

Chrysler Corp. 1.7L
Engine Firing Order: 1-3-4-2
Distributor Rotation: Clockwise

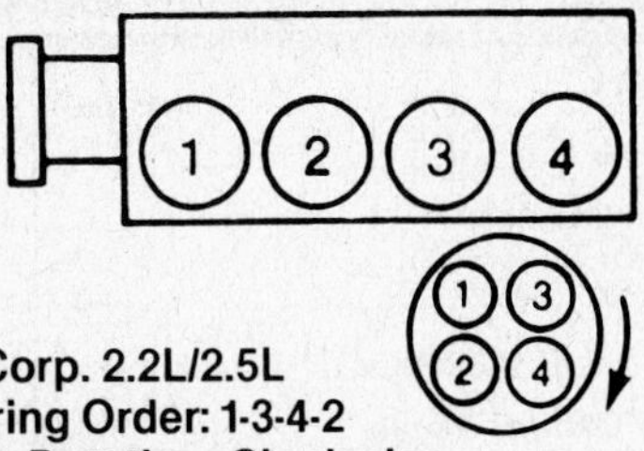

Chrysler Corp. 2.2L/2.5L
Engine Firing Order: 1-3-4-2
Distributor Rotation: Clockwise

WHEEL ALIGNMENT SPECIFICATIONS

Caster is not adjustable

Year and Model	Caster	Front Camber Range (deg.)	Front Camber Preferred	Rear Camber Range (deg.)	Rear Camber Preferred	Toe-In (inches) Front	Toe-In (inches) Rear
'83–'85 Omni, 024, Rampage, Charger	1 7/8P ②	1/4N–3/4P	5/16P	1 1/4N–1/4N	3/4P ③	1/16	3/32
'86–'87 Omni, Charger	1 7/8P	1/4N–3/4P	5/16P	1 1/4N–1/4N	3/4N	1/16	3/32
'83–'85 Horizon, TC3, Turismo, Scamp	1 7/8P	1/4N–3/4P	5/16P	1 1/4N–1/4N	3/4N ③	1/16	3/32
'86–'87 Horizon, Turismo	1 7/8P	1/4N–3/4P	5/16P	1 1/4N–1/4N	3/4N	1/16	3/32

① Wagon—7/8P°
② 4 door—1 3/8P°
③ Rampage, Scamp—Rear Camber
Min.—1 1/8N°
Max.—1/8N°
Pref—5/8N°

LABOR — SERVICE BAY OPERATIONS — LABOR

(Factory Time) — Chilton Time

COOLING

(M) Winterize Cooling System

Includes: Run engine to check for leaks, tighten all hose connections. Test radiator and pressure cap, drain radiator and engine block. Add anti-freeze and refill system.

All models 5

(M) Thermostat, Renew

1983-87 (.4) 6

FUEL

(M) Carburetor Air Cleaner, Service

All models (.3) 3

(G) Carburetor, Adjust (On Car)

Includes: Adjust idle mixture and idle speed. Check and reset ignition timing.

All models 6

(G) Electric Assist (Automatic) Choke, Renew

1983-87 (.7) 1.0

BRAKES

(G) Brakes, Adjust (Minor)

Includes: Adjust brakes, fill master cylinder.

two wheels 4

CHILTON'S 10 POINT SAFETY CHECK

CHECK OPERATION & CONDITION OF THE FOLLOWING ITEMS:

1. Legal Registration (serial no.)
2. Tires & Wheels
3. Brake System (R&R all wheels)
4. Light Systems & Signals
5. Accelerator Linkage, Neutral Safety Switch, Shift Indicator Pointer & Seat Position Locks
6. Glass, Mirrors, Door Locks, Seat Belts & Harness
7. Wipers, Washers & Defrosters
8. Frame, Steering, Shocks, Front & Rear Suspension
9. Fuel & Exhaust Systems
10. Road Test Vehicle

All models 1.0
Exhaust Smog Analysis, add 4

(Factory Time) — Chilton Time

(G) Bleed Brakes (Four Wheels)

Includes: Fill master cylinder.

All models (.4) 6

(M) Parking Brake, Adjust

All models (.3) 4

LUBRICATION SERVICE

(M) Lubricate Chassis, Change Oil & Filter

Includes: Inspect and correct all fluid levels.

All models 6
Install grease fittings add 1

(M) Lubricate Chassis

Includes: Inspect and correct all fluid levels.

All models 4
Install grease fittings add 1

(M) Engine Oil & Filter, Change

Includes: Inspect and correct all fluid levels.

All models 4

WHEELS

(M) Wheels, Rotate (All)

All models 5

(M) Wheel, Renew

one (.3) 5

LABOR — SERVICE BAY OPERATIONS — LABOR

	(Factory Time)	Chilton Time
(G) Wheels, Balance		
one		.3
each adtnl		.2
ELECTRICAL		
(M) Battery Cables, Renew		
1983-87-ground	(.2)	.2
positive	(.5)	.6
(G) Aim Headlamps		
two		.4
four		.6
(M) Headlamp Sealed Beam Bulb, Renew		
Does not include aim headlamps.		
All models-each	(.2)	.3
(G) Headlight Switch, Renew		
All models	(.3)	.4
(G) Headlamp Dimmer Switch, Renew (Column Mounted)		
All models	(.3)	.6
(G) Stop Light Switch, Renew		
All models	(.3)	.4
w/Cruise control add	(.1)	.1
(G) Back-Up Lamp Switch, Renew (w/Manual Trans)		
All models	(.2)	.4
(G) Neutral Safety Switch, Renew		
All models	(.3)	.4
(G) Turn Signal Switch, Renew		
All models-std column	(.5)	1.0
tilt column	(.8)	1.5
(M) Tail and Stop Lamp Lens, Renew		
All models	(.4)	.5
(M) License Lamp Assembly, Renew		
All models	(.2)	.3
(M) Park and Turn Signal Lamp Assy., Renew		
All models-each	(.2)	.3
(M) Park and Turn Signal Lamp Lens, Renew		
All models-each	(.4)	.5
(M) Tail Lamp Assembly, Renew		
All models-each	(.6)	.7
(M) Turn Signal or Hazard Warning Flasher, Renew		
All models	(.2)	.3
(G) Horn Relay, Renew		
All models	(.2)	.3
(G) Horn, Renew		
All models-one	(.2)	.4

LABOR — 1 TUNE UP 1 — LABOR

	(Factory Time)	Chilton Time
(G) Compression Test		
1983-87		.6

(G) Engine Tune Up, (Electronic Ignition)

Includes: Test battery and clean connections. Tighten manifold and carburetor mounting bolts. Check engine compression, clean and adjust or renew spark plugs. Test resistance of spark plug cables. Inspect distributor cap and rotor. Adjust air gap. Check vacuum advance operation. Reset ignition timing. Adjust idle mixture and idle speed. Service air cleaner. Inspect and adjust drive belts. Inspect choke operation and adjust or free up. Check operation of EGR valve.

	(Factory Time)	Chilton Time
1983-87		1.5
w/Turbo add		.5

LABOR — 2 IGNITION SYSTEM 2 — LABOR

	(Factory Time)	Chilton Time
(G) Spark Plugs, Clean and Reset or Renew		
1983-87	(.5)	.6
(G) Ignition Timing, Reset		
1983-87	(.3)	.4
(G) Spark Control Computer, Renew		
1983-87	(.3)	1.0
(G) Distributor, Renew		
Includes: Reset ignition timing.		
1983-87	(.4)	.6
(G) Distributor, R&R and Recondition		
Includes: Reset ignition timing.		
1983-87	(.9)	1.5
(G) Distributor Pick-Up Plate and Coil Assy., Renew (Hall Effect)		
Does not require R&R of distributor.		
1983-87	(.3)	.6
(G) Distributor Cap and/or Rotor, Renew		
1983-87	(.2)	.4
(G) Ignition Coil, Renew		
1983-87	(.2)	.4
(G) Ignition Cables, Renew		
1983-87	(.2)	.4
(G) Ignition Switch, Renew		
1983-87	(.4)	.8
(G) Ignition Key Buzzer Switch, Renew		
1983-87	(.3)	.5
(G) Ignition Key Warning Buzzer, Renew		
1983-87	(.2)	.3
(G) Ignition Lock Housing, Renew		
Does not include painting.		
1983-87	(.9)	1.6

PARTS — 2 IGNITION SYSTEM 2 — PARTS

	Part No.	Price
(1) Distributor Assy.		
1.6L		
1983-87	5213575	55.00
1.7L		
1983	5206945	55.00
2.2L		
1983-85-exc. Turbo	4240470	66.25
1986-87-exc. Turbo	5226575	N.L.
Turbo	5226525	N.L.
(2) Distributor Cap		
1983-87-exc. below	4240446	8.25
1986-87-2.2L	5226527	N.L.
(3) Rotor Assy.		
1983-87-exc. below	5213728	8.25
1986-87-2.2L	5226535	8.25
(4) Switch Assy.		
1983	4240471	30.50
1984-87-exc. below	5213522	32.00
1986-87-2.2L	5226616	26.50

Control Unit (Elect. Spark Advance)

Part numbers shown are for price reference only. Order with complete year, model, type transmission, engine and unit I.D. number information.

	Part No.	Price
1.6L		
1983-M.T.	5213641	110.00

PARTS 2 IGNITION SYSTEM 2 PARTS

	Part No.	Price
Canada	5213679	N.L.
1984	5226106	N.L.
Canada	5226164	N.L.
1985-87	5226411	110.00
Canada	5226429	110.00
1.7L		
1983-M.T.	5213542	110.00
Canada	5313441	N.L.
2.2L		
1983	5213868	110.00
Canada	5213753	N.L.
Shelby	5213974	110.00
1984-M.T.	5213854	110.00
Canada	5213753	N.L.
Shelby	5213974	110.00
1985-A.T.	5226451	110.00
Canada	5226507	N.L.
Shelby	5226449	110.00
1986-87-M.T.	5226439	110.00
Canada	5226507	N.L.
Shelby (Calif.)	5226765	105.00

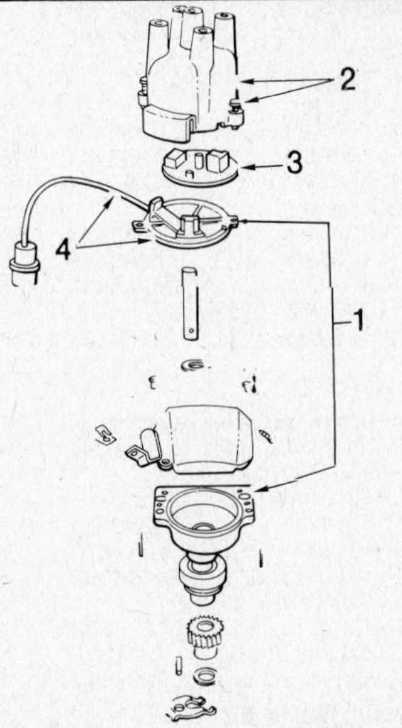

	Part No.	Price
Power Module (EFI)		
1985-87-exc. Calif.	5226765	105.00
Calif.	5226648	140.00
Ignition Wire Set		
1.6L		
1983-87-No. 1, 4	5213361	5.00
No. 2, 3	5213363	4.75
1.7L		
1983	4240432	18.00
2.2L		
1983	4240435	19.75
1984-85-No. 1, 4	5213373	3.00
No. 2, 3	5213372	3.00
1986-87-No. 1, 4	5226785	3.00
No. 2, 3	5226786	3.00
Ignition Coil		
1983-87	4176009	26.75
Ignition Switch		
1983-87	5209891	14.00
Ignition Warning Buzzer		
1983-87	4221309	7.00

LABOR 3 FUEL SYSTEM 3 LABOR

(Factory Time) Chilton Time

(G) Fuel Pump, Test
Includes: Disconnect line at carburetor, attach pressure gauge.
All models 3

(M) Carburetor Air Cleaner, Service
All models (.3) 3

(G) Carburetor, Adjust (On Car)
Includes: Adjust idle mixture and idle speed. Check and reset ignition timing.
All models 6

(G) Electric Assist (Automatic) Choke, Renew
1983-87 (.7) 1.0

(G) Idle Solenoid, Renew
1983-87 (.4) 8

(G) Coolant Temperature Sensor/Switch, Renew
1983-87 (.2) 4

(G) Anti-Dieseling Relay, Renew
1983-87 (.2) 4

(M) Fuel Filter, Renew
1983-87
in line (.2) 3
in tank (.5) 8

(G) Choke Vacuum Kick, Adjust
1983-87
Holly (.2) 3

(G) Choke Vacuum Kick Diaphragm, Renew
1983-87
Holly (.2) 4

(G) Accelerator Pump, Renew
1983-87
Holly (.4) 6

(G) Carburetor Float Level, Adjust
Includes: Adjust idle speed.
1983-87 (.7) 1.3

(G) Carburetor, Renew
Includes: Adjust idle speed and mixture.
1983-87 (.8) 1.6

(Factory Time) Chilton Time

(G) Carburetor, R&R and Clean or Recondition
Includes: Adjust idle speed and mixture.
1983-87 (1.6) 2.4

(G) Fuel Pump, Renew
1983-87
mechanical (.5) 9
electric (.6) 9
Add pump test if performed.

(G) Flexible Fuel Line, Renew
1983-87-one (.3) 4

(G) Fuel Tank, Renew
1983-87 (.9) 1.5

(G) Fuel Gauge (Tank), Renew
1983-87 (.7) 1.0

(G) Fuel Gauge (Dash), Renew
1983-87 (.2) 5

(G) Intake Manifold, Renew
1983-87-1.7 L eng-w/M.T. (2.4) 3.4
w/A.T. (2.0) 2.9
2.2 L eng (2.0) 3.7
1.6 L eng (1.1) 1.5
w/P.S. add (.4) 4
w/Air inj add (.1) 1
w/Turbo add (.6) 6

(G) Intake and Exhaust Manifold Gaskets, Renew
1983-87-1.7 L eng
w/M.T. (2.1) 2.9
w/A.T. (2.7) 3.5
2.2 L eng (1.9) 3.5
w/P.S. add (.4) 4
w/Air inj add (.1) 1
w/Turbo add (.6) 6

(G) Intake Manifold Gasket, Renew
1983-87
1.6L eng (1.0) 1.6

TURBOCHARGER

(P) Turbocharger Assembly, Renew
Includes: Renew gaskets.
1985-87 (2.7) 3.5

(Factory Time) Chilton Time

(G) Fuel Pressure Regulator, Renew
1985-87 (.3) 5

(G) Vehicle Speed Sensor, Renew
1985-87 (.3) 6

(G) Detonation Sensor, Renew
1985-87 (.2) 4

(G) Change Temperature Sensor, Renew
1985-87 (.2) 4

(G) Fuel Pump, Renew (In Tank)
1985-87 (1.0) 1.6

ELECTRONIC FUEL INJECTION

(G) Throttle Body, Renew
1985-87 (.5) 9

(G) Fuel Pressure Regulator, Renew
1985-87 (.3) 5

(G) Automatic Idle Speed Assy., Renew
1985-87 (.3) 5

(G) Fuel Injector Rail, Renew
1985-87 (.6) 1.0

(G) Fuel Injector, Renew
1985-87
one (.4) 6
each adtnl (.1) 1

(G) Logic Module, Renew
1985-87 (.2) 3

(G) Power Module, Renew
1985-87 (.3) 4

(G) M.A.P. Sensor, Renew
1985-87 (.4) 6

(G) Throttle Position Sensor (Potentiometer), Renew
1985-87 (.2) 3

PARTS 3 FUEL SYSTEM 3 PARTS

	Part No.	Price
Carburetor Assy. (Holley New)		
1983-1.6L (w/5220 carb.)		
(M.T.)		
R-40036-1	4227391	325.75
1983-2.2L (w/5220 carb.)		
(M.T.)		
R-40020-1	4300017	325.75
R-40023-1	4227382	325.75
R-40024-1	4227383	325.75
R-40039-1	4227386	325.75
(A.T.)		
R40022-1	4300018	325.75
R-40025-1	4227384	325.75
R-40026-1	4227385	325.75
R-40041-1	4227387	325.75
1983-1.6L (w/6520 carb.)		
(M.T.)		
R-40015-1	4227388	325.75
R-40053-1	4227389	325.75
R-40035-1	4227390	325.75
1983-1.7L (w/6520 carb.)		
(M.T.)		
R-40080-1	4227361	325.75
R-40081-1	4227362	327.75
1983-2.2L (w/6520 carb.)		
(M.T.)		
R-40003-1	4227365	325.75
R-40046-1	4227368	325.75
R-40007-1	4227371	325.75
R-40005-1	4227374	325.75
R-40050-1	4227377	325.75
(A.T.)		
R-40010-1	4287087	325.75
R-40004-1	4287087	325.75
R-40047-1	4227369	325.75
R-40048-1	4227370	325.75
R-40012-1	4227372	325.75
R-40008-1	4287093	325.75
R-40014-1	4227375	325.75
R-40006-1	4293879	326.00
R-40051-1	4227378	325.75
R-40052-1	4227379	325.75
1984-1.6L (w/5220 carb.)		
(M.T.)		
R-40060-1	4288438	Disc.
R-40060-2	4288484	325.75
(A.T.)		
R-40085-1	4288439	Disc.
1984-2.2L (w/5220 carb.)		
(M.T.)		
R-40067-1	4288450	325.75
(A.T.)		
R-40068-1	4288451	325.75
1984-1.6L (w/6520 carb.)		
R-40058-1	4288436	325.75
R-40107-1	4288437	Disc.

	Part No.	Price
1984-2.2L (w/6520 carb.)		
(Hi Altitude)		
R-40064-1	4288440	325.75
R-40065-1	4288441	325.75
R-40071	4288414	325.75
(Calif. em.)		
R-40061-1	4288444	325.75
R-40062-1	4288445	325.75
R-40122	4288433	325.75
1985-87-1.6L		
5220 carb	4288484	325.75
6520 carb	4288436	325.75
1985-87-2.2L		

Part number are for price reference only. Order by carb. stamped number (on carburetor) and year/model.

	Part No.	Price
(w/5220 carb.)		
R-40142	4288521	N.S.S.
R-40116	4324670	N.L.
R-40117	4324669	N.L.
(w/6520 carb.)		
R-40230	4324608	N.L.
R-40232	4324610	N.L.
R-40234	4324612	N.L.

Carburetor Repair Kit

Order by carb. I.D. number.

	Part No.	Price
1983 (w/5220 carb.)		
1.6L eng.	4293725	41.25
2.2L eng.		
exc. below	4293767	31.00
Hi alt.	4293726	41.25
1983-1.6L (w/6520 carb.)		
exc. below	4267177	31.00
Hi alt.	4240199	27.00
1983-1.7L		
6520 carb.	4293767	31.00
1983-2.2L (w/6520 carb.)		
exc. below	4240199	27.00
Hi alt.	4293776	31.00
1984 (w/5220 carb.)		
1.6L	4293851	26.25
2.2L	4293853	26.25
1984 (w/6520 carb.)		
1.6L	4293839	28.25
2.2L	4293856	31.00
1985-87-5220 carb	4397666	52.00
6520 carb	4397657	31.75
Carburetor Gasket Set		
1983-5220 carb	4271875	6.75
6520 carb.	4267174	6.75
1984-5220 carb	4293850	7.25
6520 carb.	4293838	7.25
1985-87-5220 carb	4342872	7.00
6520 carb	4293838	7.25
Carburetor Needle and Seat		
1983-87	4131116	6.50

	Part No.	Price
Fuel Pump Assy.		
1.6L		
1983	4271946	36.00
1984-87	4293801	36.00
1.7L		
1983	4271891	36.00
2.2L		
1983	4271892	35.00
1984-85-exc.		
below	4293802	36.00
EFI	4279951	225.25
Turbo	4203652	169.75
Tank (Shelby)	4279949	238.00
1986-87-exc.		
below	4293802	36.00
EFI	4075445	36.00
Turbo	4203652	169.75
Tank (Shelby)	4279949	238.00
Fuel Line Hoses		
Order by length.		
Fuel Tank		
1983-84	4279499	139.75
1985-87-exc.		
below	4279896	139.75
EFI	4279657	141.75
Turbo	4279661	139.75
Fuel Gauge (Tank)		
1983	5211383	30.25
1984	4051720	30.50
1985-87-exc.		
below	4203540	30.50
EFI	4279950	32.50
Turbo	4279949	238.00
Fuel Gauge (Dash)		
(wo/Rallye package)		
1983	5211437	15.00
1984	4051745	16.50
1985-87	4051885	33.75
(w/Rallye package)		
1983	5209694	15.00
1984-87	4051833	70.00
Fuel Filter Pkg.		
1.6L		
1983-87	4240049	5.75
1.7L		
1983	4186209	5.75
2.2L		
1983-87-exc.		
below	4240102	5.75
EFI & Turbo	4279898	23.25
Manifold Gasket Intake & Exh.		
1.6L		
1983-87-Intake	4273787	1.75
Exhaust	4273793	1.75
1.7L		
1983	5240311	2.00
2.2L		
1983-87	4105745	6.75

PARTS 3 TURBOCHARGER SYSTEM 3 PARTS

(1) E.G.R. Valve

Replacement E.G.R. valves must be ordered according to the stamping number on the original valve.

	Part No.	Price
(2) Elbow (Compressor Inlet)		
1985-87	4105461	30.50
(3) Gasket (Inlet Elbow)		
1985-87	4227973	.50
(4) Turbocharger Assy.		
1985-87	4105800	567.00
(5) Oxygen Sensor		
1985-87	4301346	36.75
(6) Hose Connector		
1985-87	4323444	6.00
(7) Strap (Vane Hose)		
1985-87	4105719	2.00
(8) Vane (Air Flow)		
1985-87	4105465	3.00

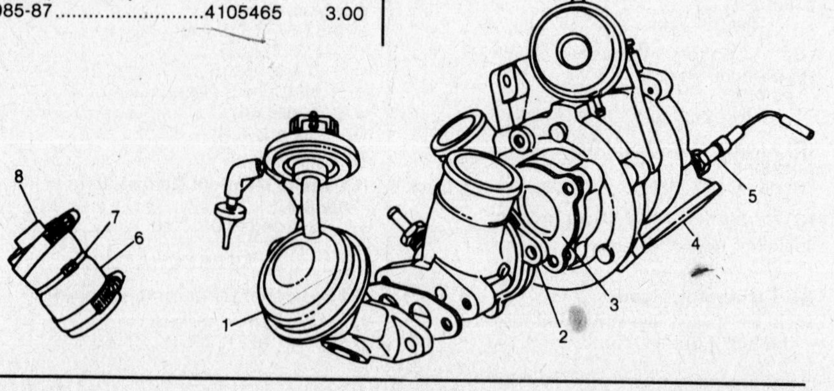

PARTS 3 ELECTRONIC FUEL INJECTION 3 PARTS

	Part No.	Price
Throttle Body Assy.		
1985	4342948	N.L.
(1) Fitting Kit (Hose)		
1985	4287316	11.00
1986-87	4300252	6.75
(2) Injector Kit		
1985	4275985	160.00
1986-87	4300257	53.55
(3) Seal Kit (Pressure Regulator)		
1985	4287324	5.25
1986-87	4300253	3.00
(4) Gasket (Intake Mounting)		
1985-87	4275531	1.75
(5) Potentiometer Kit		
1985	4179848	32.00
(6) Housing Kit (AIS Motor)		
1985	4287730	17.75
(7) Regulator Kit		
1985	4287320	53.25
1986-87	4300263	60.00
(8) Motor Kit (AIS)		
1985	4287712	64.00
1986-87	4300264	N.L.
(9) "O" Ring Kit (AIS Motor)		
1985	4287714	3.50
M.A.P. Sensor		
1985-wo/Turbo	5226223	51.00
Turbo	5226224	56.25
1986-87-wo/Turbo	4419315	51.00
Turbo	4419316	54.75
Logic Module		
(wo/Turbo)		
1985-exc. Calif.	5226608	130.00
Calif.	5226648	140.00
(Turbo)		
1985-A.T.	5226611	140.00
M.T.	5226794	140.00
1986-87	5227371	140.00
Auto. Shutdown Relay		
1985-87	4221279	13.75
Detonation Sensor		
1985-87-wo/Turbo	5213629	23.75
Turbo	4318118	23.75
Vehicle Speed Sensor		
1985-87	4312032	33.50

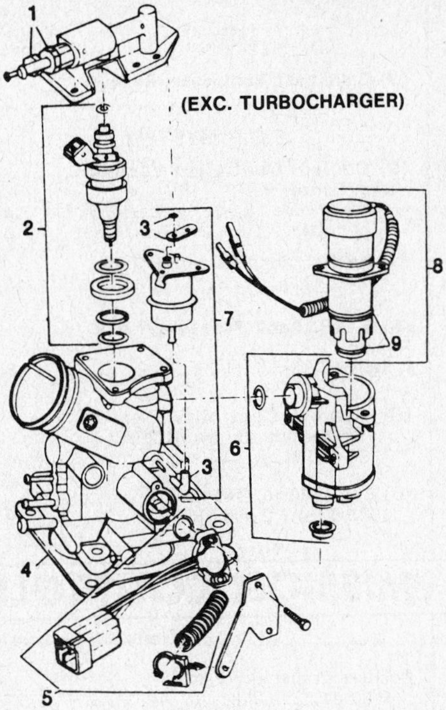

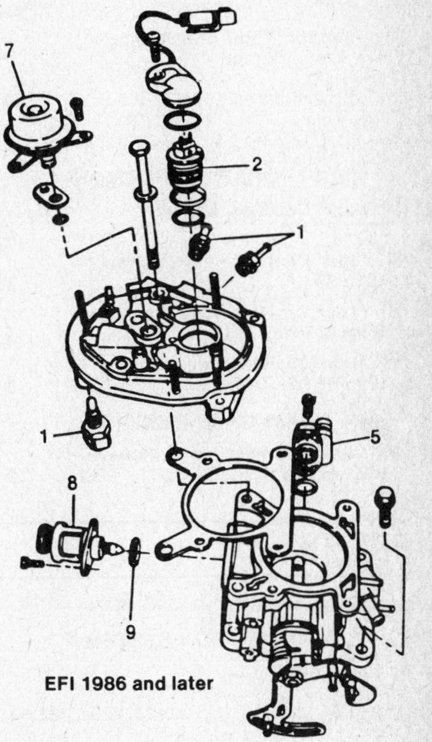

EFI 1986 and later

	Part No.	Price
Throttle Body Assy.		
1985	4288277	325.00
1986-87	4307257	325.00
AIS Motor		
1985	4275651	63.50
1986-87	4288088	63.50
O-Ring Package (AIS Motor)		
1985-87	4287714	3.50
Potentiometer Package		
1985-87	4179849	32.00

	Part No.	Price
Gasket (Mounting Throttle Body)		
1985-87	4268804	1.50
Injector Mounting O-Rings		
1985-87	4275594	4.25
Injectors		
1985-87	4306024	53.75
Pressure Regulator		
Fuel Rail		
1985-87	4275555	39.25

LABOR 3A EMISSION CONTROLS 3A LABOR

(Factory Time)	Chilton Time
AIR INJECTION SYSTEM	
(G) Aspirator Valve, Renew	
1983-87 (.2)	.4
(G) Aspirator Tube, Renew	
1983-87 (.7)	1.0
(G) Air Pump, Renew	
1983-87 (.6)	.9
(M) Air Pump Hose, Renew	
1983-87-one (.2)	.3
(G) Air Injection Pump Belt, Renew	
1983-87	
1.6-2.2 L engs (.3)	.4
1.7 L eng (.5)	.7
w/A.C. add (.1)	.1
(G) Air Pump Diverter/Switching Valve, Renew	
1983-87 (.3)	.7

CHILTON'S EMISSION CONTROL TUNE-UP

1. Clean or renew P.C.V. valve, hoses and filter.
2. Check fuel tank cap for sealing ability.
3. Check fuel tank and fuel lines for leakage.
4. Check evaporation canister and filter. Replace if necessary.
5. Check engine compression to determine leakage of unburned gases. (Add time for items of interference).
6. Test and clean or renew spark plugs.
7. Check engine oil dipstick for sealing ability.
8. Test exhaust system with analyzer and check system for leakage.
9. Check exhaust manifold heat valve for operation.
10. Adjust ignition timing and carburetor idle speed and mixture.
11. Check automatic choke mechanism for free operation.
12. Inspect air cleaner and element.
13. On models so equipped, test distributor vacuum control switch and transmission control switch.

Four 1.3

LABOR 3A EMISSION CONTROLS 3A LABOR

(Factory Time) Chilton Time

(G) Injection Tube and Aspirator Valve Assy., Renew
1983-87
ex manif mount (.5) 8
to conv
one or both (.4).... .6

EVAPORATIVE EMISSION

(M) Vapor Canister, Renew
1983-87 (.4).... .6

(M) Vapor Canister Filter, Renew
1983-87 (.2).... .3

(M) Vapor Canister Hose, Renew
1983-87-one (.2).... .3

(M) Vapor Canister Valve, Renew
1985-87 (.2).... .3

CRANKCASE EMISSION

(M) Crankcase Vent Valve, Renew
1983-87 (.2).... .3

(M) Crankcase Vent Hose, Renew
1983-87-one (.2).... .2

E.G.R. SYSTEM

(G) Coolant Controlled Vacuum Valve, Renew
1983-87-one (.3).... .4
both (.4).... .6

(G) E.G.R. Solenoid Bank, Renew
1984-87 (.2).... .3

(G) E.G.R. Back Pressure Valve, Renew
1984-87 (.2).... .3

(G) Coolant Controlled Engine Vacuum Switch, Renew (CCEVS)
1983-87 (.3).... .4

(G) E.G.R. Valve, Renew
1983-87-1.7 L eng (.3).... .6
2.2 L eng (.6).... .8
1.6 L eng (.3).... .6
w/Turbo add (.1).... .1

(G) Exhaust Gas Recirculation Coolant Valve, Renew (CCEGR)
1983-87 (.3).... .5

HEATED INLET AIR SYSTEM

(G) Heated Air Door Delay Valve, Renew
1983-87 (.3).... .3

(G) Heated Air Door Sensor, Renew
1983-87 (.2).... .3

EFE SYSTEM

(G) Oxygen Sensor, Renew

(G) High Altitude Compensator, Renew
1986-87 (.3).... .5

PARTS 3A EMISSION CONTROLS 3A PARTS

	Part No.	Price
AIR INJECTION SYSTEM		
Air Pump Assy.		
1.6L		
1983-87	4267228	162.50
1.7L		
1983	4268924	162.50
2.2L		
1983-87	4267227	162.50
Air Pump Pulley		
1.6L		
1983-87	4268416	7.50
1.7L		
1983	4240629	30.50
2.2L		
1983-87	5203585	4.75
Air Pump Diverter Valve		
1983-84	4179719	30.50
Aspirator Valve		
1983-84-wo/EFI	4041966	10.75
1985-87-1.6L	4300376	19.50
1985-EFI	4271931	20.75
1986-87-EFI	4300376	19.50
Positive Crankcase Valve		
1983-87	4273145	4.00
EVAPORATIVE EMISSION		
Vapor Canister		
1983-3 port	4241836	47.25
4 port	4241838	52.75
1984-87-3 port	4271982	49.25
4 port	4241838	52.75
Canister Filter		
1983-87	3577586	1.75
Vent Valve (Bowl)		
1984-87	5214336	4.75
Vent Valve (Tank bypass)		
1984-87	4185414	15.50
E.G.R. SYSTEM		
E.G.R. Valve		

Replacement E.G.R. valves must be ordered according to the stamping number on the original valve.

	Part No.	Price
Switch (CCEGR)		
1983-87-yellow	4213597	18.75
black	4049277	17.50
Oxygen Sensor		
1983	4301175	34.00
1984-85	4301346	36.75
1986-87-exc. Turbo	4301375	40.00
Turbo	4301346	36.75
Switch (CCEV)		
1983-87-orange	3879736	17.50
natural	3879707	17.50
Vacuum Solenoid Valve (Idle Spd.)		
1983-84	5213348	16.00
1985	5213749	16.00
Vacuum Delay Valve		
1983-87	4173433	4.25
Dual Vacuum Solenoid Valve		
1985-87-wo/EFI	5226347	28.75
EFI	5213957	28.50
Canada	5213749	16.00
Quad Vacuum Solenoid		
1985-87-Turbo	5226352	57.00

LABOR 4 ALTERNATOR AND REGULATOR 4 LABOR

(Factory Time) Chilton Time

(G) Alternator Circuit Test
Includes: Test battery, regulator and alternator output.
All models.... .6

(M) Alternator Drive Belt, Renew
1983-87 (.3).... .4
w/A.C. add (.1).... .1

(G) Alternator, Renew
Includes: Transfer pulley if required.
1983-87 (.8).... 1.2
w/A.C. add (.5).... .5
Add circuit test if performed.

(G) Alternator, R&R and Recondition
Includes: Test and disassemble, renew parts as required.
1983-87 (1.5).... 2.1
w/A.C. add (.5).... .5

(G) Alternator Front Bearing or Retainer, Renew
Includes: R&R alternator.
1983-87 (.8).... 1.3
w/A.C. add (.5).... .5
Renew rear brg add.... .2

(G) Alternator Regulator, Renew
Includes: Test.
1983-87 (.2).... .6

(G) Alternator Gauge, Renew
1983 (.2).... .5
1984-87 (.3).... .6

(G) Instrument Cluster Voltage Limiter, Renew
1983 (.3).... .5

PARTS 4 ALTERNATOR AND REGULATOR 4 PARTS

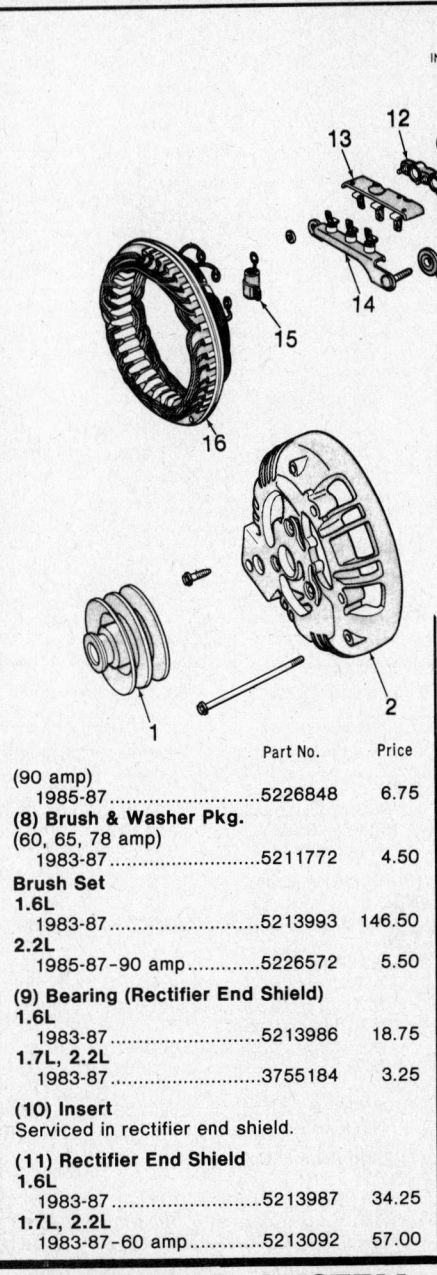

	Part No.	Price
Alternator Assembly (New)		
1.6L		
1983-87	5213831	129.00
1.7L, 2.2L		
1983-84-60 amp	5213079	129.00
65, 78 amp	5213053	129.00
1985-87-60 amp	5213762	129.00
78 amp	5213763	129.00
90 amp	4339440	154.50
100 amp	5213847	161.50
Regulator Assembly		
1983-87	4111990	29.00
Instrument Voltage Regulator		
1983-87	2258413	8.25
(1) Pulley		
1.6L		
1983-87	5226019	23.75
1.7L, 2.2L		
1983	4205845	7.50
1984-87-exc. below	5213760	15.00
EFI	5213764	129.00
Turbo	5226324	25.00
(2) Drive End Shield		
1.6L		
1983-87	5213964	32.25
1.7L, 2.2L		
1983-87-60 amp	5206421	20.00
65, 78 amp	5206422	20.25
90 amp	5226840	39.50
(3) Drive End Shield Bearing		
1.6L		
1983-87	5213982	26.50
1.7L, 2.2L		
1983-87	3656444	8.75
(4) Plate (Bearing Retainer)		
1983-84	4091398	1.25
1985-87	5226156	2.00
(5) Retainer & Slip Ring Pkg.		
1983-87	3744889	5.50
(6) Rotor Assy.		
1.6L		
1983-87	5213984	70.25
1.7L, 2.2L		
1983-87-60 amp	4240413	62.00
65, 78 amp	4240414	62.00
90 amp	5226841	102.25
(7) Brush Holder		
1.6L		
1983-87	5213991	14.25
1.7L, 2.2L		
(60, 65, 78 amp)		
1983-87-radial	4091667	.75
axial	3438159	1.50

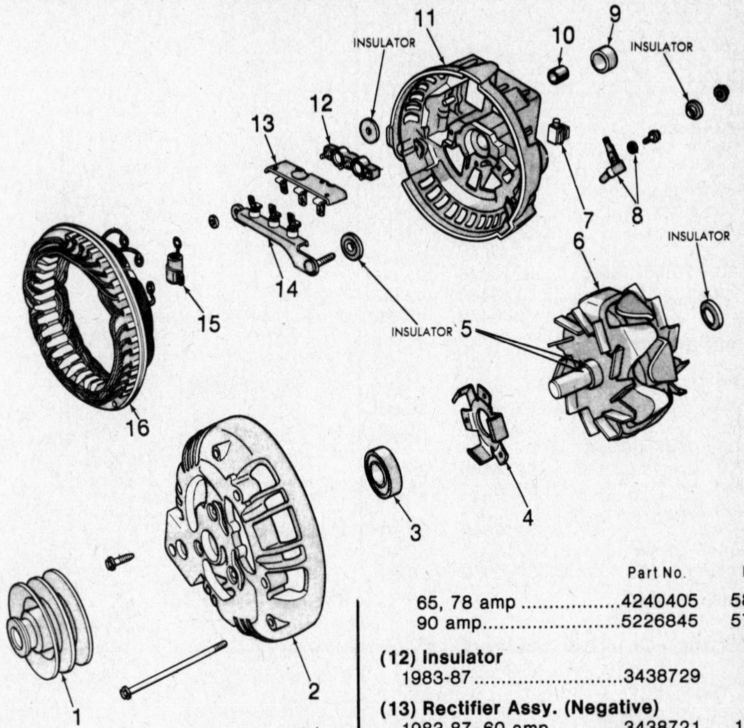

	Part No.	Price
(90 amp)		
1985-87	5226848	6.75
(8) Brush & Washer Pkg.		
(60, 65, 78 amp)		
1983-87	5211772	4.50
Brush Set		
1.6L		
1983-87	5213993	146.50
2.2L		
1985-87-90 amp	5226572	5.50
(9) Bearing (Rectifier End Shield)		
1.6L		
1983-87	5213986	18.75
1.7L, 2.2L		
1983-87	3755184	3.25
(10) Insert		
Serviced in rectifier end shield.		
(11) Rectifier End Shield		
1.6L		
1983-87	5213987	34.25
1.7L, 2.2L		
1983-87-60 amp	5213092	57.00

	Part No.	Price
65, 78 amp	4240405	58.75
90 amp	5226845	57.50
(12) Insulator		
1983-87	3438729	2.25
(13) Rectifier Assy. (Negative)		
1983-87-60 amp	3438721	17.75
65 & 78 amp	3755114	17.75
(14) Rectifier Assy. (Positive)		
1983-87-60 amp	4026082	17.50
65 & 78 amp	4026083	17.50
Rectifier Assy.		
1.6L		
1983-87	5213988	60.50
2.2L		
1985-87-90 amp	5226846	118.50
(15) Capacitor		
1.6L		
1983-87	5213997	15.50
1.7L, 2.2L		
1983-87-exc. below	3620793	4.75
90 amp	5226856	16.50
(16) Stator		
1.6L		
1983-87	5213994	151.00
1.7L, 2.2L		
1983-87-60 amp	4091515	36.75
65 & 78 amp	4091517	36.75

LABOR 5 STARTING SYSTEM 5 LABOR

(Factory Time)	Chilton Time
(G) Starter Draw Test (On Car)	
All models	.3
(G) Starter, Renew	
Includes: Test starter relay, starter solenoid and amperage draw.	
1983-87	
1.6L eng (.8)	1.1
2.2L eng (1.0)	1.3
w/Turbo add (.5)	.5
(G) Starter, R&R and Recondition	
Includes: Test relay, starter solenoid and amperage draw.	
1983-87	
1.6L eng	2.5
2.2L eng	2.8

(Factory Time)	Chilton Time
w/Turbo add (.5)	.5
Renew field coils add (.5)	.5
(G) Starter Drive, Renew	
Includes: R&R starter.	
1983-87	
1.6L eng (1.2)	1.6
2.2L eng (1.4)	1.8
w/Turbo add (.5)	.5
(G) Starter Relay, Renew	
1983-87 (.2)	.3
(G) Starter Motor Pilot Bushing, Renew	
Includes: R&R starter.	
1983 (.8)	1.2

(Factory Time)	Chilton Time
(G) Starter Solenoid, Renew	
Includes: R&R starter.	
1983-87	
1.6L eng (.8)	1.2
2.2L eng (1.0)	1.4
w/Turbo add (.5)	.5
(G) Neutral Safety Switch, Renew	
1983-87 (.3)	.4
(G) Ignition Switch, Renew	
1983-87 (.4)	.8
(M) Battery Cables, Renew	
1983-87-ground (.2)	.2
positive (.5)	.6

PARTS 5 STARTING SYSTEM 5 PARTS

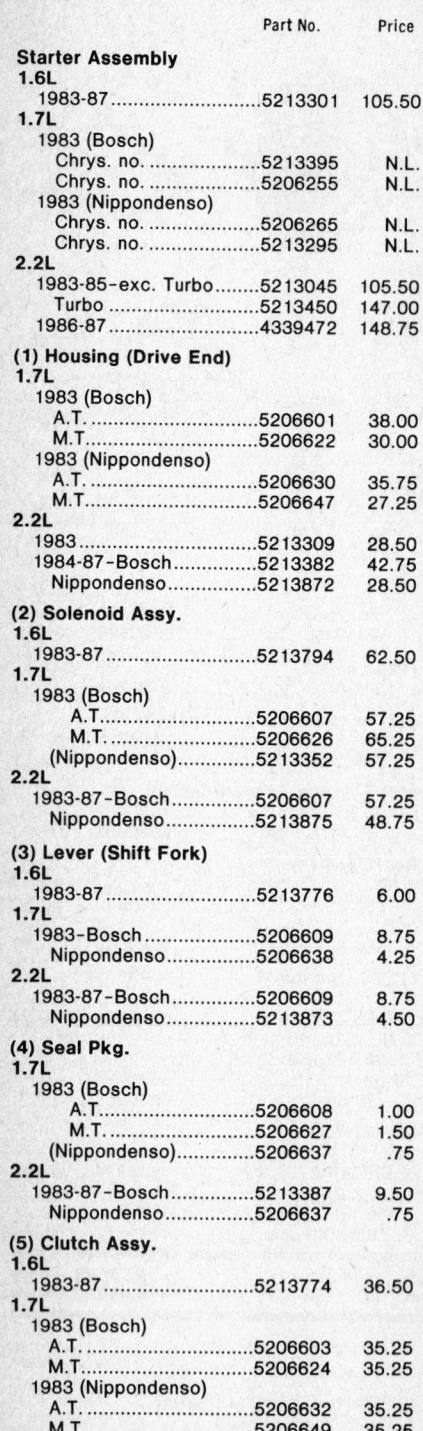

	Part No.	Price
Starter Assembly		
1.6L		
1983-87	5213301	105.50
1.7L		
1983 (Bosch)		
Chrys. no.	5213395	N.L.
Chrys. no.	5206255	N.L.
1983 (Nippondenso)		
Chrys. no.	5206265	N.L.
Chrys. no.	5213295	N.L.
2.2L		
1983-85-exc. Turbo	5213045	105.50
Turbo	5213450	147.00
1986-87	4339472	148.75
(1) Housing (Drive End)		
1.7L		
1983 (Bosch)		
A.T.	5206601	38.00
M.T.	5206622	30.00
1983 (Nippondenso)		
A.T.	5206630	35.75
M.T.	5206647	27.25
2.2L		
1983	5213309	28.50
1984-87-Bosch	5213382	42.75
Nippondenso	5213872	28.50
(2) Solenoid Assy.		
1.6L		
1983-87	5213794	62.50
1.7L		
1983 (Bosch)		
A.T.	5206607	57.25
M.T.	5206626	65.25
(Nippondenso)	5213352	57.25
2.2L		
1983-87-Bosch	5206607	57.25
Nippondenso	5213875	48.75
(3) Lever (Shift Fork)		
1.6L		
1983-87	5213776	6.00
1.7L		
1983-Bosch	5206609	8.75
Nippondenso	5206638	4.25
2.2L		
1983-87-Bosch	5206609	8.75
Nippondenso	5213873	4.50
(4) Seal Pkg.		
1.7L		
1983 (Bosch)		
A.T.	5206608	1.00
M.T.	5206627	1.50
(Nippondenso)	5206637	.75
2.2L		
1983-87-Bosch	5213387	9.50
Nippondenso	5206637	.75
(5) Clutch Assy.		
1.6L		
1983-87	5213774	36.50
1.7L		
1983 (Bosch)		
A.T.	5206603	35.25
M.T.	5206624	35.25
1983 (Nippondenso)		
A.T.	5206632	35.25
M.T.	5206649	35.25

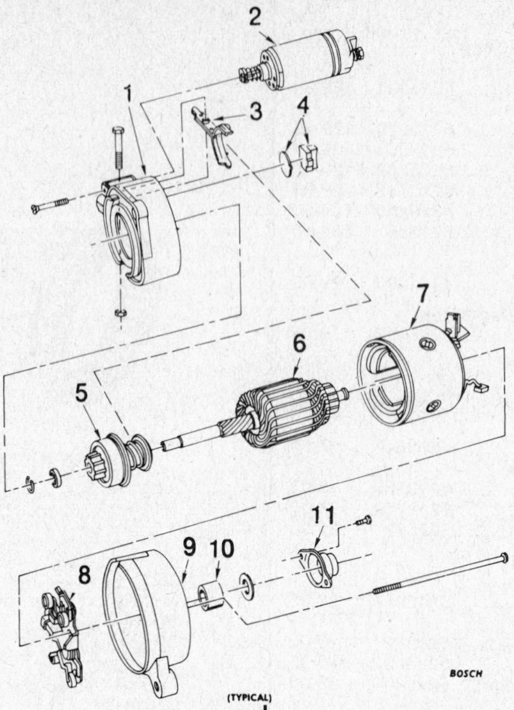

	Part No.	Price
2.2L		
1983	5213310	35.25
1984-87-Bosch	5213384	35.25
Nippodenso	5213850	35.25
(6) Armature Assy.		
1.6L		
1983-87	5213780	78.50
1.7L		
1983 (Bosch)		
A.T.	5206602	25.00
M.T.	5206623	25.00
1983 (Nippondenso)		
A.T.	5206631	78.50
M.T.	5206648	25.00
2.2L		
1983-87-Bosch	5213383	78.50
Nippondenso	5206631	78.50
(7) Field Frame Assy.		
1.7L		
1983 (Bosch)		
A.T.	5206604	67.75
M.T.	5206625	61.75
1983 (Nippondenso)		
A.T.	5213353	56.75
M.T.	5206650	46.00
2.2L		
1983-87-Bosch	5213385	69.00
Nippondenso	5213311	56.75
(8) Brush Holder Assy.		
1.6L		
1983-87	5213785	14.25

	Part No.	Price
1.7L		
1983 (Nippondenso)		
A.T.	5206634	10.75
M.T.	5206564	10.75
(Bosch)	5206605	21.75
2.2L		
1983-87-Bosch	5206605	21.75
Nippondenso	5206634	10.75
(9) End Head Assy.		
1.6L		
1983-87	5213788	8.75
1.7L, 2.2L		
1983-87-Bosch	5206606	27.00
Nippondenso	5213312	16.25
(10) Bearing (End Head)		
1983-87	5206610	2.25
(11) Cover Bearing		
1.7L		
1983 (Nippondenso)		
A.T.	5206641	N.S.S.
M.T.	5213315	1.00
(Bosch)	5206612	1.25
2.2L		
1983-87-Bosch	5206612	1.25
Nippondenso	5213315	1.00
Battery Ground Cable		
1983-87	4274814	8.00
Battery Positive Cable		
Order by year and model.		
Ignition Switch		
1983-87	5209891	14.00

LABOR 6 BRAKE SYSTEM 6 LABOR

	(Factory Time)	Chilton Time
(G) Brake Pedal Free Play, Adjust		
All models		.3
(G) Brakes, Adjust (Minor)		
Includes: Adjust brakes, fill master cylinder.		
two wheels		.4
(G) Bleed Brakes (Four Wheels)		
Includes: Fill master cylinder.		
All models	(.4)	.6
(G) Brake Shoes and/or Pads, Renew		
Includes: Install new or exchange shoes or pads, adjust service and hand brake. Bleed system.		
1983-87-front-disc	(.5)	.8
rear-drum	(.8)	1.5
all four wheels		2.2
Resurface disc rotor, add-each		.9
Resurface brake drum, add-each		.5

LABOR — 6 BRAKE SYSTEM 6 — LABOR

(Factory Time)	Chilton Time
(G) Brake Drum, Renew	
1983-87-one (.5)	.6

BRAKE HYDRAULIC SYSTEM

(Factory Time)	Chilton Time
(G) Wheel Cylinder, Renew	
Includes: Bleed system.	
1983-87-one (.7)	1.1
both (1.3)	2.1
(G) Wheel Cylinder, R&R and Recondition	
Includes: Bleed system.	
1983-87-one	1.2
both	2.3
(G) Brake Hose, Renew (Flex)	
Includes: Bleed system.	
1983-87-front-one (.4)	.8
rear-one (.4)	.8
(G) Master Cylinder, Renew	
Includes: Bleed complete system.	
1983-87-w/Pwr brks (.5)	.9
w/Manual brks (.7)	1.1
(G) Master Cylinder, R&R and Recondition	
Includes: Bleed complete system.	
1983-87	
w/Manual brks	1.9
w/Power brks	1.6
(G) Master Cylinder Reservoir, Renew	
Includes: Bleed complete system.	
1983-87 (.6)	1.0

POWER BRAKES

(Factory Time)	Chilton Time
(G) Brake Booster Assembly, Renew	
1983-87 (.8)	1.1

COMBINATIONS

Add to Brakes, Renew

See Machine Shop Operations

(Factory Time)	Chilton Time
(G) RENEW WHEEL CYLINDER	
Each (.3)	.3
(G) REBUILD WHEEL CYLINDER	
Each	.4
(G) REBUILD CALIPER ASSEMBLY	
Each	.5
(G) RENEW MASTER CYLINDER	
All models (.5)	.6
(G) REBUILD MASTER CYLINDER	
All models	.8
(G) RENEW BRAKE HOSE	
Each (.3)	.3
(G) RENEW REAR WHEEL GREASE SEALS	
One side (.2)	.3
(G) RENEW BRAKE DRUM	
Each (.3)	.3
(G) RENEW DISC BRAKE ROTOR	
Each (.2)	.2
(G) DISC BRAKE ROTOR STUDS, RENEW	
Each	.1

(Factory Time)	Chilton Time
(G) Brake Booster Check Valve, Renew	
1983-87 (.2)	.2
(G) Brake Booster Vacuum Hose, Renew	
1983-87 (.2)	.2

DISC BRAKES

(Factory Time)	Chilton Time
(G) Brake Shoes and/or Pads, Renew	
Includes: Install new or exchange shoes or pads, adjust service and hand brake. Bleed system.	
1983-87-front-disc (.5)	.8
rear-drum (.8)	1.5
all four wheels	2.2
Resurface disc rotor, add-each	.9
Resurface brake drum, add-each	.5
(G) Disc Brake Rotor w/Hub, Renew	
1983-87-each (1.0)	1.4
(G) Disc Brake Rotor, Renew	
1983-87 (.3)	.6
(G) Caliper Assembly, Renew	
Includes: Bleed system.	
1983-87-one (.5)	.9
both	1.7
(G) Caliper Assembly, R&R and Recondition	
Includes: Bleed system.	
1983-87-one (.8)	1.4
both	2.7
(G) Brake System Combination Valve, Renew	
Includes: Bleed system.	
1983-87 (1.2)	1.5

PARKING BRAKE

(Factory Time)	Chilton Time
(M) Parking Brake, Adjust	
1983-87 (.3)	.4
(G) Parking Brake Warning Lamp Switch, Renew	
1983-87 (.2)	.3
(G) Parking Brake Lever, Renew	
1983-87 (.4)	.7
(G) Parking Brake Cables, Renew	
1983-87-front (.7)	1.0
rear-each (.4)	.6

PARTS — 6 BRAKE SYSTEM 6 — PARTS

	Part No.	Price
Brake Shoes & Lining Set (Rear)		
1983-87-Std.	4238827	36.25
H.D.	4238826	39.75
Wheel Cylinder (Rear)		
1983-87-Std.	4238701	22.50
H.D.	4238706	22.50
Hub & Drum (Rear)		
1983-87-Std.	4238531	89.75
H.D.		
4 blt	4238538	100.50
5 blt	4313635	100.50
Brake Hose (Rear)		
1983-87	5204264	16.00
Brake Hose (Front)		
1983-84-right	5204260	18.75
left	5204261	18.75
1985-87-right	4313772	18.75
left	4313773	18.75
Master Cylinder Assy.		
1983-84	4271388	70.50
1985-87	4294268	80.00
Indictor Switch (Brake Warning)		
1983-87	3620790	4.25
Metering Valve		
1983	5204080	35.75
1984-87	4313266	48.50

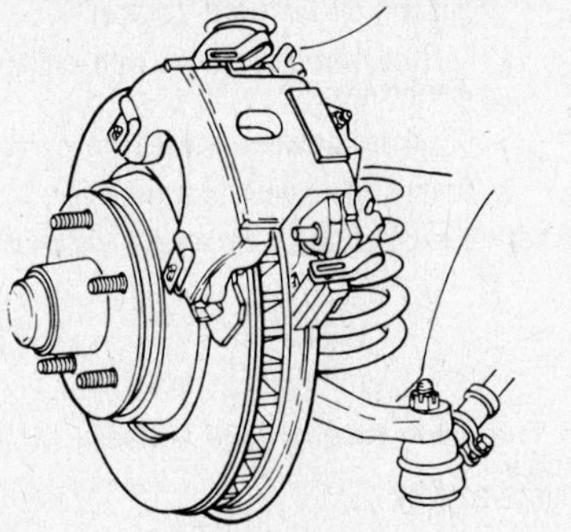

FRONT BRAKE

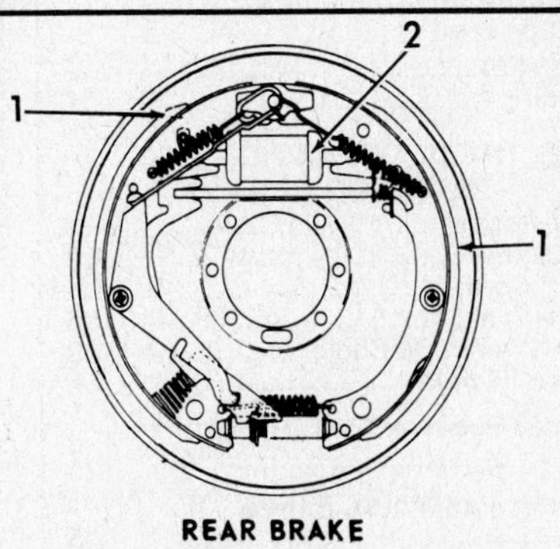

REAR BRAKE

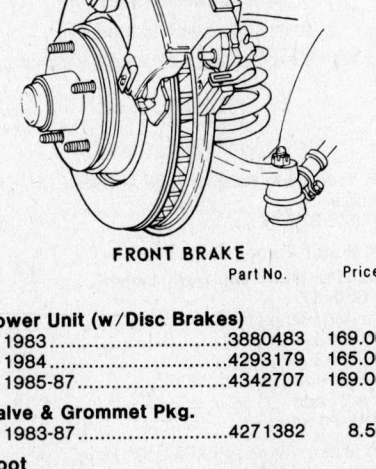

	Part No.	Price
Power Unit (w/Disc Brakes)		
1983	3880483	169.00
1984	4293179	165.00
1985-87	4342707	169.00
Valve & Grommet Pkg.		
1983-87	4271382	8.50
Boot		
1983-87	5204069	3.50
Parking Brake Lever		
1983-87	5211931	31.00

	Part No.	Price
Parking Brake Cable (Front)		
(2-door)		
1983-84	3880427	14.50
1985-87	5204120	14.50
(4-door)		
1983-87	5204111	14.50
Parking Brake Cable (Rear)		
1983-84-2 dr	4294049	9.00
4 dr	4294051	7.50
1985-87-Std.	4294411	7.25
H.D.	4294412	7.50

PARTS — 6 DISC BRAKES 6 — PARTS

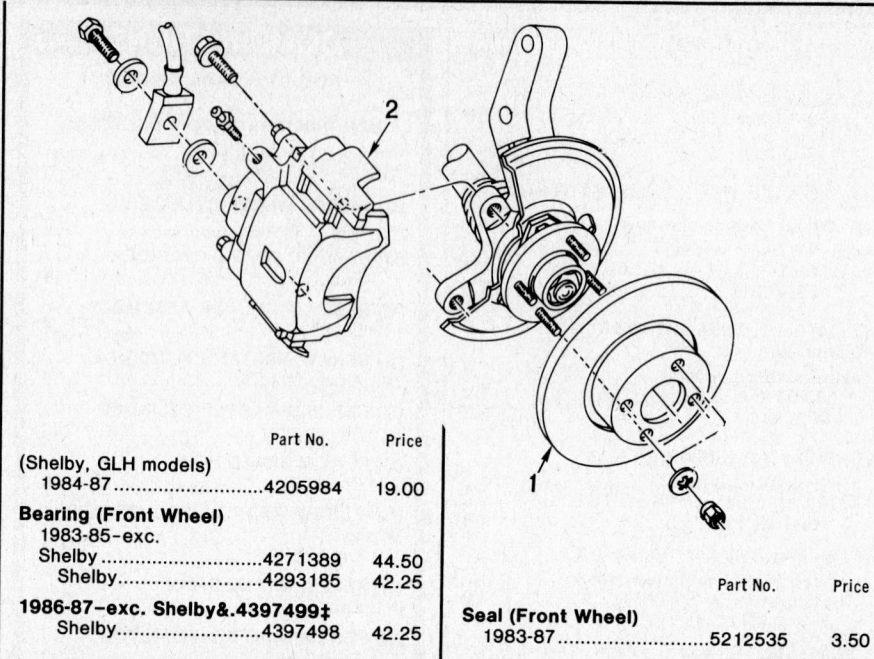

	Part No.	Price
(1) Rotor		
(exc. Shelby, GLH models)		
1983	5204255	44.50
1984-87	4313591	44.50
(Shelby, GLH models)		
1984-85-4 stud	4313593	56.00
5 stud	4313633	56.00
(2) Housing (Partial)		
(exc. Shelby, GLH models)		
1983-87-right	4238676	114.75
left	4238677	114.75
(Shelby, GLH models)		
1984-87-right	4238710	114.75
left	4238711	114.75
Brake Pads		
1983-87-exc. below	4238786	55.25
Shelby, GLH	4313429	72.25
Boot & Seal Pkg.		
(exc. Shelby, GLH models)		
1983-87	4364779	5.50
(Shelby, GLH models)		
1984-87	4205985	3.75
Piston Pkg.		
(exc. Shelby, GLH models)		
1983-87	4364778	22.00

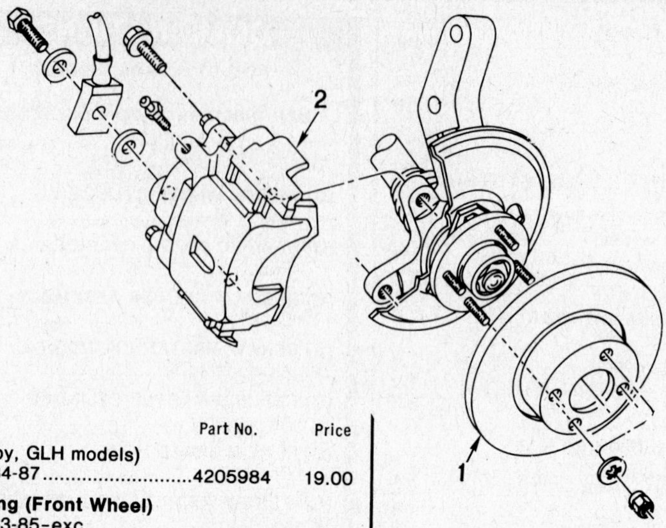

	Part No.	Price
(Shelby, GLH models)		
1984-87	4205984	19.00
Bearing (Front Wheel)		
1983-85-exc. Shelby	4271389	44.50
Shelby	4293185	42.25
1986-87–exc. Shelby	**4397499‡**	
Shelby	4397498	42.25

	Part No.	Price
Seal (Front Wheel)		
1983-87	5212535	3.50

LABOR — 7 COOLING SYSTEM 7 — LABOR

(Factory Time)	Chilton Time
(M) Winterize Cooling System	
Includes: Run engine to check for leaks, tighten all hose connections. Test radiator and pressure cap, drain radiator and engine block. Add anti-freeze and refill system.	
All models	.5
(M) Thermostat, Renew	
1983-87 (.4)	.6
(G) Thermostat Water Box and/or Gasket, Renew	
1983 (.8)	1.2
(M) Radiator Assembly, R&R or Renew	
1983-87 (.5)	.9
w/A.T. add (.1)	.1
ADD THESE OPERATIONS TO RADIATOR R&R	
(G) Boil & Repair	1.5
(G) Rod Clean	1.9
(G) Repair Core	1.3
(G) Renew Tank	1.6
(G) Renew Trans. Oil Cooler	1.9
(G) Recore Radiator	1.7
(M) Coolant Reserve Tank, Renew	
1983-87 (.5)	.7
(G) Radiator Fan Motor, Renew	
1983-87 (.4)	.5
(G) Radiator Fan Motor Relay, Renew	
1983-87 (.2)	.3
(G) Radiator Fan Switch, Renew	
1983-87 (.3)	.6
(M) Radiator Hoses, Renew	
1983-87-upper (.3)	.4
lower (.5)	.6
by-pass (.4)	.6
(G) Radiator Fan Coolant Sensor, Renew	
1983-87 (.2)	.3

COOLING SYSTEM TUNE-UP

An Annual Cooling System Tune-Up Suggestion List should include (with some exceptions):

1. A visual check of the cooling system for indications of leaks or excessive oil content.
2. Pressure check the cooling system for internal and external leaks with filler cap and neck adapter and tester.
3. Check crankcase and automatic transmission oil for water content.
4. Test coolant thermostat with radiator thermometer.
5. Check temperature gauge for accuracy.
6. Drain system and flush till clean.
7. Clean foreign matter from radiator fins.
8. Test radiator pressure cap with cap tester.
9. Check fan blades and pulleys for alignment and damage.
10. Internal and external inspection of all hoses for cracks and deterioration.
11. Check core plugs (where possible) for seepage.
12. Refill system with correct coolant and check for air locks.
13. Check condition and tension of drive belts with tension gauge.

All models **1.5**

(Factory Time)	Chilton Time
(G) Transaxle Auxiliary Oil Cooler, Renew	
1983-87 (.3)	.6
(G) Water Pump, Renew	
Includes: Drain and refill coolant.	
1983-87	
1.7 L eng (1.5)	2.0
2.2 L eng (1.1)	1.6
1.6 L eng (.7)	1.1
w/P.S. add (.3)	.3
w/A.C. add (.7)	.7
w/Air inj add (.4)	.4
(G) Water Pump Housing 'O' Ring, Renew	
1983-87	
1.7 L eng (1.5)	2.0
2.2 L eng (.9)	1.6

(Factory Time)	Chilton Time
w/P.S. add (.3)	.3
w/A.C. add (.7)	.7
w/Air inj add (.4)	.4
(G) Water Jacket Expansion Plugs, Renew (Cylinder Block)	
1983-87	
1.7 L engine	
front side (.8)	1.2
center-side (.7)	1.1
rear side (.6)	1.0
2.2 L engine	
left side	
front (.7)	1.1
rear (.4)	.7
right side	
front or center (.6)	1.0
rear (1.0)	1.4

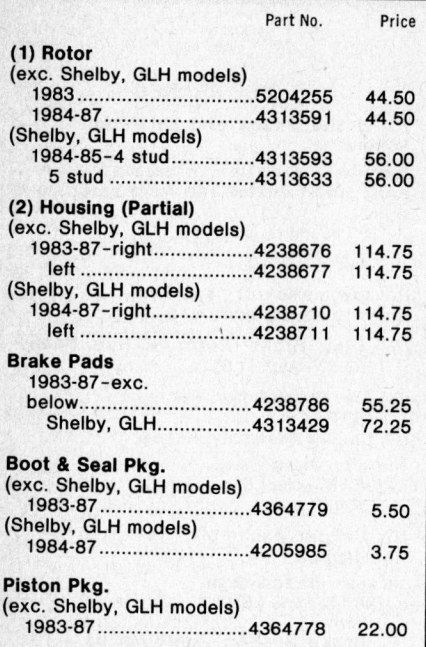

LABOR 7 COOLING SYSTEM 7 LABOR

(Factory Time)	Chilton Time
w/P.S. add (.3)	.3
w/A.T. add (.4)	.4
w/Pulse air add (.6)	.6
(G) Water Jacket Expansion Plugs, Renew (Cylinder Head)	
1983-87	
1.7 L engine	
front (.9)	1.3
2.2 L engine	
front (.6)	1.0
rear (.8)	1.2
(M) Fan Blades, Renew	
1983-87 (.2)	.5
(M) Drive Belt, Renew	
1983-87 (.3)	.4
w/A.C. add (.1)	.1
(M) Drive Belt, Adjust	
All models-one	.3
each adtnl	.1
(G) Temperature Gauge (Engine Unit), Renew	
1983-87 (.3)	.4
(G) Temperature Gauge (Dash Unit), Renew	
1984-87 (.3)	.6
(M) Heater Hoses, Renew	
1983-87-one (.4)	.4
both (.5)	.6
(G) Heater Core, R&R or Renew	
1983-87-wo/A.C. (1.0)	1.7
w/A.C. (2.5)	*4.2

*Includes recharge A.C. system.

ADD THESE OPERATIONS TO HEATER CORE R&R

(Factory Time)	Chilton Time
(G) Boil & Repair	1.2
(G) Repair Core	.9
(G) Recore	1.2
(G) Heater Control Assembly, Renew	
1983-87 (.4)	.7
(G) Heater Blower Motor, Renew	
1983-87 (.4)	.6
(G) Heater Blower Motor Resistor, Renew	
1983-87 (.2)	.3
(G) Heater Blower Motor Switch, Renew	
1983-87 (.4)	.7
(G) Water Valve, Renew (With Air Conditioning)	
1983-87 (.3)	.5

PARTS 7 COOLING SYSTEM 7 PARTS

	Part No.	Price
Radiator Assy.		
Order by year and model.		
Thermostat		
1.6L, 2.2L		
1983-87	4105768	.75
1.7L		
1983		
up to 9-21-81	5214513	8.25
from 9-21-81	4105436	8.25
Radiator Hose (Upper)		
1.6L		
1983	4266271	9.25
1984-85	4266345	10.25
1.7L		
1983	4266298	6.75
2.2L		
1983	4266285	4.75
1984-85	4266346	5.50
Radiator Hose (Lower)		
1.6L		
1983	4266281	13.50
1984-87	4266723	9.75
1.7L		
1983	4140547	14.00
2.2L		
1983-87-wo/A.C. & Turbo	4266739	13.00
A.C. & Turbo	4266262	14.00
By-Pass Hose (Water Pump)		
1.6L		
1983-87	4105421	1.75
1.7L		
1983	5214521	4.00
2.2L		
1983-87	4273486	4.75
Water Pump		
1.6L		
1983-87	4173703	50.00
1.7L		
1983	5214490	48.00
2.2L		
1983	5203432	N.L.
1984-87	4293898	48.00
Motor, Fan & Shroud Assy.		
Order by number stamped on motor or shroud assembly.		
Relay (Rad. Motor Fan)		
1983	4057981	16.50
1984	4221542	15.00
1985-87	4221615	18.75
Heat Indicator (Engine Unit)		
1983-84-1.6L eng.	4267281	16.25
1983-1.7L eng.		
98°	4145348	6.75
150°	4091719	6.75
1983-2.2L eng.		
125°	4145716	6.75
150°	4091719	6.75
1984-2.2L eng.	4051687	10.25
1985-87-wo/Gauges	4221071	6.75
w/Gauges	4051687	10.25
Sensor (Coolant Temp)		
1986-87	5213737	11.30
Sensor (Dual Temp)		
1986-87	5226356	22.00
Heat Indicator (Dash)		
1983	5211439	4.00
1984	4051744	27.25
1985-87	4375008	27.25
Heater Core		
1983-87-wo/A.C.	4240448	83.25
A.C.	3847943	90.75
Blower Motor		
1983-87-wo/A.C.	4057933	54.25
A.C.	4240426	66.25
Resistor (Heater Motor)		
1983-87-wo/A.C.	5210365	6.25
A.C.	3848995	7.75
Blower Motor Switch		
1983-87-wo/A.C.	3847940	10.25
Heater Valve		
1983-87-1.7L eng.	4240422	29.25
2.2L eng.	3848136	27.75
Turbo	3848114	27.75
Trans. Auxiliary Oil Cooler		
1983-84	4266294	76.25
1985-87	4266350	76.25

LABOR 8 EXHAUST SYSTEM 8 LABOR

(Factory Time)	Chilton Time
(G) Muffler, Renew	
1983-87 (.4)	.8
Cut exhaust pipe add (.2)	.2
(G) Tail Pipe, Renew	
1983 (.4)	.5
Cut at muffler add (.2)	.2
(G) Catalytic Converter, Renew	
1983-87 (.7)	.9
(G) Exhaust Pipe Extension, Renew	
1983-87 (.6)	1.0
(G) Exhaust Pipe, Renew	
1983-87 (.7)	1.1
Cut at muffler add (.2)	.2
(G) Intake and Exhaust Manifold Gaskets, Renew	
1983-87-1.7 L eng	
w/M.T. (2.1)	2.9
w/A.T. (2.7)	3.5
2.2 L eng (1.9)	3.5
w/P.S. add (.4)	.4
w/Air inj add (.1)	.1
w/Turbo add (.6)	.6
(G) Exhaust Manifold, Renew	
1983-87-1.7 L eng	
w/M.T. (2.2)	3.0
w/A.T. (2.8)	3.6
2.2 L eng (2.7)	3.7
1.6 L eng (.6)	1.0
w/P.S. add (.4)	.4
w/Air inj add (.1)	.1
w/Turbo add (.6)	.6
(G) Exhaust Pipe Flange Gasket or Ring, Renew	
1983-87 (.4)	.6

COMBINATIONS

(G) Muffler, Exhaust and Tail Pipe, Renew	
1983-87 (1.0)	1.5

PARTS 8 EXHAUST SYSTEM 8 PARTS

	Part No.	Price
Muffler		
Order by year and model.		
Tail Pipe		
1.6L, 2.2L		
1983-87-2 dr	4150438	19.75
4 dr	4150439	18.75
1.7L		
1983-2 dr	5217136	16.50
4 dr	5217088	17.25
Exhaust Pipe (wo/Resonator)		
1.7L		
1983-exc. below	4150792	19.00
w/A412 trans.	4150793	18.50
2.2L		
1985-87	4301394	15.25
Exhaust Pipe (w/Resonator)		
2.2L		
1984	4150833	N.L.
1985-87	4301560	48.00
Catalytic Converter & Pipes (Front)		
1.6L		
1983	4301091	284.25
1984-87	4301324	285.50
Canada	4150965	N.L.
2.2L		
1983	4150823	307.25
1984	4301262	285.50
1985-87	4301470	280.00
Canada	4301425	N.L.
Catalytic Converter & Pipes (Rear)		
1.6L		
1983-2 dr	4301087	184.50
4 dr	4301088	184.50
1.7L		
1983-2 dr	4150624	348.25
4 dr	4150625	335.00
2.2L		
1985-87-2 dr	4301395	257.00
4 dr	4301396	244.75
Exhaust Pipe Extension		
1.6L, 2.2L		
(wo/Resonator)		
1983-87-2 dr	4301220	27.75
4 dr	4301221	27.75
(w/Resonator)		
1983-84		
up to 6-1-83	4150989	N.L.
from 6-1-83	4301223	57.75
1985-87-2 dr	4301223	57.75
Canada	4301223	57.75
4 dr	4301224	56.50
Canada	4301224	56.50

LABOR 9 FRONT SUSPENSION 9 LABOR

(Factory Time)	Chilton Time
Note: On all front suspension operations alignment charges must be added if performed. Time given does not include alignment.	
(M) Wheel, Renew	
one (.3)	.5
(G) Wheels, Rotate (All)	
All models	.5
(G) Wheels, Balance	
one	.3
each adtnl	.2
(G) Check Alignment of Front End	
All models	.5
Note: Deduct if alignment is performed.	
(G) Toe-Out, Adjust	
All models	.6
(G) Align Front End	
Includes: Adjust camber, toe-out and center steering wheel.	
All models (.8)	1.4
(G) Steering Knuckle, Renew (One)	
Add alignment charges.	
1983-87 (1.0)	1.6
(G) Front Strut Assembly, R&R or Renew	
Add alignment charges.	
1983-87-one (.8)	1.4
both (1.5)	2.7
(G) Lower Control Arm, Renew (One)	
Includes: Reset toe-in.	
1983-87 (1.1)	1.6
(G) Lower Control Arm Strut Bushings, Renew	
Add alignment charges.	
1984-87-one side (.6)	.9
(G) Lower Ball Joint, Renew (One)	
Includes: Reset toe-in.	
1983-87 (.8)	1.2
(G) Front Spring or Strut Bearing, Renew (One)	
Add alignment charges.	
1983-87 (.8)	1.5
(G) Steering Knuckle Bearing, Renew (Wheel Bearing)	
Add alignment charges.	
1983-87-one (1.2)	1.6
(G) Front Sway Bar, Renew	
1983-87 (.4)	.7
(G) Sway Bar Bracket and Bushings, Renew	
1983-87-both (.5)	.9
(P) K-Frame Assembly, Renew	
Add alignment charges.	
All models (2.5)	4.0
A-412 MANUAL TRANSAXLE	
(G) Drive Shaft Boot, Renew	
Includes: Clean and lubricate C/V joint.	
1983	
one-inner or outer (.8)	1.2
both-one side (1.0)	1.5
(G) Drive Shaft C/V Joint, Renew	
1983	
one-inner or outer (.8)	1.2
both-one side (1.0)	1.5
(G) Front Wheel Drive Shaft Assy., Renew	
1983-each (.9)	1.3
Renew shaft seal	
add-each (.2)	.3
(G) Drive Shaft Flange, Renew	
Includes: Renew oil seal.	
1983-one (.9)	1.3
A-460-A-465-A-525 MANUAL TRANSAXLES & AUTOMATIC TRANSAXLES	
(G) Drive Shaft Boot, Renew	
Includes: Clean and lubricate C/V joint.	
1983-87	
one-inner or outer (.7)	1.0
both-one side (1.0)	1.4
Renew shaft seal, add	
right side (.1)	.1
left side (.3)	.3
(G) Drive Shaft C/V Joint, Renew	
1983-87	
one-inner or outer (.7)	1.0
both-one side (1.0)	1.4
inter shaft U-joint (.6)	1.0
Renew shaft seal, add	
right side (.1)	.1
left side (.3)	.3
(G) Front Wheel Drive Shaft Assy., Renew	
1983-87	
inter spline yoke (.6)	1.0
inter stub shaft (.6)	1.0
all others-each (1.0)	1.4
Renew shaft seal, add	
right side (.1)	.1
left side (.3)	.3
(G) Intermediate Shaft Support Bearing, Renew	
1984-87-each (.6)	1.0
(G) Drive Shaft Oil Seal, Renew	
All models	
right side (.5)	.8
left side (.7)	1.1

PARTS 9 FRONT SUSPENSION 9 PARTS

	Part No.	Price
(1) Steering Knuckle		
1983-right	4052580	89.75
left	4052581	89.75
1984-87 (exc. Shelby & perf. pkg.)		
right	4052844	89.75
left	4052845	89.75
1985-87 (Shelby & perf. pkg.)		
right	4322756	89.75
left	4322757	89.75
(2) Shock Absorber Pkg.		
1983-87-exc. below	4052647	40.00
Firm susp.	5204734	43.25
Shelby & perf. pkg	4322271	50.00
(3) Coil Spring		
Order by year and model.		

PARTS 9 FRONT SUSPENSION 9 PARTS

	Part No.	Price
(4) Bumper (Jounce)		
1983-87-exc. below	5204608	3.25
Shelby & perf. pkg	4052996	3.25
(5) Seat (Shock Upper)		
1983	4014325	5.75
1984-87	4052931	6.00
(6) Ball Bearing		
1983-87	5204595	4.50
(7) Front Shock Mount (Upper)		
1983-87	4318717	18.25
(8) Retainer Pkg.		
1983-87	4052680	4.25
(9) Bushing (Strut Arm Rear)		
1983-84	4052672	2.00
(10) Bushing (Strut Arm Front)		
1983	5204537	2.00
1984	4052671	2.00
1985-87	4322285	2.00
(11) Ball Joint Pkg.		
1983	4014323	37.25
1984-85	4052583	32.75
1986-87	4364782	37.25
(12) Lower Control Arm		
1983-right	4052634	92.75
left	4052635	92.75
1984-87-right	4322154	92.75
left	4322155	92.75
(13) Bushing (Pivot Shaft)		
1983-87	5204622	8.00

Part numbers shown are for pricing reference only. Order by year model and type.

Driveshaft

1.6L

1983-Right	5212676	137.50
Left	5212677	76.00
1984-87-Right	5212862	137.50
Left	5212863	76.00

1.7L

1983-Right	5212646	137.50
Left	5212647	72.50

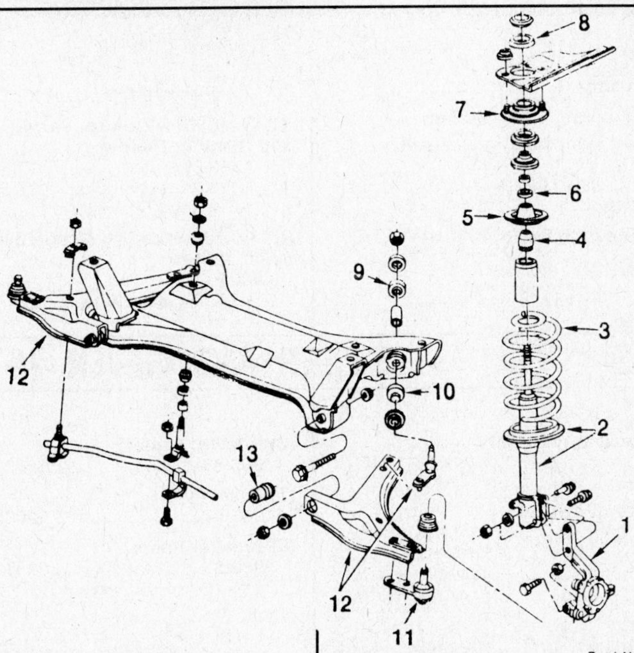

	Part No.	Price
2.2L, 2.5L & 2.6L		
Horizon, Omni, 024, TC3, Turismo, Charger		
(G.K.N.)		
1983-Right	5212660	137.50
Left	5212661	76.00
1984-87-Right	5212862	137.50
Left	5212863	76.00
1986-87-H/P		
Right	5212862	137.50
Left	5212933	76.00
(Citroen)		
1985-wo/Turbo		
Right	5212766	85.00
Left	5212765	52.25
Turbo	5212765	52.25
1986-87-Right	5212766	85.00
Left	5212935	52.25
Turbo	5212935	52.25

	Part No.	Price
Exc. Horizon, Omni, TC3, 024, Turismo, Charger		
(G.K.N.)		
1983-Right	5212662	137.50
Left	5212663	76.00
1984-87-Right	5212872	123.00
Left	5212913	76.00
(Citroen)		
1983-Right	5212744	85.00
Left	5212745	52.50
1984-wo/Turbo		
right	5212798	85.00
left	5212799	N.L.
Turbo	5212799	N.L.
1985-87-wo/Turbo		
Right	5212798	85.00
Left	5212763	52.25
Turbo	5212763	52.25
(A.C.I.)		
1984-87-Right	5212826	123.00
Left	5212827	76.00

LABOR 11 STEERING GEAR 11 LABOR

(Factory Time)	Chilton Time
(G) Tie Rod Ends, Renew	
Includes: Adjust toe, replace tie rod if necessary.	
1983-87	
outer-one (.9)	1.2
Inner and Outer	
w/P.S.-one (1.9)	2.5

STANDARD STEERING

(Factory Time)	Chilton Time
(G) Horn Contact, Renew	
1983-87-exc below (.2)	.3
cable & ring (.2)	.5
(G) Horn Switch, Renew	
1983-87 (.2)	.3
(G) Steering Wheel, Renew	
1983-87 (.2)	.3
(G) Steering Column Jacket, Renew	
Does not include painting.	
1983-87 (1.0)	1.9
(G) Upper Mast Jacket Bearing, Renew	
Includes: Replace insulators if necessary.	
1983-87 (.8)	1.7
(G) Steering Column Lower Shaft Bearing, Renew	
Includes: Replace support if necessary.	
1983-87 (.4)	.7
(G) Steering Column Shaft, Renew	
1983-87 (.8)	2.0
(G) Steering Column Flexible Coupling, Renew	
1983-87 (1.0)	1.3
(G) Steering Gear Assembly, Renew	
1983-87 (1.7)	3.0

POWER STEERING

(Factory Time)	Chilton Time
(G) Power Steering Pump Pressure Check	
All models	.5
(M) Power Steering Pump Belt, Renew	
1983-87 (.5)	.6
w/Air inj add (.1)	.1
w/A.C. add (.1)	.1
(G) Power Steering Gear Assembly, Renew	
1983-87 (2.3)	3.1
(G) Steering Gear Oil Seals, Renew (All)	
Includes: R&R gear assy. and reset toe-in.	
1983-87 (3.5)	5.1
(G) Upper and Lower Valve Pinion Seals, Renew	
1983-87 (1.4)	2.0

LABOR 11 STEERING GEAR 11 LABOR

	(Factory Time)	Chilton Time
Renew brgs add (.3)		.5
(G) Power Steering Pump, Renew		
Includes: Test pump and transfer pulley.		
1983-87		
1.7-2.2 L engs (1.2)		1.9
1.6 L eng (.6)		.9
(G) Power Steering Pump, R&R and Recondition		
1983-87		
1.7-2.2 L engs (1.5)		2.8
1.6 L eng (1.1)		1.8
(G) Pump Flow Control Valve, Test and Clean or Renew		
1983-87		
1.7-2.2 L engs (.6)		1.0
1.6 L eng (.5)		.9
(G) Power Steering Reservoir or Seals, Renew		
1983-87		
1.7-2.2 L eng (.9)		1.4
1.6 L eng (.6)		1.0
(G) Pump Drive Shaft Oil Seal, Renew		
1983-87		
1.7-2.2 L engs (1.1)		1.9
1.6 L eng (.5)		.8
(M) Power Steering Hoses, Renew		
1983-87-each (.4)		.5

PARTS 11 STEERING GEAR-(STANDARD) 11 PARTS

	Part No.	Price
(1) Steering Gear (Manual)		
1983	4188856	242.75
1984-87	4147230	242.75
(2) Clamp (Boot To Tube)		
1983-84-right	3815816	1.50
left	3815811	1.50
1985-87-right	4147140	N.L.
left	4147139	N.L.
(3) Boot Kit		
1983-87-right	4131348	13.50
left	4131349	13.50
(4) Clamp (Boot to Tie Rod)		
1983-87	5205313	1.25
(5) Tie Rod (Outer)		
1983-87	4106180	39.75
(6) Bracket (Outer)		
1983-87	5205225	4.00
(7) Bushing		
1983-87	5205227	2.00
(8) Bracket (Inner)		
1983-87	5205226	1.00

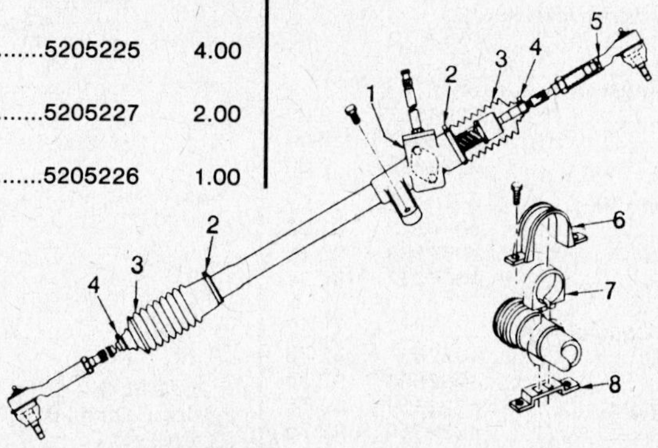

PARTS 11 POWER STEERING GEAR 11 PARTS

	Part No.	Price
Steering Gear Assy.		
1983	4293168	343.50
1984-exc. below	4147225	343.50
Shelby	4147228	275.50
1985-87-exc. below	4318726	284.25
Shelby & perf. pkg	4333149	275.50
(1) Housing Assy.		
1983-87	4147082	178.00
(2) Cylinder Oil Kit		
1983-87-right	4147089	8.25
left	4147090	8.25
(3) Dust Cover		
1983-87	5205284	3.50
(4) Pinion Bearing Kit		
1983-87	5205295	25.50
(5) Ring (Shock Dampener)		
1983-87-exc. below	4147088	2.00
Shelby & perf. pkg	4333101	2.75
(6) Valve Kit (Pinion Assy.)		
(Std. susp.)		
1983-84	5205328	150.50
1985-87	3815947	150.50
(H.D. susp.)		
1983	5205336	150.50
1984	4147091	150.50
1985-87	4333340	150.50
(7) Spool Shaft Bearing Kit		
1983-87	5205299	19.25
(8) Retainer Ring		
1983-87	5205278	1.75
(9) Seal (Inner Rack)		
1983-87	4147098	33.75

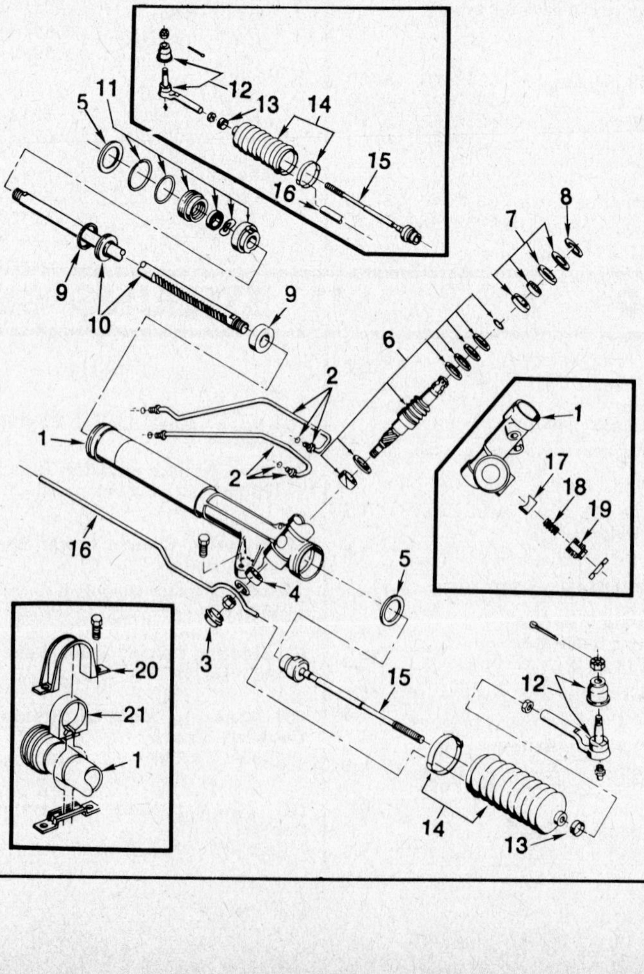

PARTS 11 POWER STEERING GEAR 11 PARTS

	Part No.	Price
(10) Rack Assy. (W/Piston)		
1983	4147079	128.75
1984-87-exc. below	4147079	128.75
Shelby	4147224	146.00
(11) Bulkhead Assy. Kit		
1983-87-exc. Firm	4147096	41.50
Firm	4333103	41.50
(12) Tie Rod Assy. (Outer)		
1983-87	4106180	39.75
(13) Clamp (Tie Rod End)		
1983-87	4147085	5.00

	Part No.	Price
(14) Boot Service Kit		
1983-87-right	4147092	30.75
left	4147093	28.75
(15) Tie Rod Assy. (Inner)		
1983-87 (exc. Shelby & perf. pkg.)		
right	4147094	48.75
left	4147133	48.75
1985-87 (Shelby & perf. pkg.)		
right	4333124	46.25
left	4333125	46.25
(16) Breather Tube		
1983-87	4147086	9.00

	Part No.	Price
(17) Rack Bearing		
1983-87	5205282	5.25
(18) Spring (Adjuster)		
1983-87	5205280	2.00
(19) Plug (Adjuster)		
1983-87	5205286	7.75
(20) Bracket (Outer)		
1983-87-right	3643470	4.00
left	3643424	4.00
(21) Bushing		
1983-87-right	3643471	4.00
left	3643425	4.00

PARTS 11 POWER STEERING PUMP 11 PARTS

	Part No.	Price
Power Steering Pump		
1.6L		
1983-87	3815982	170.25
1.7L, 2.2L		
1983-87-exc. below	3815956	170.25
Shelby & perf. pkg	4188832	170.25
Oil Pressure Hose		
1983-1.7L eng	3815841	27.75
2.2L eng.	3815839	29.25
1984-87-1.6L eng.	3815980	27.75
2.2L eng.	3815987	30.25
(1) Reservoir		
1983	3643453	60.75
1984-87-1.6L eng.	2891741	61.75
2.2L eng.	3643453	60.75
(2) Union Assy. (Fitting)		
1983-87-exc. below	5205267	7.00
H.D. susp	3815983	6.00
(3) Seal		
1983-87	2537838	11.00
(4) Retaining Ring (End Plate)		
1983-87	2537823	1.00
(5) End Plate		
1983-87	2537820	3.50

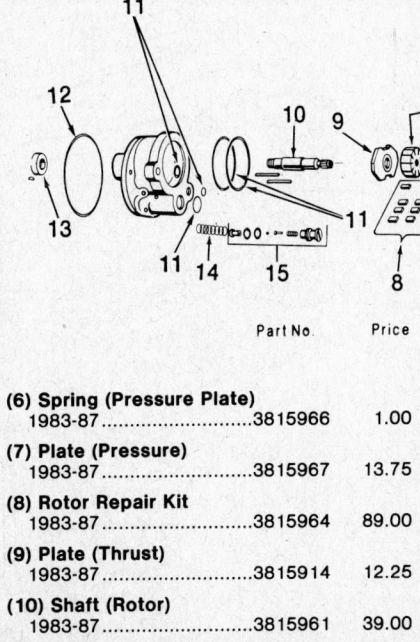

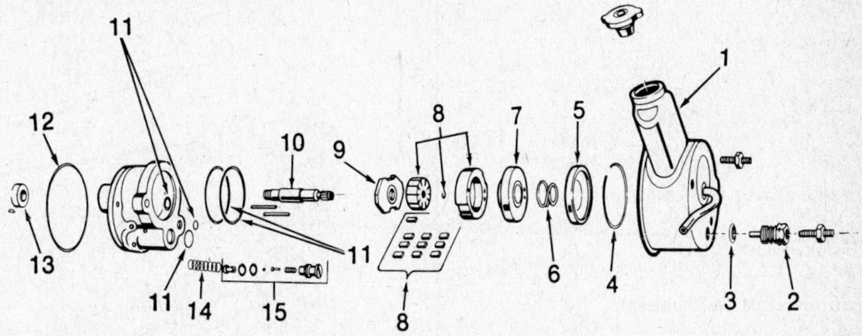

	Part No.	Price
(6) Spring (Pressure Plate)		
1983-87	3815966	1.00
(7) Plate (Pressure)		
1983-87	3815967	13.75
(8) Rotor Repair Kit		
1983-87	3815964	89.00
(9) Plate (Thrust)		
1983-87	3815914	12.25
(10) Shaft (Rotor)		
1983-87	3815961	39.00

	Part No.	Price
(11) Seal Kit		
1983-87	2537838	11.00
(12) "O" Ring		
1983-87	2537828	3.25
(13) Seal (Drive Shaft)		
1983-87	2537899	4.50
(14) Spring (Control Valve)		
1983-87	2537833	1.50
(15) Control Valve		
1983-87-exc. below	3815965	12.50
H.D. susp	2891695	13.00

LABOR 12 CYLINDER HEAD & VALVE SYSTEM 12 LABOR

(Factory Time)	Chilton Time
(G) Compression Test	
1983-87	.6
(G) Cylinder Head Gasket, Renew	
Includes: Clean carbon.	
1983-87	
1.7 L eng (3.3)	4.7
2.2 L eng (3.4)	4.8
1.6 L eng (1.7)	2.4
w/A.C. add (.4)	.4
w/Air inj add (.3)	.3
w/P.S. add (.1)	.1
w/Turbo add (.5)	.5
(G) Cylinder Head, Renew	
Includes: Transfer all necessary parts. Clean carbon, make all necessary adjustments.	
1983-87	
1.7 L eng (6.5)	9.2
2.2 L eng (5.3)	8.0
1.6 L eng (2.7)	3.8
w/A.C. add (.4)	.4
w/Air inj add (.3)	.3

COMBINATIONS

Add to Valve Job

See Machine Shop Operations

(Factory Time)	Chilton Time
(G) DRAIN, EVACUATE & RECHARGE AIR CONDITIONING SYSTEM	
All models	1.0
(G) DISTRIBUTOR, RECONDITION	
All models (.7)	.7
(G) CARBURETOR, RECONDITION	
All models (.8)	1.1

w/P.S. add (.1)	.1
w/Turbo add (.5)	.5
(P) Clean Carbon and Grind Valves	
Includes: R&R cylinder head, adjust valve clearance when required. Minor engine tune up.	
1983-87	
1.7 L eng (6.8)	9.9

(Factory Time)	Chilton Time
2.2 L eng (4.8)	8.7
1.6 L eng (2.9)	4.0
w/A.C. add (.4)	.4
w/Air inj add (.1)	.3
w/P.S. add (.1)	.1
w/Turbo add (.5)	.5
(G) Cylinder Head Cover Gasket, Renew or Reseal	
1983-87	
1.7 L eng (.7)	1.0
2.2 L eng (.8)	1.1
1.6 L eng (.5)	.7
(G) Valve Tappets or Rocker Arms, Renew	
1983-87	
2.2 L eng-one (1.0)	1.5
all (1.7)	2.9
1.6 L eng	
one or all (1.7)	2.8

LABOR 12 CYLINDER HEAD & VALVE SYSTEM 12 LABOR

	(Factory Time)	Chilton Time
(G) Valve Push Rods, Renew		
1983-87		
1.6L eng	(.6)	1.0
(G) Valve Springs, Renew		
Includes: Adjust valve clearance when required.		
1983-87-1.7 L eng-one	(1.7)	4.0
all	(2.6)	5.3
2.2 L eng-one	(1.2)	1.5
all	(1.9)	2.9
1.6 L eng-one	(.8)	1.2
all	(1.7)	2.8
w/A.C. add	(.4)	.4
w/Air inj add	(.1)	.3
(G) Valve Stem Oil Seals, Renew		
1983-87		
1.7 L eng-all	(2.8)	5.9
2.2 L eng-all	(1.9)	2.9
1.6 L eng-one or all	(1.7)	2.8
w/A.C. add	(.4)	.4
w/Air inj add	(.1)	.1
(G) Valve Tappets, Adjust		
1983-87		
1.6 L eng	(.9)	1.5

PARTS 12 CYLINDER HEAD & VALVE SYSTEM 12 PARTS

1.6L ENGINE

	Part No.	Price
Engine Gasket Set (Complete)		
1983-87	4271980	42.75
(1) Cylinder Head		
1983-84	4273603	432.00
1985-87	4273884	419.25
(2) Cylinder Head Gasket		
1983-85	4273608	11.00
1986-87	4273883	11.25
(3) Valve Cover Gasket		
1983-87	4273621	5.50
(4) Rocker Arm Shaft		
1983-87	4273679	17.50
(5) Spring (Rocker Spacer)		
1983-87	4273536	1.00
(6) Rocker Arm		
1983-87-right	4273678	9.50
left	4273677	9.50
(7) Adjusting Screw (Rocker Arm)		
1983-87	4273686	1.50
(8) Push Rod		
1983-87	4273676	3.75
(9) Valve Retainer		
1983-87	4273663	2.00
(10) Valve Spring		
1983-87	4273657	2.50
(11) Oil Seal (Valve Stem)		
1983-87	4273515	1.75
(12) Lower Washer (Valve Spring)		
1983-87	4273660	1.75
(13) Intake Valve		
1983-84	4273645	8.25
1985-87	4273874	8.25
(14) Exhaust Valve		
1983-84	4273651	13.50
1985-87	4273879	13.50
(15) Valve Tappet		
1983-87	4273601	9.25
(16) "O" Ring (Block Heater)		
1983-87	6027513	1.00

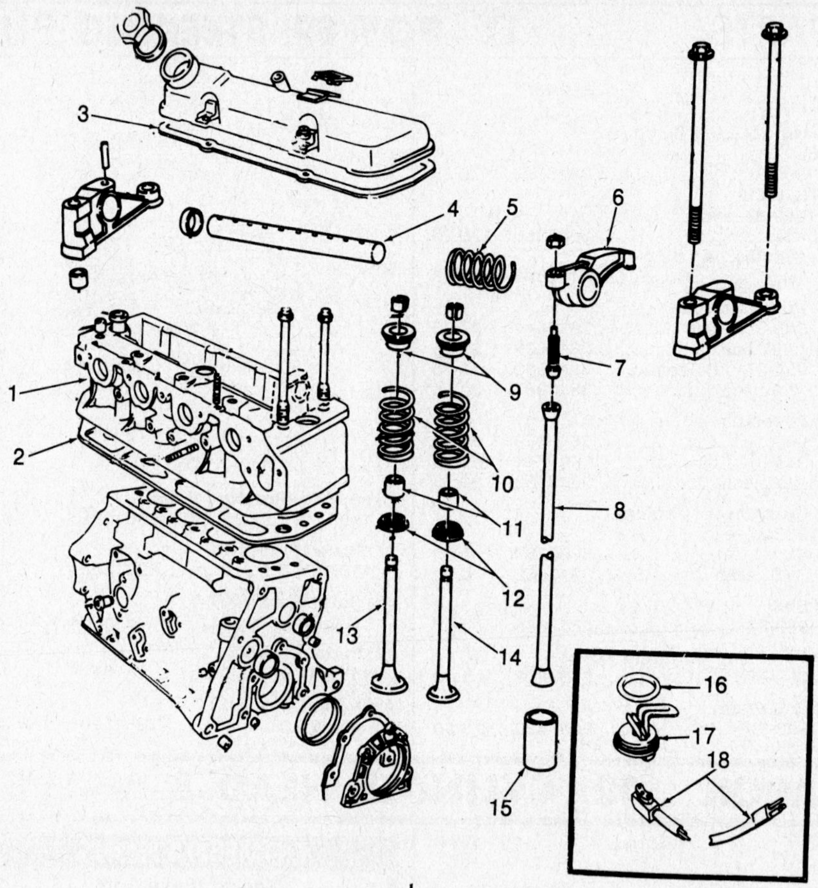

	Part No.	Price
(17) Engine Block Heater		
1983-87	5213548	28.50
(18) Block Heater Cord		
1983-87	5213549	20.50

PARTS 12 CYLINDER HEAD & VALVE SYSTEM 12 PARTS

1.7L ENGINE

	Part No.	Price
Engine Gasket Set (Complete)		
1983	4267197	93.25
(1) Cylinder Head		
1983	5240996	577.75
(2) Cylinder Head Gasket		
1983	4240141	21.25
(3) Camshaft Seal		
1983	4186220	9.25
(4) Camshaft Seal (Journal No. 1)		
1983	5240468	2.00
(5) Valve Cover Gasket		
1983	4201755	2.50
(6) Spacer (Valve Tappet)		
1983	5240946	3.50
(7) Valve Tappet		
1983	5240508	3.50
(8) Valve Lock		
1983	4201761	.50
(9) Retainer (Valve Spring)		
1983-Early	5240505	1.50
Late	4210760	15.50
(10) Valve Spring (Outer)		
1983	5240503	1.00
(11) Valve Spring (Inner)		
1983	5240504	1.50

PARTS 12 CYLINDER HEAD & VALVE SYSTEM 12 PARTS

	Part No.	Price
(12) Oil Seal (Valve Stem)		
1983	4186331	12.00
(13) Seat (Valve Spring)		
1983	5240507	1.25
(14) Exhaust Valve		
1983	4267225	30.25
(15) Intake Valve		
1983	4267222	12.75
(16) Valve Guide		
1983-intake	5240925	5.50
exhaust	5240998	7.00
(17) Insert (Valve Seat)		
1983-Intake	5240923	1.00
Exhaust	5240924	1.25
(18) Valve Cover Seal (Rear)		
1983	5240524	2.25
(19) Oil Seal (Rear)		
1983	4094810	20.75
(20) Oil Seal Retainer (Rear)		
1983	5240433	5.00
(21) Retainer Gasket (Rear)		
1983	5214198	1.00
(22) Engine Block Heater		
1983	5206360	33.50
(23) Heater Cord (Eng. Block)		
1983	5206359	19.50
(24) Retainer Gasket (Front)		
1983	5240431	1.00
(25) Oil Seal Retainer (Front)		
1983	5240427	5.00

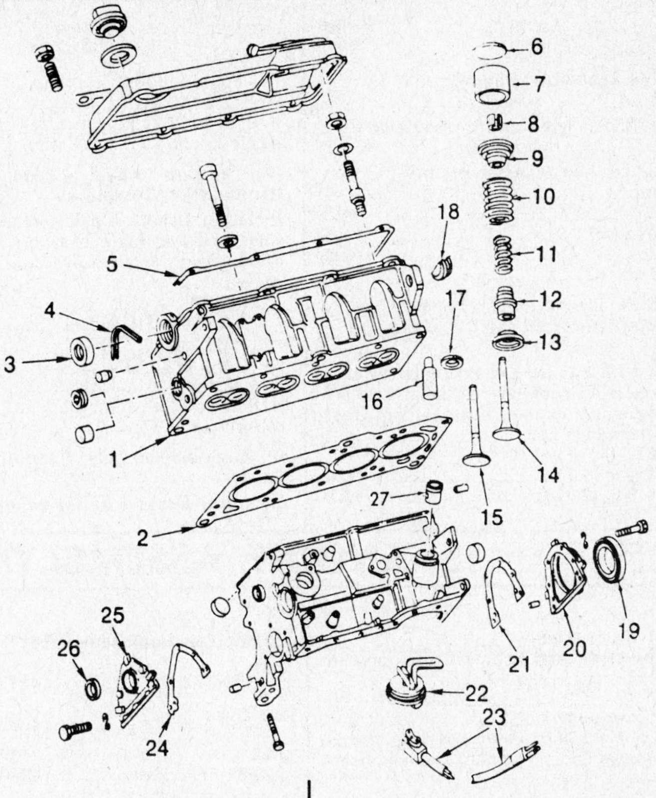

	Part No.	Price
(26) Oil Seal (Front)		
1983	4186220	9.25
(27) Drive Shaft Sleeve (Oil Pump)		
1983	5240416	2.00

PARTS 12 CYLINDER HEAD & VALVE SYSTEM 12 PARTS

2.2L ENGINE

	Part No.	Price
Cylinder Head Gasket Pkg.		
1983-85-wo/Turbo	4271994	30.50
Turbo	4271926	29.25
1986-87-wo/Turbo	4397680	28.25
Turbo	4397681	28.25

Use R.T.V. sealer for gaskets not supplied.

	Part No.	Price
(1) Cylinder Head (Partial)		
1983	4105399	340.25
1984	4105443	340.25
1985	4323288	340.25
1986-87-wo/Turbo	4387614	340.25
Turbo	4343627	340.25
(2) Cylinder Head Gasket		
1983-85	4105468	11.50
1986-87	4387319	11.50
(3) End Seal (Head Cover)		
1983-87	5214479	2.25
(4) Valve Spring		
1983-84	4105755	2.25
1985-87-wo/Turbo	4323225	2.25
Turbo	4105793	2.25
(5) Valve Guide		
1983-87-Exhaust	4105715	7.75
Intake	4105716	7.75
(6) Exhaust Valve (Std.)		
1983-87-wo/Turbo	5214866	9.00
Turbo (84-85)	5214959	21.00
Turbo (86-87)	4323249	21.00

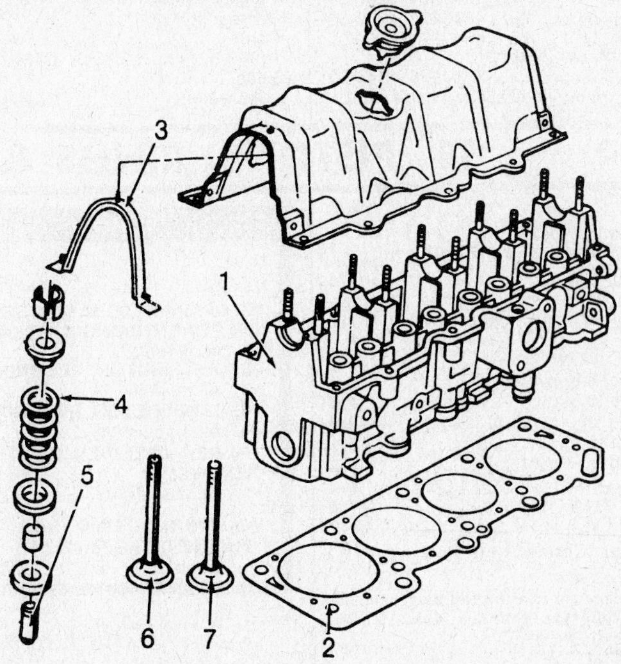

	Part No.	Price
(7) Intake Valve (Std.)		
1983-87-wo/Turbo	5214861	8.25
Turbo (84-85)	5214895	8.75
Turbo (86-87)	4323244	8.75

LABOR 13 ENGINE ASSEMBLY & MOUNTS 13 LABOR

(Factory Time)	Chilton Time

(G) Engine Assembly, Remove and Install

Includes: R&R engine and transmission as a unit.

Does not include transfer of any parts or equipment.

1983-87	4.5
w/A.C. add (.3)	.5
w/P.S. add (.2)	.2
w/Air inj add (.7)	.7

(P) Short Engine Assembly, Renew (w/All Internal Parts Less Cyl. Head and Oil Pan)

Includes: R&R engine and transmission as a unit. Transfer all necessary parts not supplied with replacement engine, clean carbon, grind valves. Minor tune up.

1983-87	
1.7 L eng (9.7)	16.0
2.2 L eng (9.1)	15.0
1.6 L eng (9.2)	15.3
w/A.C. add (.3)	.5
w/P.S. add (.2)	.2
w/Air inj add (.7)	.7

(P) Engine Assy., R&R and Recondition (Complete)

Includes: Rebore block, install new pistons, rings, rod and main bearings. Clean carbon, grind valves, replace valve stem oil seals. Tune engine.

1983-87	
1.7 L eng (19.9)	27.0
2.2 L eng (17.8)	25.2
1.6 L eng (13.8)	19.3
w/A.C. add (.3)	.5
w/P.S. add (.2)	.2
w/Air inj add (.7)	.7

(P) Engine Assembly, Recondition (In Car)

Includes: Expand or renew pistons, install rings, pins, rod and main bearings, clean carbon and grind valves. Tune engine.

1983-87	
1.7 L eng (14.0)	19.6
2.2 L eng (15.2)	20.8
1.6 L eng (9.4)	13.1
w/A.C. add (.4)	.5
w/Air inj add (.7)	.7

(G) Engine Support, Renew

1983-87-1.6-1.7 L eng	
right side (.4)	.6
left side (.4)	.6
center (.5)	.8
2.2 L eng-right side (.3)	.5
left side (.3)	.5
center (.4)	.6
Trans/Axle	
Roll rod (.3)	.5
Head	
Roll rod (.5)	.7

PARTS 13 ENGINE ASSEMBLY & MOUNTS 13 PARTS

	Part No.	Price
Engine Assy. (Partial)		
Consist of block and head with all internal parts.		
1983-1.7L	5240405	1701.00
Short Engine Assy.		
Consists of block with piston and rings, crankshaft, bearings and connecting rods and bearings.		
1.6L		
1983-87	4173751	1151.00
2.2L		
1983-84-exc. H/P	5214968	1200.50
H/P	4201991	N.L.
1985-exc. H/P	4387201	1200.50
H/P	4387203	N.L.
Turbo	4387202	1200.50
1986-87-exc. H/P	4343874	1200.50
H/P	4343873	1200.50
Turbo	4343871	1200.50
Cylinder Block (w/Pistons)		
1983-1.7L	5240986	1144.50
1.6L eng. & 2.2L serviced in short engine assy.		
Engine Overhaul Gasket Set		
1.6L		
1983-87	4271980	42.75
1.7L		
1983	4267197	93.25
2.2L		
1983-85-Lower	4240098	5.75
(Upper)		
wo/Turbo	4271994	30.50
Turbo	4271926	29.25
1986-87-Lower	4240098	5.75
(Upper)		
wo/Turbo	4397680	28.25
Turbo	4397681	28.25
Engine Mounts		
1.6L		
(Front)		
1983-87	4269354	22.50
(Sides)		
1983-Right	5209928	2.25
Left	4295198	12.50
1984-Right	4295173	N.L.
Left	4295237	9.00
1985-87-Right	4295260	12.50
Left	4295237	9.00
1.7L		
(Front)		
1983-exc. below	4269277	22.50
A412 trans	5202975	27.75
(Sides)		
1983	4295198	12.50
2.2L		
(Front)		
1983-87-wo/Turbo	4269279	22.50
Turbo	4377449	25.25
(Sides)		
1983	4295198	12.50
1984-87-Right	4295260	12.50
Left	4295237	9.00

LABOR 14 PISTONS, RINGS & BEARINGS 14 LABOR

(Factory Time)	Chilton Time

(P) Rings, Renew (See Engine Combinations)

Includes: Replace connecting rod bearings, deglaze cylinder walls, clean carbon. Minor tune up.

1983-87	
1.7 L eng-one cyl (4.7)	6.3
all cyls (5.8)	8.0
2.2 L eng-one cyl (4.6)	6.9
all cyls (5.9)	8.1
1.6 L eng-one cyl (3.5)	4.9
all cyls (5.0)	6.4
w/A.C. add (.2)	.2
w/Air inj add (.2)	.2

(P) Piston or Connecting Rod, Renew

Includes: Replace connecting rod bearings and piston rings, deglaze cylinder walls. Clean carbon from cylinder head.

1983-87	
1.7 L eng-one cyl (4.4)	6.6
all cyls (5.6)	9.2
2.2 L eng-one cyl (4.9)	7.2
all cyls (6.1)	9.3
1.6 L eng-one cyl (3.2)	5.2
all cyls (4.6)	7.6
w/A.C. add (.2)	.2
w/Air inj add (.2)	.2

COMBINATIONS

Add to Engine Work
See Machine Shop Operations

(G) DRAIN, EVACUATE & RECHARGE AIR CONDITIONING SYSTEM	
All models	1.0
(G) DISTRIBUTOR, RECONDITION	
All models (.7)	.7
(G) CARBURETOR, RECONDITION	
All models (.8)	1.1
(G) R&R CYLINDER HEAD (ENGINE REMOVED)	
All models	1.5
(G) CONNECTING ROD, RENEW (ENGINE DISASSEMBLED)	
Each	.4
(G) DEGLAZE CYLINDER WALLS	
Each (.1)	.1
(G) REMOVE CYLINDER TOP RIDGE	
Each (.1)	.1
(G) MAIN BEARINGS, RENEW (PAN REMOVED)	
All models (.9)	1.4
(G) PLASTIGAUGE BEARINGS	
Each (.1)	.1
(M) OIL FILTER ELEMENT, RENEW	
All models (.3)	.3

(P) Connecting Rod Bearings, Renew

1983-87	
1.7 L eng-one (1.1)	1.5
all (1.7)	2.5
2.2 L eng-one (1.5)	1.9
all (2.1)	3.0
1.6 L eng-all (1.6)	2.2

PARTS 14 PISTONS, RINGS & BEARINGS 14 PARTS

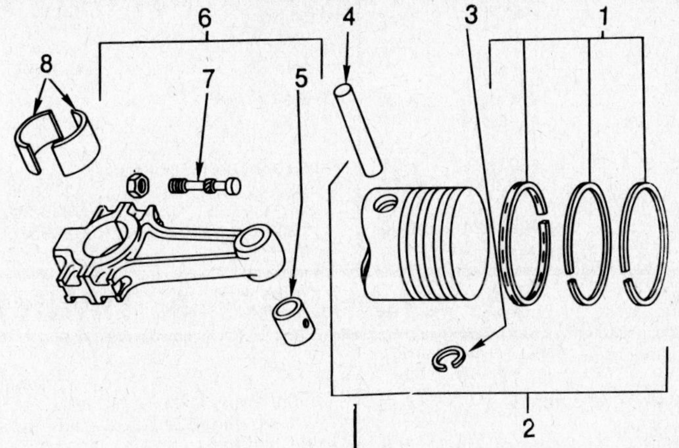

	Part No.	Price
(1) Piston Ring Set		
1.6L		
1983-87	4271995	15.75
1.7L		
1983	4186268	114.50
2.2L		
1983-87-wo/Turbo	4240137	54.00
Turbo	4293799	54.00
(2) Piston Assy.		
1.6L		
1983-87	4173739	31.25
1.7L		
1983	4186275	61.50
2.2L		
1983-87-wo/Turbo	4271929	33.00
Turbo (84-85)	4271927	33.00
Turbo (86-87)	4397634	33.00
(3) Retainer (Piston Pin)		
1983-1.7L eng	5240442	.50
(4) Piston Pin		
1983-87-1.6L eng	4273561	5.75
1.7L eng.	5240441	1.00
2.2L eng.	5203800	3.75
(5) Bushing (Connecting Rod)		
1983-1.7L eng.	4131202	3.50
(6) Connecting Rod Assy.		
1.6L		
1983-87	4173775	56.25
1.7L		
1983	4094874	58.50
2.2L		
1983-85-wo/Turbo	5203384	35.00
Turbo	4105486	35.00
1986-87	4343725	35.00
(7) Screw (Connecting Rod & Cap)		
1983-1.7L eng	5240449	2.75
(8) Connecting Rod Brg. Pkg.		
1.6L		
1983-87	4273551	3.25
1.7L		
1983	4094818	43.00
2.2L		
1983-87-wo/Turbo	4240025	4.00
Turbo	4342751	4.00

LABOR 15 CRANKSHAFT & DAMPER 15 LABOR

(Factory Time)	Chilton Time
(P) Crankshaft and Main Bearings, Renew	
Includes: R&R engine assy.	
1983-87	
1.7 L eng (8.8)	13.3
2.2 L eng (6.7)	11.2
1.6 L eng (5.9)	8.2
w/A.C. add (.4)	.4
w/P.S. add (.3)	.3
w/Air inj add (.7)	.7
(P) Main Bearings, Renew (All)	
1983-87	
1.7 L eng (3.7)	4.7
2.2 L eng (7.0)	11.0
1.6 L eng (2.5)	3.5
w/A.C. add (.2)	.2
w/P.S. add (.3)	.3
(P) Main and Rod Bearings, Renew (All)	
1983-87	
1.7 L eng (4.4)	5.9
2.2 L eng (7.7)	12.2
1.6 L eng (3.2)	4.7
w/A.C. add (.2)	.2
w/P.S. add (.3)	.3
(G) Rear Main Bearing Oil Seals, Renew (Complete)	
1983-87	
1.7 L eng	
w/M.T. (3.0)	4.2
w/A.T. (3.6)	5.1
2.2 L eng (3.5)	5.4
1.6 L eng	
w/M.T. (2.7)	3.8
w/A.T. (2.4)	3.4
w/Cruise control add (.2)	.2
(G) Crankshaft Rear Bearing Oil Seal Retainer, Renew	
Includes: Replace oil seal complete.	
1983-87	
1.7 L eng	
w/M.T. (3.1)	4.3
w/A.T. (3.7)	5.2
2.2 L eng (4.1)	6.0
1.6 L eng (2.6)	3.6
w/Cruise control add (.2)	.2
(G) Crankshaft Pulley, Renew	
1983-87 (.5)	.8
w/A.C. add (.1)	.1
w/P.S. add (.1)	.1
w/Air inj add (.1)	.1
(G) Crankshaft Front Oil Seal, Renew	
1983-87	
1.7 L eng (1.2)	1.9
2.2 L eng (1.3)	2.0
w/A.C. add (.7)	.7
w/P.S. add (.2)	.2

PARTS 15 CRANKSHAFT & DAMPER 15 PARTS

	Part No.	Price
(1) Crankshaft (New)		
1.6L		
1983-87	4273530	321.25
1.7L		
1983	5240417	464.25
2.2L		
1983-85	5214737	317.50
Turbo	4105498	317.50
1986-87	4343407	317.50
(2) Crankshaft Bearing Pkg.		
1.6L		
1983-87 (Upper)		
No. 1, 2, 4, 5	4173757	5.50
No. 3	4173758	4.25
1983-87 (Lower)		
No. 1, 5	4173756	4.25
No. 2, 4	4173757	5.50
No. 3	4173755	4.25
1.7L		
1983 (Set)	4131062	91.50

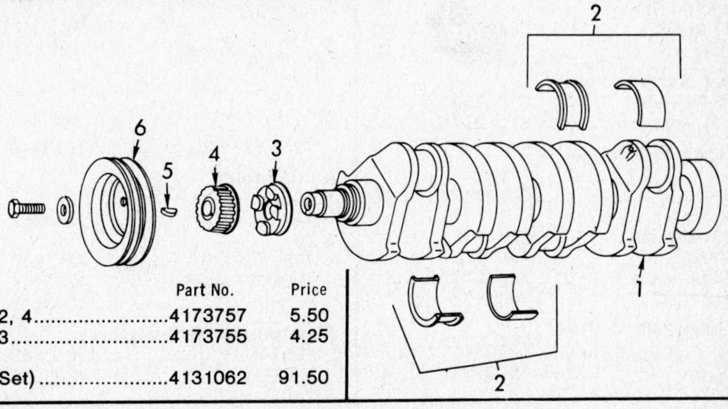

PARTS 15 CRANKSHAFT & DAMPER 15 PARTS

	Part No.	Price
2.2L		
(wo/Turbo)		
1983-85-No. 1, 2, 4, 5	4240013	6.00
No. 3	4240019	6.00
(Turbo)		
1985-No. 1, 2, 4, 5	4293824	6.00
No. 3	4293830	12.75
1986-87-No. 1, 2, 4, 5	4293824	6.00
No. 3	4293830	12.75
(3) Belt Guide		
1983-1.7L	5240700	1.00
(4) Crankshaft Sprocket		
1983-87-1.6L	4273535	16.75
1.7L	5240370	14.00
2.2L	5203575	14.00
(5) Key (Crank. Sprocket)		
1983-87	6500150	.25
(6) Pulley		
1.6L		
1983-87	4273803	54.00
1.7L		
1983-wo/A.C.	5214486	19.00
A.C.	4241150	28.50

LABOR 16 CAMSHAFT & TIMING GEARS 16 LABOR

	(Factory Time)	Chilton Time
(G) Intermediate Shaft, Renew		
1983-87		
1.7 L eng	(2.1)	2.8
2.2 L eng	(1.3)	2.5
w/A.C. add	(.6)	.6
w/P.S. add	(.1)	.1
w/Air inj add	(.2)	.2
(G) Intermediate Shaft Oil Seal, Renew		
1983-87		
1.7 L eng	(1.2)	2.0
2.2 L eng	(1.1)	1.8
w/A.C. add	(.6)	.6
w/P.S. add	(.1)	.1
w/Air inj add	(.2)	.2
(G) Intermediate Shaft Sprocket, Renew		
1983-87		
1.7 L eng	(1.8)	2.5
2.2 L eng	(1.7)	2.7
w/A.C. add	(.6)	.6
w/P.S. add	(.1)	.1
w/Air inj add	(.2)	.2
(G) Intermediate Shaft Plug, Renew		
1983-1.7 L eng		
w/M.T.	(2.8)	4.0
w/A.T.	(3.6)	5.1
(G) Camshaft, Renew		
1983-87		
1.7 L eng	(2.6)	4.0
2.2 L eng	(1.7)	2.8
1.6 L eng	(3.5)	4.8
w/A.C. add	(.6)	.6
w/P.S. add	(.1)	.1
w/Air inj add	(.2)	.2
(G) Camshaft Sprocket, Renew		
Includes: Replace cover oil seal.		
1983-87		
1.7 L eng	(1.8)	2.5
2.2 L eng	(1.7)	2.4
1.6 L eng	(1.3)	1.9
w/A.C. add	(.6)	.6
w/P.S. add	(.2)	.2
w/Air inj add	(.2)	.2
(G) Timing Belt, Renew		
1983-87		
1.7 L eng	(1.7)	2.4
2.2 L eng	(1.6)	2.3
w/A.C. add	(.4)	.4
w/P.S. add	(.2)	.2
w/Air inj add	(.1)	.1
(G) Timing Belt Cover, Renew		
1983-87		
1.7 L eng-upper	(.3)	.6
lower	(1.2)	1.6
2.2 L eng-upper	(.2)	.4
lower	(.6)	1.0
w/A.C. add	(.5)	.5
w/P.S. add	(.2)	.2
w/Air inj add	(.1)	.1
(G) Timing Belt Tensioner, Renew		
1983-87		
1.7 L eng	(.7)	1.2
2.2 L eng	(.9)	1.5
w/A.C. add	(.4)	.4
w/P.S. add	(.2)	.2
w/Air inj add	(.1)	.1
(G) Camshaft Oil Seal, Renew		
1983-87		
1.7 L eng	(.8)	1.5
2.2 L eng-front	(.7)	1.1
rear	(.4)	.8
(G) Timing Chain Cover and/or Gasket, Renew		
1983-87		
1.6L eng	(1.2)	1.7
w/P.S. add	(.1)	.1
(G) Timing Chain Cover Oil Seal, Renew		
1983-87		
1.6L eng	(.4)	.8
w/P.S. add	(.1)	.1
(G) Timing Chain, Renew		
1983-87		
1.6 L eng	(1.3)	1.8
w/P.S. add	(.1)	.1

PARTS 16 CAMSHAFT & TIMING GEARS 16 PARTS

1.7L & 2.2L ENGS.

	Part No.	Price
(1) Timing Belt Cover (Upper)		
1.7L		
1983	5240793	10.00
2.2L		
1983-87	4105714	10.00
(2) Tension Pulley		
1983-87-1.7L	5240607	41.75
2.2L	5203469	41.75
(3) Stud (Tension Pulley)		
1983-87-1.7L	6100750	1.00
2.2L eng	6101277	1.00
(4) Camshaft Sprocket		
1.7L		
1983	5240369	16.25
2.2L		
1983-exc. below	5214870	16.25
Shelby	4201992	22.50
1984-87-exc. H/P	4201974	16.50
H/P	4201992	22.50
(5) Timing Belt		
1983-1.7L	5240346	22.75
1983-85-2.2L	5203401	22.75

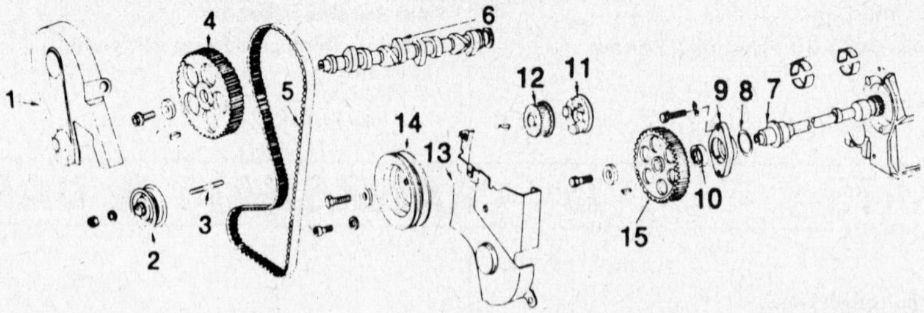

	Part No.	Price
1986-87-2.2L	4343946	22.75
(6) Camshaft		
1.7L		
1983	5240967	145.00
2.2L		
1983	4271910	154.00
1984-87-wo/Turbo	4293817	161.50
Turbo	4293819	161.50
(7) Intermediate Shaft Assy.		
1983-87-1.7L	5240469	111.25
2.2L	4293815	95.75
1986-87-Turbo	4343428	86.75
(8) 'O' Ring		
1983-1.7L	5240440	1.00
(9) Retainer (Interm. Shaft)		
1983-87-1.7L	5240522	11.50
2.2L	5203325	8.50
(10) Seal (Interm. Shaft)		
1983-87-1.7L	4186220	9.25
2.2L	4105395	2.75
(11) Belt Guide		
1983-1.7L	5240700	1.00

PARTS 16 CAMSHAFT & TIMING GEARS 16 PARTS

	Part No.	Price
(12) Crankshaft Sprocket		
1983-87-1.7L	5240370	14.00
2.2L	5203575	14.00
(13) Timing Belt Cover (Lower)		
1.7L		
1983	5240794	10.00
2.2L		
1983-84	4105293	10.00
1985-87	4343639	10.50
(14) Pulley		
1983-1.7L		
wo/A.C.	5214486	19.00
A.C.	4241150	28.50
(15) Sprocket (Interm. Shaft)		
1.7L		
1983	5240369	16.25
2.2L		
1983-87-wo/Turbo	4201974	16.50
Turbo	4201992	22.50

PARTS 16 CAMSHAFT & TIMING GEARS 16 PARTS

1.6L ENGINE

	Part No.	Price
(1) Timing Chain Cover		
1983-87	4273842	82.75
(2) Front Cover Gasket		
1983-87	4273519	1.25
(3) Timing Chain		
1983-87	4273635	23.25
(4) Sprocket (Crankshaft)		
1983-87	4273535	16.75
(5) Sprocket (Camshaft)		
1983-87	4273847	22.50
(6) Plate		
1983-87	4273590	11.00
(7) Camshaft		
1983-87	4273587	110.50
(8) Camshaft Bearing		
1983-87-No. 1	4173752	4.75
No. 2	4173753	4.75
No. 3	4173754	4.75

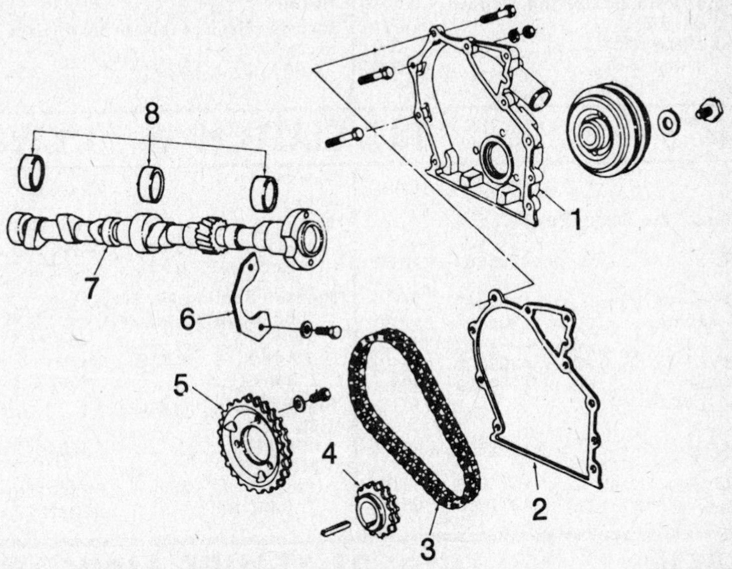

LABOR 17 ENGINE OILING SYSTEM 17 LABOR

(Factory Time)	Chilton Time
(G) Oil Pan or Gasket, Renew or Reseal	
1983-87-1.7 L eng (.8)	1.2
2.2 L eng (1.0)	1.4
1.6 L eng (.5)	.9
(P) Pressure Test Engine Bearings (Pan Off)	
All models	1.0
(G) Oil Pump, Renew	
1983-87	
1.7 L eng (1.0)	1.4
2.2 L eng (1.3)	1.7
1.6 L eng (.6)	1.0
(G) Oil Pump, R&R and Recondition	
1983-87	
1.7 L eng (1.3)	1.7
2.2 L eng (1.7)	2.2
1.6 L eng (.8)	1.2
(G) Oil Pump Drive Shaft, Renew	
Includes: Renew drive gear.	
1983-87	
1.6L eng (.8)	1.1
(G) Oil Pressure Gauge (Dash), Renew	
1984-87 (.3)	.6
(G) Oil Pressure Gauge (Engine), Renew (Light Switch)	
1983-87 (.2)	.4
(M) Oil Filter Element, Renew	
All models (.2)	.3

PARTS 17 ENGINE OILING SYSTEM 17 PARTS

	Part No.	Price
Oil Pan Gasket		
1983-87-1.7L	4131166	10.50
1.6L	4273722	3.25
R.T.V. sealer is used with the 2.2 liter engine oil pan.		
Oil Pump Assy.		
1.6L		
1983-87	4273802	40.50
1.7L		
1983	5240510	118.00
2.2L		
1983	5203415	N.L.
1984	4323327	58.50
1985	4293888	N.L.
1986-87	4397827	66.00
Oil Pump Housing		
1983-1.7L	5240511	43.00
Oil Pump Drive Shaft		
1983-87-1.7L	5240515	20.25
1.6L	4273761	16.75
Drive Shaft & Rotor Pkg.		
1983-85-2.2L	4240008	24.25
1986-87-2.2L	4342940	24.50
Oil Pump Drive Gear		
1983-1.7L eng.	5240985	3.50
1.6L & 2.2L liter engine serviced in oil pump assy.		
Oil Pump Cover Assy.		
1983-87-1.7L	5240594	52.00
2.2L (83-85)	5203322	7.75
(86-87)	4323030	7.75
Oil Pump Baffle		
1983-1.7L	5240918	1.50
Baffle Screen		
1983	5240988	1.00
Relief Valve Plunger (Oil Pressure)		
1983-87-2.2L	2120764	3.00
Relief Valve Spring (Oil Pressure)		
2.2L		
1983-87	2402473	2.25
Oil Pump Strainer Assy.		
1983-87-1.6L	4273768	27.75
2.2L (83-85)	5203324	7.75
(86-87)	4343198	7.65
Oil Filter Assy.		
1983-87-1.6L	4105409	5.50
1.7L	4105409	5.50
2.2L	4105409	5.50

LABOR 18 CLUTCH & FLYWHEEL 18 LABOR

(Factory Time)	Chilton Time
(G) Clutch Pedal Free Play, Adjust	
All models	.4
(G) Clutch Assembly, Renew	
1983-87-5 Spd	
1.6 L eng (2.1)	3.2
1.7 L eng (2.9)	4.0
2.2 L eng (3.3)	4.6
4 spd	
All models (2.7)	4.0
w/Cruise control add (.2)	.2
Renew input shaft seal add	.2
(G) Clutch Release Bearing, Renew	
1983-87-5 Spd	
1.6 L eng (2.0)	3.0
1.7 L eng (2.8)	3.8
2.2 L eng (3.2)	4.4
4 Spd	
All models (.5)	.8
w/Cruise control add (.2)	.2
(G) Clutch Release Lever Arm, Renew	
1983-87 (.2)	.5
(G) Clutch Release Arm Seal, Renew	
1983-87 (.5)	.8
(G) Clutch Release Push Rod, Renew	
Includes: Replace release bearing and sleeve if necessary.	
1983 (.6)	1.0
(G) Clutch Release Cable, Renew	
1983-87 (.3)	.5
(G) Clutch Self-Adjusting Mechanism, Renew	
1983-87 (.3)	.6
(G) Flywheel, Renew	
1983-87-5 Spd	
1.6 L eng (2.2)	3.5
1.7 L eng (3.0)	4.2
2.2 L eng (3.4)	4.7
4 Spd	
All models (2.7)	3.9
w/Cruise control add (.2)	.2
Renew ring gear add	.5

PARTS 18 CLUTCH & FLYWHEEL 18 PARTS

	Part No.	Price
Pressure Plate Assy. (New)		
1.6L		
1983-87	4205864	122.50
1.7L		
1983-A-412 trans	4186867	N.L.
A-460 trans	4205864	122.50
2.2L		
1983-87-wo/Turbo	4295007	122.50
Turbo	4269309	122.50
Clutch Disc (New)		
1.6L		
1983-87	4205865	66.50
1.7L		
1983-A-412 trans	4186868	66.50
A-460 trans	4205865	66.50
2.2L		
1983-87-wo/Turbo	4295006	66.50
Turbo	4269308	68.25
Release Bearing (w/Sleeve)		
1983-87-A412 trans	4094827	7.50
A460 & A525 trans.	4202378	44.00
Flywheel (w/Ring Gear)		
1.6L		
1983-87	4202927	149.50
1.7L		
1983-A-412 trans	5240156	142.75
A-460 trans	5222972	150.75
2.2L		
1983-84	4329177	142.75
1985-wo/Turbo	4348312	142.50
Turbo	4348314	142.75
1986-87-wo/Turbo	4338874	142.75
Turbo	4338872	142.75
Clutch Control Cable		
1.6L & 2.2L		
1983	4019750	N.L.
1984	4188672	18.50
1985-87	4377771	18.50
1.7L		
1983	5206246	18.50

LABOR 21 SHIFT LINKAGE 21 LABOR

(Factory Time)	Chilton Time
MANUAL	
(G) Gearshift Linkage, Adjust	
All models (.2)	.4
(G) Gearshift Control Rod and/or Swivel, Renew	
1983-87 (.3)	.4
(G) Crossover Rod, Renew	
1983-87 (.3)	.4
(G) Gearshift Outside Lever, Renew	
1983-87 (.3)	.4
(G) Gearshift Lever, Renew	
Includes: Replace boot if necessary.	
1983-87 (.4)	.6
(G) Gearshift Mechanism, Renew	
1983-87 (.6)	.9
w/Console add (.1)	.1
(G) Gearshift Selector Tube Assembly, Renew	
1983-87 (.4)	.6
(G) Selector Shaft Seal, Renew	
1983-87 (.8)	1.1
(G) Trans/Axle Selector Shaft, Renew	
1983-87-w/A 412 (.8)	1.1
w/A 460-A 465-A 525 (1.3)	1.7
AUTOMATIC	
(G) Throttle Linkage, Adjust	
All models (.2)	.4
(G) Gearshift Mechanism, Renew	
Includes: Replace knob and push button if necessary.	
1983-87 (.5)	.8
(G) Gearshift Control Cable, Renew	
1983-87 (.7)	1.0
(G) Gear Selector, Renew	
1983-87 (.3)	.5
(G) Throttle Lever Control Cable, Renew	
Includes: Adjust cable.	
1983-87 (.3)	.6
(G) Gear Selector Dial, Renew	
1983-87 (.2)	.4

LABOR 26 REAR WHEEL & SUSPENSION 26 LABOR

(Factory Time)	Chilton Time
(G) Rear Wheel Bearing, Renew or Repack	
Includes: Replace bearing cups and grease seal.	
1983-87-each (.6)	.9
(G) Rear Wheel Grease Seal, Renew	
1983-87-one side (.4)	.7
(G) Rear Spring, Renew	
1983-87	
2 Dr-one (.6)	1.0
both (1.2)	1.7
4 Dr-one (.4)	.6
both (.7)	1.1
(G) Rear Shock Absorber, Renew	
1983-87	
2 Dr-one (.6)	1.0
both (1.2)	1.7
4 Dr-one (.3)	.6
both (.7)	1.1
(G) Stub Axle Spindle, Renew	
1983-87-each (.5)	.7
(G) Rear Wheel Mounting Studs, Renew	
1983-87-one (.5)	.8
each adtnl	.1

PARTS 26 REAR AXLE AND SUSPENSION 26 PARTS

	Part No.	Price
(1) Wheel Spindle (Rear)		
1983-84	4228123	62.75
1985-87	4228117	50.50
(2) Brake Support		
1983-87	4238697	28.00
(3) Dust Seal		
1983-87	4238570	3.50
(4) Wheel Bearing (Inner)		
1983-87	4238567	14.75
(5) Bearing Cup (Inner)		
1983	2203353	4.50
1984-87	4238567	14.75
(6) Hub & Drum		
1983-87-H.D.	4238531	89.75
H.D.		
4 blt	4238538	100.50
5 blt	4313635	100.50
(7) Bearing Cup (Outer)		
1983-87	3683974	13.25
(8) Wheel Bearing (Outer)		
1983	3580888	9.25
1984-87	4293196	9.25
(9) Lock		
1983-87	1673324	2.75

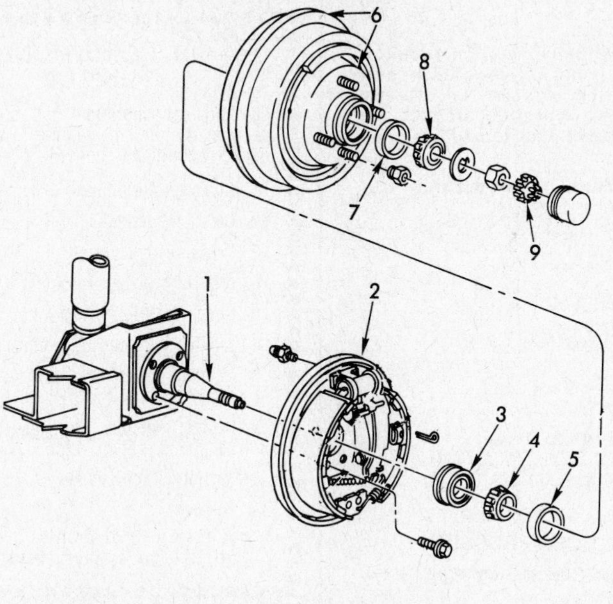

PARTS 26 REAR AXLE AND SUSPENSION 26 PARTS

	Part No.	Price
(1) Retainer (Upper)		
1983-87	5205032	1.00
(2) Isolator (Upper)		
1983-87	5204969	3.25
(3) Isolator (Lower)		
1983-87	5204932	3.75
(4) Sleeve (Seat)		
1983-87	5204939	2.75
(5) Seat (Upper)		
1983-84	5205185	4.00
1985-87	4228083	4.50
(6) Coil Spring		
1983-87-exc. below	5205154	46.50
H.D. susp	5205174	49.00
Shelby & perf. pkg	4228324	49.00
(7) Bumper (Jounce)		
1983-87-exc. below	5205182	3.25
Shelby & perf. pkg	4228330	3.25
(8) Dust Shield		
1983-87	5204937	1.75
(9) Seat (Lower)		
1983-87	5205186	5.00
(10) Shock Absorber		
1983-87 (Std. susp.)		
2 door	5205195	30.00
4 door	5205194	30.00
1985-87 (H.D. susp.)		
2 door	5205191	30.00
4 door	5205189	30.00
1985-87-Shelby	4228401	30.00
Perf. pkg	4228450	30.00
(11) Spindle Assy.		
1983-84	4228123	62.75
1985-87	4228117	50.50

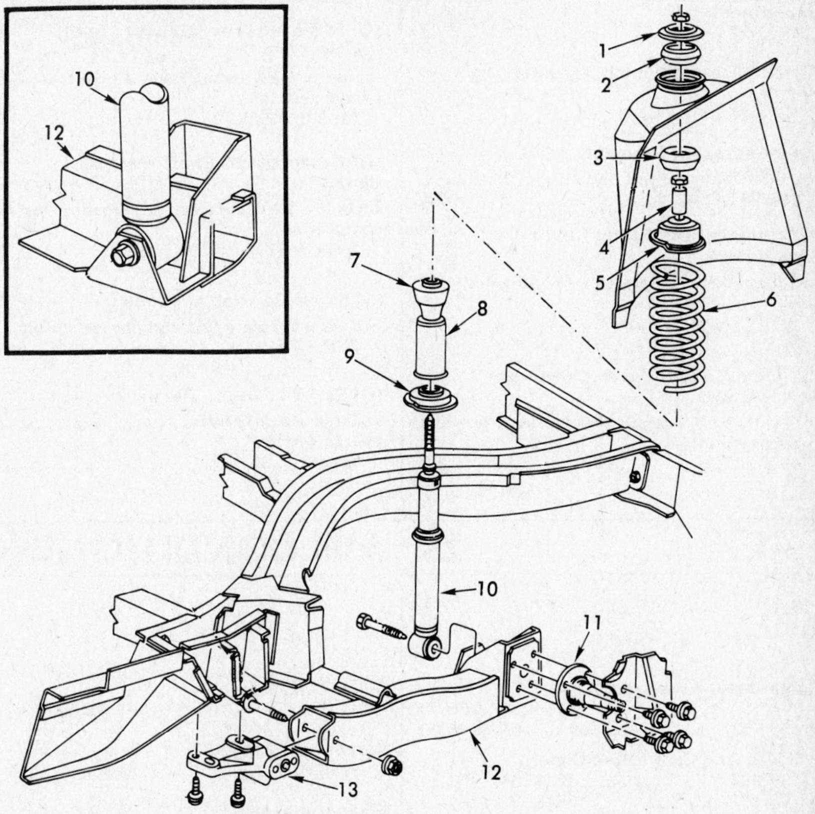

	Part No.	Price
(12) Lower Control Arm (w/Crossmember)		
1983-wo/Sway bar	5205038	199.50
Sway bar	5205149	193.75
1984-exc. below	5205149	193.75
Shelby	4228310	193.75
1985-87-exc. below	5205038	199.50
Firm susp	4228396	199.50

	Part No.	Price
(13) Pivot Hanger (w/Bushing)		
1983-85-exc. below	5205097	51.00
Firm susp	5205142	49.50
1986-87-exc. below	4228562	51.00
Firm susp	4228563	51.00

LABOR 28 AIR CONDITIONING 28 LABOR

(Factory Time) Chilton Time

Note: If more than one item requires replacement where evacuation and discharging the system is already included in the operation, deduct 1.0 hour for each additional item to the times listed.

(G) Drain, Evacuate, Leak Test and Charge System
All models.. 1.0

(G) Partial Charge
Includes: Leak test.
All models (.4).. .6

(G) Performance Test
All models.. .8

(G) Vacuum Leak Test
All models.. .8

(G) Compressor Belt, Renew
1983-87 (.2).. .5
w/Air inj add (.1).. .1

C-171 COMPRESSOR

(G) Compressor Clutch Field Coil, Renew
Includes: Replace pulley w/hub if necessary.
1983-87 (.6).. .9

(G) Compressor Clutch Pulley (W/Hub), Renew
1983-87 (.4).. .7

(G) Compressor Clutch Assembly, Renew
1983-87 (.6).. .9

(G) Compressor Assembly, Renew
Includes: Pressure test and charge system.
1983-87 (1.4).. 2.5

(G) Compressor Front Cover or Seal, Renew
Includes: R&R compressor. Pressure test and charge system.
1983-87 (2.1).. 3.4

(G) Compressor Rear Cover or Seal, Renew
Includes: R&R compressor. Pressure test and charge system.
1983-87 (2.0).. 3.3

AIR CONDITIONER TUNE-UP

For efficient operation and satisfactory performance in hot weather. The following air conditioner tune-up is suggested:

1. Clean intake filter
2. Clean condenser fins
3. Pressure test system
4. Adjust drive belt tension
5. Check antifreeze/coolant
6. Tighten compressor mounts
7. Tighten condenser and evaporator mounts
8. Inspect system for leaks (hoses, couplings, valves, etc.)
9. Partial charge system

All models 1.0
If necessary to evacuate and charge system, add 1.0

(Factory Time) Chilton Time

(G) Compressor Center Seal, Renew
Includes: R&R compressor. Pressure test and charge system.
1983-87 (2.2).. 3.5

(G) Compressor Shaft Gas Seal, Renew
Includes: R&R compressor. Pressure test and charge system.
1983-87 (2.1).. 3.4

(G) Expansion Valve, Renew
Includes: Pressure test and charge system.
1983-87 (1.0).. 1.7

(G) Receiver Dryer, Renew
Includes: Add partial charge, leak test and charge system.
1983-87 (.9).. 1.6

(Factory Time) Chilton Time

(G) Low Pressure Cut Off Switch, Renew
Includes: Charge system.
1983-87 (.9).. 1.4

(G) Clutch Cycling (Thermostatic Control) Switch, Rnew
1983-87 (.3).. .6

(G) Condenser Assembly, Renew
Includes: Add partial charge, leak test and charge system.
1983-87 (1.5).. 2.2
Renew receiver drier add.. .2

(G) Temperature Control Assembly, Renew
1983-87 (.4).. .7

(G) Push Button Vacuum Switch, Renew
1983-87 (.5).. .9

(G) Temperature Control Cable, Renew
1983-87 (.6).. .9

(G) Vacuum Hose Control Assy., Renew
1983-87
main assy (2.0).. 3.0

(G) Evaporator Coil, Renew
Includes: Add partial charge, leak test and charge system.
1983-87 (2.7).. 3.9

(G) Vacuum Actuator, Renew
1983-87
outside air door (.3).. .6
heater/defroster door (.3).. .6
A/C mode door (.6).. 1.0

(G) Blower Motor, Renew
1983-87 (.6).. .9

(G) Blower Motor Resistor, Renew
1983-87 (.3).. .4

(G) Blower Motor Switch, Renew
1983-87 (.4).. .8

(G) Air Conditioning Hoses, Renew
Includes: Add partial charge, leak test and charge system.
1983-87-one (1.1).. 1.6
each adtnl (.3).. .5
Renew receiver drier add.. .2

PARTS 28 AIR CONDITIONING 28 PARTS

	Part No.	Price
Compressor Assy.		
1983-84	4176059	275.00
1985-87	4339456	275.00
Pulley & Armature (Drive Clutch)		
1983-84	5210384	101.50
1985-87	3848982	101.75
Field Coil (Drive Clutch)		
1983	3846845	60.75
1984	3848673	60.75
1985-87	3848969	29.50
Check Valve (Suction & Disch. Line)		
1983-87	3847576	1.75
Expansion Valve (H-Type)		
1983-87	4176999	59.75
Filter Drier Assy.		
1983-87	5210438	39.00
Condenser Assy.		
1983-87	5210420	222.00
Evaporator Assy.		
1983	4339422	312.25
1984-87	3848854	312.25
Blower Motor		
1983-87	4240426	66.25
Blower Motor Resistor		
1983-84	3848807	7.75
1985-87	3848995	7.75
Blower Motor Switch		
1983-87	3847940	10.25
Push Button Vacuum Switch		
1983-87	3847512	26.25
Temp. Sensing Switch (Suct. Line)		
1983-84	4205830	33.75
1985-87	4339411	33.50
Low Pressure Cut Off Switch		
1983-87	5210377	17.25
Water Valve		
1983-87-exc. Turbo	3848136	27.75
Turbo	3848114	27.75

LABOR 29 LOCKS, HINGES & WIND. REGULATORS 29 LABOR

(Factory Time)	Chilton Time
(G) Hood Latch, Renew	
1983-87 (.2)	.4
(G) Hood Latch Release Cable, Renew	
1983-87 (.4)	.6
(G) Hood Hinge, Renew (One)	
Does not include painting.	
1983-87 (.3)	.4
(G) Door Lock or Remote Control, Renew (Front or Rear)	
1983-87 (.4)	.6
(G) Door Handle (Outside), Renew (Front or Rear)	
1983-87 (.5)	.7
(G) Lock Striker Plate, Renew	
1983-87 (.2)	.3
(G) Door Window Regulator, Renew	
1983-87	
Front	
2 DR (.5)	1.0
4 DR (.8)	1.2
Rear (.6)	1.0
(G) Lift Gate Lock, Renew	
1983-87 (.2)	.4
(G) Lift Gate Hinge, Renew	
1983-87-each (.3)	.5
(G) Door Lock Cylinder, Renew (Front or Rear)	
1983-87 (.4)	.5
Recode cylinder add (.2)	.3

PARTS 29 LOCKS, HINGES & WIND. REGULATORS 29 PARTS

	Part No.	Price
Hood Hinge (Hood Half)		
1983-87-right	5201084	9.25
left	5201085	9.25
Hood Lock (Inside Release)		
1983-87-2 door	5232057	13.00
4 door	5207088	13.00
Door Lock (Outside)		
1983-87-right	4184776	17.00
left	4184777	17.00
Front Door Lock (Manual)		
1983-87-right (wo/override)		
2 door	4184748	19.50
4 door	4184750	26.50
1983-87-left (w/override)		
2 door	4184747	19.50
4 door	4184753	26.50
Rear Door Lock (Inside)		
1983-87-right	5231650	35.25
left	5231651	35.25
Door Lock Cylinder & Key		
1983-87	5207203	20.50
Lift Gate Lock		
(2 door)		
1983-87-Manual	5207345	10.75
Power	4246675	40.50
(4 door)		
1983-87	5207383	12.25
Liftgate Hinges		
(2 door)		
1983-87		
up to 9-12-83	5232101	N.L.
from 9-12-83	4246776	13.00
(4 door)		
1983-84 (up to 9-12-83)		
right	5207340	13.00
left	5207341	12.75
1984-87 (from 9-12-83)		
right	4246774	13.00
left	4246775	13.00
Lift Gate Cylinder & Key		
1983-2 door	5207386	21.25
4 door	4132000	8.50
Sta. wagon	5207386	21.25
1984-87-2 door	4246630	36.50
4 door	4246646	12.75
Manual Window Regulator		
Front		
1983-87 (2 door)		
right	5231046	49.00
left	5231047	49.00
1983-87 (4 door)		
right	5231742	49.00
left	5231743	49.00
Rear		
1983-87-right	5200722	49.00
left	5200723	49.00

LABOR 30 HEAD AND PARKING LAMPS 30 LABOR

(Factory Time)	Chilton Time
(G) Aim Headlamps	
two	.4
four	.6
(M) Headlamp Sealed Beam Bulb, Renew	
Does not include aim headlamps.	
All models-each (.2)	.3
(M) Tail and Stop Lamp Lens, Renew	
All models (.4)	.5
(M) License Lamp Assembly, Renew	
All models (.2)	.2
(G) Side Marker Lamp Assy., Renew	
All models (.2)	.3

PARTS 30 HEAD AND PARKING LAMPS 30 PARTS

	Part No.	Price
Sealed Beam Bulb		
1983-87-Hi beam	153440	16.00
Hi & Low beam	153481	16.00
Halogen	153590	31.00
R.T. way shift	153199	16.00
Parking & Turn Signal Lamp Assy.		
(2 door)		
1983-right	5207568	13.25
left	5207569	13.25
1984-87 (exc. Shelby)		
right	5207722	13.25
left	5207723	13.25
1985-87 (Shelby)		
right	5207568	13.25
left	5207569	13.25
(4 door)		
1983-87-right	4103216	30.00
left	4103217	30.00
Tail & Stop Lamp Assy.		
Horizon		
(2 door)		
1983-right	5207674	45.50
left	5207675	45.50
1984-right	5207766	42.25
left	5207767	43.75
1985-87-right	5207788	79.50
left	5207789	79.50
(4 door)		
1983-87-right	5207648	33.50
left	5207649	33.50
Omni		
(2 door)		
1983-right	5207686	45.50
left	5207687	45.50
1984-right	5207736	43.75
left	5207737	43.75
1985-87-right	5207786	79.50
left	5207787	79.50
(4 door)		
1983-87-right	5207656	38.25
left	5207657	38.25
High Mount Stop Light Assy.		
1986-87	X135EX8	N.L.
License Lamp Assy.		
1983-87	5207516	8.50

LABOR 31 WINDSHIELD WIPER & SPEEDOMETER 31 LABOR

(Factory Time) — Chilton Time

(G) Windshield Wiper Motor, Test and Renew
1983-87 (.4) 7

(G) Rear Window Motor, Renew
1983-87 (.3) 5

(G) Windshield Wiper Switch, Renew
1983-87 (.4) 9

(G) Rear Window Wiper/Washer Switch, Renew
1983-87 (.3) 4

(G) Wiper Pivot, Renew (One)
1983-87 (.3) 5

(G) Wiper Links, Renew
1983-87 (.3) 6

(G) Windshield Washer Pump, Renew (Front or Rear)
1983-87 (.3) 4

(G) Speedometer Head, R&R or Renew
Does not include reset odometer.
1983-87 (.4) 7
Reset odometer add 2

(G) Speedometer Cable and Casing, Renew
1983
speed control to trans (.2) 6
speed control to speedo (.3) 6
trans to speedo (.4) 9
1984-87
upper (.3) 6
lower (.5) 9
one piece (.5) 9

(G) Speedometer Cable (Inner), Renew or Lubricate
1983
speed control to trans (.2) 5
speed control to speedo (.3) 5
trans to speedo (.3) 7
1984-87
upper (.3) 5
lower (.4) 8
one piece (.4) 8

(G) Intermittent Wiper Control Module, Renew
1983-87 (.2) 4

(G) Speedometer Drive Pinion, Renew
Includes: Replace oil seal.
1983-87 (.3) 4

(G) Radio, R&R
1983-87 (.3) 7

PARTS 31 WINDSHIELD WIPER & SPEEDOMETER 31 PARTS

Part No. — Price

Wiper Motor (Windshield)
1983-84 .... 4205951 106.75
1985-87 .... 4339449 106.75

Wiper Pivot
1983-87-right 5211008 14.75
left 5211009 14.75

Link w/Crank (Windshield Wiper)
1983-87-right 5211004 14.25

Link w/Bushing (Windshield Wiper)
1983-87-left 5211003 6.75

Wiper & Washer Switch (Windshield)
1983-87-exc.
below 5209863 25.25
w/interm. 4221282 34.25

Wiper Motor (Lift Gate)
1983-87 .... 4240492 106.75

Pump & Seal Pkg. (Windshield Washer)
1983-87 .... 3799090 21.50

Reservoir w/Cap (Windshield Washer)
1983 .... 5211084 18.50
1984 .... 3799791 18.25
1985-87 .... 4334190 18.25

Pump & Seal Pkg. (Lift Gate Washer)
1983-87 .... 3799462 21.25

Reservoir Pkg. (Lift Gate Washer)
1983-87 .... 5211087 14.00

Wiper & Washer Switch (Lift Gate)
1983-87 .... 5209875 6.50

Speedometer Cable & Casing
1.6L
1983 .... 4220740 14.25
1984-85 .... 4312327 13.25
1.7L
1983-37" long 4220740 14.25
41" long 4220892 13.25
2.2L
1983-upper 4220741 15.25
lower 4220742 14.75
1984-87-upper 4312328 13.25
lower 4312334 12.75

Speedometer Drive Cable
1983-87-80" long 2448294 6.50
113" long 2448295 8.75

Speedometer Assy.
(wo/Rallye Panel)
1983-wo/Clock 4051455 62.00
Clock 4051454 62.00
1984-87 .... 4051734 62.00
(w/Rallye Panel)
1983 .... 4220107 64.75
1984-87 .... 4051737 64.75

LABOR 32 LIGHT SWITCHES & WIRING 32 LABOR

(Factory Time) — Chilton Time

(G) Headlamp Switch, Renew
1983-87 (.3) 4

(G) Headlamp Dimmer Switch, Renew (Column Mounted)
1983-87 (.3) 6

(G) Stop Light Switch, Renew
1983-87 (.3) 4
w/Cruise control add (.1) 1

(G) Back Up Lamp Switch, Renew (w/Manual Trans)
1983-87 (.2) 4

(G) Neutral Safety Switch, Renew
1983-87 (.3) 4

(G) Turn Signal Switch, Renew
1983-87-std column (.5) 1.0
tilt column (.8) 1.5

(M) Turn Signal or Hazard Warning Flasher, Renew
1983-87 (.2) 3

(G) Horn Switch, Renew
1983-87 (.2) 3

(G) Horn Relay, Renew
1983-87 (.2) 3

(G) Horn, Renew
1983-87-one (.2) 4

(G) Wiring Harness, Renew
(Instrument Panel)
1983-87 (2.1) 3.4
(Body)
1983-87 (1.1) 1.8

PARTS 32 LIGHT SWITCHES & WIRING 32 PARTS

Part No. — Price

Headlamp Switch
1983-87 .... 4221223 17.25

Stoplight Switch
1983-exc. below 2926275 5.25
w/Spd. cont. 5209994 8.00
1984-87-exc.
below 2926275 5.25
Spd. cont. 4221438 15.50

Back-Up Lamp Switch
(A.T.)
1983-87 .... 4057750 8.75
(M.T.)
1983-84-exc.
below 2258404 9.50
A-412 trans 4057983 5.75
1985-87 .... 4221587 10.00

Turn Signal & Warning Switch
1983-87 .... 4221339 34.75

Hazard Warning Flasher
1983-87 .... 2932877 4.50

Turn Signal Flasher
1983-87-2 lamps 3837161 4.25
3 lamps 3837162 4.25

Horn Assy.
1983-87-Low note 2808868 24.00
Hi note 2808869 24.00

Wiring Harness
Order by model and description.

LABOR 33 GLASS 33 LABOR

	(Factory Time)	Chilton Time
(G) Windshield Glass, Renew		
Includes: Replace weatherstrip if necessary, where applicable.		
1983-87	(1.4)	2.0
(G) Front Door Glass, Renew		
1983-87		
2 DR	(.7)	1.0
4 DR	(.8)	1.1
(G) Rear Door Glass, Renew		
1983-87	(.6)	.9
(G) Stationary Door Glass, Renew		
1983-87	(.6)	1.0
(G) Quarter Window Stationary Glass, Renew		
1983-87	(1.0)	1.7
(G) Rear Window Glass, Renew		
1983-87	(.8)	1.2
w/Heated rear window add		.2

LABOR 34 CRUISE CONTROL 34 LABOR

	(Factory Time)	Chilton Time
(G) Speed Control Switch, Renew (Turn Signal Lever)		
1983-87	(.3)	.6
(G) Speed Control Servo Assy., Renew		
1983-87	(.3)	.5
(G) Speed Control Cable, Renew		
1983-87	(.4)	.7
(G) Speed Control Vacuum, Hose, Renew		
1983-87	(.2)	.3
(G) Speed Control Wiring Harness, Renew		
1983-87	(.3)	.6
(G) Speed Control Safety (Cut-Off) Switch, Renew		
1983-87	(.3)	.5

PARTS 34 CRUISE CONTROL 34 PARTS

	Part No.	Price
Speed Control Switch		
(A-412 trans.)		
1983-87	4221416	8.00
(A-460 trans.)		
1983-84	4221415	14.25
1985-87	4221696	21.75
Speed Control Servo Assy.		
1983-87	4241551	129.75
Speed Control Cables		
1983-87-1.7L	5214342	16.00
2.2L	4288054	14.50
Speed Control Vacuum Hose		
1983-87	3744933	40.50
Switch (Electronic Speed Control)		
1986-87	4342209	41.75
Module (ESC)		
1986-87	4318829	116.50
Stoplight Switch (ESC)		
1986-87	4221980	15.50
Sensor (A.T.)		
1986-87	4312032	33.50
Vacuum Motor (ESC)		
1986-87	4318819	27.50
Clutch Switch (ESC)		
1986-87	4221696	21.75

GROUP INDEX

ALPHABETICAL INDEX

Chrysler Corporation
Front Wheel Drive Cars

SUNDANCE • SHADOW

YEAR IDENTIFICATION

1987 Shadow

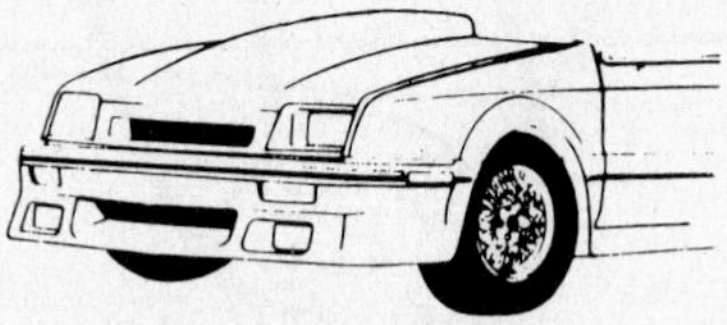

1987 Shadow D.C.

1987 Sundance

VEHICLE IDENTIFICATION NUMBER (VIN)

It is important for servicing and ordering parts to be certain of the vehicle and engine identification. The VIN (vehicle identification number) is a 13 or 17 digit number visible through the windshield on the driver's side of the dash, and contains the vehicle and engine identification codes. It can be interpreted as follows:

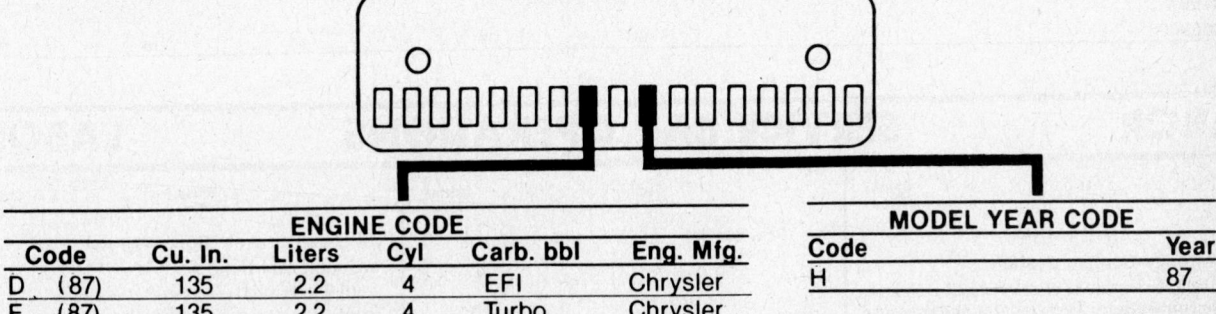

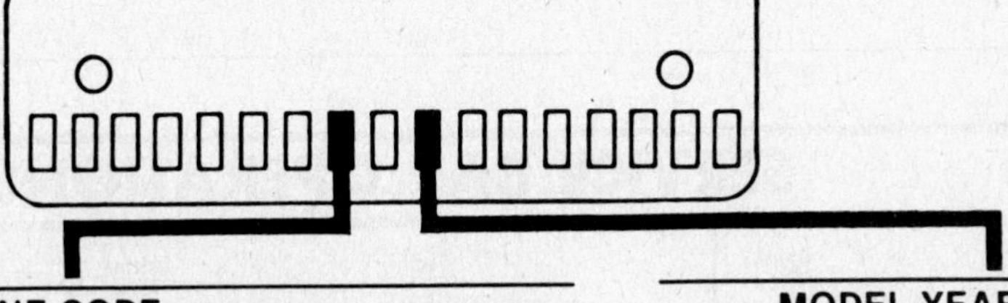

ENGINE CODE

Code	Cu. In.	Liters	Cyl	Carb. bbl	Eng. Mfg.
D (87)	135	2.2	4	EFI	Chrysler
E (87)	135	2.2	4	Turbo	Chrysler

MODEL YEAR CODE

Code	Year
H	87

The seventeen digit Vehicle Identification Number can be used to determine engine application and model year. The tenth indicates the model year, and the eighth digit identifies engine displacement.

TUNE-UP SPECIFICATIONS

Eng. V.I.N. Code	No. Cyl. Displ. Cu. In.	Eng. Mfg.	h.p.	Spark Plugs Orig. Type	Spark Plugs Gap (in.)	Ignition Timing (deg.) ▲ Man. Trans.	Ignition Timing (deg.) ▲ Auto Trans.	Intake Valve Opens (deg.)▪	Fuel Pump Pressure (psi)	Idle Speed (rpm) Man. Trans.	Idle Speed (rpm) Auto Trans.	Valve Lash (in.) Intake	Valve Lash (in.) Exhaust
D	4-135	Chrysler	99	RN12YC	.035	12B	12B	10.5	36	850	750	Hyd.	Hyd.
E	4-135	Chrysler	146	RN12YC	.035	12B	12B	10	53	950	950	Hyd.	Hyd.

NOTE: The underhood specifications sticker often reflects tune-up specification changes made in production. Sticker figures must be used if they disagree with those in this chart. Part numbers in this chart are not recommendations by Chilton for any product by brand name.

▲ See text for procedure
▪ Before top dead center
Hyd.—Hydraulic

FIRING ORDERS

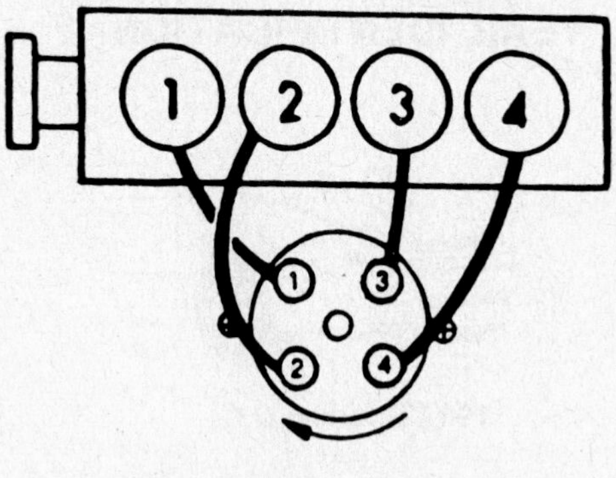

Chrysler Corp. 2.2L/2.5L
Engine Firing Order: 1-3-4-2
Distributor Rotation: Clockwise

WHEEL ALIGNMENT SPECIFICATIONS

Caster is not adjustable

Year and Model	Caster	Front Camber Range (deg.)	Front Camber Preferred	Rear Camber Range (deg.)	Rear Camber Preferred	Toe-In (inches) Front	Toe-In (inches) Rear
'87 Shadow, Sundance	1³⁄₁₆P	¼N–¾P	⁵⁄₁₆P	1¼N–¼P	½P	¹⁄₁₆	0

LABOR — SERVICE BAY OPERATIONS — LABOR

(Factory Time) Chilton Time

COOLING

(M) Winterize Cooling System
Includes: Run engine to check for leaks, tighten all hose connections. Test radiator and pressure cap, drain radiator and engine block. Add antifreeze and refill system.
All models 5

(M) Thermostat, Renew
1986-87 (.4) 6

(M) Drive Belts, Adjust
All models-one 2
each adtnl 1

(M) Drive Belt, Renew
1986-87
Fan & Alter (.2) .... *.3
Pow str (.4) 6
A.C. (.2) 3
*w/A.C. add (.1) 1

(M) Radiator Hoses, Renew
1986-87-upper (.3) 4
lower (.4) 6

BRAKES

(G) Brake Pedal Free Play, Adjust
All models 3

(G) Brakes, Adjust (Minor)
Includes: Adjust brake shoes, fill master cylinder.
two wheels 4

(G) Bleed Brakes (Four Wheels)
Includes: Add fluid.
All models (.4) 6

(G) Parking Brake, Adjust
All models (.3) 4

LUBRICATION SERVICE

(M) Lubricate Chassis, Change Oil & Filter
Includes: Inspect and correct all fluid levels.
All models 6
Install grease fittings add 1

(M) Engine Oil & Filter, Change
Includes: Inspect and correct all fluid levels.
All models 4

LABOR — SERVICE BAY OPERATIONS — LABOR

(Factory Time) Chilton Time

(M) Lubricate Chassis
Includes: Inspect and correct all fluid levels.
All models 4
Install grease fittings add 1

WHEELS

(G) Wheels, Balance
one 3
each adtnl 2

(M) Wheel, Renew
one 5

(M) Wheels, Rotate (All)
All models 5

ELECTRICAL

(G) Aim Headlamps
two 4
four 6

(M) Headlamp Sealed Beam Bulb, Renew
Does not include aim headlamps.
All models-each (.2) 3

CHILTON'S 10 POINT SAFETY CHECK

CHECK OPERATION & CONDITION OF THE FOLLOWING ITEMS:

1. Legal Registration (serial no.)
2. Tire & Wheels
3. Brake System (R&R all wheels)
4. Light Systems & Signals
5. Accelerator Linkage, Neutral Safety Switch, Shift Indicator Pointer & Seat Position Locks
6. Glass, Mirrrors, Door Locks, Seat Belts & Harness
7. Wipers, Washers & Defrosters
8. Frame, Steering, Shocks, Front & Rear Suspension
9. Fuel & Exhaust Systems
10. Road Test Vehicle

All models 1.0
Exhaust Smog Analysis, add...... .4

(Factory Time) Chilton Time

(M) License Lamp Lens, Renew
All models (.2) 2

(Factory Time) Chilton Time

(M) License Lamp Assembly, Renew
All models (.2) 3

(M) Turn Signal and Parking Lamp Assy., Renew
All models (.3) 4

(M) Tail Lamp Assembly, Renew
All models (.3) 4

(M) Side Marker Lamp Assy., Renew
All models-each (.2) 3

(M) Turn Signal or Hazard Warning Flasher, Renew
All models (.2) 3

(G) Horn Relay, Renew
All models (.2) 3

(G) Horn, Renew
All models-one (.2) 4
each adtnl 1

(M) Battery Cables, Renew
All models
positive (.5) 6
negative (.2) 2

(M) Battery Terminals, Clean
All models 3

LABOR — 1 TUNE UP 1 — LABOR

(Factory Time) Chilton Time

(G) Compression Test
Four–1986-87

(G) Engine Tune Up (Electronic Ignition)
Includes: Test battery and clean connections. Tighten manifold mounting bolts. Check engine compression, clean and adjust or renew spark plugs. Test resistance of spark plug cables. Inspect distributor cap and rotor, reluctor and pick up plate. Check vacuum advance operation. Reset ignition timing. Service air cleaner. Inspect crankcase ventilation system. Inspect and adjust drive belts. Check operation of EGR valve.
Four–1986-87 .... 1.5
w/Turbo add 5

LABOR — 2 IGNITION SYSTEM 2 — LABOR

(Factory Time) Chilton Time

(G) Spark Plugs, Clean and Reset or Renew
1986-87 (.5) 6

(G) Ignition Timing, Reset
1986-87 (.3) 4

(G) Distributor Assembly, Renew
Includes: Reset ignition timing.
1986-87 (.4) 6

(G) Distributor, R&R and Recondition
Includes: Reset ignition timing.
1986-87 (.9) 1.5

(G) Distributor Pick-Up Plate and Coil Assy., Renew (Hall Effect)
Does not require R&R of distributor.
1986-87
2.2L eng (.3) 6

(G) Distributor Cap and/or Rotor, Renew
1986-87 (.2) 4

(G) Ignition Coil, Renew
1986-87 (.2) 4

(G) Ignition Cables, Renew
1986-87 (.2) 4

(G) Ignition Switch, Renew
1986-87
std column (.4) 8
tilt columnn (.4) 9

(G) Ignition Key Warning Buzzer, Renew
1986-87 (.2) 4

(G) Ignition Switch Time Delay Relay, Renew
1986-87 (.2) 3

(G) Ignition Key Buzzer/Chime Switch, Renew
1986-87
std column (.6) 1.2
tilt column (.5) 1.0

(G) Ignition Lock Housing, Renew
1986-87-std colm (.8) 1.3
Tilt Column
console shift (1.1) 1.7

PARTS — 2 IGNITION SYSTEM 2 — PARTS

	Part No.	Price
(1) Distributor Assy.		
1986-87-exc. Turbo	5226575	N.L.
Turbo	5213525	79.75
(2) Distributor Cap		
1986-87	5226527	N.L.
(3) Rotor		
1986-87	5226535	8.25

PARTS 2 IGNITION SYSTEM 2 PARTS

	Part No.	Price
(4) Switch		
1986-87-exc. Turbo	5226616	26.50
Turbo	5226617	N.L.
Coil		
1986-87	4176009	26.75
Ignition Wires (Spark Plug)		
1986-87		
Nos. 1 & 4	5226785	3.00
Nos. 2 & 3	5226786	3.00
Ignition Switch		
1986-87		
exc. Tilt whl.	4221779	16.25
Tilt whl.	4221780	27.25
Ignition Warning Buzzer		
1986-87	4221954	10.25

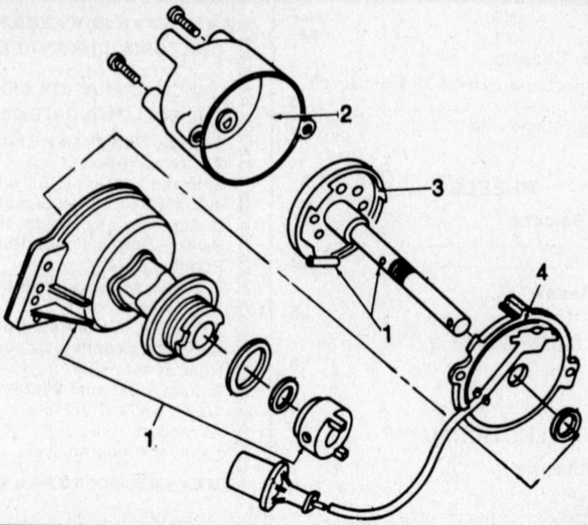

LABOR 3 FUEL SYSTEM 3 LABOR

(Factory Time)	Chilton Time
ELECTRONIC FUEL INJECTION	
(G) Throttle Body, Renew	
1986-87 (.5)	.9
(G) Fuel Pressure Regulator, Renew	
1986-87 (.2)	4
(G) Fuel Pump, Renew	
1986-87 (.6)	.9
(G) Fuel Pump Relay, Renew	
1986-87 (.3)	..4
(G) Fuel Inlet Chamber, Renew	
1986-87 (.4)	.7
(G) Automatic Idle Speed Assy., Renew	
1986-87	
motor (.3)	.5
adapter (.3)	.5
(G) Fuel Injector Rail, Renew	
1986-87 (.6)	1.0
(G) Fuel Injector, Renew	
1986-87	
wo/Turbo (.3)	.5
w/Turbo	
one (.4)	.6
each adtnl (.1)	.2
(G) Throttle Body Temperature Sensor, Renew	
1986-87 (.2)	.3
(G) Logic Module, Renew	
1986-87 (.2)	.3
(G) Power Module, Renew	
1986-87 (.3)	.4
(G) M.A.P. Sensor, Renew	
1986-87 (.4)	.6
(G) Throttle Position Sensor (Potentiometer), Renew	
1986-87 (.2)	.3
(G) Fuel Tank, Renew	
1986-87 (1.2)	1.6
(G) Fuel Gauge (Tank Unit), Renew	
1986-87 (.7)	1.0
(G) Fuel Gauge (Dash Unit), Renew	
1986-87 (.3)	.6
(G) Intake Manifold, Renew	
1986-87	
2.2L eng (2.0)	3.7
w/Turbo add (.6)	.6
(G) Intake and Exhaust Manifold Gaskets, Renew	
1986-87	
2.2L eng (1.9)	3.5
w/Turbo add (.6)	.6
w/P.S. add (.4)	.4
TURBOCHARGER	
(G) Turbocharger Assy., Renew	
1986-87 (2.2)	3.5
(G) Fuel Pressure Regulator, Renew	
1986-87 (.3)	.5
(G) Vehicle Speed Sensor, Renew	
1986-87 (.3)	.6
(G) Change Temperature Sensor, Renew	
1986-87 (.2)	.4
(G) Fuel Pump, Renew (In Tank)	
1986-87 (1.0)	1.6
(G) Throttle Body, Renew	
1986-87 (.5)	.9

PARTS 3 TURBOCHARGER SYSTEM 3 PARTS

	Part No.	Price
(1) E.G.R. Valve		
Order by number stamped on the valve.		
(2) Elbow (Compressor Inlet)		
1986-87	4105461	30.50
(3) Gasket (Inlet Elbow)		
1986-87	4227973	.50
(4) Turbocharger Assy.		
1986-87	4105800	567.00
(5) Oxygen Sensor		
1986-87	4301346	36.75
(6) Hose Connector		
1986-87	4323444	6.00
(7) Strap (Vane Hose)		
1986-87	4105719	2.00
(8) Vane (Air Flow)		
1986-87	4105465	3.00

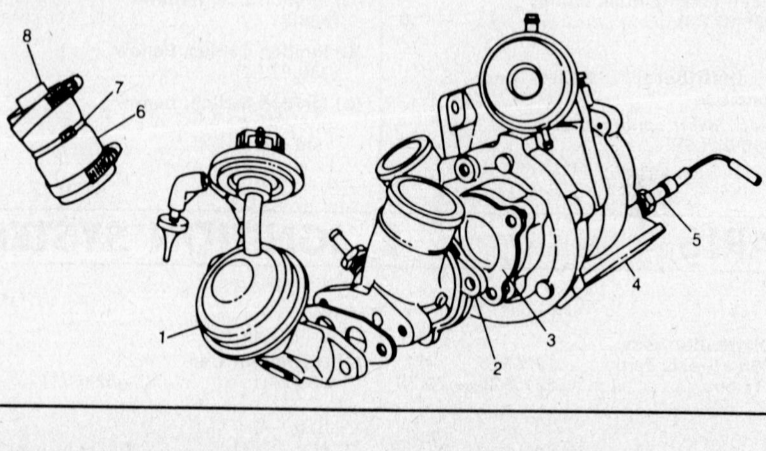

PARTS 3 ELECTRONIC FUEL INJECTION 3 PARTS

	Part No.	Price
Throttle Body Assy.		
1986-87-exc. Turbo	4300265	290.00
Turbo	4307255	325.00
Fuel Pump Assy.		
1986-87		
exc. Turbo	4075445	36.00
Turbo	4279917	217.00
Power Module		
1986-87-exc. Turbo	5226765	105.00
Turbo	5226766	105.00
(1) Fitting Kit (Hose)		
1986-87	4300252	6.75
(2) Injector (w/o O-rings)		
1986-87	4300257	53.55
(Nos. 3 & 4 not listed.)		
(5) Potentiometer (Kit)		
1986-87-Turbo	4179849	32.00
Throttle Position Sensor		
1986-87-exc. Turbo	5226509	29.00
(No. 6 not listed.)		
(7) Regulator Kit		
1986-87	4300263	60.00
AIS Motor (w/o O-ring)		
1986-87	4300264	N.L.
Fuel Injectors (Turbo)		
1986-87	4306024	53.75
Regulator (Fuel Pressure-Turbo)		
1986-87	4275313	53.75

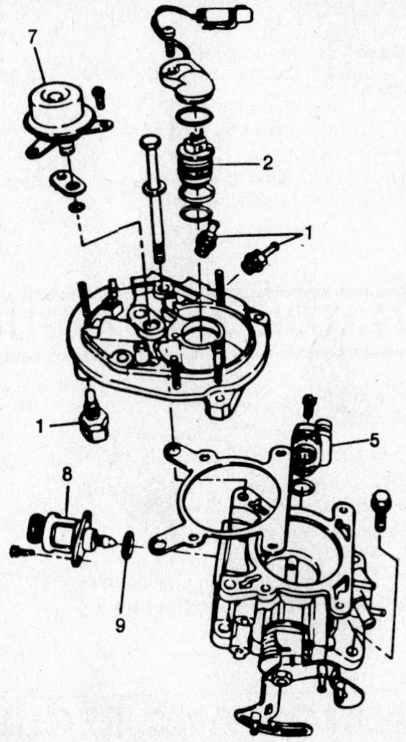

	Part No.	Price
Fuel Rail (Turbo)		
1986-87	4275555	39.25
Air Cleaner Element		
1986-87-exc. Turbo	4288009	9.00
Turbo	4306113	N.L.
Fuel Tank		
1986-87	4279603	140.00
Fuel Tank Sending Unit		
1986-87		
exc. Turbo	4203774	N.L.
Turbo	4501663	N.L.
Fuel Pump Relay (Turbo)		
1986-87	4221279	13.75
Detonation Sensor		
1986-87-exc. Turbo	5213629	23.75
Turbo	4318118	23.75
Temperature Sensor		
1986-87	4330251	52.50
M.A.P. Sensor		
1986-87-exc. Turbo	4419315	51.00
Turbo	4419316	54.75
Logic Module		
1986-87		
exc. Turbo		
A.T.	5227160	N.L.
M.T.	5227400	140.00
Turbo		
A.T.	5227255	140.00
M.T.	5227371	140.00

LABOR 3A EMISSION CONTROLS 3A LABOR

(Factory Time)	Chilton Time
CRANKCASE EMISSION	
(M) Crankcase Vent Valve, Renew	
All models (.2)	.3
AIR INJECTION SYSTEM	
(G) Injection Tube and Aspirator Valve Assy., Renew	
1986-87	
2.2L eng-to conv (.5)	.8
(G) Pulse Air Feeder/Aspirator Tube, Renew	
1986-87 (.4)	.7
(G) Aspirator Valve, Renew	
1986-87 (.3)	.5
EVAPORATIVE EMISSION	
(M) Vapor Canister, Renew	
All models (.3)	.4
E.G.R. SYSTEM	
(G) Exhaust Gas Recirculation Control Valve, Renew	
1986-87	
2.2L eng (.6)	.8
w/Turbo add (.1)	.2
(G) Change Temperature Sensor, Renew	
1986-87 (.2)	.3

CHILTON'S EMISSION CONTROL TUNE-UP

1. Clean or renew P.C.V. valve, hoses and filter
2. Check fuel tank cap for sealing ability
3. Check fuel tank and fuel lines for leakage
4. Check evaporation canister and filter. Replace if necessary
5. Check engine compression to determine leakage of unburned gases. (Add time for items of interference
6. Test and clean or renew spark plugs
7. Check engine oil dipstick for sealing ability
8. Test exhaust system with analyzer and check system for leakage
9. Check exhaust manifold heat valve for operation
10. Adjust ignition timing and carburetor idle speed and mixture
11. Check automatic choke mechanism for free operation
12. Inspect air cleaner and element
13. On models so equipped test distributor vacuum control switch and transmission control switch

All models
Four **1.2**
For repairs made charge accordingly

(Factory Time)	Chilton Time
(G) E.G.R. Back Pressure Valve, Renew	
1986-87 (.2)	.3
(G) E.G.R. and Purge Control Solenoid Bank, Renew	
1986-87 (.2)	.3
EFE SYSTEM	
(G) Oxygen Sensor, Renew	
1986-87 (.2)	.4

(Factory Time)	Chilton Time
(G) Detonation Sensor, Renew	
1986-87 (.2)	.4
HEATED INLET AIR SYSTEM	
(M) Air Cleaner, Service	
All models	.3
(G) Heated Air Door Sensor, Renew	
1986-87 (.2)	.3

PARTS 3A EMISSION CONTROLS 3A PARTS

	Part No.	Price
CRANKCASE EMISSION SYSTEM		
Crankcase Vent Valve		
1986-87-exc. Turbo	4343766	7.00
Turbo	3671076	4.25

	Part No.	Price
AIR INJECTION SYSTEM		
Aspirator Valve		
1986-87	4300376	19.50

	Part No.	Price
Silencer		
1986-87	4300382	4.50

PARTS 3A EMISSION CONTROLS 3A PARTS

	Part No.	Price
Tube (Air Cleaner to Silencer)		
1986-87	4300381	2.75
Tube (Silencer to Aspirator)		
1986-87	4300383	6.00
EVAPORATIVE EMISSION SYSTEM		
Vapor Canister		
1986-87	4241838	52.75
Vacuum Solenoid		
1986-87-exc. Turbo	5227169	20.50
Quad Vacuum Solenoid		
1986-87-Turbo	5226352	57.00

E.G.R. SYSTEM

E.G.R. Valve
Order by number stamped on valve. Transducer valve is serviced with the E.G.R. valve.

	Part No.	Price
Check Valve		
1986-87	4306923	1.50
EFE SYSTEM		
Oxygen Sensor		
1986-87-exc. Turbo	4301375	40.00
Turbo	4301346	36.75
Detonation Sensor		
1986-87-exc. Turbo	5213629	23.75
Turbo	4318118	23.75
Sensor (Air Cleaner Temp.)		
1986-87-exc. Turbo	4342765	7.00

LABOR 4 ALTERNATOR AND REGULATOR 4 LABOR

(Factory Time)	Chilton Time
(G) Alternator Circuits, Test	
Includes: Test battery, regulator and alternator output.	
All models	.6
(M) Alternator Drive Belt, Renew	
1986-87 (.2)	.3
w/A.C. add (.1)	.1
(G) Alternator Assembly, Renew	
Includes: Transfer pulley if required.	
1986-87 (.8)	1.2
w/A.C. add (.3)	.3
Add circuit test if performed.	
(G) Alternator, R&R and Recondition	
Includes: Test and disassemble.	
1986-87 (1.5)	2.1
w/A.C. add (.3)	.3
(G) Alternator Front Bearing or Retainer, Renew	
1986-87 (.8)	1.1
w/A.C. add (.3)	.3
Renew rear brg add	.2
(G) Voltage Regulator, Test and Renew	
1986-87	
internal type (1.0)	1.6
w/A.C. add (.3)	.3
(G) Gauge Alert Module, Renew	
1986-87 (.7)	1.1

PARTS 4 ALTERNATOR AND REGULATOR 4 PARTS

	Part No.	Price
Alternator Assy. (90 amp.)		
1986-87	4339440	154.50
(1) Drive End Shield		
1986-87	5226840	39.50
(2) Drive End Bearing		
1986-87	3656444	8.75
(3) Rotor Assy.		
1986-87	5226841	102.25
(4) Stator		
1986-87	5226315	151.00
Rectifier		
1986-87	5226096	61.75
Terminal Parts Kit		
1986-87	5226020	8.25
Brush Holder		
1986-87	5226084	6.75
Voltage Regulator		
1986-87	4379100	29.00

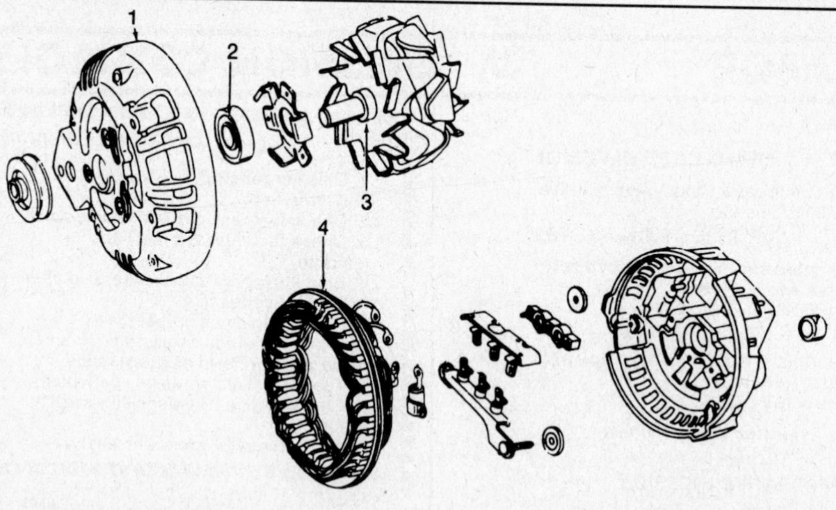

LABOR 5 STARTING SYSTEM 5 LABOR

(Factory Time)	Chilton Time
(G) Starter Draw Test (On Car)	
All models	.3
(G) Starter Assy., Renew	
Includes: Test starter relay, starter solenoid and amperage draw.	
1986-87 (1.0)	1.3
w/Turbo add (.5)	.5
(G) Starter, R&R and Recondition	
Includes: Turn down armature.	
1986-87	2.8
w/Turbo add (.5)	.5
Renew field coils add (.5)	.5
(G) Starter Drive, Renew	
Includes: R&R starter.	
1986-87 (1.4)	1.8
w/Turbo add (.5)	.5
(G) Starter Solenoid, Renew	
Includes: R&R starter.	
1986-87 (1.0)	1.4
w/Turbo add (.5)	.5
Starter Relay, Renew	
1986-87 (.2)	.3
(G) Neutral Start and Back-Up Lamp Switch, Renew	
1986-87 (.3)	.4
(G) Ignition Switch, Renew	
1986-87	
std colm (.4)	.8
tilt colm (.4)	.9
(M) Battery Cables, Renew	
1986-87	
positive (.5)	.6
negative (.2)	.2
(M) Battery Terminals, Clean	
All models	.3

PARTS 5 STARTING SYSTEM 5 PARTS

	Part No.	Price
Starter Assy.		
1986-87	4339472	148.75
(1) Drive End Housing		
1986-87	5213382	42.75
(2) Clutch Starter Drive		
1986-87	5213384	35.25
(3) Armature		
1986-87	5213383	78.50
(4) Solenoid		
1986-87	5206607	57.25
(5) Field Frame		
1986-87	5213385	69.00
(6) Brush Holder		
1986-87	5206605	21.75
(7) Head End		
1986-87	5206606	27.00
Neutral Safety Switch		
1986-87	4057750	8.75

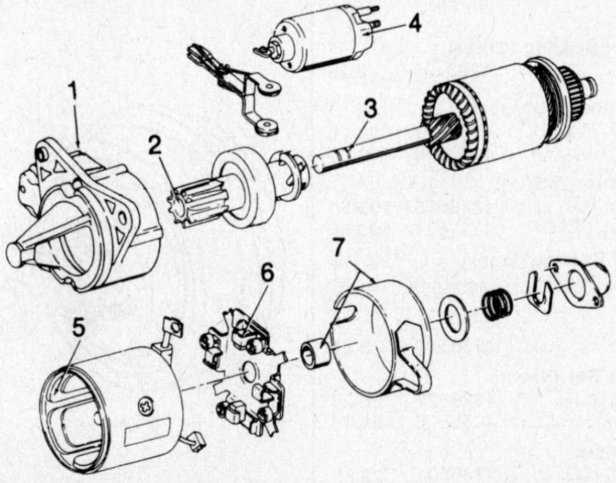

LABOR 6 BRAKE SYSTEM 6 LABOR

(Factory Time) — Chilton Time

(G) Brake Pedal Free Play, Adjust
All models 3

(G) Brakes, Adjust (Minor)
two wheels 4

(G) Bleed Brakes (Four Wheels)
Includes: Add fluid.
All models (.4) 6

(G) Brake Shoes and/or Pads, Renew
Includes: Install new or exchange brake shoes or pads. Adjust service and hand brake. Bleed system.
1986-87-front-disc (.5) 8
rear-drum (.8) 1.5
all four wheels (1.3) 2.2
Resurface disc rotor, add-each 9
Resurface brake drum, add-each 5

(G) Rear Brake Drum, Renew (One)
1986-87 (.5) 6

BRAKE HYDRAULIC SYSTEM

(G) Wheel Cylinder, Renew
Includes: Bleed system.
1986-87-one (.7) 1.1
both (1.3) 2.1

(G) Wheel Cylinder, R&R and Rebuild
Includes: Hone cylinder and bleed system.
1986-87-one 1.2
both 2.3

(G) Brake Hose, Renew (Flex)
Includes: Bleed system.
1986-87-front-one (.4) 8
rear-one (.4) 8

(G) Master Cylinder, Renew
Includes: Bleed complete system.
1986-87 (.5) 9

(G) Master Cylinder, R&R and Rebuild
Includes: Bleed complete system.
1986-87 .... 1.6

COMBINATIONS

Add to Brakes, Renew

See Machine Shop Operations

(Factory Time) — Chilton Time

(G) RENEW WHEEL CYLINDER
Each 3

(G) REBUILD WHEEL CYLINDER
Each 4

(G) REBUILD CALIPER ASSEMBLY
Each 5

(G) RENEW MASTER CYLINDER
All models 6

(G) REBUILD MASTER CYLINDER
All models 8

(G) RENEW BRAKE HOSE
Each 3

(G) RENEW REAR WHEEL GREASE SEALS
One side 3

(G) RENEW DISC BRAKE ROTOR
Each 2

(G) RENEW BRAKE DRUM
Each 3

(G) DISC BRAKE ROTOR STUDS, RENEW
Each 1

(Factory Time) — Chilton Time

(G) Master Cylinder Reservoir, Renew
Includes: Bleed complete system.
1986-87 (.6) 1.0

(G) Brake System, Flush and Refill
All models 1.2

POWER BRAKES

(G) Brake Booster Assembly, Renew
1986-87 (1.3) 1.6

(Factory Time) — Chilton Time

(G) Brake Booster Check Valve, Renew
1986-87 (.2) 2

DISC BRAKES

(G) Disc Brake Pads, Renew
Includes: Install new disc brake pads only.
1986-87 (.5) 8

(G) Disc Brake Rotor, Renew
1986-87-one (.3) 6

(G) Disc Brake Rotor and Hub, Renew
1986-87-one (1.0) 1.4

(G) Caliper Assembly, Renew
Includes: Bleed system.
1986-87-one (.5) 9
both 1.7

(G) Caliper Assy., R&R and Recondition
Includes: Bleed system.
1986-87-one (.8) 1.4
both 2.7

(G) Brake System Combination Valve, Renew
Includes: Bleed complete system.
1986-87 (1.2) 1.5

PARKING BRAKE

(G) Parking Brake, Adjust
All models (.3) 4

(G) Parking Brake Warning Lamp Switch, Renew
1986-87 (.2) 3

(G) Parking Brake Control, Renew
1986-87 (.5) 7

(G) Parking Brake Cables, Renew
1986-87
assy (1.0) 1.5

PARTS 6 BRAKE SYSTEM 6 PARTS

	Part No.	Price
(1) Rear Wheel Bearing (Outer)		
1986-87	4293196	9.25
(2) Hub and Drum (4 Stud)		
1986-87-exc. H.D.	4238531	89.75
H.D.	4238538	100.50
(2) Hub and Drum (5 Stud)		
1986-87-exc. H.D.	4313635	100.50
H.D.	4313634	100.50
(3) Rear Wheel Bearing (Inner)		
1986-87	4238567	N.L.
(4) Dust Seal		
1986-87	4238570	3.50
(5) Brake Shoe Set (Rear)		
1986-87-exc. H.D.	4238827	36.25
H.D.	4238826	39.75
(6) Wheel Cylinder		
1986-87-exc. H.D.	4238701	22.50
H.D.	4238706	22.50

The following part numbers are for pricing reference only.

	Part No.	Price
Master Cylinder		
1986-87	4294268	80.00
Reservoir (Master Cylinder)		
1986-87	4294495	N.L.
Mounting Grommets (Reservoir)		
1986-87	5204149	1.00
Proportioning Valve		
1986-87-exc. H.D.	4238588	35.75
H.D.	4313054	28.50

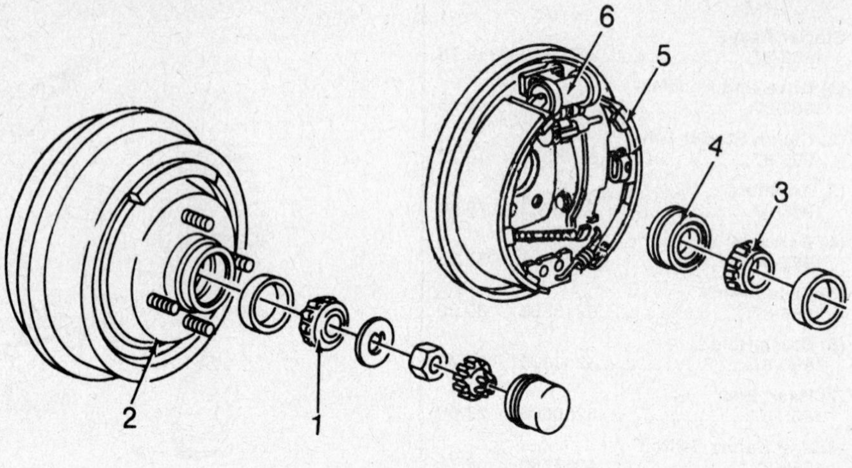

	Part No.	Price
Power Brake Booster		
1986-87-M.T.	4364773	169.00
A.T.	4342709	218.25
Booster Check Valve		
1986-87	4271382	8.50

PARKING BRAKE

The following part numbers are for pricing reference only.

	Part No.	Price
Front Cable		
1986-87	3766435	14.75
Intermediate Cable		
1986-87	4294172	24.75
Rear Cable		
1986-87	4318708	24.75
Parking Brake Assy.		
1986-87	4294136	40.00

PARTS 6 DISC BRAKES 6 PARTS

The following part numbers are for pricing reference only.

	Part No.	Price
(1) Pin Pkg.		
1986-87-exc. H.D.	4267330	9.00
H.D.	4267329	12.25
(2) Bushing Pkg.		
1986-87-exc. H.D.	4267331	3.00
H.D.	4205982	1.75
(3) Inner Brake Pads		
Refer to (10) Brake Pad Set		
(4) Disc Rotor		
1986-87-4 stud	4313593	56.00
5 stud	4313633	56.00
(5) Hub		
1986-87-4 stud	5212545	60.00
5 stud	5212770	60.00
(6) Retainer		
1986-87	5212980	3.00
(7) Gasket		
1986-87	5212559	.50
(8) Bearing		
1986-87	4397498	42.25
(9) Seal		
1986-87	5212535	3.50
(10) Brake Pad Set		
1986-87-exc. H.D.		
w/o Sensor	4313238	72.25
w/Sensor	4313642	N.L.
H.D.	4313429	72.25
(11) Sensor		
Included with pad (10).		

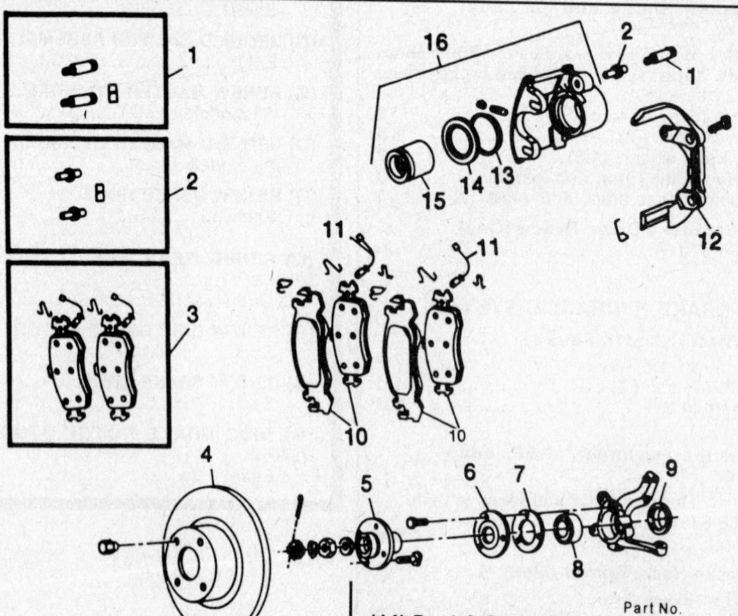

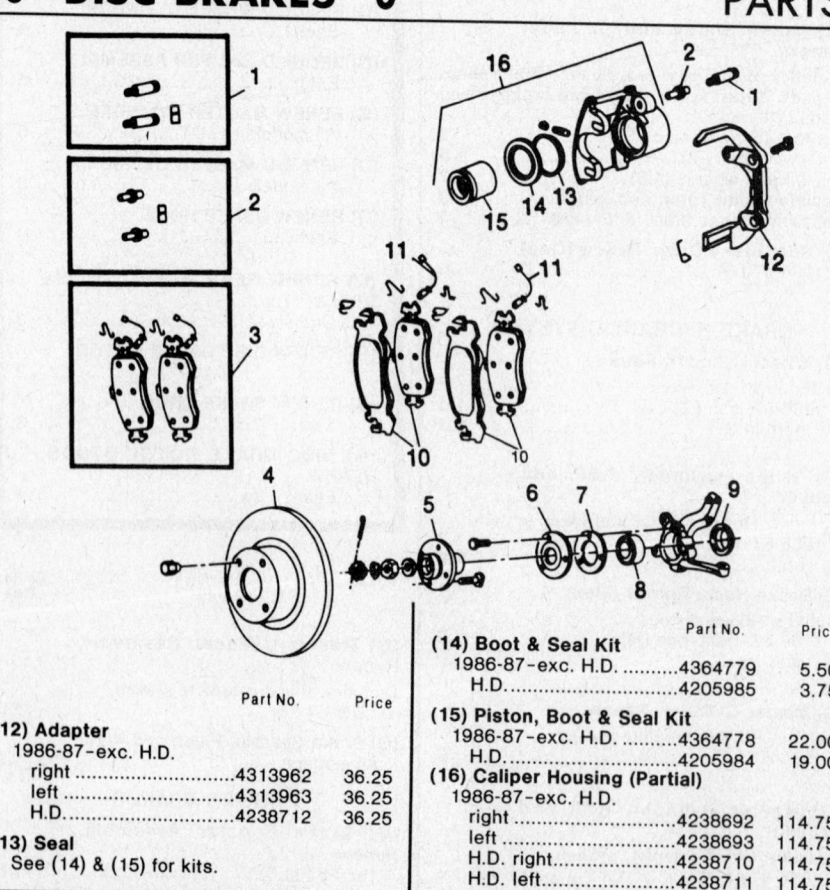

	Part No.	Price
(12) Adapter		
1986-87-exc. H.D.		
right	4313962	36.25
left	4313963	36.25
H.D.	4238712	36.25
(13) Seal		
See (14) & (15) for kits.		

	Part No.	Price
(14) Boot & Seal Kit		
1986-87-exc. H.D.	4364779	5.50
H.D.	4205985	3.75
(15) Piston, Boot & Seal Kit		
1986-87-exc. H.D.	4364778	22.00
H.D.	4205984	19.00
(16) Caliper Housing (Partial)		
1986-87-exc. H.D.		
right	4238692	114.75
left	4238693	114.75
H.D. right	4238710	114.75
H.D. left	4238711	114.75

LABOR 7 COOLING SYSTEM 7 LABOR

(Factory Time) Chilton Time

(M) Winterize Cooling System

Includes: Run engine to check for leaks, tighten all hose connections. Test radiator and pressure cap. Drain radiator and engine block. Add antifreeze and refill system.

All models 5

(M) Thermostat, Renew
1986-87 (.4) 6

(M) Radiator Assembly, R&R or Renew
1986-87 (.5) 9
w/A.T. add (.1) 1

ADD THESE OPERATIONS TO RADIATOR R&R

(G) Boil & Repair 1.5
(G) Rod Clean 1.9
(G) Repair Core 1.3
(G) Renew Tank 1.6
(G) Renew Trans. Oil Cooler 1.9
(G) Recore Radiator 1.7

(M) Fan Blades, Renew
1986-87 (.2) 5

(G) Drive Belts, Renew
1986-87
Fan & Alter (.2) .... *.3
Pow str (.4) 6
A.C. (.2) 3
*w/A.C. add (.1) 1

(M) Drive Belts, Adjust
All models-one 2
each adtnl 1

(M) Radiator Hoses, Renew
1986-87-upper (.3) 4
lower (.4) 6

(G) Water Pump, Renew
1986-87 (1.0) 1.6
w/A.C. add 5

(G) Radiator Fan Motor, Renew
1986-87-wo/A.C. (.4) 5
w/A.C. (.4) 5

(G) Radiator Fan Switch, Renew
1986-87 (.3) 6

(G) Radiator Fan Motor Relay, Renew
1986-87 (.2) 3

COOLING SYSTEM TUNE-UP

An Annual Cooling System Tune-up Suggestion List should include (with some exceptions):
1. A visual check of the cooling system for indications of leaks or excessive oil content
2. Pressure check the cooling system for internal and external leaks with filler cap and neck adapter and tester
3. Check crankcase and automatic transmission oil for water content
4. Test coolant thermostat with radiator thermometer
5. Check temperature gauge for accuracy
6. Drain system and flush till clean
7. Clean foreign matter from radiator fins
8. Test radiator pressure cap with cap tester
9. Check fan blades and pulleys for alignment and damage
10. Internal and external inspection of all hoses for cracks and deterioration
11. Check core plugs (where possible) for seepage
12. Refill system with correct coolant and check for air locks
13. Check condition and tension of drive belts with tension gauge

All models 1.5

(Factory Time) Chilton Time

(G) Water Jacket Expansion Plugs, Renew (Cylinder Block)
1986-87
2.2L eng
left side
front (.7) 1.0
rear (.4) 6
right side
front or center (.6) 9
rear (1.0) 1.4
w/P.S. add (.3) 3

(G) Water Jacket Expansion Plugs, Renew (Cylinder Head)
2.2L eng
front (.6) 9
rear (.8) 1.1

(G) Temperature Gauge (Dash Unit), Renew
1986-87 (.3) 5

(G) Temperature Gauge (Engine Unit), Renew
1986-87
sending unit (.3) 4
light switch (.3) 4

(G) Heater Hoses, Renew
1986-87-one (.4) 4
each adtnl (.1) 2

(Factory Time) Chilton Time

(G) Heater Water Valve, Renew
1986-87-w/A.C. (.3) 5

(G) Heater Control Assembly, Renew
1986-87-wo/A.C. (.4) 7
w/A.C. (.3) 6

(G) Vacuum Switch (Push Button), Renew
1986-87-w/A.C. (.5) 9

(G) Blower Motor Switch, Renew
1986-87-wo/A.C. (.5) 8
w/A.C. (.4) 7

(G) Heater Core, R&R or Renew
1986-87-wo/A.C. (1.0) 1.7
w/A.C. (2.4) *5.5
*Includes recharge A.C. system.

ADD THESE OPERATIONS TO HEATER CORE R&R

(G) Boil & Repair 1.2
(G) Repair Core 9
(G) Recore 1.2

(G) Heater Blower Motor, Renew
1986-87-wo/A.C. (.4) 6
w/A.C. (.6) 1.2

(G) Blower Motor Resistor, Renew
1986-87-wo/A.C. (.2) 3
w/A.C. (.3) 4

PARTS 7 COOLING SYSTEM 7 PARTS

Part No. Price

The following part numbers are for pricing reference only.

(1) Radiator Assy.
Order by year and model.

(2) Radiator Hose (Upper)
1986-87-exc.
Silicone 4266696 6.25
Silicone .... 4266692 N.L.

(3) Radiator Hose (Lower)
1986-87-exc.
Silicone 4266697 13.75
Silicone 4266954 38.75

(4) Radiator Fan
Order by number stamped on assy.
1986-87-w/o A.C. 4266069 16.75
A.C. 4266282 17.75

(5) Motor (Radiator Fan)
1986-87-w/o A.C. 4240493 83.00
w/A.C. 4240494 83.00

Water Pump
1986-87 .... 4293898 48.00

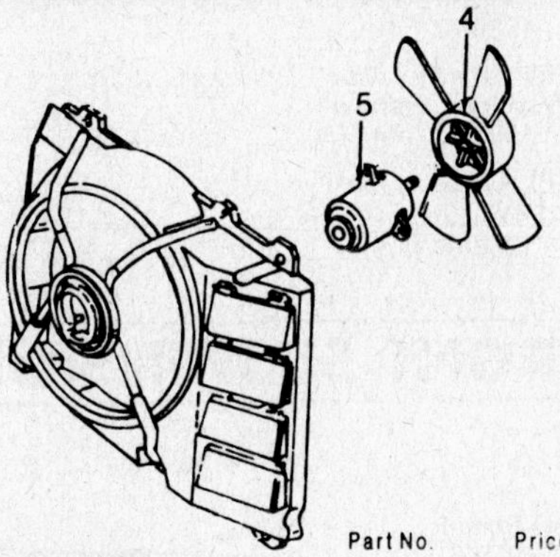

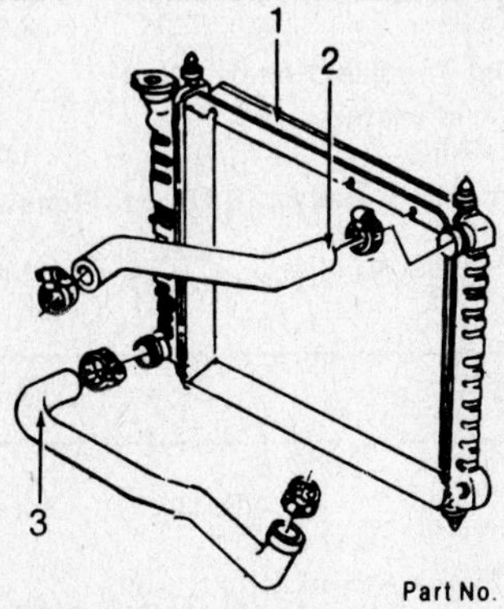

Part No. Price

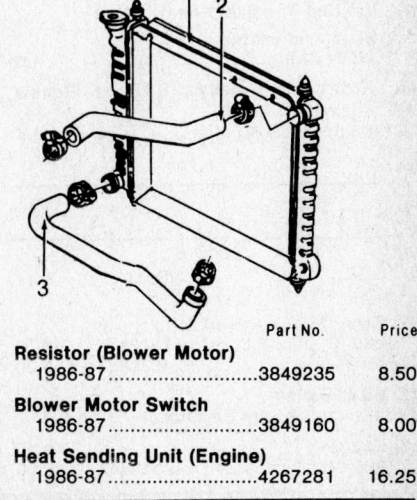

By-Pass Hose
1986-87 .... 4273488 1.75

Heater Core
1986-87 .... 3847943 90.75

Blower Motor Assy.
1986-87 .... 3849266 59.00

Part No. Price

Resistor (Blower Motor)
1986-87 .... 3849235 8.50

Blower Motor Switch
1986-87 .... 3849160 8.00

Heat Sending Unit (Engine)
1986-87 .... 4267281 16.25

LABOR 8 EXHAUST SYSTEM 8 LABOR

	(Factory Time)	Chilton Time
(G) Muffler, Renew		
1986-87	(.4)	.7
Cut exhaust pipe add	(.2)	.2
(G) Exhaust Pipe, Renew		
1986-87	(.7)	1.1
Cut at muffler add	(.2)	.2
(G) Exhaust Pipe Extension, Renew		
1986-87	(.6)	1.0
(G) Catalytic Converter, Renew		
1986-87		
exh pipe mount	(.7)	.9
(G) Exhaust Manifold or Gasket, Renew		
1986-87		
2.2L eng	(2.7)	3.7
w/Turbo add	(.6)	.6
COMBINATIONS		
(G) Exhaust System, Renew (Complete)		
1986-87		1.5

PARTS 8 EXHAUST SYSTEM 8 PARTS

System part numbers shown are for pricing reference only.

	Part No.	Price
Front Converter (w/Pipes)		
1986-87-Calif.	4301658	255.75
exc. Calif.	4301657	255.75
Pipe Exhaust Extension		
1986-87	4301453	36.25
Canada	4301492	N.L.
Rear Converter (w/Pipes)		
1986-87	4301460	244.50
Muffler & Tailpipe		
1986-87-exc. Turbo	4301653	56.50
Turbo	4301655	115.50

LABOR 9 FRONT SUSPENSION 9 LABOR

Note: On all front suspension operations alignment charges must be added if performed. Time given does not include alignment.

	(Factory Time)	Chilton Time
(M) Wheel, Renew		
one		.5
(M) Wheels, Rotate (All)		
All models		.5
(G) Wheels, Balance		
one		.3
each adtnl		.2
(G) Check Alignment of Front End		
All models		.5
Note: Deduct if alignment is performed.		
(G) Toe-Out, Adjust		
All models		.6
(G) Align Front End		
Includes: Adjust camber, toe, car height and center steering wheel.		
All models	(.8)	1.4
(G) Steering Knuckle Bearing, Renew (Wheel Bearing)		
Add alignment charges.		
1986-87-one	(1.2)	1.6
both	(2.3)	3.0
(G) Steering Knuckle, Renew (One)		
Add alignment charges.		
1986-87	(1.0)	1.6
(G) Front Strut Assy., R&R or Renew		
Add alignment charges.		
1986-87-one	(.8)	1.4
both	(1.5)	2.7
(G) Front Suspension Strut Mount Assy., Renew		
Includes: Renew bearing.		
1986-87	(.8)	1.5
(G) Lower Control Arm Assy., Renew		
Includes: Reset toe-in.		
1986-87-one	(1.1)	1.6
(G) Lower Control Arm Strut Bushings, Renew		
Add alignment charges.		
1986-87-one side	(.6)	.9
(G) Lower Ball Joint, Renew (One)		
Add alignment charges.		
1986-87	(.8)	1.2
(G) Front Coil Spring or Strut Bearing, Renew		
Includes: R&R front strut.		
Add alignment charges.		
1986-87-one	(.8)	1.5
both	(1.5)	2.8
(G) Front Sway Bar, Renew		
1986-87	(.4)	.7
(G) Sway Bar Bracket and Bushings, Renew		
1986-87-both	(.5)	.9
(P) K-Frame, Renew		
Add alignment charges.		
1986-87	(2.5)	4.0
(G) Drive Shaft Boot, Renew		
Includes: Clean and lubricate C/V joint.		
1986-87		
one-inner or outer	(.7)	1.0
both-one side	(1.0)	1.4
Renew shaft seal, add		
right side	(.1)	.1
left side	(.3)	.3
(G) Drive Shaft C/V Joint, Renew		
1986-87		
one-inner or outer	(.7)	1.0
both-one side	(1.0)	1.4
inter shaft U-joint	(.6)	1.0
Renew shaft seal, add		
right side	(.1)	.1
left side	(.3)	.3
(G) Front Wheel Drive Shaft Assy., Renew		
1986-87		
inter spline yoke	(.6)	1.0
inter stub shaft	(.6)	1.0
all others-each	(1.0)	1.4
Renew shaft seal, add		
right side	(.1)	.1
left side	(.3)	.3
(G) Intermediate Shaft Support Bearing, Renew		
1986-87-each	(.6)	1.0
(G) Drive Shaft Oil Seals, Renew		
1986-87		
right side	(.5)	.8
left side	(.7)	1.1

PARTS 9 FRONT SUSPENSION 9 PARTS

	Part No.	Price
(1) Strut (Shock Absorber)		
1986-87-exc. H.D.	4322641	40.00
H.D.	4322881	50.00
(2) Strut Spring		
Order by model and description.		
(3) Spacer		
1986-87	4014441	5.00
(4) Shield		
1986-87	4322704	1.50
(5) Bumper		
1986-87	4322610	N.L.
(6) Seat Assy.		
1986-87	4322678	4.75
(7) Bearing Assy.		
1986-87	5204595	4.50
Spacer		
1986-87	5204615	.75
Mount Assy.		
1986-87	4322601	N.L.

PARTS 9 FRONT SUSPENSION 9 PARTS

	Part No.	Price
(8) Knuckle Assy.		
Part number shown for pricing reference only.		
R.H. (86-87)	4052838	89.75
L.H. (86-87)	4052839	89.75
(9) Ball Joint		
1986-87	4364782	37.25
(10) Bushing		
1986-87	4322285	2.00
(11) Bushing		
1986-87-exc. H.D.	5204622	8.00
H.D.	4052646	8.00
(12) Sway Bar		
1986-87	4322014	81.25
(13) Bushing		
1986-87-exc. H.D.	4322017	3.25
H.D.	4352613	N.L.
(14) Bushing		
1986-87	4322751	3.75
(15) Lower Control Arm Assy.		
1986-87-R.H.	4322154	92.75
L.H.	4322155	92.75

Part numbers shown are for pricing reference only. Order by year model and type.

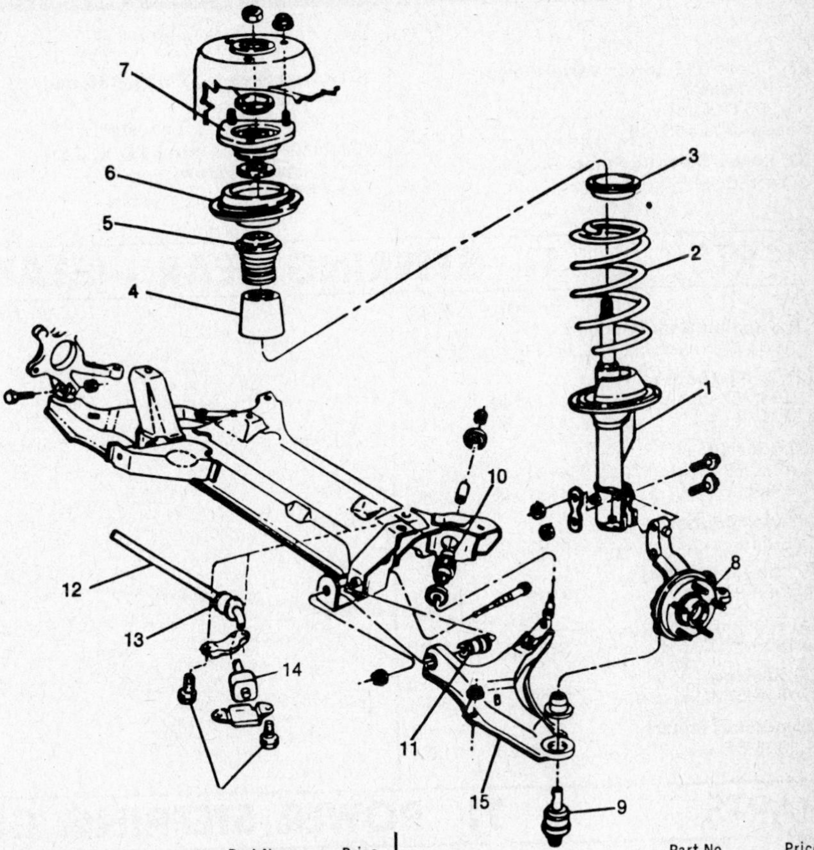

	Part No.	Price
Driveshaft		
1.6L		
1983-Right	5212676	137.50
Left	5212677	76.00
1984-87-Right	5212862	137.50
Left	5212863	76.00
1.7L		
1983-Right	5212646	137.50
Left	5212647	72.50
2.2L, 2.5L & 2.6L		
Horizon, Omni, 024, TC3, Turismo, Charger		
(G.K.N.)		
1983-Right	5212660	137.50
Left	5212661	76.00
1984-87-Right	5212862	137.50
Left	5212863	76.00
1986-87-H/P		
Right	5212862	137.50
Left	5212933	76.00
(Citroen)		
1985-wo/Turbo		
Right	5212766	85.00
Left	5212765	52.25
Turbo	5212765	52.25
1986-87-Right	5212766	85.00
Left	5212935	52.25
Turbo	5212935	52.25
Exc. Horizon, Omni, TC3, 024, Turismo, Charger		
(G.K.N.)		
1983-Right	5212662	137.50
Left	5212663	76.00
1984-87-Right	5212872	123.00
Left	5212913	76.00
(Citroen)		
1983-Right	5212744	85.00
Left	5212745	52.50
1984-wo/Turbo		
right	5212798	85.00
left	5212799	N.L.
Turbo	5212799	N.L.
1985-87-wo/Turbo		
Right	5212798	85.00
Left	5212763	52.25
Turbo	5212763	52.25
(A.C.I.)		
1984-87-Right	5212826	123.00
Left	5212827	76.00

LABOR 11 STEERING GEAR 11 LABOR

(Factory Time)	Chilton Time
(G) Tie Rods or Tie Rod Ends, Renew	
Includes: Reset toe-out.	
1986-87	
outer-one (.9)	1.2
inner and outer-w/P.S. one side (1.9)	2.5
(G) Horn Contact Cable or Ring, Renew	
1986-87 (.2)	.4
(G) Horn Switch, Renew	
1986-87 (.2)	.3
(G) Steering Column Jacket, Renew	
Does not include painting.	
1986-87	
Std Column	
console shift (1.1)	1.8
Tilt Column	
console shift (1.5)	2.6
(G) Upper Mast Jacket Bearing, Renew	
Includes: Replace insulators if necessary.	
1986-87	
std column (.4)	.9
tilt column (1.2)	2.0
(G) Steering Column Lower Shaft Bearing, Renew	
Includes: Replace support if necessary.	
1986-87	
Std Column	
console shift (.8)	1.6
Tilt Column	
console shift (.6)	1.0

POWER STEERING

(Factory Time)	Chilton Time
(G) Power Steering Pump Pressure Check	
All models	.5
(M) Power Steering Pump Belt, Renew	
1986-87 (.4)	.6
w/A.C. add (.1)	.1
(G) Power Steering Gear, R&R or Renew	
Includes: Reset toe-in.	
1986-87 (1.7)	2.4
Renew gear add (.6)	1.0
(G) Steering Gear Oil Seals, Renew (All)	
Includes: R&R gear assy. and reset toe-in.	
1986-87 (2.9)	5.1

LABOR 11 STEERING GEAR 11 LABOR

	(Factory Time)	Chilton Time
(G) Upper and Lower Valve Pinion Seals, Renew		
1986-87	(1.4)	2.0
Renew brgs add	(.3)	.5
(G) Power Steering Pump, Renew		
1986-87	(1.0)	1.4
(G) Power Steering Pump, R&R and Recondition		
1986-87	(1.5)	2.3
(G) Pump Flow Control Valve, Test and Clean or Renew		
1986-87	(.6)	1.0
(G) Power Steering Reservoir or Seals, Renew		
1986-87	(.7)	1.1
(G) Pump Drive Shaft Oil Seal, Renew		
1986-87	(.9)	1.4
(M) Power Steering Hoses, Renew		
1986-87-each	(.4)	.5

PARTS 11 STEERING GEAR - (STANDARD) 11 PARTS

	Part No.	Price
(1) Steering Gear (Manual)		
1986-87	4147415	242.75
(2) Clamp (Boot to Tube)		
1986-87-right	4147140	N.L.
left	4147139	N.L.
(3) Boot Kit		
1986-87-right	4131348	13.50
left	4131349	13.50
(4) Clamp (Boot to Tie Rod)		
1986-87	5205313	1.25
(5) Tie Rod (Outer)		
1986-87	4106180	39.75
(6) Bracket (Outer)		
1986-87	5205225	4.00
(7) Bushing		
1986-87	5205227	2.00
(8) Bracket (Inner)		
1986-87	5205226	1.00

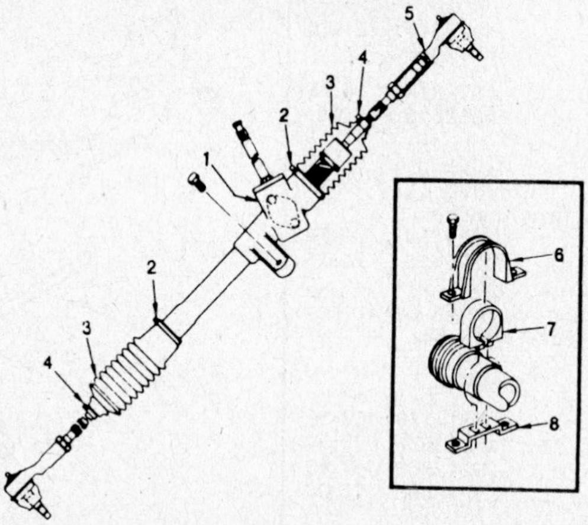

PARTS 11 POWER STEERING GEAR 11 PARTS

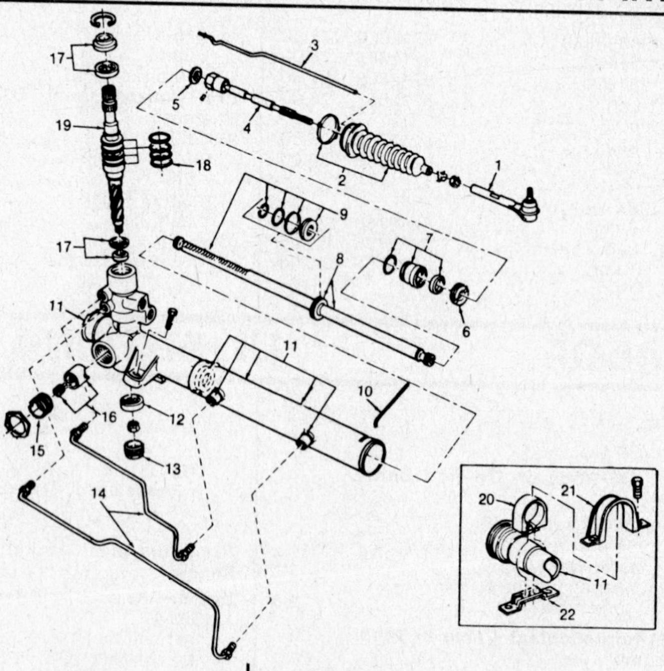

TRW TYPE

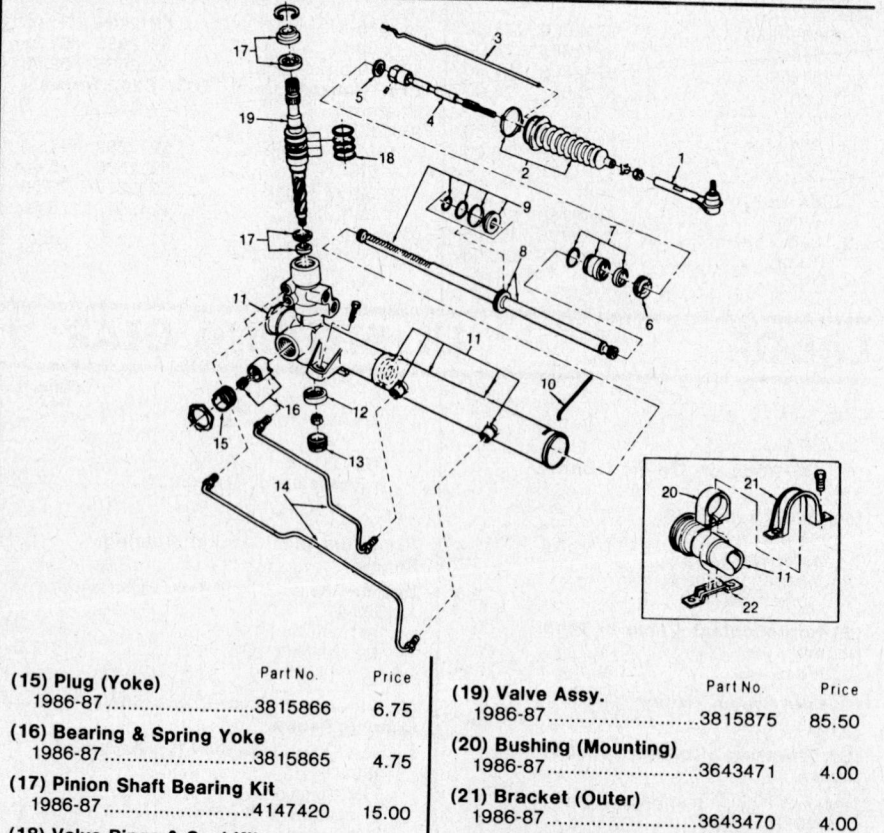

	Part No.	Price
(1) Tie Rod End (Outer)		
1986-87	4106180	39.75
(2) Boot Service Kit		
1986-87	4147303	14.75
(3) Breather Tube		
1986-87	3815871	2.00
(4) Horizontal Socket Assy.		
1986-87	4333450	50.00
(5) Service Ring Kit		
1986-87	3815874	2.75
(6) Lock Ring Bushing		
1986-87	3815874	2.75
(7) Bushing Rack Service Kit		
1986-87	3815881	6.00
(8) Rack Assy.		
1986-87	3815861	103.00
(9) Rack Seal Service Kit		
1986-87	3815878	2.75
(10) Retaining Wire		
1986-87	3815884	.50
(11) Housing (Rack & Pinion)		
1986-87-Std.	4333275	125.75
H.D.	4333148	275.50
(12) Bearing Assy.		
1986-87	3815868	4.75
(13) Plug (Pinion)		
1986-87	4147306	3.75
(14) Cylinder Line Assy.		
1986-87-right	3815873	3.75
left	3815872	3.75
(15) Plug (Yoke)		
1986-87	3815866	6.75
(16) Bearing & Spring Yoke		
1986-87	3815865	4.75
(17) Pinion Shaft Bearing Kit		
1986-87	4147420	15.00
(18) Valve Rings & Seal Kit		
1986-87	4147421	5.50
(19) Valve Assy.		
1986-87	3815875	85.50
(20) Bushing (Mounting)		
1986-87	3643471	4.00
(21) Bracket (Outer)		
1986-87	3643470	4.00
(22) Bracket (Inner)		
1986-87	3643469	1.00

PARTS 11 POWER STEERING GEAR 11 PARTS

	Part No.	Price
SAGINAW TYPE		
Steering Gear Assy.		
1986-87-Std.	4293164	343.50
H.D.	4364785	343.50
(1) Housing Assy.		
1986-87	4147083	178.00
(2) Cylinder Lines		
1986-87-right	4147089	8.25
left	4147090	8.25
(3) Dust Cover		
1986-87	5205284	3.50
(4) Pinion Bearing Kit		
1986-87	5205295	25.50
(5) Ring (Shock Damper)		
1986-87	5205287	2.50
(6) Valve Kit (Pinion Assy.)		
1986-87-Std.	3815947	150.50
H.D.	4333434	150.50
(7) Spool Shaft Bearing Kit		
1986-87	5205299	19.25
(8) Retainer Ring		
1986-87	5205278	1.75
(9) Seal Kit (Inner Rack)		
1986-87	4147098	33.75
(10) Rack Assy. (w/Piston)		
1986-87-Std.	4147000	N.L.
H.D.	4147081	128.75
(11) Bulkhead Assy. Kit		
1986-87-Std.	4147096	41.50
H.D.	4333147	41.50
(12) Tie Rod Assy. (Outer)		
1986-87	4106180	39.75
(13) Clamp (Tie Rod End)		
1986-87	4147085	5.00
(14) Boot Service Kit		
1986-87-right	4147092	30.75
left	4147093	28.75
(15) Tie Rod Assy. (Inner)		
1986-87-right	4147095	48.50
left	4333104	46.25

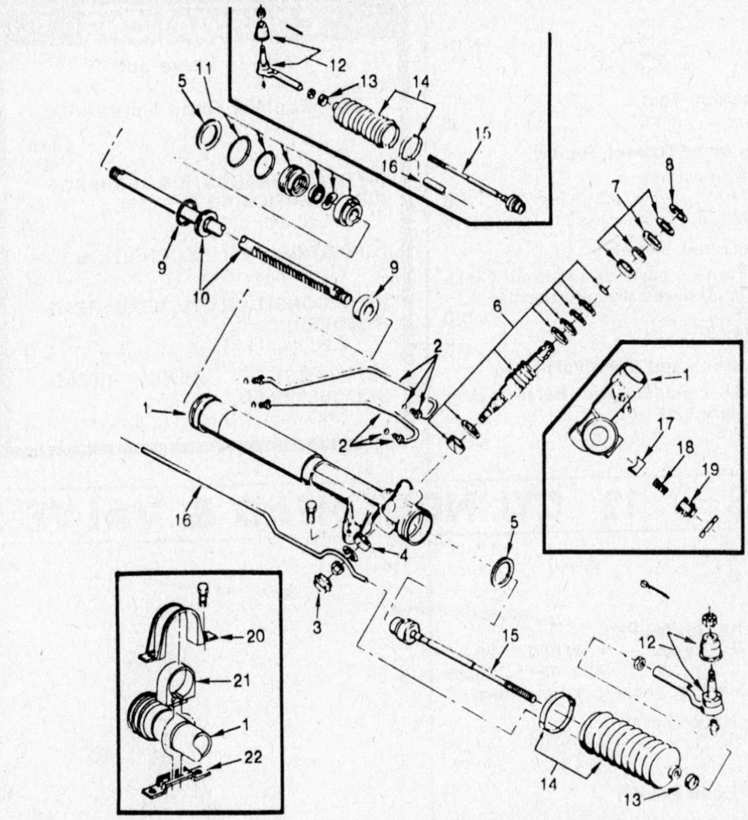

	Part No.	Price
(16) Breather Tube		
1986-87	4147087	9.00
(17) Rack Bearing		
1986-87	5205282	5.25
(18) Spring (Adjuster)		
1986-87	5205280	2.00
(19) Plug (Adjuster)		
1986-87	5205286	7.75

	Part No.	Price
(20) Bracket (Outer)		
1986-87-right	3643470	4.00
left	3643424	4.00
(21) Bushing		
1986-87-right	3643471	4.00
left	3643425	4.00
(22) Bracket (Inner)		
1986-87-right	3643469	1.00
left	3643423	1.00

PARTS 11 POWER STEERING PUMP 11 PARTS

	Part No.	Price
Pump Assy.		
1986-87-Std.	3815956	170.25
H.D.	4188832	170.25
Pressure Hose		
1986-87	4333130	25.25
Return Hose		
Serviced with cut bulk hose.		
(1) Reservoir		
1986-87	3643453	60.75
(2) Union Assy. (Fitting)		
1986-87-Std.	5205267	7.00
H.D.	3815983	6.00
(3) Seal		
1986-87	2537838	11.00
(4) Retaining Ring (End Plate)		
1986-87	2537823	1.00
(5) End Plate		
1986-87	2537820	3.50
(6) Spring (Pressure Plate)		
1986-87	3815966	1.00
(7) Plate (Pressure)		
1986-87	3815967	13.75

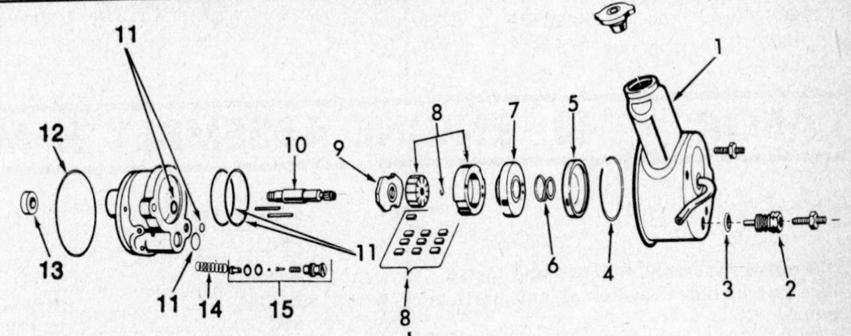

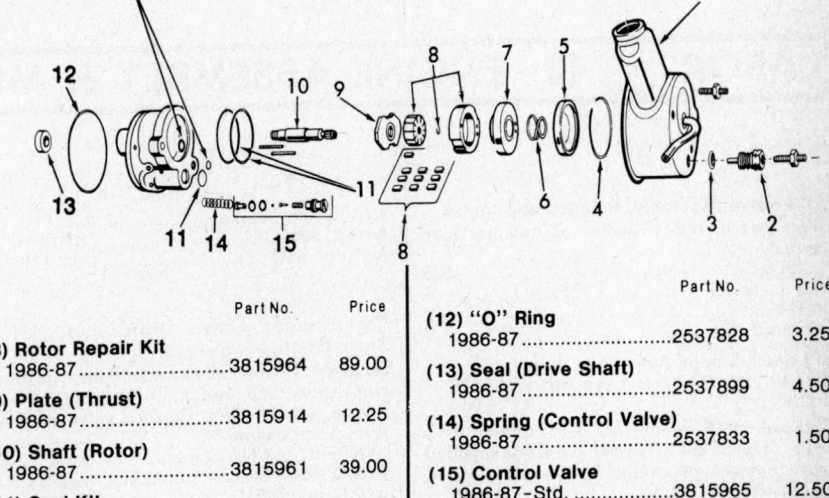

	Part No.	Price
(8) Rotor Repair Kit		
1986-87	3815964	89.00
(9) Plate (Thrust)		
1986-87	3815914	12.25
(10) Shaft (Rotor)		
1986-87	3815961	39.00
(11) Seal Kit		
1986-87	2537838	11.00

	Part No.	Price
(12) "O" Ring		
1986-87	2537828	3.25
(13) Seal (Drive Shaft)		
1986-87	2537899	4.50
(14) Spring (Control Valve)		
1986-87	2537833	1.50
(15) Control Valve		
1986-87-Std.	3815965	12.50
H.D.	2891695	13.00

LABOR 12 CYLINDER HEAD & VALVE SYSTEM 12 LABOR

(Factory Time) Chilton Time

(G) Compression Test
1986-87 6

(G) Cylinder Head Gasket, Renew
Includes: Clean carbon.
1986-87 (3.4) 4.8
w/Turbo add (.5) 5

(G) Cylinder Head, Renew
Includes: Transfer parts as required. Clean carbon, make all necessary adjustments.
1986-87 (5.3) 8.0
w/Turbo add (.5) 5

(G) Clean Carbon and Grind Valves
Includes: R&R cylinder head. Reface valves and seats. Minor tune up.
1986-87 (4.8) 6.8

COMBINATIONS

Add to Valve Job

See Machine Shop Operations

(Factory Time) Chilton Time

(G) DRAIN, EVACUATE & RECHARGE AIR CONDITIONING SYSTEM
All models 1.0

(G) DISTRIBUTOR, RECONDITION
All models (.7) 7

(G) RECONDITION CYL. HEAD (HEAD REMOVED)
2.2L eng (1.4) 2.0

(G) CAMSHAFT, RENEW (HEAD DISASSEMBLED)
OHC engs (.1) 2

(Factory Time) Chilton Time

w/Turbo add (.5) 5

(G) Cylinder Head Cover Gasket, Renew or Reseal
1986-87 (.8) 1.1

(G) Valve Rocker Arms or Shafts, Renew
1986-87-all arms (1.2) 1.6

(G) Valve Tappets, Renew
1986-87-one (1.0) 1.4
each adtnl (.1) 1

(G) Valve Springs and/or Valve Stem Oil Seals, Renew (Head on Car)
1986-87-one (1.2) 1.5
all (1.9) 2.9

PARTS 12 CYLINDER HEAD & VALVE SYSTEM 12 PARTS

	Part No.	Price
2.2L		
Cylinder Head Gasket Pkg.		
1986-87-wo/Turbo	4397680	28.25
Turbo	4397681	28.25
Use RTV sealant for gaskets not provided.		
(1) Cylinder Head (Bare)		
1986-87-wo/Turbo	4105783	340.25
Turbo	4343627	340.25
(2) Cylinder Head Gasket		
1986-87	4387319	11.50
(3) End Seal (Head Cover)		
1986-87-wo/Turbo	5214479	2.25
Turbo	4105475	2.25
(4) Valve Spring		
1986-87-wo/Turbo	4323225	2.25
Turbo	4105793	2.25
(5) Valve Guide		
1986-87-Exhaust	4105715	7.75
Intake	4105716	7.75
(6) Exhaust Valve (Std.)		
1986-87-wo/Turbo	4298142	9.00
Turbo	4323249	21.00
(7) Intake Valve (Std.)		
1986-87-wo/Turbo	4298137	8.25
Turbo	4323244	8.75

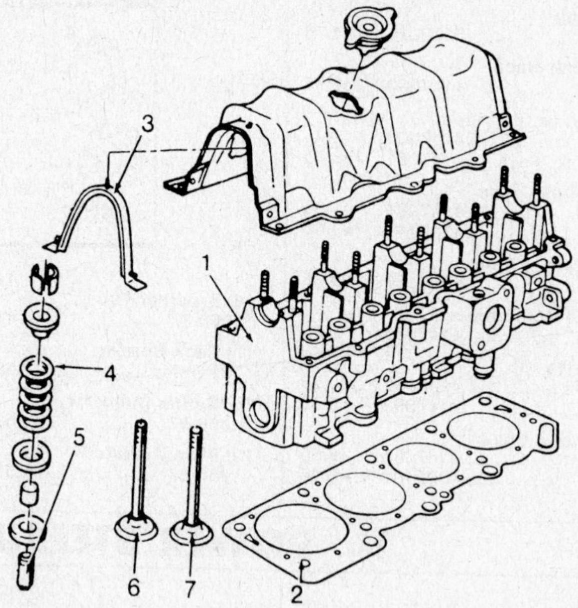

LABOR 13 ENGINE ASSEMBLY & MOUNTS 13 LABOR

(Factory Time) Chilton Time

(G) Engine Assembly, Remove and Install
Does not include transfer of any parts or equipment.
1986-87 .... 6.0
w/A.C. add 5
w/P.S. add 2
w/Turbo add 5

(P) Short Engine Assembly, Renew (w/All Internal Parts Less Head and Oil Pan)
Includes: R&R engine and transmission as a unit. Transfer all necessary parts not supplied with replacement engine. Clean carbon, grind valves. Minor tune up.
1986-87 (9.1) 15.0

(Factory Time) Chilton Time

w/A.C. add (.5) 5
w/P.S. add (.2) 2
w/Turbo add (.5) 5

(P) Engine Assy., R&R and Recondition
Includes: Rebore block, install new pistons, rings, pins, rod and main bearings. Clean carbon, grind valves. Replace valve stem oil seals. Tune engine.
1986-87 (17.8) 25.2
w/A.C. add (.5) 5
w/P.S. add (.2) 2
w/Turbo add (.5) 5

(Factory Time) Chilton Time

(P) Engine Assembly, Recondition (In Car)
Includes: Expand or renew pistons, install new pistons, rings, pins, rod and main bearings. Clean carbon, grind valves. Tune engine.
1986-87 (15.2) 20.8
w/A.C. add (.1) 1
w/Turbo add (.5) 5

(G) Engine Support, Renew
1986-87
right side (.3) 5
left side (.3) 5
center (.4) 6
Trans/Axle
Roll rod (.2) 5

PARTS 13 ENGINE ASSEMBLY & MOUNTS 13 PARTS

	Part No.	Price
2.2L		
Engine Assy.		
Consists of block, pistons, rings, connecting rods, crankshaft, bearings & caps.		
1986-87-wo/Turbo	4343590	1200.50
Turbo	4343871	1200.50
Engine Overhaul Gasket Kit		
1986-87-wo/Turbo		
upper	4397680	28.25
lower	4240098	5.75
1986-87-Turbo		
upper	4397681	28.25
lower	4240098	5.75
Use RTV sealant for gaskets not provided.		
Engine Insulator (Front)		
1986-87-wo/Turbo	4295018	25.25
Turbo	4377458	25.25
Engine Insulator (Right Side)		
1986-87		
Bracket	4295265	11.50
Bushing	4295260	12.50
Engine Insulator (Left Side)		
1986-87		
Bracket	4295255	9.75
Bushing	4295237	9.00

LABOR 14 PISTONS, RINGS & BEARINGS 14 LABOR

(Factory Time)	Chilton Time
(P) Rings, Renew	
(See Engine Combinations)	
Includes: Replace connecting rod bearings, deglaze cylinder walls, clean carbon. Minor tune up.	
1986-87-one cyl (4.6)	6.9
all cyls (5.9)	8.1
w/A.C. add (.1)	.1
w/Turbo add (.5)	.5
(P) Pistons or Connecting Rods, Renew	
Includes: Replace connecting rod bearings and piston rings, deglaze cylinder walls. Clean carbon from cylinder head. Minor tune up.	
1986-87-one cyl (4.9)	7.2
all cyls (6.1)	9.3
w/A.C. add (.1)	.1
w/Turbo add (.5)	.5
(P) Connecting Rod Bearings, Renew	
1986-87 (2.1)	3.0

COMBINATIONS

Add To Engine Work

See Machine Shop Operations

(G) DRAIN, EVACUATE & RECHARGE AIR CONDITIONING SYSTEM	
All models	1.0
(G) DISTRIBUTOR, RECONDITION	
All models (.7)	.7
(G) RECONDITION CYL. HEAD (HEAD REMOVED)	
2.2L eng (1.4)	2.0
(G) R&R CYLINDER HEAD (ENGINE REMOVED)	
All models	1.5
(G) CONNECTING ROD, RENEW (ENGINE DISASSEMBLED)	
Each	.4
(G) CAMSHAFT, RENEW (HEAD DISASSEMBLED)	
OHC engs (.1)	.2
(G) REMOVE CYLINDER TOP RIDGE	
Each (.1)	.1
(G) RENEW OIL PUMP	
All engs (.2)	.3
(G) ROD BEARINGS, RENEW (PAN REMOVED)	
All engs (.7)	1.2
(G) DEGLAZE CYLINDER WALLS	
Each (.1)	.1
(G) PLASTIGAUGE BEARINGS	
Each (.1)	.1
(G) OIL FILTER ELEMENT, RENEW	
All models (.3)	.3

PARTS 14 PISTONS, RINGS & BEARINGS 14 PARTS

	Part No.	Price
2.2L		
(1) Piston Ring Set (Std.)		
1986-87-wo/Turbo	4240137	54.00
Turbo	4293799	54.00
(2) Piston Assy. (Std.)		
1986-87-wo/Turbo	4397632	33.00
Turbo	4397634	33.00
(3) Connecting Rod		
1986-87	4343725	35.00
(4) Connecting Rod Bearing (Std.)		
1986-87-wo/Turbo	4240025	4.00
Turbo	4342751	4.00

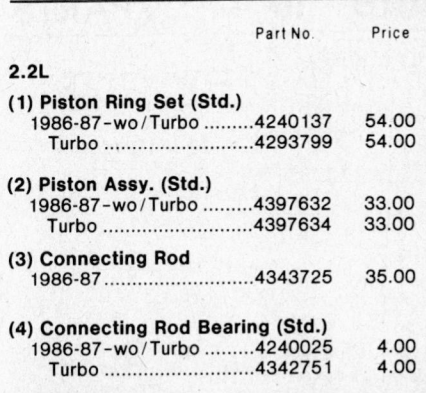

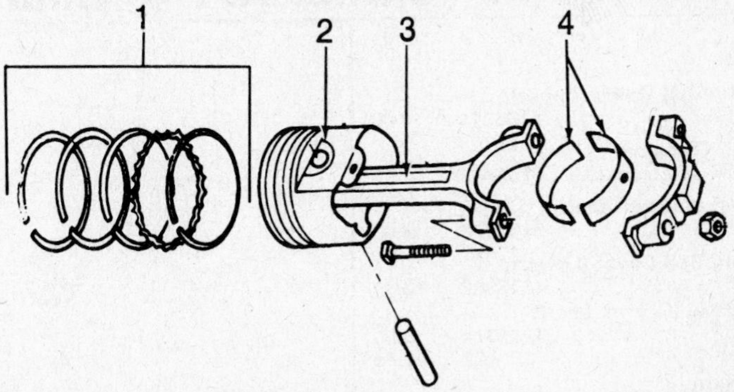

LABOR 15 CRANKSHAFT & DAMPER 15 LABOR

(Factory Time)	Chilton Time
(P) Crankshaft and Main Bearings, Renew	
Includes: R&R engine assembly.	
1986-87 (6.7)	11.2
w/A.C. add (.2)	.2
w/P.S. add (.2)	.2
w/Turbo add (.5)	.5
(P) Main Bearings, Renew	
1986-87	
No-2-3 or 4 (1.8)	2.8
No 1 (3.0)	4.0
No 5 (5.6)	8.8
all (7.0)	11.0
(G) Rear Main Bearing Oil Seals, Renew (Complete)	
1986-87 (3.0)	5.4
(G) Crankshaft Pulley, Renew	
1986-87 (.5)	.7
w/A.C. add (.1)	.1
w/P.S. add (.1)	.1
(G) Crankshaft Front Oil Seal, Renew	
1986-87 (1.1)	2.0
w/A.C. add (.2)	.2
w/P.S. add (.2)	.2

PARTS 15 CRANKSHAFT & DAMPER 15 PARTS

2.2L

	Part No.	Price
(1) Pulley		
1986-87-w/A.C.	4298125	19.00
wo/A.C.	4273184	14.25
(2) Crankshaft		
1986-87	4343407	317.50
(3) Main Bearings		
1986-87-wo/Turbo		
Nos. 1, 2, 4, 5	4240013	6.00
No. 3	4240019	6.00
1986-87-Turbo		
Nos. 1, 2, 4, 5	4293824	6.00
No. 3	4293830	12.75
Oil Seal (Front)		
1986-87	4105395	2.75
Oil Seal (Rear)		
1986-87	5203590	6.25

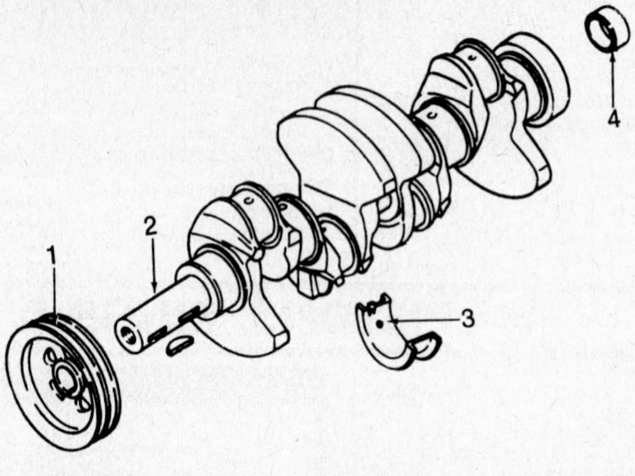

LABOR 16 CAMSHAFT & TIMING GEARS 16 LABOR

(Factory Time)	Chilton Time
(G) Timing Belt Case/Cover, Renew	
Includes: Renew gasket.	
1986-87	
upper cover (.2)	.4
lower cover (.6)	1.0
w/A.C. add (.2)	.2
w/P.S. add (.1)	.1
(G) Timing Belt, Renew	
1986-87 (1.6)	2.2
w/A.C. add (.2)	.2
w/P.S. add (.1)	.1
(G) Timing Belt Tensioner, Renew	
1986-87 (.9)	1.5
w/A.C. add (.2)	.2
w/P.S. add (.2)	.2
(G) Camshaft Sprocket, Renew	
1986-87 (1.7)	2.4
w/A.C. add (.2)	.2
w/P.S. add (.2)	.2
(G) Camshaft Oil Seal, Renew	
1986-87-front (.7)	1.1
rear (.4)	.8
(G) Camshaft, Renew	
1986-87 (1.7)	2.8
Renew valve springs add (1.1)	1.1
(G) Intermediate Shaft, Renew	
1986-87 (1.3)	2.5
w/A.C. add (.2)	.2
w/P.S. add (.1)	.1
(G) Intermediate Shaft Oil Seal, Renew	
1986-87 (1.1)	2.0
w/A.C. add (.2)	.2
w/P.S. add (.2)	.2
(G) Intermediate Shaft Sprocket, Renew	
1986-87 (1.7)	2.7
w/A.C. add (.2)	.2
w/P.S. add (.2)	.2

PARTS 16 CAMSHAFT & TIMING GEARS 16 PARTS

2.2L

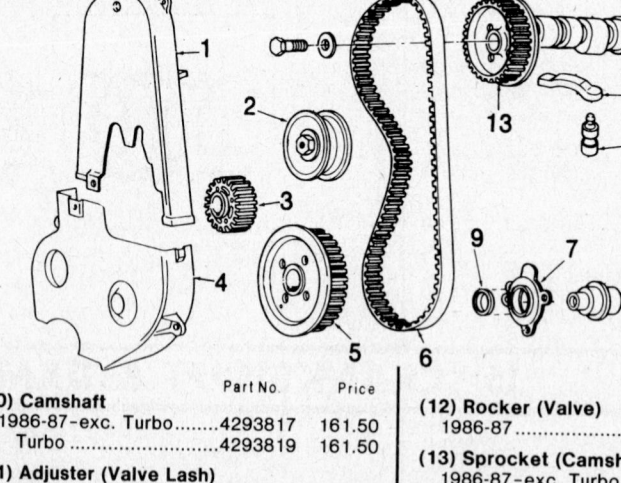

	Part No.	Price
(1) Timing Belt Cover (Upper)		
1986-87	4105714	10.00
(2) Pulley (Tension)		
1986-87	5203469	41.75
(3) Sprocket (Crankshaft)		
1986-87	5203575	14.00
(4) Timing Belt Cover (Lower)		
1986-87	4343639	10.50
(5) Sprocket (Interm. Shaft)		
1986-87-exc. Turbo	4201974	16.50
Turbo	4201992	22.50
(6) Timing Belt		
1986-87	4343946	22.75
(7) Retainer Assy. (Interm. Shaft)		
1986-87	5203325	8.50
(8) Intermediate Shaft		
1986-87	4343428	86.75
(9) Seal (Interm. Shaft)		
1986-87	4105395	2.75

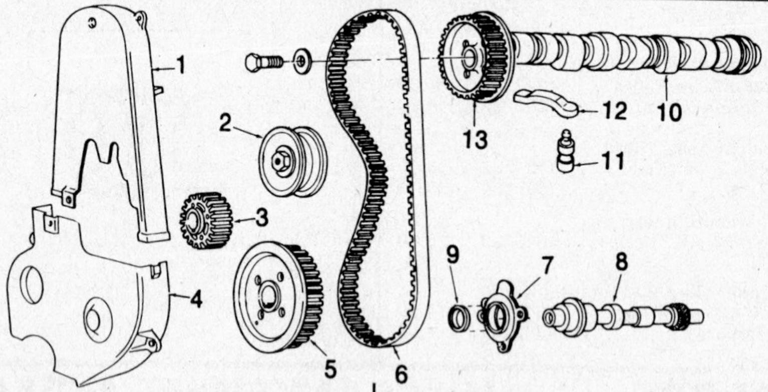

	Part No.	Price
(10) Camshaft		
1986-87-exc. Turbo	4293817	161.50
Turbo	4293819	161.50
(11) Adjuster (Valve Lash)		
1986-87	4240007	12.50
(12) Rocker (Valve)		
1986-87	4173390	7.00
(13) Sprocket (Camshaft)		
1986-87-exc. Turbo	4201974	16.50
Turbo	4201992	22.50

LABOR 17 ENGINE OILING SYSTEM 17 LABOR

	Chilton Time
(G) Oil Pan or Gasket, Renew or Reseal	
1986-87 (1.0)	1.4
(P) Pressure Test Engine Bearings (Pan Off)	
All models	1.0
(G) Oil Pump, Renew	
Includes: R&R oil pan.	
1986-87 (1.3)	1.7

LABOR 17 ENGINE OILING SYSTEM 17 LABOR

	(Factory Time)	Chilton Time
(G) Oil Pump, R&R and Recondition		
Includes: R&R oil pan.		
1986-87	(1.7)	2.2
(G) Oil Pressure Relief Valve Spring, Renew		
1986-87	(1.6)	2.2
(G) Oil Pressure Gauge Sending Unit, Renew		
1986-87	(.2)	.4
(G) Oil Pressure Gauge (Dash Unit), Renew		
1986-87	(.3)	.6
(M) Oil Filter Element, Renew		
1986-87	(.2)	.3

PARTS 17 ENGINE OILING SYSTEM 17 PARTS

	Part No.	Price
2.2L		
Oil Pump Assy.		
1986-87	4397827	66.00
Oil Pan Gasket		
Use RTV sealer.		
Pan Seal (Front & Rear)		
1986-87	5203778	1.75
Pump Screen Assy.		
1986-87	4343198	7.65

LABOR 18 CLUTCH & FLYWHEEL 18 LABOR

	(Factory Time)	Chilton Time
(G) Clutch Self-Adjusting Mechanism, Renew		
1986-87	(.3)	.6
(G) Clutch Release Cable, Renew		
1986-87	(.3)	.5
(G) Clutch Release Arm Seal, Renew		
1986-87	(.5)	.8
(G) Clutch Release Bearing or Fork, Renew		
1986-87	(2.8)	3.8
(G) Clutch Assembly, Renew		
1986-87	(2.9)	4.0
Renew input seal add	(.2)	.2
(G) Flywheel, Renew		
1986-87	(3.0)	4.2

PARTS 18 CLUTCH & FLYWHEEL 18 PARTS

	Part No.	Price
Pressure Plate		
1986-87-exc. Turbo	4295007	122.50
Turbo	4269309	122.50
Clutch Disc		
1986-87-exc. Turbo	4295006	66.50
Turbo	4269308	68.25
Flywheel (w/Ring gear)		
1986-87-exc. Turbo	4338874	142.75
Turbo	4338872	142.75
Clutch Release Bearing		
1986-87	4202378	44.00
Clutch Control Cable		
1986-87	4377769	18.50

LABOR 21 SHIFT LINKAGE 21 LABOR

	(Factory Time)	Chilton Time
MANUAL		
(G) Gearshift Linkage, Adjust		
1986-87	(.9)	1.2
(G) Gearshift Lever, Renew		
1986-87	(.4)	.6
(G) Gearshift Mechanism, Renew		
1986-87	(1.1)	1.6
(G) Selector Shaft Seal, Renew		
1986-87	(.8)	1.1
(G) Trans/Axle Selector Cable, Renew		
1986-87	(1.7)	2.4
(G) Gearshift Crossover Cable, Renew		
1986-87	(1.7)	2.4
AUTOMATIC		
(G) Throttle Linkage, Adjust		
1986-87	(.2)	.4
(G) Selector Lever, Renew		
1986-87	(.3)	.4
(G) Gearshift Mechanism, Renew		
1986-87	(.4)	.8
(G) Gearshift Control Cable, Renew		
1986-87	(.5)	.8
(G) Throttle Lever Control Cable, Renew		
1986-87	(.3)	.6
(G) Gearshift Selector Dial, Renew		
1986-87	(.7)	1.1

LABOR 26 REAR AXLE AND SUSPENSION 26 LABOR

	(Factory Time)	Chilton Time
(G) Rear Wheel Bearings, Renew or Repack		
1986-87-one side	(.6)	.9
both sides	(1.1)	1.7
(G) Rear Wheel Grease Seal, Renew		
1986-87-one side	(.4)	.7
(G) Rear Shock Absorbers, Renew		
1986-87-one	(.3)	.5
both	(.4)	.7
(G) Rear Springs, Renew		
1986-87-one	(.3)	.6
both	(.5)	.8
(G) Lower Control Arm Bushings, Renew		
1986-87-one side	(.6)	1.0
(G) Stub Axle Spindle, Renew		
1986-87-each	(.5)	.7
(G) Rear Sway Bar, Renew		
1986-87	(.4)	.7
(G) Rear Wheel Mounting Studs, Renew		
1986-87-one	(.5)	.8
each adtnl		.1

PARTS 26 REAR AXLE AND SUSPENSION 26 PARTS

	Part No.	Price
(1) Rear Spindle		
1986-87	4228117	50.50
(2) Shim (Whl. Alignment)		
1986-87	5205114	2.25
(3) Shock Absorber		
1986-87-Std.	4147848	15.00
H.D.	4228377	30.00
X.H.D.	4228335	30.00
(4) Track Bar Pkg.		
1986-87	4228256	63.25
(5) Brace (Track Bar Mtg.)		
1986-87	4228251	17.75
(6) Pivot Bolt		
1986-87	6500415	1.25
(7) Cup (Jounce Bumper)		
1986-87		
one notch	4228096	7.00
three notch	4228440	7.00
(8) Isolator (Spring Upper)		
1986-87	4147759	2.75
(9) Bumper (Jounce)		
1986-87	4228159	6.50
(10) Coil Spring		
Order by model and description.		
(11) Bushing (Control Arm)		
1986-87	4147857	9.25
(12) Control Arm & Axle Assy.		
1986-87		
Std. w/Frt. Sway Bar	4228501	199.50
Std. wo/Frt. Sway Bar	4228502	N.L.
H.D.	4228504	199.50
(13) Hanger (Front)		
1986-87-right	4228452	N.L.
left	4228453	N.L.

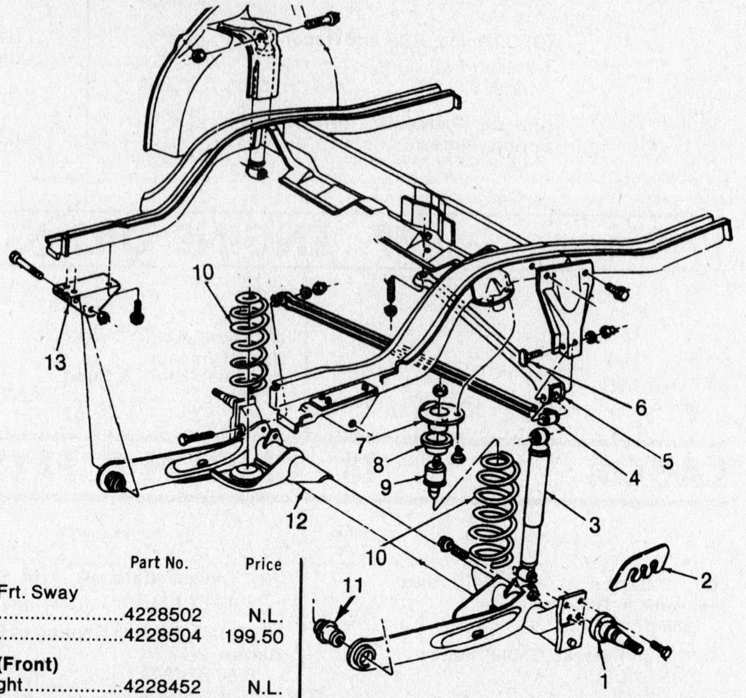

LABOR 28 AIR CONDITIONING 28 LABOR

	(Factory Time)	Chilton Time
Note: If more than one item requires replacement where evacuation and discharging the system is already included in the operation, deduct 1.0 hour for each additional item to the times listed.		
(G) Drain, Evacuate, Leak Test and Charge System		
All models		1.0
(G) Partial Charge		
Includes: Leak test.		
All models	(.5)	.6
(G) Performance Test		
All models		.8
(G) Vacuum Leak Test		
All models		.8
(G) Compressor Drive Belt, Renew		
1986-87	(.2)	.3

C-171 COMPRESSOR

	(Factory Time)	Chilton Time
(G) Compressor Assembly, Renew		
Includes: Transfer parts as required. Pressure test and charge system.		
1986-87	(1.4)	2.5
(G) Compressor Clutch Field Coil, Renew		
1986-87	(.6)	.9
(G) Compressor Clutch Pulley (w/Hub), Renew		
1986-87	(.4)	.5
(G) Compressor Clutch Assembly, Renew		
1986-87	(.6)	.8

AIR CONDITIONER TUNE-UP

For efficient operation and satisfactory performance in hot weather. The following air conditioner tune-up is suggested:

1. Clean intake filter
2. Clean condenser fins
3. Pressure test system
4. Adjust drive belt tension
5. Check antifreeze/coolant
6. Tighten compressor mounts
7. Tighten condenser and evaporator mounts
8. Inspect system for leaks (hoses, couplings, valves, etc.)
9. Partial charge system

All models 1.0

If necessary to evacuate and charge system, add 1.0

	(Factory Time)	Chilton Time
(G) Compressor Front Cover Seal, Renew		
Includes: R&R compressor. Pressure test and charge system.		
1986-87	(1.8)	3.1
(G) Compressor Rear Cover Seal, Renew		
Includes: R&R compressor. Pressure test and charge system.		
1986-87	(1.7)	3.0
(G) Compressor Center Seal, Renew		
Includes: R&R compressor. Pressure test and charge system.		
1986-87	(1.9)	3.2
(G) Compressor Shaft Gas Seal, Renew		
Includes: R&R compressor. Pressure test and charge system.		
1986-87	(1.8)	3.1
(G) Expansion Valve, Renew		
Includes: Pressure test and charge system.		
1986-87	(1.0)	1.7
Renew receiver drier add	(.2)	.2
(G) Receiver Drier, Renew		
Includes: Pressure test and charge system.		
1986-87	(.9)	1.6
(G) Low Pressure Cut Off Switch, Renew		
Includes: Charge system.		
1986-87	(.9)	1.4

LABOR 28 AIR CONDITIONING 28 LABOR

(Factory Time) Chilton Time

(G) Clutch Cycling (Thermostatic Control) Switch, Renew
1986-87 (.3) .6
pressure activated (.2) .4

(G) Condenser Assembly, Renew
Includes: Add partial charge, leak test and charge system.
1986-87 (1.5) 2.5
Renew receiver drier add (.2) .2

(G) Evaporator Coil, Renew
Includes: Add partial charge, leak test and charge system.
1986-87 (2.6) 4.5
w/Console add (.2) .2

(G) Temperature Control Assembly, Renew
1986-87 (.3) .6

(G) Push Button Vacuum Switch, Renew
1986-87 (.5) .9

(G) Blower Motor Switch, Renew
1986-87 (.5) .8

(G) Temperature Control Cable, Renew
1986-87 (.6) .9

(G) Blower Motor, Renew
1986-87 (.6) .9

(G) A.C. On-Off Switch, Renew
1986-87 (.5) .8

(G) Vacuum Actuators, Renew
1986-87
outside air door (.2) .4
heater/defroster door (.3) .6
A/C mode door (.8) 1.5

(G) Air Conditioning Hoses, Renew
Includes: Add partial charge, leak test and charge system.
1986-87-one (1.1) 1.6
each adtnl (.3) .5
Renew receiver drier add (.2) .2

PARTS 28 AIR CONDITIONING 28 PARTS

Part numbers shown are for pricing reference only.

	Part No.	Price
Compressor Assy.		
1986-87	4339456	275.00
Compressor Seal Pkg.		
1986-87	3847916	7.75
Pulley & Armature (Drive Clutch)		
1986-87	3848982	101.75
Field Coil (Drive Clutch)		
1986-87	3848969	29.50
Expansion Valve		
1986-87	3849240	59.75
Receiver Drier		
1986-87	3848217	37.25
Low Pressure Cut Off Switch		
1986-87	5210377	17.25
High Pressure Cut Off Switch		
1986-87	3849335	45.50
Condenser Assy.		
1986-87	3848530	219.75
Evaporator Coil		
1986-87	4339423	317.25
Heater Core		
1986-87	3847943	90.75
Blower Motor		
1986-87	8349266	N.L.
Blower Motor Resistor		
1986-87	3849235	8.50
Blower Motor Switch		
1986-87	3849139	10.25
Push Button Vacuum Switch		
1986-87	3849140	28.50
Water Control Valve		
1986-87-exc. Turbo	3849199	27.75
Turbo	3848460	27.75

LABOR 29 LOCKS, HINGES & WIND. REGULATORS 29 LABOR

(Factory Time) Chilton Time

(G) Hood Hinge, Renew
Does not include painting.
1986-87 (.3) .4

(G) Hood Latch, Renew
1986-87 (.2) .4

(G) Hood Release Cable, Renew
1986-87 (.3) .6

(G) Door Latch, Renew
1986-87 (.5) .7

(G) Lock Striker Plate, Renew
1986-87 (.2) .3

(G) Door Lock Remote Control, Renew
1986-87 (.3) .7

(G) Front Door Window Regulator, Renew
1986-87
manual (.5) .9
electric (.7) 1.3

(G) Rear Door Window Regulator, Renew
1986-87
manual (.5) .9
electric (.8) 1.5

(G) Door Handle (Outside), Renew
1986-87 (.5) .7

(G) Liftgate Latch, Renew
1986-87 (.3) .5

(G) Liftgate Hinge, Renew
1986-87-one (.3) .5

PARTS 29 LOCKS, HINGES & WIND. REGULATORS 29 PARTS

	Part No.	Price
Hood Lock		
1986-87	4341952	9.50
Hood Latch Release (w/Cable)		
1986-87	4341462	23.50
Hood Hinges		
1986-87-right	4386556	20.50
left	4386557	20.50
Front Door Latch		
1986-87-right	4365414	N.L.
left	4365415	N.L.
Rear Door Latch		
1986-87-right	4415410	21.75
left	4415411	21.75
Lock Solenoid-Front		
1986-87	4396017	60.00
Lock Solenoid-Rear		
1986-87	4396737	N.L.
Door Handle-Outside		
Front		
1986-87-right	4419012	26.75
left	4419013	26.75
Rear		
1986-87-right	4419014	26.75
left	4419015	26.75
Window Regulator		
Front		
1986-87-right	4315408	N.L.
left	4315409	N.L.
Rear		
1986-87-right	4396208	67.50
left	4396209	67.50
Power Window Motor		
Front		
1986-87-right	4336766	N.L.
left	4336767	N.L.
Rear		
1986-87-right	4336782	173.25
left	4336783	173.25
Latch Liftgate		
1986-87	4246940	N.L.
Liftgate Hinges		
1986-87-right	4378038	11.00
left	4378039	11.00

LABOR 30 HEAD AND PARKING LAMPS 30 LABOR

(Factory Time) — Chilton Time

(G) Aim Headlamps
two 4
four 6

(M) Headlamp Sealed Beam Bulb, Renew
Does not include aim headlamps.
All models-each (.2).... .3

(M) License Lamp Lens, Renew
All models (.2).... .2

(M) License Lamp Assembly, Renew
All models (.2).... .3

(M) Turn Signal and Parking Lamp Assy., Renew
All models (.3).... .4

(M) Turn Signal and Parking Lamp Lens, Renew
All models-each (.2).... .3

(M) Tail Lamp Assembly, Renew
All models (.3).... .4

(M) Side Marker Lamp Assy., Renew
All models-each (.2).... .3

PARTS 30 HEAD AND PARKING LAMPS 30 PARTS

	Part No.	Price
Parking & Turn Signal Front Assy.		
1986-87-right	4328690	11.00
left	4328691	11.00
Side Marker Front Assy.		
1986-87	4328698	7.00
Lens Taillight		
Sundance		
1986-87-right	4321514	27.25
left	4321515	27.25
Shadow		
1986-87-right	4321516	18.75
left	4321517	18.75
High Mount Stoplight		
1986-87	4321717	11.75

LABOR 31 WINDSHIELD WIPER & SPEEDOMETERS 31 LABOR

(Factory Time) — Chilton Time

(G) Windshield Wiper Motor, Test and Renew
1986-87 (.6).... .8

(G) Wiper/Washer Switch Assy., Renew
1986-87
std column (.8).... 1.2
tilt column (1.1).... 1.5

(G) Rear Window Wiper/Washer Switch, Renew
1986-87 (.3).... .5

(G) Rear Window Wiper Motor, Renew
1986-87 (.5).... .7

(G) Washer Pump, Renew
1986-87
front (.3).... .4
rear (.7).... 1.0

(G) Wiper Link Assembly, Renew
1986-87 (.5).... .7

(G) Windshield Wiper Pivot, Renew
1986-87-one (.5).... .8

(G) Intermittent Wiper Control Module, Renew
1986-87 (.2).... .4

(G) Speedometer Head, R&R or Renew
1986-87 (.5).... .8
Reset odometer add.... .2

(G) Speedometer Cable and Casing, Renew
1986-87
upper (.3).... .6
lower (.5).... .9
one piece (.6).... 1.0

(G) Speedometer Cable (Inner), Renew or Lubricate
1986-87
upper (.3).... .5
lower (.4).... .8
one piece (.4).... .8

(G) Speedometer Drive Pinion, Renew
Includes: Renew oil seal.
1986-87 (.3).... .4

(G) Radio, R&R
1986-87 (.3).... .7

(G) Electronic Instrument Cluster Assy., R&R or Renew
1986-87 (.4).... .6

(G) Odometer Memory Chip, Renew (Electronic Cluster)
1986-87 (.4).... .6

PARTS 31 WINDSHIELD WIPER & SPEEDOMETER 31 PARTS

Part numbers shown are for pricing reference only.

	Part No.	Price
Wiper Motor Front		
1986-87	4339449	106.75
Wiper Pivot		
1986-87-right	4240511	17.00
left	4240512	17.00
Wiper Motor Liftgate		
1986-87	4240484	106.75
Speedometer Assy.		
1986-87		
85 mph wo/ Odometer	4375064	N.L.
85 mph w/ Odometer	4375034	79.25
125 mph w/Tach	4375032	88.75

LABOR 32 LIGHT SWITCHES & WIRING 32 LABOR

(Factory Time) — Chilton Time

(G) Headlamp Switch, Renew
1986-87 (.3).... .4

(G) Headlamp Dimmer Switch, Renew
1986-87 (.3).... .6

(G) Back-Up Lamp Switch, Renew (w/Manual Trans)
1986-87 (.2).... .4

(G) Stop Lamp Switch, Renew
1986-87 (.3).... .4
w/Cruise control add (.1).... .1

(G) Neutral Safety Switch, Renew
1986-87 (.3).... .4

(G) Parking Brake Warning Lamp Switch, Renew
1986-87 (.2).... .3

(G) Turn Signal Switch, Renew
1986-87
std column (.6).... 1.0
tilt column (.8).... 1.5

(M) Turn Signal or Hazard Warning Flasher, Renew
1986-87 (.2).... .3

(G) Horn, Renew
1986-87-one (.2).... .4
each adtnl.... .1

(G) Horn Relay, Renew
1986-87 (.2).... .3

(G) Horn Switch, Renew
1986-87 (.2).... .3

(G) Wiring Harness, Renew
1986-87
Main harness to dash (1.2).... 3.0
Body harness (.7).... 1.3
Intermediate harness (.9).... 1.7

PARTS 32 LIGHT SWITCHES & WIRING 32 PARTS

	Part No.	Price
Headlamp Switch		
1986-87	4221405	17.25
Stoplight Switch		
1986-87	4221976	15.50
Turn Signal & Hazard Warning		
1986-87-wo/Tilt	4221955	38.00
w/Tilt	4221956	37.50
Back-Up Lamp Switch		
1986-87-M.T.	4221949	10.00
A.T.	4057750	8.75

LABOR 33 GLASS 33 LABOR

	(Factory Time)	Chilton Time
(G) Windshield Glass, Renew		
Includes: Replace weatherstrip if necessary, where applicable.		
1986-87	(1.8)	2.8
(G) Front Door Glass, Renew		
1986-87	(.7)	1.0
(G) Rear Door Glass, Renew		
1986-87	(.7)	1.2
(G) Rear Door Vent Glass, Renew		
1986-87	(.8)	1.2
(G) Quarter Window Glass, Renew		
1986-87	(1.4)	2.0
(G) Liftgate Glass, Renew		
1986-87	(1.1)	1.5

LABOR 34 CRUISE CONTROL 34 LABOR

	(Factory Time)	Chilton Time
(G) Speed Control Servo/Motor Assy., Renew		
1986-87	(.5)	.6
w/Turbo add	(.1)	.1
(G) Speed Control Cable, Renew		
1986-87	(.4)	.7
(G) Speed Control Turn Signal Lever Switch, Renew		
1986-87		
std column	(.5)	.9
tilt column	(1.0)	1.5
(G) Speed Control Wiring Harness, Renew		
1986-87	(.3)	.6
(G) Speed Control Safety (Cut-Out) Switch, Renew		
1986-87	(.3)	.5
(G) Electronic Speed Control Module, Renew		
1986-87	(.2)	.4

PARTS 34 CRUISE CONTROL 34 PARTS

Part numbers are for pricing reference only.

	Part No.	Price
Cruise Control Servo		
1986-87	4307221	130.00
Clutch Switch		
1986-87	4221697	21.75
Switch and Lever		
1986-87		
w/Tilt wheel	3747881	41.75
wo/Tilt wheel	4221482	41.75
Brake Switch		
1986-87	4221651	15.50
Control Cable		
1986-87	4307565	24.75

Chrysler • Cordoba • Imperial • Mirada

GROUP INDEX

ALPHABETICAL INDEX

Chrysler Corporation

Real Wheel Drive Cars

CHRYSLER • CORDOBA • IMPERIAL • MIRADA

YEAR IDENTIFICATION

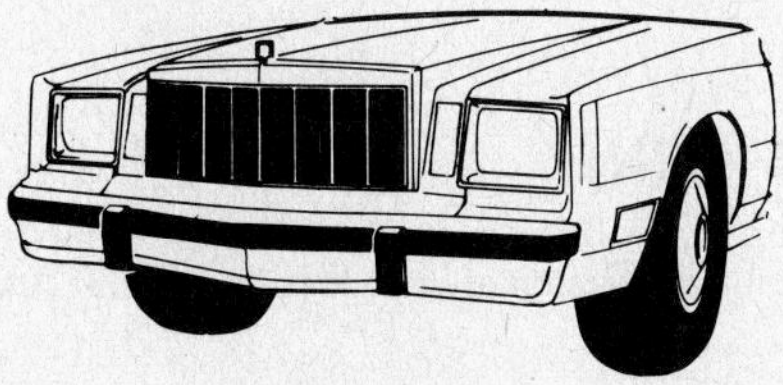

1983 Cordoba

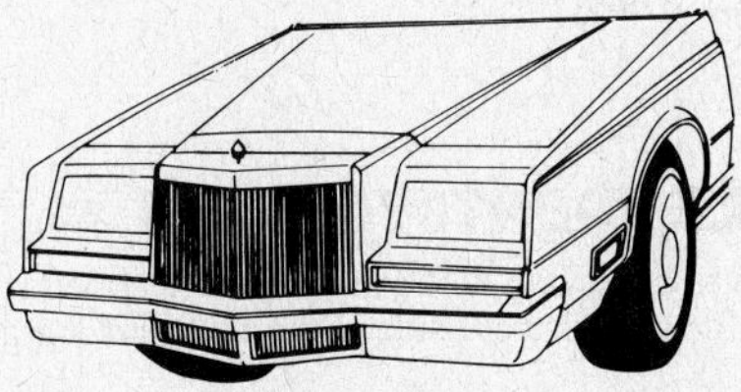

1983 Imperial

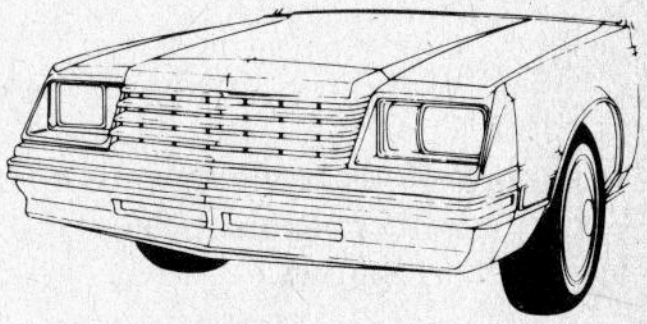

1983 Mirada

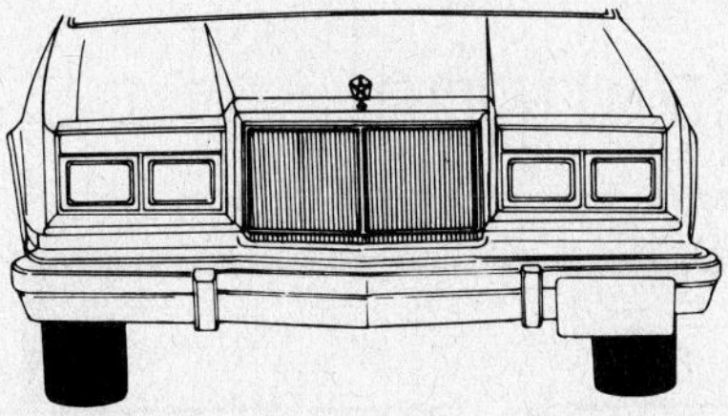

1983 New Yorker, Fifth Avenue

1984-87 Fifth Avenue

TUNE-UP SPECIFICATIONS

When analyzing compression test results, look for uniformity among cylinders rather than specific pressures

Year	Eng. V.I.N. Code	Engine No. Cyl. Displacement (cu. in.)	Carb. (bbl.)	Spark Plugs Orig. Type	Spark Plugs Gap (in.)	Distributor Point Dwell (deg)	Distributor Point Gap (in.)	Ignition Timing (deg.)	Valves Intake Opens ■(deg.)	Fuel Pump Pressure (psi)	Idle Speed (rpm)
'83	H,J,K,L	6-225	1 & 2	RBL-16Y	.035	Electronic		⑤	6	4.0–5.5	750
	N,P,R,S	8-318	2 & 4	RN-12Y	.035	Electronic		⑤	10	5.75–7.25	700
'84–'87	P,R,S	8-318	2 & 4	RN-12Y	.035	Electronic		⑤	10	5.75–7.25	700

NOTE: The underhood specifications sticker often reflects tune-up specification changes made in production. Sticker figures must be used if they disagree with those in this chart.

Part numbers in this chart are not recommended by Chilton for any product by brand name.

■All figures Before Top Dead Center

EFI Electronic Fuel Injection

⑤ See underhood sticker

FIRING ORDERS

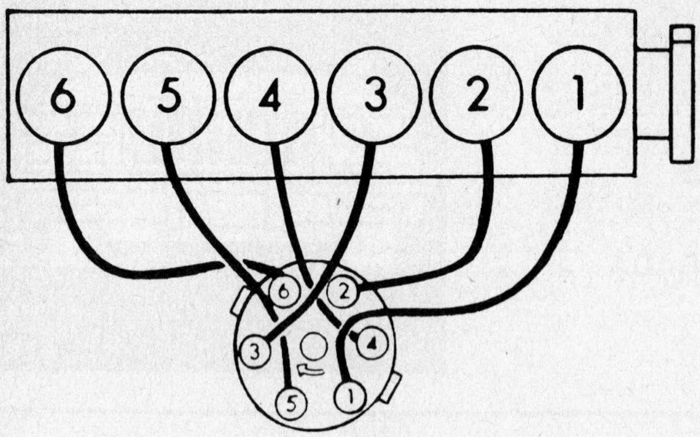

Chrysler Corp. 6-cyl.
Engine firing order: 1–5–3–6–2–4
Distributor rotation: clockwise

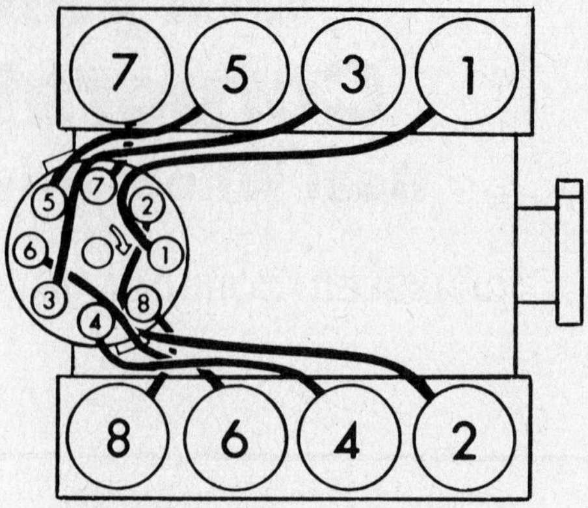

Chrysler Corp. 318, V8
Engine firing order:1–8–4–3–6–5–7–2
Distributor rotation: clockwise

VEHICLE IDENTIFICATION NUMBER (VIN)

It is important for servicing and ordering parts to be certain of the vehicle and engine identification. The VIN (vehicle identification number) is a 17 digit number visible through the windshield on the driver's side of the dash and contains the vehicle and engine identification codes. It can be interpreted as follows:

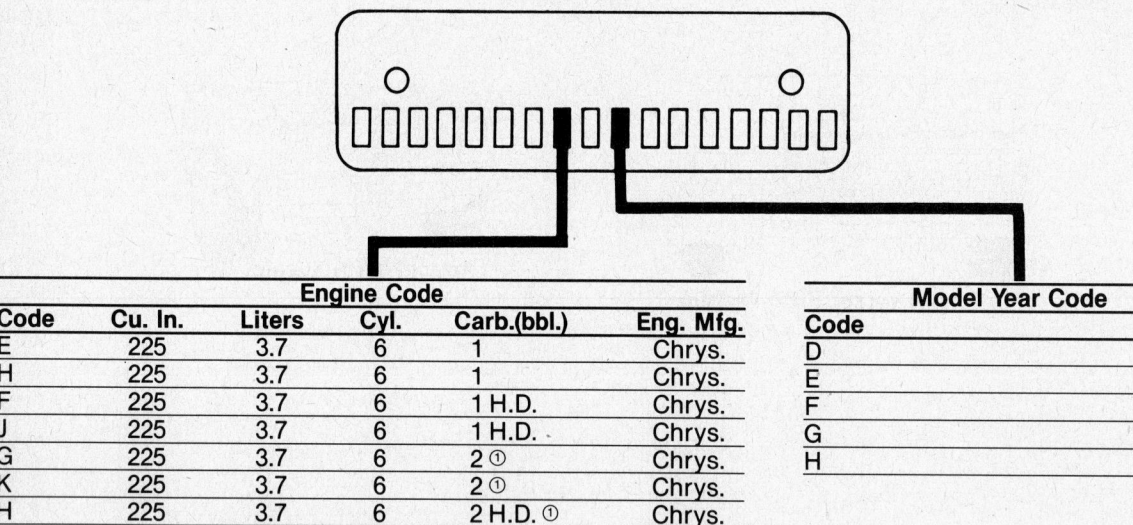

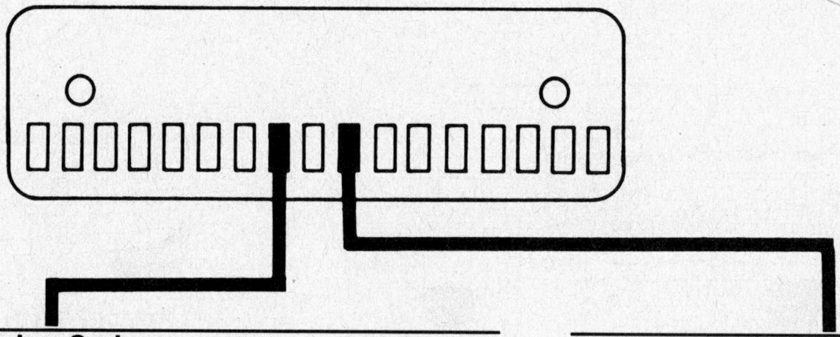

Engine Code

Code	Cu. In.	Liters	Cyl.	Carb.(bbl.)	Eng. Mfg.
E	225	3.7	6	1	Chrys.
H	225	3.7	6	1	Chrys.
F	225	3.7	6	1 H.D.	Chrys.
J	225	3.7	6	1 H.D.	Chrys.
G	225	3.7	6	2 ①	Chrys.
K	225	3.7	6	2 ①	Chrys.
H	225	3.7	6	2 H.D. ①	Chrys.
L	225	3.7	6	2 H.D. ①	Chrys.
K	318	5.2	8	2	Chrys.
P	318	5.2	8	2	Chrys.
L	318	5.2	8	2 H.D.	Chrys.
J	318	5.2	8	EFI	Chrys.
N	318	5.2	8	EFI	Chrys.
R	318	5.2	8	4	Chrys.
M	318	5.2	8	4	Chrys.
N	318	5.2	8	4 H.D.	Chrys.
S	318	5.2	8	4 H.D.	Chrys.

H.D. = Heavy Duty
EFI = Electronic Fuel Injection
① = Canada Only
The seventeen digit Vehicle Identification Number can be used to determine engine application and model year.
The 10th digit indicates the model year, and the 8th digit identifies the factory installed engine.
EFI Electronic Fuel Injection

Model Year Code

Code	Year
D	1983
E	1984
F	1985
G	1986
H	1987

WHEEL ALIGNMENT SPECIFICATIONS

Year	Model	Caster Range (deg.)	Caster Pref. Setting (deg.)	Camber Range (deg.)	Camber Pref. Setting (deg.)	Toe-in (in.)	Steering Axis Inclin. (deg.)	Wheel Pivot Ratio Inner Wheel	Wheel Pivot Ratio Outer Wheel
'83-'87	Diplomat, Gran Fury, Newport, 5th Avenue	1¼P to 3¾P	2½±1	1.4N-1¼P	1/2P±1/2	1/8+1/16	8	20	18

FRONT END HEIGHT

Year	Model	Front End Height (±1/8 in.)
'83-'87	5th Avenue	12½ ①②

① ± 1/4 in.
② Measured from the head of the suspension crossmember front isolater bolt to ground

LABOR SERVICE BAY OPERATIONS LABOR

(Factory Time) Chilton Time

COOLING

(M) Winterize Cooling System
Includes: Run engine to check for leaks, tighten all hose connections. Test radiator and pressure cap, drain radiator and engine block. Add anti-freeze and refill system.
All models .5

(M) Thermostat, Renew
All models (.4) .6
w/A.C. add (.3) .3

(M) Drive Belt, Renew
All models (.2) .3
w/A.C. add (.1) .1
w/Air inj add (.1) .1
w/P.S. add (.1) .1

FUEL

(M) Carburetor Air Cleaner, Service
All models (.3) .3

(G) Carburetor, Adjust (On Car)
All models (.6) .6

(G) Automatic Choke, Renew
1 bbl (.2) .4
2 bbl (.2) .4
4 bbl (.5) .7

BRAKES

(G) Brakes, Adjust (Minor)
Includes: Adjust brakes, fill master cylinder.
two wheels .4

(M) Parking Brake, Adjust
All models (.3) .4

LUBRICATION SERVICE

(M) Lubricate Chassis, Change Oil & Filter
Includes: Inspect and correct all fluid levels.
All models .6
Install grease fittings add .1

CHILTON'S 10 POINT SAFETY CHECK

CHECK OPERATION & CONDITION OF THE FOLLOWING ITEMS:

1. Legal Registration (serial no.)
2. Tires & Wheels
3. Brake System (R&R all wheels)
4. Light Systems & Signals
5. Accelerator Linkage, Neutral Safety Switch, Shift Indicator Pointer & Seat Position Locks
6. Glass, Mirrors, Door Locks, Seat Belts & Harness
7. Wipers, Washers & Defrosters
8. Frame, Steering, Shocks, Front & Rear Suspension
9. Fuel & Exhaust Systems
10. Road Test Vehicle

All models 1.0
Exhaust Smog Analysis, add .4

(Factory Time) Chilton Time

(M) Lubricate Chassis
Includes: Inspect and correct all fluid levels.
All models .4
Install grease fittings add .1

(M) Engine Oil & Filter, Change
Includes: Inspect and correct all fluid levels.
All models .4

WHEELS

(M) Wheel, Renew
one (.3) .3

(G) Wheels, Balance
one .3
each adtnl .2

(Factory Time) Chilton Time

(G) Front Wheel Bearings, Clean and Repack (Both Wheels)
1983-87 (.9) 1.4

(G) Front Wheel Grease Seals, Renew
1983-87-one whl (.5) .6
both whls (.9) 1.0

ELECTRICAL

(M) Battery Cables, Renew
ground (.2) .3
batt to starter relay (.5) .5
positive (.4) .4

(G) Aim Headlamps
two .4
four .6

(M) Headlamp Sealed Beam Bulb, Renew
Does not include aim headlamps.
All models-each (.2) .3

(M) Parking Lamp Assembly, Renew
All models (.3) .4

(M) Tail & Stop Lamp Lens, Renew
All models (.3) .4

(G) Headlamp Dimmer Switch, Renew
All models-floor mount (.3) .5
column mount (.5) 1.0

(G) Stop Light Switch, Renew
All models (.3) .4
w/Cruise control add (.1) .1

(M) Turn Signal or Hazard Warning Flasher, Renew
All models (.2) .3

(G) Horn Relay, Renew
All models (.2) .3

(M) License Lamp Assembly, Renew
All models (.3) .4

(G) Horn, Renew
All models-one (.2) .3

LABOR 1 TUNE UP 1 LABOR

	(Factory Time)	Chilton Time
(G) Compression Test		
Six–1983	(.5)	.6
V-8–1983-87		
318-360 engs	(.6)	.8
w/A.C. add	(.3)	.3
w/Air inj add	(.3)	.3

(G) Engine Tune Up, (Electronic Ignition)

Includes: Test battery and clean connections. Tighten manifold bolts and carburetor mounting bolts. Check engine compression, clean and adjust or renew spark plugs. Test resistance of spark plug cables. Inspect distributor cap, rotor, reluctor and pick up plate. Adjust air gap. Check vacuum advance operation. Inspect and free up exhaust manifold heat valve. Reset ignition timing. Adjust idle mixture and idle speed. Service air cleaner. Inspect crankcase ventilation system. Inspect and adjust drive belts. Inspect choke operation and adjust or free up. Check operation of EGR valve.

	(Factory Time)	Chilton Time
Six–1983		2.0
V-8–1983-87		2.5
w/A.C. add		.6

LABOR 2 IGNITION SYSTEM 2 LABOR

	(Factory Time)	Chilton Time
(G) Spark Plugs, Clean and Reset or Renew		
Six–1983	(.4)	.5
V-8–1983-87		
318-360 engs	(.5)	.7
w/Air inj add	(.3)	.3
w/A.C. add	(.3)	.3
(G) Ignition Timing, Reset		
1983-87	(.3)	.3
(G) Electronic Ignition Control Unit, Renew		
1983-87	(.2)	.3
(G) Distributor, Renew		
Includes: Reset ignition timing.		
Six–1983	(.6)	.8
V-8–1983-87		
318-360 engs	(.5)	.8
(G) Distributor, R&R and Recondition		
Includes: Reset ignition timing.		
Six–1983	(1.0)	1.6
V-8–1983-87		
318-360 engs	(1.0)	1.6
(G) Distributor Reluctor, Renew		
Includes: R&R distributor and reset ignition timing.		
Six–1983	(.6)	.9
V-8–1983-87		
318-360 engs	(.6)	.9
(G) Distributor Pick-Up Plate and Coil Assy., Renew		
Includes: R&R distributor and reset ignition timing.		
Six–1983	(.7)	1.0
V-8–1983-87		
318-360 engs	(.7)	1.0
w/Dual coil add	(.2)	.2
(G) Vacuum Control Unit, Renew		
Includes: R&R distributor and reset ignition timing.		
Six–1983	(.6)	1.0
V-8–1983-87		
318-360 engs	(.6)	1.0
(G) Distributor Cap and/or Rotor, Renew		
1983-87	(.2)	.5
(G) Dual Ballast Resistor, Renew		
1983-87	(.2)	.3
1983-Imperial	(.6)	.8
(G) Ignition Coil, Renew		
Six–1983	(.4)	.5
V-8–1983-87	(.2)	.4
(G) Ignition Cables, Renew		
Six–1983	(.5)	.6
V-8–1983-87		
318-360 engs	(.3)	.8
w/A.C. add	(.5)	.5
(G) Spark Control Computer, Renew		
Includes: Test computer. Does not include test fuel injection system.		
1983-87	(.2)	.8
1983-Imperial	(1.3)	1.8
(G) Ignition Switch, Renew		
Includes: Replace and recode lock cylinder if necessary.		
Chrysler		
1983-87-std column	(.5)	1.3
tilt column	(.4)	1.0
Cordoba-Mirada		
1983-std column	(.6)	1.1
tilt column	(.5)	1.0
Imperial		
1983	(.5)	1.0
(G) Ignition Key Buzzer Switch, Renew		
Chrysler		
1983-87-std column	(1.1)	1.5
tilt column	(.5)	1.0
Cordoba-Mirada		
1983-std column	(1.1)	1.5
tilt column	(.6)	1.0
Imperial		
1983	(.6)	1.1
(G) Ignition Key Warning Buzzer, Renew		
1983-87	(.2)	.4
1983-Imperial	(1.3)	1.8
(G) Ignition Switch Time Delay Relay, Renew		
1983-87	(.2)	.5

PARTS 2 ELECTRONIC IGNITION 2 PARTS

	Part No.	Price
Distributor Assy. (New)		
Six–225 engine		
1983-exc. below	4145955	72.00
Lean burn	4145613	72.00
California	4145752	60.00
V-8–318 engine		
1983-87-Single pickup	4091142	81.50
Dual pickup	4145754	71.00
(1) Distributor Cap		
1983-Six	4111630	8.25
1983-87-V-8	4111640	8.50
(2) Rotor		
1983-87	3874401	2.75
(3) Reluctor		
1983-Six	3656862	4.50
1983-87-V-8	3656017	4.50
(4) Pick Up & Plate & Assy.		
Six–225 engine		
1983-exc. Calif.	4145210	27.50
California	4145239	30.00

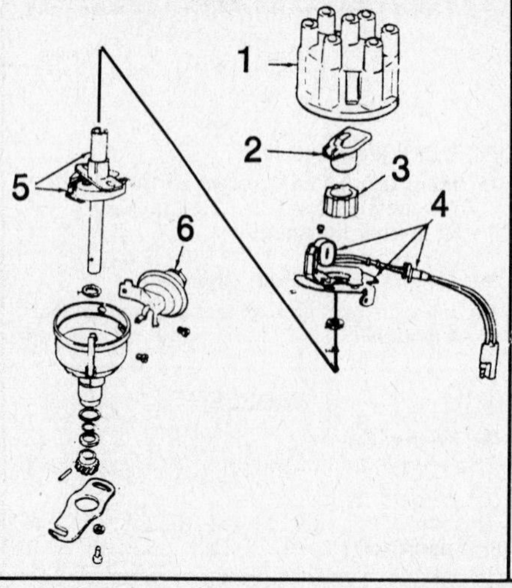

	Part No.	Price
V-8–318 engine		
1983-87-Dual pickup	4145239	30.00
Single pickup	4091147	18.00
(5) Shaft (Dist.)		
Note: Serviced in distributor assy.		
(6) Vacuum Control		
Six–225 engine		
1983	3874878	13.50
V-8–318 engine		
1983-87	3755474	13.50
Coil		
1983-87	4176009	26.75
Ignition Wire Set		
1983-87-V-8	4339401	27.00
Ignition Switch		
1983-87-wo/Tilt whl.	4131367	13.00
w/Tilt whl.	3747529	14.50
Control Unit (Elect. Ignition)		
1983-87	4111850	45.00

LABOR — 3 FUEL SYSTEM 3 — LABOR

(Factory Time) Chilton Time

(G) Fuel Pump, Test
Includes: Disconnect line at carburetor, attach pressure gauge.
All models 2

(M) Carburetor Air Cleaner, Service
1983-87 (.3) 3

(G) Air Cleaner Vacuum Diaphragm, Renew
Includes: Renew sensor if necessary.
1983-87 (.2) 5

(G) Air Cleaner Vacuum Sensor, Renew
1983-87-one (.2) 5
1983-Imperial (.6) 8

(G) Coolant Temperature Sensor/Switch (ESC), Renew
Includes: Test.
1983 (.6) 1.0
1984-87 (.3) 6
1983-Imperial (1.3) 1.8

(M) Fuel Filter, Renew
1983-87 (.2) 3

(G) Carburetor, Adjust (On Car)
All models
w/Catalytic converter (.6) 6
wo/Catalytic converter (.5) 6

(G) Automatic Choke, Renew
1983-85
1 bbl (.2) 4
2 bbl (.2) 4
4 bbl (.5) 7

(G) Automatic Choke Diaphragm, Renew
1983-85
Holly (.2) 4
Carter-2 bbl (.5) 7
4 bbl (.6) 9

(G) Choke Control Switch, Renew
1983-87 (.2) 3

(G) Choke Vacuum Kick, Renew
1983-85
2 bbl (.2) 4
4 bbl (.6) 8

(G) Choke Vacuum Kick, Adjust
1983-87
2 bbl (.2) 3
4 bbl (.5) 6

(G) Automatic Choke/Cover or Float Chamber, Renew
1985-87 (.3) 5

(G) Carburetor, Renew
Includes: Adjust idle speed and mixture with analyzer.
1983-87
1 bbl (.7) 1.3
2 bbl (.7) 1.3
4 bbl (.6) 1.3

(G) Carburetor, R&R and Clean or Recondition
Includes: Adjust idle speed and mixture with analyzer.
1983-87
Holly (1.8) 2.8
Carter-2 bbl (2.2) 3.2
4 bbl (2.5) 3.5

(G) Carburetor Needle and Seat, Renew
Includes: Adjust float level, adjust idle speed and mixture with analyzer.
1983-87-1 bbl (.5) 7
2 bbl (.6) 8
4 bbl (.9) 1.2

(G) Float, Renew or Adjust Level
Includes: Adjust idle speed.
1983-87
1 bbl (.9) 1.2
2 bbl (.9) 1.2
4 bbl (1.2) 1.5
Thermo-Quad (1.2) 1.5

(G) Accelerator Pump, Renew
1983-87-1 bbl (.5) 8
2 bbl (.5) 8
4 bbl (.9) 1.2

(G) Fuel Pump, Renew
Six-1983 (.8) 1.1
V-8-1983-87
318-360 engs (.5) 8
Add pump test if performed.

(G) Flexible Fuel Line, Renew
1983-87-each (.3) 4

(G) Fuel Tank, Renew
Chrysler-Imperial
1983-87 (1.0) 1.5
Cordoba-Mirada
1983 (1.0) 1.5

(G) Fuel Gauge (Tank), Renew
Chrysler-Imperial
1983-87 (1.0) 1.2
Cordoba-Mirada
1983 (.9) 1.2

(G) Fuel Gauge (Dash), Renew
Chrysler
1983 (.4) 1.0
1984-87 (.7) 1.2
Cordoba-Mirada
1983 (.4) 1.0

(G) Electronic Instrument Cluster Assy., Renew
Includes: Speedometer, odometer, fuel gauge, clock and gear selector assy.
1983-Imperial (.9) 1.7

(G) Intake Manifold or Gaskets, Renew
Six-1983 (2.1) 3.0
V-8-1983-87
318-360 engs (2.4) 3.5
w/A.C. add (.4) 4
w/Air inj add (.2) 3
Renew manifold add (.4) 5

(G) Intake and Exhaust Manifold Gaskets, Renew
Six-1983 (1.7) 2.3
w/A.C. add (.4) 4

ELECTRONIC FUEL INJECTION COMPONENTS

(P) Hydraulic Support Plate, Test and Renew
1983 (1.7) 2.5

(P) Power Module, Test and Renew
1983 (1.1) 1.6

(P) Air Flow Module, Test and Renew
1983 (1.1) 1.7

(P) Automatic Shut Down Module, Test and Renew
1983 (.9) 1.4

(P) Throttle Position Potentiometer, Test and Renew
1983 (1.2) 1.7

(P) Automatic Idle Speed Motor, Test and Renew
1983 (.8) 1.3

(P) Heated Air Door/Vacuum Diaphragm Assy., Test and Renew
1983 (.5) 1.0

(P) Air Flow Meter Body, Renew
1983 (.3) 6

(P) Throttle Body Spacer, Renew
Includes: Renew gaskets.
1983 (.7) 1.2

(P) Fuel Pump Resistor, Test and Renew (In Tank)
1983 (.9) 1.9

(P) Fuel Pump Relay, Test and Renew (In Tank)
1983 (.9) 1.9

(P) Fuel Filters, Renew
1983-in tank (1.8) 2.2
under body (1.1) 1.5

(P) Fuel Check Valve, Renew (In Tank)
1983 (1.8) 2.3

(P) Fuel Pump, Renew (In Tank)
1983 (1.9) 2.4

PARTS — 3 FUEL SYSTEM 3 — PARTS

	Part No.	Price
Air Cleaner Temperature Sensor		
1983-87	4240062	7.50
Carburetor Assy. (Carter) (New)		
Note: Order by tag number.		
Six-225 engine		
1983	4179128	243.00
V-8-318 engine		
1983-2 bbl (w/Lean burn)		
BBD-8291	4287089	231.50
BBD-8292	4179130	332.25
BBD-8369	4287023	310.25
4 bbl		
exc. below	4287051	407.00
w/Hi Alt.	4227251	407.00
Lean burn	4179177	364.00
1984-2 bbl		
exc. Calif.	4287023	310.25
Calif.	4300011	243.00
1984-4 bbl		
exc. Calif.	4300012	407.00
Calif.	4179177	364.00
Carburetor Assy. (Holley) (New)		
Note: Order by tag number.		
Six-225 engine		
1983	4287073	243.00
V-8-318 engine		
1985-R-40121	4288576	325.75
R-40157	4288578	N.S.S.
1986-87-R40245	4288581	N.L.
R40276	4324647	325.75

PARTS 3 FUEL SYSTEM 3 PARTS

	Part No.	Price
Carburetor Assy. (Rochester) (New)		
1985-exc. below	4342808	N.L.
electronic	4342805	698.75
1986-87-5411	4306411	N.L.
5433	4306433	N.L.
Carburetor Repair Kit (Carter)		
Six-225 engine		
1983	4271962	28.25
V-8-318 engine		
1983-84-2 bbl	4271962	28.25
Carburetor Repair Kit (Holley)		
Six-225 engine		
1983	4293773	22.25
V-8-318 engine		
1985-87 (Canada)	4267245	47.50
Federal	4342860	47.50
Carburetor Repair Kit (Rochester)		
1985-87-exc. below	4342832	50.50
electronic	4342812	50.50
Choke Assy.		
Carter		
(6 cyl.)		
1983	4095337	17.75
(V-8 eng.)		
1983-2 bbl.	4095338	21.00
4 bbl	4095984	22.25
1984-2 bbl	4271956	10.25
4 bbl	4267133	10.00
Holley		
1983	4095330	26.50
1985-87	4293895	11.50
Rochester		
1985-87-exc. below	4342819	38.75
electronic	4342934	39.00
Fuel Pump Assy. (New)		
1983-Six	4271893	35.50
V-8	4271894	35.50
1984-87-V-8	4293803	35.25
Fuel Gauge (Tank)		
1983-exc. below	4051399	34.75
New Yorker	4051398	34.75
1983-Imperial	4051415	33.75
1984	4051867	30.50
1985-87	4051398	34.75
Fuel Gauge (Dash)		
1983 (Miriada)		
wo/Console	4047534	30.25
w/Console	4047537	31.25
1983 (Imperial)		
wo/E.F.I.	4222447	644.75
w/E.F.I.	4342203	125.00
1983-87 (New Yorker, Newport & Fifth Ave.)		
unleaded fuel	4051388	24.50
leaded fuel	4051389	26.50
Intake Manifold Gaskets		
Six-225 engine		
1983	4186180	7.00
V-8-318 engine		
1983-85-2 bbl	3837605	7.75
4 bbl	3514187	11.25
1986-87-2 bbl	4397643	7.75
4 bbl	4397642	7.75

PARTS 3 ELECTRONIC FUEL INJECTION 3 PARTS

	Part No.	Price
Control & Throttle Body Assy.		
1983	4271868	485.50
(1) Pump		
1983	4051583	135.25
(2) Check valve		
1983	4111747	16.50
(3) Flowmeter		
1983	4267128	199.50
(4) Module (Power)		
1983	4091383	173.00
(5) Sensor		
1983	4240147	7.50
(6) Speed control motor (Automatic)		
1983	4145049	75.00
(7) Throttle body		
1983	4145061	182.00
(8) Spacer		
1983	4145070	11.75
(9) Potentiometer		
1983	4267126	61.50
Fuel Sending Unit		
1983	4051674	46.00

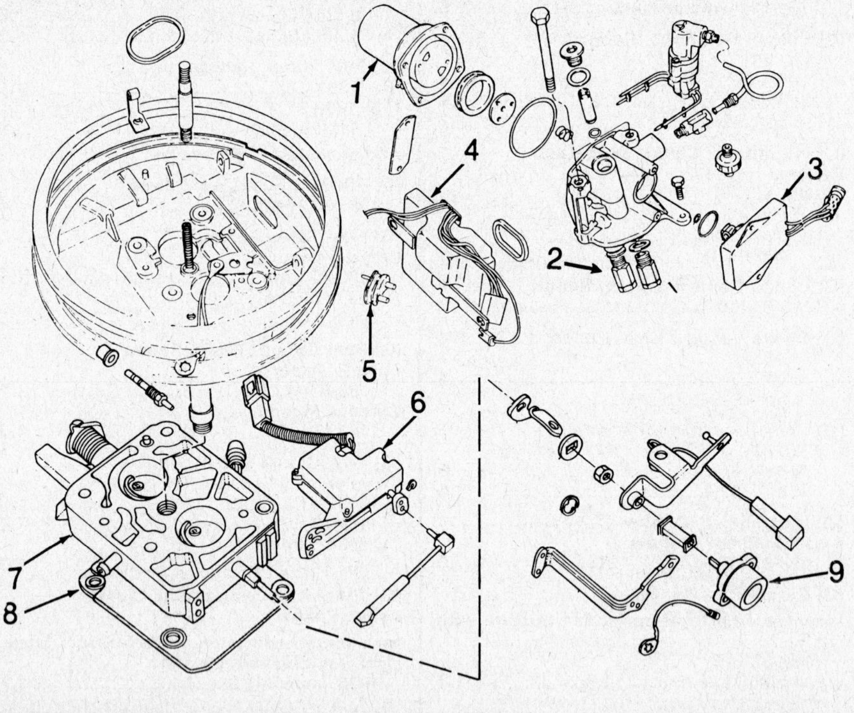

LABOR 3A EMISSION CONTROLS 3A LABOR

(Factory Time)	Chilton Time
AIR INJECTION SYSTEM	
(G) Air Pump, Renew	
Six-1983 (.7)	1.2
V-8-1983-87 (.5)	.9
(M) Air Injection Pump Belt, Renew	
1983-87 (.3)	.4
(G) Aspirator Assembly, Renew	
1983-87 (.2)	.3
(G) Air Pump Diverter/Switching Valve, Renew	
Six-1983 (.3)	.6
V-8-1983-87 (.3)	.6
(G) Injection Tube and Check Valve Assy., Renew	
Six-1983-to exh pipe (.4)	.7
to cyl head (.9)	1.2
V-8-1983-87	
exh manif mount (.9)	1.3
to converter (.4)	.7
(M) Air Pump Hoses, Renew	
1983-87-one (.2)	.3
(G) Orifice Spark Advance Control Valve, Renew	
1983-87 (.3)	.4

LABOR 3A EMISSION CONTROLS 3A LABOR

(Factory Time) Chilton Time

(G) Pulse Air Feeder/Aspirator Tube, Renew
1983-87 (.2) 4

EVAPORATIVE EMISSION

(M) Vapor Canister, Renew
1983-87 (.3) 4

(M) Vapor Canister Hoses, Renew
1983-87-one (.2) 2

(M) Vapor Canister Filter, Renew
1983-87 (.2) 3

CRANKCASE EMISSION

(M) Crankcase Vent Valve, Renew
1983-87 (.2) 3

(M) Positive Crankcase Vent Hose, Renew
1983-87 (.2) 3

(M) Crankcase Vent Air Cleaner, Renew
1983-87 (.2) 3

E.G.R. SYSTEM

(G) Exhaust Gas Recirculation Control Valve, Renew
Does not include test fuel injection system.
1983-87 (.3) 6

(G) Coolant Control Valve (CCEGR), Renew
1983-87 (.4) 4

CHILTON'S EMISSION CONTROL TUNE-UP

1. Clean or renew P.C.V. valve, hoses and filter.
2. Check fuel tank cap for sealing ability.
3. Check fuel tank and fuel lines for leakage.
4. Check evaporation canister and filter. Replace if necessary.
5. Check engine compression to determine leakage of unburned gases. (Add time for items of interference).
6. Test and clean or renew spark plugs.
7. Check engine oil dipstick for sealing ability.
8. Test exhaust system with analyzer and check system for leakage.
9. Check exhaust manifold heat valve for operation.
10. Adjust ignition timing and carburetor idle speed and mixture.
11. Check automatic choke mechanism for free operation.
12. Inspect air cleaner and element.
13. On models so equipped, test distributor vacuum control switch and transmission control switch.

Six **1.5**
V-8 .... **1.8**

For repairs made, charge accordingly.

(Factory Time) Chilton Time

(G) Recirculation Vacuum Amplifier, Renew
1983-87 (.2) 3

(G) Time Delay Timer, Renew
1983-87 (.2) 3

(G) Time Delay Solenoid, Renew
Does not include test fuel injection system.
1983-87 (.2) 3

(G) Engine Coolant Control Vacuum or Change Temperature Switch, Renew (CCEVS)
1983-87 (.4) 6

(G) Exhaust Manifold Power Heat Valve Actuator, Renew
1983-87 (.8) 1.2

EFE SYSTEM

(G) Oxygen Sensor, Renew
Does not include test fuel injection system.
1983-87 (.2) 4

(G) Detonation Switch, Renew
1983-87 (.2) 4

(G) High Altitude Compensator, Renew
1983-87 (.3) 5

(G) Oxygen Sensor Maintenance Lamp Switch, Renew or Reset
1983-87 (.2) 4

(G) Electronic Speed Switch, Renew
1984-87 (.2) 4

PARTS 3A EMISSION CONTROLS 3A PARTS

	Part No.	Price
Air Pump Assy.		
1983-exc. below	4268963	162.50
Six (wo/A.C.)	4268961	162.50
1984-87-V-8	4268963	162.50
Air Pump Pulley		
1983-Six	4241645	11.00
1983-87-V-8	3870088	10.50
Air Pump Diverter Valve		
1983-87-Six	4227670	30.50
V-8	4179719	30.50
Aspirator Valve		
1983-85	4041966	10.75
1986-87	4300376	19.50
Air Switch & Relief Valve		
1983-85	4227670	30.50
1986-87	4227672	30.50
Crossover and Check Valve Assy.		
1983-87	4179893	38.75

EVAPORATIVE EMISSION

	Part No.	Price
Vapor Canister		
1983-84	4241842	52.75
1985-87 (4227010)	4241839	49.75
(4227009)	4241838	52.75
Vapor Canister Filter		
1983	3577586	1.75

CRANKCASE EMISSION

	Part No.	Price
Positive Crankcase Vent Valve		
1983-87	3671076	4.25
Positive Crankcase Vent Air Cleaner		
1983-87	4273322	4.50

E.G.R. System

E.G.R. Valve

Replacement E.G.R. valves must be ordered according to the stamping number on the original valve.

	Part No.	Price
Vacuum Amplifier		
1983-85 (amplifier stamped)		
stamped	4041733	41.50
stamped	4241995	41.50
1986-87-4 bbl	4041737	41.50
Engine Coolant Control Vacuum Switch		
1983-225 eng.		
w/A.C.	3879736	17.50
wo/A.C.	4049208	17.50
1983-84-318 eng.		
2 bbl	3837622	17.50
4 bbl	4049276	17.50
1985-87-black	3879736	17.50
red	4095231	17.50
2 bbl	4049277	17.50
Time Delayed E.G.R. Solenoid Valve		
1983-225 eng (w/2 bbl carb)		
exc below	4240415	16.00
Stamped 4145631	4240149	15.25
Stamped 4145731	4240149	15.25
1983-84-318 eng.		
wo/E.F.I.	4240416	16.00
w/E.F.I.	4240415	16.00
1986-87	2 bbl&.416	
Dual Vacuum Solenoid		
1985	4289087	28.75
1986-87-exc. Calif.	6032473	.25
Calif.-2 bbl.	4289087	28.75
Manifold Heat Control Valve		
1983-Six	4186175	12.25
1983-87-V-8	3683947	15.00
Time Delay Control (E.G.R.)		
1983-87-blue	4145202	45.25
red	4111481	43.00
Oxygen Sensor Switch		
1983	4301175	34.00
1984-87	4301375	40.00
Detonation Sensor		
1983-87	5213629	23.75

LABOR 4 ALTERNATOR AND REGULATOR 4 LABOR

	(Factory Time)	Chilton Time
(G) Alternator Circuits, Test		
Includes: Test battery, regulator and alternator output.		
All models		.6
(M) Alternator Drive Belt, Renew		
1983-87	(.2)	.3
w/A.C. add	(.1)	.1
w/P.S. add	(.1)	.1
w/Air inj add	(.1)	.1
(G) Alternator, Renew		
Includes: Transfer pulley if required.		
1983-87	(.4)	.6
w/A.C. add	(.1)	.1
w/Air inj add	(.2)	.2
w/100 amp alter add	(.1)	.1
Add circuit test if performed.		
(G) Alternator, R&R and Recondition		
Includes: Test and disassemble.		
1983-87	(1.4)	2.0
w/A.C. add	(.1)	.1
w/Air inj add	(.2)	.2
w/100 amp alter add	(.1)	.1
(G) Alternator Front Bearing or Retainer, Renew		
1983-87	(.7)	1.0
w/A.C. add	(.1)	.1
w/Air inj add	(.2)	.2
w/100 amp alter add	(.1)	.1
Renew rear brg add		.2
(G) Alternator Regulator, Renew		
Includes: Test.		
1983-87	(.2)	.6
(G) Alternator Gauge, Renew		
Chryler		
1983-87	(.5)	1.0
Cordoba-Mirada		
1983	(.4)	.8
(G) Instrument Cluster Voltage Limiter, Renew		
Chrysler		
1983-87	(.3)	.7
Cordoba-Mirada		
1983	(.4)	.7

PARTS 4 ALTERNATOR AND REGULATOR 4 PARTS

	Part No.	Price
Alternator Assembly (New)		
(60 & 78 amp)		
1983-87-stamped ident.		
4091565	4091565	129.00
4091566	4176007	129.00
4111266	4176004	129.00
4111204	4176006	129.00
(114 amp)		
1983-87	4091460	252.25
Regulator Assembly (New)		
1983-87	4111990	29.00
(1) Brush Pkg.		
1983-87-exc. 114 amp	4057928	4.50
114 amp	3838079	4.75
(2) Drive End Shield Brg.		
(60 & 78 amp)		
1983-87-exc. below	3656444	8.75
stamped 4091565	2098478	N.L.
(114 amp)		
1983-87	3755951	24.00
(3) Rotor		
1983-87-exc. below	4240414	62.00
60 amp	4240413	62.00
114 amp	4026048	62.00
(4) Stator		
1983-87-exc. below	4091517	36.75
60 amp	4091515	36.75
114 amp	3879401	55.50
(5) Rectifier End Shield Brg.		
1983-87-exc below	3755184	3.25
114 amp	3874074	4.00

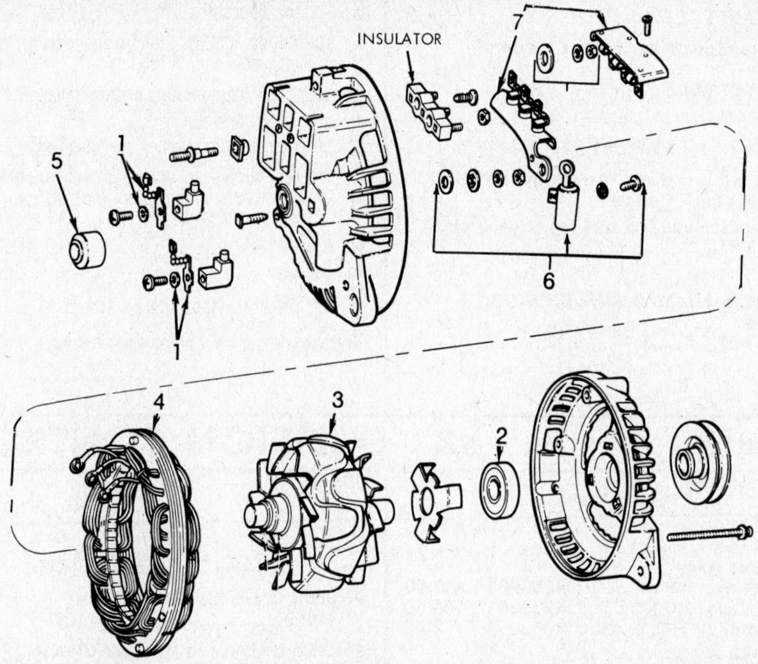

	Part No.	Price
(6) Capacitor and Bolt Pkg.		
1983-87-exc below	3620793	4.75
114 amp	3838078	4.75
(7) Rectifier Heat Sink Pkg.		
(60 amp)		
1983-87-positive	4240488	17.50
negative	3438721	17.75
(78 amp)		
1983-87-positive	4240488	17.50
negative	3755114	17.75
(114 amp)		
1983-87-positive	4026303	28.25
negative	3755627	22.75

LABOR 5 STARTING SYSTEM 5 LABOR

	(Factory Time)	Chilton Time
(G) Starter Draw Test (On Car)		
All models		.3
(G) Starter, Renew		
Includes: Test starter relay, starter solenoid and amperage draw.		
Six–1983	(.8)	1.2
V-8–1983-87	(.7)	1.3
(G) Starter, R&R and Recondition		
Includes: Test relay, starter solenoid and amperage draw.		
Six–1983	(1.4)	2.0
V-8–1983-87	(1.5)	2.1
Renew field coils add	(.5)	.5
(G) Starter Drive, Renew		
Includes: R&R starter.		
Six–1983	(1.2)	1.7
V-8–1983-87	(1.1)	1.8
(G) Starter Relay, Renew		
1983-87	(.2)	.4

LABOR 5 STARTING SYSTEM 5 LABOR

(Factory Time) Chilton Time

(G) Starter Solenoid, Renew
Includes: R&R starter.
Six–1983 (1.2) 1.7
V-8–1983-87 (1.0) 1.8

(G) Starter Neutral Switch, Renew
1983-87 (.3) 4

(Factory Time) Chilton Time

(G) Ignition Switch, Renew
Includes: Replace and recode lock cylinder if necessary.
Chrysler
1983-87-std column (.5) 1.3
tilt column (.4) 1.0
Cordoba-Mirada
1983-std column (.6) 1.1

(Factory Time) Chilton Time

tilt column (.5) 1.0
Imperial
1983 (.5) 1.0

(M) Battery Cables, Renew
ground (.2) 3
battery to starter relay (.5) 5
positive (.4) 4

PARTS 5 STARTING SYSTEM 5 PARTS

	Part No.	Price
Ignition Switch		
1983-87-wo/tilt whl	4131367	13.00
w/tilt whl	3747529	14.50
Starter Assy. (New)		
1983-87	4145360	149.00
(1) Starter Armature (New)		
1983-87	3837334	66.25
(2) Shaft (Pinion)		
1983-87	4091914	11.00
(3) Gear & Snap Ring Pkg.		
1983-87	4106092	11.25
(4) Starter Clutch Assy.		
1983-87	4145978	23.50
(5) Core and Shifting Fork Pkg.		
1983-87	4057940	12.75
(6) Bearing		
1983-87		
pinion housing	3874817	1.75
gear housing	3874818	2.25
(7) Contact & Spring Pkg.		
1983-87	2932814	5.50

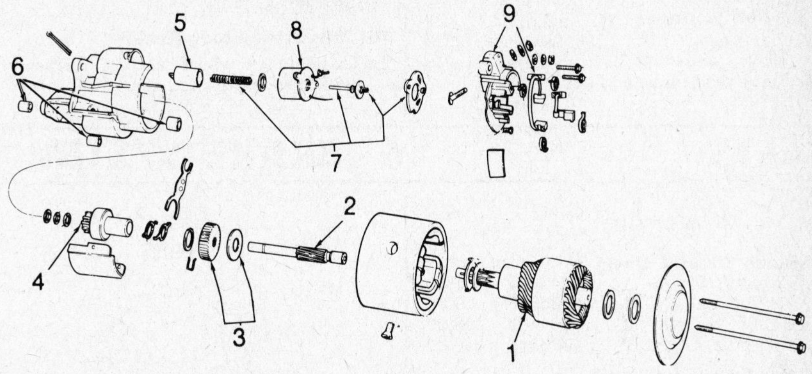

	Part No.	Price
(8) Solenoid Switch (New)		
1983-87	3837337	27.00
(9) Plate & Brush Pkg.		
1983-87	3874345	20.00

	Part No.	Price
Relay Switch		
1983-87	4111971	11.25
Battery Cables		
Order by year and model.		

LABOR 6 BRAKE SYSTEM 6 LABOR

(Factory Time) Chilton Time

(G) Brake Pedal Free Play, Adjust
All models 4

(G) Brakes, Adjust (Minor)
Includes: Adjust brake shoes, fill master cylinder.
two wheels 4

(G) Bleed Brakes (Four Wheels)
Includes: Add fluid.
All models (.4) 6

(G) Self Adjustor Cable and Guide or Lever, Renew
1983-87-one (.3) 7
each adtnl 4

(G) Brakes Shoes and/or Pads, Renew
Includes: Install new or exchange shoes or pads, adjust service and hand brake. Bleed system.
1983-87-front-disc (.6) 1.1
rear-drum (.7) 1.5
all four wheels (1.3) 2.5
Resurface disc rotor, add-each 9
Resurface brake drum, add-each 5

(G) Brake Drum, Renew (One)
1983-87 (.4) 5

COMBINATIONS

Add To Brakes, Renew

See Machine Shop Operations

(G) RENEW WHEEL CYLINDER
Each 2

(G) REBUILD WHEEL CYLINDER
Each 3

(G) REBUILD CALIPER ASSEMBLY
Each 5

(G) RENEW MASTER CYLINDER
All models 6

(G) REBUILD MASTER CYLINDER
All models 1.0

(G) RENEW BRAKE HOSE
Each (.3) 3

(G) RENEW REAR WHEEL GREASE SEALS
One side (.4) 4

(G) REPACK FRONT WHEEL BEARINGS (BOTH WHEELS)
All models 6

(G) RENEW DISC BRAKE ROTOR
Each 5

(G) RENEW BRAKE DRUM
Each 1

(Factory Time) Chilton Time

BRAKE HYDRAULIC SYSTEM

(G) Wheel Cylinder, Renew
Includes: Bleed system.
1983-87-one (.7) 1.1
both (1.3) 2.1

(G) Wheel Cylinder, R&R and Rebuild
Includes: Hone cylinder & bleed system.
1983-87-one 1.2
both 2.3

(G) Brake Hose, Renew (Flex)
Includes: Bleed system.
1983-87-each (.4) 6

(G) Master Cylinder, Renew
Includes: Bleed complete system.
1983-87 (.5) 9

(G) Master Cylinder, R&R and Rebuild
Includes: Bleed complete system.
1983-87 .... 1.7

(G) Master Cylinder Reservoir, Renew
Includes: Bleed complete system.
1983-87 (.6) 1.0

LABOR — 6 BRAKE SYSTEM 6 — LABOR

(Factory Time)	Chilton Time
POWER BRAKES	
(G) Brake Booster Assembly, Renew	
1983-87 (.6)	1.0
(G) Brake Booster Check Valve, Renew	
1983-87 (.2)	.3
DISC BRAKES	
(G) Brake Shoes and/or Pads, Renew	
Includes: Install new or exchange shoes or pads, adjust service and hand brake. Bleed system.	
1983-87-front-disc (.6)	1.1
rear-drum (.7)	1.5
all four wheels (1.3)	2.5
Resurface disc rotor, add-each	.9
Resurface brake drum, add-each	.5
(G) Caliper Assembly, Renew	
Includes: Bleed system.	
1983-87-one (.5)	1.0
both (.9)	1.8
(G) Caliper Assy., R&R And Recondition	
Includes: Bleed system.	
1983-87-one (.8)	1.5
both (1.5)	2.8
(G) Brake System Combination Valve Assy., Renew	
Includes: Bleed system.	
1983-87 (.8)	1.2
(G) Disc Brake Rotor, Renew	
Includes: Renew wheel bearings if necessary.	
1983-87-one (.6)	.9
both (1.1)	1.7
PARKING BRAKE	
(M) Parking Brake, Adjust	
1983-87 (.3)	.4
(G) Parking Brake Lever, Renew	
Chrysler-Imperial	
1983-87 (.7)	1.2
Cordoba-Mirada	
1983 (.7)	1.2
(G) Parking Brake Cables, Renew	
1983-87-front (.6)	.9
rear (.5)	.7
intermediate (.4)	.6
(G) Parking Brake Warning Lamp Switch, Renew	
1983-87 (.3)	.4

PARTS — 6 BRAKE SYSTEM 6 — PARTS

	Part No.	Price
(1) Brake Shoes & Lining Set (Rear)		
1983-84-10″ brks	4049682	55.00
11″ brks	4026648	50.00
1985-86-10″ brks	4364786	55.00
11″ brks	4026648	50.00
(2) Wheel Cylinder (Rear)		
1983-87	3780525	21.25
Brake Hose (Front)		
1983-87-right	4240508	19.25
left	4240509	19.25
Brake Hose (Rear)		
1983-87	4126502	16.00
Master Cylinder Assy.		
1983-87	3880289	79.75
Reservoir		
1983-87	3766448	4.75
Reservoir Grommets		
1983-87	5204149	1.00
Brake Booster Assy.		
1983-87	3880348	218.25
Check Valve Kit		
1983-87	3420973	8.50
Hub & Disc Rotor (Front)		
Except Imperial		
1983-87-Std	4131251	118.00
H.D.	3880685	112.75

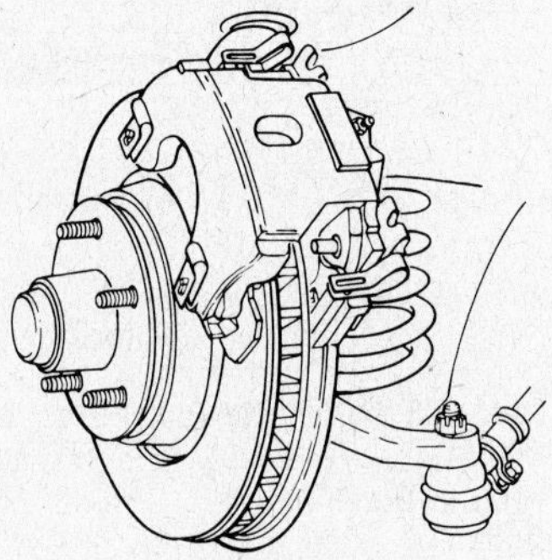

FRONT BRAKE

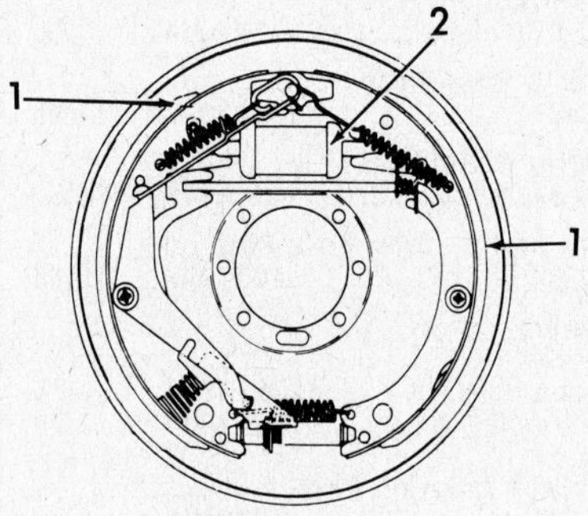

REAR BRAKE

	Part No.	Price
Imperial		
1983	4126886	118.00
Brake Drum		
1983-87-10″ brks	4049661	97.75
11″ brks	3780537	102.75
Oil Seal (Front)		
1983-87	3580723	6.00
PARKING BRAKE		
Parking Brake Lever		
1983	4019851	32.50
1984-87	4019369	37.75
Parking Brake Cable		
1983-87-front	3766292	17.25
interm.	3880072	5.75
rear-exc. H.D.	3880074	19.50
H.D.	3880075	19.50
Brake System Indicator Switch		
1983-87	3620790	4.25
Proportioning Valve		
1983-87-exc.		
Police	4176794	60.75
Police	3880038	56.75

PARTS — 6 DISC BRAKES 6 — PARTS

	Part No.	Price
(1) Brake Pads		
1983-87-Std.	4176778	47.50
H.D.	4049699	47.50
(2) Boot & Seal Pkg.		
1983-87	4186990	4.50
Piston, Boot & Seal Pkg.		
1983-87	4186989	19.25
(3) Caliper Housing		
1983-87-right	4126842	126.00
left	4126843	126.00

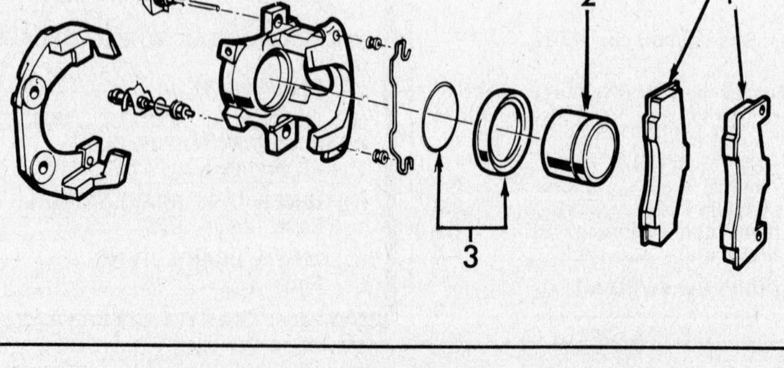

LABOR 7 COOLING SYSTEM 7 LABOR

	(Factory Time)	Chilton Time
(M) Winterize Cooling System		
Includes: Run engine to check for leaks, tighten all hose connections. Test radiator and pressure cap, drain radiator and engine block. Add anti-freeze and refill system.		
All models		.5
(M) Thermostat, Renew		
1983-87	(.4)	.6
w/A.C.	(.3)	.3
(M) Radiator Assembly, R&R or Renew		
1983-87	(.8)	1.2
w/A.C. add	(.1)	.2
w/A.T. add	(.1)	.2

ADD THESE OPERATIONS TO RADIATOR R&R

(G) Boil & Repair	1.5
(G) Rod Clean	1.9
(G) Repair Core	1.3
(G) Renew Tank	1.6
(G) Renew Trans. Oil Cooler	1.9
(G) Recore Radiator	1.7

	(Factory Time)	Chilton Time
(M) Radiator Hoses, Renew		
1983-87-upper	(.4)	.5
lower	(.4)	.5
by-pass-Six	(.6)	.9
V-8	(.3)	.6
w/A.C. add	(.1)	.1
(G) Transmission Auxiliary Oil Cooler, Renew		
1983-87-Chrysler	(.3)	.8
Imperial	(.6)	.9
Cordoba-Mirada		
1983	(.6)	.9
(G) Water Pump, Renew		
Includes: Drain and refill coolant.		
Six-1983	(.9)	1.3
V-8-1983-87		
318-360 engs	(1.0)	1.4
w/P.S. add	(.2)	.2
w/A.C. add	(.4)	.4
(M) Fan Blades, Renew		
1983-87	(.3)	.4
w/A.C. add		.1
w/Air inj add	(.1)	.1
(M) Drive Belt, Renew		
1983-87	(.2)	.3
w/A.C. add	(.1)	.1
w/Air inj add	(.1)	.1
w/P.S. add	(.1)	.1

COOLING SYSTEM TUNE-UP

An Annual Cooling System Tune-Up Suggestion List should include (with some exceptions):

1. A visual check of the cooling system for indications of leaks or excessive oil content.
2. Pressure check the cooling system for internal and external leaks with filler cap and neck adapter and tester.
3. Check crankcase and automatic transmission oil for water content.
4. Test coolant thermostat with radiator thermometer.
5. Check temperature gauge for accuracy.
6. Drain system and flush till clean.
7. Clean foreign matter from radiator fins.
8. Test radiator pressure cap with cap tester.
9. Check fan blades and pulleys for alignment and damage.
10. Internal and external inspection of all hoses for cracks and deterioration.
11. Check core plugs (where possible) for seepage.
12. Refill system with correct coolant and check for air locks.
13. Check condition and tension of drive belts with tension gauge.

All models 1.5

	(Factory Time)	Chilton Time
(M) Fluid Fan Drive, Renew		
1983-87	(.3)	.6
w/A.C. add	(.3)	.3
w/Air inj add	(.1)	.1
(G) Temperature Gauge (Engine Unit), Renew		
1983-87	(.3)	.5
(G) Temperature Gauge (Dash Unit), Renew		
Chrysler		
1983-87	(.5)	.9
Cordoba-Mirada		
1983	(.4)	.6
(G) Water Jacket Expansion Plugs, Renew (Engine Block)		
Six-1983-one	(2.3)	2.8
V-8-1983-87-front		
right or left side-one	(1.3)	1.5
center-one	(.6)	.8
rear side-one	(.7)	.9
all-both sides	(2.3)	2.8
engine rear-one or both	(2.7)	3.5
(G) Water Jacket Expansion Plugs, Renew (Cylinder Head)		
Six-1983-front-one	(.5)	.7
V-8-1983-87		
318-360 engs-front-one	(.5)	.7
rear-one	(3.4)	4.1
(G) Heater Hoses, Renew		
1983-87-one	(.3)	.6
both	(.5)	.8
(G) Heater Core, R&R or Renew		
Without Air Conditioning		
1983-87	(1.9)	3.0
With Air Conditioning		
1983-87-Chrysler	(3.0)	*4.5
Cordoba-Mirada-Imperial	(2.6)	*4.0

*Includes: Charge A.C. system.

ADD THESE OPERATIONS TO HEATER CORE R&R

(G) Boil & Repair	1.2
(G) Repair Core	.9
(G) Recore	1.2

	(Factory Time)	Chilton Time
(G) Heater Control Assembly, Renew		
1983-87	(.4)	.9
(G) Temperature Control Cable, Renew		
1983-87	(1.0)	1.6
(G) Heater Mode Control Cable, Renew		
1983-87	(.4)	.6
(G) Heater Blower Motor, Renew		
Chrysler-Imperial		
1983-87	(1.9)	3.0
Cordoba-Mirada		
1983	(.6)	1.1
(G) Heater Blower Motor Switch, Renew		
1983-87	(.4)	.7
(G) Heater Water Valve, Renew		
1983-87	(.4)	.6
(G) Heater Blower Motor Resistor, Renew		
1983-87	(.4)	.6

PARTS 7 COOLING SYSTEM 7 PARTS

	Part No.	Price
Radiator Assy.		
Order by year and model.		
(1) Thermostat		
1983-87	4131240	6.50
(2) Radiator Hoses		
Order by year and model.		
(3) Water Pump Assy. (New)		
Six-225 engine		
1983	4131243	54.00
V-8-318 engine		
1983-87	3837641	60.25
(4) Fan Belt		
Order by year and model.		
Heat Indicator (Engine Unit)		
1983-87	4091471	16.25
Heat Indicator (Dash Unit)		
Cordoba & Mirada		
New Yorker, Fifth Ave.		
1983-87	4051348	22.00
Note: Imperial is serviced in electronic instrument cluster.		
Heater Core		
1983	3847600	106.75
1984	3848455	106.50
1985-87	4339438	106.50

PARTS 7 COOLING SYSTEM 7 PARTS

	Part No.	Price
Blower Motor		
1983-exc. below	4240425	74.25
Imperial	3847997	74.25
1984	4049797	56.50
1985-87	4240425	74.25
Blower Motor Resistor		
1983-84	3847910	12.75
1985-87	3848996	13.25
Heater Switch		
1983-87	3847940	10.25
Heater Valve		
1983-87	3847475	28.25
Transmission Auxiliary Oil Cooler		
1983	4266033	111.50
1984-87	4266038	99.75
Engine Oil Cooler		
1983-87	4140394	262.00
Transmission Oil Cooler (Radiator)		
1983-87 (Length X Outside Dia.)		
12" x 1.00"	4140380	56.25
12" x 1.25"	4140383	56.25
12" x 1.50"	4140382	56.25
14.40" x 1.50"	4140381	56.25

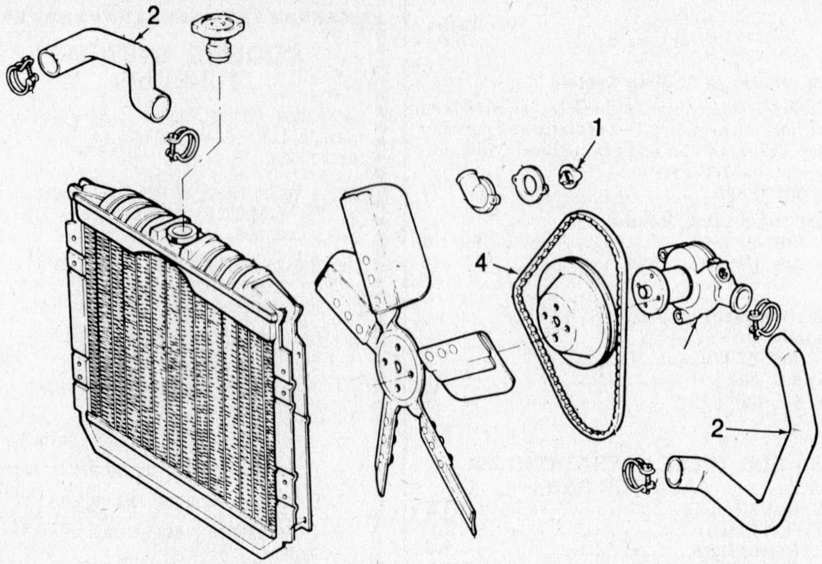

LABOR 8 EXHAUST SYSTEM 8 LABOR

(Factory Time)	Chilton Time
(G) Muffler, Renew	
1983-87-each (.6)	.9
(G) Tail Pipe, Renew	
1983-87-one (.4)	.6
(G) Catalytic Converter, Renew	
1983-87-one (.7)	1.2
both (1.3)	2.0
(G) Catalytic Converter Heat Shield, Renew	
1983-87-front (.8)	1.2
intermediate (.4)	.8
rear (.6)	1.0
(G) Exhaust Pipe Flange Gasket, Renew	
1983 (.3)	.6
(G) Exhaust Pipe, Renew	
1983-87-Six (.7)	1.1
V-8-one piece (1.3)	1.8
two piece-each (.5)	.8
Cut at muffler add (.2)	.2
(G) Exhaust Pipe Extension, Renew	
1983-87-front-one (.6)	1.1
both (1.2)	1.8
(G) Manifold Heat Valve, Recondition	
Includes: R&R exhaust manifold, where required.	
Six-1983 (2.2)	3.2
V-8-1983-87	
318-360 engs (1.4)	1.9
w/A.C. add (.4)	.4
(G) Manifold Heat Control Valve Counterweight & Spring, Renew	
Six (.3)	.6
V-8 (.5)	.8
(G) Power Heat Control Valve, Renew	
1983-87 (.8)	1.2
(G) Exhaust Manifold or Gaskets, Renew	
Six-1983 (1.9)	3.0
V-8	
1983-87-right side (.7)	1.0
left side (.6)	.9
w/Air inj add (.4)	.4
w/A.C. add (.4)	.4
(G) Intake and Exhaust Manifold Gaskets, Renew	
Six-1983 (1.7)	2.3
w/A.C. add (.4)	.4

COMBINATIONS

(G) Muffler, Exhaust and Tail Pipe, Renew	
one side	2.0
both sides	3.5
(G) Muffler and Tail Pipe, Renew	
front one	1.5
rear one	1.2
one side two	1.6
one each side	2.0

PARTS 8 EXHAUST SYSTEM 8 PARTS

	Part No.	Price
Muffler		
Order by year and model.		
1984-87	4150553	71.00
Tail Pipe		
V-8-318 engine		
1983	4150170	21.25
1984-87-2 bbl	4150170	21.25
4 bbl	4301339	63.25
Tail Pipe & Resonator		
Six-225 engine		
1983	4150186	65.50
V-8-318 engine		
1983	4301339	63.25
Exhaust Pipe		
Six-225 engine		
1983	4150462	51.00
V-8-318 engine		
1983	4150324	81.00
1984-87-2 bbl	4150342	74.75
4 bbl	4150324	81.00
Heat Control Valve		
1983-87-Six	4186175	12.25
V-8 engs.	3683947	15.00
Catalytic Convertor		
Six-225 engine		
1983-front	4301100	328.25
rear	4150715	276.50
V-8-318 engine		
1983 (New Yorker, Cordoba & Mirada)		
exc. Calif.	4150744	307.25
Calif.	4150718	338.00
1983 (Imperial)		
E.F.I.	4150722	338.00
1984-87 (Front)		
2 bbl	4150524	366.75
4 bbl	4150330	280.00
1984-87 (Rear)		
2 bbl	4150744	307.25
4 bbl	4150718	338.00

LABOR 9 FRONT SUSPENSION 9 LABOR

(Factory Time) Chilton Time

Note: On all front suspension operations alignment charges must be added if performed. Time given does not include alignment.

(M) Wheel, Renew
one (.3) 3

(M) Wheels, Rotate (All)
All models 5

(G) Wheels, Balance
one 3
each adtnl 2

(G) Check Alignment of Front End
All models 5
Note: Deduct if alignment is performed.

(G) Toe-In, Adjust
All models (.4) 6

(G) Align Front End
Includes: Adjust caster, camber, toe, car height and center steering wheel.
All models (1.1) 1.4
Adjust headlamps add 4
w/A.C. interference add 5

(G) Car Height, Adjust
1983-87 (.3) 6
Adjust headlamps add 3

(G) Front Wheel Bearings, Clean and Repack (Both Wheels)
1983-87 (.9) 1.4

(G) Front Wheel Bearings and Cups, Renew
Includes: R&R dust seal.
1983-87-one whl (.6) 7
both whls (1.1) 1.3

(G) Front Wheel Grease Seals, Renew
1983-87-one whl (.5) 6
both whls (.9) 1.0

(G) Front Shock Absorber or Bushings, Renew
1983-87-one (.3) 4
both (.5) 7

(G) Rebuild Front Suspension
Includes: Disassemble, renew necessary parts, reassemble, lubricate and align front end.
1983-87
one side 5.2
both sides 7.4

(G) Upper and Lower Ball Joints, Renew (One Side)
Add alignment charges.
1983-87 .... 2.1

(G) Upper Ball Joint, Renew
Add alignment charges.
1983-87-one (.7) 1.0
both (1.3) 2.0

(G) Lower Ball Joint, Renew
Add alignment charges.
1983-87-one (.7) 1.1
both (1.3) 2.1
1983-Imperial-one (.7) 1.1
both (1.3) 2.1

(G) Steering Knuckle, Renew (One)
Add alignment charges.
1983-87 (.7) 1.1
1983-Imperial (.7) 1.1

(G) Upper Control Arm, Renew (One)
Includes: Align front end.
1983-87 (1.8) 2.7

(G) Lower Control Arm, Renew (One)
Add alignment charges.
1983-87 (1.0) 1.4
1983-Imperial (1.0) 1.4

(G) Lower Control Arm Bushings, Renew
Add alignment charges.
1983-87-one side (1.1) 1.6

(G) Lower Control Arm Struts or Bushings, Renew
Add alignment charges.
1983-one (.5) 8
both (.9) 1.4

(G) Upper Control Arm Bushings, Renew
1983-87-one side (1.0) 1.5

(G) Torsion Bar, Renew
Includes: Adjust car height.
1983-87-one side (.7) 1.1
both sides (.9) 1.5

(G) Torsion Bar Bolt & Swivel, Renew
1983-87-one (.7) 9

(G) Front Sway Bar, Renew
1983-87 (.6) 1.0

(G) Front Sway Bar Bushings, Renew
Includes: Replace retainers and insulators.
1983-87 (.4) 6

(G) Front Sway Bar Links, Renew
1983-87-one (.6) 8
both (.7) 1.0

(G) 'K' Frame, Renew
Includes: Align front end.
1983-87 (5.7) 9.0

PARTS 9 FRONT SUSPENSION 9 PARTS

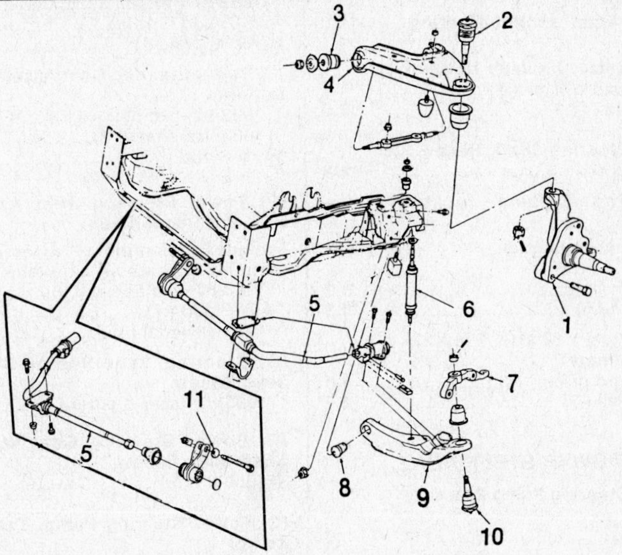

	Part No.	Price
Front Wheel Bearing Pkg.		
1983-87-outer	1671465	12.25
inner	3683975	14.75
(1) Steering Knuckle		
1983-87-right	3402640	109.00
Left	3402641	109.00
(2) Upper Ball Joint		
1983-87	2298534	33.75
(3) Bushing (Control Arm)		
1983-87	4106195	14.75
(4) Control Arm (Upper)		
1983-87-right	4014368	76.00
Left	4014369	76.00
(5) Torsion Bar Or Spring		
1983-87-Right	4014142	179.75
Left	4014143	179.75
(6) Shock Absorber		
1983-exc. below	3879932	16.25
Sta. Wagon	3879281	16.25
1983-Imperial	4342716	15.25
1984-87-Std.	4228410	16.25
H.D.	4228411	16.25
(7) Steering Knuckle Arm		
1983-87-Right	3815712	83.25
Left	3815713	83.25
(8) Bushing (Lower Arm)		
1983-87	3815688	8.50
(9) Control Arm (Lower)		
1983-87-Right	4014004	127.25
Left	4014005	127.25
(10) Lower Ball Joint		
1983-87	3837087	35.50
(11) Bearing (Adjusting Bolt)		
1983-87	4014100	5.50

LABOR 10 STEERING LINKAGE 10 LABOR

	(Factory Time)	Chilton Time
(G) Tie Rod Ends, Renew		
Includes: Adjust toe-in. Replace tie rod if necessary.		
1983-87		
inner or outer-both	(.7)	1.0
(G) Pitman Arm, Renew		
1983-87	(.3)	.6
(G) Idler Arm, Renew		
1983-87	(.4)	.6
(G) Steering Gear Center Link, Renew		
1983-87	(.4)	.7
(G) Steering Knuckle Arm, Renew (One)		
1983-87	(.7)	1.1
1983-Imperial	(.7)	1.1

PARTS 10 STEERING LINKAGE 10 PARTS

	Part No.	Price
(1) Steering Arm		
1983-87-right	3815712	83.25
left	3815713	83.25
(2) Tie Rod End Pkg.		
1983-87-inner	3420155	20.50
outer	3420154	20.50
(3) Tie Rod Tube		
1983-87	4014085	11.50
(4) Steering Arm (Pitman Arm)		
1983-87	3815777	56.25
(5) Idler Arm		
1983-87	4014089	53.25
(6) Center Link		
1983-87	3815727	51.50

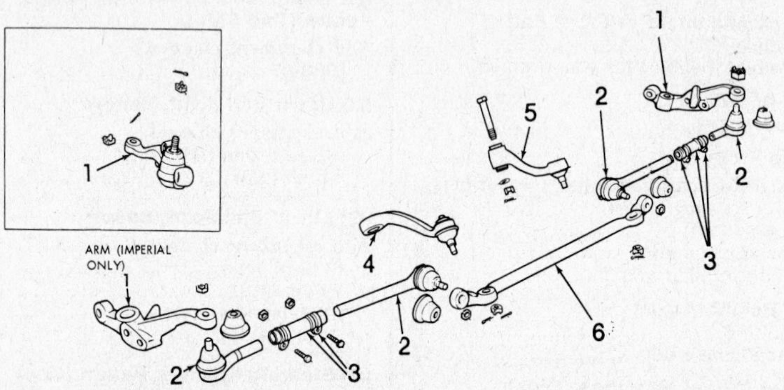

LABOR 11 STEERING GEAR 11 LABOR

	(Factory Time)	Chilton Time
(G) Horn Blowing Ring, Renew		
Cable & Ring		
1983-87-std colm	(.4)	.5
tilt colm	(.2)	.4
(G) Steering Wheel, Renew		
1983-87	(.2)	.4
(G) Upper Mast Jacket Bearing, Renew		
Includes: Replace insulator if necessary.		
1983-87-std column	(.7)	1.2
tilt column	(1.3)	2.0
(G) Upper Steering Shaft, Renew		
1983-87	(1.5)	2.1
(G) Steering Column Jacket, Renew		
Does not include painting.		
1983-87		
std colm	(2.3)	3.2
tlt colm	(2.6)	3.3
(G) Steering Shaft Flexible Coupling, Renew		
1983-87-std column	(.8)	1.4
tilt column	(.7)	1.1
POWER STEERING		
(G) Power Steering Pump Pressure Check		
All models		.5
(G) Power Steering Gear Sector Shaft, Adjust		
All models	(.5)	.8
(G) Power Steering Gear Control Valve, Adjust		
All models	(.3)	.6
(G) Power Steering Gear Control Valve, Renew		
All models	(.6)	.9
(M) Power Steering Pump Drive Belt, Renew		
1983-87	(.2)	.3
w/A.C. add	(.1)	.1
w/Air inj add	(.1)	.1
(G) Power Steering Gear Assembly, Renew		
1983-87-exc below	(1.2)	*2.0
1983-Imperial	(2.6)	4.0
*w/V-8 add	(.7)	.7
(P) Power Steering Gear Assy., R&R and Recondition		
Includes: Complete disassembly, and assembly, perform all adjustments.		
1983-87-exc below	(2.8)	*4.0
*w/V-8 add	(.7)	.7
1983-Imperial	(4.2)	6.0
(G) Steering Gear Sector Shaft Seal, Renew		
1983-87-inner & outer	(.5)	.9
(G) Power Steering Gear Worm Shaft Seal, Renew		
1983-87	(.9)	1.3
(G) Power Steering Pump, Test & Renew		
Includes: Transfer or renew pulley.		
1983-87	(.8)	1.2
(G) Power Steering Pump, R&R and Recondition		
1983-87	(1.3)	2.0
Add pressure check if performed.		
(G) Power Steering Reservoir or Seals, Renew		
1983-87	(.6)	1.0
(G) Pump Drive Shaft Seal, Renew		
1983-87	(1.0)	1.6
(G) Pump Flow Control Valve, Test and Clean or Renew		
1983-87	(.6)	1.0
(G) Pressure Control Valve, Renew		
1983-87	(.5)	.9
(M) Power Steering Hoses, Renew		
1983-87-pressure	(.3)	.5
return	(.2)	.4
cooling	(.4)	.6
TILT & TELESCOPIC STEERING COLUMN		
(G) Tilt Steering Wheel, Renew		
1983-87	(.3)	.6
(G) Upper Steering Shaft, Renew		
1983-87-to yoke	(1.4)	2.3
to coupling	(2.1)	2.9
(G) Steering Column Jacket, Renew		
Does not include painting.		
1983-87-column shift	(2.6)	3.3
console shift	(1.6)	2.5
(G) Steering Column Upper Bearing, Renew		
Includes: Replace insulator if necessary.		
1983-87	(1.3)	2.0

PARTS 11 POWER STEERING GEAR 11 PARTS

	Part No.	Price
(1) Sector Shaft		
1983-87	3643302	113.75
(2) Lower Seal Pkg.		
1983-87	3879921	6.50
(3) Valve Assembly		
1983-87	3643280	92.00
(4) Valve Lever		
1983-87	1822380	10.50
(5) Worm w/Piston		
1983-87-exc. Imp.	2948855	176.25
Imperial	3815854	176.25
(6) Piston 'O' Ring Pkg.		
1983-87	3879924	14.50
(7) Bearing (Worm)		
1983-87	2537796	3.00
(8) Cylinder Head		
1983-87	3643173	41.50
(9) Thrust Bearing Race		
1983-87-inner	1856292	3.00
outer	1822156	1.75
(10) Thrust Bearing		
1983-87	1822158	1.75

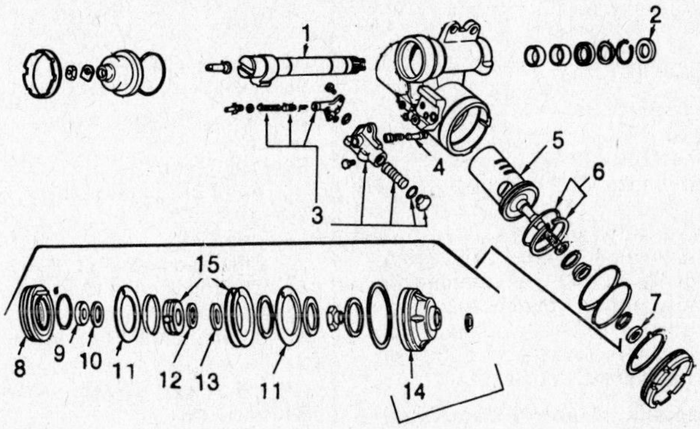

	Part No.	Price
(11) Reaction Spring		
1983-87	3643129	2.25
(12) Bearing (Thrust)		
1983-87	1822158	1.75

	Part No.	Price
(13) Bearing Race (Outer)		
1983-87	1822156	1.75
(14) Head (Housing)		
1983-87	3643315	60.00
(15) Spacer (w/Center Race)		
1983-87	1822390	56.00

PARTS 11 POWER STEERING PUMP 11 PARTS

	Part No.	Price
Pump Assy.		
1983-87	3815971	246.25
Seal Kit		
1983-87	2537838	11.00
(1) Plate (Pressure)		
1983-87	3815967	13.75
(2) Rotor Repair Kit		
1983-87	3815962	89.00
(3) Plate (Thrust)		
1983-87	3815914	12.25
(4) Shaft (Rotor)		
1983-87	3815961	39.00
(5) Housing		

Note: Serviced only in pump assembly.

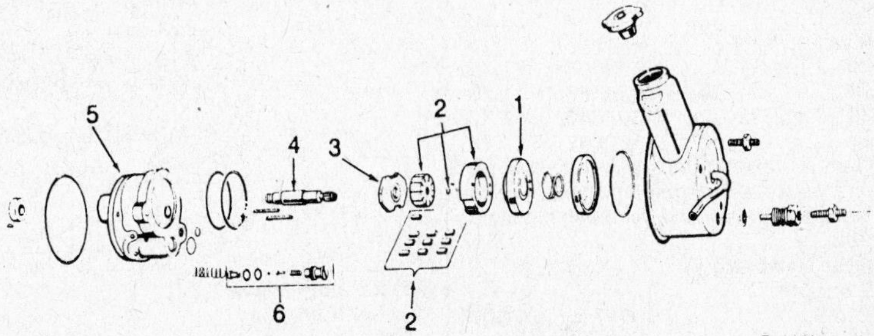

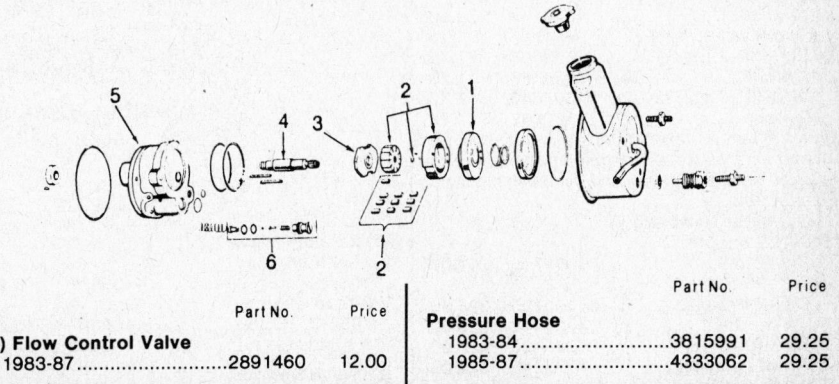

	Part No.	Price
(6) Flow Control Valve		
1983-87	2891460	12.00

	Part No.	Price
Pressure Hose		
1983-84	3815991	29.25
1985-87	4333062	29.25

LABOR 12 CYLINDER HEAD & VALVE SYSTEM 12 LABOR

	(Factory Time)	Chilton Time
(G) Compression Test		
Six-1983	(.5)	.6
V-8-1983-87		
318-360 engs	(.8)	1.1
w/A.C. add	(.3)	.3
w/Air inj add	(.3)	.3
(G) Cylinder Head Gasket, Renew		
Includes: Clean carbon.		
Six-1983	(3.1)	4.3
V-8-1983-87		
318-360 engs-one	(3.4)	4.7
both	(4.3)	6.0
w/A.C. add	(.4)	.5
(G) Cylinder Head, Renew		
Includes: Reface and adjust valves, clean carbon.		
Six-1983	(5.7)	8.0
V-8-1983-87		
318-360 engs-one	(4.9)	6.8
both	(7.2)	10.0
w/A.C. add	(.4)	.5

COMBINATIONS
Add to Valve Job

See Machine Shop Operations

(G) DRAIN, EVACUATE & RECHARGE AIR CONDITIONING SYSTEM	
All models	1.0
(G) ROCKER ARMS & SHAFT ASSY., DISASSEMBLE AND CLEAN OR OVERHAUL	
Six	.5
V-8-One side	.5
Both sides	.9
(G) HYDRAULIC VALVE LIFTERS, DISASSEMBLE AND CLEAN	
Each	.2
(G) DISTRIBUTOR, RECONDITION	
All models (1.0)	1.0
(G) CARBURETOR, RECONDITION	
1 BBL (.8)	1.2
2 BBL (1.7)	2.0
4 BBL (2.4)	2.7
(P) VALVE GUIDES, REAM OVERSIZE	
Each (.2)	.2

	(Factory Time)	Chilton Time
(P) Clean Carbon and Grind Valves		
Includes: R&R cylinder heads, adjust valve clearance when required. Minor engine tune up.		
Six-1983	(5.1)	7.4
V-8-1983-87		
318-360 engs	(6.9)	11.0
w/A.C. add	(.4)	.5
w/100 amp alter add	(.4)	.4
(G) Rocker Arm Cover or Gasket, Renew		
Six-1983	(.8)	1.1
V-8-1983-87		
318-360 engs-one	(.4)	.6
both	(.7)	1.0
w/A.C. add	(.4)	.5
w/100 amp alter add	(.4)	.4
w/Air inj add	(.3)	.3
(G) Valve Tappets, Renew		
Includes: R&R cylinder head on 6 cyl engine.		
Six-1983		
mechanical-one or all	(3.5)	4.4

LABOR 12 CYLINDER HEAD & VALVE SYSTEM 12 LABOR

(Factory Time)	Chilton Time
hydraulic-one or all (2.5)	4.4
V-8–1983-87	
318-360 engs	
one (2.0)	3.0
one-each bank (2.1)	3.4
all-both banks (2.2)	3.9
w/A.C. add (.4)	.5
w/100 amp alter add (.4)	.4

Note: Factory time based on using magnetic tool thru push rod opening to remove lifters. Chilton experience finds it better and safer to R&R intake manifold, since the lifters have a tendency to stick in the block and sometimes come apart.

(G) Valve Tappets, Renew (Roller Type)

(Factory Time)	Chilton Time
V-8–1985-87	
one (2.6)	3.6
each adtnl (.1)	.1

(G) Valve Spring and/or Valve Stem Oil Seal, Renew (Head on Car)

Includes: Adjust valve clearance when required.

(Factory Time)	Chilton Time
Six–1983-one (.9)	1.2
all (2.2)	3.2
V-8–1983-87	
one (.7)	1.0
one-each bank (1.3)	1.7
all-both banks (3.2)	4.0
w/A.C. add (.4)	.5
w/100 amp alter add (.4)	.4

(G) Rocker Arm Assembly, Recondition

Includes: Renew arms as required and shaft if necessary.

(Factory Time)	Chilton Time
Six–1983 (.9)	1.5
V-8–1983-87	
318-360 engs	
one side (.6)	1.3
both sides (1.0)	2.1
w/A.C. add (.4)	.5
w/100 amp alter add (.4)	.4

(G) Valve Push Rods, Renew

(Factory Time)	Chilton Time
Six–1983-one (.8)	1.0
all (1.1)	1.4
V-8–1983-87	
318-360 engs	
one (.5)	1.0
one-each bank (.8)	1.6
all-both banks (1.3)	2.0
w/A.C. add (.4)	.5
w/Air inj add (.3)	.3

PARTS 12 CYLINDER HEAD & VALVE SYSTEM 12 PARTS

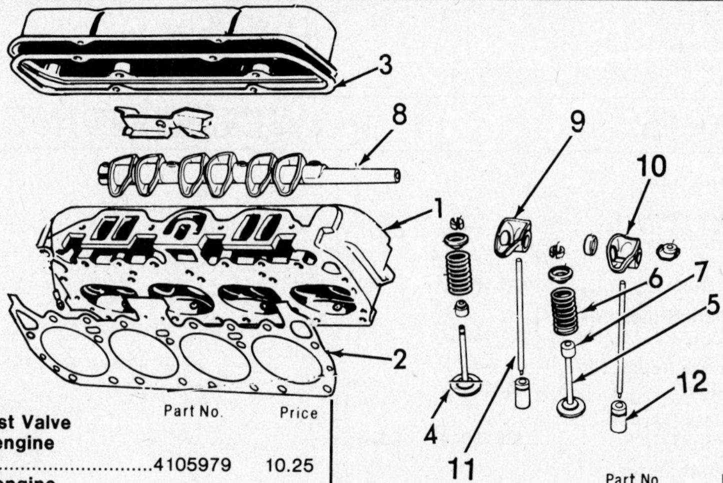

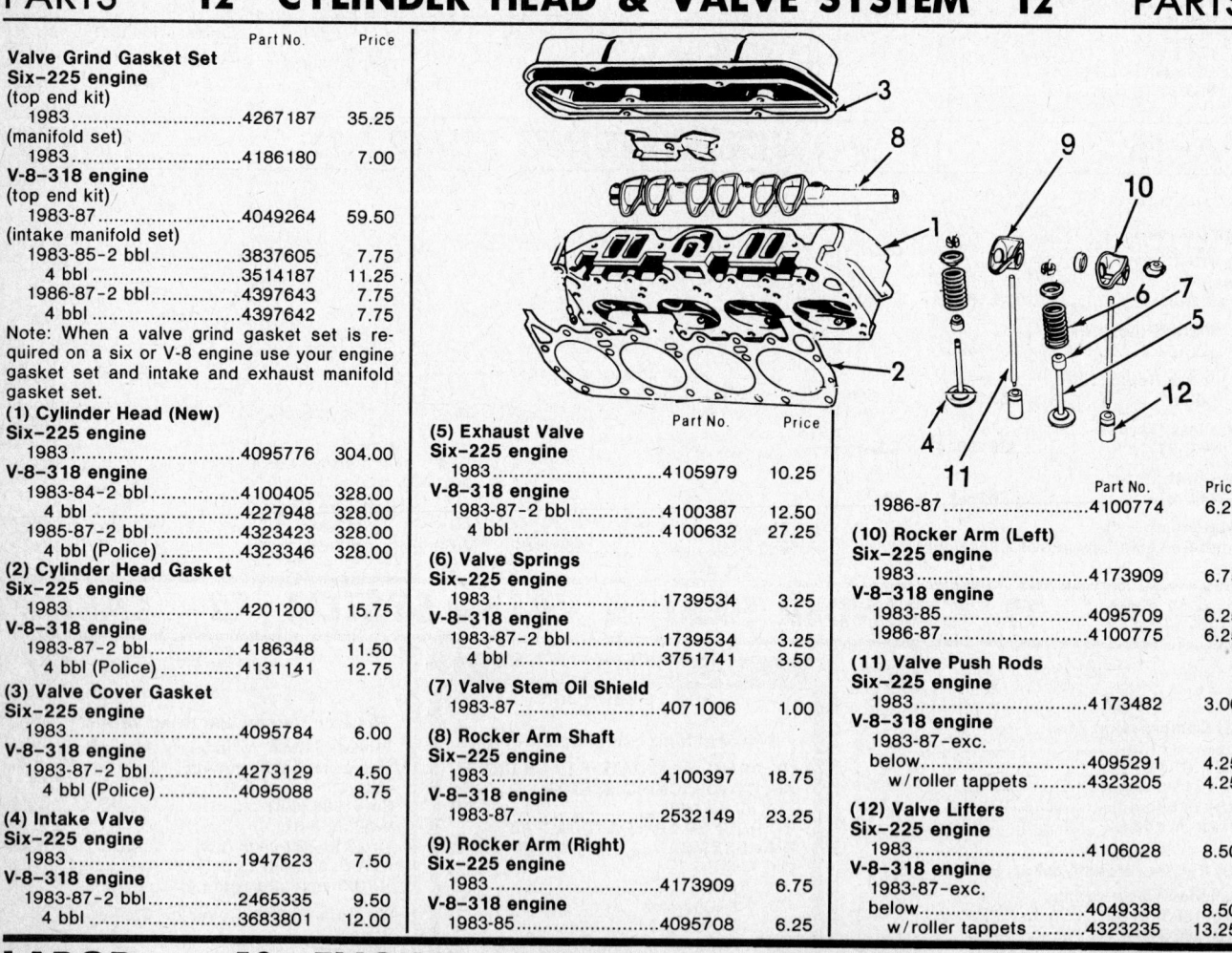

	Part No.	Price
Valve Grind Gasket Set		
Six–225 engine		
(top end kit)		
1983	4267187	35.25
(manifold set)		
1983	4186180	7.00
V-8–318 engine		
(top end kit)		
1983-87	4049264	59.50
(intake manifold set)		
1983-85-2 bbl	3837605	7.75
4 bbl	3514187	11.25
1986-87-2 bbl	4397643	7.75
4 bbl	4397642	7.75

Note: When a valve grind gasket set is required on a six or V-8 engine use your engine gasket set and intake and exhaust manifold gasket set.

	Part No.	Price
(1) Cylinder Head (New)		
Six–225 engine		
1983	4095776	304.00
V-8–318 engine		
1983-84-2 bbl	4100405	328.00
4 bbl	4227948	328.00
1985-87-2 bbl	4323423	328.00
4 bbl (Police)	4323346	328.00
(2) Cylinder Head Gasket		
Six–225 engine		
1983	4201200	15.75
V-8–318 engine		
1983-87-2 bbl	4186348	11.50
4 bbl (Police)	4131141	12.75
(3) Valve Cover Gasket		
Six–225 engine		
1983	4095784	6.00
V-8–318 engine		
1983-87-2 bbl	4273129	4.50
4 bbl (Police)	4095088	8.75
(4) Intake Valve		
Six–225 engine		
1983	1947623	7.50
V-8–318 engine		
1983-87-2 bbl	2465335	9.50
4 bbl	3683801	12.00
(5) Exhaust Valve		
Six–225 engine		
1983	4105979	10.25
V-8–318 engine		
1983-87-2 bbl	4100387	12.50
4 bbl	4100632	27.25
(6) Valve Springs		
Six–225 engine		
1983	1739534	3.25
V-8–318 engine		
1983-87-2 bbl	1739534	3.25
4 bbl	3751741	3.50
(7) Valve Stem Oil Shield		
1983-87	4071006	1.00
(8) Rocker Arm Shaft		
Six–225 engine		
1983	4100397	18.75
V-8–318 engine		
1983-87	2532149	23.25
(9) Rocker Arm (Right)		
Six–225 engine		
1983	4173909	6.75
V-8–318 engine		
1983-85	4095708	6.25
1986-87	4100774	6.25
(10) Rocker Arm (Left)		
Six–225 engine		
1983	4173909	6.75
V-8–318 engine		
1983-85	4095709	6.25
1986-87	4100775	6.25
(11) Valve Push Rods		
Six–225 engine		
1983	4173482	3.00
V-8–318 engine		
1983-87-exc.		
below	4095291	4.25
w/roller tappets	4323205	4.25
(12) Valve Lifters		
Six–225 engine		
1983	4106028	8.50
V-8–318 engine		
1983-87-exc.		
below	4049338	8.50
w/roller tappets	4323235	13.25

LABOR 13 ENGINE ASSEMBLY & MOUNTS 13 LABOR

(G) Engine Assembly, Remove & Install

Does not include transfer of any parts or equipment.

(Factory Time)	Chilton Time
Six–1983	5.0
V-8–1983-87	5.9
w/A.C. add	1.0

(G) Engine Assembly, Replace with New or Rebuilt Unit

Includes: R&R engine assembly, transfer all necessary parts, fuel and electrical units. Minor tune up.

(Factory Time)	Chilton Time
Six–1983 (7.3)	8.9
V-8–1983-87	
318-360 engs (8.4)	9.7
w/A.C. add (1.0)	1.0

LABOR 13 ENGINE ASSEMBLY & MOUNTS 13 LABOR

(Factory Time) Chilton Time

(P) Short Engine Assy., Renew (w/All Internal Parts Less Cylinder Head(s) and Oil Pan)

Includes: R&R engine, transfer all necessary parts not supplied with replacement engine, clean carbon, grind valves. Minor tune up.

Six–1983 (9.7)	12.5
V-8–1983-87	
318-360 engs (14.4)	18.4
w/A.C. add (1.0)	1.0

(P) Cylinder Block, Renew (w/Pistons, Rings and Pins)

Includes: R&R engine, transfer all necessary parts, clean carbon, grind valves. Minor tune up.

Six–1983 (12.7)	15.4
w/A.C. add (.4)	.4

(P) Engine Assy., R&R and Recondition (Complete)

Includes: Rebore block, install new pistons, rings, rod and main bearings. Clean carbon and grind valves, replace valve stem oil seals. Tune engine.

Six–1983 (23.2)	28.2
V-8–1983-87	
318-360 engs (28.3)	34.3
w/A.C. add (1.0)	1.0

(P) Engine Assembly, Recondition (In Car)

Includes: Expand or renew pistons, install rings, pins, rod and main bearings, clean carbon and grind valves. Tune engine.

Six–1983 (17.1)	23.2
V-8–1983-87	
318-360 engs (21.0)	25.6
w/A.C. add (.4)	.5
w/P.S. add (.4)	.4

(G) Engine Mounts, Renew

Front	
Six–1983	
right side (.6)	.8
left side (.4)	.6
V-8	
Chrysler-Imperial	
1983-87–right side (1.1)	1.6
left side (.9)	1.1
Cordoba-Mirada	
1983–right side (1.4)	1.7
left side (1.1)	1.4
Rear	
Six (.4)	.6
V-8-318-360 engs (.4)	.6

PARTS 13 ENGINE ASSEMBLY & MOUNTS 13 PARTS

Short Block (New)

Includes: Pistons, Pins, Rings, Crankshaft and bearings, Connecting rods and bearings.

	Part No.	Price
Six–225 engine		
1983	4227894	1503.50
V-8–318 engine		
1983-84–2 bbl	4105987	1757.50
4 bbl	4105989	1757.50
1985-87–2 bbl	4323619	1757.50
4 bbl	4323621	1757.50
Engine Gasket Set		
Six–225 engine		
1983–upper	4267187	35.25
lower	4106048	12.00
V-8–318 engine		
1983-85–upper	4049264	59.50
lower	3837644	12.75
1985-87–upper		
2 bbl	4049264	59.50
4 bbl	4049265	59.50
lower	3837644	12.75
Engine Mounts (Front)		
Six–225 engine		
1983–right	4295459	30.00
left	3642821	32.50
V-8–318 engine		
1983-87–right	3642818	21.75
left	3817237	21.75
Engine Mounts (Rear)		
(Exc. Imperial)		
1983-87–Std	4001801	20.25
H.D.	3817295	17.25
(Imperial)		
1983–Std	4001861	15.50
H.D.	3817295	17.25

LABOR 14 PISTONS, RINGS & BEARINGS 14 LABOR

(Factory Time) Chilton Time

(P) Rings, Renew (See Engine Combinations)

Includes: Replace connecting rod bearings, deglaze cylinder walls, clean carbon. Minor tune up.

Six–1983 (7.7)	10.2
V-8–1983-87	
318-360 engs (8.8)	12.5
w/A.C. add (.4)	.5
w/100 amp alter add (.4)	.4

(P) Piston or Connecting Rod, Renew

Includes: Replace connecting rod bearings and piston rings, deglaze cylinder walls.

Six–1983–one (5.6)	7.7
all (8.1)	11.2
V-8–1983-87	
318-360 engs–one (5.4)	7.3
one-each side (6.7)	9.4
all (8.9)	12.2
w/A.C. add (.4)	.5
w/100 amp alter add (.4)	.4

(P) Connecting Rod Bearings, Renew

Includes: Plastigauge all bearings.

Six–1983–one (2.4)	3.4
all (3.4)	4.4
V-8–1983-87–one (2.9)	4.0
all (4.3)	6.0

COMBINATIONS

Add to Engine Work

See Machine Shop Operations

(Factory Time) Chilton Time

(G) DRAIN, EVACUATE & RECHARGE AIR CONDITIONING SYSTEM

All models	1.0

(G) ROCKER ARM & SHAFT ASSEMBLY, DISASSEMBLE AND CLEAN OR OVERHAUL

Six	.5
V-8–One side	.5
Both sides	.9

(G) HYDRAULIC VALVE LIFTERS, DISASSEMBLE AND CLEAN

Each	.2

(G) DISTRIBUTOR, RECONDITION

All models (1.0)	1.0

(G) CARBURETOR, RECONDITION

1 BBL (.8)	1.2
2 BBL (1.7)	2.0
4 BBL (2.4)	2.7

(G) DEGLAZE CYLINDER WALLS

Each (.1)	.1

(G) REMOVE CYLINDER TOP RIDGE

Each (.1)	.1

(G) MAIN BEARINGS, RENEW (PAN REMOVED)

Six (1.3)	1.8
V-8 (1.8)	2.5

(G) PLASTIGAUGE BEARINGS

Each (.1)	.1

(G) OIL PUMP, RECONDITION

Six (1.4)	1.8
V-8 (.7)	.9

(M) OIL FILTER ELEMENT, RENEW

All models (.2)	.2

PARTS 14 PISTONS, RINGS & BEARINGS 14 PARTS

	Part No.	Price
(1) Piston Ring Set		
Six-225 engine		
1983	4131203	87.50
V-8-318 engine		
1983-85-2 bbl	2808550	93.50
4 bbl	2808553	102.75
1986-87	2808553	102.75
(2) Piston Assy. (Std.)		
Six-225 engine		
1983	2084384	33.00
V-8-318 engine		
1983-84	3685751	35.75
1985-87	4342772	35.75
(3) Connecting Rod (New)		
Six-225 engine		
1983	4041994	35.00
V-8-318 engine		
1983-87	3751015	38.75

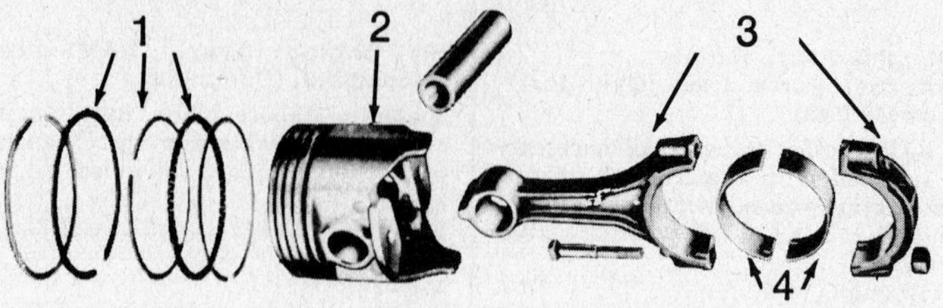

	Part No.	Price
(4) Connecting Rod Bearing (Std.)		
Six-225 engine		
1983	4049256	5.25
V-8-318 engine		
1983-87-2 bbl	4186118	6.50
4 bbl	2421305	9.00

LABOR 15 CRANKSHAFT & DAMPER 15 LABOR

(Factory Time)	Chilton Time
(P) Crankshaft & Main Bearings, Renew	
Includes: Replace rod bearings.	
Six-1983 (8.3)	**10.4**
V-8-1983-87	
318-360 engs (9.4)	**12.6**
Plastigauge bearings add, each (.1)	**.1**
(P) Main Bearings, Renew	
Includes: Replace pan gasket and seals, plastigauge all bearings.	
Six-1983 (4.1)	**5.7**
V-8-1983-87	
318-360 engs (4.4)	**6.0**
Renew rod bearings add, each (.3)	**.4**
(P) Rear Main Bearing Oil Seals, Renew (Upper & Lower)	
Six-1983 (2.3)	**3.2**
V-8-1983-87	
318-360 engs (2.5)	**3.5**
Note: Upper seal removed using special tool. If necessary to R&R crankshaft use crankshaft and main bearings, renew.	
(G) Vibration Damper, Renew	
Six-1983 (.9)	**1.4**
V-8-1983-87 (.6)	**1.0**
w/A.C. add (.3)	**.3**
w/Air inj add (.1)	**.1**

PARTS 15 CRANKSHAFT & DAMPER 15 PARTS

	Part No.	Price
(1) Crankshaft (New)		
Six-225 engine		
1983	4100646	578.25
V-8-318 engine		
1983-87-2 bbl	3751831	540.00
4 bbl	4227880	540.00
(2) Main Bearing Set (Std.)		
Six-225 engine		
1983-No. 1-2-4	4049242	8.75
No. 3	4049249	14.50
V-8-318 engine		
1983-87-2 bbl.		
No. 1	4106009	10.00
No. 2-4	4186194	9.75
No. 3	3780075	14.50
No. 5	3514151	12.25
1983-87-4 bbl		
No. 1-2-4	4240083	9.75

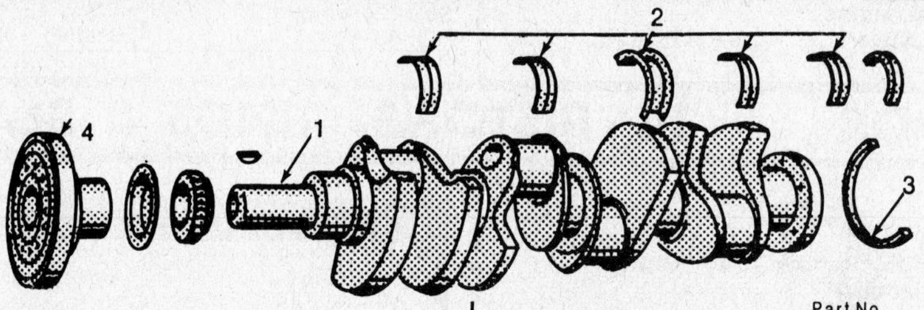

	Part No.	Price
No. 3	3780075	14.50
No. 5	3514151	12.25
(3) Rear Bearing Oil Seal		
Six-225 engine		
1983	4240150	6.50
V-8-318 engine		
1983-87	4240044	4.75
Front Oil Seal		
1983-87-Six	3830108	6.00
V-8	3830109	6.50
(4) Vibration Damper Or Pulley		
Six-225 engine		
1983-w/M.T.	4100696	71.00
w/A.T.	4095527	86.50
V-8-318 engine		
1983-87	4173443	81.00

LABOR 16 CAMSHAFT & TIMING GEARS 16 LABOR

(Factory Time)	Chilton Time
(G) Timing Cover Oil Seal, Renew	
V-8-1983-87 (.8)	**1.2**
w/A.C. add (.2)	**.2**
w/P.S. add (.2)	**.2**
(G) Timing Case Seal and Gaskets, Renew	
Six-1983 (1.5)	**2.5**
V-8-1983-87 (2.1)	**3.1**
w/P.S. add (.2)	**.2**
w/A.C. add (.4)	**.5**
w/Air inj add (.1)	**.1**
(G) Camshaft Gear or Timing Chain, Renew	
Includes: Renew cover oil seal and crankshaft gear if necessary.	
Six-1983 (2.1)	**3.1**
V-8-1983-87	
318-360 engs (2.6)	**3.6**
w/P.S. add (.2)	**.2**
w/A.C. add (.4)	**.5**
w/Air inj add (.1)	**.1**
(G) Camshaft, Renew	
Includes: Renew valve tappets and adjust valve clearance when required.	
Six-1983 (5.1)	**8.0**
V-8-1983-87 (5.5)	**8.4**
w/A.C. add (.8)	**1.3**
w/P.S. add (.2)	**.2**
w/Air inj add (.1)	**.1**
(P) Camshaft Bearings, Renew	
Six-1983 (5.9)	**10.8**
V-8-1983-87	
318-360 engs (6.3)	**9.1**
w/A.C. add (1.0)	**1.3**
(G) Camshaft Rear Bearing Welsh Plug, Renew	
Six-1983 (2.5)	**3.5**
V-8-1983-87 (2.5)	**3.5**

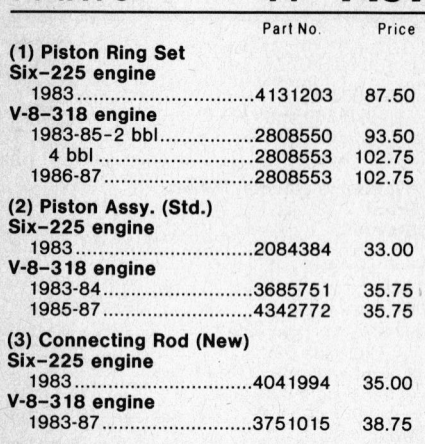

PARTS 16 CAMSHAFT & TIMING GEARS 16 PARTS

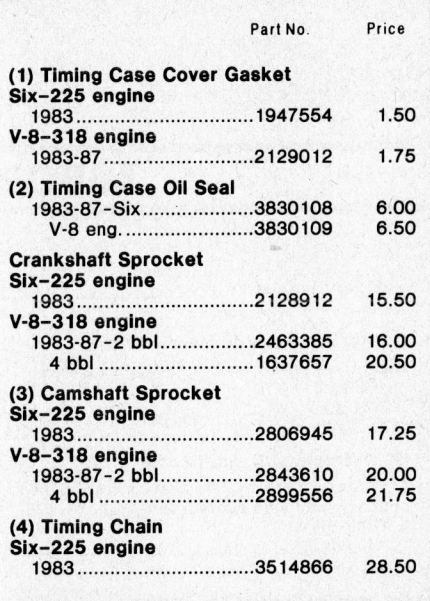

	Part No.	Price
(1) Timing Case Cover Gasket		
Six-225 engine		
1983	1947554	1.50
V-8-318 engine		
1983-87	2129012	1.75
(2) Timing Case Oil Seal		
1983-87-Six	3830108	6.00
V-8 eng.	3830109	6.50
Crankshaft Sprocket		
Six-225 engine		
1983	2128912	15.50
V-8-318 engine		
1983-87-2 bbl	2463385	16.00
4 bbl	1637657	20.50
(3) Camshaft Sprocket		
Six-225 engine		
1983	2806945	17.25
V-8-318 engine		
1983-87-2 bbl	2843610	20.00
4 bbl	2899556	21.75
(4) Timing Chain		
Six-225 engine		
1983	3514866	28.50

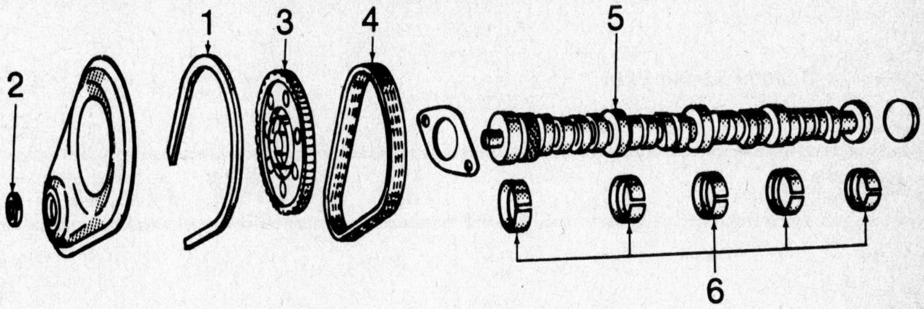

	Part No.	Price
V-8-318 engine		
1983-87-2 bbl	3514182	32.50
4 bbl	1327319	36.00
(5) Camshaft		
Six-225 engine		
1983	4105275	113.25
V-8-318 engine		
(2 bbl.)		
1983-84	4227879	131.00
1985-87	4323239	205.25
(4 bbl.)		
1983-87	4227879	131.00

	Part No.	Price
(6) Camshaft Bearings		
Six-225 engine		
1983-No. 1	4100754	5.50
No. 2	4100755	5.50
No. 3	4100756	5.50
No. 4	2121727	5.50
V-8-318 engine		
1983-87-No. 1	3830603	6.50
No. 2	4179776	10.00
No. 3	4179777	10.00
No. 4	4179778	10.00
No. 5	1632526	6.50

LABOR 17 ENGINE OILING SYSTEM 17 LABOR

(Factory Time)	Chilton Time
(G) Oil Pan or Gasket, Renew	
Six-1983 (1.8)	2.3
V-8-1983-87 (2.0)	2.8
(P) Pressure Test Engine Bearings (Pan Off)	
All models	1.0
(G) Oil Pump, Renew	
Six-1983 (1.1)	1.8
V-8-1983-87 (2.2)	3.0
(G) Oil Pump, R&R and Recondition	
Six-1983 (1.4)	2.5
V-8-1983-87 (2.6)	3.5
(G) Oil Pressure Relief Valve Spring, Renew	
Six-1983 (.3)	.5
V-8-1983-87 (2.3)	*3.2
*Includes: R&R oil pump.	
(G) Oil Pressure Gauge (Engine), Renew	
1983-87 (.4)	.6
w/A.C. add (.1)	.1
(G) Oil Pressure Gauge (Dash), Renew	
1983-87 (.5)	1.0
(M) Oil Filter Element, Renew	
1983-87 (.2)	.3

PARTS 17 ENGINE OILING SYSTEM 17 PARTS

	Part No.	Price
Oil Pan Gasket		
Six-225 engine		
1983	4049287	9.50
V-8-318 engine		
1983-87	4240153	9.50
Oil Pump Assy. (New)		
Six-225 engine		
1983	4186182	60.00
V-8-318 engine		
1983-87	2806270	53.50
Oil Pump Shaft w/Inner Rotor		
Six-225 engine		
1983	4186183	24.00
V-8-318 engine		
1983-87	3837648	24.00
Oil Pressure Sender (w/Gauge)		
1983-87	2427237	13.50
Oil Pressure Sender (w/Light)		
Six-225 engine		
1983	4205921	6.50
V-8-318 engine		
1983-87	4186352	6.50
Oil Pressure Gauge (Dash)		
1983-87	4196430	24.75
Oil Filter Assy.		
1983-87	3549957	5.50
Oil Pump Strainer Assy.		
1983-87-Six	2780999	15.25
V-8	2468849	16.75

LABOR 21 SHIFT LINKAGE 21 LABOR

(Factory Time)	Chilton Time
(G) Steering Column Gear Shift Tube, Renew	
1983-87-std column (2.4)	3.1
tilt column (2.7)	4.0
(G) Steering Column Lock Lever, Renew	
1983-87 (.9)	1.3
(G) Shift Lever Gate, Renew	
1983-87-std column (1.1)	2.0
tilt column (2.3)	2.7
Tilt-Tel column (2.5)	3.0
(G) Steering Column Shift Housing, Renew (Standard Column)	
1983-87 (2.4)	3.2
(G) Gear Selector Indicator, Renew	
Panel Mounted	
1983-87 (.2)	.4
Console Mounted	
1983 (.2)	.4

LABOR 25 U-JOINTS & DRIVESHAFT 25 LABOR

(G) Universal Joints, Renew	
Includes: R&R drive shaft.	
1983-87-front (.4)	.6
rear (.5)	.8
both (.7)	1.1
(G) Driveshaft, Renew	
1983-87-w/Joints (.3)	.6
(G) Driveshaft Sliding Yoke, Renew	
1983-87 (.4)	.6
(G) Driveshaft Flange, Renew	
1983-85 (.5)	.7

PARTS 25 UNIVERSAL JOINTS & DRIVE SHAFT 25 PARTS

	Part No.	Price
U/Joint Repair Pkg.		
1983-87	3780250	20.25
Companion Flange		
1983-87-front	4137452	68.50
1983-87-rear	3723251	29.25

LABOR 26 REAR AXLE 26 LABOR

(Factory Time)	Chilton Time
INTEGRAL TYPE	
(M) Differential, Drain & Refill	
All models	.6
(M) Axle Housing Cover, Renew or Reseal	
1983-87 (.4)	.6
(G) Axle Shaft Oil Seals, Renew	
1983-87	
7¼ axle-one (.4)	.7
8¼-9¼ axle-one (.6)	1.3
(G) Axle Shaft or Bearing, Renew	
Includes: Replace gasket and oil seal.	
1983-87	
7¼ axle-one (.6)	.9
8¼-9¼ axle-one (.8)	1.5
(G) Pinion Shaft Oil Seal, Renew	
1983-87 (.6)	1.0
(P) Differential Backlash, Adjust	
1983-87	
7¼ axle (1.1)	1.5
8¼-9¼ axles (1.3)	1.8
(G) Rear Axle Assembly, Renew	
Includes: Replace axle shaft oil seals and qaskets.	
1983-87 (2.0)	4.0
(P) Differential Side Bearings, Renew	
Includes: Replace pinion and side bearings, inner oil seal and pinion seal.	
1983-87	
7¼ axle (2.3)	3.5
8¼-9¼ axle (2.4)	3.6
(P) Ring Gear and Pinion Set, Renew	
Includes: Replace axle shaft oil seals and gaskets.	
1983-87	
7¼ axle (3.5)	6.1
8¼-9¼ axle (3.7)	6.3
Renew side brgs add (.4)	.4
(P) Differential Side Gears, Renew	
Includes: Replace axle oil seal and gasket.	
1983-87	
7¼ axle (1.2)	2.2
8¼-9¼ axle (1.3)	2.4
(P) Differential Case, Renew	
Includes: Replace ring gear and pinion, bearings and side gears if necessary.	
1983-87	
7¼ axle (3.2)	5.4
8¼-9¼ axle (3.0)	5.2
(P) Rear Axle Housing, Renew	
Includes: Replace axle shaft oil seals, pinion seal and gaskets.	
1983-87	
7¼ axle (4.0)	6.6
8¼-9¼ axle (4.2)	6.8

PARTS 26 REAR AXLE 26 PARTS

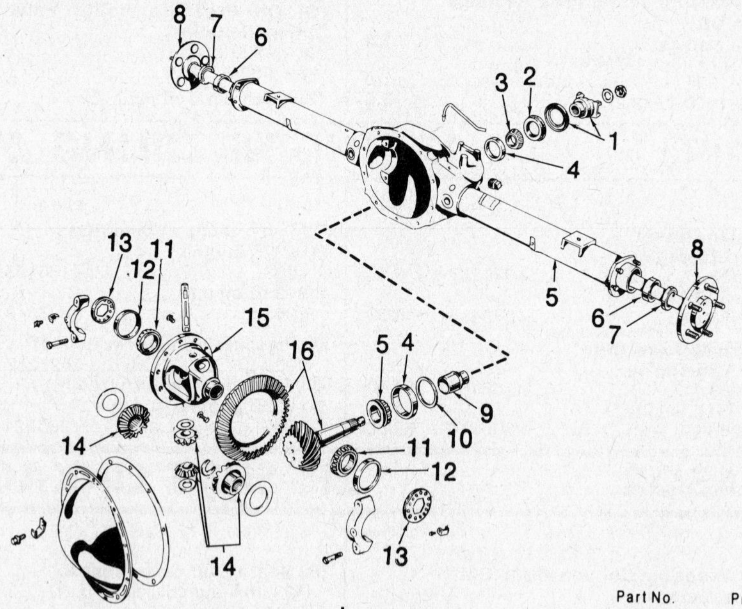

	Part No.	Price
(1) Companion Flange		
1983-87	3723251	29.25
(2) Pinion Oil Seal		
1983-87	2881041	7.00
(3) Drive Pinion Bearing		
7¼" dia. gear		
1983-87-front	2070316	13.50
rear	2070318	16.00
8¼" dia. gear		
1983-87-front	2070316	13.50
rear	2800484	19.25
(4) Pinion Bearing Cup		
7¼" dia. gear		
1983-87-front	2070317	6.75
rear	2070319	9.00
8¼" dia. gear		
1983-87-front	2070317	6.75
rear	2800485	9.50
(5) Axle Housing		
7¼" dia. gear		
1983-87	4137623	471.25
8¼" dia. gear		
1983-87	3723967	533.50
(6) Axle Shaft Bearing Pkg.		
1983-87	3744495	18.00
(7) Oil Seal		
1983-84	2931875	6.25
1985-87	4137426	6.25
(8) Axle Shaft		
7¼" dia. gear		
1983-87	4137621	131.75
8¼" dia. gear		
1983-87	3723982	138.00
(9) Front Bearing Spacer		
1983-87	3507575	3.00
(10) Rear Bearing Shims		
7¼" dia. gear		
1983-87	3723020	2.50
8¼" dia. gear		
1983-87	3723620	2.50
(11) Carrier Bearing		
7¼" dia. gear		
1983-87	1937771	13.25
8¼" dia. gear		
1983-87	1790541	15.00
(12) Carrier Bearing Cup		
7¼" dia. gear		
1983-87	1937770	6.25
8¼" dia. gear		
1983-87	3723569	8.25
(13) Adjuster		
1983-87	3507876	5.00
(14) Differential Side Gear Pkg.		
7¼" dia. gear		
1983-87	4205888	133.25
8¼" dia. gear		
1983-87	4176754	142.75

Note: Side gear package includes side gears, pinion gears, shaft and washers.

PARTS 26 REAR AXLE 26 PARTS

	Part No.	Price
(15) Differential Case		
7¼″ dia. gear		
1983-87 (casting no.)		
4137052	4137051	136.00
4137014	4137013	N.L.
8¼″ dia. gear		
1983-87-exc. below	3432435	117.50
2.94 to 1 ratio	2881423	153.25
(16) Ring & Pinion Gear Set		
7¼″ dia. gear		
1983-87-2.71	3621939	326.00
2.24, 2.26	4186969	386.00
2.94	3723672	326.00
8¼″ dia. gear		
1983-87-2.45	3837579	335.50
2.24, 2.26	4186957	335.50
2.71	3837580	387.00
2.93, 2.94	3837581	335.50
3.21	3837582	335.50

Sure Grip Differential
Note: Sure Grip Differential must be bought as a complete assembly.

LABOR 27 REAR SUSPENSION 27 LABOR

(Factory Time)	Chilton Time
(G) Rear Spring, Renew (One)	
Chrysler-Imperial	
1983-87 (.6)	1.0
Cordoba-Mirada	
1983 (.6)	1.0
(G) Rear Spring Front Bushing and Pin, Renew (One)	
Chrysler-Imperial	
1983-87 (.9)	1.3
Cordoba-Mirada	
1983 (.9)	1.3
(G) Rear Spring Center Bolt, Renew	
1983-87-one (.9)	1.1
both (1.6)	2.0
(G) Rear Spring Shackle or Bushing, Renew (One)	
Chrysler-Imperial	
1983-87 (.5)	1.0
Cordoba-Mirada	
1983 (.4)	.8
(G) Rear Shock Absorber or Rubber Bushing, Renew	
1983-87-one (.2)	.4
both (.3)	.6

PARTS 27 REAR SUSPENSION 27 PARTS

	Part No.	Price
(1) Rear Shock Absorber		
1983-exc. below	4026825	18.25
Imperial	4267310	31.50
1984-87-Std	4228413	16.50
H.D.	4228414	16.25
Extra duty	4057094	20.00
(2) Rear Spring		
Order by year and model.		
(3) Shackle Pkg.		
1983-87-wo/sway bar	3780515	14.75
w/sway bar	4094060	14.75
(4) Shackle Bushing Pkg.		
1983-87	3643989	1.50

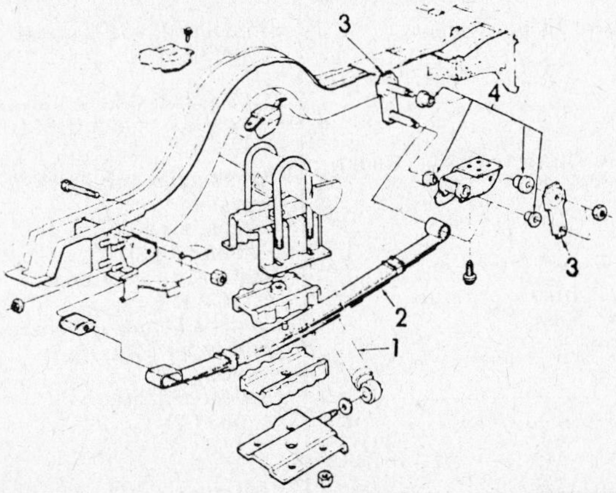

LABOR 28 AIR CONDITIONING 28 LABOR

(Factory Time)	Chilton Time
Note: If more than one item requires replacement where evacuation and discharging the system is already included in the operation, deduct 1.0 hour for each additional item to the times listed.	
(G) Drain, Evacuate, Leak Test and Charge System	
All models	1.0
(G) Partial Charge	
Includes: Leak test.	
All models (.5)	.6
(G) Performance Test	
All models	.8
(G) Vacuum Leak Test	
All models	.8
(G) Compressor Belt, Renew	
Six-1983-87 (.4)	.6
V-8-1983-87 (.2)	.3
w/Air inj add (.1)	.1
(G) Compressor, R&R for Engine Work	
Includes: Purging compressor of air.	
1983-87 (.9)	1.4
C-171 COMPRESSOR	
(G) Compressor Assembly, Renew	
Includes: Add partial charge, leak test and charge system.	
1983-87 (1.7)	3.1
(G) Compressor Clutch Field Coil, Renew	
Includes: Replace pulley w/hub if necessary.	
1983-87 (.5)	.9
(G) Compressor Clutch Pulley (w/Hub), Renew	
1983-87 (.4)	.7
(G) Compressor Clutch Assembly, Renew	
1983-87 (.5)	.7
(G) Compressor Front Cover or Seal, Renew	
Includes: R&R compressor. Evacuate and charge system.	
1983-87 (2.1)	3.4
(G) Compressor Rear Cover or Seal, Renew	
Includes: R&R compressor. Evacuate and charge system.	
1983-87 (2.0)	3.3
(G) Compressor Center Seal, Renew	
Includes: R&R compressor. Evacuate and charge system.	
1983-87 (2.2)	3.5
(G) Compressor Shaft Gas Seal, Renew	
Includes: R&R compressor. Evacuate and charge system.	
1983-87 (2.1)	3.4

LABOR 28 AIR CONDITIONING 28 LABOR

(Factory Time) Chilton Time

(G) Condenser Assembly, Renew
Includes: Add partial charge, leak test and charge system.
Chrysler-Imperial
1983-87 (1.4)........ 2.8
Cordoba-Mirada
1983 (1.4)........ 2.8

(G) Evaporator Coil, Renew
Includes: Add partial charge, leak test and charge system.
Chrysler-Imperial
1983-87 (3.2)........ 4.5
Cordoba-Mirada
1983 (2.8)........ 4.4

(G) Expansion Valve, Renew
1983-87 (1.0)........ 2.0

(G) Receiver Drier, Renew
Includes: Add partial charge, leak test and charge system.
1983-87 (.9)........ 2.0

(G) Low Pressure Cut Off Switch, Renew
Includes: Charge system.
1983-87 (.9)........ 1.8

(G) Thermostatic Control Clutch Cycling Switch, Renew
1983-87 (.3)........ .6

(G) Vacuum Control Switch, Renew
Chrysler-Imperial
1983-87 (.5)........ 1.0
Cordoba-Mirada
1983 (.5)........ .9

(G) Temperature Control Cable, Renew
Chrysler-Imperial
1983-87 (1.0)........ 1.6
Cordoba-Mirada
1983 (.6)........ 1.0

(G) Vacuum Control Hose Assembly, Renew (Main)
Chrysler
1983-87
wo/A.C. (.4)........ .5
w/A.C. (1.1)........ 1.7

AIR CONDITIONER TUNE-UP

For efficient operation and satisfactory performance in hot weather. The following air conditioner tune-up is suggested:

1. Clean intake filter
2. Clean condenser fins
3. Pressure test system
4. Adjust drive belt tension
5. Check antifreeze/coolant
6. Tighten compressor mounts
7. Tighten condenser and evaporator mounts
8. Inspect system for leaks (hoses, couplings, valves, etc.)
9. Partial charge system

All models 1.0
If necessary to evacuate and charge system, add 1.0

(Factory Time) Chilton Time

Cordoba-Mirada-Imperial
1983 (.5)........ .8

(G) Vacuum Check Valves, Renew
1983-87-one or both (.3)........ .6

(G) Vacuum Actuators, Renew
Chrysler
Outside air door
1983-87 (.3)........ .6
Heater/Defroster door
1983-87 (.4)........ .8
Cordoba-Mirada-Imperial
Outside air door
1983 (.3)........ .6
Heater/Defroster door
1983 (.2)........ .5

(Factory Time) Chilton Time

(G) Blower Motor, Renew
Chrysler-Imperial
1983-87 (.6)........ 1.1
Cordoba-Mirada
1983 (.6)........ 1.1

(G) Blower Motor Resistor, Renew
Chrysler-Imperial
1983-87 (.5)........ .9
Cordoba-Mirada
1983 (.3)........ .6
w/A.T.C. (.5)........ .9
w/S.A.T.C. (.3)........ .5

(G) Blower Motor Switch, Renew
Chrysler-Imperial
1983-87 (.4)........ .7
Cordoba-Mirada
1983 (.5)........ 1.0

(G) Air Conditioning Hoses, Renew
Includes: Add partial charge, leak test and charge system.
1983-87-one (1.0)........ 1.6
each adtnl (.3)........ .5

AUTO-TEMP COMPONENTS

(G) Aspirator, Renew
1983-87 (.4)........ .6

(G) Sensor Assembly (In Car), Renew
1983-87 (.4)........ .7

(G) Ambient Sensor, Renew
1983-87 (.3)........ .5

(G) Sliding Rheostat Assembly, Renew
1983-87 (.5)........ .9

(G) Electronic Servomotor, Renew
1983-87 (1.1)........ 1.7

(G) A.T.C. Hoses, Renew
1983-87
compensator to aspirator (.2)........ .4
sensing valve to aspirator (.2)........ .4
in-car sensor (.4)........ .7

PARTS 28 AIR CONDITIONING 28 PARTS

	Part No.	Price
Compressor Assy.		
1983-87	4176059	275.00
Pulley & Armature (Drive Clutch)		
Six-225 engine		
1983	3847178	101.50
V-8-318 engine		
1983-84	3847179	101.50
1985-87	3848981	101.75
Field Coil (Drive Clutch)		
1983	3846845	60.75
1984	3848673	60.75
1985-87	3848969	29.50
Switch High Pressure Cut-off		
1983-87	3848674	45.50
Lower Pressure Cut-off Switch		
1983-87	5210377	17.25
Condenser		
1983-85	3847789	225.00
1986-87	3848374	219.75
Receiver Drier		
1983-87	3847830	40.25
Evaporator Coil Assy.		
1983-87	3847256	341.75
Expansion Valve		
1983-87	4176999	59.75
Control Valve (Water Temp)		
1983-87	3847475	28.25
Push Button Vacuum and Electrical Switch		
1983-87	3847742	27.50
Blower Motor		
1983-87-exc. below	4240425	74.25
Imperial	3847997	74.25
Blower Motor Switch		
1983-87	3847940	10.25
Blower Motor Resistor		
1983-84	3847910	12.75
1985-87	3848996	13.25
Air Condition Hoses		
Order by year and model.		

AUTOMATIC TEMPERATURE CONTROL

	Part No.	Price
Potentiometer (Rheostat)		
1983-87	3847435	29.00
Aspirator		
1983-87	3847766	8.00
Sensor Assembly (Ambient)		
1983-87	3847589	12.25
Servo Actuator Assy.		
1983-87	3847296	70.00
Sensor Assy.		
1983-87	3847291	14.50

LABOR 29 LOCKS, HINGES & WIND. REGULATORS 29 LABOR

(Factory Time) — Chilton Time

(G) Hood Latch, Renew
1983-87 (.3) 5

(G) Hood Release Cable, Renew
1983-87 (.4) 6

(G) Hood Hinge, Renew (One)
Does not include painting.
1983-87 (.4) 6

(G) Door Lock or Remote Control, Renew
1983-87-exc below (.4) 9
1983-Imperial (.6) 9

(G) Door and Ignition Lock Cylinders, Renew
Includes: R&R door lock cylinders to recode or replace.
1983-87-w/Tilt column (1.4) 2.3
w/Tilt-Tel (1.3) 2.0
Recode door cyls add (.3) 3

(G) Door Handle (Outside), Renew (Front or Rear)
1983-87 (.4) 6
1983-Imperial (.6) 9

(G) Lock Striker Plate, Renew
1983-87 (.2) 3

(G) Front Door Window Regulator (Manual), Renew
1983-87 (.5) 9

(G) Front Door Window Regulator (Electric), Renew
1983-87 (1.0) 1.5

(G) Rear Door Window Regulator (Manual), Renew
1983-87 (.5) 9

(G) Rear Door Window Regulator (Electric), Renew
1983-87 (.5) 9

(G) Trunk Lock Cylinder and Key, Renew
1983-87 (.3) 5
vacuum (complete) (1.7) 2.0
Recode cyl add 3

(G) Trunk Hinge Assembly, Renew (One)
Chrysler-Imperial
1983-87 (.3) 5
Cordoba-Mirada
1983 (.3) 5

PARTS 29 LOCKS, HINGES & WIND. REGULATORS 29 PARTS

	Part No.	Price
Upper Hood Lock		
1983-87	3861819	25.50
Hood Hinge (Right)		
1983	4103904	37.25
1984-87	4103428	38.25
Front Door Lock		
1983-right	3882800	35.25
left	3882805	35.25
1984-87-right	4310526	35.25
left	4310529	35.25
Rear Door Lock		
1983-right	4184710	35.25
left	4184711	35.25
1984-87-right	4310532	35.25
left	4310533	35.25
Remote Control Door Lock		
1983-87-right	3871274	16.25
left	3871275	16.25
Lock Cylinder & Key		
(wo/illuminated entry)		
1983-87-wo/tilt whl	4054805	20.50
w/tilt whl	3548955	18.25
(w/illuminated entry)		
1983-87-wo/tilt whl	4172348	36.50
w/tilt whl	4172305	36.50
Trunk Lock		
(Exc. Imperial)		
1983-87-manual	4054825	29.00
electric	4054962	49.72
(Imperial)		
1983	4172826	56.00
Trunk Lock Cyl. & Key		
1983-87-exc. below	4267850	30.00
Imperial	4172663	29.50
Trunk Hinges (Right)		
1983-87-exc. below	4134518	19.25
Imperial	4129638	46.75
Manual Window Regulator		
Front		
(Cordoba, Imperial, Mirada)		
1983-right	3882648	60.00
left	3882649	60.00
(Newport, New Yorker, Fifth Ave.)		
1983-87-right	3882274	54.50
left	3882275	54.50
Rear		
1983-87-right	3882290	54.50
left	3882291	54.50
Power Window Regulator		
(Cordoba, Imperial, Mirada)		
1983-right	3882742	80.75
left	3882743	80.75
(Newport, New Yorker, Fifth Ave.)		
1983-87-right	3882350	72.75
left	3882351	72.75
Power Window Motor		
(Cordoba, Imperial, Mirada)		
1983-right	4240416	16.00
left	4240415	16.00
(Newport, New Yorker, Fifth Ave.)		
1983-87-right	4240519	173.25
left	4240520	173.25

LABOR 30 HEAD AND PARKING LAMPS 30 LABOR

(Factory Time) — Chilton Time

(G) Aim Headlamps
two 4
four 6

(M) Headlamp Sealed Beam Bulb, Renew
Does not include aim headlamps.
1983-87-each (.2) 3

(M) Parking Lamp Assembly, Renew
1983-87 (.2) 4

(M) Tail, Stop and Turn Signal Lamp Assy., Renew
1983-87-each (.2) 4

(M) Tail & Stop Lamp Lens, Renew
1983-87 (.3) 4

(M) License Lamp Assembly, Renew
1983-87 (.2) 4

(M) Side Marker Lamp, Renew
1983-87 (.2) 4

(M) Cornering Lamp, Renew
1983-85 (.2) 4

(G) Headlamp Rotating Motor, Renew
1983 (.4) 7

(G) Headlamp Rotating Motor Relay, Renew
1983 (.3) 5

PARTS 30 HEAD AND PARKING LAMPS 30 PARTS

	Part No.	Price
Sealed Beam Bulb		
(Cordoba, Mirada)		
1983 (Rt way shift)		
exc below	153199	16.00
Halogen	153590	31.00
(Imperial, Newport, New Yorker & Fifth Ave.)		
(exc. Halogen)		
1983-87-Hi/Low	153201	11.00
Hi beam	153200	11.00
(w/Halogen)		
1983-87-Hi/Low	153481	16.00
Hi beam	153440	16.00
Parking & Turn Signal Lamp Assy.		
Cordoba, Mirada		
1983-right	4076988	12.25
left	4076989	12.25
Imperial		
1983-right	4174008	28.50
left	4174009	28.50
Newport, New Yorker, Fifth Ave.		
1983-87-right	4174364	31.75
left	4174365	31.75

PARTS 30 HEAD AND PARKING LAMPS 30 PARTS

	Part No.	Price
Tail Lamp Lens		
Cordoba		
1983-right	4076714	17.25
left	4076715	17.25
Imperial		
1983-right	4174070	76.50
left	4174071	76.50
Newport, New Yorker, Fifth Ave.		
1983-87-right	4076892	38.75
left	4076893	38.75
Mirada		
1983-right	4076704	41.75
left	4076705	39.00
High Mount Stop Light		
1986-87		
Bracket	4399100	N.L.
Cover	H201EK1	N.L.
License Plate Lamp Assy.		
Cordoba, Mirada		
1983	4076850	4.25
Imperial		
1983	4174042	8.75
Newport, New Yorker, Fifth Ave.		
1983-87	4076808	3.25

LABOR 31 WINDSHIELD WIPER & SPEEDOMETER 31 LABOR

(Factory Time)	Chilton Time
(G) Windshield Wiper Motor, Renew	
1983-87 (.5)	.9
(G) Wiper Pivot, Renew (One)	
1983-87 (.5)	.9
(G) Intermittent Windshield Wiper Control Module, Renew	
1983-87 (.4)	.6
(G) Wiper Links, Renew	
1983-87 (.4)	.7
(G) Windshield Wiper and Washer Switch, Renew	
1983-87-std column (.8)	1.5
tilt column (1.2)	1.6
(G) Windshield Washer Pump, Renew	
1983-87 (.3)	.5
(G) Electronic Instrument Cluster Assy., Renew	
Includes: Speedometer, odometer, fuel gauge, clock and gear selector assy.	
1983-Imperial (.9)	1.7
(G) Speedometer Head, R&R or Renew	
Does not include reset odometer.	
1983-87 (.7)	1.1
Reset odometer add	.2
(G) Speedometer Cable and Casing, Renew	
1983	
Cruise control to trans (.3)	.6
Cruise control to speedo (.3)	.6
Trans to speedo (.4)	.8
1984-87	
upper (.3)	.6
lower (.7)	1.1
one piece (.7)	1.1
(G) Speedometer Cable (Inner), Renew or Lubricate	
1983	
Cruise control to trans (.3)	.6
Cruise control to speedo (.5)	.7
Trans to speedo (.4)	.7
1984-87	
upper (.3)	.5
lower (.7)	1.0
one piece (.7)	1.0
(G) Speedometer Drive Pinion, Renew	
Includes: Replace oil seal.	
1983-87 (.3)	.5
(G) Radio, R&R	
1983-87 (.3)	.8
w/A.C. add	.3

PARTS 31 WINDSHIELD WIPER & SPEEDOMETER 31 PARTS

	Part No.	Price
Wiper Motor		
1983-exc. below	4186956	106.75
Imperial	4240528	110.00
1984	4205951	106.75
1985-87	4339449	106.75
Wiper Pivot		
1983-87-right	4026046	17.00
left	3799479	17.00
Wiper Switch		
(wo/intermitten wipers)		
1983-exc. New Yorker	3747654	39.75
New Yorker	3747653	39.75
1984-87	3747653	39.75
(w/intermitten wipers)		
1983 (New Yorker)		
wo/tilt whl	4221042	36.00
w/tilt whl	4293110	67.50
1983 (exc. New Yorker)		
wo/tilt whl	4221051	49.50
w/tilt whl	4293111	60.25
1984-wo/tilt whl	4221042	36.00
w/tilt whl	4293310	29.25
1985-87-wo/tilt whl	4221500	36.00
w/tilt whl	4221486	36.00
Intermitten Wiper Control		
1983-87	4222060	28.25
Washer Fluid Level Sensor		
1983-87	3746813	22.75
Windshield Washer Pump		
1983-87	3799462	21.25
Speed. Cable & Housing		
Order by year and model.		
Inner Speed. Cable		
1983-87-80" long	2448294	6.50
113" long	2448295	8.75
Speedometer Assy.		
Order by year and model.		

LABOR 32 LIGHT SWITCHES & WIRING 32 LABOR

(Factory Time)	Chilton Time
(G) Headlamp Switch, Renew	
Chrysler-Imperial	
1983-87 (.3)	.5
Cordoba-Mirada	
1983 (.4)	.7
w/A.C. add (.2)	.2
(G) Headlamp Dimmer Switch, Renew	
1983-87-floor mount (.3)	.5
column mount (.5)	1.0
(G) Stop Light Switch, Renew	
1983-87 (.3)	.4
w/Cruise control add (.1)	.1
(G) Turn Signal Switch, Renew	
1983-87-std column (.7)	1.0
tilt column (1.0)	1.6
Tilt-Tel column (.9)	1.7
(G) Turn Signal/Washer Wiper Combination Lever Assy., Renew	
1983-87 (.2)	.5
(G) Neutral Safety (w/Back-Up Lamp) Switch, Renew	
1983-87 (.3)	.4
(M) Turn Signal or Hazard Warning Flasher, Renew	
1983-87 (.2)	.3
(G) Parking Brake Warning Lamp Switch, Renew	
1983-87 (.3)	.4

LABOR 32 LIGHT SWITCHES & WIRING 32 LABOR

	(Factory Time)	Chilton Time
(G) Printed Circuit Boards, Renew		
Chrysler		
1983-87	(.4)	.7
Cordoba-Mirada-Imperial		
1983	(1.1)	1.6
(G) Horns, Renew		
1983-87-one	(.2)	.3
(G) Horn Relay, Renew		
1983-87	(.2)	.3
(G) Wiring Harness, Renew		
(Instrument Panel)		
1983-87	(3.4)	4.9
(Body)		
1983-87	(2.7)	4.0

PARTS 32 LIGHT SWITCHES & WIRING 32 PARTS

	Part No.	Price
Headlamp Switch		
Cordoba, Mirada		
1983	4221223	17.25
New Yorker, Imperial, Newport, Fifth Ave.		
1983-87	4221248	16.00
Beam Selector Lamp Switch		
1983-87-wo/Tilt whl	4131373	11.00
w/Tilt whl	4131525	13.25
Stop Light Switch		
(wo/speed control)		
1983-85	2926275	5.25
(w/speed control)		
1983	5209994	8.00
1984-85	4221438	15.50
Turn Signal Flasher		
1983-87-w/2 lamps	3837161	4.25
w/3 lamps	3837162	4.25
Hazard Warning Flasher		
1983-87	2932877	4.50
Wiring Harness		
Order by year and model.		
Turn Signal Switch		
(wo/cornering lamps)		
1983-84-wo/tilt whl	4221337	38.50
w/tilt whl	4221304	47.00
1985-87-wo/tilt whl	4221682	42.50
w/tilt whl	4221485	37.25
(w/cornering lamps)		
1983-84-wo/tilt whl	4221338	40.75
w/tilt whl	4221305	53.50
1985-87-wo/tilt whl	4221681	52.00
w/tilt whl	4221305	53.50
Neutral Safety & Back-Up Switch		
1983-87	4057750	8.75
Horn Assembly		
1983-87-high note	2808869	24.00
low note	2808868	24.00
Horn Relay		
1983-87	3747298	6.25
Brake System Indicator Switch		
1983-87	3620790	4.25

LABOR 33 GLASS 33 LABOR

	(Factory Time)	Chilton Time
(G) Windshield Glass, Renew		
Includes: Replace weatherstrip if necessary, where applicable.		
1983	(1.7)	3.0
w/Cabriolet roof add	(.6)	1.0
1984-87	(1.5)	2.5
(G) Front Door Glass, Renew		
1983-87-hardtops	(.9)	1.4
4 D sedan	(.6)	1.0
sedan w/Vent	(1.2)	1.7
(G) Rear Door Glass, Renew		
1983-87-exc below	(.5)	1.0
4 D hdtp	(.9)	1.4
(G) Stationary Door Glass, Renew		
1983-87	(.7)	1.1
(G) Rear Quarter Glass, Renew		
1983		
2 D-movable	(1.0)	1.4
opera glass	(1.0)	1.7
sta wag	(2.1)	2.8
fixed	(1.4)	1.8
(G) Rear Window Glass, Renew		
Includes: Replace weatherstrip if necessary, where applicable.		
1983-87	(1.6)	2.5
heated back window	(2.7)	3.5
Cordoba-w/Landau crown roof, add	(7.4)	8.5
Cordoba-w/Cabriolet roof, add	(2.5)	4.0
Chrysler-w/Stainless steel roof, add	(5.4)	7.0
Cordoba-w/Padded Landau roof, add	(7.4)	8.5
Le Baron-New Yorker w/5th Ave option add	(3.3)	4.5

LABOR 34 CRUISE CONTROL 34 LABOR

	(Factory Time)	Chilton Time
(G) Speed Control Servo, Renew		
1983-87	(.3)	.5
(G) Speed Control Cable, Renew		
1983-87	(.3)	.5
(G) Speed Control Vacuum Hoses, Renew		
1983-87	(.2)	.3
(G) Speed Control Wiring Harness, Renew		
1983-87	(.3)	.6
(G) Speed Control Switch (Turn Signal Lever), Renew		
1983-87-std colm	(.5)	.9
tilt colm	(1.0)	1.5

PARTS 34 CRUISE CONTROL 34 PARTS

	Part No.	Price
ELECTRO MECHANICAL		
Speed Control Servo Assy.		
1983-87	4241551	129.75
Speed Control Cable		
1983 (w/225 eng)		
1 bbl	4104331	18.25
2 bbl	4104330	22.00
1983 (w/318 eng.)		
2 bbl	5214339	22.00
4 bbl	4241249	22.00
1984-87	4241249	22.00
Speed Control Link (Lost Motion)		
1983-exc. below	3769261	6.75
1 bbl	4095071	10.50
2 bbl	4027798	6.75
1983-Imperial	4095107	6.50
1984-87	3769261	6.75
ELECTRONIC		
Electronic Module		
1985-87	4318829	116.50
Sensor		
1985-87	4312186	30.25
Control Switch		
1985-87	4342209	41.75
Vacuum Motor		
1985-87	4318819	27.50
Stop Light Switch		
1985-87	4241438	N.L.
Valve Body		
1985-87	4318818	103.75

GROUP INDEX

ALPHABETICAL INDEX

Chrysler Corporation
Rear Wheel Drive Cars

DODGE & PLYMOUTH

YEAR IDENTIFICATION

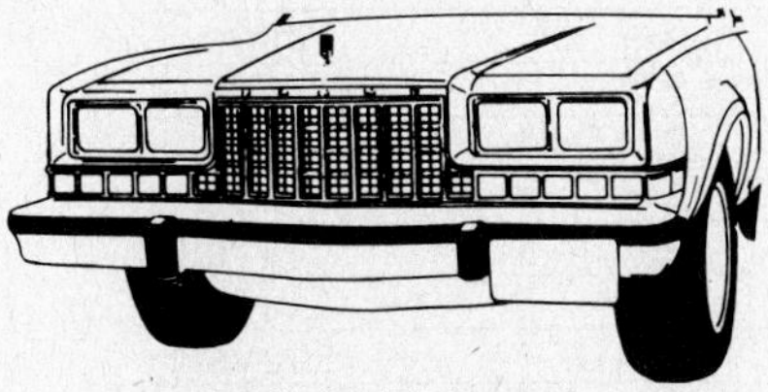

1983-84 Diplomat

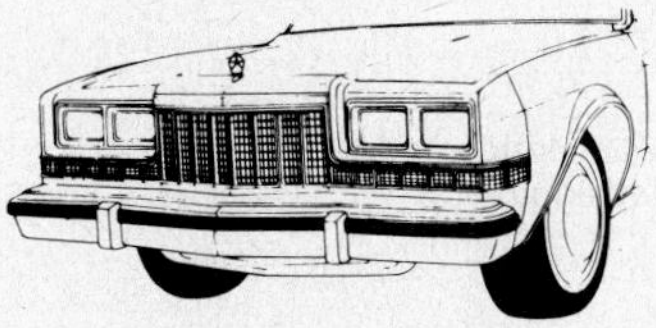

1983-87 Gran Fury

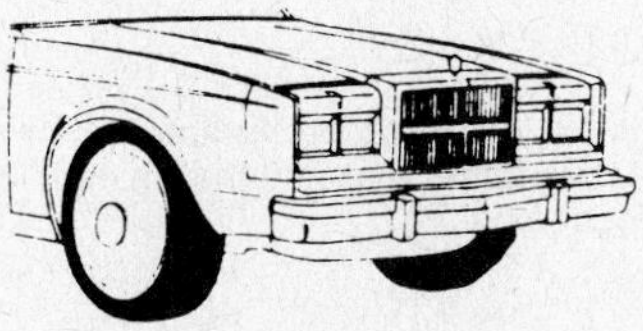

1985-87 Diplomat SE

TUNE-UP SPECIFICATIONS

When analyzing compression test results, look for uniformity among cylinders rather than specific pressures

Year	Engine: Eng. V.I.N. Code	Engine: No. Cyl. Displacement (cu. in.)	Carb. (bbl.)	Spark Plugs: Orig. Type	Spark Plugs: Gap (in.)	Distributor: Point Dwell (deg)	Distributor: Point Gap (in.)	Ignition Timing (deg.)	Valves Intake Opens ▪(deg.)	Fuel Pump Pressure (psi)	Idle Speed (rpm)
'83	H,J,K,L	6-225	1 & 2	RBL-16Y	.035	Electronic		⑤	6	4.0–5.5	750
	N,P,R,S	8-318	2 & 4	RN-12Y	.035	Electronic		⑤	10	5.75–7.25	700
'84–'87	P,R,S	8-318	2 & 4	RN-12Y	.035	Electronic		⑤	10	5.75–7.25	700

NOTE: The underhood specifications sticker often reflects tune-up specification changes made in production. Sticker figures must be used if they disagree with those in this chart.
Part numbers in this chart are not recommended by Chilton for any product by brand name.
▪All figures Before Top Dead Center
EFI Electronic Fuel Injection
⑤ See underhood sticker

VEHICLE IDENTIFICATION NUMBER (VIN)

It is important for servicing and ordering parts to be certain of the vehicle and engine identification. The VIN (vehicle identification number) is a 17 digit number visible through the windshield on the driver's side of the dash and contains the vehicle and engine identification codes. It can be interpreted as follows:

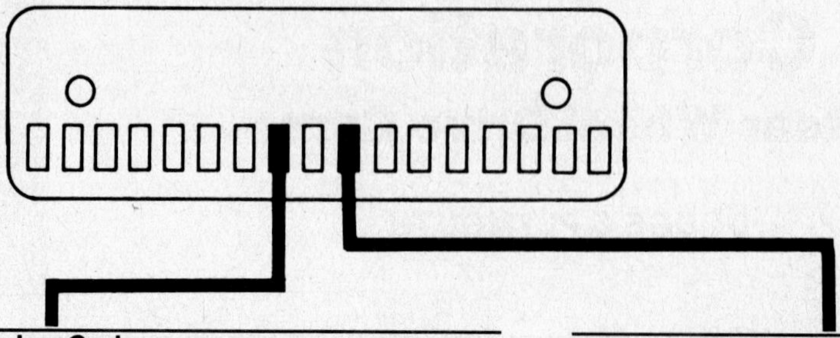

Engine Code

Code	Cu. In.	Liters	Cyl.	Carb.(bbl.)	Eng. Mfg.
E	225	3.7	6	1	Chrys.
H	225	3.7	6	1	Chrys.
F	225	3.7	6	1 H.D.	Chrys.
J	225	3.7	6	1 H.D.	Chrys.
G	225	3.7	6	2 ①	Chrys.
K	225	3.7	6	2 ①	Chrys.
H	225	3.7	6	2 H.D. ①	Chrys.
L	225	3.7	6	2 H.D. ①	Chrys.
K	318	5.2	8	2	Chrys.
P	318	5.2	8	2	Chrys.
L	318	5.2	8	2 H.D.	Chrys.
J	318	5.2	8	EFI	Chrys.
N	318	5.2	8	EFI	Chrys.
R	318	5.2	8	4	Chrys.
M	318	5.2	8	4	Chrys.
N	318	5.2	8	4 H.D.	Chrys.
S	318	5.2	8	4 H.D.	Chrys.

H.D. = Heavy Duty
EFI = Electronic Fuel Injection
① = Canada Only
The seventeen digit Vehicle Identification Number can be used to determine engine application and model year.
The 10th digit indicates the model year, and the 8th digit identifies the factory installed engine.
EFI Electronic Fuel Injection

Model Year Code

Code	Year
D	1983
E	1984
F	1985
G	1986
H	1987

FIRING ORDERS

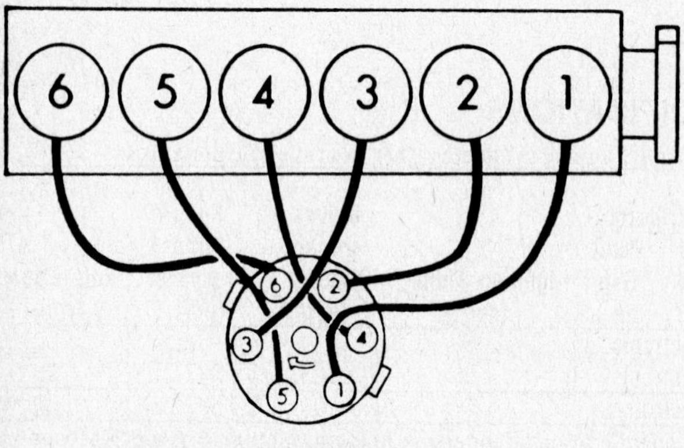

Chrysler Corp. 6-cyl.
Engine firing order: 1–5–3–6–2–4
Distributor rotation: clockwise

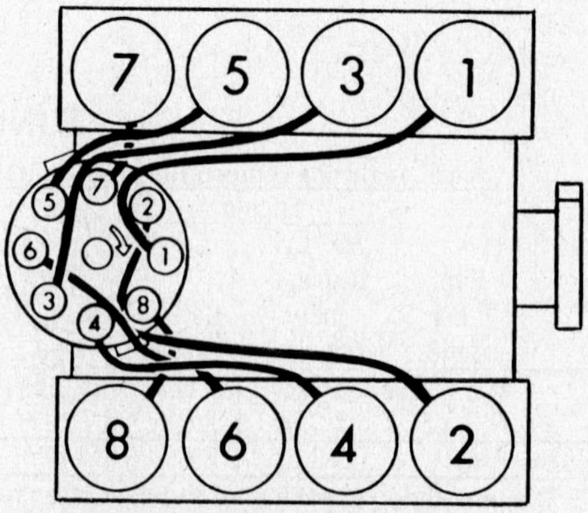

Chrysler Corp. 318, V8
Engine firing order: 1–8–4–3–6–5–7–2
Distributor rotation: clockwise

WHEEL ALIGNMENT SPECIFICATIONS

Year	Model	Caster Range (deg.)	Caster Pref. Setting (deg.)	Camber Range (deg.)	Camber Pref. Setting (deg.)	Toe-in (in.)	Steering Axis Inclin. (deg.)	Wheel Pivot Ratio Inner Wheel	Wheel Pivot Ratio Outer Wheel
'83-'87	Diplomat, Gran Fury, Newport, 5th Avenue	1¼P to 3¾P	2½ ± 1	1.4N-1¼P	1/2P ± 1/2	1/8 + 1/16	8	20	18

FRONT END HEIGHT

Year	Model	Front End Height (± 1/8 in.)
'83-'87	5th Avenue	12½ ①②

① ± 1/4 in.
② Measured from the head of the suspension crossmember front isolater bolt to ground

LABOR SERVICE BAY OPERATIONS LABOR

(Factory Time) Chilton Time

COOLING

(M) Winterize Cooling System
Includes: Run engine to check for leaks, tighten all hose connections. Test radiator and pressure cap, drain radiator and engine block. Add anti-freeze and refill system.
All models 5

(M) Thermostat, Renew
All models (.4) 6
w/A.C. add (.3) 3

(M) Drive Belt, Renew
All models (.2) 3
w/A.C. add (.1) 1
w/Air inj add (.1) 1
w/P.S. add (.1) 1

FUEL

(M) Carburetor Air Cleaner, Service
All models (.3) 3

(G) Carburetor, Adjust (On Car)
All models (.6) 6

(G) Automatic Choke, Renew
1 bbl (.2) 4
2 bbl (.2) 4
4 bbl (.5) 7

BRAKES

(G) Brakes, Adjust (Minor)
Includes: Adjust brakes, fill master cylinder.
two wheels 4

(M) Parking Brake, Adjust
All models (.3) 4

LUBRICATION SERVICE

(M) Lubricate Chassis, Change Oil & Filter
Includes: Inspect and correct all fluid levels.
All models 6
Install grease fittings add 1

CHILTON'S 10 POINT SAFETY CHECK

CHECK OPERATION & CONDITION OF THE FOLLOWING ITEMS:

1. Legal Registration (serial no.)
2. Tires & Wheels
3. Brake System (R&R all wheels)
4. Light Systems & Signals
5. Accelerator Linkage, Neutral Safety Switch, Shift Indicator Pointer & Seat Position Locks
6. Glass, Mirrors, Door Locks, Seat Belts & Harness
7. Wipers, Washers & Defrosters
8. Frame, Steering, Shocks, Front & Rear Suspension
9. Fuel & Exhaust Systems
10. Road Test Vehicle

All models 1.0
Exhaust Smog Analysis, add 4

(Factory Time) Chilton Time

(M) Lubricate Chassis
Includes: Inspect and correct all fluid levels.
All models 4
Install grease fittings add 1

(M) Engine Oil & Filter, Change
Includes: Inspect and correct all fluid levels.
All models 4

WHEELS

(M) Wheel, Renew
one (.3) 3

(G) Wheel, Balance
one 3
each adtnl 2

(Factory Time) Chilton Time

(G) Front Wheel Bearings, Clean and Repack (Both Wheels)
1983-87 (.9) 1.4

(G) Front Wheel Grease Seals, Renew
1983-87-one whl (.5) 6
both wheels (.9) 1.0

ELECTRICAL

(M) Battery Cables, Renew
ground (.2) 3
batt to starter relay (.5) 5
positive (.4) 4

(G) Aim Headlamps
two 4
four 6

(M) Headlamp Sealed Beam Bulb, Renew
Does not include: Aim headlamps.
All models-each (.2) 3

(M) Parking Lamp Assembly, Renew
All models (.3) 4

(M) Tail & Stop Lamp Lens, Renew
All models (.3) 4

(G) Headlamp Dimmer Switch, Renew
All models-floor mount (.3) 5
column mount (.5) 1.0

(G) Stop Light Switch, Renew
All models (.3) 4
w/Cruise control add (.1) 1

(M) Turn Signal or Hazard Warning Flasher, Renew
All models (.2) 3

(G) Horn Relay, Renew
All models (.2) 3

(G) License Lamp Assembly, Renew
All models (.3) 4

(G) Horn, Renew
All models-one (.2) 3

LABOR 1 TUNE UP 1 LABOR

(Factory Time)	Chilton Time
(G) Compression Test	
Six–1983 (.5)	.6
V-8–1983-87–318, 360 engs (.6)	.8
w/A.C. add (.3)	.3

(G) Engine Tune Up, (Electronic Ignition)

Includes: Test battery and clean connections. Tighten manifold bolts and carburetor mounting bolts. Check engine compression, clean and adjust or renew spark plugs. Test resistance of spark plug cables. Inspect distributor cap, rotor, reluctor and pick up plate. Adjust air gap. Check vacuum advance operation. Inspect and free up exhaust manifold heat valve. Reset ignition timing. Adjust idle mixture and idle speed. Service air cleaner. Inspect crankcase ventilation system. Inspect and adjust drive belts. Inspect choke operation and adjust or free up. Check operation of EGR valve.

(Factory Time)	Chilton Time
Six–1983	2.0
V-8–1983-87	2.5
w/A.C. add	.6

LABOR 2 IGNITION SYSTEM 2 LABOR

(Factory Time)	Chilton Time
(G) Spark Plugs, Clean and Reset or Renew	
Six–1983 (.4)	.5
V-8–1983-87–318, 360 engs (.5)	.7
(G) Ignition Timing, Adjust	
1983-87 (.3)	.3
(G) Electronic Ignition Control Unit, Renew	
1983-87 (.2)	.3
(G) Distributor, Renew	
Includes: Reset ignition timing.	
1983-87	
225, 318, 360 engs (.5)	.8
(G) Distributor, R&R and Recondition	
Includes: Reset ignition timing.	
1983-87	
225, 318, 360 engs (1.0)	1.6
(G) Distributor Reluctor, Renew	
Includes: R&R distributor and reset ignition timing.	
1983-87	
225, 318, 360 engs (.6)	.9
(G) Distributor Pick-Up Plate and Coil Assy., Renew	
Includes: R&R distributor and reset ignition timing.	
1983-87	
225, 318, 360 engs (.7)	1.0
w/Dual coil add (.2)	.2
(G) Vacuum Control Unit, Renew	
Includes: R&R distributor and reset ignition timing.	
1983-87	
225, 318, 360 engs (.6)	1.0
(G) Distributor Cap and/or Rotor, Renew	
1983-87 (.2)	.5
(G) Dual Ballast Resistor, Renew	
1983-87 (.2)	.3
(G) Ignition Coil, Renew	
1983-87 (.2)	.4
(G) Ignition Cables, Renew	
Six–1983 (.5)	.6
V-8–1983-87	
318, 360 engs (.3)	.8
w/A.C. add (.5)	.5
(G) Spark Control Computer, Renew	
Includes: Test.	
1983-87 (.2)	.8
(G) Ignition Switch, Renew	
Includes: Replace and recode lock cylinder if necessary.	
1983-87 (.6)	1.0
(G) Ignition Key Buzzer Switch, Renew	
1983-87–std column (1.1)	1.5
w/Tilt column (.6)	1.0
w/Tilt-Tel (.5)	1.0
(G) Ignition Key Warning Buzzer, Renew	
1983-87 (.2)	.4
(G) Ignition Switch Time Delay Relay, Renew	
1983-87 (.2)	.5

PARTS 2 ELECTRONIC IGNITION 2 PARTS

	Part No.	Price
Distributor Assy.		
Six–225 engine		
1983-exc.Calif.	4145955	72.00
Calif.	4145752	60.00
V-8–318 engine		
1983-87-exc. Dual pickup	4145754	71.00
Single pickup	4091142	81.50
(1) Distributor Cap		
1983-Six	4111630	8.25
1983-87-V-8	4111640	8.50
(2) Rotor		
1983-87	3874401	2.75
(3) Reluctor		
1983-Six	3656862	4.50
1983-87-V-8	3656017	4.50
(4) Pick-Up & Plate Assy.		
1983-87-Dual pickup	4145239	30.00
Single pickup	4091147	18.00
(5) Shaft (Dist.)		
Note: Serviced in distributor assy.		

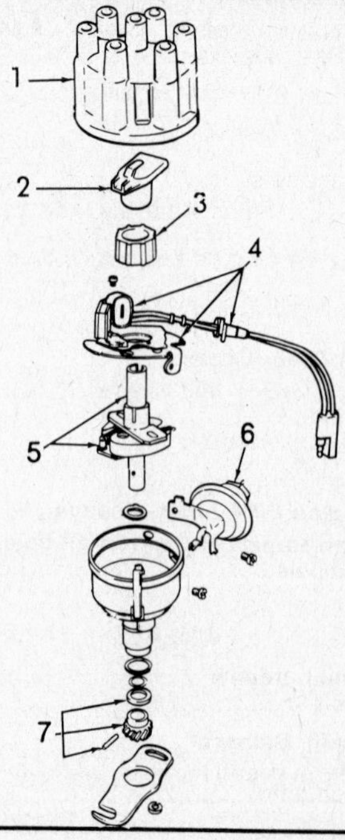

	Part No.	Price
(6) Vacuum Control		
Six–225 engine		
1983	3874878	13.50
V-8–318 engine		
1983-87	3755474	13.50
(7) Gear & Pin Pkg.		
1983-87	2084653	4.25
Control Unit (Elect. Ignition)		
1983-87	4111850	45.00
Coil		
1983-87	4176009	26.75
Ignition Wire Set		
1983-225 eng.	4240433	23.75
1983-87-w/318 eng.	4339401	27.00
Ignition Switch		
1983-87-wo/Tilt whl	4131367	13.00
w/Tilt whl	3747529	14.50
Ignition Buzzer Switch		
1983-87-wo/Tilt whl	4131522	11.75
w/Tilt whl	3488432	7.50

LABOR — 3 FUEL SYSTEM 3 — LABOR

(Factory Time)	Chilton Time

(G) Fuel Pump, Test
Includes: Disconnect line at carburetor, attach pressure gauge.

All models	.2

(M) Carburetor Air Cleaner, Service

1983-87 (.3)	.3

(G) Air Cleaner Vacuum Diaphram, Renew
Includes: Renew sensor if necessary.

1983-87 (.2)	.5

(G) Air Cleaner Vacuum Sensor, Renew

1983-87-one (.2)	.5

(M) Fuel Filter, Renew

1983-87 (.2)	.3

(G) Coolant Temperature Sensor/Switch (ESC), Renew
Includes: Test.

1983 (.5)	1.0
1984-87 (.3)	.6

(G) Carburetor, Adjust (On Car)

All models	
w/Catalytic converter (.6)	.6
wo/Catalytic converter (.5)	.6

(G) Automatic Choke, Renew

1 bbl (.2)	.4
2 bbl (.2)	.4
4 bbl (.5)	.7

(G) Automatic Choke/Cover or Float Chamber, Renew

1985-87 (.3)	.5

(G) Automatic Choke Diaphragm, Renew

1983-85	
Holly (.2)	.4
Carter-2 bbl (.5)	.7
4 bbl (.6)	.9

(G) Choke Control Switch, Renew

1983-87 (.2)	.3

(G) Choke Vacuum Kick, Renew

1983-87	
2 bbl (.2)	.4
4 bbl (.6)	.8

(G) Choke Vacuum Kick, Adjust

1983-85	
2 bbl (.2)	.3
4 bbl (.5)	.6

(G) Carburetor, Renew
Includes: Adjust idle speed and mixture with analyzer.

1983-87 (.7)	1.3

(G) Carburetor, R&R and Clean or Recondition
Includes: Adjust idle speed and mixture with analyzer.

1983-87-Holly (1.8)	2.8
Carter-2 bbl (2.2)	3.2
4 bbl (2.5)	3.5
Thermo-Quad (2.4)	4.0

(G) Carburetor Needle and Seat, Renew
Includes: Adjust float level, adjust idle speed and mixture with analyzer.

1983-87-1 bbl (.5)	.7
2 bbl (.6)	.8
4 bbl (.9)	1.2

(G) Float, Renew or Adjust Level
Includes: Adjust idle speed.

1983-87-exc below (.9)	1.2
4 bbl (1.2)	1.5

(G) Accelerator Pump, Renew

1983-87-exc below (.5)	.8
4 bbl (.9)	1.1

(G) Fuel Pump, Renew

Six-1983 (.8)	1.1
V-8-1983-87	
318, 360 engs (.5)	.8

Add pump test if performed.

(G) Flexible Fuel Line, Renew

1983-87-each (.3)	.4

(G) Fuel Tank, Renew

1983-87 (1.0)	1.5

(G) Fuel Gauge (Tank), Renew

1983-87 (1.0)	1.2

(G) Fuel Gauge (Dash), Renew

1983 (.5)	1.0
1984-87 (.7)	1.2

(G) Intake Manifold or Gaskets, Renew

Six-1983 (2.1)	3.0
V-8-1983-87	
318, 360 engs (2.4)	3.5
w/A.C. add (.4)	.4
w/Air inj add (.3)	.3
Renew manif add (.4)	.5

(G) Intake and Exhaust Manifold Gaskets, Renew

Six-1983 (1.7)	2.3
w/A.C. add (.4)	.4

PARTS — 3 FUEL SYSTEM 3 — PARTS

	Part No.	Price
Air Cleaner Temperature Sensor		
1983-87	4240062	7.50
Carburetor Assy. (Carter) (New)		
Six-225 engine		
1983	4179128	243.00
V-8-318 engine		
1983-2 bbl		
BBD-8291	4287089	231.50
BBD-8369	4287023	310.25
1983-4 bbl		
TQ-9385	4287051	407.00
TQ-9364	4179177	364.00
TQ-9374	4227251	407.00
1984-2 bbl		
BBD-8369	4287023	310.25
BBD-8385	4300011	243.00
1984-4 bbl		
TQ-9364	4179177	364.00
TQ-9389	4300012	407.00
Carburetor Assy. (Holley) (New)		
Six-225 engine		
1983 (1 bbl carb)		
R-40032	4227337	325.75
R-40042	4287073	243.00
V-8-318 engine		
1985-2 bbl.		
R-40121	4288576	325.75
R-40157	4288578	N.S.S.
1986-87-R40245	4288581	N.L.
R40276	4324647	325.75
Carburetor Assy. (Rochester) (New)		
V-8-318 engine		
1985-87-exc. below	4342808	N.L.
electronic	4342805	698.75
1986-87-5411	4306411	N.L.
5433	4306433	N.L.
Carburetor Repair Kit (Carter)		
1983-87-2 bbl	4271962	28.25
4 bbl	4271945	33.00
Carburetor Repair Kit (Holley)		
Six-225 engine		
1983	4267155	28.50
V-8-318 engine		
1985-87-R-40121	4342860	47.50
R-40157	4267245	47.50
Carburetor Repair Kit (Rochester)		
V-8-318 engine		
1985-87-exc. below	4342832	50.50
electronic	4342812	50.50
Choke Assembly		
Carter		
(6 cyl.)		
1983	4095337	17.75
(V-8)		
1983-2 bbl	4095338	21.00
4 bbl	4095984	22.25
1984-2 bbl	4271956	10.25
4 bbl	4267133	10.00
Holley		
1983	4095330	26.50
1985-87	4293895	11.50
Rochester		
1985-87-exc below	4342819	38.75
electronic	4342934	39.00
Fuel Pump Assy. (New)		
Six-225 engine		
1983	4271893	35.50
V-8-318 engine		
1983	4271894	35.50
1984-87	4293803	35.25
Fuel Tank		
Order by year and model.		
Fuel Gauge (Tank Unit)		
1983-87	4051398	34.75
Fuel Gauge (Dash Unit)		
1983-87-unleaded	4051388	24.50
leaded	4051389	26.50
Intake Manifold Gasket		
Six-225 engine		
1983	4186180	7.00
V-8-318 engine		
1983-85-2 bbl	3837605	7.75
4 bbl	3514187	11.25
1986-87-2 bbl	4397643	7.75
4 bbl	4397642	7.75
Throttle Position Transducer (ESA)		
1983	4049198	17.25

LABOR 3A EMISSION CONTROLS 3A LABOR

	(Factory Time)	Chilton Time
AIR INJECTION SYSTEM		
(G) Air Pump, Renew		
Six–1983	(.7)	1.2
V-8–1983-87	(.5)	.9
(M) Air Injection Pump Belt, Renew		
1983-87	(.3)	.4
(G) Aspirator Assembly, Renew		
1983-87	(.2)	.3
(G) Air Pump Diverter/Switching Valve, Renew		
Six–1983	(.3)	.6
V-8–1983-87-318, 360 engs	(.3)	.6
(G) Injection Tube and Check Valve Assy., Renew		
Six–1983		
to exh pipe	(.4)	.6
to cyl head	(.9)	1.2
w/A.C. add	(.1)	.1
V-8–1983-87-318, 360 engs		
exh manif mount	(.9)	1.3
to converter	(.4)	.7
(M) Air Pump Hoses, Renew		
1983-87-one	(.2)	.3
(G) Orifice Spark Advance Control Valve, Renew		
1983-87	(.3)	.4
(G) Pulse Air Feeder/Aspirator Tube, Renew		
1983-87	(.2)	.4
EVAPORATIVE EMISSION		
(M) Vapor Canister, Renew		
1983-87	(.3)	.4
(M) Vapor Canister Hoses, Renew		
1983-87-one	(.2)	.2
(M) Vapor Canister Filter, Renew		
1983-87	(.2)	.3
CRANKCASE EMISSION		
(M) Crankcase Vent Valve, Renew		
1983-87	(.2)	.3

CHILTON'S EMISSION CONTROL TUNE-UP

1. Clean or renew P.C.V. valve, hoses and filter.
2. Check fuel tank cap for sealing ability.
3. Check fuel tank and fuel lines for leakage.
4. Check evaporation canister and filter. Replace if necessary.
5. Check engine compression to determine leakage of unburned gases. (Add time for items of interference).
6. Test and clean or renew spark plugs.
7. Check engine oil dipstick for sealing ability.
8. Test exhaust system with analyzer and check system for leakage.
9. Check exhaust manifold heat valve for operation.
10. Adjust ignition timing and carburetor idle speed and mixture.
11. Check automatic choke mechanism for free operation.
12. Inspect air cleaner and element.
13. On models so equipped, test distributor vacuum control switch and transmission control switch.

Six **1.5**

V-8 .... **1.8**

For repairs made, charge accordingly.

	(Factory Time)	Chilton Time
(M) Positive Crankcase Vent Hose, Renew		
1983-87	(.2)	.3
(M) Crankcase Vent Air Cleaner, Renew		
1983-87	(.2)	.3
E.G.R. SYSTEM		
(G) Exhaust Gas Recirculation Control Valve, Renew		
1983-87	(.4)	.6
(G) Coolant Control Valve (CCEGR), Renew		
1983-87	(.4)	.4
(G) Recirculation Vacuum Amplifier, Renew		
1983-87	(.2)	.3
(G) Time Delay Timer, Renew		
1983-87	(.2)	.3
(G) Time Delay Solenoid, Renew		
1983-87	(.2)	.3

	(Factory Time)	Chilton Time
(G) Engine Coolant Control Vacuum or Change Temperature Switch, Renew		
1983-87	(.4)	.6
(G) Exhaust Manifold Power Heat Valve Actuator, Renew		
1983-87	(.8)	1.2
EFE SYSTEM		
(G) Oxygen Sensor, Renew		
1983-87	(.2)	.4
(G) Detonation Switch, Renew		
1983-87	(.2)	.4
(G) High Altitude Compensator, Renew		
1983-87	(.3)	.5
(G) Oxygen Sensor Maintenance Lamp Switch, Renew or Reset		
1983-87	(.2)	.4
(G) Electronic Speed Switch, Renew		
1984-87	(.2)	.4

PARTS 3A EMISSION CONTROLS 3A PARTS

	Part No.	Price
AIR INJECTION SYSTEM		
Air Pump		
Six–225 engine		
1983-wo/Air cond	4268963	162.50
w/Air cond	4268961	162.50
V-8–318 engine		
1983-87	4268963	162.50
Air Pump Pulley		
1983	4241645	11.00
1983-87	3870088	10.50
Air Pump Diverter Valve		
1983-87-V-8	4179719	30.50
Aspirator Valve		
1983-85	4041966	10.75
1986-87	4300376	19.50
Air Switch & Relief Valve		
1983-85	4227670	30.50
1986-87	4227672	30.50
Crossover & Check Valve		
1983-87-318 eng	4179893	38.75

	Part No.	Price
Orifice Spark Control Valve		
Six–225 engine		
1983 (number stamped on decal)		
blue decal	3755711	23.50
black decal	4111935	23.50
pink decal	4091994	23.50
V-8–318 engine		
1983	3755727	23.50
EVAPORATIVE EMISSION		
Fuel Vapor Canister		
1983-87-3 port	4271982	49.25
4 port	4241838	52.75
5 port	4241841	52.75
Vapor Canister Filter		
1983	3577586	1.75
CRANKCASE EMISSION		
Positive Crankcase Vent Valve		
1983-87	3671076	4.25
Crankcase Vent Air Cleaner		
1983-87	4273322	4.50

E.G.R. SYSTEM

E.G.R. Valve

Replacement E.G.R. valves must be ordered according to the stamping number on the original valve.

	Part No.	Price
E.G.R. Vacuum Amplifier		
Six–225 engine		
1983 (no. stamped on amplifier)		
stamped	4041733	41.50
stamped	4241995	41.50
V-8–318 engine		
1983-85 (no. stamped on amplifier)		
stamped	4041733	41.50
stamped	4241995	41.50
1986-87-4 bbl	4041737	41.50
Coolant Control Vacuum Switch		
Six–225 engine		
1983	3879736	17.50
V-8–318 engine		
1983-84	3837622	17.50
1985-87-black	3879736	17.50

PARTS 3A EMISSION CONTROLS 3A PARTS

	Part No.	Price
red	4095231	17.50
2 bbl	4049277	17.50
Time Delayed E.G.R. Solenoid Valve		
1983-black	4111179	43.00
orange	4111180	43.00
red	4111481	43.00
1984-85-blue	4145202	45.25
red	4111482	7.00
1986-87-2 bbl	4167046	4.25
Dual Vacuum Solenoid		
1985	4289087	28.75
1986-87-exc Calif.	6032473	.25
Calif. 2 bbl	4289087	28.75
Oxygen Sensor Switch		
1983	4301175	34.00
1984-87	4301375	40.00
Detonation Sensor		
1983-87	5213629	23.75

LABOR 4 ALTERNATOR AND REGULATOR 4 LABOR

	(Factory Time)	Chilton Time
(G) Alternator Circuits, Test		
Includes: Test battery, regulator and alternator output.		
All models		.6
(M) Alternator Drive Belt, Renew		
1983-87	(.2)	.3
w/A.C. add	(.1)	.1
w/P.S. add	(.1)	.1
w/Air inj add	(.1)	.1
(G) Alternator, Renew		
Includes: Transfer pulley if required.		
1983-87	(.4)	.6
w/A.C. add	(.1)	.1
w/Air inj add	(.2)	.2
w/100 amp alter add	(.1)	.1
Add circuit test if performed.		
(G) Alternator, R&R and Recondition		
Includes: Test and disassemble.		
1983-87	(1.4)	2.0
w/A.C. add	(.1)	.1
w/Air inj add	(.2)	.2
w/100 amp alter add	(.1)	.1
(G) Alternator Front Bearing or Retainer, Renew		
1983-87	(.7)	1.0
w/A.C. add	(.1)	.1
w/Air inj add	(.2)	.2
w/100 amp alter add	(.1)	.1
Renew rear brg add		.2
(G) Alternator Regulator, Renew		
Includes: Test.		
1983-87	(.2)	.6
(G) Alternator Gauge, Renew		
1983-87	(.5)	.8
(G) Instrument Cluster Voltage Limiter, Renew		
1983-87	(.3)	.7

PARTS 4 ALTERNATOR AND REGULATOR 4 PARTS

	Part No.	Price
Alternator Assembly (New)		
(60 & 78 amp)		
1983-87 (Stamped ident.)		
4091565	4091565	129.00
4091566	4176007	129.00
4111266	4176004	129.00
4111204	4176006	129.00
(114 amp)		
1983-87	4091460	252.25
Regulator Assembly		
1983-87	4111990	29.00
(1) Insulator Brush. Pkg.		
1983-87-exc 114 amp	4057928	4.50
114 amp	3838079	4.75
(2) Brush Holder		
(60 & 78 amp)		
1983-87-axial	3438159	1.50
radial	4091667	.75
(114 amp)		
1983-87	3755773	1.50
(3) Drive End Shield Brg.		
(60 & 78 amp)		
1983-87-exc. below	3656444	8.75
4091566	2098478	N.L.
(114 amp)		
1983-87	3755951	24.00
(4) Drive End Shield		
1983-87-exc below	4091534	19.25
65 amp	4091533	19.75
114 amp	3874995	34.75
(5) Rotor		
1983-87-exc. below	4240414	62.00
60 amp	4240413	62.00
114 amp	4026048	62.00
(6) Stator		
1983-87-exc. below	4091517	36.75
60 amp	4091515	36.75
114 amp	3879401	55.50

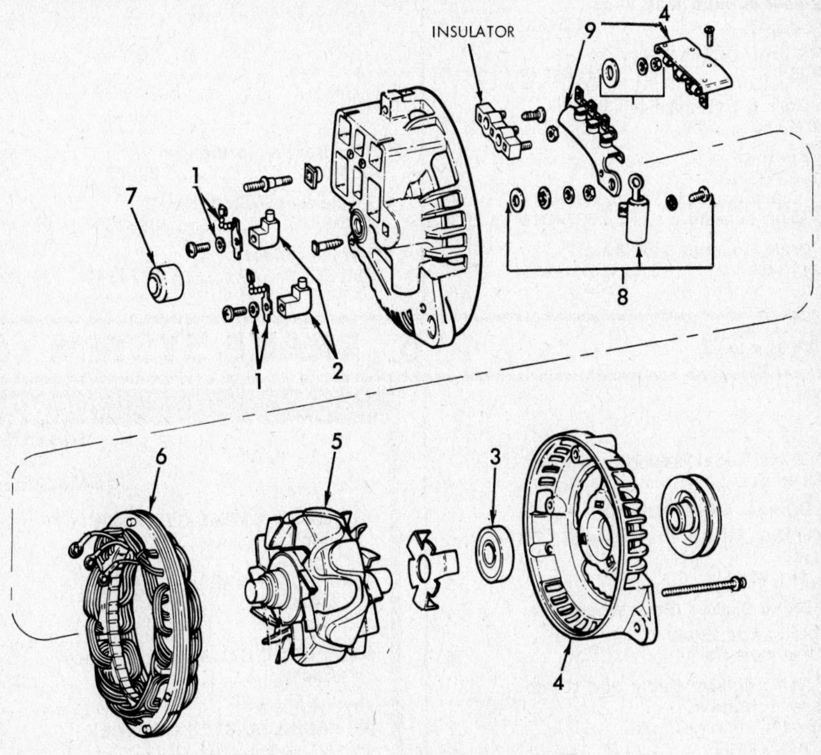

	Part No.	Price
(7) Rectifier End Shield Brg.		
1983-87-exc 114 amp	3755184	3.25
114 amp	3874074	4.00
(8) Capacitor and Bolt Pkg.		
1983-87-exc 114 amp	3620793	4.75
114 amp	3838078	4.75
(9) Rectifier Heat Sink Pkg.		
1983-87 (negative)		
exc. below	3755114	17.75
60 amp	3438721	17.75
114 amp	3755627	22.75
1983-87 (positive)		
exc. below	4240488	17.50
114 amp	4026303	28.25

LABOR 5 STARTING SYSTEM 5 LABOR

	(Factory Time)	Chilton Time
(G) Starter Draw Test (On Car)		
All models		.3
(G) Starter, Renew		
Includes: Test starter relay, starter solenoid and amperage draw.		
Six–1983	(.8)	1.2
V-8–1983-87	(.7)	1.3
(G) Starter, R&R and Recondition		
Includes: Test relay, starter solenoid and amperage draw.		
Six–1983	(1.4)	2.0
V-8–1983-87-318, 360 engs	(1.5)	2.1
Renew field coils add	(.5)	.5
(G) Starter Drive, Renew		
Six–1983	(1.2)	1.7
V-8–1983-87	(1.1)	1.8
(G) Starter Relay, Renew		
1983-87	(.2)	.4
(G) Starter Solenoid, Renew		
Six–1983	(1.2)	1.7
V-8–1983-87	(1.0)	1.8
(G) Starter Neutral Switch, Renew		
1983-87	(.3)	.4
(G) Ignition Switch, Renew		
Includes: Replace and recode lock cylinder if necessary.		
1983-87	(.6)	1.0
(M) Battery Cables, Renew		
ground	(.2)	.3
batt to starter relay	(.5)	.5
positive	(.4)	.4

PARTS 5 STARTING SYSTEM 5 PARTS

	Part No.	Price
Starter Assy. (New)		
1983-87	4145360	149.00
(1) Thrust Washer Pkg.		
1983-87	3837340	2.25
(2) Starter Armature (New)		
1983-87	3837334	66.25
(3) Frame & Field Coil Assy.		
1983-87	4111959	54.50
(4) Shaft (Pinion)		
1983-87	4091914	11.00
(5) Gear & Snap Ring Pkg.		
1983-87	4106092	11.25
(6) Starter Clutch Assy.		
1983-87	4145978	23.50
(7) Core & Shifting Fork Pkg.		
1983-87	4057940	12.75
(8) Bearing		
1983-87		
pinion housing	3874817	1.75
gear housing	3874818	2.25
(9) Drive Housing & Bearing		
1983-87	3755261	28.75

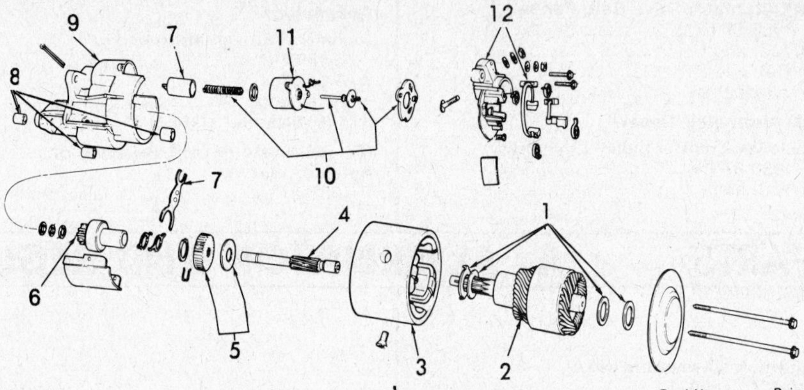

	Part No.	Price
(10) Contact & Spring Pkg.		
1983-87	2932814	5.50
(11) Solenoid Switch (New)		
1983-87	3837337	27.00
(12) Brush Holder		
1983-87	3874345	20.00
Starter Relay		
1983-87	4111971	11.25
Battery Cables		
Order by year and model.		
Ignition Switch		
1983-87-wo/tilt whl	4131367	13.00
w/tilt whl	3747529	14.50

LABOR 6 BRAKE SYSTEM 6 LABOR

	(Factory Time)	Chilton Time
(G) Brake Pedal Free Play, Adjust		
All models		.4
(G) Brakes, Adjust (Minor)		
Includes: Adjust brake shoes, fill master cylinder.		
two wheels		.4
(G) Bleed Brakes (Four Wheels)		
Includes: Add fluid.		
All models	(.4)	.6
(G) Self Adjustor Cable and Guide or Lever, Renew		
1983-87-one	(.4)	.7
each adtnl		.4
(G) Brake Shoes and/or Pads, Renew		
Includes: Install new or exchange shoes or pads, adjust service and hand brake. Bleed system.		
1983-87-front-disc	(.6)	1.1
rear-drum	(.7)	1.5
all four wheels	(1.3)	2.5
Resurface disc rotor, add-each		.9
Resurface brake drum, add-each		.5

COMBINATIONS

Add to Brakes, Renew

See Machine Shop Operations

(G) RENEW WHEEL CYLINDER		
Each		.2
(G) REBUILD WHEEL CYLINDER		
Each		.3
(G) REBUILD CALIPER ASSEMBLY		
Each		.5
(G) RENEW MASTER CYLINDER		
All models	(.6)	.6
(G) REBUILD MASTER CYLINDER		
All models		1.0
(G) RENEW BRAKE HOSE		
Each	(.3)	.3
(G) RENEW REAR WHEEL GREASE SEALS		
One side	(.4)	.4
(G) REPACK FRONT WHEEL BEARINGS (BOTH WHEELS)		
All models		.6
(G) RENEW DISC BRAKE ROTOR		
Each		.5
(G) RENEW BRAKE DRUM		
Each		.1

	(Factory Time)	Chilton Time
(G) Brake Drum, Renew (One)		
1983-87	(.4)	.5
(G) Brake System Indicator Switch, Renew		
1983-87	(.2)	.4

LABOR 6 BRAKE SYSTEM 6 LABOR

(Factory Time)	Chilton Time

BRAKE HYDRAULIC SYSTEM

(G) Wheel Cylinder, Renew
Includes: Bleed system.

1983-87-one (.7)	1.1
both (1.3)	2.1

(G) Wheel Cylinder, R&R and Rebuild
Includes: Hone cylinder & bleed system.

1983-87-one	1.2
both	2.3

(G) Brake Hose, Renew (Flex)
Includes: Bleed system.

1983-87-each (.4)	.6

(G) Master Cylinder, Renew
Includes: Bleed complete system.

1983-87 (.5)	.9

(G) Master Cylinder, R&R and Rebuild
Includes: Bleed complete system.

1983-87	1.7
w/P.B. add	.2

(G) Master Cylinder Reservoir, Renew
Includes: Bleed complete system.

1983-87 (.6)	1.0

POWER BRAKES

(G) Brake Booster Assembly, Renew

1983-87 (.6)	1.0

(G) Brake Booster Check Valve, Renew

1983-87 (.2)	.3

DISC BRAKES

(G) Front Brake Disc Pads, Renew
Includes: Install new disc brake pads only.

1983-87 (.6)	1.1

(G) Brake Shoes and/or Pads, Renew
Includes: Install new or exchange shoes or pads, adjust service and hand brake. Bleed system.

1983-87-front-disc (.6)	1.1
rear-drum (.7)	1.5
all four wheels (1.3)	2.5
Resurface disc rotor, add-each	.9
Resurface brake drum, add-each	.5

(G) Disc Brake Rotor, Renew
Includes: Replace inner and outer bearings if necessary.

1983-87-one (.6)	.9
both (1.1)	1.7

(G) Caliper Assembly, Renew
Includes: Bleed system.

1983-87-one (.6)	1.0
both (1.0)	1.8

(G) Caliper Assembly, R&R and Recondition
Includes: Bleed system.

1983-87-one (.9)	1.5
both (1.6)	2.8

(G) Brake System Combination Valve Assy., Renew
Includes: Bleed system.

1983-87 (.8)	1.2

PARKING BRAKE

(M) Parking Brake, Adjust

1983-87 (.3)	.4

(G) Parking Brake Lever, Renew

1983-87 (.7)	1.2

(G) Parking Brake Cables, Renew

1983-87-front (.6)	.9
rear (.5)	.7
intermediate (.4)	.6

PARTS 6 BRAKE SYSTEM 6 PARTS

	Part No.	Price
(1) Brake Shoes & Lining (Rear)		
1983-84-10″ brks	4049682	55.00
11″ brks	4026648	50.00
1985-86-10″ brks	4364786	55.00
11″ brks	4026648	50.00
(2) Wheel Cylinder (Rear)		
1983-87	3780525	21.25
Brake Hose (Front)		
1983-87-right	4240508	19.25
left	4240509	19.25
Brake Hose (Rear)		
1983-87	4126502	16.00
Master Cylinder Assy.		
1983-87	3880289	79.75
Reservoir		
1983-87	3766448	4.75
Reservoir Grommets		
1983-87	5204149	1.00
Brake Booster Assy.		
1983-87	3880348	218.25
Check Valve Kit		
1983-87	3420973	8.50

FRONT BRAKE

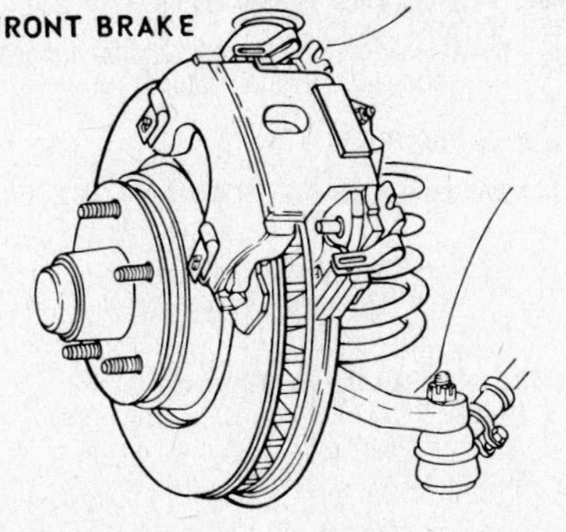

REAR BRAKE

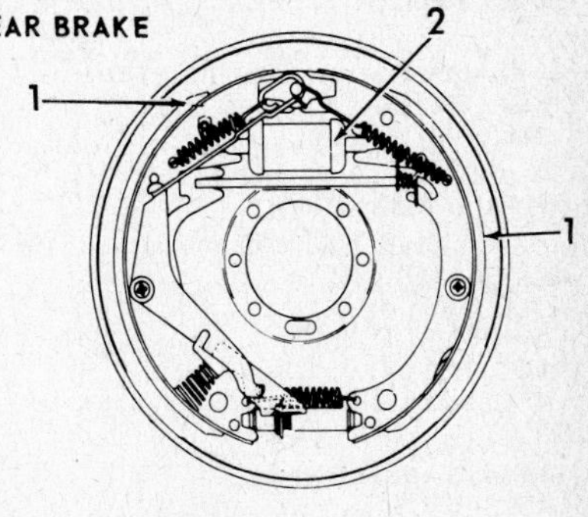

	Part No.	Price
Brake Drum (Rear)		
1983-87-10″ brake	4049661	97.75
11″ brake	3780537	102.75
Oil Seal (Front)		
1983-87	3580723	6.00
Oil Seal (Rear)		
1983-87	2931875	6.25

PARKING BRAKE

	Part No.	Price
Parking Brake Lever		
1983-87	4019369	37.75
Hand Brake Cable		
1983-87-Front	3766292	17.25
interm	3880072	5.75
rear	3880074	19.50
H.D.	3880075	19.50

PARTS 6 DISC BRAKES 6 PARTS

	Part No.	Price
(1) Piston, Seal & Boot Pkg.		
1983-87	4186989	19.25
(2) Boot & Seal Pkg.		
1983-87	4186990	4.50
(3) Caliper Housing		
1983-87-right	4126842	126.00
left	4126843	126.00
(4) Brake Pads		
1983-87-Std.	4176778	47.50
H.D.	4049699	47.50
(5) Plate (Retaining)		
1983-87	3580824	2.50
(6) Adapter		
1983-87	4267344	30.00
Front Hub & Disc		
1983-87-Std	4131251	118.00

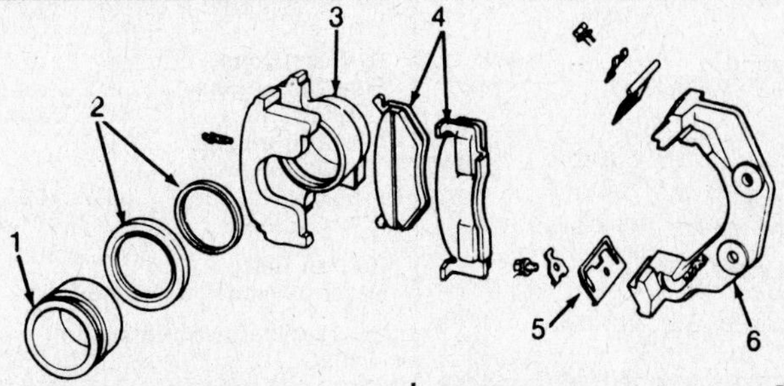

	Part No.	Price
H.D.	3880685	112.75
Brake System Indicator Switch		
1983-87	3620790	4.25

	Part No.	Price
Proportioning Valve		
1983-87-exc Police	4176794	60.75
Police	3880038	56.75

LABOR 7 COOLING SYSTEM 7 LABOR

	(Factory Time)	Chilton Time
(M) Winterize Cooling System		
Includes: Run engine to check for leaks, tighten all hose connections. Test radiator pressure cap, drain radiator and engine block. Add anti-freeze and refill system.		
All models		.5
(M) Thermostat, Renew		
1983-87	(.4)	.6
w/A.C. add	(.3)	.3
(M) Radiator Assembly, R&R or Renew		
1983-87	(.8)	1.2
w/A.C. add	(.1)	.2
w/A.T. add	(.1)	.2

ADD THESE OPERATIONS TO RADIATOR R&R

	Chilton Time
(G) Boil & Repair	1.5
(G) Rod Clean	1.9
(G) Repair Core	1.3
(G) Renew Tank	1.6
(G) Renew Trans. Oil Cooler	1.9
(G) Recore Radiator	1.7

	(Factory Time)	Chilton Time
(M) Radiator Hoses, Renew		
1983-87-upper	(.4)	.5
lower	(.4)	.5
by-pass-Six	(.6)	.9
V-8	(.3)	.6
w/A.C. add	(.1)	.1
(G) Transmission Auxiliary Oil Cooler, Renew		
1983-87	(.3)	.9
(G) Water Pump, Renew		
Includes: Drain and refill coolant.		
Six-1983	(.9)	1.3
w/A.C. add	(.4)	.4
V-8-1983-87	(1.0)	1.3
w/A.C. add	(.4)	.4
w/P.S. add	(.2)	.2
(M) Fan Blades, Renew		
1983-87	(.3)	.4
w/A.C. add		.1
w/Air inj add		.1
(M) Drive Belt, Renew		
1983-87	(.2)	.3
w/A.C. add	(.1)	.1
w/Air inj add	(.1)	.1
w/P.S. add	(.1)	.1

COOLING SYSTEM TUNE-UP

An Annual Cooling System Tune-Up Suggestion List should include (with some exceptions):

1. A visual check of the cooling system for indications of leaks or excessive oil content.
2. Pressure check the cooling system for internal and external leaks with filler cap and neck adapter and tester.
3. Check crankcase and automatic transmission oil for water content.
4. Test coolant thermostat with radiator thermometer.
5. Check temperature gauge for accuracy.
6. Drain system and flush till clean.
7. Clean foreign matter from radiator fins.
8. Test radiator pressure cap with cap tester.
9. Check fan blades and pulleys for alignment and damage.
10. Internal and external inspection of all hoses for cracks and deterioration.
11. Check core plugs (where possible) for seepage.
12. Refill system with correct coolant and check for air locks.
13. Check condition and tension of drive belts with tension gauge.

All models 1.5

	(Factory Time)	Chilton Time
(M) Fluid Fan Drive, Renew		
1983-87	(.3)	.6
w/A.C. add	(.3)	.3
w/Air inj add	(.1)	.1
(G) Temperature Gauge (Engine Unit), Renew		
1983-87	(.3)	.5
(G) Temperature Gauge (Dash Unit), Renew		
1983-87	(.5)	.8
(G) Water Jacket Expansion Plugs, Renew (Engine Block)		
Six-1983-left side		
one	(1.9)	2.3
all	(2.1)	2.9
V-8-1983-87-front		
right or left	(1.3)	1.5
center	(.6)	.8
rear	(.7)	.9
eng rear-one or both	(2.9)	3.6
all-both sides	(2.3)	2.8
(G) Water Jacket Expansion Plugs, Renew (Cylinder Head)		
Six-1983-front		
one	(.5)	.7
rear-one	(3.1)	3.8
V-8-1983-87-318, 360 engs		
front-one	(.5)	.7
rear-one	(3.4)	4.1
(G) Heater Hoses, Renew		
1983-87-one	(.3)	.6
both	(.5)	.8
(G) Heater Core, R&R or Renew		
Without Air Conditioning		
1983-87	(1.9)	3.0
With Air Conditioning		
1983-87	(3.0)	*4.5

*Includes charge A.C. system.

ADD THESE OPERATIONS TO HEATER CORE R&R

	Chilton Time
(G) Boil & Repair	1.2
(G) Repair Core	.9
(G) Recore	1.2

	(Factory Time)	Chilton Time
(G) Temperature Control Cable, Renew		
1983-87	(1.0)	1.6
(G) Heater Mode Control Cable, Renew		
1983-87	(.4)	.6
(G) Heater Control Assembly, Renew		
1983-87	(.4)	.9
(G) Heater Blower Motor, Renew		
1983-87	(1.9)	3.0
(G) Heater Blower Motor Resistor, Renew		
1983-87	(.4)	.6
(G) Heater Blower Motor Switch, Renew		
1983-87	(.4)	.7
(G) Heater Water Valve, Renew		
1983-87	(.4)	.6

PARTS 7 COOLING SYSTEM 7 PARTS

	Part No.	Price
(1) Radiator Assembly		
Order by year and model.		
(2) Thermostat		
1983-87	4131240	6.50
(3) Radiator Hoses		
Order by year and model.		
(4) Water Pump Assy. (New)		
Six-225 engine		
1983	4131243	54.00
V-8-318 engine		
1983-87	3837641	60.25
By-Pass Hose		
Six-225 engine		
1983	5214521	4.00
V-8-318 engine		
1983-87-exc. below	4095227	5.50
silicone	4012595	12.00
(5) Fan Belt		
Order by model and description.		
Heat Indicator Sending Unit		
1983	4051140	6.00
1984-87	4051141	5.50
Heat Indicator (Dash Unit)		
1983-87	4051348	22.00
Heater Core		
1983	3847600	106.75
1984	3848455	106.50
1985-87	4339438	106.50
Blower Motor		
1983-84	4049797	56.50
1985-87	4240425	74.25
Heater Switch (Blower)		
1983-87	3847940	10.25

PARTS 7 COOLING SYSTEM 7 PARTS

	Part No.	Price
Heater Vacuum Control Switch		
1983-87	3846895	12.00
Blower Motor Resistor		
1983-84	3847910	12.75
1985-87	3848996	13.25
Transmission Auxiliary Oil Cooler		
1983	4266033	111.50
1984-87	4266038	99.75
Engine Oil Cooler		
1983-87	4140394	262.00
Transmission Oil Cooler (Radiator)		
1983-87 (Length X Outside Dia.)		
12″ x 1.00″	4140380	56.25
12″ x 1.25″	4140383	56.25
12″ x 1.50″	4140382	56.25
14.40″ x 1.50″	4140381	56.25

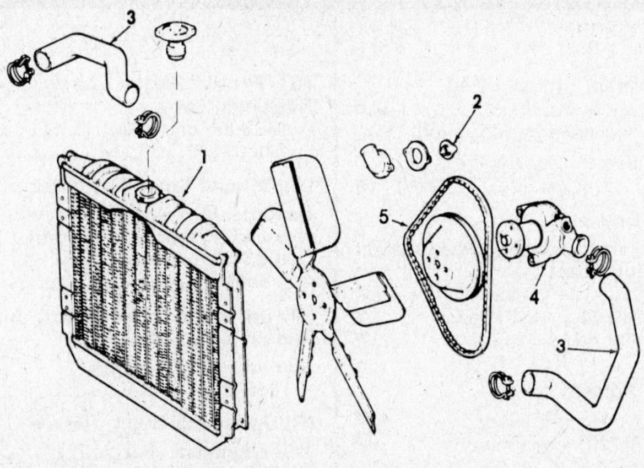

LABOR 8 EXHAUST SYSTEM 8 LABOR

(Factory Time)	Chilton Time
(G) Muffler, Renew	
1983-87-each (.6)	.9
(G) Tail Pipe, Renew	
1983-87-one (.4)	.6
(G) Exhaust Pipe Extension, Renew	
1983-87-front-one (.6)	1.1
both (1.2)	1.8
(G) Catalytic Converter, Renew	
1983-87-one (.7)	1.2
both (1.3)	2.0
(G) Catalytic Converter Heat Shield, Renew	
1983-87-front (.8)	1.2
intermediate (.4)	.8
rear (.6)	1.0
(G) Exhaust Pipe Flange Gasket, Renew	
Six-1983 (.3)	.6
(G) Exhaust Pipe, Renew	
Six-1983 (.7)	.9
V-8-1983-87 (1.3)	1.8
Cut at muffler add (.2)	.2
(G) Manifold Heat Valve, Recondition	
Includes: R&R exhaust manifold.	
Six-1983 (2.2)	3.2
V-8-1983-87	
318, 360 engs (1.4)	1.9
w/A.C. add (.4)	.4
(G) Manifold Heat Control Valve Counterweight & Spring, Renew	
Six (.3)	.6
V-8 (.5)	.8
(G) Power Heat Control Valve, Renew	
1983-87 (.8)	1.2
(G) Exhaust Manifold or Gaskets, Renew	
Six-1983 (1.9)	3.0
V-8-318, 360 engs	
1983-87-right side (.7)	1.0
left side (.6)	.9
w/A.C. add (.4)	.4
w/Air inj add (.4)	.4
(G) Intake and Exhaust Manifold Gaskets, Renew	
Six-1983 (1.7)	2.3
w/A.C. add (.4)	.4

COMBINATIONS

(G) Muffler, Exhaust and Tail Pipe, Renew	
one side	2.0
both sides	3.5
(G) Muffler and Tail Pipe, Renew	
front-one	1.5
rear-one	1.2
one side	2.0
both side	3.2

PARTS 8 EXHAUST SYSTEM 8 PARTS

	Part No.	Price
Muffler		
Six-225 engine		
1983	4150280	52.75
V-8-318 engine		
1983-2 bbl	4150280	52.75
4 bbl	4150425	45.75
1984-2 bbl	4150280	52.75
4 bbl	4301341	45.75
1985-87-2 bbl	4301534	52.75
4 bbl	4301341	45.75
Tail Pipe		
Six-225 engine		
1983	4150186	65.50
V-8-318 engine		
1983	4150170	21.25
1984-87-2 bbl	4150170	21.25
4 bbl	4301339	63.25
Exhaust Pipe		
V-8-318 engine		
1984-87-2 bbl	4150342	74.75
4 bbl	4150324	81.00

Note: Exhaust Pipes not listed are part of Catalytic Converter Assy.

	Part No.	Price
Heat Control Valve Pkg.		
Six-225 engine		
1983	4186175	12.25
V-8-318 engine		
1983-87	3683947	15.00
Catalytic Converter		
Six-225 engine		
1983	4150715	276.50
V-8-318 engine		
1983-87 (Rear)		
2 bbl	4150744	307.25
4 bbl	4150718	338.00
1983-87 (Front)		
2 bbl	4150524	366.75
4 bbl	4150330	280.00
Exhaust Manifold Gasket		
Six-225 engine		
1983	4186180	7.00

LABOR 9 FRONT SUSPENSION 9 LABOR

Note: On all front suspension operations alignment charges must be added if performed. Time given does not include alignment.

(Factory Time)	Chilton Time
(M) Wheel, Renew	
one	.3
(M) Wheels, Rotate (All)	
All models	.5
(G) Wheels, Balance	
one	.3
each adtnl	.2

LABOR 9 FRONT SUSPENSION 9 LABOR

(Factory Time)	Chilton Time
(G) Check Alignment of Front End	
All models	.5
Note: Deduct if alignment is performed.	
(G) Toe-In, Adjust	
All models (.4)	.6
(G) Align Front End	
Includes: Adjust caster, camber, toe, car height and center steering wheel.	
All models (1.1)	1.4
Adjust headlamps add	.3
w/A.C. interference add	.5
(G) Car Height, Adjust	
1983-87 (.3)	.6
Adjust headlamps add	.3
(G) Front Wheels Bearings, Clean and Repack (Both Wheels)	
Includes: R&R dust seal.	
1983-87 (.9)	1.4
(G) Front Wheel Bearings and Cups, Renew	
Includes: R&R dust seal.	
1983-87-one whl (.6)	.7
both whls (1.1)	1.3
(G) Front Wheel Grease Seals, Renew	
1983-87-one whl (.5)	.6
both whls (.9)	1.0
(G) Front Shock Absorber or Bushings, Renew	
1983-87-one (.3)	.4
both (.5)	.7
(G) Rebuild Front Suspension	
Includes: Disassemble, renew necessary parts, reassemble, lubricate and align front end.	
1983-87-one side	4.8
both sides	6.6
(G) Upper and Lower Ball Joints, Renew (One Side)	
Add alignment charges.	
1983-87	2.1
(G) Upper Ball Joint, Renew	
Add alignment charges.	
1983-87-one (.7)	1.0
both (1.3)	2.0
(G) Lower Ball Joint, Renew	
Add alignment charges.	
1983-87-one (.7)	1.1
both (1.3)	2.0
(G) Steering Knuckle, Renew (One)	
Add alignment charges.	
1983-87 (.7)	1.1
(G) Upper Control Arm, Renew (One)	
Includes: Align front end.	
1983-87 (1.8)	2.7
(G) Lower Control Arm, Renew (One)	
Add alignment charges.	
1983-87 (1.0)	1.4
Renew bushings add (.2)	.2
(G) Upper Control Arm Bushings, Renew	
1983-one side (1.0)	1.5
(G) Torsion Bar, Renew	
Includes: Adjust car height.	
1983-87-each (.7)	1.1
(G) Front Sway Bar, Renew	
1983-87 (.6)	1.0
(G) Front Sway Bar Bushings, Renew	
Includes: Replace retainers and insulators.	
1983-87 (.4)	.6
(G) Front Sway Bar Links, Renew	
1983-87-one (.6)	.8
both (.7)	1.0
(G) 'K' Frame, Renew	
Includes: Align front end.	
1983-87 (5.7)	9.0

PARTS 9 FRONT SUSPENSION 9 PARTS

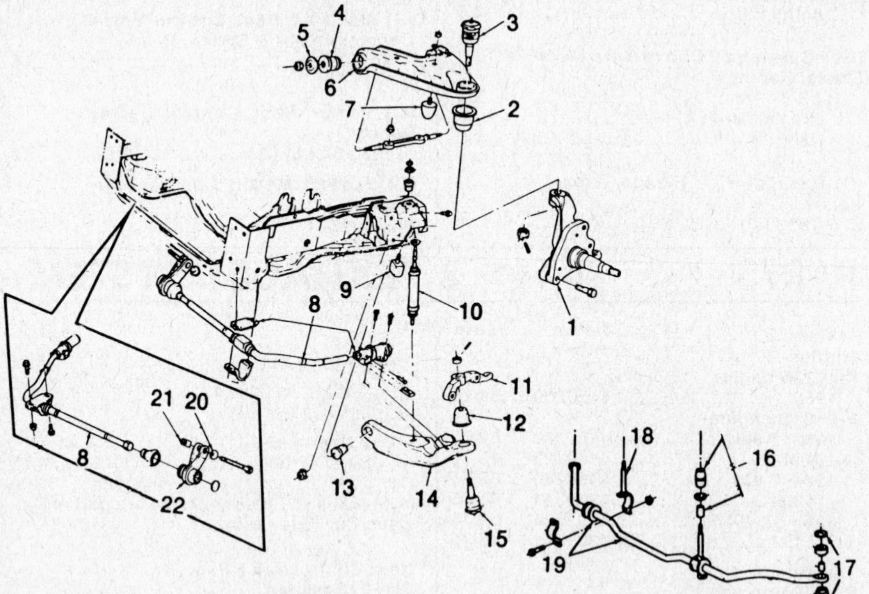

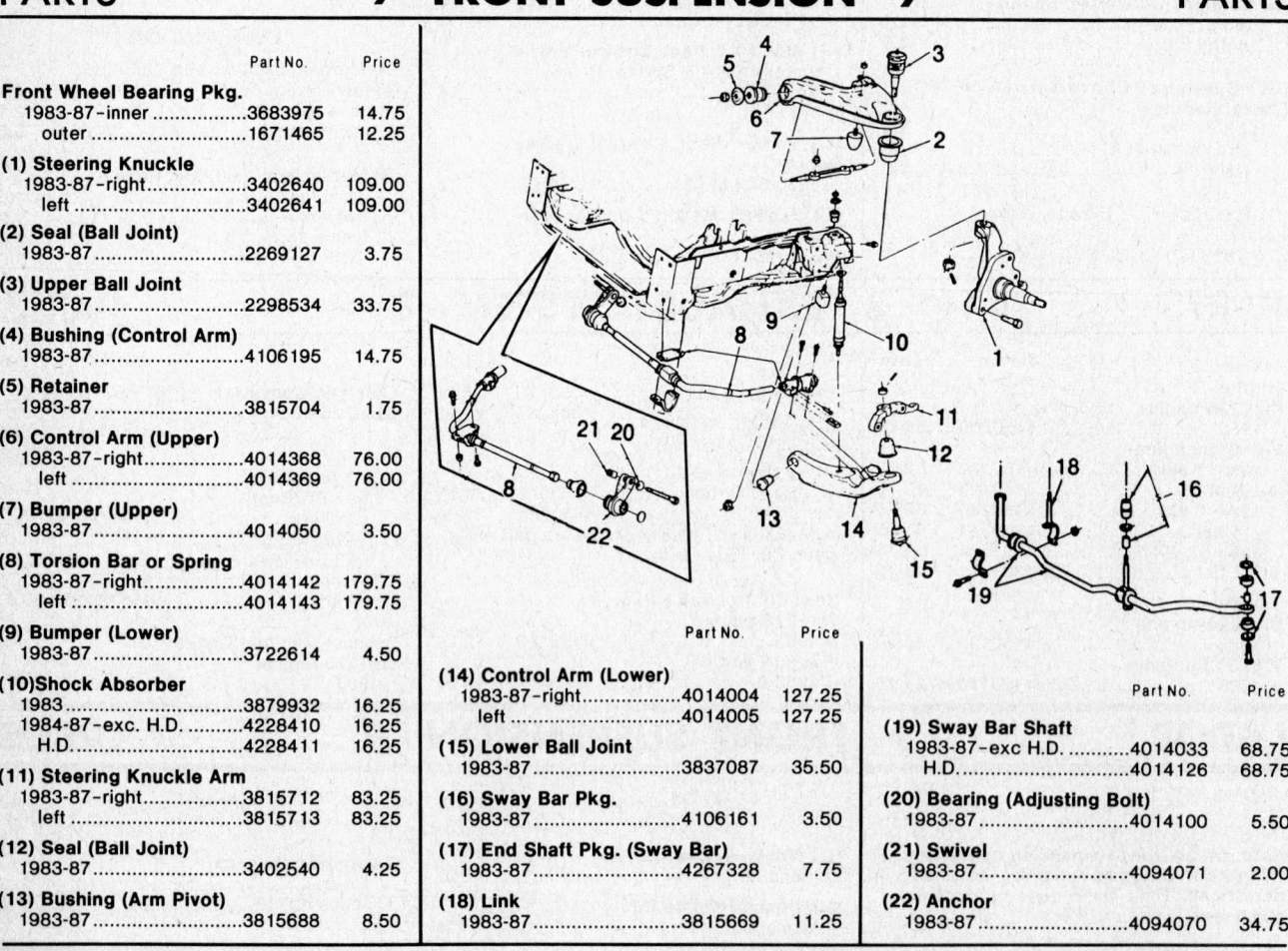

	Part No.	Price
Front Wheel Bearing Pkg.		
1983-87-inner	3683975	14.75
outer	1671465	12.25
(1) Steering Knuckle		
1983-87-right	3402640	109.00
left	3402641	109.00
(2) Seal (Ball Joint)		
1983-87	2269127	3.75
(3) Upper Ball Joint		
1983-87	2298534	33.75
(4) Bushing (Control Arm)		
1983-87	4106195	14.75
(5) Retainer		
1983-87	3815704	1.75
(6) Control Arm (Upper)		
1983-87-right	4014368	76.00
left	4014369	76.00
(7) Bumper (Upper)		
1983-87	4014050	3.50
(8) Torsion Bar or Spring		
1983-87-right	4014142	179.75
left	4014143	179.75
(9) Bumper (Lower)		
1983-87	3722614	4.50
(10)Shock Absorber		
1983	3879932	16.25
1984-87-exc. H.D.	4228410	16.25
H.D.	4228411	16.25
(11) Steering Knuckle Arm		
1983-87-right	3815712	83.25
left	3815713	83.25
(12) Seal (Ball Joint)		
1983-87	3402540	4.25
(13) Bushing (Arm Pivot)		
1983-87	3815688	8.50
(14) Control Arm (Lower)		
1983-87-right	4014004	127.25
left	4014005	127.25
(15) Lower Ball Joint		
1983-87	3837087	35.50
(16) Sway Bar Pkg.		
1983-87	4106161	3.50
(17) End Shaft Pkg. (Sway Bar)		
1983-87	4267328	7.75
(18) Link		
1983-87	3815669	11.25
(19) Sway Bar Shaft		
1983-87-exc H.D.	4014033	68.75
H.D.	4014126	68.75
(20) Bearing (Adjusting Bolt)		
1983-87	4014100	5.50
(21) Swivel		
1983-87	4094071	2.00
(22) Anchor		
1983-87	4094070	34.75

LABOR 10 STEERING LINKAGE 10 LABOR

	(Factory Time)	Chilton Time
(G) Tie Rod Ends, Renew		
Includes: Adjust toe-in. Replace tie rod if necessary.		
1983-87		
inner and outer-both	(.7)	1.0
(G) Pitman Arm, Renew		
1983-87	(.3)	.6
(G) Idler Arm, Renew		
1983-87	(.4)	.6
(G) Steering Gear Center Link, Renew		
1983-87	(.4)	.7
(G) Steering Knuckle Arm, Renew (One)		
1983-87	(.7)	1.1

PARTS 10 STEERING LINKAGE 10 PARTS

	Part No.	Price
(1) Steering Arm		
1983-87-right	3815712	83.25
left	3815713	83.25
(2) Tie Rod End Pkg.		
1983-87-outer	3420154	20.50
inner	3420155	20.50
(3) Tie Rod Tube		
1983-87	4014085	11.50
(4) Pitman Arm		
1983-87	3815777	56.25
(5) Idler Arm		
1983-87	4014089	53.25
(6) Center Link		
1983-87	3815727	51.50

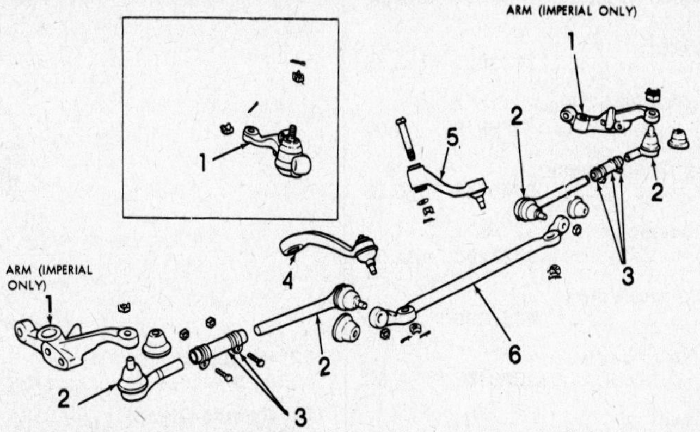

LABOR 11 STEERING GEAR 11 LABOR

	(Factory Time)	Chilton Time
(G) Horn Blowing Ring, Renew		
Cable & Ring		
1983-87-std colm	(.4)	.5
tilt colm	(.2)	.4
(G) Steering Wheel, Renew		
1983-87	(.2)	.4
(G) Upper Mast Jacket Bearing, Renew		
Includes: Replace insulator if necessary.		
1983-87		
std column	(.7)	1.2
tilt column	(1.3)	2.0
(G) Upper Steering Shaft, Renew		
1983-87	(1.5)	2.1
(G) Steering Column Jacket, Renew		
Does not include painting.		
1983-87	(2.3)	3.2
(G) Steering Shaft Flexible Coupling, Renew		
1983-87-std column	(1.0)	1.4
w/Tilt column	(.7)	1.1
w/Tilt-Tel	(.9)	1.3

POWER STEERING

	(Factory Time)	Chilton Time
(G) Power Steering Pump Pressure Check		
All models		.5
(G) Power Steering Gear Sector Shaft, Adjust		
All models	(.5)	.8
(G) Power Steering Gear Control Valve, Adjust		
All models	(.3)	.6
(G) Power Steering Gear Control Valve, Renew		
All models	(.6)	.9
(M) Power Steering Pump Drive Belt, Renew		
1983-87	(.2)	.3
w/A.C. add	(.1)	.1
w/Air inj add	(.1)	.1
(G) Power Steering Gear Assembly, Renew		
1983-87	(1.2)	2.0
w/V-8 add	(.7)	.7
(P) Power Steering Gear Assembly, R&R and Recondition		
Includes: Complete disassembly and assembly, preform all adjustments.		
1983-87	(2.8)	4.0
w/V-8 add	(.7)	.7
(G) Steering Gear Sector Shaft Seal, Renew		
1983-87	(.5)	.9
(G) Power Steering Gear Worm Shaft Seal, Renew		
1983-87	(.9)	1.3
(G) Power Steering Pump, Test & Renew		
Includes: Transfer or renew pulley.		
1983-87	(.8)	1.2
(G) Power Steering Pump, R&R and Recondition		
1983-87	(1.3)	2.0
Add pump pressure check if performed.		
(G) Power Steering Reservoir or Seals, Renew		
1983-87	(.6)	1.0
(G) Pump Drive Shaft Seal, Renew		
1983-87	(1.0)	1.6
(G) Pump Flow Control Valve, Test & Clean or Renew		
1983-87	(.6)	1.0
(G) Pressure Control Valve, Renew		
1983-87	(.5)	.9
(M) Power Steering Hoses, Renew		
1983-87-pressure	(.3)	.5
return	(.2)	.4
cooler	(.4)	.6

TILT & TELESCOPIC STEERING COLUMN

	(Factory Time)	Chilton Time
(G) Tilt Steering Wheel, Renew		
1983-87	(.3)	.6
(G) Upper Steering Shaft, Renew		
1983-87-to yoke	(1.4)	2.3
to coupling	(2.1)	2.9
(G) Steering Column Jacket, Renew		
Does not include painting.		
1983-87	(2.6)	3.3
(G) Steering Column Upper Bearings, Renew		
Includes: Replace insulator if necessary.		
1983-87	(1.3)	2.0

PARTS 11 POWER STEERING GEAR 11 PARTS

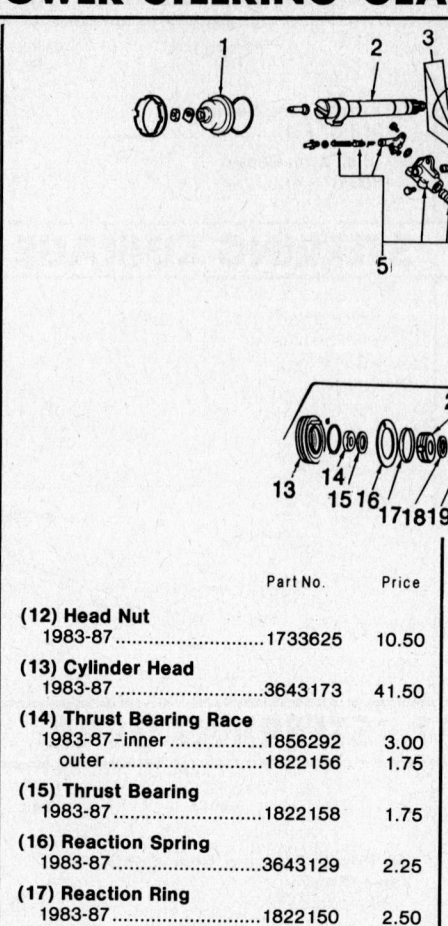

	Part No.	Price
Sector Seal Cover Pkg.		
1983-87	3879920	5.25
Lower Sector Seal Pkg.		
1983-87	3879921	6.50
Gear Power Train Pkg.		
1983-87	3879924	14.50
(1) Shaft Bearing Cover		
1983-87	3643301	34.50
Note: Serviced in Sector Seal Cover Package.		
(2) Sector Shaft		
1983-87	3643302	113.75
(3) Housing 'O' Ring (Pkg.)		
1983-87	3879919	3.00
(4) Steering Gear Housing		
1983-87	3643317	180.25
(5) Valve Assembly		
1983-87	3643280	92.00
Pressure Control Valve		
1983-87	4057085	30.00
(6) Spring Valve Lever		
1983-87	1823151	1.00
(7) Valve Lever		
1983-87	1822380	10.50
(8) Worm w/Piston		
1983-87	2948855	176.25
(9) Piston 'O' Ring (Pkg.)		
1983-87	3879924	14.50
(10) Worm Seal Ring		
1983-87	1822406	1.00
(11) Bearing (Worm)		
1983-87	2537796	3.00

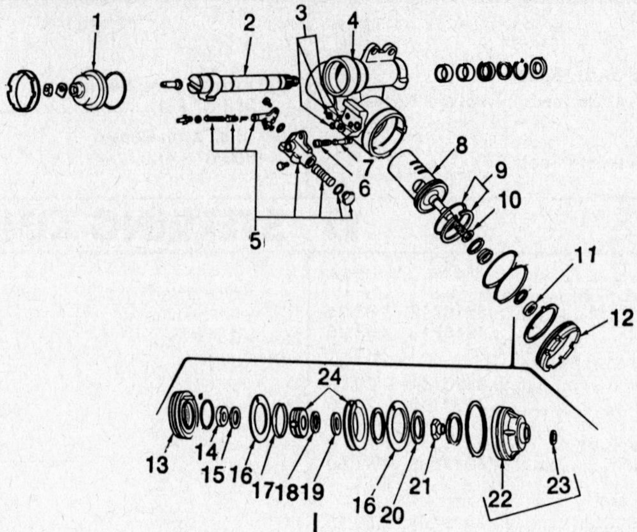

	Part No.	Price
(12) Head Nut		
1983-87	1733625	10.50
(13) Cylinder Head		
1983-87	3643173	41.50
(14) Thrust Bearing Race		
1983-87-inner	1856292	3.00
outer	1822156	1.75
(15) Thrust Bearing		
1983-87	1822158	1.75
(16) Reaction Spring		
1983-87	3643129	2.25
(17) Reaction Ring		
1983-87	1822150	2.50

	Part No.	Price
(18) Bearing (Thrust)		
1983-87	1822158	1.75
(19) Bearing Race (Outer)		
1983-87	1822156	1.75
(20) Washer (Reaction)		
1983-87	1733790	1.00
(21) Nut (Thrust Bearing)		
1983-87	1822157	7.00
(22) Head (Housing)		
1983-87	3643315	60.00
(23) Seal		
1983-87	3643321	3.25
(24) Spacer (w/Center Race)		
1983-87	1822390	56.00

PARTS 11 POWER STEERING PUMP 11 PARTS

	Part No.	Price
Pump Assy.		
1983-87	3815971	246.25
(1) Seal Kit		
1983-87	2537838	11.00
(2) Plate (Cover)		
1983-87	2537820	3.50
(3) Spring (Pressure Plate)		
1983-87	3815966	1.00
(4) Plate (Pressure)		
1983-87	3815967	13.75
(5) Rotor Repair Kit		
1983-87	3815962	89.00
(6) Plate (Thrust)		
1983-87	3815914	12.25
(7) Shaft (Rotor)		
1983-87	3815961	39.00
(8) Seal Kit		
1983-87	2537838	11.00

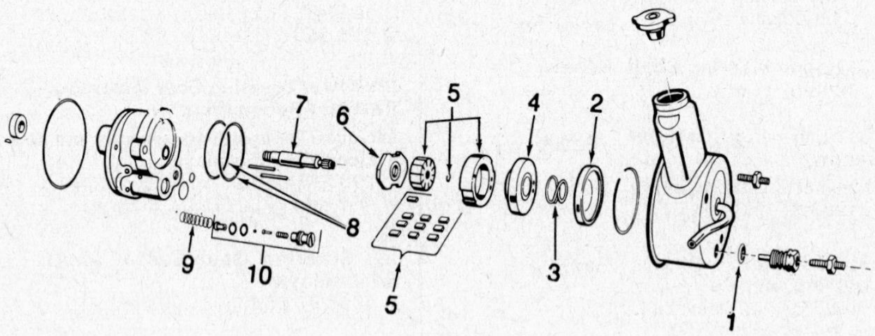

	Part No.	Price
(9) Spring (Control Valve)		
1983-87	2537833	1.50
(10) Valve Assy.		
1983-87	2891460	12.00

	Part No.	Price
Pressure Hose		
1983-84	3815991	29.25
1985-87	4333062	29.25
Return Hose		
Order by length.		

LABOR 12 CYLINDER HEAD & VALVE SYSTEM 12 LABOR

(Factory Time) Chilton Time

(G) Compression Test
Six–1983 (.5) 6
V-8–1983-87-318, 360 engs (.6) 8
w/A.C. add (.3) 3

(G) Cylinder Head Gasket, Renew
Includes: Clean carbon.
Six–1983 (3.1) 4.3
V-8–318-360 engs
1983-87-one (3.4) 4.7
both (4.3) 6.0
w/A.C. add (.4) 5
w/100 amp alter add (.4) 4

(G) Cylinder Head, Renew
Includes: Reface and adjust valves, clean carbon.
Six–1983 (5.7) 8.0
V-8–1983-87
318, 360 engs
one (4.9) 6.8
both (7.2) 10.0
w/A.C. add (.4) 5
w/100 amp alter add (.4) 4

(P) Clean Carbon and Grind Valves
Includes: R&R cylinder heads, adjust valve clearance when required. Minor engine tune up.
Six–1983 (5.1) 7.4
V-8–318-360 engs
1983-87 (6.7) 11.0
w/A.C. add (.4) 5
w/100 amp alter add (.4) 4

(G) Rocker Arm Cover or Gasket, Renew
Six–1983 (.8) 1.1
V-8–318-360 engs
1983-87-one (.4) 6
both (.6) 1.0
w/A.C. add (.1) 1
w/100 amp alter add (.4) 4

(G) Valve Tappets, Renew
Includes: R&R head and adjust valve clearance on 6 cyl. R&R intake manifold and clean carbon on V-8's.
Six–1983-one or all (3.3) 4.4

COMBINATIONS

Add to Valve Job

See Machine Shop Operations

(G) DRAIN, EVACUATE & RECHARGE AIR CONDITIONING SYSTEM
All models 1.0

(G) DISTRIBUTOR, RECONDITION
All models (1.0) 1.0

(G) ROCKER ARMS & SHAFT ASSY., DISASSEMBLE AND CLEAN OR OVERHAUL
Six 5
V-8-One side 5
Both sides 9

(G) HYDRAULIC VALVE LIFTERS, DISASSEMBLE AND CLEAN
Each 2

(G) CARBURETOR, RECONDITION
Exc below (1.7) 2.0
4 BBL (2.4) 2.7

(P) VALVE GUIDES, REAM OVERSIZE
Each (.2) 2

(Factory Time) Chilton Time

V-8–1983-87
318, 360 engs
one (2.0) 3.0
all (2.2) 3.9
w/A.C. add (.4) 5
w/100 amp alter add (.4) 4

*Note: Factory time based on using magnetic tool thru push rod opening to remove lifters. Chilton experience finds it better and safer to R&R intake manifold, since the lifters have a tendency to stick in the block and sometimes come apart.

(G) Valve Tappets, Renew (Roller Type)
V-8–1985-87
one (2.6) 3.6
each adtnl (.1) 1

(G) Valve Spring or Valve Stem Oil Seals, Renew (Head on Car)
Includes: Adjust valve clearance when required.
Six–1983-one (.9) 1.2
all (2.2) 3.2

(Factory Time) Chilton Time

V-8–318, 360 engs
1983-87-one (.7) 1.0
all (3.2) 4.0
w/A.C. add (.5) 5
w/100 amp alter add (.4) 4

(G) Rocker Arm Assembly, Recondition
Includes: Renew arms as required and shaft if necessary.
Six–1983 (.9) 1.5
V-8–1983-87-318, 360 engs
one side (.6) 1.3
both sides (1.0) 2.1
w/A.C. add (.5) 5
w/100 amp alter add (.4) 4

(G) Valve Push Rods, Renew
Includes: Adjust valve clearance when required.
Six–1983-one (.8) 1.0
all (1.1) 1.4
V-8–1983-87-one (.5) 1.0
one each bnk (.8) 1.6
all both bnks (1.3) 2.0
w/A.C. add (.5) 5

PARTS 12 CYLINDER HEAD & VALVE SYSTEM 12 PARTS

	Part No.	Price
Valve Grind Gasket Set		
Note: When a valve grinding gasket set is required, use the upper engine gasket kit along with the manifold gasket kits.		
Six–225 engine		
(upper eng. set)		
1983	4267187	35.25
(manifold set)		
1983	4186180	7.00
V-8-318 engine		
(upper eng. set)		
1983-87-2 bbl	4049264	59.50
4 bbl	4049265	59.50
(intake manifold set)		
1983-85-2 bbl	3837605	7.75
4 bbl	3514187	11.25
1986-87-2 bbl	4397643	7.75
4 bbl	4397642	7.75
(1) Cylinder Head (New)		
Six–225 engine		
1983	4095776	304.00
V-8–318 engine		
1983-84-2 bbl	4100405	328.00
4 bbl	4227948	328.00

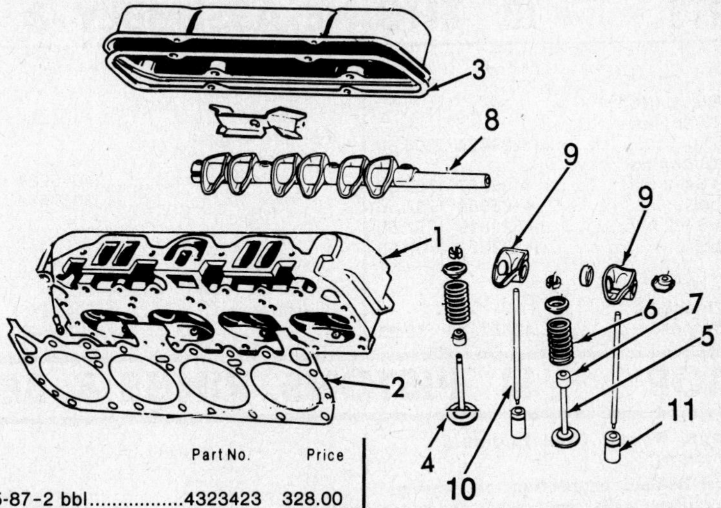

	Part No.	Price
1985-87-2 bbl	4323423	328.00
4 bbl (Police)	4323346	328.00

PARTS 12 CYLINDER HEAD & VALVE SYSTEM 12 PARTS

	Part No.	Price
(2) Cylinder Head Gasket		
Six-225 engine		
1983	4201200	15.75
V-8-318 engine		
1983-87-2 bbl	4186348	11.50
4 bbl (Police)	4131141	12.75
(3) Valve Cover Gasket		
Six-225 engine		
1983	4095784	6.00
V-8-318 engine		
1983-87-2 bbl	4273129	4.50
4 bbl	4095088	8.75
(4) Intake Valve (Std.)		
Six-225 engine		
1983	1947623	7.50
V-8-318 engine		
1983-87-2 bbl	2465335	9.50
4 bbl	3683801	12.00
(5) Exhaust Valve (Std.)		
Six-225 engine		
1983	4105979	10.25
V-8-318 engine		
1983-87-2 bbl	4100387	12.50
4 bbl	4100632	27.25
(6) Valve Spring		
Six-225 engine		
1983	1739534	3.25
V-8-318 engine		
1983-87-2 bbl	1739534	3.25
4 bbl	3751741	3.50
(7) Valve Stem Oil Shield		
1983-87	4071006	1.00
(8) Rocker Arm Shaft		
Six-225 engine		
1983	4100397	18.75
V-8-318 engine		
1983-87	2532149	23.25
(9) Rocker Arm		
Six-225 engine		
1983	4173909	6.75
V-8-318 engine		
1983-85-right	4095708	6.25
left	4095709	6.25
1986-87-right	4100774	6.25
left	4100775	6.25
(10) Valve Push Rods		
Six-225 engine		
1983	4173482	3.00
V-8-318 engine		
1983-87-exc. below	4095291	4.25
w/roller tappets	4323205	4.25
(11) Valve Lifters		
Six-225 engine		
1983	4106028	8.50
V-8-318 engine		
1983-87-exc. below	4049338	8.50
w/roller tappets	4323235	13.25

LABOR 13 ENGINE ASSEMBLY & MOUNTS 13 LABOR

(Factory Time) — Chilton Time

(G) Engine Assembly, Remove & Install

Does not include transfer of any parts or equipment.

	Chilton Time
Six-1983 (4.0)	5.0
V-8-1983-87	
318, 360 engs (4.8)	5.9
w/A.C. add (1.0)	1.0
w/A.T. add (.8)	.8
w/4 spd trans add (.6)	.6

(G) Engine Assembly, Replace with New or Rebuilt Unit

Includes: R&R engine assembly, transfer all necessary parts, fuel and electrical units. Minor tune up.

	Chilton Time
Six-1983 (7.3)	8.9
V-8-1983-87	
318, 360 engs (7.4)	9.0
w/A.C. add (1.0)	1.0

(P) Short Engine Assembly, Renew (w/All Internal Parts Less Head and Oil Pan)

Includes: R&R engine, transfer all necessary parts not supplied with replacement engine, clean carbon, grind valves, minor tune up.

	Chilton Time
Six-1983 (9.7)	12.5
V-8-1983-87	
318, 360 engs (11.7)	18.0
w/P.S. add (.2)	.2
w/A.C. add (.4)	.3

(P) Cylinder Block, Renew (w/Pistons, Rings & Pins)

Includes: R&R engine, transfer all necessary parts, clean carbon, grind valves. Minor tune up.

	Chilton Time
Six-1983 (12.7)	15.4
w/A.C. add (1.0)	1.0
Renew head add (1.9)	*2.5

*Includes transfer or replace all parts.

(P) Engine Assy., R&R and Recondition (Complete)

Includes: Rebore block, install new pistons, rings, rod and main bearings. Clean carbon and grind valves, replace valve stem oil seals. Tune engine.

	Chilton Time
Six-1983 (23.2)	28.2
V-8-1983-87	
318, 360 engs (28.3)	34.3
w/A.C. add (1.0)	1.0

(P) Engine Assembly, Recondition (In Car)

Includes: Expand or renew pistons, install rings, pins, rod and main bearings, clean carbon and grind valves. Tune engine.

	Chilton Time
Six-1983 (14.0)	16.7
V-8-1983-87	
318, 360 engs (21.0)	25.6
w/A.C. add (.5)	.5
w/P.B. add (.4)	.4

(G) Engine Mounts, Renew

	Chilton Time
Front	
Six-1983-left (.4)	.5
right (.6)	.7
both (.9)	1.1
V-8-1983-87-left (1.1)	1.6
right (.9)	1.1
both (1.4)	1.8
Rear	
1983-87 (.4)	.5

PARTS 13 ENGINE ASSEMBLY & MOUNTS 13 PARTS

	Part No.	Price
Short Block (New)		
Six-225 engine		
1983	4227894	1503.50
V-8-318 engine		
1983-84-2 bbl	4105987	1757.50
4 bbl	4105989	1757.50
1985-87-2 bbl	4323619	1757.50
4 bbl	4323621	1757.50
Engine Gasket Set		
Six-225 engine		
1983-upper	4267187	35.25
lower	4106048	12.00
V-8-318 engine		
1983-87-2 bbl		
upper	4049264	59.50
lower	3837644	12.75
1983-87-4 bbl		
upper	4049265	59.50
lower	3837644	12.75
Engine Mounts (Front)		
Six-225 engine		
1983-right	4295459	30.00
left	3642821	32.50
V-8-318 engine		
1983-87-right	3642818	21.75
left	3817237	21.75
Engine Mounts (Rear)		
1983-87-Std	4001801	20.25
H.D.	3817295	17.25

LABOR 14 PISTONS, RINGS & BEARINGS 14 LABOR

(P) Rings, Renew (See Engine Combinations)

Includes: Replace connecting rod bearings, deglaze cylinder walls, clean carbon and minor tune up.

(Factory Time)	Chilton Time
Six-1983 (7.7)	10.2
V-8-318, 360 engs	
1983-87 (8.8)	12.5

LABOR 14 PISTONS, RINGS & BEARINGS 14 LABOR

(Factory Time) Chilton Time

w/A.C. add (.5) 5
w/100 amp alter add (.4) 4

(P) Piston or Connecting Rod, Renew

Includes: Replace connecting rod bearings and piston rings, deglaze cylinder walls.

Six–1983-one (5.6) 7.7
all (8.1) 11.2
V-8–318, 360 engs
1983-87-one (5.4) 7.3
one-each side (6.7) 9.4
all (8.9) 12.2
w/A.C. add (.4) 5
w/100 amp alter add (.4) 4

(P) Connecting Rod Bearings, Renew

Includes: Plastigauge all bearings.

Six–1983-one (2.0) 3.0
all (3.0) 4.0
V-8–318, 360 engs
1983-87-one (2.9) 4.0
all (4.3) 6.0
w/A.C. add (.4) 5

COMBINATIONS

Add to Engine Work
See Machine Shop Operations

(G) DRAIN, EVACUATE & RECHARGE AIR CONDITIONING SYSTEM
All models 1.0

(G) ROCKER ARM & SHAFT ASSEMBLY, DISASSEMBLE & CLEAN OR OVERHAUL
Six 5
V-8-One side 5
Both sides 9

(G) HYDRAULIC VALVE LIFTERS, DISASSEMBLE & CLEAN
Each 2

(G) DISTRIBUTOR, RECONDITION
All models (1.0) 1.0

(G) CARBURETOR, RECONDITION
Exc below (1.7) 2.0
4 BBL (2.4) 2.7

(G) DEGLAZE CYLINDER WALLS
Each (.1) 1

(G) REMOVE CYLINDER TOP RIDGE
Each (.1) 1

(G) MAIN BEARINGS, RENEW (PAN REMOVED)
Six (1.3) 1.8
V-8 (1.8) 2.5

(G) PLASTIGAUGE BEARINGS
Each (.1) 1

(G) OIL PUMP, RECONDITION
Six (1.4) 1.8
V-8 (.7) 9

(M) OIL FILTER ELEMENT, RENEW
All models (.2) 2

PARTS 14 PISTONS, RINGS & BEARINGS 14 PARTS

	Part No.	Price
(1) Piston Ring Set		
Six–225 engine		
1983	4131203	87.50
V-8–318 engine		
1983-85-2 bbl	2808550	93.50
4 bbl	2808553	102.75
1986-87	2808553	102.75
(2) Piston Pin (Std.)		
1983-87-V-8	2658878	3.75
(3) Piston Assembly (Std.)		
Six–225 engine		
1983	2084384	33.00
V-8–318 engine		
1983-84	3685751	35.75
1985-87	4342772	35.75
(4) Connecting Rod (New)		
Six–225 engine		
1983	4041994	35.00
V-8–318 engine		
1983-87	3751015	38.75

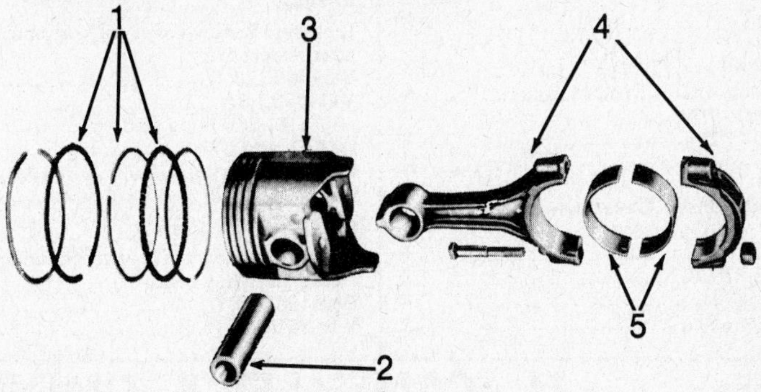

	Part No.	Price
(5) Connecting Rod Brg. (Std.)		
Six–225 engine		
1983	4049256	5.25
V-8–318 engine		
1983-87-2 bbl	4186118	6.50
4 bbl	2421305	9.00

LABOR 15 CRANKSHAFT & DAMPER 15 LABOR

(Factory Time) Chilton Time

(P) Crankshaft & Main Bearings, Renew

Includes: Replace rod bearings.

Six–1983 (8.3) 10.4
V-8–318, 360 engs
1983-87 (9.4) 12.6
Plastigauge bearings each add (.1) 1

(P) Main Bearings, Renew

Includes: Replace pan gasket and seals, plastigauge all bearings.

Six–1983 (4.1) 5.7
V-8–1983-87
318, 360 engs (4.4) 6.0
Renew rod bearings each add (.3) 4

(P) Rear Main Bearing Oil Seals, Renew (Upper & Lower)

Six–1983 (2.3) 3.2
V-8–1983-87
318, 360 engs (2.5) 3.5

Note: Upper seal removed using special tool. If necessary to R&R crankshaft use Crankshaft and Main Bearings, Renew.

(G) Vibration Damper, Renew

Six–1983 (.9) 1.4
V-8–1983-87 (.6) 1.0
w/A.C. add (.3) 3
w/Air inj add (.1) 1

PARTS 15 CRANKSHAFT & DAMPER 15 PARTS

	Part No.	Price
(1) Crankshaft (New)		
Six–225 engine		
1983	4100646	578.25
V-8–318 engine		
1983-87-2 bbl	3751831	540.00
4 bbl	4227880	540.00
(2) Main Bearings (Standard)		
Six–225 engine		
1983-No. 1, 2, 4	4049242	8.75

PARTS 15 CRANKSHAFT & DAMPER 15 PARTS

	Part No.	Price
No. 3	4049249	14.50
V-8-318 engine		
1983-87-2 bbl		
No. 1	4106009	10.00
No. 2, 4	4186194	9.75
No. 3	3780075	14.50
No. 5	3514151	12.25
1983-87-4 bbl		
No. 1, 2, 4	4240083	9.75
No. 3	3780075	14.50
No. 5	3514151	12.25
(3) Rear Bearing Oil Seal Pkg.		
Six-225 engine		
1983	4240150	6.50
V-8-318 engine		
1983-87	4240044	4.75
Front Oil Seal		
Six-225 engine		
1983	3830108	6.00
V-8-318 engine		
1983-87	3830109	6.50

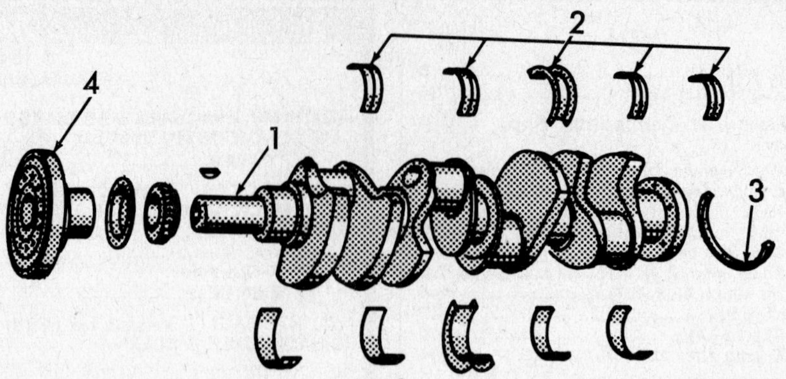

	Part No.	Price
(4) Vibration Damper		
Six-225 engine		
1983-87-M.T.	4100696	71.00
A.T.	4095527	86.50
V-8-318 engine		
1983-87	4173443	81.00

LABOR 16 CAMSHAFT & TIMING GEARS 16 LABOR

(Factory Time)	Chilton Time
(G) Timing Case Seal and Gaskets, Renew	
Six-1983 (1.5)	2.5
V-8-1983-87	
318, 360 engs (2.1)	3.1
w/A.C. add (.4)	.5
w/Air inj add (.1)	.1
w/P.S. add (.2)	.2
(G) Timing Chain Cover Oil Seal, Renew	
Six-1983 (1.0)	1.5
V-8-1983-87 (.8)	1.2
w/A.C. add (.4)	.4
w/P.S. add (.2)	.2
(G) Camshaft Gear or Timing Chain, Renew	
Includes: Renew cover oil seal and crankshaft gear if necessary.	
Six-1983 (2.1)	3.1
V-8-1983-87	
318, 360 engs (2.6)	3.6
w/A.C. add (.4)	.5
w/Air inj add (.1)	.1
w/P.S. add (.2)	.2
(G) Camshaft, Renew	
Includes: Renew valve tappets and adjust valve clearance when required.	
Six-1983 (5.1)	8.0
V-8-1983-87 (5.5)	8.4
w/A.C. add (.8)	1.3
w/Air inj add (.1)	.1
w/P.S. add (.2)	.2
(P) Camshaft Bearings, Renew	
Six-1983 (7.4)	12.3
V-8-1983-87	
318, 360 engs (6.3)	9.1
w/A.C. add (1.0)	1.3
w/P.S. add (.2)	.2
(G) Camshaft Rear Bearing Welsh Plug, Renew	
Six-1983 (2.2)	3.5
V-8-1983-87 (2.2)	3.5

PARTS 16 CAMSHAFT & TIMING GEARS 16 PARTS

	Part No.	Price
(1) Timing Case Cover Gasket		
Six-225 engine		
1983	1947554	1.50
V-8-318 engine		
1983-87	2129012	1.75
(2) Timing Cover Oil Seal		
Six-225 engine		
1983	3830108	6.00
V-8-318 engine		
1983-87	3830109	6.50
Crankshaft Sprocket		
Six-225 engine		
1983	2128912	15.50
V-8-318 engine		
1983-87-2 bbl	2463385	16.00
4 bbl	1637657	20.50
(3) Camshaft Sprocket		
Six-225 engine		
1983	2806945	17.25
V-8-318 engine		
1983-87-2 bbl	2843610	20.00
4 bbl	2899556	21.75

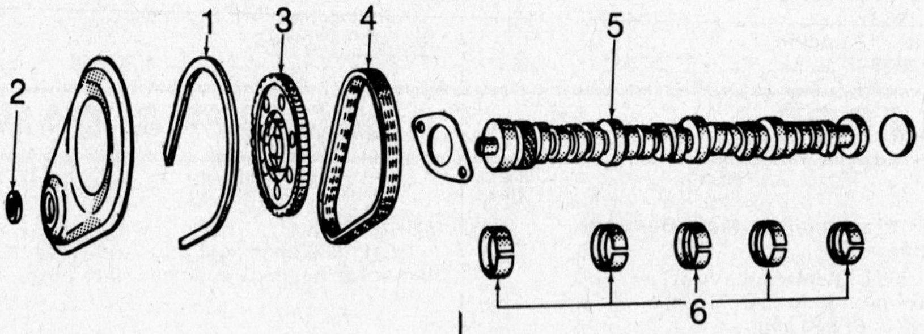

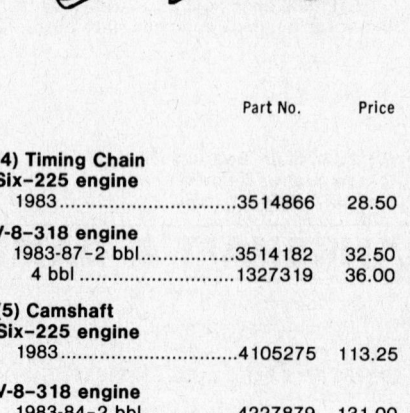

	Part No.	Price
(4) Timing Chain		
Six-225 engine		
1983	3514866	28.50
V-8-318 engine		
1983-87-2 bbl	3514182	32.50
4 bbl	1327319	36.00
(5) Camshaft		
Six-225 engine		
1983	4105275	113.25
V-8-318 engine		
1983-84-2 bbl	4227879	131.00
4 bbl	4227879	131.00
1985-87-2 bbl	4323239	205.25
4 bbl	4227879	131.00
(6) Camshaft Bearings (Set)		
Six-225 engine		
1983-No. 1	4100754	5.50
No. 2	4100755	5.50
No. 3	4100756	5.50
rear	2121727	5.50
V-8-318 engine		
1983-87-No. 1	3830603	6.50
No. 2	4179776	10.00
No. 3	4179777	10.00
No. 4	4179778	10.00
No. 5	1632526	6.50

LABOR 17 ENGINE OILING SYSTEM 17 LABOR

(Factory Time)	Chilton Time
(G) Oil Pan or Gasket, Renew	
Six–1983 (1.8)	2.3
V-8–318, 360 engs	
1983-87 (2.0)	2.8
(P) Pressure Test Engine Bearings (Pan Off)	
All models	1.0
(G) Oil Pump, Renew	
Six–1983 (1.1)	1.8
V-8–318, 360 engs	
1983-87 (2.2)	3.0
(G) Oil Pump, R&R & Recondition	
Six–1983 (1.4)	2.5
V-8–318, 360 engs	
1983-87 (2.6)	3.5
(G) Oil Pressure Relief Valve Spring, Renew	
Six–1983 (.3)	.5
V-8–318, 360 engs	
1983-87 (2.3)	*3.2
*Includes R&R oil pump.	
(G) Oil Pressure Gauge (Engine), Renew	
1983-87 (.4)	.6
w/A.C. add (.1)	.1
(G) Oil Pressure Gauge (Dash), Renew	
1983-87 (.5)	1.0
(M) Oil Filter Element, Renew	
1983-87 (.2)	.3

PARTS 17 ENGINE OILING SYSTEM 17 PARTS

	Part No.	Price
Oil Pan Gasket		
Six-225 engine		
1983	4049287	9.50
V-8-318 engine		
1983-87	4240153	9.50
Oil Pump Assy. (New)		
Six-225 engine		
1983	4186182	60.00
V-8-318 engine		
1983-87	2806270	53.50
Oil Pump Shaft and Rotor Pkg.		
Six-225 engine		
1983	4186183	24.00
V-8-318 engine		
1983-87	3837648	24.00
Oil Pump Shaft & Drive Gear		
Six-225 engine		
1983-gear	1947225	7.75
V-8-318 engine		
1983-87	4095260	27.50
Oil Pressure Gauge (Dash)		
1983	4047724	16.25
1984-87	4196430	24.75
Oil Pressure Sending Unit		
1983-87	2427237	13.50
Oil Pressure Relief Valve		
Six-225 engine		
1983-87	2120764	3.00
V-8-318 engine		
1983-87	2843208	3.00
Oil Filter Assy.		
1983-87	3549957	5.50
Oil Pump Strainer Assy.		
Six-225 engine		
1983	2780999	15.25
V-8-318 engine		
1983-87	2468849	16.75

LABOR 21 SHIFT LINKAGE 21 LABOR

(Factory Time)	Chilton Time
AUTOMATIC	
(G) Steering Column Gearshift Tube, Renew	
1983-87-std column (2.4)	3.7
w/Tilt column (2.5)	3.8
(G) Gearshift Lever and/or Spring Column Shift, Renew	
1983-87 (.3)	.5
(G) Gearshift Lower Rod or Swivel, Renew	
1983-87 (.3)	.6
(G) Gear Selector Indicator, Renew	
1983-87 (.2)	.4
(G) Shift Lever Gate, Renew	
1983-87-std column (1.1)	2.0
Tilt column (2.3)	2.7
Tilt-Tel (2.5)	3.0

LABOR 25 U-JOINTS & DRIVESHAFT 25 LABOR

(Factory Time)	Chilton Time
(G) Universal Joints, Renew	
Includes: R&R driveshaft.	
1983-87-front (.4)	.6
rear (.5)	.8
both (.7)	1.1
(G) Driveshaft, Renew	
1983-87-w/Joints (.3)	.6
(G) Driveshaft Sliding Yoke, Renew	
1983-87 (.4)	.6
(G) Driveshaft Flange, Renew	
1983-85 (.5)	.7

PARTS 25 UNIVERSAL JOINTS & DRIVE SHAFT 25 PARTS

	Part No.	Price
U/Joints Package		
1983-87	3780250	20.25
Companion Flange		
1983-87-front	4137452	68.50
1983-87-rear	3723251	29.25

LABOR — 26 REAR AXLE 26 — LABOR

(Factory Time)	Chilton Time
INTEGRAL TYPE	
(M) Differential, Drain & Refill	
All models	.6
(M) Axle Housing Cover, Renew or Reseal	
1983-87 (.4)	.6
(G) Axle Shaft Oil Seals, Renew	
1983-87	
7¼" axle-one (.4)	.7
both (.6)	1.0
8¼-9¼" axles-one (.6)	1.3
both (1.0)	1.6
(G) Axle Shaft or Bearing, Renew	
Includes: Replace gasket and oil seal.	
1983-87	
7¼" axle-one (.6.)	.9
8¼-9¼" axles-one (.8)	1.5
(G) Pinion Shaft Oil Seal, Renew	
1983-87 (.6)	1.0

(Factory Time)	Chilton Time
(P) Differential Backlash, Adjust	
1983-87	
7¼ axle (1.1)	1.5
8¼-9¼ axles (1.3)	1.8
(P) Differential Side Bearings, Renew	
Includes: Replace axle shaft oil seals.	
1983-87	
7¼" axle (2.3)	3.5
8¼-9¼" axles (2.4)	3.6
(P) Differential Case, Renew	
Includes: Replace ring gear and pinion, bearings and side gears if necessary.	
1983-87	
7¼" axle (3.2)	5.4
8¼-9¼" axles (3.0)	5.4
(P) Differential Side Gears, Renew	
Includes: Replace axle shaft oil seals.	
1983-87-7¼" axle (1.2)	2.2
8¼-9¼" axles (1.3)	2.4

(Factory Time)	Chilton Time
(P) Ring Gear and Pinion Set, Renew	
Includes: Replace axle shaft oil seals and pinion bearings.	
1983-87	
7¼" axle (3.5)	6.1
8¼-9¼" axles (3.7)	6.3
Renew side brgs add (.4)	.4
(P) Rear Axle Housing, Renew	
Includes: Replace axle shaft or wheel bearing oil seals, pinion seal and gaskets and collapsible spacer.	
1983-87-7¼" axle (4.0)	6.6
8¼-9¼" axles (4.2)	6.8
(G) Rear Axle Assembly, Renew	
Includes: Replace axle shaft oil seals and gaskets.	
1983-87-7¼" axle (2.0)	3.0
8¼-9¼" axles (2.0)	3.4

PARTS — 26 REAR AXLE 26 — PARTS

	Part No.	Price
(1) Companion Flange		
1983-87	3723251	29.25
(2) Pinion Oil Seal		
1983-87	2881041	7.00
(3) Drive Pinion Bearing		
7¼" dia. gear		
1983-87-front	2070316	13.50
rear	2070318	16.00
8¼" dia. gear		
1983-87-front	2070316	13.50
rear	2800484	19.25
(4) Pinion Bearing Cup		
7¼" dia. gear		
1983-87-front	2070317	6.75
rear	2070319	9.00
8¼" dia. gear		
1983-87-front	2070317	6.75
rear	2800485	9.50
(5) Axle Shaft Housing		
7¼" dia. gear		
1983-87	4137623	471.25
8¼" dia. gear		
1983-87	3723967	533.50
(6) Axle Shaft Bearing Pkg.		
1983-87	3744495	18.00
(7) Oil Seal		
1983-84	2931875	6.25
1985-87	4137426	6.25
(8) Axle Shaft		
7¼" dia. gear		
1983-87	4137621	131.75
8¼" dia. gear		
1983-87	3723982	138.00
(9) Front Bearing Spacer		
1983-87	3507575	3.00
(10) Rear Bearing Shims		
7¼" dia. gear		
1983-87	3723020	2.50
8¼" dia gear		
1983-87	3723620	2.50

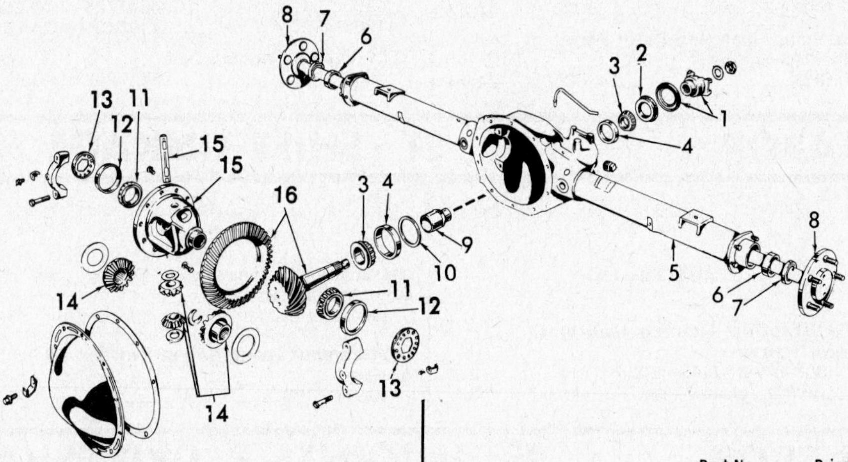

	Part No.	Price
(11) Carrier Bearing		
7¼" dia. gear		
1983-87	1937771	13.25
8¼" dia. gear		
1983-87	1790541	15.00
(12) Carrier Bearing Cup		
7¼" dia. gear		
1983-87	1937770	6.25
8¼" dia. gear		
1983-87	3723569	8.25
(13) Adjuster		
1983-87	3507876	5.00
(14) Differential Side Gear Pkg.		
7¼" dia. gear		
1983-87	4205888	133.25
8¼" dia. gear		
1983-87	4176754	142.75

Note: Side gear package includes side gears, pinion gears, shaft and washers.

	Part No.	Price
(15) Differential Case		
7¼" dia. gear		
1983-87 (casting no.)		
4137052	4137051	136.00
4137014	4137013	N.L.
8¼" dia. gear		
1983-87-exc. below	2881423	153.25
w/2.45R	3432435	117.50
(16) Ring & Pinion Gear Set		
7¼" dia. gear		
1983-87-2.71	3621939	326.00
2.24, 2.26	4186969	386.00
2.94	3723672	326.00
8¼" dia. gear		
1983-87-2.45	3837579	335.50
2.24, 2.26	4186957	335.50
2.71	3837580	387.00
2.93, 2.94	3837581	335.50

Sure Grip Differential

Note: Sure Grip Differential must be bought as a complete assembly.

LABOR 27 REAR SUSPENSION 27 LABOR

	(Factory Time)	Chilton Time
(G) Rear Spring, Renew		
1983-87-one	(.6)	1.0
both	(1.0)	1.8
(G) Rear Spring Front Bushing and Pin, Renew (One Side)		
1983-87	(.9)	1.3
(G) Rear Spring Center Bolt, Renew (One)		
1983-87-one	(.9)	1.3
both	(1.6)	2.0
(G) Rear Spring Shackle or Bushing, Renew (One)		
1983-87	(.5)	1.0
(G) Rear Shock Absorber or Rubber Bushing, Renew		
Standard		
1983-87-one	(.2)	.4
both	(.3)	.6

PARTS 27 REAR SUSPENSION 27 PARTS

	Part No.	Price
(1) Rear Shock Absorber		
1983	4026825	18.25
1984-87-Std	4228413	16.50
H.D.	4228414	16.25
Extra Duty	4057094	20.00
(2) Rear Spring		
Note: Order by model & description.		
(3) Rear Spring Isolators		
1983-87	3815207	12.50
(4) Shackle Pkg.		
1983-87-wo/Sway Bar	3780515	14.75
w/Sway Bar	4094060	14.75
(5) Shackle Bushing Pkg.		
1983-87	3643989	1.50
(6) Pivot Bushing		
1983-87-Std	3815210	8.75
H.D.	4052125	12.75

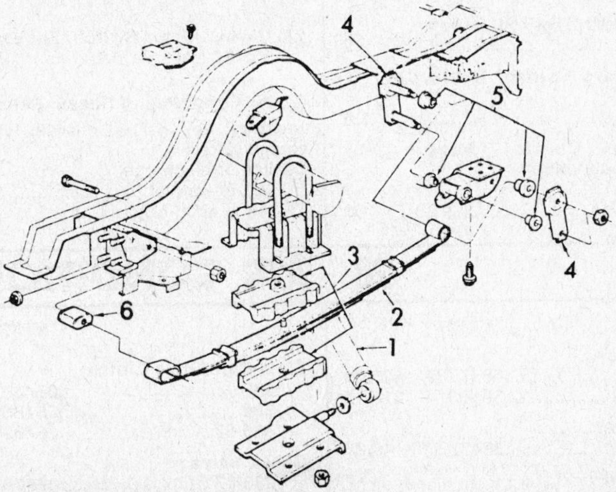

LABOR 28 AIR CONDITIONING 28 LABOR

	(Factory Time)	Chilton Time
Note: If more than one item requires replacement where evacuation and discharging the system is already included in the operation, deduct 1.0 hour for each additional item to the times listed.		
(G) Drain Evacuate, Leak Test & Charge System		
All models		1.0
(G) Partial Charge		
Includes: Leak test.		
All models	(.5)	.6
(G) Performance Test		
All models		.8
(G) Vacuum Leak Test		
All models		.8
(G) Compressor Belt, Renew		
Six-1983	(.4)	.6
V-8-1983-87	(.2)	.3
w/Air inj add	(.1)	.1
(G) Compressor R&R for Engine Work		
Includes: Purging compressor of air.		
1983-87	(.9)	1.4

C-171 COMPRESSOR

	(Factory Time)	Chilton Time
(G) Compressor Clutch Field Coil, Renew		
Includes: Replace pulley w/hub if necessary.		
1983-87	(.5)	.9
(G) Compressor Clutch Pulley (w/Hub), Renew		
1983-87	(.4)	.7

AIR CONDITIONER TUNE-UP

For efficient operation and satisfactory performance in hot weather. The following air conditioner tune-up is suggested:

1. Clean intake filter
2. Clean condenser fins
3. Pressure test system
4. Adjust drive belt tension
5. Check antifreeze/coolant
6. Tighten compressor mounts
7. Tighten condenser and evaporator mounts
8. Inspect system for leaks (hoses, couplings, valves, etc.)
9. Partial charge system

All models 1.0

If necessary to evacuate and charge system, add 1.0

	(Factory Time)	Chilton Time
(G) Compressor Clutch Assembly, Renew		
1983-87	(.5)	.7
(G) Compressor Assembly, Renew		
Includes: Pressure test and charge system.		
1983-87	(1.7)	3.1
(G) Compressor Front Cover or Seal, Renew		
Includes: R&R compressor. Evacuate and charge system.		
1983-87	(2.1)	3.4
(G) Compressor Rear Cover or Seal, Renew		
Includes: R&R compressor. Evacuate and charge system.		
1983-87	(2.0)	3.3
(G) Compressor Center Seal, Renew		
Includes: R&R compressor. Evacuate and charge system.		
1983-87	(2.2)	3.5
(G) Compressor Shaft Gas Seal, Renew		
Includes: R&R compressor. Evacuate and charge system.		
1983-87	(2.1)	3.4
(G) Condenser Assembly, Renew		
Includes: Add partial charge, leak test and charge system.		
1983-87	(1.4)	2.8
(G) Evaporator Coil, Renew		
Includes: Add partial charge, leak test and charge system.		
1983-87	(3.2)	4.5
(G) Receiver Drier, Renew		
Includes: Add partial charge, leak test and charge system.		
1983-87	(.9)	2.0

LABOR 28 AIR CONDITIONING 28 LABOR

	(Factory Time)	Chilton Time
(G) Expansion Valve, Renew		
Includes: Add partial charge, leak test and charge system.		
1983-87	(1.0)	2.0
(G) Low Pressure Cut Off Switch, Renew		
Includes: Charge system.		
1983-87	(.9)	1.8
(G) Thermostatic Control Clutch Cycling Switch, Renew		
1983-87	(.3)	.6
(G) Vacuum Control Switch, Renew		
1983-87	(.5)	.9
(G) Temperature Control Cable, Renew		
1983-87	(1.0)	1.6
(G) Vacuum Control Hose Assembly, Renew (Main)		
1983-87		
wo/A.C.	(.4)	.5
w/A.C.	(1.1)	1.7
(G) Vacuum Actuators, Renew		
1983-87-outside air door	(.3)	.8
heater/defrost door	(.3)	.8
(G) Blower Motor, Renew		
1983-87	(.6)	1.1
(G) Blower Motor Resistor, Renew		
1983-87	(.5)	.7
w/S.A.T.C.	(.3)	.5
(G) Blower Motor Switch, Renew		
1983-87	(.4)	.7
(G) Air Conditioning Hoses, Renew		
Includes: Add partial charge, leak test and charge system.		
Suction or discharge		
1983-87-one	(1.0)	1.6
each adtnl	(.3)	.5

SATC COMPONENTS

	(Factory Time)	Chilton Time
(G) Aspirator, Renew		
1983-87	(.4)	.6
(G) In-Car Sensor Assy., Renew		
1983-87	(.4)	.7
(G) Ambient Sensor, Renew		
1983-87	(.3)	.5
(G) Electronic Servomotor, Renew		
1983-87	(1.1)	1.7
(G) SATC Hoses, Renew		
1983-87		
each	(.4)	.6
(G) Sliding Rheostat Assembly, Renew		
1983-87	(.5)	.9

PARTS 28 AIR CONDITIONING 28 PARTS

	Part No.	Price
Condenser Assy.		
1983-85	3847789	225.00
1986-87	3848374	219.75
Receiver & Drier		
1983-87	3847830	40.25
Evaporator Coil		
1983-87	3847256	341.75
Expansion Valve		
1983-87	4176999	59.75
Compressor Assy.		
1983-87	4176059	275.00
Pulley & Armature (Drive Clutch)		
Six-225 engine		
1983	3847178	101.50
V-8-318 engine		
1983-84	3847179	101.50
1985-87	3848981	101.75
Field Coil (Drive Clutch)		
1983	3846845	60.75
1984	3848673	60.75
1985-87	3848969	29.50
Check Valve		
1983-87	3847576	1.75
Low Pressure Cut Off Switch		
1983-87	5210377	17.25
High Pressure Cut Off Switch		
1983	3846898	45.50
1984-87	3848674	45.50
Blower Motor		
1983-87	4240425	74.25
Blower Motor Switch		
1983-87	3847940	10.25
Blower Motor Resistor		
1983-84	3847910	12.75
1985-87	3848996	13.25
Air Condition Hoses		
Order by model and description.		
Push Button Switch		
1983-87	3847742	27.50

SATC COMPONENTS

	Part No.	Price
Aspirator		
1983-87	3847766	8.00
Servo Actuator Assy.		
1983-87	3847296	70.00
In-Car Sensor		
1983-87	3847291	14.50
Ambient Sensor		
1983-87	3847589	12.25
Rheostat Assy.		
1983-87	3847435	29.00

LABOR 29 LOCKS, HINGES & WIND. REGULATORS 29 LABOR

	(Factory Time)	Chilton Time
(G) Hood Latch, Renew		
1983-87	(.3)	.5
(G) Hood Hinge, Renew (One)		
Does not include painting.		
1983-87	(.2)	.4
(G) Hood Release Cable, Renew		
1983-87	(.3)	.6
(G) Door Lock or Remote Control, Renew		
1983-87	(.4)	.9
(G) Door and Ignition Lock Cylinder, Renew		
Includes: R&R door lock cylinders to recode or replace.		
1983-87-w/Tilt column	(1.4)	2.3
w/Tilt-Tel	(1.3)	2.0
Recode door cyls add	(.3)	.3
(G) Door Handle (Outside), Renew (Front or Rear)		
1983-87	(.4)	.6
(G) Lock Striker Plate, Renew		
1983-87	(.2)	.3
(G) Door Window Regulator (Manual), Renew		
1983-87	(.5)	1.1
(G) Door Window Regulator (Electric), Renew		
1983-87	(.6)	1.1
(G) Trunk Lock Cylinder and Key, Renew		
1983-87	(.3)	.5
Recode cyl add		.3
(G) Trunk Hinge Assembly, Renew (One)		
1983-87	(.3)	.5

PARTS 29 LOCKS, HINGES & WIND. REGULATORS 29 PARTS

	Part No.	Price
Hood Lock (Upper)		
1983-87	3861819	25.50
Hood Hinge		
1983-87-right	4103428	38.25
left	4103429	38.25
Front Door Lock		
1983-right	3882800	35.25
left	3882801	37.00

PARTS 29 LOCKS, HINGES & WIND. REGULATORS 29 PARTS

	Part No.	Price
1984-87-right	4310526	35.25
left	4310529	35.25
Rear Door Lock		
1983 (up to 4-19-82)		
right	3882808	35.25
left	3882809	35.25
1983 (after 4-19-82)		
right	4184710	35.25
left	4184711	35.25
1984-87-right	4310532	35.25
left	4310533	35.25
Door Lock Cyl. & Key		
1983-87-wo/Tilt whl	4054805	20.50
w/Tilt whl	3548955	18.25
Trunk Lock		
1983-87-manual	4054825	29.00
electric	4054962	49.72
Trunk Lock Cyl. & Key		
1983-87	4267850	30.00
Outer Door Handle		
1983-87	3882621	28.50
Trunk Lid Hinge		
(wo/cam)		
1983-87-right	4134518	19.25
left	4134519	19.25
(w/cam)		
1983-87-right	4129804	43.50
left	4129805	43.50
Manual Window Regulator		
(Front)		
1983-87-right	3882274	54.50
left	3882275	54.50
(Rear)		
1983-87-right	3882290	54.50
left	3882291	54.50
Electric Window Regulator		
1983-87-right	3882350	72.75
left	3882351	72.75
Window Regulator Motor		
1983-87-right	4240519	173.25
left	4240520	173.25

LABOR 30 HEAD AND PARKING LAMPS 30 LABOR

	(Factory Time)	Chilton Time
(G) Aim Headlamps		
two		.4
four		.6
(M) Headlamp Sealed Beam Bulb, Renew		
Does not include aim headlamps.		
1983-87-each	(.2)	.3
(M) Parking Lamp Assembly, Renew		
1983-87	(.3)	.4
(M) Tail & Stop Lamp Lens, Renew		
1983-87	(.3)	.4
(M) Tail, Stop and Turn Signal Lamp Assy., Renew		
1983-87-each	(.2)	.4
(M) License Lamp Assembly, Renew		
1983-87	(.3)	.4
(M) Side Marker Lamp, Renew		
1983-87	(.4)	.5

PARTS 30 HEAD AND PARKING LAMPS 30 PARTS

	Part No.	Price
Sealed Beam Bulb		
(high & low beam)		
1983-87-exc below	153201	11.00
halogen	153481	16.00
(high beam)		
1983-87-exc below	153200	11.00
halogen	153440	16.00
Parking & Turn Signal Lamp Assy.		
1983-87-right	4076566	31.75
left	4076567	31.75
Side Marker Lamp Assy.		
1983-87-right	4076570	7.25
left	4076571	7.25
Tail & Stop Lamp Lens		
1983-87-right	4076688	36.00
left	4076689	36.00
High Mount Stop Light		
1986-87		
Bracket	4399100	N.L.
Cover	H201EK1	N.L.
License Plate Lamp Assy.		
1983-87	4076812	2.50

LABOR 31 WINDSHIELD WIPER & SPEEDOMETER 31 LABOR

	(Factory Time)	Chilton Time
(G) Windshield Wiper Motor, Renew		
1983-87	(.5)	.9
(G) Wiper Pivot, Renew (One)		
1983-87	(.5)	.9
(G) Wiper Links, Renew		
1983-87	(.4)	.7
(G) Windshield Wiper and Washer Switch, Renew		
1983-87-std column	(.8)	1.5
tilt column	(1.2)	1.6
(G) Intermittent Windshield Wiper Control Module, Renew		
1983-87	(.4)	.6
(G) Windshield Washer Pump, Renew		
1983-87	(.3)	.5
(G) Speedometer Head, R&R or Renew		
Does not include reset odometer.		
1983-87	(.6)	1.0
Reset odometer add		.2
(G) Speedometer Cable & Casing, Renew		
1983		
Cruise control to trans	(.3)	.6
Cruise control to speedo	(.3)	.6
Trans to speedo	(.4)	.8
1984-87		
upper	(.3)	.6
lower	(.7)	1.1
one piece	(.7)	1.1
Speedometer Cable (Inner), Renew or Lubricate		
1983		
Cruise control to trans	(.3)	.6
Cruise control to speedo	(.4)	.7
Trans to speedo	(.4)	.7
1984-87		
upper	(.3)	.5
lower	(.7)	1.0
one piece	(.7)	1.0
(G) Speedometer Drive Pinion, Renew		
Includes: Replace oil seal.		
1983-87	(.3)	.5
(G) Radio, R&R		
1983-87	(.3)	.7

PARTS 31 WINDSHIELD WIPER & SPEEDOMETER 31 PARTS

	Part No.	Price
Wiper Motor		
1983-84	4205951	106.75
1985-87	4339449	106.75
Wiper Pivot		
1983-87-right	4026046	17.00
left	3799479	17.00
Wiper Switch		
(wo/intermitten wipers)		
1983-87	3747653	39.75

PARTS 31 WINDSHIELD WIPER & SPEEDOMETER 31 PARTS

	Part No.	Price
(w/intermitten wipers)		
1983-wo/tilt whl	4221042	36.00
w/tilt whl.	4293110	67.50
1984-87-wo/tilt whl	4221500	36.00
w/tilt whl.	4221486	36.00
Windshield Wiper Control Module		
1983-87	4222060	28.25
Windshield Washer Pump		
1983-87	3799462	21.25
Washer Fluid Level Sensor		
1983-87	3746813	22.75
Speed. Cable & Housing		
Order by year and model.		
Speed. Cable		
1983-87-80" long	2448294	6.50
113" long	2448295	8.75
Speedometer Assembly		
Order by year and model.		

LABOR 32 LIGHT SWITCHES & WIRING 32 LABOR

	(Factory Time)	Chilton Time
(G) Headlamp Switch, Renew		
1983-87	(.3)	.5
w/A.C. add	(.2)	.2
(G) Headlamp Dimmer Switch, Renew		
1983-87-floor mount	(.3)	.5
column mount	(.5)	1.0
(G) Stop Light Switch, Renew		
1983-87	(.3)	.4
w/Cruise control add	(.1)	.1
(G) Parking Brake Warning Lamp Switch, Renew		
1983-87	(.3)	.4
(G) Turn Signal Switch, Renew		
1983-87-std column	(.7)	1.2
Tilt column	(1.0)	1.5
Tilt-Tel column	(.9)	1.7
(G) Turn Signal/Washer Wiper Combination Lever Assy., Renew		
1983-87	(.2)	.5
(M) Turn Signal or Hazard Warning Flasher, Renew		
1983-87	(.2)	.3
(G) Neutral Safety (w/Back-Up Lamp) Switch, Renew		
1983-87	(.3)	.4
(G) Horns, Renew		
1983-87-one	(.2)	.3
(G) Horn Relay, Renew		
1983-87	(.2)	.3
(G) Wiring Harness, Renew		
(Instrument Panel)		
1983-87	(3.4)	4.9
(Body)		
1983-87		
2 & 4 Dr models	(1.8)	2.8
sta wagons	(2.4)	3.5
w/Electric gate add	(.3)	.3

PARTS 32 LIGHT SWITCHES & WIRING 32 PARTS

	Part No.	Price
Headlamp Switch		
1983-87	4221248	16.00
Headlamp Dimmer Switch		
1983-87-wo/Tilt whl	4131373	11.00
w/Tilt whl	4131525	13.25
Stop Light Switch		
(wo/speed control)		
1983-87	2926275	5.25
(w/speed control)		
1983	5209994	8.00
1984-85	4221438	15.50
Directional Switch Assembly		
(wo/cornering lamps)		
1983-84-wo/tilt whl	4221498	36.75
w/tilt whl	4221485	37.25
1985-87-wo/tilt whl	4221337	38.50
w/tilt whl	4221205	47.00
(w/cornering lamps)		
1983-84-wo/tilt whl	4221338	40.75
w/tilt whl	4221305	53.50
1985-87-wo/tilt whl	4221338	40.75
w/tilt whl	4221206	53.50
Neutral Safety & Back-Up Switch		
1983-87	4057750	8.75
Chassis Wiring Harness		
Order by model & description.		
Brake System Indicator Switch		
1983-87	3620790	4.25
Horn Relay		
1983-87	3747298	6.25
Horn Assy.		
1983-87-hi note	2808869	24.00
low note	2808868	24.00

LABOR 33 GLASS 33 LABOR

	(Factory Time)	Chilton Time
(G) Windshield Glass, Renew		
Includes: Replace weatherstrip if necessary, where applicable.		
1983-87	(1.5)	2.5
(G) Front Door Glass, Renew		
1983-87-hardtops	(.9)	1.4
4 D sedan	(.5)	1.0
sedan w/Vent	(1.2)	1.7
(G) Rear Door Glass, Renew		
1983-87-exc below	(.5)	1.0
hardtops	(.9)	1.6
(G) Rear Door Stationary Glass, Renew		
1983-87	(.7)	1.2
(G) Rear Window Glass, Renew		
Includes: Replace weatherstrip if necessary, where applicable.		
1983-87-exc below	(1.6)	2.5
heated back window	(1.9)	3.0

LABOR 34 CRUISE CONTROL 34 LABOR

	(Factory Time)	Chilton Time
(G) Speed Control Servo, Renew		
1983-87	(.3)	.5
(G) Speed Control Cable, Renew		
1983-87	(.3)	.5
(G) Speed Control Vacuum Hoses, Renew		
1983-87	(.2)	.3
(G) Speed Control Wiring Harness, Renew		
1983-87	(.3)	.6
(G) Speed Control Switch (Turn Signal Lever), Renew		
1983-87-std colm	(.5)	.9
tilt colm	(1.0)	1.5

	Part No.	Price
ELECTRO MECHANICAL		
Speed Control Servo Assy.		
1983-87	4241551	129.75
Speed Control Cable		
Six-225 engine		
1983-1 bbl	4104331	18.25
2 bbl	4104330	22.00
V-8-318 engine		
1983-87	4241249	22.00
Speed Control Link (Lost Motion)		
1983-exc 225	3769261	6.75
225 eng (1 bbl)	4095071	10.50
225 eng (2 bbl)	4027798	6.75
1984-87	3769261	6.75
ELECTRONIC		
Electronic Module		
1985-87	4318829	116.50
Vacuum Motor		
1985-87	4318819	27.50
Control Switch		
1985-87	4342209	41.75
Sensor		
1985-87	4312186	30.25
Valve Body		
1985-87	4318818	103.75
Stop Light Switch		
1985-87	4241438	N.L.
Servo Cable		
1985-87	4241249	22.00

GROUP INDEX

ALPHABETICAL INDEX

Ford Motor Company
Front Wheel Drive Cars

ESCORT • LYNX • EXP • LN7

YEAR IDENTIFICATION

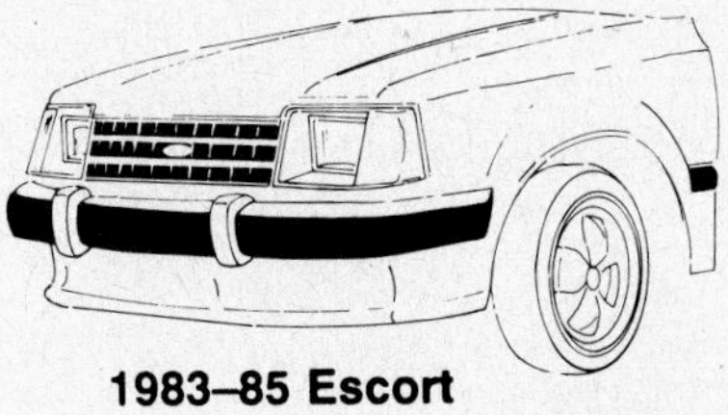

1983–85 Escort

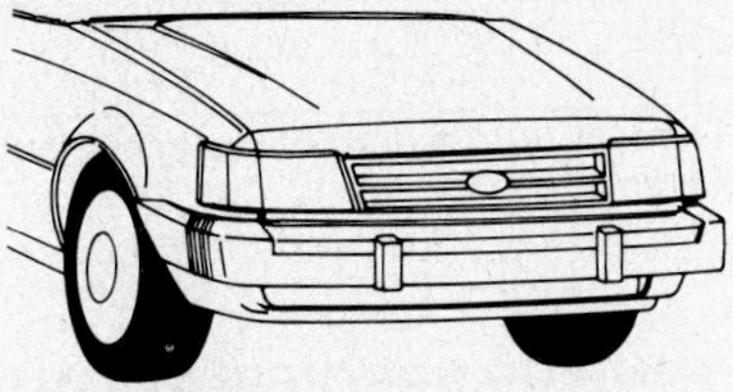

1985½–87 Escort

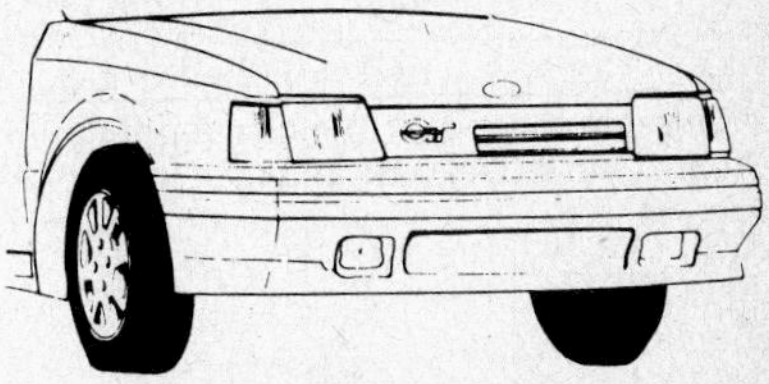

1987 Escort GT

1983 EXP

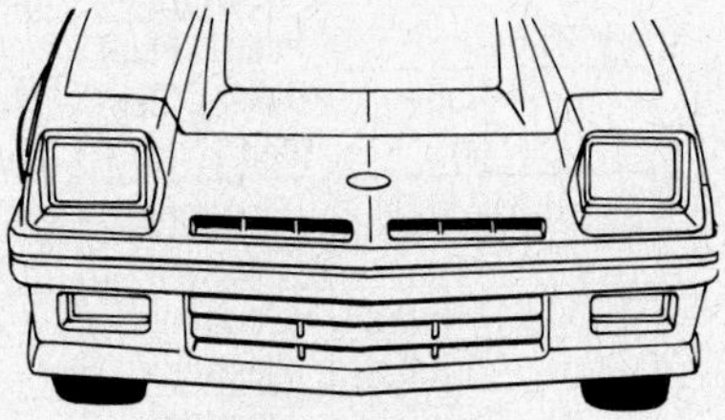

1984–85 EXP

1987 EXP

1983–84 Lynx

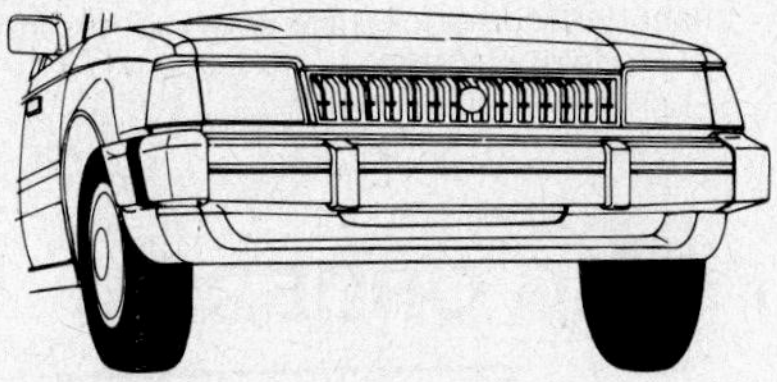

1985½–87 Lynx

1986–87 Lynx XR3

1983 LN7

VEHICLE IDENTIFICATION NUMBER (VIN)

It is important for servicing and ordering parts to be certain of the vehicle and engine identification. The VIN (vehicle identification number) is a 13 or 17 digit number visible through the windshield on the driver's side of the dash and contains the vehicle and engine identification codes. It can be interpreted as follows:

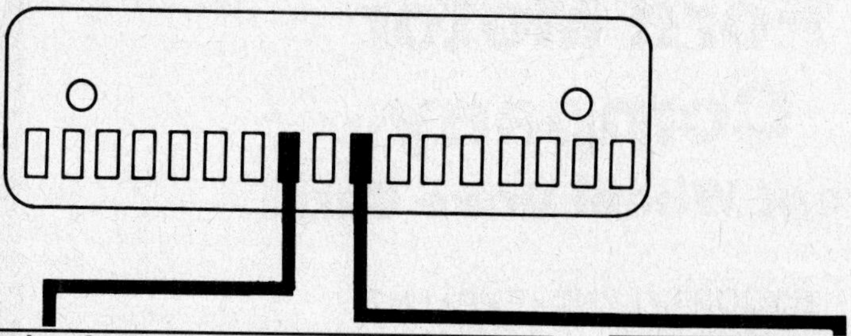

Engine Code

Code	Cu. In.	Liters	Cyl.	Carb.	Eng. Mfg.
2	98	1.6	4	2	Ford
5	98	1.6	4	EFI	Ford
4	98	1.6 HO	4	2	Ford
H	121	2.0	4	Diesel	Mazda
R	140	2.3 (HSC)	4	1/EFI	Ford
9	116	1.9	4	2	Ford
D	153	2.5 (HSC)	4	CFI	Ford
U	182	3.0	6	EFI	Ford

Model Year Code

Code	Year
D	'83
E	'84
F	'85
G	'86
H	'87

The seventeen digit Vehicle Identification Number can be used to determine engine application and model year. The tenth digit indicates the model year, and the eighth digit identifies engine code.

TUNE-UP SPECIFICATIONS

When analyzing compression test results, look for uniformity among cylinders rather than specific pressures.

	Engine			Spark Plugs		Distributor		Ignition Timing (deg.)		Valves	Fuel	Idle Speed (rpm)	
Year	Eng. VIN Code	No. Cyl Displacement cu. in. (cc)	Eng. Mfg.	Orig. Type •	Gap (in.)	Point Dwell (deg.)	Point Gap (in.)	Man. Trans •	Auto Trans	Intake Opens ■ (deg.)	Pump Pressure (psi)	Man Trans	Auto Trans
'83–'87	—	4-97.6 (1597)	Ford	AWSF-34 ②	0.042–0.046	Electronic		①	①	—	4–6 ③	①	①
'84–'87	R	4-140 (2300)	Ford	AWSF-62	.044	Electronic		10B	15B	—	5	①	①
'85–'87	9	4-116 (1901)	Ford	AWSF-34C ②	0.042–0.046	Electronic		①	①	—	5–6	①	①
'86–'87	0	4-153 (2508)	Ford	AWSF-32C	0.042–0.046	Electronic		①	①	—	35–45	①	①
'86–'87	U	6-182 (2983)	Ford	AWSF-32C	0.042–0.046	Electronic		①	①	—	35–45	①	①

NOTE: The underhood specifications sticker often reflects tune-up specification changes made in production. Sticker figures must be used if they disagree with those in this chart. Part numbers in this chart are not recommended by Chilton for any product by brand name.

■ All figures Before Top Dead Center
• Figure in parenthesis is for California
B Before Top Dead Center
— Not applicable

① Calibration levels vary from model to model. Always refer to the underhood sticker for your car requirements.
② EFI Models: AWSF24
③ EFI pressure: 35–45 psi

FIRING ORDERS

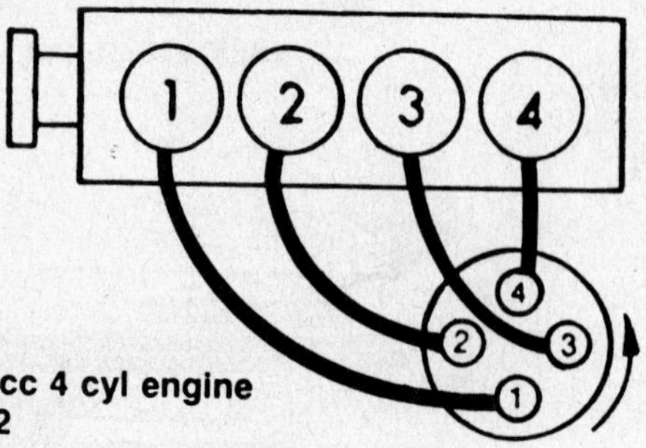

Ford Motor Co. 1600cc 4 cyl engine
Firing order: 1–3–4–2
Distributor rotation: counterclockwise

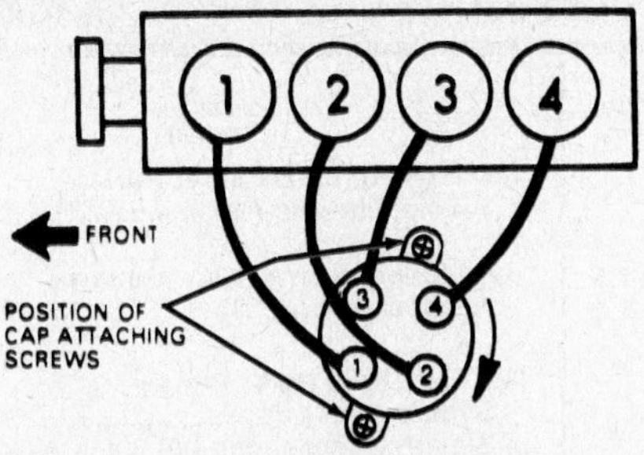

Ford 2500 cc 4 cyl (2.5L)
Firing order: 1–3–4–2
Distributor rotation: clockwise

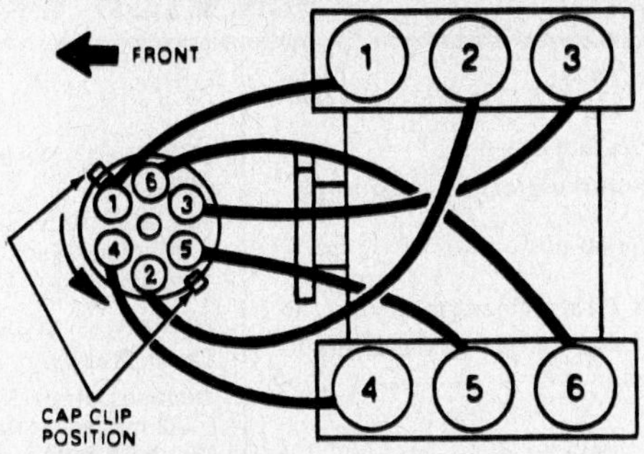

Ford 3000 cc 6 cyl (3.0L)
Firing order: 1–4–2–5–3–6
Distributor rotation: counterclockwise

WHEEL ALIGNMENT SPECIFICATIONS

Year	Model	Caster Range (deg)■▲	Caster Pref. Setting (deg)	Camber Range (deg)■	Camber Pref. Setting (deg)	Toe-in (in.)	Steering Axis Inclin. (deg)
'83	Escort, Lynx, EXP/LN7	$\frac{9}{16}$P to $2\frac{1}{16}$P	$1\frac{5}{16}$P	—	—	$\frac{1}{32}$ to $\frac{7}{32}$	—
		—	—	(Left) $1\frac{13}{32}$P to $2\frac{29}{32}$P	$2\frac{5}{32}$P	—	$14\frac{21}{32}$
		—	—	(Right) $\frac{31}{32}$P to $2\frac{15}{32}$P	$1\frac{23}{32}$P	—	$15\frac{3}{32}$
'84–'87	Escort, Lynx, EXP	$\frac{5}{8}$P to $2\frac{1}{8}$P	$1\frac{2}{3}$P	—	—	$\frac{1}{64}$ (in) to $\frac{7}{32}$ (out)	—
				(Left) $1\frac{3}{8}$P to $2\frac{7}{8}$P	$2\frac{1}{8}$P	—	$14\frac{21}{32}$
				(Right) $1\frac{5}{16}$P to $2\frac{7}{16}$P	$1\frac{11}{16}$P	—	$15\frac{3}{32}$

■ Caster and chamber are pre-set at the factory and cannot be adjusted
▲ Caster measurements must be made on the left side by turning left wheel through the prescribed angle of sweep and on the right side by turning right wheel through prescribed angle of sweep for the equipment being used. When using alignment equipment designed to measure caster on both the right and left side, turning only one wheel will result in a significant error in caster angle for the opposite side.

LABOR — SERVICE BAY OPERATIONS — LABOR

(Factory Time) — Chilton Time

COOLING

(M) Winterize Cooling System
Includes: Run engine to check for leaks, tighten all hose connections. Test radiator and pressure cap. Drain radiator and engine block. Add anti-freeze and refill system.
All models.. .5

(M) Thermostat, Renew
All models
wo/EFI (.5).. .7
w/EFI (.8).. 1.0
Diesel (.4).. .5

(M) Drive Belts, Adjust
All models-one (.2)........................... .3
each adtnl (.1)................................ .1
Note: If necessary to R&R any component to gain access to belts, add appropriate time.

(M) Radiator Hoses, Renew
All models
upper (.3).. .4
lower (.4).. .5
both (.5).. .6

CHILTON'S 10 POINT SAFETY CHECK
CHECK OPERATION & CONDITION OF THE FOLLOWING ITEMS:
1. Legal Registration (serial no.)
2. Tires & Wheels
3. Brake System (R&R all wheels)
4. Light Systems & Signals
5. Accelerator Linkage, Neutral Safety Switch, Shift Indicator Pointer & Seat Position Locks
6. Glass, Mirrors, Door Locks, Seat Belts & Harness
7. Wipers, Washers & Defrosters
8. Frame, Steering, Shocks, Front & Rear Suspension
9. Fuel & Exhaust Systems
10. Road Test Vehicle
All models.. 1.0
Exhaust Smog Analysis, add...... .4

(Factory Time) — Chilton Time

FUEL

(M) Carburetor Air Cleaner, Service
All models.. .2

(Factory Time) — Chilton Time

(G) Carburetor, Adjust (On Car)
Includes: Adjust idle speed and ignition timing.
All models (.7)................................... 1.0

BRAKES

(G) Brakes, Adjust (Minor)
Includes: Adjust brakes, fill master cylinder.
two wheels.. .4

(G) Bleed Brakes (Four Wheels)
Includes: Fill master cylinder.
All models (.3)................................... .5

(G) Brake Pedal Free Play, Adjust
All models.. .4

(M) Parking Brake, Adjust
All models (.3)................................... .5
w/Console add (.1)............................ .1

LUBRICATION SERVICE

(M) Lubricate Chassis, Change Oil & Filter
Includes: Inspect and correct all fluid levels.
All models.. .7
Install grease fittings add.................. .1

LABOR — SERVICE BAY OPERATIONS — LABOR

(Factory Time) Chilton Time

(M) Lubricate Chassis
Includes: Inspect and correct all fluid levels.
All models 4
Install grease fittings add 1

(M) Engine Oil & Filter, Change
Includes: Inspect and correct all fluid levels.
All models 6

WHEELS

(M) Wheel, Renew
one 5

(G) Wheels, Balance
one 3
each adtnl 2

(G) Wheels, Rotate (All)
All models (.5) 5

(G) Front Wheel Grease Seals, Renew
Includes: Repack bearings.
All models-one side (1.4) 1.9
both sides (2.5) 3.2

(G) Front Wheel Bearings and Cups, Renew
Includes: Repack bearings.
All models-one side (1.6) 2.0
both sides (2.9) 3.5

ELECTRICAL

(G) Aim Headlamps
two 4
four 6

(M) Headlamp Sealed Beam Bulb, Renew
All models-each (.3) 3

(M) Parking Lamp Bulb, Renew
All models-one (.3) 3

(M) License Lamp Bulb, Renew
All models-one (.3) 3

(M) Tail Lamp Bulb, Renew
Sedans-one (.2) 2
Station wagons-one (.3) 3

(M) Back-Up Lamp Bulb, Renew
All models-one (.3) 3

(M) Battery Cables, Renew
Batt to Relay
Gas (.3) 3
Diesel (1.2) 1.5
Negative (.3) 3
Relay to Starter (.7) 1.0

LABOR — 1 TUNE UP 1 — LABOR

(Factory Time) Chilton Time

(G) Compression Test
All models (.3) 6
w/A.C. add 2

(G) Engine Tune Up, (Electronic Ignition)
Includes: Test battery and clean connections. Tighten manifold and carburetor mounting bolts. Check engine compression, clean and adjust or renew spark plugs. Test resistance of spark plug cables. Inspect distributor cap and rotor. Adjust air gap. Check vacuum advance operation. Reset ignition timing. Adjust idle mixture and idle speed. Service air cleaner. Inspect and adjust drive belts. Inspect choke operation and adjust or free up. Check operation of EGR valve.
1983-87 .... 1.5
w/A.C. add 2
Perform EEC IV system test add 1.0

LABOR — 2 IGNITION SYSTEM 2 — LABOR

(Factory Time) Chilton Time

GASOLINE ENGINE

(G) Spark Plugs, Clean and Reset or Renew
1983-87 (.3) 5

(G) Ignition Timing, Reset
All models (.3) 4

(G) Distributor, R&R or Renew
Includes: Reset ignition timing.
1983-87
w/Dura Spark (.3) 6
w/CFI (.3) 6
w/TFI (.4) 8
w/EFI (.5) 9
w/EFI turbo (.6) 1.0
Renew vacuum diaph add (.1) 2

(G) Distributor Armature, Renew
1983-84 (.3) 5

(G) Distributor Stator, Renew
Includes: R&R distributor armature.
1983-84 (.6) 1.2

(G) Distributor Cap and/or Rotor, Renew
1983-87 (.3) 4

(G) Profile Ignition Pick-Up Sensor, Renew (Duraspark)
1983-87 (.6) 1.0
Perform system test add (.3) 3

(G) Ignition Coil, Renew
Includes: Test.
1983-87 (.4) 6
w/EFI (.5) 7

(G) Ignition Module Assembly, Renew
Note: Fender mount type. For TFI unit, refer to Emission Control section.
1983-84 (.3) 5
w/TFI (.6) 9
w/EFI (.5) 7
1985-87
w/EFI (.3) 7
Turbo (.4) 8
All others (.6) 9
Perform system test add (.3) 3

(G) Ignition Cables, Renew
Includes: Test wiring.
1983-87 (.4) 6

(G) Ignition Switch, Renew
1983-87 (.6) 1.0

(G) Ignition Key Indicator Buzzer, Renew
1983-87 (.2) 4

DIESEL ENGINE

(G) Glow Plug System Test
All models (.2) 4

(G) Glow Plugs, Renew
1984-87
one (.2) 4
each adtnl (.1) 3
all (.4) 1.0

(G) Glow Plug Relay, Renew
1984-87 (.3) 4

PARTS — 2 IGNITION SYSTEM 2 — PARTS

	Part No.	Price
(1) Distributor Assy. (New)		
1983 (wo/Hi output & E.F.I.)		
MTX	▲E3FZ-12127P	155.50
ATX	▲E3FZ-12127H	155.50
1983 (w/Hi output)		
MTX	▲E3FZ-12127T	144.00
ATX	▲E3FZ-12127Y	155.50
1983-85 (w/MTX & ATX)		
E.F.I.	▲E3FZ-12127B	155.50
1986-87	▲E6FZ-12127E	155.50

PARTS 2 IGNITION SYSTEM 2 PARTS

	Part No.	Price
1984-85 (wo/Hi output & E.F.I.)		
exc. below	▲E3FZ-12127P	155.50
wo/A.C. & P.S.	▲E4FZ-12127G	155.50
1986-87-wo/E.F.I.		
MTX	▲E6FZ-12127D	155.50
ATX	▲E6FZ-12127C	155.50
1984-85 (w/Hi output)		
MTX	▲E4FZ-12127F	155.50
ATX	▲E3FZ-12127Y	155.50
(2) Distributor Cap		
1983-87	▲E5FZ-12106C	8.75
(3) Rotor		
1983-85-w/E.F.I. (exc. 1.6 eng.)	▲E5FZ-12200A	3.25
1985-87-wo/E.F.I. (w/1.6 eng.)	▲E6AZ-12200C	2.50
(4) Vacuum Diaphragm Assy.		
1983-MTX	▲E1FZ-12370A	31.25
ATX		
wo/H.O.	▲E3FZ-12370B	31.25
w/H.O.	▲E3FZ-12370F	31.25
1984-85 (wo/Hi output & EFI)		
exc. below	▲E1FZ-12370A	31.25
wo/A.C. & P.S.	▲E2FZ-12370D	31.25
1986-87-wo/E.F.I.		
MTX	▲N.L.	
ATX	▲E6FZ-12370A	31.25
1984-85-w/H.O.	▲E3FZ-12370F	31.25

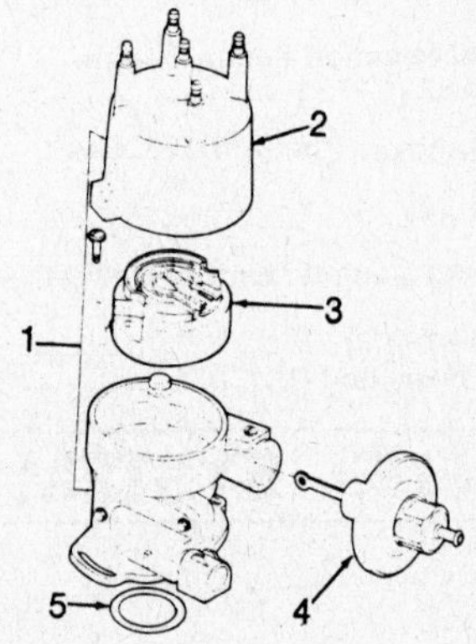

	Part No.	Price
(5) Gasket (Dist. Base)		
1983-87	▲E1FZ-12143A	1.00
Modulator Assy.		
1983-87-wo/E.C.C. IV	▲E3FZ-12A297B	104.00
w/E.E.C. IV	▲E43Z-12A297A	106.00
Ignition Coil		
1983-87	▲E3FZ-12029A	33.75

	Part No.	Price
Ignition Wire Set		
1983 (wo/Rubber boots)		
wo/E.F.I.	▲E3PZ-12259AAR	30.25
w/E.F.I.	▲E3PZ-12259U	39.50
1983-85 (w/Rubber boots)		
wo/turbo	▲E3PZ-12259AK	35.25
w/turbo	▲E4PZ-12259K	39.00
1986-87	▲E6PZ-12259C	30.75
Ignition Switch		
1983-87	▲E4FZ-11572A	11.50

IGNITION SYSTEM DIESEL

	Part No.	Price
Module (Glow Plug Control)		
1984-87	▲E43Z-12B533A	168.50
Switch (Glow Plug)		
1984-87	▲E3TZ-9A444B	20.25
Glow Plug		
1984-87	▲E43Z-12A342A	24.75
Glow Plug Relay		
1984-87-white label	▲E43Z-12A343B	38.50
brown label	▲E43Z-12A343C	38.50
Resister Assy. (Glow Plug)		
1984-87	▲E43Z-12A344A	40.50

LABOR 3 FUEL SYSTEM 3 LABOR

(Factory Time) — Chilton Time

GASOLINE ENGINE

(G) Fuel Pump, Test (On Car)
Includes: Disconnect line at carburetor, attach pressure gauge.
All models
mechanical (.3) 3
electric (.4) 4

(M) Carburetor Air Cleaner, Service
All models 2

(G) Fuel Filter, Renew
All models (.3) 4

(G) Carburetor, Adjust (On Car)
Includes: Adjust idle speed and ignition timing.
All models (.7) 1.0

(G) Carburetor Assembly, R&R or Renew
Includes: All necessary adjustments.
1983-87 (.6) 1.0
Renew carb add (.4) 4

(G) Carburetor, R&R and Clean or Recondition
Includes: All necessary adjustments.
1983-87
Motorcraft 740 (1.5) 2.5

(G) Fuel Enrichment Valve Assy., Renew
1983-87 (.7) 1.1

(G) Thermostatic Choke Housing, Renew
1983-87 (.6) 1.0

(G) Float Level, Adjust
1983-87 (.5) 7

(G) Float or Needle Valve and Seat, Renew
1983-87 (.5) 8

CHILTON'S EMISSION CONTROL TUNE-UP

1. Clean or renew P.C.V. valve, hoses and filter
2. Check fuel tank cap for sealing ability
3. Check fuel tank and fuel lines for leakage
4. Check evaporation canister and filter. Replace if necessary
5. Check engine compression to determine leakage of unburned gases. (Add time for items of interference)
6. Test and clean or renew spark plugs
7. Check engine oil dipstick for sealing ability
8. Test exhaust system with analyzer and check system for leakage
9. Check exhaust manifold heat valve for operation
10. Adjust ignition timing and carburetor idle speed and mixture
11. Check automatic choke mechanism for free operation
12. Inspect air cleaner and element
13. On models so equipped test distributor vacuum control switch and transmission control switch

Four 1.3
For repairs made charge accordingly.

(Factory Time) — Chilton Time

(G) Accelerator Pump Assy., Renew
1983-87 (.4) 7

(G) Fuel Tank, Renew
Includes: Drain and refill tank, transfer tank gauge unit.
1983-87 (.9) 1.3
w/EFI add (.2) 2
w/Elec fuel pump add (.2) 2

(G) Fuel Gauge (Tank Unit), Renew
1983-87 (.9) 1.2
w/EFI add (.3) 3

(G) Fuel Gauge (Dash Unit), Renew
1983-87 (.4) 7

(G) Fuel Pump, Renew
1983-87
mechanical (.4) 6
electric (.6) 9
Add pump test if performed.

(Factory Time) — Chilton Time

(G) Intake Manifold and/or Gasket, Renew
1983-87
w/CVH (1.6) 2.3
w/EFI
upper (1.0) 1.4
lower (1.7) 2.4
Renew manif add (.4) 5

ELECTRONIC FUEL INJECTION

(G) Fuel Injection Manifold Assy., Renew
1983-87 (1.2) 1.8

(G) Fuel Injector Assy., Renew
1983-87-one (1.2) 1.7
all (1.3) 2.0

(G) Air Intake Throttle Body, Renew
1983-87 (.6) 1.0

(G) Fuel Charging Wiring Assy., Renew
1983-87 (.3) 6

LABOR — 3 FUEL SYSTEM 3 — LABOR

(Factory Time) Chilton Time

(G) Fuel Pressure Regulator Assy., Renew
1983-87 (1.2)....... 1.7

DIESEL FUEL INJECTION

(G) Fuel Injection Nozzle, Renew
1984-87
one (.6)....... .9
each adtnl (.2)....... .3
all (.7)....... 1.6

(G) Fuel Injection Pump, Renew
1984-87 (1.7)....... 2.5

(G) Injection Pump Drive Gear, Renew
1984-87 (1.1)....... 1.5

(G) Intake Manifold and/or Gasket, Renew
1984-87 (1.8)....... 3.0
Renew manif add (.2)....... .5

TURBOCHARGER

(G) Turbocharger Assy., R&R or Renew
1984-85 (.9)....... 1.5

(G) Turbocharger Wastegate Actuator, Renew
Includes: R&R turbocharger.
1984-85 (1.1)....... 1.7

PARTS — 3 FUEL SYSTEM 3 — PARTS

Part No. Price

Carburetor Air Cleaner Element
1983 .... ▲E1FZ-9601AR 11.75
1984-85-1.6 eng.
exc. below....... ▲E1FZ-9601AR 11.75
w/E.F.I. & T.C. .... ▲E4FZ-9601A 12.00
1983-85-w/E.F.I. & exc. T.C....... ▲E3FZ-9601B 9.25
1986-87-1.9 eng.
exc. E.F.I....... ▲E4FZ-9601CR N.L.
w/E.F.I. .... ▲E59Z-9601A 12.00
1984-87-w/ diesel....... ▲E4FZ-9601B 17.25

Carburetor Assembly (New)
Note: New carburetor assy. must be ordered by stamping on tag attached to carburetor. If tag is missing order by calibration code on engine.
1983-w/MTX (wo/Hi output)
(carb. stamped E3EE-)
C1A....... ▲E3FZ-9510C 357.00
D1A....... ▲E3FZ-9510D 357.00
E1A, E2A....... ▲E3FZ-9510E 357.00
1983-w/ATX (wo/Hi output)
(carb. stamped E3EE-)
A1A .... ▲E3FZ-9510A 357.00
B1A .... ▲E3FZ-9510B 357.00
J1A, J2A....... ▲E3FZ-9510J 357.00
K1A .... ▲E3FZ-9510K 357.00
N1A .... ▲E3FZ-9510N 378.75
P1A .... ▲E3FZ-9510P 378.75
1983-w/MTX (w/Hi output)
(carb. stamped E3GE-)
C1A....... ▲E3GZ-9510C 357.00
M1A....... ▲E3GZ-9510M 357.00
P1A....... ▲E3GZ-9510P 392.75
U1A....... ▲E3GZ-9510U 357.00
R1A....... ▲E3GZ-9510R 403.75
S1A....... ▲E3GZ-9510S 392.75
1983-w/ATX (w/Hi output)
(carb. stamped E3GE-)
D1A....... ▲E3GZ-9510D 426.75
F1A....... ▲E3GZ-9510F 392.75
H1A....... ▲E3GZ-9510H 357.00
J1A....... ▲E3GZ-9510J 392.75
1984-85-1.6 eng. w/MTX (wo/Hi output)
(carb. stamped E4EE-)
AC1A .... ▲E4FZ-9510AC 369.50
AB1A....... ▲E4FZ-9510AB 369.50
Y1A .... ▲E4FZ-9510Y 369.50
AA1A....... ▲E4FZ-9510AA 406.50
1984-85-1.6 eng. w/MTX (w/Hi output)
(carb, stamped E4GE-)
K1A....... ▲E4GZ-9510K 369.50
L1A....... ▲E4GZ-9510L 369.50
M1A....... ▲E4GZ-9510M 406.50
1984-85-1.6 eng. w/ATX (w/Hi output)
(carb. stamped E4GE-)
U1A....... ▲E4GZ-9510Z 369.50
Z1A....... ▲E4GZ-9510Z 369.50
AAA .... ▲E4GZ-9510AA 406.50
ACA .... ▲E5GZ-9510AC 409.75
1985-87-1.9 eng.-MTX
(carb. stamped E5GE)
AAA....... ▲E6FZ-9510AA 331.75
ADA....... ▲E6FZ-9510AD 331.75
1985-87-1.9 eng.-ATX
AEE .... ▲E6FZ-9510AEE N.L.

Float Needle & Seat Assy.
1983-85-w/1.6 eng....... ▲E2PZ-9564A 7.00
1985-87-w/1.9 eng....... ▲E6PZ-9564A 14.50

Carburetor Tune-up Kit
1983 .... ▲E3PZ-9A586W 48.00
1984-85-w/1.6 eng. .... ▲E4PZ-9A586C 49.75
1985-87-w/1.9 eng. .... ▲E6PZ-9A586A 48.00

Carburetor Gasket Kit
1983 .... ▲E3PZ-9502A 25.50
1984-85-w/1.6 eng. .... ▲E4PZ-9502C N.L.
1985-87-w/1.9 eng....... ▲E6PZ-9502A 23.25

Choke Diaphragm & Shaft
1983
exc. below....... ▲E2PZ-9J549A 7.50
(Tag code E3EE)
D1A .... ▲E1PZ-9J549D 6.75
(Tag code E3GE)
C1A .... ▲E3PZ-9J549E 13.50
1984-87-wo/Hi output....... ▲E4PZ-9J549B 7.50
w/Hi output .... ▲E4PZ-9J549C 7.50

Dashpot Assy.
1983-87
exc. below .... ▲E2PZ-9B549B 19.00
(Tag code E3EE)
A1A, B1A, N1A, J1A, J2A, K1A .. ▲E2PZ-9B549A 16.75

Fuel Tank
1983-85 (10 gal.)....... ▲E3FZ-9002E 67.50
(13 gallon)-bef. 3-85
wo/E.F.I. .... ▲E3FZ-9002B 78.50
w/E.F.I. .... ▲E3FZ-9002D 78.50
1985-87-from 3-85-wo/E.F.I....... ▲E6FZ-9002B 87.75
diesel .... ▲E6FZ-9002A 87.75

Fuel Pump
1983-w/vapor return tube
wo/E.F.I. .... ▲E3FZ-9350C 29.00
1983-87-wo/vapor return tube
wo/E.F.I. .... ▲E3FZ-9350D 37.25
w/E.F.I. .... ▲E3FZ-9350B 235.50

Fuel Gauge (Tank Unit)
Gasoline engine
1983 (10 gal.)....... ▲E2FZ-9275A 42.25
(13 gal. tank)
wo/E.F.I. .... ▲E3FZ-9275C 42.25
w/E.F.I. .... ▲E3FZ-9275B 42.25
1984 (10 gal.)....... ▲E4FZ-9275B 42.25
(13 gal. tank)
wo/E.F.I. .... ▲E3FZ-9275D 42.25
w/E.F.I. .... ▲E3FZ-9275B 42.25
1985-87 (10 gal.)....... ▲E5FZ-9275D 42.25
(13 gal. tank)
wo/E.F.I. .... ▲E5FZ-9275A 42.25
w/E.F.I. .... ▲E5FZ-9275B 42.25
Diesel engine
1984 .... ▲E4FZ-9275A 42.25
1985-87 .... ▲E5FZ-9275C 42.25

Fuel Gauge (Dash)
1983 (wo/Tach.)
before 10-4-82 .... ▲E3FZ-9305B 35.00
from 10-4-82 .... ▲E3FZ-9305D 35.00
1983 (w/Tach.)
white lettering .... ▲E3FZ-9305E 35.00
orange lettering....... ▲E3FZ-9305A 33.00
1984-87-Escort & Lynx
wo/Tach....... ▲E4FZ-9305A 34.75
w/Tach. .... ▲E4FZ-9305D 36.25
w/diesel eng....... ▲E4FZ-9305D 36.25
1984-85-EXP....... ▲E4GY-9305A 35.00

PARTS — 3 ELECTRONIC FUEL INJECTION 3 — PARTS

Part No. Price

(1) Manifold (Intake)
1983-85-1.6 eng.
upper .... ▲E3FZ-9424A 106.00
lower .... ▲E3FZ-9424B 143.75
1986-87-1.9 eng., upper....... ▲E6FZ-9424B 106.00
lower .... ▲E6FZ-9424C 143.75

(2) Manifold Gasket (Upper)
1983-85-1.6 eng.. ▲E3FZ-9H486A .75
1986-87-1.9 eng.. ▲E6FZ-9H486A 2.25

PARTS 3 ELECTRONIC FUEL INJECTION 3 PARTS

	Part No.	Price
(3) Pressure Regulator (Fuel Charging)		
1983-87	▲E3FZ-9C968A	68.50
(4) Fuel Supply Manifold		
1983-85-wo/ Turbo	▲E3FZ-9D280G	61.75
1984-85-w/ Turbo	▲E4FZ-9D280D	63.50
1986-87	▲E6FZ-9D280A	64.00
(5) Injector Assy. (Fuel)		
1983-85-wo/ Turbo	▲E4FZ-9F593A	147.75
1984-85-w/ Turbo	▲E4FZ-9F593B	147.75
1986-87	▲E6FZ-9F593A	63.50
(6) Wiring Assy. (Fuel Charging)		
1983-85	▲E3FZ-9D930A	67.75
1986-87	▲E6FZ-9D930B	52.25
(7) Relief Valve Assy. (Pressure)		
1983-87	▲E0AY-9H321A	6.50
(8) Potentiometer Assy. (Throttle)		
1983-85	▲E5FZ-9B989C	29.25
1986-87	▲E6FZ-9B989A	28.25
1985-87	▲E5FZ-9B989C	29.25
(9) Throttle Body Assy.		
1983-w/MTX	▲E3FZ-9E926D	251.00
w/ATX	▲E3FZ-9E926C	252.25
1984-85-w/MTX	▲E4FZ-9E926B	250.75
w/ATX	▲E4FZ-9E926A	252.25
w/Turbo	▲E4FZ-9E926C	250.75
1986-87-w/MTX	▲E6FZ-9E926D	252.25
w/ATX	▲E6FZ-9E926C	N.L.
(10) Manifold Gasket		
1983-85	▲E3FZ-9E936A	.75
(11) Gasket (By-Pass Valve)		
1983-87	▲E3FZ-9F670A	1.25
(12) By-Pass Valve Assy. (Throttle)		
1983-87	▲E3FZ-9F715A	33.25
(13) Lever & Shaft Assy. (Throttle)		
1983-w/MTX	▲E3FZ-9E926D	251.00
w/ATX	▲E3FZ-9E926C	252.25
1984-85-w/ATX	▲E4FZ-9E926A	252.25
w/MTX	▲E4FZ-9E926B	250.75
w/turbo	▲E4FZ-9E926C	250.75
1986-87-w/ATX	▲E6FZ-9E926C	N.L.
w/MTX	▲E6FZ-9E926D	252.25

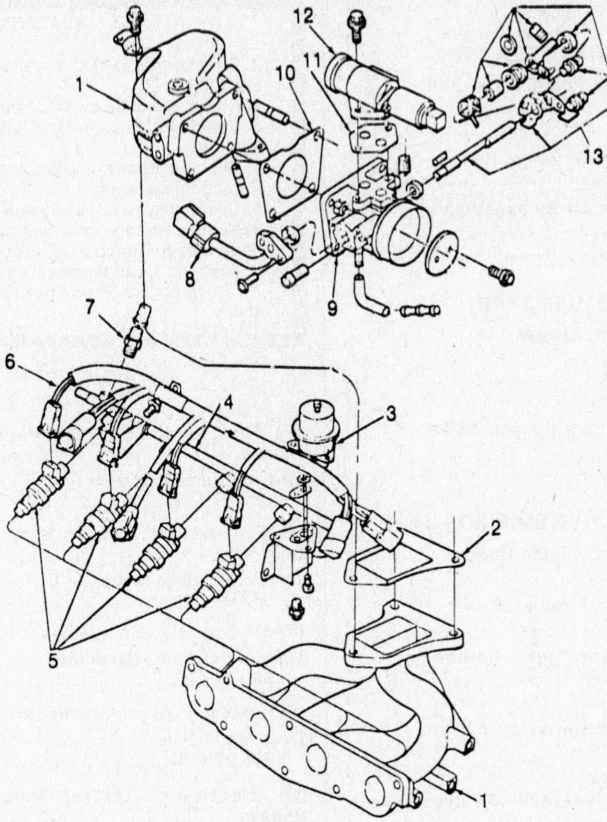

DIESEL FUEL INJECTION

	Part No.	Price
Fuel Injection Pump (exc. Calif.)		
1984 (bef. 3-1-84)	▲E43Z-9A543B	411.00
(from 3-1-84)	▲E43Z-9A543D	411.00
1985 (bef. 3-85)	▲E5FZ-9A543A	411.00
1985-87 (from 3-85)	▲E6FZ-9A543A	411.00
(Calif.)		
1984-85 (bef. 3-85)	▲E43Z-9A543C	411.00
1985-87 (from 3-85)	▲E53Z-9A543A	411.00
Nozzle Holder Assy.		
1984-87	▲E43Z-9E527B	22.50
Engine Idle Control		
1984-87 (I.D. plate color code)		
blue	▲E43Z-9L513A	11.50
white	▲E43Z-9L513B	11.50
Switch Assy. (Eng. Idle Cont.)		
1984-87-wo/ cruise cont.	▲E4FZ-12B537A	15.00
w/cruise cont.	▲E4FZ-12B537B	20.25
Intake Manifold		
1984-87	▲E43Z-9424B	84.50

PARTS 3 TURBOCHARGER SYSTEM 3 PARTS

	Part No.	Price
(1) Turbocharger Assy.		
1984-85 (bef. 2-85)	▲E4FZ-9G438A	325.25
1985 (from 2-85)	▲E4FZ-9G438AB	336.25
(2) Oil Return Tube		
1984-85	▲E4FZ-9G441A	12.25
(3) Intake Manifold		
1984-85-upper	▲E3FZ-9424A	106.00
lower	▲E3FZ-9424B	143.75
(4) Tube (E.G.R. Valve to Exh. Man.)		
1984-85	▲E3FZ-9D477A	25.50

(5) E.G.R. Valve
Note: Replacement E.G.R. valves must be ordered according to the stamping number on the original valve.

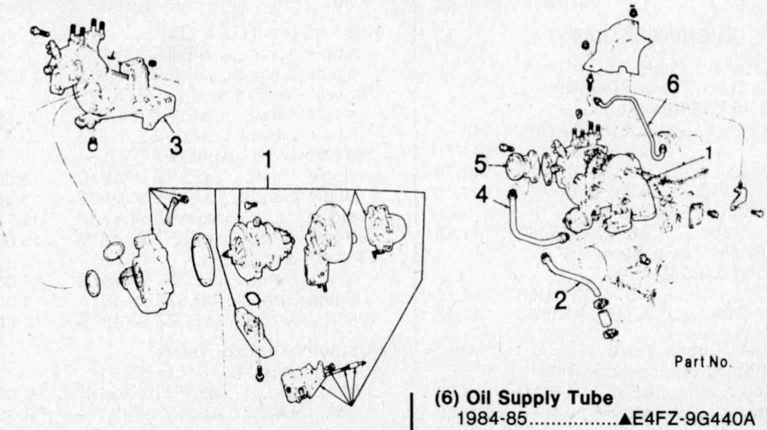

	Part No.	Price
(6) Oil Supply Tube		
1984-85	▲E4FZ-9G440A	3.25

LABOR 3A EMISSION CONTROLS 3A LABOR

(Factory Time) Chilton Time

THERMACTOR TYPE

(G) Thermactor Pump Drive Belt, Renew
1983-87 (.6) 9

(G) Thermactor Air Pump, Renew
1983-87 (.6) 1.1

(G) Thermactor Air By-Pass Valve, Renew
1983-87 (.4) 6

E.G.R. TYPE

(G) E.G.R. Valve, Renew
1983-87
w/MTX (.4) 6
w/ATX (.5) 7

(G) E.G.R. Vacuum Control Valve, Renew
1983-87 (.3) 4

EVAPORATIVE EMISSION TYPE

(G) Fuel Vapor Canister, Renew
1983-87 3

(G) Purge Control Valve, Renew
1983-87 4

(M) Carburetor Air Cleaner Element, Renew
1983-87 (.2) 2

(M) Crankcase Emission Filter, Renew
1983-87 3

(M) Crankcase Ventilation Valve, Renew
1983-87 (.2) 2

ELECTRONIC ENGINE CONTROL IV

(P) E.E.C. System, Test
1983-87 (.6) 1.0

(P) Throttle Position Sensor, Renew
Does not include system test.
1983-87 (.2) 3

(P) E.G.R. Shut Off Solenoid, Renew
Does not include system test.
1983-87 (.1) 2

CHILTON'S EMISSION CONTROL TUNE-UP

1. Clean or renew P.C.V. valve, hoses and filter
2. Check fuel tank cap for sealing ability
3. Check fuel tank and fuel lines for leakage
4. Check evaporation canister and filter. Replace if necessary
5. Check engine compression to determine leakage of unburned gases. (Add time for items of interference)
6. Test and clean or renew spark plugs
7. Check engine oil dipstick for sealing ability
8. Test exhaust system with analyzer and check system for leakage
9. Check exhaust manifold heat valve for operation
10. Adjust ignition timing and carburetor idle speed and mixture
11. Check automatic choke mechanism for free operation
12. Inspect air cleaner and element
13. On models so equipped test distributor vacuum control switch and transmission control switch

Four 1.3

For repairs made charge accordingly.

(Factory Time) Chilton Time

(P) Throttle Air By-Pass Valve, Renew
Does not include system test.
1983-87 (.1) 3

(P) Exhaust Gas Oxygen Sensor, Renew
Does not include system test.
1983-87 (.1) 3

(P) Air Control Sensor, Renew
Does not include system test.
1983-87 (.3) 5

(P) Processor Assembly, Renew
Does not include system test.
1983-87 (.2) 3

(P) Electronic Control Relay, Renew
Does not include system test.
1983-87 (.1) 2

(P) Back Pressure Variable Transducer Valve, Renew
Does not include system test.
1983-87 (.1) 2

(P) Engine Coolant Temperature Sensor, Renew
Does not include system test.
1983-87 (.1) 2

(P) Fuel Pump Relay, Renew
Does not include system test.
1983-87 (.1) 2

(Factory Time) Chilton Time

(P) Fuel Pump Inertia Switch, Renew
Does not include system test.
1983-87 (.3) 5

(P) Barometric Manifold Absolute Pressure Sensor, Renew
Does not include system test.
1983-87 (.1) 3

(P) Canister Purge Valve, Renew
Does not include system test.
1983-87 (.1) 2

(P) Fuel Injector Assembly, Renew
Does not include system test.
1983-87-one (1.1) 1.5
all (1.2) 1.7

(P) Thick Film Ignition Module, Renew
Does not include system test.
1983-87 (.6) 8

(P) Profile Ignition Pick-Up Sensor, Renew
Does not include system test.
1983-87 (.7) 9

(P) E.G.R. Valve, Renew
Does not include system test.
1983-87 (.3) 5

(P) Cooling Fan Control Module or Relay, Renew
Does not include system test.
1985-87 (.1) 2

PARTS 3A EMISSION CONTROLS 3A PARTS

THERMACTOR TYPE

	Part No.	Price
Thermactor Air Pump		
1983-87 (wo/Power Steering)		
(stamped E1EE-9A486-)		
J2A	▲E1FZ-9A486J	141.75
LA	▲E1FZ-9A486L	141.75
E3A	▲E1FZ-9A486B	141.75
F1A, F2A	▲E1FZ-9A486F	141.75
(stamped E1ZE-9A486-)		
D1B, D2B	▲E1ZZ-9A486D	141.75
1983-87 (w/Power Steering)		
(stamped E1EE-9A486-)		
K2A	▲E1FZ-9A486K	141.75
R1A, R2A	▲E1FZ-9A486C	141.75
Thermactor Check Valve		
1983 (Fitting or clamp one end)		
Fitting	▲E3FZ-9A487G	13.00
Clamp	▲E3FZ-9A487E	13.25
1984-85 (wo/H.O & EFI)		
nipple 1 end	▲E3FZ-9A487G	13.00
nipple 2 ends	▲E3FZ-9A487E	13.25
1984-85-w/Hi output (w/MTX)		
nipple 1 end	▲E3FZ-9A487F	13.00
nipple 2 ends	▲E3FZ-9A487E	13.25
1984-85-w/Hi output (w/ATX)		
nipple 1 end	▲E3FZ-9A487G	13.00
nipple 2 ends	▲E3FZ-9A487E	13.25
4 port	▲D8BZ-9D473A	36.75
1984-85-w/E.F.I.	▲E3FZ-9A487B	18.50
1986-87-exc. E.F.I.		
nipple 1 end	▲E3FZ-9A487G	13.00
nipple 2 ends	▲E3TZ-9A487A	13.25
1986-87-w/E.F.I.	▲E3FZ-9A487B	18.50
Thermactor Control Valve		
1983 (stamped no. E1EE-9F491)		
B3A, B4A	▲E1FZ-9F491-B	56.00
C3A, C4A	▲E1FZ-9F491-C	56.00
D3A, D4A	▲E1FZ-9F491-D	56.00
EA	▲E2FZ-9F491-A	56.00
G3A, G4A	▲E1FZ-9F491-G	56.00
M3A, M4A	▲E1FZ-9F491-M	56.00
1984-85-exc.		
below	▲E3FZ-9F491E	52.25
w/Hi output	▲E3FZ-9F491D	56.00
1986-87	▲E6FZ-9F491A	56.00

E.G.R. TYPE

	Part No.	Price
Intergral E.G.R. Valve (w/Transducer)		
1983	▲E2GZ-9D448J	60.75
1984-85	▲E4FZ-9D448A	61.00
1986-87	▲E6FZ-9D475G	47.75
Vacuum Control Valve (E.G.R.)		
1983-85-2 port	▲D7BZ-9D473A	28.50
4 port	▲D8BZ-9D473A	36.75
1986-87-2 port	▲D3TZ-9D473A	33.00

PARTS 3A EMISSION CONTROLS 3A PARTS

	Part No.	Price
Solenoid Valve (E.G.R. Vacuum)		
1983 (Stamped No. E1EE 9D474-)		
CC	▲E1FZ-9D474C	16.25
B2A, B3A	▲E1FZ-9D474B	32.50
B2C, B3C	▲E1FZ-9D474D	32.50
1984-87 (Stamped No. E3ZZ-9D474)		
A2A, A3A	▲E1FZ-9D474C	16.25
B2A, B3A	▲E3FZ-9D474B	16.25
C3A	▲E3FZ-9D474C	16.25
EVAPORATIVE EMISSON TYPE		
Fuel Vapor Canister		
1983-87-exc. E.F.I.	▲D8AZ-9D653C	53.25
w/E.F.I.	▲E3FZ-9D653B	53.25
Sensor Assy.		
1983-87-exc. E.F.I.	▲D4FZ-9E607A	7.00
1983-85-w/E.F.I.	▲D7FZ-9E607A	7.25
Compensator Assy. (Carb. Altitude)		
1986-87	▲E6FZ-9A950B	54.75
Crankcase Emission Filter		
1983-85	▲E1FZ-9D697A	1.00
1986-87	▲E6FZ-9D697A	1.25
Crankcase Air Cleaner Filter		
1983-87	▲E1FZ-9D695B	3.50

	Part No.	Price
Purge Control Valve		
1983	▲D9AZ-9B963B	7.25
1984-87	▲E3TZ-9B963B	7.25
ELECTRONIC ENGINE CONTROL IV		
Throttle Position Sensor		
1983-84	▲E3FZ-9B989A	N.L.
1985	▲E5FZ-9B989C	29.25
1986-87	▲E6FZ-9B989A	28.25
Exhaust Gas Oxygen Sensor		
1983 (stamped 9F472)		
E3EF-AA	▲E3FZ-9F472A	48.50
E47F-AA	▲E3TZ-9F472B	N.L.
E3BF-AA	▲E4BZ-9F472A	N.L.
1984-85	▲E3FZ-9F472A	48.50
1986-87	▲E59Z-9F472A	48.50
Processor Assy.		
1984-85-wo/turbo	▲E4GZ-12A650A	167.75
1984-w/turbo	▲E4ZZ-12A650A	167.75
1985-w/turbo	▲E5ZZ-12A650HA	167.75
1986-87-w/MTX	▲E6FZ-12A650BA	167.75
w/ATX	▲E6FZ-12A650AA	N.L.
Engine Coolant Temperature Sensor		
1983-87	▲E1AZ-12A648A	32.00

	Part No.	Price
Barometric Manifold Absolute Pressure Sensor		
1984-87	▲E3ZZ-12A644A	59.75
Fuel Injector Assy.		
1984-85-wo/Turbo	▲E4FZ-9F593A	147.75
w/Turbo	▲E4FZ-9F593B	147.75
1986-87	▲E6FZ-9F593A	63.50
Canister Purge Valve		
1984-85	▲E3TZ-9C915B	21.75
E.G.R. Shut Off Solenoid		
1984-87	▲E3FZ-9D474C	16.25
Throttle Air By Pass Valve		
1983-87	▲E3FZ-9F715A	33.25
Relay, Electronic Control		
1983-87	▲E3AZ-12A646A	15.50

Back Pressure Variable Tranducer Valve
Note: 1983-84 must be ordered by stamping on valve.

	Part No.	Price
Air Control Sensor		
1983-85-wo/turbo	▲E3GZ-12B529B	192.00
w/turbo	▲E3SZ-12B529A	199.75
1986-87	▲E6FZ-12B259B	N.L.

LABOR 4 ALTERNATOR AND REGULATOR 4 LABOR

	(Factory Time)	Chilton Time
(G) Alternator Circuits, Test		
Includes: Test battery, regulator and alternator output.		
All models	(.3)	.6
(M) Alternator Drive Belt, Renew		
1983-87	(.3)	.4
(G) Alternator Assembly, Renew		
1983-87	(.4)	.7
Transfer pulley add	(.1)	.1
Add circuit test if performed.		

	(Factory Time)	Chilton Time
(G) Alternator, R&R and Recondition		
Includes: Complete disassembly, replacement of parts as required. Test validity of rotor field, stator and diodes.		
1983-87	(.9)	1.5
(G) Alternator Brushes, Renew		
Includes: R&R alternator.		
1983-87	(.7)	1.2
Add circuit test if performed.		
(G) Alternator Front Bearing or End Plate, Renew		
Includes: R&R alternator.		
1983-87	(.7)	1.1

	(Factory Time)	Chilton Time
(G) Alternator Rear Bearing, Renew		
Includes: R&R alternator.		
1983-87	(.6)	1.0
(G) Alternator Regulator, Renew		
1983-87	(.3)	.5
Add circuit test if performed.		
(G) Instrument Cluster Voltage Regulator, Renew		
1983-87	(.4)	.6
(G) Ammeter, Renew		
1983-87	(.4)	.7

PARTS 4 ALTERNATOR AND REGULATOR 4 PARTS

	Part No.	Price
Alternator Assy. (New)		
40 amp		
1983	▲E1ZZ-10346A	203.50
1984-85-std.	▲E2DZ-10346A	N.L.
hi efficiency	▲E43Z-10346A	203.50
1986-87	▲E6FZ-10346A	N.L.
60 amp		
1983-85-w/1.6 eng.	▲E2GZ-10346B	233.50
1985-87-w/1.9 eng.	▲E6FZ-10346C	N.L.
65 amp		
1984-85-wo/diesel	▲E2GZ-10346A	233.50
1984-85-w/diesel	▲E43Z-10346A	203.50
1986-87	▲E63Z-10346A	232.75
(1) Pulley		
40 amp		
1983-87	▲E1FZ-10344B	12.25

	Part No.	Price
60 amp		
1983-87	▲E1FZ-10344C	10.00
1984-87-w/diesel	▲D9AZ-10344A	17.75
65 amp		
1983-87-wo/diesel	▲E1FZ-10344C	10.00
1984-87-w/diesel	▲E4FZ-10344A	9.75
(2) Fan		
1983-87	▲D9ZZ-10A310A	4.50
(3) Spacer		
1983-87	▲C5AZ-10A344B	.50
(4) Housing (Front)		
1983-w/40 Amp.	▲D3OZ-10333B	17.75
1984-87-w/40 Amp.	▲E1FZ-10333A	21.25
1983-87-w/60 amp	▲E1FZ-10333A	21.25
w/65 amp	▲E1FZ-10333A	21.25

	Part No.	Price
(5) Front Bearing		
1983-87	▲C9ZZ-10094A	9.00
(6) Bearing Retainer (Front)		
1983-87	▲D20Z-10A355A	1.75
(7) Stop (Rotor)		
1983-87	▲C5AZ-10A360A	1.00
(8) Rotor Assy.		
1983-87-exc. 40 amp	▲E1ZZ-10335B	45.75
w/40 amp	▲E1ZZ-10335A	45.75
(9) Slip Ring (Rotor)		
1983-87	▲C3SZ-10328A	N.L.
(10) Shaft (Rotor)		
1983-87	▲C5AZ-10330A	N.L.
(11) Stator Assy.		
40 amp		
1983-84	▲E3FZ-10336A	31.25
1985	▲D8ZZ-10336A	74.00
1986-87	▲E43Z-10336C	41.25

PARTS 4 ALTERNATOR AND REGULATOR 4 PARTS

	Part No.	Price
60 amp		
1983-85	▲E3FZ-10336A	31.25
1986-87	▲E43Z-10336B	N.L.
65 amp		
1983-85	▲D8ZZ-10336A	74.00
1986-87	▲E6DZ-10336D	33.50
(12) Insulator Kit		
1983-87	▲C9SZ-10A383A	1.75
(13) Rectifier Assy.		
1983-w/40 amp	▲D6AZ-10304A	48.00
1984-exc. 40 amp.	▲D9VY-10304A	47.25
1985-w/40 amp	▲D9VY-10304A	47.25
exc. 40 amp.	▲D9VY-10304A	47.25
1986-87	▲E43Z-10304A	47.25
(14) Capacitor (Radio)		
1983-85	▲C6AZ-18827A	2.25
(15) Insulator Kit		
1983-85	▲C9SZ-10A383A	1.75
(16) Brush Set		
1983-85	▲C6VY-10347A	3.50
(17) Brush Holder		
1983-87	▲C5AZ-10351A	2.00
(18) Spring (Brush)		
1983-87	▲C5AZ-10349A	.75
(19) Housing (Rear)		
1983-w/40 & 65 amp	▲D7ZZ-10334A	26.25
w/60 amp.	▲D7AZ-10334A	23.25
1984	▲D7ZZ-10334A	26.25
1985-w/40 & 65 amp	▲D7ZZ-10334A	26.25
w/60 amp.	▲D7AZ-10334A	23.25

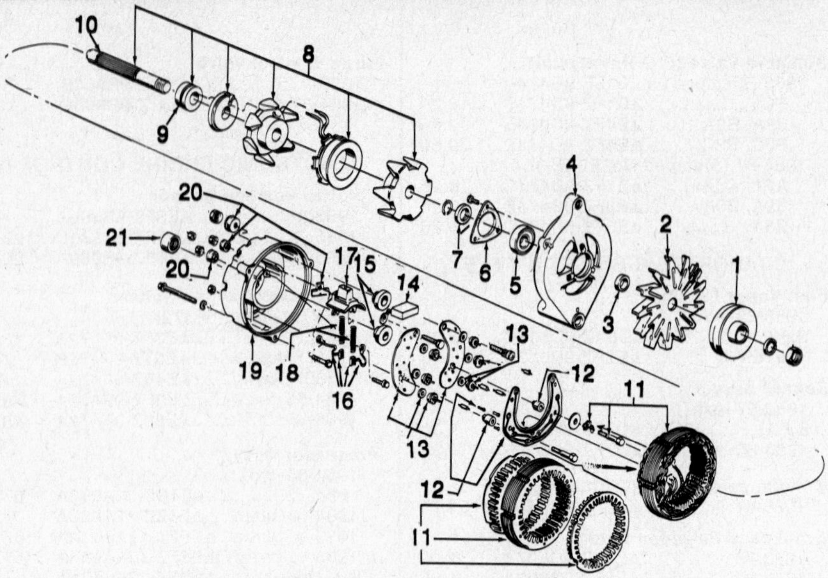

	Part No.	Price
1986-87	▲E6FZ-10334A	36.75
(20) Insulator (Terminal)		
1983-87	▲C5AZ-10329D	2.25
(21) Rear Bearing		
1983-87	▲D2OZ-10A304A	5.25

	Part No.	Price
Alternator Regulator		
1983-85	▲E2PZ-10316A	36.75
1986-87	▲E43Z-10316A	29.75
Instrument Cluster Voltage Regulator		
1983-87-Escort & Lynx-wo/Tach.	▲C9AZ-10804A	10.25
inc. EXP & LN7-w/Tach.	▲D1AZ-10804A	10.25

LABOR 5 STARTING SYSTEM 5 LABOR

(Factory Time)	Chilton Time
(G) Starter Draw Test (On Car)	
All models (.3)	.3
(G) Starter Assembly, Renew	
1983-87	
Gas (.4)	.7
Diesel (.8)	1.1
Add draw test if performed.	
(G) Starter, R&R and Recondition	
Includes: Turn down armature.	
1983-87	
Gas (1.6)	2.8
Diesel (2.3)	3.5
Renew field coils add	.4
Add draw test if performed.	
(G) Starter Drive, Renew	
Includes: R&R starter.	
1983-87	
Gas (.6)	.9
Diesel (1.4)	1.8
(G) Starter Solenoid Relay, Renew	
1983-87 (.3)	.4
(G) Ignition Switch, Renew	
1983-87 (.6)	1.0
(M) Battery Cables, Renew	
Batt to Relay	
Gas (.3)	.3
Diesel (1.2)	1.5
Negative (.3)	.3
Relay to Starter (.7)	1.0

PARTS 5 STARTING SYSTEM 5 PARTS

	Part No.	Price
Starter Assy. (New)		
1983-85-w/1.6 eng.	▲E3FZ-11002A	159.25
1985-87-w/1.9 eng.	▲E6FZ-11002A	159.25
diesel eng.	▲E4FZ-11002A	231.25
(1) Plate (Brush End)		
1983-87-exc. diesel	▲E3FZ-11049A	7.75
diesel eng.	▲E4FZ-11049A	14.50
(2) Plate Bushing (Brush End)		
1983-87-exc. diesel	▲D3AZ-11052A	1.50
diesel eng.	▲E4FZ-11052A	9.50
(3) Insulator (Brush Holder)		
1983-87	▲E2BZ-11062A	2.00
(4) Spring (Brush)		
1983-87	▲D7AZ-11059A	1.00
(5) Brush Holder		
1983-87-exc. diesel	▲E3FZ-11061A	3.00
diesel eng.	▲E4FZ-11061A	4.25
(6) Brush Set		
1983-87	▲E4PZ-11057A	13.00
(7) Grommet		
1983-87-exc. diesel	▲E3FZ-11A120A	1.75
diesel eng.	▲E4FZ-11A120A	1.25
(8) Field Coil (Complete)		
1983-85-w/1.6 eng.	▲E3FZ-11082A	45.25
1985-87-w/1.9 eng.	▲E6FZ-11082A	45.25
diesel eng.	▲E4FZ-11082A	50.00
(9) Contact Point Kit		
1983-87	▲E2PZ-11134A	24.75
(10) Cover (Plunger)		
1983-87	▲E2BZ-11060A	2.75
(11) Gasket (Cover)		
1983-87	▲C2DF-11065A	1.00
(12) Spring (Plunger Return)		
1983-87-exc. diesel	▲C2DF-11103A	1.50
1984-87-diesel eng.	▲E4FZ-11103A	1.75
(13) Lever & Pin Kit		
1983-87-exc. diesel	▲E2BZ-11067A	14.25

LABOR 5 STARTING SYSTEM 5 LABOR

	Part No.	Price
1984-87-diesel eng.	▲E4FZ-11067A	14.25
(14) Retaining Flange (Coil)		
1983-87		▲N.L.
(15) Retaining Sleeve (Coil)		
1983-87	▲E2BZ-11105A	1.50
(16) Armature		
1983-87-exc. below	▲E3FZ-11005A	66.75
diesel eng.	▲E4FZ-11005A	66.75
(17) Drive Assy.		
1983-85-w/1.6 eng.	▲D6PZ-11350B	17.50
1985-87-w/1.9 eng.	▲E6FZ-11350A	16.75
diesel eng.	▲E4FZ-11350A	21.00
(18) Housing Kit (Drive End)		
1983-85-w/1.6 eng.	▲E2FZ-11130A	21.75
1985-87-w/1.9 eng.	▲E6FZ-11130A	21.75
diesel eng.	▲E4FZ-11130A	23.00

(19) Seal (Rear Bearing)
Note: Serviced in Housing Kit No. 18

	Part No.	Price
(20) Bearing (Drive Housing)		
1983-87-exc. diesel	▲D0AZ-11135B	N.L.
1984-87-diesel eng.	▲E4FZ-11135A	2.75
Battery to Starter Relay Cable		
1983-87-exc. diesel	▲E1FZ-14300A	6.25
1984-87-diesel eng.	▲E4FZ-14300A	7.50

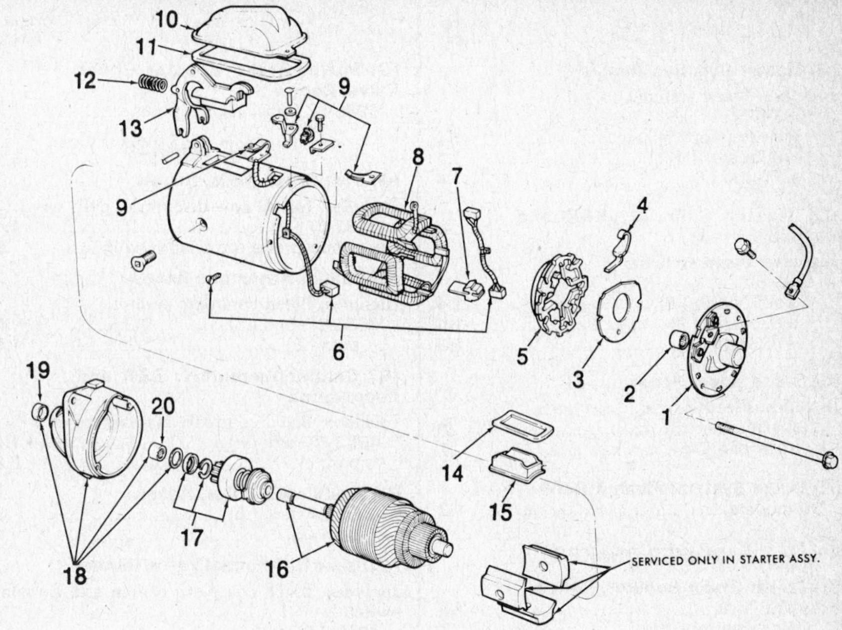

	Part No.	Price
Battery to Ground Cable		
1983-exc. E.F.I.	▲E3FZ-14301B	N.L.
w/E.F.I.	▲E3FZ-14301A	N.L.
1984-85-exc. E.F.I.	▲E3FZ-14301D	12.50
w/E.F.I.	▲E3FZ-14301C	12.50
1986-87	▲E6FZ-14301A	12.50
1984-87-diesel eng.	▲E4FZ-14301A	19.75

	Part No.	Price
Relay to Starter Cable		
1983-87-w/E.F.I.	▲E4FZ-14431C	21.75
1984-85-w/turbo	▲E4FZ-14431E	36.25
diesel eng.	▲E4FZ-14431A	44.25
Ignition Switch		
1983-87	▲E4FZ-11572A	11.50

LABOR 6 BRAKE SYSTEM 6 LABOR

(Factory Time)	Chilton Time
(G) Brake Pedal Free Play, Adjust	
All models	.4
(G) Brakes, Adjust (Minor)	
Includes: Adjust brakes, fill master cylinder.	
two wheels	.4
(G) Bleed Brakes (Four Wheels)	
Includes: Fill master cylinder.	
All models (.3)	.5
(G) Brake Self Adjustors, Disassemble and Clean	
one wheel	.8
both wheels	1.5
(G) Brake Shoes and/or Pads, Renew	
Includes: Install new or exchange brake shoes or pads. Adjust service and hand brake. Bleed system.	
1983-87	
front-disc (.7)	1.1
rear-drum (1.0)	1.5
all four wheels (1.4)	2.5
Resurface brake rotor, add-each	.9
Resurface brake drum, add-each	.5
(G) Brake Drum, Renew	
1983-87-one (.3)	.6
both (.5)	.9
(G) Brake Pressure Warning Light Switch, Renew	
1983-87 (.3)	.5

COMBINATIONS
Add To Brakes, Renew

See Machine Shop Operations

(G) RENEW WHEEL CYLINDER	
Each (.3)	.5
(G) REBUILD WHEEL CYLINDER	
Each (.3)	.5
(G) REBUILD CALIPER ASSEMBLY	
Each (.3)	.5
(G) RENEW MASTER CYLINDER	
All models	1.0
(G) REBUILD MASTER CYLINDER	
All models	1.4
(G) RENEW BRAKE HOSE	
Each (.3)	.3
(G) RENEW REAR WHEEL GREASE SEALS	
One (.2)	.3
Both (.3)	.4
(G) RENEW BRAKE DRUM	
Each (.2)	.2
(G) RENEW DISC BRAKE ROTOR	
Each (.1)	.2
(G) REPACK FRONT WHEEL BEARINGS (BOTH WHEELS)	
All models	2.0
(G) REPACK REAR WHEEL BEARINGS (BOTH WHEELS)	
All models	.5

BRAKE HYDRAULIC SYSTEM

(Factory Time)	Chilton Time
(G) Wheel Cylinder, Renew	
Includes: Bleed system.	
1983-87-one (1.0)	1.4
both (1.8)	2.4
(G) Wheel Cylinder, R&R and Rebuild	
Includes: Hone cylinder and bleed system.	
1983-87-one (1.2)	1.7
both (2.1)	3.0

LABOR — 6 BRAKE SYSTEM 6 — LABOR

(Factory Time)	Chilton Time
(G) Master Cylinder, Renew	
Includes: Bleed system.	
1983-87	
wo/Booster (.5)	1.0
w/Booster (.6)	1.1
w/Turbo (.8)	1.4
(G) Master Cylinder, R&R and Rebuild	
Includes: Bleed system.	
1983-87	
wo/Booster (.8)	1.4
w/Booster (.9)	1.5
w/Turbo (1.1)	1.8
(G) Brake Hose, Renew	
Includes: Bleed system.	
1983-87-rear (.5)	.8
front-one (.4)	.7
(G) Brake System, Flush & Refill	
All models	1.2
POWER BRAKES	
(G) Power Brake Booster, Renew	
1983-87 (.9)	1.3
w/Cruise control add	.2
w/Turbo add (.2)	.2

(Factory Time)	Chilton Time
(G) Power Brake Booster Check Valve, Renew	
1983-87 (.3)	.4
DISC BRAKES	
(G) Disc Brake Pads, Renew	
Includes: Install new disc brake pads only.	
1983-87 (.7)	1.1
Resurface brake rotor, add-each	.9
(G) Caliper Assembly, Renew	
Includes: Bleed complete system.	
1983-87-one (.6)	.9
both (.8)	1.6
(G) Caliper Assembly, R&R and Recondition	
Includes: Bleed complete system.	
1983-87-one (.8)	1.4
both (1.2)	2.6
(G) Disc Brake Rotor, Renew	
1983-87-one (.3)	.5
both (.5)	.8
(G) Brake Differential Valve, Renew	
Includes: Bleed complete system and transfer switch.	
1983-87	
one (.5)	.8

(Factory Time)	Chilton Time
two (.6)	1.0
w/Turbo add (.2)	.2
(G) Vacuum Pump, Renew	
1984-87 (.4)	.6
PARKING BRAKE	
(M) Parking Brake, Adjust	
1983-87 (.3)	.5
w/Console add (.1)	.1
(G) Parking Brake Control, Renew	
1983-87	
wo/Console (.5)	.7
w/Console (.6)	1.0
(G) Parking Brake Cables, Renew	
Includes: Adjust parking brake.	
1983-87	
front (.5)	.9
rear	
wo/Console	
one (.6)	.9
both (.9)	1.3
w/Console	
one (.7)	1.0
both (1.0)	1.4

PARTS — 6 BRAKE SYSTEM 6 — PARTS

	Part No.	Price
(1) Brake Shoe Set (Rear)		
1983-87		
7" x 1¼" Brk.	▲E1FZ-2200A	33.00
8" x 1⅓" Brk.	▲E2FZ-2200A	47.25
sta. wag. (from 4-83 to 10-83)	▲E3FZ-2200A	40.25
(from 10-83)	▲E2FZ-2200A	47.25
Brake Lining Kit		
1983-87		
8" x 1⅓" Brk.	▲E2FZ-2007A	20.00
(2) Rear Wheel Cylinder Assy.		
1983-87-Right	▲E2FZ-2261B	17.25
Left	▲E2FZ-2262B	21.25
1983-84-sta. wagon R.H.	▲E43Z-2261A	17.25
left	▲E43Z-2262A	17.25
Repair Kit Wheel Cylinder		
1983-87	▲E1FZ-2128A	5.00
1983-84-sta. wagon	▲E43Z-2128A	4.75
Brake Hose (Front)		
1983-bef 2-83-Right	▲E1FZ-2078A	15.75
left	▲E1FZ-2078C	15.75
1983-87-from 2/83-Right	▲E43Z-2078A	15.75
left	▲E43Z-2078B	15.25
Master Cylinder Assy.		
Manual disc.		
1983 (bef. 2-83)	▲E1FZ-2140B	90.00
1983-87 (from 2-83)	▲E3FZ-2140A	89.00
Power disc.		
1983 (bef 2-83)	▲E1FZ-2140A	93.00
1983-87 (from 2-83)	▲E3FZ-2140B	89.00
Repair Kit (Master Cylinder)		
Manual disc.		
1983 (bef. 2-83)	▲E1FZ-2004B	26.75
1983-87	▲E3FZ-2004A	62.75

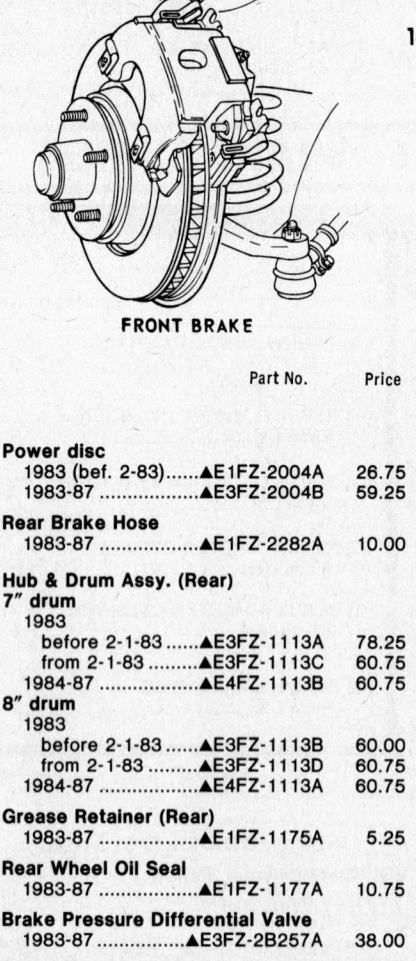

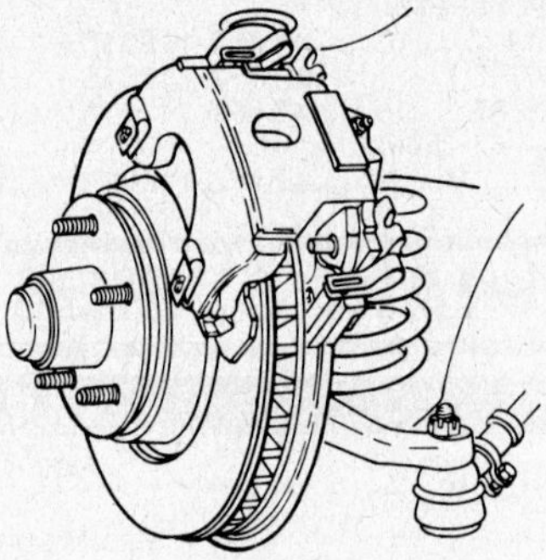

FRONT BRAKE

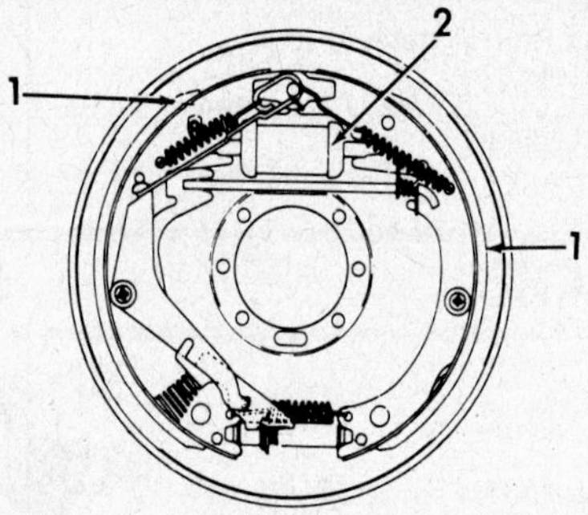

REAR BRAKE

	Part No.	Price
Power disc		
1983 (bef. 2-83)	▲E1FZ-2004A	26.75
1983-87	▲E3FZ-2004B	59.25
Rear Brake Hose		
1983-87	▲E1FZ-2282A	10.00
Hub & Drum Assy. (Rear)		
7" drum		
1983		
before 2-1-83	▲E3FZ-1113A	78.25
from 2-1-83	▲E3FZ-1113C	60.75
1984-87	▲E4FZ-1113B	60.75
8" drum		
1983		
before 2-1-83	▲E3FZ-1113B	60.00
from 2-1-83	▲E3FZ-1113D	60.75
1984-87	▲E4FZ-1113A	60.75
Grease Retainer (Rear)		
1983-87	▲E1FZ-1175A	5.25
Rear Wheel Oil Seal		
1983-87	▲E1FZ-1177A	10.75
Brake Pressure Differential Valve		
1983-87	▲E3FZ-2B257A	38.00

	Part No.	Price
Brake Booster Assy. (New)		
Gasoline engine		
1983-87		
before 2-1-83	▲E2FZ-2005A	150.00
from 2-1-83	▲E3FZ-2005A	131.75
Diesel engine		
1984-87	▲E4FZ-2005A	131.75
Brake Pressure Warning Light Switch		
1983-87	▲E2FZ-2B264B	7.50
Parking Brake Lever		
1983-87	▲E3FZ-2780A	38.00
Parking Brake Cable (Rear)		
1983-85 (bef. 2-85)	▲E3FZ-2A635A	18.75
1985-87 (from 2-85)	▲E6FZ-2A635A	15.75
Equalizer & Rod Assy.		
1983-87	▲E1FZ-2A794A	4.25

PARTS 6 DISC BRAKES 6 PARTS

	Part No.	Price
(1) Caliper Assy. (Front)		
1983 (bef. 4-83)		
R.H.	▲E1FZ-2B120A	92.25
left	▲E1FZ-2B121A	92.25
1983-87 (from 4-83) R.H.	▲E43Z-2B120A	89.50
left	▲E43Z-2B121A	89.50
(2) Pad Set		
1983-87-exc. diesel	▲E3FZ-2001A	40.25
w/diesel	▲E4FZ-2201A	N.L.
w/SVO	▲E4FZ-2001A	40.25
(3) Caliper Repair Kit		
1983-87	▲E43Z-2221A	8.00
(4) Caliper Piston (Front)		
1983-87	▲E43Z-2196A	11.75
(5) Locating Pin (Caliper)		
1983-87	▲E43Z-2B296A	6.50
(6) Grease Shield		
1983		
before 2-1-83	▲E1FZ-3K070A	2.50
from 2-1-83	▲E3FZ-3K070A	2.50
(7) Brake Bearing Kit		
1983-87	▲E3FZ-2C134A	39.25
(8) Bearing Cup (Outer)		
1983	▲E1FZ-1217B	N.L.
1984-87	▲D0AZ-1217A	8.25
(9) Caliper Support Spring		
1983	▲E1FZ-2B486A	2.75

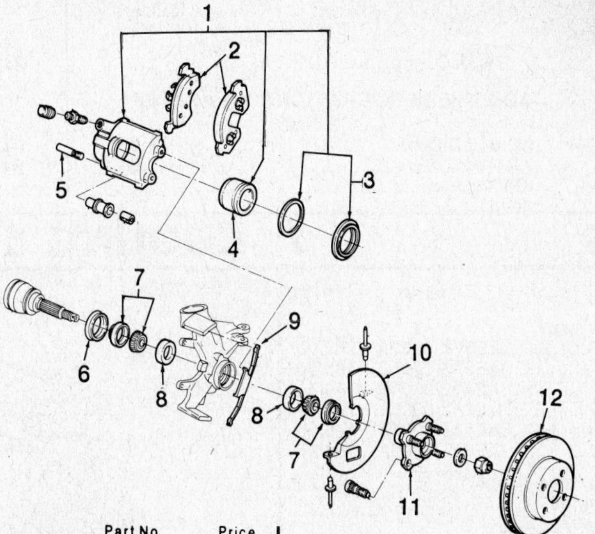

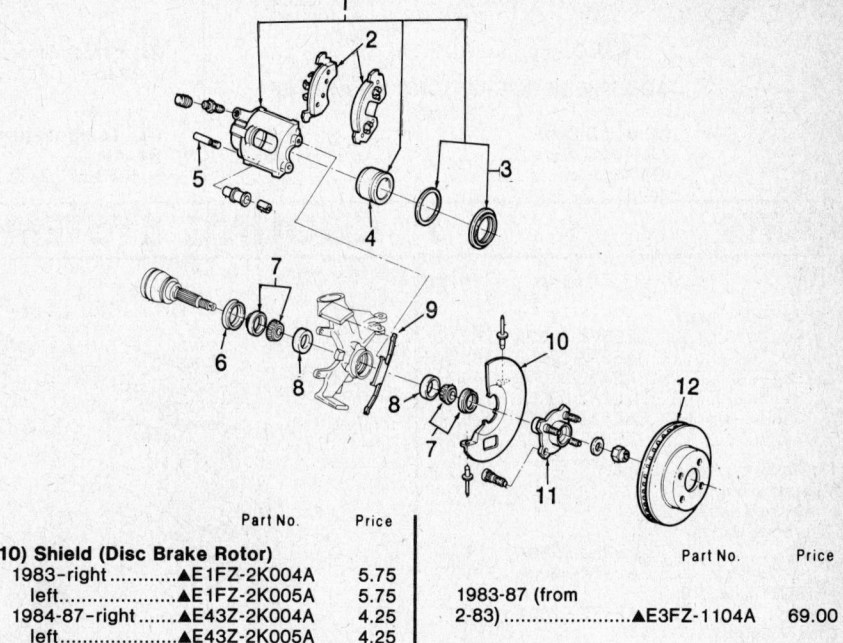

	Part No.	Price
(10) Shield (Disc Brake Rotor)		
1983-right	▲E1FZ-2K004A	5.75
left	▲E1FZ-2K005A	5.75
1984-87-right	▲E43Z-2K004A	4.25
left	▲E43Z-2K005A	4.25
(11) Front Wheel Hub		
1983 (bef. 2-83)	▲E1FZ-1104A	44.75
1983-87 (from 2-83)	▲E3FZ-1104A	69.00
(12) Rotor		
1983-87	▲E43Z-1125A	81.00

LABOR 7 COOLING SYSTEM 7 LABOR

(Factory Time)	Chilton Time
(M) Winterize Cooling System	
Includes: Run engine to check for leaks, tighten all hose connections. Test radiator and pressure cap, drain radiator and engine block. Add anti-freeze and refill system.	
All models	.5
(M) Thermostat, Renew	
1983-87	
wo/EFI (.5)	.7
w/EFI (.8)	1.0
Diesel (.4)	.5
(M) Radiator Assembly, R&R or Renew	
Includes: Drain and refill cooling system.	
1983-87 (.7)	1.1
Renew side tank add	
one (.5)	.7
both (.9)	1.3
w/A.C. add (.1)	.1
(M) Radiator Hoses, Renew	
1983-87	
upper (.3)	.4
lower (.4)	.5
both (.5)	.6
(G) Water Pump, Renew	
1983-87	
Gas (1.5)	2.2
Diesel (1.5)	*2.2
*Note: If necessary to R&R engine, add	5.0
w/A.C. add (.3)	.4
(M) Fan Blade, Renew	
1983-87 (.3)	.4
(M) Drive Belt, Renew	
1983-87	
A.C. (.3)	.5
Alter (.3)	.5
P.S. (.6)	.8
Thermactor (.6)	.9

COOLING SYSTEM TUNE-UP

An Annual Cooling System Tune-Up Suggestion List should include (with some exceptions):
1. A visual check of the cooling system for indications of leaks or excessive oil content
2. Pressure check the cooling system for internal and external leaks with filler cap and neck adapter and tester
3. Check crankcase and automatic transmission oil for water content
4. Test coolant thermostat with radiator thermometer
5. Check temperature gauge for accuracy
6. Drain system and flush till clean
7. Clean foreign matter from radiator fins
8. Test radiator pressure cap with cap tester
9. Check fan blades and pulleys for alignment and damage
10. Internal and external inspection of all hoses for cracks and deterioration
11. Check core plugs (where possible) for seepage
12. Refill system with correct coolant and check for air locks
13. Check condition and tension of drive belts with tension gauge

All models 1.5

(Factory Time)	Chilton Time
Note: If necessary to R&R any component to gain access to belts, add appropriate time.	
(M) Drive Belt, Adjust	
1983-87-one (.2)	.3
each adtnl (.1)	.1

(Factory Time)	Chilton Time
Note: If necessary to R&R any component to gain access to belts, add appropriate time.	
(G) Water Jacket Expansion Plugs, Renew (Side of Block)	
each	*.5
*Add time to gain accessibility.	
(G) Electric Cooling Fan Motor, Renew	
1983-87 (.4)	.6
(G) Engine Cooling Fan Relay, Renew	
1983-87 (.3)	.4
(G) Temperature Gauge (Engine Unit), Renew	
1983-87 (.3)	.4
(G) Temperature Gauge (Dash Unit), Renew	
Includes: R&R instrument panel pad when required.	
1983-87 (.5)	.9
w/Sport cluster (.9)	1.7
(G) Heater Hoses, Renew	
1983-87-each (.4)	.5
(G) Heater Control Assembly, Renew	
1983-87 (.5)	.9
(G) Heater Blower Motor Switch, Renew	
1983-87 (.4)	.9
(G) Heater Blower Motor Resistor, Renew	
1983-87 (.3)	.5
(G) Heater Core, R&R or Renew	
1983-87	
wo/A.C. (.6)	1.2

LABOR 7 COOLING SYSTEM 7 LABOR

(Factory Time)	Chilton Time
w/A.C. (1.0)	3.0
ADD THESE OPERATIONS TO HEATER CORE R&R	
(G) Boil & Repair	1.2
(G) Repair Core	.9
(G) Recore	1.2
(G) Heater Blower Motor, Renew	
1983-87 (.4)	.8
(G) Temperature Control Cable, Renew	
1983-87 (.4)	.6

PARTS 7 COOLING SYSTEM 7 PARTS

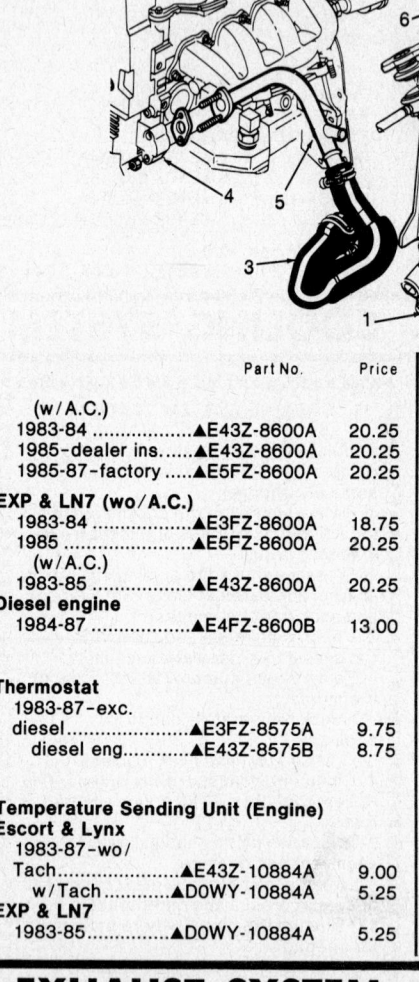

	Part No.	Price
(1) Radiator Assy.		
1983-w/A.C.	▲E3FZ-8005A	202.00
wo/A.C.	▲E3FZ-8005B	168.50
1984-wo/A.C.	▲E43Z-8005B	176.25
w/A.C.	▲E3FZ-8005A	202.00
1985-87-wo/A.C.	▲E43Z-8005B	176.25
w/A.C.	▲E53Z-8005A	188.25
(2) Radiator Hose (Upper)		
Gasoline engine		
1983-85-wo/turbo & w/1.6 eng.	▲E3FZ-8260A	6.50
w/turbo	▲E4FZ-8260A	19.00
1985-87-w/1.9 eng.	▲E6FZ-8260A	9.75
Diesel engine		
1984-85	▲E4FZ-8260B	9.75
(3) Radiator Hose (Lower)		
Gasoline engine		
1983-85-wo/A.C. & w/1.6 eng.	▲E3FZ-8286A	18.25
w/A.C.	▲E1FZ-8286A	10.75
1985-87-w/1.9 eng.	▲E6FZ-8286A	18.50
Diesel engine		
1984-85-front	▲E4FZ-8286A	10.00
rear	▲E4FZ-8286B	7.25
(4) Water Pump Assy.		
1983-85-w/1.6 eng.	▲E3FZ-8501B	82.25
1985-87-w/1.9 eng.	▲E6FZ-8501A	82.25
diesel eng.	▲E43Z-8501B	54.25
(5) Tube & Flange Assy. (Water Pump Inlet)		
1983	▲E2FZ-8A573A	N.L.
1984-87	▲E4FZ-8A573A	12.50
(6) Electric Motor Assy. (Radiator)		
(wo/A.C.)		
1983-85	▲E3FZ-8K621A	72.50
1986-87	▲E6FZ-8K621A	72.50
(w/A.C.)		
1983-85	▲E3FZ-8K621B	72.50
1986-87	▲E6FZ-8K621B	72.50
(7) Fan		
Gasoline engine		
Escort & Lynx (wo/A.C.)		
1983-87	▲E3FZ-8600A	18.75

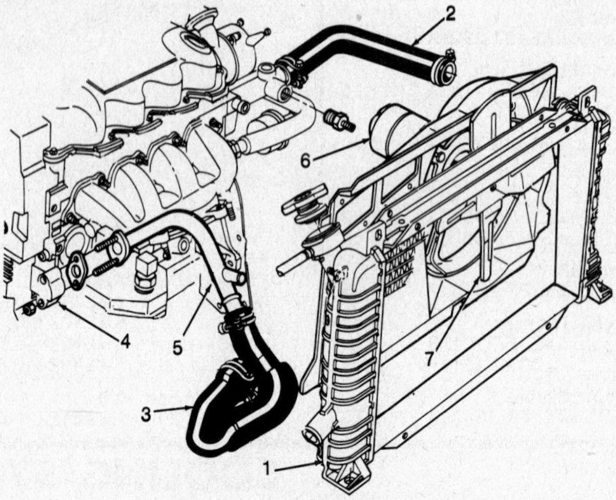

	Part No.	Price
(w/A.C.)		
1983-84	▲E43Z-8600A	20.25
1985-dealer ins.	▲E43Z-8600A	20.25
1985-87-factory	▲E5FZ-8600A	20.25
EXP & LN7 (wo/A.C.)		
1983-84	▲E3FZ-8600A	18.75
1985	▲E5FZ-8600A	20.25
(w/A.C.)		
1983-85	▲E43Z-8600A	20.25
Diesel engine		
1984-87	▲E4FZ-8600B	13.00
Thermostat		
1983-87-exc. diesel	▲E3FZ-8575A	9.75
diesel eng.	▲E43Z-8575B	8.75
Temperature Sending Unit (Engine)		
Escort & Lynx		
1983-87-wo/Tach	▲E43Z-10884A	9.00
w/Tach	▲D0WY-10884A	5.25
EXP & LN7		
1983-85	▲D0WY-10884A	5.25

	Part No.	Price
Heater Core		
Gasoline engine		
1983-85-dealer ins. A.C.	▲E2FZ-18476A	59.50
w/factory A.C.	▲E1FZ-18476B	45.50
1986-87	▲E6FZ-18476A	45.50
Diesel engine		
1984-87-wo/A.C.	▲E4FZ-18476C	65.50
w/A.C.	▲E4FZ-18476B	45.50
Blower Motor		
(wo/Air conditioning)		
1983-84	▲E1FZ-18527A	71.50
1985-87	▲E43Z-18527A	62.25
(w/Air conditioning)		
1983	▲E3FZ-19805A	109.50
1984-87	▲E43Z-19805A	87.50
Blower Motor Resistor		
1983-wo/A.C.	▲E1FZ-18591A	8.50
1984-wo/A.C.	▲E4ZZ-18591A	8.00
1983-w/A.C.	▲E2FZ-19A706A	9.00
1984-87-w/A.C.	▲E43Z-19A706A	8.75
Switch Assy (Heater)		
1983	▲E2FZ-18578A	4.50
1984-87-std.	▲E4FZ-18578A	4.50
Hi capacity	▲E4FZ-18578B	14.00

LABOR 8 EXHAUST SYSTEM 8 LABOR

(Factory Time)	Chilton Time
(G) Muffler, Renew	
1983-87 (.4)	.8
(G) Inlet or Intermediate Pipe, Renew	
1983-84 (.7)	1.1
1985-87 (.5)	.9
(G) Catalytic Converter, Renew	
1983-87 (.6)	1.0
(G) Exhaust Manifold or Gasket, Renew	
1983-87	
1.6-1.9 CVH (1.8)	2.6
1.6 HO-1.6 EFI (1.3)	2.1
1.6 Turbo (1.6)	2.4
1.9 EFI (1.3)	2.1
w/A.C. add (.7)	.7
Diesel (1.0)	1.7
COMBINATIONS	
(G) Muffler, Exhaust and Tail Pipe, Renew	
1983-87 (1.0)	1.5

PARTS 8 EXHAUST SYSTEM 8 PARTS

	Part No.	Price
Muffler		
Note: Order by year and model.		
Catalytic Converter (Escort & Lynx)		
(wo/H.O. engine)		
1983-wo/E.F.I.	▲E3FZ-5E212M	382.25
w/E.F.I.	▲E3FZ-5E212N	401.50
1984-85-w/1.6 eng. & wo/E.F.I.	▲E4FZ-5E212A	421.50
w/E.F.I.	▲E3FZ-5E212N	401.50
1985-87-w/1.9 eng	▲E6FZ-5E212A	377.50
(EXP & LN7)		
1983-w/ATX	▲E3FZ-5E212G	382.25
w/MTX	▲E3FZ-5E212F	220.75
1984	▲E4FZ-5E212A	421.50
1985	▲E5FZ-5E212A	391.50
Muffler Inlet Pipe		
Gasoline engine		
1983-85-wo/turbo	▲E3FZ-5246C	34.00
w/turbo	▲E4FZ-5246B	108.25
1986-87	▲E5FZ-5246A	46.50
Diesel engine		
1984-87	▲E4FZ-5246A	56.50

LABOR 9 FRONT SUSPENSION 9 LABOR

(Factory Time)	Chilton Time
Note: On all front suspension operations alignment charges must be added if performed. Time given does not include alignment.	
(M) Wheel, Renew	
one	.5
(G) Wheels, Rotate (All)	
All models (.5)	.5
(G) Wheels, Balance	
one	.3
each adtnl	.2
(G) Check Alignment of Front End	
All models	.5
Note: Deduct if alignment is performed.	
(G) Front Toe-In, Adjust	
All models (.6)	.8
(G) Rear Toe-In, Check and Adjust	
All models	
one side (.5)	.8
both sides (.6)	.9
(G) Rear Camber, Check and Adjust	
All models	
one side (.5)	.8
both sides (.8)	1.4
(G) Front Wheel Grease Seals, Renew	
Includes: Repack bearings.	
1983-84-one side (1.4)	1.9
both sides (2.5)	3.2
(G) Front Wheel Bearings and Cups, Renew	
Includes: Repack bearings.	
1983-84-one side (1.6)	2.0
both sides (2.9)	3.5
(G) Lower Control Arm Assy., Renew	
Add alignment charges.	
1983-one side (1.0)	1.6
both sides (1.4)	2.5
1984-87-one side (.7)	1.0
both sides (1.1)	1.5
(G) Front Spindle Carrier/Knuckle, Renew	
Add alignment charges.	
1983-84-one side (1.9)	2.5
both sides (3.2)	4.3
1985-87-one (1.5)	2.0
both (2.8)	3.8
Renew hub brg add each	.4
(G) Front Coil Springs, Renew	
Includes: R&R front strut.	
1983-84-one (1.1)	1.8
both (1.9)	3.2
1985-87-one (.7)	1.1
both (1.2)	2.0
(G) Front Stabilizer Bar, Renew	
1983-87 (.6)	1.0
(G) Front Strut Shock Absorber Assy., R&R or Renew	
1983-84-one (.9)	1.7
both (1.6)	3.0
1985-87-left (.8)	1.1
right (.6)	.9
both (1.0)	1.8
(G) Halfshaft Assy., R&R or Renew	
1983-87-one (1.0)	1.2
both (1.7)	2.2
(G) C.V. Joint, Renew or Recondition	
Includes: R&R halfshaft.	
1983-87-one (1.2)	1.5
two (2.0)	2.8
each adtnl	.3
(G) Differential Oil Seal, Renew	
Includes: R&R halfshaft.	
1983-87-one (1.2)	1.6
both (2.2)	3.0

PARTS 9 FRONT SUSPENSION 9 PARTS

	Part No.	Price
(1) Knuckle Assy. (Front Wheel)		
1983 (bef. 2-83) R.H.	▲E1FZ-3K185A	118.50
left	▲E1FZ-3K186A	118.50
1983-87-(from 3-83) right	▲E3FZ-3K185-A	136.75
left	▲E3FZ-3K186-A	136.75
(2) Lower Arm Assy.		
1983-right	▲E1FZ-3078A	88.00
left	▲E1FZ-3079A	88.00
1984-85-(bef. 2-25-85) right	▲E43Z-3078B	88.00
left	▲E43Z-3079B	88.00
1985-87 (from 2-25-85) right	▲E6FZ-3078A	88.00
left	▲E6FZ-3079A	88.00
(3) Spacer		
1983-85	▲E1FZ-5490B	1.75
1986-87	▲E1FZ-5490D	1.75
(4) Stabilizer Bar (Front)		
1983-7/8" thk	▲E3FZ-5482C	106.00
15/16" thk.	▲E3FZ-5482B	N.L.
1" thk.	▲E3FZ-5482A	98.75
1984-87-1" thk	▲E43Z-5482A	106.00
7/8" thk.	▲E43Z-5482C	106.00
15/16" thk.	▲E43Z-5482D	106.00
1⅛" thk.	▲E43Z-5482B	106.00
(5) Insulator (Stabilizer)		
1983-7/8" thk.	▲E43Z-5493B	3.25
15/16" thk.	▲E2FZ-5493B	2.50
1" thk.	▲E2FZ-5493A	3.75
1984-87-1" thk	▲E43Z-5493A	3.25
7/8" tnk.	▲E43Z-5493C	3.25
15/16" thk.	▲E43Z-5493D	2.75
1⅛" thk.	▲E43Z-5493B	3.25
(6) Bracket (Stabilizer)		
1983-right	▲E1FZ-5486A	30.75
left	▲E1FZ-5486D	30.00
1984-85 (bef. 2-25-85)	▲E43Z-5486A	5.25
1985-87 (from 2-25-85)	▲E5FZ-5486F	5.25
(7) Shock Absorber		
Escort, Lynx		
1983 (bef. 2-83) 4 dr.	▲E2FZ-18124A	73.25
2 dr.	▲E2FZ-18124B	73.00
w/TRX susp.	▲E3FZ-18124E	73.25
sta. wag.	▲E2FZ-18124A	73.25
(from 2-83) 4 dr.	▲E3FZ-18124G	73.25
2 dr.	▲E3FZ-18124F	73.25
w/TRX susp.	▲E3FZ-18124K	73.25
sta. wag.	▲E3FZ-18124G	73.25
1984-85-4 dr. & wag.	▲E4FZ-18124C	73.00
2 dr.	▲E3FZ-18124F	73.25
4 dr. & wag.-w/TRX	▲E3FZ-18124F	73.25
2 dr.-w/TRX	▲E4FZ-18124D	73.00
1986-87-2 dr. GT	▲E6FZ-18124D	73.25
exc. GT	▲E6FZ-18124A	73.25
4 dr. & wag.	▲E6FZ-18124B	73.25
EXP, LN7		
1983 (bef. 2-83)	▲E2GZ-18124A	74.00
1983-85-(from 2-83) wo/TRX	▲E3FZ-18124F	73.25
w/TRX	▲E4FZ-18124D	73.00
(8) Spring		
Note: Order by model and description.		
(9) Insulator		
1983-85 (bef. 2-25-85)	▲E1FZ-5415A	8.50
1985-87 (from 2-25-85)	▲E5FZ-5415A	N.L.

PARTS 9 FRONT SUSPENSION 9 PARTS

	Part No.	Price
(10) Spring Seat		
1983-87	▲N.L.	N.L.
(11) Bearing & Seal Assy.		
1983-85 (bef. 2-25-85)	▲E1FZ-3B455B	5.25
1985-87 (from 2-25-85)	▲E43Z-3B355C	12.50
(12) Mounting Plate (Thrust Bearing)		
1983-87	▲E1FZ-3K048A	3.75
(13) Mounting Bracket (Shock)		
1983-85	▲E3FZ-18183A	18.25
1986-87	▲E6FZ-18183A	13.75
(14) Strut Cover Cup (Shock)		
1983-87	▲E3FZ-18A179A	1.00

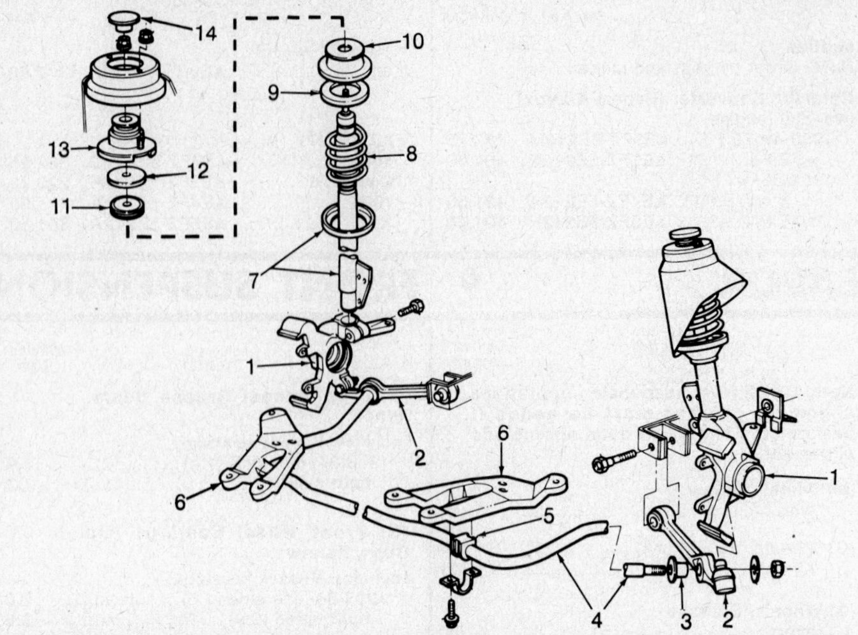

LABOR 11 STEERING GEAR 11 LABOR

(Factory Time) — Chilton Time

(G) Tie Rod End, Renew
Includes: Reset toe-in.
1983-87-one (.8) **1.1**
two (.9) **1.2**

(G) Horn Button or Ring, Renew
1983-87 (.5) .... **.7**

(G) Steering Wheel, Renew
1983-87 (.3) .... **.4**

(G) Upper Mast Jacket Bearing, Renew
1983-87
std colm (.5) .... **.9**
tilt colm (.6) **1.1**

(G) Steering Column Lock Actuator, Renew
1985-87-std colm (1.0) **1.4**
tilt colm (1.3) **2.0**

STANDARD STEERING

(G) Manual Rack and Pinion Assy., R&R or Renew
1983-87 (1.8) **3.5**

(P) Manual Rack and Pinion Assy., R&R and Recondition
Includes: Disassemble, renew necessary parts, reassemble and adjust.
1983-87 (1.9) **3.8**

(G) Manual Rack and Pinion Assy., R&R and Adjust
1983-87 (2.0) **2.7**

(G) Ball Joints, Tie Rod Ends and Bellows, Renew (Both Sides)
Includes: R&R rack and pinion assy. Does not include reset toe-in.
1983-87 (1.6) **2.5**

(G) Manual Rack and Pinion Assy., Adjust (On Car)
All models (.3) .... **.6**

(P) Input Shaft and Valve Assy., Recondition
Includes: R&R rack and pinion assy.
1983-87 (1.7) **2.7**

(G) Input Shaft Seals, Renew (In Chassis)
1983-87 (1.3) **2.0**

POWER STEERING

(G) Trouble Shoot Power Steering
Includes: Test pump and system pressure. Check pounds pull on steering wheel and check for leaks.
All models .... **.5**

(M) Check and Fill Reservoir
All models .... **.2**

(G) Pump Pressure Check & Flow Test
All models **1.0**

(M) Pump Drive Belt, Renew or Adjust
1983-87-renew (.6) .... **.8**
adjust (.5) .... **.6**

Note: If necessary to R&R any component to gain access to belt, add appropriate time.

(G) Power Rack and Pinion Assy., Adjust (On Car)
All models (.3) .... **.6**

(P) Input Shaft and Valve Assy., Recondition
Includes: R&R rack and pinion assy.
1983-87 (2.8) **4.0**
w/Turbo add .... **.7**

(G) Input Shaft Seals, Renew (In Chassis)
1983-87 (1.3) **2.0**

(G) Power Rack and Pinion Assy., R&R or Renew
1983-87 (3.5) **5.0**
w/Turbo add .... **.7**

(P) Short Rack Assembly, Renew
Includes: R&R rack and pinion, transfer or renew all parts not supplied with replacement unit. Does not include pressure check or alignment charges.
1983-87 .... **4.5**
w/Turbo add .... **.7**

(P) Power Rack and Pinion Assy., R&R and Recondition
Includes: Disassemble, renew necessary parts, reassemble and adjust. Does not include pressure check or alignment charges.
1983-87 (3.6) **5.8**
w/Turbo add .... **.7**

(G) Power Rack and Pinion Assy., R&R and Adjust
1983-87 (3.1) **4.0**
w/Turbo add .... **.7**

(G) Ball Joints, Tie Rod Ends and Bellows, Renew (Both Sides)
Includes: R&R rack and pinion assy. Does not include reset toe-in.
1983-87 (2.7) **4.4**
w/Turbo add .... **.7**

(G) Power Steering Oil Pump, R&R or Renew
Includes: Bleed system.
1983-87
wo/EFI (1.4) **2.0**
w/EFI (.8) **1.2**
Diesel (1.5) **2.1**
Turbo (1.7) **2.5**
Renew shaft seal add .... **.2**

(G) Power Steering Oil Pump, R&R and Recondition
Includes: Bleed system.
1983-87
wo/EFI (1.8) **2.5**
w/EFI (1.2) **1.7**
Diesel (1.9) **2.7**

LABOR 11 STEERING GEAR 11 LABOR

	(Factory Time)	Chilton Time
Turbo (2.1)		3.0
(G) Power Steering Hoses, Renew		
Includes: R&R air pump and air cleaner. Bleed system.		
1983-87		
Pressure-to pump (.8)		1.2
to gear (.8)		1.2
Return-from pump (.7)		1.1
from gear (.7)		1.1
Cooling (.6)		1.0

PARTS 11 STEERING GEAR - (STANDARD) 11 PARTS

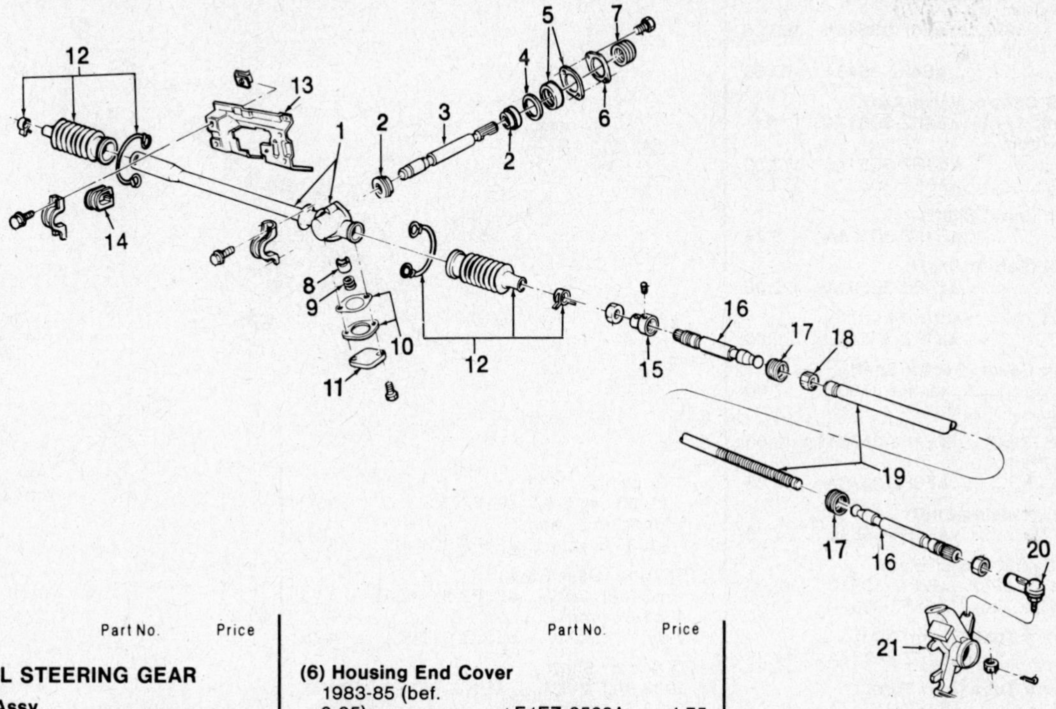

	Part No.	Price
MANUAL STEERING GEAR		
Steering Gear Assy.		
EXP & LN7		
1983 (bef. 7-83)	▲E5FZ-3504B	237.75
1983-84 (from 7-83)	▲E3FZ-3504D	N.L.
1985	▲E5FZ-3504B	237.75
Escort & Lynx		
1983-84 (bef. 4-84)	▲E3FZ-3504A	N.L.
1984 (from 4-84)	▲E3FZ-3504D	N.L.
1985 (bef. 6-85)	▲E5FZ-3504B	237.75
1985-87 (from 6/85)	▲E5FZ-3504C	255.50
(1) Steering Gear Housing		
1983-85 (bef. 6-85)	▲E1FZ-3548C	57.00
1985-87 (from 6-85)	▲E5FZ-3548A	57.00
(2) Cup (Worm Bearing)		
1983-87	▲E1FZ-3552C	14.25
(3) Shaft Assy. (Upper)		
1983-85-wo/Tilt whl.	▲E43Z-3524B	43.75
1984-87-w/Tilt whl.	▲E5FZ-3524A	175.00
(4) Shim Kit		
1983-before 2-1-83	▲E1FZ-3763A	3.50
1983-87-from 2-1-83	▲E3FZ-3763A	3.50
(5) Gasket		
1983-87	▲E1FZ-3581B	4.50
(6) Housing End Cover		
1983-85 (bef. 6-85)	▲E1FZ-3568A	4.75
1985-87 (from 6-85)	▲E5FZ-3568A	4.75
(7) Oil Seal (Sector Shaft Housing)		
1983-before 2-1-83	▲E1FZ-3591-B	3.50
1983-85-from 2-1-83	▲E5FZ-3591A	4.00
1985-87 (from 6-85)	▲E5FZ-3591A	4.00
(8) Support Yoke (Sector Shaft)		
1983-87	▲E1FZ-3F515A	2.25
(9) Spring		
Note: Spring is included in support yoke.		
(10) Gasket & Shim Kit		
1983-87	▲E1FZ-3F518A	6.50
(11) Housing Cover (Sector Shaft)		
1983-85 (bef. 6-85)	▲E1FZ-3580B	8.50
1985-87 (from 6-85)	▲E5FZ-3580A	8.50
(12) Dust Seal Kit (Ball Stud)		
1983-85-(bef. 6-85) right	▲E2FZ-3332B	10.25
left	▲E2FZ-3332A	10.00
1985-87 (from 6-85)	▲E5FZ-3332A	10.25
(13) Mounting Bracket Assy.		
1983-87	▲E3FZ-3K571A	14.75
(14) Insulator (Support End)		
1983-87	▲E1FZ-3C716A	3.00
(15) Socket (Ball Stud)		
1983-87	▲E2FZ-3A754A	22.25
(16) Connecting Rod Assy.		
1983-85 (bef. 6-85)	▲E2FZ-3280A	19.50
1985-87 (from 6-85)	▲E5FZ-3280A	8.50
(17) Seat (Ball Spring)		
1983-84 (bef. 3-84)	▲E1FZ-3F513A	3.25
1984-87 (from 3-84)	▲E4FZ-3F513A	3.25
(18) Bushing		
1983-87	▲E1FZ-3576B	8.50
(19) Sector Shaft		
1983-85 (bef. 6-85)	▲E1FZ-3575A	54.00
1985-87 (from 6-85)	▲E5FZ-3575A	54.00
(20) Tie Rod End		
1983-87	▲E3FZ-3A130A	38.75
(21) Knuckle Assy.		
1983 (bef. 3-83) R.H.	▲E1FZ-3K185A	118.50
left	▲E1FZ-3K186A	118.50
1983-87-(from 3-83) right	▲E3FZ-3K185A	136.75
left	▲E3FZ-3K186A	136.75

PARTS 11 POWER STEERING GEAR 11 PARTS

	Part No.	Price
Steering Gear Assy.		
1983-87	▲E5FZ-3504A	521.00
(1) Cover (Input Shaft)		
1983 (bef. 2-83)	▲E1FZ-3568B	N.L.
1983-87 (from 2-83)	▲E3FZ-3568A	4.75
(2) Cup (Worm Bearing)		
1983-87	▲D8BZ-3552A	13.25
(3) Housing Assy.		
1983 (bef. 2-83)	▲E1FZ-3548D	267.00
1983-84 (from 2-83 to 11-83)	▲E3FZ-3548A	100.25
1984-87 (from 11-83)	▲E4FZ-3548A	107.50
(4) Shaft & Control Valve Assy.		
1983 (bef. 11-82)	▲E3FZ-3D517A	N.L.
1983-84 (from 11-82)	▲E3GZ-3D517B	173.00
1985-87	▲E5FZ-3D517A	173.00
(5) Bearing (Input Shaft)		
1983-87	▲E1FZ-3D525A	8.25
(6) Seal Kit (Sector Shaft)		
1983-87	▲E3FZ-3E501A	22.00
(7) Support Yoke (Sector Shaft)		
1983-87	▲E1FZ-3F515B	6.00
(8) Housing Cover (Sector Shaft)		
1983-87	▲E1FZ-3580A	7.00
(9) Bushing		
1983 (bef. 2-83)	▲E1FZ-3576A	12.00
1983-87 (from 2-83)	▲E3FZ-3576A	10.25
(10) Cover (Housing End)		
1983-87	▲E1FZ-3568C	4.75
(11) Dust Seal Kit (Ball Stud)		
1983 (bef. 2-83)	▲E1FZ-3332C	10.00
1983-85	▲E3FZ-3332A	10.00
(12) Pressure Tube (Right Turn)		
1983-87	▲E1FZ-3A717A	14.25
(13) Pressure Tube (Left Turn)		
1983-87	▲E1FZ-3A714A	12.75
(14) Mounting Bracket		
1983-87	▲E3FZ-3K571A	14.75
(15) Insulator		
1983-87 Housing end	▲E1FZ-3C716B	7.25

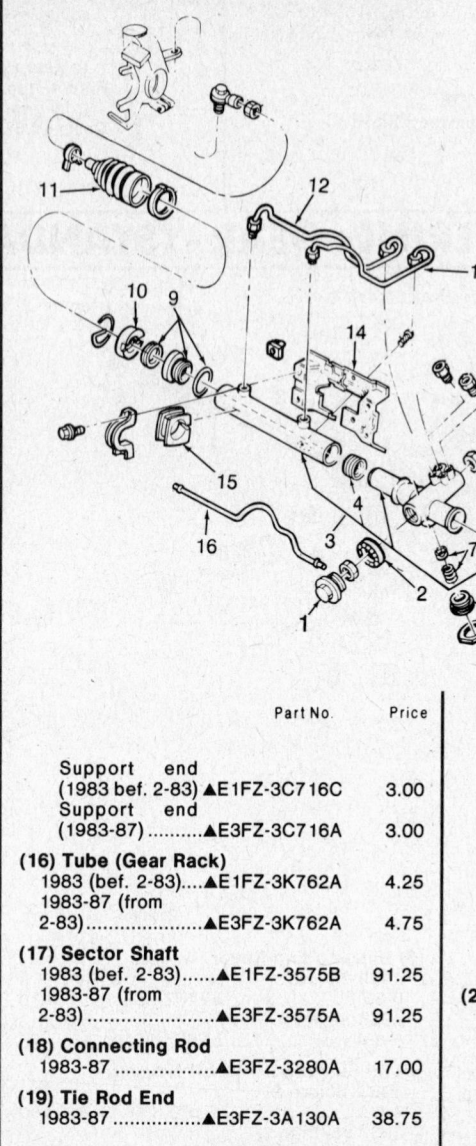

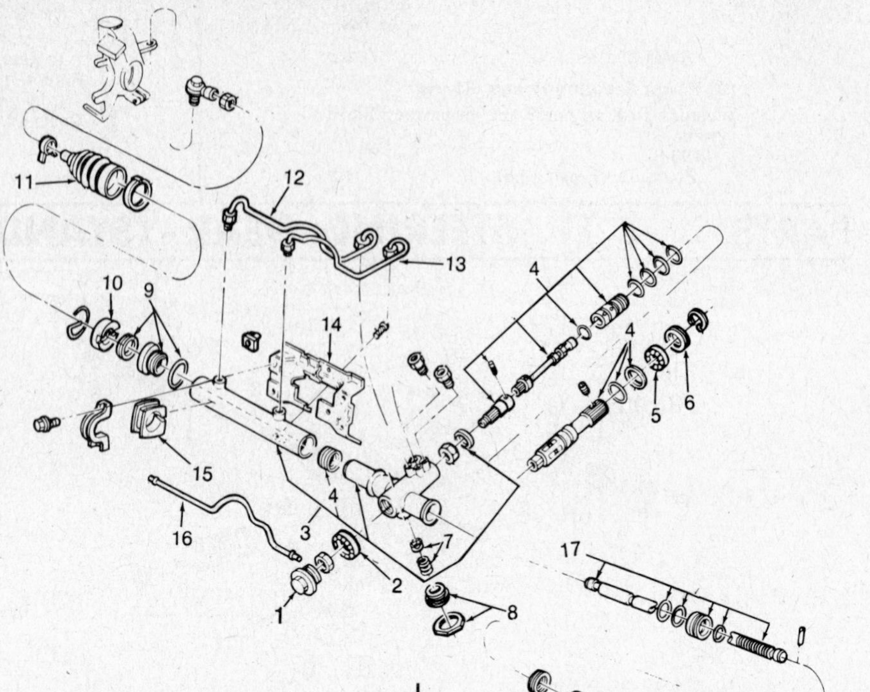

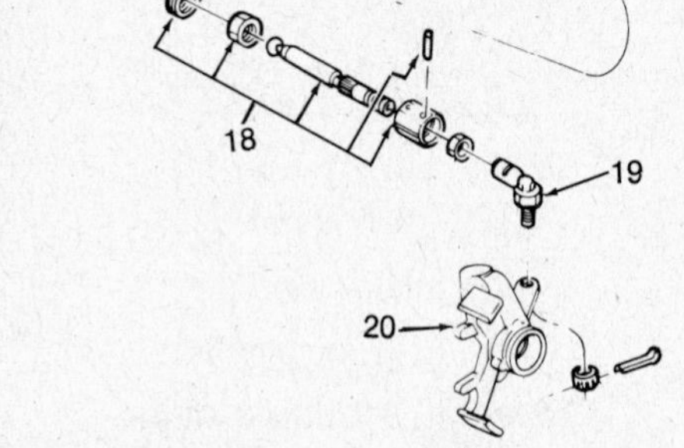

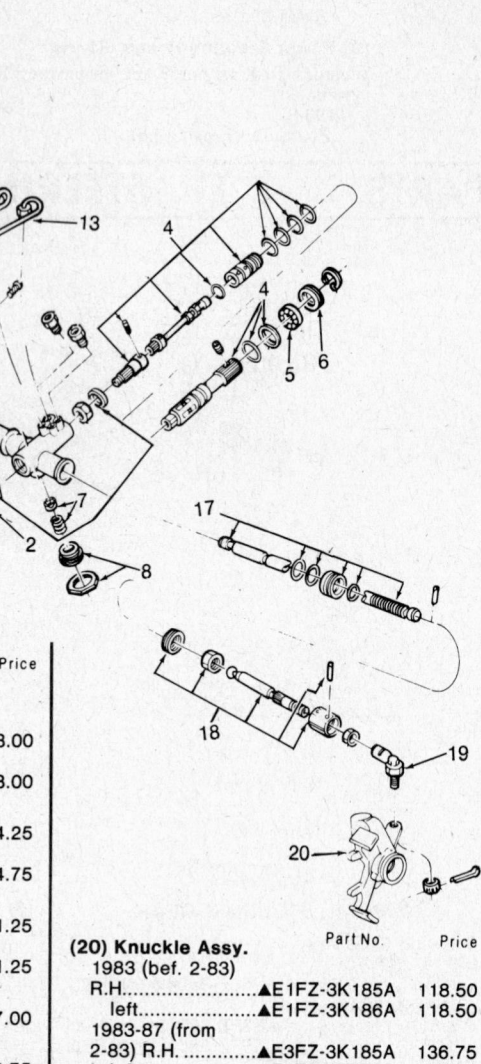

	Part No.	Price
Support end (1983 bef. 2-83)	▲E1FZ-3C716C	3.00
Support end (1983-87)	▲E3FZ-3C716A	3.00
(16) Tube (Gear Rack)		
1983 (bef. 2-83)	▲E1FZ-3K762A	4.25
1983-87 (from 2-83)	▲E3FZ-3K762A	4.75
(17) Sector Shaft		
1983 (bef. 2-83)	▲E1FZ-3575B	91.25
1983-87 (from 2-83)	▲E3FZ-3575A	91.25
(18) Connecting Rod		
1983-87	▲E3FZ-3280A	17.00
(19) Tie Rod End		
1983-87	▲E3FZ-3A130A	38.75

	Part No.	Price
(20) Knuckle Assy.		
1983 (bef. 2-83) R.H.	▲E1FZ-3K185A	118.50
left	▲E1FZ-3K186A	118.50
1983-87 (from 2-83) R.H.	▲E3FZ-3K185A	136.75
left	▲E3FZ-3K186A	136.75

PARTS 11 POWER STEERING PUMP 11 PARTS

	Part No.	Price
Power Steering Pump Hoses		
Order by year and model.		
Power Steering Pump		
Gasoline engine		
1983-87	▲E5FZ-3A674A	194.50
Diesel engine		
1984 (bef. 6-84)	▲E4FZ-3A674A	194.50
1984-85 (from 6-84)	▲E5FZ-3A674B	194.50
(1) Tube Connector		
1983-87	▲D8BZ-3R608A	3.25
(2) Washer		
1983-87	▲87004-S100	.50
(3) Outlet Fitting		
1983-84	▲E1FZ-3D654B	20.25
1985-87	▲E5FZ-3D654A	20.25
(4) Seal & Gasket Kit		
1983-87	▲E1AZ-3D684A	3.00

	Part No.	Price
(5) Valve Assy.		
1983-87-exc. diesel	▲E1FZ-3A561B	9.50
diesel eng.	▲E43Z-3A561A	16.00
(6) Valve Spring (Flow Control)		
1983-87	▲D8AZ-3D586A	1.50
(7) Cap Assy. (Reservoir)		
1983-84-w/E.F.I. & Turbo	▲E3FZ-3A006A	5.00
1985-wo/E.F.I. & Turbo	▲E5FZ-3A006A	5.00
1986-87	▲E6DZ-3A006A	5.00
(8) Reservoir Assy.		
1983-85	▲E1FZ-3A697B	15.50
1986-87	▲E6FZ-3A697A	15.50
(9) Retaining Ring		
1983-87	▲387573-S	1.50

	Part No.	Price
(10) Housing Assy.		
1983-87	▲E1AZ-3A643A	42.25
(11) Pressure Plate (Front)		
1983-84	▲D8AZ-3D590A	N.L.
1984-87	▲E5FZ-3D590A	13.75
(12) Rotor Assy.		
1983-84	▲E3FZ-3B607A	52.50
1985-87	▲E5FZ-3D607A	56.25
(13) Rotor Shaft		
1983-87	▲D8AZ-3B559A	18.00
(14) Pressure Plate (Rear)		
1983	▲D8AZ-3D590B	13.75
1984-87	▲E5FZ-3D590B	13.75
(15) Pin		
1983-87	▲387579-S	1.00
(16) Seal & Gasket Kit		
1983-87	▲E1AZ-3B584A	8.75

PARTS 11 POWER STEERING PUMP 11 PARTS

	Part No.	Price
(17) Spring (Pressure Plate)		
1983-87	▲D8AZ-3D596A	2.50
(18) Plate & Bushing		
1983-87	▲E1AZ-3D643A	42.25
(19) Oil Seal (Rotor)		
1983-87	▲D9AZ-3B592A	9.25

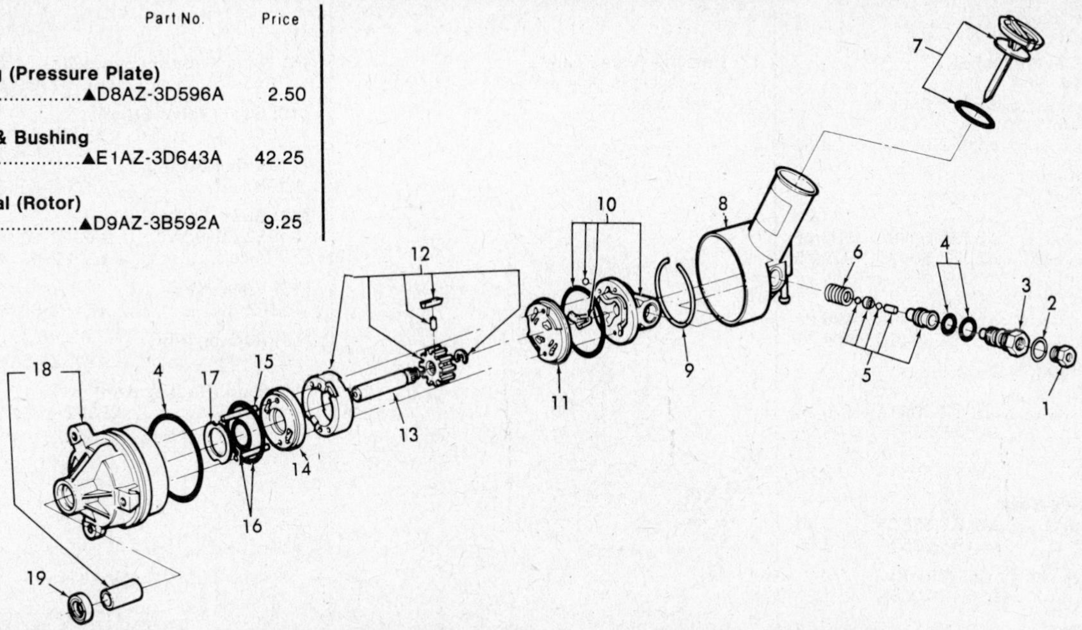

LABOR 12 CYLINDER HEAD & VALVE SYSTEM 12 LABOR

(Factory Time) Chilton Time

GASOLINE ENGINE

(G) Compression Test
1983-87 (.3)........ .6
w/A.C. add 2

(G) Cylinder Head Gasket, Renew
Includes: Check cylinder head and block flatness. Clean carbon and make all necessary adjustments.
1983-87 (3.2)........ 5.0
w/A.C. add (.6)........ .6
w/P.S. add (.3)........ .3
w/EFI add (.3)........ .3

(G) Cylinder Head, Renew
Includes: Transfer all components, clean carbon. Reface valves, check valve spring tension, assembled height and valve head runout.
1983-87 (4.4)........ 6.5
w/A.C. add (.6)........ .6
w/P.S. add (.3)........ .3
w/EFI add (.3)........ .3

(P) Clean Carbon and Grind Valves
Includes: R&R cylinder head, check valve spring tension, valve seat and head runout, stem to guide clearance and spring assembled height. Minor tune up.
1983-87 (5.8)........ 8.0
w/A.C. add (.6)........ .6
w/P.S. add (.3)........ .3
w/EFI add (.3)........ .3

(G) Valve Tappets, Renew
Includes: Adjust carburetor and ignition timing.
1983-87
one (.8)........ 1.1

COMBINATIONS

Add To Valve Job
See Machine Shop Operations

(Factory Time) Chilton Time

(G) DRAIN, EVACUATE & RECHARGE AIR CONDITIONING SYSTEM
All models (.7)........ 1.2

(G) CARBURETOR, RECONDITION
All models (1.4)........ 1.9

(G) HYDRAULIC VALVE LIFTERS, DISASSEMBLE AND CLEAN
Each........ .2

(P) CYLINDER HEAD, RECONDITION (HEAD REMOVED)
All models (2.6)........ 3.5

(P) VALVE GUIDES, REAM OVERSIZE
Each (.1)........ .2

(Factory Time) Chilton Time

all (1.3)........ 2.1
w/Cruise control add (.1)........ .1

(G) Rocker Arm Cover Gasket, Renew
1983-87 (.6)........ .8
w/Cruise control add (.1)........ .1

(G) Rocker Arms, Renew (All)
1983-87 (1.1)........ 1.7
w/Cruise control add (.1)........ .1

(G) Valve Springs and/or Valve Stem Oil Seals, Renew (Head On Car)
1983-87-one (.8)........ 1.4

(Factory Time) Chilton Time

DIESEL ENGINE

(G) Compression Test
1984-87........ 1.2

(G) Cylinder Head Gasket, Renew
Includes: Clean carbon and make all necessary adjustments.
1984-87 (4.3)........ 6.0

(G) Cylinder Head, Renew
Includes: Transfer all components, clean carbon. Make all necessary adjustments.
1984-87 (5.2)........ 7.3

(P) Clean Carbon and Grind Valves
Includes: R&R cylinder head. Grind valves and seats. Make all necessary adjustments.
1984-87 (6.8)........ 9.5

(G) Rocker Arm Cover Gasket, Renew
1984-87 (.4)........ .6

(G) Valve Springs and/or Valve Stem Oil Seals, Renew
1984-87-one (3.6)........ 5.0
each adtnl (.2)........ .3
all (4.0)........ 7.0

(G) Valve Tappets, Renew
1984-87-one (3.5)........ 4.9
all (3.7)........ 5.2

each adtnl (.2)........ .2
all (1.8)........ 2.7
w/Cruise control add (.1)........ .1

PARTS 12 CYLINDER HEAD & VALVE SYSTEM 12 PARTS

98 (1.6) GASOLINE ENGINE

	Part No.	Price
Valve Grind Gasket Set		
1983-84-before 1-20-84	▲E2GZ-6079A	79.50
1984 (from 1-20-84)	▲E4FZ-6079B	79.50
1985	▲E5FZ-6079A	79.50

PARTS 12 CYLINDER HEAD & VALVE SYSTEM 12 PARTS

	Part No.	Price
Rocker Arm Cover Gasket		
1983-84 (bef. 1-20-84)	▲E3FZ-6584A	4.50
1984-85 (from 1-20-84)	▲E4FZ-6584A	4.50
(1) Cylinder Head		
(wo/H.O. engine)		
1983-85-wo/valves	▲E2FZ-6049A	596.25
w/valves	▲E3FZ-6049B	909.75
(w/H.O. engine)		
1983-85-wo/valves	▲E3FZ-6049A	496.25
w/valves	▲E3FZ-6049C	909.75
(2) Cylinder Head Gasket		
(wo/turbo)		
1983-84	▲E2GZ-6051A	29.25
1985	▲E5FZ-6051C	29.25
(w/Turbo)		
1984-85	▲E4FZ-6051A	29.75
(3) Insert (Valve Seat)		
1983-85-Intake	▲E1FZ-6057A	3.50
Exhaust	▲E1FZ-6057C	3.50
(4) Dowel (Cyl. Hd. to Cyl. Block)		
1983-85	▲E2FZ-6A008A	1.25
(5) Intake Valve		
1983-85	▲E4FZ-6507A	8.75
(6) Exhaust Valve		
1983-85	▲E4FZ-6505A	19.25

(7) Bushing (Valve Guide)
Note: Bushing is only available in 6049 cylinder head assy.

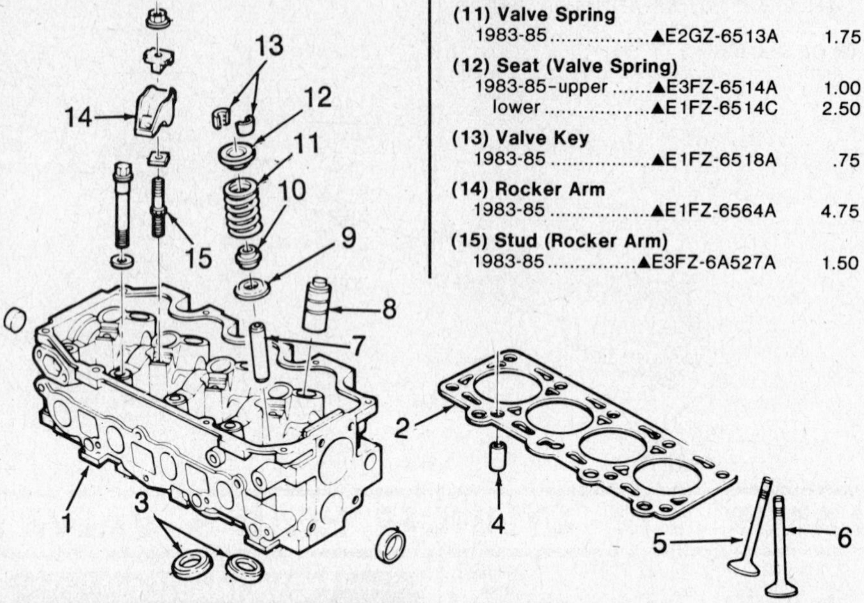

	Part No.	Price
(8) Valve Tappet (Hydraulic)		
1983-85	▲E2FZ-6500B	9.00
(10) Seal (Valve Stem)		
1983-85	▲E4FZ-6571A	1.25
(11) Valve Spring		
1983-85	▲E2GZ-6513A	1.75
(12) Seat (Valve Spring)		
1983-85-upper	▲E3FZ-6514A	1.00
lower	▲E1FZ-6514C	2.50
(13) Valve Key		
1983-85	▲E1FZ-6518A	.75
(14) Rocker Arm		
1983-85	▲E1FZ-6564A	4.75
(15) Stud (Rocker Arm)		
1983-85	▲E3FZ-6A527A	1.50

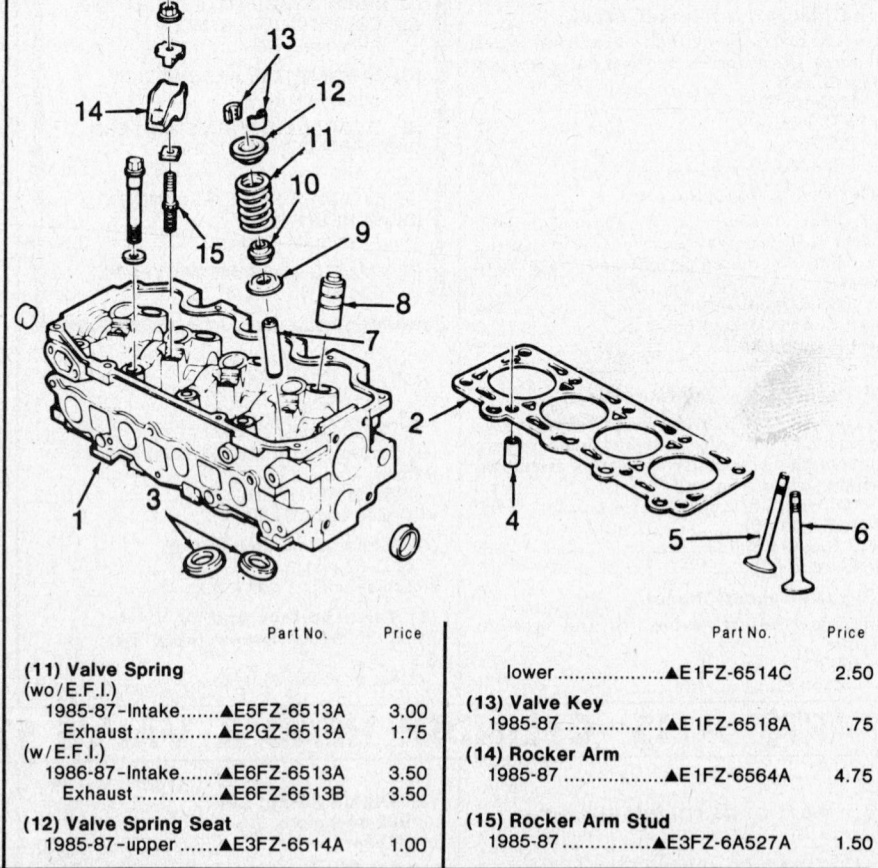

PARTS 12 CYLINDER HEAD & VALVE SYSTEM 12 PARTS

116 (1.9) GASOLINE ENGINE

	Part No.	Price
Valve Grind Gasket Set		
1985-87-exc. E.F.I.	▲E5FZ-6079B	N.L.
1986-87-w/E.F.I.	▲E6FZ-6079A	84.50
Rocker Arm Cover Gasket		
1985-exc. E.F.I.	▲E4FZ-6584A	4.50
1985-87-w/E.F.I.	▲E5FZ-6584B	N.L.
(1) Cylinder Head		
(wo/E.F.I.)		
1985-87-wo/valves	▲E5FZ-6049A	496.25
w/valves	▲E5FZ-6049C	909.75
(w/E.F.I.)		
1986-87-wo/valves	▲E5FZ-6049B	626.25
(2) Cylinder Head Gasket		
1985-87-wo/E.F.I.	▲E5FZ-6051D	N.L.
w/E.F.I.	▲E6FZ-6051A	N.L.
(3) Insert (Valve Seat)		
1985-87-Intake	▲E1FZ-6057A	N.L.
Exhaust	▲E1FZ-6057C	3.50
(4) Dowel (Cyl. Head to Block)		
1985-87	▲E2FZ-6A008A	1.25
(5) Intake Valve		
1985-87	▲E5FZ-6507A	8.75
(6) Exhaust Valve		
1985-87	▲E4FZ-6505A	19.25

(7) Valve Guide Bushing
Note: Bushing is only available in 6049 cylinder head assy.

	Part No.	Price
(8) Valve Tappet		
1985-87	▲E5FZ-6500A	7.75
(10) Valve Stem Seal		
1985-87	▲E4FZ-6571A	1.25

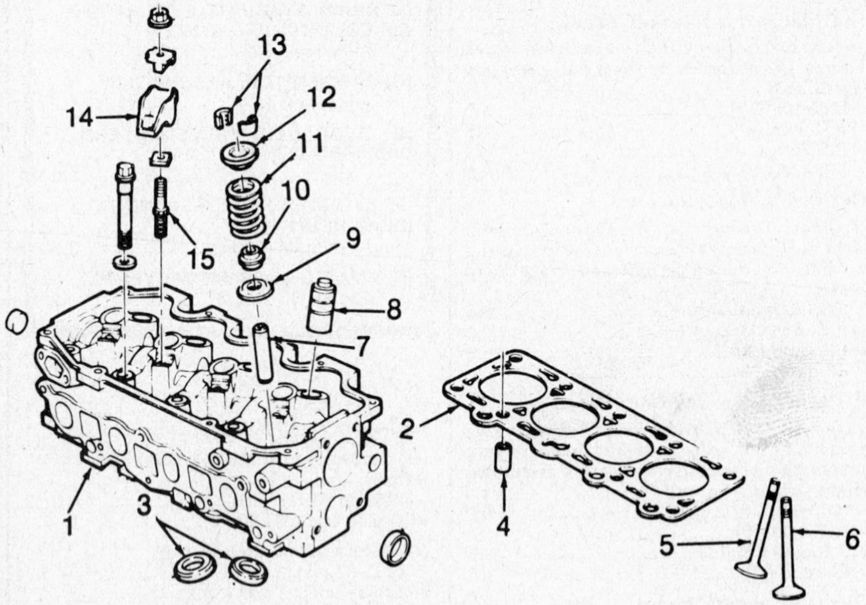

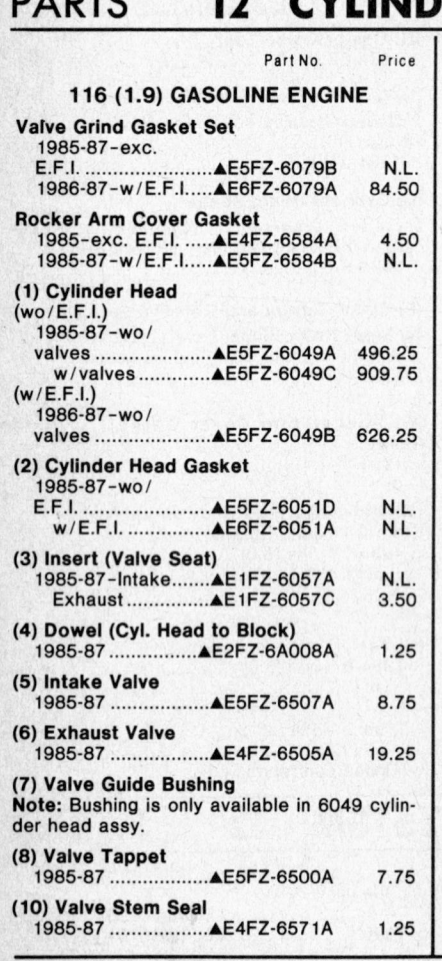

	Part No.	Price
(11) Valve Spring		
(wo/E.F.I.)		
1985-87-Intake	▲E5FZ-6513A	3.00
Exhaust	▲E2GZ-6513A	1.75
(w/E.F.I.)		
1986-87-Intake	▲E6FZ-6513A	3.50
Exhaust	▲E6FZ-6513B	3.50
(12) Valve Spring Seat		
1985-87-upper	▲E3FZ-6514A	1.00
lower	▲E1FZ-6514C	2.50
(13) Valve Key		
1985-87	▲E1FZ-6518A	.75
(14) Rocker Arm		
1985-87	▲E1FZ-6564A	4.75
(15) Rocker Arm Stud		
1985-87	▲E3FZ-6A527A	1.50

LABOR 12 CYLINDER HEAD & VALVE SYSTEM 12 LABOR

	Part No.	Price
122 (2.0) DIESEL ENGINE		
Overhaul Gasket Set (Partial)		
1984-85	▲E43Z-6008B	88.25
(1) Cylinder Head		
1984-85-(bef. 4-1-85)	▲E43Z-6049D	425.25
1985-87 (from 4-1-85)	▲E5BZ-6049C	N.L.
(2) Cylinder Head Gasket		
1984-87	▲E53Z-6051B	29.25
(3) Valve Cover Gasket		
1984-87	▲E43Z-6584B	4.50
(4) Valve Tappet Assy.		
1984-87	▲E43Z-6500A	5.50
(5) Spring Retainer (Valve)		
1984-87	▲E43Z-6514B	1.25
(6) Valve Springs (Int. & Exh.)		
1984-87	▲E43Z-6513B	1.75
(7) Spring Seat (Valve)		
1984-87	▲E43Z-6A536A	.75
(8) Seal (Valve Stem)		
1984-87	▲E43Z-6571D	2.75
(9) Valve Guide Assy.		
1984-87-intake	▲E43Z-6510A	2.25
exhaust	▲E43Z-6510B	2.25
(10) Intake Valve		
1984-87	▲E43Z-6507D	7.25
(11) Exhaust Valve		
1984	▲E43Z-6505D	12.00
1985-87	▲E43Z-6505E	11.75
(12) Insert Assy. (Comb. Chamber)		
1984	▲E43Z-6057A	18.00
1985-87	▲E43Z-6057B	19.00
(13) Glow Plug		
1984-87	▲E43Z-12A342A	24.75

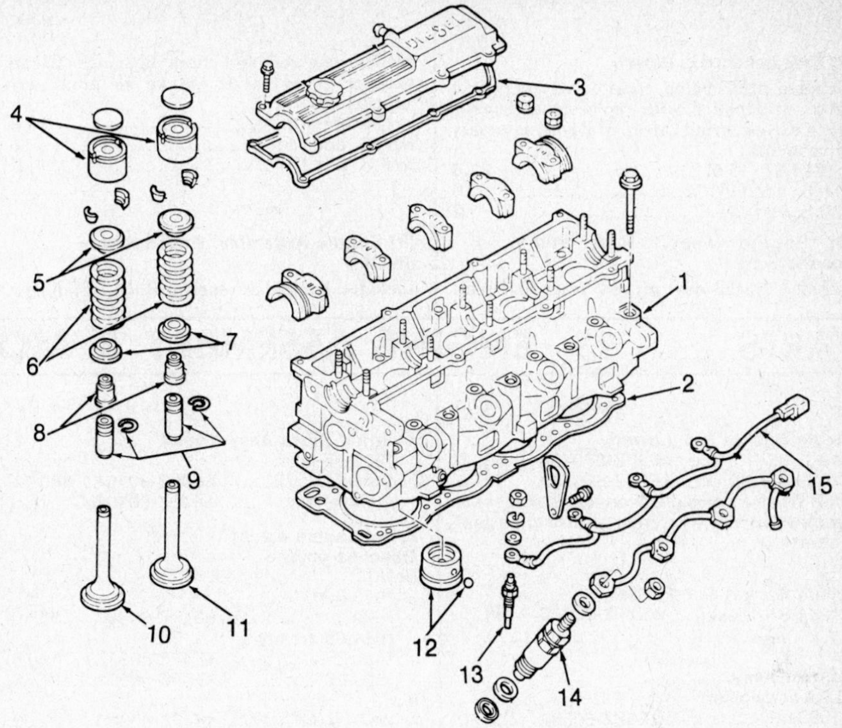

	Part No.	Price
(14) Nozzle Holder Assy.		
1984-87	▲E43Z-9E527A	64.00

	Part No.	Price
(15) Wire Assy. (Glow Plug)		
1984-87	▲E43Z-9A451A	5.00

LABOR 13 ENGINE ASSEMBLY & MOUNTS 13 LABOR

(Factory Time) — Chilton Time

GASOLINE ENGINE

(G) Engine Assembly, Remove & Install

Does not include transfer of any parts or equipment. Does not include R&R trans/axle assy.

	Chilton Time
1983-84	
w/MTX (4.3)	6.4
w/ATX (4.1)	5.9
1985-87	
w/MTX (4.9)	7.0
w/ATX (4.7)	6.8
w/A.C. add (.5)	.5
w/P.S. add (.3)	.3
w/EFI or Turbo add (.2)	.2

(P) Cylinder Assembly, Renew (w/All Internal Parts Less Head and Oil Pan)

Includes: R&R engine, transfer all component parts not supplied with replacement engine, clean carbon, grind valves. Minor tune up.

	Chilton Time
1983-84	
w/MTX (12.4)	17.9
w/ATX (12.2)	17.4
1985-87	
w/MTX (11.1)	18.5
w/ATX (10.9)	18.3
w/A.C. add (.5)	.5
w/P.S. add (.3)	.3
w/EFI or Turbo add (.2)	.2

(P) Cylinder Block, Renew

Includes: R&R engine, transfer all component parts, renew rings and bearings, clean carbon, grind valves. Minor tune up.

	Chilton Time
1983-84	
w/MTX (15.8)	22.1
w/ATX (15.6)	21.6
1985-87	
w/MTX (14.5)	22.7
w/ATX (14.3)	22.5
w/A.C. add (.5)	.5
w/P.S. add (.3)	.3
w/EFI or Turbo add (.2)	.2

(P) Engine Assy., R&R and Recondition

Includes: Rebore block, install new pistons, rings, rod and main bearings. Clean carbon, grind valves. Tune engine.

	Chilton Time
1983-84	
w/MTX (23.9)	30.9
w/ATX (23.7)	30.4
1985-87	
w/MTX (22.6)	30.9
w/ATX (22.4)	30.4
w/A.C. add (.5)	.5
w/P.S. add (.3)	.3
w/EFI or Turbo add (.2)	.2

(P) Engine Assembly, Recondition (In Car)

Includes: Expand or renew pistons, install new rings, pins, rod and main bearings. Clean carbon, grind valves. Tune engine.

	Chilton Time
1983-87 (16.1)	22.5

(G) Engine Mounts, Renew

	Chilton Time
FRONT	
1983-87-one (.6)	.9
both	1.4
REAR	
1983-87 (.5)	.8

DIESEL ENGINE

(G) Engine Assembly, Remove & Install

Does not include transfer of any parts or equipment.

	Chilton Time
1984-87 (4.1)	5.9
w/A.C. add (.6)	.6
w/P.S. add (.2)	.2

(P) Cylinder Assembly, Renew (w/All Internal Parts Less Cyl. Head and Oil Pan)

Includes: R&R engine, transfer all component parts not supplied with replacement engine. Clean carbon, grind valves. Make all necessary adjustments.

	Chilton Time
1984-87 (10.2)	18.0
w/A.C. add (.6)	.6
w/P.S. add (.2)	.2

LABOR 13 ENGINE ASSEMBLY & MOUNTS 13 LABOR

	(Factory Time)	Chilton Time
(P) Cylinder Block, Renew		
Includes: R&R engine, transfer all component parts not supplied with replacement engine. Clean carbon, grind valves. Make all necessary adjustments.		
1984-87	(15.6)	22.6
w/A.C. add	(.6)	.6
w/P.S. add	(.2)	.2
(P) Engine Assy., R&R and Recondition		
Includes: Install new pistons, rings and pins. Install new rod and main bearings. Clean carbon, grind valves. Make all necessary adjustments.		
1984-87	(16.4)	23.8
w/A.C. add	(.6)	.6
w/P.S. add	(.2)	.2
(P) Engine Assembly, Recondition (In Car)		
Includes: Expand or renew pistons, install new rings, pins, rod and main bearings. Clean carbon, grind valves. Make all necessary adjustments.		
1984-87	(14.6)	21.1
(G) Engine Mounts, Renew (Front)		
1984-87	(.6)	.9

PARTS 13 ENGINE ASSEMBLY & MOUNTS 13 PARTS

	Part No.	Price
Engine Gasket Set (Lower)		
1983-85-1.6 eng.	▲E1FZ-6E078A	50.75
1985-87-1.9 eng.	▲E5FZ-6E078A	50.75
Note: When a complete overhaul gasket set is required you must also order a valve grind gasket set.		
Engine Gasket Set, Partial		
1984-87 (Diesel)	▲E43Z-6008B	88.25
Cylinder Assy.		
(Gasoline engine)		
1983	▲E3FZ-6009A	1403.50
1984-85--1.6 eng.-wo/Turbo	▲E4FZ-6009B	1508.75
w/Turbo	▲E4FZ-6009A	1544.00
1985-87-1.9 eng.	▲E5FZ-6009A	1748.00
(Diesel engine)		
1984-85 (bef. 4-1-85)	▲E43Z-6009B	2125.75
1985-87 (from 4-1-85)	▲E53Z-6009B	2125.75
Cylinder Block Assy. (New)		
1983-85-exc. diesel	▲E4FZ-6010A	680.25
diesel eng.	▲E43Z-6010B	N.L.
Front Engine Mount		
Gasoline engine		
(R.H.)		
1983 (bef. 9-1-83)	▲E1FZ-6038A	23.50
1984-85-from 9-1-83	▲E4FZ-6038B	37.75
1986-87	▲E6FZ-6038A	37.75
(L.H.)		
1983-w/MTX	▲E1FZ-6038B	23.50
w/ATX	▲E1FZ-6038C	28.50
1984-85-1.6 eng.		
w/4 sp.	▲E4FZ-6038D	23.50
w/5 sp.	▲E4FZ-6038C	24.50
w/ATX	▲E4FZ-6038E	31.00
1985-87-1.9 eng		
w/4 sp.	▲E6FZ-6038B	23.50
w/5 sp.	▲E6FZ-6038C	23.50
w/ATX	▲E6FZ-6038D	30.00
Diesel engine		
(R.H.)		
1984-87	▲E4FZ-6038A	37.75
(L.H.)		
1984-w/4 sp.	▲E43Z-6038C	23.50
1984-87-w/5 spd.	▲E43Z-6038E	23.50
1984-w/ATX	▲E43Z-6038D	23.00
Rear Engine Mount		
Gasoline engine		
1983-L.H.	▲E1FZ-6068A	26.00
1984-85-1.6 eng.		
w/4 sp.	▲E4FZ-6068D	24.00
w/5 sp.	▲E4FZ-6068C	23.00
w/ATX	▲E4FZ-6068B	22.00
1985-87-1.9 eng.		
w/ATX	▲E6FZ-6068C	29.25
w/4 sp.	▲E6FZ-6068A	31.25
w/5 sp.	▲E6FZ-6068B	29.00
Diesel engine		
1984-87-L.H.	▲E4FZ-6068A	28.25

LABOR 14 PISTONS, RINGS & BEARINGS 14 LABOR

	(Factory Time)	Chilton Time
GASOLINE ENGINE		
(P) Rings, Renew (See Engine Combinations)		
Includes: Remove cylinder top ridge, deglaze cylinder walls, replace rod bearings, clean carbon. Minor tune up.		
1983-84		
one	(5.7)	7.8
all	(7.0)	9.9
1985-87		
one	(6.0)	8.4
all	(7.4)	10.3
w/A.C. add	(.6)	.6
(P) Piston or Connecting Rod, Renew		
Includes: Remove cylinder top ridge, deglaze cylinder walls, replace rod bearings, clean carbon. Minor tune up.		
1983-84		
one	(6.0)	8.1
all	(8.2)	11.1
1985-87		
one	(6.3)	8.7
all	(8.6)	11.4
w/A.C. add	(.6)	.6
(P) Connecting Rod Bearings, Renew		
1983-84	(2.5)	3.3

COMBINATIONS

Add To Engine Work

See Machine Shop Operations

	(Factory Time)	Chilton Time
(G) DRAIN, EVACUATE & RECHARGE AIR CONDITIONING SYSTEM		
All models	(.7)	1.2
(G) CARBURETOR, RECONDITION		
All models	(1.4)	1.9
(G) HYDRAULIC VALVE LIFTERS, DISASSEMBLE AND CLEAN		
Each		.2
(G) CYLINDER HEAD, R&R (ENGINE REMOVED)		
Four		
Gas		3.0
Diesel		4.0
(G) CONNECTING ROD, RENEW (ENGINE DISASSEMBLED)		
Four		
Each		.4
(P) CYLINDER HEAD, RECONDITION (HEAD REMOVED)		
Gas models	(2.6)	3.5
(P) VALVE GUIDES, REAM OVERSIZE		
Each	(.1)	.2
(G) REMOVE CYLINDER TOP RIDGE		
Each	(.1)	.1
(G) DEGLAZE CYLINDER WALLS		
Each	(.1)	.1
(G) MAIN BEARINGS, RENEW (PAN REMOVED)		
All models	(1.9)	2.5
(G) ROD BEARINGS, RENEW (PAN REMOVED)		
All models	(.9)	1.2
(G) PLASTIGAUGE BEARINGS		
Each		.1
(M) OIL FILTER ELEMENT, RENEW		
All models	(.6)	.6

LABOR 14 PISTONS, RINGS & BEARINGS 14 LABOR

(Factory Time) Chilton Time

1985-87
wo/EFI (3.1)................................ 4.3
w/EFI (3.8)................................ 5.3

DIESEL ENGINE

(P) Rings, Renew (See Engine Combinations)
Includes: Remove cylinder top ridge, deglaze cylinder walls. Renew rod bearings and clean carbon from cylinder head. Make all necessary adjustments.
1984-87
one cyl (5.8)................................ 8.5
all cyls (7.4)................................ 10.8

(P) Pistons or Connecting Rods, Renew
Includes: Remove cylinder top ridge, deglaze cylinder walls. Renew rod bearings and clean carbon from cylinder head. Make all necessary adjustments.
1984-87
one cyl (6.1)................................ 8.8
all cyls (8.6)................................ 12.0

(P) Connecting Rod Bearings, Renew
1984-87 (2.2)................................ 3.2

PARTS 14 PISTONS, RINGS & BEARINGS 14 PARTS

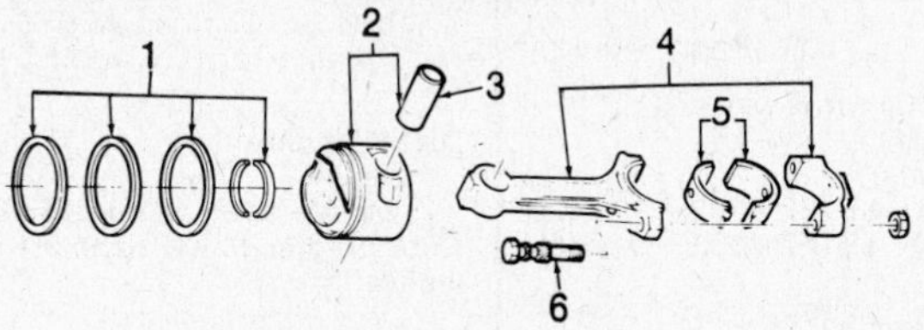

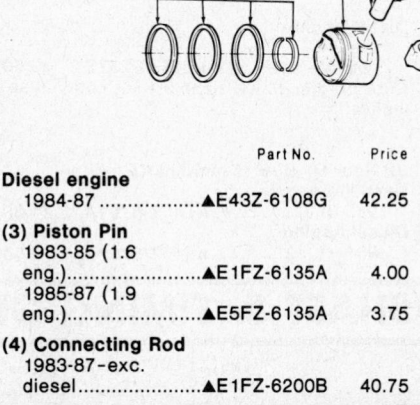

	Part No.	Price
(1) Piston Ring Set (Partial)		
Gasoline engine		
1983-85-1.6 eng. wo/Turbo	▲E1FZ-6148A	36.00
1984-85-w/Turbo	▲E4FZ-6148A	41.75
1985-87-w/1.9 eng.	▲E5FZ-6148A	43.25
Diesel engine		
1984-87	▲E43Z-6148A	106.75
(2) Piston Assy.		
Gasoline engine (wo/turbo)		
1983	▲E3FZ-6108A	26.25
1984-85	▲E3FZ-6108B	26.25
1985-87	▲E5FZ-6108A	24.50
(w/turbo)		
1984	▲E4FZ-6108A	25.50
1985	▲E4FZ-6108B	25.50
Diesel engine		
1984-87	▲E43Z-6108G	42.25
(3) Piston Pin		
1983-85 (1.6 eng.)	▲E1FZ-6135A	4.00
1985-87 (1.9 eng.)	▲E5FZ-6135A	3.75
(4) Connecting Rod		
1983-87-exc. diesel	▲E1FZ-6200B	40.75
1984-diesel eng.	▲E43Z-6200B	58.25
1985-87	▲E43Z-6200C	62.50
(5) Connecting Rod Bearings		
1983-87-exc. diesel	▲E1FZ-6211A	3.75
diesel eng.	▲E43Z-6211A	29.00
(6) Connecting Rod Bolt		
1983-87	▲E1FZ-6214A	1.75

LABOR 15 CRANKSHAFT & DAMPER 15 LABOR

(Factory Time) Chilton Time

GASOLINE ENGINE

(P) Crankshaft and Main Bearings, Renew
Includes: R&R engine, check all bearing clearances.
1983-84
w/MTX (8.1)................................ 10.9
w/ATX (7.9)................................ 10.7
1985-87
w/MTX (8.5)................................ 11.9
w/ATX (8.3)................................ 11.7
w/A.C. add (.5)................................ .5
w/P.S. add (.3)................................ .3
w/EFI or Turbo add (.2)................................ .2

(P) Main Bearings, Renew
Includes: Check all bearing clearances.
1983-84 (3.5)................................ 4.7
1985-87
wo/EFI (4.0)................................ 5.6
w/EFI (4.7)................................ 6.5

(P) Main and Rod Bearings, Renew
Includes: Check all bearing clearances.
1983-87 (4.4)................................ 5.9

(G) Crankshaft Front Oil Seal, Renew
1983-87 (1.5)................................ 2.4
w/A.C. add (.4)................................ .4

(G) Crankshaft Pulley or Damper, Renew
1983-87 (.7)................................ 1.0

(G) Rear Main Bearing Oil Seal, Renew
(Full Circle Type)
1983-87
w/MTX (2.4)................................ 3.8
w/ATX (3.3)................................ 5.3

DIESEL ENGINE

(P) Crankshaft and Main Bearings, Renew
Includes: R&R engine, check all bearing clearances.
1984-87 (8.0)................................ 12.0
w/A.C. add (.6)................................ .6
w/P.S. add (.2)................................ .2

(P) Main Bearings, Renew
Includes: Check all bearing clearances.
1984-87 (3.1)................................ 4.5

(P) Main and Rod Bearings, Renew
Includes: Check all bearing clearances.
1984-87 (4.1)................................ 5.7

(P) Crankshaft Front Seal, Renew
Includes: R&R engine assy.
1984 (4.4)................................ 6.4
1985-87 (2.4)................................ 6.4
w/A.C. add (.6)................................ .6

(G) Crankshaft Rear Main Seal, Renew
(Full Circle Type)
Includes: R&R trans and clutch assy's.
1984-87 (4.3)................................ 6.7
w/A.C. add (.6)................................ .6

(G) Crankshaft Damper or Pulley, Renew
Includes: R&R engine assy.
1984 (4.0)................................ 5.8
1985-87 (1.9)................................ 5.8
w/A.C. add (.6)................................ .6

LABOR 15 CRANKSHAFT & DAMPER 15 LABOR

	Part No.	Price
(1) Pulley Assy.		
Gasoline engine		
1983-87	▲E2FZ-6A312A	45.50
Diesel engine		
1984-87	▲E43Z-6A312B	34.25
(2) Timing Belt		
Gasoline engine		
1983-87	▲E3FZ-6268A	20.75
Diesel engine		
1984-87-front	▲E43Z-6268B	25.75
rear	▲E43Z-6268C	13.00
(3) Guide (Timing Belt)		
1983-87	▲E1FZ-6K297B	1.50

PARTS 15 CRANKSHAFT & DAMPER 15 PARTS

	Part No.	Price
(4) Sprocket (Crankshaft)		
1983-87-exc.		
diesel	▲E2FZ-6306A	17.25
diesel eng.	▲E43Z-6306B	9.75
(5) Front Oil Seal (Crankshaft)		
1983-87-exc.		
diesel	▲E1FZ-6700A	9.50
diesel eng.	▲E43Z-6700D	2.00
(6) Crankshaft		
Gasoline engine		
1983-1.6 eng.		
(bef. 5-14-83)	▲E1FZ-6303B	336.00
(from 5-14-83)	▲E4FZ-6303A	336.00
1984-85-1.6 eng.		
Diesel engine		
1984-87	▲E43Z-6303C	669.75
(7) Main Bearings (Upper & Lower)		
1.6 Gasoline engine		
1983-85 (exc. center)		
Red (upper)	▲E1FZ-6333A	3.25
Blue (upper)	▲E1FZ-6333B	3.25
1983-85 (center)		
Red (upper)	▲E2FZ-6337A	6.25
Blue (upper)	▲E2FZ-6337B	6.25
1983-85 (lower bearing)		
Red	▲E1FZ-6333A	3.25
Blue	▲E1FZ-6333B	3.25
1985-87-w/1.9 eng.		
red	▲E5FZ-6333A	3.25

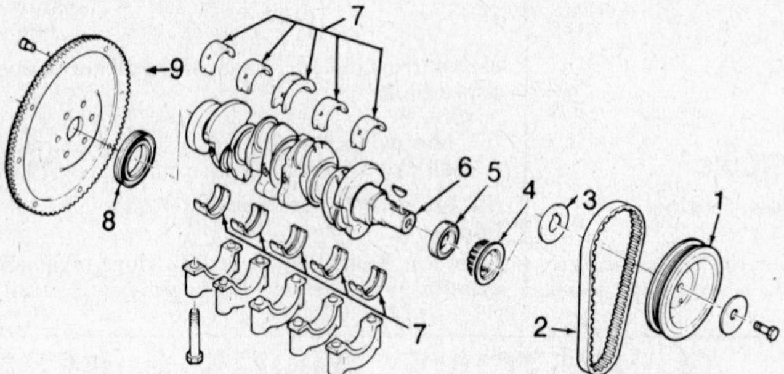

	Part No.	Price
blue	▲E5FZ-6333B	3.25
center	▲E5FZ-6337A	6.25
Diesel engine		
1984-87-		
complete set	▲E43Z-6333G	39.50

Note: Red and blue sizes are for optional selective fit.

	Part No.	Price
(8) Rear Oil Seal (Crankshaft)		
Gasoline engine		
1983-87	▲E4FZ-6701A	11.50
Diesel engine		
1984-87	▲E43Z-6701A	6.50

	Part No.	Price
(9) Flywheel Assy		
Gasoline engine		
(w/A.T.)		
1983-87	▲E53Z-6375B	79.00
(w/M.T.)		
1983-w/1.6 eng.	▲E1FZ-6375A	90.75
1984-85	▲E4FZ-6375B	147.00
1985-87-w/1.9		
eng., wo/E.F.I.	▲E5FZ-6375B	147.00
w/E.F.I.	▲E6FZ-6375A	N.L.
Diesel engine		
1984-87-w/MTX	▲E43Z-6375B	161.25
Flywheel Ring Gear		
1983-87	▲D4FZ-6384A	34.25
diesel eng.	▲E43Z-6384A	50.00

LABOR 16 CAMSHAFT & TIMING GEARS 16 LABOR

(Factory Time)	Chilton Time
GASOLINE ENGINE	
(G) Timing Belt Cover, R&R or Renew	
1983-87	1.2
w/A.C. add (.6)	.6
(G) Timing Belt and/or Tensioner, Renew	
Includes: R&R front cover and reset valve timing.	
1983-87 (1.5)	2.5
w/A.C. add (.6)	.6
(G) Camshaft Seal, Renew	
1983-87	
1.6 CVH eng (1.2)	1.7
1.9 eng (1.2)	1.7
(G) Camshaft, Renew	
1983-87 (2.6)	3.5
w/A.C. add (.4)	.4
w/P.S. add (.2)	.2
w/EFI or Turbo add (.3)	.3
DIESEL ENGINE	
(G) Front Timing Belt, Renew	
Includes: R&R engine assy.	
1984 (4.2)	6.0
1985-87 (2.2)	6.0
w/A.C. add (.6)	.6
(G) Rear Timing Belt or Tensioner, Renew	
1984-87 (1.0)	1.5
(G) Front Timing Belt Tensioner, Renew	
Includes: R&R upper cover.	
1984-87 (2.0)	3.0
(G) Camshaft Seal, Renew	
1984-87 (3.5)	4.9
(P) Camshaft, Renew	
1984-87 (3.5)	5.0
Note: If necessary to R&R engine add	3.6

PARTS 16 CAMSHAFT & TIMING GEARS 16 PARTS

	Part No.	Price
(1) Camshaft		
(wo/H.O. & E.F.I. engine)		
1983-85	▲E3FZ-6250A	141.25
(w/H.O. & E.F.I. engine)		
1983-85	▲E2GZ-6250-A	149.00
1985-87-wo/		
E.F.I.	▲E5FZ-6250A	140.00
w/E.F.I.	▲E6FZ-6250A	149.00
(2) Thrust Plate		
1983-84	▲E1FZ-6269A	4.75
1985-87	▲E5FZ-6269A	4.75
(3) Seal Assy. (Front)		
1983-87	▲E1FZ-6K292A	5.75
(4) Sprocket (Camshaft)		
1983-85 (1.6		
eng.)	▲E1FZ-6256D	14.50
1985-87 (1.9		
eng.)	▲E5FZ-6256A	14.50
(5) Washer		
1983-87	▲E1FZ-6278A	1.00
(6) Timing Belt		
1983-87	▲E3FZ-6268A	20.75

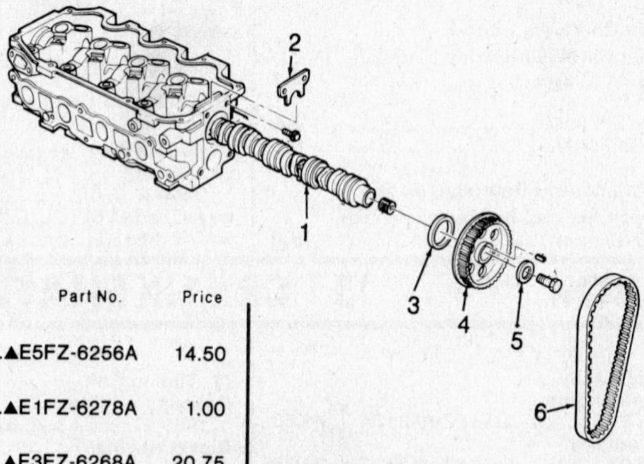

PARTS 16 CAMSHAFT & TIMING GEARS 16

	Part No.	Price
122 (2.0) DIESEL ENGINE		
(1) Front Cover Assy. (Outer)		
1984-R.H.	▲E43Z-6019B	15.25
L.H.	▲E43Z-6019C	11.00
1985-87	▲E43Z-6019E	27.75
(2) Seal (Timing Belt Cover) (Inner)		
1984-87-R.H.	▲E43Z-6020B	1.75
L.H.	▲E43Z-6020D	1.00
(Outer)		
1984-87-R.H.	▲E43Z-6020C	2.25
L.H.	▲E43Z-6020E	1.75
(3) Camshaft Sprocket		
1984-87-front	▲E43Z-6256B	22.75
rear	▲E43Z-6256C	20.25
(4) Tensioner (Timing Belt)		
1984-87-front	▲E43Z-6K254B	29.00
rear	▲E43Z-6K254C	20.00
(5) Crankshaft Sprocket		
1984-87	▲E43Z-6306B	9.75
(6) Timing Belt		
1984-87-front	▲E43Z-6268B	25.75
rear	▲E43Z-6268C	13.00
(7) Spring (Tensioner)		
1984-87-front	▲E43Z-6L273A	1.25
rear	▲E43Z-6L273B	1.50
(8) Front Cover (Inner)		
1984-87	▲E43Z-6019D	15.50
(9) Oil Seal (Crankshaft)		
1984-87-front	▲E43Z-6700D	2.00
rear	▲E43Z-6701A	6.50
(10) Camshaft		
1984-87	▲E43Z-6250B	151.25
(11) Bearing Caps (Camshaft)		
1984-87-front	▲E43Z-6A258A	6.25
center	▲E43Z-6L285A	3.00
rear	▲E43Z-6A284A	6.25
(12) Rear Cover Assy. (Inner)		
1984-87	▲E43Z-6E004A	3.75
(13) Drive Pulley (Injection Pump)		
1984-87	▲E43Z-9M564A	27.25
(14) Rear Cover Assy. (Outer)		
1984-87	▲E43Z-6E006A	10.00

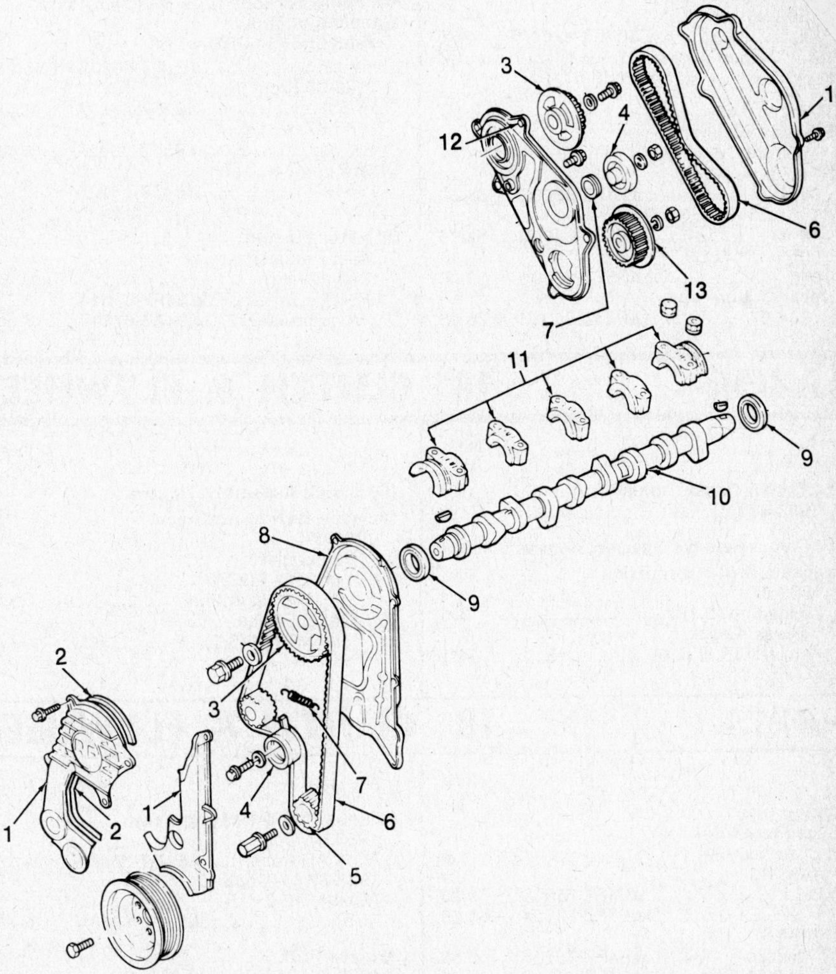

LABOR 17 ENGINE OILING SYSTEM 17 LABOR

	(Factory Time)	Chilton Time
GASOLINE ENGINE		
(G) Oil Pan or Gasket, Renew		
1983-84	(1.6)	2.1
1985-87		
wo/EFI	(2.1)	2.9
w/EFI	(2.8)	3.9
w/P.S. add	(.1)	.1
(P) Pressure Test Engine Bearings (Pan Off)		
All models		1.0
(G) Oil Pump, Renew		
Includes: R&R timing belt, starter and oil pan. Reset valve timing.		
1983-84	(3.0)	4.8
w/A.C. add		.4
1985-87		
wo/EFI	(3.5)	5.3
w/EFI	(4.2)	6.0
Recond pump add	(.3)	.3
w/P.S. add	(.1)	.1
(G) Oil Pressure Gauge (Engine), Renew		
1983-87	(.3)	.4
(G) Oil Pressure Gauge (Dash), Renew		
1983-87	(.4)	.7
(M) Oil Filter Element, Renew		
1983-84	(.6)	.6
1985-87	(.3)	.4
DIESEL ENGINE		
(G) Oil Pan or Gasket, Renew		
1984-87	(1.2)	1.7
(P) Pressure Test Engine Bearings (Pan Off)		
All models		1.0
(G) Oil Pump, Renew		
Includes: R&R engine assy.		
1984	(5.0)	7.2
1985-87	(3.7)	7.2
w/A.C. add	(.6)	.6
(M) Oil Filter Element, Renew		
1984-87		
oil filter	(.3)	.3
by-pass filter	(.4)	.4

PARTS 17 ENGINE OILING SYSTEM 17 PARTS

	Part No.	Price
Oil Pan Gasket Set		
1983-85-w/1.6 eng.	▲E1FZ-6781A	13.75

Note: Oil pan gasket for 1.9 engine is a one piece design. Part no. E5FZ-6710A.

	Part No.	Price
Oil Pump Assy.		
Gasoline engine		
1983 (bef. 5-14-83) w/1.6 eng.	▲E1FZ-6600B	57.50
1984-85 (from 5-14-83)	▲E3FZ-6600A	53.75
1985-87-w/1.9 eng.	▲E5FZ-6600A	59.25
Diesel engine		
1984-87	▲E43Z-6600B	76.25
Oil Pump Screen, Tube & Cover Assy.		
Gasoline engine		
1983 (bef. 5-14-83) w/1.6 eng.	▲E1FZ-6622A	15.25
1983-85 (from 5-14-83)	▲E3FZ-6622A	15.25
1985-87-w/1.9 eng.	▲E5FZ-6622A	15.25
Diesel engine		
1984-87	▲E43Z-6622B	7.00
Oil Filter Element		
Gasoline engine		
1983-87-wo/turbo.	▲E4FZ-6731A	8.25
w/turbo.	▲D4ZZ-6731B	8.50
Diesel engine		
1984-87	▲E43Z-6731A	12.50
Oil Pressure Gauge (Engine Unit)		
Gasoline engine		
(w/gauge)		
1983-84	▲E2GZ-9278A	14.50
1985-87	▲E4GZ-9278A	15.50
(w/light)		
1983-87	▲D4AZ-9278A	3.50
Diesel engine		
1984-85 (bef. 6-85)	▲D27Z-9278A	6.75
1985-87 (from 6-85)	▲E53Z-9278A	6.50

LABOR 18 CLUTCH & FLYWHEEL 18 LABOR

(Factory Time)	Chilton Time
(G) Clutch Cable, Renew	
1983-87 (.5)	.8
(G) Clutch Release Bearing, Renew	
Includes: R&R transmission.	
1983-87	
Gas Eng (2.1)	3.5
Diesel Engine	
w/MTX III (2.9)	4.1
(G) Clutch Assembly, Renew	
Includes: R&R transmission.	
1983-87	
Gas Engine	
w/MTX I (2.2)	3.8
w/MTX III (2.2)	3.8
Diesel Engine	
w/MTX III (3.0)	4.4
(G) Flywheel, Renew	
Includes: R&R transmission.	
1983-87	
Gas Engine	
w/MTX I (2.5)	4.1
w/MTX III (2.5)	4.1
Diesel Engine	
w/MTX III (4.1)	5.5
Renew ring gear add (.2)	.4

PARTS 18 CLUTCH & FLYWHEEL 18 PARTS

	Part No.	Price
Clutch Disc		
Gasoline engine		
(1.6 wo/turbo)		
1983-85-wo/E.F.I.	▲E4FZ-7550D	55.25
w/E.F.I.	▲E3FZ-7550A	55.25
1984-87		
before 4-1-84	▲E4FZ-7550B	55.50
from 4-1-84	▲E4FZ-7550D	55.25
(1.6 w/turbo)		
1984-85	▲E4FZ-7550C	55.25
1.9 engine		
1985-87	▲E5FZ-7550A	44.00
Diesel engine		
1984-87	▲E4FZ-7550A	55.25
Pressure Plate		
Gasoline engine		
1983-85-1.6 eng.		
wo/turbo	▲E1FZ-7563B	56.25
w/turbo	▲E4FZ-7563B	53.50
Diesel engine		
1984-87	▲E4FZ-7563A	53.75
Release Hub & Bearing Assy.		
1983 (w/Code AC & AG trans.)	▲E1FZ-7548A	29.75
1983-87 (w/Code AE, AH, AL & RUB)	▲E3FZ-7548A	26.75
Release Fork		
1983 (w/Code AC & AG)	▲E1FZ-7N515A	21.50
1983-85 (w/Code AE, AH & AL)	▲E3FZ-7N515A	21.50
1986-87 (w/Code AB)	▲E3FZ-7N515A	21.50
(w/Code AD & AE)	▲E6FZ-7N515A	21.50
Release Cable Assy.		
1983-84-4 sp.	▲E3FZ-7K553B	26.75
5 sp.	▲E3FZ-7K553A	26.75
1985-w/1.6 eng.	▲E5FZ-7K553A	24.25
1985-87-w/1.9 eng.	▲E5FZ-7K553B	26.00
Flywheel Ring Gear		
1983-87-exc. diesel	▲D4FZ-6384A	34.25
diesel eng.	▲E43Z-6384A	50.00
Flywheel Assy.		
Gasoline engine		
(A.T.)		
1983-(bef. 12-6-82) wo/H.O.	▲E1FZ-6375C	79.25
w/H.O.	▲E2FZ-6375A	85.00
1983-87 (from 12-6-82)	▲E53Z-6375B	79.00
(M.T.)		
1983	▲E1FZ-6375A	147.00
1984-85-1.6 eng.	▲E4FZ-6375B	147.00
1985-87-1.9 eng. (exc. E.F.I.)	▲E5FZ-6375B	147.00
1986-87-w/E.F.I.	▲E6FZ-6375A	N.L.
Diesel engine		
1984-87	▲E43Z-6375B	161.25

LABOR 21 SHIFT LINKAGE 21 LABOR

(Factory Time)	Chilton Time
STANDARD	
(G) Gear Selector Lever, Renew	
1983-87 (.7)	1.0
AUTOMATIC	
(G) Linkage, Adjust	
1983-87	
manual (.3)	.6
throttle valve control (.3)	.6
(G) Gear Selector Lever, Renew	
1983-87 (.5)	.9
w/Console add (.1)	.1

LABOR — 26 REAR AXLE 26 — LABOR

(Factory Time)	Chilton Time
(G) Rear Wheel Bearing Grease Seal, Renew	
1983-87-one (.5)	.7
both (.7)	1.1
(G) Rear Wheel Bearings, Adjust	
1983-87-both (.3)	.5
(G) Rear Wheel Bearings and Cups, Clean and Repack or Renew	
1983-87-one side (.6)	.9
both sides (.9)	1.5
(G) Lower Control Arm Assy., Renew	
1983-87-one (.6)	.9
both (1.0)	1.6
(G) Rear Springs, Renew	
1983-87-one (.4)	.7
both (.6)	1.0
(G) Rear Shock Absorbers, Renew	
1983-87	
sedan-one (.6)	.9
both (.9)	1.4
sta wagon-one (.6)	.9
both (.9)	1.4
(G) Rear Tie Rod, Renew	
1983-87-one (.3)	.4
both (.5)	.7
(G) Rear Wheel Spindle, Renew	
1983-87-one (.9)	1.3
both (1.7)	2.5
Renew brgs and cups add	
one side (.3)	.3
both sides (.4)	.4

PARTS — 26 REAR AXLE 26 — PARTS

	Part No.	Price
(1) Shock Mounting Kit (Rear)		
1983-87	▲E3FZ-18198B	N.L.
(2) Plate (Lower)		
Note: Serviced in number 1.		
(3) Shock Absorber		
Escort & Lynx		
2 door hatchback		
1983 (wo/TRX susp.)		
before 3-83	▲E2FZ-18125B	74.00
from 3-83	▲E3FZ-18125F	68.50
1983 (w/TRX susp.)		
before 3-83	▲E3FZ-18125E	73.00
from 3-83	▲E3FZ-18125K	73.00
1984-85-wo/TRX	▲E4FZ-18125C	31.00
(w/TRX susp.)		
wo/turbo	▲E4FZ-18125D	31.00
w/turbo	▲E4FZ-18125A	99.00
1986-87-exc.		
G.T. model	▲E6FZ-18125A	68.50
G.T. model R.H.	▲E6FZ-18125D	73.25
left	▲E6FZ-18125E	73.25
4 door & sta. wagon		
1983 (wo/TRX susp.)		
before 3-83	▲E2FZ-18125A	74.00
from 3-83	▲E3FZ-18125G	68.50
1983 (w/TRX susp.)		
before 3-83	▲E3FZ-18125E	73.00
from 3-83	▲E3FZ-18125K	73.00
1984-85-wo/TRX	▲E4FZ-18125C	31.00
w/TRX	▲E3FZ-18125F	68.50
1986-87	▲E6FZ-18125B	68.50
EXP & LN7		
(wo/TRX susp.)		
1983-85	▲E2GZ-18125C	73.25
(w/TRX susp.)		
1983-85-wo/turbo	▲E2GZ-18125D	73.25

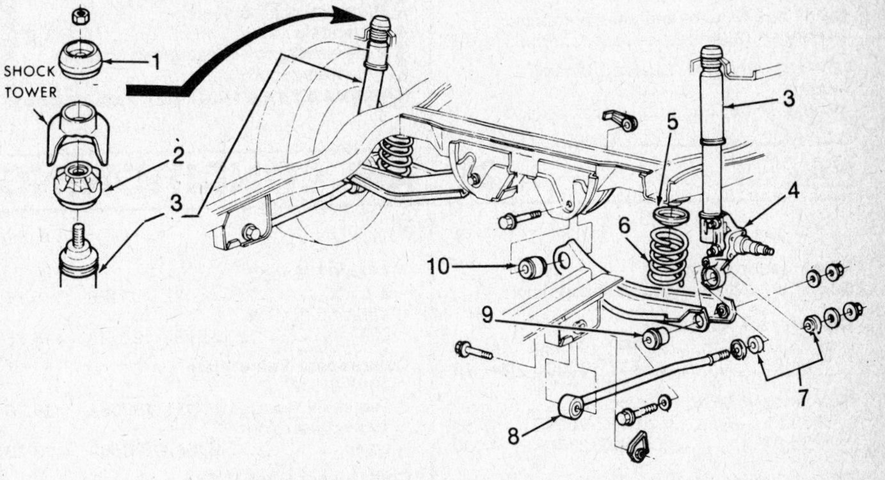

	Part No.	Price
w/turbo	▲E4FZ-18125A	99.00
(4) Spindle (Rear)		
1983	▲E1FZ-4A013B	91.25
1984-85	▲E43Z-4A013A	94.50
(5) Insulator (Upper)		
1983-85	▲E3FZ-5536A	7.25
(6) Spring Assy.		
Note: Order by year model and spring code on door.		
(7) Bushing (Tie Rod)		
1983-wo/TRX	▲E2FZ-5K897A	3.00
w/TRX	▲E2FZ-5K897B	3.00
1984-85-wo/TRX	▲E43Z-5K897A	3.00
w/TRX	▲E5FZ-5K897A	3.00
(8) Tie Rod Assy. (w/Bushing)		
1983-85	▲E4FZ-5K898A	45.00
(9) Arm Bushing (Spindle End)		
1983-85	▲E1FZ-5A638B	6.75
(10) Arm Bushing (Body End)		
1983-85	▲E1FZ-5A638A	7.50

LABOR — 28 AIR CONDITIONING 28 — LABOR

Note: If more than one item requires replacement where evacuation and discharging the system is already included in the operation, deduct 1.0 hour for each additional item to the times listed.

(Factory Time)	Chilton Time
(G) Drain, Evacuate & Recharge System	
Includes: Check for leaks.	
All models (.7)	1.2
(G) Pressure Test System	
All models	.6
(G) Compressor Drive Belt, Renew	
1983-87 (.3)	.5

Note: If necessary to R&R any component to gain access to belt, add appropriate time.

(Factory Time)	Chilton Time
(G) Compressor Assembly, Renew	
Includes: Transfer parts as required. Evacuate and charge system.	
1983-87	
Gas (2.4)	4.0
Diesel (2.3)	3.7
(G) Compressor Clutch and Pulley, Renew	
Includes: Evacuate and charge system.	
1983-87	
Gas (2.3)	3.5
Diesel (2.3)	3.0
Renew clutch brg add (.1)	.1
Renew clutch field add (.1)	.1
(G) Compressor Shaft Seal Kit, Renew	
Includes: R&R compressor. Evacuate and charge system.	
1983-87	
Gas (2.8)	4.5
Diesel (2.9)	4.7
(G) Compressor Assy., R&R and Recondition	
Includes: Evacuate and charge system.	
1983-87	
Gas (3.5)	4.8

LABOR 28 AIR CONDITIONING 28 LABOR

	(Factory Time)	Chilton Time
Diesel	(3.4)	4.5
(G) Condenser Assembly, Renew		
Includes: Evacuate and charge system.		
1983-87	(1.3)	2.4
(G) Accumulator Assembly, Renew		
Includes: Evacuate and charge system.		
1983-87	(1.6)	2.0
(G) Orifice Valve, Renew		
Includes: Evacuate and charge system.		
1983-87	(1.2)	1.6
(G) Clutch Cycling Pressure Switch Assy., Renew		
1983-87	(.3)	.4
(G) Evaporator Core, Renew		
Includes: Evacuate and charge system.		
1983-87	(3.9)	6.5
(G) A.C./Heater Blower Motor, Renew		
1983-87	(.5)	.8

AIR CONDITIONER TUNE-UP

For efficient operation and satisfactory performance in hot weather. The following Air Conditioner tune-up is suggested:

1. Clean intake filter
2. Clean condenser fins
3. Pressure test system
4. Adjust drive belt tension
5. Check anti freeze/coolant
6. Tighten compressor mounts
7. Tighten condenser and evaporator mounts
8. Inspect system for leaks (hoses, couplings, valves, etc.)
9. Partial charge system

All models 1.0

If necessary to evacuate and charge system, add 1.0

	(Factory Time)	Chilton Time
(G) Blower Motor Switch, Renew		
1983-87	(.4)	.7
(G) Blower Motor Resistor, Renew		
1983-87	(.3)	.6
(G) A.C. Vacuum Motor, Renew		
1983-84		
Recirculating door	(.6)	1.1
A/C Defroster door	(.4)	.8
A/C Heat door	(.5)	.9
Heat Defrost door	(.3)	.6
(G) Suction or Discharge Manifold Assy. Kit, Renew		
Includes: Evacuate and charge system.		
1983-87	(.8)	1.5
(G) Air Conditioning Hoses, Renew		
Includes: Evacuate and charge system.		
1983-87		
Cond. to Evap.	(1.0)	1.7
Suction	(1.7)	2.4
Comp. to Cond.	(.8)	1.5

PARTS 28 AIR CONDITIONING 28 PARTS

	Part No.	Price
Compressor Drive Belt		
Note: Order by model and description.		
Compressor Assembly		
1983	▲E4FZ-19703A	192.50
1984-87	▲E43Z-19703C	247.75
Compressor Clutch (Complete)		
1983	▲E1FZ-2884E	107.50
1984-87	▲E43Z-2884A	47.00
Clutch Cycling Pressure Switch		
1983-87	▲E35Y-19E561A	23.75
Compressor Shaft Seal		
1983-87	▲C9AZ-19655A	17.75
Condenser Assembly		
1983	▲E3FZ-19712A	126.25
1984-87 (Escort & Lynx)	▲E43Z-19712A	115.75
1984-85 (EXP & LN7)	▲E43Z-19712A	115.75
Compressor Valve Plate		
1983-87-w/ Tecumseh comp.	▲C3GY-19656A	26.25
1983-87-w/York comp.	▲D5AZ-19656A	23.25
Compressor Gasket Set		
1983-87	▲C3GY-19B684A	9.00
Evaporator Core		
1983	▲E2FZ-19860A	N.L.
1984-87	▲E3FZ-19860A	162.75
Orifice Valve		
1983-87	▲E1FZ-19D990A	5.25
Blower Motor		
1983	▲E3FZ-19805A	107.75
1984-87	▲E43Z-19805A	86.25
Blower Motor Resistor		
1983	▲E2FZ-19A706A	9.00
1984-87	▲E43Z-19A706A	8.75
Blower Motor Switch		
1983	▲E1FZ-19986A	10.00
1984	▲E4FZ-19986A	15.50
1985-87	▲E5FZ-19986A	15.50
Manifold Suction Kit		
1983-87	▲E2FZ-19E583A	36.75
Manifold Discharge Kit		
1983-87	▲E2FZ-19E582A	52.75

LABOR 29 LOCKS, HINGES & WIND. REGULATORS 29 LABOR

	(Factory Time)	Chilton Time
(G) Hood Latch Assembly, Renew		
1983-87	(.3)	.5
(G) Hood Hinge, Renew (One)		
Includes: Adjust hood and latch.		
1983-87	(.3)	.6
(G) Hood Release Cable, Renew		
1983-87	(.6)	1.0
(G) Front Door Latch, Renew		
Includes: R&R trim panel and weathersheet.		
1983-87	(.6)	.9
(G) Door Lock Remote Control, Renew (Front or Rear)		
Includes: R&R trim panel and weathersheet.		
1983-87	(.4)	.8
(G) Lock Striker Plate, Renew		
1983-87	(.2)	.3
(G) Front Door Handle (Outside), Renew		
Includes: R&R trim panel and weathersheet.		
1983-87	(.6)	.8
(G) Front Door Window Regulator, Renew		
Includes: R&R trim panel and weathersheet.		
1983-87	(.7)	1.1
(G) Rear Door Window Regulator, Renew		
Includes: R&R trim pad and weathersheet.		
1983-87	(.7)	1.1
(G) Rear Door Handle (Outside), Renew		
Includes: R&R trim panel and weathersheet.		
1983-87	(.5)	.8
(G) Rear Door Latch, Renew		
Includes: R&R trim panel and weathersheet.		
1983-87	(.5)	.9
(G) Tailgate or Liftgate Latch, Renew		
1983-87	(.3)	.5
(G) Rear Compartment Hydraulic Lift, Renew		
1983-87-one	(.3)	.4
both	(.3)	.5

PARTS 29 LOCKS, HINGES & WIND. REGULATORS 29 PARTS

	Part No.	Price
Hood Latch		
1983-85	▲E2FZ-16700A	11.50
1986-87	▲E6DZ-16700A	14.75
Hood Hinge		
1983-87-right	▲E1FZ-16796A	9.00
left	▲E1FZ-16797A	9.00
Door Lock (Front)		
1983-85 (before 3-85)		
right	▲E3GZ-6721812A	36.00

PARTS 29 LOCKS, HINGES & WIND. REGULATORS 29 PARTS

	Part No.	Price
left	▲E3GZ-6721813A	36.00
1985-87 (from 3-85)		
right	▲E59Z-1121812A	21.50
left	▲E59Z-1121813A	21.50
Door Lock (Rear)		
1983-right	▲E3FZ-5826412A	31.00
left	▲E3FZ-5826413A	31.00
1984-right	▲E43Z-5426412A	23.00
left	▲E43Z-5426413A	23.00
1985-87-right	▲E3FZ-5426412A	N.L.
left	▲E3FZ-5426413A	N.L.
Door Lock (Electric)		
Escort & Lynx		
1983-right	▲E3TZ-1021818A	N.L.
left	▲E3TZ-1021819A	N.L.
1984-87-right	▲E4FZ-5821818A	9.25
left	▲E4FZ-5821819A	9.25
EXP & LN7		
1983-right	▲E4GZ-6721818A	10.50
left	▲E4GZ-6721819A	10.50
1984-85-right	▲E4GZ-6721818A	10.50
left	▲E4GZ-6721819A	10.50
Lock Striker Plate		
1983	▲E1FZ-6122008B	4.25
1984-85	▲E1FZ-6122008B	4.25
1985-86	▲E69Z-1122008A	3.75

	Part No.	Price
Front Window Regulator (Manual)		
Escort & Lynx		
2 door sedan-hatchback		
1983-right	▲E3FZ-6123200A	59.25
left	▲E3FZ-6123201A	59.25
1984-87-right	▲E4FZ-6123200A	59.25
left	▲E4FZ-6123201A	59.25
4 door sedan-sta. wagon		
1983-right	▲E3FZ-7423200A	55.25
left	▲E3FZ-7423201A	55.25
1984-87-right	▲E4FZ-5823200A	59.25
left	▲E4FZ-5823201A	59.25
EXP & LN7		
1983-right	▲E3GZ-6723200A	59.25
left	▲E3GZ-6723201A	59.25
1984-86-right	▲E4FZ-6123200A	59.25
left	▲E4FZ-6123201A	59.25
Rear Window Regulator (Manual)		
1983-87-right	▲E3FZ-7427000A	53.00
left	▲E3FZ-7427001A	53.00
Front & Rear Door Handles (Outside)		
Bright finish		
1983 (bef. 3-1-83)		
right	▲E3FZ-5822404A	21.50
left	▲E3FZ-5822405A	21.50
1983-87 (from 3-1-83)		
right	▲E3FZ-5822404A	21.50
left	▲E3FZ-5822405A	21.50

	Part No.	Price
Black finish		
1984-87-right	▲E3FZ-6122404B	21.50
left	▲E3FZ-6122405B	21.50
Black plastic		
1984-87-right	▲E4FZ-6122404A	20.75
left	▲E4FZ-6122405A	20.75
Trunk Lid Lock		
(wo/power locks)		
1983-87	▲E3FZ-5843200A	15.00
(w/power locks)		
1983-87	▲E3FZ-5423200B	N.L.
Trunk Lid Hinge		
1983-87	▲E1FZ-6142700A	18.50
Liftgate Lock		
1983-87	▲E1FZ-7443150A	20.75
Door Lock Cylinder & Key		
(w/bright cyl.)		
1983-87-right	▲E1FZ-6121984A	10.75
left	▲E1FZ-6121985A	10.75
(w/black cyl.)		
1983-87-right	▲E1FZ-6121984B	10.75
left	▲E1FZ-6121985B	10.75
Trunk Lock Cylinder & Key		
1983-87-w/black cyl.	▲E1FZ-6143505A	10.75
w/bright cyl.	▲E1FZ-6143505B	10.75

LABOR 30 HEAD AND PARKING LAMPS 30 LABOR

(Factory Time)	Chilton Time
(G) Aim Headlamps	
two	.4
four	.6
(M) Headlamp Sealed Beam Bulb, Renew	
1983-87-each (.3)	.3

(Factory Time)	Chilton Time
(M) Parking Lamp Housing, Renew	
1983-87 (.3)	.4
(M) Rear Lamp Body, Renew	
Escort-Lynx	
1983-87 (.3)	.5
3 Dr. Coupe (.5)	.7
EXP-LN7	
1983-87 (.5)	.7

(Factory Time)	Chilton Time
(M) License Lamp Assembly, Renew	
1983-87 (.2)	.3
(M) Side Marker Lamps, Renew	
1983-87-each (.2)	.3

PARTS 30 HEAD AND PARKING LAMPS 30 PARTS

	Part No.	Price
Seal Beam Bulbs		
1983-85 (bef. 3-85)	▲E1FZ-13007A	24.25
1985-87 (from 3-85) R.H.	▲E6FZ-13007A	25.50
left	▲E6FZ-13007B	25.50
Parking Lamp Assy.		
Escort		
1983-85-(bef. 3-85) right	▲E1FZ-13200A	19.75
left	▲E1FZ-13201A	19.75
1985-87-(from 3-85) right	▲E6FZ-13200A	19.75
left	▲E6FZ-13201A	19.75
Lynx		
1983-85-(bef. 3-85) right	▲E1YY-13200A	19.75
left	▲E1YY-13201A	19.75
1985-87 (from 3-85) R.H.	▲E6YY-13200A	19.75
left	▲E6YY-13201A	19.75
EXP & LN7		
1983-85-right	▲E2GZ-13200A	15.50
left	▲E2GZ-13201A	15.50
Rear Lamp Assy.		
Escort		
(exc. station wagon)		
1983-85 (bef. 3-85) (wo/black taillamp ext.)		
right	▲E1FZ-13404A	69.75

	Part No.	Price
left	▲E1FZ-13405A	69.75
1983-85 (bef. 3-85) (w/black taillamp ext.)		
(wo/sports group)		
right	▲E2FZ-13404A	78.25
left	▲E2FZ-13405A	78.25
(w/Sports group)		
right	▲E3FZ-13404A	104.75
left	▲E3FZ-13405A	104.75
1985-87-from 3-85 (exc. sport group) right	▲E6FZ-13404A	69.75
left	▲E6FZ-13405A	69.75
1986-87 (w/sport group)		
black R.H.	▲E6FZ-13404B	104.75
left	▲E6FZ-13405B	104.75
blue R.H.	▲E6FZ-13404C	104.75
left	▲E6FZ-13405C	104.75
red R.H.	▲E6FZ-13404D	104.75
left	▲E6FZ-13405D	104.75
ox-white R.H.	▲E6FZ-13404E	104.75
left	▲E6FZ-13405E	104.75
(Station wagon)		
(exc. Squire model)		
1983-85 (bef. 4-85) right	▲E1FZ-13404B	75.25
left	▲E1FZ-13405B	75.25
(w/Squire model)		
1983-85 (bef. 4-85) right	▲E1FZ-13404C	82.75

	Part No.	Price
left	▲E1FZ-13405C	82.75
1985-87 (from 4-85) R.H.	▲E6FZ-13404F	75.25
left	▲E6FZ-13405F	75.25
(Three Door Hatchback)		
1986-87-R.H.	▲E20Y-13404A	141.25
left	▲E20Y-13405A	141.25
Lynx		
(exc. Station wagon)		
1983-85-bef. 3-85 (exc. Sport group)		
right	▲E1YY-13404A	97.75
left	▲E1YY-13405A	97.75
1985-87 (from 3-85) R.H.	▲E6YY-13404A	97.75
left	▲E6YY-13405A	97.75
1983-85-bef. 3-85 (Sport group)		
right	▲E3FZ-13404A	104.75
left	▲E3FZ-13405A	104.75
1985-87 (from 3-85) R.H.	▲E6YY-13404B	104.75
left	▲E6YY-13404B	104.75
(Station wagon)		
(exc. Squire model)		
1983-85-(bef. 4-85) right	▲E1YY-13404B	75.25
left	▲E1YY-13405B	75.25
(Squire model)		
1983-85 (bef. 4-85) right	▲E1YY-13404C	82.75
left	▲E1YY-13405C	82.75

PARTS 30 HEAD AND PARKING LAMPS 30 PARTS

	Part No.	Price
1985-87 (from 4-85) R.H.	▲E6YY-13404C	82.75
left	▲E6YY-13405C	82.75
EXP		
1983-right	▲E2GZ-13404A	123.75
left	▲E2GZ-13405A	124.00
1984-85-right	▲E2OY-13404A	141.25
left	▲E2OY-13405A	141.25
LN7		
1983-right	▲E2OY-13404A	141.25
left	▲E2OY-13405A	141.25
Rear Lamp Lens		
Escort		
(exc. Station wagon)		
1983-85-bef. 3-85 (wo/Sports group)		
right	▲E1FZ-13450A	24.75
left	▲E1FZ-13451A	24.75
1985-87 (from 3-85) R.H.	▲E6FZ-13450A	24.75
left	▲E6FZ-13451A	24.75
1983-85-bef. 3-85 (w/Sports group)		
right	▲E3FZ-13450A	51.50
left	▲E3FZ-13451A	51.50
1986-87-black-right	▲E6FZ-13450B	51.50
left	▲E6FZ-13451B	51.50
1986-87-Blue R.H.	▲E6FZ-13450C	51.50
left	▲E6FZ-13451C	51.50
1986-87-Red R.H.	▲E6FZ-13450D	51.50
left	▲E6FZ-13451D	51.50
1986-87-Ox-White R.H.	▲E6FZ-13450E	51.50
left	▲E6FZ-13451E	51.50
3 door hatchback		
1986-87-R.H.	▲E20Y-13450A	79.75
left	▲E20Y-13451A	79.75
Lynx		
(exc. Station wagon)		
1983-85-bef. 3-85 (exc. Sport group)		
right	▲E1YY-13450A	44.50
left	▲E1YY-13451A	44.50
1985-87 (from 3-85) R.H.	▲E6YY-13450A	44.50
left	▲E6YY-13451A	44.50
1983-85-bef. 3-85 (Sport group)		
right	▲E3FZ-13450A	51.50
left	▲E3FZ-13451A	51.50
1985-87 (from 3-85) R.H.	▲E6YY-13450B	51.50
left	▲E6YY-13451B	51.50
EXP		
1983-right	▲E2GZ-13450A	46.50
left	▲E2GZ-13451A	46.50
1984-85-right	▲E2OY-13405A	141.25
left	▲E2OY-13451A	79.75
LN7		
1983-right	▲E2OY-13450A	79.75
left	▲E2OY-13451A	79.75
License Plate Lamp Assy.		
1983-87	▲E2FZ-13550A	4.00
Back Up Lamp Assy.		
1983-87 (sta. wagon)	▲E1FZ-15500B	21.25
Marker Lamp Assy.		
1983-85 (EXP & LN7)		
right	▲E2GZ-15A201A	12.50
left	▲E2GZ-15A201B	12.50
Rear Hi-Mount Lamp Assy.		
1985-87-exc. Sta. wagon	▲E6FZ-13A613A	25.00
Station wagon	▲E6FZ13A613B	25.00

LABOR 31 WINDSHIELD WIPER & SPEEDOMETER 31 LABOR

(Factory Time)	Chilton Time
(G) Windshield Wiper Motor, Renew	
1983-87 (.4)	.7
(G) Windshield Wiper Switch, Renew	
1983-87 (.5)	.9
(G) Wiper Pivot Shaft and Link Assy., Renew	
1983-87 (.4)	.9
(G) Windshield Washer Pump, Renew	
1983-87	
sdn (.3)	.4
wagon (.5)	.7
(G) Windshield Wiper Governor, Renew	
1983-87 (.5)	.9
(G) Rear Window Wiper Motor, Renew	
1983-87	
3 & 5 Dr. (.4)	.6
(G) Rear Window Wiper Switch, Renew	
1983-87 (.3)	.4
(G) Rear Window Washer Pump, Renew	
1983-87	
3 & 5 Dr. (.3)	.4
sta wag (.5)	.7
(G) Speedometer Head, R&R or Renew	
1983-87	
standard (.5)	1.0
performance (.9)	1.7
Reset odometer add	.2
(G) Speedometer Cable and Casing, Renew	
1983-87	
one piece (.3)	.5
upper (.3)	.5
lower (.3)	.5
(G) Speedometer Cable (Inner), Renew or Lubricate	
1983-87-each (.3)	.5
(G) Speedometer Driven Gear, Renew	
1983-87	
w/MTX (.3)	.5
w/ATX (3.1)	4.9
(G) Tachometer, R&R or Renew	
1983-84 (.5)	1.0
1985-87 (.9)	1.7
(G) Radio, R&R	
1983-87 (.4)	.8
w/Console add (.1)	.1

PARTS 31 WINDSHIELD WIPER & SPEEDOMETER 31 PARTS

	Part No.	Price
Wiper Motor Assy. (Front)		
1983	▲E1FZ-17508B	94.25
1984-87	▲E4FZ-17508A	101.25
Wiper Motor Assy. (Rear)		
(wo/sta. wagon)		
1983-87	▲D8BZ-17508A	75.75
(w/sta. wagon)		
1983-85	▲E1FZ-17508A	126.00
1986-87	▲E6FZ-17508A	126.00
Wiper Arm & Pivot Shaft		
1983-87-front	▲E1FZ-17566A	26.75
rear	▲E1FZ-17566B	46.00
Wiper Arm (Front)		
1983-84-before 6-84	▲E1FZ-17526A	10.00
1984-87-from 6-84	▲E4FZ-17526A	10.00
Wiper Arm (Rear Exc. Sta. Wag.)		
1983-84 (bef. 6-84)	▲E1FZ-17526B	10.00
1984-87 (from 6-84)	▲E4FZ-17526B	9.75
Wiper Arm (Rear Sta. Wagon)		
1983-84 (bef. 6-84)	▲E1FZ-17526C	10.00
1984-85 (from 6-84)	▲E4FZ-17526C	9.75
1986-87	▲E6FZ-17526A	9.75
Wiper Switch (Front)		
1983-wo/interm.	▲E3DZ-17A553C	18.50
w/interm.	▲E3DZ-17A553A	25.75
1984-85-wo/interm.	▲E4FZ-17A553C	18.50
w/interm.	▲E4FZ-17A553A	41.00
1986-87-wo/Interm.	▲E6FZ-17A553A	18.50
w/Interm.	▲E6FZ-17A553B	41.00
Wiper Switch (Rear)		
1983	▲E1FZ-17A553C	12.25
1984-87	▲E4FZ-17A553B	16.25
Windshield Wiper Govenor		
1983	▲E43Z-17C476B	74.00
1984-85-exc. tilt	▲E43Z-17C476B	74.00
w/tilt whl.	▲E43Z-17C476A	74.00
1986-87-w/Tilt	▲E6FZ-17C476B	74.00
wo/Tilt	▲E6FZ-17C476A	74.00
Windshield Washer Pump		
1983-87-front	▲E0AZ-17664A	20.00
rear	▲E1FZ-17664A	18.75

PARTS 31 WINDSHIELD WIPER & SPEEDOMETER 31 PARTS

	Part No	Price
Windshield Washer Reservoir		
(Front)		
1983-wo/sensor	▲E2FZ-17618A	17.25
w/sensor	▲E2FZ-17618B	21.50
1984-87-wo/ sensor	▲E4FZ-17618A	16.50
w/sensor	▲E4FZ-17618C	20.75
(Rear)		
1983-87	▲E1FZ-17618C	15.00
Speedometer Head Assy.		
Order by year and model.		
Speedometer Core Kit		
1983-87 (Must cut to fit)		
up to 81" long	▲D4AZ-17262A	7.75
up to 135" long	▲C5AZ-17262B	8.75
Speedometer Speed Control Cable		
1983-upper	▲E2FZ-9A820A	15.00
lower	▲E2FZ-9A820B	15.00
1984-87	▲E43Z-9A820A	13.25
Speedometer Cable (wo/Speed Control)		
1983-87	▲E3FZ-17260A	8.25

LABOR 32 LIGHT SWITCHES & WIRING 32 LABOR

(Factory Time)	Chilton Time
(G) Headlamp Switch, Renew	
1983-84-w/A.C. (.3)	.5
wo/A.C. (.5)	.7
1985-87 (.4)	.7
(G) Headlamp Dimmer Switch, Renew	
1983-87 (.5)	.9
(G) Turn Signal Switch, Renew	
1983-87 (.5)	.9
(M) Turn Signal or Hazard Warning Flasher, Renew	
1983-87 (.2)	.3
(G) Stop Light Switch, Renew	
1983-87 (.3)	.5
(G) Back-Up Lamp Switch, Renew	
1983-87 (.3)	.5
(G) Parking Brake Warning Lamp Switch, Renew	
1983-87 (.3)	.5
(G) Horn, Renew	
1983-87 (.3)	.3
(G) Wiring Harness, Renew	
Alternator to Regulator	
1983-87 (.3)	.6

PARTS 32 LIGHT SWITCHES & WIRING 32 PARTS

	Part No	Price
Headlamp Switch		
1983		
wo/visib. lite	▲E0AZ-11654C	16.50
w/visib. lite	▲E0AZ-11654D	17.50
1984 (bef. 2-84)	▲E43Z-11654C	N.L.
1984-85 (from 2-84 & bef 3-85)	▲E53Z-11654A	20.00
1985-87 (from 3-85)	▲E6FZ-11654A	16.75
Stop Light Switch		
1983-85 (bef. 3-85)	▲E3FZ-13480A	5.75
1985-87 (from 3-85)	▲E6FZ-13480A	5.75
Turn Signal & Warning Switch		
1983-84	▲E2FZ-13341A	41.25
1985-87	▲E5FZ-13341A	41.25
Brake Warning Light Switch		
1983-87	▲E2FZ-2B264B	7.50
Turn Signal Flasher		
1983-87	▲C5AZ-13350B	3.75
Emergency Flasher		
1983-87	▲D1FZ-13350A	4.25
Horn		
1983-87-low pitch	▲E3AZ-13833A	17.00
high pitch	▲E3AZ-13832A	17.00
Wiring Harness		
Note: Order by model and description.		

LABOR 33 GLASS 33 LABOR

(Factory Time)	Chilton Time
(G) Windshield Glass, Renew	
1983-87 (1.9)	3.0
R&R mldgs add	.3
(G) Front Door Glass, Renew	
Includes: R&R trim panel and weathersheet.	
1983-87 (.5)	.9
(G) Rear Door Glass, Renew	
Includes: R&R trim panel and weathersheet.	
1983-87 (.6)	1.0
(G) Rear Quarter Window Glass, Renew	
1983-87	
sdn (.7)	1.0
sta wagon (.6)	.9
(G) Rear Door Stationary Glass, Renew	
1983-87 (.7)	1.0
(G) Rear Window or Tailgate Glass, Renew	
1983-87-3 Dr. (.8)	1.2
sta wagon (.8)	1.2
Renew butyl tape add (.2)	.2

LABOR 34 CRUISE CONTROL 34 LABOR

(Factory Time)	Chilton Time
(G) Cruise Control System Diagnosis	
1983-87 (.4)	.6
(G) Cruise Control Chain/Cable, Renew	
1983-87 (.2)	.4
(G) Speed Control Servo Assy., Renew	
1983-87 (.4)	.6
Road test add (.3)	.3
(G) Speed Control Relay, Renew	
1983-87 (.3)	.4
Road test add (.3)	.3
(G) Speed Control Sensor Assy., Renew	
1983-87 (.3)	.5
Road test add (.3)	.3
(G) Speed Control Amplifier Assy., Renew	
1983-87 (.3)	.6
Road test add (.3)	.3
(G) Speed Control Actuator Switch, Renew	
1983-87 (.3)	.6
Road test add (.3)	.3
(G) Speed Control Metering (Dump) Valve, Renew	
1983-87 (.2)	.4
(G) Speed Control Clutch Switch, Renew	
1983-87 (.1)	.3
Road test add (.3)	.3

	Part No.	Price
Speed Control Amplifier Assy.		
1983-87	▲E0AZ-9D843A	161.50
Speed Control Servo Assy.		
1983-87	▲E2FZ-9C735A	120.25

	Part No.	Price
Speed Control Sensor		
1983	▲D4AZ-9E731B	47.25
1984-87	▲E43Z-9E731A	20.75
Speed Control Actuator Switch		
1983-87	▲E3SZ-9C888A	45.75

GROUP INDEX

ALPHABETICAL INDEX

Ford Motor Company
Front Wheel Drive Cars

TAURUS • SABLE

YEAR IDENTIFICATION

1987 Taurus

1987 Sable

VEHICLE IDENTIFICATION NUMBER (VIN)

It is important for servicing and ordering parts to be certain of the vehicle and engine identification. The VIN (vehicle identification number) is a 13 or 17 digit number visible through the windshield on the driver's side of the dash and contains the vehicle and engine identification codes. It can be interpreted as follows:

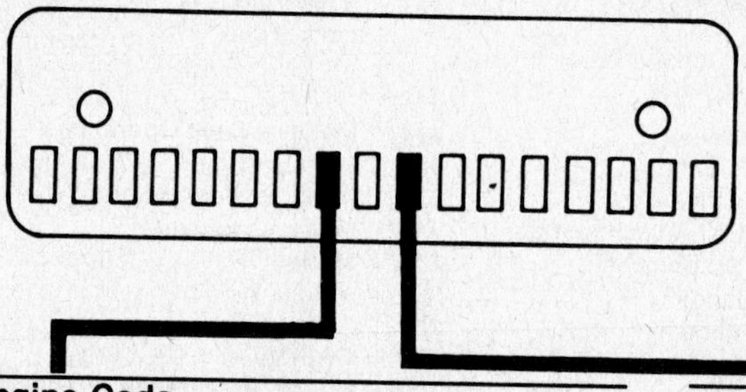

Engine Code

Code	Cu. In.	Liters	Cyl.	Carb.	Eng. Mfg.
D	153	2.5 (HSC)	4	CFI	Ford
U	182	3.0	6	EFI	Ford

Model Year Code

Code	Year
H	'87

The seventeen digit Vehicle Identification Number can be used to determine engine application and model year. The tenth digit indicates the model year, and the eighth digit identifies engine code.

TUNE-UP SPECIFICATIONS

When analyzing compression test results, look for uniformity among cylinders rather than specific pressures.

Year	Engine: Eng. VIN Code	Engine: No. Cyl Displacement cu. in. (cc)	Eng. Mfg.	Spark Plugs: Orig. Type •	Spark Plugs: Gap (in.)	Distributor: Point Dwell (deg.)	Distributor: Point Gap (in.)	Ignition Timing (deg.): Man. Trans •	Ignition Timing (deg.): Auto Trans	Valves Intake Opens ▪ (deg.)	Fuel Pump Pressure (psi)	Idle Speed (rpm): Man Trans	Idle Speed (rpm): Auto Trans
'86–'87	0	4-153 (2508)	Ford	AWSF-32C	0.042–0.046	Electronic		①	①	—	35–45	①	①
'86–'87	U	6-182 (2983)	Ford	AWSF-32C	0.042–0.046	Electronic		①	①	—	35–45	①	①

NOTE: The underhood specifications sticker often reflects tune-up specification changes made in production. Sticker figures must be used if they disagree with those in this chart. Part numbers in this chart are not recommended by Chilton for any product by brand name.

- ▪ All figures Before Top Dead Center
- • Figure in parenthesis is for California
- B Before Top Dead Center

① Calibration levels vary from model to model. Always refer to the underhood sticker for your car requirements.

FIRING ORDERS

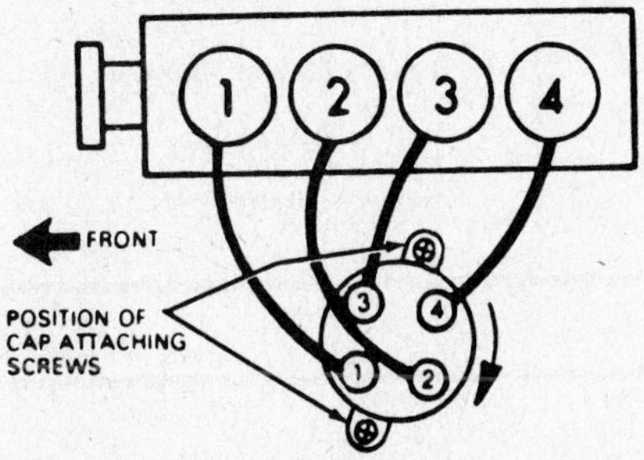

Ford 2500 cc 4 cyl (2.5L)
Firing order: 1–3–4–2
Distributor rotation: clockwise

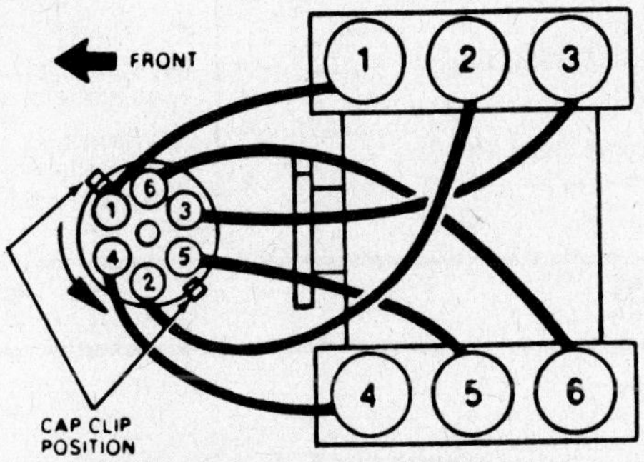

Ford 3000 cc 6 cyl (3.0L)
Firing order: 1–4–2–5–3–6
Distributor rotation: counterclockwise

WHEEL ALIGNMENT SPECIFICATIONS

Year	Model	Caster Range (deg)■▲	Caster Pref. Setting (deg)	Camber Range (deg)■	Camber Pref. Setting (deg)	Toe-in (in.)	Steering Axis Inclin. (deg)
'86–'87	Taurus/Sable Front	3P to 6P	4P	1 3/32N to 3/32P	1/2N	7/32 (out) to 1/64 (in)	15 3/8
'86–'87	Taurus/Sable Rear	■	■	■ ■	■	1/16 (out) to 3/16 (in)	N/A

■ Caster and chamber are pre-set at the factory and cannot be adjusted
▲ Caster measurements must be made on the left side by turning left wheel through the prescribed angle of sweep and on the right side by turning right wheel through prescribed angle of sweep for the equipment being used. When using alignment equipment designed to measure caster on both the right and left side, turning only one wheel will result in a significant error in caster angle for the opposite side.

LABOR SERVICE BAY OPERATIONS LABOR

(Factory Time) Chilton Time

COOLING

(M) Winterize Cooling System
Includes: Run engine to check for leaks, tighten all hose connections. Test radiator and pressure cap. Drain radiator and engine block. Add antifreeze and refill system.
All models 5

(M) Thermostat, Renew
1986-87
V-6 (.7) 1.0

(M) Drive Belt, Adjust
1986-87
V-6 (.2) 3

(M) Radiator Hoses, Renew
1986-87-upper (.4) 4
lower (.5) 5
both (.6) 6

BRAKES

(G) Brakes, Adjust (Minor)
Includes: Adjust brakes, fill master cylinder.
two wheels 4

(G) Bleed Brakes (Four Wheels)
Includes: Fill master cylinder.
All models (.3) 5

(G) Brake Pedal Free Play, Adjust
All models 4

CHILTON'S 10 POINT SAFETY CHECK
CHECK OPERATION & CONDITION OF THE FOLLOWING ITEMS:
1. Legal Registration (serial no.)
2. Tires & Wheels
3. Brake System (R&R all wheels)
4. Light Systems & Signals
5. Accelerator Linkage, Neutral Safety Switch, Shift Indicator Pointer & Seat Position Locks
6. Glass, Mirrors, Door Locks, Seat Belts & Harness
7. Wipers, Washers & Defrosters
8. Frame, Steering, Shocks, Front & Rear Suspension
9. Fuel & Exhaust Systems
10. Road Test Vehicle
All models 1.0
Exhaust Smog Analysis, add 4

(Factory Time) Chilton Time

(M) Parking Brake, Adjust
All models (.3) 5

LUBRICATION SERVICE

(M) Lubricate Chassis, Change Oil & Filter
Includes: Inspect and correct all fluid levels.
All models 6

(Factory Time) Chilton Time

Install grease fittings add 1

(M) Lubricate Chassis
Includes: Inspect and correct all fluid levels.
All models 4
Install grease fittings add 1

(M) Engine Oil & Filter, Change
Includes: Inspect and correct all fluid levels.
All models 4

WHEELS

(M) Wheel, Renew
one 5

(G) Wheels, Balance
one 3
each adtnl 2

(G) Wheels, Rotate (All)
All models 5

ELECTRICAL

(G) Aim Headlamps
two 4
four 6

(M) Headlamp Sealed Beam Bulb, Renew
All models-each (.2) 3

LABOR — SERVICE BAY OPERATIONS — LABOR

(Factory Time)	Chilton Time
(M) Parking Lamp Bulb, Renew	
Taurus (.2)	.3
Sable (.3)	.4
(M) License Lamp Bulb, Renew	
All models-one (.2)	.2
(M) Back-Up Lamp Bulb, Renew	
All models-one (.3)	.3
(M) Rear Lamp Bulb, Renew	
All models-one (.3)	.3
each adtnl	.1
(M) Battery Cables, Renew	
All models	
Batt to Relay (.3)	.4
Negative (.3)	.3
Relay to Starter (.4)	.5

LABOR — 1 TUNE UP 1 — LABOR

(G) Compression Test

Four–1986-87	.6
V-6–1986-87	.8

(G) Engine Tune Up, (Electronic Ignition)

Includes: Test battery and clean connections. Check engine compression, clean and adjust or renew spark plugs. Test resistance of spark plug cables. Inspect distributor cap and rotor. Check vacuum advance operation. Reset ignition timing. Service air cleaner. Inspect and adjust drive belts. Inspect choke operation and adjust or free up. Check operation of EGR valve.

Four–1986-87	1.5
V-6–1986-87	1.8
Perform EEC IV system test add	1.0

LABOR — 2 IGNITION SYSTEM 2 — LABOR

(Factory Time)	Chilton Time
(G) Spark Plugs, Clean and Reset or Renew	
1986-87	
V-6 (.5)	.7
(G) Ignition Timing, Reset	
All models (.4)	.6
(G) Distributor, Renew	
Includes: Reset ignition timing.	
1986-87	
V-6 (.4)	.7
Renew vacuum diaph add (.1)	.2
(G) Distributor Cap and/or Rotor, Renew	
1986-87 (.3)	.4
(G) Ignition Coil, Renew	
1986-87 (.3)	.4
(G) Ignition Cables, Renew	
1986-87 (.3)	.5
(G) Ignition Switch, Renew	
1986-87 (.5)	.9

PARTS — 2 ELECTRONIC IGNITION 2 — PARTS

	Part No.	Price
Distributor Assembly		
Four		
1986-87	▲E63Z-12127B	136.75
V-6-183		
1986-87	▲E6AZ-12127C	136.75
(1) Cap		
Four		
1986-87	▲E5FZ-12106C	8.75
V-6-183		
1986-87	▲E6AZ-12106A	12.50
(2) Rotor		
1986-87	▲E6AZ-12200C	2.50
(3) Stator Assembly		
1986-87	▲E3ZZ-12A112C	25.00
Ignition Coil		
1986-87	▲E3FZ-12029A	33.75
Ignition Wire Set		
Four		
1986-87	▲E6PZ-12259D	41.00

Note: Spark plug wires for V-6 eng. are sold separately and not available as a set.

Ignition Switch		
1986-87	▲E6DZ-11572A	10.25

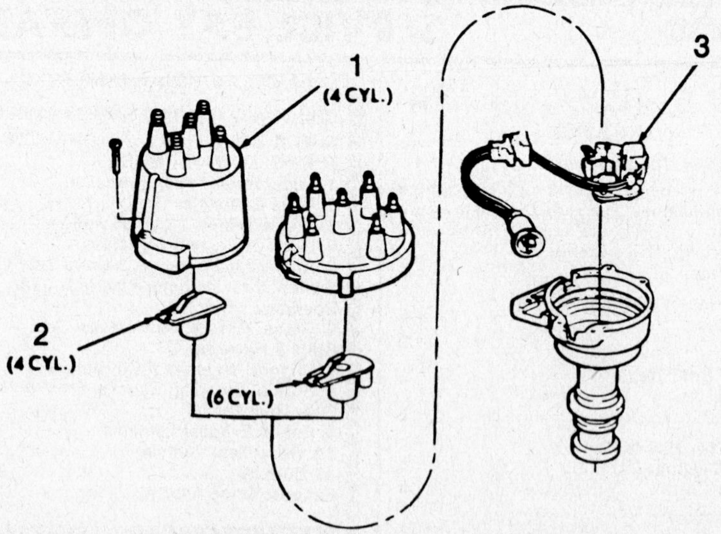

LABOR — 3 FUEL SYSTEM 3 — LABOR

FUEL INJECTION

(Factory Time)	Chilton Time
(G) Fuel Injection Manifold Assy., Renew	
1986-87	
w/EFI (1.2)	1.7
(G) Air Intake Charge Throttle Body, Renew	
1986-87	
V-6 (1.1)	1.6
(G) Fuel Charging Wiring Assy., Renew	
1986-87	
w/EFI (1.0)	1.5

LABOR — 3 FUEL SYSTEM 3 — LABOR

(Factory Time)	Chilton Time
w/CFI (.3)	.6
(G) Fuel Pressure Regulator Assy., Renew	
1986-87	
w/EFI (.5)	.9
w/CFI (.7)	1.2
(G) Fuel Charging Assy., R&R or Renew	
1986-87	
Four (.5)	.8
(G) Fuel Charging Assy., R&R and Recondition	
1986-87	
Four (1.3)	2.0
(G) Fuel Injector Assembly, Renew	
Does not include system test.	
1986-87	
V-6-one (1.4)	2.0
all (1.5)	2.2
(G) Fuel Tank, Renew	
Includes: Drain and refill tank, transfer tank gauge unit.	
1986-87	
Sdn (1.2)	1.6
Sta wagon (1.2)	1.6
(G) Fuel Gauge (Tank Unit), Renew	
1986-87	
Sdn (1.0)	1.4
Sta wagon (1.0)	1.4
(G) Fuel Gauge (Dash Unit), Renew	
1986-87	
Std. cluster (1.0)	1.7
Elec. cluster (.8)	1.2
(G) Fuel Pump, Renew (In Tank)	
1986-87 (1.0)	1.4
(G) Intake Manifold Gasket, Renew	
V-6–1986-87 (2.6)	3.7
Renew manif add (.2)	.5

PARTS — 3 FUEL SYSTEM 3 — PARTS

	Part No.	Price
Air Cleaner Element		
Four & V-6		
1986-87	▲E6AZ-9601B	10.25
Sender & Pump Assy. (Fuel Tank)		
w/16 gal. tank		
Four		
1986-87	▲E6DZ-9H307F	93.75
V-6-183		
1986-87	▲E6DZ-9H307C	93.75
w/18.6 gal. tank & wo/Elect. Inst. Clust.		
Four		
1986-87	▲E6DZ-9H307A	93.75
V-6-183		
1986-87	▲E6DZ-9H307B	93.75
w/18.6 gal. tank & w/Elec. Inst. Clust.		
Four		
1986-87	▲E6DZ-9H307E	93.75
V-6-183		
1986-87	▲E6DZ-9H307D	93.75
Fuel Tank		
1986-87		
16 gal. tank	▲E6DZ-9002A	118.00
18.6 gal. tank	▲E6DZ-9002B	136.25
Fuel Gauge (Dash)		
1986-87-wo/Elect. Inst. Cluster		
wo/Tach	▲E6DZ-9305A	30.75
w/Tach	▲E64Z-9305A	30.75
w/Electronic Inst. Cluster		
1986-87	▲E6DZ-9305B	30.75

PARTS — 3 ELECTRONIC FUEL INJECTION 3 — PARTS

	Part No.	Price
(1) Intake Manifold		
1986-87		
Four	▲E63Z-9424A	133.75
V-6-183	▲E6AZ-9424A	224.00
(2) Manifold Gasket		
1986-87-V-6	▲E6AZ-9H486A	4.50
(3) Throttle Body Assy.		
1986-87-V-6	▲E6AZ-9E926B	253.75
(4) Potentiometer Assy.		
1986-87-V-6	▲E6DZ-9B989B	N.L.
(5) Throttle By-pass Valve Assy.		
1986-87-V-6	▲E6AZ-9F715D	56.75
(6) Fuel Charging Wiring		
1986-87-V-6	▲E6DZ-9D930A	39.25
(7) Manifold Crossover Tube Assy.		
1986-87-V-6	▲E6AZ-9F792A	138.00
(8) Injector Assy.		
1986-87-V-6	▲E5TZ-9F593A	133.75

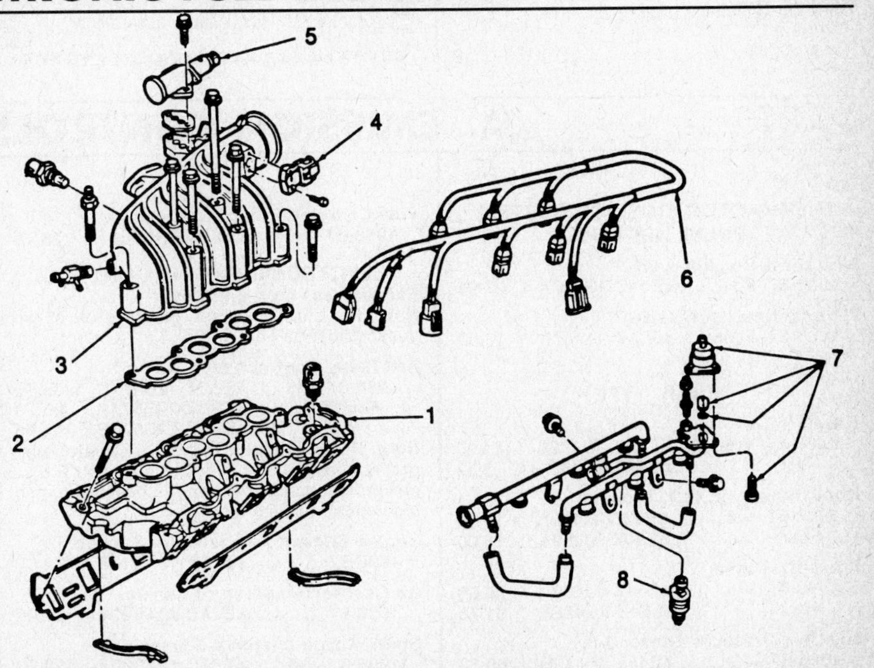

LABOR — 3A EMISSION CONTROLS 3A — LABOR

(Factory Time)	Chilton Time
ELECTRONIC ENGINE CONTROL IV	
(P) E.E.C. System Test	
1986-87 (.5)	1.0
(P) Throttle Position Sensor, Renew	
Does not include system test.	
1986-87	
V-6 (.2)	.3
(P) Throttle Air By-Pass Valve, Renew	
Does not include system test.	
1986-87	
V-6 (.2)	.3

LABOR 3A EMISSION CONTROLS 3A LABOR

(Factory Time) Chilton Time

(P) Exhaust Gas Oxygen Sensor, Renew
Does not include system test.
1986-87
V-6 (.3) 5

(P) Processor Assembly, Renew
Does not include system test.
1986-87
V-6 (.2) 3

(P) Engine Coolant Temperature Sensor, Renew
Does not include system test.
1986-87
V-6 (.2) 3

(P) Fuel Pump Relay, Renew
Does not include system test.
1986-87
V-6 (.1) 2

(P) Fuel Pump Inertia Switch, Renew
Does not include system test.
1986-87
V-6 (.1) 2

(P) Manifold Absolute Pressure Sensor, Renew
Does not include system test.
1986-87
V-6 (.1) 2

(P) Thick Film Ignition Module, Renew
Does not include system test.
1986-87
V-6 (.5) 7

(P) Profile Ignition Pick-Up Sensor, Renew
Does not include system test.
1986-87
V-6 (.6) 8

CHILTON'S EMISSION CONTROL TUNE-UP

1. Clean or renew P.C.V. valve, hoses and filter.
2. Check fuel tank cap for sealing ability.
3. Check fuel tank and fuel lines for leakage.
4. Check evaporation canister and filter. Replace if necessary.
5. Check engine compression to determine leakage of unburned gases. (Add time for items of interference).
6. Test and clean or renew spark plugs.
7. Check engine oil dipstick for sealing ability.
8. Test exhaust system with analyzer and check system for leakage.
9. Check exhaust manifold heat valve for operation.
10. Adjust ignition timing and carburetor idle speed and mixture.
11. Check automatic choke mechanism for free operation.
12. Inspect air cleaner and element.
13. On models so equipped, test distributor vacuum control switch and transmission control switch.

Four **1.3**
V-6 .... **1.7**
For repairs made, charge accordingly.

(Factory Time) Chilton Time

(P) E.G.R. Control Solenoids, Renew
Does not include system test.
1986-87
V-6 (.3) 4

(P) Canister Purge Solenoid, Renew
Does not include system test.
1986-87
V-6 (.1) 2

(P) Fuel Injector Assy., Renew
Does not include system test.
1986-87
V-6-one (1.4) 2.0
all (1.5) 2.2

(P) Knock Sensor, Renew
Does not include system test.
1986-87
V-6 (.3) 4

(P) Electronic Control Relay, Renew
Does not include system test.
1986-87
V-6 (.1) 2

(P) E.G.R. Valve, Renew
Does not include system test.
1986-87
V-6 (.1) 3

(P) Air Change Temperature Sensor, Renew
Does not include system test.
1986-87
V-6 (.1) 2

PARTS 3A EMISSION CONTROLS 3A PARTS

	Part No.	Price
THERMACTOR EMISSION SYSTEM PULSE AIR TYPE		
Silencer & Bracket Assy.		
1986-87-Four	▲E6AZ-9G427A	27.25
Thermactor Check Valve		
1986-87-Four	▲E6AZ-9A487B	18.50
E.G.R. TYPE		
E.G.R. Valve		
1986-87-V-6	▲E6AZ-9D475B	41.25
Four	▲E53Z-9F483A	N.L.
Control Assy. (E.G.R. Vacuum)		
1986-87-V-6	▲E63Z-9J459A	15.00
Four	▲E63Z-9J459A	15.00
Pressure Sensor		
1986-87-V-6	▲E6AZ-9J460A	78.00
Four	▲E5AZ-9G428A	31.75
Manifold Pressure Sensor Assy.		
1986-87	▲E43Z-9F479B	68.50
Throttle Air By-pass Valve		
1986-87-V-6	▲E6AZ-9F715D	56.75

	Part No.	Price
Fuel Charging Pressure Regulator		
1986-87-V-6	▲E6AZ-9C968A	25.75
ELECTRONIC ENGINE CONTROL		
Exhaust Gas Oxygen Sensor		
Note: For correct sensor, numbers off of old sensor must be obtained.		
Fan Relay Control Assy.		
1986-87-V-6	▲E6DZ-12B577C	96.75
Four, A.T.	▲E6DZ-12B577A	96.75
M.T.	▲E6DZ-12B577B	96.75
Note: Relay control attaches to radiator support & consists of 4 electronic relays. E.E.C. power, fuel pump, low speed cooling fan, and high speed cooling fan.		
Engine Coolant Temperature Sensor		
1986-87	▲E1AZ-12A648A	32.00
Air Charge Temperature Sensor		
1986-87	▲E1AZ-12A697A	27.00
Spark Knock Intensity Sensor		
1986-87-V-6	▲E5TZ-12A699A	33.00
Cooling Fan Motor Resistor		
1986-87	▲E6DZ-8L603A	14.25

	Part No.	Price
Processor Assembly		
1986-87-V-6		
4 dr., exc. Cal.	▲E6DZ-12A650HH	N.L.
Canada	▲E6DZ-12A650AFH	N.L.
Calif.	▲E6DZ-12A650CH	N.L.
Sta. Wagon, exc. Calif.	▲E6DZ-12A650MH	167.75
Canada	▲E6DZ-12A650AFH	N.L.
Calif.	▲E6DZ-12A650AH	N.L.
1986-87-Four cyl.		
4 dr., exc. Cal.	▲E6DZ-12A650DA	167.75
Calif.	▲E6DZ-12A650EA	167.75
sta. wag.	▲E6DZ-12A650RA	167.75
1986-87-Taurus w/MTX		
4 dr. exc. Cal.	▲E6DZ-12A650FA	167.75
Sta. Wag., exc. Calif.	▲E6DZ-12A650UA	167.75
Calif.	▲E6DZ-12A650GA	167.75
EVAPORATIVE EMISSION TYPE		
Fuel Vapor Canister Assy.		
1986-87	▲E6AZ-9D653A	27.50
Sensor Assy.		
1986-87	▲D7FZ-9E607B	7.25

LABOR 4 ALTERNATOR & REGULATOR 4 LABOR

(Factory Time) Chilton Time

(G) Alternator Circuits, Test
Includes: Test battery, regulator and alternator output.
All models (.3) 6

(M) Alternator Drive Belt, Renew
1986-87 (.3) 5

(G) Alternator Assembly, Renew
V-6–1986-87 (.4) 7
Transfer pulley add (.1) 1

LABOR 4 ALTERNATOR & REGULATOR 4 LABOR

	(Factory Time)	Chilton Time
(G) Alternator, R&R and Recondition		
Includes: Complete disassembly, replacement of parts as required. Test validity of rotor field, stator and diodes.		
V-6–1986-87	(.9)	1.5
(G) Alternator Brushes, Renew		
Includes: R&R alternator.		
V-6–1986-87	(.7)	1.2
(G) Alternator Front Bearing or End Plate, Renew		
Includes: R&R alternator.		
V-6–1986-87	(.7)	1.1
(G) Alternator Rear Bearing, Renew		
Includes: R&R alternator.		
V-6–1986-87	(.7)	1.1
(G) Alternator Regulator, Renew		
1986-87	(.3)	.5

PARTS 4 ALTERNATOR AND REGULATOR 4 PARTS

	Part No.	Price
Alternator Assy. (New)		
64 amp.		
1986-87	▲E6DZ-10346B	232.75
75 amp.		
1986-87	▲E6DZ-10346C	232.75
70 amp.		
1986-87	▲E1BZ-10346A	265.00
(1) Pulley		
1986-87		
w/64 & 75 amp.	▲E6DZ-10344C	17.75
w/70 amp.	▲E6DZ-10344D	9.75
(2) Fan		
1986-87		
w/64 & 75 amp	▲E6DZ-10A310A	5.50
w/70 amp.	▲E6DZ-10A310C	4.50
(3) Front Housing		
1986-87		
w/64 & 75 amp.	▲E6DZ-10333C	21.25
w/70 amp.	▲D3VY-10333A	72.75
(4) Bearing (Front)		
1986-87	▲C9ZZ-10094A	9.00
(5) Rotor Assy.		
1986-87		
w/64 & 75 amp.	▲E6DZ-10335A	56.75
w/70 amp.	▲E1ZZ-10335C	68.00
(6) Stator Assy.		
1986-87-w/64 amp.	▲E6DZ-10336E	37.00
w/75 amp.	▲E6DZ-10336A	37.00
w/70 amp.	▲D2OZ-10336A	74.75
(7) Rectifier Assy.		
1986-87-w/64 amp.	▲E6DZ-10304A	47.25
w/75 amp.	▲E43Z-10304A	47.25
w/70 amp.	▲D2OZ-10304A	33.00
(8) Rear Housing		
1986-87		
w/64 & 75 amp.	▲E6FZ-10334A	36.75
w/70 amp.	▲D7VZ-10334A	49.25

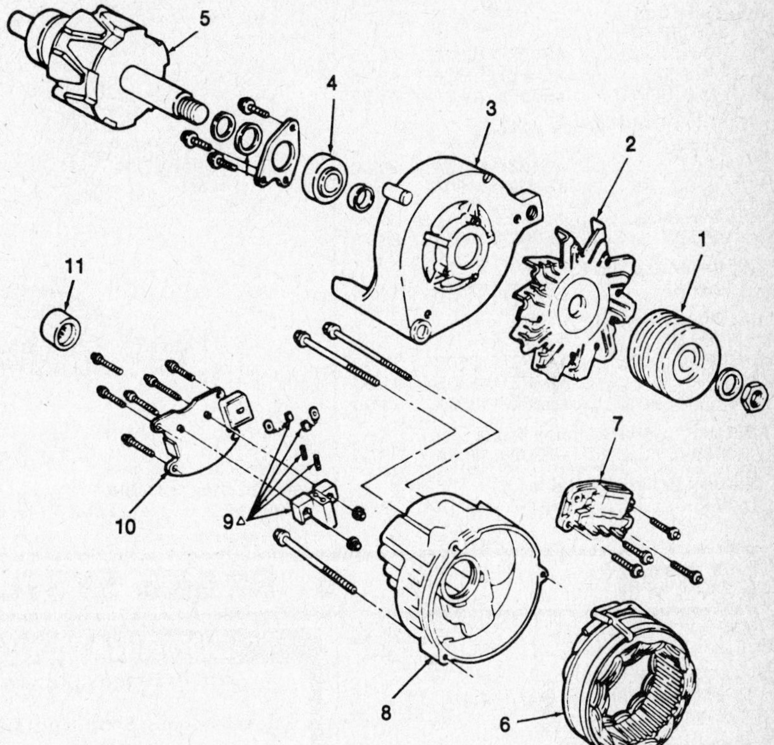

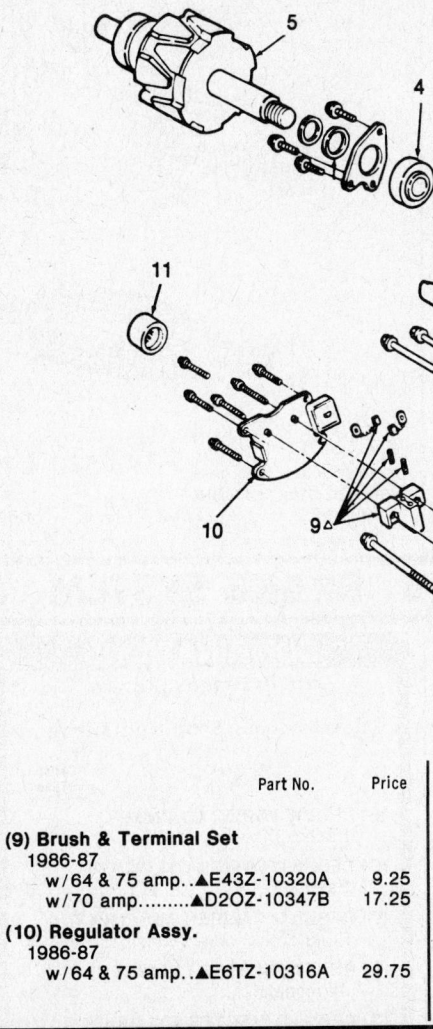

	Part No.	Price
(9) Brush & Terminal Set		
1986-87		
w/64 & 75 amp.	▲E43Z-10320A	9.25
w/70 amp.	▲D2OZ-10347B	17.25
(10) Regulator Assy.		
1986-87		
w/64 & 75 amp.	▲E6TZ-10316A	29.75
(11) Bearing (Rear)		
1986-87	▲D2OZ-10A304A	5.25
Alternator Regulator		
1986-87-w/70 amp.	▲E2PZ-10316A	36.75

Note: 64 & 75 amp. alternators have an integral regulator.

LABOR 5 STARTING SYSTEM 5 LABOR

	(Factory Time)	Chilton Time
(G) Starter Draw Test (On Car)		
All models	(.3)	.3
(G) Starter Assembly, Renew		
V-6–1986-87	(.5)	.7
Add draw test if performed.		
(G) Starter, R&R and Recondition		
Includes: Turn down armature.		
V-6–1986-87	(1.5)	2.6
Renew field coils add		.5
Add draw test if performed.		
(G) Starter Drive, Renew		
Includes: R&R starter.		
V-6–1986-87	(.7)	1.0
(G) Starter Solenoid Relay, Renew		
1986-87	(.3)	.4
(G) Ignition Switch, Renew		
1986-87	(.5)	.9
(M) Battery Cables, Renew		
1986-87		
Batt to Relay	(.3)	.4
Negative	(.3)	.3
Relay to Starter	(.4)	.5
(M) Battery Terminals, Clean		
All models		.3

PARTS 5 STARTING SYSTEM 5 PARTS

	Part No.	Price
Starter Assy. (New)		
1986-87		
Four	▲E6DZ-11002B	132.50
V-6-exc. Hi-Perf.	▲E6DZ-11002A	N.L.
Hi-Perf.	▲E6DZ-11002C	132.50
(1) Plate & Bushing (Brush End)		
1986-87	▲E6DZ-11049A	8.00
(2) Brush Set		
1986-87	▲E4PZ-11057A	13.00
(3) Brush Holder		
1986-87	▲E3FZ-11061A	3.00
(4) Field Coil		
1986-87		
Four	▲E6FZ-11082A	45.25
V-6	▲E6FZ-11082A	45.25
V-6-Hi-Perf.	▲E6DZ-11082A	45.25
(5) Drive End Housing Assy.		
1986-87		
Four	▲E43Z-11130A	29.00
V-6	▲E6DZ-11130A	N.L.
(6) Armature		
1986-87	▲E3FZ-11005A	66.75
(7) Lever and Pin Kit		
1986-87	▲E2BZ-11067A	14.25
(8) Drive Assy.		
1986-87		
Four	▲D6PZ-11350B	17.50
V-6	▲D6PZ-11350B	17.50
Hi-Perf.	▲E2PZ-11350A	21.00
Battery to Starter Relay Cable		
1986-87	▲E6DZ-14300A	6.00
Battery to Ground Cable		
1986-87	▲E6DZ-14301A	8.50

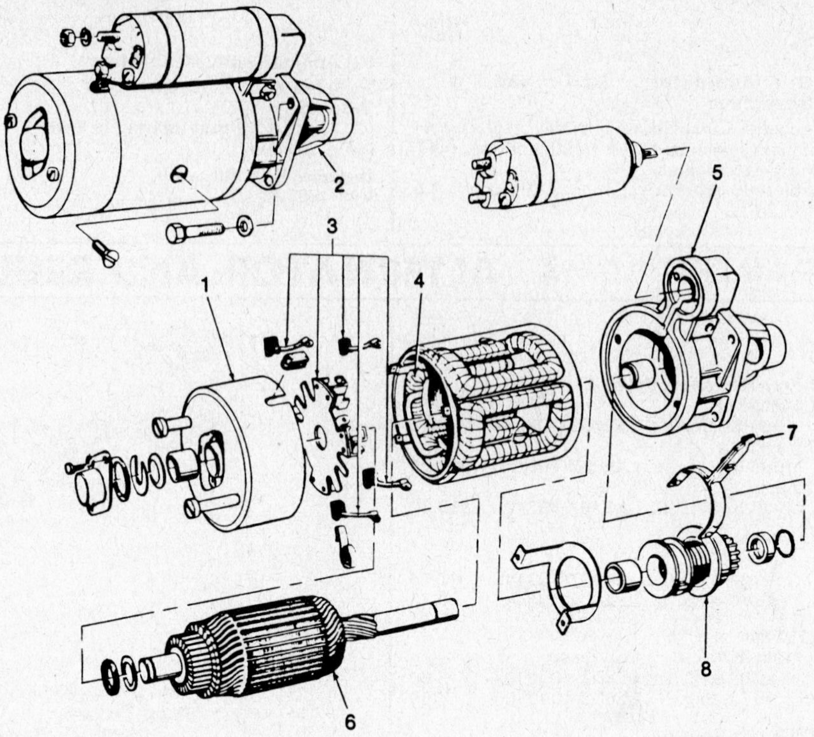

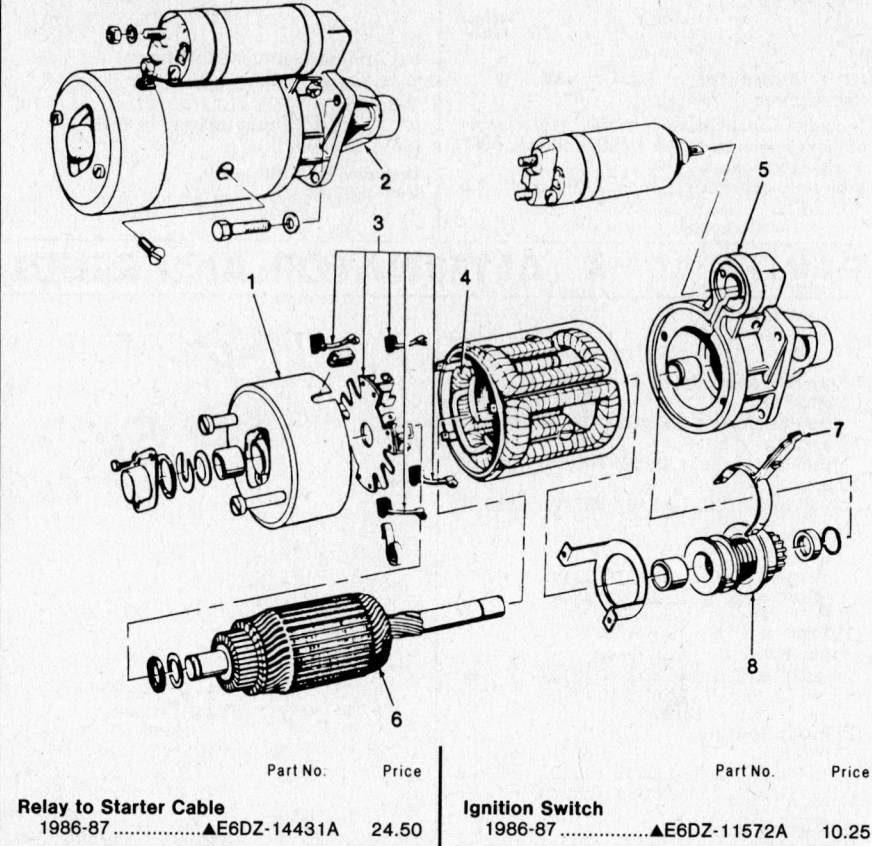

	Part No.	Price
Relay to Starter Cable		
1986-87	▲E6DZ-14431A	24.50

	Part No.	Price
Ignition Switch		
1986-87	▲E6DZ-11572A	10.25

LABOR 6 BRAKE SYSTEM 6 LABOR

	(Factory Time)	Chilton Time
(G) Brake Pedal Free Play, Adjust		
All models		.4
(B) Brakes, Adjust (Minor)		
Includes: Adjust brakes, fill master cylinder.		
two wheels		.4
(G) Bleed Brakes (Four Wheels)		
Includes: Fill master cylinder.		
All models	(.3)	.5
(G) Brake Shoes and/or Pads, Renew		
Includes: Install new or exchange brake shoes or pads. Adjust service and hand brake. Bleed system.		
1986-87		
front-disc	(.7)	1.1
rear-drum	(1.0)	1.5
all four wheels	(1.4)	2.5
Resurface brake rotor, add-each		.9
Resurface brake drum, add-each		.5
(G) Brake Drum, Renew		
1986-87-one	(.4)	.6
both	(.5)	.9

BRAKE HYDRAULIC SYSTEM

	(Factory Time)	Chilton Time
(G) Wheel Cylinder, Renew		
Includes: Bleed system.		
1986-87-one	(.8)	1.2
both	(1.4)	2.2

COMBINATIONS

Add to Brakes, Renew

See Machine Shop Operations

	(Factory Time)	Chilton Time
(G) RENEW WHEEL CYLINDER		
Each		.4
(G) REBUILD WHEEL CYLINDER		
Each		.5
(G) REBUILD CALIPER ASSEMBLY		
Each		.5
(G) RENEW MASTER CYLINDER		
All models		.8
(G) REBUILD MASTER CYLINDER		
All models		1.2
(G) RENEW BRAKE HOSE		
Each		.3
(G) RENEW REAR WHEEL GREASE SEALS		
One	(.2)	.3
Both	(.3)	.4
(G) RENEW BRAKE DRUM		
Each	(.2)	.2
(G) RENEW DISC BRAKE ROTOR		
Each	(.1)	.2
(G) REPACK REAR WHEEL BEARINGS (BOTH WHEELS)		
All models		.5

	(Factory Time)	Chilton Time
(G) Wheel Cylinder, R&R and Rebuild		
Includes: Bleed system.		
1986-87-one	(1.1)	1.6
both	(1.8)	3.0
(G) Master Cylinder, Renew		
Includes: Bleed system.		
1986-87	(.6)	1.0
(G) Master Cylinder, R&R and Rebuild		
Includes: Bleed system.		
1986-87	(.9)	1.4
(G) Brake Hose, Renew		
Includes: Bleed system.		
1986-87-front-one	(.4)	.7
rear-one	(.5)	.8
(G) Brake System, Flush and Refill		
All models		1.2

POWER BRAKES

	(Factory Time)	Chilton Time
(G) Power Brake Booster, Renew		
V-6–1986-87	(1.3)	1.8
(G) Power Brake Booster Check Valve, Renew		
1986-87	(.3)	.4

DISC BRAKES

	(Factory Time)	Chilton Time
(G) Disc Brake Pads, Renew		
Includes: Install new disc brake pads only.		
1986-87	(.7)	1.1

LABOR 6 BRAKE SYSTEM 6 LABOR

	(Factory Time)	Chilton Time
Resurface brake rotor, add-each		.9
(G) Caliper Assembly, Renew		
Includes: Bleed system.		
1986-87-one	(.6)	.9
both	(.8)	1.6
(G) Caliper Assy., R&R and Reconditon		
Includes: Bleed system.		
1986-87-one	(.8)	1.4
both	(1.2)	2.6
(G) Disc Brake Rotor, Renew		
1986-87-one	(.4)	.5
both	(.5)	.8
(G) Brake Differential Valve, Renew		
Includes: Bleed complete system and transfer switch.		
1986-87		
Sdn	(.6)	.9
Sta wag-one	(.5)	.8
both	(.6)	1.0
PARKING BRAKE		
(M) Parking Brake, Adjust		
1986-87	(.3)	.5
(G) Parking Brake Control, Renew		
1986-87	(.7)	1.1
(G) Parking Brake Control to Equalizer Cable, Renew		
1986-87	(.6)	.8
(G) Parking Brake Power Vacuum Unit, Renew		
1986-87	(.3)	.5
(G) Parking Brake Cables, Renew		
1986-87-one	(.7)	.9
both	(1.1)	1.3

PARTS 6 BRAKE SYSTEM 6 PARTS

	Part No.	Price
Brake Shoe Set (Rear)		
1986-87-exc. Sta. Wag.	▲E6DZ-2200A	59.75
Station wag.	▲E6DZ-2200B	73.50
Brake Lining Kit		
1986-87-exc. Sta. Wag.	▲E6DZ-2007B	27.50
Station wag.	▲E6DZ-2007A	29.50
Rear Wheel Cylinder Assy.		
1986-87	▲E6DZ-2261A	17.25
Wheel Cylinder Repair Kit		
1986-87	▲E6DZ-2128A	4.75
Brake Hose (Front)		
1986-87-R.H.	▲E6DZ-2078A	15.75
left	▲E6DZ-2078B	15.75
Master Cylinder Assy.		
1986-87-sedan	▲E6DZ-2140A	90.75
Station wag.	▲E6DZ-2140B	90.75
Repair Kit (Master Cyl.)		
1986-87-sedan	▲E6DZ-2004A	31.75
Station wag.	▲E6DZ-2004B	N.L.
Rear Brake Hose		
1986-87-R.H.	▲E6DZ-2282B	12.75
left	▲E6DZ-2282A	12.75
Hub & Drum Assy. (Rear)		
1986-87-w/o alum. whls.		
exc. Sta. Wag.	▲E6DZ-1113B	N.L.
Station wag.	▲E6DZ-1113A	60.75
1986-87-w/alum. whls.		
exc. Sta. Wag.	▲E6DZ-1113C	60.75
Station wag.	▲E6DZ-1113D	60.75
Rear Wheel Oil Seal		
1986-87	▲E6DZ-1249A	3.25
Brake Booster Assy. (New)		
1986-87	▲E6DZ-2005A	156.75
Parking Brake Control		
1986-87		
w/manual release	▲E6DZ-2780A	34.50
w/auto release	▲E6DZ-2780B	69.25
Parking Brake Cable (Rear)		
1986-87-R.H.	▲E6DZ-2A635B	16.25
left	▲E6DZ-2A635C	16.25

PARTS 6 DISC BRAKES 6 PARTS

	Part No.	Price
(1) Caliper Assy. (Front)		
1986-87-R.H.	▲E6DZ-2B120B	87.00
left	▲E6DZ-2B121B	87.00
(2) Brake Pads		
1986-87		
exc. Sta. Wag.	▲E6DZ-2001A	46.75
Sta. wag.	▲E6DZ-2001B	N.L.
(3) Caliper Repair Kit		
1986-87	▲E6DZ-2221A	8.00
(4) Front Caliper Piston		
1986-87	▲N.L.	
(5) Knuckle Assy. (Front Whl.)		
1986-87-R.H.	▲E6DZ-3K185A	118.50
left	▲E6DZ-3K186A	118.50
(6) Shield (Front Brake Rotor)		
1986-87-R.H.	▲E6DZ-2K004A	6.50
left	▲E6DZ-2K005A	6.50
(7) Drive Hub (Front Whl.)		
1986-87	▲E6DZ-1104A	69.00
(8) Rotor		
1986-87	▲E6DZ-1125A	48.75

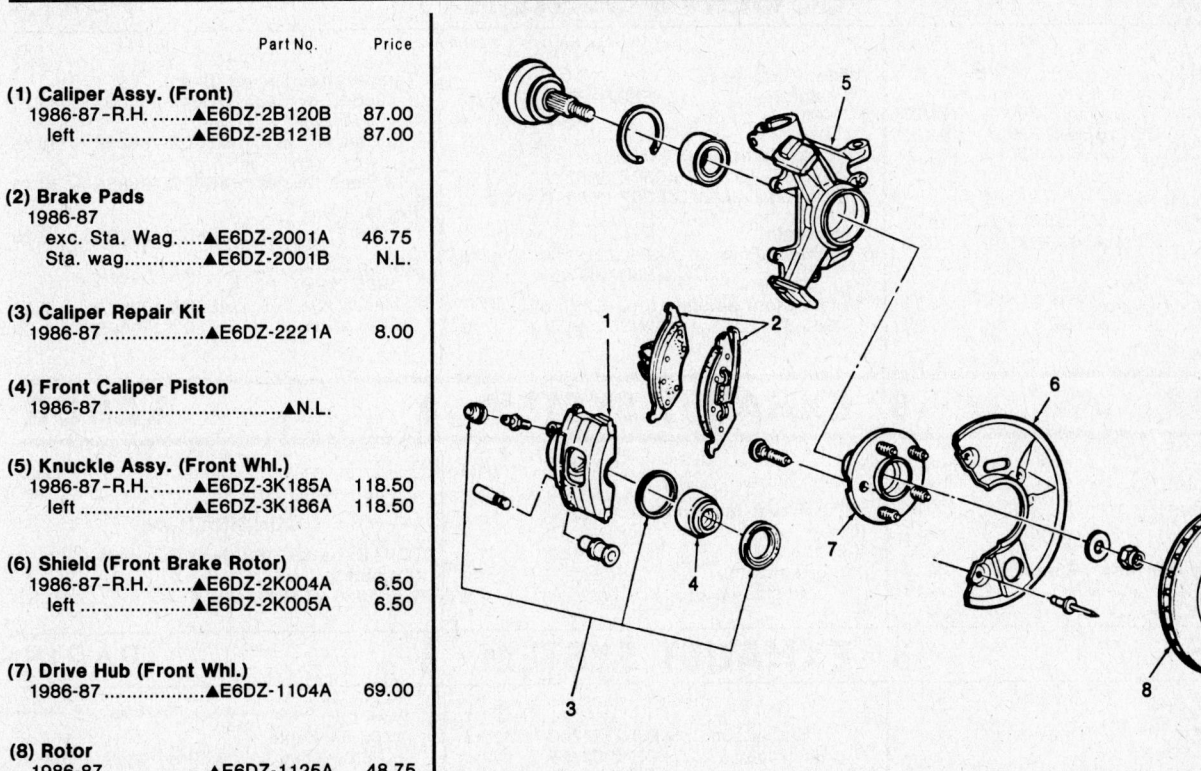

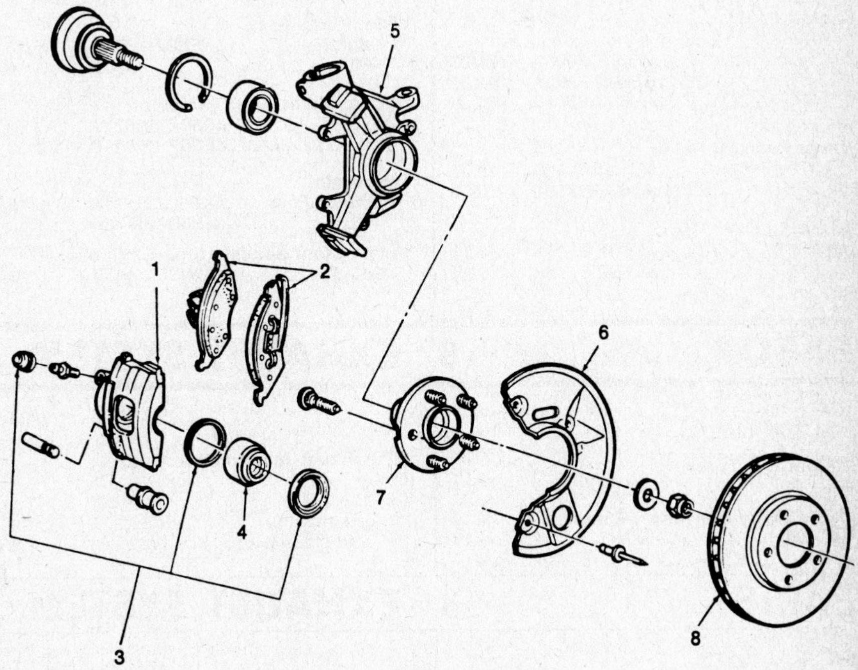

LABOR 7 COOLING SYSTEM 7 LABOR

(Factory Time) Chilton Time

(M) Winterize Cooling System

Includes: Run engine to check for leaks, tighten all hose connections. Test radiator and pressure cap, drain radiator and engine block. Add anti-freeze and refill system.

All models .5

(M) Thermostat, Renew

V-6–1986-87 (.7) 1.0

(M) Radiator Assembly, R&R or Renew

Includes: Drain and refill cooling system.

V-6–1986-87 (.9) 1.4

Renew side tank add

one (.5) .7

both (.9) 1.3

(M) Radiator Hoses, Renew

1986-87

upper (.4) .4

lower (.5) .5

both (.6) .6

(G) Water Pump, Renew

V-6–1986-87 (1.3) 2.0

(G) Fan Blade, Renew

1986-87 (.4) .6

Renew motor add (.1) .1

(M) Drive Belt, Renew

1986-87

V-6 (.3) .5

(M) Drive Belt, Adjust

1986-87

V-6 (.2) .3

COOLING SYSTEM TUNE-UP

An Annual Cooling System Tune-Up Suggestion List should include (with some exceptions):

1. A visual check of the cooling system for indications of leaks or excessive oil content
2. Pressure check the cooling system for internal and external leaks with filler cap and neck adapter and tester
3. Check crankcase and automatic transmission oil for water content
4. Test coolant thermostat with radiator thermometer
5. Check temperature gauge for accuracy
6. Drain system and flush till clean
7. Clean foreign matter from radiator fins
8. Test radiator pressure cap with cap tester
9. Check fan blades and pulleys for alignment and damage
10. Internal and external inspection of all hoses for cracks and deterioration
11. Check core plugs (where possible) for seepage
12. Refill system with correct coolant and check for air locks
13. Check condition and tension of drive belts with tension gauge

All models 1.5

(Factory Time) Chilton Time

(G) Water Jacket Expansion Plugs, Renew (Side of Block)

each .5

Add time to gain accessibility.

(Factory Time) Chilton Time

(G) Electric Cooling Fan Motor, Renew

1986-87 (.5) .7

(G) Temperature Gauge (Dash Unit), Renew

1986-87

Std cluster (1.0) 1.7

Sport cluster (.7) 1.2

(G) Temperature Gauge (Engine Unit), Renew

1986-87 (.3) .4

(G) Heater Hoses, Renew

1986-87–each (.4) .5

(G) Heater Control Assembly, Renew

1986-87 (1.0) 1.5

(G) Heater Blower Motor Switch, Renew

1986-87 (1.0) 1.5

(G) Heater Blower Motor Resistor, Renew

1986-87 (.3) .5

(G) Heater Core, R&R or Renew

1986-87

wo/A.C. (2.3) 5.0

w/A.C. (3.1) 6.0

ADD THESE OPERATIONS TO HEATER CORE R&R

(G) Boil & Repair 1.2

(G) Repair Core .9

(G) Recore 1.2

(G) Heater Blower Motor, Renew

1986-87 (.8) 1.5

(G) Temperature Control Cable, Renew

1986-87 (.8) 1.5

PARTS 7 COOLING SYSTEM 7 PARTS

	Part No.	Price
Radiator Assy.		
1986-87		
four	▲E6DZ-8005A	194.25
V-6-exc. A.C	▲E6DZ-8005A	194.25
w/A.C.	▲E6DZ-8005B	194.25
Upper Radiator Hose		
1986-87-Four	▲E6DZ-8260A	16.00
V-6	▲E6DZ-8260B	16.00
Lower Radiator Hose		
1986-87-Four	▲E6DZ-8286A	14.25
V-6	▲E6DZ-8286B	18.25

	Part No.	Price
Water Pump Assy.		
1986-87-V-6	▲E6DZ-8501A	65.75
Four	▲N.L.	
Electric Motor Assy. (Radiator)		
1986-87-A.T.	▲E6DZ-8K621A	72.50
M.T.	▲E6DZ-8K621B	72.50
Thermostat		
1986-87-Four	▲E63Z-8575A	5.75
V-6	▲E6DZ-8575A	N.L.
Temperature Sending Unit (Engine)		
1986-87	▲D0WY-10884A	5.25

	Part No.	Price
Temperature Gauge (Dash)		
1986-87-w/Tach.	▲E64Z-10883A	30.25
w/Elect. Cluster	▲E6DZ-10883B	30.25
wo/Tach or Elect. Cluster	▲E6DZ-10883A	30.25
Heater Core		
1986-87	▲E6DZ-18476A	59.25
Switch Assy.		
1986-87-w/ manual	▲E6DZ-19986A	7.50
w/A.T.C.	▲E6DZ-19986B	12.00

LABOR 8 EXHAUST SYSTEM 8 LABOR

(Factory Time) Chilton Time

(G) Muffler, Renew

V-6–1986-87 (.8) 1.1

(G) Catalytic Converter, Renew

V-6–1986-87 (.6) .9

(Factory Time) Chilton Time

(G) Exhaust Manifold or Gasket, Renew

V-6–1986-87

one side (.9) 1.2

both sides (1.6) 2.2

(Factory Time) Chilton Time

COMBINATIONS

(G) Exhaust System, Renew (Complete)

V-6–1986-87 (1.3) 1.8

PARTS 8 EXHAUST SYSTEM 8 PARTS

	Part No.	Price
Muffler Assy.		
1986-87-Taurus		
Four-sedan	▲E6DZ-5230A	98.75
Sta. wagon	▲E6DZ-5230C	112.75
V-6-sedan	▲E6DZ-5230B	98.75
Sta. wagon	▲E6DZ-5230D	112.75
1986-87-Sable		
Four-sedan	▲E64Y-5230A	98.75
V-6-sedan	▲E64Y-5230B	98.75

PARTS 8 EXHAUST SYSTEM 8 PARTS

	Part No.	Price
Sta. wagon	▲E6DZ-5230D	112.75
Catalytic Converter		
1986-87-Four	▲E6DZ-5E212A	377.50
V-6	▲E6DZ-5F250A	231.75

	Part No.	Price
Inlet Pipe		
1986-87-Four		
M.T.	▲E6DZ-5246A	56.50
A.T.	▲E6DZ-5246B	56.50
1986-87-V-6	▲E6DZ-5A289A	27.50

	Part No.	Price
Exhaust Manifold		
1986-87-Four	▲E6AZ-9430E	110.50
V-6-L.H.	▲E6AZ-9431D	119.50
exc. Canada,		
R.H.	▲E6AZ-9430D	119.50
Canada R.H.	▲E6AZ-9430H	N.L.

LABOR 9 FRONT SUSPENSION 9 LABOR

(Factory Time) Chilton Time

Note: On all front suspension operations alignment charges must be added if performed. Time given does not include alignment.

	Chilton Time
(M) Wheel, Renew	
one	.5
(M) Wheels, Rotate (All)	
All models	.5
(G) Wheels, Balance	
one	.3
each adtnl	.2
(G) Check Alignment of Front End	
All models	.5
Note: Deduct if alignment is performed.	
(G) Front Toe-In, Check and Adjust	
All models (.6)	.8
(G) Rear Toe-In, Check and Adjust	
All models	
one side (.6)	.8
both sides (.7)	.9
(G) Lower Control Arm Assy., Renew	
Add alignment charges.	
1986-87-one side (.7)	1.0
both sides (1.1)	1.5
(G) Front Spindle Carrier/Knuckle, Renew	
Add alignment charges.	
1986-87-one side (1.3)	1.8
both sides (2.4)	3.3
(G) Front Coil Springs, Renew	
Includes: R&R front strut.	
1986-87-one (1.2)	1.6
both (2.1)	2.9
(G) Front Stabilizer Bar, Renew	
1986-87 (1.0)	1.3
(G) Front Strut Shock Absorber Assy., R&R or Renew	
1986-87-one (1.2)	1.6
both (2.2)	3.0
(G) Halfshaft Assy., R&R or Renew	
1986-87-one (1.0)	1.4
both (1.8)	2.5
(G) C.V. Joint, Renew or Recondition	
Includes: R&R halfshaft.	
1986-87-one (1.2)	1.6
two (2.1)	2.9
each adtnl	.3
(G) Differential Oil Seal, Renew	
Includes: R&R halfshaft.	
1986-87-one (1.1)	1.5
both (1.9)	2.6

PARTS 9 FRONT SUSPENSION 9 PARTS

	Part No.	Price
(1) Knuckle Assy. (Front Whl.)		
1986-87-R.H.	▲E6DZ-3K185A	118.50
left	▲E6DZ-3K186A	118.50
(2) Lower Arm Assy.		
1986-87-R.H.	▲E6DZ-3078A	99.25
left	▲E6DZ-3079A	99.25
(3) Lower Arm Strut		
1986-87	▲E6DZ-3468A	20.75
(4) Stabilizer Bar Assy.		
1986-87-sedan	▲E6DZ-5482A	38.50
Station wag.	▲E6DZ-5482B	38.50
(5) Insulator (Stabilizer)		
1986-87-sedan	▲E6DZ-5493C	8.50
Station wag.	▲E6DZ-5493B	8.50
(6) Stabilizer Bar Bracket		
1986-87	▲E6DZ-5486A	6.75
(7) Link Assy.		
1986-87	▲E6DZ-5K484A	11.50
(8) Shock Absorber		
1986-87	▲E6DZ-18124A	N.L.
(9) Bearing and Seal Assy.		
1986-87	▲E6DZ-3B455A	9.50
(10) Mounting Bracket (Shock)		
1986-87	▲E6DZ-18183A	13.75

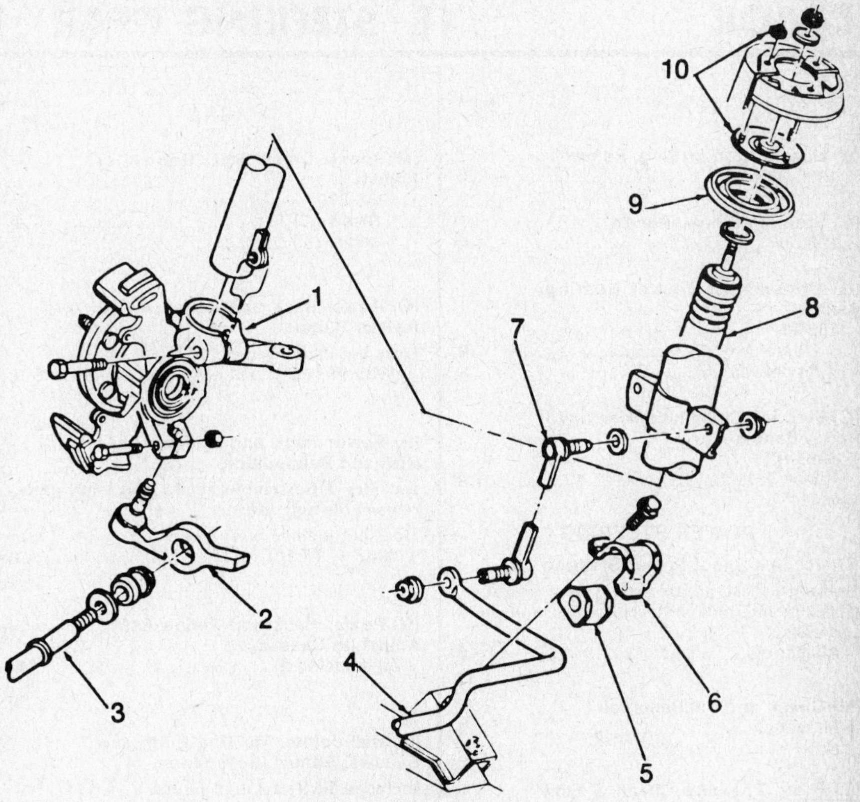

	Part No.	Price
(1) Joint Assy.		
1986-87-Four		
Outer	▲E6DZ-3B413B	212.50
Inner R.H.	▲E6DZ-3B414A	214.25
left-ATX	▲E6DZ-3B414C	N.L.
MTX	▲E6DZ-3B414B	214.25
1986-87-V-6		
T & C Type		
Outer	▲E6DZ-3B413A	212.50
Inner R.H.	▲E6DZ-3B414E	214.25
left	▲E6DZ-3B414F	214.25
G.K.N. Type		
Outer	▲E6DZ-3B413B	212.50
Inner R.H.	▲E6DZ-3B414D	214.25
left	▲E6DZ-3B414A	214.25
(2) Boot Kit		
1986-87-Four		
Outer	▲E6DZ-3A331A	7.75
Inner	▲E6DZ-3A331B	7.75
1986-87-V-6		
Outer	▲E6DZ-3A331A	7.75
Inner G.K.N. type		
R.H.	▲E6DZ-3A331D	7.75
L.H.	▲E6DZ-3A331B	7.75
Inner T & C Type		
R.H.	▲E6DZ-3A331C	7.75
L.H.	▲E6DZ-3A331E	7.75
(3) Axle Shaft		
1986-87-Four		
ATX	▲E6DZ-3A329B	133.00
MTX-R.H.	▲E6DZ-3A329A	133.00
left	▲E6DZ-3A329C	37.75

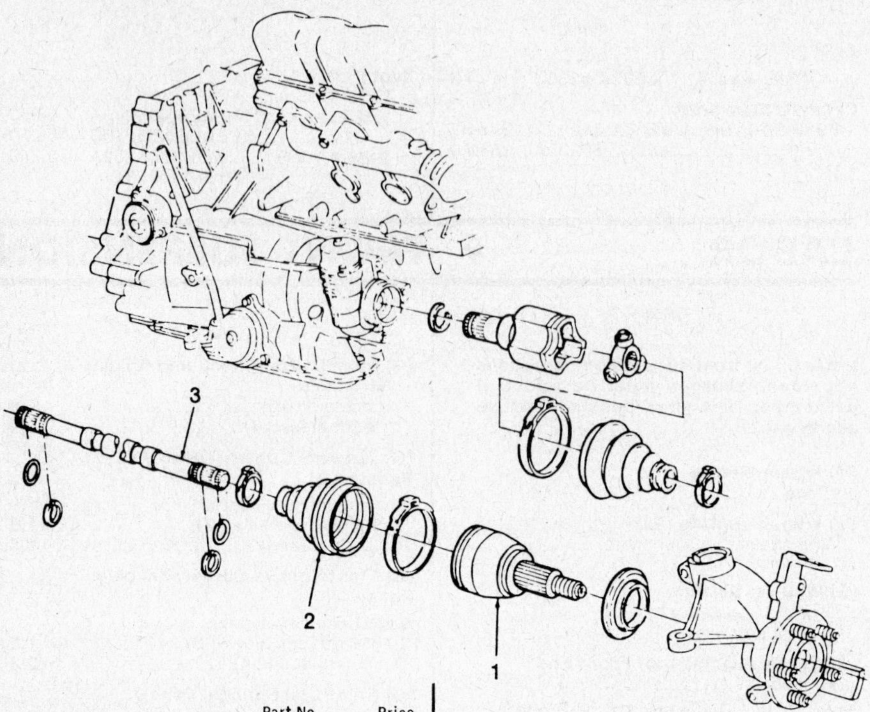

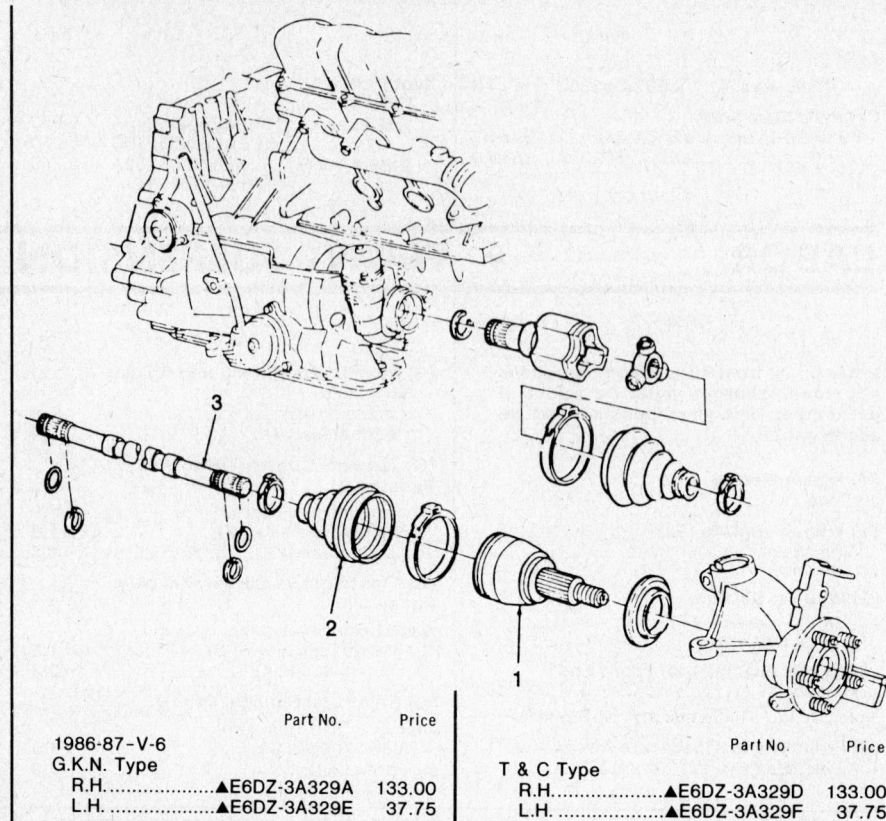

	Part No.	Price
1986-87-V-6		
G.K.N. Type		
R.H.	▲E6DZ-3A329A	133.00
L.H.	▲E6DZ-3A329E	37.75

	Part No.	Price
T & C Type		
R.H.	▲E6DZ-3A329D	133.00
L.H.	▲E6DZ-3A329F	37.75

LABOR 11 STEERING GEAR 11 LABOR

(Factory Time) — Chilton Time

(G) Horn Button or Ring, Renew
1986-87 (.3) 5

(G) Steering Wheel, Renew
1986-87 (.3) 4

(G) Upper Mast Jacket Bearing, Renew
1986-87
std column (.5) 9
tilt column (.5) 9

(G) Steering Column Lock Actuator Parts, Renew
1986-87
w/A.T. (1.2) 1.8

POWER STEERING

(G) Trouble Shoot Power Steering
Includes: Test pump and system pressure. Check pounds pull on steering wheel and check for leaks.
All models 5

(M) Check and Fill Reservoir
All models 2

(G) Pump Pressure Check & Flow Test
All models 1.0

(M) Pump Drive Belt, Renew or Adjust
1986-87
renew (.3) 4
adjust (.2) 3

(G) Power Rack and Pinion Assy., R&R or Renew
Does not include reset toe-in.
1986-87 (2.6) 3.8

(P) Power Rack and Pinion Assy., R&R and Recondition
Includes: Disassemble, renew necessary parts, reassemble and adjust.
Does not include reset toe-in.
1986-87 (3.1) 5.1

(G) Power Rack and Pinion Assy., Adjust (In Chassis)
All models (.3) 6

(G) Ball Joints, Tie Rod Ends and Bellows, Renew (Both Sides)
Includes: R&R rack and pinion assy. Does not include reset toe-in.
1986-87 (2.2) 3.1

(G) Input Shaft Seals, Renew (In Chassis)
1986-87 (1.3) 2.0

(G) Power Steering Oil Pump, Renew
Includes: Bleed system.
1986-87
V-6 (1.3) 1.8

(G) Power Steering Oil Pump, R&R and Recondition
Includes: Bleed system.
1986-87
V-6 (1.7) 2.4

(G) Power Steering Pump Shaft Oil Seal, Renew
Includes: R&R pump and bleed system.
1986-87
V-6 (1.4) 1.9

(G) Power Steering Reservoir Seal Kit, Renew
Includes: Bleed system.
1986-87 (1.6) 2.1

(G) Power Steering Hoses, Renew
1986-87
Pressure-V-6 (1.0) 1.4
Return-V-6 (1.0) 1.4

PARTS 11 POWER STEERING GEAR 11 PARTS

	Part No.	Price
Steering Gear Assy.		
1986-87	▲E6DZ-3504A	559.75
(1) End Cover		
1986-87	▲D8BZ-3568A	5.00
(2) Worm Bearing Cup		
1986-87	▲D8BZ-3552A	13.25
(3) Housing Assy.		
1986-87	▲N.L.	
(4) Shaft and Control Valve Assy.		
1986-87	▲N.L.	
(5) Input Shaft Bearing		
1986-87	▲D8AZ-3D525A	8.75
(6) Seal Kit (Sector Shaft)		
1986-87	▲E6DZ-3E501A	12.50
(7) Support Yoke		
1986-87	▲D8BZ-3F515B	7.00
(8) Housing Cover (Sector Shaft)		
1986-87	▲E6DZ-3580A	8.50
(9) Bushing		
1986-87	▲E6DZ-3576A	N.L.
(10) Cover (Housing End)		
1986-87	▲D8BZ-3568B	5.00
(11) Dust Seal Kit (Ball Stud)		
1986-87	▲E69Z-3332A	10.25
(12) Pressure Tube (Left Turn)		
1986-87	▲E6DZ-3A714A	14.25
(13) Pressure Tube (Right Turn)		
1986-87	▲E6DZ-3A717A	14.25
(14) Tube (Gear Rack)		
1986-87	▲E6DZ-3K762A	4.75
(15) Sector Shaft		
1986-87	▲E6DZ-3575A	91.25
(16) Connecting Rod		
1986-87	▲E6DZ-3280A	19.50
(17) Tie Rod End		
1986-87	▲E6DZ-3A130A	38.75

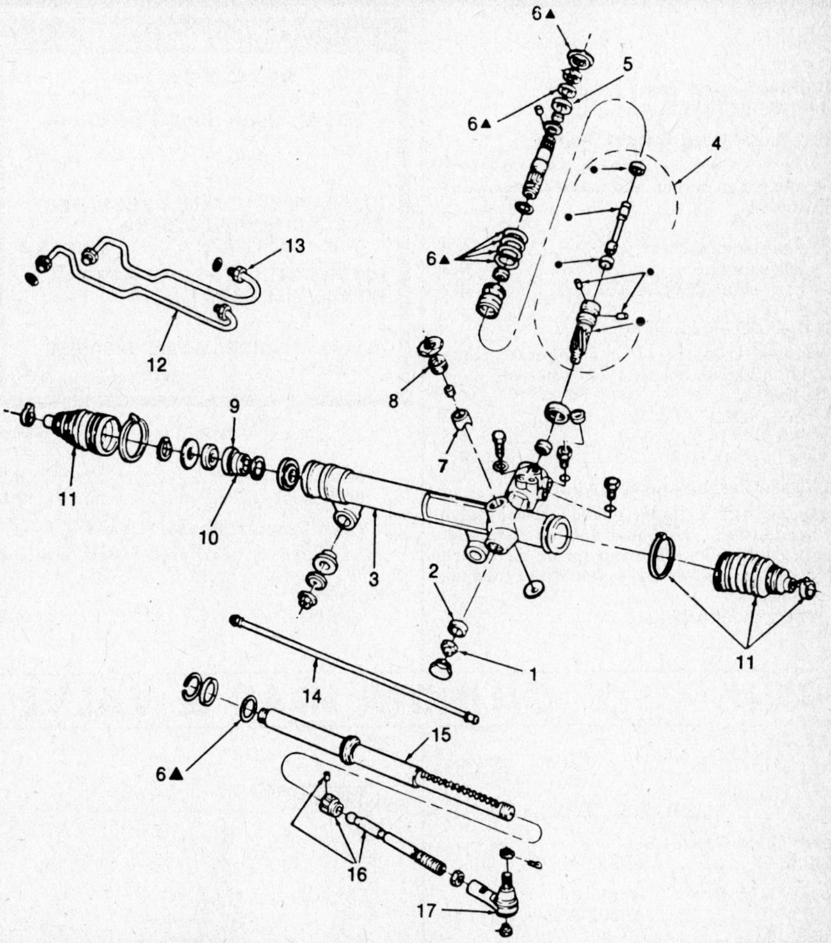

PARTS 11 POWER STEERING PUMP 11 PARTS

	Part No.	Price
Power Steering Pump		
1986-87	▲E6DZ-3A674A	194.50
(1) Valve Spring (Flow Control)		
1986-87	▲D8AZ-3D586A	1.50
(2) Housing Assy.		
1986-87	▲E1AZ-3A643A	42.25
(3) Pressure Plate (Rear)		
1986-87	▲D8AZ-3D590B	13.75
(4) Oil Filler Cap Assy.		
1986-87	▲E6DZ-3A006A	5.00
(5) Rotor Shaft		
1986-87	▲D8AZ-3B559A	18.00
(6) Pressure Plate (Front)		
1986-87	▲E5FZ-3D590A	13.75
(7) Spring (Pressure Plate)		
1986-87	▲E6FZ-3D596A	2.50
(8) Plate and Bushing Assy.		
1986-87	▲E1AZ-3D643A	38.50

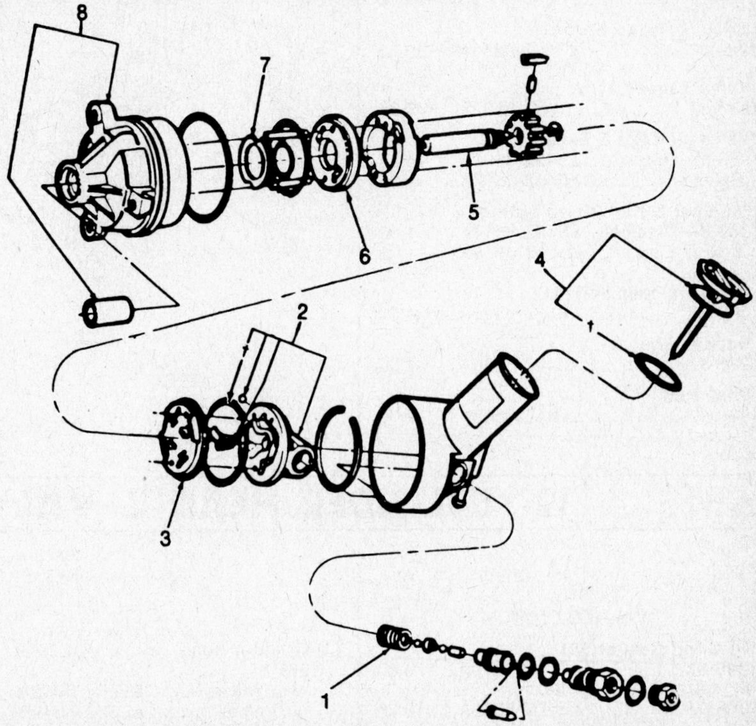

LABOR 12 CYLINDER HEAD & VALVE SYSTEM 12 LABOR

(Factory Time) — Chilton Time

(G) Compression Test
V-6–1986-87 (.4)................................ .6

(G) Cylinder Head Gasket, Renew
Includes: Check cylinder head and block flatness. Clean carbon and make all necessary adjustments.
V-6–1986-87
right side (4.2) 5.8
left side (4.6).............................. 6.3
both sides (5.9)............................ 8.2

(G) Cylinder Head, Renew
Includes: Transfer all components, clean carbon. Make all necessary adjustments.
V-6–1986-87
right side (4.4) 6.3
left side (4.8).............................. 6.8
both sides (6.2)............................ 9.2

(G) Clean Carbon and Grind Valves
Includes: R&R cylinder head(s), check valve spring tension, valve seat and head runout, stem to guide clearance and spring assembled height. Grind valves and seats. Minor tune up.
V-6–1986-87
right side (5.6) 7.5
left side (6.0)............................... 8.3
both sides (8.7)............................ 12.0

(G) Valve Tappets, Renew (Lifters)
Includes: Adjust carburetor and ignition timing.
V-6–1986-87
one cyl (2.9)................................ 4.2
all cyls-one side (3.2)................ 4.6
all cyls-both sides (3.5)............... 5.0

(G) Rocker Arm Cover Gasket, Renew
V-6–1986-87
right side (.6) 9
left side (.5)............................... .8
both sides (.9)............................ 1.5

(G) Valve Push Rods and/or Rocker Arms, Renew
V-6–1986-87
right side-one cyl (.7)................ 1.1
right side-all cyls (.9)................ 1.4
left side-one cyl (.6)................... 1.0
left side-all cyls (.8).................. 1.3
all cyls-both sides (1.5) 2.2

(G) Valve Springs and/or Valve Stem Oil Seals, Renew (Head on Car)
V-6–1986-87
right side-one cyl (.9)................ 1.3
left side-one cyl (.8).................. 1.2
each adtnl cyl (.3)...................... .3
all cyls-both sides (3.1) 4.1

COMBINATIONS

Add to Valve Job

See Machine Shop Operations

(Factory Time) — Chilton Time

(G) DRAIN, EVACUATE & RECHARGE AIR CONDITIONING SYSTEM
All models (.7).................... 1.2

(G) HYDRAULIC VALVE LIFTERS, DISASSEMBLE AND CLEAN
Each 2

(G) VALVE GUIDES, REAM OVERSIZE
Each (.1)............................. .2

PARTS 12 CYLINDER HEAD & VALVE SYSTEM 12 PARTS

FOUR–2.5 (153)

	Part No.	Price
Valve Grind Gasket Set		
1986-87	▲E53Z-6079B	49.00
Rocker Arm Cover Gasket		
1986-87	▲E63Z-6584A	11.25
(1) Cylinder Head		
1986-87		
wo/valves	▲E63Z-6049A	387.75
w/valves	▲E63Z-6049B	590.00
(2) Cylinder Head Gasket		
1986-87	▲E53Z-6051A	12.75
(3) Valve Tappet Assy.		
1986-87	▲D9HZ-6500A	9.25
(4) Valves (Intake & Exhaust)		
1986-87-Intake	▲E43Z-6505A	14.25
Exhaust	▲E43Z-6507A	9.00
(5) Retainer & Key (Valve Spring)		
1986-87-Retainer	▲E43Z-6514A	1.00
Key	▲D0AZ-6518A	1.00
(6) Valve Damper Spring		
1986-87	▲E53Z-6513A	4.50
(7) Rocker Arm		
1986-87	▲E43Z-6564A	7.00
(8) Push Rod		
1986-87	▲E6AZ-6565A	2.00

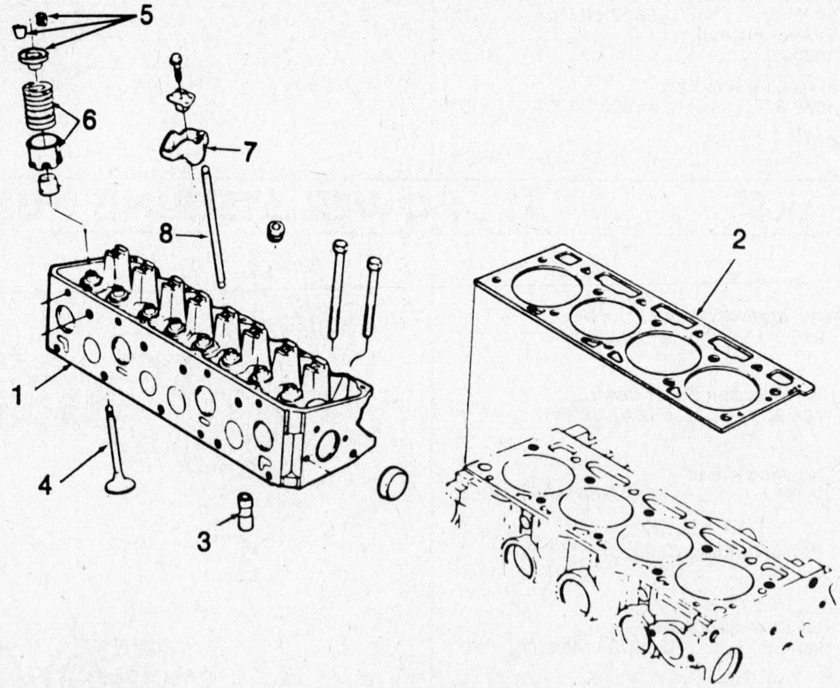

PARTS 12 CYLINDER HEAD & VALVE SYSTEM 12 PARTS

V-6–3.0 (183)

	Part No.	Price
Valve Grind Gasket Set		
1986-87	▲E6DZ-6079A	75.00
Rocker Arm Cover Gasket		
1986-87	▲E6DZ-6584A	8.25
(1) Cylinder Head		
1986-87		
wo/Valves	▲E6DZ-6049A	286.50
w/Valves	▲E6DZ-6049B	
(2) Cylinder Head Gasket		
1986-87	▲E6DZ-6051A	12.50
(3) Valve Tappet Assy.		
1986-87	▲D9HZ-6500A	9.25

PARTS 12 CYLINDER HEAD & VALVE SYSTEM 12 PARTS

	Part No.	Price
(4) Valves (Intake & Exhaust)		
1986-87-Intake	▲E6DZ-6507A	8.25
Exhaust	▲E6DZ-6505A	9.00
(5) Retainer & Key (Valve Spring)		
1986-87-Retainer	▲E3FZ-6514A	1.00
Key	▲E1FZ-6518A	.75
(6) Valve Damper Spring		
1986-87	▲E6DZ-6513A	4.75
(7) Bolt (Cylinder Head)		
1986-87	▲E43Z-6065A	1.50
(8) Rocker Arm		
1986-87	▲E6DZ-6564A	6.50
(9) Push Rod		
1986-87	▲E6DZ-6565A	2.00

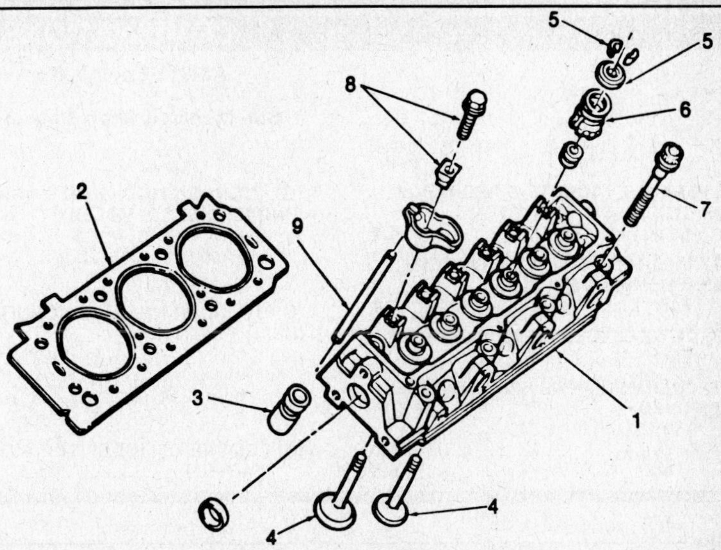

LABOR 13 ENGINE ASSEMBLY & MOUNTS 13 LABOR

(Factory Time) Chilton Time

(G) Engine Assembly, Remove and Install

Does not include transfer of any parts or equipment.

V-6–1986-87 (4.6)	6.5
w/A.C. add (.7)	.7

(P) Cylinder Assembly, Renew (w/All Internal Parts Less Head(s) and Oil Pan)

Includes: R&R engine, transfer all component parts not supplied with replacement engine. Make all necessary adjustments.

V-6–1986-87 (9.7)	13.5
w/A.C. add (.7)	.7
Recond valves add (2.8)	3.8

(P) Cylinder Block, Renew

Includes: R&R engine, transfer all component parts, renew rings and bearings, clean carbon, grind valves. Minor tune up.

V-6–1986-87 (13.9)	19.6
w/A.C. add (.7)	.7

(P) Engine Assy., R&R and Recondition

Includes: Rebore block, install new pistons, rings, rod and main bearings. Clean carbon, grind valves. Tune engine.

V-6–1986-87 (19.7)	27.5
w/A.C. add (.7)	.7

(P) Engine Assembly, Recondition (In Car)

Includes: Expand or renew pistons, install new rings, rod and main bearings. Clean carbon, grind valves. Tune engine.

V-6–1986-87 (18.3)	26.5

(G) Engine Mounts, Renew

Front	
V-6–1986-87	
right (.4)	.6
left (.5)	.7
both (.7)	1.1
Rear	
V-6–1986-87 (1.3)	1.7

PARTS 13 ENGINE ASSEMBLY & MOUNTS 13 PARTS

	Part No.	Price
Engine Gasket Set (Lower)		
Four		
1986-87	▲E43Z-6E078A	26.75
V-6	▲E6DZ-6E078A	30.25

Note: When a complete overhaul gasket set is required you must also order a valve grind gasket set.

	Part No.	Price
Cylinder Assy.		
1986-87-Four	▲E63Z-6009A	1529.00
V-6	▲E6DZ-6009A	1885.00
Cylinder Block Assy.		
1986-87-Four	▲E63Z-6010A	688.25
V-6	▲E6DZ-6010A	848.25
Front Engine Mount (R.H.)		
1986-87	▲E6DZ-6038B	31.25
V-6	▲E6DZ-6038A	41.25
Rear Engine Mount (R.H.)		
1986-87-Four	▲E6DZ-6068B	35.50
V-6	▲E6DZ-6068A	35.50
Engine & Trans. Mount		
1986-87-Four	▲E6DZ-6F065B	71.50
V-6	▲E6DZ-6F065A	68.75

LABOR 14 PISTONS, RINGS & BEARINGS 14 LABOR

(Factory Time) Chilton Time

(P) Rings, Renew (See Engine Combinations)

Includes: Remove cylinder top ridge, deglaze cylinder walls, replace rod bearings, clean carbon. Minor tune up.

V-6–1986-87	
one cyl-right side (6.4)	9.2
one cyl-left side (6.8)	9.8
one cyl-each side (8.6)	12.4
all cyls-both sides (10.7)	15.5

(P) Piston or Connecting Rod, Renew

Includes: Remove cylinder top ridge, deglaze cylinder walls, replace rod bearings, clean carbon. Minor tune up.

V-6–1986-87	
one cyl-right side (6.7)	9.7
one cyl-left side (7.1)	10.2
one cyl-each side (9.2)	13.3
all cyls-both sides (12.5)	18.1

(P) Connecting Rod Bearings, Renew

Includes: Check all bearing clearances.

V-6–1986-87 (3.3)	4.5

LABOR 14 PISTONS, RINGS & BEARINGS 14 LABOR

COMBINATIONS

Add to Engine Work

See Machine Shop Operations

	(Factory Time)	Chilton Time
(G) DRAIN, EVACUATE & RECHARGE AIR CONDITIONING SYSTEM		
All models	(.7)	1.2
(G) HYDRAULIC VALVE LIFTERS, DISASSEMBLE AND CLEAN		
Each		.2
(G) VALVE GUIDES, REAM OVERSIZE		
Each	(.1)	.2
(G) CYLINDER HEAD, R&R (ENGINE REMOVED)		
V-6		
one		4.0
both		5.5
(G) CONNECTING ROD, RENEW (ENGINE DISASSEMBLED)		
V-6		
Each		.4
(G) CYLINDER HEAD, RECONDITION (HEAD REMOVED)		
V-6		
one	(1.4)	1.9
both	(2.8)	3.8
(G) REMOVE CYLINDER TOP RIDGE		
Each	(.1)	.1
(G) DEGLAZE CYLINDER WALLS		
Each	(.1)	.1
(G) MAIN BEARINGS, RENEW (PAN REMOVED)		
V-6	(1.5)	1.8
(G) ROD BEARINGS, RENEW (PAN REMOVED)		
V-6	(1.5)	1.8
(G) PLASTIGAUGE BEARINGS		
Each		.1
(M) OIL FILTER ELEMENT, RENEW		
All models	(.3)	.3

PARTS 14 PISTONS, RINGS & BEARINGS 14 PARTS

	Part No.	Price
(1) Piston Ring Set		
1986-87-Four	▲E63Z-6148A	32.75
V-6	▲E6DZ-6148A	29.00
(2) Piston Assy.		
1986-87-Four	▲E63Z-6108A	
V-6	▲E6DZ-6108A	25.50
(3) Pin (Piston)		
1986-87-Four	▲E6DZ-6135A	4.50
V-6	▲E6DZ-6135A	4.50
(4) Connecting Rod		
1986-87-Four	▲E63Z-6200A	47.00
V-6	▲E6DZ-6200A	47.00
(5) Connecting Rod Bearings		
1986-87-Four	▲E63Z-6211A	2.75
V-6	▲E6DZ-6211A	2.75

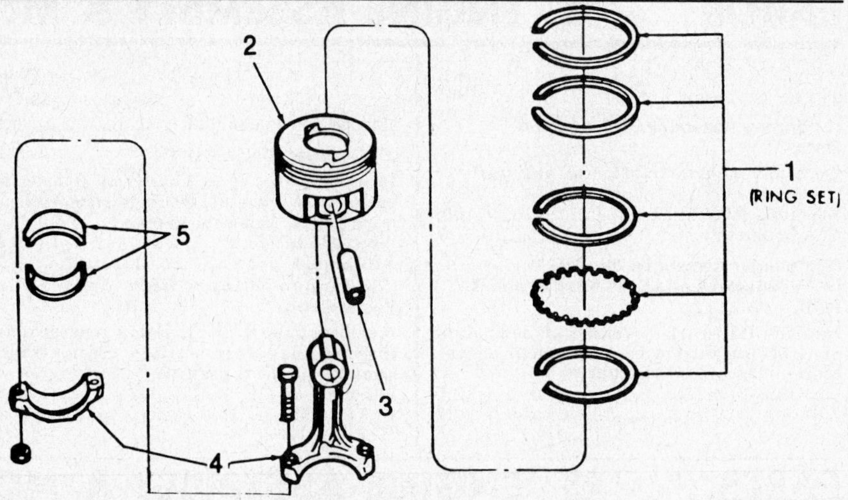

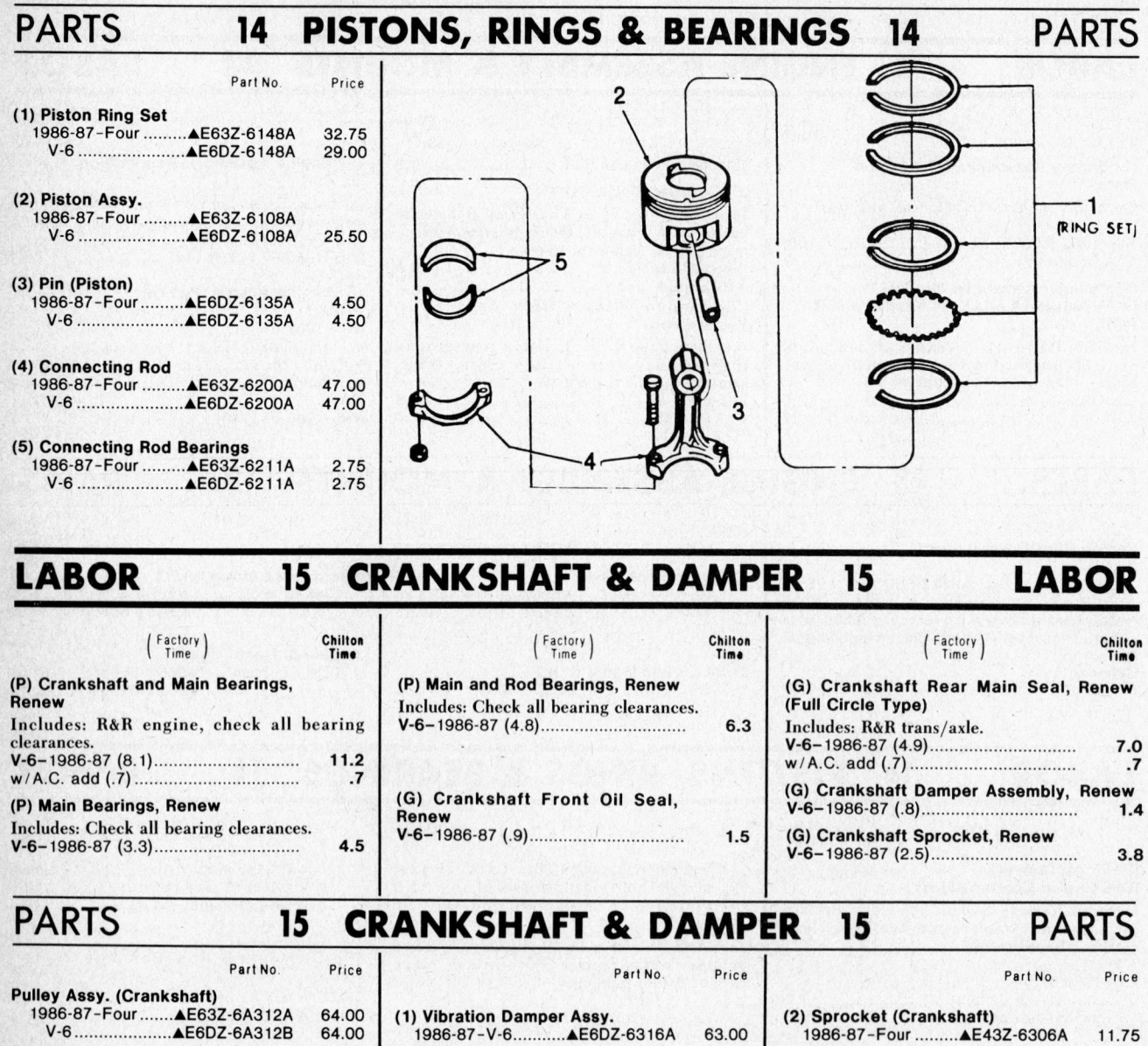

LABOR 15 CRANKSHAFT & DAMPER 15 LABOR

	(Factory Time)	Chilton Time
(P) Crankshaft and Main Bearings, Renew		
Includes: R&R engine, check all bearing clearances.		
V-6–1986-87	(8.1)	11.2
w/A.C. add	(.7)	.7
(P) Main Bearings, Renew		
Includes: Check all bearing clearances.		
V-6–1986-87	(3.3)	4.5
(P) Main and Rod Bearings, Renew		
Includes: Check all bearing clearances.		
V-6–1986-87	(4.8)	6.3
(G) Crankshaft Front Oil Seal, Renew		
V-6–1986-87	(.9)	1.5
(G) Crankshaft Rear Main Seal, Renew (Full Circle Type)		
Includes: R&R trans/axle.		
V-6–1986-87	(4.9)	7.0
w/A.C. add	(.7)	.7
(G) Crankshaft Damper Assembly, Renew		
V-6–1986-87	(.8)	1.4
(G) Crankshaft Sprocket, Renew		
V-6–1986-87	(2.5)	3.8

PARTS 15 CRANKSHAFT & DAMPER 15 PARTS

	Part No.	Price
Pulley Assy. (Crankshaft)		
1986-87-Four	▲E63Z-6A312A	64.00
V-6	▲E6DZ-6A312B	64.00
(1) Vibration Damper Assy.		
1986-87-V-6	▲E6DZ-6316A	63.00
(2) Sprocket (Crankshaft)		
1986-87-Four	▲E43Z-6306A	11.75

PARTS 15 CRANKSHAFT & DAMPER 15 PARTS

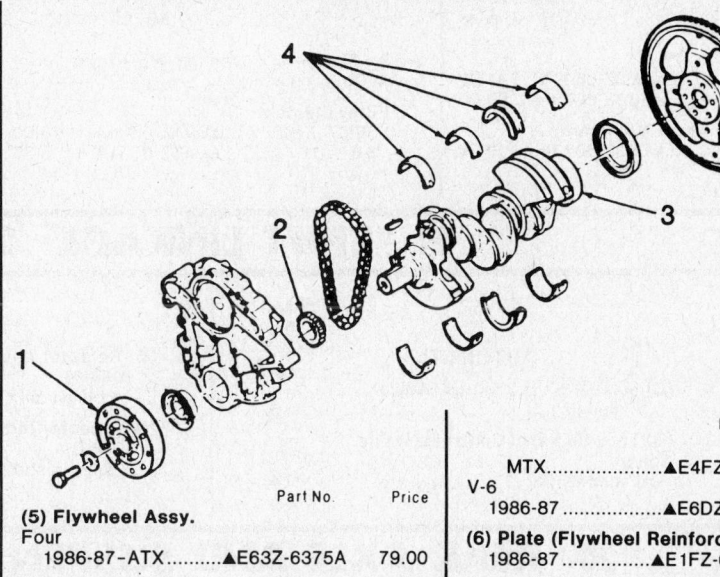

	Part No.	Price
V-6	▲E6DZ-6306A	22.50
(3) Crankshaft		
1986-87-Four	▲E63Z-6303A	418.50
V-6	▲E6DZ-6303A	423.25
(4) Main Bearings		
Four		
1986-87-Lower (All)	▲D5DZ-6333D	4.75
Upper Front	▲E43Z-6333B	2.75
Intermediate	▲D5DZ-6333A	4.75
Center	▲D5DZ-6337A	7.25
Rear	▲D5DZ-6333A	4.75
Rear Intermediate	▲D5DZ-6333A	4.75
V-6		
1986-87		
Upper (exc. below)	▲E6DZ-6333A	3.25
Rear Thrust	▲E6DZ-6337A	8.25
Rear	▲E6DZ-6333J	3.25
Lower (exc. below)	▲E6DZ-6333E	3.25
Rear Thrust	▲E6DZ-6337E	8.25
Rear	▲E6DZ-6333N	3.25

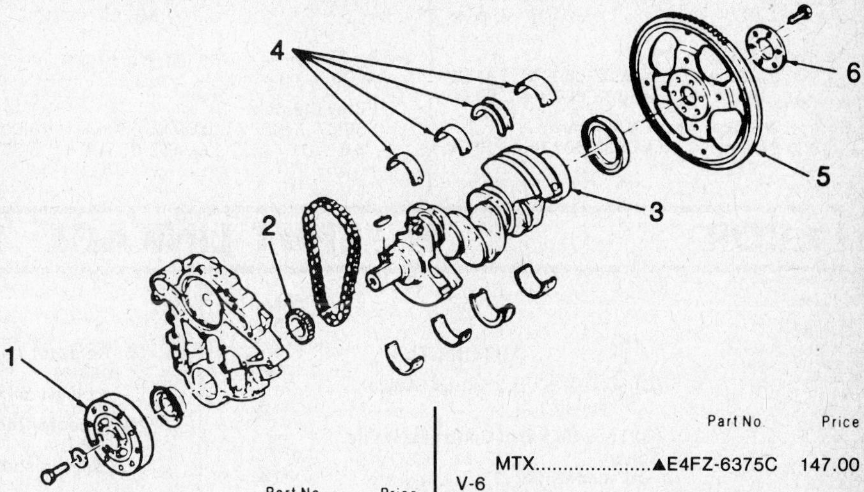

	Part No.	Price
(5) Flywheel Assy.		
Four		
1986-87-ATX	▲E63Z-6375A	79.00
MTX	▲E4FZ-6375C	147.00
V-6		
1986-87	▲E6DZ-6375A	93.50
(6) Plate (Flywheel Reinforcing)		
1986-87	▲E1FZ-6A366A	5.00

LABOR 16 CAMSHAFT & TIMING GEARS 16 LABOR

(Factory Time)	Chilton Time
(G) Timing Chain Cover Gasket and/or Seal, Renew	
V-6–1986-87 (2.4)	3.3
(G) Timing Chain, Renew	
V-6–1986-87 (2.5)	3.8
(G) Timing Chain Tensioner, Renew	
V-6–1986-87 (1.3)	1.8
w/A.C. add (.2)	.2
(G) Camshaft, Renew	
Includes: R&R engine.	
V-6–1986-87 (8.5)	11.8
w/A.C. add (.7)	.7
Renew cam brgs add (.7)	1.0
(G) Camshaft Sprocket, Renew	
V-6–1986-87 (2.5)	3.8

PARTS 16 CAMSHAFT & TIMING GEARS 16 PARTS

	Part No.	Price
Front Cover Gasket		
1986-87-Four	▲E43Z-6020A	1.75
V-6	▲E6DZ-6020A	3.00
Timing Cover Oil Seal		
1986-87-Four	▲E43Z-6700A	N.L.
V-6	▲E6DZ-6700A	6.75
(1) Camshaft		
1986-87-Four	▲E43Z-6250A	146.00
V-6	▲E6DZ-6250A	148.25
(2) Camshaft Bearings		
Four		
1986-87-Front	▲E43Z-6261A	13.50
Center	▲E43Z-6262A	10.75
Rear	▲E43Z-6263A	10.75

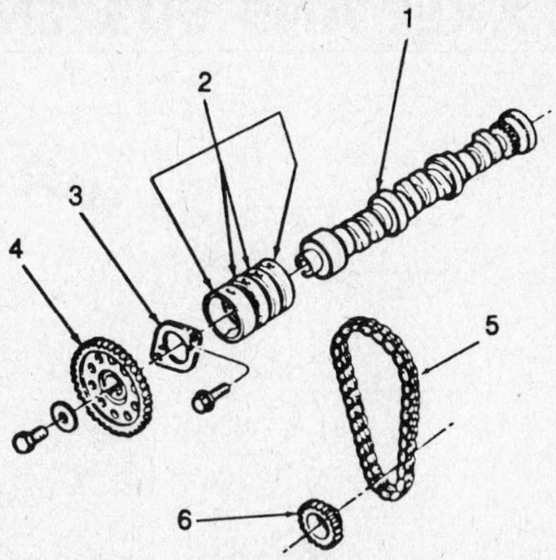

	Part No.	Price
V-6		
1986-87-Front	▲E6DZ-6261A	8.50
Center	▲E6DZ-6262A	7.00
Rear	▲E6DZ-6263A	7.25
(3) Thrust Plate		
1986-87-Four	▲E43Z-6269A	4.75
V-6	▲E6DZ-6269A	7.25
(4) Sprocket		
1986-87-Four	▲E43Z-6256A	15.00
V-6	▲E6DZ-6256A	32.25
(5) Timing Chain		
1986-87-Four	▲E43Z-6268A	19.50
V-6	▲E6DZ-6268A	25.00
(6) Sprocket (Crankshaft)		
1986-87-Four	▲E43Z-6306A	11.75
V-6	▲E6DZ-6306A	22.50

LABOR 17 ENGINE OILING SYSTEM 17 LABOR

(Factory Time)	Chilton Time
(G) Oil Pan and/or Gasket, Renew	
V-6–1986-87 (1.8)	2.5
(P) Pressure Test Engine Bearings (Pan Off)	
All models	1.0
(G) Oil Pump, Renew	
V-6–1986-87 (1.9)	2.7
(G) Oil Pump, R&R and Recondition	
V-6–1986-87 (2.2)	3.0
(G) Oil Pressure Sending Unit, Renew	
V-6–1986-87 (.3)	.4
(M) Oil Filter Element, Renew	
V-6–1986-87 (.3)	.3

PARTS 17 ENGINE OILING SYSTEM 17 PARTS

	Part No	Price
Oil Pump Assy.		
1986-87-Four	▲E63Z-6600A	41.00
V-6	▲E6DZ-6600A	69.00
Screen & Cover Assy. (Oil Pump)		
1986-87-Four	▲E63Z-6622A	19.00

Note: Screen & cover for V-6 engine is included with oil pump.

	Part No	Price
Oil Filter Element		
1986-87-Four	▲D9AZ-6731A	8.00
V-6	▲E4FZ-6731A	8.25
Oil Pressure Gauge (Engine Unit)		
1986-87	▲D4AZ-9278A	3.50
Oil Pan Gasket		
1986-87-Four	▲E63Z-6710A	21.50
V-6	▲E6DZ-6710A	11.25

LABOR 21 SHIFT LINKAGE 21 LABOR

(Factory Time)	Chilton Time
AUTOMATIC	
(G) Manual Shift Linkage, Adjust	
All models (.3)	.5
(G) Throttle Valve Control Linkage, Adjust	
All models (.3)	.4
(G) Selector Lever, Renew	
1986-87	
column shift (.4)	.6
(G) Selector Indicator, Renew	
1986-87	
column shift (.7)	1.1

LABOR 26 REAR AXLE AND SUSPENSION 26 LABOR

(Factory Time)	Chilton Time
(G) Rear Wheel Bearings, Adjust	
1986-87-both (.3)	.5
(G) Rear Wheel Bearing Grease Seal, Renew	
1986-87-one (.5)	.7
both (.7)	1.1
(G) Rear Wheel Bearings and Cups, Clean and Repack or Renew	
1986-87-one side (.5)	.9
both sides (.7)	1.5
(G) Rear Stabilizer Bar, Renew	
1986-87 (.6)	.9
(G) Lower Control Arm Assy., Renew	
1986-87	
all-one side (.4)	.7
(G) Rear Springs, Renew	
1986-87-left (.9)	1.2
right (.8)	1.1
both (1.4)	2.0
(G) Rear Shock Absorbers, Renew	
1986-87	
Sdn-left (.9)	1.2
right (.8)	1.1
both (1.5)	2.1
Wagon-one (.4)	.6
both (.5)	.8
(G) Rear Tie Rods, Renew	
1986-87-one (.5)	.7
both (.8)	1.2
(G) Rear Wheel Spindle, Renew	
1986-87-one (.7)	1.2
both (1.2)	2.2
Renew brgs and cups add	
one side (.3)	.3
both sides (.4)	.4

PARTS 26 REAR AXLE AND SUSPENSION 26 PARTS

	Part No	Price
Bushing Repair Kit (Shock)		
1986-87-exc.		
Sta. Wag.	▲E6DZ-18198B	6.75
Sta. wagon	▲E6DZ-18198C	10.00
(1) Bracket (Shock Absorber)		
1986-87	▲E6DZ-18192A	10.50
(2) Insulator (Rear Spring)		
1986-87-exc.		
Sta. Wag.	▲E6DZ-5536A	9.50
Sta. wagon	▲E6DZ-5536B	9.50
(3) Shock Absorber		
4 dr sedan		
1986-87-Four	▲E6DZ-18125A	N.L.
V-6	▲E6DZ-18125B	N.L.
Station Wagon		
1986-87-Four	▲E6DZ-18125C	N.L.
V-6	▲E6DZ-18125D	N.L.
(4) Spindle (Wheel)		
4 dr. sedan		
1986-87-R.H.	▲E6DZ-4A013D	91.25
left	▲E6DZ-4A013A	91.25
Sta. Wagon		
1986-87-R.H.	▲E6DZ-4A013C	91.25
left	▲E6DZ-4A013B	91.25
(5) Stabilizer Bar Assy.		
1986-87-exc.		
Sta. Wag.	▲E6DZ-5A772A	67.75

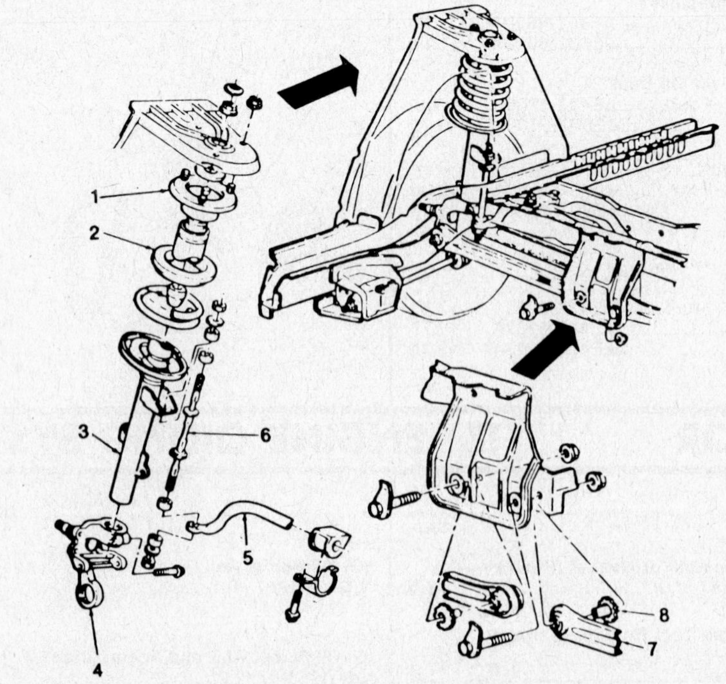

PARTS 26 REAR AXLE AND SUSPENSION 26 PARTS

	Part No.	Price
Sta. wagon		
(Four)	▲E6DZ-5A772B	67.75
V-6	▲E6DZ-5A772C	67.75
(6) Link Assy. (Stabilizer Bar)		
1986-87-exc.		
Sta. Wag.	▲E6DZ-5K484B	11.50
(7) Arm & Bushing Assy.		
Station Wagon		
1986-87-R.H.	▲E6DZ-5500A	82.00
left	▲E6DZ-5500B	82.00
4 dr. sedan		
1986-87-Std.		
Front	▲E6DZ-5500C	53.25
H.D. front	▲E6DZ-5500D	48.25
Std. rear	▲E6DZ-5500E	48.25
H.D. rear	▲E6DZ-5500F	48.25
(8) Cam Kit (Arm Adjusting)		
1986-87	▲E6DZ-5K751A	3.50

LABOR 28 AIR CONDITIONING 28 LABOR

(Factory Time) Chilton Time

Note: If more than one item requires replacement where evacuation and discharging the system is already included in the operation, deduct 1.0 hour for each additional item to the times listed.

	Chilton Time
(G) Drain, Evacuate & Recharge System	
Includes: Check for leaks.	
All models (.7)	1.2
(G) Refrigerant, Add (Partial Charge)	
All models	.6
(G) Compressor Drive Belt, Renew	
1986-87 (.3)	.5
(G) Compressor Assembly, Renew	
Includes: Transfer parts as required. Evacuate and charge system.	
V-6-1986-87 (2.7)	3.6
(G) Compressor Clutch and Pulley, Renew	
Includes: R&R compressor. Evacuate and charge system, if required.	
V-6-1986-87 (2.6)	3.5
(G) Compressor Shaft Seal Kit, Renew	
Includes: R&R compressor. Evacuate and charge system.	
V-6-1986-87 (3.1)	4.1
(G) Compressor Assy., R&R and Recondition	
Includes: Evacuate and charge system.	
V-6-1986-87 (3.9)	5.2

AIR CONDITIONER TUNE-UP

For efficient operation and satisfactory performance in hot weather. The following Air Conditioner tune-up is suggested:

1. Clean intake filter
2. Clean condenser fins
3. Pressure test system
4. Adjust drive belt tension
5. Check anti freeze/coolant
6. Tighten compressor mounts
7. Tighten condenser and evaporator mounts
8. Inspect system for leaks (hoses, couplings, valves, etc.)
9. Partial charge system

All models 1.0
If necessary to evacuate and charge system, add 1.0

	Chilton Time
(G) Condenser Assembly, Renew	
Includes: Evacuate and charge system.	
V-6-1986-87 (1.3)	2.2
(G) Orifice Valve, Renew	
Includes: Evacuate and charge system.	
1986-87 (.9)	1.5
(G) Evaporator Core, Renew	
Includes: Evacuate and charge system.	
1986-87 (3.4)	6.5
(G) A.C./Heater Blower Motor, Renew	
1986-87 (.8)	1.5
w/EATC (1.0)	1.7
(G) Blower Motor Switch, Renew	
1986-87 (1.0)	1.5
(G) Blower Motor Resistor, Renew	
1986-87 (.3)	.5
(G) A.C. Clutch Cycling Switch, Renew	
1986-87 (.3)	.4
(G) A.C. Door Actuator Motor, Renew	
1986-87	
Temp. Door (3.0)	6.0
(G) EATC Ambient Sensor, Renew	
1986-87 (.3)	.6
(G) Blower Motor Speed Control, Renew	
1986-87 (.3)	.5
(G) Blower Motor Relay, Renew	
1986-87 (.3)	.4
(G) Compressor Suction and Discharge Tube Assembly, Renew	
Includes: Evacuate and charge system.	
1986-87 (1.7)	2.4
(G) A.C. Control Assy., Renew	
1986-87 (1.0)	1.5
(G) Air Conditioning Hoses, Renew	
Includes: Evacuate and charge system.	
1986-87	
Cond. to Evap. (.9)	1.5
Suction line (1.4)	2.1

PARTS 28 AIR CONDITIONING 28 PARTS

	Part No.	Price
Compressor Assy.		
1986-87	▲E6DZ-19703A	221.50
Condensor Core Assy.		
1986-87	▲E6DZ-19712A	143.25
Valve Plate Replacement Kit		
1986-87	▲E6VY-19B685A	49.00
Front Head Gasket & Shaft Seal Kit		
1986-87	▲E6VY-19E579A	19.75
Head Front Kit		
1986-87	▲E6VY-19E580A	20.25
Head Rear Kit		
1986-87	▲E6VY-19E581A	31.00
Manifold Discharge Kit		
1986-87	▲E3VY-19E582A	21.00
Evaporator Core Assy.		
1986-87	▲E6DZ-19860A	132.25
Blower Motor Assy.		
1986-87	▲E6DZ-19805A	143.25
Switch Assy.		
1986-87-manual		
A.C.	▲E6DZ-19986A	7.50
w/A.T.C.	▲E6DZ-19986B	12.00

LABOR 29 LOCKS, HINGES & WIND. REGULATORS 29 LABOR

(Factory Time)	Chilton Time
(G) Hood Latch Assembly, Renew	
1986-87 (.3)	.5
(G) Hood Hinge, Renew (One)	
Includes: Adjust hood and latch.	
1986-87 (.4)	.6
(G) Hood Release Cable, Renew	
1986-87 (.7)	1.1
(G) Front Door Latch, Renew	
1986-87 (.7)	1.0
(G) Front Door Lock Remote Control, Renew	
1986-87 (.6)	.9
(G) Lock Striker Plate, Renew	
1986-87 (.2)	.3
(G) Front Door Handle (Outside), Renew	
1986-87 (.6)	.9
(G) Front Door Window Regulator, Renew	
Includes: R&R trim panel and weathersheet.	
1986-87	
manual (.7)	1.2
electric (.9)	1.4

LABOR 29 LOCKS, HINGES & WIND. REGULATORS 29 LABOR

(Factory Time) — Chilton Time

(G) Rear Door Latch, Renew
1986-87 (.5) 8

(G) Rear Door Window Regulator, Renew
1986-87
manual (.6) 1.0
electric (.8) 1.2

(G) Rear Door Handle (Outside), Renew
1986-87 (.4) 7

(G) Luggage Compartment Hydraulic Lift, Renew
1986-87-one (.3) 4
both (.3) 5

(G) Luggage Compartment Torsion Bar, Renew
1986-87 (.3) 4

(G) Tailgate/Liftgate Hinge, Renew
1986-87-one (.3) 4
both (.4) 6

PARTS 29 LOCKS, HINGES & WIND. REGULATORS 29 PARTS

	Part No	Price
Hood Latch		
1986-87	▲E6DZ-16700A	14.75
Hood Hinge		
1986-87-R.H.	▲E6DZ-16796A	13.25
left	▲E6DZ-16797A	10.00
Door Latch Assy. (Front)		
1986-87-R.H.	▲E6DZ-5421812A	28.00
left	▲E6DZ-5421813A	28.00
Door Latch Assy. (Rear)		
1986-87-R.H.	▲E6DZ-5426412A	N.L.
left	▲E6DZ-5426413A	N.L.
Door Lock (Electric)		
1986-87-R.H.	▲E6DZ-542818A	15.25
left	▲E6DZ-5421819A	8.00
Front Door Window Regulator (Manual)		
1986-87-R.H.	▲E6DZ-5423200A	36.00
left	▲E6DZ-5423201A	54.50
Rear Door Window Regulator (Manual)		
1986-87-R.H.	▲E6DZ-5427000A	32.25
left	▲E6DZ-5427001A	32.25
Front Window Regulator (Electric)		
1986-87-R.H.	▲E6DZ-5423208A	120.75
left	▲E6DZ-5423209A	120.75
Rear Window Regulator (Electric)		
1986-87-R.H.	▲E6DZ-5427008A	35.00
left	▲E6DZ-5427009A	35.00
Luggage Compartment Door Lock		
1986-87	▲E6DZ-5443200A	11.25
Hinge		
1986-87-R.H.	▲E6DZ-5442700A	15.25
left	▲E6DZ-5442701A	15.25
Door Lock Cylinder & Key		
wo/Lighted key		
1986-87	▲E6DZ-5422050A	30.00
w/Bright cyl, 4 dr. sedan		
1986-87	▲E6DZ-5443507A	N.L.
Station Wagon		
1986-87	▲E6DZ-7443505A	13.00

LABOR 30 HEAD AND PARKING LAMPS 30 LABOR

(Factory Time) — Chilton Time

(G) Aim Headlamps
two 4
four 6

(M) Headlamp Sealed Beam Bulb, Renew
1986-87-each (.3) 3

(M) Parking Lamp Housing, Renew
1986-87 (.3) 4

(M) Front Side Marker Lamp, Renew
1986-87-one (.2) 3
both (.3) 4

(M) Rear Side Marker Lamp, Renew
1986-87
Sta wagon (.3) 4

(M) Parking Lamp Assembly, Renew (Lighted Grille)
1986-87 (.3) 5

(G) Rear Lamp Body, Renew
1986-87-Sdn (.4) 6
Sta wagon (.3) 5
Sable add (.1) 1

(M) License Lamp Assembly, Renew
1986-87 (.2) 3

(G) High Mount Stop Lamp, Renew
1986-87
Sdn (.3) 4
Sta wagon (.5) 6

PARTS 30 HEAD AND PARKING LAMPS 30 PARTS

	Part No	Price
Seal Beam Bulbs		
Taurus		
1986-87-R.H.	▲E6DZ-13007A	49.50
left	▲E6DZ-13007B	49.50

Note: Seal beam bulbs do not include filament. It can be obtained in a headlamp kit. Or separate part no. E5LY-13N021-A.

	Part No	Price
Sable		
1986-87-R.H.	▲E64Y-13007A	25.50
left	▲E64Y-13007B	25.50
Parking Lamp Assy.		
Sable		
1986-87-R.H.	▲E64Y-13200C	28.75
left	▲E64Y-13201C	28.75
center	▲E64Y-13200B	134.00
Rear Lamp Assy.		
Taurus (exc. Decor group)		
1986-87-R.H.	▲E6DZ-13404A	91.50
left	▲E6DZ-13405A	91.50
(w/Decor group)		
1986-87-R.H.	▲E6DZ-13404B	91.50
left	▲E6DZ-13405B	91.50
Station Wagon		
1986-87-R.H.	▲E6DZ-13404C	57.50
left	▲E6DZ-13405C	57.50
Sable (Sedan)		
1986-87-R.H.	▲E64Y-13404A	68.75
left	▲E64Y-13405A	68.75
Station Wagon		
1986-87-R.H.	▲E6DZ-13404C	57.50
left	▲E6DZ-13405C	57.50
License Plate Lamp Assy.		
Sedan		
1986-87	▲E6DZ-13550B	11.25
Station Wagon		
1986-87	▲E6DZ-13550A	11.25
Rear Lamp Lens		
Taurus (exc. Decor group)		
1986-87-R.H.	▲E6DZ-13450A	38.00
left	▲E6DZ-13451A	38.00
(w/Decor group)		
1986-87-R.H.	▲E6DZ-13450B	38.00
left	▲E6DZ-1341B	
Sable		
1986-87-R.H.	▲E64Y-13450A	23.75
left	▲E64Y-13451A	23.75
Rear Hi-Mount Lamp Assy.		
Sedan		
1986-87	▲E6DZ-13A613D	41.75
Station wagon		
1986-87-exc. rear window wiper	▲E6DZ-13A613B	25.00
w/rear window wiper	▲E6DZ-13A613C	25.00
Marker Lamp Assy.		
Taurus (Bumper mounted lamps)		
1986-87-R.H.	▲E6DZ-15A201A	16.50
left	▲E6DZ-15A201B	16.50
(Fender mounted lamps)		
1986-87-R.H.	▲E6DZ-15A201C	28.75
left	▲E6DZ-15A201D	28.75
Station Wagon		
1986-87-R.H.	▲E6DZ-15A201E	9.75
left	▲E6DZ-15A201F	9.75
Sable		
1986-87-R.H.	▲E64Y-15A201A	30.75
left	▲E64Y-15A201B	30.75

LABOR 31 WINDSHIELD WIPER & SPEEDOMETER 31 LABOR

(Factory Time)	Chilton Time
(G) Windshield Wiper Motor, Renew	
1986-87 (.3)	.6
(G) Windshield Wiper Switch, Renew (Combination Switch)	
1986-87 (.5)	.9
(G) Windshield Wiper Governor, Renew	
1986-87 (.5)	.9
(G) Wiper Pivot Shaft and Link Assy., Renew	
1986-87 (.6)	.9
(G) Windshield Washer Pump, Renew	
1986-87 (.3)	.4
(G) Rear Window Wiper Motor, Renew	
1986-87 (.3)	.5
(G) Rear Window Wiper Switch, Renew	
1986-87 (.3)	.5
(G) Rear Window Washer Pump, Renew	
1986-87	
sdn (.5)	.7
sta wagon (.8)	1.1
(G) Speedometer Head, R&R or Renew	
1986-87	
Standard Cluster (1.0)	1.8
Performance Cluster (1.0)	1.8
Electronic Cluster (.8)	1.3
Reset odometer add	.2
(G) Speedometer Cable and Casing, Renew	
1986-87	
upper (.6)	1.0
lower (.3)	.6
(G) Speedometer Cable (Inner), Renew or Lubricate	
1986-87	
upper (.6)	1.0
lower (.4)	.7
(G) Speedometer Driven Gear, Renew	
1986-87 (.3)	.4
(G) Radio, R&R	
1986-87 (.6)	1.0

PARTS 31 WINDSHIELD WIPER & SPEEDOMETER 31 PARTS

	Part No.	Price
Wiper Motor Assy. (Front)		
1986-87	▲E6DZ-17508B	94.25
Wiper Motor Assy. (Rear)		
1986-87	▲E6DZ-17508A	126.00
Wiper Arm & Pivot Shaft		
1986-87	▲E6DZ-17566A	27.50
Wiper Arm		
1986-87-R.H.	▲E6DZ-17526A	13.25
left	▲E6DZ-17527A	13.25
rear	▲E6DZ-17526B	11.25
Wiper Switch		
Sedan		
wo/Intermittent wipers		
1986-87	▲E6DZ-13K359A	45.00
w/Intermittent wipers		
1986-87	▲E6DZ-13K359B	47.75
Taurus (Station Wagon)		
1986-87	▲E6DZ-17A553A	15.00
Sable (Station Wagon)		
1986-87	▲E64Y-17A553A	15.00
Windshield Wiper Governor		
1986-87	▲E6DZ-17C476A	77.50
Windshield Washer Pump		
1986-87	▲E1FZ-17664A	18.75
Windshield Washer Reservoir		
w/Low fluid sensor		
1986-87	▲E6DZ-17618B	20.75
wo/Low fluid sensor		
1986-87	▲E6DZ-17618A	20.75
w/Back window washer		
1986-87	▲E6DZ-17618C	14.50
Speedometer Head Assy.		
Note: Order by year & model.		
Speed Control Cable		
wo/AXOD		
1986-87	▲E6DZ-9A820A	15.00
w/AXOD		
1986-87	▲E6DZ-9A820B	15.00

LABOR 32 LIGHT SWITCHES & WIRING 32 LABOR

(Factory Time)	Chilton Time
(G) Windshield Wiper/Turn Indicator/Headlamp Dimmer Switch Assy., Renew	
1986-87 (.5)	.9
(G) Headlamp Switch, Renew	
1986-87-Taurus (.4)	.6
Sable (.3)	.5
(G) Stop Lamp Switch, Renew	
1986-87 (.3)	.5
(G) Back-Up Lamp Switch, Renew	
1986-87 (.3)	.5
(G) Parking Brake Lamp Switch, Renew	
1986-87 (.3)	.5
(M) Turn Signal or Hazard Warning Flasher, Renew	
1986-87 (.3)	.4

PARTS 32 LIGHT SWITCHES & WIRING 32 PARTS

	Part No.	Price
Head Lamp Switch		
Taurus		
1986-87	▲E6DZ-11654A	17.00
Sable		
1986-87	▲E64Y-11654A	17.00
Stop Light Switch		
1986-87	▲E6FZ-13480A	6.00
Turn Signal Flasher		
1986-87	▲E6DZ-13350A	14.25
Horn Assy.		
1986-87-Low	▲E3AZ-13833A	17.00
High	▲E3AZ-13832A	17.00

LABOR 33 GLASS 33 LABOR

(Factory Time)	Chilton Time
(G) Windshield Glass, Renew	
1986-87 (2.3)	3.0
(G) Front Door Glass, Renew	
Includes: R&R trim panel and weathersheet.	
1986-87 (.7)	1.1
(G) Rear Door Glass, Renew	
Includes: R&R trim panel and weathersheet.	
1986-87 (.8)	1.2
(G) Tailgate Window Glass, Renew	
1986-87	
movable (.4)	.6

LABOR 34 CRUISE CONTROL 34 LABOR

	(Factory Time)	Chilton Time
(G) Cruise Control System Diagnosis		
1986-87	(.5)	.6
(G) Cruise Control Chain/Cable, Renew		
1986-87	(.3)	.4
(G) Cruise Control Servo Assy., Renew		
1986-87	(.2)	.4
Road test add	(.3)	.3
(G) Cruise Control Relay, Renew		
1986-87	(.1)	.2
Road test add	(.3)	.3
(G) Cruise Control Sensor Assy., Renew		
1986-87	(.2)	.4
Road test add	(.3)	.3
(G) Cruise Control Amplifier Assy., Renew		
1986-87	(.2)	.4
Road test add	(.3)	.3
(G) Cruise Control Actuator Switch, Renew		
1986-87	(.2)	.4
Road test add	(.3)	.3
(G) Cruise Control Metering (Dump) Valve, Renew		
1986-87	(.2)	.4
Road test add	(.3)	.3
(G) Cruise Control Clutch Switch, Renew		
1986-87	(.3)	.4

PARTS 34 CRUISE CONTROL 34 PARTS

	Part No.	Price
Speed Control Servo. Assy.		
1986-87-Four	▲E6DZ-9C735A	120.25
V-6	▲E6DZ-9C735C	116.25
Speed Control Sensor		
Four		
1986-87-w/		
Elect. orn	▲E6DZ-9E731B	20.75
wo/Elect. orn	▲E43Z-9E731A	20.75
V-6		
1986-87-w/		
Elect. orn	▲E6DZ-9E731D	20.75
wo/Electronic orn.	▲E6DZ-9E731C	20.75

GROUP INDEX

ALPHABETICAL INDEX

Ford Motor Company

Front Wheel Drive Cars

FORD TEMPO • MERCURY TOPAZ •

YEAR IDENTIFICATION

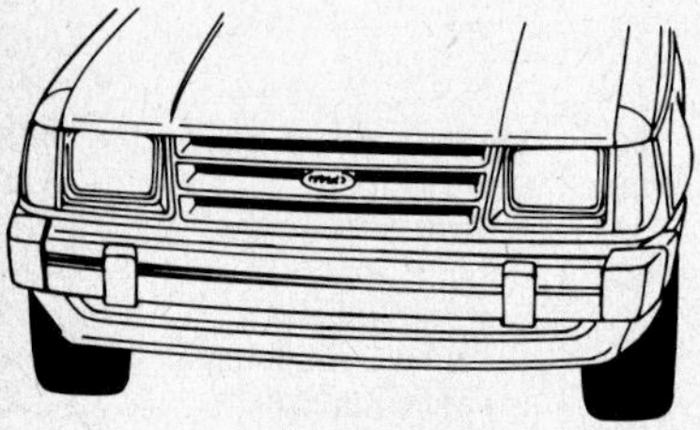

1984 Tempo

1985 Tempo

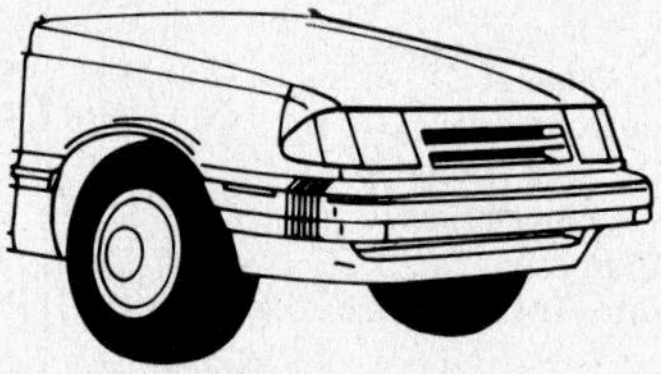

1986–87 Tempo

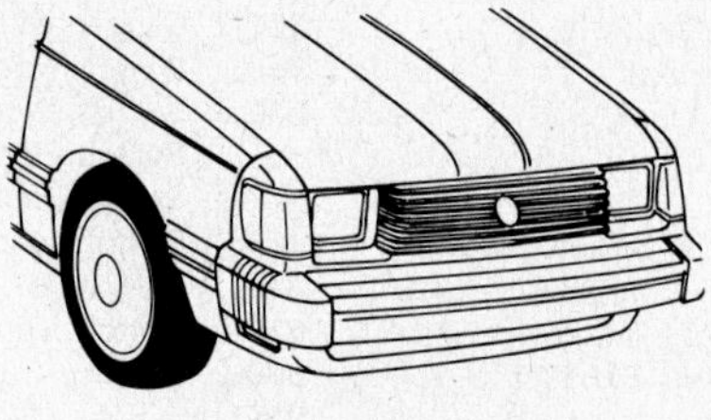

1984–85 Topaz

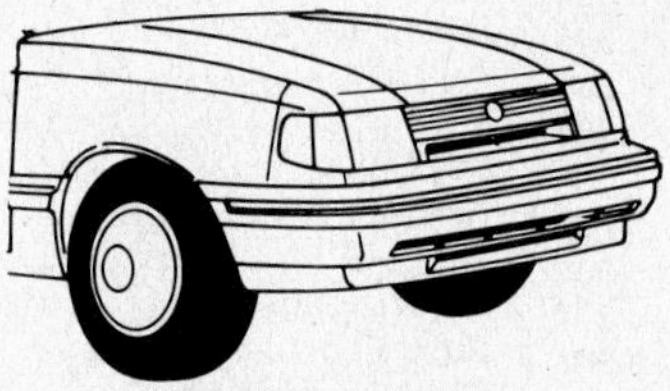

1986–87 Topaz

VEHICLE IDENTIFICATION NUMBER (VIN)

It is important for servicing and ordering parts to be certain of the vehicle and engine identification. The VIN (vehicle identification number) is a 13 or 17 digit number visible through the windshield on the driver's side of the dash and contains the vehicle and engine identification codes. It can be interpreted as follows:

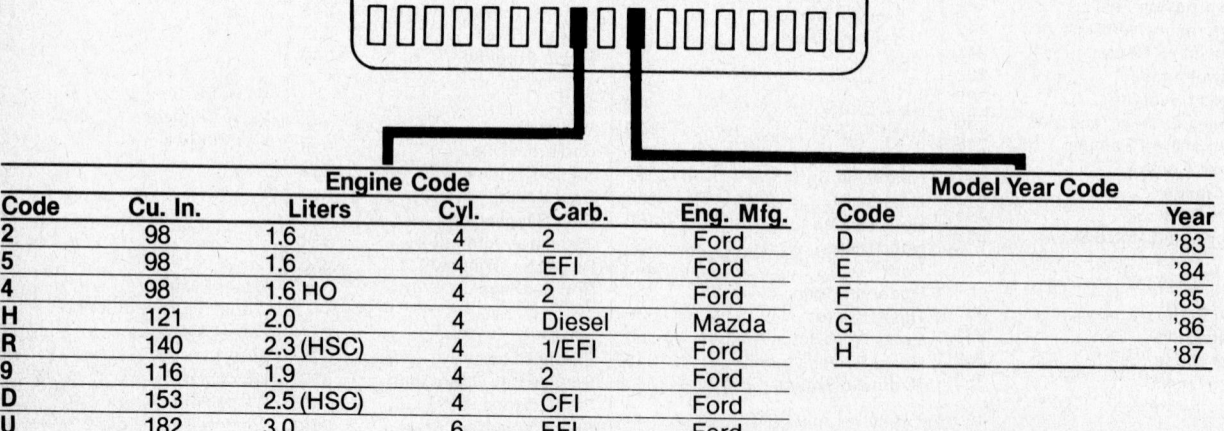

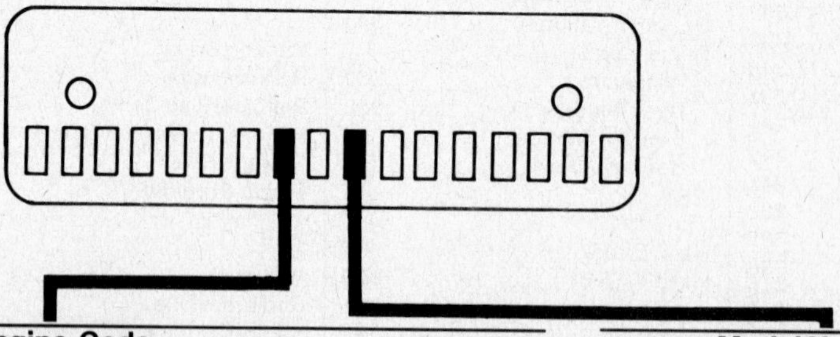

Engine Code

Code	Cu. In.	Liters	Cyl.	Carb.	Eng. Mfg.
2	98	1.6	4	2	Ford
5	98	1.6	4	EFI	Ford
4	98	1.6 HO	4	2	Ford
H	121	2.0	4	Diesel	Mazda
R	140	2.3 (HSC)	4	1/EFI	Ford
9	116	1.9	4	2	Ford
D	153	2.5 (HSC)	4	CFI	Ford
U	182	3.0	6	EFI	Ford

Model Year Code

Code	Year
D	'83
E	'84
F	'85
G	'86
H	'87

The seventeen digit Vehicle Identification Number can be used to determine engine application and model year. The tenth digit indicates the model year, and the eighth digit identifies engine code.

TUNE-UP SPECIFICATIONS

When analyzing compression test results, look for uniformity among cylinders rather than specific pressures.

	Engine			Spark Plugs		Distributor		Ignition Timing (deg.)		Valves	Fuel	Idle Speed (rpm)	
Year	Eng. VIN Code	No. Cyl Displace-ment cu. in. (cc)	Eng. Mfg.	Orig. Type •	Gap (in.)	Point Dwell (deg.)	Point Gap (in.)	Man. Trans •	Auto Trans	Intake Opens ▪ (deg.)	Pump Pressure (psi)	Man Trans	Auto Trans
'83-'85	—	4-97.6 (1597)	Ford	AWSF-34 ②	0.042-0.046	Electronic		①	①	—	4-6 ③	①	①
'84-'87	R	4-140 (2300)	Ford	AWSF-62	.044	Electronic		10B	15B	—	5	①	①
'85-'87	9	4-116 (1901)	Ford	AWSF-34C ②	0.042-0.046	Electronic		①	①	—	5-6	①	①
'86-'87	0	4-153 (2508)	Ford	AWSF-32C	0.042-0.046	Electronic		①	①	—	35-45	①	①
'86-'87	U	6-182 (2983)	Ford	AWSF-32C	0.042-0.046	Electronic		①	①	—	35-45	①	①

NOTE: The underhood specifications sticker often reflects tune-up specification changes made in production. Sticker figures must be used if they disagree with those in this chart. Part numbers in this chart are not recommended by Chilton for any product by brand name.

▪ All figures Before Top Dead Center
• Figure in parenthesis is for California
B Before Top Dead Center
— Not applicable

① Calibration levels vary from model to model. Always refer to the underhood sticker for your car requirements.
② EFI Models: AWSF24
③ EFI pressure: 35-45 psi

FIRING ORDERS

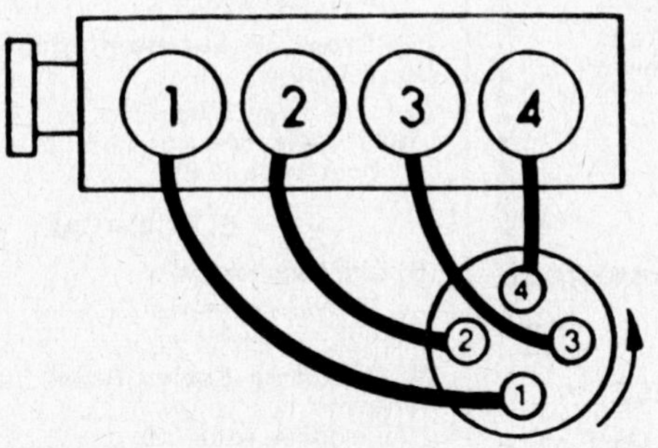

Ford Motor Co. 1600cc 4 cyl engine
Firing order: 1–3–4–2
Distributor rotation: counterclockwise

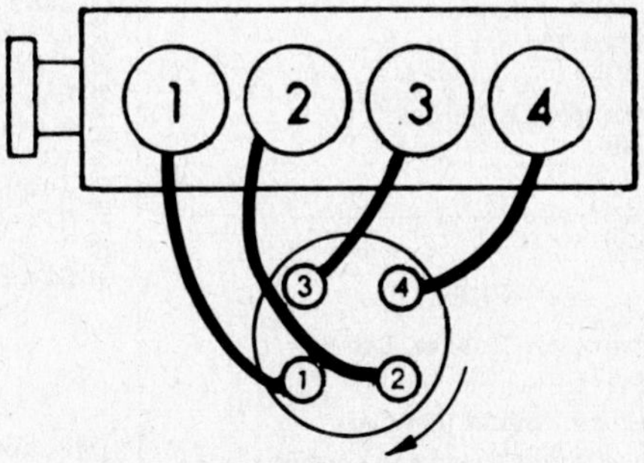

Tempo/Topaz 2300 HSC engine
Firing order 1–3–4–2
Distributor rotation: clockwise

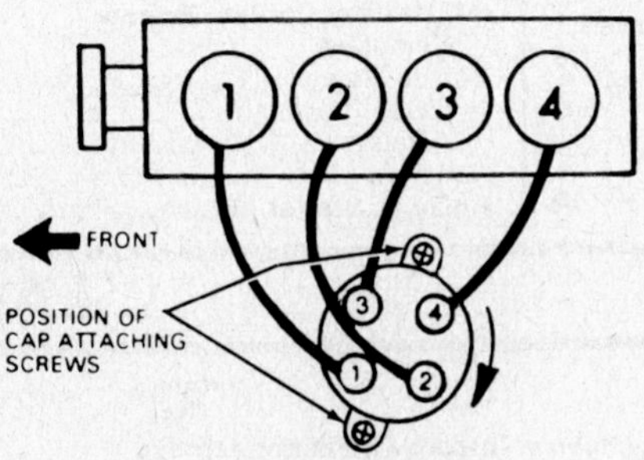

Ford 2500 cc 4 cyl (2.5L)
Firing order: 1–3–4–2
Distributor rotation: clockwise

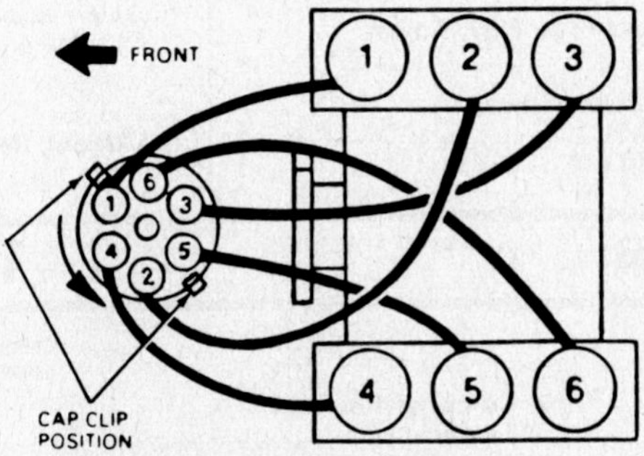

Ford 3000 cc 6 cyl (3.0L)
Firing order: 1–4–2–5–3–6
Distributor rotation: counterclockwise

WHEEL ALIGNMENT SPECIFICATIONS

Year	Model	Caster Range (deg)▪▲	Caster Pref. Setting (deg)	Camber Range (deg)▪	Camber Pref. Setting (deg)	Toe-in (in.)	Steering Axis Inclin. (deg)
'84–'87	Tempo, Topaz	$^{9}/_{16}$P to $2^{1}/_{16}$P	$1^{5}/_{16}$P	—	—	$^{1}/_{32}$ (in) to $^{7}/_{32}$ (out)	—
				(Left) $1^{1}/_{8}$P to $2^{5}/_{8}$P	$1^{7}/_{8}$P	—	$14^{5}/_{8}$
				(Right) $^{11}/_{16}$P to $2^{3}/_{16}$P	$1^{1}/_{2}$P	—	$15^{1}/_{8}$

▪ Caster and chamber are pre-set at the factory and cannot be adjusted
▲ Caster measurements must be made on the left side by turning left wheel through the prescribed angle of sweep and on the right side by turning right wheel through prescribed angle of sweep for the equipment being used. When using alignment equipment designed to measure caster on both the right and left side, turning only one wheel will result in a significant error in caster angle for the opposite side.

LABOR — SERVICE BAY OPERATIONS — LABOR

(Factory Time) — Chilton Time

COOLING

(M) Winterize Cooling System
Includes: Run engine to check for leaks, tighten all hose connections. Test radiator and pressure cap. Drain radiator and engine block. Add anti-freeze and refill system.
All models.......... .5

(M) Thermostat, Renew
All models (.4).......... .6

(M) Drive Belts, Adjust
All models-one (.2).......... .3
each adtnl (.1).......... .1

(M) Radiator Hoses, Renew
All models
upper (.3).......... .4
lower (.4).......... .5
both (.5).......... .6

FUEL

(M) Carburetor Air Cleaner, Service
All models.......... .2

(G) Carburetor, Adjust (On Car)
Includes: Adjust idle speed and ignition timing.
All models (.7).......... 1.0

BRAKES

(G) Brakes, Adjust (Minor)
Includes: Adjust brakes, fill master cylinder.
two wheels.......... .4

(G) Bleed Brakes (Four Wheels)
Includes: Fill master cylinder.
All models (.3).......... .5

(G) Brake Pedal Free Play, Adjust
All models.......... .4

(M) Parking Brake, Adjust
All models (.3).......... .5
w/Console add (.1).......... .1

CHILTON'S 10 POINT SAFETY CHECK
CHECK OPERATION & CONDITION OF THE FOLLOWING ITEMS:
1. Legal Registration (serial no.)
2. Tires & Wheels
3. Brake System (R&R all wheels)
4. Light Systems & Signals
5. Accelerator Linkage, Neutral Safety Switch, Shift Indicator Pointer & Seat Position Locks
6. Glass, Mirrors, Door Locks, Seat Belts & Harness
7. Wipers, Washers & Defrosters
8. Frame, Steering, Shocks, Front & Rear Suspension
9. Fuel & Exhaust Systems
10. Road Test Vehicle
All models.......... 1.0
Exhaust Smog Analysis, add.......... .4

(Factory Time) — Chilton Time

LUBRICATION SERVICE

(M) Lubricate Chassis, Change Oil & Filter
Includes: Inspect and correct all fluid levels.
All models.......... .6
Install grease fittings add.......... .1

(M) Lubricate Chassis
Includes: Inspect and correct all fluid levels.
All models.......... .4
Install grease fittings add.......... .1

(M) Engine Oil & Filter, Change
Includes: Inspect and correct all fluid levels.
All models.......... .6

WHEELS

(M) Wheel, Renew
one.......... .5

(Factory Time) — Chilton Time

(G) Wheels, Balance
one.......... .3
each adtnl.......... .2

(G) Wheels, Rotate (All)
All models (.5).......... .5

(G) Front Wheel Grease Seals, Renew
Includes: Repack bearings.
All models-one side (1.4).......... 1.9
both sides (2.5).......... 3.2

(G) Front Wheel Bearings and Cups, Renew
Includes: Repack bearings.
All models-one side (1.4).......... 2.0
both sides (2.6).......... 3.5

ELECTRICAL

(G) Aim Headlamps
two.......... .4
four.......... .6

(M) Headlamp Sealed Beam Bulb, Renew
All models-each (.3).......... .3

(M) Parking Lamp Bulb, Renew
All models-one (.3).......... .3

(M) License Lamp Bulb, Renew
All models-one (.2).......... .2

(M) Tail Lamp Bulb, Renew
All models-one (.3).......... .3

(M) Back-Up Lamp Bulb, Renew
All models-one (.3).......... .3

(M) Battery Cables, Renew
All models
Batt to Relay
Gas (.3).......... .3
Diesel (1.2).......... 1.5
Negative (.3).......... .3
Relay to Starter (.7).......... 1.0

LABOR — 1 TUNE UP 1 — LABOR

(Factory Time) — Chilton Time

(G) Compression Test
All models (.3).......... .6
w/A.C. add.......... .2

(G) Engine Tune Up, (Electronic Ignition)
Includes: Test battery and clean connections. Tighten manifold and carburetor mounting bolts. Check engine compression, clean and adjust or renew spark plugs. Test resistance of spark plug cables. Inspect distributor cap and rotor. Adjust air gap. Check vacuum advance operation. Reset ignition timing. Adjust idle mixture and idle speed. Service air cleaner. Inspect and adjust drive belts. Inspect choke operation and adjust or free up. Check operation of EGR valve.
All models.......... 1.5
w/A.C. add.......... .2
Perform EEC IV system test add.......... 1.0

LABOR 2 IGNITION SYSTEM 2 LABOR

(Factory Time) Chilton Time

GASOLINE ENGINE

(G) Spark Plugs, Clean and Reset or Renew
1984-87 (.3) 5

(G) Ignition Timing, Reset
All models (.3) 4

(G) Distributor, Renew
Includes: Reset ignition timing.
1984-87 (.4) 6
Renew vacuum diaph add (.1) 2

(G) Distributor Armature, Renew
1984 (.3) 5

(G) Distributor Stator, Renew
Includes: R&R distributor armature.
1984 (.6) 9

(G) Distributor Cap and/or Rotor, Renew
1984-87 (.3) 4

(G) Ignition Coil, Renew
Includes: Test.
1984-87 (.3) 4

(G) Profile Ignition Pick-Up Sensor, Renew (Duraspark)
1984-87 (.5) 9
Perform system test add (.3) 3

(G) Ignition Module Assembly, Renew
Note: Fender mount type. For TFI unit, refer to Emission Control section.
1984-87 (.4) 6
Perform system test add 3

(G) Ignition Cables, Renew
Includes: Test wiring.
1984-87 (.4) 6

(G) Ignition Switch, Renew
1984-87 (.6) 1.0

(G) Ignition Key Indicator Buzzer, Renew
1984-87 (.3) 4

DIESEL ENGINE

(G) Glow Plug System Test
All models (.2) 4

(G) Glow Plugs, Renew
1984-87
one (.2) 4
each adtnl (.1) 3
all (.4) 1.0

(G) Glow Plug Relay, Renew
1984-87 (.3) 4

PARTS 2 IGNITION SYSTEM 2 PARTS

	Part No.	Price
(1) Distributor Assy. (New)		
1984-87-exc.		
below	▲E43Z-12127C	136.75
Canada MTX	▲E43Z-12127D	N.L.
ATX	▲E43Z-12127G	N.L.
C.F.I. w/MTX	▲E43Z-12127C	136.75
w/ATX	▲E63Z-12127B	136.75
C.F.I. w/H.O.	▲E63Z-12127B	136.75
(2) Distributor Cap		
1984-85-wo/EEC IV	▲E5BZ-12106A	17.00
1984-87-w/ E.E.C. IV	▲E5FZ-12106C	8.75
(3) Rotor		
1984-87-wo/ E.E.C. IV	▲D7FZ-12200C	4.75
1984-w/E.E.C. IV	▲E5FZ-12200A	3.25
1985-w/E.E.C. IV	▲E59Z-12200A	3.25
1986-87-w/ E.E.C. IV	▲E6AZ-12200C	2.50
(4) Gasket (Dist. Base)		
1984-87	▲E43Z-12143A	1.00
Modulator Assy.		
1984-87-wo/ E.E.C. IV	▲D9VZ-12A199A	83.50
w/E.E.C. IV	▲E43Z-12A297A	106.00

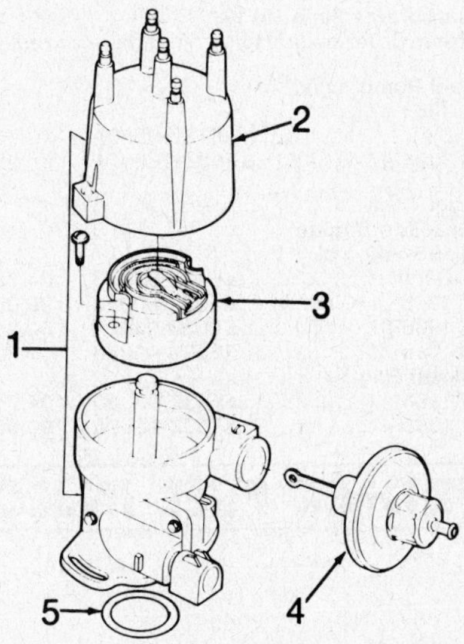

	Part No.	Price
Ignition Coil		
1984-85-wo/ E.E.C. IV	▲D5AZ-12029A	31.25
w/E.E.C. IV	▲E3FZ-12029A	33.75
1986-87-Canada	▲D5AZ-12029A	31.25
exc. Canada	▲E3FZ-12029A	33.75
Ignition Wire Set		
1984-85-wo/ E.E.C. IV	▲E4PZ-12259E	41.25
w/E.E.C. IV	▲E4PZ-12259A	31.75
1986-87	▲E6PZ-12259D	41.00
Ignition Switch		
1984-87	▲E4FZ-11572A	11.50
IGNITION SYSTEM DIESEL		
Module (Glow Plug Control)		
1984-87	▲E43Z-12B533A	168.50
Switch (Glow Plug)		
1984-87	▲E3TZ-9A444B	20.25
Glow Plug		
1984-87	▲E43Z-12A342A	24.75
Glow Plug Relay		
1984-87-white	▲E43Z-12A343B	38.50
brown	▲E43Z-12A343C	38.50
Resister Assy. (Glow Plug.)		
1984-85	▲E43Z-12A344A	40.50
1986-87	▲E63Z-12A344A	40.50

LABOR 3 FUEL SYSTEM 3 LABOR

(Factory Time) Chilton Time

GASOLINE ENGINE

(G) Fuel Pump, Test (On Car)
Includes: Disconnect line at carburetor, attach pressure gauge.
All models
mechanical (.3) 3
electric (.5) 5

(M) Carburetor Air Cleaner, Service
All models 2

(G) Carburetor, Adjust (On Car)
Includes: Adjust idle speed and ignition timing.
All models (.7) 1.0

(G) Fuel Filter, Renew
All models-Gas (.4) 5

(G) Carburetor Assembly, R&R or Renew
Includes: All necessary adjustments.
1984-87 (.6) 1.0
Renew carb add (.4) 4

(G) Carburetor, R&R and Clean or Recondition
Includes: All necessary adjustments.
1984-87
Holly 1949 (2.0) 2.8
6149-1V (2.1) 3.0

(G) Float Level, Adjust
Holly 1949 (.6) 9

(G) Float or Needle Valve and Seat, Renew
Includes: Set float level and adjust idle speed.
Holly 1949 (.7) 1.0

(G) Thermostatic Choke Housing and/or Gasket, Renew
1984-87
Holly 1949 (.4) 6

(G) Accelerator Pump Assy., Renew
1984-87
Holly 1949 (.8) 1.1

(G) Fuel Tank, Renew
Includes: Drain and refill tank, transfer tank gauge unit.
1984-87 (.9) 1.3

LABOR — 3 FUEL SYSTEM 3 — LABOR

(Factory Time)	Chilton Time
(G) Fuel Gauge (Tank Unit), Renew	
1984-87 (.8)	1.2
(G) Fuel Gauge (Dash Unit), Renew	
1984-87 (.7)	1.2
(G) Fuel Pump, Renew	
1984-87	
on block (.4)	.6
on frame (.4)	.6
in tank (.9)	1.4
Add pump test if performed.	
(G) Intake Manifold Gasket, Renew	
1984-87	
w/Carb (2.3)	3.2
w/CFI (1.0)	1.5
Renew manif add (.3)	.5

ELECTRONIC FUEL INJECTION

(Factory Time)	Chilton Time
(G) Fuel Pressure Regulator Assy., Renew	
1985-87 (.7)	1.2
(G) Fuel Charging Assy., R&R or Renew	
1985-87 (.5)	.8
(G) Fuel Charging Assy., R&R and Recondition	
1985-87 (1.3)	2.0
(G) Fuel Injector Assy., Renew	
1985-87 (1.3)	1.8
Perform EEC system test add	1.0

DIESEL FUEL INJECTION

(Factory Time)	Chilton Time
(G) Fuel Injection Nozzle, Renew	
1984-87	
one (.6)	.9
each adtnl (.2)	.3
all (.7)	1.6
(G) Fuel Injection Pump, Renew	
1984-87 (1.7)	2.5
(G) Injection Pump Drive Gear, Renew	
1984-87 (1.1)	1.5
(G) Intake Manifold and/or Gasket, Renew	
1984-87 (1.8)	3.0
Renew manif add (.2)	.5

PARTS — 3 FUEL SYSTEM 3 — PARTS

	Part No.	Price
Carburetor Air Cleaner Element		
1984-87-exc.		
below	▲E43Z-9601C	10.25
diesel	▲E4FZ-9601B	17.25
Carburetor Assy. (New)		
1984-w/MTX		
w/4 spd	▲E43Z-9510V	211.50
(w/5 speed stamped)		
E43E-VB	▲E43Z-9510VB	240.75
E43E-VA	▲E43Z-9510V	211.50
E43E-AEA	▲E43Z-9510AE	N.L.
E43E-ADA	▲E43Z-9510AD	N.L.
1984 (w/ATX stamped)		
E43E-ZA	▲E43Z-9510Z	240.75
E43E-ZD	▲E43Z-9510ZD	239.75
E43E-ZG	▲E43Z-9510Z	240.75
E43E-ZH	▲E43Z-9510ZH	240.75
E43E-ACA	▲E43Z-9510AC	N.L.
E43E-ACB	▲E43Z-9510AB	N.L.
E43Z-ABB	▲E43Z-9510ABB	N.L.
Carburetor Tune Up Kit		
Note: Order by stamping on carburetor tag.		
Fuel Pump Assy.		
1984-87-exc.		
C.F.I.	▲E43Z-9350A	40.75
1985-87-w/C.F.I.	▲E53Z-9H307A	91.25
Fuel Tank		
Gasoline Engine		
1984-85-wo/		
C.F.I.	▲E43Z-9002C	104.75
1985-w/C.F.I.	▲E53Z-9002A	90.00
1986-87-w/C.F.I.	▲E63Z-9002A	90.00
wo/C.F.I.	▲E63Z-9002B	N.L.
Diesel Engine		
1984	▲E43Z-9002D	104.75
1985	▲E53Z-9002A	90.00
1986-87	▲E63Z-9002A	90.00
Fuel Gauge (Tank Unit)		
Gasoline Engine		
1984-85-wo/		
C.F.I.	▲E43Z-9275C	42.25
1986-87-wo/		
C.F.I.	▲E63Z-9275A	N.L.
1985-87-w/E.F.I.	▲E53Z-9H307A	91.25
Diesel Engine		
1984-87	▲E53Z-9275A	42.25
Fuel Gauge (Dash)		
(wo/Tachometer)		
1984-gas	▲E46Y-9305A	30.75
diesel	▲E46Y-9305C	30.75
1985-87	▲E53Z-9305A	30.75
(w/Tachometer)		
1984	▲E46Z-9305D	31.75
1985-87	▲E56Z-9305C	31.75

PARTS — 3 ELECTRONIC FUEL INJECTION 3 — PARTS

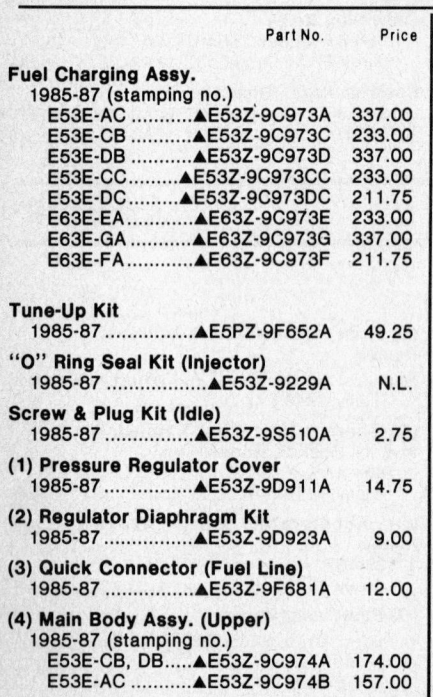

	Part No.	Price
Fuel Charging Assy.		
1985-87 (stamping no.)		
E53E-AC	▲E53Z-9C973A	337.00
E53E-CB	▲E53Z-9C973C	233.00
E53E-DB	▲E53Z-9C973D	337.00
E53E-CC	▲E53Z-9C973CC	233.00
E53E-DC	▲E53Z-9C973DC	211.75
E63E-EA	▲E63Z-9C973E	233.00
E63E-GA	▲E63Z-9C973G	337.00
E63E-FA	▲E63Z-9C973F	211.75
Tune-Up Kit		
1985-87	▲E5PZ-9F652A	49.25
"O" Ring Seal Kit (Injector)		
1985-87	▲E53Z-9229A	N.L.
Screw & Plug Kit (Idle)		
1985-87	▲E53Z-9S510A	2.75
(1) Pressure Regulator Cover		
1985-87	▲E53Z-9D911A	14.75
(2) Regulator Diaphragm Kit		
1985-87	▲E53Z-9D923A	9.00
(3) Quick Connector (Fuel Line)		
1985-87	▲E53Z-9F681A	12.00
(4) Main Body Assy. (Upper)		
1985-87 (stamping no.)		
E53E-CB, DB	▲E53Z-9C974A	174.00
E53E-AC	▲E53Z-9C974B	157.00

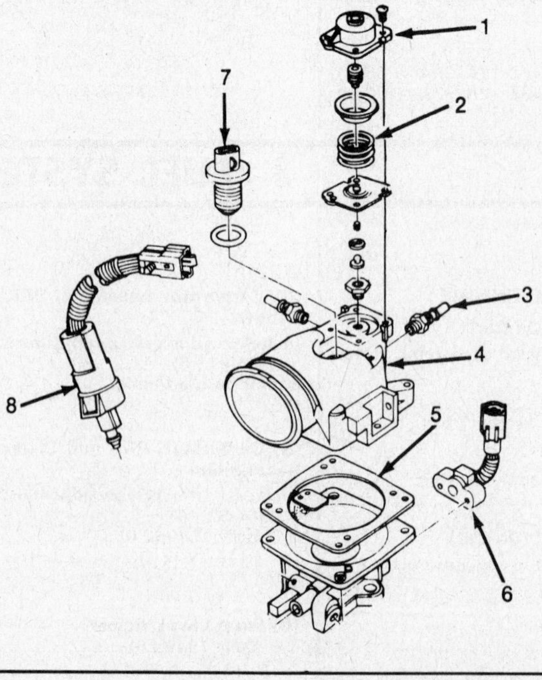

PARTS 3 ELECTRONIC FUEL INJECTION 3 PARTS

	Part No.	Price
(5) Gasket (Charging Body)		
1985-87	▲E53Z-9C983A	.75
(6) Potentiometer Assy. (Throttle)		
1985	▲E53Z-9B989B	29.25
1986-87	▲E6DZ-9B989A	29.25
(7) Fuel Injector		
1985-87 (stamping no.)		
exc. below	▲E53Z-9F593A	147.75
E53E-AC & E63E-GA	▲E53Z-9F593B	147.75
(8) Actuator Assy. (Throttle Control)		
1985	▲E53Z-9N825A	88.00
1986-87	▲E6DZ-9N825A	88.00

DIESEL FUEL INJECTION

	Part No.	Price
Fuel Injection Pump		
1984-85-exc. Fuel Econo. Leader bef. 3/85	▲E43Z-9A543C	478.50
1985-87 from 3/85	▲E53Z-9A543A	411.00
1984-Fuel Econo. Leader bef. 3/84	▲E43Z-9A543B	411.00
1985-87	▲E6FZ-9A543A	411.00
Nozzle Holder Assy.		
1984-87	▲E43Z-9E527A	64.00
Engine Idle Control		
1984-87-blue	▲E43Z-9L513A	11.50
white	▲E43Z-9L513B	11.50
Switch Assy. (Eng. Idle Cont.)		
1984-87-wo/ speed control	▲E4FZ-12B537A	15.00
w/speed control	▲E4FZ-12B537D	N.L.

LABOR 3A EMISSION CONTROLS 3A LABOR

(Factory Time) — Chilton Time

THERMACTOR TYPE

(G) Thermactor Pump Drive Belt, Renew
1984-87 (.3) 5

(G) Thermactor Air Pump, Renew
1984-87 (.4) 6

(G) Thermactor Air By-Pass Valve, Renew
1984-87 (.6) 9

E.G.R. TYPE

(G) E.G.R. Valve, Renew
1984-87 (.5) 7

(G) E.G.R. Vacuum Control Valve, Renew
1984-87 (.6) 9

EVAPORATIVE EMISSION TYPE

(G) Fuel Vapor Canister, Renew
1984-87 3

(G) Purge Control Valve, Renew
1984-87 4

(M) Carburetor Air Cleaner Element, Renew
1984-87 (.2) 2

(M) Crankcase Emission Filter, Renew
1984-87 3

(M) Crankcase Ventilation Valve, Renew
1984-87 (.2) 2

ELECTRONIC ENGINE CONTROL IV

(P) E.E.C. System, Test
1984-87 (.5) 1.0

(P) Throttle Position Sensor, Renew
Does not include system test.
1984-87 (.4) 6

(P) Exhaust Gas Oxygen Sensor, Renew
Does not include system test.
1984-87 (.3) 5

(P) Processor Assembly, Renew
Does not include system test.
1984-87 (.3) 4

CHILTON'S EMISSION CONTROL TUNE-UP

1. Clean or renew P.C.V. valve, hoses and filter
2. Check fuel tank cap for sealing ability
3. Check fuel tank and fuel lines for leakage
4. Check evaporation canister and filter. Replace if necessary
5. Check engine compression to determine leakage of unburned gases. (Add time for items of interference)
6. Test and clean or renew spark plugs
7. Check engine oil dipstick for sealing ability
8. Test exhaust system with analyzer and check system for leakage
9. Check exhaust manifold heat valve for operation
10. Adjust ignition timing and carburetor idle speed and mixture
11. Check automatic choke mechanism for free operation
12. Inspect air cleaner and element
13. On models so equipped test distributor vacuum control switch and transmission control switch

Four 1.3
For repairs made charge accordingly.

(Factory Time) — Chilton Time

(P) Engine Coolant Temperature Sensor, Renew
Does not include system test.
1984-87 (.1) 2

(P) Barometric Manifold Absolute Pressure Sensor, Renew
Does not include system test.
1984-87 (.1) 3

(P) E.G.R. Position Sensor, Renew
Does not include system test.
1984-87 (.2) 3

(P) Thick Film Ignition Module, Renew
Does not include system test.
1984-87 (.5) 7

(P) Profile Ignition Pick-Up Sensor, Renew
Does not include system test.
1984-87 (.6) 8

(P) E.G.R. Control Solenoids, Renew
Does not include system test.
1984-87 (.1) 2

(P) Tad/Tab Solenoids, Renew
Does not include system test.
1984-87 (.1) 2

(P) Canister Purge Valve or Solenoid, Renew
Does not include system test.
1984-87 (.1) 2

(P) Throttle Kicker Actuator, Renew
Does not include system test.
1984 (.2) 3

(P) Throttle Kicker Solenoid, Renew
Does not include system test.
1984-87 (.1) 2

(P) Feedback Control Solenoid, Renew
Does not include system test.
1984 (.2) 3

(P) A.C. Cooling Fan Controller Module, Renew
Does not include system test.
1984-87 (.1) 2

(P) Electronic Control Relay, Renew
Does not include system test.
1984-87 (.3) 4

(P) E.G.R. Valve, Renew
Does not include system test.
1984-87 (.3) 5

(P) Throttle Positioner Assy., Renew
Does not include system test.
1985-87 (.9) 1.2

(P) Air Change Temperature Sensor, Renew
Does not include system test.
1985-87 (.1) 2

PARTS 3A EMISSION CONTROLS 3A PARTS

	Part No.	Price
THERMACTOR TYPE		
Thermactor Air Pump		
1984-87-exc. below	▲E43Z-9A486B	141.75
1984-Tempo ATX.	▲E43Z-9A486C	141.75
Thermactor Check Valve		
1984-nipple 1 end	▲E43Z-9A487A	11.25
nipple 2 ends	▲E3TZ-9A487A	13.25
1985-87-w/C.F.I.	▲E3FZ-9A487B	18.50
1986-87-exc. C.F.I.	▲E53Z-9A487B	N.L.
Thermactor Control Valve		
1984 (MTX)		
w/4 spd.	▲E43Z-9F491C	56.00
w/5 spd.	▲E43Z-9F491D	56.00
1984 (ATX)		
exc. Calif.	▲E43Z-9F491D	56.00
Calif.	▲E43Z-9F491B	56.00
E.G.R. TYPE		
E.G.R. Valve		
Replacement E.G.R. valve must be ordered according to stamping number on the original valve.		
Solenoid Vacuum Valve (E.G.R.)		
1984 (stamped on valve) (E43Z-9F474)		
B2A, B3A	▲E43Z-9D474B	48.75
FA, FB	▲E43Z-9D474F	32.50
Pressure External Valve Assy. (E.G.R.)		
1984	▲E43Z-9H473A	68.50
1985-87-w/MTX	▲E53Z-9F483A	100.25
w/ATX	▲E53Z-9F483B	100.25
EVAPORATIVE EMISSION TYPE		
Fuel Vapor Canister		
1984-87-inc. Canada	▲E3FZ-9D653B	53.25
1984-87-exc. Canada	▲D8AZ-9D653C	53.25
Sensor Assy. (Air Cleaner)		
1984	▲E43Z-9E607A	7.25
1985-87-wo/C.F.I.	▲D4FZ-9E607A	7.00
1985-87-wo/H.O. eng.	▲D7DZ-9E607A	7.25
w/H.O. eng.	▲D7FZ-9E607B	7.25
Carburetor Air Cleaner Filter		
1984-87-exc. below	▲E43Z-9601C	10.25
diesel	▲E4FZ-9601B	17.25
ELECTRONIC ENGINE CONTROL E.E.C. IV		
Processor & Calibrator Assy. (E.E.C.-IV)		
(w/MTX)		
1984 (stamped E43F-12A650)		
F1A, F2A, F1B, F2B	▲E43Z-12A650FA	167.75
G1A, G2A, G1B, G2B	▲E43Z-12A650G	167.75
AK1A, AK2A	▲E43Z-12A650AKA	167.75
K1A, K2A, K1B, K2B	▲E43Z-12A650KA	167.75
T1A, T2A, T1B, T2B	▲E43Z-12A650TA	167.75
1985-87 (stamped E53F-12A650)		
K1A, K2A	▲E53Z-12A650KA	168.00
K1B, K2B	▲E53Z-12A650KB	167.75
H1B, H2B, H1C, H2C	▲E53Z-12A650HC	N.L.
M1A, M2A	▲E53Z-12A650MA	168.00
M1B, M2B	▲E53Z-12A650MB	167.75
G1B, G2B, G1C, G2C	▲E53Z-12A650GC	168.00
H1D, H2D	▲E53Z-12A650HD	167.75
G1D, G2D	▲E53Z-12A650GD	167.75
(w/ATX)		
1984 (stamped E43F-12A650)		
AH1A	▲E43Z-12A650AHA	167.75
AG1A	▲E43Z-12A650AGA	167.75
P1A, P2A	▲E43Z-12A650PA	167.75
S1A, S2A	▲E43Z-12A650SA	167.75
1985-87 (stamped E53F, E63F-12A650)		
D1B, D2B	▲E53Z-12A650DB	167.75
E1B, E2B	▲E53Z-12A650EB	168.00
D1C, D2C	▲E53Z-12A650DC	168.00
E1C, E2C	▲E53Z-12A650EC	168.00
D1D, D2D	▲E53Z-12A650DD	167.75
E1D, E2D	▲E53Z-12A650ED	167.75
T1E, T2E	▲E63Z-12A650TE	N.L.
U1E, U2E	▲E63Z-12A650UE	167.75
Oxygen Sensor (Exh. Gas)		
1984	▲E43Z-9F472A	63.00
1985-87	▲E53Z-9F472B	63.00
Purge Regulator Valve (Canister)		
1984-87-natural	▲E4AZ-9C915A	21.75
green	▲E4AZ-9C915B	21.75
black	▲E4AZ-9C915C	21.75
Mid Temperature Switch		
1984-87	▲D5DZ-9E862A	7.25
Sensor Assy. (Cont. Coolant Temp.)		
1984-87	▲E1AZ-12A648A	32.00
Throttle Position Sensor		
1984-87	▲E43Z-9B989A	29.25
Manifold Absolute Pressure Sensor		
1984-87	▲E43Z-9F479B	68.50
E.G.R. Position Sensor		
1984	▲E43Z-9G428B	31.75
1985-87	▲E5AZ-9G428A	31.75
Thick Film Ignition Module		
1984-87-w/E.E.C. IV	▲E43Z-12A297A	106.00
wo/E.E.C. IV	▲D9VZ-12A199A	83.50
Air Charge Temperature Sensor		
1984-87	▲E1AZ-12A697A	27.00
Feed Back Control Solenoid		
1984-85-exc. Canada	▲E43Z-9B998A	69.25

LABOR 4 ALTERNATOR AND REGULATOR 4 LABOR

	(Factory Time)	Chilton Time
(G) Alternator Circuits, Test		
Includes: Test battery, regulator and alternator output.		
All models	(.3)	.6
(M) Alternator Drive Belt, Renew		
1984-87	(.3)	.4
(G) Alternator Assembly, Renew		
1984-87	(.4)	.7
Transfer pulley add	(.1)	.1
Add circuit test if performed.		
(G) Alternator, R&R and Recondition		
Includes: Complete disassembly, replacement of parts as required. Test validity of rotor field, stator and diodes.		
1984-87	(.9)	1.5
(G) Alternator Brushes, Renew		
Includes: R&R alternator.		
1984-87	(.7)	1.2
Add circuit test if performed.		
(G) Alternator Front Bearing or End Plate, Renew		
Includes: R&R alternator.		
1984-87	(.7)	1.1
(G) Alternator Rear Bearing, Renew		
Includes: R&R alternator.		
1984-87	(.6)	1.0
(G) Alternator Regulator, Renew		
1984-87	(.3)	.5
Add circuit test if performed.		
(G) Instrument Cluster Voltage Regulator, Renew		
1984-87	(.6)	1.0
(G) Ammeter, Renew		
1984-87-Topaz	(.7)	1.2

PARTS 4 ALTERNATOR AND REGULATOR 4 PARTS

	Part No.	Price
Alternator Assy.		
Gasoline Engine		
1984-exc. 4 sp.	▲E2GZ-10346B	233.50
w/4 sp.	▲E43Z-10346A	203.50
1985-wo/A.C.	▲E43Z-10346D	232.75
w/A.C.	▲E43Z-10346A	203.50
1986-87-wo/A.C.	▲E63Z-10346A	232.75
w/A.C. & P.S.	▲E63Z-10346B	232.75
Diesel Engine		
1984-85-w/60 amp.	▲E2GZ-10346B	233.50
w/65 amp.	▲E43Z-10346C	203.50
1986-87-60 amp.	▲E63Z-10346A	232.75
65 amp.	▲E6TZ-10346B	232.75
(1) Front Bearing		
1984-87	▲C9ZZ-10094A	9.00
(2) Rotor Assy. (Gasoline Engine)		
1984-exc. 4 sp.	▲E1ZZ-10335B	45.75
w/4 sp.	▲E1ZZ-10335A	45.75
1985-wo/A.C.	▲E43Z-10335C	60.50
w/A.C.	▲E53Z-10335A	56.00
1986-87-wo/A.C.	▲E43Z-10335A	60.50
w/A.C.	▲E53Z-10335A	56.00

PARTS 4 ALTERNATOR AND REGULATOR 4 PARTS

	Part No.	Price
Diesel Engine		
1984-85	▲E1ZZ-10335B	45.75
1986-87-wo/A.C.	▲E43Z-10335A	60.50
w/A.C.	▲E53Z-10335A	56.00
(3) Shaft (Rotor)		
1984-87	▲C5AZ-10330A	N.L.
(4) Stator Assy.		
Gasoline Engine		
1984-exc. 4 sp.	▲E3FZ-10336A	31.25
w/4 sp.	▲E43Z-10336A	72.50
1985-wo/A. C.	▲E43Z-10336C	41.25
w/A.C.	▲E53Z-10336A	33.50
1986-87-wo/A.C.	▲E69Z-10336B	37.50
w/A.C.	▲E6DZ-10336D	33.50
Diesel Engine		
1984-85-w/60 amp	▲E3FZ-10336A	31.25
w/65 amp.	▲D8ZZ-10336A	74.00
1986-87-60 amp	▲E69Z-10336B	37.50
w/65 amp.	▲E6DZ-10336D	33.50
(5) Rectifier Assy.		
Gasoline Engine		
1984	▲D9VY-10304A	47.25
1985-87	▲E43Z-10304A	47.25
Diesel Engine		
1984-85	▲D6AZ-10304A	48.00
1986-87	▲E43Z-10304A	47.25
(6) Capacitor (Radio)		
1984-87	▲C6AZ-18827A	2.25

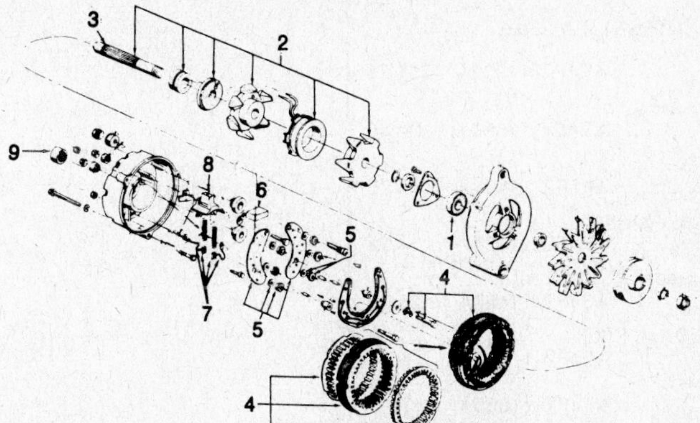

	Part No.	Price
(7) Brush Set		
1984	▲C6VY-10347A	3.50

Note: Brush set for 1985-87 models is included in the holder assy. part no. E43Z-10320A.

	Part No.	Price
(8) Brush Holder		
1984	▲C5AZ-10351A	2.00
(9) Rear Bearing		
1984-87	▲D20Z-10A304A	5.25

	Part No.	Price
Alternator Regulator		
Gasoline Engine		
1984-87-exc. integral regulator	▲E2PZ-10316A	36.75
1984-87-w/ integral regulator	▲E43Z-10316A	29.75
1986-87	▲E6TZ-10316A	29.75
Diesel Engine		
1984-85	▲E4FZ-10316A	29.75
1986-87	▲E6TZ-10316A	29.75
Instrument Cluster Voltage Regulator		
1984-87	▲C9AZ-10804A	10.25

LABOR 5 STARTING SYSTEM 5 LABOR

(Factory Time)	Chilton Time
(G) Starter Draw Test (On Car)	
All models (.3)	.3
(G) Starter Assembly, Renew	
1984-87-Gas	
w/MTX (.5)	.8
w/ATX (.4)	.7
Diesel (.8)	1.1
Add draw test if performed.	
(G) Starter, R&R and Recondition	
Includes: Turn down armature.	
1984-87-Gas	
w/MTX (1.5)	2.6
w/ATX (1.4)	2.5
Diesel (2.3)	3.5
Renew field coils add	.4
Add draw test if performed.	
(G) Starter Drive, Renew	
Includes: R&R starter.	
1984-87-Gas	
w/MTX (.7)	1.0
w/ATX (.6)	.9
Diesel (1.4)	1.8
(G) Starter Solenoid, Renew	
Includes: R&R starter.	
1984-87-Diesel (.9)	1.2
(G) Starter Solenoid Relay, Renew	
1984-87 (.3)	.4
(G) Ignition Switch, Renew	
1984-87 (.6)	1.0
(M) Battery Cables, Renew	
1984-87	
Batt to Relay	
Gas (.3)	.3
Diesel (1.2)	1.5
Negative (.3)	.3
Relay to Starter (.7)	1.0

PARTS 5 STARTING SYSTEM 5 PARTS

GASOLINE ENGINE

	Part No.	Price
Starter Assy.		
1984-87	▲E43Z-11002A	132.50
(1) Armature		
1984-87	▲E3FZ-11005A	66.75
(2) Drive Assy.		
1984-87	▲D6PZ-11350B	17.50
(3) Field Coil (Complete)		
1984-87	▲E3FZ-11082A	45.25
(4) Brush Set		
1984-87	▲E4PZ-11057A	13.00
(5) Seal (Rear Bearing)		
1984-87	▲D0AZ-11K013A	.50
(6) Plate Bushing (Brush End)		
1984-87	▲D3AZ-11052A	1.50
Battery Cable (Ground)		
1984-87-exc. Canada	▲E43Z-14301B	13.00
Canada	▲E43Z-14301A	N.L.

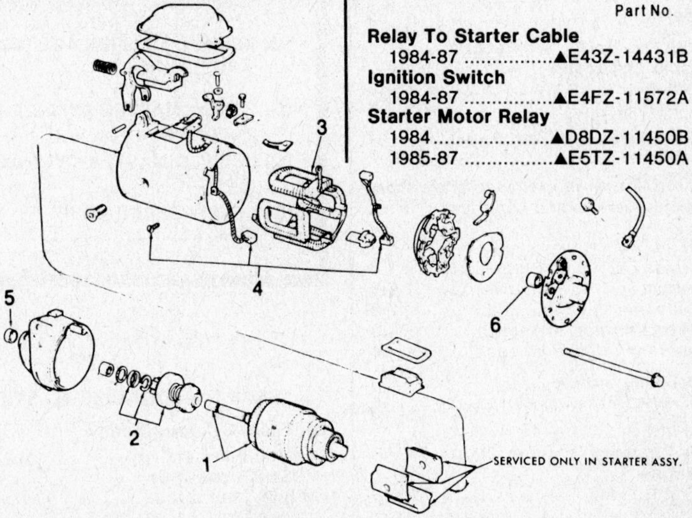

	Part No.	Price
Relay To Starter Cable		
1984-87	▲E43Z-14431B	19.25
Ignition Switch		
1984-87	▲E4FZ-11572A	11.50
Starter Motor Relay		
1984	▲D8DZ-11450B	12.00
1985-87	▲E5TZ-11450A	13.25

PARTS 5 STARTING SYSTEM 5 PARTS

	Part No.	Price
DIESEL ENGINE		
Starter Assy.		
1984-87	▲E4FZ-11002A	231.25
(1) Solenoid Assy.		
1984-87	▲E4FZ-11390A	34.50
(2) Spring (Solenoid)		
1984-87	▲E4FZ-11103A	1.75
(3) Lever Assy. (Drive)		
1984-87	▲E4FZ-11067A	14.25
(4) Housing Assy. (Drive End)		
1984-87	▲E4FZ-11130A	23.00
(5) Bearing (Drive End)		
1984-87	▲E4FZ-11135A	2.75
(6) Drive Shaft		
1984-87	▲E4FZ-11355A	7.25
(7) Drive Assy.		
1984-87	▲E4FZ-11350A	21.00
(8) Drive Gear		
1984-87	▲E4FZ-11A067A	24.75
(9) Housing Assy. (Drive Gear)		
1984-87	▲E4AZ-11A149A	13.75
(10) Bushing (End Plate)		
1984-87	▲E4FZ-11052A	9.50
(11) Brush Holder		
1984-87	▲E4FZ-11061A	4.25
(12) Armature		
1984-87	▲E4FZ-11005A	66.75
(13) Brush Set		
1984-87	▲E4PZ-11057A	13.00
(14) Field Coil (Complete)		
1984-87	▲E4FZ-11082A	50.00
(15) Plate End		
1984-87	▲E4FZ-11049A	14.50

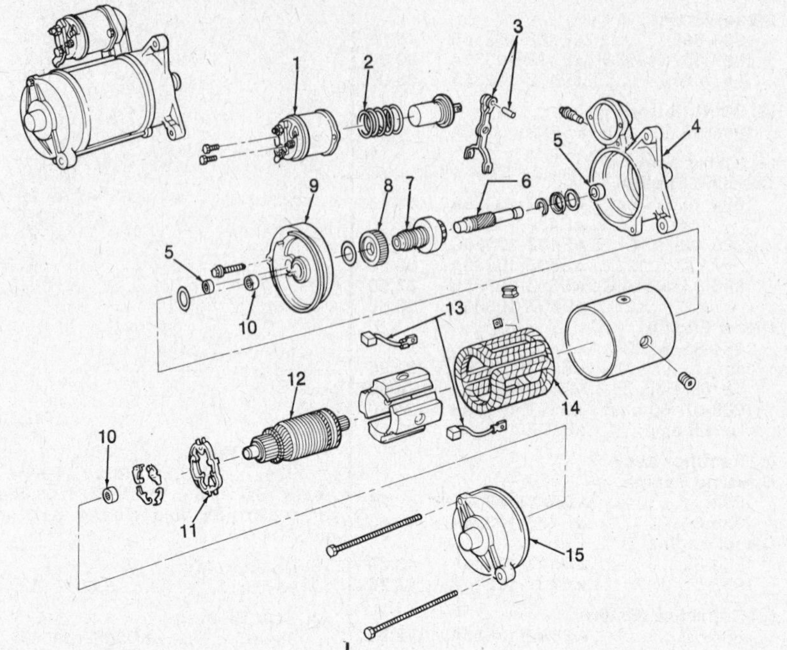

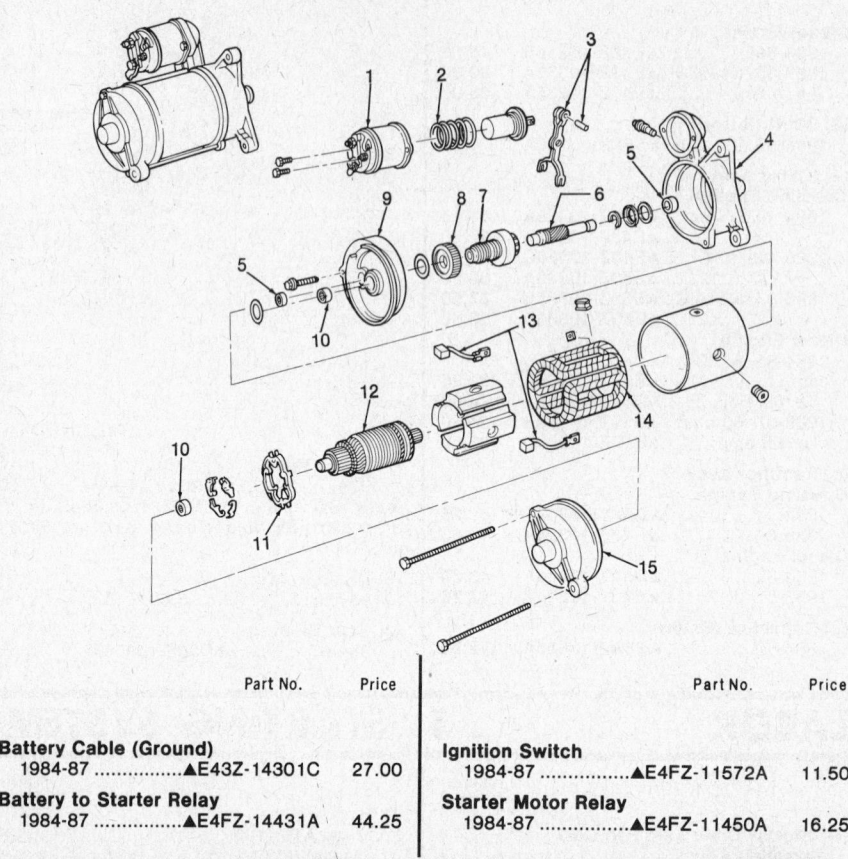

	Part No.	Price
Battery Cable (Ground)		
1984-87	▲E43Z-14301C	27.00
Battery to Starter Relay		
1984-87	▲E4FZ-14431A	44.25
Ignition Switch		
1984-87	▲E4FZ-11572A	11.50
Starter Motor Relay		
1984-87	▲E4FZ-11450A	16.25

LABOR 6 BRAKE SYSTEM 6 LABOR

	(Factory Time)	Chilton Time
(G) Brake Pedal Free Play, Adjust		
All models		.4
(G) Brakes, Adjust (Minor)		
Includes: Adjust brakes, fill master cylinder.		
two wheels		.4
(G) Bleed Brakes (Four Wheels)		
Includes: Fill master cylinder.		
All models	(.3)	.5
(G) Brake Self Adjustors, Disassemble and Clean		
one wheel		.8
both wheels		1.5
(G) Brake Shoes and/or Pads, Renew		
Includes: Install new or exchange brake shoes or pads. Adjust service and hand brake. Bleed system.		
1984-87		
front-disc	(.7)	1.1
rear-drum	(1.0)	1.5
all four wheels	(1.4)	2.5
Resurface brake rotor, add-each		.9
Resurface brake drum, add-each		.5
(G) Brake Drum, Renew		
1984-87-one	(.3)	.6
both	(.5)	.9
(G) Brake Pressure Warning Light Switch, Renew		
1984-87	(.3)	.5

COMBINATIONS

Add To Brakes, Renew

See Machine Shop Operations

	(Factory Time)	Chilton Time
(G) RENEW WHEEL CYLINDER		
Each	(.3)	.5
(G) REBUILD WHEEL CYLINDER		
Each	(.3)	.5
(G) REBUILD CALIPER ASSEMBLY		
Each	(.3)	.5
(G) RENEW MASTER CYLINDER		
All models		1.0
(G) REBUILD MASTER CYLINDER		
All models		1.4
(G) RENEW BRAKE HOSE		
Each	(.3)	.3
(G) RENEW REAR WHEEL GREASE SEALS		
One	(.2)	.3
Both	(.3)	.4
(G) RENEW BRAKE DRUM		
Each	(.2)	.2
(G) RENEW DISC BRAKE ROTOR		
Each	(.1)	.2
(G) REPACK FRONT WHEEL BEARINGS (BOTH WHEELS)		
All models		2.0
(G) REPACK REAR WHEEL BEARINGS (BOTH WHEELS)		
All models		.5

BRAKE HYDRAULIC SYSTEM

	(Factory Time)	Chilton Time
(G) Wheel Cylinder, Renew		
Includes: Bleed system.		
1984-87-one	(1.0)	1.4
both	(1.8)	2.4
(G) Wheel Cylinder, R&R and Rebuild		
Includes: Hone cylinder and bleed system.		
1984-87-one	(1.2)	1.7
both	(2.1)	3.0

LABOR 6 BRAKE SYSTEM 6 LABOR

	(Factory Time)	Chilton Time
(G) Master Cylinder, Renew		
Includes: Bleed system.		
1984-87		
wo/Booster	(.5)	.9
w/Booster	(.6)	1.0
(G) Master Cylinder, R&R and Rebuild		
Includes: Bleed system.		
1984-87		
wo/Booster	(.8)	1.3
w/Booster	(.9)	1.4
(G) Brake Hose, Renew		
Includes: Bleed system.		
1984-87-rear-one	(.5)	.8
front-one	(.4)	.7
(G) Brake System, Flush & Refill		
All models		1.2

POWER BRAKES

	(Factory Time)	Chilton Time
(G) Power Brake Booster, Renew		
1984-87	(.9)	1.3
w/Cruise control add		.2
(G) Power Brake Booster Check Valve, Renew		
1984-87	(.3)	.4
(G) Vacuum Pump, Renew		
1984-87	(.4)	.6

DISC BRAKES

	(Factory Time)	Chilton Time
(G) Disc Brake Pads, Renew		
Includes: Install new disc brake pads only.		
1984-87	(.7)	1.1
Resurface brake rotor, add-each		.9
(G) Caliper Assembly, Renew		
Includes: Bleed complete system.		
1984-87-one	(.6)	.9
both	(.8)	1.6
(G) Caliper Assembly, R&R and Recondition		
Includes: Bleed complete system.		
1984-87-one	(.8)	1.4
both	(1.2)	2.6
(G) Disc Brake Rotor, Renew		
1984-87-one	(.3)	.5
both	(.5)	.8
(G) Brake Differential Valve, Renew		
Includes: Bleed complete system and transfer switch.		
1984-87		
one	(.5)	.8
two	(.6)	1.0

PARKING BRAKE

	(Factory Time)	Chilton Time
(M) Parking Brake, Adjust		
1984-87	(.3)	.5
w/Console add	(.1)	.1
(G) Parking Brake Control, Renew		
1984-87		
wo/Console	(.5)	.7
w/Console	(.6)	1.0
(G) Parking Brake Cables, Renew		
Includes: Adjust parking brake.		
1984-87		
rear-one	(.6)	.9
both	(.9)	1.3
w/Console add		.1

PARTS 6 DISC BRAKES 6 PARTS

	Part No.	Price
(1) Caliper Assy. (Front)		
1984-87-right	▲E43Z-2B120A	89.50
left	▲E43Z-2B121A	89.50
(2) Brake Pads Kit		
1984-87	▲E3FZ-2001A	40.25
(3) Caliper Repair Kit		
1984-87	▲E43Z-2221A	8.00
(4) Caliper Piston (Front)		
1984-87	▲E43Z-2196A	11.75
(5) Locating Pin (Caliper)		
1984-87	▲E43Z-2B296A	6.50
(6) Brake Bearing Kit (Front Whl.)		
1984-87	▲E3FZ-2C134A	39.25
(7) Knuckle Assy. (Front Whl.)		
1984-87-right	▲E3FZ-3K185A	136.75
left	▲E3FZ-3K186A	136.75
(8) Shield (Disc Brake Rotor)		
1984-87-right	▲E43Z-2K004A	4.25
left	▲E43Z-2K005A	4.25
(9) Drive Hub (Front Whl.)		
1984-87	▲E3FZ-1104A	69.00
(10) Rotor		
1984-87	▲E43Z-1125A	81.00

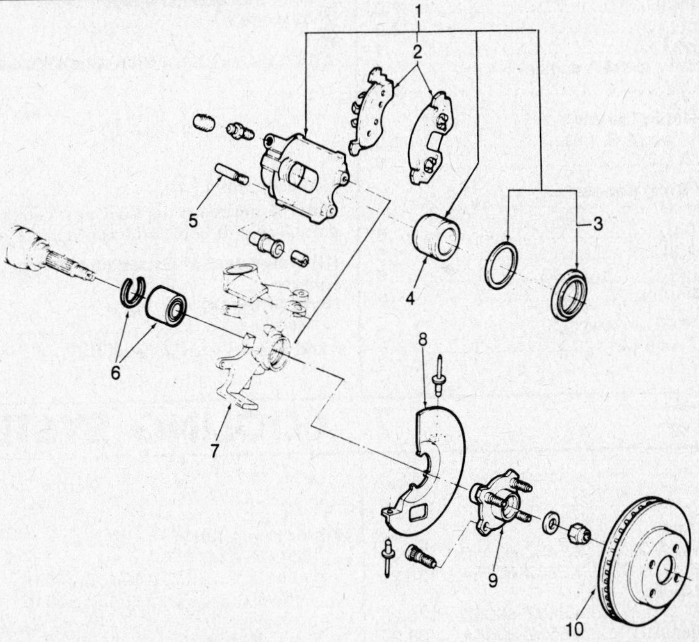

PARTS 6 BRAKE SYSTEM 6 PARTS

	Part No.	Price
Brake Shoe Set (Rear)		
1984-87	▲E2FZ-2200A	47.25
Brake Lining Kit		
1984-87	▲E2FZ-2007A	20.00
Rear Wheel Cylinder Assy.		
1984-87-right	▲E43Z-2261A	17.25
left	▲E43Z-2262A	17.25
Repair Kit (Wheel Cylinder)		
1984-87	▲E43Z-2128A	4.75
Brake Hose (Front)		
1984-87-right	▲E43Z-2078A	15.75
left	▲E43Z-2078B	15.25
Brake Hose (Rear)		
1984-87	▲E43Z-2282A	12.00
Master Cylinder Assy.		
1984-87	▲E43Z-2140A	89.00
Repair Kit (Master Cylinder)		
1984-87	▲E3FZ-2004B	59.25
Hub & Drum Assy. (Rear)		
1984	▲E43Z-1113A	79.25
1985-87-from 2/85	▲E43Z-1113B	60.75
Rear Wheel Oil Seal		
1984-87	▲E1FZ-1177A	10.75
Brake Booster Assy. (New)		
1984-87-exc. diesel	▲E43Z-2005A	131.75
diesel	▲E43Z-2005B	131.75

PARKING BRAKE

	Part No.	Price
Parking Brake Lever		
1984-87	▲E43Z-2780A	33.25
Parking Brake Cable (Rear)		
1984	▲E43Z-2A635A	16.25
1985-87	▲E53Z-2A635A	16.25
Equalizer & Rod Assy.		
1984-87	▲E1FZ-2A794A	4.25

LABOR 7 COOLING SYSTEM 7 LABOR

	(Factory Time)	Chilton Time
(M) Winterize Cooling System		
Includes: Run engine to check for leaks, tighten all hose connections. Test radiator and pressure cap, drain radiator and engine block. Add anti-freeze and refill system.		
All models		.5
(M) Thermostat, Renew		
1984-87	(.4)	.6
(M) Radiator Assembly, R&R or Renew		
Includes: Drain and refill cooling system.		
1984-87	(.6)	1.0
w/A.C. add		.2
Renew side tanks add		
one	(.3)	.4
both	(.6)	.8
(M) Radiator Hoses, Renew		
1984-87		
upper	(.3)	.4
lower	(.4)	.5
both	(.5)	.6
(M) Water Pump Drive Belt, Renew		
1984-87-wo/A.C.	(.4)	.6
w/A.C.	(.5)	.7
(G) Water Pump, Renew		
1984-87		
Gas	(1.2)	2.0
Diesel	(1.5)	*2.2
w/A.C. add	(.1)	.1
*If necessary to R&R engine, add		5.0
(M) Fan Blade, Renew		
1984-87-wo/A.C.	(.5)	1.0
w/A.C.	(.3)	.6
(M) Drive Belt, Renew		
1984-87		
A.C.	(.4)	.6
Alter	(.3)	.5
P.S.	(.4)	.6
Thermactor	(.3)	.5
(M) Drive Belt, Adjust		
1984-87-one	(.2)	.3

COOLING SYSTEM TUNE-UP

An Annual Cooling System Tune-Up Suggestion List should include (with some exceptions):

1. A visual check of the cooling system for indications of leaks or excessive oil content
2. Pressure check the cooling system for internal and external leaks with filler cap and neck adapter and tester
3. Check crankcase and automatic transmission oil for water content
4. Test coolant thermostat with radiator thermometer
5. Check temperature gauge for accuracy
6. Drain system and flush till clean
7. Clean foreign matter from radiator fins
8. Test radiator pressure cap with cap tester
9. Check fan blades and pulleys for alignment and damage
10. Internal and external inspection of all hoses for cracks and deterioration
11. Check core plugs (where possible) for seepage
12. Refill system with correct coolant and check for air locks
13. Check condition and tension of drive belts with tension gauge

All models 1.5

	(Factory Time)	Chilton Time
each adtnl	(.1)	.1
Note: If necessary to R&R any component to gain access to belts, add appropriate time.		
(G) Water Jacket Expansion Plugs, Renew (Side of Block)		
each		*.5
*Add time to gain accessibility.		

	(Factory Time)	Chilton Time
(G) Electric Cooling Fan Relay, Renew		
1984-87	(.4)	.5
(G) Electric Cooling Fan Motor, Renew		
1984-87	(.4)	.6
wo/A.C. add	(.1)	.1
(G) Temperature Gauge (Engine Unit), Renew		
1984-87	(.3)	.4
(G) Temperature Gauge (Dash Unit), Renew		
Includes: R&R instrument panel pad when required.		
1984-87-Topaz	(.7)	1.2
(G) Heater Hoses, Renew		
1984-87		
wo/A.C.	(.6)	.8
w/A.C.	(.5)	.6
(G) Heater Control Assembly, Renew		
1984-87		
wo/A.C.	(.7)	1.1
w/A.C.	(.8)	1.2
(G) Heater Blower Motor Switch, Renew		
1984-87	(.6)	1.2
(G) Heater Blower Motor Resistor, Renew		
1984-87	(.3)	.5
(G) Heater Core, R&R or Renew		
1984-87		
wo/A.C.	(1.0)	1.9
w/A.C.	(1.1)	3.0
ADD THESE OPERATIONS TO HEATER CORE R&R		
(G) Boil & Repair		1.2
(G) Repair Core		.9
(G) Recore		1.2
(G) Heater Blower Motor, Renew		
1984-87	(.5)	.9
(G) Temperature Control Cable, Renew		
1984-87	(.7)	1.1

PARTS 7 COOLING SYSTEM 7 PARTS

	Part No.	Price
Radiator Assy.		
1984-wo/A.C.	▲E43Z-8005B	176.25
1984-85-w/A.C.	▲E53Z-8005A	188.25
1985-2.3-wo/A.C.	▲E43Z-8005B	176.25
1985-diesel	▲E53Z-8005A	188.25
1986-87-2.3-wo/A.C.	▲E63Z-8005B	188.25
w/A.C.	▲E63Z-8005A	188.25
diesel	▲E63Z-8005C	188.25
Upper Radiator Hose		
Gasoline Engine		
1984-85	▲E43Z-8260A	12.50
1986-87	▲E63Z-8260A	N.L.
Diesel Engine		
1984-87	▲E4FZ-8260B	9.75
Lower Radiator Hose		
Gasoline Engine		
1984-87	▲E43Z-8286A	18.25
Diesel Engine		
1984-87-front	▲E4FZ-8286A	10.00
rear	▲E4FZ-8286B	7.25

	Part No.	Price
Water Pump Assy.		
1984-87-exc. diesel	▲E43Z-8501A	85.00
diesel	▲E43Z-8501B	54.25
Electric Motor Assy. (Radiator)		
Gasoline Engine		
1984-wo/A.C. bef 9.83	▲E43Z-8K621A	72.50
1984-85-from 9/83	▲E3FZ-8K621A	72.50
1984-87-w/A.C.	▲E43Z-8K621B	72.50
1986-87-wo/A.C.	▲E6FZ-8K621A	72.50
Diesel engine		
1984-85-wo/A.C.	▲E3FZ-8K621A	72.50
w/A.C.	▲E3FZ-8K621B	72.50
1986-87-wo/A.C.	▲E6FZ-8K621A	72.50
w/A.C.	▲E6FZ-8K621B	72.50
Thermostat		
1984-87-gas eng.	▲E43Z-8575A	5.75
diesel eng.	▲E43Z-8575B	8.75

	Part No.	Price
Temperature Sending Unit (Engine)		
1984-87-wo/gauges	▲E43Z-10884A	9.00
w/gauges	▲D0WY-10884A	5.25
diesel	▲D0ZZ-10884A	5.00
Temperature Gauge (Dash)		
1984-87-w/Tach.	▲E46Z-10883A	28.00
Heater Core		
1984-87-wo/A.C.	▲E2FZ-18476A	59.50
w/A.C.	▲E1FZ-18476B	45.50
Blower Motor		
1984-87	▲E43Z-18527A	62.25
Blower Motor Resistor		
1984-87-w/integral A.C.	▲E43Z-19A706A	8.75
1984-w/hang-on A.C.	▲D8RZ-19A706B	21.50
1985-w/hang-on A.C.	▲E53Z-19A706A	14.75
Switch Assy. (Heater)		
1984-87	▲E43Z-18578A	4.50

LABOR 8 EXHAUST SYSTEM 8 LABOR

	(Factory Time)	Chilton Time
(G) Muffler, Renew		
1984-87	(.4)	.8
(G) Inlet or Intermediate Pipe, Renew		
1984-87-Diesel	(.5)	.8
(G) Catalytic Converter, Renew		
1984-87	(.7)	1.0
(G) Exhaust Manifold or Gasket, Renew		
1984-87		
Gas	(3.3)	4.5
Diesel	(1.0)	1.7
COMBINATIONS		
(G) Muffler, Exhaust and Tail Pipe, Renew		
1984-87		1.2

PARTS 8 EXHAUST SYSTEM 8 PARTS

	Part No.	Price
Muffler		
Gasoline Engine		
1984	▲E43Z-5230A	N.L.
1985	▲E53Z-5230A	110.25
1986-87	▲E63Z-5230A	110.25
(Diesel Engine)		
1984	▲E43Z-5230D	110.50
1985	▲E53Z-5230B	108.75
1986-87	▲E63Z-5230C	110.25
Catalytic Converter		
1984-w/A.T. (exc. Canada)	▲E43Z-5E212A	401.50
Canada	▲E43Z-5E212C	N.L.
w/M.T. (exc. Canada)	▲E43Z-5E212D	441.50
1985	▲E53Z-5E212B	401.50
w/M.T. (Canada)	▲E43Z-5E212C	N.L.
1986-87-w/A.T.	▲E63Z-5E212A	377.50
w/M.T.	▲E43Z-5E212C	N.L.
Resonator & Inlet Pipe		
1984-87-gas	▲E53Z-5A289A	N.L.
1984-85-diesel	▲E4FZ-5A289A	27.50
1986-87	▲E6FZ-5A289A	27.50
Exhaust Manifold		
Gasoline Engine		
1984	▲E43Z-9430E	110.50
1985-87-exc. C.F.I.	▲E53Z-9430C	N.L.
C.F.I.	▲E53Z-9430A	110.50
Diesel Engine		
1984	▲E43Z-9430A	46.25
1985-bef. 5/85	▲E53Z-9430B	46.25
1985-87-from 5/85	▲E53Z-9430D	46.25

LABOR 9 FRONT SUSPENSION 9 LABOR

Note: On all front suspension operations alignment charges must be added if performed. Time given does not include alignment.

	(Factory Time)	Chilton Time
(M) Wheel, Renew		
one		.5
(G) Wheels, Rotate (All)		
All models	(.5)	.5
(G) Wheels, Balance		
one		.3
each adtnl		.2
(G) Check Alignment of Front End		
All models		.5
Note: Deduct if alignment is performed.		
(G) Front Toe-In, Adjust		
All models	(.6)	.8
(G) Rear Toe-In, Check and Adjust		
All models		
one side	(.5)	.8
both sides	(.6)	.9
(G) Rear Camber, Check and Adjust		
All models		
one side	(.5)	.8
both sides	(.8)	1.4
(G) Front Wheel Grease Seals, Renew		
Includes: Repack bearings.		
1984-one side	(1.4)	1.9
both sides	(2.5)	3.2
(G) Front Wheel Bearings and Cups, Renew		
Includes: Repack bearings.		
1984-one side	(1.4)	2.0
both sides	(2.6)	3.5
(G) Lower Control Arm Assy., Renew		
Add alignment charges.		
1984-87-one side	(.7)	1.0
both sides	(1.1)	1.5
(G) Front Spindle Carrier/Knuckle, Renew		
Add alignment charges.		
1984-87-one side	(1.5)	2.0
both sides	(2.8)	3.8
Renew hub brg add, each		.4
(G) Front Coil Springs, Renew		
Includes: R&R front strut.		
1984-one	(1.2)	1.8
both	(2.1)	3.2
1985-87-one	(.8)	1.1
both	(1.2)	2.0
(G) Front Stabilizer Bar, Renew		
1984-87	(.6)	1.0
(G) Front Strut Shock Absorber Assy., R&R or Renew		
1984-one	(1.2)	1.7
both	(2.1)	3.0
1985-87-left	(.8)	1.1
right	(.6)	.9
both	(1.0)	1.8
(G) Halfshaft Assy., R&R or Renew		
1984-87-one	(.9)	1.2
both	(1.7)	2.2
(G) C.V. Joint, Renew or Recondition		
Includes: R&R halfshaft.		
1984-87-one	(1.1)	1.5
two	(2.0)	2.8
each adtnl		.3
(G) Differential Oil Seal, Renew		
Includes: R&R halfshaft.		
1984-87-one	(1.0)	1.6
both	(1.9)	3.0

PARTS 9 FRONT SUSPENSION 9 PARTS

	Part No.	Price
(1) Knuckle Assy. (Front Wheel)		
1984-87-right	▲E3FZ-3K185A	136.75
left	▲E3FZ-3K186A	136.75
(2) Lower Control Arm Assy.		
1984-87-right	▲E43Z-3078B	88.00
left	▲E43Z-3079B	88.00
(3) Spacer		
1984-85	▲E1FZ-5490B	1.75
1986-87	▲E1FZ-5490D	1.75

PARTS 9 FRONT SUSPENSION 9 PARTS

	Part No.	Price
(4) Stabilizer Bar (Front)		
1984-87	▲E43Z-5482B	106.00
(5) Insulator (Stabilizer)		
1984-87	▲E43Z-5493A	3.25
(6) Bracket (Stabilizer)		
1984	▲E43Z-5486A	5.25
1984 (H.D. & Diesel)	▲E43Z-5493E	3.50
1985	▲E53Z-5493A	3.25
1985 (H.D. & Diesel)	▲E53Z-5493B	3.50
1986	▲E43Z-5493A	3.25
(7) Shock Absorber		
(wo/TRX susp.)		
1984-85-bef. 3/85	▲E43Z-18124B	73.25
diesel	▲E43Z-18124E	73.00
1986-87-wo/LX & GT	▲E63Z-18124A	73.00
H.D.	▲E63Z-18124B	73.00
w/LX	▲E63Z-18124C	73.00
w/GT	▲E63Z-18124D	73.00
(w/TRX susp.)		
1984-85-bef. 3/85	▲E43Z-18124D	73.25
1985-from 3/85	▲E53Z-18124B	73.25
(8) Spring		
Note: Order by model and description.		
(9) Bearing & Seal Assy.		
1984-87	▲E43Z-3B455C	12.50
(10) Mounting Bracket (Shock)		
1984-87	▲E43Z-18183A	13.50

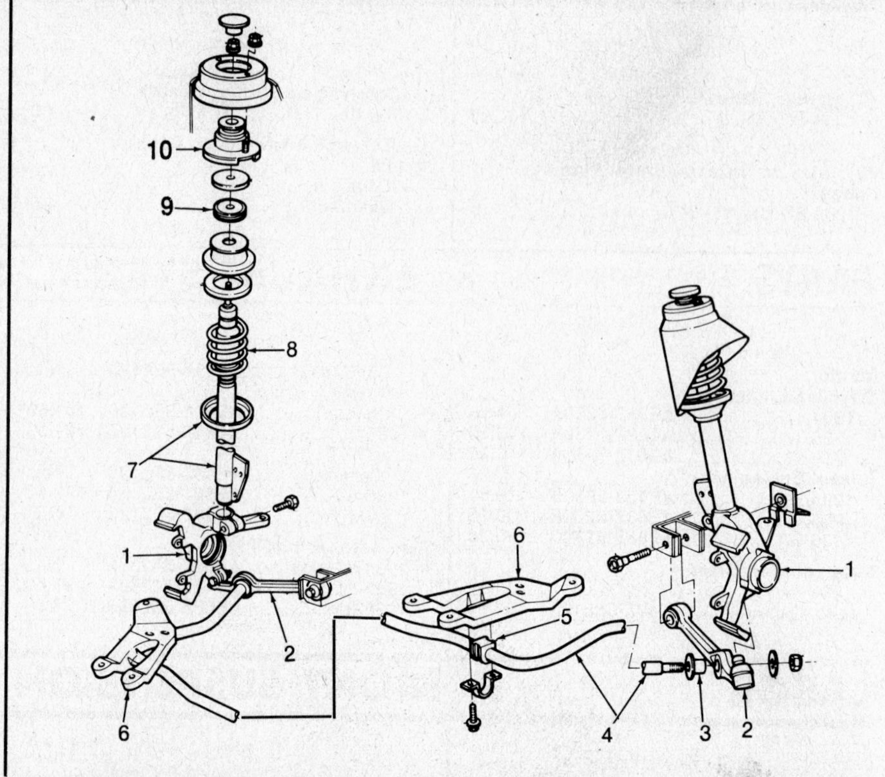

LABOR 11 STEERING GEAR 11 LABOR

(Factory Time) — Chilton Time

(G) Horn Button or Ring, Renew
1984-87 (.3) 5

(G) Steering Wheel, Renew
1984-87 (.3) 4

(G) Upper Mast Jacket Bearing, Renew
1984-87
std colm (.5) 9
tilt colm (.6) 1.1

(G) Stalk Horn Assembly, Renew
1984-87 (.5) 6

(G) Steering Column Lock Actuator Parts, Renew
1984-87
std colm (1.2) 1.6
tilt colm (1.5) 2.1
w/Cruise control add (.1) 1

(G) Tie Rod End, Renew
Includes: Reset toe-in.
1984-87-one (.8) 1.1
two (.9) 1.2

STANDARD STEERING

(G) Manual Rack and Pinion Assy., R&R or Renew
1984-87 (2.9) 4.0

(P) Manual Rack and Pinion Assy., R&R and Recondition
Includes: Disassemble, renew necessary parts, reassemble and adjust.
1984-87 (3.1) 4.4

(G) Manual Rack and Pinion Assy., Adjust (In Chassis)
1984-87 (.3) 6

(G) Ball Joints, Tie Rod Ends and Bellows, Renew (Both Sides)
Includes: R&R rack and pinion assy. Does not include reset toe-in.
1984-87 (2.0) 2.8

(G) Input Shaft Seals, Renew (In Chassis)
1984-87 (1.3) 2.0

POWER STEERING

(G) Trouble Shoot Power Steering
Includes: Test pump and system pressure. Check pounds pull on steering wheel and check for leaks.
All models 5

(M) Check and Fill Reservoir
All models 2

(G) Pump Pressure Check & Flow Test
All models 1.0

(M) Pump Drive Belt, Renew or Adjust
1984-87-renew (.4) 6
adjust (.2) 3

(G) Power Rack and Pinion Assy., R&R or Renew
Does not include reset toe-in.
1984-87 (3.0) 4.7

(P) Power Rack and Pinion Assy., R&R and Recondition
Includes: Disassemble, renew necessary parts, reassemble and adjust.
Does not include reset toe-in.
1984-87 (3.3) 5.5

(G) Power Rack and Pinion Assy., Adjust (In Chassis)
1984-87 (.3) 6

(G) Ball Joints, Tie Rod Ends and Bellows, Renew (Both Sides)
Includes: R&R rack and pinion assy. Does not include reset toe-in.
1984-87 (2.4) 3.4

(G) Input Shaft Seals, Renew (In Chassis)
1984-87 (1.3) 2.0

(G) Power Steering Oil Pump, R&R or Renew
Includes: Bleed system.
1984-87
Gas (1.0) 1.4
Diesel (1.5) 2.1
Renew shaft seal add 2

(G) Power Steering Oil Pump, R&R and Recondition
Includes: Bleed system.
1984-87
Gas (1.4) 2.0
Diesel (1.9) 2.7

(G) Power Steering Hoses, Renew
Includes: R&R air pump and air cleaner. Bleed system.
1984-87
Pressure
each (.7) 1.0
Return
front (.7) 1.0
center (.5) 7
rear (.5) 7
Cooling (.6) 9

PARTS 11 STEERING GEAR-(STANDARD) 11 PARTS

	Part No.	Price
Steering Gear Assy.		
1984-85-before 6-85	▲E5FZ-3504B	237.75
1985-87-from 6-85	▲E5FZ-3504C	255.50
(1) Steering Gear Housing		
1984-85	▲E1FZ-3548C	57.00
1986-87	▲E5FZ-3548A	57.00
from 2-85	▲E5FZ-3548A	57.00
(2) Cup (Worm Bearing)		
1984-87-upper	▲E1FZ-3552C	14.25
lower	▲E1FZ-3552B	15.75
(3) Shaft Assy. (Upper)		
(wo/tilt wheel)		
1984-85	▲E43Z-3524B	43.75
1986-87-w/air bag	▲E63Z-3524A	59.50
wo/air bag	▲E63Z-3524B	43.75
(w/tilt wheel)		
1984-85-wo/air bag	▲E5FZ-3524A	175.00
1985-w/air bag	▲E53Z-3524A	59.50
1986	▲E63Z-3524C	59.50
(4) Shim Kit		
1984-87	▲E3FZ-3763A	3.50
(5) Gasket		
1984-87	▲E1FZ-3581B	4.50
(6) Housing End Cover		
1984-85-before 6-85	▲E1FZ-3568A	4.75
1985-87-from 6-85	▲E5FZ-3568A	4.75
(7) Oil Seal (Sector Shaft Housing)		
1984-85-before 6-85	▲E2FZ-3591A	N.L.
1985-87-from 6-85	▲E5FZ-3591A	4.00
(8) Support Yoke (Sector Shaft)		
1984-87	▲E1FZ-3F515A	2.25

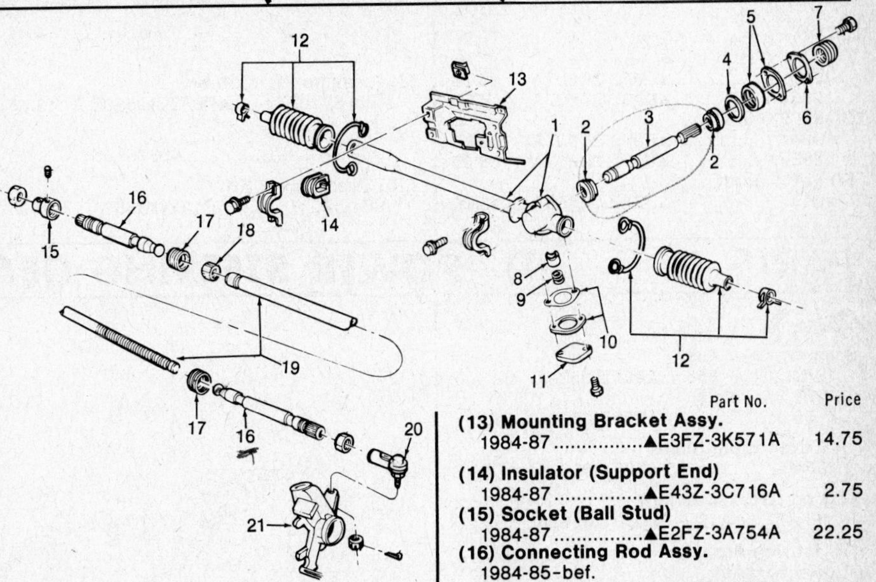

	Part No.	Price
(9) Spring		
Note: Spring is included with sector shaft support yoke.		
(10) Gasket & Shim Kit		
1984-87	▲E1FZ-3F518A	6.50
(11) Housing Cover (Sector Shaft)		
1984-85-before 6-85	▲E1FZ-3580B	8.50
from 6-85	▲E5FZ-3580A	8.50
(12) Dust Seal Kit		
1984-85 (before 6-85) right	▲E2FZ-3332B	10.25
left	▲E2FZ-3332A	10.00
1985-87 (from 6-85) right & left	▲E5FZ-3332A	10.25

	Part No.	Price
(13) Mounting Bracket Assy.		
1984-87	▲E3FZ-3K571A	14.75
(14) Insulator (Support End)		
1984-87	▲E43Z-3C716A	2.75
(15) Socket (Ball Stud)		
1984-87	▲E2FZ-3A754A	22.25
(16) Connecting Rod Assy.		
1984-85-bef. 6/85	▲E2FZ-3280A	19.50
1985-87-from 6/85	▲E5FZ-3280A	8.50
(17) Seat (Ball Spring)		
1984-87	▲E4FZ-3F513A	3.25
(18) Bushing		
1984-87	▲E1FZ-3576B	8.50
(19) Sector Shaft		
1984-85-before 6-85	▲E1FZ-3575A	54.00
from 6-85	▲E5FZ-3575A	54.00
(20) Tie Rod End		
1984-85	▲E1FZ-3A130A	38.75
1986-87	▲E3FZ-3430A	N.L.
(21) Knuckle Assy.		
1984-87-right	▲E3FZ-3K185A	136.75
left	▲E3FZ-3K186A	136.75

PARTS 11 POWER STEERING PUMP 11 PARTS

	Part No.	Price
Oil Pressure Hose		
Note: Order by year and model.		
Power Steering Pump		
Gasoline Engine		
1984-exc. 4 sp.	▲E43Z-3A674A	N.L.
w/4 sp.	▲E2FZ-3A674A	181.25
1985-exc. 4 sp.	▲E53Z-3A674A	181.25
1986-87	▲E63Z-3A674A	194.50
Diesel Engine		
1984	▲E4FZ-3A674A	194.50
1985	▲E5FZ-3A674B	194.50
1986-87	▲E6FZ-3A674B	194.50
(1) Valve Assy.		
1984-87-exc. 4 sp	▲E43Z-3A561A	16.00
w/4 sp.	▲E1FZ-3A561B	9.50
(2) Valve Spring (Flow Control)		
1984-87	▲D8AZ-3D586A	1.50
(3) Retaining Ring		
1984-87	▲387573S	1.50
(4) Housing Assy.		
1984-87	▲E1AZ-3A643A	42.25
(5) Pressure Plate (Front)		
1984-87	▲E5FZ-3D590A	13.75
(6) Rotor Assy.		
Gasoline Engine		
1984	▲E35Z-3B607A	N.L.
1984-w/4 sp. MTX	▲E3FZ-3B607A	52.50

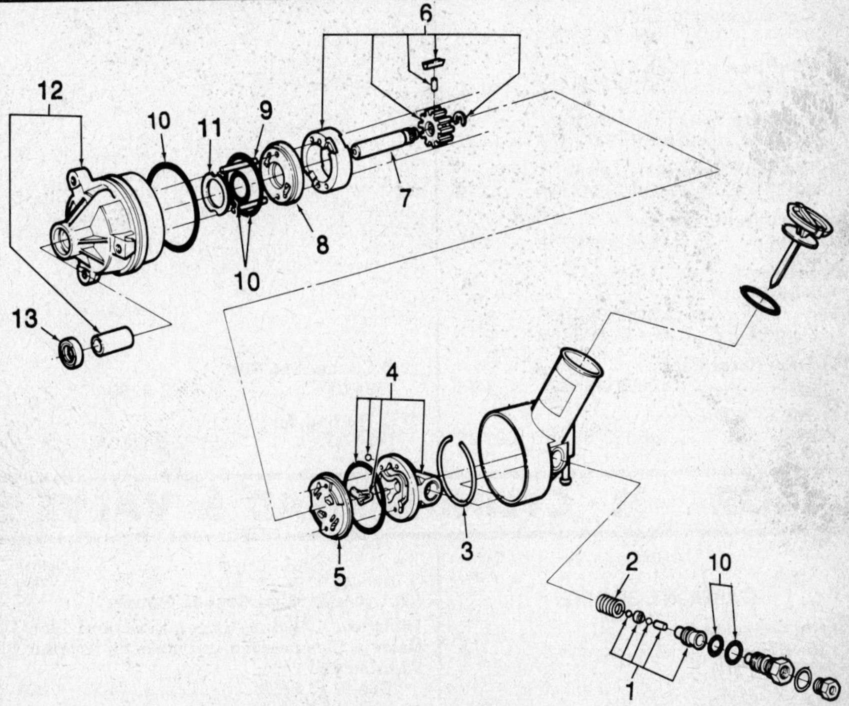

PARTS 11 POWER STEERING PUMP 11 PARTS

	Part No.	Price
1985	▲E53Z-3D607A	36.25
1986-87	▲E6DZ-3D607A	4.50
Diesel Engine		
1984	▲E3FZ-3D607A	52.50
1985-87	▲E5FZ-3D607A	56.25
(7) Rotor Shaft		
1984-87	▲D8AZ-3B559A	18.00
(8) Pressure Plate (Rear)		
1984-87	▲D8AZ-3D590B	13.75
(9) Pin		
1984-87	▲387579S	1.00
(10) Seal Gasket Kit		
1984-87	▲E1AZ-3B584A	8.75
(11) Spring (Pressure Plate)		
1984-87	▲D8AZ-3D596A	2.50
(12) Plate & Bushing		
1984-87	▲E1AZ-3D643A	42.25
(13) Oil Seal (Rotor)		
1984-87	▲D9AZ-3B592A	9.25

PARTS 11 POWER STEERING GEAR 11 PARTS

	Part No.	Price
Steering Gear Assy.		
1985-bef. 8/85	▲E5FZ-3504A	521.00
1985-87-from 8/85	▲E6FZ-3504A	559.75
(1) Cover (Input Shaft)		
1984-87	▲E3FZ-3568A	4.75
(2) Cup (Worm Bearing)		
1984-87	▲D8BZ-3552A	13.25
(3) Housing Assy.		
1984-85-bef. 8/85	▲E4FZ-3548A	107.50
1985-87-from 8/85	▲E6FZ-3548A	107.50
(4) Shaft & Control Valve Assy.		
1984-85-bef. 8/85	▲E5FZ-3D517A	173.00
1985-87-from 8/85	▲E6FZ-3D517A	173.00
(5) Bearing (Input Shaft)		
1984-87	▲E1FZ-3D525A	8.25
(6) Seal Kit (Sector Shaft)		
1984-87	▲E3FZ-3E501A	22.00
(7) Support Yoke (Sector Shaft)		
1984-87	▲E1FZ-3F515B	6.00
(8) Housing Cover (Sector Shaft)		
1984-87	▲E1FZ-3580A	7.00
(9) Bushing		
1984	▲E3FZ-3576A	10.25
1985-87	▲E4FZ-3576A	8.50
(10) Cover (Housing End)		
1984-87	▲E1FZ-3568C	4.75
(11) Dust Seal Kit (Ball Stud)		
1984-87	▲E3FZ-3332A	10.00
(12) Pressure Tube (Right Turn)		
1984-87	▲E1FZ-3A717A	14.25
(13) Pressure Tube (Left Turn)		
1984-87	▲E1FZ-3A714A	12.75
(14) Mounting Bracket		
1984-87	▲E3FZ-3K571A	14.75
(15) Insulator		
1984-87-Housing end	▲E1FZ-3C716B	7.25
Support end	▲E43Z-3C716B	2.75
(16) Tube (Gear Rack)		
1984-87	▲E3FZ-3K762A	4.75
(17) Sector Shaft		
1984-87	▲E3FZ-3575A	91.25

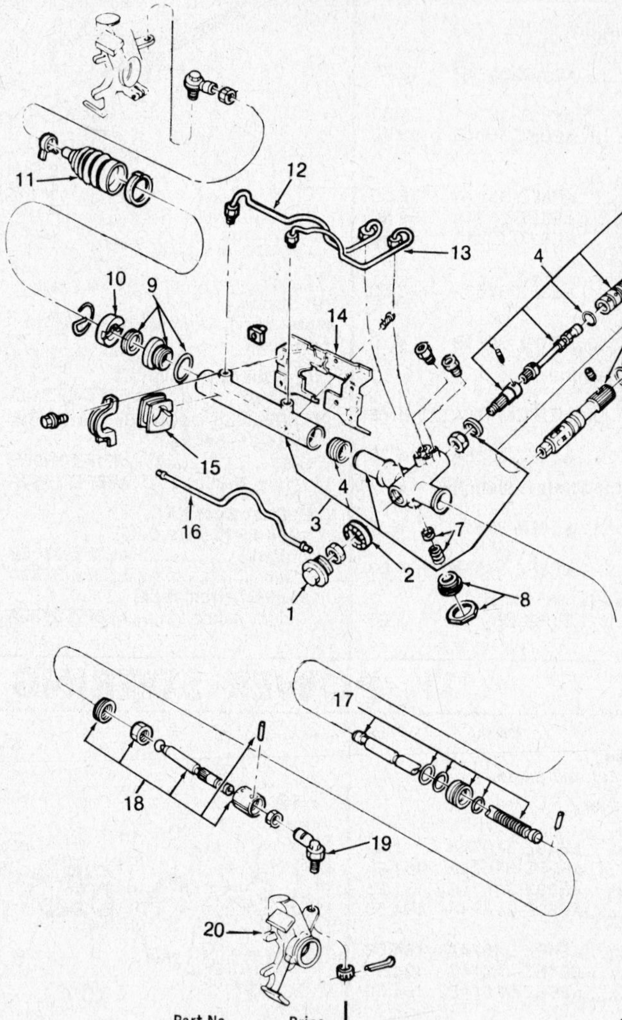

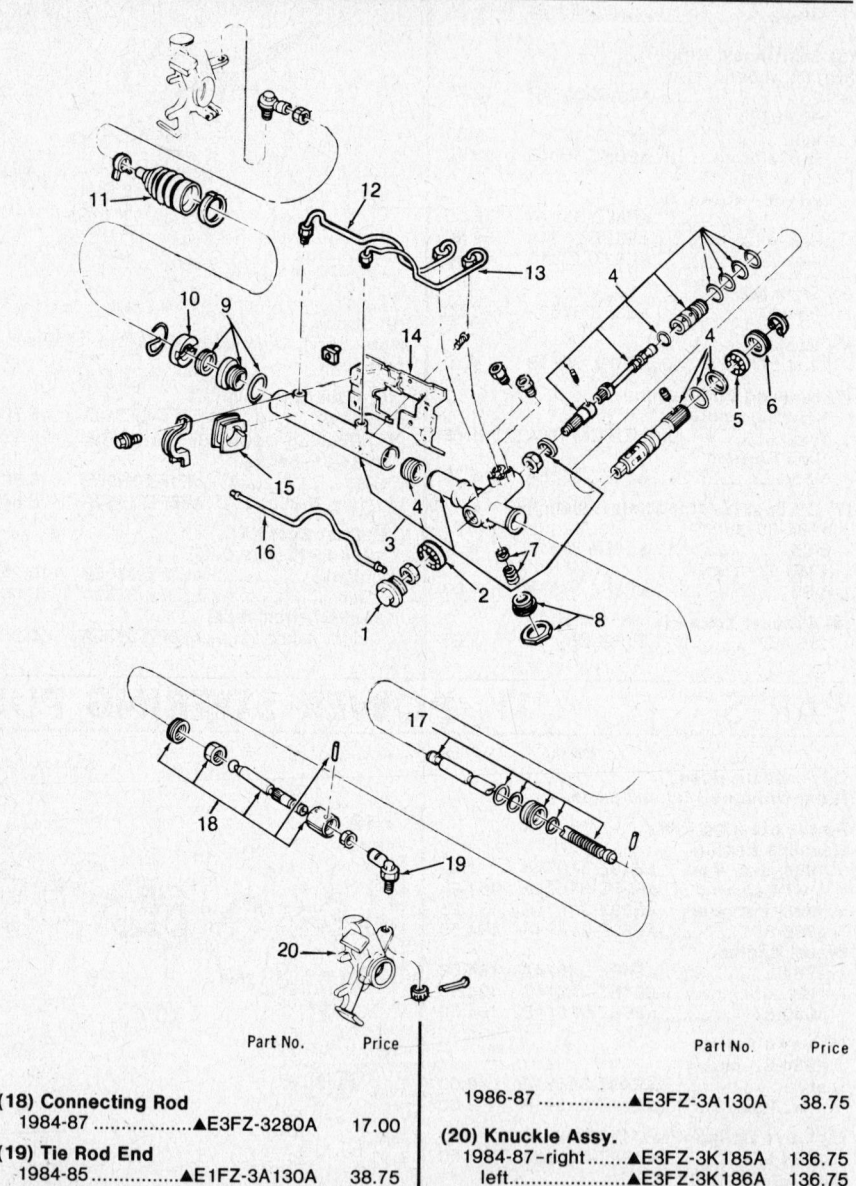

	Part No.	Price
(18) Connecting Rod		
1984-87	▲E3FZ-3280A	17.00
(19) Tie Rod End		
1984-85	▲E1FZ-3A130A	38.75
1986-87	▲E3FZ-3A130A	38.75
(20) Knuckle Assy.		
1984-87-right	▲E3FZ-3K185A	136.75
left	▲E3FZ-3K186A	136.75

LABOR 12 CYLINDER HEAD & VALVE SYSTEM 12 LABOR

(Factory Time) Chilton Time

GASOLINE ENGINE

(G) Compression Test
1984-87 (.3) .... **.6**

(G) Cylinder Head Gasket, Renew
Includes: Check cylinder head and block flatness. Clean carbon and make all necessary adjustments.
1984-87 (3.5) **4.9**

(G) Cylinder Head, Renew
Includes: Transfer all components, clean carbon. Reface valves, check valve spring tension, assembled height and valve head runout.
1984-87 (4.2) **5.9**

LABOR 12 CYLINDER HEAD & VALVE SYSTEM 12 LABOR

(Factory Time) Chilton Time

(P) Clean Carbon and Grind Valves
Includes: R&R cylinder head, check valve spring tension, valve seat and head runout, stem to guide clearance and spring assembled height. Minor tune up.
1984-87 (5.4) 7.5

(G) Valve Tappets, Renew
Includes: Adjust carburetor and ignition timing.
1984-87-one (3.5) 5.0
all (3.8) 5.5

(G) Rocker Arm Cover Gasket, Renew
1984-87 (.5) 8

(G) Valve Springs and/or Valve Stem Oil Seals, Renew (Head On Car)
1984-87-one (.7) 1.1
each adtnl (.2) 2
all (1.5) 2.5

(G) Valve Push Rods and/or Rocker Arms, Renew
1984-87-one (.6) 1.0
all (.8) 1.5

COMBINATIONS
Add To Valve Job

See Machine Shop Operations

(G) DRAIN, EVACUATE & RECHARGE AIR CONDITIONING SYSTEM
All models (.7) 1.2

(G) CARBURETOR, RECONDITION
Holly-1949 (1.4) 1.9
6149-1V (1.5) 2.0

(G) HYDRAULIC VALVE LIFTERS, DISASSEMBLE AND CLEAN
Each 2

(P) CYLINDER HEAD, RECONDITION (HEAD REMOVED)
Gas models (1.9) 2.5

(P) VALVE GUIDES, REAM OVERSIZE
Each (.1) 2

(Factory Time) Chilton Time

DIESEL ENGINE

(G) Compression Test
1984-87 .... 1.2

(Factory Time) Chilton Time

(G) Cylinder Head Gasket, Renew
Includes: Clean carbon and make all necessary adjustments.
1984-87 (4.3) 6.0

(G) Cylinder Head, Renew
Includes: Transfer all components, clean carbon. Make all necessary adjustments.
1984-87 (5.2) 7.3

(P) Clean Carbon and Grind Valves
Includes: R&R cylinder head. Grind valves and seats. Make all necessary adjustments.
1984-87 (6.8) 9.5

(G) Rocker Arm Cover Gasket, Renew
1984-87 (.4) 6

(G) Valve Springs and/or Valve Stem Oil Seals, Renew
1984-87-one (3.6) 5.0
each adtnl (.2) 3
all (4.0) 7.0

(G) Valve Tappets, Renew
1984-87-one (3.5) 4.9
all (3.7) 5.2

PARTS 12 CYLINDER HEAD & VALVE SYSTEM 12 PARTS

	Part No.	Price
122 (2.0) DIESEL ENGINE		
Overhaul Gasket Set (Partial)		
1984-87	▲E43Z-6008B	88.25
(1) Cylinder Head		
1984-87	▲E53Z-6049C	457.00
(2) Cylinder Head Gasket		
1984-87	▲E53Z-6051B	29.25
(3) Valve Cover Gasket		
1984-87	▲E43Z-6584B	4.50
(4) Valve Tappet Assy.		
1984-87	▲E43Z-6500A	5.50
(5) Spring Retainer (Valve)		
1984-87	▲E43Z-6514B	1.25
(6) Valve Springs (Int. & Exh.)		
1984-87	▲E43Z-6513B	1.75
(7) Spring Seat (Valve)		
1984-87	▲E43Z-6A536A	.75
(8) Seal (Valve Stem)		
1984-87	▲E43Z-6571D	2.75
(9) Valve Guide Assy.		
1984-87-Intake	▲E43Z-6510A	2.25
Exhaust	▲E43Z-6510B	2.25
(10) Intake Valve		
1984-87	▲E43Z-6507D	7.25
(11) Exhaust Valve		
1984	▲E43Z-6505D	12.00
1985-87	▲E43Z-6505E	11.75
(12) Insert Assy. (Comb. Chamber)		
1984-87	▲E43Z-6057A	18.00
(13) Glow Plug		
1984-87	▲E43Z-12A342A	24.75
(14) Nozzle Holder Assy.		
1984-87	▲E43Z-9E527B	22.50
(15) Wire Assy. (Glow Plug)		
1984-85	▲E43Z-9A451A	5.00
1986-87	▲E53Z-9A451A	5.00

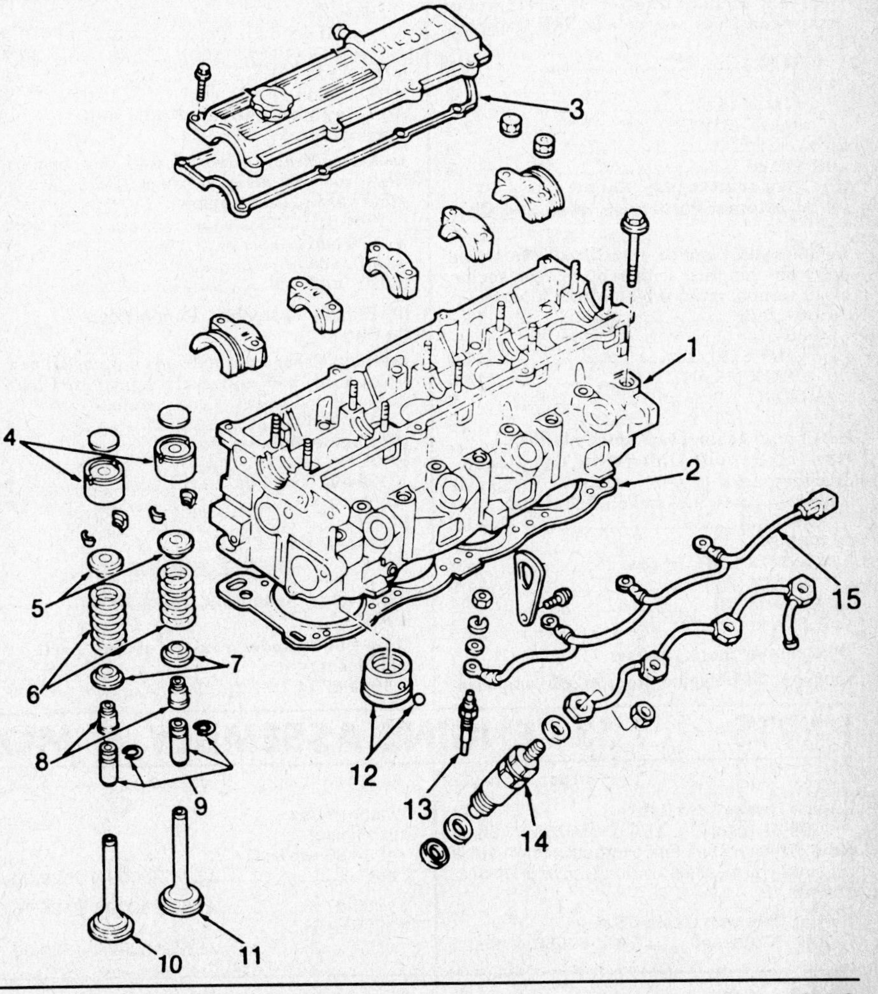

PARTS 12 CYLINDER HEAD & VALVE SYSTEM 12 PARTS

	Part No.	Price
GASOLINE ENGINE		
Valve Grind Gasket Set		
1984-87-exc. H.O.	▲E53Z-6079A	48.75
1985-87-w/H.O.	▲E53Z-6079B	49.00
Rocker Arm Cover Gasket		
1984	▲E43Z-6584A	4.50
1985	▲E53Z-6584A	4.50
1986	▲E63Z-6584A	11.25
(1) Cylinder Head (wo/H.O. engine)		
1984-85-wo/ Valves	▲E43Z-6049A	369.25
w/Valves	▲E43Z-6049B	562.00
1986-87-wo/ valves	▲E53Z-6049F	369.25
w/valves	▲E53Z-6049G	562.00
(w/H.O. engine)		
1985-wo/Valves	▲E53Z-6049A	387.75
w/Valves	▲E53Z-6049B	590.00
1986-87-wo/ valves	▲E53Z-6049D	387.75
w/valves	▲E53Z-6049E	590.00

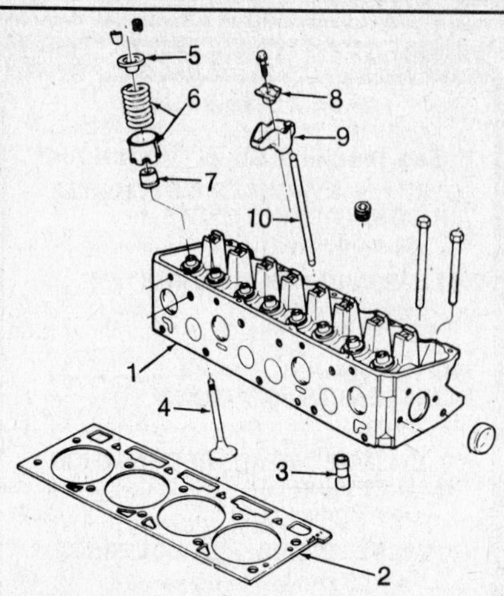

	Part No.	Price
(2) Cylinder Head Gasket		
1984	▲E43Z-6051A	12.75
1985-87	▲E53Z-6051A	12.75

	Part No.	Price
(3) Valve Tappets		
1984-87	▲D9HZ-6500A	9.25
(4) Valves (Intake & Exhaust)		
1984-87-exhaust	▲E43Z-6505A	14.25
intake	▲E43Z-6507A	9.00
(5) Seat (Valve Spring)		
1984-87	▲E43Z-6514A	1.00
(6) Spring (Valve Damper)		
1984-87	▲E53Z-6513A	4.50
(7) Seal (Valve Stem)		
1984-87-intake	▲E43Z-6571A	2.25
exhaust	▲D4FZ-6571A	1.25
(8) Seat (Rocker Arm Fulcrum)		
1984	▲E43Z-6A528B	1.00
1985-87	▲E53Z-6A528A	1.00
(9) Rocker Arm		
1984-87	▲E43Z-6564A	7.00
(10) Push Rod		
1984-87	▲E43Z-6565A	2.00

LABOR 13 ENGINE ASSEMBLY & MOUNTS 13 LABOR

(Factory Time)	Chilton Time
GASOLINE ENGINE	
(G) Engine Assembly, Remove & Install	
Does not include transfer of any parts or equipment. Does not include R&R trans/axle assy.	
1984 (4.4)	6.0
1985-87	
w/MTX (4.8)	7.0
w/ATX (5.1)	7.4
w/A.C. add	.8
w/P.S. add	.2
(P) Cylinder Assembly, Renew (w/All Internal Parts Less Head and Oil Pan)	
Includes: R&R engine, transfer all component parts not supplied with replacement engine, clean carbon, grind valves. Minor tune up.	
1984 (9.8)	14.2
1985-87	
w/MTX (10.1)	14.6
w/ATX (10.4)	15.0
w/A.C. add (.8)	.8
w/P.S. add (.2)	.2
(G) Engine Assembly, Replace With New or Rebuilt Unit (With Cyl. Head)	
Includes: R&R engine assembly, transfer all necessary parts, fuel and electrical units.	
1984 (7.3)	11.3
1985-87	
w/MTX (7.4)	11.5
w/ATX (7.7)	11.9
w/A.C. add (.8)	.8
w/P.S. add (.2)	.2
(P) Cylinder Block, Renew	
Includes: R&R engine, transfer all component parts, renew rings and bearings, clean carbon, grind valves. Minor tune up.	
1984 (13.3)	19.2
1985-87	
w/MTX (13.2)	19.8
w/ATX (13.5)	20.2
w/A.C. add (.8)	.8
w/P.S. add (.2)	.2
(P) Engine Assy., R&R and Recondition	
Includes: Rebore block, install new pistons, rings, rod and main bearings. Clean carbon, grind valves. Tune engine.	
1984-87 (17.0)	25.3
w/ATX add (.4)	.4
w/A.C. add (.8)	.8
w/P.S. add (.2)	.2
(P) Engine Assembly, Recondition (In Car)	
Includes: Expand or renew pistons, install new rings, pins, rod and main bearings. Clean carbon, grind valves. Tune engine.	
1984-87 (11.4)	17.8
(G) Engine Mounts, Renew	
FRONT	
1984-87-one (.6)	.9
both	1.4
REAR	
1984-87 (.4)	.6
DIESEL ENGINE	
(G) Engine Assembly, Remove & Install	
Does not include transfer of any parts or equipment.	
1984-87 (4.1)	5.9
w/A.C. add (.6)	.6
w/P.S. add (.2)	.2
(P) Cylinder Assembly, Renew (w/All Internal Parts Less Cyl. Head and Oil Pan)	
Includes: R&R engine, transfer all component parts not supplied with replacement engine. Clean carbon, grind valves. Make all necessary adjustments.	
1984-87 (10.2)	18.0
w/A.C. add (.6)	.6
w/P.S. add (.2)	.2
(P) Cylinder Block, Renew	
Includes: R&R engine, transfer all component parts not supplied with replacement engine. Clean carbon, grind valves. Make all necessary adjustments.	
1984-87 (15.6)	22.6
w/A.C. add (.6)	.6
w/P.S. add (.2)	.2
(P) Engine Assy., R&R and Recondition	
Includes: Install new pistons, rings and pins. Install new rod and main bearings. Clean carbon, grind valves. Make all necessary adjustments.	
1984-87 (16.4)	23.8
w/A.C. add (.6)	.6
w/P.S. add (.2)	.2
(G) Engine Mount, Renew	
FRONT	
1984-87 (.6)	.9

PARTS 13 ENGINE ASSEMBLY & MOUNTS 13 PARTS

	Part No.	Price
Engine Gasket Set (Lower)		
1984-87 (gas)	▲E43Z-6E078A	26.75

Note: When a complete overhaul gasket set is required you must also order a valve grind gasket set.

	Part No.	Price
Partial Overhaul Gasket Set		
1984-87 (diesel)	▲E43Z-6008B	88.25
Cylinder Assy. (gas engine)		
1984-85-wo/H.O. eng.	▲E43Z-6009A	1529.00
1986-87	▲E53Z-6009B	2125.75
1985-w/H.O. eng.	▲E53Z-6009A	1529.00
1986-87	▲E63Z-6009C	1529.00
(diesel engine)		
1984-85-bef. 4/85	▲E43Z-6009B	2125.75
1985-87-from 4/85	▲E53Z-6009B	2125.75

PARTS 13 ENGINE ASSEMBLY & MOUNTS 13 PARTS

	Part No.	Price
Cylinder Block Assy.		
1984-85-gas eng.	▲E43Z-6010A	688.25
1986-87	▲E63Z-6010B	688.25
1984-85-diesel eng.-bef. 4/85	▲E43Z-6010C	1067.75
1985-87-from 4/85	▲E53Z-6010A	1067.75
Front Engine Mounts		
(Right)		
1984-87	▲E53Z-6038D	21.75
(Left)		
(ATX)		
1984-85	▲E53Z-6038A	22.25
1986-87	▲E63Z-6038A	22.25
(MTX-4 sp.)		
1984-85	▲E43Z-6038C	23.50
(MTX-5 sp.)		
1984	▲E43Z-6038B	23.50
1985-87-Gas	▲E53Z-6038C	23.50
Diesel	▲E43Z-6038E	23.50
Rear Engine Mounts Gas engine		
(ATX)		
1984	▲E43Z-6068A	22.75
1985	▲E53Z-6068A	22.00
1986-87-Canada	▲E53Z-6068A	22.00
exc. Canada	▲E63Z-6068A	22.00
(MTX-4 sp.)		
1984-85	▲E43Z-6068C	24.00
(MTX-5 sp.)		
1984	▲E43Z-6068B	23.00
1985-87	▲E53Z-6068C	23.00
Diesel engine		
1984-87	▲E4FZ-6068A	28.25

LABOR 14 PISTONS, RINGS & BEARINGS 14 LABOR

(Factory Time) Chilton Time

GASOLINE ENGINE

(P) Rings, Renew (See Engine Combinations)

Includes: Remove cylinder top ridge, deglaze cylinder walls, replace rod bearings, clean carbon. Minor tune up.

	Chilton Time
1984-87	
one (4.7)	**6.5**
all (6.2)	**8.6**
w/A.C. add (1.1)	**1.1**

(P) Piston or Connecting Rod, Renew

Includes: Remove cylinder top ridge, deglaze cylinder walls, replace rod bearings, clean carbon. Minor tune up.

	Chilton Time
1984-87	
one (5.0)	**6.8**
all (7.4)	**9.8**
w/A.C. add (1.1)	**1.1**

(P) Connecting Rod Bearings, Renew

	Chilton Time
1984-87 (2.3)	**3.2**
w/A.C. add (1.1)	**1.1**

DIESEL ENGINE

(P) Rings, Renew (See Engine Combinations)

Includes: Remove cylinder top ridge, deglaze cylinder walls. Renew rod bearings and clean carbon from cylinder head. Make all necessary adjustments.

	Chilton Time
1984-87	
one cyl (5.8)	**8.5**
all cyls (7.4)	**10.8**

COMBINATIONS

Add To Engine Work

See Machine Shop Operations

(Factory Time) Chilton Time

	Chilton Time
(G) DRAIN, EVACUATE & RECHARGE AIR CONDITIONING SYSTEM	
All models (.7)	**1.2**
(G) CARBURETOR, RECONDITION	
Holly 1949 (1.4)	**1.9**
6149-1V (1.5)	**2.0**
(G) HYDRAULIC VALVE LIFTERS, DISASSEMBLE AND CLEAN	
Each	**.2**
(G) CYLINDER HEAD, R&R (ENGINE REMOVED)	
Four	
Gas	**3.0**
Diesel	**4.0**
(G) CONNECTING ROD, RENEW (ENGINE DISASSEMBLED)	
Four	
each	**.4**
(P) CYLINDER HEAD, RECONDITION (HEAD REMOVED)	
Gas models (1.9)	**2.5**
(P) VALVE GUIDES, REAM OVERSIZE	
Each (.1)	**.2**
(G) REMOVE CYLINDER TOP RIDGE	
Each (.1)	**.1**
(G) DEGLAZE CYLINDER WALLS	
Each (.1)	**.1**
(G) MAIN BEARINGS, RENEW (PAN REMOVED)	
All models (1.9)	**2.5**
(G) ROD BEARINGS, RENEW (PAN REMOVED)	
All models (.9)	**1.2**
(G) PLASTIGAUGE BEARINGS	
Each	**.1**
(M) OIL FILTER ELEMENT, RENEW	
All models (.3)	**.3**

(P) Pistons or Connecting Rods, Renew

Includes: Remove cylinder top ridge, deglaze cylinder walls. Renew rod bearings and clean carbon from cylinder head. Make all necessary adjustments.

	Chilton Time
1984-87	
one cyl (6.1)	**8.8**
all cyls (8.6)	**12.0**

(P) Connecting Rod Bearings, Renew

	Chilton Time
1984-87 (2.2)	**3.2**

PARTS 14 PISTONS, RINGS & BEARINGS 14 PARTS

	Part No.	Price
(1) Piston Ring Set		
1984-87-Gas eng.	▲C30Z-6148E	32.75
Diesel eng.	▲E43Z-6148A	106.75
(2) Pin (Piston)		
1984-87	▲E3TZ-6135A	4.50
(3) Piston Assy.		
1984-87-Gas eng.	▲E43Z-6108A	32.75
Diesel eng.	▲E43Z-6108G	42.25
(4) Connecting Rod		
1984-85-Gas eng.	▲E43Z-6200A	47.00
1986-87	▲E63Z-6200A	47.00
1984-Diesel eng.	▲E43Z-6200B	58.25
1985-87	▲E43Z-6200C	62.50

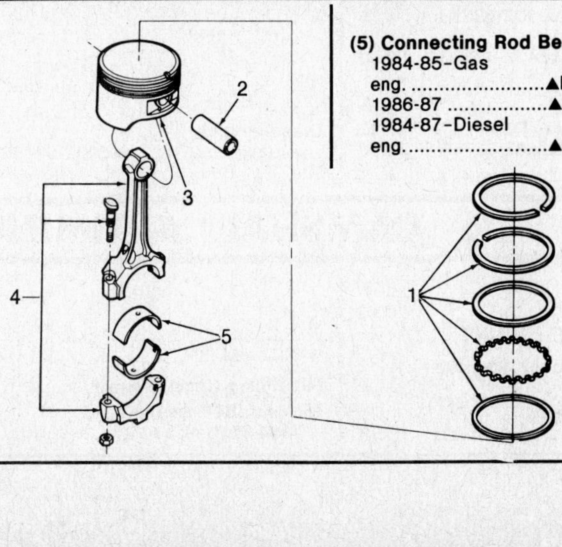

	Part No.	Price
(5) Connecting Rod Bearings		
1984-85-Gas eng.	▲D7BZ-6211A	2.75
1986-87	▲E63Z-6211A	2.75
1984-87-Diesel eng.	▲E43Z-6211A	29.00

LABOR 15 CRANKSHAFT & DAMPER 15 LABOR

(Factory Time)	Chilton Time

GASOLINE ENGINE

(P) Crankshaft and Main Bearings, Renew
Includes: R&R engine, check all bearing clearances.

1984 (8.2)	11.8
1985-87	
w/MTX (8.4)	12.2
w/ATX (8.7)	12.5
w/A.C. add (.8)	.8
w/P.S. add (.2)	.2

(P) Main Bearings, Renew
Includes: Check all bearing clearances.

1984-87 (3.3)	4.6
w/A.C. add (1.1)	1.1

(P) Main and Rod Bearings, Renew
Includes: Check all bearing clearances.

1984-87 (4.2)	5.8
w/A.C. add (1.1)	1.1

(G) Crankshaft Front Oil Seal, Renew
Includes: R&R engine assy.

1984-87 (4.6)	6.4
w/A.C. add (.9)	.9

(G) Crankshaft Pulley or Damper Assy., Renew
Includes: R&R engine assy.

1984-87 (5.0)	7.3
w/A.C. add (.9)	.9
w/P.S. add (.2)	.2

(G) Crankshaft Rear Main Seal, Renew (Full Circle Type)
Includes: R&R trans or engine as required.

1984-87	
w/MTX (2.8)	4.0
w/ATX (5.3)	*7.6
*w/A.C. add (.8)	.8

DIESEL ENGINE

(P) Crankshaft and Main Bearings, Renew
Includes: R&R engine, check all bearing clearances.

1984-87 (8.0)	12.0
w/A.C. add (.6)	.6
w/P.S. add (.2)	.2

(P) Main Bearings, Renew
Includes: Check all bearing clearances.

1984-87 (3.1)	4.5

(P) Main and Rod Bearings, Renew
Includes: Check all bearing clearances.

1984-87 (4.1)	5.7

(P) Crankshaft Front Seal, Renew
Includes: R&R engine assy.

1984 (4.4)	6.4
1985-87 (2.4)	6.4
w/A.C. add (.6)	.6

(G) Crankshaft Rear Main Seal, Renew (Full Circle Type)
Includes: R&R trans and clutch assy's.

1984-87	
w/M.T. (4.3)	6.7
w/A.T. (5.3)	7.4
w/A.C. add (.6)	.6

(G) Crankshaft Damper or Pulley, Renew
Includes: R&R engine assy.

1984 (4.0)	5.8
1985-87 (1.9)	5.8
w/A.C. add (.6)	.6

PARTS 15 CRANKSHAFT & DAMPER 15 PARTS

	Part No.	Price
(1) Pulley Assy. (Crankshaft)		
Gas engine		
1984-87		
before 11-15-83	▲E43Z-6A312A	64.00
from 11-15-83	▲E43Z-6A312C	64.00
Diesel engine		
1984-87	▲E43Z-6A312B	34.25
(2) Sprocket (Crankshaft)		
1984-87-Gas eng.	▲E43Z-6306A	11.75
Diesel eng.	▲E43Z-6306B	9.75
(3) Crankshaft		
1984-87-Gas eng.	▲E43Z-6303A	406.25
Diesel eng.	▲E43Z-6303C	669.75
(4) Main Bearing		
Gas engine		
(upper)		
1984-87-exc. below	▲D5DZ-6333A	4.75
front	▲E43Z-6333B	2.75
center	▲D5DZ-6337A	7.25
(lower)		
1984-87	▲D5DZ-6333B	4.75
Diesel engine		
1984-87	▲E43Z-6333G	39.50
(5) Flywheel Assy.		
Gas engine		
1984-87-MTX	▲E4FZ-6375C	147.00
ATX	▲E53Z-6375B	79.00

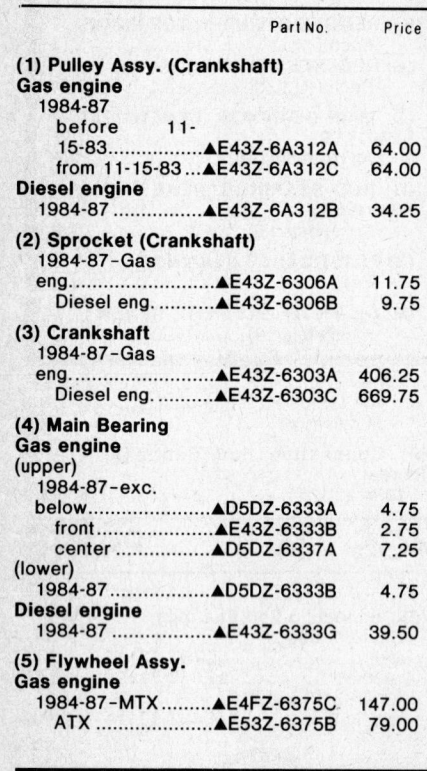

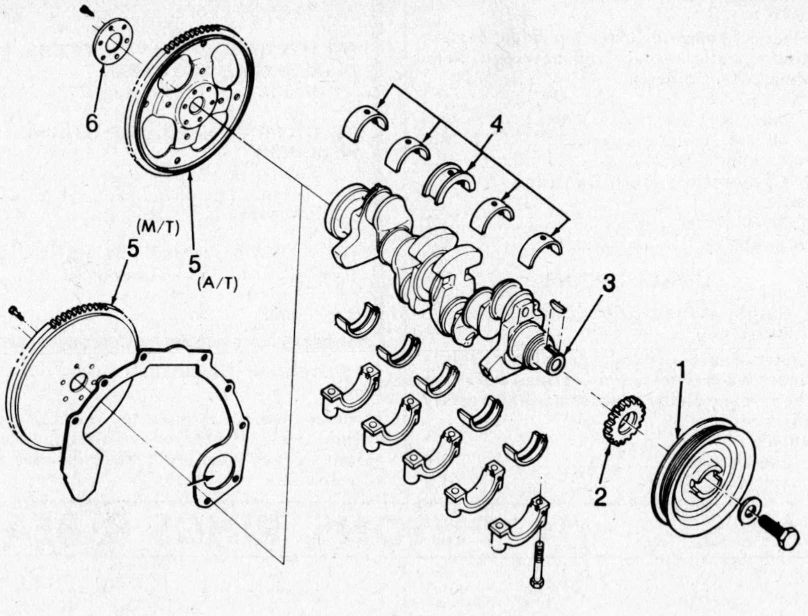

	Part No.	Price
Diesel engine		
1984-87	▲E43Z-6375B	161.25
(6) Plate (Flywheel Reinforcing)		
1984-87	▲E1FZ-6A366A	5.00

LABOR 16 CAMSHAFT & TIMING GEARS 16 LABOR

(Factory Time)	Chilton Time

GASOLINE ENGINE

(G) Timing Chain Cover Gasket and/or Seal, Renew
Includes: R&R engine assy.

1984-87 (5.0)	6.8
w/A.C. add (.8)	.8
w/P.S. add (.2)	.2

(G) Timing Chain, Renew
Includes: R&R engine assy.

1984-87 (5.4)	7.4
w/A.C. add (.8)	.8
w/P.S. add (.2)	.2

(G) Timing Chain Tensioner, Renew
Includes: R&R engine assy.

1984-87 (5.1)	7.0

LABOR 16 CAMSHAFT & TIMING GEARS 16 LABOR

(Factory Time)	Chilton Time
w/A.C. add (.8)	.8
w/P.S. add (.2)	.2
(G) Camshaft, Renew	
Includes: R&R engine assy.	
1984-87 (8.3)	11.6
w/A.C. add (.8)	.8
w/P.S. add (.2)	.2
w/MTX add (.3)	.3
Renew cam brgs add	.9
DIESEL ENGINE	
(G) Front Timing Belt, Renew	
Includes: R&R engine assy.	
1984 (4.2)	6.0
1985-87 (2.2)	6.0
w/A.C. add (.6)	.6
(G) Rear Timing Belt or Tensioner, Renew	
1984-87 (1.0)	1.5
(G) Front Timing Belt Tensioner, Renew	
Includes: R&R upper cover.	
1984-87 (2.0)	3.0
(G) Camshaft Seal, Renew	
1984-87 (3.5)	4.9
(P) Camshaft, Renew	
1984-87 (3.5)	5.0
Note: If necessary to R&R engine add	3.6

PARTS 16 CAMSHAFT & TIMING GEARS 16 PARTS

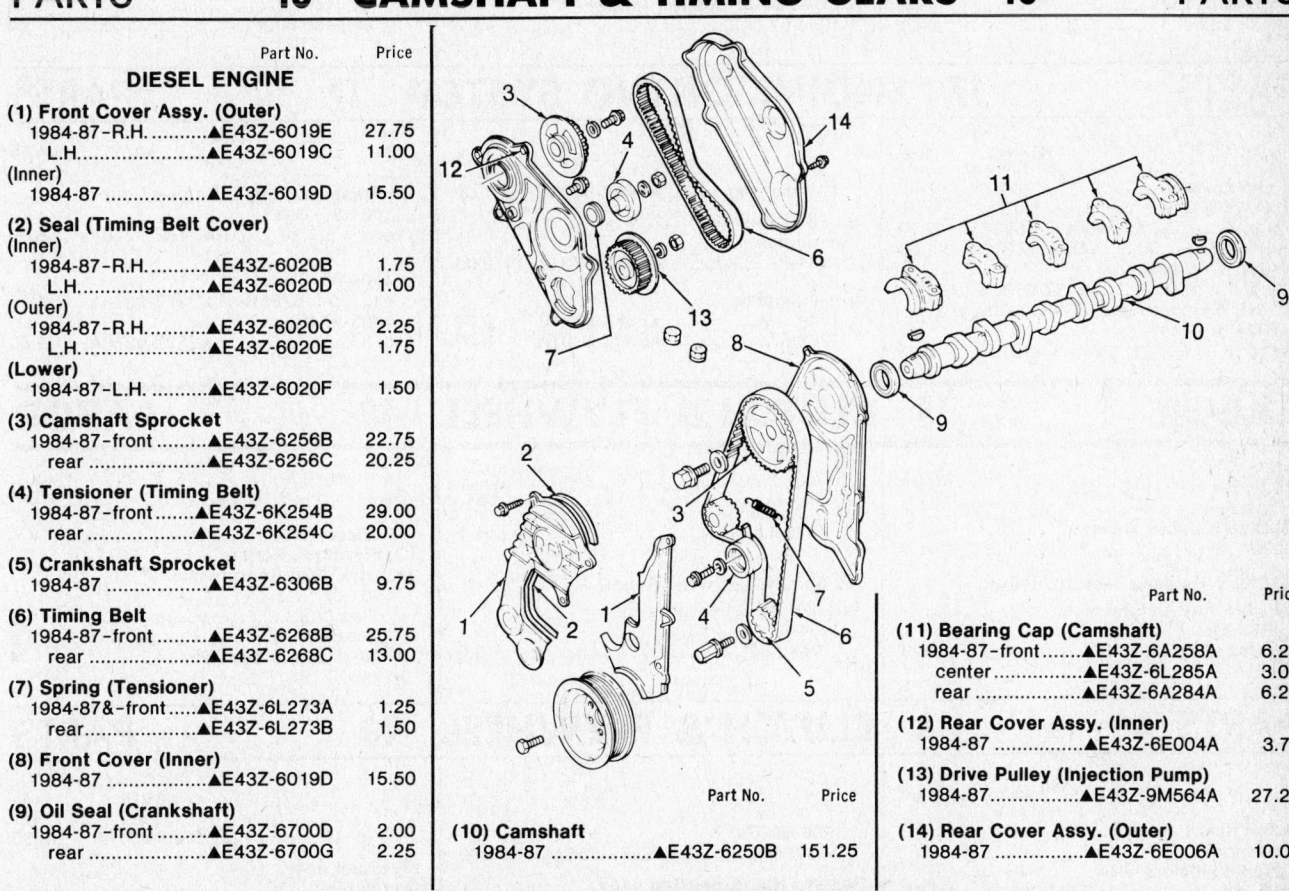

	Part No.	Price
DIESEL ENGINE		
(1) Front Cover Assy. (Outer)		
1984-87-R.H.	▲E43Z-6019E	27.75
L.H.	▲E43Z-6019C	11.00
(Inner)		
1984-87	▲E43Z-6019D	15.50
(2) Seal (Timing Belt Cover)		
(Inner)		
1984-87-R.H.	▲E43Z-6020B	1.75
L.H.	▲E43Z-6020D	1.00
(Outer)		
1984-87-R.H.	▲E43Z-6020C	2.25
L.H.	▲E43Z-6020E	1.75
(Lower)		
1984-87-L.H.	▲E43Z-6020F	1.50
(3) Camshaft Sprocket		
1984-87-front	▲E43Z-6256B	22.75
rear	▲E43Z-6256C	20.25
(4) Tensioner (Timing Belt)		
1984-87-front	▲E43Z-6K254B	29.00
rear	▲E43Z-6K254C	20.00
(5) Crankshaft Sprocket		
1984-87	▲E43Z-6306B	9.75
(6) Timing Belt		
1984-87-front	▲E43Z-6268B	25.75
rear	▲E43Z-6268C	13.00
(7) Spring (Tensioner)		
1984-87&-front	▲E43Z-6L273A	1.25
rear	▲E43Z-6L273B	1.50
(8) Front Cover (Inner)		
1984-87	▲E43Z-6019D	15.50
(9) Oil Seal (Crankshaft)		
1984-87-front	▲E43Z-6700D	2.00
rear	▲E43Z-6700G	2.25

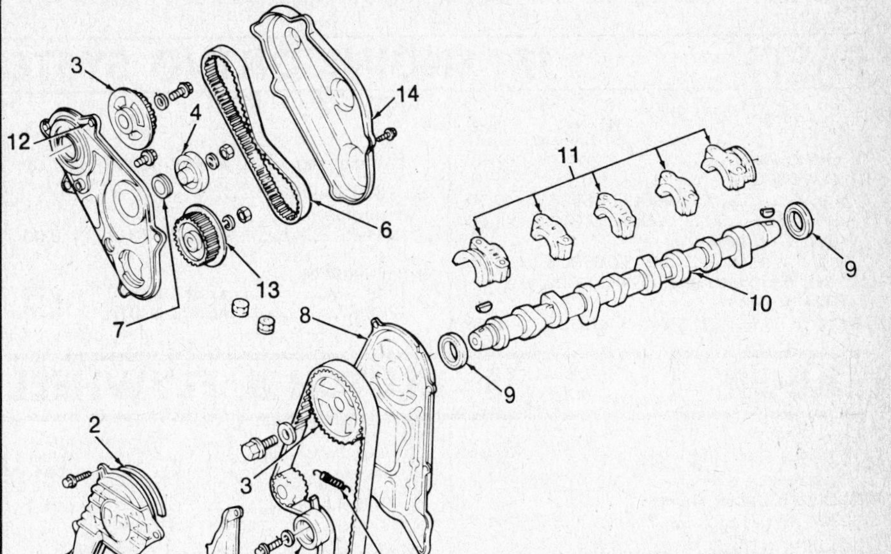
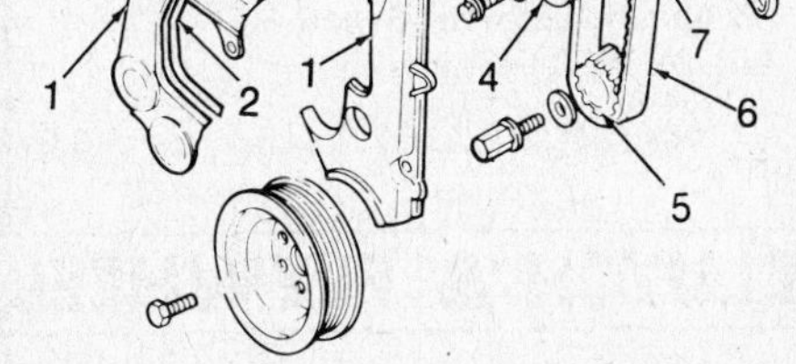

	Part No.	Price
(10) Camshaft		
1984-87	▲E43Z-6250B	151.25
(11) Bearing Cap (Camshaft)		
1984-87-front	▲E43Z-6A258A	6.25
center	▲E43Z-6L285A	3.00
rear	▲E43Z-6A284A	6.25
(12) Rear Cover Assy. (Inner)		
1984-87	▲E43Z-6E004A	3.75
(13) Drive Pulley (Injection Pump)		
1984-87	▲E43Z-9M564A	27.25
(14) Rear Cover Assy. (Outer)		
1984-87	▲E43Z-6E006A	10.00

PARTS 16 CAMSHAFT & TIMING GEARS 16 PARTS

	Part No.	Price
GASOLINE ENGINE		
Cover Gasket		
1984-87	▲E43Z-6020A	1.75
Timing Cover Oil Seal		
1984-87	▲E43Z-6700E	4.25
(1) Camshaft		
1984-87-wo/H.O. eng.	▲E43Z-6250A	146.00
1985-87-w/H.O. eng.	▲E53Z-6250A	168.25
(2) Camshaft Bearings		
1984-87-front	▲E43Z-6261A	13.50
center	▲E43Z-6262A	10.75
rear	▲E43Z-6263A	10.75
(3) Thrust Plate		
1984-87	▲E43Z-6269A	4.75
(4) Tensioner Assy. (Timing Chain)		
1984-87	▲E43Z-6K254A	15.75
(5) Sprocket (Crankshaft)		
1984-87	▲E43Z-6306A	11.75
(6) Sprocket (Camshaft)		
1984-87	▲E43Z-6256A	15.00
(7) Timing Chain		
1984-87	▲E43Z-6268A	19.50
(8) Damper Assy. (Timing Chain)		
1984-87	▲E43Z-6284A	3.75

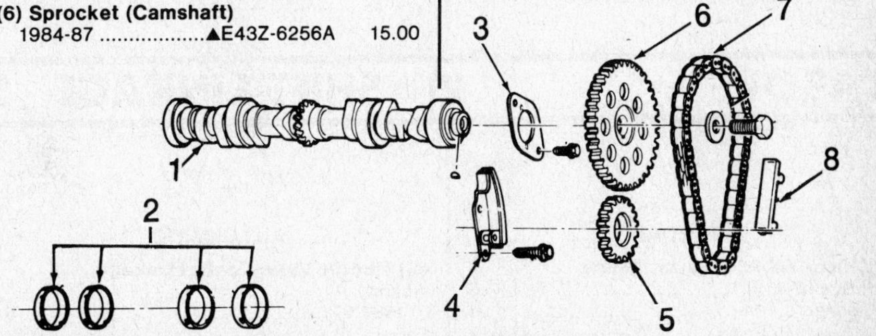

LABOR 17 ENGINE OILING SYSTEM 17 LABOR

	(Factory Time)	Chilton Time
GASOLINE ENGINE		
(G) Oil Pan or Gasket, Renew		
1984-87	(1.4)	2.0
w/A.C. add	(1.1)	1.1
(P) Pressure Test Engine Bearings (Pan Off)		
All models		1.0
(G) Oil Pump, Renew		
1984-87	(1.5)	2.2
w/A.C. add	(1.1)	1.1
(G) Oil Pump, R&R and Recondition		
1984-87	(1.8)	2.5
w/A.C. add	(1.1)	1.1
(G) Oil Pressure Gauge (Engine), Renew		
1984-87	(.3)	.4
(M) Oil Filter Element, Renew		
1984-87	(.3)	.3
DIESEL ENGINE		
(G) Oil Pan or Gasket, Renew		
1984-87	(1.2)	1.7
(P) Pressure Test Engine Bearings (Pan Off)		
All models		1.0
(G) Oil Pump, Renew		
Includes: R&R engine assy.		
1984	(5.0)	7.2
1985-87	(3.7)	7.2
w/A.C. add	(.6)	.6
(M) Oil Filter Element, Renew		
1984-87		
oil filter	(.3)	.3
by-pass filter	(.4)	.4

PARTS 17 ENGINE OILING SYSTEM 17 PARTS

	Part No.	Price
Oil Pump Assy.		
1984-85-Gas eng.	▲E43Z-6600A	40.50
1986-87	▲E63Z-6600A	41.00
1984-87-Diesel eng.	▲E43Z-6600B	76.25
Screen & Cover Assy. (Timing Chain)		
1984-87-Gas eng.	▲E43Z-6622A	18.50
Diesel eng.	▲E43Z-6622B	7.00
Oil Filter Element		
Gas engine		
1984-87	▲D9AZ-6731A	8.00
Diesel engine		
1984	▲E3TZ-6731C	9.00
1985-87	▲E5FZ-6731A	9.00
Oil Pressure Gauge (Engine Unit)		
1984-87-Gas eng.	▲D4AZ-9278A	3.50
1984-85-Diesel eng. (bef. 6/85)	▲D27Z-9278A	6.75
1985-87 (from 6/85)	▲E53Z-9278A	6.50

LABOR 18 CLUTCH & FLYWHEEL 18 LABOR

	(Factory Time)	Chilton Time
(G) Clutch Cable, Renew		
1984-87	(.7)	1.1
(G) Clutch Release Bearing, Renew		
Includes: R&R transmission.		
1984-87		
Gas	(2.4)	3.6
Diesel	(2.9)	4.1
(G) Clutch Assembly, Renew		
Includes: R&R transmission.		
1984-87		
Gas	(2.5)	3.9
Diesel	(3.0)	4.4
(G) Flywheel, Renew		
Includes: R&R transmission.		
1984-87		
Gas	(2.8)	4.2
Diesel	(4.1)	5.5
Renew ring gear add	(.2)	.4

PARTS 18 CLUTCH & FLYWHEEL 18 PARTS

	Part No.	Price
Clutch Disc		
Gas engine		
1984-85-before 3-5-85	▲E43Z-7550A	63.75
1985-87-from 3-5-85	▲E53Z-7550A	63.75
Diesel engine		
1984-87	▲E4FZ-7550A	55.25
Pressure Plate		
1984-85-Gas eng.	▲E43Z-7563A	57.50
Diesel eng.	▲E4FZ-7563A	53.75
1986-87-Gas & Diesel eng.	▲E5FZ-7563A	53.50
Release Hub & Bearing Assy.		
1984-87	▲E3FZ-7548A	26.75
Release Fork		
1984-87	▲E3FZ-7N515A	21.50
Release Cable Assy.		
1984	▲E43Z-7K553A	26.00
1985-87	▲E5FZ-7K553A	24.25
Plate Assy. (Clutch Release)		
1984	▲E1FZ-7B517A	5.50
1985-87	▲E5FZ-7B517A	8.50
Flywheel Assy.		
Gas engine		
1984-87-MTX	▲E4FZ-6375C	147.00
ATX	▲E53Z-6375B	79.00
Diesel engine		
1984-87	▲E43Z-6375B	161.25
Flywheel Ring Gear		
1984-87-Gas eng.	▲D4FZ-6384A	34.25
Diesel eng.	▲E43Z-6384A	50.00

LABOR 21 SHIFT LINKAGE 21 LABOR

	(Factory Time)	Chilton Time
STANDARD		
(G) Gear Selector Lever, Renew		
1984-87	(.4)	.6
w/Console add	(.1)	.1
AUTOMATIC		
(G) Throttle Valve Control Linkage, Adjust		
1984-87	(.3)	.6
(G) Gear Selector Lever, Renew		
1984-87	(.5)	.9
w/Console add	(.1)	.1

LABOR 26 REAR AXLE AND SUSPENSION 26 LABOR

(Factory Time)	Chilton Time
(G) Rear Wheel Bearing Grease Seal, Renew	
1984-87-one (.5)	.7
both (.7)	1.1
(G) Rear Wheel Bearings, Adjust	
1984-87-both (.3)	.5
(G) Rear Wheel Bearings and Cups, Clean and Repack or Renew	
1984-87-one side (.6)	.9
both sides (.9)	1.5
(G) Lower Control Arm Assy., Renew	
1984-87	
all-one side (.4)	.7
(G) Rear Springs, Renew	
1984-87-one (.8)	1.2
both (1.2)	1.8
(G) Rear Shock Absorbers, Renew	
1984-87-one (.7)	1.2
both (1.2)	1.8
(G) Rear Tie Rod, Renew	
1984-87-one (.5)	.7
both (.8)	1.2
(G) Rear Wheel Spindle, Renew	
1984-87-one (.8)	1.2
both (1.4)	2.2
Renew brgs and cups add	
one side (.3)	.3
both sides (.4)	.4

PARTS 26 REAR AXLE AND SUSPENSION 26 PARTS

	Part No.	Price
(1) Bushing Repair Kit (Shock Absorber)		
1984-87	▲E43Z-18198A	6.75
(2) Shock Absorber		
(wo/TRX susp.)		
1984-85-Gas eng.	▲E43Z-18125B	73.25
Diesel eng.	▲E43Z-18125E	73.00
(w/TRX susp.)		
1984-85	▲E43Z-18125D	78.50
1986-87-w/sport susp.	▲E63Z-18125C	73.25
w/GT susp.	▲E63Z-18125D	73.25
wo/sport & GT susp.	▲E63Z-18125A	73.25
(3) Spindle (Rear)		
1984-87	▲E43Z-4A013A	94.50
(4) Insulator (Upper)		
1984-87	▲E3FZ-5536A	7.25
(5) Spring Assy.		
Note: Order by year and model.		
(6) Bushing (Tie Rod)		
1984-87-body end	▲E43Z-5K897A	3.00
1984-85-spindle end	▲E43Z-5K897B	10.50
1986-87	▲E5FZ-5K897A	3.00
(7) Tie Rod Assy. (w/Bushing)		
1984-87	▲E43Z-5K848A	14.00

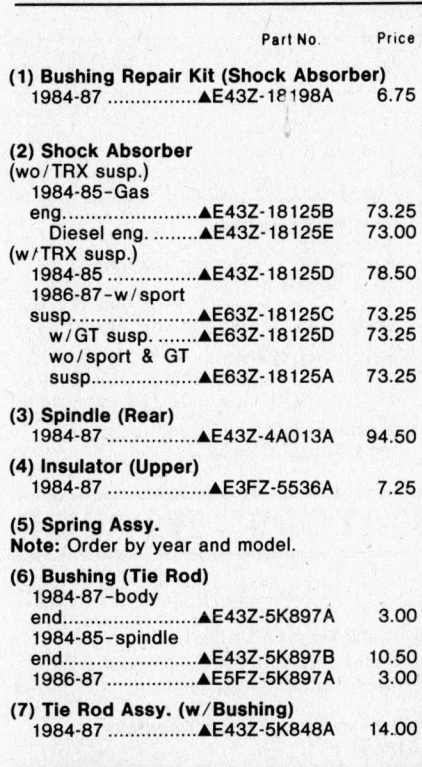

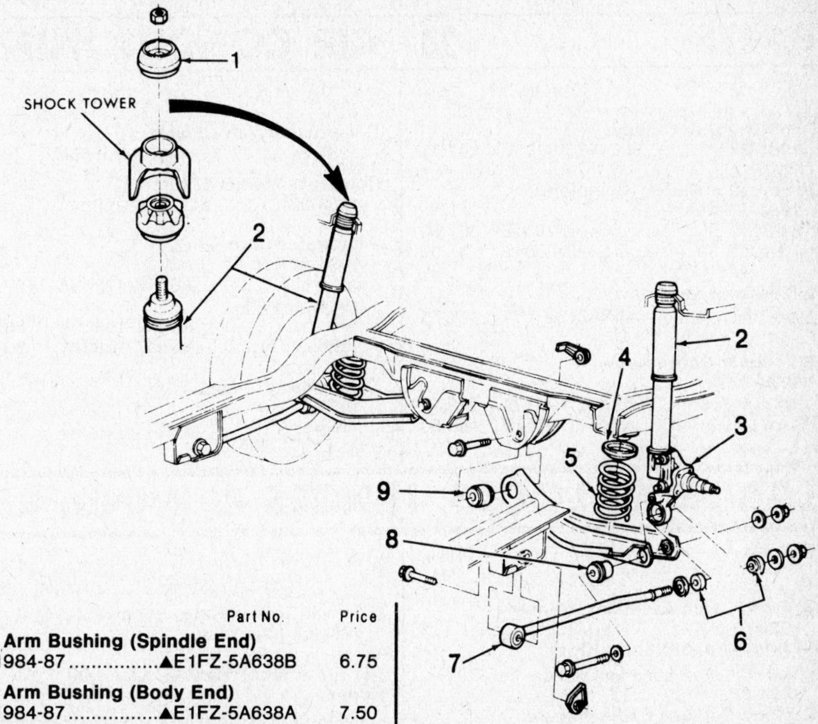

	Part No.	Price
(8) Arm Bushing (Spindle End)		
1984-87	▲E1FZ-5A638B	6.75
(9) Arm Bushing (Body End)		
1984-87	▲E1FZ-5A638A	7.50

LABOR 28 AIR CONDITIONING 28 LABOR

(Factory Time)	Chilton Time
Note: If more than one item requires replacement where evacuation and discharging the system is already included in the operation, deduct 1.0 hour for each additional item to the times listed.	
(G) Drain, Evacuate & Recharge System	
Includes: Check for leaks.	
All models (.7)	1.2
(G) Pressure Test System	
All models	.6
(G) Compressor Drive Belt, Renew	
1984-87 (.4)	.6
(G) Compressor Assembly, Renew	
Includes: Transfer parts as required. Evacuate and charge system.	
1984-87	
Gas (2.5)	3.6

AIR CONDITIONER TUNE-UP

For efficient operation and satisfactory performance in hot weather. The following Air Conditioner tune-up is suggested:

1. Clean intake filter
2. Clean condenser fins
3. Pressure test system
4. Adjust drive belt tension
5. Check anti freeze/coolant
6. Tighten compressor mounts
7. Tighten condenser and evaporator mounts
8. Inspect system for leaks (hoses, couplings, valves, etc.)
9. Partial charge system

All models	1.0
If necessary to evacuate and charge system, add	1.0

(Factory Time)	Chilton Time
Diesel (1.8)	2.9
(G) Compressor Clutch and Pulley, Renew	
Includes: Evacuate and charge system, if required.	
1984-87	
Gas (2.2)	3.3
Diesel (2.3)	3.4
Renew clutch brg add (.1)	.1
Renew clutch field add (.1)	.1
(G) Compressor Shaft Seal Kit, Renew	
Includes: R&R compressor. Evacuate and charge system.	
1984-87	
Gas (2.6)	3.8
Diesel (2.9)	4.1

LABOR 28 AIR CONDITIONING 28 LABOR

(Factory Time)	Chilton Time
(G) Compressor Assy., R&R and Recondition	
Includes: Evacuate and charge system.	
1984-87	
Gas (3.7)	4.8
Diesel (3.4)	4.5
(G) Condenser Assembly, Renew	
Includes: Evacuate and charge system.	
1984-87 (1.5)	2.4
(G) Accumulator Assembly, Renew	
Includes: Evacuate and charge system.	
1984-87 (1.2)	2.0
(G) Orifice Valve, Renew	
Includes: Evacuate and charge system.	
1984-87 (1.5)	2.1
(G) Clutch Cycling Pressure Switch Assy., Renew	
1984-87 (.4)	.6
(G) Evaporator Core, Renew	
Includes: Evacuate and charge system.	
1984-87 (3.2)	6.5
(G) A.C./Heater Blower Motor, Renew	
1984-87 (.5)	.8
(G) Blower Motor Switch, Renew	
1984-87 (.6)	1.0
(G) Blower Motor Resistor, Renew	
1984-87 (.3)	.6
(G) Suction or Discharge Manifold Assy. Kit, Renew	
Includes: Evacuate and charge system.	
1983-87 (.8)	1.5
(G) Air Conditioning Hoses, Renew	
Includes: Evacuate and charge system.	
1984-87	
Cond. to Evap. (1.3)	2.0
Suction line (1.3)	2.0
Comp. to Cond. (1.0)	1.7

PARTS 28 AIR CONDITIONING 28 PARTS

	Part No.	Price
Compressor Assembly		
1984-87	▲E43Z-19703C	247.75
Compressor Clutch (Complete)		
1984-87-before 8-83	▲E1FZ-2884E	107.50
from 8-83	▲E43Z-2884A	47.00
Compressor Shaft Seal		
1984-87	▲C9AZ-19655A	17.75
Condensor Core Assy.		
1984-87-w/ integral A.C.	▲E3FZ-19712A	126.25
w/built-in A.C.	▲E1FZ-19712B	168.50
Compressor Valve Plate		
1984-87	▲C3GY-19656A	26.25
Compressor Gasket Kit		
1984-87	▲C3GY-19B684A	9.00
Evaporator Core Assy.		
1984-87-w/ integral A.C.	▲E3FZ-19860A	162.75
1984-w/built-in A.C.	▲E43Z-19860A	86.00
1985	▲E53Z-19860B	86.00
Blower Motor Assy.		
1984-87-w/ integral A.C.	▲E43Z-19805A	86.25
1984-w/built-in A.C.	▲E0TZ-19805B	N.L.
1985	▲E53Z-19805A	75.50
Blower Motor Resister		
1984-87-w/ integral A.C.	▲E43Z-19A706A	8.75
1984-w/built-in A.C.	▲D8RZ-19A706A	N.L.
1985	▲E53Z-19A706A	14.75
Blower Motor Switch		
1984	▲E43Z-19986A	16.50
1985-87	▲E53Z-19986A	16.50
Pressure Relief Valve (Compressor)		
1984-87	▲D2AZ-19D644A	9.00

LABOR 29 LOCKS, HINGES & WIND. REGULATORS 29 LABOR

(Factory Time)	Chilton Time
(G) Hood Latch Assembly, Renew	
1984-87 (.3)	.5
(G) Hood Hinge, Renew (One)	
Includes: Adjust hood and latch.	
1984-87 (.4)	.6
(G) Hood Release Cable, Renew	
1984-87 (.6)	1.0
(G) Front Door Latch, Renew	
Includes: R&R trim panel and weathersheet.	
1984-87 (.6)	.9
(G) Front Door Lock Remote Control, Renew	
Includes: R&R trim panel and weathersheet.	
1984-87 (.5)	.8
(G) Lock Striker Plate, Renew	
1984-87 (.2)	.3
(G) Front Door Handle (Outside), Renew	
Includes: R&R trim panel and weathersheet.	
1984-87 (.6)	.9
(G) Front Door Window Regulator, Renew	
Includes: R&R trim panel and weathersheet.	
1984-87	
manual (.6)	1.0
electric (.7)	1.2
(G) Rear Door Latch, Renew	
Includes: R&R trim panel and weathersheet.	
1984-87 (.5)	.9
(G) Rear Door Window Regulator, Renew	
Includes: R&R trim panel and weathersheet.	
1984-87-manual (.6)	1.0
electric (.6)	1.2
(G) Rear Door Handle (Outside), Renew	
Includes: R&R trim panel and weathersheet.	
1984-87 (.5)	.8

PARTS 29 LOCKS, HINGES & WIND. REGULATORS 29 PARTS

	Part No.	Price
Hood Latch		
1984-85	▲E4DZ-16700A	14.75
1986-87	▲E6DZ-16700A	14.75
Hood Hinge		
1984-87-right	▲E43Z-16796A	8.75
left	▲E43Z-16797A	8.75
Door Lock (Front)		
1984-right	▲E3GZ-6721812A	36.00
left	▲E3GZ-6721813A	36.00
1985-87-right	▲E59Z-1121812A	21.50
left	▲E59Z-1121813A	21.50
Door Lock (Rear)		
1984-right	▲E43Z-5426412A	23.00
left	▲E43Z-5426413A	23.00
1985-right	▲E53Z-5426412A	23.75
left	▲E53Z-5426413A	23.75
1986-87-right	▲E6DZ-5426412A	N.L.
left	▲E6DZ-5426413A	N.L.
Door Lock (Electric)		
1984-87	▲E43Z-5421818B	9.25
Front Door Window Regulator (Manual)		
(4 door sedan)		
1984-87-right	▲E43Z-5423200B	43.25
left	▲E43Z-5423201B	43.25
(2 door sedan)		
1984-87-right	▲E43Z-6623200B	52.75
left	▲E43Z-6623201B	52.75
Rear Window Regulator (Manual)		
1984-87-right	▲E43Z-5427000B	31.25
left	▲E43Z-5427001B	31.25
Front Window Regulator (Electric)		
1984-87-right	▲E43Z-5423208A	55.50
left	▲E43Z-5423209A	55.50
Rear Window Regulator (Electric)		
1984-87-right	▲E43Z-5427008A	94.50
left	▲E43Z-5427009A	91.50

PARTS 29 LOCKS, HINGES & WIND. REGULATORS 29 PARTS

	Part No.	Price
Trunk Lid Lock		
1984-87-w/		
manual	▲D9ZZ-6643200A	22.00
w/power	▲D9BZ-5443200A	57.50
Trunk Lid Hinge		
1984-87-right	▲E43Z-5442700A	18.75
left	▲E43Z-5442701A	18.75
Door Lock Cylinder & Key		
(wo/anti-theft)		
1984-87	▲E1DZ-5421984C	10.75
(w/anti-theft)		
1984-87-right	▲E43Z-5421984F	32.00
left	▲E43Z-5421985F	32.00
Trunk Lock Cylinder & Key		
1984-87-exc.		
below	▲D6ZZ-6943505A	10.75
w/anti-theft	▲E3SZ-6943505B	N.L.

LABOR 30 HEAD AND PARKING LAMPS 30 LABOR

(Factory Time)	Chilton Time
(G) Aim Headlamps	
two	.4
four	.6
(M) Headlamp Sealed Beam Bulb, Renew	
1984-87-each (.3)	.3
(M) Parking Lamp Housing, Renew	
1984-87 (.3)	.4
(M) Rear Lamp Body, Renew	
1984-87 (.4)	.6
(M) License Lamp Assembly, Renew	
1984-87 (.2)	.3

PARTS 30 HEAD & PARKING LAMPS 30 PARTS

	Part No.	Price
Seal Beam Bulbs		
1984-85	▲E1FZ-13007A	24.25
1986-87-R.H.	▲E63Z-13007A	25.50
left	▲E63Z-13007B	25.50
Parking Lamps Assy.		
Tempo		
1984-85-right	▲E43Z-13200A	18.00
left	▲E43Z-13201A	18.00
1986-87-right	▲E63Z-13200A	18.00
left	▲E63Z-13201A	18.00
Topaz		
1984-85-right	▲E46Y-13200A	19.25
left	▲E46Y-13201A	19.25
1986-87-right	▲E66Y-13200A	19.25
left	▲E66Y-13201A	19.25
Rear Lamp Assy.		
Tempo		
1984-85-right	▲E43Z-13404A	89.50
left	▲E43Z-13405A	89.50
1986-87-right	▲E63Z-13404A	89.50
left	▲E63Z-13405A	89.50
Topaz		
(2 door wo/trim)		
1984-85-right	▲E46Y-13404B	92.25
left	▲E46Y-13405B	92.25
(2 door w/trim)		
1984-85-right	▲E46Y-13404D	92.25
left	▲E46Y-13405D	92.25
(Exc. LS)		
1986-87-right	▲E66Y-13404B	92.25
left	▲E66Y-13405B	92.25
(w/LS)		
1986-87-right	▲E66Y-13404C	92.25
left	▲E66Y-13404C	92.25
(4 door wo/trim)		
1984-85-right	▲E46Y-13404A	88.50
left	▲E46Y-13405A	88.50
(4 door w/trim)		
1984-85-right	▲E46Y-13404C	88.50
left	▲E46Y-13405C	88.50
(exc. LS)		
1986-87-right	▲E66Y-13404A	88.50
left	▲E66Y-13405A	88.50
(w/LS)		
1986-87-right	▲E66Y-13404D	88.50
left	▲E66Y-13405D	88.50
Rear Lamp Lens		
Tempo		
1984-85-right	▲E43Z-13450A	44.50
left	▲E43Z-13451A	44.50
1986-87-right	▲E63Z-13450A	44.50
left	▲E63Z-13451A	44.50
Topaz		
(2 door wo/trim)		
1984-85-right	▲E46Y-13450B	30.50
left	▲E46Y-13451B	30.50
(2 door w/trim)		
1984-85-right	▲E46Y-13450D	30.50
left	▲E46Y-13451D	30.50
(2 dr. exc. LS)		
1986-87-right	▲E66Y-13450B	30.50
left	▲E66Y-13451B	30.50
(2 dr. w/LS)		
1986-87-right	▲E66Y-13450C	30.50
left	▲E66Y-13451C	30.50
(4 door wo/trim)		
1984-85-right	▲E46Y-13450A	26.75
left	▲E46Y-13451A	26.75
(4 door w/trim)		
1984-85-right	▲E46Y-13450C	26.75
left	▲E46Y-13451C	26.75
(4 dr exc. LS)		
1986-87-right	▲E66Y-13450A	26.75
left	▲E66Y-13451A	26.75
(4 dr w/LS)		
1986-87-right	▲E66Y-13450D	26.75
left	▲E66Y-13451D	26.75
License Plate Lamp Assy.		
1984-85	▲D9AZ-13550A	5.75
1986-87	▲E69Z-13550A	5.75
Rear Hi-Mount Lamp Assy.		
1985-w/air bags		
(bef. 8/85)	▲E53Z-13A613A	41.75
1985-87-4 dr.		
(from 8/85)	▲E63Z-13A613B	41.75
2 dr.	▲E63Z-13A613A	41.75

LABOR 31 WINDSHIELD WIPER & SPEEDOMETER 31 LABOR

(Factory Time)	Chilton Time
(G) Windshield Wiper Motor, Renew	
1984-87 (.3)	.6
(G) Windshield Wiper Switch, Renew	
1984-87 (.5)	.9
(G) Windshield Wiper Governor, Renew	
1984-87 (.5)	.9
(G) Wiper Pivot Shaft and Link Assy., Renew	
1984-87 (.5)	.9
(G) Windshield Washer Pump, Renew	
1984-87 (.3)	.4
(G) Speedometer Head, R&R or Renew	
1984-87 (.7)	1.2
Reset odometer add (.2)	.2
(G) Speedometer Cable and Casing, Renew	
1984-87 (.4)	.7
(G) Speedometer Cable (Inner), Renew or Lubricate	
1984-87-one piece (.4)	.7
(G) Radio, R&R	
1984-87 (.5)	.9
w/Console (1.4)	2.2

PARTS 31 WINDSHIELD WIPER & SPEEDOMETER 31 PARTS

	Part No.	Price
Wiper Motor Assy.		
1984	▲E43Z-17508A	106.25
1985	▲E53Z-17508A	106.25
1986-87	▲E63Z-17508A	106.25
Wiper Arm & Pivot Shaft Assy.		
1984-85	▲E43Z-17566A	26.75
1986-87	▲E63Z-17566A	27.50
Wiper Arm		
1984	▲E43Z-17526A	10.00
1985-right	▲E53Z-17526A	10.50
left	▲E53Z-17527A	10.50
1986-87	▲E63Z-17526A	10.50
Wiper Switch		
(wo/intermittent wiper)		
1984-85-wo/tilt whl.	▲E3DZ-17A553C	18.50
w/tilt whl.	▲E43Z-17A553B	25.00
1986-87	▲E63Z-17A553A	18.50
(w/intermittent wiper)		
1984-85-wo/tilt whl.	▲E3DZ-17A553A	25.75
w/tilt whl.	▲E43Z-17A553A	25.00
1986-87	▲E63Z-17A553B	25.75
Windshield Wiper Governor		
1984-85-wo/tilt whl.	▲E43Z-17C476B	74.00
w/tilt whl.	▲E43Z-17C476A	74.00
1986-87	▲E63Z-17C476A	74.00
Windshield Washer Pump		
1984-87	▲E0AZ-17664A	20.00
Windshield Washer Reservoir		
1984-87-wo/sensor	▲E4FZ-17618A	16.50
w/sensor	▲E4FZ-17618B	20.75
Speedometer Head Assy.		
Order by year and model.		
Speedometer Case & Shaft		
1984-87	▲E3FZ-17260A	8.25
Speed Control Cable (Speedo.)		
1984-87	▲E43Z-9A820A	13.25

LABOR 32 LIGHT SWITCHES & WIRING 32 LABOR

(Factory Time)	Chilton Time
(G) Headlamp Switch, Renew	
1984-87 (.3)	.5
(G) Headlamp Dimmer Switch, Renew	
1984-87 (.5)	.9
(G) Turn Signal Switch, Renew	
1984-87 (.5)	.9
(M) Turn Signal or Hazard Warning Flasher, Renew	
1984-87	
turn signal (.2)	.3
hazard (.3)	.4
(G) Stop Light Switch, Renew	
1984-87 (.3)	.5
(G) Back-Up Lamp Switch, Renew	
1984-87 (.3)	.5
(G) Parking Brake Warning Lamp Switch, Renew	
1984-87 (.3)	.5
(G) Horn, Renew	
1984-87 (.5)	.6
(G) Wiring Harness, Renew	
Alternator to Regulator	
1984-87 (.3)	.6

PARTS 32 LIGHT SWITCHES & WIRING 32 PARTS

	Part No.	Price
Head Lamp Switch		
1984-85	▲E53Z-11654A	20.00
1986-87	▲E6FZ-11654A	16.75
Stop Light Switch		
1984-85-bef. 3-85-	▲E3FZ-13480A	5.75
1985-87-from 3-85	▲E6FZ-13480A	6.00
Turn Signal & Warning Switch		
1984-87-w/air bags	▲E2FZ-13341A	41.25
wo/air bags	▲E5FZ-13341A	41.25
Turn Signal Flasher		
1984-87	▲C5AZ-13350B	3.75
Emergency Flasher		
1984-87	▲D1FZ-13350A	4.25
Horn		
1984-87-low pitch	▲E3AZ-13833A	17.00
high pitch	▲E3AZ-13832A	17.00
Wiring Harness		
Note: Order by year and model.		

LABOR 33 GLASS 33 LABOR

(Factory Time)	Chilton Time
(G) Windshield Glass, Renew	
1984-87 (2.3)	3.0
(G) Front Door Glass, Renew	
Includes: R&R trim panel and weathersheet.	
1984-87 (.6)	.9
(G) Rear Quarter Window Glass, Renew	
1984-87 (.4)	.7
(G) Rear Door Glass, Renew	
Includes: R&R trim panel and weathersheet.	
1984-87 (.5)	.8
(G) Rear Window Glass, Renew	
1984-87 (1.0)	1.5
Renew butyl tape add (.2)	.2

LABOR 34 CRUISE CONTROL 34 LABOR

(Factory Time)	Chilton Time
(G) Cruise Control System Diagnosis	
1984-87 (.5)	.6
(G) Cruise Control Chain/Cable, Renew	
1984-87 (.2)	.4
(G) Speed Control Servo Assy., Renew	
1984-87 (.3)	.6

LABOR 34 CRUISE CONTROL 34 LABOR

(Factory Time)	Chilton Time
Road test add (.3)	.3
(G) Speed Control Relay, Renew	
1984-87 (.3)	.4
Road test add (.3)	.3
(G) Speed Control Sensor Assy., Renew	
1984-87 (.3)	.5
Road test add (.3)	.3
(G) Speed Control Amplifier Assy., Renew	
1984-87 (.3)	.6
Road test add (.3)	.3
(G) Speed Control Actuator Switch, Renew	
1984-87 (.4)	.6
Road test add (.3)	.3
(G) Speed Control Metering (Dump) Valve, Renew	
1984-87 (.3)	.4
(G) Speed Control Clutch Switch, Renew	
1984-87 (.3)	.4

PARTS 34 CRUISE CONTROL 34 PARTS

	Part No.	Price
Speed Control Amplifier Assy.		
1984-87	▲E0AZ-9D843A	161.50
Speed Control Servo Assy.		
1984-w/dealer speed cont.	▲D9AZ-9C735B	86.75
1984-87-w/ factory speed cont.	▲E2FZ-9C735A	120.25
Speed Control Sensor		
1984-87-w/ dealer speed cont.	▲E4AZ-9E731A	20.75
1984-87-w/ factory speed cont.	▲E43Z-9E731A	20.75
Speed Control Actuator Switch		
1984-87-w/ dealer speed cont.	▲E4FZ-9C888A	34.25
1984-85-w/ factory speed cont.	▲E3SZ-9C888A	45.75
1986-87	▲E63Z-9C888A	45.75

GROUP INDEX

ALPHABETICAL INDEX

Ford Motor Company

Rear Wheel Drive Cars

CAPRI • MUSTANG

YEAR IDENTIFICATION

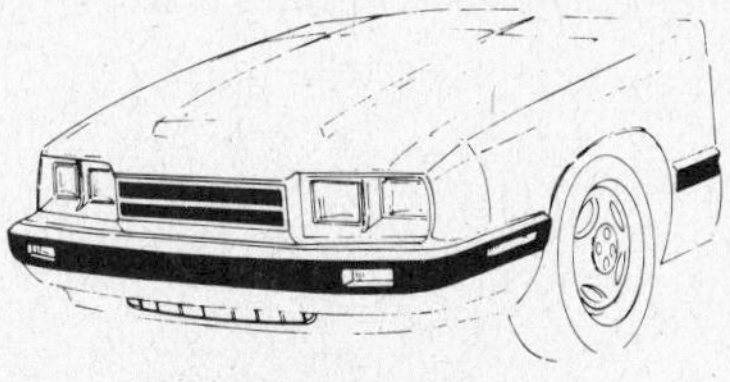

1983–86 Capri

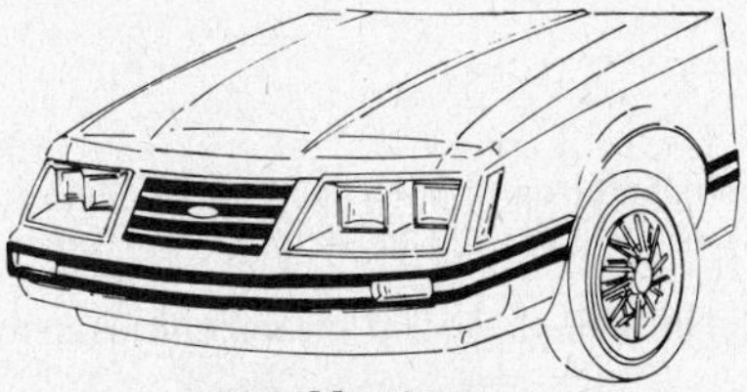

1983 Mustang

1984–86 Mustang

1985–86 Mustang GT

1984–86 Mustang SVO

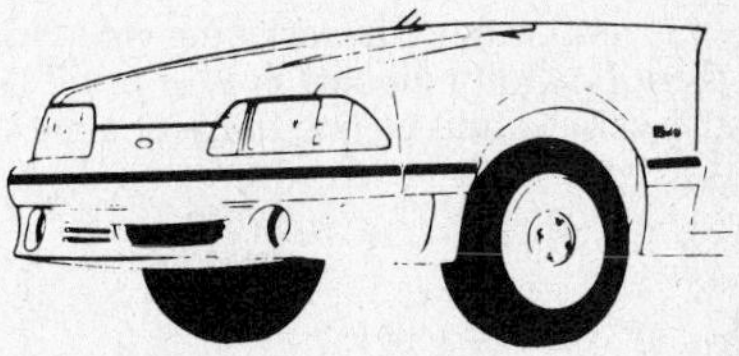

1987 Mustang GT

TUNE-UP SPECIFICATIONS

When analyzing compression test results, look for uniformity among cylinders rather than specific pressures

Year	Engine: Eng. VIN Code	Engine: No. Cyl. Displacement (cu. in.)	Engine: Eng. mfg.	Spark Plugs: Orig. Type	Spark Plugs: Gap (in.)•	Distributor: Point Dwell (deg)	Distributor: Point Gap (in.)	Ignition Timing (deg): Man. Trans.	Ignition Timing (deg): Auto. Trans.	Valves Intake Opens (deg)	Fuel Pump Pressure (psi)	Idle Speed (rpm): Man. Trans.	Idle Speed (rpm): Auto. Trans.
'83	A	4-140	Ford	AWSF-44	.044	Electronic		①	①	16	5.5–6.5	850	800
	X	6-200	Ford	BSF-92	.050	Electronic		①	①	20	6–8	600	600
	3	V-6-232	Ford	AWSF-52	.044	Electronic		①	①	13	39	550	550
	F	8-302	Ford	ASF-52 ②	.050	Electronic		①	①	16	6–8 ③	—	550
	G	8-351	Ford	ASF-42	.044	Electronic		①	①	23	6–8	—	700/600
'84	A	4-140	Ford	AWSF-44	.044	Electronic		①	①	16	5–7	850	750
	W	4-140-T	Ford	AWSF-32	.034	Electronic		①	①	—	39	①– ④	①– ④
	T	4-140-T ⑤	Ford	AWSF-32	.034	Electronic		①	①	—	39	① ④	① ④
	3	V6-232	Ford	AWSF-54	.044	Electronic		①	①	13	39	—	550
	F	8302	Ford	ASF-52	.050	Electronic		①	①	16	39	550	550
	M	8302HO	Ford	ASF-42	.044	Electronic		①	①	—	6–8	700	700
	G	8-351	Ford	ASF-42	.044	Electronic		①	①	23	6–8	—	600 ⑥

TUNE-UP SPECIFICATIONS

When analyzing compression test results, look for uniformity among cylinders rather than specific pressures

Year	Engine: Eng. VIN Code	Engine: No. Cyl. Displacement (cu. in.)	Eng. mfg.	Spark Plugs: Orig. Type	Spark Plugs: Gap (in.)•	Distributor: Point Dwell (deg)	Distributor: Point Gap (in.)	Ignition Timing (deg): Man. Trans.	Ignition Timing (deg): Auto. Trans.	Valves Intake Opens (deg)	Fuel Pump Pressure (psi)	Idle Speed (rpm): Man. Trans.	Idle Speed (rpm): Auto. Trans.
'85	A	4-140	Ford	AWSF-44	.044	Electronic		①	①	16	6–8	850	750
	W	4-140T	Ford	AWSF-32	.034	Electronic		①	①	—	39	750	750
	T	4-140-T ⑤	Ford	AWSF-32	.034	Electronic		①	①	—	39	① ④	① ④
	R	4-140-HSC	Ford	AWSF-52	.044	Electronic		①	①	—	39	800	700
	3	V6-232	Ford	AGSP-52	.044	Electronic		①	①	13	6–8	600	600
	C	V6-232	Ford	AWSF-54	.044	Electronic		①	①	13	39	—	550
	F	8-302	Ford	ASF-52	.050	Electronic		①	①	—	39	550	550
	M	8-302 HO	Ford	ASF-42	.044	Electronic		①	①	—	6–8	700	700
	G	8-351	Ford	ASF-42	.044	Electronic		①	①	—	6–8	—	600 ⑥
'86–'87	A	4-140	Ford	AWSF-44C	.044	Electronic		①	①	16	6–8	750	750
	T	4-140-T	Ford	AWSF-32C	.034	Electronic		①	①	—	39	825/975	825/975
	W	4-140-T	Ford	AWSF-32C	.034	Electronic		①	①	—	39	825/975	825/975
	3	V6-232	Ford	AWSF-54	.044	Electronic		①	①	13	39	—	550
	F	8-302	Ford	ASF-32C	.044	Electronic		①	①	—	39	① ④	① ④
	M	8-302 HO	Ford	ASF-42	.044	Electronic		①	①	—	6–8	700	700
	G	8-351	Ford	ASF-32C	.044	Electronic		①	①	—	6–8	650	650

NOTE: The underhood calibrations sticker often reflects tune-up specification changes made in production. Sticker figures must be used if they disagree with those in this chart.

T Turbocharger
HO High output
HSC High swirl combustion
① Calibrations vary depending upon the model; refer to the underhood calibration sticker.
② The carbureted models use spark plug ASF-42 (.044) and the idle speed rpm is 700 rpm.
③ On fuel injected models the pressure is 39 psi.
④ Electronic engine control models the ignition timing, idle speed and idle mixture is not adjustable.
⑤ SVO
⑥ 700 rpm with the VOTM on.

VEHICLE IDENTIFICATION NUMBER (VIN)

It is important for servicing and ordering parts to be certain of the vehicle and engine identification. The VIN (vehicle identification number) is a 13 or 17 digit number visible through the windshield on the driver's side of the dash and contains the vehicle and engine identification codes. It can be interpreted as follows:

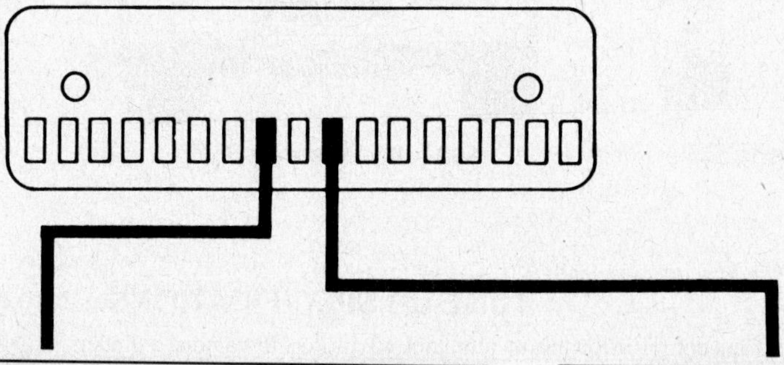

Engine Code

Code	Cu. In.	Liters	Cyl.	Carb.	Eng. Mfg.
A	140	2.3	4	1	Ford
W	140-T	2.3	4	Turbo.	Ford
T	140-T SVO	2.3	4	Turbo.	Ford
R	140-HSC	2.3	4	①	Ford
T,B,X	200	3.3	6	1	Ford
3	232	3.8	V6	①	Ford
C	232	3.8	V6	①	Ford
F	302	5.0	V8	1	Ford
M	302-H.O.	5.0	V8	①	Ford
G	351-W	5.8	V8	①	Ford
G	351-H.O.	5.8	V8	①	Ford

Model Year Code

Code	Year
D	1983
E	1984
F	1985
G	1986
H	1987

The seventeen digit Vehicle Identification Number can be used to determine engine application and model year. The tenth digit indicates the model year, and the eighth digit identifies the engine code.
① EFI, VV, 2 bbl. or 4 bbl. depending on model

FIRING ORDERS

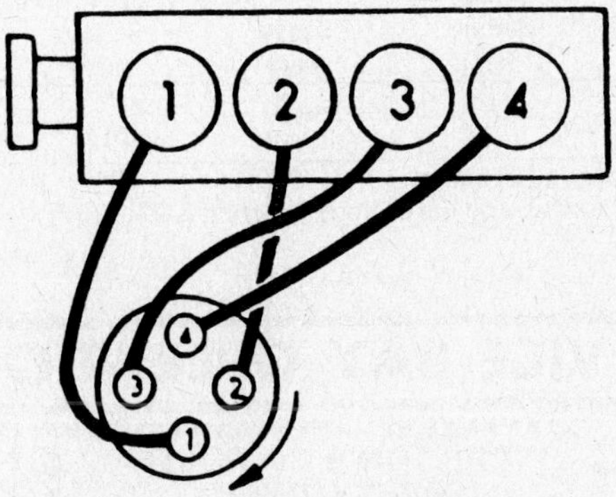

FORD MOTOR CO. 2300 cc 4-cyl.
Engine firing order: 1–3–4–2
Distributor rotation: clockwise

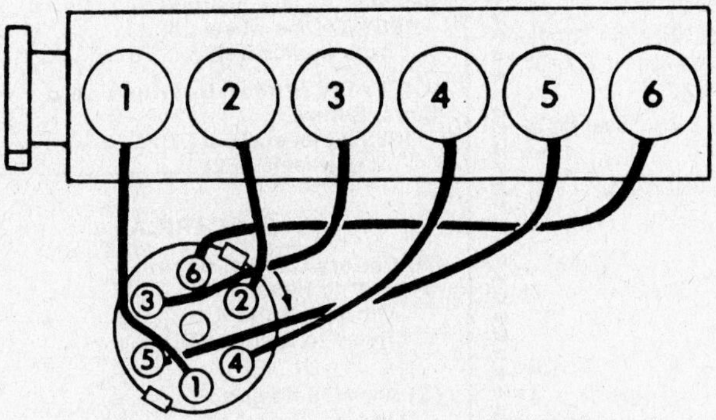

FORD MOTOR CO. 200, 250 6-cyl.
Engine firing order: 1–5–3–6–2–4
Distributor rotation: clockwise

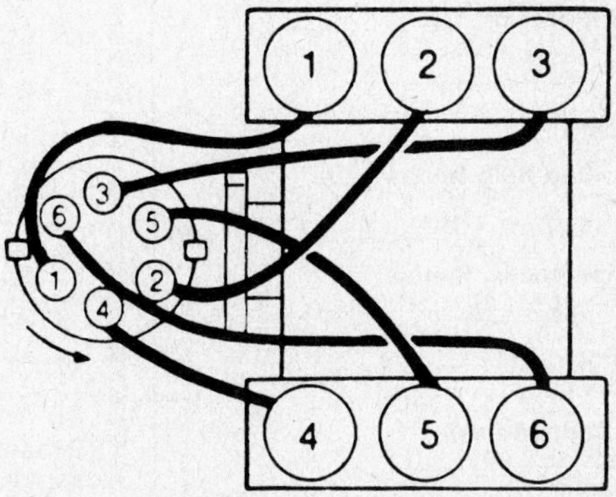

FORD MOTOR CO. 232 V6
Engine firing order 1–4–2–5–3–6
Distributor rotation: counterclockwise

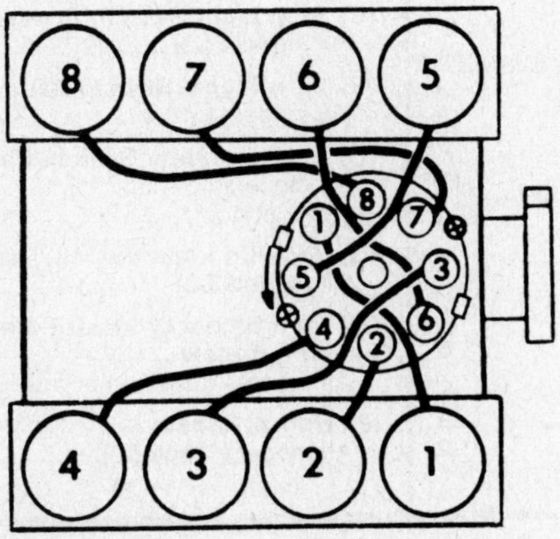

FORD MOTOR CO. 255, 302 (exc. HO) 460
V8 Engine firing order: 1–5–4–2–6–3–7–8
Distributor rotation: counterclockwise

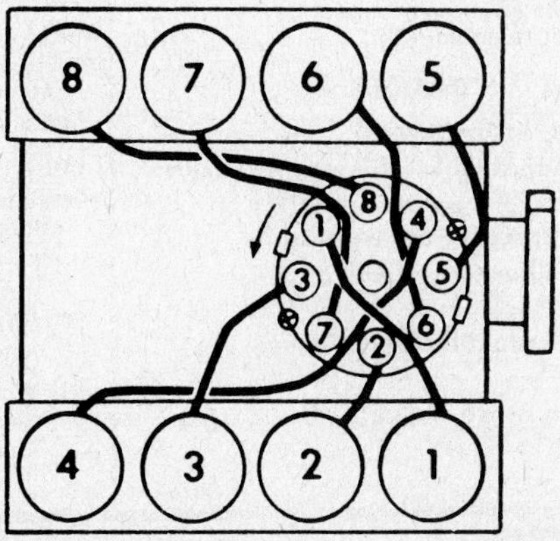

FORD MOTOR CO. 302HO, 351, 400
Engine firing order: 1–3–7–2–6–5–4–8
Distributor rotation: counterclockwise

WHEEL ALIGNMENT SPECIFICATIONS

Year	Model	Caster Range (deg)	Caster Pref. Setting (deg)	Camber Range (deg)	Camber Pref. Setting (deg)	Toe-in (in.)	Steering Axis Inclin. (deg)	Wheel Pivot Ratio (deg) Inner Wheel	Wheel Pivot Ratio (deg) Outer Wheel
'83-'84	Mustang/Capri	1/2P to 2P	1 1/4P	3/4N to 3/4P	0P	1/16 to 5/16	15 23/32	20	19 27/32
'85-'87	Mustang/Capri	1/4P to 1 3/4P	1P	3/4N to 3/4P	0P	1/16 to 5/16	15 23/32	20	19 27/32

① Set the vehicle height before making the alignment check.
② On the 84 models the caster range is 2 3/8P to 4 1/8P and the preferred setting is 3 1/8P.

LABOR — SERVICE BAY OPERATIONS — LABOR

(Factory Time) — Chilton Time

COOLING

(M) Winterize Cooling System
Includes: Run engine to check for leaks, tighten all hose connections. Test radiator and pressure cap. Drain radiator and engine block. Add anti-freeze and refill system.
All models 5

(M) Thermostat, Renew
1983-87-Four (.5) 7
Six (.4) 6
V-6 (.5) 7
V-8 (.6) 8
w/A.C. add 2

(M) Serpentine Belt, Renew
1983-87
V-6 & V-8 (.3) 5

(M) Radiator Hoses, Renew
1983-87-upper (.3) 4
lower (.4) 5
both (.5) 8
by-pass (.3) 5

(M) Drive Belts, Adjust
All models-one (.2) 3
each adtnl (.1) 1

FUEL

(M) Carburetor Air Cleaner, Service
All models (.2) 3

(G) Carburetor, Adjust (On Car)
All models (.4) 5
Propane enrichment method (1.0) 1.5

(G) Thermostatic Choke Cover and/or Gasket, Renew
All models (.5) 7
Tamper resistant (.9) 1.4

BRAKES

(G) Brakes, Adjust (Minor)
Includes: Adjust brakes, fill master cylinder.
two wheels 4

(G) Bleed Brakes (Four Wheels)
Includes: Fill master cylinder.
All models (.3) 5

(G) Brake Pedal Free Play, Adjust
All models 4

(M) Parking Brake, Adjust
All models (.3) 4

CHILTON'S 10 POINT SAFETY CHECK

CHECK OPERATION & CONDITION OF THE FOLLOWING ITEMS:

1. Legal Registration (serial no.)
2. Tires & Wheels
3. Brake System (R&R all wheels)
4. Light Systems & Signals
5. Accelerator Linkage, Neutral Safety Switch, Shift Indicator Pointer & Seat Position Locks
6. Glass, Mirrors, Door Locks, Seat Belts & Harness
7. Wipers, Washers & Defrosters
8. Frame, Steering, Shocks, Front & Rear Suspension
9. Fuel & Exhaust Systems
10. Road Test Vehicle

All models 1.0
Exhaust Smog Analysis, add 4

(Factory Time) — Chilton Time

LUBRICATION SERVICE

(M) Lubricate Chassis, Change Oil & Filter
Includes: Inspect and correct all fluid levels.
All models 6
Install grease fittings add 1

(M) Lubricate Chassis
Includes: Inspect and correct all fluid levels.
All models 4
Install grease fittings add 1

(M) Engine Oil & Filter, Change
Includes: Inspect and correct all fluid levels.
All models 4

WHEELS

(M) Wheel, Renew
one (.5) 5

(G) Wheels, Balance
one 3
each adtnl 2

(Factory Time) — Chilton Time

(M) Wheels, Rotate (All)
All models 5

(G) Front Wheel Bearings, Clean and Repack (Both Wheels)
All models 1.3

(G) Front Wheel Grease Seals, Renew
Includes: Repack bearings.
1983-87-one wheel (.5) 7
both wheels (.8) 1.1

(G) Front Wheel Bearings and Cups, Renew
1983-87-one wheel (.7) 9
both wheels (1.2) 1.5

ELECTRICAL

(M) Battery Cables, Renew
Batt to Relay (.3) 3
Ground (.3) 3
Relay to Starter (.4) 5

(G) Aim Headlamps
two 4
four 6

(M) Headlamp Sealed Beam Bulb, Renew
All models-each (.3) 3

(G) Headlamp Switch, Renew
All models (.3) 5

(G) Headlamp Dimmer Switch, Renew
All models (.4) 7

(G) Stop Light Switch, Renew
All models (.3) 4

(G) Turn Signal Switch, Renew
All models (.4) 1.0

(G) Neutral Safety Switch, Renew
All models (.3) 4
w/AOD add (.1) 1

(G) Back-Up Light Switch, Renew
All models (.3) 5

(M) Turn Signal or Hazard Warning Flasher, Renew
All models (.3) 4

(G) Horns, Renew
All models-each (.3) 4

LABOR — 1 TUNE UP 1 — LABOR

(Factory Time) — Chilton Time

(G) Compression Test
Four-1983-87 (.3) 6
V-6-1983-87 (.4) 9
V-8-1983-87 (.5) 9
w/A.C. add 2

LABOR 1 TUNE UP 1 LABOR

(Factory Time)	Chilton Time
(G) Engine Tune Up, (Electronic Ignition)	
Includes: Test battery and clean connections. Tighten manifold and carburetor mounting bolts. Check engine compression, clean and adjust or renew spark plugs. Test resistance of spark plug cables. Inspect distributor cap and rotor. Adjust air gap. Check vacuum advance operation. Reset ignition timing. Adjust idle mixture and idle speed. Service air cleaner. Inspect and adjust drive belts. Inspect choke operation and adjust or free up. Check operation of EGR valve.	
Four–1983-87	1.5
V-6–1983-87	2.0
V-8–1983-87	2.4
w/A.C. add	.2
Perform EEC IV system test add	1.0

LABOR 2 IGNITION SYSTEM 2 LABOR

(Factory Time)	Chilton Time
(G) Spark Plugs, Clean and Reset or Renew	
1983-87-Four (.3)	.5
Six (.4)	.6
V-6	
2.8 L eng (.8)	1.1
3.8 L eng (.7)	1.0
V-8 (.7)	1.0
w/A.C. add	.2
(G) Ignition Timing, Reset	
1983-87 (.3)	.4
(G) Distributor, Renew	
Includes: Reset ignition timing.	
1983-87 (.4)	.7
(G) Ignition Module Assembly, Renew	
Note: Fender mount type. For TFI unit, refer to Emission Control section.	
1983-87 (.3)	.6
Perform system test add (.3)	.3
(G) Profile Ignition Pick-Up Sensor, Renew (Duraspark)	
1983-87 (.5)	.9
Perform system test add (.3)	.3
(G) Distributor Armature, Renew	
1983-87 (.3)	.6
(G) Distributor Stator, Renew	
Includes: R&R armature.	
1983-84 (.4)	.8
2.3L OHC eng add (.2)	.2
(G) Distributor Cap and/or Rotor, Renew	
1983-87 (.3)	.5
(G) Vacuum Control Unit, Renew	
Includes: R&R distributor and reset ignition timing.	
1983-87 (.5)	.8
(G) Ignition Coil, Renew	
Includes: Test.	
1983-87 (.3)	.6
(G) Ignition Cables, Renew	
Includes: Test wiring.	
1983-87 (.4)	.6
(G) Ignition Switch, Renew	
1983-87 (.4)	.7
(G) Ignition Key Indicator Buzzer, Renew	
1983-87 (.3)	.5

PARTS 2 ELECTRONIC IGNITION 2 PARTS

	Part No.	Price
Distributor Assy. (New)		
4 cyl.–140 eng.		
1983-exc. below	▲E3ZZ-12127D	136.75
w/E.F.I.	▲E3ZZ-12127B	155.50
1984	▲E3ZZ-12127B	155.50
1985-87	▲E59Z-12127C	136.75
V-6–230 eng.		
1983-exc. Calif.	▲E3ZZ-12127F	136.75
w/Calif.	▲E2SZ-12127B	136.75
w/hi alt.	▲E3ZZ-12127C	155.50
1984-85-exc. Canada	▲E4ZZ-12127A	155.50
Canada	▲E4AZ-12127A	155.50
1986-87	▲E6SZ-12127C	155.50
V-8–302 eng.		
1983-wo/conv.	▲E3ZZ-12127J	136.75
w/conv.	▲E3ZZ-12127H	136.75
1984-w/A.T.	▲E4TZ-12127B	136.75
w/M.T.	▲E4ZZ-12127D	136.75
1985-w/A.T.	▲E5TZ-12127B	136.75
w/M.T.	▲E5ZZ-12127B	136.75
1986-87	▲E6AZ-12127D	136.75
(1) Distributor Cap		
4 cyl.–140 eng.		
1983-85-wo/EEC IV	▲E3BZ-12106A	16.25
1984-87-w/ E.E.C. IV	▲E5FZ-12106C	8.75
V-6–230 eng.		
1983-85-wo/ E.E.C. IV	▲E5DZ-12106A	19.50
1984-87-w/ E.E.C. IV	▲E6AZ-12106A	12.50
V-8–302 Eng.		
1983-84	▲E2ZZ-12106A	20.00
1985	▲E5ZZ-12106A	N.L.
1986-87	▲E6TZ-12106A	20.00

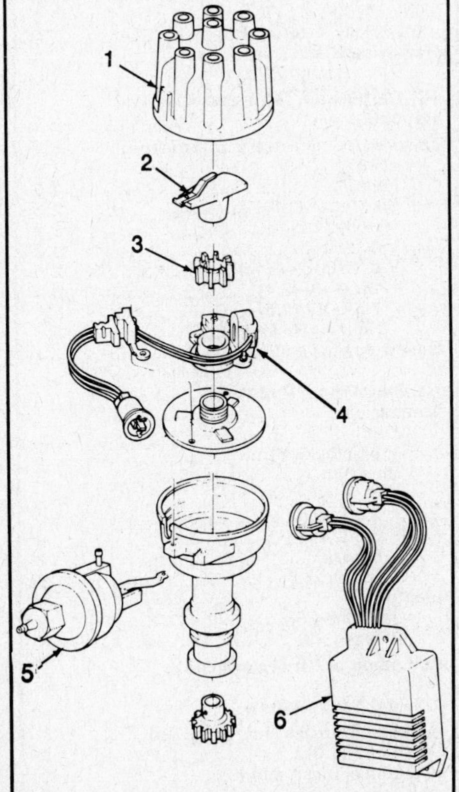

	Part No.	Price
(2) Rotor		
4 cyl.–140 eng.		
1983-87-wo/ E.E.C. IV	▲D7FZ-12200C	4.75
1983-84-w/ E.E.C. IV	▲E5FZ-12200A	3.25
1985-w/E.E.C. IV	▲E59Z-12200A	3.25
1986-87-w/ E.E.C. IV	▲E6AZ-12200C	2.50
6 cyl.–230 eng.		
1983-87-wo/ E.E.C. IV	▲E3DZ-12200A	2.75
1984-85-w/ E.E.C. IV	▲E5FZ-12200A	3.25
1986-87	▲E6AZ-12200C	2.50
V-8–302 eng.		
1984-85-wo/ E.E.C.	▲E4HZ-12200A	3.50
1984-w/E.E.C. IV	▲E4TZ-12200B	4.00
1985-87	▲E5TZ-12200B	2.50
(3) Armature		
4 cyl.–140 eng.		
1983-85	▲D7FZ-12A099A	3.75
V-6–230 eng.		
1983-87	▲D4DZ-12A099A	5.50
V-8–302 eng.		
1983-85	▲D3AZ-12A099A	6.00
(4) Stator Assy.		
140 eng.		
1983-87-wo/ E.E.C. IV	▲D5TZ-12A112B	25.25
w/E.E.C. IV	▲E3ZZ-12A112C	25.00
230, 302 engs.		
1983-85-wo/ E.E.C. IV	▲D4PZ-12A112A	25.50
1983-87-w/ E.E.C. IV	▲E3ZZ-12A112C	25.00

PARTS 2 ELECTRONIC IGNITION 2 PARTS

	Part No.	Price
(5) Vacuum Diaphragm Assy.		
4 cyl.-140 eng.		
1983	▲E2BZ-12370F	31.25
V-6-230 eng.		
1983-exc. Calif.	▲E1SZ-12370A	31.25
w/Calif.	▲D5TZ-12370N	N.L.
1984-85	▲E1SZ-12370A	31.25
V-8-302 eng.		
1983-wo/conv.	▲E2DZ-12370A	31.25
w/conv.	▲E1SZ-12370A	31.25
1984-87	▲D3AZ-12370C	33.25
(6) Modulator Assy.		
1983-wo/turbo	▲D9VZ-12A199A	83.50
w/turbo	▲E43Z-12A297A	106.00
1984-85-wo/ E.E.C. IV	▲D9VZ-12A199A	83.50
1984-87-w/ E.E.C. IV	▲E43Z-12A297A	106.00

	Part No.	Price
Ignition Coil		
1983-exc. Turbo	▲D5AZ-12029A	31.25
w/turbo	▲E3FZ-12029A	33.75
1984-85-wo/ E.E.C. IV	▲D5AZ-12029A	31.25
1984-87-w/ E.E.C. IV	▲E3FZ-12029A	33.75
Ignition Wire Set		
4 cyl.-140 eng.		
(wo/E.E.C. IV)		
1983-87-wo/ turbo	▲E3PZ-12259ABR	31.75
1983-w/turbo	▲E3PZ-12259AH	41.25
(w/E.E.C. IV)		
1984	▲E3PZ-12259AH	41.25
1985	▲E5PZ-12259D	49.50
1986-87	▲E6PZ-12259H	49.50

	Part No.	Price
V-6-230 eng.		
1983	▲E4PZ-12259AFR	53.75
1984-87-wo/ E.E.C. IV	▲E4PZ-12259FR	53.50
w/E.E.C. IV	▲E4PZ-12259B	42.75
V-8-302 engs.		
1983	▲E3PZ-12259ADR	57.50
1984	▲E5PZ-12259B	75.50
1986-87	▲E6PZ-12259G	75.25
Ignition Switch		
1983-87	▲E4FZ-11572A	11.50
Ignition Warning Switch		
1983	▲D9AZ-11A127A	5.50
1984-85	▲E25Y-11A127A	5.50
1986-87	▲D9AZ-11A127A	5.50

LABOR 3 FUEL SYSTEM 3 LABOR

(Factory Time)	Chilton Time
(G) Fuel Pump, Test	
Includes: Disconnect line at carburetor, attach pressure gauge.	
All models	
mechanical	.3
electric	.5
(M) Carburetor Air Cleaner, Service	
1983-87 (.2)	.3
(G) Carburetor, Adjust (On Car)	
1983-87 (.4)	.5
Propane enrichment method (1.0)	1.5
(M) Fuel Filter, Renew	
1983-87 (.4)	.5
Holly 4180 4V (.4)	.6
w/EFI Turbo add (.2)	.2
(G) Float Level, Adjust	
Includes: Set idle speed and mixture.	
All models	
Carter YFA 1V (.6)	.8
Holly 1946 1V (.5)	.7
Weber 740 2V (.5)	.7
Motorcraft 2150 2V (.4)	.6
Weber 5200-6500 2V (.5)	.7
2700-7200 VV (.5)	.7
Holly 4180 4V (.4)	.6
(G) Float or Needle Valve and Seat, Renew	
Includes: Set idle speed and mixture.	
All models	
Carter YFA 1V (.5)	.8
Holly 1946 1V (.6)	.9
Weber 740 2V (.5)	.8
Motorcraft 2150 2V (.4)	.7
Weber 5200-6500 2V (.5)	.8
2700-7200 VV (.5)	.8
Holly 4180 4V	
primary (.5)	.8
secondary (.5)	.8
both (.7)	1.3
(G) Accelerator Pump Diaphragm, Piston or Rod, Renew	
All models	
Four (.4)	.6
Six (.6)	.8
V-6 (.6)	.8
V-8-2 bbl (.3)	.5
4 bbl (.5)	.7
(G) Fuel Enrichment Valve Assy., Renew	
1983-87	
2150 2V (.8)	1.3

(Factory Time)	Chilton Time
Holly 4180 4V (.4)	.6
(G) Thermostatic Choke Housing and/or Gasket, Renew	
1983-87	
Carter YFA 1V (.4)	.6
2150 2V (.8)	1.3
Holly 4180 4V (.3)	.5
(G) Carburetor, R&R or Renew	
Includes: All necessary adjustments.	
1983-87	
Four (.4)	.8
Six (.5)	.8
V-6 (.6)	1.0
V-8-2150-2-V (.6)	.9
2700-VV (.6)	1.0
7200-VV (.7)	1.1
Holly 4180-4V (.6)	1.0
Renew carb add (.4)	.4
(G) Carburetor, R&R and Clean or Recondition	
Includes: All necessary adjustments.	
1983-87	
Four (1.2)	2.5
Six-Carter (1.8)	2.8
Holly (2.2)	3.2
V-6 (1.6)	3.0
V-8-2150-2-V (1.6)	2.5
2700-VV (2.4)	3.5
7200-VV (2.5)	3.6
Holly 4180-4V (1.8)	3.6
Renew spacer add (.2)	.2
(G) Fuel Pump, Renew	
Mechanical	
Four	
on block (.6)	.8
Six (.3)	.5
V-6	
2.8 L eng (.6)	1.0
3.8 L eng (.5)	.9
V-8 (.4)	.7
HO eng (.5)	.9
Electric	
on frame (.6)	.8
in tank (.9)	1.4
Add pump test if performed.	
(G) Fuel Tank, Renew	
Includes: Transfer tank gauge unit.	
1983-87 (1.0)	1.5
w/Elec fuel pump add (.2)	.2

(Factory Time)	Chilton Time
(G) Fuel Gauge (Tank), Renew	
Includes: Drain and refill tank.	
1983-87 (.9)	1.4
(G) Fuel Gauge (Dash), Renew	
1983-87 (.4)	.9
(G) Intake Manifold or Gaskets, Renew	
1983-87-Four (1.1)	2.0
w/EFI Turbo	
upper (1.0)	1.4
lower (2.1)	3.0
V-6	
2.8 L eng (2.4)	3.0
3.8 L eng (2.2)	3.3
V-8-255 eng (2.3)	3.3
302 eng (2.1)	3.0
w/Turbocharger add (.3)	.3
Renew manif add (.4)	.5
TURBOCHARGER COMPONENTS	
(G) Turbocharger Assembly, Renew	
1983-87 (2.5)	3.4
w/EFI turbo (1.4)	2.0
(G) Turbocharger Wastegate, Renew	
Includes: R&R turbocharger.	
1983-87 (2.7)	3.8
w/EFI Turbo (1.6)	2.2
ELECTRONIC FUEL INJECTION	
(G) Fuel Injection Manifold Assy., Renew	
1983-87	
Four (.8)	1.2
(G) Fuel Injector Assy., Renew	
1983-87	
Four-one (.8)	1.2
all (.9)	1.5
V-6-V-8-w/CFI	
one (.8)	1.2
all (.9)	1.5
V-8-w/SEFI	
one (1.8)	2.4
all (2.0)	2.7
(G) Air Intake Throttle Body, Renew	
1983-87	
Four (.7)	1.1
(G) Fuel Charging Wiring Assy., Renew	
1983-87 (.3)	.6

LABOR 3 FUEL SYSTEM 3 LABOR

	(Factory Time)	Chilton Time
(G) Fuel Pressure Regulator Assy., Renew		
1983-87		
Four	(.9)	1.4
V-6-V-8	(.8)	1.3
(G) Fuel Charging Assy., R&R or Renew		
1983-87		
V-6-V-8	(.7)	1.2
(G) Fuel Charging Assy., R&R and Recondition		
1983-87		
V-6	(1.5)	2.2
V-8	(1.8)	2.5

PARTS 3 FUEL SYSTEM 3 PARTS

	Part No.	Price
Air Cleaner Element (Carb.)		
4 cyl.-140 eng.		
(wo/turbo)		
1983-87	▲C8TZ-9601AR	8.50
(w/turbo)		
1983-87	▲E3ZZ-9601A	9.25
V-6-230 eng.		
1983-87	▲D3ZZ-9601AR	9.75
V-8-302 eng.		
1984-85-w/A.T.	▲D7AZ-9601AR	9.25
1983-85-w/M.T.	▲E3ZZ-9601B	17.25
1986-87	▲E6SZ-9601B	11.50
Carburetor Assy. (New)		
Four-140 eng.		
1983-w/4 spd. trans. (exc. Calif. & Canada)		
wo/A.C.	▲E3ZZ-9510M	221.50
w/A.C.	▲E3ZZ-9510L	221.50
1983-w/5 spd. trans. (exc. Calif.)		
wo/A.C.	▲E3ZZ-9510T	221.50
w/A.C.	▲E3ZZ-9510U	221.50
1983-Stand. trans. (Calif.)		
wo/A.C.	▲E3ZZ-9510Y	298.00
w/A.C.	▲E3ZZ-9510V	221.50
1983-Stand. trans. (w/Hi alt.)		
wo/A.C.	▲E3ZZ-9510AE	221.50
w/A.C.	▲E3ZZ-9510AD	221.50
1983-Stand. Trans. (Canada)		
wo/A.C.	▲E3ZZ-9510AR	N.L.
w/A.C.	▲E3ZZ-9510AP	N.L.
1983 (w/Auto. trans.)		
(wo/Calif. em.)		
wo/A.C.	▲E3ZZ-9510AT	221.50
w/A.C.	▲E3ZZ-9510AS	221.50
(w/Calif. em.)		
wo/A.C.	▲E3ZZ-9510AB	221.50
w/A.C.	▲E3ZZ-9510AC	221.50
(Canada)		
wo/A.C.	▲E3ZZ-9510PB	N.L.
w/A.C.	▲E3ZZ-9510NB	N.L.
1984-w/A.T.	▲E4ZZ-9510H	228.75
w/M.T. (exc. Calif.)	▲E4ZZ-9510D	228.75
1985-87-w/A.T.	▲E5ZZ-9510C	246.50
(Canada) wo/ A.C.	▲E4ZZ-9510R	N.L.
w/A.C.	▲E4ZZ-9510P	N.L.
w/M.T.	▲E5ZZ-9510A	253.00
(Canada) wo/ A.C.	▲E4ZZ-9501N	N.L.
w/A.C.	▲E4ZZ-9510M	N.L.
V-6-230 eng.		
1983 (wo/Calif. em.)		
wo/A.C.	▲E3CZ-9510B	392.75
w/A.C.	▲E3CZ-9510A	392.75
1983 (w/Calif. em.)		
wo/A.C.	▲E3CZ-9510H	392.75
w/A.C.	▲E3CZ-9510G	421.00
1983-w/hi alt.	▲E3CZ-9510E	392.75
1983-85 (w/Canada)		

Note: Canadian models must be ordered by identification no. on carb. or by calibration code.

	Part No.	Price
V-8-302 eng.		
1983-4 spd.	▲E3ZZ-9510AU	N.L.
5 spd.	▲E3ZZ-9510BG	N.L.
1984	▲E4ZZ-9510S	475.25
1985	▲E5ZZ-9510G	471.50
Fuel Pump Assy. (New)		
4 cyl.-140 eng.		
(wo/turbo)		
1983-87	▲E0FZ-9350A	39.25
(w/turbo)		
1983-85-before 11/84	▲E3ZZ-9350A	127.00
1985-87-from 11/84	▲E5ZZ-9A407B	184.75
V-6-230 eng.		
(wo/C.F.I.)		
1983-87	▲E2AZ-9350B	26.25
(w/C.F.I.)		
1984-85	▲E4DZ-9350B	184.75
1985-87-from 11/84	▲E5ZZ-9A407A	184.75
V-8-302 eng.		
(wo/C.F.I.)		
1983-87	▲E2ZZ-9350B	30.75
(w/C.F.I.)		
1984-85-before 11/84	▲E4DZ-9350B	184.75
1985-87-from 11/84	▲E5ZZ-9A407A	184.75
Fuel Tank		
1983-exc. E.F.I.	▲E4ZZ-9002B	104.75
w/E.F.I.	▲E4ZZ-9002A	104.75
1984-87 (w/140 & 230 eng.)		
exc. C.F.I. Turbo	▲E4ZZ-9002B	104.75
w/C.F.I. turbo	▲E4ZZ-9002A	104.75
1984-87 (w/302 eng.)		
stand. trans.	▲E4ZZ-9002B	104.75
auto. trans.	▲E4ZZ-9002A	104.75
Fuel Gauge (Tank Unit)		
140, 230 engs.		
(exc. C.F.I., turbo)		
1983	▲E1ZZ-9275B	42.25
1984	▲E1ZZ-9275A	42.25
1985-87	▲E4ZZ-9275A	42.25
(w/C.F.I., turbo)		
1983-87	▲E3ZZ-9275C	42.25
(V-8-302 eng.)		
(exc. C.F.I.)		
1983	▲E1ZZ-9275A	42.25
1984-85	▲E4ZZ-9275B	42.25
(w/C.F.I.)		
1984-87	▲E3ZZ-9275C	42.25
Fuel Gauge (Dash)		
1983-87	▲E3ZZ-9305A	28.00

PARTS 3 ELECTRONIC FUEL INJECTION 3 PARTS

230 & 302 ENGINES

	Part No.	Price
Charging Assy. (Fuel)		
V-6-230 engine		
1984 (stamping no.)		
E4AE-CC	▲E4AZ-9C973A	643.75
E4AE-CE	▲E4AZ-9C973E	643.75
E4AE-DC	▲E4AZ-9C973B	598.50
E4AE-DE	▲E4AZ-9C973D	643.75
1985-87 (stamping no.)		
E5SE-HA	▲E5SZ-9C973H	598.25
E5SE-GA	▲E5SZ-9C973G	570.25
E5SE-JA	▲E5SZ-9C973J	337.00
E5SE-KA	▲E5SZ-9C973K	570.25
E6SE-AA	▲E65Z-9C973A	N.L.
E6SE-BA	▲E65Z-9C973B	N.L.
V-8-302 engine		
1984	▲E4ZZ-9C973B	643.75
1985 (stamping no.)		
E5ZE-BA	▲E5ZZ-9C973B	598.25
E5ZE-CA	▲E5ZZ-9C973C	598.25
Throttle Body Assy.		
1986-87	▲E6ZZ-9E926A	239.75
(1) Plug (Pressure Regulator)		
1984-85	▲E0AY-9E938A	.75
(2) Pressure Regulator Assy. (Fuel)		
1984-85	▲E3FZ-9C968A	68.50
(3) Body (Upper)		

Note: Serviced in charging assembly.

	Part No.	Price
(4) Relief Valve Assy. (Pressure)		
1984-85	▲E0AY-9H321A	6.50
(5) Cap (Relief Valve)		
1984-85	▲E0VY-9H323A	1.50
(6) Charging Wiring Assy.		
1984-85	▲E6SZ-9D930A	70.00
(7) Injector Assy.		
V-8-302 engine		
1986-87	▲E6ZZ-9F593A	72.50
(8) Retainer (Fuel Injector)		
1984-87	▲E0AY-9C976A	11.25
(9) Retainer Screw (Fuel Injector)		
1984-87	▲E0AY-9D927A	8.50
(10) Gasket (Charging Body)		
1984-85	▲E0AY-9C983A	1.00
(11) Control Rod Positioner (Fast Idle)		
1984-85	▲E0AY-9D993A	7.75
(12) Cam & Shaft Assy. (Choke)		
1984-85	▲E1VZ-9A753A	12.25
(13) Control Rod (Fast Idle)		
1984-85	▲E0AY-9E524A	3.00
(14) Diaphragm Assy. (Choke Control)		
1984-85	▲D9AZ-9J549A	10.00
(15) Modulator Spring (Choke Control)		
1984-85	▲E0AY-9J547F	9.75

PARTS 3 ELECTRONIC FUEL INJECTION 3 PARTS

	Part No.	Price
(16) Cover Assy. (Choke Control)		
1984-85	▲E1VZ-9B580A	14.50
(17) Lever & Shaft Assy. (Throttle)		
V-6-230 engine		
1984-exc. below	▲E4SZ-9581A	38.50
w/C-5 trans.	▲E4AZ-9581A	38.50
1985-87	▲E4SZ-9581A	38.50
V-8-302 engine		
1984-85	▲E3VY-9581A	38.50
(18) Throttle Plate		
1984	▲D7ZZ-9585A	1.50
1985	▲E2BZ-9585A	5.00
(19) Bracket Kit (Throttle Positioner)		
1984-85	▲E4AZ-9J586A	34.25
(20) Dashpot & Control Assy.		
V-6-230 engine		
1984-87	▲E1VY-9S520D	42.75
V-8-302 engine		
1984-85	▲E3VY-9S520D	N.L.
(21) Potentiometer Assy. (Throttle)		
V-6-230 engine		
1984-exc. below	▲E3TZ-9B989B	27.25
w/C-5 trans.	▲E45Z-9B989A	29.25
1985-87	▲E5ZZ-9B989B	27.50
V-8-302 engine		
1984	▲E3TZ-9B989B	27.25
1985	▲E5AZ-9B989A	27.25
(22) Adjusting Lever (Fast Idle)		
1984-87	▲E0VZ-9538A	7.00
(23) Bushing		
Note: Serviced in charging assembly.		
(24) Lever Fast (Idle Cam)		
1984-87	▲E0AY-9F577A	5.75
(25) Thermostat Lever (Choke Control)		
1984-87	▲E0AY-9A754A	1.50
(26) Housing Gasket (Choke Thermostat)		
1984-87	▲C1AZ-9871A	1.00

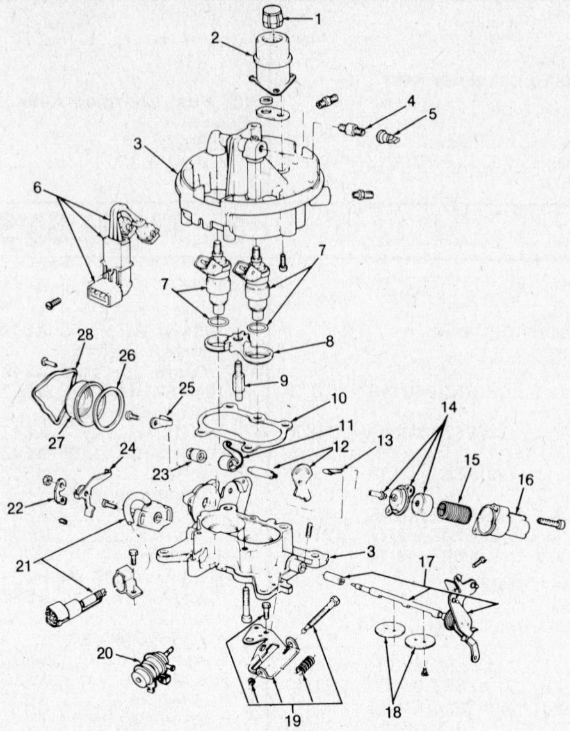

	Part No.	Price
(27) Thermostat Housing Assy. (Choke)		
1984-87	▲E35Y-9848A	33.25
(28) Clamp (Thermostat Housing)		
1984-87	▲E2AZ-9842A	6.75

PARTS 3 ELECTRONIC FUEL INJECTION 3 PARTS

302 ENGINE

	Part No.	Price
(1) Intake Manifold (Upper)		
1986-87	▲E6SZ-9424B	257.00
(2) Upper Manifold Cover		
1986-87	▲E6SZ-9E434A	16.00
(3) E.G.R. Spacer Assy.		
1986-87	▲E6ZZ-9H474A	18.75
(4) Throttle Body Gasket		
1986-87	▲E6ZZ-9E933A	1.25
(5) Throttle Body Assy.		
1986-87	▲E6ZZ-9E926A	239.75
(6) Throttle Air-Bypass Valve		
1986-87	▲E6ZZ-9F715A	56.50
(7) Throttle Position Sensor		
1986-87	▲E6AZ-9B989C	29.25
(8) E.G.R. Valve Assy.		
1986-87	▲E6AZ-9F483C	100.00
(9) Intake Manifold Gasket		
1986-87	▲E6SZ-9H486A	N.L.
(10) Lower Intake Manifold		
1986-87	▲E6SZ-9424A	276.25
(11) Fuel Rail Assy.		
1986-87	▲E6SZ-9F792D	166.00
(12) Schrader Valve		
1986-87	▲N.L.	

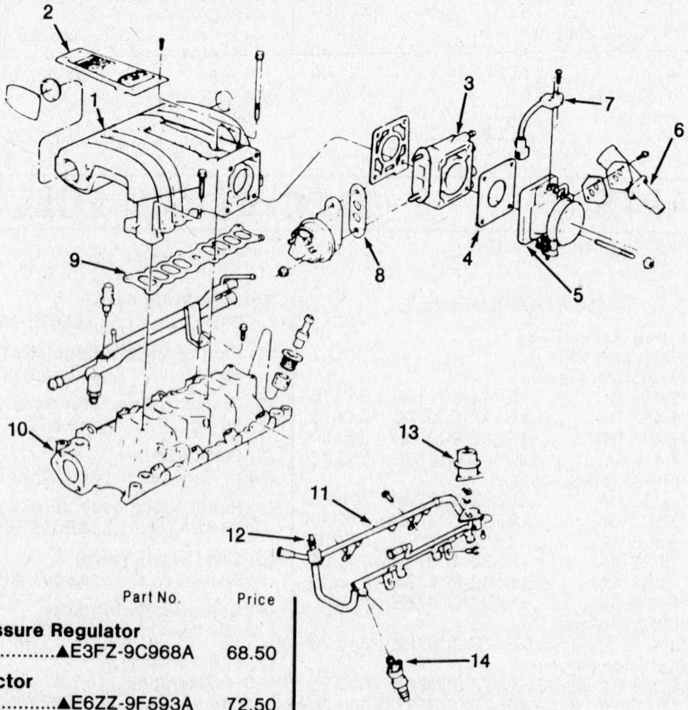

	Part No.	Price
(13) Fuel Pressure Regulator		
1986-87	▲E3FZ-9C968A	68.50
(14) Fuel Injector		
1986-87	▲E6ZZ-9F593A	72.50

PARTS 3 ELECTRONIC FUEL INJECTION 3 PARTS

Part No. Price

140 ENGINE

(1) Fuel Injector Assy.
Note: Injector assy. basic part no. 9F593 must be ordered from identification no. on fuel charging assy.

(2) Intake Manifold
1983-87-exc.
T.C. ▲E1ZZ-9424B 90.50
1983-84-w/T.C.
upper ▲E3ZZ-9424B 165.50
lower ▲E3ZZ-9424A 127.00
1985-87-upper ▲E5ZZ-9424B 165.50
lower ▲E5ZZ-9424C 127.00

(3) Manifold Assy. (Fuel Injection)
1983-84 ▲E3ZZ-9D280B 46.50
1985 ▲E5ZZ-9D280A 61.75

(4) Gasket (Pressure Regulator)
1983-87 ▲E0AY-9C977A 1.00

(5) Regulator Assy. (Pressure)
1983-87 ▲E3FZ-9C968A 68.50

(6) Throttle Body Assy.
(exc. SVO)
1983-84 ▲E4SZ-9E926A 239.75
1985-87 ▲E5SZ-9E926A 177.50
(SVO)
1984-bef. 5-85 ▲E4ZZ-9E926A 239.75
1985-87-from
5-85 ▲E5ZZ-9E926C 239.75

(7) Wiring Assy. (Fuel Charging)
1983-85-bef.
2-85 ▲E3ZZ-9D930A 51.00
1985-87-from
2-85 ▲E5ZZ-9D930A 51.00

(8) Gasket (Charge Cont. Manifold)
1983-84 ▲E3ZZ-9E936A 1.00
1985-87 ▲E5TZ-9E936A 6.50

(9) Gasket (Air By Pass Valve)
1983-84 ▲E3FZ-9F670A 1.25

(10) Shaft Seal (Throttle Control)
1983-87 ▲E3FZ-9C753A 4.25

(11) Throttle Valve (Air By Pass)
1983-87-exc.
SVO ▲E3FZ-9F715A 33.25
SVO ▲E4ZZ-9F715A 64.00

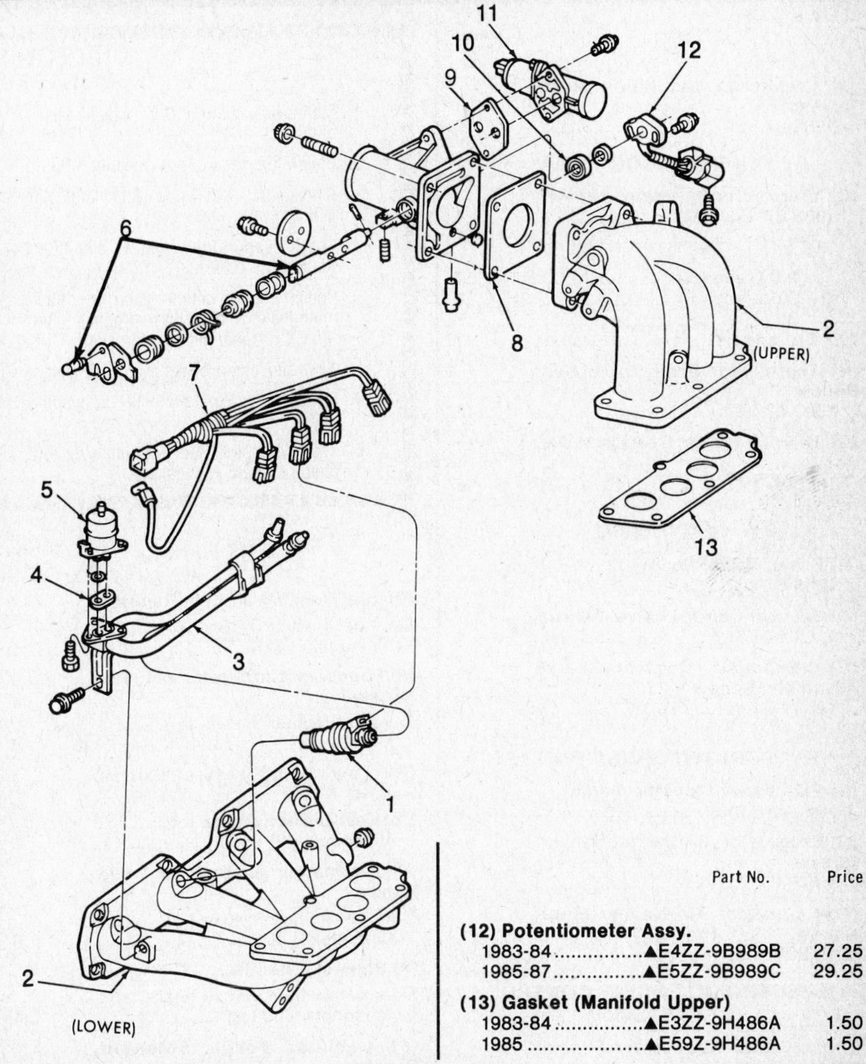

Part No. Price

(12) Potentiometer Assy.
1983-84 ▲E4ZZ-9B989B 27.25
1985-87 ▲E5ZZ-9B989C 29.25

(13) Gasket (Manifold Upper)
1983-84 ▲E3ZZ-9H486A 1.50
1985 ▲E59Z-9H486A 1.50

PARTS 3 TURBOCHARGER SYSTEM 3 PARTS

Part No. Price

140 ENGINE

(1) Turbocharger Assy.
exc. SVO
1983-84 ▲E4ZZ-9G438C 352.00
SVO
1984-85-before
4/85 ▲E4ZZ-9G438B 349.25
1985-87-from
4/85 ▲E5ZZ-9G438B 349.25

(2) Oil Return Tube
1983-87 ▲E3ZZ-9G441A 22.75

(3) Intake Manifold
1983-84-lower ▲E3ZZ-9424A 127.00
upper ▲E3ZZ-9424B 165.50
1985-87-lower ▲E5ZZ-9424C 127.00
upper ▲E5ZZ-9424B 165.50

(4) Tube (E.G.R. Valve to Exh. Man.)
1983-84 ▲E3ZZ-9D477A 26.75
1985 ▲E5ZZ-9D477B 5.75

(5) E.G.R. Valve
Replacement E.G.R. valves must be ordered according to the stamping number on the original valve.

(6) Oil Supply Tube
1983-87 ▲E3ZZ-9G439A 6.50

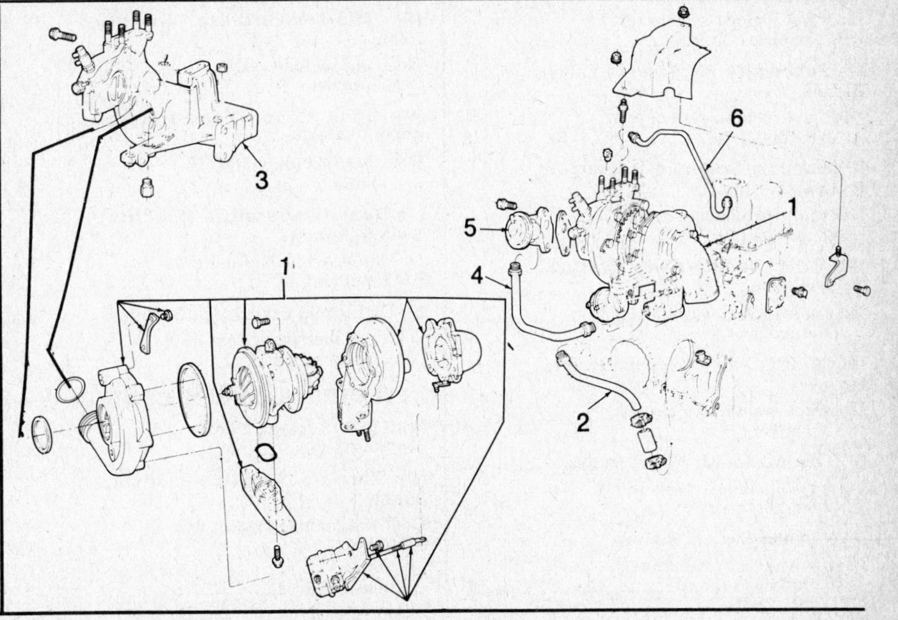

(Factory Time)	Chilton Time
(M) Crankcase Ventilation Valve, Renew	
1983-87 (.2)	.2

THERMACTOR TYPE

(Factory Time)	Chilton Time
(G) Thermactor Air Pump, Renew	
1983-87-Four (.7)	*1.1
Six (.4)	.7
V-6	
2.8 L eng (.4)	.7
3.8 L eng (.5)	.8
V-8 (.4)	.7
*w/A.C. add (.1)	.1
(G) Thermactor Pump Drive Belt, Renew	
1983-87 (.3)	.5
(G) Thermactor Air By-Pass Valve, Renew	
1983-87 (.4)	.6

E.G.R. TYPE

(Factory Time)	Chilton Time
(G) E.G.R. Valve, Renew	
1983-87 (.3)	.4
(G) Vacuum Control Valve, Renew	
1983-87 (.3)	.4
(G) Exhaust Control Valve Assembly, Renew	
1983-87 (.4)	.7

EVAPORATIVE EMISSION TYPE

(Factory Time)	Chilton Time
(G) Fuel Vapor Canister, Renew	
1983-87 (.3)	.4
(G) Carburetor Air Cleaner Sensor, Renew	
1983-87 (.2)	.3
(G) Carburetor Air Cleaner Filter, Renew	
1983-87 (.2)	.3

ELECTRONIC ENGINE CONTROL SYSTEM

(Factory Time)	Chilton Time
(P) Feed Back Carburetor Control System, Test	
All models (.5)	.8
(P) Oxygen Sensor, Renew	
Does not include system test.	
All models (.3)	.7
(P) Secondary Air Control Valve, Renew	
Does not include system test.	
All models (.4)	.6
(P) Vacuum Solenoid Regulator, Renew	
Does not include system test.	
All models (.3)	.5
(P) Cold Temperature Switch, Renew	
Does not include system test.	
All models (.4)	.6
(P) Throttle Angle Vacuum Switch, Renew	
Does not include system test.	
All models (.3)	.6
(P) Thermactor Air Valve, Renew	
Does not include system test.	
All models-one (.4)	.6
(P) Vacuum Switch, Renew	
Does not include system test.	
All models-one (.3)	.5

CHILTON'S EMISSION CONTROL TUNE-UP

1. Clean or renew P.C.V. valve, hoses and filter.
2. Check fuel tank cap for sealing ability.
3. Check fuel tank and fuel lines for leakage.
4. Check evaporation canister and filter. Replace if necessary.
5. Check engine compression to determine leakage of unburned gases. (Add time for items of interference).
6. Test and clean or renew spark plugs.
7. Check engine oil dipstick for sealing ability.
8. Test exhaust system with analyzer and check system for leakage.
9. Check exhaust manifold heat valve for operation.
10. Adjust ignition timing and carburetor idle speed and mixture.
11. Check automatic choke mechanism for free operation.
12. Inspect air cleaner and element.
13. On models so equipped, test distributor vacuum control switch and transmission control switch.

Four	1.3
Six	1.5
V-6	1.7
V-8	1.8

For repairs made, charge accordingly.

(Factory Time)	Chilton Time
(P) Idle Tracking Switch, Renew	
Does not include system test.	
All models (.3)	.5
(P) Feedback Carburetor Actuator, Renew	
Does not include system test.	
All models (.3)	.5
(P) Low Temperature Switch, Renew	
Does not include system test.	
All models (.3)	.6
(P) Thermactor Air By-Pass Valve, Renew	
Does not include system test.	
All models (.4)	.6
(P) Solenoid, Renew	
Does not include system test.	
All models-one (.3)	.4
(P) Canister Purge Solenoid, Renew	
Does not include system test.	
All models (.3)	.4
(P) Mid-Temperature Switch, Renew	
Does not include system test.	
All models (.3)	.4
(P) Open Loop (Temperature) Switch, Renew	
Does not include system test.	
All models (.3)	.4
(P) Dual Temperature (Electric) Switch, Renew	
Does not include system test.	
All models (.3)	.5
(P) Electronic Control Unit, Renew	
Does not include system test.	
All models (.3)	.5

ELECTRONIC ENGINE CONTROL IV

(Factory Time)	Chilton Time
(P) E.E.C. System, Test	
1984-87 (.5)	1.0
(P) Throttle Position Sensor, Renew	
Does not include system test.	
1984-87	
Four	
w/FBC (.2)	.3
w/EFI (.4)	.6
V-6 (.3)	.4
V-8 (.7)	1.0
(P) E.G.R. Shut Off Solenoid, Renew	
Does not include system test.	
1984-87	
Four (.1)	.2
(P) Throttle Air By-Pass Valve, Renew	
Does not include system test.	
1983-87	
Four (.1)	.2
Must. SVO (.3)	.5
(P) Exhaust Gas Oxygen Sensor, Renew	
Does not include system test.	
1984-87	
Four (.1)	.3
V-6-left (.3)	.5
right (.7)	1.0
both (1.0)	1.4
V-8 (.2)	.5
V-8-w/SEFI	
left (.4)	.6
right (.2)	.3
both (.5)	.8
Must. SVO (.3)	.6
(P) Processor Assembly, Renew	
Does not include system test.	
1984-87	
All models (.3)	.4
(P) Air Control Sensor, Renew	
Does not include system test.	
1983-87	
Four (.3)	.4
(P) Engine Coolant Temperature Sensor, Renew	
Does not include system test.	
1984-87	
All models (.2)	.3
(P) Fuel Pump Relay, Renew	
Does not include system test.	
1983-87	
Four (.2)	.3
(P) Barometric Manifold Absolute Pressure Sensor, Renew	
Does not include system test.	
1984-87	
All models (.1)	.2

LABOR 3A EMISSION CONTROLS 3A LABOR

(Factory Time) — Chilton Time

(P) E.G.R. Position Sensor, Renew
Does not include system test.
1984-87
V-6 (.3) 4
V-8 (.3) 4

(P) Thick Film Ignition Module, Renew
Does not include system test.
1984-87
All models (.5) 7

(P) Profile Ignition Pick-Up Sensor, Renew
Does not include system test.
1983-87
All models (.6) 8

(P) Throttle Positioner Assembly, Renew
Does not include system test.
1984-87
All models (.2) 3

(P) E.G.R. Control Solenoids, Renew
Does not include system test.
1984-87
V-6 (.1) 2
V-8 (.1) 2

(P) Tad/Tab Solenoids, Renew
Does not include system test.
1984-87
All models (.1) 2

(P) Cooling Fan Controller, Module or Relay, Renew
Does not include system test.
1985-87 (.1) 2

(P) Fuel Injector Assembly, Renew
Does not include system test.
1984-87
Four-one (.8) 1.2
all (.9) 1.5
Must. SVO-one (.8) 1.2
all (.9) 1.5
V-6-V-8-w/CFI
one or both (.8) 1.2
V-8-w/SEFI
one (1.8) 2.4
all (2.0) 2.7

(P) Knock Sensor, Renew
Does not include system test.
1983-87
All models (.1) 2

(P) Intake Manifold Heat Control Valve, Renew
Does not include system test.
1984-87
V-6 (.2) 4

(P) Air Change Temperature Sensor, Renew
Does not include system test.
1984-87
V-6-V-8 (.2) 3

(P) Throttle Kicker Actuator, Renew
Does not include system test.
1984-87
V-8 (.2) 3

(P) Exhaust Heat Control Valve, Renew
Does not include system test.
1984-87
V-8 (.3) 6

(P) Electronic Control Relay, Renew
Does not include system test.
All models (.3) 4

(P) Back Pressure Variable Transducer, Renew
Does not include system test.
All models (.1) 2

(P) Fuel Pump Inertia Switch Assy., Renew
Does not include system test.
All models (.2) 3

(P) Canister Purge Valve or Solenoid, Renew
Does not include system test.
All models (.1) 2

(P) Feed Back Control Solenoid, Renew
Does not include system test.
1985-87
Four (.2) 3

(P) E.G.R. Valve, Renew
Does not include system test.
All models (.2) 4

PARTS 3A EMISSION CONTROLS 3A PARTS

	Part No.	Price
Crankcase Ventilation Valve		
4 cyl.–140 eng.		
(wo/turbo)		
1983-87	▲E1ZZ-6A666A	3.75
(w/turbo)		
1983-84	▲D9DZ-6A666A	3.50
1985-87	▲E5ZZ-6A666A	3.75
V-6–230 eng.		
1983-87	▲E1DZ-6A666A	3.75
V-8–302 engs.		
1983-87	▲D9ZZ-6A666A	3.50

THERMACTOR TYPE

	Part No.	Price
Thermactor Air Pump		
4 cyl.–140 eng.		
1983-87	▲E3ZZ-9A486A	141.75
V-6–230 eng.		
1983-exc. Canada	▲E2SZ-9A486A	N.L.
Canada	▲E3SZ-9A486B	141.75
1984-87	▲E3SZ-9A486C	141.75
V-8–302 eng.		
1983	▲E1ZZ-9A486L	141.75
1984	▲E3ZZ-9A486E	141.75
1985-87-w/M.T.	▲E5SZ-9A486A	141.75
w/A.T.	▲E3ZZ-9A486E	141.75
Air Supply Check Valve		
140 eng.		
(nipple 1 end)		
1983	▲D8FZ-9A487A	24.50
1984	▲E4ZZ-9A487B	14.50
1985-87	▲E5ZZ-9A487A	14.50
(nipple 2 ends)		
1983-87	▲D9AZ-9A487C	11.25
1983-84 (Canadian Models)	▲E3FZ-9A487B	18.50
V-8–302 eng.		
(nipple 1 end)		
1983-87	▲D4VY-9A487A	14.25
(nipple 2 ends)		
1983-85	▲D9AZ-9A487C	11.25
1986-87	▲E3TZ-9A487A	13.25
V-6–230 eng.		
(nipple 1 end)		
1983	▲E2AZ-9A487A	18.50
1984-87	▲D4AZ-9A487A	14.25
(nipple 2 ends)		
1983-87	▲D9AZ-9A487C	11.25
Air By-Pass Valve		
1983-exc. 140	▲E1TZ-9B289C	28.75
140 eng.	▲E1ZZ-9B289A	32.50
1984-87	▲E1TZ-9B289C	28.75

EVAPORATIVE EMISSION TYPE

	Part No.	Price
Vapor Canister Assy.		
(exc. turbo)		
1983-87-exc Calif.	▲D8AZ-9D653C	53.25
Calif.	▲E0AZ-9D653A	53.25
(w/turbo)		
1984-87	▲E2VY-9D653A	72.75
(Canada)		
1984-85-w/230 eng.	▲E2VY-9D653A	72.75
1986-87-w/302 eng.	▲E2ZZ-9D653A	55.50
Sensor Assy.		
140 eng.		
1983-87	▲D7FZ-9E607A	7.25
V-8–302 eng.		
1983-85-w/A.T.	▲D4ZZ-9E607A	7.00
w/M.T.	▲D7FZ-9E607B	7.25
V-6–230 eng.		
1983	▲D4ZZ-9E607A	7.00
1984-87	▲D7FZ-9E607B	7.25

E.G.R. CONTROL SYSTEM

E.G.R. Valve
Replacement E.G.R. valves must be ordered according to the stamping number on the original valve.

	Part No.	Price
Control Valve Assy.		
1983 (w/140 eng.)		
w/4 spd.	▲D7BZ-9D473A	28.50
w/5 spd.	▲D8TZ-9D473B	36.75
w/hi alt.	▲D8BZ-9D473A	36.75
1983-w/302 eng.	▲D3TZ-9D473A	33.00
1984-87-w/140 eng.	▲D7BZ-9D473A	28.50
Solenoid Valve (E.G.R. Vacuum)		
4 cyl.–140 eng.		
(exc. SVO)		
1983-(stamped)		
E1ZE-A2A, A3a	▲E1ZZ-9D474A	16.25
E3ZE-C2A	▲E3ZZ-9D474C	16.25
E2SE-A2A, A3A	▲E2SZ-9D474A	16.25
1984-87	▲E4ZZ-9D474H	32.50
(SVO)		
1984	▲E3ZZ-9D474B	16.25
1985-87	▲E5ZZ-9D474A	16.25
V-6–230 eng.		
1983-(stamped)		
E3SE-A2A, A3A	▲E3SZ-9D474A	32.50
E3SE-B2A, B3A	▲E3SZ-9D474B	16.25

PARTS 3A EMISSION CONTROLS 3A PARTS

	Part No.	Price
1984-87-(stamped)		
E4ZE-G2A, G3A	▲E4ZZ-9D474G	16.25
E4ZE-E2A, E3A	▲E4ZZ-9D474E	32.50
E4ZE-FA	▲E4ZZ-9D474F	32.50
E5TE-AA	▲E5TZ-9D474AA	32.50
V-8-302 eng.		
1984-87 (stamped)		
E35E-A2A, FA	▲E35Y-9D474A	32.50
E4ZE-E2A, E3A	▲E4ZZ-9D474E	32.50
E4ZE-FA	▲E4ZZ-9D474F	32.50
E4ZE-G2A, G3A	▲E4ZZ-9D474G	16.25
E5ZE-B2A, B3A	▲E5ZZ-9D474B	32.50
E65E-A2A	▲E65Z-9D474A	N.L.

ELECTRONIC ENGINE CONTROL SYSTEM

	Part No.	Price
Oxygen Sensor (Exh. Gas.)		
140, 230 engs.		
1983 (stamped)		
E1AF-AA	▲E1AZ9F472A	95.00
E3EF-AA	▲E3FZ-9F472A	48.50
1984-87-wo/ turbo	▲E3FZ-9F472A	48.50
w/turbo	▲E4ZZ-9F472A	69.00
302 engine		
(wo/E.F.I.)		
1984-85	▲E3FZ-9F472A	48.50
(w/E.F.I.)		
1984-87 (stamped)		
E4ZF-AA	▲E4ZZ-9F472A	69.00
E59F-A1A, A2A, A3A	▲E59Z-9F472A	48.50
E67F-AA, CA	▲E6TZ-9F472A	48.50
E67F-BA	▲E6TZ-9F472B	48.50
Air Control Valve (Secondary)		
4 cyl.-140 eng.		
1983	▲E3TZ-9F491A	56.00
1984-87 (stamped)		
E3EE-C3A	▲E43Z-9F491C	56.00
E4SE-A3A	▲E4SZ-9F491A	56.00
E4SE-BA	▲E4SZ-9F491B	56.00
V-6-230 eng.		
1983-exc. hi. alt	▲E3TZ-9F491A	56.00
w/hi alt.	▲E3SZ-9F491C	27.25
1984-87	▲E4SZ-9F491A	56.00
V-8-302 eng.		
1983-(stamped)		
E1SE-F3A, F4A	▲E1SZ-9F491F	56.00
E3SE-AA	▲E3SZ-9F491C	27.25
1984-87-exc. Calif.	▲E5ZZ-9F491A	27.25
Calif.	▲E3TZ-9F491A	56.00

	Part No.	Price
Cold Temperature Vacuum Switch		
4 cyl.-140 eng.		
1983-(stamped)		
E1ZE-A1A, A2A, A3A	▲E1ZZ-12A182A	41.25
E1ZE-B1A	▲E1ZZ-12A182B	25.25
E2ZE-B1A	▲E2ZZ-12A182B	41.25
E2ZE-C1A	▲E2ZZ-12A182C	41.25
V-8-302 eng.		
1983-exc. Calif.	▲E3ZZ-12A182A	41.25
Calif.	▲E3ZZ-12A182C	41.25
1984-Calif.	▲E3ZZ-12A182C	41.25
(exc. Calif.)		
(stamped E4ZE)		
A1A, A2A	▲E4ZZ-12A182A	41.25
B1A, B2A	▲E4ZZ-12A182B	41.25
1985-(color coded)		
brown	▲E4ZZ-12A182B	41.25
green	▲E5ZZ-12A182B	41.25
violet	▲E5ZZ-12A182A	41.25
Electronic Control Unit		
4 cyl.-140 eng.		
1983	▲E3ZZ-12A651B	212.25
Purge Regulator Valve Assy. (Canister)		
1983-exc. hi. alt.	▲E0AZ-9C915A	21.75
w/hi alt.	▲E1TZ-9C915B	21.75
1984-87-(stamped)		
E4ZE-AA	▲E4ZZ-9C915A	56.25
E4AE-AA	▲E4AZ-9C915A	21.75
E4AE-BA	▲E4AZ-9C915B	21.75
E4AE-CA	▲E4AZ-9C915C	21.75
Idle Tracking Switch		
4 cyl.-140 eng.		
(wo/Calif. em.)		
1983-87	▲E0FZ-9D944A	22.75
(w/Calif. em.)		
1983-87-w/M.T.	▲E1ZZ-9D944A	22.75
w/A.T.	▲E1PZ-9D944A	38.25
Dual Coolant Switch Assy.		
1983	▲E1AZ-12B513A	71.50

ELECTRONIC ENGINE CONTROL IV

	Part No.	Price
Throttle Position Sensor		
4 cyl.-140 eng.		
1983-84	▲E4ZZ-9B989B	29.25
1985-87	▲E5ZZ-9B989C	29.25
Exhaust Gas Oxygen Sensor		
1984-87-exc. Turbo	▲E3FZ-9F472A	48.50
w/turbo	▲E4ZZ-9F472A	69.00
Processor Assy.		
4 cyl.-140 eng.		
1984 (stamped)		
E4EF-G1A, G2A	▲E4FZ-12A650GA	167.75
H1A, H2A	▲E4FZ-12A650HA	167.75
AAA	▲E4FZ-12A650AAA	167.75
AD1A	▲E4FZ-12A650ADA	167.75
E4ZF-B1A, B2A	▲E4ZZ-12A650BA	168.00
D1A, D2A	▲E4ZZ-12A650DA	N.L.
E1A, E2A	▲E4ZZ-12A650EA	N.L.
1985-87 (stamped)		
E5DF-F1A, F2A	▲E5DZ-12A650FA	168.00
F1B, F2B	▲E5DZ-12A650FB	167.75
K1A, K2A	▲E5DZ-12A650KA	167.75
K1B, K2B	▲E5DZ-12A650KB	167.75
N1A, N2A	▲E5DZ-12A650NA	167.75
N1B, N2B	▲E5DZ-12A650NB	167.75
E5ZF-E1A, E2A	▲E5ZZ-12A650EA	167.75
J1A, J2A	▲E5ZZ-12A650JA	167.75
V-6-230 eng.		
1984-(stamping no. E4VF)		
A1A, A2A	▲E4VZ-12A650A	167.75
B1A, B2A	▲E4VZ-12A650BA	167.75
1985-87-(stamping no. E4VF)		
A1B, A2B	▲E5VZ-12A650AB	167.75
B1B, B2B	▲E5VZ-12A650BB	167.75
(stamping no. E53F)		
AR1A, AR2A	▲E53Z-12A650ARA	167.75
AS1A, AS2A	▲E53Z-12A650ASA	167.75
(stamping no. E63F)		
A1A, A2A	▲E63Z-12A650AA	167.75
B1A, B2A	▲E63Z-12A650BA	167.75
V-8-302 eng.		
1984-(stamping no. E4VF)		
A1A, A2A	▲E4VZ-12A650MA	167.75
M1A, M2A	▲E4VZ-12A650MA	167.75
T1A, T2A	▲E4VZ-12A650TA	167.75
1985-87	▲E53Z-12A650FB	167.75
Back Pressure Variable Tranducer		
1984-87-w/140 eng.	▲E4ZZ-9J431B	33.75
Engine Coolant Temperature Sensor		
1984-87	▲E1AZ-12A648A	32.00
Barometric Manifold Pressure Sensor		
1984-87-w/140 eng	▲E3ZZ-12A644A	59.75
Ignition Modulator Assy.		
1984-87	▲E43Z-12A297A	106.00
E.G.R. Position Sensor		
1984-87	▲E43Z-9G428B	31.75
Canister Purge Valve		
1984-87-exc. below	▲D9AZ-9B963B	7.25
1983-Calif. w/ 302	▲E1TZ-9B963A	7.25
1984-85-Canada	▲E1TZ-9B963A	7.25
1983-w/230 eng.	▲E3TZ-9B963B	7.25
w/hi. alt carb.	▲E3UZ-9B963A	7.25
Intake Manifold Heat Control Valve		
V-6-230 eng.		
1984	▲E4AZ-9G464A	27.50
1985-87	▲E5AZ-9G464A	27.50
Air Change Temperature Sensor		
1984-87	▲E1AZ-12A697A	27.00
Exhaust Heat Control Valve		
1984-87-V-6	▲E1SZ-9A427A	86.50
V-8	▲E4ZZ-9A427A	86.50

LABOR 4 ALTERNATOR AND REGULATOR 4 LABOR

(Factory Time) — Chilton Time

(G) Alternator Circuits, Test
Includes: Test battery, regulator and alternator output.
All models (.3) 6

(M) Alternator Drive Belt, Renew
1983-87 (.3) 4

(G) Alternator, Renew
1983-87 (.4) 7
Transfer pulley add (.1) 1
Circuit test add 6

(G) Alternator, R&R and Recondition
Includes: Complete disassembly, replacement of parts as required. Test validity of rotor fields, stator and diodes.
1983-87 (.9) 1.5
Circuit test add 6

(G) Alternator Front Bearing or End Plate, Renew
1983-87 (.7) 1.0

(G) Alternator Rear Bearing, Renew
1983-87 (.6) 9

(G) Alternator Regulator, Renew
1983-87 (.3) 4
Circuit test add 6

(G) Ammeter, Renew
1983-87 (.4) 9

(G) Instrument Cluster Voltage Regulator, Renew
1983-87 (.4) 6

PARTS 4 ALTERNATOR AND REGULATOR 4 PARTS

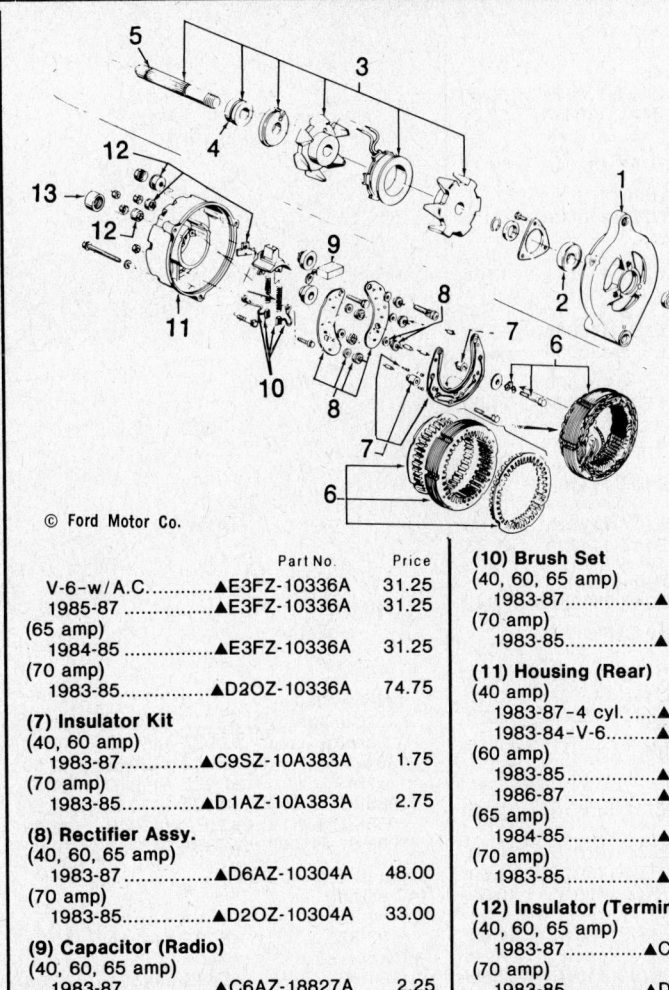

	Part No.	Price
Alternator Assy. (New)		
(40 amp)		
1983-87-4 cyl		
wo/A.C.	▲E1ZZ-10346A	203.50
1983-85-V-6	▲E2GZ-10346B	233.50
(60 amp)		
1983-84-wo/A.C.	▲E2GZ-10346C	233.50
w/A.C.	▲E2GZ-10346B	233.50
1985-87-V-6	▲E5SZ-10346A	232.75
1985-V-8	▲E2GZ-10346C	233.50
1986-87-V-8	▲E6TZ-10346A	232.75
(65 amp)		
1984-85	▲E1BZ-10346B	233.50
(70 amp)		
1985 (M.T.)	▲E1BZ-10346A	265.00
(1) Housing (Front)		
(40, 60 amp)		
1983-87-4 cyl.	▲D3OZ-10333B	17.75
V-6	▲E1FZ-10333A	21.25
(65 amp)		
1984-87	▲E1FZ-10333A	21.25
(70 amp)		
1983-85	▲D3VY-10333A	72.75
(2) Front Bearing		
1983-87	▲C9ZZ-10094A	9.00
(3) Rotor Assy.		
(40 amp)		
1983-87-4 cyl.	▲E1ZZ-10335A	45.75
V-6	▲E1ZZ-10335B	45.75
(60, 65 amp)		
1983-87	▲E1ZZ-10335B	45.75
(70 amp)		
1983-85	▲E1ZZ-10335C	68.00
(4) Slip Ring (Rotor)		
(40, 60 amp)		
1983-87	▲C3SZ-10328A	N.L.
(70 amp)		
1983-85	▲D2OZ-10328A	16.00
(5) Shaft (Rotor)		
1983-87	▲C5AZ-10330A	N.L.
Note: 70 amp serviced in Rotor Assembly.		
(6) Stator Assy.		
(40, 60 amp)		
1983-84-4 cyl.	▲E3FZ-10336A	31.25
V-6-wo/A.C.	▲D8ZZ-10336A	74.00

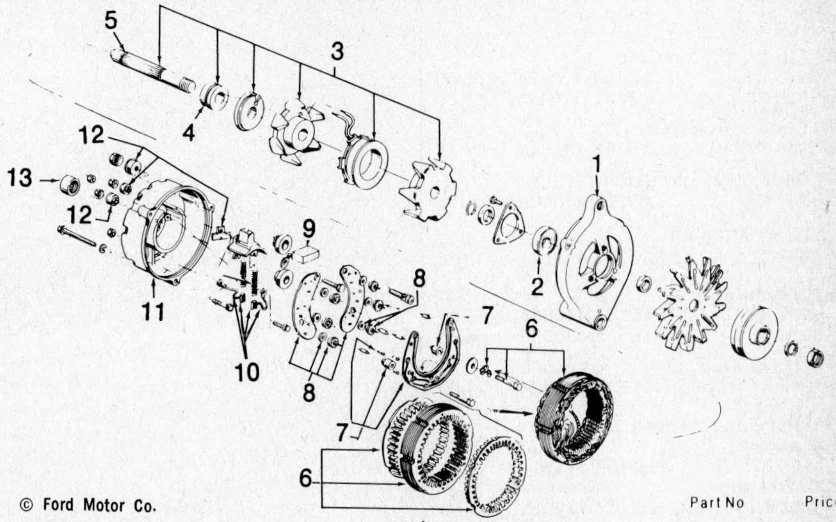

© Ford Motor Co.

	Part No.	Price
V-6-w/A.C.	▲E3FZ-10336A	31.25
1985-87	▲E3FZ-10336A	31.25
(65 amp)		
1984-85	▲E3FZ-10336A	31.25
(70 amp)		
1983-85	▲D2OZ-10336A	74.75
(7) Insulator Kit		
(40, 60 amp)		
1983-87	▲C9SZ-10A383A	1.75
(70 amp)		
1983-85	▲D1AZ-10A383A	2.75
(8) Rectifier Assy.		
(40, 60, 65 amp)		
1983-87	▲D6AZ-10304A	48.00
(70 amp)		
1983-85	▲D2OZ-10304A	33.00
(9) Capacitor (Radio)		
(40, 60, 65 amp)		
1983-87	▲C6AZ-18827A	2.25
(70 amp)		
1983-85	▲D2OZ-18827A	2.25

	Part No.	Price
(10) Brush Set		
(40, 60, 65 amp)		
1983-87	▲C6VY-10347A	3.50
(70 amp)		
1983-85	▲D2OZ-10347B	17.25
(11) Housing (Rear)		
(40 amp)		
1983-87-4 cyl.	▲D7ZZ-10334A	26.25
1983-84-V-6	▲D7AZ-10334A	23.25
(60 amp)		
1983-85	▲D7AZ-10334A	23.25
1986-87	▲D7ZZ-10334A	26.25
(65 amp)		
1984-85	▲D7ZZ-10334A	26.25
(70 amp)		
1983-85	▲D7VZ-10334A	49.25
(12) Insulator (Terminal)		
(40, 60, 65 amp)		
1983-87	▲C9SZ-10A383A	1.75
(70 amp)		
1983-85	▲D1AZ-10A383A	2.75
(13) Rear Bearing		
1983-87	▲D2OZ-10A304A	5.25

LABOR 5 STARTING SYSTEM 5 LABOR

	(Factory Time)	Chilton Time
(G) Starter Draw Test (On Car)		
All models	(.3)	.3
(G) Starter, Renew		
1983-87		
Four	(.3)	.6
Six	(1.0)	1.4
V-6	(.4)	.6
V-8	(.4)	.6
w/Turbo add	(.1)	.1
(G) Starter, R&R and Recondition		
Includes: Turn down armature.		
1983-87		
positive engagement starter	(1.7)	2.4
solenoid actuated starter	(1.5)	2.2
Motorcraft	(1.4)	2.1
w/Turbo add	(.1)	.1
Renew field coils add		.5
Add draw test if performed.		
(G) Starter Drive, Renew		
Includes: R&R starter.		
1983-87		
Four	(.5)	.8
Six	(1.2)	1.6
V-6	(.5)	.8
V-8	(.6)	.9
w/Turbo add	(.1)	.1
(G) Starter Solenoid Relay, Renew		
1983-87	(.3)	.4
(G) Neutral Safety Switch, Renew		
1983-87	(.3)	.4
w/AOD add	(.1)	.1
(G) Ignition Switch, Renew		
1983-87	(.4)	.7
(M) Battery Cables, Renew		
1983-87		
Batt to Relay	(.3)	.3
Ground	(.3)	.3
Relay to Starter	(.4)	.5

PARTS 5 STARTING SYSTEM 5 PARTS

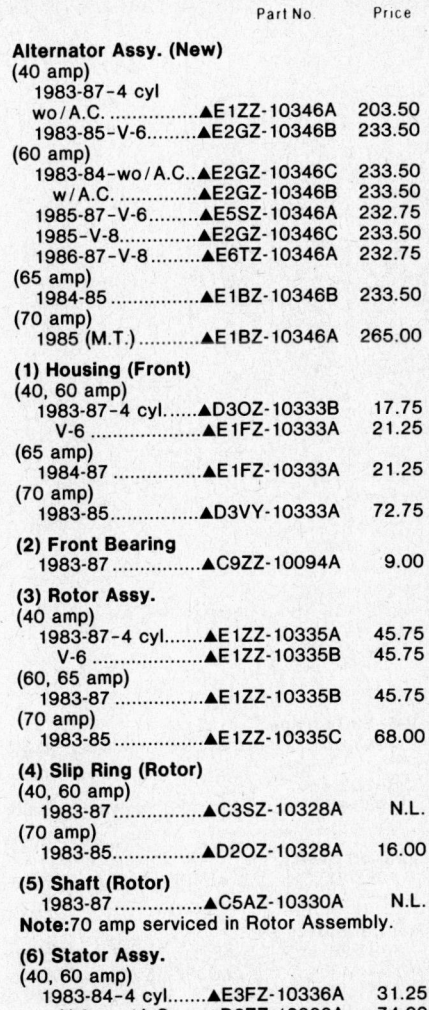

	Part No.	Price
Starter Assy. (New)		
140 engine		
1983-84	▲E3TZ-11002D	N.L.
1985-87	▲E4TZ-11002B	203.50
230, 302 engs.		
1983-87	▲E4DZ-11002B	185.50
(1) Plate (Brush End)		
1983-84	▲E2BZ-11049A	14.50
1985-87	▲E4AZ-11049A	14.50
(2) Plate Bushing (Brush End)		
1983-87	▲D3AZ-11052A	1.50
(3) Brush Holder		
1983-84	▲E2BZ-11061A	4.25
1985-87	▲E4AZ-11061A	4.25
(4) Brush Set		
1983-87	▲E4PZ-11057A	13.00

PARTS 5 STARTING SYSTEM 5 PARTS

	Part No.	Price
(5) Field Coil (Complete)		
1983-84	▲E2BZ-11082A	50.00
1985-87	▲E4AZ-11082A	50.00
(6) Contact Point Kit		
1983-87	▲E2PZ-11134A	24.75
(7) Spring (Plunger Return)		
1983-87	▲C2DF-11103A	1.50
(8) Lever & Pin Kit		
1983-87	▲E2BZ-11067A	14.25
(9) Armature		
1983-84	▲E2BZ-11005A	77.00
1985-87	▲E3FZ-11005A	66.75
(10) Drive Assy.		
1983-87	▲E2PZ-11350A	21.00
(11) Housing Kit (Drive End)		
140 engine		
1983-87	▲E4DZ-11130A	27.75
230, 302 engs.		
1983-84	▲E25Y-11130A	45.00
1985-87	▲E4AZ-11130A	41.75
(12) Bearing (Drive Housing)		
1983-87	▲D0AZ-11135B	N.L.
Battery to Starter Relay Cable		
1983-87-wo/ turbo	▲D1PZ-14300E	6.25
w/turbo	▲E3SZ-14300A	8.50
1986-87-V-8	▲E3SZ-14300A	8.50
Battery to Ground Cable		
140 engine		
(wo/turbo)		
1983	▲D9ZZ-14301C	12.50
1984-exc. Canada	▲E0ZZ-14301B	12.50
1984-Canada	▲D9ZZ-14301C	12.50
1985	▲E5ZZ-14301A	12.50
(w/turbo)		
1983-84	▲E3SZ-14301A	10.00
230, 302 engs.		
1983	▲D9ZZ-14301C	12.50

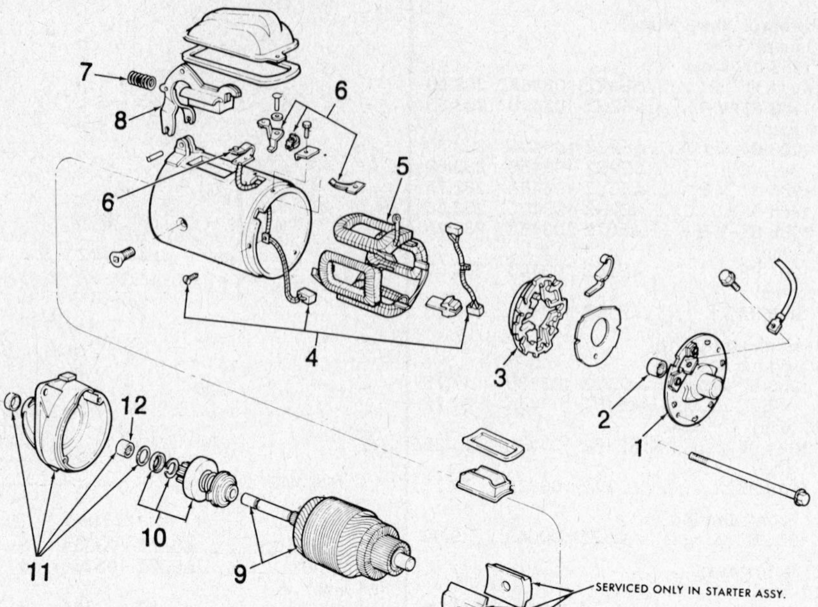

	Part No.	Price
1984-w/230, exc. Canada	▲E0ZZ-14301B	12.50
Canada	▲D9ZZ-14301C	12.50
1984-302 w/A.T.	▲E0ZZ-14301B	12.50
w/M.T.	▲D9ZZ-14301C	12.50
1985-87-w/230	▲E0ZZ-14301B	12.50
1985-w/302	▲E0ZZ-14301B	12.50
1986-87-w/302	▲E3SZ-14301A	10.00
Relay to Starter Cable		
140 engine		
(wo/turbo)		
1983-87	▲E0BZ-14431A	10.25
(w/turbo)		
1984-87	▲E4SZ-14431A	30.00

	Part No.	Price
V-6–230 engine		
1983-87	▲E2DZ-14431A	10.25
V-8–302 eng.		
1983-87	▲D1PZ-14431J	11.00
Ignition Switch		
1983-87	▲E4FZ-11572A	11.50
Neutral Safety Switch		
1983-87-w/A.T.	▲E2DZ-7A247A	38.50
w/M.T.	▲D3FZ-15520A	6.00

LABOR 6 BRAKE SYSTEM 6 LABOR

(Factory Time)	Chilton Time
(G) Brake Pedal Free Play, Adjust	
All models	.4
(G) Brakes, Adjust (Minor)	
Includes: Adjust brakes, fill master cylinder.	
two wheels	.4
(G) Bleed Brakes (Four Wheels)	
Includes: Fill master cylinder.	
All models (.3)	.5
(G) Brake Self Adjustors, Disassemble & Clean	
one wheel	.7
each adtnl	.4
(G) Brake Shoes and/or Pads, Renew	
Includes: Install new or exchange shoes or pads. Adjust service and hand brake. Bleed system.	
1983-87-front-disc (.7)	1.1
rear-drum (1.0)	1.5
all four wheels (1.4)	2.5
Resurface disc rotor, add-each	.9
Resurface brake drum, add-each	.5
(G) Brake Drum, Renew	
Includes: Remove wheel and adjust brakes.	
1983-87-one (.3)	.6

(Factory Time)	Chilton Time
both (.4)	.8
(G) Brake Pressure Warning Light Switch, Renew	
1983-87 (.3)	.5
BRAKE HYDRAULIC SYSTEM	
(G) Wheel Cylinder, Renew	
Includes: Bleed system.	
1983-87-one (.9)	1.4
both (1.5)	2.1
(G) Wheel Cylinder, R&R and Rebuild	
Includes: Hone cylinder and bleed system.	
1983-87-one (.9)	1.7
both (1.5)	2.7
(G) Brake Hose, Renew	
Includes: Bleed system.	
1983-87-front-one (.4)	.6
both (.5)	.7
rear-one (.5)	.8
(G) Master Cylinder, Renew	
Includes: Bleed complete system.	
1983-87	
w/Booster (.5)	1.0

(Factory Time)	Chilton Time
w/Hydra-boost (.7)	1.2
(G) Master Cylinder, R&R and Rebuild	
Includes: Hone cylinder and bleed complete system.	
1983-87	
w/Booster (.7)	1.5
w/Hydra-boost (.9)	1.7
POWER BRAKES	
(G) Power Brake Booster, Renew	
1983-87	
Four (1.3)	1.8
V-6 (.9)	1.3
V-8 (1.0)	1.4
Hydra boost (1.3)	1.8
w/EFI Turbo add (.6)	.6
w/Cruise control add	.2
(G) Power Brake Booster Check Valve, Renew	
1983-87 (.3)	.4
DISC BRAKES	
(G) Disc Brake Pads, Renew	
1983-87	
front (.7)	1.1

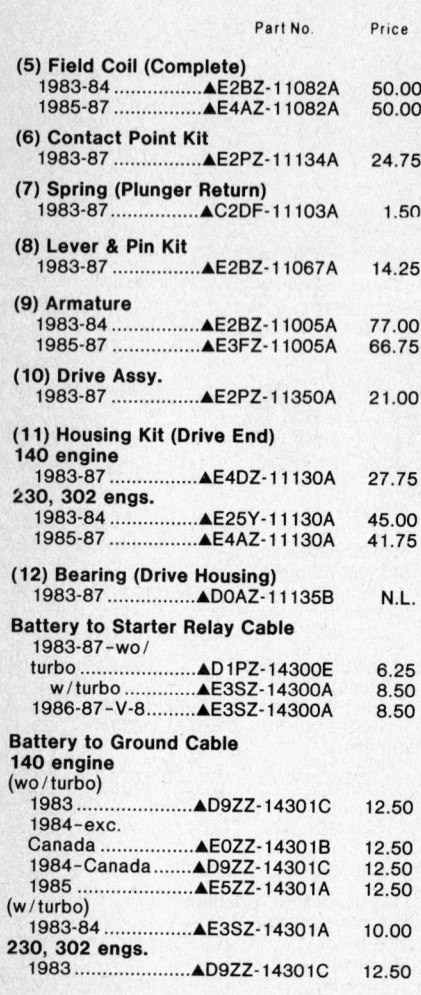

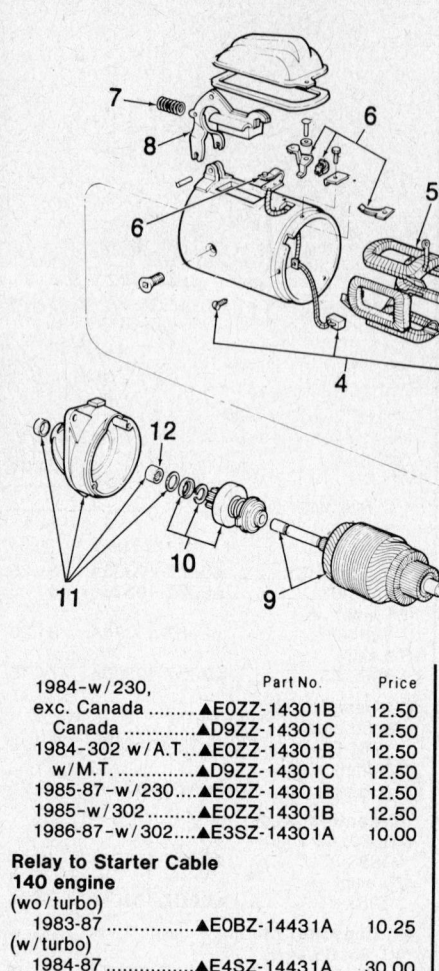

LABOR — 6 BRAKE SYSTEM 6 — LABOR

(Factory Time) Chilton Time

rear (.8) 1.2
all four wheels (1.2) 2.0
Resurface brake rotor, add-each 9

(G) Caliper Assembly, Renew
Includes: Bleed complete system.
1983-87-front-one (.6) 1.0
both (.8) 1.5
rear-one (.7) 1.1
both (1.0) 1.8

(G) Caliper Assy., R&R and Recondition
Includes: Bleed complete system.
1983-87-front-one (.8) 1.5
both (1.2) 2.5
rear-one (1.0) 1.6
both (1.6) 2.8

(G) Brake Rotor, Renew
Includes: Renew wheel bearings and grease retainer and repack bearings.
1983-87-front-one (.5) 7
both (.7) 1.2
rear-one (.4) 6
both (.5) 9

(G) Brake Differential Valve, Renew
Includes: Bleed complete system and transfer switch.
1983-87 (.7) 1.0

COMBINATIONS
Add to Brakes, Renew

See Machine Shop Operations

(Factory Time) Chilton Time

(G) RENEW WHEEL CYLINDER
Each (.3) 3

(G) REBUILD WHEEL CYLINDER
Each (.3) 3

(G) REBUILD CALIPER ASSEMBLY
Each (.2) 5

(G) RENEW MASTER CYLINDER
All models (.6) 6

(G) REBUILD MASTER CYLINDER
All models (.8) 1.0

(G) RENEW REAR WHEEL GREASE SEALS
One (.3) 4
Both (.4) 6

(G) REPACK FRONT WHEEL BEARINGS (BOTH WHEELS)
All models (.3) 6

(G) RENEW BRAKE DRUM
Each (.2) 2

(G) RENEW DISC BRAKE ROTOR
Each (.2) 4

(G) RENEW BRAKE HOSE
Each (.3) 3

(Factory Time) Chilton Time

PARKING BRAKE

(M) Parking Brake, Adjust
1983-87 (.3) 4

(G) Parking Brake Indicator Switch, Renew
1983-87 (.3) 4

(G) Parking Brake Control, Renew
1983-87 (.3) 5
w/Console add 2

(G) Parking Brake Cable, Renew
Includes: Adjust parking brake.
1983-87-one (.4) 7
both (.6) 1.0
w/Console add 2

PARTS — 6 BRAKE SYSTEM 6 — PARTS

	Part No.	Price
(1) Brake Shoe Set (Rear)		
1983-87		
9 x 1¾″ Brk.	▲D9ZZ-2200A	35.50
Brake Lining Kit		
1983-87		
9 x 1¾″ Brk.	▲D9ZZ-2007A	22.25
(2) Rear Wheel Cylinder Assy.		
w/9 x 1¾″ Brk.		
1983-87	▲E0ZZ-2261A	29.75
Repair Kit Wheel Cylinder		
1983-87		
9 x 1¾″ Brk.	▲E0ZZ-2128A	4.50
Brake Hose (Front)		
(exc. SVO)		
1983-84	▲E3DZ-2078A	15.25
1985	▲E5DZ-2078A	12.75
(SVO)		
1984-87-(before 5-84)		
right	▲E25Y-2078A	23.75
left	▲E25Y-2078B	23.75
(from 5-84)		
right	▲E5ZZ-2078B	23.75
left	▲E5ZZ-2078C	23.75
Brake Hose (Rear)		
1983-87-exc.		
Dual exh.	▲E3SZ-2282A	17.25
1984-w/dual		
exh.	▲E4ZZ-2282A	13.25
1985-w/5.0 eng.	▲E5ZZ-2282A	13.25
Master Cylinder Assy.		
(Manual disc brakes)		
1983	▲E2ZZ-2140A	89.00
1984-87	▲E4ZZ-2140A	89.00
(Power Disc Brakes)		
1983-87-exc.		
SVO	▲E4DZ-2140A	93.00
SVO	▲E25Y-2140A	102.50

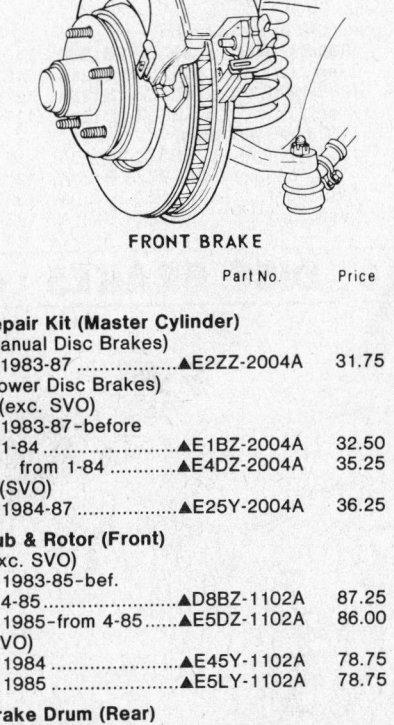

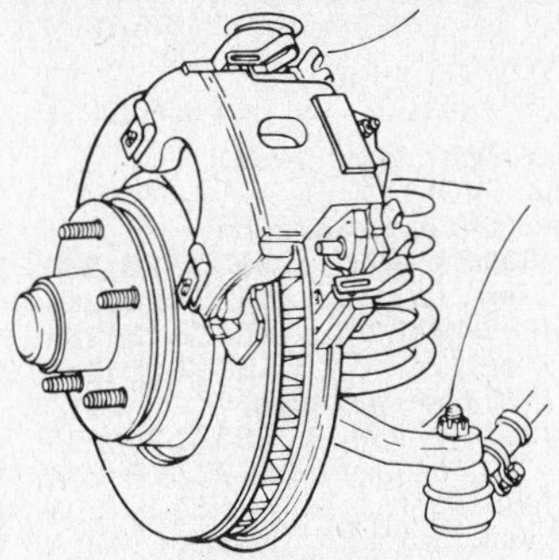

FRONT BRAKE

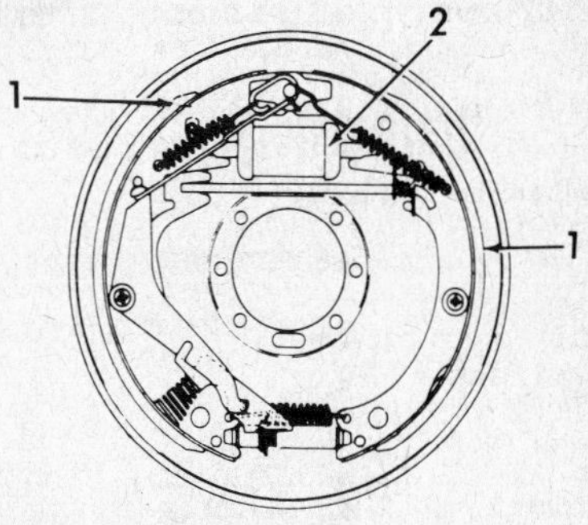

REAR BRAKE

	Part No.	Price
Repair Kit (Master Cylinder)		
(Manual Disc Brakes)		
1983-87	▲E2ZZ-2004A	31.75
(Power Disc Brakes)		
(exc. SVO)		
1983-87-before		
1-84	▲E1BZ-2004A	32.50
from 1-84	▲E4DZ-2004A	35.25
(SVO)		
1984-87	▲E25Y-2004A	36.25
Hub & Rotor (Front)		
(exc. SVO)		
1983-85-bef.		
4-85	▲D8BZ-1102A	87.25
1985-from 4-85	▲E5DZ-1102A	86.00
(SVO)		
1984	▲E45Y-1102A	78.75
1985	▲E5LY-1102A	78.75
Brake Drum (Rear)		
(w/9″ x 1¾″ brakes)		
1983-87-cast		
iron	▲D9ZZ-1126A	60.50

	Part No.	Price
1983-aluminum	▲D9ZZ-1126B	60.50
(w/10″ x 1¾″ brakes)		
1983	▲D9BZ-1126A	76.00
Grease Retainer (Front)		
1983-87-exc.		
SVO	▲C8AZ-1190A	3.00
SVO	▲C6AZ-1190A	7.75

PARKING BRAKE

	Part No.	Price
Parking Brake Lever		
1983-87-exc.		
below	▲E3ZZ-2780A	43.50
w/SVO	▲E4ZZ-2780A	64.00
Parking Brake Cable (Rear)		
(exc. SVO)		
1983-84	▲E3ZZ-2A635A	13.25
1985	▲E5ZZ-2A635A	17.75
(SVO)		
1984-87	▲E4ZZ-2A635A	17.75

PARTS 6 BRAKE SYSTEM 6 PARTS

	Part No.	Price
POWER BRAKE BOOSTER		
Brake Booster Assy. (New)		
1983-wo/turbo	▲E1BZ-2005E	117.00
w/turbo	▲E2ZZ-2005A	204.25
1984-87-3.8, 5.0 & SVO	▲E1BZ-2005B	178.50
w/140 eng.	▲E1BZ-2005E	117.00
Brake Pressure Warning Light Switch		
1983-87	▲D9BZ-2B264A	7.50
Brake Booster Check Valve		
1983-87	▲D0AZ-2365A	5.50
Brake Differential Valve		
1983-87-exc. below	▲E0ZZ-2B257A	48.75
SVO	▲E4ZZ-2B257A	34.00
Turbo 2.3	▲E2ZZ-2B257A	48.75

PARTS 6 DISC BRAKES 6 PARTS

	Part No.	Price
(1) Wheel Bearing (Outer)		
1983-87	▲D0AZ-1216A	8.25
Bearing Cup (Outer)		
1983-87	▲D0AZ-1217B	3.75
(2) Hub & Rotor Assy.		
(exc. SVO)		
1983-85-bef. 4-85	▲D8BZ-1102A	87.25
1985-from 4-85	▲E5DZ-1102A	86.00
(SVO)		
1984	▲E45Y-1102A	78.75
1985-87	▲E5LY-1102A	78.75
(3) Wheel Bearing (Inner)		
1983-87-exc. SVO	▲D0AZ-1201A	9.50
w/SVO	▲B7C-1201A	10.00
(4) Grease Retainer (Wheel Hub)		
1983-87-exc. SVO	▲C8AZ-1190A	3.00
w/SVO	▲C6AZ-1190A	7.75
(5) Spindle Assy. (Front)		
(exc. SVO)		
1983-87-right	▲E1SZ-3105A	137.00
left	▲E1SZ-3106A	137.00
(SVO)		
1984-87-right	▲E25Y-3105A	188.00
left	▲E25Y-3106A	188.00
(6) Caliper Piston (Front)		
(exc. SVO)		
1983-87	▲E3SZ-2196A	12.75
(SVO)		
1984-87	▲E1AZ-2196A	14.25
(7) Brake Pads		
(exc. SVO)		
1983-87-wo/turbo	▲E3ZZ-2001A	27.00
w/turbo	▲E3SZ-2001A	48.75

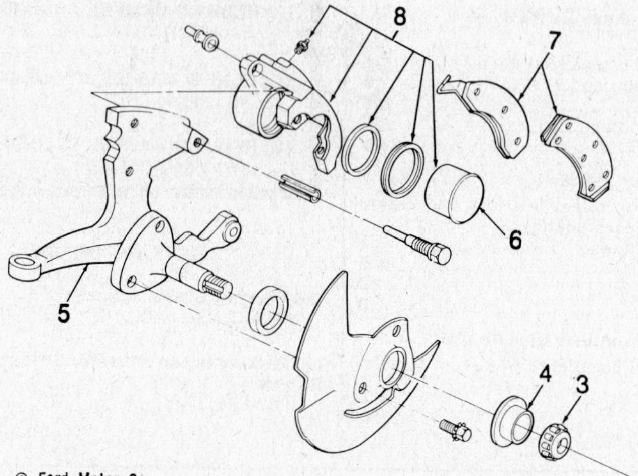

© Ford Motor Co.

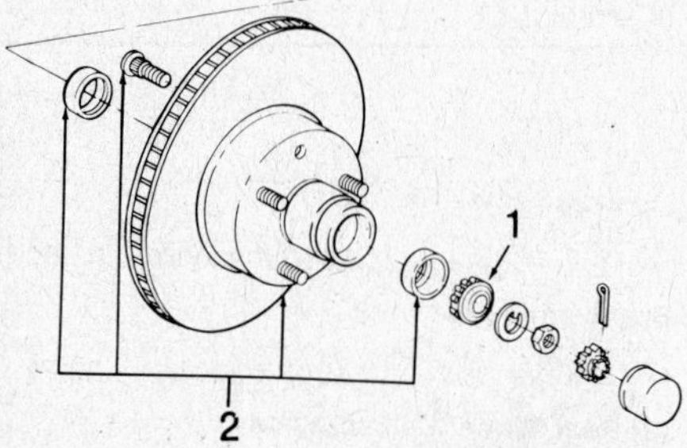

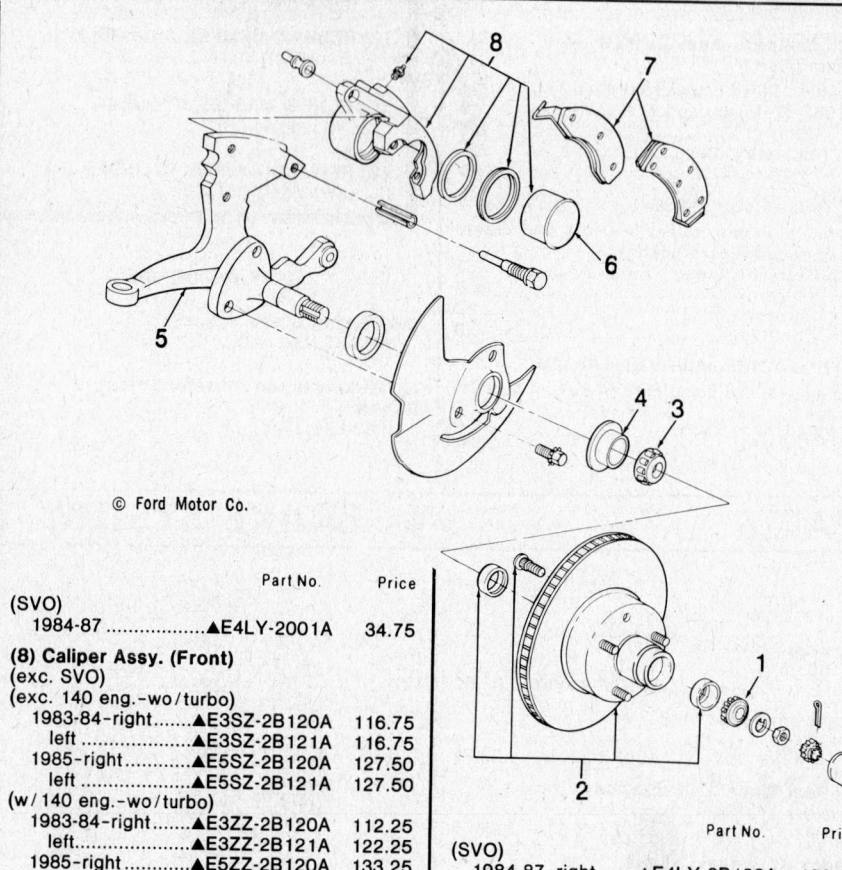

	Part No.	Price
(SVO)		
1984-87	▲E4LY-2001A	34.75
(8) Caliper Assy. (Front)		
(exc. SVO)		
(exc. 140 eng.-wo/turbo)		
1983-84-right	▲E3SZ-2B120A	116.75
left	▲E3SZ-2B121A	116.75
1985-right	▲E5SZ-2B120A	127.50
left	▲E5SZ-2B121A	127.50
(w/140 eng.-wo/turbo)		
1983-84-right	▲E3ZZ-2B120A	112.25
left	▲E3ZZ-2B121A	122.25
1985-right	▲E5ZZ-2B120A	133.25
left	▲E5ZZ-2B121A	127.50
(SVO)		
1984-87-right	▲E4LY-2B120A	120.00
left	▲E4LY-2B121A	120.00

PARTS 6 DISC BRAKES 6 PARTS

	Part No.	Price
REAR DISC BRAKES		
SVO		
(1) Rotor Assy.		
1984-87-right	▲E25Y-2C026A	105.50
left	▲E25Y-2C027A	105.50
(2) Anchor Plate (Caliper)		
1984-87	▲E4LY-2B582A	35.00
(3) Clip (Anti-Rattle)		
1984-87	▲E35Y-2B164A	1.50
(4) Brake Pads		
1984-87	▲E4LY-2200A	42.75
(5) Adapter (Rear Axle)		
1984-87-right	▲E25Y-4A404B	20.75
left	▲E25Y-4A405B	20.75

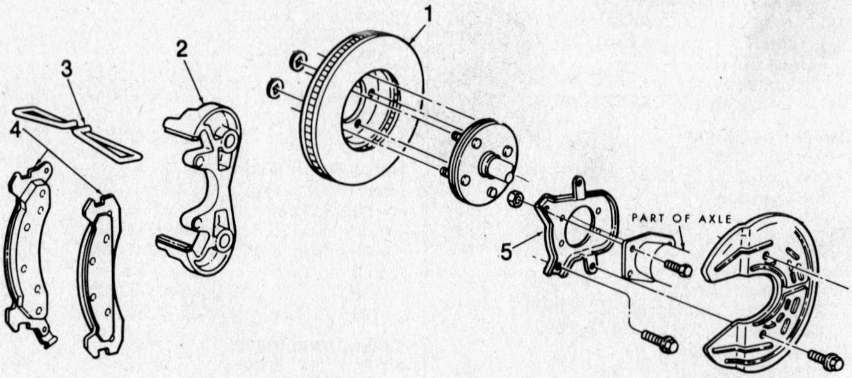

PARTS 6 DISC BRAKES 6 PARTS

	Part No.	Price
(6) Seal Kit		
1984-87	▲D5DZ-2B595A	20.75
(7) Piston & Adjuster Assy.		
1984-87	▲E25Y-2B588A	36.00
(8) Insulator		
1984-87	▲E25C-2B299A	5.00
(9) Locating Pin		
1984-87	▲E25Y-2B296A	4.75
(10) Ball Ramp Kit		
1984-87-right	▲E25Y-2A870A	20.75
left	▲E25Y-2A871A	20.75
(11) Caliper Assy. (Rear)		
1984-87-right	▲E4LY-2552A	219.00
left	▲E4LY-2553A	219.00
Caliper Repair Kit		
1984-87	▲D5DZ-2221A	20.75
(12) Bearing & Retainer Kit		
1984-87	▲E25Y-2B598A	11.00
(13) Actuating Lever (Parking Brake)		
1984-87-right	▲E4LY-2B596A	4.25
left	▲E4LY-2B597A	4.25

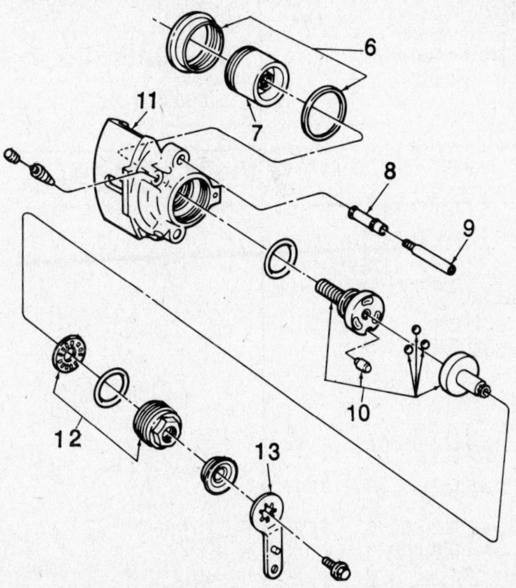

LABOR 7 COOLING SYSTEM 7 LABOR

	(Factory Time)	Chilton Time
(M) Winterize Cooling System		
Includes: Run engine to check for leaks, tighten all hose connections. Test radiator and pressure cap, drain radiator and engine block. Add anti-freeze and refill system.		
All models		.5
(M) Thermostat, Renew		
1983-87-Four	(.5)	.7
Six	(.4)	.6
V-6	(.5)	.7
V-8	(.6)	.8
w/A.C. add		.2
(M) Radiator Assembly, R&R or Renew		
Includes: Drain and refill cooling system.		
1983-87	(.6)	1.0
w/EFI Turbo add	(.1)	.1
w/A.C. add	(.1)	.1
ADD THESE OPERATIONS TO RADIATOR R&R		
(G) Boil & Repair		1.5
(G) Rod Clean		1.9
(G) Repair Core		1.3
(G) Renew Tank		1.6
(G) Renew Trans. Oil Cooler		1.9
(G) Recore Radiator		1.7
(M) Radiator Hoses, Renew		
1983-87-upper	(.3)	.4
lower	(.4)	.5
both	(.5)	.8
(M) Radiator By-Pass Hose, Renew		
V-8-1983-87	(.3)	.5
(G) Water Pump, Renew		
Four-1983-87	(.8)	1.2
V-6-1983-87	(1.1)	1.7
V-8-1983-87	(.8)	1.6
w/A.C. add	(.1)	.2
(M) Drive Belts, Adjust		
All models-one	(.2)	.3
each adtnl	(.1)	.1
(G) Engine Cooling Fan Relay, Renew		
1983-87	(.3)	.4

COOLING SYSTEM TUNE-UP

An Annual Cooling System Tune-Up Suggestion List should include (with some exceptions):

1. A visual check of the cooling system for indications of leaks or excessive oil content.
2. Pressure check the cooling system for internal and external leaks with filler cap and neck adapter and tester.
3. Check crankcase and automatic transmission oil for water content.
4. Test coolant thermostat with radiator thermometer.
5. Check temperature gauge for accuracy.
6. Drain system and flush till clean.
7. Clean foreign matter from radiator fins.
8. Test radiator pressure cap with cap tester.
9. Check fan blades and pulleys for alignment and damage.
10. Internal and external inspection of all hoses for cracks and deterioration.
11. Check core plugs (where possible) for seepage.
12. Refill system with correct coolant and check for air locks.
13. Check condition and tension of drive belts with tension gauge.

All models 1.5

	(Factory Time)	Chilton Time
(G) Electric Cooling Fan Motor, Renew		
1983-87	(.3)	.5
(M) Clutch Fan, Renew		
1983-87	(.4)	.6
(M) Serpentine Belt, Renew		
1983-87		
V-6 & V-8	(.3)	.5
(G) Temperature Gauge (Engine Unit), Renew		
1983-87	(.3)	.4
(G) Temperature Gauge (Dash Unit), Renew		
1983-87	(.4)	.7
(G) Water Jacket Expansion Plugs, Renew (Side of Block)		
each	(.3)	*.5

*Add time to gain accessibility.

	(Factory Time)	Chilton Time
(G) Heater Hoses, Renew		
1983-87-each	(.3)	.5
(G) Heater Core, R&R or Renew		
1983-87	(2.4)	6.0
Add time to recharge A.C. system, if required.		
ADD THESE OPERATIONS TO HEATER CORE R&R		
(G) Boil & Repair		1.2
(G) Repair Core		.9
(G) Recore		1.2
(G) Heater Control Assembly, Renew		
1983-87	(.4)	.7
(G) Heater Blower Motor, Renew		
1983-87	(.6)	1.1

LABOR 7 COOLING SYSTEM 7 LABOR

	(Factory Time)	Chilton Time
(G) Heater Blower Motor Resistor, Renew		
1983-87	(.3)	.5
(G) Heater Blower Motor Switch, Renew		
1983-87	(.3)	.6
(G) Temperature Control Cable, Renew		
1983-87	(.3)	.6

PARTS 7 COOLING SYSTEM 7 PARTS

	Part No.	Price
(1) Radiator Assy.		
Order by year and model.		
(2) Radiator Hoses		
Order by year and model.		
(3) Fan Blade		
140 engine		
(wo/fuel option)		
1983-87	▲D4ZZ-8600A	41.75
(w/fuel option)		
1983-87	▲E3ZZ-8600B	31.25
230 engine		
1983	▲E3ZZ-8600B	31.25
1984-87	▲E4ZZ-8600A	28.75
302 eng.		
1983-87-wo/H.O.	▲E1ZZ-8600B	54.75
1985-87-w/H.O.	▲E5ZZ-8600A	27.75
(4) Spacer (Fan)		
140 engine		
1983-87-wo/A.C.	▲C9TZ-8546A	6.00
w/A.C.	▲E3ZZ-8546B	5.25
230 engine		
1983-87	▲E3ZZ-8546A	5.75
(5) Pulley		
140 engine		
1983-84-wo/A.C.	▲E3ZZ-8509B	34.75
w/A.C.	▲E3ZZ-8509C	10.00
1985-87-wo/P.S.	▲E5ZZ-8509B	44.00
w/P.S.	▲E5ZZ-8509C	44.00
230 engine		
1983-87	▲E3DZ-8509A	28.50
302 engine		
1983-84	▲E1ZZ-8509A	28.50
1985-87-w/A.T.	▲E1ZZ-8509A	28.50
1985-w/M.T.	▲E5ZZ-8509A	33.50
1986-87-w/M.T.	▲D9ZZ-8509A	36.50
(6) Fan Belt		
Order by year and model.		

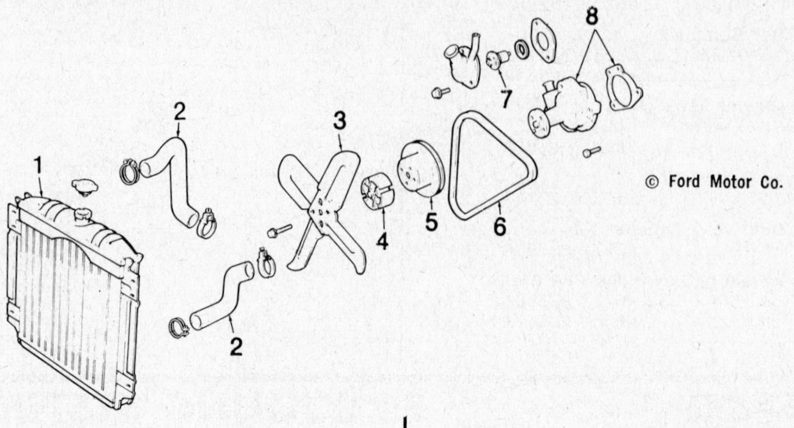

	Part No.	Price
(7) Thermostat		
140 engine		
1983-87	▲E3FZ-8575A	9.75
230 engine		
1983-87	▲E2DZ-8575A	6.00
302 engine		
1983-87	▲D9AZ-8575A	6.00
(8) Water Pump Assy. (New)		
140 engine		
1983-87	▲E4BZ-8501A	88.25
230 engine		
1983-87	▲E2DZ-8501A	65.75
302 engine		
1983	▲E2ZZ-8501A	59.25
1984-85	▲E4ZZ-8501A	59.00
1986-87	▲E6AZ-8501A	59.00

	Part No.	Price
Temperature Sending Unit (Engine)		
1983-87	▲D0WY-10884A	5.25
1985-87-w/T.C.	▲D0ZZ-10884A	5.00
Heater Core		
1983-87-wo/A.C.	▲E2FZ-18476A	59.50
w/A.C.	▲D9BZ-18476A	63.50
Blower Motor		
(wo/A.C.)		
1983-84	▲E1FZ-18527A	71.50
1985-87	▲E43Z-18527A	62.25
(w/A.C.)		
1983-87	▲E35Y-19805A	91.75
Blower Motor Resistor		
1983	▲E1FZ-18591A	8.50
1984-87	▲E4ZZ-18591A	8.50
Switch Assy. (Heater)		
1983-87	▲E2FZ-18578A	4.50

LABOR 8 EXHAUST SYSTEM 8 LABOR

	(Factory Time)	Chilton Time
(G) Muffler, Renew		
1983-84-Four	(.4)	.8
w/EFI Turbo	(.6)	.9
Six	(.4)	.8
V-6		
2.8 L eng	(.7)	1.2
3.8 L eng	(.5)	.9
V-8	(.5)	.9
1985-87	(.6)	1.0
Welded type add		.3
(G) Catalytic Converter, Renew		
1983-84-Four	(.6)	1.0
Six	(1.7)	2.4
V-6 & V-8-one	(.8)	1.2
both	(1.2)	1.9
center	(.5)	.8
1985-87		
Four		
wo/Turbo	(.7)	1.1
w/Turbo	(.6)	1.0
V-6 & V-8		
Y-Pipe	(.8)	1.1
underbody	(.5)	.8
both	(1.2)	1.8
(G) Inlet Exhaust Pipe, Renew		
Includes: Replace exhaust control valve if required.		
1983-87	(.5)	.9
w/EFI Turbo	(.6)	1.0
(G) Exhaust Control Valve Assy., Renew		
1983-87	(.4)	.7
(G) Exhaust Manifold, Renew		
1983-87-Four	(1.0)	1.5
w/EFI Turbo	(1.6)	2.2
Six	(1.2)	1.9
w/Lite off cat	(3.5)	4.5
V-6-2.8 L eng		
right	(1.4)	1.9
left	(1.2)	1.7
3.8 L eng		
right	(1.4)	2.1
left	(.8)	1.3
both	(1.9)	3.1
V-8-255 eng-right	(.6)	1.1
left	(.8)	1.3
both	(1.1)	2.0
302 eng-right	(.7)	1.3
left	(.6)	1.1
both	(1.0)	1.8
302 CFI eng		
right	(1.3)	1.8
left	(.8)	1.1
both	(1.9)	2.7
302 HO eng		
right	(1.3)	1.8
left	(.8)	1.1
both	(1.8)	2.7
w/A.C. add	(.2)	.2

COMBINATIONS

	(Factory Time)	Chilton Time
(G) Muffler, Exhaust and Tail Pipe, Renew		
1983-87		1.6

PARTS 8 EXHAUST SYSTEM 8 PARTS

	Part No.	Price
Muffler		
140 engine		
1983-2		
Converters	▲E3ZZ-5230C	135.75
E.F.I. turbo	▲E3ZZ-5230A	140.25
1 Converter	▲E3ZZ-5230D	136.25
1984-exc. below	▲E4ZZ-5230B	97.00
E.F.I. turbo	▲E4ZZ-5230F	140.25
SVO	▲E4ZZ-5230D	139.25
Canada	▲E4ZZ-5230C	N.L.
1985-exc. SVO	▲E5ZZ-5230F	97.00
SVO	▲E5ZZ-5230A	145.25
1986-87	▲E6ZZ-5230D	96.00
230 engine		
1983	▲E3ZZ-5230B	135.75
1984	▲E4ZZ-5230E	134.25
1985	▲E5ZZ-5230B	132.25
1986-87	▲E6ZZ-5230F	132.25
302 engine		
(single exh.)		
1983	▲E3ZZ-5230H	140.25
1984-w/A.T.	▲E4ZZ-5230A	140.50
w/M.T.	▲E3ZZ-5230H	140.25
1985	▲E5ZZ-5230C	138.50
(dual exh.)		
(w/A.T.)		
1985-right	▲E5ZZ-5230E	87.00
left	▲E4ZZ-5230H	96.00
(w/M.T.)		
1984-85-right	▲E4ZZ-5230G	96.00
left	▲E4ZZ-5230H	96.00
1986-87-R.H.	▲E6ZZ-5230A	87.00
left	▲E6ZZ-5230C	96.00
Catalytic Converter		
140 engine		
1983-exc. below	▲E3ZZ-5E212C	191.25
Calif.	▲E3DZ-5E212A	382.25
Canada	▲E3DZ-5E212C	N.L.
1984-exc. below	▲E3DZ-5E212A	382.25
Canada	▲E3DZ-5E212C	N.L.
SVO	▲E3ZZ-5E212K	401.50
1985-87-exc.		
SVO	▲E3DZ-5E212A	382.25
SVO	▲E5ZZ-5E212A	401.50
230 engine		
1983-Front	▲E2DZ-5F250C	200.75
1983-Rear	▲E3DZ-5E212B	382.25
1984-Front	▲E4ZZ-5F250A	415.25
1985-Front	▲E5ZZ-5F250A	401.50
1984-87-Rear	▲E4DZ-5E212C	207.75

Note: For front converter on 1986-87 models with V-6 230 eng. stamped I.D. on old converter must be used.

	Part No.	Price
302 engine		
(single exh rear conv.)		
1983-85-w/A.T.	▲E4ZZ-5E212A	401.50
w/M.T.	▲E3ZZ-5E212L	401.50
(dual exh rear conv.)		
1985-w/M.T.	▲E3ZZ-5E212L	401.50
1983-84-front		
conv.	▲E3ZZ-5F250A	200.75

LABOR 9 FRONT SUSPENSION 9 LABOR

Note: On all front suspension operations alignment charges must be added if performed. Time given does not include alignment.

(Factory Time)	Chilton Time
(M) Wheel, Renew	
one (.5)	.5
(G) Wheels, Rotate (All)	
All models (.5)	.5
(G) Wheels, Balance	
one	.3
each adtnl	.2
(G) Check Alignment of Front End	
All models (.4)	.5
Note: Deduct if alignment is performed.	
(G) Toe-In, Adjust	
All models (.4)	.6
(G) Align Front End	
Includes: Adjust front wheel bearings.	
All models (1.0)	1.5
w/A.C. interference add	.5
(G) Front Wheel Bearings, Clean and Repack (Both Wheels)	
All models	1.3
(G) Front Wheel Grease Seals, Renew	
Includes: Repack bearings.	
1983-87-one wheel (.6)	.7
both wheels (.9)	1.1
(G) Front Wheel Bearings and Cups, Renew	
1983-87-one wheel (.7)	.9
both wheels (1.2)	1.5
(G) Front Strut Shock Absorbers, Renew	
1983-87-one (.7)	1.1
both (1.1)	1.9
(G) Front Spindle Assembly, Renew (One)	
Add alignment charges.	
1983-87 (.8)	1.2
(G) Lower Control Arm Assy., Renew (One)	
Add alignment charges.	
1983-87 (1.1)	1.5
(G) Ball Joints, Renew	
Add alignment charges.	
1983-87	
one side	1.2
both sides	1.9
(G) Front Spring, Renew	
1983-87-one (1.0)	1.5
both (1.7)	2.7
(G) Front Stabilizer Bar, Renew	
1983-87 (.6)	.9
(G) Control Arm Bumpers, Renew	
1983-87-one (.3)	.5
both (.4)	.6

PARTS 9 FRONT SUSPENSION 9 PARTS

	Part No.	Price
(1) Plate (Camber Adjusting)		
1983-85	▲D8BZ-3B391A	8.25
1986-87	▲E3DZ-3B391A	2.00
(2) Bracket Assy. (Upper Mounting)		
(exc. SVO)		
1983-87-exc.		
below	▲E2DZ-18A161A	41.25
w/G.T.	▲E4ZZ-18A161A	41.25
(SVO)		
1984-87	▲D8BZ-18A161B	14.50
(3) Shock Absorber (Front)		
(exc. SVO)		
1983-87-exc.		
below	▲E3ZZ-18124A	91.50
w/GT	▲E5ZZ-18124B	91.50
(SVO)		
1985-87	▲E5ZZ-18124A	91.50
(4) Spindle Assy.		
(exc. SVO)		
1983-87-right	▲E1SZ-3105A	137.00
left	▲E1SZ-3106A	137.00
(SVO)		
1984-87-right	▲E25Y-3105A	188.00
left	▲E25Y-3106A	188.00

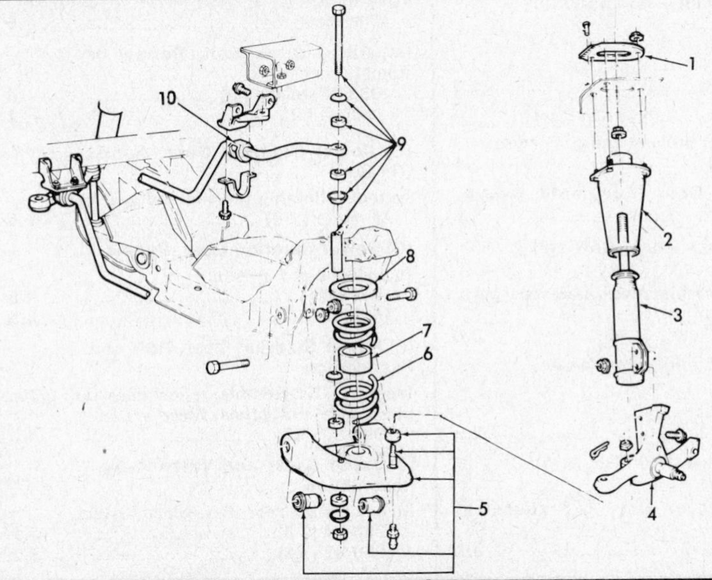

PARTS 9 FRONT SUSPENSION 9 PARTS

	Part No.	Price
(5) Lower Control Arm Assy.		
(exc. SVO)		
(wo/handling susp.)		
1983-87-right	▲E3ZZ-3078A	99.25
left	▲E3ZZ-3079A	99.25
(w/handling susp.)		
1983-right	▲E3ZZ-3078B	99.25
left	▲E3ZZ-3079B	99.25
1984-87-right	▲E3SZ-3078C	99.25
left	▲E3SZ-3079C	99.25
(SVO)		
1984-87-right	▲E4ZZ-3078A	266.25
left	▲E4ZZ-3079A	266.25
(6) Coil Spring		
Order by year and model.		
(8) Insulator (Upper)		
1983-87	▲E1SZ-5415A	9.00
(9) Stabilizer Repair Kit		
1983	▲E2AZ-5A486C	20.75
1984-87	▲E4ZZ-5A486A	20.75
(10) Insulator (Stabilizer)		
Order by year and model.		

LABOR 10 STEERING LINKAGE 10 LABOR

	(Factory Time)	Chilton Time
(G) Tie Rod Ends, Renew		
Includes Reset toe-in.		
1983-87-one	(.8)	1.2
each adtnl	(.2)	.2

PARTS 10 STEERING LINKAGE 10 PARTS

	Part No.	Price
Tie Rod Ends (Outer)		
1983-87-exc.		
SVO	▲E2DZ-3A130A	36.00
w/SVO	▲E2SZ-3A130A	36.25
Tie Rod Kit		
1983-87	▲E2SZ-3280A	66.25
Sector Shaft		
(Man. steering)		
1983-87	▲D8BZ-3575B	62.00
(Power steering)		
1983-84-exc.		
H.D. susp.	▲D8BZ-3575A	36.50
w/H.D. susp.	▲E3SZ-3575A	31.75
1985-87-exc.		
H.D. susp.	▲E5DZ-3575A	36.50
w/H.D. susp.	▲E5DZ-3575B	36.50

LABOR 11 STEERING GEAR 11 LABOR

	(Factory Time)	Chilton Time
STANDARD STEERING		
(G) Horn Button or Ring, Renew		
1983-87	(.4)	.6
(G) Steering Wheel, Renew		
1983-87	(.3)	.5
(G) Upper Mast Jacket Bearing, Renew		
1983-87-std column	(.4)	.9
tilt column	(.6)	1.1
(G) Steering Column Lock Actuator Parts, Renew		
1983-87		
fixed colm	(1.1)	1.5
tilt colm	(1.7)	2.3
(G) Steering Gear, Adjust (On Car)		
Includes: Bearing preload and gear mesh.		
All models	(.3)	.5
(G) Steering Gear Assembly, Renew		
1983	(1.1)	1.5
(P) Steering Gear Assy., R&R and Recondition		
Includes: Disassemble, renew necessary parts, reassemble and adjust.		
1983	(2.2)	3.0
(G) Input Shaft and Valve Assy., Recondition		
Includes: R&R gear assy.		
1983	(1.7)	2.3
(G) Tie Rod Ends and Ball Joint Sockets, Renew		
Includes: R&R gear assy. Add alignment charges.		
1983	(1.6)	2.2
POWER STEERING		
(G) Trouble Shoot Power Steering		
Includes: Test pump and system pressure. Check pounds pull on steering wheel and check for leaks.		
All models		.5
(M) Check and Fill Reservoir		
All models		.2
(G) Pump Pressure Check & Flow Test		
All models		.5
(M) Pump Drive Belt, Renew or Adjust		
1983-87-renew	(.3)	.4
adjust	(.2)	.2
(G) Power Steering Gear, Adjust (On Car)		
Includes: Bearing preload and gear mesh.		
All models	(.3)	.5
(G) Power Steering Gear, Renew		
Includes: Bleed system.		
1983-84	(1.7)	2.5
1985-87	(2.2)	2.5
(P) Power Steering Gear, R&R and Recondition		
Includes: Disassemble, renew necessary parts, reassemble and adjust. Bleed system.		
1983-87	(3.2)	4.5
(G) Input Shaft and Valve Assy., Recondition		
Includes: R&R gear assy. Bleed system.		
1983-84	(2.3)	3.2
1985-87	(1.8)	3.2
(G) Tie Rod Ends and Ball Joint Sockets, Renew		
Includes: R&R gear assy. Renew tie rod ends and bellows. Add alignment charges.		
1983-84	(1.9)	2.6
1985-87	(1.4)	2.6
(G) Power Steering Oil Pump, Renew		
Includes: Bleed system.		
1983-87-Four	(.9)	1.3
w/Turbo add		.1
Six	(.9)	1.3
V-6	(1.1)	1.5
V-8	(1.0)	1.4
(G) Power Steering Oil Pump, R&R and Recondition		
Includes: Bleed system.		
1983-87-Four	(1.3)	1.8
w/Turbo add		.1
Six	(1.3)	1.8
V-6	(1.5)	2.1
V-8	(1.4)	1.9
(G) Power Steering Pump Shaft Seal, Renew		
Includes: Bleed system.		
1983-87		
Four	(1.0)	1.4
w/Turbo add		.1
Six	(1.0)	1.4
V-6	(1.2)	1.6
V-8	(1.1)	1.5
(M) Power Steering Hoses, Renew		
1983-87-pressure	(.6)	.8
return	(.5)	.7
cooling	(.4)	.5

PARTS 11 STEERING GEAR - (STANDARD) 11 PARTS

	Part No.	Price
(1) Steering Gear Assy.		
1983-87	▲E2DZ-3504B	385.50
(2) Insulator		
1983-87	▲E0SZ-3C716A	7.50
(3) Oil Seal (Sector Shaft)		
1983-87	▲D1FZ-3738A	1.25
(4) Spacer (Pinion Bearing)		
1983-87	▲D4FZ-3K599A	2.75
(5) Cover (Housing End)		
1983-87	▲D8BZ-3568C	8.50
(6) Cup (w/worm Bearing)		
1983-87	▲D1FZ-3552A	13.75
(7) Shaft Assy. (Upper)		
(wo/tilt wheel)		
1983-85	▲E3SZ-3524B	47.25
1986-87	▲E6SZ-3524B	47.25
(w/tilt wheel)		
1983-84	▲E3SZ-3524A	193.50
1985	▲E5DZ-3524A	200.00
1986-87	▲E6SZ-3524A	193.50
(8) Bearing (Rack Adjustment)		
1983-87	▲D8BZ-3F515B	7.00
(9) Gasket & Shim Kit		
1983-87	▲D3FZ-3F518A	1.00
(10) Housing Cover (Sector Shaft)		
1983-87	▲D3FZ-3580A	8.75
(11) Clamp		
1983-87	▲385951-S	2.00
(12) Dust Seal		
1983-87	▲D9BZ-3332B	5.50
(13) Clamp		
1983-87	▲385950-S	2.50

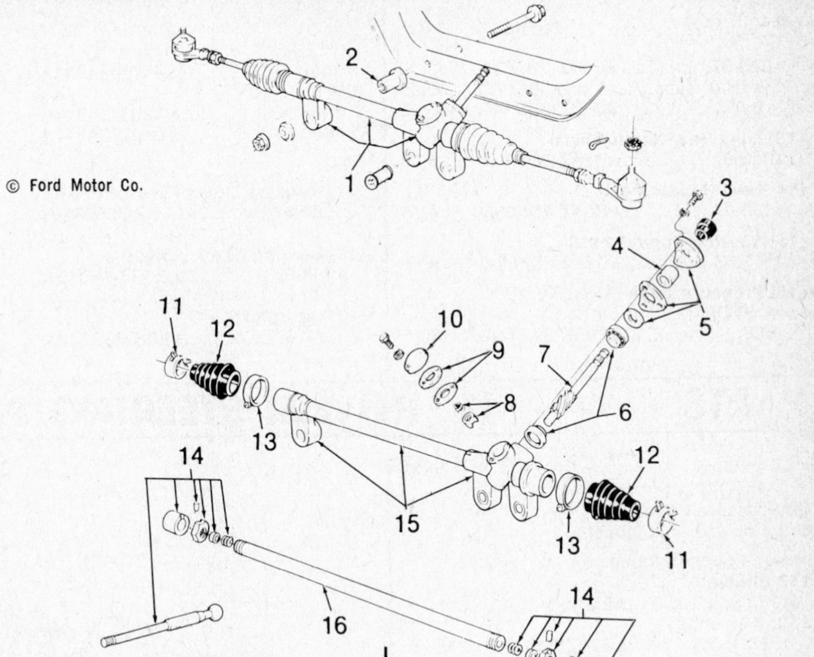

	Part No.	Price
(14) Connecting Rod Assy.		
1983-87	▲E2SZ-3280A	66.25
(15) Housing Assy. (Steering Gear)		
1983-87	▲D8BZ-3548C	128.50
(16) Sector Shaft		
1983-87	▲D8BZ-3575B	62.00
(17) Tie Rod End		
1983-87	▲E2DZ-3A130A	36.00

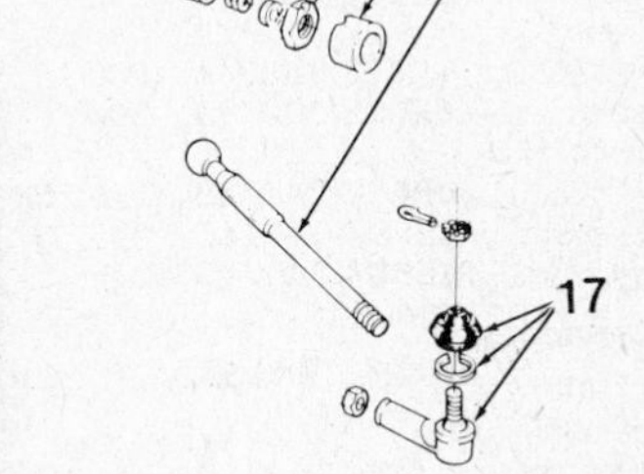

PARTS 11 POWER STEERING GEAR 11 PARTS

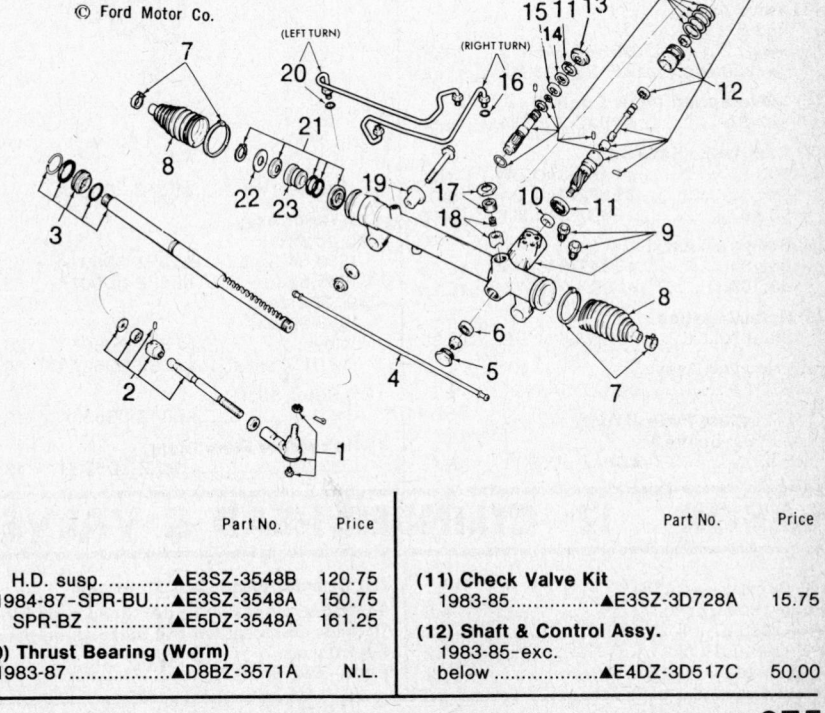

	Part No.	Price
(1) Tie Rod End		
1983-87-exc.		
SVO	▲E2DZ-3A130A	36.00
SVO	▲E2SZ-3A130A	36.25
(2) Connecting Rod Assy.		
1983-87	▲E2SZ-3280A	66.25
(3) Sector Shaft Assy.		
1983-84-exc.		
H.D. susp.	▲D8BZ-3575A	36.50
w/H.D. susp.	▲E3SZ-3575A	31.75
1985-87-exc.		
H.D. susp.	▲E5DZ-3575A	36.50
w/H.D. susp.	▲E5DZ-3575B	36.50
(4) Gear Rack Tube		
1983-87	▲D8BZ-3K762A	2.25
(5) Cover (Housing End)		
1983-87	▲D8BZ-3568B	5.00
(6) Cup (Worm Bearing)		
1983-87	▲D8BZ-3552A	13.25
(7) Clamps (Gear Boot)		
1983-87	▲D8BZ-3C650B	.75
(8) Boot (Dust Seal)		
1983	▲D9BZ-3332A	5.50
1984-85	▲E3SZ-3K661A	6.25
1986-87	▲E69Z-3332A	10.25
(9) Housing Assy.		
1983-exc. H.D.		
susp.	▲E3SZ-3548A	150.75

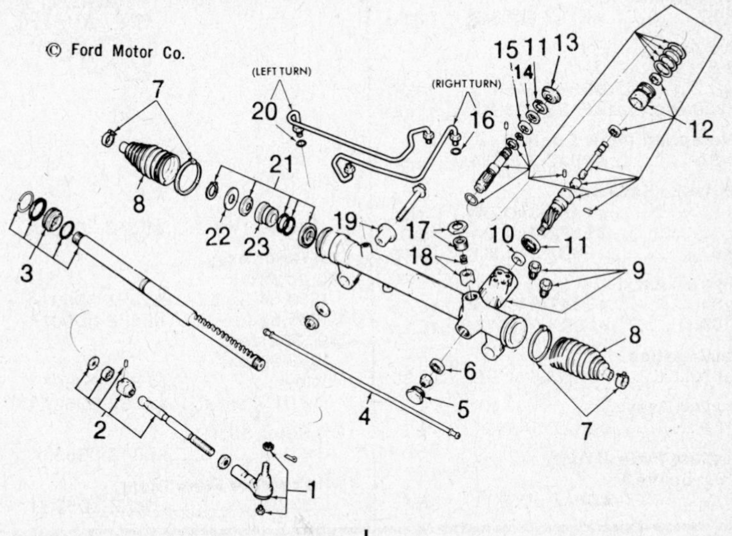

	Part No.	Price
H.D. susp.	▲E3SZ-3548B	120.75
1984-87-SPR-BU	▲E3SZ-3548A	150.75
SPR-BZ	▲E5DZ-3548A	161.25
(10) Thrust Bearing (Worm)		
1983-87	▲D8BZ-3571A	N.L.

	Part No.	Price
(11) Check Valve Kit		
1983-85	▲E3SZ-3D728A	15.75
(12) Shaft & Control Assy.		
1983-85-exc.		
below	▲E4DZ-3D517C	50.00

PARTS 11 POWER STEERING GEAR 11 PARTS

	Part No.	Price
1986-87	▲E5DZ-3D517A	50.00
w/H.D. susp.	▲E4SZ-3D517C	50.00
SVO	▲E5ZZ-3D517A	50.00
(13) Dust Seal (Input Shaft)		
1983-87	▲D5AZ-3D527A	5.00
(14) Seal (Input Shaft)		
1983-87	▲D6AZ-3D526A	4.75
(15) Bearing (Input Shaft)		
1983-87	▲D8AZ-3D525A	8.75
(16) Pressure Tube (Right Turn)		
(exc. SVO)		
1983	▲D9BZ-3A717A	15.25
1984-87	▲E4DZ-3A717A	14.25
(SVO)		
1984	▲D8BZ-3A714B	16.00
1985-87	▲E4DZ-3A717A	14.25
(17) Housing Cover (Sector Shaft)		
1983-87	▲E0BZ-3580AMR	7.00
(18) Bearing (Rack Adjust)		
1983-87	▲E0SZ-3F515A	8.25
(19) Insulator		
1983-87	▲E0SZ-3C716A	7.50
(20) Pressure Tube (Left Turn)		
(exc. SVO)		
1983	▲D9BZ-3A714A	18.00
1984-87	▲E4DZ-3A714A	14.25
(SVO)		
1984	▲D8BZ-3A717B	19.75
1985-87	▲E4DZ-3A714A	14.25
(21) Seal Kit (Rack Shaft)		
1983-87	▲E3SZ-3E501A	12.00
(22) Cover (Housing End)		
1983-87	▲D8BZ-3568B	5.00
(23) Bushing (Sector Shaft)		
1983-87	▲D9BZ-3576A	4.25

PARTS 11 POWER STEERING PUMP 11 PARTS

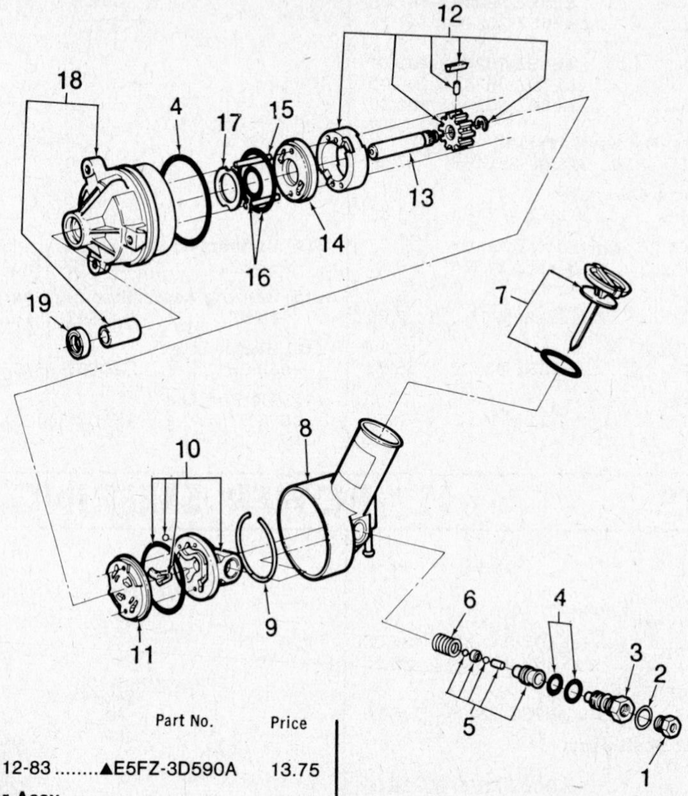

	Part No.	Price
Oil Pressure Hose		
Order by year and model.		
Power Steering Pump		
140 engine		
1983-85	▲E5DZ-3A674A	215.75
230, 302 engs.		
1983	▲E2DZ-3A674B	215.75
1984-85-exc.		
H.D. susp.	▲E5ZZ-3A674A	200.75
H.D. susp.	▲E5SZ-3A674A	200.75
1986-87-wo/H.D.		
susp.	▲E6SZ-3A674B	215.75
w/H.D. susp.	▲E6SZ-3A674C	215.75
V-8 Eng.	▲E6SZ-3A674C	215.75
(1) Tube Connector		
1983-87	▲D8BZ-3R608A	3.25
(2) Washer		
1983-87	▲87004-S100	.50
(3) Outlet Fitting		
1983-84	▲E1TZ-3D654B	18.50
1985-87	▲E5DZ-3D654A	18.50
(4) Seal & Gasket Kit		
1983-87	▲E1AZ-3D684A	3.00
(5) Valve Assy.		
1983-87-exc.		
below	▲D8BZ-3A561A	11.00
w/230 eng.	▲E1SZ-3A561A	11.00
(6) Valve Spring (Flow Control)		
1983-87	▲D8AZ-3D586A	1.50
(7) Cap Assy. (Reservoir)		
1983-84	▲E1AZ-3A006B	N.L.
1985	▲E5FZ-3A006A	5.00
1986-87	▲E6DZ-3A006A	5.00
(8) Reservoir Assy.		
1983-84	▲E1AZ-3A697A	15.25
1985-87	▲E5DZ-3A697A	16.25
(9) Retaining Ring		
1983-87	▲387573-S	1.50
(10) Housing Assy.		
1983-87	▲E1AZ-3A643A	42.25
(11) Pressure Plate (Front)		
1983-84-before		
12-83	▲D8AZ-3D590A	N.L.
from 12-83	▲E5FZ-3D590A	13.75
(12) Rotor Assy.		
140 engine		
1983-84	▲E3FZ-3D607A	52.50
1985-87	▲E5FZ-3D607A	56.25
230, 302 engs.		
1983-87-exc.		
below	▲E53Z-3D607A	36.25
w/H.D. susp.	▲E5SZ-3D607A	38.75
(13) Rotor Shaft		
1983-87	▲D8AZ-3B559A	18.00
(14) Pressure Plate (Rear)		
1983-87	▲D8AZ-3D590B	13.75
(15) Pin		
1983-87	▲387579-S	1.00
(16) Seal & Gasket Kit		
1983-87	▲E1AZ-3B584A	8.75
(17) Spring (Pressure Plate)		
1983-87	▲D8AZ-3D596A	2.50
(18) Plate & Bushing		
1983-87	▲E1AZ-3D643A	42.25
(19) Oil Seal (Rotor Shaft)		
1983-87	▲D9AZ-3B592A	9.25

LABOR 12 CYLINDER HEAD & VALVE SYSTEM 12 LABOR

(G) Compression Test

Four–1983-87 (.3)	.6
V-6–1983-87 (.4)	.9
V-8–1983-87 (.5)	.9
w/A.C. add	.2

(G) Cylinder Head Gasket, Renew

Includes: Check cylinder head and block flatness. Clean carbon and make all necessary adjustments.

Four–1983-87 (3.7)	5.1
w/Turbocharger add	1.3
1983-87	
EFI Turbo (4.3)	6.0
w/A.C. add (.1)	.1
V-6–1983-87-one (4.7)	6.6

LABOR 12 CYLINDER HEAD & VALVE SYSTEM 12 LABOR

(Factory Time)	Chilton Time
both (6.0)	8.4
V-8–1983-87-one (3.6)	4.9
both (5.0)	6.8
w/A.C. add	.3
w/P.S. add	.2

(G) Cylinder Head, Renew

Includes: Transfer all components, clean carbon. Reface valves, check valve spring tension, assembled height and valve head runout.

Four–1983-87 (5.8)	7.5
w/Turbocharger add	1.3
1983-87	
EFI Turbo (5.2)	7.2
w/A.C. add (.1)	.1
V-6–1983-87-one (5.7)	8.0
both (8.0)	11.2
V-81983-87-one (4.8)	6.5
both (7.5)	9.4
w/A.C. add	.3
w/P.S. add	.2

(P) Clean Carbon and Grind Valves

Includes: R&R cylinder heads, check valve spring tension, valve seat and head runout, stem to guide clearance and spring assembled height. Minor tune up.

Four–1983-87 (6.3)	8.0
w/Turbocharger add	1.3
1983-87	
EFI Turbo (6.9)	9.6
w/A.C. add (.1)	.1
V-6–1983-87 (8.9)	12.4
V-8–1983-87 (8.5)	11.0
w/A.C. add	.3
w/P.S. add	.2

(G) Rocker Arm Cover or Gasket, Renew

Four–1983-87 (.7)	1.0
w/Turbocharger add (.2)	.2
1983-87	
EFI Turbo (1.0)	1.4
V-6–1983-87-one (.6)	1.0
both (1.0)	1.6
V-8–1983-87	
255 eng-one (.6)	.8
both (.9)	1.2
302 eng-one (.8)	1.1
both (1.3)	1.8

COMBINATIONS

Add to Valve Job

See Machine Shop Operations

(G) DRAIN, EVACUATE & RECHARGE AIR CONDITIONING SYSTEM

All models (.7)	1.2

(G) ROCKER ARMS & SHAFT ASSY., DISASSEMBLE AND CLEAN OR OVERHAUL

V-6-one (.5)	.8
both (1.0)	1.4

(G) HYDRAULIC VALVE LIFTERS, DISASSEMBLE AND CLEAN

Each	.2

(G) DISTRIBUTOR, RECONDITION

All models (.7)	1.0

(G) CARBURETOR, RECONDITION

1983-87	
Four (1.1)	1.6
Six-Carter (1.3)	1.8
Holly (1.7)	2.2
V-6 (1.0)	1.5
V-8-2 V (1.0)	1.5
2700-VV (1.8)	2.4
7200-VV (1.9)	2.5
4180-4V (1.9)	2.5

(P) VALVE GUIDES, REAM OVERSIZE

Each (.1)	.1

(G) Valve Push Rod, Renew

(Factory Time)	Chilton Time
V-6–1983-87-one (.7)	1.1
all-one side (.8)	1.2
all-both sides (1.3)	1.9
V-8–1983-87-one	
255 eng-one (.7)	.9
all-one side (.8)	1.0
all-both sides (1.2)	1.7
302 eng-one (1.1)	1.5
all-one side (1.2)	1.7
all-both sides (1.8)	2.4

(G) Rocker Arm Stud, Renew

V-8–1983-87-one (1.0)	1.4
each adtnl (.2)	.2

(G) Rocker Arm, Renew

Four–1983-87-one (1.1)	1.6
all (1.4)	2.0
V-6–1983-87-one (.7)	1.1
all-one side (.8)	1.4
all-both sides (1.3)	2.0
V-8–1983-87	
255 eng-one (.7)	.9
all-one side (.8)	1.0
all-both sides (1.2)	1.7
302 eng-one (1.1)	1.5
all-one side (1.2)	1.7
all-both sides (1.8)	2.4

(G) Valve Tappets, Renew

Includes: R&R intake manifold where required. Make all necessary adjustments.

(Factory Time)	Chilton Time
Four–1983-87 (1.3)	2.5
w/Turbocharger add (.2)	.2
1983-87	
EFI Turbo-one (1.0)	1.6
all (1.5)	2.4
V-6–1983-87-one (2.6)	3.9
all (3.2)	4.5
V-8–1983-87-all (3.3)	4.5
w/Cruise control add (.1)	.1

(G) Valve Springs and/or Valve Stem Oil Seals, Renew (Head on Car)

Four–1983-87-one (.9)	1.3
each adtnl (.1)	.2
w/Turbocharger add	.2
1983-87	
EFI Turbo-one (1.2)	1.7
each adtnl (.2)	.2
all (2.2)	3.2
V-6–1983-87-one (.8)	1.4
all (2.8)	4.0
V-8–1983-87	
255 eng-one (.8)	1.1
one-each side (1.3)	1.9
all-both sides (2.7)	3.8
302 eng-one (1.0)	1.4
one-each side (1.7)	2.4
all-both sides (3.7)	5.2

PARTS 12 CYLINDER HEAD & VALVE SYSTEM 12 PARTS

SIX & V-8 ENGINES

	Part No.	Price
Valve Grind Gasket Set		
230 engine		
1983		
before 2-83	▲E2DZ-6079A	61.00
from 2-83	▲E3DZ-6079A	71.50
1984	▲E4DZ-6079A	65.25
1985-87	▲E5DZ-6079A	71.50
302 engine		
1983-84-wo/H.O.	▲E1AZ-6079A	61.00
H.O. eng.	▲E2ZZ-6079B	52.50
1985	▲E5ZZ-6079C	52.50
(1) Cylinder Head Gasket		
230 engine		
1983-87	▲E3DZ-6051A	12.75
302 engine		
(wo/H.O. eng.)		
1983-84	▲D7OZ-6051C	12.50
1985	▲E5ZZ-6051A	13.75
1986-87	▲E5ZZ-6051B	13.75

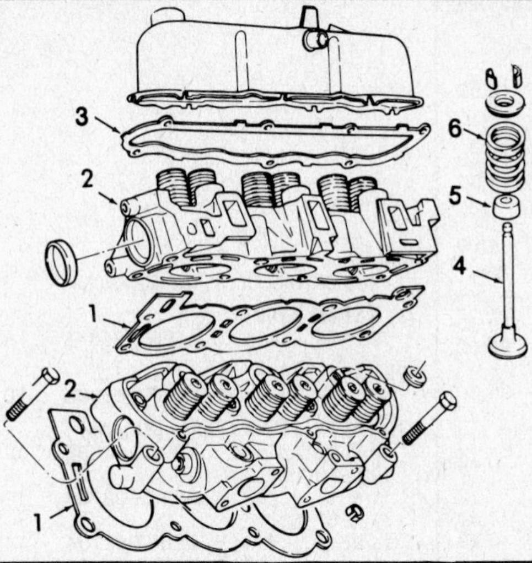

© Ford Motor Co.

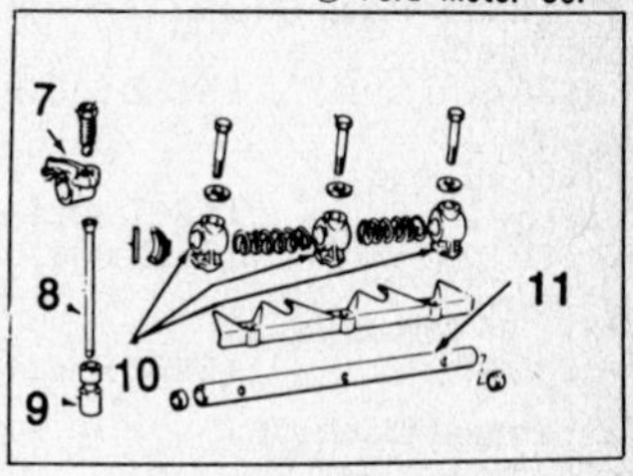

VALVE RELATED PARTS

PARTS 12 CYLINDER HEAD & VALVE SYSTEM 12 PARTS

	Part No.	Price
(w/H.O. eng.)		
1983-84	▲E2ZZ-6051A	13.75
1985-87	▲E5ZZ-6051B	13.75
(2) Cylinder Head		
230 engine		
1983-wo/valves	▲E3DZ-6049C	377.00
w/valves	▲E3DZ-6049D	505.25
1984-87-wo/ valves	▲E4DZ-6049A	377.00
w/valves	▲E4DZ-6049B	505.25
302 engine		
1983-84-wo/ valves	▲D84Y-6049C	281.25
w/valves	▲E2AZ-6049A	461.50
1985-wo/valves	▲E5AZ-6049A	302.25
w/valves	▲E5AZ-6049B	429.25
1986-87-wo/ valves	▲E6AZ-6049A	302.25
w/valves	▲E6ZZ-6049A	429.25
(3) Valve Cover Gasket		
230 engine		
1983-87	▲E3DZ-6584A	5.25
V-8-302 engine		
1983-85	▲E3AZ-6584A	4.75
1986-87-wo/H.O.	▲E5TZ-6584C	4.75
1985-87-w/H.O. eng.	▲E5ZZ-6584A	4.75

	Part No.	Price
(4) Valves (Std.)		
230 engine		
1983-intake	▲E2DZ-6507A	9.50
exhaust	▲E2DZ-6505A	11.75
1984-87-intake	▲E4DZ-6507A	9.50
exhaust	▲E2DZ-6505A	11.75
302 engine		
1983-84-intake	▲E3ZZ-6507A	7.75
1985	▲E5ZZ-6507G	7.25
1986-87	▲E6AZ-6507A	7.50
1983-85-exhaust	▲E2AZ-6505D	8.25
1986-87	▲E6AZ-6505A	8.00
(5) Valve Stem Seal		
230 engine		
1983-87-intake	▲E3DZ-6571A	.75
exhaust	▲D9OZ-6571A	.75
V-8-302 engine		
1983-84-intake	▲E0SZ-6571A	.75
1985-87	▲E43Z-6571A	2.25
1983-87-exhaust wo/H.O.	▲D9OZ-6571A	.75
H.O. eng.	▲E2ZZ-6571A	1.00
(6) Valve Spring		
230 engine		
1983-84-bef. 6-1-84	▲E2DZ-6513A	5.50
1984-87-from 6-1-84	▲E4DZ-6513A	4.75

	Part No.	Price
V-8-302 engine		
(wo/H.O. eng.)		
1983-87-intake	▲D8AZ-6513B	5.75
exhaust	▲D5OZ-6513A	6.75
(w/H.O. eng.)		
1983-87-intake	▲E3ZZ-6513B	5.75
exhaust	▲E3ZZ-6513C	6.75
(7) Rocker Arm		
1983-87-w/230 eng.	▲E2DZ-6564A	7.75
w/V-8 eng.	▲E0AZ-6564A	11.00
(8) Push Rod		
230 engine		
1983-87	▲E2DZ-6565A	2.75
V-8-302 engine		
1983-85	▲C9OZ-6565B	2.75
1985-87-w/H.O. eng.	▲E5AZ-6565A	4.00
(9) Valve Tappet		
230 engine		
1983-87-exc. Canada	▲D9HZ-6500A	9.25
Canada	▲CE2DZ-6500A	N.L.
V-8-302 engine		
1983-85	▲D9HZ-6500A	9.25
1985-87	▲E5AZ-6500A	7.00

PARTS 12 CYLINDER HEAD & VALVE SYSTEM 12 PARTS

O.H.C. 140 ENGINE

	Part No.	Price
Valve Grind Gasket Set		
1983-87	▲E5ZZ-6079A	42.00
(1) Cylinder Head (New)		
(exc. turbo)		
(wo/valves)		
1983	▲E1BZ-6049C	351.75
1984	▲E4ZZ-6049A	351.75
1985-87	▲E5ZZ-6049B	351.75
(w/valves)		
1983	▲E1BZ-6049B	521.25
1984	▲E4ZZ-6049B	521.25
1985-87	▲E5ZZ-6049C	869.75
(turbo)		
(wo/valves)		
1983-84	▲E1BZ-6049C	351.75
1985	▲E4ZZ-6049A	351.75
1986-87	▲E5ZZ-6049A	351.75
(w/valves)		
1983-84	▲E1BZ-6049B	521.25
(2) Cylinder Head Gasket		
(exc. turbo)		
1983-87	▲E5FZ-6051A	13.50
(turbo)		
1983-87-exc. below	▲E5FZ-6051A	13.50
1985-87-SVO	▲E5ZZ-6051C	13.50
(3) Valve Cover Gasket		
1983-87	▲E2ZZ-6584A	1.00
(4) Exhaust Manifold		
(exc. turbo)		
1983-exc. below	▲E3ZZ-9430A	110.50
pulsed air type	▲E3ZZ-9430J	96.00
1984-87-exc. below	▲E4ZZ-9430C	96.00
pulsed air type	▲E4ZZ-9430D	N.L.
(turbo)		
1983-87	▲E3ZZ-9430A	110.50
(5) Shroud & Tube Assy.		
1983-85-outer	▲E5TZ-9A603C	12.50
inner	▲E5TZ-9A603D	9.75

	Part No.	Price
(6) Seal (Valve Stem)		
1983-84	▲D4FZ-6571A	1.25
1985-87-Intake	▲E43Z-6571A	2.25
Exhaust	▲D4FZ-6571A	1.25
(7) Valve Spring		
(exc. turbo)		
1983-84	▲E4ZZ-6513A	6.25
1985-87	▲E5ZZ-6513A	5.25

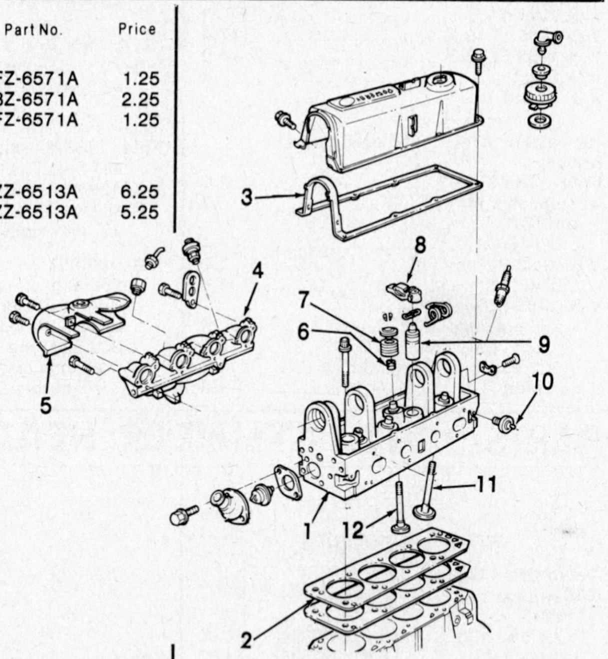

	Part No.	Price
(turbo)		
1983-87	▲E4ZZ-6513A	6.25
(8) Rocker Arm		
1983-87	▲D8FZ-6564A	8.00
(9) Valve Tappet		
1983-87	▲D6FZ-6500A	10.00
(10) Oil Pressure Gauge (Engine)		
1983-84	▲D9ZZ-9278B	12.75
1985-86-bef. 11-85	▲E4ZZ-9278A	12.75
1986-87-from 11-85	▲E6ZZ-9278A	14.50

	Part No.	Price
(11) Intake Valve		
(exc. turbo)		
1983-87	▲E5ZZ-6507A	9.75
(turbo)		
1983-85	▲D9ZZ-6507A	12.00
1985-87-SVO	▲E5ZZ-6507D	9.25
(12) Exhaust Valve		
(exc. turbo)		
1983-87	▲E43Z-6505A	14.25
(turbo)		
1983-84	▲D9ZZ-6505A	21.75
1985-87	▲E5ZZ-6505A	16.75

LABOR 13 ENGINE ASSEMBLY & MOUNTS 13 LABOR

	(Factory Time)	Chilton Time
(G) Engine Assembly, Remove & Install		
Does not include transfer of any parts or equipment.		
Four–1983-87	(3.0)	4.9
1983-87 EFI Turbo	(3.7)	5.2
w/A.C. add		.7
V-6–1983-87	(4.2)	5.9
V-8–1983-87-255 eng	(3.5)	5.2
302 eng	(4.5)	6.1
w/A.C. add		.6
w/P.S. add		.3
(G) Engine Assembly, Replace with New or Rebuilt Unit (With Cyl. Heads)		
Includes: R&R engine assembly, transfer all necessary parts, fuel and electrical units. Minor tune up.		
V-8–1983-87-302 eng	(6.7)	11.0
w/A.C. add		.6
w/P.S. add		.3
(G) Cylinder Assembly, Renew (w/All Internal Parts Less Head(s) and Oil Pan)		
Includes: R&R engine, transfer all component parts not supplied with replacement engine, clean carbon, grind valves. Minor tune up.		
Four–1983-87	(10.5)	15.0
V-6–1983-87	(11.0)	15.4
V-8–1983-87-255 eng	(12.1)	16.6
302 eng	(13.0)	17.5
w/A.C. add		.6
w/P.S. add		.3
(P) Cylinder Block, Renew		
Includes: R&R engine, transfer all component parts, renew rings and bearings, clean carbon, grind valves. Minor tune up.		
Four–1983-87	(14.0)	19.6
1983-87 EFI Turbo	(13.5)	18.9
w/A.C. add	(.7)	.7
V-6–1983-87	(15.8)	22.0
V-8–1983-87-255 eng	(17.4)	24.3
302 eng	(18.3)	25.6
w/A.C. add		.6
w/P.S. add		.3
(P) Engine Assy., R&R and Recondition (Complete)		
Includes: Rebore block, install new pistons, rings, rod and main bearings. Clean carbon, grind valves. Tune engine.		
Four–1983-87	(23.1)	28.3
1983-87 EFI Turbo	(24.1)	28.7
w/A.C. add	(.7)	.7
V-6–1983-87	(23.1)	32.3
V-8–1983-87	(28.0)	34.0
w/A.C. add		.6
w/P.S. add		.3
(P) Engine Assembly, Recondition (In Car)		
Includes: Expand or renew pistons, install new rings, pins, rod and main bearings. Clean carbon and grind valves. Tune engine.		
Four–1983-87	(16.7)	19.5
1983-87 EFI Turbo	(17.7)	20.6
V-6–1983-87	(19.6)	27.4
V-8–1983-87	(23.5)	27.9
w/A.C. add		.3
w/P.S. add		.2
(G) Engine Mounts, Renew		
Front		
Four–1983-87-one	(.5)	.7
both	(.8)	1.2
1983-87 EFI Turbo-one	(.7)	1.0
both	(.9)	1.4
V-6–1983-87-one	(.6)	.8
both	(.8)	1.0
V-8–1983-87-one	(.6)	.9
both	(.7)	1.2
Rear		
1983-87	(.4)	.7

PARTS 13 ENGINE ASSEMBLY & MOUNTS 13 PARTS

	Part No.	Price
Engine Overhaul Gasket Set		
140 engine		
1983-84	▲E2PZ-6E078A	25.50
1985-87	▲E5ZZ-6E078A	25.50
230 engine		
1983-87	▲E3DZ-6E078B	23.50
302 engine		
1983-87	▲E3AZ-6E078A	27.75
Note: When a complete overhaul gasket set is required you must also order a valve grind gasket set.		
Cylinder Assembly		
140 engine		
(exc. turbo)		
1983-84	▲E2ZZ-6009A	1506.00
1985-87	▲E5ZZ-6009A	1506.00
(turbo)		
1983-87	▲E4ZZ-6009A	1534.50
230 engine		
1983-87	▲E4DZ-6009A	2000.50
302 engine		
(wo/H.O. eng.)		
1983-84	▲E3AZ-6009A	2044.75
1985	▲E5ZZ-6009C	2253.25
(w/H.O. eng.)		
1983-84-w/A.T.	▲E4ZZ-6009B	2253.25
w/M.T.	▲E3ZZ-6009B	2253.25
1985	▲E5ZZ-6009B	2253.25
1986-87	▲E6ZZ-6009A	2253.25
Cylinder Block Assy. (New)		
140 engine		
(exc. turbo)		
1983-84	▲E3ZZ-6010A	671.75
1985-87	▲E5ZZ-6010A	671.75
(turbo)		
1983-87	▲E3ZZ-6010B	671.75
230 engine		
1983	▲E3DZ-6010A	837.75
1984-87	▲E4DZ-6010A	900.25
302 engine		
1983-85	▲E5AZ-6010A	920.25
1986-87	▲E6AZ-5010A	N.L.
Front Engine Mount		
140 engine		
(exc. convertible)		
1983-right	▲E3ZZ-6038C	29.75
left	▲E3DZ-6038F	30.50
1984-87-right	▲E4ZZ-6038C	24.50
left	▲E4ZZ-6038D	24.50
(convertible)		
1983-right	▲E4ZZ-6038A	30.50
left	▲E4ZZ-6038B	30.50
230 engine		
(exc. convertible)		
1983-right	▲E3DZ-6038C	25.75
left	▲E2DZ-6038B	25.75
1984-87-right	▲E3SZ-6038G	37.75
left	▲E3SZ-6038H	37.75
(convertible)		
1983-87-right	▲E3ZZ-6C38F	24.50
left	▲E2ZZ-6038G	
302 engine		
(exc. convertible)		
1983-right	▲E3ZZ-6038H	29.75
left	▲E3ZZ-6038J	30.50
1984-85-right	▲E3SZ-6038A	39.00
left	▲E3SZ-6038B	39.00
(convertible)		
1983-87-right	▲E3ZZ-6038D	24.50
left	▲E3ZZ-6038E	24.50
Rear Engine Mount		
140 engine		
1983-85-wo/turbo	▲E2SZ-6068B	22.50
1986-87	▲E5SZ-6068C	23.00
1983-87-w/turbo	▲E3ZZ-6068A	20.75
V-8-302 engine		
1983-M.T.	▲E2SZ-6068B	22.50
1984-85	▲E4ZZ-6068A	20.75
1986-87	▲E6ZZ-6068A	33.00
230 engine		
1983-84-AOD trans.	▲E2SZ-6068B	22.50
C5 trans.	▲E2SZ-6068C	19.50
1985-87-AOD trans.	▲E5SZ-6068C	23.00
C5 trans.	▲E5SZ-6068D	18.75

LABOR 14 PISTONS, RINGS & BEARINGS 14 LABOR

	(Factory Time)	Chilton Time
(P) Rings, Renew (See Engine Combinations)		
Includes: Remove cylinder top ridge, deglaze cylinder walls, replace rod bearings. Clean carbon from cylinder head and pistons. Minor tune up.		
Four–1983-87	(7.1)	9.6
w/Turbocharger add		1.5
1983-87 EFI Turbo	(8.2)	11.4
V-6–1983-87	(10.3)	14.5
V-8–1983-87	(10.1)	14.0
w/A.C. add		.3
w/P.S. add		.2
Clean or renew spark plugs add		.3

LABOR 14 PISTONS, RINGS & BEARINGS 14 LABOR

(Factory Time)	Chilton Time
(P) Piston or Connecting Rod, Renew (One)	
Includes: Remove cylinder top ridge, deglaze cylinder walls, replace rod bearings. Clean carbon from cylinder head and pistons. Minor tune up.	
Four–1983-87 (6.1)	8.3
w/Turbocharger add	1.5
1983-87	
EFI Turbo (9.4)	12.6
V-6–1983-87 (6.9)	9.7
V-8–1983-87 (5.7)	8.5
w/A.C. add	.3
w/P.S. add	.2
Clean or renew spark plugs add	.3
(P) Connecting Rod Bearings, Renew	
Four–1983-87 (2.5)	3.8
1983-87	
EFI Turbo (3.7)	5.3
V-6–1983-87 (3.5)	4.7
V-8–1983-87–255 eng (3.5)	5.1
302 eng (4.4)	6.1

COMBINATIONS

Add to Engine Work
See Machine Shop Operations

(G) DRAIN, EVACUATE & RECHARGE AIR CONDITIONING SYSTEM	
All models (.7)	1.2
(G) ROCKER ARMS, RENEW OR DISASSEMBLE AND CLEAN	
Each (.1)	.1
(G) HYDRAULIC VALVE LIFTERS, DISASSEMBLE AND CLEAN	
Each	.2
(G) ROCKER ARM STUD, RENEW	
Each (.2)	.2
(G) DISTRIBUTOR, RECONDITION	
All models (.7)	1.0
(G) CARBURETOR, RECONDITION	
1983-87	
Four (1.1)	1.6
Six-Carter (1.3)	1.8
Holly (1.7)	2.2
V-6 (1.0)	1.5
V-8-2V (1.0)	1.5
2700-VV (1.8)	2.4
7200-VV (1.9)	2.5
4180-4V (1.9)	2.5
(G) CYLINDER HEAD, R&R (ENGINE REMOVED)	
Four	
wo/Turbo	3.5
w/Turbo	4.0
V-6	
one	4.0
both	5.5
V-8	
one	3.2
both	4.7
(G) CONNECTING ROD, RENEW (ENGINE DISASSEMBLED)	
All engines	
each	.4
(G) DEGLAZE CYLINDER WALLS	
Each (.1)	.1
(G) REMOVE CYLINDER TOP RIDGE	
Each (.1)	.1
(G) TIMING CHAIN OR GEARS, RENEW (COVER REMOVED)	
All models (.3)	.5
(G) MAIN BEARINGS, RENEW (PAN REMOVED)	
Four (1.9)	2.5
Six (2.7)	3.4
V-6 (1.5)	2.0
V-8 (1.9)	2.5
(G) PLASTIGAUGE BEARINGS	
Each (.1)	.1
(G) OIL PUMP, RECONDITION	
All models (.3)	.6
(M) OIL FILTER ELEMENT, RENEW	
All models (.3)	.3

PARTS 14 PISTONS, RINGS & BEARINGS 14 PARTS

	Part No	Price
(1) Piston Ring Set (Partial)		
140 engine		
(exc. turbo)		
1983-84	▲D4FZ-6148A	31.75
1985-87	▲E5ZZ-6148A	32.00
(turbo)		
1983-87	▲D9ZZ-6148A	29.25
230 engine		
1983-87	▲E2DZ-6148A	29.00
302 engine		
1983-85	▲C3AZ-6148F	31.75
1986-87	▲E6AZ-6148A	31.75
(2) Piston Assy.		
140 engine		
(wo/turbo)		
1983-84	▲D4FZ-6108A	21.75
1985-87	▲E5ZZ-6108A	20.75
(w/turbo)		
1983-87	▲E3ZZ-6108A	45.00
230 engine		
1983	▲E2DZ-6108AB	25.75
1984-87	▲E4DZ-6108A	25.50
302 engine		
1983-85	▲D9AZ-6108A	35.00
1986-87	▲E6ZZ-6108A	34.50
(3) Connecting Rod Assy.		
1983-87–140 eng	▲D7FZ-6200A	47.00
230 eng	▲E2DZ-6200A	47.00
V-8 eng	▲D3OZ-6200A	44.00
(4) Connecting Rod Bearing		
1983-87–140 eng	▲D7FZ-6211A	2.50
230 eng	▲E2DZ-6211A	2.75
V-8 eng	▲C2OZ-6211R	2.25

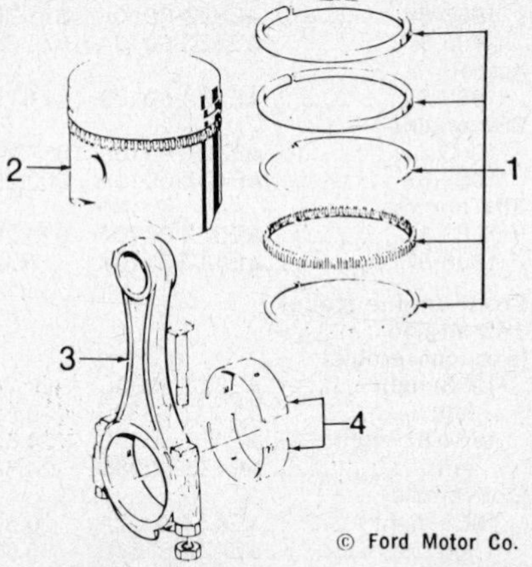

© Ford Motor Co.

LABOR 15 CRANKSHAFT & DAMPER 15 LABOR

(Factory Time)	Chilton Time
(P) Crankshaft and Main Bearings, Renew	
Includes: R&R engine, check all bearing clearances.	
Four–1983-87 (6.8)	9.7
1983-87	
EFI Turbo (7.5)	10.5
w/A.C. add (.7)	.7
V-6–1983-87 (7.5)	10.5
V-8–1983-87–255 eng (7.3)	10.8
302 eng (8.2)	11.5
w/A.C. add	.6
w/P.S. add	.3
(P) Main Bearings, Renew	
Includes: Check all bearing clearances.	
Four–1983-87 (3.5)	4.6
1983-87	
EFI Turbo (4.7)	6.7
V-6–1983-87 (3.6)	4.9
V-8–1983-87–255 eng (3.6)	4.7
302 eng (4.5)	6.2
w/A.C. add	.6

°Includes R&R engine.

(Factory Time)	Chilton Time
(P) Main and Rod Bearings, Renew	
Includes: Check all bearing clearances.	
Four–1983-87 (4.4)	5.8
1983-87	
EFI Turbo (5.6)	7.9
V-6–1983-87 (5.0)	6.7

LABOR 15 CRANKSHAFT & DAMPER 15 LABOR

(Factory Time)	Chilton Time
V-8–1983-87-255 eng (5.4)	7.1
302 eng (6.4)	8.6
w/A.C. add	.6

°Includes R&R engine.

(G) Rear Main Bearing Oil Seals, Renew (Upper & Lower)
Split Lip Type

Includes: R&R oil pan or trans., as required.

(Factory Time)	Chilton Time
Four–1983 (2.4)	3.6
V-6–1983 (2.8)	3.9
V-8–1983	
255 eng (2.4)	3.5
302 eng (2.8)	4.0

(G) Rear Main Bearing Oil Seal, Renew (Full Circle Type)

(Factory Time)	Chilton Time
Four–1983-87	
4 sp-ET (2.1)	2.8
4 sp-RAD (1.8)	2.4
5 sp-RAD (2.1)	2.9
C-3 (2.2)	3.0
EFI Turbo	
5 sp-REP (2.3)	3.3
V-6–1985-87 (3.5)	4.9
V-8–1983-87	
w/M.T. (2.2)	3.1
w/A.T. (3.3)	4.6

(G) Vibration Damper or Pulley, Renew

(Factory Time)	Chilton Time
Four–1983-87 (.8)	1.1
1983-87	
EFI Turbo (.4)	.8
w/A.C. add (.1)	.1
V-6–1983-87 (.8)	1.2
V-8–1983-87 (.8)	1.2

(G) Crankshaft Front Oil Seal, Renew

(Factory Time)	Chilton Time
Four–1983-87	
crank (1.3)	1.8
aux drive (1.0)	1.5
1983-87	
EFI Turbo	
crank (1.3)	1.8
aux drive (1.2)	1.7
w/A.C. add (.1)	.1
V-6–1983-87 (1.0)	1.5
V-8–1983-87 (.9)	1.4
w/A.C. add (.1)	.1

PARTS 15 CRANKSHAFT & DAMPER 15 PARTS

O.H.C. 140 ENGINE

	Part No.	Price
(1) Pulley Assy. (Outer)		
(wo/A.C.)		
1983-87	▲E2BZ-6A312A	51.50
(w/A.C.)		
1983-84	▲E3ZZ-6A312A	51.50
1985-87	▲E5ZZ-6A312A	48.00
(2) Spacer (Belt Cover)		
1983-87	▲D4FZ-6K297B	1.75
(3) Crankshaft Gear		
1983-87	▲D9FZ-6306A	11.50
(4) Front Cover Assy. (Lower)		
1983-84	▲E3TZ-6019A	45.25
1985-87	▲E5ZZ-6019A	45.25
(5) Gasket (Front Cover)		
1983-87-outer	▲D4FZ-6020A	2.25
inner	▲D4FZ-6020B	1.50
(6) Rear Packing (Crankshaft)		
1983-87	▲E5ZZ-6701A	6.25
(7) Pilot Bearing (Clutch)		
1983-87	▲D4ZZ-7600A	5.25

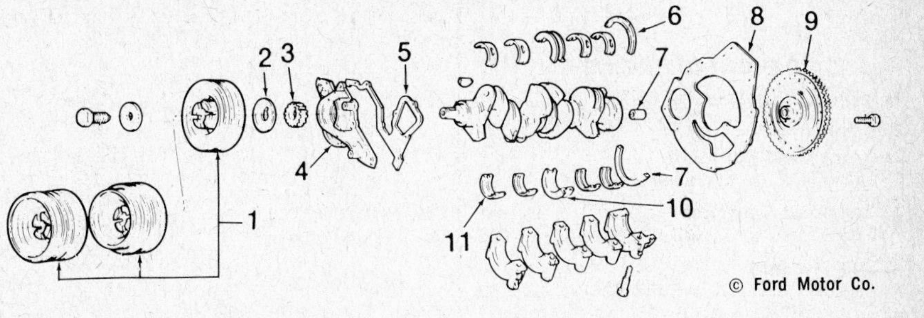

	Part No.	Price
(8) Cover Plate (Rear)		
1983-87	▲E3TZ-7007A	21.75
(9) Flywheel		
(w/A.T.)		
1983-87	▲D5FZ-6375A	81.75
(w/M.T.)		
(wo/turbo)		
1983-5 sp.	▲E2ZZ-6375B	185.75
(w/turbo)		
1983-87	▲E3TZ-6375A	162.50
(10) Main Bearing (Center)		
1983-87-upper	▲D4FZ-6337A	9.75
lower	▲D4FZ-6337G	9.75
(11) Main Bearing (Exc. Center)		
1983-87	▲D4FZ-6333A	3.75

PARTS 15 CRANKSHAFT & DAMPER 15 PARTS

SIX & V-8 ENGS.

	Part No.	Price
(1) Vibration Damper or Pulley		
230 engine		
1983-87-AOD	▲E3SZ-6B321B	88.00
C5 trans.	▲E3DZ-6B321B	88.00
V-8-302 eng.		
1983-87	▲D9ZZ-6A312A	33.50
(2) Crankshaft Gear		
230 engine		
1983-87	▲E2DZ-6306A	22.50
V-8-302 eng.		
1983-87-wo/H.O.	▲D5OZ-6306A	11.25
H.O. eng.	▲E0AZ-6306A	18.50
(3) Crankshaft		
230 engine		
1983-87	▲E3DZ-6303A	423.25
302 engine		
1983-87	▲E3AZ-6303A	500.75
(4) Main Bearings, Upper & Lower		
230 engine		
(exc. rear intermediate)		
1983-87-upper	▲E2DZ-6333A	3.25
lower	▲E2DZ-6333D	3.25
(rear intermediate)		
1983-87-upper	▲E2DZ-6337A	8.25

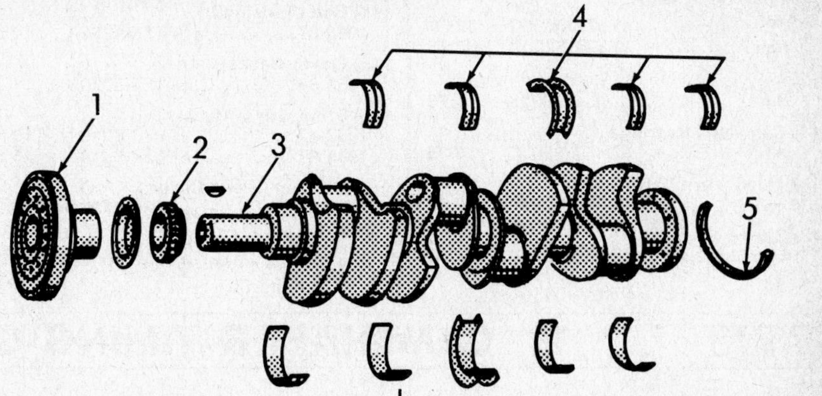

	Part No.	Price
lower	▲E2DZ-6337D	8.25
V-8-302 eng.		
(exc. center)		
1983-87-upper	▲C3AZ-6333P	3.50
lower	▲C3AZ-6333AA	3.50
(center)		
1983-87-upper	▲C3AZ-6337P	8.00
lower	▲C3AZ-6337AA	8.00
(5) Rear Main Bearing Oil Seal (230, 302 engs.)		
1983-rope type	▲C9OZ-6701A	2.00
1983-split type	▲D4FZ-6701A	6.25
1983-87-one piece	▲E5ZZ-6701A	6.25

LABOR 16 CAMSHAFT & TIMING GEARS 16 LABOR

	(Factory Time)	Chilton Time
(G) Timing Case Seal and Gaskets, Renew		
Includes: R&R radiator and oil pan where required.		
Four–1983-87	(1.6)	2.1
1983-87 EFI Turbo	(1.7)	2.4
w/A.C. add	(.1)	.1
V-6–1983-87	(4.1)	5.7
V-8–1983-87	(2.0)	2.9
w/A.C. add		.3
w/P.S. add		.2
(G) Timing Chain or Sprockets, Renew		
Includes: Adjust timing.		
V-6–1983-87	(4.4)	6.2
V-8–1983-87	(2.6)	3.4
w/A.C. add		.3
w/P.S. add		.2
(G) Timing Belt, Renew		
Four–1983-87	(1.1)	2.0
1983-87 EFI Turbo	(1.0)	1.5
w/A.C. add	(.1)	.1
Renew tensioner add		.2
(G) Camshaft, Renew		
Four–1983-87	(2.9)	4.1
w/Turbocharger add		.2
1983-87 EFI Turbo	(3.3)	4.6
V-6–1983-87	(7.5)	10.7
V-8–1983-87–255 eng	(5.0)	7.0
302 eng	(5.4)	7.5
w/A.C. add		.3
w/P.S. add		.2
(P) Camshaft Bearings, Renew		
Includes: R&R engine and crankshaft where required.		
Four–1983-87	(3.4)	5.5
w/Turbocharger add		.2
1983-87 EFI Turbo	(3.8)	5.6
V-6–1983-87	(8.7)	12.1
V-8–1983-87–255 eng	(8.1)	11.0
302 eng	(9.0)	12.0
w/A.C. add		.6
w/P.S. add		.3

PARTS 16 CAMSHAFT & TIMING GEARS 16 PARTS

O.H.C. 140 ENGINE

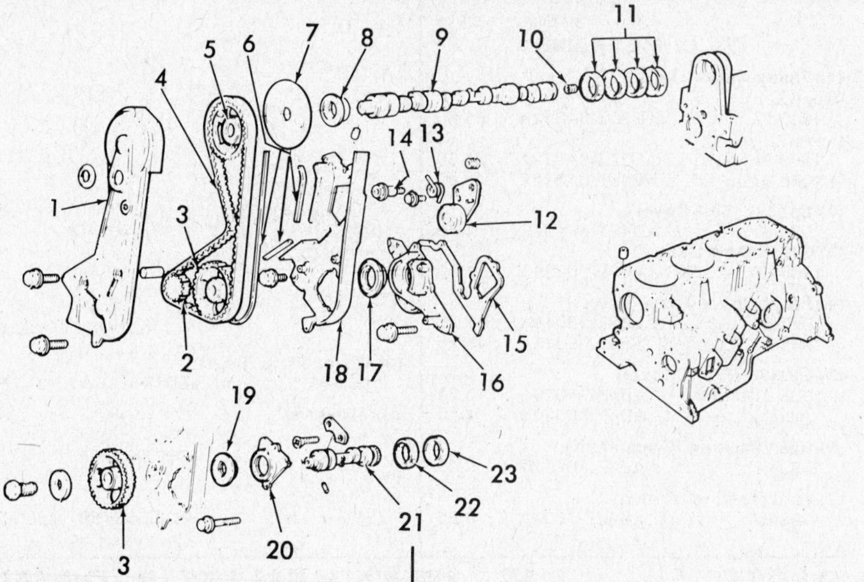

	Part No.	Price
(1) Cylinder Cover Assy. (Front)		
1983-87	▲E3ZZ-6019A	38.50
(2) Crankshaft Sprocket		
1983-87	▲D9FZ-6306A	11.50
(3) Camshaft Sprocket		
1983-87	▲D4FZ-6256A	13.75
(4) Belt (Timing)		
1983-87	▲E5ZZ-6268A	21.50
(5) Camshaft Gear		
1983-87	▲D4FZ-6256A	13.75
(6) Cover Gasket (Front)		
1983-87-outer	▲D4FZ-6020A	2.25
inner	▲D4FZ-6020B	1.50
(7) Guide (Timing Belt)		
1983-87	▲D4FZ-6B260A	4.75
(8) Oil Seal (Front Cover)		
1983-87	▲D4FZ-6700A	5.75
(9) Camshaft		
(exc. SVO)		
1983-84	▲E1ZZ-6250A	158.75
1985-87	▲E5ZZ-6250B	148.75
(SVO)		
1984	▲E5ZZ-6250C	162.25
1985-87	▲E5ZZ-6250D	162.25
(10) Plug		
1983-87	▲87837S	1.75
(11) Camshaft Bearings		
1983-87	▲D4FZ-6261C	3.25
(12) Tensioner (Pulley Assy.)		
1983-87	▲D4FZ-6K254A	23.00
(13) Spring (Tensioner)		
1983-87	▲D4FZ-6L273A	7.50
(14) Bolt (Tensioner)		
1983-87	▲D7FZ-6K282A	4.25
(15) Cover Gasket (Inner)		
1983-87	▲D4FZ-6020B	1.50
(16) Front Cover (Lower)		
1983-84	▲E3TZ-6019A	45.25
1985-87	▲E5ZZ-6019A	45.25
(17) Oil Seal (Front Cover)		
1983-87	▲D4FZ-6700A	5.75
(18) Front Cover (Inner)		
1983-87	▲E3ZZ-6019B	43.00
(19) Oil Seal (Front Cover)		
1983-87	▲D4FZ-6700A	5.75
(20) Front Cover (Upper)		
1983-87	▲D4FZ-6019B	22.75
(21) Drive Shaft (Dist. Fuel & Oil Pump)		
1983-87	▲E4FZ-6A739A	63.25
(22) Auxiliary Shaft Bearing (Front)		
1983-87	▲D4FZ-6A753A	5.00
(23) Auxiliary Shaft Bearing (Rear)		
1983-87	▲D4FZ-6A738A	5.00

PARTS 16 CAMSHAFT & TIMING GEARS 16 PARTS

V-6 & V-8 ENGS.

	Part No.	Price
(1) Timing Cover (Front)		
230 engine		
1983	▲E2DZ-6019A	132.25
1984-87	▲E4DZ-6019A	132.25
V-8-302 eng.		
1983-wo/EEC	▲E0AZ-6019B	126.50
w/EEC	▲E3AZ-6019A	118.00
1984-87-wo/CFI	▲E4AZ-6019C	126.50
w/CFI	▲E4AZ-6019B	126.50
(2) Timing Cover Gasket		
w/230 eng.	▲E2DZ-6020A	4.75
w/V-8 eng.	▲E3AZ-6020A	1.50
(3) Timing Cover Oil Seal		
1983-87-exc. below	▲D0AZ-6700A	6.75
(4) Timing Chain		
230 engine		
1983-87	▲E2DZ-6268A	28.00

PARTS 16 CAMSHAFT & TIMING GEARS 16 PARTS

	Part No.	Price
V-8–302 eng.		
1983-87-wo/H.O.	▲C3OZ-6268A	19.25
H.O. eng.	▲E0AZ-6268A	22.25
(5) Camshaft Gear		
230 engine		
1983-87	▲E2DZ-6256A	32.25
V-8–302 eng.		
(wo/H.O. eng.)		
1983-87	▲D3AZ-6256B	22.25
(w/H.O. eng.)		
1983-84	▲E0AZ-6256A	26.00
1985-87	▲E4AZ-6256A	26.00
(6) Camshaft		
230 engine		
1983	▲E2DZ-6250A	133.00
1984	▲E4DZ-6250A	151.00
1985-87	▲E5DZ-6250A	N.L.
302 engine		
(wo/H.O. eng.)		
1983-84	▲D5OZ-6250A	138.25
1985-w/2 V Carb	▲E5ZZ-6250A	148.75
1985-w/C.F.I.	▲D3OZ-6250A	141.50

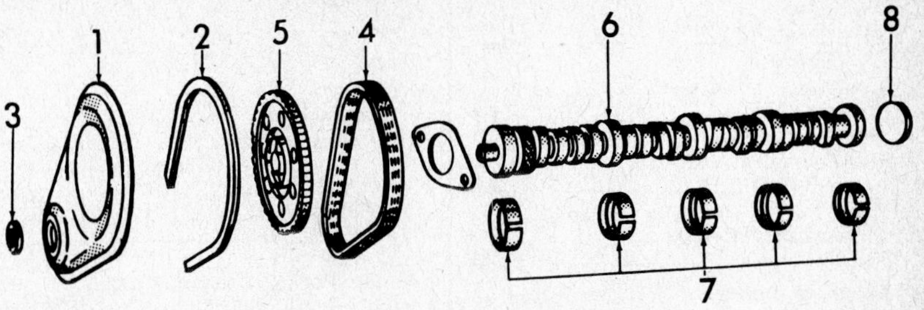

	Part No.	Price
(w/H.O. eng.)		
1983-84	▲D3OZ-6250A	141.50
1985-w/C.F.I.	▲D3OZ-6250A	141.50
1985-w/4 V Carb	▲E5ZZ-6250A	148.75
1986-87	▲E5ZZ-6250A	148.75
(7) Bearings (Camshaft)		
230 engine		
1983-87-exc. below	▲E2DZ-6267A	6.50

	Part No.	Price
frt & rear	▲E2DZ-6261A	9.00
V-8–302 eng.		
1983-87-front	▲C2OZ-6261A	5.00
center	▲C2OZ-6262A	5.00
front inter	▲C2OZ-6267A	5.00
rear inter	▲C2OZ-6270A	5.00
rear	▲C2OZ-6263A	5.00
(8) Welsh Plug		
1983-87	▲D7AZ-6026A	1.00

LABOR 17 ENGINE OILING SYSTEM 17 LABOR

(Factory Time)	Chilton Time
(G) Oil Pan or Gasket, Renew	
Four–1983-87 (1.6)	2.6
1983-87 EFI Turbo (2.8)	3.8
V-6–1983-87 (2.1)	2.9
V-8–1983-87-255 eng (1.7)	2.4
302 eng w/M.T. (2.7)	3.7
w/A.T. (2.4)	3.3
(P) Pressure Test Engine Bearings (Pan Off)	
All models	1.0
(G) Oil Pump, Renew	
Four–1983-87 (1.7)	2.8
1983-87 EFI Turbo (2.9)	4.0
V-6–1983-87 (.7)	1.1
V-8–1983-87-255 eng (1.8)	2.6
302 eng w/M.T. (2.8)	3.9
w/A.T. (2.5)	3.5
(G) Oil Pump, R&R and Recondition	
Four–1983-87 (2.0)	3.1
1983-87 EFI Turbo (3.2)	4.4
V-6–1983-87 (.7)	1.2
V-8–1983-87-255 eng (2.1)	3.0
302 eng w/M.T. (3.1)	4.3
w/A.T. (2.8)	3.9
(G) Oil Pressure Gauge (Engine), Renew	
1983-87-exc below (.3)	.4
2.8 L-V-6 (.7)	1.0
(G) Oil Pressure Gauge (Dash), Renew	
1983-87 (.4)	.7
(M) Oil Filter Element, Renew	
1983-87 (.3)	.3

PARTS 17 ENGINE OILING SYSTEM 17 PARTS

	Part No.	Price
Oil Pan Gasket Set		
1983-84-140 eng	▲E2ZZ-6781A	10.75
1985-87	▲E5ZZ-6781A	10.75
1983-87-230 eng.	▲E2DZ-6781A	9.00
1983-87-V-8 eng.	▲D9AZ-6781A	11.50
Oil Pump Assy.		
140 engine		
1983-85-wo/ Turbo (bef. 4-8-85)	▲D5FZ-6600A	66.00
1985-87 (from 4-8-85)	▲E5ZZ-6600A	44.25
1983-85-w/ Turbo (bef. 4-8-85)	▲D9ZZ-6600A	58.00
1985-87 (from 4-8-85)	▲E5ZZ-6600A	44.25
V-8–302 eng.		
1983-87	▲C2OZ-6600A	52.50
Oil Pump Screen		
1983-84-140 eng	▲E3ZZ-6622A	19.50
1985-87	▲E5ZZ-6622A	19.50
1983-87-230 eng.	▲E3DZ-6622A	28.00
1983-87-V-8 eng.	▲E0SZ-6622A	28.00
Oil Filter Assy.		
1983-87	▲D9AZ-6731A	8.00
Oil Pressure Gauge (Engine Unit)		
1983-84	▲D9ZZ-9278B	12.75
1985-87 (bef. 11-85)	▲E4ZZ-9278A	12.75
1986-87 (from 11-85)	▲E6ZZ-9278A	14.50

LABOR 18 CLUTCH & FLYWHEEL 18 LABOR

(G) Clutch Pedal Free Play, Adjust

(Factory Time)	Chilton Time
All models (.3)	.5

(G) Clutch Assembly, Renew

Includes: R&R flywheel housing and adjust free play.

(Factory Time)	Chilton Time
1983-87	
4 Speed	
German (1.8)	2.4
Borg Warner (2.0)	2.5
RUG (2.0)	2.5
5 Speed	
RAP (2.6)	3.5
REP	
Four (1.8)	2.4
V-8 (1.9)	2.5
T50D (2.2)	2.9

(G) Clutch Release Bearing, Renew

Includes: R&R trans and adjust free play.

(Factory Time)	Chilton Time
1983-87	
4 Speed	
German (1.6)	2.1
Borg Warner (1.4)	2.0
RUG (1.5)	2.0

LABOR 18 CLUTCH & FLYWHEEL 18 LABOR

(Factory Time)	Chilton Time
5 Speed	
RAP (1.2)	1.7
REP	
Four (1.3)	2.0
V-8 (1.8)	2.3
(G) Clutch Cable, Renew	
1983-87 (.5)	.8
(G) Flywheel, Renew	
Includes: R&R starter and flywheel housing.	
1983-87	
4 Speed	
German (1.9)	2.7
Borg Warner (2.2)	2.8
RUG (2.2)	2.8
5 Speed	
RAP (2.9)	3.8
REP	
Four (2.1)	2.9
V-8 (2.2)	3.0
T50D (2.5)	3.4
Renew ring gear add (.3)	.5
(G) Flywheel Housing, Renew	
1983-87	
4 Speed	
German (2.1)	3.0
Borg Warner (2.2)	3.1
5 Speed	
RAP (3.4)	4.6
REP	
Four (2.9)	3.9
V-8 (2.8)	3.9

PARTS 18 CLUTCH & FLYWHEEL 18 PARTS

	Part No.	Price
Clutch Disc		
140 engine		
(exc. SVO)		
1983-w/Ford 4 sp.	▲D9ZZ-7550B	44.00
1983-87-w/German 4 sp.	▲D8BZ-7550B	44.00
1983-RAP-5 sp.	▲E3ZZ-7550B	39.75
1983-87-REP-5 sp.	▲E3ZZ-7550D	44.00
(SVO)		
1984-87	▲E4ZZ-7550A	40.50
302 engine		
1983-87	▲E4ZZ-7550B	45.25
Pressure Plate		
140 engine		
(exc. SVO)		
1983-87-exc. below	▲D8BZ-7563B	58.75
REP-5 sp.	▲E3ZZ-7563A	58.50
(SVO)		
1984-87	▲E4ZZ-7563A	62.75
302 engine		
1983	▲D9ZZ-7563A	73.75
1984-87	▲E4ZZ-7563B	73.75
Release Bearing & Hub Assy.		
1983-87-exc below	▲D9ZZ-7548A	29.50
Germ. type	▲D9ZZ-7548B	37.75
Pilot Bearing		
1983-87-exc. 140	▲D4DZ-7600A	12.75
140 eng.	▲D4ZZ-7600A	5.25
Release Lever Assy.		
140 engine		
1983-87-exc. below	▲D9ZZ-7515C	12.75
REP-5 sp.	▲E3ZZ-7515A	10.00
302 engine		
1983-85	▲D9ZZ-7515B	15.75
1986-87	▲E6ZZ-7515A	15.75
Cable Assy.		
140 engine		
1983-87-exc. below	▲E2DZ-7K553A	37.50
REP-5 sp.	▲E3SZ-7K553B	45.75
302 engine		
1983-87	▲E4ZZ-7K553A	55.00
Flywheel Assy.		
140 engine		
(w/A.T.)		
1983-87	▲D5FZ-6375A	81.75
(w/M.T.)		
(exc. SVO)		
1983-wo/turbo, w/5 sp.	▲E2ZZ-6375B	185.75
1983-87-wo/turbo, w/4 sp.	▲E2ZZ-6375C	185.75
1983-87-w/turbo	▲E3TZ-6375A	162.50
230 engine		
1983-84-C5 trans.	▲E3DZ-6375B	94.75
1985-87-AOD trans.	▲E5SZ-6375A	94.75
V-8-302 eng.		
1983-87-w/A.T.	▲E2AZ-6375A	94.75
1983-85-w/M.T.	▲E2ZZ-6375A	177.50
1986-87-w/M.T.	▲E6ZZ-6375A	177.50

LABOR 21 SHIFT LINKAGE 21 LABOR

(Factory Time)	Chilton Time
STANDARD	
(G) Shift Linkage, Adjust	
All models (.3)	.5
(G) Gear Selector Lever, Renew	
1983-87 (.4)	.6
AUTOMATIC	
(G) Linkage, Adjust	
manual (.3)	.4
throttle (.3)	.5
manual & throttle (.5)	.7
downshift (.3)	.4
(G) Gear Selector Lever, Renew	
1983-87-floor shift (1.0)	1.4
console (.8)	1.2
(G) Transmission Control Selector Indicator, Renew	
1985-87	
floor shift (.3)	.4

LABOR 25 U-JOINTS & DRIVESHAFT 25 LABOR

(Factory Time)	Chilton Time
(G) Driveshaft, Renew	
1983-87 (.3)	.5
(G) Universal Joints, Renew or Recondition	
Includes: R&R driveshaft.	
1983-87 Double Cardan	
front or rear (.9)	1.3
all (1.5)	2.0
Single Cardan	
front or rear (.6)	.9
both (.8)	1.3

PARTS 25 UNIVERSAL JOINTS & DRIVE SHAFT 25 PARTS

	Part No.	Price
Universal Joint (Front & Rear)		
1983-87	▲C3AZ-4635E	15.25
Pinion Shaft Oil Slinger		
1983-87	▲D5AZ-4670A	1.50
Yoke		
1983-87	▲E1DZ-4782A	14.25

LABOR — 26 REAR AXLE 26 — LABOR

	(Factory Time)	Chilton Time
(M) Differential, Drain & Refill		
All models		.6
(M) Axle Housing Cover or Gasket, Renew		
All models	(.4)	.6
(G) Axle Shaft Inner Oil Seal, Renew		
Includes: R&R wheel, drum and axle shaft.		
1983-84		
6.75 axle-one	(.5)	.7
both	(.7)	.9
7.5 axle-one	(.6)	.9
both	(.8)	1.3
1985-87		
w/Drum brks-one	(.7)	.9
both	(.9)	1.3
w/Disc brks-one	(.8)	1.0
both	(1.1)	1.5
(G) Rear Wheel Bearings, Renew		
Includes: Renew oil seal.		
1983-84		
6.75 axle	(.6)	.8
both	(1.0)	1.3
7.5 axle-one	(.7)	1.0
both	(.9)	1.5
1985-87		
w/Drum brks-one	(.7)	1.0
both	(1.0)	1.5
w/Disc brks-one	(.8)	1.1
both	(1.1)	1.6
(G) Axle Shaft, Renew		
1983-84		
6.75 axle-one	(.4)	.6
both	(.6)	1.0
7.5 axle-one	(.6)	.8
both	(.8)	1.2
1985-87		
w/Drum brks-one	(.6)	.8
both	(.8)	1.2
w/Disc brks-one	(.6)	.8
both	(1.0)	1.4
(G) Axle Shaft Wheel Mounting Studs, Renew		
All models-one		.8
all		1.2
(G) Pinion Shaft Oil Seal, Renew		
1983-87	(.8)	1.3
w/Disc brks add	(.2)	.2
(P) Differential Case Assy., Recondition (In Chassis)		
Includes: Drain and refill axle, renew necessary parts. Renew axle shaft oil seals. Road test.		
1983-87		
6.75 axle	(2.3)	4.5
7.5 axle		
std	(1.2)	2.1
lock	(2.1)	3.3
w/Rear disc brks add	(.3)	.3
(P) Axle Housing, Renew		
Includes: Transfer all necessary parts, adjust ring gear and pinion. Does not include disassembly of differential case.		
1983-87		
6.75 axle	(3.3)	4.6
7.5 axle	(3.5)	4.9
Recondition diff assy. add	(.4)	.8
(P) Ring and Pinion Set, Renew		
Includes: R&R axle shafts, drain and refill unit. Road test.		
1983-87		
6.75 axle	(2.6)	3.5
7.5 axle	(2.8)	3.8
w/Rear disc brks add	(.2)	.2
O/Haul diff assy add	(.4)	.8
Renew diff brgs add	(.2)	.2
(P) Ring and Pinion, Adjust (In Chassis)		
Includes: Remove axle shafts, drain and refill unit. Road test.		
1983-87		
6.75 axle	(1.6)	2.4
7.5 axle	(1.5)	2.3
w/Rear disc brks add	(.2)	.2

PARTS — 26 REAR AXLE 26 — PARTS

	Part No.	Price
(1) Pinion Kit		
(wo/locking rear)		
1983-87		
w/7.5″ gear	▲E4DZ-4215A	20.00
(w/locking rear)		
1985-87	▲E4DZ-4215A	20.00
1986-87	▲E3TZ-4215A	34.50

Note: On 1983-84 models with locking rears, pinion kit is not available. It is only serviced in the differential assy. basic part no. 4026.

	Part No.	Price
(2) Side Gear		
1985-87-w/7.5″ gear	▲E4DZ-4236A	40.25
1986-87-w/8.8 gear	▲E0AZ-4236A	102.25
(3) Shim		
1983-87	▲D8BZ-4067	3.25

Note: Shims must be ordered according to thickness needed.

	Part No.	Price
(4) Bearing Cup		
1983-87	▲C6TZ-4222A	6.00
1986-87-w/8.8	▲D9AZ-4222A	7.25
(5) Bearing Assy.		
1983-87	▲B7A-4221A	11.50
1986-87-w/8.8	▲B7A-4221B	12.50
(6) Pinion Shaft		
(wo/locking rear)		
1983-87		
w/7.5″ gear	▲D8BZ-4211A	13.75
(w/locking rear)		
1983-84	▲Not Serviced	
1985-87-exc. 3.73	▲D8BZ-4211A	13.75
w/3.73R	▲E4SZ-4211A	13.75
1986-87-w/8.8	▲B7AZ-4211A	9.00
(7) Case Assy.		
(wo/locking rear)		
1983-87		
w/7.5″ gear	▲D9AZ-4204A	104.50

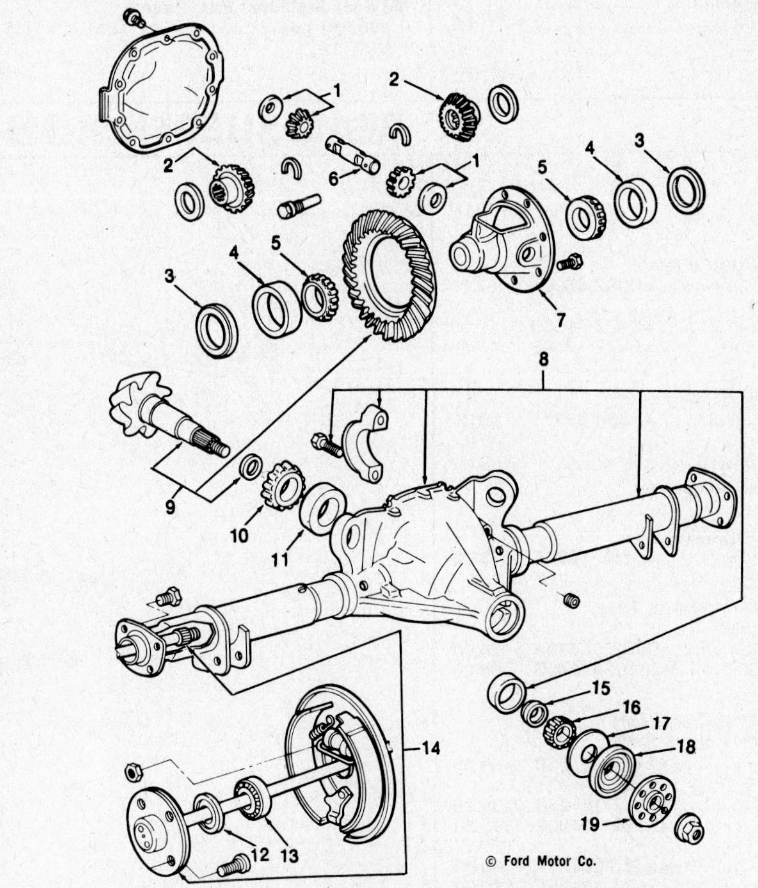

PARTS 26 REAR AXLE 26 PARTS

	Part No.	Price
(w/locking rear)		
1983-84	▲Not Serviced	
1985-87	▲E4DZ-4204A	105.75
1986-87-w/8.8	▲E3AZ-4204B	169.50
(8) Housing Assy. Order by year and model.		
(9) Ring Gear & Pinion Kit (w/7.5" ring gear)		
1983-87-2.47R	▲D8BZ-4209C	352.50
2.73R	▲E5SZ-4209A	352.50
3.08R	▲E25Y-4209A	352.50
3.27R (1983-84)	▲E35Y-4209A	381.75
3.27R (1985-87)	▲E5LY-4209A	381.75
3.45R	▲E25Y-4209B	401.25
3.73R (SVO)	▲E4SZ-4209A	381.75
(w/8.8 ring gear)		
1986-87-w/ 2.73R	▲E3AZ-4209A	319.25
3.08R	▲E3TZ-4209H	381.75
3.27R	▲E6LY-4209A	319.25
(10) Pinion Bearing (Rear)		
1983-87 w/7.5" & 8.8 gear	▲C7AZ-4630A	15.75
(11) Bearing Cup (Rear)		
1983-87 w/7.5" & 8.8 gear	▲C7AZ-4628A	8.00
(12) Axle Shaft Oil Seal		
1983-87 w/7.5" & 8.8 gear	▲E1AZ-1177B	3.50
(13) Axle Shaft Bearing		
1983-87 w/7.5" & 8.8 gear	▲C7AZ-1225A	15.75
(14) Axle Shaft Assy. (Rear) (w/7.5" & 8.8 ring gear)		
1983-87-exc. SVO	▲D9BZ-4234C	80.00
w/SVO	▲E25Y-4234A	134.00
(15) Spacer		
1983-87 w/7.5" & 8.8 gear	▲B7A-4662A	4.00
(16) Pinion Bearing (Front)		
1983-87 w/7.5" & 8.8 gear	▲C7AZ-4628A	8.00
(17) Oil Slinger		
1983-87	▲D5AZ-4670A	1.50
(18) Pinion Oil Seal		
1983-87 w/7.5" & 8.8 gear	▲E3TZ-4676A	11.25
(19) Flange Assy. (U-Joint)		
1983-87 w/7.5" gear	▲D8BZ-4851A	17.00
w/8.8 gear	▲E3AZ-4851A	20.75

LABOR 27 REAR SUSPENSION 27 LABOR

(Factory Time)	Chilton Time
(G) Rear Springs, Renew	
1983-87	
wo/Stabilizer (.8)	1.0
w/Stabilizer (.9)	1.2
(G) Rear Suspension Upper Arm, Renew	
1983-87-one (.4)	.7
both (.6)	1.0
(G) Rear Suspension Lower Arm, Renew	
1983-87-wo/Stabilizer-one (.6)	1.1
both (.9)	1.5
w/Stabilizer-one (.7)	1.2
both (1.0)	1.7
(G) Rear Stabilizer Bar, Renew	
1983-87 (.4)	.5
(G) Rear Shock Absorber or Rubber Bushing, Renew	
1983-87	
Vertical	
one (.3)	.5
both (.4)	.8
Horizontal	
one (.4)	.6
both (.6)	.9

PARTS 27 REAR SUSPENSION 27 PARTS

	Part No.	Price
(1) Upper Control Arm		
1983-exc. below	▲D9BZ-5500A	37.00
w/rear stabilizer	▲D9ZZ-5500D	37.00
1984-87	▲E4ZZ-5500B	38.25
(2) Insulator (Upper)		
1983-87	▲D9BZ-5536A	3.00
(4) Coil Spring Order by year and model.		
(5) Insulator (Lower)		
1983-87	▲D8BZ-5536A	3.00
(6) Lower Control Arm Assy.		
1983-87-exc below	▲D9BZ-5A649A	66.00
w/V-8 eng	▲D9BZ-5A649B	66.00
(7) Shock Absorber (Rear) (exc. special hndlg. & SVO)		
1983-87	▲E4ZZ-18125B	38.25
(w/special hndlg.)		
1984	▲E4ZZ-18125C	38.75
1985-87	▲E5ZZ-18125B	41.50
(SVO)		
1984	▲E4ZZ-18125A	80.00
1985-87	▲E5ZZ-18125A	80.00

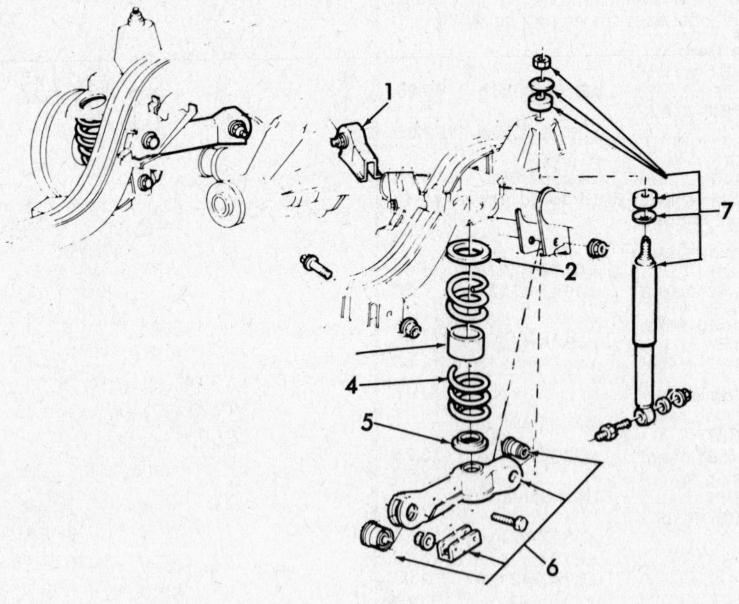

LABOR 28 AIR CONDITIONING 28 LABOR

(Factory Time) Chilton Time

Note: If more than one item requires replacement where evacuation and discharging the system is already included in the operation, deduct 1.0 hour for each additional item to the times listed.

(G) Drain, Evacuate and Recharge System
Includes: Check for leaks.
All models (.7) 1.2

(G) Pressure Test System
All models 6

(G) Compressor Belt, Renew
All models (.3) 5

(G) Compressor Assembly, Renew
Includes: Evacuate and charge system.
1983-84
York (1.5) 2.3
HR 980 (1.6) *2.4
6 P 148 (1.7) 2.5
1985-87
Four (1.6) *2.4
V-6 (1.7) 2.5
V-8 (1.5) 2.3
*w/EFI Turbo add 7
Recond comp add (.7) 1.0

(G) Compressor Shaft Seal Kit, Renew
Includes: R&R compressor where required. Evacuate and charge system.
1983-84
York (1.1) 1.7
HR 980 (1.5) 2.3
6 P 148 (2.0) 3.0
1985-87
Four (1.5) *2.3
V-6 (2.0) 3.0
V-8 (1.8) 2.8
*w/EFI Turbo add 7

(G) Compressor Clutch and Pulley, Renew
Includes: R&R compressor when required.
1983-84
York (.4) 7
HR 980 (.6) 9

AIR CONDITIONER TUNE-UP

For efficient operation and satisfactory performance in hot weather. The following air conditioner tune-up is suggested:

1. Clean intake filter
2. Clean condenser fins
3. Pressure test system
4. Adjust drive belt tension
5. Check antifreeze/coolant
6. Tighten compressor mounts
7. Tighten condenser and evaporator mounts
8. Inspect system for leaks (hoses, couplings, valves, etc.)
9. Partial charge system

All models 1.0
If necessary to evacuate and charge system, add 1.0

(Factory Time) Chilton Time

6 P 148 (.5) 8
1985-87
Four (.5) .... *.8
V-6 (.5) 8
V-8 (.4) 7
*w/EFI Turbo add 7
Renew clutch brg add (.1) 1
Renew clutch field add (.1) 1

(G) Compressor Service Valve or Gasket, Renew
Includes: Evacuate and charge system.
1983-87 (1.4) 2.0

(G) Condenser Assembly, Renew
Includes: Evacuate and charge system.
1983-87 (.9) 2.0

(G) Evaporator Core, Renew
Includes: Renew or transfer valve, evacuate and charge system.
1983-87 (2.3) 6.0

(Factory Time) Chilton Time

(G) A.C. Clutch Cycling Pressure Switch, Renew
1983-87 (.2) 4

(G) Accumulator Assy., Renew
Includes: Evacuate and charge system.
1983 (1.0) 1.5

(G) Orifice Valve, Renew
Includes: Evacuate and charge system.
1983-87 (.9) 1.5

(G) Pressure Relief Valve, Renew
Includes: Evacuate and charge system.
1985-87 (.8) 1.6

(G) Door Vacuum Motor, Renew A/C Defroster Door
1983-85 (.4) 9
Restrictor Door Recirculating
1983-87 (.3) 8
Heat Defrost Door
1983-87 (1.3) *2.1
Defroster Door-Floor
1985-87 (2.0) 3.0
*Add time to recharge A.C. system.

(G) Temperature Control Cable, Renew
1983-87 (.3) 6

(G) Blower Motor, Renew
1983-87 (.4) 8

(G) Blower Motor Switch, Renew
1983-87 (.3) 5

(G) Blower Motor Resistor, Renew
1983-87 (.3) 4

(G) Suction or Discharge Manifold Assy. Kit, Renew
Includes: Evacuate and charge system.
1983-87 (.8) 1.5

(G) Air Conditioning Hoses, Renew
Includes: Evacuate and charge system.
1983-87
Cond. to Evap. (.8) 1.7
Suction line (1.0) 1.9
Comp. to Cond. (.7) 1.6

PARTS 28 AIR CONDITIONING 28 PARTS

	Part No.	Price
Compressor Drive Belt		
Order by year and model.		
Compressor Assembly		
1983-87-exc. below	▲E4FZ-19703A	192.50
w/140 eng.	▲E3DZ-19703A	221.50
Compressor Shaft Seal		
1983-87	▲C9AZ-19655A	17.75
Compressor Clutch Brush Assy.		
1983-87	▲C8SZ-2979A	24.50
Compressor Clutch (Complete)		
140 engine		
1983-84	▲E3SZ-2884A	47.00
1985-87	▲E4SZ-2884A	47.00
230, 302 engs.		
1983-87	▲E2ZZ-2884A	141.50
Compressor Clutch Pulley Bearing		
1983-87	▲C9AZ-2990A	27.25
Compressor Valve Plate Kit		
1983-87	▲C3GY-19656A	26.25
Condenser Assy.		
(exc. V-8 eng.)		
1983-87	▲E2ZZ-19712A	180.75
(V-8 engine)		
1983-84	▲E2ZZ-19712A	180.75
1985-87	▲E5LY-19712A	241.50
Evaporator Core		
1983-84	▲E25Y-19860A	139.50
1985-87	▲E4LY-19860A	141.00
Blower Motor		
1983-87	▲E35Y-19805A	90.50
Blower Motor Resister		
1983-87	▲E35Y-19A706A	11.00
Blower Motor Switch		
1983-87	▲E1FZ-19986A	10.00

LABOR 29 LOCKS, HINGES & WIND. REGULATORS 29 LABOR

(Factory Time) Chilton Time

(G) Hood Release Cable, Renew
1983-87 (.3) 6

(G) Hood Latch, Renew
1983-87 (.3) 5

(G) Hood Hinge, Renew
Includes: Adjust hood and latch.
1983-87 (.4) 6

LABOR 29 LOCKS, HINGES & WIND. REGULATORS 29 LABOR

	(Factory Time)	Chilton Time
(G) Door Latch, Renew		
Includes: R&R trim panel and weathersheet.		
1983-87	(.5)	.8
(G) Door Lock Remote Control, Renew		
Includes: R&R trim panel and weathersheet.		
1983-87	(.4)	.7
(G) Door Handle (Outside), Renew		
Includes: R&R trim panel and weathersheet.		
1983-87	(.5)	.7
(G) Lock Striker Plate, Renew		
1983-87	(.2)	.3
(G) Door Window Regulator, Renew		
Includes: R&R trim panel and weathersheet.		
1983-87		
manual	(.5)	.9
electric	(.6)	1.0
(G) Quarter Window Regulator, Renew		
1983-87	(.7)	1.2
(G) Luggage Compartment Lift Cylinder, Renew		
1983-87	(.2)	.4
(G) Liftgate Hinges, Renew		
1983-87-upper-one	(.3)	.5
both	(.4)	.6

PARTS 29 LOCKS, HINGES & WIND. REGULATORS 29 PARTS

	Part No.	Price
Hood Latch		
1983-85	▲E4DZ-16700A	14.75
1986-87	▲E6DZ-16700A	14.75
Hood Hinge		
1983-87	▲D9ZZ-16796A	13.25
Door Lock		
1983-87-right	▲E3BZ-3621812A	30.50
left	▲E3BZ-3621813A	30.50
Door Lock Cylinder & Key		
(w/Bright cylinder)		
1983-87-right	▲E1FZ-6121984A	10.75
left	▲E1FZ-6121985A	10.75
(w/Black cylinder)		
1983-87-right	▲E1FZ-6121984B	10.75
left	▲E1FZ-6121985B	10.75
Outer Door Handle		
(bright finish)		
1983-87-right	▲E3FZ-5822404A	21.50
left	▲E3FZ-5822405A	21.50
(w/black finish)		
1983-87-right	▲E3FZ-6122404B	21.50
left	▲E3FZ-6122405B	21.50
Front Door Hinge (On Door)		
1983-87-upper	▲E1ZZ-6622814A	17.00
lower	▲E2ZZ-6122814A	17.50
Front Door Hinge (On Body)		
1983-87-lower	▲E4ZZ-6122820B	10.50
upper	▲E4ZZ-6122820A	10.50
Front Window Regulator		
Manual		
1983-87	▲D9ZZ-6623200C	62.75
Power		
1983-87-right	▲E1ZZ-6623208B	73.50
left	▲E1ZZ-6623209B	73.50
Trunk Lid Lock		
(2-door sedan)		
1983-87-manual	▲D9ZZ-6643200A	22.00
power	▲D9BZ-5443200A	57.50
(3-door sedan)		
1983-87-manual	▲E3FZ-5843200A	15.00
power	▲E3FZ-5843200B	16.00
Trunk Lock Cylinder & Key		
1983-87-bright cyl.	▲E1ZZ-6643505A	10.75
black cyl.	▲E1ZZ-6643505B	10.75
Trunk Lid Hinge		
(2 door sedan)		
1983-87-right	▲D9ZZ-6642700A	27.25
left	▲D9ZZ-6642701A	27.25
(3 door sedan)		
(wo/convertible)		
1983-87	▲D9ZZ-6142700A	26.00
(w/convertible)		
1983-87-right	▲E3ZZ-7642700A	28.00
left	▲E3ZZ-7642701A	28.00

LABOR 30 HEAD AND PARKING LAMPS 30 LABOR

	(Factory Time)	Chilton Time
(G) Aim Headlamps		
two		.4
four		.6
(M) Headlamp Sealed Beam Bulb, Renew		
1983-87-each	(.3)	.4
(M) Tail Lamp Assembly, Renew		
1983-87	(.3)	.4
(M) License Lamp Assembly, Renew		
1983-87	(.2)	.3
(M) Tail Lamp Lens, Renew		
1983-87	(.2)	.3
(M) Parking Lamp Assembly, Renew		
1983-87	(.4)	.5
(M) Parking Lamp Lens, Renew		
1983-87	(.2)	.3
(M) Side Marker Lamp Assy., Renew		
1983-87	(.3)	.4

PARTS 30 HEAD & PARKING LAMPS 30 PARTS

	Part No.	Price
Seal Beam Bulbs		
(exc. SVO)		
1983-87-high	▲D94Y-13007C	12.75
low	▲D94Y-13007A	12.75
(SVO)		
1984-85 (bef. 2/85)	▲E1FZ-13007A	24.25
1985-87 (from 2-85) R.H.	▲E5ZZ-13007A	25.50
left	▲E5ZZ-13007B	25.50
Parking Lamp Assy.		
(exc. SVO)		
1983-84	▲D9ZZ-13200A	21.25
1985-87	▲E5ZZ-13200A	21.25
(SVO)		
1984 (bef. 4-85) R.H.	▲E4ZZ-13200A	21.50
left	▲E5ZZ-13201B	21.25
1985-87 (from 4-85) R.H.	▲E5ZZ-13200B	21.25
left	▲E5ZZ-13201B	21.25
Tail Lamp Assy.		
Mustang		
(exc. SVO)		
1983-84-right	▲E3ZZ-13404A	120.50
left	▲E3ZZ-13405A	120.50
1985-87-right	▲E5ZZ-13404A	114.00
left	▲E5ZZ-13405A	114.00
(SVO)		
1984-right	▲E4ZZ-13404A	101.50
left	▲E4ZZ-13405A	101.50
1985-87-right	▲E5ZZ-13404B	114.00
left	▲E5ZZ-13405B	114.00
Capri		
(Black)		
1983-84-right	▲E3CY-13404B	93.00
left	▲E3CY-13405B	93.00
(Silver)		
1983-right	▲E3CY-13404D	113.75
left	▲E3CY-13405D	113.75
(Charcoal)		
1985-87-right	▲E5CY-13404A	88.00
left	▲E5CY-13405A	88.00
Tail Lamp Lens		
Mustang		
(exc. SVO)		
1983-84-right	▲E3ZZ-13450A	39.50
left	▲E3ZZ-13451A	39.50
1985-87-right	▲E5ZZ-13450A	52.25
left	▲E5ZZ-13451A	52.25
(SVO)		
1984-right	▲E4ZZ-13450A	66.75
left	▲E4ZZ-13451A	66.75
1985-87-right	▲E5ZZ-13450B	52.25
left	▲E5ZZ-13451B	52.25
Capri		
(Black)		
1983-84-right	▲E3CY-13450A	46.00
left	▲E3CY-13451A	46.00

PARTS 30 HEAD AND PARKING LAMPS 30 PARTS

	Part No.	Price
(Silver)		
1983-right	▲E3CY-13450B	54.25
left	▲E3CY-13451B	54.25
(Charcoal)		
1985-87-right	▲E5CY-13450A	34.50
left	▲E5CY-13451A	34.50
License Plate Lamp Assy.		
1983-87	▲D9ZZ-13550A	6.25
Rear Hi-Mount Lamp Assy.		
1985-87-3 dr. hatchback	▲E6ZZ-13A613E	25.00
2 dr. sedan (exc. conv.)	▲E6ZZ-13A613G	41.75
convertible	▲E6ZZ-13A613F	41.75

LABOR 31 WINDSHIELD WIPER & SPEEDOMETER 31 LABOR

	(Factory Time)	Chilton Time
(G) Windshield Wiper Motor, Renew		
1983-87	(.4)	.6
(G) Wiper Pivot, Renew (One)		
1983-87	(.4)	.6
(G) Wiper Switch, Renew		
1983-87	(.4)	.7
(G) Windshield Wiper Governor Assy., Renew		
1983-87	(.4)	.6
(G) Windshield Washer Pump, Renew		
1983-87	(.3)	.5
under fender	(.5)	.7
(G) Rear Window Wiper Motor, Renew		
1983-84	(.4)	.6
(G) Rear Window Wiper Switch, Renew		
1983-84	(.4)	.6
(G) Speedometer Head, R&R or Renew		
Includes: R&R instrument panel pad when required.		
1983-87	(.4)	.8
Reset odometer add		.2
(G) Speedometer Cable and Casing, Renew		
Includes: R&R instrument panel pad when required.		
1983-87		
one piece	(.4)	.7
upper	(.3)	.6
lower	(.3)	.6
(G) Speedometer Cable (Inner), Renew or Lubricate		
1983-87		
one piece	(.3)	.5
upper	(.3)	.5
lower	(.4)	.6
(G) Speedometer Driven Gear, Renew		
1983-87	(.3)	.4
(G) Radio, R&R		
Includes: R&R instrument panel pad when required.		
1983-84	(.5)	1.0
1985-87	(1.1)	2.0
w/Console add	(.2)	.3

PARTS 31 WINDSHIELD WIPER & SPEEDOMETER 31 PARTS

	Part No.	Price
Wiper Motor Assy.		
(Front)		
1983	▲D8BZ-17508B	94.25
1984-87	▲E4ZZ-17508A	94.25
Arm & Pivot Shaft		
1983-87-front	▲D9ZZ-17566A	32.50
rear	▲D9ZZ-17566C	48.00
Wiper Switch		
(Front)		
(wo/interm. wprs.)		
1983-87	▲E3DZ-17A553C	18.50
(w/interm. wprs.)		
1983-87	▲E3DZ-17A553A	25.75
(Rear)		
Windshield Wiper Governor		
1983	▲D8BZ-17C476A	77.50
1984-87	▲E4ZZ-17C476A	72.50
Windshield Washer Pump		
1983-87-front	▲E0AZ-17664A	20.00
rear	▲E1FZ-17664A	18.75
Speedometer Cable (Inner)		
1983-87	▲D4AZ-17262A	7.75
Speedometer Case & Shaft		
(wo/turbo)		
1983-87	▲E3BZ-17260A	22.75
(w/turbo)		
1983-87	▲E0ZZ-17260A	21.75
Speedometer Head Assy.		
(exc. SVO)		
1983-87	▲E3ZZ-17255A	99.75
(SVO)		
1984-87-85 m.p.h.	▲E4ZZ-17255A	99.75
140 m.p.h.	▲E4ZZ-17255B	99.75

LABOR 32 LIGHT SWITCHES & WIRING 32 LABOR

	(Factory Time)	Chilton Time
(G) Headlamp Switch, Renew		
1983-87	(.3)	.5
(G) Headlamp Dimmer Switch, Renew		
1983-87	(.4)	.7
(G) Stop Light Switch, Renew		
1983-87	(.3)	.4
(G) Turn Signal Switch Assy., Renew		
1983-87	(.4)	1.0
(G) Back-Up Lamp Switch, Renew		
1983-87	(.3)	.5
(M) Turn Signal or Hazard Warning Flasher, Renew		
1983-87	(.3)	.4
(G) Horns, Renew		
1983-87-each	(.3)	.4
(G) Wiring Harness, Renew		
Dash to Engine Gauge Feed		
1983-87	(.3)	.8
Alternator to Regulator		
1983-87	(.3)	.7

PARTS 32 LIGHT SWITCHES & WIRING 32 PARTS

	Part No.	Price
Headlamp Switch		
1983-87-wo/light	▲E0AZ-11654C	16.50
w/light	▲E0AZ-11654D	17.50
Turn Signal & Warning Switch		
1983-85	▲E2FZ-13341A	41.25
1985-87	▲E5FZ-13341A	41.25
Stop Light Switch		
1983-85	▲E3ZZ-13480A	7.25
1986-87	▲E6ZZ-13480A	7.50
Back-Up Lamp Switch		
(w/A.T.)		
1983-87-C3 trans.	▲D6RY-7A247B	31.75
C5 trans.	▲E2DZ-7A247A	36.50

PARTS 32 LIGHT SWITCHES & WIRING 32 PARTS

	Part No.	Price
(w/M.T.)		
1983-87-5 sp.		
O.D. (T5)	▲E0ZZ-15520A	21.25
RAP	▲D3FZ-15520A	6.00
German	▲D3FZ-15520A	6.00
Turn Signal Flasher		
1983-87	▲C6AZ-13350B	3.75
Emergency Warning Flasher		
1983-87	▲D1FZ-13350A	4.25
Horn Assy.		
Mustang		
1983-87-high	▲E3AZ-13832A	17.00
low	▲E3AZ-13833A	17.00
Capri		
1983-84-wo/ turbo	▲D9CY-13832A	27.00
w/turbo	▲E3CY-13832A	27.00
1983-87-high	▲E3AZ-13832A	17.00
low	▲E3AZ-13833A	17.00
Wiring Harness		
Note: Order by model and description.		

LABOR 33 GLASS 33 LABOR

(Factory Time)	Chilton Time
(G) Windshield Glass, Renew	
1983-87	
sdn (1.0)	**1.5**
convertible (2.2)	**3.0**
Renew butyl tape add (.2)	**.2**
(G) Door Glass, Renew	
Includes: R&R trim panel and weathersheet.	
1983-87 (.5)	**1.0**
(G) Rear Quarter Window Glass, Renew	
Includes: R&R trim panel and weathersheet.	
1983-87	
sdn (.9)	**1.3**
convertible (.8)	**1.2**
(G) Rear Window Glass, Renew	
1983-87	
sdn (.8)	**1.4**
convertible (3.7)	**5.0**
Renew butyl tape add (.2)	**.2**

LABOR 34 CRUISE CONTROL 34 LABOR

(Factory Time)	Chilton Time
(G) Cruise Control System Diagnosis	
1983-87 (.4)	**.6**
(G) Speed Control Amplifier, Assy., Renew	
1983-87 (.3)	**.6**
Road test add (.3)	**.3**
(G) Speed Control Sensor Assy., Renew	
1983-87 (.3)	**.5**
Road test add (.3)	**.3**
(G) Speed Control Servo Assy., Renew	
1983-87 (.4)	**.6**
under fender	
w/Conn (.6)	**.9**
wo/Conn (.6)	**.9**
Road test add (.3)	**.3**
(G) Speed Control Relay, Renew	
1983-87 (.3)	**.5**
Road test add (.3)	**.3**
(G) Speed Control Actuator Switch, Renew	
1983-87 (.3)	**.6**
Road test add (.3)	**.3**
(G) Speed Control Metering (Dump) Valve, Renew	
1983-87 (.4)	**.6**
(G) Cruise Control Chain/Cable, Renew	
1983-87 (.6)	**.8**
(G) Cruise Control Clutch Switch, Renew	
1983-87 (.1)	**.3**
Road test add (.3)	**.3**

PARTS 34 CRUISE CONTROL 34 PARTS

	Part No.	Price
Speed Control Amplifier Assy.		
1983-87-exc. 302	▲E0AZ-9D843A	161.50
1986-87-w/302	▲E6AZ-9D843A	161.50
Speed Control Servo Assy.		
1983-w/140 eng.		
wo/Turbo	▲E2FZ-9C735A	120.25
w/Turbo	▲E3ZZ-9C735A	120.25
1983-w/230 eng.	▲E3ZZ-9C735B	120.25
w/302 eng.	▲E2FZ-9C735A	120.25
1984-87	▲E4LY-9C735A	120.25
Speed Control Sensor		
1983-87	▲E3AZ-9E731A	20.75
Speed Control Actuator Switch		
1983-84	▲E3SZ-9C888A	45.75
1985-87	▲E53Z-9C888A	42.75

GROUP INDEX

ALPHABETICAL INDEX

Ford Motor Company
Rear Wheel Drive Cars

COUGAR • XR7 • THUNDERBIRD

YEAR IDENTIFICATION

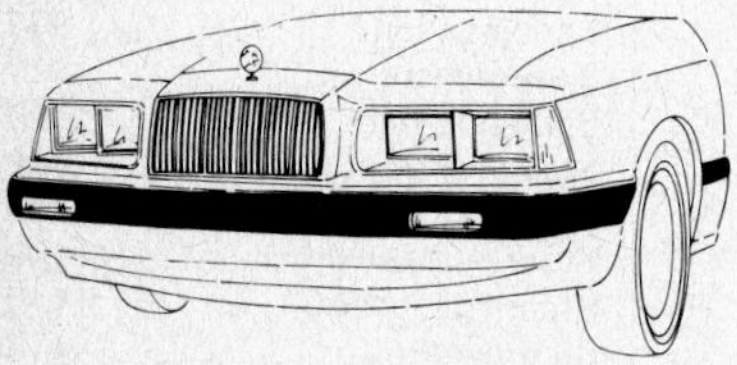

1983–86 Cougar

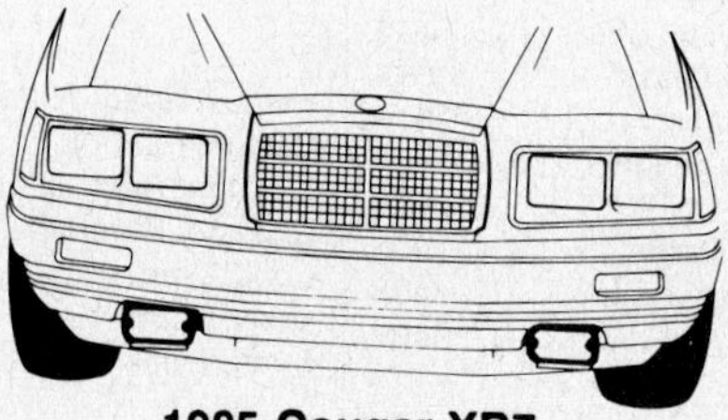

1985 Cougar XR7

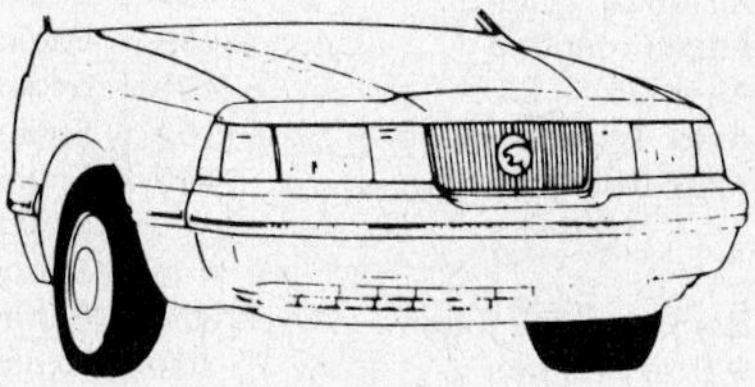

1987 Cougar

1983–86 Thunderbird

1985–86 Thunderbird Turbo Coupe

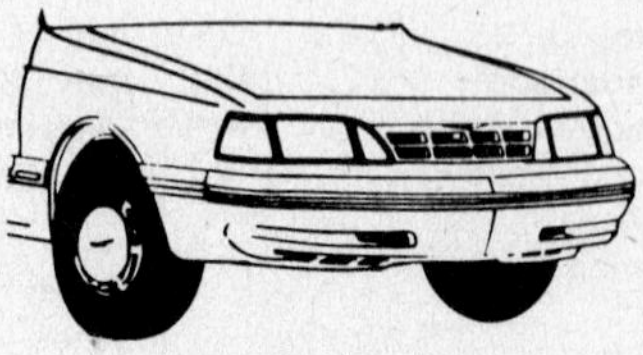

1987 Thunderbird

1987 Thunderbird Turbo

VEHICLE IDENTIFICATION NUMBER (VIN)

It is important for servicing and ordering parts to be certain of the vehicle and engine identification. The VIN (vehicle identification number) is a 13 or 17 digit number visible through the windshield on the driver's side of the dash and contains the vehicle and engine identification codes. It can be interpreted as follows:

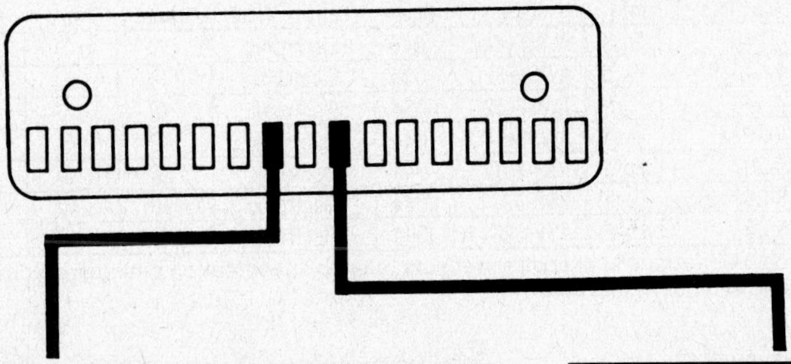

Engine Code					
Code	Cu. In.	Liters	Cyl.	Carb.	Eng. Mfg.
A	140	2.3	4	1	Ford
W	140-T	2.3	4	Turbo.	Ford
T	140-T SVO	2.3	4	Turbo.	Ford
R	140-HSC	2.3	4	①	Ford
T,B,X	200	3.3	6	1	Ford
3	232	3.8	V6	①	Ford
C	232	3.8	V6	①	Ford
F	302	5.0	V8	1	Ford
M	302-H.O.	5.0	V8	①	Ford
G	351-W	5.8	V8	①	Ford
G	351-H.O.	5.8	V8	①	Ford

Model Year Code	
Code	Year
D	1983
E	1984
F	1985
G	1986
H	1987

The seventeen digit Vehicle Identification Number can be used to determine engine application and model year. The tenth digit indicates the model year, and the eighth digit identifies the engine code.

① EFI, VV, 2 bbl. or 4 bbl. depending on model

TUNE-UP SPECIFICATIONS

When analyzing compression test results, look for uniformity among cylinders rather than specific pressures

Year	Engine: Eng. VIN Code	Engine: No. Cyl. Displacement (cu. in.)	Eng. mfg.	Spark Plugs: Orig. Type	Spark Plugs: Gap (in.)•	Distributor: Point Dwell (deg)	Distributor: Point Gap (in.)	Ignition Timing (deg): Man. Trans.	Ignition Timing (deg): Auto. Trans.	Valves Intake Opens (deg)	Fuel Pump Pressure (psi)	Idle Speed (rpm): Man. Trans.	Idle Speed (rpm): Auto. Trans.
'83	A	4-140	Ford	AWSF-44	.044	Electronic		①	①	16	5.5–6.5	850	800
	X	6-200	Ford	BSF-92	.050	Electronic		①	①	20	6–8	600	600
	3	V-6-232	Ford	AWSF-52	.044	Electronic		①	①	13	39	550	550
	F	8-302	Ford	ASF-52 ②	.050	Electronic		①	①	16	6–8 ③	—	550
	G	8-351	Ford	ASF-42	.044	Electronic		①	①	23	6–8	—	700/600
'84	A	4-140	Ford	AWSF-44	.044	Electronic		①	①	16	5–7	850	750
	W	4-140-T	Ford	AWSF-32	.034	Electronic		①	①	—	39	①–④	①–④
	T	4-140-T ⑤	Ford	AWSF-32	.034	Electronic		①	①	—	39	① ④	① ④
	3	V6-232	Ford	AWSF-54	.044	Electronic		①	①	13	39	—	550
	F	8302	Ford	ASF-52	.050	Electronic		①	①	16	39	550	550
	M	8302HO	Ford	ASF-42	.044	Electronic		①	①	—	6–8	700	700
	G	8-351	Ford	ASF-42	.044	Electronic		①	①	23	6–8	—	600 ⑥
'85	A	4-140	Ford	AWSF-44	.044	Electronic		①	①	16	6–8	850	750
	W	4-140T	Ford	AWSF-32	.034	Electronic		①	①	—	39	750	750
	T	4-140-T ⑤	Ford	AWSF-32	.034	Electronic		①	①	—	39	① ④	① ④
	R	4-140-HSC	Ford	AWSF-52	.044	Electronic		①	①	—	39	800	700
	3	V6-232	Ford	AGSP-52	.044	Electronic		①	①	13	6–8	600	600
	C	V6-232	Ford	AWSF-54	.044	Electronic		①	①	13	39	—	550
	F	8-302	Ford	ASF-52	.050	Electronic		①	①	—	39	550	550
	M	8-302 HO	Ford	ASF-42	.044	Electronic		①	①	—	6–8	700	700
	G	8-351	Ford	ASF-42	.044	Electronic		①	①	—	6–8	—	600 ⑥

TUNE-UP SPECIFICATIONS

When analyzing compression test results, look for uniformity among cylinders rather than specific pressures

Year	Engine: Eng. VIN Code	Engine: No. Cyl. Displacement (cu. in.)	Engine: Eng. mfg.	Spark Plugs: Orig. Type	Spark Plugs: Gap (in.)•	Distributor: Point Dwell (deg)	Distributor: Point Gap (in.)	Ignition Timing (deg): Man. Trans.	Ignition Timing (deg): Auto. Trans.	Valves Intake Opens (deg)	Fuel Pump Pressure (psi)	Idle Speed (rpm): Man. Trans.	Idle Speed (rpm): Auto. Trans.
'86–'87	A	4-140	Ford	AWSF-44C	.044	Electronic		①	①	16	6–8	750	750
	T	4-140-T	Ford	AWSF-32C	.034	Electronic		①	①	—	39	825/975	825/975
	W	4-140-T	Ford	AWSF-32C	.034	Electronic		①	①	—	39	825/975	825/975
	3	V6-232	Ford	AWSF-54	.044	Electronic		①	①	13	39	—	550
	F	8-302	Ford	ASF-32C	.044	Electronic		①	①	—	39	① ④	① ④
	M	8-302 HO	Ford	ASF-42	.044	Electronic		①	①	—	6–8	700	700
	G	8-351	Ford	ASF-32C	.044	Electronic		①	①	—	6–8	650	650

NOTE: The underhood calibrations sticker often reflects tune-up specification changes made in production. Sticker figures must be used if they disagree with those in this chart.

T Turbocharger
HO High output
HSC High swirl combustion
① Calibrations vary depending upon the model; refer to the underhood calibration sticker.
② The carbureted models use spark plug ASF-42 (.044) and the idle speed rpm is 700 rpm.
③ On fuel injected models the pressure is 39 psi.
④ Electronic engine control models the ignition timing, idle speed and idle mixture is not adjustable.
⑤ SVO
⑥ 700 rpm with the VOTM on.

FIRING ORDERS

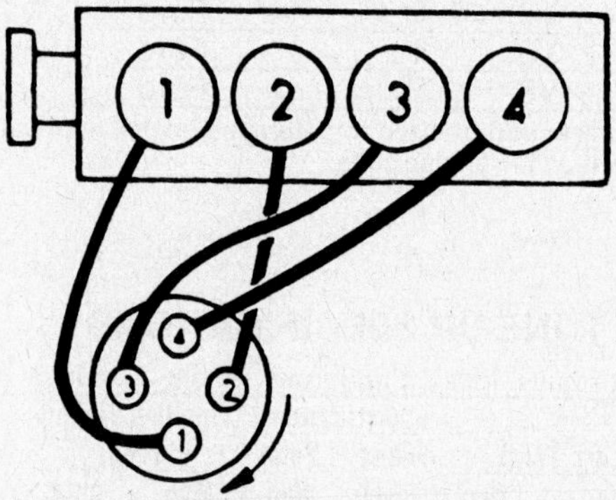

FORD MOTOR CO. 2300 cc 4-cyl.
Engine firing order: 1–3–4–2
Distributor rotation: clockwise

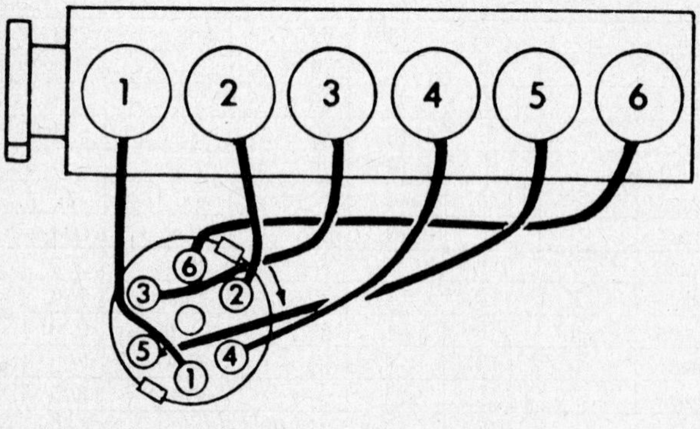

FORD MOTOR CO. 200, 250 6-cyl.
Engine firing order: 1–5–3–6–2–4
Distributor rotation: clockwise

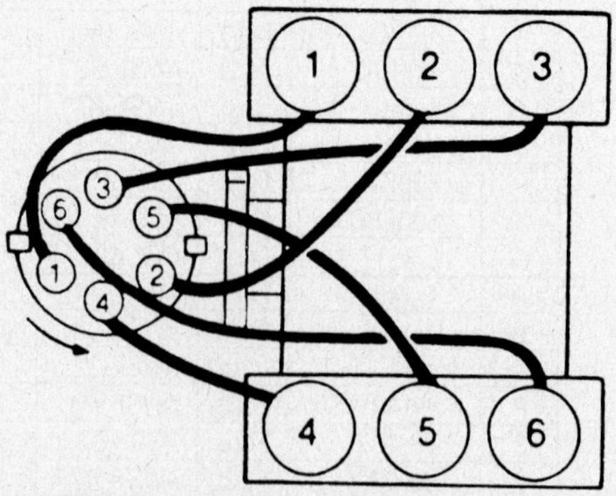

FORD MOTOR CO. 232 V6
Engine firing order 1–4–2–5–3–6
Distributor rotation: counterclockwise

FIRING ORDERS

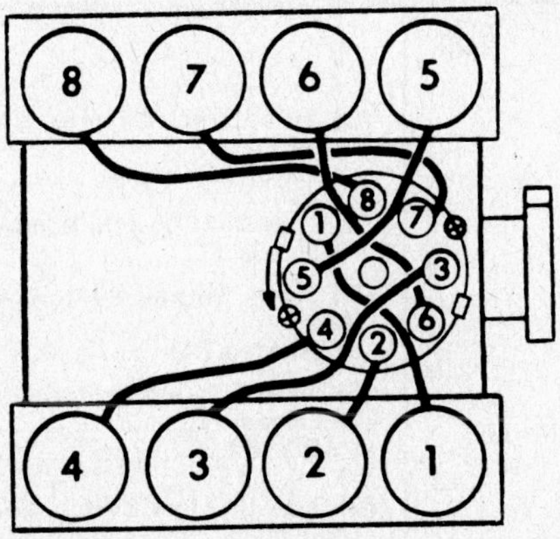

FORD MOTOR CO. 255, 302 (exc. HO) 460
V8 Engine firing order: 1–5–4–2–6–3–7–8
Distributor rotation: counterclockwise

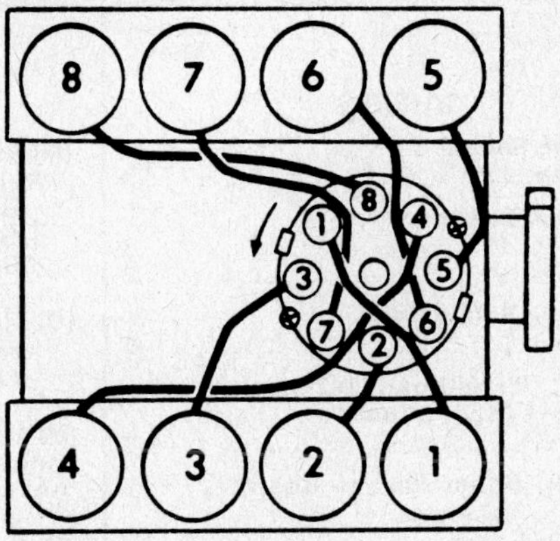

FORD MOTOR CO. 302HO, 351, 400
Engine firing order: 1–3–7–2–6–5–4–8
Distributor rotation: counterclockwise

WHEEL ALIGNMENT SPECIFICATIONS

		Caster		Camber				Wheel Pivot Ratio (deg)	
Year	Model	Range (deg)	Pref. Setting (deg)	Range (deg)	Pref. Setting (deg)	Toe-in (in.)	Steering Axis Inclin. (deg)	Inner Wheel	Outer Wheel
'83	Cougar XR7 Thunderbird	$\frac{1}{2}$P to 2P	$1\frac{1}{4}$P	$\frac{1}{2}$N to 1P	$\frac{1}{4}$P	$\frac{1}{16}$ to $\frac{5}{16}$	$15\frac{23}{32}$	20	$19\frac{23}{32}$
'84	Thunderbird Cougar	$\frac{1}{4}$P to $1\frac{3}{4}$P	1P	$\frac{1}{2}$N to 1P	$\frac{1}{4}$P	$\frac{1}{16}$ to $\frac{5}{16}$	$15\frac{23}{32}$	20	$19\frac{23}{32}$
'85-'87	Thunderbird Cougar	0P to $1\frac{1}{2}$P	$\frac{3}{4}$P	$\frac{1}{2}$N to 1P	$\frac{1}{4}$P	$\frac{1}{16}$ to $\frac{5}{16}$	$15\frac{23}{32}$	20	$19\frac{23}{32}$

LABOR — SERVICE BAY OPERATIONS — LABOR

(Factory Time) — Chilton Time

COOLING

(M) Winterize Cooling System
Includes: Run engine to check for leaks, tighten all hose connections. Test radiator and pressure cap. Drain radiator and engine block. Add anti-freeze and refill system.
All models 5

(M) Thermostat, Renew
1983-87-Four (.5) 7
V-6 (.5) 7
V-8-255 eng (.5) 7
302 eng (.4) 6

(M) Drive Belt, Renew
1983-87-one (.3) 4
each adtnl (.1) 1

(M) Drive Belt, Adjust
1983-87-one (.2) 3
each adtnl (.1) 1

(M) Radiator Hoses, Renew
All models
upper (.3) 4
lower (.4) 6
both (.5) 7

FUEL

(G) Carburetor Air Cleaner, Service
All models (.2) 3

(G) Carburetor Adjust (On Car)
All models (.4) 5
Propane enrichment method (1.0) 1.5

CHILTON'S 10 POINT SAFETY CHECK

CHECK OPERATION & CONDITION OF THE FOLLOWING ITEMS:

1. Legal Registration (serial no.)
2. Tires & Wheels
3. Brake System (R&R all wheels)
4. Light Systems & Signals
5. Accelerator Linkage, Neutral Safety Switch, Shift Indicator Pointer & Seat Position Locks
6. Glass, Mirrors, Door Locks, Seat Belts & Harness
7. Wipers, Washers & Defrosters
8. Frame, Steering, Shocks, Front & Rear Suspension
9. Fuel & Exhaust Systems
10. Road Test Vehicle

All models 1.0
Exhaust Smog Analysis, add 4

(Factory Time) — Chilton Time

(G) Thermostatic Choke Cover and/or Gasket, Renew
All models (.8) 1.3

(Factory Time) — Chilton Time

BRAKES

(G) Brakes, Adjust (Minor)
Includes: Adjust brakes, fill master cylinder.
two wheels 4

(G) Bleed Brakes (Four Wheels)
Includes: Fill master cylinder.
All models (.3) 5

(G) Brake Pedal Free Play, Adjust
All models 4

(M) Parking Brake, Adjust
All models (.2) 4

LUBRICATION SERVICE

(M) Lubricate Chassis, Change Oil & Filter
Includes: Inspect and correct all fluid levels.
All models 6
Install grease fittings add 1

(M) Lubricate Chassis
Includes: Inspect and correct all fluid levels.
All models 4
Install grease fittings add 1

(M) Engine Oil & Filter, Change
Includes: Inspect and correct all fluid levels.
All models 4

LABOR SERVICE BAY OPERATIONS LABOR

(Factory Time) Chilton Time

WHEELS

(M) Wheel, Renew
one (.5) 5

(G) Wheels, Balance
one 3
each adtnl 2

(G) Wheels, Rotate (All)
All models (.5) 5

(G) Front Wheel Bearings, Clean and Repack (Both Wheels)
All models 1.3

(G) Front Wheel Grease Seals, Renew
Includes: Repack bearings.
All models-one whl (.5) 7
both whls (.8) 1.1

(G) Front Wheel Bearings and Cups, Renew
All models-one whl (.7) 9
both whls (1.2) 1.5

ELECTRICAL

(M) Battery Cables, Renew
All models
Batt to Relay (.3) 3
Ground (.3) 3
Relay to Starter (.4) 5

(G) Aim Headlamps
two 4
four 6

(M) Headlamp Sealed Beam Bulb, Renew
All models-each (.3) 3

(M) Parking Lamp Lens, Renew
All models (.3) 4

(M) Stop Lamp Lens, Renew
All models (.2) 3

(G) Headlamp Switch, Renew
1983-87 (.4) 6

(G) Headlamp Dimmer Switch, Renew
1983-87 (.6) 1.0

(G) Stop Light Switch, Renew
All models (.3) 4

(G) Turn Signal Switch Assy., Renew
All models (.4) 1.0

(G) Neutral Safety Switch, Renew
All models (.3) 4
w/AOD add 2

(G) Back-Up Light Switch, Renew
All models (.3) 5

(M) Turn Signal or Hazard Warning Flasher, Renew
All models (.3) 4

(G) Horn, Renew
All models-each (.3) 4

LABOR 1 TUNE UP 1 LABOR

(Factory Time) Chilton Time

(G) Compression Test
Four–1983-87 (.3) 6
V-6–1983-87 (.4) 8
V-8–1983-87 (.5) 9
w/A.C. add 2

(G) Engine Tune Up, (Electronic Ignition)
Includes: Test battery and clean connections. Tighten manifold and carburetor mounting bolts. Check engine compression, clean and adjust or renew spark plugs. Test resistance of spark plug cables. Inspect distributor cap and rotor. Adjust air gap. Check vacuum advance operation. Reset ignition timing. Adjust idle mixture and idle speed. Service air cleaner. Inspect and adjust drive belts. Inspect choke operation and adjust or free up. Check operation of EGR valve.

Four–1983-87 .... 1.5
V-6–1983-87 .... 2.0
V-8–1983-87 .... 2.4
w/A.C. add 2
Perform EEC IV system test add 1.0

LABOR 2 IGNITION SYSTEM 2 LABOR

(Factory Time) Chilton Time

(G) Spark Plugs, Clean and Reset or Renew
1983-87-Four (.3) 5
V-6 (.6) 8
V-8 (.6) 8
w/A.C. add 2

(G) Ignition Timing, Reset
1983-87 (.4) 4

(G) Distributor, Renew
Includes: Reset ignition timing.
1983-87 (.4) 7

(G) Distributor Cap and/or Rotor, Renew
1983-87 (.3) 5

(G) Vacuum Control Unit, Renew
Includes: R&R distributor and reset ignition timing.
1983-87 (.5) 8

(G) Profile Ignition Pick-Up Sensor, Renew (Duraspark)
1983-87 (.5) 9
Perform system test add (.3) 3

(G) Ignition Coil, Renew
Includes: Test.
1983-87 (.3) 6

(G) Ignition Cables, Renew
Includes: Test wiring.
1983-87 (.4) 6

(G) Ignition Switch, Renew
1983-87 (.6) 1.0

(G) Ignition Key Indicator Buzzer or Chime, Renew
1983-87 (.6) 8

(G) Ignition Module Assembly, Renew
Note: Fender mount type. For TFI unit, refer to Emission Control section.
1983-87 (.3) 6
Perform system test add (.3) 3

(G) Distributor Armature, Renew
1983-84 (.3) 6

(G) Distributor Stator, Renew
Includes: R&R armature.
1983-84 (.4) 8

PARTS 2 ELECTRONIC IGNITION 2 PARTS

	Part No.	Price
Distributor Assy. (New)		
140 engine		
1983	▲E3ZZ-12127B	155.50
1984 (stamped)		
E3ZE-BA	▲E3ZZ-12127B	155.50
E4ZE-FA	▲E4ZZ-12127F	N.L.
1985-87	▲E59Z-12127C	136.75

PARTS 2 ELECTRONIC IGNITION 2 PARTS

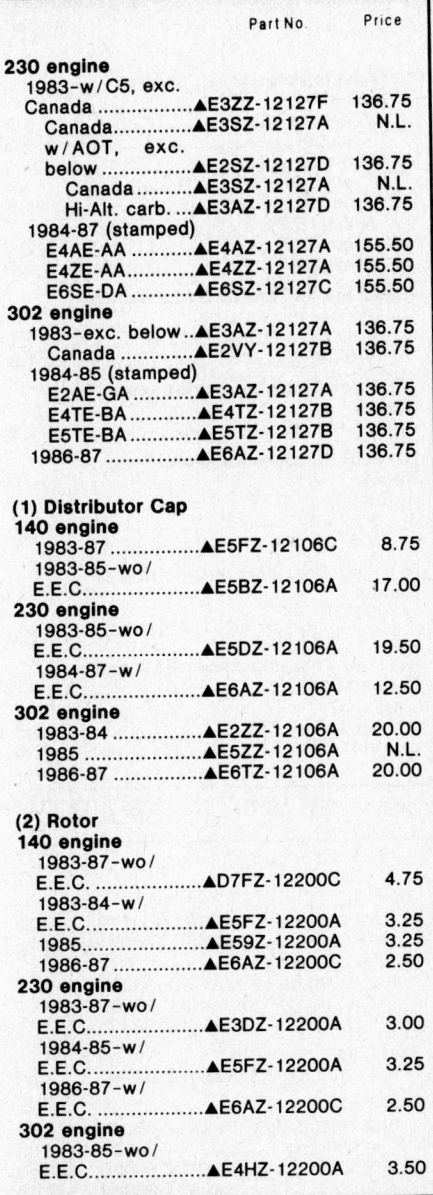

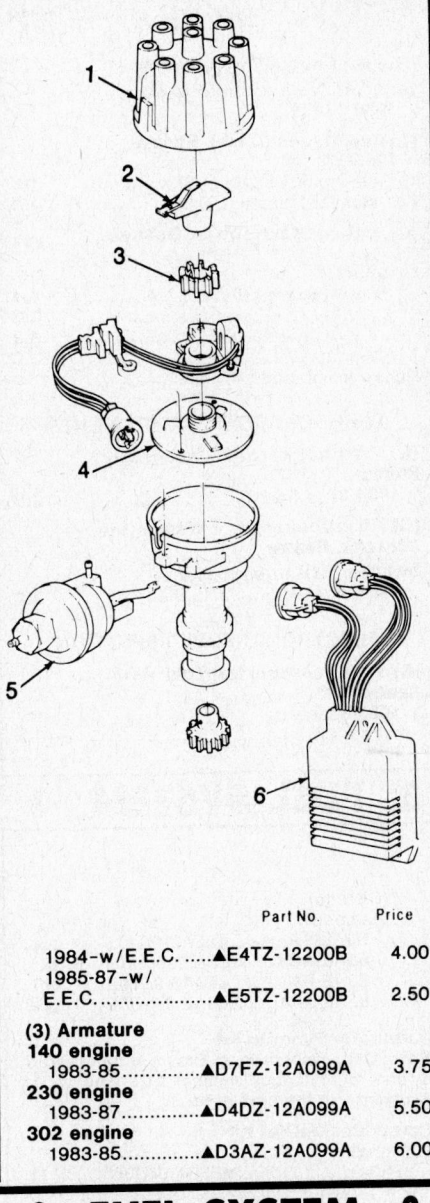

	Part No.	Price
230 engine		
1983-w/C5, exc.		
Canada	▲E3ZZ-12127F	136.75
Canada	▲E3SZ-12127A	N.L.
w/AOT, exc.		
below	▲E2SZ-12127D	136.75
Canada	▲E3SZ-12127A	N.L.
Hi-Alt. carb.	▲E3AZ-12127D	136.75
1984-87 (stamped)		
E4AE-AA	▲E4AZ-12127A	155.50
E4ZE-AA	▲E4ZZ-12127A	155.50
E6SE-DA	▲E6SZ-12127C	155.50
302 engine		
1983-exc. below	▲E3AZ-12127A	136.75
Canada	▲E2VY-12127B	136.75
1984-85 (stamped)		
E2AE-GA	▲E3AZ-12127A	136.75
E4TE-BA	▲E4TZ-12127B	136.75
E5TE-BA	▲E5TZ-12127B	136.75
1986-87	▲E6AZ-12127D	136.75
(1) Distributor Cap		
140 engine		
1983-87	▲E5FZ-12106C	8.75
1983-85-wo/		
E.E.C.	▲E5BZ-12106A	17.00
230 engine		
1983-85-wo/		
E.E.C.	▲E5DZ-12106A	19.50
1984-87-w/		
E.E.C.	▲E6AZ-12106A	12.50
302 engine		
1983-84	▲E2ZZ-12106A	20.00
1985	▲E5ZZ-12106A	N.L.
1986-87	▲E6TZ-12106A	20.00
(2) Rotor		
140 engine		
1983-87-wo/		
E.E.C.	▲D7FZ-12200C	4.75
1983-84-w/		
E.E.C.	▲E5FZ-12200A	3.25
1985	▲E59Z-12200A	3.25
1986-87	▲E6AZ-12200C	2.50
230 engine		
1983-87-wo/		
E.E.C.	▲E3DZ-12200A	3.00
1984-85-w/		
E.E.C.	▲E5FZ-12200A	3.25
1986-87-w/		
E.E.C.	▲E6AZ-12200C	2.50
302 engine		
1983-85-wo/		
E.E.C.	▲E4HZ-12200A	3.50

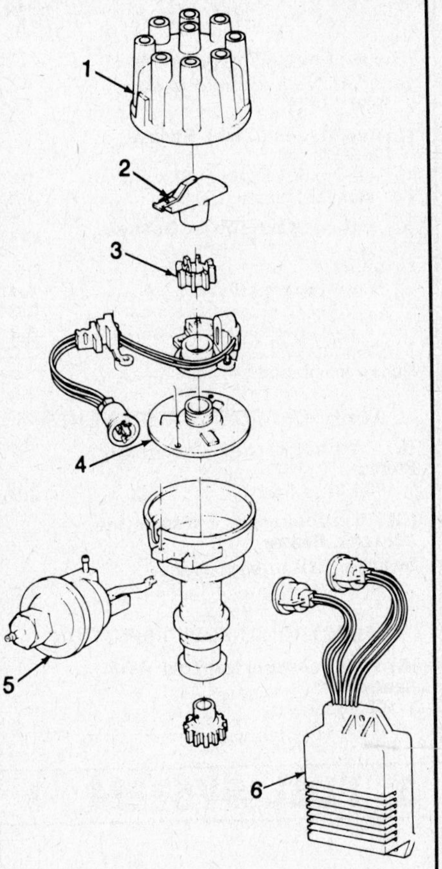

	Part No.	Price
1984-w/E.E.C.	▲E4TZ-12200B	4.00
1985-87-w/		
E.E.C.	▲E5TZ-12200B	2.50
(3) Armature		
140 engine		
1983-85	▲D7FZ-12A099A	3.75
230 engine		
1983-87	▲D4DZ-12A099A	5.50
302 engine		
1983-85	▲D3AZ-12A099A	6.00

	Part No.	Price
(4) Stator Assy.		
140 eng.		
1983-87	▲D5TZ-12A112B	25.25
230, 302 engs.		
1983-87	▲D4PZ-12A112A	25.50
(5) Vacuum Diaphragm Assy.		
230 engine		
1983-85-exc. C5		
& Canada	▲E1AZ-12370K	34.00
w/C5, &		
Canada	▲E1SZ-12370A	31.25
(6) Modulator Assy.		
140 engine		
1983-87-w/turbo	▲E43Z-12A297A	106.00
230 eng.		
1983-exc.		
Canada	▲E1AZ-12A199A	101.50
Canada	▲D9VZ-12A199A	83.50
1984-87-wo/		
E.E.C. IV	▲D9VZ-12A199A	83.50
w/EEC IV	▲E43Z-12A297A	106.00
302 engine		
1983-87-exc.		
Canada	▲D9AZ-12A199B	83.50
1983-Canada	▲D9VZ-12A199A	83.50
1984-87-w/EEC		
IV	▲E43Z-12A297A	106.00
Ignition Coil		
1983-87-wo/EEC		
IV	▲D5AZ-12029A	31.25
w/EEC IV	▲E3FZ-12029A	33.75
Ignition Wire Set		
140 engine		
1983-84	▲E3PZ-12259AH	41.25
1985	▲E5PZ-12259D	49.50
1986-87	▲E6PZ-12259H	49.50
230 engine		
1983	▲E4PZ-12259AFR	53.75
1984-87-wo/EEC		
IV	▲E4PZ-12259FR	53.50
w/EEC IV	▲E4PZ-12259B	42.75
302 engine		
1983	▲E3PZ-12259ADR	57.50
1984-85	▲E4PZ-12259C	58.75
1986-87	▲E6PZ-12259F	58.75
Ignition Switch		
1983-87	▲E4FZ-11572A	11.50
Ignition Warning Switch		
1983	▲D9AZ-11A127A	5.50
1984-87	▲E5SZ-11A127A	5.00

LABOR 3 FUEL SYSTEM 3 LABOR

(Factory Time) — Chilton Time

(G) Fuel Pump, Test
Includes: Disconnect line at carburetor, attach pressure gauge.

	Chilton Time
All models	
mechanical	.3
electric	.5

(G) Carburetor Air Cleaner, Service

	Chilton Time
1983-87 (.2)	.3

(G) Carburetor, Adjust (On Car)

	Chilton Time
1983-87 (.4)	.5
Propane enrichment method (1.0)	1.5

(M) Fuel Filter, Renew

	Chilton Time
1983-87 (.4)	.5
w/Turbo add	.2

(G) Carburetor, R&R or Renew
Includes: All necessary adjustments.

	Chilton Time
1983-87-Four (.5)	.8
V-6 (.6)	.8
V-8-2150-2 V (.6)	9
2700 VV (1.3)	2.0
7200 VV (1.2)	1.9
Renew carb add (.4)	.4

(G) Carburetor, R&R and Clean or Recondition
Includes: All necessary adjustments.

	Chilton Time
1983-87-Four (1.6)	2.2
V-6 (1.6)	2.5
V-8-2150-2 V (1.6)	2.5
2700 VV (2.4)	3.5
7200 VV (2.5)	3.5
Renew spacer add (.2)	.2
Transfer choke add (.1)	.1

(G) Float Level, Adjust
Includes: Set idle speed and mixture.

	Chilton Time
All models	
Holly 1946 1V (.5)	.7
Weber 740 2V (.5)	.7
Motorcraft 2150 2V (.4)	.6
Weber 5200-6500 2V (.5)	.7
2700-7200 VV (.5)	.7

(G) Float or Needle Valve and Seat, Renew
Includes: Set idle speed and mixture.

	Chilton Time
All models	
Holly 1946 1V (.6)	.9
Weber 740 2V (.5)	.8
Motorcraft 2150 2V (.4)	.7
Weber 5200-6500 2V (.5)	.8
2700-7200 VV (.5)	.8

LABOR — 3 FUEL SYSTEM 3 — LABOR

(Factory Time)	Chilton Time
(G) Accelerator Pump Diaphragm, Piston or Rod, Renew	
All models	
Four (.4)	.6
V-6 (.6)	.8
V-8-2 bbl (.3)	.5
4 bbl (.5)	.7
(G) Fuel Enrichment Valve Assy., Renew	
1983-87	
2150 2V (.8)	1.3
(G) Thermostatic Choke Housing and/or Gasket, Renew	
1983-87	
2150 2V (.8)	1.3
(G) Fuel Pump, Renew	
1983-84-Four (.5)	.8
V-6 (.5)	.7
V-8	
on block (.5)	.9
frame mount (.6)	.8
in tank (.9)	1.4
1985-87	
on frame (.6)	.8
in tank (.9)	1.4
Add pump test if performed.	
(G) Fuel Tank, Renew	
Includes: Transfer tank gauge unit.	
1983-87 (1.0)	1.5
w/Elec fuel pump add	.2
(G) Fuel Gauge (Tank), Renew	
Includes: Drain and refill tank.	
1983-87 (.9)	1.4
(G) Fuel Gauge (Dash), Renew	
1983-87	
electronic cluster (1.2)	1.8
standard cluster (.7)	1.2
(G) Intake Manifold or Gaskets, Renew	
1983-87	
Four-upper (1.0)	1.4
lower (2.1)	3.0
V-6 (2.2)	3.2
V-8 (2.1)	3.0
Renew manif. add (.4)	.5

TURBOCHARGER COMPONENTS

(Factory Time)	Chilton Time
(G) Turbocharger Assembly, Renew	
1983-87 (1.5)	2.0
(G) Turbocharger Wastegate Actuator, Renew	
Includes: R&R turbocharger.	
1983-87 (1.7)	2.2

ELECTRONIC FUEL INJECTION

(Factory Time)	Chilton Time
(G) Fuel Injection Manifold Assy., Renew	
1983-87	
Four (.8)	1.2
(G) Fuel Injector Assy., Renew	
1983-87	
Four-one (.8)	1.2
all (.9)	1.5
V-6-V-8-w/CFI	
one (.8)	1.2
all (.9)	1.5
V-8-w/SEFI	
one (1.8)	2.4
all (2.0)	2.7
(G) Air Intake Throttle Body, Renew	
1983-87	
Four (.7)	1.1
V-8 (.9)	1.3
(G) Fuel Charging Wiring Assy., Renew	
1983-87 (.3)	.6
(G) Fuel Pressure Regulator Assy., Renew	
1983-87	
Four (.9)	1.4
V-6-V-8 (.8)	1.3
(G) Fuel Charging Assy., R&R or Renew	
1983-87	
V-6-V-8 (.7)	1.2
(G) Fuel Charging Assy., R&R and Recondition	
1983-87	
V-6 (1.5)	2.2
V-8 (1.8)	2.5

PARTS — 3 FUEL SYSTEM 3 — PARTS

	Part No.	Price
Air Cleaner Element (Carb.)		
140 engine		
1983-87	▲E3ZZ-9601A	9.25
230 engine		
1983-87	▲D3ZZ-9601A	10.75
302 engine		
1983-exc. Canada	▲D2AZ-9601AR	8.50
Canada	▲D7ZZ-9601AR	11.00
1984-85	▲D2AZ-9601AR	8.50
1986-87	▲E6SZ-9601B	11.50
Carburetor Assy. (New)		
230 engine		
1983 (w/C5 trans.)		
(exc. California)		
wo/A.C.	▲E3SZ-9510BE	392.75
w/A.C.	▲E3SZ-9510BD	392.75
(California)		
wo/A.C.	▲E3SZ-9510BG	392.75
w/A.C.	▲E3SZ-9510BF	277.00
1983 (w/A.O.T.)		
(exc. Calif.)		
stamped		
E3SE-FA	▲E3SZ-9510F	391.25
E3SE-AUA	▲E3SZ-9510AU	391.25
E3SE-EA	▲E3SZ-9510E	392.75
E3SE-ATA	▲E3SZ-9510AT	392.75
(California)		
stamped		
E3SE-KA	▲E3SZ-9510K	392.75
E3SE-APA	▲E3SZ-9510AP	432.00
E3SE-JA	▲E3SZ-9510J	392.75
E3SE-ANA	▲E3SZ-9510AN	392.75
(w/hi alt. carb.)		
stamped		
E3SE-HA	▲E3SZ-9510H	Disc.
E3SE-GA	▲E3SZ-9510G	444.00
E3SE-ARA	▲E3SZ-9510AR	432.00
(Canada)		
stamped		
E3AE-SA	▲E3AZ-9510S	N.L.
E3AE-AGA	▲E3AZ-9510AG	N.L.
E3AE-RA	▲E3AZ-9510R	N.L.
E3AE-AFA	▲E3AZ-9510AF	N.L.

Carburetor Tune-Up Kit

Note: Carburetor tune-up kits must be ordered by the identification number attached to or stamped into the carburetor.

	Part No.	Price
Carburetor Gasket Kit		
230 engine		
1983	▲E3PZ-9502B	35.75
Fuel Pump Assy. (New)		
140 engine		
(fuel tank unit)		
1984	▲E4SZ-9H307C	93.75
1985	▲E5SZ-9A407B	184.75
1986-87	▲E6LZ-9A407A	161.00
(engine mounted)		
1983	▲E3SZ-9350A	101.25
1984-before 2-84	▲E3ZZ-9350B	190.75
from 2-84	▲E4ZZ-9350B	190.75
230 engine		
(fuel tank unit)		
1984-exc. below	▲E4SZ-9H307A	93.75
elec. cluster	▲E4SZ-9H307B	93.75
1985-87	▲E5SZ-9A407A	184.75
(engine mounted)		
1983-87-exc. C.F.I.	▲E2AZ-9350B	26.25
1984-85	▲E4DZ-9350B	184.75
1985-87	▲E5SZ-9A407A	184.75
302 engine		
(fuel tank unit)		
1984-exc. below	▲E4SZ-9H307A	93.75
elec. cluster	▲E4SZ-9H307B	93.75
1985-87	▲E5SZ-9A407A	184.75
(engine mounted)		
1983-exc. below	▲E3SZ-9350C	114.00
elec. cluster	▲E3SZ-9350D	114.00
1983-84	▲E4DZ-9350B	184.75
Fuel Line		
1983-87	▲E1PZ-9324C	1.50
Fuel Tank		
1983-exc. below	▲E4SZ-9002B	138.50
w/230 eng.	▲E3SZ-9002B	115.00
1984	▲E4SZ-9002B	138.50
1985	▲E5SZ-9002B	138.50
1986-87	▲E5LY-9002A	152.00

Fuel Gauge (Tank Unit)

Order by year and model.

	Part No.	Price
Fuel Gauge (Dash)		
1983 (wo/elect. inst. cluster)		
Cougar	▲E3WY-9305A	40.75
Thunderbird (exc. 140 eng.)	▲E3SZ-9305A	31.75
w/140 eng.	▲E3SZ-9305D	31.75
1983-84 (w/elect. inst. cluster)		
V-6 & V-8 eng.	▲E3SZ-9305CR	124.75
1984 (wo/elect. inst. cluster)		
Cougar (exc. 140 eng.)	▲E4WY-9305A	40.75
w/140 eng.	▲E3SZ-9305D	31.75
Thunderbird	▲E3SZ-9305A	31.75
1985-87-w/140 eng.	▲E5SZ-9305B	40.75
w/230, 302 engs. wo/elec. cluster	▲E5SZ-9305A	31.75
1985-w/elec. cluster	▲E5SZ-10D898AR	124.75
1986-87	▲E6SZ-10D898AR	181.00

PARTS 3 FUEL SYSTEM 3 PARTS

	Part No.	Price
Intake Manifold Gaskets		
140 engine		
1983-84	▲D4FZ-9441A	4.75
1985-87	▲E59Z-9439A	3.50
230 engine		
1983	▲E2AZ-9439A	2.75
1984-87	▲E4AZ-9439A	2.75
302 engine		
1983-87	▲D9AZ-9433B	7.50

PARTS 3 ELECTRONIC FUEL INJECTION 3 PARTS

140 ENGINE

	Part No.	Price
(1) Fuel Injector Assy.		
1983-84	▲E4ZZ-9F593A	147.75
1985	▲E5ZZ-9F593A	147.75
(2) Intake Manifold		
1983-84-upper	▲E3ZZ-9424B	165.50
lower	▲E3ZZ-9424A	127.00
1985-87-upper	▲E5ZZ-9424B	165.50
lower	▲E5ZZ-9424C	127.00
(3) Manifold Assy. (Fuel Injection)		
1983-84	▲E3ZZ-9D280B	46.50
1985	▲E5ZZ-9D280A	61.75
(4) Gasket (Pressure Regulator)		
1983-87	▲E0AY-9C977A	1.00
(5) Regulator Assy. (Pressure)		
1983-87	▲E3FZ-9C968A	68.50
(6) Lever, Shaft & Body Assy.		
1984-w/A.T.	▲E4ZZ-9E926C	239.75
1983-84-w/M.T.	▲E45Z-9E926A	N.L.
1985-87-w/A.T.	▲E5SZ-9E926B	177.50
w/M.T.	▲E5SZ-9E926A	177.50
(7) Wiring Assy. (Fuel Charging)		
1983-84	▲E3ZZ-9D930A	51.00
1985-87	▲E5ZZ-9D930A	51.00
(8) Gasket (Charge Cont. Manifold)		
1983-87	▲E3ZZ-9E936A	1.00
(9) Gasket (Air By Pass Valve)		
1983-84	▲E3FZ-9F670A	1.25
(10) Shaft Seal (Throttle Control)		
1983-87	▲E3FZ-9C753A	4.25
(11) Throttle Valve (Air By Pass)		
1983-87	▲E3FZ-9F715A	33.25
(12) Potentiometer Assy.		
1983-84	▲E4ZZ-9B989B	27.25
1985-87	▲E5ZZ-9B989C	29.25

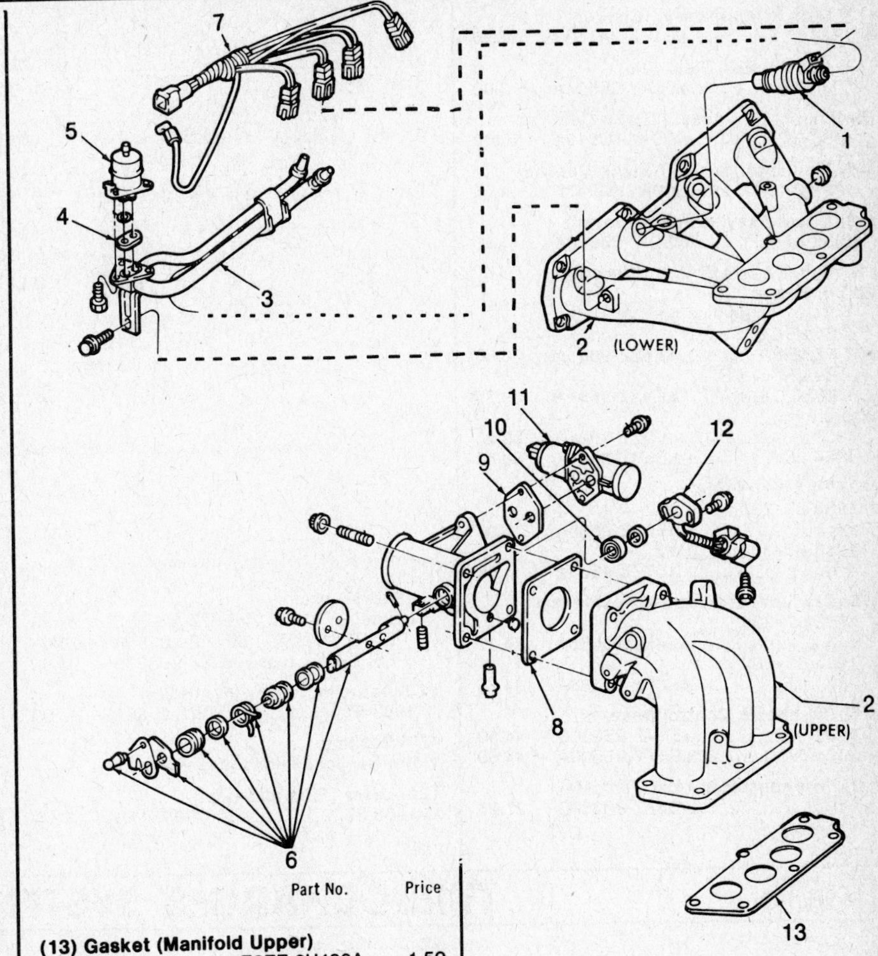

	Part No.	Price
(13) Gasket (Manifold Upper)		
1983-84	▲E3ZZ-9H486A	1.50
1985	▲E59Z-9H486A	1.50

PARTS 3 ELECTRONIC FUEL INJECTION 3 PARTS

230 & 302 ENGINE

	Part No.	Price
Charging Assy. (Fuel)		
230 engine		
1984-(stamping no.)		
E4AE-CC	▲E4AZ-9C973A	643.75
E4AE-CE, CF	▲E4AZ-9C973E	643.75
E4AE-DC	▲E4AZ-9C973B	598.50
E4AE-DE, DF	▲E4AZ-9C973D	643.75
1985-(stamping no.)		
E5SE-HA	▲E5SZ-9C973H	598.25
E5SE-JA	▲E5SZ-9C973J	337.00
E5SE-GA	▲E5SZ-9C973G	570.25
E5SE-KA	▲E5SZ-9C973K	570.25
1986-87-(stamping no.)		
E6SE-AA	▲E6SZ-9C973A	337.00
E6SE-BA	▲E6SZ-9C973B	402.25
302 engine		
1983 (stamping no.)		
E35E-AA	▲E35Y-9C973A	749.00
E35E-AB	▲E35Z-9C973C	N.L.
E35E-BA	▲E35Y-9C973B	749.00
E35E-BB	▲E35Y-9C973D	N.L.
1984-(stamping no.)		
E4AE-FA, FB	▲E4AZ-9C973C	643.75
E4AE-NA	▲E4AZ-9C973N	643.75
E45E-EA	▲E45Z-9C973A	708.25
1985	▲E5SZ-9C973F	598.25
(1) Plug (Pressure Regulator)		
1983-87	▲E0AY-9E938A	.75
(2) Pressure Regulator Assy. (Fuel)		
1983-87	▲E0SY-9C968A	101.00
(3) Body (Upper)		
Serviced in charging assembly.		
(4) Relief Valve Assy. (Pressure)		
1983-87	▲E0AY-9H321A	6.50
(5) Cap (Relief Valve)		
1983-87	▲E0VY-9H323A	1.50
(6) Charging Wiring Assy.		
1983-87-exc. below	▲E0VY-9D930A	43.50
E4AE-CE	▲E4DZ-9D930A	14.75
(7) Injector Assy.		
1983-87-230 eng.	▲E3VY-9F593A	147.75
1983-85-302 eng.	▲E0SY-9F593A	147.75
(8) Retainer (Fuel Injector)		
1983-87	▲E0AY-9C976A	11.25

PARTS 3 ELECTRONIC FUEL INJECTION 3 PARTS

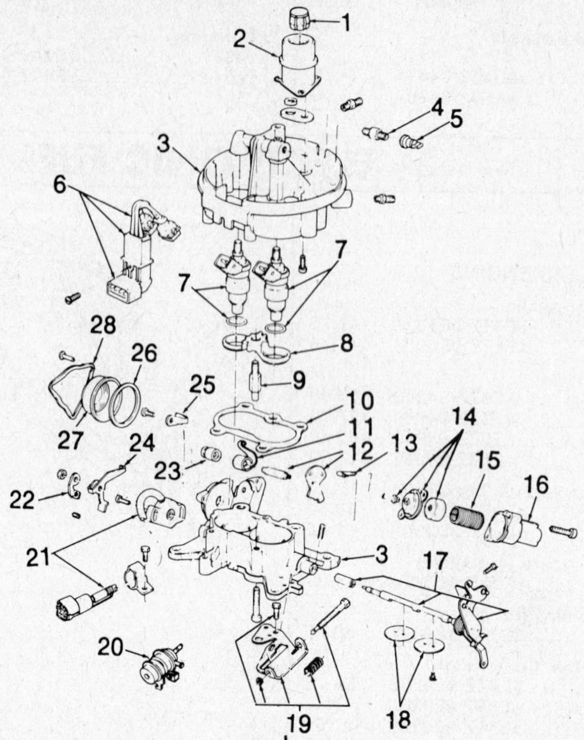

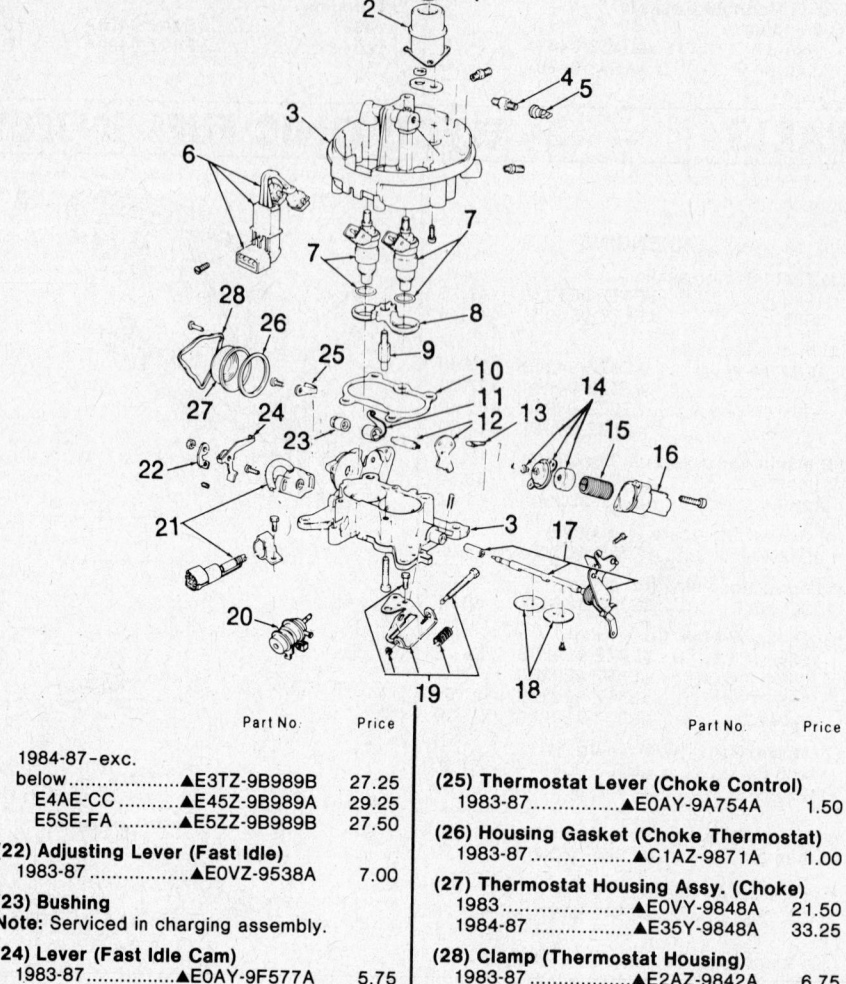

	Part No.	Price
(9) Retainer Screw (Fuel Injector)		
1983-87	▲E0AY-9D927A	8.50
(10) Gasket (Charging Body)		
1983-87	▲E0AY-9C983A	1.00
(11) Control Rod Positioner (Fast Idle)		
1983-87	▲E0AY-9D993A	7.75
(12) Cam & Shaft Assy. (Choke)		
1983-87	▲E1VZ-9A753A	12.25
(13) Control Rod (Fast Idle)		
1983-87	▲E0AY-9E524A	3.00
(14) Diaphragm Assy. (Choke Control)		
1983-87	▲D9AZ-9J549A	10.00
(15) Modulator Spring (Choke Control)		
1983-87	▲E0AY-9J547F	9.75
(16) Cover Assy. (Choke Control)		
1983-87	▲E1VZ-9B580A	14.50
(17) Lever & Shaft Assy. (Throttle)		
230 engine		
1984-87-(stamping no.) E4AE-CC, CF, E5SE-HA, HJ	▲E4SZ-9581A	38.50
E4AE-DC, DF, E5SE-GA, KA	▲E4AZ-9581A	38.50
302 engine		
1983	▲E0VY-9581D	39.25
1984-85	▲E3VY-9581A	38.50
(18) Throttle Plates		
1983-87-230 eng.	▲E2BZ-9585A	5.00
1983-85-302 eng.	▲D7ZZ-9585A	1.50
(19) Bracket Kit (Throttle Positioner)		
1983-87-230 eng.	▲E4AZ-9J586A	34.25
1983-85-302 eng.	▲E0VY-9J586A	34.25
(20) Dashpot & Control Assy.		
1983	▲E1VZ-9S520D	44.50
1984-87	▲E3VY-9S520A	44.50
(21) Potentiometer Assy. (Throttle)		
1983	▲E4ZZ-9B989B	27.25
1984-87-exc. below	▲E3TZ-9B989B	27.25
E4AE-CC	▲E45Z-9B989A	29.25
E5SE-FA	▲E5ZZ-9B989B	27.50
(22) Adjusting Lever (Fast Idle)		
1983-87	▲E0VZ-9538A	7.00
(23) Bushing		
Note: Serviced in charging assembly.		
(24) Lever (Fast Idle Cam)		
1983-87	▲E0AY-9F577A	5.75
(25) Thermostat Lever (Choke Control)		
1983-87	▲E0AY-9A754A	1.50
(26) Housing Gasket (Choke Thermostat)		
1983-87	▲C1AZ-9871A	1.00
(27) Thermostat Housing Assy. (Choke)		
1983	▲E0VY-9848A	21.50
1984-87	▲E35Y-9848A	33.25
(28) Clamp (Thermostat Housing)		
1983-87	▲E2AZ-9842A	6.75

PARTS 3 TURBOCHARGER SYSTEM 3 PARTS

© Ford Motor Co.

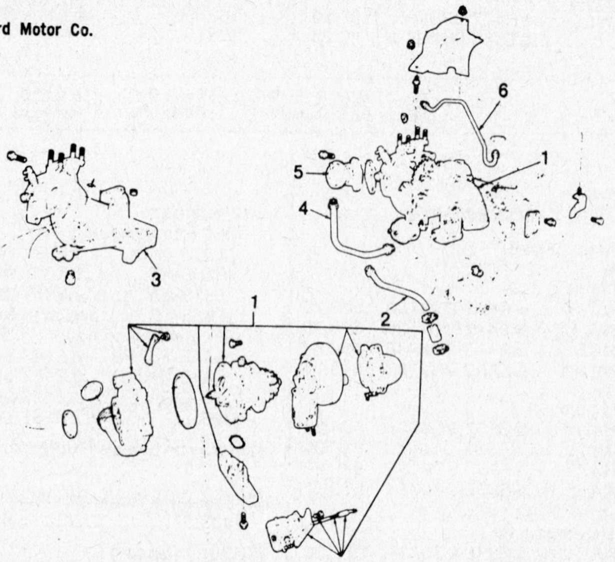

140 ENGINE

	Part No.	Price
(1) Turbocharger Assy.		
1983-84	▲E4ZZ-9G438C	349.25
1985-87-w/A.T.	▲E5ZZ-9G438A	349.25
w/M.T.	▲E5SZ-9G438A	349.25
(2) Oil Return Tube		
1983-87	▲E3ZZ-9G441A	22.75
(3) Intake Manifold		
1983-84-upper	▲E3ZZ-9424B	165.50
lower	▲E3ZZ-9424A	127.00
1985-87-upper	▲E5ZZ-9424B	165.50
lower	▲E5ZZ-9424C	127.00
(4) Tube (E.G.R. Valve to Exh. Man.)		
1983-84	▲E3ZZ-9D477A	26.75
1985	▲E5ZZ-9D477B	26.75
(5) E.G.R. Valve		
Order by year and model.		
(6) Oil Supply Tube		
1983-87	▲E3ZZ-9G439A	6.50

PARTS 3 ELECTRONIC FUEL INJECTION 3 PARTS

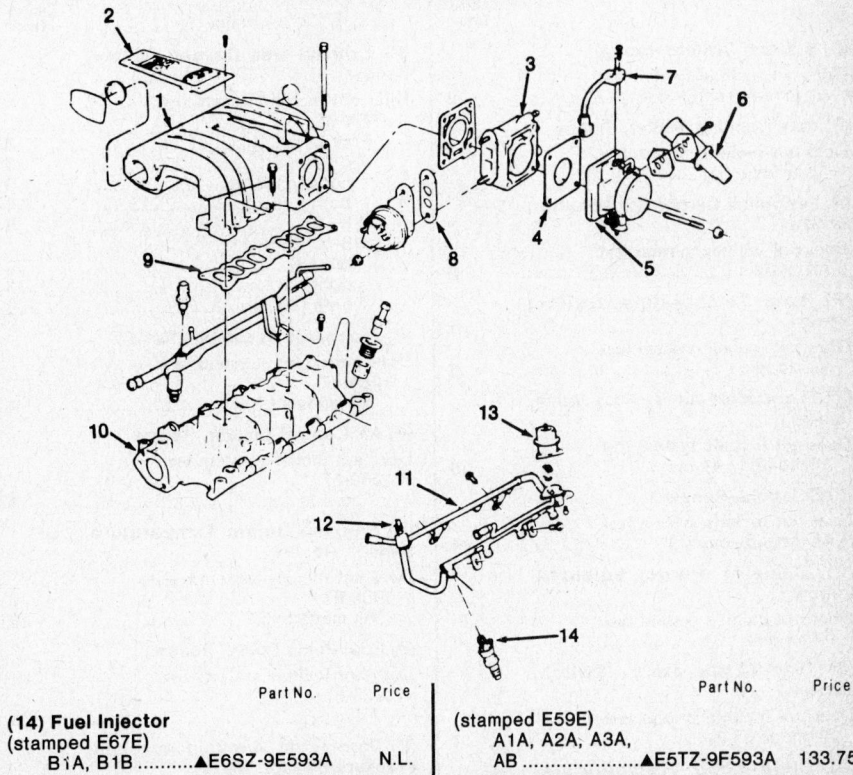

	Part No.	Price
302 ENGINE		
(1) Intake Manifold (Upper)		
1986-87	▲E6SZ-9424B	257.00
(2) Upper Manifold Cover		
1986-87	▲E6SZ-9E434A	16.00
(3) E.G.R. Spacer Assy.		
1986-87	▲E6SZ-9H474A	20.75
(4) Throttle Body Gasket		
1986-87	▲E6SZ-9E933A	1.25
(5) Throttle Body Assy.		
1986-87	▲E6SZ-9E926D	239.75
(6) Throttle Air Bypass Valve		
1986-87	▲E6ZZ-9F715A	56.50
(7) Throttle Position Sensor		
1986-87	▲E6AZ-9B989C	29.25
(8) E.G.R. Valve Assy.		
1986-87	▲E6AZ-9F483C	100.00
(9) Intake Manifold Gasket		
1986-87	▲E6SZ-9H486A	N.L.
(10) Lower Intake Manifold		
1986-87	▲E6SZ-9424A	276.25
(11) Fuel Rail Assy.		
1986-87	▲E6SZ-9F792D	166.00
(12) Schrader Valve		
1986-87	▲N.L.	
(13) Fuel Pressure Regulator		
1986-87	▲E3FZ-9C968A	68.50

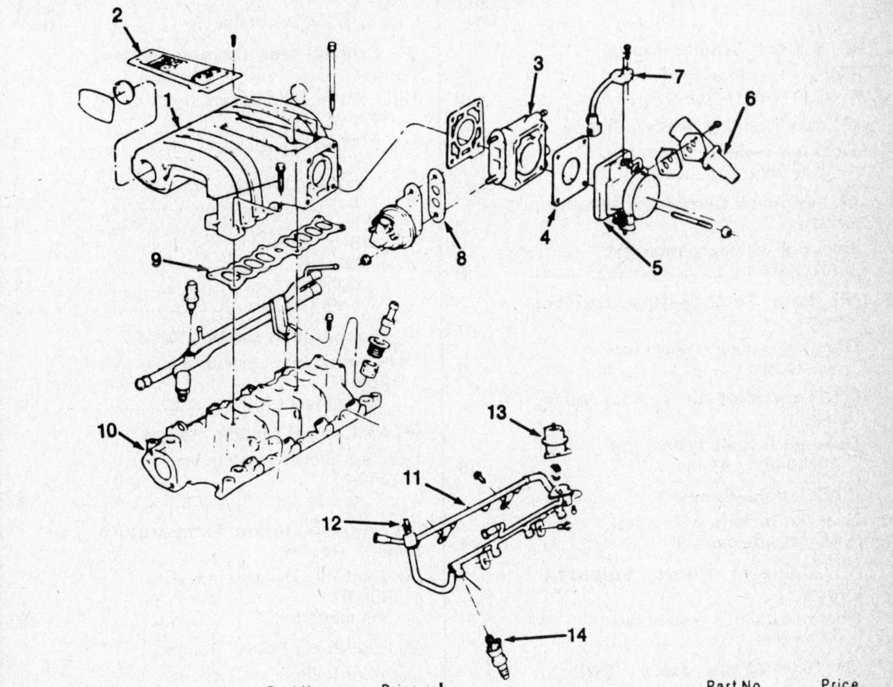

	Part No.	Price
(14) Fuel Injector		
(stamped E67E)		
B1A, B1B	▲E6SZ-9E593A	N.L.
(stamped E59E)		
A1A, A2A, A3A, AB	▲E5TZ-9F593A	133.75

LABOR 3A EMISSION CONTROLS 3A LABOR

	(Factory Time)	Chilton Time
CRANKCASE EMISSION		
(M) Crankcase Ventilation Valve, Renew		
1983-87	(.2)	.2
THERMACTOR TYPE		
(G) Thermactor Air Pump, Renew		
1983-87	(.5)	.7
(G) Thermactor Pump Drive Belt, Renew		
1983-87	(.3)	.6
(G) Thermactor Air By-Pass Valve, Renew		
1983-87	(.4)	.6
E.G.R. TYPE		
(G) E.G.R. Valve, Renew		
1983-87	(.3)	.4
(G) Vacuum Control Valve, Renew		
1983-87	(.3)	.4
(G) Exhaust Control Valve Assy., Renew		
1983-87	(.4)	.7
EVAPORATIVE EMISSION TYPE		
(M) Fuel Vapor Canister, Renew		
1983-87	(.3)	.4
(G) Carburetor Air Cleaner Sensor, Renew		
1983-87	(.2)	.3
(G) Carburetor Air Cleaner Filter, Renew		
1983-87	(.2)	.3

CHILTON'S EMISSION CONTROL TUNE-UP

1. Clean or renew P.C.V. valve, hoses and filter.
2. Check fuel tank cap for sealing ability.
3. Check fuel tank and fuel lines for leakage.
4. Check evaporation canister and filter. Replace if necessary.
5. Check engine compression to determine leakage of unburned gases. (Add time for items of interference).
6. Test and clean or renew spark plugs.
7. Check engine oil dipstick for sealing ability.
8. Test exhaust system with analyzer and check system for leakage.
9. Check exhaust manifold heat valve for operation.
10. Adjust ignition timing and carburetor idle speed and mixture.
11. Check automatic choke mechanism for free operation.
12. Inspect air cleaner and element.
13. On models so equipped, test distributor vacuum control switch and transmission control switch.

Six 1.5
V-8 .... 1.8

For repairs made, charge accordingly.

	(Factory Time)	Chilton Time
ELECTRONIC ENGINE CONTROL SYSTEM		
(P) Feed Back Carburetor Control System, Test		
All models	(.5)	.8
(P) Oxygen Sensor, Renew		
Does not include system test.		
All models	(.3)	.7
(P) Thermactor Air Valve, Renew		
Does not include system test.		
All models	(.4)	.6
(P) Vacuum Solenoid, Renew		
Does not include system test.		
All models	(.3)	.4
(P) Electronic Control Module, Renew		
Does not include system test.		
All models	(.3)	.5
(P) Thermactor Air Valve, Renew		
Does not include system test.		
All models-one	(.4)	.6

LABOR 3A EMISSION CONTROLS 3A LABOR

(Factory Time) — Chilton Time

(P) Vacuum Switch, Renew
Does not include system test.
All models-one (.3) 5

(P) Idle Tracking Switch, Renew
Does not include system test.
All models (.3) 5

(P) Feedback Carburetor Actuator, Renew
Does not include system test.
All models (.3) 5

(P) Low Temperature Switch, Renew
Does not include system test.
All models (.3) 6

(P) Thermactor Air By-Pass Valve, Renew
Does not include system test.
All models (.4) 6

(P) Solenoid, Renew
Does not include system test.
All models-one (.3) 4

(P) Canister Purge Solenoid, Renew
Does not include system test.
All models (.3) 4

(P) Mid-Temperature Switch, Renew
Does not include system test.
All models (.3) 4

(P) Open Loop (Temperature) Switch, Renew
Does not include system test.
All models (.3) 4

(P) Dual Temperature (Electric) Switch, Renew
Does not include system test.
All models (.3) 5

ELECTRONIC ENGINE CONTROL IV

(P) E.E.C. System, Test
1984-87 (.5) 1.0

(P) Throttle Position Sensor, Renew
Does not include system test.
1984-87
Four (.2) 3
V-6 (.3) 4
V-8 (.7) 1.0

(P) E.G.R. Shut Off Solenoid, Renew
Does not include system test.
1984-87
Four (.1) 2

(P) Throttle Air By-Pass Valve, Renew
Does not include system test.
1983-87
Four (.1) 2

(P) Exhaust Gas Oxygen Sensor, Renew
Does not include system test.
1984-87
Four (.1) 3
V-6-left (.3) 5
right (.7) 1.0
both (.8) 1.4
V-8 (.3) 5
V-8-w/SEFI
left (.4) 6
right (.2) 3
both (.5) 8

(P) Processor Assembly, Renew
Does not include system test.
1984-87
All models (.3) 4

(P) Air Control Sensor, Renew
Does not include system test.
1983-87
Four (.3) 4

(P) Engine Coolant Temperature Sensor, Renew
Does not include system test.
1984-87
All models (.2) 3

(P) Fuel Pump Relay, Renew
Does not include system test.
1983-87
Four (.2) 3

(P) Barometric Manifold Absolute Pressure Sensor, Renew
Does not include system test.
1984-87
All models (.1) 2

(P) E.G.R. Position Sensor, Renew
Does not include system test.
1984-87
V-6 (.3) 4
V-8 (.3) 4

(P) Thick Film Ignition Module, Renew
Does not include system test.
1984-87
All models (.5) 7

(P) Profile Ignition Pick-Up Sensor, Renew
Does not include system test.
1983-87
All models (.6) 8

(P) Throttle Positioner Assembly, Renew
Does not include system test.
1984-87
All models (.2) 3

(P) E.G.R. Control Solenoids, Renew
Does not include system test.
1984-87
V-6 (.1) 2
V-8 (.2) 3

(P) Tad/Tab Solenoids, Renew
Does not include system test.
1984-87
All models (.1) 2

(P) Fuel Injector Assembly, Renew
Does not include system test.
1984-87
Four-one (.8) 1.2
all (.9) 1.5
V-6-V-8-w/CFI
one or both (.8) 1.2
V-8-w/SEFI
one (1.8) 2.4
all (2.0) 2.7

(P) Intake Manifold Heat Control Valve, Renew
Does not include system test.
1984-87
V-6 (.2) 4

(P) Air Change Temperature Sensor, Renew
Does not include system test.
1984-87
V-6-V-8 (.2) 3

(P) Throttle Kicker Solenoid, Renew
Does not include system test.
1984-85
V-8 (.1) 2

(P) Exhaust Heat Control Valve, Renew
Does not include system test.
1984-87
V-8 (.3) 6

(P) Canister Purge Valve or Solenoid, Renew
Does not include system test.
1984-87
V-6-V-8 (.1) 2

(P) Throttle Kicker Actuator, Renew
Does not include system test.
1984-85
V-8 (.2) 3

(P) Electronic Control Relay, Renew
Does not include system test.
All models (.3) 4

(P) Fuel Pump Inertia Switch Assy., Renew
Does not include system test.
All models (.2) 3

(P) E.G.R. Valve, Renew
Does not include system test.
All models (.2) 4

PARTS 3A EMISSION CONTROLS 3A PARTS

	Part No.	Price
Crankcase Ventilation Valve		
140 engine		
(wo/turbo)		
1983-87	▲E1ZZ-6A666A	3.75
(w/turbo)		
1983-84	▲D9DZ-6A666A	3.50
1985-87	▲E5ZZ-6A666A	3.75
230 engine		
1983-87	▲E1DZ-6A666A	3.75
302 engine		
1983-87	▲D9ZZ-6A666A	3.50

PARTS 3A EMISSION CONTROLS 3A PARTS

	Part No.	Price
THERMACTOR TYPE		
Thermactor Air Pump		
Note: Thermactor air pump, Basic part no. 9A486 must be ordered by identification no. attached to pump.		
Air By-Pass Valve		
1983-87	▲E1TZ-9B289C	28.75
Air Supply Check Valve		
1983 (ex. w/230 eng.)		
exc below	▲D4VY-9A487A	14.25
No. CX-385	▲D9AZ-9A487C	11.25
1983 (w/230 eng.)		
nipple 1 end	▲E2AZ-9A487A	18.50
nipple 2 ends	▲D9AZ-9A487C	11.25
1984-87 (w/230 eng.)		
upstream	▲D4AZ-9A487A	14.25
downstream	▲E3TZ-9A487A	13.25
1984-87 (w/302 eng.)		
upstream	▲D4VY-9A487A	14.25
downstream	▲E3TZ-9A487A	13.25
E.G.R. CONTROL SYSTEM		
Integral E.G.R. Valve (w/Transducer)		
1983 (w/230 eng.)		
exc. Calif.	▲E3SZ-9D448A	61.00
Calif.	▲E3ZZ-9D448B	60.75
Vacuum Control Valve		
1983-w/230 eng.	▲D3TZ-9D473A	33.00
EVAPORATIVE EMISSION TYPE		
Vapor Canister Assy.		
140 engine		
1983-87	▲E2VY-9D653A	72.75
230 engine		
1984-87-exc. Canada	▲D8AZ-9D653C	53.25
Canada	▲E2VY-9D653A	72.75
302 engine		
1983-85-exc. Canada	▲D8AZ-9D653C	53.25
1983-Canada	▲E2VY-9D653A	72.75
1984-w/EEC III	▲E3FZ-9D653B	53.25
1986-87	▲E2ZZ-9D653A	55.50
Air Cleaner Sensor		
1983-87	▲D7FZ-9E607B	7.25
ELECTRONIC ENGINE CONTROL SYSTEM		
Oxygen Sensor (Exh. Gas)		
140 engine		
1983 (stamped)		
E1AF-AA	▲E1AZ-9F472A	95.00
E3EF-AA	▲E3FZ-9F472A	48.50
1984	▲E4ZZ-9F472A	69.00
1985-87 (stamped)		
E3EF-AA	▲E3FZ-9F472A	48.50
E47F-BA	▲E43Z-9F472A	63.00
E53F-BA	▲E53Z-9F472A	N.L.
(230, 302 engs.)		
1983-87	▲E3FZ-9F472A	48.50

	Part No	Price
Thermactor Control Valve		
230 engine		
1983-(stamped)		
E3SE-AA	▲E3SZ-9F491C	27.25
E1TE-AB	▲E3TZ-9F491A	56.00
1984-87	▲E4SZ-9F491A	56.00
302 engine		
1983	▲E1SZ-9F491A	56.00
1984-87-exc. below	▲E3TZ-9F491A	56.00
E4SE-BA	▲E4SZ-9F491B	N.L.
E4PE-FA	▲E3SZ-9F491A	24.75
Purge Regulator Valve (Canister)		
1983	▲E0AZ-9C915A	21.75
1984-87-green	▲E4AZ-9C915B	21.75
black	▲E4AZ-9C915C	21.75
natural	▲E4AZ-9C915A	21.75
Mid-Temperature Switch		
1983-87 (stamped on valve)		
D7ZE-AA	▲D7ZZ-9E862A	7.50
D5DF-AA	▲D5DZ-9E862A	7.25
Dual Coolant Switch Assy.		
1983-87	▲E1AZ-12B513A	71.50
ELECTRONIC ENGINE CONTROL IV		
Throttle Position Sensor		
140 engine		
1984	▲E4ZZ-9B989B	29.25
1985	▲E5ZZ-9B989C	29.25
1986-87	▲E6ZZ-9B989A	29.25
Throttle Air By-Pass Valve		
1983-87-w/140 eng	▲E3FZ-9F715A	33.25
Processor Assy.		
140 engine		
1984-(stamped E4FZ)		
B1A, B2A	▲E4ZZ-12A650BA	168.00
E1A, E2A	▲E4PZ-12A650A	167.75
1985-87-(stamped E5ZF)		
C1A, C2A, C1B, C2B	▲E5ZZ-12A650CB	167.75
A1A. A2A, K1A, K2A	▲E5ZZ-12A650KA	167.75
K1B, K2B	▲E5ZZ-12A650KB	167.75
230 engine		
1984-(stamped E4VF)		
C1A, C2A	▲E4VZ-12A650CA	167.75
D1A, D2A	▲E4VZ-12A650DA	167.75
E1A, E2A	▲E4VZ-12A650EA	N.L.
F1A, F2A	▲E4VZ-12A650FA	167.75
1985-(stamped E4VF)		
C1B, C2B	▲E5VZ-12A650CB	167.75
D1B, D2B	▲E5VZ-12A650DB	167.75
(stamped E53F)		
AL1A, AL2A	▲E53Z-12A650ALA	167.75
AM1A, AM2A	▲E53Z-12A650AMA	168.00
1986-87 (stamped E53F)		
AN1B, AN2B	▲E53Z-12A650ANB	167.75
(stamped E63F)		
A1A, A2A	▲E63Z-12A650AA	167.75

	Part No.	Price
302 engine		
1984-85-(stamped E4VF)		
P1A, P2A	▲E4VZ-12A650PA	167.75
R1A, R2A	▲E4VZ-12A650RA	167.75
(stamped E53F)		
C1B, C2B	▲E53Z-12A650CB	167.75
C1C, C2C	▲E53Z-12A650CC	167.75
1986-87 (stamped E6SF)		
Y1B, Y2B	▲E6SZ-12A650YB	N.L.
V1B, V2B	▲E65Z-12A650VB	N.L.
U1B, U2B	▲E65Z-12A650UB	N.L.
Air Control Sensor		
140 engine		
1983-87	▲E3SZ-12B529A	199.75
1985-87	▲E5ZZ-12B529A	160.50
Engine Coolant Temperature Sensor		
1984-87	▲E1AZ-12A648A	32.00
Barometric Pressure Sensor		
140 engine		
1984-87	▲E3ZZ-12A644A	59.75
E.G.R. Position Sensor		
1984-87	▲E43Z-9G428A	32.00
Thick Film Ignition Module		
1984-87-all	▲E43Z-12A297A	106.00
E.G.R. Control Solenoid		
140 engine		
1983-84	▲E3ZZ-9D474B	16.25
1985-87	▲E5ZZ-9D474A	16.25
230 engine		
(therm.)		
1984-87	▲E4ZZ-9D474E	32.50
(fuel)		
1984-87	▲E4ZZ-9D474G	16.25
(E.G.R.)		
1984-87-(stamped)		
E4ZE-FA	▲E4ZZ-9D474F	32.50
E5TE-AA	▲E5TZ-9D474AA	32.50
302 engine		
1984-85 (stamped)		
E1SE-C2A, C3A	▲E1SZ-9D474C	16.25
E1TE-C2A, C3A.	▲E1TZ-9D474C	32.50
E4ZE-D2A, D3A	▲E4ZZ-9D474D	32.50
E4ZE-E2A, E3A.	▲E4ZZ-9D474E	32.50
E4ZE-FA	▲E4ZZ-9D474F	32.50
E4SE-A3A	▲E3SZ-9D474C	32.50
E35E-D2A, D3A, E3A	▲E35Y-9D474D	28.00
E35E-A2A, FA	▲E35Y-9D474A	32.50
E5TE-AA	▲E5TZ-9D474AA	32.50
1986-87	▲E6SZ-9D474A	N.L.
Knock Sensor		
140 engine		
1983-87	▲E3ZZ-12A699A	33.00
Intake Manifold Heat Control Valve		
230 engine		
1984	▲E4AZ-9G464A	27.50
1985-87	▲E5AZ-9G464A	27.50
Air Charge Temperature Sensor		
1984-87	▲E1AZ-12A697A	27.00
Exhaust Heat Control Valve		
1984-87	▲E1SZ-9A427A	86.50

LABOR 4 ALTERNATOR AND REGULATOR 4 LABOR

	(Factory Time)	Chilton Time
(G) Alternator Circuits, Test		
Includes: Test battery, regulator and alternator output.		
All models	(.3)	.6
(M) Alternator Drive Belt, Renew		
1983-87	(.3)	.4
(G) Alternator, Renew		
1983-87	(.4)	.7
Transfer pulley add	(.1)	.1
Circuit test add		.6

LABOR 4 ALTERNATOR AND REGULATOR 4 LABOR

	(Factory Time)	Chilton Time
(G) Alternator, R&R and Recondition		
Includes: Complete disassembly, replacement or parts as required. Test validity of rotor fields, stator and diodes.		
1983-87	(1.0)	1.5
Circuit test add		.6
(G) Alternator Front Bearing or End Plate, Renew		
1983-87	(.7)	1.0
(G) Alternator Rear Bearing, Renew		
1983-87	(.6)	.9
(G) Alternator Regulator, Renew		
1983-87	(.3)	.6
Circuit test add		.6
(G) Instrument Cluster Voltage Regulator, Renew		
Includes: Remove instrument panel pad when required.		
1985-87	(1.1)	1.8

PARTS 4 ALTERNATOR AND REGULATOR 4 PARTS

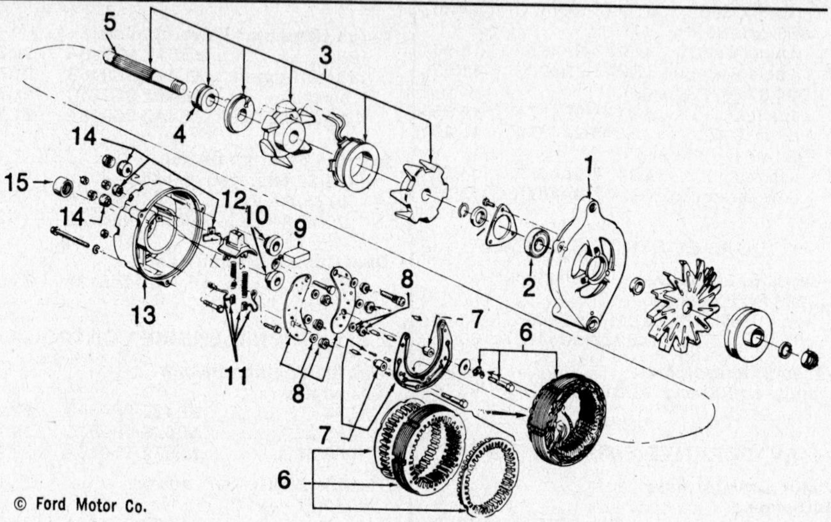

© Ford Motor Co.

	Part No.	Price
Alternator Assy. (New)		
40 amp		
1983	▲E2GZ-10346B	233.50
60 amp		
1983-84-wo/A.C.	▲E2GZ-10346C	233.50
w/A.C.	▲E2GZ-10346B	233.50
1985-87-exc. below	▲E2GZ-10346C	233.50
w/230 eng.	▲E5SZ-10346A	232.75
65 amp		
1983-87	▲E1BZ-10346B	233.50
(1) Housing (Front)		
40, 60 amp		
1983-87-wo/A.C.	▲D3OZ-10333B	17.75
w/A.C.	▲E1FZ-10333A	21.25
65 amp		
1983-87	▲E1FZ-10333A	21.25
(2) Front Bearing		
1983-87	▲C9ZZ-10094A	9.00
(3) Rotor Assy.		
40 amp		
1983-84	▲E1ZZ-10335A	45.75
60 amp		
1983-87-exc. below	▲E1ZZ-10335B	45.75
w/230 eng.	▲E5SZ-10335A	56.00
65 amp		
1983-87	▲E1ZZ-10335B	45.75
(4) Slip Ring (Rotor)		
1983-87	▲C3SZ-10328A	N.L.
(5) Shaft (Rotor)		
1983-87	▲C5AZ-10330A	N.L.
(6) Stator Assy.		
1983-87	▲E3FZ-10336A	31.25
(7) Insulator Kit		
1983-87	▲C9SZ-10A383A	1.75
(8) Rectifier Assy.		
1983-87	▲D6AZ-10304A	48.00
(9) Capacitor (Radio)		
1983-87	▲C6AZ-18827A	2.25
(10) Insulator Kit		
1983-87	▲C9SZ-10A383A	1.75
(11) Brush Set		
1983-87	▲C6VY-10347A	3.50
(12) Brush Holder		
1983-87	▲C5AZ-10351A	2.00
(13) Housing (Rear)		
40, 60 amp		
1983-87	▲D7AZ-10334A	23.25
65 amp		
1983-87	▲D7ZZ-10334A	26.25
(14) Insulator (Terminal)		
1983-87	▲C9SZ-10A383A	1.75
(15) Rear Bearing		
1983-87	▲D2OZ-10A304A	5.25
Regulator Assy.		
1983-87	▲E2PZ-10316-A	36.75
Instrument Cluster Voltage Regulator		
1983-87-wo/ Elec. Cluster	▲D1AZ-10804A	10.25
1983-84-w/Tach, w/Turbo	▲C9AZ-10804A	10.25

LABOR 5 STARTING SYSTEM 5 LABOR

	(Factory Time)	Chilton Time
(G) Starter Draw Test (On Car)		
All models	(.3)	.3
(G) Starter, Renew		
1983-87	(.4)	.6
Add draw test if performed.		
(G) Starter, R&R and Recondition		
Includes: Turn down armature.		
1983-87		
positive engagement starter	(1.7)	2.4
solenoid engagement starter	(1.5)	2.2
Motorcraft	(1.4)	2.1
Renew field coils add		.5
Add draw test if performed.		
(G) Starter Drive, Renew		
Includes: R&R starter.		
1983-87	(.6)	.8
(G) Starter Solenoid Relay, Renew		
1983-87	(.3)	.4
(G) Neutral Safety Switch, Renew		
1983-87	(.3)	.4
w/AOD add		.2
(G) Ignition Switch, Renew		
1938-87	(.6)	1.0
(M) Battery Cables, Renew		
1983-87		
Batt. to Relay	(.3)	.3
Ground	(.3)	.3
Relay to Starter	(.4)	.5

PARTS 5 STARTING SYSTEM 5 PARTS

	Part No.	Price
Starter Assy. (New)		
140 engine		
1983	▲E3TZ-11002D	N.L.
1984-87	▲E4TZ-11002B	203.50
230, 302 engs.		
1983-w/302 eng.	▲E25Z-11002A	N.L.
1983-87	▲E4DZ-11002B	185.50
Starter Relay Switch		
1983-84	▲D8DZ-11450B	12.00
1985-87	▲E5TZ-11450A	13.25
Ignition Starter Switch		
1983-87	▲E4FZ-11572A	11.50
(1) Starter Armature (New)		
1983-87-exc. below	▲E2BZ-11005A	77.00
1984-87-w/140 eng	▲E3FZ-11005A	66.75
(2) Starter Drive Assy.		
1983-87	▲E2PZ-11350A	21.00
(3) Rear Plate (Housing)		
140 engine		
1983-87	▲E4DZ-11130A	27.75
230, 302 engs.		
1983-87	▲E25Y-11130A	45.00
(4) Front Plate Assy.		
1983-87-exc. below	▲E2BZ-11049A	14.50
1984-87-w/140 eng	▲E4AZ-11049A	14.50
(5) Field Coil Assy.		
1983-87-exc. below	▲E2BZ-11082A	50.00
1984-87-w/140 eng	▲E4AZ-11082A	50.00
(6) Starter Brush Set		
1983-87	▲E4PZ-11057A	13.00
Brush Holder		
1983-87-exc. below	▲E2BZ-11061A	4.25
1984-87-w/140 eng	▲E4AZ-11061A	4.25
Bearing (Drive End Plate)		
1983-87	▲D3AZ-11052A	1.50

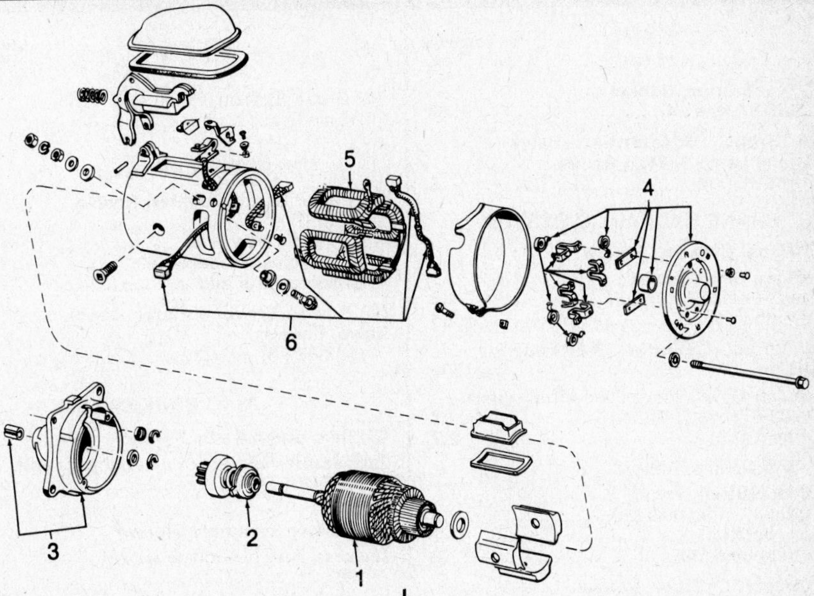

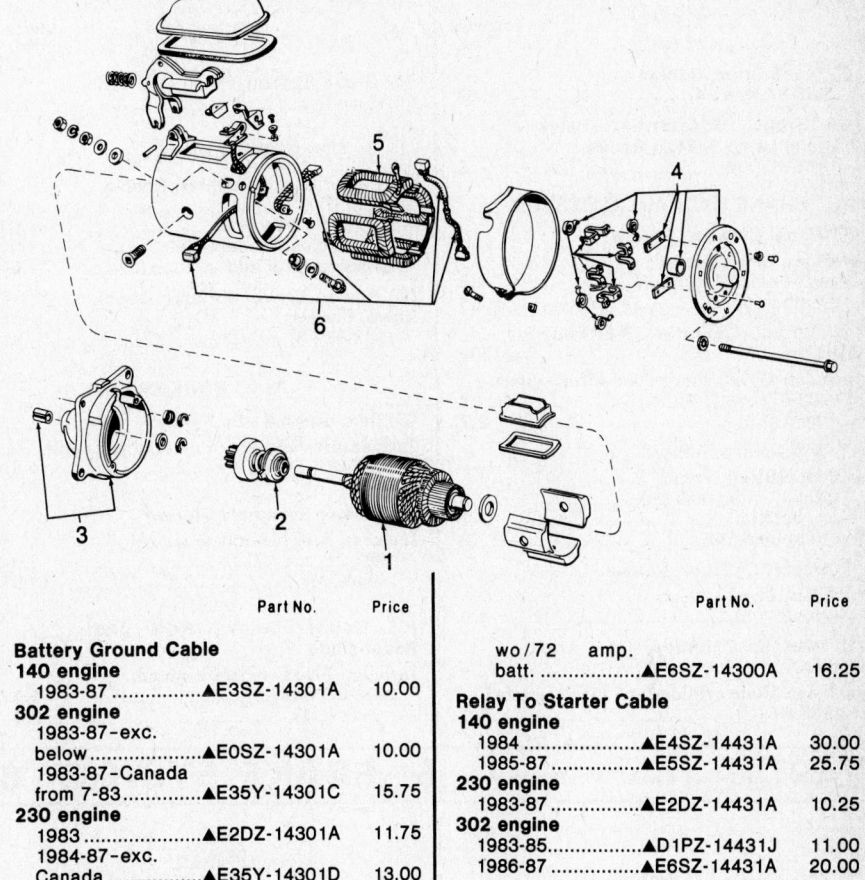

	Part No.	Price
Battery Ground Cable		
140 engine		
1983-87	▲E3SZ-14301A	10.00
302 engine		
1983-87-exc. below	▲E0SZ-14301A	10.00
1983-87-Canada from 7-83	▲E35Y-14301C	15.75
230 engine		
1983	▲E2DZ-14301A	11.75
1984-87-exc. Canada	▲E35Y-14301D	13.00
Canada	▲E2DZ-14301A	11.75
Battery To Starter Relay		
1983-87-exc. below	▲E35Y-14300A	6.25
w/140 eng.	▲E3SZ-14300A	8.50
1986-87-w/302 engine w/72 amp. batt.	▲E6SZ-14300B	7.25
wo/72 amp. batt.	▲E6SZ-14300A	16.25
Relay To Starter Cable		
140 engine		
1984	▲E4SZ-14431A	30.00
1985-87	▲E5SZ-14431A	25.75
230 engine		
1983-87	▲E2DZ-14431A	10.25
302 engine		
1983-85	▲D1PZ-14431J	11.00
1986-87	▲E6SZ-14431A	20.00
Neutral Safety Switch		
(w/A.T.)		
1983-87-exc. below	▲D6RY-7A247B	33.25
C4 & C5 trans.	▲E2DZ-7A247A	38.50
(w/M.T.)		
1983-87	▲E0ZZ-15520A	21.50

LABOR 6 BRAKE SYSTEM 6 LABOR

(Factory Time)	Chilton Time
(G) Brake Pedal Free Play, Adjust	
All models	.4
(G) Brakes, Adjust (Minor)	
Includes: Adjust brakes, fill master cylinder.	
two wheels	.4
(G) Bleed Brakes (Four Wheels)	
Includes: Fill master cylinder.	
All models (.3)	.5
(G) Brake Self Adjustors, Disassemble & Clean	
one wheel	.7
each adtnl	.4
(G) Brake Shoes and/or Pads, Renew	
Includes: Install new or exchange shoes or pads. Adjust service and hand brake. Bleed system.	
1983-87-front-disc (.7)	1.1
rear-drum (1.0)	1.5
all four wheels (1.4)	2.5
Resurface disc rotor, add-each	.9
Resurface brake drum, add-each	.5

COMBINATIONS

Add to Brakes, Renew

See Machine Shop Operations

(Factory Time)	Chilton Time
(G) RENEW WHEEL CYLINDER	
Each (.3)	.3
(G) REBUILD WHEEL CYLINDER	
Each (.3)	.3
(G) REBUILD CALIPER ASSEMBLY	
Each (.2)	.5
(G) RENEW MASTER CYLINDER	
All models	.6
(G) REBUILD MASTER CYLINDER	
All models	1.0
(G) RENEW BRAKE HOSE	
Each (.3)	.3
(G) RENEW REAR WHEEL GREASE SEALS	
One (.3)	.4
Both (.4)	.6
(G) REPACK FRONT WHEEL BEARINGS (BOTH WHEELS)	
All models (.3)	.6
(G) RENEW BRAKE DRUM	
Each (.2)	.2
(G) RENEW DISC BRAKE ROTOR	
Each (.2)	.4

LABOR — 6 BRAKE SYSTEM 6 — LABOR

(Factory Time)	Chilton Time
(G) Brake Drum, Renew	
1983-87-one (.4)	.6
(G) Brake Differential Valve Warning Lamp Switch, Renew	
1983-87 (.3)	.5
BRAKE HYDRAULIC SYSTEM	
(G) Wheel Cylinder, Renew	
Includes: Bleed system.	
1983-87-one (1.0)	1.4
both (1.5)	2.1
(G) Wheel Cylinder, R&R and Rebuilt	
Includes: Hone cylinder and bleed system.	
1983-87-one (1.0)	1.7
both (1.5)	2.7
(G) Brake Hose, Renew	
Includes: Bleed system.	
1983-87-front-one (.4)	.6
both (.5)	.7
rear-one (.5)	.8
(G) Master Cylinder, Renew	
Includes: Bleed system.	
1983-87 (.5)	1.0
(G) Master Cylinder, R&R and Rebuild	
Includes: Hone cylinder and bleed system.	
1983-87 (.7)	1.6
(G) Brake System, Flush and Refill	
All models	1.2
POWER BRAKES	
(G) Power Brake Booster, Renew	
1983-87	
T/Bird Turbo (1.3)	1.9
All other models (.9)	1.3
w/Cruise control add	.2
(G) Power Brake Booster Check Valve, Renew	
1983-87 (.3)	.4
DISC BRAKES	
(G) Disc Brake Pads, Renew	
Includes: Install new disc brake pads only.	
1983-87 (.7)	1.1
(G) Caliper Assembly, Renew	
Includes: Bleed complete system.	
1983-87-one (.6)	1.0
both (.8)	1.5
(G) Caliper Assy., R&R and Recondition	
Includes: Bleed complete system.	
1983-87-one (.8)	1.5
both (1.2)	2.5
(G) Disc Brake Rotor, Renew	
Includes: Renew front wheel bearings and grease retainer and repack bearings.	
1983-87-one (.5)	.7
both (.7)	1.2
(G) Brake Differential Valve, Renew	
Includes: Bleed complete system and transfer switch.	
1983-87 (.7)	1.0
PARKING BRAKE	
(M) Parking Brake, Adjust	
1983-87 (.2)	.4
(G) Parking Brake Indicator Switch, Renew	
1983-87 (.3)	.4
(G) Parking Brake Control, Renew	
1983-87 (.6)	1.0
(G) Parking Brake Cables, Renew	
Includes: Adjust parking brake.	
1983-87-front-one (.3)	.6
rear-one (.5)	.7
(G) Parking Brake Power Vacuum Unit, Renew	
1983-87 (.7)	1.1

PARTS — 6 BRAKE SYSTEM 6 — PARTS

	Part No.	Price
(1) Brake Shoe Set (Rear)		
1983-87-w/9" brk	▲D9ZZ-2200A	35.50
1983-w/10" brk	▲D6DZ-2200A	37.00
Brake Lining Kit		
1983-87-w/9" brk	▲D9ZZ-2007A	22.25
w/10" brk	▲D6DZ-2007A	21.75
(2) Rear Wheel Cylinder Assy.		
9" brakes		
1983-87	▲E0ZZ-2261A	29.75
10" brakes		
1983-R.H.	▲D8BZ-2261B	19.75
left	▲D8BZ-2262A	19.75
Repair Kit Wheel Cylinder		
9" brakes		
1983-87	▲E0ZZ-2128A	4.50
10" brakes		
1983	▲D8BZ-2128B	5.50
Brake Hose (Front)		
1983-84	▲E3SZ-2078A	16.50
1985-87	▲E5SZ-2078A	16.50
Brake Hose (Rear)		
1983-87	▲E3SZ-2282A	17.25
Master Cylinder Assy.		
1983-87	▲E4DZ-2140A	93.00

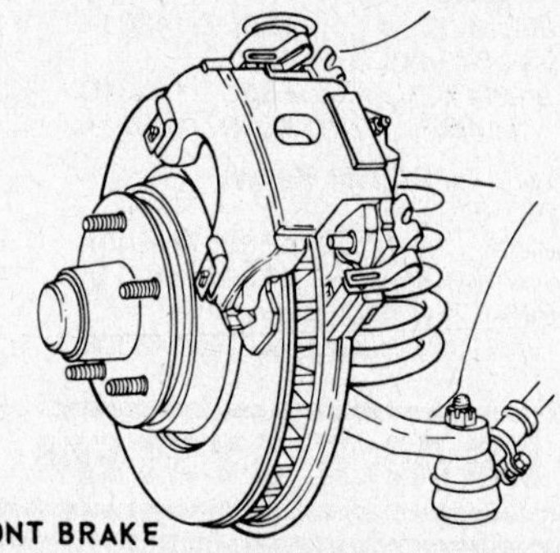

FRONT BRAKE

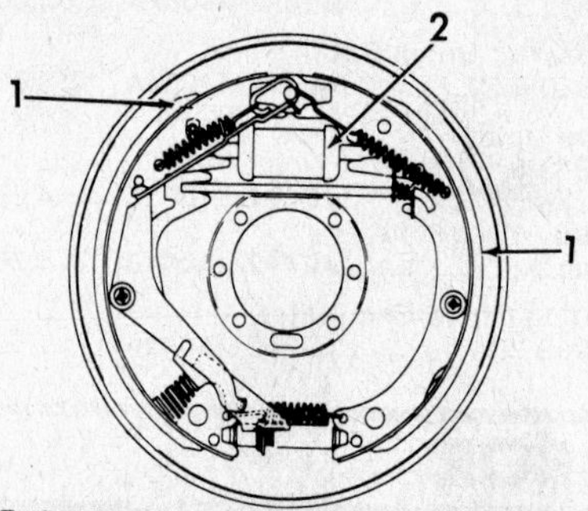

REAR BRAKE

	Part No.	Price
Repair Kit (Master Cylinder)		
1983-87	▲E4DZ-2004A	35.25
Brake Drum (Rear)		
9" brakes		
1983-84	▲E3SZ-1126A	48.50
1985-87	▲D9ZZ-1126A	60.50
10" brakes		
1983-85	▲D9BZ-1126A	76.00
Grease Retainer (Front)		
1983-87	▲C8AZ-1190A	3.00
Rear Wheel Oil Seal		
1983-87	▲E1AZ-1177B	3.50
Brake Booster Assy. (New)		
1983-87	▲E3SZ-2005A	156.75

PARKING BRAKE

	Part No.	Price
Parking Brake Lever		
Manual release		
1983	▲E3SZ-2780A	38.50
1984	▲E4SZ-2780A	69.25
1985-87	▲E5SZ-2780A	38.50
Auto. release		
1983	▲E3SZ-2780B	69.25
1984	▲E4DZ-2780A	69.25
1985-87	▲E5SZ-2780B	69.25
Parking Brake Cable (Front)		
1983-87	▲E3SZ-2853A	16.00
Parking Brake Cable (Rear)		
1983-84	▲E3SZ-2A635A	21.75
1985-87	▲E3DZ-2A635A	18.50

PARTS — 6 DISC BRAKES 6 — PARTS

	Part No.	Price
(1) Wheel Bearing (Outer)		
1983-87	▲D0AZ-1216A	8.25
Bearing Cup (Outer)		
1983-87	▲D0AZ-1217B	3.75
(2) Hub & Rotor Assy.		
1983-84	▲D8BZ-1102A	87.25
1985-87	▲E5DZ-1102A	86.00

PARTS 6 DISC BRAKES 6 PARTS

	Part No.	Price
(3) Wheel Bearing (Inner)		
1983-87	▲D0AZ-1201A	9.50
(4) Grease Retainer (Wheel Hub)		
1983-87	▲C8AZ-1190A	3.00
(5) Caliper Piston (Front)		
1983-87	▲E3SZ-2196A	12.75
(6) Brake Pad Set		
1983	▲E3SZ-2001A	48.75
1984-87-exc. turbo	▲E4SZ-2001A	47.50
turbo	▲E3SZ-2001A	48.75
(7) Caliper Assy. (Front)		
1983-84-right	▲E3SZ-2B120A	116.75
left	▲E5SZ-2B121A	127.50
1985-87-right	▲E5SZ-2B120A	127.50
left	▲E5SZ-2B121A	127.50

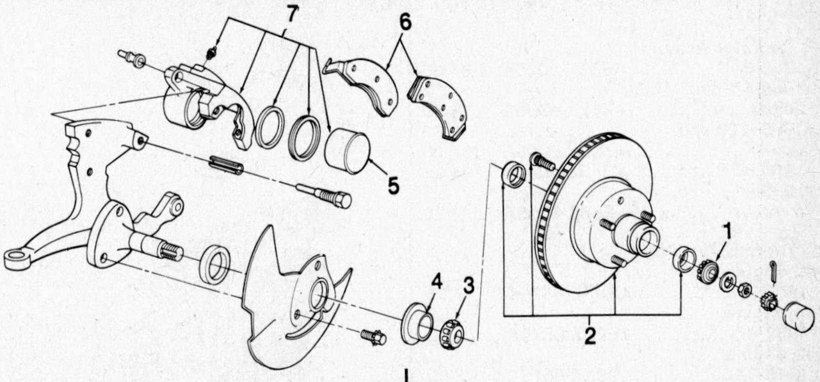

	Part No.	Price
Caliper Assy. Repair Kit		
1983-87	▲D9BZ-2221A	8.25
1 kit required for car.		

	Part No.	Price
Brake Differential Valve		
1983-87	▲E3SZ-2B257B	46.50

LABOR 7 COOLING SYSTEM 7 LABOR

(Factory Time) — Chilton Time

(M) Winterize Cooling System
Includes: Run engine to check for leaks, tighten all hose connections. Test radiator and pressure cap, drain radiator and engine block. Add anti-freeze and refill system.

All models	.5

(M) Thermostat, Renew

1983-87-Four (.5)	.7
V-6 (.5)	.7
V-8-255 eng (.5)	.7
302 eng (.4)	.6

(M) Radiator Assembly, R&R or Renew
Includes: Drain and refill cooling system.

1983-87 (.6)	1.0
w/A.C. add (.1)	.1
w/Turbo add (.1)	.1

ADD THESE OPERATIONS TO RADIATOR R&R

(G) Boil & Repair	1.5
(G) Rod Clean	1.9
(G) Repair Core	1.3
(G) Renew Tank	1.6
(G) Renew Trans. Oil Cooler	1.9
(G) Recore Radiator	1.7

(M) Radiator Hoses, Renew

1983-87	
upper (.3)	.4
lower (.4)	.6
both (.5)	.7

(M) Radiator By-Pass Hose, Renew

V-6-1983-87 (.5)	.7
V-8-1983-87 (.3)	.5

(G) Water Pump, Renew

Four-1983-87 (.7)	1.2
V-6-1983-87 (1.1)	1.6
V-8-1983-87 (1.6)	2.5
w/A.C. and P.S. add (.2)	.2

(M) Fan Blades, Renew

1983-87 (.4)	.5
w/Clutch fan add	.1

(M) Drive Belt, Renew

1983-87-one (.3)	.4
each adtnl (.1)	.1

(M) Drive Belt, Adjust

1983-87-one (.2)	.3
each adtnl (.1)	.1

COOLING SYSTEM TUNE-UP

An Annual Cooling System Tune-Up Suggestion List should include (with some exceptions):

1. A visual check of the cooling system for indications of leaks or excessive oil content.
2. Pressure check the cooling system for internal and external leaks with filler cap and neck adapter and tester.
3. Check crankcase and automatic transmission oil for water content.
4. Test coolant thermostat with radiator thermometer.
5. Check temperature gauge for accuracy.
6. Drain system and flush till clean.
7. Clean foreign matter from radiator fins.
8. Test radiator pressure cap with cap tester.
9. Check fan blades and pulleys for alignment and damage.
10. Internal and external inspection of all hoses for cracks and deterioration.
11. Check core plugs (where possible) for seepage.
12. Refill system with correct coolant and check for air locks.
13. Check condition and tension of drive belts with tension gauge.

All models 1.5

(Factory Time) — Chilton Time

(M) Serpentine Belt, Renew

All models (.3)	.5

(G) Electric Cooling Fan Motor, Renew

Four-1983-87 (.3)	.5

(G) Engine Cooling Fan Relay, Renew

1983-87 (.3)	.4

(Factory Time) — Chilton Time

(M) Clutch Fan, Renew

1983-87 (.4)	.6

(G) Temperature Gauge (Engine Unit), Renew

1983-87 (.3)	.4

(G) Temperature Indicator, Renew

1983-87	
Sport cluster (1.2)	1.8

(G) Water Jacket Expansion Plugs, Renew (Side of Block)

each (.3)	*.5

*Add time to gain accessibility.

(G) Heater Hoses, Renew

1983-87-each (.3)	.4

(G) Heater Core, R&R or Renew

1983-87 (3.6)	7.5

Add time to recharge A.C. system.

ADD THESE OPERATIONS TO HEATER CORE R&R

(G) Boil & Repair	1.2
(G) Repair Core	.9
(G) Recore	1.2

(G) Heater or A.C. Control Assembly, Renew

1983-87 (.5)	.9

(G) Heater or A.C. Blower Motor, Renew
Includes: Transfer blower wheel when required.

1983-87 (1.0)	1.6

(G) Heater or A.C. Blower Motor Resistor, Renew

1983-87 (.3)	.5

(G) Heater or A.C. Blower Motor Switch, Renew

1983-87 (.4)	.7

(G) Temperature Control Cable, Renew

1983-87-wo/A.T.C. (.5)	.8
w/A.T.C. (.8)	1.2

PARTS 7 COOLING SYSTEM 7 PARTS

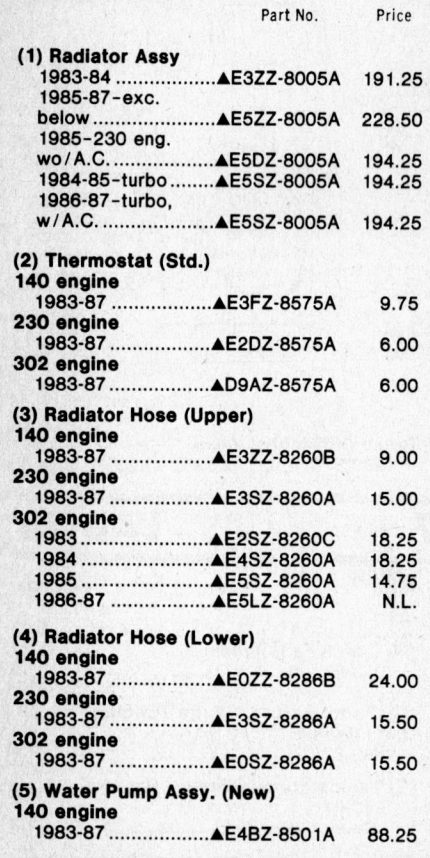

	Part No.	Price
(1) Radiator Assy		
1983-84	▲E3ZZ-8005A	191.25
1985-87-exc. below	▲E5ZZ-8005A	228.50
1985-230 eng. wo/A.C.	▲E5DZ-8005A	194.25
1984-85-turbo	▲E5SZ-8005A	194.25
1986-87-turbo, w/A.C.	▲E5SZ-8005A	194.25
(2) Thermostat (Std.)		
140 engine		
1983-87	▲E3FZ-8575A	9.75
230 engine		
1983-87	▲E2DZ-8575A	6.00
302 engine		
1983-87	▲D9AZ-8575A	6.00
(3) Radiator Hose (Upper)		
140 engine		
1983-87	▲E3ZZ-8260B	9.00
230 engine		
1983-87	▲E3SZ-8260A	15.00
302 engine		
1983	▲E2SZ-8260C	18.25
1984	▲E4SZ-8260A	18.25
1985	▲E5SZ-8260A	14.75
1986-87	▲E5LZ-8260A	N.L.
(4) Radiator Hose (Lower)		
140 engine		
1983-87	▲E0ZZ-8286B	24.00
230 engine		
1983-87	▲E3SZ-8286A	15.50
302 engine		
1983-87	▲E0SZ-8286A	15.50
(5) Water Pump Assy. (New)		
140 engine		
1983-87	▲E4BZ-8501A	88.25

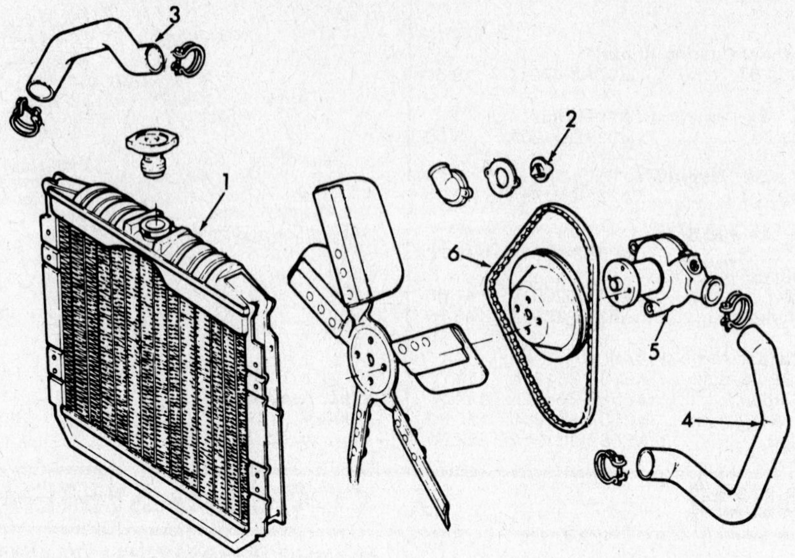

	Part No.	Price
230 engine		
1983-87	▲E2DZ-8501A	65.75
302 engine		
1983-84	▲E0AZ-8501A	89.25
1985	▲E1AZ-8501A	91.00
1986-87	▲E6AZ-8501A	59.00
(6) Fan Belt		
Order by model and description.		

	Part No.	Price
Heater Core		
1983-87	▲D9BZ-18476A	63.50
Blower Motor		
1983-87	▲E35Y-19805A	91.75
Blower Motor Resistor		
1983-87	▲E35Y-19A706A	11.00
Switch Assy. (Heater)		
1983-87	▲D5AZ-19986A	12.75

LABOR 8 EXHAUST SYSTEM 8 LABOR

(Factory Time)	Chilton Time
(G) Muffler, Renew	
1983-87 (.6)	.9
Welded type add	.3
(G) Tail Pipe, Renew	
1983-87 (.2)	.5
Welded type add	.3
(G) Catalytic Converter, Renew	
1983-84	
Four (.6)	.9
V-6 (.5)	.8
V-8 (1.0)	1.4
1985	
Four (.6)	.9
V-6 & V-8 (.5)	.8
1986-87	
Four (.6)	.9
V-6	
Y-Pipe (.8)	1.1
underbody (.5)	.8
both (1.2)	1.8
V-8 (1.0)	1.4
(G) Inlet Exhaust Pipe, Renew	
Includes: Replace exhaust control valve if required.	
1983-84-Four (.6)	1.0
V-6 (.7)	1.1
V-8 (.5)	.9
(G) Manifold Heat Valve, Renew	
1983-87 (.4)	.7
(G) Exhaust Manifold, Renew	
Four-1983-87 (1.8)	2.4
V-6-1983-87	
right (1.6)	2.4
left (.9)	1.3
both (2.2)	3.5
V-8-1983-87 (1.3)	1.9
left (.8)	1.2
both (1.9)	3.0
w/A.C. add (.2)	.2

COMBINATIONS

(Factory Time)	Chilton Time
(G) Muffler, Exhaust and Tail Pipe, Renew	
1983-87	1.2

PARTS 8 EXHAUST SYSTEM 8 PARTS

	Part No.	Price
Muffler		
140 engine		
1983-84	▲E3SZ-5230D	96.25
1985-87	▲E4SZ-5230C	96.75
230 engine		
1983	▲E3SZ-5230B	139.25
1984	▲E4SZ-5230A	132.25
1985-87	▲E4SZ-5230D	135.75
302 engine		
1983-84	▲E3SZ-5230E	137.75
1985	▲E4SZ-5230B	135.75
1986-87	▲E6SZ-5230A	135.75
Converter Air Tube		
230 engine		
1983-84	▲E2SZ-5F235A	27.25
1985-87	▲E5SZ-5F235B	27.25
302 engine		
1983-84	▲E3SZ-5F235A	13.75
1985	▲E5SZ-5F235A	27.25
1986-87	▲E6LY-5F235B	27.25
Catalytic Converter		
140 engine		
1983	▲E3SZ-5E212D	373.75
1984-w/A.T.	▲E4SZ-5E212C	373.75
w/M.T.	▲E3SZ-5E212D	373.75
1985-w/A.T.	▲E5SZ-5E212B	373.75
w/M.T.	▲E5SZ-5E212A	401.50
1986-87	▲E6SZ-5E212D	419.25
230 engine		
(front)		
1983	▲E2DZ-5F250C	200.75
1984	▲E4DZ-5F250A	456.75
1985	▲E5DZ-5F250A	397.75
1986-87	▲E6SZ-5F250B	427.25
(rear)		
1983	▲E3SZ-5E212B	382.25
1984-87	▲E4SZ-5E212B	207.75

PARTS 8 EXHAUST SYSTEM 8 PARTS

	Part No.	Price
(Canada)		
1983	▲E2SZ-5E212E	N.L.
1984-87	▲E4SZ-5E212A	N.L.
302 engine		
1983	▲E3SZ-5F250A	764.50
1984-85	▲E4SZ-5F250A	415.25
1986-87	▲E6SZ-5F250A	377.50
1983-Canada	▲E2DZ-5F250C	200.75

LABOR 9 FRONT SUSPENSION 9 LABOR

(Factory Time) — Chilton Time

Note: On all front suspension operations alignment charges must be added if performed. Time given does not include alignment.

(M) Wheel, Renew
- one (.5) 5

(G) Wheels, Rotate (All)
- All models (.5) 5

(G) Wheels, Balance
- one 3
- each adtnl 2

(G) Check Alignment of Front End
- All models (.4) 5

Note: Deduct if alignment is performed.

(G) Toe-In, Adjust
- All models (.4) 6

(G) Align Front End

Includes: Adjust front wheel bearings.
- All models (1.0) 1.5
- w/A.C. interference add 5

(G) Front Wheel Bearing, Clean and Repack (Both Wheels)
- All models 1.3

(G) Front Wheel Bearings and Cups, Renew
- 1983-87-one whl (.7) 9
- both whls (1.2) 1.5

(G) Front Wheel Grease Seals, Renew

Includes: Repack bearings.
- 1983-87-one whl (.6) 7
- both whls (.9) 1.1

(G) Front Strut Shock Absorbers, R&R or Renew
- 1983-87-one (.7) 1.0
- both (1.2) 1.9

(G) Front Spindle Assembly, Renew (One)

Add alignment charges.
- 1983-87 (.8) 1.2

(G) Lower Control Arm Assy., Renew (One)

Add alignment charges.
- 1983-87 (1.1) 1.5

(G) Ball Joints, Renew

Add alignment charges.
- 1983-87
  - one side 1.2
  - both sides 1.9

(G) Lower Control Arm Bushings, Renew

Add alignment charges.
- 1983-87-one side (1.4) 1.9
- both sides (2.5) 3.5

(G) Front Spring, Renew
- 1983-87-one (1.0) 1.5
- both (1.7) 2.7

(G) Front Stabilizer Bar, Renew
- 1983-87 (.6) 9

(G) Control Arm Rubber Bumpers, Renew
- one (.3) 4
- each adtnl (.1) 1

PARTS 9 FRONT SUSPENSION 9 PARTS

	Part No.	Price
(1) Plate (Camber Adjusting)		
1983-87	▲E0SZ-3B391A	5.50
(2) Bracket Assy. (Upper Mounting)		
1983-87	▲E3SZ-18A161A	41.25
(3) Shock Absorber (Front)		
1983-84	▲E3SZ-18124C	N.L.
1985-87-exc.		
140 eng.	▲E5SZ-18124A	91.50
w/140 eng. bef.		
5-85	▲E5SZ-18124C	N.L.
from 5-85	▲E3SZ-18124D	N.L.
(4) Spindle Assy.		
1983-87-right	▲E1SZ-3105A	137.00
left	▲E1SZ-3106A	137.00
(5) Lower Control Arm Assy.		
1983-84-right	▲E3SZ-3078B	99.25
left	▲E3SZ-3079B	99.25
1985-87-exc. 140 turbo		
right	▲E3SZ-3078B	99.25
left	▲E3SZ-3079B	99.25
1985-87-w/140 turbo		
right	▲E5SZ-3078A	99.25
left	▲E5SZ-3079A	99.25
(6) Coil Spring		
Order by model and description.		
(7) Insulator (Upper)		
1983-87	▲E1SZ-5415A	9.00
(8) Stabilizer Repair Kit		
1983-87	▲E3AZ-5A486A	20.75

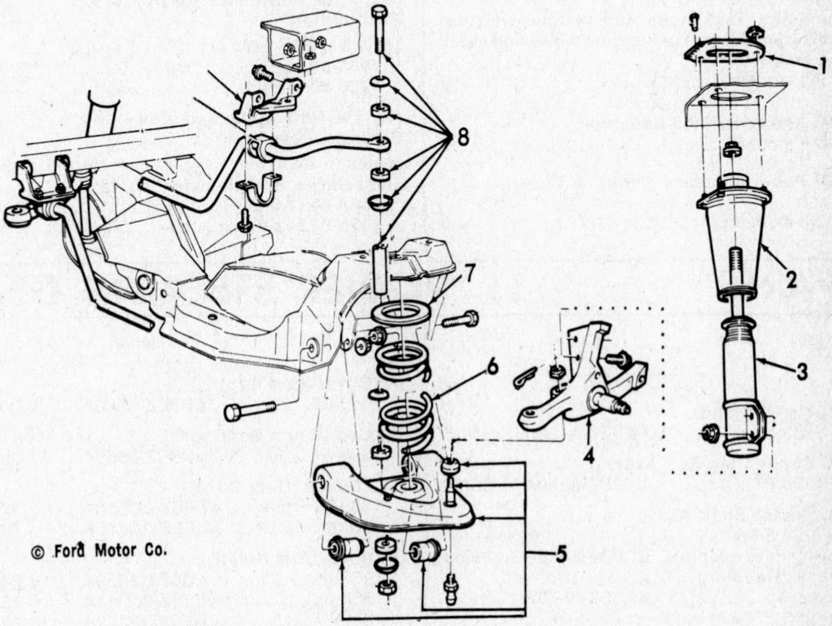

LABOR 10 STEERING LINKAGE 10 LABOR

	Factory Time	Chilton Time
(G) Tie Rod Ends, Renew		
Includes: Reset toe-in.		
1983-87-one	(.8)	1.2
each adtnl	(.2)	.2

PARTS 10 STEERING LINKAGE 10 PARTS

	Part No.	Price
Tie Rod End (Outer)		
1983-87	▲E2SZ-3A130A	36.25
Connecting Rod Assy.		
1983-87	▲E2SZ-3280A	66.25
Sector Shaft		
1983-84-w/ Standard susp.	▲D8BZ-3575A	36.50
w/Handling susp.	▲E3SZ-3575A	31.75
1985-87-w/ Standard susp.	▲E5DZ-3575A	36.50
w/Handling susp.	▲E5DZ-3575B	36.50

LABOR 11 STEERING GEAR 11 LABOR

	Factory Time	Chilton Time
(G) Horn Button or Ring, Renew		
1983-87	(.3)	.6
(G) Steering Wheel, Renew		
1983-87	(.3)	.5
(G) Upper Mast Jacket Bearing, Renew		
1983-87-std column	(.4)	.9
tilt column	(.6)	1.1
(G) Steering Column Lock Actuator, Renew		
1983-87-std colm	(1.1)	1.5
tilt colm	(1.7)	2.3

POWER STEERING

	Factory Time	Chilton Time
(G) Trouble Shoot Power Steering		
Includes: Test pump and system pressure. Check pounds pull on steering wheel and check for leaks.		
All models		.5
(M) Check and Fill Reservoir		
All models		.2
(G) Pump Pressure Check & Flow Test		
All models		.5
(M) Pump Drive Belt, Renew or Adjust		
1983-87-renew	(.3)	.4
adjust	(.2)	.2
(G) Power Steering Gear, Adjust (On Car)		
Includes: Bearing preload and gear mesh.		
All models	(.3)	.5
(G) Power Steering Gear, Renew		
Includes: Bleed system.		
1983-84	(1.7)	2.5
1985-87	(2.2)	2.5
(P) Steering Gear, R&R and Recondition		
Includes: Disassemble, renew necessary parts, reassemble and adjust.		
1983-87	(3.2)	4.5
(G) Input Shaft and Valve Assy., Recondition		
Includes: R&R gear assy. Bleed system.		
1983-84	(2.3)	3.2
1985-87	(1.8)	3.2
(G) Tie Rod Ends and Ball Joint Sockets, Renew		
Includes: R&R gear assy. Renew tie rod ends and bellows. Add alignment charges.		
1983-84	(1.9)	2.6
1985-87	(1.4)	2.6
(G) Power Steering Pump, Renew		
Includes: Bleed system.		
1983-87		
Four	(1.1)	1.5
V-6	(1.1)	1.5
V-8	(.9)	1.3
(G) Power Steering Pump, R&R and Recondition		
Includes: Bleed system.		
1983-87		
Four	(1.5)	2.1
V-6	(1.5)	2.1
V-8	(1.3)	1.8
(G) Power Steering Pump Shaft Oil Seal, Renew		
Includes: Bleed system.		
1983-87		
Four	(1.2)	1.6
V-6	(1.2)	1.6
V-8	(1.0)	1.4
(M) Power Steering Hoses, Renew		
Includes: Bleed system.		
1983-87-pressure	(.5)	.8
return	(.6)	.8
cooling	(.4)	.6

PARTS 11 POWER STEERING GEAR 11 PARTS

FORD TYPE

	Part No.	Price
(1) Tie Rod End		
1983-87	▲E2SZ-3A130A	36.25
(2) Connecting Rod Assy.		
1983-87	▲E2SZ-3280A	66.25
(3) Sector Shaft Assy.		
1983-84-w/ Standard susp.	▲D8BZ-3575A	36.50
w/Handling susp.	▲E3SZ-3575A	31.75
1985-87-w/ Standard susp.	▲E5DZ-3575A	36.50
w/Handling susp.	▲E5DZ-3575B	36.50
(4) Gear Rack Tube		
1983-87	▲D8BZ-3K762A	2.25
(5) Cover (End Cap)		
1983-87	▲D8BZ-3568A	5.00
(6) Cup (Worm Bearing)		
1983-87	▲D8BZ-3552A	13.25
(7) Clamps (Gear Boot)		
1983-87-inner	▲D8BZ-3C650A	2.00
outer	▲D8BZ-3C650B	.75
(8) Boot (Dust Seal)		
1983	▲D9BZ-3332A	5.50
1984-85	▲E3SZ-3K661A	6.25
1986-87	▲E69Z-3332A	10.25
(9) Housing Assy.		
1983-wo/ Handling susp.	▲E3SZ-3548A	150.75
1983-w/Handling susp.	▲E3SZ-3548B	120.75
1984-87		
thru SPR-BT	▲E4DZ-3548A	161.25
from SPR-BZ	▲E5DZ-3548A	161.25
(11) Check Valve Kit		
1983-87	▲E3SZ-3D728A	15.75
(12) Shaft & Control Assy.		
w/std. susp.		
1983	▲E5SZ-3D517C	50.00
1984-85	▲E4DZ-3D517B	50.00
1986-87	▲E5SZ-3D517A	50.00
w/handling susp.		
1983-84-bef. 2-84	▲E4SZ-3D517C	50.00
1984-85-from 2-84	▲E4SZ-3D517F	50.00
1986-87	▲E5SZ-3D517B	50.00

PARTS 11 POWER STEERING GEAR 11 PARTS

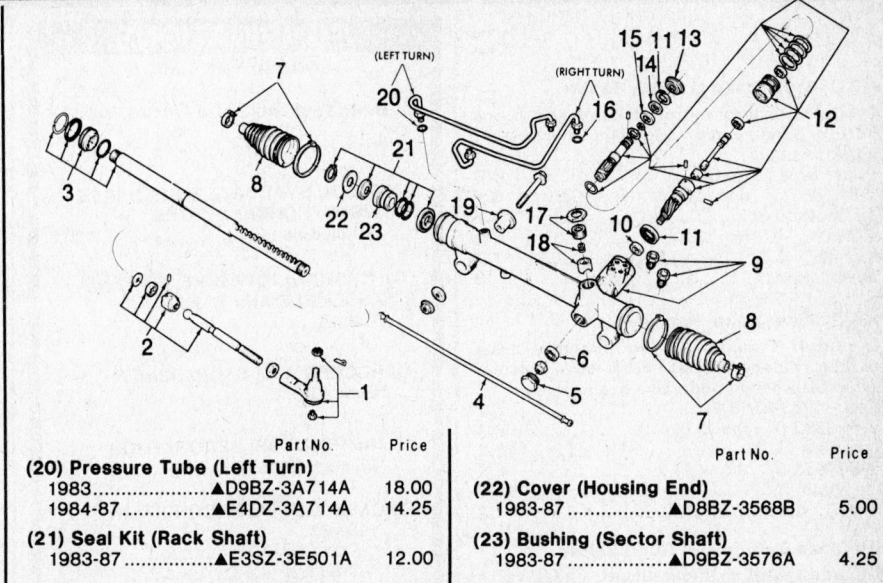

	Part No	Price
(13) Dust Seal (Input Shaft)		
1983-87	▲D5AZ-3D527A	5.00
(14) Seal (Input Shaft)		
1983-87	▲D6AZ-3D526A	4.75
(15) Bearing (Input Shaft)		
1983-87	▲D8AZ-3D525A	8.75
(16) Pressure Tube (Right Turn)		
1983	▲D9BZ-3A717A	15.25
1984-87	▲E4DZ-3A717A	14.25
(17) Housing Cover (Sector Shaft)		
1983-87	▲E0BZ-3580AMR	7.00
(18) Bearing (Rack Adjust)		
1983	▲E0SZ-3F515A	8.25
1986-87	▲E69Z-3F515A	9.00
(19) Insulator		
1983-87	▲E0SZ-3C716A	7.50

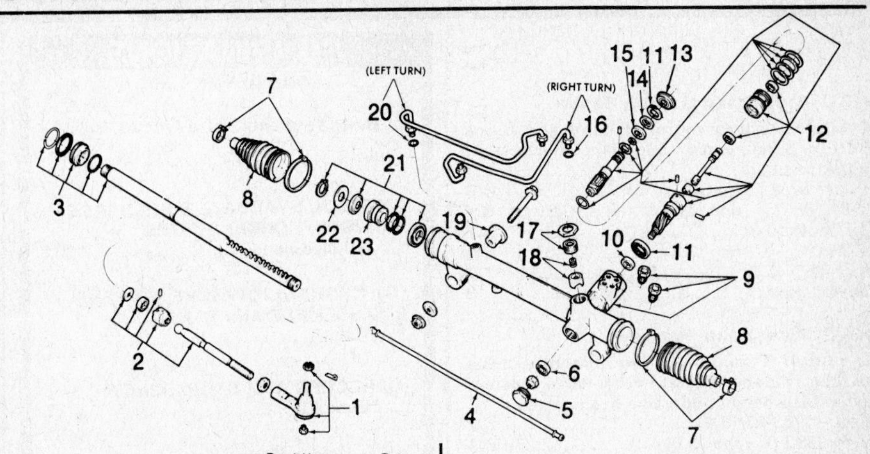

	Part No.	Price
(20) Pressure Tube (Left Turn)		
1983	▲D9BZ-3A714A	18.00
1984-87	▲E4DZ-3A714A	14.25
(21) Seal Kit (Rack Shaft)		
1983-87	▲E3SZ-3E501A	12.00

	Part No.	Price
(22) Cover (Housing End)		
1983-87	▲D8BZ-3568B	5.00
(23) Bushing (Sector Shaft)		
1983-87	▲D9BZ-3576A	4.25

PARTS 11 POWER STEERING PUMP 11 PARTS

	Part No.	Price
Oil Pressure Hose		
1983-right turn	▲D9BZ-3A717A	15.25
left turn	▲D9BZ-3A714A	18.00
1984-87-right turn	▲E4DZ-3A717A	14.25
left turn	▲E4DZ-3A714A	14.25
Oil Return Hose		
1983-87	▲E2SZ-3A713B	15.25
Power Steering Pump		
140 engine		
1983-85	▲E5DZ-3A674A	215.75
1986-87	▲E6SZ-3A674A	215.75
230 engine		
1983-85-exc. Handling susp.	▲E5DZ-3A674B	215.75
1983-85-w/ Handling susp.	▲E5SZ-3A674A	200.75
1986-87-exc. Handling susp.	▲E6SZ-3A674B	215.75
w/Handling susp.	▲E6SZ-3A674C	215.75
302 engine		
1983-85	▲E5SZ-3A674A	200.75
1986-87	▲E6SZ-3A674C	215.75
(1) Seal & Gasket Kit		
1983-87	▲E1AZ-3D684A	3.00
(2) Valve Assy.		
140 engine		
1983-87	▲D8BZ-3A561A	11.00
230 engine		
1983-87-Std. susp.	▲D8BZ-3A561A	11.00
H.D. susp.	▲E1SZ-3A561A	11.00
302 engine		
1983-87	▲E1SZ-3A561A	11.00
(3) Valve Spring (Flow Control)		
1983-87	▲D8AZ-3D586A	1.50
(4) Housing Assy.		
1983-87	▲E1AZ-3A643A	42.25

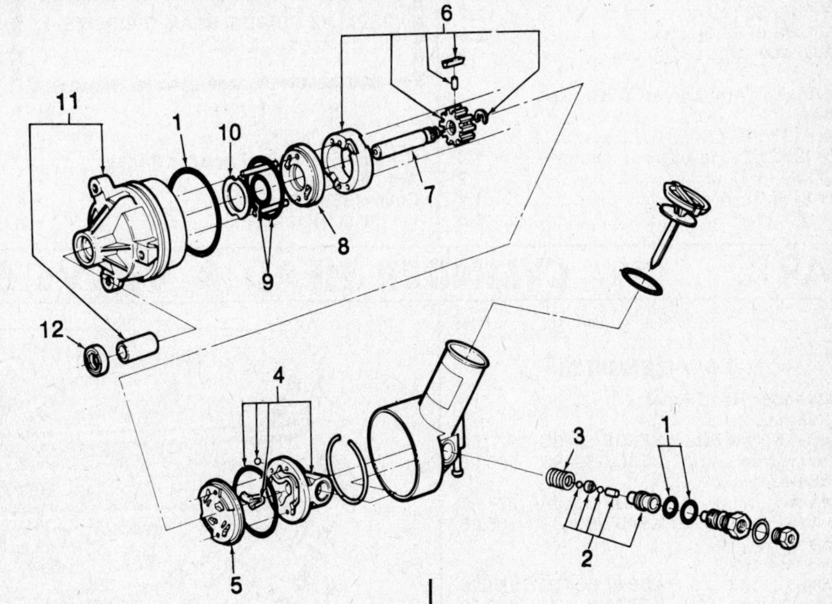

	Part No.	Price
(5) Pressure Plate (Front)		
1983	▲D8AZ-3D590A	N.L.
1984-87	▲E5FZ-3D590A	13.75
(6) Rotor Assy.		
1983-87-(wo/turbo) wo/H.D. susp.	▲E53Z-3D607A	36.25
w/H.D. susp.	▲E5SZ-3D607A	38.75
1985-87-w/turbo	▲E5FZ-3D607A	56.25
(7) Rotor Shaft		
1983-87	▲D8AZ-3B559A	18.00

	Part No.	Price
(8) Pressure Plate (Rear)		
1983-87	▲D8AZ-3D590B	13.75
(9) Seal & Gasket Kit		
1983-87	▲E1AZ-3B584A	8.75
(10) Spring (Pressure Plate)		
1983-87	▲D8AZ-3D596A	2.50
(11) Plate & Bushing		
1983-87	▲E1AZ-3D643A	42.25
(12) Oil Seal (Rotor Shaft)		
1983-87	▲D9AZ-3B592A	9.25

LABOR 12 CYLINDER HEAD & VALVE SYSTEM 12 LABOR

(Factory Time)	Chilton Time
(G) Compression Test	
Four–1983-87 (.3)	.6
V-6–1983-87 (.4)	.8
V-8–1983-87 (.5)	.9
w/A.C. add	.2

LABOR 12 CYLINDER HEAD & VALVE SYSTEM 12 LABOR

	(Factory Time)	Chilton Time

(G) Cylinder Head Gasket, Renew

Includes: Check cylinder head and block flatness. Clean carbon and make all necessary adjustments.

Four–1983-87	(4.3)	6.0
V-6–1983-87-one	(4.6)	6.4
both	(6.2)	8.7
V-8–1983-87-one	(3.7)	5.2
both	(5.5)	7.7
w/A.C. add		.3

(G) Cylinder Head, Renew

Includes: Transfer all components, clean carbon. Reface valves, check valve tension, assembled height and valve head runout.

Four–1983-87	(5.2)	7.2
V-6–1983-87-one	(5.8)	8.1
both	(8.7)	12.1
V-8–1983-87-one	(4.9)	6.8
both	(8.0)	11.2
w/A.C. add		.3

(P) Clean Carbon and Grind Valves

Includes: R&R cylinder heads, check valve spring tension, valve seat and head runout, stem to guide clearance and spring assembled height. Minor tune up.

Four–1983-87	(6.9)	9.6
V-6–1983-87	(9.1)	12.7
V-8–1983-87	(9.0)	12.6
w/A.C. add		.3

(G) Rocker Arm Cover or Gasket, Renew

Four–1983-87	(1.0)	1.4
V-6–1983-87-one	(.8)	1.1
both	(1.2)	1.7
V-8–1983-87-one	(.7)	1.1
both	(1.2)	1.8

COMBINATIONS

Add to Valve Job

See Machine Shop Operations

	(Factory Time)	Chilton Time
(G) DRAIN, EVACUATE & RECHARGE AIR CONDITIONING SYSTEM		
All models	(.7)	1.2
(G) HYDRAULIC VALVE LIFTERS, DISASSEMBLE AND CLEAN		
Each		.2
(G) ROCKER ARM STUD, RENEW		
Each	(.2)	.2
(G) DISTRIBUTOR, RECONDITION		
All models	(1.1)	1.5
(G) CARBURETOR, RECONDITION		
1983-87		
Four	(1.1)	1.6
V-6	(1.2)	1.7
V-8-2150-2 V	(1.5)	2.0
2700 VV	(2.2)	2.7
7200 VV	(2.3)	2.8
(P) VALVE GUIDES, REAM OVERSIZE		
Each	(.1)	.1

	(Factory Time)	Chilton Time

(G) Valve Push Rod and/or Rocker Arm, Renew

Four–1983-87-one	(1.1)	1.6
all	(1.4)	2.0
V-6–1983-87-one	(.9)	1.3
one-each side	(1.4)	2.0
all-both sides	(1.5)	2.2
V-8–1983-87-one	(.9)	1.3
all-one side	(1.0)	1.4
all-both sides	(1.6)	2.2

(G) Rocker Arm Stud, Renew

V-8–1983-87-one	(1.0)	1.4
one-each side	(1.7)	2.4
each adtnl	(.2)	.2

(G) Valve Spring and/or Valve Stem Oil Seals, Renew (Head on Car)

Four–1983-87-one	(1.2)	1.7
each adtnl	(.2)	.2
all	(2.2)	3.2
V-6–1983-87-one	(1.0)	1.4
one-each side	(1.6)	2.2
all-both sides	(3.0)	4.2
V-8–1983-87-one	(1.0)	1.4
one-each side	(1.7)	2.4
all-both sides	(3.7)	5.2

(G) Valve Tappets, Renew

Includes: R&R intake manifold where required. Make all necessary adjustments.

Four–1983-87-one	(1.0)	1.6
all	(1.5)	2.4
V-6–1983-87-one	(2.6)	3.9
all	(3.2)	4.5
V-8–1983-87-one	(2.1)	2.9
all	(2.8)	4.0
w/Cruise control add	(.1)	.1

PARTS 12 CYLINDER HEAD & VALVE SYSTEM 12 PARTS

V-6 & V-8 ENGINES

	Part No.	Price
(1) Cylinder Head Assy.		
230 engine		
1983-wo/valves	▲E3DZ-6049C	377.00
w/valves	▲E3DZ-6049D	505.25
1984-87-wo/valves	▲E4DZ-6049A	377.00
w/valves	▲E4DZ-6049B	505.25
302 engine		
1983-84-wo/valves	▲D84Y-6049C	281.25
w/valves	▲E2ZZ-6049A	429.50
1985-wo/valves	▲E5AZ-6049A	302.25
w/valves	▲E5AZ-6049B	429.25
1986-87-w/valves	▲E6AZ-6049A	302.25
w/valves	▲E6AZ-6049B	429.25
(2) Cylinder Head Gasket		
230 engine		
1983-87	▲E3DZ-6051A	12.75
302 engine		
1983-84-wo/H.O.	▲D7OZ-6051C	12.50
w/H.O.	▲E2ZZ-6051A	13.75
1985	▲E5AZ-6051A	11.50
1986-87	▲E5ZZ-6051B	13.75
Valve Grind Gasket Set		
1983	▲E3DZ-6079A	71.50
1984	▲E4DZ-6079A	65.25
1985-87	▲E5DZ-6079A	71.50
302 engine		
1983-84-wo/H.O.	▲E1AZ-6079A	61.00
w/H.O.	▲E2ZZ-6079B	52.50
1985-w/H.O.	▲E5ZZ-6079B	52.50

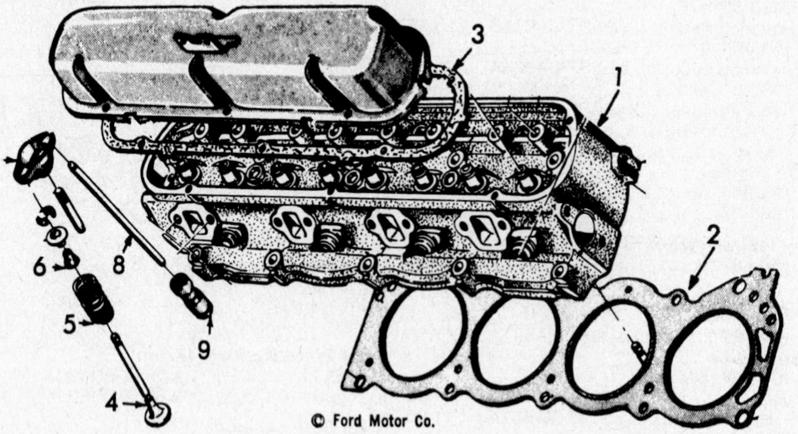

© Ford Motor Co.

	Part No.	Price
(3) Valve Cover Gasket		
1983-87-Six	▲E3BZ-6584A	7.50
1983-87-V-6	▲E3DZ-6584A	5.25
1983-85-V-8	▲E3AZ-6584A	4.75
1986-87	▲E5TZ-6584C	4.75
(4) Intake Valve (Std.)		
230 engine		
1983	▲E2DZ-6507A	9.50
1984-87	▲E4DZ-6507A	9.50
302 engine		
1983-85	▲E3ZZ-6507A	7.75
1986-87	▲E6AZ-6507A	7.50

	Part No.	Price
Exhaust Valve (Std.)		
1983-87-Six	▲E2DZ-6505A	11.75
1983-85-V-8	▲E4AZ-6505A	8.00
1986-87	▲E6AZ-6505A	8.00
(5) Valve Spring		
230 engine		
1983	▲E2DZ-6513A	5.50
1984-87	▲E4DZ-6513A	4.75
302 engine		
1983-87-intake	▲D8AZ-6513A	4.50
exhaust	▲D5OZ-6513A	6.75

PARTS 12 CYLINDER HEAD & VALVE SYSTEM 12 PARTS

	Part No.	Price
(6) Valve Stem Oil Seal		
230 engine		
1983-87-intake	▲E3DZ-6571A	.75
exhaust	▲D9OZ-6571A	.75
302 engine		
1983-85-intake	▲E0SZ-6571A	.75
1983-87-exhaust	▲D9OZ-6571A	.75
1986-87	▲E43Z-6571A	2.25
(7) Rocker Arm		
1983-87-V-6	▲E2DZ-6564A	7.75
V-8	▲E0AZ-6564A	11.00
(8) Valve Push Rods (Std.)		
1983-87-V-6	▲E2DZ-6565A	2.75
1983-85-V-8	▲C9OZ-6565B	2.75
1986-87	▲E5AZ-6565A	4.00
(9) Valve Tappet		
1983-87-V-6		
(exc. Canada)	▲D9HZ-6500A	9.25
Canada	▲CE2DZ-6500A	N.L.
1983-85-V-8	▲D9HZ-6500A	9.25
1986-87	▲E5AZ-6500A	7.00

PARTS 12 CYLINDER HEAD & VALVE SYSTEM 12 PARTS

	Part No.	Price
2.3L ENGINE		
1983-87	▲E5ZZ-6079A	42.00
(1) Cylinder Head (New)		
wo/Turbo		
(wo/valves)		
1983	▲E1BZ-6049C	351.75
1984	▲E4ZZ-6049A	351.75
1985-87	▲E5ZZ-6049B	351.75
(w/valves)		
1983-84	▲E1BZ-6049B	521.25
1984	▲E4ZZ-6049B	521.25
1985-87	▲E5ZZ-6049C	869.75
Turbo		
(wo/valves)		
1983-84	▲E1BZ-6049C	351.75
1985-87	▲E5ZZ-6049A	351.75
(w/valves)		
1983-84	▲E1BZ-6049B	521.25
(2) Cylinder Head Gasket		
1983-87	▲E5FZ-6051A	13.50
(3) Valve Cover Gasket		
1983-87	▲E2ZZ-6584A	1.00
(4) Exhaust Manifold		
1983-87	▲E3ZZ-9430A	110.50
(5) Seal (Valve Stem)		
1983-84	▲D4FZ-6571A	1.25
1985-87-intake	▲E43Z-6571A	2.25
exhaust	▲D4FZ-6571A	1.25
(6) Valve Spring		
wo/Turbo		
1983-84	▲E4ZZ-6513A	6.25
1985-87	▲E5ZZ-6513A	N.L.
Turbo		
1983-87	▲E4ZZ-6513A	6.25
(7) Rocker Arm		
1983-87	▲D8FZ-6564A	8.00

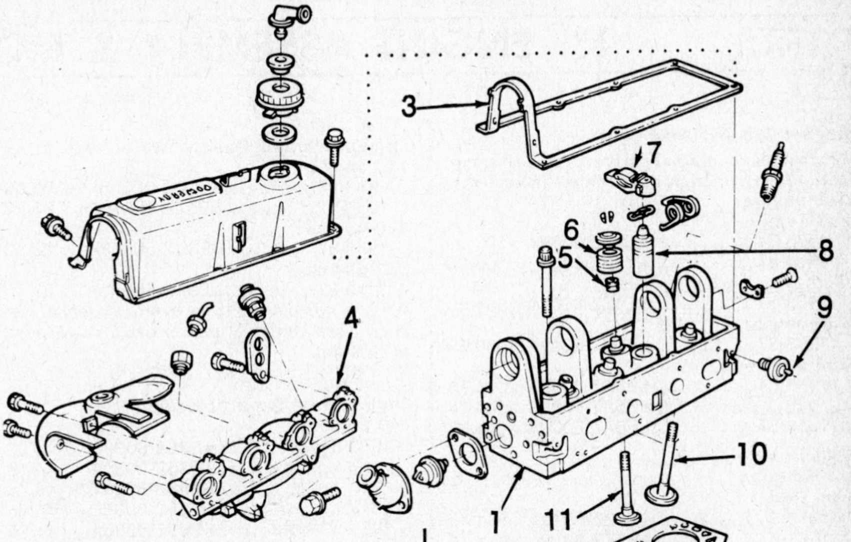

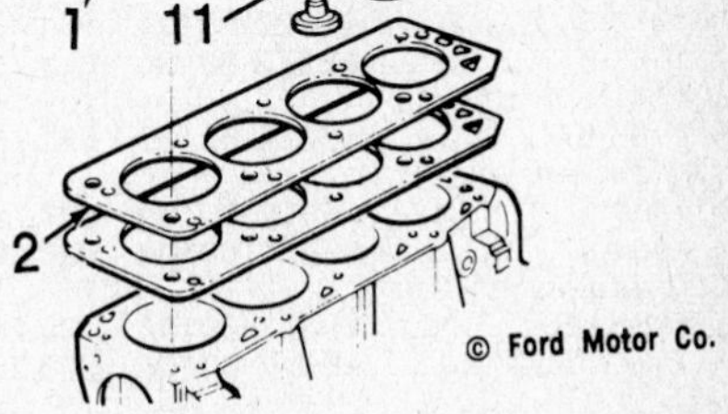

© Ford Motor Co.

	Part No.	Price
(8) Valve Tappet		
1983-87	▲D6FZ-6500A	10.00
(9) Oil Pressure Gauge (Engine)		
1983-84	▲D4AZ-9278A	3.50
1985	▲E4ZZ-9278A	12.75
1986-87	▲E6ZZ-9278A	14.50
(10) Intake Valve		
wo/Turbo		
1983-87	▲E5ZZ-6507A	9.75
Turbo		
1983-84	▲D9ZZ-6507A	12.00
1985-87	▲E5ZZ-6507D	9.25
(11) Exhaust Valve		
wo/Turbo		
1983-87	▲E43Z-6505A	14.25
Turbo		
1983-84	▲D9ZZ-6505A	21.75
1985-87	▲E5ZZ-6505A	16.75

LABOR 13 ENGINE ASSEMBLY & MOUNTS 13 LABOR

(Factory Time) — Chilton Time

(G) Engine Assembly, Remove & Install

Does not include transfer of any parts or equipment.

	Chilton Time
Four–1983-87 (4.2)	**5.9**
w/A.C. add (.7)	**.7**
V-6–1983-87 (4.5)	**6.3**
V-8–1983-87 (4.5)	**6.3**
w/A.C. add (.3)	**.3**
w/P.S. add (.3)	**.3**

(G) Engine Assembly, Replace With New or Rebuilt Unit (With Cyl. Heads)

Includes: R&R engine assembly, transfer all necessary parts, fuel and electrical units. Minor tune up.

	Chilton Time
V-8–1983-87 (6.8)	**9.5**
w/A.C. add (.3)	**.3**
w/P.S. add (.3)	**.3**

(P) Cylinder Assembly, Renew (w/All Internal parts Less Cyl. Heads and Oil Pan)

Includes: R&R engine, transfer all component parts not supplied with replacement engine, clean carbon, grind valves. Tune engine.

	Chilton Time
V-6–1983-87 (11.3)	**15.8**
V-8–1983-87 (12.3)	**17.5**
w/A.C. add (.3)	**.3**
w/P.S. add (.3)	**.3**

(P) Cylinder Block, Renew

Includes: R&R engine, transfer all component parts, renew rings and bearings, clean carbon, grind valves. Tune engine.

	Chilton Time
V-6–1983-87 (12.5)	**17.5**
V-8–1983-87 (17.6)	**25.6**
w/A.C. add (.3)	**.3**
w/P.S. add (.3)	**.3**

(P) Engine Assy., R&R and Recondition (Complete)

Includes: Rebore block, install new pistons, rings, rod and main bearings. Clean carbon, grind valves. Tune engine.

	Chilton Time
Four–1983-87 (18.0)	**24.4**
V-6–1983-87 (25.0)	**29.9**
V-8–1983-87 (23.1)	**33.4**
w/A.C. add (.3)	**.3**
w/P.S. add (.3)	**.3**

LABOR 13 ENGINE ASSEMBLY & MOUNTS 13 LABOR

	(Factory Time)	Chilton Time
(P) Engine Assembly, Recondition (In Car)		
Includes: Expand or renew pistons, install new rings, pins, rod and main bearings. Clean carbon, grind valves. Tune engine.		
Four–1983-87	(18.1)	24.3
w/A.C. add	(.7)	.7
V-6–1983-87	(18.0)	26.1
V-8–1983-87	(19.9)	29.8
w/A.C. add	(.3)	.3

	(Factory Time)	Chilton Time
(G) Engine Mounts, Renew		
Front		
Four–1983-87–one	(.8)	1.1
both	(1.2)	1.6
V-6–1983-87–one	(.6)	.8
both	(.9)	1.2
V-8–1983-87–one	(.7)	.9
both	(.9)	1.2
Rear		
1983-87	(.5)	.8

PARTS 13 ENGINE ASSEMBLY & MOUNTS 13 PARTS

	Part No.	Price
Engine Cylinder Assembly		
Block with all internal parts except, heads, tappets, oil pan or front cover unless indicated.		
140 engine		
(wo/Turbo)		
1983-84	▲E2ZZ-6009A	1506.00
1985-87	▲E5ZZ-6009A	1506.00
(Turbo)		
1983-87	▲E4ZZ-6009A	1534.50
230 engine		
1983-87	▲E4DZ-6009A	2000.50
302 engine		
1983-84	▲E3AZ-6009A	2044.75
1985	▲E5AZ-6009B	2044.75
1986-87	▲E6AZ-6009A	2044.75
Cylinder Block		
140 engine		
(wo/Turbo)		
1983-84	▲E3ZZ-6010A	671.75
1985-87	▲E5ZZ-6010A	671.75
(Turbo)		
1983-87	▲E3ZZ-6010B	671.75
230 engine		
1983	▲E3DZ-6010A	837.75
1984-87	▲E4DZ-6010A	900.25
302 engine		
1983-85	▲E5AZ-6010A	920.25
1986-87	▲E6AZ-6010A	920.25

	Part No.	Price
Engine Overhaul Gasket Set		
140 engine		
1983-84	▲E2PZ-6E078A	25.50
1985-87	▲E5ZZ-6E078A	25.50
230 engine		
1983-87	▲E3DZ-6E078B	23.50
302 engine		
1983-87	▲E3AZ-6E078A	27.75

When a complete engine overhaul gasket set is required you must also order a valve grind gasket set.

	Part No.	Price
Engine Front Support Insulator		
140 engine		
1983-84-right	▲E3SZ-6038C	44.75
left	▲E3SZ-6038D	44.75
1985-left	▲E5SZ-6038A	44.75
right	▲E5SZ-6038B	44.75
1986-87-right	▲E6SZ-6038A	44.50
left	▲E6SZ-6038B	44.75
230 engine		
1983-right	▲E3SZ-6038J	37.75
left	▲E3SZ-6038K	37.75
1984-85-right	▲E3SZ-6038G	37.75
left	▲E3SZ-6038H	37.75
1986-87-right	▲E6SZ-6038C	46.75
left	▲E65Z-6038D	N.L.
302 engine		
1983-right	▲E3SZ-6038E	34.75
left	▲E3SZ-6038F	34.75
1984-right	▲E4SZ-6038A	34.75
left	▲E4SZ-6038B	34.75
1985-right	▲E4DZ-6038C	35.75
left	▲E4DZ-6038D	35.75
1986-87	▲E6SZ-6038E	50.25
left	▲E6SZ-6038F	50.25

	Part No.	Price
Engine Rear Support Insulator		
140 engine		
1983	▲E3ZZ-6068A	20.75
1984-w/A.T.	▲E2SZ-6068C	19.50
w/M.T.	▲E2SZ-6068B	22.50
1985-w/A.T.	▲E5SZ-6068B	33.00
w/M.T.	▲E5SZ-6068A	33.00
1986-87-w/A.T.	▲E6SZ-6068B	33.00
w/M.T.	▲E6SZ-6068A	33.00
230 engine		
1983-84-w/		
A.O.D.	▲E2SZ-6068B	22.50
C5 trans.	▲E2SZ-6068C	19.50
1985-87-w/		
A.O.D.	▲E5SZ-6068C	23.00
w/C5 trans.	▲E5SZ-6068D	18.75
302 engine		
1983-85	▲E3SZ-6068A	20.75
1986-87	▲E6SZ-6068C	20.75

LABOR 14 PISTONS, RINGS & BEARINGS 14 LABOR

COMBINATIONS

Add to Engine Work

See Machine Shop Operations

	(Factory Time)	Chilton Time
(G) DRAIN, EVACUATE & RECHARGE AIR CONDITIONING SYSTEM		
All models	(.7)	1.2
(G) HYDRAULIC VALVE LIFTERS, DISASSEMBLE AND CLEAN		
Each		.2
(G) ROCKER ARM STUD, RENEW		
Each	(.2)	.2
(G) TIMING CHAIN OR GEARS, RENEW (COVER REMOVED)		
All models	(.3)	.5
(G) DISTRIBUTOR, RECONDITION		
All models	(1.1)	1.5
(G) CARBURETOR, RECONDITION		
1983-87		
Four	(1.1)	1.6
Six-Carter	(1.3)	1.8
Holly	(1.7)	2.2
V-6	(1.2)	1.7
V-8-2150-2 V	(1.5)	2.0

	(Factory Time)	Chilton Time
2700 VV	(2.2)	2.7
7200 VV	(2.3)	2.8
(G) CYLINDER HEAD, R&R (ENGINE REMOVED)		
Four		
wo/Turbo		3.5
w/Turbo		4.0
V-6		
one		4.0
both		5.5
V-8		
one		3.2
both		4.7
(G) CONNECTING ROD, RENEW (ENGINE DISASSEMBLED)		
All engines		
each		.4
(G) DEGLAZE CYLINDER WALLS		
Each	(.1)	.1
(G) REMOVE CYLINDER TOP RIDGE		
Each	(.1)	.1

	(Factory Time)	Chilton Time
(P) RECONDITION CYLINDER HEADS (HEADS REMOVED)		
Four	(2.6)	3.0
V-6-one	(1.5)	2.0
both	(2.9)	3.9
V-8-one	(1.8)	2.5
both	(3.5)	4.5
(P) MAIN BEARINGS, RENEW (PAN REMOVED)		
Four	(1.9)	2.5
V-6	(1.5)	2.0
V-8	(1.9)	2.5
(P) CONNECTING ROD BEARINGS, RENEW (PAN REMOVED)		
Four	(.9)	1.2
V-6	(1.4)	1.8
V-8	(1.8)	2.4
(G) PLASTIGAUGE BEARINGS		
Each	(.1)	.1
(G) OIL PUMP, RECONDITION		
All models	(.3)	.4
(M) OIL FILTER ELEMENT, RENEW		
All models	(.3)	.3

LABOR 14 PISTONS, RINGS & BEARINGS 14 LABOR

	(Factory Time)	Chilton Time
(P) Rings, Renew (See Engine Combinations)		
Includes: Remove cylinder top ridge, deglaze cylinder walls, replace rod bearing, clean carbon. Minor tune up.		
Four–1983-87	(8.5)	11.9
V-6–1983-87	(10.6)	14.8
V-8–1983-87	(12.6)	17.6
w/A.C. add	(.3)	.3
w/P.S. add	(.3)	.3
(P) Piston or Connecting Rod, Renew (One)		
Includes: Remove cylinder top ridge, deglaze cylinger walls, replace rod bearings, clean carbon. Minor tune up.		
Four–1983-87	(7.5)	10.5
V-6–1983-87	(6.8)	9.5
V-8–1983-87	(8.7)	12.1
w/A.C. add	(.3)	.3
w/P.S. add	(.3)	.3
(P) Connecting Rod Bearings, Renew		
Four–1983-87	(3.8)	5.3
V-6–1983-87	(3.7)	5.2
V-8–1983-87	(5.4)	8.4

PARTS 14 PISTONS, RINGS & BEARINGS 14 PARTS

	Part No	Price
(1) Piston Ring Set (Partial)		
140 engine		
(wo/Turbo)		
1983-84	▲D4FZ-6148A	31.75
1985-87	▲E5ZZ-6148A	32.00
(Turbo)		
1983-87	▲D9ZZ-6148A	29.25
230 engine		
1983-87	▲E2DZ-6148A	29.00
302 engine		
1983-85	▲C3AZ-6148F	31.75
1986-87	▲E6AZ-6148A	31.75
Piston ring set consists of the necessary rings for (2) pistons.		
(2) Piston Assy. (Std.)		
140 engine		
(wo/Turbo)		
1983-84	▲D4FZ-6108A	21.75
1985-87	▲E5ZZ-6108A	20.75

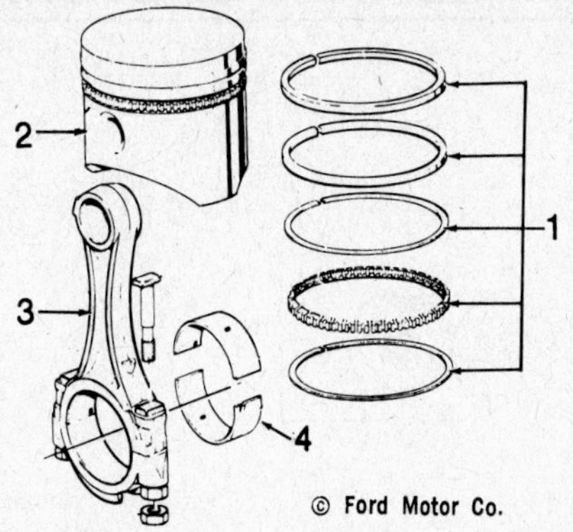

© Ford Motor Co.

	Part No.	Price
(Turbo)		
1983-87	▲E3ZZ-6108A	45.00
230 engine		
1983	▲E2DZ-6108AB	25.75
1984-87	▲E4DZ-6108A	25.50
302 engine		
1983-85	▲D9AZ-6108A	35.00
1986-87	▲E6AZ-6108A	35.50
(3) Connecting Rod Assy.		
1983-87-Four	▲D7FZ-6200A	47.00
V-6	▲E2DZ-6200A	47.00
V-8	▲D3OZ-6200A	44.00
(4) Connecting Rod Bearing		
1983-87-Four	▲D7FZ-6211A	2.50
V-6	▲E2DZ-6211A	2.75
V-8	▲C2OZ-6211R	2.25

LABOR 15 CRANKSHAFT & DAMPER 15 LABOR

	(Factory Time)	Chilton Time
(P) Crankshaft and Main Bearings, Renew		
Includes: R&R engine, check all bearing clearances.		
Four–1983-87	(8.0)	11.2
w/A.C. add	(.7)	.7
V-6–1983-87	(7.8)	11.7
V-8–1983-87	(8.3)	12.0
w/A.C. add	(.3)	.3
w/P.S. add	(.3)	.3
(P) Main Bearings, Renew		
Includes: Check all bearing clearances.		
Four–1983-87	(4.8)	6.7
V-6–1983-87	(3.8)	5.3
V-8–1983-87	(5.4)	8.5
(P) Main and Rod Bearings, Renew		
Includes: Check all bearing clearances.		
Four–1983-87	(5.7)	7.9
V-6–1983-87	(5.2)	7.1
V-8–1983-87	(7.2)	10.9
(G) Rear Main Bearing Oil Seals, Renew (Upper & Lower) (Split Lip Type)		
V-6–1983	(3.0)	4.2
(G) Rear Main Bearing Oil Seal, Renew (Full Circle Type)		
Four–1983-87	(2.3)	3.1
V-6–1983-87	(3.5)	4.9
V-8–1983-87	(3.3)	4.6
(G) Vibration Damper or Pulley, Renew		
Four–1983-87	(.4)	.8
V-6–1983-87	(.8)	1.2
V-8–1983-87	(.8)	1.2
w/A.C. or P.S. add	(.1)	.1
(G) Crankshaft Front Oil Seal, Renew		
Four–1983-87		
crank	(1.3)	1.8
aux drive	(1.2)	1.7
V-6–1983-87	(1.0)	1.5
V-8–1983-87	(.9)	1.4
w/A.C. add	(.1)	.1

Note: R&R front cover not required.

PARTS 15 CRANKSHAFT & DAMPER 15 PARTS

	Part No.	Price
V-6 & V-8 ENGS.		
(1) Vibration Damper or Pulley		
230 engine		
1983-87-C5 trans.	▲E3SZ-6B321A	88.00
AOD trans.	▲E3SZ-6B321B	88.00
302 engine		
1983	▲E2TZ-6316B	74.00
1984-87	▲E4TZ-6316A	67.75
(2) Crankshaft Gear		
1983-87-V-6	▲E2DZ-6306A	22.50
V-8	▲D5OZ-6306A	11.25
V-8-w/H.O.	▲E0AZ-6306A	18.50

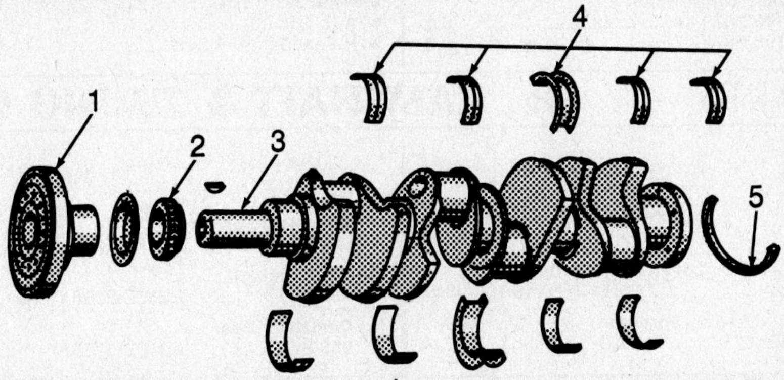

PARTS 15 CRANKSHAFT & DAMPER 15 PARTS

	Part No.	Price
(3) Crankshaft		
230 engine		
1983	▲E2DZ-6303B	423.25
1984-87	▲E3DZ-6303A	423.25
302 engine		
1983-87	▲E3AZ-6303A	500.75
(4) Main Bearing (Upper & Lower)		
230 engine		
(exc. rear intermediate)		
1983-87-upper	▲E2DZ-6333A	3.25
lower	▲E2DZ-6333D	3.25
(rear intermediate)		
1983-87-upper	▲E2DZ-6337A	8.25
lower	▲E2DZ-6337D	8.25
302 engine		
(exc. center)		
1983-87-upper	▲C3AZ-6333P	3.50
lower	▲C3AZ-6333AA	3.50
(center)		
1983-87-upper	▲C3AZ-6337P	8.00
lower	▲C3AZ-6337AA	8.00
(5) Rear Main Bearing Oil Seal		
rope type		
1983	▲C9OZ-6701A	2.00
split lip type		
1983	▲D4FZ-6701A	6.25
one piece type		
1983-87	▲E5ZZ-6701A	6.25

PARTS 15 CRANKSHAFT & DAMPER 15 PARTS

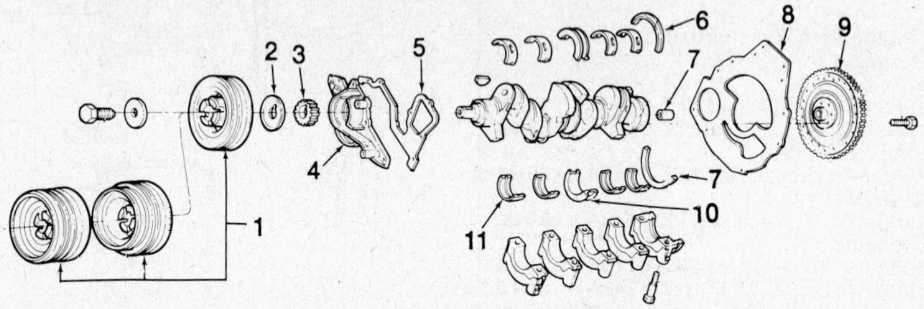

	Part No.	Price
2.3L ENGINE		
Crankshaft		
1983-87	▲E2ZZ-6303A	387.00
(1) Pulley Assy. (Outer)		
wo/A.C.		
1983-87	▲E2BZ-6A312A	51.50
w/A.C.		
1983-84	▲E3ZZ-6A312A	51.50
1985-87	▲E5ZZ-6A312A	48.00
(2) Spacer (Belt Cover)		
1983-87	▲D4FZ-6K291A	1.25
(3) Crankshaft Sprocket		
1983-87	▲D9FZ-6306A	11.50
(4) Front Cover Assy. (Lower)		
1983-84	▲E3TZ-6019A	45.25
1985-87	▲E5ZZ-6019A	45.25
1983-87-w/T.C.	▲E3TZ-6019A	45.25
(5) Gasket (Front Cover)		
1983-87 inner	▲D4FZ-6020B	1.50
outer	▲D4FZ-6020A	2.25
(6) Rear Packing (Crankshaft)		
1983-87	▲E5ZZ-6701A	6.25
(7) Pilot Bearing (Clutch)		
1983-87	▲D4ZZ-7600A	5.25
(8) Cover Plate (Rear)		
1983-87	▲E3TZ-7007A	21.75
(9)Flywheel		
A.T.		
1983-87	▲D5FZ-6375A	81.75
M.T.		
1983-87-wo/ turbo	▲E2ZZ-6375C	185.75
w/turbo	▲E3TZ-6375A	162.50
(10) Main Bearing (Center)		
1983-87-upper	▲D4FZ-6337A	9.75
lower	▲D4FZ-6337G	9.75
(11) Main Bearing (Exc. Center)		
1983-87	▲D4FZ-6333A	3.75

LABOR 16 CAMSHAFT & TIMING GEARS 16 LABOR

	(Factory Time)	Chilton Time
(G) Timing Case Seal and Gaskets, Renew		
Includes: R&R radiator and oil pan where required.		
Four–1983-87	(1.7)	**2.4**
V-6–1983-87	(4.1)	**5.7**
V-8–1983-87	(2.4)	**3.4**
w/A.C. add	(.2)	**.2**
w/P.S. add	(.3)	**.3**
(G) Timing Chain or Sprockets, Renew		
Includes: Adjust timing.		
V-6–1983-87	(4.4)	**6.2**
V-8–1983-87	(2.7)	**3.9**
w/A.C. add	(.2)	**.2**
w/P.S. add	(.3)	**.3**
(G) Timing Belt, Renew		
Four–1983-87	(1.0)	**1.5**
w/A.C. add	(.1)	**.1**
Renew tensioner add		**.2**
(G) Camshaft, Renew		
Four–1983-87	(3.3)	**4.6**
V-6–1983-87	(7.3)	**10.2**
V-8–1983-87	(5.5)	**8.0**
w/A.C. add	(.3)	**.3**
w/P.S. add	(.3)	**.3**
(P) Camshaft Bearings, Renew		
Includes: R&R engine and crankshaft where required.		
Four–1983-87	(3.8)	**5.6**
V-6–1983-87	(9.0)	**12.6**
V-8–1983-87	(9.1)	**12.7**
w/A.C. add	(.3)	**.3**
w/P.S. add	(.3)	**.3**
(G) Camshaft Rear Welsh Plug, Renew		
Includes: R&R trans. and flywheel for accessibility.		
Four–1983-87	(2.9)	**3.9**
V-6–1983-87	(3.9)	**5.5**
V-8–1983-87	(3.7)	**5.2**

PARTS 16 CAMSHAFT & TIMING GEARS 16 PARTS

	Part No.	Price
140 ENGINE		
(1) Cylinder Cover Assy. (Front)		
1983-87	▲E3ZZ-6019A	38.50
(2) Crankshaft Sprocket		
1983-87	▲D9FZ-6306A	11.50
(3) Camshaft Sprocket		
1983-87	▲D4FZ-6256A	13.75
(4) Belt (Timing)		
1983-87	▲E5ZZ-6268A	21.50
(5) Camshaft Gear		
1983-87	▲D4FZ-6256A	13.75
(6) Cover Gasket (Front)		
1983-87	▲D4FZ-6020A	2.25
(7) Guide (Timing Belt)		
1983-87	▲D4FZ-6B260A	4.75
(8) Oil Seal (Front Cover)		
1983-87	▲D4FZ-6700A	5.75

PARTS 16 CAMSHAFT & TIMING GEARS 16 PARTS

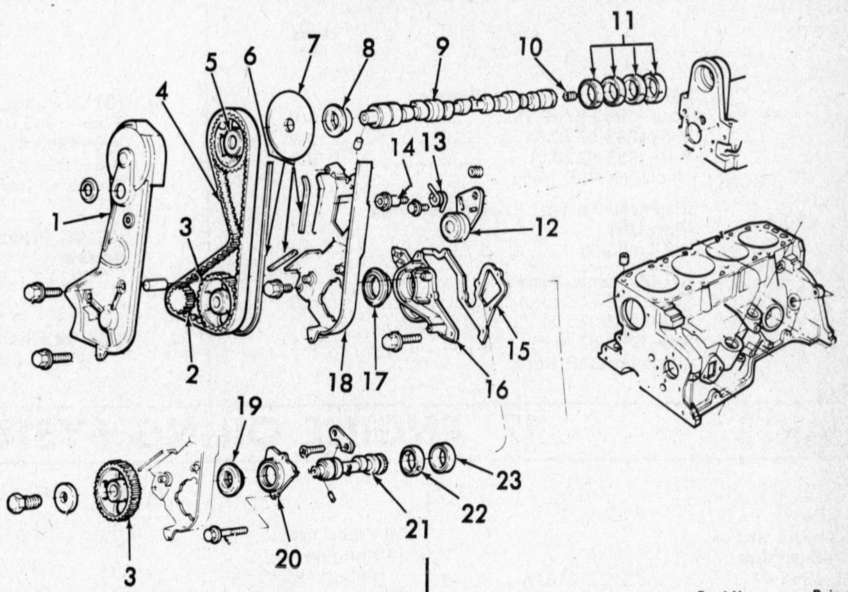

	Part No.	Price
(9) Camshaft		
wo/Turbo		
1983-84	▲E1ZZ-6250A	158.75
1985-87	▲E5ZZ-6250B	148.75
Turbo		
1983-87	▲E5ZZ-6250C	162.25
(10) Plug		
1983-87	▲87837S	1.75
(11) Camshaft Bearings (Front)		
1983-87	▲D4FZ-6261C	3.25
(12) Tensioner (Pulley Assy.)		
1983-87	▲D4FZ-6K254A	23.00
(13) Spring (Tensioner)		
1983-87	▲D4FZ-6L273A	7.50
(14) Bolt (Tensioner)		
1983-87	▲D7FZ-6K282A	4.25
(15) Cover Gasket (Inner)		
1983-87	▲D4FZ-6020B	1.50
(16) Front Cover (Lower)		
1983-84	▲E3TZ-6019A	45.25
1985-87	▲E5ZZ-6019A	45.25
1983-87-Turbo	▲E3TZ-6019A	45.25
(17) Oil Seal (Front Cover)		
1983-87	▲D4FZ-6700A	5.75
(18) Front Cover (Inner)		
1983-87	▲E3ZZ-6019B	43.00
(19) Oil Seal (Front Cover)		
1983-87	▲D4FZ-6700A	5.75

	Part No.	Price
(20) Front Cover (Upper)		
1983-87	▲D4FZ-6019B	22.75
(21) Drive Shaft (Dist. Fuel & Oil Pump)		
1983-87	▲E4FZ-6A739A	63.25

	Part No.	Price
(22) Auxiliary Shaft Bearing (Front)		
1983-87	▲D4FZ-6A753A	5.00
(23) Auxiliary Shaft Bearing (Rear)		
1983-87	▲D4FZ-6A738A	5.00

PARTS 16 CAMSHAFT & TIMING GEARS 16 PARTS

V-6 & V-8 ENGINES

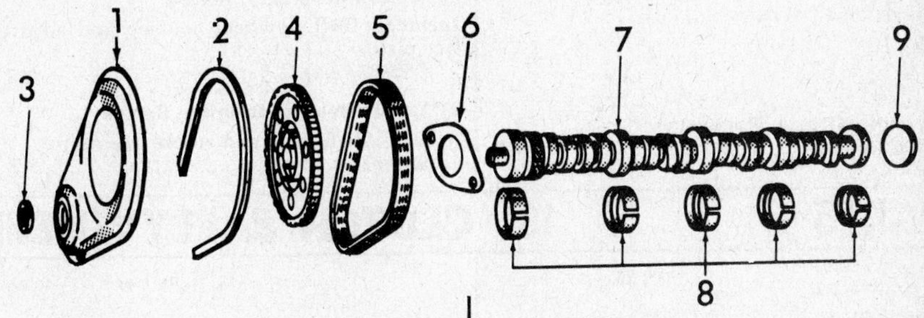

	Part No.	Price
(1) Timing Cover (Front)		
230 engine		
1983	▲E2DZ-6019A	132.25
1984-87	▲E4DZ-6019A	132.25
1984-87-Canada	▲E2DZ-6019A	132.25
302 engine		
1983-wo/EEC	▲E0AZ-6019B	126.50
w/EEC	▲E4AZ-6019C	126.50
1984-87	▲E4AZ-6019B	126.50
(2) Timing Cover Gasket		
1983-87-V-6	▲E2DZ-6020A	4.75
V-8	▲E3AZ-6020A	1.50
(3) Timing Cover Oil Seal		
1983-87	▲D0AZ-6700A	6.75
(4) Camshaft Gear		
1983-87-V-6	▲E2DZ-6256A	32.25
V-8	▲D3AZ-6256B	22.25
(5) Timing Chain		
1983-87-V-6	▲E2DZ-6268A	28.00
V-8	▲C3OZ-6268A	19.25
V-8-w/H.O.	▲E0AZ-6268A	22.25
(6) Thrust Plate		
230 engine		
1983-87	▲E4DZ-6269A	7.75

	Part No.	Price
302 engine		
1983	▲C9OZ-6269A	5.50
1984-87	▲C5OZ-6269D	7.75
(7) Camshaft		
230 engine		
1983	▲E2DZ-6250A	133.00
1984	▲E4DZ-6250A	151.00
1985-87	▲E5DZ-6250A	N.L.
302 engine		
1983-85	▲D5OZ-6250A	138.25
1986-87	▲E5AZ-6259A	138.75
(8) Bearing (Camshaft)		
230 engine		
1983-87-front & rear	▲E2DZ-6261A	9.00
front & rear interm.	▲E2DZ-6267A	6.50

	Part No.	Price
302 engine		
1983-87-front	▲C2OZ-6261A	5.00
front inter	▲C2OZ-6267A	5.00
center	▲C2OZ-6262A	5.00
rear inter	▲C2OZ-6270A	5.00
rear	▲C2OZ-6263A	5.00
(9) Welsh Plug		
1983-87	▲D7AZ-6026A	1.00
Oil Pressure Gauge (Engine Unit)		
1983-84-oil light	▲D4AZ-9278A	3.50
oil gauge	▲D9ZZ-9278B	12.75
1985-87-exc. below	▲D4AZ-9278A	3.50
w/elec. cluster (bef. 11/85)	▲E4ZZ-9278A	12.75
1986-87	▲E6ZZ-9278A	14.50

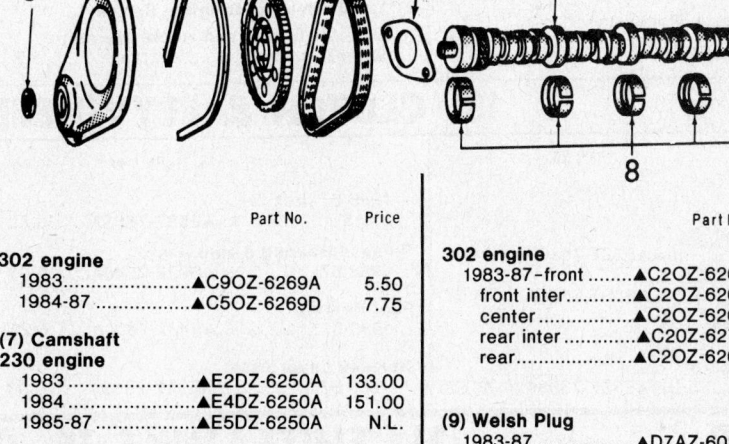

LABOR 17 ENGINE OILING SYSTEM 17 LABOR

	(Factory Time)	Chilton Time
(G) Oil Pan or Gasket, Renew		
Four–1983-87	(2.9)	3.8
V-6–1983-87	(2.3)	3.2
V-8–1983-87	(3.5)	*5.9
*Includes R&R trans.		
(P) Pressure Test Engine Bearings (Pan Off)		
All models		1.0
(G) Oil Pump, Renew		
Four–1983-87	(3.0)	4.0
V-6–1983-87	(.7)	1.1
V-8–1983-87	(3.6)	*6.1
*Includes R&R trans.		
(G) Oil Pump, R&R and Recondition		
Four–1983-87	(3.3)	4.4
V-6–1983-87	(.7)	1.2
V-8–1983-87	(3.9)	*6.5
*Includes R&R trans.		
(G) Oil Pressure Gauge (Engine), Renew		
1983-87	(.3)	.4
(M)) Oil Filter Element, Renew		
1983-87	(.3)	.3

PARTS 17 ENGINE OILING SYSTEM 17 PARTS

	Part No.	Price
Oil Pan Gasket		
140 engine		
1983-84	▲E2ZZ-6781A	10.75
1985-87	▲E5ZZ-6781A	10.75
230 engine		
1983-87	▲E2DZ-6781A	9.00
302 engine		
1983-87	▲D9AZ-6781A	11.50
Oil Pump assy.		
140 engine		
1983-85-wo/turbo	▲D5FZ-6600A	66.00
w/turbo	▲D9ZZ-6600A	58.00
1986-87	▲E5ZZ-6600A	44.25
302 engine		
1983-87	▲C2OZ-6600A	52.50
Oil Pump Screen		
1983-85-Four	▲E3ZZ-6622A	19.50
1986-87-Four	▲E5ZZ-6622A	19.50
1983-87-V-6	▲E3DZ-6622A	28.00
V-8	▲E0SZ-6622A	28.00
Oil Filter Assy.		
1983-87-wo/Turbo	▲D9AZ-6731A	8.00
Turbo	▲D4ZZ-6731B	8.50

LABOR 18 CLUTCH & FLYWHEEL 18 LABOR

	(Factory Time)	Chilton Time
(G) Clutch Pedal Free Play, Adjust		
All models	(.4)	.5
(G) Clutch Cable, Renew		
1983-87	(.5)	.8
(G) Clutch Assembly, Renew		
Includes: R&R flywheel housing and adjust free play.		
1983-87	(2.1)	2.7
(G) Clutch Release Bearing, Renew		
Includes: R&R trans and adjust free play.		
1983-87	(1.3)	1.7
(G) Flywheel Housing, Renew		
Includes: R&R transmission.		
1983-87	(2.7)	3.5
(G) Flywheel, Renew		
Includes: R&R transmission.		
1983-87	(2.4)	3.1
Renew ring gear add	(.2)	.4

PARTS 18 CLUTCH & FLYWHEEL 18 PARTS

	Part No.	Price
Clutch Disc		
140 engine		
1983-85 (bef. 3-20-85)	▲E3ZZ-7550D	44.00
1985-87 (from 3-20-85)	▲E5SZ-7550A	44.00
Pressure Plate		
140 engine		
1983-85 (bef. 3-20-85)	▲E3ZZ-7563A	58.50
1985-87 (from 3-20-85)	▲E5SZ-7563A	58.50
Release Bearing & Hub Assy.		
1983-87	▲D9ZZ-7548A	29.50
Pilot Bearing		
1983-87	▲D4ZZ-7600A	5.25
Release Lever Assy.		
1983-87	▲E3ZZ-7515A	10.00
Cable Assy.		
1983-87	▲E3SZ-7K553B	45.75
Flywheel Assy.		
1983-87	▲E3TZ-6375A	162.50
Flywheel Ring Gear		
1983-87	▲D4FZ-6384A	34.25

LABOR 21 SHIFT LINKAGE 21 LABOR

	(Factory Time)	Chilton Time
STANDARD		
(G) Shift Linkage, Adjust		
All models	(.3)	.5
(G) Gear Selector Lever, Renew		
1983-87	(.5)	.7
w/Console add	(.1)	.1
AUTOMATIC		
(G) Linkage, Adjust		
manual,	(.3)	.4
throttle	(.3)	.5
manual & throttle	(.6)	.7
downshift	(.3)	.4
(G) Kickdown Linkage, Adjust		
All models	(.3)	.5
(G) Gear Selector Lever, Renew		
1983-87		
column shift	(.4)	.6
floor shift	(.5)	.8

LABOR 21 SHIFT LINKAGE 21 LABOR

(G) Tilt Wheel Pivot, Recondition (In Chassis)
1983-87 (.7) 1.0

(G) Transmission Control Selector Indicator, Renew
1985-87
colm shift (.9) 1.4

LABOR 25 U-JOINTS & DRIVESHAFT 25 LABOR

(Factory Time) — Chilton Time

(G) Universal Joints, Renew or Recondition
Includes: R&R drive shaft.
1983-87
Double Cardan
front or rear (.9) 1.3
all (1.5) 2.0
Single Cardan
front or rear (.6) 9
both (.8) 1.3

(G) Driveshaft, Renew
1983-87 (.3) 5

PARTS 25 UNIVERSAL JOINTS & DRIVE SHAFT 25 PARTS

	Part No.	Price
Universal Joint Kit		
1983-87	▲C3AZ-4635E	15.25
Pinion Bearing Spacer		
1983-87	▲B7A-4662A	4.00
Yoke		
1983-87	▲E1DZ-4782A	14.25

LABOR 26 REAR AXLE 26 LABOR

(Factory Time) — Chilton Time

(M) Differential, Drain & Refill
All models 6

(M) Axle Housing Cover or Gasket, Renew
All models (.4) 6

(G) Axle Shaft Inner Oil Seal, Renew
Includes: R&R wheel, drum and axle shaft.
1983-87-one (.7) 9
both (.9) 1.3

(G) Rear Wheel Bearings, Renew
Includes: Renew oil seal.
1983-87-one (.7) 1.0
both (1.0) 1.5

(G) Axle Shaft, Renew
Includes: Renew inner oil seal.
1983-87-one (.6) 1.0
both (.8) 1.4

(G) Axle Shaft Wheel Mounting Studs, Renew
All models-one 8
all 1.2

(G) Pinion Shaft Oil Seal, Renew
1983-87 (.8) 1.3

(G) Axle Housing and Differential Assy., Remove and Reinstall (Complete)
Includes: Drain and refill axle, remove wheels and hubs, axle shafts, replace inner oil seals. Remove backing plates without disconnecting brake lines. Road test.
1983-87 (1.7) 2.8

(P) Differential Case Assy., Recondition (In Chassis)
Includes: Drain and refill axle, renew necessary parts. Renew axle shaft oil seals. Road test.
1983-87
std (1.2) 2.1
lock (2.1) 3.3

(P) Axle Housing, Renew
Includes: Transfer all necessary parts, adjust ring gear and pinion. Does not include disassembly of differential case.
1983-87 (3.5) 4.9

(P) Ring and Pinion Set, Renew
Includes: R&R axle shafts, drain and refill unit. Road test.
1983-87 (2.8) 3.8
O/Haul diff assy add (.4) 8
Renew diff brgs add (.2) 2

(P) Ring and Pinion, Adjust (In Chassis)
Includes: Remove axle shafts, drain and refill unit. Road test.
1983-87 (1.5) 2.3

PARTS 26 REAR AXLE 26 PARTS

	Part No.	Price
(1) Pinion Kit		
1983-87	▲E4DZ-4215A	20.00
(2) Side Gear		
wo/locking rear		
1983-87	▲D9AZ-4236A	40.00
w/locking rear		
1983-84	▲Not Serviced	
1985-87	▲E4DZ-4236A	40.25
(3) Shim (2.43" Thick)		
1983-87	▲D8BZ-4067BS	3.25
Other sizes available.		
(4) Bearing Cup		
1983-87	▲C6TZ-4222A	6.00
(5) Bearing Assy.		
1983-87	▲B7A-4221A	11.50
(6) Pinion Shaft		
1983-87	▲D8BZ-4211A	13.75
(7) Case Assy.		
wo/locking rear		
1983-87	▲D9AZ-4204A	104.50
w/locking rear		
1983-84	▲Not Serviced	
1985-87	▲E4DZ-4204A	105.75
(8) Housing Assy.		
wo/quad shocks		
(9) Ring Gear & Pinion Kit		
1983-87		
2.47R	▲D8BZ-4209C	352.50
2.73R	▲E5SZ-4209A	352.50
3.08R	▲E25Y-4209A	352.50
3.27R (1983-84)	▲E35Y-4209A	381.75
3.27R (1985-87)	▲E5LY-4209A	381.75
1983-84	▲E2BZ-4010A	457.75
1985-87	▲E5SZ-4010C	457.75
w/quad shocks		
1983-84	▲E3SZ-4010A	457.75
1985-87		
before 2/85	▲E5SZ-4010A	457.75
from 2/85	▲E5SZ-4010B	457.75
(10) Pinion Bearing (Rear)		
1983-87	▲C7AZ-4630A	15.75
(11) Bearing Cup (Rear)		
1983-87	▲C7AZ-4628A	8.00

PARTS 26 REAR AXLE 26 PARTS

	Part No.	Price
(12) Axle Shaft Oil Seal		
1983-87	▲E1AZ-1177B	3.50
(13) Axle Shaft Bearing		
1983-87	▲C7AZ-1225A	15.75
(14) Axle Shaft Assy. (Rear)		
1983-84	▲E3SZ-4234A	154.75
1985-87	▲E5SZ-4234A	70.25
(15) Spacer		
1983-87	▲B7A-4662A	4.00
(16) Pinion Bearing (Front)		
1983-87	▲C7AZ-4628A	8.00
(17) Pinion Oil Seal		
1983-87	▲E3TZ-4676A	11.25
(18) Flange Assy. (U-Joint)		
1983-87	▲D8BZ-4851A	17.00

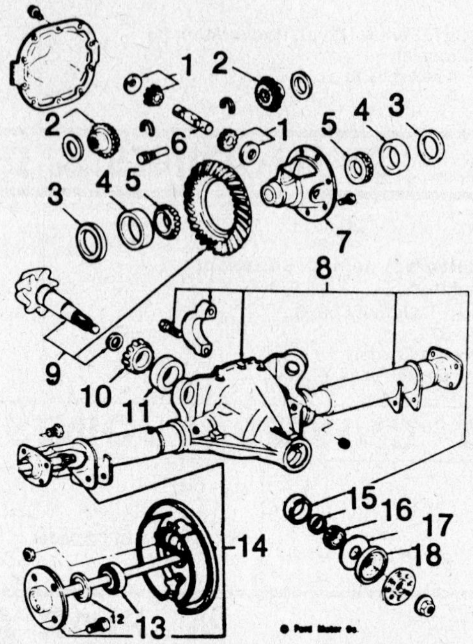

LABOR 27 REAR SUSPENSION 27 LABOR

	(Factory Time)	Chilton Time
(G) Rear Spring, Renew		
1983-87		
wo/Stabilizer		
both	(.8)	1.0
w/Stabilizer		
both	(.9)	1.2
(G) Rear Shock Absorber or Rubber Bushing, Renew		
1983-87		
Vertical		
one	(.3)	.5
both	(.4)	.8
Horizontal		
one	(.4)	.6
both	(.6)	.9
(G) Rear Suspension Upper Arm, Renew		
1983-87-one	(.4)	.7
both	(.6)	1.0
(G) Rear Suspension Lower Arm, Renew		
1983-87-wo/stabilizer		
one	(.6)	1.1
both	(.9)	1.5
w/stabilizer-one	(.7)	1.2
both	(1.0)	1.7
(G) Rear Stabilizer Bar, Renew		
1983-87	(.4)	.5

PARTS 27 REAR SUSPENSION 27 PARTS

	Part No.	Price
(1) Upper Control Arm		
1983-87	▲E4SZ-5500A	37.00
(2) Insulator (Upper)		
1983-87	▲D9BZ-5536A	3.00
(4) Coil Spring		
Order by model and description.		
(5) Insulator (Lower)		
1983-87	▲D8BZ-5536A	3.00
(6) Lower Control Arm		
1983-87-		
exc.below	▲E3SZ-5A649A	93.25
w/alum. whl.	▲E3SZ-5A649B	93.25
(7) Shock Absorber (Rear)		
140 engine		
1983-84	▲E3SZ-18125F	38.25
1985-87	▲E5SZ-18125A	41.25

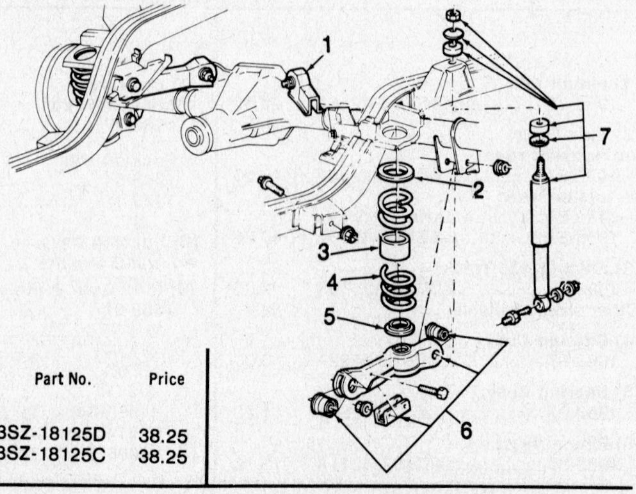

	Part No.	Price
V-6 & V-8 engs.		
1983-87-exc.	▲E3SZ-18125D	38.25
w/towing pkg.	▲E3SZ-18125C	38.25

LABOR 28 AIR CONDITIONING 28 LABOR

(Factory Time) Chilton Time

Note: If more than one item requires replacement where evacuation and discharging the system is already included in the operation, deduct 1.0 hour for each additional item to the times listed.

(G) Drain, Evacuate and Recharge System
Includes: Check for leaks.
All models (.7) 1.2

(G) Pressure Test System
All models 6

(G) Compressor Drive Belt, Renew
1983-87 (.3) 4

(G) Compressor Assembly, Renew
Includes: Evacuate and charge system.
1983-87
Four (2.3) 3.1
V-6 (1.6) 2.4
V-8 (1.7) 2.5
Recond comp add (.7) 1.0

(G) Compressor Shaft Seal Kit, Renew
Includes: R&R compressor when required. Evacuate and charge system.
1983-87
Four (1.5) 2.4
V-6 (1.5) 2.4
V8 (2.0) 2.9

(G) Compressor Clutch and Pulley, Renew
1983-87
Four (.6) 8
V-6 (.6) 8
V-8 (.6) 8
Renew clutch brg add (.1) 1
Renew clutch field add (.1) 1

(G) Compressor Service Valve or Gasket, Renew
Includes: Evacuate and charge system.
1983-87 (.8) 1.5

AIR CONDITIONER TUNE-UP

For efficient operation and satisfactory performance in hot weather. The following air conditioner tune-up is suggested:

1. Clean intake filter
2. Clean condenser fins
3. Pressure test system
4. Adjust drive belt tension
5. Check antifreeze/coolant
6. Tighten compressor mounts
7. Tighten condenser and evaporator mounts
8. Inspect system for leaks (hoses, couplings, valves, etc.)
9. Partial charge system

All models 1.0
If necessary to evacuate and charge system, add 1.0

(Factory Time) Chilton Time

(G) Condenser Assembly, Renew
Includes: Evacuate and charge system.
1983-87 (.9) 2.0

(G) Evaporator Core, Renew
Includes: Renew or transfer valve. Evacuate and charge system.
1983-87 (4.6) 7.5

(G) A.C. Clutch Cycling Pressure Switch, Renew
1983-87 (.2) 4

(G) A.T.C. Sensor, Renew
1983-87
inst panel (.8) 1.3

(Factory Time) Chilton Time

(G) A.C. Automatic Temperature Servo Assy., Renew
1985-87 (.4) 6

(G) Accumulator Assy., Renew
Includes: Evacuate and charge system.
1983 (1.0) 1.5

(G) Orifice Valve, Renew
Includes: Evacuate and charge system.
1983-87 (.9) 1.5

(G) Door Vacuum Motor, Renew
1983-87
Recirculation door (.3) 6
Heat defrost door (3.6) *5.0
ATC servo (.4) 8
A.C. defrost door (2.8) *4.5
*Add time to recharge A.C. system, if required.

(G) Temperature Control Cable, Renew
1983-87-w/ATC (.8) 1.2
wo/ATC (.5) 8

(G) Blower Motor, Renew
1983-87 (1.0) 1.6

(G) Blower Motor Switch, Renew
1983-87 (.4) 7

(G) Blower Motor Resistor, Renew
1983-87 (.3) 5

(G) Suction or Discharge Manifold Assy. Kit, Renew
Includes: Evacuate and charge system.
1983-87 (.8) 1.5

(G) Air Conditioning Hoses, Renew
Includes: Evacuate and charge system.
1983-87
Cond. to Evap. (.8) 1.7
Suction line (1.0) 1.9
Comp. to Cond. (.8) 1.7

PARTS 28 AIR CONDITIONING 28 PARTS

	Part No.	Price
Compressor Drive Belt		
Note: Order by model and description.		
Compressor Assy.		
140 engine		
1983-87	▲E3DZ-19703A	221.50
230 engine		
1983-85	▲E3SZ-19703A	268.75
1985-87	▲E4FZ-19703A	192.50
302 engine		
1983-85	▲E4VY-19703A	315.00
1986-87	▲E6VY-19703A	315.00
Compressor Shaft Seal		
1983-87	▲C9AZ-19655A	17.75
Compressor Clutch (Complete)		
140 engine		
1983	▲E3SZ-2884A	47.00
1984-87	▲E4SZ-2884A	47.00
230 engine		
1983	▲E3AZ-2884A	69.75
1984-87	▲E4SZ-2884A	47.00
302 engine		
1983	▲E0VY-2884A	149.00
1984	▲E3AZ-2884A	69.75
1985	▲E3SZ-2884A	47.00
Compressor Clutch Pulley Bearing		
1983-87	▲D1VY-2990A	32.50
Compressor Gasket Set		
1983	▲C8AZ-19B684A	10.75
Condenser Assy.		
1983-87-exc. V-8	▲E2ZZ-19712A	180.75
V-8	▲E5LY-19712A	241.50
Evaporator Core		
1983-84	▲E25Y-19860A	139.50
1985-87	▲E4LY-19860A	141.00
Blower Motor		
1983-87	▲E35Y-19805A	90.50
Blower Motor Resistor		
1983-87	▲E35Y-19A706A	11.00
Blower Motor Switch		
1983-87	▲D5AZ-19986A	12.75

LABOR 29 LOCKS, HINGES & WIND. REGULATORS 29 LABOR

(Factory Time) Chilton Time

(G) Hood Release Cable, Renew
1983-87 (.4) 6

(G) Hood Latch, Renew
1983-87 (.3) 5

(G) Hood Hinge, Renew
Includes: Adjust hood and latch.
1983-87 (.4) 6

LABOR 29 LOCKS, HINGES & WIND. REGULATORS 29 LABOR

	Part No.	Price
(G) Door Lock, Renew		
Includes: R&R trim panel and weathersheet.		
1983-87 (.8)		1.2
(G) Door Lock Remote Control, Renew		
Includes: R&R trim panel and weathersheet.		
1983-87 (.7)		1.1
(G) Lock Striker Plate, Renew		
1983-87 (.2)		.3
(G) Door Handle (Outside), Renew		
1983-87 (.8)		1.2
(G) Door Window Regulator (Manual), Renew		
Includes: R&R trim panel and weathersheet.		
1983-87 (.8)		1.3
(G) Door Window Regulator (Electric), Renew		
Includes: R&R trim panel and weathersheet.		
1983-87 (1.0)		1.5
(G) Trunk Hinge Assembly, Renew (One)		
1983-87		.6

PARTS 29 LOCKS, HINGES & WIND. REGULATORS 29 PARTS

	Part No.	Price
Hood Hinge		
1983-right	▲E3SZ-16796A	11.75
left	▲E3SZ-16797A	11.75
Hood Latch		
1983-85	▲E4DZ-16700A	14.75
1986-87	▲E6DZ-16700A	14.75
1984-right (w/ Clock Spring)	▲E4LY-16796A	19.50
left	▲E4LY-16797A	19.50
1984-87-(wo/clock spring)		
right	▲E5SZ-16796A	11.75
left	▲E5SZ-16797A	12.00
Door Lock Cylinder & Key		
1983-84 (w/bright cyl.)		
right	▲E1FZ-6121984A	10.75
left	▲E1FZ-6121985A	10.75
1983-84 (w/black cyl.)		
right	▲E1FZ-6121984B	10.75
left	▲E1FZ-6121985B	10.75
1985-87 (wo/anti-theft)		
black cyl.	▲E5SZ-6322050C	30.00
bright cyl.	▲E5SZ-6322050A	30.00
1985-87 (w/anti-theft)		
black cyl.	▲E5SZ-6322050G	72.50
bright cyl.	▲E5SZ-6322050E	72.50
Door Lock		
1983-84-right	▲E3GZ-6721812A	36.00
left	▲E3GZ-6721813A	36.00
1985-87-right	▲E59Z-1121812A	21.50
left	▲E59Z-1121813A	21.50
Outer Door Handle w/bright finish		
1983-87-right	▲E3FZ-5822404A	21.50
left	▲E3FZ-5822405A	21.50
w/black finish		
1983-87-right	▲E3FZ-6122404B	21.50
left	▲E3FZ-6122405B	21.50
Front Door Hinge upper		
1983-87-right	▲E3SZ-6322800A	11.25
left	▲E3SZ-6322801A	11.25
lower		
1983-87-right	▲E3SZ-6322810A	19.50
left	▲E3SZ-6322811A	19.50
Front Window Regulator (Manual)		
1983-87-right	▲E3SZ-6323200A	27.75
left	▲E3SZ-6323201A	27.75
Front Window Regulator (Electric)		
1983-87-right	▲E3SZ-6323208A	53.25
left	▲E3SZ-6323209A	53.25
Power Window Motor		
1983-87-right	▲D3AZ-5723395A	131.50
left	▲D8TZ-9823394A	134.00
Power Window Gear Kit		
1983-87	▲D0AZ-62234A24B	39.00
Trunk Lid & Lock		
1983-87-wo/ Power	▲D9ZZ-6643200A	22.00
w/power	▲D9BZ-5443200A	57.50
Trunk Lock Cylinder & Key wo/anti-theft		
1983-84-bright cyl.	▲D6ZZ-6943505A	10.75
black cyl.	▲E3SZ-6943505A	10.00
1985-87-bright cyl.	▲E5SZ-6343507A	16.50
black cyl.	▲E5SZ-6343507B	16.50
w/anti-theft		
1983-84-bright cyl.	▲E3SZ-6343505B	18.50
black cyl.	▲E4SZ-6343505A	18.50
1985-87-bright cyl.	▲E5SZ-6343507C	24.25
black cyl.	▲E5SZ-6343507D	24.25
Trunk Lid Hinge		
1983-87 (Cougar)		
right	▲E3WY-6642700A	23.00
left	▲E3WY-6642701A	23.00
1983-87 (Thunderbird)		
right	▲E3SZ-6342700A	26.75
left	▲E3SZ-6342701A	26.75

LABOR 30 HEAD AND PARKING LAMPS 30 LABOR

	(Factory Time)	Chilton Time
(G) Aim Headlamps		
two		.4
four		.6
(M) Headlamp Sealed Beam Bulb, Renew		
1983-87-each	(.3)	.3
(M) Parking Lamp Lens, Renew		
1983-87	(.3)	.4
(M) Stop Lamp Lens, Renew		
1983-87	(.2)	.3
(M) License Lamp Assembly, Renew		
1983-87	(.3)	.4
(M) Side Marker Lamp Assembly, Renew		
1983-87	(.3)	.4
(M) Rear Lamp Body Assy., Renew		
1985-87	(.4)	.6
(M) High Mount Stop Lamp, Renew		
1986-87	(.3)	.5

PARTS 30 HEAD AND PARKING LAMPS 30 PARTS

	Part No.	Price
Seal Beam Bulbs		
1983-87		
low beam	▲D94Y-13007A	12.75
Hi beam	▲D94Y-13007C	12.75
Parking Lamp Assy.		
1983-right	▲E3SZ-13200A	31.25
left	▲E3SZ-13201A	31.25
1984-87-right	▲E4SZ-13200A	31.25
left	▲E4SZ-13201A	31.25
Rear Lamp Assy.		
Cougar		
1983-84-right	▲E3WY-13404A	111.25
left	▲E3WY-13405A	111.25
1985-87-right	▲E5WY-13404B	115.00
left	▲E5WY-13405B	115.00
Thunderbird		
1983-(wo/chrome on lens)		
right	▲E3SZ-13404A	114.00
left	▲E3SZ-13405A	114.00
1983-(w/chrome on lens)		
right	▲E3SZ-13404B	126.00
left	▲E3SZ-13405B	126.00
1984-(wo/chrome on lens)		
right	▲E4SZ-13404A	114.00
left	▲E4SZ-13405A	114.00
1984-(w/chrome on lens)		
right	▲E4SZ-13404B	126.00
left	▲E4SZ-13405B	126.00

PARTS 30 HEAD AND PARKING LAMPS 30 PARTS

	Part No.	Price
1985-87-(chrome mldgs. on lamp)		
right	▲E5SZ-13404A	92.75
left	▲E5SZ-13405A	92.75
1985-87-(charcoal mldgs. on lamp)		
right	▲E5SZ-13404B	92.75
left	▲E5SZ-13405B	92.75
1985-87-(blue mldgs. on lamp)		
right	▲E5SZ-13404C	114.00
left	▲E5SZ-13405C	114.00
License Plate Lamp Assy.		
1983-87	▲D7AZ-13550A	6.00
Rear Lamp Lens		
Cougar		
1983-84-right	▲E3WY-13450A	56.25
left	▲E3WY-13451A	56.25
1985-87-right	▲E5WY-13450A	53.25
left	▲E5WY-13451A	53.25
Thunderbird		
1983-(wo/chrome on lens)		
right	▲E3SZ-13450A	67.00
left	▲E3SZ-13451A	53.75
1983-(w/chrome on lens)		
right	▲E3SZ-13450B	67.00
left	▲E3SZ-13451B	67.00
1984-(wo/chrome on lens)		
right	▲E4SZ-13450A	53.75
left	▲E4SZ-13451A	53.75
1984-(w/chrome on lens)		
right	▲E4SZ-13450B	67.00
left	▲E4SZ-13451B	67.00
1985-87-right	▲E5SZ-13450B	31.25
left	▲E5SZ-13451B	31.25
Rear Hi-Mount Lamp Assy.		
1985-87	▲E6SZ-13A613B	41.75

LABOR 31 WINDSHIELD WIPER & SPEEDOMETER 31 LABOR

(Factory Time)	Chilton Time
(G) Windshield Wiper Motor, Renew	
1983-87 (.4)	.6
(G) Wiper Pivot, Renew	
1983-87 (.4)	.6
(G) Windshield Wiper Governor, Renew	
1983-87 (.6)	.8
(G) Wiper Switch, Renew	
1983-87 (.6)	1.0
(G) Windshield Washer Pump, Renew	
1983-87 (.3)	.5
under fender (.7)	1.0
(G) Speedometer Head, R&R or Renew	
Includes: R&R instrument panel pad when required.	
1983-87	
standard cluster (.7)	1.5
electronic cluster (1.3)	2.0
Reset odometer add	.2
(G) Speedometer Cable and Casing, Renew	
1983-87	
one piece (.9)	1.5
(G) Speedometer Cable (Inner), Renew or Lubricate	
1983-87	
one piece (.9)	1.4
(G) Speedometer Driven Gear, Renew	
1983-87 (.3)	.4
(G) Radio, R&R	
1983-87 (.3)	.6

PARTS 31 WINDSHIELD WIPER & SPEEDOMETER 31 PARTS

	Part No.	Price
Wiper Motor Assy.		
1983-87	▲E3SZ-17508A	141.75
Arm & Pivot Shaft		
1983-85	▲E3SZ-17566A	25.50
1986-87	▲E6SZ-17566A	N.L.
Wiper Arm		
1983-84 (bef. 6-84) Right	▲E3SZ-17526A	13.00
left	▲E3SZ-17527A	19.00
1984-85 (from 6-84) Right	▲E4SZ-17526A	13.25
left	▲E4SZ-17527A	19.00
1986-87-Right	▲E4SZ-17526A	13.25
left	▲E6SZ-17527A	19.50
Wiper Blade Assy.		
1983-87	▲E3DZ-17528A	4.75
Wiper Switch		
wo/intermitten wipers		
1983-84	▲E3SZ-17A553A	22.25
1985	▲E5SZ-17A553A	22.25
w/intermitten wipers		
1983-84	▲E3SZ-17A553B	49.00
1985	▲E5SZ-17A553B	29.75
Windshield Wiper Governor		
1983	▲E0VY-17C476A	77.50
1984-87	▲E3SZ-17C476A	77.50
Windshield Washer Pump		
1983-87	▲E0AZ-17664A	20.00
Windshield Washer Reservoir		
1983-wo/sensor, exc. Turbo	▲E3ZZ-17618C	16.50
w/sensor	▲E4ZZ-17618B	20.75
w/Turbo	▲E3SZ-17618C	20.75
1984-87-wo/sensor	▲E4SZ-17618A	16.50
w/sensor	▲E4SZ-17618B	20.75
Speedometer Head Assy.		
Order by year and model.		
Speedometer Cable (Inner)		
1983-87 (must cut to fit)		
81″ long	▲D4AZ-17262A	7.75
135″ long	▲C5AZ-17262B	8.75

LABOR 32 LIGHT SWITCHES & WIRING 32 LABOR

(Factory Time)	Chilton Time
(G) Headlamp Switch, Renew	
1983-87 (.4)	.6
(G) Headlamp Dimmer Switch, Renew	
1983-87 (.6)	1.0
(G) Stop Light Switch, Renew	
1983-87 (.3)	.4
(G) Back-Up Lamp Switch, Renew	
1983-87 (.3)	.5
(G) Parking Brake Indicator Switch, Renew	
1983-87 (.3)	.4
(G) Turn Signal Switch and Wire Assy., Renew	
1983-87	
switch only (.6)	1.0
(M) Turn Signal or Hazard Warning Flasher, Renew	
1983-87 (.3)	.4
(G) Horns, Renew	
1983-87-each (.3)	.4

PARTS 32 LIGHT SWITCHES & WIRING 32 PARTS

	Part No.	Price
Headlamp Switch		
1983-84 (wo/auto. lamp on & off delay)		
wo/Warning lights	▲E0AZ-11654C	16.50
w/Warning lights	▲E0AZ-11654D	17.50
1983-84 (w/auto. lamp on & off delay)		
Thunderbird & Cougar	▲E1WZ-11654A	47.25
1985-87	▲E5SZ-11654A	47.25
Turn Signal Switch		
1983-84	▲E2FZ-13341A	41.25
1985-87	▲E5LY-13341A	41.25
Stop Light Switch		
1983-85	▲E3ZZ-13480A	7.25
1986-87	▲E6ZZ-13480A	7.50
Back-Up Lamp Switch		
A.T.		
1983-87-exc. C5 trans.	▲D6RY-7A247B	31.75
w/C5 trans.	▲E2DZ-7A247A	36.50
M.T.		
1983-87	▲E0ZZ-15520A	21.25
Turn Signal Flasher		
1983-87	▲C6AZ-13350B	3.75
Emergency Warning Flasher		
1983-87	▲D1FZ-13350A	4.25
Horn Assy.		
1983-87-low pitch	▲E3AZ-13833A	17.00
high pitch	▲E3AZ-13832A	17.00

LABOR 33 GLASS 33 LABOR

	(Factory Time)	Chilton Time
(G) Windshield Glass, Renew		
1983-87	(2.3)	3.0
Renew butyl tape add	(.2)	.2
(G) Front Door Glass, Renew		
Includes: R&R trim panel and weathersheet.		
1983-87	(1.0)	1.5
(G) Rear Quarter Window Stationary Glass, Renew		
1983-87	(.4)	.7
(G) Rear Window Glass, Renew		
1983-87-T-Bird	(2.2)	3.2
Cougar	(1.8)	2.7
Renew butyl tape add	(.2)	.2

LABOR 34 CRUISE CONTROL 34 LABOR

	(Factory Time)	Chilton Time
(G) Cruise Control System Diagnosis		
1983-87	(.4)	.6
(G) Speed Control Amplifier Assy., Renew		
1983-87	(.3)	.6
Road test add	(.3)	.3
(G) Speed Control Sensor Assy., Renew		
1983-87	(.3)	.5
Road test add	(.3)	.3
(G) Speed Control Servo Assy., Renew		
1983-87		
w/Conn	(.6)	.9
wo/Conn	(.7)	1.0
Road test add	(.3)	.3
(G) Speed Control Relay, Renew		
1983-87	(.3)	.5
Road test add	(.3)	.3
(G) Speed Control Actuator Switch, Renew		
1983-87	(.3)	.6
Road test add	(.3)	.3
(G) Speed Control Metering (Dump) Valve, Renew		
1983-87	(.4)	.6
(G) Cruise Control Chain/Cable, Renew		
1983-87	(.6)	.8
(G) Cruise Control Clutch Switch, Renew		
1983-87	(.1)	.3
Road test add	(.3)	.3

PARTS 34 CRUISE CONTROL 34 PARTS

	Part No.	Price
Speed Control Amplifier Assy.		
1983-87	▲E0AZ-9D843A	161.50
Speed Control Servo Assy.		
1983	▲E3ZZ-9C735A	120.25
1984-87	▲E4LY-9C735A	120.25
Speed Control Sensor		
1983-84	▲E3AZ-9E731A	20.75
1985-87	▲E45Y-9E731A	20.75
Speed Control Actuator Switch		
1983	▲E3SZ-9C888A	45.75
1984-87	▲E4SZ-9C888A	45.75

GROUP INDEX

ALPHABETICAL INDEX

Ford Motor Company

Rear Wheel Drive Cars

FAIRMONT • ZEPHYR

YEAR IDENTIFICATION

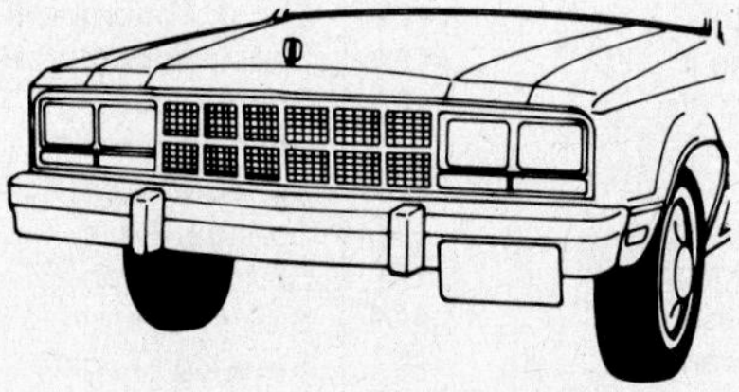

1983 Fairmont Futura

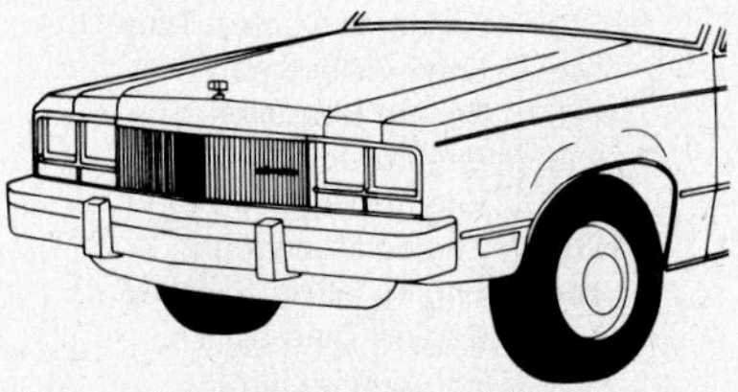

1983 Zephyr

VEHICLE IDENTIFICATION NUMBER (VIN)

It is important for servicing and ordering parts to be certain of the vehicle and engine identification. The VIN (vehicle identification number) is a 13 or 17 digit number visible through the windshield on the driver's side of the dash and contains the vehicle and engine identification codes. It can be interpreted as follows:

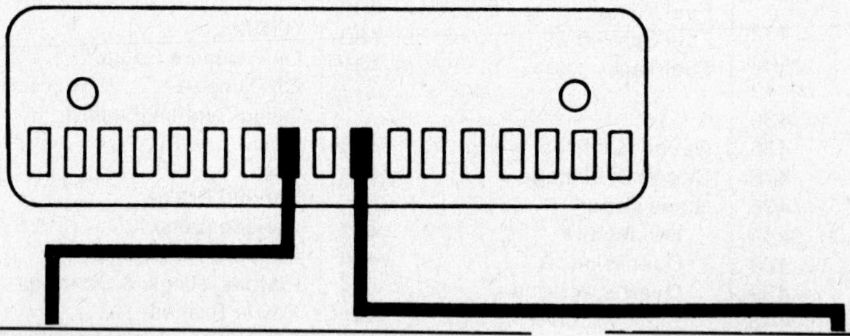

Engine Code

Code	Cu. In.	Liters	Cyl.	Carb.	Eng. Mfg.
A	140	2.3	4	1	Ford
W	140-T	2.3	4	Turbo.	Ford
T	140-T SVO	2.3	4	Turbo.	Ford
R	140-HSC	2.3	4	①	Ford
T,B,X	200	3.3	6	1	Ford
3	232	3.8	V6	①	Ford
C	232	3.8	V6	①	Ford
F	302	5.0	V8	1	Ford
M	302-H.O.	5.0	V8	①	Ford
G	351-W	5.8	V8	①	Ford
G	351-H.O.	5.8	V8	①	Ford

Model Year Code

Code	Year
D	1983
E	1984
F	1985
G	1986
H	1987

The seventeen digit Vehicle Identification Number can be used to determine engine application and model year. The tenth digit indicates the model year, and the eighth digit identifies the engine code.

① EFI, VV, 2 bbl. or 4 bbl. depending on model

TUNE-UP SPECIFICATIONS

When analyzing compression test results, look for uniformity among cylinders rather than specific pressures

Year	Engine: Eng. VIN Code	Engine: No. Cyl. Displacement (cu. in.)	Engine: Eng. mfg.	Spark Plugs: Orig. Type	Spark Plugs: Gap (in.)•	Distributor: Point Dwell (deg)	Distributor: Point Gap (in.)	Ignition Timing (deg): Man. Trans.	Ignition Timing (deg): Auto. Trans.	Valves Intake Opens (deg)	Fuel Pump Pressure (psi)	Idle Speed (rpm): Man. Trans.	Idle Speed (rpm): Auto. Trans.
'83	A	4-140	Ford	AWSF-44	.044	Electronic		①	①	16	5.5–6.5	850	800
	X	6-200	Ford	BSF-92	.050	Electronic		①	①	20	6–8	600	600
	3	V-6-232	Ford	AWSF-52	.044	Electronic		①	①	13	39	550	550
	F	8-302	Ford	ASF-52 ②	.050	Electronic		①	①	16	6–8 ③	—	550
	G	8-351	Ford	ASF-42	.044	Electronic		①	①	23	6–8	—	700/600

NOTE: The underhood calibrations sticker often reflects tune-up specification changes made in production. Sticker figures must be used if they disagree with those in this chart.

T Turbocharger
HO High output
HSC High swirl combustion
① Calibrations vary depending upon the model; refer to the underhood calibration sticker.
② The carbureted models use spark plug ASF-42 (.044) and the idle speed rpm is 700 rpm.
③ On fuel injected models the pressure is 39 psi.

FIRING ORDERS

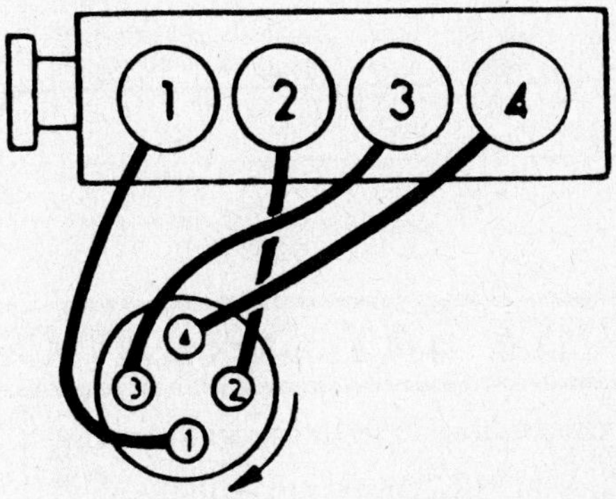

FORD MOTOR CO. 2300 cc 4-cyl.
Engine firing order: 1–3–4–2
Distributor rotation: clockwise

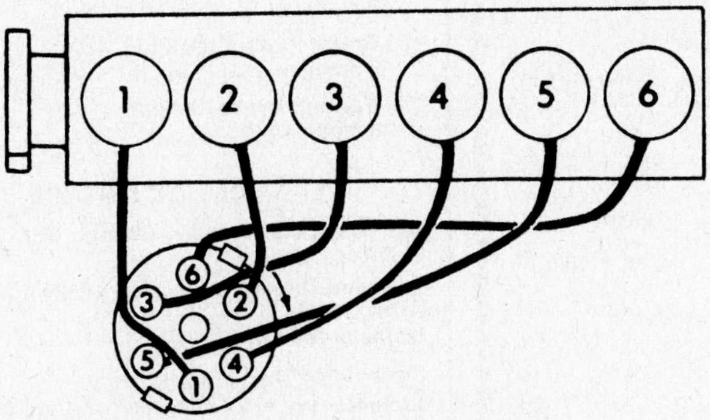

FORD MOTOR CO. 200, 250 6-cyl.
Engine firing order: 1–5–3–6–2–4
Distributor rotation: clockwise

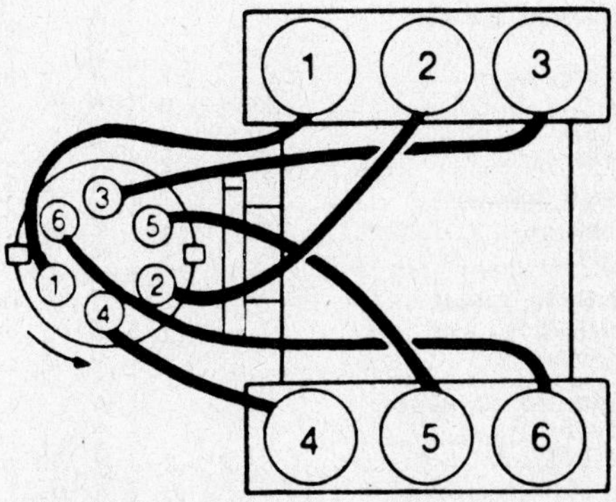

FORD MOTOR CO. 232 V6
Engine firing order 1–4–2–5–3–6
Distributor rotation: counterclockwise

FIRING ORDERS

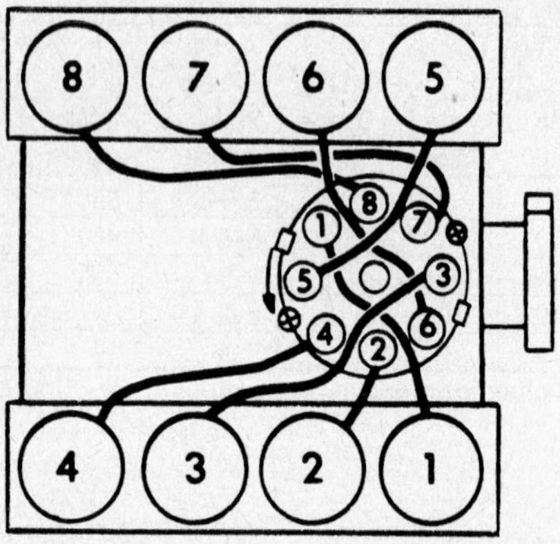

FORD MOTOR CO. 255, 302 (exc. HO) 460 V8 Engine firing order: 1–5–4–2–6–3–7–8
Distributor rotation: counterclockwise

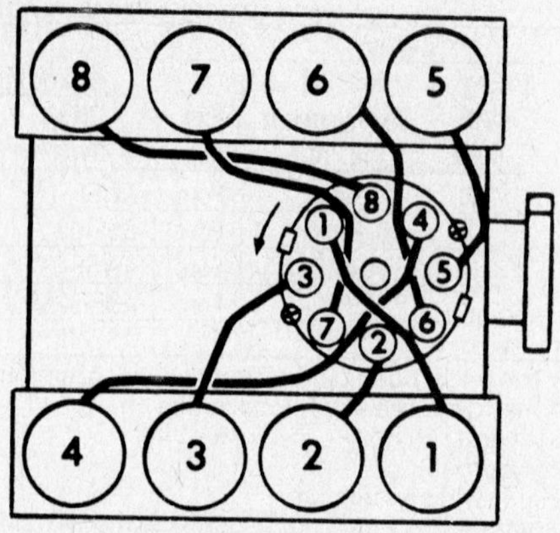

FORD MOTOR CO. 302HO, 351,400 V8 Engine firing order: 1–3–7–2–6–5–4–8
Distributor rotation: counterclockwise

WHEEL ALIGNMENT SPECIFICATIONS

		Caster		Camber				Wheel Pivot Ratio (deg)	
Year	Model	Range (deg)	Pref. Setting (deg)	Range (deg)	Pref. Setting (deg)	Toe-in (in.)	Steering Axis Inclin. (deg)	Inner Wheel	Outer Wheel
'83	Fairmont, Zephyr	1/8P to 2 1/8P	1 1/8P	15/16N to 1 13/16P	7/16P	1/16 to 5/16	15 23/32	20	19 27/32

LABOR — SERVICE BAY OPERATIONS — LABOR

(Factory Time) — Chilton Time

COOLING

(M) Winterize Cooling System
Includes: Run engine to check for leaks, tighten all hose connections. Test radiator and pressure cap. Drain radiator and engine block. Add anti-freeze and refill system.
All models 5

(M) Thermostat, Renew
1983
Four (.5) 7
Six (.4) 6
V-8 (.4) 6
w/A.C. add 2

(M) Fan Belt, Renew
All models (.5) 6
w/A.C. add 2

(M) Drive Belts, Adjust
All models-one (.2) 3
each adtnl (.1) 1

(M) Radiator Hoses, Renew
All models
upper (.3) 4
lower (.5) 6
both (.6) 7

FUEL

(M) Carburetor Air Cleaner, Service
All models (.2) 3

(G) Carburetor, Adjust (On Car)
All models (.4) 5
Propane enrichment method (1.0) 1.5

CHILTON'S 10 POINT SAFETY CHECK

CHECK OPERATION & CONDITION OF THE FOLLOWING ITEMS:

1. Legal Registration (serial no.)
2. Tires & Wheels
3. Brake System (R&R all wheels)
4. Light Systems & Signals
5. Accelerator Linkage, Neutral Safety Switch, Shift Indicator Pointer & Seat Position Locks
6. Glass, Mirrors, Door Locks, Seat Belts & Harness
7. Wipers, Washers & Defrosters
8. Frame, Steering, Shocks, Front & Rear Suspension
9. Fuel & Exhaust Systems
10. Road Test Vehicle

All models 1.0
Exhaust Smog Analysis, add 4

(Factory Time) — Chilton Time

(G) Thermostatic Choke Cover and/or Gasket, Renew
All models (.3) 4
Tamper resistant (.9) 1.4

(Factory Time) — Chilton Time

BRAKES

(G) Brakes, Adjust (Minor)
Includes: Adjust brakes, fill master cylinder.
two wheels 4

(G) Bleed Brakes (Four Wheels)
Includes: Fill master cylinder.
All models (.3) 5

(G) Brake Pedal Free Play, Adjust
All models 4

(M) Parking Brake, Adjust
All models (.3) 4

LUBRICATION SERVICE

(M) Lubricate Chassis, Change Oil & Filter
Includes: Inspect and correct all fluid levels.
All models 6
Install grease fittings add 1

(M) Lubricate Chassis
Includes: Inspect and correct all fluid levels.
All models 4
Install grease fittings add 1

(M) Engine Oil & Filter, Change
Includes: Inspect and correct all fluid levels.
All models 4

WHEELS

(M) Wheel, Renew
one (.5) 5

LABOR SERVICE BAY OPERATIONS LABOR

	(Factory Time)	Chilton Time
(G) Wheels, Balance		
one		.3
each adtnl		.2
(G) Wheels, Rotate (All)		
All models	(.5)	.5
(G) Front Wheel Bearings, Clean and Repack (Both Wheels)		
All models		1.3
(G) Front Wheel Grease Seals, Renew		
Includes: Repack bearings.		
All models		
one wheel	(.5)	.7
both wheels	(.8)	1.1
(G) Front Wheel Bearings and Cups, Renew		
All models		
one wheel	(.7)	.9
both wheels	(1.2)	1.5
ELECTRICAL		
(M) Battery Cables, Renew		
each	(.3)	.3
(G) Aim Headlamps		
two		.4
four		.6
(M) Headlamp Sealed Beam Bulb, Renew		
All models-each	(.3)	.3
(M) Parking Lamp Lens, Renew		
All models	(.3)	.4
(G) Stop Lamp Lens, Renew		
All models	(.2)	.3
(G) Headlamp Switch, Renew		
All models	(.4)	.5
(G) Headlamp Dimmer Switch, Renew		
All models	(.4)	.7
(G) Stop Light Switch, Renew		
All models	(.3)	.4
(G) Turn Signal Switch Assy., Renew		
All models	(.4)	.6
(G) Neutral Safety Switch, Renew		
All models	(.3)	.4
(G) Back-Up Light Switch, Renew		
All models	(.3)	.5
(M) Turn Signal or Hazard Warning Flasher, Renew		
All models	(.3)	.4
(G) Horns, Renew		
All models-each	(.2)	.4

LABOR 1 TUNE UP 1 LABOR

	(Factory Time)	Chilton Time
(G) Compression Test		
Four-1983	(.3)	.6
Six-1983	(.3)	.6
w/A.C. add		.2
(G) Engine Tune Up, (Electronic Ignition)		
Includes: Test battery and clean connections. Tighten manifold and carburetor mounting bolts. Check engine compression, clean and adjust or renew spark plugs. Test resistance of spark plug cables. Inspect distributor cap and rotor. Adjust air gap. Check vacuum advance operation. Reset ignition timing. Adjust idle mixture and idle speed. Service air cleaner. Inspect and adjust drive belts. Inspect choke operation and adjust or free up. Check operation of EGR valve.		
Four-1983		1.5
Six-1983		1.5
w/A.C. add		.2

LABOR 2 IGNITION SYSTEM 2 LABOR

	(Factory Time)	Chilton Time
(G) Spark Plugs, Clean and Reset or Renew		
1983-Four	(.3)	.5
Six	(.4)	.6
V-6	(.8)	1.1
V-8	(.6)	.8
w/A.C. add		.2
(G) Ignition Timing, Reset		
1983	(.4)	.4
(G) Distributor, Renew		
Includes: Reset ignition timing.		
1983	(.4)	.7
w/A.C. add		.2
(G) Distributor Cap, Renew		
1983	(.3)	.5
(G) Vacuum Control Unit, Renew		
Includes: R&R distributor and reset ignition timing.		
1983	(.5)	.8
(G) Ignition Coil, Renew		
Includes: Test.		
1983	(.4)	.6
(G) Ignition Cables, Renew		
Includes: Test wiring.		
1983	(.4)	.6
(G) Ignition Switch, Renew		
1983	(.4)	.6
(G) Ignition Key Indicator Buzzer, Renew		
1983	(.3)	.5
(G) Ignition Modulator Assembly, Renew		
1983	(.3)	.6
(G) Distributor Armature, Renew		
1983	(.3)	.6
(G) Distributor Stator, Renew		
Includes: R&R armature.		
1983	(.4)	.8

PARTS 2 ELECTRONIC IGNITION 2 PARTS

	Part No.	Price
Distributor Assy. (New)		
Four-140 engine		
1983	▲E3ZZ-12127D	136.75
Six-200 engine		
1983 (auto. trans.)		
exc. Calif.	▲E2BZ-12127C	136.75
w/Hi alt.	▲E2BZ-12127A	136.75
Calif.	▲E2BZ-12127C	136.75
(1) Distributor Cap		
Four-140 engine		
1983	▲E3BZ-12106A	16.25
Six-200 eng.		
1983	▲D7DZ-12106A	18.75
(2) Rotor		
Four-140 engine		
1983	▲D7FZ-12200C	4.75
Six-200 eng.		
1983	▲E3DZ-12200A	3.00
(3) Armature		
Four-140 engine		
1983	▲D7FZ-12A099A	3.75
Six-200 eng.		
1983	▲D5DZ-12A099A	5.00
(4) Stator Assy.		
Four-140 engine		
1983	▲D5TZ-12A112B	25.25
Six-200 engine		
1983	▲D5TZ-12A112B	25.25
(5) Vacuum Control Unit		
Four-140 engine		
1983	▲E2BZ-12370F	31.25

PARTS 2 ELECTRONIC IGNITION 2 PARTS

	Part No.	Price
Six-200 engine		
1983 (w/auto trans.)		
exc. Calif.	▲D8BZ-12370A	32.75
California	▲D6FZ-12370A	32.00
w/Hi alt. carb.	▲D8BZ-12370A	32.75
(6) Modulator Assy.		
Four-140 engine		
1983	▲D9VZ-12A199A	83.50
Six-200 engine		
1983	▲D9VZ-12A199A	83.50
Coil		
1983	▲D5AZ-12029A	31.25
Ignition Resistor		
1983	▲C0LF-12250A	4.75
Ignition Wire Set		
Four-140 engine		
1983	▲E3PZ-12259ABR	31.75
Six-200 engine		
1983	▲E3PZ-12259ER	34.75
Ignition Switch		
1983	▲E4FZ-11572A	11.50

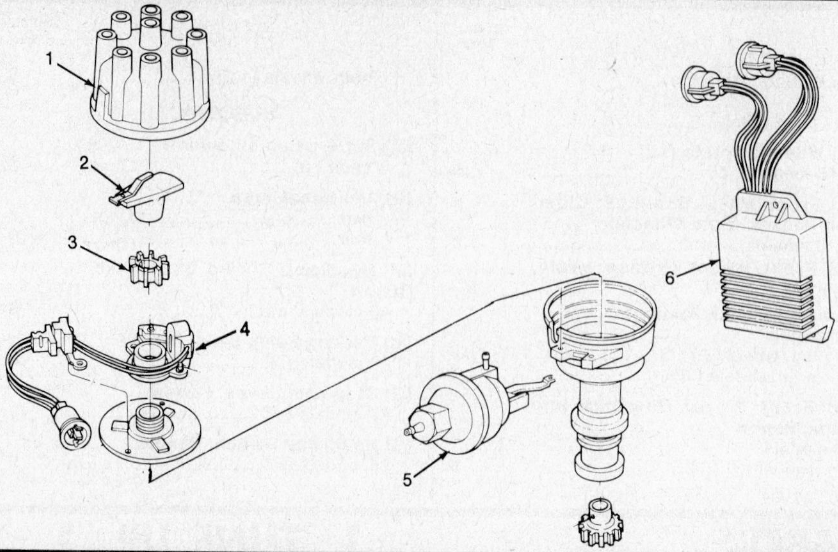

LABOR 3 FUEL SYSTEM 3 LABOR

(Factory Time)	Chilton Time
(G) Fuel Pump, Test	
Includes: Disconnect line at carburetor, attach pressure gauge.	
All models (.3)	.3
(M) Carburetor Air Cleaner, Service	
1983 (.2)	.3
(G) Carburetor, Adjust (On Car)	
1983 (.4)	.5
Propane enrichment method (1.0)	1.5
(M) Fuel Filter, Renew	
1983 (.3)	.4
(G) Carburetor, Renew	
Includes: Necessary adjustments.	
1983 (.5)	.9
(G) Carburetor, R&R and Clean or Recondition	
Includes: Necessary adjustments.	
1983	
Four (1.6)	2.2
Six-Carter (1.8)	2.4
Holly (2.2)	2.8
Renew spacer add (.2)	.2
Transfer choke add (.1)	.1
(G) Float Level, Adjust	
Includes: Set idle speed and mixture.	
All models	
Holly 1946 1V (.5)	.7
Weber 740 2V (.5)	.7
Motorcraft 2150 2V (.4)	.6
Weber 5200-6500 2V (.5)	.7
2700-7200 VV (.5)	.7
(G) Float or Needle Valve and Seat, Renew	
Includes: Set idle speed and mixture.	
All models	
Holly 1946 1V (.6)	.9
Weber 740 2V (.5)	.8
Motorcraft 2150 2V (.4)	.7
Weber 5200-6500 2V (.5)	.8
2700-7200 VV (.5)	.8
(G) Accelerator Pump Diaphragm, Piston or Rod, Renew	
All models	
Four (.4)	.6
Six (.6)	.8
V-6 (.6)	.8
(G) Fuel Pump, Renew	
1983-Four (.4)	.7
Six (.3)	.6
V-6 (.6)	1.0
Add pump test if performed.	
(G) Fuel Tank, Renew	
Includes: Transfer tank gauge unit.	
1983 (.8)	1.1
(G) Fuel Gauge (Tank), Renew	
Includes: Drain and refill tank.	
1983 (.5)	.8
(G) Fuel Gauge (Dash), Renew	
1983 (.5)	.9
(G) Intake Manifold or Gaskets, Renew	
1983-Four (1.1)	1.6
w/Turbocharger add (.3)	.3
Six (1.1)	1.7
V-6 (2.2)	2.7
Renew manif add (.4)	.5

PARTS 3 FUEL SYSTEM 3 PARTS

	Part No.	Price
Air Cleaner Element (Carb.)		
Four-140 engine		
1983	▲C8TZ-9601AR	8.50
Six-200 engine		
1983	▲D4ZZ-9601AR	9.00
Carburetor Assy. (New)		
Four-140 engine		
1983 (stand. trans.)		
wo/A.C.	▲E3ZZ-9510Y	298.00
w/A.C.	▲E3ZZ-9510V	221.50
(w/Hi altitude carb.)		
wo/A.C.	▲E3ZZ-9510AE	221.50
w/A.C.	▲E3ZZ-9510AD	221.50
(w/Auto. trans.)		
exc. Calif.		
wo/A.C.	▲E3ZZ-9510AT	221.50
w/A.C.	▲E3ZZ-9510AS	221.50
(California)		
wo/A.C.	▲E3ZZ-9510AB	221.50
w/A.C.	▲E3ZZ-9510AC	221.50
Six-200 engine		
1983 (auto. trans.)		
exc. hi altitude carb.		
wo/A.C.	▲E2BZ-9510B	277.00
w/A.C.	▲E2BZ-9510C	277.00
(w/Hi altitude carb.)		
wo/A.C.	▲E2BZ-9510S	284.75
w/A.C.	▲E2BZ-9510T	277.00
Carburetor Valve Seat Assy.		
Four-140 engine		
1983	▲E4PZ-9564A	8.25
Six-200 engine		
1983	▲E0PZ-9564B	12.25
Fuel Pump Assy. (New)		
Four-140 engine		
1983	▲D6FZ-9350A	38.25
Six-200 engine		
1983	▲D6DZ-9350B	34.75
Fuel Flex Line		
1983	▲E1PZ-9324C	1.50
Fuel Tank		
1983	▲E4DZ-9002D	135.00
Fuel Gauge (Tank Unit)		
1983 (w/std. fuel range)		
w/140 eng.	▲E2BZ-9275A	42.25
w/200 eng.	▲E2BZ-9275C	42.25
(w/Extended fuel range)		
w/140 eng.	▲E2BZ-9275B	42.25
w/200 eng.	▲E2BZ-9275D	42.25
Fuel Gauge (Dash)		
1983 (wo/tach)		
wo/clock	▲E0BZ-9305C	38.00
w/clock	▲E0BZ-9305D	39.50
w/tach	▲D9ZZ-9305A	28.00

LABOR 3A EMISSION CONTROLS 3A LABOR

(Factory Time) Chilton Time

CRANKCASE EMISSION

(M) Crankcase Ventilation Valve, Renew
1983 (.2) 2

THERMACTOR TYPE

(G) Thermactor Air Pump, Renew
1983 (.4) 7

(G) Thermactor Pump Drive Belt, Renew
1983 (.4) 6

(G) Thermactor Air By-Pass Valve, Renew
1983 (.4) 6

E.G.R. TYPE

(G) E.G.R. Valve, Renew
1983 (.3) 4

(G) Vacuum Control Valve, Renew
1983 (.3) 4

(G) Thermactor Air By-Pass Valve, Renew
1983 (.4) 6

EVAPORATIVE EMISSION TYPE

(G) Fuel Vapor Canister, Renew
1983 (.3) 4

(G) Carburetor Air Cleaner Sensor, Renew
1983 (.2) 3

(G) Carburetor Air Cleaner Filter, Renew
1983 (.2) 3

ELECTRONIC ENGINE CONTROL SYSTEM

(P) Feed Back Carburetor Control System, Test
All models (.5) 8

(P) Oxygen Sensor, Renew
Does not include system test.
All models (.3) 7

(P) Secondary Air Control Valve, Renew
Does not include system test.
All models (.4) 6

(P) Thermactor Air Valve, Renew
Does not include system test.
All models-one (.4) 6

CHILTON'S EMISSION CONTROL TUNE-UP

1. Clean or renew P.C.V. valve, hoses and filter.
2. Check fuel tank cap for sealing ability.
3. Check fuel tank and fuel lines for leakage.
4. Check evaporation canister and filter. Replace if necessary.
5. Check engine compression to determine leakage of unburned gases. (Add time for items of interference).
6. Test and clean or renew spark plugs.
7. Check engine oil dipstick for sealing ability.
8. Test exhaust system with analyzer and check system for leakage.
9. Check exhaust manifold heat valve for operation.
10. Adjust ignition timing and carburetor idle speed and mixture.
11. Check automatic choke mechanism for free operation.
12. Inspect air cleaner and element.
13. On models so equipped, test distributor vacuum control switch and transmission control switch.

Four 1.3
Six 1.5
V-6 .... 1.7
V-8 .... 1.8

For repairs made, charge accordingly.

(Factory Time) Chilton Time

(P) Vacuum Switch, Renew
Does not include system test.
All models-one (.3) 5

(P) Idle Tracking Switch, Renew
Does not include system test.
All models (.3) 5

(P) Feedback Carburetor Actuator, Renew
Does not include system test.
All models (.3) 5

(P) Low Temperature Switch, Renew
Does not include system test.
All models (.3) 6

(P) Thermactor Air By-Pass Valve, Renew
Does not include system test.
All models (.4) 6

(P) Solenoid, Renew
Does not include system test.
All models-one (.3) 4

(P) Canister Purge Solenoid, Renew
Does not include system test.
All models (.3) 4

(Factory Time) Chilton Time

(P) Mid-Temperature Switch, Renew
Does not include system test.
All models (.3) 4

(P) Open Loop (Temperature) Switch, Renew
Does not include system test.
All models (.3) 4

(P) Dual Temperature (Electric) Switch, Renew
Does not include system test.
All models (.3) 5

(P) Vacuum Solenoid Regulator, Renew
Does not include system test.
All models (.3) 5

(P) Cold Temperature Switch, Renew
Does not include system test.
All models (.4) 6

(P) Throttle Angle Vacuum Switch, Renew
Does not include system test.
All models (.3) 6

(P) Electronic Control Unit, Renew
Does not include system test.
All models (.3) 5

PARTS 3A EMISSION CONTROLS 3A PARTS

EVAPORATIVE EMISSION TYPE

	Part No.	Price
Vapor Canister Assy.		
1983-w/140 eng.	▲D8AZ-9D653C	53.25
w/200 eng.		
wo/Hi alt.	▲D8AZ-9D653C	53.25
w/Hi alt.	▲E0AZ-9D653A	53.25

THERMACTOR TYPE

	Part No.	Price
Thermactor Air Pump		
1983 (w/200 eng.)		
exc. below	▲E1ZZ-9A486G	141.75
(stamped EOEE)		
B1A, B2A	▲E1TZ-9A486-D	141.75
1983-w/140 eng.	▲E3ZZ-9A486A	141.75

	Part No.	Price
Crankcase Ventilator Valve		
1983		
w/140 eng.	▲E1ZZ-6A666A	3.75
1983		
w/200 eng.	▲E1DZ-6A666A	3.75

ELECTRONIC ENGINE CONTROL

	Part No.	Price
Oxygen Sensor (Exh. Gas)		
1983 (w/140 eng.)		
exc. below	▲E3FZ-9F472A	48.50
(stamped E1AF)		
AA	▲E1AZ-9F472A	95.00

	Part No.	Price
Secondary Air Control Valve		
1983 (w/200 eng.)		
(stamped)		
E1BE-BA	▲E2BZ-9F491-C	30.25
E1BE-BB	▲E2BZ-9F491C	30.25
E1BE-DA	▲E2BZ-9F491C	30.25
E1BE-DB	▲E2BZ-9F491B	27.25
E1BE-JA	▲E2BZ-9F491J	27.25
E1BE-JB	▲E2BZ-9F491J	27.25
E1ZE-BC	▲E2ZZ-9F491B	13.50
1983 (w/140 eng.)		
stand. trans.	▲E3TZ-9F491A	56.00
(auto. trans.)		
exc. below	▲E3ZZ-9F491D	27.25
(stamped)		
E1TE-AB	▲E3TZ-9F491A	56.00

PARTS 3A EMISSION CONTROLS 3A PARTS

	Part No.	Price
Vacuum Solenoid Regulator		
1983 (w/140 eng.)		
Calif.	▲E2ZZ-9B998A	55.75
Modulator Valve Switch Assy.		
1983 (w/140 eng.)		
(stamped E1ZE)		
A1A, A2A, A3A	▲E1ZZ-12A182A	41.25
(stamped E2ZE)		
C1A	▲E2ZZ-12A182C	41.25
Electronic Control Unit		
1983-w/140 eng	▲E3ZZ-12A651B	212.25
Mid Temperature Switch		
1983-w/140 eng. (stamped on valve)		
D7ZE-AA	▲D7ZZ-9E862A	7.50
E0EE-AA	▲E0FZ-9E862A	7.50
Canister Purge Solenoid		
1983	▲E0AZ-9C915A	21.75

LABOR 4 ALTERNATOR AND REGULATOR 4 LABOR

(Factory Time) Chilton Time

(G) Alternator Circuits, Test
Includes: Test battery, regulator and alternator output.
All models (.3) 6

(G) Alternator, Renew
1983 (.4) 8
Transfer pulley add (.1) 1
Circuit test add 6

(G) Alternator, R&R and Recondition
Includes: Complete disassembly, replacement of parts as required. Test validity of rotor fields, stator and diodes.
1983 (.9) 1.7
Circuit test add 6

(G) Alternator Front Bearing or End Plate, Renew
1983 (.7) 1.0

(G) Alternator Rear Bearing, Renew
1983 (.6) 9

(G) Alternator Regulator, Renew
1983 (.3) 4
Circuit test add 6

(G) Instrument Cluster Voltage Regulator, Renew
Includes: Remove instrument panel pad when required.
1983 (.4) 6

PARTS 4 ALTERNATOR AND REGULATOR 4 PARTS

	Part No.	Price
Alternator Assy. (New)		
1983-40 amp	▲E1ZZ-10346A	203.50
60 amp	▲E2GZ-10346C	233.50
(1) Pulley		
1983-40 amp	▲C5AZ-10344L	18.50
60 amp	▲D9ZZ-10344A	10.00
(2) Fan		
1983	▲C9ZZ-10A310A	6.00
(3) Front Housing		
1983	▲D30Z-10333B	17.75
(4) Front Bearing		
1983	▲C9ZZ-10094A	9.00
(5) Rotor		
1983-40 amp	▲E1ZZ-10335A	45.75
60 amp	▲E1ZZ-10335B	45.75
(6) Stator		
1983	▲E3FZ-10336A	31.25
(7) Rectifier Assy.		
1983	▲D6AZ-10304A	48.00
(8) Brushes		
1983	▲C6VY-10347A	3.50
(9) Rear Housing		
1983-40 amp	▲D7ZZ-10334A	26.25
60 amp	▲D7AZ-10334A	23.25

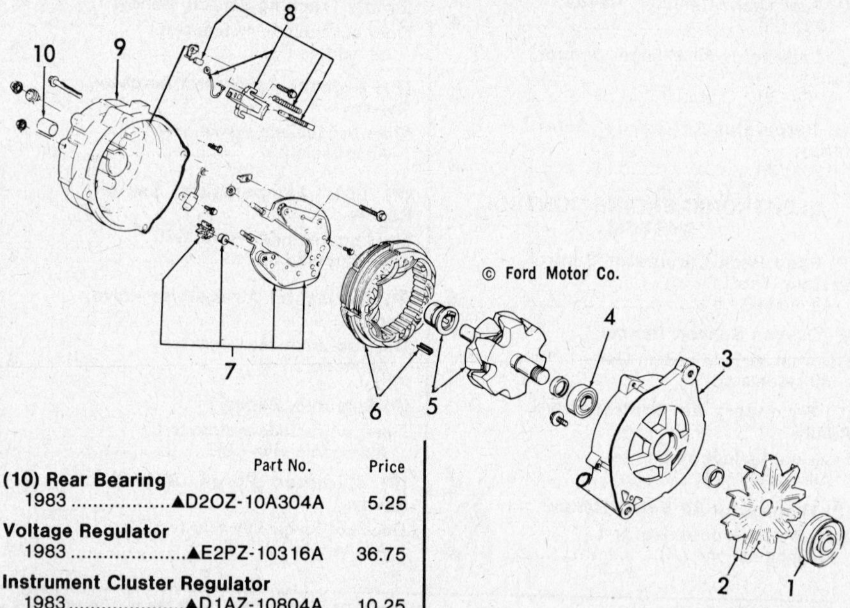

	Part No.	Price
(10) Rear Bearing		
1983	▲D2OZ-10A304A	5.25
Voltage Regulator		
1983	▲E2PZ-10316A	36.75
Instrument Cluster Regulator		
1983	▲D1AZ-10804A	10.25

LABOR 5 STARTING SYSTEM 5 LABOR

(Factory Time) Chilton Time

(G) Starter Draw Test (On Car)
All models (.3) 3

(G) Starter, Renew
1983-exc below (.4) 9
Six-w/Lite off converter (1.0) 1.5

(G) Starter, R&R and Recondition
Includes: Turn down armature.
1983
positive engagement starter (1.7) 2.4
solenoid actuated starter (1.5) 2.2
brush end terminal (1.4) 2.1
w/Lite off converter add (.7) 7
Renew field coils add 5
Add draw test if performed.

(G) Starter Drive, Renew
1983 (.5) 1.3
w/Lite off converter add (.7) 7

(G) Starter Solenoid, Renew
Includes: R&R starter.
1983 (.6) 1.1
w/Lite off converter add (.7) 7

(G) Starter Solenoid Relay, Renew
1983 (.3) 4

(G) Neutral Safety Switch, Renew
1983 (.3) 4

(G) Ignition Switch, Renew
1983 (.4) 6

(M) Battery Cables, Renew
1983-each (.3) 3

PARTS 5 STARTING SYSTEM 5 PARTS

	Part No.	Price
Starter Assy. (New)		
1983-w/140 eng.	▲E4TZ-11002B	203.50
(w/200 eng.)		
wo/Hi alt.	▲E4DZ-11002B	185.50
w/Hi alt.	▲E1BZ-11002B	201.75
Starter Relay Switch		
1983	▲D8DZ-11450B	12.00
Ignition & Starter Switch		
1983	▲E4FZ-11572A	11.50
(1) Starter Armature (New)		
1983-w/140 eng.	▲E2BZ-11005A	77.00
(w/200 eng.)		
wo/Hi alt.	▲E2BZ-11005A	77.00
w/Hi alt.	▲D7AZ-11005A	60.25
(2) Starter Drive Assy.		
1983-w/140 eng.	▲E2PZ-11350A	21.00
(w/200 eng.)		
w/Hi alt.	▲D6PZ-11350B	17.50
wo/Hi alt.	▲E2PZ-11350A	21.00
(3) Rear Plate (Housing)		
1983-w/140 eng.	▲E4DZ-11130A	27.75
(w/200 eng.)		
wo/Hi alt	▲E2FZ-11130A	21.75
w/Hi alt.	▲E4DZ-11130A	27.75
(4) Front Plate		
1983		
exc below	▲D7AZ-11049A	8.00
140 eng.	▲E2BZ-11049A	14.50
(5) Field Coil Assy.		
1983		
exc below	▲D7AZ-11049A	8.00
140 eng.	▲E2BZ-11082A	50.00

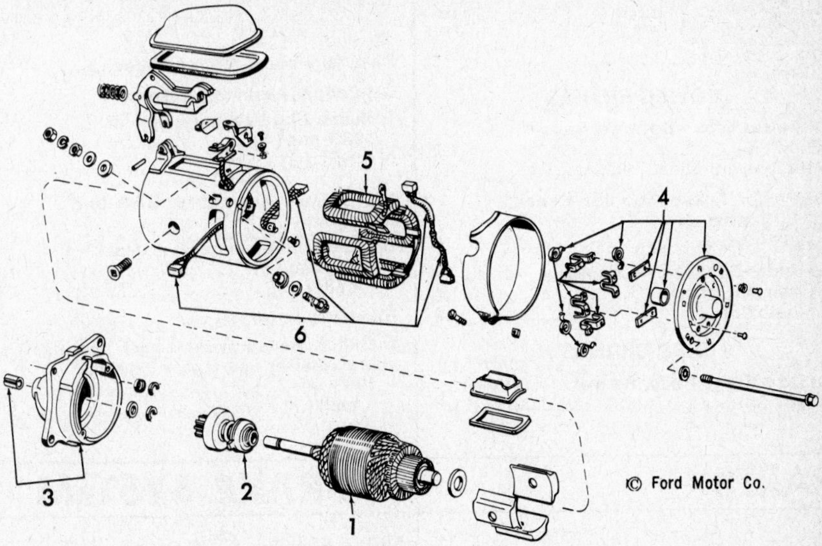

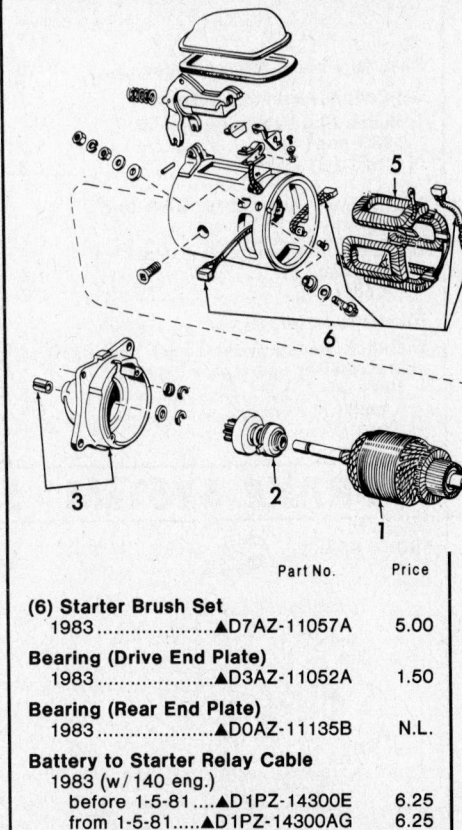

	Part No.	Price
(6) Starter Brush Set		
1983	▲D7AZ-11057A	5.00
Bearing (Drive End Plate)		
1983	▲D3AZ-11052A	1.50
Bearing (Rear End Plate)		
1983	▲D0AZ-11135B	N.L.
Battery to Starter Relay Cable		
1983 (w/140 eng.)		
before 1-5-81	▲D1PZ-14300E	6.25
from 1-5-81	▲D1PZ-14300AG	6.25
1983-200 eng.	▲D1PZ-14300E	6.25
Battery to Ground Cable		
1983		
exc below	▲E35Y-14301C	15.75
140 eng.	▲E1DZ-14301B	12.50
Relay to Starter Cable		
1983-w/140 eng.	▲E0BZ-14431A	10.25
w/200 eng.	▲E0BZ-14431B	11.00
Switch (Dash)		
1983	▲E4FZ-11572A	11.50

LABOR 6 BRAKE SYSTEM 6 LABOR

(Factory Time)	Chilton Time
(G) Brake Pedal Free Play, Adjust	
All models	.4
(G) Brakes, Adjust (Minor)	
Includes: Adjust brakes, fill master cylinder.	
two wheels	.4
(G) Bleed Brakes (Four Wheels)	
Includes: Fill master cylinder.	
All models (.3)	.5
(G) Brake Self Adjustors, Disassemble & Clean	
one wheel	.7
each adtnl	.4
(G) Brake Shoes and/or Pads, Renew	
Includes: Install new or exchange brake shoes or pads. Adjust service and hand brake. Bleed system.	
1983-front-disc (.6)	1.1
rear-drum (1.1)	1.5
all four wheels (1.4)	2.5
Resurface disc rotor, add-each	.9
Resurface brake drum, add-each	.5
(G) Brake Drum, Renew	
1983-one (.4)	.6
(G) Brake Pressure Warning Light Switch, Renew	
1983 (.3)	.5

COMBINATIONS

Add to Brakes, Renew

See Machine Shop Operations

(Factory Time)	Chilton Time
(G) RENEW WHEEL CYLINDER	
Each (.3)	.3
(G) REBUILD WHEEL CYLINDER	
Each (.3)	.3
(G) REBUILD CALIPER ASSEMBLY	
Front-one (.2)	.5
Rear-one (.2)	.5
(G) RENEW MASTER CYLINDER	
All models (.6)	.6
(G) REBUILD MASTER CYLINDER	
All models	1.0
(G) RENEW BRAKE HOSE	
Each (.3)	.3
(G) RENEW REAR WHEEL GREASE SEALS	
One (.3)	.4
Both (.4)	.6
(G) REPACK FRONT WHEEL BEARINGS (BOTH WHEELS)	
All models (.3)	.6
(G) RENEW BRAKE DRUM	
Each (.2)	.2
(G) RENEW DISC BRAKE ROTOR	
Each (.2)	.4

BRAKE HYDRAULIC SYSTEM

(Factory Time)	Chilton Time
(G) Wheel Cylinder, Renew	
Includes: Bleed system.	
1983-rear-one (.9)	1.4
both (1.5)	2.1
(G) Wheel Cylinder, R&R and Rebuild	
Includes: Hone cylinder and bleed system.	
1983-rear-one (.9)	1.7
both (1.5)	2.7
(G) Brake Hose, Renew	
Includes: Bleed system.	
1983-front-one (.4)	.6
both (.5)	.7
rear-one (.6)	.8
(G) Master Cylinder, Renew	
Includes: Bleed complete system.	
1983 (.6)	1.0
(G) Master Cylinder, R&R and Rebuild	
Includes: Hone cylinder and bleed complete system.	
1983 (.8)	1.6
(G) Brake System, Flush and Refill	
All models	1.2
(G) Brake Hydraulic System, Recondition (Complete)	
Includes: Renew all rubber parts in brake system and bleed all lines.	
1983	4.8

LABOR 6 BRAKE SYSTEM 6 LABOR

(Factory Time)	Chilton Time
w/Pwr brks add	.5

POWER BRAKES

(G) Power Brake Booster, Renew

1983 (.8)	1.2
1983-Hydra-boost (.9)	1.4

(G) Power Brake Booster Check Valve, Renew

1983 (.3)	.5

(G) Hydra-Boost Hose, Renew

1983-one (.4)	.6
both (.5)	.8

DISC BRAKES

(G) Disc Brake Pads, Renew

1983 (.6)	1.1

(Factory Time)	Chilton Time
Resurface brake rotor, add-each	.9

(G) Caliper Assembly, Renew

Includes: Bleed complete system.

1983-one (.6)	1.0
both (.8)	1.5

(G) Caliper Assembly, R&R and Recondition

Includes: Bleed complete system.

1983-one (.8)	1.5
both (1.2)	2.5

(G) Brake Rotor, Renew

Includes: Renew front wheel bearings and grease retainer and repack bearings.

1983-one (.5)	.7
both (.7)	1.2

(Factory Time)	Chilton Time

(G) Brake Differential Valve, Renew

Includes: Bleed complete system and transfer switch.

1983 (.7)	1.2

PARKING BRAKE

(M) Parking Brake, Adjust

1983 (.3)	.4

(G) Parking Brake Control, Renew

1983 (.6)	1.0

(G) Parking Brake Cable, Renew

Includes: Adjust parking brake.

1983	
one (.4)	.7
both (.5)	.9

PARTS 6 BRAKE SYSTEM 6 PARTS

	Part No.	Price
(1) Brake Shoe Set (Rear)		
1983		
9" x 1¾"	▲D9ZZ-2200A	35.50
10" x 1¾"	▲D6DZ-2200A	37.00
Brake Lining Kit		
1983		
9" x 1¾"	▲D9ZZ-2007A	22.25
10" x 1¾"	▲D6DZ-2007A	21.75
(2) Rear Wheel Cylinder Assy.		
1983-exc below	▲D8BZ-2261A	17.75
(w/10" x 1¾" brakes)		
R.H.	▲D8BZ-2261B	19.75
L.H.	▲D8BZ-2262A	19.75
Repair Kit Wheel Cylinders		
1983		
9" x 1¾"	▲D8BZ-2128A	5.75
10" x 1¾"	▲D8BZ-2128B	5.50
Brake Hose (Front)		
1983	▲E3DZ-2078A	15.25
Brake Hose (Rear)		
1983	▲E3SZ-2282A	17.25
Master Cylinder Assy.		
1983-man. disc	▲D8BZ-2140B	104.50
power disc	▲E4DZ-2140A	93.00
Repair Kit (Master Cyl.)		
1983-man. disc	▲D8BZ-2004B	34.25
power disc	▲E1BZ-2004A	32.50

FRONT BRAKE

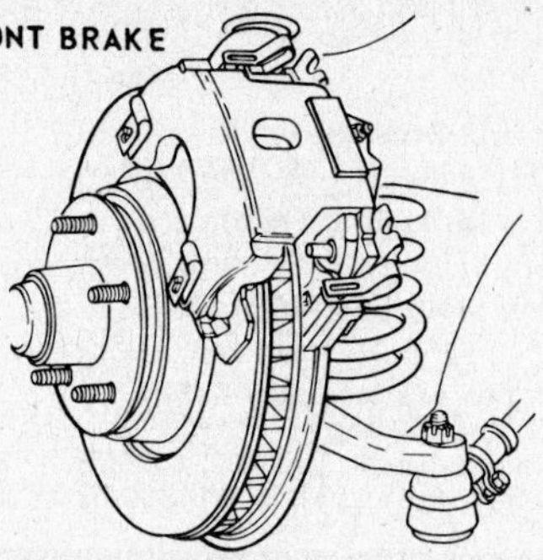

REAR BRAKE

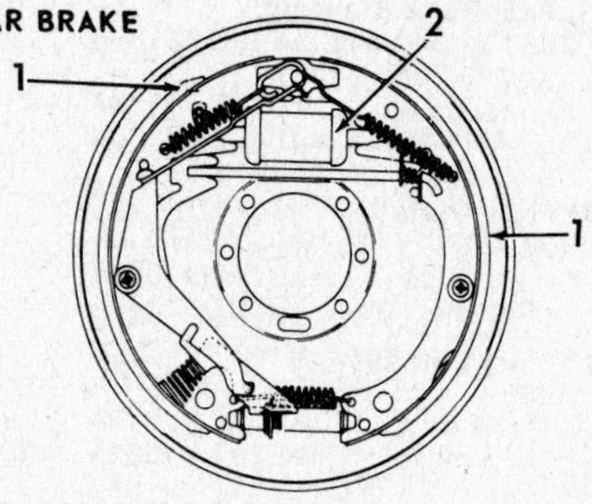

	Part No.	Price
Hub & Brake Drum (Front)		
1983	▲D8BZ-1126A	60.50
Brake Drum (Rear)		
1983		
10¾" O.D.	▲D9ZZ-1126A	60.50
11⅝" O.D.	▲D9BZ-1126A	76.00
Grease Retainer (Front Wheel)		
1983	▲C8AZ-1190A	3.00

	Part No.	Price
Rear Wheel Oil Seal		
1983		
w/6¾" R/gear	▲D9BZ-1177B	4.25
w/7½" R/gear	▲E1AZ-1177B	3.50
w/8½" R/gear	▲E1AZ-1177B	3.50
PARKING BRAKE		
Parking Brake Control Assy.		
1983	▲E3SZ-2780A	38.50
Parking Brake Cable (Rear)		
1983	▲E3SZ-2A635A	21.75

PARTS 6 DISC BRAKES 6 PARTS

	Part No.	Price
FAIRMONT & ZEPHYR		
(1) Hub and Rotor		
1983	▲D8BZ-1102A	87.25
(2) Piston Assembly		
1983	▲D8BZ-2196A	13.00
(3) Brake Pads		
1983		
before 11-2-82	▲D9BZ-2001G	43.75
from 11-2-82	▲E3SZ-2001A	48.75
(4) Caliper Assembly		
1983-right	▲E3SZ-2B120A	116.75
left	▲E3SZ-2B121A	116.75

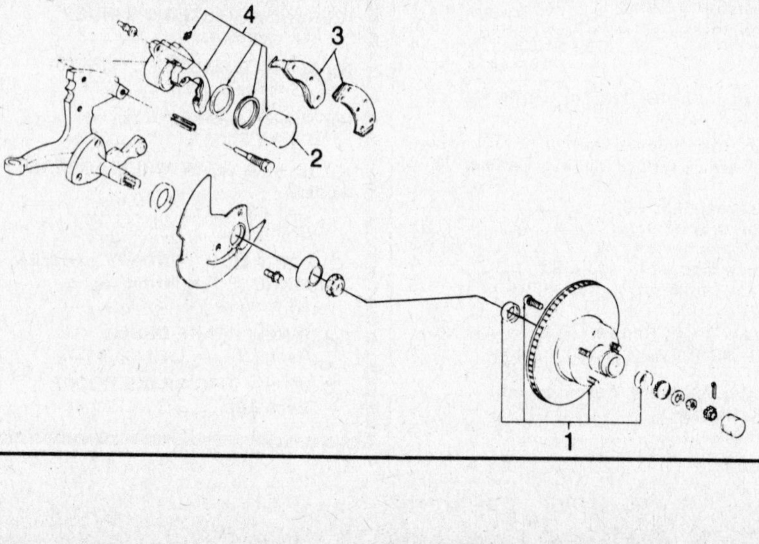

LABOR 7 COOLING SYSTEM 7 LABOR

	(Factory Time)	Chilton Time
(M) Winterize Cooling System		
Includes: Run engine to check for leaks, tighten all hose connections. Test radiator and pressure cap, drain radiator and engine block. Add anti-freeze and refill system.		
All models		.5
(M) Thermostat, Renew		
1983		
Four	(.5)	.7
Six	(.4)	.6
w/A.C. add		.2
(M) Radiator Assembly, R&R or Renew		
Includes: Drain and refill cooling system.		
1983	(.6)	1.1

ADD THESE OPERATIONS TO RADIATOR R&R

(G) Boil & Repair		1.5
(G) Rod Clean		1.9
(G) Repair Core		1.3
(G) Renew Tank		1.6
(G) Renew Trans. Oil Cooler		1.9
(G) Recore Radiator		1.7
(M) Radiator Hoses, Renew		
1983		
upper	(.3)	.4
lower	(.5)	.6
both	(.6)	.7
(G) Water Pump, Renew		
Four–1983	(1.0)	1.7
Six–1983	(.9)	1.6
w/A.C. add	(.2)	.3
w/P.S. add		.2
(M) Fan Blades, Renew		
1983	(.4)	.7
w/Clutch fan add		.2
(M) Drive Belt, Renew		
1983-one	(.3)	.4
each adtnl	(.1)	.1

COOLING SYSTEM TUNE-UP

An Annual Cooling System Tune-Up Suggestion List should include (with some exceptions):

1. A visual check of the cooling system for indications of leaks or excessive oil content.
2. Pressure check the cooling system for internal and external leaks with filler cap and neck adapter and tester.
3. Check crankcase and automatic transmission oil for water content.
4. Test coolant thermostat with radiator thermometer.
5. Check temperature gauge for accuracy.
6. Drain system and flush till clean.
7. Clean foreign matter from radiator fins.
8. Test radiator pressure cap with cap tester.
9. Check fan blades and pulleys for alignment and damage.
10. Internal and external inspection of all hoses for cracks and deterioration.
11. Check core plugs (where possible) for seepage.
12. Refill system with correct coolant and check for air locks.
13. Check condition and tension of drive belts with tension gauge.

All models 1.5

	(Factory Time)	Chilton Time
(M) Drive Belt, Adjust		
1983-one	(.2)	.3
each adtnl	(.1)	.1
(G) Electric Cooling Fan Motor, Renew		
1983	(.3)	.5
(M) Clutch Fan, Renew		
1983	(.4)	.8
(G) Temperature Gauge (Engine Unit), Renew		
1983	(.3)	.4
(G) Water Jacket Expansion Plugs, Renew (Side of Block)		
each	(.3)	*.5
*Add time to gain accessibility.		
(G) Heater Hoses, Renew		
1983-each	(.3)	.5
(G) Heater Core, R&R or Renew		
1983		
wo/A.C.	(.5)	.9
w/A.C.	(3.3)	*6.0
*Includes recharge A.C. system.		

ADD THESE OPERATIONS TO HEATER CORE R&R

(G) Boil & Repair		1.2
(G) Repair Core		.9
(G) Recore		1.2
(G) Heater Control Assembly, Renew		
1983	(.4)	.7
(G) Heater Blower Motor, Renew		
Includes: Transfer blower wheel when required.		
1983	(.6)	1.1
(G) Heater Blower Motor Resistor, Renew		
1983	(.3)	.5
(G) Heater Blower Motor Switch, Renew		
1983	(.4)	.6

PARTS 7 COOLING SYSTEM 7 PARTS

	Part No.	Price
(1) Radiator Assy.		
Order by year and model.		
(2) Thermostat		
Four–140 engine		
1983	▲E3FZ-8575A	9.75
Six–200 engine		
1983	▲E1BZ-8575A	6.00
(3) Radiator Hoses		
Order by year and model.		
(4) Water Pump Assy. (New)		
Four–140 engine		
1983	▲E4BZ-8501A	88.25
Six–200 engine		
1983	▲D8BZ-8501A	62.50
(5) Fan Belt		
Order by model & description.		
Heat Indicator (Engine)		
1983-exc. below	▲E43Z-10884A	9.00
(w/140 eng.)		
wo/Tach	▲C8GY-10884A	9.25
w/Tach	▲D0WY-10884A	5.25
Heater Core		
1983-wo/A.C.	▲E2FZ-18476A	59.50
w/A.C.	▲D9BZ-18476A	63.50

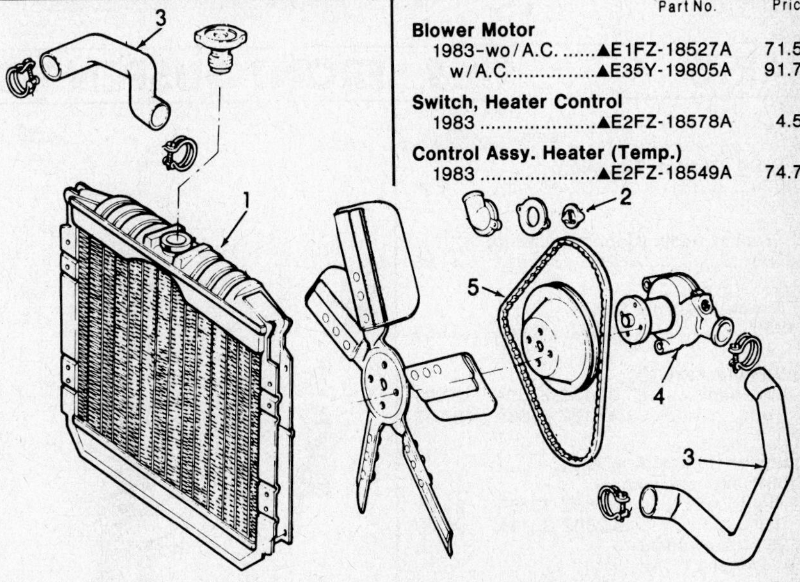

	Part No.	Price
Blower Motor		
1983-wo/A.C.	▲E1FZ-18527A	71.50
w/A.C.	▲E35Y-19805A	91.75
Switch, Heater Control		
1983	▲E2FZ-18578A	4.50
Control Assy. Heater (Temp.)		
1983	▲E2FZ-18549A	74.75

LABOR 8 EXHAUST SYSTEM 8 LABOR

(Factory Time) Chilton Time

(G) Muffler, Renew
1983-single inlet (.5) 8
dual inlet (.6) 1.0
Welded type add 3

(G) Tail Pipe, Renew
1983 (.2) 5
Welded type add 3

(G) Catalytic Converter, Renew
1983
Four (.6) 9
Six (1.7) 2.3

(G) Exhaust Pipe, Renew
Includes: Replace exhaust control valve if required.
1983-single (.6) 9
dual (.9) 1.2

(G) Manifold Heat Valve, Renew
1983 (.3) 7

(G) Exhaust Manifold, Renew
1983
Four (1.1) 1.7
Six (1.2) 1.9
w/Lite-off conv (3.5) 4.5
w/A.C. add 3

COMBINATIONS

(G) Muffler, Exhaust and Tail Pipe, Renew
1983 .... 1.7

PARTS 8 EXHAUST SYSTEM 8 PARTS

	Part No.	Price
Muffler		
Order by year and model.		
Catalytic Converter		
Four-140 engine		
1983 exc. Calif.	▲E3DZ-5E212D	191.25
Calif.	▲E3DZ-5E212A	382.25
Six-200 engine		
1983		
single conv.	▲E2BZ-5E212D	373.75
(Dual converter)		
before 10-4-82	▲E1BZ-5E212E	187.50
from 10-4-82	▲E3ZZ-5E212C	191.25

LABOR 9 FRONT SUSPENSION 9 LABOR

(Factory Time) Chilton Time

Note: On all front suspension operations alignment charges must be added if performed. Time given does not include alignment.

(M) Wheel, Renew
one (.5) 5

(G) Wheels, Rotate (All)
All models (.5) 5

(G) Wheels, Balance
one 3
each adtnl 2

(G) Check Alignment of Front End
All models (.4) 5
Note: Deduct if alignment is performed.

(G) Toe-In, Adjust
All models (.4) 5

(G) Align Front End
Includes: Adjust front wheel bearings.
All models (1.2) 1.4
w/A.C. interference add 5

(G) Front Wheel Bearings, Clean and Repack (Both Wheels)
All models 1.3

(G) Front Wheel Bearings and Cups, Renew
Includes: Repack bearings.
All models
one wheel (.7) 9
both wheels (1.2) 1.5

(G) Front Wheel Grease Seals, Renew
Includes: Repack bearings.
All models
one wheel (.5) 7
both wheels (.8) 1.1

(G) Front Shock Absorber or Bushings, Renew
1983
one (.7) 1.1
both (1.1) 1.9

(G) Front Spindle Assembly, Renew
Add alignment charges.
1983-one (.8) 1.2

(G) Lower Control Arm Assy., Renew (One)
Add alignment charges.
1983 (1.0) 1.5

(G) Ball Joints, Renew
Add alignment charges.
1983-upper or lower
one side 1.2
both sides 1.9
upper & lower
one side 1.6
both sides 2.5

(G) Lower Control Arm Struts or Bushings, Renew
Add alignment charges.
1983
one (1.4) 2.2
both (2.5) 4.0

(G) Front Stabilizer Bushings, Renew
1983 (.5) 7

(G) Front Spring, Renew
1983-one (1.0) 1.5
both (1.7) 2.7

(G) Control Arm Rubber Bumpers, Renew
one (.3) 4
each adtnl (.1) 1

PARTS 9 FRONT SUSPENSION 9 PARTS

	Part No.	Price
(1) Plate (Camber Adjusting)		
1983	▲D8BZ-3B391A	8.25
(2) Bracket Assy. (Upper Mounting)		
1983	▲E2DZ-18A161A	41.25
(3) Shock Absorber (Front)		
1983	▲E3BZ-18124A	91.50
(4) Spindle Assy.		
1983-right	▲E1SZ-3105A	137.00
left	▲E1SZ-3106A	137.00
(5) Lower Control Arm Assy.		
1983 (exc. sta. wagon)		
right	▲D8BZ-3078A	99.25
left	▲D8BZ-3079A	99.25
1983 (sta. wagon)		
(w/140 eng.)		
right	▲D9BZ-3078A	115.00

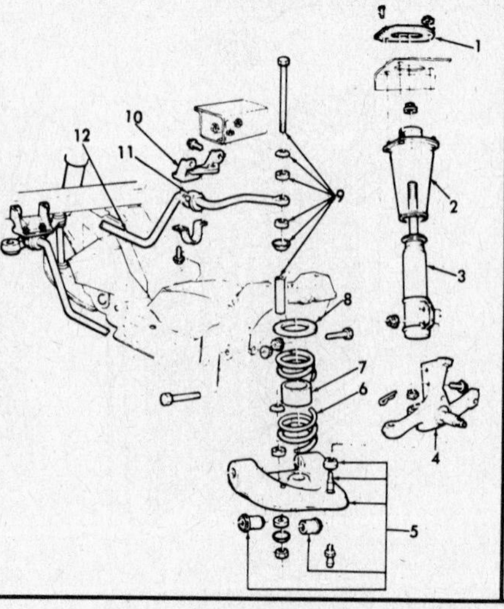

	Part No.	Price
left	▲D9BZ-3079A	115.00
(w/200 eng.)		
right	▲D8BZ-3078A	99.25
left	▲D8BZ-3079A	99.25
(6) Coil Spring		
Order by model and description.		
(7) Damper (Front Spring)		
1983	▲D8BZ-5A669A	6.75
(8) Insulator (Upper)		
1983	▲D4ZZ-5415A	5.25
(9) Stabilizer Repair Kit		
1983	▲E3AZ-5A486A	20.75
(11) Insulator (Stabilizer)		
1983 (Four & six cylinder)		
wo/TRX	▲E1BZ-5493C	5.50
w/TRX	▲E1BZ-5493E	5.50

LABOR 10 STEERING LINKAGE 10 LABOR

(Factory Time) Chilton Time

(G) Tie Rod Ends, Renew
Includes: Reset toe-in.

	Chilton Time
1983-one (.9)	1.2
each adtnl (.2)	.2

(G) Tie Rod Ball Joint Sockets, Renew
Includes: R&R gear assy. Renew tie rod ends and bellows.

	Chilton Time
1983-manual (1.6)	2.1
power (1.9)	2.6

PARTS 10 STEERING LINKAGE 10 PARTS

	Part No.	Price
Tie Rod Ends (Outer)		
1983	▲E2DZ-3A130A	36.00
Tie Rod Kit		
1983-manual strg.	▲D8BZ-3280B	71.75
power strg.	▲E2SZ-3280A	66.25
Sector Shaft		
1983-exc. below	▲D8BZ-3575B	62.00
power strg.	▲D8BZ-3575A	36.50

LABOR 11 STEERING GEAR 11 LABOR

(Factory Time) Chilton Time

STANDARD STEERING

(G) Horn Button or Ring, Renew
1983 (.4) 5

(G) Steering Wheel, Renew
1983 (.3) 5

(G) Upper Mast Jacket Bearing, Renew
1983 std column (.5) 9
tilt column (.6) 1.1

(G) Steering Gear, Adjust (Off Car)
Includes: Bearing preload and gear mesh.
1983 (1.4) 1.9

(G) Steering Gear Assembly, Renew
1983 (1.1) 1.5

(P) Steering Gear Assembly, R&R and Recondition
Includes: Disassemble, renew necessary parts, reassemble and adjust.
1983 (2.2) 3.0

POWER STEERING

(G) Trouble Shoot Power Steering
Includes: Test pump and system pressure. Check pounds pull on steering wheel and check for leaks.
All models 5

(M) Check and Fill Reservoir
All models 2

(G) Pump Pressure Check
All models 5

(M) Pump Drive Belt, Renew or Adjust
1983-renew (.3) 4
adjust (.2) 2

(G) Power Steering Gear, Adjust (Off Car)
Includes: Bearing preload and gear mesh.
1983 (1.7) 2.2

(G) Power Steering Gear, Renew
1983 (1.4) 1.9

(P) Steering Gear Assy., R&R and Recondition
Includes: Disassemble, renew necessary parts, reassemble and adjust.
1983 (2.9) 3.9

(G) Power Steering Oil Pump, Renew
Includes: Bleed system.
1983 (.6) 9

(G) Power Steering Pump, R&R and Recondition
Includes: Bleed system.
1983 (1.2) 1.7

(G) Power Steering Reservoir Seals, Renew
Includes: R&R pump and reservoir. Bleed system.
1983 (.9) 1.6

(G) Power Steering Pump Shaft Seal, Renew
Includes: Bleed system.
1983 (.7) 1.2

(M) Power Steering Hoses, Renew
Includes: Bleed system.
1983-pressure (.5) 9
return (.5) 9
cooling (.3) 7

PARTS 11 POWER STEERING GEAR 11 PARTS

	Part No.	Price
(1) Tie Rod End		
1983	▲E2DZ-3A130A	36.00
(2) Connecting Rod		
1983	▲E2SZ-3280A	66.25
(3) Sector Shaft Assy.		
1983	▲D8BZ-3575A	36.50
(4) Gear Rack Tube		
1983	▲D8BZ-3K762A	2.25
(5) Cover (Housing End)		
1983	▲D8BZ-3568A	5.00
(6) Cup (Worm Bearing)		
1983	▲D8BZ-3552A	13.25
(7) Clamps (Gear Boot)		
1983	▲D8BZ-3C650B	.75
(8) Boot (Dust Seal)		
1983	▲D9BZ-3332A	5.50

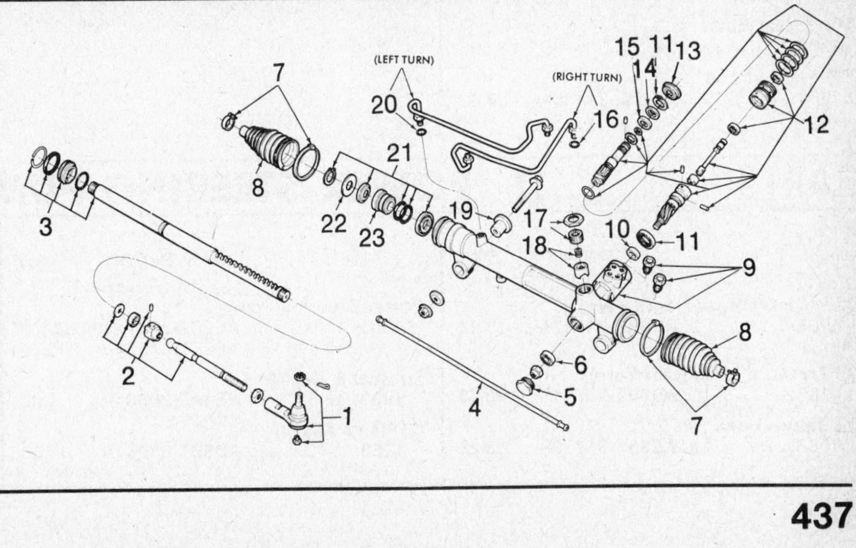

PARTS 11 POWER STEERING GEAR 11 PARTS

	Part No.	Price
(9) Housing Assy.		
1983	▲E3SZ-3548A	150.75
(11) Check Valve Kit		
1983	▲E3SZ-3D728A	15.75
(12) Shaft & Control Assy.		
1983		
before 12-1-82	▲E4DZ-3D517C	50.00
from 12-1-82	▲E4DZ-3D517C	50.00
(13) Dust Seal (Input Shaft)		
1983	▲D5AZ-3D527A	5.00
(14) Seal (Input Shaft)		
1983	▲D6AZ-3D526A	4.75
(15) Bearing (Input Shaft)		
1983	▲D8AZ-3D525A	8.75
(16) Pressure Tube (Right Turn)		
1983	▲D9BZ-3A717A	15.25
(17) Housing Cover (Sector Shaft)		
1983	▲E0BZ-3580AMR	7.00
(18) Bearing (Rack Adjust.)		
1983	▲E0SZ-3F515A	8.25
(19) Insulator		
1983	▲E3DZ-3C716A	6.50
(20) Pressure Tube (Left Turn)		
1983	▲D9BZ-3A714A	18.00
(21) Seal Kit (Rack Shaft)		
1983-87	▲E3SZ-3E501A	12.00
(22) Cover (Housing End)		
1983	▲D8BZ-3568B	5.00
(23) Bushing (Sector Shaft)		
1983	▲D9BZ-3576A	4.25

PARTS 11 STEERING GEAR - (STANDARD) 11 PARTS

	Part No.	Price
(1) Steering Gear Assy.		
1983	▲E2DZ-3504B	385.50
(2) Insulator (Steering Gear)		
1983	▲E0SZ-3C716A	7.50
(3) Oil Seal (Sector Shaft)		
1983	▲D1FZ-3738A	1.25
(4) Spacer (Pinion Bearing)		
1983	▲D4FZ-3K599A	2.75
(5) End Cover (Gear Housing)		
1983	▲D8BZ-3568C	8.50
(6) Bearing Cup (Worm)		
1983	▲D1FZ-3552A	13.75
(7) Shaft Assy. (Upper)		
1983-wo/Tilt whl	▲E3SZ-3524B	47.25
w/Tilt whl.	▲E3SZ-3524A	193.50
(8) Yoke (Shaft Support)		
1983	▲D8BZ-3F515B	7.00
(9) Gasket & Shim Kit		
1983	▲D3FZ-3F518A	1.00
(10) Housing Cover (Sector Shaft)		
1983	▲D3FZ-3580A	8.75
(11) Clamp		
1983	▲385951-S	2.00
(12) Dust Seal (Ball Stud)		
1983	▲D9BZ-3332B	5.50
(13) Clamp		
1983	▲385950-S	2.50
(14) Connecting Rod Assy.		
1983	▲E2SZ-3280A	66.25
(15) Housing Assy. (Steering Gear)		
1983	▲D8BZ-3548C	128.50
(16) Sector Shaft		
1983	▲D8BZ-3575B	62.00
(17) Tie Rod End		
1983	▲E2DZ-3A130A	36.00

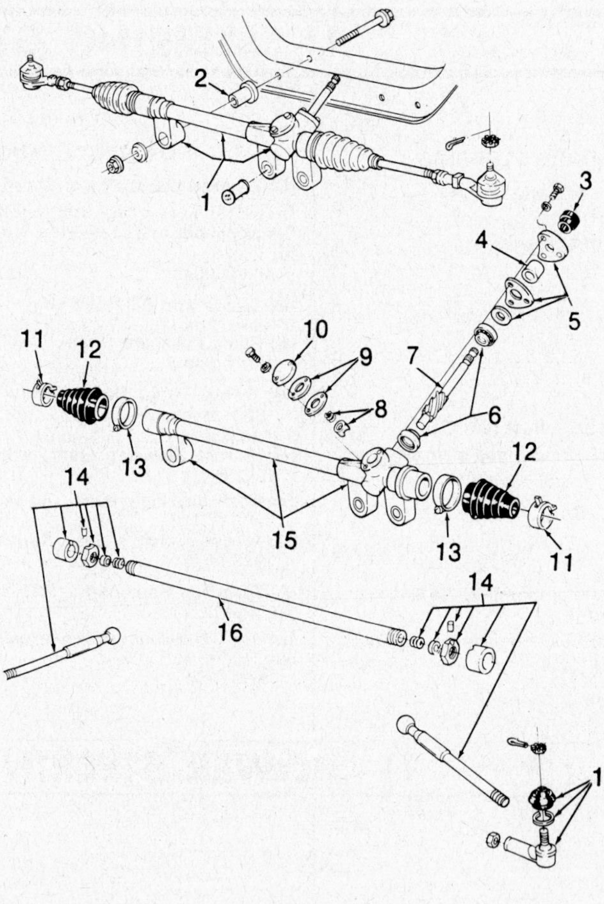

PARTS 11 POWER STEERING PUMP 11 PARTS

	Part No.	Price
Oil Pressure Hose (Right Turn)		
1983	▲D9BZ-3A717A	15.25
Oil Pressure Hose (Left Turn)		
1983	▲D9BZ-3A714A	18.00
Oil Return Hose		
1983	▲E2SZ-3A713B	15.25
Power Steering Pump		
1983-w/140 eng.	▲E2DZ-3A674A	200.75
w/200 eng.	▲E2DZ-3A674B	215.75
(1) Seal & Gasket Kit		
1983	▲E1AZ-3D684A	3.00
(2) Valve Assy.		
1983	▲D8BZ-3A561A	11.00
(3) Valve Spring (Flow Control)		
1983	▲D8AZ-3D586A	1.50
(4) Housing Assy.		
1983	▲E1AZ-3A643A	42.25
(5) Pressure Plate (Front)		
1983	▲E5FZ-3D590A	13.75

PARTS 11 POWER STEERING PUMP 11 PARTS

	Part No.	Price
(6) Rotor Assy.		
1983-w/140 eng.	▲E3FZ-3D607A	52.50
w/200 eng.	▲E53Z-3B607A	38.75
(7) Rotor Shaft		
1983	▲D8AZ-3B559A	18.00
(8) Pressure Plate (Rear)		
1983	▲D8AZ-3D590B	13.75
(9) Seal & Gasket Kit		
1983	▲E1AZ-3B584A	8.75
(10) Spring (Pressure Plate)		
1983	▲D8AZ-3D596A	2.50
(11) Plate & Bushing		
1983	▲E1AZ-3D643A	42.25
(12) Oil Seal (Rotor Shaft)		
1983	▲D9AZ-3B592A	9.25

FORD MODEL C II PUMP

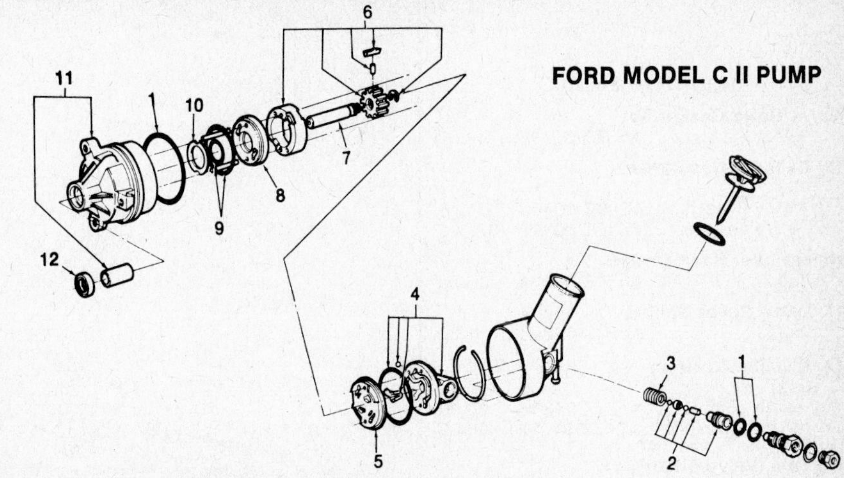

© Ford Motor Co.

LABOR 12 CYLINDER HEAD & VALVE SYSTEM 12 LABOR

(Factory Time)	Chilton Time
(G) Compression Test	
Four-1983 (.3)	.6
Six-1983 (.3)	.6
w/A.C. add	.2
(G) Cylinder Head Gasket, Renew	
Includes: Check cylinder head and block flatness. Clean carbon and make all necessary adjustments.	
Four-1983 (3.7)	5.1
w/Turbocharger add	1.3
Six-1983 (2.1)	3.8
w/P.S. add (.3)	.3
w/A.C. add (.2)	.2
(G) Cylinder Head, Renew	
Includes: Transfer all components, clean carbon. Reface valves, check valve spring tension, assembled height and valve head runout.	
Four-1983 (5.8)	7.5
w/Turbocharger add	1.3
Six-1983 (4.5)	6.2
w/P.S. add (.3)	.3
w/A.C. add (.2)	.2
(P) Clean Carbon and Grind Valves	
Includes: R&R cylinder heads, check valve spring tension, valve seat and head runout, stem to guide clearance and spring assembled height. Minor tune up.	
Four-1983 (6.3)	8.0
w/Turbocharger add	1.3
Six-1983 (4.8)	7.9

COMBINATIONS

Add to Valve Job

See Machine Shop Operations

(Factory Time)	Chilton Time
(G) DRAIN, EVACUATE & RECHARGE AIR CONDITIONING SYSTEM	
All models (.7)	1.2
(G) ROCKER ARMS & SHAFT ASSY., DISASSEMBLE AND CLEAN OR OVERHAUL	
Six (.5)	.8
V-6-one (.5)	.8
both (1.0)	1.4
(G) HYDRAULIC VALVE LIFTERS, DISASSEMBLE AND CLEAN	
Each	.2
(G) ROCKER ARM STUD, RENEW	
Each (.1)	.1
(G) DISTRIBUTOR, RECONDITION	
All models (.7)	1.0
(G) CARBURETOR, RECONDITION	
1983	
Four (1.1)	1.6
Six-Carter (1.3)	1.8
Holly (1.7)	2.2
(P) VALVE GUIDES, REAM OVERSIZE	
Each (.1)	.1

(Factory Time)	Chilton Time
w/P.S. add (.3)	.3
w/A.C. add (.2)	.2
(G) Valve Tappets, Adjust	
Four-1983 (1.0)	1.6
(G) Rocker Arm Cover or Gasket, Renew	
Four-1983 (.7)	1.0
w/Turbocharger add (.2)	.2
Six-1983 (.5)	.8
(G) Valve Tappets, Renew (Lifters)	
Includes: R&R intake manifold where required. Adjust carburetor and ignition timing.	
Four-1983 (1.3)	2.5
w/Turbocharger add (.2)	.2
Six-1983 (2.3)	*3.4
*If necessary to R&R head add (2.5)	3.8
(G) Valve Spring or Valve Stem Oil Seals, Renew (Head on Car)	
Four-1983-one (.9)	1.2
all (1.7)	2.3
Six-1983-one (.7)	1.1
all (1.9)	3.0
(G) Rocker Arm, Renew	
Four-1983-one (.8)	1.1
all (1.1)	1.5
(G) Valve Push Rod, Renew	
Six-1983-one (.7)	.9
all (.7)	1.4
(G) Rocker Arm Shaft Assy., Recondition	
Six-1983 (1.0)	1.6

PARTS 12 CYLINDER HEAD & VALVE SYSTEM 12 PARTS

	Part No.	Price
SIX 200 ENGINE		
Valve Grind Gasket		
1983	▲C9OZ-6079A	37.25
Cylinder Head Assy.		
1983		
wo/Valves	▲E0BZ-6049A	709.50
w/Valves	▲E0BZ-6049B	Disc.
Cylinder Head Gasket		
1983	▲E3BZ-6051A	N.L.
Valve Cover Gasket		
1983	▲E3BZ-6584A	7.50
Valve (Standard)		
1983-intake	▲D7BZ-6507A	8.50
exhaust	▲E1AZ-6505A	10.00
Valve Spring		
1983	▲C3DZ-6513A	2.50
Valve Key		
1983	▲C0DE-6518A	.75
Rocker Arm		
1983	▲C4DZ-6564A	8.75
Valve Push Rod		
1983	▲C4DZ-6565A	2.75
Valve Tappet		
1983	▲C8AZ-6500A	9.25
Rocker Arm Shaft		
1983	▲C3DZ-6563A	27.25

PARTS 12 CYLINDER HEAD & VALVE SYSTEM 12 PARTS

	Part No.	Price
FOUR 140 ENGINE		
Valve Grind Gasket Set		
1983	▲E5ZZ-6079A	42.00
(1) Cylinder Head (New)		
1983		
wo/Valves	▲E1BZ-6049C	351.75
w/Valves	▲E1BZ-6049B	521.25
(2) Cylinder Head Gasket		
1983	▲E5FZ-6051A	13.50
(3) Valve Cover Gasket		
1983	▲E2ZZ-6584A	1.00
(4) Exhaust Manifold		
1983		
w/Air pump	▲E3ZZ-9430H	96.00
w/Pulsed pump	▲E3ZZ-9430J	96.00
(5) Seal (Valve Stem)		
1983	▲D4FZ-6571A	1.25
(6) Valve Spring		
1983	▲D8FZ-6513A	4.25
(7) Rocker Arm		
1983	▲D8FZ-6564A	8.00
(8) Valve Tappet		
1983	▲D6FZ-6500A	10.00
(9) Intake Valve		
1983	▲D9ZZ-6507A	12.00
(10) Exhaust Valve		
1983	▲E43Z-6505A	14.25

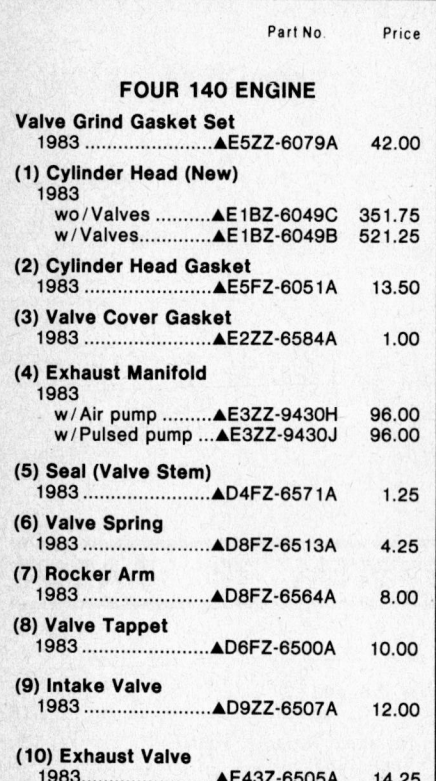

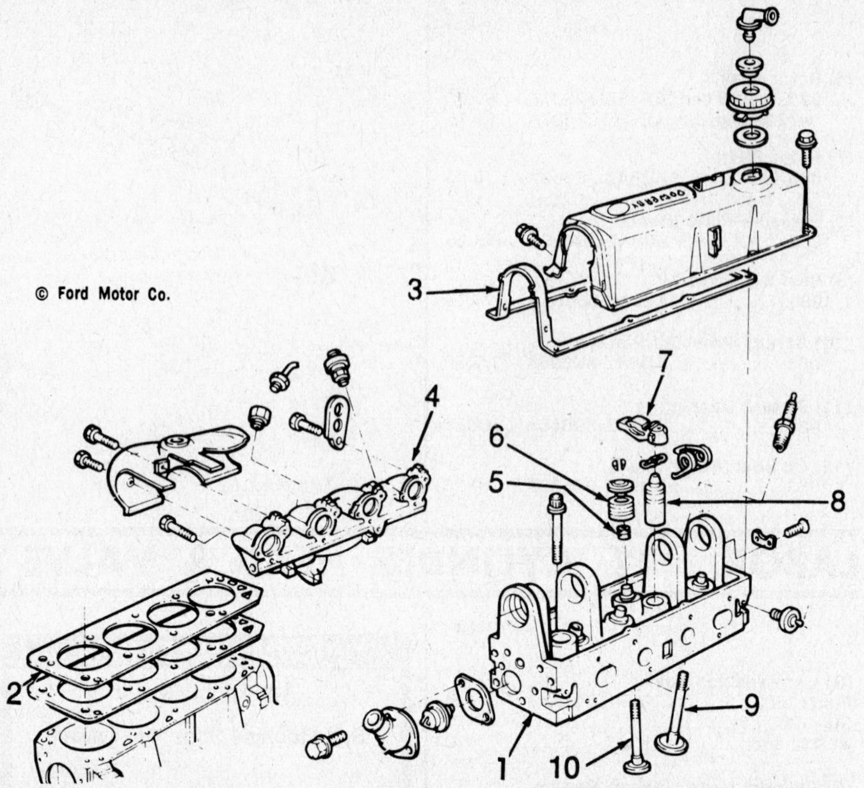

LABOR 13 ENGINE ASSEMBLY & MOUNTS 13 LABOR

(Factory Time)	Chilton Time
(G) Engine Assembly, Remove & Install	
Does not include transfer of any parts or equipment.	
Four–1983 (3.0)	4.9
Six–1983 (2.6)	4.2
w/P.S. add	.3
w/A.C. add	.7
(G) Engine Assembly, Replace with New or Rebuilt Unit (with Cyl. Heads)	
Includes: R&R engine assembly, transfer all necessary parts, fuel and electrical units. Minor tune up.	
Four–1983 (6.2)	9.0
Six–1983 (6.0)	9.9
w/P.S. add	.3
w/A.C. add	.7
(G) Cylinder Assembly, Renew (w/All Internal Parts Less Head(s) and Oil Pan)	
Includes: R&R engine, transfer all component parts not supplied with replacement engine, clean carbon, grind valves. Minor tune up.	
Four–1983 (10.5)	15.0
Six–1983 (10.9)	15.4
w/P.S. add	.3
w/A.C. add	.7
Clean oil pump add (.3)	.3
(P) Cylinder Block, Renew	
Includes: R&R engine, transfer all component parts, renew rings and bearings, clean carbon, grind valves. Minor tune up.	
Four–1983 (14.0)	19.6
Six–1983 (14.9)	20.8
w/P.S. add	.3
w/A.C. add	.7
Clean oil pump add (.3)	.3
(P) Engine Assy., R&R and Recondition (Complete)	
Includes: Rebore block, install new pistons, rings, rod and main bearings. Clean carbon, grind valves. Tune engine.	
Four–1983 (23.1)	28.3
Six–1983 (25.7)	30.1
w/P.S. add	.3
w/A.C. add	.7
(P) Engine Assembly, Recondition (In Car)	
Includes: Expand or renew pistons, install new rings, pins, rod and main bearings. Clean carbon and grind valves. Tune engine.	
Four–1983 (16.7)	19.5
Six–1983 (17.8)	22.5
w/P.S. add	.3
w/A.C. add	.7
(G) Engine Mounts, Renew	
Front	
Four–1983–one (.6)	1.0
both (1.0)	1.4
Six–1983–one (.4)	.6
both (.6)	.9
Rear	
1983 (.6)	.9

PARTS 13 ENGINE ASSEMBLY & MOUNTS 13 PARTS

	Part No.	Price
Cylinder Block (New)		
Four–140 engine		
1983		
before 11-15-82	▲E3ZZ-6010A	671.75
from 11-15-82	▲E3ZZ-6010A	671.75
Six–200 engine		
1983		
C3 trans.	▲E1BZ-6010B	724.25
C5 trans.	▲E2BZ-6010A	674.00
Cylinder Assy.		
Four–140 engine		
1983	▲E2ZZ-6009A	1506.00
Six–200 engine		
1983		
C3 trans.	▲E1DZ-6009A	1609.50
C5 trans.	▲E3BZ-6009A	1609.50
Engine Overhaul Gasket Set		
Four–140 engine		
1983	▲E2PZ-6E078A	25.50

PARTS 13 ENGINE ASSEMBLY & MOUNTS 13 PARTS

	Part No.	Price
Six-200 engine		
1983	▲D5PZ-6E078H	27.50

Note: When a complete overhaul gasket set is required on a V-8 engine you must also order a valve grind gasket set.

	Part No.	Price
Cylinder Cover Assembly		
Four-140 engine		
1983-upper	▲D4FZ-6019B	22.75
lower	▲E3TZ-6019A	45.25
1983-outer	▲E3ZZ-6019A	38.50
inner	▲E3ZZ-6019B	43.00
Six-200 engine		
1983	▲D7DZ-6019A	34.25
Engine Mount (Front)		
1983 (w/140 eng.)		
right	▲E3DZ-6038D	29.75
(left hand)		
exc. below	▲E3DZ-6038E	24.50
floorshift	▲E3DZ-6038F	30.50
1983-w/200 eng.	▲E1BZ-6038A	19.00
Engine Mount (Rear)		
1983		
140 eng.	▲E3ZZ-6068A	20.75
200 eng.	▲E2SZ-6068B	22.50

LABOR 14 PISTONS, RINGS & BEARINGS 14 LABOR

(Factory Time)	Chilton Time
(P) Rings, Renew (See Engine Combinations)	
Includes: Remove cylinder top ridge, deglaze cylinder walls, replace rod bearings, clean carbon. Minor tune up.	
Four-1983 (7.1)	9.6
w/Turbocharger add	.7
Six-1983 (6.4)	8.9
w/P.S. add	.3
w/A.C. add	.4
Clean or renew spark plugs add	.3
(P) Piston or Connecting Rod, Renew (One)	
Includes: Remove cylinder top ridge, deglaze cylinder walls, replace rod bearings, clean carbon. Minor tune up.	
Four-1983 (6.1)	8.3
w/Turbocharger add	.7
Six-1983 (4.3)	7.1
w/P.S. add	.3
w/A.C. add	.4
Clean or renew spark plugs add	.3
(P) Connecting Rod Bearings, Renew	
Four-1983 (2.8)	3.8
Six-1983 (3.2)	4.5

COMBINATIONS

Add to Engine Work

See Machine Shop Operations

(Factory Time)	Chilton Time
(G) DRAIN, EVACUATE & RECHARGE AIR CONDITIONING SYSTEM	
All models (.7)	1.2
(G) ROCKER ARMS, RENEW OR DISASSEMBLE AND CLEAN	
Each (.1)	.1
(G) HYDRAULIC VALVE LIFTERS, DISASSEMBLE AND CLEAN	
Each	.2
(G) ROCKER ARM STUD, RENEW	
(G) DISTRIBUTOR, RECONDITION	
All models (.7)	1.0
(G) CARBURETOR, RECONDITION	
1983	
Four-(1.1)	1.6
Six-Carter (1.3)	1.8
Holly (1.7)	2.2
(G) DEGLAZE CYLINDER WALLS	
Each (.1)	.1
(G) REMOVE CYLINDER TOP RIDGE	
Each (.1)	.1
(G) TIMING CHAIN OR GEARS, RENEW (COVER REMOVED)	
All models (.3)	.5
(G) MAIN BEARINGS, RENEW (PAN REMOVED)	
Four(1.9)	2.5
Six(2.7)	3.4
(G) PLASTIGAUGE BEARINGS	
Each (.1)	.1
(G) OIL PUMP, RECONDITION	
All models (.3)	.6
(M) OIL FILTER ELEMENT, RENEW	
All models (.3)	.3

PARTS 14 PISTONS, RINGS & BEARINGS 14 PARTS

	Part No.	Price
(1) Piston Ring Set		
Four-140 engine		
1983-exc. below	▲D4FZ-6148A	31.75
w/Turbo.	▲D9ZZ-6148A	29.25
Six-200 engine		
1983	▲C3OZ-6148E	32.75
(2) Piston Pin (Std.)		
1983	▲B2AZ-6135A	5.25

Note: With some engines pin is included with piston assembly.

	Part No.	Price
(3) Connecting Rod Assy.		
Four-140 engine		
1983	▲D7FZ-6200A	47.00
Six-200 engine		
1983	▲D8BZ-6200A	41.75
(4) Connecting Rod Bearings		
Four-140 engine		
1983	▲D7FZ-6211A	2.50
Six-200 engine		
1983	▲D7BZ-6211A	2.75

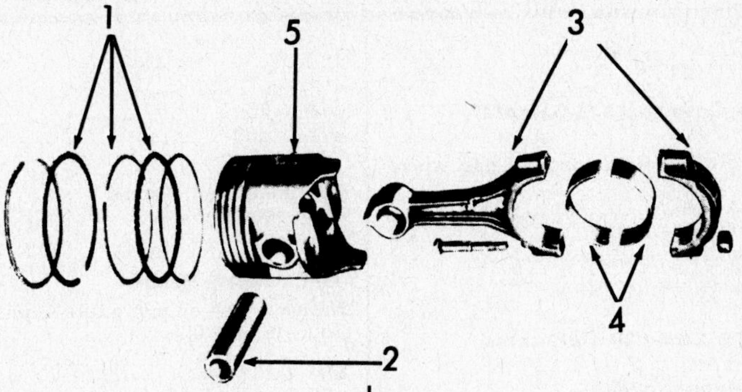

	Part No.	Price
(5) Piston Assy.		
Four-140 engine		
1983	▲D4FZ-6108A	21.75
Six-200 engine		
1983	▲C9DZ-6108A	25.75

LABOR 15 CRANKSHAFT & DAMPER 15 LABOR

(Factory Time)	Chilton Time
(P) Crankshaft and Main Bearings, Renew	
Includes: R&R engine, check all bearing clearances.	
Four-1983 (6.8)	9.7
Six-1983 (6.4)	8.9
w/P.S. add	.3
w/A.C. add	.7
w/M.T. add	.2
(P) Main Bearings, Renew	
Includes: Check all bearing clearances.	
Four-1983 (3.8)	4.9

LABOR 15 CRANKSHAFT & DAMPER 15 LABOR

(Factory Time)	Chilton Time
Six–1983 (4.5)	5.8
w/P.S. add	.3
w/A.C. add	.7

(P) Main and Rod Bearings, Renew
Includes: Check all bearing clearances.

(Factory Time)	Chilton Time
Four–1983 (4.7)	6.1
Six–1983 (5.9)	7.6
w/P.S. add	.3
w/A.C. add	.7

(G) Rear Main Bearing Oil Seals, Renew (Upper & Lower)
Includes: R&R oil pan on 4, 6, and 8 cylinder engines. R&R of transmission on V-6 engines.

(Factory Time)	Chilton Time
Four–1983 (2.7)	3.6
Six–1983 (2.6)	3.7

(G) Vibration Damper or Pulley, Renew

(Factory Time)	Chilton Time
Four–1983 (1.0)	1.4
Six–1983 (.5)	.8

(G) Crankshaft Front Oil Seal, Renew

(Factory Time)	Chilton Time
Four–1983 (1.3)	*1.8
Six–1983 (1.6)	1.9
w/P.S. add	.2
w/A.C. add	.2

*R&R front cover not required.

PARTS 15 CRANKSHAFT & DAMPER 15 PARTS

	Part No.	Price
(1) Crankshaft (New)		
Four–140 engine		
1983	▲E2ZZ-6303A	387.00
Six–200 engine		
1983-exc. below	▲E1BZ-6303A	476.50
w/PEN trans.	▲E1BZ-6303B	476.50
(2) Main Bearings		
Four–140 engine		
1983 (upper)		
exc. below	▲D4FZ-6333A	3.75
center	▲D4FZ-6337A	9.75
(lower)		
exc. below	▲D4FZ-6333A	3.75
center	▲D4FZ-6337G	9.75
Six–200 engine		
1983 (upper)		
exc. below	▲D5DZ-6333A	4.75
No. 5	▲D5DZ-6337A	7.25
(lower) exc. below	▲D5DZ-6333B	4.75
No. 5	▲D5DZ-6337B	7.25
(3) Main Bearing Oil Seal (Rear)		
Four–140 engine		
1983	▲E2ZZ-6701A	6.00

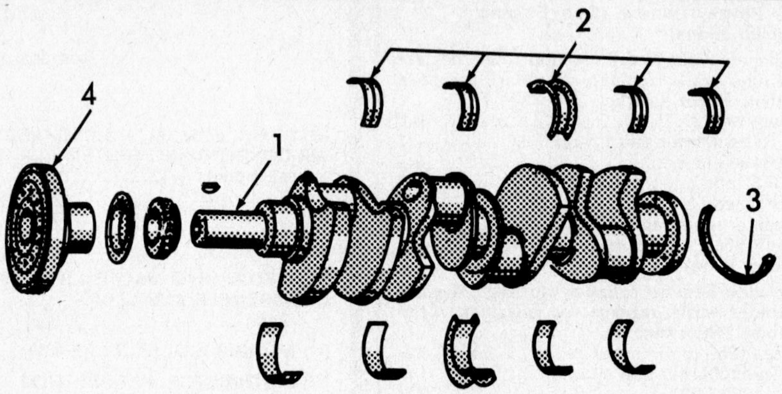

	Part No	Price
Six–200 engine		
1983-exc. below	▲C9AZ-6701B	8.00
rope type	▲C9OZ-6701A	2.00

	Part No	Price
(4) Crankshaft Pulley		
Four–140 engine		
1983-wo/A.C.	▲E2BZ-6A312A	51.50
w/A.C.	▲E2BZ-6A312B	51.50
Six–200 engine		
1983	▲D8BZ-6A312A	33.50

LABOR 16 CAMSHAFT & TIMING GEARS 16 LABOR

(G) Timing Case Seal and Gaskets, Renew
Includes: R&R radiator and oil pan where required.

(Factory Time)	Chilton Time
Four–1983 (1.6)	2.1
Six–1983 (1.3)	1.8
w/P.S. add	.2
w/A.C. add	.3

(G) Timing Chain or Sprockets, Renew
Includes: Adjust timing.

(Factory Time)	Chilton Time
Six–1983 (1.6)	2.4
w/P.S. add	.2
w/A.C. add	.3

(G) Timing Belt, Renew

(Factory Time)	Chilton Time
Four–1983 (1.5)	2.0

(G) Camshaft, Renew
Includes: R&R oil pan where required.

(Factory Time)	Chilton Time
Four–1983 (2.9)	4.1
Six–1983 (4.4)	6.1
w/P.S. add	.2
w/A.C. add	.4

(P) Camshaft Bearings, Renew
Includes: R&R engine and crankshaft, where required.

(Factory Time)	Chilton Time
Four–1983 (3.4)	5.5
Six–1983 (6.6)	9.9

(G) Camshaft Rear Welsh Plug, Renew
Includes: R&R trans and flywheel for accessibility.

(Factory Time)	Chilton Time
w/Std trans	
Four–1983 (2.3)	3.1
Six–1983 (2.3)	3.1
w/Auto trans	
Four–1983 (3.3)	4.2
Six–1983 (2.9)	3.8

PARTS 16 CAMSHAFT & TIMING GEARS 16 PARTS

	Part No.	Price
FOUR 140 ENGINE		
(1) Cylinder Cover Assy. (Front)		
1983-upper	▲D4FZ-6019B	22.75
(2) Crankshaft Sprocket		
1983	▲D9FZ-6306A	11.50
(3) Camshaft Sprocket		
1983	▲D4FZ-6256A	13.75
(4) Belt (Timing)		
1983	▲E5ZZ-6268A	21.50
(5) Camshaft Gear		
1983	▲D4FZ-6256A	13.75
(6) Cover Gasket (Front)		
1983-outer	▲D4FZ-6020A	2.25
(7) Guide (Timing Belt)		
1983	▲D4FZ-6B260A	4.75
(8) Oil Seal (Front Cover)		
1983	▲D4FZ-6700A	5.75

PARTS 16 CAMSHAFT & TIMING GEARS 16 PARTS

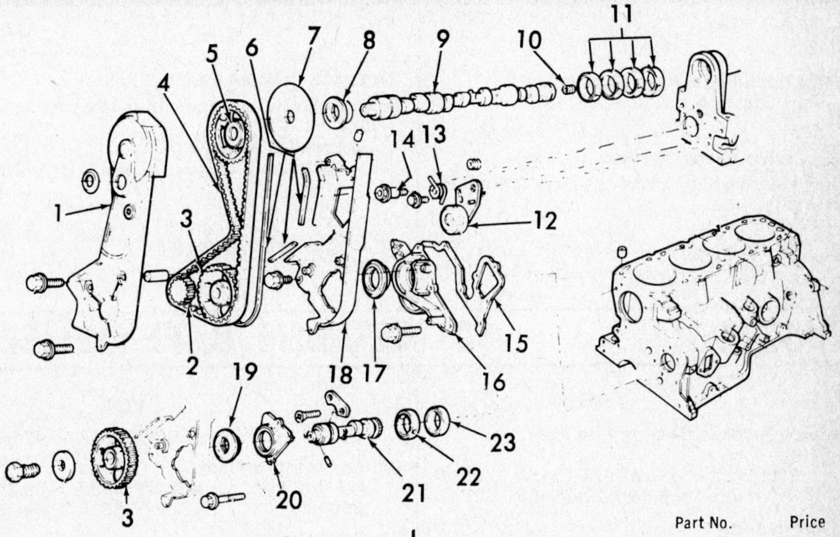

	Part No.	Price
(9) Camshaft		
1983	▲E1ZZ-6250A	158.75
(10) Plug		
1983	▲87837S	1.75
(11) Camshaft Bearings		
1983	▲D4FZ-6261C	3.25
(12) Tensioner (Pulley Assy.)		
1983	▲D4FZ-6K254A	23.00
(13) Spring (Tensioner)		
1983	▲D4FZ-6L273A	7.50
(14) Bolt (Tensioner)		
1983	▲D7FZ-6K282A	4.25
(15) Cover Gasket (Inner)		
1983	▲D4FZ-6020B	1.50
(16) Front Cover (Lower)		
1983	▲E3TZ-6019A	45.25
(17) Oil Seal (Front Cover)		
1983	▲D4FZ-6700A	5.75
(18) Front Cover (Inner)		
1983	▲E3ZZ-6019B	43.00
(19) Oil Seal (Front Cover)		
1983	▲D4FZ-6700A	5.75
(20) Front Cover (Upper)		
1983	▲D4FZ-6019B	22.75
(21) Drive Shaft (Dist., Fuel & Oil Pump)		
1983	▲E4FZ-6A739A	63.25
(22) Auxiliary Shaft Bearing (Front)		
1983	▲D4FZ-6A753A	5.00
(23) Auxiliary Shaft Bearing (Rear)		
1983	▲D4FZ-6A738A	5.00

PARTS 16 CAMSHAFT & TIMING GEARS 16 PARTS

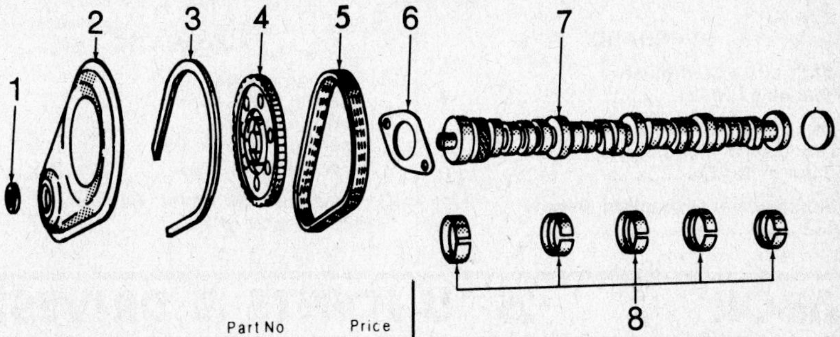

SIX & 200 ENGINE

	Part No.	Price
(1) Timing Cover Oil Seal		
1983-200 eng	▲C0DE-6700A	4.25
(2) Timing Cover		
1983-200 eng	▲D7DZ-6019A	34.25
(3) Timing Cover Gasket		
1983-200 eng	▲C0DE-6020B	1.75
(4) Camshaft Gear		
1983-200 eng	▲D8BZ-6256B	13.75
(5) Timing Chain		
1983-200 eng	▲C0DZ-6268A	14.00
(6) Thrust Plate		
1983-200 eng	▲C0DE-6269A	5.00
(7) Camshaft		
1983-200 eng	▲D5DZ-6250B	123.00
(8) Camshaft Bearings		
1983-200 eng		
front	▲E3BZ-6261A	11.50
front inter	▲D9BZ-6267A	7.25
rear inter	▲D9BZ-6270A	12.25
rear	▲D9BZ-6263A	6.25
Crankshaft Gear		
1983-200 eng	▲C0DZ-6306A	10.25

LABOR 17 ENGINE OILING SYSTEM 17 LABOR

(Factory Time)	Chilton Time
(G) Oil Pan or Gasket, Renew	
Four–1983 (1.9)	2.4
Six–1983 (1.8)	2.3
(P) Pressure Test Engine Bearings (Pan Off)	
All models	1.0
(G) Oil Pump, Renew	
Four–1983 (2.0)	2.6
Six–1983 (1.9)	2.5
(G) Oil Pump, R&R and Recondition	
Four–1983 (2.3)	3.0
Six–1983 (2.2)	2.9
(G) Oil Pressure Gauge (Engine), Renew	
1983 (.3)	.4
(G) Oil Pressure Gauge (Dash), Renew	
1983 (.4)	.7
(M) Oil Filter Element, Renew	
1983 (.3)	.3

PARTS 17 ENGINE OILING SYSTEM 17 PARTS

	Part No.	Price
Oil Pan Gasket Set		
1983-200 eng	▲D0DZ-6781A	10.75
1983-140 eng	▲E2ZZ-6781A	10.75
Oil Pump Assy. (New)		
1983-200 eng	▲C5DZ-6600A	54.50
1983-140 eng		
wo/Turbo	▲D5FZ-6600A	66.00
w/Turbo	▲D9ZZ-6600A	58.00
Oil Pressure Gauge (Engine Unit)		
1983-All	▲D4AZ-9278A	3.50
Oil Filter Assy.		
1983	▲D9AZ-6731A	8.00

LABOR 18 CLUTCH & FLYWHEEL 18 LABOR

	(Factory Time)	Chilton Time
(M) Clutch Pedal Free Play, Adjust		
All models	(.4)	.5
(G) Clutch Assembly, Renew		
Includes: R&R flywheel housing and adjust free play.		
1983		
3 speed	(2.1)	3.0
4 speed	(2.7)	3.6
(G) Clutch Release Bearing, Renew		
Includes: R&R trans and adjust free play.		
1983		
3 speed	(1.3)	2.1
4 speed	(1.8)	2.6
(G) Clutch Cable, Renew		
1983	(.5)	.8
(G) Flywheel, Renew		
Includes: R&R starter and flywheel housing.		
1983		
3 speed	(2.5)	3.4
4 speed	(3.0)	4.0
A.T.	(3.3)	4.9
(G) Flywheel Housing, Renew		
1983		
3 speed	(2.7)	3.6
4 speed	(3.2)	4.2

PARTS 18 CLUTCH & FLYWHEEL 18 PARTS

	Part No.	Price
Clutch Release Bearing Hub Assy.		
1983		
200 eng.	▲D9ZZ-7548A	29.50
140 eng.	▲D9ZZ-7548B	37.75
Pilot Bearing		
1983-200 eng	▲D4DZ-7600A	12.75
140 eng.	▲D4ZZ-7600A	5.25
Clutch Disc		
1983-140 eng.	▲D8BZ-7550B	44.00
200 eng.	▲D9BZ-7550A	42.50
Clutch Pressure Plate		
1983-140 eng.	▲D8BZ-7563B	58.75
200 eng.	▲D8BZ-7563A	69.75
Flywheel Housing		
1983-140 eng.	▲E0BZ-6392A	108.75
200 eng.		
exc. below	▲E1ZZ-6392A	107.00
w/overdrive	▲D9BZ-6392B	107.00
Release Lever Assy.		
1983	▲D9ZZ-7515C	12.75
Cable Assy.		
1983	▲E2DZ-7K553A	37.50
Flywheel Assy.		
1983-140 eng.	▲E2ZZ-6375C	185.75
Flywheel Ring Gear		
1983-140 eng	▲D4FZ-6384A	34.25

LABOR 21 SHIFT LINKAGE 21 LABOR

	(Factory Time)	Chilton Time
STANDARD		
(G) Shift Linkage, Adjust		
All models	(.3)	.4
(G) Gear Selector Lever, Renew		
1983-column shift	(.3)	.4
floor shift	(.7)	1.0
(G) Shift Rods or Grommets, Renew		
1983		.5
AUTOMATIC		
(G) Linkage, Adjust		
manual	(.3)	.4
throttle	(.3)	.5
manual & throttle	(.5)	.7
kickdown	(.3)	.5
(G) Gear Selector Lever, Renew		
1983-console	(.6)	1.1
floor	(.7)	1.2
column	(.3)	.4
(G) Gearshift Tube Assembly, Renew		
Includes: Adjust neutral switch when required.		
1983	(.9)	1.5
(G) Tilt Wheel Pivot, Recondition (In Chassis)		
1983	(.6)	1.0

LABOR 25 U-JOINTS & DRIVESHAFT 25 LABOR

	(Factory Time)	Chilton Time
(G) Universal Joints, Renew or Recondition		
Includes: R&R drive shaft.		
1983		
front	(.8)	1.1
rear	(.7)	1.1
both	(1.1)	1.7
(G) Driveshaft, Renew		
1983	(.3)	.5

PARTS 25 UNIVERSAL JOINTS & DRIVE SHAFT 25 PARTS

	Part No.	Price
Universal Joint		
1983	▲C3AZ-4635E	15.25

LABOR 26 REAR AXLE 26 LABOR

	(Factory Time)	Chilton Time
INTEGRAL TYPE		
(M) Differential, Drain & Refill		
All models		.6
(M) Axle Housing Cover or Gasket, Renew		
All models	(.4)	.6
(G) Axle Shaft Inner Oil Seal, Renew		
Includes: R&R wheel, drum and axle shaft.		
1983-one	(.6)	.9
both	(.8)	1.3
(G) Axle Shaft, Renew		
Includes: Renew inner oil seal.		
1983-one	(.4)	.6
both	(.6)	1.0

LABOR — 26 REAR AXLE 26 — LABOR

(Factory Time) — Chilton Time

(G) Rear Wheel Bearings, Renew
Includes: Renew inner oil seal.
1983-one (.7) 9
both (.9) 1.3

(G) Axle Shaft Wheel Mounting Studs, Renew
All models-one 8
all 1.2

(G) Pinion Shaft Oil Seal, Renew
1983 (.9) 1.3

(G) Axle Housing and Differential Assy., Remove and Reinstall (Complete)
Includes: Drain and refill axle, remove wheel and hubs, axle shafts, replace inner oil seals. Remove backing plates without disconnecting brake lines. Road test.
1983
6.75 axle (1.6) 3.8
7.5 axle (1.7) 3.8

(P) Differential Carrier Assy., Recondition (In Chassis)
Includes: Drain and refill axle, renew necessary parts. Renew axle shaft oil seals. Road test.
1983 (2.9) 5.0

(P) Axle Housing, Renew
Includes: Transfer all necessary parts, adjust ring gear and pinion.
Does not include disassembly of differential case.
1983 (3.5) 4.9
Recond diff assy. add (.4) 8

(P) Pinion Shaft Bearings, Renew
1983 .... 4.1

(P) Carrier Bearings, Renew
1983 .... 3.6

(P) Ring and Pinion Set, Renew
Includes: R&R axle shafts, drain and refill unit. Road test.
1983 (2.6) 3.8

(P) Ring and Pinion, Adjust (In Chassis)
Includes: Remove axle shafts, drain and refill unit. Road test.
1983 (1.6) 2.4

PARTS — 26 REAR AXLE 26 — PARTS

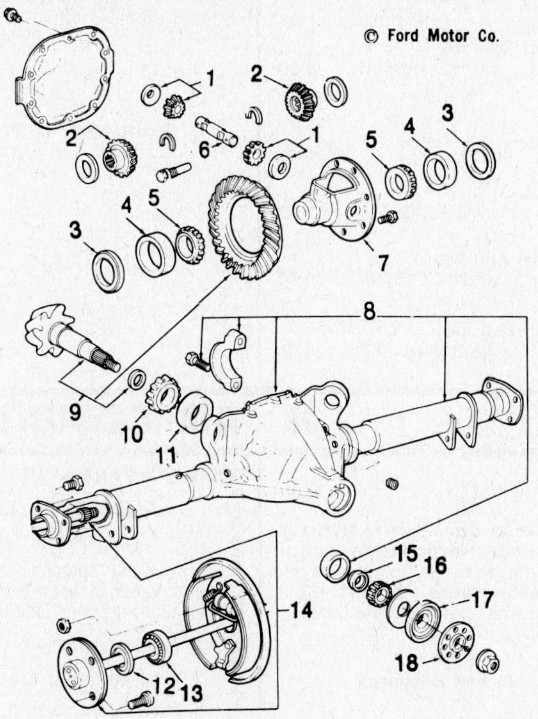

© Ford Motor Co.

	Part No.	Price
(1) Pinion Kit		
1983		
w/7.5″ R/Gear	▲E4DZ-4215A	20.00
w/6¾″ R/Gear	▲E0BZ-4215A	21.00
(2) Side Gear		
1983		
w/6¾″ R/Gear	▲D9BZ-4236A	43.25
w/7.5″ R/Gear	▲D9AZ-4236A	40.00
(3) Shim		
1983		
w/6¾″ R/Gear	▲D8BZ-4067BS	3.25
w/7.5″ R/Gear	▲D8BZ-4067AH	3.25
(4) Bearing Cup		
1983	▲C6TZ-4222A	6.00
(5) Bearing Assy.		
1983	▲B7A-4221A	11.50
(6) Pinion Shaft		
1983		
w/7.5″ R/Gear	▲D8BZ-4211A	13.75
1983-(w/6¾″ R/Gear)		
exc. below	▲E1FZ-4211A	13.75
WGG-E axle	▲D9BZ-4211A	31.50
(7) Case Assy.		
1983		
w/6¾″ R/Gear	▲D9BZ-4204A	92.00
w/7.5″ R/Gear	▲D9AZ-4204A	104.50
(8) Housing Assy.		
1983		
w/6¾″ R/Gear	▲D9BZ-4010C	505.00
w/7.5″ R/Gear	▲E2BZ-4010A	457.75
(9) Ring Gear & Pinion Kit		
1983 (w/7.5″ ring gear)		
2.26 to 1	▲E0AZ-4209A	352.50
2.47 to 1	▲D8BZ-4209C	352.50
2.73 to 1	▲D8BZ-4209A	328.00
3.08 to 1	▲E25Y-4209A	352.50
3.45 to 1	▲E25Y-4209B	401.25
(10) Pinion Bearing (Rear)		
1983		
w/6¾″ R/Gear	▲D9BZ-4630A	15.25
w/7.5″ R/Gear	▲C7AZ-4630A	15.75
(11) Bearing Cup (Rear)		
1983		
w/6¾″ R/Gear	▲C0DW-4628A	7.50
w/7.5″ R/Gear	▲C7AZ-4628A	8.00
(12) Axle Shaft Oil Seal		
1983		
w/6¾″ R/Gear	▲D9BZ-1177B	4.25
w/7.5″ R/Gear	▲E1AZ-1177B	3.50
(13) Axle Shaft Bearing		
1983		
w/6¾″ R/Gear	▲D8DZ-1225B	41.75
w/7.5″ R/Gear	▲C7AZ-1225A	15.75
(14) Axle Shaft Assy. (Rear)		
1983		
w/7.5″ R/Gear	▲D9BZ-4234C	80.00
(15) Spacer		
1983		
w/6¾″ R/Gear	▲D9BZ-4662A	4.00
w/7.5″ R/Gear	▲B7A-4662A	4.00
(16) Pinion Bearing (Front)		
1983		
w/6¾″ R/Gear	▲C0DW-4628A	7.50
w/7.5″ R/Gear	▲C7AZ-4628A	8.00
(17) Pinion Oil Seal		
1983		
w/6¾″ R/Gear	▲D9BZ-4676A	5.75
w/7.5″ R/Gear	▲E3TZ-4676A	11.25
(18) Flange Assy. (U-Joint)		
1983		
w/7.5″ R/Gear	▲D8BZ-4851A	17.00
w/6¾″ R/Gear	▲D9BZ-4851A	16.50
Traction Lok Assy.		
1983		
w/7.5″ R/Gear	▲E3TZ-4026B	386.25

LABOR 27 REAR SUSPENSION 27 LABOR

(Factory Time) Chilton Time

(G) Rear Spring, Renew
1983 (.4) 6

(G) Rear Spring Rubber Bumper, Renew
1983-one 4

(G) Rear Shock Absorber or Rubber Bushing, Renew
1983-one (.3) 5
both (.4) 8

(G) Rear Suspension Upper Arm, Renew
1983
one (.4) 7
both (.6) 1.0

(G) Rear Suspension Lower Arm, Renew
1983-wo/Stabilizer-one (.6) 1.1
both (.9) 1.5
w/Stabilizer-one (.7) 1.2
both (1.1) 1.7

(G) Rear Stabilizer Bar, Renew
1983 (.3) 5

PARTS 27 REAR SUSPENSION 27 PARTS

	Part No.	Price
(1) Upper Control Arm Assy.		
1983		
wo/Stabilizer	▲D9BZ-5500A	37.00
w/Stabilizer	▲D9BZ-5500B	37.00
(2) Insulator (Upper)		
1983	▲D9BZ-5536A	3.00
(3) Damper (Rear Spring)		
1983	▲D8BZ-5A669C	8.50
(4) Coil Spring		
Order by model and description.		
(5) Insulator (Lower)		
1983	▲D8BZ-5536A	3.00
(6) Lower Control Arm Assy.		
1983	▲D9BZ-5A649A	66.00
(7) Shock Absorber (Rear)		
1983	▲E2DZ-18125C	29.00

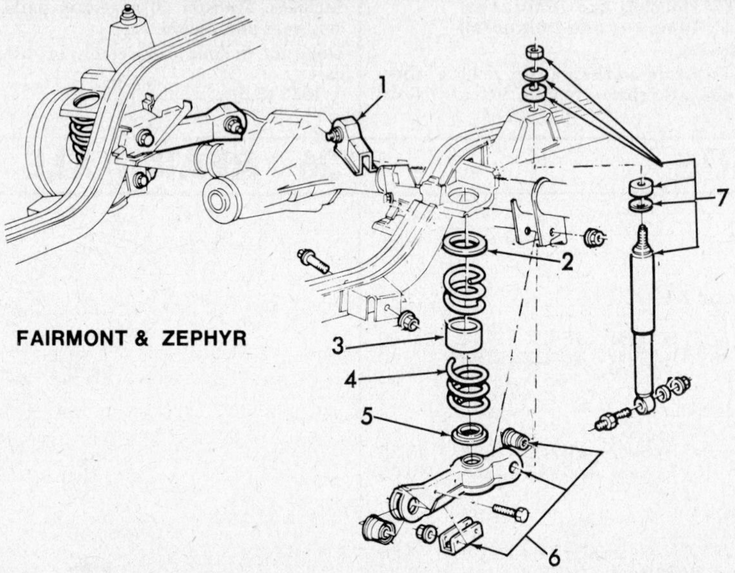

LABOR 28 AIR CONDITIONING 28 LABOR

(Factory Time) Chilton Time

Note: If more than one item requires replacement where evacuation and discharging the system is already included in the operation, deduct 1.0 hour for each additional item to the times listed.

(G) Drain, Evacuate and Recharge System
Includes: Check for leaks.
All models (.7) 1.2

(G) Pressure Test System
All models 6

(G) Compressor Belt, Renew
All models (.3) 6

(G) Compressor Assembly, Renew
Includes: Evacuate and charge system.
1983 (1.5) 2.2

(G) Compressor Shaft Seal Kit, Renew
Includes: R&R compressor when required. Evacuate and charge system.
1983 (1.0) 1.9

(G) Compressor Clutch and Pulley, Renew
Includes: R&R compressor when required. Evacuate and charge system.
1983 (.3) 6

AIR CONDITIONER TUNE-UP

For efficient operation and satisfactory performance in hot weather. The following air conditioner tune-up is suggested:

1. Clean intake filter
2. Clean condenser fins
3. Pressure test system
4. Adjust drive belt tension
5. Check antifreeze/coolant
6. Tighten compressor mounts
7. Tighten condenser and evaporator mounts
8. Inspect system for leaks (hoses, couplings, valves, etc.)
9. Partial charge system

All models 1.0
If necessary to evacuate and charge system, add 1.0

(Factory Time) Chilton Time

(P) Compressor Valve Plate Kit, Renew (On Car)
Includes: Evacuate and charge system.
1983-Two cyl comp (1.3) 1.9
Six cyl comp (1.9) 2.5

(G) Compressor Service Valve or Gasket, Renew
Includes: Evacuate and charge system.
1983 (.9) 1.3

(G) Condenser Assembly, Renew
Includes: Evacuate and charge system.
1983 (1.3) 2.4

(G) Evaporator Core, Renew
Includes: Renew or transfer valve. Evacuate and charge system.
1983 (2.6) 4.0

(G) Evaporator Thermostatic Switch, Renew
1983 (.3) 5

(G) A.C. Clutch Cycling Pressure Switch, Renew
1983 (.2) 4

(G) Accumulator Assy., Renew
Includes: Evacuate and charge system.
1983 (.9) 1.4

(G) Orifice Valve, Renew
Includes: Evacuate and charge system.
1983 (1.0) 1.5

(G) Door Vacuum Motor, Renew
1983
Restrictor door (1.4) 2.5
Heat defrost door (1.3) 2.2

LABOR 28 AIR CONDITIONING 28 LABOR

	(Factory Time)	Chilton Time
(G) Temperature Control Cable, Renew		
1983	(.4)	.7
(G) Blower Motor, Renew		
1983	(.4)	.8
(G) Blower Motor Switch, Renew		
1983	(.3)	.5
(G) Blower Motor Resistor, Renew		
1983	(.3)	.5
(G) Air Conditioning Hoses, Renew		
Includes: Evacuate and charge system.		
1983-one	(1.2)	1.7
each adtnl	(.3)	.5

PARTS 28 AIR CONDITIONING 28 PARTS

	Part No.	Price
Compressor Drive Belt		
Order by model & description.		
Compressor Assembly		
1983		
FS-6 comp.	▲E4VY-19703A	315.00
York comp.	▲D4FZ-19703B	322.25
Compressor Shaft Seal		
1983	▲C9AZ-19655B	18.25
Compressor Clutch Brush Assy.		
1983	▲C8SZ-2979A	24.50
Compressor Clutch (Complete)		
1983		
FS-6 comp.	▲E3DZ-2884A	71.50
York comp	▲E3SZ-2884A	47.00
Compressor Clutch Pulley Bearing		
1983	▲C9AZ-2990A	27.25
Compressor Service Valve		
1983	▲D0AZ-19752A	15.25
Compressor Valve Plate Kit		
1983		
exc below	▲C3GY-19656A	26.25
York comp	▲D5AZ-19656A	23.25
Compressor Gasket Set		
1983		
exc below	▲C3GY-19B684A	9.00
York comp	▲C8AZ-19B684A	10.75
Condenser Assy.		
1983	▲E25Y-19712A	180.75
Evaporator Core		
1983	▲E25Y-19860A	139.50
Blower Motor		
1983		
before 9-6-82	▲E0SZ-19805A	82.00
from 9-6-82	▲E3SY-19805A	90.50
Blower Motor Switch		
1983	▲E1FZ-19986A	10.00

LABOR 29 LOCKS, HINGES & WIND. REGULATORS 29 LABOR

	(Factory Time)	Chilton Time
(G) Hood Release Cable, Renew		
1983	(.3)	.6
(G) Hood Lock, Renew		
1983	(.3)	.5
(G) Hood Hinge, Renew		
Includes: Adjust hood and latch.		
1983	(.3)	.6
(G) Door Latch, Renew		
Includes: R&R trim panel and weathersheet.		
1983	(.5)	.8
(G) Door Lock Remote Control, Renew		
Includes: R&R trim panel and weathersheet.		
1983	(.4)	.7
(G) Door Handle (Outside), Renew (Front or Rear)		
Includes: R&R trim panel and weathersheet.		
1983	(.5)	.8
(G) Lock Striker Plate, Renew		
1983	(.2)	.3
(G) Door Window Regulator (Manual), Renew (Front or Rear)		
Includes: R&R trim panel and weathersheet.		
1983	(.5)	.9
(G) Door Window Regulator (Electric), Renew (Front or Rear)		
1983	(.6)	1.0
(G) Trunk Hinge Assembly, Renew (One)		
1983	(.6)	.8
(G) Tail Gate Latch, Renew		
1983	(.4)	.6
(G) Tail Gate Hinge, Renew		
1983-one	(.6)	1.0
both	(.7)	1.2

PARTS 29 LOCKS, HINGES & WIND. REGULATORS 29 PARTS

	Part No.	Price
Hood Latch		
1983	▲E4DZ-16700A	14.75
Hood Hinge		
1983	▲E0SZ-16796A	13.25
Door Lock		
(front door)		
1983 (before 11-1-82)		
right	▲E3BZ-3621812A	30.50
left	▲E3BZ-3621812A	30.50
1983 (from 11-1-82)		
right	▲E3BZ-3621812A	30.50
left	▲E3BZ-3621813A	30.50
Lock Cylinder & Key (Front Door)		
1983	▲E1DZ-5421984C	10.75
Outer Door Handle		
1983-right	▲D8BZ-5422404A	25.00
left	▲D8BZ-5422405A	25.00
Door Hinge (Front)		
1983-upper	▲E3BZ-3622800A	25.75
lower	▲E1DZ-5422811A	32.25
Front Door Window Regulator		
1983		
(2 door) right	▲E2BZ-3623200A	54.50
left	▲E2BZ-3623201A	54.50
(4 door) right	▲E2BZ-5423200A	54.50
left	▲E2BZ-5423201A	54.50
Trunk Lid Lock		
1983-wo/Power	▲D9ZZ-6643200A	22.00
w/Power	▲D9BZ-5443200A	57.50
Trunk Lid Lock Cylinder & Key		
1983	▲D6ZZ-6943505A	10.75
Trunk Lid Hinge		
1983-right	▲D8BZ-5442700A	26.00
left	▲D8BZ-5442701A	26.00

LABOR 30 HEAD AND PARKING LAMPS 30 LABOR

	(Factory Time)	Chilton Time
(G) Aim Headlamps		
two		.4
four		.6
(M) Headlamp Sealed Beam Bulb, Renew		
All models-each	(.3)	.3
(M) Parking Lamp Lens, Renew		
1983	(.3)	.4
(M) Stop Lamp Lens, Renew		
1983	(.2)	.3
(M) License Lamp Assembly, Renew		
1983	(.3)	.4
(M) Side Marker Lamp Assy., Renew		
1983	(.2)	.4

PARTS 30 HEAD AND PARKING LAMPS 30 PARTS

	Part No.	Price
Seal Beam Bulbs		
1983		
single lamp	▲D8BZ-13007A	16.50
dual lamps		
low beam	▲D94Y-13007A	12.75
high beam	▲D94Y-13007C	12.75
Rear Lamp Lens		
1983-Fairmont		
(exc 4 door sport coupe)		
right	▲D8BZ-13450A	48.00
left	▲D8BZ-13451A	48.00
(4 door sport coupe)		
right	▲D9BZ-13450A	133.75
left	▲D9BZ-13451A	133.75
1983-Zephyr		
(exc 4 door sport coupe)		
right	▲D8KY-13450A	48.00
left	▲D8KY-13451A	48.00
(4 door sport coupe)		
right	▲D9KY-13450A	133.75
left	▲D9KY-13451A	133.75
Turn Signal Lamp Lens (Rear)		
1983 (Zephyr)		
right	▲D8KY-13B328B	24.50
left	▲D8KY-13B329B	24.50
1983 (Fairmont)		
right	▲D8BZ-13B328A	24.50
left	▲D8BZ-13B329A	24.50
Parking Lamp Assy.		
1983 (Fairmont)		
(single lamp)		
right	▲D9BZ-13200A	21.50
left	▲D9BZ-13201A	21.50
(dual lamps)		
right	▲D9KY-13200A	34.25
left	▲D9KY-13201A	34.25
1983 (Zephyr)		
right	▲D9KY-13200A	34.25
left	▲D9KY-13201A	34.25
License Lamp Assy. (Rear)		
1983	▲D7AZ-13550A	6.00

LABOR 31 WINDSHIELD WIPER & SPEEDOMETER 31 LABOR

(Factory Time) — Chilton Time

(G) Windshield Wiper Motor, Renew
1983 (.5) 9

(G) Wiper Pivot, Renew (One)
1983-each (.4) 6

(G) Windshield Wiper Governor Assy., Renew
1983 (.4) 8

(G) Wiper Switch, Renew
Includes: R&R instrument panel pad when required.
1983 (.4) 6

(G) Windshield Washer Pump, Renew
1983 (.3) 5

(G) Speedometer Head, R&R or Renew
Includes: R&R instrument panel pad when required.
1983 (.5) 9

(G) Speedometer Cable and Casing, Renew
Includes: R&R instrument panel pad when required.
1983-each (.4) 7

(G) Speedometer Cable (Inner), Renew or Lubricate
1983-each (.3) 6

(G) Speedometer Driven Gear, Renew
1983 (.3) 4

(G) Radio, R&R
Includes: R&R instrument panel pad when required.
1983 (.5) 8

PARTS 31 WINDSHIELD WIPER & SPEEDOMETER 31 PARTS

	Part No.	Price
Wiper Motor		
1983	▲D8BZ-17508B	94.25
Arm & Pinion Shaft		
1983	▲D9BZ-17566A	32.50
Wiper Switch		
1983-exc. below	▲E1DZ-17A553A	18.50
intermittent	▲E1DZ-17A553B	29.25
Wiper Arm		
1983	▲E3ZZ-17526A	12.75
Wiper Blade Assy.		
1983	▲E3DZ-17528B	12.75
Windshield Wiper Governor		
1983	▲D8BZ-17C476A	77.50
Windshield Washer Pump		
1983	▲E0AZ-17664A	20.00
Speedometer Cable (Inner)		
1983	▲D4AZ-17262A	7.75
Speedometer Casing & Shaft		
1983	▲E3BZ-17260A	22.75
Speedometer Head Assy.		
Order by year and model.		

LABOR 32 LIGHT SWITCHES & WIRING 32 LABOR

(Factory Time) — Chilton Time

(G) Headlamp Switch, Renew
1983 (.3) 5

(G) Headlamp Dimmer Switch, Renew
1983 (.4) 7

(G) Stop Light Switch, Renew
1983 (.3) 4

(G) Brake Warning Light Switch, Renew
1983 (.3) 5

(G) Turn Signal Switch Assy., Renew
1983 (.4) 6

(M) Turn Signal or Hazard Warning Flasher, Renew
1983 (.3) 4

(G) Back-Up Light Switch, Renew
1983 (.3) 5

(G) Horns, Renew
1983-each (.2) 4

(G) Wiring Harness, Renew
Alternator to Regulator
1983 (.3) 7
Dash to Headlight Junction
Fairmont & Zephyr (1.0) 1.7

PARTS 32 LIGHT SWITCHES & WIRING 32 PARTS

	Part No.	Price
Headlamp Switch		
1983	▲E0AZ-11654C	16.50
Turn Signal & Warning Switch		
1983	▲E0AZ-13341A	41.25
Turn Signal Flasher		
1983-exc sta wag	▲C6AZ-13350B	3.75
sta wagon	▲C5AZ-13350B	3.75
Emergency Warning Flasher		
1983	▲D1FZ-13350A	4.25
Stop Light Switch		
1983	▲E3ZZ-13480A	7.25

PARTS 32 LIGHT SWITCHES & WIRING 32 PARTS

	Part No.	Price
Back-Up Lamp Switch		
1983		
(4 spd. trans.)		
four cyl.	▲D3FZ-15520A	6.00
six cyl.	▲E3TZ-15520B	18.50
(auto trans)		
C3 trans	▲D6RY-7A247B	31.75
C4 trans	▲E2DZ-7A247A	36.50
C5 trans	▲E2DZ-7A247A	36.50
Horn		
1983-low pitch	▲E3AZ-13833A	17.00

Wiring Harness
Order by model and description.

LABOR 33 GLASS 33 LABOR

	(Factory Time)	Chilton Time
(G) Windshield Glass, Renew		
1983	(1.0)	1.5
Renew butyl tape add	(.2)	.2
(G) Front Door Glass, Renew		
Includes: R&R trim panel and weathersheet.		
1983		
wo/Vent	(.5)	.7
w/Vent	(.7)	.9
(G) Rear Door Glass, Renew		
Includes: R&R trim panel and weathersheet.		
1983	(.7)	1.2
(G) Rear Window Glass, Renew		
1983	(1.0)	1.5
Renew butyl tape add	(.2)	.2
(G) Tail Gate Glass, Renew		
1983	(.8)	1.2

LABOR 34 CRUISE CONTROL 34 LABOR

	(Factory Time)	Chilton Time
(G) Speed Control Amplifier Assy., Renew		
1983	(.3)	.6
Road test add	(.3)	.3
(G) Speed Control Sensor Assy., Renew		
1983	(.3)	.5
Road test add	(.3)	.3
(G) Speed Control Servo Assy., Renew		
1983	(.4)	.6
Road test add	(.3)	.3
(G) Speed Control Relay, Renew		
1983	(.3)	.5
(G) Speed Control Actuator Switch, Renew		
1983	(.3)	.6
Road test add	(.3)	.3
(G) Speed Control Metering (Dump) Valve, Renew		
1983	(.4)	.6

PARTS 34 CRUISE CONTROL 34 PARTS

	Part No.	Price
Speed Control Sensor		
1983	▲D4AZ-9E731B	47.25
Speed Control Actuator Switch		
1983	▲E3SZ-9C888A	45.75
Speed Control Amplifier Assy.		
1983	▲E0AZ-9D843A	161.50
Speed Control Servo Assy.		
1983	▲E2FZ-9C735A	120.25

GROUP INDEX

ALPHABETICAL INDEX

Ford Motor Company

Rear Wheel Drive Cars

FORD & MERCURY

YEAR IDENTIFICATION

1983–86 Grand Marquis & Colony Park

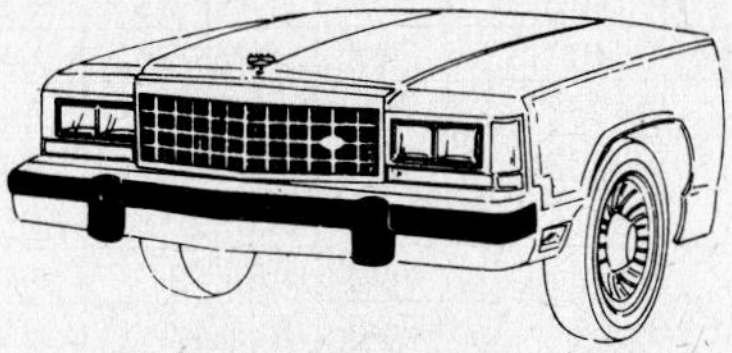

1983–86 Crown Victoria & Country Squire

VEHICLE IDENTIFICATION NUMBER (VIN)

It is important for servicing and ordering parts to be certain of the vehicle and engine identification. The VIN (vehicle identification number) is a 13 or 17 digit number visible through the windshield on the driver's side of the dash and contains the vehicle and engine identification codes. It can be interpreted as follows:

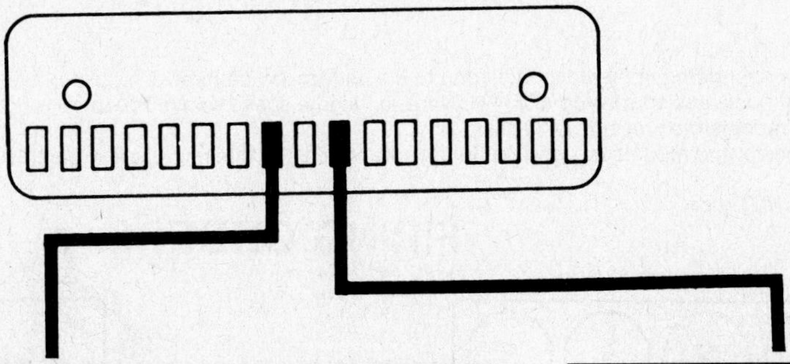

Engine Code					
Code	**Cu. In.**	**Liters**	**Cyl.**	**Carb.**	**Eng. Mfg.**
A	140	2.3	4	1	Ford
W	140-T	2.3	4	Turbo.	Ford
T	140-T SVO	2.3	4	Turbo.	Ford
R	140-HSC	2.3	4	①	Ford
T,B,X	200	3.3	6	1	Ford
3	232	3.8	V6	①	Ford
C	232	3.8	V6	①	Ford
F	302	5.0	V8	1	Ford
M	302-H.O.	5.0	V8	①	Ford
G	351-W	5.8	V8	①	Ford
G	351-H.O.	5.8	V8	①	Ford

Model Year Code	
Code	**Year**
D	1983
E	1984
F	1985
G	1986
H	1987

The seventeen digit Vehicle Identification Number can be used to determine engine application and model year. The tenth digit indicates the model year, and the eighth digit identifies the engine code.

① EFI, VV, 2 bbl. or 4 bbl. depending on model

TUNE-UP SPECIFICATIONS

When analyzing compression test results, look for uniformity among cylinders rather than specific pressures

Year	Engine: Eng. VIN Code	Engine: No. Cyl. Displacement (cu. in.)	Eng. mfg.	Spark Plugs: Orig. Type	Spark Plugs: Gap (in.)•	Distributor: Point Dwell (deg)	Distributor: Point Gap (in.)	Ignition Timing (deg): Man. Trans.	Ignition Timing (deg): Auto. Trans.	Valves Intake Opens (deg)	Fuel Pump Pressure (psi)	Idle Speed (rpm): Man. Trans.	Idle Speed (rpm): Auto. Trans.
'83	A	4-140	Ford	AWSF-44	.044	Electronic		①	①	16	5.5–6.5	850	800
	X	6-200	Ford	BSF-92	.050	Electronic		①	①	20	6–8	600	600
	3	V-6-232	Ford	AWSF-52	.044	Electronic		①	①	13	39	550	550
	F	8-302	Ford	ASF-52 ②	.050	Electronic		①	①	16	6–8 ③	—	550
	G	8-351	Ford	ASF-42	.044	Electronic		①	①	23	6–8	—	700/600
'84	A	4-140	Ford	AWSF-44	.044	Electronic		①	①	16	5–7	850	750
	W	4-140-T	Ford	AWSF-32	.034	Electronic		①	①	—	39	①–④	①–④
	T	4-140-T ⑤	Ford	AWSF-32	.034	Electronic		①	①	—	39	① ④	① ④
	3	V6-232	Ford	AWSF-54	.044	Electronic		①	①	13	39	—	550
	F	8302	Ford	ASF-52	.050	Electronic		①	①	16	39	550	550
	M	8302HO	Ford	ASF-42	.044	Electronic		①	①	—	6–8	700	700
	G	8-351	Ford	ASF-42	.044	Electronic		①	①	23	6–8	—	600 ⑥
'85	A	4-140	Ford	AWSF-44	.044	Electronic		①	①	16	6–8	850	750
	W	4-140T	Ford	AWSF-32	.034	Electronic		①	①	—	39	750	750
	T	4-140-T ⑤	Ford	AWSF-32	.034	Electronic		①	①	—	39	① ④	① ④
	R	4-140-HSC	Ford	AWSF-52	.044	Electronic		①	①	—	39	800	700
	3	V6-232	Ford	AGSP-52	.044	Electronic		①	①	13	6–8	600	600
	C	V6-232	Ford	AWSF-54	.044	Electronic		①	①	13	39	—	550
	F	8-302	Ford	ASF-52	.050	Electronic		①	①	—	39	550	550
	M	8-302 HO	Ford	ASF-42	.044	Electronic		①	①	—	6–8	700	700
	G	8-351	Ford	ASF-42	.044	Electronic		①	①	—	6–8	—	600 ⑥
'86–'87	A	4-140	Ford	AWSF-44C	.044	Electronic		①	①	16	6–8	750	750
	T	4-140-T	Ford	AWSF-32C	.034	Electronic		①	①	—	39	825/975	825/975
	W	4-140-T	Ford	AWSF-32C	.034	Electronic		①	①	—	39	825/975	825/975
	3	V6-232	Ford	AWSF-54	.044	Electronic		①	①	13	39	—	550
	F	8-302	Ford	ASF-32C	.044	Electronic		①	①	—	39	① ④	① ④
	M	8-302 HO	Ford	ASF-42	.044	Electronic		①	①	—	6–8	700	700
	G	8-351	Ford	ASF-32C	.044	Electronic		①	①	—	6–8	650	650

NOTE: The underhood calibrations sticker often reflects tune-up specification changes made in production. Sticker figures must be used if they disagree with those in this chart.

T Turbocharger

HO High output

HSC High swirl combustion

① Calibrations vary depending upon the model; refer to the underhood calibration sticker.

② The carbureted models use spark plug ASF-42 (.044) and the idle speed rpm is 700 rpm.

③ On fuel injected models the pressure is 39 psi.

④ Electronic engine control models the ignition timing, idle speed and idle mixture is not adjustable.

⑤ SVO

⑥ 700 rpm with the VOTM on.

FIRING ORDERS

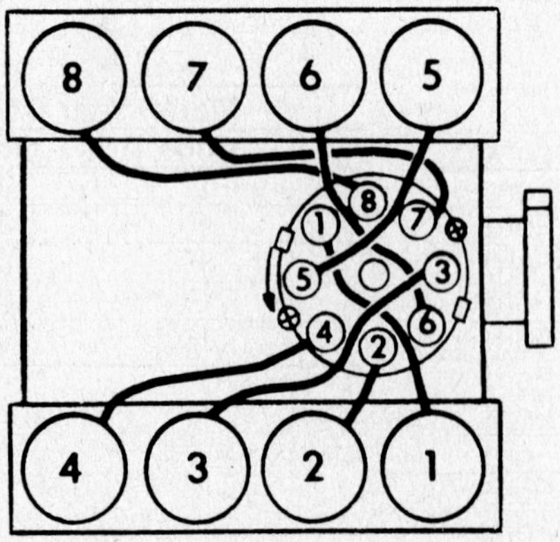

FORD MOTOR CO. 255, 302 (exc. HO) 460 V8 Engine firing order: 1–5–4–2–6–3–7–8 Distributor rotation: counterclockwise

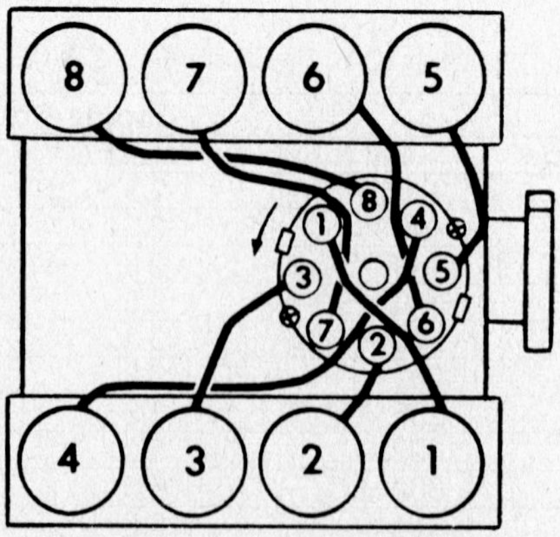

FORD MOTOR CO. 302HO, 351,400 V8 Engine firing order: 1–3–7–2–6–5–4–8 Distributor rotation: counterclockwise

WHEEL ALIGNMENT SPECIFICATIONS

Year	Model	Caster Range (deg)	Caster Pref. Setting (deg)	Camber Range (deg)	Camber Pref. Setting (deg)	Toe-in (in.)	Steering Axis Inclin. (deg)	Wheel Pivot Ratio (deg) Inner Wheel	Wheel Pivot Ratio (deg) Outer Wheel
'83-'84	LTD, Marquis (Sedan)	1/8P to 2 1/8P	1 1/8P	15/16N to 1 13/16P	7/16P	1/16 to 5/16	15 23/32	20	19 27/32
'83-'84	LTD, Marquis (Wagon)	1/8N to 1 7/8P	1P	1/4N to 1 1/4P	1/2P	1/16 to 5/16	15 23/32	20	19 27/32
'85-'87	LTD, Marquis (Sedan)	1/8P to 2 1/8P	7/8P	3/8N to 1 1/8P	3/8P	1/16 to 5/16	15 23/32	20	19 27/32
'85-'87	LTD, Marquis (Wagon)	0P to 2P	3/4P	15/16N to 1 13/16P	7/16P	1/16 to 5/16	15 23/32	20	19 27/32
'83-'87	Ford/Mercury ②	2 1/4P to 4P	3P	1/4N to 1 1/4P	1/2P	1/16 to 3/16	11	20	18 1/2

① Set the vehicle height before making the alignment check.
② On the 84 models the caster range is 2 3/8P to 4 1/8P and the preferred setting is 3 1/8P.

LABOR SERVICE BAY OPERATIONS LABOR

(Factory Time) Chilton Time

COOLING

(M) Winterize Cooling System
Includes: Run engine to check for leaks, tighten all hose connections. Test radiator and pressure cap. Drain radiator and engine block. Add anti-freeze and refill system.
All models 5

(M) Thermostat, Renew
All models (.4) 6
w/A.C. add 2

(M) Drive Belt, Renew
All models-one (.3) 4
each adtnl 1

(M) Drive Belt, Adjust
All models-one (.2) 3
each adtnl (.1) 1

(M) Radiator Hoses, Renew
All models
upper (.4) 4
lower (.5) 6
both (.6) 9

FUEL

(M) Carburetor Air Cleaner, Service
All models (.2) 3

(G) Carburetor, Adjust (On Car)
All models (.4) 5
Propane enrichment method (1.0) 1.5

(G) Thermostatic Choke Cover and/or Gasket, Renew
All models (.8) 1.3

BRAKES

(G) Brakes, Adjust (Minor)
Includes: Adjust brakes, fill master cylinder.
two wheels 4

(G) Bleed Brakes (Four Wheels)
Includes: Fill master cylinder.
All models (.3) 5

(G) Brake Pedal Free Play, Adjust
All models 4

(M) Parking Brake, Adjust
All models (.3) 4

CHILTON'S 10 POINT SAFETY CHECK

CHECK OPERATION & CONDITION OF THE FOLLOWING ITEMS:

1. Legal Registration (serial no.)
2. Tires & Wheels
3. Brake System (R&R all wheels)
4. Light Systems & Signals
5. Accelerator Linkage, Neutral Safety Switch, Shift Indicator Pointer & Seat Position Locks
6. Glass, Mirrors, Door Locks, Seat Belts & Harness
7. Wipers, Washers & Defrosters
8. Frame, Steering, Shocks, Front & Rear Suspension
9. Fuel & Exhaust Systems
10. Road Test Vehicle

All models 1.0
Exhaust Smog Analysis, add 4

(Factory Time) Chilton Time

LUBRICATION SERVICE

(M) Lubricate Chassis, Change Oil & Filter
Includes: Inspect and correct all fluid levels.
All models 6
Install grease fittings add 1

(M) Lubricate Chassis
Includes: Inspect and correct all fluid levels.
All models 4
Install grease fittings add 1

(M) Engine Oil & Filter, Change
Includes: Inspect and correct all fluid levels.
All models 4

WHEELS

(M) Wheel, Renew
one (.5) 5

(Factory Time) Chilton Time

(G) Wheels, Balance
one 3
each adtnl 2

(G) Wheels, Rotate (All)
All models (.5) 5

(G) Front Wheel Bearings, Clean and Repack (Both Wheels)
All models 1.3

(G) Front Wheel Grease Seals, Renew
Includes: Repack bearings.
All models-one wheel (.6) 7
both wheels (.9) 1.1

(G) Front Wheel Bearings and Cups, Renew
All models-one wheel (.7) 9
both wheels (1.2) 1.5

ELECTRICAL

(M) Battery Cables, Renew
Batt. to Relay (.3) 3
Ground (.3) 3
Relay to Starter (.4) 5

(G) Aim Headlamps
two 4
four 6

(M) Headlamp Sealed Beam Bulb, Renew
All models-each (.3) 3

(M) Parking Lamp Lens, Renew
All models (.3) 4

(G) Stop Lamp Lens, Renew
All models (.2) 3

(G) Headlamp Switch, Renew
All models (.3) 5

(G) Headlamp Dimmer Switch, Renew
All models (.3) 6

(G) Stop Light Switch, Renew
All models (.3) 4

(G) Turn Signal Switch Assy., Renew
All models (.6) 1.0
switch only (.3) 5

LABOR — SERVICE BAY OPERATIONS — LABOR

	(Factory Time)	Chilton Time
(G) Neutral Safety Switch, Renew		
All models	(.4)	.6
(M) Turn Signal or Hazard Warning Flasher, Renew		
All models	(.2)	.4
(G) Horns, Renew		
All models-each	(.3)	.4

LABOR — 1 TUNE UP 1 — LABOR

	(Factory Time)	Chilton Time
(G) Compression Test		
1983-87	(.5)	1.0
w/A.C. add		.3

(G) Engine Tune Up, (Electronic Ignition)

Includes: Test battery and clean connections. Tighten manifold and carburetor mounting bolts. Check engine compression, clean and adjust or renew spark plugs. Test resistance of spark plug cables. Inspect distributor cap and rotor. Adjust air gap. Check vacuum advance operation. Reset ignition timing. Adjust idle mixture and idle speed. Service air cleaner. Inspect and adjust drive belts. Inspect choke operation and adjust or free up. Check operation of EGR valve.

	(Factory Time)	Chilton Time
V-8–1983-87		3.0
w/A.C. add		.6
Perform EEC IV system test add		1.0

LABOR — 2 IGNITION SYSTEM 2 — LABOR

	(Factory Time)	Chilton Time
(G) Spark Plugs, Clean and Reset or Renew		
1983-87	(.7)	1.0
w/A.C. add		.3
(G) Ignition Timing, Reset		
1983-87	(.4)	.4
(G) Distributor, Renew		
Includes: Reset ignition timing.		
1983-87	(.4)	.8
(G) Distributor Cap and/or Rotor, Renew		
1983-87	(.2)	.5
(G) Vacuum Control Unit, Renew		
Includes: R&R distributor and reset ignition timing.		
1983-87	(.5)	.8
(G) Profile Ignition Pick-Up Sensor, Renew (Duraspark)		
1983-87	(.5)	.9
Perform system test add	(.3)	.3
(G) Ignition Coil, Renew		
Includes: Test.		
1983-87	(.3)	.5
(G) Ignition Cables, Renew		
Includes: Test wiring.		
1983-87	(.4)	.6
(G) Ignition Switch, Renew		
1983-87	(.4)	.7
(G) Ignition Key Indicator Buzzer or Chime, Renew		
1983-87	(.2)	.4
(G) Ignition Module Assembly, Renew		
Note: Fender mount type. For TFI unit, refer to Emission Control section.		
1983-87	(.3)	.6
Perform system test add	(.3)	.3
(G) Distributor Armature, Renew		
1983-84	(.3)	.6
(G) Distributor Stator, Renew		
Includes: R&R armature.		
1983-84	(.4)	.8

PARTS — 2 ELECTRONIC IGNITION 2 — PARTS

ELECTRONIC IGNITION SYSTEM

	Part No.	Price
Distributor Assy. (New)		
V-8–302 engine		
1983	▲E3AZ-12127A	136.75
1984	▲E4TZ-12127B	136.75
1985	▲E5TZ-12127B	136.75
1986-87	▲E6AZ-12127D	136.75
(Canada)		
1983-85	▲E2VY-12127B	136.75
V-8–351 engine		
1983-87	▲E2AZ-12127E	136.75
(1) Distributor Cap		
1983-84	▲E2ZZ-12106A	20.00
1985	▲E5ZZ-12106A	N.L.
1986-87	▲E6TZ-12106A	20.00
(2) Rotor		
V-8–302 engine		
1983-85-wo/ E.E.C.	▲E4HZ-12200A	3.50
1984-w/E.E.C.	▲E4TZ-12200B	4.00
1985-87-w/ E.E.C.	▲E5TZ-12200B	2.50

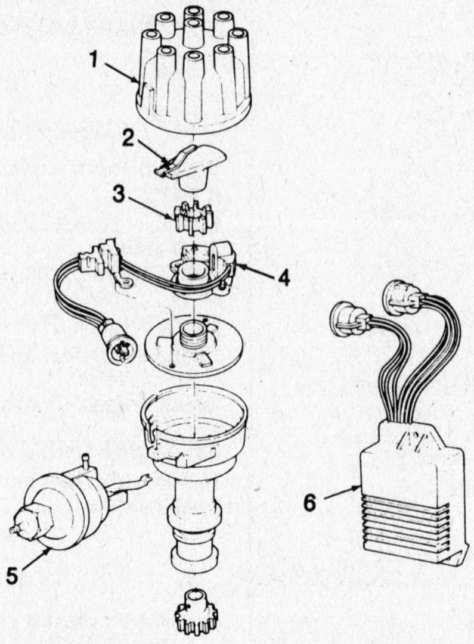

PARTS 2 ELECTRONIC IGNITION 2 PARTS

	Part No.	Price
V-8-351 engine		
1983-85-wo/ E.E.C.	▲E4HZ-12200A	3.50
1984-w/E.E.C.	▲E4TZ-12200B	4.00
(3) Armature		
1983-85	▲D3AZ-12A099A	6.00
(4) Stator Assy.		
1983-85-exc. E.E.C. IV	▲D4PZ-12A112A	25.50
1983-87-w/EEC IV	▲E3ZZ-12A112C	25.00
(5) Vacuum Diaphragm Assy.		
V-8-351 engine		
1983-87	▲E2SZ-12370B	31.25
(6) Modulator Assy.		
V-8-302 engine		
1983-exc. Canada	▲D9AZ-12A199B	83.50
1983-Canada	▲D9VZ-12A199A	83.50
1984-87-exc. E.E.C. IV	▲D9VZ-12A199A	83.50
w/EEC IV	▲E43Z-12A297A	106.00
V-8-351 engine		
1983-87	▲E1AZ-12A199A	101.50
Coil		
1983-87-exc. below	▲D5AZ-12029A	31.25
w/EEC IV	▲E3FZ-12029A	33.75
Ignition Wire Set		
V-8-302 engine		
1983-85-wo/ E.E.C. IV	▲E3PZ-12259ADR	57.50
1984-85-w/EEC IV	▲E4PZ-12259C	58.75
1986-87	▲E6PZ-12259E	58.75
V-8-351 engine		
1983	▲E3PZ-12259J	56.50
1984-85	▲E4PZ-12259G	70.75
1986-87	▲E6PZ-12259G	75.25
Ignition Resistor		
1983-87	▲D7AZ-12250A	9.50
Ignition Switch		
1983-87	▲E4FZ-11572A	11.50

LABOR 3 FUEL SYSTEM 3 LABOR

(Factory Time)	Chilton Time
(G) Fuel Pump, Test	
Includes: Disconnect line at carburetor, attach pressure gauge.	
All models	
mechanical	.3
electric	.5
(M) Carburetor Air Cleaner, Service	
1983-87 (.2)	.3
(G) Carburetor, Adjust (On Car)	
1983-87 (.4)	.5
Propane enrichment method (1.0)	1.5
(M) Fuel Filter, Renew	
1983-84 (.3)	.4
1985-87 (.6)	.8
(G) Carburetor, R&R or Renew	
Includes: All necessary adjustments.	
1983-87	
Motorcraft (.5)	.8
2150 - 2V (.6)	.9
2700 - VV	
wo/EEC (.6)	1.0
w/EEC (.5)	.9
7200 - VV (.7)	1.2
Renew carb add (.4)	.4
(G) Carburetor, R&R and Clean or Recondition	
Includes: All necessary adjustments.	
1983-87	
Motorcraft (1.4)	2.3
2150 - 2V (1.6)	2.5
2700 - VV (2.4)	3.5
7200 - VV (2.5)	3.6
Renew spacer add (.2)	.2
Transfer choke add (.1)	.1
(G) Float Level, Adjust	
Includes: Set idle speed and mixture.	
All models	
Holly 1946 1V (.5)	.7
Weber 740 2V (.5)	.7
Motorcraft 2150 2V (.4)	.6
Weber 5200-6500 2V (.5)	.7
2700-7200 VV (.5)	.7
(G) Float or Needle Valve and Seat, Renew	
Includes: Set idle speed and mixture.	
All models	
Holly 1946 1V (.6)	.9
Weber 740 2V (.5)	.8
Motorcraft 2150 2V (.4)	.7
Weber 5200-6500 2V (.5)	.8
2700-7200 VV (.5)	.8
(G) Accelerator Pump Diaphragm, Piston or Rod, Renew	
All models	
Four (.4)	.6
Six (.6)	.8
V-6 (.6)	.8
V-8-2 bbl (.3)	.5
4 bbl (.5)	.7
(G) Economizer or Power Valve, Renew	
1983-84	
2 bbl (.6)	1.2
(G) Fuel Enrichment Valve Assy., Renew	
1983-87 (.8)	1.3
(G) Thermostatic Choke Housing and/or Gasket, Renew	
1983-87 (.8)	1.3
(G) Cold Enrichment System, Adjust	
7200 VV	
wo/Limiter (.6)	1.0
w/Limiter (1.3)	1.9
(G) Fuel Pump, Renew	
1983-87	
mechanical (.5)	.9
electric	
on frame (.6)	.8
in tank (1.4)	1.8
Add pump test if performed.	
(G) Fuel Tank, Renew	
Includes: Transfer tank gauge unit.	
1983-87-exc below (.7)	1.2
sta wag (1.0)	1.3
w/Feedback system (1.1)	1.4
(G) Fuel Gauge (Tank), Renew	
Includes: Drain and refill tank.	
1983-87-sdn (.5)	.8
sta wag (.6)	.9
(G) Fuel Gauge (Dash), Renew	
1983-87 (.6)	1.0
(G) Intake Manifold or Gaskets, Renew	
1983-87	
255 eng (2.3)	3.3
302-351W engs (2.1)	3.0
Renew manif add (.4)	.5
FUEL INJECTION SYSTEM	
(G) Air Intake Throttle Body, Renew	
1984-87 (.8)	1.3
(G) Fuel Injector Assembly, Renew	
1984-87-w/CFI	
one (.8)	1.2
all (.9)	1.5
w/SEFI	
one (1.8)	2.4
all (2.0)	2.7
(G) Fuel Charging Wiring Assy., Renew	
1984-87 (.3)	.6
(G) Fuel Charging Regulator Assy., Renew	
1984-87 (.8)	1.3
(G) Fuel Charging Assy., R&R or Renew	
1984-87 (.7)	1.2
(G) Fuel Charging Assy., R&R and Recondition	
1984-87 (1.8)	2.5

PARTS 3 FUEL SYSTEM 3 PARTS

	Part No.	Price
Carburetor Assy.		
V-8-302 engine		
1983-85-Canada	▲E3AZ-9510E	N.L.
V-8-351 engine		
1983-87 (stamped E2AE)		
NA	▲E2AZ-9510N	N.L.
AJA	▲E2AZ-9510AJ	813.25
APA	▲E2AZ-9510AP	N.L.
Carburetor Tune Up Kit		
1983-85-Canada	▲E2PZ-9A586P	28.50
1983-87	▲E3PZ-9A586A	69.00
Carburetor Gasket Set		
1983-85-Canada	▲E2PZ-9502A	38.00
1983-87	▲E2PZ-9502F	41.25

PARTS 3 FUEL SYSTEM 3 PARTS

	Part No.	Price
Fuel Pump		
V-8-302 engine		
1983-85-wo/ C.F.I.	▲D6OZ-9350A	34.75
1983-87-w/C.F.I. exc. sta. wagon	▲E3VY-9350A	247.50
sta. wagon	▲E3AZ-9350A	235.50
V-8-351 engine		
1983-87	▲E0AZ-9350C	32.75
Fuel Tank Assy.		
wo/E.F.I.		
(exc. sta. wag.)		
1983-87	▲E4AZ-9002C	147.50
(sta. wag.)		
1983-87	▲E4AZ-9002D	115.00
w/E.F.I.		
(exc. sta. wag.)		
1983-87	▲E4AZ-9002A	132.75
(sta. wag.)		
1983-85	▲E4AZ-9002B	136.25
1986-87	▲E6AZ-9002B	125.00
Fuel Gauge (Tank Unit)		
wo/E.F.I.		
(wo/Tripminder)		
1983-exc. below	▲E0AZ-9275D	42.25
sta. wag.	▲D9AZ-9275B	42.25
(w/Tripminder)		
1983-exc. below	▲E0LY-9275A	42.25
sta. wag.	▲E0AZ-9275C	42.25
1984-85-w/302, exc. sta. wag	▲E0AZ-9275D	42.25
sta. wag.	▲D9AZ-9275B	42.25
1984-87-w/351, exc. sta. wag	▲E0LY-9275A	42.25
sta. wag.	▲E0AZ-9275C	42.25
w/E.F.I.		
1983-87-w/302 exc. below	▲E0LY-9275B	42.25
sta. wag.	▲E1AZ-9275A	43.50
Fuel Gauge (Dash Unit)		
Ford		
1983-87	▲E1AZ-9305A	22.00
Mercury		
(wo/Tripodometer)		
1983-87	▲E1MY-9305E	41.25
(w/Tripodometer)		
1983	▲E1MY-9305F	41.25
1984-87-exc. Canada	▲E4MY-9305A	40.00
Canada, w/351	▲E4MY-9305C	N.L.
Intake Manifold Gasket Set		
V-8-302 engine		
1983-87	▲D9AZ-9433B	7.50
V-8-351 engine		
1983-87	▲D9AZ-9433A	7.50

PARTS 3 ELECTRONIC FUEL INJECTION 3 PARTS

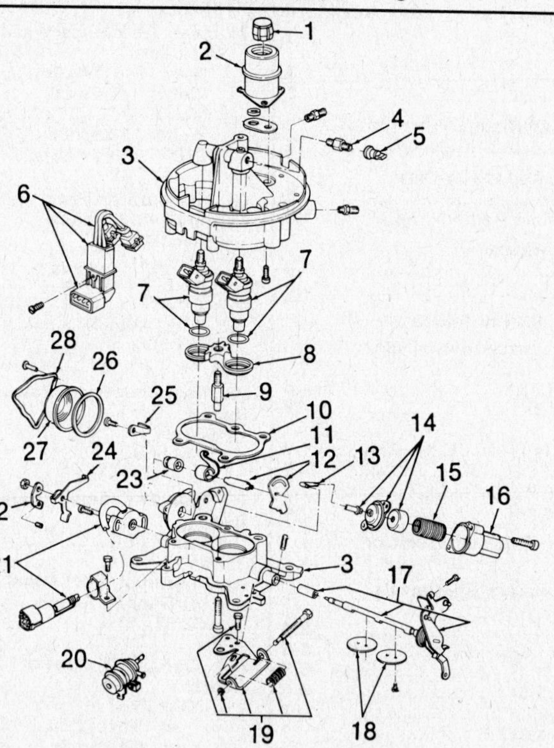

	Part No.	Price
Charging Assy. (Fuel)		
1984-(stamping no.)		
E4AE-FB	▲E4AZ-9C973C	643.75
E4AE-NA	▲E4AZ-9C973N	643.75
1985	▲E5AZ-9C973E	632.75
1983-(stamping no.)		
E3VE-EA	▲E3VY-9C973E	749.00
E3VE-EB	▲E3VZ-9C973F	N.L.
E3VE-CA	▲E3VY-9C973C	749.00
E3VE-CB	▲E3VZ-9C973D	N.L.
E3AE-AA	▲E3AZ-9C973A	749.00
E3AE-AB	▲E3AZ-9C973B	N.L.
(1) Plug (Pressure Regulator)		
1983-85	▲E0AY-9E938A	.75
(2) Pressure Regulator Assy. (Fuel)		
1983-85	▲E0SY-9C968A	101.00
(3) Body (Upper)		
Serviced in charging assembly.		
(4) Relief Valve Assy. (Pressure)		
1983-85	▲E0AY-9H321A	6.50
(5) Cap (Relief Valve)		
1983-85	▲E0VY-9H323A	1.50
(6) Charging Wiring Assy.		
1983-85	▲E0VY-9D930A	43.50
(7) Injector Assy.		
1983-85	▲E0SY-9F593A	147.75
(8) Retainer (Fuel Injector)		
1983-85	▲E0AY-9C976A	11.25
(9) Retaining Screw (Fuel Injector)		
1983-85	▲E0AY-9D927A	8.50
(10) Gasket (Charging Body)		
1983-85	▲E0AY-9C983A	1.00
(11) Control Rod Positioner (Fast Idle)		
1983-85	▲E0AY-9D993A	7.75
(12) Cam & Shaft Assy. (Choke)		
1983-84	▲E1VZ-9A753A	12.25
1985	▲E5AZ-9A753A	12.25
(13) Control Rod (Fast Idle)		
1983-85	▲E0AY-9E524A	3.00
(14) Diaphragm Assy. (Choke Control)		
1983-85	▲D9AZ-9J549A	10.00
(15) Modulator Spring (Choke Control)		
1983-85	▲E0AY-9J547F	9.75
(16) Cover Assy. (Choke Control)		
1983-85	▲E1VZ-9B580A	14.50
(17) Lever & Shaft Assy. (Throttle)		
1983-85	▲E3VY-9581A	38.50
(18) Throttle Plates		
1983-84	▲D7ZZ-9585A	1.50
1985	▲E2BZ-9585A	5.00
(19) Bracket Kit (Throttle Positioner)		
1983-84	▲E0VY-9J586A	34.25
1985	▲E4AZ-9J586A	34.25
(20) Dashpot & Control Assy.		
1983-85	▲E3VY-9S520A	44.50
(21) Potentiometer Assy. (Throttle)		
1983-84	▲E3TZ-9B989B	27.25
1985	▲E5AZ-9B989A	27.25
(22) Adjusting Lever (Fast Idle)		
1983-85	▲E0VZ-9538A	7.00
(23) Bushing		
Serviced in charging assembly.		
(24) Lever (Fast Idle Cam)		
1983-85	▲E0AY-9F577A	5.75
(25) Thermostat Lever (Choke Control)		
1983-85	▲E0AY-9A754A	1.50
(26) Housing Gasket (Choke Thermostat)		
1983-85	▲C1AZ-9871A	1.00
(27) Thermostat Housing Assy. (Choke)		
1983-85	▲E35Y-9848A	33.25
(28) Clamp (Thermostat Housing)		
1983-85	▲E2AZ-9842A	6.75

PARTS 3 ELECTRONIC FUEL INJECTION 3 PARTS

	Part No.	Price
302 ENGINE		
(1) Intake Manifold (Upper)		
1986-87	▲E6SZ-9424B	257.00
(2) Upper Manifold Cover		
1986-87	▲E6AZ-9E434B	16.00
(3) E.G.R. Spacer Assy.		
1986-87	▲E6AZ-9H474A	2.25
(4) Throttle Body Gasket		
1986-87	▲E6SZ-9E933A	1.25
(5) Throttle Body Assy.		
1986-87	▲E6AZ-9E926D	183.75
(6) Throttle Air-Bypass Valve		
1986-87	▲E6AZ-9F715C	56.50
(7) Throttle Position Sensor		
1986-87	▲E6AZ-9B989C	29.25
(8) E.G.R. Valve Assy.		
1986-87	▲E6AZ-9F483C	100.00
(9) Intake Manifold Gasket		
1986-87	▲E6SZ-9H486A	N.L.
(10) Lower Intake Manifold		
1986-87	▲E6SZ-9424A	276.25
(11) Fuel Rail Assy.		
1986-87	▲E6AZ-9F792D	121.75
(12) Schrader Valve		
1986-87	▲N.L.	
(13) Fuel Pressure Regulator		
1986-87	▲E3FZ-9C968A	68.50

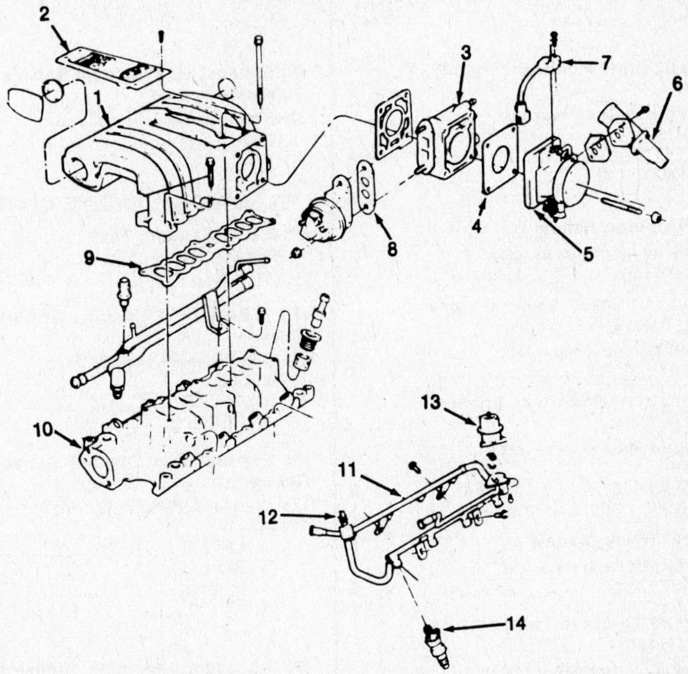

	Part No.	Price
(14) Fuel Injector		
(stamped E67E)		
B1B, B1A	▲E6SZ-9F593A	59.50
(stamped E59E)		
A1A, A2A, A3A, AB	▲E5TZ-9F593A	133.75

LABOR 3A EMISSION CONTROLS 3A LABOR

(Factory Time)	Chilton Time
CRANKCASE EMISSION	
(M) Crankcase Ventilation Valve, Renew	
1983-87 (.2)	.2
THERMACTOR TYPE	
(G) Thermactor Air Pump, Renew	
1983-87 (.4)	.7
(G) Thermactor Pump Drive Belt, Renew	
1983-87 (.3)	.6
(G) Thermactor Air By-Pass Valve, Renew	
1983-87 (.4)	.6
E.G.R. TYPE	
(G) E.G.R. Valve, Renew	
1983-87	
w/E.G.R. cooler (.5)	.9
wo/E.G.R. cooler (.3)	.4
(G) E.G.R. Switch, Renew	
1983-87 (.3)	.4
(G) E.G.R. Vacuum Control Valve, Renew	
1983-87 (.3)	.4
(G) Exhaust Control Valve Assembly, Renew	
1983-87 (.4)	.7

CHILTON'S EMISSION CONTROL TUNE-UP

1. Clean or renew P.C.V. valve, hoses and filter.
2. Check fuel tank cap for sealing ability.
3. Check fuel tank and fuel lines for leakage.
4. Check evaporation canister and filter. Replace if necessary.
5. Check engine compression to determine leakage of unburned gases. (Add time for items of interference).
6. Test and clean or renew spark plugs.
7. Check engine oil dipstick for sealing ability.
8. Test exhaust system with analyzer and check system for leakage.
9. Check exhaust manifold heat valve for operation.
10. Adjust ignition timing and carburetor idle speed and mixture.
11. Check automatic choke mechanism for free operation.
12. Inspect air cleaner and element.
13. On models so equipped, test distributor vacuum control switch and transmission control switch.

V-8 .... **1.8**

For repairs made, charge accordingly.

(Factory Time)	Chilton Time
EVAPORATIVE EMISSION TYPE	
(M) Fuel Vapor Canister, Renew	
1983-87 (.3)	.4
(G) Carburetor Air Cleaner Sensor, Renew	
1983-87 (.2)	.3

(Factory Time)	Chilton Time
(G) Carburetor Air Cleaner Filter, Renew	
1983-87 (.2)	.3
ELECTRONIC ENGINE CONTROL	
(P) E.E.C. System, Test	
1983-87	
w/EEC I (.8)	1.3
w/EEC II (.8)	1.3
w/EEC III (.7)	1.5

(Factory Time) Chilton Time

(P) Crankshaft Position Sensor, Renew

Does not include system test.

1983-87
- w/EEC I (.9) ... 1.4
- w/EEC II (.3) 7
- w/EEC III (1.1) ... 1.8

(P) EGR Cooler, Renew

Does not include system test.

1983-87 (.6) 8

(P) Air Charge Temperature Sensor, Renew

Does not include system test.

1983-87 (.3) 4

(P) Throttle Position Sensor, Renew

Does not include system test.

1983-87
- w/FBC (.3) 5
- w/C.F.I. (.7) ... 1.1

(P) Power Relay, Renew

Does not include system test.

1983-87 (.2) 4

(P) Engine Coolant Temperature Sensor, Renew

Does not include system test.

1983-87 (.3) 5

(P) Calibrator Assembly, Renew

Does not include system test.

1983-87 (.3) 6

(P) Processor Assembly, Renew

Does not include system test.

1983-87 (.3) 6

(P) Canister Purge Solenoid Valve, Renew

Does not include system test.

1983-87 (.3) 4

(P) Feedback Carburetor Actuator, Renew

Does not include system test.

1983-87 (.3) 4

(P) Exhaust Gas Oxygen Sensor, Renew

Does not include system test.

1983-87 (.3) 7

(P) Barometric Manifold Absolute Pressure Sensor, Renew

Does not include system test.

1983-87 (.3) 6

(P) E.G.R. Valve Position Sensor, Renew

Does not include system test.

1983-87 (.3) 4

(P) Thermactor Air Bypass and Air Diverter Solenoid Valve, Renew

Does not include system test.

1983-87 (.3) 5

(P) Throttle Kicker Solenoid, Renew

Does not include system test.

1983-87 (.3) 4

(P) Thermactor Air Solenoid, Renew

Does not include system test.

1983 (.3) 4

(Factory Time) Chilton Time

(P) Exhaust Gas Vacuum and Vent Solenoid, Renew

Does not include system test.

1983-87 (.3) 5

ELECTRONIC ENGINE CONTROL IV

(P) E.E.C. System, Test

1984-87
- w/E.E.C. IV (.6) ... 1.0

(P) Throttle Position Sensor, Renew

Does not include system test.

1984-87
- w/CFI (.7) ... 1.0
- w/SEFI (.1) 2

(P) Exhaust Gas Oxygen Sensor, Renew

Does not include system test.

1984-87
- w/CFI (.2) 5
- w/SEFI
  - right (.4) 6
  - left (.2) 3
  - both (.5) 8

(P) Processor Assembly, Renew

Does not include system test.

1984-87
- w/CFI (.3) 4
- w/SEFI (.3) 4

(P) Engine Coolant Temperature Sensor, Renew

Does not include system test.

1984-87
- w/CFI (.2) 3
- w/SEFI (.2) 3

(P) Barometric Manifold Absolute Pressure Sensor, Renew

Does not include system test.

1984-87
- w/CFI (.1) 2
- w/SEFI (.1) 2

(P) E.G.R. Position Sensor, Renew

Does not include system test.

1984-87
- w/CFI (.3) 4
- w/SEFI (.3) 4

(P) Thick Film Ignition Module, Renew

Does not include system test.

1984-87
- w/CFI (.5) 7
- w/SEFI (.5) 7

(P) Profile Ignition Pick-Up Sensor, Renew

Does not include system test.

1984-87
- w/CFI (.6) 8
- w/SEFI (.6) 8

(P) E.G.R. Control Solenoids, Renew

Does not include system test.

1984-87
- w/CFI (.1) 2
- w/SEFI (.1) 2

(P) Tab/Tad Solenoids, Renew

Does not include system test.

1984-87
- w/CFI (.1) 2
- w/SEFI (.1) 2

(Factory Time) Chilton Time

(P) Fuel Injector Assembly, Renew

Does not include system test.

1984-87
- w/CFI-one or both (.7) ... 1.0
- w/SEFI
  - one (1.8) ... 2.4
  - all (2.0) ... 2.7

(P) Canister Purge Valve, Renew

Does not include system test.

1984-87
- w/CFI (.1) 2
- w/SEFI (.1) 2

(P) Air Change Temperature Sensor, Renew

Does not include system test.

1984-87
- w/CFI (.2) 3
- w/SEFI (.2) 3

(P) Throttle Kicker Actuator, Renew

Does not include system test.

1984
- w/CFI (.2) 3

(P) Throttle Kicker Solenoid, Renew

Does not include system test.

1984
- w/CFI (.1) 2

(P) Exhaust Heat Control Valve, Renew

Does not include system test.

1984
- w/CFI (.3) 6

(P) Throttle Air By-Pass Valve, Renew

Does not include system test.

1986-87
- w/SEFI (.2) 3

(P) Fuel Pump Relay, Renew

Does not include system test.

1986-87
- w/SEFI (.1) 2

(P) Electronic Control Relay, Renew

Does not include system test.

1984-87 (.1) 2

(P) Fuel Pump Inertia Switch, Renew

Does not include system test.

1984-87
- sdn (.1) 2
- sta wag (.3) 4

(P) E.G.R. Valve, Renew

Does not include system test.

1984-87 (.2) 4

ELECTRONIC ENGINE CONTROL SYSTEM

(P) Feedback Carburetor Control System, Test

All models (.3) 8

(P) Oxygen Sensor, Renew

Does not include system test.

All models (.3) 7

(P) Thermactor Air Valve, Renew

Does not include system test.

All models (.3) 6

LABOR 3A EMISSION CONTROLS 3A LABOR

(Factory Time) Chilton Time

(P) Vacuum Regulator Solenoid, Renew
Does not include system test.
All models (.3) 4

(P) Electronic Control Module, Renew
Does not include system test.
All models (.3) 5

(P) Vacuum Switch, Renew
Does not include system test.
All models-one (.3).... .5

(P) Idle Tracking Switch, Renew
Does not include system test.
All models (.3) 5

(P) Feedback Carburetor Actuator, Renew
Does not include system test.
All models (.3) 5

(P) Low Temperature Switch, Renew
Does not include system test.
All models (.3) 6

(P) Thermactor Air By-Pass Valve, Renew
Does not include system test.
All models (.4) 6

(P) Solenoid, Renew
Does not include system test.
All models-one (.3).... .4

(P) Canister Purge Solenoid, Renew
Does not include system test.
All models (.3) 4

(P) Mid-Temperature Switch, Renew
Does not include system test.
All models (.3) 4

(P) Open Loop (Temperature) Switch, Renew
Does not include system test.
All models (.3) 4

(P) Dual Temperature (Electric) Switch, Renew
Does not include system test.
All models (.3) 5

(P) Distributor Modulator Valve Switch Assy., Renew
Does not include system test.
All models (.3) 4

(P) E.G.R. Valve, Renew
Does not include system test.
All models (.3) 5

PARTS 3A EMISSION CONTROLS 3A PARTS

	Part No.	Price
CRANKCASE EMISSION		
Crankcase Ventilation Valve		
V-8-302 engine		
1983-87	▲D9ZZ-6A666A	3.50
V-8-351 engine		
1983-87-exc Calif.	▲D9OZ-6A666A	3.00
Calif.	▲D9ZZ-6A666A	3.50
THERMACTOR TYPE		
Thermactor Air Pump		
1983-85-exc. below	▲E1AZ-9A486A	141.75
1984-85-Canada	▲E4AZ-9A486A	N.L.
1983 (Stamped, E0AE) B1A, B2A	▲E1TZ-9A486A	141.75
1986-87 (stamped) E3ZE-EA, EB	▲E3ZZ-9A486E	141.75
E5AE-AA	▲E5AZ-9A486A	N.L.
E6VE-AA	▲E6VZ-9A486A	141.75
Check Valve		
1983-87 Nipple 1 end	▲D4VY-9A487A	14.25
Nipple 2 ends	▲D9AZ-9A487C	11.25
downstream	▲E3TZ-9A487A	13.25
EVAPORATIVE EMISSION TYPE		
Vapor Canister Assy.		
1983-w/hi-alt. carb	▲E0AZ-9D653A	53.25
1984-85-w/302, exc. Canada	▲D8AZ-9D653C	53.25
Canada	▲E2VY-9D653A	72.75
1986-87	▲E2ZZ-9D653A	55.50
1983-87-w/351 eng.	▲E0AZ-9D653A	53.25
Sensor Assy.		
1983-w/302 eng.	▲D4ZZ-9E607A	7.00
w/351 eng.	▲D7FZ-9E607B	7.25
1984-87	▲D7FZ-9E607B	7.25
E.G.R. SYSTEM		
Integral E.G.R. Valve (w/Transducer)		
V-8-351 eng		
1983-87-(stamping no.) E1AE-K1A, K2A	▲E1AZ-9D448K	60.75
E2TE-G1A, G2A	▲E2TZ-9D448G	60.75

	Part No.	Price
ELECTRONIC ENGINE CONTROL		
Crankshaft Position Sensor		
1983-87	▲E0AZ-6C315A	42.50
Throttle Position Sensor		

Note: Throttle position sensor basic part no. 9B989 must be ordered by identification tag or number stamped on fuel charging assy.

	Part No.	Price
Power Relay Assy.		
1983-87 (w/elect. fuel pump) w/302 eng.	▲E3AZ-12A646A	15.50
Engine Coolant Temperature Sensor		
1983-87	▲E1AZ-12A648A	32.00
Calibrator Assy.		
1983 (w/302 eng.) wo/hi alt.	▲E2VY-12A649JB	140.50
w/hi alt.	▲E2VY-12A649HA	140.50
Calif. (stamped) E2VF-S1A, S2A	▲E3VZ-12A649A	140.50
E3AF-A1A, A2A	▲E3AZ-12A649A	140.50
Processor Assy. (EEC IV)		
1984-85-(stamped E4VF) G1A, G2A	▲E4VZ-12A650GA	167.75
H1A, H2A	▲E4VZ-12A650HA	167.75
J1A, J2A	▲E4VZ-12A650JA	167.75
(stamped E53F) N1B, N2B	▲E53Z-12A650NB	167.75
1986-87-(stamped E6SF) E1B, E2B	▲E6SZ-12A65-EB	N.L.
F1B, F2B	▲E6SZ-12A650FB	N.L.
A1B, A2B	▲E6SZ-12A650AB	N.L.
G1B, G2B	▲E6SZ-12A650GB	N.L.
B1B, B2B	▲E6SZ-12A650BB	N.L.
H1B, H2B	▲E6SZ-12A650HB	N.L.
C1B, C2B	▲E6SZ-12A650CB	N.L.
AM1B, AM2B	▲E6SZ-12A650AMB	N.L.
S1B, S2B	▲E6SZ-12A650SB	N.L.
T1B, T2B	▲E6SZ-12A650TB	N.L.
Solenoid Valve (Canister Purge)		
1983	▲E0AZ-9C915A	21.75
1984-87-(color coded) black	▲E4AZ-9C915C	21.75
green	▲E4AZ-9C915B	21.75
natural	▲E4AZ-9C915A	21.75
Feedback Carburetor Actuator		
1983-87	▲D9AZ-9C908A	56.25

	Part No.	Price
Exhaust Gas Oxygen Sensor		
1983-85	▲E3FZ-9F472A	48.50
1986-87 (stamping E59F) A1A, A2A, A3A	▲E59Z-9F472A	48.50
(stamping E67F) AA, CA	▲E6TZ-9F472A	48.50
BA	▲E6TZ-9F472B	48.50
Barometric Manifold Absolute Pressure Sensor		
1983-84	▲E1AZ-12A680A	169.50
Position Sensor (E.G.R. Valve)		
1983-85	▲E43Z-9G428B	31.75
1986-87	▲E5AZ-9G428A	31.75
Thermactor Air By-Pass & Air Diverter Solenoid Valve		
V-8-302 engine		
1983-85	▲E1AZ-9F491A	56.00
1986-87	▲E3TZ-9F491A	56.00
V-8-351 engine		
1983-87	▲E1AZ-9F491D	56.00
Dual Temperature Switch (Electric)		
1983-w/302 eng	▲E1AZ-12B513A	71.50
1983-87-w/351 eng.	▲E1AZ-12B513A	71.50
Solenoid Valve Assy. (E.G.R. Vacuum)		
1983-exc. below	▲E0AZ-9D474B	32.50
(Stamped, E1SE) C2A, C3A	▲E1SZ-9D474C	16.25
1984-85-fuel	▲E1SZ-9D474C	16.25
Therm.	▲E0AZ-9D474B	32.50
E.G.R. valve	▲E0AZ-9D474D	32.50
1986-87	▲E6AZ-9D474A	32.50
Ignition Module Assy.		
1984-87	▲E43Z-12A297A	106.00
Exhaust Heat Control Valve		
1984-87	▲E1SZ-9A427A	86.50
Air Charge Temperature Sensor		
1984-87	▲E1AZ-12A697A	27.00
Engine Spark Knock Sensor		
V-8-351 engine		
1983-87	▲E3AZ-12A699A	33.00

LABOR 4 ALTERNATOR AND REGULATOR 4 LABOR

	(Factory Time)	Chilton Time
(G) Alternator Circuits, Test		
Includes: Test battery, regulator and alternator output.		
All models	(.3)	.6
(M) Alternator Drive Belt, Renew		
1983-87	(.3)	.4
(G) Alternator, Renew		
1983-87	(.3)	.6
Transfer pulley add	(.1)	.1
Circuit test add	(.3)	.6
(G) Alternator, R&R and Recondition		
Includes: Complete disassembly, replacement of parts as required. Test validity of rotor fields, stator and diodes.		
1983-87	(.8)	1.5
Circuit test add	(.3)	.6
(G) Alternator Front Bearing or End Plate, Renew		
1983-87	(.6)	1.0
(G) Alternator Rear Bearing, Renew		
1983-87	(.5)	.9
(G) Alternator Regulator, Renew		
1983-87	(.3)	.6
Circuit test add	(.3)	.6
(G) Instrument Cluster Voltage Regulator, Renew		
Includes: Remove instrument panel pad when required.		
1983-87		
Ford	(.5)	.8
Mercury	(.6)	.9
(G) Ammeter, Renew		
1985-87	(1.2)	1.9

PARTS 4 ALTERNATOR AND REGULATOR 4 PARTS

	Part No.	Price
Alternator, Assy. (New)		
1983-85-60 amp.	▲E2GZ-10346C	233.50
1986-87-65 amp.	▲E6ZZ-10346B	418.75
1983-87-100 amp	▲E1VZ-10346A	418.75
(1) Front Housing		
1983-85-60 amp	▲D3OZ-10333B	17.75
1986-87-65 amp	▲E6AZ-10333A	18.50
1983-87-100 amp	▲D3VY-10333A	72.75
(2) Front Bearing		
1983-87	▲C9ZZ-10094A	9.00
(3) Rotor		
1983-85-60 amp.	▲E1ZZ-10335B	45.75
1986-87-65 amp.	▲E53Z-10335A	56.00
1983-87-100 amp	▲E1VZ-10335A	120.50
(4) Stator		
1983-85-60 amp.	▲E3FZ-10336A	31.25
1986-87-65 amp.	▲E6DZ-10336D	33.50
1983-87-100 amp.	▲D3VY-10336A	74.75
(5) Rectifier Kit		
1983-85-60 amp.	▲D6AZ-10304A	48.00
1986-87-65 amp.	▲E43Z-10304A	47.25
1983-87-100 amp.	▲D4VY-10304A	88.25
(6) Brushes		
1983-85-60 amp.	▲C6VY-10347A	3.50
1983-87-100 amp.	▲D2OZ-10347B	17.25

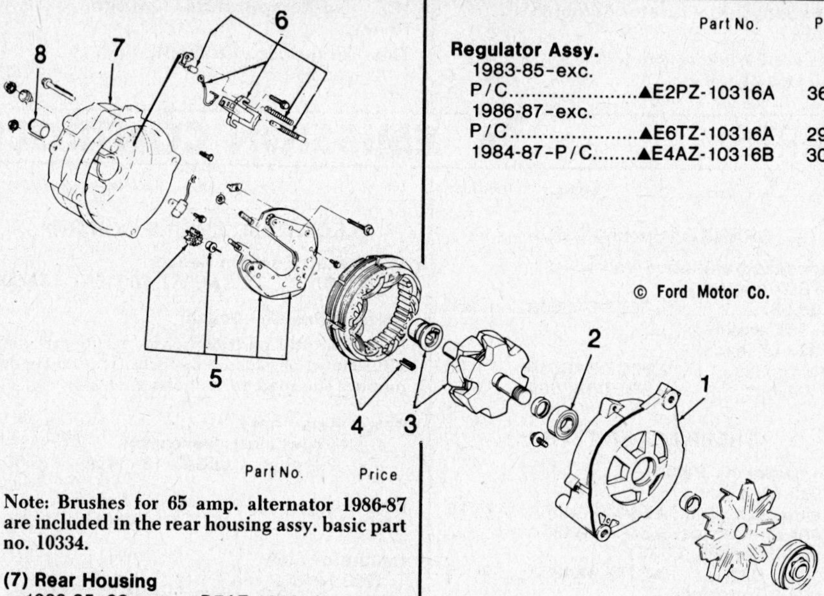

© Ford Motor Co.

Note: Brushes for 65 amp. alternator 1986-87 are included in the rear housing assy. basic part no. 10334.

	Part No.	Price
(7) Rear Housing		
1983-85-60 amp.	▲D7AZ-10334A	23.25
1986-87-65 amp.	▲E6FZ-10334A	36.75
1983-87-100 amp.	▲D7VZ-10334A	49.25
(8) Rear Bearing		
1983-87	▲D2OZ-10A304A	5.25
Regulator Assy.		
1983-85-exc. P/C	▲E2PZ-10316A	36.75
1986-87-exc. P/C	▲E6TZ-10316A	29.75
1984-87-P/C	▲E4AZ-10316B	30.00
Instrument Cluster Voltage Regulator		
1983-87	▲D1AZ-10804A	10.25

LABOR 5 STARTING SYSTEM 5 LABOR

	(Factory Time)	Chilton Time
(G) Starter Draw Test (On Car)		
All models	(.3)	.3
(G) Starter, Renew		
1983-87	(.3)	.6
Add draw test if performed.		
(G) Starter, R&R and Recondition		
Includes: Turn down armature.		
1983-87		
positive engagement starter	(1.6)	2.3
solenoid actuated starter	(1.4)	2.1
Motorcraft	(1.4)	2.1
Renew field coils add		.5
Add draw test if performed.		
(G) Starter Drive, Renew		
Includes: R&R starter.		
1983-87	(.5)	.8
(M) Starter Solenoid Relay, Renew		
1983-87	(.3)	.4
(M) Neutral Safety Switch, Renew		
1983-87	(.4)	.6
(G) Ignition Switch, Renew		
1983-87	(.4)	.7
(M) Battery Cables, Renew		
Batt. to Relay	(.3)	.3
Ground	(.3)	.3
Relay to Starter	(.4)	.5

PARTS 5 STARTING SYSTEM 5 PARTS

	Part No.	Price
Starter Assy. (New)		
1983	▲E25Z-11002A	N.L.
1984-87	▲E4DZ-11002B	185.50
Starter Relay Switch		
1983-84-w/302, exc. Canada	▲D8VY-11450A	12.25
1983-84-w/302, Canada	▲D8DZ-11450B	12.00

PARTS 5 STARTING SYSTEM 5 PARTS

	Part No.	Price
1985-exc. Canada	▲E5AZ-11450A	13.25
Canada	▲E5TZ-11450A	13.25
1986-87-w/302	▲E5AZ-11450A	13.25
w/351	▲E5TZ-11450A	13.25
Ignition & Starter Switch		
1983-87	▲E4FZ-11572A	11.50
(1) Starter Armature (New)		
1983	▲E2BZ-11005A	77.00
1984-87	▲E3FZ-11005A	66.75
(2) Starter Drive Assy.		
1983-87	▲E2PZ-11350A	21.00
(3) Rear Plate (Housing)		
1983	▲E25Y-11130A	45.00
1984-87	▲E4AZ-11130A	41.75
(4) Front Plate		
1983	▲E2BZ-11049A	14.50
1984-87	▲E4AZ-11049A	14.50
(5) Field Coil Assy.		
1983	▲E2BZ-11082A	50.00
1984-87	▲E4AZ-11082A	50.00
(6) Starter Brush Set		
1983	▲D7AZ-11057A	5.00
1984-87	▲E4PZ-11057A	13.00
Bearing (Drive End Plate)		
1983-87	▲D3AZ-11052A	1.50
Battery Ground Cable		
1983-87-w/302 exc. Canada	▲D9AZ-14301B	10.00

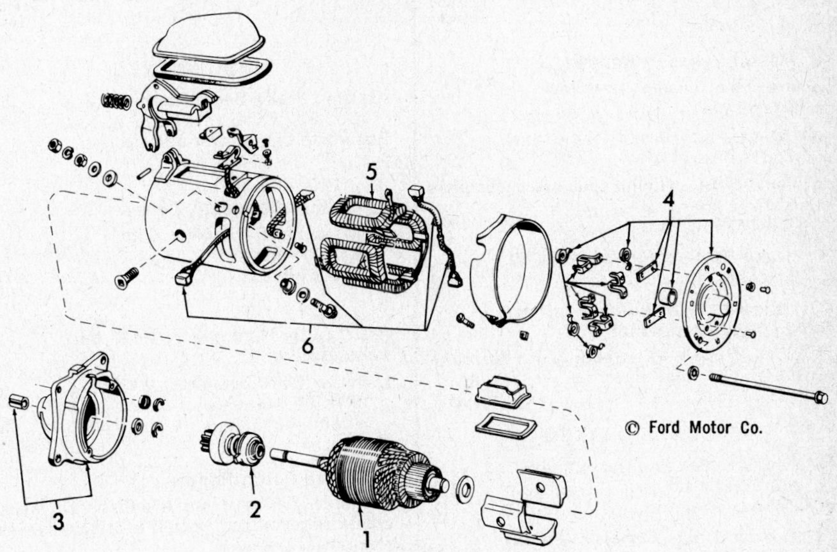

	Part No.	Price
1983-85-w/302, Canada	▲D9AZ-14301B	10.00
1983-87-w/351	▲D9AZ-14301B	10.00
Battery to Starter Relay Cable		
1983-87	▲D1PZ-14300A	6.25

	Part No.	Price
Starter to Relay Cable		
1983-87	▲E0VY-14431B	28.25
Starter Neutral Switch		
1983-87	▲D6RY-7A247B	33.25

LABOR 6 BRAKE SYSTEM 6 LABOR

COMBINATIONS

Add to Brakes, Renew

See Machine Shop Operations

(Factory Time)	Chilton Time
(G) RENEW WHEEL CYLINDER	
Each (.3)	.3
(G) REBUILD WHEEL CYLINDER	
Each (.3)	.3
(G) REBUILD CALIPER ASSEMBLY	
Front-one (.5)	.5
Rear-one (.3)	.6
(G) RENEW MASTER CYLINDER	
All models (.6)	.6
(G) REBUILD MASTER CYLINDER	
All models (.8)	1.0
(G) RENEW BRAKE HOSE	
Each (.3)	.3
(G) RENEW REAR WHEEL GREASE SEALS	
One (.4)	.4
Both (.5)	.6
(G) REPACK FRONT WHEEL BEARINGS (BOTH WHEELS)	
All models (.4)	.6
(G) RENEW BRAKE DRUM	
Each (.2)	.2
(G) RENEW DISC BRAKE ROTOR	
Each (.2)	.4

(Factory Time)	Chilton Time
(G) Brake Pedal Free Play, Adjust	
All models	.4
(G) Brakes, Adjust (Minor)	
Includes: Adjust brakes, fill master cylinder.	
two wheels	.4
(G) Bleed Brakes (Four Wheels)	
Includes: Fill master cylinder.	
All models (.3)	.5
(G) Brake Self Adjustors, Disassemble & Clean	
one wheel	.7
each adtnl	.4
(G) Brake Shoes and/or Pads, Renew	
Includes: Install new or exchange brake shoes or pads. Adjust service and hand brake. Bleed system.	
1983-87-front-disc (.7)	1.1
rear-drum (1.0)	1.5
all four wheels (1.4)	2.5
Resurface disc rotor add-each	.9
Resurface brake drum add-each	.5
(G) Brake Drum, Renew	
1983-87-one (.3)	.6
both (.4)	.8
(G) Brake Pressure Warning Light Switch, Renew	
1983-87 (.3)	.5

BRAKE HYDRAULIC SYSTEM

(Factory Time)	Chilton Time
(G) Wheel Cylinder, Renew	
Includes: Bleed system.	
1983-87-one (.9)	1.4
both (1.5)	2.1
(G) Wheel Cylinder, R&R and Rebuild	
Includes: Hone cylinder and bleed system.	
1983-87-one (.9)	1.7
both (1.5)	2.7
(G) Brake Hose, Renew	
Includes: Bleed system.	
1983-87-front-one (.4)	.7
both (.5)	.8
rear-one (.5)	.8

LABOR — 6 BRAKE SYSTEM 6 — LABOR

(Factory Time)	Chilton Time
(G) Master Cylinder, Renew	
Includes: Bleed complete system.	
1983-87 (.5)	.9
(G) Master Cylinder, R&R and Rebuild	
Includes: Hone cylinder and bleed complete system.	
1983-87 (.7)	1.6
(G) Brake System, Flush and Refill	
All models	1.2
(G) Brake Hydraulic System, Recondition (Complete)	
Includes: Renew all rubber parts in brake system and bleed all lines.	
1983-87 (5.2)	6.1
POWER BRAKES	
(G) Power Brake Booster, Renew	
1983-87-vacuum (.6)	1.0
w/Cruise control add	.2
(G) Power Brake Booster Check Valve, Renew	
1983-87 (.3)	.4

(Factory Time)	Chilton Time
DISC BRAKES	
(G) Disc Brake Pads, Renew	
1983-87 (.7)	1.1
Resurface brake rotor add-each	.9
(G) Caliper Assembly, Renew	
Includes: Bleed complete system.	
1983-87-one (.6)	1.0
both (.8)	1.5
(G) Caliper Assembly, R&R and Recondition	
Includes: Bleed complete system.	
1983-87-one (.8)	1.5
both (1.2)	2.5
(G) Brake Rotor, Renew	
Includes: Renew front wheel bearings and grease retainer and repack bearings. Remove rear wheel assembly.	
1983-87-one (.5)	.7
both (.8)	1.2

(Factory Time)	Chilton Time
(G) Brake Differential Valve, Renew	
Includes: Bleed complete system and transfer switch.	
1983-87 (.7)	1.0
PARKING BRAKE	
(M) Parking Brake, Adjust	
All models (.2)	.4
(G) Parking Brake Indicator Switch, Renew	
1983-87 (.3)	.4
(G) Parking Brake Control, Renew	
1983-87 (.5)	1.0
(G) Parking Brake Cable, Renew	
Includes: Adjust parking brake.	
All models-one (.5)	.8
both (.8)	1.0
(G) Parking Brake Power Vacuum Unit, Renew	
1983-87 (.3)	.5

PARTS — 6 BRAKE SYSTEM 6 — PARTS

	Part No.	Price
(1) Brake Shoe Set (2 Wheels)		
1983-87-10″ brks.	▲D9AZ-2200A	42.50
11″ brks.	▲D9AZ-2200B	47.25
Brake Lining Sets (Rear)		
1983-87-10″ brks.	▲D9AZ-2007A	26.25
11″ brks.	▲D9AZ-2007B	29.25
(2) Wheel Cylinder		
1983-87	▲D9AZ-2261B	25.75
Wheel Cylinder Repair Kit		
1983-87	▲D9AZ-2128B	6.00
Brake Hose, (Front)		
1983-87-right	▲E0AZ-2078A	18.00
left	▲E0AZ-2078B	18.00
Brake Hose, (Rear)		
1983-87	▲D9AZ-2282B	19.25
Master Cylinder Repair Kit		
1983-87	▲D9AZ-2004A	41.25
Master Cylinder Assembly, Power		
1983-87	▲D9AZ-2140A	93.50
Brake Booster Assy. (New)		
1983-87-exc. P/C, Taxi	▲D9AZ-2005A	236.25
P/C, Taxi	▲D9AZ-2005B	213.00

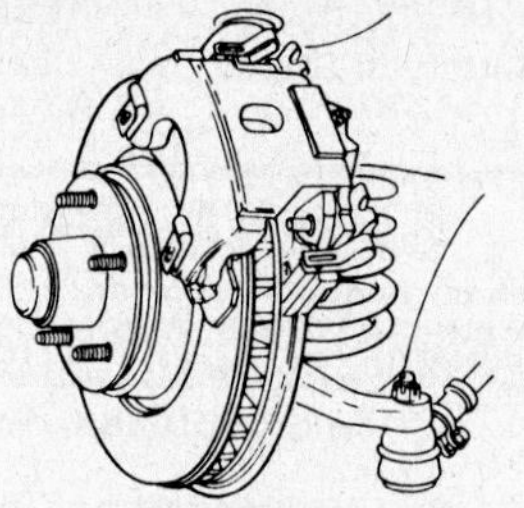

FRONT BRAKE

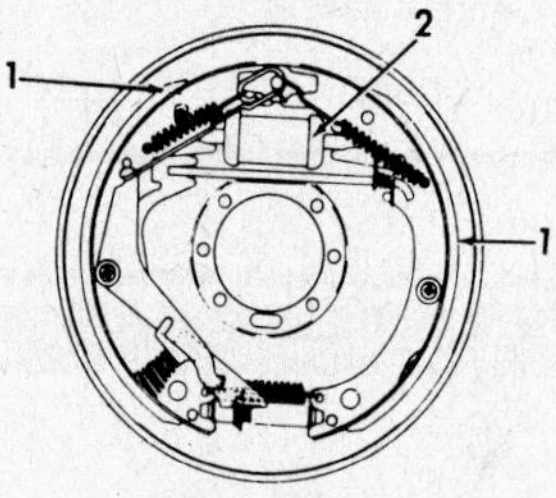

REAR BRAKE

	Part No.	Price
Brake Drum, Rear		
1983-87-10″ brks.	▲D9AZ-11264	N.L.
11″ brks.	▲D9AZ-1126B	111.75
Oil Seal, Front		
1983-87	▲C8AZ-1190A	3.00
Oil Seal, Rear		
1983-87	▲E1AZ-1177B	3.50
Brake Pressure Warning Light Switch		
1983-87	▲D9BZ-2B264A	7.50
Brake Booster Check Valve		
1983-87	▲D0AZ-2365A	5.50

	Part No.	Price
Brake Differential Valve		
1983-87-exc. below	▲E0AZ-2B257A	73.75
Sta. wagon	▲D9AZ-2B257D	40.00
PARKING BRAKE		
Parking Brake Lever		
1983-85 (type of release) manual	▲D9AZ-2780A	53.00
auto	▲E0AZ-2780A	65.25
1986-87-Auto	▲E6AZ-2780A	69.25
Front Brake Cable		
1983-87	▲D9AZ-2853A	16.00
Rear Brake Cable		
1983-87-right	▲E2AZ-2A635A	25.00
left	▲E2LY-2A635A	17.75

PARTS — 6 DISC BRAKES 6 — PARTS

	Part No.	Price
(1) Wheel Bearing (Outer)		
1983-87	▲D0AZ-1216A	8.25
(3) Hub & Rotor Assy.		
1983-87	▲D9AZ-1102A	73.00
(4) Cup (Inner)		
1983-87	▲D4AZ-1202A	5.00
(5) Wheel Bearing (Inner)		
1983-87	▲D4AZ-1201A	9.75
(6) Retainer (Grease)		
1983-87	▲C8AZ-1190A	3.00

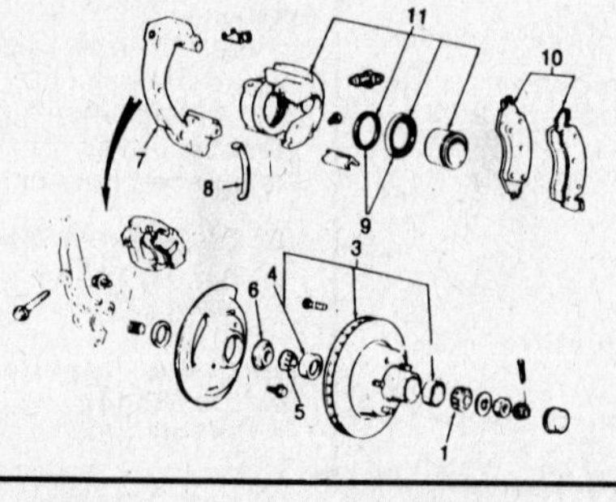

PARTS 6 DISC BRAKES 6 PARTS

	Part No.	Price
(9) Seal Kit		
1983-87	▲D9AZ-2221A	6.25
(10) Brake Pad Set		
1983-87	▲E2AZ-2001A	27.00
(11) Caliper Assembly		
1983-87-right		
exc. (P/C)	▲E4LY-2B120A	120.00
left	▲E4LY-2B121A	120.00
1983-87-right		
(P/C)	▲E0AZ-2B120A	112.25
left	▲E0AZ-2B121A	112.25

LABOR 7 COOLING SYSTEM 7 LABOR

	(Factory Time)	Chilton Time
(M) Winterize Cooling System		
Includes: Run engine to check for leaks, tighten all hose connections. Test radiator and pressure cap, drain radiator and engine block. Add anti-freeze and refill system.		
All models		.5
(M) Thermostat, Renew		
1983-87	(.4)	.6
w/A.C. add		.2
(M) Radiator Assembly, R&R or Renew		
Includes: Drain and refill cooling system.		
1983-87	(.5)	1.0
w/A.C. add		.2

ADD THESE OPERATIONS TO RADIATOR R&R

(G) Boil & Repair		1.5
(G) Rod Clean		1.9
(G) Repair Core		1.3
(G) Renew Tank		1.6
(G) Renew Trans. Oil Cooler		1.9
(G) Recore Radiator		1.7
(M) Radiator Hoses, Renew		
1983-87		
upper	(.4)	.4
lower	(.5)	.6
both	(.6)	.9
(M) Radiator By-Pass Hose, Renew		
1983-87	(.3)	.6
(G) Water Pump, Renew		
1983-87	(1.1)	1.9
w/A.C. add	(.1)	.1
(M) Fan Blades, Renew		
1983-87	(.3)	.6
w/Clutch fan add		.2
(M) Drive Belt, Renew		
1983-87-one	(.3)	.4
each adtnl		.1
(M) Drive Belt, Adjust		
All models-one	(.2)	.3
each adtnl		.1
(M) Clutch Fan, Renew		
1983-87	(.4)	.6

COOLING SYSTEM TUNE-UP

An Annual Cooling System Tune-Up Suggestion List should include (with some exceptions):

1. A visual check of the cooling system for indications of leaks or excessive oil content.
2. Pressure check the cooling system for internal and external leaks with filler cap and neck adapter and tester.
3. Check crankcase and automatic transmission oil for water content.
4. Test coolant thermostat with radiator thermometer.
5. Check temperature gauge for accuracy.
6. Drain system and flush till clean.
7. Clean foreign matter from radiator fins.
8. Test radiator pressure cap with cap tester.
9. Check fan blades and pulleys for alignment and damage.
10. Internal and external inspection of all hoses for cracks and deterioration.
11. Check core plugs (where possible) for seepage.
12. Refill system with correct coolant and check for air locks.
13. Check condition and tension of drive belts with tension gauge.

All models 1.5

	(Factory Time)	Chilton Time
(G) Temperature Gauge (Engine Unit), Renew		
1983-87	(.3)	.7
(G) Water Jacket Expansion Plugs, Renew (Side of Block)		
each	(.3)	*.5
*Add time to gain accessibility.		
(G) Heater Hoses, Renew		
1983-87-each	(.3)	.4
(G) Heater Core, R&R or Renew		
1983-84	(1.4)	5.0
1985-87-wo/A.C.	(1.5)	3.0
w/A.C.	(1.5)	5.0
Add time to recharge A.C. system if required.		

ADD THESE OPERATIONS TO HEATER CORE R&R

(G) Boil & Repair		1.2
(G) Repair Core		.9
(G) Recore		1.2

	(Factory Time)	Chilton Time
(G) Heater Control Assembly, Renew		
1983-87	(.5)	.9
(G) Heater Blower Motor, Renew		
Includes: Transfer blower wheel when required.		
1983-87	(.4)	.9
(G) Heater Blower Motor Resistor, Renew		
1983-87	(.3)	.5
(G) Heater Blower Motor Switch, Renew		
1983-87	(.4)	.7
(G) Temperature Control Cable, Renew		
1983-87		
wo/A.T.C.	(.4)	.7
w/A.T.C.	(.8)	1.4

PARTS 7 COOLING SYSTEM 7 PARTS

	Part No.	Price
(1) Radiator Assembly		
Order by year and model.		
(2) Thermostat		
V-8-302, 351 engs.		
1983-87	▲D9AZ-8575A	6.00
(3) Radiator Hose, Upper		
1983-87-exc.		
below	▲D9AZ-8260A	11.50
1986-87-w/302	▲E6AZ-8260A	30.00
(4) Radiator Hose, Lower		
1983-87-exc.		
below	▲D9AZ-8286A	18.00
1986-87-w/302		
eng	▲E6AZ-8286A	18.00
(5) Water Pump Assy. (New)		
1983-85-Alum	▲E0AZ-8501A	89.25
1983-85-cast		
iron	▲E1AZ-8501A	91.00
1986-87-exc.		
below	▲E1AZ-8501A	91.00
Mercury, w/LS		
option	▲E6MY-8501A	N.L.
(6) Fan Belts		
Note: Order by model & description.		
Fan Clutch Assy.		
1983-85-exc.		
P/C	▲E0MY-8A616A	57.25
P/C	▲E1AZ-8A616A	71.00
1984-Canada	▲E0MY-8A616A	57.25
1985-Canada	▲E1AZ-8A616A	71.00
1986-87-exc.		
P/C	▲E6AZ-8A616A	50.50
P/C	▲E6AZ-8A616B	71.00
Heat Indicator Sending Unit		
1983-87	▲E43Z-10884A	9.00

PARTS 7 COOLING SYSTEM 7 PARTS

	Part No.	Price
Heater Core		
1983-87	▲E3AZ-18476E	62.00
Heater Core Seal Kit		
1983-87	▲D9AZ-18658A	13.75
Blower Motor		
1983-87	▲E0VY-19805A	86.50
Switch Assy. Heater		
1983-87-exc. below	▲D5AZ-19986A	12.75
w/ATC	▲E4VY-19986A	5.25
Blower Motor Resistor		
1983-87-exc. below	▲E3AZ-19A706A	11.00
w/ATC	▲E4VY-19A706A	11.00

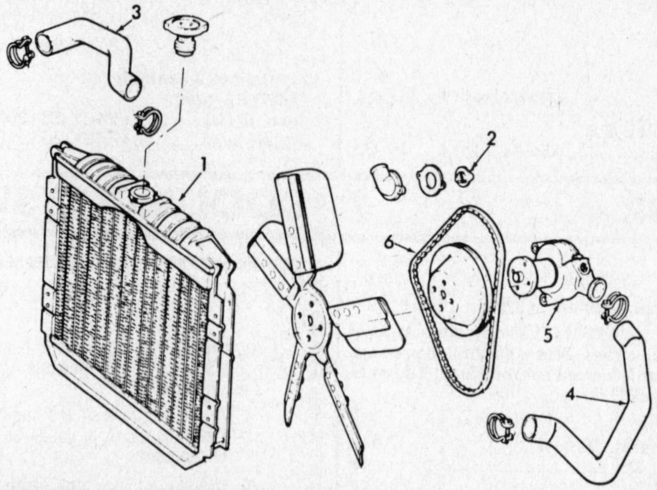

LABOR 8 EXHAUST SYSTEM 8 LABOR

(Factory Time)	Chilton Time
(G) Muffler, Renew	
1983-84-one (.6)	1.0
1985-87-one (.8)	1.2
Welded type add	.3
(G) Tail Pipe, Renew	
1983-87-one (.2)	.5
both (.3)	.8
Welded type add	.3
(G) Catalytic Converter, Renew	
1983-87-one (.6)	.9
both (1.0)	1.6
(G) Muffler Inlet Pipe, Renew	
Includes: Replace exhaust control valve if required.	
1983-87 (.6)	1.0
(G) Manifold Heat Valve, Renew	
1983-87 (.4)	.7
(G) Exhaust Manifold, Renew	
1983-87	
255, 302 engs-right (.7)	1.1
left (.9)	1.3
both (1.3)	2.0
351W eng-right (.9)	1.3
left (.8)	1.2
both (1.5)	2.1

COMBINATIONS

(Factory Time)	Chilton Time
(G) Muffler, Exhaust and Tail Pipe, Renew	
1983-87	
one side (1.0)	1.4
both sides (1.4)	1.9
Welded type add	.3
(G) Muffler and Tail Pipe, Renew	
1983-87	
one side (.8)	1.2
both sides (1.3)	1.7
Welded type add	.3

PARTS 8 EXHAUST SYSTEM 8 PARTS

	Part No.	Price
Muffler		
Order by year and model.		
Exhaust Pipe		
(Single exhaust)		
1983-85	▲E1AZ-5246A	128.00
1986-87	▲E6AZ-5246A	128.00
(dual exhaust)		
1983-84	▲E0AZ-5246A	116.75
1985-87	▲E5AZ-5246A	119.50
Catalytic Converter		
V-8-302 engine		
1983-right	▲E3MY-5E212C	401.50
left	▲E1MY-5E212G	401.50
1984-85-right	▲E4MY-5E212B	401.50
left	▲E4MY-5E212A	401.50
1986-87-right	▲E6AZ-5E212A	377.00
left	▲E6AZ-5E212B	377.50
Canada		
(FORD)		
1983-84-right	▲E1AZ-5E212P	N.L.
left	▲E1AZ-5E212R	N.L.
(MERCURY)		
1983-84-right	▲E1MY-5E212L	N.L.
left	▲E1MY-5E212M	N.L.
1985-right	▲E1AZ-5E212P	N.L.
left	▲E1AZ-5E212R	N.L.
V-8-351 engine		
1983-right	▲E3MY-5E212A	382.25
left	▲E3MY-5E212B	382.25
1984-85-right	▲E3AZ-5E212A	356.00
left	▲E3AZ-5E212B	356.00
1986-87-right	▲E3MY-5E212A	382.25
left	▲E3MY-5E212B	382.25
Converter Shield (Lower)		
1983-84	▲E4SZ-5E258A	19.25
1985-87	▲E4SZ-5E258A	19.25
Converter Shield (Upper)		
1983-87	▲E0AZ-5F223B	17.25

LABOR 9 FRONT SUSPENSION 9 LABOR

Note: On all front suspension operations alignment charges must be added if performed. Time given does not include alignment.

(Factory Time)	Chilton Time
(M) Wheel, Renew	
one (.5)	.5
(G) Wheels, Rotate (All)	
All models (.5)	.5
(G) Wheels, Balance	
one	.3
each adtnl	.2
(G) Check Alignment of Front End	
All models (.4)	.5
Note: Deduct if alignment is performed.	
(G) Toe-In, Adjust	
All models (.4)	.6
(G) Align Front End	
Includes: Adjust front wheel bearings.	
All models (1.1)	1.5
w/A.C. interference add	.5
(G) Front Wheel Bearings, Clean and Repack (Both Wheels)	
1983-87	1.3

LABOR 9 FRONT SUSPENSION 9 LABOR

(Factory Time)	Chilton Time
(G) Front Wheel Bearings and Cups, Renew	
Includes: Repack bearings.	
1983-87-one (.7)	.9
both (1.2)	1.5
(G) Front Wheel Grease Seals, Renew	
Includes: Repack bearings.	
1983-87-one (.6)	.7
both (.9)	1.1
(G) Front Shock Absorber or Bushings, Renew	
1983-87-one (.4)	.6
both (.6)	.8
(G) Rebuild Front Suspension	
Includes: Disassemble, renew necessary parts, reassemble, lubricate and align front end.	
1983-87-one side (4.6)	6.1
both sides (7.8)	9.5
(G) Front Spindle Assembly, Renew (One)	
Add alignment charges.	
1983-87 (1.2)	2.0
(G) Upper Control Arm Assy., Renew (One)	
Add alignment charges.	
1983-87 (1.0)	1.9
(G) Lower Control Arm Assy., Renew (One)	
Add alignment charges.	
1983-87 (1.2)	2.0
(G) Ball Joints, Renew	
Add alignment charges.	
1983-87-upper or lower	
one side	1.2
both sides	1.9
upper or lower	
one side	1.6
both sides	2.5
(G) Upper Control Arm Shaft or Bushings, Renew	
Add alignment charges.	
1983-87-one (1.2)	1.6
both (1.9)	2.8
(G) Front Stabilizer Bar, Renew	
1983-87 (.6)	1.0
(G) Front Stabilizer Bushings, Renew	
1983-87 (.5)	.7
(G) Front Spring, Renew	
1983-87-one (1.1)	1.5
both (2.0)	2.7
(G) Control Arm Rubber Bumpers, Renew	
one (.3)	.4
each adtnl (.1)	.1

PARTS 9 FRONT SUSPENSION 9 PARTS

	Part No.	Price
Front Wheel Bearing		
1983-87-inner	▲D4AZ-1201A	3.75
outer	▲D0AZ-1216A	8.25
Wheel Bearing Cup		
1983-87-inner	▲D4AZ-1202A	5.00
outer	▲D0AZ-1217B	10.00
Front Wheel Oil Seal		
1983-87	▲C8AZ-1190A	3.00
(1) Lower Control Arm & Joint Assy.		
1983-87-right,		
exc. P/C	▲E0VY-3078A	115.00
left	▲E0VY-3079A	115.00
1983-87-Right,		
P/C	▲E0AZ-3078B	115.00
left	▲E0AZ-3079B	115.00
(2) Seal (Lower Arm)		
1983-87	▲D9AZ-3A105A	4.00
(3) Bumper (Lower)		
1983-87	▲D9AZ-3020A	5.75
(4) Shock Absorber		
(exc./sta. wagon)		
1983-84-exc.		
P/C	▲E1AZ-18124A	25.75
1985	▲E5AZ-18124A	38.75
1983-87-P/C	▲E4AZ-18124A	29.00
(sta. wagon)		
1983-84	▲E1AZ-18124C	25.75
1985	▲E5AZ-18124B	38.50
(5) Spindle Assy.		
1983-87-right	▲D9AZ-3105A	188.00
left	▲D9AZ-3106A	188.00
(6) Insulator (Front Spring)		
1983-87	▲C9AZ-5415B	2.25
(7) Bumper (Upper)		
1983-87	▲D9AZ-3020C	4.75
(8) Seal (Upper Arm)		
1983-87	▲D9AZ-3A105A	4.00
(9) Upper Control Arm & Joint Assy.		
1983-87-right,		
exc. P/C	▲E1AZ-3082A	103.00
left	▲E1AZ-3083A	103.00
1983-87-Right,		
P/C	▲E1AZ-3082B	103.00
left	▲E1AZ-3083B	103.00

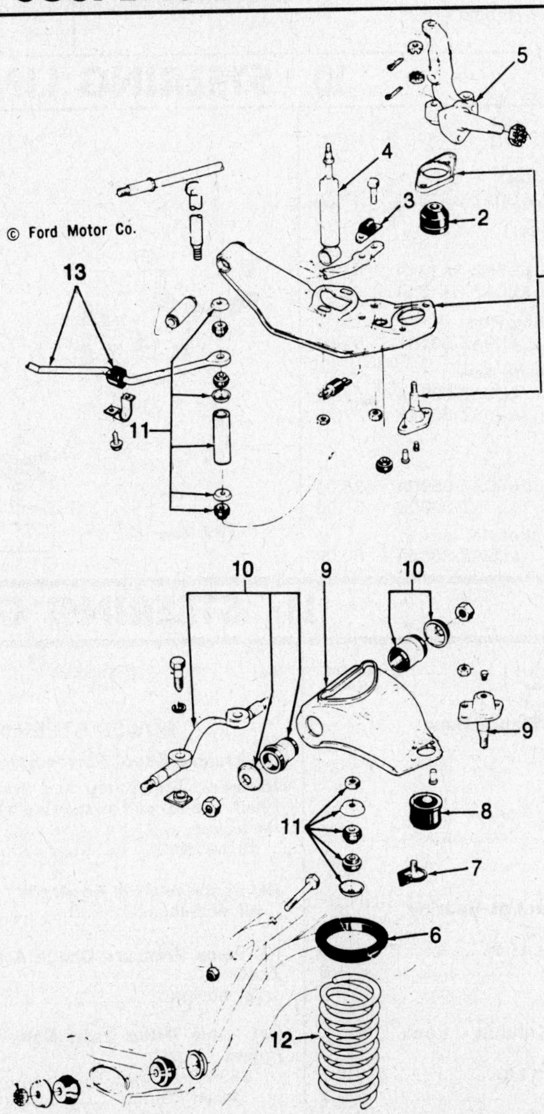

PARTS 9 FRONT SUSPENSION 9 PARTS

	Part No.	Price
(10) Shaft Kit (Upper Arm)		
1983-87-exc.		
P/C	▲D9AZ-3047A	28.75
P/C	▲D9AZ-3047B	48.75
(11) Bushing Kit		
1983-87-exc.		
P/C	▲D7AZ-18198A	2.00
P/C	▲E5AZ-18198A	2.00

(12) Coil Spring
Note: Coil springs must be ordered by the spring identification code on the vehicle certification label located on left door.

	Part No.	Price
(13) Stabilizer Assy.		
(exc./sta. wagon)		
1983-87-Std. susp.	▲D9AZ-5482A	55.75
H.D. susp.	▲D9AZ-5482B	55.75
(sta. wagon)		
1983-87	▲D9AZ-5482C	66.75

LABOR 10 STEERING LINKAGE 10 LABOR

	(Factory Time)	Chilton Time
(G) Tie Rod Ends, Renew		
Includes: Reset toe-in.		
1983-87-one	(.8)	1.2
each adtnl	(.2)	.2
(G) Pitman Arm, Renew		
1983-87-wo/Frame	(.4)	.6
w/Frame	(.5)	.7
(G) Idler Arm, Renew		
Add alignment charges.		
1983-87	(.7)	1.2
Renew bushing add	(.2)	.2
(G) Sector Arm Rod, Renew		
Add alignment charges.		
1983-87	(.8)	1.2

PARTS 10 STEERING LINKAGE 10 PARTS

	Part No.	Price
(1) Tie Rod End (Outer)		
1983-87	▲D9AZ-3A130A	47.00
(2) Tie Rod End (Inner)		
1983-87-exc.		
P/C	▲D9AZ-3A131A	41.00
P/C	▲E0AZ-3A131A	35.75
(3) Sleeve Connecting Rod		
1983-87	▲D9AZ-3310A	11.00
(4) Rod Assy.-Steering Arm		
1983-85	▲D9AZ-3304A	51.75
1986-87	▲E6AZ-3304A	51.75
(5) Pitman Arm		
1983-87-exc.		
P/C	▲E0AZ-3590A	38.00
P/C	▲E0AZ-3590B	37.00
(6) Idler Arm & Bracket Kit		
1983-87	▲D9AZ-3355A	50.00

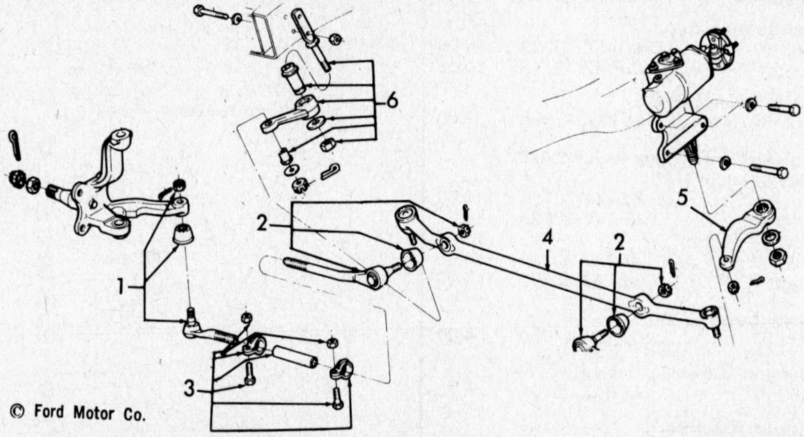

© Ford Motor Co.

LABOR 11 STEERING GEAR 11 LABOR

	(Factory Time)	Chilton Time
(G) Horn Button or Ring, Renew		
1983-87	(.3)	.4
(G) Steering Wheel, Renew		
1983-87	(.3)	.5
(G) Upper Mast Jacket Bearing, Renew		
1983-87-std column	(.5)	.9
tilt column	(.6)	1.0
(G) Steering Column Lock Actuator, Renew		
1983-87-std colm	(1.1)	1.5
tilt colm	(1.7)	2.3

POWER STEERING

	(Factory Time)	Chilton Time
(G) Trouble Shoot Power Steering		
Includes: Test pump and system pressure. Check pounds pull on steering wheel and check for leaks.		
All models		.5
(M) Check and Fill Reservoir		
All models		.2
(G) Pump Pressure Check & Flow Test		
All models		.5
(M) Pump Drive Belt, Renew or Adjust		
1983-87-renew	(.3)	.4
adjust	(.2)	.2
(P) Power Steering Gear, Adjust (On Car)		
Includes: Bearing preload and gear mesh.		
1983-87	(.6)	1.0
(G) Power Steering Gear, Renew		
1983-87	(.8)	1.2
(P) Steering Gear Assy., R&R and Recondition		
Includes: Disassemble, renew necessary parts, reassemble and adjust.		
1983-87	(2.2)	3.5
(G) Sector Shaft and/or Seals, Renew		
Includes: R&R gear and all necessary adjustments.		
1983-87	(1.6)	2.2

LABOR 11 STEERING GEAR 11 LABOR

	(Factory Time)	Chilton Time
(G) Power Steering Oil Pump, Renew		
Includes: Bleed system.		
1983-87	(.7)	1.1
w/A.C. add		.3
(G) Power Steering Pump, R&R and Recondition		
Includes: Bleed system.		
1983-87	(1.1)	1.7
w/A.C. add		.3
(G) Power Steering Reservoir Seals, Renew		
Includes: R&R pump and reservoir. Bleed system.		
1983-87	(1.0)	1.4
w/A.C. add		.3
(G) Power Steering Pump Shaft Seal, Renew		
Includes: R&R pump and bleed system.		
1983-87	(.9)	1.3
w/A.C. add		.3
(M) Power Steering Hoses, Renew		
Includes: Bleed system.		
1983-87-pressure	(.4)	.7
return	(.4)	.5
cooling	(.4)	.5

PARTS 11 POWER STEERING GEAR 11 PARTS

	Part No.	Price
(1) Cover		
1983-87	▲E3AZ-3580A	23.00
(2) Sector Shaft		
1983-87	▲E0AZ-3575A	120.75
(3) Seal Kit (Sector Shaft)		
1983-87	▲D7AZ-3E501B	10.00
(4) Seal Kit (Input Shaft)		
1983-87	▲D7AZ-3E502A	11.00
(5) Housing Assy.		
1983-87	▲D9AZ-3548A	134.75
(6) Input Shaft & Control Assy.		
1983-87	▲E0AZ-3D517B	402.75
(7) Nut (Steering Gear Race)		
1983-87	▲C8AZ-3D627A	6.50
(8) Bearing (Input Shaft)		
1983-87	▲D8AZ-3D525A	8.75

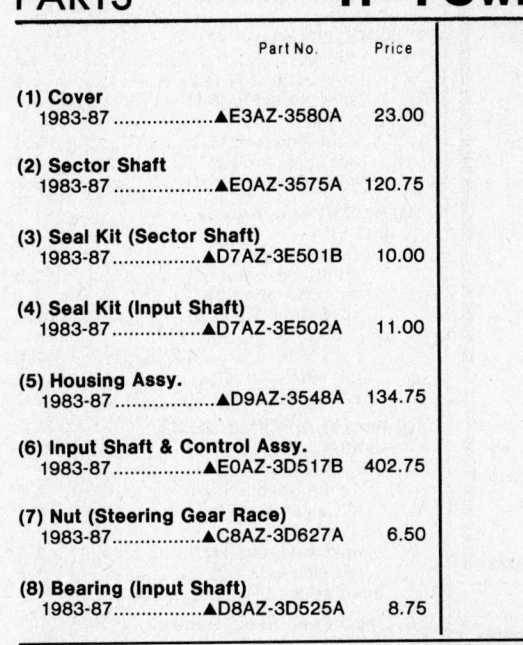

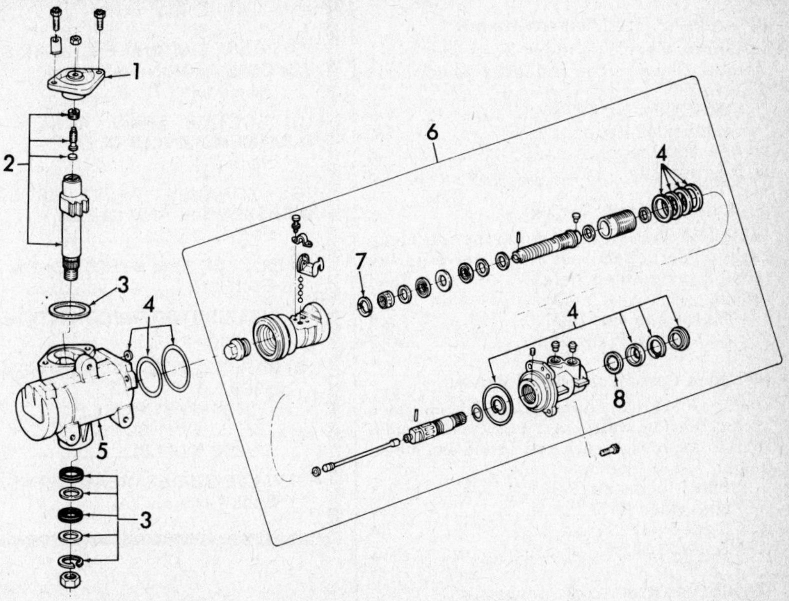

PARTS 11 POWER STEERING PUMP 11 PARTS

	Part No.	Price
Oil Pressure Hose		
1983-87	▲E0AZ-3A719A	26.75
Oil Return Hose		
1983-87	▲E0AZ-3A713A	13.75
Power Steering Pump		
1983-85-exc. P/C	▲E5AZ-3A674A	215.75
1986-87	▲E6AZ-3A674A	215.75
1983-84-P/C	▲E1LY-3A674A	N.L.
1985	▲E5VY-3A674A	220.00
1986-87	▲E6VY-3A674A	220.00
(1) Seal & Gasket Kit		
1983-87	▲E1AZ-3D684A	3.00
(2) Valve Assy.		
1983-87	▲E1AZ-3A561A	11.00
(3) Valve Spring (Flow Control)		
1983-87	▲D8AZ-3D586A	1.50
(4) Housing Assy.		
1983-87	▲E1AZ-3A643A	42.25
(5) Pressure Plate (Front)		
1983	▲D8AZ-3D590A	N.L.
1984-87	▲E5FZ-3D590A	13.75
(6) Rotor Assy.		
1983-87	▲E5SZ-3D607A	38.75

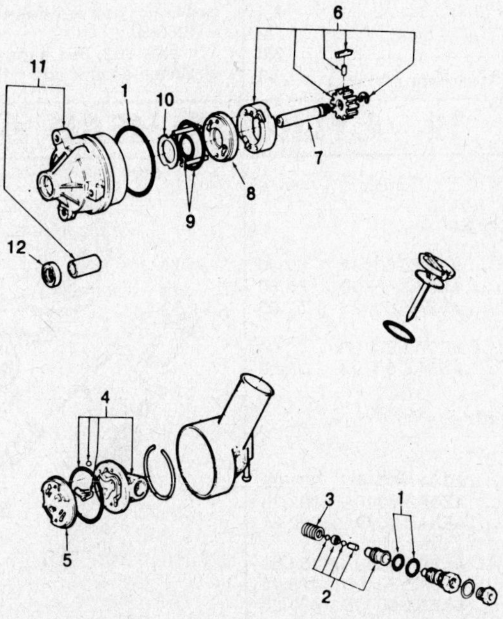

PARTS 11 POWER STEERING PUMP 11 PARTS

	Part No.	Price
(7) Rotor Shaft		
1983-87	▲D8AZ-3B559A	18.00
(8) Pressure Plate (Rear)		
1983-87	▲D8AZ-3D590B	13.75
(9) Seal & Gasket Kit		
1983-87	▲E1AZ-3B584A	8.75
(10) Spring (Pressure Plate)		
1983-85	▲D8AZ-3D596A	2.50
1986-87	▲E6FZ-3D596A	2.50
(11) Plate & Bushing		
1983-87	▲E1AZ-3D643A	42.25
(12) Oil Seal (Rotor Shaft)		
1983-87	▲D9AZ-3B592A	9.25

LABOR 12 CYLINDER HEAD & VALVE SYSTEM 12 LABOR

(Factory Time)	Chilton Time
(G) Compression Test	
1983-87 (.5)	.9
w/A.C. add	.3
(G) Cylinder Head Gasket, Renew	
Includes: Check cylinder head and block flatness. Clean carbon and make all necessary adjustments.	
1983-87-one side (3.9)	5.4
both sides (5.0)	7.0
w/A.C. add (.4)	.4
w/P.S. add (.3)	.3
(G) Cylinder Head, Renew	
Includes: Transfer all components, clean carbon. Reface valves, check valve spring tension, assembled height and valve head runout.	
1983-87-one side (5.1)	7.1
both sides (7.4)	10.3
(P) Clean Carbon and Grind Valves	
Includes: R&R cylinder heads, check valve spring tension, valve seat and head runout, stem to guide clearance and spring assembled height. Minor tune up.	
1983-87-one side (5.8)	8.1
both sides (8.7)	12.1
w/A.C. add (.4)	.4
w/P.S. add (.3)	.3
(G) Rocker Arm Cover or Gasket, Renew	
1983-87	
255, 302, engs-right (.9)	1.2
left (.7)	1.0
both (1.2)	1.7
351 eng-right (1.5)	2.1
left (.6)	.9
both (1.7)	2.5
w/Cruise control add (.1)	.1

COMBINATIONS

Add to Valve Job

See Machine Shop Operations

(Factory Time)	Chilton Time
(G) DRAIN, EVACUATE & RECHARGE AIR CONDITIONING SYSTEM	
All models (.7)	1.2
(G) ROCKER ARMS, RENEW OR DISASSEMBLE AND CLEAN	
Each (.1)	.1
(G) HYDRAULIC VALVE LIFTERS, DISASSEMBLE AND CLEAN	
Each	.2
(G) ROCKER ARM STUD, RENEW	
Each (.2)	.2
(G) DISTRIBUTOR, RECONDITION	
All models (.7)	1.0
(G) CARBURETOR, RECONDITION	
1983-87	
2150-2V (1.0)	1.5
2700 VV (1.8)	2.4
7200 VV (1.9)	2.5
(P) VALVE GUIDES, REAM OVERSIZE	
Each (.1)	.1

(Factory Time)	Chilton Time
(G) Valve Tappets, Renew	
Includes: R&R intake manifold, adjust carburetor and ignition timing.	
1983-87	
255, 302, 351 engs (3.4)	5.0
w/Cruise control add (.1)	.1

(Factory Time)	Chilton Time
(G) Valve Spring or Valve Stem Oil Seals, Renew (Head on Car)	
1983-87	
255, 302 engs	
one (.8)	1.4
one-each side (1.2)	1.9
all-both sides (3.2)	4.8
351 eng	
right side-one (1.7)	2.4
left side-one (.8)	1.2
all-both sides (4.1)	5.7
(G) Rocker Arm, Renew	
1983-87	
255, 302 engs	
right side-one (1.0)	1.3
left side-one (.8)	1.1
all-both sides (1.5)	2.0
351 eng	
right side-one (1.6)	2.2
left side-one (.7)	1.0
all-both sides (2.0)	2.9
(G) Rocker Arm Stud, Renew	
1983-87	
255, 302 engs	
right side-one (.8)	1.4
left side-one (.7)	1.2
351 eng	
right side-one (1.7)	2.4
left side-one (.8)	1.2
each adtnl (.2)	.2
(G) Valve Push Rods, Renew	
1983-87	
255, 302 engs	
right side-one (.7)	1.4
left side-one (.6)	1.2
all-both sides (1.1)	2.2
351 eng	
right side-one (1.6)	2.2
left side-one (.7)	1.0
all-both sides (2.0)	3.0

PARTS 12 CYLINDER HEAD & VALVE SYSTEM 12 PARTS

	Part No.	Price
Valve Grind Gasket Set		
V-8-302 engine		
1983-84-wo/H.O.	▲E1AZ-6079A	61.00
1985	▲E5ZZ-6079B	52.50
1983-84-w/H.O.	▲E2ZZ-6079B	52.50
V-8-351 engine		
1983-84	▲D9AZ-6079B	70.00
1985-87	▲E5AZ-6079A	70.00
(1) Cylinder Head (New)		
V-8-302 engine		
(wo/valves)		
1983-84	▲D84Y-6049C	281.25
1985	▲E5AZ-6049A	302.25
1986-87	▲E6AZ-6049A	302.25
(w/valves)		
1983-84	▲E2AZ-6049A	461.50
1985	▲E5AZ-6049B	429.25
1986-87	▲E6AZ-6049B	429.25

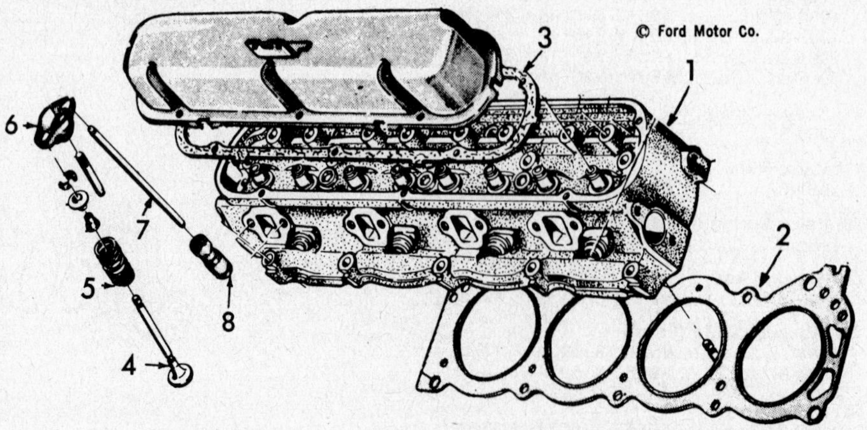

PARTS 12 CYLINDER HEAD & VALVE SYSTEM 12 PARTS

	Part No.	Price
V-8-351 engine		
(exc. H.O. eng.)		
1983-84 (wo/E.E.C.)		
wo/Valves	▲D9TZ-6049A	N.L.
w/Valves	▲D9TZ-6049B	524.25
1983-84 (w/E.E.C.)		
wo/Valves	▲D9AZ-6049A	N.L.
w/Valves	▲D8UZ-6049A	487.75
1985-87-wo/valves	▲E5TZ-6049D	365.25
w/valves	▲E5TZ-6049J	524.25
(w/H.O. eng.)		
1983-84-exc. P/C	▲E0AZ-6049A	524.25
P/C	▲E1AZ-6049A	524.25
1985-87-wo/valves	▲E5TZ-6049D	365.25
w/valves	▲E5TZ-6049J	524.25
(2) Cylinder Head Gasket		
V-8-302 engine		
1983-84	▲D7OZ-6051C	12.50
1985	▲E5AZ-6051A	11.50
1986-87	▲E5ZZ-6051B	13.75
V-8-351 engine		
1983-87-w/351W eng	▲D7OZ-6051C	12.50

	Part No.	Price
(3) Valve Cover Gasket		
1983-85-w/302	▲E3AZ-6584A	4.75
1986-87	▲E5TZ-6584C	4.75
1983-84-w/351	▲E3AZ-6584A	4.75
1985-87	▲E5TZ-6584C	4.75
(4) Intake Valve		
V-8-302 engine		
1983-85	▲E3ZZ-6507A	7.75
1986-87	▲E6AZ-6507A	7.50
V-8-351 engine		
1983-87-exc. P/C	▲E3ZZ-6507A	7.75
P/C	▲E0AZ-6507A	8.75
Exhaust Valve		
V-8-302 engine		
1983-85	▲E4AZ-6505A	8.00
1986-87	▲E6AZ-6505A	8.00
V-8-351 engine		
1983	▲E2AZ-6505D	8.25
1984-87	▲E4AZ-6505A	8.00

	Part No.	Price
(5) Valve Springs		
1983-87-intake	▲D8AZ-6513B	5.75
exhaust	▲D5OZ-6513A	6.75
1983-87-w/351 H.O.		
intake	▲E0AZ-6513A	3.00
exhaust	▲D74Y-6513A	6.75
(6) Rocker Arms		
1983-87	▲E0AZ-6564A	11.00
Rocker Arm Stud		
1983-87	▲D8AZ-6A527A	2.25
(7) Valve Push Rod		
V-8-302 engine		
1983-85	▲C9OZ-6565B	2.75
1986-87	▲E5AZ-6565A	4.00
V-8-351 engine		
1983-87	▲D8AZ-6565A	2.75
(8) Valve Lifters–Hydraulic		
1983-85-w/302	▲D9HZ-6500A	9.25
1986-87	▲E5AZ-6500A	7.00
1983-87-w/351	▲D9HZ-6500A	9.25

LABOR 13 ENGINE ASSEMBLY & MOUNTS 13 LABOR

(Factory Time) Chilton Time

(G) Engine Assembly, Remove and Install

Does not include transfer of any parts or equipment.

	Chilton Time
1983-87 (4.8)	**6.2**
w/A.C. add (.5)	**.5**
w/P.S. add	**.2**

(G) Engine Assembly, Replace with New or Rebuilt Unit (with Cyl Heads)

Includes: R&R engine assembly, transfer all necessary parts, fuel and electrical units. Minor tune up.

	Chilton Time
1983-87 (7.1)	**9.6**
w/A.C. add	**.5**
w/P.S. add	**.2**

(G) Cylinder Assembly, Renew (w/All Internal Parts Less Head(s) and Oil Pan)

Includes: R&R engine, transfer all component parts not supplied with replacement engine, clean carbon, grind valves. Minor tune up.

	Chilton Time
1983-87 (14.7)	**20.0**
w/A.C. add	**.5**
w/P.S. add	**.2**
Clean oil pump add (.3)	**.3**

(P) Cylinder Block, Renew

Includes: R&R engine, transfer all component parts, renew rings and bearings, clean carbon, grind valves. Minor tune up.

	Chilton Time
1983-87 (19.1)	**26.1**
w/A.C. add	**.5**
w/P.S. add	**.2**
Clean oil pump add (.3)	**.3**

(P) Engine Assy., R&R and Recondition (Complete)

Includes: Rebore block, install new pistons, rings, rod and main bearings. Clean carbon, grind valves. Tune engine.

	Chilton Time
1983-87 (26.8)	**31.8**
w/A.C. add	**.5**
w/P.S. add	**.2**

(P) Engine Assembly, Recondition (In Car)

Includes: Expand or renew pistons, install new rings, pins, rod and main bearings. Clean carbon and grind valves. Tune engine.

	Chilton Time
1983-87 (23.6)	**29.4**
w/A.C. add	**.5**
w/P.S. add	**.2**

(G) Engine Mounts, Renew

	Chilton Time
Front	
1983-87-one (.7)	**.9**
both (1.0)	**1.3**
Rear	
1983-87 (.3)	**.6**

PARTS 13 ENGINE ASSEMBLY & MOUNTS 13 PARTS

	Part No.	Price
Engine Assembly (New)		
V-8-302 engine		
1983-84	▲E3AZ-6009A	2044.75
1985-wo/CFI	▲E5AZ-6009A	2044.75
w/CFI	▲E5AZ-6009B	2044.75
1986-87	▲E6AZ-6009A	2044.75
V-8-351 engine		
1983-87	▲D9AZ-6009A	2164.00
Cylinder Block Stripped (New)		
V-8-302 engine		
1983-85	▲E3AZ-6010A	856.25
1986-87	▲E6AZ-6010A	920.25

	Part No.	Price
V-8-351 engine		
1983-w/2 piece seal	▲D9UZ-6010A	1011.25
1983-87-w/1 piece seal	▲E3AZ-6010B	1011.25
Engine Overhaul Seal & Gasket Set		
V-8-302 engine		
1983-87	▲E3AZ-6E078A	27.75
V-8-351 engine		
1983-87	▲E3AZ-6E078B	21.25

When a complete overhaul gasket set is required you must also order a valve grind gasket set.

	Part No.	Price
Engine Mounts–Front		
1983-87-right	▲D9AZ-6038A	35.25
left	▲D9AZ-6038B	40.50
Engine Mounts–Rear		
1983-87-exc. sta. wagon	▲D9AZ-6068A	22.50
1985-87-sta. wagon	▲E0LZ-6068A	22.50

LABOR 14 PISTONS, RINGS & BEARINGS 14 LABOR

(Factory Time) Chilton Time

(P) Rings, Renew (See Engine Combinations)

Includes: Remove cylinder top ridge, deglaze cylinder walls, replace rod bearings. Clean carbon from cyl head and pistons. Minor tune up.

1983-87 (11.5)	16.6
w/A.C. add	.5
w/P.S. add	.2
Clean, test or renew spark plugs, add	.3

(P) Piston or Connecting Rod, Renew (One)

Includes: Remove cylinder top ridge, deglaze cylinder walls, replace rod bearings, clean carbon. Minor tune up.

1983-87 (7.4)	10.7
w/A.C. add	.5
w/P.S. add	.2
Clean, test or renew spark plugs, add	.3

(P) Connecting Rod Bearings, Renew

1983-87 (4.2)	5.8
w/P.S. add	.1
Clean oil pump add	.3

COMBINATIONS
Add to Engine Work
See Machine Shop Operations

(G) DRAIN, EVACUATE & RECHARGE AIR CONDITIONING SYSTEM
All models (.7) 1.2

(G) ROCKER ARMS, RENEW OR DISASSEMBLE AND CLEAN
Each (.1) 1

(G) HYDRAULIC VALVE LIFTERS, DISASSEMBLE AND CLEAN
Each 2

(G) ROCKER ARM STUD, RENEW
Each (.2) 2

(G) DISTRIBUTOR, RECONDITION
All models (.7) 1.0

(G) CARBURETOR, RECONDITION
1983-87
2150-2V (1.0) 1.5
2700-VV (1.8) 2.4
7200 VV (1.9) 2.5

(G) CYLINDER HEAD, R&R (ENGINE REMOVED)
V-8
one 3.5
both 5.0

(G) CONNECTING ROD, RENEW (ENGINE DISASSEMBLED)
V-8
each 4

(G) DEGLAZE CYLINDER WALLS
Each (.1) 1

(G) REMOVE CYLINDER TOP RIDGE
Each (.1) 1

(G) TIMING CHAIN OR GEARS, RENEW (COVER REMOVED)
All models (.3) 5

(G) MAIN BEARINGS, RENEW (PAN REMOVED)
All models (1.9) 2.5

(G) PLASTIGAUGE BEARINGS
Each (.1) 1

(G) OIL PUMP, RECONDITION
All models (.3) 5

(M) OIL FILTER ELEMENT, RENEW
All models (.3) 3

PARTS 14 PISTONS, RINGS & BEARINGS 14 PARTS

	Part No.	Price
(1) Piston Ring Set		
V-8-302 engine		
1983-85	▲C3AZ-6148F	31.75
1986-87	▲E6AZ-6148A	31.75
V-8-351 engine		
1983-87	▲C3AZ-6148F	31.75
(2) Piston Pin		
1983-87	▲B2AZ-6135A	5.25
(3) Piston Assembly (Std.)		
V-8-302 engine		
1983-85	▲D9AZ-6108A	35.00
1986-87	▲E6AZ-6108A	35.50
V-8-351 engine		
1983-87	▲D9AZ-6108G	36.75
(4) Connecting Rod Assy.		
V-8-302 engine		
1983-87	▲D3OZ-6200A	44.00
V-8-351 engine		
1983-87	▲D5UZ-6200A	47.00

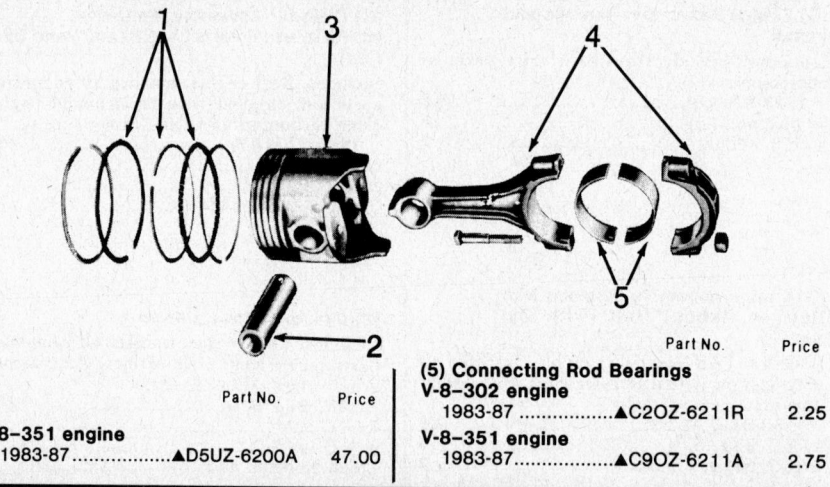

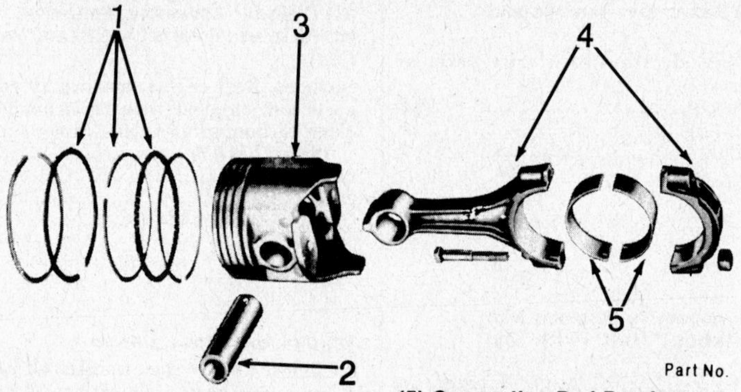

	Part No.	Price
(5) Connecting Rod Bearings		
V-8-302 engine		
1983-87	▲C2OZ-6211R	2.25
V-8-351 engine		
1983-87	▲C9OZ-6211A	2.75

LABOR 15 CRANKSHAFT & DAMPER 15 LABOR

(Factory Time) Chilton Time

(P) Crankshaft and Main Bearings, Renew

Includes: R&R engine, check all bearing clearances.

1983-87 (8.1)	12.0
w/A.C. add	.3
w/P.S. add	.2
Clean oil pump add	.3

(P) Main Bearings, Renew

Includes: Check all bearing clearances.

1983-87 (4.3)	6.0

(P) Main and Rod Bearings, Renew

Includes: Check all bearing clearances.

1983-87 (6.1)	8.4

(G) Rear Main Bearing Oil Seals, Renew (Upper & Lower) Split Lip Type

1983 (3.0)	4.3

(G) Rear Main Bearing Oil Seal, Renew Full Circle Type

1983-87	
w/AOD (2.8)	4.2

(G) Vibration Damper or Pulley, Renew

1983-87 (.8)	1.4
w/A.C. add	.1
w/P.S. add	.1

(G) Crankshaft Front Oil Seal, Renew

1983-87 (.9)	1.5
w/A.C. add	.1
w/P.S. add	.1

PARTS 15 CRANKSHAFT & DAMPER 15 PARTS

	Part No.	Price
(1) Crankshaft (New)		
V-8-302 engine		
1983-87	▲E3AZ-6303A	500.75
V-8-351 engine		
1983-87	▲E3AZ-6303B	484.25
(2) Main Bearings		
V-8-302 engine		
1983-87 (Upper bearing)		
exc. center	▲C3AZ-6333P	3.50
center	▲C3AZ-6337P	8.00
1983-87 (Lower bearing)		
exc. center	▲C3AZ-6333AA	3.50
center	▲C3AZ-6337AA	8.00
V-8-351 engine		
1983-87 (Upper bearing)		
exc. center	▲D7AZ-6333A	3.75
center	▲D1AZ-6337A	8.75
1983-87 (Lower bearing)		
exc. center	▲D7AZ-6333G	3.75
center	▲D1AZ-6337A	8.75
(3) Rear Main Bearing Oil Seal		
V-8-302 engine		
1983-rope type	▲C9OZ-6701A	2.00
1983-split type	▲D4FZ-6701A	6.25

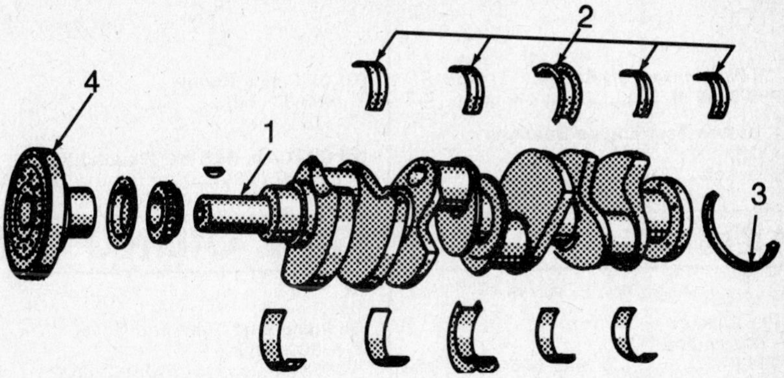

	Part No.	Price
1983-87-one piece	▲E5ZZ-6701A	6.25
V-8-351 engine		
1983-rope type	▲C9OZ-6701A	2.00
1983-split type	▲D0OZ-6701A	5.00
1983-87-one piece	▲E3TZ-6701A	19.50

	Part No.	Price
(4) Vibration Damper or Pulley		
V-8-302 engine		
1983-exc. Canada	▲E2TZ-6316B	74.00
1983-Canada	▲E1TZ-6316A	65.00
1984-87	▲E4TZ-6316A	67.75
V-8-351 engine		
1983-87	▲E4TZ-6316B	67.75

LABOR 16 CAMSHAFT & TIMING GEARS 16 LABOR

	(Factory Time)	Chilton Time
(G) Timing Case Seal and Gaskets, Renew		
Includes: R&R radiator and oil pan where required.		
1983-87	(2.3)	**3.4**
w/A.C. add		**.5**
w/P.S. add		**.2**
(G) Timing Chain or Sprockets, Renew		
Includes: Adjust timing.		
1983-87	(2.6)	**3.8**
w/A.C. add		**.5**
w/P.S. add		**.2**

	(Factory Time)	Chilton Time
(G) Camshaft, Renew		
Includes: R&R oil pan where required.		
1983-87	(5.8)	**8.1**
w/A.C. add		**.5**
w/P.S. add		**.3**
(P) Camshaft Bearings, Renew		
Includes: R&R engine and crankshaft.		
1983-87	(9.1)	**12.9**
w/A.C. add		**.5**
w/P.S. add		**.3**
(G) Camshaft Rear Welsh Plug, Renew		
Includes: R&R trans and flywheel for accessibility.		
1983-87	(3.3)	**4.5**

PARTS 16 CAMSHAFT & TIMING GEARS 16 PARTS

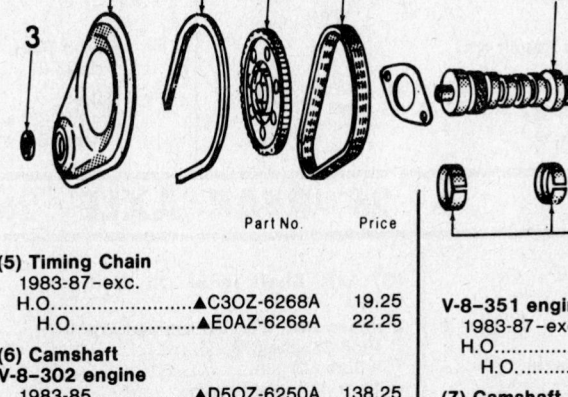

	Part No.	Price
(1) Timing Case Cover		
1983-wo/E.E.C.	▲E0AZ-6019B	126.50
1983-85-w/E.E.C.	▲E4AZ-6019C	126.50
1984-85-w/CFI	▲E4AZ-6019C	126.50
1984-87	▲E4AZ-6019B	126.50
(2) Timing Case Cover Gasket		
1983-87	▲E3AZ-6020A	1.50
(3) Timing Case Cover Oil Seal		
1983-87	▲D0AZ-6700A	6.75
(4) Camshaft Sprocket		
1983-87-exc. P/C	▲D3AZ-6256B	22.25
P/C	▲E4AZ-6256A	26.00
Crankshaft Sprocket		
1983-87-exc. H.O.	▲D5OZ-6306A	11.25
H.O.	▲E0AZ-6306A	18.50

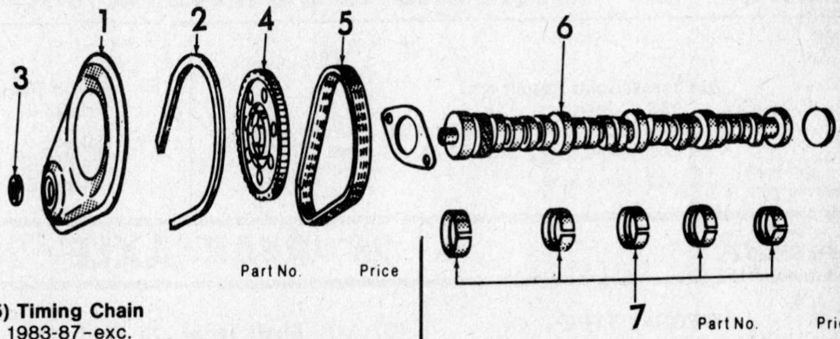

	Part No.	Price
(5) Timing Chain		
1983-87-exc. H.O.	▲C3OZ-6268A	19.25
H.O.	▲E0AZ-6268A	22.25
(6) Camshaft		
V-8-302 engine		
1983-85	▲D5OZ-6250A	138.25
1986-87	▲E5AZ-6250A	138.75

	Part No.	Price
V-8-351 engine		
1983-87-exc. H.O.	▲D6OZ-6250C	141.50
H.O.	▲E0AZ-6250A	141.50
(7) Camshaft Bearing Set		
1983-87	▲C2OZ-6A251A	23.50

LABOR 17 ENGINE OILING SYSTEM 17 LABOR

	(Factory Time)	Chilton Time
(G) Oil Pan or Gasket, Renew		
1983-87	(2.4)	3.2
(P) Pressure Test Engine Bearings (Pan Off)		
All models		1.0
(G) Oil Pump, Renew		
1983-87	(2.5)	3.4
(G) Oil Pump, R&R and Recondition		
1983-87	(2.8)	3.7
(G) Oil Pressure Gauge (Engine), Renew		
1983-87	(.3)	.4
(M) Oil Filter Element, Renew		
1983-87	(.3)	.3

PARTS 17 ENGINE OILING SYSTEM 17 PARTS

	Part No.	Price
Oil Pan Gasket		
V-8-302 engine		
1983-87	▲D9AZ-6781A	11.50
V-8-351 engine		
1983-87	▲D0AZ-6781C	11.50
Oil Pump (New)		
V-8-302 engine		
1983-87	▲C2OZ-6600A	52.50
V-8-351 engine		
1983-87	▲D9AZ-6600A	53.25
Oil Pump Inlet Tube and Cover		
V-8-302 engine		
1983-87	▲E0SZ-6622A	28.00
V-8-351 engine		
1983-87	▲D9AZ-6622B	18.50
Oil Pressure Gauge-Engine Unit		
1983-87-w/302 eng.	▲D4AZ-9278A	3.50
w/351 eng.	▲E0AZ-9278A	5.75
Oil Filter Element		
1983-87	▲D9AZ-6731A	8.00
Oil Pump Shaft		
V-8-302 engine		
1983-87	▲D8AZ-6A618A	7.50
V-8-351 engine		
1983-87	▲D9AZ-6A618A	6.75

LABOR 21 SHIFT LINKAGE 21 LABOR

	(Factory Time)	Chilton Time
AUTOMATIC		
(G) Linkage, Adjust		
manual	(.3)	.4
throttle	(.3)	.5
manual & throttle	(.5)	.7
kickdown	(.3)	.5
(G) Gear Selector Lever, Renew		
1983-87	(.4)	.5
(G) Gearshift Tube Assembly, Renew		
Includes: Adjust neutral switch when required.		
1983-87	(1.3)	1.8
Tilt wheel	(1.2)	1.7
(G) Tilt Wheel Pivot, Recondition (In Chassis)		
1983-87	(.7)	1.0

LABOR 25 U-JOINTS & DRIVESHAFT 25 LABOR

	(Factory Time)	Chilton Time
(G) Universal Joints, Renew or Recondition		
Includes: R&R drive shaft.		
1983-87		
Double Cardan		
front or rear	(.9)	1.3
all	(1.5)	2.0
Single Cardan		
front or rear	(.6)	.9
both	(.8)	1.3
(G) Driveshaft, Renew		
1983-87	(.3)	.5

PARTS 25 UNIVERSAL JOINTS & DRIVE SHAFT 25 PARTS

	Part No.	Price
Universal Joint Repair Kit		
1983-87-exc below	▲D3AZ-4635E	15.00
w/Towing pkg	▲D3AZ-4635G	17.25
Pinion Bearing Spacer		
1983-87	▲B7A-4662A	4.00
Yoke		
1983-87-w/302	▲E1DZ-4782A	14.25
1983-87-w/351	▲D9AZ-4782B	13.50

LABOR 26 REAR AXLE 26 LABOR

	(Factory Time)	Chilton Time
INTEGRAL TYPE		
(M) Differential, Drain & Refill		
All models		.6
(M) Axle Housing Cover or Gasket, Renew		
All models	(.4)	.6
(G) Axle Shaft Inner Oil Seal, Renew		
Includes: R&R wheel, drum and axle shaft.		
1983-87-one	(.7)	.9
both	(.9)	1.3
w/Rear disc brakes add		
each side	(.3)	.3
(G) Rear Wheel Bearings, Renew		
1983-87-one	(.7)	1.0
both	(1.0)	1.5
(G) Axle Shaft, Renew		
Includes: Renew inner oil seal.		
1983-87-one	(.6)	.8
both	(.8)	1.2

LABOR 26 REAR AXLE 26 LABOR

	(Factory Time)	Chilton Time
(G) Axle Shaft Wheel Mounting Studs, Renew		
1983-87-one		.8
all		1.2
(G) Pinion Shaft Oil Seal, Renew		
1983-87	(.8)	1.3
(P) Differential Carrier Assy., Recondition (In Chassis)		
Includes: Drain and refill axle, renew necessary parts. Renew axle shaft oil seals. Road test.		
1983-87	(3.9)	5.6
(P) Differential Case, Recondition		
Does not include overhaul of pinion assembly.		
1983-87		
std	(1.2)	2.1
lock	(2.1)	3.3
(P) Axle Housing, Renew		
Includes: Transfer all necessary parts, adjust ring gear and pinion.		
Does not include disassembly of differential case.		
1983-87	(3.6)	5.2
Recond diff assy add	(.4)	.8
(P) Pinion Shaft Bearings, Renew		
1983-87		4.5
(P) Carrier Bearings, Renew		
1983-87		2.6
(P) Ring and Pinion Set, Renew		
Includes: R&R axle shafts, drain and refill unit. Road test.		
1983-87	(2.7)	3.8
(P) Ring and Pinion, Adjust (In Chassis)		
Includes: Remove axle shafts, drain and refill unit. Road test.		
1983-87	(1.5)	2.3

PARTS 26 REAR AXLE 26 PARTS

	Part No.	Price
(1) Cover Assy.		
1983-87	▲E3AZ-4033A	15.00
Serviced with silicone rubber instead of gasket.		
(2) Pinion Kit		
1983-87	▲E3TZ-4215A	34.50
(3) Side Gear		
1983-87	▲E0AZ-4236A	102.25
(4) Shim		
1983-87	▲D9AZ-4067A	3.25
Smallest sizes listed larger sizes available.		
(5) Bearing Cup		
1983-87	▲D9AZ-4222A	7.25
(6) Bearing Assy.		
1983-87	▲B7A-4221B	12.50
(7) Pinion Shaft		
1983-87	▲B7AZ-4211A	9.00
(8) Case Assy.		
1983-87	▲E3AZ-4204A	105.75
(9) Housing Assy.		
1983-87	▲D9AZ-4010B	712.75
(10) Ring Gear & Pinion Kit w/8.8" ring gear		
1983-87-2.73 to 1	▲E3AZ-4209A	319.25
3.08 to 1	▲E3TZ-4209H	381.75
3.55 to 1	▲E3TZ-4209J	381.75
1986-87-3.27 to 1	▲E6LY-4209A	319.25
(11) Pinion Bearing (Rear)		
1983-87	▲C7AZ-4630A	15.75
(12) Bearing Cup (Rear)		
1983-87	▲C7AZ-4628A	8.00
(13) Axle Shaft Oil Seal		
1983-87	▲E1AZ-1177B	3.50
(14) Axle Shaft Bearing		
1983-87	▲C7AZ-1225A	15.75
(15) Axle Shaft Assy. (Rear)		
1983-87	▲D9AZ-4234A	132.00

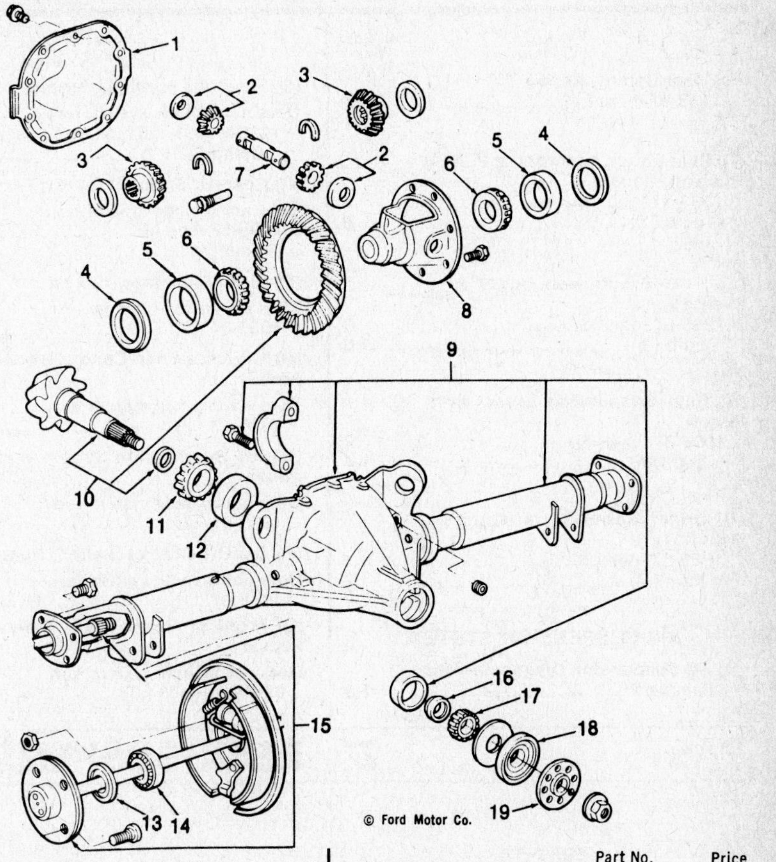

	Part No.	Price
(16) Spacer		
1983-87	▲B7A-4662A	4.00
(17) Pinion Bearing (Front)		
1983-87	▲B7A-4621A	11.50
(18) Pinion Oil Seal		
1983-87	▲E3TZ-4676A	11.25
(19) Flange Assy. (U-Joint)		
1983	▲D8BZ-4851A	17.00
1984-87	▲E3AZ-4851A	20.75

PARTS 26 NON-SLIP DIFFERENTIAL 26 PARTS

	Part No.	Price
(1) Case Assy.		
1983-87	▲E3AZ-4204B	169.50
(2) Bearing (Case)		
1983-87	▲B7A-4221B	12.50
(3) Cup		
1983-87	▲D9AZ-4222A	7.25
(4) Shim (Bearing)		
1983-87	▲D9AZ-4067A	3.25
Smallest size listed, larger sizes available.		
(5) Clutch Shim		
1983-87	▲E0AZ-4A324A	1.00
Smallest size listed, larger sizes available.		
(6) Clutch Plate Kit		
1983-87	▲E2AZ-4947A	31.75

PARTS 26 NON-SLIP DIFFERENTIAL 26 PARTS

	Part No.	Price
(7) Side Gear		
1983-87	▲E0AZ-4236A	102.25
(8) Pinion Kit		
1983-87	▲E3TZ-4215A	34.50
(9) U Washer (Retaining)		
1983-87	▲C7AZ-4N237A	1.50
(10) Pinion Shaft		
1983-87	▲B7AZ-4211A	9.00
(11) Lock Pin (Pinion Shaft)		
1983-87	▲D8BZ-4241A	2.00

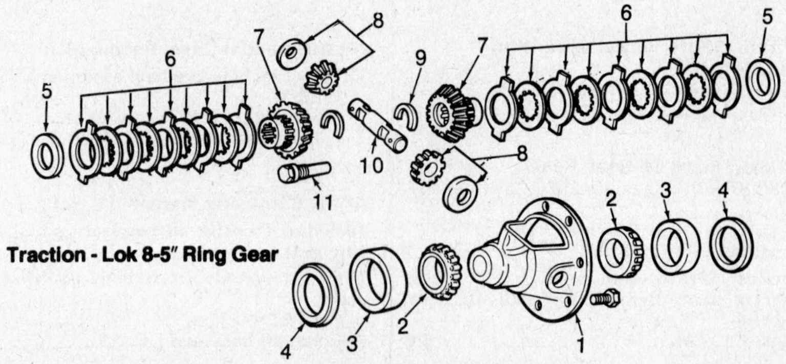

LABOR 27 REAR SUSPENSION 27 LABOR

	(Factory Time)	Chilton Time
(G) Rear Spring, Renew		
1983-87-both	(.4)	.6
(G) Rear Shock Absorber or Rubber Bushing, Renew		
1983-87-one	(.4)	.6
both	(.5)	.8
(G) Rear Suspension Upper Arm, Renew		
1983-87-one	(.5)	.9
both	(.8)	1.5
(G) Rear Suspension Lower Arm, Renew		
1983-87-one	(.5)	.9
both	(.7)	1.4
(G) Upper Control Arm Bushings, Renew		
1983-87-one	(.5)	1.1
both	(.7)	1.4
AIR SUSPENSION SYSTEM		
(G) Air Suspension Diagnosis Test		
All models		1.0
(G) Front Air Springs, Renew		
Does not include system test.		
1985-87-one	(.3)	.5
both	(.5)	.9
(G) Rear Air Springs, Renew		
Does not include system test.		
1985-87-one	(.5)	.8
both	(.9)	1.5
(G) Air Compressor, Renew		
Does not include system test.		
1985-87	(.3)	.5
(G) Air Suspension Control Module, Renew		
Does not include system test.		
1985-87	(.2)	.4
(G) Air Suspension Dryer Assy., Renew		
Does not include system test.		
1985-87	(.2)	.4
(G) On/Off Control Switch, Renew		
Does not include system test.		
1985-87	(.1)	.3
(G) Front or Rear Height Sensor, Renew		
Does not include system test.		
1985-87-each	(.3)	.4
(G) Air Spring Valve, Renew		
Does not include system test.		
1985-87	(.3)	.4
(G) Air Compressor Relay, Renew		
Does not include system test.		
1985-87	(.2)	.3
(G) Rear Suspension Lower Control Arms, Renew		
1985-87-both	(2.4)	3.3
(G) Rear Suspension Upper Control Arms, Renew		
1985-87-both	(1.0)	1.5
(G) Upper Control Arm Bushings, Renew		
1985-87-upper	(.6)	.9
lower	(.5)	.8
both	(.8)	1.4
(G) Rear Sway Bar, Renew		
1985-87	(.6)	.9
(G) Rear Shock Absorbers, Renew		
1985-87-one	(.5)	.7
both	(.6)	.9

PARTS 27 REAR SUSPENSION 27 PARTS

	Part No.	Price
1983-87		
(1) Lower Control Arm		
1983-87-exc. below	▲D9AZ-5A649E	49.25
Sta. wagon	▲D9AZ-5A649B	49.25
P/C-right	▲D9AZ-5A649C	49.25
left	▲D9AZ-5A649D	49.25
(2) Coil Spring		
Order by model and description.		
(3) Insulator (Spring)		
1983-87	▲D9AZ-5536A	3.00
(4) Shock Absorber		
1983-84-exc. below	▲E1AZ-18125A	31.00

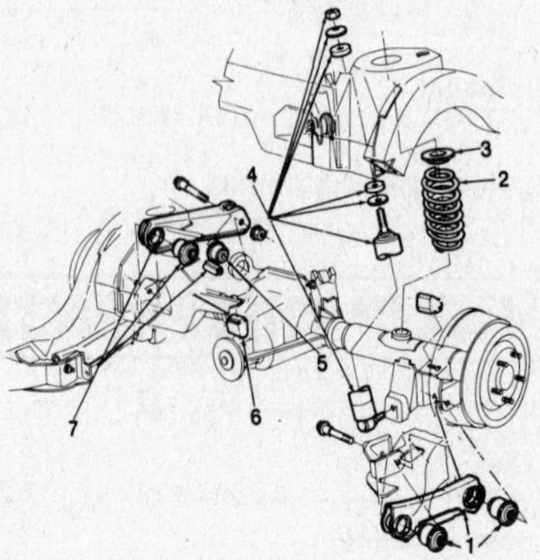

	Part No.	Price
sta. wagon	▲E2AZ-18125A	31.00
P/C	▲E4AZ-18125A	31.00
1985-87-exc. below	▲E5AZ-18125A	41.25
sta. wagon	▲E5AZ-18125B	41.25
P/C	▲E4AZ-18125A	31.00
(5) Bushing (Rear Arm)		
1983-85	▲E0AZ-5A638A	10.00
1986-87	▲E6AZ-5A638A	10.00
(6) Bumper		
1983-87	▲D9AZ-4730A	5.50
(7) Upper Control Arm		
1983-84	▲D9AZ-5500C	42.50
1985-87	▲E5AZ-5500A	42.50

LABOR 28 AIR CONDITIONING 28 LABOR

(Factory Time) Chilton Time

Note: If more than one item requires replacement where evacuation and discharging the system is already included in the operation, deduct 1.0 hour for each additional item to the times listed.

(G) Drain, Evacuate and Recharge System
Includes: Check for leaks.
All models (.7) 1.2

(G) Pressure Test System
All models 6

(G) Compressor Belt, Renew
All models (.3) 6

(G) Compressor Assembly, Renew
Includes: Evacuate and charge system.
1983-87 (1.5) 3.0

(P) Compressor Assembly, R&R and Recondition
Includes: Evacuate and charge system.
1983-87 (2.6) 3.8

(G) Compressor Shaft Seal Kit, Renew
Includes: R&R compressor when required. Evacuate and charge system.
1983-87
Frigidaire (1.2) 1.8
FS6 (1.9) 2.5

(G) Compressor Clutch and Pulley, Renew
1983-87 (.7) 1.1
Renew clutch brg add (.1) 1
Renew clutch field add (.1) 1

(G) Compressor Service Valve or Gasket, Renew
Includes: Evacuate and charge system.
1983-87 (.9) 1.3

(G) Condenser Assembly, Renew
Includes: Evacuate and charge system.
1983-87 (.9) 2.0

AIR CONDITIONER TUNE-UP

For efficient operation and satisfactory performance in hot weather. The following air conditioner tune-up is suggested:

1. Clean intake filter
2. Clean condenser fins
3. Pressure test system
4. Adjust drive belt tension
5. Check antifreeze/coolant
6. Tighten compressor mounts
7. Tighten condenser and evaporator mounts
8. Inspect system for leaks (hoses, couplings, valves, etc.)
9. Partial charge system

All models 1.0
If necessary to evacuate and charge system, add 1.0

(Factory Time) Chilton Time

(G) Evaporator Core, Renew
Includes: Renew or transfer valve. Evacuate & charge system.
1983-87 (2.1) 6.0

(G) Clutch Cycling Pressure Switch Assy., Renew
1983-87 (.2) 4

(G) Accumulator Assy., Renew
Includes: Evacuate and charge system.
1983 (.9) 1.5

(G) Orifice Valve, Renew
Includes: Evacuate and charge system.
1983-87 (.9) 1.5

(Factory Time) Chilton Time

(G) Pressure Relief Valve, Renew
Includes: Evacuate and charge system.
1983-87-two cyl comp (.9) 1.6
six cyl comp (.8) 1.5

(G) Door Vacuum Motor, Renew
1983-87-each (.3) 7
Panel door (1.3) 2.0

(G) Temperature Control Cable, Renew
1983-87 (.3) 7
w/ATC (.8) 1.4

(G) Temperature Control Assy., Renew
1983-87 (.5) 9

(G) Blower Motor, Renew
1983-87 (.4) 8

(G) Blower Motor Switch, Renew
1983-87 (.4) 7

(G) Blower Motor Resistor, Renew
1983-87 (.3) 5

(G) Suction or Discharge Manifold Assy. Kit, Renew
Includes: Evacuate and charge system.
1983-87 (.8) 1.5

(G) Air Conditioning Hoses, Renew
Includes: Evacuate and charge system.
1983-87
Cond. to Evap. (.8) 1.7
Suction line (1.0) 1.9
Comp. to Cond. (.8) 1.7

(G) A.T.C. Sensor, Renew
1983-87 (.5) 9

(G) A.C. Automatic Temperature Servo Assy., Renew
1985-87 (.4) 6

PARTS 28 AIR CONDITIONING 28 PARTS

	Part No.	Price
Compressor Belt		
Order by model & description.		
Compressor Assembly		
1983-85-w/ factory A/C	▲E4VY-19703A	315.00
1986-87	▲E6VY-19703A	315.00
built-in A/C		
1983-87-w/York comp.	▲D2AZ-19703C	171.50
1984-85-w/ Tecumseh	▲E4TZ-19703B	268.75
Compressor Gasket Kit		
Tecumseh Comp.		
1983	▲C3GY-19B684A	9.00
York Comp.		
1983	▲C8AZ-19B684A	10.75
Compressor Shaft Oil Seal (Kit)		
York Comp.		
1983-87	▲C9AZ-19655B	18.25
Tecumseh Comp.		
1983-87	▲C9AZ-19655A	17.75
Compressor Clutch Brush Assy.		
1983-87	▲C8SZ-2979A	24.50
Compressor Clutch Pulley Bearing		
1983-87	▲C9AZ-2990A	27.25
Compressor Clutch & Pulley Assy.		
1983	▲E0VY-2884A	149.00
1984-87	▲E3AZ-2884A	69.75
Compressor Valve Plate Kit		
Tecumseh Comp.		
1983-87	▲C3GY-19656A	26.25
York Comp.		
1983-87	▲D5AZ-19656A	23.25
Condenser Assy.		
1983	▲E0AZ-19712A	325.25
1984	▲E0AZ-19712B	325.25
1985	▲E5AZ-19712A	355.75
1986-87	▲E6AZ-19712A	355.75
Evaporator Core		
1983-85	▲E0VY-19860A	164.75
1986-87	▲E6VY-19860A	180.25
Blower Motor Assembly		
1983-87w/ factory A/C	▲E0VY-19805A	77.75
w/built-in A/C	▲D2AZ-19805A	71.50
Blower Motor Switch		
1983-87-exc. below	▲D5AZ-19986A	12.75
w/A.T.C.	▲E4VY-19986A	5.25
Air Conditioning Hoses		
Order by model and description.		
A.T.C. Sensor Assy.		
1983-87	▲E3VY-19C734A	21.50

LABOR 29 LOCKS, HINGES & WIND. REGULATORS 29 LABOR

	(Factory Time)	Chilton Time
(G) Hood Latch, Renew		
1983-87	(.3)	.5
(G) Hood Hinge, Renew		
Includes: Adjust hood and latch.		
1983-87	(.4)	.6
(G) Hood Release Cable, Renew		
1983-87	(.4)	.7
(G) Door Latch, Renew		
Includes: R&R trim panel and weathersheet.		
1983-87	(.5)	.9
(G) Door Lock Remote Control, Renew		
Includes: R&R trim panel and weathersheet.		
1983-87	(.4)	.8
(G) Door Handle (Outside), Renew (Front or Rear)		
Includes: R&R trim panel and weathersheet.		
1983-87	(.5)	.9
(G) Lock Striker Plate, Renew		
1983-87	(.2)	.3
(G) Door Window Regulator (Manual), Renew		
Includes: R&R trim panel and weathersheet.		
1983-87	(.5)	1.0
(G) Door Window Regulator (Electric), Renew		
Includes: R&R trim panel and weathersheet.		
1983-87	(.6)	1.2
(G) Trunk Hinge Assembly, Renew (One)		
1983-87	(.5)	.6
(G) Tail Gate Latch, Renew		
1983-87-upper	(.4)	.6
lower	(.3)	.5
(G) Tail Gate Hinge, Renew		
1983-87-upper	(.3)	.6
lower	(.9)	1.4
one piece	(1.5)	2.0
(G) Tail Gate Window Regulator (Electric), Renew		
1983-87	(.7)	1.2

PARTS 29 LOCKS, HINGES & WIND. REGULATORS 29 PARTS

	Part No.	Price
Hood Lock		
1983	▲E4DZ-16700A	14.75
1984-87	▲E1DZ-16700A	16.50
Hood Hinge		
1983-87-right	▲D9AZ-16796A	13.25
left	▲D9AZ-16797A	13.25
Door Lock, Front		
1983-87-right	▲E3AZ-5421812A	31.75
left	▲E3AZ-5421813A	31.75
Door Lock, Rear		
1983-87-right	▲E3AZ-5426412A	41.50
left	▲E3AZ-5426413A	41.50
Door Lock Remote Control		
1983-right	▲E0VY-5421818A	17.00
left	▲E0VY-5421819A	17.00
1984-87-right	▲E3SZ-6321818A	12.00
left	▲E3SZ-6321819A	12.00
Services both front and rear doors.		
Lock Cylinder & Keys (Front)		
1983-87 (w/or wo/illuminated entry)		
wo/illum.	▲E1DZ-5421984C	10.75
w/illum.	▲E1DZ-5421984D	15.50
Trunk Lock		
1983-87-wo/ Power	▲D5DZ-6643200A	15.50
w/Power	▲D6LZ-6543200A	56.25
Window Regulator–Manual Front Door		
(4 door sedan & sta wag)		
1983-87-right	▲D9AZ-5423200B	55.75
left	▲D9AZ-5423201B	55.75
(2 door sedan)		
1983-87-right	▲D9AZ-6623200B	55.75
left	▲D9AZ-6623201B	55.75
Rear Door		
1983-87-right	▲E3AZ-5427000A	55.75
left	▲E3AZ-5427001A	55.75
Window Regulator–Electric Front Door		
(2 door sedan)		
1983-87-right	▲D9AZ-6623208A	120.75
left	▲D9AZ-6623209A	120.75
(4 door sedan & sta wag)		
1983-87-right	▲D9AZ-5423208A	120.75
left	▲D9AZ-5423209A	120.75
Rear Door		
1983-87-right	▲D9AZ-5427008A	94.50
left	▲D9AZ-5427009A	94.50
Tail Gate Window Regulator		
1983-87	▲D9AZ-7444000A	83.25
Trunk Lock Cylinder & Keys		
1983-87-exc. below	▲D6DZ-6643505A	10.75
sta. wagon	▲E1AZ-7443505A	9.75
Door Handle (Outside)		
1983-87-right	▲E3FZ-5822404A	21.50
left	▲E3FZ-5822405A	21.50
Trunk Hinges		
1983-87-right	▲D9AZ-5442700B	50.00
left	▲D9AZ-5442701B	50.00

LABOR 30 HEAD & PARKING LAMPS 30 LABOR

	(Factory Time)	Chilton Time
(G) Aim Headlamps		
two		.4
four		.6
(M) Headlamp Sealed Beam Bulb, Renew		
All models-each	(.3)	.3
(M) Parking Lamp Lens, Renew		
1983-87	(.3)	.4
(M) Stop Lamp Lens, Renew		
1983-87	(.2)	.3
(M) License Lamp Assembly, Renew		
1983-87	(.3)	.4
(M) Side Marker Lamp Assy., Renew		
1983-87	(.3)	.4

PARTS 30 HEAD AND PARKING LAMPS 30 PARTS

	Part No.	Price
Sealed Beam Bulb		
1983-87-high beam	▲D94Y-13007C	12.75
low beam	▲D94Y-13007A	12.75
Parking Lamp Assy.		
Ford		
1983-87-right	▲E0AZ-13200A	54.75
left	▲E0AZ-13201A	54.75
Mercury		
1983-87-right	▲D9MY-13200A	32.75
left	▲D9MY-13201A	32.75
Tail Lamp Lens		
Ford		
1983-87-right	▲E3AZ-13450A	19.00
left	▲E3AZ-13451A	19.00
Mercury		
1983-87-right	▲E3MY-13450A	58.25
left	▲E3MY-13451A	58.00
Tail Lamp Assy.		
Ford		
(exc./sta. wagon)		
1983-87-right	▲E3AZ-13404A	72.50
left	▲E3AZ-13405A	72.50
(sta. wagon)		
1983-87-right	▲D9AZ-13404B	81.00
left	▲D9AZ-13405B	81.00
Mercury		
(exc./sta. wagon)		
1983-87-right	▲E3MY-13404A	119.75
left	▲E3MY-13405A	119.75
(sta. wagon)		
1983-87-right	▲E2MY-13404A	75.00
left	▲E2MY-13405A	75.00

PARTS 30 HEAD AND PARKING LAMPS 30 PARTS

	Part No.	Price
Rear License Plate Lamp Assy.		
(exc./sta. wagon)		
1983-87-Ford	▲D4ZZ-13550A	13.00
Mercury	▲D9MY-13550A	11.00
(sta. wagon)		
1983-85	▲D9AZ-13550A	5.75
1986-87	▲E69Z-13550A	5.75
Rear Hi-Mount Lamp Assy.		
1985-87-wo/		
custom top	▲E6AZ-13A613A	41.75
w/custom top	▲E6AZ-13A613C	41.75
station wagon	▲E6AZ-13A613B	33.50

LABOR 31 WINDSHIELD WIPER & SPEEDOMETER 31 LABOR

(Factory Time)	Chilton Time
(G) Windshield Wiper Motor, Renew	
1983-87 (.4)	.7
(G) Wiper Pivot, Renew (One)	
1983-87 (.3)	.5
(G) Windshield Wiper Governor Assy., Renew	
1983-87 (.3)	.6
(G) Wiper Switch, Renew	
Includes: R&R instrument panel pad when required.	
1983-87 (.4)	.7
(G) Windshield Washer Pump, Renew	
1983-87 (.3)	.4
(G) Speedometer Head, R&R or Renew	
Includes: R&R instrument panel pad when required.	
1983-87 (.7)	1.4
Reset odometer add	.2
(G) Speedometer Cable and Casing, Renew	
Includes: R&R instrument panel pad when required.	
1983-87-wo/Cruise control (.4)	.8
w/Cruise control	
upper (.3)	.6
lower (.4)	.7
(G) Speedometer Cable (Inner), Renew or Lubricate	
1983-87	
one piece (.4)	.7
upper (.3)	.5
lower (.5)	.8
(G) Speedometer Driven Gear, Renew	
1983-87 (.3)	.4
(G) Radio, R&R	
Includes: R&R instrument panel pad when required.	
1983-87 (.3)	.6

PARTS 31 WINDSHIELD WIPER & SPEEDOMETER 31 PARTS

	Part No.	Price
Windshield Wiper Motor		
1983-85	▲D9AZ-17508A	97.75
1986-87	▲E6AZ-17508A	97.75
Wiper Pivot		
1983-87	▲D9AZ-17566B	26.75
Wiper Switch		
1983-87-wo/		
interm.	▲E1AZ-17A553A	30.00
w/interm.	▲E1AZ-17A553C	32.75
Windshield Wiper Governor		
1983-87	▲D9AZ-17C476A	77.50
Windshield Washer Pump		
1983-87	▲E0AZ-17664A	20.00
Windshield Washer Reservoir		
1983-sensor	▲D9AZ-17618A	16.50
w/sensor	▲E1AZ-17618A	20.75
1984-87-wo/		
sensor	▲E4AZ-17618A	16.50
w/sensor	▲E4AZ-17618B	20.75
Speedometer Head		
Mercury		
1983-87-wo/		
Tripo	▲E1MY-17255A	82.00
w/Tripo	▲E1MY-17255B	99.75
Ford		
1983-87-wo/		
Tripo	▲E2AZ-17255K	90.75
w/Tripo	▲E2AZ-17255P	108.75
1983-87-P/C	▲E2AZ-17255J	90.75
Speedometer Cable & Casing		
(wo/speed cont)		
1983-87	▲E0AZ-17260B	15.25
(w/speed cont.)		
1983-87	▲E3MZ-9A820A	13.50
Speedometer Cable Kit		
1983-87 (cut to fit)		
81″ long	▲D4AZ-17262A	7.75
135″ long	▲C5AZ-17262B	8.75

LABOR 32 LIGHT SWITCHES & WIRING 32 LABOR

(Factory Time)	Chilton Time
(G) Headlamp Switch, Renew	
1983-87 (.3)	.5
(G) Headlamp Dimmer Switch, Renew	
1983-87 (.3)	.6
(G) Stop Light Switch, Renew	
1983-87 (.3)	.4
(G) Parking Brake Indicator Switch, Renew	
1983-87 (.3)	.4
(G) Turn Signal Switch Assy., Renew	
1983-87 (.6)	1.0
switch only (.3)	.5
(M) Turn Signal or Hazard Warning Flasher, Renew	
1983-87 (.2)	.4
(G) Horns, Renew	
1983-87-each (.3)	.4
(G) Wiring Harness, Renew	
Alternator to Regulator	
1983-87 (.5)	.9

PARTS 32 LIGHT SWITCHES & WIRING 32 PARTS

	Part No.	Price
Headlamp Switch		
1983-87-exc		
below	▲E0AZ-11654C	16.50
wo/Delay sys	▲E0AZ-11654D	17.50
w/Delay sys	▲E1WZ-11654A	47.25
Stop Light Switch		
1983-85	▲E3VY-13480A	6.25
1986-87	▲E6AZ-13480A	6.50
Turn Signal & Warning Switch		
1983-84	▲E0AZ-13341A	41.25
1985-87	▲E5FZ-13341A	41.25

PARTS 32 LIGHT SWITCHES & WIRING 32 PARTS

	Part No.	Price
Turn Signal Flasher		
1983-87	▲C6AZ-13350B	3.75
Emergency Flasher		
1983-85	▲D1FZ-13350A	4.25
1985-87-from 8-85	▲E6AZ-13350A	10.75
Back-Up Light Switch		
1983-87	▲D6RY-7A247B	31.75
Horns		
1983-87-high pitch	▲E3AZ-13832A	17.00
low pitch	▲E3AZ-13833A	17.00

LABOR 33 GLASS 33 LABOR

(Factory Time) — Chilton Time

(G) Windshield Glass, Renew
1983-87 (2.1) 3.5
Renew butyl tape add (.2) 2

(G) Front Door Glass, Renew
Includes: R&R trim panel and weathersheet.
1983-87 (.8) 1.1

(G) Rear Door Glass, Renew
Includes: R&R trim panel and weathersheet.
1983-87 (.8) 1.1

(G) Rear Quarter Window Glass, Renew
Includes: R&R trim panel and weathersheet.
1983-87-sta wag (.8) 1.3
sdn (.8) 1.3

(G) Rear Door Stationary Glass, Renew
1983-87-sta wags (.7) 1.2

(G) Tail Gate Glass, Renew
1983-84 (.6) 1.0
1985-87 (.8) 1.2

(G) Rear Window Glass, Renew
1983-87 (.9) 1.7
Renew butyl tape add (.2) 2

LABOR 34 CRUISE CONTROL 34 LABOR

(Factory Time) — Chilton Time

(G) Cruise Control System Diagnosis
1983-87 (.4) 6

(G) Cruise Control Chain/Cable, Renew
1983-87 (.3) 5

(G) Speed Control Amplifier Assy., Renew
1983-87 (.3) 6
Road test add (.3) 3

(G) Speed Control Sensor Assy., Renew
1983-87 (.3) 5
Road test add (.3) 3

(G) Speed Control Servo Assy., Renew
1983-87 (.3) 6
Road test add (.3) 3

(G) Speed Control Relay, Renew
1983-87 (.3) 5

(G) Speed Control Actuator Switch, Renew
1983-87 (.3) 6
Road test add (.3) 3

(G) Speed Control Metering (Dump) Valve, Renew
1983-87 (.4) 6

PARTS 34 CRUISE CONTROL 34 PARTS

	Part No.	Price
Speed Control Amplifier Assy.		
1983-87	▲E0AZ-9D843A	161.50
Speed Control Servo Assy.		
1983-85	▲E2FZ-9C735A	120.25
1986-87	▲E6AZ-9C735A	120.25
Speed Control Sensor Assy.		
1983-87	▲E3AZ-9E731A	20.75
Speed Control Actuator Switch factory A/C		
1983-84	▲E3SZ-9C888A	45.75
1985-87	▲E5AZ-9C888A	45.75
built-in A/C		
1983-84	▲E2AZ-9C888A	45.75
1985-87	▲E4AZ-9C888A	34.25

GROUP INDEX

ALPHABETICAL INDEX

Ford Motor Company

Rear Wheel Drive Cars

LINCOLN • CONTINENTAL • MARK VI • VII

YEAR IDENTIFICATION

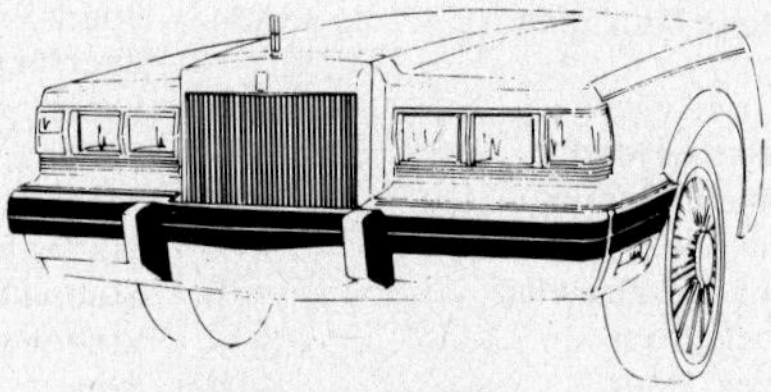

1983 Continental

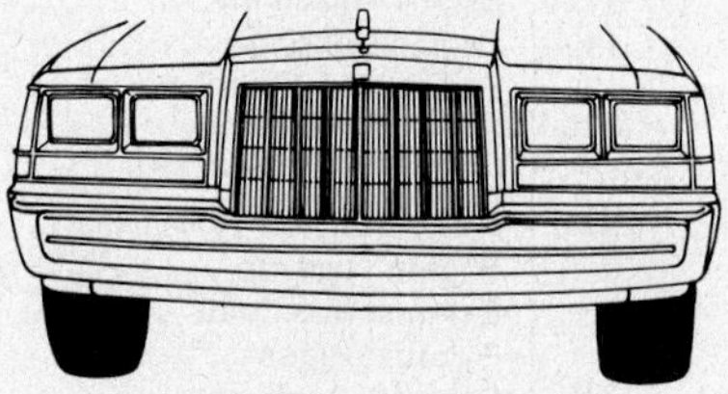

1984–85 Continental

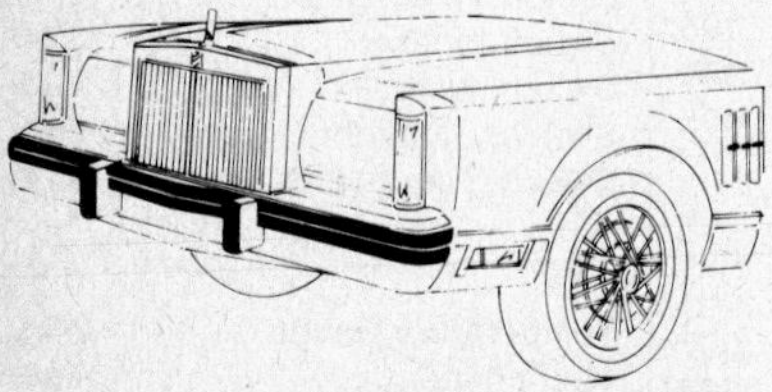

1983 Continental Mark VII LSC

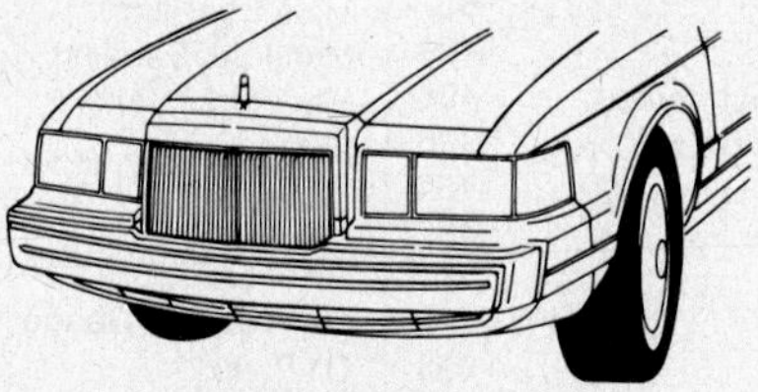

1984–86 Mark VII

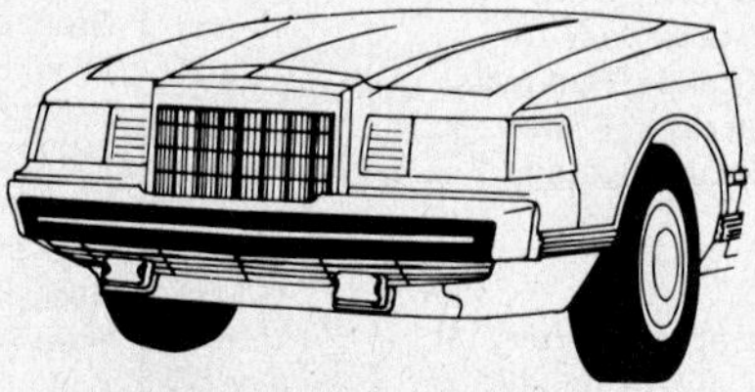

1985–86 Mark VII LSC

1987 Mark VII LSC

1983–84 Town Car

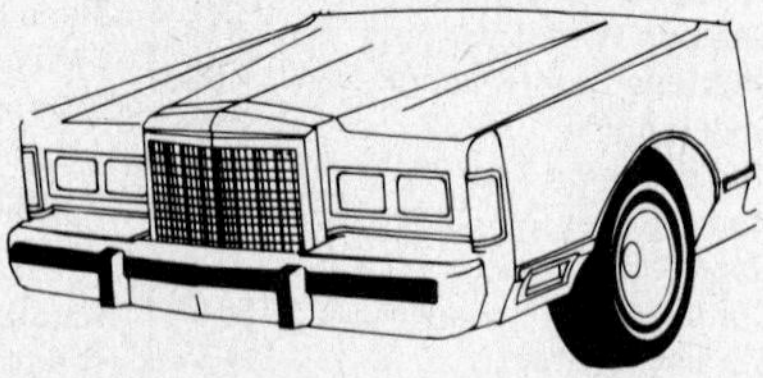

1985–86 Lincoln Town Car

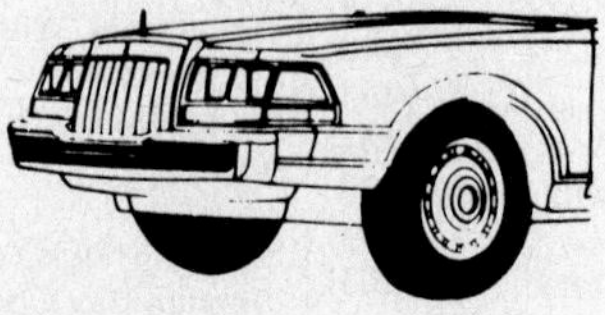

1987 Lincoln Continental

VEHICLE IDENTIFICATION NUMBER (VIN)

It is important for servicing and ordering parts to be certain of the vehicle and engine identification. The VIN (vehicle identification number) is a 13 or 17 digit number visible through the windshield on the driver's side of the dash and contains the vehicle and engine identification codes. It can be interpreted as follows:

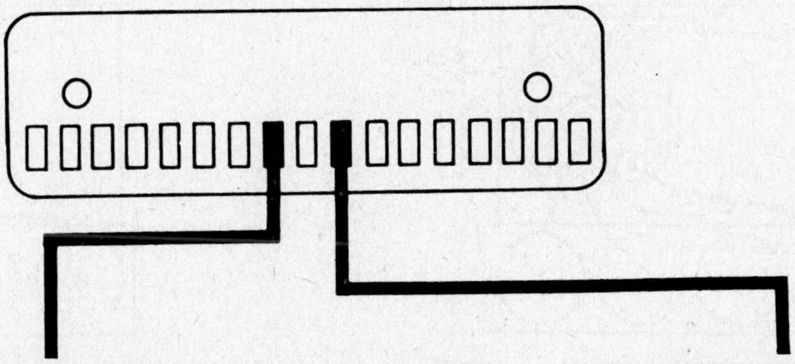

Engine Code					
Code	Cu. In.	Liters	Cyl.	Carb.	Eng. Mfg.
A	140	2.3	4	1	Ford
W	140-T	2.3	4	Turbo.	Ford
T	140-T SVO	2.3	4	Turbo.	Ford
R	140-HSC	2.3	4	①	Ford
T,B,X	200	3.3	6	1	Ford
3	232	3.8	V6	①	Ford
C	232	3.8	V6	①	Ford
F	302	5.0	V8	1	Ford
M	302-H.O.	5.0	V8	①	Ford
G	351-W	5.8	V8	①	Ford
G	351-H.O.	5.8	V8	①	Ford

Model Year Code	
Code	Year
D	1983
E	1984
F	1985
G	1986
H	1987

The seventeen digit Vehicle Identification Number can be used to determine engine application and model year. The tenth digit indicates the model year, and the eighth digit identifies the engine code.
① EFI, VV, 2 bbl. or 4 bbl. depending on model

TUNE-UP SPECIFICATIONS

When analyzing compression test results, look for uniformity among cylinders rather than specific pressures

Year	Engine: Eng. VIN Code	Engine: No. Cyl. Displacement (cu. in.)	Eng. mfg.	Spark Plugs: Orig. Type	Spark Plugs: Gap (in.)•	Distributor: Point Dwell (deg)	Distributor: Point Gap (in.)	Ignition Timing (deg): Man. Trans.	Ignition Timing (deg): Auto. Trans.	Valves Intake Opens (deg)	Fuel Pump Pressure (psi)	Idle Speed (rpm): Man. Trans.	Idle Speed (rpm): Auto. Trans.
'83	F	8-302	Ford	ASF-52 ②	.050	Electronic		①	①	16	6-8 ③	—	550
	G	8-351	Ford	ASF-42	.044	Electronic		①	①	23	6-8	—	700/600
'84	F	8302	Ford	ASF-52	.050	Electronic		①	①	16	39	550	550
	M	8302HO	Ford	ASF-42	.044	Electronic		①	①	—	6-8	700	700
	G	8-351	Ford	ASF-42	.044	Electronic		①	①	23	6-8	—	600 ⑥
'85	F	8-302	Ford	ASF-52	.050	Electronic		①	①	—	39	550	550
	M	8-302 HO	Ford	ASF-42	.044	Electronic		①	①	—	6-8	700	700
	G	8-351	Ford	ASF-42	.044	Electronic		①	①	—	6-8	—	600 ⑥
'86–'87	F	8-302	Ford	ASF-32C	.044	Electronic		①	①	—	39	① ④	① ④
	M	8-302 HO	Ford	ASF-42	.044	Electronic		①	①	—	6-8	700	700
	G	8-351	Ford	ASF-32C	.044	Electronic		①	①	—	6-8	650	650

NOTE: The underhood calibrations sticker often reflects tune-up specification changes made in production. Sticker figures must be used if they disagree with those in this chart.
T Turbocharger
HO High output
HSC High swirl combustion
① Calibrations vary depending upon the model; refer to the underhood calibration sticker.
② The carbureted models use spark plug ASF-42 (.044) and the idle speed rpm is 700 rpm.
③ On fuel injected models the pressure is 39 psi.
④ Electronic engine control models the ignition timing, idle speed and idle mixture is not adjustable.
⑥ 700 rpm with the VOTM on.

FIRING ORDERS

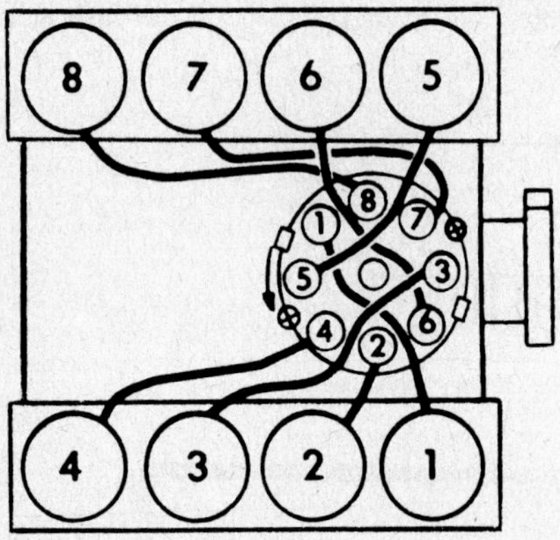

FORD MOTOR CO. 255, 302 (exc. HO) 460 V8 Engine firing order: 1–5–4–2–6–3–7–8
Distributor rotation: counterclockwise

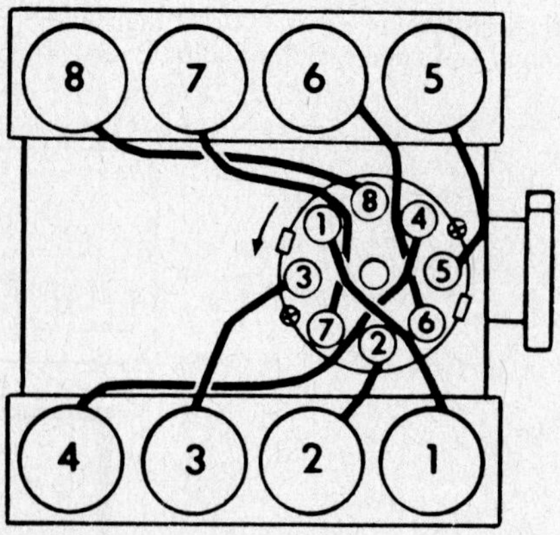

FORD MOTOR CO. 302HO, 351,400 V8 Engine firing order: 1–3–7–2–6–5–4–8
Distributor rotation: counterclockwise

WHEEL ALIGNMENT SPECIFICATIONS

Year	Model	Caster Range (deg)	Caster Pref. Setting (deg)	Camber Range (deg)	Camber Pref. Setting (deg)	Toe-in (in.)	Steering Axis Inclin. (deg)	Wheel Pivot Ratio (deg) Inner Wheel	Wheel Pivot Ratio (deg) Outer Wheel
'83	Continental	3/8P to 2 1/8P	1 1/4P	1/2N to 1 1/4P	3/8P	0 to 1/4	N/A	20	19 1/8
'84	Continental Mark VII ①	7/8P to 2 15/16P	1 3/4P	7/8N to 7/8P	0P	0 to 1/4	11	20	17 1/8
'85-'87	Continental Mark VII ①	5/8P to 2 3/4P	1 1/2P	3/4N to 3/4P	0P	0 to 1/4	11	20	17 1/8
'83-'87	Town Car Mark VI ②	2 1/4P to 4P	3P	1/4N to 1 1/4P	1/2P	1/16 to 3/16	11	20	18 1/2
'83-'87	Ford/Mercury ②	2 1/4P to 4P	3P	1/4N to 1 1/4P	1/2P	1/16 to 3/16	11	20	18 1/2

① Set the vehicle height before making the alignment check.
② On the 84 models the caster range is 2 3/8P to 4 1/8P and the preferred setting is 3 1/8P.

LABOR — SERVICE BAY OPERATIONS — LABOR

(Factory Time) — Chilton Time

COOLING

(M) Winterize Cooling System
Includes: Run engine to check for leaks, tighten all hose connections. Test radiator and pressure cap. Drain radiator and engine block. Add anti-freeze and refill system.
All models 5

(M) Thermostat, Renew
All models-Gas (.5) 6
Diesel (.8) 1.0
w/A.C. add 2

(M) Drive Belt, Renew
All models-one (.3) 4
each adtnl 1

(M) Drive Belt Adjust
All models-one (.2) 3
each adtnl (.1) 1

(M) Radiator Hoses, Renew
All models
upper (.4) 4
lower (.5) 6
both (.6) 9

CHILTON'S 10 POINT SAFETY CHECK

CHECK OPERATION & CONDITION OF THE FOLLOWING ITEMS:

1. Legal Registration (serial no.)
2. Tires & Wheels
3. Brake System (R&R all wheels)
4. Light Systems & Signals
5. Accelerator Linkage, Neutral Safety Switch, Shift Indicator Pointer & Seat Position Locks
6. Glass, Mirrors, Door Locks, Seat Belts & Harness
7. Wipers, Washers & Defrosters
8. Frame, Steering, Shocks, Front & Rear Suspension
9. Fuel & Exhaust Systems
10. Road Test Vehicle

All models 1.0
Exhaust Smog Analysis, add 4

(Factory Time) — Chilton Time

FUEL

(M) Carburetor Air Cleaner, Service
All models (.2) 3

(G) Carburetor, Adjust (On Car)
All models (.4) 5
Propane enrichment method (1.0)...... 1.5

(G) Thermostatic Choke Cover and/or Gasket, Renew
All models (.8) 1.3

BRAKES

(G) Brakes, Adjust (Minor)
Includes: Adjust brakes, fill master cylinder.
two wheels 4

(G) Bleed Brakes (Four Wheels)
Includes: Fill master cylinder.
All models (.3) 5

(G) Brake Pedal Free Play, Adjust
All models 4

(M) Parking Brake, Adjust
drum brakes (.3) 4
w/Rear disc brakes (.3) 5

LABOR — SERVICE BAY OPERATIONS — LABOR

(Factory Time) — Chilton Time

LUBRICATION SERVICE

(M) Lubricate Chassis, Change Oil & Filter
Includes: Inspect and correct all fluid levels.
All models 6
Install grease fittings add 1

(M) Lubricate Chassis
Includes: Inspect and correct all fluid levels.
All models 4
Install grease fittings add 1

(M) Engine Oil & Filter, Change
Includes: Inspect and correct all fluid levels.
All models 4

WHEELS

(M) Wheel, Renew
one (.5) 5

(G) Wheels, Balance
one 3
each adtnl 2

(G) Wheels, Rotate (All)
All models (.5) 5

(G) Front Wheel Bearings, Clean and Repack (Both Wheels)
All models 1.3

(G) Front Wheel Grease Seals, Renew
Includes: Repack bearings.
one wheel (.6) 7
both wheels (.9) 1.1

(G) Front Wheel Bearings and Cups, Renew
one wheel (.7) 9
both wheels (1.2) 1.5

ELECTRICAL

(M) Battery Cables, Renew
Batt. to Relay (.3) 3
Ground (.3) 3
Relay to Starter (.4) 5

(G) Aim Headlamps
two 4
four 6

(M) Headlamp Sealed Beam Bulb, Renew
All models-each (.3) 3

(M) Parking Lamp Lens, Renew
All models (.3) 4

(G) Stop Lamp Lens, Renew
All models (.2) 3

(G) Headlamp Switch, Renew
1983-87-exc below (.4) 6
1983-84-Continental (.7) 1.1

(G) Headlamp Dimmer Switch, Renew
All models (.5) 9

(G) Stop Light Switch, Renew
All models (.3) 4

(G) Turn Signal Switch Assy., Renew
1983-87 (.4) 1.0

(M) Turn Signal or Hazard Warning Flasher, Renew
All models (.2) 3

LABOR — 1 TUNE UP 1 — LABOR

(Factory Time) — Chilton Time

(G) Compression Test
V-8–1983-87 (.5) 1.0
w/A.C. add 3

(G) Engine Tune Up, (Electronic Ignition)
Includes: Test battery and clean connections. Tighen manifold and carburetor mounting bolts. Check engine compression, clean and adjust or renew spark plugs. Test resistance of spark plug cables. Inspect distributor cap and rotor. Adjust air gap. Check vacuum advance operation. Reset ignition timing. Adjust idle mixture and idle speed. Service air cleaner. Inspect and adjust drive belts. Inspect choke operation and adjust or free up. Check operation of EGR valve.
V-8–1983-87 .... 3.0
w/A.C. add 6
Perform EEC IV system test add 1.0

LABOR — 2 IGNITION SYSTEM 2 — LABOR

(Factory Time) — Chilton Time

GASOLINE ENGINES

(G) Spark Plugs, Clean and Reset or Renew
1983-87 (.6) 1.0
w/A.C. add 3

(G) Ignition Timing, Reset
1983-87 (.4) 4

(G) Distributor, Renew
Includes: Reset ignition timing.
1983-87 (.3) 7

(G) Distributor Cap and/or Rotor, Renew
1983-87 (.2) 5

(G) Vacuum Control Unit, Renew
Includes: R&R distributor and reset ignition timing.
1983-87 (.4) 8

(G) Ignition Coil, Renew
Includes: Test.
1983-87 (.3) 5

(G) Ignition Cables, Renew
Includes: Test wiring.
1983-87 (.4) 6

(G) Ignition Switch, Renew
1983-87 (.5) 9

(G) Ignition Key Indicator Buzzer or Chime, Renew
1983-87
Lincoln (.3) 4
Continental (.4) 6
Mark VII (.5) 7

(G) Ignition Module Assembly, Renew
Note: Fender mount type. For TFI unit, refer to Emission Control section.
1983-87 (.3) 6
Perform system test add (.3) 3

(G) Profile Ignition Pick-Up Sensor, Renew (Duraspark)
1983-87 (.5) 9
Perform system test add (.3) 3

(G) Distributor Armature, Renew
1983-84 (.3) 6

(G) Distributor Stator, Renew
Includes: R&R armature.
1983-84 (.4) 8

DIESEL ENGINE

(G) Glow Plug System, Test
All models (.4) 5

(G) Glow Plugs, Renew
Does not include system test.
All models
one (.2) 3
each adtnl (.1) 2
all (.6) 1.0

(G) Glow Plug Module, Renew
All models (.2) 4

PARTS 2 ELECTRONIC IGNITION 2 PARTS

	Part No.	Price
GASOLINE ENGINE		
Distributor Assy.		
V-8-302 eng		
1983-exc		
Canada	▲E3AZ-12127A	136.75
Canada	▲E2VY-12127B	136.75
1984	▲E4TZ-12127B	136.75
1985	▲E5TZ-12127B	136.75
1986-87	▲E6AZ-12127D	136.75
(1) Distributor Cap		
1983-84	▲E2ZZ-12106A	20.00
1985	▲E5ZZ-12106A	N.L.
1986-87	▲E6TZ-12106A	20.00
(2) Rotor		
1983-85-wo/		
E.E.C.	▲E4HZ-12200A	3.50
1984-w/E.E.C.	▲E4TZ-12200B	4.00
1985-87-w/		
E.E.C.	▲E5TZ-12200B	2.50
(3) Armature		
1983-85	▲D3AZ-12A099A	6.00
(4) Stator Assy.		
1983-85-wo/		
E.E.C.	▲D4PZ-12A112A	25.50
1983-85-w/		
E.E.C.	▲E3ZZ-12A112C	25.00
1986-87	E5PZ-12A112A	25.00
(6) Modulator Assy.		
1983-exc.		
Canada	▲D9AZ-12A199B	83.50
1983-Canada	▲D9VZ-12A199A	83.50

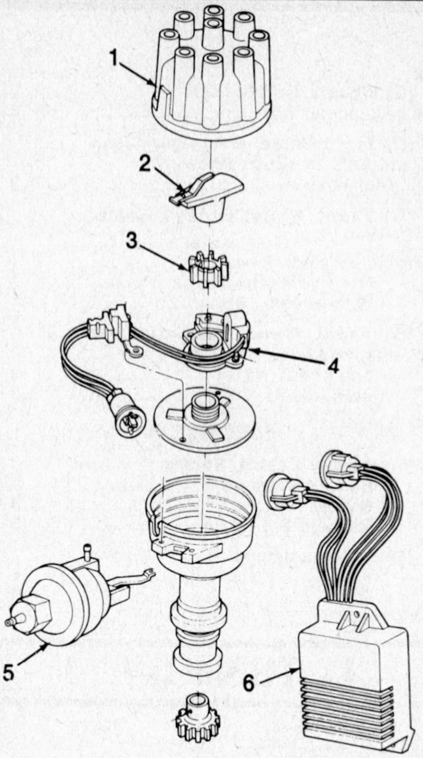

	Part No.	Price
1984-87-w/E.E.C		
IV	▲E43Z-12A297A	106.00
Coil		
1983	▲D5AZ-12029A	31.25
1984-85-wo/		
E.E.C. IV	▲D5AZ-12029A	31.25
1984-87-w/E.E.C		
IV	▲E3FZ-12029A	33.75
Ignition Coil Resistor		
1983-87		
57″ long	C9OZ-12250A	5.00
60″ long	D1AZ-12250A	4.75
61″ long	▲C0LF-12250A	4.75
Ignition Wire Set		
V-8-302 eng		
1983-exc. below	▲E3PZ-12259ADR	57.50
Continental	E3PZ-12259H	57.50
1984-85	▲E4PZ-12259C	58.75
1986-87-exc.		
Lincoln	▲E6PZ-12259F	58.75
Lincoln	▲E6PZ-12259E	58.75
Ignition Switch		
1983-87	▲E4FZ-11572A	11.50
Ignition Switch Warning Assy.		
1983	▲E25Y-11A127A	5.50
1984-87	▲E5SZ-11A127A	5.00
IGNITION SYSTEM DIESEL		
Module (Glow Plug Control)		
1984	E45Y-12A510A	1462.00
Glow Plug (Intake Manifold)		
1984-85	E45Y-12A342A	9.00

LABOR 3 FUEL SYSTEM 3 LABOR

(Factory Time) — Chilton Time

GASOLINE ENGINES

(G) Fuel Pump, Test

Includes: Disconnect line at carburetor, attach pressure gauge.

All models	
mechanical	.3
electric	.5

(M) Carburetor Air Cleaner, Service

1983-87 (.2)	.3
Propane enrichment method (1.0)	1.5

(M) Fuel Filter Assembly, Renew

All models (.6)	.8

(G) Carburetor, R&R or Renew

Includes: All necessary adjustments.

All models (.6)	1.0
Renew assy add (.4)	.4

(G) Carburetor, R&R and Clean or Recondition

Includes: All necessary adjustments.

All models (1.6)	2.5

(G) Fuel Enrichment Valve Assy., Renew

All models (.8)	1.3

(G) Thermostatic Choke Housing and/or Gasket, Renew

All models (.8)	1.3

(G) Float Level, Adjust

Includes: Set idle speed and mixture.

All models	
Holly 1946 1V (.5)	.7
Weber 740 2V (.5)	.7
Motorcraft 2150 2V (.4)	.6
Weber 5200-6500 2V (.5)	.7
2700-7200 VV (.5)	.7

(G) Float or Needle Valve and Seat, Renew

Includes: Set idle speed and mixture.

All models	
Holly 1946 1V (.6)	.9
Weber 740 2V (.5)	.8
Motorcraft 2150 2V (.4)	.7
Weber 5200-6500 2V (.5)	.8
2700-7200 VV (.5)	.8

(G) Accelerator Pump Diaphragm, Piston or Rod, Renew

All models	
Four (.4)	.6
Six (.6)	.8
V-6 (.6)	.8
V-8-2 bbl (.3)	.5
4 bbl (.5)	.7

(G) Fuel Pump Relay, Renew

1983-87 (.2)	.3

(G) Fuel Pump, Renew

Includes: R&R fuel tank where required.

1983-87	
Lincoln	
mechanical (.4)	.8
on frame (.6)	.8
in tank (1.4)	1.8
Cont & Mark VII	
on frame (.6)	.8
in tank (.9)	1.4

Add pump test if performed.

(G) Fuel Tank, Renew

Includes: Drain and refill tank. Transfer tank gauge unit and fuel pump where required.

Lincoln	
1983-87-w/EFI (1.3)	1.9
w/FBC (1.1)	1.7
1983-87	
Cont & Mark VII (1.1)	1.7

(G) Fuel Gauge (Tank), Renew

Includes: Drain and refill tank.

Lincoln & Mark VI	
1983-87 (.5)	.8
Continental & Mark VII	
1983-87 (.9)	1.4

(G) Electronic Instrument Display Assy., Renew

Lincoln-Mark VI	
1983-87 (.8)	1.5
Continental	
1983 (.6)	1.1
1984-87 (.4)	.7
Mark VII	
1984-87 (.4)	.7

(G) Fuel Gauge (Dash), Renew

1983-87	
Standard Cluster (.8)	1.5
Electronic Cluster (.9)	1.7

(G) Intake Manifold or Gaskets, Renew

1983-87 (2.1)	3.5
Renew manif add (.4)	.5

LABOR 3 FUEL SYSTEM 3 LABOR

(Factory Time)	Chilton Time
ELECTRONIC FUEL INJECTION	
(G) Fuel Injector Assy., Renew	
1983-87-w/CFI	
one (.8)	1.2
all (.9)	1.5
w/SEFI	
one (1.8)	2.4
all (2.0)	2.7
(G) Fuel Charging Wiring Assy., Renew	
1983-87 (.3)	.6
(G) Fuel Pressure Regulator, Renew	
1983-87 (.8)	1.3
(G) Fuel Charging Assy., R&R or Renew	
1983-87 (.7)	1.2
(G) Fuel Charging Assy., R&R and Recondition	
1983-87 (1.8)	2.5
DIESEL ENGINE	
(G) Fuel Filter/Conditioner, Renew	
1984-85 (.3)	.5
(G) Turbocharger Assy., R&R or Renew	
1984-85 (1.3)	2.5
(G) Turbocharger Wastegate Actuator, Renew	
Includes: R&R turbocharger.	
1984-85 (1.5)	2.7
(G) Fuel Injection Pump, Renew	
1984-85 (2.6)	3.7
(G) Injection Pump Drive Gear, Renew	
1984-85 (.8)	1.2
(G) Injector Nozzles, Renew	
1984-85	
one (.5)	.7
each adtnl (.2)	.2
all (.6)	1.2
(G) Intake Manifold and/or Gasket, Renew	
1984-85 (.9)	1.5

PARTS 3 FUEL SYSTEM 3 PARTS

	Part No.	Price
GASOLINE ENGINE		
Carburetor Air Cleaner Element		
1983-85-exc.		
below	▲D2AZ-9601AR	8.50
LSC (1985)	▲D7AZ-9601AR	9.25
Continental (Canada 1983)	▲D7ZZ-9601AR	11.00
1986-87-exc.		
Lincoln	▲E6SZ-9601B	11.50
Lincoln	E5TZ-9601B	10.00
Fuel Pump Assy. (New)		
Continental		
(Externally Mounted)		
1983-wo/C.F.I.	E25Z-9350A	29.00
1983-84-w/C.F.I.	▲E4DZ-9350B	184.75
(In-tank Mounted)		
1983	E35Y-9350A	97.00
1984	E4LY-9H307A	93.75
1985-87	E55Y-9A407A	184.75
Mark VI, VII		
(Externally Mounted)		
1983-wo/C.F.I.	▲D6OZ-9350A	34.75
1983-87	E0VZ-9350A	254.75
(In-tank Mounted)		
1984	E4LY-9H307A	93.75
1985-87-exc.		
H.O.	E5SY-9A407A	184.75
H.O.	▲E6LZ-9A407A	161.00
Lincoln		
1983-wo/C.F.I.	▲D6OZ-9350A	34.75
C.F.I.	▲E3VY-9350A	247.50
1984-87	E0VZ-9350A	254.75
Fuel Tank		
Order by year and model.		
Fuel Gauge (Tank)		
Lincoln		
(wo/Electronic cluster)		
1983-87-exc.		
Canada	▲E0LY-9275B	42.25
1983-Canada	▲E0AZ-9275D	42.25
(w/Electronic cluster)		
1983-84-exc.		
Canada	E1LY-9275C	42.25
1983-Canada	E1LY-9275D	N.L.
1985-87	E5VY-9275A	42.25
Mark VI & VII		
(wo/Electronic cluster)		
1983-exc.		
Canada	▲E0LY-9275B	42.25
Canada	▲E0AZ-9275D	42.25
(w/Electronic cluster)		
1983-exc.		
Canada	E1LY-9275C	42.25
Canada	E1LY-9275D	N.L.
1984	E4LY-9H307A	93.75
1985	E5LY-9275A	42.25
1986-87	E6LY-9275A	42.25
Continental		
1983-exc.		
Canada	E35Y-9350A	97.00
Canada	E25Y-9275B	68.25
1984	E4LY-9H307A	93.75
1985	E5LY-9275A	42.25
Fuel Gauge (Dash)		
Lincoln		
(wo/Electronic cluster)		
1983-84	E2LY-9305A	46.00
1985-87	E5VY-9305A	40.75
(w/Electronic cluster)		
1983-84	E0LY-9305AR	125.50
1985-87	E4VY-9305A	124.75
Mark VI & VII		
1983-exc. below	E2LY-9305A	46.00
w/Elec. cluster	E0LY-9305AR	125.50
1984-87-exc.		
Canada	E4LY-10D922AR	124.75
Canada	E4LY-10D922BR	N.L.
Continental		
1983-exc.		
Canada	E25Y-10D922AR	124.75
Canada	E25Y-10D922BR	N.L.
1984-85-exc.		
Canada	E45Y-10D922AR	124.75
Canada	E45Y-10D922BR	N.L.
1986-87-exc.		
Canada	E65Y-10D922AR	181.00
Canada	E65Y-10D922BR	N.L.
Intake Manifold Gasket		
V-8-302 eng		
1983-87	▲D9AZ-9433B	7.50
DIESEL FUEL SYSTEM		
Fuel Injection Pump		
1984-exc. Calif.	E45Y-9A543A	478.50
Calif.	E45Y-9A543B	478.50
Nozzle Holder Assy.		
1984-exc. below	E45Y-9E527A	64.00
w/lift sensor	E45Y-9E527B	64.00
Turbocharger Assy.		
1984	E45Y-9G438A	N.L.
Fuel Pump		
1984	E4LY-9350A	55.50
Fuel Gauge (Tank)		
1984	E4LY-9275A	42.25
1985	E5LY-9275B	42.25
Intake Manifold Gasket		
1984	E45Y-9439A	.50

PARTS 3 ELECTRONIC FUEL INJECTION 3 PARTS

	Part No.	Price
Charging Assy. (Fuel)		
1983 (Stamped on assy.)		
E3VE-CA	▲E3VY-9C973C	749.00
E3VE-CB	▲E3VZ-9C973D	N.L.
E3VE-EA	▲E3VY-9C973E	749.00
E3VE-EB	▲E3VZ-9C973F	N.L.
E3AE-AA	▲E3AZ-9C973A	749.00
E3AE-AB	▲E3AZ-9C973B	N.L.
E35E-AA	▲E35Y-9C973A	749.00
E35E-AB	▲E35Z-9C973C	N.L.
E35E-BA	▲E35Y-9C973B	749.00
E35E-BB	E35Z-9C973D	N.L.
1984 (Stamped on assy.)		
E4AE-KB	E4AZ-9C973K	643.75
E45E-EA	▲E45Z-9C973A	708.25
E4AE-FB	▲E4AZ-9C973C	643.75
E4AE-NA	▲E4AZ-9C973N	643.75
1985 (Stamped on assy.)		
E5AE-EA	▲E5AZ-9C973E	632.75
E5LE-AA	▲E5LY-9C973A	598.25
E55E-EA	E55Y-9C973E	N.L.
E55E-EB	E55Y-9C973EB	598.25
E55E-EC	E55Y-9C973EC	598.25
E5ZE-BA	▲E5ZZ-9C973B	598.25
E5ZE-CA	▲E5ZZ-9C973C	598.25
(1) Plug (Pressure Regulator)		
1983-85	▲E0AY-9E938A	.75
(2) Pressure Regulator Assy. (Fuel)		
1983-85	▲E0SY-9C968A	101.00
(3) Body (Upper)		
Serviced in charging assembly.		
(4) Relief Valve Assy. (Pressure)		
1983-85	▲E0AY-9H321A	6.50
(5) Cap (Relief Valve)		
1983-85	▲E0VY-9H323A	1.50
(6) Charging Wiring Assy.		
1983-85	▲E0VY-9D930A	43.50

	Part No.	Price
(7) Injector Assy. Injector assy. must be ordered by identification no. on tag attached to charging assy.		
(8) Retainer (Fuel Injector)		
1983-85	▲E0AY-9C976A	11.25
(9) Retaining Screw (Fuel Injection)		
1983-85	▲E0AY-9D927A	8.50
(10) Gasket (Charging Body)		
1983-85	▲E0AY-9C983A	1.00
(11) Control Rod Positioner (Fast Idle)		
1983-85	▲E0AY-9D993A	7.75
(12) Cam & Shaft Assy. (Choke)		
1983-85-exc. below	E0PY-9A753A	12.25
Stamped		
E5AE-EA	▲E5AZ-9A753A	12.25
E55E-FA	▲E5AZ-9A753A	12.25
E5ZE-BA, CA, DA	▲E1VZ-9A753A	12.25
E55E-EB, EA, EC	E55Y-9A753A	N.L.
E5LE-AA	▲E1VZ-9A753A	12.25
(13) Control Rod (Fast Idle)		
1983-85	▲E0AY-9E524A	3.00
(14) Diaphragm Assy. (Choke Control)		
1983-85	▲D9AZ-9J549A	10.00
(15) Modulator Spring (Choke Control)		
1983-85	▲E0AY-9J547F	9.75
(16) Cover Assy. (Choke Control) Choke control cover assy. must be ordered by identification no. on charging assy.		
(17) Lever & Shaft Assy. (Throttle)		
1983	▲E3VY-9581A	38.50
(18) Throttle Plates		
1983-84	▲D7ZZ-9585A	1.50
1984-85	▲E2BZ-9585A	5.00
(19) Bracket Kit (Throttle Positioner)		
1983-85	▲E0VY-9J586A	34.25
(20) Dashpot & Control Assy.		
1983-87	▲E3VY-9S520A	44.50

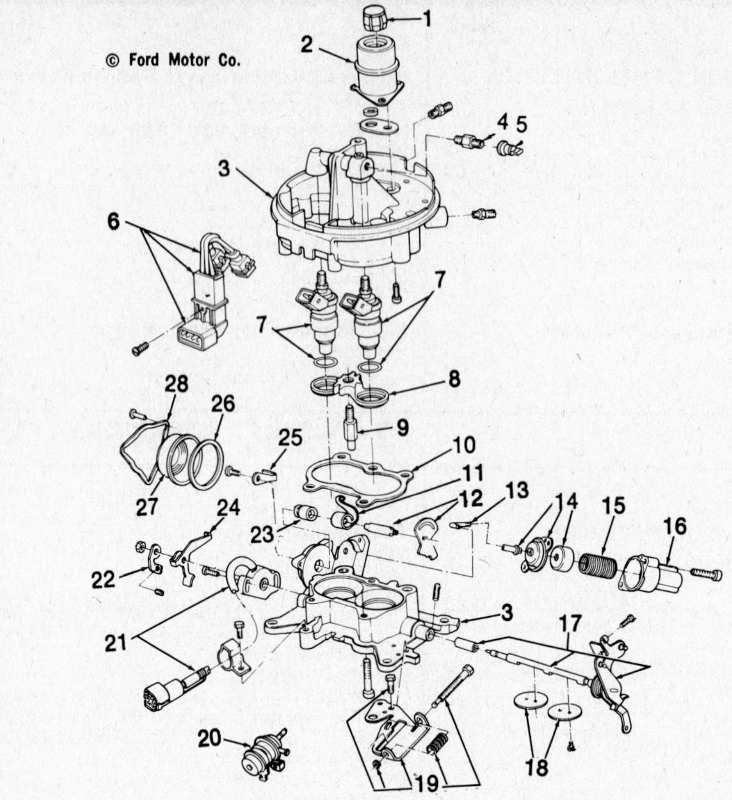

	Part No.	Price
(21) Potentiometer Assy. (Throttle)		
1983-85 (stamped 9E957)		
E0AE-CA	E0AZ-95520C	39.75
E0VE-DA	E1VZ-95520D	44.50
E2VE-AB	E3VY-95520A	44.50
(22) Adjusting Lever (Fast Idle)		
1983-85	▲E0VZ-9538A	7.00
(23) Bushing Serviced in charging assembly.		
(24) Lever (Fast Idle Cam)		
1983-85	▲E0AY-9F577A	5.75

	Part No.	Price
(25) Thermostat Lever (Choke Control)		
1983-85	▲E0AY-9A754A	1.50
(26) Housing Gasket (Choke Thermostat)		
1983-85	▲C1AZ-9871A	1.00
(27) Thermostat Housing Assy. (Choke) Order by identification no. stamped on fuel charging assy.		
(28) Clamp (Thermostat Housing)		
1983-85	▲E2AZ-9842A	6.75

PARTS 3 ELECTRONIC FUEL INJECTION 3 PARTS

SEQUENTIAL ELECTRONIC FUEL INJECTION SYSTEM

302 ENGINE

	Part No.	Price
(1) Intake Manifold (Upper)		
1986-87	E65Z-9424B	N.L.
(2) Upper Manifold Cover		
1986-87-exc. below	▲E6SZ-9E434A	16.00
Lincoln	▲E6AZ-9E434B	16.00
Mark-w/H.O.	E6ZZ-9E434A	16.00
(3) E.G.R. Spacer Assy.		
1986-87-exc. below	E63Z-9H474A	N.L.
Lincoln	▲E6AZ-9H474A	2.25
Mark-w/H.O.	▲E6ZZ-9H474A	18.75
(4) Throttle Body Gasket		
1986-87-exc. LSC	▲E6SZ-9E933A	1.25
LSC	▲E6ZZ-9E933A	1.25
(5) Throttle Body Assy.		
1986-87-exc. below	▲E6SZ-9E926D	239.75

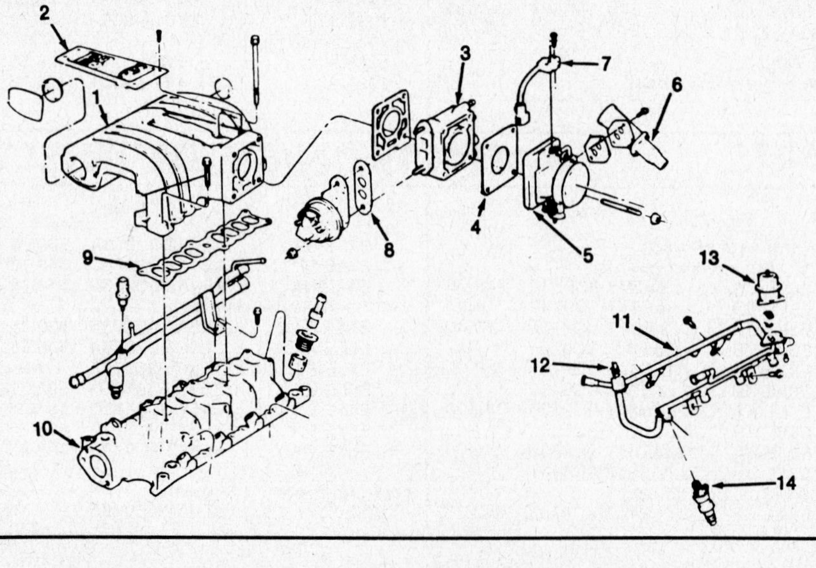

PARTS 3 ELECTRONIC FUEL INJECTION 3 PARTS

	Part No.	Price
Lincoln	▲E6AZ-9E926D	183.75
Mark w/LSC	▲E6ZZ-9E926A	239.75
(6) Throttle Air By-Pass Valve		
1986-87-exc.		
Lincoln	▲E6ZZ-9F715A	56.50
Lincoln	▲E6AZ-9F715C	56.50
(7) Throttle Position Sensor		
1986-87	▲E6AZ-9B989C	29.25
(8) E.G.R. Valve Assy.		
Order by identification no. stamped on valve.		
(9) Intake Manifold Gasket		
1986-87	E6SZ-9H486C	4.50
(10) Lower Intake Manifold		
1986-87	▲E6SZ-9424A	276.25
(11) Fuel Rail Assy.		
1986-87-exc.		
Lincoln	▲E6SZ-9F792D	166.00
Lincoln	▲E6AZ-9F792D	121.75
(12) Schrader Valve		
1986-87	▲N.L.	
(13) Fuel Pressure Regulator		
1986-87	▲E3FZ-9C968A	68.50
(14) Fuel Injector		
(stamped E67E)		
B1A, B1B	▲E6SZ-9F593A	59.50
(stamped E59E)		
A1A, A2A,		
A3A, AB	▲E5TZ-9F593A	133.75

LABOR 3A EMISSION CONTROLS 3A LABOR

(Factory Time) — Chilton Time

CRANKCASE EMISSION

(M) Crankcase Ventilation Valve, Renew
1983-87 (.2) 3

THERMACTOR TYPE

(G) Thermactor Air Pump, Renew
1983-87 (.4) 7

(G) Thermactor Pump Drive Belt, Renew
1983-87 (.3) 5

(G) Thermactor Air By-Pass Valve, Renew
1983-87 (.4) 6

E.G.R. TYPE

(G) E.G.R. Valve, Renew
1983-87 (.3) 4

(G) Vacuum Control Valve, Renew
1983-87 (.3) 4

(G) Exhaust Control Valve Assy., Renew
1983-87 (.4) 7

EVAPORATIVE EMISSION TYPE

(M) Fuel Vapor Canister, Renew
1983-87 (.3) 4

(G) Carburetor Air Cleaner Sensor, Renew
1983-87 (.2) 3

(G) Carburetor Air Cleaner Filter, Renew
1983-87 (.2) 3

ELECTRONIC ENGINE CONTROL

(P) E.E.C. System, Test
1983
w/EEC I (1.0) 1.5
w/EEC III (1.1) 1.7

(P) Crankshaft Position Sensor, Renew
Does not include system test.
1983
w/EEC I (.9) 1.4
w/EEC III (1.1) 1.8

(P) E.G.R. Cooler, Renew
Does not include system test.
1983 (.6) 8

(P) Thermactor Air By-Pass and Diverter Valve Solenoid, Renew
Does not include system test.
1983 (.3) 5

CHILTON'S EMISSION CONTROL TUNE-UP

1. Clean or renew P.C.V. valve, hoses and filter.
2. Check fuel tank cap for sealing ability.
3. Check fuel tank and fuel lines for leakage.
4. Check evaporation canister and filter. Replace if necessary.
5. Check engine compression to determine leakage of unburned gases. (Add time for items of interference).
6. Test and clean or renew spark plugs.
7. Check engine oil dipstick for sealing ability.
8. Test exhaust system with analyzer and check system for leakage.
9. Check exhaust manifold heat valve for operation.
10. Adjust ignition timing and carburetor idle speed and mixture.
11. Check automatic choke mechanism for free operation.
12. Inspect air cleaner and element.
13. On models so equipped, test distributor vacuum control switch and transmission control switch.

V-8 .... 1.8
For repairs made, charge accordingly.

(Factory Time) — Chilton Time

(P) Throttle Position Sensor, Renew
Does not include system test.
1983-exc below (.3) 5
w/CFI (.8) 1.1

(P) Power Relay, Renew
Does not include system test.
1983 (.2) 4

(P) Engine Coolant Temperature Sensor, Renew
Does not include system test.
1983 (.3) 5

(P) Calibrator Assembly, Renew
Does not include system test.
1983 (.3) 5

(P) Processor Assembly, Renew
Does not include system test.
1983 (.3) 4

(P) E.G.R. Value Positive Sensor, Renew
Does not include system test.
1983 (.3) 4

(P) Canister Purge Solenoid Valve, Renew
Does not include system test.
1983 (.2) 4

(P) Exhaust Gas Oxygen Sensor, Renew
Does not include system test.
1983 (.3) 7

(P) Barometric Manifold Absolute Pressure Sensor, Renew
Does not include system test.
1983 (.3) 6

(Factory Time) — Chilton Time

(P) Throttle Kicker Solenoid, Renew
Does not include system test.
1983 (.3) 4

(P) Air Change Temperature Sensor, Renew
Does not include system test.
1983 (.3) 4

ELECTRONIC ENGINE CONTROL IV

(P) E.E.C. System, Test
1984-87
w/E.E.C. IV (.5) 1.0

(P) Throttle Position Sensor, Renew
Does not include system test.
1984-87
w/CFI (.7) 1.0
w/SEFI (.1) 2

(P) Exhaust Gas Oxygen Sensor, Renew
Does not include system test.
1984-87
w/CFI (.2) 5
w/SEFI
right (.4) 6
left (.2) 3
both (.5) 8

(P) Processor Assembly, Renew
Does not include system test.
1984-87
w/CFI (.3) 4
w/SEFI (.3) 4

LABOR 3A EMISSION CONTROLS 3A LABOR

(Factory Time) Chilton Time

(P) Engine Coolant Temperature Sensor, Renew
Does not include system test.
1984-87
w/CFI (.2) 3
w/SEFI (.2) 3

(P) Barometric Manifold Absolute Pressure Sensor, Renew
Does not include system test.
1984-87
w/CFI (.2) 3
w/SEFI (.2) 3

(P) E.G.R. Position Sensor, Renew
Does not include system test.
1984-87
w/CFI (.3) 4
w/SEFI (.3) 4

(P) Thick Film Ignition Module, Renew
Does not include system test.
1984-87
w/CFI (.5) 7
w/SEFI (.5) 7

(P) Profile Ignition Pick-Up Sensor, Renew
Does not include system test.
1984-87
w/CFI (.6) 8
w/SEFI (.6) 8

(P) E.G.R. Control Solenoids, Renew
Does not include system test.
1984-87
w/CFI (.2) 3
w/SEFI (.2) 3

(P) Tab/Tad Solenoids, Renew
Does not include system test.
1984-87
w/CFI (.2) 3
w/SEFI (.2) 3

(P) Fuel Injector Assembly, Renew
Does not include system test.
1984-87
w/CFI-one or both (.7) 1.0
w/SEFI
one (1.8) 2.0
all (2.0) 2.7

(P) Canister Purge Valve or Solenoid, Renew
Does not include system test.
1984-87
w/CFI (.1) 2
w/SEFI (.1) 2

(P) Air Change Temperature Sensor, Renew
Does not include system test.
1984-87
w/CFI (.2) 3
w/SEFI (.2) 3

(P) Throttle Kicker Actuator, Renew
Does not include system test.
1984
w/CFI (.2) 3

(P) Throttle Kicker Solenoid, Renew
Does not include system test.
1984
w/CFI (.1) 2

(P) Exhaust Heat Control Valve, Renew
Does not include system test.
1984
w/CFI (.3) 6

(P) Throttle Air By-Pass Valve, Renew
Does not include system test.
1985-87
w/SEFI (.2) 3

(P) Fuel Pump Relay, Renew
Does not include system test.
1985-87
w/SEFI (.1) 2

(P) Fuel Pump Inertia Switch, Renew
Does not include system test.
1985-87
w/SEFI (.1) 2

(P) Electronic Control Relay, Renew
Does not include system test.
1984-87 (.1) 2

(P) E.G.R. Valve, Renew
Does not include system test.
1984-87 (.2) 4
w/EGR Cooler add (.1) 1

PARTS 3A EMISSION CONTROLS 3A PARTS

	Part No.	Price
THERMACTOR TYPE		
Thermactor Air Pump		
1983-87 (stamped)		
(E1AE-A1A, A2A)	▲E1AZ-9A486A	141.75
(E0RE-B1A, B2A)	▲E1TZ-9A486A	141.75
(E1DE-A1A, A2A)	E1DZ-9A486A	N.L.
(E2AE-BA)	E3AZ-9A586B	N.L.
(E3ZE-EB)	E3ZZ-9A586E	N.L.
(E2AE-CA)	▲E4AZ-9A486A	N.L.
(E5AE-AA)	▲E5AZ-9A486A	N.L.
(E6VE-AA)	▲E6VZ-9A486A	141.75
Air Supply Check Valve		
1983-87 (302 eng)		
nipple 1 end	▲D4VY-9A487A	14.25
nipple 2 ends	▲D9AZ-9A487C	11.25
downstream	▲E3TZ-9A487A	13.25
EVAPORATIVE EMISSION TYPE		
Canister Assy.		
1983 (Lincoln & Mark VI)		
exc. Calif.	▲E2VY-9D653A	72.75
Calif.	▲E0AZ-9D653A	53.25
1983 (Continental)		
exc. Canada	▲E3FZ-9D653B	53.25
Canada	▲E2VY-9D653A	72.75
1984-85	▲D8AZ-9D653C	53.25
1986-87	▲E2ZZ-9D653A	55.50
Crankcase Ventilator Valve		
1983-87-exc.		
Canada	▲D9ZZ-6A666A	3.50
Canada	▲D9OZ-6A666A	3.00

	Part No.	Price
E.G.R. SYSTEM		
ELECTRONIC ENGINE CONTROL I, III, IV		
Crankshaft Position Sensor		
1983-84	▲E0AZ-6C315A	42.50
Cooler Assy. (E.G.R.)		
1983-85 (Intake manifold)		
Cast iron	E1TZ-9F464A	109.25
Aluminum	E1TZ-9F464B	117.75
Manifold Absolute Pressure Sensor		
E1AF-AA	▲E1AZ-9F472A	95.00
1984-87	▲E43Z-9F479B	68.50
Throttle Position Sensor		
Order by identification code. Stamped on assy.		
Exhaust Gas Oxygen Sensor		
1983-87 (stamped)		
E3EF-AA	▲E3FZ-9F472A	48.50
E4ZF-AA	▲E4ZZ-9F472A	69.00
E59F-A1A, A2A	▲E59Z-9F472A	48.50
E6DF-AA	▲E6DZ-9F472A	N.L.
E67F-AA, CA	▲E6TZ-9F472A	48.50
BA	▲E6TZ-9F472B	48.50
Power Relay Assy.		
1983-87-exc.		
below	▲E3AZ-12A646A	15.50
1984-85-w/tow		
pkg.	E0BZ-12A646A	15.50
1984-diesel	E45Y-12A646A	15.50
Engine Coolant Temperature Sensor		
1983-87	▲E1AZ-12A648A	32.00

	Part No.	Price
Thick Film Ignition Module		
1984-87	▲E43Z-12A297A	106.00
Canister Purge Valve		
1984-87 (w/E.E.C. IV)		
natural	▲E4AZ-9C915A	21.75
green	▲E4AZ-9C915B	21.75
black	▲E4AZ-9C915C	21.75
Air Charge Temperature Sensor		
1984-87	▲E1AZ-12A697A	27.00
Calibrator Assy.		
1983 (Lincoln Town Car, Mark VI)		
exc. Calif.	▲E2VY-12A649HA	140.50
Calif.	▲E3VZ-12A649A	140.50
Hi Alt.	▲E2VY-12A649JB	140.50
1983 (Continental)		
exc. hi alt.	E35Y-12A649E	140.50
w/hi alt.	E35Y-12A649G	140.50
Exhaust Heat Control Valve		
1984-87-exc.		
H.O.	▲E1SZ-9A427A	86.50
H.O.	▲E4ZZ-9A427A	86.50
Processor Assy.		
1984-85 (stamped)		
E4VF-L1A, L2A	E4VZ-12A650LA	N.L.
E4VF-S1A, S2A	E4VZ-12A650SA	167.75
E53F-L1B, L2B	E53Z-12A650LB	167.75
E53F-R1B, R2B	E53Z-12A650RB	167.75
E53F-U1B, U2B	E53Z-12A650UB	167.75
E53F-U1C, U2C	E53Z-12A650UC	167.75
E53F-V1C, V2C	E53Z-12A650VC	167.75

PARTS 3A EMISSION CONTROLS 3A PARTS

	Part No.	Price
E53F-V1D, V2D	E53Z-12A650VD	167.75
1986-87 (stamped E6SF)		
E1B, E2B	E6SZ-12A650EB	N.L.
D1B, D2B	E6SZ-12A650DB	N.L.
L1A, L2A	E6SZ-12A650LA	N.L.
S1B, S2B	▲E6SZ-12A650SB	N.L.
T1B, T2B	▲E6SZ-12A650TB	N.L.
X1B, X2B	E6SZ-12A650XB	N.L.
Y1B, Y2B	▲E6SZ-12A650YB	N.L.
Position Sensor (E.G.R. Valve)		
1983-84	▲E43Z-9G428B	31.75
1985-87	▲E43Z-9G428B	31.75
Solenoid Vacuum Valve		
1983-85 (stamped)		
E1SE-C2A, C3A	▲E1SZ-9D474C	16.25
E1TE-C2A, C3A	▲E1TZ-9D474C	32.50
E0AE-B2A, B3A, E2A, E3A	▲E0AZ-9D474B	32.50
E9AE-B2A, B3A	▲E0AZ-9D474D	32.50
E35E-A2A, FA	▲E35Y-9D474A	32.50
E35E-D2A, D3A, E3A	▲E35Y-9D474D	28.00
E4SE-A3A	▲E3SZ-9D474C	32.50
E4AE-A2A, A3A	E4AZ-9D474A	16.25
E4ZE-D2A, D3A	▲E4ZZ-9D474D	32.50
E4ZE-E2A, E3A	▲E4ZZ-9D474E	32.50
E4ZE-FA	▲E4ZZ-9D474F	32.50
E45E-AA	E45Y-9D474A	32.50
E5VE-AA	E5VZ-9D474A	35.75
1986-87 (stamped)		
E6AE-A3A	▲E6AZ-9D474A	32.50
E65E-A2A	▲E65Z-9D474A	N.L.

LABOR 4 ALTERNATOR AND REGULATOR 4 LABOR

(Factory Time)	Chilton Time
(G) Alternator Circuits, Test	
Includes: Test battery, regulator and alternator output.	
All models (.3)	.6
(M) Alternator Drive Belt, Renew	
1983-87 (.3)	.4
(G) Alternator, Renew	
1983-87 (.4)	.6
w/Diesel eng add (.1)	.1
Transfer pulley add (.1)	.1
Circuit test add (.4)	.6
(G) Alternator, R&R and Recondition	
Includes: Complete disassembly, replacement of parts as required. Test validity of rotor fields, stator and diodes.	
1983-87 (.9)	1.5
w/Diesel eng add (.1)	.1
Circuit test add (.4)	.6
(G) Alternator Front Bearing or End Plate, Renew	
1983-87 (.7)	1.1
w/Diesel eng add (.1)	.1
(G) Alternator Rear Bearing, Renew	
1983-87 (.6)	1.0
w/Diesel eng add (.1)	.1
(G) Alternator Regulator, Renew	
1983-87 (.3)	.5
Circuit test add (.4)	.6
(G) Instrument Cluster Voltage Regulator, Renew	
Includes: Remove instrument panel pad when required.	
Lincoln & Continental	
1983-87 (.7)	1.1
Mark VI, VII	
1983-87 (.7)	1.1

PARTS 4 ALTERNATOR AND REGULATOR 4 PARTS

	Part No.	Price
Alternator Assy. (New)		
Lincoln		
(60 amp.)		
1983-85	▲E2GZ-10346C	233.50
(65 amp.)		
1986-87	▲E6ZZ-10346B	418.75
(70 amp.)		
1984	▲E1BZ-10346A	265.00
(100 amp.)		
1983-87 (exc. 1985)	▲E1VZ-10346A	418.75
Continental		
(60 amp.)		
1983-84	▲E2GZ-10346A	233.50
(70 amp.)		
1984-85	▲E1BZ-10346A	265.00
(100 amp.)		
1984-87	▲E1VZ-10346A	418.75
Mark VI & VII		
(60 amp.)		
1983-84	▲E2GZ-10346C	233.50
(70 amp.)		
1984-85	▲E1BZ-10346A	265.00
(100 amp.)		
1983-87	▲E1VZ-10346A	418.75

1984 Continental & Mark VII with 100 amp. alternator have diesel engine.

	Part No.	Price
Regulator Assy.		
1983-85-exc. below	▲E2PZ-10316-A	36.75
1986-87-65 amp	▲E6TZ-10316A	29.75
1983-87-100 amp	▲E2PZ-10316A	36.75
Instrument Cluster Voltage Regulator		
1983-87	▲D1AZ-10804A	10.25
(1) Front Housing		
1983-85-60 amp	▲D3OZ-10333B	17.75
1986-87-65 amp	▲E6AZ-10333A	18.50
1983-87-70, 100 amp	▲D3VY-10333A	72.75

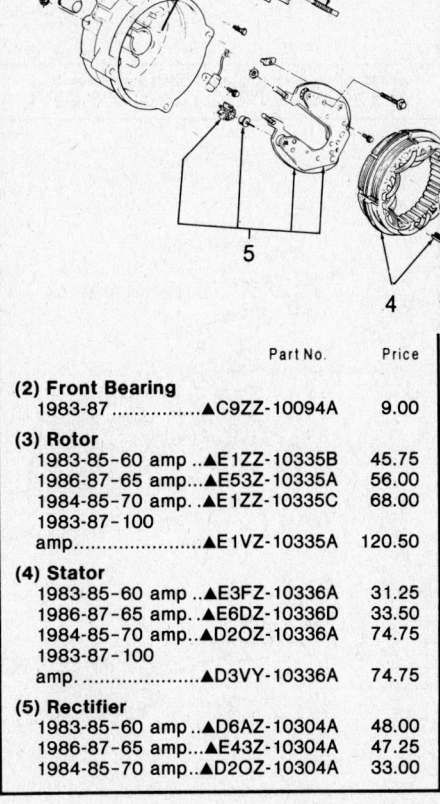

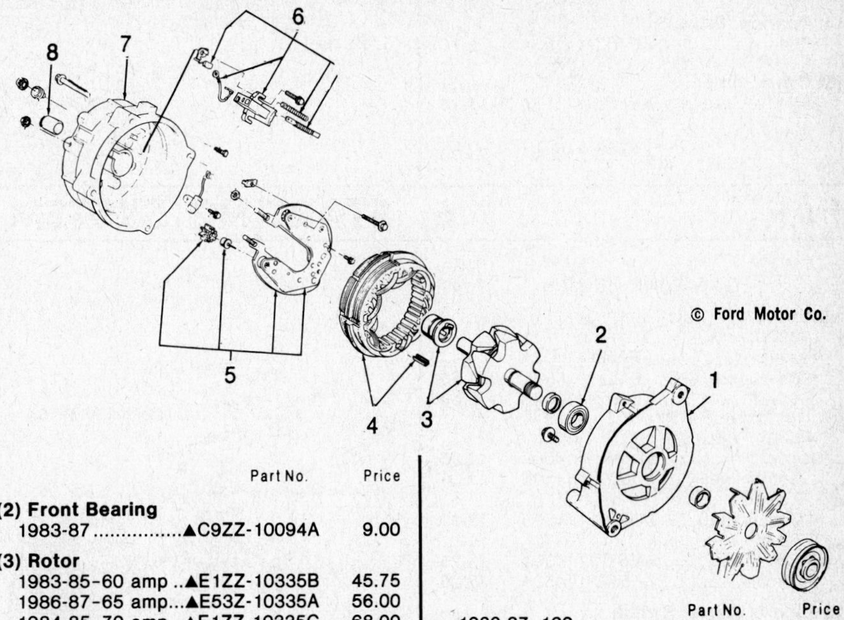

© Ford Motor Co.

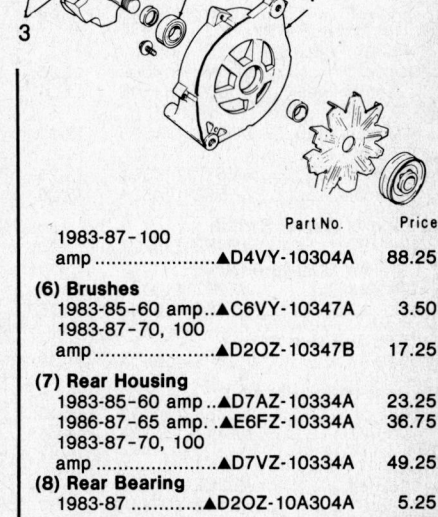

	Part No.	Price
(2) Front Bearing		
1983-87	▲C9ZZ-10094A	9.00
(3) Rotor		
1983-85-60 amp	▲E1ZZ-10335B	45.75
1986-87-65 amp	▲E53Z-10335A	56.00
1984-85-70 amp	▲E1ZZ-10335C	68.00
1983-87-100 amp	▲E1VZ-10335A	120.50
(4) Stator		
1983-85-60 amp	▲E3FZ-10336A	31.25
1986-87-65 amp	▲E6DZ-10336D	33.50
1984-85-70 amp	▲D2OZ-10336A	74.75
1983-87-100 amp	▲D3VY-10336A	74.75
(5) Rectifier		
1983-85-60 amp	▲D6AZ-10304A	48.00
1986-87-65 amp	▲E43Z-10304A	47.25
1984-85-70 amp	▲D2OZ-10304A	33.00
1983-87-100 amp	▲D4VY-10304A	88.25
(6) Brushes		
1983-85-60 amp	▲C6VY-10347A	3.50
1983-87-70, 100 amp	▲D2OZ-10347B	17.25
(7) Rear Housing		
1983-85-60 amp	▲D7AZ-10334A	23.25
1986-87-65 amp	▲E6FZ-10334A	36.75
1983-87-70, 100 amp	▲D7VZ-10334A	49.25
(8) Rear Bearing		
1983-87	▲D2OZ-10A304A	5.25

LABOR 5 STARTING SYSTEM 5 LABOR

(Factory Time)	Chilton Time
(G) Starter Draw Test (On Car)	
All models (.3)	.3
(G) Starter, Renew	
Lincoln	
1983-87 (.3)	.6
Mark VI	
1983 (.3)	.6
Continental & Mark VII	
1983-87-Gas (.4)	.6
Diesel (.6)	.9
Add draw test if performed.	
(G) Starter, R&R and Recondition	
Includes: Turn down armature.	
Lincoln	
1983-87 (1.5)	2.3
Mark VI	
1983 (1.6)	2.7
Continental & Mark VII	
1983-87-Gas (1.6)	2.4
Diesel (2.1)	3.0
Renew field coils add	.5
Add draw test if performed.	
(G) Starter Drive, Renew	
Lincoln	
1983-87 (.5)	.9
Mark VI	
1983 (.5)	1.1
Continental & Mark VII	
1983-87-Gas (.6)	1.0
Diesel (1.2)	1.5
(G) Starter Solenoid Relay, Renew	
1983-87 (.3)	.4
(G) Neutral Safety Switch, Renew	
1983-87 (.4)	.6
(G) Ignition Switch, Renew	
1983-87 (.5)	.9
(M) Battery Cables, Renew	
Batt to Relay (.3)	.3
Ground (.3)	.3
Relay to Starter (.4)	.5

PARTS 5 STARTING SYSTEM 5 PARTS

DIESEL ENGINE

	Part No.	Price
Starter Assy.		
1984	E4LY-11002A	231.25
(1) Solenoid Assy.		
1984	▲E4FZ-11390A	34.50
(2) Spring (Plunger)		
1984	▲E4FZ-11103A	1.75
(3) Lever Assy. (Drive)		
1984	▲E4FZ-11067A	14.25
(4) Housing Assy. (Drive End)		
1984	E4LY-11130A	29.25
(5) Bearing (Drive End)		
1984	▲E4FZ-11135A	2.75
(6) Drive Shaft		
1984	▲E4FZ-11355A	7.25
(7) Drive Assy.		
1984	▲E4FZ-11350A	21.00

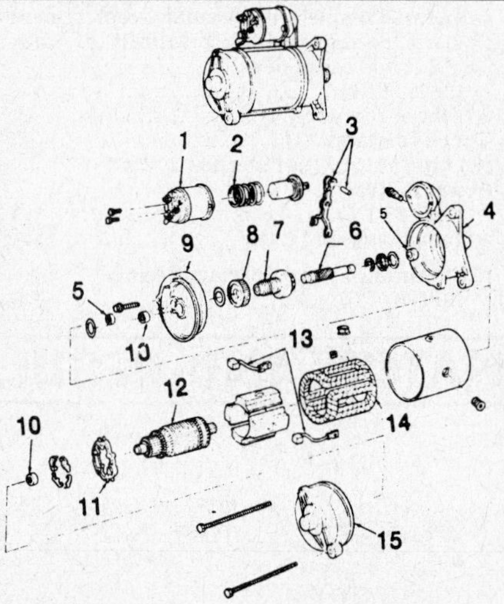

	Part No.	Price
(8) Drive Gear (Armature)		
1984	▲E4FZ-11A067A	24.75
(9) Housing Assy. (Gear)		
1984	▲E4AZ-11A149A	13.75
(10) Bushing		
1984	▲E4FZ-11052A	9.50
(11) Brush Holder		
1984	▲E4FZ-11061A	4.25
(12) Armature		
1984	▲E4FZ-11005A	66.75
(13) Brush Assy.		
1984	▲E4PZ-11057A	13.00
(14) Field Coil (Complete)		
1984	▲E4FZ-11082A	50.00
(15) Plate Assy.		
1984	▲E4FZ-11049A	14.50
Ignition Switch		
1984	▲E4FZ-11572A	11.50

PARTS 5 STARTING SYSTEM 5 PARTS

GASOLINE ENGINE

	Part No.	Price
Starter Assy. (New)		
1983-84-exc. diesel	▲E25Z-11002A	N.L.
1984-Diesel	E4LY-11002A	231.25
1985-87	▲E4DZ-11002B	185.50
Starter Relay Switch		
1983-84-exc. below	▲D8VY-11450A	12.25
Continental	▲D8DZ-11450B	12.00
Canada (exc. Continental)	▲D8DZ-11450B	12.00
1985-87-exc. below	▲E5TZ-11450A	13.25
Lincoln	▲E5AZ-11450A	13.25
Ignition & Starter Switch		
1983-87	▲E4FZ-11572A	11.50
(1) Starter Armature (New)		
1983-84	▲E2BZ-11005A	77.00
1985-87	▲E3FZ-11005A	66.75
(2) Starter Drive Assy.		
1983-87	▲E2PZ-11350A	21.00
(3) Rear Plate (Housing)		
1983-84	▲E25Y-11130A	45.00
1985-87	▲E4AZ-11130A	41.75
(4) Front Plate		
1983-84	▲E2BZ-11049A	14.50
1985-87	▲E4AZ-11049A	14.50

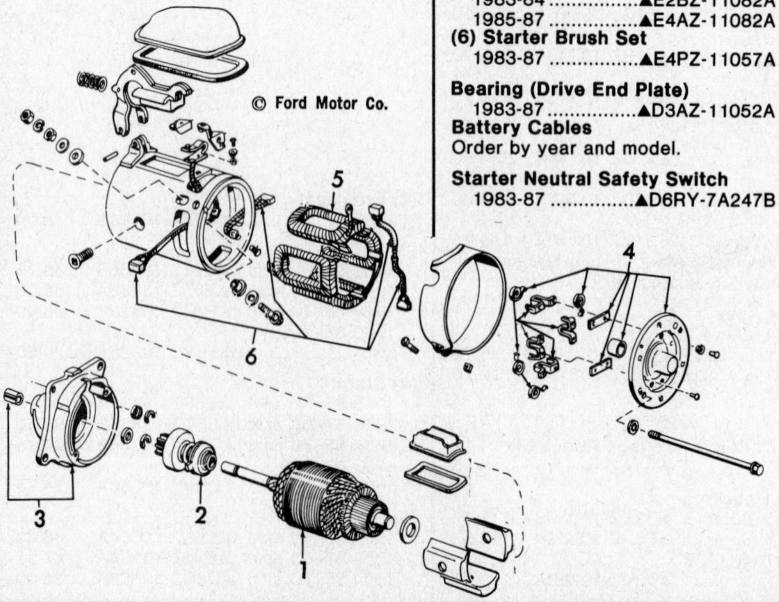

	Part No.	Price
(5) Field Coil Assy.		
1983-84	▲E2BZ-11082A	50.00
1985-87	▲E4AZ-11082A	50.00
(6) Starter Brush Set		
1983-87	▲E4PZ-11057A	13.00
Bearing (Drive End Plate)		
1983-87	▲D3AZ-11052A	1.50
Battery Cables		
Order by year and model.		
Starter Neutral Safety Switch		
1983-87	▲D6RY-7A247B	33.25

LABOR 6 BRAKE SYSTEM 6 LABOR

(Factory Time) Chilton Time

(G) Brake Pedal Free Play, Adjust
All models 4

(G) Brakes, Adjust (Minor)
Includes: Adjust brakes, fill master cylinder.
two wheels 4

(G) Bleed Brakes (Four Wheels)
Includes: Fill master cylinder.
All models (.3) 5

(G) Brake Self Adjustors, Disassemble & Clean
one wheel 7
each adtnl 4

(G) Brake Shoes and/or Pads, Renew
Includes: Install new or exchange brake shoes or pads. Adjust service and hand brake. Bleed system.
1983-87-front-disc (.7) 1.1
rear-drum (1.0) 1.5
all four wheels (1.4) 2.5
Resurface disc rotor add-each 9
Resurface brake drum add-each 5

(G) Brake Drum, Renew
1983-87-one (.3) 6
both (.4) 8

(G) Brake Pressure Warning Light Switch, Renew
1983-87 (.3) 5

BRAKE HYDRAULIC SYSTEM

(G) Wheel Cylinder, Renew
Includes: Bleed system.
1983-87-one (.9) 1.4
both (1.5) 2.1

(G) Wheel Cylinder, R&R and Rebuild
Includes: Hone cylinder and bleed system.
1983-87-one (.9) 1.7
both (1.5) 2.7

(G) Brake Hose, Renew
Includes: Bleed system.
1983-87-front-one (.4) 7
both (.5) 8
rear-one (.5) 8

(G) Master Cylinder, Renew
Includes: Bleed complete system.
1983-87 (.5) 1.0
w/Hyd Boost add (.2) 2

(G) Master Cylinder, R&R and Rebuild
Includes: Hone cylinder and bleed complete system.
1983-87 (.7) 1.6
w/Hyd Boost add (.2) 2

(G) Brake System, Flush and Refill
All models 1.2

(G) Brake Hydraulic System, Recondition (Complete)
Includes: Renew all rubber parts in brake system and bleed all lines.
1983-87 (4.8) 5.5

POWER BRAKES

(G) Vacuum Pump, Renew
1984-85 (.7) 1.1

(G) Power Brake Booster, Renew
Lincoln
1983-87 (.6) 1.1
Mark VI, VII
1983 (.5) 1.1

COMBINATIONS
Add to Brakes, Renew

See Machine Shop Operations

(G) RENEW WHEEL CYLINDER
Each (.3) 3

(G) REBUILD WHEEL CYLINDER
Each (.3) 3

(G) REBUILD CALIPER ASSEMBLY
Front-one (.5) 5
Rear-one (.6) 6

(G) RENEW MASTER CYLINDER
All models (.6) 6

(G) REBUILD MASTER CYLINDER
All models (.8) 1.0

(G) RENEW BRAKE HOSE
Each (.3) 3

(G) RENEW REAR WHEEL GREASE SEALS
One (.4) 4
Both (.5) 6

(G) REPACK FRONT WHEEL BEARINGS (BOTH WHEELS)
All models (.4) 6

(G) RENEW BRAKE DRUM
Each (.2) 2

(G) RENEW DISC BRAKE ROTOR
Each (.2) 4

(Factory Time) Chilton Time

1984-87
H/Boost (1.3) 2.0
Continental
1983-87 (.8) 1.3
H/Boost (1.3) 2.0
w/Cruise control add (.2) 2

(G) Power Brake Booster Check Valve, Renew
1983-87 (.3) 4

(G) Hydra-boost Hose, Renew
1983-87-one (.4) 6
both (.5) 8

DISC BRAKES

(G) Disc Brake Pads, Renew
1983-87-front (.7) 1.1
rear (.8) 1.2
all four wheels (1.2) 2.0
Resurface brake rotor add-each 9

(G) Caliper Assembly, Renew
Includes: Bleed complete system.
1983-87-front-one (.6) 1.0
both (.8) 1.5
rear-one (.7) 1.1
both (1.0) 1.7

(G) Caliper Assembly, R&R and Recondition
Includes: Bleed system.
1983-87-front-one (.9) 1.5
both (1.2) 2.5
rear-one (1.0) 1.7
both (1.7) 2.9

(G) Brake Rotor, Renew
Includes: Renew front wheel bearings and grease retainer and repack bearings. Remove rear wheel assembly.
1983-87-front-one (.5) 7
both (.8) 1.2

(Factory Time) Chilton Time

rear-one (.4) 6
both (.5) 1.0

(G) Brake Differential Valve, Renew
Includes: Bleed complete system and transfer switch.
1983-87 (.7) 1.0

PARKING BRAKE

(M) Parking Brake, Adjust
drum brakes (.3) 4
w/Rear disc brakes (.3) 5

(G) Parking Brake Indicator Switch, Renew
1983-87 (.3) 4

(G) Parking Brake Control, Renew
1983-87-Lincoln (.5) 1.0
Cont & Mark VII (1.0) 1.5

(G) Parking Brake Cable, Renew
Includes: Adjust parking brake.
drum brakes-one (.6) 8
both (.8) 1.1
w/Rear disc brakes-one (.5) 7
both (.6) 1.0

(G) Parking Brake Power Vacuum Unit, Renew
1985-87
Lincoln (.3) 5
Cont. & Mark VII (1.1) 1.6

ANTI-LOCK BRAKE SYSTEM

(G) Brake System Diagnosis
1985-87 (.4) 5

(G) Front Sensor Rings, Renew
Does not include system test.
1985-87-one (.4) 6
both (.8) 1.2

(G) Front Sensor Assemblies, Renew
Does not include system test.
1985-87-one (.3) 4
both (.4) 6

(G) Rear Sensor Rings, Renew
Does not include system test.
1985-87-one (.7) 9
both (1.1) 1.5

(G) Rear Sensor Assemblies, Renew
Does not include system test.
1985-87-one (.4) 6
both (.8) 1.2

(G) Hydraulic Booster Assy., Renew
Does not include system test.
1985-87 (1.6) 2.0

(G) Anti-Lock Module, Renew
Does not include system test.
1985-87 (.1) 2

(G) Accumulator, Renew
Does not include system test.
1985-87 (.1) 2

(G) Pressure Switch, Renew
Does not include system test.
1985-87 (.2) 3

(G) Reservoir Assy., Renew
1985-87 (.5) 7

(G) Hydraulic Pump Motor, Renew
Does not include system test.
1985-87 (.6) 8

PARTS 6 BRAKE SYSTEM 6 PARTS

	Part No.	Price
Brake Pressure Warning Light Switch		
1983-87	▲D9BZ-2B264A	7.50
Brake Booster Check Valve		
1983-87	▲D0AZ-2365A	5.50
Brake Differential Valve		
Lincoln		
1983-87	▲E0AZ-2B257A	73.75
Continental & Mark VI		
1983		
(Continental)	E1DZ-2B25A	N.L.
(Mark)	▲E0AZ-2B257A	73.75
1984-87-exc. anti-skid	E4LY-2B257A	40.00
1985-87-w/anti-skid	E5LY-2B257A	46.50
(1) Brakes Shoes (New)		
Lincoln & Mark VI (1983)		
1983-87-10″ brks.	▲D9AZ-2200A	42.50
11″ brks.	▲D9AZ-2200B	47.25
Continental & Mark VII		
1983-87	▲E4LY-2200A	42.75

1983-87-Continental and 1984-87-Mark VI have rear disc brakes.

	Part No.	Price
Brake Lining Kit		
1983-87-10″ brks.	▲D9AZ-2007A	26.25
11″ brks.	▲D9AZ-2007B	29.25
(2) Wheel Cylinder Assy. (Rear)		
1983-87	▲D9AZ-2261B	25.75
Wheel Cylinder Repair Kit		
1983-87	▲D9AZ-2128B	6.00
Brake Hose (Front)		
1983 (Lincoln & Mark VI)		
right	▲E0AZ-2078A	18.00
left	▲E0AZ-2078B	18.00
1983 (Continental)		
right	▲E25Y-2078A	23.75
left	▲E25Y-2078B	23.75
1984-87 (Continental & Mark VII)		
right	E45Y-2078A	16.25
left	E45Y-2078B	12.25
1984-87 (Lincoln Town Car)		
right	▲E0AZ-2078A	18.00
left	▲E0AZ-2078B	18.00
Brake Hose (Rear)		
Lincoln		
1983-87	▲D9AZ-2282B	19.25
Mark VI & VII		
1983	▲D9AZ-2282B	19.25

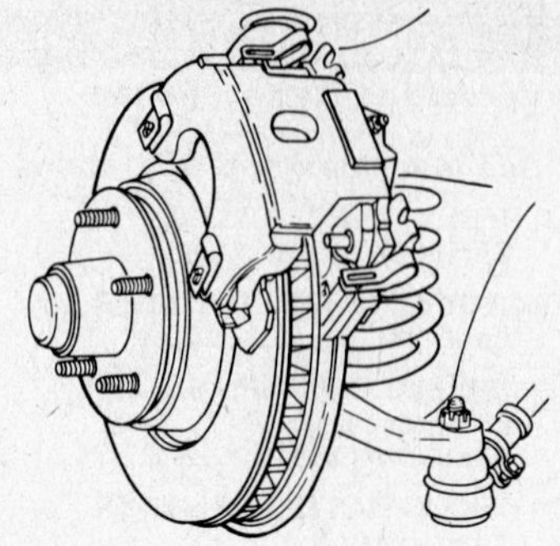

FRONT BRAKE

	Part No.	Price
1984-87-exc. anti-skid	E45Y-2282A	14.00
Anti skid	E5LY-2282A	14.00
Continental		
1983	▲E3SZ-2282A	17.25
1984-87-exc. anti-skid	E45Y-2282A	14.00
Anti-skid	E5LY-2282A	14.00
Master Cylinder Assy.		
Lincoln		
1983-87	▲D9AZ-2140A	93.50
Mark VI, VII		
1983	▲D9AZ-2140A	93.50
1984-87	▲E25Y-2140A	102.50
Continental		
1983-87	▲E25Y-2140A	102.50
Power Brake Unit (New)		
Lincoln		
1983-87	▲D9AZ-2005A	236.25
Mark VI & VII		
1983	▲D9AZ-2005A	236.25
1984-87	E35Y-2005A	427.75
Continental		
1983-87-exc. below	E35Y-2005A	427.75
w/anti-skid	E5LY-2005A	N.L.
Brake Drum Rear		
(10″ brakes)		
1983-87-cast iron	D9AZ-1126A	87.00
aluminum	E0VZ-1126A	161.75
(11″ brakes)		
1983-87	▲D9AZ-1126B	111.75
Oil Seal, Front		
1983-87	▲C8AZ-1190A	3.00

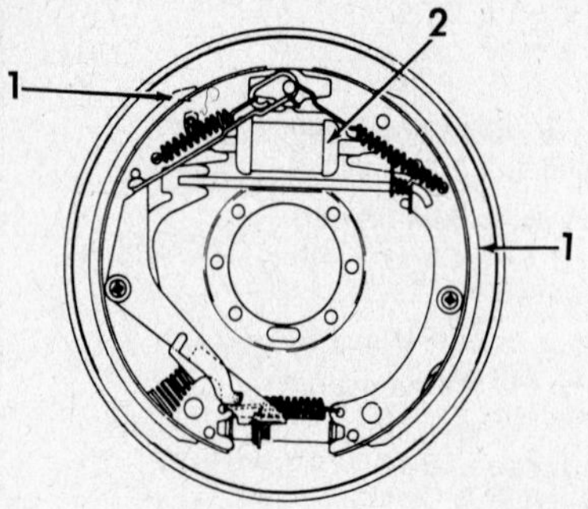

REAR BRAKE

	Part No.	Price
Oil Seal, Rear		
1983-87	▲E1AZ-1177B	3.50

PARKING BRAKE

	Part No.	Price
Front Cable, Hand Brake		
Lincoln		
1983-87	▲D9AZ-2853A	16.00
Mark VI & VII		
1983	▲D9AZ-2853A	16.00
1984-87	E4LY-2853A	7.75
Continental		
1983	E25Y-2853A	18.25
1984-87	E4LY-2853A	7.75
Rear Cable, Hand Brake		
Lincoln		
1983-87-R.H.	▲E2AZ-2A635A	25.00
L.H.	▲E2LY-2A635A	17.75
Mark VI & VII		
1983-R.H.	▲E2AZ-2A635A	25.00
L.H.	▲E2LY-2A635A	17.75
1984-87	E4LY-2A635A	13.25
Continental		
1983	E25Y-2A635A	17.75
1984-87	E4LY-2A635A	13.25
Lever, Hand or Foot (Parking Brake)		
Lincoln		
1983-87-exc. auto release	E0LY-2780A	84.50
1986-87-w/auto release	▲E6AZ-2780A	69.25
Mark VI & VII		
1983	E0LY-2780A	84.50
1984-87	E35Y-2780A	69.25
Continental		
1983-84	E35Y-2780A	69.25
1985-87	E4LY-2780A	69.25

PARTS 6 DISC BRAKES 6 PARTS

FRONT

	Part No.	Price
Continental & Mark VII		
(1) Hub and Rotor		
1983-84	▲E45Y-1102A	78.75
1985-87	▲E5LY-1102A	78.75
(2) Piston Assembly		
1983-87	▲E1AZ-2196A	14.25
(3) Brake Pad Set		
1983-Continental	E35Y-2001A	N.L.
Mark	▲E2AZ-2001A	27.00
1984-87	▲E4LY-2001A	34.75
(4) Caliper Assembly		
1983-87-right	▲E4LY-2B120A	120.00
left	▲E4LY-2B121A	120.00

FRONT DISC BRAKES

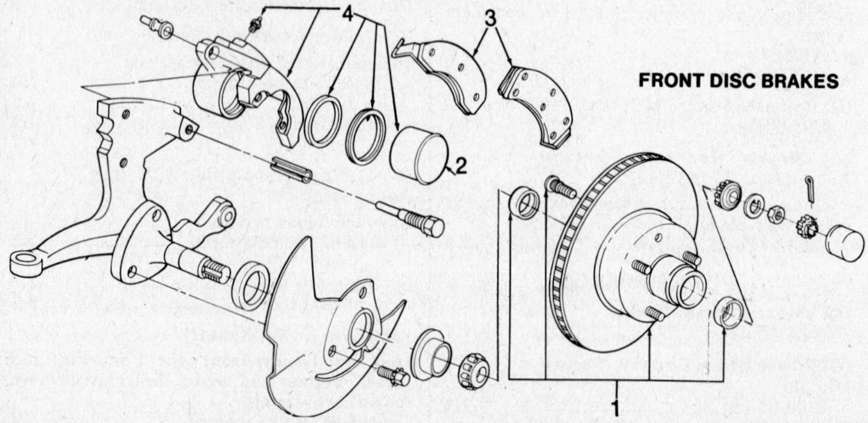

PARTS 6 DISC BRAKES 6 PARTS

FRONT
Lincoln & Mark VI

	Part No.	Price
(1) Hub & Rotor Assy.		
1983-87	▲D9AZ-1102A	73.00
(2) Seal Kit		
1983-87	▲D9AZ-2221A	6.25
(3) Brake Pad Set		
1983-87	▲E2AZ-2001A	27.00
(4) Caliper Assembly		
1983-87-right	▲E4LY-2B120A	120.00
left	▲E4LY-2B121A	120.00

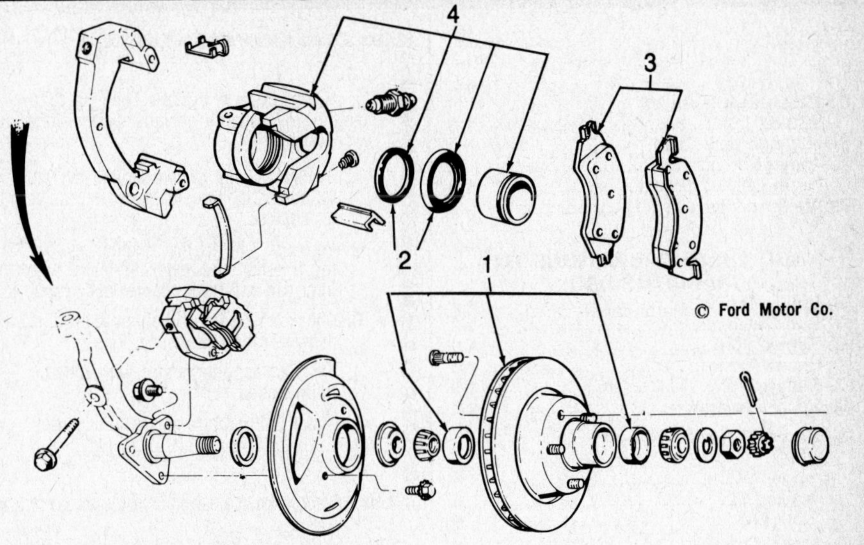

PARTS 6 DISC BRAKES 6 PARTS

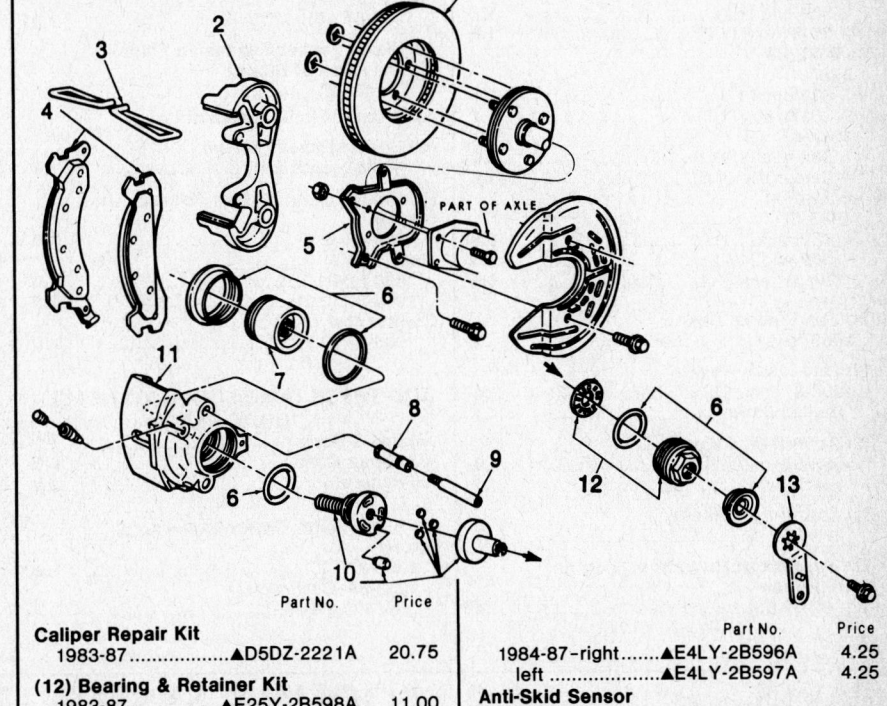

REAR
Continental & Mark VII

	Part No.	Price
(1) Rotor Assy.		
1983-87-right	▲E25Y-2C026A	105.50
left	E25Y-2C027A	105.50
(2) Anchor Plate (Caliper)		
1983-right	▲E4LY-2B582A	35.00
left	E25Y-2B583A	34.00
1984-87	▲E4LY-2B582A	35.00
(3) Clip (Anti-Rattle)		
1983-87	▲E35Y-2B164A	1.50
(4) Pad Set		
1983-87	▲E4LY-2200A	42.75
(5) Adapter (Rear Axle)		
wo/anti-skid		
1983-87-right	▲E25Y-4A404B	20.75
left	▲E25Y-4A405B	20.75
w/anti-skid		
1985-87-right	E5LY-4A404A	22.00
left	E5LY-4A405A	22.00
(6) Seal Kit		
1983-87	▲D5DZ-2B595A	20.75
(7) Piston & Adjuster Assy.		
1983-87	▲E25Y-2B588A	36.00
(8) Insulator		
1983-87	C8AZ-2B299A	1.75
(9) Locating Pin		
1983-87	▲E25Y-2B296A	4.75
(10) Ball Ramp Kit		
1983-87-right	▲E25Y-2A870A	20.75
left	▲E25Y-2A871A	20.75
(11) Caliper Assy.		
1983-87-right	▲E4LY-2552A	219.00
left	▲E4LY-2553A	219.00

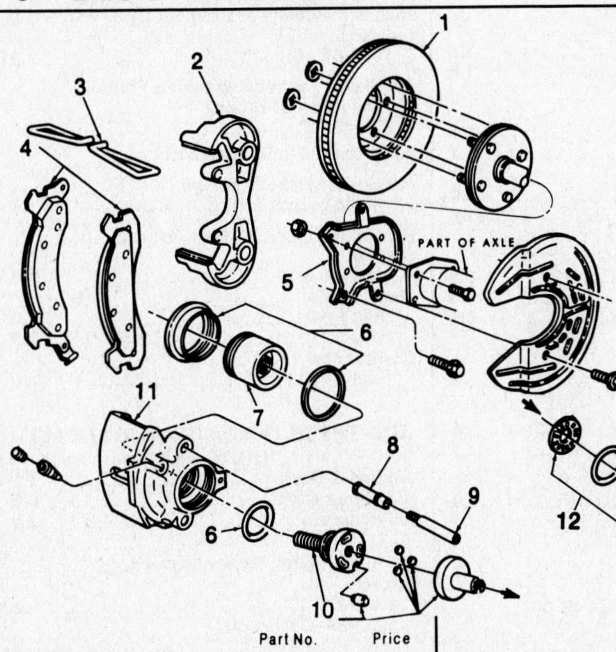

	Part No.	Price
Caliper Repair Kit		
1983-87	▲D5DZ-2221A	20.75
(12) Bearing & Retainer Kit		
1983-87	▲E25Y-2B598A	11.00
(13) Actuating Lever (Parking Brake)		
1983-right	E25Y-2B596A	4.25
left	E25Y-2B597A	4.25

	Part No.	Price
1984-87-right	▲E4LY-2B596A	4.25
left	▲E4LY-2B597A	4.25
Anti-Skid Sensor		
1985-87-right	E5LY-2C190A	30.00
left	E5LY-2C190B	30.00
Anti-Skid Sensor Indicator		
1985-87	E5LY-2C189A	53.50

LABOR 7 COOLING SYSTEM 7 LABOR

	(Factory Time)	Chilton Time
(M) Winterize Cooling System		
Includes: Run engine to check for leaks, tighten all hose connections. Test radiator and pressure cap, drain radiator and engine block. Add anti-freeze and refill system.		
All models		.5

	(Factory Time)	Chilton Time
(M) Thermostat, Renew		
1983-87-Gas	(.5)	.6
Diesel	(.8)	1.0

	(Factory Time)	Chilton Time
(M) Radiator Assembly, R&R or Renew		
Includes: Drain and refill cooling system.		
Lincoln & Mark VI		
1983-87	(.5)	.9

LABOR 7 COOLING SYSTEM 7 LABOR

(Factory Time) Chilton Time

Continental & Mark VII
1983-87 (.6).................................... 1.0
Renew side tanks add
one (.5).................................... .7
both (.9).................................... 1.3
Renew oil cooler add (.1).................... .1

ADD THESE OPERATIONS TO RADIATOR R&R
(G) Boil & Repair.................................... 1.5
(G) Rod Clean.................................... 1.9
(G) Repair Core.................................... 1.3
(G) Renew Tank.................................... 1.6
(G) Renew Trans. Oil Cooler.................... 1.9
(G) Recore Radiator.................................... 1.7

(M) Radiator Hoses, Renew
1983-87
upper (.4).................................... .4
lower (.5).................................... .6
both (.6).................................... .9

(M) Radiator By-Pass Hose, Renew
1983-87 (.3).................................... .7

(G) Water Pump, Renew
Lincoln
1983-87
302 eng (1.2).................................... 1.7
351W eng (1.2).................................... 1.7
Mark VI, VII
1983
302 eng (1.0).................................... 1.5
351W eng (1.2).................................... 1.7
1984-87
302 eng (1.9).................................... 3.0
Diesel eng (1.0).................................... 1.6
Continental
1983-87
232 eng (1.2).................................... 1.8
302 eng (1.7).................................... 2.5
Diesel eng (1.0).................................... 1.6

(M) Fan Blades, Renew
1983-87 (.4).................................... .6

(M) Drive Belt, Renew
1983-87-one (.3).................................... .4
each adtnl.................................... .1

(M) Drive Belt, Adjust
1983-87-one (.2).................................... .3
each adtnl.................................... .1

(M) Clutch Fan, Renew
1983-87 (.4).................................... .7

(G) Temperature Gauge (Engine Unit), Renew
1983-87 (.3).................................... .4

COOLING SYSTEM TUNE-UP

An Annual Cooling System Tune-Up Suggestion List should include (with some exceptions):

1. A visual check of the cooling system for indications of leaks or excessive oil content.
2. Pressure check the cooling system for internal and external leaks with filler cap and neck adapter and tester.
3. Check crankcase and automatic transmission oil for water content.
4. Test coolant thermostat with radiator thermometer.
5. Check temperature gauge for accuracy.
6. Drain system and flush till clean.
7. Clean foreign matter from radiator fins.
8. Test radiator pressure cap with cap tester.
9. Check fan blades and pulleys for alignment and damage.
10. Internal and external inspection of all hoses for cracks and deterioration.
11. Check core plugs (where possible) for seepage.
12. Refill system with correct coolant and check for air locks.
13. Check condition and tension of drive belts with tension gauge.

All models 1.5

(Factory Time) Chilton Time

(G) Temperature Indicator (Dash Unit), Renew
Includes: Remove instrument panel pad when required.
1983-87 (.8).................................... 1.5

(G) Water Jacket Expansion Plugs, Renew (Side of Block)
each (.3).................................... *.5
*Add time to gain accessibility.

(G) Heater Hoses, Renew
1983-87-each (.4).................................... .6

(G) Heater Core, R&R or Renew
Lincoln
1983-87 (2.6).................................... 5.0
Mark VI, VII
1983 (2.6).................................... 5.0
1984-87 (2.8).................................... 5.5
Continental
1983-87 (3.7).................................... *7.0

ADD THESE OPERATIONS TO HEATER CORE R&R
(G) Boil & Repair.................................... 1.2
(G) Repair Core.................................... .9
(G) Recore.................................... 1.2

(G) A.C./Heater Control Assembly, Renew
1983-87 (.7).................................... 1.2
1983-84-Continental
w/A.C. (.5).................................... .9

(Factory Time) Chilton Time

(G) A.C./Heater Blower Motor, Renew
Includes: Transfer blower wheel when required.
Lincoln
1983-87 (.4).................................... .8
Mark VI, VII
1983 (.4).................................... .8
1984-87 (1.1).................................... 1.9
Continental
1983-87 (.9).................................... 1.5

(G) Heater Blower Motor Resistor, Renew
1983-87 (.3).................................... .6

(G) A.C./Heater Blower Motor Switch, Renew
Lincoln & Mark Series
1983-87 (.5).................................... .9
Continental
1983-84 (.4).................................... .7

(G) Blower Motor Speed Control, Renew
1985-87 (.4).................................... .6

(G) Temperature Lock-Out Switch, Renew
Lincoln
1984-87 (.4).................................... .6

(G) Temperature Control Cable, Renew
Lincoln
1984-87-w/ATC (.8).................... 1.4

PARTS 7 COOLING SYSTEM 7 PARTS

	Part No.	Price
(1) Radiator Assembly		
Order by year and model.		
(2) Thermostat		
1983-87-gas		
eng.	▲D9AZ-8575A	6.00
1984-diesel eng.	E45Y-8575A	13.50
(3) Radiator Hoses		
Order by year and model.		
Radiator Hose, By-Pass		
6 cyl.-diesel eng.		
1984	E45Y-8597A	6.00
V-8-302 eng		
1983-87	D0OZ-8597B	6.50
(4) Water Pump Assembly (New)		
6 cyl.-diesel eng.		
1984	E45Y-8501A	55.25
V-8-302 eng		
1983-84-alum.	▲E0AZ-8501A	89.25
1984-87-cast iron (exc. below)	▲E1AZ-8501A	91.00
1986-87 (Continental & Mark)	▲E6AZ-8501A	59.00
(5) Fan Belts		
Order by model & description.		
Fan Clutch Assy.		
Lincoln, Mark VI		
1983-85	▲E0MY-8A616A	57.25
1986-87	▲E6AZ-8A616B	71.00
Mark VII		
(gasoline engine)		
1984	E45Y-8A616B	42.00
1985	E5LY-8A616A	66.50
1986-87	E6SZ-8A616A	45.25

PARTS 7 COOLING SYSTEM 7 PARTS

	Part No.	Price
(diesel engine)		
1984	E45Y-8A616A	62.50
Continental		
(gasoline engine)		
1983-V-6 eng.	E2DZ-8A616A	61.25
V-8 eng.	E35Y-8A616A	41.25
1983-84	E45Y-8A616B	42.00
1985	E5LY-8A616A	66.50
1986-87	E6SZ-8A616A	45.25
(diesel engine)		
1984	E45Y-8A616A	62.50
Temperature, Sending Unit		
Lincoln		
1983-87-exec. below	▲D0WY-10884A	5.25
w/Elec. clusters	▲E43Z-10884A	9.00
Continental		
1983	▲E1AZ-12A648A	32.00
1984-87-gas	D6LZ-10884A	14.25
diesel	E45Y-10884A	27.00
Mark VI & VII		
1983-84-exc. below	▲D0WY-10884A	5.25
w/Elec. cluster	▲E43Z-10884A	9.00
1985	D6LZ-10884A	14.25
1986-87-wo/ A.T.C.	▲E43Z-10884A	9.00
A.T.C.	D6LZ-10884A	14.25
Heat Indicator, Dash Unit		
Lincoln & Mark VI		
1983-84	E3LY-10883A	21.25
1985-87	E5VY-10883A	21.25
Mark VII		
1984-87-exc. Canada	E4LY-10D922AR	124.75
Canada	E4LY-10D922BR	N.L.
Continental		
1983-exc. Canada	E25Y-10D922AR	124.75

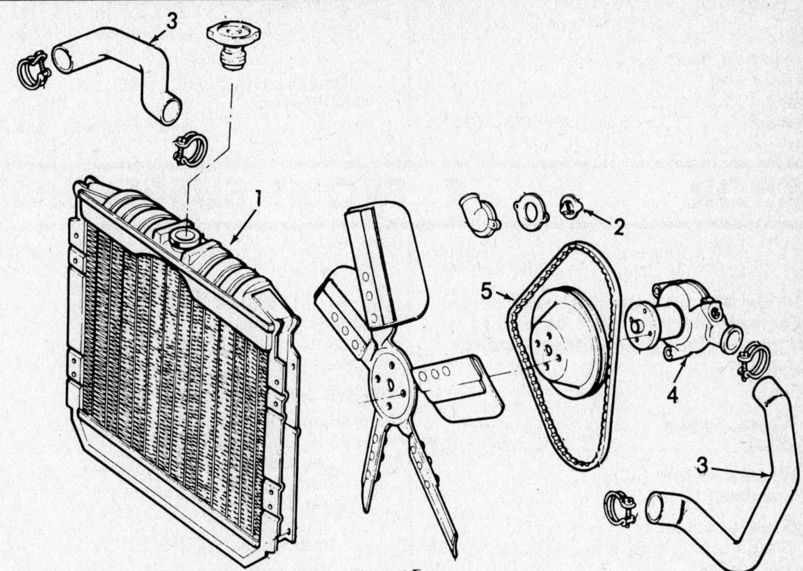

	Part No.	Price
Canada	E25Y-10D922BR	N.L.
1984-85-exc. Canada	E45Y-10D922AR	124.75
Canada	E45Y-10D922BR	N.L.
1986-87-exc. Canada	E65Y-10D922AR	181.00
Canada	E65Y-10D922BR	N.L.
Electronic Sensor (Temperature Control)		
1983-87	▲E1AZ-12A648A	32.00
Heater Core		
Lincoln, Mark VI		
1983-87	▲E3AZ-18476E	62.00

	Part No.	Price
Continental, Mark VII		
1983-87	▲D9BZ-18476A	63.50
Blower Motor		
Lincoln, Mark VI		
1983-87	▲E0VY-19805A	86.50
Continental, Mark VII		
1983-87	▲E35Y-19805A	91.75
Switch, Heater Control		
1983	▲D5AZ-19986A	12.75
1984-87-w/ A.T.C.	▲E4VY-19986A	5.25

LABOR 8 EXHAUST SYSTEM 8 LABOR

(Factory Time)	Chilton Time
(G) Muffler, Renew	
1983-87-one (.8)	**1.1**
both (.9)	**1.4**
Welded type add	**.3**
(G) Catalytic Converter, Renew	
Lincoln & Mark VI	
1983-85-one (.6)	**1.0**
both (1.0)	**1.7**
1986-87-one (.9)	**1.3**
both (1.3)	**1.8**
Continental-Mark VII	
1983-87 (1.0)	**1.4**
(G) Inlet Pipe, Renew	
Includes: Replace exhaust control valve if required.	
1983-87-one (.6)	**1.1**

(Factory Time)	Chilton Time
(G) Manifold Heat Valve, Renew	
1983-87 (.4)	**.7**
(G) Exhaust Manifold, Renew	
Lincoln & Mark VI	
1983-87	
302 eng-right (.7)	**1.1**
left (.9)	**1.3**
both (1.3)	**2.0**
351 W eng-right (.9)	**1.3**
left (.8)	**1.2**
both (1.5)	**2.1**
Mark VII	
1984-87	
302 eng-right (1.3)	**1.9**

(Factory Time)	Chilton Time
left (.8)	**1.2**
both (1.9)	**3.0**
Diesel (1.9)	**2.7**
Continental	
1983-87	
302 eng-right (1.3)	**1.9**
left (.8)	**1.2**
both (1.9)	**2.1**
Diesel (1.9)	**2.7**

COMBINATIONS

(G) Muffler, Resonator and Exhaust Pipe, Renew	
1983-87-one side (1.4)	**1.9**

PARTS 8 EXHAUST SYSTEM 8 PARTS

	Part No.	Price
Muffler		
Order by year and model.		
Inlet Pipe		
Lincoln, Mark VI		
(single exhaust)		
1983-87	E1LY-5246A	113.75
(dual exhaust)		
1983-84	E2LY-5246A	106.00
1985-87	E5VY-5246A	108.50

	Part No.	Price
Continental, Mark VII		
(gas engine)		
1983-85-right	E35Y-5E256A	45.25
left	E45Y-5E257A	45.25
1986-87	▲E6LY-5F235B	27.25
(diesel engine)		
1984	E45Y-5246A	69.25
Catalytic Converter Lincoln, Mark VI		
1983-right exc. Canada	▲E3MY-5E212C	401.50

	Part No.	Price
left	▲E1MY-5E212G	401.50
Canada-right	▲E1MY-5E212L	N.L.
left	▲E1MY-5E212M	N.L.
1984-85-right	▲E4MY-5E212B	401.50
left	▲E4MY-5E212A	401.50
1986-87-right	▲E6AZ-5E212A	377.00
left	▲E6AZ-5E212B	377.50

PARTS 8 EXHAUST SYSTEM 8 PARTS

	Part No.	Price
Continental, Mark VII		
V-8-302 eng		
1983-exc.		
Canada	E35Y-5F250D	764.50
Canada	E25Y-5E212C	N.L.
1984-85-sngl.		
exh.	E45Y-5F250A	415.25
dual exh.	E5LY-5F250A	401.50
1986-87-sngl.		
exh.	E6LY-5E212A	188.75
dual exh.	E6LY-5F250B	377.50

LABOR 9 FRONT SUSPENSION 9 LABOR

	(Factory Time)	Chilton Time
Note: On all front suspension operations alignment charges must be added if performed. Time given does not include alignment.		
(M) Wheel, Renew		
one	(.5)	.5
(G) Wheels, Rotate (All)		
All models	(.5)	.5
(G) Wheels, Balance		
one		.3
each adtnl		.2
(G) Check Alignment of Front End		
All models	(.4)	.5
Note: Deduct if alignment is performed.		
(G) Toe-In, Adjust		
All models	(.4)	.6
(G) Align Front End		
Includes: Adjust front wheel bearings.		
All models	(1.3)	1.5
w/A.C. interference add		.5
LINCOLN AND MARK VI		
(G) Front Wheel Bearings, Clean and Repack (Both Wheels)		
All models		1.3
(G) Front Wheel Bearings and Cups, Renew		
Includes: Repack bearings.		
one wheel	(.7)	.9
both wheels	(1.2)	1.5
(G) Front Wheel Grease Seals, Renew		
Includes: Repack bearings.		
one wheel	(.6)	.7
both wheels	(.9)	1.1
(G) Front Shock Absorber or Bushings, Renew		
1983-87-one	(.4)	.6
both	(.6)	.8
(G) Ball Joints, Renew		
Add alignment charges.		
1983-87-upper or lower		
one side		1.2
both sides		1.9
upper & lower		
one side		1.6
both sides		2.5
(G) Front Spindle Assembly, Renew (One)		
Add alignment charges.		
1983-87	(1.2)	2.0
(G) Upper Control Arm Assy., Renew (One)		
Add alignment charges.		
Lincoln & Mark VI		
1983-87	(1.0)	1.8
(G) Lower Control Arm Assy., Renew (One)		
Add alignment charges.		
Lincoln		
1983-87	(1.2)	2.0
Mark VI		
1983	(1.2)	2.0
(G) Upper Control Arm Shaft or Bushings, Renew		
Add alignment charges.		
1983-87-one side	(1.2)	1.7
both sides	(1.9)	2.9
(G) Front Stabilizer Bar, Renew		
1983-87	(.6)	.9
(G) Front Spring, Renew		
Lincoln & Mark VI		
1983-87-one	(1.2)	1.5
both	(2.0)	2.7
(G) Control Arm Rubber Bumpers, Renew		
one	(.3)	.4
each adtnl	(.1)	.1
CONTINENTAL AND MARK VII		
(G) Front Wheel Bearings, Clean and Repack (Both Wheels)		
All models		1.3
(G) Front Wheel Grease Seals, Renew		
Includes: Repack bearings.		
1983-87-one whl	(.6)	.7
both whls	(.9)	1.1
(G) Front Wheel Bearings and Cups, Renew		
1983-87-one whl	(.7)	.9
both whls	(1.2)	1.5
(G) Front Strut Shock Absorbers, R&R or Renew		
1983-one	(.7)	1.0
both	(1.2)	1.9
(G) Front Spindle Assembly, Renew (One)		
Add alignment charges.		
1983	(.8)	1.2
1984-87	(1.3)	1.8
(G) Lower Control Arm Assy., Renew (One)		
Add alignment charges.		
1983		
Cont	(1.1)	1.5
Mark VII	(1.4)	2.0
1984-87	(1.4)	2.0
(G) Front Spring, Renew		
1983		
Cont-one	(1.0)	1.5
both	(1.7)	2.7
(G) Front Stabilizer Bar, Renew		
1983-87	(.7)	1.0

PARTS 9 FRONT SUSPENSION 9 PARTS

	Part No.	Price
CONTINENTAL & MARK VII		
(1) Spindle Assy.		
1984-right	E4LY-3105A	N.L.
left	E5LY-3106A	188.00
1985-87-right	E5LY-3105A	188.00
left	E5LY-3106A	188.00
(2) Shock Absorber		
1984-87-exc.		
below	E4LY-18124A	73.00
H.D. susp.	E4LY-18124D	73.00
(3) Dust Tube Kit		
1984-87	▲N.L.	N.L.
(4) Front Bumper (Jounce)		
1984-87	E4LY-18A085A	5.00
(5) Upper Shock Mounting Bracket		
1984-87	E4LY-18A161A	49.75
(6) Stabilizer End Kit		
1984-87	▲E2AZ-5A486C	20.75

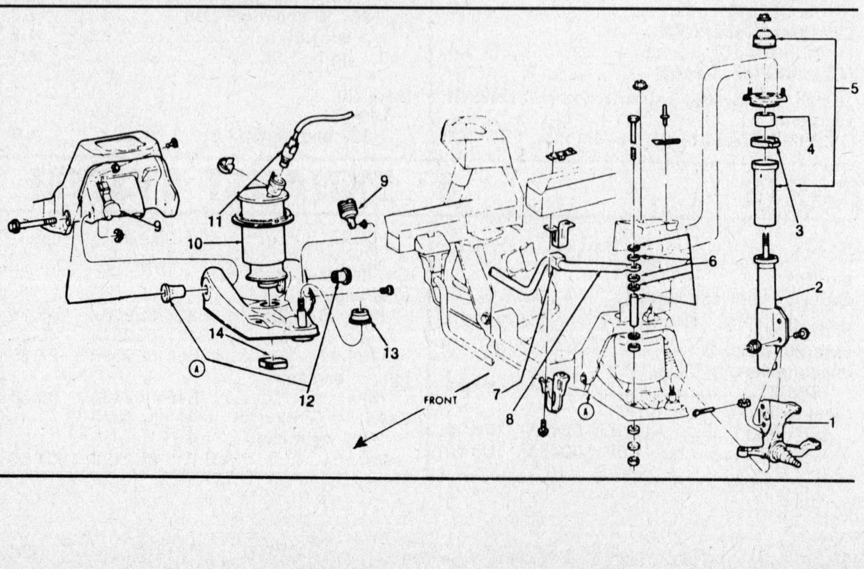

PARTS 9 FRONT SUSPENSION 9 PARTS

	Part No.	Price
(7) Stabilizer Insulator		
1984-87-exc.		
below	E4LY-5493D	8.50
w/Hand. pkg.	E3SZ-5493C	8.50
(8) Stabilizer Bar		
1984-87 (Mark VII)		
1″ dia.	E4LY-5482A	55.75
1⅛″ dia.	E4LY-5482C	76.25
1984-87 (Continental)		
1″ dia.	E4LY-5482B	72.75
1¹⁄₁₈″ dia.	E4LY-5482C	76.25
(9) Sensor Assy.		
1984-87	E4LY-5359C	74.00
(10) Spring Assy. (Air)		
1984-87-std.	E4LY-5310E	264.25
H.D. susp.	E4LY-5310F	264.25
1986-87-LSC	E6LY-5310A	264.25
(11) Solenoid Assy.		
1984-87	E4LY-5311B	44.50
(12) Lower Control Arm		
1984-87-right	E4LY-3078A	166.25
left	E4LY-3079A	166.25
(13) Dust Seal (Ball Joint)		
1984-87	D8BZ-3A105A	3.25
(14) Retainer		
1984-87	E4LY-5C560A	6.00

PARTS 9 FRONT SUSPENSION 9 PARTS

LINCOLN TOWN CAR, MARK VI

	Part No.	Price
Front Wheel Bearing		
1983-87-inner	▲D4AZ-1201A	3.75
outer	▲D0AZ-1216A	8.25
Wheel Bearing Cup		
1983-87-inner	▲D4AZ-1202A	5.00
outer	▲D0AZ-1217B	10.00
Front Wheel Oil Seal		
1983-87	▲C8AZ-1190A	3.00
(1) Lower Control Arm & Joint Assy.		
1983-87-right	▲E0VY-3078A	115.00
left	▲E0VY-3079A	115.00
(2) Shock Absorber		
1983	E1VY-18124A	25.75
1984-85	E4VY-18124A	38.25
1986-87	E6VY-18124A	38.25
(3) Spindle Assy.		
1983-87-right	▲D9AZ-3105A	188.00
left	▲D9AZ-3106A	188.00
(4) Upper Control Arm & Joint Assy.		
1928-87-right	E0AZ-3082B	96.00
left	▲E1AZ-3083A	103.00
(5) Shaft Kit (Upper)		
1983-87	▲D9AZ-3047A	28.75
(6) Bushing Kit (Shock Absorber)		
1983-87	▲D7AZ-18198A	2.00
(8) Coil Spring		
Order by model and description.		

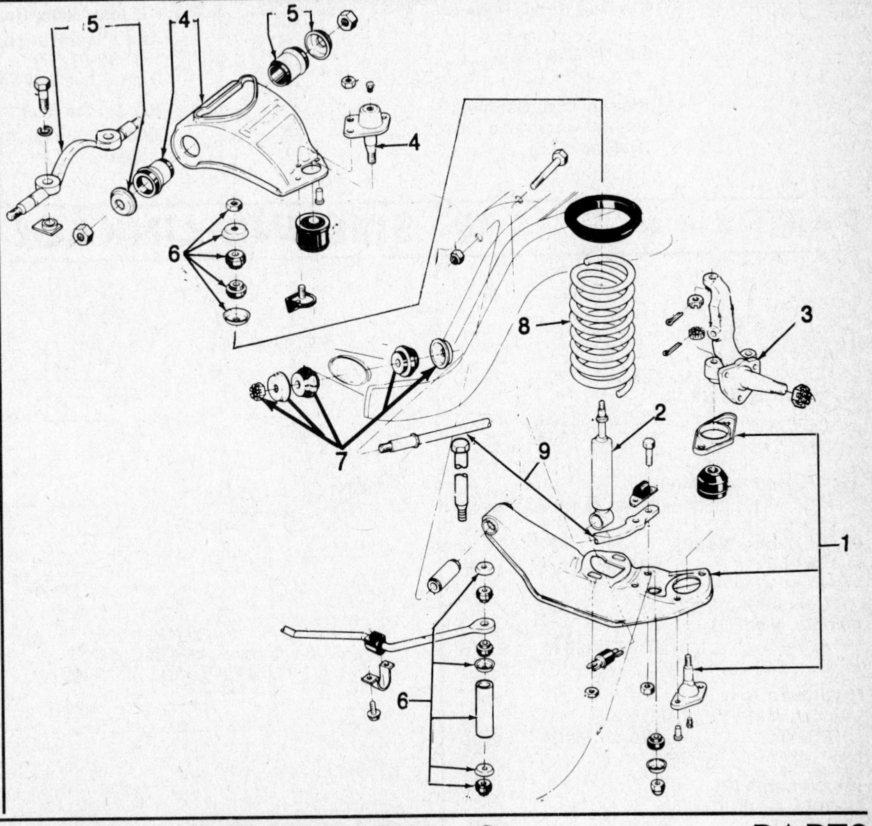

PARTS 9 FRONT SUSPENSION 9 PARTS

CONTINENTAL (1983)

	Part No.	Price
Front Wheel Bearing		
1983-inner	▲B7C-1201A	10.00
outer	▲D0AZ-1216A	8.25
Wheel Bearing Cup		
1983-inner	B7C-1202A	5.00
outer	▲D0AZ-1217B	3.75
Front Wheel Oil Seal		
1983	▲C6AZ-1190A	7.75
(1) Spindle Assy.		
1983-right	▲E25Y-3105A	188.00
left	▲E25Y-3106A	188.00
(2) Shock Absorber		
1983	E25Y-18124C	82.50
(3) Adjusting Plate (Camber)		
1983	▲E0SZ-3B391A	5.50
(4) Bracket Assy. (Upper Mounting)		
1983	E25Y-18A161A	50.25

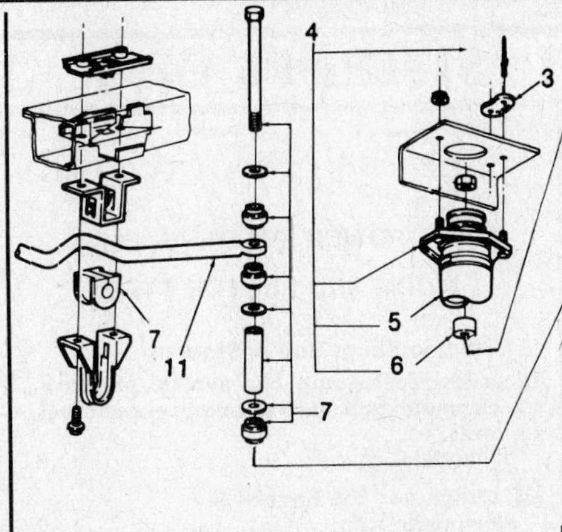

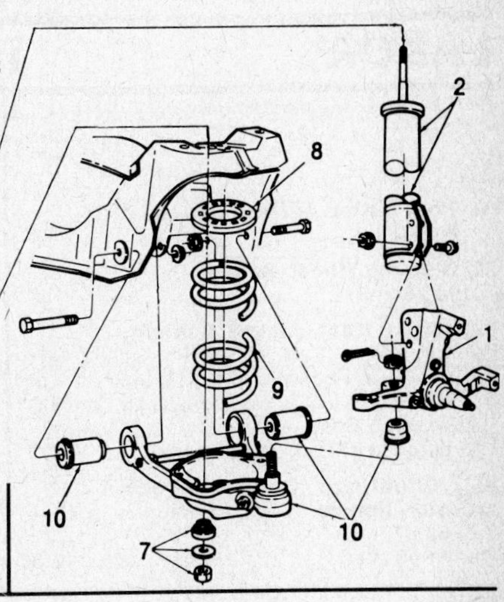

	Part No.	Price
(5) Dust Tube Kit (Shock Absorber)		
1983	E0SZ-18A047A	6.75

PARTS 9 FRONT SUSPENSION 9 PARTS

	Part No.	Price
(6) Bumper (Shock Jounce)		
1983	E1SZ-18A085A	2.25
(7) End Repair Kit (Stabilizer Bar)		
1983	▲E2AZ-5A486C	20.75
(8) Insulator (Front Spring)		
1983-upper	E25Y-5415A	9.50
lower	E25Y-5415B	8.00
(9) Coil Spring		
Order by model and description.		
(10) Lower Control Arm Assy.		
1983-right	E25Y-3078A	267.50
left	E25Y-3079A	267.50
(11) Stabilizer Bar Assy. (Front)		
1983	E35Y-5482A	69.00

LABOR 10 STEERING LINKAGE 10 LABOR

	(Factory Time)	Chilton Time
(G) Tie Rod Ends, Renew		
Includes: Reset toe-in.		
1983-87-one	(.8)	1.2
each adtnl	(.2)	.2
(G) Pitman Arm, Renew		
1983-87-wo/Frame	(.4)	.6
w/Frame	(.5)	.7
(G) Idler Arm, Renew		
Add alignment charges.		
1983-87	(.7)	1.2
Renew bushing add	(.2)	.2
(G) Sector Arm Rod, Renew		
Add alignment charges.		
1983-87	(.8)	1.2

PARTS 10 STEERING LINKAGE 10 PARTS

	Part No.	Price
(1) Tie Rod End (Outer)		
Lincoln, Mark VI		
1983-87	▲D9AZ-3A130A	47.00
Continental, Mark VII		
1983	▲E2SZ-3A130A	36.25
1984-87	E45Y-3A130A	26.75
(2) Tie Rod End (Inner)		
1983-87	▲D9AZ-3A131A	41.00
(3) Adjusting Sleeve		
1983-87	▲D9AZ-3310A	11.00
(4) Connecting Link		
Lincoln, Mark VI		
1983-87	▲D9AZ-3304A	51.75
(5) Pitman Arm		
Lincoln, Mark VI		
1983-87	▲E0AZ-3590A	38.00
(6) Idler Arm Kit		
Lincoln, Mark VI		
1983-87	▲D9AZ-3355A	50.00

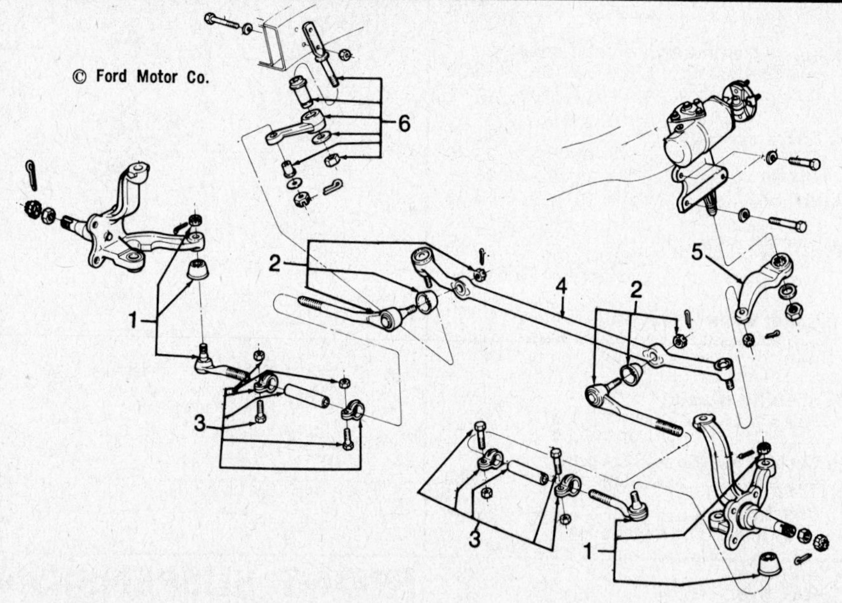

LABOR 11 STEERING GEAR 11 LABOR

	(Factory Time)	Chilton Time
(G) Horn Button or Ring, Renew		
1983-87	(.3)	.4
(G) Steering Wheel, Renew		
1983-87	(.3)	.5
(G) Upper Mast Jacket Bearing, Renew.		
1983-87-std column	(.5)	.9
tilt column	(.6)	1.0
Mark VII & Cont.		
tilt colm	(.7)	1.0
(G) Steering Column Lock Actuator, Renew		
1983-87		
tilt colm	(1.7)	2.3

POWER STEERING

WORM AND SECTOR TYPE

	(Factory Time)	Chilton Time
(G) Trouble Shoot Power Steering		
Includes: Test pump and system pressure. Check pounds pull on steering wheel and check for leaks.		
All models		.5
(M) Check and Fill Reservoir		
All models		.2
(G) Pump Pressure Check & Flow Test		
All models		.5
(M) Pump Drive Belt, Renew or Adjust		
1983-87-renew	(.3)	.4
adjust	(.2)	.3
(G) Power Steering Gear, Adjust (On Car)		
Includes: Bearing preload and gear mesh.		
1983-87	(.7)	1.2
(G) Power Steering Gear, Renew		
1983-87	(.8)	1.2
(P) Steering Gear Assy., R&R and Recondition		
Includes: Disassemble, renew necessary parts, reassemble and adjust.		
1983-87	(2.2)	3.5

LABOR 11 STEERING GEAR 11 LABOR

	(Factory Time)	Chilton Time
(G) Sector Shaft and/or Seals, Renew		
Includes: R&R gear and make all necessary adjustments.		
1983-87	(1.6)	2.2
RACK AND PINION TYPE		
(G) Steering Gear Assy., R&R or Renew		
1983-84	(1.7)	3.2
1985-87	(2.3)	3.2
w/Diesel eng add	(.5)	.5
(P) Steering Gear, R&R and Recondition		
Includes: Disassemble, renew necessary parts, reassemble and adjust.		
1983-87	(3.0)	4.2
w/Diesel eng add	(.5)	.5
(G) Steering Gear, Adjust (On Car)		
1984-87	(.3)	.6
(G) Ball Joints, Tie Rod Ends and Bellows, Renew (Both Sides)		
Includes: R&R rack and pinion assy. Does not include reset toe-in.		
1983-84	(2.0)	2.7
1985-87	(1.5)	2.7
w/Diesel eng add	(.5)	.5
(G) Power Steering Oil Pump, Renew		
Includes: Bleed system.		
Lincoln & Mark VI		
1983-87	(1.0)	1.4
Mark VII		
1984-87	(1.0)	1.4
Continental		
1983-87	(1.0)	1.4
(G) Power Steering Pump, R&R and Recondition		
Includes: Bleed system.		
Lincoln & Mark VI		
1983-87	(1.4)	2.0
Continental		
1983-87	(1.4)	2.0
Mark VII		
1984-87	(1.4)	2.0
(G) Power Steering Reservoir Seals, Renew		
Includes: R&R pump and reservoir. Bleed system.		
Lincoln & Mark VI		
1983-87	(1.3)	1.8
Mark VII		
1984-87	(1.3)	1.8
Continental		
1983-87	(1.3)	1.8
(M) Power Steering Hoses, Renew		
Includes: Bleed system.		
Lincoln & Mark VI		
Pressure		
to booster	(.8)	1.2
to gear	(.4)	.6
Return		
from booster	(.3)	.5
from gear	(.4)	.6
Cooling	(.2)	.3
Mark VII-Cont		
Cooling	(.5)	.7
Return		
from gear	(.6)	.8
from H/Boost	(.4)	.6
Pressure		
to H/Boost	(.5)	.7
to gear	(.6)	.9

PARTS 11 POWER STEERING GEAR 11 PARTS

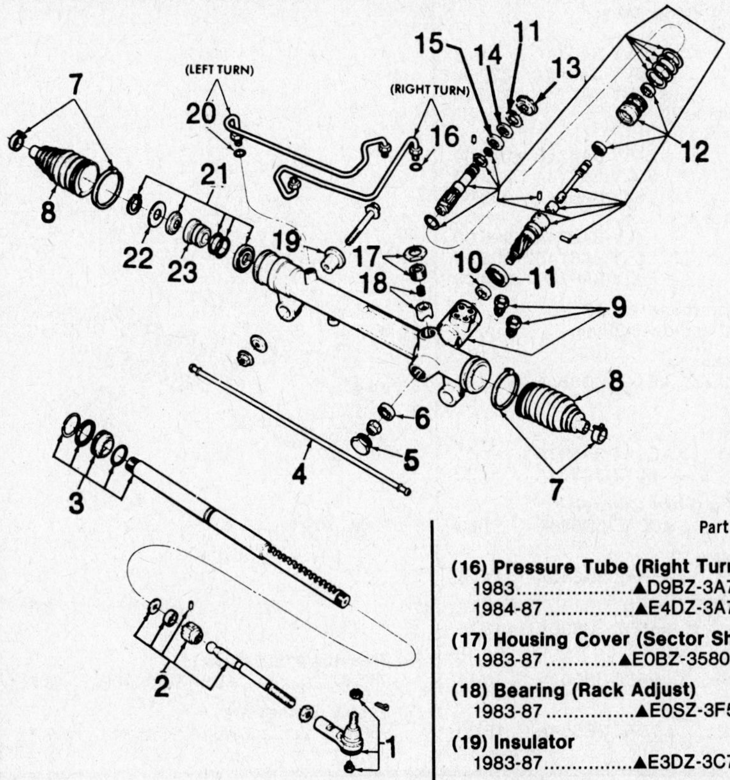

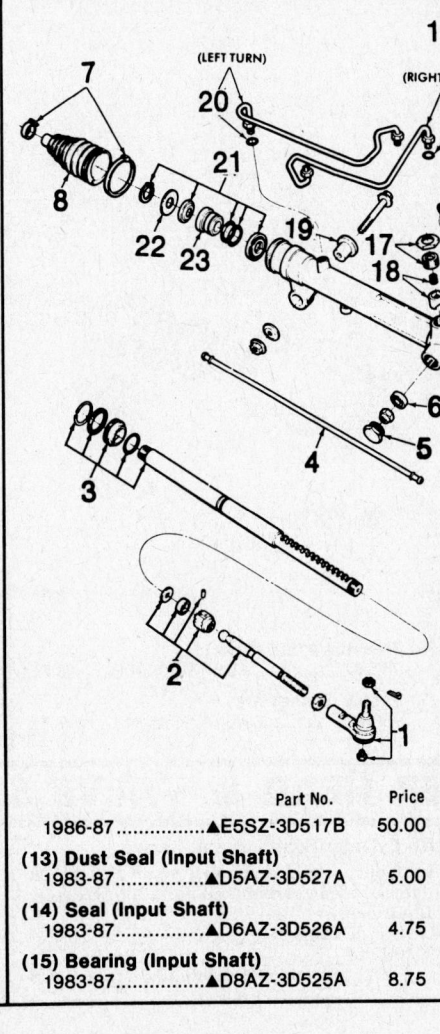

	Part No.	Price
CONTINENTAL, MARK VII		
(1) Tie Rod End (Outer)		
1983	▲E2SZ-3A130A	36.25
1984-87	E45Y-3A130A	26.75
(2) Connecting Rod Assy.		
1983-87	▲E2SZ-3280A	66.25
(3) Sector Shaft Assy.		
1983-84-exc. below	▲D8BZ-3575A	36.50
H.D. susp.	▲E3SZ-3575A	31.75
1985-87-exc. below	▲E5DZ-3575A	36.50
H.D. susp.	▲E5DZ-3575B	36.50
(4) Gear Rack Tube		
1983-87	▲D8BZ-3K762A	2.25
(5) Cover (Housing End)		
1983-87	▲D8BZ-3568B	5.00
(6) Cup (Worm Bearing)		
1983-87	▲D8BZ-3552A	13.25
(7) Clamps (Gear Boot)		
1983-87	▲D8BZ-3C650B	.75
(8) Boot (Dust Seal)		
1983	▲D9BZ-3332A	5.50
1984-85	▲E3SZ-3K661A	6.25
1986-87	▲E69Z-3332A	10.25
(9) Housing Assy.		
1983	▲E3SZ-3548A	150.75
1984-87		
1984	▲E4DZ-3548A	161.25
1985-87	▲E5DZ-3548A	161.25
(10) Thrust Bearing (Worm)		
1983-87	▲D8BZ-3571A	N.L.
(11) Check Valve Kit		
1983-87	▲E3SZ-3D728A	15.75
(12) Shaft & Control Assy.		
Stand. suspension		
1984-85	▲E4DZ-3D517B	50.00
1986-87	▲E5SZ-3D517A	50.00
Handling suspension		
1984-85	▲E4SZ-3D517F	50.00
1986-87	▲E5SZ-3D517B	50.00
(13) Dust Seal (Input Shaft)		
1983-87	▲D5AZ-3D527A	5.00
(14) Seal (Input Shaft)		
1983-87	▲D6AZ-3D526A	4.75
(15) Bearing (Input Shaft)		
1983-87	▲D8AZ-3D525A	8.75
(16) Pressure Tube (Right Turn)		
1983	▲D9BZ-3A717A	15.25
1984-87	▲E4DZ-3A717A	14.25
(17) Housing Cover (Sector Shaft)		
1983-87	▲E0BZ-3580AMR	7.00
(18) Bearing (Rack Adjust)		
1983-87	▲E0SZ-3F515A	8.25
(19) Insulator		
1983-87	▲E3DZ-3C716A	6.50
(20) Pressure Tube (Left Turn)		
1983	▲D9BZ-3A714A	18.00
1984-87	▲E4DZ-3A714A	14.25
(21) Seal Kit (Rack Shaft)		
1983-87	▲E3SZ-3E501B	12.50
(22) Cover (Housing End)		
1983-87	▲D8BZ-3568A	5.00
(23) Bushing (Sector Shaft)		
1983-87	▲D9BZ-3576A	4.25

PARTS 11 POWER STEERING GEAR 11 PARTS

LINCOLN TOWN CAR, MARK VI

	Part No.	Price
Seal Kit		
1983-87	▲D7AZ-3E501B	10.00
(1) Cover		
1983-87	▲E3AZ-3580A	23.00
(2) Sector Shaft		
1983-87	▲E0AZ-3575A	120.75
(3) Seal Kit (Sector Shaft)		
1983-87	▲D7AZ-3E501B	10.00
(4) Seal Kit (Input Shaft)		
1983-87	▲D7AZ-3E502A	11.00
(5) Housing Assy.		
1983-87	▲D9AZ-3548A	134.75
(6) Input Shaft & Control Assy.		
1983-87	▲E0AZ-3D517B	402.75
(7) Nut (Steering Gear Race)		
1983-87	▲C8AZ-3D627A	6.50
(8) Bearing (Input Shaft)		
1983-87	▲D8AZ-3D525A	8.75

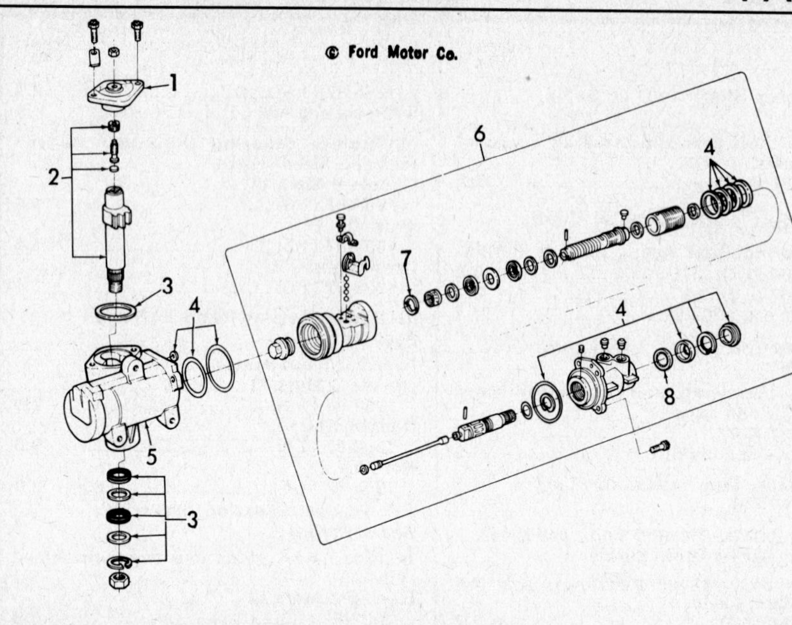

PARTS 11 POWER STEERING PUMP 11 PARTS

	Part No.	Price
Power Steering Pump Assy.		
Lincoln, Mark VI		
1983-84	▲E1LY-3A674A	N.L.
1985	▲E5VY-3A674A	220.00
1986-87	▲E6VY-3A674A	220.00
Continental, Mark VII		
(wo/Handling susp.)		
1983-84	E45Y-3A674B	220.00
1985	E5LY-3A674A	220.00
1986-87	E6LY-3A674A	220.00
(w/Handling susp.)		
1984	E4LY-3A674A	205.00
1985	E5LY-3A674B	205.00
1986-87	E6LY-3A674B	220.00
Power Steering Hoses		
Order by model and description.		
(1) Seal & Gasket Kit		
1983-87	▲E1AZ-3D684A	3.00
(2) Valve Assy.		
1983-87-Std. susp	▲E1AZ-3A561A	11.00
H.D. susp.	E0TZ-3A561A	11.00
(3) Valve Spring (Flow Control)		
1983-87	▲D8AZ-3D586A	1.50
(4) Housing Assy.		
1983-87	▲E1AZ-3A643A	42.25
(5) Pressure Plate (Front)		
1983-87	▲E5FZ-3D590A	13.75
(6) Rotor Assy.		
1983-87	E5SZ-3B607A	38.75
(7) Rotor Shaft		
1983-87	▲D8AZ-3B559A	18.00

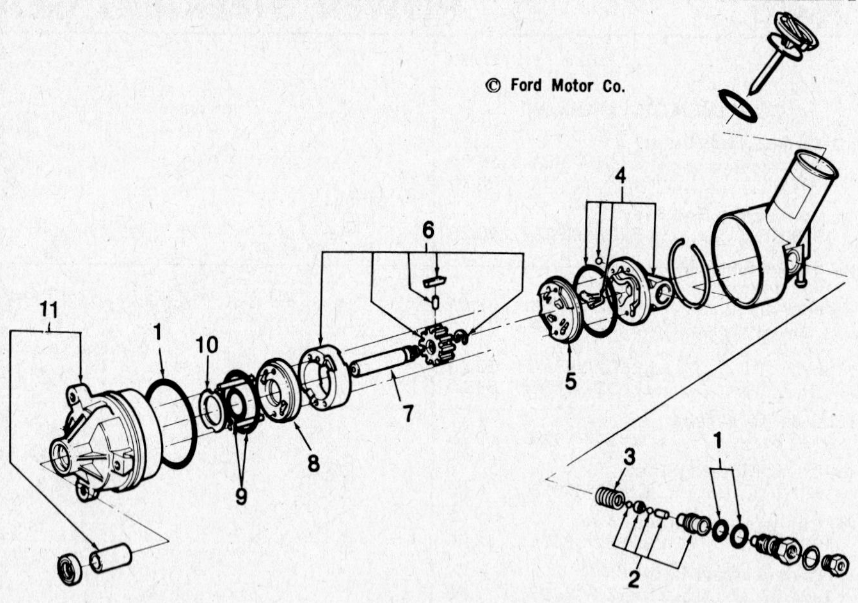

	Part No.	Price
(8) Pressure Plate (Rear)		
1983-87	▲D8AZ-3D590B	13.75
(9) Seal & Gasket Kit		
1983-87	▲E1AZ-3B584A	8.75
(10) Spring (Pressure Plate)		
1983-87	▲D8AZ-3D596A	2.50
(11) Plate & Bushing		
1983-87	▲E1AZ-3D643A	42.25

LABOR 12 CYLINDER HEAD & VALVE SYSTEM 12 LABOR

(Factory Time) Chilton Time

GASOLINE ENGINES

(G) Compression Test

	Chilton Time
V-8-1983-87 (.4)	1.0
w/A.C. add	.3

(G) Cylinder Head Gasket, Renew

Includes: Check cylinder head and block flatness. Clean carbon and make all necessary adjustments.

	Chilton Time
Lincoln & Mark VI	
1983-87	
302, 351 engs-one side (3.6)	4.8
both sides (4.8)	6.2
Mark VII	
1984-87	
302 eng-one (3.7)	5.2

LABOR 12 CYLINDER HEAD & VALVE SYSTEM 12 LABOR

(Factory Time) Chilton Time

both (5.6) 7.8
Continental
1983-87
302 eng-one (3.6) 4.9
both (5.0) 7.0

(G) Cylinder Head, Renew
Includes: Transfer all components, clean carbon. Reface valves, check valve spring tension, assembled height and valve head runout.
Lincoln & Mark VI
1983-87
302, 351 engs-one side (4.8) 6.6
both sides (7.3) 9.2
Mark VII
1984-87
302 eng-one (4.9) 6.8
both (8.1) 11.3
Continental
1983-87
302 eng-one (4.8) 6.6
both (7.5) 10.5

(P) Clean Carbon and Grind Valves
Includes: R&R cylinder heads, check valve spring tension, valve seat and head runout, stem to guide clearance and spring assembled height. Minor tune up.
Lincoln & Mark VI
1983-87
302, 351 engs
one side (5.4) 7.4
both sides (8.4) 11.5
Mark VII
1984-87
302 eng
one side (5.6) 7.7
both sides (9.3) 12.8
Continental
1983-87
302 eng
one side (5.5) 7.5
both sides (8.7) 12.0

(G) Rocker Arm Cover or Gasket, Renew
Lincoln
1983-87-302, 351 engs
one (.9) 1.2
both (1.2) 1.7
Mark VI, VII
1983
302, 351 engs-one (.9) 1.2
both (1.2) 1.7
1984-87
302 eng-one (.8) 1.2
both (1.3) 1.9
Continental
1983-87
302 eng-one (.8) 1.2
both (1.1) 1.7

(G) Valve Tappets, Renew
Includes: R&R intake manifold, adjust carburetor and ignition timing.
Lincoln & Mark VI
1983-87-one (2.3) 3.1
all (3.3) 4.5

COMBINATIONS

Add to Valve Job

See Machine Shop Operation

(Factory Time) Chilton Time

(G) DRAIN, EVACUATE & RECHARGE AIR CONDITIONING SYSTEM
All models (.7) 1.2

(G) ROCKER ARMS, RENEW OR DISASSEMBLE AND CLEAN
Each (.1) 1

(G) HYDRAULIC VALVE LIFTERS, DISASSEMBLE AND CLEAN
Each 2

(G) ROCKER ARM STUD, RENEW
Each (.2) 2

(G) DISTRIBUTOR, RECONDITION
All models (.7) 1.0

(P) VALVE GUIDES, REAM OVERSIZE
Each (.1) 1

(Factory Time) Chilton Time

Mark VII
1984-87
302 eng-one (2.2) 3.0
all (2.9) 4.0
Continental
1983-87
302 eng-one (2.2) 3.0
all (2.9) 4.0

(G) Valve Spring or Valve Stem Oil Seals, Renew (Head On Car)
Lincoln & Mark VI
1983-87
302, 351 engs-one (1.1) 1.4
one-each side (1.6) 1.9
all-both sides (3.0) 4.2
Mark VII
1984-87
302 eng-one (1.0) 1.5
one-each side (1.7) 2.5
all-both sides (3.7) 5.3
Continental
1983-87
302 eng
one (1.0) 1.5
one-each side (1.7) 2.5
all-both sides (3.7) 5.3

(G) Rocker Arm, Renew
Lincoln & Mark VI
1983-87
302, 351 engs-one (1.0) 1.3
all-one side (1.1) 1.4
all-both sides (1.6) 2.3
Mark VII
1984-87
302 eng-one (.9) 1.2
all-one side (1.0) 1.5
all-both sides (1.6) 2.5

(Factory Time) Chilton Time

Continental
1983-87
302 eng
one (.9) 1.2
all-one side (1.0) 1.5
all-both sides (1.6) 2.5

(G) Rocker Arm Stud, Renew (One)
Lincoln & Mark VI
1983-87
302, 351 engs-one (1.1) 1.4
each adtnl 2
Mark VII
1984-87
302 eng-one (1.0) 1.5
each adtnl (.2) 2
Continental
1983-87-302 eng
one (1.0) 1.5
each adtnl 2

(G) Valve Push Rods, Renew
Lincoln & Mark VI
1983-87
302, 351 engs-one (1.0) 1.3
all-one side (1.1) 1.4
all-both sides (1.5) 2.2
Mark VII
1984-87
302 eng-one (.9) 1.2
all-one side (1.0) 1.5
all-both sides (1.6) 2.5
Continental
1983-87
302 eng
right side-one (1.2) 1.6
left side-one (.8) 1.2
all-both sides (1.9) 2.7

DIESEL ENGINE

(G) Compression Test
1984-85 (.7) 1.0

(G) Cylinder Head Gasket, Renew
Includes: Clean carbon and make all necessary adjustments.
1984-85 (3.5) 4.9

(G) Cylinder Head, Renew
Includes: Transfer all components, clean carbon. Make all necessary adjustments.
1984-85 (5.9) 8.2

(P) Clean Carbon and Grind Valves
Includes: R&R cylinder head. Grind valves and seats. Make all necessary adjustments.
1984-85 (7.5) 10.5

(G) Rocker Arm Cover or Gasket, Renew
1984-85 (.6) 8
(G) Valve Clearance, Adjust
1984-85 (1.2) 1.7
(G) Valve Rocker Arms, Renew
1984-85-one (.8) 1.1
all (2.3) 3.0

(G) Valve Springs and/or Valve Stem Oil Seals, Renew (Head On Car)
1984-85-one (.8) 1.2
each adtnl (.2) 3
all (2.4) 3.5

PARTS 12 CYLINDER HEAD & VALVE SYSTEM 12 PARTS

	Part No.	Price
Valve Grind Gasket Set		
V-8–302 eng		
1983-84-exc.		
H.O.	▲E1AZ-6079A	61.00
H.O.	▲E2ZZ-6079B	52.50
1985-87	▲E5ZZ-6079B	52.50
(1) Cylinder Head (New)		
V-8–302 eng		
(wo/valves)		
1983-84	E84Y-6049C	N.L.
1985	▲E5AZ-6049A	302.25
1986-87	▲E6AZ-6049A	302.25
(w/valves)		
1983-84	▲E2AZ-6049A	461.50
1985	▲E5AZ-6049B	429.25
1986-87	▲E6AZ-6049B	429.25

PARTS 12 CYLINDER HEAD & VALVE SYSTEM 12 PARTS

	Part No.	Price
(2) Cylinder Head Gasket		
V-8-302 eng		
1983-84-exc.		
H.O.	▲D7OZ-6051C	12.50
H.O.	▲E2ZZ-6051A	13.75
1985-exc. LSC	▲E5AZ-6051A	11.50
LSC	▲E5ZZ-6051A	N.L.
1986-87	▲E5ZZ-6051B	13.75
(3) Valve Cover Gasket		
V-8-302 eng		
1983-85	▲E3AZ-6584A	4.75
1986-87	▲E5TZ-6584C	4.75
(4) Intake Valve (Std.)		
V-8-302 eng		
1983-85-exc.		
LSC	▲E3ZZ-6507A	7.75
LSC	▲E5ZZ-6507G	7.25
1986-87	▲E6AZ-6507A	7.50
Exhaust Valve (Std.)		
V-8-302 eng		
1983-85	▲E4AZ-6505A	8.00
1986-87	▲E6AZ-6505A	8.00
(5) Valve Spring		
V-8-302 eng		
1983-87-intake	▲D8AZ-6513B	5.75
exhaust	▲D5OZ-6513A	6.75
(6) Valve Stem Oil Seal		
V-8-302 eng		
(Intake)		
1983-85-exc.		
LSC	▲E0SZ-6571A	.75

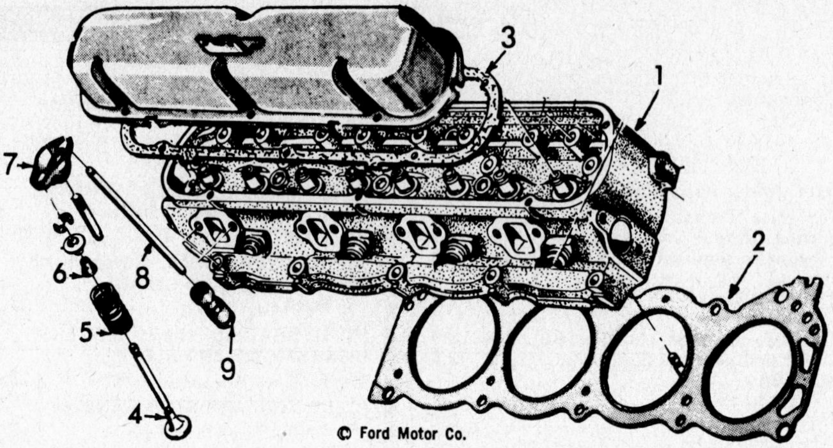

	Part No.	Price
LSC	▲E43Z-6571A	2.25
1986-87	▲E43Z-6571A	2.25
(Exhaust)		
1983-87-exc.		
H.O.	▲D9OZ-6571A	.75
H.O.	▲E2ZZ-6571A	1.00
(7) Rocker Arm		
V-8-302 eng		
1983-87	▲E0AZ-6564A	11.00

	Part No.	Price
(8) Valve Push Rod		
V-8-302 eng		
1983-85-exc.		
below	▲C9OZ-6565B	2.75
1985-87-w/roller		
lifters	▲E5AZ-6565A	4.00
(9) Valve Lifters (Hydraulic)		
1983-85-exc.		
below	▲D9HZ-6500A	9.25
1986-87-w/roller		
lifters	▲E5AZ-6500A	7.00

PARTS 12 CYLINDER HEAD & VALVE SYSTEM 12 PARTS

DIESEL ENGINE

	Part No.	Price
Valve Grind Gasket Set		
1984	E45Y-6079A	63.25
(1) Cylinder Head		
1984-head only	E45Y-6049A	1051.00
complete	E45Y-6049B	2042.50
(2) Cylinder Head Gasket		
1984	E45Y-6051A	42.50
(3) Insert (Valve Seat)		
1984-intake	E45Y-6057A	7.50
exhaust	E45Y-6057C	7.50
(4) Exhaust Valve		
1984	E45Y-6505A	16.50
(5) Intake Valve		
1984	E45Y-6507A	15.75
(6) Gasket (Water Outlet)		
1984	E45Y-8255A	.25
(7) Vacuum Pump Assy.		
1984	E45Y-6F049A	219.25
(8) Valve Cover Gasket		
1984	E45Y-6584A	8.25
(9) Valve Spring Retainer (Upper)		
1984	E45Y-6514B	1.50
(10) Valve Spring		
1984	E45Y-6513A	2.25
(11) Seal (Valve Stem)		
1984	E45Y-6571A	2.00
(12) Valve Spring Retainer (Lower)		
1984	E45Y-6514A	.75
(13) Front Seal (Camshaft)		
1984	E45Y-6700A	5.00

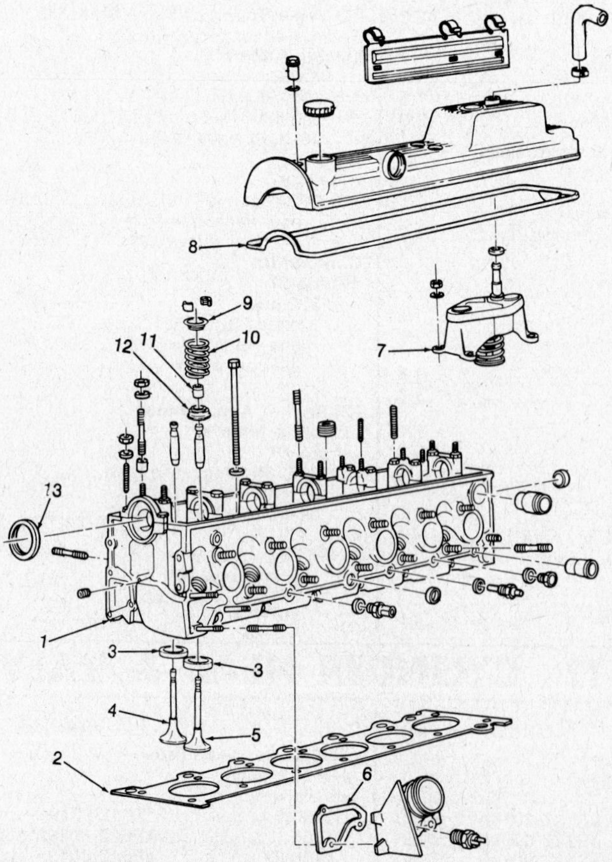

LABOR 13 ENGINE ASSEMBLY & MOUNTS 13 LABOR

(Factory Time) Chilton Time

GASOLINE ENGINES

(G) Engine Assembly, Remove and Install

Does not include transfer of any parts or equipment.

Lincoln & Mark VI
1983-87
302, 351 engs (4.7) 6.8
Mark VII
1984-87
302 eng (4.7)........ 6.8
Continental
1983-87
302 eng (4.7)........ 6.8
w/P.S. add........ .2

(G) Engine Assembly, Replace with New or Rebuilt Unit (with Cyl. Heads)

Includes: R&R engine assembly, transfer all necessary parts, fuel and electrical units. Minor tune up.

1983-87
302, 351 engs (7.3) 11.0
w/P.S. add........ .2

(G) Cylinder Assembly, Renew (w/All Internal Parts Less Head(s) and Oil Pan)

Includes: R&R engine, transfer all component parts not supplied with replacement engine, clean carbon, grind valves. Minor tune up.

Lincoln & Mark VI
1983-87
302, 351 engs (14.9)........ 21.3
Mark VII
1984-87
302 eng (14.7)........ 21.3
Continental
1983-87
302 eng (12.1)........ 21.3

(P) Cylinder Block, Renew

Includes: R&R engine, transfer all component parts, renew rings and bearings, clean carbon, grind valves. Minor tune up.

Lincoln & Mark VI
1983-87
302, 351 engs (19.3)........ 27.6
Mark VII
1984-87
302 eng (19.1)........ 27.6
Continental
1983-87
302 eng (17.4)........ 27.6

(P) Engine Assy., R&R and Recondition (Complete)

Includes: Rebore block, install new pistons, rings, rod and main bearings. Clean carbon, grind valves. Tune engine.

1983-87
302, 351 engs (26.8)........ 31.8

(P) Engine Assembly, Recondition (In Car)

Includes: Expand or renew pistons, install new rings, pins, rod and main bearings. Clean carbon and grind valves. Tune engine.

Lincoln & Mark Series
1983-87
302, 351 engs (27.2)........ 32.2

(G) Engine Mounts, Renew

FRONT
Lincoln & Mark Series
1983-87
302, 351 engs-one (.7)........ .9
both (1.0)........ 1.3
Continental
FRONT
1983-87-one (.6)........ .8
both (.8)........ 1.0
REAR
1983-87
All models (.5)........ .9

DIESEL ENGINE

(G) Engine Assembly, Remove & Install

Does not include transfer of any parts or equipment.

1984-85 (6.1)........ 8.8

(P) Cylinder Assembly, Renew (w/All Internal Parts Less Head and Oil Pan)

Includes: R&R engine, transfer all component parts not supplied with replacement engine. Make all necessary adjustments.

1984-85 (12.9)........ 18.7
Recond cyl head add (4.0)........ 4.0

(P) Cylinder Block, Renew

Includes: R&R engine, transfer all component parts, renew rings and bearings. Make all necessary adjustments.

1984-85 (15.2)........ 22.0
Recond cyl head add (4.0)........ 4.0

(P) Engine Assy., R&R and Recondition

Includes: Rebore block, install new pistons, rings, rod and main bearings. Clean carbon, grind valves. Make all necessary adjustments.

1984-85 (24.6)........ 30.7

(G) Engine Mounts, Renew

Front
1984-85-one (1.3)........ 1.8
both (1.5)........ 2.0
Rear
1984-85 (.4)........ .6

PARTS 13 ENGINE ASSEMBLY & MOUNTS 13 PARTS

	Part No.	Price
Partial Engine (Block w/All Internal Parts, Less Heads, Oil Pan) (New)		
6 cyl. diesel eng.		
1984	E45Y-6010A	1830.00
V-8-302 eng		
1983-84	▲E3AZ-6009A	2044.75
1985-exc. Lincoln	E5LY-6009A	2253.25
Lincoln	▲E5AZ-6009B	2044.75
1986-87	▲E6AZ-6009A	2044.75
Engine Assy.		
6 cyl. diesel eng.		
1984-exc. Calif.	E45Y-6007A	6576.25
Calif.	E45Y-6007B	6576.25
Cylinder Block (New)		
6 cyl. diesel eng.		
1984	E45Y-6009B	2795.00
V-8-302 eng		
1983-85-w/roller lifters	▲E5AZ-6010A	920.25
1986-87	▲E6AZ-6010A	920.25
Engine Overhaul Gasket Set		
6 cyl. diesel eng.		
1984	E45Y-6E078A	31.25
V-8-302 eng		
1983-87	▲E3AZ-6E078A	27.75

When a complete engine overhaul set is required you must also order a valve grind gasket set.

	Part No.	Price
Engine Mounts, Front		
6 cyl. diesel eng.		
1984-R.H.	E45Y-6038B	33.25
L.H.	E45Y-6038A	33.25
V-8-302 eng		
(Lincoln, Mark VI)		
1983-87-R.H.	E0LZ-6038A	38.00
L.H.	E0LZ-6038B	36.75
(Continental, Mark VII)		
(exc. LSC)		
1983-R.H.	E25Y-6038C	31.75
L.H.	E35Y-6038A	29.75
1984-87-R.H.	E45Y-6038D	25.50
L.H.	E45Y-6038C	25.50
(LSC)		
1984-87-R.H.	E45Y-6038F	25.50
L.H.	E45Y-6038E	25.50
Engine Mounts, Rear		
6 cyl. diesel eng.		
1984	E45Y-6068A	35.00
V-8-302 eng		
(Lincoln, Mark VI)		
1983-87	▲E0LZ-6068A	22.50
(Continental, Mark VII)		
1983-87-exc. LSC	E25Y-6068A	8.50
LSC	E45Y-6068D	8.00

LABOR 14 PISTONS, RINGS & BEARINGS 14 LABOR

GASOLINE ENGINES

(P) Rings, Renew (See Machine Shop Operations)

Includes: Remove cylinder top ridge, deglaze cylinder walls, replace rod bearings. Clean carbon from cylinder heads and pistons. Minor tune up.

(Factory Time) Chilton Time

Lincoln & Mark VI
1983-87
302, 351 engs (10.7)........ 15.7

Mark VII
1984-87
302 eng (12.8)........ 18.0

LABOR 14 PISTONS, RINGS & BEARINGS 14 LABOR

	(Factory Time)	Chilton Time
Continental		
1983-87		
302 eng	(10.1)	18.0

(P) Piston or Connecting Rod, Renew (One)

Includes: Remove cylinder top ridge, deglaze cylinder walls, replace rod bearings, clean carbon. Minor tune up.

	(Factory Time)	Chilton Time
Lincoln & Mark VI		
1983-87		
302, 351 engs	(7.1)	9.9
Mark VII		
1984-87		
302 eng	(8.9)	12.4
Continental		
1983-87		
302 eng	(5.7)	12.4

(P) Connecting Rod Bearings, Renew

	(Factory Time)	Chilton Time
Lincoln & Mark VI		
1983-87	(5.3)	6.8
Mark VII		
1984-87		
302 eng	(6.1)	8.5
Continental		
1983-87		
302 eng	(4.4)	5.9
w/P.S. add		.1
Clean oil pump add		.3

DIESEL ENGINE

(P) Piston Rings, Renew

Includes: R&R engine. Remove cylinder top ridge, deglaze cylinder walls. Replace rod bearings, clean carbon from cylinder head and pistons. Make all necessary adjustments.

	(Factory Time)	Chilton Time
1984-85-one cyl	(9.2)	13.3
all cyls	(11.1)	16.0

COMBINATIONS

Add to Engine Work

See Machine Shop Operations

		Chilton Time
(G) DRAIN, EVACUATE & RECHARGE AIR CONDITIONING SYSTEM		
All models	(.7)	1.2
(G) ROCKER ARMS, RENEW OR DISASSEMBLE AND CLEAN		
Each	(.1)	.1
(G) HYDRAULIC VALVE LIFTERS, DISASSEMBLE AND CLEAN		
Each		.2
(G) ROCKER ARM STUD, RENEW		
Each	(.2)	.2
(G) DISTRIBUTOR, RECONDITION		
All models	(.7)	1.0
(G) CARBURETOR, RECONDITION		
2150 2V	(1.0)	1.5
(G) CYLINDER HEAD, R&R (ENGINE REMOVED)		
Six		
Diesel		3.0
V-8		
one		3.2
both		4.7
(G) CONNECTING ROD, RENEW (ENGINE DISASSEMBLED)		
All engines		
each		.4
(G) DEGLAZE CYLINDER WALLS		
Each	(.1)	.1
(G) REMOVE CYLINDER TOP RIDGE		
Each	(.1)	.1
(G) TIMING CHAIN OR GEARS, RENEW (COVER REMOVED)		
All models	(.3)	.5
(G) MAIN BEARINGS, RENEW (PAN REMOVED)		
V-8	(1.9)	2.5
(G) PLASTIGAUGE BEARINGS		
Each	(.1)	.1
(G) OIL PUMP, RECONDITION		
All models	(.3)	.5
(M) OIL FILTER ELEMENT, RENEW		
All models	(.3)	.3

(P) Piston or Connecting Rod, Renew (One)

Includes: R&R engine. Remove cylinder top ridge, deglaze cylinder wall, replace rod bearing, clean carbon from cylinder head. Make all necessary adjustments.

	(Factory Time)	Chilton Time
1984-85	(9.5)	13.6

(G) Connecting Rod Bearings, Renew

Includes: R&R engine assembly.

	(Factory Time)	Chilton Time
1984-85	(7.9)	11.5

PARTS 14 PISTONS, RINGS & BEARINGS 14 PARTS

	Part No.	Price
(1) Piston Ring Set (Std.)		
6 cyl. diesel eng.		
1984	E45Y-6148A	37.50
V-8–302 eng		
1983-85	▲C3AZ-6148F	31.75
1986-87	▲E6AZ-6148A	31.75
(2) Piston & Pin Assy. (Std.)		
6 cyl. diesel eng.		
1984	E45Y-6108A	140.25
V-8–302 eng		
1983-85	▲D9AZ-6108A	35.00
1986-87-exc.		
LSC	▲E6AZ-6108A	35.50
LSC	▲E6ZZ-6108A	34.50

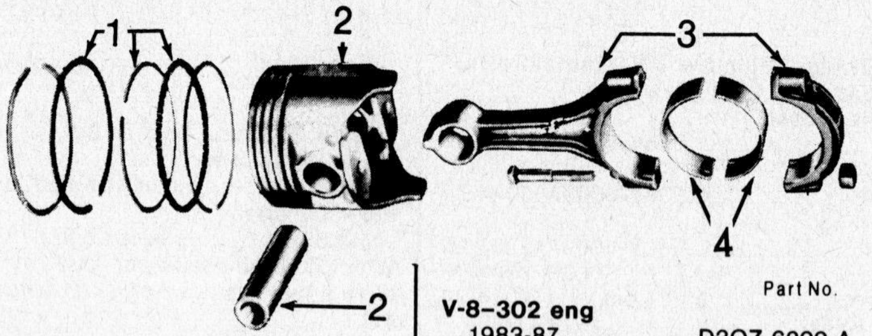

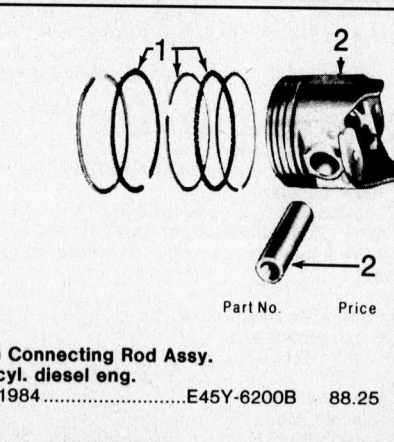

	Part No.	Price
(3) Connecting Rod Assy.		
6 cyl. diesel eng.		
1984	E45Y-6200B	88.25
V-8–302 eng		
1983-87	D3OZ-6200-A	44.00
(4) Connecting Rod Bearings (Std.)		
6 cyl. diesel eng.		
1984	E45Y-6211A	3.25
V-8–302 eng		
1983-87	▲C2OZ-6211R	2.25

LABOR 15 CRANKSHAFT & DAMPER 15 LABOR

GASOLINE ENGINES

(P) Crankshaft and Main Bearings, Renew

Includes: R&R engine, check all bearing clearances.

	(Factory Time)	Chilton Time
Lincoln & Mark VI		
1983-87		
302, 351 engs	(8.8)	12.4
Mark VII		
1984-87		
302 eng	(8.8)	12.4
Continental		
1983-87	(8.8)	12.4

(P) Main Bearings, Renew

Includes: Check all bearing clearances.

	(Factory Time)	Chilton Time
Lincoln & Mark VI		
1983-87		
302, 351 engs	(5.4)	6.5

LABOR 15 CRANKSHAFT & DAMPER 15 LABOR

(Factory Time) Chilton Time

Mark VII
1984-87
302 eng (6.2) 8.7
Continental
1983-87
302 eng (4.5) 6.0

(P) Main and Rod Bearings, Renew
Includes: Check all bearing clearances.
Lincoln & Mark VI
1983-87
302, 351 engs (7.2) 8.9
Mark VII
1984-87
302 eng (8.0) 11.1
Continental
1983-87
302 eng (6.3) 8.4

(G) Rear Main Bearing Oil Seals, Renew (Upper & Lower) (Split Lip Type)
Lincoln & Mark Series
1983
302, 351 engs (4.2) 5.4
Continental
1983
302 eng (3.3) 4.5

(G) Crankshaft Rear Main Seal, Renew
(Full Circle Type)
Lincoln-Mark VI
1983-87
302 eng (2.8) 3.9

(Factory Time) Chilton Time

Mark VII
1984-87
302 eng (3.3) 4.6
Continental
1983-87
302 eng (3.3) 4.6

(G) Vibration Damper or Pulley, Renew
Lincoln & Mark VI
1983-87
302, 351 engs (.6) 1.0
Mark VII
1984-87
302 eng (.8) 1.4
Continental
1983-87
302 eng (.8) 1.4

(G) Crankshaft Front Oil Seal, Renew
Lincoln
1983-84
302, 351 engs (2.3) 3.4
1985-87 (.9) 1.5
Mark VI, VII
1983-84
302, 351 engs (2.3) 3.4
1985-87 (.9) 1.5
Continental
1983-84
302 eng (2.7) 3.7

(Factory Time) Chilton Time

1985-87 (.9) 1.5

DIESEL ENGINE

(P) Crankshaft and Main Bearings, Renew
Includes: R&R engine assy., check all bearing clearances.
1984-85 (9.9) 14.5

(G) Main Bearings, Renew
Includes: R&R engine assy., check all bearing clearances.
1984-85 (8.9) 12.9

(G) Main and Rod Bearings, Renew
Includes: R&R engine assy., check all bearing clearances.
1984-85 (10.4) 14.7

(G) Crankshaft Rear Main Seal, Renew
(Full Circle Type)
1984-85 (3.8) 5.5

(G) Crankshaft Front Seal, Renew
1984-85
crankshaft (1.8) 2.5
aux. drive (1.8) 2.5

(G) Vibration Damper or Pulley, Renew
1984-85 (.4) 6

PARTS 15 CRANKSHAFT & DAMPER 15 PARTS

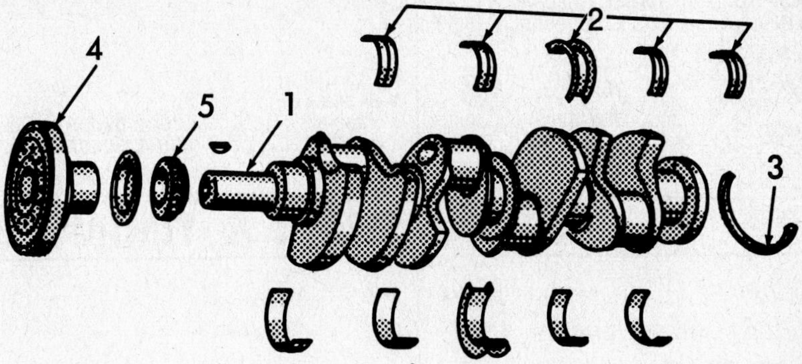

Part No. / Price

(1) Crankshaft (New)
6 cyl. diesel engine
1984 .... E45Y-6303A 810.00
V-8-302 eng
1983-87 .... ▲E3AZ-6303A 500.75

(2) Main Bearing (Upper or Lower)
6 cyl. diesel engine
1984 (exc. rear intermediate)
upper E45Y-6333A 5.00
lower E45Y-6333G 4.75
1984 (rear intermediate)
upper E45Y-6337A 11.50
lower E45Y-6337G 11.25
V-8-302 eng
1983-87 (center)
upper .... ▲C3AZ-6337P 8.00
lower .... ▲C3AZ-6337AA 8.00
1983-87 (exc. center)
upper .... ▲C3AZ-6333P 3.50
lower .... ▲C3AZ-6333AA 3.50

(3) Rear Oil Seal
Gasoline engine
1983-rope type .... ▲C9OZ-6701A 2.00
1983-split lip type .... ▲D4FZ-6701A 6.25

Part No. / Price

1983-87-one piece type .... ▲E5ZZ-6701A 6.25
Diesel engine
1984 .... E45Y-6701A 12.25
Front Oil Seal
1983-87-gas .... ▲D0AZ-6700A 6.75
diesel E45Y-6700B 8.00
(4) Vibration Damper
6 cyl. diesel engine
1984-87 .... E45Y-6316A 222.75

Part No. / Price

V-8-302 engine
1983 .... ▲E2TZ-6316B 74.00
1984-87 .... ▲E4TZ-6316A 67.75
(5) Crankshaft Sprocket
6 cyl. diesel engine
1984 .... E45Y-6306A 13.00
V-8-302 engine
1983-87-exc.
H.O. .... ▲D5OZ-6306A 11.25
H.O. .... ▲E0AZ-6306A 18.50

LABOR 16 CAMSHAFT & TIMING GEARS 16 LABOR

(Factory Time) Chilton Time

GASOLINE ENGINES

(G) Timing Case Seal and Gaskets, Renew
Includes: R&R radiator and oil pan where required.
Lincoln
1983-87
302, 351 engs (2.3) 3.4

(Factory Time) Chilton Time

Mark VI, VII
1983
302, 351 engs (2.3) 3.4
1984-87
302 eng (2.6) 3.6
Continental
1983-87
302 eng (2.7) 3.7

(Factory Time) Chilton Time

(G) Timing Chain or Sprockets, Renew
Includes: Adjust timing.
Lincoln
1983-87
302, 351 engs (2.6) 3.9

LABOR 16 CAMSHAFT & TIMING GEARS 16 LABOR

	(Factory Time)	Chilton Time
Mark VI, VII		
1983		
302, 351 engs	(2.6)	3.9
1984-87		
302 eng	(2.9)	4.1
Continental		
1983-87		
302 eng	(3.0)	4.2

*Includes R&R oil pan.

(G) Camshaft, Renew

Includes: R&R oil pan where required.

	(Factory Time)	Chilton Time
Lincoln		
1983-87	(5.6)	7.6
Mark VI, VII		
1983		
302, 351 engs	(5.6)	7.6
1984-87		
302 eng	(5.7)	8.2
Continental		
1983-87		
302 eng	(5.4)	7.6

(P) Camshaft Bearings, Renew

Includes: R&R engine and crankshaft.

	(Factory Time)	Chilton Time
1983-87		
302, 351 engs	(8.9)	12.5

(G) Camshaft Rear Welsh Plug, Renew

Includes: R&R trans and flywheel for accessibility.

	(Factory Time)	Chilton Time
Lincoln & Mark VI		
1983-87	(3.1)	4.5
Continental & Mark VII		
1983-87	(4.2)	5.3

DIESEL ENGINE

	(Factory Time)	Chilton Time
(G) Timing Case Seal and Gaskets, Renew		
1984-85	(1.7)	2.4
(G) Timing Belt, Renew		
1984-85	(1.2)	1.7
(G) Camshaft, Renew		
1984-85	(3.3)	4.6
(G) Camshaft Sprocket, Renew		
1984-85	(1.0)	1.6
(G) Camshaft Seal, Renew		
1984-85	(1.0)	1.5

PARTS 16 CAMSHAFT & TIMING GEARS 16 PARTS

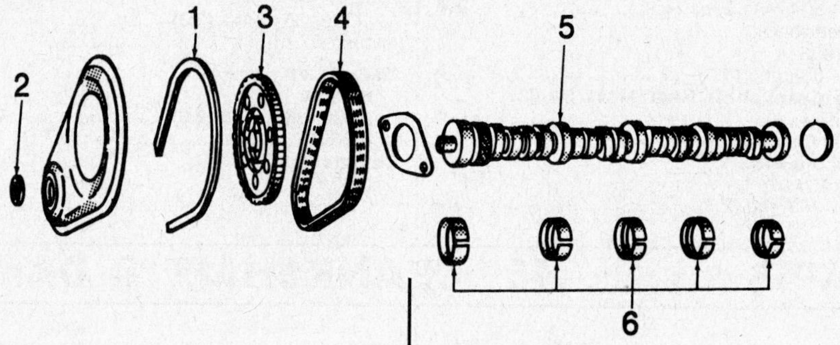

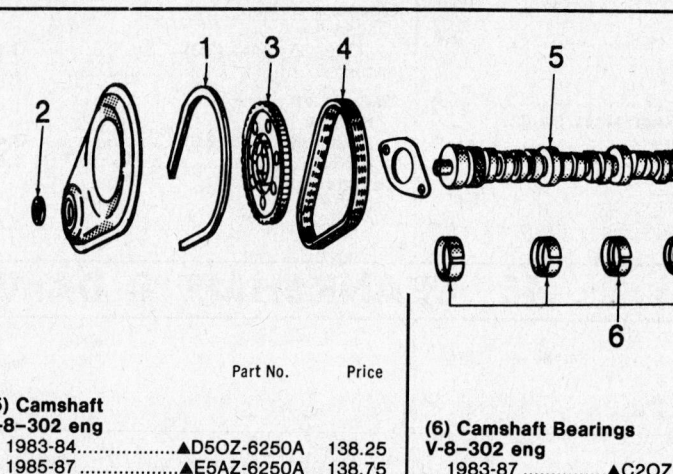

	Part No.	Price
(1) Timing Case Gasket		
V-8-302 eng		
1983-87	▲E3AZ-6020A	1.50
(2) Timing Case Oil Seal		
1983-87	▲D0AZ-6700A	6.75
(3) Timing Gears		
(Camshaft)		
V-8-302 eng		
1983-87	▲D3AZ-6256B	22.25
(Crankshaft)		
V-8-302 eng		
1983-87-exc.		
H.O.	▲D5OZ-6306A	11.25
H.O.	E0AZ-6306	18.50
(4) Timing Chain		
V-8-302 eng		
1983-87-exc.		
H.O.	▲C3OZ-6268A	19.25
H.O.	▲E0AZ-6268A	22.25
(5) Camshaft		
V-8-302 eng		
1983-84	▲D5OZ-6250A	138.25
1985-87	▲E5AZ-6250A	138.75
(6) Camshaft Bearings		
V-8-302 eng		
1983-87	▲C2OZ-6A251A	23.50

PARTS 16 CAMSHAFT & TIMING GEARS 16 PARTS

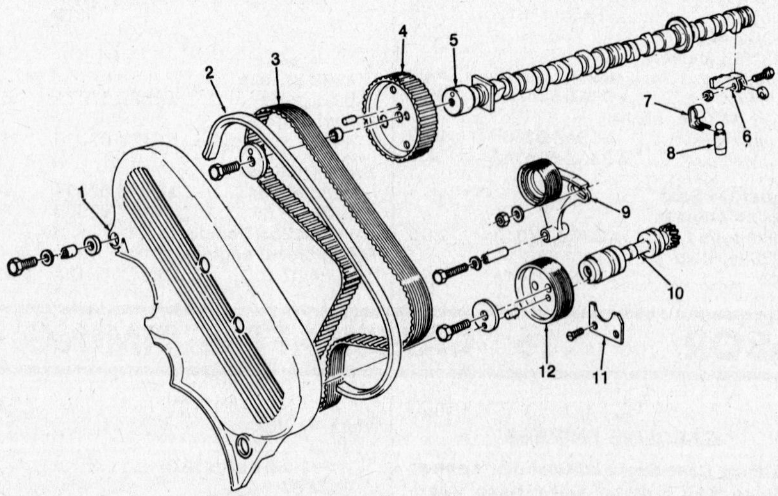

	Part No.	Price
2.4L DIESEL ENGINE		
(1) Timing Case Cover		
1984	E45Y-6019B	55.75
(2) Timing Cover Seal		
1984	E45Y-6020B	4.50
(3) Timing Belt		
1984	E45Y-6268A	41.25
(4) Camshaft Sprocket		
1984	E45Y-6256A	14.00
(5) Camshaft		
1984	E45Y-6250A	282.00
(6) Rocker Arm Assy.		
1984	E45Y-6564A	16.00
(7) Retaining Spring (Rocker Arm Pin)		
1984	E45Y-6K532A	.50
(8) Pin (Rocker Arm Fulcrum)		
1984	E45Y-6A527A	2.75
(9) Tensioner Assy. (Timing Belt)		
1984	E45Y-6K254A	43.00
(10) Auxiliary Shaft Assy.		
1984	E45Y-6A739A	76.00
(11) Retaining Plate (Auxiliary Shaft)		
1984	E45Y-6613A	3.00
(12) Auxiliary Shaft Sprocket		
1984	E45Y-6256B	8.75

LABOR 17 ENGINE OILING SYSTEM 17 LABOR

(Factory Time) Chilton Time

GASOLINE ENGINES

(G) Oil Pan or Gasket, Renew
Lincoln
1983-87
302, 351 engs (3.5) 4.4
Mark VI, VII
1983
302, 351 engs (3.5) 4.4
1984-87
302 eng (4.3).............................. 6.0
Continental
1983-87
302 eng (2.6).............................. 3.5

(P) Pressure Test Engine Bearings (Pan Off)
All models.................................... 1.0

(G) Oil Pump, Renew
Lincoln
1983-87
302, 351 engs (3.6) 4.6
Mark VI, VII
1983
302, 351 engs (3.6) 4.6
1984-87
302 eng (4.4).............................. 6.2
Continental
1983-87
302 eng (2.7).............................. 3.7

(G) Oil Pump, R&R and Recondition
Lincoln
1983-87
302, 351 engs (3.9) 5.0
Mark VI, VII
1983
302, 351 engs (3.9) 5.0
1984-87
302 eng (4.7).............................. 6.6
Continental
1983-87
302 eng (3.0).............................. 4.2

(G) Oil Pressure Gauge (Engine), Renew
1983-87 (.3).................................. .5

(G) Oil Filter Element, Renew
1983-87 (.3).................................. .3

DIESEL ENGINE

(G) Oil Pan or Gasket, Renew
Includes: R&R engine assy.
1984-85 (6.4).................................. 9.3

(P) Pressure Test Engine Bearings (Pan Off)
All models.................................... 1.0

(G) Oil Pump, Renew
Includes: R&R engine assy.
1984-85 (6.5).................................. 9.5

(G) Oil Pump, R&R and Recondition
Includes: R&R engine assy.
1984-85 (6.8).................................. 9.9

(G) Oil Cooler, Renew
1984-85 (.6).................................. 1.0

(M) Oil Filter Element, Renew
1984-85 (.4).................................. .4

PARTS 17 ENGINE OILING SYSTEM 17 PARTS

	Part No.	Price
Oil Pan Gasket		
V-8–302 eng		
1983-87	▲D9AZ-6781A	11.50
Oil Pump Assy. (New)		
6 cyl. diesel engine		
1984	E45Y-6600A	130.50
V-8–302 eng		
1983-87	▲C2OZ-6600A	52.50
Oil Pressure Gauge (Engine Unit)		
6 cyl. diesel engine		
1984	E45Y-9278A	6.50
V-8–302 eng		
1983-87-exc. below	▲D4AZ-9278A	3.50
1985-87-elec. image car	▲D9ZZ-9278B	12.75
Oil Filter Element Assy.		
1983-87-exc. below	▲D9AZ-6731A	8.00
1984-diesel eng	E45Y-6731A	15.50

LABOR 21 SHIFT LINKAGE 21 LABOR

(Factory Time) Chilton Time

AUTOMATIC

(G) Linkage, Adjust
manual (.3).................................. .4
throttle (.3).................................. .5
manual & throttle (.5) 7
kickdown (.3).................................. .5

(G) Gearshift Tube Assembly, Renew
Includes: Adjust neutral switch when required.
Lincoln
1983-87 (1.0).................................. 1.7
Mark VI
1983 (1.4).................................. 2.2

(G) Gear Selector Lever, Renew
1983-87
Mark VII & Cont. (.4).................. .6
All other models (.2).................. .5

(G) Tilt Wheel Pivot, Recondition (In Chassis)
1983-87 (.7).................................. 1.0

LABOR 25 U-JOINTS & DRIVESHAFT 25 LABOR

(Factory Time) Chilton Time

(G) Universal Joints, Renew or Recondition
Includes: R&R drive shaft.
1983-87
Double Cardan
front or rear (.9)........................ 1.3
all (1.5).................................. 2.0
Single Cardan
front or rear (.6)........................ .9
both (.8).................................. 1.3

(G) Driveshaft, Renew
1983-87 (.3).................................. .5

PARTS 25 UNIVERSAL JOINTS & DRIVE SHAFT 25 PARTS

	Part No.	Price
Universal Joint Kit		
1983-87 (front & rear) wo/Towing pkg.	▲C3AZ-4635E	15.25
Towing pkg.	C3AZ-4635G	17.25
Pinion Bearing Spacer		
1983-87	▲B7A-4662A	4.00
Yoke		
Lincoln, Mark VI		
1983-87	▲E1DZ-4782A	14.25
Continental, Mark VII		
1983-87	E0WY-4782A	55.50

LABOR 26 REAR AXLE 26 LABOR

(Factory Time) Chilton Time

INTEGRAL CARRIER TYPE

(M) Differential, Drain & Refill
All models .6

(M) Axle Housing Cover or Gasket, Renew
All models (.4) .6

(G) Axle Shaft Inner Oil Seals, Renew
Includes: R&R wheel, drum and axle shaft.
1983-87-one (.7) .9
both (.9) 1.3
w/Rear disc brakes
one (.8) 1.0
both (1.1) 1.5

(G) Axle Shaft, Renew
Includes: Renew inner oil seal.
1983-87-one (.6) .8
both (.8) 1.2
w/Rear disc brakes
one (.6) .8
both (1.0) 1.4

(G) Rear Wheel Bearings, Renew
Includes: Renew oil seal.
1983-87-one (.7) 1.0
both (1.0) 1.5
w/Rear disc brakes
one (.8) 1.1
both (1.1) 1.6

(G) Axle Shaft Wheel Mounting Studs, Renew
All models-one .8
all 1.2

(G) Pinion Shaft Oil Seal, Renew
1983-87 (.8) 1.3

(P) Differential Carrier Assy., Recondition (In Chassis)
Includes: Drain and refill axle, renew necessary parts. Renew axle shaft oil seals. Road test.
Cont. & Mark VII
1984-87 (4.7) 6.5
All other models
1983-87 (3.9) 5.6

(P) Axle Housing, Renew
Includes: Transfer all necessary parts, adjust ring gear and pinion. Does not include disassembly of differential case.
Cont. & Mark VII
1984-87 (4.8) 7.0
All other models
1983-87 (3.6) 5.2
Recond diff assy add (.4) .8

(P) Ring and Pinion Set, Renew
Includes: R&R axle shafts, drain and refill unit. Road test.
Cont. & Mark VII
1984-87 (3.7) 5.5
All other models
1983-87 (2.7) 3.8

(P) Ring and Pinion, Adjust (In Chassis)
Includes: Remove axle shafts, drain and refill unit. Road test.
1983-87 (1.5) 2.3
w/Rear disc brks add (.1) .1

(P) Differential Case, Recondition
1983-87 (2.1) 3.3
w/Rear disc brks add .5

PARTS 26 REAR AXLE 26 PARTS

CONVENTIONAL

	Part No.	Price
(1) Pinion Kit		
7.5" dia. ring gear		
1983-87	▲E4DZ-4215A	20.00
8.5", 8.8" dia. ring gear		
1983-87	▲E3TZ-4215A	34.50
(2) Side Gear		
1983-87-exc.		
below	D9AZ-4236B	40.00
7.5"	▲D9AZ-4236A	40.00
Includes, gears and washer.		
(3) Shim		
1983-87	▲D9AZ-4067A	3.25
(4) Bearing Cup		
1983-87-exc.		
below	▲D9AZ-4222A	7.25
7.5"	▲C6TZ-4222A	6.00
(5) Bearing Assy.		
1983-87-exc.		
below	▲B7A-4221B	12.50
7.5"	▲B7A-4221A	11.50
(6) Pinion Shaft		
1983-87-exc.		
below	▲B7AZ-4211A	9.00
7.5"	▲D8BZ-4211A	13.75
(7) Case Assy.		
1983-87-exc.		
below	▲E3AZ-4204A	105.75
7.5"	▲D9AZ-4204A	104.50
(8) Housing Assy.		
7.5" dia. ring gear		
1983	▲E2BZ-4010A	457.75
1984	E4LY-4010A	457.75
1985-87	E5LY-4010A	457.75
8.5", 8.8" dia. ring gear		
1983-87	▲D9AZ-4010B	712.75
1986-87-8.8"	E6LY-4010A	457.75
(9) Ring Gear & Pinion Kit		
7.5" dia. ring gear		
1983-87-2.73R	▲E5SZ-4209A	352.50
3.08R	▲E25Y-4209A	352.50
3.27R (1983-84)	▲E35Y-4209A	381.75

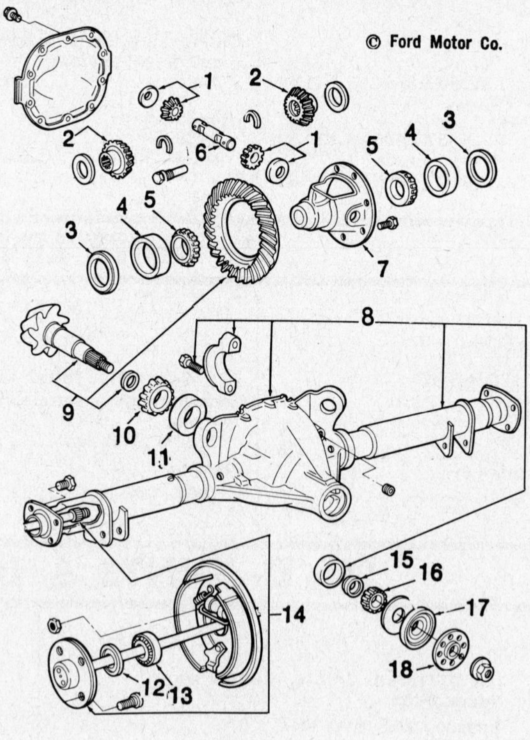

	Part No.	Price
3.27R (1985-87)	▲E5LY-4209A	381.75
3.45R	▲E25Y-4209B	401.25
8.5" dia. ring gear		
1983-2.73R	D9AZ-4209G	328.00
3.08R	D9AZ-4209H	328.00
3.42R	E2AZ-4209A	328.00
8.8" dia. ring gear		
1983-87-2.73R	▲E3AZ-4209A	319.25
3.08R	▲E3TZ-4209H	381.75
3.55R	▲E3TZ-4209J	381.75

	Part No.	Price
(10) Pinion Bearing (Rear)		
1983-87	▲C7AZ-4630A	15.75
(11) Bearing Cup (Rear)		
1983-87	▲C7AZ-4628A	8.00
(12) Axle Shaft Oil Seal		
1983-87	▲E1AZ-1177B	3.50
(13) Axle Shaft Bearing		
1983-87	▲C7AZ-1225A	15.75

PARTS 26 REAR AXLE 26 PARTS

	Part No.	Price
(14) Axle Shaft Assy.		
7.5" dia. ring gear		
1983-87-exc.		
below	▲E25Y-4234A	134.00
w/anti-skid brks	E5LY-4234A	134.00
8.5", 8.8." dia. ring gear		
1983-87	▲D9AZ-4234A	132.00
(15) Spacer		
1983-87	▲B7A-4662A	4.00
(16) Pinion Bearing (Front)		
1983-87	▲B7A-4621A	11.50
(17) Pinion Oil Seal		
1983-87	▲E3TZ-4676A	11.25
(18) Flange Assy. (U-Joint)		
1983-87-exc.		
below	▲D8BZ-4851A	17.00
8.8"	▲E3AZ-4851A	20.75

PARTS 26 REAR AXLE (TRAC-LOK) 26 PARTS

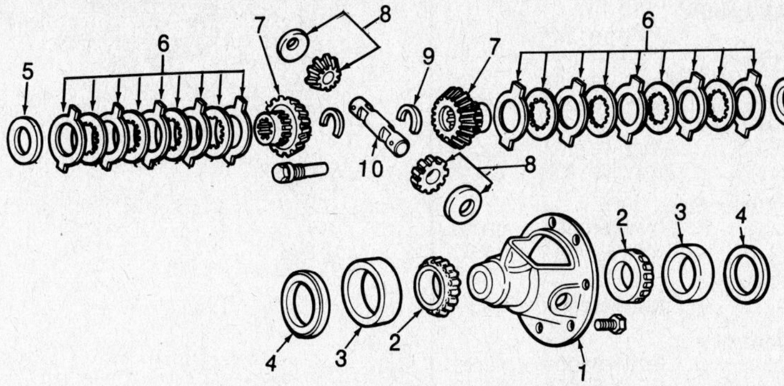

	Part No.	Price
(1) Case Assy.		
7.5" dia. ring gear		
1983-84	▲Not Serviced	
1985-87	▲E4DZ-4204A	105.75
8.5", 8.8" ring gear		
1983-87	▲E3AZ-4204B	169.50
(2) Bearing (Side)		
1983-87-exc.		
below	▲B7A-4221B	12.50
7.5"	▲B7A-4221A	11.50
(3) Bearing Cup		
1983-87-exc.		
below	▲D9AZ-4222A	7.25
7.5"	▲C6TZ-4222A	6.00
(4) Bearing Adjuster		
1983-87-exc.		
below	▲D9AZ-4067A	3.25
7.5"	D8BZ-4067BR	3.25
(5) Shim (.025" Thick)		
1983-87-exc.		
below	▲E0AZ-4A324A	1.00
7.5"	E4DZ-4A324A	1.00
Other sizes available.		
(6) Clutch Plate Kit		
1983-87-exc.		
below	▲E2AZ-4947A	31.75
7.5"	E4DZ-4947A	31.25

1983-84 cars with 7.5", clutch plate kit is only serviced in the differential assy. basic part No. 4026.

	Part No.	Price
(7) Side Gear		
1983-87-exc.		
below	▲E0AZ-4236A	102.25
7.5"	▲E4DZ-4236A	40.25
(8) Pinion Kit		
1983-87-exc.		
below	▲E3TZ-4215A	34.50
7.5"	▲E4DZ-4215A	20.00
(9) U-Washer (Retaining)		
1983-87	▲C7AZ-4N237A	1.50
(10) Pinion Shaft		
7.5" dia. ring gear		
1983-84	▲Not Serviced	
1985-87-exc.		
below	▲D8BZ-4211A	13.75
3.73R	▲E4SZ-4211A	13.75
8.5", 8.8" dia. ring gear		
1983-87	▲B7AZ-4211A	9.00
(11) Lock Pin (Pinion Shaft)		
1983-87	▲D8BZ-4241A	2.00

LABOR 27 REAR SUSPENSION 27 LABOR

(Factory Time)	Chilton Time
LINCOLN & MARK VI	
(G) Rear Spring, Renew	
1983-87-both (.4)	.6
(G) Rear Shock Absorber or Rubber Bushing, Renew	
1983-87-one (.4)	.6
both (.5)	.8
(G) Rear Suspension Upper Arm, Renew	
1983-87-one (.5)	1.2
both (.8)	1.5
(G) Rear Suspension Lower Arm, Renew	
1983-87-one (.5)	.7
both (.7)	1.3
(G) Upper Control Arm Bushings, Renew	
1983-87-one (.5)	1.0
both (.7)	1.4
CONTINENTAL (1983)	
(G) Rear Spring, Renew	
1983-both (.5)	.9
(G) Rear Suspension Upper Arm, Renew	
1983-one (.6)	.9
both (.9)	1.5
(G) Rear Suspension Lower Arm, Renew	
1983-right (.6)	.9
left (.8)	1.2
both (1.2)	1.7
(G) Rear Shock Absorbers, Renew	
1983-one (.3)	.5
both (.4)	.8
CONTINENTAL AND MARK VII AIR SUSPENSION SYSTEM	
(G) Air Suspension Diagnosis Test	
All models	1.0
(G) Front Air Springs, Renew	
Does not include system test.	
1984-87-one (.3)	.5
both (.5)	.9
(G) Rear Air Springs, Renew	
Does not include system test.	
1984-87-one (.5)	.8
both (.9)	1.5
(G) Air Compressor, Renew	
Does not include system test.	
1984-87 (.3)	.5
(G) Air Suspension Control Module, Renew	
Does not include system test.	
1984-87 (.3)	.4
(G) Air Suspension Dryer Assy., Renew	
Does not include system test.	
1984-87 (.2)	.4
(G) On/Off Control Switch Assy., Renew	
Does not include system test.	
1984-87 (.1)	.3
(G) Front or Rear Height Sensor, Renew	
Does not include system test.	
1984-87-each (.2)	.3
(G) Air Spring Valve, Renew	
Does not include system test.	
1984-87 (.3)	.4
(G) Air Compressor Relay, Renew	
Does not include system test.	
1984-87 (.1)	.3
(G) Rear Suspension Upper Control Arm, Renew	
1984-87-both (1.0)	1.5
(G) Rear Suspension Lower Control Arm, Renew	
1984-87-both (2.4)	3.3
(G) Upper Control Arm Bushings, Renew	
1984-87-upper (.6)	.9
lower (.5)	.8
both (.8)	1.4
(G) Rear Sway Bar, Renew	
1984-87 (.6)	.9
(G) Rear Shock Absorbers, Renew	
1984-87-one (.3.)	.4
both (.4)	.6

PARTS 27 REAR SUSPENSION 27 PARTS

	Part No.	Price
LINCOLN & MARK VI		
(1) Lower Control Arm		
1983-87	E0VY-5A649A	99.25
(2) Bumper (Axle)		
1983-87	▲D9AZ-4730A	5.50
(3) Coil Spring		
Order by model and description.		
(4) Insulator (Spring)		
1983-87	▲D9AZ-5536A	3.00
(5) Shock Absorber		
1983	E1VY-18125A	29.00
1984-wo/Tow pkg.	E4VY-18125A	41.25
Tow pkg.	E4VY-18125B	41.25
1985-87-wo/Tow pkg.	E5VY-18125A	29.75
Tow pkg.	E5VY-18125B	29.75
(6) Bushing (Rear Arm)		
1983-85	E0VY-5A638A	10.00
1986-87	E6VY-5A638A	10.00
(7) Bumper (Pinion)		
1983-87	D5DZ-4730A	3.25
(8) Upper Control Arm		
1983-84	E0VY-5500A	42.50
1985-87	E5VY-5500A	42.50

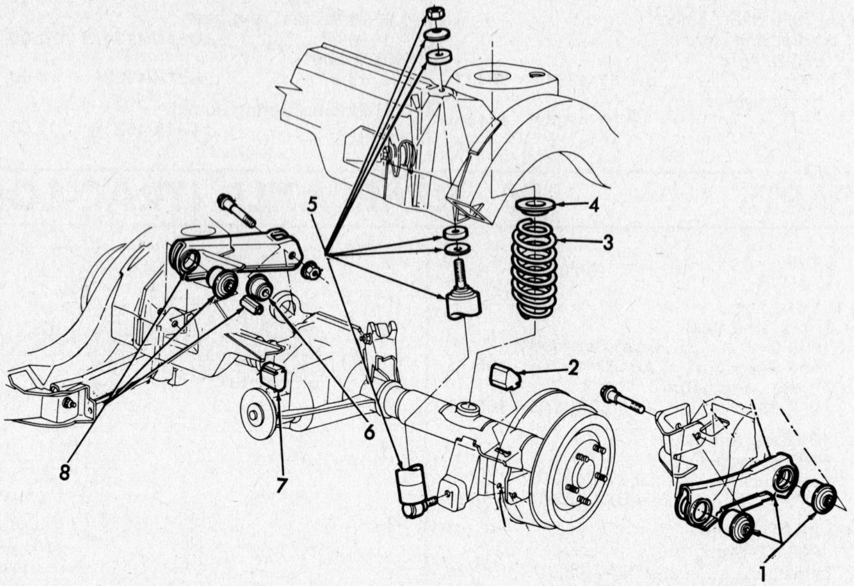

PARTS 27 REAR SUSPENSION 27 PARTS

	Part No.	Price
CONTINENTAL & MARK VII (1984-87)		
(1) Upper Control Arm		
1984-87-right	E4LY-5500A	42.50
left	E4LY-5500B	38.25
(2) Bushing (Control Arm)		
1984-87	E25Y-5A638B	16.75
(3) Sensor Assy.		
1984-87	E4LY-5359B	74.00
(4) Bumper (Rear Axle)		
1984-87	E25Y-4730B	3.50
(5) Lower Control Arm		
1984-87	E4LY-5A649A	93.25
(6) Spring Assy. (Air)		
1984-87-Std.	E4LY-5560E	264.25
1984-85-H.D.	E4LY-5560F	264.25
1986-87-H.D.	E6LY-5560A	264.25
(7) "O" Ring (Compressor Piston)		
1984-87	E4LY-5308B	1.75
(8) Solenoid Assy. (Valve)		
1984-87	E4LY-5311B	44.50
(9) Shock Absorber		
1984-87	E4LY-18125A	38.25
(10) Bushing Repair Kit (Shock Absorber)		
1984-87	E3SZ-18198B	17.25

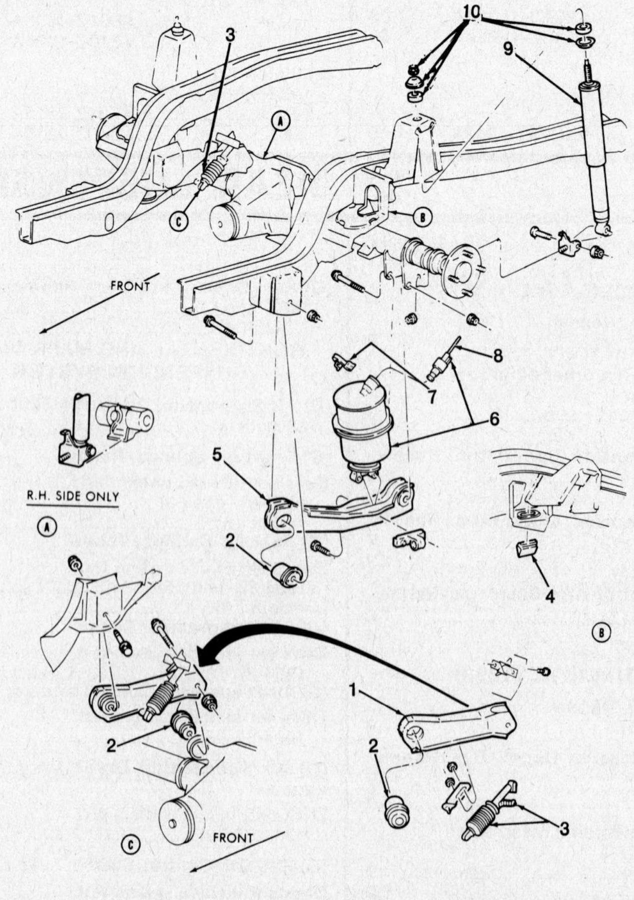

PARTS 27 REAR SUSPENSION 27 PARTS

CONTINENTAL (1983)

	Part No.	Price
(1) Upper Control Arm Assy.		
1983	E25Y-5500A	37.00
(2) Insulator (Upper)		
1983	▲E25Y-5536A	9.50
(3) Damper (Rear Spring)		
1983	▲D8BZ-5A669C	8.50
(4) Coil Spring		
Order by model and description.		
(5) Insulator (Lower)		
1983	▲D8BZ-5536A	3.00
(6) Lower Control Arm Assy.		
1983	E35Y-5A649A	93.25
(7) Shock Absorber (Rear)		
1983	E35Y-18125A	N.L.

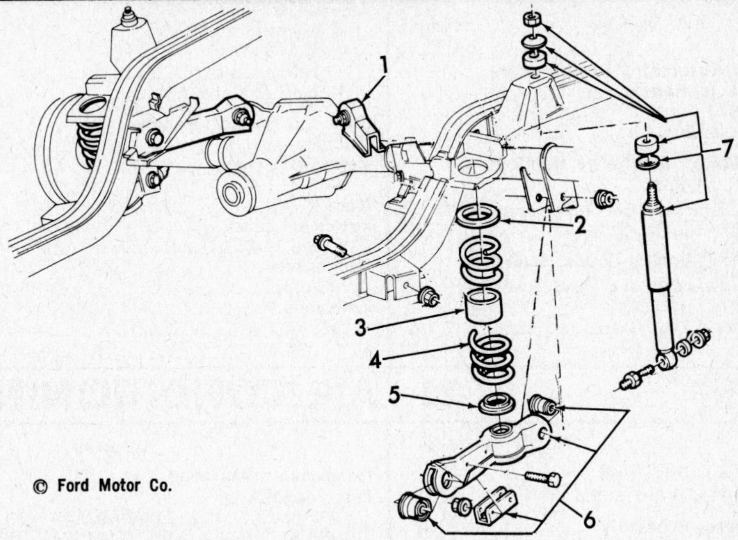

LABOR 28 AIR CONDITIONING 28 LABOR

(Factory Time) Chilton Time

Note: If more than one item requires replacement where evacuation and discharging the system is already included in the operation, deduct 1.0 hour for each additional item to the times listed.

(G) Drain, Evacuate and Recharge System
Includes: Check for leaks.
All models (.7)........ 1.2

(G) Pressure Test System
All models........ .8

(G) Compressor Belt, Renew
All models (.3)........ .6

(G) Compressor Assembly, Renew
Includes: Evacuate and charge system.
1983-87 (2.0)........ 3.0

(P) Compressor Assembly, R&R and Recondition
Includes: Evacuate and charge system.
1983-87
Frigidaire (2.5)........ 3.5
FS6 (2.7)........ 4.0

(G) Compressor Shaft Seal Kit, Renew
Includes: R&R compressor when required. Evacuate and charge system.
1983-87
Frigidaire (1.2)........ 2.3
FS6 (2.0)........ 3.0

(G) Compressor Clutch and Pulley, Renew
Includes: R&R compressor when required. Evacuate and charge system.
Lincoln & Mark Series
1983-87 (.7)........ 1.1
Continental
1983-84 (.5)........ .8
1985-87 (.8)........ 1.2
Renew clutch brg add (.1)........ .1
Renew clutch field add (.1)........ .1

(G) Compressor Service Valve or Gasket, Renew
Includes: Evacuate and charge system.
1983-87 (.9)........ 1.3

AIR CONDITIONER TUNE-UP

For efficient operation and satisfactory performance in hot weather. The following air conditioner tune-up is suggested:

1. Clean intake filter
2. Clean condenser fins
3. Pressure test system
4. Adjust drive belt tension
5. Check antifreeze/coolant
6. Tighten compressor mounts
7. Tighten condenser and evaporator mounts
8. Inspect system for leaks (hoses, couplings, valves, etc.)
9. Partial charge system

All models........ 1.0
If necessary to evacuate and charge system, add........ 1.0

(Factory Time) Chilton Time

(G) Condenser Assembly, Renew
Includes: Evacuate and charge system.
Lincoln
1983-87 (.9)........ 2.1
Mark VI, VII
1983 (1.0)........ 2.1
1984-87 (1.2)........ 2.1
Continental
1983-87 (1.0)........ 2.1

(G) Evaporator Core, Renew
Includes: Renew or transfer valve. Evacuate and charge system.
Lincoln
1983-87 (2.1)........ 6.0
Mark VI, VII
1983 (2.1)........ 4.5
1984-87 (4.6)........ 8.0

(Factory Time) Chilton Time

Continental
1983-87 (4.6)........ 8.0

(G) Pressure Relief Valve, Renew
Includes: Evacuate and charge system.
1983-87-two cyl comp (.9)........ 1.6
six cyl comp (.8)........ 1.5

(G) A.C. Clutch Cycling Switch Assy., Renew
1983-87 (.2)........ .4

(G) Accumulator Assembly, Renew
Includes: Evacuate and charge system.
1983 (1.0)........ 1.5

(G) Orifice Valve, Renew
Includes: Evacuate and charge system.
1983-87 (1.0)........ 1.5

(G) Door Vacuum Motor, Renew
1983-87-each-exc below (.4)........ .8
by-pass door (.7)........ 1.3
A/C heat door (1.1)........ 2.0
panel door (2.6)........ 4.5
heat/defrost door (3.1)........ *5.0
A.C./Defrost (3.1)........ *5.0
ATC servo (.3)........ .6
*Add time to recharge A.C. system.

(G) Blower Motor, Renew
Lincoln
1983-87 (.4)........ .8
Mark VI, VII
1983 (.4)........ .8
1984-87 (1.1)........ 1.9
Continental
1983-87 (.9)........ 1.5

(G) Blower Motor Switch, Renew
Lincoln & Mark Series
1983-87 (.5)........ .9
Continental
1983-84 (.4)........ .7

(G) Blower Motor Speed Control, Renew
1985-87 (.4)........ .6

(G) Blower Motor Resistor, Renew
1983-87 (.3)........ .5

LABOR 28 AIR CONDITIONING 28 LABOR

(Factory Time)	Chilton Time
(G) A.C. Automatic Temperature Servo Assy., Renew	
1985-87	
Lincoln (.3)	.5
(G) Suction or Discharge Manifold Assy. Kit, Renew	
Includes: Evacuate and charge system.	
1983-87 (.8)	1.5
(G) Air Conditioning Hoses, Renew	
Includes: Evacuate and charge system.	
1983-87	
Cond. to Evap. (.9)	1.8
Suction line (1.0)	1.9
Comp. to Cond. (.8)	1.7
(P) A.T.C. Sensor, Renew	
Lincoln	
Instrument panel	
1983-87 (.4)	.7
Mark VI, VII	
Instrument panel	
1983-87 (.4)	.7
Condenser	
Continental	
Instrument Panel	
1983-87 (.9)	1.4
(G) A.C. Control Assembly, Renew	
Mark VII-Cont	
1984-87 (.4)	.7
(G) Actuator Doors, Renew	
Mark VII	
1984-87	
Outside/Recirculation (.6)	1.1
Panel/Defrost (2.3)	4.0
Temp. Blend (.7)	1.3
Floor/Panel (2.8)	*5.0

*Add time to recharge A.C. system.

PARTS 28 AIR CONDITIONING 28 PARTS

	Part No.	Price
Compressor Drive Belt		
Order by model & description.		
Compressor Assembly		
1983-85	▲E4VY-19703A	315.00
1986-87	▲E6VY-19703A	315.00
Compressor Shaft Oil Seal		
1983-87-York	▲C9AZ-19655B	18.25
Tecumseh	▲C9AZ-19655A	17.75
Clutch Bearing		
1983-87-York	▲D5AZ-19656A	23.25
Tecumseh	▲C3GY-19656A	26.25
Compressor Clutch Assembly		
1983	▲E0VY-2884A	149.00
1984-87	▲E3AZ-2884A	69.75
Condenser Assembly		
Lincoln, Mark VI		
1983-85	E0VZ-19712A	393.25
1986-87	▲E6AZ-19712A	355.75
Continental		
1983-85	▲E25Y-19712A	180.75
1986-87	E65Y-19712A	180.75
Mark VII		
1984	▲E2ZZ-19712A	180.75
1985-87	▲E5LY-19712A	241.50
Evaporator Core		
Lincoln, Mark VI		
1983-85	▲E0VY-19860A	164.75
1986-87	▲E6VY-19860A	180.25
Continental, Mark VII		
1983	▲E25Y-19860A	139.50
1984-87	▲E4LY-19860A	141.00
Blower Motor		
Lincoln, Mark VI		
1983-87	▲E0VY-19805A	77.75
Continental, Mark VII		
1983-87	▲E35Y-19805A	90.50
Air Conditioning Hose		
Order by model and description.		
Blower Motor Switch		
1983	▲D5AZ-19986A	12.75
1984-87-w/ A.T.C.	▲E4VY-19986A	5.25

LABOR 29 LOCKS, HINGES & WIND. REGULATORS 29 LABOR

(Factory Time)	Chilton Time
(G) Hood Latch, Renew	
1983-87 (.3)	.5
(G) Hood Hinge, Renew	
Includes: Adjust hood and latch.	
1983-87 (.4)	.7
(G) Hood Release Cable, Renew	
1983-84	
Mark VII (1.0)	1.6
All other models (.4)	.7
1985-87	
Lincoln (.4)	.7
All other models (1.0)	1.6
(G) Door Latch, Renew	
Includes: R&R trim panel and weathersheet.	
1983-87 (.7)	1.0
(G) Door Lock Remote Control, Renew	
Includes: R&R trim panel and weathersheet.	
1983-87	
Mark VII (.7)	1.1
All other models (.5)	.9
(G) Door Handle (Outside), Renew (Front or Rear)	
Includes: R&R trim panel and weathersheet.	
1983-87	
Mark VII (.7)	1.1
All other models (.5)	.9
(G) Lock Striker Plate, Renew	
1983-87 (.2)	.3
(G) Door Window Regulator (Electric), Renew	
Includes: R&R trim panel and weathersheet.	
Lincoln	
1983-87 (1.0)	1.5
Mark VI, VII	
1983-87 (1.0)	1.5
Continental	
1983-87 (.8)	1.2
(G) Trunk Lock Cylinder and Key, Renew	
1983-87 (.3)	.5
(G) Trunk Hinge Assembly, Renew (One)	
1983-87 (.5)	.8

PARTS 29 LOCKS, HINGES & WIND. REGULATORS 29 PARTS

	Part No.	Price
Hood Lock		
1983-85	▲E4DZ-16700A	14.75
1986-87	▲E6DZ-16700A	14.75
Rear Door Lock		
exc. Continental		
1983-87-right	▲E3AZ-5426412A	41.50
left	▲E3AZ-5426413A	41.50
Continental		
1983-84-right	E35Y-5426412A	30.25
left	E35Y-542626413A	28.25
1985-87-right	E55Y-5426412A	30.25
left	E55Y-5426413A	30.25
Door Lock Remote Control		
Lincoln, Mark VI		
1983-87-right	▲E3SZ-6321818A	12.00
left	▲E3SZ-6321819A	12.00
Continental		
1983-right	E35Y-5421818A	21.50
left	E35Y-5421819A	21.50
1984-87-right	E45Y-5421818A	21.50
left	E45Y-5421819A	20.75
Mark VII		
1984-87-right	E4LY-6321818A	9.75
left	E4LY-6321819A	9.75
Door Lock Cylinder & Keys		
Lincoln		
(Non-illuminated)		
1983	E1VY-5421984C	10.75
1984-exc. below	E1VY-5421984A	32.00
w/anti-theft	E3VY-5421984A	82.00
1985-87-exc. below	E5VY-5422050A	30.00
w/anti-theft	E5VY-5422050C	72.25
(Illuminated entry)		
1984-exc. below	E1VY-5421984B	32.00
w/anti-theft	E3VY-5421984B	82.00

PARTS 29 LOCKS, HINGES & WIND. REGULATORS 29 PARTS

	Part No.	Price
1985-87-exc.		
below	E5VY-5422050B	39.50
w/anti-theft	E5VY-5422050D	72.25
Mark VI, VII		
(Non-illuminated)		
1983	E1VY-5421984C	10.75
1984	E4LY-6321984G	10.75
1985-87-exc.		
below	E5LY-6322050A	30.00
w/anti-theft	E5LY-6322050C	72.50
(Illuminated entry)		
1984-exc. below	E1VY-5421984D	15.50
w/anti-theft	E4LY-6321984F	82.00
1985-87-exc.		
below	E5LY-6322050B	39.50
w/anti-theft	E5LY-6322050D	72.50
Continental		
(wo/Anti-theft)		
1983-84	E1VY-5421984D	15.50
1985-87	E55Y-5422050A	39.50
(Anti-theft)		
1983-84	E35Y-5421984A	82.00
1985-87	E55Y-5422050B	72.25
Door Outside Handle Assy.		
exc. Mark VII		
1983-87-right	E25Y-5422404A	31.75
left	E25Y-5422405A	31.75
Mark VII		
1984-87-right	E4LY-6322404A	31.75
left	E4LY-6322405A	31.75
Lock Striker Plate		
Lincoln, Mark VI		
1983-87	D2AZ-6522008A	6.00
Continental, Mark VII		
1983-85	▲E1FZ-6122008B	4.25
1986-87	▲E69Z-1122008A	3.75

	Part No.	Price
Hood Hinge		
Lincoln, Mark VI		
1983-85-right	E0VY-16796B	13.25
left	E0VY-16797A	13.50
1986-87-right	E6VY-16796A	13.25
left	E6VY-16797A	13.25
Continental		
1983-87	E25Y-16796A	13.25
Mark VII		
1984-87-right	▲E4LY-16796A	19.50
left	▲E4LY-16797A	19.50
Front Door Lock		
Lincoln, Mark VI		
1983-87-right	▲E3AZ-5421812A	31.75
left	▲E3AZ-5421813A	31.75
Continental		
1983-84-right	E25Y-5421812A	30.50
left	E25Y-5421813A	30.50
1985-87-right	E55Y-5421812A	30.50
left	E55Y-5421813A	30.50
Mark VII		
1984-right	▲E3GZ-6721812A	36.00
left	▲E3GZ-6721813A	36.00
1985-87-right	▲E59Z-1121812A	21.50
left	▲E59Z-1121813A	21.50
Electric Window Regulator (Front)		
Lincoln, Mark VI		
1983-87-right	E1VY-5423208A	135.50
left	E1VY-5423209A	135.50
Mark VII		
1984-87-right	▲E3SZ-6323208A	53.25
left	▲E3SZ-6323209A	53.25
Continental		
1983-right	E25Y-5423208A	70.25
left	E25Y-5423209A	70.25
1984-87-right	E45Y-5423208A	97.25
left	E45Y-5423209A	97.25
Electric Window Regulator (Rear)		
1983-87-right	▲D9AZ-5427008A	94.50

	Part No.	Price
left	▲D9AZ-5427009A	94.50
Trunk Lock		
(wo/Power latch)		
1983-87	▲D9ZZ-6643200A	22.00
(Power latch)		
1983-87-exc.		
below	E0VY-5443200D	62.00
w/Trunk ajar		
sw.	E0VY-5443200C	49.75
(Power pull down)		
1984-87	E4LY-6343200A	65.50
Trunk Lock Cylinder & Keys		
1983-84-exc.		
below	E0VY-5443505A	10.75
w/anti-theft	E3VY-5443505A	18.50
1985-87 (Lincoln)		
wo/anti-theft	E5VY-5443507B	16.50
w/anti-theft	E5VY-5443507A	24.25
1985-87 (Continental)		
wo/anti-theft	E55Y-5443507A	16.50
w/anti-theft	E55Y-5443507B	24.25
1985-87 (Mark VII)		
wo/anti-theft	E5LY-6343507A	22.25
w/anti-theft	E5LY-6343507B	30.00
Trunk Hinge		
Lincoln, Mark VI		
1983-right	E2VY-5442700A	18.75
left	E2VY-5442701A	27.75
1984-87-right	E4VY-5442700A	27.75
left	E4VY-5442701A	27.75
Mark VII		
1984-87-right	E4LY-5442700A	26.00
left	E4LY-5442701A	N.L.
Continental		
1983-right	E25Y-5442700B	27.75
left	E25Y-5442701B	27.75
1984-87-right	E45Y-5442700A	27.75
left	E45Y-5442701A	27.75

LABOR 30 HEAD AND PARKING LAMPS 30 LABOR

(Factory Time)	Chilton Time
(M) Headlamp Sealed Beam Bulb, Renew	
All models-each (.3)	.3
(M) Stop Lamp Lens, Renew	
1983-87 (.2)	.3
(G) Aim Headlamps	
two	.4
four	.6
(M) License Lamp Assembly, Renew	
1983-87 (.3)	.4
(M) Side Marker Lamp Assy., Renew	
1983-87 (.4)	.5

PARTS 30 HEAD AND PARKING LAMPS 30 PARTS

	Part No.	Price
Sealed Beam Bulb		
Lincoln & Continental		
1983-87-Low		
beam	▲D94Y-13007A	12.75
High beam	▲D94Y-13007C	12.75
Mark VI		
1983-Low beam	E0LY-13007A	11.50
High beam	E0LY-13007B	11.50
Mark VII		
1984-right	E4LY-13007A	26.00
left	E4LY-13007B	26.00
1985-87-right	E5LY-13007A	25.50
left	E5LY-13007B	25.50
Parking Lamp Assy.		
Lincoln		
1983-84	E0VY-13200A	65.00
1985-87-right	E5VY-13200A	45.50
left	E5VY-13201A	45.50
Mark VI & VII		
1983 (clear lens)		
chrome	E0VY-13200A	65.00

	Part No.	Price
1984-87	E4LY-13200B	26.75
Continental		
1983-right	E35Y-13200-A	77.75
left	E35Y-13201A	77.75
1984-87-right	E45Y-13200A	41.75
left	E45Y-13201A	41.75
Tail Lamp Lens		
Lincoln		
1983-84-right	E0VY-13450A	17.00
left	E0VY-13451A	17.00
1985-87-right	E5VY-13450A	20.00
left	E5VY-13451A	20.00
Mark VI & VII		
1983-right	E0LY-13450A	14.00
left	E0LY-13451A	14.00
1984-87-right	E4LY-13450A	17.50
left	E4LY-13451A	17.50
Continental		
1983-right	E25Y-13450A	27.00
left	E25Y-13451A	27.00

	Part No.	Price
1984-87-right	E45Y-13450A	34.25
left	E45Y-13451A	34.25
Tail Lamp Assy.		
Lincoln		
1983-84-right	E0VY-13404A	101.25
left	E0VY13405A	101.25
1985-87-right	E5VY-13404A	73.50
left	E5VY-13405A	73.50
Mark VI & VII		
1983-right	E0LY-13404A	72.50
left	E0LY-13405A	72.50
1984-87-right	E4LY-13404A	79.25
left	E4LY-13405A	79.25
Continental		
1983-right	E25Y-13404B	97.50
left	E25Y-13405B	97.50
1984-87-right	E45Y-13404A	96.00
left	E45Y-13405A	96.00

PARTS 30 HEAD AND PARKING LAMPS 30 PARTS

	Part No.	Price
Rear License Lamp Assy.		
exc. Mark VII		
1983-87	▲D7AZ-13550A	6.00
Mark VII		
1984-87	▲D9MY-13550A	11.00
Hi-Mount, Lamp Assy. (Rear)		
Lincoln		
1985-87-exc. vinyl top	E6VY-13A613C	41.75
Vinyl top	E6VY-13A613B	41.75
Continental		
1985-87	E65Y-13A613A	41.75
Mark VII		
1985-87	E6LY-13A613A	41.75

LABOR 31 WINDSHIELD WIPER & SPEEDOMETER 31 LABOR

	(Factory Time)	Chilton Time
(G) Windshield Wiper Motor, Renew		
1983-87	(.5)	.8
(G) Wiper Pivot, Renew (One)		
Lincoln & Mark Series		
1983-87	(.5)	.9
Continental		
1983-87	(.3)	.5
(G) Windshield Wiper Governor Assy., Renew		
1983-87-exc below	(.3)	.6
1983-87-Continental	(.6)	1.0
1984-87-Mark VII	(.5)	.9
(G) Wiper Switch, Renew		
Includes: R&R instrument panel pad when required.		
1983-87	(.5)	.9
(G) Windshield Washer Pump, Renew		
1983-87-exc below	(.3)	.5
Mark VII under fender	(1.0)	1.5
Continental under fender	(.7)	1.0
(G) Speedometer Head, R&R or Renew		
Includes: R&R instrument panel pad when required.		
Lincoln		
Standard Cluster		
1983-87	(.8)	1.5
Electronic Cluster		
1983	(.9)	1.7
1984-87	(.7)	1.2
Mark VI, VII		
1983	(.9)	1.7
1984-87	(.7)	1.2
Continental		
1983-87	(.9)	1.7
Reset odometer add	(.2)	.2
(G) Speedometer Cable and Casing, Renew		
Includes: R&R instrument panel pad when required.		
Lincoln & Mark Series		
1983-84-one piece	(.4)	.7
upper	(.3)	.6
lower	(.4)	.7
1985-87-Lincoln		
one piece	(1.0)	1.9
upper	(.3)	.6
lower	(.4)	.7
Continental		
1983-84 one piece	(.9)	1.8
(G) Speedometer Cable (Inner), Renew or Lubricate		
1983-84-exc below	(.4)	.7
1983-84-Continental	(1.0)	1.7
1985-87-Lincoln		
one piece	(1.0)	1.9
upper	(.3)	.6
lower	(.4)	.7
(G) Speedometer Driven Gear, Renew		
1983-87	(.3)	.5
(G) Electronic Instrument Display Assy., Renew		
Lincoln-Mark VI		
1983-87	(.8)	1.5
Continental		
1983-87	(.6)	1.1
Mark VII		
1984-87	(.4)	.7
(G) Radio, R&R		
Includes: R&R instrument panel pad when required.		
Lincoln		
1983-87	(.4)	.8
Mark VI, VII		
1983-87	(.4)	.8
Continental		
1983-87	(.3)	.6

PARTS 31 WINDSHIELD WIPER & SPEEDOMETER 31 PARTS

	Part No.	Price
Windshield Wiper Motor		
Lincoln, Mark VI		
1983-85	▲D9AZ-17508A	97.75
1986-87	E6VY-17508A	97.75
Mark VII		
1984-87	▲E3SZ-17508A	141.75
Continental		
1983-87-exc. below	E25Y-17508A	141.75
1984-diesel	E45Y-17508A	141.75
Windshield Wiper Pivot Shaft Housing		
Lincoln, Mark VI		
1983-85	E0VY-17566A	32.25
1986-87	E6VY-17566A	27.50
Mark VII		
1984-85	▲E3SZ-17566A	25.50
1986-87	▲E6SZ-17566A	N.L.
Continental		
1983-87	E25Y-17566A	32.25
Windshield Wiper Governor		
Lincoln, Mark VI		
1983-87	▲E0VY-17C476A	77.50
Continental		
1983-87	E25Y-17C476A	77.75
Mark VII		
1984-87	E4LY-17C476A	77.50
Windshield Wiper Control Assy.		
Lincoln, Mark VI		
1983-87-exc. below	E1AZ-17A553B	30.00
intermittent wprs.	▲E1AZ-17A553C	32.75
Continental, Mark VII		
1983	E25Y-17A553A	33.50
1984-87	E4LY-17A553A	33.50
Windshield Washer Pump		
1983-87	▲E0AZ-17664A	20.00
Speedometer Cable & Casing		
Order by year and model.		

LABOR 32 LIGHT SWITCHES & WIRING 32 LABOR

	(Factory Time)	Chilton Time
(G) Headlamp Switch, Renew		
1983-87	(.4)	.6
1983-84-Continental	(.7)	1.1
(G) Headlamp Dimmer Switch, Renew		
1983-87	(.5)	.9
(G) Stop Light Switch, Renew		
1983-87	(.3)	.4
(G) Parking Brake Indicator Switch, Renew		
1983-87	(.3)	.4
(G) Turn Signal Switch Assy., Renew		
1983-87	(.4)	1.0
(M) Turn Signal or Hazard Warning Flasher, Renew		
1983-87	(.2)	.3
(G) Horns, Renew		
1983-87-exc below	(.3)	.5
Cont. & Mark VII	(.9)	1.2
(G) Wiring Harness, Renew		
Alternator to Reg.		
1983-87	(.3)	.6

PARTS 32 LIGHT SWITCHES & WIRING 32 PARTS

	Part No.	Price
Turn Signal and Hazard Switch		
1983-84-exc. Continental		
wo/dimmer	▲E0AZ-13341A	41.25
w/dimmer	E0LY-13341A	41.25
Continental	▲E2FZ-13341A	41.25
1985-87	▲E5LY-13341A	41.25
Turn Signal Flasher		
1983-87	▲C6AZ-13350B	3.75
Hazard Flasher		
1983-85	▲D1FZ-13350A	4.25
1986-87	▲E6AZ-13350A	10.75
Headlamp Switch		
Lincoln		
(wo/auto. headlamp dimmer)		
1983-87-exc.		
below	E0VY-11654A	38.00
w/elec. cluster	E0VY-11654E	47.25
(w/auto. headlamp dimmer)		
1983-84	E0VY-11654F	61.75
1985-87	E5VY-11654A	61.75
Mark VI, VII		
1983-exc. below	E0LY-11654C	38.00
w/auto. dimmer	E0LY-11654D	61.75
1984-87-exc.		
below	E4LY-11654A	26.75
comtech	E5LY-11654A	34.50
Continental		
1983	E25Y-11654A	130.00
1984-87	E4LY-11654A	26.75
Stop Light Switch		
Lincoln, Mark VI		
1983-87	▲E6AZ-13480A	6.50
Continental, Mark VII		
1983-85	E3TZ-13480B	6.50
1986-87	E6LY-13480A	6.75
Horns		
1983-87-high	▲E3AZ-13832A	17.00
low	▲E3AZ-13833A	17.00
Brake Warning Light Switch		
1983-87	▲D9BZ-2B264A	7.50

LABOR 33 GLASS 33 LABOR

(Factory Time)	Chilton Time
(G) Windshield Glass, Renew	
Lincoln & Mark Series	
1983-87 (2.1)	3.5
Continental	
1983-87 (2.1)	3.5
Renew butyl tape add (.2)	.2
(G) Front Door Glass, Renew	
Includes: R&R trim panel and weathersheet.	
Lincoln	
1983-87-wo/Vent (.8)	1.2
w/Vent (.7)	1.2
Mark VI, VII	
1983-door glass (.7)	1.3
vent glass (.7)	1.0
1984-87 (1.0)	1.5
Continental	
1983-87 (.5)	1.0
(G) Rear Door Glass, Renew	
Includes: R&R trim panel and weathersheet.	
1983-87 (.8)	1.3
(G) Rear Door Stationary Glass, Renew	
1983-87 (.7)	1.2
(G) Rear Quarter Window Glass, Renew	
1983-87 (.8)	1.3
(G) Back Window Glass, Renew	
Lincoln & Mark Series	
1983-87-exc below (1.1)	1.8
Mark VII (2.1)	3.0
Heated glass add (.5)	.7
Continental	
1983-84 (.8)	1.5
1985-87 (2.5)	3.5
Renew butyl tape add (.2)	.2

LABOR 34 CRUISE CONTROL 34 LABOR

(Factory Time)	Chilton Time
(G) Cruise Control System, Diagnosis	
1985-87 (.4)	.6
(G) Cruise Control Chain/Cable, Renew	
1985-87	
Lincoln (.3)	.5
Mark VII & Cont. (.6)	.8
(G) Speed Control Amplifier Assy., Renew	
1983-87 (.3)	.5
Road test add (.3)	.3
(G) Speed Control Sensor Assy., Renew	
1983-87 (.3)	.5
Road test add (.3)	.3
(G) Speed Control Servo Assy., Renew	
1983-87 (.3)	.6
under fender	
w/Conn (.6)	.9
wo/Conn (1.0)	1.4
Road test add (.3)	.3
(G) Speed Control Relay, Renew	
1983-87 (.3)	.5
Road test add (.3)	.3
(G) Speed Control Actuator Switch, Renew	
1983-87 (.3)	.6
Road test add (.3)	.3

PARTS 34 CRUISE CONTROL 34 PARTS

	Part No.	Price
Speed Control Amplifier Assy.		
1983-87-exc.		
below	▲E0AZ-9D843A	161.50
1986-87-		
Continental, Mark		
VII	▲E6AZ-9D843A	161.50
Speed Control Servo Assy.		
1983	▲E2FZ-9C735A	120.25
1984-85-exc.		
below	E45Y-9C735A	120.25
Lincoln	▲E2FZ-9C735A	120.25
1986-87-Lincoln	▲E6AZ-9C735A	120.25
Continental	E45Y-9C735A	120.25
Mark	▲E4LY-9C735A	120.25
Speed Control Sensor Assy.		
1983-87-exc.		
below	▲E3AZ-9E731A	20.75
1984-87-		
Continental &		
Mark	▲E45Y-9E731A	20.75
Speed Control On & Off Switch		
Lincoln, Mark VI		
1983-84	▲E3SZ-9C888A	45.75
1985-87	▲E5AZ-9C888A	45.75
Continental, Mark VII		
1983	▲E3SZ-9C888A	45.75
1984-87	▲E4SZ-9C888A	45.75

GROUP INDEX

ALPHABETICAL INDEX

Ford Motor Company

Rear Wheel Drive Cars

FORD LTD • MERCURY MARQUIS

YEAR IDENTIFICATION

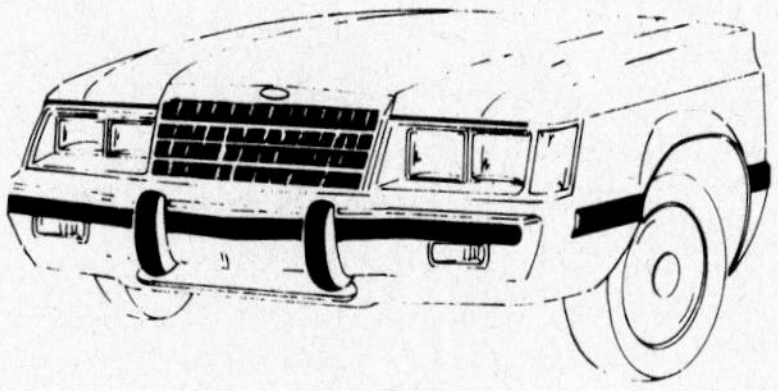

1983 LTD

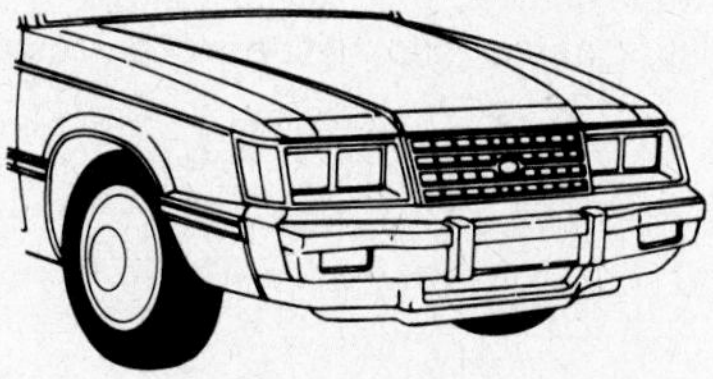

1984–86 LTD

1983–86 Marquis

VEHICLE IDENTIFICATION NUMBER (VIN)

It is important for servicing and ordering parts to be certain of the vehicle and engine identification. The VIN (vehicle identification number) is a 13 or 17 digit number visible through the windshield on the driver's side of the dash and contains the vehicle and engine identification codes. It can be interpreted as follows:

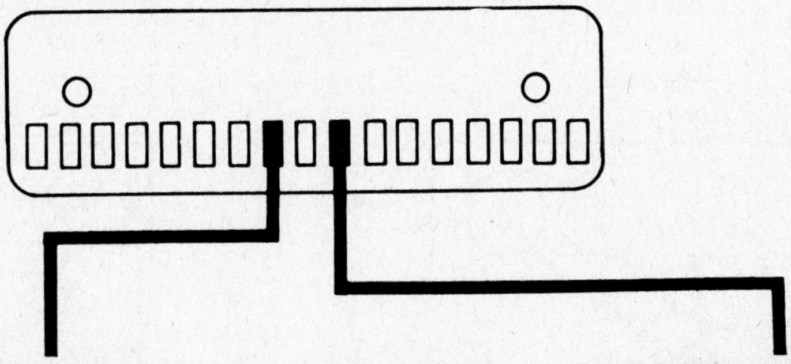

Engine Code

Code	Cu. In.	Liters	Cyl.	Carb.	Eng. Mfg.
A	140	2.3	4	1	Ford
W	140-T	2.3	4	Turbo.	Ford
T	140-T SVO	2.3	4	Turbo.	Ford
R	140-HSC	2.3	4	①	Ford
T,B,X	200	3.3	6	1	Ford
3	232	3.8	V6	①	Ford
C	232	3.8	V6	①	Ford
F	302	5.0	V8	1	Ford
M	302-H.O.	5.0	V8	①	Ford
G	351-W	5.8	V8	①	Ford
G	351-H.O.	5.8	V8	①	Ford

Model Year Code

Code	Year
D	1983
E	1984
F	1985
G	1986
H	1987

The seventeen digit Vehicle Identification Number can be used to determine engine application and model year. The tenth digit indicates the model year, and the eighth digit identifies the engine code.

① EFI, VV, 2 bbl. or 4 bbl. depending on model

TUNE-UP SPECIFICATIONS

(When analyzing compression test results, look for uniformity among cylinders rather than specific pressures.)

Year	Engine No. Cyl. Displacement (cu. in.)	Engine Eng. V.I.N. Code	hp	Eng. MFG	Spark Plugs Orig. Type	Spark Plugs Gap • (in.)	Distributor Point Dwell (deg)	Distributor Point Gap (in.)	Ignition Timing (deg) Man. Trans. •	Ignition Timing (deg) Auto. Trans.	Valves Intake Opens ■ (deg)	Fuel Pump Pressure (psi)	Idle Speed (rpm) Man. Trans.*	Idle Speed (rpm) Auto. • Trans.
'83-'86	A	4-140		Ford	AWSF-44	.044	Electronic		①	①	22	5½-6½	850	800
	—	4-140P		Ford	AWSF-34	.034	Electronic		①	①	—	—	—	750
	W	4-140T		Ford	AWSF32C	.034	Electronic		①	①	—	—	①④	①④
	B	6-200		Ford	BSF-92	.050	Electronic		①	①	20	6-8	—	550
	3	6-232		Ford	AWSF-52 ⑪	.044	Electronic		①	①	13	6-8 ⑨	—	700(650) ①
	F	8-302		Ford	ASF-42 ①⑫	.044	Electronic		①	①④	16	6-8 ⑧⑩	700 ①	550 ①

NOTE: The underhood specifications sticker often reflects tune-up specification changes. Sticker data must be used if they disagree with those shown in this chart.

NOTE: Part numbers listed in this chart are not recommendations by Chilton for any product by part number or brand name.

■ All figures are in degrees Before Top Dead Center

T Turbocharged

P Propane

① Calibrations vary depending upon model: refer to the underhood specifications sticker

④ EEC equipped depending on model—Ignition timing, idle speed and mixture are non-adjustable.

⑧ EFI models; 39 psi

⑨ In tank pump 40-45

⑩ 6 low pressure pump 39 EFI pressure

⑪ CFI model: AWSF-54

⑫ '85—ASF52, HO—ASF42

FIRING ORDERS

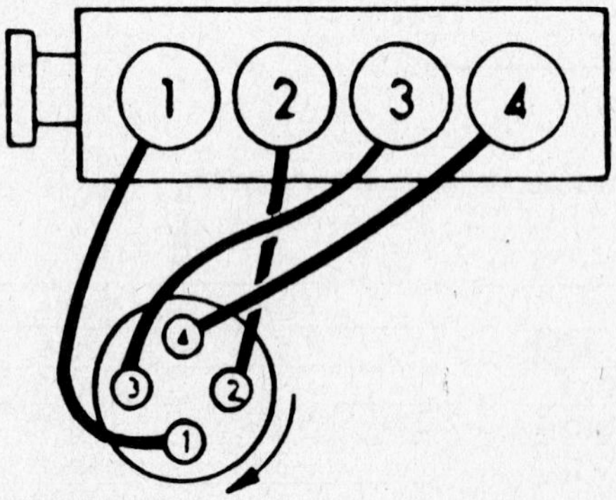

FORD MOTOR CO. 2300 cc 4-cyl.
Engine firing order: 1–3–4–2
Distributor rotation: clockwise

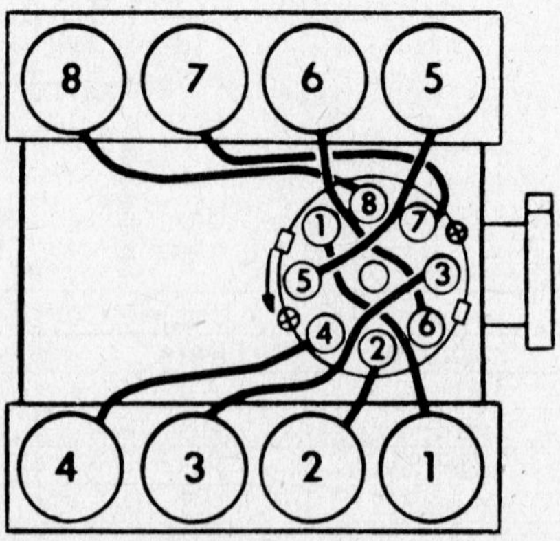

FORD MOTOR CO. 255, 302 (exc. HO) 460
V8 Engine firing order: 1–5–4–2–6–3–7–8
Distributor rotation: counterclockwise

FIRING ORDERS

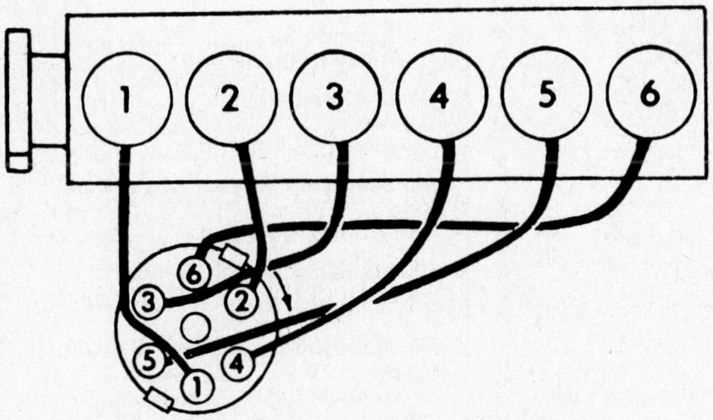

FORD MOTOR CO. 200, 250 6-cyl.
Engine firing order: 1–5–3–6–2–4
Distributor rotation: clockwise

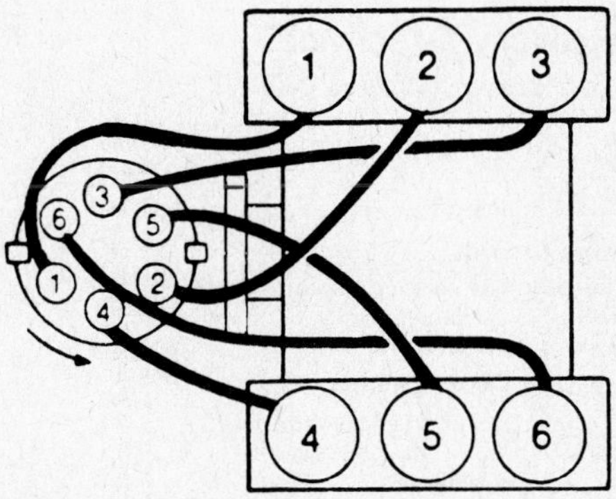

FORD MOTOR CO. 232 V6
Engine firing order 1–4–2–5–3–6
Distributor rotation: counterclockwise

WHEEL ALIGNMENT SPECIFICATIONS

Year	Model	Caster Range (deg)	Caster Pref. Setting (deg)	Camber Range (deg)	Camber Pref. Setting (deg)	Toe-in (in.)	Steering Axis Inclin. (deg)	Wheel Pivot Ratio (deg) Inner Wheel	Wheel Pivot Ratio (deg) Outer Wheel
'83-'84	LTD, Marquis (Sedan)	1⅛P to 2⅛P	1⅛P	5/16N to 1 3/16P	7/16P	1/16 to 5/16	—	20	19.84
'83-'84	LTD, Marquis (Station Wagon)	⅛N to 1⅞P	⅞P	¼N to 1¼P	½P	1/16 to 5/16	—	20	19.84
'85-'86	LTD/Marquis Sedan	⅞P to 2⅛P	③④	¾N to 1⅛P	④	1/16 to 5/16	—	20	19.84
'85-'86	LTD/Marquis Station Wagon	¾P to 2P	③④	5/16N to 1 3/16P	④	1/16 to 5/16	—	20	19.84

N Negative P Positive

① Caster is set at the factory and cannot be adjusted

② Maximum side to side difference between wheels (left minus right) to be within ⅞N to ⅞P with the caster and camber set to specifications

LABOR SERVICE BAY OPERATIONS LABOR

(Factory Time) Chilton Time

COOLING

(M) Winterize Cooling System

Includes: RUn engine to check for leaks, tighten all hose connections. Test radiator and pressure cap. Drain radiator and engine block. Add anti-freeze and refill system.

All models 5

(M) Thermostat, Renew

1983-86-Four (.5) 7
Six (.4) 6
V-6 (.5) 7
V-8 (.6) 8

(M) Radiator Hoses, Renew

1983-86-upper (.3) 4
lower (.5) 6
both (.6) 8

(Factory Time) Chilton Time

(M) Drive Belts, Adjust

All models-one (.2) 3
each adtnl (.1) 1

(M) Drive Belts, Renew

All models-one (.3) 4
each adtnl (.1) 1

(M) Serpentine Belt, Renew

All models (.3) 5

FUEL

(M) Carburetor Air Cleaner, Service

All models (.2) 3

(G) Carburetor, Adjust (On Car)

All models (.4) 5
Propane enrichment method (1.0) 1.5

(Factory Time) Chilton Time

(G) Carburetor Float Level, Adjust

Holly 1946 (.5) 7
Weber 740 (.5) 7
Motorcraft 2150 (.4) 6
Weber 5200-6500 (.5) 7

BRAKES

(G) Brakes, Adjust (Minor)

Includes: Adjust brakes, fill master cylinder.

two wheels 4

(G) Bleed Brakes (Four Wheels)

Includes: Fill master cylinder.

All models (.3) 5

(G) Brake Pedal Free Play, Adjust

All models 4

LABOR SERVICE BAY OPERATIONS LABOR

(Factory Time) Chilton Time

LUBRICATION SERVICE

(M) Lubricate Chassis, Change Oil & Filter

Includes: Inspect and correct all fluid levels.

All models.. .6
Install grease fittings add.......................... .1

(M) Lubricate Chassis

Includes: Inspect and correct all fluid levels.

All models.. .4
Install grease fittings add.......................... .1

(M) Engine Oil & Filter, Change

Includes: Inspect and correct all fluid levels.

All models.. .4

WHEELS

(M) Wheel, Renew

one (.5).. .5

(G) Wheels, Balance

one.. .3
each adtnl.. .2

(G) Front Wheel Bearings, Clean and Repack (Both Wheels)

All models.. 1.3

(G) Front Wheel Grease Seals, Renew

1983-86-one whl (.6).......................... .7
both whls (.9).......................... 1.1

(G) Front Wheel Bearings and Cups, Renew

1983-86-one whl (.7).......................... .9
both whls (1.2).......................... 1.5

CHILTON'S 10 POINT SAFETY CHECK

CHECK OPERATION & CONDITION OF THE FOLLOWING ITEMS:

1. Legal Registration (serial no.)
2. Tires & Wheels
3. Brake System (R&R all wheels)
4. Light Systems & Signals
5. Accelerator Linkage, Neutral Safety Switch, Shift Indicator Pointer & Seat Position Locks
6. Glass, Mirrors, Door Locks, Seat Belts & Harness
7. Wipers, Washers & Defrosters
8. Frame, Steering, Shocks, Front & Rear Suspension
9. Fuel & Exhaust Systems
10. Road Test Vehicle

All models.......................... 1.0
Exhaust Smog Analysis, add.......... .4

(Factory Time) Chilton Time

ELECTRICAL

(M) Battery Cables, Renew

Batt. to Relay (.3).......................... .3
Ground (.3).......................... .3
Relay to Starter (.4).......................... .5

(G) Aim Headlamps

two.. .4
four.. .6

(M) Headlamp Sealed Beam Bulb, Renew

All models-each (.3).......................... .3

(G) Headlamp Switch, Renew

All models (.3).......................... .5

(G) Headlamp Dimmer Switch, Renew

All models (.4).......................... .7

(G) Stop Light Switch, Renew

All models (.3).......................... .4

(G) Turn Signal Switch, Renew

All models (.4).......................... 1.0

(G) Neutral Safety Switch, Renew

All models (.3).......................... .4
w/AOD add.......................... .1

(G) Back-Up Lamp Switch, Renew

All models (.3).......................... .5

(M) Turn Signal or Hazard Warning Flasher, Renew

1983-86
turn signal (.3).......................... .4
hazard (.5).......................... .7

(G) Horns, Renew

All models-each (.3).......................... .4

LABOR 1 TUNE UP 1 LABOR

(Factory Time) Chilton Time

(G) Compression Test

Four-1983-86 (.3).......................... .6
Six-1983 (.3).......................... .6
V-6-1983-86 (.4).......................... .9
V-8-1983-86.......................... 1.0
w/A.C. add.......................... .2

(G) Engine Tune Up, (Electronic Ignition)

Includes: Test battery and clean connections. Tighten manifold and carburetor mounting bolts. Check engine compression, clean and adjust or renew spark plugs. Test resistance of spark plug cables. Inspect distributor cap and rotor. Adjust air gap. Check vacuum advance operation. Reset ignition timing. Adjust idle mixture and idle speed. Service air cleaner. Inspect and adjust drive belts. Inspect choke operation and adjust or free up. Check operation of EGR valve.

Four-1983-86.......................... 1.5
Six-1983.......................... 1.5
V-6-1983-86.......................... 2.0
V-8-1983-86.......................... 2.4
w/A.C. add.......................... .2
Perform EEC IV system test add.......... 1.0

LABOR 2 IGNITION SYSTEM 2 LABOR

(Factory Time) Chilton Time

(G) Spark Plugs, Clean and Reset or Renew

1983-86-Four (.3).......................... .5
Six (.4).......................... .6
V-6 (.6).......................... .8
V-8 (.7).......................... 1.0
w/A.C. add.......................... .2

(G) Ignition Timing, Reset

1983-86 (.3).......................... .4

(G) Distributor, Renew

Includes: Reset ignition timing.

1983-86 (.4).......................... .7

(G) Ignition Module Assembly, Renew

Note: Fender mount type. For TFI unit, refer to Emission Control section.

1983-86 (.3).......................... .6

Perform system test add (.3).......................... .3

(G) Distributor Armature, Renew

1983-84 (.3).......................... .6

(G) Distributor Stator, Renew

Includes: R&R armature.

1983-84
Four (.6).......................... 1.0
Six (.4).......................... .8
V-6 (.4).......................... .8
V-8 (.4).......................... .8

(G) Distributor Cap and/or Rotor, Renew

1983-86 (.3).......................... .5

(G) Vacuum Control Unit, Renew

Includes: R&R distributor and reset ignition timing.

1983-86 (.5).......................... .8

(G) Profile Ignition Pick-Up Sensor, Renew (Duraspark)

1983-86 (.5).......................... .9
Perform system test add (.3).......................... .3

(G) Ignition Coil, Renew

Includes: Test.

1983-86 (.3).......................... .6

(G) Ignition Cables, Renew

Includes: Test wiring.

1983-86 (.4).......................... .6

(G) Ignition Switch, Renew

1983-86 (.4).......................... .9

PARTS 2 ELECTRONIC IGNITION 2 PARTS

	Part No.	Price
Distributor Assy. (New)		
Four–140		
1983–exc. below	▲E3ZZ-12127D	136.75
Calif.	▲E0FZ-12127B	136.75
Canada	▲E3ZZ-12127E	136.75
1984 (stamped)		
E3ZE-BA	▲E3ZZ-12127B	155.50
E4ZE-FA	▲E4ZZ-12127F	N.L.
E4ZE-CA	▲E4ZZ-12127C	N.L.
1985-86	▲E59Z-12127C	136.75
Six–200		
1983–exc. below	▲E3AZ-12127E	136.75
Calif.	▲E3AZ-12127C	136.75
V-6–230		
1983 (stamped)		
E2SE-DA	▲E2SZ-12127D	136.75
E3AE-DA	▲E3AZ-12127D	136.75
E3SE-AA	▲E3SZ-12127A	N.L.
E3ZE-FA	▲E3ZZ-12127F	136.75
1984-85–exc. below	▲E4ZZ-12127A	155.50
Canada	▲E4AZ-12127A	155.50
1986	▲E6SZ-12127C	155.50
V-8–302		
1984	▲E4TZ-12127B	136.75
1985	▲E5TZ-12127B	136.75
(1) Distributor Cap		
Four–140		
1984-86–w/ E.E.C. IV	▲E5FZ-12106C	8.75
1983-85–wo/ E.E.C. IV	▲E5BZ-12106A	17.00
Six–200		
1983	▲E3DZ-12106A	18.75
V-6–230		
1983-85–wo/ E.E.C. IV	▲E5DZ-12106A	19.50
1984-86–w/ E.E.C. IV	▲E6AZ-12106A	12.50
V-8–302		
1984	▲E2ZZ-12106A	20.00
1985	▲E5ZZ-12106A	N.L.
(2) Rotor		
Four–140		
1983-86–wo/ E.E.C. IV	▲D7FZ-12200C	4.75

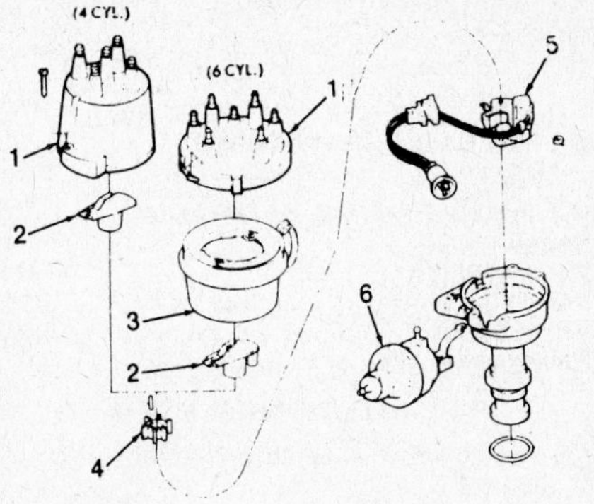

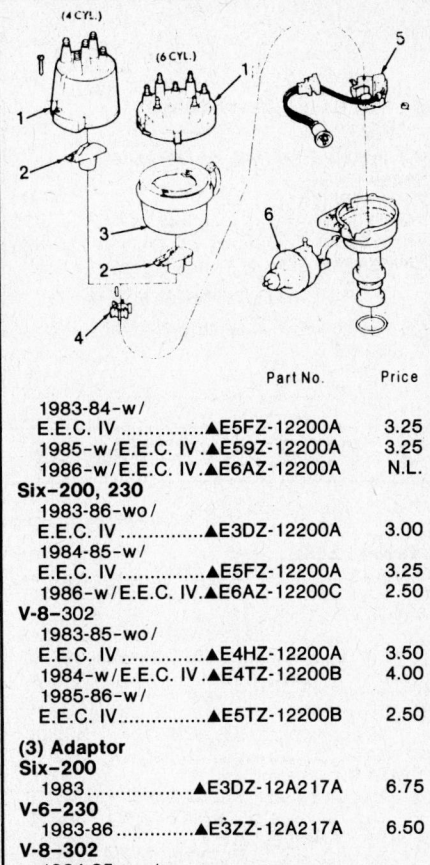

	Part No.	Price
1983-84–w/ E.E.C. IV	▲E5FZ-12200A	3.25
1985–w/E.E.C. IV	▲E59Z-12200A	3.25
1986–w/E.E.C. IV	▲E6AZ-12200A	N.L.
Six–200, 230		
1983-86–wo/ E.E.C. IV	▲E3DZ-12200A	3.00
1984-85–w/ E.E.C. IV	▲E5FZ-12200A	3.25
1986–w/E.E.C. IV	▲E6AZ-12200C	2.50
V-8–302		
1983-85–wo/ E.E.C. IV	▲E4HZ-12200A	3.50
1984–w/E.E.C. IV	▲E4TZ-12200B	4.00
1985-86–w/ E.E.C. IV	▲E5TZ-12200B	2.50
(3) Adaptor		
Six–200		
1983	▲E3DZ-12A217A	6.75
V-6–230		
1983-86	▲E3ZZ-12A217A	6.50
V-8–302		
1984-85–wo/ E.E.C. IV	▲E2ZZ-12A217B	7.50
1984-85–w/ E.E.C. IV	▲E3TZ-12A217A	14.50
(4) Armature (Dist.)		
1983-86–140 eng.	▲D7FZ-12A099A	3.75

	Part No.	Price
200 eng.	▲D5DZ-12A099A	5.00
230 eng.	▲D4DZ-12A099A	5.50
1984-85-302 eng.	▲D3AZ-12A099A	6.00
(5) Stator Assy. (Dist.)		
(wo/EEC IV)		
140, 200		
1983-86	▲D5TZ-12A112B	25.25
230, 302		
1983-86	▲D4PZ-12A112A	25.50
(w/EEC IV)		
1983-86	▲E3ZZ-12A112C	25.00
(6) Vacuum Diaphragm Assy.		
1983–140 (exc. Calif.)	▲E2BZ-12370F	31.25
Calif.	▲E0FZ-12370B	31.25
200	▲D5TZ-12370J	33.25
230–exc. C5, Canada	▲E1AZ-12370K	34.00
C5 & Canada	▲E1SZ-12370A	31.25
1984-86–Canada	▲E4TZ-12370A	31.25
Canada, w/C5	▲E1SZ-12370A	31.25
Ignition Coil		
1983-86		
wo/E.E.C. IV	▲D5AZ-12029A	31.25
w/E.E.C. IV	▲E3FZ-12029A	33.75
Ignition Switch		
1983-86	▲E4FZ-11572A	11.50
Ignition Wire Set		
Four–140		
(wo/EEC IV)		
1983-85	▲E3PZ-12259ABR	31.75
(w/EEC IV)		
1984	▲E3PZ-12259AH	41.25
1985	▲E5PZ-12259D	49.50
1986	▲E6PZ-12259H	49.50
Six–200		
1983	▲E3PZ-12259ER	34.75
V-6–230		
(wo/EEC IV)		
1983-86	▲E4PZ-12259FR	53.50
(w/EEC IV)		
1984-86	▲E4PZ-12259B	42.75
V-8–302		
1984-85	▲E5PZ-12259B	75.50

LABOR 3 FUEL SYSTEM 3 LABOR

(Factory Time)	Chilton Time
(G) Fuel Pump, Test	
Includes: Disconnect line at carburetor, attach pressure gauge.	
All models	
mechanical	.3
electric	.5
(M) Carburetor Air Cleaner, Service	
1983-86 (.2)	.3
(G) Carburetor, Adjust (On Car)	
1983-86 (.4)	.5
Propane enrichment method (1.0)	1.5
(M) Fuel Filter, Renew	
1983-86 (.4)	.5
(G) Carburetor, R&R or Renew	
Includes: All necessary adjustments.	
Four–1983-86 (.5)	.8
Six–1983(.4)	.7
V-6–1983-86 (.6)	.9
V-8–1984-86 (.6)	.9
Renew carb add (.4)	.4
(G) Carburetor, R&R and Clean or Recondition	
Includes: All necessary adjustments.	
Four–1983-86 (1.4)	2.4
Six–1983 (1.6)	2.5
V-6–1983-86 (1.6)	2.5
V-8–1984-86 (1.6)	2.5
Renew spacer add (.2)	.2
(G) Float Level, Adjust	
Includes: Set idle speed and mixture.	
All models	
Carter YFA 1V (.6)	.8
Holly 1946 1V (.5)	.7
Weber 740 2V (.5)	.7
Motorcraft 2150 2V (.4)	.6
Weber 5200-6500 2V (.5)	.7
2700-7200 VV (.5)	.7
(G) Float or Needle Valve and Seat, Renew	
Includes: Set idle speed and mixture.	
All models	
Carter YFA 1V (.5)	.8
Holly 1946 1V (.6)	.9
Weber 740 2V (.5)	.8
Motorcraft 2150 2V (.4)	.7
Weber 5200-6500 2V (.5)	.8
2700-7200 VV (.5)	.8
(G) Accelerator Pump Diaphragm, Piston or Rod, Renew	
All models	
Four (.4)	.6
Six (.6)	.8
V-6 (.6)	.8
V-8-2 bbl (.3)	.5
4 bbl (.5)	.7
(G) Fuel Enrichment Valve Assy., Renew	
1983-86	
2150 2V (.8)	1.3
(G) Thermostatic Choke Housing and/or Gasket, Renew	
1983-86	
Carter YFA 1V (.4)	.6
2150 2V (.8)	1.3
(G) Fuel Pump, Renew	
Mechanical	
Four (.4)	.8
Six (.3)	.5

LABOR — 3 FUEL SYSTEM 3 — LABOR

(Factory Time)	Chilton Time
V-6 (.5)	.9
Electric	
in tank (.9)	1.4
on frame (.6)	.8
Add pump test if performed.	

(G) Fuel Tank, Renew
Includes: Transfer tank gauge unit.

1983-86	
sdn (1.0)	1.4
station wag (.8)	1.2
w/Elec fuel pump add	.2

(G) Fuel Gauge (Tank), Renew
Includes: Drain and refill tank.

1983-86	
sdn (.9)	1.3
station wag (.5)	.8

(G) Fuel Gauge (Dash), Renew

1983-86 (.7)	1.2

(G) Intake Manifold or Gaskets, Renew

Four–1983-86 (1.1)	1.6
V-6–1983-86 (2.2)	3.3
V8–1984-86 (2.1)	3.0
Renew manif add (.4)	.5

FUEL INJECTION SYSTEM

(G) Fuel Injector Assembly, Renew

1984-86	
one (.8)	1.2
all (.9)	1.5

(G) Fuel Charging Wiring Assy., Renew

1984-86 (.3)	.6

(G) Fuel Charging Regulator Assy., Renew

1984-86 (.8)	1.3

(G) Fuel Charging Assy., R&R or Renew

1984-86 (.7)	1.2

(G) Fuel Charging Assy., R&R and Recondition

1984-86	
V-6 (1.5)	2.2
V-8 (1.8)	2.5

PARTS — 3 FUEL SYSTEM 3 — PARTS

	Part No.	Price
Carburetor Assy. (New)		
Four–140		
1983 (M.T.)		
wo/A.C.	▲E3ZZ-9510Y	298.00
A.C.	▲E3ZZ-9510V	221.50
(w/Hi Alt. Carb)		
wo/A.C	▲E3ZZ-9510AE	221.50
A.C.	▲E3ZZ-9510AD	221.50
1983-A.T. (Exc. Calif.)		
wo/A.C.	▲E3ZZ-9510AT	221.50
A.C.	▲E3ZZ-9510AS	221.50
1983-A.T. (Calif.)		
wo/A.C.	▲E3ZZ-9510AB	221.50
A.C.	▲E3ZZ-9510AC	221.50
1983-Canada		
wo/A.C.	▲E3ZZ-9510PB	N.L.
w/A.C.	▲E3ZZ-9510NB	N.L.
1984-exc.		
Canada	▲E4ZZ-9510H	228.75
Canada-wo/		
A.C.	▲E4ZZ-9510R	N.L.
A.C.	▲E4ZZ-9510P	N.L.
1985	▲E5ZZ-9510C	246.50
1986	▲E6ZZ-9510D	260.75
Six–200		
1983 (Exc. Calif.)		
wo/A.C.	▲E3SZ-9510D	234.00
w/A.C.	▲E3SZ-9510C	234.00
1983 (Calif.)		
wo/A.C.	▲E3SZ-9510B	277.00
w/A.C.	▲E3SZ-9510A	277.00
V-6–230		
1983 (W/Auto. Overdrive Trans.)		
(wo/A.C.-Exc. Calif.)		
stamped E3SE		
AUA	▲E3SZ-9510AV	N.L.
FA	▲E3SZ-9510F	391.25
(w/A.C.)		
ATA	▲E3SZ-9510ATA	N.L.
EA	▲E3SZ-9510E	392.75
(wo/A.C.-Calif.)		
stamped E3SE		
APA	▲E3SZ-9510AP	432.00
KA	▲E3SZ-9510K	392.75
(w/A.C.)		
ANA	▲E3SZ-9510AN	392.75
JA	▲E3SZ-9510J	392.75
(w/Hi Alt Carb.)		
wo/A.C	▲E3SZ-9510H	Disc.
w/A.C.	▲E3SZ-9510G	444.00
stamped E3SE-		
ARA	▲E3SZ-9510AR	432.00
(wo/A.C. Canada)		
stamped E3AE		
SA	▲E3AZ-9510S	N.L.
AGA	▲E3AZ-9510AG	N.L.
(w/A.C.)		
RA	▲E3AZ-9510R	N.L.
AFA	▲E3AZ-9510AF	N.L.
(w/C5-exc. Calif. & Canada)		
wo/A.C.	▲E3SZ-9510BD	392.75
w/A.C.	▲E3SZ-9510BE	392.75
(w/C5 trans. Canada)		
stamped E3AE		
UA	▲E3AZ-9510U	N.L.
AEA	▲E3AZ-9510AE	N.L.
TA	▲E3AZ-9510T	N.L.
ADA	▲E3AZ-9510AD	N.L.
1984 (w/C5 trans.)		
(exc. Calif.)		
wo/A.C.	▲E4CZ-9510B	406.50
A.C.	▲E4CZ-9510A	406.50
(Canada)		
wo/A.C.	▲E4SZ-9510D	N.L.
A.C.	▲E4SZ-9510C	N.L.
Carburetor Tune Up Kit		
Four–140		
1983-86	▲E5PZ-9A586E	36.25
Six–200		
1983	▲E1PZ-9A586F	31.00
Tune up kit for V-6 230 eng. must be order by identification no. on carb.		
Fuel Pump Assy. (New)		
Four–140		
1983-86	▲E0FZ-9350A	39.25
Six–200		
1983	▲D6DZ-9350B	34.75
V-6 230 & V-8 302		
(wo/C.F.I.)		
1983-84	▲E2AZ-9350B	26.25
(w/C.F.I.)		
1984-86	▲E4DZ-9350B	184.75
Fuel Gauge (Dash)		
(wo/elec. inst. cluster)		
1983-86	▲E3DZ-9305C	31.75
1984-85-302		
eng. w/tach	▲E4DZ-9305A	34.50
1984-85-302 w/Tach		
(w/elec. inst. cluster)		
1983	▲E0SZ-9305AR	125.50
1984	▲E3SZ-9305CR	124.75
Fuel Gauge (Tank)		
Order by year and model.		

PARTS — 3 ELECTRONIC FUEL INJECTION 3 — PARTS

	Part No.	Price
Charging Assy. (Fuel)		
V-6–230		
1984 (stamping no.)		
E4AE-CC	▲E4AZ-9C973A	643.75
E4AE-CE	▲E4AZ-9C973E	643.75
E4AE-DC	▲E4AZ-9C973B	598.50
E4AE-DE	▲E4AZ-9C973D	643.75
1985 (stamping no.)		
E5SE-HA	▲E5SZ-9C973H	598.25
E5SE-JA	▲E5SZ-9C973J	337.00
E5SE-GA	▲E5SZ-9C973G	570.25
E5SE-KA	▲E5SZ-9C973K	570.25
1986 (stamping)		
E6SE-AA	▲E6SZ-9C973A	337.00
E6SZ-BA	▲E6SZ-9C973B	402.25
V-8–302		
1984	▲E4ZZ-9C973B	643.75
1985 (stamping no.)		
E5ZE-BA	▲E5ZZ-9C973B	598.25
E5ZE-DA	▲E5ZZ-9C973D	598.25
(1) Plug (Pressure Regulator)		
1984-86	▲E0AY-9E938A	.75
(2) Pressure Regulator Assy. (Fuel)		
1984-86	▲E0SY-9C968A	101.00
(3) Body (Upper)		
Serviced in charging assembly.		
(4) Relief Valve Assy. (Pressure)		
1984-86	▲E0AY-9H321A	6.50
(5) Cap (Relief Valve)		
1984-86	▲E0VY-9H323A	1.50

PARTS 3 ELECTRONIC FUEL INJECTION 3 PARTS

	Part No.	Price
(6) Charging Wiring Assy.		
1984-86	▲E0VY-9D930A	43.50
(7) Injector Assy.		
1984-86-V-6 eng.	▲E3VY-9F593A	147.75
V-8 eng.	▲E4ZZ-9F593C	147.75
(8) Retainer (Fuel Injector)		
1984-86	▲E0AY-9C976A	11.25
(9) Retainer Screw (Fuel Injection)		
1984-86	▲E0AY-9D927A	8.50
(10) Gasket (Charging Body)		
1984-86	▲E0AY-9C983A	1.00
(11) Control Rod Positioner (Fast Idle)		
1984-86	▲E0AY-9D993A	7.75
(12) Cam & Shaft Assy. (Choke)		
Order by identification tag code number.		
(13) Control Rod (Fast Idle)		
1984-86	▲E0AY-9E524A	3.00
(14) Diaphragm Assy. (Choke Control)		
1984-86	▲D9AZ-9J549A	10.00
(15) Modulator Spring (Choke Control)		
1984-86	▲E0AY-9J547F	9.75
(16) Cover Assy. (Choke Control)		
1984-86	▲E1VZ-9B580A	14.50
(17) Lever & Shaft Assy. (Throttle)		
1984-86-exc. below	▲E0VY-9581D	39.25
E4AE-CC, E5SE-HA, JA	▲E4SZ-9581A	38.50
E4AE-DC, E5SE-GA, KA	▲E4AZ-9581A	38.50
(18) Throttle Plate		
1984-86-V-6	▲E2BZ-9585A	5.00
V-8	▲D7ZZ-9585A	1.50
(19) Bracket Kit (Throttle Plate)		
1984-86-V-6	▲E4AZ-9J586A	34.25
V-8	▲E0VY-9J586A	34.25
(20) Dashpot & Control Assy.		
1984-86	▲E3VY-9S520A	44.50

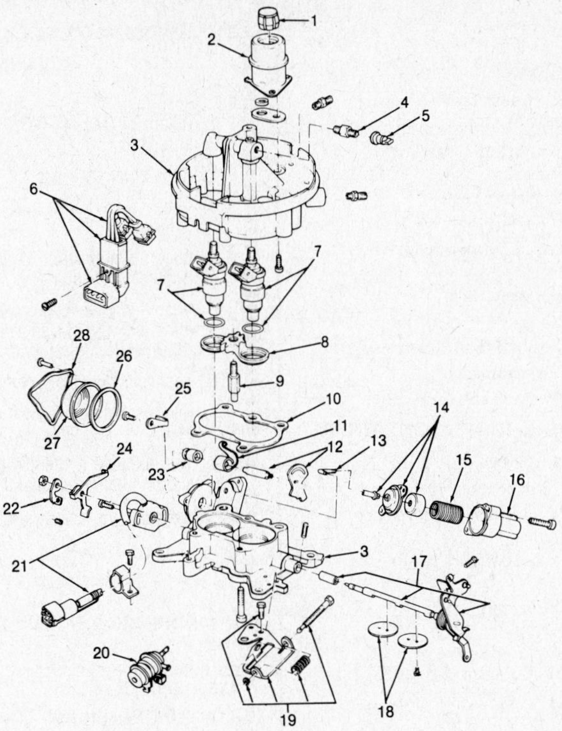

	Part No.	Price
(21) Potentiometer Assy. (Throttle)		
V-6-230		
1984-exc. below	▲E3TZ-9B989B	27.25
w/C-5 trans.	▲E45Z-9B989A	29.25
1985-86	▲E5ZZ-9B989B	27.50
V-8-302		
1984	▲E3TZ-9B989B	27.25
1985-86	▲E5AZ-9B989A	27.25
(22) Adjusting Lever (Fast Idle)		
1984-86	▲E0VZ-9538A	7.00
(23) Bushing		
Serviced in charging assembly.		

	Part No.	Price
(24) Lever (Fast Idle Cam)		
1984-86	▲E0AY-9F577A	5.75
(25) Thermostat Lever (Choke Control)		
1984-86	▲E0AY-9A754A	1.50
(26) Housing Gasket		
1984-86	▲C1AZ-9871A	1.00
(27) Thermostat Housing Assy. (Choke)		
1984-86	▲E35Y-9848A	33.25
(28) Clamp (Thermostat Housing)		
1984-86	▲E2AZ-9842A	6.75

LABOR 3A EMISSION CONTROLS 3A LABOR

(Factory Time)	Chilton Time
(M) Crankcase Ventilation Valve, Renew	
1983-86 (.2)	.2
THERMACTOR TYPE	
(G) Thermactor Air Pump, Renew	
1983-86-Four (.4)	.7
Six (.4)	.7
V-6 (.5)	.8
V-8 (.4)	.7
(G) Thermactor Pump Drive Belt, Renew	
1983-86 (.3)	.5
(G) Thermactor Air By-Pass Valve, Renew	
1983-86 (.4)	.6
E.G.R. TYPE	
(G) E.G.R. Valve, Renew	
1983-86 (.3)	.4
(G) E.G.R. Vacuum Control Valve, Renew	
1983-86 (.3)	.4

(Factory Time)	Chilton Time
(G) Exhaust Control Valve Assy., Renew	
1983-86 (.4)	.7
EVAPORATIVE EMISSION TYPE	
(G) Fuel Vapor Canister, Renew	
1983-86	.4
(G) Carburetor Air Cleaner Sensor, Renew	
1983-86	.4
(G) Carburetor Air Cleaner Filter, Renew	
1983-86	.3
ELECTRONIC ENGINE CONTROL SYSTEM	
(P) Feed Back Carburetor Control System, Test	
All models (.5)	.8
(P) Oxygen Sensor, Renew	
Does not include system test.	
All models (.3)	.7

(Factory Time)	Chilton Time
(P) Vacuum Solenoid Regulator, Renew	
Does not include system test.	
All models (.3)	.5
(P) Thermactor Air Valve, Renew	
Does not include system test.	
All models-one (.4)	.6
(P) Vacuum Switch, Renew	
Does not include system test.	
All models-one (.3)	.5
(P) Idle Tracking Switch, Renew	
Does not include system test.	
All models (.3)	.5
(P) Low Temperature Switch, Renew	
Does not include system test.	
All models (.3)	.6
(P) Thermactor Air By-Pass Valve, Renew	
Does not include system test.	
All models (.4)	.6

LABOR 3A EMISSION CONTROLS 3A LABOR

(Factory Time) Chilton Time

(P) Solenoid, Renew
Does not include system test.
All models-one (.3) 4

(P) Mid-Temperature Switch, Renew
Does not include system test.
All models (.3) 4

(P) Open Loop (Temperature) Switch, Renew
Does not include system test.
All models (.3) 4

(P) Electronic Control Unit, Renew
Does not include system test.
All models (.3) 5

ELECTRONIC ENGINE CONTROL IV

(P) E.E.C. System, Test
1984-86 (.5) 1.0

(P) Throttle Position Sensor, Renew
Does not include system test.
1984-86
Four (.2) 3
V-6 (.3) 4
V-8 (.7) 1.0

(P) Exhaust Gas Oxygen Sensor, Renew
Does not include system test.
1984-86
Four (.1) 3
V-6-left (.3) 5
right (.7) 1.0
both (.8) 1.4
V-8 (.2) 5

(P) Processor Assembly, Renew
Does not include system test.
1984-86
All models (.3) 4

(P) Back Pressure Variable Transducer Valve, Renew
Does not include system test.
1984-86
Four (.1) 2

(P) Engine Coolant Temperature Sensor, Renew
Does not include system test.
1984-86
All models (.2) 3

(P) Barometric Manifold Absolute Pressure Sensor, Renew
Does not include system test.
1984-86
All models (.2) 3

(P) E.G.R. Position Sensor, Renew
Does not include system test.
1984-86
V-6 (.3) 4
V-8 (.3) 4

(P) Thick Film Ignition Module, Renew
Does not include system test.
1984-86
All models (.5) 7

CHILTON'S EMISSION CONTROL TUNE-UP

1. Clean or renew P.C.V. valve, hoses and filter.
2. Check fuel tank cap for sealing ability.
3. Check fuel tank and fuel lines for leakage.
4. Check evaporation canister and filter. Replace if necessary.
5. Check engine compression to determine leakage of unburned gases. (Add time for items of interference).
6. Test and clean or renew spark plugs.
7. Check engine oil dipstick for sealing ability.
8. Test exhaust system with analyzer and check system for leakage.
9. Check exhaust manifold heat valve for operation.
10. Adjust ignition timing and carburetor idle speed and mixture.
11. Check automatic choke mechanism for free operation.
12. Inspect air cleaner and element.
13. On models so equipped, test distributor vacuum control switch and transmission control switch.

Four **1.3**
V-6 .... **1.7**
V-8 .... **1.8**

For repairs made, charge accordingly.

(Factory Time) Chilton Time

(P) Profile Ignition Pick-Up Sensor, Renew
Does not include system test.
1983-86 (.6) 8

(P) Throttle Positioner Assembly, Renew
Does not include system test.
1984-86
All models (.2) 3

(P) E.G.R. Control Solenoids, Renew
Does not include system test.
1984-86
V-6 (.2) 3
V-8 (.2) 3

(P) Tad/Tab Solenoids, Renew
Does not include system test.
1984-86
All models (.2) 3

(P) Fuel Injector Assembly, Renew
Does not include system test.
1984-86
V-6-V-8
one or both (.7) 1.0

(P) Canister Purge Valve or Solenoid, Renew
Does not include system test.
1984-86
V-6 (.1) 2
V-8 (.1) 2

(P) Intake Manifold Heat Control Valve, Renew
Does not include system test.
1984-86
V-6 (.2) 4

(P) Air Change Temperature Sensor, Renew
Does not include system test.
1984-86
V-6 (.2) 3

(Factory Time) Chilton Time

V-8 (.2) 3

(P) Fuel Pump Relay, Renew
Does not include system test.
1985-86 (.1) 2

(P) Cooling Fan Controller, Module or Relay, Renew
Does not include system test.
1985-86 (.1) 2

(P) Throttle Kicker Actuator, Renew
Does not include system test.
1984-86
V-8 (.2) 3

(P) Throttle Kicker Solenoid, Renew
Does not include system test.
1984-86
V-8 (.1) 2

(P) Exhaust Heat Control Valve, Renew
Does not include system test.
1984-86
V-8 (.3) 6

(P) Feedback Control Solenoid, Renew
Does not include system test.
1984-86
Four (.2) 3

(P) Electronic Control Relay, Renew
Does not include system test.
All models (.3) 4

(P) Fuel Pump Inertia Switch Assy., Renew
Does not include system test.
All models (.2) 3

(P) E.G.R. Valve, Renew
Does not include system test.
All models (.2) 4

PARTS 3A EMISSION CONTROLS 3A PARTS

CRANKCASE EMISSION

	Part No.	Price
Crankcase Ventilation Valve		
Four-140 engine		
1983-86	▲E1ZZ-6A666A	3.75
Six-200, 230 eng.		
1983-86	▲E1DZ-6A666A	3.75
V-8-302 engine		
1984-85	▲D9ZZ-6A666A	3.50

THERMACTOR TYPE

Item	Part No.	Price
Thermactor Air Pump		
1983-86-w/140 eng.	▲E3ZZ-9A486A	141.75
w/230 eng.	▲E3SZ-9A486C	141.75
w/302 eng.	▲E3ZZ-9A486E	141.75
Air By Pass Valve		
Four-140		
1983-Stand Trans.	▲E1ZZ-9B289A	32.50
(Auto. Trans.)		
exc. Calif.	▲E3ZZ-9B289B	28.75
Calif.	▲E1ZZ-9B289A	32.50
1983-200 eng.	▲E3TZ-9B289E	35.25
1983-230 eng.	▲E1TZ-9B289C	28.75
1984-86	▲E1TZ-9B289C	28.75
Air Supply Check Valve		
Four-140		
(hose nipple 1 end)		
1983	▲D8FZ-9A487A	24.50
1984	▲E4ZZ-9A487B	14.50
1985-86	▲E5ZZ-9A487A	14.50
(hose nipple 2 ends)		
1983-86	▲D9AZ-9A487C	11.25
Six-200		
1983 (hose nipple)		
1 end	▲D4VY-9A487A	14.25
2 ends	▲D9AZ-9A487C	11.25
V-6-230		
(hose nipple 1 end)		
1983	▲E2AZ-9A487A	18.50
1984-86	▲D4AZ-9A487A	14.25
(hose nipple 2 ends)		
1983-86	▲D9AZ-9A487C	11.25
V-8-302		
1984-85 (hose nipple)		
1 end	▲D4VY-9A487A	14.25
2 ends	▲D9AZ-9A487C	11.25

E.G.R. CONTROL SYSTEM

E.G.R. Valve

Replacement E.G.R. Valves must be ordered according to the stamping number on the Original Valve.

Item	Part No.	Price
Vacuum Control Valve		
1983-140 eng.		
exc. below	▲D8BZ-9D473A	36.75
(Stamped D8TE)		
BIA, B2A	▲D8TZ-9D473B	36.75
1983-200 eng.	▲D5FZ-9D473A	29.75
1983-230 eng.	▲D8TZ-9D473B	36.75
1984-86-w/140 eng.	▲D7BZ-9D473A	28.50
Solenoid Valve (E.G.R. Vacuum)		
1983-140 eng. (M.T.)		
(Stamped E1ZE)		
A2A, A3A	▲E1ZZ-9D474A	16.25
(Stamped E3ZE)		
C2A	▲E3ZZ-9D474C	16.25
(Stamped E2SE)		
A2A, A3A	▲E2SZ-9D474A	16.25
1983-140 eng. (A.T.)		
(Stamped E2DE)		
A2A, A3A	▲E2DZ-9D474A	16.25
(Stamped E3ZE)		
C2A	▲E3ZZ-9D474C	16.25
(Stamped E1ZE)		
A2A, A3A	▲E1ZZ-9D474A	16.25
1983-200 eng.	▲E1DZ-9D474A	16.25
1983-230 eng.		
exc. below	▲E3SZ-9D474A	32.50
Calif.	▲E3SZ-9D474B	16.25

EVAPORATIVE EMISSION TYPE

Item	Part No.	Price
Vapor Canister Assy.		
Four-140		
1983-exc. Calif.	▲D8AZ-9D653C	53.25
Calif.	▲E0AZ-9D653A	53.25
1984-85-exc. Canada	▲E0AZ-9D653A	53.25
Canada	▲D8AZ-9D653C	53.25
1986	▲E0AZ-9D653A	53.25
V-6-230		
1983-exc. Calif.	▲D8AZ-9D653C	53.25
Calif.	▲E0AZ-9D653A	53.25
1984-86	▲D8AZ-9D653C	53.25
V-8-302		
1984-85	▲D8AZ-9D653C	53.25
Sensor Assy.		
Four-140		
1983-86	▲D7FZ-9E607A	7.25
Six-200, 230		
1983	▲D4ZZ-9E607A	7.00
1984-86	▲D7FZ-9E607B	7.25
V-8-302		
1984-85	▲D4ZZ-9E607A	7.00
Air Cleaner Filter		
1983-86-140 eng.	▲C8TZ-9601AR	8.50
200 eng.	▲D4ZZ-9601AR	9.00
230 eng.	▲D3ZZ-9601AR	9.75
302 eng.	▲D7AZ-9601AR	9.25

ELECTRONIC ENGINE CONTROL SYSTEM

Item	Part No.	Price
Oxygen Sensor (Exh. Gas)		
1983 (140 eng.)		
(Stamped)		
E1AF-AA	▲E1AZ-9F472A	95.00
E3EF-AA	▲E3FZ-9F472A	48.50
1984-85-all	▲E3FZ-9F472A	48.50
1986	▲E6DZ-9F472A	N.L.
Thermactor Control Valve		
1983 (140 eng.)		
(Stamped)		
E1TE-AB	▲E2TZ-9F491A	N.L.
E4SE-BA	▲E4SZ-9F491B	N.L.
1983 (200 eng.)		
exc. Calif.	▲E3SZ-9F491A	24.75
Calif.	▲E3SZ-9F491B	27.25
1983 (230 eng.)		
exc. Calif.	▲E3TZ-9F491A	56.00
w/Hi Alt.	▲E3SZ-9F491C	27.25
Calif.	▲E3SZ-9F491C	27.25
1984-86-(stamped on valve)		
E1TE-AB	▲E3TZ-9F491A	56.00
E3EE-C3A	▲E43Z-9F491C	56.00
E4SE-BA	▲E3TZ-9F491A	56.00
E4SE-A3A	▲E4SZ-9F491A	56.00
Cold Temperature Vacuum Switch		
1983-140 eng.	▲E1ZZ-12A182A	41.25
Electronic Control Unit		
1983-140 eng.	▲E3ZZ-12A651B	212.25
Purge Regulator Valve (Canister)		
1983	▲E0AZ-9C915A	21.75
1984-86-natural	▲E4AZ-9C915A	21.75
green	▲E4AZ-9C915B	21.75
black	▲E4AZ-9C915C	21.75
Dual Coolant Switch Assy.		
1983-86	▲E1AZ-12B513A	71.50
Mid Temperature Switch		
1983 (Stamped on Valve)		
D5DF-AA	▲D5DZ-9E862A	7.25
D7ZE-AA	▲D7ZZ-9E862A	7.50
E0EE-AA	▲E0FZ-9E862A	7.50
1984-86 (stamped on valve)		
D5DF-AA	▲D5DZ-9E862A	7.25
D7ZE-AA	▲D7ZZ-9E862A	7.50

ELECTRONIC ENGINE CONTROL IV

Item	Part No.	Price
Throttle Position Sensor		
Four-140		
1984	▲E4TZ-9B989A	29.25
1985-86	▲E5DZ-9B989A	29.25
V-6-230		
1984-exc. below	▲E3TZ-9B989B	27.25
C-5 trans.	▲E45Z-9B989A	29.25
1985-86	▲E5ZZ-9B989B	27.00
V-8-302		
1984	▲E3TZ-9B989B	27.25
1985-86	▲E5AZ-9B989A	27.25
Exhaust Gas Oxygen Sensor		
1984-86	▲E3TZ-9F472A	N.L.
1986	▲E6DZ-9F472A	N.L.
Processor Assy.		
Four-140		
1984-exc. Calif.	▲E4FZ-12A650AAA	167.75
Calif.	▲E4FZ-12A650ADA	167.75
1985-exc. Calif	▲E5DZ-12A650NA	167.75
Calif.	▲E5DZ-12A650KA	167.75
1986-exc. Calif	▲E5DZ-12A650NB	167.75
Calif.	▲E5DZ-12A650KB	167.75
V-6-230		
1984-86 (stamping no.)		
E53F-AL1A, AL2A	▲E53Z-12A650ALA	167.75
E4VF-F1A, F2A	▲E4VZ-12A650FA	167.75
E4VF-C1A, C2A	▲E4VZ-12A650CA	167.75
E4VF-D1A, D2A	▲E4VZ-12A650DA	167.75
E4VF-C1B, C2B	▲E5VZ-12A650CB	167.75
E4VF-D1B, D2B	▲E5VZ-12A650DB	167.75
E4VF-E1A, E2A	▲E4VZ-12A650EA	N.L.
E53F-AM1A, AM2A	▲E53Z-12A650AMA	168.00
E53F-AN1B, AN2B	▲E53Z-12A650ANB	167.75
E53F-AP1B, AP2B	▲E53Z-12A650APB	167.75
E63F-A1A, A2A	▲E63Z-12A650AA	167.75
E63F-B1A, B2A	▲E63Z-12A650BA	167.75
V-8-302		
1984-85 (stamping no.)		
E4VF-M12, M2A	▲E4VZ-12A650MA	167.75
E4VF-T12, T2A	▲E4VZ-12A650TA	167.75
Back Pressure Variable Transducer Valve		
1984-86-140 eng.	▲E4ZZ-9J431B	33.75
Engine Coolant Temperature Sensor		
1984-86	▲E1AZ-12A648A	32.00
Barometric Manifold Absolute Pressure Sensor		
1984-86	▲E43Z-9F479B	68.50
E.G.R. Position Sensor		
1984-86	▲E43Z-9G428B	31.75
Ignition Module Assy.		
1984-86	▲E43Z-12A297A	106.00
E.G.R. Control Solenoid		
1984-86 (stamping no.)		
E35E-FA	▲E35Y-9D474A	32.50
E4ZE-FA	▲E4ZZ-9D474F	32.50
E4ZE-H2A, H3A	▲E4ZZ-9D474H	32.50
E4ZE-E2A, E3A	▲E4ZZ-9D474E	32.50
E4ZE-G2A, G3A	▲E4ZZ-9D474G	16.25
E5TE-AA	▲E5TZ-9D474AA	32.50
Canister Purge Valve		
1984-86-natural	▲E4AZ-9C915A	21.75
green	▲E4AZ-9C915B	21.75
black	▲E4AZ-9C915C	21.75
Manifold Heat Control Valve (Intake)		
V-6-230		
1984	▲E4AZ-9G464A	27.50
1985-86	▲E5AZ-9G464A	27.50
Air Charge Temperature Sensor		
1984-86	▲E1AZ-12A697A	27.00
Throttle Kicker Actuator		
1984-85-V-8	▲E3VY-9S520A	44.50
Exhaust Heat Control		
V-8	▲E15Z-9A427A	N.L.

LABOR 4 ALTERNATOR & REGULATOR 4 LABOR

	(Factory Time)	Chilton Time
(G) Alternator Circuits, Test		
Includes: Test battery, regulator and alternator output.		
All models		.6
(M) Alternator Drive Belt, Renew		
1983-86	(.3)	.4
(G) Alternator Assy., Renew		
1983-86	(.4)	.7
Transfer pulley add	(.1)	.1
Circuit test add		.6
(G) Alternator, R&R and Recondition		
Includes: Complete disassembly, replacement of parts as required. Test validity of rotor fields, stator and diodes.		
1983-86	(.9)	1.5
Circuit test add		.6
(G) Alternator Front Bearing or End Plate, Renew		
Includes: R&R alternator.		
1983-86	(.7)	1.0
(G) Alternator Rear Bearing, Renew		
Includes: R&R alternator.		
1983-86	(.6)	.9
(G) Alternator Regulator, Renew		
1983-86	(.3)	.4
Circuit test add		.6
(G) Instrument Cluster Voltage Regulator, Renew		
1983-86	(.7)	1.1

PARTS 4 ALTERNATOR & REGULATOR 4 PARTS

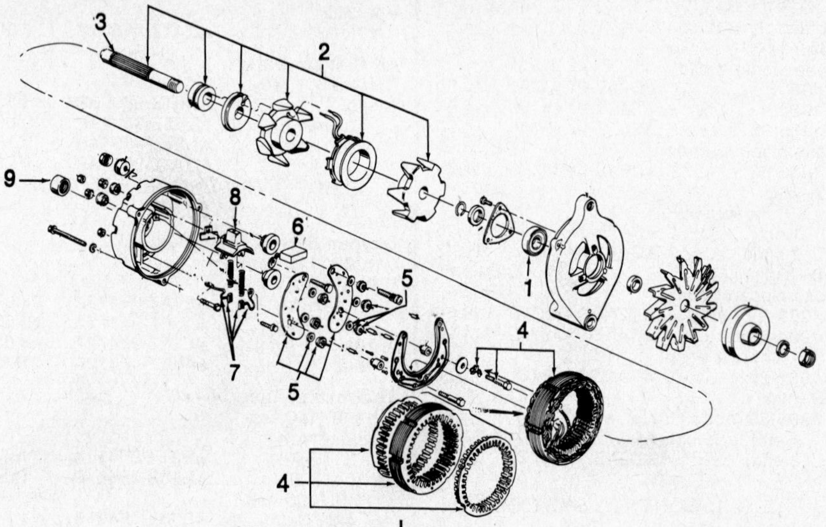

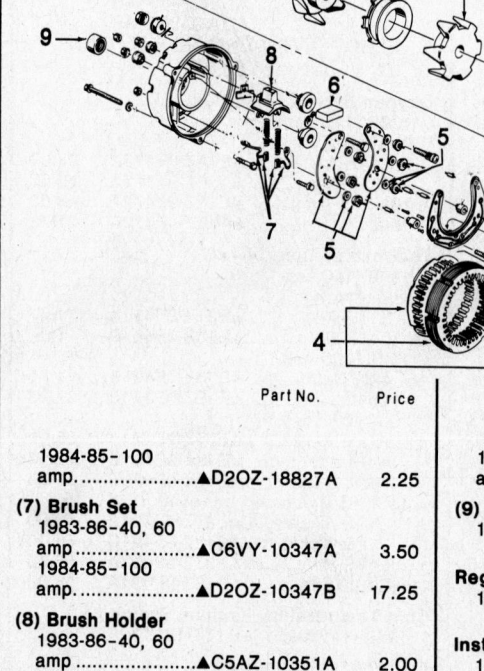

	Part No.	Price
Alternator Assy. (New)		
40 amp		
1983-84	▲E1ZZ-10346A	203.50
60 amp		
(140, 302 engs.)		
1983-86	▲E2GZ-10346C	233.50
(230 engine)		
1983-84	▲E2GZ-10346B	233.50
1985-86	▲E5SZ-10346A	232.75
100 amp		
1984-85	▲E1VZ-10346A	418.75
(1) Front Bearing		
1983-86	▲C9ZZ-10094A	9.00
(2) Rotor Assy.		
40 amp		
1983-84	▲E1ZZ-10335A	45.75
60 amp		
1983-86-exc. V-6	▲E1ZZ-10335B	45.75
V-6 eng.	▲E5SZ-10335A	56.00
100 amp		
1984-85	▲E1VZ-10335A	120.50
(3) Shaft (Rotor)		
1983-86	▲C5AZ-10330A	N.L.
(4) Stator Assy.		
1983-86-exc. 100 amp	▲E3FZ-10336A	31.25
1984-85-100 amp	▲D3VY-10336A	74.75
(5) Rectifier Assy.		
1983-86-40, 60 amp	▲D6AZ-10304A	48.00
1984-85-100 amp	▲D4VY-10304A	88.25
(6) Capacitor (Radio)		
1983-86-40, 60 amp	▲C6AZ-18827A	2.25
1984-85-100 amp	▲D2OZ-18827A	2.25
(7) Brush Set		
1983-86-40, 60 amp	▲C6VY-10347A	3.50
1984-85-100 amp	▲D2OZ-10347B	17.25
(8) Brush Holder		
1983-86-40, 60 amp	▲C5AZ-10351A	2.00
1984-85-100 amp	▲D2OZ-10347B	17.25
(9) Rear Bearing		
1983-86	▲D2OZ-10A304A	5.25
Regulator Assy.		
1983-86	▲E2PZ-10316A	36.75
Instrument Cluster Voltage Regulator		
1983-86	▲D1AZ-10804A	10.25

LABOR 5 STARTING SYSTEM 5 LABOR

	(Factory Time)	Chilton Time
(G) Starter Draw Test (On Car)		
All models	(.3)	.3
(G) Starter Assy., Renew		
1983-86	(.4)	.6
Add draw test if performed.		
(G) Starter, R&R and Recondition		
Includes: Turn down armature.		
1983-86 positive engagement starter	(1.7)	2.4
Motorcraft	(1.4)	2.1
Renew field coils add		.5
Add draw test if performed.		
(G) Starter Drive, Renew		
Includes: R&R starter.		
1983-86	(.6)	.8
(G) Starter Solenoid Relay, Renew		
1983-86	(.3)	.4
(G) Neutral Safety Switch, Renew		
1983-86	(.3)	.4
w/AOD add		.1
(G) Ignition Switch, Renew		
1983-86	(.4)	.9
(M) Battery Cables, Renew		
Batt to Relay	(.3)	.3
Ground	(.3)	.3
Relay to Starter	(.4)	.5

PARTS 5 STARTING SYSTEM 5 PARTS

	Part No.	Price
Starter Assy.		
Four-140		
1983-84	▲E3TZ-11002D	N.L.
1985-86	▲E4TZ-11002B	203.50
200, 230 eng.		
1983-86	▲E4DZ-11002B	185.50
V-8-302		
1984	▲E25Z-11002A	N.L.
1985	▲E4DZ-11002B	185.50
Starter Relay Switch		
1983-84	▲D8DZ-11450B	12.00
1985-86	▲E5TZ-11450A	13.25
Ignition Starter Switch		
1983-86	▲E4FZ-11572A	11.50
(1) Starter Armature		
1983-84	▲E2BZ-11005A	77.00
1985-86	▲E3FZ-11005A	66.75
(2) Starter Drive		
1983-86	▲E2PZ-11350A	21.00
(3) Field Coil Assy. (Complete)		
1983-84	▲E2BZ-11082A	50.00
1985-86	▲E4AZ-11082A	50.00
(4) Starter Brush Set		
1983-86	▲E4PZ-11057A	13.00
(5) Bearing (Drive End)		
1983-86	▲D0AZ-11135B	N.L.
(6) Plate Bushing (Brush End.)		
1983-86	▲D3AZ-11052A	1.50

Battery Cables
Order by Year and Model.

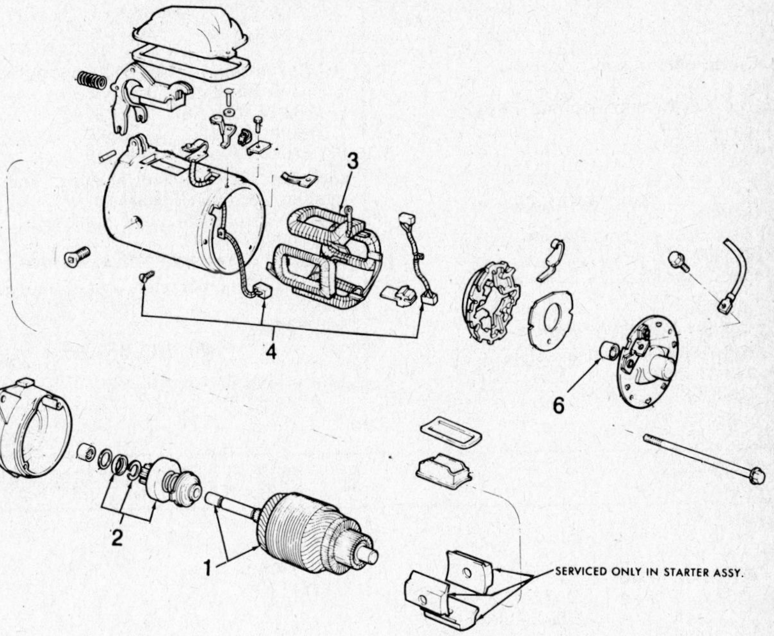

	Part No.	Price
Ignition Switch		
1983-86	▲E4FZ-11572A	11.50

	Part No.	Price
Neutral Safety Switch		
1983-86-exc.		
below	▲D6RY-7A247B	33.25
w/C 5 Trans.	▲E2DZ-7A247A	38.50

LABOR 6 BRAKE SYSTEM 6 LABOR

(Factory Time) — Chilton Time

(G) Brake Pedal Free Play, Adjust
All models 4

(G) Brakes, Adjust (Minor)
Includes: Adjust brakes, fill master cylinder.
two wheels 4

(G) Bleed Brakes (Four Wheels)
Includes: Fill master cylinder.
All models (.3) 5

(G) Brake Self Adjustors, Disassemble & Clean
one wheel 7
each adtnl 4

(G) Brake Shoes and/or Pads, Renew
Includes: Install new or exchange shoes or pads. Adjust service and hand brake. Bleed system.
1983-86-front-disc (.7) 1.1
rear-drum (1.0) 1.5
all four wheels (1.4) 2.5
Resurface disc rotor, add-each 9
Resurface brake drum, add-each 5

(G) Brake Drum, Renew
Includes: Remove wheel and adjust brakes.
1983-86-one (.3) 6
both (.4) 8

(G) Brake Pressure Warning Light Switch, Renew
1983-86 (.3) 5

COMBINATIONS
Add to Brakes, Renew
See Machine Shop Operations

(Factory Time) — Chilton Time

(G) RENEW WHEEL CYLINDER
Each (.3) 3

(G) REBUILD WHEEL CYLINDER
Each (.3) 3

(G) REBUILD CALIPER ASSEMBLY
Each (.4) 5

(G) RENEW MASTER CYLINDER
All models (.6) 6

(G) REBUILD MASTER CYLINDER
All models (.8) 1.0

(G) RENEW REAR WHEEL GREASE SEALS
One (.2) 3
Both (.3) 4

(G) REPACK FRONT WHEEL BEARINGS (BOTH WHEELS)
All models (.4) 6

(G) RENEW BRAKE DRUM
Each (.2) 2

(G) RENEW DISC BRAKE ROTOR
Each (.2) 4

(G) RENEW BRAKE HOSE
Each (.3) 3

(Factory Time) — Chilton Time

BRAKE HYDRAULIC SYSTEM

(G) Wheel Cylinder, Renew
Includes: Bleed system.
1983-86-one (.9) 1.4
both (1.5) 2.1

(G) Wheel Cylinder, R&R and Recondition
Includes: Bleed system.
1983-86-one (.9) 1.7
both (1.5) 2.7

(G) Brake Hose, Renew
Includes: Bleed system.
1983-86-front-one (.4) 6
both (.5) 7
rear-one (.5) 8

(G) Master Cylinder, Renew
Includes: Bleed complete system.
1983-86 (.5) 1.0

(G) Master Cylinder, R&R and Rebuild
Includes: Hone cylinder and bleed complete system.
1983-86 (.7) 1.6

POWER BRAKES

(G) Power Brake Booster, Renew
1983-86 (1.0) 1.4

LABOR 6 BRAKE SYSTEM 6 LABOR

	(Factory Time)	Chilton Time
w/Cruise control add		.2
(G) Power Brake Booster Check Valve, Renew		
1983-86	(.3)	.4

DISC BRAKES

	(Factory Time)	Chilton Time
(G) Disc Brake Pads, Renew		
1983-86	(.7)	1.1
Resurface brake rotor, add-each		.9
(G) Caliper Assembly, Renew		
Includes: Bleed complete system.		
1983-86-one	(.6)	1.0
both	(.8)	1.5
(G) Caliper Assy., R&R and Recondition		
Includes: Bleed complete system.		
1983-86-one	(.8)	1.5
both	(1.2)	2.5
(G) Brake Rotor, Renew		
Includes: Renew wheel bearings and grease retainer and repack bearings.		
1983-86-one	(.5)	.7
both	(.7)	1.2
(G) Brake Differential Valve, Renew		
Includes: Bleed complete system and transfer switch.		
1983-86	(.7)	1.0

PARKING BRAKE

	(Factory Time)	Chilton Time
(M) Parking Brake, Adjust		
1983-86	(.3)	.4
(G) Parking Brake Indicator Switch, Renew		
1983-86	(.3)	.4
(G) Parking Brake Control, Renew		
1983-86	(.6)	1.0
(G) Parking Brake Cables, Renew		
Includes: Adjust parking brake.		
1983-86-front-one	(.3)	.5
both	(.3)	.6
rear-one	(.5)	.8
both	(.8)	1.0
(G) Parking Brake Power Vacuum Unit, Renew		
1983-86	(.3)	.5

PARTS 6 BRAKE SYSTEM 6 PARTS

	Part No.	Price
(1) Brake Shoe Set		
1983-86-9" brks.	▲D9ZZ-2200A	35.50
10" brks.	▲D6DZ-2200A	37.00
(2) Rear Wheel Cylinder		
1983-86-9" brks.	▲D8BZ-2261A	17.75
10" brks.-right	▲D8BZ-2261B	19.75
left	▲D8BZ-2262A	19.75
Repair Kit (Wheel Cylinder)		
1983-86-9" brks.	▲D8BZ-2128A	5.75
10" brks.	▲D8BZ-2128B	5.50
Brake Hose (Front)		
1983-84	▲E3DZ-2078A	15.25
1985-86	▲E5DZ-2078A	12.75
Brake Hose (Rear)		
1983-86	▲E3SZ-2282A	17.25
Master Cylinder Assy.		
1983-86	▲E4DZ-2140A	93.00

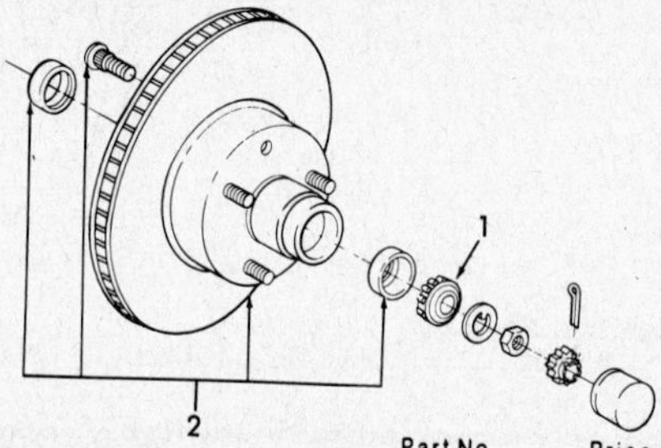

	Part No.	Price
Repair Kit (Master Cylinder)		
1983-86	▲E4DZ-2004A	35.25
Brake Drum (Rear)		
1983-86-9" brks.	▲D9ZZ-1126A	60.50
10" brks.	▲D9BZ-1126A	76.00
Brake Booster Assy. (New)		
1983-86-V-6 230	▲E1BZ-2005B	178.50
140 eng.	▲E1BZ-2005E	117.00
302 eng.	▲E4DZ-2005A	142.00

PARKING BRAKE

	Part No.	Price
Parking Brake Control		
Manual release		
1983	▲E3SZ-2780A	38.50
1984-86	▲E4SZ-2780A	69.25
Auto. release		
1983	▲E3SZ-2780B	69.25
1984-86	▲E4DZ-2780A	69.25
Parking Brake Cable (Front)		
1983-86	▲E3SZ-2853A	16.00
Parking Brake Cable (Rear)		
1983-84-exc. below	▲E3SZ-2A635A	21.75
Sta. Wagon	▲E3DZ-2A635A	18.50
1985-86	▲E3DZ-2A635A	18.50

PARTS 6 DISC BRAKES 6 PARTS

	Part No.	Price
(1) Wheel Bearing (Outer)		
1983-86	▲D0AZ-1216A	8.25
Wheel Bearing Cup (Outer)		
1983-86	▲D0AZ-1217B	3.75
(2) Hub Rotor Assy.		
1983-84	▲D8BZ-1102A	87.25
1985-86	▲E5DZ-1102A	86.00
(3) Wheel Bearing (Inner)		
1983-86	▲D0AZ-1201A	9.50
(4) Grease Retainer		
1983-86	▲C8AZ-1190A	3.00
(5) Shield (Rotor)		
1983-86-right	▲E0SZ-2K004A	11.75
left	▲E0SZ-2K005A	11.75
(6) Spindle Assy.		
1983-86-right	▲E1SZ-3105A	137.00
left	▲E1SZ-3106A	137.00
(7) Locating Pin		
1983-86	▲E3SZ-2B296A	3.00
(8) Caliper Piston (Front)		
1984-86	▲E3SZ-2196A	12.75
(9) Brake Pad Set		
1983-86	▲E3SZ-2001A	48.75

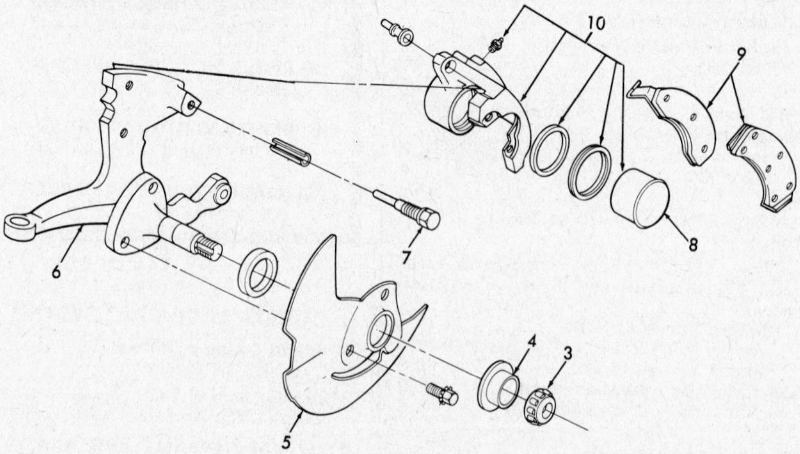

	Part No.	Price
(10) Caliper Assy. (Front)		
1983-84-right	▲E3SZ-2B120A	116.75
left	▲E3SZ-2B121A	116.75
1985-86-right	▲E5SZ-2B120A	127.50
left	▲E5SZ-2B121A	127.50
Brake Differential Valve		
wo/Sta. wagon		
1983-86	▲E1DZ-2B257A	40.00
Sta. wagon		
1983-86	▲E3SZ-2B257B	46.50
Caliper Assy. Repair Kit		
1983-86	▲D9BZ-2221A	8.25

LABOR 7 COOLING SYSTEM 7 LABOR

(Factory Time) Chilton Time

(M) Winterize Cooling System
Includes: Run engine to check for leaks, tighten all hose connections. Test radiator and pressure cap, drain radiator and engine block. Add anti-freeze and refill system.
All models 5

(M) Thermostat, Renew
1983-86-Four (.5) 7
Six (.4) 6
V-6 (.5) 7
V-8 (.6) 8

(M) Radiator Assembly, R&R or Renew
Includes: Drain and refill cooling system.
1983-86 (.6) 1.0
w/A.C. add (.1) 1

ADD THESE OPERATIONS TO RADIATOR R&R
(G) Boil & Repair 1.5
(G) Rod Clean 1.9
(G) Repair Core 1.3
(G) Renew Tank 1.6
(G) Renew Trans. Oil Cooler 1.9
(G) Recore Radiator 1.7

(M) Radiator Hoses, Renew
1983-86-upper (.3) 4
lower (.5) 6
both (.6) 8

(G) Water Pump, Renew
Four-1983-86 (.8) 1.2
Six-1983 (.9) 1.4
V-6-1983-86 (1.1) 1.7
V-8-1984-86 (.8) 1.6
w/A.C. add (.1) 2

(M) Drive Belts, Adjust
All models-one (.2) 3
each adtnl (.1) 1

(M) Drive Belts, Renew
All models-one (.3) 4
each adtnl (.1) 1

(G) Electric Cooling Fan Motor, Renew
1983-86 (.3) 5

COOLING SYSTEM TUNE-UP

An Annual Cooling System Tune-Up Suggestion List should include (with some exceptions):

1. A visual check of the cooling system for indications of leaks or excessive oil content.
2. Pressure check the cooling system for internal and external leaks with filler cap and neck adapter and tester.
3. Check crankcase and automatic transmission oil for water content.
4. Test coolant thermostat with radiator thermometer.
5. Check temperature gauge for accuracy.
6. Drain system and flush till clean.
7. Clean foreign matter from radiator fins.
8. Test radiator pressure cap with cap tester.
9. Check fan blades and pulleys for alignment and damage.
10. Internal and external inspection of all hoses for cracks and deterioration.
11. Check core plugs (where possible) for seepage.
12. Refill system with correct coolant and check for air locks.
13. Check condition and tension of drive belts with tension gauge.

All models 1.5

(Factory Time) Chilton Time

(G) Electric Cooling Fan Relay, Renew
1983-86 (.3) 4

(Factory Time) Chilton Time

(M) Serpentine Belt, Renew
1983-86 (.3) 5

(G) Temperature Gauge (Engine Unit), Renew
1983-86 (.3) 4

(G) Temperature Indicator (Dash Unit), Renew
1983-84 (.3) 5
1985-86 (.7) 1.1

(G) Water Jacket Expansion Plugs, Renew (Side of Block)
each (.3) .... *.5
*Add time to gain accessibility.

(G) Heater Hoses, Renew
1983-86-each (.3) 4

(G) Heater Core, R&R or Renew
1983-86
wo/A.C. (2.1) 5.0
w/A.C. (2.9) 6.0
Add time to recharge A.C. system if required.

ADD THESE OPERATIONS TO HEATER CORE R&R
(G) Boil & Repair 1.2
(G) Repair Core 9
(G) Recore 1.2

(G) Heater Control Assembly, Renew
1983-86 (.5) 9

(G) Heater Blower Motor, Renew
1983-86 (.6) 8

(G) Heater Blower Motor Resistor, Renew
1983-86 (.3) 5

(G) Heater Blower Motor Switch, Renew
1983-86 (.4) 7

(G) Temperature Control Cable, Renew
1983-86 (.5) 8

PARTS 7 COOLING SYSTEM 7 PARTS

	Part No.	Price
Radiator Assy.		
1983-84	▲E3ZZ-8005A	191.25
1985-wo/A.C.	▲E5DZ-8005A	194.25
w/A.C.	▲E4DZ-8005A	194.25
1984-85-302	▲E4DZ-8005A	194.25
1986-140 & 230	▲E4DZ-8005A	194.25
Radiator Hoses		
Order by year and model.		
Water Pump Assy.		
1983-86-140 eng	▲E4BZ-8501A	88.25
200 eng	▲D8BZ-8501A	62.50
230 eng	▲E2DZ-8501A	65.75
1984-85-302 eng	▲E4ZZ-8501A	59.00
Thermostat		
1983-86-140 eng	▲E3FZ-8575A	9.75
200 eng	▲D9BZ-8575A	6.00
230 eng	▲E2DZ-8575A	6.00
1984-85-302 eng.	▲D9AZ-8575A	6.00
Temperature Sending Unit (Engine)		
1983-86-exc. 140 eng	▲E43Z-10884A	9.00
140 eng.	▲C8GY-10884A	9.25
Heater Core		
1983-86-wo/A.C.	▲E2FZ-18476A	59.50
A.C.	▲D9BZ-18476A	63.50
Blower Motor		
1983-86	▲E35Y-19805A	91.75
Resistor (Blower Motor)		
1983-86	▲E35Y-19A706A	11.00
Switch Assy. (Blower Motor)		
1983-86	▲D5AZ-19986A	12.75

LABOR 8 EXHAUST SYSTEM 8 LABOR

(Factory Time) Chilton Time

(G) Muffler, Renew
1983-86 (.6) 9
Welded type add 3

(G) Catalytic Converter, Renew
Four-1983-86 (.7) 1.0
Six-1983 (1.2) 1.7

V-6-1983-86
Light off (.8) 1.2
center (.5) 8

LABOR 8 EXHAUST SYSTEM 8 LABOR

(Factory Time)	Chilton Time
both (1.2)	1.9
V-8–1984-86 (.5)	.8
(G) Exhaust Control Valve Assy., Renew	
1983-86 (.4)	.7
(G) Exhaust Manifold, Renew	
Four–1983-86 (1.0)	1.5
Six–1983 (3.2)	4.5
V-6–1983-86	
right (1.4)	2.1
left (.8)	1.3
both (1.9)	3.1
V-8–1984-86	
right (1.3)	1.8
left (.8)	1.1
both (1.9)	2.7
w/A.C. add (.3)	.3

COMBINATIONS

(Factory Time)	Chilton Time
(G) Muffler, Exhaust and Tail Pipe, Renew	
1983-86	1.6

PARTS 8 EXHAUST SYSTEM 8 PARTS

	Part No.	Price
Muffler Assy.		
Four–140		
1983-exc. Calif.	▲E3DZ-5230A	123.75
Calif.	▲E3DZ-5230G	98.75
1984-86	▲E3DZ-5230G	98.75
Six–200		
1983-exc. below	▲E3DZ-5230C	123.75
Sta. wag.	▲E3DZ-5230E	128.75
V-6–230		
(exc. Sta. wagon)		
1983-84-wo/EEC	▲E3DZ-5230J	128.75
EEC	▲E4DZ-5230D	131.75
1985-86	▲E5DZ-5230A	112.75
(Sta. wagon)		
1983-84-wo/EEC	▲E3DZ-5230L	133.50
EEC	▲E4DZ-5230D	131.75
1985-86	▲E5DZ-5230B	112.75
V-8-302		
1984-85	▲E4DZ-5230F	114.50
Catalytic Converter		
Four–140		
1983-exc. Calif.	▲E3DZ-5E212D	191.25
Calif.	▲E3DZ-5E212A	382.25
1984-wo/E.E.C.	▲E3DZ-5E212B	382.25
E.E.C.	▲E4DZ-5E212C	207.75
1985-86	▲E3DZ-5E212A	382.25
Six–200		
1983	▲E3DZ-5E212E	226.75
V-6–230		
(front)		
1983-84-wo/EEC.	▲E2DZ-5F250C	200.75
EEC	▲E4DZ-5F250A	456.75
1985	▲E5DZ-5F250A	397.75
1986	▲E6SZ-5F250B	427.25
(rear)		
1983-exc. Calif.	▲E3DZ-5E212B	382.25
Calif.	▲E3DZ-5E212G	401.50
1984-86-wo/EEC.	▲E3DZ-5E212B	382.25
EEC	▲E4DZ-5E212C	207.75
V-8-302		
1984-85	▲E4DZ-5E212A	401.50

LABOR 9 FRONT SUSPENSION 9 LABOR

Note: On all front suspension operations alignment charges must be added if performed. Time given does not include alignment.

(Factory Time)	Chilton Time
(M) Wheel, Renew	
one (.5)	.5
(G) Wheels, Rotate (All)	
All models (.5)	.5
(G) Wheels, Balance	
one	.3
each adtnl	.2
(G) Check Alignment of Front End	
All models (.4)	.5
Note: Deduct if alignment is performed.	
(G) Toe-In, Adjust	
All models (.6)	.6
(G) Align Front End	
Includes: Adjust front wheel bearings.	
All models (1.1)	1.5
w/A.C. interference add	.5
(G) Front Wheel Bearings, Clean and Repack (Both Wheels)	
All models	1.3
(G) Front Wheel Grease Seals, Renew	
Includes: Repack bearings.	
1983-86-one whl (.6)	.7
both whls (.9)	1.1
(G) Front Wheel Bearings and Cups, Renew	
1983-86-one whl (.7)	.9
both whls (1.2)	1.5
(G) Front Strut Shock Absorbers, Renew	
1983-86-one (.7)	1.1
both (1.1)	1.9
(G) Front Spindle Assembly, Renew (One)	
Add alignment charges.	
1983-86 (.8)	1.2
(G) Lower Control Arm Assy., Renew (One)	
Add alignment charges.	
1983-86 (1.1)	1.5
(G) Ball Joints, Renew	
Add alignment charges.	
1983-86	
one side	1.2
both sides	1.9
(G) Front Spring, Renew	
1983-86-one (1.0)	1.5
both (1.7)	2.7
(G) Front Stabilizer Bar, Renew	
1983-86 (.6)	.9

PARTS 9 FRONT SUSPENSION 9 PARTS

	Part No.	Price
(1) Plate (Camber Adjusting)		
1983-86	▲E3DZ-3B391A	2.00
(2) Bracket Assy. (Upper Mounting)		
140 & 6 cyl.		
1983-84	▲E3DZ-18A161A	41.25
1985-86	▲E5DZ-18A161A	41.25
V-8-302		
1984-85	▲E4ZZ-18A161A	41.25
(3) Shock Absorber (Front)		
1983-84-exc. V-8.	▲E3DZ-18124D	91.50
V-8	▲E4DZ-18124B	91.50
1985-86	▲E5DZ-18124A	91.50
(4) Spindle Assy.		
1983-86-right	▲E1SZ-3105A	137.00
left	▲E1SZ-3106A	137.00
(5) Lower Control Arm Assy.		
(exc. Touring car)		
1983-84-right	▲E3DZ-3078A	92.50

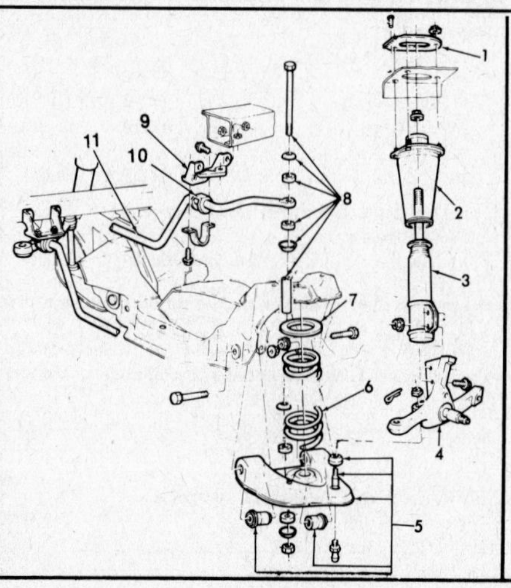

	Part No.	Price
left	▲E3DZ-3079A	92.50
1985-86-right	▲E3SZ-3078B	99.25
left	▲E3SZ-3079B	99.25
(Touring car)		
1984-85-right	▲E3SZ-3078C	99.25
left	▲E3SZ-3079B	99.25
(6) Coil Spring		
Order by year and model.		
(7) Insulator (Upper)		
1983-86	▲E1SZ-5415A	9.00
(8) Stabilizer Repair Kit		
1984-85	▲E3AZ-5A486A	20.75
(9) Bracket (Stabilizer)		
1983-86	▲E25Y-5B482A	1.25
(10) Insulator (Stabilizer)		
1983-86 (bar dia.)		
15/16″	▲E3SZ-5493D	8.50

PARTS 9 FRONT SUSPENSION 9 PARTS

	Part No.	Price
7/8"	▲E3DZ-5493C	8.50
1"	▲E3DZ-5493E	8.50
1 1/16"	▲E3DZ-5493B	8.50

	Part No.	Price
(11) Stabilizer Bar Assy.		
1983-86 (bar dia.)		
15/16"	▲E4ZZ-5482B	85.50

	Part No.	Price
7/8"	▲E3DZ-5482C	35.75
1"	▲E3DZ-5482D	47.00
1 1/16"	▲E3DZ-5482F	49.50

LABOR 11 STEERING GEAR 11 LABOR

(Factory Time) — Chilton Time

(G) Tie Rod Ends, Renew
Includes: Reset toe-in.
1983-86-one (.8) 1.2
each adtnl (.2) 2

STANDARD STEERING

(G) Horn Button or Ring, Renew
1983-86 (.4) 5

(G) Steering Wheel, Renew
1983-86 (.3) 5

(G) Steering Column Lock Actuator, Renew
1983-86-std colm (1.1) 1.5
tilt colm (1.7) 2.3

(G) Upper Mast Jacket Bearing, Renew
1983-86-std column (.4) 9
tilt column (.6) 1.1

(G) Steering Gear, Adjust (On Car)
Includes: Bearing preload and gear mesh.
All models (.3) 5

(G) Steering Gear Assembly, Renew
1983-84 (1.1) 2.0
1985-86 (1.6) 2.0

(P) Steering Gear Assy., R&R and Recondition
Includes: Disassemble, renew necessary parts, reassemble and adjust.
1983-86 (2.2) 3.0

(G) Input Shaft and Valve Assy., Recondition
Includes: R&R gear assy.
1983-84 (1.7) 2.3
1985-86 (1.5) 2.3

(G) Tie Rod Ends and Ball Joint Sockets, Renew
Includes: R&R gear assy. Add alignment charges.
1983-84 (1.6) 2.2
1985-86 (1.1) 2.2

POWER STEERING

(G) Trouble Shoot Power Steering
Includes: Test pump and system pressure. Check pounds pull on steering wheel and check for leaks.
All models 5

(G) Pump Pressure Check and Flow Test
All models 5

(M) Pump Drive Belt, Renew or Adjust
1983-86-renew (.3) 4
adjust (.2) 3

(G) Power Steering Gear, Adjust (On Car)
Includes: Bearing preload and gear mesh.
All models (.3) 5

(G) Power Steering Gear, Renew
Includes: Bleed system.
1983-84 (1.7) 2.5
1985-86 (2.2) 2.5

(P) Power Steering Gear, R&R and Recondition
Includes: Disassemble, renew necessary parts, reassemble and adjust. Bleed system.
1983-86 (3.2) 4.5

(G) Input Shaft and Valve Assy., Recondition
Includes: R&R gear assy. Bleed system.
1983-84 (2.3) 3.2
1985-86 (1.8) 3.2

(G) Tie Rod Ends and Ball Joint Sockets, Renew
Includes: R&R gear assy. Renew tie rod ends and bellows. Add alignment charges.
1983-84 (1.9) 2.6
1985-86 (1.4) 2.6

(G) Power Steering Oil Pump, Renew
Includes: Bleed system.
1983-86-Four (.9) 1.3
Six (.9) 1.3
V-6 (1.1) 1.5
V-8 (1.0) 1.4

(G) Power Steering Oil Pump, R&R and Recondition
Includes: Bleed system.
1983-86-Four (1.3) 1.8
Six (1.3) 1.8
V-6 (1.5) 2.1
V-8 (1.4) 1.9

(G) Power Steering Pump Shaft Seal, Renew
Includes: Bleed system.
1983-86
Four (1.0) 1.4
Six (1.0) 1.4
V-6 (1.2) 1.6
V-8 (1.1) 1.5

(M) Power Steering Hoses, Renew
1983-86-pressure (.6) 8
return (.6) 8
cooling (.4) 5

PARTS 11 POWER STEERING GEAR 11 PARTS

	Part No.	Price
(1) Tie Rod End		
1983-86	▲E2DZ-3A130A	36.00
(2) Connecting Rod Assy.		
1983-86	▲E2SZ-3280A	66.25
(3) Sector Shaft Assy.		
1983-84-exc. below	▲D8BZ-3575A	36.50
1984-85-Touring sed.	▲E3SZ-3575A	31.75
1985-86	▲E5AZ-3575A	N.L.
(4) Gear Rack Tube		
1983-86	▲D8BZ-3K762A	2.25
(5) Cup (Worm Bearing)		
1983-86	▲D8BZ-3552A	13.25
(6) Thrust Bearing (Worm)		
1983-86	▲D8BZ-3571A	N.L.
(7) Check Valve Kit		
1983-86	▲E3SZ-3D728A	15.75

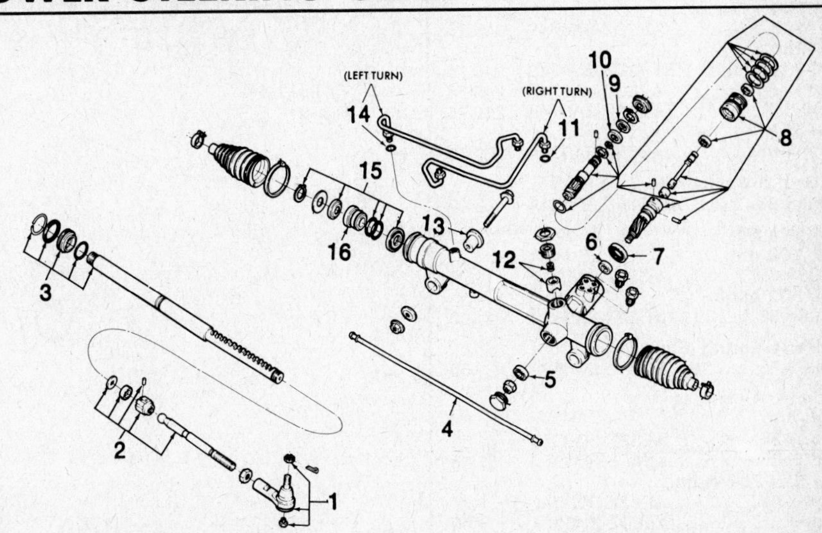

PARTS 11 POWER STEERING GEAR 11 PARTS

	Part No.	Price
(8) Shaft & Control Assy.		
1983-85-exc. below	▲E4DZ-3D517C	50.00
Touring sed.	▲E4SZ-3D517F	50.00
1986	▲E5DZ-3D517A	50.00
(9) Seal (Input Shaft)		
1983-86	▲D6AZ-3D526A	4.75
(10) Bearing (Input Shaft)		
1983-86	▲D8AZ-3D525A	8.75
(11) Pressure Tube (Right Turn)		
1983	▲D9BZ-3A717A	15.25
1984-86	▲E4DZ-3A717A	14.25
(12) Bearing (Rack Adjustment)		
1983-86	▲E0SZ-3F515A	8.25
(13) Insulator		
1983-86	▲E3DZ-3C716A	6.50
(14) Pressure Tube (Left Turn)		
1983	▲D9BZ-3A714A	18.00
1984-86	▲E4DZ-3A714A	14.25
(15) Seal Kit (Rack Shaft)		
1983-87	▲E3SZ-3E501B	12.50
(16) Bushing (Sector Shaft)		
1983-86	▲D9BZ-3576A	4.25

PARTS 11 STEERING GEAR-(STANDARD) 11 PARTS

	Part No.	Price
(1) Steering Gear		
1983-86	▲E2DZ-3504B	385.50
(2) Insulator		
1983-86	▲E3DZ-3C716A	6.50
(3) Oil Seal (Sector Shaft)		
1983-86	▲D1FZ-3738A	1.25
(4) Cup (Worm Bearing)		
1983-86	▲D1FZ-3552A	13.75
(5) Shaft Assy. (Upper)		
(wo/Tilt wheel)		
1983-86	▲E3SZ-3524B	47.25
(Tilt wheel)		
1983-84	▲E3SZ-3524A	193.50
1985-86	▲E5DZ-3524A	200.00
(6) Bearing (Rack Adjustment)		
1983-86	▲D8BZ-3F515B	7.00
(7) Gasket & Shim Kit		
1983-86	▲D3FZ-3F518A	1.00
(8) Connecting Rod Assy.		
1983-86	▲E2SZ-3280A	66.25
(9) Sector Shaft		
1983-86	▲D8BZ-3575B	62.00
(10) Tie Rod End		
1983-86	▲E2DZ-3A130A	36.00

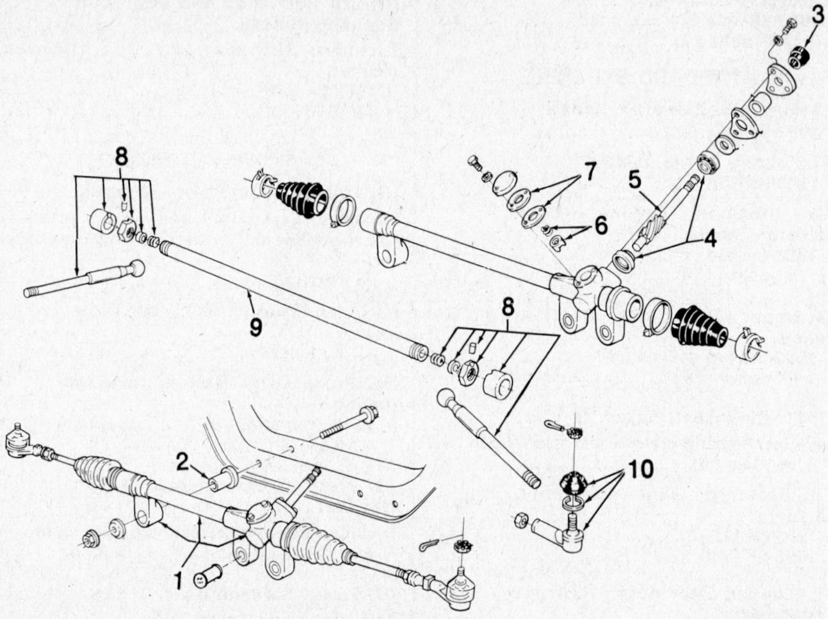

PARTS 11 POWER STEERING PUMP 11 PARTS

	Part No.	Price
Power Steering Pump		
Four-140		
1983-85	▲E5DZ-3A674A	215.75
1986	▲E6SZ-3A674A	215.75
Six-200		
1983	▲E2DZ-3A674B	215.75
V-6-230		
1983	▲E2DZ-3A674B	215.75
1984-85	▲E5DZ-3A674B	215.75
1986	▲E6SZ-3A674B	215.75
V-8-302		
1984-85	▲E5SZ-3A674A	200.75
(1) Seal & Gasket Kit		
1983-86	▲E1AZ-3D684A	3.00
(2) Valve Assy.		
140, 200 eng.		
1983-86	▲D8BZ-3A561A	11.00
230, 302 engs.		
1983-86	▲E1SZ-3A561A	11.00
(3) Valve Spring (Flow Control)		
1983-86	▲D8AZ-3D586A	1.50
(4) Rotor Assy.		
Four-140		
1983-84	▲E3FZ-3D607A	52.50
1985-86	▲E5FZ-3D607A	56.25
Six-200, 230 engs.		
1983-85	▲E53Z-3D607A	N.L.
1986	▲E6DZ-3D607A	4.50

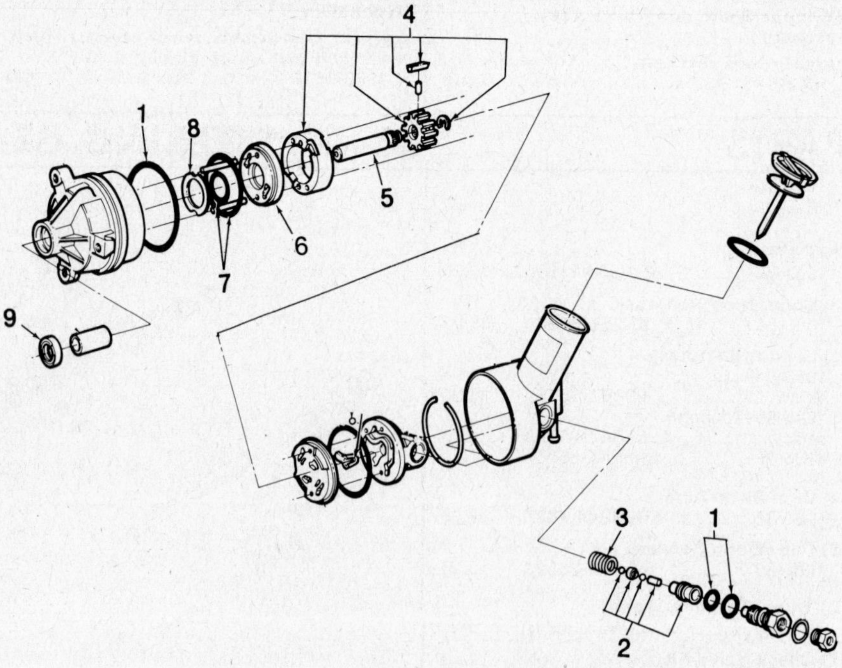

PARTS 11 POWER STEERING PUMP 11 PARTS

	Part No.	Price
V-8-302		
1984-85	▲E5SZ-3D607A	38.75
(5) Rotor Shaft		
1983-86	▲D8AZ-3B559A	18.00
(6) Pressure Plate (Rear)		
1983-87	▲D8AZ-3D590B	13.75
(7) Seal Gasket Kit		
1983-86	▲E1AZ-3B584A	8.75
(8) Spring (Pressure Plate)		
1983-85	▲D8AZ-3D596A	2.50
1986	▲E6FZ-3D596A	2.50
(9) Oil Seal (Rotor Shaft)		
1983-86	▲D9AZ-3B592A	9.25

LABOR 12 CYLINDER HEAD & VALVE SYSTEM 12 LABOR

(Factory Time)	Chilton Time
(G) Compression Test	
Four-1983-86 (.3)	.6
Six-1983 (.3)	.6
V-6-1983-86 (.4)	.9
V-8-1984-86 (.5)	.9
w/A.C. add	.2

(G) Cylinder Head Gasket, Renew

Includes: Check cylinder head and block flatness. Clean carbon and make all necessary adjustments.

Four-1983-86 (3.7)	5.1
Six-1983 (2.6)	3.8
V-6-1983-86-one (4.7)	6.6
both (6.0)	8.4
V-8-1984-86-one (3.6)	4.9
both (5.0)	6.8
w/A.C. add (.3)	.3
w/P.S. add (.3)	.3

(G) Cylinder Head, Renew

Includes: Transfer all components, clean carbon. Reface valves, check valve spring tension, assembled height and valve head runout.

Four-1983-86 (5.8)	7.5
Six-1983 (4.9)	6.2
V-6-1983-86-one (5.7)	8.0
both (8.0)	11.2
V-8-1984-86-one (4.8)	6.5
both (7.5)	9.4
w/A.C. add (.3)	.3
w/P.S. add (.3)	.3

(P) Clean Carbon and Grind Valves

Includes: R&R cylinder head(s), check valve spring tension, valve seat and head runout, stem to guide clearance and spring assembled height. Minor tune up.

Four-1983-86 (6.3)	8.0
Six-1983 (5.3)	7.9
V-6-1983-86	
one side (6.2)	8.6
both sides (8.9)	12.4
V-8-1984-86	
one side (5.5)	7.7

COMBINATIONS

Add to Valve Job

See Machine Shop Operations

(Factory Time)	Chilton Time
(G) DRAIN, EVACUATE & RECHARGE AIR CONDITIONING SYSTEM	
All models (.7)	1.2
(G) ROCKER ARMS & SHAFT ASSY., DISASSEMBLE AND CLEAN OR RECONDITION	
Six (.5)	.8
(G) HYDRAULIC VALVE LIFTERS, DISASSEMBLE AND CLEAN	
Each	.2
(G) DISTRIBUTOR, RECONDITION	
All models (.7)	1.0
(G) CARBURETOR, RECONDITION	
Four (.8)	1.3
Six (1.2)	1.7
V-6 (1.0)	1.5
V-8 (1.0)	1.5
(P) VALVE GUIDES, REAM OVERSIZE	
Each (.1)	.1

(Factory Time)	Chilton Time
both sides (8.7)	12.1
w/A.C. add (.3)	.3
w/P.S. add (.3)	.3
(G) Rocker Arm Cover or Gasket, Renew	
Four-1983-86 (.7)	1.0
Six-1983 (.7)	1.0
V-6-1983-86-one (.8)	1.1
both (1.2)	1.8
V-8-1984-86-one (.8)	1.1
both (1.1)	1.7
(G) Rocker Arm Shaft Assy., Recondition	
Six-1983 (1.2)	1.5

(Factory Time)	Chilton Time
(G) Valve Push Rods, Renew	
Six-1983-one (.9)	1.2
all (.9)	1.4
V-6-1983-86-one (.9)	1.3
all-one side (1.0)	1.5
all-both sides (1.5)	2.1
V-8-1984-86-one (.9)	1.3
all-one side (1.0)	1.5
all-both sides (1.4)	2.0
(G) Rocker Arm(s), Renew	
Four-1983-86-one (.8)	1.2
all (1.1)	1.7
V-6-1983-86-one (.9)	1.3
all-one side (1.0)	1.5
all-both sides (1.5)	2.1
V-8-1984-86-one (.9)	1.3
all-one side (1.0)	1.5
all-both sides (1.4)	2.0

(G) Valve Tappets, Renew

Includes: R&R intake manifold where required. Make all necessary adjustments.

Four-1983-86-one (.8)	1.4
all (1.2)	2.5
Six-1983	
one or all (2.2)	3.4
V-6-1983-86-one (2.6)	3.9
all (3.2)	4.5
V-8-1984-86-one (2.3)	3.1
all (3.3)	4.5
w/Cruise control add (.1)	.1
(G) Valve Springs and/or Valve Stem Oil Seals, Renew (Head on Car)	
Four-1983-86-one (.9)	1.5
each adtnl (.2)	.2
Six-1983-one (.9)	1.5
each adtnl (.2)	.2
V6-1983-86-one (1.0)	1.4
each adtnl (.2)	.2
all (3.0)	4.0
V-8-1984-86-one (1.0)	1.4
each adtnl (.2)	.2
all (3.5)	4.7

PARTS 12 CYLINDER HEAD & VALVE SYSTEM 12 PARTS

FOUR CYLINDER 140 ENG.

	Part No.	Price
Valve Grind Gasket Set		
1983-86	▲E5ZZ-6079A	42.00
(1) Cylinder Head		
wo/Valves		
1983	▲E1BZ-6049C	351.75
1984	▲E4ZZ-6049A	351.75
1985-86	▲E5ZZ-6049B	351.75
w/Valves		
1983	▲E1BZ-6049B	521.25
1984	▲E4ZZ-6049B	521.25
1985-86	▲E5ZZ-6049C	869.75
(2) Cylinder Head Gasket		
1983-86	▲E5FZ-6051A	13.50

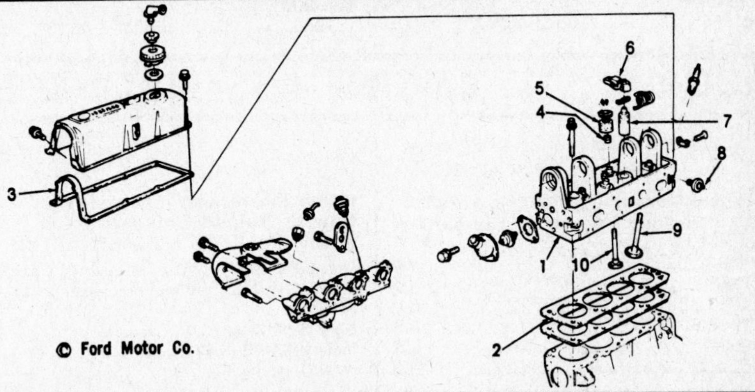

PARTS 12 CYLINDER HEAD & VALVE SYSTEM 12 PARTS

	Part No.	Price
(3) Valve Cover Gasket		
1983-86	▲E2ZZ-6584A	1.00
(4) Seal (Valve Stems)		
1983-84	▲D4FZ-6571A	1.25
1985-86-Intake	▲E43Z-6571A	2.25
Exhaust	▲D4FZ-6571A	1.25
(5) Valve Spring		
1983-84	▲E4ZZ-6513A	6.25
1985-86	▲E5ZZ-6513A	N.L.
(6) Rocker Arm		
1983-86	▲D8FZ-6564A	8.00
(7) Valve Tappet		
1983-86	▲D6FZ-6500A	10.00
(8) Oil Pressure Gauge (Engine)		
1983-86	▲D4AZ-9278A	3.50
(9) Intake Valve		
1983-86	▲E5ZZ-6507A	9.75
(10) Exhaust Valve		
1983-86	▲E43Z-6505A	14.25

PARTS 12 CYLINDER HEAD & VALVE SYSTEM 12 PARTS

SIX & V-8 ENGS.

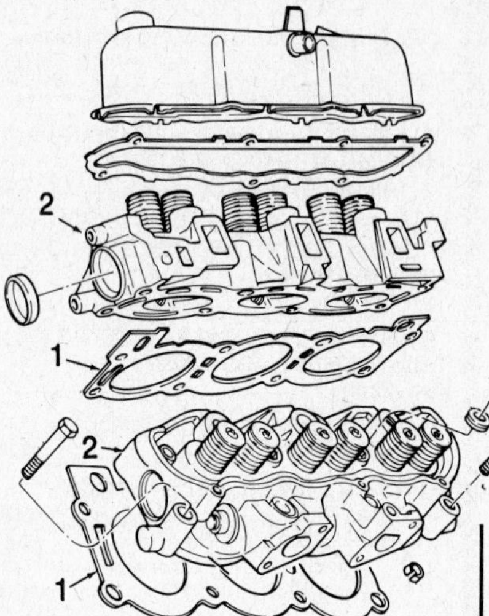

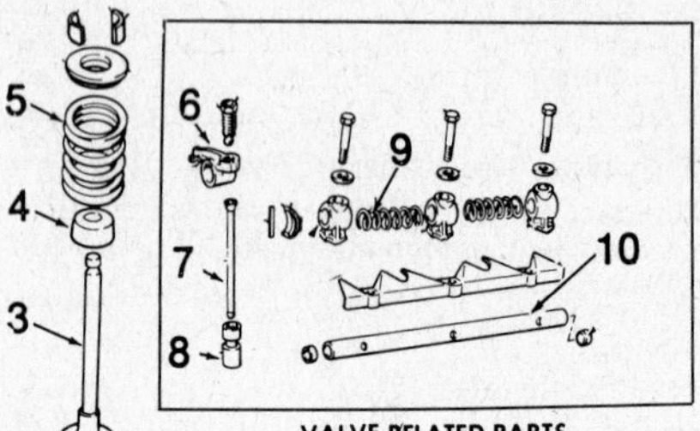

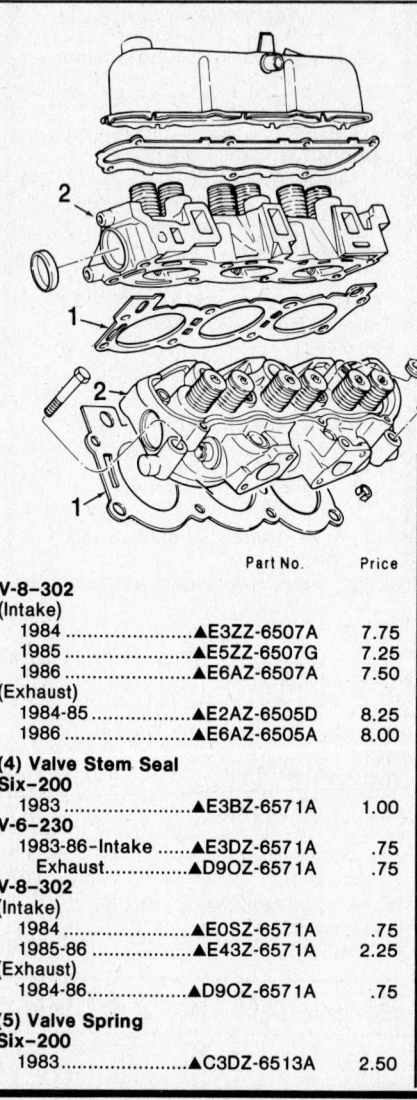

VALVE RELATED PARTS

	Part No.	Price
Valve Grind Gasket Set		
Six-200		
1983	▲C9OZ-6079A	37.25
V-6-230		
1983	▲E3DZ-6079A	71.50
1984	▲E4DZ-6079A	65.25
1985-86	▲E5DZ-6079A	71.50
V-8-302		
1984	▲E1AZ-6079A	61.00
1985-86	▲E5ZZ-6079C	52.50
(1) Cylinder Head Gasket		
Six-200		
1983	▲C9DZ-6051B	20.25
V-6-230		
1983-86	▲E3DZ-6051A	12.75
V-8-302		
1984	▲D7OZ-6051C	12.50
1985	▲E5ZZ-6051A	13.75
1986	▲E5ZZ-6051B	13.75
(2) Cylinder Head		
Six-200		
1983-wo/Valves	▲E0BZ-6049A	709.50
w/Valves	▲E0BZ-6049B	Disc.
V-6-230		
1983-wo/Valves	▲E3DZ-6049C	377.00
w/Valves	▲E3DZ-6049D	505.25
1984-86-wo/Valves	▲E4DZ-6049A	377.00
w/Valves	▲E4DZ-6049B	505.25
V-8-302		
1984-wo/Valves	▲D84Y-6049C	281.25
w/Valves	▲E2AZ-6049A	461.50
1985-wo/Valves	▲E5AZ-6049A	302.25
w/Valves	▲E5AZ-6049B	429.25
1986	▲E6AZ-6049A	302.25
(3) Valves (Std.)		
Six-200		
1983-Intake	▲D7BZ-6507A	8.50
Exhaust	▲E1AZ-6505A	10.00
V-6-230		
(Intake)		
1983	▲E2DZ-6507A	9.50
1984-86	▲E4DZ-6507A	9.50
(Exhaust)		
1983-86	▲E2DZ-6505A	11.75
V-8-302		
(Intake)		
1984	▲E3ZZ-6507A	7.75
1985	▲E5ZZ-6507G	7.25
1986	▲E6AZ-6507A	7.50
(Exhaust)		
1984-85	▲E2AZ-6505D	8.25
1986	▲E6AZ-6505A	8.00
(4) Valve Stem Seal		
Six-200		
1983	▲E3BZ-6571A	1.00
V-6-230		
1983-86-Intake	▲E3DZ-6571A	.75
Exhaust	▲D9OZ-6571A	.75
V-8-302		
(Intake)		
1984	▲E0SZ-6571A	.75
1985-86	▲E43Z-6571A	2.25
(Exhaust)		
1984-86	▲D9OZ-6571A	.75
(5) Valve Spring		
Six-200		
1983	▲C3DZ-6513A	2.50
V-6-230		
1983-84	▲E2DZ-6513A	5.50
1985-86	▲E4DZ-6513A	4.75
V-8-302		
1984-86-Intake	▲D8AZ-6513B	5.75
Exhaust	▲D5OZ-6513A	6.75
(6) Rocker Arm		
1983-200 eng.	▲C4DZ-6564A	8.75
1983-86-230 eng.	▲E2DZ-6564A	7.75
1984-86-302 eng	▲E0AZ-6564A	11.00
(7) Push Rod		
1983-200 eng.	▲C4DZ-6565A	2.75
1983-86-230 eng.	▲E2DZ-6565A	2.75
1984-86-302 eng.	▲C9OZ-6565B	2.75
(8) Valve Tappet		
1983-86-exc. below	▲D9HZ-6500A	9.25
200 eng	▲C8AZ-6500A	9.25
(9) Spring (Rocker Shaft)		
1983-200 eng.	▲C0DE-6587A	.75
(10) Rocker Arm Shaft		
1983-200 eng.	▲C3DZ-6563A	27.25

LABOR 13 ENGINE ASSEMBLY & MOUNTS 13 LABOR

(Factory Time) Chilton Time

(G) Engine Assembly, Remove & Install

Does not include transfer of any parts or equipment.

	Chilton Time
Four-1983-86 (3.0)	4.9
Six-1983 (3.1)	5.0
V-6-1983-86 (4.3)	6.0
V-8-1984-86 (4.5)	6.3
w/A.C. add (.3)	.3
w/P.S. add (.3)	.3

(G) Engine Assembly, Replace with New or Rebuilt Unit (With Cyl. Heads)

Includes: R&R engine assembly, transfer all necessary parts, fuel and electrical units. Minor tune up.

	Chilton Time
Six-1983 (5.4)	8.9
V-8-1984-86 (6.8)	11.0
w/A.C. add (.3)	.3
w/P.S. add (.3)	.3

(P) Cylinder Assembly, Renew (w/All Internal Parts Less Head(s) and Oil Pan)

Includes: R&R engine, transfer all component parts not supplied with replacement engine. Clean carbon, grind valves. Tune engine.

	Chilton Time
Four-1983-86 (9.7)	15.0

LABOR 13 ENGINE ASSEMBLY & MOUNTS 13 LABOR

(Factory Time)	Chilton Time
Six–1983 (9.2)	14.5
V-6–1983-86 (11.1)	15.6
V-8–1984-86 (14.7)	19.8
w/A.C. add (.3)	.3
w/P.S. add (.3)	.3

(P) Cylinder Block, Renew

Includes: R&R engine, transfer all component parts, renew rings and bearings. Clean carbon, grind valves. Tune engine.

Four–1983-86 (12.8)	19.6
Six–1983 (13.7)	20.8
V-6–1983-86 (15.9)	22.1
V-8–1984-86 (19.3)	25.6
w/A.C. add (.3)	.3
w/P.S. add (.3)	.3

(P) Engine Assy., R&R and Recondition (Complete)

Includes: Rebore block, install new pistons, rings, rod and main bearings. Clean carbon, grind valves. Tune engine.

(Factory Time)	Chilton Time
Four–1983-86 (20.1)	28.3
Six–1983 (24.2)	29.7
V-6–1983-86 (23.1)	32.3
V-8–1984-86 (28.0)	34.0
w/A.C. add (.3)	.3
w/P.S. add (.3)	.3

(P) Engine Assembly, Recondition (In Car)

Includes: Expand or renew pistons, install new rings, pins, rod and main bearings. Clean carbon, grind valves. Tune engine.

(Factory Time)	Chilton Time
Four–1983-86 (16.7)	19.5
Six–1983 (17.7)	22.5
V-6–1983-86 (19.6)	27.4
V-8–1984-86 (23.5)	27.9

(G) Engine Mounts, Renew

FRONT	
Four–1983-86-one (.6)	.8
both (.8)	1.0
Six–1983-one (.4)	.6
both (.6)	.9
V-6–1983-86-one (.6)	.8
both (.8)	1.0
V-8–1984-86-one (.6)	.9
both (.7)	1.2
REAR	
1983-86 (.4)	.7

PARTS 13 ENGINE ASSEMBLY & MOUNTS 13 PARTS

Engine Overhaul Gasket

	Part No.	Price
Four–140		
1983-84	▲E2PZ-6E078A	25.50
1985-86	▲E5ZZ-6E078A	25.50
Six–200		
1983	▲D5PZ-6E078H	27.50
V-6–230		
1983-86	▲E3DZ-6E078B	23.50
V-8–302		
1984-86	▲E3AZ-6E078A	27.75

When a complete overhaul gasket set is required you must also order a Valve Grind Gasket Set.

Cylinder Assembly

Includes Cylinder block with all internal part of engine except cylinder head, tappets, oil pan or cylinder front cover.

	Part No.	Price
Four–140		
1983-84	▲E2ZZ-6009A	1506.00
1985-86	▲E5ZZ-6009A	1506.00
Six–200		
1983	▲E3BZ-6009A	1609.50
V-6–230		
1983-86	▲E4DZ-6009A	2000.50
V-8–302		
1984	▲E3AZ-6009A	2044.75
1985-86	▲E5ZZ-6009C	2253.25

Cylinder Block

	Part No.	Price
Four–140		
1983-84	▲E3ZZ-6010A	671.75
1985-86	▲E5ZZ-6010A	671.75
Six–200		
1983	▲E3BZ-6010A	724.25
V-6–230		
1983	▲E3DZ-6010A	837.75
1984-86	▲E4DZ-6010A	900.25
V-8–302		
1984-85	▲E5AZ-6010A	920.25
1986	▲E6AZ-6010A	920.25

Front Engine Mount

	Part No.	Price
Four–140		
1983-right	▲E3DZ-6038D	29.75
left (M.T.)	▲E3DZ-6038E	24.50
left (A.T.)	▲E3DZ-6038F	30.50
1984-86-right	▲E4DZ-6038A	25.75
left	▲E4DZ-6038B	24.50
Six–200		
1983-right	▲E3DZ-6038A	33.00
left	▲E3DZ-6038B	33.00
V-6–230		
1983-right	▲E3DZ-6038C	25.75
left	▲E2DZ-6038B	25.75
1984-86-right	▲E3SZ-6038G	37.75
left	▲E3SZ-6038H	37.75
V-8–302		
1984-86-right	▲E4DZ-6038C	35.75
left	▲E4DZ-6038D	35.75

Rear Engine Mount

	Part No.	Price
Four–140		
1983-86	▲E3ZZ-6068A	20.75
Six–200		
1983	▲E2SZ-6068B	22.50
V-6–230		
1983-86-C-5	▲E2SZ-6068C	19.50
A.O.D.	▲E2SZ-6068B	22.50
V-8–302		
1984-86	▲E4ZZ-6068A	20.75

LABOR 14 PISTONS, RINGS & BEARINGS 14 LABOR

COMBINATIONS

Add to Engine Work

See Machine Shop Operations

(Factory Time)	Chilton Time
(G) DRAIN, EVACUATE & RECHARGE AIR CONDITIONING SYSTEM	
All models (.7)	1.2
(G) ROCKER ARMS & SHAFT ASSY., DISASSEMBLE AND CLEAN OR RECONDITION	
Six (.5)	.8
(G) HYDRAULIC VALVE LIFTERS, DISASSEMBLE AND CLEAN	
Each	.2
(G) DISTRIBUTOR, RECONDITION	
All models (.7)	1.0
(G) CARBURETOR, RECONDITION	
Four (.8)	1.3
Six (1.2)	1.7
V-6 (1.0)	1.5
V-8 (1.0)	1.5
(G) CYLINDER HEAD, R&R (ENGINE REMOVED)	
Four	
wo/Turbo	3.5
w/Turbo	4.0
V-6	
one	4.0
both	5.5
V-8	
one	3.2
both	4.7
(G) CONNECTING ROD, RENEW (ENGINE DISASSEMBLED)	
All engines	
each	.4
(P) VALVE GUIDES, REAM OVERSIZE	
Each (.1)	.1
(G) DEGLAZE CYLINDER WALLS	
Each (.1)	.1
(G) REMOVE CYLINDER TOP RIDGE	
Each (.1)	.1
(G) TIMING CHAIN OR GEARS, RENEW (COVER REMOVED)	
All models (.3)	.5
(G) MAIN BEARINGS, RENEW (PAN REMOVED)	
Four (1.9)	2.5
Six (2.7)	3.4
V-6 (1.5)	2.0
V-8 (1.9)	2.5
(G) PLASTIGAUGE BEARINGS	
Each (.1)	.1
(G) OIL PUMP, RECONDITION	
All models (.3)	.6
(M) OIL FILTER ELEMENT, RENEW	
All models (.3)	.3

LABOR 14 PISTONS, RINGS & BEARINGS 14 LABOR

(Factory Time)	Chilton Time
(P) Rings, Renew	
(See Engine Combinations)	
Includes: Remove cylinder top ridge, deglaze cylinder walls, replace rod bearings, clean carbon. Minor tune up.	
Four–1983-86 (7.2)	9.6
Six–1983 (6.9)	8.9
V-6–1983-86 (10.3)	14.5
V-8–1984-86 (10.1)	14.0
w/A.C. add (.3)	.3
w/P.S. add (.2)	.2
(P) Piston or Connecting Rod, Renew (One)	
Includes: Remove cylinder top ridge, deglaze cylinder walls, replace rod bearings, clean carbon. Minor tune up.	
Four–1983-86 (6.2)	8.3
Six–1983 (4.7)	7.1
V-6–1983-86 (6.9)	9.7
V-8–1984-86 (5.4)	8.5
w/A.C. add (.3)	.3
w/P.S. add (.2)	.2
(P) Connecting Rod Bearings, Renew	
Four–1983-86 (2.8)	3.9
Six–1983 (3.2)	4.1
V-6–1983-86 (3.5)	4.7
V-8–1984-86 (4.2)	6.1

PARTS 14 PISTONS, RINGS & BEARINGS 14 PARTS

	Part No.	Price
(1) Piston Ring Set (Partial)		
Four–140		
1983-84	▲D4FZ-6148A	31.75
1985-86	▲E5ZZ-6148A	32.00
Six–200		
1983	▲C3OZ-6148E	32.75
V-6–230		
1983-86	▲E2DZ-6148A	29.00
V-8–302		
1984-85	▲C3AZ-6148F	31.75
1986	▲E6AZ-6148A	31.75
(2) Piston Assy.		
Four–140		
1983-84	▲D4FZ-6108A	21.75
1985-86	▲E5ZZ-6108A	20.75
Six–200		
1983	▲C9DZ-6108A	25.75
V-6–230		
1983	▲E2DZ-6108AB	25.75
1984-86	▲E4DZ-6108A	25.50
V-8–302		
1984-86	▲D9AZ-6108A	35.00
(3) Connecting Rod Assy.		
1983-86-140 eng.	▲D7FZ-6200A	47.00
1983-200 eng.	▲D8BZ-6200A	41.75
1983-86-230 eng.	▲E2DZ-6200A	47.00
1984-86-302 eng.	▲D3OZ-6200A	44.00
(4) Connecting Rod Bearing		
1983-86-140 eng.	▲D7FZ-6211A	2.50
1983-200 eng.	▲D7BZ-6211A	2.75
1983-86-230 eng.	▲E2DZ-6211A	2.75
1984-86-302 eng.	▲C2OZ-6211R	2.25

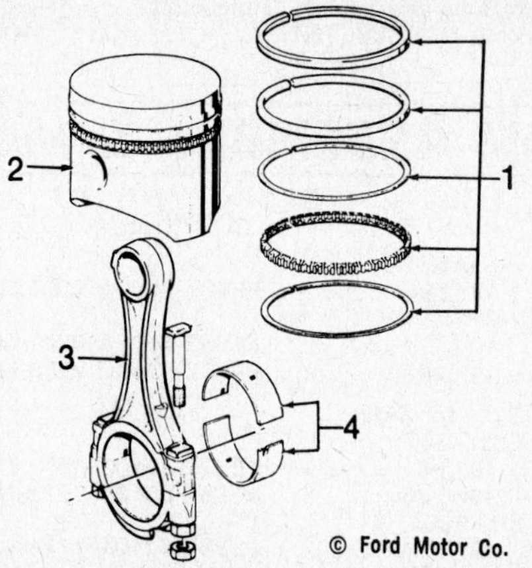

© Ford Motor Co.

LABOR 15 CRANKSHAFT & DAMPER 15 LABOR

(Factory Time)	Chilton Time
(P) Crankshaft and Main Bearings, Renew	
Includes: R&R engine, check all bearing clearances.	
Four–1983-86 (6.8)	9.7
Six–1983 (6.9)	10.0
V-6–1983-86 (7.5)	10.5
V-8–1984-86 (8.3)	11.5
w/A.C. add (.3)	.3
w/P.S. add (.3)	.3
(P) Main Bearings, Renew	
Includes: Check all bearing clearances.	
Four–1983-86 (3.8)	5.2
Six–1983 (4.5)	6.0
V-6–1983-86 (3.6)	4.9
V-8–1984-86 (4.3)	6.2
(P) Main and Rod Bearings, Renew	
Includes: Check all bearing clearances.	
Four–1983-86 (4.7)	6.4
Six–1983 (5.9)	7.8
V-6–1983-86 (5.0)	6.7
V-8–1984-86 (6.1)	8.6
(G) Rear Main Bearing Oil Seals, Renew (Upper & Lower)	
Note: Split lip type.	
Includes: R&R oil pan.	
Four–1983 (2.7)	3.9
Six–1983 (2.6)	3.8
V-6–1983 (2.8)	4.0
(G) Rear Main Bearing Oil Seal, Renew	
Full Circle Type	
Four–1984-86	
w/M.T. (1.8)	2.5
w/A.T. (2.3)	3.2
V-6–1984-86 (3.5)	4.9
V-8–1984-86 (3.3)	4.6
(G) Vibration Damper or Pulley, Renew	
Four–1983-86 (.5)	.9
Six–1983 (.5)	.9
V-6–1983-86 (.8)	1.2
V-8–1984-86 (.8)	1.2
w/A.C. add (.1)	.1
w/P.S. add (.1)	.1
(G) Crankshaft Front Oil Seal, Renew	
Four–1983-86	
crank or cam (1.3)	1.8
aux. drive (1.0)	1.5
Six–1983 (1.6)	2.3
V-6–1983-86 (1.0)	1.5
V-8–1984-86 (.9)	1.4
w/A.C. add (.1)	.1

PARTS 15 CRANKSHAFT & DAMPER 15 PARTS

	Part No.	Price
FOUR–140		
(1) Pulley Assy. (Outer)		
1983-86-wo/A.C.	▲E2BZ-6A312A	51.50
1983-84-w/A.C.	▲E3ZZ-6A312A	51.50
1985-86	▲E5ZZ-6A312A	48.00
(2) Spacer (Belt Cover)		
1983-86	▲D4FZ-6K297A	N.L.
(3) Crankshaft Gear		
1983-86	▲D9FZ-6306A	11.50
(4) Front Cover Assy. (Lower)		
1983-84	▲E3TZ-6019A	45.25
1985-86	▲E5ZZ-6019A	45.25

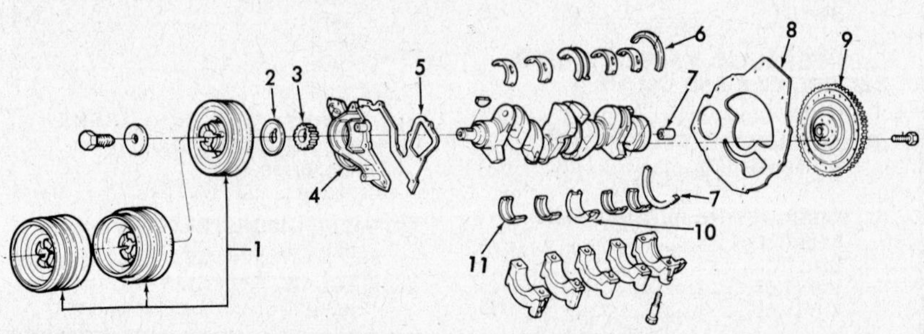

PARTS 15 CRANKSHAFT & DAMPER 15 PARTS

	Part No.	Price
(5) Gasket (Front Cover)		
1983-86-outer	▲D4FZ-6020A	2.25
inner	▲D4FZ-6020B	1.50
(6) Rear Packing (Crankshaft)		
1983-86	▲E5ZZ-6701A	6.25
(7) Pilot Bearing (Clutch)		
1983-86	▲D4ZZ-7600A	5.25
(8) Cover Plate (Rear)		
1983-86	▲E3TZ-7007A	21.75
(9) Flywheel		
1983-86-A.T.	▲D5FZ-6375A	81.75
M.T.	▲E2ZZ-6375C	185.75
(10) Main Bearing (Center)		
1983-86-Upper	▲D4FZ-6337A	9.75
Lower	▲D4FZ-6337G	9.75
(11) Main Bearing (Exc. Center)		
1983-86-Upper	▲D4FZ-6333A	3.75
Lower	▲D4FZ-6333A	3.75

PARTS 15 CRANKSHAFT & DAMPER 15 PARTS

	Part No.	Price
SIX & V-8 ENGS.		
(1) Vibration Damper or Pulley		
Six-200		
1983	▲D8BZ-6312A	86.25
V-6-230		
1983-86-C-5	▲E3DZ-6B321B	88.00
A.O.D.	▲E3DZ-6B321A	88.00
V-8-302		
1984-86	▲D9ZZ-6A312A	33.50
(2) Crankshaft Gear		
1983-200 eng.	▲C0DZ-6306A	10.25
1983-86-230 eng.	▲E2DZ-6306A	22.50
1984-86-302 eng.	▲D5OZ-6306A	11.25
(3) Crankshaft		
1983-200 eng. (exc. below)	▲E1BZ-6303A	476.50
w/trans. code-PEN or PEP	▲E1BZ-6303B	476.50
1983-86-230 eng.	▲E3DZ-6303A	423.25
1984-86-302 eng	▲E3AZ-6303A	500.75
(4) Main Bearing (Upper & Lower)		
Six-200		
(exc. rear intermediate)		
1983-upper	▲D5DZ-6333A	4.75
lower	▲D5DZ-6333B	4.75
(rear intermediate)		
1983 (upper)		
No. 5	▲D5DZ-6337A	7.25

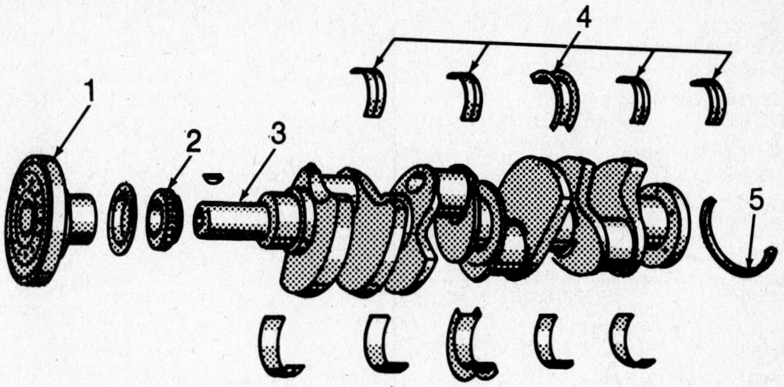

	Part No.	Price
No. 6	▲D5DZ-6333A	4.75
1983 (lower)		
No. 5	▲D5DZ-6337B	7.25
No. 6	▲D5DZ-6333B	4.75
V-6-230		
(exc. rear intermediate)		
1983-86-upper	▲E2DZ-6333A	3.25
lower	▲E2DZ-6333D	3.25
(rear intermediate)		
1983-86-upper	▲E2DZ-6337A	8.25
lower	▲E2DZ-6337D	8.25
V-8-302		
(upper)		
1984-86-exc. below	▲C3AZ-6333P	3.50
center	▲C3AZ-6337P	8.00
(lower)		
1984-86-exc. below	▲C3AZ-6333AA	3.50
center	▲C3AZ-6337AA	8.00
(5) Rear Main Bearing Oil Seal		
(rope type)		
1983	▲C9OZ-6701A	2.00
(split type)		
1983-exc. below	▲D4FZ-6701A	6.25
200 eng	▲C9AZ-6701B	8.00
(one-piece type)		
1983-86	▲E2ZZ-6701A	6.00

LABOR 16 CAMSHAFT & TIMING GEARS 16 LABOR

(Factory Time)	Chilton Time
(G) Timing Case Seal and Gaskets, Renew	
Four-1983-86 (1.6)	2.1
Six-1983 (1.2)	1.8
V-6-1983-86 (4.1)	5.7
V-8-1984-86	2.9
w/A.C. add (.3)	.3
w/P.S. add (.2)	.2
(G) Timing Chain or Sprockets, Renew	
Includes: Adjust timing.	
Six-1983 (1.5)	2.3
V-6-1983-86 (4.4)	6.2
V-8-1984-86 (2.6)	3.4
w/A.C. add (.3)	.3
w/P.S. add (.2)	.2
(G) Timing Belt, Renew	
Four-1983-86 (1.1)	2.0
Renew tensioner add	.2
(G) Camshaft, Renew	
Four-1983-86 (2.9)	4.1
Six-1983 (4.5)	6.1
V-6-1983-86 (7.4)	10.7
V-8-1984-86 (5.4)	7.5
w/A.C. add (.2)	.2
w/P.S. add (.2)	.2
(G) Camshaft Bearings, Renew	
Includes: R&R engine and crankshaft, where required.	
Four-1983-86 (3.4)	5.5
Six-1983 (6.8)	8.5
V-6-1983-86 (8.8)	12.1
V-8-1984-86 (9.1)	12.0
w/A.C. add (.3)	.3
w/P.S. add (.3)	.3

PARTS 16 CAMSHAFT & TIMING GEARS 16 PARTS

	Part No.	Price
FOUR-140		
(1) Cylinder Cover Assy. (Front)		
1983-86	▲E3ZZ-6019A	38.50
(2) Crankshaft Sprocket		
1983-86	▲D9FZ-6306A	11.50
(3) Camshaft Sprocket		
1983-86	▲D4FZ-6256A	13.75
(4) Belt (Timing)		
1983-86	▲E5ZZ-6268A	21.50
(5) Camshaft Gear		
1983-86	▲D4FZ-6256A	13.75
(6) Cover Gasket (Front)		
1983-86-Outer	▲D4FZ-6020A	2.25

PARTS 16 CAMSHAFT & TIMING GEARS 16 PARTS

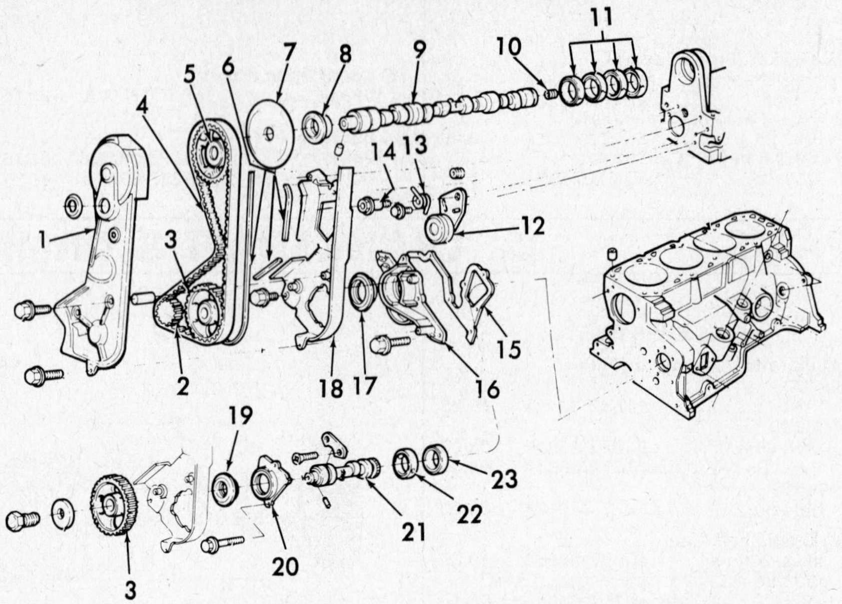

	Part No.	Price
(7) Guide (Timing Belt)		
1983-86	▲D4FZ-6B260A	4.75
(8) Oil Seal (Front Cover)		
1983-86	▲D4FZ-6700A	5.75
(9) Camshaft		
1983-84	▲E1ZZ-6250A	158.75
1985-86	▲E5ZZ-6250B	148.75
(10) Plug		
1983-86	▲87837-S	1.75
(11) Camshaft Bearing		
1983-86	▲D4FZ-6261C	3.25
(12) Tensioner (Pulley Assy.)		
1983-86	▲D4FZ-6K254A	23.00
(13) Spring (Tensioner)		
1983-86	▲D4FZ-6L273A	7.50
(14) Bolt (Tensioner)		
1983-86	▲D7FZ-6K282A	4.25
(15) Cover Gasket (Inner)		
1983-86	▲D4FZ-6020B	1.50
(16) Front Cover (Lower)		
1983-84	▲E3TZ-6019A	45.25
1985-86	▲E5ZZ-6019A	45.25
(17) Oil Seal (Front Cover)		
1983-86	▲D4FZ-6700A	5.75
(18) Front Cover (Inner)		
1983-86	▲E3ZZ-6019B	43.00
(19) Oil Seal (Front Cover)		
1983-86	▲D4FZ-6700A	5.75

	Part No.	Price
(20) Front Cover (Upper)		
1983-86	▲D4FZ-6019B	22.75
(21) Drive Shaft (Dist., Fuel, Oil Pump)		
1983-86	▲E4FZ-6A739A	63.25

	Part No.	Price
(22) Auxiliary Shaft Bearing (Front)		
1983-86	▲D4FZ-6A753A	5.00
(23) Auxiliary Shaft Bearing (Rear)		
1983-86	▲D4FZ-6A738A	5.00

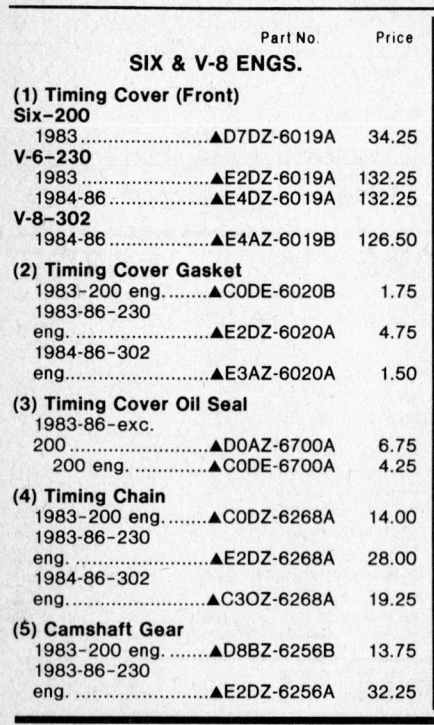

PARTS 16 CAMSHAFT & TIMING GEARS 16 PARTS

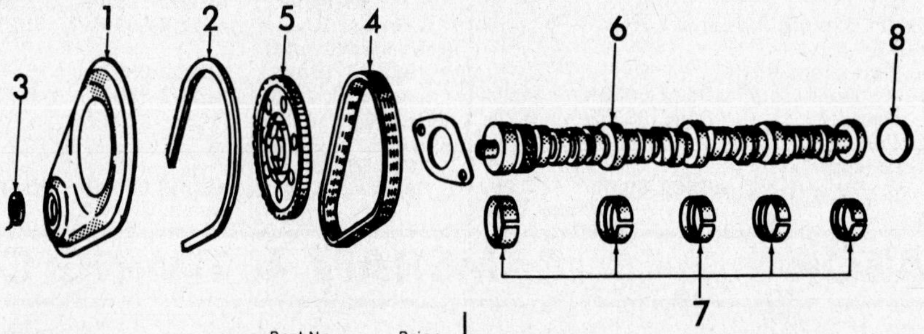

SIX & V-8 ENGS.

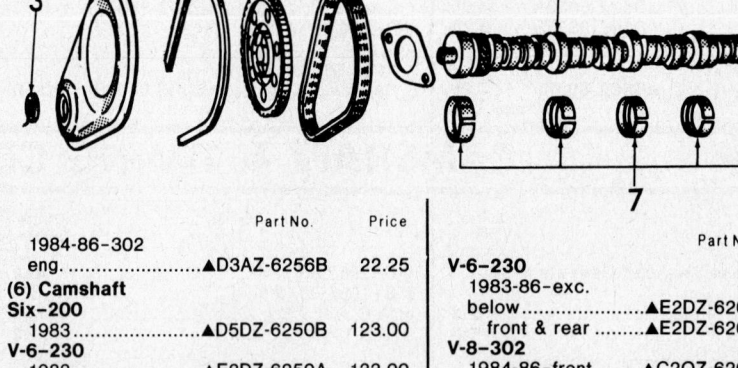

	Part No.	Price
(1) Timing Cover (Front)		
Six-200		
1983	▲D7DZ-6019A	34.25
V-6-230		
1983	▲E2DZ-6019A	132.25
1984-86	▲E4DZ-6019A	132.25
V-8-302		
1984-86	▲E4AZ-6019B	126.50
(2) Timing Cover Gasket		
1983-200 eng.	▲C0DE-6020B	1.75
1983-86-230 eng.	▲E2DZ-6020A	4.75
1984-86-302 eng.	▲E3AZ-6020A	1.50
(3) Timing Cover Oil Seal		
1983-86-exc. 200	▲D0AZ-6700A	6.75
200 eng.	▲C0DE-6700A	4.25
(4) Timing Chain		
1983-200 eng.	▲C0DZ-6268A	14.00
1983-86-230 eng.	▲E2DZ-6268A	28.00
1984-86-302 eng.	▲C3OZ-6268A	19.25
(5) Camshaft Gear		
1983-200 eng.	▲D8BZ-6256B	13.75
1983-86-230 eng.	▲E2DZ-6256A	32.25

	Part No.	Price
1984-86-302 eng.	▲D3AZ-6256B	22.25
(6) Camshaft		
Six-200		
1983	▲D5DZ-6250B	123.00
V-6-230		
1983	▲E2DZ-6250A	133.00
1984	▲E4DZ-6250A	151.00
1985-86	▲E5DZ-6250A	N.L.
V-8-302		
1984-86	▲D5OZ-6250A	138.25
(7) Bearings (Camshaft)		
Six-200		
1983-front	▲E3BZ-6261A	11.50
front inter.	▲E3BZ-6267A	10.50
rear inter.	▲E3BZ-6270A	10.00
rear	▲E3BZ-6263A	10.75

	Part No.	Price
V-6-230		
1983-86-exc. below	▲E2DZ-6267A	6.50
front & rear	▲E2DZ-6261A	9.00
V-8-302		
1984-86-front	▲C2OZ-6261A	5.00
front inter.	▲C2OZ-6267A	5.00
rear inter.	▲C2OZ-6270A	5.00
center	▲C2OZ-6262A	5.00
rear	▲C2OZ-6263A	5.00
(8) Welsh Plug		
1983-200 eng.	▲C8DZ-6026A	.50
1983-86-230 eng.	▲E2DZ-6026A	2.25
1984-86-302 eng.	▲D7AZ-6026A	1.00

LABOR 17 ENGINE OILING SYSTEM 17 LABOR

(Factory Time)	Chilton Time
(G) Oil Pan or Gasket, Renew	
Four-1983-86 (1.9)	2.7
Six-1983 (1.8)	2.6
V-6-1983-86 (2.1)	2.9
V-8-1984-86 (2.4)	3.3

LABOR 17 ENGINE OILING SYSTEM 17 LABOR

	(Factory Time)	Chilton Time
(P) Pressure Test Engine Bearings (Pan Off)		
All models		1.0
(G) Oil Pump, Renew		
Four–1983-86	(2.0)	2.9
Six–1983	(1.9)	2.8
V-6–1983-86	(.7)	1.1
V-8–1984-86	(2.5)	3.5
(G) Oil Pump, R&R and Recondition		
Four–1983-86	(2.3)	3.2
Six–1983	(2.2)	3.1
V-6–1983-86	(.7)	1.2
V-8–1984-86	(2.8)	3.9
(G) Oil Pressure Gauge (Engine), Renew		
1983-86	(.3)	.4
(M) Oil Filter Element, Renew		
1983-86	(.3)	.3

PARTS 17 ENGINE OILING SYSTEM 17 PARTS

	Part No.	Price
Oil Pan Gasket Set		
1983-84-140 eng.	▲E2ZZ-6781A	10.75
1985-86-140 eng.	▲E5ZZ-6781A	10.75
1983-200 eng.	▲D0DZ-6781A	10.75
1983-86-230 eng.	▲E2DZ-6781A	9.00
1984-86-302 eng.	▲D9AZ-6781A	11.50
Oil Pump Assy.		
1983-84-140 eng.	▲D5FZ-6600A	66.00
1985-86	▲E5ZZ-6600A	44.25
1983-200 eng.	▲C5DZ-6600A	54.50
1984-86-302 eng.	▲C2OZ-6600A	52.50
Oil Pump Screen		
1983-84-140 eng.	▲E3ZZ-6622A	19.50
1985-86-140 eng.	▲E5ZZ-6622A	19.50
1983-200 eng.	▲E3BZ-6622A	19.00
1983-86-230 eng.	▲E3DZ-6622A	28.00
1984-86-302 eng.	▲E0SZ-6622A	28.00
Oil Filter Assy.		
1983-86-all	▲D9AZ-6731A	8.00
Oil Pressure Gauge (Engine Unit)		
1983-86	▲D4AZ-9278A	3.50

LABOR 18 CLUTCH & FLYWHEEL 18 LABOR

	(Factory Time)	Chilton Time
(G) Clutch Assembly, Renew		
1983	(1.8)	2.3
(G) Clutch Release Bearing, Renew		
1983	(1.7)	2.1
(G) Clutch Cable, Renew		
1983	(.5)	.8
(G) Flywheel, Renew Includes: R&R trans.		
1983	(1.9)	2.5
Renew ring gear add	(.3)	.5
(G) Flywheel Housing, Renew Includes: R&R trans.		
1983	(2.1)	2.7

PARTS 18 CLUTCH & FLYWHEEL 18 PARTS

	Part No.	Price
Clutch Disc		
1983	▲D8BZ-7550B	44.00
Pressure Plate		
1983	▲D8BZ-7563B	58.75
Release Bearing & Hub Assy.		
1983	▲D9ZZ-7548B	37.75
Pilot Bearing		
1983	▲D4ZZ-7600A	5.25
Release Lever Assy.		
1983	▲D9ZZ-7515C	12.75
Cable Assy.		
1983	▲E2DZ-7K553A	37.50
Flywheel Assy.		
1983	▲E2ZZ-6375C	185.75
Flywheel Ring Gear		
1983	▲D4FZ-6384A	34.25

LABOR 21 SHIFT LINKAGE 21 LABOR

	(Factory Time)	Chilton Time
STANDARD		
(G) Shift Linkage, Adjust		
All models	(.3)	.5
(G) Gear Selector Lever, Renew		
1983-86	(.4)	.6
AUTOMATIC		
(G) Linkage, Adjust		
manual	(.3)	.4
kickdown	(.3)	.4
manual & kickdown	(.6)	.8
downshift	(.3)	.4
(G) Gear Selector Lever, Renew		
1983-86-floor shift	(.4)	.6
column shift	(.4)	.6
(G) Transmission Control Selector Indicator, Renew		
1985-86 colm shift	(.8)	1.2
(G) Tilt Wheel Pivot, Recondition (In Chassis)		
1983-86	(.7)	1.0

LABOR 25 U-JOINTS & DRIVESHAFT 25 LABOR

	(Factory Time)	Chilton Time
(G) Driveshaft, Renew		
1983-86	(.3)	.5
(G) Universal Joints, Renew or Recondition Includes: R&R driveshaft.		
1983-86		
Double Cardan		
front or rear	(.9)	1.3
all	(1.5)	2.0
Single Cardan		
front or rear	(.6)	.9
both		1.3

PARTS 25 U-JOINTS & DRIVESHAFT 25 PARTS

	Part No.	Price
Universal Joint Kit		
1983-86	▲C3AZ-4635E	15.25
Pinion Bearing Spacer		
1983-86	▲B7A-4662A	4.00
Yoke		
1983-86	▲E1DZ-4782A	14.25

LABOR 26 REAR AXLE 26 LABOR

(Factory Time)	Chilton Time
(M) Differential, Drain & Refill	
All models	.6
(M) Axle Housing Cover or Gasket, Renew	
All models (.4)	.6
(G) Axle Shaft Inner Oil Seal, Renew	
Includes: R&R wheel, drum and axle shaft.	
1983-86	
7.5 axle-one (.6)	.9
both (.8)	1.3
(G) Rear Wheel Bearings, Renew	
Includes: Renew inner oil seal.	
1983-86	
7.5 axle-one (.7)	1.0
both (.9)	1.5
(G) Axle Shaft, Renew	
Includes: Renew inner oil seal.	
1983-86	
7.5 axle-one (.6)	1.0
both (.8)	1.4
(G) Axle Shaft Wheel Mounting Studs, Renew	
All models-one	.8
all	1.2
(G) Pinion Shaft Oil Seal, Renew	
1983-86 (.8)	1.3
(P) Differential Case Assy., Recondition	
Includes: Drain and refill axle, renew necessary parts. Renew axle shaft oil seals. Road test.	
1983-86	
7.5 axle-std (1.2)	2.1
7.5 axle-lock (2.1)	3.3
(P) Axle Housing, Renew	
Includes: Transfer all necessary parts, adjust ring gear and pinion. Does not include disassembly of differential case.	
1983-86	
7.5 axle (3.5)	4.9
Recond diff assy. add (.4)	.8
(P) Ring and Pinion Set, Renew	
Includes: R&R axle shafts, drain and refill unit. Road test.	
1983-86	
7.5 axle (2.7)	3.8
O/Haul diff assy add (.4)	.8
Renew diff brgs add (.2)	.2
(P) Ring and Pinion, Adjust (In Chassis)	
Includes: Remove axle shafts, drain and refill unit. Road test.	
1983-86	
7.5 axle (1.5)	2.3

PARTS 26 REAR AXLE 26 PARTS

	Part No.	Price
(1) Pinion Kit		
1983-86	▲E4DZ-4215A	20.00
(2) Thrust Washer (Side Gear)		
1983-86	▲D8BZ-4228A	.75
(3) Side Gears		
1983-86	▲D9AZ-4236A	40.00
(4) Bearing Cup		
1983-86	▲C6TZ-4222A	6.00
(5) Bearing Assy.		
1983-86	▲B7A-4221A	11.50
(6) Pinion Shaft		
1983-86	▲D8BZ-4211A	13.75
(7) Case Assy.		
1983-86-exc. below	▲D9AZ-4204A	104.50
Traction-Loc	▲E4DZ-4204A	105.75
(8) Ring Gear & Pinion Kit		
1983-86-2.47R	▲D8BZ-4209C	352.50
2.73R	▲E5SZ-4209A	352.50
3.08R	▲E25Y-4209A	352.50
3.27R (1983-84)	▲E35Y-4209A	381.75
3.27R (1985-86)	▲E5LY-4209A	381.75
3.45R	▲E25Y-4209B	401.25
(9) Pinion Bearing (Rear)		
1983-86	▲C7AZ-4630A	15.75
(10) Bearing Cup		
1983-86	▲C7AZ-4628A	8.00
(11) Axle Shaft Oil Seal		
1983-86	▲E1AZ-1177B	3.50
(12) Axle Shaft Bearing		
1983-86	▲C7AZ-1225A	15.75
(13) Axle Shaft Assy.		
1983-86	▲D9BZ-4234C	80.00
(14) Pinion Bearing (Front)		
1983-86	▲C7AZ-4628A	8.00
(15) Oil Slinger		
1983-86	▲D5AZ-4670A	1.50

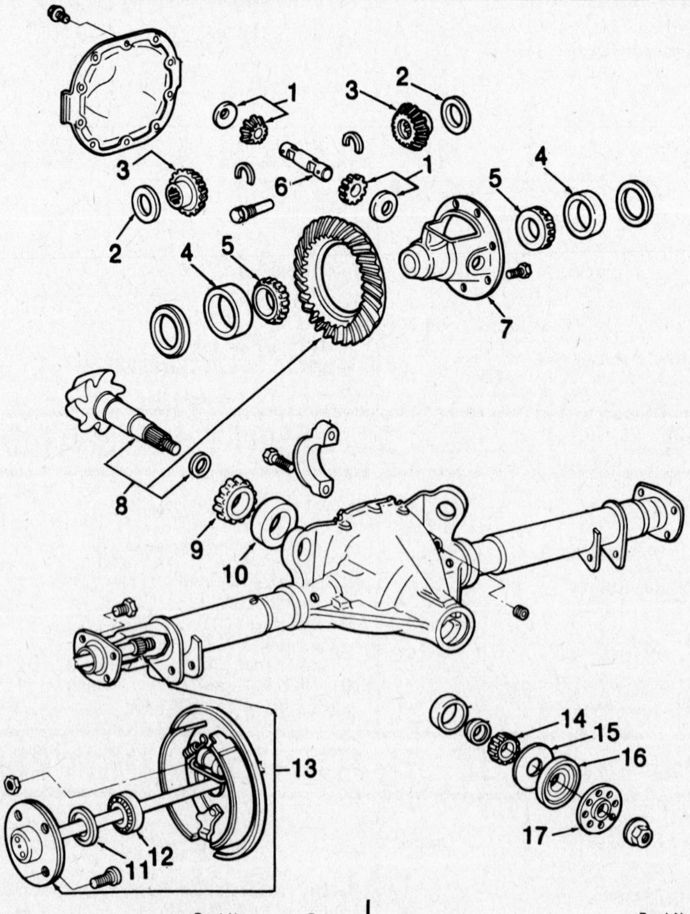

	Part No.	Price
(16) Pinion Oil Seal		
1983-86	▲E3TZ-4676A	11.25
(17) Flange Assy.		
1983-86	▲D8BZ-4851A	17.00

LABOR 27 REAR SUSPENSION 27 LABOR

	(Factory Time)	Chilton Time
(G) Rear Springs, Renew		
1983-86-both		
wo/Stabilizer bar	(.8)	1.0
w/Stabilizer bar	(.9)	1.2
(G) Rear Suspension Upper Arm, Renew		
1983-86-one	(.5)	.9
both	(.6)	1.1
(G) Rear Suspension Lower Arm, Renew		
1983-86		
wo/Stabilizer-one	(.6)	1.1
both	(.9)	1.5
w/Stabilizer-one	(.7)	1.2
both	(1.0)	1.7
(G) Rear Shock Absorbers, Renew		
1983-86-one	(.3)	.5
both	(.4)	.8

PARTS 27 REAR SUSPENSION 27 PARTS

	Part No.	Price
(1) Upper Control Arm		
1983-86	▲D9BZ-5500A	37.00
(2) Insulator (Upper)		
1983-86	▲E25Y-5536A	9.50
(3) Damper (Rear Spring.)		
1983-86	▲D8BZ-5A669C	8.50
(4) Coil Spring		
Order by model and description.		
(5) Insulator (Lower)		
1983-86	▲D8BZ-5536A	3.00
(6) Lower Control Arm		
1983-86-exc.		
Sta. wag.	▲E1DZ-5A649A	66.00
Sta. wag.	▲D9BZ-5A649A	66.00
302 eng.	▲E4BZ-5A649A	93.25
(7) Shock Absorber (Rear)		
1983-84-exc.		
below	▲E5DZ-18125A	41.25
Sta. wagon	▲E3DZ-18125G	26.00
1985-86	▲E5DZ-18125A	41.25

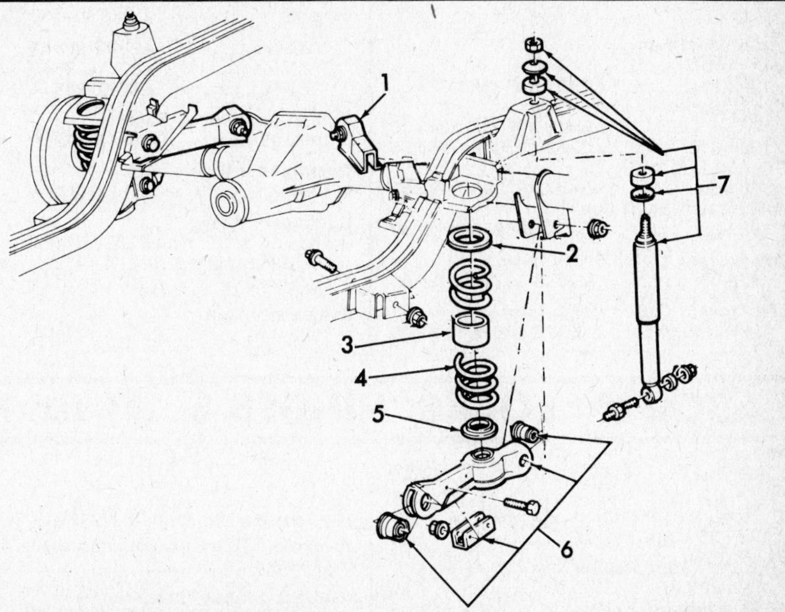

LABOR 28 AIR CONDITIONING 28 LABOR

Note: If more than one item requires replacement where evacuation and discharging the system is already included in the operation, deduct 1.0 hour for each additional item to the times listed.

	(Factory Time)	Chilton Time
(G) Drain, Evacuate and Recharge System		
Includes: Check for leaks.		
All models	(.7)	1.2
(G) Pressure Test System		
All models		.6
(G) Compressor Belt, Renew		
All models	(.3)	.6
(G) Compressor Assembly, Renew		
Includes: Evacuate and charge system.		
1983-86		
Four	(1.6)	2.5
V-6	(1.6)	2.5
V-8	(1.5)	2.4
Recond comp add	(.7)	1.0
(G) Compressor Shaft Seal Kit, Renew		
Includes: R&R compressor where required. Evacuate and charge system.		
1983-86		
Four	(1.4)	2.3

AIR CONDITIONER TUNE-UP

For efficient operation and satisfactory performance in hot weather. The following air conditioner tune-up is suggested:

1. Clean intake filter
2. Clean condenser fins
3. Pressure test system
4. Adjust drive belt tension
5. Check antifreeze/coolant
6. Tighten compressor mounts
7. Tighten condenser and evaporator mounts
8. Inspect system for leaks (hoses, couplings, valves, etc.)
9. Partial charge system

All models 1.0

If necessary to evacuate and charge system, add 1.0

	(Factory Time)	Chilton Time
V-6	(1.4)	2.3
V-8	(1.8)	3.0
(G) Compressor Clutch and Pulley Assy., Renew		
1983-86	(.5)	.8
Renew clutch brg. add	(.1)	.1
Renew clutch field add	(.1)	.1
(G) A.C. Clutch Cycling Pressure Switch, Renew		
1983-86	(.2)	.4
(G) Condenser Assembly, Renew		
Includes: Evacuate and charge system.		
1983-86	(1.3)	2.4
(G) Accumulator Assembly, Renew		
Includes: Evacuate and charge system.		
1983	(1.0)	1.5
(G) Orifice Valve, Renew		
Includes: Evacuate and charge system.		
1983-86	(.9)	1.5
(G) Evaporator Core, Renew		
Includes: Renew or transfer valve. Evacuate and charge system.		
1983-86	(2.7)	6.0
(G) Door Vacuum Motor, Renew		
1983-86		
Recirculation	(.3)	.6
A/C Defrost	(.5)	.9
ATC Servo	(.5)	.9

LABOR 28 AIR CONDITIONING 28 LABOR

(Factory Time)	Chilton Time
Heat Defrost (2.7)	*6.0
*Add time to recharge A.C. system, if required.	
(G) A.C. Blower Motor Switch, Renew	
1983-86 (.4)	.7
(G) A.C./Heater Blower Motor, Renew	
1983-86 (.7)	1.2
(G) Blower Motor Resistor, Renew	
1983-86 (.3)	.4
(G) Suction or Discharge Manifold Assy. Kit, Renew	
Includes: Evacuate and charge system.	
1983-86 (.8)	1.5
(G) Air Conditioning Hoses, Renew	
Includes: Evacuate and charge system.	
1983-86	
Cond. to Evap. (.8)	1.7
Suction line (1.0)	1.9
Comp. to Cond (.8)	1.7

PARTS 28 AIR CONDITIONING 28 PARTS

	Part No.	Price
Compressor Assy.		
Four-140		
1983-86	▲E3DZ-19703A	221.50
Six-200, 230		
1983	▲E4VY-19703A	315.00
1984-86	▲E3SZ-19703A	268.75
V-8-302		
1984-86	▲E4FZ-19703A	192.50
Compressor Shaft Seal		
1983-86	▲E3SZ-19655A	12.50
Compressor Clutch Brush Assy.		
1983-86	▲C8SZ-2979A	24.50
Compressor Clutch (Complete)		
1983-140 eng.	▲E3SZ-2884A	47.00
200 eng.	▲E3DZ-2884A	71.50
230 eng.	▲E0VY-2884A	149.00
1984-86	▲E4SZ-2884A	47.00
Compressor Pulley Bearing		
1983-86	▲C9AZ-2990A	27.25
Compressor Gasket Set		
1983	▲C3GY-19B684A	9.00
Condenser Assy.		
1983-84	▲E2ZZ-19712A	180.75
1985-86-exc. V-8	▲E2ZZ-19712A	180.75
V-8	▲E5LY-19712A	241.50
Evaporator Core		
1983-84	▲E25Y-19860A	139.50
1985-86	▲E4LY-19860A	141.00
Sensor Assy. (Temperature Cont.)		
1983-86	▲E3DZ-19C734A	38.50
Blower Motor		
1983-86	▲E35Y-19805A	90.50
Blower Motor Resister		
1983-86	▲E35Y-19A706A	11.00
Blower Motor Switch		
1983-86	▲D5AZ-19986A	12.75
Clutch Cycling Pressure Switch		
1983-86	▲E35Y-19E561A	23.75

LABOR 29 LOCKS, HINGES & WIND. REGULATORS 29 LABOR

(Factory Time)	Chilton Time
(G) Hood Release Cable, Renew	
1983-86 (.3)	.6
(G) Hood Latch, Renew	
1983-86 (.3)	.5
(G) Hood Hinge, Renew	
Includes: Adjust hood and latch.	
1983-86 (.3)	.5
(G) Door Latch, Renew	
Includes: R&R trim panel and weathersheet.	
1983-86-front (.5)	.8
rear (.8)	1.2
(G) Door Lock Remote Control, Renew	
Includes: R&R trim panel and weathersheet.	
1983-86 (.4)	.7
(G) Door Handle (Outside), Renew	
Includes: R&R trim panel and weathersheet.	
1983-86 (.6)	.9
(G) Lock Striker Plate, Renew	
1983-86 (.2)	.3
(G) Door Window Regulator (Manual), Renew	
Includes: R&R trim panel and weathersheet.	
1983-86 (.6)	1.0
(G) Door Window Regulator (Electric), Renew	
Includes: R&R trim panel and weathersheet.	
1983-86 (.7)	1.2
(G) Trunk Lock Cylinder and Key, Renew	
1983-86 (.3)	.4
(G) Tailgate/Liftgate Hinge, Renew	
1983-86	
upper (.3)	.5
both (.3)	.7
(G) Tailgate/Liftgate Latch, Renew	
1983-86 (.4)	.6
(G) Rear Compartment Hydraulic Lift, Renew	
1983-86-one (.3)	.4
both (.3)	.5

PARTS 29 LOCKS, HINGES & WIND. REGULATORS 29 PARTS

	Part No.	Price
Hood Latch		
1983-85	▲E4DZ-16700A	14.75
1986	▲E6DZ-16700A	14.75
Front Door Lock (Manual)		
1983-86-right	▲E3BZ-3621812A	30.50
left	▲E3BZ-3621813A	30.50
Rear Door Lock (Manual)		
1983-86-right	▲E3BZ-5426412A	41.50
left	▲E3BZ-5426413A	41.50
Front & Rear Door Lock (Electric)		
1983-right	▲E3TZ-1021818A	N.L.
left	▲E3TZ-1021819A	N.L.
1984-86-right	▲E4TZ-1021818A	9.25
left	▲E4TZ-1021819A	9.25
Door Lock Cylinder & Key		
1983-86	▲E1DZ-5421984C	10.75
Trunk Lock Cylinder & Key		
1983-86	▲D6ZZ-6943505A	10.75
Trunk Lid Latch		
1983-86-wo/		
Power	▲D9ZZ-6643200A	22.00
Power	▲D9BZ-5443200A	57.50
Front Window Regulator (Manual)		
1983-86-right	▲E2BZ-5423200A	54.50
left	▲E2BZ-5423201A	54.50
Rear Window Regulator (Manual)		
1983-86	▲E2BZ-5427000A	32.25
left	▲E2BZ-5427001A	32.25
Front Window Regulator (Electric)		
1983-86-right	▲D8BZ-5423208A	120.75
left	▲D8BZ-5423209A	120.75
Rear Window Regulator (Electric)		
1983-86-right	▲D8BZ-5427008A	94.50
left	▲D8BZ-5427009A	94.50

LABOR 30 HEAD AND PARKING LAMPS 30 LABOR

(Factory Time)	Chilton Time
(G) Aim Headlamps	
two	.4
four	.6
(M) Headlamp Sealed Beam Bulb, Renew	
1983-86-each (.3)	.4
(M) Parking Lamp Housing, Renew	
1983-86 (.7)	1.0
(M) Parking Lamp Bulb, Renew	
1983-86 (.2)	.3

LABOR 30 HEAD & PARKING LAMPS 30 LABOR

	(Factory Time)	Chilton Time
(M) Side Marker Lamp Bulb, Renew		
1983-86	(.2)	.3
(M) Tail Lamp Body, Renew		
1983-86	(.3)	.4
(M) Tail Lamp Bulb, Renew		
1983-86	(.2)	.3
(M) License Lamp Assembly, Renew		
1983-86	(.2)	.3

PARTS 30 HEAD & PARKING LAMPS 30 PARTS

	Part No.	Price
Seal Beam Bulb		
1983-86-Low beam	▲D94Y-13007A	12.75
Hi beam	▲D94Y-13007C	12.75
Parking Lamp Assy.		
1983-right	▲E3DZ-13200A	25.25
left	▲E3DZ-13201A	25.25
1984-86-right	▲E1DZ-13200A	25.25
left	▲E1DZ-13201A	25.25
Tail Lamp Lens Assy.		
LTD		
(exc. LX)		
1983-right	▲E3DZ-13450A	48.50
left	▲E3DZ-13451A	48.50
1984-right	▲E4DZ-13450A	56.75
left	▲E4DZ-13451A	48.50
1985-86-right	▲E5DZ-13450A	48.50
left	▲E5DZ-13451A	56.75
(LX)		
1984-right	▲E4DZ-13450B	48.50
left	▲E4DZ-13451B	48.50
1985-right	▲E5DZ-13405B	118.50
left	▲E5DZ-13451B	56.75
Marquis		
(exc. LTS)		
1983-right	▲E34Y-13450A	47.75
left	▲E34Y-13451A	47.75
1984-right	▲E44Y-13450A	47.75
left	▲E44Y-13451A	47.75
1985-86-right	▲E54Y-13450A	56.75
left	▲E54Y-13451A	57.00
(LTS)		
1984-right	▲E44Y-13450B	47.75
left	▲E44Y-13451B	47.75
1985-right	▲E54Y-13450B	56.75
left	▲E54Y-13451B	56.75
Tail Lamp Assy.		
LTD		
(exc. LX)		
1983-right	▲E3DZ-13404A	104.00
left	▲E3DZ-13405A	104.00
1984-right	▲E4DZ-13404A	104.00
left	▲E4DZ-13405A	104.00
1985-86-right	▲E5DZ-13404A	118.50
left	▲E5DZ-13405A	118.50
(LX)		
1984-right	▲E4DZ-13404B	104.00
left	▲E4DZ-13405B	104.00
1985-right	▲E5DZ-13404B	118.50
left	▲E5DZ-13405B	118.50
(Sta. wagon)		
1983-86-right	▲E3DZ-13404B	66.75
left	▲E3DZ-13405B	66.75
Marquis		
(exc. LTS)		
1983-right	▲E34Y-13404A	125.50
left	▲E34Y-13405A	125.50
1984-right	▲E44Y-13404A	125.50
left	▲E44Y-13405A	125.50
1985-86-right	▲E54Y-13404A	118.50
left	▲E54Y-13405A	118.50
(LTS)		
1984-right	▲E44Y-13404B	125.50
left	▲E44Y-13405B	125.50
1985-right	▲E54Y-13404B	118.50
left	▲E54Y-13405B	118.50
(Sta. wagon)		
1983-86-right	▲E34Y-13404B	65.00
left	▲E34Y-13405B	65.00
License Plate Lamp Assy.		
wo/Sta. wagon		
(exc. LX, LTS)		
1983-right	▲E3DZ-13550A	11.25
left	▲E3DZ-13550B	11.25
1984-86-right	▲E4DZ-13550A	11.25
left	▲E4DZ-13550B	11.25
(LX, LTS)		
1984-86-right	▲E4DZ-13550C	11.25
left	▲E4DZ-13550D	11.25
Sta. wagon		
1983-86	▲D7AZ-13550A	6.00
Rear Hi-Mount Lamp Assy.		
1986-exc. Sta. wagon	▲E6KZ-13A613A	41.75
Station wagon	▲E6KZ-13A613C	41.75

LABOR 31 WINDSHIELD WIPER & SPEEDOMETER 31 LABOR

	(Factory Time)	Chilton Time
(G) Windshield Wiper Motor, Renew		
1983-86	(.5)	.7
(G) Windshield Wiper Switch, Renew		
1983-86	(.4)	.7
(G) Windshield Wiper Governor Assy., Renew		
1983-86	(.4)	.6
(G) Wiper Pivot, Renew		
1983-86-one piece	(.4)	.7
(G) Windshield Washer Pump, Renew		
1983-86	(.3)	.5
under fender	(.5)	.7
(G) Rear Window Wiper Motor, Renew		
1983-86-sta wag	(.5)	.8
(G) Rear Window Wiper Switch, Renew		
1983-86-sta wag	(.3)	.5
(G) Rear Window Washer Pump, Renew		
1983-86-sta wag	(.3)	.4
(G) Speedometer Head, R&R or Renew		
Includes: R&R instrument panel pad when required.		
1983-86	(.7)	1.2
Reset odometer add		.2
(G) Speedometer Cable and Casing, Renew		
1983-86		
one piece	(.4)	.7
(G) Speedometer Cable (Inner), Renew or Lubricate		
1983-86		
one piece	(.4)	.6
(G) Speedometer Driven Gear, Renew		
1983-86	(.3)	.4
(G) Radio, R&R		
1983-86	(.3)	.6

PARTS 31 WINDSHIELD WIPER & SPEEDOMETER 31 PARTS

	Part No.	Price
Wiper Motor Assy.		
(front)		
1983	▲D8BZ-17508B	94.25
1984-86	▲E4DZ-17508A	94.25
(rear)		
1983-86	▲D8BZ-17508A	75.75
Arm Pivot Shaft		
1983-86-front	▲E3DZ-17566A	27.50
rear	▲D8BZ-17566C	27.50
Windshield Wiper Governor		
1983	▲D8BZ-17C476A	77.50
1984-86	▲E4ZZ-17C476A	72.50
Windshield Washer Pump		
1983-86-front	▲E0AZ-17664A	20.00
Rear	▲E1FZ-17664A	18.75
Wiper & Washer Switch Assy.		
(Front Wiper)		
1983-86-wo/Interm.	▲E3DZ-17A553C	18.50

PARTS 31 WINDSHIELD WIPER & SPEEDOMETER 31 PARTS

	Part No.	Price
w/Interm.	▲E3DZ-17A553A	25.75
(rear wiper)		
1983-86	▲E3DZ-17A553B	13.75
Speedometer Head		
Order by year and model.		
Speedometer Case & Shaft		
1983-86-wo/		
Speed control	▲E3BZ-17260A	22.75
Speedo. Control Cable		
1983-86-140		
eng.	▲E3ZZ-9A820B	11.00
200, 230 engs.	▲E3SZ-9A820A	11.00
302 eng.	▲E3ZZ-9A820A	11.00
Speedometer Cable (Inner)		
1983-86		
81″ Long	▲D4AZ-17262A	7.75
135″ Long	▲C5AZ-17262B	8.75

LABOR 32 LIGHT SWITCHES & WIRING 32 LABOR

(Factory Time)	Chilton Time
(G) Headlamp Switch, Renew	
1983-86 (.3)	.7
(G) Headlamp Dimmer Switch, Renew	
1983-86 (.4)	.7
(G) Turn Signal Switch, Renew	
1983-86 (.4)	1.0
(G) Stop Lamp Switch, Renew	
1983-86 (.3)	.4
(G) Back-Up Lamp Switch, Renew	
1983-86 (.3)	.5
(G) Parking Brake Indicator Switch, Renew	
1983-86 (.3)	.4
(M) Turn Signal or Hazard Warning Flasher, Renew	
1983-86	
turn signal (.3)	.4
hazard (.5)	.7
(G) Horns, Renew	
1983-86-each (.3)	.4

PARTS 32 LIGHT SWITCHES & WIRING 32 PARTS

	Part No.	Price
Headlamp Switch		
1983-86 (w/or wo/Diagnostic Light)		
wo/Light	▲E0AZ-11654C	16.50
w/Light	▲E0AZ-11654D	17.50
w/Delay sys.	▲E1WZ-11654A	47.25
Turn Signal & Warning Switch		
1983-84	▲E2FZ-13341A	41.25
1985-86	▲E5FZ-13341A	41.25
Stop Light Switch		
1983-85	▲E3ZZ-13480A	7.25
1986	▲E6ZZ-13480A	7.50
Back-Up Lamp Switch		
(w/M.T.)		
1983	▲D3FZ-15520A	6.00
(w/A.T.)		
1983-86-C5		
trans.	▲E2DZ-7A247A	36.50
A.O.D. trans.	▲D6RY-7A247B	31.75
Turn Signal Flasher		
1983-86-wo/		
Corn Lite	▲C5AZ-13350B	3.75
w/Corn Lite	▲C6AZ-13350B	3.75
Hazard Warning Flasher		
1983-85	▲D1FZ-13350A	4.25
1986	▲E6AZ-13350A	10.75
Horn Assy.		
1983-86-Hi Pitch	▲E3AZ-13832A	17.00
Low Pitch	▲E3AZ-13833A	17.00
Wiring Harness		
Order by year and model.		

LABOR 33 GLASS 33 LABOR

(Factory Time)	Chilton Time
(G) Windshield Glass, Renew	
1983-86 (1.0)	1.5
Renew butyl tape add (.2)	.2
(G) Front Door Glass, Renew	
1983-86	
wo/vent (.6)	.9
w/vent (.8)	1.3
(G) Rear Door Glass, Renew	
1983-86 (.8)	1.2
(G) Quarter Window Stationary Glass, Renew	
1983-86-sta wag (.7)	1.2
(G) Tail Gate Window Glass, Renew	
1983-86	
fixed (.8)	1.2
movable (.3)	.5
(G) Back Window Glass, Renew	
1983-86 (1.0)	1.5
Renew butyl tape add (.2)	.2

LABOR 34 CRUISE CONTROL 34 LABOR

(G) Cruise Control System Diagnosis	
1983-86 (.4)	.6
(G) Speed Control Amplifier Assy., Renew	
1983-86 (.3)	.5
Road test add (.3)	.3
(G) Speed Control Sensor Assy., Renew	
1983-86 (.3)	.5
Road test add (.3)	.3
(G) Speed Control Servo Assy., Renew	
1983-86 (.4)	.6
under fender (.6)	.9
Road test add (.3)	.3
(G) Speed Control Relay, Renew	
1983-86 (.3)	.5
Road test add (.3)	.3
(G) Speed Control Actuator Switch, Renew	
1983-86 (.3)	.6
Road test add (.3)	.3
(G) Speed Control Metering (Dump) Valve, Renew	
1983-86 (.3)	.6
(G) Cruise Control Chain/Cable, Renew	
1983-86 (.6)	.8
(G) Cruise Control Clutch Switch, Renew	
1983 (.1)	.3
Road test add (.3)	.3

PARTS 34 CRUISE CONTROL 34 PARTS

	Part No.	Price
Speed Control Amplifier Assy.		
1983-86	▲E0AZ-9D843A	161.50
Speed Control Servo Assy.		
1983-140 & 200		
engs.	▲E2FZ-9C735A	120.25
230 eng.	▲E3ZZ-9C735B	120.25
1984-86	▲E4LY-9C735A	120.25
Speed Control Sensor		
1983-86	▲E3AZ-9E731A	20.75
Speed Control Actuator Switch		
1983-86	▲E3SZ-9C888A	45.75

GROUP INDEX

ALPHABETICAL INDEX

General Motors
Front Wheel Drive Cars

BUICK LESABRE • OLDS 88

YEAR IDENTIFICATION

1986 LeSabre Limited

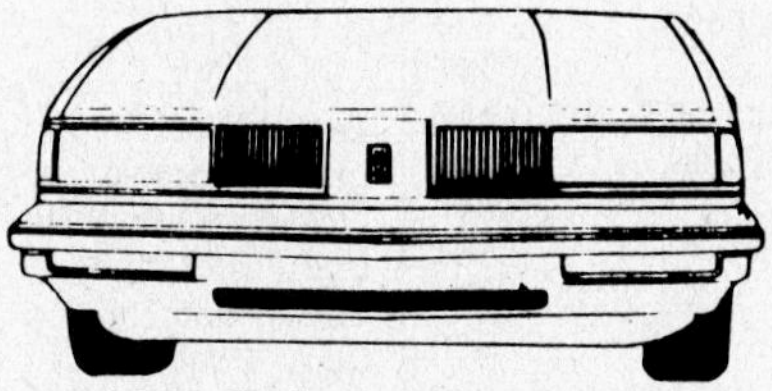

1987 Oldsmobile Delta 88

1987 LeSabre Sedan

VEHICLE IDENTIFICATION NUMBER (VIN)

It is important for servicing and ordering parts to be certain of the vehicle and engine identification. The VIN (vehicle identification number) is a 13 or 17 digit number visible through the windshield on the driver's side of the dash and contains the vehicle and engine identification codes. It can be interpreted as follows:

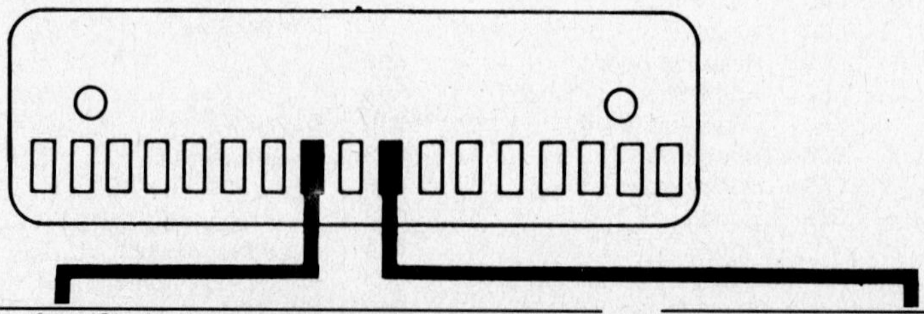

Engine Code					
Code	Cu. In.	Liters	Cyl.	Fuel Delivery	Eng. Mfg.
L	181	3.0	6	MFI	Buick
B,3	231	3.8	6	SFI	Buick

Model Year Code	
Code	Year
G	1986
H	1987

The seventeen digit Vehicle Identification Number can be used to determine engine application and model year. The 10th digit indicates the model year and the 8th digit identifies the factory installed engine.
MFI Multiport Fuel Injection
SFI Sequential Fuel Injection

TUNE-UP SPECIFICATIONS

When analyzing compression test results, look for uniformity among cylinders rather than specific pressures

Year	VIN Code	Eng. No. Cyl. Displ. (cu. in.)	Eng. Mfg.	hp	Spark Plugs Orig. Type	Spark Plugs Gap (in.)	Ignition Timing (deg.)	Fuel Pump Pressure (psi)	Idle Speed (rpm)
'86	L	6-181	Buick	125	R44LTS	.045	①	34-44	①
	B,3	6-231	Buick	150	R44LTS	.045	①	26-36	①
'87	All	See Underhood Specifications Sticker							

NOTE: The underhood specifications sticker often reflects tune-up specification changes made in production. Sticker figures must be used if they disagree with those in this chart.

Part numbers in this chart are not recommendations by Chilton for any product by brand name.

① Idle speed and ignition timing are computer-controlled and not adjustable

FIRING ORDER

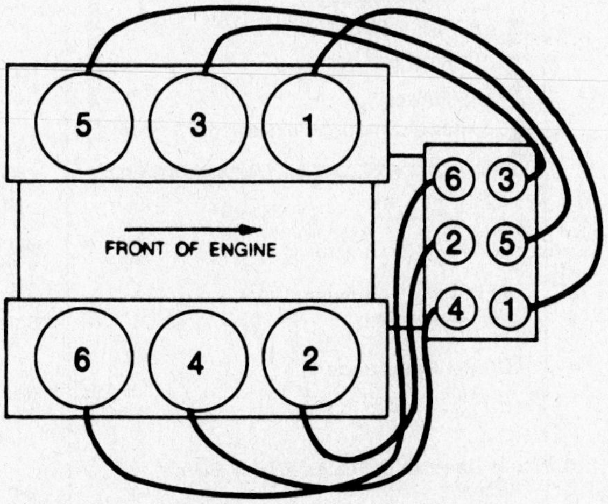

183 cu. in. (3.0L) and 231 cu. in. (3.8L) engines
Firing Order: 1-6-5-4-3-2

WHEEL ALIGNMENT SPECIFICATIONS

Year	Model	Caster Range (deg.)	Caster Pref. Setting (deg.)	Camber Range (deg.)	Camber Pref. Setting (deg.)	Toe (in.)
'86–'87	Buick	2–3	2 1/2	L–1–0 R 0–1	1/2	7/32 ①
'86–'87	Olds	2–3	2 1/2	L–1–0 R 0–1	–1/2 1/2	3/32 ①

L Left
R Right
① In or out. Pref: 0

LABOR — SERVICE BAY OPERATIONS — LABOR

(Factory Time) Chilton Time

COOLING

(M) Winterize Cooling System
Includes: Run engine to check for leaks, tighten all hose connections. Test radiator and pressure cap, drain radiator and engine block. Add anti-freeze and refill system.
All models 5

(G) Thermostat, Renew
1986-87
V-6 (.5) 7

(M) Radiator Hoses, Renew
Includes: Drain and refill cooling system.
1986-87-upper (.3) 4
lower (.4) 5
both (.4) 7
by-pass (.5) 7

(M) Serpentine Drive Belt, Renew
1986-87
V-6 (.3) 5

(M) Serpentine Belt Tensioner, Renew
1986-87
V-6 (.5) 7

FUEL

(M) Air Cleaner, Service
All models 3

(G) Minimum Idle Speed, Adjust
All models (.4) 6

LABOR SERVICE BAY OPERATIONS LABOR

(Factory Time) Chilton Time

BRAKES

(G) Bleed Brakes (Four Wheels)
Includes: Fill master cylinder.
All models (.4) 5

(G) Brake Pedal Free Play, Adjust
All models 3

(G) Parking Brake, Adjust
All models (.3) 4

LUBRICATION SERVICE

(M) Lubricate Chassis, Change Oil & Filter
Includes: Inspect and correct all fluid levels.
All models 6
Install grease fittings add 1

(M) Lubricate Chassis
Includes: Inspect and correct all fluid levels.
All models 4
Install grease fittings add 1

(M) Engine Oil & Filter, Change
Includes: Inspect and correct all fluid levels.
All models 4

WHEELS

(M) Wheel, Renew
one 5

(G) Wheels, Balance
one 3
each adtnl 2

(M) Wheels, Rotate (All)
All models 5

ELECTRICAL

(M) Battery Cables, Renew
All models
positive (.3) 4
negative (.3) 3
to start connector (.2) 3

CHILTON'S 10 POINT SAFETY CHECK

CHECK OPERATION & CONDITION OF THE FOLLOWING ITEMS:

1. Legal Registration (serial no.)
2. Tires & Wheels
3. Brake System (R&R all wheels)
4. Light Systems & Signals
5. Accelerator Linkage, Neutral Safety Switch, Shift Indicator Pointer & Seat Position Locks
6. Glass, Mirrors, Door Locks, Seat Belts & Harness
7. Wipers, Washers & Defrosters
8. Frame, Steering, Shocks, Front & Rear Suspension
9. Fuel & Exhaust Systems
10. Road Test Vehicle

All models 1.0
Exhaust Smog Analysis, add 4

(Factory Time) Chilton Time

(M) Battery Terminals, Clean
All models 3

(G) Aim Headlamps
two 4
four 6

(M) Headlamp Sealed Beam Bulb, Renew
1986-87-each (.3) 3

(Factory Time) Chilton Time

(M) Park and Turn Signal Lamp Assy., Renew
1986-87
right (.2) 3
left (.3) 4

(M) Side Marker Lamp Assy., Renew
1986-87
front-each (.2) 3
rear-each (.3) 4

(M) License Lamp Assembly, Renew
1986-87 (.2) 3

(M) Back-Up Lamp Assembly, Renew
1986-87 (.3) 4

(M) Cornering Lamp Bulb, Renew
All models-each (.2) 3

(M) High Level Stop Lamp Assy., Renew
All models (.2) 4

(M) High Level Stop Lamp Bulb, Renew
All models (.2) 3

(M) License Lamp Bulb, Renew
All models-one or all (.2) 3

(M) Park and Turn Signal Lamp Bulb, Renew
All models-each 2

(M) Rear Combination Lamp Bulb, Renew
All models-one 2
each adtnl 1

(M) Side Marker Lamp Bulb, Renew
All models-each 2

LABOR 1 TUNE UP 1 LABOR

(Factory Time) Chilton Time

(G) Compression Test
V-6–1986-87 7

(G) Engine Tune Up, (Electronic Ignition)
Includes: Test battery and clean connections. Tighten manifold mounting bolts. Check engine compression, clean and adjust or renew spark plugs. Reset ignition timing. Adjust minimum idle speed. Service air cleaner. Inspect and adjust drive belts. Check operation of EGR valve.
V-6–1986-87 .... 1.4

LABOR 2 IGNITION SYSTEM 2 LABOR

(Factory Time) Chilton Time

(G) Spark Plugs, Clean and Reset or Renew
V-6–1986-87 (.3) 6

(G) Ignition Timing, Reset
All models (.3) 4

(G) Ignition Cables, Renew
V-6–1986-87 (.4) 6

(G) Ignition Switch, Renew
1986-87 (.6) 9

(Factory Time) Chilton Time

(G) Ignition Key Warning Switch, Renew
1986-87
LeSabre (.5) 1.0
Olds 88 (.6) 1.0

DISTRIBUTORLESS IGNITION SYSTEM

(G) Electronic Spark Control Module, Renew
1986-87 (.5) 7

(Factory Time) Chilton Time

(G) Electronic Spark Control Knock Sensor, Renew
1986-87 (.3) 5

(G) Crankshaft Sensor, Renew
1986-87 (.6) 9

(G) Camshaft Sensor, Renew
1986-87 (.6) 9

(G) Ignition Coil and/or Module, Renew
1986-87 (.5) 8

PARTS 2 IGNITION SYSTEM 2 PARTS

	Part No.	Price
Electronic Spark Control Module		
1986-87	◆16049534	70.00
Electronic Spark Control Knock Sensor		
1986-87	◆1997562	37.00
Crankshaft Position Sensor		
1986-87-3.0	◆25526124	20.25
3.8	◆25526123	20.25
Camshaft Position Sensor		
1986-87	◆25523227	27.50
Ignition Coil		
1986-87	◆25526448	109.00
Ignition Module		
1986-87	◆25526449	215.00
Ignition Switch		
1986-87-exc. Tilt whl.	◆1990115	N.L.
Tilt whl. exc. Digital	◆1990116	N.L.
Digital	◆1990118	12.75

LABOR 3 FUEL SYSTEM 3 LABOR

(Factory Time) — Chilton Time

(M) Air Cleaner, Service
All models 3

(G) Throttle Body, Remove and Install
1986-87
V-6 (.3) 5
Renew throttle body add (.3) 3
Renew fuel meter body add (.3) 3

(G) Idle Air Control Valve, Renew
1986-87
V-6 (.2) 3

(G) Minimum Idle Speed, Adjust
All models (.4) 6

(G) Fuel Pressure Regulator and/or Gaskets, Renew
1986-87
V-6 (.3) 5
Perform balance test add (.4) 4

(G) Fuel Pump Relay, Renew
1986-87
V-6 (.3) 4

(G) Fuel Injector, Renew
1986-87
V-6-one (.6) 1.0
each adtnl (.1) 2
Perform balance test add (.4) 4

(G) Fuel Rail, Renew
1986-87
V-6 (.6) 1.0

(G) Mass Air Sensor, Renew
1986-87
V-6 (.3) 4

(G) Fuel Gauge (Dash Unit), Renew
1986-87
Olds 88 (.6) 1.0

(G) Fuel Gauge (Tank Unit), Renew
1986-87 (.9) 1.3
Transfer elec pump add (.1) 1

(G) Fuel Tank, Renew
Includes: Drain and refill tank, transfer sending unit.
1986-87 (.8) 1.2

(G) Intake Manifold and/or Gaskets, Renew
V-6-1986-87 (1.5) 2.1
Renew manif add (.3) 5

PARTS 3 FUEL SYSTEM 3 PARTS

	Part No.	Price
Fuel Pump		
1986-87	◆25115190	89.50
Fuel Pump Relay		
1986-87-exc. Digital	◆10038490	7.25
Digital	◆25520316	8.75
Fuel Tank		
1986-87	◆25527547	205.00
Fuel Gauge (Tank)		
(wo/Digital cluster)		
1986-87	◆25092116	147.75
(Digital cluster)		
1986-87	◆25092119	156.75
Fuel Gauge (Dash)		
1986-87	◆6433447	25.00
Intake Manifold Gasket Kit		
1986-87-3.0	◆25524292	14.75
3.8	◆1264924	N.L.

PARTS 3 ELECTRONIC FUEL INJECTION 3 PARTS

3.0 MULTIPORT FUEL INJECTION

	Part No.	Price
Throttle Body Kit		
1986-87	◆17111590	147.00
(1) Throttle Body Assembly		
1986-87	◆17086041	N.L.
(2) Coolant Cover Kit		
1986-87	◆17110820	21.75
(3) Idle Air Housing Assembly		
1986-87	◆17110821	26.75
(4) Throttle Position Sensor		
1986-87	◆17111293	62.75
(5) Idle Air Control Valve		
1986-87	◆17111286	58.00

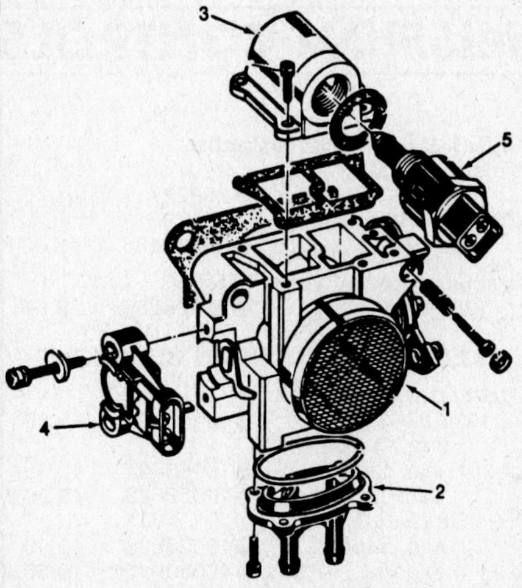

	Part No.	Price
Fuel Injector		
1986-87	◆25527181	79.00
Fuel Injection Rail		
1986-87	◆25521323	174.00
Pressure Regulator		
1986-87	◆25523720	44.75

3.8 SEQUENTIAL FUEL INJECTION

	Part No.	Price
(1) Throttle Body Assembly		
1986-87	◆25524565	150.00
(2) Idle Air Control Motor		
1986-87	◆25527077	29.00
(3) Throttle Position Sensor		
1986-87	◆25036663	23.50

PARTS 3 ELECTRONIC FUEL INJECTION 3 PARTS

	Part No.	Price
(4) Throttle Body Gasket		
1986-87	◆25517008	.75
Fuel Injector		
1986-87	◆25519366	85.50

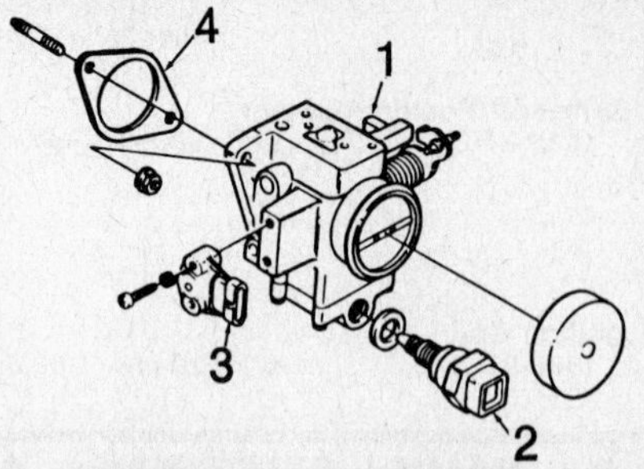

	Part No.	Price
Fuel Injection Rail		
1986-87	◆25526902	144.00
Pressure Regulator		
1986-87	◆25519368	42.25

LABOR 3A EMISSION CONTROLS 3A LABOR

(Factory Time) — Chilton Time

(G) Emission Control Check

Includes: Check and adjust engine idle speed and mixture and ignition timing. Check P.C.V. valve.

All models 6

POSITIVE CRANKCASE VENTILATION

(M) Positive Crankcase Ventilation Valve, Renew

All models (.2) 3

EXHAUST GAS RECIRCULATION SYSTEM

(G) E.G.R. Valve, Renew

1986-87
V-6 (.3) 5

EVAPORATIVE EMISSION TYPE

(G) Charcoal Canister, Renew

All models (.3) 4

ELECTRONIC EMISSION CONTROLS

(P) Throttle Position Sensor, Adjust

1986-87
V-6 (.4) 6

(P) ECM Controller, Renew

1986-87
V-6 (.6) 8

(P) Prom Calibrator, Renew

1986-87
V-6 (.6) 8

(P) Barometric Pressure Sensor, Renew

1986-87
V-6 (.4) 6

CHILTON'S EMISSION CONTROL TUNE-UP

1. Clean or renew P.C.V. valve, hoses and filter.
2. Check fuel tank cap for sealing ability.
3. Check fuel tank and fuel lines for leakage.
4. Check evaporation canister and filter. Replace if necessary.
5. Check engine compression to determine leakage of unburned gases. (Add time for items of interference).
6. Test and clean or renew spark plugs.
7. Check engine oil dipstick for sealing ability.
8. Test exhaust system with analyzer and check system for leakage.
9. Check exhaust manifold heat valve for operation.
10. Adjust ignition timing and carburetor idle speed and mixture.
11. Check automatic choke mechanism for free operation.
12. Inspect air cleaner and element.
13. On models so equipped, test distributor vacuum control switch and transmission control switch.

V-6 .... **1.7**

For repairs made, charge accordingly.

(Factory Time) — Chilton Time

(P) Coolant Temperature Sensor, Renew

1986-87
V-6 (.4) 6

(P) Manifold Absolute Pressure Sensor, Renew

1986-87
V-6 (.4) 6

(P) Manifold Temperature Sensor, Renew

1986-87
V-6 (.4) 6

(P) Oxygen Sensor, Renew

1986-87
V-6 (.5) 7

(P) Vehicle Speed Sensor, Renew

1986-87
V-6 (.5) 7

(P) Throttle Position Sensor, Renew

1986-87
V-6 (.9) 1.2

(P) Calpak, Renew

1986-87
V-6 (.3) 5

(P) Back-Up Lamp and Park/Neutral Switch, Renew

1986-87
V-6 (.5) 7

(P) E.G.R. Vacuum Control Solenoid, Renew

1986-87
V-6 (.3) 4

(P) Fuel Vapor Canister Purge Solenoid, Renew

1986-87
V-6 (.3) 4

PARTS 3A EMISSION CONTROLS 3A PARTS

	Part No.	Price
POSITIVE CRANKCASE VENTILATION		
P.C.V. Valve		
1986-87	◆6487936	N.L.
EVAPORATIVE EMISSION TYPE		
Fuel Vapor Canister		
1986-87-3.0	◆17075856	60.00
3.8	◆17085935	44.75
Canister Filter		
1986-87	◆7026014	N.L.
EXHAUST GAS RECIRCULATION SYSTEM		
E.G.R. Valve		
1986-87-3.0	◆17111571	37.25
3.8	◆17111583	37.25

	Part No.	Price
E.G.R. Valve Vacuum Control		
(Stamped 25522717)		
1986-87	◆25522717	41.75
(Stamped 25527186)		
1986-87	◆25527186	45.00
Vacuum Control Valve Filter		
1986-87	◆25526889	2.00
ELECTRONIC EMISSION CONTROLS		
Calibrator (PROM)		
1986-87-3.0	◆16055132	40.50
3.8 (2.73 axle ratio)		
exc. Calif.	◆16055821	40.50
Calif.	◆16057846	40.50
3.8 (2.84 axle ratio)		
exc. export	◆16055825	40.50
export	◆16059913	40.50

	Part No.	Price
Calpak (ECM)		
1986-87-3.0	◆16047428	5.75
3.8	◆16036494	6.75
Controller (ECM)		
1986-87-3.0	◆1227153	110.00
3.8	◆1227148	110.00
Exhaust Oxygen Sensor		
1986-87	◆8990741	28.75
Coolant Temperature Sensor		
1986-87	◆25036708	12.75
Vehicle Speed Sensor		
1986-87	◆25007335	44.00

LABOR 4 ALTERNATOR AND REGULATOR 4 LABOR

(Factory Time) Chilton Time

(G) Delcotron Circuits, Test
Includes: Test battery, regulator, Delcotron output.
All models 6

(M) Alternator Drive Belt, Renew
V-6–1986-87 (.3) 5

(G) Delcotron Assembly, Renew
Includes: Transfer fan and pulley.
V-6–1986-87 (.5) 7

(G) Delcotron, R&R and Recondition
Includes: Completely disassemble, inspect, test, replace parts as required, reassemble.
V-6–1986-87 (1.4) 2.1

(G) Delcotron Front Bearing, Renew
Includes: R&R Delcotron, separate end frames.
V-6–1986-87 (.5) 1.0
Renew rear brg add 2

(G) Delcotron Voltage Regulator, Test and Renew
Includes: R&R, disassemble and reassemble Delcotron.
V-6–1986-87 (.8) 1.2

(G) Voltmeter, Renew
1986-87
Olds 88 (.6) 1.0

PARTS 4 ALTERNATOR AND REGULATOR 4 PARTS

	Part No.	Price
Alternator Assy.		
1986-87-108 amp	◆10456319	173.50
120 amp.		
3.0	◆10497110	191.75
3.8	◆10497108	191.75
Alternator Drive Belt		
1986-87-3.0	◆25529593	22.50
3.8	◆25529592	22.50
Alternator Brace		
1986-87-R.H.	◆25518826	3.00
L.H.	◆25518771	5.00
Alternator Support		
1986-87	◆25518827	6.25

Alternator must be replaced as a unit. Replacement parts are not yet available.

LABOR 5 STARTING SYSTEM 5 LABOR

(Factory Time) Chilton Time

(G) Starter Draw Test (On Car)
All models 3

(G) Starter Assembly, Renew
Includes: Transfer solenoid.
V-6–1986-87 (.6) 1.0

(G) Starter, R&R and Recondition
Includes: Turn down armature.
V-6–1986-87 (1.4) 2.1
Renew field coils add (.3) 5
Add draw test if performed.

(G) Starter Drive, Renew
Includes: R&R starter and solenoid.
V-6–1986-87 (.7) 1.2

(G) Starter Motor Solenoid, Renew
Includes: R&R starter.
V-6–1986-87 (.6) 1.0

(G) Ignition Switch, Renew
1986-87 (.6) 9

(M) Battery Cables, Renew
All models
positive (.3) 4
negative (.3) 3
to start connector (.2) 3

(M) Battery Terminals, Clean
All models 3

PARTS 5 STARTING SYSTEM 5 PARTS

	Part No.	Price
Starter Assy.		
1986-87-3.0	◆1998526	189.50
3.8 (stamped 1998521)	◆1998521	179.75
(stamped 1998544)	◆1998544	192.25
Armature		
1986-87-3.0	◆10497046	76.75
3.8	◆10495881	73.00
Commutator End Roller Bearing		
1986-87	◆9441607	3.75
Brush		
1986-87	◆1893296	.75
Drive Assembly		
1986-87	◆10498407	33.50
Commutator End Frame		
1986-87-3.0	◆1978292	6.50
3.8	◆10496330	9.50
Field Frame		
1986-87-3.0	◆1987277	71.00
3.8	◆10495885	94.75
Brush Holder Kit		
1986-87	◆10497180	9.75
Drive Housing		
1986-87-3.0	◆1985148	25.50
3.8	◆10495877	28.25
Plunger		
1986-87	◆1987391	6.75
Shift Lever Shaft		
1986-87	◆1945804	1.25
Plunger Return Spring		
1986-87	◆1978281	1.75
Solenoid Switch		
1986-87	◆1114531	N.L.
Battery Cable (Positive)		
1986-87	◆12042315	39.00
Battery Cable (Negative)		
1986-87	◆12046243	24.50

LABOR 6 BRAKE SYSTEM 6 LABOR

(Factory Time) Chilton Time

(G) Brake Pedal Free Play, Adjust
All models 3

(G) Brakes, Adjust (Minor)
Includes: R&R wheels and adjust brakes thru access holes in drums. Fill master cylinder.
two wheels
Remove knock out plugs, add-each.. .1

(G) Bleed Brakes (Four Wheels)
Includes: Fill master cylinder.
All models (.4) 5

(G) Free Up or Renew Brake Self-Adjusting Units
All models-one 6
each adtnl 4

(G) Brake Shoes and/or Pads, Renew
Includes: Install new or exchange brake shoes or pads. Adjust service and hand brake. Bleed system.
1986-87-front-disc (.6) 9
rear-drum (.9) 1.5
all four wheels 2.3
Resurface disc rotor add-each 5
Resurface brake drum add-each 5

(G) Brake Drums, Renew
1986-87-one (.3) 5
both (.5) 8

(G) Brake System Failure Warning Switch, Renew
1986-87 (.2) 3

BRAKE HYDRAULIC SYSTEM

(G) Wheel Cylinder, Renew
Includes: Bleed system.
1986-87-one (.7) 1.0
both (1.1) 1.9

(G) Wheel Cylinder, R&R and Rebuild
Includes: Hone cylinder and bleed system.
1986-87-one (.9) 1.3
both (1.5) 2.1

(G) Master Cylinder, Renew
Includes: Bleed system.
1986-87 (.8) 1.2

COMBINATIONS

Add to Brakes, Renew

See Machine Shop Operations

(G) RENEW WHEEL CYLINDER
Each (.2) 2

(G) REBUILD WHEEL CYLINDER
Each (.2) 3

(G) REBUILD CALIPER ASSEMBLY
Each (.5) 5

(G) RENEW MASTER CYLINDER
All models (.5) 8

(G) REBUILD MASTER CYLINDER
All models (.8) 1.0

(G) RENEW BRAKE HOSE
Each 3

(G) RENEW BRAKE DRUM
Each (.1) 1

(G) RENEW DISC BRAKE ROTOR
Each (.2) 3

(Factory Time) Chilton Time

(G) Master Cylinder, R&R and Rebuild
Includes: Bleed complete system.
1986-87 (1.6) 2.0

(G) Brake Hose, Renew (Flex)
Includes: Bleed system.
1986-87-front-one (.7) 9
both (.8) 1.1
rear-each (.7) 9
center-both (.7) 1.0

(G) Brake System, Flush and Refill
All models 1.2

POWER BRAKES

(G) Power Brake Cylinder, Renew
1986-87 (.6) 1.0

(G) Power Brake Cylinder, R&R and Recondition
1986-87 (1.3) 2.0
Recond m/Cyl add (.8) 8

(Factory Time) Chilton Time

(G) Low Vacuum Switch, Renew
1986-87 (.2) 3

(G) Low Vacuum Brake Indicator Module Assy., Renew
1986-87 (.2) 3

(G) Vacuum Check Valve, Renew
1986-87 (.3) 3

DISC BRAKES

(G) Disc Brake Pads, Renew
Includes: Install new disc brake pads only.
1986-87 (.6) 9

(G) Disc Brake Rotor, Renew
1986-87-one (.4) 6
both (.8) 1.2

(G) Caliper Assembly, Renew
Includes: Bleed complete system.
1986-87-one (.4) 7
both (.6) 1.2

(G) Caliper Assy., R&R and Recondition
Includes: Bleed complete system.
1986-87-one (.9) 1.2
both (1.6) 2.2

(G) Brake Proportioner Valves, Renew
Includes: Bleed system.
1986-87-one (.3) 6
both (.5) 8

PARKING BRAKE

(M) Parking Brake, Adjust
All models (.3) 4

(G) Parking Brake Control, Renew
1986-87 (.5) 8

(G) Parking Brake Cables, Renew
1986-87-front (.6) 9
rear-right (.7) 1.0
left (.5) 8

(G) Parking Brake Equalizer, Renew
1986-87 (.3) 5

(G) Parking Brake Lamp Switch, Renew
1986-87 (.3) 4

PARTS 6 BRAKE SYSTEM 6 PARTS

	Part No.	Price
Shoe & Lining Kit (Rear)		
1986-87	◆12321420	N.L.
Rear Wheel Cylinder		
1986-87	◆18012582	31.50
Rear Cyl. Repair Kit		
1986-87	◆18013501	11.50
Front Brake Hose		
1986-87-R.H.	◆9769366	14.00
L.H.	◆9769365	14.00
Rear Brake Hose		
1986-87-R.H.	◆25522528	N.L.
L.H.	◆25522287	9.75
Master Cylinder Assy.		
1986-87	◆18013495	201.00
Master Cylinder Repair Kit		
1986-87	◆18010085	20.75
Rear Brake Drum		
1986-87 (Alum.)	◆25509919	90.00
(Cast iron)	◆25518892	69.25
POWER BRAKE UNIT		
Power Head Booster		
1986-87	◆18008736	250.25
Power Head Repair Kit		
1986-87	◆18007897	47.50
PARKING BRAKE		
Parking Brake Lever		
1986-87	◆18013489	6.75
Pedal		
1986-87	◆25515136	23.50
Release Handle		
1986-87	◆22529763	4.75
Front Cable		
1986-87	◆25523196	11.25
Intermediate Cable		
1986-87	◆25519956	22.00

PARTS 6 DISC BRAKES 6 PARTS

	Part No.	Price
(1) Brake Pad Set		
1986-87	◆12321410	N.L.
(2) Caliper Piston		
1986-87	◆18003155	11.00
(3) Caliper Repair Kit		
1986-87	◆18003724	8.75
(4) Caliper Housing		
1986-R.H.	◆18008319	142.00
L.H.	◆18008318	142.00
1987-R.H.	◆18013999	142.00
L.H.	◆18013998	142.00

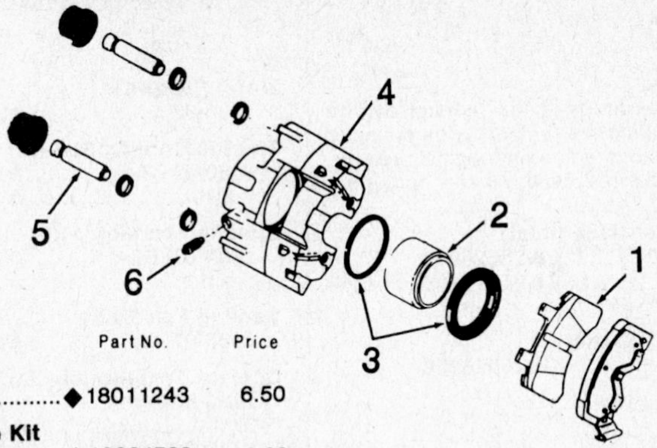

	Part No.	Price
(5) Mounting Bolt		
1986-87	◆18011243	6.50
(6) Bleeder Valve Kit		
1986-87	◆18004702	1.00

LABOR 7 COOLING SYSTEM 7 LABOR

(Factory Time) — Chilton Time

(M) Winterize Cooling System

Includes: Run engine to check for leaks, tighten all hose connections. Test radiator and pressure cap, drain radiator and engine block. Add antifreeze and refill system.

All models 5

(G) Thermostat, Renew

Includes: Drain and refill cooling system.

1986-87
V-6 (.5) 7

(G) Radiator Assy., R&R or Renew

Includes: Drain and refill cooling system.

1986-87
LeSabre (1.1) 1.8
Olds 88 (.6) 1.0
Renew side tank and/or gskt add
one side (.7) 7
both sides (1.2) 1.2

ADD THESE OPERATIONS TO RADIATOR R&R

(G) Boil & Repair 1.5
(G) Rod Clean 1.9
(G) Repair Core 1.3
(G) Renew Trans. Oil Cooler 1.9
(G) Recore Radiator 1.7

(M) Radiator Hoses, Renew

Includes: Drain and refill cooling system.

1986-87-upper (.3) 4
lower (.4) 5
both (.5) 7
by-pass (.5) 7

(M) Serpentine Drive Belt, Renew

1986-87 (.3) 5

(G) Serpentine Belt Tensioner, Renew

1986-87 (.5) 7

(G) Water Pump, Renew

Includes: Drain and refill cooling system.

1986-87 (1.7) 2.8

(G) Engine Coolant Fan Relay, Renew

1986-87 (.2) 3

(G) Engine Cooling Fan Resistor, Renew

1986-87 (.2) 3

(G) Coolant Fan Switch, Renew

1986-87 (.4) 5

(G) Engine Coolant Fan Electronic Control Module Assy., Renew

1986-87 (.3) 4

COOLING SYSTEM TUNE-UP

An Annual Cooling System Tune-Up Suggestion List should include (with some exceptions):

1. A visual check of the cooling system for indications of leaks or excessive oil content.
2. Pressure check the cooling system for internal and external leaks with filler cap and neck adapter and tester.
3. Check crankcase and automatic transmission oil for water content.
4. Test coolant thermostat with radiator thermometer.
5. Check temperature gauge for accuracy.
6. Drain system and flush till clean.
7. Clean foreign matter from radiator fins.
8. Test radiator pressure cap with cap tester.
9. Check fan blades and pulleys for alignment and damage.
10. Internal and external inspection of all hoses for cracks and deterioration.
11. Check core plugs (where possible) for seepage.
12. Refill system with correct coolant and check for air locks.
13. Check condition and tension of drive belts with tension gauge.

All models 1.5

(Factory Time) — Chilton Time

(G) Electronic Cooling Fan Blade and/or Motor, Renew

1986-87 (.3) 4

(G) Engine Coolant Temperature Switch (Engine Unit), Renew

1986-87 (.3) 5

(G) Temperature Gauge (Dash Unit), Renew

1986-87
Olds 88 (.6) 1.0

(G) Water Jacket Expansion Plugs, Renew (Side of Block)

each 5

Note: If necessary to R&R any component to gain access to plug, add appropriate time.

(M) Heater Hoses, Renew

Includes: Drain and refill cooling system.

1986-87-one (.3) 4
all (.9) 1.2

(G) Heater Core, R&R or Renew

1986-87 (1.6) 3.0

Add time to evacuate and charge A.C. system if required.

(Factory Time) — Chilton Time

ADD THESE OPERATIONS TO HEATER CORE R&R

(G) Boil & Repair 1.2
(G) Repair Core 9
(G) Recore 1.2

(G) Heater Control Assembly, Renew

1986-87 (.6) 9

(G) Heater Blower Motor, Renew

1986-87 (.3) 5

(G) Heater Blower Motor Relay, Renew

1986-87 (.2) 3

(G) Heater Blower Motor Switch, Renew

1986-87 (.4) 6

(G) Heater Blower Motor Resistor, Renew

1986-87 (.2) 3

(G) Heater Water Control Valve, Renew

1986-87 (.4) 6

PARTS 7 COOLING SYSTEM 7 PARTS

	Part No.	Price
Radiator Assy.		
Accurate replacement of the radiator can be done only by using the radiator code stamped on a metal tag located on the original radiator. Order by year, model, and radiator code no.		
Upper Radiator Hose (Inlet)		
1986-87-3.0	◆25526969	7.75
3.8	◆25527496	6.50
Radiator Hose (Outlet)		
1986-87	◆25526890	12.50
Thermostat		
1986-87	◆3037747	6.75
Water Pump Kit		
1986-87	◆25527537	63.00
Electric Cooling Fan Kit		
1986-87-R.H.	◆22036293	27.00
L.H.	◆22049520	26.75
Cooling Fan Motor Kit		
1986-87-R.H.	◆22048577	86.75
L.H.	◆22049519	67.00
Cooling Fan Relay		
1986-87	◆25522339	16.50
Coolant Temperature Switch (Engine)		
1986-87-w/ Digital	◆25036628	19.75
Digital	◆25036629	9.75
Fan Control Switch		
1986-87	◆3040674	N.L.
Heater Core		
1986-87 (1st des.)	◆3058630	114.00
(2nd des.)	◆3093683	N.L.
1st design has 64.0 m.m. center distance. 2nd design has 38.5 m.m. center distance.		
Blower Motor		
1986-87	◆22049769	52.00
Heater Control		
1986-87	◆16022134	47.00

LABOR 8 EXHAUST SYSTEM 8 LABOR

(Factory Time)	Chilton Time
(G) Muffler, Renew	
1986-87 (.5)	.8
(G) Intermediate Exhaust Pipe, Renew	
1986-87 (.4)	.7
(G) Front Exhaust Pipe Seal, Renew	
1986-87 (.4)	.7
(G) Crossover Exhaust Pipe, Renew	
1986-87 (.4)	.7
(G) Front Exhaust Pipe, Renew (To Converter)	
1986-87 (.4)	.7
(G) Catalytic Converter, Renew	
1986-87 (.8)	1.0
(G) Exhaust Manifold, Renew	
1986-87-right (1.7)	2.5
left (.5)	.9
COMBINATIONS	
(G) Exhaust System, Renew (Complete)	
1986-87	1.3

PARTS 8 EXHAUST SYSTEM 8 PARTS

	Part No.	Price
Exhaust Manifold		
1986-87-3.0 R.H.	◆25527106	202.00
L.H.	◆25527105	N.L.
1986-87-3.8 R.H.	◆25527098	105.00
L.H.	◆25527101	130.00
Crossover Pipe		
1986-87-3.0	◆25527594	32.00
3.8	◆25523739	19.00
Catalytic Converter		
1986-87	◆25056944	348.00
Manifold Pipe		
1986-3.0	◆25528758	N.L.
1986-87-3.8	◆25528757	N.L.
Intermediate Pipe		
1986-87	◆25528692	N.L.
Muffler & Tailpipe		
1986-87-3.0	◆25528697	N.L.
3.8 (exc. Sport)	◆25528695	N.L.
(Sport)	◆25528696	N.L.

LABOR 9 FRONT SUSPENSION 9 LABOR

(Factory Time)	Chilton Time
Note: On all front suspension operations alignment charges must be added if performed. Time given does not include alignment.	
(M) Wheel, Renew	
one	.5
(M) Wheels, Rotate (All)	
All models	.5
(G) Wheels, Balance	
one	.3
each adtnl	.2
(G) Check Alignment of Front End	
All models	.5
Note: Deduct if alignment is performed.	
(G) Toe-In, Adjust	
All models (.5)	.6
(G) Caster and Camber, Check	
Includes: Check and adjust toe-in.	
All models (1.2)	1.6
Adjust caster and camber add-each side	*.5
*Includes time to file struts as needed.	
(G) Front Wheel Hub and Bearing Assy., Renew	
1986-87-one side (.7)	1.1
both sides (1.2)	2.0
(G) Lower Control Arm Assy., Renew	
Add alignment charges.	
1986-87-one (.7)	1.0
both (1.2)	1.8
(G) Lower Control Arm Bushings, Renew	
Add alignment charges.	
1986-87-one side (1.0)	1.4
both sides (1.9)	2.6
(G) Lower Ball Joints, Renew	
Add alignment charges.	
1986-87-one side (.9)	1.3
both sides (1.7)	2.4
(G) Front Coil Springs, Renew	
Add alignment charges.	
1986-87-one (.8)	1.3
both (1.4)	2.3
(G) Front Shock Absorber Strut, Renew	
Add alignment charges.	
1986-87-one (.8)	1.3
both (1.4)	2.3
(G) Front Spring Seat and/or Insulator, Renew (Upper or Lower)	
Add alignment charges.	
1986-87-one side (.8)	1.3
both sides (1.4)	2.4

LABOR 9 FRONT SUSPENSION 9 LABOR

(Factory Time) Chilton Time

(G) Front Strut Bearing Mount Assy., Renew
Add alignment charges.

1986-87-one side (.8)	1.3
both sides (1.4)	2.4

(G) Steering Knuckle Assy., Renew
Add alignment charges.

1986-87-one (1.0)	1.5
both (1.9)	2.6

(G) Steering Knuckle Inner Dust Seal, Renew

1986-87-one (.8)	1.3
both (1.4)	2.3

(G) Front Stabilizer Shaft, Renew

1986-87 (1.0)	1.4

(G) Front Stabilizer Shaft Bushings, Renew

1986-87-one (.3)	.4
both (.4)	.6

(G) Engine Cradle, Renew (Complete)
Add alignment charges.

1986-87 (3.1)	5.0

FRONT DRIVE AXLE

(G) Front Drive Axle, R&R or Renew

1986-87-one (1.1)	1.4
both (1.6)	2.2
Renew shaft add-each (.3)	.4
Renew C/V Joint add each (.3)	.4
Renew D/O Joint add each (.3)	.4
Renew Tri-Pot Joint add each side (.3)	.4
Renew C/V Joint seal add each (.2)	.2

(G) Axle Shaft Oil Seal, Renew

1986-87-one (.8)	1.1
both (1.4)	2.0

PARTS 9 FRONT SUSPENSION 9 PARTS

	Part No.	Price
(1) Hub Bearing Kit		
1986-87	◆7470003	184.50
(2) Steering Knuckle		
1986-87-R.H.	◆25525862	173.00
L.H.	◆25525863	173.00
(3) Wheel Bearing Seal Kit		
1986-87	◆14084119	3.75
(4) Drive Axle Kit		
1986-87-R.H.	◆26003284	475.00
L.H.	◆26000329	544.00
(5) Lower Control Arm		
1986-87-R.H.	◆14089118	219.00
L.H.	◆14089117	219.00
(6) Lower Control Arm Bushing		
1986-87	◆14076627	6.50
(7) Stabilizer Shaft Bolt		
1986-87	◆561891	1.00
(8) Stabilizer Shaft		
1986-87	◆14081410	55.25
Other sizes available. Order by thickness of shaft.		
(9) Stabilizer Shaft Link Kit		
1986-87	◆14083559	4.25
(10) Upper Bracket		
1986-87	◆14086860	2.50
(11) Insulator Lower Clamp		
1986-87	◆14081620	1.25
(12) Insulator		
1986-87	◆14086877	2.00
(13) Strut Mount		
1986-87	◆17983307	53.50
(14) Front Spring Seat		
1986-87	◆14041893	5.75
(15) Front Spring Upper Insulator		
1986-87	◆14081609	4.50
(16) Strut Bumper		
1986-87	◆14081493	6.00

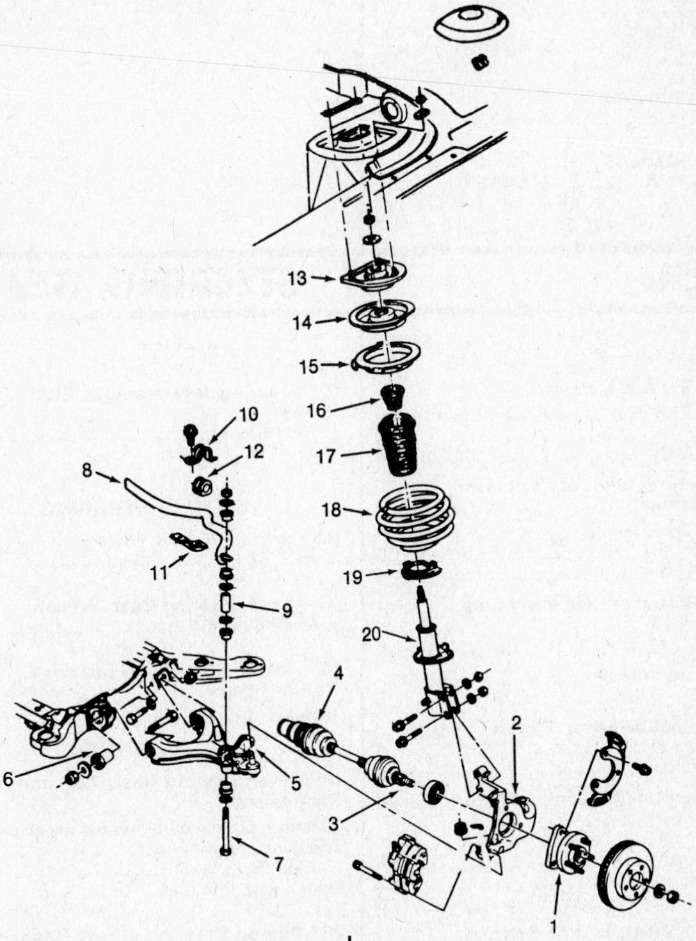

	Part No.	Price
(17) Strut Shield		
1986-87	◆14082814	5.50
(18) Spring		
For accurate replacement of coil springs the I.D. code must obtained from the spring tag.		

	Part No.	Price
(19) Lower Insulator		
1986-87	◆14063507	3.50
(20) Front Strut		
1986-87-exc. H.D.	◆22041011	88.25
H.D.	◆22047914	88.50

PARTS 9 FRONT DRIVE AXLE 9 PARTS

	Part No.	Price
(1) Joint Kit		
1986-87	◆26000318	385.00
(2) Seal Retaining Clamp		
Order according to diameter of axle shaft.		
C.V. Joint Seal		
1986-87	◆26000317	21.50
(4) Axle Shaft		
1986-87-R.H.	◆26002694	N.L.
(5) Tripot Seal Kit		
1986-87	◆26001938	21.50
(6) Tripot Bushing		
1986-87	◆7845165	5.00
(7) Spider Kit		
1986-87	◆26001939	N.L.
(8) Seal Retaining Clamp		
Order according to diameter of axle shaft.		
(9) Tripot Housing		
1986-87-R.H.	◆7843920	N.L.
(10) Tripot Housing		
1986-87-L.H.	◆7843922	N.L.
(11) Axle Shaft		
1986-87-L.H.	◆7846210	71.50

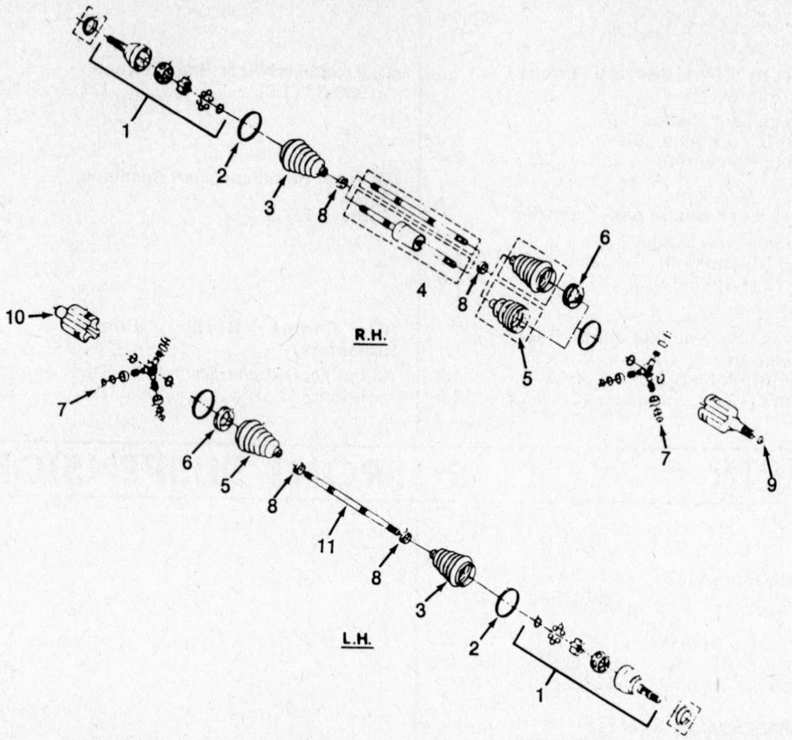

LABOR 11 STEERING GEAR 11 LABOR

(Factory Time)	Chilton Time
(G) Inner Tie Rods, Renew	
Includes: R&R gear as necessary. Reset toe-in.	
1986-87-one (2.0)	3.2
both (2.2)	3.4
(G) Tie Rod and/or Adjustor Sleeve, Renew	
Includes: Reset toe-in.	
1986-87-one (.7)	1.0
both (1.0)	1.4
(G) Horn Button or Cancelling Cam, Renew	
1986-87 (.4)	.6
(G) Steering Wheel, Renew	
1986-87 (.3)	.5
(G) Multifunction Lever, Renew	
1986-87 (.2)	.4
w/Cruise control add (.3)	.3
(G) Steering Column Lock Actuator Parts, Renew	
1986-87	
std colm (1.1)	1.6
tilt colm (.8)	1.3
Renew actuator rod add (.6)	.6
(G) Upper Mast Jacket Bearing, Renew	
1986-87	
std colm (1.1)	1.6
tilt colm (.5)	.9
(G) Steering Intermediate Shaft, Renew	
1986-87 (.4)	.7
POWER STEERING	
(M) Pump Drive Belt, Renew	
1986-87 (.3)	.5
(G) Power Steering Gear, Adjust	
All models (.3)	.6
(G) Power Steering Gear Assy., R&R or Renew	
Includes: Reset toe-in.	
1986-87 (1.8)	3.0
(P) Power Steering Gear, R&R and Recondition	
Includes: Disassemble, renew necessary parts, reassemble and adjust.	
1986-87 (3.1)	5.0
Bench leak test add	.5
(G) Power Steering Short Rack Assy., Renew	
Includes: Transfer parts as required. Reset toe-in.	
1986-87 (2.0)	3.9
(G) Power Steering Gear Boot Seals, Renew	
Includes: Reset toe-in.	
1986-87-one (1.2)	1.6
both (1.5)	2.0
(G) Power Steering Pump, Renew	
1986-87 (.5)	.8
(G) Power Steering Pump, R&R and Recondition	
1986-87 (1.0)	1.6
(G) Power Steering Pump Shaft Oil Seal, Renew	
1986-87 (.6)	1.0
(G) Power Steering Pump Flow Control Valve, Renew	
1986-87 (.6)	1.0
(G) Power Steering Reservoir, Renew (Remote)	
1986-87 (.4)	.6
(M) Power Steering Gear Cylinder Lines, Renew	
1986-87-one (.3)	.5
both (.5)	.8

PARTS 11 POWER STEERING GEAR 11 PARTS

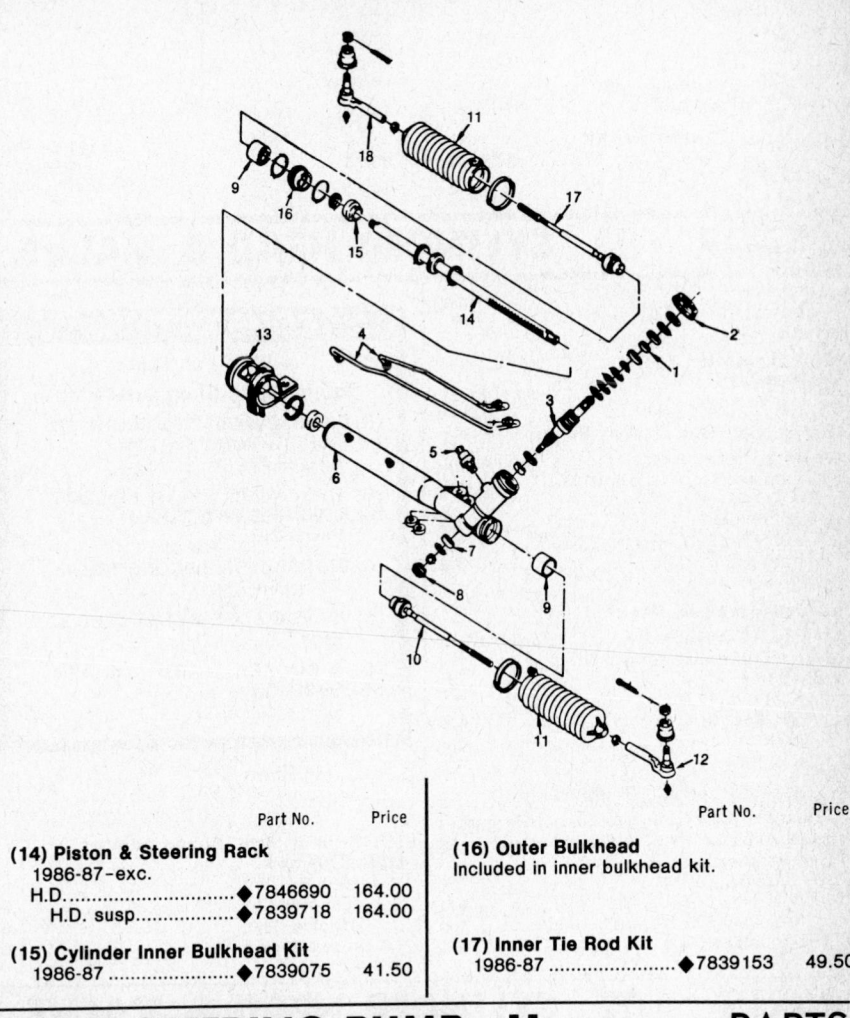

	Part No.	Price
Steering Gear Kit		
1986-87-exc.		
H.D.	◆26000072	191.00
H.D. susp.	◆26000098	191.00
(1) Stub Shaft Seal Adapter		
1986-87	◆7833732	6.75
(2) Bearing Annulus		
1986-87	◆7829888	19.25
(3) Pinion Valve Kit		
1986-87-exc.		
H.D.	◆7843191	263.00
H.D. susp.	◆26001767	263.00
(4) Line Kit		
1986-87-R.H.	◆7843187	15.75
L.H.	◆7843188	15.75
(5) Idle Speed Switch		
1986-87	◆10038601	14.75
(6) Housing		
1986-87	◆7847407	195.00
(7) Pinion Bearing Kit		
1986-87	◆7829884	53.50
(8) Dust Cover		
1986-87	◆7846884	7.00
(9) Shock Dampener Ring		
1986-87	◆7831234	1.75
(10) Outer Tie Rod Kit		
1986-87	◆7843189	52.75
(11) Boot Kit		
1986-87	◆7843190	24.00
(12) Tie Rod Ball Stud		
Included in outer tie rod kit.		
(13) Mounting Bracket		
1986-87	◆7842146	12.25

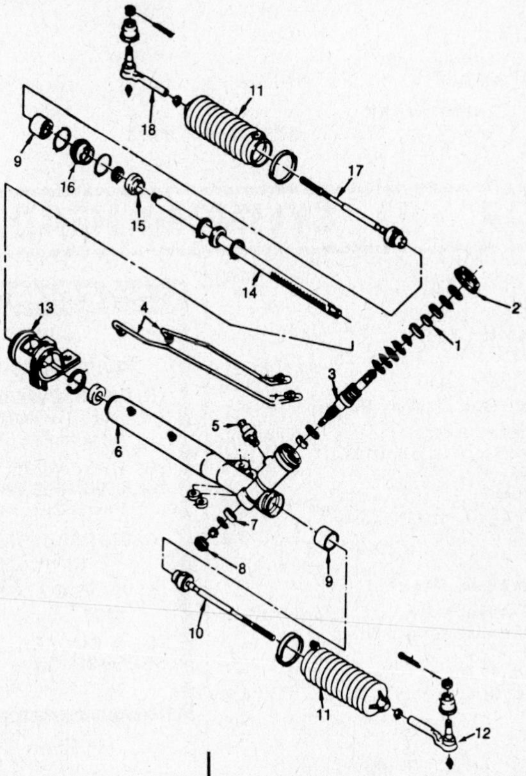

	Part No.	Price
(14) Piston & Steering Rack		
1986-87-exc.		
H.D.	◆7846690	164.00
H.D. susp.	◆7839718	164.00
(15) Cylinder Inner Bulkhead Kit		
1986-87	◆7839075	41.50

	Part No.	Price
(16) Outer Bulkhead		
Included in inner bulkhead kit.		
(17) Inner Tie Rod Kit		
1986-87	◆7839153	49.50

PARTS 11 POWER STEERING PUMP 11 PARTS

	Part No.	Price
Power Steering Pump		
1986-87-3.0	◆7848110	199.00
3.8	◆7848115	199.00
Seal Kit		
1986-87	◆7840566	11.00
(1) Thrust Plate		
1986-87	◆7840139	14.25
(2) Ring Kit (Rotor & Vane)		
1986-87-3.0	◆7841845	92.00
3.8	◆7840567	92.00
(3) Pressure Plate		
1986-87	◆7840080	14.25
(4) Pressure Plate Spring		
1986-87	◆7839989	3.00
(5) Sleeve Kit		
1986-87	◆7842086	9.75
(6) Reservoir Retaining Clip		
1986-87-R.H.	◆7844813	3.25
L.H.	◆7844812	3.25
(7) Pump Housing		
1986-87-3.0	◆7845378	62.75
3.8	◆7849050	110.00
(8) Bearing Shaft		
1986-87	◆26001375	42.00

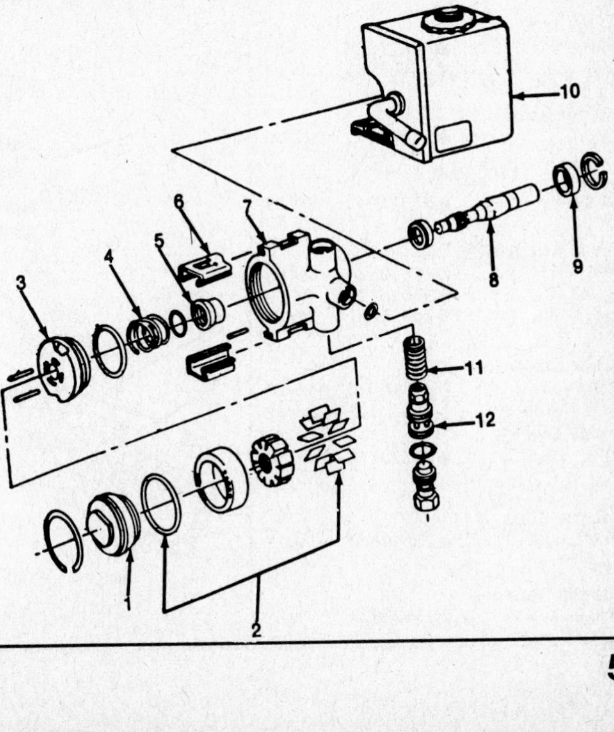

PARTS 11 POWER STEERING PUMP 11 PARTS

	Part No.	Price
(9) Bearing		
1986-87	◆26001378	16.00
(10) Reservoir Kit		
1986-87	◆7849244	63.75
(11) Flow Control Spring		
1986-87	◆5688037	1.25
(12) Control Valve		
1986-87	◆7841851	15.75

LABOR 12 CYLINDER HEAD & VALVE SYSTEM 12 LABOR

(Factory Time) — Chilton Time

(G) Compression Test
V-6–1986-87 7

(G) Cylinder Head Gasket, Renew
Includes: Clean gasket surfaces. Clean carbon. Make all necessary adjustments.
V-6–1986-87
right side (2.1) 3.0
left side (2.6) 3.8
both sides (3.6) 5.2

(G) Cylinder Head, Renew
Includes: Transfer all parts, reface valves. Make all necessary adjustments.
V-6–1986-87
right side (2.6) 3.7
left side (3.1) 4.5
both sides (4.4) 6.3

(P) Clean Carbon and Grind Valves
Includes: R&R cylinder heads, clean gasket surfaces, clean carbon, reface valves and seats. Minor tune up.
V-6–1986-87
right side (2.8) 4.0
left side (3.3) 4.8
both sides (4.6) 6.6

COMBINATIONS

Add to Valve Job
See Machine Shop Operations

(G) DRAIN, EVACUATE & RECHARGE AIR CONDITIONING SYSTEM
All models (.5) 1.0

(G) HYDRAULIC VALVE LIFTERS, DISASSEMBLE AND CLEAN
Each (.2) 2

(G) DISTRIBUTOR, RECONDITION
All models (.5) 8

(G) VALVE GUIDES, REAM OVERSIZE
Each (.2) 2

(G) ROCKER ARM SHAFT, RECONDITION
Each side (.2) 3

(Factory Time) — Chilton Time

(G) Rocker Arm Cover and/or Gasket, Renew
V-6–1986-87
right side (.5) 9
left side (.3) 6
both sides (.6) 1.0

(G) Rocker Arm Shafts and/or Assy., Renew
V-6–1986-87
right side (.7) 1.1
left side (.5) 8
both sides (.8) 1.5

(G) Valve Springs and/or Valve Stem Oil Seals, Renew (Head on Car)
V-6–1986-87
one cyl-right side (1.0) 1.5
one cyl-left side (.8) 1.2
one cyl-each side (1.4) 2.0
each adtnl cyl (.3) 3

(G) Vavle Tappets, Renew (Lifters)
Includes: Drain and refill cooling system, R&R intake manifold. Make all necessary adjustments.
V-6–1986-87
right side (2.3) 3.3
left side (2.1) 3.0
both sides (2.4) 3.4

(G) Rocker Arms and/or Push Rods, Renew
V-6–1986-87
right side (.8) 1.2
left side (.6) 9
both sides (.9) 1.6

PARTS 12 CYLINDER HEAD & VALVE SYSTEM 12 PARTS

	Part No.	Price
Gasket Kit		
1986-87-3.0	◆25527305	67.50
3.8	◆25527308	74.25
(1) Cylinder Head		
1986-87	◆25524543	217.00
(2) Gasket		
1986-87	◆25525919	21.25
(3) Rocker Arm Cover		
1986-87-R.H.	◆25518546	24.00
L.H. (3.0)	◆25525799	24.00
(3.8)	◆25525797	28.50
(4) Rocker Cover Gasket		
1986-87	◆25518526	5.75
(5) Rocker Arm Kit		
1986-87	◆25523770	4.50
(6) Pedestal Stud		
1986-87	◆25519860	2.75
(7) Pedestal Retainer		
1986-87	◆25522837	N.L.

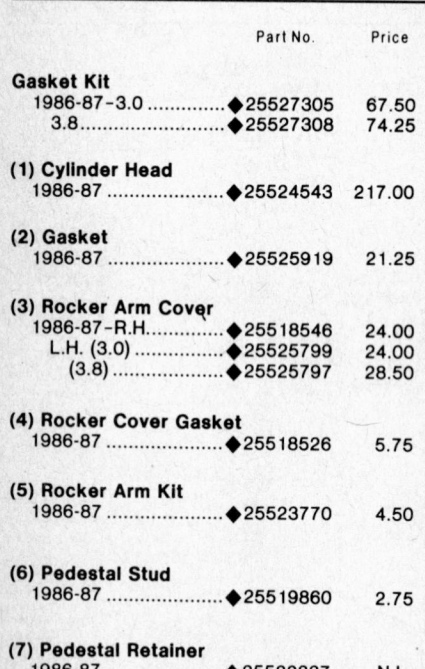

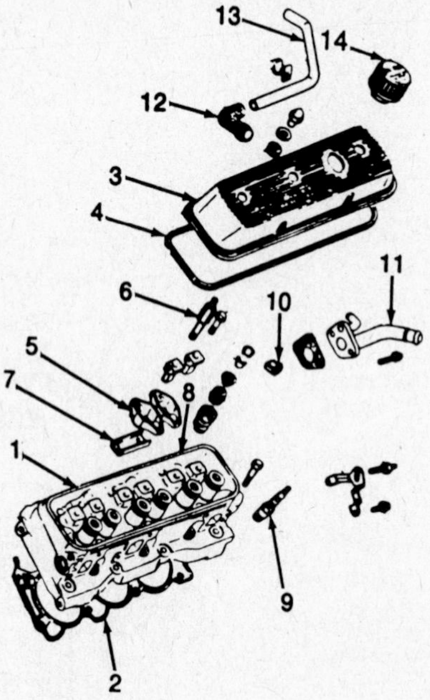

	Part No.	Price
(8) Valve Spring		
1986-87-3.0	◆25512551	2.75
3.8	◆25523695	3.00
(9) Spark Plug		
1986-87	◆5613611	N.L.
(10) Thermostat		
1986-87	◆3037747	6.75
(11) Coolant Outlet		
1986-87-3.0	◆25526957	11.75
3.8	◆25522194	5.75
(12) Vent Pipe Elbow		
1986-87	◆391095	1.75
(13) Vent Tube		
1986-87-3.0	◆25527150	5.25
3.8	◆25522041	4.00
(14) Oil Filler Cap		
1986-87	◆25525796	2.25

LABOR 13 ENGINE ASSEMBLY & MOUNTS 13 LABOR

(Factory Time) Chilton Time

(G) Engine Assembly, Remove and Install

Does not include transfer of any parts or equipment.

V-6–1986-87 .... 6.5

(P) Cylinder Block, Renew (Partial) (Less Head(s) and Oil Pan)

Includes: R&R engine, transfer all component parts not supplied with replacement engine. Minor tune up.

V-6–1986-87 (12.2) 18.9

Recond valves add (1.6) 1.6

(P) Engine Assy., R&R and Recondition

Includes: Rebore block, install new pistons, rings, rod and main bearings. Clean carbon, grind valves. Tune engine.

V-6–1986-87 (15.6) 24.1

(P) Engine Assembly, Recondition (In Car)

Includes: Expand or renew pistons, install new rings, pins, rod and main bearings. Clean carbon, grind valves. Tune engine.

V-6–1986-87 (14.2) 22.0

(P) Cylinder Block, Renew (Fitted) (w/Pistons, Rings and Bearings)

Includes: R&R engine assy. Transfer all component parts not supplied with replacement engine. Clean carbon, grind valves. Tune engine.

V-6–1986-87 (14.6) 22.6

(G) Engine Mount, Renew

V-6–1986-87

right (.4) 6

PARTS 13 ENGINE ASSEMBLY & MOUNTS 13 PARTS

	Part No.	Price
Engine Overhaul Gasket Kit		
1986-87-3.0	◆25530151	84.75
3.8	◆25530152	96.00
Engine Assy		
1986-87-3.0	◆966520	2250.00
3.8 (FHC)	◆966534	2650.00
(FKC)	◆966535	2550.00
Partial Engine Assy		
1986-87-3.0	◆25527472	1195.00
3.8 (Code 3)	◆25527480	1275.00
(Code B)	◆25527478	1263.00
Cylinder Block		
1986-87-3.0	◆25527473	949.00
3.8 (Code 3)	◆25527481	925.00
(Code B)	◆25527479	950.00
Engine Mount-R.H.		
1986-87	◆17983797	42.50
Transmission Mount		
1986-87-Front-L.H.	◆17986404	N.L.
Rear L.H.	◆17986405	N.L.
Rear R.H.	◆17983799	42.50

LABOR 14 PISTONS, RINGS & BEARINGS 14 LABOR

(Factory Time) Chilton Time

(P) Rings, Renew (See Engine Combinations)

Includes: Remove cylinder top ridge, deglaze cylinder walls. Minor tune up.

V-6–1986-87

one cyl-right side (3.5) 5.1
one cyl-left side (4.0) 5.9
one cyl-each side (6.0) 8.8
all cyls-both sides (7.9) 11.6

(P) Piston or Connecting Rod, Renew

Includes: Remove cylinder top ridge, deglaze cylinder walls. Minor tune up.

V-6–1986-87

one cyl-right side (4.2) 6.2
one cyl-left side (4.7) 6.9
one cyl-each side (7.4) 10.9
all cyls-both sides (8.6) 12.7

(G) Connecting Rod Bearings, Renew

Includes: R&R oil pan, check all bearing clearances.

V-6–1986-87 (2.2) 3.0

COMBINATIONS

See Machine Shop Operations

(G) DRAIN, EVACUATE & RECHARGE AIR CONDITIONING SYSTEM
All models (.5) 1.0

(G) HYDRAULIC VALVE LIFTERS, DISASSEMBLE AND CLEAN
Each (.2) 2

(G) DISTRIBUTOR, RECONDITION
All models (.5) 8

(G) VALVE GUIDES, REAM OVERSIZE
Each (.2) 2

(G) ROCKER ARM SHAFT ASSY., DISASSEMBLE AND CLEAN OR RECONDITION
Each side (.2) 3

(G) CYLINDER HEAD, R&R (ENGINE REMOVED)
V-6
one (1.7) 2.2
both (2.8) 3.6

(G) CONNECTING ROD, RENEW (ENGINE DISASSEMBLED)
V-6
Each (.5) 6

(G) DEGLAZE CYLINDER WALLS
Each (.1) 1

(G) REMOVE CYLINDER TOP RIDGE
Each (.1) 1

(G) PLASTIGAUGE BEARINGS
Each (.1) 1

(M) OIL FILTER ELEMENT, RENEW
All models (.3) 3

PARTS 14 PISTONS, RINGS & BEARINGS 14 PARTS

	Part No.	Price
(1) Piston Ring Kit		
1986-87-3.0	◆25526600	17.50
3.8	◆25528822	17.50
(2) Piston		
1986-87-3.0	◆25522584	49.00
3.8	◆25527178	48.25

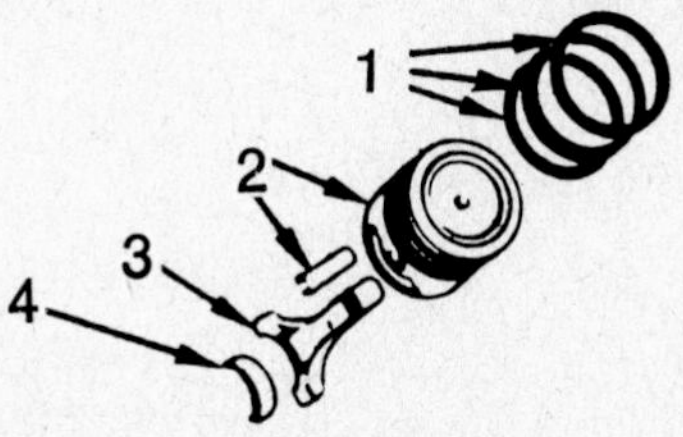

	Part No.	Price
(3) Connecting Rod		
1986-87-3.0	◆25518462	39.00
3.8	◆25506520	39.00
(4) Bearing Kit		
1986-87	◆18005399	N.L.

LABOR 15 CRANKSHAFT & DAMPER 15 LABOR

	(Factory Time)	Chilton Time
(P) Crankshaft and Main Bearings, Renew		
Includes: R&R engine, check all bearing clearances.		
V-6–1986-87	(6.3)	10.8
(P) Main Bearings, Renew		
Includes: R&R oil pan and bearing caps. Check all bearing clearances.		
V-6–1986-87	(1.8)	2.5
(P) Main and Rod Bearings, Renew		
Includes: R&R oil pan and bearing caps. Check all bearing clearances.		
V-6–1986-87	(3.0)	4.3
(G) Rear Main Bearing Oil Seal, Renew or Repack		
V-6–1986-87	(1.2)	2.2
(G) Crankshaft Pulley and/or Balancer, Renew		
V-6–1986-87 balancer	(1.0)	1.5

PARTS 15 CRANKSHAFT & DAMPER 15 PARTS

	Part No.	Price
(1) Crankshaft		
1986-87-3.0	◆25519733	385.00
3.8	◆25516025	405.00
(2) Sprocket		
1986-87	◆25528628	16.00
(3) Balancer Hub Seal		
1986-87	◆25523377	1.00
(4) Bearing Kit		
1986-87-No. 1	◆18009457	12.00
No. 2	◆18004602	20.00
No. 3	◆18002950	12.50
No. 4	◆5468578	13.00
(5) Rear Main Bearing Packing		
1986-87	◆9772831	1.50

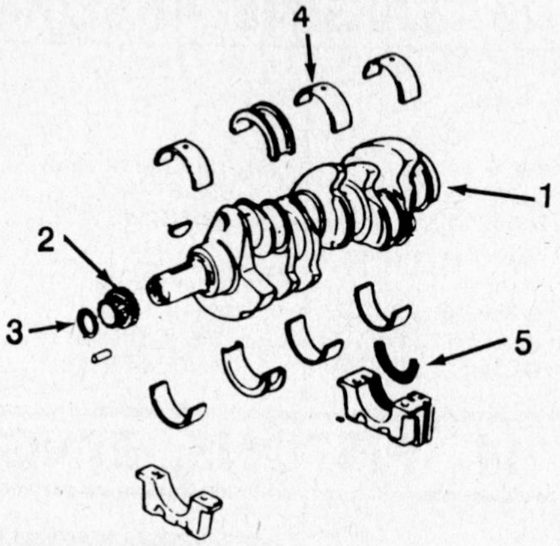

LABOR 16 CAMSHAFT & TIMING GEARS 16 LABOR

	(Factory Time)	Chilton Time
(G) Timing Case Cover Gasket, Renew		
Includes: Renew cover oil seal.		
V-6–1986-87	(3.8)	5.3
Renew cover add	(.4)	.4
(G) Timing Chain and/or Gears, Renew		
V-6–1986-87	(4.1)	5.6
(G) Camshaft, Renew		
V-6–1986-87	(6.2)	8.6
(G) Camshaft Rear Bearing Plug, Renew		
V-6–1986-87	(3.7)	5.0

PARTS 16 CAMSHAFT & TIMING GEARS 16 PARTS

	Part No.	Price
(1) Timing Chain		
1986-87	◆1257650	N.L.
(2) Camshaft Sprocket		
1986-87	◆25523115	17.50
(3) Damper Spring		
1986-87	◆1358909	.75
(4) Timing Chain Damper		
1986-87	◆1356634	N.L.

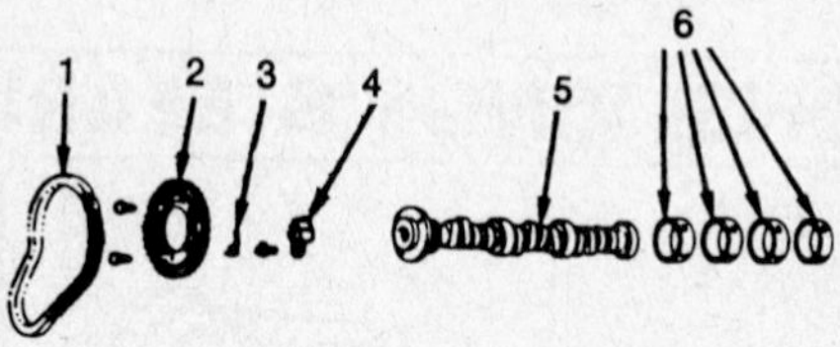

	Part No.	Price
(5) Camshaft		
1986-87-3.0	◆25526849	130.00
3.8 (Code 3)	◆25522674	119.00
(Code B)	◆25523930	124.00
(6) Bearings		
1986-87-Nos. 2, 3,RR	◆1231142	7.75
Nos. 1 & 4	◆25524301	7.25

LABOR 17 ENGINE OILING SYSTEM 17 LABOR

	(Factory Time)	Chilton Time
(G) Oil Pan and/or Gasket, Renew		
V-6–1986-87	(.9)	1.5
(P) Pressure Test Engine Bearings (Pan Off)		
All models		1.0
(G) Oil Pump Cover and/or Gears, R&R and Recondition		
V-6–1986-87	(.8)	1.2
(G) Oil Pressure Gauge (Engine), Renew		
1986-87	(.4)	.5
(G) Oil Pressure Gauge (Dash), Renew		
1986-87		
Olds 88	(.6)	1.0
(M) Oil Filter Element, Renew		
1986-87	(.3)	.3

PARTS 17 ENGINE OILING SYSTEM 17 PARTS

	Part No.	Price
Oil Pan		
1986-87	◆25522149	57.00
Oil Pan Gasket		
1986-87	◆25526425	7.50
Oil Pump		
1986-87	◆25525965	11.25
Pump Cover		
1986-87	◆25521935	9.00
Oil Pressure Regulator Valve		
1986-87	◆25515390	1.25
Filter By-Pass Valve		
1986-87	◆25011523	4.00
Oil Pressure Switch		
1986-87-Digital	◆10030963	20.75
exc. Digital		
1986	◆1623576	6.00
1987	◆25036925	7.50
Oil Pressure Gage (Dash)		
1986-87	◆25026385	68.50
Oil Filter		
1986-87	◆25010792	N.L.

LABOR 21 SHIFT LINKAGE 21 LABOR

	(Factory Time)	Chilton Time
(G) Shift Linkage, Adjust		
All models		
Neutral Safety Switch	(.3)	.4
Shift Indicator Needle	(.2)	.3
Shift Linkage	(.4)	.5
T.V. Cable	(.2)	.4
(G) Gear Selector Lever, Renew		
1986-87	(.2)	.4
(G) Gear Selector Indicator Needle and/or Assy., Renew		
1986-87	(.6)	.9
(G) Shift Control Cable, Renew		
1986-87		
colm shift	(.5)	.8

LABOR 26 REAR AXLE AND SUSPENSION 26 LABOR

	(Factory Time)	Chilton Time
(G) Rear Suspension, Align		
All models	(1.0)	1.3
(G) Rear Stabilizer Bar, Renew		
1986-87	(.9)	1.2
(G) Rear Tie Rod Ends, Renew		
Includes: Adjust toe-in.		
1986-87-one	(.9)	1.2
both	(1.2)	1.6
(G) Rear Wheel Bearing and Hub Assy., Renew		
1986-87-one side	(.5)	.7
both sides	(.8)	1.2
(G) Rear Wheel Knuckle Assy., Renew		
Add alignment charges.		
1986-87-one	(1.0)	1.3
both	(1.7)	2.2
w/H/duty susp add		
one side	(.2)	.2
both sides	(.3)	.3
(G) Rear Coil Springs, Renew		
1986-87-one	(.9)	1.2
both	(1.6)	2.2
w/H/duty susp add		
one side	(.2)	.2
both sides	(.3)	.3
(G) Rear Control Arm Bushings, Renew		
1986-87		
upper-one	(.6)	.8
both	(1.0)	1.3
lower-one	(.6)	.8
both	(1.0)	1.3
w/H/duty susp add		
one side	(.2)	.2
both sides	(.3)	.3
(G) Rear Control Arms, Renew		
1986-87		
upper-one	(.5)	.7
both	(.8)	1.2
lower-one	(.4)	.6
both	(.5)	.8
w/H/duty susp add		
one side	(.2)	.2
both sides	(.3)	.3
(G) Control Arm Ball Joint, Renew		
1986-87-one	(.8)	1.0
(G) Rear Strut Mounts, Renew		
1986-87-one	(.8)	1.1
both	(1.3)	1.9
(G) Rear Struts, Renew		
1986-87-one	(.6)	.9
both	(1.2)	1.7
ELECTRONIC LEVEL CONTROL		
(G) Compressor Assembly, Renew		
1986-87	(.5)	.7
(G) Compressor Relay, Renew		
1986-87	(.2)	.4
(G) Height Sensor, Renew		
1986-87	(.4)	.6
(G) Height Sensor, Adjust		
1986-87	(.4)	.6
(G) Electronic Level Control Dryer, Renew		
1986-87	(.3)	.4
(G) Electronic Level Control Head, Renew		
1986-87	(.5)	.8
(G) Electronic Level Control Motor and Cylinder Assy., R&R and Recondition		
1986-87	(.6)	1.0
(G) Pressure Limiter Valve, Renew		
1986-87	(.3)	.4

PARTS 26 REAR AXLE AND SUSPENSION 26 PARTS

	Part No.	Price
(1) Strut		
wo/Electronic level control		
1986-87-wo/H.D. susp.	◆22047954	N.L.
H.D. susp.	◆22047955	N.L.
Electronic Level Control		
1986-87-wo/H.D. susp.	◆22047949	144.75
H.D. susp.	◆22047948	144.75
(2) Knuckle		
1986-87-R.H.	◆25522880	47.50
L.H.	◆25522881	47.50
(3) Control Arm		
1986-87-R.H.	◆25527786	77.50
L.H.	◆25527787	77.50
(4) Adjusting Link		
1986-87	◆7845426	40.75
(5) Rear Spring		
Replacement springs must be ordered according to code on spring tag.		
(6) Spring Insulator		
1986-87-upper	◆10028860	4.25
lower	◆10027268	2.50
(7) Stabilizer Shaft		
1986-87	◆25523281	50.00
(8) Bolt		
1986-87	◆10026678	.50
(9) Brake Drum		
1986-87 (Alum.)	◆25509919	90.00
(Cast iron)	◆25518892	69.25

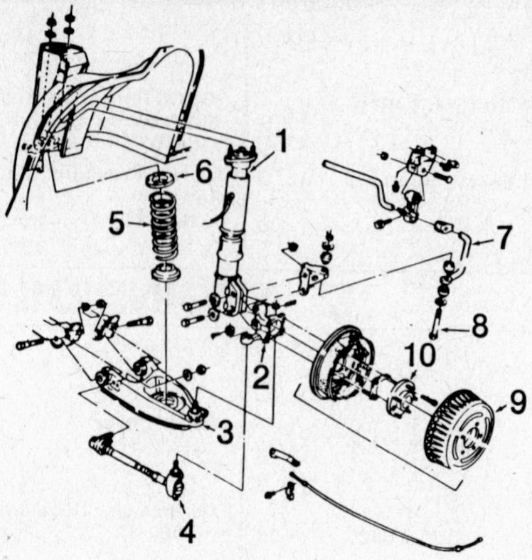

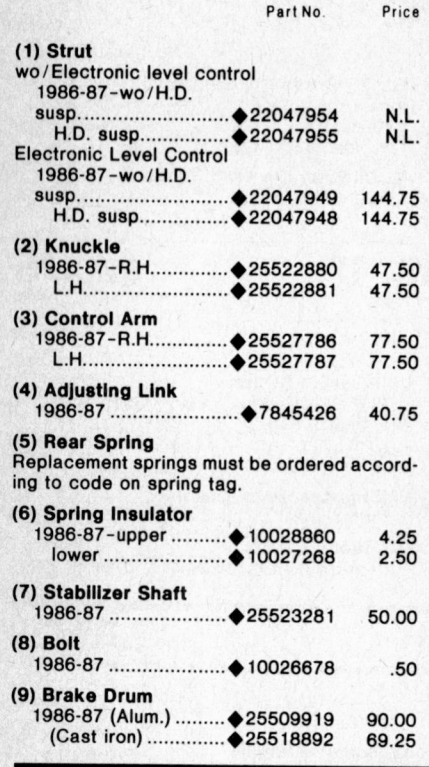

	Part No.	Price
(10) Wheel Bearing		
1986-87	◆7466926	198.00
ELECTRONIC LEVEL CONTROL		
Compressor Assy		
1986-87	◆22062531	233.00
Relay		
1986-87	◆25516613	9.75
Level Control Sensor		
1986-87	◆22048625	200.00
Air Dryer Kit		
1986-87	◆22009035	41.50
Level Control Head		
1986-87	◆22062535	68.50
Pressure Limiter Valve		
1986-87	◆22016688	31.00

LABOR 28 AIR CONDITIONING 28 LABOR

(Factory Time) — Chilton Time

Note: If more than one item requires replacement where evacuation and discharging the system is already included in the operation, deduct 1.0 hour for each additional item to the times listed.

(G) Drain, Evacuate and Recharge System
All models (.5) 1.0

(G) Refrigerant, Add (Partial Charge)
All models 6

(G) Leak Check
Includes: Check all lines and connections.
All models 5

(G) Compressor Belt, Renew
1986-87 (.3) 5

DA-6 COMPRESSOR

(G) Compressor Assembly, Renew
Includes: Transfer parts as required. Evacuate and charge system.
1986-87 (1.1) 1.9

(G) Compressor Clutch Plate and Hub Assy., Renew
1986-87 (.6) 9
Add time to evacuate and charge system if required.

(G) Compressor Clutch Rotor and/or Bearing, Renew
1986-87 (1.0) 1.5
Add time to evacuate and charge system if required.

AIR CONDITIONER TUNE-UP

For efficient operation and satisfactory performance in hot weather. The following air conditioner tune-up is suggested:

1. Clean intake filter
2. Clean condenser fins
3. Pressure test system
4. Adjust drive belt tension
5. Check antifreeze/coolant
6. Tighten compressor mounts
7. Tighten condenser and evaporator mounts
8. Inspect system for leaks (hoses, couplings, valves, etc.)
9. Partial charge system

All models 1.0
If necessary to evacuate and charge system, add 1.0

(G) Compressor Clutch Coil and/or Pulley Rim Assembly, Renew
1986-87 (1.0) 1.3
Renew pulley or brg add 2
Add time to evacuate and charge system if required.

(G) Compressor Front Seal, Seat and 'O' Ring, Renew
Includes: R&R clutch hub and drive plate assy. Evacuate and charge system.
1986-87 (1.4) 2.4

(Factory Time) — Chilton Time

(G) Compressor Front Head and/or Seal, Renew
Includes: R&R compressor. R&R clutch and pulley assy. R&R shaft seal assy. Clean and inspect parts. Evacuate and charge system.
1986-87 (1.7) 2.7

(G) Compressor Shaft and Cylinder Assy., Renew
Includes: R&R compressor. Clean and inspect parts. Evacuate and charge system.
1986-87 (1.8) 2.8

(G) Condenser, Renew
Includes: Evacuate and charge system.
1986-87 (1.2) 2.0

(G) Evaporator Core, Renew
Includes: Evacuate and charge system.
1986-87
LeSabre (1.3) 2.5
Olds 88 (1.9) 3.7

(G) Accumulator Assembly, Renew
Includes: Evacuate and charge system.
1986-87 (.8) 1.5

(G) Expansion Tube (Orifice), Renew
Includes: Evacuate and charge system.
1986-87 (.7) 1.4

(G) Vacuum Selector Valve, Renew
1986-87 (.4) 6

LABOR 28 AIR CONDITIONING 28 LABOR

(Factory Time)	Chilton Time
(G) A.C. Blower Motor Switch, Renew	
1986-87	
LeSabre (.5)	.7
Olds 88 (.3)	.5
(G) Master Electrical Switch, Renew	
1986-87 (.4)	.6
(G) A.C. Blower Motor Resistor, Renew	
1986-87 (.3)	.4
(G) A.C. Blower Motor Relay, Renew	
1986-87 (.3)	.4
(G) Refrigerant Switch, Renew	
1986-87	
High Pressure (.3)	.4
Low Pressure (.2)	.4
Add time to evacuate and charge system if required.	
(G) Temperature Control Assy., Renew	
1986-87-exc Touch Control (.5)	.8
Touch Control (.4)	.7
(G) A.C. Blower Motor, Renew	
1986-87 (.4)	.6
(G) Vacuum Actuators, Renew	
1986-87	
Defroster (.8)	1.4
Upper or Lower Mode (.8)	1.4
Air Inlet (.6)	1.0
(G) Electric Actuators, Renew	
LeSabre	
1986-87	
Defroster (.8)	1.2
(G) Heater Water Control Valve, Renew	
1986-87 (.4)	.6
(G) Air Conditioning Hoses, Renew	
Includes: Evacuate and charge system.	
1986-87	
liquid line (.8)	1.5
evap. to accum (.8)	1.5
suction & discharge (1.0)	1.7
AUTOMATIC TEMPERATURE CONTROL	
(G) Programmer, R&R or Renew	
1986-87 (.7)	1.1
Renew motor add (.1)	.1
(G) A.C. Aspirator, Renew	
1986-87	
LeSabre (.4)	.7
Olds 88 (1.1)	1.5
(G) Aspirator Hose, Renew	
1986-87	
LeSabre (.6)	.9
Olds 88 (1.3)	1.9
(G) In-Car Sensor, Renew	
1986-87 (.6)	.9
(G) Ambient Sensor, Renew	
1986-87 (.8)	1.1
(G) Outside Temperature Sensor, Renew	
1986-87 (.3)	.5

PARTS 28 AIR CONDITIONING 28 PARTS

	Part No.	Price
Compressor		
1986-87	◆12323604	N.L.
Clutch Drive		
1986-87	◆2724325	51.50
Pulley		
1986-87	◆6551983	115.25
Coil		
1986-87	◆6551997	47.50
Discharge Valve Plate		
1986-87-front	◆6551700	25.00
rear	◆6551702	25.00
Shaft Seal Kit		
1986-87	◆2724319	11.25
Compressor Head		
1986-87-Front	◆6557775	44.25
Rear	◆6557378	36.25
Shaft & Cylinder Assy.		
1986-87	◆6551952	307.75
Hi-Pressure Cut Off Switch		
1986-87	◆2724333	27.25
Pressure Relief Valve		
1986-87	◆5914435	13.25
Condenser		
1986-87-exc.		
H.D.	◆3058662	141.75
H.D.	◆3058661	145.00
Evaporator Core		
1986-87	◆3058764	220.75
Accumulator		
1986-87	◆3092035	85.50
Control Assy.		
LeSabre		
1986-87	◆16022134	47.00
Delta 88		
1986-87	◆16025803	51.25
Blower Motor		
1986-87	◆22049769	51.75
Blower Motor Relay		
1986-87	◆10026578	7.75
Blower Motor Resistor		
1986-87	◆10027029	4.25
Switch		
1986-87	◆16033615	7.25

LABOR 29 LOCKS, HINGES & WIND. REGULATORS 29 LABOR

(Factory Time)	Chilton Time
(G) Hood Latch Assembly, Renew	
1986-87 (.3)	.4
(G) Hood Hinge, Renew	
1986-87-one (.5)	.6
both (.6)	.8
(G) Hood Release Cable, Renew	
1986-87	
LeSabre (.4)	.6
Olds 88 (.5)	.8
(G) Hood Support Tube, Renew	
1986-87-each (.2)	.3
(G) Door Handle (Outside), Renew	
1986-87 (.6)	.9
Renew insert add	.1
(G) Front Door Lock Assembly, Renew	
1986-87 (.6)	.9
(G) Rear Door Lock Assembly, Renew	
1986-87	
LeSabre (.8)	1.2
Olds 88 (.6)	.9
(G) Front Door Lock Cylinder, Renew	
1986-87 (.4)	.7
Recode cyl add (.3)	.3
w/Ill entry system add (.2)	.2
(G) Door Lock Remote Control, Renew (Front or Rear)	
1986-87 (.4)	.6
(G) Lock Striker Plate, Renew	
1986-87 (.2)	.3
(G) Trunk Hinge or Strap, Renew	
1986-87 (.8)	1.2
(G) Rear Compartment Lid Lock Cylinder, Renew	
1986-87 (.3)	.4
Recode cyl add (.3)	.3
(G) Front Door Window Regulator, Renew	
1986-87-manual (.7)	*1.2
electric (.9)	1.4
*Recond add (.2)	.2
(G) Rear Door Window Regulator, Renew	
1986-87-manual (.6)	1.1
electric (.8)	1.3

PARTS 29 LOCKS, HINGES & WIND. REGULATORS 29 PARTS

	Part No.	Price
Hood Latch (Primary)		
1986-87	◆14039229	4.75
Hood Latch (Secondary)		
LeSabre		
1986-87	◆25522740	6.25
Delta 88		
1986-87	◆14039230	6.50
Hood Hinge		
LeSabre		
1986-87	◆25516653	23.50
Delta 88		
1986-87-R.H.	◆14039220	4.75
left	◆14039219	4.75
Front Door Lock		
1986-87-R.H.	◆20475164	39.25
L.H.	◆20475165	39.25
Rear Door Lock		
1986-87-R.H.	◆20482494	39.25
L.H.	◆20482495	39.25
Door Handle (Outside)		
1986-87-R.H.	◆20479794	28.25
L.H.	◆20479795	28.25
Window Regulator Front (Manual)		
(2 Door)		
1986-87-R.H.	◆20643060	64.25
L.H.	◆20643061	64.25
(4 Door)		
1986-87-R.H.	◆20643062	64.25
L.H.	◆20643063	64.25
Window Regulator Front (Power)		
(2 Door)		
1986-87-R.H.	◆20480596	64.25
L.H.	◆20480597	64.25
(4 Door)		
1986-R.H.	◆20304754	64.25
L.H.	◆20304755	64.25
1987-R.H.	◆20611636	64.25
L.H.	◆20611637	64.25
Window Regulator Rear (Manual)		
1986-87-R.H.	◆20457822	57.75
L.H.	◆20457823	57.75
Rear (Power)		
1986-R.H.	◆20611674	57.75
L.H.	◆20611675	57.75
1987-R.H.	◆20611642	50.50
L.H.	◆20611643	50.50
Power Window Regulator Motor		
1986	◆22062528	80.25
1987-R.H.	◆22062567	80.25
L.H.	◆22062568	80.25
Trunk Lock		
1986-87	◆20513755	11.25
Trunk Lock Cylinder		
1986-87	◆3910570	6.50
Trunk Hinge		
(2 Door)		
1986-87-R.H.	◆20453916	22.50
L.H.	◆20453917	22.50
(4 Door)		
1986-87-R.H.	◆20453912	38.75
L.H.	◆20453913	38.75

LABOR 30 HEAD AND PARKING LAMPS 30 LABOR

(Factory Time)	Chilton Time
(G) Aim Headlamps	
two	.4
four	.6
(M) Headlamp Sealed Beam Bulb, Renew	
1986-87-each (.3)	.3
(M) Park and Turn Signal Lamp Assy., Renew	
1986-87	
right (.2)	.3
left (.3)	.4
(M) Side Marker Lamp Assy., Renew	
1986-87	
front-each (.2)	.3
rear-each (.3)	.4
(M) License Lamp Assembly, Renew	
1986-87 (.2)	.3
(M) Back-Up Lamp Assembly, Renew	
1986-87 (.3)	.4
(M) Cornering Lamp Bulb, Renew	
All models-each (.2)	.3
(M) High Level Stop Lamp Assy., Renew	
All models (.2)	.4
(M) High Level Stop Lamp Bulb, Renew	
All models (.2)	.3
(M) License Lamp Bulb, Renew	
All models-one or all (.2)	.3
(M) Park and Turn Signal Lamp Bulb, Renew	
All models-each	.2
(M) Rear Combination Lamp Bulb, Renew	
All models-one	.2
each adtnl	.1
(M) Side Marker Lamp Bulb, Renew	
All models-each	.6

PARTS 30 HEAD AND PARKING LAMPS 30 PARTS

	Part No.	Price
Headlamp Sealed Beam		
LeSabre		
1986-87-exc. quartz		
inboard	◆5966201	N.L.
outboard	◆5966200	N.L.
1986-87-w/quartz		
inboard	◆5930567	N.L.
outboard	◆16502327	N.L.
Delta 88		
1986-87-inboard	◆5930567	N.L.
outboard	◆5966200	N.L.
Parking & Turn Signal Lamp Assy.		
LeSabre		
1986-87-R.H.	◆918308	28.50
L.H.	◆918307	28.50
Delta 88		
1986-87-R.H.	◆918182	28.50
L.H.	◆918181	28.50
Side Marker Lamp (Front)		
LeSabre		
1986-87	◆917984	8.50
Delta 88		
1986-87-R.H.	◆920136	10.00
L.H.	◆920135	10.00
Side Marker Lamp (Rear)		
LeSabre		
1986-87	◆917985	8.50
Delta 88		
1986-87	◆919989	9.75
License Lamp Assy.		
LeSabre		
1986-87	◆929475	3.75
Delta 88		
1986-87-R.H.	◆917936	4.00
L.H.	◆917935	4.00
Tail Lamp Housing		
LeSabre		
1986-87	◆16503835	47.50
Delta 88		
1986-87-R.H.	◆5974540	73.25
L.H.	◆5974539	73.25

Delta 88 model tail lamp is serviced as a complete assy. Lesabre is serviced only in parts.

	Part No.	Price
Back-Up Lamp		
LeSabre (Housing)		
1986-87	◆16503951	78.50
Delta 88 (Lamp)		
1986-87	◆918304	20.75
Cornering Lamp		
LeSabre		
1986-87-R.H.	◆918066	25.50
L.H.	◆918065	25.50
Delta 88		
1986-87-R.H.	◆5974398	20.50
L.H.	◆5974397	20.50
High Mounted Stop Lamp		
(2 Door)		
1986-87-exc.		
Lug. rack	◆5974465	36.00
Lug. rack	◆920116	36.00
(4 Door)		
1986-87-exc.		
Lug. rack	◆5974468	36.00
Lug. rack	◆920116	36.00

LABOR 31 WINDSHIELD WIPER & SPEEDOMETER 31 LABOR

(Factory Time)	Chilton Time
(G) Windshield Wiper Motor, Renew	
1986-87 (.6)	.8
w/Inter wiper add (.1)	.1
(G) Windshield Wiper Motor, R&R and Recondition	
1986-87 (1.1)	1.5
(G) Wiper Transmission, Renew	
1986-87 (.6)	1.0
(G) Wiper Switch, Renew	
1986-87	
std colm (.9)	1.3
tilt colm (1.2)	1.7
(G) Windshield Washer Pump, Renew	
1986-87 (.6)	.8
w/Pulse wipe add (.1)	.1
Recond pump add (.3)	.3
(G) Windshield Washer Pump Valve, Renew	
1986-87 (.2)	.3
(G) Wiper Motor Terminal Board and/or Timing Delay Switch, Renew	
1986-87 (.6)	1.0
(G) Wiper Motor Main Drive Gear (Depressed Park), Renew	
Includes: R&R wiper motor.	
1986-87 (1.0)	1.5
(G) Pulse Wipe Control Module, Renew	
1986-87 (.2)	.3
(G) Intermittent Wiper Controller Assy, Renew	
1986-87 (.3)	.4
(G) Instrument Panel Cluster Assy., Renew	
1986-87	
LeSabre (.4)	.7
Olds 88 (.6)	1.1
(G) Speedometer Signal Generator, Renew	
1986-87	
LeSabre (.3)	.5
(G) Speedometer Head, R&R or Renew	
1986-87	
LeSabre (.4)	.7
Olds 88 (.5)	.9
Reset odometer add	.2
(G) Radio, R&R	
1986-87	
LeSabre (.4)	.7
Olds 88 (.6)	1.1

PARTS 31 WINDSHIELD WIPER & SPEEDOMETER 31 PARTS

	Part No.	Price
Windshield Wiper Motor		
1986-87	◆22039328	117.75
Wiper Transmission		
1986-87-R.H.	◆22039330	19.25
L.H.	◆22039331	19.25
Wiper Switch		
1986-87-w/Corn. lamp	◆7837280	N.L.
exc. Tilt whl	◆7842714	44.75
Tilt whl	◆7843683	56.25
Wiper Arm		
1986-87-R.H.	◆20634672	25.25
L.H.	◆20634673	25.25
Windshield Washer Pump		
1986-87	◆22039041	18.50
Speedometer Head		
Order according to year, model and options.		

LABOR 32 LIGHT SWITCHES & WIRING 32 LABOR

(Factory Time)	Chilton Time
(G) Headlamp Switch, Renew	
1986-87 (.3)	.6
(G) Headlamp Dimmer Switch, Renew	
1986-87 (.6)	1.0
(G) Stop Light Switch, Renew	
1986-87 (.3)	.4
(G) Turn Signal or Hazard Warning Switch, Renew	
1986-87	
std whl (.6)	1.0
tilt whl (.7)	1.1
(G) Parking Brake Lamp Switch, Renew	
1986-87 (.3)	.4
(G) Back-Up Lamp Switch, Renew	
1986-87	
LeSabre (.6)	1.0
(G) Neutral Start Switch, Renew	
1986-87	
LeSabre-colm mount (.6)	1.0
(M) Turn Signal or Hazard Warning Flasher, Renew	
1986-87 (.2)	.3
(G) Horn Relay, Renew	
1986-87 (.3)	.4
(G) Horn, Renew	
1986-87-one (.3)	.4
each adtnl	.1

PARTS 32 LIGHT SWITCHES & WIRING 32 PARTS

	Part No.	Price
Head Lamp Switch		
LeSabre		
1986-87	◆1995241	14.75
Delta 88		
1986-87	◆1972717	16.75
Headlamp Dimmer Switch		
1986-87	◆7841238	9.75
Stop Lamp Switch		
1986-87-exc. Cruise	◆25523464	8.00
Cruise cont	◆25523462	8.00
Back-up Lamp Switch		
1986-87-exc. Digital	◆1994253	13.00
Digital	◆1994258	25.00
Turn Signal Switch		
1986-87-exc. Corn. lamp	◆1997983	N.L.
Corn. lamp	◆1997984	N.L.
Turn Signal Lamp Flasher		
1986	◆10041074	3.75
1987	◆10041073	N.L.
Parking Brake Alarm Switch		
1986-87	◆1264464	1.50
Hazard Lamp Flasher		
1986-87	◆6450089	N.L.
Horn Assy.		
1986-87-Low	◆1892163	N.L.
High	◆1892164	N.L.
Horn Relay		
1986-87	◆25523703	N.L.

LABOR 33 GLASS 33 LABOR

	(Factory Time)	Chilton Time
(G) Windshield Glass, Renew		
1986-87	(1.6)	2.2
Renew caulk bead add	(.4)	.4
(G) Front Door Glass, Renew		
1986-87-2 Dr	(1.0)	1.6
4 Dr	(1.0)	1.6
(G) Rear Quarter Stationary Glass, Renew		
1986-87-2 Dr	(1.5)	2.0
4 Dr	(.7)	1.0
(G) Rear Door Glass, Renew		
1986-87	(.8)	1.3
(G) Rear Door Vent Glass, Renew		
1986-87		
LeSabre	(1.1)	1.5
Olds 88	(.6)	.8
(G) Rear Window Glass, Renew		
1986-87	(1.3)	2.0
w/Elec Defogger add	(.6)	.6
w/3/4 plug, unpadded add	(1.3)	2.0
w/3/4 plug, padded add	(2.6)	4.0
w/Full plug, padded add	(2.8)	4.4

LABOR 34 CRUISE CONTROL 34 LABOR

	(Factory Time)	Chilton Time
(G) Cruise Control Engagement Switch, Renew		
Includes: Renew turn signal lever.		
1986-87	(.5)	.9
(G) Cruise Control Servo, Renew		
1986-87	(.5)	.8
(G) Cruise Control Vacuum Hoses, Renew		
1986-87	(.3)	.4
(G) Cruise Control Chain or Cable, Renew		
1986-87	(.3)	.4
(G) Cruise Control Module, Renew		
1986-87	(.5)	.7

PARTS 34 CRUISE CONTROL 34 PARTS

	Part No.	Price
Cruise Control Module		
1986-87-3.0	◆25074738	101.00
3.8	◆25074736	101.00
Cruise Control Servo		
1986-87	◆25074625	119.75
Servo Cable		
1986-87	◆25523976	6.50
Vacuum Release Valve		
1986-87	◆25523376	14.00
Vacuum Hose Check Value		
1986-87	◆14056648	1.75

GROUP INDEX

ALPHABETICAL INDEX

General Motors
Front Wheel Drive Cars

BUICK RIVIERA • CADILLAC ELDORADO • SEVILLE • OLDSMOBILE TORONADO

1983–85

YEAR IDENTIFICATION

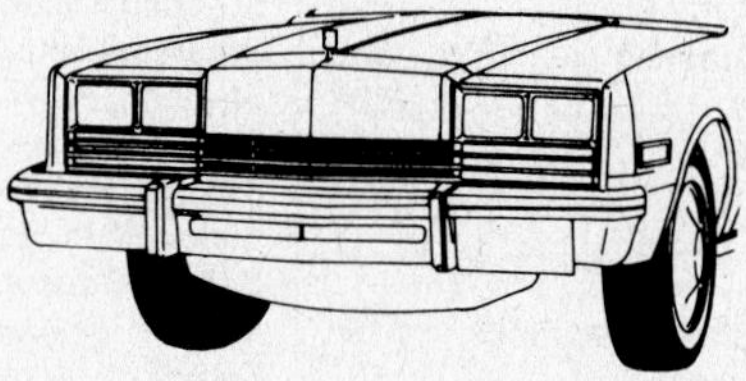

1983–84 Toronado

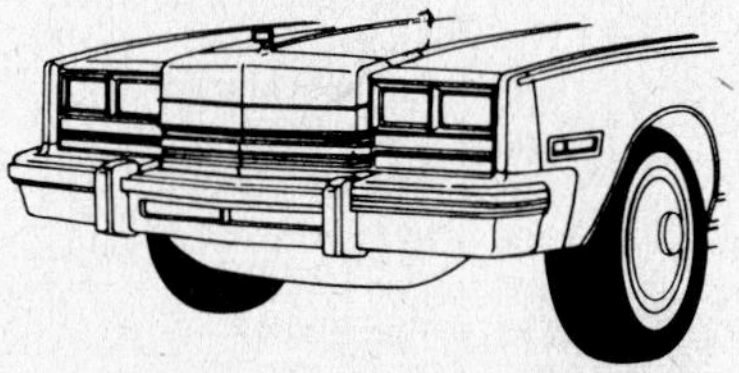

1984–85 Toronado Calienta

1983–84 Eldorado

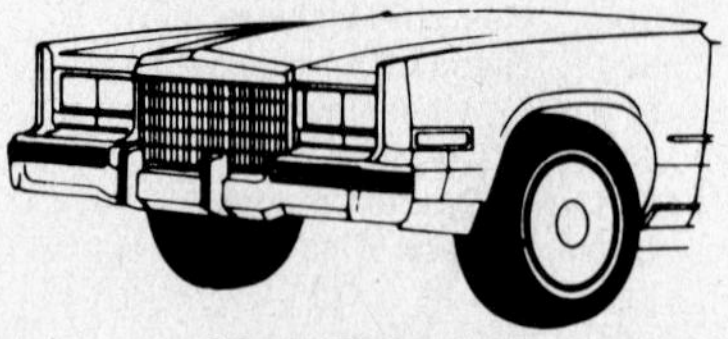

1985 Eldorado

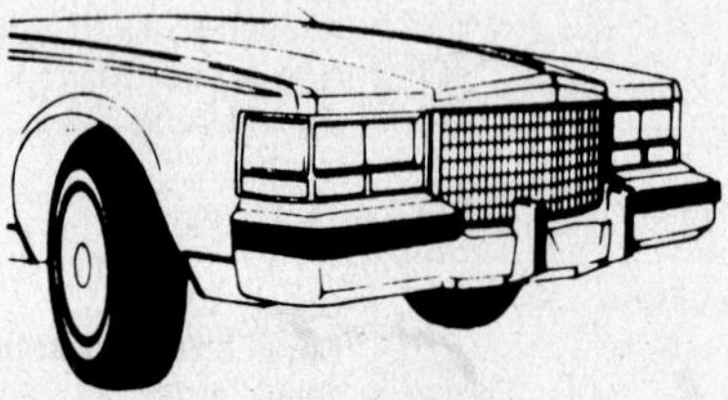

1985 Seville

VEHICLE IDENTIFICATION NUMBER (VIN)

It is important for servicing and ordering parts to be certain of the vehicle and engine identification. The VIN (vehicle identification number) is a 13 or 17 digit number visible through the windshield on the driver's side of the dash and contains the vehicle and engine identification codes. It can be interpreted as follows:

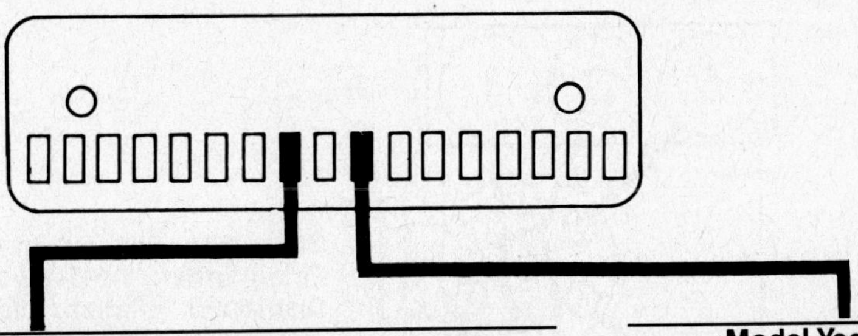

Engine Code

Code	Cu. In.	Liters	Cyl.	Carb.	Eng. Mfg.
8, B	231	3.8	6	SFI	Buick
3	231	3.8	6	4	Buick
9	231	3.8	6	FI-Turbo	Buick
8	250	4.1	8	DFI	Cad.
8	250	4.1	8	4	Cad.
4	252	4.1	6	4	Buick
4	252	4.1	6	DFI	Buick
Y	307	5.0	8	4	Olds.
N	350	5.7	8	Diesel	Olds.

Model Year Code

Code	Year
D	83
E	84
F	85
G	86
H	87

The seventeen digit Vehicle Identification Number can be used to determine engine application and model year. The 10th digit indicates the model year, and the 8th digit identifies the factory installed engine.
EFI Electronic Fuel Injection
DFI Digital Fuel Injection

GASOLINE ENGINE TUNE-UP SPECIFICATIONS

When analyzing compression test results, look for uniformity among cylinders rather than specific pressures.

Year	Eng. Code	Engine No. Cyl. Displacement (cu. in.)	Liters	Eng. Mfg.	Spark Plugs Orig. Type	Spark Plugs Gap (in.)	Distributor	Ignition Timing (deg.) *Auto Trans.•	Valves Intake Opens (deg.) •	Fuel Pump Pressure (psi)	Idle Speed (rpm) Auto Trans.•
					TORONADO						
'83	4	6-252	4.1	Buick	R-45TS8	.080	Electronic	15B	16	6-7.5	①
	Y	8-307	5.0	Olds.	R-46SX	.080	Electronic	15B	20	6-7.5	①
'84–'85	4	6-252	4.1	Buick	R-45TS8	.080	Electronic	①	16	6-7.5	①
	Y	8-307	5.0	Olds.	R-46SX	.080	Electronic	①	20	6-7.5	①
					RIVIERA						
'83	8	6-231 Turbo	3.8	Buick	R-45TS	.040	Electronic	15B	16	4.2-5.8	①
	4	6-252	4.1	Buick	R-45TS8	.080	Electronic	15B	16	6-7.5	①
	Y	8-307	5.0	Olds.	R-46SX	.080	Electronic	15B @ 1100	20	6-7.5	①
'84–'85	8 ③	6-231 Turbo	3.8	Buick	R-45TS	.040	Electronic	①	16	4.2-5.8	①
	4	6-252	4.1	Buick	R-45TS8	.080	Electronic	①	16	6-7.5	①
	Y	8-307	5.0	Olds.	R-46SX	.080	Electronic	①	20	6-7.5	①
					ELDORADO AND SEVILLE						
'83	8	8-250	4.1	Cadillac	R-43NTS6	.060	Electronic	①	37	40	②
'84–'85	8	8-250	4.1	Cadillac	R-43NTS6 ④	.060	Electronic	①	37	40	②

*Set timing with carburetor adjusted to 1100 rpm, unless sticker specifies otherwise.

• Where two figures appear separated by a slash, the first is idle speed with solenoid energized, the second is idle speed with solenoid disconnected. Figure in parenthesis indicates California engine.
B Before Top Dead Center
Part numbers in this chart are not recommendations by Chilton for any product by brand name.
① See Underhood Sticker
② Electronic controlled idle, no adjustment
③ 85; VIN9
④ R42CLTS6

FIRING ORDERS

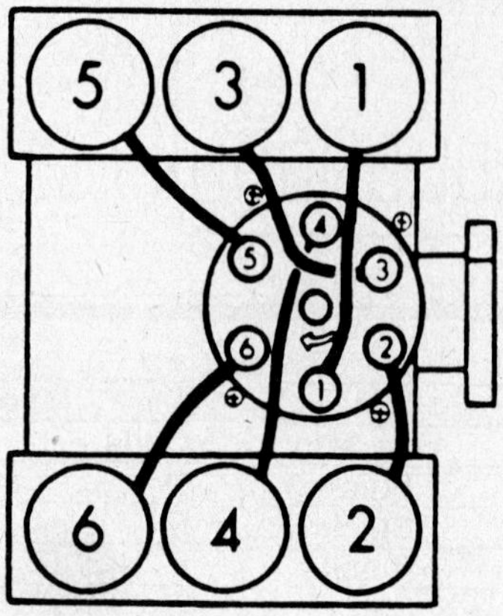

Buick 231, 252 cu. in. V6 (3.8, 4.1L)
Firing order: 1-6-5-4-3-2
Distributor rotation: clockwise

V6 Harmonic balancers have two timing marks: one is 1/8 in. wide, and one is 1/16 in. wide. Use the 1/16 in. mark for timing with a hand held light. The 1/8 in. mark is used only with a magnetic timing pick-up probe.

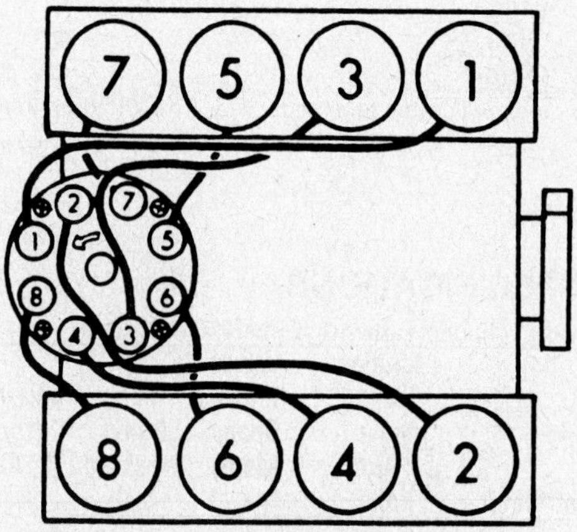

GM 250, 307, 350 cu. in. V8 (4.1, 5.0, 5.7L)
Firing order: 1-8-4-3-6-5-7-2
Distributor rotation: counterclockwise

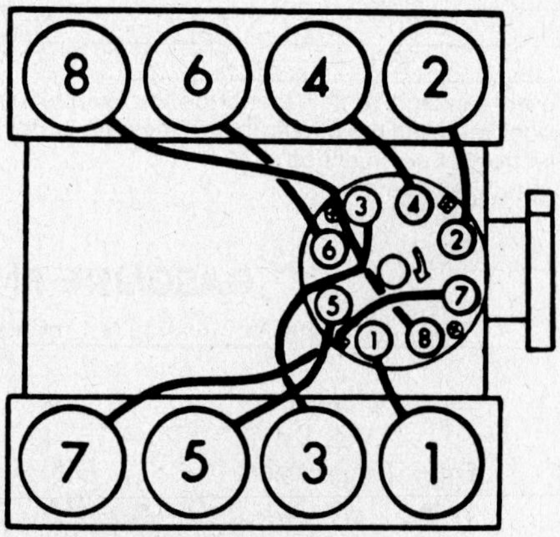

GM 368 cu. in. V8 (6.0L)
Firing order: 1-5-6-3-4-2-7-8
Distributor rotation: clockwise

WHEEL ALIGNMENT SPECIFICATIONS

Year	Caster Range (deg.)	Caster Pref. Setting (deg.)	Camber Range (deg.)	Camber Pref. Setting (deg.)	Toe in (in.)	Steering Axis Inclin. (deg.)
			TORONADO			
'83–'85	1 1/2P to 3 1/2P	2 1/2P	1/2N to 1/2P	0	1/8 in to 1/8 out	11
			ELDORADO AND SEVILLE			
'83–'85	2P to 3P	2 1/2P	1/2N to 1/2P	0	1/8 in to 1/8 out	—
			RIVIERA			
'83–'85	2P to 3P	2 1/2P	1/2N to 1/2P	0	1/8 in to 1/8 out	—

LABOR SERVICE BAY OPERATIONS LABOR

(Factory Time) Chilton Time

COOLING

(M) Winterize Cooling System

Includes: Run engine to check for leaks, tighten all hose connections. Test radiator and pressure cap, drain radiator and engine block. Add anti-freeze and refill system.

All models	.5

(G) Thermostat, Renew

Includes: Test thermostat.

V-6–1983-85 (.7)	.8
V-8–1983-85 (.5)	.6
Diesel–1983-85 (.5)	.8
w/Turbocharger and A.I.R. add (.4)	.6

(M) Drive Belt, Renew

1983-85-one (.3)	.5
each adtnl	.1
w/Eng. Code 8	
A.C. (.6)	.8
AIR (.5)	.7
Alter (.3)	.4
Vacuum pump (.2)	.3

(M) Drive Belt, Adjust

1983-85-one (.3)	.4
each adtnl	.1

(M) Radiator Hoses, Renew

1983-85-upper (.3)	.4
lower (.4)	.6
both (.5)	.8
w/Turbocharger and A.I.R. add (.3)	.4

FUEL

(G) Carburetor Air Cleaner, Service

1983-85 (.2)	.3

(G) Air Cleaner Vacuum Motor, Renew

1983-85 (.3)	.5

(G) Air Cleaner Temperature Sensor, Renew

1983-85 (.2)	.3

(G) Carburetor, Adjust (On Car)

Includes: Adjust pump rod, idle vent, air valve, fast idle, choke rod, vacuum brake, unloader, secondary lockout, idle speed and mixture.

1983-85	
Slow & Fast Idle (.3)	.4
Vacuum Brake-one (.4)	.6
both (.6)	.8
Choke (.6)	1.0
Complete (1.3)	1.8

(G) Automatic Choke Cover and/or Coil, Renew

1983-85 (.6)	1.0

(G) Automatic Choke Vacuum Brake Diaphragm, Renew or Adjust

1983-85-one (.4)	.6
both (.6)	.8

CHILTON'S 10 POINT SAFETY CHECK

CHECK OPERATION & CONDITION OF THE FOLLOWING ITEMS:

1. Legal Registration (serial no.)
2. Tires & Wheels
3. Brake System (R&R all wheels)
4. Light Systems & Signals
5. Accelerator Linkage, Neutral Safety Switch, Shift Indicator Pointer & Seat Position Locks
6. Glass, Mirrors, Door Locks, Seat Belts & Harness
7. Wipers, Washers & Defrosters
8. Frame, Steering, Shocks, Front & Rear Suspension
9. Fuel & Exhaust Systems
10. Road Test Vehicle

All models	1.0
Exhaust Smog Analysis, add	.4

(Factory Time) Chilton Time

BRAKES

(G) Brakes, Adjust (Minor)

Includes: R&R wheels and adjust brakes thru access holes in drums. Fill master cylinder.

two wheels	.4
Remove knock out plugs add, each	.1

(G) Bleed Brakes (Four Wheels)

Includes: Fill master cylinder.

All models (.4)	.5

(G) Brake Pedal Free Play, Adjust

All models	.3

(G) Parking Brake, Adjust

All models (.3)	.4

LUBRICATION SERVICE

(M) Lubricate Chassis, Change Oil & Filter

Includes: Inspect and correct all fluid levels.

All models	.6
Install grease fittings add	.1

(M) Lubricate Chassis

Includes: Inspect and correct all fluid levels.

All models	.4
Install grease fittings add	.1

(M) Engine Oil & Filter, Change

Includes: Inspect and correct all fluid levels.

All models	.4

(Factory Time) Chilton Time

WHEELS

(M) Wheel, Renew

one	.5

(G) Wheels, Balance

one	.3
each adtnl	.2

(G) Wheels, Rotate (All)

All models	.5

(G) Front Hub and Bearing Assy., Renew

1983-85-one side (.7)	.9
both sides (1.1)	1.6

ELECTRICAL

(M) Battery Cables, Renew

1983-85-negative (.2)	.3
positive (.6)	.8
batt to batt (.3)	.4

(M) Battery Terminals, Clean

All models	.3

(G) Aim Headlamps

two	.4
four	.6

(M) Headlamp Sealed Beam Bulb, Renew

1983-85-each (.3)	.3

(G) Headlamp Switch, Renew

1983-85 (.3)	.7

(G) Headlamp Dimmer Switch, Renew

1983-85 (.5)	.9

(G) Dimmer Switch Pivot Assy., Renew

1983-85 (.6)	1.2
w/Cruise Control add (.2)	.2

(G) Neutral Safety Switch, Renew

1983-85	
Riviera-colm mounted (.6)	.8

(G) Stop Light Switch, Renew

1983-85-exc below (.3)	.4
Riviera (.6)	.8

(G) Turn Signal Switch, Renew

1983-85 (.7)	1.1

(G) Back-Up Lamp and Park/Neutral Switch, Renew

1983-85 (.3)	.4

(M) Turn Signal or Hazard Warning Flasher, Renew

1983-85 (.2)	.2

(G) Horn, Renew

1983-85-each (.3)	.4

(G) Horn Relay, Renew

1983-85 (.2)	.3

LABOR 1 TUNE UP 1 LABOR

(Factory Time)	Chilton Time
(G) Compression Test	
V-6–1983-85	.8
V-8–1983-85	.9
w/A.C. add	.3

(G) Engine Tune Up, (Electronic Ignition)

Includes: Test battery and clean connections. Tighten manifold and carburetor mounting bolts. Check engine compression, clean and adjust or renew spark plugs. Test resistance of spark plug cables. Inspect distributor cap and rotor. Adjust air gap. Check vacuum advance operation. Reset ignition timing. Adjust idle mixture and idle speed. Service air cleaner. Inspect and adjust drive belts. Inspect choke operation and adjust or free up. Check operation of EGR valve.

(Factory Time)	Chilton Time
V-6–1983-85	2.0
V-8–1983-85	3.0
To perform C.C.C. system test add	1.0

LABOR 2 IGNITION SYSTEM 2 LABOR

GASOLINE ENGINES

(Factory Time)	Chilton Time
(G) Spark Plugs, Clean and Reset or Renew	
V-6–1983-85 (.4)	.6
V-8–1983-85 (.5)	.7
w/A.C. add (.2)	.3
w/Turbocharger add (.2)	.3
To clean add (.2)	.2
(G) Ignition Timing, Reset	
All models (.3)	.3
(G) Distributor, Renew	
Includes: Reset ignition timing.	
1983-85 (.5)	.8
w/Turbocharger add (.3)	.3
w/AIR add (.3)	.3
w/Vacuum pump add (.2)	.2
(G) Distributor, R&R and Recondition	
Includes: Reset ignition timing.	
1983-85 (.9)	1.4
w/Turbocharger add (.3)	.3
w/AIR add (.3)	.3
w/Vacuum pump add (.2)	.2
(G) Distributor Cap and/or Rotor, Renew	
1983-85 (.5)	.7
w/Turbocharger add (.2)	.2
w/AIR add (.3)	.3
w/Vacuum pump add (.2)	.2
(G) Distributor Module, Renew	
Includes: Test module.	
1983-85 (.4)	.7
w/Turbocharger add (.2)	.2
w/AIR add (.3)	.3
w/Vacuum pump add (.2)	.2
Perform C.C.C. system test add	1.0
(G) Distributor Pick-Up Coil and/or Pole Piece, Renew	
Includes: R&R distributor and reset ignition timing.	
1983-85 (.6)	.9
w/Turbocharger add (.3)	.3
w/AIR add (.3)	.3
w/Vacuum pump add (.2)	.2
(G) Distributor Capacitor and/or Module Wiring Harness, Renew	
Includes: R&R distributor cap and rotor, reset ignition timing.	
1983-85 (.4)	.5
w/Turbocharger add (.2)	.2
w/AIR add (.3)	.3
w/Vacuum pump add (.2)	.2
(G) Ignition Coil, Renew	
Includes: Test.	
1983-85 (.4)	.5
w/AIR add (.3)	.3
w/Vacuum pump add (.2)	.2
w/Turbocharger add (.2)	.2
(G) Ignition Cables, Renew	
1983-85	
V-6 (.9)	1.4
V-8 (.3)	.7
(G) ESC Detonation Sensor, Renew	
1983-85	
wo/Turbo (.7)	1.0
w/Turbo (2.5)	3.4
(G) ESC Module, Renew	
1983-85 (.5)	.7
(G) Ignition Switch, Renew	
1983-85 (.6)	.9
(G) Ignition Lock Cylinder and/or Buzzer Switch, Renew	
1983-85 (.4)	.7
w/Tilt colm add (.1)	.4
w/Cruise control add (.1)	.1
Recode cyl add (.5)	.5

DISTRIBUTORLESS IGNITION SYSTEM

(Factory Time)	Chilton Time
(G) Crankshaft Sensor, Renew	
1984-85 (.5)	.8
(G) Camshaft Sensor, Renew	
1984-85 (.6)	.9
(G) Ignition Coil and/or Module, Renew	
1984-85 (.5)	.7

DIESEL IGNITION COMPONENTS

(Factory Time)	Chilton Time
(G) Glow Plugs, Renew	
1983-85	
one	.4
all-one bank (.5)	.7
all-both banks (.7)	1.3
(G) Glow Plug Module, Renew	
1983-84 (.3)	.5
(G) Glow Plug Relay, Renew	
1983-84 (.3)	.5
(G) Coolant Fast Idle Temperature Switch, Renew	
1983-85 (.2)	.4
(G) Fast Idle Solenoid, Renew	
1983-85 (.3)	.4
(G) Glow Plug Control Module, Renew (Controller)	
1983-85 (.4)	.6
(G) Fast Idle Relay, Renew	
1983-84 (.3)	.4

PARTS 2 ELECTRONIC IGNITION 2 PARTS

	Part No.	Price
Distributor Assy.		
Buick Riviera & Olds. Toronado		
V-6		
1983-85	◆1103470	351.25
V-8–307		
1983-84	◆1103457	333.50
1985	◆1103602	275.00
Cadillac Eldorado & Seville		
V-8–250		
1983-85-exc. below	◆1103541	198.50
1985-Calif.	◆1103038	N.L.
(1) Distributor Cover		
1983-85-V-6	◆1894209	6.00
V-8	◆1875960	6.00
(2) Coil		
Buick Riviera & Olds. Toronado		
1983-87	◆1985474	36.00
Cadillac Eldorado & Seville		
1983-85-V-6	◆1985474	36.00
V-8	◆1985473	36.00
(3) Cap		
Buick Riviera & Olds. Toronado		
1983-85-V-6	◆1894979	17.00
V-8	◆1974408	17.00
Cadillac Eldorado & Seville		
1983-85-V-6	◆1894979	17.00
V-8 eng.	◆1977046	24.50
(4) Rotor		
1983-85	◆1977026	6.50

PARTS 2 ELECTRONIC IGNITION 2 PARTS

	Part No.	Price
(5) Mainshaft (Dist.)		
Buick Riviera & Olds. Toronado		
V-6		
1983-85	◆1976930	38.50
V-8-307		
1983-85	◆1979955	42.50
Cadillac Eldorado & Seville		
1983-85-V-6	◆1976930	38.50
V-8	◆1979556	38.00
(6) Pole Piece and Plate Assy.		
Buick Riviera & Olds. Toronado		
V-6		
1983-85	◆1976925	30.25
V-8		
1983-85	◆1977207	32.00
Cadillac Eldorado & Seville		
1983-85-V-6	◆1976925	30.25
V-8	◆1976897	30.25
(7) Module		
Buick Riviera		
1983-85	◆1976908	60.00
Cadillac Eldorado & Seville		
1983-85-exc. below	◆1976908	60.00
1985-V-8 Calif.	◆1987744	N.L.
1985-231	◆16022614	66.75

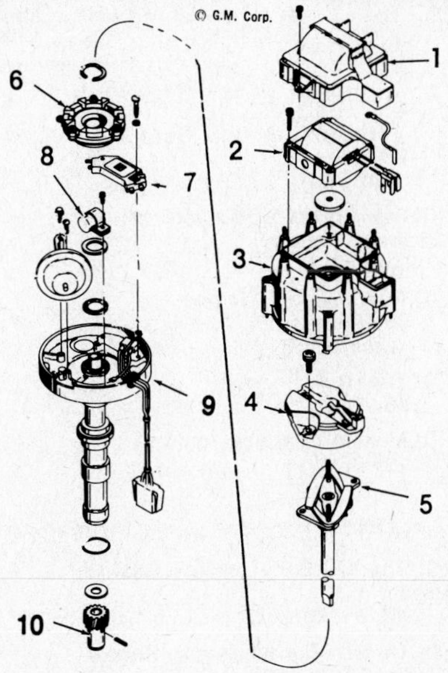

	Part No.	Price
(8) Capacitor		
1983-85	◆1876154	4.50

	Part No.	Price
(9) Housing (Dist)		
Buick Riviera & Olds. Toronado		
V-6		
1983-85	◆1976928	36.25
V-8		
1983-85	◆1977208	34.00
Cadillac Eldorado & Seville		
1983-85-V-6	◆1976928	36.25
V-8	◆1979554	66.50
(10) Gear		
Buick Riviera & Olds. Toronado		
1983-85-V-6	◆1892082	15.25
V-8	◆1979948	22.25
Cadillac Eldorado & Seville		
1983-85-V-6	◆1892082	15.25
V-8	◆1979546	37.00
Ignition Switch		
1983-wo/Tilt whl.	◆1990109	11.50
Tilt whl.	◆1990110	11.50
1984-85-wo/Tilt whl.	◆1990115	11.50
Tilt whl.	◆1990116	11.50
Ignition Warning Buzzer Switch		
1983-85-wo/Tilt whl	◆7804414	6.25
Tilt whl.	◆7811092	4.75

Spark Plug Wire Set
Order by year and model.

LABOR 3 FUEL SYSTEM 3 LABOR

	(Factory Time)	Chilton Time
GASOLINE ENGINES		
(G) Fuel Pump, Test		
Includes: Disconnect line at carburetor, attach pressure gauge.		
All models		.2
(M) Carburetor Air Cleaner, Service		
1983-85	(.2)	.3
(G) Air Cleaner Vacuum Motor, Renew		
1983-85	(.3)	.5
(G) Air Cleaner Temperature Sensor, Renew		
1983-85	(.2)	.3
(G) Carburetor, Adjust (On Car)		
Includes: Adjust vacuum brake, choke coil, fast idle and idle speed, dash pot or solenoid.		
1983-85		
Slow & Fast Idle	(.3)	.4
Vacuum Brake-one	(.4)	.6
both	(.6)	.8
Choke	(.6)	1.0
Complete	(1.3)	1.8
(G) Automatic Choke Cover and/or Coil, Renew		
1983-85	(.6)	1.0
(G) Throttle Control Solenoid, Renew		
1983-84	(.3)	.3
(G) Automatic Choke Vacuum Brake Diaphragm, Renew or Adjust		
1983-85-one	(.4)	.6
both	(.6)	.8
(G) Carburetor, Renew		
Includes: All necessary adjustments.		
1983-85	(.6)	1.0
To perform C.C.C. system check, add	(.5)	1.0
(G) Electric Choke Relay, Renew		
1983-84	(.2)	.3
(G) Carburetor, R&R and Clean or Recondition		
Includes: All necessary adjustments.		
1983-85	(2.1)	3.2
To perform C.C.C. system check add	(.5)	1.0
(G) Fuel Pump, Renew		
V-6-1983-85	(.7)	1.0
V-8-1983-85	(1.0)	1.4
Diesel-1983-85	(1.0)	1.4
w/A.C. add	(.5)	.5
w/P.S. add	(.3)	.3
Add pump test if performed.		
(G) Carburetor Needle Valve and Seat, Renew		
Includes: Adjust float level.		
All models		
2 bbl	(.7)	1.2
4 bbl	(.9)	1.5
To perform C.C.C. system check, add	(.5)	1.0
(G) Accelerator Pump, Renew		
All models		
2 bbl	(.7)	1.0
4 bbl	(.8)	1.2
(G) Water In Fuel Detector, Renew (WIF)		
All models	(.9)	1.2
(G) Fuel Tank, Renew		
Includes: Drain and refill tank. Test gauge.		
1983-85	(.8)	1.1
(G) Fuel Gauge (Tank), Renew		
Includes: R&R tank and test gauge.		
1983-85	(.9)	1.3
(G) Fuel Gauge (Dash), Renew		
Includes: Disconnect battery cable.		
1983-85	(.3)	.9
(G) Intake Manifold Gaskets and/or Seals, Renew		
Includes: Drain and refill cooling system. Make all necessary adjustments.		
V-6-1983-85		
Code A	(2.0)	3.0
Code 4	(2.1)	3.0
Code 9	(1.9)	2.9
V-8-1983-85		
250 eng-Code 8	(4.5)	6.4
368 eng-Code 6 or 9	(1.0)	1.5
350 eng-Code 8	(1.6)	2.3
307-350 engs Code Y or R	(1.8)	2.5
Renew manif add,		
w/E.F.I.	(.8)	1.3
wo/E.F.I.	(.2)	.5
w/A.C. add	(.4)	.4
E.F.E. SYSTEM		
(G) E.F.E. Valve, Renew		
Includes: Disconnect crossover pipe.		
1983-85	(.5)	1.0
(G) E.F.E. Thermal Vacuum Switch, Renew		
1983-85	(.3)	.5
w/Turbocharger add	(.6)	.6
(G) E.F.E. Vacuum Check Valve, Renew		
1983-85	(.2)	.4

LABOR 3 FUEL SYSTEM 3 LABOR

(Factory Time) Chilton Time

TURBOCHARGER COMPONENTS

(G) Turbocharger Carburetor Air Intake Assembly, Renew
V-6–1983-85 (.2) .4

(G) Turbocharger Vacuum Bleed Valve or Power Enrichment Valve, Renew
V-6–1983 (.5) .9

(G) Turbocharger Detonation Sensor, Renew
*Includes: R&R turbocharger.

(G) Turbocharger Assembly, Renew
Includes: Transfer all necessary parts.
V-6–1983-85 (2.0) 2.8

(G) Turbocharger Thermo Purge Switch, Renew
V-6–1983 (.4) .6

(G) Turbocharger Waste Gate Actuator, Renew
V-6–1983-85 (.3) .5

(G) Turbocharger Waste Gate Elbow, Renew
V-6–1983-85 (.8) 1.0

(G) Turbocharger Turbine Housing, Renew
Includes: R&R turbine housing and central housing rotating assembly as a unit. Separate and replace turbine housing.
V-6–1983-85 (2.3) 3.1

(G) Turbocharger Central Housing Rotating Assembly, Renew
Includes: R&R rotating assy., at compressor housing, transfer turbine housing.
V-6–1983-85 (2.3) 3.2

(G) Turbocharger Compressor Housing, Renew
Includes: R&R turbine housing and central housing rotating assembly as a unit.
V-6–1983-85 (2.2) 3.1

(G) Turbocharger Plenium, Renew
Includes: Drain and refill cooling system. R&R carburetor, transfer E.G.R. manifold and all attaching parts.
V-6–1983-85 (2.2) 3.1

(G) Turbocharger Outlet Pipe, Renew
Includes: Hoist car, R&R turbocharger inlet pipe.
V-6–1983-85 (.7) 1.3

(G) Turbocharger Inlet Pipe, Renew
V-6–1983 (2.1) 2.7
1984-85 (.9) 1.3

FUEL INJECTION (SFI)

(G) Throttle Body Unit, Renew
1984-85
Turbo (.4) .7

(G) Fuel Pressure Regulator and/or Gaskets, Renew
1984-85 (.3) .5

(G) Fuel Injector, Renew
1984-85–one (.6) 1.0
each adtnl (.1) .2

(G) Fuel Rail, Renew
1984-85 (.6) 1.0

(G) Mass Air Sensor, Renew
1984-85 (.2) .4

THROTTLE BODY INJECTION (DFI)

(G) Throttle Body and/or Gasket, Renew
1983-85 (.6) .9

(G) Throttle Body Injector, Renew
1983-85–one (.5) .6
both (.5) .8

(G) Injector Relay, Renew
1983-85 (.3) .4

(G) Fuel Pressure Regulator or Meter Assy., Renew
Includes: Renew gasket.
1983-85 (.4) .6

(G) Fuel Pump, Renew (In Tank)
1983-85 (1.0) 1.4

(G) Fuel Pump Relay, Renew
1983-85 (.2) .3

(G) Intake Manifold or Gasket, Renew
1983-85 (4.5) 6.4
Renew manif add (.5) .5

DIESEL FUEL INJECTION

(M) Air Cleaner, Service
1983-85 (.2) .4

(G) Air Intake Crossover, Renew
1983-85
w/Ext E.G.R. (.3) .5
w/Int E.G.R. (.4) .6

(G) Injection Pump Timing, Adjust
1983-85 (.7) .9

(G) Fuel Supply Pump, Renew
1983-85 (1.0) 1.4

(G) Fuel Filter, Renew
1983-85 (.2) .4

(G) Fuel Solenoid, Renew
1983-85 (.5) .7

(G) Cold Advance Solenoid, Renew
1983-85 (.6) 1.0

(G) Fuel Injection Head Seal, Renew
Includes: Renew head and drive shaft seals, renew governor weight retaining ring.
1983-85 (2.7) 3.9

(G) Fuel Injection Pump, Renew
Includes: Pressure and electrical tests. Adjust timing.
1983-85 (2.2) 3.4

(G) Injection Pump Adapter and/or Seal, Renew
1983-85 (1.8) 2.5

(G) Fuel Return Lines (At Nozzles), Renew
1983-85–one side (.3) .5
both sides (.4) .7
return hose (.2) .3
w/A.C. add (.2) .2

(G) Injection Pump Drive and/or Driven Gears, Renew
1983-85 (4.3) 7.0
w/A.C. add (.2) .2

(G) Fuel Injection Pump Throttle Shaft Seal, Renew
1983-85 (.8) 1.3

(G) High Pressure Fuel Lines, Renew
1983-85–one .8
one-each bank 1.0
all 2.5

(G) Injector Nozzle and/or Seal, Renew
1983-85–one (.8) 1.0
one-each bank (1.0) 1.3
all-both banks (2.4) 3.0
w/A.C. add (.2) .2
Clean nozzles add, each .2

(G) Intake Manifold or Gaskets, Renew
1983-85 (2.9) 3.5
Renew manif add (.2) .5

(G) Vacuum Pump, Renew
Includes: Vacuum test.
1983-85
gear driven (.4) .6
belt driven (.6) .8

V-8-6-4–COMPONENTS

(G) Valve Selector Solenoid, Renew
Includes. R&R valve cover.
All models–one side (.6) 1.1

(G) Modulated Displacement Driver Assy. (M.D.D.A.), Renew
All models (.5) .9

(G) Range Module, Renew
All models (.4) .6

(G) Electronic Control Module, Renew
All models (.5) .8

PARTS 3 FUEL SYSTEM 3 PARTS

	Part No.	Price
Carburetor Assy.		
V-6		
1983-231	◆17079412	969.50
252	◆17079266	767.25
1984	◆17110448	974.00
V-8		
1983	◆17079672	817.00
1984	◆17110444	823.50
1985	◆17111105	887.00

	Part No.	Price
Carburetor Repair Kit (Major Overhaul)		
V-6		
1983	◆17069095	55.00
V-8		
1983	◆17076044	32.00

PARTS 3 FUEL SYSTEM 3 PARTS

	Part No.	Price
1984	◆17069115	45.50
1985	◆17076141	49.50
Carburetor Gasket Kit		
V-6		
1983-84	◆17067277	41.75
V-8		
1983-84	◆17068938	36.50
1985	◆17111092	40.25
Needle Valve & Seat Assy.		
1983-85-V-6	◆7035150	6.50
V-8	◆7035134	6.00
Choke Thermostat		
V-6		
1983-84-231	◆17079035	72.50
252	◆17068871	35.00
V-8		
1983-84	◆17068941	20.25
1985	◆17110646	26.25
Fuel Pump		
V-6-231		
1983	◆6472026	34.50
1984	◆6472529	131.25
1985	◆6472230	131.00
V-6-252		
1983-84	◆6471554	33.50
V-8-250		
1983-85	◆6472009	92.00
V-8-307		
1983-85	◆6471743	35.00
V-8-350 Diesel		
1983-84	◆6471317	N.L.
1985	◆6442228	59.25
Fuel Tank		
Order by year and model.		

	Part No.	Price
Fuel Gauge (Tank Unit)		
Buick Riviera		
Gasoline Engines		
1983-84-exc.		
below	◆25002573	55.75
1984-85-231	◆25003923	138.75
1985-307		
Digital	◆25090034	N.L.
wo/Digital	◆25002474	N.L.
Diesel Engine		
(w/Water-in-fuel indicator)		
1983-84	◆25003272	94.50
1985-Digital	◆25090030	95.75
wo/Digital	◆25004278	77.00
(wo/Water-in-fuel indicator)		
Cadillac Eldorado & Seville		
1983-85-307	◆250002276	N.L.
1984-85-350 Diesel		
Digital	◆25003272	94.50
wo/Digital	◆25003273	94.50
1985-350 Diesel		
Digital	◆25004279	81.50
wo/Digital	◆25004278	77.00
Olds. Toronado		
1983-84-exc.		
below	◆25002573	55.75
Diesel	◆25003272	94.50
1985-307		
Digital	◆25002474	N.L.
wo/Digital	◆25090034	N.L.
1985-350 Diesel		
Digital	◆25090030	95.75
wo/Digital	◆25094278	N.L.
Fuel Gauge (Dash)		
Buick Riviera		
V-6-231		
1983	◆6433326	41.50
1984-85	◆6434009	45.50

	Part No.	Price
V-6-252		
1983-84	◆6433329	38.75
V-8-Gas		
1983-85	◆6433329	38.75
V-8-Diesel		
1983-85	◆6433323	24.50
Cadillac Eldorado & Seville		
1983-85-exc.		
below	◆6433050	63.00
Diesel	◆6433052	65.75
Olds. Toronado		
1983-85 (Gauge package)		
Gas	◆6433064	41.50
Diesel	◆6433065	46.25
1983-85 (wo/Gauge package)		
Gas	◆6433063	21.50
Diesel	◆6433062	20.75
Intake Manifold Gaskets		
V-6-231		
1983	◆25505397	15.75
1984-85	◆1264924	14.50
V-6-252		
1983-84	◆25505397	15.75
V-8-250		
1983-85	◆3634619	16.50
V-8-307		
1983-84	◆557866	20.00
1985	◆22527545	31.25
V-8-350 Diesel		
1983-84	◆22516344	12.00
1985	◆22527544	16.50

PARTS 3 TURBOCHARGER SYSTEM 3 PARTS

	Part No	Price
Turbocharger (Rebuilt)		
1983	◆25512716	325.25
1984-85	◆25519875	352.25
Seal and Bolt Kit (Turbine)		
1983-85	◆25509647	48.50
(1) Housing Kit		
1983	◆25501289	137.25
(2) Center Housing (Rebuilt)		
1983	◆25516899	243.75
1984-85	◆25519876	243.75
(3) Housing Kit (Turbine)		
1983	◆25512717	201.00
(4) Elbow Kit (Turbine)		
1983	◆25501290	160.00
1984-85	◆25520378	287.00
(5) Actuator Kit (Turbine)		
1983	◆25505451	115.00
1984-85	◆25520376	132.00

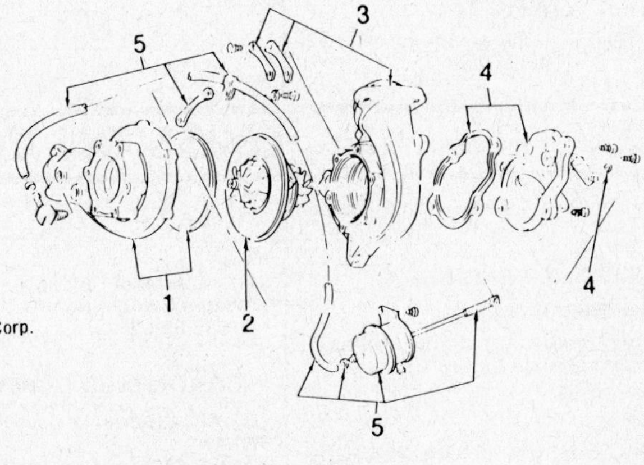

© G.M. Corp.

PARTS 3 FUEL SYSTEM (DIESEL) 3 PARTS

	Part No	Price
Air Cleaner Element		
1983-85	◆8996990	N.L.
Air Intake Crossover		
1983-85	◆22509735	109.00

	Part No.	Price
Injection Pump		
1983-exc. below	◆22518688	763.00
Hi alt	◆22518689	763.00
1984-exc. below	◆22520938	763.00
Hi alt	◆22520999	763.00
1985	◆22524423	763.00

Part number is stamped on a tag attached to the left side of the injection pump.

PARTS 3 FUEL SYSTEM (DIESEL) 3 PARTS

	Part No.	Price
Injection Pump Adaptor		
1983-85	◆558768	21.75
Injection Nozzles		
1983	◆22520378	60.00
1984-85	◆22521207	89.50
Injection Pump Adap. to Mfld. Seal		
1983-85	◆559697	2.00
Injection Pump Pressure Tap Seal		
1983-85	◆22507974	3.75
Injection Pump Driven Gear Bearing		
1983-85-Front	◆559256	3.00
Rear	◆559255	3.00
Vacuum Pump (w/Drive)		
1983-85	◆7839413	116.00

PARTS 3 ELECTRONIC FUEL INJECTION 3 PARTS

CADILLAC ELDORADO & SEVILLE 8-250

	Part No.	Price
(1) Throttle Body Injection Unit		
1983	◆17079495	753.75
1984	◆17110353	877.25
1985	◆17110662	678.00
(2) Throttle Body Kit		
1983	◆17079498	216.25
1984	◆17110354	187.25
1985	◆17110663	185.75
(3) Idle Speed Control Kit		
1983-84	◆17079663	123.50
1985	◆17111169	103.00
(4) Fuel Meter Kit		
1983-84	◆17079496	873.75
1985	◆17110657	424.50
Two injectors and pressure regulator included.		
(5) Throttle Position Sensor		
1983	◆17078259	106.00
1984-85	◆17110352	100.50
Fuel Injector Kit		
1983-84	◆17079500	191.50
1985	◆17110659	179.50
Gasket Kit		
1983-85	◆17078257	17.75

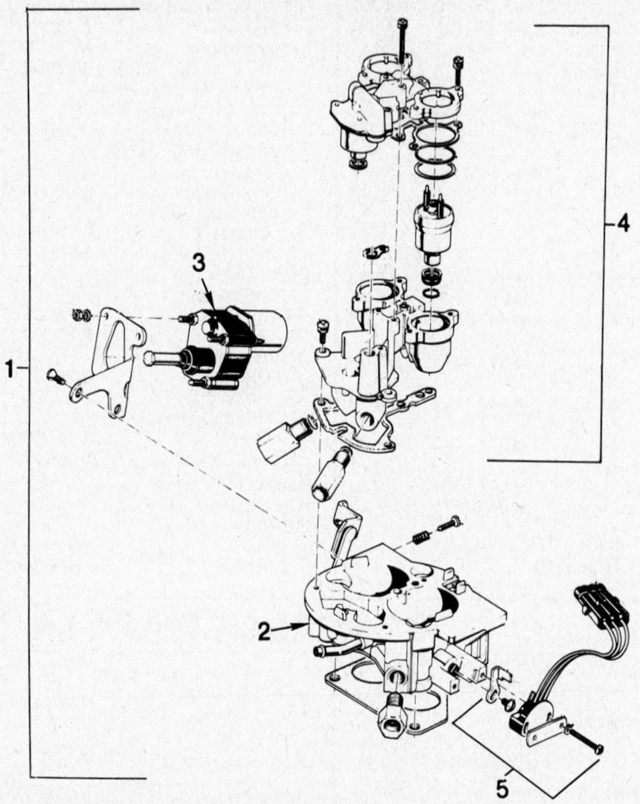

LABOR 3A EMISSION CONTROLS 3A LABOR

(Factory Time) — Chilton Time

GASOLINE ENGINES

(G) Emission Control Check
Includes: Check and adjust engine idle speed and mixture and ignition timing. Check P.C.V. valve.

	Chilton Time
All models	.6

POSITIVE CRANKCASE VENTILATION

	Chilton Time
(M) Positive Crankcase Ventilation Valve, Renew	
1983-85 (.2)	.3
w/Turbocharger add (.1)	.1
(M) Crankcase Ventilation Filter Assy., Renew	
All models (.2)	.3

EVAPORATIVE EMISSION TYPE

	Chilton Time
(G) Charcoal Canister, Renew	
1983-85 (.2)	.3
(G) Canister Purge Thermal Vacuum Switch, Renew	
1983-85 (.2)	.3

CONTROLLED COMBUSTION TYPE

	Chilton Time
(G) Air Cleaner Vacuum Motor, Renew	
1983-85 (.3)	.5
(G) Air Cleaner Temperature Sensor, Renew	
1983-85 (.2)	.3

EXHAUST GAS RECIRCULATION SYSTEM

	Chilton Time
(G) E.G.R. Valve, Renew	
1983-85-Gas (.4)	.6
Diesel (.5)	.8
(G) Thermal Control Valve, Renew	
1983-85 (.3)	.4
(G) E.G.R. Vacuum Delay Valve, Renew	
1983-85 (.2)	.3
(G) E.G.R. Thermal Vacuum Switch, Renew	
1983-85	
V-6 (.5)	.7
V-8 (.3)	.4
(G) Thermostatic Vacuum Control Switch, Renew	
1983-85 (.3)	.4

AIR INJECTOR REACTOR TYPE

	Chilton Time
(G) Air Pump, Renew	
1983-85	
V-6 (.3)	.5
V-8 (.4)	.6
w/Vacuum pump add (.2)	.2

(Factory Time) Chilton Time

(G) Check Valve, Renew
1983-85-one (.2) 3
each adtnl 1

(G) Air Pump Centrifugal Filter, Renew
1983-85 (.3) 5

(G) A.I.R. Air Cleaner, Renew
1983-85 (.2) 3

(G) A.I.R. Drive Belt, Renew
1983-85 (.2) 3

(G) Catalytic Converter Air Pipe, Renew
1983-85
one piece (.5) 7

COMPUTER COMMAND CONTROL SYSTEM (C.C.C.)

(P) Throttle Position Sensor, Adjust
Does not include system performance check.
All models 9

(P) Electronic Control Module, Renew
Does not include system performance check.
1983-85 (.5) 6

(P) Mixture Control Solenoid, Renew
Does not include system performance check.
1983-85-2 BBL (1.1) 1.5
4 BBL (1.2) 1.6

(P) Prom, Renew
Does not include system performance check.
Includes: R&R electronic module.
1983-85 (.5) 8

(P) EGR/EFE Purge Solenoid, Renew
Does not include system performance check.
1983-85 (.4) 6

(P) Air Control/Air Switching Valve, Renew
Does not include system performance check.
1983-85 (.5) 6

(P) Air Switching Valve, Renew
Does not include system performance check.
1983-85 (.4) 6

(P) Canister Purge Control Valve, Renew
Does not include system performance check.
1983-85 (.4) 6

(P) Air Control Valve, Renew
Does not include system performance check.
1983-85 (.4) 6

(P) Air Switching Valve Solenoid, Renew
Does not include system performance check.
1983-85 (.5) 8

(P) E.G.R. Vacuum Control Solenoid, Renew
Does not include system performance check.
1983-85 (.3) 5

(P) E.F.E. Vacuum Control Solenoid, Renew
Does not include system performance check.
1983-85 (.3) 5

(P) Back-Up Lamp and Park/Neutral Switch, Renew
Does not include system performance check.
1984-85 (.5) 7

CHILTON'S EMISSION CONTROL TUNE-UP

1. Clean or renew P.C.V. valve, hoses and filter.
2. Check fuel tank cap for sealing ability.
3. Check fuel tank and fuel lines for leakage.
4. Check evaporation canister and filter. Replace if necessary.
5. Check engine compression to determine leakage of unburned gases. (Add time for items of interference).
6. Test and clean or renew spark plugs.
7. Check engine oil dipstick for sealing ability.
8. Test exhaust system with analyzer and check system for leakage.
9. Check exhaust manifold heat valve for operation.
10. Adjust ignition timing and carburetor idle speed and mixture.
11. Check automatic choke mechanism for free operation.
12. Inspect air cleaner and element.
13. On models so equipped, test distributor vacuum control switch and transmission control switch.

V-6 .... 1.7
V-8 .... 1.8

For repairs made, charge accordingly.

(Factory Time) Chilton Time

(P) Vacuum Control Purge Solenoid, Renew
Does not include system performance check.
1983-85 (.3) 5

(P) Idle Speed Control Motor, Renew or Adjust
Does not include system performance check.
1983-85 (.6) 8
Recond motor add (.3) 3

(G) Idle Load Compensator, Renew or Adjust
Does not include system performance check.
1983-85 (.4) 6

(G) Vehicle Speed Sensor, Renew
Does not include system performance check.
1983-85 (.7) 1.5

(P) Barometric Sensor, Renew
Does not include system performance check.
1983-85 (.5) 7

(P) Manifold Pressure Sensor, Renew
Does not include system performance check.
1983-85 (.5) 6

(P) Tachometer Filter, Renew
Does not include system performance check.
1983-85 (.3) 3

(P) Coolant Temperature Sensor, Renew
Does not include system performance check.
Includes: Drain and refill cooling system.
1983-85 (.6) 9

(Factory Time) Chilton Time

(P) Oxygen Sensor, Renew
Does not include system performance check.
1983-85 (.5) 7

(P) Throttle Position Sensor, Renew
Does not include system performance check.
1983-85
2 BBL (1.0) 1.4
4 BBL (1.1) 1.5

(P) Computer Command Control System Performance Check
1983-85 (.5) 1.0

EMISSION CONTROLS

DIESEL ENGINE

(G) Crankcase Depression Regulator Valve, Renew
1983-85 (.2) 3

(G) Crankcase Ventilation Flow Control Valve, Renew
1983-85 (.2) 3

(G) Crankcase Ventilation Filter, Renew
1983-85 (.2) 3

(G) E.G.R. Valve and/or Gasket, Renew
1983-85 (.5) 8

(G) E.G.R. Control Valve Switch, Renew
1983-85 (.2) 3

(G) E.G.R. Control Valve Solenoid, Renew
1983-85 (.2) 3

(G) E.P.R. Control Valve Solenoid, Renew
1983-85 (.4) 6
Renew ECM add 1

(G) E.P.R. Control Valve Switch, Renew
1983-85 (.3) 4

(G) E.P.R. Exhaust Pressure Regulator Valve, Renew
1983-85 (.3) 4

(G) Altitude Fuel Limiter, Renew
1985-85 (.6) 8

(G) Housing Pressure Cold Advance Solenoid, Renew
1985-85 (.5) 6

(G) Housing Pressure Altitude Advance Solenoid, Renew
1985-85 (.2) 3

(G) Housing Pressure Altitude Advance Relay, Renew
1985-85 (.4) 5

(G) Vacuum Regulator Valve, Renew
1983-85 (.6) 8

EMISSION CONTROLS

DIGITAL FUEL INJECTION (DFI)

(P) Electronic Control Module, Renew
1983-85 (.5) 7

(P) Prom, Renew
1983-85 (.4) 8

(P) Barometric Sensor, Renew
1983-85 (.4) 6

LABOR 3A EMISSION CONTROLS 3A LABOR

(Factory Time)	Chilton Time
(P) Coolant Temperature Sensor, Renew	
1983-85 (.3)	.4
(P) Manifold Pressure Sensor, Renew	
1983-85 (.4)	.5
(P) Manifold Absolute Temperature Sensor, Renew	
1983-85 (.3)	.4
(P) Oxygen Sensor, Renew	
1983-85 (.4)	.6
(P) Vehicle Speed Sensor, Renew	
1983-85 (.6)	1.0
(P) Throttle Position Sensor, Renew	
1983-85 (.5)	.7
(P) Air Control/Air Switching Valve, Renew	
1983-85 (.4)	.6
(P) EGR Vacuum Control Solenoid, Renew	
1983-85 (.3)	.4
(P) Vacuum Control Purge Solenoid, Renew	
1983-85 (.3)	.4
(P) Idle Speed Control Motor, Renew or Adjust	
1983-85 (.5)	.8

PARTS 3A EMISSION CONTROLS 3A PARTS

	Part No.	Price
Positive Crankcase Vent. Valve		
V-6-231		
1983-84	◆6487936	3.50
1985	◆6487534	3.00
V-6-252		
1983-84	◆6487534	3.00
V-8-250		
1983-84	◆6487532	3.00
1985	◆6487779	2.50
V-8-307		
1983-85	◆8997683	3.50
V-8-350 Diesel		
1983-85	◆25041678	34.50

EVAPORATIVE EMISSION TYPE

	Part No.	Price
Charcoal Canister		
Buick Riviera & Olds. Toronado		
1983-85	◆17064622	39.50
Cadillac Eldorado & Seville		
1983-85-250	◆17075825	46.25
307	◆17064622	39.50
Vapor Canister Filter		
1983-85	◆7026014	2.50
E.F.E. Valve (w/Actuator)		
V-6		
1983-85	◆5233155	58.00
V-8		
1983-250	◆5234104	64.00
307	◆5233475	52.00
1984-85-250	◆5234104	64.00
307	◆5234580	68.75

CONTROLLED COMBUSTION TYPE

	Part No.	Price
Air Cleaner Motor		
1983-85-exc. below	◆8994333	18.75
Air Cleaner Sensor		
V-6-231		
1983	◆8997493	18.75
1984-85	◆25007653	196.25
V-6-252		
1983	◆8997493	18.75
1984-85	◆8997916	18.75
V-8		
1983-85	◆8997574	18.75

EXHAUST GAS RECIRCULATION SYSTEM

E.G.R. Valve

Replacement E.G.R. valves must be ordered according to the stamping number on the original valve.

	Part No.	Price
E.G.R. & E.F.E. Thermo Vacuum Switch		
Buick Riviera & Olds. Toronado		
V-8-307		
1983	◆3048786	14.50
1984-85	◆3055550	13.75
V-8-350 Diesel		
1983-84	◆22521799	35.00
Cadillac Eldorado & Seville		
1983-85-250	◆3049626	29.25
1984-350 Diesel	◆22521799	35.00

AIR INJECTOR REACTOR TYPE

	Part No.	Price
Air Pump		
Buick Riviera & Olds. Toronado		
V-6		
1983-231	◆7835314	192.00
1983-84-252	◆7835397	131.00
V-8		
1983-85-307	◆7838575	158.00
Check Valve		
Buick Riviera		
1983-84-V-6	◆22034703	12.75
V-8	◆22034702	10.25
Cadillac Eldorado & Seville		
1983-V-6	◆22034703	12.75
V-8	◆22034704	12.75
1984-85	◆22048210	13.00
Olds. Toronado		
1983-85-V-6	◆22034703	12.75
V-8	◆22034702	10.25
Injection Manifold Assy.		
Buick Riviera & Olds. Toronado		
1983-85-right	◆22514382	23.50
left	◆22514383	19.50
Air Injection Control Valve		
Buick Riviera & Olds. Toronado		
1983-231	◆17072786	52.00
252	◆17071525	99.00
307	◆17064379	51.50
1984-85-307	◆17075081	59.00
Cadillac Eldorado & Seville		
1983-87-V-6	◆17071525	99.00
V-8	◆17071106	100.25

COMPUTER COMMAND CONTROLLED EMISSION SYSTEM

	Part No.	Price
Electronic Control Module (E.C.M.) Remanufactured		
Buick Riviera & Olds. Toronado		
1983-231	◆1226025	110.25
252	◆1225500	110.25
307	◆1225450	110.25
1984-V-6	◆1226519	110.25
V-8	◆1226457	110.25
1985-V-6	◆1226459	110.25
V-8 eng.	◆1226866	110.00
Cadillac Eldorado & Seville		
1983-85	◆1226028	110.25
1st design	◆1226028	110.25
2nd design	◆1226930	110.00
Calibration Unit (PROM)		
Buick Riviera & Olds. Toronado		
V-6		
1983-231	◆1226509	40.50
(252)		
Fed.	◆1226662	40.50
Calif.	◆1225977	40.50
1984-Fed.	◆16037849	40.50
Calif.	◆16037674	40.50
1985-87	◆16041935	40.50
V-8		
1983-Fed.	◆1226436	40.50
Calif.	◆1226286	40.50
1984-Fed.	◆16045629	40.50
Calif.	◆16040802	N.L.
1985-Fed.	◆16039649	40.50
Calif.	◆16048879	40.50
Cadillac Eldorado & Seville		
1983 (Mech. Speedo Display)		
Federal	◆1226532	40.50
Hi alt	◆1226539	40.50
Calif.	◆1226533	40.50
1983 (Digital Speedo Display)		
Federal	◆1226535	40.50
Hi alt	◆1226540	40.50
Calif.	◆1226536	40.50
1984-85 (Mech. Speedo. Display)		
Code 6578 CTX, 3223 CCS	◆1226539	40.50
Code 2012DLZ	◆16042010	40.50
Code 2015 DMA	◆16042014	40.50
Code 2022 DMC	◆16042020	40.50
Code 2043 DMM	◆16042042	40.50
Code 2070 DMY	◆16042069	40.50
1985 (Mech. Speedo. Display)		
Code 3793 DKF	◆16043792	40.50
Code 3805 DKJ	◆16043804	40.50
1984-85 (Digital Speedo. Display)		
Code 0948 AXM, 6573 CTY, 3229 CCT	◆1226540	40.50
Code 2002 DLW	◆16042000	40.50
Code 2018 DMB	◆16042017	40.50
Code 2025 DMD	◆16042024	40.50
Code 2046 DMN	◆16042045	40.50
Code 2067 DMX	◆16042066	40.50
1985 (Digital Speedo Display)		
Code 3812 DKK	◆16043810	40.50
Code 3817 DKL	◆16043816	40.50
Code 3799 DKH	◆16043798	40.50
Code 3787 DKD	◆16043785	40.50

PARTS 3A EMISSION CONTROLS 3A PARTS

	Part No.	Price
E.G.R. Solenoid		
Buick Riviera & Olds. Toronado		
V-8		
1983	◆1997636	13.25
1984	◆1997665	43.50
1985	◆1997126	43.00
Mixture Control Solenoid (Kit)		
1983-85	◆17067343	71.00
Barometric Sensor		
V-8		
1983-85	◆16006833	62.25
Coolant Temperature Sensor		
1983-84	◆25036092	22.00
1985	◆25036708	12.75
Manifold Air Temp. Sensor		
Cadillac Eldorado & Seville		
1983-85	◆25036094	17.25
Manifold Pressure Sensor		
Buick Riviera & Olds. Toronado		
1983-85-231	◆16009886	62.25
252	◆16006835	62.25
V-8	◆16006834	62.25
Cadillac Eldorado & Seville		
1983-85	◆16006832	62.25
Oxygen Sensor		
1983-85	◆5613959	29.00
Throttle Position Sensor		
Buick Riviera & Olds. Toronado		
1983	◆17078448	40.50
1984-85	◆25036658	20.75
Cadillac Eldorado & Seville		
1983-exc. below	◆17078448	40.50
Fuel inj.	◆17078259	106.00
1984-85	◆17110352	100.75
Air Switching Valve		
Buick Riviera & Olds. Toronado		
1983-85-V-8	◆17064880	46.00
V-6	◆17071991	26.25

LABOR 4 ALTERNATOR & REGULATOR 4 LABOR

(Factory Time)	Chilton Time
(G) Delcotron Circuits, Test	
Includes: Test battery, regulator, Delcotron output.	
All models	.6
(G) Delcotron Assembly, Renew	
Includes: Transfer fan and pulley.	
1983-85 (.5)	.7
w/A.C. and Turbocharger	
add (.2)	.3
(G) Delcotron, R&R and Recondition	
Includes: Complete disassembly, inspect, test, replace parts as required, reassemble.	
1983-85 (1.0)	1.7
w/A.C. and Turbocharger	
add (.2)	.3
w/Diesel eng add	.6
(G) Delcotron Front Bearing, Renew	
Includes: R&R Delcotron, separate end frames.	
1983-85 (.8)	1.0
w/A.C. and Turbocharger	
add (.2)	.3
Renew rear brg add	.2
(G) Delcotron Voltage Regulator, Test and Renew	
Includes: R&R, disassemble and reassemble Delcotron.	
1983-85 (.7)	1.2
w/A.C. and Turbocharger	
add (.2)	.3
w/Diesel eng add (.1)	.1

PARTS 4 ALTERNATOR AND REGULATOR 4 PARTS

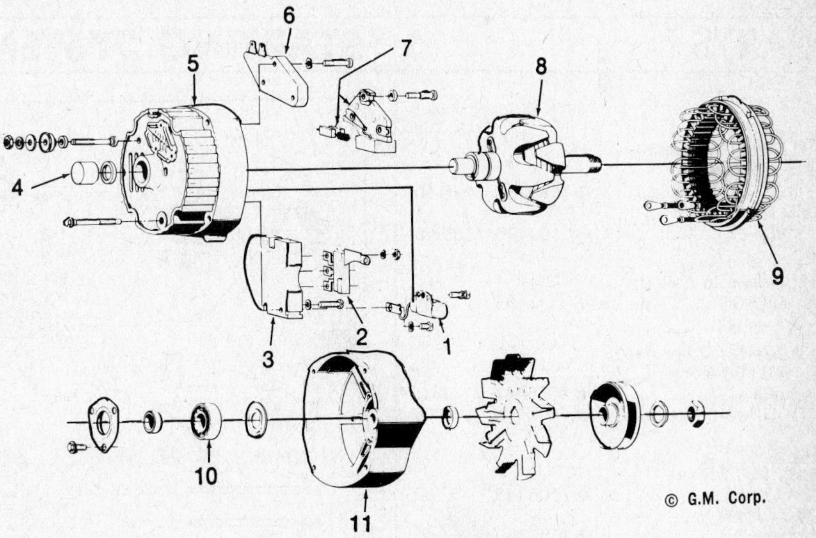

	Part No.	Price
Delcotron Assy. (New)		
Buick Riviera & Olds. Toronado		
1983-85		
70 amp	◆1105335	265.00
78 amp (1983)	◆1100250	225.00
78 amp (1984-85)	◆1105369	228.75
85 amp	◆1105339	326.50
(94 amp)		
231	◆1105492	228.50
307, 350N	◆1105480	232.00
108 amp	◆1105481	218.50
Cadillac Eldorado & Seville		
1983-85		
55, 63 amp	◆1105360	206.00
70 amp	◆1101040	257.00
80, 85, 100 amp	◆1101050	536.00
(1) Capacitor		
1983-87	◆1978146	4.75
(2) Diode Trio		
Buick Riviera & Olds. Toronado		
1983-85	◆1984459	5.00
Cadillac Eldorado & Seville		
1983-85-exc. below	◆1985348	7.00
70, 85 amp	◆1984459	5.00
80, 100 amp	◆1977064	7.00
(3) Rectifier Bridge		
1983-85-exc. below	◆1975313	24.50
80, 100 amp	◆1875645	42.00
108 amp	◆1985801	29.75
(4) Bearing		
1983-85-exc. below	◆9436831	5.50
70, 85 amp	◆1975322	5.50
(5) Frame (Slip Ring End)		
Buick Riviera & Olds. Toronado		
1983-85-exc. below	◆1975310	31.00
63, 78 amp	◆1984460	47.75
94 amp	◆1987073	28.00
108 amp	◆1985671	21.00
Cadillac Eldorado & Seville		
1983-85-exc. below	◆1975310	31.00
80, 100 amp	◆1976141	38.50
(6) Regulator		
1983-87	◆1116387	25.00

PARTS 4 ALTERNATOR AND REGULATOR 4 PARTS

	Part No.	Price
(7) Brush Holder		
Buick Riviera & Olds. Toronado		
1983-85-exc.		
below	◆1975323	10.00
78, 94 amp	◆1984462	9.00
Cadillac Eldorado & Seville		
1983-85-exc.		
below	◆1984462	9.00
70, 85 amp	◆1975323	10.00
(8) Rotor Assy.		
Buick Riviera & Olds. Toronado		
1983-85-exc.		
below	◆1975333	65.00
78, 94 amp	◆1984466	77.25
108 amp	◆1985646	79.25

	Part No.	Price
Cadillac Eldorado & Seville		
1983-85-exc.		
below	◆1978876	138.00
70 amp.	◆1975333	65.00
(9) Stator Assy.		
Buick Riviera & Olds. Toronado		
1983-85-exc.		
below	◆1971639	41.00
37, 42 amp.	◆1971986	31.00
70 amp.	◆1975303	48.75
78 amp	◆1984445	37.25
85 amp.	◆1875987	N.L.
80, 100 amp.	◆801818	82.25
94 amp	◆1987074	41.50
108 amp	◆1985625	52.00

	Part No.	Price
Cadillac Eldorado & Seville		
1983-85-exc.		
below	◆801818	82.25
70 amp.	◆1975303	48.75
100 amp	◆1892941	106.75
(10) Bearing (Front End)		
1983-85-exc.		
below	◆908419	10.00
80, 100 amp	◆907998	7.00
(11) Frame (Drive End)		
1983-85-78 amp	◆1986206	24.00
70, 85 amp.	◆1986590	30.00
80, 100 amp	◆1976049	30.00
94 amp	◆1987997	27.50
108 amp	◆1985669	21.50

LABOR 5 STARTING SYSTEM 5 LABOR

(Factory Time)	Chilton Time
(G) Starter Draw Test	
All Models	.3
(G) Starter, Renew	
Includes: R&R solenoid.	
V-6–1983-85 (.6)	1.0
V-8–1983-85 (.5)	.9
Diesel–1983-85 (.5)	.9
Add draw test if performed.	
(G) Starter, R&R and Recondition	
Includes: Turn down armature.	
V-6–1983-85 (1.4)	1.7
V-8–1983-85 (1.3)	1.9
Diesel–1983-85 (1.3)	2.0
Renew field coils add (.4)	.5
Add draw test if performed.	

(Factory Time)	Chilton Time
(G) Starter Drive, Renew	
Includes: R&R starter and solenoid.	
V-6–1983-85 (.9)	1.3
V-8–1983-85 (.6)	1.2
Diesel–1983-85 (.7)	1.2
(G) Starter Solenoid Switch, Renew	
Includes: R&R starter.	
V-6–1983-85 (.5)	1.0
V-8–1983-85 (.5)	1.0
Diesel–1983-85 (.5)	1.0
(G) Ignition Switch, Renew	
1983-85 (.6)	.9

(Factory Time)	Chilton Time
(M) Battery Cables, Renew	
1983-85-positive (.6)	.8
negative (.2)	.3
batt to batt (.3)	.4
(M) Battery Terminals, Clean	
All models	.3
(G) Back-Up Lamp and Park/Neutral Switch, Renew	
1983-85 (.3)	.4
(G) Ignition Lock Cylinder and/or Buzzer, Renew	
1983-85 (.4)	.7
w/Tilt colm add (.1)	.4
w/Cruise control add (.1)	.1
Recode cyl add (.5)	.5

PARTS 5 STARTING SYSTEM 5 PARTS

	Part No.	Price
(1) Starter Assembly		
exc. 350 Diesel		
1983-85	◆1998237	245.00
350 Diesel		
1983-85	◆1109495	585.25
(2) Solenoid Switch		
1983-85	◆1114531	N.L.
(3) Starter Drive Assy.		
1983-85-exc.		
below	◆1875687	N.L.
Diesel	◆1893445	65.00
(4) Brush Set		
exc. 350 Diesel		
1983-85	◆1906945	.50
350 Diesel		
1983-85	◆1852880	1.50
(5) Drive End Bushing		
1983-85-exc.		
below	◆1932190	.50
Diesel	◆1839345	1.00
(6) Commutator End Frame		
1983-85-exc.		
below	◆1974157	7.00
Diesel	◆1978137	N.L.

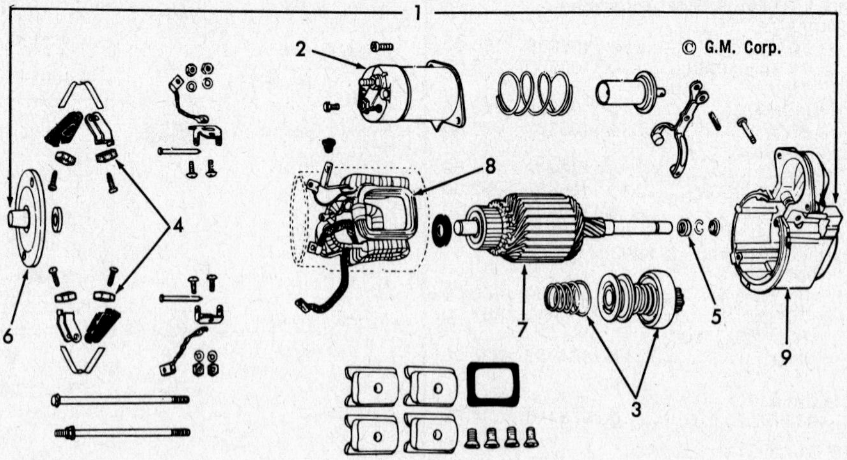

	Part No.	Price
(7) Armature		
1983-85-exc.		
below	◆1970548	52.00
252	◆1971568	57.00
Diesel	◆1974786	170.00

	Part No.	Price
(8) Field Coils		
exc. 350 Diesel		
1983-85-exc.		
below	◆1877306	26.00
252	◆1974123	N.L.

PARTS 5 STARTING SYSTEM 5 PARTS

	Part No.	Price
350 Diesel		
1983-85	◆1978123	56.25
(9) Drive End Housing (w/Bushing)		
1983-85-exc. below	◆1974897	73.75
Diesel	◆1975336	73.75
Ignition Switch		
1983-exc. below	◆1990109	N.L.
Tilt whl	◆1990110	N.L.
1984-85-exc. below	◆1990115	11.50
Tilt whl	◆1990116	11.50
Neutral Safety Switch		
Buick Riviera & Olds. Toronado		
1983-85-exc. below	◆22509632	5.50
Elec. dr. lcks.	◆22514861	7.00
Cadillac Eldorado & Seville		
1983-85	◆1619499	26.00
Battery Cables		
Order by year and model.		

LABOR 6 BRAKE SYSTEM 6 LABOR

	(Factory Time)	Chilton Time
(G) Brake Pedal Free Play, Adjust		
All models		.3
(G) Brakes, Adjust (Minor)		
Includes: R&R wheels and adjust brakes thru access holes in drums. Fill master cylinder.		
two wheels		.4
Remove knock out plugs, add each		.1
(G) Bleed Brakes (Four Wheels)		
Includes: Fill master cylinder.		
All models	(.4)	.5
(G) Free-Up or Renew Brake Self Adjusting Units		
one wheel		.5
each adtnl		.4
(G) Brake Shoes and/or Pads, Renew		
Includes: Install new or exchange shoes or pads. Adjust service and hand brake. Bleed system.		
1983-85-front-disc	(.8)	1.1
rear-drum	(.9)	1.5
all four wheels		2.5
Resurface disc rotor add, each		.9
Resurface brake drum add, each		.5
(G) Brake Drum, Renew (One)		
1983-85	(.3)	.5
(G) Brake Combination Valve, Renew		
Includes: Bleed system.		
1983-85	(.7)	1.0

BRAKE HYDRAULIC SYSTEM

	(Factory Time)	Chilton Time
(G) Wheel Cylinder, Renew		
Includes: Bleed system.		
1983-85-one	(1.0)	1.4
both	(1.3)	2.0
(G) Wheel Cylinder, R&R and Rebuild		
Includes: Hone cylinder and bleed system.		
1983-85-one	(1.2)	1.7
both	(1.7)	2.6
(G) Brake Hose, Renew		
Includes: Bleed system.		
1983-85-front-one	(.6)	.8
both	(.8)	1.2
rear-one	(.7)	1.0
(G) Master Cylinder, Renew		
Includes: Bleed complete system.		
1983-85	(.6)	1.0
(G) Master Cylinder, R&R and Rebuild		
Includes: Hone cylinder and bleed complete system.		
1983-85	(1.4)	2.0
Powermaster	(1.4)	2.2

COMBINATIONS

Add to Brakes, Renew

See Machine Shop Operations

	(Factory Time)	Chilton Time
(G) RENEW WHEEL CYLINDER		
Each	(.3)	.2
(G) REBUILD WHEEL CYLINDER		
Each	(.2)	.3
(G) REBUILD CALIPER ASSEMBLY		
Each	(.5)	.6
(G) RENEW MASTER CYLINDER		
All models	(.3)	.8
(G) REBUILD MASTER CYLINDER		
All models	(.8)	1.0
(G) RENEW BRAKE HOSE		
Each	(.3)	.3
(G) RENEW REAR WHEEL GREASE SEALS		
Each	(.1)	.1
(G) REPACK FRONT WHEEL BEARINGS (BOTH WHEELS)		
All models	(.3)	.6
(G) RENEW BRAKE DRUM		
Each	(.1)	.2
(G) RENEW DISC BRAKE ROTOR		
Each	(.2)	.3

	(Factory Time)	Chilton Time
(G) Brake System, Flush and Refill		
All models		1.2

DISC BRAKES

	(Factory Time)	Chilton Time
(G) Brake Shoes and/or Pads, Renew		
Includes: Install new or exchange shoes or pads. Adjust service and hand brake. Bleed system.		
1983-85-front-disc	(.8)	1.1
rear-drum	(.9)	1.5
all four wheels		2.5
Resurface rotor add, each		.9
Resurface drum add, each		.5
(G) Disc Brake Pads, Renew		
Includes: Install new brake pads only.		
1983-85-front	(.8)	1.1
rear	(1.0)	1.3
all four wheels		2.3
Resurface disc rotor add, each		.9
(G) Disc Brake Rotor, Renew		
Includes: R&R wheel, transfer bearings and races. Clean and repack wheel bearings.		
1983-85-front-one	(.5)	.8
both	(.8)	1.4
rear-one	(.6)	.9
both	(.9)	1.4
all four wheels		2.5
(G) Caliper Assembly, Renew		
Includes: Remove brake shoes. Bleed complete system.		
1983-85-front-one	(.7)	1.0
both	(1.0)	1.5
rear-one	(.7)	1.0
both	(1.2)	1.5
all four wheels		2.5
(G) Caliper Assy., R&R and Recondition		
Includes: Remove brake shoes, renew parts as required and bleed system.		
1983-85-front-one	(1.2)	1.5
both	(2.0)	2.5
rear-one	(1.2)	1.6
both	(2.2)	2.7
all four wheels		5.0

PARKING BRAKE

	(Factory Time)	Chilton Time
(M) Parking Brake, Adjust		
All models	(.3)	.4
(G) Parking Brake Control, Renew		
Toronado		
1983-85	(.6)	1.0
Riviera		
1983-85	(.6)	1.0
Eldorado & Seville		
1983-85	(.6)	1.0
Renew vacuum diaph add		.3
(G) Parking Brake Equalizer, Renew		
1983-85	(.3)	.5
(G) Parking Brake Cables, Renew		
1983-85-front-one	(.8)	1.0
rear-one	(.7)	1.1

LABOR 6 BRAKE SYSTEM 6 LABOR

(Factory Time)	Chilton Time
POWER BRAKES	
(G) Power Brake Cylinder, Renew	
Includes: R&R master cylinder.	
1983-85 (.6)	1.0
(G) Power Brake Cylinder, R&R and Recondition	
Includes: R&R master cylinder.	
1983-85-single cyl (1.1)	1.8
tandem cyl (1.3)	2.0
Recond m/Cyl add (.8)	.8

(Factory Time)	Chilton Time
(G) Power Brake Check Valve, Renew	
1983-85 (.3)	.3
(G) Low Vacuum Switch, Renew	
1983-85 (.2)	.3
(G) Low Vacuum Brake Indicator Module Assy., Renew	
1983-85 (.3)	.4

(Factory Time)	Chilton Time
HYDRA-BOOST SYSTEM	
(G) Hydra-Boost Unit, Renew	
Includes: Bleed system.	
1983-85 (1.2)	1.8
(G) Hydra-Boost Unit, R&R and Recondition	
Includes: Bleed system.	
1983-85 (1.6)	2.3
(G) Hydra-Boost Pressure Lines, Renew	
Includes: Bleed system.	
1983-85-each (.3)	.6

PARTS 6 BRAKE SYSTEM 6 PARTS

	Part No.	Price
Brake Shoe Set (Rear)		
1983-85	◆12300219	41.00
Wheel Cylinder (Rear)		
1983-85	◆18003905	28.00
Wheel Cylinder Repair Kit		
1983-85	◆18005281	7.25
Front Brake Hose		
1983-85-right	◆9762702	18.00
left	◆9762703	18.00
Rear Brake Hose		
1983-85	◆1261559	9.50
Master Cylinder Assy.		
Buick Riviera		
1983-85-exc. below	◆18009373	134.50
wo/Rr. disc brks.	◆18009816	171.25
231	◆18010591	112.00
Cadillac Eldorado, Seville & Olds. Toronado		
1983-85-exc. below	◆18009369	189.25
Diesel	◆18009373	134.50
Master Cylinder Repair Kit		
Buick Riviera		
1983-85-exc. below	◆18009375	20.50
wo/Rr. disc. brks.	◆18010083	22.75
Cadillac Eldorado, Seville & Olds. Toronado		
1983-85-exc. below	◆18009364	20.50
Diesel	◆18009375	20.50

	Part No.	Price
Rear Brake Drum		
1983-85-Alum.	◆1255496	90.00
Cast Iron	◆1249146	73.00
Front Wheel Grease Retainer		
1983-85	◆560680	4.75
Power Brake Booster (Vacuum Operated)		
Buick Riviera		
1983-252	◆18008743	271.25
307	◆18010249	271.25
1984-85-252	◆18007627	250.25
307	◆18010249	271.25
Cadillac Eldorado & Seville		
1983	◆18008673	271.25
1984-85	◆18007280	250.25
Olds. Toronado		
1983-85-252	◆18008673	271.25
307	◆18010263	271.25
Hydraulic Power Brake Booster Assy.		
1983-85	◆25511547	265.00
Vacuum Power Brake Cyl. Repair Kit		
1983-85	◆18007865	47.50
Hydraulic Booster Seal Kit		
1983-85	◆22506710	16.50
Hydraulic Booster Accumulator Kit		
1983-85-w/ Piston	◆22506439	128.00
Hydraulic Booster Piston Kit		
1983-85	◆22506438	5.50

	Part No.	Price
Vacuum Booster Piston Kit		
Buick Riviera		
1983-85	◆18009419	40.75
Cadillac Eldorado, Seville & Olds. Toronado		
1983-85	◆18007877	40.50
PARKING BRAKE		
Parking Brake Lever		
1983-85 (Drum brakes)		
right	◆458484	10.00
left	◆458483	10.00
1983-85 (Rear disc brakes)		
right	◆18003045	7.75
left	◆18003044	7.75
Parking Brake Control		
Buick Riviera & Olds. Toronado		
1983-85	◆1261850	N.L.
Cadillac Eldorado & Seville		
1983-85	◆1613714	54.75
Parking Brake Cable (Front)		
1983	◆25517514	11.75
1984-85	◆25517514	11.75
Parking Brake Cable (Rear)		
(Drum Brakes)		
1983-85-right	◆25517518	18.00
left	◆25517519	15.00
(Rear Disc Brakes)		
1983-85-right	◆25517516	22.00
left	◆25517517	13.75

PARTS 6 DISC BRAKES 6 PARTS

	Part No.	Price
FRONT DISC BRAKES		
Front Rotor		
1983-85	◆14056179	70.50
(1) Brake Pad Set		
Buick Riviera		
1983-85-exc. below	◆12300228	47.00
Rr. disc brks.	◆12300210	42.00
Cadillac Eldorado, Seville & Olds. Toronado		
1983-85	◆12300228	47.00
(2) Spring Kit (Anti-Rattle)		
1983-85	◆18006810	3.00
(3) Piston Seals (Repair Kit)		
1983-85	◆18003724	8.75
(4) Piston		
1983-85	◆18003155	11.00

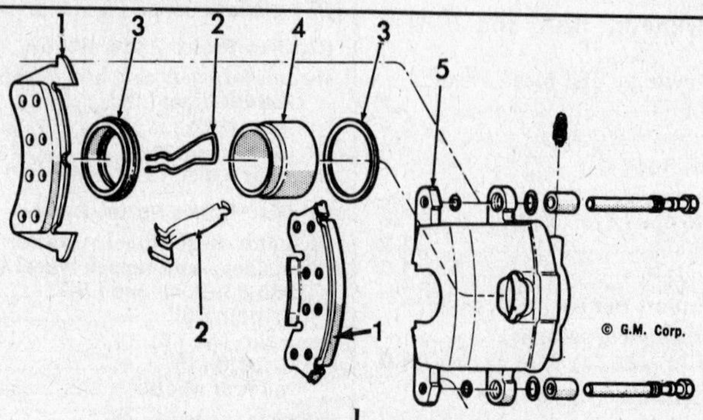

	Part No.	Price
(5) Caliper		
1983-85-right	◆18008846	137.00
left	◆18008845	137.00

	Part No.	Price
Hub and Bearing (Front)		
1983-85	◆7466907	240.50

PARTS 6 DISC BRAKES 6 PARTS

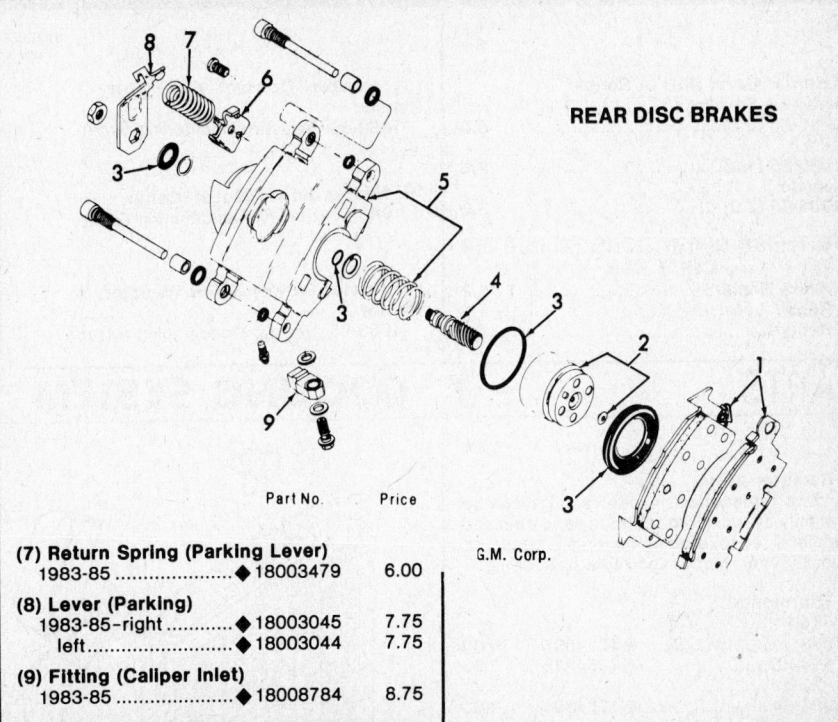

	Part No.	Price
REAR DISC BRAKES		
Rear Disc Rotor		
1983-85	◆14056179	70.50
(1) Brake Shoe Kit (Rear)		
Buick Riviera		
1983-85	◆12300220	47.00
Cadillac Eldorado, Seville & Olds. Toronado		
1983-85	◆12300221	40.00
(2) Actuator Assy. (Caliper Piston)		
1983-85-right	◆18009167	75.00
left	◆18009166	75.00
(3) Boot & Seal Pkg.		
Buick Riviera & Olds. Toronado		
1983-85	◆18007696	15.00
Cadillac Eldorado & Seville		
1983-85	◆18007696	15.00
(4) Screw & Locknut Pkg.		
1983-85-right	◆18005297	15.75
left	◆18005296	15.75
(5) Caliper Assy.		
1983-85-right	◆18008848	290.75
left	◆18008847	290.75
(6) Bracket & Bolt Pkg.		
1983-85-right	◆18005312	5.50
left	◆18005311	5.50

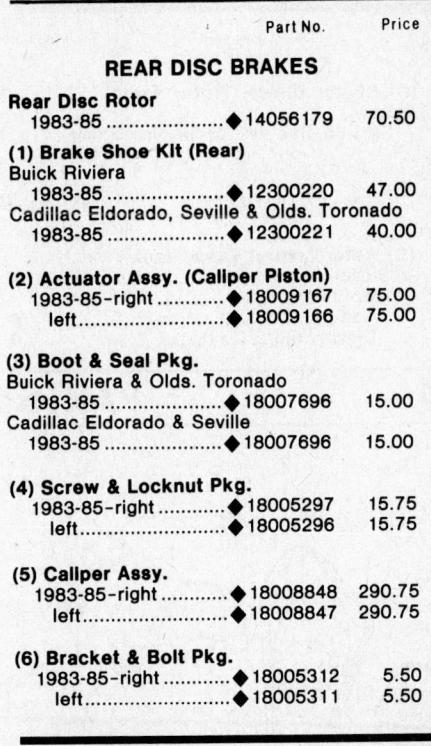

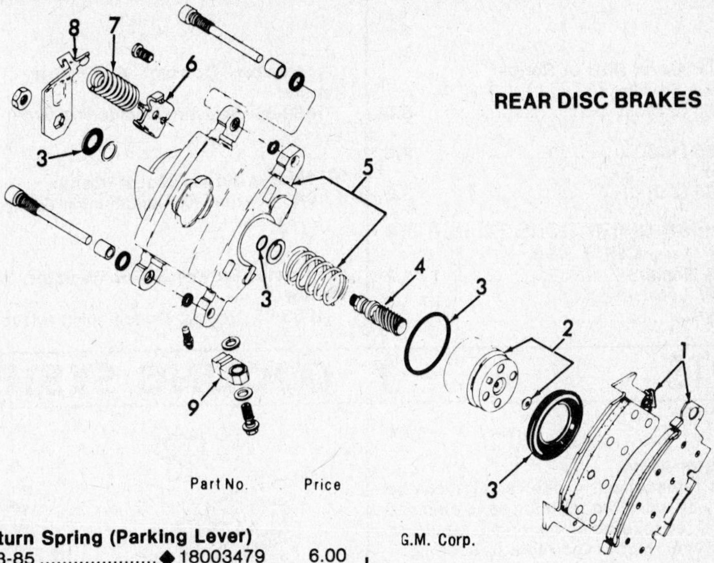

REAR DISC BRAKES

G.M. Corp.

	Part No.	Price
(7) Return Spring (Parking Lever)		
1983-85	◆18003479	6.00
(8) Lever (Parking)		
1983-85-right	◆18003045	7.75
left	◆18003044	7.75
(9) Fitting (Caliper Inlet)		
1983-85	◆18008784	8.75

LABOR 7 COOLING SYSTEM 7 LABOR

(Factory Time)	Chilton Time
(M) Winterize Cooling System	
Includes: Run engine to check for leaks, tighten all hose connections. Test radiator and pressure cap, drain radiator and engine block. Add anti-freeze and refill system.	
All models	.5
(G) Thermostat, Renew	
V-6–1983-85 (.7)	.8
V-8–1983-85 (.5)	.6
Diesel–1983-85 (.5)	.8
w/Turbocharger and A.I.R. add (.4)	.6
(M) Radiator Assembly, R&R or Renew	
Includes: Drain and refill cooling system.	
V-6–1983-85 (.8)	1.2
V-8–1983-85 (.7)	1.1
Diesel–1983-85 (.7)	1.1
ADD THESE OPERATIONS TO RADIATOR R&R	
(G) Boil & Repair	1.5
(G) Rod Clean	1.9
(G) Repair Core	1.3
(G) Renew Tank	1.6
(G) Renew Trans. Oil Cooler	1.9
(G) Recore Radiator	1.7
(G) Thermostat Housing and/or Gasket, Renew	
Includes: Partial removal of water pump and renew 'O' rings.	
1983-85	
250 eng-Code 8	
w/DFI-lower (2.0)	3.0
(M) Radiator Hoses, Renew	
1983-85-upper (.3)	.4
lower (.4)	.5
both (.6)	.7
by-pass (.4)	.6

COOLING SYSTEM TUNE-UP

An Annual Cooling System Tune-Up Suggestion List should include (with some exceptions):

1. A visual check of the cooling system for indications of leaks or excessive oil content.
2. Pressure check the cooling system for internal and external leaks with filler cap and neck adapter and tester.
3. Check crankcase and automatic transmission oil for water content.
4. Test coolant thermostat with radiator thermometer.
5. Check temperature gauge for accuracy.
6. Drain system and flush till clean.
7. Clean foreign matter from radiator fins.
8. Test radiator pressure cap with cap tester.
9. Check fan blades and pulleys for alignment and damage.
10. Internal and external inspection of all hoses for cracks and deterioration.
11. Check core plugs (where possible) for seepage.
12. Refill system with correct coolant and check for air locks.
13. Check condition and tension of drive belts with tension gauge.

All models 1.5

(Factory Time)	Chilton Time
w/Turbocharger and A.I.R. add (.3)	.4
(M) Drive Belt, Adjust	
1983-85-one (.3)	.4
each adtnl	.1
(M) Drive Belt, Renew	
1983-85 (.3)	.5
each adtnl	.1
w/Eng Code 8	
A.C. (.6)	.8

(Factory Time)	Chilton Time
AIR (.5)	.7
Alter (.3)	.4
Vacuum pump (.2)	.3
(G) Water Pump, Renew	
Includes: R&R fan and pulleys.	
V-6–1983-84 (1.1)	1.5
1985 (.9)	1.5
V-8–1983-85 (2.0)	3.0
Diesel–1983-85 (1.8)	2.7
w/P.S. add (.1)	.1
w/A.I.R. add (.1)	.1
w/A.C. add (.2)	.2
(G) Temperature Gauge (Engine Unit), Renew	
1983-85-V-6 (.5)	.7
V-8 (.3)	.5
(G) Temperature Gauge (Dash Unit), Renew	
1983-85 (.4)	.7
(G) Thermostat By-Pass Hose, Renew	
1983-85 (.3)	.6
(G) Fan Blades or Pulley, Renew	
1983-85 (.3)	.5
w/Thermo fan clutch add (.1)	.1
w/P.S. add (.1)	.1
w/A.I.R. add (.1)	.1
w/A.C. add (.1)	.1
(G) Water Jacket Expansion Plugs, Renew	
1983-85-each (.5)	.7
Note: If necessary to R&R any component to gain access to plug, add appropriate time.	
(G) Heater Hoses, Renew	
Includes: Drain and refill coolant.	
1983-85-one (.3)	.5
all (.6)	.8

LABOR 7 COOLING SYSTEM 7 LABOR

	(Factory Time)	Chilton Time
(G) Heater Core, R&R or Renew		
Eldorado & Seville		
1983-85	(3.5)	6.0
Riviera		
1983-85	(1.9)	3.5
Toronado		
1983-85	(2.0)	3.5
ADD THESE OPERATIONS TO HEATER CORE R&R		
(G) Boil & Repair		1.2
(G) Repair Core		.9
(G) Recore		1.2

(G) Heater Control Assembly, Renew
1983-85–See Air Conditioning Group.

(G) Heater Blower Motor, Renew
1983-85–See Air Conditioning Group.

(G) Heater Blower Motor Resistor, Renew
1983-85–See Air Conditioning Group.

(G) Heater Blower Motor Switch, Renew
1983-85–See Air Conditioning Group.

	(Factory Time)	Chilton Time
(G) Water Control Valve, Renew		
w/Diesel eng add	(.3)	.3
1983-85		
Gas	(.4)	.4
Diesel	(.6)	.6

PARTS 7 COOLING SYSTEM 7 PARTS

(1) Radiator Assy.
Accurate replacement of the radiator can be done only by using the radiator code stamped on a metal tag located on the original radiator. Order by year, model and radiator code no.

	Part No.	Price
(2) Thermostat		
V-6–231		
1983	◆1254894	9.00
1984-85	◆3054228	6.50
V-6–252		
1983-84	◆1254894	9.00
V-8		
1983-85–exc. below	◆3051139	5.00
250	◆1622630	4.50

(3) Radiator Hoses
Order by year and model.

	Part No.	Price
(4) Water Pump Assy.		
V-6		
1983-85	◆1260709	61.75
V-8–250		
1983-85	◆3634580	125.00
V-8–307		
1983-85–wo/A.C.	◆231886	96.50
A.C.	◆556283	95.00

(5) Fan Belts
Order by year and model.

	Part No.	Price
Fan Clutch Assy.		
Buick Riviera & Olds. Toronado		
V-6		
1983-85	◆22008492	87.50
V-8–Gas		
1983-85–exc. below	◆4974367	84.50
H.D. cooling	◆22008668	N.L.
V-8–Diesel		
1983-85–exc. below	◆22008668	N.L.
H.D. cooling	◆561826	122.00
Cadillac Eldorado & Seville		
1983-85–Diesel	◆1625161	80.50
V-6	◆22008492	87.50
V-8	◆22008464	84.50

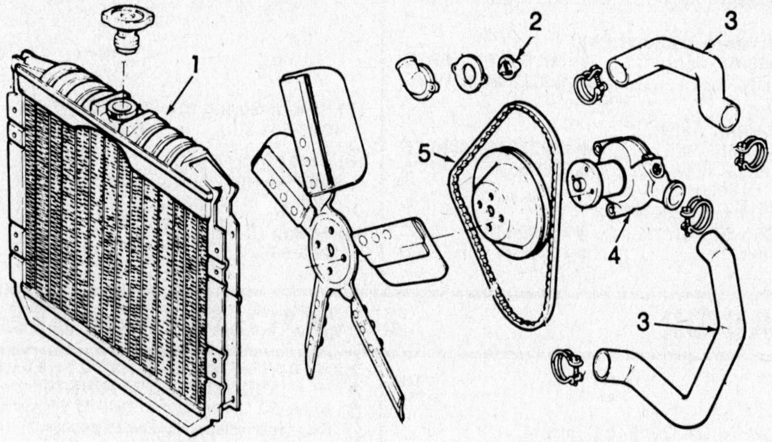

	Part No.	Price
Water Temperature Switch		
Buick Riviera & Olds. Toronado		
V-6		
1983	◆25036371	8.00
1984-85–231	◆25036371	8.00
252	◆25036629	9.75
V-8		
1983	◆25036506	8.75
1984-85	◆25036628	19.75
Cadillac Eldorado & Seville		
V-8 Gas		
1983-85	◆25036335	21.00
V-8 Diesel		
1983-85	◆25036588	9.00
Heater Core		
1983-85	◆3040690	61.00
Blower Motor		
1983-85	◆22020945	60.00

	Part No.	Price
Water Control Valve		
Buick Riviera		
1983-85		
(Without Electronic Climate Control)		
231	◆25508956	32.75
252	◆14032007	22.50
V-8 (1983)	◆22502236	18.00
V-8 (1984-85)	◆22502236	18.00
(With Electronic Climate Control)		
231 (1983)	◆25508960	23.50
231 (1984-85)	◆25506254	14.50
252	◆25506254	14.50
V-8	◆25506256	21.50
Cadillac Eldorado & Seville		
1983-85–wo/Diesel	◆14032007	22.50
Diesel	◆411283	N.L.
Olds. Toronado		
1983-85–V-6	◆14032007	22.50
V-8	◆22502236	18.00

LABOR 8 EXHAUST SYSTEM 8 LABOR

	(Factory Time)	Chilton Time
(G) Muffler, Renew		
1983-84	(.5)	.9
1985	(.7)	1.0
(G) Exhaust 'Y' Pipe, Renew		
1983-85	(.7)	1.2
(G) Tail Pipe and Resonator Assy., Renew		
1983-85	(.4)	.7

LABOR 8 EXHAUST SYSTEM 8 LABOR

(Factory Time) Chilton Time

(G) Exhaust Crossover Pipe, Renew
1983-Gas (.4) 7
Diesel (1.4) 1.9

(G) Front Exhaust Pipe, Renew
1983-85-one (.6) 9
both (.7) 1.1

(G) Catalytic Converter, Renew
1983 (.5) 8
1984-85 (.8) 1.0
w/AIR add 1

(G) Intermediate Pipe, Renew
1983-85 (.5) 7

(G) E.F.E. Valve (Heat Riser), Renew
1983-85 (.5) 1.0

(G) E.F.E. Vacuum Check Valve, Renew
1983-85 (.2) 4

(G) Turbocharger Outlet Pipe, Renew
1983-85 (.7) 1.3

(G) Turbocharger Inlet Pipe, Renew
1983 (2.1) 2.7
1984-85 (.9) 1.3

(G) Exhaust Manifold, Renew
V-6–1983-85
Code A
right side (1.3) 1.7
left side (.6) 1.0
Code 4
right side (1.3) 1.8
left side (.5) 1.0
Code 9
right side (.8) 1.2
left side (.8) 1.2
w/A.C. add (.3) 3
V-8–1983-85
250 eng-Code 8
right side (1.0) 1.4
left side (.8) 1.1
350-368 engs
Code 8-6 or 9
right side (.8) 1.4
left side (.7) 1.3
350 eng-Code R
right side (.9) 1.3
left side (.6) 1.0
307 eng-Code Y
right side (.8) 1.3
left side (.7) 1.2
w/A.C. add (.4) 4
Diesel–1983
right side (.9) 1.2
left side (.7) 1.1
1984-85
right side (1.2) 1.7
left side (.8) 1.2

COMBINATIONS

(G) Exhaust System, Renew (Complete)
1983-85
V-6 .... 1.3
V-8 .... 1.5

PARTS 8 EXHAUST SYSTEM 8 PARTS

	Part No.	Price
Muffler		
Order by year and model.		
Resonator (w/Pipe)		
Buick Riviera		
V-6		
1983-85	◆1263020	89.25
V-8 Gas		
1983-85	◆22500630	95.75
V-8 Diesel		
1983-85	◆22510564	89.25
Cadillac Eldorado & Seville		
V-6		
1983-85	◆1622802	88.75
V-8 Diesel		
1983-85	◆1621280	74.00
Olds. Toronado		
V-6		
1983-84	◆1263020	89.25
V-8 Gas		
1983-85	◆563634	89.25
V-8 Diesel		
1983-85	◆22510564	89.25
Exhaust Pipe (Front)		
V-6-231		
1983-85	◆25513257	82.25
V-6-252		
1983	◆25508196	37.50
1984	◆25518882	35.00
V-8-250		
1983-right	◆1622006	37.50
left	◆1622005	37.50
1984-exc. Calif.		
L.H.	◆1627642	23.25
R.H.	◆1627641	12.50
1984-Calif.		
L.H.	◆1622005	37.50
R.H.	◆1622006	37.50
1985-L.H.	◆1631190	19.25
R.H.	◆1631193	37.50
V-8-307		
1983-right	◆562622	31.25
left	◆22504832	19.00
1984-85	◆22522087	23.25
V-8-350 Diesel		
1983-84-right	◆562622	31.25
left	◆22504832	19.00
1985-right	◆22505220	31.25
left	◆22527465	21.50
Front "Y" Pipe		
V-6-231		
1983	◆25513237	158.00
1984-85	◆25520078	155.00
V-6-252		
1983	◆25508195	37.50
1984-85	◆25518881	26.75
V-8-Gas		
1983-85-exc. below	◆22510562	48.75
1983-Eldorado & Seville	◆1619814	55.50
1984-Eldorado & Seville		
Fed.	◆1627643	35.75
Calif.	◆1619814	55.50
1985-Eldorado & Seville	◆1631192	66.00
V-8-Diesel		
1983-85-exc. below	◆22510562	48.75
1983-84-Fed. & Calif. exc. Hi Alt.	◆22517996	48.75
Intermediate Pipe		
Buick Riviera & Olds. Toronado		
V-6		
1983	◆25505905	53.00
1984-85	◆25508667	53.00
V-8 Gas		
1983	◆22512351	24.25
1984-85	◆22524715	53.00
V-8 Diesel		
1983-85	◆22512352	46.75
Cadillac Eldorado & Seville		
V-8		
1983-85-250 exc. below	◆1618323	29.00
1984-85-Fed. & Hi Alt.	◆1627644	23.00
1983-85-Diesel	◆22512352	46.75
Catalytic Converter		
Buick Riviera		
V-6-231		
1983	◆25056345	319.25
1984-85	◆25056546	357.25
V-6-252		
1983-84	◆8999596	N.L.
V-8		
1983	◆25056622	308.25
1984-85-Calif.	◆25056562	313.25
1984-85-exc. Calif.	◆25056634	335.00
Cadillac Eldorado & Seville		
1983-V-6	◆8999596	N.L.
V-8	◆25056623	349.25
1984-85	◆25056586	337.25
Olds. Toronado		
1983-V-6	◆8999596	N.L.
1984-V-6	◆8999615	312.25
1983-V-8	◆25056622	308.25
1984-85-V-8		
exc. below	◆25056634	335.00
Calif.	◆25056562	313.25

LABOR 9 FRONT SUSPENSION 9 LABOR

(Factory Time) Chilton Time

Note: On all front suspension operations alignment charges must be added if performed. Time given does not include alignment.

(M) Wheel, Renew
one (.5) 5

(M) Wheels, Rotate (All)
All models 5

LABOR 9 FRONT SUSPENSION 9 LABOR

(Factory Time) Chilton Time

(G) Wheels, Balance
one 3
each adtnl 2

(G) Check Alignment of Front End
All models 5
Note: Deduct if alignment is performed.

(G) Toe-In Adjust
All models (.5) 6

(G) Align Front End
Includes: Adjust front wheel bearings and check carrying height.
All models (1.1) 1.7
w/A.C. interference add 5

(G) Front Wheel Bearing and Hub Assy., Renew
1983-85-one side (.7) 9
both sides (1.1) 1.6

(G) Lower Control Arm Assy., Renew
Add alignment charges.
1983-85-one (1.0) 2.0
both (2.0) 3.7

(G) Lower Control Arm Bushings, Renew
Add alignment charges.
1983-85-one side (.8) 1.6
both sides (1.5) 2.9

(G) Upper Control Arm Assy., Renew
Includes: Alignment charges.
1983-85-one (1.5) 2.0
both (1.9) 2.9

(G) Upper Control Arm Bushings, Renew
Includes: Alignment charges.
1983-85-one side (1.6) 2.4
both sides (2.2) 3.7

(G) Upper Ball Joint, Renew
Add alignment charges.
1983-85-one (.5) 1.0
both (.9) 1.8

(G) Lower Ball Joint, Renew
Add alignment charges.
1983-85-one (1.0) 1.4
both (1.8) 2.7

(G) Torsion Bar, Adjust
All models (.3) 5

(G) Front Torsion Bar, Renew
Includes: Adjust trim height.
Add alignment charges.
1983-85-one (.4) 7
both (.8) 1.4

(G) Torsion Bar Pivot Arm, Renew
Includes: Adjust trim height.
Add alignment charges.
1983-85-one (.3) 6
both (.7) 1.3

(G) Torsion Bar Support Member, Renew
Includes: Adjust trim height.
1983-85 (1.9) 3.0

(G) Torsion Bar Support Member Cushions, Renew (One or Both)
Add alignment charges.
1983-85 (.9) 1.3

(G) Front Shock Absorbers, Renew
1983-85-one (.3) 4
both (.5) 7

(G) Front Stabilizer Shaft, Renew
1983-85 (.5) 8

(G) Front Stabilizer Shaft Link or Link Bushings, Renew
1983-85-one (.3) 4
both (.4) 6

(G) Steering Knuckle, Renew
Add alignment charges.
1983-85-one (.7) 1.4
both (1.4) 2.5

(G) Steering Knuckle Inner Dust Seal, Renew
Add alignment charges.
1983-85-one (.7) 1.4
both (1.4) 2.5

FINAL DRIVE

(G) Drive Axle Shaft, R&R
1983-85-one side (.8) 1.1
both sides (1.4) 2.0
Overhaul or repack
outer C/V joint add, each (.6) 8
Overhaul or repack
inner C/V joint add, each (.4) 6
Renew drive axle assy.,
with inner and outer joints
add, each (1.0) 1.0

(G) Output Shaft, Renew
V-6–1983-85
right side (1.6) 2.0
left side (1.0) 1.4
both sides (2.4) 3.2
V-8–1983-85
right side (1.2) 1.6
left side (1.0) 1.4
both sides (1.9) 2.8
Renew output shaft bearing
add (.3) 4
Renew output shaft seal add,
each (.1) 2

(G) Final Drive Cover and/or Gasket, Renew
1983-85 (.5) 6

(G) Final Drive Assembly, Renew
V-6–1983-85 (2.0) 3.0
V-8–1983-85 (2.1) 3.0

(G) Final Drive Pinion Oil Seal, Renew
Includes: R&R final drive and refill.
V-6–1983-85 (3.8) 5.7
V-8–1983-85 (3.6) 5.2

(P) Final Drive Pinion Bearings, Renew
Includes: R&R final drive. Make all necessary adjustments.
V-6–1983-85 (3.8) 5.7
V-8–1983-85 (3.7) 5.4

(P) Final Drive Side Bearings, Renew
Includes: R&R final drive. Make all necessary adjustments.
V-6–1983-85 (3.1) 4.6
V-8–1983-85 (3.2) 4.6

(P) Final Drive Ring Gear and Pinion, Renew
Includes: R&R final drive. Renew pinion bearings and make all necessary adjustments.
V-6–1983-85 (3.8) 5.7
V-8–1983-85 (3.7) 5.4
Recond diff case add (.3) 5

(P) Final Drive Case, Renew
Includes: R&R final drive. Transfer or renew ring gear and pinion, pinion shaft, pinion and side gears. Make all necessary adjustments.
V-6–1983-85 (3.2) 4.8
V-8–1983-85 (3.3) 4.7

(P) Final Drive Ring Gear and Pinion, Adjust
Includes: R&R final drive and refill.
V-6–1983-85 (3.4) 4.5
V-8–1983-85 (3.0) 4.0

PARTS 9 FRONT SUSPENSION 9 PARTS

	Part No.	Price
(1) Hub (Front Wheel)		
1983-85	◆7466907	240.50
(2) Steering Knuckle		
1983-right	◆22522938	158.00
left	◆22522937	158.00
1984-85-right	◆22522938	158.00
left	◆22522937	158.00
(3) Seal Inner		
1983-85	◆560680	4.75
(4) Shock Absorber		
Buick Riviera		
1983-85	◆4993587	24.50
Cadillac Eldorado, Seville & Olds. Toronado		
1983-85	◆4993587	24.50
(5) Drive Axle		
Component parts serviced.		
(6) Torsion Bar Anchor Bearing		
1983-85	◆563432	10.50
(7) Torsion Bar (Front)		
1983-85 (34 rate)		
right	◆22511564	95.25
left	◆22511565	95.25
1983-85 (36 rate)		
right	◆562088	95.25
left	◆562089	95.25
1983-85 (40 rate)		
right	◆562090	94.75
left	◆562091	95.25
1983-85 (45 rate)		
right	◆562092	95.25
left	◆562093	95.25
1983-85 (50 rate)		
right	◆562094	105.00
left	◆562095	105.00

PARTS 9 FRONT SUSPENSION 9 PARTS

	Part No.	Price
(8) Lower Control Arm		
Buick Riviera		
1983-85-right	◆562354	219.00
left	◆562355	219.00
Cadillac Eldorado & Seville		
1983-85-right	◆22514732	219.00
left	◆22514733	219.00
Olds. Toronado		
1983-85-right	◆22514732	219.00
left	◆22514733	219.00
(9) Front Anchor Arm (Torsion Bar)		
1983-85	◆561756	35.75
(10) Stabilizer Shaft Bushing		
Buick Riviera & Cadillac Eldorado		
1983-85 (wo/Rally Suspension)		
exc. below	◆370283	1.00
1″ hole	◆371773	1.00
Rally Susp.	◆22501022	2.00
Olds. Toronado		
1983-85	◆371773	1.00
(11) Stabilizer Link Pkg. (Front)		
1983-85	◆22500910	4.25
(12) Upper Control Arm		
1983-85-right	◆22504368	97.25
left	◆22504369	97.25

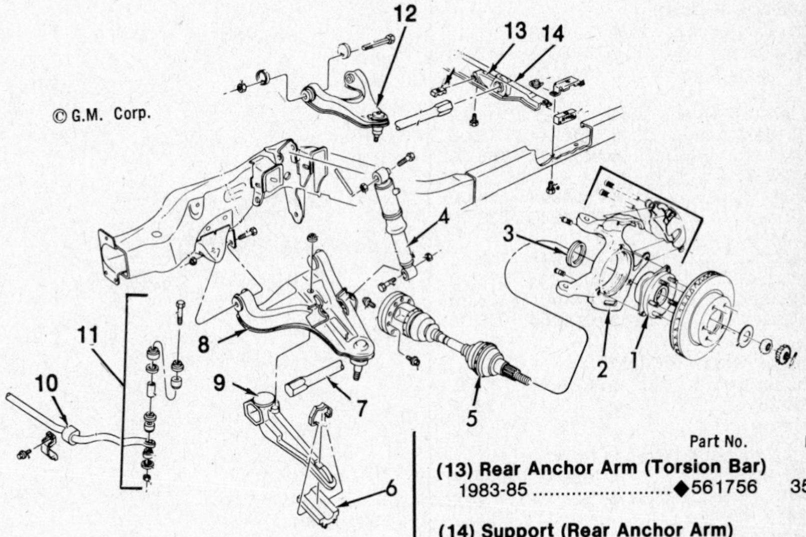

	Part No.	Price
(13) Rear Anchor Arm (Torsion Bar)		
1983-85	◆561756	35.75
(14) Support (Rear Anchor Arm)		
1983-85	◆22514725	64.25

PARTS 9 FINAL DRIVE 9 PARTS

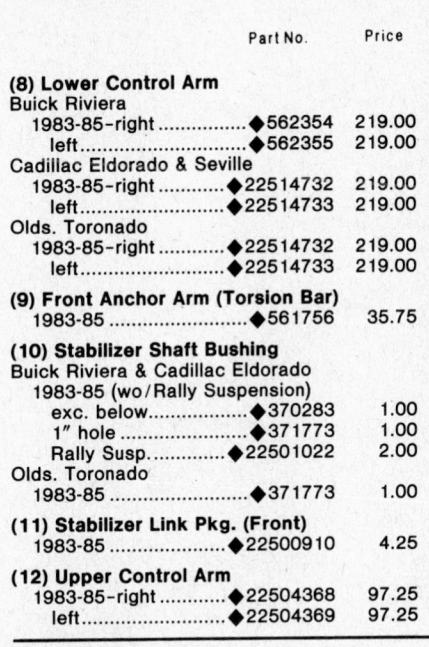

	Part No.	Price
(1) Ring Gear & Pinion Kit		
1983-85-2.19 ratio	◆1615579	309.00
2.41 ratio	◆1615578	309.00
2.73 ratio	◆1622622	324.00
2.93 ratio	◆1615577	309.00
3.15 ratio	◆1622623	324.00
3.36 ratio	◆1625764	370.00
(2) Shim Kit (Drive Pinion)		
1983-85 (.020-.028)	◆484365	6.50
(.030-.038)	◆484366	6.50
(3) Bearing Assy. (Front)		
1983-85	◆7451409	35.50
(4) Housing Assy. (Final Drive)		
1983-85	◆1621460	262.00
(5) Output Shaft Seal (Right)		
1983-85	◆1614579	6.50
(6) Seal (Pinion Gear)		
1983-85	◆1615116	8.00
(7) Spacer (Pinion Bearing)		
1983-85	◆1612360	1.50
(8) Bearing Assy. (Rear)		
1983-85	◆9418356	16.25
(9) Output Shaft Seal (Left)		
1983-85	◆1614578	6.75
(10) Drive Shaft (Front Wheel)		
1983-85-right	◆1612377	115.00
left	◆1612376	89.00

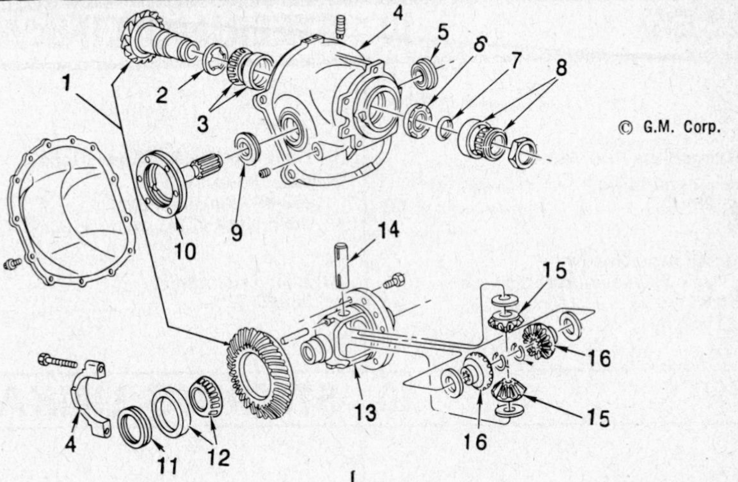

	Part No.	Price
(11) Shim Kit (Diff. Bearing)		
1983-85		
.040-.044	◆3995791	6.50
.046-.050	◆3995792	6.50
.052-.056	◆3907088	4.25
.058-.063	◆3907089	4.25
.064-.070	◆3853759	4.00
.072-.078	◆3853760	4.00
.080-.086	◆3853761	3.75
.088-.094	◆3853762	4.00
.096-.100	◆3853912	3.25

	Part No.	Price
(12) Bearing Assy. (Side)		
1983-85	◆7451281	14.00
(13) Differential Case		
1983-85	◆1612337	231.00
(14) Pinion Shaft		
1983-85	◆22507586	11.00
(15) Pinion Gear		
1983-85	◆1613620	19.50
(16) Side Gear		
1983-85	◆1612338	49.00

PARTS 9 FRONT DRIVE AXLE 9 PARTS

	Part No.	Price
(1) Joint Assy.		
1983	◆7835070	225.25
1984-85-right	◆7843739	278.00
left	◆7835070	225.25

	Part No.	Price
(2) Retainer (Seal)		
1983-85	◆7830137	6.50

	Part No.	Price
(3) Seal Kit		
(For use w/Tri-Pot Joint)		
1983	◆7834238	N.L.
1984	◆7845012	29.00
1985	◆7844067	N.L.

PARTS 9 FRONT DRIVE AXLE 9 PARTS

	Part No.	Price
(For use w/C.V. Joint)		
1983	◆7834239	N.L.
1984	◆7845013	17.00
1985	◆7844066	36.25
(4) Axle Kit (Replacement)		
1983-right	◆7834244	718.00
left	◆7834245	638.00
1984-V-6		
right	◆7844064	506.00
left	◆7834245	638.00
1984-V-8		
right	◆7834244	718.00
left	◆7834245	638.00
1985-right	◆7844064	506.00
left	◆7844065	500.00
(5) Spider Kit (Tripot Joint)		
1983	◆7834241	N.L.
1984-85	◆7845014	92.00
(6) Housing Kit (w/Grease Retainer)		
1983-right	◆7830112	222.00
left	◆7834082	115.00
1984-V-6		
right	◆7846610	196.00
left	◆7834082	115.00
1984-V-8		
right	◆7830112	222.00
left	◆7834082	115.00

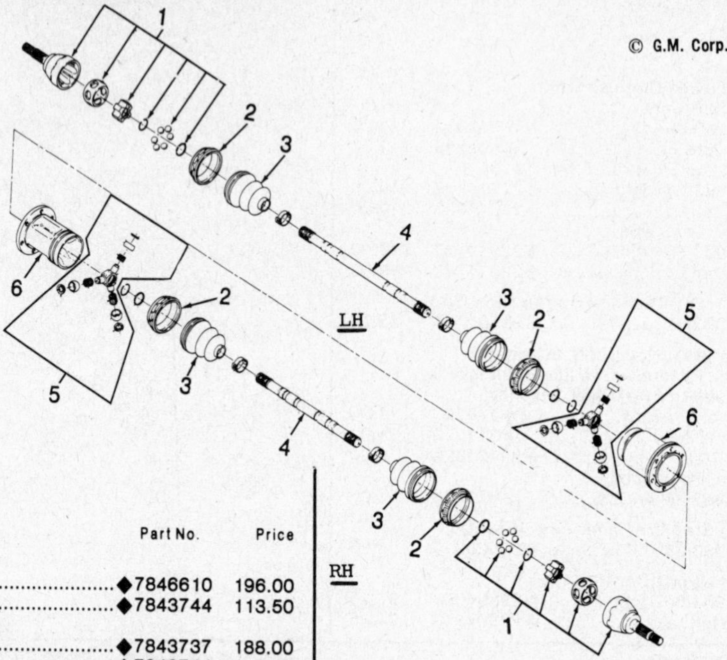

	Part No.	Price
1985-V-6		
right	◆7846610	196.00
left	◆7843744	113.50
1985-V-8		
right	◆7843737	188.00
left	◆7843744	113.50

LABOR 10 STEERING LINKAGE 10 LABOR

(Factory Time)	Chilton Time
(G) Intermediate Rod, Renew	
Includes: Reset toe-in.	
1983-85 (1.1)	1.6
(G) Pitman Arm, Renew	
Note: Does not require resetting toe-in.	
1983-85 (.8)	1.4
(G) Tie Rod or Tie Rod Ends, Renew	
Includes: Reset toe-in.	
1983-85-one side (.8)	1.0
both sides (1.0)	1.4
(G) Idler Arm, Adjust	
1983-85 (.7)	1.0
(G) Idler Arm, Renew	
Includes: Reset toe-in.	
1983-85 (.9)	1.6
(G) Steering Shock Absorber, Renew	
1983-85 (.3)	.5

PARTS 10 STEERING LINKAGE 10 PARTS

	Part No.	Price
(1) Shield (Tie Rod End)		
1983-85-right	◆22500606	2.25
left	◆22500607	2.25
(2) Tie Rod (Outer)		
1983-85	◆7830666	49.00
(3) Tube Kit (Adjuster)		
1983-85	◆7826714	15.50
(4) Tie Rod (Inner)		
1983-85	◆7833122	51.00
(5) Pitman Arm Kit		
1983-85	◆7831535	63.50
(6) Intermediate Rod		
1983-85	◆7834621	102.00
(7) Idler Arm Kit		
1983-85	◆7830667	71.00
(8) Shock Absorber (Linkage)		
1983-85	◆4993543	42.00

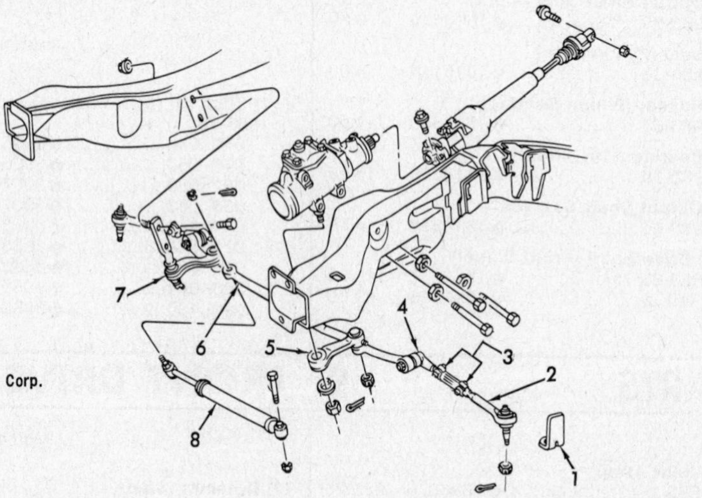

LABOR 11 STEERING GEAR 11 LABOR

(Factory Time)	Chilton Time
(G) Horn Contact or Cancelling Cam, Renew	
1983-85 (.4)	.6
w/Tilt-Tel (.5)	.7
(G) Steering Wheel, Renew	
1983-85 (.3)	.5
w/Tilt-Tel (.4)	.6
(G) Multifunction Lever, Renew	
All models (.2)	.4
w/Cruise control add (.5)	.5
(G) Steering Column Lock Actuator Parts, Renew	
1983-85	
std colm (1.0)	1.5
tilt colm (.8)	1.3
Tilt Tel (.7)	1.2
(G) Dimmer Switch Pivot Assy., Renew	
1983-85 (.6)	1.2
w/Cruise control add (.2)	.2
(G) Steering Column Shift Bowl, Renew	
1983-85 (1.5)	2.2
w/Tilt-Tel (1.8)	2.4
(G) Upper Mast Jacket Bearing, Renew	
1983-85	
std colm (.8)	1.4
tilt colm (1.1)	1.7
w/Cruise control add (.2)	.2
(G) Steering Column Lower Bearing, Renew	
1983-85 (.4)	.7
(G) Intermediate Shaft Assy., Renew	
1983-85 (.4)	.6
(G) Steering Flex Coupling, Renew (Rag Joint)	
1983-85 (.3)	.6
(G) Universal Joint (Pot Joint), Renew	
1983-84 (.3)	.8

POWER STEERING

(Factory Time)	Chilton Time
(G) Trouble Shoot Power Steering	
Includes: Test pump and system pressure. Check pounds pull on steering wheel and check system for leaks.	
All models	.6
(M) Pump Drive Belt, Renew	
1983-85 (.4)	.5
w/A.C. add (.1)	.1
w/A.I.R. add (.1)	.1
(M) Check Reservoir and Add Fluid	
All models	.2
(G) Power Steering Gear, Adjust	
Includes: R&R gear assy.	
1983-85 (.8)	1.2
(G) Power Steering Gear Assembly, Renew	
1983-85 (.7)	1.3
(G) Power Steering Gear Assy., R&R and Recondition	
Includes: Disassemble, renew necessary parts, reassemble and adjust.	
1983-85 (1.7)	2.5
(G) End Cover and/or Seal, Renew	
Includes: R&R gear assy.	
1983-85 (.8)	1.2
(G) Pitman Shaft or Bearing, Renew	
Includes: R&R gear assy.	
1983-85 (1.1)	1.6
(G) Adjuster Plug, R&R and Recondition	
Includes: R&R gear assy.	
1983-85 (1.1)	1.6
(G) Valve Body, Renew or Recondition	
Includes: R&R gear assy.	
1983-85 (1.3)	1.8
(G) Rack Piston and Worm Shaft, Renew	
Includes: R&R gear assy.	
1983-85 (1.5)	2.2
(G) Gear Housing, Renew	
Includes: R&R gear assy.	
1983-85 (1.4)	2.1
(G) Power Steering Oil Pump, Renew	
1983-85-V-6 (.9)	1.3
V-8 (1.1)	1.5
Diesel (1.1)	1.5
w/eng Code R add (.2)	.2
(P) Power Steering Pump, R&R and Recondition	
Includes: R&R reservoir.	
1983-85-V-6 (1.4)	2.1
V-8 (1.6)	2.3
Diesel (1.6)	2.3
w/eng Code R add (.2)	.2
(G) Power Steering Pump Seal, Renew	
Includes: R&R pump pulley.	
1983-85 (.7)	1.1
w/eng Code R add (.2)	.2
(G) Pump Flow Control Valve, Renew	
1983-85 (.7)	1.1
(G) Power Steering Reservoir, Renew (Remote)	
1983-85 (.3)	.6
(M) Power Steering Hoses, Renew	
1983-85-each (.4)	.6
(M) Hydra-Boost Hoses, Renew	
1983-85-each (.3)	.5

TILT AND TELESCOPIC COLUMN

(Factory Time)	Chilton Time
(G) Steering Column Shift Bowl, Renew	
Includes: R&R steering wheel and turn signal housing support assy.	
1983-85 (1.8)	2.4
(G) Steering Shaft and Upper Bearing, Renew	
Includes: R&R steering wheel, horn contact, turn signal lever, upper column cover, turn signal switch, and tilt actuator.	
1983-85 (1.1)	1.6
Recond shaft add (.2)	.3
(G) Tilt Column, R&R and Recondition	
1983-85 (1.9)	2.5
Recond add (.2)	.4
(G) Steering Column Assy., Renew	
Does not include color coat.	
1983-85 (1.1)	2.2
(G) Upper Bearing and Turn Signal Housing, Renew	
1983-85 (1.1)	2.0
Recond housing add (.2)	.4
(G) Steering Column Lock Shoes, Renew	
1983-85 (1.3)	2.2
Polish shoes add (.2)	.3

PARTS 11 POWER STEERING PUMP 11 PARTS

	Part No.	Price
Oil Pressure Hose		
V-6		
1983-85		
exc. RR. disc brks.	◆7833039	36.00
RR. disc brks.		
Booster to gear (1983-87)	◆7843875	57.00
Pump to booster	◆7840807	57.00
V-8		
1983-85-Diesel		
Pump to booster	◆7833361	48.25
Booster to gear (1983-85)	◆7837182	50.50
1983-85-exc. Diesel		
Pump outlet	◆7833360	36.00
Booster to gear	◆7833362	50.50
Oil Return Hose		
Order by length.		
Power Steering Pump		
Buick Riviera		
V-6		
1983-85-231	◆7839796	199.00
V-6-252		
exc. below	◆7839794	199.00
Rear disc brks.	◆7839796	199.00
V-8 Gas		
1983-85-exc. below	◆7840244	199.00
Rr. disc brks.	◆7839790	213.00
V-8 Diesel		
1983-85	◆7839790	213.00
Cadillac Eldorado & Seville		
V-8 Gas		
1983-85	◆7842624	199.00
V-8 Diesel		
1983-85	◆7839790	213.00
Olds. Toronado		
V-6		
1983-85	◆7839794	199.00
V-8 Gas		
1983-85	◆7840244	199.00
V-8 Diesel		
1983-85	◆7839790	213.00

PARTS 11 POWER STEERING PUMP 11 PARTS

	Part No.	Price
(1) Oil Seal Kit		
1983-85-exc. below	◆5688044	10.75
V-8-250	◆7834853	11.00
(2) Pressure Plate		
1983-85	◆7839669	14.25
(3) Spring (Pressure Plate)		
1983-85	◆7839667	1.00
(4) End Plate		
1983-85	◆5689358	3.50
(5) Rotor and Vane Kit		
1983-85	◆7837322	75.00
(6) Thrust Plate (Pump)		
Buick Riviera		
1983-85	◆7839366	25.75
Cadillac Eldorado & Olds. Toronado		
1983-85	◆7839366	25.75
(7) Flow Control Valve		
Buick Riviera & Olds. Toronado		
1983-85	◆7809232	10.75
Cadillac Eldorado & Seville		
1983-85	◆7809232	10.75
(8) Pump Housing		
1983-85-exc. below	◆7830236	62.75
1983-85-252	◆7840520	62.75

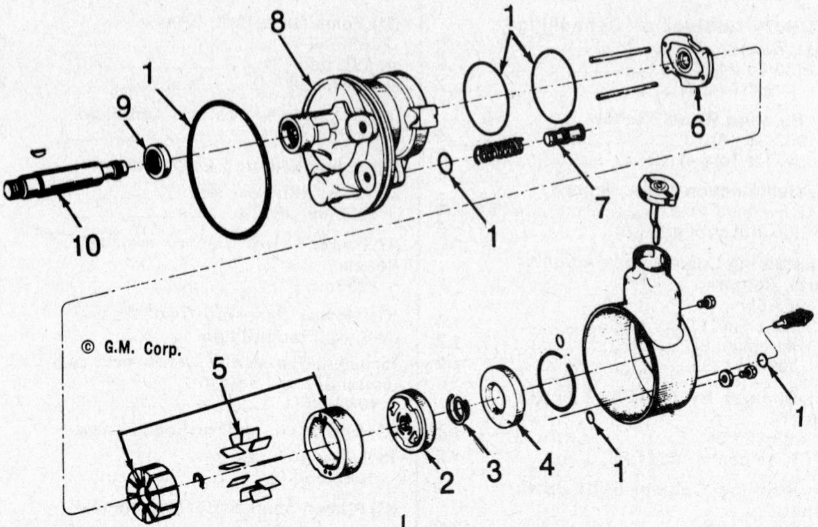

	Part No.	Price
(9) Seal (Drive Shaft)		
1983-85	◆7808195	4.50
(10) Drive Shaft		
1983-85	◆7837321	39.50

PARTS 11 POWER STEERING GEAR 11 PARTS

	Part No.	Price
(1) Seal (Side Cover)		
1983-85	◆7817486	9.00
(2) Pitman Shaft (w/Gear)		
1983-85	◆7815885	87.50
(3) Check Valve Unit		
1983-85	◆7834284	5.25
(4) Bearing Kit		
1983-85	◆7826850	11.00
(5) Housing Assy.		
1983-85	◆7834135	174.25
(6) Bearing (Pitman Shaft)		
1983-85	◆5697804	15.00
(7) Seal Kit (Pitman Shaft)		
1983-85	◆7826470	17.00
(8) Seal Kit (Adjuster Plug)		
1983-85	◆7832730	8.25
(9) Adjuster Plug Bearing		
1983-85	◆7828012	7.25
(10) Plug Assy. (Adjuster)		
1983-85	◆7832731	53.50
(11) Seal Kit		
1983-85	◆5687182	12.50
(12) Valve Kit		
Includes: Valve assembly, torsion bar stub-shaft, spool, pins, rings and seals.		
1983-85		
Rally Susp.	◆7832945	212.00
wo/Rally Susp.	◆7832036	212.00
(13) Seal Kit		
1983-85	◆7817485	6.50
(14) Plug		
1983-85	◆7805168	7.50
(15) Rack Kit		
1983-85-exc. below	◆7827170	154.25
convertible	◆7817526	151.00

Consists of piston ring, seal, worm, balls, guides, clamp & screws.

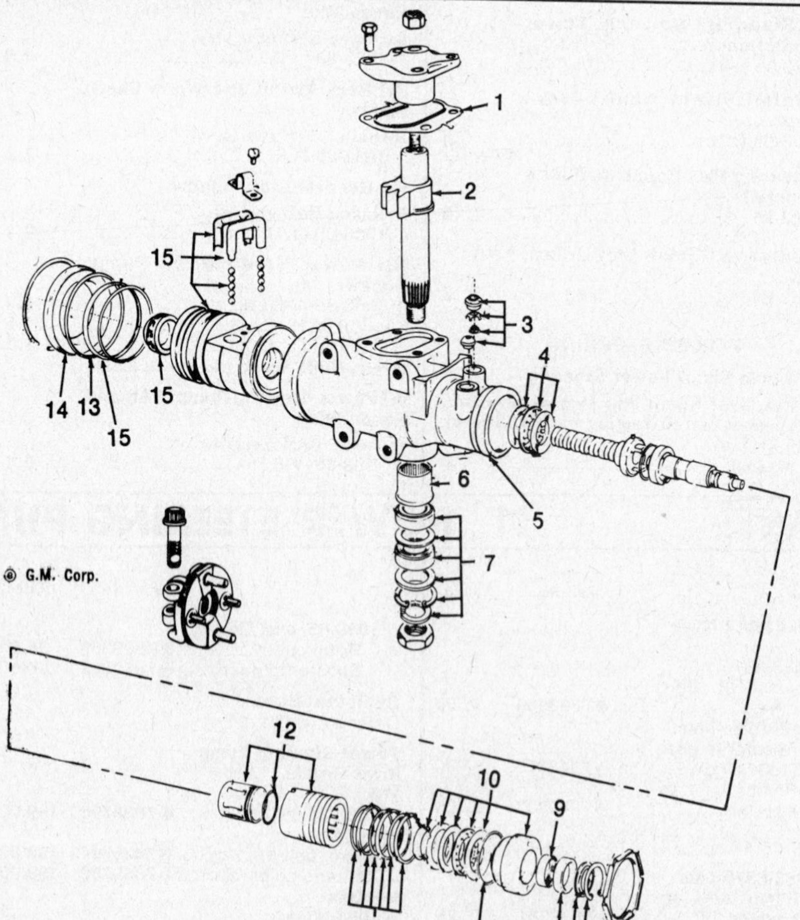

(Factory Time) Chilton Time

GASOLINE ENGINES

(G) Compression Test

V-6–1983-85	.8
V-8–1983-85	.9
w/A.C. add	.3

(G) Cylinder Head Gasket, Renew

Includes: Clean gasket surfaces, clean carbon. Make all necessary adjustments.

V-6–1983-85	
Code A	
right side (4.0)	5.6
left side (4.4)	6.2
both sides (5.7)	8.0
Code 4	
one side (4.4)	6.1
both sides (6.0)	8.4
Code 9	
right side (3.4)	4.8
left side (2.2)	3.1
both sides (4.1)	5.7
V-8–1983-85	
250 eng-Code 8	
one side (5.4)	7.0
both sides (6.3)	8.2
350-368 engs	
Code 6, 8 or 9	
one side (3.3)	4.7
both sides (4.9)	6.9
w/A.I.R. add (.3)	.3
307-350 engs	
Code Y or R	
one side (4.5)	6.3
both sides (5.7)	8.0
w/A.I.R. add (.3)	.3
w/A.C. add (.3)	.3
w/P.S. add (.2)	.2

(G) Cylinder Head, Renew

Includes: Transfer all parts, reface valves. Make all necessary adjustments.

V-6–1983-85	
Code A	
right side (4.6)	6.5
left side (4.9)	6.8
both sides (6.3)	8.8
Code 4	
one side (5.0)	7.0
both sides (7.2)	10.0
Code 9	
right side (4.0)	5.6
left side (2.8)	3.9
both sides (5.3)	7.4
V-8–1983-85	
250 eng-Code 8	
one side (5.8)	7.5
both sides (7.1)	9.2
350-368 engs	
Code 6, 8 or 9	
one side (4.7)	6.3
both sides (7.7)	10.6
307-350 engs	
Code Y or R	
one side (4.8)	6.7
both sides (6.4)	8.9
w/A.I.R. add (.3)	.3
w/A.C. add (.3)	.3
w/P.S. add (.2)	.2

(P) Clean Carbon and Grind Valves

Includes: R&R cylinder heads, clean gasket surfaces, clean carbon, reface valves and seats. Minor tune up.

V-6–1983-85	
Code A (8.0)	11.2
Code 4 (7.5)	10.5
Code 9 (6.0)	8.4
V-8–1983-85	
250 eng-Code 8	
one side (6.2)	8.0
both sides (7.9)	10.3
350-368 engs	
Code 6, 8 or 9 (6.2)	11.4
307-350 engs	
Code Y or R (7.4)	10.3
w/A.I.R. add (.3)	.3
w/A.C. add (.3)	.3
w/P.S. add (.2)	.2

COMBINATIONS

Add to Valve Job

See Machine Shop Operations

(Factory Time) Chilton Time

(G) DRAIN, EVACUATE & RECHARGE AIR CONDITIONING SYSTEM	
All models (.5)	1.0
(G) HYDRAULIC VALVE LIFTERS, DISASSEMBLE AND CLEAN	
Each (.2)	.2
(G) DISTRIBUTOR, RECONDITION	
All models (.5)	.8
(G) CARBURETOR, RECONDITION	
2 bbl	1.2
4 bbl	1.5
(P) VALVE GUIDES, REAM OVERSIZE	
Each (.2)	.2
(G) ROCKER ARM SHAFT, RECONDITION	
Each side (.2)	.3

(G) Valve Tappets, Renew (Lifters)

Includes: Drain and refill cooling system, R&R intake manifold. Make all necessary adjustments.

V-6–1983-85	
Code A	
one bank (2.6)	3.6
both banks (2.9)	4.0
Code 4	
one bank (1.8)	3.0
both banks (2.1)	3.6
Code 9	
one bank (2.5)	3.5
both banks (2.7)	3.8
V-8–1983-85	
250 eng-Code 8	
one or all (4.6)	6.0
350 eng-Code 8	
one cyl (2.4)	3.1
all cyls-one bank (2.6)	3.3
all cyls-both banks (3.0)	4.0
368 eng-Code 6 or 9	
one cyl (1.3)	1.9
all cyls-one bank (1.6)	2.2
all cyls-both banks (1.9)	3.0
307-350 engs	
Code Y or R	
one cyl (2.2)	2.8
one cyl-each bank (2.5)	3.8
each adtnl cyl (.1)	.1
w/A.I.R. add (.4)	.4
w/A.C. add (.3)	.3

(G) Rocker Arm Cover and/or Gasket, Renew

V-6–1983-85	
Code A	
one side (.4)	.7
both sides (.6)	1.2
Code 4	
one (.3)	.5
both (.5)	.8
Code 9	
one side (.3)	.6
both sides (.5)	1.1
V-8–1983-85	
250 eng-Code 8	
right side (.8)	1.1
left side (.5)	.7
both sides (1.1)	1.6
350 eng-Code 8	
each (.8)	1.1
368 eng-Code 6 or 9	
each (.5)	.7
307-350 engs	
Code Y or R	
one (.5)	.7
both (.9)	1.2
w/A.I.R. add (.3)	.3
w/A.C. add (.3)	.3

(G) Valve Springs and/or Valve Stem Oil Seals, Renew (Head On Car)

V-6–1983-85	
Code A	
one cyl (.6)	1.0
one cyl-each bank (1.0)	1.8
w/Turbocharger add (1.3)	1.4
Code 4	
one cyl (.6)	1.0
one cyl-each bank (1.0)	1.8
Code 9	
one cyl (.6)	1.0
one cyl-each bank (1.1)	1.9
V-8–1983-85	
250 eng-Code 8	
right side-one (1.3)	1.7
left side-one (1.0)	1.3
350 eng-Code 8	
one cyl (1.0)	1.4
one cyl-each bank (1.6)	2.0
368 eng-Code 6 or 9	
one cyl (.7)	1.1
one cyl-each bank (1.1)	1.7
307-350 engs	
Code Y or R	
one cyl (.6)	1.0
one cyl-each bank (1.0)	1.8
each adtnl cyl	
all engs (.2)	.3
w/A.I.R. add (.3)	.3
w/A.C. add (.3)	.3

(G) Rocker Arm Shafts and/or Assy., Renew

V-6.–1983-85	
Code A	
one side (.7)	1.1
both sides (1.1)	1.9
w/Turbocharger add (1.3)	1.4
Code 4	
one side (.4)	.6
both sides (.7)	.9
Code 9	
one side (.5)	.9
both sides (.9)	1.7
V-8–1983-85	
307-350 engs	
Code Y or R	
one side (.6)	.8
both sides (1.0)	1.3
w/A.I.R. add (.3)	.3
w/A.C. add (.3)	.3
Recond each side add (.2)	.3

LABOR 12 CYLINDER HEAD & VALVE SYSTEM 12 LABOR

(Factory Time)	Chilton Time
(G) Rocker Arms and/or Pivots, Renew	
V-8–1983-85	
250 eng-Code 8	
right side-one (1.1)	1.4
left side-one (.8)	1.0
both sides all cyls (1.7)	2.4
307-350 engs Code Y or R	
one cyl (.6)	.9
one cyl-each bank (1.0)	1.2
each adtnl cyl (.1)	.1
w/A.C. add (.3)	.3
(G) Valve Push Rods, Renew	
V-6–1983-85	
Code A	
one side (.6)	1.0
both sides (.7)	1.3
w/Turbocharger add (1.3)	1.4
Code 4	
one side (.4)	.6
both sides (.7)	.9
Code 9	
one side (.5)	.9
both sides (1.0)	1.8
V-8–1983-85	
250 eng-Code 8	
right side (1.0)	1.3
left side (.7)	.9
both sides (1.6)	2.1
350 eng-Code 8	
one cyl (.9)	1.3
one cyl-each side (1.1)	1.8
368 eng-Code 6 or 9	
one cyl (.6)	.9
one cyl-each side (.8)	1.4
307-350 engs Code Y or R	
one cyl (.6)	.8
one cyl-each side (1.0)	1.1
each adtnl cyl all engs (.1)	.1
w/A.I.R. add (.3)	.3
w/A.C. add (.3)	.3

DIESEL ENGINE

(Factory Time)	Chilton Time
(G) Compression Test	
1983-85	1.3

(G) Cylinder Head Gasket, Renew

Includes: R&R injector pump and lines. R&R intake manifold and disconnect exhaust manifolds. Clean gasket surfaces, bleed lifters and adjust timing. Drain and refill cooling system.

(Factory Time)	Chilton Time
1983-85-left side (6.1)	7.9
right side (6.5)	8.4
both sides (8.0)	10.4
w/A.C. add (.3)	.3

(G) Cylinder Head, Renew

Includes: R&R injector pump and lines. R&R intake manifold and disconnect exhaust manifolds. Clean gasket surfaces. Transfer parts, reface valves. Bleed lifters and adjust timing. Drain and refill cooling system.

(Factory Time)	Chilton Time
1983-85-left side (6.5)	8.4
right side (6.9)	8.9
both sides (8.8)	11.4
w/A.C. add (.3)	.3

(P) Clean Carbon and Grind Valves

Includes: R&R injector pump and lines. R&R cylinder heads, clean carbon. Recondition valves and seats. Check and adjust valve stem length. Bleed lifters, drain and refill cooling system.

(Factory Time)	Chilton Time
1983-85-left side (6.2)	7.9
right side (6.6)	8.2
both sides (9.7)	12.6
w/A.C. add (.3)	.3

(G) Valve Tappets, Renew (Lifters)

Includes: R&R injector pump and lines, intake manifold and rocker arms. Drain and refill cooling system.

(Factory Time)	Chilton Time
1983-85-one cyl (3.5)	4.5
one cyl-each side (3.9)	5.0
each adtnl cyl (.1)	.1

(G) Rocker Arm Cover or Gasket, Renew

Includes: R&R injector pump and lines.

(Factory Time)	Chilton Time
1983-85-one side (1.2)	2.4
both sides (2.0)	2.9

(G) Valve Springs and/or Valve Stem Oil Seals, Renew (Head on Car)

Includes: R&R injector pump and lines.

(Factory Time)	Chilton Time
1983-85-one cyl (1.6)	3.0
one cyl-each side (2.4)	3.7
each adtnl cyl (.3)	.3
w/A.C. add (.3)	.3

(G) Rocker Arm, Pivot and/or Push Rod, Renew

Includes: R&R injector pump and lines.

(Factory Time)	Chilton Time
1983-85-one cyl (1.5)	2.5
one cyl-each side (2.3)	3.0
each adtnl cyl (.1)	.2

PARTS 12 CYLINDER HEAD & VALVE SYSTEM 12 PARTS

	Part No.	Price
Valve Grind Gasket Set		
V-6-231		
1983	◆25503372	2.75
1984	◆25523724	N.L.
1985	◆25525121	N.L.
V-6-252		
1983-84	◆25518568	N.L.
V-8-307		
1983-84	◆22507725	48.75
1985	◆22527542	46.00
V-8 Diesel		
1983-84	◆22522053	94.50
1985	◆22527541	N.L.
(1) Cylinder Head		
V-6		
1983-85	◆25518679	217.00
V-8-250		
1983	◆1617594	314.00
1984	◆1626693	N.L.
1985-Fed.	◆1628559	296.00
Calif.	◆1628557	296.00
V-8-307		
1983-84	◆22511238	247.00
1985	◆22527549	N.L.
V-8 Diesel		
1983-85	◆22515038	387.00
(2) Cylinder Head Gasket		
V-6		
1983-84-231	◆1261403	8.50
252	◆25518453	8.25
1985	◆25524597	N.L.

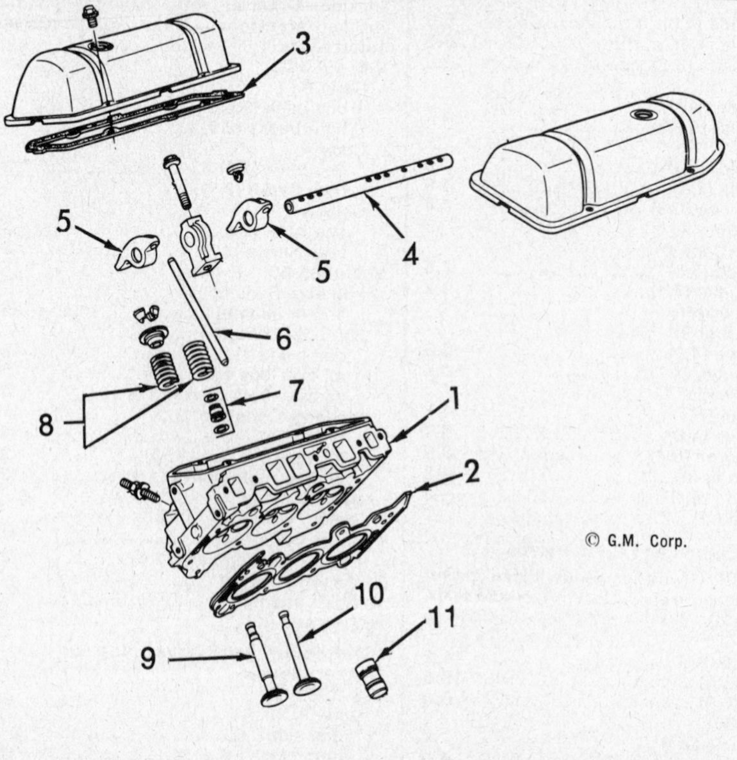

PARTS 12 CYLINDER HEAD & VALVE SYSTEM 12 PARTS

	Part No.	Price
V-8–250		
1983-85	◆1619040	24.00
V-8–307		
1983-85	◆22503500	9.25
V-8 Diesel		
1983-85	◆22519416	30.75

(3) Valve Cover Gasket

	Part No.	Price
1983-85		
V-6	◆25505889	6.00

Use R.T.V. Sealer (P/N 1052289) on V-8 engines in place of gaskets.

(4) Rocker Arm Shaft

	Part No.	Price
1983-85-V-6	◆1254201	15.75

(5) Rocker Arm

	Part No.	Price
V-6		
1983-85-right	◆1241850	4.50
left	◆1241851	4.50
V-8–250		
1983-85	◆1618802	4.75
V-8–307		
1983-85	◆22505583	N.L.

Rocker arm locations on the V-6 engines are referred to by right and left sides of each cylinder pair, not by right and left side cylinder banks.

(6) Valve Push Rod

	Part No.	Price
V-6		
1983-85-231	◆25510025	4.25
252	◆1249139	4.00
V-8–250		
1983-85	◆1618805	2.50
V-8–307		
1983-85	◆22505582	2.50
V-8–Diesel		
1983-85	◆22511044	3.25

(7) Seal (Valve Stem)

	Part No.	Price
V-6		
1983-85	◆25518390	2.50
V-8–250		
1983-85	◆1622249	3.25
V-8–307		
1983-85-intake	◆406595	1.00
exhaust	◆401823	1.00

(8) Valve Spring

	Part No.	Price
V-6–231		
1983-85	◆25512551	3.00
V-6–252		
1983-85	◆1249267	2.75
V-8–250		
1983-85	◆1622834	4.00
V-8–307		
1983-85	◆411226	4.00
V-8–Diesel		
1983-85	◆22510372	4.00

(9) Exhaust Valve

	Part No.	Price
V-6		
1983-85	◆1261380	13.50
V-8–250		
1983-85	◆1621321	15.25
V-8–307		
1983-85	◆555456	13.50
V-8–Diesel		
1983-85	◆558873	13.00

(10) Intake Valve

	Part No.	Price
V-6		
1983-85	◆25512098	11.25
V-8–250		
1983-85	◆1618837	12.00
V-8–307		
1983-85	◆22503324	11.00
V-8–Diesel		
1983-85	◆22519914	20.00

(11) Valve Lifter

	Part No.	Price
V-6		
1983-85-231	◆5234330	N.L.
252	◆5232765	9.00
V-8–250		
1983-85	◆5234360	8.50
V-8–307		
1983-85	◆5232750	N.L.
V-8–Diesel		
1983-85	◆5234470	38.10

LABOR 13 ENGINE ASSEMBLY & MOUNTS 13 LABOR

(Factory Time) — Chilton Time

GASOLINE ENGINES

(G) Engine Assembly, Remove & Install

Does not include transfer of any parts or equipment.

	Chilton Time
V-6–1983-85	
Code A	7.8
Code 4	7.1
Code 9	6.9
V-8–1983-85	
250 eng–Code 8	7.0
350-368 engs	
Code 6, 8 or 9	6.1
307-350 engs	
Code Y or R	5.0
w/A.I.R. add	.6
w/A.C. add	.4
w/P.S. add	.3
w/Cruise control add	.1
w/E.F.I. add	.2

(G) Engine Assembly, Renew

Includes: R&R engine assembly, transfer all component parts not supplied with replacement engine. Minor tune up.

	Chilton Time
V-6–1983-85	
Code A (8.7)	11.3
Code 4 (8.0)	10.6
Code 9 (7.2)	10.4
w/Turbo add	1.2
V-8–1983-85	
250 eng–Code 8 (7.3)	10.5
350-368 engs	
Code 6, 8 or 9 (6.3)	10.8
307-350 engs	
Code Y or R (4.4)	10.0
w/A.I.R. add (.6)	.6
w/A.C. add (.4)	.4
w/P.S. add (.3)	.3
w/Cruise control add (.1)	.1
w/E.F.I. add (.2)	.2

(P) Cylinder Block, Renew (w/All Internal Parts Less Cylinder Heads and Oil Pan)

Includes: R&R engine, transfer all component parts not supplied with replacement engine. Clean carbon and grind valves. Minor tune up.

	Chilton Time
V-6–1983-85	
Code A (10.4)	15.0
Code 4 (9.2)	15.0
Code 9 (10.6)	15.4
V8–1983-85	
250 eng–Code 8 (13.2)	17.5
350-368 engs	
Code 6, 8 or 9 (10.4)	15.4
307-350 engs	
Code Y or R (17.0)	21.6
w/A.I.R. add (.6)	.6
w/A.C. add (.4)	.4
w/P.S. add (.3)	.3
w/Cruise control add (.1)	.1
w/E.F.I. add (.2)	.2

(P) Engine Assy., R&R and Recondition (Complete)

Includes: Rebore block, install new pistons, rings, rod and main bearings. Clean carbon and grind valves. Tune engine.

	Chilton Time
V-6–1983-85	
Code A (19.6)	28.4
Code 4 (24.8)	31.3
Code 9 (17.4)	25.2
V-8–1983-85	
250 eng–Code 8 (17.0)	25.1
350-368 engs	
Code 6, 8 or 9 (26.7)	31.9
307-350 engs	
Code Y or R (31.4)	38.5
w/A.I.R. add (.6)	.6
w/A.C. add (.4)	.4
w/P.S. add (.3)	.3
w/Cruise control add (.1)	.1
w/E.F.I. add (.2)	.2

(P) Engine Assembly, Recondition (In Car)

Includes: Expand or renew pistons, install new rings, pins, rod and main bearings. Clean carbon and grind valves. Tune engine.

	Chilton Time
V-6–1983-85	
Code A (15.7)	22.7
Code 4 (15.9)	20.9
Code 9 (15.1)	21.8
V-8–1983-85	
250 eng–Code 8 (14.7)	21.7
350-368 engs	
Code 6, 8 or 9 (20.8)	25.2
307-350 engs	
Code Y or R (23.1)	28.7
w/A.I.R. add (.6)	.6
w/A.C. add (.4)	.4
w/P.S. add (.3)	.3
w/Cruise control add (.1)	.1
w/E.F.I. add (.3)	.3

(P) Cylinder Block, Renew (w/Pistons, Rings and Bearings)

Includes: Transfer all component parts. Clean carbon and grind valves. Minor tune up.

	Chilton Time
V-6–1983-85	
Code A (13.3)	19.2
Code 4 (13.5)	19.3
Code 9 (12.9)	18.7
V-8–1983-85	
350-368 engs	
Code 6, 8 or 9 (13.1)	18.8
w/A.I.R. add (.2)	.2
w/Cruise control add (.1)	.1
w/E.F.I. add (.2)	.2

(G) Engine Mounts, Renew

	Chilton Time
V-6–1983-85	
Front	
Code A, 4 or 9	
one (.5)	.7
both (1.1)	1.4

LABOR 13 ENGINE ASSEMBLY & MOUNTS 13 LABOR

	(Factory Time)	Chilton Time
Rear		
one	(.5)	.7
both	(.8)	1.1
V-8–1983-85		
250 eng-Code 8		
one	(.4)	.7
both	(.6)	.9
350-368 engs		
Code 6, 8 or 9		
Front		
one	(.4)	.6
both	(.5)	.9
350 eng-Code R		
Front		
single front mount	(.5)	.9
307-350 engs		
Code Y or R		
Rear		
one	(.3)	.5
both	(.5)	.8

DIESEL ENGINE

(G) Engine Assembly, Remove & Install

Does not include transfer of any parts or equipment.

	(Factory Time)	Chilton Time
1983-85		5.7
w/A.C. add	(.4)	.4

(G) Engine Assembly, Renew (Universal)

Includes: R&R engine assembly. Transfer all component parts not supplied with replacement engine. Make all necessary adjustments.

	(Factory Time)	Chilton Time
1983-85	(9.8)	20.0
w/A.C. add	(.4)	.4

(P) Cylinder Block, Renew (w/All Internal Parts Less Heads and Oil Pan)

Includes: R&R engine. Transfer all component parts not supplied with replacement engine. Clean carbon and grind valves. Make all necessary adjustments.

	(Factory Time)	Chilton Time
1983-85	(16.8)	24.0
w/A.C. add	(.4)	.4

(P) Cylinder Block, Renew (w/Pistons, Rings and Bearings)

Includes: Transfer all component parts. Clean carbon and grind valves. Make all necessary adjustments.

	(Factory Time)	Chilton Time
1983-85	(18.9)	26.0

(P) Engine Assy., R&R and Recondition (Complete)

Includes: Rebore block, install new pistons, rings, pins, rod and main bearings. Clean carbon and grind valves. Make all necessary adjustments.

	(Factory Time)	Chilton Time
1983-85	(29.5)	36.0
w/A.C. add	(.4)	.4

(P) Engine Assembly, Recondition (In Car)

Includes: Expand or renew pistons, install new rings, pins, rod and main bearings. Clean carbon and grind valves. Make all necessary adjustments.

	(Factory Time)	Chilton Time
1983-85	(23.2)	27.3
w/A.C. add	(.4)	.4

(G) Engine Mounts, Renew

Front

	(Factory Time)	Chilton Time
1983-85-one	(.3)	.6
both	(.4)	.8

PARTS 13 ENGINE ASSEMBLY & MOUNTS 13 PARTS

Cylinder Block

Includes: Piston, connecting rods and crankshaft.

	Part No.	Price
V-6-231		
1983	◆25516157	1305.25
1984	◆25519451	1305.25
1985	◆25524286	1263.00
V-6-252		
1983-84	◆25516158	1319.25
V-8-250		
1983-85	◆1623537	2039.25
V-8-307		
1983-84	◆22504938	1397.00
1985	◆22527863	1397.00
V-8-Diesel		
1983-85	◆22518906	1950.00

Front Engine Mount

	Part No.	Price
V-6		
1983-85-exc. below	◆25511568	27.50
Eldorado	◆1622125	29.75
V-8		
1983-85	◆1620158	27.50

Rear Engine Mount

	Part No.	Price
Buick Riviera		
1983-85-R.H.	◆25511570	35.00
L.H.	◆25515793	18.50
Cadillac Eldorado & Seville		
1983-85-V-8		
R.H.	◆1623384	26.50
L.H.	◆1626753	17.75
Olds. Toronado		
1983-85-R.H.	◆25511570	35.00
L.H.	◆25515793	18.50

Engine Overhaul Gasket Kit

	Part No.	Price
V-6-231		
1983	◆25505370	52.50
1984	◆25523723	N.L.
1985	◆25525119	58.25
V-6-252		
1983-84	◆25518567	53.25
V-8-307		
1983-84	◆22506498	58.75
1985	◆22527539	62.50
V-8-Diesel		
1983-84	◆22521786	90.00
1985	◆22527538	N.L.

When a complete overhaul gasket set is required you must also order a Valve Grind gasket set.

LABOR 14 PISTONS, RINGS & BEARINGS 14 LABOR

GASOLINE ENGINES

(P) Rings, Renew (See Engine Combinations)

Includes: Remove cylinder top ridge, deglaze cylinder walls. Minor tune up.

	(Factory Time)	Chilton Time
V-6–1983-85		
Code A		
one cyl	(8.2)	9.9
one cyl-each side	(10.5)	12.2
all cyls-both sides	(11.4)	14.2
Code 4		
one cyl	(8.1)	11.7
one cyl-each side	(10.2)	14.7
all cyls-both sides	(12.1)	17.5
Code 9		
one cyl	(6.5)	9.1
one cyl-each side	(8.0)	11.2
all cyls-both sides	(9.9)	13.7
V-8–1983-85		
250 eng-Code 8		
one cyl	(8.3)	10.8
one cyl-each side	(9.3)	12.1
all cyls-both sides	(9.7)	13.9
Renew piston liner		
add-each	(.2)	.3
350-368 engs		
Code 6, 8 or 9	(8.0)	11.0
307-350 engs		
Code Y or R		
one cyl	(7.5)	10.8
one cyl-each side	(9.1)	13.1
all cyls-both sides	(11.4)	16.5
w/A.I.R. add	(.3)	.3
w/A.C. add	(.4)	.4
w/P.S. add	(.2)	.2

(P) Piston or Connecting Rod, Renew

Includes: Remove cylinder top ridge, deglaze cylinder walls. Minor tune up.

	(Factory Time)	Chilton Time
V-6–1983-85		
Code A		
one cyl	(8.4)	10.2
one cyl-each side	(10.9)	12.8
all cyls-both sides	(12.1)	15.4
Code 4		
one cyl	(8.1)	12.0
one cyl-each side	(10.2)	15.3
all cyls-both sides	(12.8)	19.3
Code 9		
one cyl	(7.2)	9.4
one cyl-each side	(9.4)	11.8
all cyls-both sides	(10.6)	15.5

LABOR 14 PISTONS, RINGS & BEARINGS 14 LABOR

	(Factory Time)	Chilton Time
V-8–1983-85		
250 eng–Code 8		
one cyl	(8.3)	11.1
one cyl–each side	(9.3)	12.7
all cyls–both sides	(9.7)	16.3
Renew piston liner		
add–each	(.2)	.3
350-368 engs		
Code 6, 8 or 9	(8.0)	13.4
307-350 engs		
Code Y or R		
one cyl	(7.5)	11.1
one cyl–each side	(9.1)	13.7
all cyls–both sides	(12.5)	18.9
w/A.I.R. add	(.3)	.3
w/A.C. add	(.4)	.4
w/P.S. add	(.2)	.2

(P) Connecting Rod Bearings, Renew

Includes: R&R oil pan, check all bearing clearances.

	(Factory Time)	Chilton Time
V-6–1983-85		
Code A, 4 or 9	(4.1)	5.7
V-8–1983-85		
250 eng–Code 8	(4.3)	5.7
350-368 engs		
Code 6, 8 or 9	(4.5)	5.7
307-350 engs		
Code Y or R	(4.7)	6.5

DIESEL ENGINE

(P) Rings, Renew (See Engine Combinations)

Includes: Remove cylinder top ridge, deglaze cylinder walls. Clean piston and ring grooves. Make all necessary adjustments.

	(Factory Time)	Chilton Time
1983-85	(13.9)	17.0
w/A.C. add	(.3)	.3

COMBINATIONS

Add to Engine Work
See Machine Shop Operations

(G) DRAIN, EVACUATE & RECHARGE AIR CONDITIONING SYSTEM
All models (.5) 1.0

(G) HYDRAULIC VALVE LIFTERS DISASSEMBLE AND CLEAN
Each (.2) 2

(G) DISTRIBUTOR, RECONDITION
All models (.5) 8

(G) CARBURETOR, RECONDITION
2 bbl 1.2
4 bbl 1.5

(P) VALVE GUIDES, REAM OVERSIZE
Each (.2) 2

(G) ROCKER ARM SHAFT ASSY., DISASSEMBLE AND CLEAN OR RECONDITION
Each side (.2) 3

(G) PISTON LINER, RENEW
Each (.2) 3

(G) DEGLAZE CYLINDER WALLS
Each (.1) 1

(G) REMOVE CYLINDER TOP RIDGE
Each (.1) 1

(G) MAIN BEARINGS, RENEW (PAN REMOVED)
V-6 (1.5) 2.0
V-8 (1.5) 2.0

(G) PLASTIGAUGE BEARINGS
Each (.1) 1

(G) OIL PUMP, RECONDITION
V-6 (.5) 8
V-8-Eng Code R (.1) 3

(M) OIL FILTER ELEMENT, RENEW
V-6 (.2) 2
V-8 (.3) 3

(P) Pistons or Connecting Rods, Renew

Includes: Remove cylinder top ridge, deglaze cylinder walls. Clean piston and ring grooves. Make all necessary adjustments.

	(Factory Time)	Chilton Time
1983-85	(14.4)	19.4
w/A.C. add	(.3)	.3

(P) Connecting Rod Bearings, Renew

Includes: Raise engine and clean oil pump screen.

	(Factory Time)	Chilton Time
1983-85	(5.4)	7.2

PARTS 14 PISTONS, RINGS & BEARINGS 14 PARTS

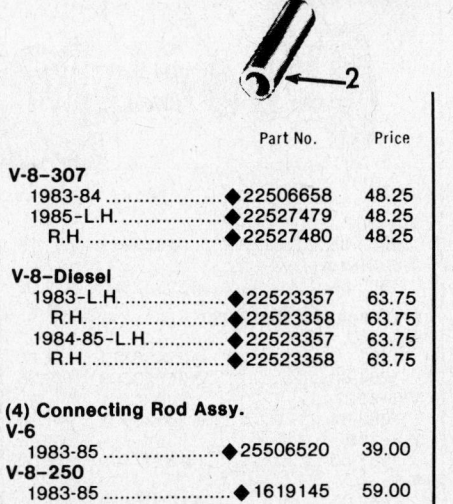

	Part No.	Price
(1) Piston Ring Set (Std.)		
V-6-231		
1983	◆1261407	N.L.
1984-85	◆25519462	16.50
V-6-252		
1983-84	◆25505382	17.25
V-8-250		
1983-85	◆1623817	20.25
V-8-307		
1983-84	◆22506536	16.00
1985	◆22529562	18.25
V-8-Diesel		
1983	◆22515964	21.00
1984-85	◆22523733	21.00
(2) Piston Pin (Std.)		
1983-85-307	◆398295	4.50
(3) Piston & Pin Assy. (Std.)		
V-6-231		
1983	◆25515840	52.75
1984-85	◆25519444	52.75
V-6-252		
1983-84	◆25505374	54.00
V-8-250		
1983-85	◆1623538	107.00

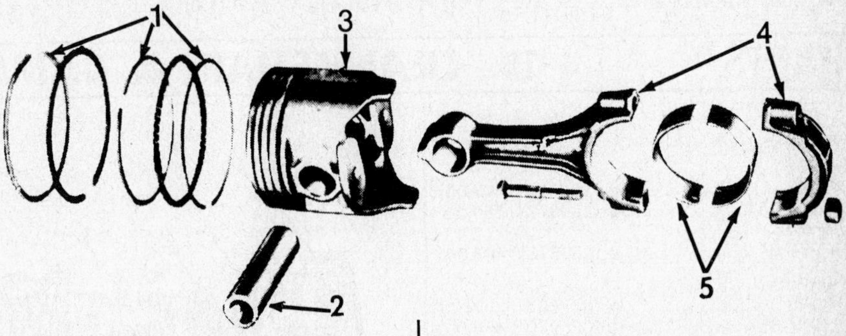

	Part No.	Price
V-8-307		
1983-84	◆22506658	48.25
1985-L.H.	◆22527479	48.25
R.H.	◆22527480	48.25
V-8-Diesel		
1983-L.H.	◆22523357	63.75
R.H.	◆22523358	63.75
1984-85-L.H.	◆22523357	63.75
R.H.	◆22523358	63.75
(4) Connecting Rod Assy.		
V-6		
1983-85	◆25506520	39.00
V-8-250		
1983-85	◆1619145	59.00

	Part No.	Price
V-8-307		
1983-84	◆554976	45.00
1985	◆22527025	45.00
V-8-Diesel		
1983-85	◆22515313	50.50
(5) Connecting Rod Bearing (Std.)		
V-6		
1983-85	◆18005399	11.00
V-8-250		
1983-85	◆18009085	11.00
V-8-307		
1983-85	◆18008494	10.50
V-8-Diesel		
1983-85	◆18008494	10.50

LABOR 15 CRANKSHAFT & DAMPER 15 LABOR

(Factory Time)	Chilton Time

GASOLINE ENGINES

(P) Crankshaft and Main Bearings, Renew

Includes: R&R engine. Check all bearing clearances.

V-6–1983-85	
Code A or 4 (9.7)	**14.0**
Code 9 (7.2)	**10.4**
V-8–1983-85	
250 eng-Code 8 (8.8)	**12.0**
350-368 engs	
Code 6, 8 or 9 (6.4)	**9.0**
307-350 engs	
Code Y or R (8.8)	**12.7**
w/A.I.R. add (.6)	**.6**
w/A.C. add (.4)	**.4**
w/P.S. add (.3)	**.3**
w/Cruise control add (.1)	**.1**

(P) Main Bearings, Renew

Includes: R&R oil pan and bearing caps. Check all bearing clearances.

V-6–1983-85	
Code A or 4 (3.8)	**5.3**
Code 9 (2.2)	**5.3**
V-8–1983-85	
250 eng-Code 8 (3.7)	**4.8**
350-368 engs	
Code 6, 8 or 9 (3.9)	**4.8**
307-350 engs	
Code Y or R (3.8)	**5.3**

(P) Main and Rod Bearings, Renew

Includes: R&R oil pan and bearing caps. Check all bearing clearances.

V-6–1983-85	
Code A or 4 (5.0)	**7.0**
Code 9 (3.4)	**7.0**
V-8–1983-85	
250 eng-Code 8 (5.3)	**7.2**
350-368 engs	
Code 6, 8 or 9 (5.5)	**7.2**
307-350 engs	
Code Y or R (5.2)	**7.7**

(G) Rear Main Bearing Oil Seal, Renew or Repack

Includes: R&R oil pan and rear main bearing cap.

V-6–1983-85	
Code A or 4 (3.3)	**5.0**
Code 9 (2.9)	**5.0**
V-8–1983-85	
250 eng-Code 8 (2.9)	**4.0**
350-368 engs	
Code 6, 8 or 9 (3.7)	**5.5**
307-350 engs	
Code Y or R (3.5)	**5.0**

(G) Crankshaft Pulley and/or Harmonic Balancer, Renew

V-6–1983-85	
Code A (.4)	**.8**
Code 4	
pulley (1.0)	**1.5**
balancer (1.1)	**1.7**
Code 9	
pulley (.7)	**1.2**
balancer (.8)	**1.3**
V-8–1983-85	
250 eng-Code 8	
pulley (.7)	**1.2**
balancer (.7)	**1.3**
350-368 engs	
Code 6, 8 or 9	
pulley (.5)	**.9**
balancer (.8)	**1.2**
307-350 engs	
Code Y or R (.6)	***1.0**
w/A.I.R. add (.1)	**.1**
w/A.C. add (.1)	**.1**
w/P.S. add (.1)	**.1**
*Renew balancer add (.2)	**.2**

(G) Crankshaft Front Oil Seal, Renew

V-8–1983-85	
250 eng-Code 8 (1.0)	**1.5**
307-350 engs	
Code Y or R (.9)	**1.5**
w/A.C. add (.1)	**.1**

DIESEL ENGINE

(P) Crankshaft and Main Bearings, Renew

Includes: R&R engine. Check all bearing clearances.

1983-85 (11.0)	**15.0**
w/A.C. add (.4)	**.4**

(P) Main Bearings, Renew

Includes: Check all bearing clearances.

1983-85 (4.6)	**6.3**

(P) Main and Rod Bearings, Renew

Includes: Check all bearing clearances.

1983-85 (7.0)	**8.7**

(G) Rear Main Bearing Oil Seals, R&R and Repack

Includes: R&R oil pan and rear main bearing cap.

1983-85 (3.5)	**4.7**

(G) Crankshaft Rear Main Seals, Renew

Includes: R&R engine assy.

1983-85 (10.1)	**14.6**

(G) Crankshaft Pulley or Balancer, Renew

1983-85-pulley (.8)	**1.2**
balancer (1.0)	**1.4**
w/A.C. add (.1)	**.1**

(G) Crankshaft Front Oil Seal, Renew

1983-85 (1.1)	**1.5**
w/A.C. add (.1)	**.1**

PARTS 15 CRANKSHAFT & DAMPER 15 PARTS

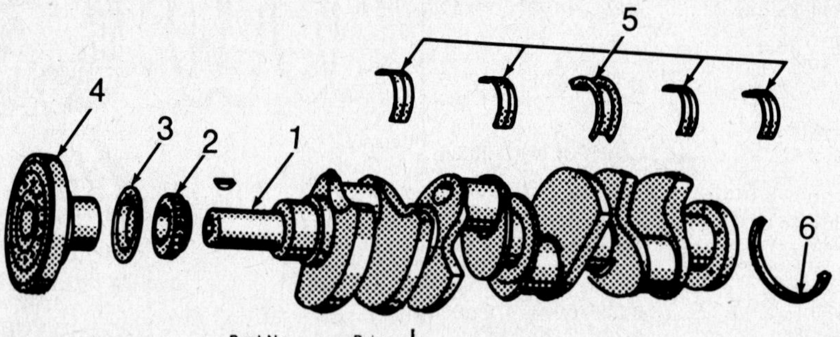

	Part No.	Price
(1) Crankshaft		
V-6-231		
1983	◆1260873	407.00
1984-85	◆1260877	385.00
V-6-252		
1983-84	◆1260873	407.00
V-8-250		
1983	◆1617591	N.L.
1984-85	◆1628920	473.00
V-8-307		
1983-84	◆22505615	403.00
1985	◆22527438	403.00
V-8-Diesel		
1983-85	◆22511035	439.00
(2) Crankshaft Sprocket		
V-6		
1983-85	◆1192916	16.00
V-8-250		
1983-85	◆1618159	13.25
V-8-307		
1983-85	◆382880	16.75
V-8-Diesel		
1983-85	◆558489	44.25
(3) Oil Slinger		
V-6		
1983-85	◆1193967	1.00
V-8-250		
1983-85	◆1618692	2.00
V-8-307		
1983-85	◆382572	.75
V-8-Diesel		
1983-85	◆22513590	2.00
(4) Crankshaft Balancer		
V-6-231		
1983	◆25506571	42.75
1984-85	◆25523503	46.25
V-6-252		
1983-84	◆25523502	41.25
V-8-250		
1983-85	◆3517492	117.00
V-8-307		
1983-85	◆22506730	31.75
V-8-Diesel		
1983-85	◆559131	63.25
(5) Main Bearing Set (Std.)		
V-6		
1983-85		
No. 1	◆18009457	12.00
No. 2	◆18004602	20.00
No. 3	◆18002950	12.50
No. 4	◆5468578	13.00
V-8-250		
1983-85		
Nos. 1, 2, 4	◆18009086	18.75
No. 3	◆18009088	23.75
Rear	◆18009087	16.50

PARTS 15 CRANKSHAFT & DAMPER 15 PARTS

	Part No.	Price
V-8-307		
1983-85		
No. 1	◆5466211	13.00
Nos. 2, 4	◆5466089	13.00
No. 3	◆5466090	20.00
No. 5	◆5466091	17.00
V-8-Diesel		
1983-85		
No. 1	◆5466312	16.00
Nos. 2, 4	◆5458657	15.00
No. 3	◆5463797	26.25
No. 5	◆5466314	19.75
(6) Rear Bearing Packing		
1983-85-exc.		
below	◆9772831	1.50
250	◆1627821	7.00
Rear Bearing Oil Seal		
1983-85-V-6	◆1193151	1.50
Front Oil Seal (Crankshaft)		
V-6		
1983-85	◆1305044	1.00
V-8-250		
1983	◆1627827	4.50
1984-85	◆1627827	4.50
V-8-307		
1983-85	◆552711	4.25

LABOR 16 CAMSHAFT & TIMING GEARS 16 LABOR

(Factory Time) Chilton Time

GASOLINE ENGINES

(G) Timing Case Cover Gasket, Renew

Includes: R&R fan blade, crankshaft pulley and balancer. Drain and refill oil and coolant.

	Chilton Time
V-6-1983-85	
Code A (2.2)	3.0
Code 4 (2.5)	3.5
Code 9 (2.8)	4.0
V-8-1983-85	
250 eng-Code 8 (2.4)	3.1
350 eng-Code 8 (1.7)	2.6
368 eng-Code 6 or 9 (2.5)	3.4
307-350 engs	
Code Y or R (3.6)	5.0
w/A.C. add (.2)	.2
w/P.S. add (.2)	.2
Renew cover add (.4)	.6
Renew oil seal add (.2)	.2

(G) Timing Chain or Gears, Renew

Includes: R&R fan blade, crankshaft pulley and balancer, engine front cover. Drain and refill oil and coolant.

	Chilton Time
V-6-1983-85	
Code A (2.4)	3.5
Code 4 (2.7)	4.0
Code 9 (3.0)	4.5
V-8-1983-85	
250 eng-Code 8 (2.5)	3.5
350 eng-Code 8 (2.1)	3.0
368 eng-Code 6 or 9 (2.8)	3.8
307-350 engs	
Code Y or R (4.0)	5.5
w/A.I.R. add (.2)	.2
w/A.C. add (.2)	.2
w/P.S. add (.2)	.2

(G) Camshaft, Renew

Includes: R&R pulleys, radiator, harmonic balancer, fuel pump, distributor, timing chain cover, intake manifold, rocker arms, push rods and lifters.

	Chilton Time
V-6-1983-85	
Code A (5.5)	8.0
Code 4 (5.1)	7.5
Code 9 (6.0)	8.7
V-8-1983-85	
250 eng-Code 8 (7.7)	10.8
350-368 engs	
Code 6, 8 or 9 (5.9)	9.3
307-350 engs	
Code Y or R (6.5)	9.4
w/A.I.R. add (.2)	.2
w/A.C. add (.4)	.4
w/P.S. add (.2)	.2
Renew cam brgs add (3.1)	4.0

(G) Camshaft Rear Bearing Plug, Renew

Includes: R&R trans for accessibility.

	Chilton Time
V-6-Code A or 4	
1983-84 (4.8)	5.9
1985 (5.9)	7.9
V-8-1983-85	
307-350 engs	
Code Y or R (3.1)	4.5
250 eng-Code 8	
Rear (3.7)	5.1
Top (.5)	.9

DIESEL ENGINE

(G) Timing Case Cover or Gasket, Renew

Includes: R&R fan blade, crankshaft pulley and balancer. Drain and refill oil and coolant.

	Chilton Time
1983-85 (2.4)	3.4
w/A.C. add (.2)	.2
Renew cover add (.2)	.3

(G) Timing Chain or Gears, Renew

Includes: R&R fan blade, crankshaft pulley and balancer. Drain and refill oil and coolant.

	Chilton Time
1983-85 (2.6)	3.7
w/A.C. add (.2)	.2

(G) Injector Pump Drive Gear, Renew

Includes: R&R timing gear and chain. R&R intake manifold and lifters. Drain and refill oil and coolant.

	Chilton Time
1983-85 (4.3)	7.0
Renew driven gear add (.1)	.1
w/A.C. add (.2)	.2

(G) Camshaft, Renew

Includes: R&R radiator, front cover, fuel pump, timing gear and chain, R&R injector pump, intake manifold and lifters. Disconnect exhaust system. Drain and refill oil and coolant. Make all necessary adjustments.

	Chilton Time
1983-85 (8.3)	11.4
w/A.C. add (1.0)	1.0
Renew camshaft brgs add (2.8)	3.8

PARTS 16 CAMSHAFT & TIMING GEARS 16 PARTS

	Part No.	Price
(1) Timing Cover Gasket		
V-6		
1983-85	◆25512861	3.00
V-8-250		
1983	◆1619361	3.50
1984-85	◆1628915	2.75
V-8-307		
1983-85	◆22505997	1.25
(2) Front Cover Oil Seal		
V-6		
1983-85	◆1305044	1.00
V-8-250		
1983	◆1627827	4.50
1984-85	◆1627827	4.50
V-8-307		
1983-85	◆552711	4.25

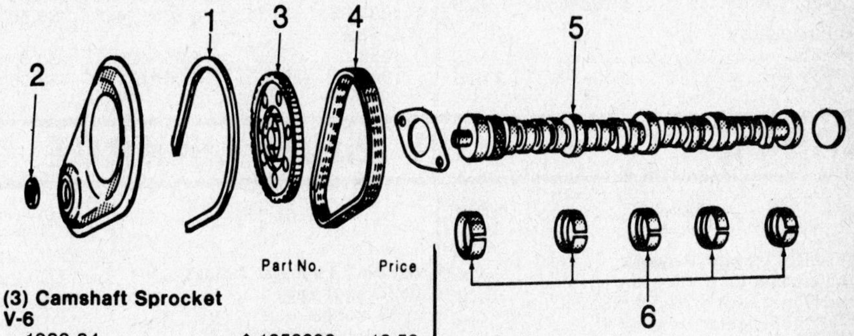

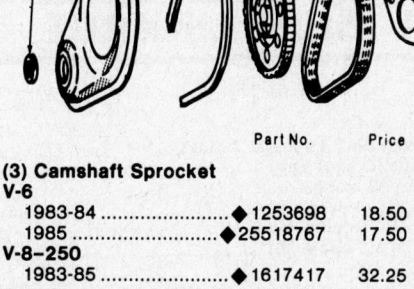

	Part No.	Price
(3) Camshaft Sprocket		
V-6		
1983-84	◆1253698	18.50
1985	◆25518767	17.50
V-8-250		
1983-85	◆1617417	32.25
V-8-307		
1983-85	◆381263	25.25

PARTS 16 CAMSHAFT & TIMING GEARS 16 PARTS

	Part No.	Price
V-8-Diesel		
1983-85	◆558767	58.75
(4) Timing Chain		
V-6		
1983-85	◆1257650	26.00
V-8-250		
1983-85	◆1618157	31.75
V-8-307		
1983-85	◆401584	31.75
V-8-Diesel		
1983-85	◆558484	N.L.
(5) Camshaft		
V-6-231		
1983-84	◆25510019	119.00
1985	◆25518609	N.L.
V-6-252		
1983-84	◆1262835	119.00
V-8-250		
1983-85	◆1628822	334.00
V-8-307		
1983	◆22506227	121.00
1984	◆22521997	124.00
1985	◆22527149	256.00
V-8-Diesel		
1983-85	◆22510099	266.00
(6) Camshaft Bearings		
V-6		
1983-85-exc. below	◆1231142	7.75
Front	◆1231141	N.L.
V-8		
1983-87-No. 1	◆561077	11.50
No. 2	◆390300	11.50
No. 3	◆390301	11.75
No. 4	◆390302	11.50
No. 5	◆390303	11.50

LABOR 17 ENGINE OILING SYSTEM 17 LABOR

	(Factory Time)	Chilton Time
GASOLINE ENGINES		
(G) Oil Pan or Gasket, Renew		
V-6-1983-85		
Code A, 4 or 9	(2.8)	3.5
V-8-1983-85		
250 eng-Code 8	(2.5)	3.3
350 eng-Code 8	(2.5)	3.3
368 eng-Code 6 or 9	(2.7)	3.5
307-350 engs Code Y or R	(2.8)	3.9
(P) Pressure Test Engine Bearings (Pan Off)		
All models		1.0
(G) Oil Pump Cover and/or Gears, R&R and Recondition		
V-6-1983-85		
Code A, 4 or 9	(.5)	.8
V-8-1983-85		
368 eng-Code 6 or 9	(.5)	.8
(G) Oil Pump, Renew		
Includes: R&R oil pan.		
V-8-1983-85		
250 eng-Code 8	(2.6)	3.5
350 eng-Code 8	(2.7)	3.6
307-350 engs Code Y or R	(2.9)	4.1
(G) Oil Pump, R&R and Recondition		
Includes: R&R oil pan.		
V-8-1983-85		
250 eng-Code 8	(2.9)	3.9
350 eng-Code 8	(3.0)	4.0
307-350 engs Code Y or R	(3.0)	4.4
(G) Oil Pressure Gauge (Engine), Renew		
1983-84	(.5)	.7
1985	(.3)	.7
(M) Oil Filter Element, Renew		
1983-85-V-6	(.2)	.2
V-8	(.3)	.3
DIESEL ENGINE		
(G) Oil Pan or Gasket, Renew		
1983-85	(2.8)	3.5
(P) Pressure Test Engine Bearings (Pan Off)		
All models		1.0
(G) Oil Pump, Renew		
1983-85	(2.9)	3.8
(G) Oil Pump, R&R and Recondition		
1983-85	(3.2)	4.2
(G) Oil Pressure Sending Unit, Renew		
1983-85	(.2)	.3
(G) Vacuum Pump, Renew		
Includes: Test.		
1983-85		
gear driven	(.4)	.6
belt driven	(.6)	.8
Recond pump add		.3
(M) Oil Filter Element, Renew		
1983-85	(.3)	.3

PARTS 17 ENGINE OILING SYSTEM 17 PARTS

	Part No.	Price
Oil Pan Gasket		
V-6		
1983	◆1260771	3.00
1984-85	◆25521994	8.50
V-8		
1983-85-exc. below	◆22519181	7.00
1985-250	◆1629459	9.75
Oil Pump Assy.		
V-8-250		
1983-85	◆3517442	71.25
V-8-307		
1983-85	◆22524583	61.50
V-8-Diesel		
1983-85	◆22525288	61.50
Oil Pump Overhaul Kit		
V-6-231		
1983	◆25519448	38.00
1984-85	◆25519447	36.50
V-6-252		
1983	◆25519447	36.50
1984	◆25519448	38.00
Oil Pressure Gauge (Engine)		
V-6		
1983	◆25500672	5.50
1984	◆1623576	6.00
1985	◆25036378	8.75
V-8		
1983-85-exc. below	◆3815936	3.50
250	◆1623576	6.00

LABOR 21 SHIFT LINKAGE 21 LABOR

	(Factory Time)	Chilton Time
(G) Shift Linkage, Adjust		
All models		
Neutral Safety Switch	(.3)	.4
Shift Indicator Needle	(.2)	.3
Shift Linkage	(.4)	.5
T.V. Cable	(.3)	.4
(G) Shift Linkage, Adjust (w/Diesel Eng)		
All models		
Fast idle speed	(.2)	.3
Throttle rod/T.V. cable	(.5)	.6
Trans vacuum valve	(.6)	.6
Vacuum regul valve	(.6)	.8
Complete	(1.0)	1.0
(G) Gear Selector Lever, Renew		
1983-85	(.3)	.5

LABOR 21 SHIFT LINKAGE 21 LABOR

(Factory Time) — Chilton Time

(G) Gear Selector Indicator Needle, Renew
1983-85 (.4) 6

(G) Shift Control Cable or Rods, Renew
1983-85 (.5) 7

(G) Steering Column Shift Bowl, Renew
1983-85 (1.5) 2.2
w/Tilt-tel (1.8) 2.4

LABOR 26 REAR AXLE AND SUSPENSION 26 LABOR

(Factory Time) — Chilton Time

(G) Rear Suspension, Align
1983-85 (.5) 8

(G) Rear Wheel Hub or Bearing, Renew
Includes: Renew seal and repack bearing.
1983-85-one (.8) 1.1
both (1.5) 2.1

(G) Rear Stabilizer Bar, Renew
1983-85 (.5) 9

(G) Rear Stabilizer Bar Bushings, Renew
1983-85 (.5) 8

(G) Rear Spring, Renew
1983-85-one (.6) 1.0
both (.8) 1.5

(G) Rear Shock Absorbers, Renew
1983-85-one (.4) 5
both (.5) 8

(G) Rear Control Arm, Renew
1983-85-one (1.4) 1.8
both (2.5) 3.3
Renew bush add, each 2

ELECTRONIC LEVEL CONTROL

(G) Compressor Assembly, Renew
1983-85 (.3) 5

(G) Compressor Relay, Renew
1983-85 (.2) 4

(G) Height Sensor, Renew
1983-85 (.6) 9

(G) Height Sensor, Adjust
1983-85 (.3) 6

(G) Electronic Level Control Dryer, Renew
1983-85 (.2) 4

(G) Electronic Level Control Head, Renew
Includes: Renew cover gasket, solenoid and valves.
1983-85 (.5) 9

(G) Electronic Level Control Motor and Cylinder Assy., R&R and Recondition
1983-85 (.5) 1.2

(G) Level Control Tubing, Renew
comp to valve (.6) 8
valve to shock (.3) 5
valve to bumper (.3) 5
comp to shock (.5) 7
shock to shock (.3) 4

(G) Compressor Dryer, Renew
1983-85 (.2) 4

(G) Super Lift Shock Absorbers, Renew
1983-85-one (.4) 6
both (.6) 1.0

(G) Pressure Limiter Valve, Renew
1983-85 (.2) 4

PARTS 26 REAR AXLE AND SUSPENSION 26 PARTS

	Part No.	Price
(1) Rotor (Rear Brake)		
1983-85	◆14056179	70.50
(2) Bearing Assy. (w/Hub)		
1983-85-Drum brk.	◆7466903	202.75
Disc brk.	◆7466902	200.50
(3) Plate Assy. (Caliper Suppt.)		
1983-85	◆1613288	33.25
(4) Shock Absorber		
Buick Riviera		
1983-85-right	◆22012064	57.00
left	◆22012063	57.00
Cadillac Eldorado & Seville		
1983-85-right	◆22012064	57.00
left	◆22012063	57.00
Olds. Toronado		
1983-85-right	◆22012064	57.00
left	◆22012063	57.00
(5) Link Kit		
1983-85	◆3634475	2.25
(6) Bushing (Stablizer)		
1983-85-exc. below	◆1614067	2.00
Rally Susp.	◆1614068	2.00
(7) Coil Spring		
Order by year and model.		

ELECTRONIC LEVEL CONTROL

	Part No.	Price
Compressor		
1983-85	◆22020538	176.25
Valve Assy. (Pressure Limited)		
1983-85	◆22017155	42.00

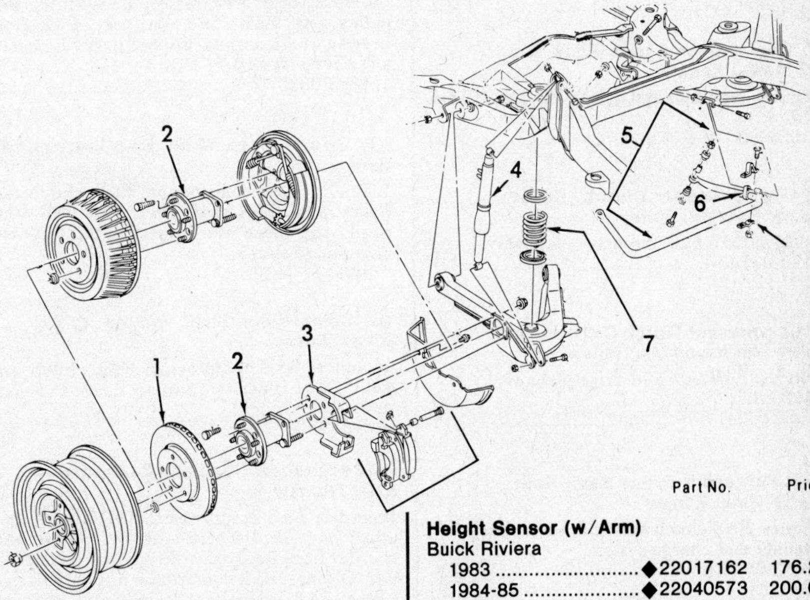

	Part No.	Price
Tube Assy. (Shock Absorber)		
1983-85-770.0M	◆1615530	4.75
3280.0M	◆10005354	7.75
Link (Height Sensor)		
1983-85	◆1615321	4.50

	Part No.	Price
Height Sensor (w/Arm)		
Buick Riviera		
1983	◆22017162	176.25
1984-85	◆22040573	200.00
Cadillac Eldorado & Seville		
1983	◆22017481	N.L.
1984-85	◆22040574	200.00
Olds. Toronado		
1983	◆22017162	176.25
1984-85	◆22040573	200.00
Air Dryer Kit		
1983-85	◆22020540	41.50

(Factory Time) Chilton Time

Note: If more than one item requires replacement where evacuation and discharging the system is already included in the operation, deduct 1.0 hour for each additional item to the times listed.

(G) Drain, Evacuate and Recharge System
All models (.5) 1.0

(G) Refrigerant, Add (Partial Charge)
All models.................................... .6

(G) Pressure Test System
All models.................................... .6

(G) Leak Check
Includes: Check all lines and connections.
All models.................................... .5

(G) Performance Test
Includes: Gauge hook up.
All models.................................... .8

(G) Compressor Belt, Renew
V-6–1983-85 (.4)............................ .5
V-8–1983-85 (.5)............................ .8
Diesel–1983-85 (.5)......................... .6

(G) Compressor R&R, Partial for Engine Work
Note: Hoses remain attached to compressor.
1983-85 (.5).................................. .8

COMPRESSOR 4 CYLINDER RADIAL

(G) Compressor Assembly, Renew
Includes: Transfer parts as required. Evacuate and charge system.
1983-85
Gas (1.2)..................................... 2.5
Diesel (.9)................................... 2.2

(G) Compressor Clutch Plate and Hub Assy., Renew
Includes: R&R hub and drive plate assy. Check air gap.
1983-85 (.4).................................. .6

(G) Compressor Clutch Rotor and/or Bearing, Renew
Includes: R&R hub and drive plate assy.
1983-85 (.8).................................. 1.1

(G) Compressor Clutch Coil and/or Pulley Rim Assembly, Renew
Includes: R&R hub and drive plate assy.
1983-85 (.5).................................. 1.0
Renew pulley or brg add.................... .1

(G) Compressor Front Seal, Seat and 'O' Ring, Renew
Includes: R&R clutch hub and drive plate assy. Evacuate and charge system.
1983-85 (1.2)................................. 2.5

(G) Compressor Front Head and/or Seal, Renew
Includes: R&R compressor, R&R clutch and pulley assy. R&R shaft seal assy. Clean and inspect parts. Evacuate and charge system.
1983-85 (1.7)................................. 2.8

AIR CONDITIONER TUNE-UP

For efficient operation and satisfactory performance in hot weather. The following air conditioner tune-up is suggested:

1. Clean intake filter
2. Clean condenser fins
3. Pressure test system
4. Adjust drive belt tension
5. Check antifreeze/coolant
6. Tighten compressor mounts
7. Tighten condenser and evaporator mounts
8. Inspect system for leaks (hoses, couplings, valves, etc.)
9. Partial charge system

All models 1.0
If necessary to evacuate and charge system, add 1.0

(Factory Time) Chilton Time

(G) Compressor Discharge Valve Plates, Renew
Includes: R&R compressor, R&R clutch and pulley assy. R&R shell to internal mechanism. Clean and inspect parts. Evacuate and charge system.
1983-85 (1.5)................................. 2.6
Two or more add (.1) 2

(G) Compressor Thrust and/or Belleville Washers, Renew
Includes: R&R compressor, R&R clutch and pulley assy. R&R shaft seal assy. R&R front head assy. Clean and inspect parts. Evacuate and charge system.
1983-85 (1.7)................................. 2.8

(G) Compressor Main Bearing, Renew
Includes: R&R compressor, R&R clutch and pulley assy. R&R shaft seal assy. R&R front head assy. Clean and inspect parts. Evacuate and charge system.
1983-85 (1.7)................................. 2.8

(G) Compressor Shell and/or 'O' Rings, Renew
Includes: R&R compressor, R&R clutch and pulley assy. Clean and inspect parts. Evacuate and charge system.
1983-85 (1.7)................................. 2.8

(G) Compressor Shaft and Cylinder Assy., Renew
Includes: R&R compressor, R&R clutch and pulley assy. R&R shaft seal assy., remove and transfer front head assy. R&R compressor shell and 'O' rings. R&R compressor discharge valve plates, R&R super heat switch and pressure relief valve. Clean and inspect parts. Evacuate and charge system.
1983-85 (1.7)................................. 2.9

(G) Condenser, Renew
Includes: Evacuate and charge system.
1983-85 (1.5)................................. 2.6

(Factory Time) Chilton Time

(G) Evaporator Core, Renew
Includes: Evacuate and charge system.
Riviera
1983-85 (3.2)................................. 5.0
Eldorado & Seville
1983-85 (1.6)................................. 3.0
Toronado
1983 (2.7).................................... 5.0
1984-85 (1.7)................................. 3.0

(G) Accumulator Assembly, Renew
Includes: Evacuate and charge system.
1983-85 (.8).................................. 1.5

(G) Expansion Tube (Orifice), Renew
Includes: Evacuate and charge system.
1983-85 (.7).................................. 1.4

(G) Pressure Cut Off Switch, Renew
Includes: Evacuate and charge system where required.
1983-85 (.2).................................. .3

(G) Compressor Thermostatic (Clutch Cycling) Switch, Renew
1983-85 (.3).................................. .5

(G) A. C. Control Assy., Renew
1983-85 (.4).................................. 1.0

(G) Blower Motor, Renew
Eldorado, Toronado & Seville
1983-85 (.4).................................. .6
Riviera
1983-85
Gas (.5)...................................... .8
Diesel (.4)................................... .7

(G) Blower Motor Switch, Renew
1983-85 (.4).................................. .7

(G) Blower Motor Resistor, Renew
1983-85 (.2).................................. .3

(G) Blower Motor Relay, Renew
1983-85 (.2).................................. .3

(G) Air Conditioning Hoses, Renew
Includes: Evacuate and charge system.
1983-85-each-exc below (1.1)...... 1.7
receiver to exp valve (1.2).......... 2.4
cond to evaporator
(liquid line) (1.2)...................... 2.4
Mfg. hose add (.3).......................... .4

AUTOMATIC TEMPERATURE CONTROL

(G) Power Servo or Programmer, Renew
Includes: Test.
1983-85 (.6).................................. 1.1
Renew vacuum valve add (.1)........... .2
Renew vacuum motor add (.2) 3
Renew blower switch add (.2)........... .3
Renew circuit board add (.3)............ .4
Renew amplifier and/or feed
back potentiometer add (.3) 4
Renew output shaft add (.1).............. .1
Renew vacuum checking relay
add (.1)...................................... .1
Renew compensator add (.1).............. .1

(G) A.C. Control Assembly, Renew (Touch Control)
1983-85 (.4).................................. 1.0

(G) ECC Power Module, Renew
1983-85 (.3).................................. .5

PARTS 28 AIR CONDITIONING 28 PARTS

	Part No.	Price
Compressor Assy.		
Buick Riviera & Olds. Toronado		
1983-85	◆12300273	390.00
Cadillac Eldorado & Seville		
1983-85	◆12300274	390.00
Clutch Hub and Drive Plate		
1983-85	◆6551220	32.50
Rotor and Bearing		
1983-85	◆6551216	67.50
Compressor Shaft Seal Kit		
1983-85	◆9956695	13.00
Front Head		
1983-85	◆6551142	28.25
Front Head Main Bearing		
1983-85	◆6556572	4.00
Outer Shell Assy.		
1983-85	◆2724158	38.00
Valve Plate Assy.		
1983-85	◆6551141	11.50
Cylinder and Shaft Assy.		
Buick Riviera & Olds. Toronado		
1983-85	◆2724144	269.00
Cadillac Eldorado & Seville		
1983-85	◆2724060	275.00

REFRIGERANT SYSTEM

	Part No.	Price
Condenser Assy.		
Buick Riviera & Olds. Toronado		
1983-85	◆3040548	154.50
Cadillac Eldorado & Seville		
1983-85	◆3040531	162.75
Evaporator Core Assy.		
1983-85	◆3042897	196.50
Accumulator Dehydrator		
Buick Riviera & Olds. Toronado		
1983	◆2724259	87.00
1984-85-exc.		
below	◆2724261	79.75
231	◆2724260	89.50
Cadillac Eldorado & Seville		
1983	◆2724259	87.00
1984-85	◆2724259	87.00

AUTOMATIC CLIMATE CONTROL

	Part No.	Price
Programmer		
Buick Riviera		
Cadillac Eldorado & Seville		
1983-85	◆1226159	72.50
Olds. Toronado		
1983-85	◆16028093	84.25
Automatic Vacuum Motor		
1983-85	◆16004018	11.50
Sensor (In Car)		
Buick Riviera		
1983-85	◆25508293	13.50
Cadillac Eldorado & Seville		
1983-85	◆16003736	7.75
Olds. Toronado		
1984-85	◆25036390	37.00
Sensor (Ambient Air)		
Buick Riviera		
1983-85	◆25507677	16.75
Cadillac Eldorado & Seville		
1983-85	◆16015606	10.25
Olds. Toronado		
1984-85	◆25036391	59.25
Relay (Hi Blower)		
Buick Riviera & Olds. Toronado		
1983-85	◆10018449	N.L.
Linkage (Programmer)		
Cadillac Eldorado & Seville		
1983-85	◆16010356	2.50
Olds. Toronado		
1983-85	◆16004273	1.50
Blower Motor		
Buick Riviera		
1983-85	◆22020945	60.00
Cadillac Eldorado, Seville & Olds. Toronado		
1983-85	◆22020945	60.00
Blower Motor Resistor		
Buick Riviera		
1983-85	◆25503141	9.75
Olds. Toronado		
1983-85	◆25503141	9.75
Blower Motor Switch		
Buick Riviera & Olds. Toronado		
(Manual A/C)		
1983	◆16015256	6.00
1984-85	◆16032480	7.50

LABOR 29 LOCKS, HINGES & WIND. REGULATORS 29 LABOR

(Factory Time)	Chilton Time
(G) Hood Latch Assembly, Renew	
1983-85 (.2)	.4
(G) Hood Hinge, Renew	
1983-85-one (.3)	.5
both (.5)	.8
(G) Hood Release Cable, Renew	
1983-85 (.4)	.6
(G) Hood Support Tube, Renew	
1983-85 (.2)	.5
(G) Door Handle (Outside), Renew (Front or Rear)	
1983-85 (.5)	.7
Renew insert add	.1
(G) Front Door Lock Assembly, Renew	
1983-85 (.5)	1.0
w/Vacuum or elec locks add (.1)	.2
(G) Rear Door Lock Assembly, Renew	
Seville	
1983-85 (.8)	1.2
(G) Door Lock Cylinder and Keys, Renew	
1983-85 (.3)	.6
Recode cyl add (.3)	.3
(G) Door Lock Remote Control, Renew (Front or Rear)	
1983-85 (.3)	.7
(G) Lock Striker Plate, Renew	
1983-85 (.2)	.3
(G) Door Window Regulator (Electric), Renew	
1983-85 (1.0)	1.6
(G) Door Window Regulator Motor, Renew	
1983-85-exc. below (.6)	1.0
Seville (1.0)	1.5
(G) Trunk Hinge or Strap Assembly, Renew	
1983-85-one (.8)	1.2
(G) Trunk Lock Cylinder and Key, Renew	
1983-85 (.2)	.4
Recode cyl add (.3)	.3
(G) Trunk Lock Assembly, Renew	
1983-85 (.2)	.4

PARTS 29 LOCKS, HINGES & WIND. REGULATORS 29 PARTS

	Part No.	Price
Hood Latch Assy. (Lower)		
1983-85	◆14070703	16.25
Hood Latch Assy. (Secondary)		
Buick Riviera		
1983-85	◆1261535	11.50
Cadillac Eldorado & Seville		
1983-85	◆1607317	7.75
Olds. Toronado		
1983-85	◆562374	11.25
Hood Hinge		
Buick Riviera		
1983-85-right	◆1621296	30.25
left	◆1621295	30.25
Cadillac Eldorado & Seville		
1983-85-right	◆1621294	30.25
left	◆1621293	30.25
Olds. Toronado		
(Aluminum Hood)		
1983-85-right	◆1621298	43.75
left	◆1621297	43.75
(Steel Hood)		
1983-85-right	◆1621296	30.25
left	◆1621295	30.25
Front Door Lock		
Buick Riviera		
1983-right	◆20293612	33.50
left	◆20293613	33.50
1984-right	◆20479756	33.25
left	◆20479757	33.25
1985-right	◆20298852	37.25
left	◆20298853	38.50
Cadillac Eldorado & Seville		
1983-right	◆20293612	33.50
left	◆20293613	33.50
1984-right	◆20479756	33.25
left	◆20479757	33.25
1985-right	◆20298852	37.25
left	◆20298853	38.50

PARTS 29 LOCKS, HINGES & WIND. REGULATORS 29 PARTS

	Part No.	Price
Olds. Toronado		
1983-84-right	◆20293620	62.75
left	◆20293621	62.75
1985-right	◆20298852	37.25
left	◆20298853	38.50
Door Lock Cylinder (Uncoded)		
Buick Riviera		
1983-85-exc. below	◆9632728	8.25
Dr. lock light	◆9632767	9.50

*This lock cylinder is only available coded w/ Keys.

	Part No.	Price
Cadillac Eldorado & Seville		
1983-85-exc. below	◆20496702	7.00
(w/Anti-theft)		
wo/Dr. lock light	◆9632728	8.25
Dr. lock light	◆9632767	9.50
Olds. Toronado		
1983-85-exc. below	◆9632769	7.75
Elec. dr. lock	◆9632728	8.25
(w/Door lock light)		
wo/Anti-theft	◆9632766	9.50
Anti-theft	◆9632767	9.50
Front Door Outer Handle		
Buick Riviera		
1983-right	◆20273628	23.75
left	◆20273629	23.75
1984 (wo/Door lock light)		
right	◆20479794	28.25
left	◆20470543	22.75
1985 (wo/Door lock light)		
right	◆20479794	28.25
left	◆20479795	28.25
1984-85 (Door lock light)		
right	◆20480174	23.75
left	◆20480175	23.75
Cadillac Eldorado & Seville		
1983-right	◆20273628	23.75
left	◆20273629	23.75
1984-85-right	◆20479416	23.75
left	◆20479417	23.75
Olds. Toronado		
(wo/Door lock light)		
1983-85-right	◆20099257	28.00
left	◆20099256	28.00
(Door lock light)		
1983-85-right	◆20101210	44.75
left	◆20101211	44.75
Front Window Regulator (Power)		
1983-85-right	◆20151038	88.25
left	◆20151039	88.25
Window Regulator Electric Motor		
1983-85	◆22020900	73.00
Deck Lid Lock		
1983-85	◆20279741	N.L.
Deck Lid Lock Cylinder (uncoded)		
1983-85	◆3910570	6.25
Deck Lid Hinge		
1983 (Gas supports)		
right	◆20216520	28.75
left	◆20216521	28.75
1983-85 (Torque Rods)		
right	◆20434752	28.75
left	◆20434753	28.75

LABOR 30 HEAD & PARKING LAMPS 30 LABOR

(Factory Time)	Chilton Time
(G) Aim Headlamps	
two	.4
four	.6
(M) Headlamp Sealed Beam Bulb, Renew	
1983-85-each (.3)	.3
(M) Park and Turn Signal Lamp Assy., Renew	
1983-85 (.3)	.4
Renew housing add (.3)	.3
(M) Front Side Marker Lamp Assy., Renew	
1983-85 (.3)	.4
(M) License Lamp Assembly, Renew	
1983-85 (.2)	.3
(M) Rear Side Marker Lamp and/or Lens, Renew	
1983-85 (.3)	.3
(M) Park and Turn Signal Lamp Bulb, Renew	
All models-each	.2
(M) Side Marker Lamp Bulb, Renew	
All models-each	.2
(M) Stop, Tail and Turn Signal Lamp Bulb, Renew	
All models-one	.2
each adtnl	.1
(M) License Lamp Bulb, Renew	
All models-one or all (.2)	.3
(M) Cornering Lamp Bulb, Renew	
All models-each (.2)	.3
(M) Back-Up Lamp Bulb, Renew	
All models-one or all (.2)	.3
(M) Stop, Tail and Turn Signal Lamp Assy., Renew	
1983-85-exc below (.3)	.4
Seville (.5)	.7
(M) Cornering Lamp Assembly, Renew	
1983-85-each (.3)	.4
(M) Back-Up Assembly, Renew	
1983-85-each (.3)	.4

PARTS 30 HEAD AND PARKING LAMPS 30 PARTS

	Part No.	Price
Sealed Beam Bulb		
Buick Riviera		
1983-85-exc. Quartz		
inner	◆5966201	15.00
outer	◆5966200	15.00
1983-85-Quartz		
inner	◆5930567	22.50
outer (1983)	◆16502327	22.50
outer (1984-85)	◆16502327	22.50
Cadillac Eldorado, Seville & Olds. Toronado		
1983-85-inner	◆5930567	22.50
outer	◆1650327	N.L.
Parking & Turn Signal Lamp Assy.		
Buick Riviera		
(wo/Sport pkg. or lamp monitor)		
1983-85-left	◆913935	39.75
right	◆913936	39.75
(Sport pkg.)		
1983-85-left	◆914333	39.75
right	◆914334	39.75
(Lamp monitor, wo/sport pkg.)		
1983-85-left	◆914327	39.75
right	◆914328	39.75
Cadillac Eldorado & Seville		
1983-85-left	◆913963	40.00
right	◆913964	40.00
Olds. Toronado		
1983-85-left	◆915027	42.25
right	◆915028	42.25
Corner & Side Marker Lamp Assy.		
Buick Riviera		
1983-85-left	◆913937	29.50
right	◆913938	29.50
Cadillac Eldorado		
1983-85-left	◆5970535	29.50
right	◆5970536	29.50
Cadillac Seville		
1983-85-left	◆915493	43.50
right	◆915494	43.50
Olds. Toronado		
1983-85-left	◆913957	35.00
right	◆913958	35.00
Tail, Stop & Signal Lamp Lens		
Buick Riviera		
1983-right	◆5970554	71.25
left	◆5970553	71.25
1984-85-right	◆16501896	71.25
left	◆16501895	71.25
Cadillac Eldorado		
1983-85-exc. below	◆5973563	57.00
Cust. ext.	◆16500488	57.00
Cadillac Seville		
1983-right	◆5972462	80.25
left	◆5972461	80.25
1984-85-right	◆16502416	80.25
left	◆16502415	80.25
Olds. Toronado		
1983-85-right	◆5970112	61.75
left	◆5970111	61.75
Rear License Lamp Assy.		
Buick Riviera		
1983-85-left	◆913941	7.50
right	◆913942	7.50
Cadillac Eldorado		
1983-85-left	◆913979	4.00
right	◆913980	4.00

PARTS 30 HEAD AND PARKING LAMPS 30 PARTS

	Part No.	Price
Cadillac Seville		
1983-85-left	◆914691	4.00
right	◆914692	4.00
Olds. Toronado		
1983-85-Black	◆913584	6.25
Argent	◆913578	6.50
Rear Marker Lamp Assy.		
Buick Riviera		
1983-85-left	◆913807	15.00
right	◆913808	15.00
Cadillac Eldorado		
1983-85	◆913907	52.50
Cadillac Seville		
1983-85	◆914317	10.00
Olds. Toronado		
1983-85-left	◆913781	9.25
right	◆913782	9.25

LABOR 31 WINDSHIELD WIPER & SPEEDOMETER 31 LABOR

(Factory Time)	Chilton Time
(G) Windshield Wiper Motor, Renew	
1983-85 (.6)	.9
(G) Windshield Wiper Motor, R&R and Recondition	
1983-85	
round motor (.8)	1.2
rectangle motor (1.0)	1.4
(G) Wiper Transmission, Renew (Complete)	
1983-85 (.6)	1.0
Renew wiper support add (.5)	.7
(G) Wiper Switch, Renew	
Eldorado & Seville	
1983-85 (.3)	.5
Toronado	
1983-85 (.8)	1.3
Riviera	
1983-85	
std colm (.9)	1.5
tilt colm (.7)	1.3
(G) Windshield Washer Pump, Renew	
1983-85 (.2)	.4
w/Pulse wipe add (.1)	.1
(G) Windshield Washer Pump, R&R and Recondition	
1983-85 (.5)	.8
w/Pulse wipe add (.1)	.1
(G) Windshield Washer Pump Valve, Renew	
1983-85 (.2)	.4
(G) Wiper Motor Main Drive Gear (Depressed Park), Renew	
Includes: R&R wiper motor.	
1983-85 (1.0)	1.5
(G) Wiper Motor Terminal Board and/or Timing Delay Switch, Renew	
1983-85 (.5)	1.0
(G) Speedometer Head, R&R or Renew	
1983-85 (.6)	1.0
Reset odometer add	.2
(G) Speedometer Cable and Casing, Renew	
1983-85	
one piece assy. (.8)	1.3
upper assy. (.5)	.8
lower assy. (.3)	.4
(G) Speedometer Cable (Inner), Renew or Lubricate	
1983-85-each (.7)	1.2
(G) Speedometer Driven Pinion or Seal, Renew	
1983-85 (.3)	.4
(G) M.P.G. Sentinel, Renew	
1983-85 (.3)	.6
(G) Radio, R&R	
1983-85 (.5)	.8

PARTS 31 WINDSHIELD WIPER & SPEEDOMETER 31 PARTS

	Part No.	Price
Windshield Wiper Motor		
1983-85-exc.		
Pulse	◆4960974	84.00
Pulse wiper	◆4961608	80.00
Windshield Wiper Transmission		
1983-85-right	◆22010688	17.25
left	◆22010690	19.50
Windshield Wiper Motor Control Switch		
Buick Riviera & Olds. Toronado		
(wo/Pulse wiper)		
1983-85	◆7837279	41.50
(Pulse wiper)		
1983-85	◆7837280	53.50
Cadillac Eldorado & Seville		
1983-84	◆1617090	35.00
1985	◆1632569	21.75
Windshield Washer Pump Assy.		
(wo/Pulse wiper)		
1983-85	◆22029665	30.00
(Pulse wiper)		
1983	◆22029601	27.00
1984-85	◆22039321	29.00
Windshield Washer Valve Kit		
1983-85	◆22029597	4.25
Speedometer Cable & Head Assy.		
Order by year and model.		

LABOR 32 LIGHT SWITCHES & WIRING 32 LABOR

(Factory Time)	Chilton Time
(G) Headlamp Switch, Renew	
1983-85 (.3)	.7
(G) Headlamp Dimmer Switch, Renew	
1983-85 (.5)	.9
(G) Stop Light Switch, Renew	
1983-85 (.3)	.4
(G) Turn Signal or Hazard Warning Switch, Renew	
1983-85 (.7)	1.1
(G) Parking Brake Lamp Switch, Renew	
1983-85 (.3)	.4
(G) Back-Up Lamp and Park/Neutral Switch, Renew	
1983-85 (.3)	.4
(G) Neutral Safety Switch, Renew	
1983-85	
Riviera-colm mounted (.6)	.8
(G) Dimmer Switch Pivot Assy., Renew	
1983-85 (.6)	1.2
w/Cruise control add (.2)	.2
(M) Turn Signal or Hazard Warning Flasher, Renew	
1983-85 (.2)	.2
(G) Horn Relay, Renew	
1983-85 (.2)	.3
(G) Horn, Renew	
1983-85-each (.3)	.4
(G) Chassis Wiring Harness, Renew	
Fusible link	
1983-85 (.4)	.6
Headlamp harness	
1983-85 (.6)	1.1
Instrument panel	
1983-85 (2.0)	2.5
Engine harness	
1983-85 (1.1)	1.7
Fuse block	
1983-85 (.6)	1.1

PARTS 32 LIGHT SWITCHES & WIRING 32 PARTS

	Part No.	Price
Headlamp Switch		
Buick Riviera		
1983-85-exc. below	◆1995230	30.50
Twilight Sentinel	◆1995238	41.25
Cadillac Eldorado & Seville		
1983-85	◆1995225	18.00
Olds. Toronado		
1983-exc. below	◆1995212	28.00
Twilight Sentinel	◆1995232	41.50
1984-85-exc. below	◆1995283	31.00
Twilight Sentinel	◆1995284	40.50
Headlamp Dimmer Switch		
(exc. Guidematic)		
1983-85	◆7838234	12.50
(Guidematic)		
1983-85	◆7831354	21.50
Stop Light Switch		
1983-85		
wo/Cruise Cont	◆1362835	3.00
1983-84		
Cruise Cont	◆9794682	7.75
1985		
Cruise Cont.	◆25524846	6.50
Turn Signal Switch		
1983-85	◆1997984	35.00
Turn Signal Flasher		
Buick Riviera & Olds. Toronado		
1983-85	◆10029240	4.25
Cadillac Eldorado & Seville		
1983-85	◆10029240	4.25
Back-Up Light Switch		
Buick Riviera		
1983-85-w/Elec. dr. locks	◆22514861	7.00
Conv. top	◆22514861	7.00
wo/Conv. top	◆22509632	5.50
Cadillac Eldorado & Seville		
1983-85	◆1619499	26.00
Olds. Toronado		
1983-85-exc. below	◆22514861	7.00
wo/Elec. trunk lid	◆22509632	5.50
Chassis Wiring Harness		
Order by model and description.		
Horn Assy.		
1983-85		
High note (A)	◆1892164	22.00
High note (C)	◆1892246	27.50
Low note (D)	◆1892162	23.50
Low note (F)	◆1892163	22.00
Horn Relay		
Buick Riviera & Olds. Toronado		
1983-85	◆25513270	8.50
Cadillac Eldorado & Seville		
1983-85-exc. diesel	◆1626239	6.50
Diesel	◆2098912	21.50

LABOR 33 GLASS 33 LABOR

(Factory Time)	Chilton Time
(G) Windshield, Renew	
1983-85 (1.3)	1.8
Renew caulk bead add (.4)	.4
(G) Front Door Glass, Renew	
1983-85-exc below (1.0)	1.6
Seville (.7)	1.0
(G) Rear Quarter Stationary Glass, Renew	
1983-85 (.5)	1.0
(G) Rear Door Glass, Renew	
1983-85 (.8)	1.3
(G) Quarter Window Movable Glass, Renew	
1983-85 (1.1)	1.8
Renew retainer add (.2)	.2
(G) Rear Window Glass, Renew	
1983-85-exc below (2.1)	4.0
Seville (1.3)	2.0
w/Elec grid defogger add (.6)	.6
w/3/4 plug, unpadded add (1.0)	1.5
w/Full plug, padded add (2.8)	4.4
w/Cabriolet option add (5.1)	6.5

LABOR 34 CRUISE CONTROL 34 LABOR

(Factory Time)	Chilton Time
(G) Cruise Control, Adjust	
1983 (.3)	.3
(G) Cruise Control Regulator (Transducer), Renew	
Includes: R&R cover and external adjustments.	
1983 (.4)	.6
Adjust low speed switch add (.1)	.1
Overhaul vacuum regulator add (.4)	.6
(G) Cruise Control Engagement Switch, Renew	
Includes: Renew turn signal lever.	
1983-85-std colm (.6)	.9
tilt colm (.5)	.7
(G) Cruise Control Brake Release Switch, Renew	
Includes: Adjust.	
1983-85 (.2)	.4
(G) Cruise Control Servo, Renew	
Includes: External adjustments.	
1983-85 (.3)	.5
(G) Cruise Control Vacuum Hoses, Renew	
1983-85-one or all (.2)	.3
(G) Cruise Control Chain or Cable, Renew	
1983-85 (.2)	.4
(G) Cruise Control Regulator (Transducer) Filter, Renew	
1983 (.2)	.3
(G) Cruise Control Vacuum Regulator Valve, Renew (In Line)	
1983-84 (.2)	.3
(G) Cruise Control Resume Solenoid Valve, Renew	
1983-85 (.2)	.4
(G) Power Unit or Vacuum Servo Solenoid, Renew	
1983 (.2)	.5
(G) Cruise Control Controller or Module, Renew	
Eldorado & Seville	
1983-85	
w/EFI (.4)	.6
w/DFI (.5)	.7
Riviera (.3)	.5
Toronado (.3)	.5
(G) Cruise Control Speed Sensor and Wiring Harness, Renew	
1983-85 (.8)	1.2
(G) Cruise Control On-Off Switch, Renew	
1983-85 (.3)	.5
(G) Cruise Control Vacuum Control Valve, Renew	
1983-84 (.2)	.3

PARTS 34 CRUISE CONTROL 34 PARTS

	Part No.	Price
Cruise Control Power Unit		
Buick Riviera & Olds. Toronado		
V-6-231		
1983	◆25031713	27.00
1984-85	◆25074627	117.00
V-6-252		
1983	◆25031846	23.75
1984-85	◆25074630	116.25
V-8-307		
1983	◆25031316	27.00
1984-85	◆25074629	123.50
V-8-Diesel		
1983	◆25030980	32.75
1984-85	◆25074629	123.50
Cadillac Eldorado & Seville		
1983-85	◆25031423	29.00
Cruise Control Lever & Switch		
Order by year and model.		
Cruise Control Transducer		
Buick Riviera		
1983-V-6	◆25030878	158.00
V-8	◆25031261	158.00
Diesel	◆25031604	179.25
Cadillac Eldorado & Seville		
1983	◆25031699	62.50
Olds. Toronado		
231 & 307		
1983	◆25030882	158.00
V-6-252		
1983	◆25030881	160.00
350 Diesel		
1983	◆25031683	169.50
Cruise Control Brake Release Switch		
1983-85	◆9794682	8.00
Vacuum Release Valve		
1983-85	◆25509432	14.00

GROUP INDEX

ALPHABETICAL INDEX

General Motors

Front Wheel Drive Cars

BUICK RIVIERA • CADILLAC ELDORADO • SEVILLE • OLDSMOBILE TORONADO

(1986–87)

YEAR IDENTIFICATION

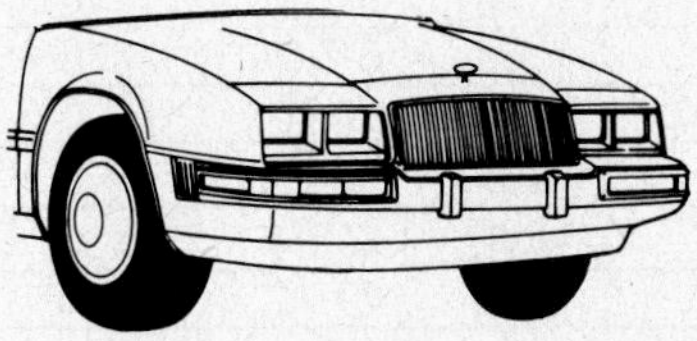

1986–87 Riviera

1986–87 Toronado

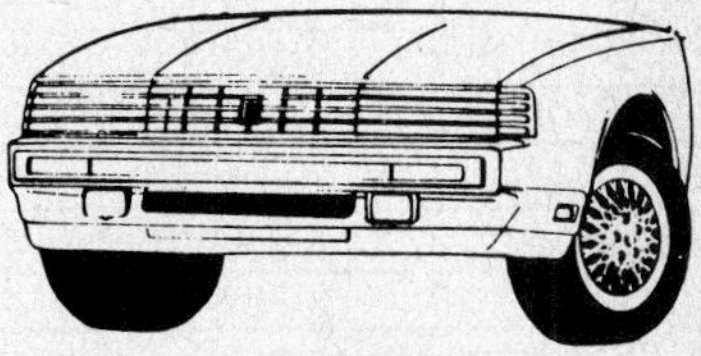

1987 Trofeo

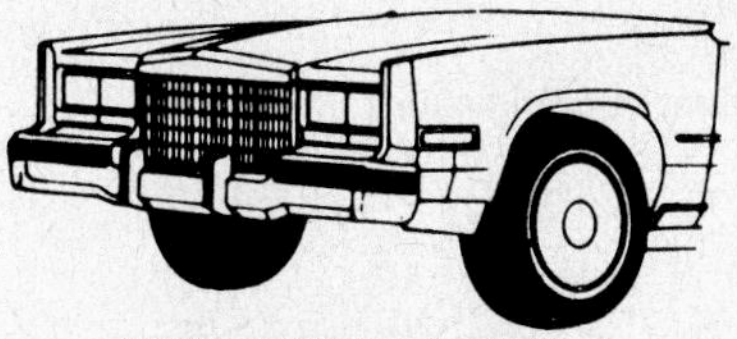

1986–87 Eldorado

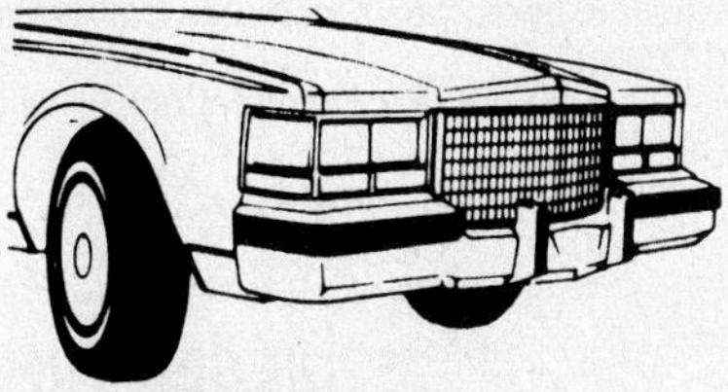

1986–87 Seville

VEHICLE IDENTIFICATION NUMBER (VIN)

It is important for servicing and ordering parts to be certain of the vehicle and engine identification. The VIN (vehicle identification number) is a 13 or 17 digit number visible through the windshield on the driver's side of the dash and contains the vehicle and engine identification codes. It can be interpreted as follows:

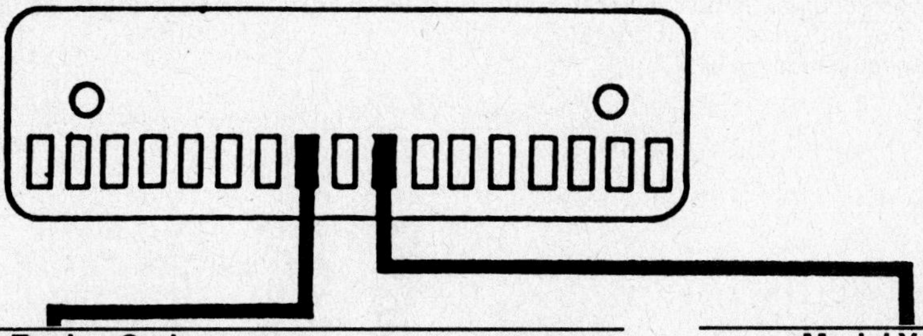

Engine Code					
Code	Cu. In.	Liters	Cyl.	Carb.	Eng. Mfg.
8, B	231	3.8	6	SFI	Buick
3	231	3.8	6	4	Buick
9	231	3.8	6	FI-Turbo	Buick
8	250	4.1	8	DFI	Cad.
8	250	4.1	8	4	Cad.
4	252	4.1	6	4	Buick
4	252	4.1	6	DFI	Buick
Y	307	5.0	8	4	Olds.
N	350	5.7	8	Diesel	Olds.

Model Year Code	
Code	Year
D	83
E	84
F	85
G	86
H	87

The seventeen digit Vehicle Identification Number can be used to determine engine application and model year. The 10th digit indicates the model year, and the 8th digit identifies the factory installed engine. EFI Electronic Fuel Injection DFI Digital Fuel Injection

GASOLINE ENGINE TUNE-UP SPECIFICATIONS

When analyzing compression test results, look for uniformity among cylinders rather than specific pressures.

Year	Eng. Code	Engine No. Cyl. Displacement (cu. in.)	Liters	Eng. Mfg.	Spark Plugs Orig. Type	Spark Plugs Gap (in.)	Distributor	Ignition Timing (deg.)▲ *Auto Trans.•	Valves Intake Opens (deg.) •	Fuel Pump Pressure (psi)	Idle Speed (rpm)▲ Auto Trans.•
TORONADO											
'83	4	6-252	4.1	Buick	R-45TS8	.080	Electronic	15B	16	6-7.5	①
	Y	8-307	5.0	Olds.	R-46SX	.080	Electronic	15B	20	6-7.5	①
'84-'85	4	6-252	4.1	Buick	R-45TS8	.080	Electronic	①	16	6-7.5	①
	Y	8-307	5.0	Olds.	R-46SX	.080	Electronic	①	20	6-7.5	①
1986-'87	B	231	3.8	Olds.	R44LTS	0.045	Electronic	①	16	34-40	①
RIVIERA											
'83	8	6-231 Turbo	3.8	Buick	R-45TS	.040	Electronic	15B	16	4.2-5.8	①
	4	6-252	4.1	Buick	R-45TS8	.080	Electronic	15B	16	6-7.5	①
	Y	8-307	5.0	Olds.	R-46SX	.080	Electronic	15B @ 1100	20	6-7.5	①
'84-'85	8 ③	6-231 Turbo	3.8	Buick	R-45TS	.040	Electronic	①	16	4.2-5.8	①
	4	6-252	4.1	Buick	R-45TS8	.080	Electronic	①	16	6-7.5	①
	Y	8-307	5.0	Olds.	R-46SX	.080	Electronic	①	20	6-7.5	①
1986-'87	B	231	3.8	Olds.	R44LTS	.045	Electronic	①	16	34-40	①
ELDORADO AND SEVILLE											
'83	8	8-250	4.1	Cadillac	R-43NTS6	.060	Electronic	①	37	40	②
'84-'87	8	8-250	4.1	Cadillac	R-43NTS6 ④	.060	Electronic	①	37	40	②

*Set timing with carburetor adjusted to 1100 rpm, unless sticker specifies otherwise.
▲ See text for procedure
• Where two figures appear separated by a slash, the first is idle speed with solenoid energized, the second is idle speed with solenoid disconnected. Figure in parenthesis indicates California engine.
B Before Top Dead Center
Part numbers in this chart are not recommendations by Chilton for any product by brand name.
① See Underhood Sticker
② Electronic controlled idle, no adjustment
③ 85; VIN9
④ R42CLTS6

DIESEL TUNE-UP SPECIFICATIONS

Year	Engine No. Cyl. Displacement (cu. in.)	Liters	Fuel Pump Pressure (psi)	Compression (lbs.)	Intake Valve Opens (deg.)	Idle Speed (rpm)
'82-'87	8-350	5.7	5.5-7.0	275 min.	16	①

NOTE: The underhood specifications sticker often reflects tune-up specification changes made in production. Sticker figures must be used if they disagree with those in this chart.
① See underhood specifications sticker

WHEEL ALIGNMENT SPECIFICATIONS

Year	Caster Range (deg.)	Caster Pref. Setting (deg.)	Camber Range (deg.)	Camber Pref. Setting (deg.)	Toe in (in.)	Steering Axis Inclin. (deg.)
TORONADO						
'83-'85	1 1/2P to 3 1/2P	2 1/2P	1/2N to 1/2P	0	1/8 in to 1/8 out	11
'86-'87	1 5/16P to 3 5/16	2 5/16	13/16N to 13/16P	0	3/32 to 3/32	—
ELDORADO AND SEVILLE						
'83-'87	2P to 3P	2 1/2P	1/2N to 1/2P	0	1/8 in to 1/8 out	—
RIVIERA						
'83-'85	2P to 3P	2 1/2P	1/2N to 1/2P	0	1/8 in to 1/8 out	—
'86-'87	1 15/16 to 3 5/16	2 5/16	13/16N to 13/16P	0	3/32 to 3/32	—

LABOR — SERVICE BAY OPERATIONS — LABOR

(Factory Time) — Chilton Time

COOLING

(M) Winterize Cooling System
Includes: Run engine to check for leaks, tighten all hose connections. Test radiator and pressure cap, drain radiator and engine block. Add anti-freeze and refill system.
All models 5

(G) Thermostat, Renew
1986-87
V-6 (.6) 8
V-8 (.3) 5

(M) Radiator Hoses, Renew
Includes: Drain and refill cooling system.
1986-87-upper (.3) 4
lower (.4) 5
both (.5) 7
by-pass (.5) 7

(M) Serpentine Drive Belt, Renew
1986-87
V-6 (.3) 5
V-8 (.2) 4

(G) Serpentine Belt Tensioner, Renew
1986-87
V-6 (.5) 7
V-8 (.2) 4

FUEL

(M) Air Cleaner, Service
All models 3

(G) Air Cleaner Vacuum Motor, Renew
All models (.3) 4

(G) Air Cleaner Temperature Sensor, Renew
All models (.3) 4

(G) Minimum Idle Speed, Adjust
All models (.4) 6

BRAKES

(G) Bleed Brakes (Four Wheels)
Includes: Fill master cylinder.
All models (.4) 5

(G) Brake Pedal Free Play, Adjust
All models 3

(G) Parking Brake, Adjust
All models (.3) 4

CHILTON'S 10 POINT SAFETY CHECK

CHECK OPERATION & CONDITION OF THE FOLLOWING ITEMS:

1. Legal Registration (serial no.)
2. Tires & Wheels
3. Brake System (R&R all wheels)
4. Light Systems & Signals
5. Accelerator Linkage, Neutral Safety Switch, Shift Indicator Pointer & Seat Position Locks
6. Glass, Mirrors, Door Locks, Seat Belts & Harness
7. Wipers, Washers & Defrosters
8. Frame, Steering, Shocks, Front & Rear Suspension
9. Fuel & Exhaust Systems
10. Road Test Vehicle

All models 1.0
Exhaust Smog Analysis, add 4

(Factory Time) — Chilton Time

LUBRICATION SERVICE

(M) Lubricate Chassis, Change Oil & Filter
Includes: Inspect and correct all fluid levels.
All models 6
Install grease fillings add 1

(M) Lubricate Chassis
Includes: Inspect and correct all fluid levels.
All models 4
Install grease fittings add 1

(M) Engine Oil & Filter, Change
Includes: Inspect and correct all fluid levels.
All models 4

WHEELS

(M) Wheel, Renew
one 5

(G) Wheels, Balance
one 3
each adtnl 2

(G) Wheels, Rotate (All)
All models 5

(Factory Time) — Chilton Time

ELECTRICAL

(M) Battery Cables, Renew
All models
positive (.6) 8
negative (.3) 3
to start connector (.2) 3

(M) Battery Terminals, Clean
All models 3

(G) Aim Headlamps
two 4
four 6

(M) Headlamp Sealed Beam Bulb, Renew
1986-87-each (.3) 3

(M) Park and Turn Signal Lamp Assy., Renew
1986-87 (.3) 4

(M) Side Marker Lamp Assy., Renew
1986-87 (.2) 3

(M) License Lamp Assembly, Renew
1986-87 (.2) 3

(M) Back-Up Lamp Assembly, Renew
1986-87 (.2) 3

(M) Cornering Lamp Bulb, Renew
All models-each (.2) 3

(M) High Level Stop Lamp Bulb, Renew
All models (.2) 3

(M) High Level Stop Lamp Assy., Renew
All models (.2) 4

(M) License Lamp Bulb, Renew
All models-one or all (.2) 3

(M) Park and Turn Signal Lamp Bulb, Renew
All models-each 2

(M) Rear Combination Lamp Bulb, Renew
All models-one 2
each adtnl 1

(M) Side Marker Lamp Bulb, Renew
All models-each 2

LABOR 1 TUNE UP 1 LABOR

	(Factory Time)	Chilton Time
(G) Compression Test		
V-6–1986-87		.7
V-8–1986-87		.9
(G) Engine Tune Up, (Electronic Ignition)		
Includes: Test battery and clean connections. Tighten manifold and carburetor mounting bolts. Check engine compression, clean and adjust or renew spark plugs. Test resistance of spark plug cables. Inspect distributor cap and rotor. Reset ignition timing. Adjust idle mixture and idle speed. Service air cleaner. Inspect and adjust drive belts. Inspect choke operation and adjust or free up. Check operation of EGR valve.		
V-6–1986-87		2.0
V-8–1986-87		3.0
To perform C.C.C. system test add		1.0

LABOR 2 IGNITION SYSTEM 2 LABOR

	(Factory Time)	Chilton Time
(G) Spark Plugs, Clean and Reset or Renew		
1986-87-V-6	(.4)	.6
V-8	(.5)	.8
(G) Ignition Timing, Reset		
All models	(.3)	.4
(G) Distributor, Renew		
Includes: Reset ignition timing.		
1986-87-V-8	(.5)	.9
(G) Distributor, R&R and Recondition		
Includes: Reset ignition timing.		
1986-87-V-8	(.8)	1.5
(G) Distributor Cap and/or Rotor, Renew		
1986-87-V-8	(.3)	.4
(G) Distributor Module, Renew		
1986-87-V-8	(.4)	.6
(G) Distributor Pick-Up Coil and/or Pole Piece, Renew		
Includes: R&R distributor and reset ignition timing.		
1986-87-V-8	(.6)	1.0
(G) Distributor Capacitor and/or Module Wiring Harness, Renew		
Includes: R&R distributor cap and rotor. Reset ignition timing.		
1986-87-V-8	(.3)	.5
(G) Ignition Coil, Renew		
1986-87-V-8	(.3)	.5
(G) Ignition Cables, Renew		
1986-87-V-6	(.4)	.6
V-8	(.5)	.7
(G) Ignition Switch, Renew		
1986-87		
Eldorado & Seville	(.6)	.9
Riviera	(.4)	.9
Toronado	(.6)	.9
(G) Ignition Key Warning Switch, Renew		
1986-87		
Riviera	(.5)	1.0
Toronado	(.6)	1.0
DISTRIBUTORLESS IGNITION SYSTEM		
(G) Electronic Spark Control Module, Renew		
1986-87	(.5)	.7
(G) Electronic Spark Control Knock Sensor, Renew		
1986-87	(.3)	.5
(G) Crankshaft Sensor, Renew		
1986-87	(.6)	.9
(G) Camshaft Sensor, Renew		
1986-87	(.6)	.9
(G) Ignition Coil and/or Module, Renew		
1986-87	(.5)	.8

PARTS 2 ELECTRONIC IGNITION 2 PARTS

	Part No.	Price
Distributor Assy.		
V-8-250		
1986-87	◆1103730	N.L.
(1) Distributor Cover		
1986-87-V-8	◆1875960	5.75
(2) Coil		
1986-87-V-8	◆1985474	N.L.
(3) Cap		
1986-87-V-8	◆1977046	24.25
(4) Rotor		
1986-87-V-8	◆1977026	N.L.
(5) Mainshaft		
1986-87-V-8	◆1979556	37.75
(6) Pole Piece & Plate Assy.		
1986-87-V-8	◆1977207	31.75
(7) Module		
1986-87-V-8	◆1987744	N.L.
(8) Capacitor (w/Terminal Block)		
1986-87-V-8	◆1892261	N.L.
(9) Housing		
1986-87-V-8	◆10497570	53.50

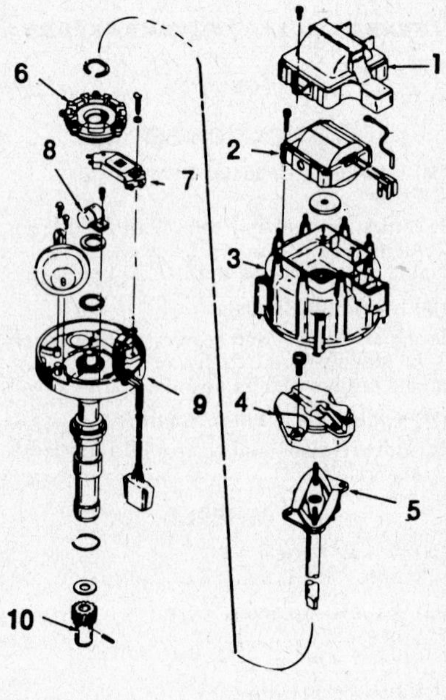

	Part No.	Price
(10) Gear		
1986-87-V-8	◆10499163	N.L.
C3I Ignition System		
V-6-231		
Coil (w/Module-C3I)		
1986-87	◆1103608	313.00
Sensor Crankshaft Position		
1986-87-C3I	◆1103691	19.00
Sensor Cam Position		
1986-87-C3I	◆25523227	27.50
Module Electric Spark Control		
1986-87	◆16049534	70.00
Ignition Switch (On Column)		
1986-87		
Buick & Cadillac	◆7846340	15.25
Olds-wo/ Console	◆1990118	12.75
Olds-w/ Console	◆1990120	12.25
Ignition Warning Buzzer Switch		
1986-87-exc. Olds	◆7846712	11.75
Olds	◆7811092	4.75

LABOR 3 FUEL SYSTEM 3 LABOR

	(Factory Time)	Chilton Time
(M) Air Cleaner, Service		
All models		.3
(G) Air Cleaner Vacuum Motor, Renew		
All models	(.3)	.4
(G) Air Cleaner Temperature Sensor, Renew		
ALI models	(.3)	.4
(G) Throttle Body, Remove and Install		
1986-87		
V-6	(.3)	.5
V-8	(.3)	.5
Renew throttle body add	(.3)	.3
Renew fuel meter body add	(.3)	.3
(G) Throttle Body Fuel Meter Assy., Renew		
1986-87		
V-8	(.4)	.6
(G) Idle Air Control Valve, Renew		
1986-87		
V-6	(.2)	.3
(G) Minimum Idle Speed, Adjust		
All models	(.4)	.6
(G) Throttle Body Injector and/or Gasket, Renew		
1986-87		
V-8-one	(.4)	.6
both	(.4)	.8
(G) Fuel Pressure Regulator and/or Gaskets, Renew		
1986-87		
V-6	(.3)	.5
Perform balance test add	(.4)	.4
(G) Fuel Pump Relay, Renew		
1986-87		
V-6	(.3)	.4
V-8	(.2)	.3
(G) Fuel Injector, Renew		
1986-87		
V-6-one	(.6)	1.0
each adtnl	(.1)	.2
Perform balance test add	(.4)	.4
(G) Fuel Rail, Renew		
1986-87		
V-6	(.6)	1.0
(G) Mass Air Flow Sensor, Renew		
1986-87		
V-6	(.3)	.4
(G) Instrument Panel Cluster Assy., Renew		
1986-87		
Eldorado & Seville	(.7)	1.2
Riviera	(.5)	.9
Toronado	(.4)	.8
(G) Fuel Tank, Renew		
Includes: Drain and refill tank, transfer sending unit.		
1986-87		
Eldorado & Seville	(.7)	1.1
Riviera	(.8)	1.2
Toronado	(1.3)	1.7
(G) Fuel Gauge (Tank Unit), Renew		
1986-87		
Eldorado & Seville	(.9)	1.3
Riviera	(1.0)	1.4
Toronado	(1.4)	1.8
(G) Intake Manifold and/or Gaskets, Renew		
V-6–1986-87	(1.5)	2.1
V-8–1986-87	(3.8)	4.9
Renew manif add		.5

PARTS 3 FUEL SYSTEM 3 PARTS

	Part No.	Price
Air Cleaner Element		
1986-87-V-6	◆25095333	13.25
V-8	◆25043852	15.25
Temperature Sensor (Air Cleaner)		
1986-87-V-6	◆25036751	21.00
V-8	◆8997787	18.50
Mass Air Flow Sensor		
1986-87-V-6	◆25007540	135.00
Vacuum Motor (Air Cleaner)		
1986-87-V-8	◆25095481	225.00
Separator Kit (Crankcase Vent)		
1986-87-V-8	◆25041743	6.00

PARTS 3 THROTTLE BODY INJECTION 3 PARTS

	Part No.	Price
V-8 THROTTLE BODY INJECTION		
(1) Throttle Body Injection Unit		
1986-87	◆17111500	650.00
(2) Throttle Body Kit		
1986-87	◆17111503	185.75
(3) Idle Speed Control Kit		
1986-87	◆17111170	108.75
(4) Fuel Meter Kit		
1986-87	◆17111501	296.75
Two injectors and pressure regulator included.		
(5) Throttle Position Sensor		
1986-87	◆17110352	100.50
Fuel Injector Kit		
1986-87	◆17111277	179.50
Gasket Kit&.17078257‡		
Fuel Pump		
1986-87	◆25115334	87.00
Fuel Tank		
1986-87	◆1638239	N.L.
Fuel Meter (Tank Unit)		
1986-87	◆25091211	156.50
Intake Gaskets		
1986-87	◆3634619	N.L.

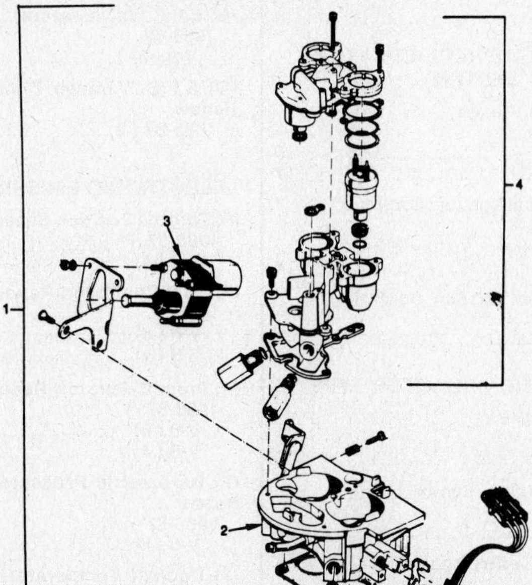

PARTS 3 ELECTRONIC FUEL INJECTION 3 PARTS

	Part No.	Price
V-6–3.8L SEQUENTIAL FUEL INJECTION		
(1) Throttle Body Assembly		
1986-87	◆25524565	150.00
(2) Idle Air Control Motor		
1986-87	◆25527077	29.00
(3) Throttle Position Sensor		
1986-87	◆25036663	23.50
(4) Throttle Body Gasket		
1986-87	◆25517008	.75
Fuel Injector		
1986-87	◆25519366	85.50
Fuel Injection Rail		
1986-87	◆25526902	144.00
Pressure Regulator		
1986-87	◆25519368	42.25
Fuel Pump Relay		
1986-87	◆25520198	5.25
Fuel Pump		
1986-87	◆25115429	79.75
Fuel Tank		
1986-87	◆1638239	N.L.
Fuel Meter (Tank Unit)		
1986-87	◆25092103	147.75
Intake Gaskets		
1986-87	◆1264924	N.L.

LABOR 3A EMISSION CONTROLS 3A LABOR

(Factory Time)	Chilton Time
(G) Emission Control Check	
Includes: Check and adjust engine idle speed and mixture and ignition timing. Check P.C.V. valve.	
All models	.6
POSITIVE CRANKCASE VENTILATION	
(M) Positive Crankcase Ventilation Valve, Renew	
All models (.2)	.3
(M) Crankcase Ventilation Filter Assy., Renew	
All models (.2)	.3
EVAPORATIVE EMISSION TYPE	
(G) Charcoal Canister, Renew	
All models (.2)	.3
(G) Charcoal Canister Filter, Renew	
All models (.5)	.3
CONTROLLED COMBUSTION TYPE	
(G) Air Cleaner Vacuum Motor, Renew	
1986-87 (.3)	.4
(G) Air Cleaner Temperature Sensor, Renew	
1986-87 (.3)	.4
EXHAUST GAS RECIRCULATION SYSTEM	
(G) E.G.R. Valve, Renew	
1986-87	
V-6 (.3)	.5
V-8 (.5)	.7
(G) E.G.R. Thermal Vacuum Switch, Renew	
1986-87	
V-8 (.2)	.4
(G) Thermostatic Vacuum Control Switch, Renew	
1986-87 (.2)	.4
AIR INJECTION REACTOR TYPE	
(G) Air Pump, Renew	
1986-87	
V-8 (.6)	.9
(G) AIR Check Valve, Renew	
1986-87	
V-8 (.2)	.3
(G) Air Pump Centrifugal Filter, Renew	
1986-87 (.4)	.6
(M) A.I.R. Drive Belt, Renew	
1986-87 (.2)	.4

CHILTON'S EMISSION CONTROL TUNE-UP

1. Clean or renew P.C.V. valve, hoses and filter.
2. Check fuel tank cap for sealing ability.
3. Check fuel tank and fuel lines for leakage.
4. Check evaporation canister and filter. Replace if necessary.
5. Check engine compression to determine leakage of unburned gases. (Add time for items of interference).
6. Test and clean or renew spark plugs.
7. Check engine oil dipstick for sealing ability.
8. Test exhaust system with analyzer and check system for leakage.
9. Check exhaust manifold heat valve for operation.
10. Adjust ignition timing and carburetor idle speed and mixture.
11. Check automatic choke mechanism for free operation.
12. Inspect air cleaner and element.
13. On models so equipped, test distributor vacuum control switch and transmission control switch.

V-6 .... **1.7**
V-8 .... **1.8**

For repairs made, charge accordingly.

(Factory Time)	Chilton Time
E.F.E. SYSTEM	
(G) E.F.E. Valve, Renew	
1986-87	
V-8 (.5)	.7
(G) E.F.E. Vacuum Check Valve, Renew	
1986-87 (.2)	.3
ELECTRONIC EMISSION CONTROLS	
(P) Throttle Position Sensor, Adjust	
1986-87	
V-6 (.4)	.6
(P) ECM Controller, Renew	
1968-87	
V-6 (.6)	.8
V-8 (.4)	.6
(P) Prom Calibrator, Renew	
1986-87	
V-6 (.6)	.8
V-8 (.4)	.6
(P) Barometric Pressure Sensor, Renew	
1986-87	
V-6 (.4)	.6
(P) Coolant Temperature Sensor, Renew	
1986-87	
V-6 (.4)	.6
V-8 (.3)	.5

(Factory Time)	Chilton Time
(P) Manifold Absolute Pressure Sensor, Renew	
1986-87	
V-8 (.4)	.6
(P) Manifold Temperature Sensor, Renew	
1986-87	
V-6 (.4)	.6
V-8 (.3)	.5
(P) Oxygen Sensor, Renew	
1986-87	
V-6 (.5)	.7
V-8 (.3)	.5
(P) Vehicle Speed Sensor, Renew	
1986-87	
V-6 (.4)	.6
V-8 (.6)	.8
(P) Throttle Position Sensor, Renew	
1986-87	
V-6 (.9)	1.2
V-8 (.5)	.7
(P) Calpak, Renew	
1986-87	
V-6 (.3)	.5
(P) Back-Up Lamp and Park/Neutral Switch, Renew	
1986-87	
V-6 (.5)	.7

LABOR 3A EMISSION CONTROLS 3A LABOR

	(Factory Time)	Chilton Time
(P) Air Control/Air Switching Valve, Renew		
1986-87		
V-8	(.4)	.6
(P) E.G.R. Vacuum Control Solenoid, Renew		
1986-87		
V-6	(.3)	.4
V-8	(.3)	.4
(P) Vacuum Control Purge Solenoid, Renew		
1986-87		
V-8	(.3)	.4
(P) Fuel Vapor Canister Purge Solenoid, Renew		
1986-87		
V-6	(.3)	.4
(P) Idle Speed Control Motor, Renew or Adjust		
1986-87		
V-8	(.5)	.7

PARTS 3A EMISSION CONTROLS 3A PARTS

	Part No.	Price
POSITIVE CRANKCASE VENTILATION		
Positive Crankcase Vent. Valve		
1986-87-V-6	◆6487936	N.L.
V-8	◆6487532	N.L.
EVAPORATIVE EMISSION TYPE		
Charcoal Canister		
1986-87-V-6	◆17085935	44.75
V-8	◆17075834	51.00
Vapor Canister Filter		
1986-87	◆7026014	N.L.
CONTROLLED COMBUSTION TYPE		
Refer to Fuel Injection Sections		
EXHAUST GAS RECIRCULATION SYSTEM		
E.G.R. Valve		
1986-87-V-6	◆17111583	37.25
V-8	◆17111584	58.75
E.G.R. Valve Control Switch		
1986-87-V-6		
stamped	◆25522717	41.75
stamped	◆25527186	45.00
E.G.R. Solenoid Valve		
1986-87-V-8	◆1997156	29.25
AIR INJECTION REACTOR TYPE		
Air Pump		
1986-87-V-8	◆7834919	149.00
Check Valve		
1986-87-V-8	◆22040899	18.75
ELECTRONIC EMISSIONS CONTROLS		
Sensor (Throttle Position)		
1986-87-V-6	◆25036663	23.25
V-8 (Kit)	◆17110352	100.50
ECM Controller		
1986-87-V-6	◆1227057	110.00
V-8	◆1227056	110.00
PROM Calibrator		
Part numbers listed are for pricing reference only. Order with complete year, model, engine and component I.D. number.		
1986-87-V-6		
Code 4435HSU	◆16054434	40.50
Code 0425CMY	◆16060423	40.50
1986-87-V-8		
Code 3049FDC	◆16053048	40.50
Code 9159AFP	◆16059158	N.L.
Sensor Coolant Temperature		
1986-87	◆25036708	12.75
MAP Sensor		
1986-87-V-8	◆16006835	N.L.
Speed Sensor		
1986-87-V-6		
Trans. Mtd.	◆25007335	44.00
Cluster Mtd.	◆25007463	44.00
1986-87-V-8	◆25007335	44.00
Oxygen Sensor		
1986-87	◆8990741	28.75
Knock Sensor		
1986-87	◆1997562	37.00

LABOR 4 ALTERNATOR AND REGULATOR 4 LABOR

	(Factory Time)	Chilton Time
(G) Delcotron Circuits, Test		
Includes: Test battery, regulator, Delcotron output.		
All models		.6
(M) Alternator Drive Belt, Renew		
1986-87		
V-6	(.3)	.5
V-8	(.2)	.4
(G) Delcotron Assembly, Renew		
Includes: Transfer fan and pulley.		
1986-87		
V-6	(.5)	.7
V-8	(.5)	.7
Delcotron, R&R and Recondition		
Includes: Completely disassemble, inspect, test, replace parts as required, reassemble.		
1986-87		
V-6	(1.4)	2.1
V-8	(1.0)	1.7
(G) Delcotron Front Bearing, Renew		
Includes: R&R Delcotron, separate end frames.		
1986-87		
V-6	(.5)	1.0
V-8	(.8)	1.0
(G) Delcotron Voltage Regulator, Test and Renew		
Includes: R&R disassemble and reassemble Delcotron.		
1986-87		
V-6	(.8)	1.3
V-8	(.7)	1.2

PARTS 4 ALTERNATOR AND REGULATOR 4 PARTS

	Part No.	Price
Delcotron Assy.		
Remanufactured.		
1986-87		
108 amp	◆10456319	173.50
120 amp (V-6)	◆10497108	191.75
120 amp (V-8)	◆10497111	191.75
New-Service Alternator		
78 amp	◆1105369	228.50
(1) Capacitor		
1986-87-78 amp	◆1978146	4.50
(2) Diode Trio		
1986-87-78 amp	◆1984459	N.L.

PARTS 4 ALTERNATOR AND REGULATOR 4 PARTS

	Part No.	Price
(3) Rectifier Bridge		
1986-87-78 amp	◆1984454	N.L.
(4) Bearing (Rear)		
1986-87-78 amp	◆9436831	N.L.
(5) Frame (Slip Ring End)		
1986-87-78 amp	◆1984460	47.75
(6) Regulator		
1986-87-78 amp	◆1116387	N.L.
(7) Brush Holder		
1986-87-78 amp	◆1984462	N.L.
(8) Rotor Assy.		
1986-87-78 amp	◆1984466	N.L.
(9) Stator Assy.		
1986-87-78 amp	◆1984445	37.25
(10) Bearing (Front)		
1986-87-78 amp	◆908419	9.75
(11) Frame (Drive End)		
1986-87-78 amp	◆1986206	23.75

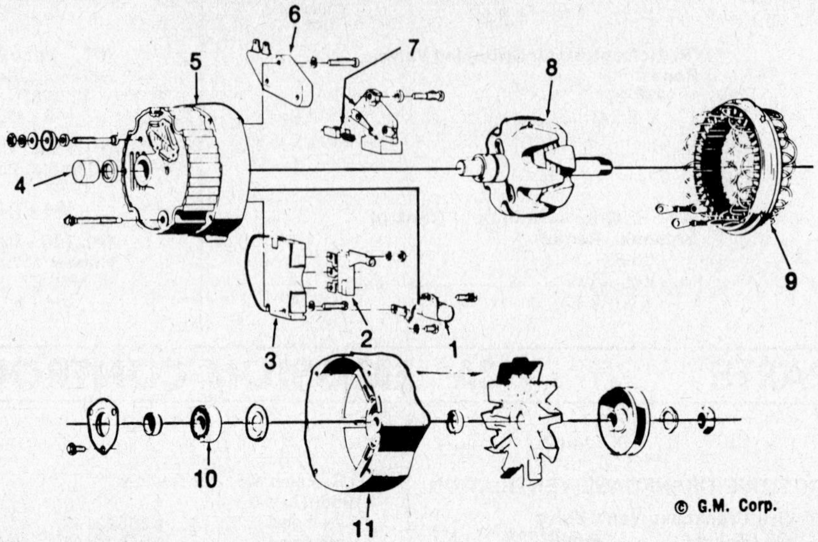

LABOR 5 STARTING SYSTEM 5 LABOR

	(Factory Time)	Chilton Time
(G) Starter Draw Test		
All models		.3
(G) Starter Assembly, Renew		
Includes: Transfer solenoid.		
1986-87		
V-6	(.6)	1.0
V-8	(.4)	.8
(G) Starter, R&R and Recondition		
Includes: Turn down armature.		
1986-87		
V-6	(1.3)	2.1
V-8	(1.3)	2.1
Add draw test if performed.		
(G) Starter Drive, Renew		
Includes: R&R starter and solenoid.		
1986-87		
V-6	(.7)	1.2
V-8	(.6)	1.0
(G) Starter Motor Solenoid, Renew		
Includes: R&R starter.		
1986-87		
V-6	(.6)	1.0
V-8	(.5)	1.0
(G) Ignition Switch, Renew		
1986-87	(.6)	.9
(M) Battery Cables, Renew		
All models		
positive	(.6)	.8
negative	(.3)	.3
to start connector	(.2)	.3
(M) Battery Terminals, Clean		
All models		.3

PARTS 5 STARTING SYSTEM 5 PARTS

	Part No.	Price
(1) Starter Assy.		
1986-87-V-6	◆1998545	247.50
V-8	◆1998509	189.00
(2) Solenoid		
1986-87-V-8	◆1114557	33.25
(3) Starter Drive Assy.		
1986-87-V-8	◆1984511	23.25
(4) Brush Set		
1986-87-V-8	◆1893296	.75
(5) Drive End Bushing		
1986-87-V-8	◆1932190	.75
(6) Commutator End Frame		
1986-87-V-8	◆1978292	6.50
(7) Armature		
1986-87-V-8	◆10495931	71.50
(8) Field Coils		
1986-87-V-8	◆1985143	71.50
Frame included.		
(9) Drive End Housing		
1986-87-V-8	◆10495253	35.75

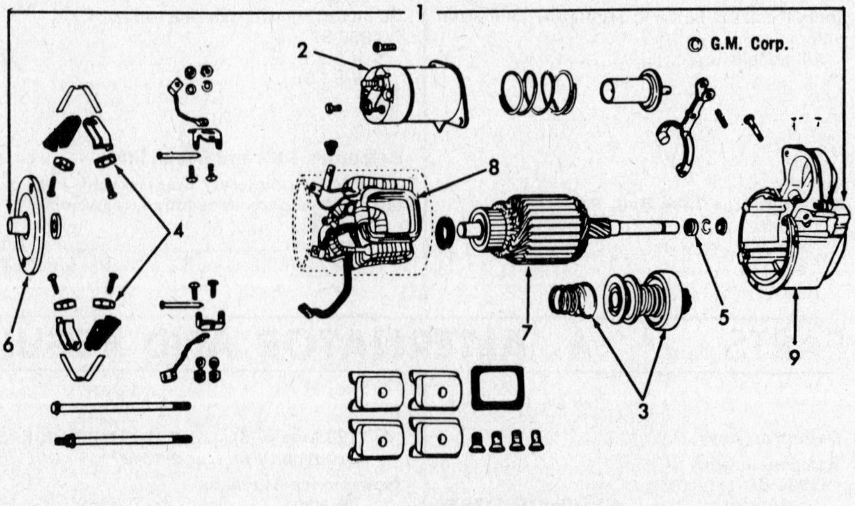

PARTS 5 STARTING SYSTEM 5 PARTS

	Part No.	Price
Ignition Switch (Column)		
1986-87		
Buick & Cadillac	◆7846340	15.25
Olds-wo/ Console	◆1990118	12.75
Olds-w/ Console	◆1990120	12.75

	Part No.	Price
Neutral Safety Switch		
1986-87		
Buick	◆1994253	12.50
Olds & Cadillac	◆1994267	86.00

Battery Cables
Order by year and model.

LABOR 6 BRAKE SYSTEM 6 LABOR

(Factory Time)	Chilton Time
(G) Brake Pedal Free Play, Adjust	
All models	.3
(G) Bleed Brakes (Four Wheels)	
Includes: Fill master cylinder.	
All models (.4)	.5
(G) Brake System Failure Warning Switch, Renew	
1986-87 (.2)	.3

BRAKE HYDRAULIC SYSTEM

(Factory Time)	Chilton Time
(G) Brake Hose, Renew (Flex)	
Includes: Bleed system.	
1986-87-front-one (.6)	.8
both (.8)	1.2
rear-one (.6)	.8
both (.8)	1.2
(G) Master Cylinder, Renew	
Includes: Bleed system.	
1986-87 (.7)	1.0
(G) Master Cylinder, R&R and Recondition	
Includes: Bleed system.	
1986-87 (1.5)	2.0
(G) Brake System, Flush & Refill	
All models	1.2

DISC BRAKES

(Factory Time)	Chilton Time
(G) Disc Brake Pads, Renew	
Includes: Install new disc brake pads only.	
1986-87	
front (.8)	1.1
rear (1.0)	1.3
all four wheels	2.3
Resurface disc rotor add, each	.9
(G) Disc Brake Rotor, Renew	
Includes: R&R wheel, transfer bearings and races. Clean and repack wheel bearings.	
1986-87	
front-one (.5)	.8
both (.8)	1.4
rear-one (.6)	.9
both (.9)	1.4
all four wheels	2.5

COMBINATIONS
Add to Brakes, Renew
See Machine Shop Operations

(G) REBUILD CALIPER ASSEMBLY	
Each (.5)	.6
(G) RENEW MASTER CYLINDER	
All models (.3)	.8
(G) REBUILD MASTER CYLINDER	
All models (.8)	1.0
(G) RENEW BRAKE HOSE	
Each (.3)	.3
(G) REPACK FRONT WHEEL BEARINGS (BOTH WHEELS)	
All models (.3)	.6
(G) RENEW DISC BRAKE ROTOR	
Each (.2)	.3

(Factory Time)	Chilton Time
(G) Caliper Assembly, Renew	
Includes: Remove brake shoes. Bleed system.	
1986-87	
front-one (.7)	1.0
both (1.1)	1.5
rear-one (.7)	1.0
both (1.1)	1.5
all four wheels	2.5
Caliper Assy., R&R and Recondition	
Includes: Remove brake shoes, renew parts as required and bleed system.	
1986-87	
front-one (1.2)	1.5
both (2.1)	2.5
rear-one (1.2)	1.5
both (2.1)	2.5
all four wheels	5.0

POWER BRAKES

(Factory Time)	Chilton Time
(G) Power Brake Cylinder, Renew	
Includes: R&R master cylinder.	
1986-87 (.7)	1.1
(G) Power Brake Cylinder, R&R and Recondition	
Includes: R&R master cylinder.	
1986-87 (1.4)	2.0
Recond m/Cyl add (.8)	.8
(G) Power Brake Check Valve, Renew	
1986-87 (.5)	.5
(G) Low Vacuum Switch, Renew	
1986-87 (.2)	.3
(G) Low Vacuum Brake Indicator Module Assy., Renew	
1986-87 (.2)	.4

PARKING BRAKE

(Factory Time)	Chilton Time
(M) Parking Brake, Adjust	
All models (.3)	.4
(G) Parking Brake Control, Renew	
Toronado	
1986-87 (1.4)	1.9
Riviera	
1986-87 (.6)	1.0
Eldorado & Seville	
1986-87 (.6)	1.0
Renew vacuum diaph add	.3
(G) Parking Brake Equalizer, Renew	
1986-87 (.4)	.5
(G) Parking Brake Warning Lamp Switch, Renew	
1986-87	
Eldorado & Seville (.3)	.4
Riviera (.3)	.4
Toronado (.5)	.7
(G) Parking Brake Cables, Renew	
1986-87-front (.8)	1.0
rear-one (.7)	1.1

PARTS 6 BRAKE SYSTEM 6 PARTS

	Part No.	Price
Master Cylinder		
1986-87	◆18013425	210.00
Repair Kit (Master Cylinder)		
1986-87	◆18012657	17.75
Reservoir & Grommet Kit		
1986-87	◆18013409	40.00

	Part No.	Price
Proportioner Valve		
1986-87		
10mm	◆18012129	21.00
13mm	◆18012130	21.00
Sensor Kit (Fluid Level)		
1986-87	◆18012132	5.75
Power Brake Booster		
1986-87-V-6	◆18011749	271.00
V-8	◆18011750	248.50

	Part No.	Price
Repair Kit (Powerhead)		
1986-87	◆18007865	47.50
Air Valve (Plunger & Valve)		
1986-87	◆18012679	28.00
Vacuum Switch Kit		
1986-87-V-8	◆18010278	10.50

PARTS 6 DISC BRAKES 6 PARTS

	Part No.	Price
FRONT DISC BRAKES		
Disc Rotor		
1986-87	◆14035588	94.25
(1) Brake Pad Set		
1986-87	◆12321415	N.L.
(2) Spring Kit (Anti-Rattle)		
1986-87 (Insulator)	◆18013564	1.75
(3) Piston Seals (Repair Kit)		
1986-87	◆18012693	8.50
(4) Piston		
1986-87	◆18011608	14.25
(5) Caliper		
1986-87-L.H.	◆18012690	152.00
R.H.	◆18012691	152.00
Bushing Kit		
1986-87	◆18013996	10.25
Hub and Bearing Kit		
1986-87	◆7470003	184.50

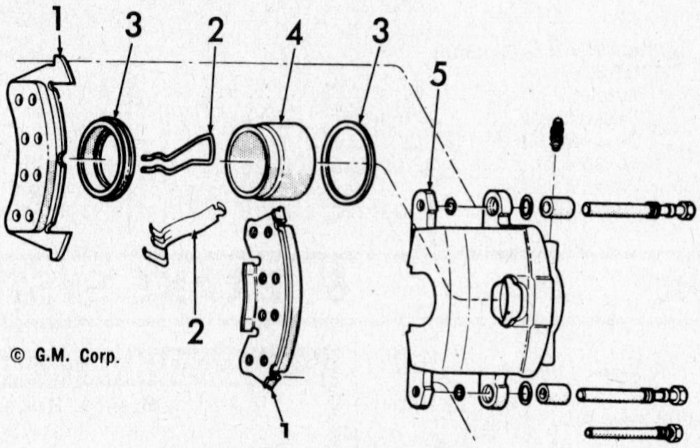

	Part No.	Price
Seal (Grease Retainer)		
1986-87	◆14084119	3.75

	Part No.	Price
Brake Hose		
1986-87-L.H.	◆17982337	18.00
R.H.	◆17982338	18.00

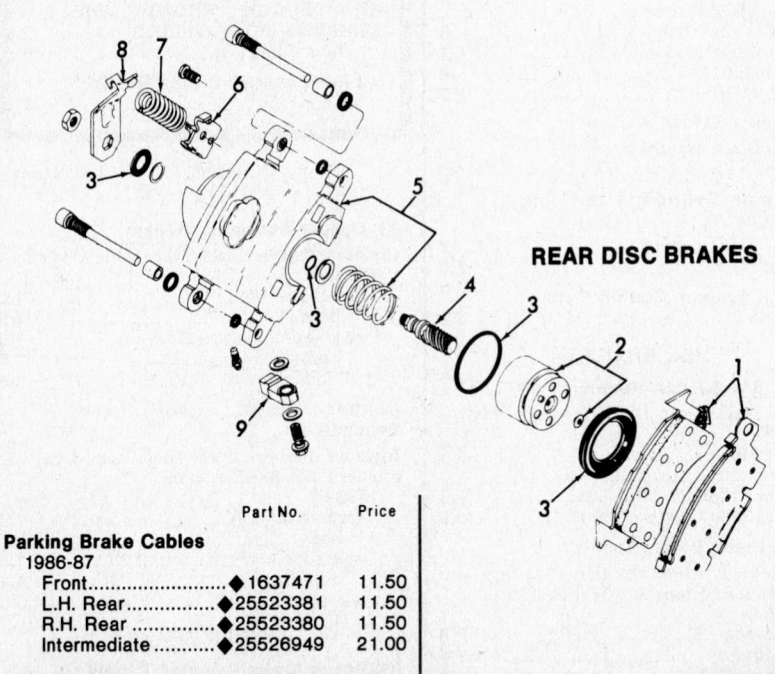

PARTS 6 DISC BRAKES 6 PARTS

	Part No.	Price
REAR DISC BRAKES		
Disc Rotor		
1986-87	◆25526230	48.50
(1) Brake Pad Set		
1986-87	◆12321416	N.L.
(2) Actuator Kit (Piston)		
1986-87	◆18013677	81.50
(3) Repair Kit (Piston Seals)		
1986-87	◆18012689	29.75
(4) Screw & Locknut Pkg.		
1986-87	◆18012703	14.50
(5) Caliper Assy.		
1986-87	◆18012692	309.00
(6) Bracket Kit		
1986-87	◆18012702	6.50
(7) Return Spring (Parking Lever)		
1986-87	◆18013882	10.75
(8) Lever (Parking Brake)		
1986-87	◆18013824	5.25
Bushing Kit		
1986-87	◆18013996	10.25
Brake Hose		
1986-87-L.H.	◆17985579	10.00
R.H.	◆17985580	9.75

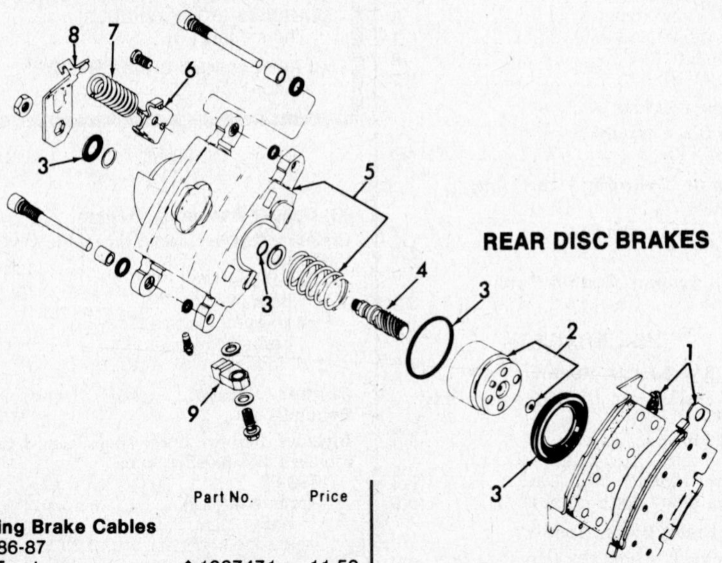

REAR DISC BRAKES

	Part No.	Price
Parking Brake Cables		
1986-87		
Front	◆1637471	11.50
L.H. Rear	◆25523381	11.50
R.H. Rear	◆25523380	11.50
Intermediate	◆25526949	21.00

LABOR 7 COOLING SYSTEM 7 LABOR

	(Factory Time)	Chilton Time
(M) Winterize Cooling System		
Includes: Run engine to check for leaks, tighten all hose connections. Test radiator and pressure cap, drain radiator and engine block. Add anti-freeze and refill system.		
All models		.5
(G) Thermostat, Renew		
1986-87		
V-6	(.6)	.8
V-8	(.3)	.5

	(Factory Time)	Chilton Time
(G) Radiator Assembly, R&R or Renew		
Includes: Drain and refill cooling system.		
1986-87		
V-6	(.5)	.9
V-8	(.8)	1.4
Renew side tank and/or gskt add		
one side	(.7)	.7.
both sides	(1.2)	1.2

	(Factory Time)	Chilton Time
ADD THESE OPERATIONS TO RADIATOR R&R		
(G) Boil & Repair		1.5
(G) Rod Clean		1.9
(G) Repair Core		1.3
(G) Renew Trans. Oil Cooler		1.9
(G) Recore Radiator		1.7

LABOR 7 COOLING SYSTEM 7 LABOR

(Factory Time) Chilton Time

(M) Radiator Hoses, Renew
Includes: Drain and refill cooling system.

1986-87-upper (.3)	.4
lower (.4)	.5
both (.5)	.7
by-pass (.5)	.7

(M) Serpentine Drive Belt, Renew
1986-87

V-6 (.3)	.5
V-8 (.2)	.4

(G) Serpentine Belt Tensioner, Renew
1986-87

V-6 (.5)	.7
V-8 (.2)	.4

(G) Water Pump, Renew
Includes: Drain and refill cooling system.
1986-87

V-6 (.6)	1.0
V-8 (1.3)	2.0

(G) Engine Coolant Fan Relay, Renew

1986-87-V-6 (.3)	.4
w/Heavy duty cool. add (.1)	.1

(G) Engine Cooling Fan Resistor, Renew

1986-87-V-6 (.4)	.6

(G) Engine Coolant Fan Electronic Control Module Assy., Renew

1986-87 (.3)	.4

(G) Electronic Cooling Fan Blade and/or Motor, Renew
1986-87

V-6 (.5)	.7
V-8-one (.3)	.5
both (.6)	.8

COOLING SYSTEM TUNE-UP

An Annual Cooling System Tune-Up Suggestion List should include (with some exceptions):

1. A visual check of the cooling system for indications of leaks or excessive oil content.
2. Pressure check the cooling system for internal and external leaks with filler cap and neck adapter and tester.
3. Check crankcase and automatic transmission oil for water content.
4. Test coolant thermostat with radiator thermometer.
5. Check temperature gauge for accuracy.
6. Drain system and flush till clean.
7. Clean foreign matter from radiator fins.
8. Test radiator pressure cap with cap tester.
9. Check fan blades and pulleys for alignment and damage.
10. Internal and external inspection of all hoses for cracks and deterioration.
11. Check core plugs (where possible) for seepage.
12. Refill system with correct coolant and check for air locks.
13. Check condition and tension of drive belts with tension gauge.

All models 1.5

(Factory Time) Chilton Time

(G) Engine Coolant Temperature Switch (Engine Unit), Renew

1986-87 (.3)	.5

(Factory Time) Chilton Time

(G) Water Jacket Expansion Plugs, Renew
(Side of Block)

each	.5

Note: If necessary to R&R any component to gain access to plug, add appropriate time.

(M) Heater Hoses, Renew
Includes: Drain and refill coolant.

1986-87-one (.3)	.4
all (.8)	1.1

(G) Heater Core, R&R or Renew

1986-87 (1.4)	2.7

Add time to evacuate and charge A.C. system if required.

ADD THESE OPERATIONS TO HEATER CORE R&R

(G) Boil & Repair	1.2
(G) Repair Core	.9
(G) Recore	1.2

(G) Heater Control Assembly, Renew
1986-87-See Air Conditioning Group.

(G) Heater Blower Motor, Renew
1986-87-See Air Conditioning Group.

(G) Heater Blower Motor Switch, Renew
1986-87-See Air Conditioning Group.

(G) Heater Water Control Valve, Renew

Eldorado & Seville	
1986-87 (.3)	.5
Toronado	
1986-87 (.5)	.6
Riviera	
1986-87 (.4)	.6

PARTS 7 COOLING SYSTEM 7 PARTS

	Part No.	Price
(1) Radiator Assy.		
Order by code. I.D. stamped on tag.		
(2) Thermostat		
1986-87-V-6	◆3037747	6.75
V-8	◆3055672	6.75
(3) Radiator Hoses		
Order by model and year.		
(4) Water Pump Assy.		
1986-87-V-6	◆25527537	63.00
V-8	◆3634606	96.50
(5) Drive Belts		
Order by model and year.		
Fan Kit (Blades)		
V-6		
1986-87-exc.		
H.D.	◆22049520	26.75
H.D. cooling	◆22054218	19.25
V-8		
1986-87-L.H.	◆22036292	26.25
R.H.	◆22054216	13.50

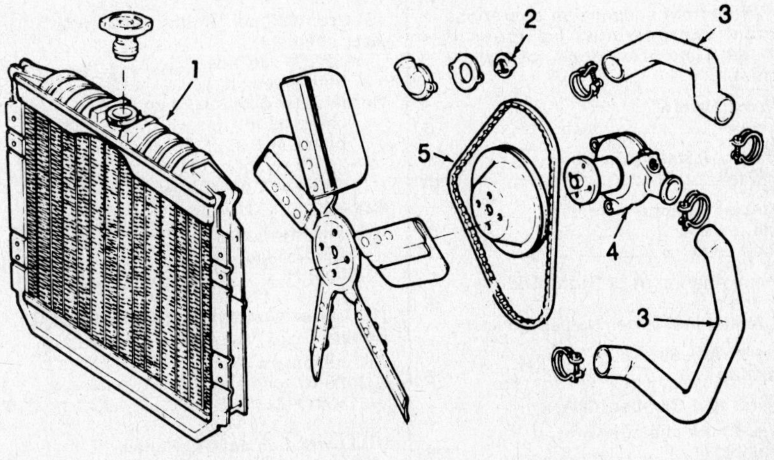

PARTS 7 COOLING SYSTEM 7 PARTS

	Part No.	Price
Fan Motor		
V-6		
1986-87		
exc. H.D.	◆22049526	86.75
H.D. cooling	◆22054217	67.00
V-8		
1986-87-L.H.	◆22048577	86.75
R.H.	◆22054220	86.75
Module (Fan Control)		
1986-87-V-8	◆1638574	134.50
Relay (Fan Control)		
1986-87	◆25520198	5.25
Resistor Kit (Fan Control)		
1986-87-V-6	◆22054222	26.75
Coolant Temperature Switch		
1986-87	◆25036708	12.75
Heater Core		
1986-87	◆3058630	114.00
Blower Motor		
1986-87	◆22049769	52.00
Control Module (Blower)		
1986-87	◆16047800	90.50
Water Control Valve		
1986-87-V-6	◆25528308	10.50
V-8	◆1631926	12.25

LABOR 8 EXHAUST SYSTEM 8 LABOR

(Factory Time)	Chilton Time
(G) Muffler, Renew	
1986-87	
V-6 (.7)	**1.0**
V-8 (.5)	**.8**
(G) Intermediate Exhaust Pipe, Renew	
1986-87	
V-6 (.5)	**.8**
V-8 (.4)	**.7**
(G) Front Exhaust Pipe Seal, Renew	
1986-87	
V-6 (.4)	**.7**
V-8 (.3)	**.6**
(G) Crossover Exhaust Pipe, Renew	
1986-87	
V-6 (.3)	**.6**
(G) Front Exhaust Pipe, Renew	
1986-87	
V-8-right (.5)	**.8**
left (.4)	**.7**
both (.6)	**1.0**
(G) Catalytic Converter, Renew	
1986-87	
V-6 (.8)	**1.0**
V-8 (.9)	**1.1**
(G) Exhaust Manifold, Renew	
1986-87	
V-6-right (1.7)	**2.5**
left (.5)	**.8**
V-8-right (1.3)	**1.9**
left (.9)	**1.4**
COMBINATIONS	
(G) Exhaust System, Renew (Complete)	
1986-87	
V-6 (.6)	**1.0**
V-8 (.6)	**1.1**

PARTS 8 EXHAUST SYSTEM 8 PARTS

	Part No.	Price
Pipe (Exhaust Manifold)		
1986-87-V-6	◆25529968	N.L.
V-8 (Front)	◆1632107	32.25
Crossover (Exhaust Pipe)		
1986-87-V-6	◆25523739	19.00
V-8 (Rear)	◆1633128	72.50
Converter		
1986-87-V-6	◆25101078	348.00
V-8	◆25057926	322.00
Intermediate Pipe		
1986-87-V-6	◆1638595	N.L.
V-8	◆1638595	N.L.
Muffler (w/Tailpipe)		
1986-87-V-6		
Buick	◆1638785	N.L.
Olds	◆1638786	N.L.
1986-87-V-8	◆1638787	N.L.

LABOR 9 FRONT SUSPENSION 9 LABOR

Note: On all front suspension operations alignment charges must be added if performed. Time given does not include alignment.

(Factory Time)	Chilton Time
(M) Wheel, Renew	
one (.5)	.5
(M) Wheels, Rotate (All)	
All models	.5
(G) Wheels, Balance	
one	.3
each adtnl	.2
(G) Check Alignment of Front End	
All models	.5
Note: Deduct if alignment is performed.	
(G) Toe-In, Adjust	
All models (.5)	.6
(G) Caster and Camber, Check	
Includes: Check and adjust toe.	
All models (1.1)	1.5
Adjust caster and camber	
add-each side	*.5
*Includes time to file struts as needed.	
(G) Front Wheel Bearing and Hub Assy., Renew	
1986-87-one side (.7)	**1.1**
both sides (1.2)	**2.0**
Renew inner dust seal, add	
one (.4)	**.4**
both (.7)	**.7**
(G) Lower Control Arm Assy., Renew	
Add alignment charges.	
1986-87-one (.7)	**1.1**
both (1.3)	**1.9**
(G) Lower Control Arm Bushings, Renew	
Add alignment charges.	
1986-87-one side (.9)	**1.4**
both sides (1.6)	**2.6**
(G) Lower Ball Joints, Renew	
Add alignment charges.	
1986-87-one side (1.1)	**1.5**
both sides (2.1)	**2.9**
(G) Front Coil Springs, Renew	
Add alignment charges.	
1986-87-one (.8)	**1.3**
both (1.4)	**2.3**
(G) Front Shock Absorber Strut, Renew	
Add alignment charges.	
1986-87-one (.8)	**1.3**
both (1.5)	**2.4**
(G) Front Spring Seat and/or Insulator, Renew (Upper or Lower)	
Add alignment charges.	
1986-87-one side (.8)	**1.3**
both sides (1.4)	**2.3**
(G) Front Strut Bearing Mount Assy., Renew	
Add alignment charges.	
1986-87-one side (.8)	**1.3**
both sides (1.5)	**2.4**

LABOR 9 FRONT SUSPENSION 9 LABOR

	(Factory Time)	Chilton Time
(G) Steering Knuckle Assy., Renew		
Add alignment charges.		
1986-87-one	(1.0)	1.4
both	(1.9)	2.7
(G) Steering Knuckle Inner Dust Seal, Renew		
1986-87-one	(1.0)	1.4
both	(1.9)	2.7
(G) Front Stabilizer Shaft, Renew		
1986-87	(1.2)	1.7
(G) Front Stabilizer Shaft Bushings, Renew		
1986-87-one	(.3)	.4
both	(.5)	.7
(G) Engine Cradle, Renew (Complete)		
Add alignment charges.		
1986-87	(3.2)	5.0

FRONT DRIVE AXLE

	(Factory Time)	Chilton Time
(G) Front Drive Axle, R&R or Renew		
1986-87-one	(1.2)	1.5
both	(1.9)	2.5
Renew shaft add-each	(.3)	.4
Renew C/V Joint add each side	(.3)	.4
Renew D/O Joint add each side	(.3)	.4
Renew Tri-Pot Joint add each side	(.3)	.4
Renew C/V Joint seal add each	(.2)	.2
(G) Axle Shaft Oil Seal, Renew		
1986-87-one	(.8)	1.1
both	(1.4)	2.0

PARTS 9 FRONT SUSPENSION 9 PARTS

	Part No.	Price
(1) Strut Mount (Upper)		
1986-87-V-6	◆1636132	53.50
V-8	◆1636275	53.50
(2) Spring Seat		
1986-87	◆22527449	8.25
(3) Insulator (Upper)		
1986-87	◆22527791	3.50
(4) Bumper		
1986-87	◆1627781	9.00
(5) Shield		
1986-87	◆22527729	9.50
(6) Spring		
Order by service I.D. code.		
(7) Insulator (Lower)		
1986-87	◆22527792	3.50
(8) Strut		
1986-87-V-6		
exc. H.D.	◆22047938	N.L.
H.D.	◆22047939	95.00
1986-87-V-8		
exc. H.D.	◆22047938	N.L.
H.D.	◆22047941	144.75
(9) Splash Shield		
1986-87-L.H.	◆14080265	7.50
R.H.	◆14080266	7.50
(10) Hub & Bearing Kit		
1986-87	◆7470003	184.50
(11) Steering Knuckle		
1986-87-L.H.	◆1634058	90.00
L.H.	◆1634059	90.00
(12) Seal		
1986-87	◆14084119	3.75
(13) Axle Kit		
1986-87-L.H.	◆26000332	544.00
R.H.-V-6	◆26000384	595.00
R.H.-V-8	◆26000375	595.00
(14-17) Link Kit (Stabilizer)		
1986-87	◆3634639	4.25
(18) Lower Control Arm Assy.		
1986-87-L.H.	◆22527859	105.00
R.H.	◆22527858	105.00
Ball Joint Kit		
1986-87	◆17983482	92.25
(19) Retainer		
1986-87	◆22528563	2.00
(20) Insulator (Inner)		
1986-87	◆22528801	2.00
(21) Insulator (Outer)		
1986-87-V-6	◆22530936	1.50
V-8	◆22528799	1.50
(22) Retainer		
1986-87	◆22528562	1.00

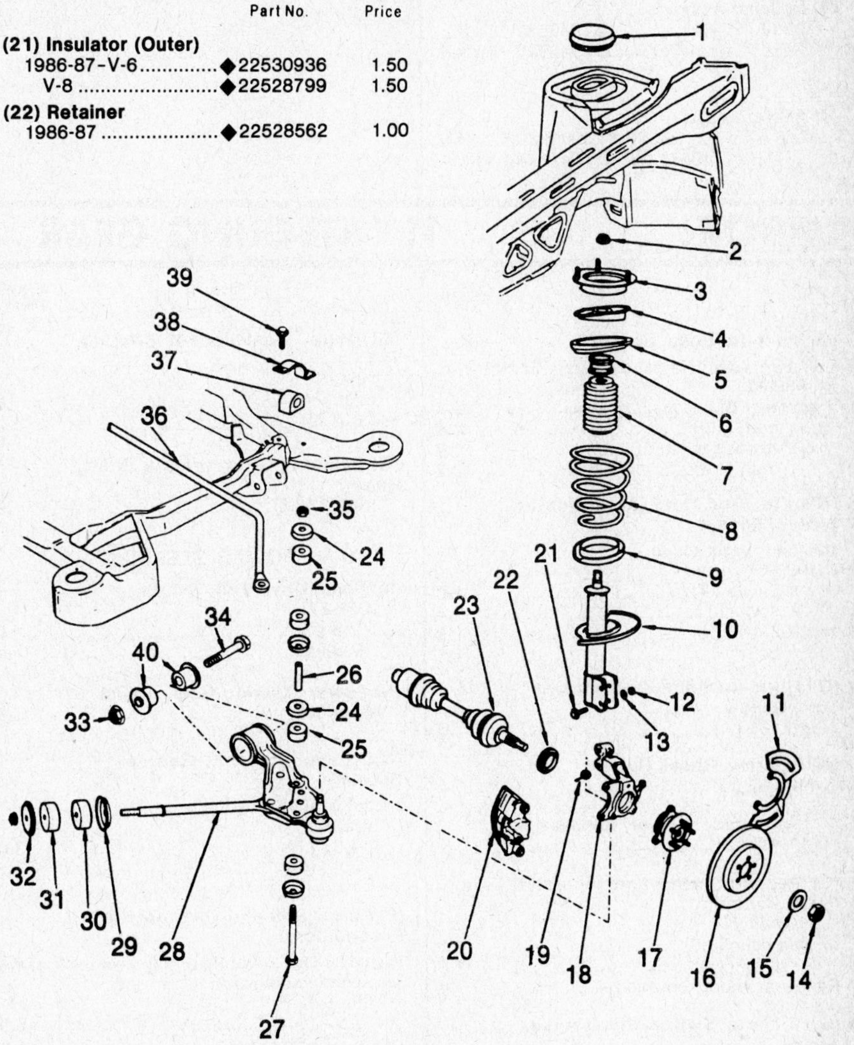

	Part No.	Price
(23) Bushing (Lower Control Arm)		
1986-87 (Front)	◆22528562	1.00
(Rear)	◆22528563	2.00
(24) Stabilizer Shaft		
1986-87-exc.		
H.D.	◆22528086	55.25
H.D.	◆22528083	55.25
(25) Stabilizer Mounting Bushing		
1986-87-exc.		
H.D.	◆22528091	2.00
H.D.	◆22528089	2.00
(26) Bracket		
1986-87	◆22528027	2.00

	Part No.	Price
(1) Joint Kit		
1986-87	◆26000322	225.00
right w/H.D.	◆26000318	385.00
(2) Seal Kit		
1986-87	◆26000317	21.50
(3) Clamp		
1986-87	◆7848880	3.25
(4) Axle Shaft		
1986-87-L.H.	◆7846210	71.50
R.H. (exc. H.D.)	◆7848444	175.00
H.D. (R.H.)	◆26002694	N.L.
(5) Housing Assy.		
1986-87-L.H.	◆7843922	N.L.
R.H.	◆7843920	N.L.
(6) Spider Assy.		
1986-87	◆26001939	N.L.
V-8 R.H. (1987)	◆7847114	110.00

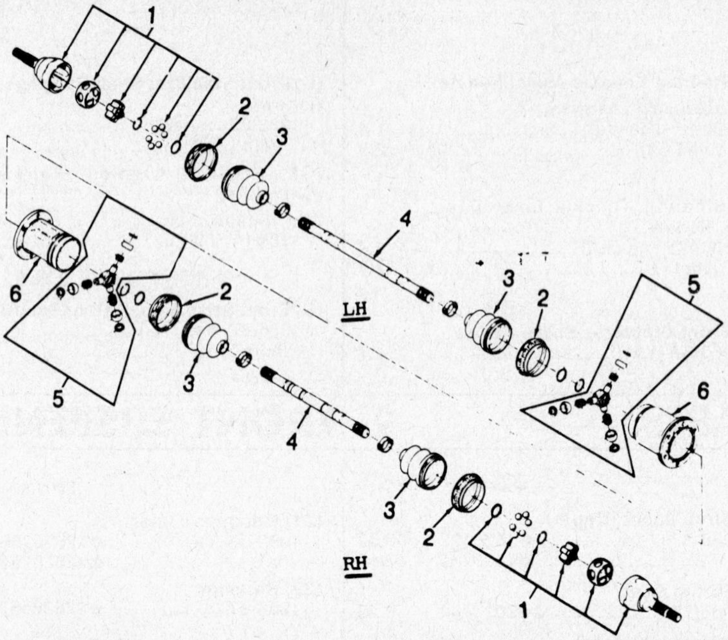

LABOR 11 STEERING GEAR 11 LABOR

(Factory Time) | Chilton Time

(G) Inner Tie Rods, Renew

Includes: R&R gear as necessary. Reset toe-in.

1986-87
- one (1.8) 2.5
- both (2.0) 2.8
- V-8-one (1.4) 1.9
- both (1.6) 2.2

(G) Tie Rod and/or Adjustor Sleeve, Renew

Includes: Reset toe-in.

1986-87
- V-6-one (.7) 1.0
- both (1.0) 1.4
- V-8-one (.5) 8
- both (.7) 1.1

(G) Horn Contact or Cancelling Cam, Renew

1986-87 (.4) 6

(G) Steering Wheel, Renew

1986-87 (.3) 5

(G) Multifunction Lever, Renew

1986-87 (.5) 9

(G) Steering Column Lock Actuator Parts, Renew

1986-87
- tilt colm (1.0) 1.5
- Tilt Tel (1.3) 1.8

Renew actuator rod add (.4) 4

(G) Dimmer Switch Pivot Assy., Renew

1986-87 (.6) 1.2

(G) Upper Mast Jacket Bearing, Renew

1986-87
- tilt colm (.5) 9
- Tilt Tel (.6) 1.0

(G) Steering Intermediate Shaft, Renew

1986-87 (.6) 9

POWER STEERING

(M) Pump Drive Belt, Renew

1986-87
- V-6 (.3) 5
- V-8 (.2) 4

(G) Power Steering Gear, Adjust

All models (.3) 6

(G) Power Steering Gear Assy., Renew

Includes: Reset toe-in.

1986-87
- V-6 (1.6) 3.0
- V-8 (1.2) 2.2

(P) Power Steering Gear, R&R and Recondition

Includes: Disassemble, renew necessary parts, reassemble and adjust.

1986-87
- V-6 (2.9) 5.3
- V-8 (2.5) 4.6

Bench leak test add 5

(G) Power Steering Short Rack Assy., Renew

Includes: Transfer parts as required. Reset toe-in.

1986-87
- V-6 (1.9) 3.9
- V-8 (1.7) 3.1

(G) Power Steering Gear Boot Seals, Renew

Includes: Reset toe-in.

1986-87
- V-6-one (1.2) 1.6
- both (1.5) 2.0
- V-8-one (1.2) 1.6
- both (1.4) 1.9

(G) Power Steering Pump, Renew

1986-87
- V-6 (.4) 7
- V-8 (.9) 1.3

(P) Power Steering Pump, R&R and Recondition

1986-87
- V-6 (.9) 1.5
- V-8 (1.5) 2.1

Renew reservoir and/or 'O' ring seal add (.1) 2

(G) Power Steering Reservoir, Renew (Remote)

1986-87 (.3) 5

(M) Power Steering Gear Cylinder Lines, Renew

1986-87-one (.4) 6
- both (.5) 8

PARTS 11 POWER STEERING GEAR 11 PARTS

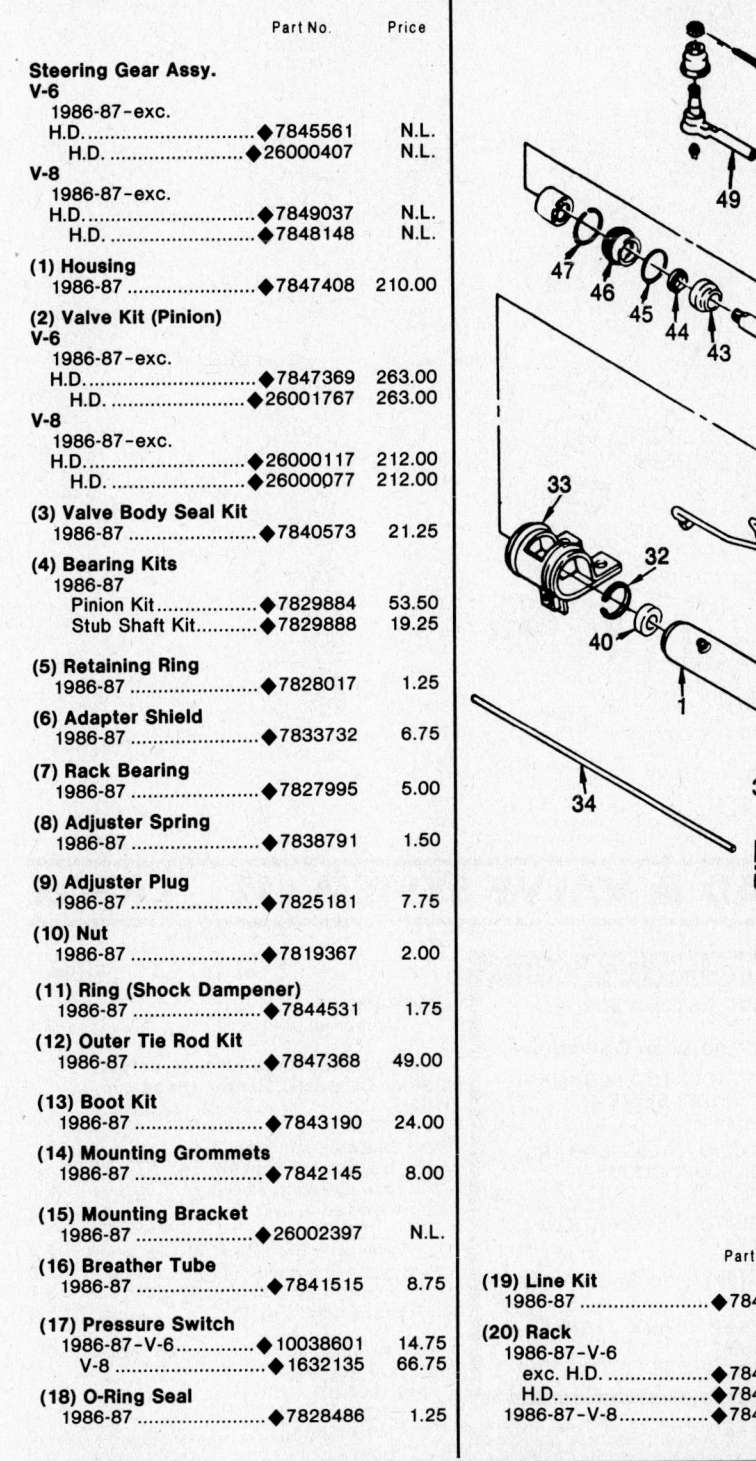

	Part No.	Price
Steering Gear Assy.		
V-6		
1986-87-exc.		
H.D.	◆7845561	N.L.
H.D.	◆26000407	N.L.
V-8		
1986-87-exc.		
H.D.	◆7849037	N.L.
H.D.	◆7848148	N.L.
(1) Housing		
1986-87	◆7847408	210.00
(2) Valve Kit (Pinion)		
V-6		
1986-87-exc.		
H.D.	◆7847369	263.00
H.D.	◆26001767	263.00
V-8		
1986-87-exc.		
H.D.	◆26000117	212.00
H.D.	◆26000077	212.00
(3) Valve Body Seal Kit		
1986-87	◆7840573	21.25
(4) Bearing Kits		
1986-87		
Pinion Kit	◆7829884	53.50
Stub Shaft Kit	◆7829888	19.25
(5) Retaining Ring		
1986-87	◆7828017	1.25
(6) Adapter Shield		
1986-87	◆7833732	6.75
(7) Rack Bearing		
1986-87	◆7827995	5.00
(8) Adjuster Spring		
1986-87	◆7838791	1.50
(9) Adjuster Plug		
1986-87	◆7825181	7.75
(10) Nut		
1986-87	◆7819367	2.00
(11) Ring (Shock Dampener)		
1986-87	◆7844531	1.75
(12) Outer Tie Rod Kit		
1986-87	◆7847368	49.00
(13) Boot Kit		
1986-87	◆7843190	24.00
(14) Mounting Grommets		
1986-87	◆7842145	8.00
(15) Mounting Bracket		
1986-87	◆26002397	N.L.
(16) Breather Tube		
1986-87	◆7841515	8.75
(17) Pressure Switch		
1986-87-V-6	◆10038601	14.75
V-8	◆1632135	66.75
(18) O-Ring Seal		
1986-87	◆7828486	1.25

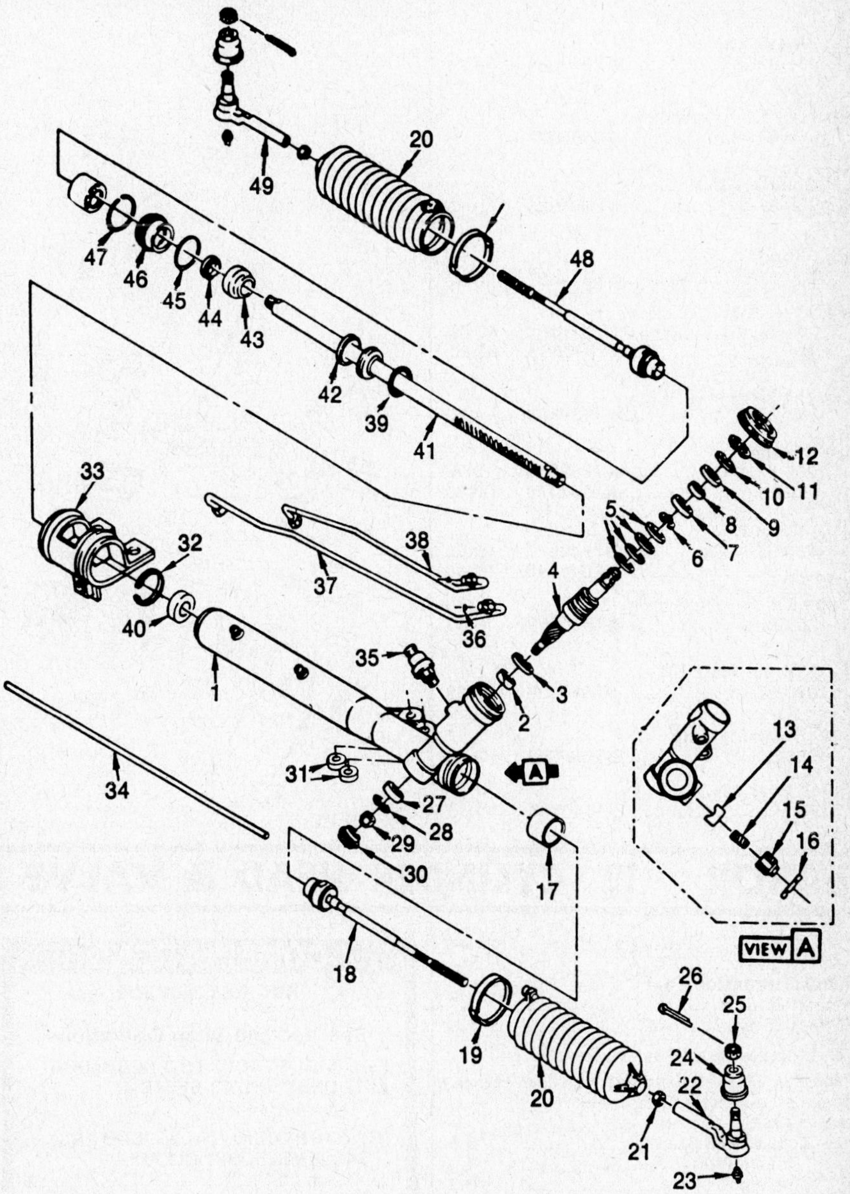

	Part No.	Price
(19) Line Kit		
1986-87	◆7843187	15.75
(20) Rack		
1986-87-V-6		
exc. H.D.	◆7846690	164.00
H.D.	◆7846691	N.L.
1986-87-V-8	◆7846691	N.L.

	Part No.	Price
(21) Bulkhead Kit		
1986-87	◆7839075	41.50
(22) Inner Tie Rod Kit		
1986-87-V-6 exc.		
H.D.	◆7839153	49.50
H.D.	◆26000076	51.00
1986-87-V-8	◆26000076	51.00

PARTS 11 POWER STEERING PUMP 11 PARTS

	Part No.	Price
Power Steering Pump		
1986-87-V-6	◆7848115	199.00
V-8	◆7841463	199.00
Pressure Hose		
1986-87-V-6	◆26001531	57.00
V-8	◆26001530	50.50

	Part No.	Price
Return Hose		
1986-87-V-6		
From gear	◆7833193	4.50
1986-87-V-8		
From gear	◆1631384	2.25
Reservoir	◆1631383	4.50

	Part No.	Price
(1) Pressure Plate		
1986-87	◆7840080	14.25
(2) Pressure Plate Spring		
1986-87	◆7839989	3.00

PARTS 11 POWER STEERING PUMP 11 PARTS

	Part No.	Price
(3) Sleeve Kit		
1986-87	◆7842086	9.75
(4) Flow Control Spring		
1986-87	◆5688037	1.25
(5) Control Valve		
1986-87	◆7841855	10.75
(6) Fitting		
1986-87	◆7841467	10.50
(7) Drive Shaft		
1986-87-V-6	◆26001375	42.00
V-8	◆7840633	58.00
(8) Seal (Driveshaft)		
1986-87	◆7839589	4.50
(9) Housing		
1986-87-V-6	◆7849050	110.00
V-8	◆7841770	68.00
(10) Rotor Kit		
1986-87-V-6	◆7840567	92.00
V-8	◆7841845	92.00
Vane Kit		
1986-87	◆7840569	13.50
(11) Thrust Plate Kit		
1986-87	◆7840139	14.25
(12) Retaining Ring		
1986-87	◆7839992	2.00
Pump Seal Kit		
1986-87	◆7840566	11.00

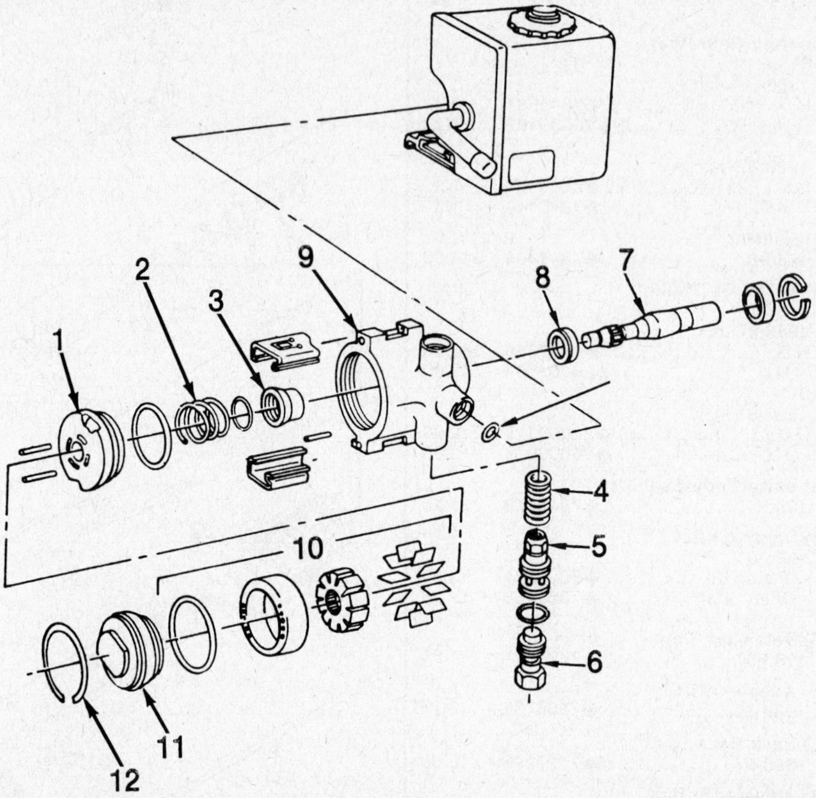

LABOR 12 CYLINDER HEAD & VALVE SYSTEM 12 LABOR

(Factory Time) — Chilton Time

(G) Compression Test
V-6–1986-87 7
V-8–1986-87 9

(G) Cylinder Head Gasket, Renew
Includes: Clean gasket surfaces. Clean carbon. Make all necessary adjustments.
V-6–1986-87
- right side (3.8) 5.5
- left side (3.7) 5.3
- both sides (4.4) 6.3

V-8–1986-87
- right sdie (5.0) 7.2
- left side (5.3) 7.6
- both sides (6.2) 8.9

(G) Cylinder Head, Renew
Includes: Transfer all parts, reface valves. Make all necessary adjustments.
V-6–1986-87
- right side (4.3) 6.2
- left side (4.2) 6.0
- both sides (5.2) 7.5

V-8–1986-87
- right side (5.4) 7.8
- left side (5.6) 8.1
- both sides (7.0) 10.1

(P) Clean Carbon and Grind Valves
Includes: R&R cylinder heads, clean gasket surfaces, clean carbon, reface valves and seats. Minor tune up.
V-6–1986-87
- right side (4.5) 6.5
- left side (4.3) 6.2
- both sides (5.3) 7.6

COMBINATIONS
Add to Valve Job

See Machine Shop Operations

(G) DRAIN, EVACUATE & RECHARGE AIR CONDITIONING SYSTEM
All models (.5) 1.0

(G) HYDRAULIC VALVE LIFTERS, DISASSEMBLE AND CLEAN
Each (.2) 2

(G) DISTRIBUTOR, RECONDITION
All models (.5) 8

(P) VALVE GUIDES, REAM OVERSIZE
Each (.2) 2

(G) ROCKER ARM SHAFT, RECONDITION
Each side (.2) 3

(Factory Time) — Chilton Time

V-8–1986-87
- right side (5.8) 8.4
- left side (6.1) 8.8
- both sides (7.8) 11.3

(G) Valve Tappets, Renew (Lifters)
Includes: Drain and refill cooling system, R&R intake manifold. Make all necessary adjustments.
V-6–1986-87
- right side (2.6) 3.7
- left side (2.1) 3.0
- both sides (2.8) 4.0

(Factory Time) — Chilton Time

V-8–1986-87
- one or all (3.8) 5.5

(G) Valve Springs and/or Valve Stem Oil Seals, Renew (Head on Car)
V-6–1986-87
- one cyl-right side (1.4) 2.0
- one cyl-left side (.8) 1.2
- one cyl-each side (1.8) 2.6
- each adtnl cyl (.3) 3

V-8–1986-87
- one cyl-right side (1.7) 2.4
- one cyl-left side (1.4) 2.0
- one cyl-each side (2.5) 3.6
- each adtnl cyl (.2) 3

(G) Rocker Arm Cover and/or Gasket, Renew
V-6–1986-87
- right side (.9) 1.3
- left side (.3) 5
- both sides (1.0) 1.5

V-8–1986-87
- right side (1.2) 1.7
- left side (.9) 1.3
- both sides (1.6) 2.3

(G) Rocker Arm Shafts and/or Assy., Renew
V-6–1986-87
- right side (1.1) 1.6
- left side (.6) 9
- both sides (1.3) 1.9

Recond each side add (.2) 3

LABOR 12 CYLINDER HEAD & VALVE SYSTEM 12 LABOR

	(Factory Time)	Chilton Time
(G) Rocker Arms and/or Push Rods, Renew		
V-6–1986-87		
right side	(1.2)	1.7
left side	(.6)	.9
both sides	(1.3)	1.9
V-8–1986-87		
right side	(1.5)	2.1
left side	(1.2)	1.7
both sides	(2.1)	3.0

PARTS 12 CYLINDER HEAD & VALVE SYSTEM 12 PARTS

	Part No.	Price
Valve Grind Gasket Kit		
1986-87-V-6	◆25527308	74.25
(1) Cylinder Head		
1986-87-V-6	◆22524543	N.L.
V-8	◆1628557	296.00
(2) Cylinder Head Gasket		
1986-87-V-6	◆25525919	21.25
V-8	◆1619040	24.00
(3) Push Rod		
1986-87-V-6	◆25524317	3.50
V-8	◆1618805	2.50
(4) Valve Lifter		
1986-87-V-6	◆5234330	N.L.
V-8	◆5234360	N.L.

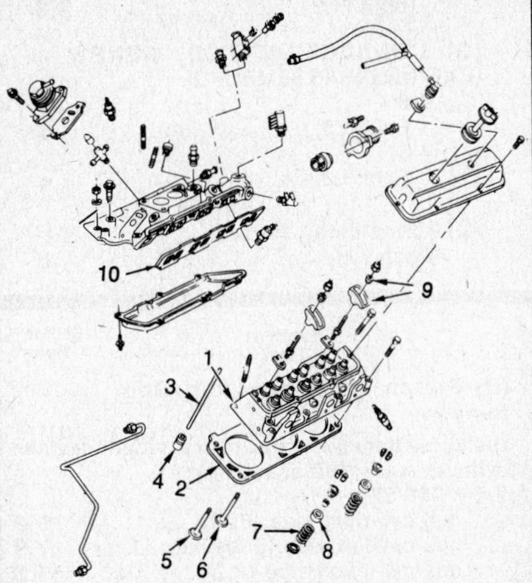

	Part No.	Price
(5) Intake Valve (Std.)		
1986-87-V-6	◆25512098	11.25
V-8	◆1618837	12.00
(6) Exhaust Valve (Std.)		
1986-87-V-6	◆25521841	13.75
V-8	◆1621321	15.25
(7) Valve Spring		
1986-87-V-6	◆25523695	3.00
V-8	◆1622834	3.75
(9) Rocker Arm		
1986-87-V-6	◆25523770	4.50
V-8	◆1618802	4.75
(10) Intake Manifold Gasket		
1986-87-V-6	◆1264924	N.L.
V-8	◆3634619	N.L.

LABOR 13 ENGINE ASSEMBLY & MOUNTS 13 LABOR

(G) Engine Assembly, Remove and Install

Does not include transfer of any parts or equipment.

	(Factory Time)	Chilton Time
V-6–1986-87		6.5
V-8–1986-87		6.0

(G) Engine Assembly, Renew

Includes: R&R engine assembly, transfer all component parts not supplied with replacement engine. Minor tune up.

	(Factory Time)	Chilton Time
V-8–1986-87	(7.8)	12.0

(P) Cylinder Block, Renew (Partial) (Less Heads and Oil Pan)

Includes: R&R engine, transfer all component parts not supplied with replacement engine. Minor tune up.

	(Factory Time)	Chilton Time
V-6–1986-87	(12.2)	18.9
Recond valves add	(1.2)	1.2
V-8–1986-87	(11.8)	18.2
Recond valves add	(1.6)	1.6

(P) Engine Assy., R&R and Recondition

Includes: Rebore block, install new pistons, rings, rod and main bearings. Clean carbon, grind valves. Tune engine.

	(Factory Time)	Chilton Time
V-6–1986-87	(15.6)	24.1
V-8–1986-87	(20.0)	31.0

(G) Engine Assembly, Recondition (In Car)

Includes: Expand or renew pistons, install new rings, pins, rod and main bearings. Clean carbon, grind valves. Tune engine.

	(Factory Time)	Chilton Time
V-6–1986-87	(14.2)	22.0
V-8–1986-87	(16.7)	25.8

(G) Cylinder Block, Renew (Fitted) (w/Pistons, Rings and Bearings)

Includes: R&R engine assy. Transfer all component parts not supplied with replacement engine. Clean carbon, grind valves. Tune engine.

	(Factory Time)	Chilton Time
V-6–1986-87	(14.6)	22.6

(G) Engine Mounts, Renew

	(Factory Time)	Chilton Time
V-6–1986-87	(.4)	.7
V-8–1986-87		
left	(.4)	.7
Renew brkt add	(.3)	.3

PARTS 13 ENGINE ASSEMBLY & MOUNTS 13 PARTS

	Part No.	Price
Engine Overhaul Gasket Kit		
1986-87-V-6	◆25530152	96.00
Engine Assy.		
Includes block and pistons.		
1986-87-V-6	◆25527479	950.00
Includes block, crank, piston assemblies; etc.		
1986-87-V-6	◆25527478	1263.00
Service Engine Assy.		
1986-87-V-8	◆3634656	2335.00
Engine Mounts (Front)		
1986-87-V-6	◆17985868	36.50
V-8	◆1634359	29.75
Transaxle Mount		
1986-87-V-6		
L.H.	◆17985122	22.50
R.H.	◆1636204	25.75
1986-87-V-8		
L.H.	◆17984350	33.50
R.H.	◆1634218	22.75

LABOR 14 PISTONS, RINGS & BEARINGS 14 LABOR

COMBINATIONS

Engine Combinations

See Machine Shop Operations

(G) DRAIN, EVACUATE & RECHARGE AIR CONDITIONING SYSTEM
All models (.5) 1.0

(G) HYDRAULIC VALVE LIFTERS, DISASSEMBLE AND CLEAN
Each (.2) 2

(G) DISTRIBUTOR, RECONDITION
All models (.5) 8

(P) VALVE GUIDES, REAM OVERSIZE
Each (.2) 2

(G) ROCKER ARM SHAFT ASSY., DISASSEMBLE AND CLEAN OR RECONDITION
Each side (.2) 3

(G) CYLINDER HEAD, R&R (ENGINE REMOVED)
V-6
one (1.7) 2.2
both (2.8) 3.6
V-8
one (1.6) 2.0
both (1.8) 2.3

(G) CONNECTING ROD, RENEW (ENGINE DISASSEMBLED)
V-6
Each (.5) 6
V-8
Each (.3) 4

(G) Piston Liner, Renew
Each (.2) 3

(G) DEGLAZE CYLINDER WALLS
Each (.1) 1

(G) REMOVE CYLINDER TOP RIDGE
Each (.1) 1

(G) PLASTIGAUGE BEARINGS
Each (.1) 1

(G) OIL PUMP, RECONDITION
V-8 (.3) 3

(M) OIL FILTER ELEMENT, RENEW
All models (.3) 3

(Factory Time) — Chilton Time

(P) Rings, Renew
(See Engine Combinations)
Includes: Remove cylinder top ridge, deglaze cylinder walls. Minor tune up.
V-6–1986-87
one cyl-right side (5.7) 8.2
one cyl-left side (4.8) 6.9
one cyl-each side (6.8) 9.8
all cyls-both sides (8.7) 12.6
V-8–1986-87
one cyl-right side (6.4) 9.2
one cyl-left side (6.8) 9.8
one cyl-each side (8.1) 11.7
all cyls-both sides (10.5) 15.2
Renew piston liner
add-each (.3) 3

(P) Piston or Connecting Rod, Renew
Includes: Remove cylinder top ridge, deglaze cylinder walls. Minor tune up.
V-6–1986-87
one cyl-right side (6.4) 9.2
one cyl-left side (5.5) 7.9
one cyl-each side (8.2) 11.8
all cyls-both sides (11.3) 16.3
V-8–1986-87
one cyl-right side (7.2) 10.4
one cyl-left side (7.2) 10.4
one cyl-each side (8.8) 12.7
all cyls-both sides (11.8) 17.1
Renew piston liner
add-each (.3) 3

(P) Connecting Rod Bearings, Renew
Includes: R&R oil pan, check all bearing clearances.
V-6–1986-87 (2.2) 3.0
V-8–1986-87 (3.1) 4.6

PARTS 14 PISTONS, RINGS, PINS & BEARINGS 14 PARTS

	Part No.	Price
(1) Piston Rings (Std.)		
1986-87-V-6	◆25528822	17.50
V-8	◆1623817	20.25
(2 & 3) Piston (w/Pin)		
1986-87-V-6	◆25527178	48.25
V-8 (w/Liner)	◆1623538	107.00

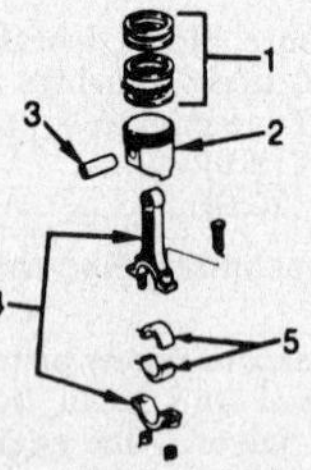

	Part No.	Price
(4) Connecting Rod		
1986-87-V-6	◆25506520	39.00
V-8	◆1619145	59.00
(5) Connecting Rod Bearings (Std.)		
1986-87-V-6	◆18005399	N.L.
V-8	◆18009085	11.00

LABOR 15 CRANKSHAFT & DAMPER 15 LABOR

(Factory Time) — Chilton Time

(P) Crankshaft and Main Bearings, Renew
Includes: R&R engine. Check all bearing clearances.
V-6–1986-87 (7.0) 10.1
V-8–1986-87 (10.0) 14.5

(P) Main Bearings, Renew
Includes: R&R oil pan and bearing caps. Check all bearing clearances.
V-6–1986-87 (1.8) 2.5
V-8–1986-87 (2.4) 3.5

(P) Main and Rod Bearings, Renew
Includes: R&R oil pan and bearing caps. Check all bearing clearances.
V-6–1986-87 (3.0) 4.3
V-8–1986-87 (4.0) 5.9

(G) Rear Main Bearing Oil Seal, Renew or Repack
V-6–1986-87 (1.2) 2.2
V-8–1986-87 (4.0) 5.8

(G) Crankshaft Pulley and/or Balancer, Renew
V-6–1986-87
balancer (.5) 8
V-8–1986-87
pulley (.4) 7
balancer (.6) 9

PARTS 15 CRANKSHAFT & DAMPER 15 PARTS

	Part No.	Price
(1) Crankshaft		
1986-87-V-6	◆25516025	405.00
V-8	◆1625959	441.00
(2) Crankshaft Gear		
1986-87-V-6	◆25528628	16.00
V-8	◆1618159	13.25
(3) Crankshaft Pulley		
See No. 4		
(4) Balancer Assy.		
1986-87-V-6	◆25527009	31.00
V-8	◆1635539	116.00
(5) Rear Main Bearing Oil Seal		
1986-87-V-6		
Packing	◆9772831	1.50
Seal	◆1193151	1.50
1986-87-V-8	◆1627806	10.75

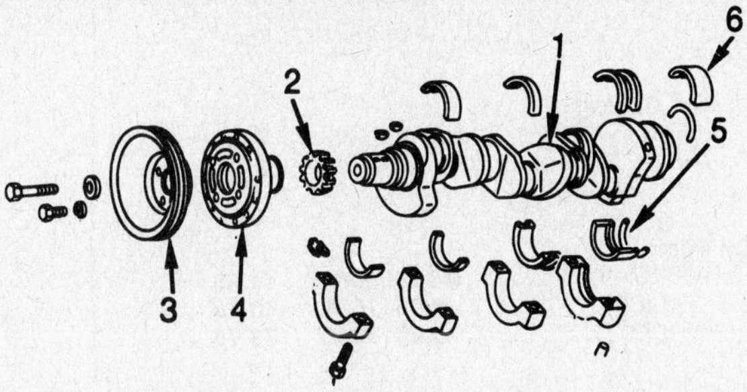

	Part No.	Price
Main Bearings (Std.)		
1986-87-V-6		
NO. 1	◆18009457	12.00
No. 2	◆18004602	20.00
No. 3	◆18002950	12.50
No. 4	◆5468578	13.00

	Part No.	Price
1986-87-V-8		
No. 1	◆18012316	17.75
Nos. 2, 4	◆18013442	17.25
No. 3	◆18009088	23.75
Rear	◆18009087	16.50

LABOR 16 CAMSHAFT & TIMING GEARS 16 LABOR

(Factory Time)	Chilton Time
(G) Timing Cover Oil Seal, Renew	
V-8–1986-87 (.8)	1.4
(G) Timing Case Cover Gasket, Renew	
V-6–1986-87 (2.4)	3.5
V-8–1986-87 (2.1)	3.0
Renew cover add (.4)	.4
Renew oil seal add (.1)	.2

(Factory Time)	Chilton Time
(G) Timing Chain or Gears, Renew	
V-6–1986-87 (2.7)	4.0
V-8–1986-87 (2.5)	3.5
(G) Camshaft, Renew	
V-6–1986-87 (7.0)	10.0
V-8–1986-87 (7.9)	11.8
(G) Camshaft Rear Bearing Plug, Renew	
V-6–1986-87 (3.7)	5.0
V-8–1986-87 (4.3)	6.2

PARTS 16 CAMSHAFT & TIMING GEARS 16 PARTS

	Part No.	Price
(1) Front Cover Oil Seal		
1986-87-V-6	◆25523327	3.25
V-8	◆1627827	4.50
(2) Front Cover		
1986-87-V-6	◆25526379	77.00
V-8	◆3517549	48.50
Timing Cover Gasket		
1986-87-V-6		
Gasket	◆25525159	3.50
Gasket & Seal Kit	◆25530153	9.75
1986-87-V-8	◆1628915	2.75
(3) Camshaft Gear		
1986-87-V-6	◆25523115	17.50
V-8	◆1617417	32.25
Cam Sensor Magnet		
1986-87-V-6	◆25523228	13.25

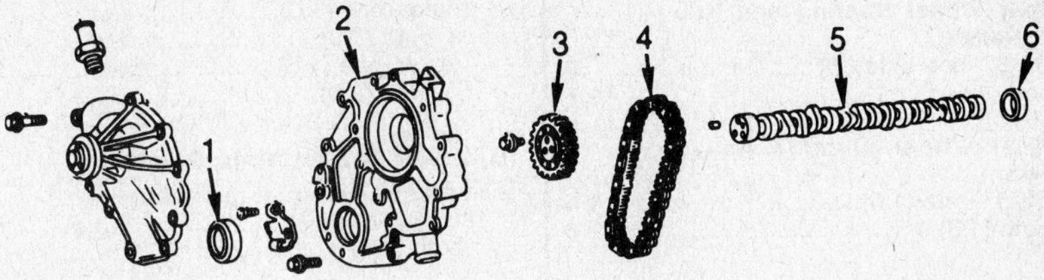

	Part No.	Price
(4) Camshaft		
1986-87-V-6	◆25523930	124.00
Camshaft Kit		
Includes lifters and lubricant.		
1986-87-V-8	◆1628822	334.00

	Part No.	Price
Button, Spring (Camshaft)		
1986-87-V-6		
Spring	◆1254199	1.00
Button	◆1250948	2.20
(6) Camshaft Bearings (Std.)		
1986-87-V-6		
Nos. 1, 4	◆25524301	7.25
Nos. 2, 3 & rear	◆1231142	7.75

LABOR 17 ENGINE OILING SYSTEM 17 LABOR

	Chilton Time
(G) Oil Pan or Gasket, Renew	
V-6–1986-87 (.9)	1.5
V-8–1986-87 (1.1)	1.8
(P) Pressure Test Engine Bearings (Pan Off)	
All models	1.0
(G) Oil Pump Cover and/or Gears, R&R and Recondition	
V-6–1986-87 (2.5)	3.6
(G) Oil Pump, Renew	
V-8–1986-87 (1.2)	2.0
Recond pump add (.3)	.3
(G) Oil Pressure Gauge (Engine), Renew	
1986-87-V-6 (.2)	.3
V-8 (.4)	.5
(M) Oil Filter Element, Renew	
1986-87-V-6 (.3)	.3
V-8 (.3)	.3

PARTS 17 ENGINE OILING SYSTEM 17 PARTS

	Part No.	Price
Oil Pan Gasket		
1986-87-V-6	◆25526425	7.50
V-8	◆1629458	9.75
Oil Pump		
1986-87-V-6	◆25525965	11.25
V-8 (86)	◆3517635	73.75
V-8 (87)	◆3517640	73.75
Shaft (Oil Pump Drive)		
1986-87-V-8	◆1619035	3.00
Oil Pressure Switch (Engine)		
1986-87-V-6	◆25036925	7.50
V-8	◆1632576	N.L.
Oil Filter		
1986-87-V-6	◆25010792	N.L.
V-8	◆25010324	N.L.

LABOR 21 SHIFT LINKAGE 21 LABOR

(Factory Time)	Chilton Time
(G) Shift Linkage, Adjust	
All models	
Neutral Safety Switch (.3)	.4
Shift Indicator Needle (.2)	.3
Shift Linkage (.4)	.5
T.V. Cable (.2)	.4
(G) Gear Selector Lever, Renew	
1986-87 (.2)	.4
(G) Gear Selector Indicator Needle and/or Assy., Renew	
1986-87 (.4)	.5
(G) Park Lock Cable, Renew	
1986-87 (.6)	1.0
(G) Shift Control Cables, Renew	
1986-87	
colm shift (.5)	.8
floor shift (.6)	.9
(G) Cable Shift Lever Assy., Renew	
1986-87 (.5)	.9
(G) Floor Shift Control Assy., Renew	
1986-87 (.5)	.9

LABOR 26 REAR AXLE 26 LABOR

(Factory Time)	Chilton Time
(G) Rear Suspension, Align	
All models (.6)	.9
(G) Rear Stabilizer Bar, Renew	
1986-87 (.7)	1.0
(G) Rear Stabilizer Bar Bushings, Renew	
1986-87-one (.4)	.6
both (.5)	.8
(G) Rear Wheel Bearing and Hub Assy., Renew	
1986-87-one side (.6)	.9
both sides (1.1)	1.7
(G) Rear Wheel Knuckle Assy., Renew	
1986-87-one (1.0)	1.4
both (1.8)	2.6
(G) Rear Leaf Spring Insulators, Renew	
1986-87	
upper-one (1.1)	1.5
both (1.3)	1.8
center (1.1)	1.5
lower-one (.4)	.6
both (.6)	1.0
(G) Rear Transverse Leaf Spring, Renew	
1986-87 (1.3)	1.9
(G) Rear Control Arm Bushings, Renew	
Includes: Align rear suspension.	
1986-87	
inner-one (1.1)	1.5
both (2.1)	2.9
outer-one (1.0)	1.4
both (1.8)	2.7
lower-one (1.5)	2.1
both (2.6)	3.8
(G) Lower Control Arms, Renew	
Includes: Align rear suspension.	
1986-87-one (.7)	1.0
both (1.3)	1.9
(G) Rear Crossmember Leading Arm Bushings, Renew	
1986-87 (1.5)	2.1
(G) Rear Crossmember, R&R or Renew	
1986-87 (2.1)	3.0
(G) Rear Struts, Renew	
1986-87-one (.9)	1.3
both (1.6)	2.5
ELECTRONIC LEVEL CONTROL	
(G) Compressor Assembly, Renew	
1986-87 (.7)	1.1
(G) Compressor Relay, Renew	
1986-87 (.2)	.4
(G) Height Sensor, Renew	
1986-87 (.4)	.6
(G) Height Sensor, Adjust	
1986-87 (.3)	.5
(G) Electronic Level Control Dryer, Renew	
1986-87 (.7)	1.1
(G) Electronic Level Control Head, Renew	
1986-87 (.7)	1.1
(G) Electronic Level Control Motor and Cylinder Assy., R&R and Recondition	
1986-87 (.9)	1.5
(G) Pressure Limiter Valve, Renew	
1986-87 (.4)	.6

PARTS 26 REAR AXLE AND SUSPENSION 26 PARTS

	Part No.	Price
(1) Insulator (Upper)		
1986-87	◆1627755	10.00
(2) Insulator (Strut Upper)		
1986-87	◆1634313	1.75
(3) Insulator (Strut Lower)		
1986-87	◆1632207	8.75
(4) Strut		
1986-87-exc.		
H.D.	◆22047940	N.L.
H.D.	◆22047941	144.75
(5) Insulator		
1986-87	◆1634312	3.50
(6) Splash Shield		
1986-87	◆25522515	16.25
(7) Knuckle		
1986-87-L.H.	◆1627298	52.00
R.H.	◆1627299	51.75

PARTS 26 REAR AXLE AND SUSPENSION 26 PARTS

	Part No.	Price
(8) Rear Wheel Bearing Assy.		
1986-87	◆7466926	198.00
(9) Control Arm Bushings (Outer)		
1986-87	◆1629205	13.00
(10) Control Arm		
1986-87-L.H.	◆1632883	335.00
R.H.	◆1632884	335.00
(11) Control Arm Bushings (Inner)		
1986-87	◆1628806	5.00
(12) Stabilizer Bar		
1986-87	◆1633804	50.00
(13) Bushing		
1986-87	◆1632195	6.25
(14) Stabilizer Link Bushing		
1986-87	◆1628813	1.00
(15) Retainer (Rear Spring)		
1986-87	◆1630283	2.25
(16) Spring Insulator		
1986-87	◆17982002	9.50
(17) Rear Spring		
Order with I.D. code number on spring.		
(18) Stabilizer Link		
1986-87	◆1627772	N.L.
(19) Suspension Support		
1986-87	◆1636120	318.00
(20) Bumper		
1986-87	◆17981778	8.75
(21) Insulator		
1986-87	◆17981840	13.00

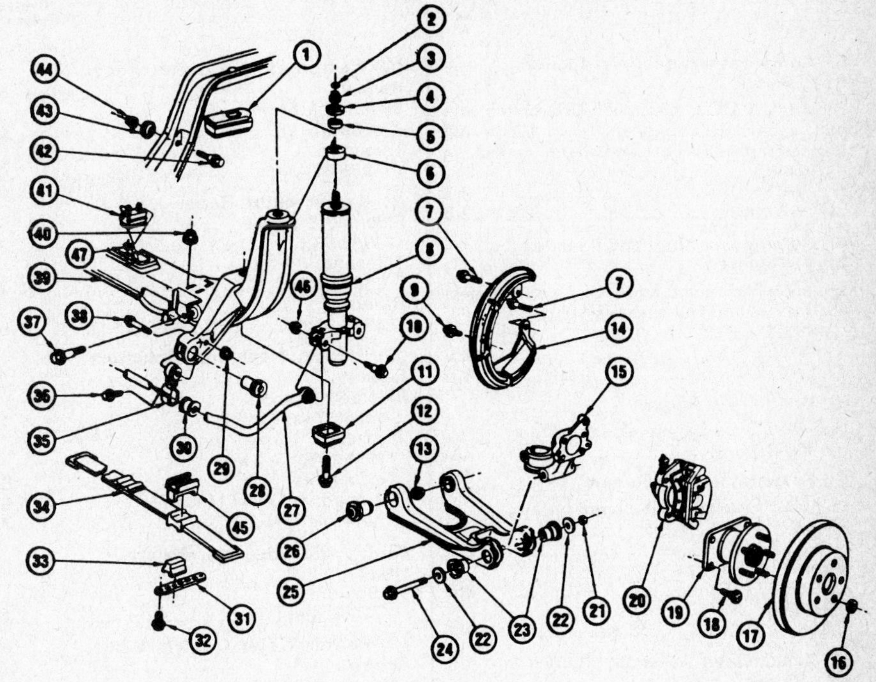

ELECTRONIC LEVEL CONTROL

	Part No.	Price
Compressor		
1986-87	◆22049808	233.00
Height Sensor		
1986-87	◆22048627	200.00
Air Dryer Kit		
1986-87	◆22054238	41.50
Compressor Head		
1986-87	◆22054244	68.50
Limiter Valve		
1986-87	◆22016688	31.00
Link Connector (Ball Stud)		
1986-87	◆1614499	1.00

LABOR 28 AIR CONDITIONING 28 LABOR

(Factory Time) Chilton Time

Note: If more than one item requires replacement where evacuation and discharging the system is already included in the operation, deduct 1.0 hour for each additional item to the times listed.

(G) Drain, Evacuate and Recharge System
All models (.5) 1.0

(G) Refrigerant, Add (Partial Charge)
All models 6

(G) Leak Check
Includes: Check all lines and connections.
All models 5

(G) Compressor Belt, Renew
1986-87
V-6 (.3) 5
V-8 (.2) 4

DA-6 COMPRESSOR

(G) Compressor Assembly, Renew
Includes: Transfer parts as required. Evacuate and charge system.
1986-87
V-6 (1.1) 1.9
V-8 (1.2) 2.0

AIR CONDITIONER TUNE-UP

For efficient operation and satisfactory performance in hot weather. The following air conditioner tune-up is suggested:

1. Clean intake filter
2. Clean condenser fins
3. Pressure test system
4. Adjust drive belt tension
5. Check antifreeze/coolant
6. Tighten compressor mounts
7. Tighten condenser and evaporator mounts
8. Inspect system for leaks (hoses, couplings, valves, etc.)
9. Partial charge system

All models 1.0
If necessary to evacuate and charge system, add 1.0

(Factory Time) Chilton Time

(G) Compressor Clutch Plate and Hub Assy., Renew
1986-87
V-6 (1.0) 1.4
V-8 (.6) 9
Add time to evacuate and charge system if required.

(G) Compressor Clutch Rotor and/or Bearing, Renew
1986-87
V-6 (1.1) 1.6
V-8 (.8) 1.1

(G) Compressor Clutch Coil and/or Pulley Rim Assembly, Renew
1986-87
V-6 (1.2) 1.5
V-8 (1.1) 1.4
Renew pulley or brg add 1
Add time to evacuate and charge system if required.

(G) Compressor Front Seal, Seat and 'O' Ring, Renew
Includes: R&R clutch hub and drive plate assy. Evacuate and charge system.
1986-87
V-6 (1.5) 2.5
V-8 (1.6) 2.6

LABOR 28 AIR CONDITIONING 28 LABOR

(Factory Time) Chilton Time

(G) Compressor Front Head and/or Seal, Renew

Includes: R&R compressor. R&R clutch and pulley assy. R&R shaft seal assy. Clean and inspect parts. Evacuate and charge system.

1986-87
- V-6 (1.8) 2.8
- V-8 (1.8) 2.8

(G) Compressor Shaft and Cylinder Assy., Renew

Includes: R&R compressor. Clean and inspect parts. Evacuate and charge system.

1986-87
- V-6 (1.9) 2.9
- V-8 (2.0) 3.0

(G) Condenser, Renew

Includes: Evacuate and charge system.

1986-87 (1.1) 2.0

(G) Evaporator Core, Renew

Includes: Evacuate and charge system.

Riviera
- 1986-87 (1.8) 3.7

Eldorado & Seville
- 1986-87 (2.6) 5.5

Toronado
- 1986-87 (1.9) 3.7

(G) Accumulator Assembly, Renew

Includes: Evacuate and charge system.

1986-87 (.9) 1.5

(G) Expansion Tube (Orifice), Renew

Includes: Evacuate and charge system.

1986-87 (.9) 1.5

(G) Refrigerant Switch, Renew

1986-87
- High Temp (.3) 4
- Low Temp (.3) 4
- Low Pressure (.2) 4

Add time to evacuate and charge system if required.

(G) Temperature Control Assy., Renew

Eldorado & Seville
- 1986-87 (.3) 6

Toronado
- 1986-87 (.4) 6

(G) Blower Motor, Renew

Eldorado & Seville
- 1986-87 (.6) 9

Toronado
- 1986-87 (.8) 1.1

Riviera
- 1986-87 (.3) 6

(G) Vacuum Diaphragm Actuators, Renew

Eldorado & Seville
- 1986-87-each (.6) 1.1

Toronado
- 1986-87
  - Defroster (.5) 9
  - Upper or Lower Mode (1.1) 1.9
  - Air Inlet (.4) 7

(G) Electric Actuators, Renew

Riviera
- 1986-87
  - Defroster (.8) 1.2

(G) Heater Water Control Valve, Renew

Eldorado & Seville
- 1986-87 (.3) 5

Toronado
- 1986-87 (.5) 6

Riviera
- 1986-87 (.4) 6

(G) Air Conditioning Hoses, Renew

Includes: Evacuate and charge system.

1986-87
- liquid line (.8) 1.5
- suction (.8) 1.5
- inlet (.8) 1.5
- evap. to accum (1.0) 1.7
- suction & discharge
  - V-6 (1.6) 2.3
  - V-8 (1.1) 1.8

AUTOMATIC TEMPERATURE CONTROL

(G) Programmer, R&R or Renew

1986-87 (.7) 1.1

Renew motor add (.1) 2

(G) A.C. Aspirator, Renew

Eldorado & Seville
- 1986-87 (.3) 4

Toronado
- 1986-87 (.9) 1.3

(G) Aspirator Hose, Renew

Eldorado & Seville
- 1986-87 (.4) 6

Toronado
- 1986-87 (.9) 1.3

(G) In-Car Sensor, Renew

1986-87 (.4) 6

(G) Refrigerant Temperature Sensor, Renew

Eldorado & Seville
- 1986-87 (.2) 4

(G) Outside Temperature Sensor, Renew

1986-87 (.3) 5

(G) ECC Power Module, Renew

Eldorado & Seville
- 1986-87 (.3) 6

(G) HVAC Power Module, Renew

Toronado
- 1986-87 (.5) 8

PARTS 28 AIR CONDITIONING 28 PARTS

	Part No.	Price
Compressor Assy.		
1986-87-V-6	◆12323602	N.L.
V-8	◆12323603	N.L.
Clutch Hub & Drive Plate		
1986-87-V-6	◆2724325	51.50
V-8	◆3092084	73.00
Coil (w/Housing)		
1986-87	◆3091128	51.50
Cylinder (w/Shaft)		
1986-87	◆6551952	307.75
Front Head (Compressor)		
1986-87	◆6557775	44.25
Rear Head		
1986-87	◆6557580	47.75
Valve Plate (Front)		
1986-87	◆6551700	25.00
Valve Plate (Rear)		
1986-87	◆6551702	25.00
Shaft Seal Kit		
1986-87	◆2724319	11.25
Pressure Relief Valve		
1986-87	◆5914435	13.25
Suction Reed Valve		
1986-87	◆6557377	8.75
Condenser		
1986-87	◆3057067	141.75
Accumulator		
1986-87	◆3059239	80.50
Evaporator Core		
1986-87	◆3092972	129.75
Blower Motor Module		
1986-87	◆16047800	90.50
Compressor Refrig. Switch		
1986-87	◆1631399	13.00

ELECTRONIC CLIMATE CONTROL

	Part No.	Price
Programmer		
1986-87-V-6	◆16054464	160.25
V-8	◆16054466	148.25
Temperature Sensor (Outside)		
1986-87	◆16047526	17.75
Temperature Sensor (Inside)		
1986-87-V-6	◆16060264	17.25
V-8	◆16033806	11.25
Motor (Programmer)		
1986-87	◆16050729	45.50

LABOR 29 LOCKS, HINGES & WIND. REGULATORS 29 LABOR

(Factory Time)	Chilton Time
(G) Hood Latch Assembly, Renew	
1986-87 (.2)	.4
(G) Hood Hinge, Renew	
1986-87-one (.3)	5
both (.4)	.7
(G) Hood Release Cable, Renew	
1986-87	
Eldorado & Seville (.4)	.6
Riviera (.8)	1.2
Toronado (.5)	.8
(G) Hood Support Tube, Renew	
1986-87-each (.2)	.3
(G) Door Handle (Outside), Renew	
1986-87 (.5)	.8
Renew insert add	.1
(G) Front Door Lock Assemlby, Renew	
1986-87 (.6)	.9
(G) Rear Door Lock Assembly, Renew	
Seville	
1986-87 (.8)	1.2
(G) Front Door Lock Cylinder, Renew	
1986-87 (.5)	.8
Recode cyl add (.3)	.3
w/Ill entry system add (.2)	.2
(G) Door Lock Remote Control, Renew (Front or Rear)	
1986-87 (.4)	.6
(G) Lock Striker Plate, Renew	
1986-87 (.2)	.3
(G) Trunk Hinge or Strap, Renew	
1986-87	
Eldorado & Seville (.8)	1.2
Riviera (.8)	1.2
Toronado-one (1.4)	1.9
(G) Rear Compartment Lid Lock Cylinder, Renew	
1986-87 (.3)	.4
Recode cyl add (.3)	.3
(G) Door Window Regulator, Renew (Electric)	
1986-87 (1.0)	1.5

PARTS 29 LOCKS, HINGES & WIND. REGULATORS 29 PARTS

	Part No.	Price
Hood Latch (Primary)		
1986-87	◆14070703	16.25
Hood Release Cable		
1986-87	◆1628539	7.75
Hood Hinge		
1986-87-L.H.	◆1636949	9.00
R.H.	◆1636950	9.00
Door Handle (Outside-Front)		
(wo/Illum.)		
1986-87-Buick & Seville		
L.H.	◆20479795	28.25
R.H.	◆20479794	28.25
1986-87-Olds.		
L.H.	◆20332645	20.00
R.H.	◆20332644	20.00
(Illum.)		
1986-87-Buick & Eldorado		
L.H.	◆20566381	44.75
R.H.	◆20566380	44.75
1986-87-Olds		
L.H.	◆20471223	27.75
R.H.	◆20471222	27.75
Door Handle (Outside-Rear)		
1986-87-Seville		
L.H.	◆20479795	28.25
R.H.	◆20479794	28.25
Door Lock Cylinder (Front)		
(wo/Illum.)		
1986-87	◆9632728	8.25
(Illum.)		
1986-87	◆9632766	9.50
Front Door Lock		
1986-87-Buick & Eldorado		
L.H.	◆20661425	39.25
R.H.	◆20661424	39.25
1986-87-Olds		
L.H.	◆20475163	39.25
R.H.	◆20475162	39.25
1986-87-Seville		
L.H.	◆20475165	39.25
R.H.	◆20475164	39.25
Rear Door Lock		
1986-87-Seville		
L.H.	◆20480449	53.25
R.H.	◆20480448	53.25
Window Regulator		
1986-87-exc. Seville		
L.H.	◆20375835	76.00
R.H.	◆20375834	76.00
1986-87-Seville (Front)		
L.H.	◆20377439	40.25
R.H.	◆20377438	40.25
1986-87-Seville (Rear)		
L.H.	◆20377441	40.25
R.H.	◆20377440	40.25
Motor (Window Regulator)		
1986-87	◆22020900	N.L.

LABOR 30 HEAD AND PARKING LAMPS 30 LABOR

(Factory Time)	Chilton Time
(G) Aim Headlamps	
two	.4
four	.6
(M) Headlamp Sealed Beam Bulb, Renew	
1986-87-each (.3)	.3
(M) Park and Turn Signal Lamp Assy., Renew	
1986-87 (.3)	.4
(M) Side Marker Lamp Assy., Renew	
1986-87 (.2)	.3
(M) License Lamp Assembly, Renew	
1986-87 (.2)	.3
(M) Back-Up Lamp Assembly, Renew	
1986-87 (.2)	.3
(M) Cornering Lamp Bulb, Renew	
All models-each (.2)	.3
(G) High Level Stop Lamp Bulb, Renew	
All models (.2)	.3
(M) High Level Stop Lamp Assy., Renew	
All models (.2)	.4
(M) License Lamp Bulb, Renew	
All models-one or all (.2)	.3
(M) Park and Turn Signal Lamp Bulb, Renew	
All models-each	.2
(M) Rear Combination Lamp Bulb, Renew	
All models-one	.2
each adtnl	.1
(M) Side Marker Lamp Bulb, Renew	
All models-each	.2

PARTS 30 HEAD AND PARKING LAMPS 30 PARTS

	Part No.	Price
Headlamp Sealbeam		
1986-87-Buick & Olds		
Inboard	◆16502681	N.L.
Outboard	◆16502682	N.L.
1986-87-Cadillac		
Inboard	◆5930567	N.L.
Outboard	◆16502327	N.L.
Parking & Turnsignal Assy.		
1986-87-Buick		
L.H. (exc. T38)	◆5974765	29.75
w/T38	◆5974767	29.75

PARTS 30 HEAD AND PARKING LAMPS 30 PARTS

	Part No.	Price
R.H. (exc. T38)	◆5974766	29.75
w/T38	◆5974768	29.75
1986-87-Olds		
L.H. (exc. B57)	◆919995	21.75
B57 (87)	◆5974659	N.L.
R.H. (exc. B57)	◆919996	21.75
B57 (87)	◆5974660	N.L.
1986-87-Eldorado		
L.H.	◆919417	28.50
R.H.	◆919418	28.50
1986-87-Seville		
L.H.	◆920027	28.50
R.H.	◆920028	28.50
Tail & Stop Light Lens		
1986-87-Buick		
L.H. (exc. T93)	◆16504685	71.25
T93	◆16504687	71.25
R.H. (exc. T93)	◆16504686	71.25
T93	◆16504688	71.25
1986-87-Olds	◆16504015	103.00
1986-87-Eldorado		
L.H.	◆16503277	18.50
R.H.	◆16503278	18.50
1986-87-Seville		
L.H.	◆16503435	47.50
R.H.	◆16503436	47.50
High Mount Stoplight		
1986-87-exc.		
Cad.	◆5974462	36.00
Cadillac	◆5974473	36.00

LABOR 31 WINDSHIELD WIPER & SPEEDOMETERS 31 LABOR

(Factory Time)	Chilton Time
(G) Windshield Wiper Motor, Renew	
1986-87 (.6)	.8
w/Inter wiper add (.1)	.1
(G) Windshield Wiper Motor, R&R and Recondition	
1986-87 (1.0)	1.4
(G) Wiper Transmission, Renew	
1986-87 (.6)	1.0
(G) Wiper Switch, Renew	
1986-87	
Riviera (.3)	.5
Toronado (1.2)	1.7
(G) Windshield Washer Pump, Renew	
1986-87 (.3)	.4
w/Pulse wipe add (.1)	.1
Recond pump add (.3)	.3
(G) Wiper Motor Main Drive Gear (Depressed Park), Renew	
Includes: R&R wiper motor.	
1986-87 (1.0)	1.5
(G) Wiper Motor Terminal Board and/or Timing Delay Switch, Renew	
1986-87 (.5)	1.0
(G) Pulse Wipe Control Module, Renew	
1986-87 (.2)	.3
(G) Instrument Panel Cluster Assy., Renew	
1986-87	
Eldorado & Seville (.7)	1.2
Riviera-Toronado (.5)	.9
(G) Speedometer Signal Generator, Renew	
1986-87	
Riviera (.3)	.5
(G) M.P.G. Sentinal, Renew	
1986-87 (.3)	.6
(G) Radio, R&R	
1986-87	
Eldorado & Seville (.3)	.5
Riviera (.4)	.7
Toronado (.4)	.7

PARTS 31 WINDSHIELD WIPER & SPEEDOMETER 31 PARTS

	Part No.	Price
Windshield Wiper Motor		
1986-87	◆22054198	118.00
Wiper Transmission		
1986-87	◆22063201	27.25
Switch (Wiper Control)		
1986-87	◆22038796	31.25
Washer Pump		
1986-87	◆22049373	9.75

Speedometer Head & Cable
Order by model, year and style.

LABOR 32 LIGHT SWITCHES & WIRING 32 LABOR

(Factory Time)	Chilton Time
(G) Headlamp Switch, Renew	
1986-87 (.3)	.6
(G) Headlamp Dimmer Switch, Renew	
1986-87 (.5)	.9
(G) Stop Light Switch, Renew	
1986-87 (.3)	.4
(G) Turn Signal or Hazard Warning Switch, Renew	
1986-87	
Riviera (.7)	1.1
Toronado (1.0)	1.5
(G) Parking Brake Lamp Switch, Renew	
1986-87	
Eldorado & Seville (.3)	.4
Riviera (.3)	.4
Toronado (.5)	.7
(G) Neutral Start Switch, Renew	
1986-87	
Riviera-colm mount (.3)	4
(M) Turn Signal or Hazard Warning Flasher, Renew	
1986-87	
hazard warning (.3)	.4
turn signal (.2)	.3
(G) Horn Relay, Renew	
1986-87 (.3)	.4
(G) Horn, Renew	
1986-87-one (.3)	.4
each adtnl. (.1)	.1

PARTS 32 LIGHT SWITCHES & WIRING 32 PARTS

	Part No.	Price
Turn Signal Switch		
1986-87-Buick	◆1997052	81.00
Olds	◆1997054	34.00
Cadillac	◆1997052	81.00
Stop Light Switch		
1986-87	◆25523462	8.00
Horn Relay		
1986-87-Buick	◆25520198	5.25
Olds & Cad.	◆1626239	6.25

LABOR 33 GLASS 33 LABOR

(Factory Time)	Chilton Time
(G) Windshield Glass, Renew	
1986-87 (1.3)	1.8
Renew caulk bead add (.4)	.4
(G) Front Door Glass, Renew	
1986-87-exc below (1.0)	1.6
Seville (.7)	1.0
(G) Rear Quarter Stationary Glass, Renew	
1986-87-2 Dr (1.5)	2.0
(G) Rear Door Glass, Renew	
1986-87-Seville (.8)	1.3
(G) Rear Window Glass, Renew	
1986-87-exc below (1.3)	2.0
Eldorado (2.1)	4.0
w/Elec Defogger add (.6)	.6
w/3/4 plug, unpadded add (1.0)	1.5

LABOR 34 CRUISE CONTROL 34 LABOR

(Factory Time)	Chilton Time
(G) Cruise Control Engagement Switch, Renew	
Includes: Renew turn signal lever.	
1986-87 (.4)	.7
(G) Cruise Control Release Switch, Renew	
1986-87 (.2)	.4
(G) Cruise Control Servo, Renew	
1986-87 (.4)	.6
(G) Cruise Control Vacuum Hoses, Renew	
1986-87 (.2)	.3
(G) Cruise Control Chain or Cable, Renew	
1986-87 (.3)	.4
(G) Cruise Control Module, Renew	
Eldorado & Seville	
1986-87 (.4)	.6
Riviera	
1986-87 (.2)	.6
Toronado	
1986-87 (.4)	.6
(G) Cruise Control On-Off Switch, Renew	
1986-87 (.3)	.5

PARTS 34 CRUISE CONTROL 34 PARTS

	Part No.	Price
Servo Assy.		
1986-87-V-6	◆25074625	119.75
V-8	◆25074786	72.25
Servo Cable		
1986-87-V-6	◆25517535	9.50
V-8	◆1629870	4.50
Vacuum Valve		
1986-87	◆25523376	14.00
Switch (Stoplight)		
1986-87-V-6	◆25523462	8.00
V-8	◆25529860	N.L.
Cruise Control Switch		
1986-87-Buick	◆17980900	18.25
Eldorado	◆17981675	50.00
Seville	◆17981674	145.00

Somerset Regal • Calais • Grand Am

GROUP INDEX

ALPHABETICAL INDEX

General Motors
Front Wheel Drive Cars

BUICK SOMERSET REGAL • OLDSMOBILE CALAIS • PONTIAC GRAND AM

YEAR IDENTIFICATION

1985–86 Grand Am

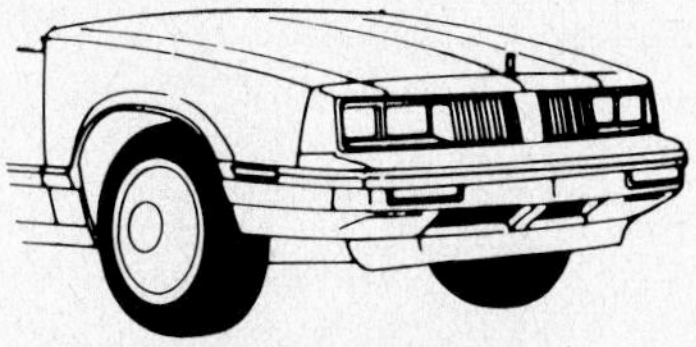

1985–86 Calais

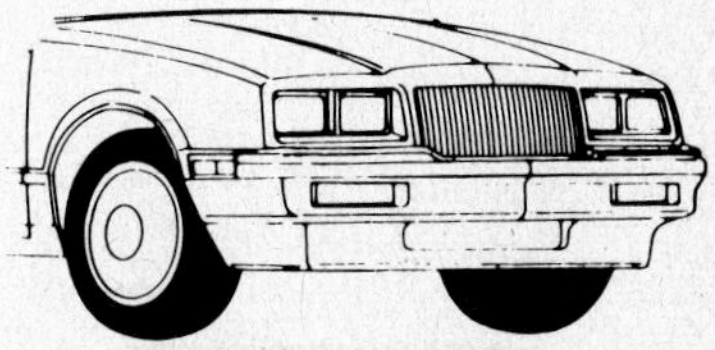

1985–86 Somerset

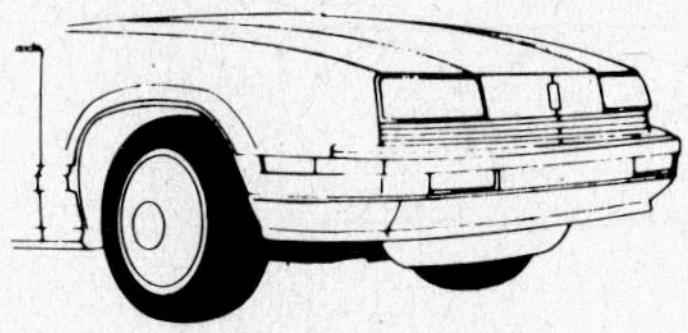

1986 Calais

1986–87 Grand Am SE

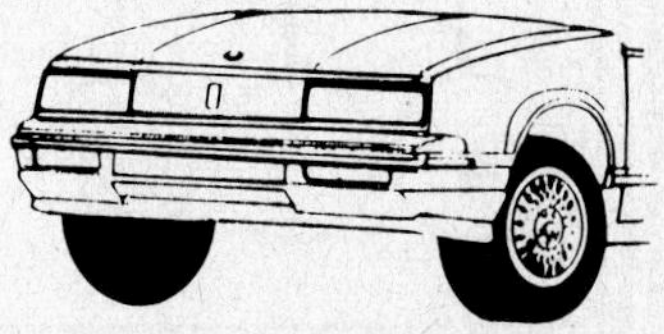

1987 Calais GT

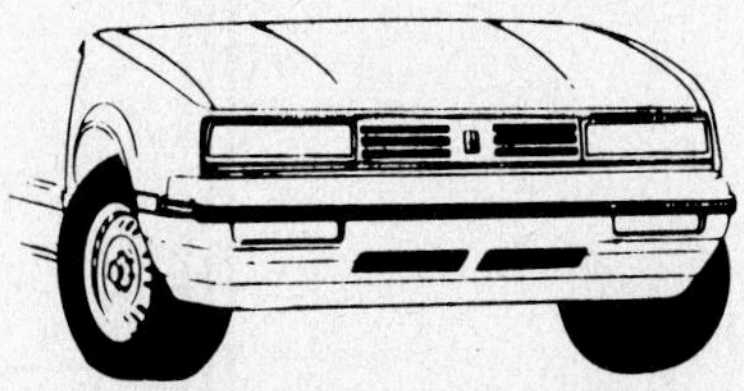

1987 Calais Supreme Coupe

VEHICLE IDENTIFICATION NUMBER (VIN)

It is important for servicing and ordering parts to be certain of the vehicle and engine identification. The VIN (vehicle identification number) is a 17 digit number visible through the windshield on the driver's side of the dash and contains the vehicle and engine identification codes. It can be interpreted as follows:

Engine Code					
Code	Cu. In.	Liters	Cyl.	Carb.	Eng. Mfg.
U	151	2.5	4	TBI	Pont.
L	183	3.0	V6	MFI	Buick

Model Year Code	
Code	Year
F	1985
G	1986
H	1987

The seventeen digit Vehicle Identification Number can be used to determine engine application and model year. The 10th digit indicates the model year and the 8th digit identifies the factory installed engine.

TBI Throttle Body Injection

MFI Multi-Port Fuel Injection

TUNE-UP SPECIFICATIONS

Year	Eng. VIN Code	Engine No. Cyl. Displacement (cu. in.)	Eng. Mfg.	Spark Plugs Orig. Type	Spark Plugs Gap (in.)	Ignition Timing (deg.) Man. Trans.	Ignition Timing (deg.) Auto. Trans.	Valves Intake Opens (deg.)	Fuel Pump Pressure (psi)	Idle Speed (rpm) Man. Trans.	Idle Speed (rpm) Auto. Trans.
'85–'86	U	4-151	Pont.	R43TSX	0.060	8B	8B	NA	12	①	①
	L	6-181	Buick	R44LTS	0.040	15B	15B	NA	34–44	①	①
'87	All	See Underhood Specifications Sticker									

NOTE: The underhood specifications sticker often reflects tune-up specification changes made in production. Sticker figures must be used if they disagree with those in this chart.
B Before Top Dead Center
Part numbers in this chart are not recommendations by Chilton for any product by brand name.
NA Not Available at time of publication
① See underhood sticker

FIRING ORDERS

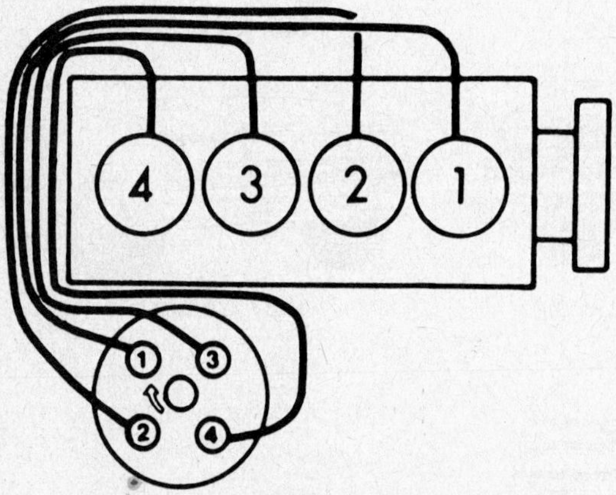

Pontiac-built 151–4 cylinder engine
Engine firing order: 1–3–4–2
Distributor rotation: clockwise

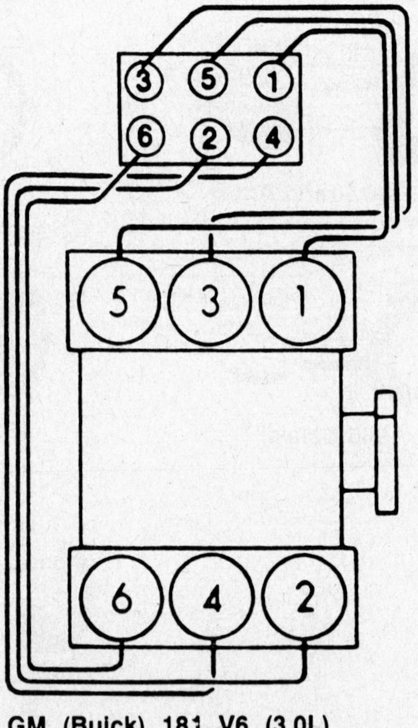

GM (Buick) 181 V6 (3.0L)
Engine firing order: 1–6–5–4–3–2
Distributor rotation: clockwise

WHEEL ALIGNMENT SPECIFICATIONS

Year	Model	Caster Range (deg)	Caster Pref. Setting (deg)	Chamber Range (deg)	Chamber Pref. Setting (deg)	Toe-In (in.)
'85	All	2/3P to 2 2/3P	1 2/3P	1/5P to 1 1/2P	5/6P	1/8 OUT
'86-'87	All	3/4P to 2 3/4P	1 3/4P	1/4P to 1 3/8P	13/16P	1/16 OUT

LABOR — SERVICE BAY OPERATIONS — LABOR

(Factory Time) — Chilton Time

COOLING

(M) Winterize Cooling System

Includes: Run engine to check for leaks, tighten all hose connections. Test radiator and pressure cap, drain radiator and engine block. Add anti-freeze and refill system.

All models 5

(G) Thermostat, Renew

1985-87
- Four (.2) 4
- V-6 (.4) 6

(M) Drive Belt, Renew

Four–1985-87
- A.C. (.5) 6
- Fan (.4) 5
- P.S. (.4) 5

w/A.C. add (.2) 2

V-6–1985-87
- Serpentine (.3) 5

(M) Drive Belt, Adjust

Four-1985-87-one (.2) 3
- all (.3) 4

(M) Radiator Hoses, Renew

1985-87-upper (.3) 4
- lower (.4) 5
- both (.5) 7

BRAKES

(G) Brake Pedal Free Play, Adjust

All models 3

(G) Brakes, Adjust (Minor)

Includes: R&R wheels and adjust brakes thru access holes in drums. Fill master cylinder,
- two wheels 4

Remove knock out plugs, add-each.. .1

(G) Bleed Brakes (Four Wheels)

Includes: Fill master cylinder.

All models (.4) 5

(M) Parking Brake, Adjust

All models (.3) 4

LUBRICATION SERVICE

(M) Lubricate Chassis, Change Oil & Filter

Includes: Inspect and correct all fluid levels.

All models 6

Install grease fittings add 1

CHILTON'S 10 POINT SAFETY CHECK

CHECK OPERATION & CONDITION OF THE FOLLOWING ITEMS:

1. Legal Registration (serial no.)
2. Tires & Wheels
3. Brake System (R&R all wheels)
4. Light Systems & Signals
5. Accelerator Linkage, Neutral Safety Switch, Shift Indicator Pointer & Seat Position Locks
6. Glass, Mirrors, Door Locks, Seat Belts & Harness
7. Wipers, Washers & Defrosters
8. Frame, Steering, Shocks, Front & Rear Suspension
9. Fuel & Exhaust Systems
10. Road Test Vehicle

All models 1.0

Exhaust Smog Analysis, add 4

(Factory Time) — Chilton Time

(M) Lubricate Chassis

Includes: Inspect and correct all fluid levels.

All models 4

Install grease fittings add 1

(M) Engine Oil & Filter, Change

Includes: Inspect and correct all fluid levels.

All models 4

WHEELS

(M) Wheel, Renew

one (.5) 5

(M) Wheels, Balance

one 3

each adtnl 2

(M) Wheels, Rotate (All)

All models 5

ELECTRICAL

(M) Battery Cables, Renew

Positive
- Four (.3) 4
- V-6 (.4) 5

Negative
- All models (.2) 3

(M) Battery Terminals, Clean

All models 3

(Factory Time) — Chilton Time

(G) Aim Headlamps

two 4

four 6

(M) Headlamp Sealed Beam Bulb, Renew

All models-one side (.3) 4

(M) Park and Turn Signal Lamp Assy., Renew

1985-87-each (.3) 4

(M) Rear Combination Lamp Assy., Renew

1985-87
- Regal-each (.5) 7
- Grand Am-each (.2) 3
- Calais-each (.5) 7

(M) Side Marker Lamp Assy., Renew (Front or Rear)

1985-87-each (.2) 3

(M) License Lamp Assembly, Renew

1985-87-each 2

(M) Back-Up Lamp Lens or Bulb, Renew

1985-87-one (.2) 3
- all (.3) 4

(M) Park and Turn Signal Lamp Bulb, Renew

1985-87-each (.2) 2

(M) Side Marker Lamp Bulb, Renew (Front or Rear)

1985-87-each (.2) 2

(M) Stop, Tail and Turn Signal Lamp Bulb, Renew

1985-87-one (.2) 3
- all (.3) 4

(M) Turn Signal or Hazard Warning Flasher, Renew

1985-87 (.2) 3

(G) Horn, Renew

1985-87-one (.2) 3
- both (.3) 4

(G) Horn Relay, Renew

1985-87 (.2) 3

LABOR — 1 TUNE UP 1 — LABOR

(Factory Time) — Chilton Time

(G) Compression Test

1985-87
- Four 6
- V-6 .... 1.0

(G) Engine Tune Up (Electronic Ignition)

Includes: Test battery and clean connections. Tighten manifold mounting bolts. Check engine compression, clean and adjust or renew spark plugs. Test resistance of spark plug cables. Inspect distributor cap and rotor. Reset ignition timing. Adjust minimum idle speed. Service air cleaner. Inspect and adjust drive belts. Check operation of EGR valve.

Four–1985-87 .... 2.0

V-6–1985-87 .... 2.5

LABOR 2 IGNITION SYSTEM 2 LABOR

	(Factory Time)	Chilton Time
(G) Spark Plugs, Clean and Reset or Renew		
1985-87-Four	(.3)	.5
V-6	(.6)	.9
(G) Ignition Timing, Reset		
All models	(.3)	.4
(G) Distributor Assy., Renew		
Includes: Reset ignition timing.		
1985-87	(.6)	1.0
(G) Distributor, R&R and Recondition		
Includes: Reset ignition timing.		
1985-87	(.9)	1.6
(G) ESC Module, Renew		
1985-87	(.5)	.7
(G) ESC Knock Sensor, Renew		
1985-87	(.3)	.5
(G) Distributor Cap and/or Rotor, Renew		
1985-87-Four	(.3)	.4
V-6	(.5)	.6
(G) Crankshaft Sensor, Renew		
1985-87	(.6)	1.0
(G) Ignition Coil, Renew		
1985-87-Four	(1.0)	1.3
V-6	(.3)	.4
(G) Ignition Coil and/or Module, Renew		
1985-87	(.5)	.7
(G) Distributor Module, Renew		
1985-87-Four	(.9)	1.2
V-6	(.4)	.6
(G) Distributor Capacitor and/or Module Wiring Harness, Renew		
1985-87-Four	(1.3)	1.8
V-6	(.4)	.8
(G) Distributor Pick-Up Coil and/or Pole Piece, Renew		
Includes: Reset ignition timing.		
1985-87-Four	(1.1)	1.6
(G) Ignition Cables, Renew		
1985-87-Four	(.3)	.5
V-6	(.4)	.6
(G) Ignition Switch, Renew		
1985-87	(.4)	.6
(G) Ignition Key Warning Switch, Renew		
1985-87	(.5)	.8
(G) Ignition Lock Cylinder, Renew		
1985-87	(.6)	.8

PARTS 2 ELECTRONIC IGNITION 2 PARTS

	Part No.	Price
FOUR CYLINDER		
Distributor Assy.		
1985-87	◆1103634	155.75
(1) Dist. Cap		
1985-87	◆10495822	10.75
(2) Rotor		
1985-87	◆10495411	3.50
(3) Main Shaft		
1985-87	◆1988077	24.75
(4) Pick-up Coil		
1985-87	◆1987964	9.75

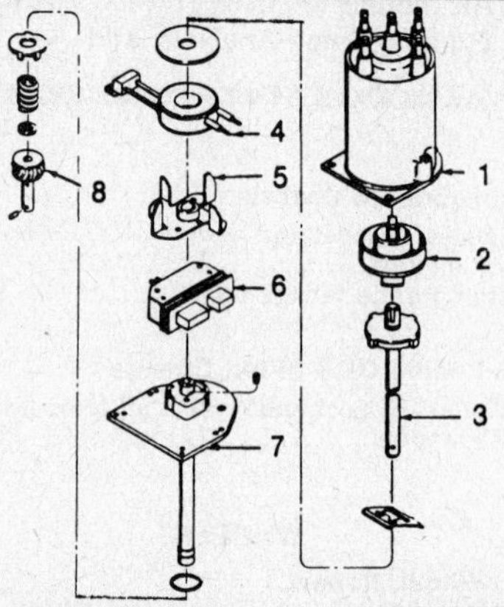

	Part No.	Price
(5) Pole Piece		
1985-87	◆1987963	3.50
(6) Module		
1985-87	◆1989747	51.50
(7) Dist. Housing		
1985-87	◆1988082	26.75
(8) Dist. Gear		
1985-87	◆1978509	13.00
Coil		
1985-86	◆1115315	39.50
1987	◆10497771	N.L.

PARTS 2 ELECTRONIC IGNITION 2 PARTS

	Part No.	Price
V-6		
Electronic Spark Control Module		
1985-87	◆16022654	51.50
Electronic Spark Control Knock Sensor		
1985-87	◆1997562	37.00
Crankshaft Position Sensor		
1985	◆25525666	52.00
1986-87	◆25526124	20.25
Ignition Coil		
1985	◆25523221	109.00
1986-87	◆25526448	109.00
Ignition Module		
1985	◆25523220	168.00
1986-87	◆25526449	215.00
Spark Plug Wire Set		
Spark plug wires are sold separately for each spark plug. Not as a set.		
Ignition Switch		
(wo/Tilt wheel)		
1985-87-A.T.	◆7843497	25.75
M.T.	◆1990115	11.50
(Tilt wheel)		
1985-87-A.T.	◆7843451	25.75
M.T.	◆1990116	11.50

LABOR 3 FUEL SYSTEM 3 LABOR

	(Factory Time)	Chilton Time
FUEL INJECTION		
(G) Throttle Body Assy., R&R or Renew		
1985-87		
Four	(.3)	.5
V-6	(.3)	.5
Renew throttle body add	(.3)	.3
Renew fuel meter body add	(.3)	.3
(G) Fuel Pump Relay, Renew		
1985-87-Four	(.7)	1.0
V-6	(.3)	.4
(G) Fuel Filter Element, Renew		
1985-87	(.3)	.4
(G) Idle Air Control Valve, Renew		
1985-87-Four	(.6)	.9
V-6	(.2)	.3
(G) Throttle Body Injector and/or Gasket, Renew		
1985-87-one	(.6)	1.0
(G) Fuel Pressure Regulator, Renew		
1985-87		
w/EFI	(.7)	1.1
w/MFI	(.3)	.6
(G) Fuel Pump, Renew (In Tank)		
1985-87	(1.2)	1.7
(G) Fuel Injector, Renew (TBI)		
1985-87-one	(.6)	1.0
each adtnl	(.1)	.2

LABOR 3 FUEL SYSTEM 3 LABOR

	(Factory Time)	Chilton Time
(G) Fuel Injector, Renew (Port)		
1985-87-one	(.6)	1.1
each adtnl	(.1)	.2
Perform balance test add	(.4)	.4
(G) Fuel Rail, Renew		
1985-87	(.6)	1.0
(G) Mass Air Sensor, Renew		
1985-87	(.2)	.4
(G) Minimum Idle Speed, Adjust		
All models		
Four	(.6)	.8
V-6	(.2)	.4
(G) Fuel Tank, Renew		
Includes: Drain and refill tank. Transfer tank gauge.		
1985-87	(.8)	1.2
(G) Fuel Gauge (Tank Unit), Renew		
Includes: Drain and refill tank.		
1985-87	(.9)	1.3
(G) Fuel Gauge (Dash Unit), Renew		
Olds Calais		
1985-87	(.5)	.9
Pontiac Grand Am		
1985-87	(.5)	.9
(G) Intake Manifold and/or Gasket, Renew		
Four-1985-87	(1.7)	2.4
V-6-1985-87	(1.5)	2.2
Renew manif add	(.3)	.5

PARTS 3 FUEL SYSTEM 3 PARTS

	Part No.	Price
Fuel Pump		
1985-151	◆6472311	56.50
1986-87-151	◆6472526	57.00
1985-181	◆6472375	79.50
1986-181	◆25115190	89.50
1987-181	◆25115429	79.75
Fuel Pump Relay		
1985-87-151	◆10034222	18.25
1985-181	◆10027719	6.00
1986-87-181	◆10038490	7.25
Fuel Tank		
1985-87	◆22527083	149.00
Fuel Gauge (Tank)		
(wo/Digital cluster)		
1985-151	◆25004390	134.25
181	◆25004392	125.25
1986-87-151	◆25091299	156.50
181	◆25091303	130.50
(Digital cluster)		
1985-151	◆25004989	131.75
181	◆25004992	121.75
1986-87-151	◆25091315	156.50
181	◆25091319	130.50
Fuel Gauge (Dash)		
1985-87-Calais	◆25078394	59.50
Grand Am	◆25077732	N.L.
Intake Manifold Gaskets		
1985-87-151	◆10026023	5.00
181	◆25524292	14.75

PARTS 3 ELECTRONIC FUEL INJECTION 3 PARTS

THROTTLE BODY FUEL INJECTION 4-151

	Part No.	Price
(1) Throttle Body Injection		
1985-87	◆17111388	513.50
(2) Fuel Injector Kit		
1985-87	◆17068993	191.75
(3) Gasket Kit		
1985-87	◆17068990	24.75
(4) Throttle Position Sensor Kit		
1985-87	◆17078274	74.75
(5) Throttle Body Kit		
1985-87	◆17111389	237.25
(6) Fastener Assortment Kit		
1985-87	◆17078276	18.25
(7) Idle Air Valve Control Kit		
1985-87	◆17079256	88.75
Fuel Meter Kit		
1985-87	◆17068992	425.75

Includes one injector & pressure regulator.

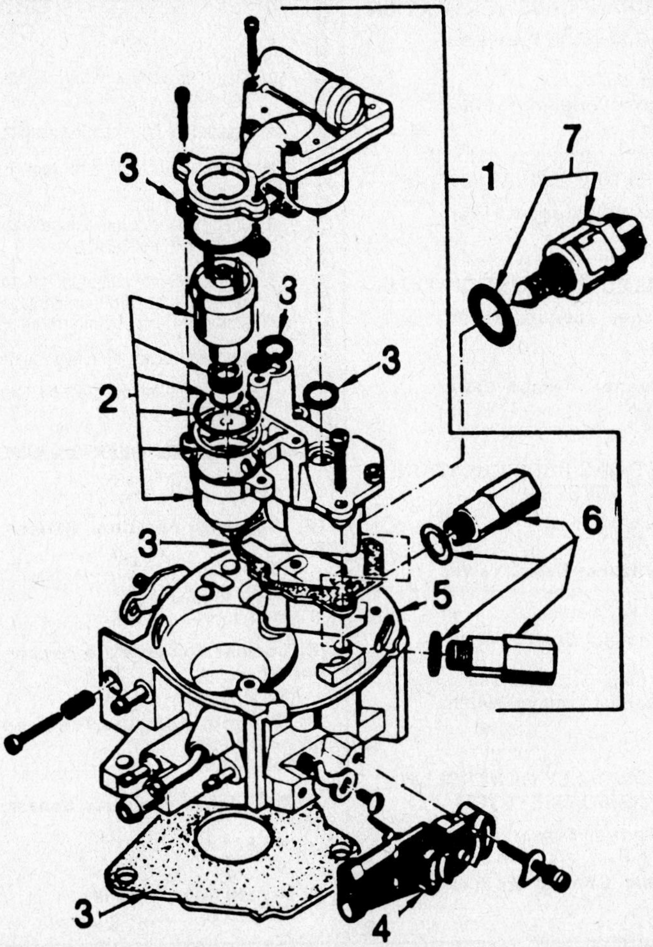

PARTS 3 ELECTRONIC FUEL INJECTION 3 PARTS

	Part No.	Price
MULTI-PORT FUEL INJECTION		
181–3.0		
(1) Throttle Body Kit		
1985-87	◆17110819	9.25
(2) Coolant Cover Kit		
1985-87	◆17110820	21.75
(3) Idle Air Housing Assy.		
1986-87	◆17110821	26.75
(4) Throttle Position Sensor		
1985-87	◆17111293	62.75
(5) Idle Air Control Valve		
1985-87	◆17111286	58.00
Fuel Injector		
1985	◆25523721	79.00
1986-87	◆25527181	79.00
Fuel Injection Rail		
1985-87	◆25521323	174.00
Pressure Regulator		
1985-87	◆25523720	44.75

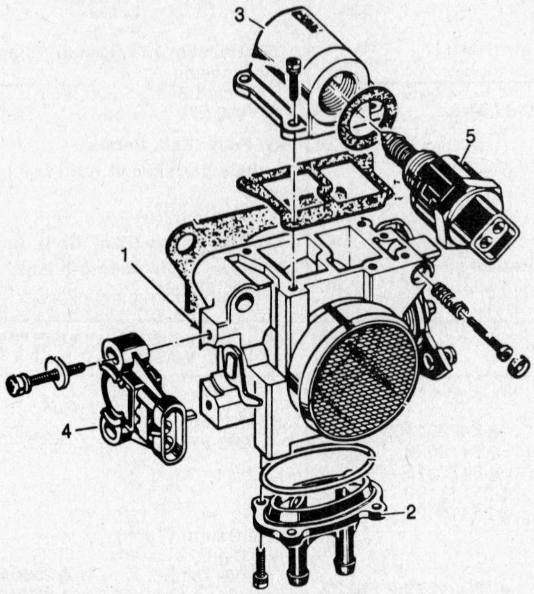

LABOR 3A EMISSION CONTROLS 3A LABOR

	(Factory Time)	Chilton Time
POSITIVE CRANKCASE VENTILATION		
(M) Positive Crankcase Ventilation Valve, Renew		
All models	(.2)	.3
(M) Crankcase Ventilation Filter Assy., Renew		
All models	(.2)	.3
EVAPORATIVE EMISSION TYPE		
(G) Charcoal Canister or Filter, Renew		
All models	(.2)	.3
CONTROLLED COMBUSTION TYPE		
(G) Air Cleaner Vacuum Motor, Renew		
All models	(.3)	.5
(G) Air Cleaner Temperature Sensor, Renew		
All models	(.2)	.3
EXHAUST GAS RECIRCULATION SYSTEM		
(G) E.G.R. Valve, Renew		
All models	(.4)	.6
(G) E.G.R. Vacuum Delay Valve, Renew		
All models	(.3)	.4
(G) E.G.R. Thermal Control Valve, Renew		
All models	(.3)	.4
(G) E.G.R. Thermal Vacuum Switch, Renew		
All models	(.3)	.4
ELECTRONICALLY CONTROLLED EMISSIONS SYSTEM		
(P) Throttle Position Sensor, Adjust		
All models	(.4)	.6
(P) Electronic Control Module, Renew		
1985-87	(.7)	.9

CHILTON'S EMISSION CONTROL TUNE-UP

1. Clean or renew P.C.V. valve, hoses and filter.
2. Check fuel tank cap for sealing ability.
3. Check fuel tank and fuel lines for leakage.
4. Check evaporation canister and filter. Replace if necessary.
5. Check engine compression to determine leakage of unburned gases. (Add time for items of interference).
6. Test and clean or renew spark plugs.
7. Check engine oil dipstick for sealing ability.
8. Test exhaust system with analyzer and check system for leakage.
9. Check exhaust manifold heat valve for operation.
10. Adjust ignition timing and carburetor idle speed and mixture.
11. Check automatic choke mechanism for free operation.
12. Inspect air cleaner and element.
13. On models so equipped, test distributor vacuum control switch and transmission control switch.

Four **1.3**
V-6 .... **1.7**

For repairs made, charge accordingly.

	(Factory Time)	Chilton Time
(P) Throttle Position Sensor, Renew		
1985-87	(.9)	1.2
(P) Prom, Renew		
1985-87	(.7)	1.0
(P) Coolant Temperature Sensor, Renew		
1985-87	(.4)	.7
(P) Manifold Absolute Pressure Sensor, Renew		
1985-87	(.5)	.6
(P) Manifold Temperature Sensor, Renew		
1985-87	(.4)	.6
(P) Oxygen Sensor, Renew		
1985-87	(.5)	.7

	(Factory Time)	Chilton Time
(P) Vehicle Speed Sensor, Renew		
1985-87	(.9)	1.4
(P) Calpak Sensor, Renew		
1985-87	(.3)	.4
(P) Back-Up Lamp and Park/Neutral Switch, Renew		
1985-87	(.5)	.7
(P) Air Control/Air Switching Valve, Renew		
1985-87	(.6)	.8
(P) Canister Purge Control Valve, Renew		
1985-87	(.4)	.6
(P) E.G.R. Vacuum Control Solenoid, Renew		
1985-87	(.3)	.5
(P) Vacuum Control Purge Solenoid, Renew		
1985-87	(.4)	.6

PARTS 3A EMISSION CONTROLS 3A PARTS

	Part No.	Price
POSITIVE CRANKCASE VENTILATION		
P.C.V. Valve		
1985-86-151	◆25043669	6.25
1987-151	◆25095452	6.00
1985-87-181	◆6487936	3.50
EVAPORATIVE EMISSION TYPE		
Fuel Vapor Canister		
1985-87-151	◆17075840	30.00
181	◆17075856	60.00
Canister Filter		
1985-151	◆7021743	1.75
1986-87-181	◆7026014	N.L.
CONTROLLED COMBUSTION TYPE		
Air Cleaner Temperature Sensor		
1985-151	◆8997787	18.50
181	◆25037034	21.25

	Part No.	Price
EXHAUST GAS RECIRCULATION SYSTEM		
E.G.R. Valve		
1985-86-151	◆17111245	67.75
1987-151	◆17110478	63.25
1985-87-181	◆17110816	49.50
E.G.R. Valve Vacuum Control		
1985-181	◆25522611	45.75
1986-87-181	◆25522717	41.75
E.G.R. Vacuum Control Switch		
1985-181	◆25523722	11.50
COMPUTER COMMAND CONTROL EMISSION SYSTEM		
Calibrator (Prom)		
151		
1985-A.T.	◆16051333	40.50
M.T.	◆16051108	40.50
1986-87-A.T.	◆16060865	40.50
M.T.	◆16052959	40.50
181		
1985	◆16049998	40.50
1986-87	◆16059958	40.50

	Part No.	Price
CalPak (ECM)		
1985-87-181	◆16047428	5.75
Controller (ECM)		
1985-87-151	◆1226864	110.25
1985-181	◆1226948	110.00
1986-87-181	◆1227153	110.00
Manifold Air Temp. Sensor		
1985-87-181	◆25036751	21.00
Exhaust Oxygen Sensor		
1985-87	◆8990741	28.75
M.A.P. Sensor		
1985-87-151	◆16017460	N.L.
Coolant Temperature Sensor		
1985-87	◆25036629	9.75
E.S.C. Knock Sensor		
1985-87-181	◆1997562	37.00
Vehicle Speed Sensor		
1985-87-A.T.	◆25007335	44.00
M.T.	◆25007336	42.25

LABOR 4 ALTERNATOR AND REGULATOR 4 LABOR

(Factory Time) — Chilton Time

(G) Delcotron Circuits, Test

Includes: Test battery, regulator, Delcotron output.

	Chilton Time
All models	.6

(M) Alternator Drive Belt, Renew

	Chilton Time
Four–1985-87 (.4)	*.5
V-6–1985-87	
Serpentine (.3)	.5
*w/A.C. add (.2)	.2

(G) Delcotron Assembly, Renew

Includes: Transfer pulley and fan if required.

	Chilton Time
Four–1985-87 (.7)	1.0
V-6–1985-87 (.5)	.8

(G) Delcotron, R&R and Recondition

Includes: Complete disassembly, replacement of parts as required, reassemble.

	Chilton Time
Four–1985-87 (1.3)	2.2
V-6–1985-87 (1.5)	2.3

(G) Delcotron Rear Bearing, Renew

Includes: R&R Delcotron, separate end frames.

	Chilton Time
Four–1985-87 (.8)	1.2
V-61985-87 (.9)	1.4
Renew front brg add	.2

(G) Delcotron Voltage Regulator, Test and Renew

Includes: R&R, disassemble and reassemble Delcotron.

	Chilton Time
Four–1985-87 (1.0)	1.5
V-6–1985-87 (.8)	1.3

PARTS 4 ALTERNATOR AND REGULATOR 4 PARTS

	Part No.	Price
Alternator Assy.		
1985-78 amp	◆1100250	225.00
94 amp	◆1105492	228.50
1986-87-85 amp.		
151	◆10497118	128.50
181	◆10497120	128.50
1876-87-100 amp		
151	◆10497119	141.00
181	◆10497121	141.00

Only remanufactured alternators as a whole unit are available for 1986-87 models.

	Part No.	Price
(1) Capacitor		
1985	◆1988873	4.00
(2) Diede Trio (Negative)		
1985	◆1984459	5.00
(3) Rectifier Bridge		
1985-78 amp	◆1984454	28.00
94 amp	◆1987061	29.25
(4) Bearing (Ring End)		
1985	◆9436831	5.50
(5) Frame (Ring End)		
1985-78 amp	◆1984460	47.75
94 amp	◆1987073	28.00
(6) Regulator		
1985	◆1116387	25.00
(7) Brush (w/Holder)		
1985	◆1984462	9.00

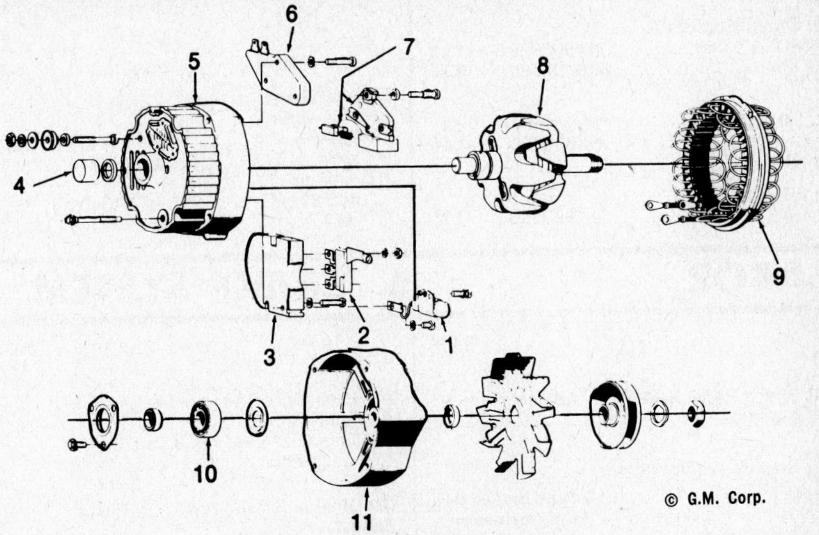

© G.M. Corp.

	Part No.	Price
(8) Rotor Assy.		
1985	◆1984466	77.25
(9) Stator Assy.		
1985-78 amp	◆1984445	37.25
94 amp	◆1987074	41.50

	Part No.	Price
(10) Bearing (Drive End)		
1985	◆908419	10.00
(11) Frame (Drive End)		
1985-78 amp	◆1984464	23.50
94 amp	◆1987054	28.00

LABOR 5 STARTING SYSTEM 5 LABOR

	(Factory Time)	Chilton Time
(G) Starter Draw Test (On Car)		
All models		.3
(G) Starter, Renew		
Four–1985-87	(.4)	.7
V-6–1985-87	(.8)	1.1
Add draw test if performed.		
(G) Starter, R&R and Recondition		
Includes: Turn down armature.		
Four–1985-87	(1.2)	2.0
V-6–1985-87	(1.4)	2.2
Renew field coils add	(.2)	.5
Add draw test if performed.		
(G) Starter Drive, Renew		
Includes: R&R starter.		
Four–1985-87	(.6)	1.0
V-6–1985-87	(1.1.)	1.5
(G) Starter Motor Solenoid, Renew		
Includes: R&R starter where required.		
Four–1985-87	(.3)	.5
V-6–1985-87	(.8)	1.1
(G) Back-Up Lamp and Park/Neutral Switch, Renew		
1985-87	(.5)	.7
(G) Ignition Switch, Renew		
1985-87	(.4)	.6
(M) Battery Cables, Renew		
Positive		
Four	(.3)	.4
V-6	(.4)	.5
Negative		
All models	(.2)	.3
(M) Battery Terminals, Clean		
All models		.3

PARTS 5 STARTING SYSTEM 5 PARTS

	Part No.	Price
Starter Assy. (New)		
1985-87-151	◆1998531	160.75
181	◆1998526	189.50
(1) Solenoid Switch		
1985-87	◆1114531	N.L.
(2) Spring		
1985-87	◆1978281	1.75
(3) Plunger		
1985-87	◆1987391	6.75
(4) Shift Lever		
1985-87	◆1945804	1.50
(5) Armature		
1985-87-151	◆10495958	85.00
181	◆10497046	76.75
(6) Drive Assy.		
1985-87	◆10498407	33.50
(7) Grommet		
1985-87	◆1984527	1.00
(8) Frame (w/Field)		
1985-87-151	◆1984522	75.00
181	◆1987277	71.25
(9) Brush Holder Kit		
1985-87-151	◆1893929	11.25
181	◆10497180	9.75
(10) Brushes		
1985-87	◆1893296	.50
(11) Holder		
1985-87	◆1893293	1.25

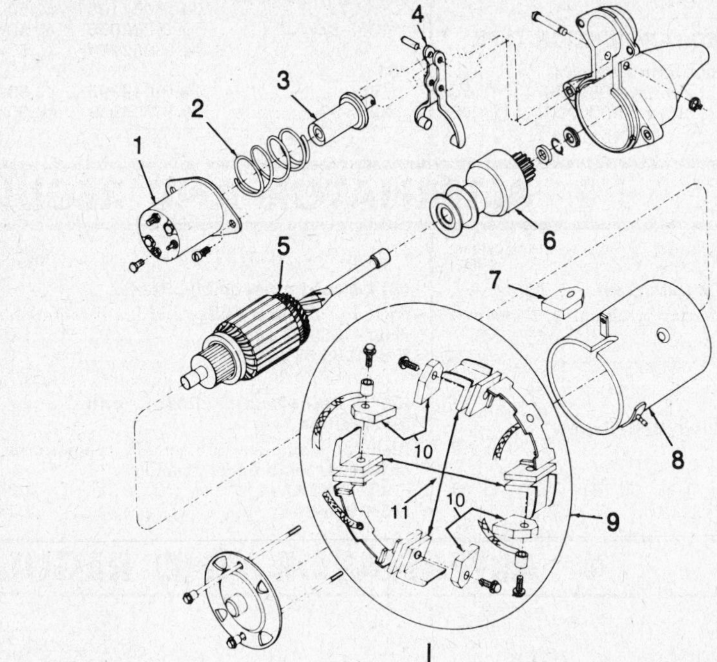

	Part No.	Price
Ignition Switch		
(wo/Tilt wheel)		
1985-87-A.T.	◆7843497	25.75
M.T.	◆1990115	11.50
(Tilt wheel)		
1985-87-A.T.	◆7843451	25.75
M.T.	◆1990116	11.50
Battery Cable (Positive)		
1985-87-151	◆12026581	20.75
181	◆12013431	23.00
Battery Cable (Negative)		
1985-87-151	◆12003646	12.00
181	◆8907035	12.25

LABOR 6 BRAKE SYSTEM 6 LABOR

	(Factory Time)	Chilton Time
(G) Brake Pedal Free Play, Adjust		
All models		.3
(G) Brakes, Adjust (Minor)		
Includes: R&R wheels and adjust brakes thru access holes in drums. Fill master cylinder.		
two wheels		.4
Remove knock out plugs, add-each		.1
(G) Bleed Brakes (Four Wheels)		
Includes: Fill master cylinder.		
All models	(.4)	.5
(G) Free Up or Renew Brake Self-Adjusting Units		
All models-one	(.4)	.6
each adtnl		.4
(G) Brake Shoes and/or Pads, Renew		
Includes: Install new or exchange shoes or pads, adjust service and hand brake. Bleed system.		
1985-87-front-disc	(.7)	1.1
rear-drum	(.9)	1.5
all four wheels		2.5
Resurface disc rotor add-each		.9
Resurface brake drum add-each		.5
(G) Brake Drum, Renew (One)		
1985-87	(.3)	.5
(G) Brake Proportioner Valves, Renew		
Includes: Bleed system.		
1985-87-one	(.4)	.6
both	(.5)	.8
(G) Brake System Failure Warning Switch, Renew		
1985-87	(.2)	.3

LABOR — 6 BRAKE SYSTEM 6 — LABOR

	(Factory Time)	Chilton Time
BRAKE HYDRAULIC SYSTEM		
(G) Wheel Cylinder, Renew		
Includes: Bleed system.		
1985-87-one	(.8)	1.0
both	(1.1)	1.9
(G) Wheel Cylinder, R&R and Rebuild		
Includes: Bleed system.		
1985-87-one	(1.0)	1.3
both	(1.5)	2.1
(G) Master Cylinder, Renew		
Includes: Bleed system.		
1985-87	(.7)	1.0
(G) Master Cylinder, R&R and Rebuild		
Includes: Bleed complete system.		
1985-87	(1.5)	1.9
(G) Brake Hose, Renew		
Includes: Bleed system.		
1985-87		
front-one	(.5)	.8
both	(.6)	1.1
rear-one	(.5)	.8
both	(.6)	1.1
(G) Brake System Flush and Refill		
All models		1.2
POWER BRAKES		
(G) Power Brake Cylinder, Renew		
1985-87	(.7)	1.1
(G) Power Brake Cylinder, R&R and Recondition		
1985-87	(1.4)	1.8
Recond m/Cyl add	(.8)	.8

COMBINATIONS
Add to Brakes, Renew

See Machine Shop Operations

	(Factory Time)	Chilton Time
(G) RENEW WHEEL CYLINDER		
Each	(.2)	.2
(G) REBUILD WHEEL CYLINDER		
Each	(.2)	.3
(G) REBUILD CALIPER ASSEMBLY		
Each	(.5)	.6
(G) RENEW MASTER CYLINDER		
All models	(.5)	.8
(G) REBUILD MASTER CYLINDER		
All models	(.8)	1.0
(G) RENEW BRAKE HOSE		
Each		.3
(G) RENEW BRAKE DRUM		
Each	(.1)	.1
(G) RENEW DISC BRAKE ROTOR		
Each	(.2)	.3

	(Factory Time)	Chilton Time
(M) Vacuum Check Valve, Renew		
1985-87	(.5)	.6
(G) Low Vacuum Brake Indicator Module Assy., Renew		
1985-87	(.2)	.3
(G) Low Vacuum Switch, Renew		
1985-87	(.2)	.3

	(Factory Time)	Chilton Time
DISC BRAKES		
(G) Disc Brake Pads, Renew		
Includes: Install new disc brake pads only.		
1985-87	(.7)	1.1
(G) Disc Brake Rotor, Renew		
1985-87-one	(.5)	.7
both	(.8)	1.2
(G) Caliper Assembly, Renew		
Includes: Bleed complete system.		
1985-87-one	(.7)	1.0
both	(1.1)	1.5
(G) Caliper Assy., R&R and Recondition		
Includes: Bleed complete system.		
1985-87-one	(1.2)	1.5
both	(2.1)	2.5
PARKING BRAKE		
(M) Parking Brake, Adjust		
All models	(.3)	.4
(G) Parking Brake Control, Renew		
1985-87	(.6)	1.0
(G) Parking Brake Equalizer, Renew		
1985-87	(.4)	.5
(G) Parking Brake Cables, Renew		
1985-87-front	(.9)	1.3
rear-right side	(.5)	.8
left side	(.5)	.8

PARTS — 6 BRAKE SYSTEM 6 — PARTS

	Part No.	Price
Shoe & Lining Kit (Rear)		
1985-87	◆12321412	43.00
Rear Wheel Cylinder Assy.		
1985-87	◆18008649	31.50
Rear Wheel Cyl. Repair Kit		
1985-87	◆18008650	7.00
Front Brake Hose		
1985-87-right	◆9768144	11.00
left	◆9768127	11.00
Rear Brake Hose		
1985-87	◆9766402	9.25

	Part No.	Price
Master Cylinder Assy.		
1985-87	◆18010087	206.50
Master Cylinder Repair Kit		
1985-87	◆18004853	22.50
Brake Drum (Rear)		
1985-87	◆1259649	69.75
Master Cylinder Warning Switch		
1985-87	◆18008614	26.00
POWER BRAKE UNIT		
Power Brake Booster (Vacuum)		
1985-87	◆18012157	238.75
Power Brake Booster Repair Kit		
1985-87	◆18013513	51.50

	Part No.	Price
Vacuum Check Valve		
1985-87	◆18003614	6.00
PARKING BRAKE		
Parking Brake Lever		
1985-87-R.H.	◆18012423	18.50
L.H.	◆18012422	18.50
Parking Brake Alarm Switch		
1985-87	◆1264464	1.50
Front Cable (Parking Brake)		
1985-87	◆25523078	14.00
Rear Cable (Parking Brake)		
1985-87-right	◆25520271	14.00
left	◆25520270	14.00

PARTS — 6 DISC BRAKES 6 — PARTS

	Part No.	Price
(1) Brake Pad Set		
1985-87	◆12321417	N.L.
(2) Caliper Piston		
1985-87	◆18002866	13.00
(3) Caliper Repair Kit		
1985-87	◆18011670	8.50
(4) Caliper Assy.		
1985-87-right	◆18011668	163.25
left	◆18011667	163.25

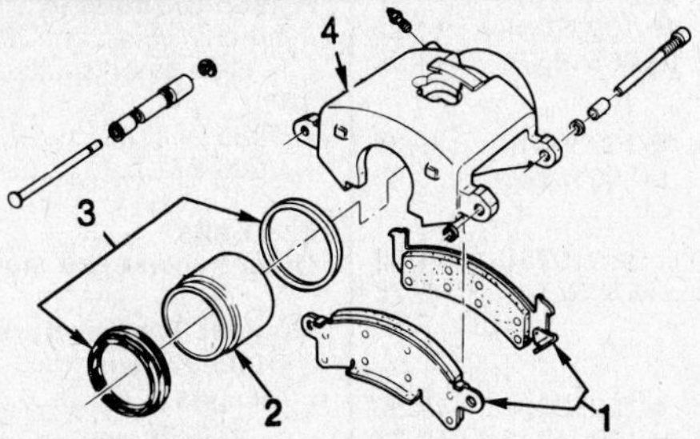

LABOR 7 COOLING SYSTEM 7 LABOR

(Factory Time) Chilton Time

(M) Winterize Cooling System

Includes: Run engine to check for leaks, tighten all hose connections. Test radiator and pressure cap, drain radiator and engine block. Add anti-freeze and refill system.

All models 5

(G) Thermostat, Renew

1985-87

Four (.2) 4

V-6 (.4) 6

(G) Radiator Assembly, R&R or Renew

Includes: Drain and refill cooling system.

1985-87 (.6) 1.1

w/A.C. add (.2) 2

Renew side tank and/or gskt add,

one side (.7) 1.0

both side (1.2) 1.7

ADD THESE OPERATIONS TO RADIATOR R&R

(G) Boil & Repair 1.5

(G) Rod Clean 1.9

(G) Repair Core 1.3

(G) Renew Tank 1.6

(G) Renew Trans. Oil Cooler 1.9

(G) Recore Radiator 1.7

(M) Radiator Hoses, Renew

1985-87-upper (.3) 4

lower (.4) 5

both (.5) 7

(M) Drive Belt, Renew

Four–1985-87

A.C. (.5) 6

Fan (.4) 5

P.S. (.4) 5

w/A.C. add (.2) 2

V-6–1985-87

Serpentine (.3) 5

(M) Drive Belt, Adjust

Four-1985-87-one (.2) 3

all (.3) 4

(G) Water Pump and/or Gasket, Renew

Four–1985-87 (1.2) 2.0

V-6–1985-87 (1.5) 2.8

w/A.C. add (.2) 2

COOLING SYSTEM TUNE-UP

An Annual Cooling System Tune-Up Suggestion List should include (with some exceptions):

1. A visual check of the cooling system for indications of leaks or excessive oil content.
2. Pressure check the cooling system for internal and external leaks with filler cap and neck adapter and tester.
3. Check crankcase and automatic transmission oil for water content.
4. Test coolant thermostat with radiator thermometer.
5. Check temperature gauge for accuracy.
6. Drain system and flush till clean.
7. Clean foreign matter from radiator fins.
8. Test radiator pressure cap with cap tester.
9. Check fan blades and pulleys for alignment and damage.
10. Internal and external inspection of all hoses for cracks and deterioration.
11. Check core plugs (where possible) for seepage.
12. Refill system with correct coolant and check for air locks.
13. Check condition and tension of drive belts with tension gauge.

All models 1.5

(Factory Time) Chilton Time

(G) Engine Coolant Fan and/or Motor, Renew

1985-87 (.3) 6

(G) Engine Coolant Fan Relay, Renew

1985-87 (.2) 3

(G) Engine Coolant Electronic Control Module, Renew

1985-87 (.3) 4

(G) Temperature Gauge (Engine Unit), Renew

1985-87 (.2) 3

(G) Water Jacket Expansion Plugs, Renew (Side of Block)

Each 5

Note: If necessary to R&R any component to gain access to plug add appropriate time.

(G) Heater Hoses, Renew

1985-87

wo/A.C.-one (.4) 6

both (.6) 8

w/A.C.-one (.6) 8

both (.8) 1.0

(Factory Time) Chilton Time

(G) Heater Core, R&R or Renew

1985-87

wo/A.C. (1.4) 3.0

w/A.C. (1.4) 3.0

ADD THESE OPERATIONS TO HEATER CORE R&R

(G) Boil & Repair 1.2

(G) Repair Core 9

(G) Recore 1.2

(G) Blower Motor, Renew

1985-87

wo/A.C. (.3) 5

w/A.C. (.5) 8

(G) Blower Motor Switch, Renew

1985-87

wo/A.C. (.6) 8

w/A.C. (.6) 8

(G) Blower Motor Resistor, Renew

1985-87 (.2) 3

(G) Temperature Control Assembly, Renew

1985-87

wo/A.C. (.7) 1.0

w/A.C. (.7) 1.0

(G) Heater Water Control Valve, Renew

1985-87 (.7) 1.0

PARTS 7 COOLING SYSTEM 7 PARTS

	Part No.	Price
Radiator Assy.		
Accurate replacement of the radiator can be done only by using the radiator code stamped on a metal tag located on the original radiator. Order by year, model, and radiator code no.		
Upper Radiator Hose		
1985-87-151	◆10037309	11.25
181	◆25519576	11.25
Lower Radiator Hose		
1985-87-151	◆10030011	7.25
181	◆25518850	10.50
Thermostat		
1985-87-151	◆3059793	11.00
181	◆3037747	6.75
Water Pump Assy.		
151		
1985-87-body	◆10013800	49.50
housing	◆10004073	59.75
181		
1985	◆25525690	63.00
1986-87	◆25527537	63.00
Eng. Coolant Fan Relay		
151		
1985-87-bolts to brkt.	◆10038311	5.50
clips to brkt.	◆10034222	7.25
181		
1985	◆10040131	20.00
1986-87	◆12034544	8.25
Fan Belts		
Order by year and model.		
Coolant Temperature Switch (Engine)		
1985-87-wo/ Gauges	◆25036629	9.75
Gauges	◆25036628	19.75
Temperature Switch (Dash)		
1985-87-Regal	◆10030963	20.75
Calais	◆25078266	64.25
Grand Am	◆25077732	162.50
Fan Control Switch		
1985-87	◆3040674	12.00
Heater Core		
1985-87	◆3058622	62.00
Blower Motor		
1985-87	◆22020945	60.00
Blower Motor Resistor		
1985	◆10024378	3.75
1986-87	◆22529266	4.50
Heater Control		
1985-87-Regal	◆16038644	46.75
Calais	◆16035393	46.75
Grand Am	◆16035382	43.00
Blower Motor Switch		
1985-87	◆16015450	6.75

LABOR 8 EXHAUST SYSTEM 8 LABOR

(Factory Time) Chilton Time

(G) Muffler, Renew
1985-87 (.6) 9

(G) Front Exhaust Pipe Seal, Renew
1985-87 (.3) 6

(G) Front Exhaust Pipe, Renew (To Converter)
1985-87 (.5) 8

(G) Intermediate Exhaust Pipe, Renew
1985-87 (.6) 1.0

(G) Catalytic Converter, Renew
1985-87 (.8) 1.0

(G) Exhaust Manifold or Gasket, Renew
Four–1985-87 (.6) 1.2
V-6–1985-87
right side (2.3) 3.1
left side (.5) 9

COMBINATIONS

(G) Muffler, Exhaust and Tail Pipe, Renew
All models 1.5

(G) Muffler and Tail Pipe, Renew
All models 1.0

PARTS 8 EXHAUST SYSTEM 8 PARTS

	Part No.	Price
Crossover Pipe		
1985-87-181	◆25523688	9.75
Catalytic Converter		
1985-87-151	◆25056706	278.00
1985-181	◆25057897	355.00
1986-87-181	◆25101076	355.00
Crossover Pipe Flange		
1985-87 (181)		
right	◆25500296	3.25
left	◆25500297	3.50
Exhaust Pipe Seal		
1985-87-151	◆10023355	6.00
181	◆1261596	4.75
Exhaust Manifold		
151		
1985-87	◆10041215	64.75
181		
1985-87 (right)		
Note 1	◆25522298	94.75
Note 2	◆25524335	94.75
(left)	◆25518779	54.00

Note 1: Oxygen sensor attaches to the top of the manifold.
Note 2: Oxygen sensor attaches to the side of the manifold.

LABOR 9 FRONT SUSPENSION 9 LABOR

(Factory Time) Chilton Time

Note: On all front suspension operations alignment charges must be added if performed. Time given does not include alignment.

(M) Wheel, Renew
one (.5) 5

(G) Wheels, Balance
one 3
each adtnl 2

(M) Wheels, Rotate (All)
All models 5

(G) Check Alignment of Front End
All models 5
Note: Deduct if alignment is performed.

(G) Toe-In, Adjust
All models (.5) 7

(G) Caster and Camber, Check
Includes: Check and adjust toe.
All models (.6) 9
Adjust caster and camber
add-each side .... *.5
*Includes time to file struts as needed.

(G) Lower Control Arm Assy., Renew
Add alignment charges.
1985-87-one (.8) 1.1
both (1.5) 2.0

(G) Lower Control Arm Bushings, Renew
Add alignment charges.
1985-87-one side (1.1) 1.5
both sides (2.0) 2.8

(G) Lower Ball Joints, Renew
Add alignment charges.
1985-87-one (.9) 1.2
both (1.7) 2.2

(G) Front Shock Absorber Strut Assy., Renew
Add alignment charges.
1985-87-one (.8) 1.1
both (1.6) 2.0

(G) Front Shock Absorber Strut Cartridge, Renew
Add alignment charges if necessary.
1985-87-one (1.0) 1.4
both (1.8) 2.7

(G) Front Spring, Seat or Insulator, Renew
Add alignment charges.
1985-87-one side (.8) 1.2
both sides (1.5) 2.3

(G) Front Strut Bearing Mount Assy., Renew
Add alignment charges.
1985-87-one side (.9) 1.2
both sides (1.6) 2.1

(G) Front Suspension Assembly Support, Renew
Add alignment charges if necessary.
1985-87-one side (.9) 1.3
both sides (1.7) 2.5

(G) Front Stabilizer Shaft, Renew
1985-87 (.8) 1.0

(G) Front Stabilizer Shaft Bushings, Renew
1985-87-one (.3) 4
both (.5) 6

(G) Steering Knuckle Assembly, Renew
Add alignment charges.
1985-87-one (1.0) 1.3
both (1.8) 2.5

(G) Steering Knuckle Inner Dust Seal, Renew
1985-87-one side (1.1) 1.2
both sides (2.1) 2.3

(G) Front Wheel Bearing and Hub Assy., Renew
1985-87-one side (.6) 1.0
both sides (1.1) 1.9

FRONT DRIVE AXLE

(G) Axle Shaft Seal, Renew
1985-87-one (.6) 1.0
both (1.1) 1.9

(G) Front Drive Axle, R&R or Renew
1985-87-one (1.2) 1.6
both (1.9) 2.4
Renew shaft add-each (.3) 4
Renew C/V Joint add
each side (.3) 4
Renew D/O Joint add
each side (.3) 4
Renew C/V Joint boots add
each (.2) 2

PARTS 9 FRONT DRIVE AXLE 9 PARTS

	Part No.	Price
(1) Joint Kit		
(A.T.)		
1985-87	◆7846867	N.L.
(M.T.)		
1985	◆7847111	N.L.
1986-87	◆26000321	205.00
(2) Seal Kit		
1985-87-A.T.	◆7845351	N.L.
M.T.	◆7845398	N.L.
(3) Seal Retaining Clamp		
1985-87-A.T.	◆7845161	3.75
M.T.	◆7843742	5.75
(4) Axle Shaft		
(A.T.)		
1985-87-right	◆7845152	44.00
left	◆7845153	41.75
(M.T.)		
1985-87-right	◆7845187	74.00
left	◆7845188	62.25
(5) Housing Assy.		
(A.T.)		
1985-87-right	◆7842378	111.00
left	◆7842380	111.00
(M.T.)		
1985-87	◆7843920	136.00
(6) Spider Assy.		
1985-87-A.T.	◆7846866	120.00
M.T.	◆7847113	120.00

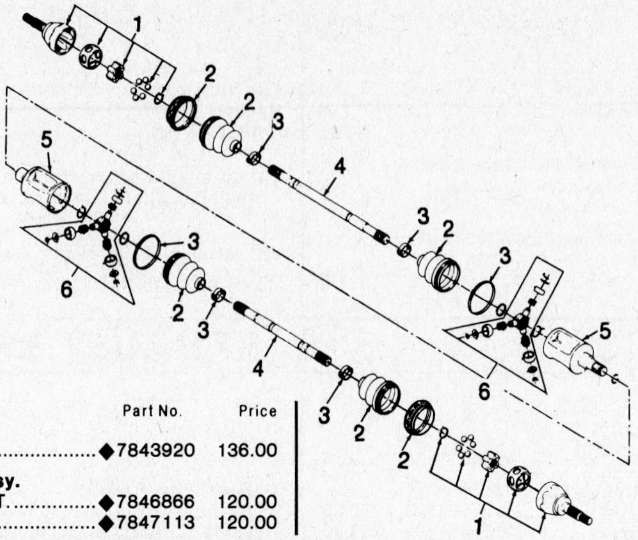

PARTS 9 FRONT SUSPENSION 9 PARTS

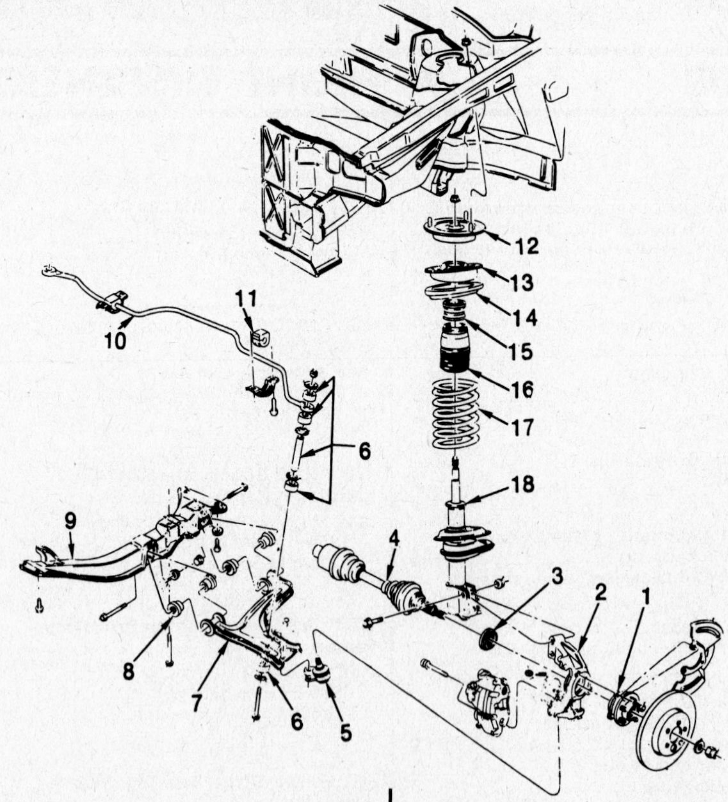

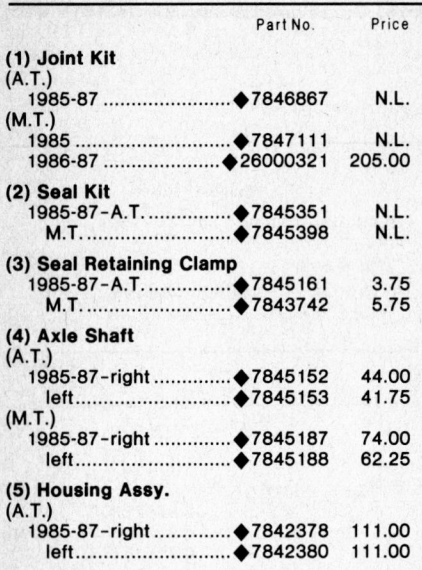

	Part No.	Price
(1) Wheel Hub Bearing		
1985-87	◆7470004	166.00
(2) Steering Knuckle		
1985-87-right	◆17066984	N.L.
left	◆17066983	31.25
(3) Front Axle Seal		
1985-87	◆14086700	4.50
(4) Drive Axle Kit		
(A.T.)		
1985-87-right	◆7845347	N.L.
left	◆7845348	N.L.
(M.T.)		
1985-87-right	◆7845395	N.L.
left	◆7845396	N.L.
(5) Ball Joint (Lower)		
1985-87	◆9767781	52.00
(6) Grommet Kit		
1985-87	◆14039143	4.75
(7) Lower Control Arm		
1985-87-right	◆14026620	93.50
left	◆14026619	93.50
(8) Lower Control Arm Bushing		
1985-87-front	◆14026628	7.00
rear	◆14026610	7.00
(9) Bracket (Support)		
151		
1985-87-right	◆14085152	53.25
left	◆14091757	82.00
181		
1985-87-right	◆14085156	64.00
left	◆14091759	82.00
(10) Stabilizer Shaft		
(wo/H.D. susp.)		
1985-87-151	◆14076605	47.50
181	◆14076607	47.50
(H.D. susp.)		
1985-87-151	◆14076612	47.50
181	◆14076613	47.50
(11) Insulator (Stabilizer)		
(wo/H.D. susp.)		
1985-87	◆14085145	1.25
(H.D. susp.)		
1985-87	◆14085147	1.25
(12) Strut Mount		
1985-87	◆17981435	48.25
(13) Spring Seat		
1985-87	◆14051008	3.75
(14) Spring Insulator		
1985-87	◆14059999	3.75
(15) Strut Bumper		
1985-87	◆14076624	18.50
(16) Strut Shield		
1985-87	◆14077713	5.25
(17) Coil Spring		
Order by year and model.		
(18) Front Strut		
(wo/H.D. susp.)		
1985-87-right	◆22047917	114.25
left	◆22047916	114.25
(H.D. susp.)		
1985-87-right	◆22047919	114.25
left	◆22047918	114.25

LABOR 11 STEERING GEAR 11 LABOR

	(Factory Time)	Chilton Time
(G) Tie Rod End, Renew		
Includes: Reset toe-in.		
1985-87-one	(.7)	.9
both	(.9)	1.2
Renew seal add-each		.1
(G) Inner Tie Rod, Renew		
Includes: Reset toe-in.		
1985-87-one	(.7)	.9
both	(1.0)	1.3
(G) Steering Wheel, Renew		
1985-87	(.3)	.4
(G) Horn Contact and Turn Signal Cancelling Cam, Renew		
1985-87	(.4)	.6
(G) Steering Column Upper Bearing, Renew		
1985-std colm	(1.1)	1.6
tilt colm	(.9)	1.4
1986-87		
std colm	(1.2)	1.7
tilt colm	(.5)	.9
(G) Steering Column Lock Actuator Parts, Renew		
1985-std colm	(1.1)	1.5
tilt colm	(1.2)	1.6
1986-87		
std colm	(1.2)	1.7
tilt colm	(.9)	1.4
Renew actuator rod add	(.5)	.5
(G) Steering Column Shift Bowl, Renew		
Does not include colorcoat.		
1985-87		
std colm	(1.2)	1.7
tilt colm	(1.3)	1.8

POWER STEERING

	(Factory Time)	Chilton Time
(G) Trouble Shoot Power Steering		
Includes: Test pump and system pressure. Check pounds pull on steering wheel and check for leaks.		
All models		.5
(M) Check and Fill Reservoir		
All models		.2
(M) Pump Drive Belt, Renew		
1985-87-Four	(.4)	.6
V-6	(.3)	.5
w/A.C. add	(.2)	.2
(G) Power Steering Gear Assy., Renew		
1985-87		
Four	(2.6)	3.7
V-6	(3.1)	4.4
(G) Power Steering Short Rack Assy., Renew		
Includes: Transfer all parts not supplied with replacement unit.		
1985-87		
Four	(2.8)	4.1
V-6	(3.3)	4.8
(P) Power Steering Gear Assy., R&R and Recondition		
1985-87		
Four	(3.9)	5.6
V-6	(4.4)	6.3
(G) Power Steering Pump, Renew		
1985-87-Four	(.6)	.9
V-6	(.5)	.8
(G) Power Steering Pump, R&R and Recondition		
1985-87-Four	(1.0)	1.6
V-6	(.9)	1.5
(G) Pump Flow Control Valve, Renew		
1985-87-Four	(.3)	.6
V-6	(.4)	.7
(G) Power Steering Reservoir 'O' Ring Seal, Renew		
1985-87-Four	(.6)	1.0
V-6	(.5)	.9
(G) Power Steering Pump Shaft Oil Seal, Renew		
1985-87-Four	(.7)	1.1
V-6	(.5)	1.0
(G) Power Steering Reservoir, Renew		
1985-87	(.5)	.7
(M) Power Steering Hoses, Renew		
1985-87		
pressure	(.3)	.5
return	(.4)	.6

PARTS 11 POWER STEERING GEAR 11 PARTS

	Part No.	Price
Steering Gear Assy.		
1985-87-wo/H.D. susp.	♦7848080	269.00
H.D. susp.	♦7848082	269.00
(1) Coupling (Flange)		
1985-87	♦7836230	38.00
(2) Seal (Dash)		
1985-87	♦7837993	12.00
(3) Bearing Kit (Stub Shaft)		
1985-87	♦7838279	19.50
(4) Line Assy. Kit (R.H.)		
1985-87	♦7846634	15.75
(5) Line Assy. Kit (L.H.)		
1985-87	♦7846633	15.75
(6) Valve Kit (Pinion)		
1985-87-wo/H.D. susp.	♦7847236	260.00
H.D. susp.	♦7844631	260.00
(7) Rack Bearing		
1985-87	♦7834432	15.00
(8) Spring (Adjuster)		
1985-87	♦7838791	1.50
(9) Plug (Adjuster)		
1985-87	♦7834435	7.75
(10) Grommet (L.H.)		
1985-87	♦7847006	9.75
(11) Rack		
1985-87-wo/H.D. susp.	♦7833655	163.00
H.D. susp.	♦7837719	163.00
(12) Housing Assy.		
1985-87	♦7846635	177.00

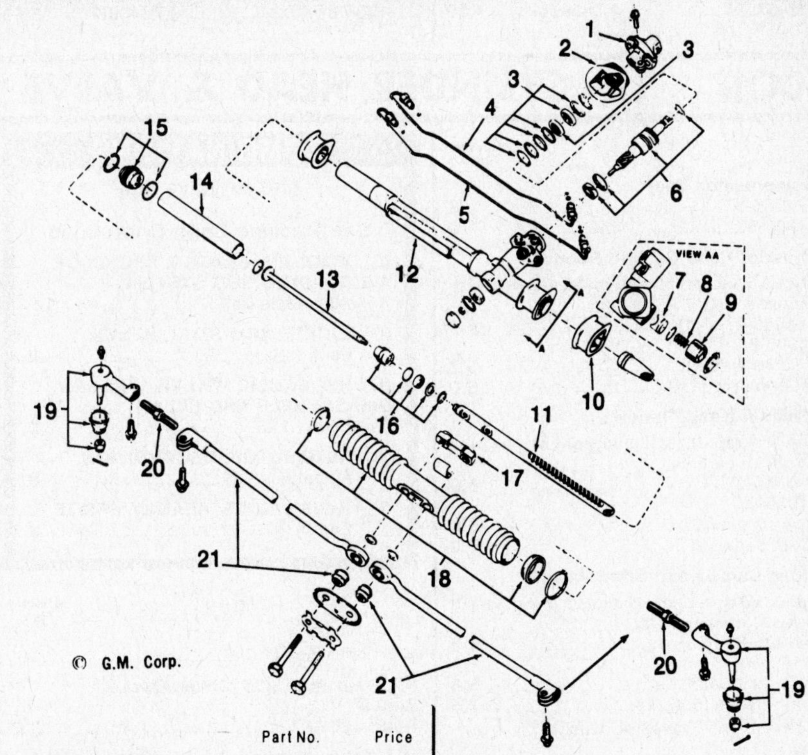

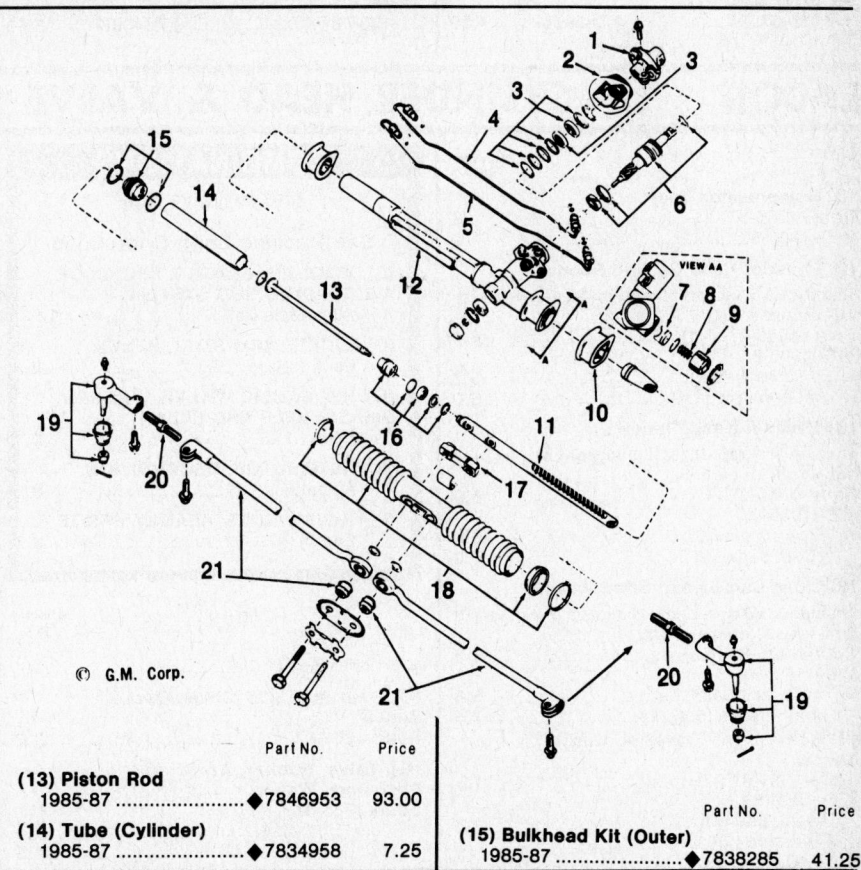

	Part No.	Price
(13) Piston Rod		
1985-87	♦7846953	93.00
(14) Tube (Cylinder)		
1985-87	♦7834958	7.25
(15) Bulkhead Kit (Outer)		
1985-87	♦7838285	41.25

PARTS 11 POWER STEERING GEAR 11 PARTS

	Part No.	Price
(16) Guide Kit		
1985-87	◆7840976	33.25
(17) Guide (Rack)		
1985-87-exc.		
below	◆7841034	15.50
Alum. whl.	◆7849750	15.50
(18) Boot Kit		
1985-87	◆7844790	24.25
(19) Tie Rod Kit (Outer)		
1985-87-right	◆7849350	49.00
left	◆7849349	49.00
(20) Adjuster (Tie Rod)		
1985-87	◆7834673	11.25
(21) Tie Rod Kit (Inner)		
1985-87-right	◆7849351	49.50
left	◆7849353	49.50

PARTS 11 POWER STEERING PUMP 11 PARTS

	Part No.	Price
Power Steering Pump		
1985-151	◆26000944	199.00
1986-87-151	◆26000944	199.00
1985-87-181	◆7849440	199.00
Power Steering Pressure Hose		
1985-87-151	◆7845577	57.00
181	◆7845409	57.00
(1) Pressure Plate		
1985-87	◆7840080	14.25
(2) Pressure Plate Spring		
1985-87	◆7839989	3.00
(3) Sleeve Kit		
1985-87	◆7842086	9.75
(4) Flow Control Spring		
1985-87	◆5688037	1.50
(5) Control Valve		
1985-87	◆7841855	10.75
(6) Fitting		
1985-87	◆7841467	10.25
(7) Drive Shaft		
1985-87-151	◆7840633	58.00
181	◆26001375	42.00
(8) Drive Shaft Seal		
1985-87	◆7839589	4.50

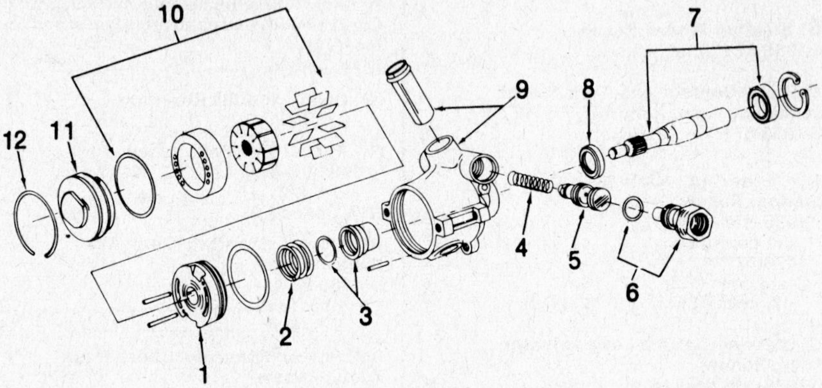

	Part No.	Price
(9) Housing		
1985-87-151	◆7844818	62.75
181	◆26001376	110.00
(10) Rotor Kit		
1985-87	◆7841845	92.00
Vane Kit		
1985-87	◆7840569	13.50
(11) Thrust Plate		
1985-87	◆7840139	14.25
(12) Retaining Ring		
1985-87	◆7839992	2.00
Pump Seal Kit		
1985-87	◆7840566	11.00

LABOR 12 CYLINDER HEAD & VALVE SYSTEM 12 LABOR

	(Factory Time)	Chilton Time
(G) Compression Test		
Four–1985-87		.6
V-6–1985-87		1.0

(G) Cylinder Head Gasket, Renew

Includes: Clean carbon and make all necessary adjustments.

	(Factory Time)	Chilton Time
Four–1985-87	(3.1)	4.4
V-6–1985-87		
one bank	(3.8)	5.2
both banks	(4.4)	6.0

(G) Cylinder Head, Renew

Includes: Transfer all components, reface valves, clean carbon.

	(Factory Time)	Chilton Time
Four–1985-87	(4.1)	5.9
V-6–1985-87		
one bank	(4.3)	6.0
both banks	(5.2)	7.2

(P) Clean Carbon and Grind Valves

Includes: R&R cylinder head(s), grind valves and seats. Minor tune up.

	(Factory Time)	Chilton Time
Four–1985-87	(4.5)	6.5
V-6–1985-87		
one bank	(4.0)	5.6
both banks	(5.4)	7.5
(G) Rocker Arm Cover or Gasket, Renew		
Four–1985-87	(.7)	1.0
V-6–1985-87		
right side	(.9)	1.3
left side	(.3)	.5

COMBINATIONS

Add to Valve Job

See Machine Shop Operations

	(Factory Time)	Chilton Time
(G) DRAIN, EVACUATE & RECHARGE AIR CONDITIONING SYSTEM		
All models	(.5)	1.0
(G) ROCKER ARM STUD, RENEW		
Each	(.2)	.2
(G) HYDRAULIC VALVE LIFTERS, DISASSEMBLE AND CLEAN		
Each	(.2)	.2
(G) DISTRIBUTOR, RECONDITION		
All models	(.3)	.8
(P) VALVE GUIDES, REAM OVERSIZE		
Each	(.2)	.2

	(Factory Time)	Chilton Time
both sides	(1.0)	1.7
(G) Push Rod Side Cover Gasket, Renew		
Four–1985-87	(2.1)	3.0
(G) Valve Rocker Arms and/or Push Rods, Renew		
Four–1985-87		
one cyl	(.7)	1.1
all cyls	(.9)	1.5
V-6–1985-87		
right side	(1.2)	1.7
left side	(.6)	.9
both sides	(1.3)	2.1
(G) Valve Rocker Arm Stud, Renew		
Four–1985-87		
one	(.9)	1.2
each adtnl	(.2)	.2
(G) Valve Springs and/or Valve Stem Oil Seals, Renew (Head on Car)		
Four–1985-87		
one cyl	(.9)	1.3
all cyls	(1.4)	2.0
V-6–1985-87		
one cyl-right bank	(1.4)	2.0
one cyl-left bank	(.8)	1.2
one cyl-each bank	(1.8)	2.6
each adtnl cyl	(.3)	.3
(G) Valve Tappets, Renew (Lifters)		
Four–1985-87		
one cyl	(2.5)	3.6
all cyls	(2.8)	4.0
V-6–1985-87		
right side	(2.6)	3.7
left side	(2.1)	3.0
both sides	(2.8)	4.0

PARTS 12 CYLINDER HEAD & VALVE SYSTEM 12 PARTS

	Part No.	Price
4-151		
Valve Grind Gasket Set		
1985-87	◆10037279	25.50
(1) Cylinder Head		
1985-87	◆10037281	296.00
(2) Cylinder Head Gasket		
1985-87	◆10035038	8.75
(3) Valve Cover Gasket		
1985-87	◆10007770	6.50
(4) Valve Keys		
1985-86	◆3947770	.50
1987	◆360505	.25
(5) Valve Stem Oil Seal		
1985-87	◆3835333	.50
(6) Valve Spring Cap		
1985-87	◆3729363	1.00

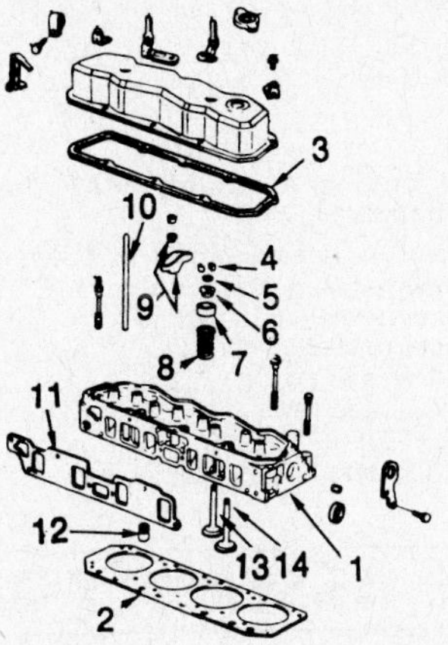

	Part No.	Price
(7) Oil Shield		
1985-87	◆10007818	.75
(8) Valve Spring & Damper		
1985	◆3735381	3.00
1986-87	◆10034268	2.75
(9) Rocker Arm & Ball Kit		
1985-87	◆10014819	7.25
(10) Push Rod		
1985-87	◆10028055	3.25
(11) Intake Manifold Gasket		
1985-87	◆10026023	5.00
(12) Lifter		
1985-87	◆5233745	32.50
(13) Intake Valve (Std.)		
1985-87	◆10022882	16.00
(14) Exhaust Valve (Std.)		
1985-87	◆10034162	16.25

PARTS 12 CYLINDER HEAD & VALVE SYSTEM 12 PARTS

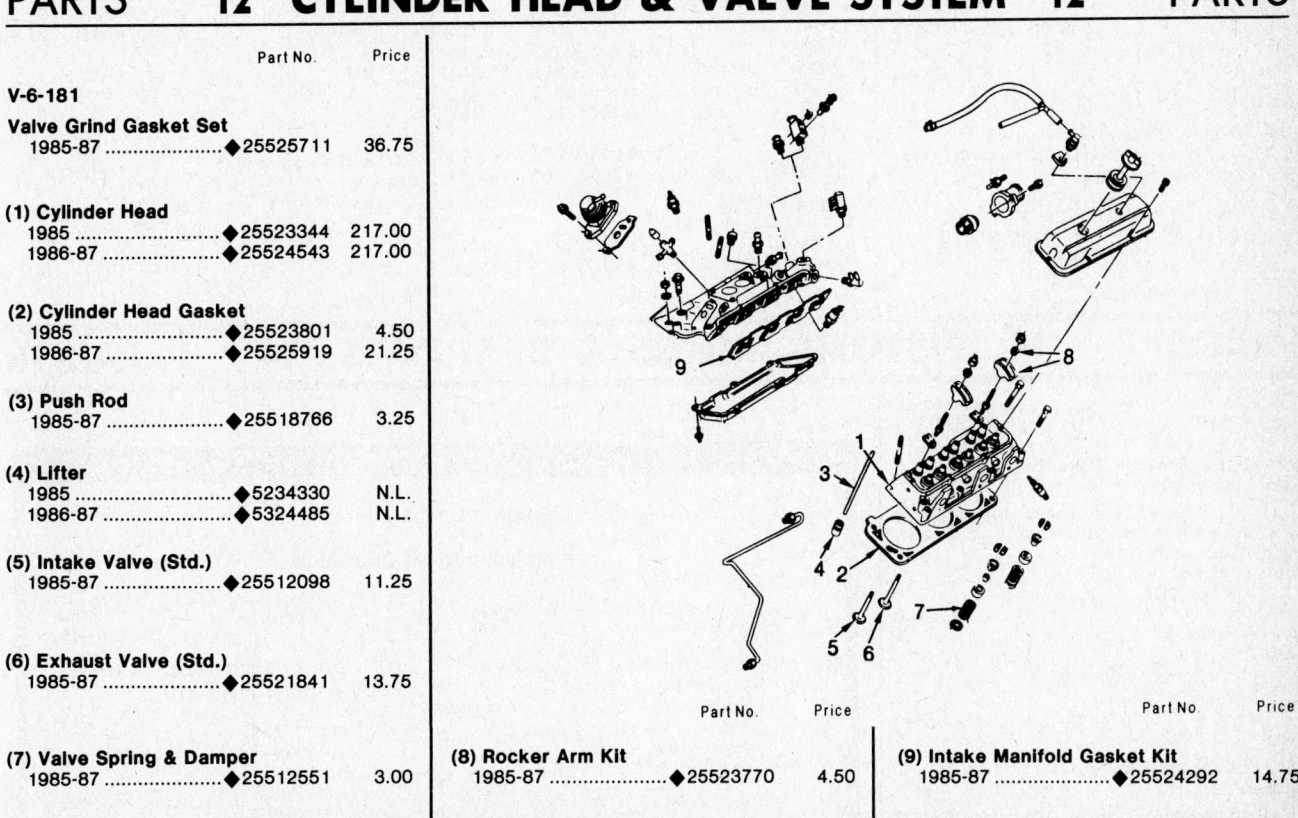

	Part No.	Price
V-6-181		
Valve Grind Gasket Set		
1985-87	◆25525711	36.75
(1) Cylinder Head		
1985	◆25523344	217.00
1986-87	◆25524543	217.00
(2) Cylinder Head Gasket		
1985	◆25523801	4.50
1986-87	◆25525919	21.25
(3) Push Rod		
1985-87	◆25518766	3.25
(4) Lifter		
1985	◆5234330	N.L.
1986-87	◆5324485	N.L.
(5) Intake Valve (Std.)		
1985-87	◆25512098	11.25
(6) Exhaust Valve (Std.)		
1985-87	◆25521841	13.75
(7) Valve Spring & Damper		
1985-87	◆25512551	3.00

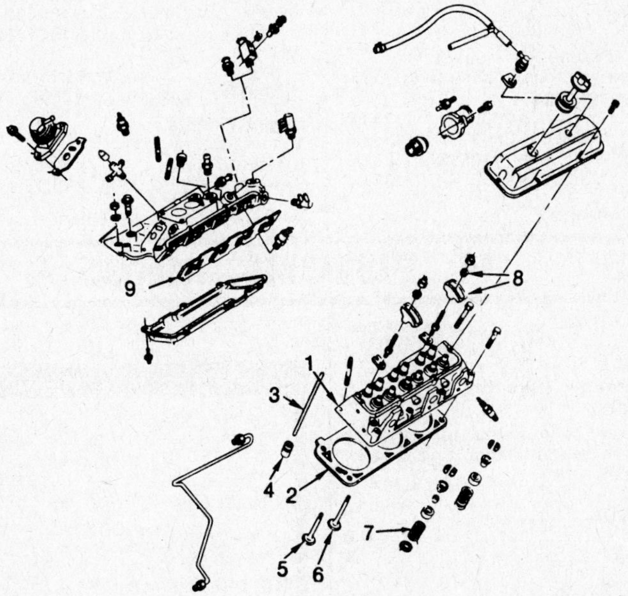

	Part No.	Price
(8) Rocker Arm Kit		
1985-87	◆25523770	4.50

	Part No.	Price
(9) Intake Manifold Gasket Kit		
1985-87	◆25524292	14.75

LABOR 13 ENGINE ASSEMBLY & MOUNTS 13 LABOR

(Factory Time) Chilton Time

(G) Engine Assembly, Remove and Install

Does not include transfer of any parts or equipment.

	Chilton Time
Four–1985-87	5.5
w/A.C. add (.4)	.4
w/A.T. add (.2)	.2
V-6–1985-87	6.0
w/A.C. add (1.3)	1.3

(G) Engine Assembly, Renew

Includes: R&R engine assembly, transfer all components not supplied with replacement engine. Minor tune up.

	Chilton Time
Four–1985-87 (8.4)	11.7
w/A.C. add (.6)	.6
w/A.T. add (.2)	.2
w/Cruise control add (.2)	.2

(P) Cylinder Block, Renew (w/All Internal Parts Less Cyl. Head(s) and Oil Pan)

Includes: R&R engine assembly, transfer all component parts not supplied with replacement engine. Clean carbon, grind valves. Minor tune up.

	Chilton Time
Four–1985-87 (13.4)	18.7
w/A.C. add (.6)	.6

LABOR 13 ENGINE ASSEMBLY & MOUNTS 13 LABOR

(Factory Time) Chilton Time

w/A.T. add (.2)........ .2
w/Cruise control add (.2)........ .2
V-6–1985-87 (11.3)........ 15.8
w/A.C. add (1.3)........ 1.3

(P) Cylinder Block, Renew (w/Pistons, Rings and Bearings)
Includes: R&R engine assembly, transfer all component parts not supplied with replacement engine. Clean carbon, grind valves. Minor tune up.
Four–1985-87 (16.0)........ 22.4
w/A.C. add (.6)........ .6
w/A.T. add (.2)........ .2
w/Cruise control add (.2)........ .2

V-6–1985-87 (13.1)........ 19.6
w/A.C. add (1.3)........ 1.3

(P) Engine Assembly, R&R and Recondition
Includes: Rebore block, install new pistons, rings, rod and main bearings. Clean carbon, grind valves. Tune engine.
Four–1985-87 (15.2)........ 21.6
w/A.C. add (.4)........ .4
w/A.T. add (.2)........ .2
V-6–1985-87 (18.7)........ 24.0
w/A.C. add (1.3)........ 1.3

(P) Engine Assembly, Recondition (In Car)
Includes: Expand or renew pistons, install new rings, pins, rod and main bearings. Clean carbon, grind valves. Tune engine.
Four–1985-87 (11.5)........ 16.3
V-6–1985-87 (13.7)........ 19.6
w/A.C. add (.4)........ .4

(G) Engine Mounts, Renew
Four–1985-87
front (.6)........ .9
rear (.9)........ 1.3
V-6–1985-87 (.8)........ *1.2
*w/A.C. add (.9)........ .9

PARTS 13 ENGINE ASSEMBLY & MOUNTS 13 PARTS

Part No. Price

Engine Overhaul Gasket Kit
1985-87-181
eng........ ◆25530151 84.75

Engine Assy. (Partial)
Includes block, pistons, connecting rods, crankshaft and bearings.
1985-151........ ◆10037144 1128.00
181........ ◆25523768 1195.00
1986-87-151........ ◆14105927 1128.00
181........ ◆25527472 1195.00

Cylinder Block Assy.
Includes block, pistons and rings.
151
1985........ ◆10037147 815.00
1986........ ◆14105928 856.00
1987-A.T........ ◆10049070 N.L.
M.T........ ◆10054506 N.L.
181
1985........ ◆25523769 949.00
1986-87........ ◆25527473 949.00

Engine Mounts
151
1985-87-front........ ◆14074074 28.00
rear........ ◆14080987 30.25
181
1985-87-front........ ◆25523523 28.00
rear........ ◆14074093 25.50

Transmission Mount
(A.T.)
1985-87-151........ ◆14074053 20.50
181........ ◆14086958 21.75
(M.T.)
1985-87........ ◆14074054 20.50

LABOR 14 PISTONS, RINGS & BEARINGS 14 LABOR

(Factory Time) Chilton Time

(P) Rings, Renew (See Engine Combinations)
Includes: Remove cylinder top ridge, deglaze cylinder walls. Clean piston and ring grooves. Minor tune up.
Four–1958-87
one cyl (5.0)........ 7.0
all cyls (6.4)........ 8.9
w/A.C. add (.4)........ .4
V-6–1985-87
one cyl-right side (5.2)........ 7.2
one cyl-left side (4.8)........ 6.7
all cyls-both sides (8.2)........ 11.4
w/A.C. add (.5)........ .5

(P) Pistons or Connecting Rods, Renew
Includes: Remove cylinder top ridge, deglaze cylinder walls. Minor tune up.
Four–1985-87
one cyl (5.0)........ 7.3
all cyls (7.0)........ 10.1
w/A.C. add (.4)........ .4
V-6–1985-87
one cyl-right side (5.2)........ 7.5
one cyl-left side (4.8)........ 7.0
all cyls-both sides (8.9)........ 12.4
w/A.C. add (.5)........ .5

(P) Connecting Rod Bearings, Renew
Includes: Plastigauge bearings.
Four–1985-87 (2.7)........ 3.7
V-6–1985-87 (2.2)........ 3.3

COMBINATIONS

Engine Combinations

See Machine Shop Operations

(Factory Time) Chilton Time

(G) DRAIN, EVACUATE & RECHARGE AIR CONDITIONING SYSTEM
All models (.5)........ 1.0

(G) ROCKER ARM STUD, RENEW
Each (.2)........ .2

(G) HYDRAULIC VALVE LIFTERS, DISASSEMBLE AND CLEAN
Each (.2)........ .2

(G) DISTRIBUTOR, RECONDITION
All models (.3)........ .8

(G) CYLINDER HEAD, R&R (ENGINE REMOVED)
Four
eng Code U (1.2)........ 1.5
V-6
eng Code L
one (1.7)........ 2.2
both (2.8)........ 3.6

(G) CONNECTING ROD, RENEW (ENGINE DISASSEMBLED)
Four
eng Code U
each (.4)........ .5
V-6
eng Code L
each (.4)........ .5

(G) VALVE GUIDES, REAM OVERSIZE
Each (.2)........ .2

(G) DEGLAZE CYLINDER WALLS
Each (.1)........ .1

(G) REMOVE CYLINDER WALL RIDGE
Each (.1)........ .1

(G) PLASTIGAUGE BEARINGS
Each (.1)........ .1

(M) OIL FILTER ELEMENT, RENEW
All models........ .3

PARTS 14 PISTONS, RINGS & BEARINGS 14 PARTS

	Part No.	Price
(1) Piston Ring Set (Std.)		
1985-87-151	◆10030202	18.00
181	◆25526600	17.50
(2) Piston Assy. (Std.)		
1985-86-151	◆10027317	53.00
1987-151	◆10044245	N.L.
1985-87-181	◆25522584	49.00
(3) Piston Pin		
1985-87-151	◆500011	5.50
(4) Connecting Rod		
1985-87-151	◆499323	39.50
181	◆25518462	39.00
(5) Connecting Rod Bearings (Std.)		
1985-87-151	◆5463932	10.50
181	◆18005399	11.00

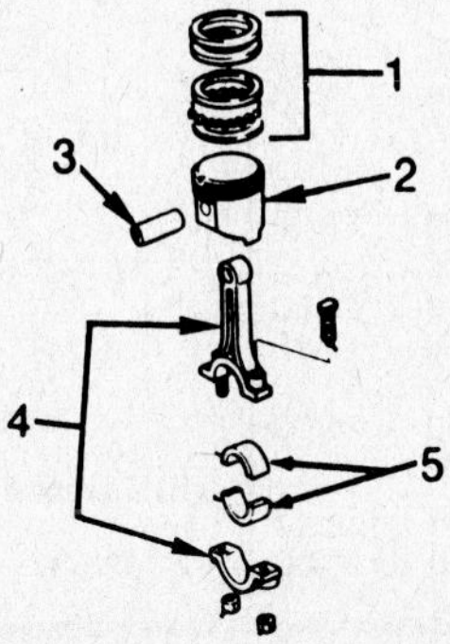

LABOR 15 CRANKSHAFT & DAMPER 15 LABOR

(Factory Time)	Chilton Time
(P) Crankshaft and Main Bearings, Renew	
Includes: R&R engine, check all bearing clearances.	
Four–1985-87 (10.5)	**15.2**
w/A.C. add (.6)	**.6**
w/Cruise control add (.2)	**.2**
w/A.T. add (.4)	**.4**
V-6–1985-87 (6.7)	**10.5**
w/A.C. add (.3)	**.3**
(P) Main Bearings, Renew	
Includes: Check all bearing clearances.	
Four–1985-87 (2.9)	**4.0**
V-6–1985-87 (1.8)	**2.5**
(P) Main and Rod Bearings, Renew	
Includes: Check all bearing clearances.	
Four–1985-87 (3.9)	**5.2**
V-6–1985-87 (3.0)	**4.3**
(G) Rear Main Bearing Oil Seal, Renew or Repack	
Includes: R&R oil pan and rear main bearing cap on V-6 engines. R&R trans on Four cyl engines.	
Four–1985-87 (3.6)	**5.2**
w/A.T. add (.4)	**.4**
V-6–1985-87 (1.2)	**2.2**
(G) Crankshaft Pulley or Balancer, Renew	
Four–1985-87	
pulley (.6)	**1.2**
balancer (.6)	**1.3**
w/A.C. add (.3)	**.3**
V-6–1985-87	
balancer (.5)	**1.0**

PARTS 15 CRANKSHAFT & DAMPER 15 PARTS

	Part No.	Price
(1) Crankshaft Assy.		
1985-87-151	◆10027772	327.00
181	◆25519733	385.00
(2) Crankshaft Gear		
1985-87-151	◆10028052	25.75
181	◆25518725	16.75
(3) Crankshaft Pulley		
1985-87-151	◆10031423	17.50
181	◆25525963	48.25
(4) Hub		
1985-87-151	◆10028930	26.75
(5) Rear Main Seal		
1985-87-151	◆10036285	10.25
181	◆1193151	1.50
(6) Main Bearings (Std.)		
151		
1985-87-exc.		
rear	◆18012433	11.25
rear	◆18012435	11.50
181		
1985-87-No. 1	◆18009457	12.00
No. 2	◆18004602	20.00
No. 3	◆18002950	12.50
No. 4	◆5468578	13.00

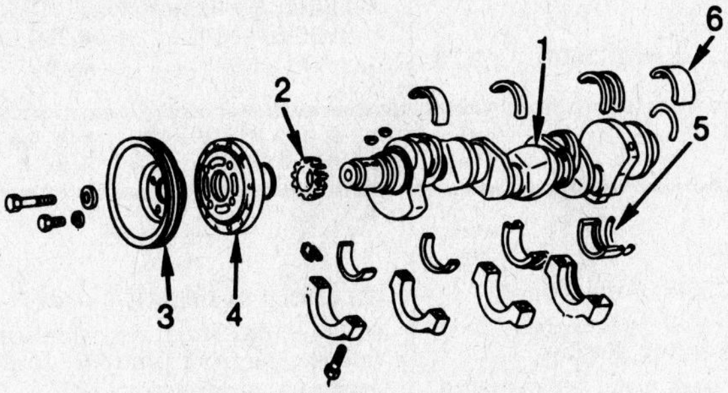

LABOR 16 CAMSHAFT & TIMING GEARS 16 LABOR

(Factory Time)	Chilton Time
(G) Timing Cover Oil Seal, Renew	
Four–1985-87 (.8)	**1.4**
w/A.C. add (.3)	**.3**
(G) Timing Cover or Gasket, Renew	
Four–1985-87 (1.2)	**1.7**
w/A.C. add (.3)	**.3**
V-6–1985-87 (2.4)	**3.4**
Renew cover add (.4)	**.6**
(G) Camshaft Timing Gear, Renew	
Four–1985-87 (9.6)	**13.9**
w/A.C. add (.6)	**.6**
(G) Timing Chain or Camshaft Gear, Renew	
V-6–1985-87 (2.7)	**3.9**
(G) Camshaft, Renew	
Four–1985-87 (9.6)	**13.9**
w/A.C. add (.6)	**.6**
Renew cam brgs add (.7)	**1.0**
V-6–1985-87 (6.5)	**9.4**
w/A.C. add (.5)	**.5**
(G) Camshaft Rear Bearing Plug, Renew	
V-6–1985-87 (3.7)	**5.1**

PARTS 16 CAMSHAFT & TIMING GEARS 16 PARTS

	Part No.	Price
(1) Front Cover Oil Seal		
1985-87-151	◆10036286	5.25
181	◆25525159	3.50
(2) Timing Case Cover		
1985-87-151	◆10036837	26.75
181	◆25526379	77.00
(3) Camshaft Gear		
1985-87-151	◆10028219	46.00
181	◆25523115	17.50
(4) Timing Chain		
1985-87-181	◆1257650	26.00
(5) Camshaft		
1985-87-151	◆10027766	127.00
181	◆25526849	130.00

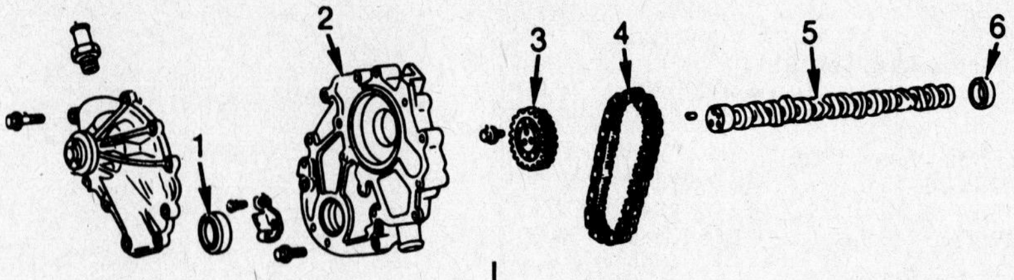

	Part No.	Price
(6) Camshaft Bearing		
151		
1985-87	◆10030873	8.75
181		
1985-87-No. 1, 4	◆25524301	7.25
No. 2, 3	◆1231142	7.75

LABOR 17 ENGINE OILING SYSTEM 17 LABOR

(Factory Time)	Chilton Time
(G) Oil Pan and/or Gasket, Renew	
Four-1985-87 (1.5)	2.1
V-6-1985-87 (.9)	1.5
(P) Pressure Test Engine Bearings (Pan Off)	
All models	1.0
(G) Oil Pump Cover and/or Gears, Renew or Recondition	
V-6-1985-87 (2.5)	3.5
(G) Oil Pump, Renew	
Four-1985-87 (1.6)	2.3
(G) Oil Pump Drive and/or Gasket, Renew	
Four-1985-87 (.5)	.7
(G) Oil Pressure Gauge (Engine), Renew	
1985-87 (.3)	.4
(M) Oil Filter Element, Renew	
Four (.3)	.3
V-6 (.3)	.3

PARTS 17 ENGINE OILING SYSTEM 17 PARTS

	Part No.	Price
Oil Pan Gasket		
1985-181	◆25519254	8.25
1986-87-181	◆25526425	7.50
Applications not listed use RTV sealant.		
Oil Pump		
1985-87-151	◆10036939	69.50
181	◆25525965	11.25
Oil Pump Cover		
1985-87-151	◆3792507	2.75
181	◆25521935	9.00
Oil Pressure Regulator Valve		
1985-87-151	◆3829433	1.50
181	◆25515390	1.25
Oil Filter By-Pass Valve		
1985-87-151	◆25010497	3.50
181	◆25011523	4.00
Oil Pressure Sender Switch		
1985-87-wo/		
Gauges	◆1623576	6.00
Gauges	◆10030963	20.75
Oil Filter Element		
151		
1985-86	◆25010792	7.50
1987-A.T.	◆25010792	N.L.
M.T.	◆25012305	N.L.
181		
1985-87	◆25010792	N.L.

LABOR 18 CLUTCH & FLYWHEEL 18 LABOR

(Factory Time)	Chilton Time
(G) Clutch Control Cable, Renew	
1985-87 (.4)	.6
(G) Clutch Release Bearing, Renew	
Includes: R&R trans and make all necessary adjustments.	
1985-87	
Four (2.4)	4.0
V-6 (2.6)	4.2
(G) Clutch Assembly, Renew	
Includes: R&R trans, renew pressure plate, disc, release bearing and/or fork. Make all necessary adjustments.	
1985-87	
Four (2.6)	4.2
V-6 (2.8)	4.4
(G) Flywheel, Renew	
Includes: R&R transmission.	
1985-87	
Four (2.8)	4.5
V-6 (3.0)	4.7
Renew ring gear add (.3)	.5
Renew shaft or bush add	.3

PARTS 18 CLUTCH & FLYWHEEL 18 PARTS

	Part No.	Price
Pressure Plate Assy.		
1985-87	◆14080212	147.00
Clutch Driven Plate		
1985-87	◆14087241	89.25
Clutch Release Bearing		
1985-87	◆94133417	43.00
Release Lever		
1985-87	◆14080232	12.50
Flywheel		
151		
1985-87-A.T.	◆10031262	70.25
M.T.	◆10004031	159.00
181		
1985-87	◆25523510	67.50
Clutch Control Cable		
1985	◆10036983	32.50

LABOR 21 SHIFT LINKAGE 21 LABOR

(Factory Time) Chilton Time

MANUAL

(G) Gearshift Linkage, Adjust
All models (.7) 9

(G) Gearshift Lever, Renew
1985-87 (.9) 1.2

(G) Floor Mounted Gearshift Control Assy., Renew
Includes: R&R console plate and rear mount. Adjust control cables.
1985-87 (.8) 1.1

(G) Gearshift Control Opening Seal, Renew
1985-87 (.4) 5

(G) Gearshift Control Cables, Renew
Includes: Raise vehicle and adjust cables.
1985-87-one cable (1.4) 1.9
two cables (1.5) 2.1

AUTOMATIC

(G) Shift Linkage, Adjust
All models
Neutral Safety Switch (.3) 4
Shift Indicator Needle (.2) 3
Shift Linkage (.4) 5
T.V. Cable (.2) 4

(G) Gearshift Selector Lever, Renew
1985-87 (.5) 8

(G) Park Lock Cable, Renew
1985-87 (.9) 1.4

(G) Shift Control Cable, Renew
Includes: Necessary adjustments.
1985-87 (.9) 1.4

(G) Floorshift Control Assembly, Renew
1985-87 (.5) 9

(G) Gear Selector Needle and/or Assy., Renew
1985-87 (.3) 5

LABOR 26 REAR AXLE AND SUSPENSION 26 LABOR

(Factory Time) Chilton Time

(G) Rear Suspension, Align
All models (.5) 6

(G) Rear Coil Springs, Renew
1985-87-one (.6) 8
both (.7) 1.0

(G) Lower Control Arm Bushings, Renew
1985-87-one side (.6) 8
both sides (.9) 1.3

(G) Rear Sway Bar, Renew
1985-87 (.4) 6

(G) Rear Shock Absorbers, Renew
1985-87-one (.4) 6
both (.7) 1.0

(G) Rear Wheel Bearing and Hub Assy., Clean and Repack or Renew
1985-87-one (.4) 6
both (.7) 1.1

(G) Rear Axle Assembly, Renew
1985-87 (2.5) 3.5

PARTS 26 REAR AXLE AND SUSPENSION 26 PARTS

	Part No.	Price
(1) Shock Absorber		
1985-87	◆22046451	24.50
(2) Spring Insulator		
1985-87	◆10017875	4.00
(3) Coil Spring		
Order by year and model.		
(4) Control Arm Bushing		
(wo/H.D. susp.)		
1985-87	◆10018021	8.00

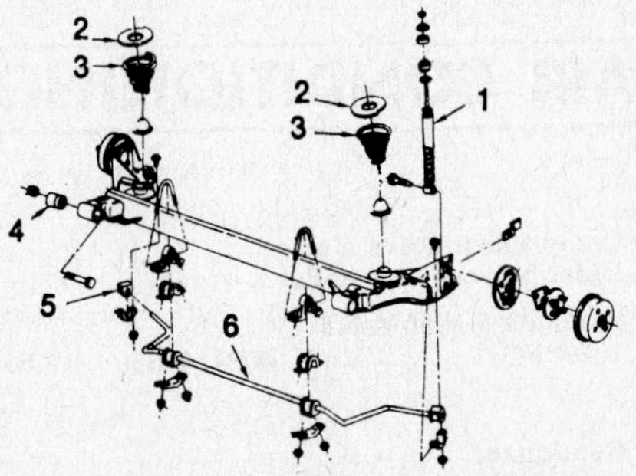

	Part No.	Price
(H.D. susp.)		
1985-87-blue	◆10018450	7.50
green	◆10019594	7.50
(5) Insulator (Stabilizer)		
1985-87 (shaft dia.)		
19mm	◆10018197	1.00
(6) Stabilizer Shaft		
1985-87 (shaft dia.)		
19mm	◆10034216	44.75

LABOR 28 AIR CONDITIONING 28 LABOR

(Factory Time) Chilton Time

Note: If more than one item requires replacement where evacuation and discharging the system is already included in the operation, deduct 1.0 hour for each additional item to the times listed.

(G) Drain, Evacuate and Recharge System
All models (.5) 1.0

(G) Leak Check
Includes: Check all lines and connections.
All models 5

(G) Refrigerant, Add (Partial Charge)
All models 6

(G) Compressor Belt, Renew
1985-87-Four (.5) 6
V-6 (.3) 5

V-5 COMPRESSOR

(G) Compressor Assembly, Renew
Includes: Transfer all necessary attaching parts. Evacuate and charge system.
1985-87
Four (1.5) 2.2

(G) Compressor Clutch Plate and Hub Assy., Renew
1985-87
Four (.8) 1.2

(G) Compressor Rotor and/or Bearing, Renew
1985-87
Four (1.0) 1.7

(G) Compressor Clutch Coil and/or Pulley Rim, Renew
1985-87
Four (1.0) 1.5
Renew pulley or brg add (.2) 2

(G) Compressor Shaft Seal Kit, Renew
Includes: Evacuate and charge system.
1985-87
Four (1.5) 2.2

LABOR 28 AIR CONDITIONING 28 LABOR

(Factory Time) Chilton Time

DA-6 COMPRESSOR

(G) Compressor Assembly, Renew
Includes: Transfer all necessary attaching parts. Evacuate and charge system.
1985-87 (1.3) 2.0

(G) Compressor Clutch Plate and Hub Assy., Renew
Includes: R&R hub and drive plate assy. Check air gap.
1985-87 (1.0) 1.3

(G) Compressor Clutch Rotor and/or Bearing, Renew
Includes: R&R hub and drive plate assy.
1985-87 (1.1) 1.7

(G) Compressor Clutch Coil and/or Pulley Rim Assy., Renew
Includes: R&R hub and drive plate assy.
1985-87 (1.2) 1.5
Renew pulley or brg add 2

(G) Compressor Front Seal, Seat and 'O' Ring, Renew
Includes: R&R clutch hub and drive plate assy. Evacuate and charge system.
1985-87 (1.8) 2.5

(G) Compressor Front Head and/or Seal, Renew
Includes: R&R compressor. R&R clutch and pulley assy. R&R shaft seal assy. Clean and inspect parts. Evacuate and charge system.
1985-87 (1.9) 2.6

(G) Compressor Cylinder and Shaft Assy., Renew
Includes: R&R compressor. Transfer all parts as required. Evacuate and charge system.
1985-87 (2.1) 2.8

AIR CONDITIONER TUNE-UP

For efficient operation and satisfactory performance in hot weather. The following air conditioner tune-up is suggested:

1. Clean intake filter
2. Clean condenser fins
3. Pressure test system
4. Adjust drive belt tension
5. Check antifreeze/coolant
6. Tighten compressor mounts
7. Tighten condenser and evaporator mounts
8. Inspect system for leaks (hoses, couplings, valves, etc.)
9. Partial charge system

All models 1.0
If necessary to evacuate and charge system, add 1.0

(Factory Time) Chilton Time

(G) Condenser Assembly, Renew
Includes: Evacuate and charge system.
1985-87 (1.6) 2.6

(G) Expansion Tube (Orifice), Renew
Includes: Evacuate and charge system.
1985-87 (.9) 1.5

(G) Accumulator Assembly, Renew
Includes: Evacuate and charge system.
1985-87 (.8) 1.4

(Factory Time) Chilton Time

(G) Evaporator Core, Renew
Includes: Evacuate and charge system.
1985-87 (2.7) 4.5

(G) Vacuum Selector Valve, Renew
1985-87 (.5) 8

(G) Blower Motor Switch, Renew
1985-87 (.6) 8

(G) Master Electrical Switch, Renew
1985-87 (.5) 8

(G) Temperature Control Assembly, Renew
1985-87 (.7) 1.0

(G) Blower Motor Resistor, Renew
1985-87 (.2) 3

(G) A.C. Relays, Renew
1985-87
Blower motor (.2) 3
Comp. cut-off (.2) 3

(G) Pressure Cycling Switch, Renew
1985-87 (.2) 3

(G) Blower Motor, Renew
1985-87
Four (.3) 5
V-6 (.5) 7

(G) Vacuum Diaphragm Actuators, Renew
1985-87
Defroster (.4) 8
Upper or Lower mode (.5) 9
Air Inlet (.5) 9

(G) Air Conditioning Hoses, Renew
1985-87-one (1.0) 1.7
each adtnl (.3) 5

PARTS 28 AIR CONDITIONING 28 PARTS

	Part No.	Price
Compressor Assy.		
1985-87-151	◆12322146	N.L.
181	◆12322327	N.L.
Clutch Drive		
1985-87 (DA-6 comp)	◆2724325	51.50
(V-5 comp)	◆6551996	41.00
Compressor Pulley		
1985-87 (DA-6 comp)	◆6551983	115.25
(V-5 comp)	◆6551713	79.75
Shaft Seal Kit		
1985-87	◆2724319	11.25
Compressor Head		
1985-87-front	◆6557775	44.25
rear	◆6557378	36.25
Cylinder & Shaft		
1985-87	◆6551952	307.75
Valve Plate		
1985-87-front	◆6551700	25.00
rear	◆6551702	25.00
Compressor Drive Belt		
Order by year and model.		
Pressure Relief Valve		
1985-87	◆5914435	13.50
Condenser		
1985-87-151	◆3055576	144.75
181	◆3059131	146.75
Evaporator		
1985-87	◆3059973	249.75
Accumulator Dehydrator		
1985-87	◆3059155	80.50
Control Assy. (Heater & A.C.)		
Somerset Regal		
1985-87	◆16038634	56.50
Calias		
1985-87	◆16035383	53.25
Grand Am		
1985-87-exc. below	◆16035392	53.25
Elec. defg.	◆16035412	65.75
Compressor Relay		
1985-87	◆10034222	N.L.
Hi Blo Relay		
1985-87	◆10019535	7.50
Blower Motor		
1985-87	◆22020945	60.00
Blower Motor Resistor		
1985	◆10039426	4.50
1986-87	◆22529265	4.50
Blower Motor Switch		
1985-87-exc. below	◆16015450	6.75
Somerset Regal	◆16033615	7.25
Reed Valve		
1985-87	◆6557377	8.75

LABOR 29 LOCKS, HINGES & WIND. REGULATORS 29 LABOR

(Factory Time) Chilton Time

(G) Hood Latch, Renew
1985-87 (.3) 4

(G) Hood Release Cable, Renew
1985-87 (.6) 1.0

(G) Hood Hinge, Renew
1985-87-one (.3) 4
both (.4) 6

LABOR 29 LOCKS, HINGES & WIND. REGULATORS 29 LABOR

(Factory Time) — Chilton Time

(G) Door Handle (Outside), Renew Front or Rear
1985-87 (.5) 8
Renew insert add (.1) 1

(G) Rear Door Lock, Renew
1985-87 (.8) 1.1

(G) Rear Door Lock Remote Control, Renew
1985-87 (.4) 6

(G) Front Door Window Regulator, Renew
1985-87
manual (.7) *1.1
power (.9) 1.3
*Recond add (.2) 2

(G) Rear Door Window Regulator, Renew
manual (.6) 1.0
power (.8) 1.2

(G) Front Door Lock Cylinder, Renew
1985-87 (.5) 8
Recode cyl add (.3) 3

(G) Front Door Lock Assembly, Renew
1985-87 (.6) 9

(G) Lock Striker Plate, Renew
1985-87 (.2) 3

(G) Front Door Lock Remote Control, Renew
1985-87 (.4) 6

(G) Rear Compartment Lid Hinge, Renew
Does not include colorcoat.
1985-87-one (1.1) 1.5

(G) Rear Compartment Lid Lock Cylinder, Renew
1985-87 (.3) 4
Recode cyl add (.3) 3

PARTS 29 LOCKS, HINGES & WIND. REGULATORS 29 PARTS

	Part No.	Price
Hood Latch (Primary)		
1985-87	◆14085142	7.50
Hood Latch (Secondary)		
1985-87-Calais	◆22519945	3.50
Grand Am	◆10027595	3.25
Somerset Regal	◆25519936	9.50
Hood Hinge (Upper)		
1985-87-right	◆14086606	4.00
left	◆14086605	4.00
Hood Hinge (Lower)		
1985-87-right	◆14086602	2.50
left	◆14086601	2.50
Front Door Lock		
1985-86 (2 door)		
R.H.	◆20531542	27.75
L.H.	◆20531543	27.75
1987 (2 door)		
R.H.	◆20618096	N.L.
L.H.	◆20618097	N.L.
1986 (4 door)		
R.H.	◆20484246	32.50
L.H.	◆20484247	32.50
1987 (4 door)		
R.H.	◆20618098	N.L.
L.H.	◆20618099	N.L.
Door Lock Cylinder		
1985-87-exc. below	◆9632769	7.75
Grand Am	◆20496703	5.75
Door Handle (Outside)		
Somerset Regal, Calais		
1985-87-right	◆20310080	20.00
left	◆20310081	20.00
Grand Am		
1985-87-right	◆20310082	20.00
left	◆20310083	20.00
Window Regulator (Manual)		
1985-87 (2 door)		
R.H.	◆20361484	45.50
L.H.	◆20361485	45.50
1986-87 (4 door)		
R.H.	◆20445880	45.50
L.H.	◆20445881	45.50
Window Regulator (Power)		
1985-87 (2 door)		
R.H.	◆20361488	65.25
L.H.	◆20361489	65.25
1986-87 (4 door)		
R.H.	◆20445878	58.50
L.H.	◆20445879	58.50
Power Window Regulator Motor		
1985-87	◆22020900	73.00
Truck Lock		
1985	◆20513752	11.25
1986-87	◆20513755	11.25
Trunk Lock Cylinder		
1985-87-exc. below	◆3910570	6.50
Dlx. dr. handle	◆20496705	3.75
Trunk Hinges		
1985-87-right	◆20361962	50.75
left	◆20361963	50.75

LABOR 30 HEAD AND PARKING LAMPS 30 LABOR

(Factory Time) — Chilton Time

(G) Aim Headlamps
two 4
four 6

(M) Headlamp Sealed Beam Bulb, Renew
All models-one side (.3) 4

(M) Park and Turn Signal Lamp Assy., Renew
1985-87 (.3) 4

(M) Rear Combination Lamp Assy., Renew
1985-87
Regal-each (.5) 7
Grand Am-each (.2) 3
Calais (.5) 7

(M) Side Marker Lamp Assy., Renew (Front or Rear)
1985-87-each (.2) 3

(M) License Lamp Lens or Bulb, Renew
1985-87-one (.2) 3
all (.3) 4

(M) Park and Turn Signal Lamp Bulb, Renew
1985-87-each (.2) 2

(M) Side Marker Lamp Bulb, Renew (Front or Rear)
1985-87-each (.2) 2

(M) Stop, Tail and Turn Signal Lamp Bulb, Renew
1985-87-one (.2) 3
all (.3) 4

(M) High Level Stop Lamp Assy., Renew
1986-87 (2.) 4

(M) High Level Stop Lamp Bulb, Renew
All models (.2) 3

PARTS 30 HEAD AND PARKING LAMPS 30 PARTS

	Part No.	Price
Headlamp Sealed Beam		
(Inner)		
1985-87	◆5930567	22.50
(Outer)		
1985-87	◆5966200	15.00
Parking & Turn Signal Lamp Assy.		
Somerset Regal		
(wo/Chrome bumper)		
1985-87-right	◆919084	20.00
left	◆919083	20.00
(Chrome bumper)		
1985-87-right	◆919688	20.00
left	◆919687	20.00
Calais		
1985-87-right	◆918410	21.75
left	◆918409	21.75
Grand Am		
1985-87-right	◆918669	16.50
left	◆918670	16.50
Tail Lamp Housing		
Somerset Regal		
1985-87	◆16503377	97.25
Calais		
1985-87-right	◆16501820	102.00
left	◆16501819	102.00
Grand Am		
1985-87-right	◆16501844	52.00
left	◆16501843	52.00
Side Marker Lamp (Front)		
Somerset Regal		
1985-87-right	◆919624	11.00
left	◆919623	11.00
Calais		
1985-87-right	◆918672	8.50
left	◆918671	8.50
Grand Am		
1985-87-right	◆919082	17.75
left	◆919081	17.75
Side Marker Lamp (Rear)		
Somerset Regal		
1985-87-right	◆918950	22.75
left	◆918949	22.75
Calais		
1985-87-right	◆918352	8.75
left	◆918351	8.75
License Plate Lamp Assy.		
1985-87-Calais	◆913061	6.25
Grand Am	◆915086	3.75
Somerset		
Regal	◆912368	6.25
Back-up Lamp Assy.		
Somerset Regal		
1985-87-exc.		
below	◆918346	14.25
Chrome bumper	◆5974199	14.25
Calais		
(Inner)		
1985-87-right	◆16501840	20.00
left	◆16501839	20.00
(Outer)		
1985-87-right	◆16502644	26.75
left	◆16501837	20.50
Grand Am		
1985-87-right	◆918564	33.25
left	◆918563	33.25
Hi-Mounted Stop Lamp		
1985	◆16506895	N.L.
1986-Lug. carr.	◆918616	36.00
1986-87-wo/Lug.		
carr.	◆5974469	36.00

LABOR 31 WINDSHIELD WIPER & SPEEDOMETER 31 LABOR

(Factory Time)	Chilton Time
(G) Windshield Wiper Motor, Renew	
1985-87 (.4)	.6
w/Inter wiper add (.1)	.1
(G) Windshield Wiper Motor, R&R and Recondition	
1985-87 (.7)	1.0
(G) Windshield Wiper Switch, Renew	
1985-87-std colm (.3)	.6
tilt colm (.3)	.6
(G) Wiper Transmission, Renew	
1985-87-one (.3)	.5
both (.4)	.7
(G) Windshield Washer Pump, Renew	
1985-87 (.3)	.4
w/Pulse wipe add (.1)	.1
(G) Wiper Motor Park Switch, Renew	
1985-87 (.3)	.5
(G) Windshield Washer Pump Valve, Renew	
1985-87 (.2)	.3
(G) Pulse Wiper Control Module, Renew	
1985-87 (.2)	.4
(G) Speedometer Head, R&R or Renew	
1985-87 (.5)	.9
w/Std colm add (.3)	.3
Reset odometer add	.2
(G) Speedometer Cable and Casing, Renew	
Regal	
1985 (.9)	1.6
(G) Speedometer Cable (Inner), Renew or Lubricate	
Regal	
1985 (.9)	1.6
(G) Speedometer Signal Generator, Renew	
Calais-Regal	
1985-87 (.3)	.5
Grand Am	
1985-87 (.6)	1.1
(G) Instrument Panel Cluster Assy., R&R or Renew	
1985-87 (.5)	.9
w/Std colm add (.3)	.3
(G) Micro Processor, Renew	
1985-87 (.4)	.7
(G) Odometer and/or Motor, Renew	
Calais-Grand Am	
1985-87 (.6)	1.1
w/Std colm add (.3)	.3
(G) Radio, R&R	
1985-87-exc below (.2)	.4
Bose Radio (.4)	.7

PARTS 31 WINDSHIELD WIPER & SPEEDOMETER 31 PARTS

	Part No.	Price
Windshield Wiper Motor		
1985-87	◆22054198	118.00
Windshield Wiper Transmission		
1985-87-right	◆22048620	20.50
left	◆22062398	17.75
Windshield Wiper Switch		
1985-87-exc.		
Pulse	◆22039693	10.25
Pulse	◆22038796	31.25
Windshield Washer Pump		
1985-87	◆22049373	9.75
Windshield Wiper Arm		
1985-87-right	◆20489074	16.50
left	◆20489075	16.50

Speedometer Head & Cable
Order by year and model.

LABOR 32 LIGHT SWITCHES & WIRING 32 LABOR

(Factory Time)	Chilton Time
(G) Headlamp Switch, Renew	
1985-87 (.3)	.6
(G) Headlamp Dimmer Switch, Renew	
1985-87 (.3)	.7
(G) Back-Up Lamp Switch, Renew	
1985-87 (.3)	.4

LABOR 32 LIGHT SWITCHES & WIRING 32 LABOR

(Factory Time)	Chilton Time
(G) Back-Up Lamp and Park/Neutral Switch, Renew	
1985-87 (.5)	.7
(G) Parking Brake Lamp Switch, Renew	
1985-87 (.2)	.3
(G) Neutral Start Switch, Renew	
1985-87 (.3)	.4
(G) Stop Lamp Switch, Renew	
1985-87 (.3)	.4
(G) Turn Signal and Hazard Warning Switch, Renew	
1985-87-std colm (.6)	1.1
tilt colm (.7)	1.2
(M) Turn Signal or Hazard Warning Flasher, Renew	
1985-87 (.2)	.3
(G) Horns, Renew	
1985-87-one (.2)	.3
both (.3)	.4
(G) Horn Relay, Renew	
1985-87 (.2)	.3

PARTS 32 LIGHT SWITCHES & WIRING 32 PARTS

	Part No.	Price
Headlamp Dimmer Switch		
1985-87	◆7832411	18.50
Stoplight Switch		
(wo/Cruise control)		
1985-A.T.	◆25524846	6.50
M.T.	◆25524844	3.00
1986-87-A.T.	◆25523464	8.00
M.T.	◆25523466	8.00
(Cruise control)		
1985	◆25524847	6.50
1986-87	◆25523462	8.00
Back-up Lamp Switch		
1985-87-A.T.	◆1994256	13.50
M.T.	◆14047186	17.75
Turn Signal Switch		
1985-87	◆1997983	30.00
Parking Brake Lamp Switch		
1985-87	◆1264464	1.50
Hazard Lamp Flasher		
1985-87	◆6450089	3.00
Turn Signal Flasher		
1985-87	◆491160	N.L.
Horn Assy.		
1985-87-Note (A)	◆1892164	22.00
Note (F)	◆1892163	22.00
Horn Relay		
1985-87	◆25523703	6.50

LABOR 33 GLASS 33 LABOR

(Factory Time)	Chilton Time
(G) Windshield Glass, Renew	
1985-87 (1.3)	1.8
Renew caulk bead add (.4)	.4
(G) Quarter Window Stationary Glass, Renew	
1985-87 (1.5)	2.0
(G) Front Door Glass, Renew	
1985-87 (.9)	1.5
(G) Rear Door Glass, Renew	
1985-87 (.9)	1.5
(G) Back Window Glass, Renew	
1985-87 (1.3)	2.0
w/Elec grid defogger add (.6)	.6

LABOR 34 CRUISE CONTROL 34 LABOR

(Factory Time)	Chilton Time
(G) Cruise Control Servo, Renew	
1985-87 (.3)	.4
(G) Brake or Clutch Release Switch, Renew	
1985-87 (.3)	.4
(G) Cruise Control Vacuum Hoses, Renew	
1985-87 (.4)	.6
(G) Cruise Control Chain or Cable, Renew	
1985-87 (.3)	.4
(G) Engagement Switch, Renew	
1985 (.5)	.9
1986-87 (.3)	.5
(G) Cruise Control Module, Renew	
1985-87 (.2)	.4

PARTS 34 CRUISE CONTROL 34 PARTS

	Part No.	Price
Cruise Control Module		
1985-87-151	◆25074704	102.00
181	◆25074717	102.00
Cruise Control Servo		
1985	◆25074627	117.00
1986-87	◆25074625	119.75
Cruise Control Cable		
1985	◆25519359	16.00
1986-87	◆25523934	7.50
Vacuum Release Valve		
1985-87-A.T.	◆25523376	14.00
M.T.	◆14046846	2.50
Cruise Control Lever		
1985-87	◆25074223	41.75
Cruise Control Release Switch		
1985-87-M.T.	◆14078922	6.00

GROUP INDEX

ALPHABETICAL INDEX

General Motors

Front Wheel Drive Cars

BUICK ELECTRA (1985–87) • PARK AVE • CADILLAC DEVILLE (1985–86) • FLEETWOOD • BROUGHAM • OLDS 98 (1985–87) • T TYPE

YEAR IDENTIFICATION

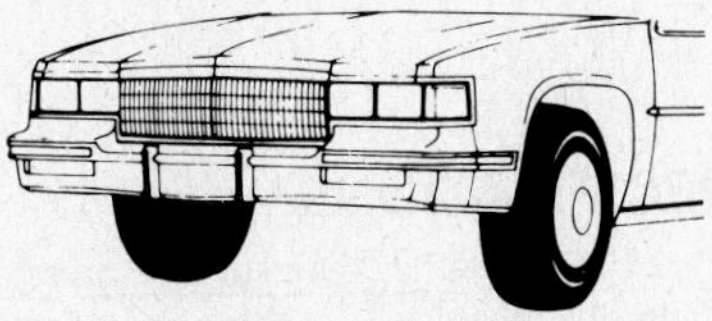

1985–86 Cadillac DeVille, Fleetwood

1985–86 Oldsmobile Ninety-Eight Regency Brougham

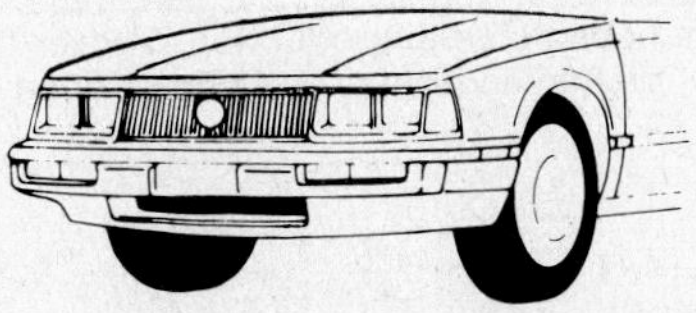

1985–86 Buick Electra, Park Avenue

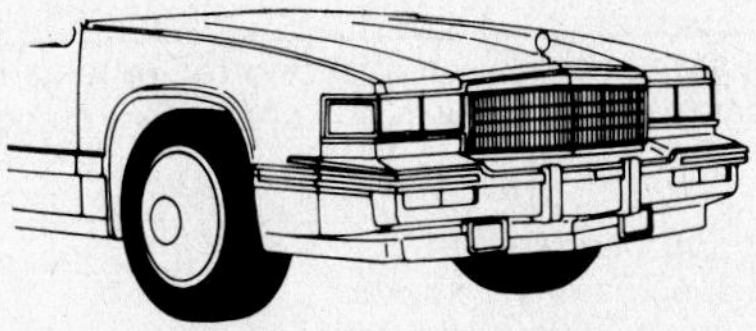

1986–87 Touring Sedan

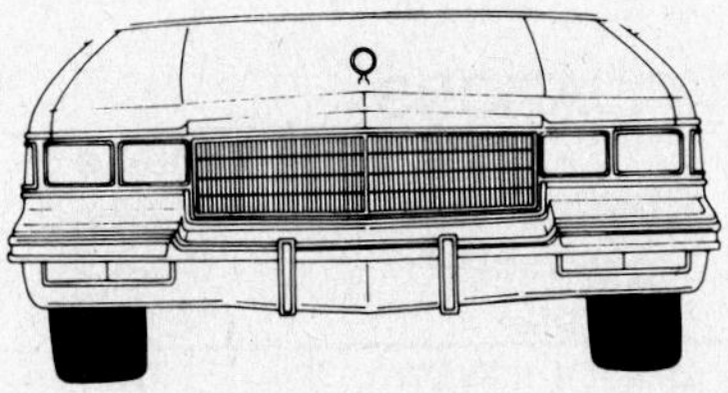

1986–87 Coupe DeVille

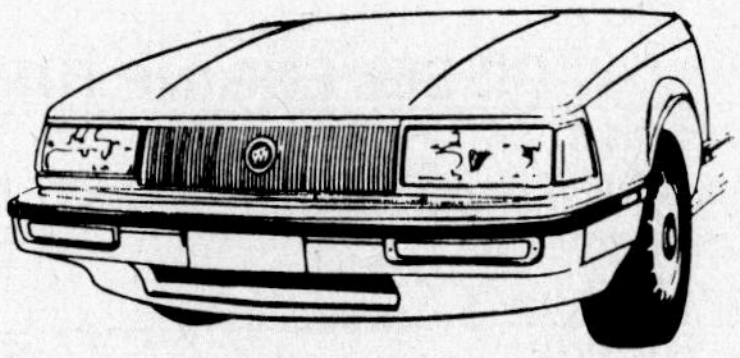

1987 Electra

VEHICLE IDENTIFICATION NUMBER (VIN)

It is important for servicing and ordering parts to be certain of the vehicle and engine identification. The VIN (vehicle identification number) is a 17 digit number visible through the windshield on the driver's side of the dash and contains the vehicle and engine identification codes. It can be interpreted as follows:

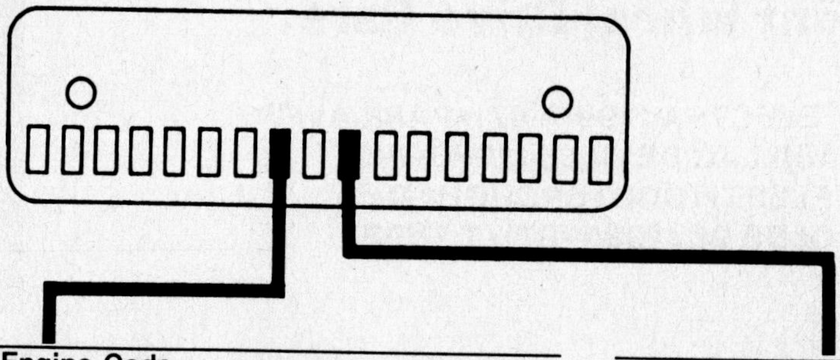

Engine Code					
Code	**Cu. In.**	**Liters**	**Cyl.**	**Carb.**	**Eng. Mfg.**
E	181	3.0	6	2	Buick
3	231	3.8	6	MFI	Buick
T	263	4.3	6	Diesel	Olds.
8	250	4.1	8	DFI	Cad.

Model Year Code	
Code	**Year**
F	85
G	86
H	87

The seventeen digit Vehicle Identification Number can be used to determine engine application and model year. The 10th digit indicates the model year and the 8th digit identifies the factory installed engine.
MFI Multiport Fuel Injection
DFI Digital Fuel Injection

GASOLINE ENGINE TUNE-UP SPECIFICATIONS

When analyzing compression test results, look for uniformity among cylinders rather than specific pressures

Year	Engine: Eng. VIN Code	Engine: No. Cyl. Displacement (cu. in.)	Engine: Liters	Engine: Eng. Mfg.	Fuel Delivery	Spark Plugs: Orig. Type	Spark Plugs: Gap (in.)	Distributor: Point Dwell (deg.)	Distributor: Point Gap (in.)	Ignition Timing (deg.) Auto. Trans.	Valves Intake Opens ■ (deg.)	Fuel Pump Pressure (psi)	Idle Speed (rpm) Auto. Trans.
'85–'87	E	6-181	3.0	Buick	2 bbl	R44TSX	.060	Electronic		①②	16	3.9–6.5	①②
'85–'87	3	6-231	3.8	Buick	MFI	R44TS8	.045	Electronic		①②	NA	28–36	①②
'85–'87	8	8-250	4.1	Cad.	DFI	R42CLTS6	.060	Electronic		①②	37	40	①②
'87	See Underhood Specifications Sticker												

NOTE: The underhood specification sticker often reflects tune-up specification changes made in production. Sticker figures must be used if they disagree with those in this chart. Part numbers in this chart are not recommendations by Chilton for any product by brand name.

■ All figures Before Top Dead Center
① See Underhood Specifications Sticker
② Only vehicles equipped with computerized emissions systems (which have no distributor vacuum advance unit), the idle speed and ignition timing are controlled by the emissions computer. These adjustments should be performed professionally on models so equipped.

DIESEL ENGINE TUNE-UP SPECIFICATIONS

Year	Engine No. of Cyl.-Displacement-Manufacturer	Liters	Fuel Pump Pressure (psi)	Compression Pressure (psi)	Intake Valve Opens (°BTDC)	Idle Speed (rpm)
'85	6-263-Olds	4.3	5.5–6.5	275 minimum	16	①

Caution: Verify the correct original equipment engine is in the vehicle by referring to the VIN engine code before torquing any bolts.
① See the Underhood Specifications Sticker

FIRING ORDERS

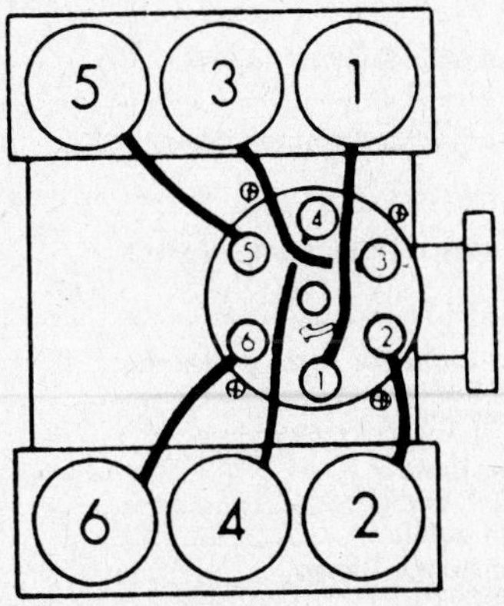

Buick 181,231, V6 (3.0L, 3.8L)
Engine firing order: 1–6–5–4–3–2
Distributor rotation: clockwise

V 6 harmonic balancers have two timing marks: one is 1/8 in. wide. Use the 1/16 in. mark for timing with a hand held light. The 1/8 in. mark is used only with a magnetic timing pick-up probe.

Cadillac 250 V8 (4.1L)
Engine firing order: 1–8–4–3–6–5–7–2
Distributor rotation: counterclockwise

WHEEL ALIGNMENT SPECIFICATIONS

Year	Model	Caster Range (deg.)	Caster Pref. Setting (deg.)	Camber Range (deg.)	Camber Pref. Setting (deg.)	Toe (in.)	Steering Axis (deg.) Inclination
'85–'87	All	1 13/16–2 13/16	2 5/16	0–1	1/2	0	—

LABOR SERVICE BAY OPERATIONS LABOR

(Factory Time) Chilton Time

COOLING

(M) Winterize Cooling System
Includes: Run engine to check for leaks, tighten all hose connections. Test radiator and pressure cap, drain radiator and engine block. Add anti-freeze and refill system.
All models 5

(G) Thermostat, Renew
V-6–1985-87
Gas (.6) 7
Diesel (.7) 8
V-8–1985-87 (.3) 4

(M) Radiator Hoses, Renew
1985-87-upper (.3) 4
lower (.4) 5
both (.5) 7

(M) Drive Belt, Adjust
V-6–1985-87
Gas-one or all (1.0) 1.4

(G) Serpentine Belt Tensioner, Renew
V-6–Diesel
1985 (.3) 5
V-8–1985-87 (.3) 5

FUEL

(M) Carburetor Air Cleaner, Service
All models 2

CHILTON'S 10 POINT SAFETY CHECK

CHECK OPERATION & CONDITION OF THE FOLLOWING ITEMS:

1. Legal Registration (serial no.)
2. Tires & Wheels
3. Brake System (R&R all wheels)
4. Light Systems & Signals
5. Accelerator Linkage, Neutral Safety Switch, Shift Indicator Pointer & Seat Position Locks
6. Glass, Mirrors, Door Locks, Seat Belts & Harness
7. Wipers, Washers & Defrosters
8. Frame, Steering, Shocks, Front & Rear Suspension
9. Fuel & Exhaust Systems
10. Road Test Vehicle

All models 1.0
Exhaust Smog Analysis, add 4

(Factory Time) Chilton Time

(G) Carburetor, Adjust (On Car)
All models
Curb & Fast Idle (.6) 8

(Factory Time) Chilton Time

Vacuum Break
both (.3) 4
Choke (.6) 1.0
Complete (1.3) 1.8

(G) Choke Vacuum Break Diaphragm, Renew
All models-one (.6) 8
both (.8) 1.0

BRAKES

(G) Brake Pedal Free Play, Adjust
All models 3

(G) Brakes, Adjust (Minor)
Includes: R&R wheels and adjust brakes thru access holes in drums. Fill master cylinder.
two wheels 4
Remove knock out plugs, add-each.. .1

(G) Bleed Brakes (Four Wheels)
Includes: Fill master cylinder.
All models (.4) 5

(M) Parking Brake, Adjust
All models (.3) 4

LUBRICATION SERVICE

(M) Lubricate Chassis, Change Oil & Filter
Includes: Inspect and correct all fluid levels.
All models 6
Install grease fittings add 1

LABOR SERVICE BAY OPERATIONS LABOR

(Factory Time) Chilton Time

(M) Lubricate Chassis
Includes: Inspect and correct all fluid levels.
All models 4
Install grease fittings add 1

(M) Engine Oil & Filter, Change
Includes: Inspect and correct all fluid levels.
All models 4

WHEELS

(M) Wheel, Renew
one (.5) 5

(M) Wheels, Balance
one 3
each adtnl 2

(M) Wheels, Rotate (All)
All models 5

ELECTRICAL

(M) Battery Cables, Renew
All models
batt to starter (.6) 8
batt to start conn (.2) 2
negative-one (.2) 3

(M) Battery Terminals, Clean
All models 3

(G) Aim Headlamps
two 4
four 6

(M) Headlamp Sealed Beam Bulb, Renew
one 3
one side 4

(G) Headlamp Switch, Renew
1985-87 (.3) 6

(G) Headlamp Dimmer Switch, Renew
1985-87 (.6) 1.0

(G) Parking Brake Lamp Switch, Renew
1985-87 (.3) 4

(M) Turn Signal or Hazard Warning Flasher, Renew
1985-87 (.2) 3

(G) Horn, Renew
1985-87-one (.3) 4
each adtnl 1

(G) Horn Relay, Renew
1985-87 (.3) 4

LABOR 1 TUNE UP 1 LABOR

(Factory Time) Chilton Time

(G) Compression Test
V-6 .... 1.2
V-8 8
w/Cruise control add 3

(G) Engine Tune Up, (Electronic Ignition)
Includes: Test battery and clean connections. Tighten manifold and carburetor mounting bolts. Check engine compression, clean and adjust or renew spark plugs. Test resistance of spark plug cables. Inspect distributor cap and rotor. Adjust air gap. Check vacuum advance operation. Reset ignition timing. Adjust idle mixture and idle speed. Service air cleaner. Inspect and adjust drive belts. Inspect choke operation and adjust or free up. Check operation of EGR valve.
V-6–1985-87 .... 3.0
V-8–1985-87 .... 2.5
w/Cruise control add 3
To perform C.C.C. system test add 1.0

LABOR 2 IGNITION SYSTEM 2 LABOR

(Factory Time) Chilton Time

GASOLINE ENGINES

(G) Spark Plugs, Clean and Reset or Renew
V-6–1985-87 (.7) 1.2
V-8–1985-87 (.6) 9
w/Cruise control add (.3) 3

(G) Ignition Timing, Reset
All models (.3) 4

(G) Distributor Assy., Renew
Includes: Reset ignition timing.
V-6–1985-87 (.6) 1.0
V-8–1985-87 (.4) 1.0

(G) Distributor, R&R and Recondition
Includes: Reset ignition timing.
V-6–1985-87 (.9) 1.5
V-8–1985-87 (.9) 1.5

(G) Distributor Cap and/or Rotor, Renew
V-6–1985-87 (.3) 4
V-81985-87 (.3) 4

(G) Ignition Coil, Renew
V-6–1985-87 (.3) 5
w/AIR add (.3) 3
V-8–1985-87 (.3) 5

(G) Distributor Capacitor and/or Module Wiring Harness, Renew
V-6–1985-87 (.3) 6
V-8–1985-87 (.4) 6

(G) Distributor Hall Effect Switch, Renew
V-6–1985-87 (1.3) 1.7

(G) ESC Knock Sensor, Renew
V-6–1985-87 (.3) 5

(G) ESC Module, Renew
V-6–1985-87 (.5) 7

(G) Distributor Module, Renew
V-6–1985-87 (.3) 6
V-8–1985-87 (.3) 6
Perform C.C.C. system check add 1.0

(G) Distributor Pick-Up Coil and/or Pole Piece, Renew
Includes: Reset ignition timing.
V-6–1985-87 (.6) 1.0
V-8–1985-87 (.6) 1.0

(G) Ignition Cables, Renew
V-6–1985-87 (.4) 6
V-8–1985-87 (.7) 1.0

(G) Ignition Switch, Renew
1985-87
All models (.6) 9

(G) Ignition Lock Cylinder, Renew
1985-87 (.6) 1.0
w/Tilt Tel add (.1) 1
Recode cyl add 3

DISTRIBUTORLESS IGNITION SYSTEM

(G) Ignition Coil and/or Module, Renew
1985-87 (.5) 7

(G) Camshaft Sensor, Renew
1985-87 (.6) 9

(G) Crankshaft Sensor, Renew
1985-87 (.6) 9

DIESEL IGNITION COMPONENTS

(G) Coolant Fast Idle Temperature Switch, Renew
All models (.2) 4

(G) Fast Idle Solenoid, Renew
All models (.4) 6

(G) Glow Plugs, Renew
All models-one bank (.4) 6
both banks (.6) 1.0

(G) Glow Plug Control Modules, Renew
All models
controller (.5) 7
relay (.5) 7

PARTS 2 IGNITION SYSTEM 2 PARTS

	Part No.	Price
Distributor Assy.		
1985-181	◆1103470	351.25
231	◆1103588	289.75
1985-87-252	◆1103683	286.00
(1) Cover		
1985-V-6	◆1894209	6.00
1985-87-V-8	◆1875960	6.00
(2) Coil		
1985-V-6	◆1985474	36.00
1985-87-V-8	◆1985473	36.00
(3) Cap		
1985-181	◆1894979	17.00
231	◆1984480	27.25
1985-87-252	◆1977046	24.50
(4) Brushes		
1985-87	◆1989880	2.50
(5) Rotor		
1985-87	◆1977026	6.50
(6) Mainshaft		
1985-V-6	◆1976930	38.50
1985-87-V-8	◆1979556	38.00
(7) Pole Piece & Plate		
1985-V-6	◆1976925	30.25
1985-87-V-8	◆1976897	30.25
(8) Module		
1985-V-6	◆1976908	60.00
1985-87-V-8	◆1987744	N.L.
(9) Housing		
1985-181	◆1976928	36.25
231	◆1987900	62.75
1985-87-252	◆10497570	53.50
(10) Gear		
1985-87-V-6	◆1892082	15.25
V-8	◆1979546	37.00
Ignition Switch		
(wo/Electronic cluster)		
1985-87-exc. Tilt whl.	◆1990115	11.50
Tilt wheel	◆1990116	11.50
(Electronic cluster)		
1985-87	◆1990118	12.75

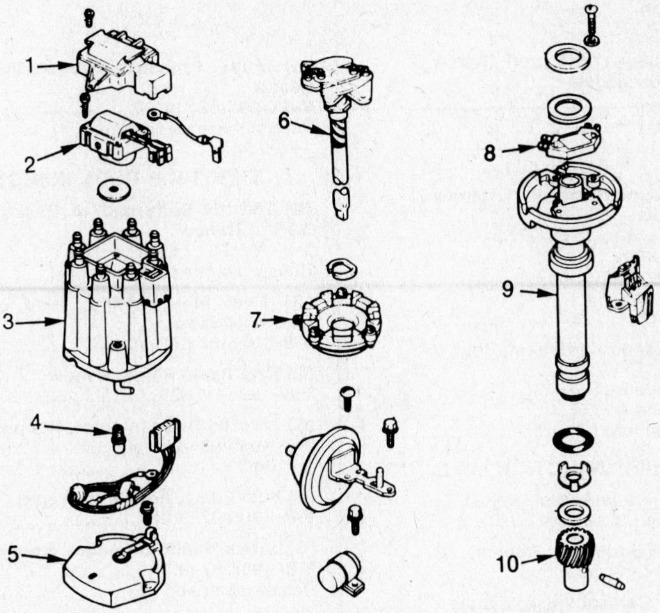

	Part No.	Price
IGNITION SYSTEM (DIESEL)		
Glow Plug Module		
1985	◆22528337	96.00
Glow Plugs		
1985	◆5613826	16.50
1985-exc. below	◆22514246	26.00
ext. EGR	◆22524391	24.75
DISTRIBUTORLESS IGNITION SYSTEM-C-3I		
Electronic Spark Control Module		
1986-87	◆16049534	70.00

	Part No.	Price
Electronic Spark Control Knock Sensor		
1986-87	◆1997562	37.00
Crankshaft Position Sensor		
1986-87	◆25526153	N.L.
Camshaft Position Sensor		
1986-87	◆25523227	27.50
Ignition Coil		
1986-87	◆25526448	109.00
Module		
1986-87	◆25526449	215.00

LABOR 3 FUEL SYSTEM 3 LABOR

(Factory Time)	Chilton Time
GASOLINE ENGINES	
(G) Fuel Pump, Test	
Includes: Disconnect line at carburetor, attach pressure gauge.	
All models	.3
(M) Carburetor Air Cleaner, Service	
All models	.2
(G) Carburetor, Adjust (On Car)	
All models	
Curb & Fast Idle (.6)	.8
Vacuum Break	
both (.3)	.4
Choke (.6)	1.0
Complete (1.3)	1.8
(G) Choke Coil, Cover and/or Gasket, Renew	
All models (.6)	1.0
(G) Choke Vacuum Break Diaphragm, Renew	
All models-one (.6)	.8
both (.8)	1.0
(G) Choke Vacuum Control Switch, Renew	
All models (.2)	.3
(G) Electric Choke Relay, Renew	
All models (.2)	.3
(G) Idle Stop Solenoid, Renew	
All models (.7)	1.0
(G) Needle Valve and Seat, Renew	
V-6–2 bbl (.9)	1.2
Perform C.C.C. system test add	1.0
(G) Carburetor Float, Renew or Adjust	
V-6–2 bbl (.9)	1.2
Perform C.C.C. system test add	1.0
(G) Accelerator Pump, Renew	
V-6–2 bbl (.7)	1.0
(G) E.F.E. Heater (Insulator), Renew	
All models (.6)	1.0
(G) Carburetor Assy., Renew	
Includes: All necessary adjustments.	
V-6 (.6)	1.0
Perform C.C.C. system test add	1.0
(G) Carburetor, R&R and Clean or Recondition	
Includes: All necessary adjustments.	
V-6	3.0
Perform C.C.C. system test add	1.0
(G) Water In Fuel Detector, Renew (WIF)	
All models (.9)	1.2
(G) Fuel Tank, Renew	
Buick & Olds models	
1985-87 (.9)	1.3
Cadillac models	
1985-87 (1.0)	1.4

LABOR 3 FUEL SYSTEM 3 LABOR

	(Factory Time)	Chilton Time
(G) Fuel Gauge (Tank Unit), Renew		
Buick & Olds models		
1985-87	(.8)	1.2
Cadillac models		
1985-87	(1.1)	1.5
Transfer elec fuel pump add		.1
(G) Fuel Gauge (Dash Unit), Renew		
Buick models		
1985-87	(.3)	.5
Cadillac models		
1985	(.3)	.5
Oldsmobile models		
1985-87	(.5)	.9
(G) Intake Manifold Gasket, Renew		
V-6–1985-87		
eng code E	(1.5)	2.1
eng code 3	(1.5)	2.1
Renew manif add	(.3)	.5

FUEL INJECTION (MFI)

	(Factory Time)	Chilton Time
(G) Minimum Idle Speed, Adjust		
All models	(.2)	.4
(G) Throttle Body Unit, Renew		
V-6–1985-87	(.3)	.5
(G) Idle Air Control Valve, Renew		
V-6–1985-87	(.2)	.3
(G) Fuel Pump, Renew (In Tank)		
1985-87	(1.0)	1.4
(G) Fuel Pump Relay, Renew		
V-6–1985-87	(.3)	.4
(G) Fuel Injector, Renew		
V-6–1985-87-one	(.6)	1.0
each adtnl	(.1)	.2
Perform balance test add	(.4)	.4
(G) Fuel Rail, Renew		
V-6–1985-87	(.6)	1.0
(G) Mass Air Sensor, Renew		
V-6–1985-87	(.2)	.4
(G) Fuel Pressure Regulator, Renew		
V-6–1985-87	(.3)	.5
Perform balance test add	(.4)	.4

THROTTLE BODY INJECTION

	(Factory Time)	Chilton Time
(G) Throttle Body and/or Gasket, R&R or Renew		
V-8–1985-87	(.6)	1.0
Renew throttle body add	(.3)	.3
(G) Fuel Meter Assy., and/or Gasket, Renew		
V-8–1985-87	(.4)	.6
(G) Fuel Pump Relay, Renew		
V-8–1985-87	(.2)	.3
(G) Throttle Body Injector, Renew		
V-8–1985-87-one	(.4)	.6
both	(.4)	.8
(G) Fuel Pump, Renew (In Tank)		
V-8–1985-87	(1.2)	1.5
(G) Intake Manifold Gasket, Renew		
V-8–1985-87	(4.7)	6.5
Renew manif add	(.5)	.5

DIESEL ENGINE

	(Factory Time)	Chilton Time
(G) Air Cleaner, Service		
All models		.4
(G) Air Intake Crossover, Renew		
All models	(.3)	.4
(G) Injection Timing, Check and Adjust		
All models	(.7)	.9
(G) Vacuum Pump, Renew (Belt Driven)		
All models	(.9)	1.2
(G) Fuel Supply Pump, Renew		
All models	(.5)	.8
(G) Fuel Injection Nozzles and/or Seals, Renew		
All models-one	(1.1)	1.6
all	(2.0)	3.0
Clean nozzles add, each		.2
(G) High Pressure Fuel Lines, Renew		
All models-one	(.6)	1.2
all	(1.2)	2.5
(G) Injection Pump Throttle Shaft Seal, Renew		
All models	(.9)	1.3
(G) Fuel Injection Pump, R&R or Renew		
All models	(2.0)	3.0
Flush meter valve sensor add	(.3)	.3
Adjust sensor add	(.2)	.2
(G) Cold Advance Solenoid, Renew		
All models	(.6)	.8
(G) Fuel Solenoid, Renew		
All models	(.5)	.7
(G) Fuel Injection Head Seal, Renew		
Includes: Renew head and drive shaft seals. Renew governor weight retaining ring.		
All models	(2.3)	3.4
(G) Injection Pump Drive Shaft Seal, Renew		
All models	(1.5)	2.1
(G) Injection Pump Adapter and/or Seal, Renew		
All models	(1.3)	2.1
(G) Intake Manifold Gasket, Renew		
All models	(2.7)	3.5
Renew manif add	(.2)	.5

PARTS 3 FUEL SYSTEM 3 PARTS

	Part No.	Price
Carburetor Assy. (Rochester)		
1985-181		
20 bolt	◆17111188	750.50
14 bolt	◆17110337	912.75
Carburetor Gasket Kit		
1985-181		
20 bolt	◆17111176	32.75
14 bolt	◆17068882	31.25
Carburetor Needle & Seat		
1985-181	◆7035157	6.00
Carburetor Power Kit		
1985-181		
20 bolt	◆17076144	57.75
14 bolt	◆17076129	51.00
Fuel Pump		
1985-181	◆6472531	39.75
1985-231 (w/ Digital)	◆6472527	134.75
(exc. Digital)	◆6472998	91.00
1985-252		
1st design	◆6472248	72.50
2nd design	◆6472358	59.00
1986-87	◆6472526	57.00

1st design has radio freq. inter. filter soldered to fuel level sender. 2nd design (RFI) filter is screwed to the top of the fuel pump.

	Part No.	Price
Fuel Gauge (Tank Unit)		
181		
1985-exc. digital	◆25090544	136.75
digital cluster	◆25003699	129.50
231		
1985-exc. digital	◆25090490	143.50
digital cluster	◆25090493	N.L.
1986-87-exc. Digital	◆25092116	147.75
Digital	◆25092119	156.75
252		
1985	◆25003686	130.50
1986-87	◆25091491	147.75
Fuel Gauge (Dash Unit)		
(Electra)		
1985-87	◆6433447	25.00
(98-Regency)		
1985-87	◆6433597	25.75
Intake Manifold Gasket Set		
1985-181	◆25505397	15.75
231	◆1264924	14.50
1985-87-252	◆3634619	N.L.

FUEL SYSTEM (DIESEL)

	Part No.	Price
Fuel pump		
1985-External E.G.R.	◆6442223	N.L.
wo/External E.G.R.	◆6472153	59.25
Air Intake Crossover		
1985-exc. below	◆22519924	109.00
Injection Pump Adapter		
1985	◆22516525	52.50
Fuel Injection Pump		
1985-Federal		
exc. below	◆22526504	763.00
external E.G.R.	◆22524419	763.00
1985-Calif.		
external EGR	◆22527910	763.00
Fuel Gauge (tank unit)		
1985-exc. external E.G.R.	◆25003684	140.75
w/external E.G.R.	◆25004981	138.50
Fuel Injection Nozzles		
1985	◆22520376	89.50
Vacuum Pump		
1985	◆7846096	119.00
Intake Manifold Gaskets		
1985	◆22514872	16.50

PARTS 3 ELECTRONIC FUEL INJECTION 3 PARTS

	Part No.	Price
V-8-252		
(1) Throttle Body Injection Unit		
1985-Fed. & Calif.	◆17110635	879.25
Canada (stamped 17085030)	◆17110656	N.L.
(stamped 17085011)	◆17111292	678.00
1986-87	◆17111500	650.00
(2) Throttle Body Kit		
1985-exc. below	◆17110636	187.00
(stamped 17085011)	◆17111290	185.75
1986-87	◆17111503	185.75
(3) Idle Speed Control Kit		
1985-exc. Canada	◆17079663	123.50
Canada	◆17111170	108.75
1986-87	◆17111170	108.75
(4) Fuel Meter Kit		
1985-exc. Canada	◆17079496	873.75
Canada	◆17110657	424.50
1986-87	◆17111501	296.75

Two injectors and pressure regulator included.

	Part No.	Price
(5) Throttle Position Sensor Kit		
1985-87	◆17110352	100.50

	Part No.	Price
Gasket Kit		
1985-87	◆17078257	17.75

PARTS 3 ELECTRONIC FUEL INJECTION 3 PARTS

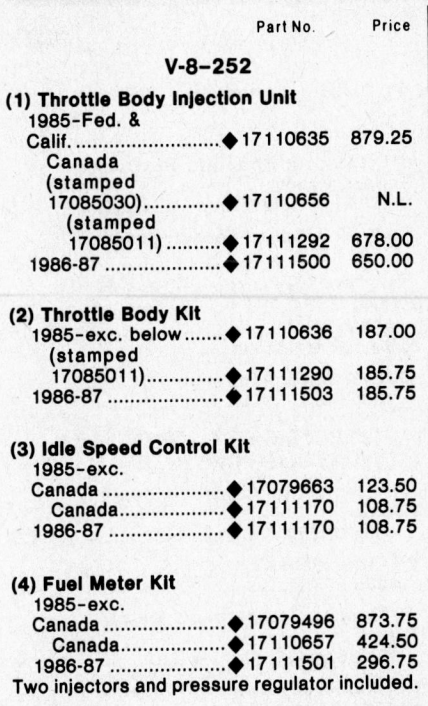

	Part No.	Price
V-6-231		
(1) Throttle Body Assm.		
1985	◆25518889	198.00
1986-87	◆25524565	150.00
(2) Idle Air Control Motor		
1985	◆22048225	64.75
1986-87	◆25527077	29.00
(3) Throttle Position Sensor		
1985-87	◆25036663	23.50

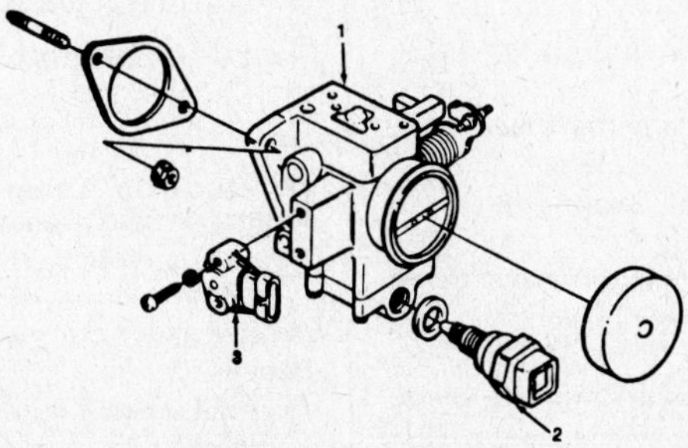

LABOR 3A EMISSION CONTROLS 3A LABOR

(Factory Time) — Chilton Time

GASOLINE ENGINES

(G) Emission Control Check

Includes: Check and adjust engine idle speed and mixture and ignition timing. Check PCV valve.

All models 6

POSITIVE CRANKCASE VENTILATION

(M) Positive Crankcase Ventilation Valve, Renew

All models (.2) 3

(M) Crankcase Vent Filter Assy., Renew

All models (.2) 3

EVAPORATIVE EMISSION TYPE

(G) Charcoal Canister, Renew

All models (.2) 3

(G) Canister Purge Thermal Vacuum Switch, Renew

All models (.2) 3

CONTROLLED COMBUSTION TYPE

(G) Air Cleaner Vacuum Motor, Renew

All models (.3) 5

(G) Air Cleaner Temperature Sensor, Renew

All models (.2) 3

EXHAUST GAS RECIRCULATION SYSTEM

(G) E.G.R. Valve, Renew

V-6–1985-87 (.3) 5
V-8–1985-87 (.4) 6

(G) E.G.R. Thermal Vacuum Switch, Renew

V-8–1985-87 (.3) 4

(G) Thermostatic Vacuum Control Switch, Renew

All models (.3) 4

(G) E.G.R. Vacuum Delay Valve, Renew

V-6-1985-87 (.3) 4

(G) Thermal Control Valve, Renew

V-6-1985-87 (.3) 4

AIR INJECTION SYSTEM

(G) Air Pump, Renew

V-6-1985-87 (.2) 5
V-8-1985-87 (.8) 1.1

(G) Air Check Valve, Renew

All models-one (.4) 5
each adtnl 2

(Factory Time) Chilton Time

(G) Vacuum Delay Valve, Renew
All models (.2) 2

(G) Air Pump Filter, Renew
All models (.4) 5

(G) Catalytic Converter Air Pipes, Renew
All models
upper (.5) 7
lower (.3) 5

EFE SYSTEM

(G) E.F.E. Valve, Renew
V-6–1985 (.7) 1.0

(G) E.F.E. Vacuum Check Valve, Renew
V-6–1985 (.2) 3

COMPUTER COMMAND CONTROL SYSTEM (C.C.C.)

(P) Computer Command Control System Performance Check
1985-87 (.5) 1.0

(P) Throttle Position Sensor, Adjust
All models
w/Carb (.7) 9
w/EFI/MFI (.4) 6
Perform C.C.C. system check add 1.0

(P) Electronic Control Module, Renew
Does not include system performance check.
1985-87 (.8) 1.1

(P) EGR/EFE Purge Solenoid, Renew
Does not include system performance check.
1985-87 (.4) 6

(P) Mixture Control Solenoid, Renew
Does not include system performance check.
1985-87 (1.1) 1.4

(P) Prom, Renew
Does not include system performance check.
1985-87 (.9) 1.2

(P) Barometric Sensor, Renew
Does not include system performance check.
1985-87 (.5) 7

(P) Coolant Temperature Sensor, Renew
Does not include system performance check.
1985-87 (.6) 8

(P) Manifold Absolute Pressure Sensor, Renew
Does not include system performance check.
1985-87 (.5) 7

(P) Oxygen Sensor, Renew
Does not include system performance check.
1985-87 (.6) 8

(P) Vehicle Speed Sensor, Renew
Does not include system performance check.
Buick models
1985 (1.3) 2.0
1986-87 (.3) 1.0
Oldsmobile models
1985-87 (.8) 1.2

(P) Throttle Position Sensor, Renew
Does not include system performance check.
1985-87 (1.1) 1.4

CHILTON'S EMISSION CONTROL TUNE-UP

1. Clean or renew P.C.V. valve, hoses and filter.
2. Check fuel tank cap for sealing ability.
3. Check fuel tank and fuel lines for leakage.
4. Check evaporation canister and filter. Replace if necessary.
5. Check engine compression to determine leakage of unburned gases. (Add time for items of interference).
6. Test and clean or renew spark plugs.
7. Check engine oil dipstick for sealing ability.
8. Test exhaust system with analyzer and check system for leakage.
9. Check exhaust manifold heat valve for operation.
10. Adjust ignition timing and carburetor idle speed and mixture.
11. Check automatic choke mechanism for free operation.
12. Inspect air cleaner and element.
13. On models so equipped, test distributor vacuum control switch and transmission control switch.

V-6 .... **1.7**
V-8 .... **1.8**

For repairs made, charge accordingly.

(Factory Time) Chilton Time

(P) Back-Up Lamp and Park/Neutral Switch, Renew
Does not include system performance check.
1985-87 (.5) 7

(P) Air Control/Air Switching Valve, Renew
Does not include system performance check.
1985-87 (.7) 1.0

(P) Canister Purge Control Valve, Renew
Does not include system performance check.
1985-87 (.4) 6

(P) EGR/EFE Vacuum Control Solenoids, Renew
Does not include system performance check.
1985-87 (.3) 4

(P) Vacuum Control Purge Solenoid, Renew
Does not include system performance check.
1985-87 (.3) 4

(P) Idle Speed Control Motor, Renew or Adjust
Does not include system performance check.
1985-87 (.7) 1.0
Recond motor add (.3) 3

(P) Idle Load Compensator, Renew
1985-87 (.4) 6

DIESEL ELECTRONIC EMISSION CONTROLS

(P) Electronic Control Module, Renew
1985 (.6) 8

(Factory Time) Chilton Time

(P) Coolant Temperature Sensor, Renew
1985 (.6) 8

(P) Manifold Absolute Pressure Sensor, Renew
1985 (.3) 5

(P) Vehicle Speed Sensor, Renew
1985 (.9) 1.4

(P) EGR Control Valve Solenoid, Renew
1985 (.4) 6
Renew ECM add (.1) 1

(P) EPR Valve, Renew
1985 (.5) 7

ELECTRICALLY CONTROLLED EMISSIONS (w/EFI)

(P) Electronic Control Module, Renew
1985-87 (.7) 1.0

(P) Prom, Renew
1985-87 (.7) 1.0

(P) Coolant Temperature Sensor, Renew
1985-87 (.4) 6

(P) Manifold Absolute Pressure Sensor, Renew
1985-87 (.5) 8

(P) Oxygen Sensor, Renew
1985-87 (.5) 7

(P) Vehicle Speed Sensor, Renew
1985-87 (.7) 1.0

(P) Throttle Position Sensor, Renew
1985-87 (.9) 1.2

(P) Manifold Temperature Sensor, Renew
1986-87 (.4) 6

DIESEL ENGINE EMISSIONS

(G) Crankcase Vent Filter, Renew
All models-each (.2) 3

(G) Crankcase Depression Regulator Valve, Renew
All models (.2) 3

(G) EGR Control Valve Switch, Renew
All models (.2) 3

(G) EGR Altitude Trim Solenoid, Renew
All models (.4) 6

(G) Housing Pressure Cold Advance Solenoid, Renew
All models (.5) 6

(G) EPR Control Valve Switch, Renew
All models (.3) 4

(G) EPR Control Valve Solenoid, Renew
All models (.3) 4

(G) Vacuum Regulator Valve, Renew
All models (.6) 8
Adj light load switch add 1

(G) EGR Valve, Renew
All models (.5) 8

(G) Metering Valve Sensor, Renew
All models (.6) 9

LABOR 3A EMISSION CONTROLS 3A LABOR

	(Factory Time)	Chilton Time
(G) Altitude Fuel Limiter, Renew		
All models	(.6)	.8
(G) EPR Valve, Renew		
All models	(.5)	.7
(G) Housing Pressure Altitude Advance Solenoid, Renew		
All models	(.2)	.3
(G) Housing Pressure Altitude Advance Relay, Renew		
All models	(.4)	.6

PARTS 3A EMISSION CONTROLS 3A PARTS

	Part No.	Price
POSITIVE CRANKCASE VENTILATION		
Positive Crankcase Valve		
1985-181	◆25043471	6.75
1985-87-231	◆6487936	3.50
1985-252	◆6487779	2.50
1986-87-252	◆6487532	N.L.
EVAPORATIVE EMISSION TYPE		
Vapor Canister		
1985-181	◆17064622	39.50
1985-231	◆17085022	48.00
1986-87-231	◆17085935	44.75
1985-87-252	◆17075834	51.25
Canister Control Valve		
1985-87-181	◆17085928	14.50
Canister Solenoid Pkg.		
1985-231	◆17110599	20.25
1986-87-231	◆25526955	13.00
1985-87-252	◆17074370	16.50
Canister Filter		
1985-87	◆7026014	2.50
CONTROLLED COMBUSTION TYPE		
Vacuum Diaphragm Motor		
1985-181	◆25043244	89.25
252	◆25043452	77.75
Air Cleaner Temperature Sensor		
1985-181	◆8997916	18.75
252	◆8997493	18.75
Vacuum Valve Kit		
1985-181	◆8997639	9.75
Exhaust Gas Recirculation System		
E.G.R. Valve		
1985-181	◆17110487	53.00
231	◆17110463	49.50
1986-87	◆17111583	37.25
1985-87-252	◆17110461	63.50
1985-Diesel eng. (wo/Ext. E.G.R.)	◆17083702	85.75
(Ext. E.G.R.)	◆17085027	63.50
E.G.R. Valve Vacuum Control		
1985-181	◆25519958	52.00
231	◆25519960	53.75
Diesel	◆1997663	32.50
1986-87 (stamped)		
(25522717)	◆25522717	41.75
(25527186)	◆2552718	N.L.
Exhaust Pressure Regulator Valve Solenoid		
1985-181	◆1997675	38.75
E.F.E. Relay		
1985-181	◆10026663	5.50
252	◆1626239	6.50
AIR INJECTOR REACTOR TYPE		
Air Injection Pump		
1985-181	◆7842853	149.00
252	◆7834919	149.00
Air Injection Pump Fan		
1985-181	◆7835231	5.75
Air Injection Control Valve		
1985-181	◆17072997	73.75
252	◆17075280	110.50
COMPUTER CONTROLLED EMISSION SYSTEM		
Controller (ecm)		
1985-181	◆1226519	110.25
1985-231 (wo/ Air temp. sensor)	◆1226461	110.25
(w/Air temp. sensor)	◆1226948	110.00
1986-87	◆1227148	110.00
1985-252	◆1226462	110.25
1986-87	◆1227056	110.00
Calibration Unit (Prom)		
181		
1985-exc. below	◆16047237	40.50
Calif.	◆16048138	40.50
231		
1985 (code)		
7216 DZX	◆16047215	40.50
3890 CMB	◆16043882	40.50
0673 HFB	◆16050672	40.50
1686 HKL	◆16051685	40.50
1986-87 (code)		
9914 BUX	◆16059913	40.50
5160 HUJ	◆16055169	N.L.
0593 CMS	◆16060592	40.50
5156 HUH	◆16055155	40.50
0588 CLK	◆16060587	40.50
252		
1985-87 (code)		
2277 HMC	◆16052276	40.50
2283 HMD	◆16052282	40.50
1151 DCR	◆16041589	40.50
3719 DSM	◆16043718	40.50
7554 BMB	◆16037553	40.50
3018 FCW	◆16053017	N.L.
7474 AHK	◆16045931	40.50
3023 FCX	◆16059163	40.50
Barometric Pressure Sensor		
1985-V-6	◆16006833	62.25
ESC Knock Sensor		
1985-87-V-6	◆1997562	37.00
Exhaust Oxygen Sensor		
1985-87	◆5613695	24.50
Coolant Temperature Sensor		
1985	◆25036092	22.00
1986-87	◆25036708	12.75
M.A.P. Sensor		
1985	◆16006835	62.25
EMISSION CONTROLS (DIESEL)		
Crankcase Depression Regulator Valve		
1985	◆25041551	28.25
Crankcase Ventilation Filter		
1985-wo/Ext. E.G.R.	◆22514303	4.00
Ext. E.G.R.	◆22525280	8.50
Electronic Control Module		
1985-wo/Ext. E.G.R.	◆22526891	300.00
Ext. E.G.R.	◆22529161	300.00
E.G.R. Valve Vacuum Control		
1985	◆1997663	32.75
E.G.R. Valve Control Switch		
1985	◆22520659	23.75
M.A.P. Sensor		
1985	◆16017460	N.L.

LABOR 4 ALTERNATOR AND REGULATOR 4 LABOR

	(Factory Time)	Chilton Time
(G) Delcotron Circuits, Test		
Includes: Test battery, regulator, Delcotron output.		
All models		.6
(M) Alternator Drive Belt, Renew		
V-6-1985-87		
Gas	(.5)	.7
Diesel	(.2)	.4
V-8-1985-87		
Serpentine	(.2)	.4
(G) Delcotron Assembly, Renew		
1985-87	(.6)	.8
(G) Delcotron, R&R and Recondition		
Includes: Complete disassembly, replacement of parts as required, reassemble.		
V-6-1985-87		
Gas	(1.6)	2.3
Diesel	(1.8)	2.5
V-8-1985-87	(1.0)	1.7

LABOR 4 ALTERNATOR AND REGULATOR 4 LABOR

(Factory Time) Chilton Time

(G) Delcotron Front Bearing, Renew

Includes: R&R Delcotron and separate end frames.

V-6–1985-87
- Gas (.7) 9
- Diesel (.5) 8

V-8–1985-87 (.8) 1.0

Renew rear brg add 2

(G) Delcotron Voltage Regulator, Test and Renew

Includes: R&R, disassemble and reassemble Delcotron.

1985-87 (.8) 1.1

(G) Voltmeter, Renew

1985-87
- Buick models (.3) 5
- Olds models (.5) 9

PARTS 4 ALTERNATOR AND REGULATOR 4 PARTS

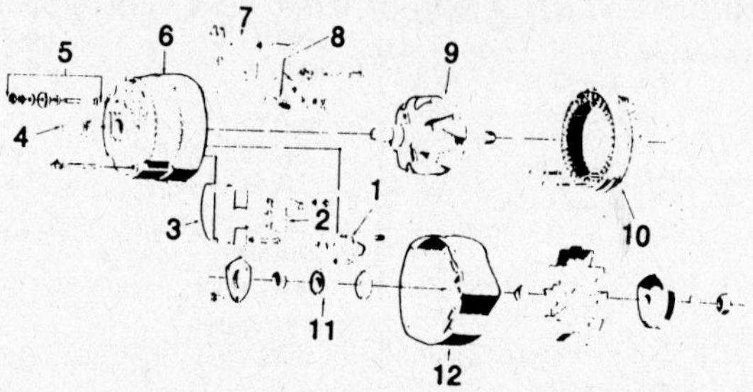

	Part No.	Price
Delcotron Assy. (New)		
1985-94 amp	◆1105402	232.00
85 amp	◆1105339	326.50
108 amp	◆1105481	218.50
1986-87	◆1101225	310.75
(1) Capacitor		
1985-87	◆1978146	4.75
(2) Diode Trio (Negative)		
1985-87	◆1984459	5.00
(3) Rectifier Bridge		
1985-87-exc. below	◆1985801	29.75
85 amp	◆1975313	24.50
94 amp	◆1987061	29.00
(4) Bearing (slip ring end)		
1985-87-exc. below	◆9436831	5.50
85 amp	◆1975322	5.50
(5) Terminal Pkg.		
1985-87	◆1975471	3.50
(6) Frame (Rear End)		
1985-94 amp	◆1987073	28.00
85 amp	◆1975310	31.00
1985-87-108 amp	◆1985671	21.00
(7) Regulator		
1985-87	◆1116387	25.00
(8) Brush w/holder		
1985-87-exc. 94 amp	◆1975323	10.00
94 amp	◆1984462	9.00
(9) Rotor Assy.		
1985-94 amp	◆1984466	77.25
85 amp	◆1975333	65.00
1985-87-108 amp	◆1985646	79.25
(10) Stator		
1985-94 amp	◆1987074	41.50
85 amp	◆1975987	83.50
97 amp	◆1987510	52.75
1986-87-108 amp	◆1985625	52.00
(11) Bearing (Drive End)		
1985-87	◆908419	10.00
(12) Frame (Drive End)		
1985-94 amp	◆1987054	28.00
85 amp	◆1986590	30.00
108 amp	◆1985669	21.50
1986-87-108 amp	◆1988983	22.25

LABOR 5 STARTING SYSTEM 5 LABOR

(Factory Time) Chilton Time

(G) Starter Draw Test (On Car)

All models 3

(G) Starter Assy., Renew

V-6–1985-87
- Gas (.8) 1.1
- Diesel (.6) 1.0

V-8–1985-87 (.5) 8

Add draw test if performed.

(G) Starter, R&R and Recondition

Includes: Turn down armature.

V-6–1985-87
- Gas (1.6) 2.2
- Diesel (1.3) 2.1

V-8–1985-87 (1.6) 2.2

Renew field coils add (.2) 5

Add draw test if performed.

(G) Starter Drive, Renew

Includes: R&R starter.

V-6–1985-87
- Gas (1.1) 1.5
- Diesel (.6) 1.1

V-8–1985-87 (.9) 1.3

(G) Starter Solenoid, Renew

Includes: R&R starter.

V-6–1985-87
- Gas (.8) 1.2
- Diesel (.6) 1.1

V-8–1985-87 (.8) 1.2

(G) Back-Up Lamp and Park/Neutral Switch, Renew

1985-87 (.3) 5

(G) Ignition Switch, Renew

1985-87
- All models (.6) 9

(M) Battery Cables, Renew

All models
- batt to starter (.6) 8
- batt to start conn (.2) 2
- negative-one (.2) 3

PARTS 5 STARTING SYSTEM 5 PARTS

	Part No.	Price
GASOLINE ENGINES		
Starter Assy. (New)		
1985-181	◆1998448	191.00
231	◆1998445	188.00
252	◆1998476	183.75
1986-87-252	◆1998534	183.50
(1) Solenoid Switch		
1985-87-V-6	◆1114531	N.L.
V-8	◆1114557	33.50
(2) Spring		
1985-87	◆1978281	1.75
(3) Plunger		
1985-87	◆1987391	6.75
(4) Shift Lever		
1985-87	◆1984501	5.00
(5) Armature		
1985-87-exc.		
252	◆10495881	73.00
252	◆10495931	71.50
(6) Drive Assy.		
1985-87-exc.		
252	◆10498407	33.50
252	◆1984511	23.25
(7) Grommet		
1985-87	◆1984527	1.00
(8) Frame (w/Field)		
1985-exc. below	◆1985143	71.50
231	◆1987277	71.25
1986-87-231	◆10495885	94.75
252	◆1985143	71.50
(9) Brush Holder Kit		
1985	◆1893929	11.25
1986-87-231	◆10497180	9.75
252	◆1893929	11.00
(10) Brushes		
1985-87	◆1893296	.50
(11) Holder		
1985-87	◆1893293	1.25

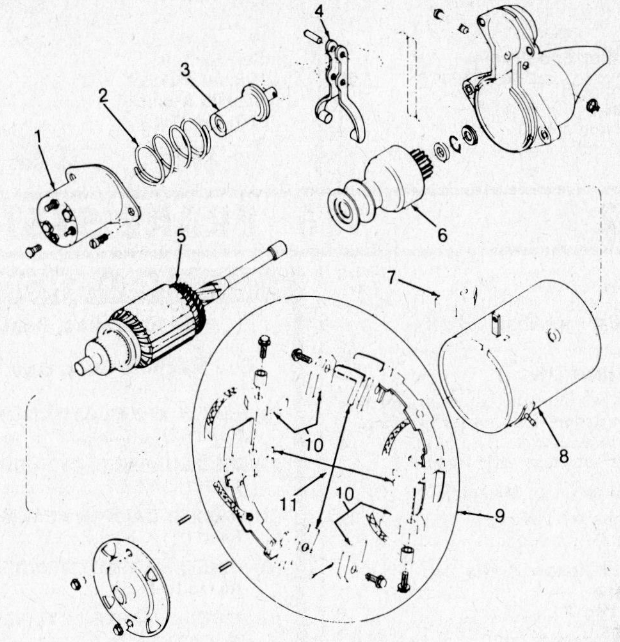

	Part No.	Price
Battery Cables		
Order by year and model.		
Ignition Switch		
Oldsmobile & Buick		
(wo/Digital cluster)		
1985-87-exc. tilt whl.	◆1990115	11.50
Tilt wheel	◆1990116	11.50
(Digital cluster)		
1985-87	◆1990118	12.75
Cadillac		
1985-87-wo/Tilt whl.	◆7804414	6.25
Tilt whl.	◆7811092	4.75

PARTS 5 STARTING SYSTEM 5 PARTS

	Part No.	Price
DIESEL ENGINE		
Starter Assy. (New)		
1985	◆22523207	389.25
(1) Drive Pinion Kit		
1985	◆22516186	8.50
(2) Drive Housing w/Bushing		
1985	◆22523730	35.00
(3) Shim Kit		
1985	◆22516175	1.50
(4) Solenoid Switch		
1985	◆22516196	44.00
(5) Lever Kit		
1985	◆22516193	3.25
(6) Drive Pinion Shaft		
1985	◆22516183	71.00
(7) Spring w/Holder		
1985	◆22516194	2.50
(8) Reduction Gear		
1985	◆22516184	9.50
(9) Shim Kit		
1985	◆22516175	1.50
(10) Gear Housing		
1985	◆22516195	28.50
(11) Pinion Shaft End Cover		
1985	◆22516182	2.00

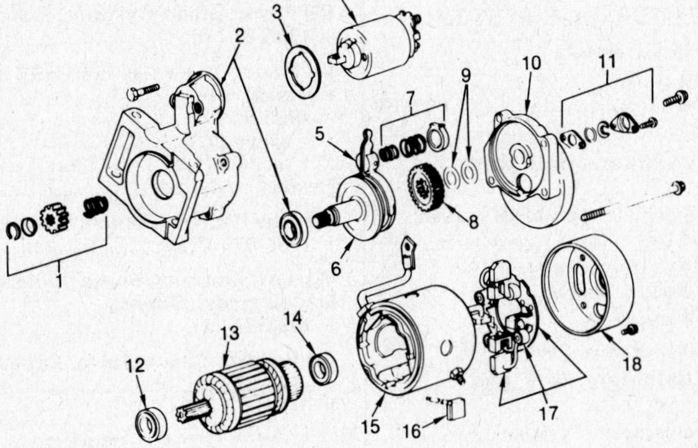

	Part No.	Price
(12) Armature Drive Gear Bearing		
1985	◆22516189	9.00
(13) Armature		
1985	◆22516197	130.00
(14) Commutator End Bearing		
1985	◆22516188	5.50
(15) Field Frame		
1985	◆22516176	7.50
(16) Positive Brush		
1985	◆22516180	3.25
(17) Negative Brush		
1985	◆22516177	3.00

PARTS 5 STARTING SYSTEM 5 PARTS

	Part No.	Price
(18) Commutator End Frame		
1985	◆22516176	7.50
Battery Cables		
Order by year and model.		
Ignition Switch		
(wo/Digital cluster)		
Oldsmobile & Buick		
1985-exc. Tilt whl.	◆1990115	11.50
Tilt wheel	◆1990116	11.50
(Digital cluster)		
1985	◆1990118	12.75
Cadillac		
1985-wo/Tilt whl.	◆7804414	6.25
Tilt whl.	◆7811092	4.75

LABOR 6 BRAKE SYSTEM 6 LABOR

	(Factory Time)	Chilton Time
(G) Brake Pedal Free Play, Adjust		
All models		.3
(G) Brakes, Adjust (Minor)		
Includes: R&R wheels and adjust brakes thru access holes in drums. Fill master cylinder.		
two wheels		.4
Remove knock out plugs, add-each		.1
(G) Bleed Brakes (Four Wheels)		
Includes: Fill master cylinder.		
All models	(.4)	.5
(G) Free Up or Renew Brake Self-Adjusting Units		
All models-one		.6
each adtnl		.4
(G) Brake Shoes and/or Pads, Renew		
Includes: Install new or exchange shoes or pads. Adjust service and hand brake. Bleed system.		
1985-87-front-disc	(.6)	.9
rear-drum	(.9)	1.5
all four wheels		2.3
Resurface disc rotor add-each		.5
Resurface brake drum add-each		.5
(G) Brake Drums, Renew		
1985-87-one	(.3)	.5
both	(.5)	.8
(G) Brake System Failure Warning Switch, Renew		
1985-87	(.2)	.3

BRAKE HYDRAULIC SYSTEM

	(Factory Time)	Chilton Time
(G) Wheel Cylinder, Renew		
Includes: Bleed system.		
1985-87-one	(.7)	1.0
both	(1.1)	1.9
(G) Wheel Cylinder, R&R and Rebuild		
Includes: Hone cylinder and bleed system.		
1985-87-one	(.9)	1.3
both	(1.5)	2.1
(G) Master Cylinder, Renew		
Includes: Bleed system.		
1985-87	(.8)	1.2
(G) Master Cylinder, R&R and Rebuild		
Includes: Bleed complete system.		
1985-87	(1.6)	2.0
(G) Brake Hose, Renew		
Includes: Bleed system.		
1985-87-front-one	(.7)	.9
both	(.8)	1.1
rear-each	(.7)	.9
center-both	(.7)	1.0

COMBINATIONS

Add to Brakes, Renew

See Machine Shop Operations

(G) RENEW WHEEL CYLINDER		
Each	(.2)	.2
(G) REBUILD WHEEL CYLINDER		
Each	(.2)	.3
(G) REBUILD CALIPER ASSEMBLY		
Each	(.5)	.5
(G) RENEW MASTER CYLINDER		
All models	(.5)	.8
(G) REBUILD MASTER CYLINDER		
All models	(.8)	1.0
(G) RENEW BRAKE HOSE		
Each	(.3)	.3
(G) RENEW BRAKE DRUM		
Each	(.1)	.1
(G) RENEW DISC BRAKE ROTOR		
Each	(.2)	.3

	(Factory Time)	Chilton Time
(G) Brake System, Flush and Refill		
All models		1.2

POWER BRAKES

	(Factory Time)	Chilton Time
(G) Power Brake Cylinder, Renew		
1985-87	(.6)	1.0
(G) Power Brake Cylinder, R&R and Recondition		
1985-87		
single	(1.1)	1.8
tandem	(1.3)	2.0
Recond m/Cyl add	(.8)	.8
(G) Low Vacuum Switch, Renew		
1985-87	(.2)	.3
(G) Low Vacuum Brake Indicator Module Assy., Renew		
1985-87	(.2)	.3
(G) Vacuum Check Valve, Renew		
1985-87	(.3)	.3

DISC BRAKES

	(Factory Time)	Chilton Time
(G) Disc Brake Pads, Renew		
Includes: Install new disc brake pads only.		
1985-87	(.6)	.9
(G) Disc Brake Rotor, Renew		
1985-87-one	(.4)	.6
both	(.5)	.9
(G) Caliper Assembly, Renew		
Includes: Bleed complete system.		
1985-87-one	(.4)	.7
both	(.6)	1.2
(G) Caliper Assy., R&R and Recondition		
Includes: Bleed complete system.		
1985-87-one	(.9)	1.2
both	(1.6)	2.2
(G) Brake Proportioner Valves, Renew		
Includes: Bleed system.		
1985-87-one	(.3)	.6
both	(.5)	.8

PARKING BRAKE

	(Factory Time)	Chilton Time
(M) Parking Brake, Adjust		
All models	(.3)	.4
(G) Parking Brake Control, Renew		
1985-87	(.5)	.8
Renew vacuum diaph add	(.3)	.3
(G) Parking Brake Vacuum Release Valve, Renew		
1986-87	(.6)	.8
(G) Parking Brake Cables, Renew		
1985-87-front	(.6)	.9
rear-right	(.7)	1.0
left	(.5)	.8
(G) Parking Brake Equalizer, Renew		
1985-87	(.3)	.5

ANTI-SKID BRAKE SYSTEM (ABS)

	(Factory Time)	Chilton Time
(G) Wheel Speed Sensors, Renew (Front or Rear)		
1986-87-one	(.3)	.5
two	(.5)	.9
Renew brkt add	(.2)	.2
(G) Hydraulic Unit, Renew		
1986-87	(1.0)	1.5
(G) Brake Controller, Renew		
1986-87	(.5)	.7
(G) Energy Unit, Renew		
1986-87	(.5)	.8
(G) Pushrod Assembly, Renew		
1986-87	(1.2)	1.6
(G) Fluid Level Sensor, Renew		
1986-87	(.2)	.3

PARTS 6 BRAKE SYSTEM 6 PARTS

	Part No.	Price
Brake Shoes Set (Rear)		
1985-86	◆12321414	N.L.
1987	◆12321420	N.L.
Wheel Cylinder Assy. (Rear)		
1985-86	◆18010106	27.50
1987	◆18012582	31.50
Wheel Cylinder Repair Kit		
1985-87	◆18010127	7.50
Front Brake Hose		
1985-87-right	◆9769366	14.50
left	◆9769365	14.50
Rear Brake Hose		
1985-87	◆25522287	10.00
Master Cylinder Assy.		
1985	◆18013423	224.50
1986-87	◆18013495	201.00
Master Cylinder Repair Kit		
1985-87	◆18010085	20.75
Brake Drum (Rear)		
1985-87	◆25509919	90.00
Oil Seal (Front)		
1985-87	◆14084119	3.75

POWER BRAKE UNIT

	Part No.	Price
Power Brake Booster (Vacuum)		
1985-87-exc.		
below	◆18008736	250.25
181, 252	◆18008777	234.25
Power Brake Booster Repair Kit		
1985-87	◆18007897	47.50
Power Brake Booster Piston Kit		
1985-87	◆18014006	48.75

PARKING BRAKE

	Part No.	Price
Parking Brake Lever		
1985-87-exc.		
below	◆25515136	23.50
1985-Cadillac	◆1630692	51.75
1986-87	◆1633850	51.75
Parking Brake Cable (Front)		
1985-87	◆25523196	11.25
Parking Brake Cable (Intermediate)		
1985-87	◆25519956	22.00
Parking Brake Cable (Rear)		
1985-87-right	◆25515026	11.50
left	◆25521417	11.50

PARTS 6 DISC BRAKES 6 PARTS

	Part No.	Price
(1) Brake Pad Set		
1985-87	◆12321410	43.50
(2) Piston Assy.		
1985-87	◆18003155	11.00
(3) Spring Kit (Anti-rattle)		
1985-87	◆18006810	3.00
(4) Caliper Repair Kit		
1985-87	◆18003724	8.75
(5) Caliper Assy.		
1985-right	◆18008319	142.00
left	◆18008318	142.00
1986-87-right	◆18013999	142.00
left	◆18013998	142.00
Disc Assy.		
1985-87	◆14035588	94.50

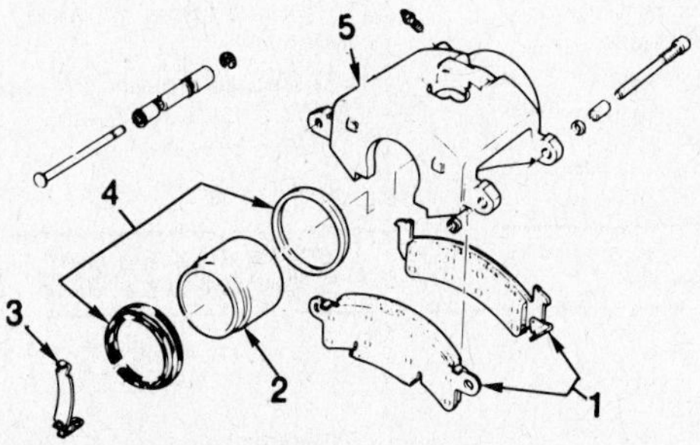

LABOR 7 COOLING SYSTEM 7 LABOR

	(Factory Time)	Chilton Time
(M) Winterize Cooling System		
Includes: Run engine to check for leaks, tighten all hose connections. Test radiator and pressure cap, drain radiator and engine block. Add anti-freeze and refill system.		
All models		.5
(G) Thermostat, Renew		
V-6–1985-87		
Gas	(.6)	.7
Diesel	(.7)	.8
V-8–1985-87	(.3)	.4
(G) Radiator Assembly, R&R or Renew		
Includes: Drain and refill cooling system.		
Cadillac models		
1985-87	(.6)	1.0
Buick & Olds models		
1985	(.6)	1.0
1986-87	(1.1)	1.8
Renew side tank and/or gskt add		
one side	(.7)	1.0
both sides	(1.2)	1.7
(M) Radiator Hoses, Renew		
1985-87-upper	(.3)	.4
lower	(.4)	.5
both	(.5)	.7
by-pass	(.5)	.7

COOLING SYSTEM TUNE-UP

An Annual Cooling System Tune-Up Suggestion List should include (with some exceptions):

1. A visual check of the cooling system for indications of leaks or excessive oil content.
2. Pressure check the cooling system for internal and external leaks with filler cap and neck adapter and tester.
3. Check crankcase and automatic transmission oil for water content.
4. Test coolant thermostat with radiator thermometer.
5. Check temperature gauge for accuracy.
6. Drain system and flush till clean.
7. Clean foreign matter from radiator fins.
8. Test radiator pressure cap with cap tester.
9. Check fan blades and pulleys for alignment and damage.
10. Internal and external inspection of all hoses for cracks and deterioration.
11. Check core plugs (where possible) for seepage.
12. Refill system with correct coolant and check for air locks.
13. Check condition and tension of drive belts with tension gauge.

All models 1.5

	(Factory Time)	Chilton Time
(M) Drive Belt, Adjust		
V-6–1985-87		
Gas-one or all	(1.0)	1.4
(G) Drive Belt, Renew		
V-6–1985-87		
Gas		
A.C.	(.7)	1.0

LABOR 7 COOLING SYSTEM 7 LABOR

(Factory Time)	Chilton Time
AIR (.2)	.3
Fan (.2)	.3
P.S. (.4)	.4
Diesel	
Vacuum pump (.4)	.6
Serpentine (.2)	.4
V-8–1985-87	
Serpentine (.2)	.4

(G) Serpentine Belt Tensioner, Renew

V-6–Diesel	
1985 (.3)	.5
V-8–1985-87 (.2)	.5

(G) Water Pump, Renew

Includes: Drain and refill cooling system.

V-6–1985-87	
Gas (1.4)	2.8
Diesel (2.0)	3.0
V-8–1985-87 (1.7)	2.7

(G) Engine Coolant Fan Relay, Renew

1986-87-Buick (.2)	.3

(G) Engine Coolant Fan Electronic Control Module Assy., Renew

Buick & Olds models	
1985-87 (.3)	.4
Cadillac models	
1985-87 (.6)	.8

(G) Electric Cooling Fan Blade and/or Motor, Renew

1985-87-one (.3)	.5
both (.4)	.6

(G) Engine Coolant Temperature Switch, Renew

V-6–1985-87	
Gas (.5)	.7
Diesel (.2)	.4
V-8–1985-87 (.2)	.4

(G) Coolant Fan Switch, Renew

1986-87-Buick (.6)	.8

(G) Temperature Gauge (Dash Unit), Renew

Buick models	
1985-87 (.3)	.5
Oldsmobile models	
1985-87 (.4)	.7

(G) Water Jacket Expansion Plugs, Renew
(Side of Block)

each	.5

Note: If necessary to R&R any component to gain access to plug, add appropriate time.

(G) Heater Hoses, Renew (w/A.C.)

Buick & Olds models	
1985-87-one (.3)	.4
all (.9)	1.2
Cadillac models	
1985-87	
water valve to core (.4)	.6
manifold to core (.4)	.6
cyl block to core (.4)	.6
cyl block to water valve (.4)	.6
all (.8)	1.2

(G) Heater Core, R&R or Renew

Buick & Olds models	
1985-87 (1.1)	2.0
Cadillac models	
1985-87 (.6)	1.1

ADD THESE OPERATIONS TO HEATER CORE R&R

(G) Boil & Repair	1.2
(G) Repair Core	.9
(G) Recore	1.2

(G) Heater Water Control Valve, Renew

1985-87	
Gas (.4)	.6
Diesel (.6)	.8

(G) Heater Blower Motor, Renew

Refer to A.C. group.

(G) Heater Blower Motor Switch, Renew

Refer to A.C. group.

PARTS 7 COOLING SYSTEM 7 PARTS

Radiator Assy.

Accurate replacement of the radiator can be done only by using the radiator code stamped on a metal tag located on the original radiator. Order by year, model, and radiator code no.

Radiator Hose (Upper)

	Part No.	Price
1985-181	◆25515308	9.75
1985-87-231	◆25527496	6.50
252	◆1626372	19.00
1985-Diesel	◆22517897	7.75

Radiator Hose (Lower)

	Part No.	Price
1985-Diesel	◆22525351	10.25
1985-181, 231	◆25515310	9.75
1986-87-231	◆25522896	.75
1985-87-252	◆1629249	17.75

Fan Belt

Order by year and model.

Water Pump Assy.

	Part No.	Price
1985-Diesel	◆22519584	83.00
181	◆25516944	70.00
1985-231	◆25525147	78.25
1986-87	◆25527537	63.00
1985-87-252	◆3634606	96.50

Thermostat

	Part No.	Price
1985-181	◆3051139	N.L.
231 (180 deg.)	◆3054228	6.50
(195 deg.)	◆3041390	5.00
1986-87-231	◆3037747	6.75
1985-87-252	◆3055672	6.75

Temperature Gauge (Engine Unit)

	Part No.	Price
(Electra, 98 Regency)		
1985-87	◆25036629	9.75
(Deville, Fleetwood Brougham)		
1985-87	◆25036335	21.00
Diesel eng.	◆25036581	7.75

Electric Cooling Motor

	Part No.	Price
(181 & 231)		
1985	◆22048577	86.75
1986-87-right	◆22048577	86.75
left	◆22049519	67.00
(252 eng.)		
1985-87	◆22048577	86.75

Engine Cooling Fan Relay

	Part No.	Price
1985-Diesel	◆22512709	12.00
181, 231	◆25522339	16.50
1986-87	◆12034544	8.25

Engine Cooling Fan Control Module

	Part No.	Price
1985-252	◆1632916	114.25
1986-87	◆16346489	N.L.

Engine Cooling Fan Switch

	Part No.	Price
181, 231		
1985-87	◆3040674	12.00
260 Diesel		
1985	◆3050223	14.00

Heater Core Assy.

	Part No.	Price
1985	◆3053452	56.75
1986-87-1st. des.	◆3058630	114.00
2nd. des.	◆3092683	65.50

1st. design has 64.0 mm center distance. 2nd design has 38.5 mm center distance.

Blower Motor

	Part No.	Price
1985	◆22020947	55.25
1986-87	◆22049769	52.00

Blower Motor Resistor

	Part No.	Price
1985-87	◆10027029	4.25

LABOR 8 EXHAUST SYSTEM 8 LABOR

(G) Muffler, Renew

(Factory Time)	Chilton Time
1985-87 (.5)	.7

(G) Intermediate Exhaust Pipe, Renew

1985-87 (.4)	.6

(G) Catalytic Converter, Renew

1985-87 (.8)	1.0

(G) Front Exhaust Pipe, Renew (To Converter)

1985-87 (.4)	.7

(G) Front Exhaust Pipe Seal, Renew

1985-87 (.4)	.7

(G) Exhaust Crossover Pipe, Renew

1985-87	
Gas (.4)	.7
Diesel (.3)	.6

(G) EFE Valve, Renew

V-6–1985 (.7)	1.0

LABOR 8 EXHAUST SYSTEM 8 LABOR

	(Factory Time)	Chilton Time
(G) EFE Check Valve, Renew		
V-6–1985	(.2)	.3
(G) Exhaust Manifold and/or Gasket, Renew		
Gas		
V-6-1985-87		
eng code E		
right side	(2.1)	3.0
left side	(1.1)	1.6
eng code 3		
right side	(1.7)	2.5
left side	(.5)	.9
V-8-1985-87		
right side	(1.2)	1.7
left side	(1.3)	1.8
Diesel		
1985		
right side	(.9)	1.4
left side	(.7)	1.1

COMBINATIONS

	(Factory Time)	Chilton Time
(G) Muffler, Exhaust and Tail Pipe, Renew		
All models		1.5
(G) Exhaust System, Renew (Complete)		
All models		1.1

PARTS 8 EXHAUST SYSTEM 8 PARTS

	Part No.	Price
Muffler (w/Tailpipe)		
1985–181	◆25518490	96.50
231	◆25518491	57.75
252	◆1633808	99.75
Diesel	◆22522801	55.25
1986-87-Sport exh.	◆25528696	N.L.
wo/Sport exh.	◆25528695	N.L.
Front Pipe		
1985-252	◆1627287	21.00
181, 231	◆25514979	19.75
Diesel	◆22523601	10.50
1986-87-231	◆25528757	N.L.
252 (Sport exh.)	◆1638555	N.L.
(wo/Sport exh.)	◆25528759	60.50
Intermediate Pipe		
1985–231	◆25518488	53.25
181	◆25518487	44.75
252	◆25516668	71.25
Diesel (frt.)	◆25514708	21.00
(rear)	◆25518487	44.75
1986-87	◆25528692	N.L.
Crossover Pipe		
181		
1985	◆25516236	31.00
231		
1985	◆25523749	22.50
1986-87	◆25523739	19.00
252		
1985	◆1621731	51.25
1986-87	◆1632333	58.75
260 Diesel		
1985-exc. below	◆22522768	15.50
ext. E.G.R.	◆22530022	46.25
Exhaust Manifold		
181		
1985-right	◆25510098	111.00
left	◆25516237	111.00
231		
1985-right	◆25527144	96.75
left-1st design	◆25516029	50.25
left-2nd design	◆25523099	78.25
1986-87-right	◆25527098	105.00
left	◆25527101	130.00
252		
1985-right	◆1626087	88.75
left	◆1626038	91.00
1986-87-right	◆1632838	148.00
left	◆1632837	148.00
260 Diesel		
1985-right	◆22524574	135.00
left	◆22524575	135.00
Catalytic Converter		
1985–181	◆25056343	299.25
231	◆25056699	347.25
252	◆25056700	337.25
1986-87-231	◆25056944	348.00
252 (Sport exh.)	◆25101933	358.00
(wo/Sport exh.)	◆25057868	318.00

LABOR 9 FRONT SUSPENSION 9 LABOR

Note: On all front suspension operations alignment charges must be added if performed. Time given does not include alignment.

	(Factory Time)	Chilton Time
(M) Wheel, Renew		
one		.5
(G) Wheels, Balance		
one		.3
each adtnl		.2
(M) Wheels, Rotate (All)		
All models		.5
(G) Check Alignment of Front End		
All models		.5
Note: Deduct if alignment is performed.		
(G) Toe-In, Adjust		
All models	(.5)	.7
(G) Align Front End		
All models	(1.4)	2.0
w/A.C. interference add		.5
(G) Front Stabilizer Shaft, Renew		
1985-87	(1.0)	1.4
(G) Front Stabilizer Shaft Bushings, Renew		
1985-87-one	(.3)	.4
both	(.4)	.6
(G) Front Wheel Bearing and Hub Assy., Renew		
1985-87-one side	(.7)	1.1
both sides	(1.3)	2.0
Renew knuckle inner seal, add-each	(.1)	.1
(G) Steering Knuckle Assy., Renew		
Add alignment charges.		
1985-87-one	(1.1)	1.5
both	(1.8)	2.6
(G) Lower Ball Joints, Renew		
Add alignment charges.		
1985-87-one	(.9)	1.3
both	(1.6)	2.4
(G) Front Coil Springs, Renew		
Add alignment charges.		
1985-87-one	(.9)	1.3
both	(1.5)	2.3
(G) Lower Control Arm Assy., Renew		
Add alignment charges.		
1985-87-one	(.6)	1.0
both	(1.0)	1.8
(G) Lower Control Arm Bushings, Renew		
Add alignment charges.		
1985-87-one side	(1.0)	1.4
both sides	(1.7)	2.6
(G) Front Strut Shock Absorbers, Renew		
Includes: Alignment charges.		
1985-87-one	(.9)	1.3
both	(1.5)	2.3
(G) Front Spring Seat and/or Insulator, Renew (Upper or Lower)		
Add alignment charges.		
1985-87-one side	(.9)	1.3
both sides	(1.6)	2.4
(G) Front Strut Bearing Mount Assy., Renew		
Add alignment charges.		
1985-87-one side	(.9)	1.3
both sides	(1.5)	2.3
(G) Engine Cradle, Renew		
Add alignment charges.		
1985-87	(4.0)	6.0

LABOR 9 FRONT SUSPENSION 9 LABOR

	(Factory Time)	Chilton Time
FRONT DRIVE AXLE		
(G) Front Drive Axle, R&R or Renew		
1985-87-one	(1.1)	1.4
both	(1.6)	2.2
Renew shaft add-each	(.3)	.4
Renew C/V Joint add each side	(.3)	.4
Renew D/O Joint add each side	(.3)	.4
Renew C/V Joint boots add each	(.2)	.2
(G) Axle Shaft Oil Seal, Renew		
1985-87-one	(.8)	1.1
both	(1.4)	2.0

PARTS 9 FRONT SUSPENSION 9 PARTS

	Part No.	Price
(1) Strut Mount		
1985-87-exc. below	◆17983307	53.50
Cadillac	◆1626705	30.50
(2) Strut Mount Bearing		
1985-87-exc. Cadillac	◆17983307	53.50
Cadillac		
1985	◆1626754	7.25
1986-87	◆1623928	N.L.
(3) Spring Seat		
1985-87-exc. Cadillac	◆14041893	5.75
Cadillac	◆1626516	5.75
(4) Spring Upper Insulator		
1985-87	◆14076647	4.50
(5) Strut Shield		
1985-87-exc. Buick	◆1626790	5.25
Buick	◆14082814	5.50
(6) Front Spring		
Order by year and model.		
(7) Spring Lower Insulator		
1985-87	◆14063507	3.50
(8) Front Strut		
1985-87-wo/H.D. susp.	◆22041011	88.50
H.D. susp.	◆22047914	88.50
(9) Steering Knuckle		
1985-right	◆14080264	144.00
left	◆25525863	173.00
1986-87-right	◆25525862	173.00
left	◆25525863	173.00
(10) Bearing Kit		
1985	◆7466922	173.00
1986-87	◆7470003	184.50
(11) Wheel Bearing Seal Kit		
1985-87	◆14084119	3.75
(12) Axle Kit		
1985-right	◆7847100	560.00
left	◆7842638	465.25
w/Electronic Brake Modulator		
1986-right	◆26003285	N.L.
left	◆26000326	544.00
wo/Electronic Brake Modulator		
1986-right	◆26003284	475.00
left	◆26000329	544.00
1987-w/Drum brks. R.H.	◆26003284	475.00
L.H.	◆26000329	544.00
(13) Lower Control Arm		
1985-87-right	◆14089118	219.00
left	◆14089117	219.00
(14) Link		
1985-87	◆14083559	4.25

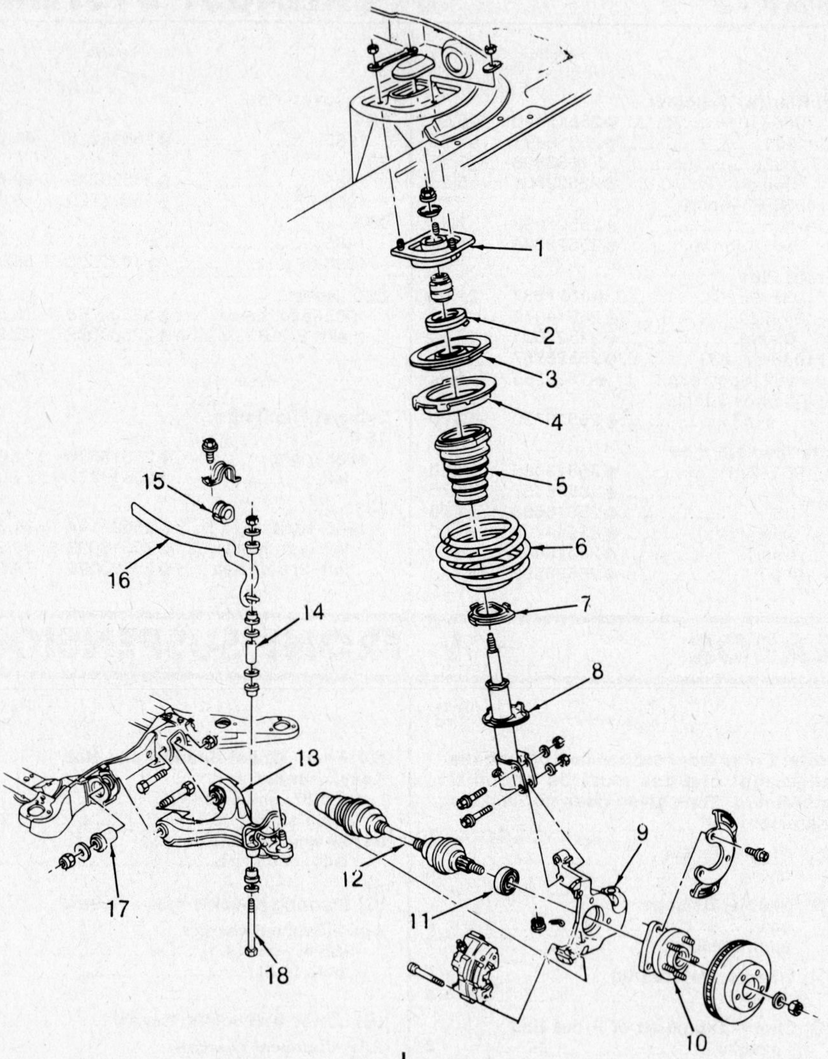

	Part No.	Price
(15) Stabilizer Shaft Insulator		
1985-exc. H.D. susp.	◆14086832	2.00
H.D. susp.	◆14085392	2.00
1986-87	◆14086877	2.00
(16) Stabilizer Shaft		
(Electra, 98 Regency) (exc. H.D. susp.)		
1985-87	◆14081408	55.25
(H.D. susp.)		
1985	◆14081410	55.25
1985-87-(32mm)	◆14081409	55.25
(Deville, Fleetwood Brougham)		
1985-87-w/ Touring susp.	◆14081408	55.25
exc. Touring susp.	◆14081407	55.25
(17) Lower Control Arm Bushing		
1985-87-exc. H.D. susp.	◆14076627	6.50
H.D. susp.	◆25526641	6.50
(18) Bolt		
1985-87	◆561891	1.00

PARTS 9 FRONT DRIVE AXLE 9 PARTS

	Part No.	Price
(1) Joint Kit		
1985-1st design	◆7845023	225.25
2nd design	◆7847112	N.L.
1986-87	◆26000318	385.00
(2) Seal Retainer		
1985-87 (32.0mm dia.)	◆7848880	3.25
Smallest size listed, other sizes available.		
(3) Seal Kit		
1985	◆7845398	N.L.
1986-87	◆26000317	21.50
(4) Seal Retaining Clamp		
See seal retainer and order according to size.		
(5) Axle Shaft		
1985-1st design		
right	◆7837084	148.25
left	◆7844994	70.25
1985-2nd design		
right	◆7846161	172.75
left	◆7846210	71.50
1986-87-right	◆26002694	N.L.
(6) Housing		
1985-87-right	◆7843920	136.00
left	◆7843922	136.00

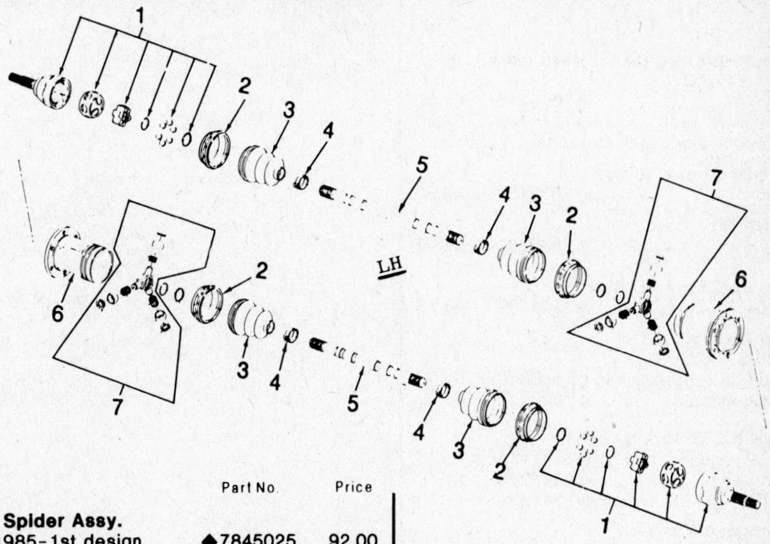

	Part No.	Price
(7) Spider Assy.		
1985-1st design	◆7845025	92.00
2nd design	◆7847113	120.00
1986-87	◆26001939	N.L.

LABOR 11 STEERING GEAR 11 LABOR

(Factory Time)	Chilton Time
(G) Inner Tie Rod, Renew	
Includes: R&R rack and pinion assy, and reset toe-in.	
1985-87-one side (1.9)	2.4
both sides (2.1)	2.7
(G) Tie Rod End, Renew	
Includes: Reset toe-in.	
1985-87-one (.7)	.9
both (.9)	1.2
Renew seal add-each	.1
(G) Steering Wheel, Renew	
1985-87 (.3)	.4
(G) Horn Contact or Cancelling Cam, Renew	
1985-87 (.5)	.6
w/Tilt Tel add (.1)	.1
(G) Multifunction Lever, Renew	
All models (.2)	.4
w/Cruise control add (.5)	.5
(G) Steering Column Lock Actuator Parts, Renew	
1985-87	
std colm (1.0)	1.5
tilt colm (.9)	1.4
tilt tel (.9)	1.4
Renew actuator rod add (.8)	.8
(G) Steering Column Shift Bowl, Renew	
1985-87	
std colm (1.4)	2.1
tilt colm (1.9)	2.7
tilt tel (2.3)	3.1
(G) Upper Mast Jacket Bearing, Renew	
1985-87	
std colm (1.1)	1.6
tilt colm (.6)	1.0
tilt tel (.6)	1.0
(G) Steering Column, R&R	
1985-87 (1.1)	1.5
Recond column add,	
std (.8)	.8
tilt (1.8)	1.8
tilt tel (1.9)	1.9
(G) Steering Intermediate Shaft, Renew	
1985-87 (.3)	.6

POWER STEERING

(Factory Time)	Chilton Time
(G) Trouble Shoot Power Steering	
Includes: Test pump and system pressure. Check pounds pull on steering wheel and check for leaks.	
All models	.5
(M) Check and Fill Reservoir	
All models	.2
(G) Pump Drive Belt, Renew	
V-6-1985	
Gas (1.1)	1.5
Diesel (.2)	.4
1986-87 (.4)	.5
V-8-1985-87 (.2)	.4
(G) Power Steering Gear Assy., R&R or Renew	
Includes: Reset toe-in.	
1985-87 (1.7)	3.0
(G) Power Steering Short Rack Assy., Renew	
Includes: Transfer parts as required. Reset toe-in.	
All models (1.9)	3.9
(P) Power Steering Gear Assy., R&R and Recondition	
Includes: Reset toe-in.	
1985-87 (3.1)	5.0
Bench leak test add	.5
(G) Power Steering Gear Boot Seals, Renew	
1985-87-one side (1.1)	1.5
both sides (1.4)	1.9
(G) Power Steering Reservoir, Renew	
1985-87 (.3)	.5
(G) Power Steering Pump, Renew	
V-6-1985	
Gas (2.0)	2.8
Diesel (1.1)	1.5
1986-87 (.5)	.8
V-8-1985-87 (.5)	.8
(G) Power Steering Pump, R&R and Recondition	
V-6-1985	
Gas (2.5)	3.6
Diesel (1.6)	2.3
1986-87 (1.0)	1.6
V-8-1985-87 (1.0)	1.6
(G) Pump Shaft Oil Seal, Renew	
V-6-1985	
Gas (2.0)	3.0
Diesel (1.1)	1.7
1986-87 (.6)	1.0
V-8-1985-87 (1.1)	1.7
(G) Pump Flow Control Valve, Renew	
V-6-1985	
Gas (2.0)	2.9
Diesel (.5)	.9
1986-87 (.6)	1.0
V-8-1985-87 (.6)	.9
(M) Power Steering Hoses, Renew	
Pressure	
Buick & Olds models	
eng code E (1.3)	1.9
eng code T (.5)	.7
all other engs (.4)	.6
Cadillac models (1.3)	1.7
Return	
All models (.4)	.6

PARTS 11 POWER STEERING GEAR 11 PARTS

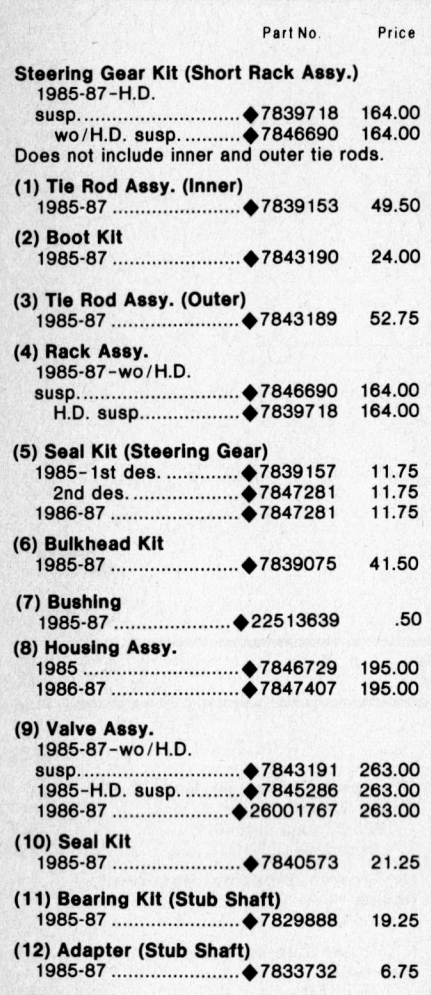

	Part No.	Price
Steering Gear Kit (Short Rack Assy.)		
1985-87-H.D.		
susp.	◆7839718	164.00
wo/H.D. susp.	◆7846690	164.00
Does not include inner and outer tie rods.		
(1) Tie Rod Assy. (Inner)		
1985-87	◆7839153	49.50
(2) Boot Kit		
1985-87	◆7843190	24.00
(3) Tie Rod Assy. (Outer)		
1985-87	◆7843189	52.75
(4) Rack Assy.		
1985-87-wo/H.D.		
susp.	◆7846690	164.00
H.D. susp.	◆7839718	164.00
(5) Seal Kit (Steering Gear)		
1985-1st des.	◆7839157	11.75
2nd des.	◆7847281	11.75
1986-87	◆7847281	11.75
(6) Bulkhead Kit		
1985-87	◆7839075	41.50
(7) Bushing		
1985-87	◆22513639	.50
(8) Housing Assy.		
1985	◆7846729	195.00
1986-87	◆7847407	195.00
(9) Valve Assy.		
1985-87-wo/H.D.		
susp.	◆7843191	263.00
1985-H.D. susp.	◆7845286	263.00
1986-87	◆26001767	263.00
(10) Seal Kit		
1985-87	◆7840573	21.25
(11) Bearing Kit (Stub Shaft)		
1985-87	◆7829888	19.25
(12) Adapter (Stub Shaft)		
1985-87	◆7833732	6.75

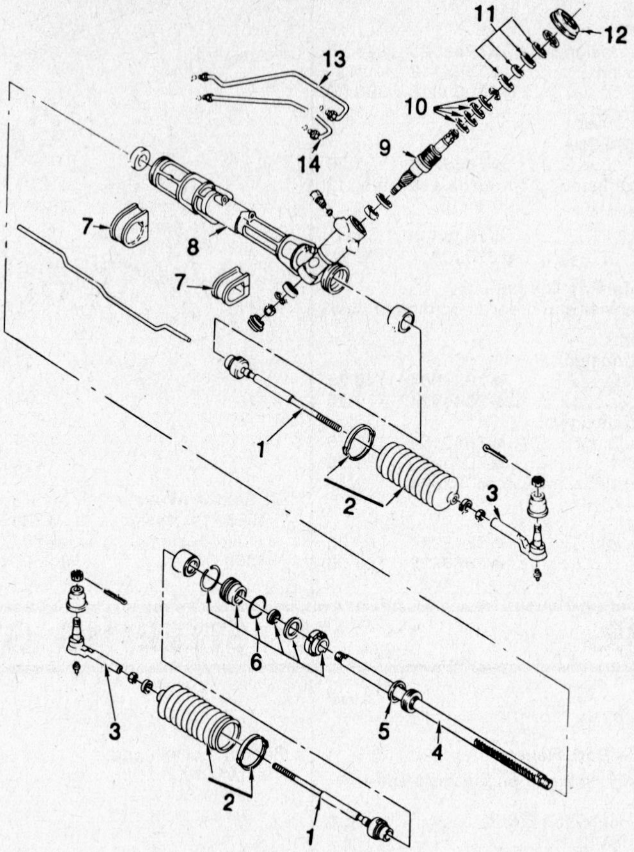

	Part No.	Price
(13) Cylinder Line Assy. (Right)		
1985-87	◆7843187	15.75
(14) Cylinder Line Assy. (Left)		
1985-87	◆7843188	15.75

PARTS 11 POWER STEERING PUMP 11 PARTS

	Part No.	Price
Power Steering Pump		
1985	◆7838469	199.00
1986-87	◆7848115	199.00
(1) Drive Shaft		
1985	◆7837321	39.50
1986-87	◆26001375	42.00
(2) Seal Kit		
1985	◆7848522	N.L.
1986-87	◆7840566	11.00
(3) Pump Housing		
1985	◆7830697	62.75
1986-87	◆7849050	110.00
(4) Thrust Plate		
1985	◆7836369	13.75
1986-87	◆7840139	14.25
(5) Control Valve		
1985	◆7809229	10.50
1986-87	◆7841851	15.75
(6) Spring (Flow Control)		
1985-87	◆5688037	1.50
(7) Rotor & Vane Kit		
1985	◆7838790	92.00
1986-87	◆7840569	13.50

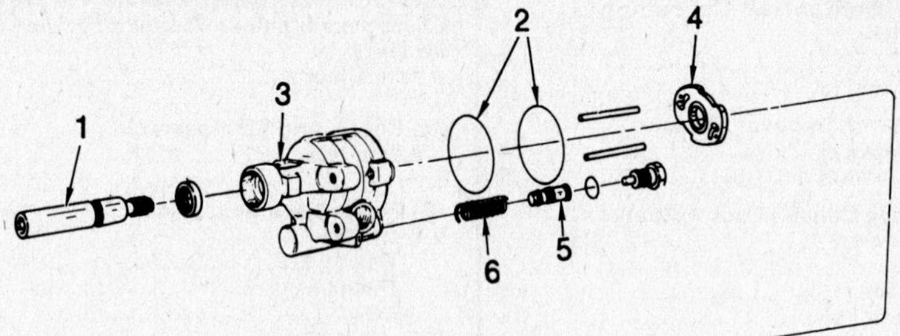

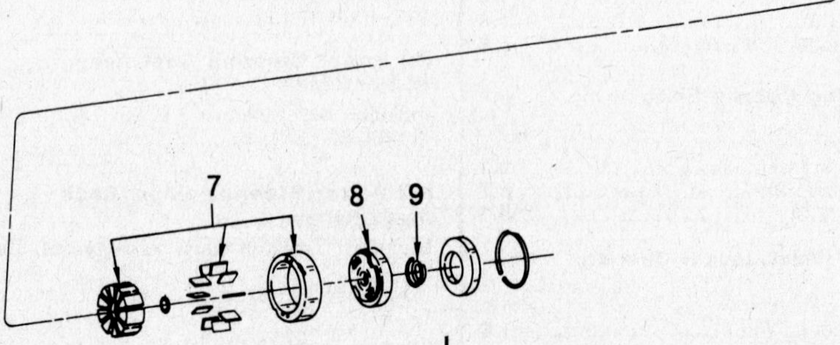

	Part No.	Price
(8) Pressure Plate		
1985	◆7839669	14.25
1986-87	◆7840080	14.25
(9) Pressure Plate Spring		
1985	◆7839667	1.00
1986-87	◆7839989	3.00

PARTS 11 POWER STEERING PUMP 11 PARTS

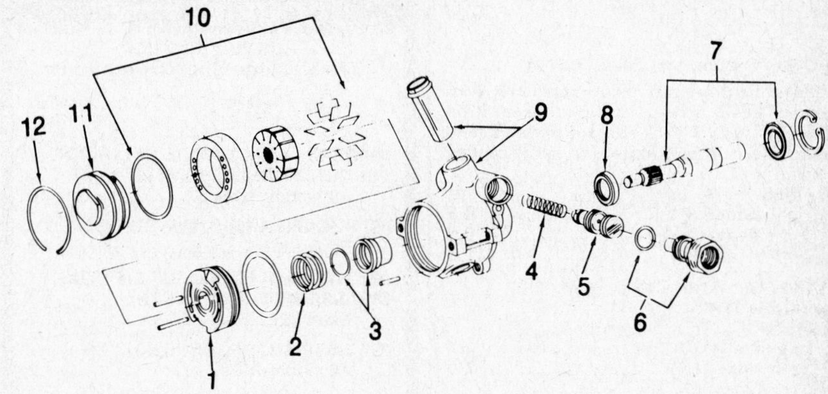

	Part No.	Price
V-6 DIESEL & V-8-252		
Power Steering Pump		
1985-87-252	◆7841463	199.00
1985-Diesel	◆7841747	199.00
(1) Pressure Plate		
1985-87	◆7840080	14.25
(2) Pressure Plate Spring		
1985-87	◆7839989	3.00
(3) Sleeve Kit		
1985-87	◆7842086	9.75
(4) Flow Control Spring		
1985-87	◆5688037	1.50
(5) Control Valve		
1985-87-252	◆7841855	10.75
1985-Diesel	◆7841853	12.00
(6) Fitting		
1985-87	◆7841467	10.25
(7) Drive Shaft		
1985-87	◆7840633	58.00
(8) Drive Shaft Seal		
1985-87	◆7839589	4.50

	Part No.	Price
(9) Housing		
1985-87	◆7841770	68.00
(10) Rotor Kit		
1985-87	◆7841845	92.00
Vane Kit		
1985-87	◆7840569	13.50

	Part No.	Price
(11) Thrust Plate		
1985-87	◆7840139	14.25
(12) Retaining Ring		
1985-87	◆7839992	2.00
Pump Seal Kit		
1985-87	◆7840566	11.00

LABOR 12 CYLINDER HEAD & VALVE SYSTEM 12 LABOR

(Factory Time)	Chilton Time
GASOLINE ENGINES	
(G) Compression Test	
V-6	1.2
V-8	.8
w/Cruise control add	.3
(G) Cylinder Head Gasket, Renew	
Includes: Clean carbon and make all necessary adjustments.	
V-6–1985-87	
eng code E	
right side (5.1)	7.0
left side (3.3)	4.5
both sides (5.8)	8.0
eng code 3	
right side (2.1)	3.0
left side (2.6)	3.8
both sides (3.6)	5.2
V-8–1985-87	
one side (6.8)	9.4
both sides (8.1)	11.2
(G) Cylinder Head, Renew	
Includes: Transfer all components, reface valves, clean carbon. Make all necessary adjustments.	
V-6–1985-87	
eng code E	
right side (5.7)	7.8
left side (3.8)	5.2
both sides (7.3)	10.0
eng code 3	
right side (2.6)	3.7
left side (3.1)	4.5
both sides (4.4)	6.3
V-8–1985-87	
one side (7.2)	10.0
both sides (8.9)	12.3
(P) Clean Carbon and Grind Valves	
Includes: R&R cylinder heads, grind valves and seats. Minor tune up.	
V-6–1985-87	
eng code E	
right side (5.8)	8.1
left side (4.0)	5.5
both sides (7.7)	10.6
eng code 3	
right side (2.8)	4.0
left side (3.3)	4.8
both sides (4.6)	6.6
V-8–1985-87	
one side (7.6)	10.5
both sides (9.7)	13.5
(G) Rocker Arm Cover or Gasket, Renew	
V-6–1985-87	
eng code E	
one side (.8)	1.2
both sides (1.3)	2.1
eng code 3	
right side (.5)	.9
left side (.3)	.6
both sides (.6)	1.0
V-8–1985-87	
one side (.7)	1.0
both sides (1.2)	1.8
(G) Valve Rocker Arms and/or Push Rods, Renew	
V-6–1985-87	
eng code E	
one side (1.0)	1.4
both sides (1.9)	2.6
eng code 3	
right side (.8)	1.2
left side (.6)	.9
both sides (.9)	1.6
V-8–1985-87	
one side (.9)	1.2
both sides (1.7)	2.3
Recond rocker arm assy	
add-each side (.2)	.2
(G) Valve Springs and/or Valve Stem Oil Seals, Renew (Head on Car)	
V-6–1985-87	
eng code E	
one cyl (1.1)	1.5
one cyl-each side (2.1)	2.9
eng code 3	
one cyl-rt side (1.0)	1.5
one cyl-lt side (.8)	1.2
one cyl-each side (1.4)	2.0
V-8–1985-87	
one cyl (1.2)	1.7
one cyl-each side (2.1)	3.1
each adtnl cyl.'	
all engs (.3)	.3
(G) Valve Tappets, Renew (Lifters)	
V-6–1985-87	
eng code E	
one bank (2.8)	3.8
both banks (3.1)	4.2
eng code 3	
right bank (2.3)	3.3
left bank (2.1)	3.0
both banks (2.4)	3.4
V-8–1985-87	
one or all (4.7)	7.0
DIESEL ENGINE	
(G) Compression Test	
V-6	1.0
(G) Cylinder Head Gasket, Renew	
Includes: R&R injector pump and lines. R&R intake manifold and disconnect exhaust manifolds. Clean gasket surfaces, bleed lifters and adjust timing. Drain and refill cooling system.	
V-6–1985	
right side (5.9)	8.2
left side (5.2)	7.3
both sides (7.2)	10.0
Renew pre-chambers add	.2
(G) Cylinder Head, Renew	
Includes: R&R injector pump and lines. R&R intake manifold and disconnect exhaust manifolds. Clean gasket surfaces. Transfer parts, reface valves. Bleed lifters and adjust timing. Drain and refill cooling system.	
V-6–1985	
right side (6.2)	8.7
left side (5.5)	7.8
both sides (7.9)	11.0

LABOR 12 CYLINDER HEAD & VALVE SYSTEM 12 LABOR

	(Factory Time)	Chilton Time
(P) Clean Carbon and Grind Valves		
Includes: R&R injector pump and lines. R&R cylinder heads, clean carbon. Recondition valves and seats. Check and adjust valve stem length. Bleed lifters, drain and refill cooling system.		
V-6-1985		
right side	(6.8)	9.5
left side	(6.1)	8.5
both sides	(9.0)	12.6
(G) Rocker Arm Cover and/or Gasket, Renew		
V-6-1985		
one side	(1.2)	1.7
both sides	(1.9)	2.5
(G) Rocker Arm, Pivot and/or Push Rod, Renew		
V-6-1985		
one cyl	(1.4)	1.9
one cyl-each side	(2.2)	2.7
each adtnl cyl		.1

COMBINATIONS
Add to Valve Job
See Machine Shop Operations

	(Factory Time)	Chilton Time
(G) DRAIN, EVACUATE & RECHARGE AIR CONDITIONING SYSTEM		
All models	(.5)	1.0
(G) ROCKER ARM STUD, RENEW		
Each	(.2)	.2
(G) HYDRAULIC VALVE LIFTERS, DISASSEMBLE AND CLEAN		
Each	(.2)	.2
(G) DISTRIBUTOR, RECONDITION		
All models	(.3)	.8
(G) CARBURETOR, RECONDITION		
2 bbl		1.2
(P) VALVE GUIDES, REAM OVERSIZE		
Each	(.2)	.2

	(Factory Time)	Chilton Time
(G) Valve Springs and/or Valve Stem Oil Seals, Renew (Head on Car)		
V-6-1985		
one cyl-rt side	(1.7)	2.2
one cyl-lt side	(1.4)	1.9
one cyl-each side	(2.5)	3.5
each adtnl cyl	(.3)	.3
(G) Valve Tappets, Renew (Lifters)		
Includes: R&R injector pump and lines, intake manifold and rocker arms. Drain and refill cooling system.		
V-6-1985		
one cyl-rt side	(3.9)	5.4
one cyl-lt side	(3.6)	5.0
one cyl-each side	(4.4)	6.0
each adtnl cyl	(.2)	.2

PARTS 12 CYLINDER HEAD & VALVE SYSTEM 12 PARTS

	Part No.	Price
Valve Grind Gasket Kit		
1985-181	◆25511669	39.00
231	◆25525121	N.L.
Diesel	◆22528684	79.50
(1) Cylinder Head		
181 & 231		
1985	◆25518679	217.00
1986-87-231	◆25524543	217.00
252		
1985-87-exc. below	◆1628557	296.00
1985-w/stl. rocker cvr.	◆1626192	314.00
260 Diesel		
1985-87-exc. below	◆22522562	357.00
ext. E.G.R.	◆22523899	357.00
(2) Cylinder Head Gasket		
1985-181 & 231	◆25524599	8.50
252	◆1619040	24.00
Diesel (exc. below)	◆22527054	30.50
w/ext. E.G.R.	◆22527030	30.50
(3) Push Rod		
1985-Diesel	◆22511044	3.25
181 & 231	◆25510025	4.25
1986-87-252	◆1618805	2.50
231	◆25524317	3.50
(4) Valve Lifter		
1985-Diesel	◆5234625	N.L.
181 & 231	◆5234330	N.L.
1985-87-252	◆5234360	8.50
231	◆5234330	N.L.
(5) Intake Valve (Std.)		
181 & 231		
1985-87	◆25512098	11.25
252		
1985-87	◆1618837	12.00
260 Diesel		
1985-exc. below	◆22513937	18.25
ext. E.G.R.	◆22524447	18.25

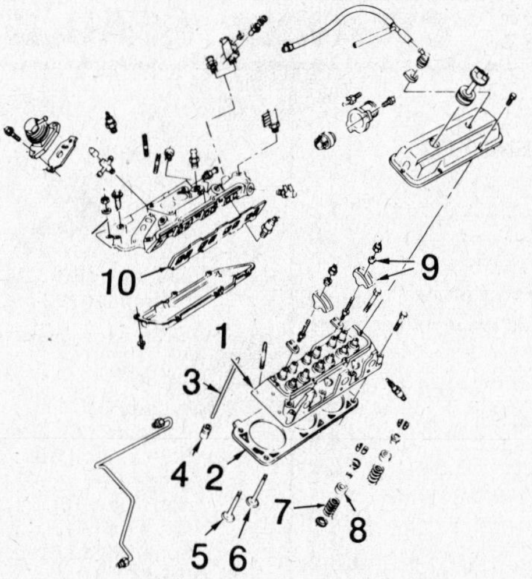

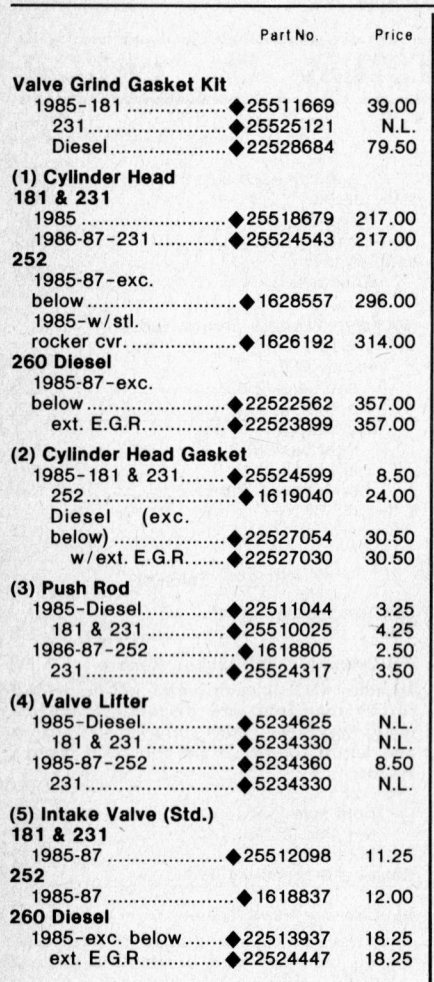

	Part No.	Price
(6) Exhaust Valve (Std.)		
181 & 231		
1985	◆1261380	13.50
1986-87-231	◆25521841	13.75
252		
1985-87	◆1621321	15.25
260 Diesel		
1985-exc. below	◆558873	13.00
ext. E.G.R.	◆22524447	18.25
(7) Valve Spring		
1985-181	◆25512551	3.00
231	◆1249267	2.75
Diesel eng.	◆22510372	4.00
1985-87-252	◆1622834	4.00
1986-87	◆25523695	3.00
(8) Rotator		
1985-Diesel	◆406996	3.50

	Part No.	Price
(9) Rocker Arm		
181 & 231		
1985-right	◆1241850	4.50
left	◆1241851	4.50
1986-87-231	◆25523770	4.50
252		
1985-87	◆1618802	4.75
260 Diesel		
1985	◆22505583	N.L.
(10) Gasket Kit (Intake Manifold)		
1985-181	◆25505397	15.50
1985-87-231	◆1264924	16.00
252	◆3634619	N.L.
1985-Diesel	◆22514872	16.50

LABOR 13 ENGINE ASSEMBLY & MOUNTS 13 LABOR

(Factory Time) Chilton Time

GASOLINE ENGINES

(G) Engine Assy., Remove and Install

Does not include transfer of any parts or equipment.

V-6–1985-87	5.5
w/A.C. add	1.5
V-8–1985-87	6.4

(G) Engine Assy., Renew (Universal) (w/Heads and Oil Pan)

Includes: R&R engine assy. Transfer all component parts not supplied with replacement engine. Minor tune up.

V-6–1985-87	
eng code E (7.0)	12.0
eng code 3 (7.9)	13.0
w/A.C. add	1.5

(P) Cylinder Block, Renew (Partial) (w/All Internal Parts Less Heads and Oil Pan)

Includes: R&R engine assy. Transfer all component parts not supplied with replacement engine. Clean carbon, grind valves. Minor tune up.

V-6–1985-87	
eng code E (9.8)	14.5
eng code 3 (11.5)	15.4
w/A.C. add	1.5
V-8–1985-87 (12.5)	18.5

(P) Cylinder Block, Renew (w/Pistons, Rings and Bearings)

Includes: R&R engine assy. Transfer all component parts not supplied with replacement engine. Clean carbon, grind valves. Minor tune up.

V-6–1985-87	
eng code E (14.5)	21.4
eng code 3 (14.4)	21.2
w/A.C. add	1.5

(P) Engine Assembly, R&R and Recondition

Includes: Rebore block, install new pistons, rings, rod and main bearings. Clean carbon, grind valves. Tune engine.

V-6–1985-87	
eng code E (21.8)	29.4
eng code 3 (21.1)	28.5
w/A.C. add	1.5
V-8–1985-87 (24.1)	32.5

(G) Engine Mount, Renew

V-6–1985-87	
right (.4)	.6
V-8–1985-87	
left (.4)	.7

DIESEL ENGINE

(G) Engine Assembly, Remove and Install

Does not include transfer of any parts or equipment.

V-6–1985	4.5

(G) Engine Assembly, Renew (Universal)

Includes: R&R engine assembly, transfer all component parts not supplied with replacement engine. Make all necessary adjustments.

V-6–1985 (7.8)	18.0

(P) Cylinder Block, Renew (w/All Internal Parts Less Heads and Oil Pan)

Includes: R&R engine assembly, transfer all component parts not supplied with replacement engine. Clean carbon, grind valves. Make all necessary adjustments.

V-6–1985 (10.8)	21.0

(P) Cylinder Block, Renew (w/Pistons, Rings and Bearings)

Includes: R&R engine assembly, transfer all component parts not supplied with replacement engine. Clean carbon, grind valves. Make all necessary adjustments.

V-6–1985 (11.6)	24.0

(P) Engine Assy., R&R and Recondition

Includes: Rebore block, install new pistons, rings, rod and main bearings. Clean carbon, grind valves. Make all necessary adjustments.

V-6–1985 (22.8)	31.4

(P) Engine Assembly, Recondition (In Car)

Includes: Expand or renew pistons, install new rings, pins, rod and main bearings. Clean carbon, grind valves. Make all necessary adjustments.

V-6–1985 (19.4)	26.1

(G) Engine Mount, Renew

Front	
1985 (.5)	.7

PARTS 13 ENGINE ASSEMBLY & MOUNTS 13 PARTS

Engine Overhaul Gasket Kit

	Part No	Price
1985-181	◆25525116	50.00
231	◆25527546	58.25
Diesel (exc. below)	◆22528685	97.50
(ext. E.G.R.)	◆22527537	99.75
1986-87	◆25530152	96.00

Cylinder Block Assy.

Includes block and pistons.

	Part No	Price
1985-181		
14 bolt pan	◆25516701	949.00
20 bolt pan	◆25524298	949.00
1985-231		
14 bolt pan	◆25519454	950.00
20 bolt pan	◆25524297	950.00
1986-87-231	◆25527479	950.00
1985-diesel eng.	◆22523727	1365.00

Engine Assy. (Partial)

Includes block, pistons, connecting rods, crankshaft, crankshaft bearings and rear seal.

	Part No	Price
1985-181		
14 bolt pan	◆25516702	1195.25
20 bolt pan	◆25524296	1195.00
1985-231		
14 bolt pan	◆25519453	1263.25
20 bolt pan	◆25524295	1263.00
1986-87	◆25527478	1263.00
1985-252	◆3634655	N.L.
1986-87	◆3634655	N.L.
1985-Diesel	◆22525606	1593.50

Engine Mount

	Part No	Price
1985	◆14069227	27.50
1986-exc. below	◆17983797	42.50
231	◆14038194	27.50
1987	◆17983797	42.50
1985-252	◆14038192	27.50
1986-87	◆25525645	36.50

Transmission Mount

	Part No	Price
1985-frt. L.H.	◆14081414	19.75
1986-87	◆17985050	19.50
1985-rear L.H.	◆14081415	21.75
1986-87	◆17985060	21.00
1985-181 & 231		
rear R.H.	◆14074042	14.25
1986-87	◆17985060	21.00
1985-Diesel		
rear R.H.	◆14085397	27.50
1985-252		
rear L.H.	◆14082893	23.75
rear R.H.	◆14082894	23.75
1986-87		
front L.H.	◆17985050	19.50
rear L.H.	◆17985370	30.25
R.H.	◆25525644	36.75

LABOR 14 PISTONS, RINGS & BEARINGS 14 LABOR

(Factory Time) Chilton Time

GASOLINE ENGINES

(P) Rings, Renew (All)
(See Engine Combinations)

Includes: Remove cylinder top ridge, deglaze cylinder walls. Clean piston and ring grooves. Minor tune up.

V-6–1985-87	
eng code E (9.7)	14.0
eng code 3 (7.9)	13.0
V-8–1985-87 (12.9)	*18.7
*Renew cyl liner, add each	.6

(P) Pistons or Connecting Rods, Renew (All)

Includes: Remove cylinder top ridge, deglaze cylinder walls. Minor tune up.

V-6–1985-87	
eng code E (10.4)	15.8
eng code 3 (8.6)	14.8
V-8–1985-87 (13.9)	*21.1
*Renew cyl liner, add each	.6

(P) Connecting Rod Bearings, Renew

Includes: Plastigauge bearings.

V-6–1985-87 (2.2)	3.0
V-8–1985-87 (3.2)	4.6

DIESEL ENGINE

(P) Rings, Renew
(See Engine Combinations)

Includes: Remove cylinder top ridge, deglaze cylinder walls. Clean piston and ring grooves. Make all necessary adjustments.

V-6–1985 (12.4)	14.9

COMBINATIONS

Engine Combinations

See Machine Shop Operations

(G) DRAIN, EVACUATE & RECHARGE AIR CONDITIONING SYSTEM

All models (.5)	1.0

(G) ROCKER ARM STUD, RENEW

Each (.2)	.2

(G) HYDRAULIC VALVE LIFTERS, DISASSEMBLE AND CLEAN

Each (.2)	.2

(G) DISTRIBUTOR, RECONDITION

All models (.3)	.8

(G) CARBURETOR, RECONDITION

2 bbl	1.2

(G) CYLINDER HEAD, R&R (ENGINE REMOVED)

V-6	
one (1.7)	2.2
both (2.8)	3.6
V-8	
one (1.8)	2.3
both (2.6)	3.3

(G) CONNECTING ROD, RENEW (ENGINE DISASSEMBLED)

V-6-each (.5)	.6
V-8-each (.4)	.5

(P) VALVE GUIDES, REAM OVERSIZE

Each (.2)	.2

(G) DEGLAZE CYLINDER WALLS

Each (.1)	.1

(G) CYLINDER LINER, RENEW

Each	.6

(G) REMOVE CYLINDER TOP RIDGE

Each (.1)	.1

(G) PLASTIGAUGE BEARINGS

Each	.1

(M) OIL FILTER ELEMENT, RENEW

V-6	.2
V-8	.3

(Factory Time) Chilton Time

(P) Pistons or Connecting Rods, Renew

Includes: Remove cylinder top ridge, deglaze cylinder walls. Make all necessary adjustments.

V-6–1985 (13.1)	16.7

(Factory Time) Chilton Time

(P) Connecting Rod Bearings, Renew

Includes: Plastigauge bearings.

V-6–1985 (4.2)	5.8

PARTS 14 PISTONS, RINGS & BEARINGS 14 PARTS

	Part No.	Price
(1) Piston Ring Set (Std.)		
1985-181 & 231	◆25519462	16.50
1985-87-252	◆1623817	20.25
1985-Diesel	◆22523733	N.L.
(2) Piston Assy.		
181		
1985	◆25516698	49.00
231		
1985	◆25518053	48.25
1986-87	◆25527178	48.25
252		
1985-87	◆1623538	107.00
260 Diesel		
1985-right	◆22523360	63.75
left	◆22523359	63.75

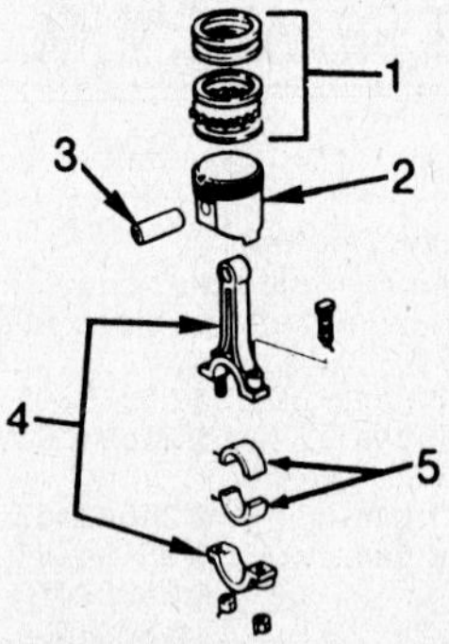

	Part No.	Price
(3) Piston Pin		
Serviced in piston assy. only.		
(4) Connecting Rod		
1985-181	◆25509405	39.00
1985-87-231	◆25506520	39.00
1985-87-252	◆1619145	59.00
1985-Diesel	◆22515315	50.50
(5) Connecting Rod Bearings (Std.)		
1985-Diesel	◆18009089	11.75
181 & 231	◆18005399	11.00
1985-87-252	◆18009085	11.00

LABOR 15 CRANKSHAFT & DAMPER 15 LABOR

(Factory Time) Chilton Time

GASOLINE ENGINES

(P) Crankshaft and Main Bearings, Renew

Includes: R&R engine, check all bearing clearances.

V-6–1985-87	
eng code E (7.7)	11.5
eng code 3 (6.3)	10.8
w/A.C. add (.3)	.3
w/AIR add (.2)	.2
V-8–1985-87 (9.1)	13.0

(Factory Time) Chilton Time

(P) Main Bearings, Renew

Includes: Check all bearing clearances.

V-6–1985-87 (1.8)	2.5
V-8–1985-87 (2.5)	3.5

(P) Main and Rod Bearings, Renew

Includes: Check all bearing clearances.

V-6–1985-87 (3.0)	4.3
V-8–1985-87 (4.1)	5.9

(Factory Time) Chilton Time

(G) Rear Main Bearing Seal, R&R and Repack or Renew

V-6–1985-87 (1.2)	2.2
V-8–1985-87 (4.0)	5.8

(G) Crankshaft Pulley or Balancer, Renew

V-6–1985-87	
balancer (1.0)	1.5
V-8–1985-87	
balancer (.8)	1.4

LABOR 15 CRANKSHAFT & DAMPER 15 LABOR

(Factory Time) Chilton Time

DIESEL ENGINE

(P) Crankshaft and Main Bearings, Renew

Includes: R&R engine, check all bearing clearances.

V-6–1985 (8.4)........ 12.5

(P) Main Bearings, Renew

Includes: Check all bearing clearances.

V-6–1985 (3.4)........ 5.2

(P) Main and Rod Bearings, Renew

Includes: Check all bearing clearances.

V-6–1985 (5.1)........ 7.6

(G) Rear Main Bearing Oil Seal, R&R and Repack

V-6–1985 (2.3)........ 3.3

(G) Rear Main Bearing Oil Seals, Renew

Includes: R&R engine assy.

V-6–1985 (7.9)........ 12.0

(G) Crankshaft Pulley or Balancer, Renew

V-6–1985

pulley (.5)........ 1.1

balancer (.6)........ 1.2

(G) Crankshaft Front Oil Seal, Renew

V-6–1985 (.7)........ 1.4

PARTS 15 CRANKSHAFT & DAMPER 15 PARTS

	Part No.	Price
(1) Crankshaft Assy.		
1985-181	◆25519733	385.00
1985-87-231	◆25516025	405.00
252	◆1625959	441.00
1985-Diesel	◆22515610	430.00
(2) Crankshaft Gear		
1985-Diesel	◆22516034	31.50
181 & 231	◆25519954	14.50
1985-87-252	◆1618159	13.25
231	◆25528628	16.00
(3) Crankshaft Pulley		
1985-181	◆25526727	45.50
231	◆25517726	1.25
1986-87-231	◆25527009	31.00
1985-87-252	◆3517546	111.25
1985-Diesel	◆22518370	78.50
(4) Hub		
1985-Diesel	◆22514399	31.75
(5) Rear Main Seal		
1985-87-Diesel	◆9772831	1.50
181 & 231	◆1193151	1.50
252	◆1627806	10.75

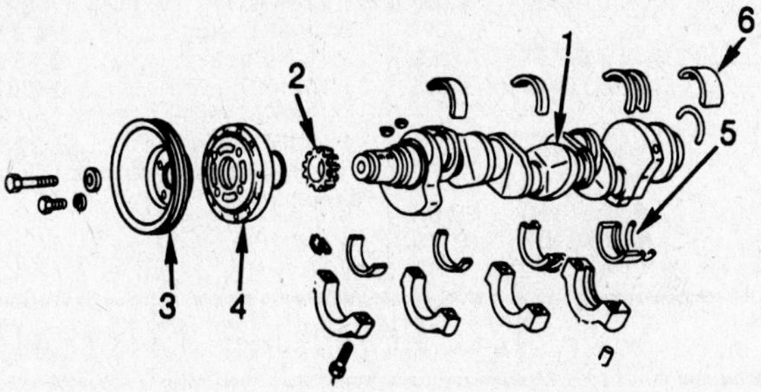

	Part No.	Price
(6) Main Bearing (Std.)		
181 & 231		
1985-87-No. 1	◆18009457	12.00
No. 2	◆18004602	20.00
No. 3	◆18002950	12.50
rear	◆5468578	13.00
252		
1985-87-No. 1	◆18012316	17.75
Nos. 2, 4	◆18013442	17.25
No. 3	◆18009088	23.75
No. 5	◆18009087	16.50
260 Diesel		
1985-No. 1	◆5466312	16.00
No. 2	◆5458657	15.00
No. 3	◆5463797	26.25
rear	◆18009091	25.75

LABOR 16 CAMSHAFT & TIMING GEARS 16 LABOR

(Factory Time) Chilton Time

GASOLINE ENGINES

(G) Timing Cover Oil Seal, Renew

V-8–1985-87 (.9)........ 1.4

(G) Timing Cover and/or Gasket, Renew

V-6–1985-87 (3.8)........ 5.3

V-8–1985-87 (2.8)........ 3.9

Renew cover add (.4)........ .4

(G) Timing Chain, Renew

V-6–1985-87

eng code E (3.9)........ 5.8

eng code 3 (4.1)........ 5.6

V-8–1985-87 (2.9)........ 4.4

(G) Camshaft, Renew

V-6–1985-87

eng code E (6.1)........ 8.4

eng code 3 (6.2)........ 8.6

w/A.C. add (.5)........ .5

w/AIR add (.4)........ .4

V-8–1985-87 (8.5)........ *11.8

*Includes R&R engine.

(G) Camshaft Rear Bearing Plug, Renew

V-6–1985-87 (3.7)........ 5.0

V-8–1985-87 (3.6)........ 5.0

DIESEL ENGINE

(G) Timing Cover and/or Gasket, Renew

Includes: R&R fan blade, crankshaft pulley and balancer. Drain and refill oil and coolant.

V-6–1985 (2.2)........ 3.4

(G) Timing Chain or Gears, Renew

Includes: R&R fan blade, crankshaft pulley and balancer. Drain and refill oil and coolant.

V-6–1985 (4.6)........ 6.4

(G) Camshaft, Renew

Includes: R&R injector pump, intake manifold and lifters. Disconnect exhaust system. Drain and refill oil and coolant. Make all necessary adjustments.

V-6–1985 (7.9)........ 11.4

Renew cam brgs add (2.8)........ 3.8

(G) Camshaft Rear Bearing Plug, Renew

Includes: R&R trans for accessibility.

V-6–1985 (3.7)........ 5.4

PARTS 16 CAMSHAFT & TIMING GEARS 16 PARTS

	Part No.	Price
(1) Front Cover Oil Seal		
1985-Diesel	◆552711	4.25
181 & 231	◆1305044	1.00
1986-87-231	◆25523327	3.25
1985-87-252	◆1627827	4.50
(2) Timing Case Cover		
1985-Diesel	◆22525285	30.75
1985-181 & 231		
14 bolt pan	◆25511672	59.00
20 bolt pan	◆25522653	59.00
1986-87-231	◆25526379	77.00
1985-87-252	◆3517549	48.50
Timing Case Cover Gasket		
1985-Diesel	◆22505997	1.25
181 & 231	◆25519994	3.25
1986-87-231	◆25530153	9.75
1985-87-252	◆1628915	2.75
(3) Camshaft Gear		
1985-Diesel	◆22516032	41.00
1985-87-181 & 231	◆25518767	17.50
252	◆1617417	32.25
(4) Timing Chain		
1985-Diesel	◆22516033	35.50
1985-87-181 & 231	◆1257650	26.00
252	◆1618157	31.75

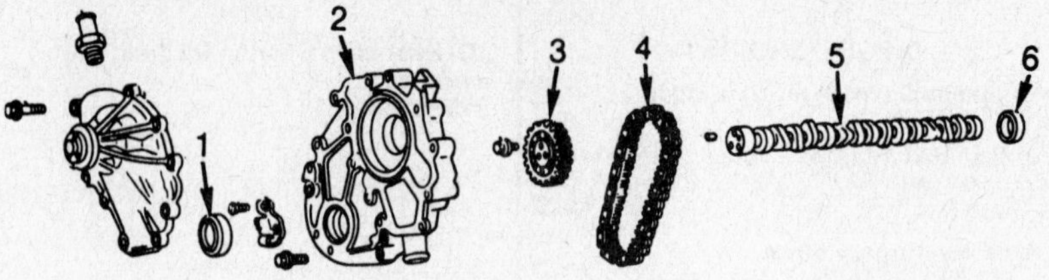

	Part No.	Price
(5) Camshaft		
1985-181	◆25510019	119.00
1985-231		
1st design	◆1262835	119.00
2nd design	◆25510049	119.00
1986-87	◆25523930	124.00
1985-87-252	◆1628822	334.00
1985-Diesel	◆22513910	266.00

1st design has two cast dimples on edge of camshaft.

	Part No.	Price
(6) Camshaft Bearings (Std.)		
181 & 231		
1985-87-exc. below		
No. 1	◆1234441	7.00
Nos. 2, 3, 4	◆1231142	7.75
1985-87-Nos. 1, 4		
20 bolt pan	◆25524301	7.25
260 Diesel		
1985-No. 1	◆561077	11.50
No. 2	◆390300	11.50
No. 3	◆390301	11.75
No. 4	◆390302	11.50

LABOR 17 ENGINE OILING SYSTEM 17 LABOR

(Factory Time)	Chilton Time
GASOLINE ENGINES	
(G) Oil Pan or Gasket, Renew	
V-6–1985-87 (.9)	1.5
V-8–1985-87 (1.3)	1.8
(P) Pressure Test Engine Bearings (Pan Off)	
All models	1.0
(G) Oil Pump Cover and/or Gears, Renew or Recondition	
V-6–1985-87 (.8)	1.2
(G) Oil Pump, Renew	
V-8–1985-87 (1.4)	2.0
Recond pump add (.3)	.3
(G) Oil Pressure Sending Unit, Renew	
1985-87 (.4)	.5
(G) Oil Pressure Gauge (Dash Unit), Renew	
Oldsmobile models	
1985-87 (.4)	.7
(M) Oil Filter Element, Renew	
V-6–1985-87 (.3)	.3
V-8–1985-87 (.3)	.3
DIESEL ENGINE	
(G) Oil Pan or Gasket, Renew	
V-6–1985 (2.2)	3.6
(P) Pressure Test Engine Bearings (Pan Off)	
All models	1.0
(G) Oil Pump, Renew	
V-6–1985 (2.3)	3.8
(G) Oil Pressure Gauge (Engine), Renew	
1985 (.3)	.4
(M) Oil Filter Element, Renew	
1985 (.3)	.3

PARTS 17 ENGINE OILING SYSTEM 17 PARTS

	Part No.	Price
Oil Pan Gasket Kit		
181		
1985		
20 bolt pan	◆25519254	8.25
14 bolt pan	◆25516877	5.50
231		
1985		
20 bolt pan	◆25519254	8.25
14 bolt pan	◆25516877	5.50
1986-87	◆25526425	7.50
252		
1985-87	◆1629458	9.75
260 Diesel		
1985	◆22520640	8.25
Oil Pump		
1985-Diesel	◆22515464	59.75
181 & 231	◆25523435	39.75
1986-87-231	◆25525965	11.25
1985-252	◆3517509	71.25
1986	◆3517635	73.75
1987	◆3517640	73.75
Oil Pump Drive Shaft		
1985-Diesel	◆22512399	11.25
1985-87-252	◆1619035	3.00
Oil Pump Gear		
1985-Diesel	◆585582	4.00
252	◆1619036	4.75
1986-87-252	◆1629251	4.75
Oil Pressure Sending Switch		
1985-181	◆25036612	6.75
231		
1985	◆25036378	8.75
1986-exc. Digital	◆25036378	8.75
w/Digital	◆10030963	20.75
1987	◆25036925	7.50
252		
1985	◆1623970	4.50
1986-87	◆25036378	8.75
260 Diesel		
1985-exc. below	◆3915936	N.L.
Oil Pump Cover		
1985-Diesel	◆22528793	2.75
181 & 231	◆966464	29.75
1986-87-231	◆25521935	9.00
1985-87-252	◆1616589	14.25
Oil Filter Element		
1985-Diesel	◆25010908	7.50
1985-87-181 & 231	◆25010792	7.50
252	◆25010324	7.50

LABOR 21 SHIFT LINKAGE 21 LABOR

(Factory Time)	Chilton Time
(G) Shift Linkage, Adjust	
All models	
Neutral Safety Switch (.3)	.4
Shift Indicator Needle (.2)	.3
Shift Linkage (.4)	.5
T.V. Cable (.3)	.4
(G) Shift Linkage, Adjust (w/Diesel Eng)	
All models	
Fast idle speed (.2)	.3
Throttle Rod/T.V. cable (.3)	.4
Vacuum regul valve (.6)	.8
Complete (.8)	1.0
(G) Shift Control Cable, Renew	
1985-87 (.4)	.6
(G) Shift Lever, Renew	
1985-87 (.2)	.4
(G) Gear Selector Needle and/or Assy., Renew	
1985-87 (.4)	.6

LABOR 26 REAR AXLE AND SUSPENSION 26 LABOR

(Factory Time)	Chilton Time
(G) Rear Suspension, Align	
All models (.8)	1.0
(G) Rear Stabilizer Bar, Renew	
1985-87 (.8)	1.2
(G) Rear Tie Rod Ends, Renew	
Includes: Alignment.	
1985-87-one (1.0)	1.4
both (1.3)	1.8
(G) Rear Wheel Bearing and Hub Assy., Clean and Repack or Renew	
1985-87-one side (.6)	.8
both sides (.8)	1.2
(G) Rear Wheel Knuckle Assy., Renew	
Includes: Alignment.	
1985-87-one (1.4)	1.9
both (2.5)	3.4
(G) Rear Coil Springs, R&R or Renew	
1985-87-one (.7)	1.1
both (1.3)	2.0
(G) Rear Control Arm Ball Joint, Renew	
1985-87-one (.9)	1.5
(G) Rear Control Arms, Renew	
1985-87-one (1.6)	2.1
both (2.4)	3.3
(G) Rear Control Arm Bushings, Renew	
1985-87-one side (1.7)	2.3
both sides (2.7)	3.7
(G) Rear Struts, R&R or Renew	
1985-87-one (.6)	1.0
both (1.0)	1.9
ELECTRONIC LEVEL CONTROL	
(G) Compressor Assembly, Renew	
1985-87 (.5)	.7
(G) Relay, Renew	
1985-87 (.2)	.4
(G) Height Sensor, Renew	
1985-87 (.5)	.6
(G) Height Sensor, Adjust	
1985-87 (.5)	.6
(G) Electronic Level Control Dryer, Renew	
1985-87 (.3)	.4
(G) Electronic Level Control Head, Renew	
Includes: Renew cover gasket, solenoid and valves.	
1985-87 (.3)	.6
(G) Electronic Level Control Motor and Cylinder Assy., R&R and Recondition	
1985-87 (.6)	1.2
(G) Pressure Limiter Valve, Renew	
1985-87 (.3)	.4

PARTS 26 REAR AXLE AND SUSPENSION 26 PARTS

	Part No.	Price
(1) Rear Wheel Bearing		
1985-87-exc. below	◆7466926	198.00
Electronic modulator	◆7466929	226.75
(2) Control Arm Support (Knuckle)		
1985-87-right	◆25522880	47.50
left	◆25522881	47.50
(3) Adjustment Link		
1985-87	◆7845426	40.75
(4) Control Arm		
1985-right	◆25523994	77.50
left	◆25523995	77.50
1986-87-right	◆25527786	77.50
left	◆25527787	77.50
(5) Lower Spring Insulator		
1985-87	◆10027268	2.25
(6) Coil Spring		
Order by year and model.		
(7) Upper Spring Insulator		
1985-87	◆10028860	4.25
(8) Grommet		
1985-87	◆6270704	1.00
(9) Stabilizer Link		
1985-87	◆10027004	4.25

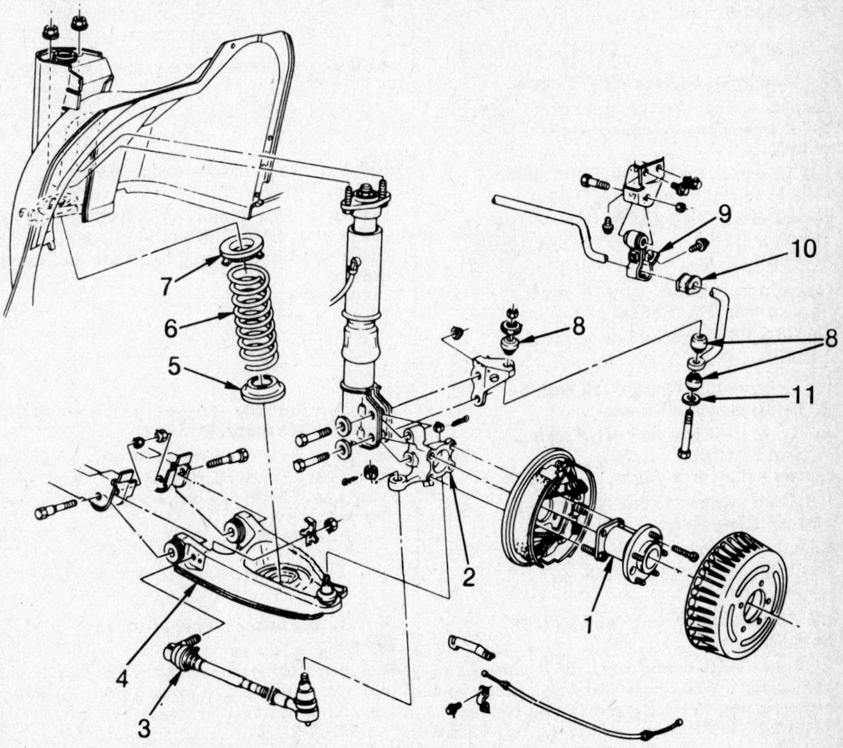

PARTS 26 REAR AXLE AND SUSPENSION 26 PARTS

	Part No.	Price
(10) Insulator (Stabilizer)		
(Deville, Fleetwood Brougham)		
1985-87	◆10026773	1.00
(Electra, 98 Regency)		
1985-87-13mm dia.	◆10026772	1.00
17mm dia.	◆10029829	1.00
(11) Retainer		
1985-87	◆4941130	1.00
Rear Strut Assy.		
1985-exc. H.D. susp.	◆22047949	144.75
H.D. susp	◆22047948	144.75
1986-87-exc. H.D. susp.	◆22047949	144.75
H.D. susp	◆22047948	144.75

ELECTRONIC LEVEL CONTROL

	Part No.	Price
Compressor		
1985	◆22049806	200.00
1986-87	◆22062531	233.00
Height Sensor		
1985-87	◆22048625	200.00
Control Relay		
1985-87-Auto cont.	◆25516613	9.75
1985-Electronic cont.	◆1620998	5.75
Air Dryer Kit		
1985-87	◆22009035	36.75
Compressor Head		
1985	◆22020539	68.50
1986-87	◆22062535	68.50
Motor (wo/Compressor Head)		
1985	◆22049807	165.00
Pressure Limiter Valve		
1985-87	◆22016688	31.00

LABOR 28 AIR CONDITIONING 28 LABOR

(Factory Time) — Chilton Time

Note: If more than one item requires replacement where evacuation and discharging the system is already included in the operation, deduct 1.0 hour for each additional item to the times listed.

(G) Drain, Evacuate and Recharge System
All models (.5) 1.0

(G) Leak Check
Includes: Check all lines and connections.
All models 5

(G) Pressure Test System
All models 8

(G) Refrigerant, Add (Partial Charge)
All models 6

(G) Compressor Belt, Renew
V-6–1985-87
Gas (.7) 1.0
Diesel (.2) 4
V-8–1985-87 (.2) 4

COMPRESSOR 4 CYLINDER RADIAL

(G) Compressor Assembly, Renew
Includes: Transfer all necessary attaching parts. Evacuate and charge system.
1985-87 (1.3) 2.0

(G) Compressor Clutch Plate and Hub Assy., Renew
Includes: R&R hub and drive plate assy. Check air gap.
1985-87 (.3) 6

(G) Compressor Clutch Rotor and/or Bearing, Renew
Includes: R&R hub and drive plate assy.
1985-87 (1.2) 1.6

(G) Compressor Clutch Coil and/or Pulley Rim Assy., Renew
Includes: R&R hub and drive plate assy.
1985-87 (1.2) 1.5
Renew pulley or brg add 1

(G) Compressor Front Seal, Seat and 'O' Ring, Renew
Includes: R&R clutch hub and drive plate assy. Evacuate and charge system.
1985-87 (1.1) 1.9

(G) Compressor Front Head and/or Seal, Renew
Includes: R&R compressor. R&R clutch and pulley assy. R&R shaft seal assy. Clean and inspect parts. Evacuate and charge system.
1985-87 (1.7) 2.8

AIR CONDITIONER TUNE-UP

For efficient operation and satisfactory performance in hot weather. The following air conditioner tune-up is suggested:

1. Clean intake filter
2. Clean condenser fins
3. Pressure test system
4. Adjust drive belt tension
5. Check antifreeze/coolant
6. Tighten compressor mounts
7. Tighten condenser and evaporator mounts
8. Inspect system for leaks (hoses, couplings, valves, etc.)
9. Partial charge system

All models 1.0
If necessary to evacuate and charge system, add 1.0

(Factory Time) — Chilton Time

(G) Compressor Discharge Valve Plates, Renew
Includes: R&R compressor. R&R clutch and pulley assy. R&R shell to internal mechanism. Clean and inspect parts. Evacuate and charge system.
1985-87 (2.1) 3.0
Two or more add (.1) 3

(G) Compressor Thrust and/or Belleville Washers, Renew
Includes: R&R compressor. R&R clutch and pulley assy. R&R shaft seal assy. R&R front head assy. Clean and inspect parts. Evacuate and charge system.
1985-87 (1.7) 2.8

(G) Compressor Main Bearing, Renew
Includes: R&R compressor. R&R clutch and pulley assy. Clean and inspect parts. Evacuate and charge system.
1985-87 (1.7) 2.8

(Factory Time) — Chilton Time

(G) Compressor Shaft and Cylinder Assy., Renew
Includes: R&R compressor. R&R clutch and pulley assy. R&R shaft seal assy, remove and transfer front head assy. R&R compressor shell and 'O' rings. R&R compressor discharge valve plates. Clean and inspect parts. Evacuate and charge system.
1985-87 (2.1) 3.1

DA-6 COMPRESSOR

(G) Compressor Assembly, Renew
Includes: Transfer all necessary attaching parts. Evacuate and charge system.
1985-87 (1.2) 2.0

(G) Compressor Clutch Plate and Hub Assy., Renew
Includes: R&R hub and drive plate assy. Check air gap.
1985-87 (.9) 1.3

(G) Compressor Clutch Rotor and/or Bearing, Renew
Includes: R&R hub and drive plate assy.
1985-87 (1.1) 1.6

(G) Compressor Clutch Coil and/or Pulley Rim Assy., Renew
Includes: R&R hub plate and drive assy.
1985-87 (1.1) 1.6
Renew pulley or brg add 1

(G) Compressor Front Seal, Seat and 'O' Ring, Renew
Includes: R&R clutch hub and drive plate assy. Evacuate and charge system.
1985-87 (1.5) 2.6

(G) Compressor Front Head and/or Seal, Renew
Includes: R&R compressor. R&R clutch and pulley assy. R&R shaft seal assy. Clean and inspect parts. Evacuate and charge system.
1985-87 (1.8) 2.8

(G) Compressor Cylinder and Shaft Assy., Renew
Includes: R&R compressor. Transfer all parts as required. Evacuate and charge system.
1985-87 (1.9) 2.9

(G) Condenser, Renew
Includes: Evacuate and charge system.
Cadillac models
1985-87 (1.3) 2.2
Buick-Olds models
1985-87 (1.4) 2.3
w/Diesel eng add (.2) 2

LABOR 28 AIR CONDITIONING 28 LABOR

	(Factory Time)	Chilton Time
(G) Accumulator Assembly, Renew		
Includes: Evacuate and charge system.		
1985-87	(.9)	1.5
(G) Expansion Tube (Orifice), Renew		
Includes: Evacuate and charge system.		
1985-87	(.7)	1.4
(G) Evaporator Core, Renew		
Includes: Evacuate and charge system.		
Buick & Olds models		
1985-87		
Gas	(1.8)	3.6
Diesel	(2.4)	4.5
Cadillac models		
1985-87	(3.4)	6.5
(G) Vacuum Actuators, Renew		
1985-87		
Defroster	(.8)	1.4
Upper or Lower mode	(.8)	1.4
Air inlet	(.6)	.9
(G) High Pressure Cut-Off Switch, Renew		
Buick-Olds models		
1985-87	(.2)	.4
(G) Pressure Cycling Switch, Renew		
Buick-Olds models		
1985-87	(.2)	.3

	(Factory Time)	Chilton Time
(G) A.C. Blower Motor, Renew		
1985-87	(.3)	.5
(G) Blower Motor Switch, Renew		
Buick-Olds models		
1985-87	(.5)	.7
(G) A.C. Control Assembly, Renew		
Buick-Olds models		
1985-87		
Custom Air	(.5)	.8
Tempmatic	(.4)	.6
(G) Vacuum Selector Valve, Renew		
Buick-Olds models		
1985-87	(.3)	.6
(G) Master Electrical Switch, Renew		
Buick-Olds models		
1985-87	(.4)	.6
(G) Air Conditioning Hoses, Renew		
Includes: Evacuate and charge system.		
1985-87		
liquid line	(1.4)	2.1
suction	(1.0)	1.7
discharge	(.9)	1.6
evap to accum	(.8)	1.5

AUTOMATIC TEMPERATURE CONTROL

	(Factory Time)	Chilton Time
(G) Programmer, R&R or Renew		
Cadillac models		
1985-87	(.4)	.6
Buick-Olds models		
1985-87	(.6)	1.0
Renew vacuum relay add	(.1)	.1
Renew motor add	(.2)	.2
Renew output shaft add	(.2)	.2
Renew compensator add	(.1)	.1
(G) Aspirator, Renew		
Cadillac models		
1985-87	(.3)	.4
Buick-Olds models		
1985-87	(.4)	.7
(G) Aspirator Hose, R&R or Renew		
Buick & Olds models		
1985-87	(.6)	.9
Cadillac models		
1985-87	(.3)	.5
(G) Ambient Sensor, Renew		
Buick & Olds models		
1985-87	(.2)	.3
(G) In-Car Sensor, Renew		
Cadillac models		
1985-87	(.3)	.5
Buick & Olds models		
1985-87	(.6)	.9
(G) EEC Power Module, Renew		
Cadillac models		
1985-87	(.3)	.6

PARTS 28 AIR CONDITIONING 28 PARTS

	Part No.	Price
Compressor Assy.		
(Buick)		
1985-exc. below	◆12322336	N.L.
w/DA6 comp.	◆12321360	N.L.
1986-87	◆12323604	N.L.
(Cadillac)		
1985-exc. below	◆12322348	N.L.
stamped 1131445	◆12321358	N.L.
1986-87	◆12323603	N.L.
(Oldsmobile)		
181		
1985	◆12322336	N.L.
Clutch Hub & Drive Plate		
1985-exc. below	◆6551220	32.50
DA-6 comp.	◆6551920	40.00
1986-87	◆2724325	51.50
Rotor (w/Bearing)		
1985-diesel eng.	◆6551884	108.50
Compressor Pulley		
1985	◆6551713	79.75
1986-87	◆6551983	115.25
Clutch Coil (w/Housing)		
1985-87-exc. below	◆6551217	44.00
DA-6 comp.	◆6551997	47.50
Shaft Seal Kit		
1985-87	◆9956695	13.00
Front Head		
1985-87-exc. below	◆6558046	40.50
DA-6 comp.	◆6557775	44.25
1985-Diesel	◆6551142	28.25
Outer Shell Assy.		
1985	◆2724158	38.00

	Part No.	Price
Cylinder & Shaft		
(Radial compressor)		
1985	◆2724060	N.L.
(DA-6 compressor)		
1985-87-exc. below	◆6551952	307.75
stamped 1131400	◆6551701	281.50
Valve Plate		
(Radial compressor)		
1985	◆6551141	11.50
(DA-6 compressor)		
1985-87-front	◆6551700	25.00
rear	◆6551702	25.00
Compressor Drive Belt		
Order by year and model.		
Pressure Relief Valve		
1985-87	◆5914435	13.50
Condenser		
181 & 231		
1985-86-exc. below	◆3053427	158.50
H.D. cooling	◆3053428	173.00
1987-exc. below	◆3058662	141.75
H.D. cooling	◆3058661	145.00
252		
1985-86	◆3053428	173.00
1987	◆3058661	145.00
260 Diesel		
1985	◆3053464	170.00
Evaporator Core		
(Buick & Oldsmobile)		
1985-exc. below	◆3050653	N.L.
1986-87	◆3058764	220.75
(Cadillac)		
1985	◆3053654	266.25
1986-87	◆3092972	129.75

	Part No.	Price
Accumulator Dehydrator		
1985	◆2724272	73.00
1986-87	◆2724259	N.L.
Blower Motor		
1985	◆22020947	55.50
1986-87	◆22049769	51.75
Blower Motor Resistor		
1985-87	◆10027029	4.25
Blower Motor Switch		
1985-87	◆16015450	6.75
Blower Motor Relay		
1985-87	◆10026578	7.75
Pressure Cut-Off Switch		
1985-87	◆3050246	23.00
Selector Valve (Vacuum)		
1985	◆16037745	3.50

ELECTRONIC CLIMATE CONTROL

	Part No.	Price
Programmer		
(Buick)		
1985	◆16038094	61.75
1986-87	◆16052184	75.00
(Cadillac)		
1985-87	◆16028106	177.75
(Oldsmobile)		
1985-87	◆16053643	157.00
Temperature Sensor (Outside)		
1985-exc. Cadillac	◆16023856	19.75
1986-87	◆16052614	17.25
1985-87-Cadillac	◆16018196	25.25

PARTS 28 AIR CONDITIONING 28 PARTS

	Part No.	Price
Temperature Sensor (Inside)		
1985-87-Cadillac	◆16023256	10.25
Electra	◆16030474	12.00
98 Regency	◆16029953	12.75
Control Module		
1985-87	◆16049206	103.00
Programmer Motor		
1985-87	◆16012468	40.75

LABOR 29 LOCKS, HINGES & WIND. REGULATORS 29 LABOR

(Factory Time)	Chilton Time
(G) Hood Latch Assembly, Renew	
1985-87 (.3)	.6
(G) Hood Release Cable, Renew	
1985-87 (.4)	.6
(G) Hood Hinge, Renew	
Cadillac models	
1985-87-each (1.0)	1.4
Buick-Olds models	
1985-87-right (.5)	.8
left (.5)	.8
both (.6)	1.0
(G) Door Handle (Outside), Renew	
Front	
1985-87 (.6)	.9
Rear	
1985-87 (.5)	.8
Renew insert add	.1
(G) Front Door Lock Cylinder, Renew	
1985-87 (.4)	.6
w/Illum entry system add (.2)	.2
Recode cyl add (.3)	.3
(G) Lock Striker Plate, Renew	
All models (.2)	.3
(G) Front Door Lock, Renew	
1985-87 (.6)	.9
(G) Door Lock Remote Control, Renew (Front or Rear)	
1985-87 (.4)	.6
(G) Rear Door Lock, Renew	
1985-87 (.8)	1.2
(G) Rear Compartment Lid Hinge Strap, Renew	
Does not include colorcoat.	
1985-87-one (.8)	1.2
(G) Rear Compartment Lid Lock and/or Cylinder, Renew	
1985-87 (.3)	.4
Recode cyl add (.3)	.3
(G) Door Window Regulator (Electric), Renew	
1985-87-front (1.0)	1.5
rear (1.0)	1.5

PARTS 29 LOCKS, HINGES & WIND. REGULATORS 29 PARTS

	Part No.	Price
Hood Latch (Primary)		
1985-87	◆14039229	4.75
Hood Latch (Secondary)		
(Deville, Fleetwood Brougham, 98 Regency)		
1985-87	◆14039230	6.50
(Electra)		
1985-87	◆25522748	171.00
Hood Hinge		
(Deville, Fleetwood Brougham, 98 Regency)		
1985-87-right	◆14039220	4.75
left	◆14039219	4.75
(Electra)		
1985-87	◆25516653	23.50
Hood Release Cable		
1985-87	◆20470537	12.50
Front Door Lock		
1985-87-right	◆20455506	39.25
left	◆20455507	39.25
Rear Door Lock		
1985-87-right	◆20455140	43.00
left	◆20455141	43.00
Door Lock Cylinder		
(wo/Door courtesy light)		
1985-87-exc. below	◆9632769	7.75
elec. dr. locks	◆9632728	8.25
(Door courtesy light)		
1985-87-exc. below	◆9632766	9.50
elec. dr. locks	◆9632767	9.50
Door Handle (Outside)		
(wo/Door courtesy light)		
1985-87-right	◆20470542	N.L.
left	◆20470543	22.75
(w/Door courtesy light)		
1985-87-right	◆20480172	53.75
left	◆20480173	53.75
Front Window Regulator (Electric)		
(2 door)		
1985-87-right	◆20303046	64.25
left	◆20303047	64.25
(4 door)		
1985-87-right	◆20304754	64.25
left	◆20304755	64.25
Rear Window Regulator (Electric)		
1985-87-right	◆20304758	57.75
left	◆20304759	57.75
Window Regulator Motor		
(Front door)		
1985-87	◆22062528	80.25
(Rear door)		
1985	◆22020900	73.00
1986-87-right	◆22062528	80.25
left	◆22062568	80.25
Trunk Lock		
1985	◆20472584	11.50
1986-87	◆20513755	11.25
Trunk Lock Cylinder		
1985-87	◆3910570	6.25
Trunk Hinges		
1985-87-right	◆20530266	22.50
left	◆20530267	22.50

LABOR 30 HEAD AND PARKING LAMPS 30 LABOR

(Factory Time)	Chilton Time
(G) Aim Headlamps	
two	.4
four	.6
(M) Headlamp Sealed Beam Bulb, Renew	
one	.3
one side	.4
(M) Park and Turn Signal Lamp Bulb, Renew	
All models-one (.2)	.3
each adtnl	.1
(M) Side Marker Lamp Bulb, Renew	
All models-one	.2
each adtnl	.1
(M) Stop, Tail and Turn Signal Lamp Bulb, Renew	
All models-one	.2
each adtnl	.1
(M) Back-Up Lamp Assy., Renew	
All models-each (.2)	.3
(M) License Lamp Assy., Renew	
All models-each (.2)	.3

LABOR 30 HEAD AND PARKING LAMPS 30 LABOR

	(Factory Time)	Chilton Time
(M) Tail, Stop and Turn Signal Lamp Assy., Renew		
All models-each	(.3)	.4
(M) High Level Stop Lamp Assy., Renew		
1986-87	(.2)	.4
(M) High Level Stop Lamp Bulb, Renew		
All models	(.2)	.3

PARTS 30 HEAD AND PARKING LAMPS 30 PARTS

	Part No.	Price
Headlamp Sealed Beam		
(wo/Quartz)		
1985-87-inner	◆5930567	N.L.
outer	◆5966200	15.00
(Quartz)		
1985-87-inner	◆5930567	22.50
outer	◆16502327	22.50
Parking & Turn Signal Lamp Assy.		
(Electra)		
1985-87-right	◆917308	N.L.
left	◆917307	N.L.
(98 Regency)		
1985-87-right	◆918182	28.50
left	◆918181	28.50
Cornering Lamp Assy.		
(Electra)		
1985-87-right	◆918068	19.50
left	◆918067	19.50
(98 Regency)		
1985-87-right	◆918236	20.50
left	◆918235	20.50
Turn Signal & Cornering Lamp Housing		
(Deville, Fleetwood Brougham)		
1985-87-right	◆16500960	29.50
left	◆16500959	29.50
License Plate Lamp Assy.		
(Deville, Fleetwood Brougham)		
1985-87	◆912366	6.25
(Electra)		
1985-87	◆929475	4.00
(98 Regency)		
1985-87-right	◆917936	4.00
left	◆917935	4.00
Tail & Stop Lamp Assy.		
(Deville, Fleetwood Brougham)		
1985-87	◆16500791	43.25
(Electra)		
(wo/External lamp monitor)		
1985-87-right	◆16501054	71.00
left	◆16501053	71.00
(External lamp monitor)		
1985-87-right	◆16501726	71.00
left	◆16501725	71.00
(98 Regency)		
1985-right	◆919804	47.00
left	◆919803	47.00
1986-87-right	◆919890	48.50
left	◆919889	48.50
Back-up Lamp Lens		
(Electra)		
1985-87-right	◆16500534	13.00
left	◆16500533	13.00
Back-up Lamp Assy.		
(Deville, Fleetwood Brougham)		
1985-87-right	◆917882	36.00
left	◆917881	36.00
(98 Regency)		
1985-87-right	◆16500680	39.00
left	◆16500679	39.00
High Mounted Stop Lamp		
1985	◆917755	N.L.
1986-87	◆5974467	36.00

LABOR 31 WINDSHIELD WIPER & SPEEDOMETER 31 LABOR

	(Factory Time)	Chilton Time
(G) Windshield Wiper Motor, Renew		
1985-87	(.6)	.8
w/Inter wiper add	(.1)	.1
(G) Windshield Wiper Motor, R&R and Recondition		
1985-87	(.9)	1.4
(G) Windshield Wiper Switch, Renew		
1985-87-std colm	(.9)	1.5
tilt colm	(.7)	1.4
(G) Wiper Transmission, Renew		
1985-87 one or both	(.5)	.8
(G) Windshield Washer Pump Valve, Renew		
1985-87	(.2)	.3
(G) Windshield Washer Pump, Renew		
1985-87	(.2)	.3
w/Pulse wipe add	(.1)	.1
(G) Speedometer Head, R&R or Renew		
1985-87	(.5)	.9
Reset odometer add		.2
(G) Speedometer Cable and Casing, Renew		
1985	(.7)	1.2
(G) Speedometer Cable (Inner), Renew or Lubricate		
1985	(.5)	.9
(G) Speedometer Signal Generator, Renew		
1985-87	(.3)	.5
(G) Radio, R&R		
Cadillac models		
1985-87	(.3)	.5
Buick-Olds models		
1985-87	(.4)	.7

PARTS 31 WINDSHIELD WIPER & SPEEDOMETER 31 PARTS

	Part No.	Price
Windshield Wiper Motor		
1985-87	◆22039328	118.00
Windshield Wiper Transmission		
1985-87-right	◆22039330	19.25
left	◆22039331	19.25
Windshield Wiper Switch		
1985-87-exc. Pulse	◆7842714	44.75
Pulse wiper	◆7843683	56.25
Windshield Washer Pump		
1985-87	◆22039041	18.50
Speedometer Head & Cable		
Order by year and model.		

LABOR 32 LIGHT SWITCHES & WIRING 32 LABOR

	(Factory Time)	Chilton Time
(G) Headlamp Switch, Renew		
1985-87	(.3)	.6
(G) Headlamp Dimmer Switch, Renew		
1985-87	(.6)	1.0
(G) Parking Brake Lamp Switch, Renew		
1985-87	(.3)	.4
(G) Stop Lamp Switch, Renew		
1985-87	(.3)	.4
(G) Back-Up Lamp and Park/Neutral Switch, Renew		
Cadillac models		
1985-87	(.3)	.5
Buick & Olds models		
1985-87	(.6)	.8
(G) Turn Signal and Hazard Warning Switch, Renew		
1985-87-std colm	(.6)	1.0
tilt colm	(.7)	1.1
(G) Horn Relay, Renew		
1985-87	(.3)	.4
(G) Horn, Renew		
1985-87-one	(.3)	.4
each adtnl		.1
(M) Turn Signal or Hazard Warning Flasher, Renew		
1985-87	(.2)	.3
(G) Wiring Harness, Renew		
1985-87		
Inst panel	(1.7)	2.9

PARTS 32 LIGHT SWITCHES & WIRING 32 PARTS

	Part No.	Price
Headlamp Switch		
(Deville, Fleetwood Brougham)		
1985-87-exc.		
below	◆1995225	18.00
Guidematic	◆16501335	29.75
Twilight sent.	◆16501334	17.25
(Electra)		
1985-87-exc.		
below	◆1995241	15.00
Twilight sent.	◆16502591	25.25
(98 Regency)		
1985-87-exc.		
below	◆1972717	17.00
Twilight sent.	◆1985219	19.75
Headlamp Dimmer Switch		
1985-87-exc.		
below	◆7841238	10.00
Guidematic	◆7841079	22.50
Stoplight Switch		
1985-exc. below	◆25524846	N.L.
(Cruise cont.)	◆25524847	N.L.
1986-87-exc.		
below	◆25523464	8.00
(Cruise cont.)	◆25523462	8.00
Turn Signal Switch		
1985-87	◆1997984	35.00
Parking Brake Lamp Switch		
1985-87	◆1264464	1.50
Back-up Lamp Switch		
1985-87	◆1994245	10.00
Turn Signal Flasher		
1985-87	◆10029240	4.25
Horn Assy.		
1985-87 (A) note	◆1892164	22.00
(C) note	◆1892246	27.50
(D) note	◆1892162	23.50
(F) note	◆1892163	22.00
Horn Relay		
1985-87-exc.		
below	◆25513270	8.50
Cadillac	◆1626239	6.50

LABOR 33 GLASS 33 LABOR

	(Factory Time)	Chilton Time
(G) Windshield Glass, Renew		
1985-87	(1.6)	2.3
Renew caulk bead add	(.4)	.4
(G) Front Door Glass, Renew		
1985-87	(1.0)	1.4
(G) Rear Door Glass, Renew		
1985-87	(.8)	1.2
(G) Rear Door Vent Glass, Renew		
1985-87	(1.1)	1.5
(G) Quarter Window Stationary Glass, Renew		
Buick models		
1985-87-4 dr	(.7)	1.1
2 dr	(1.5)	2.2
Cadillac-Olds models		
1985-87		
2 dr	(1.5)	2.2
4 dr	(1.5)	2.2
(G) Back Window Glass, Renew		
1985-87	(1.3)	2.0
w/Elec grid defogger add	(.6)	.6
w/3/4 plug, unpadded add	(1.3)	2.0
w/3/4 plug, padded add	(2.6)	4.0
w/Full plug, padded add	(2.8)	4.4

LABOR 34 CRUISE CONTROL 34 LABOR

	(Factory Time)	Chilton Time
(G) Cruise Control Servo Assy., Renew		
1985-87	(.3)	.4
(G) Cruise Control Module, Renew		
Buick-Olds models		
1985-87	(.3)	.5
Cadillac models		
1985-87	(.6)	*.8
*Note: ECM.		
(G) Cruise Control Engagement Switch, Renew		
1985-87	(.5)	.9
(G) Cruise Control Vacuum Hoses, Renew		
1985-87	(.3)	.4
(G) Cruise Control Chain, Cable or Rod, Renew		
1985-87	(.3)	.4
(G) Cruise Control Dash Switch, Renew (On-Off)		
Cadillac models		
1985-87	(.2)	.4
(G) Cruise Control Vacuum Control Valve Solenoid, Renew		
Cadillac models		
1985-87	(.2)	.3
(G) Cruise Control Speed Sensor, Renew		
1985	(.3)	.5
(G) Cruise Control Brake Release Switch, Renew		
1985-87	(.3)	.4
(G) Cruise Control Resume Solenoid Valve, Renew		
1985-87	(.2)	.3

	Part No.	Price
Cruise Control Module		
1985-181	◆25031943	123.50
1985-87-231	◆25074736	101.00
252	◆25074202	94.50
1985-Diesel	◆25074708	102.00
Cruise Control Servo		
1985-181	◆25074630	116.25
1985-87-Diesel	◆25074625	120.00
1985-252	◆25031999	30.00
1986-87	◆25074874	29.50
Vacuum Release Valve		
1985-87-exc. below	◆25523376	14.00
Cadillac	◆407437	8.00
Cruise Control Solenoid		
1985-87-Cadillac	◆25031699	62.50
Cruise Control Cable		
231		
1985	◆25517535	9.50
1986-87	◆25523976	6.50
252		
1985-87	◆1632640	4.75
260 Diesel		
1985-exc. below	◆22521988	9.00
ext. E.G.R.	◆22521739	10.00
Cruise Control Lever & Switch		
(Deville, Fleetwood Brougham)		
1985-87-wo/ Pulse wpr.	◆22510143	7.25
Pulse wipers	◆25031915	47.50
(Electra, 98 Regency)		
1985-87-wo/ Pulse wpr.	◆25031456	50.00
Pulse wipers	◆25031457	50.00

Cavalier • Cimarron • J2000 • Sunbird • Skyhawk • Firenza

GROUP INDEX

ALPHABETICAL INDEX

General Motors
Front Wheel Drive Cars

CAVALIER • CIMARRON • SUNBIRD J-2000 • SKYHAWK • FIRENZA

YEAR IDENTIFICATION

1983 Cavalier

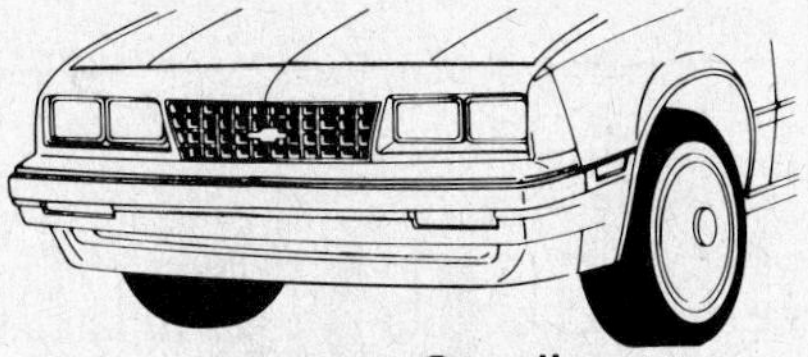

1984–87 Cavalier

1983 Cimarron

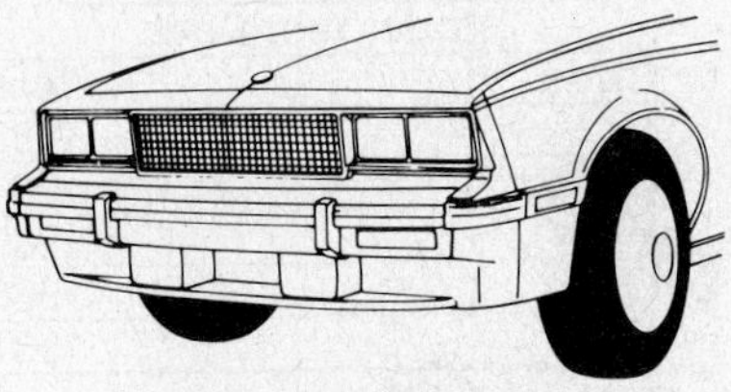

1984–85 Cimarron

1983 Firenza

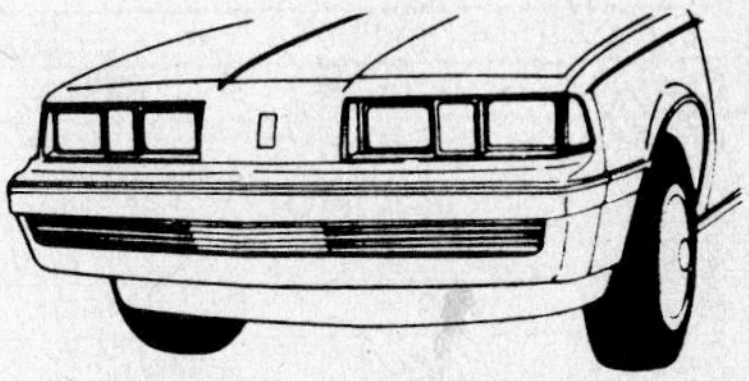

1984 Firenza

1984–87 Firenza GT

1983 2000

1984 2000 Sunbird

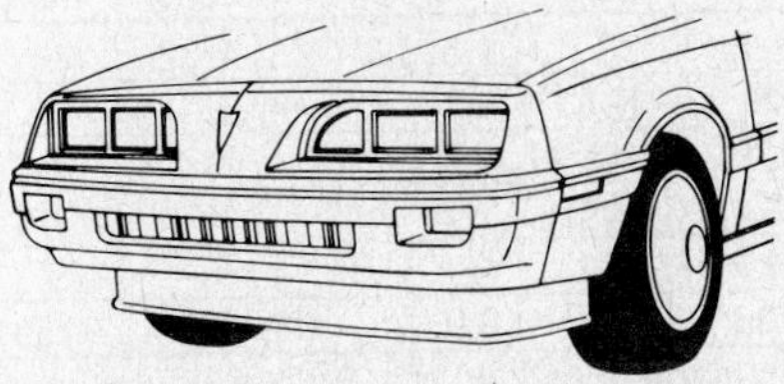

1984–85 2000 Sunbird LE, SE

1982–83 Skyhawk

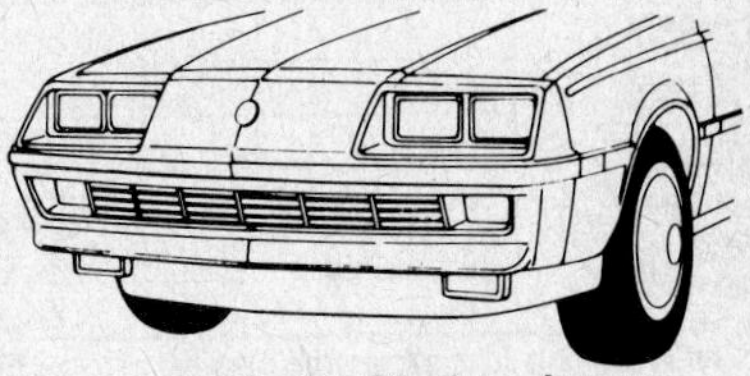

1984–85 Skyhawk

YEAR IDENTIFICATION

1986–87 Skyhawk

1986–87 Sunbird GT

1986–87 Cimarron

1986–87 Skyhawk Sedan

VEHICLE IDENTIFICATION NUMBER (VIN)

It is important for servicing and ordering parts to be certain of the vehicle and engine identification. The VIN (vehicle identification number) is a 13 or 17 digit number visible through the windshield on the driver's side of the dash and contains the vehicle and engine identification codes. It can be interpreted as follows:

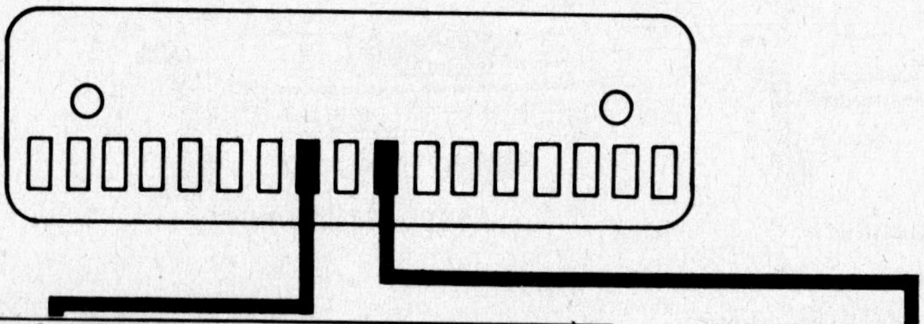

Engine Code

Code	Cu. In.	Liters	Cyl.	Carb.	Eng. Mfg.
G	110 (OHV)	1.8	4	2 bbl.	Chev.
O	110 (OHC)	1.8	4	TBI	Pontiac
J	110 (OHC)	1.8	4	MFI (Turbo)	Pontiac
B	122	2.0	4	TBI	Chev.
P	122	2.0	4	EFI	Chev.
W	173	2.8	6	MFI	Chev.

Model Year Code

Code	Year
D	1983
E	1984
F	1985
G	1986
H	1987

The seventeen digit Vehicle Identification Number can be used to determine engine application and model year. The 10th digit indicates the model year, and the 8th digit identifies the factory installed engine.

OHV—Overhead valve engine
OHC—Overhead cam engine
TBI—Throttle Body Injection
MFI—Multi-Port Fuel Injection

NOTE: Some 1983-85 Canadian models with the 2.0 Liter engine use a 2 bbl. carburetor.

TUNE-UP SPECIFICATIONS

When analyzing compression test results, look for uniformity among cylinders rather than specific pressures.

Year	Eng. VIN Code	Engine No. Cyl. Displacement (cu. in.)	Liters	Eng. Mfg.	hp	Spark Plugs Orig Type	Spark Plugs Gap (in.)	Ignition Timing (deg)▲ Man. Trans.	Ignition Timing (deg)▲ Auto. Trans.	Valves Intake Opens (deg)■	Fuel Pump Pressure (psi)	Idle Speed (rpm▲) Man. Trans.	Idle Speed (rpm▲) Auto. Trans.
1983-87	G	4-110	1.8	Chev.	88	R-42TS	0.045 ①	12B	12B	30	4.5-6.0	4F32	②
	O	4-110	1.8	Pont.	84	R-42XLS6 ④	0.060	8B	8B	N.A.	9-13	②	②
	B	4-122	2.0	Chev.	90	R-42CTS	0.035	—	12B	30	4.5-6.0 ③	②	②
	P	4-122	2.0	Chev.	86	R-42CTS	0.035	②	②	N.A.	12	②	②
	J	4-110	1.8	Pont.	150	R-42CXLS	0.035	②	②	N.A.	12	②	②
	W	6-173	2.8	Chev.	112	R42CTS	0.045	6B	10B	31	6.0	850	750

NOTE: The underhood specifications sticker often reflects tune-up specification changes made in production. Sticker figures must be used if they disagree with those in this chart.

Part numbers in this chart are not recommendations by Chilton for any product by brand name.

① Certain models may use 0.035 in. Gap—see underhood specifications sticker to be sure
② See underhood specifications sticker
③ 1983-84 w/T.B.I.—12 psi
④ 1984-85—R44XLS

■ All figures Before Top Dead Center
B Before Top Dead Center

FIRING ORDERS

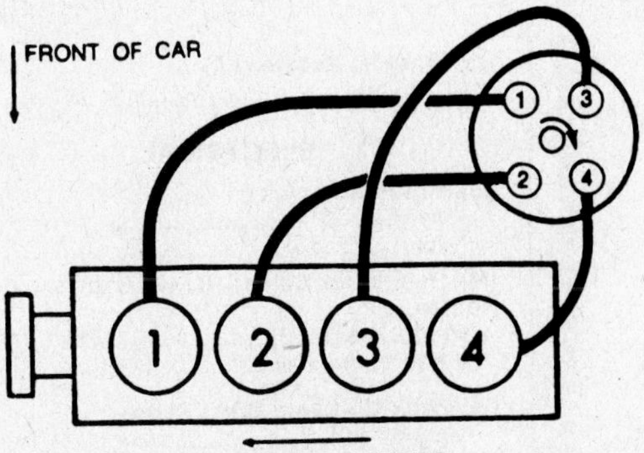

GM (Chevrolet) 110 and 122 overhead valve (OHV)
Engine firing order: 1–3–4–2
Distributor rotation: clockwise

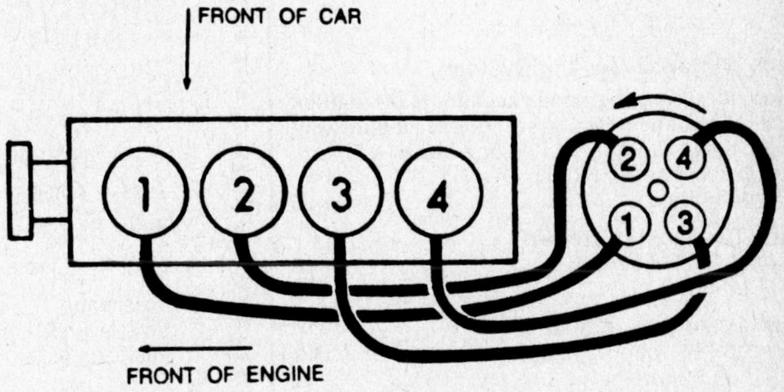

GM (Pontiac) 110 overhead camshaft (OHC)
Engine firing order: 1–3–4–2
Distributor rotation: counterclockwise

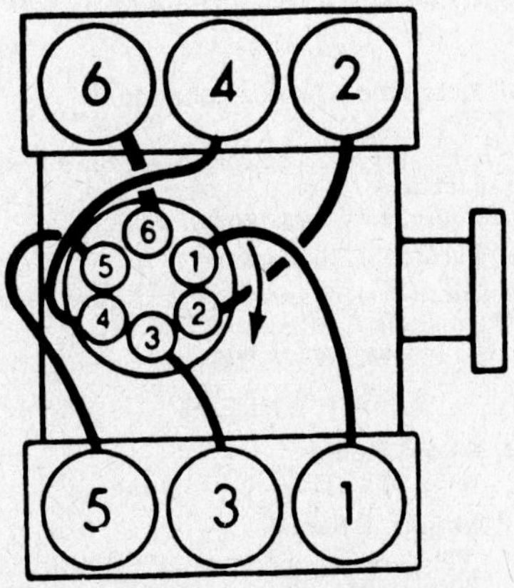

GM (Chevrolet) 173 V6 (2.8L)
Engine firing order: 1–2–3–4–5–6
Distributor rotation: clockwise

WHEEL ALIGNMENT SPECIFICATIONS

Year	Camber (postive) Range (degrees)	Camber (postive) Preferred (degrees)	Toe Range (degrees)	Toe Preferred (degrees)
'83	7/32 to 1-7/32	23/32	5/16 to 1/16	1/8 ①
'84-'85	3/16 to $1^3/_{16}$	11/16	1/4 to 0	1/8 ①
'85-'86	7/32 to $1^1/_2$	23/32 ②	5/16 to 1/16	1/8

① Out ② except '86 Firenza—27/32

LABOR — SERVICE BAY OPERATIONS — LABOR

(Factory Time) — Chilton Time

COOLING

(M) Winterize Cooling System

Includes: Run engine to check for leaks, tighten all hose connections. Test radiator and pressure cap, drain radiator and engine block. Add anti-freeze and refill system.

All models 5

(G) Thermostat, Renew

1983-87-Four (.6) 8
V-6 (.4) 5

(M) Drive Belt, Adjust

1983-87-one (.2) 3
each adtnl (.1) 1

(M) Drive Belt, Renew

1983-87-one (.3) 4
each adtnl (.3) 3
Serpentine (.3) 4

(M) Radiator Hoses, Renew

1983-87
upper (.3) 4
lower (.4) 5
both (.5) 7

BRAKES

(G) Brakes, Adjust (Minor)

Includes: R&R wheels and adjust brakes thru access holes in drums. Fill master cylinder.

two wheels 4
Remove knock out plugs add, each .. .1

(G) Bleed Brakes (Four Wheels)

Includes: Fill master cylinder.

All models (.4) 5

(G) Brake Pedal Free Play, Adjust

All models 3

(M) Parking Brake, Adjust

All models (.3) 4

LUBRICATION SERVICE

(M) Engine Oil & Filter, Change

Includes: Inspect and correct all fluid levels.

All models 4

CHILTON'S 10 POINT SAFETY CHECK

CHECK OPERATION & CONDITION OF THE FOLLOWING ITEMS:

1. Legal Registration (serial no.)
2. Tires & Wheels
3. Brake System (R&R all wheels)
4. Light Systems & Signals
5. Accelerator Linkage, Neutral Safety Switch, Shift Indicator Pointer & Seat Position Locks
6. Glass, Mirrors, Door Locks, Seat Belts & Harness
7. Wipers, Washers & Defrosters
8. Frame, Steering, Shocks, Front & Rear Suspension
9. Fuel & Exhaust Systems
10. Road Test Vehicle

All models 1.0
Exhaust Smog Analysis, add 4

(Factory Time) — Chilton Time

(M) Lubricate Chassis, Change Oil & Filter

Includes: Inspect and correct all fluid levels.

All models 6
Install grease fittings add 1

(M) Lubricate Chassis

Includes: Inspect and correct all fluid levels.

All models 4
Install grease fittings add 1

WHEELS

(M) Wheel, Renew

one (.5) 5

(G) Wheels, Balance

one 3
each adtnl 2

(Factory Time) — Chilton Time

(M) Wheels, Rotate (All)

All models 5

ELECTRICAL

(G) Aim Headlamps

two 4
four 6

(M) Headlamp Sealed Beam Bulb, Renew

1983-87-one (.2) 3
each adtnl (.1) 1

(M) Back-Up Lamp Bulb, Renew

1983-87 (.2) 2

(M) Parking Lamp Bulb, Renew

1983-87 (.2) 2

(M) Tail & Stop Lamp Bulb, Renew

1983-87 (.2) 2

(M) Side Marker Lamp Bulb, Renew

1983-87 (.2) 2

(M) License Lamp Bulb, Renew

1983-87 (.2) 2

(M) Rear Combination Lamp Assy., Renew

All models-each (.2) 3
2 Dr. Hatchback add 2

(M) Park and Turn Signal Lamp Assy., Renew

All models-each (.2) 3

(G) Horn Relay, Renew

1983-87 (.3) 3

(G) Horn, Renew

1983-87-one (.3) 4
each adtnl (.1) 1

(M) Battery Cables, Renew

1983-87
positive (.4) 5
negative (.3) 3

(M) Battery Terminals, Clean

All models 3

LABOR — 1 TUNE UP 1 — LABOR

(Factory Time) — Chilton Time

(G) Compression Test

Four–1983-87 (.3) 6
V-6–1985-87 (.3) 6

(G) Engine Tune Up, (Electronic Ignition)

Includes: Test battery and clean connections. Tighten manifold and carburetor mounting bolts. Check engine compression, clean and adjust or renew spark plugs. Test resistance of spark plug cables. Inspect distributor cap and rotor. Reset ignition timing. Adjust idle mixture and idle speed. Service carburetor air cleaner. Inspect and adjust drive belts. Inspect choke operation and adjust or free up. Check operation of EGR valve.

Four–1983-87 .... 1.6
V-6–1985-87 .... 2.0
To perform C.C.C. system test add... 1.0

LABOR — 2 IGNITION SYSTEM 2 — LABOR

(Factory Time) — Chilton Time

(G) Spark Plugs, Clean and Reset or Renew

1983-87 (.5) 6

(G) Ignition Timing, Reset

1983-87 (.3) 4

(G) Distributor, Renew

Includes: Reset ignition timing.

1983-87
Four
OHC (1.0) 1.5
In Line (.5) 7
V-6 (.5) 8

(G) Distributor, R&R and Recondition

Includes: Reset ignition timing.

1983-87
Four
OHC (1.3) 2.0
In Line (.8) 1.2
V-6 (.8) 1.4

LABOR 2 IGNITION SYSTEM 2 LABOR

(Factory Time)	Chilton Time
(G) Distributor Cap and/or Rotor, Renew	
1983-87 (.3)	.4
(G) Ignition Coil, Renew	
1983-87	
Four	
In Line eng (.8)	1.2
OHC eng (1.4)	1.8
V-6 (.3)	.5
w/A.T. add (.2)	.2
(G) ECS Module, Renew	
1983-87 (.2)	.4
(G) ESC Knock Sensor, Renew	
1983-87 (.2)	.4
(G) Distributor Module, Renew	
1983-87 (.5)	.7
(G) Distributor Capacitor and/or Module Wiring Harness, Renew	
1983-87 (.6)	.8
(G) Distributor Pick-Up Coil and/or Pole Piece, Renew	
1983-87	
Four	
OHC (1.1)	1.4
In Line (.7)	1.0
V-6 (.6)	.9
(G) Ignition Cables, Renew	
1983-87 (.3)	.4
(G) Ignition Switch, Renew	
1983-85 (.5)	.9
1986-87 (.8)	1.1
(G) Ignition Lock Cylinder, R&R or Renew	
Includes: R&R steering wheel, lock plate, cover, and turn signal switch.	
1983-85 (.4)	.7
1986-87 (.6)	1.0
w/Tilt whl add (.1)	.1
Recode cyl add (.3)	.3

PARTS 2 ELECTRONIC IGNITION 2 PARTS

	Part No.	Price
Distributor Assembly		
1.8L		
1983	◆1103585	240.75
1984-w/Turbo	◆1103589	242.25
wo/Turbo	◆1103561	236.75
1985-87-w/ Turbo	◆1103610	221.50
wo/Turbo	◆1103609	219.00
2.0L		
1983-exc. Canada	◆1103515	252.50
Canada	◆1103535	274.25
1984-85-exc. Canada	◆1103567	148.00
Canada	◆1103548	274.50
1986-87	◆1103653	155.25
2.8L		
1985	◆1103591	176.50
1986-87	◆1103704	227.50
(1) Dist. Cap		
1.8L		
1983-87	◆1985771	16.75
2.0L		
1983-84	◆1978497	16.00
1985-87	◆10495822	10.75
2.8L		
1985-87	◆1988001	9.75
(2) Rotor		
1.8L		
1983	◆1978533	9.00
1984-87	◆1988515	8.50
2.0L		
1983-84	◆1978533	9.00
1985-87	◆10495411	3.50
2.8L		
1985	◆10495408	3.50
1986-87	◆10497452	3.50
(3) Dist. Housing		
1.8L		
1983-87-exc. Turbo	◆1987007	55.50
Turbo	◆1988465	71.50
2.0L		
1983	◆1984148	57.50
1984	◆1987937	32.75
1985	◆1987968	34.75
1986-87	◆10495845	31.00
Canada		
1983-84	◆1978776	57.25
2.8L		
1985	◆1988388	34.25
1986-87	◆10496765	36.25
(4) Main Shaft		
1.8L		
1983-85	◆1985774	28.00

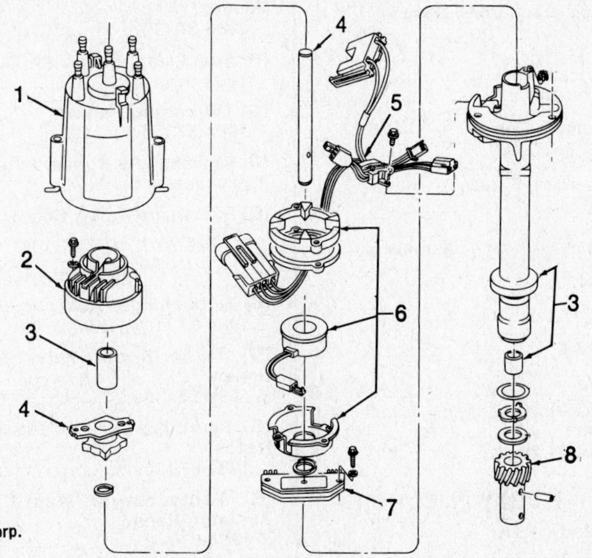

© G.M. Corp.

	Part No.	Price
2.0L		
1983	◆1978631	52.25
1984	◆1987940	30.50
1985	◆1987958	25.50
1986-87	◆10495788	28.25
Canada		
1983	◆1986102	65.75
1984-A.T. wo/ A.C.	◆1987334	65.75
A.C.	◆1986951	60.50
M.T.	◆1986951	60.50
2.8L		
1985	◆1988005	31.25
1986-87	◆10497454	27.25
(5) Terminal Block		
1.8L		
1983-84-exc. Turbo	◆1986139	27.75
Turbo	◆1987095	25.75
1985-87-exc. Turbo	◆1989284	31.00
Turbo	◆1989286	24.50
2.0L		
1983-84	◆1985749	31.75
(6) Pole Piece		
1.8L		
1983-87	◆1978503	39.25

	Part No.	Price
2.0L		
1983-84	◆1978503	39.25
1985	◆1987963	3.50
1986-87	◆10495801	4.00
Canada		
1983-84	◆1979511	39.00
2.8L		
1985-87	◆1988010	3.50
(7) Module		
1.8L		
1983	◆1979107	56.00
1984-85	◆1985342	56.50
2.0L		
1983-84	◆1979107	56.00
1984-85	◆1987465	46.00
1986-87	◆10496541	40.00
Canada		
1983-84	◆1978778	52.75
2.8L		
1985-87	◆1987466	46.00
(8) Distributor Gear		
1983-87	◆1977936	23.00
Coil		
1983-84	◆1115455	58.00
1985-87	◆1115315	39.50

PARTS 2 ELECTRONIC IGNITION 2 PARTS

	Part No.	Price
Spark Plug Wire Set		
Spark plug wires are sold separately for each spark plug and not available as a set.		
Ignition Switch		
(wo/tilt wheel)		
1983	◆1990109	11.50
1984-87-M.T.	◆1990115	11.50
A.T.	◆7843497	25.75
(w/tilt wheel)		
1983	◆1990110	11.50
1984-87-M.T.	◆1990116	11.50
A.T.	◆7843451	25.75

LABOR 3 FUEL SYSTEM 3 LABOR

	(Factory Time)	Chilton Time
(G) Fuel Tank, Renew		
Includes: Drain and refill tank. Transfer tank gauge unit.		
1983-87	(.9)	1.2
(G) Fuel Gauge (Tank Unit), Renew		
Includes: Drain and refill tank.		
1983-87	(.9)	1.1
Transfer elec pump add		.1
(G) Fuel Gauge (Dash Unit), Renew		
1983-87		
Skyhawk	(1.1)	2.0
Firenza	(.8)	1.5
All other models	(.3)	.6
(G) Intake Plenum, Renew		
V-6–1985-87	(.6)	.8
(G) Intake Runners, Renew		
V-6–1985-87	(1.4)	2.0
(G) Intake Manifold Gasket, Renew		
Four		
O.H.C. eng		
1983-87	(1.4)	2.0
w/P.S. add	(.3)	.3
w/Turbo add	(1.5)	1.5
In Line eng		
1983-87	(1.5)	2.0
V-6–1985-87	(2.9)	4.0
w/P.S. add	(.4)	.4
Renew manif add	(.2)	.5
THROTTLE BODY INJECTION		
(G) Throttle Body, R&R		
1983-87	(.7)	1.0
Renew throttle body kit add	(.3)	.3
Renew fuel meter body add	(.3)	.3
w/Turbo add	(.1)	.1
(G) Throttle Body Unit, Renew		
1983-87	(.7)	1.0
(G) Throttle Body Fuel Meter Assy, and/or Gasket, Renew		
1983-87	(.4)	.6
(G) Idle Air Control Valve, Renew		
1983-87	(.5)	.8
(G) Throttle Body Injector, Renew		
1983-87-one	(.7)	1.0
(G) Fuel Pressure Regulator, Renew		
1983-87	(.7)	1.1
(G) Fuel Pump, Renew (In Tank)		
1983-87	(1.2)	1.8
(G) TBI Heater, Renew		
1984-87	(.6)	1.0
(G) Minimun Idle Speed, Adjust		
All models	(.5)	.8
(G) Fuel Pump Relay, Renew		
1983-87	(.7)	1.0
TURBOCHARGER		
(G) Turbocharger Assy., Renew		
1984-87	(1.7)	2.5
(G) Turbo Boost Valve Assy., Renew		
1984-87	(.2)	.4
(G) Turbocharger Oil Separator, Renew		
1984-87	(.3)	.6
(G) Turbocharger Waste Gate Actuator, Renew		
1984-87	(.4)	.7
PORTED INJECTION		
(G) Throttle Body, R&R		
1985-87	(.6)	1.0
Renew throttle body kit add	(.3)	.3
Renew fuel meter body add	(.3)	.3
(G) Throttle Body Unit, Renew		
1985-87	(.6)	1.0
(G) Throttle Body Fuel Meter Assy., and/or Gasket, Renew		
1985-87	(.4)	.6
(G) Idle Air Control Valve, Renew		
1985-87	(.4)	.6
(G) Minimum Idle Speed, Adjust		
All models	(.4)	.7
(G) Throttle Body Injector and/or Gasket, Renew		
1985-87-one	(.7)	1.1
(G) Fuel Pressure Regulator, Renew		
1985-87	(.7)	.9
(G) Fuel Pump, Renew (In Tank)		
1985-87	(1.3)	1.8
(G) Fuel Pump Relay, Renew		
1985-87	(.7)	.9
(G) Cold Start Injector, Renew		
1985-87	(1.0)	1.4
(G) Thermo Start Switch, Renew		
1985-87	(.5)	.7
(G) Fuel Injector, Renew		
1985-87-one	(1.6)	2.2
each adtnl	(.1)	.1
Perform balance test add		.4
(G) Fuel Rail, Renew		
1985-87	(1.3)	1.9
(G) Mass Air Sensor, Renew		
1985-87	(.4)	.5

PARTS 3 FUEL SYSTEM 3 PARTS

	Part No.	Price
Fuel Pump		
1.8L		
1983-84-exc. Turbo	◆6472011	80.00
Turbo	◆6472143	123.00
1985-exc. Turbo	◆6472311	56.50
Turbo	◆6472375	79.50
1986-87-exc. Turbo	◆6472526	57.00
Turbo	◆6472524	45.00
2.0L		
1983-84	◆6472011	80.00
1985	◆6472311	56.50
1986-87	◆6472526	57.00
2.8L		
1985	◆6472375	79.50
1986-87	◆6472524	45.00
Fuel Tank		
1983-84	◆22518791	N.L.
1985-87	◆22527083	149.00
Meter (Fuel Tank)		
1983-84-exc. Turbo	◆25004300	132.50
Turbo	◆25003990	143.25
1985-87-exc. below	◆25004390	134.25
Turbo	◆25004392	125.25
V6 eng.	◆25004392	125.25
Dig. gauge	◆25004989	131.75
Fuel Gauge (Dash)		
Cavalier		
(2.0L wo/Gauges)		
1983	◆6433706	33.00
1984-85	◆6433874	32.00
(2.0L w/Gauges)		
1983	◆6433030	23.00
1984-85	◆6434118	24.75
1986-87	◆6434421	29.50
Canada		
1984-87	◆6434120	24.50
(2.8L wo/Gauges)		
1985	◆6434222	32.00
1986-87	◆6434423	27.25
Canada		
1985	◆6434120	24.50
1986-87	◆6434427	26.00
(2.8L w/Gauges)		
1985-87	◆6434118	24.75
Canada		
1985-87	◆6434120	24.50

PARTS 3 FUEL SYSTEM 3 PARTS

	Part No.	Price
Cimarron		
1983-87-exc.		
Canada	◆6433339	53.75
Canada	◆6433828	50.25
Firenza		
1983-87-wo/		
Gauges	◆6433385	27.50
w/Gauges	◆25048091	49.00
Canada		
J2000 & 2000		
(wo/Gauges)		
1983	◆6433817	30.25
1984-85	◆6433896	30.25
1986-87	◆25061402	47.00
Canada		
1984	◆6433897	30.25
1985	◆6434345	30.00
1986-87	◆25061403	52.25
(w/Gauges)		
1983	◆6433821	25.00
1984-85	◆6434053	24.75
1986-87	◆25061382	196.00
1984-85	◆6433898	24.75
1986-87	◆25061381	196.00
Skyhawk		
1983-87-exc. Turbo		
wo/Gauges	◆6433680	28.25
Gauges	◆6434401	53.00
1985-Turbo	◆25059071	29.50
Canada		
1983-85	◆6433807	48.25

	Part No.	Price
Manifold Gasket Set (Intake)		
1.8L		
1983	◆10019083	3.25
1984-87	◆10028243	3.50
2.0L		
1983-87	◆14018791	3.50
2.8L		
1985-87-side	◆14089022	5.75
center	◆14083328	3.50
plenum	◆14089058	2.25

PARTS 3 THROTTLE BODY INJECTION 3 PARTS

	Part No.	Price
Throttle Body Assembly		
1.8L-wo/Turbo		
1983-M.T.	◆17078272	535.00
A.T.	◆17079255	575.75
1984-M.T.	◆17110362	582.25
A.T.	◆17110368	582.25
1985-87	◆17110759	498.50
1.8L-Turbo		
1984-87	◆10026724	196.00
2.0L		
1983-M.T.	◆17079608	809.25
A.T.	◆17079596	584.00
1984-M.T.	◆17110376	552.00
A.T.	◆17110369	589.00
1985-87-M.T.	◆17110675	500.00
A.T.	◆17110671	500.00
(1) Fuel Meter Body Kit		
1983-87	◆17078222	109.75
(2) Fuel Injector Kit		
1.8L		
1983-87	◆17078273	191.50
2.0L		
1983-87	◆17079694	191.75
(3) Gasket Kit		
1.8L		
1983-87	◆17068990	24.75
2.0L		
1983	◆17079837	25.50
1984-87	◆17110370	30.25

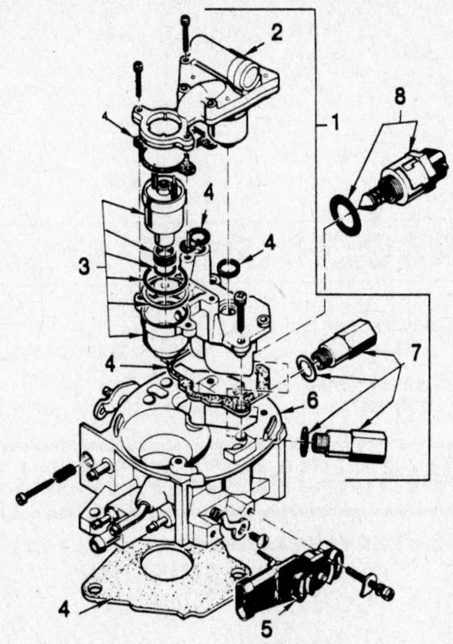

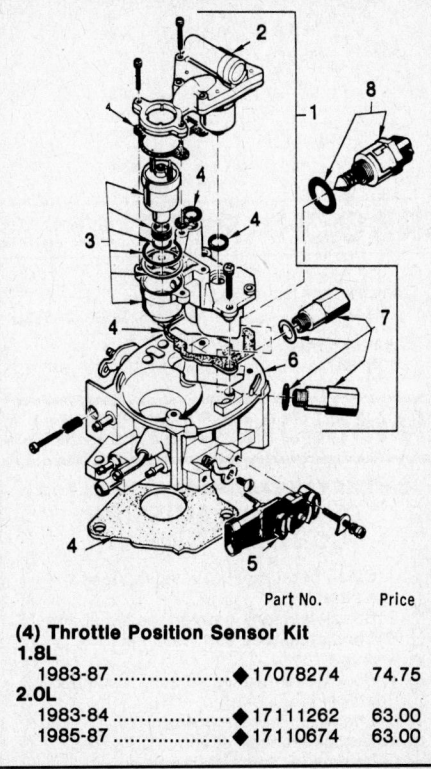

	Part No.	Price
(4) Throttle Position Sensor Kit		
1.8L		
1983-87	◆17078274	74.75
2.0L		
1983-84	◆17111262	63.00
1985-87	◆17110674	63.00

	Part No.	Price
(5) Throttle Body Kit		
1.8L-wo/Turbo		
1983	◆17078270	146.75
1984-85	◆17110363	220.25
1986-87	◆17110760	237.25
1.8L-Turbo		
1984-87	◆10031268	333.00
2.0L		
1983-M.T.	◆17079609	252.00
A.T.	◆17079597	252.00
1984-M.T.	◆17110377	248.25
A.T.	◆17110372	248.25
1985-87-M.T.	◆17110676	237.25
A.T.	◆17110672	237.25
(6) Fastener Assortment Kit		
1.8L		
1983-87	◆17078276	18.25
2.0L		
1983-87	◆17079607	16.25
(7) Idle Air Valve Control Kit		
1.8L-wo/Turbo		
1983-87	◆17079256	88.75
1.8L-Turbo		
1984-87	◆17111288	58.00
2.0L		
1983-87-M.T.	◆17079599	95.00
A.T.	◆17079256	88.75
Fuel Meter Kit		
2.0L		
1983	◆17079841	509.00
1984-87	◆17110371	510.50

Includes one injector & pressure regulator.

PARTS 3 ELECTRONIC FUEL INJECTION 3 PARTS

	Part No.	Price
2.8L		
(1) Throttle Body Assy		
1985-87-A.T.	◆17110832	193.50
M.T.	◆17110837	191.50
(2) Gasket Kit		
1985-87	◆17110827	9.00
(3) Throttle Position Sensor Kit		
1985-87	◆17111606	40.50
(4) Coolant Cover Kit		
1985-87	◆17110828	39.25
(5) Idle Air Vacuum Housing Kit		
1985-87	◆17110834	30.00
(6) Idle Air Control Valve		
1985-87	◆17111288	58.00
(7) Fuel Rail and Pressure Regulator		
1985-87	◆17110851	162.75

(2.8 liter V6 engine)

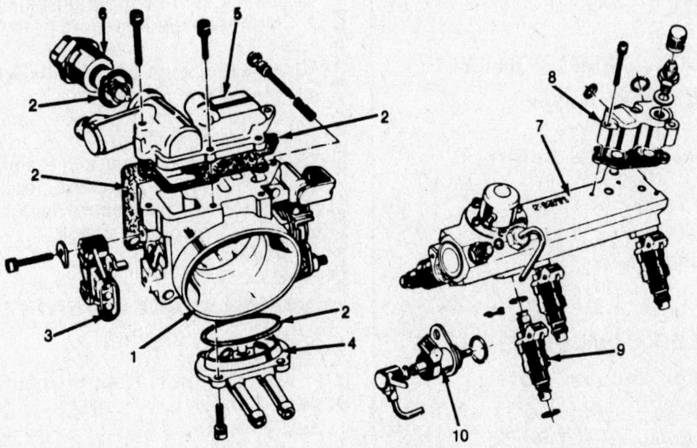

PARTS 3 ELECTRONIC FUEL INJECTION 3 PARTS

	Part No.	Price
(8) Fuel Inlet/Outlet Block		
1985-87	◆17110853	29.25
(9) Fuel Injector Kit		
1985-87	◆17111297	137.50
(10) Cold Start Valve		
1985-87	◆17110860	49.50

PARTS 3 ELECTRONIC FUEL INJECTION 3 PARTS

	Part No.	Price
1.8L		
(1) Throttle Body Assy.		
1985-87	◆10026724	196.00
(2) Sensor Kit		
1985-87	◆10031271	60.50
(3) Idle Control Motor		
1985-87	◆22048226	62.00
(4) Fuel Injector		
1985-87	◆10040095	44.00
(5) Housing w/Gasket		
1985-87	◆10031208	7.50
(6) Fuel Rail		
1985-87	◆10042008	47.50
(7) Upper Harness		
1984-87	◆12028276	90.50

(1.8 liter 4 cyl. engine)

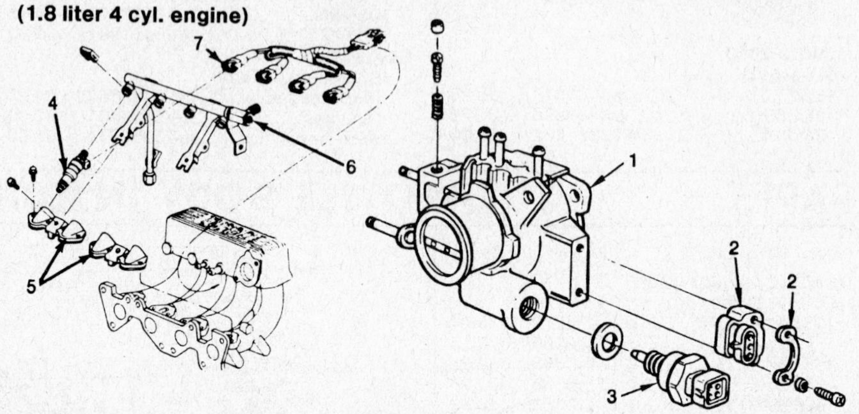

PARTS 3 TURBOCHARGER SYSTEM 3 PARTS

	Part No.	Price
Turbocharger (Rebuilt)		
1984-87	◆10031027	352.25
Actuator Kit		
1984-87	◆10031028	115.00
Compressor Housing		
1984-87	◆10031208	7.50
Exhaust Outlet Elbow		
1984-87	◆10032079	40.00
Turbo Boost Solenoid Vacuum Control Valve		
1984-85	◆1997652	16.25

LABOR 3A EMISSION CONTROLS 3A LABOR

(Factory Time) — Chilton Time

EMISSION CONTROLS

(G) Emission Control Check

Includes: Check and adjust engine idle speed and mixture and ignition timing. Check PCV valve.

All models 6

POSITIVE CRANKCASE VENTILATION

(M) Positive Crankcase Ventilation Valve, Renew
1983-87 (.2) 3

(M) Crankcase Ventilation Filter Assy., Renew
All models (.2) 3

EVAPORATIVE EMISSION TYPE

(G) Charcoal Canister, Renew
1983-87 (.3) 4

(G) Fuel Tank Pressure Control Valve, Renew
1983-87 (.2) 3

(G) Canister Purge Thermal Vacuum Switch, Renew
1983-87 (.2) 3

CONTROLLED COMBUSTION TYPE

(G) Air Cleaner Vacuum Motor, Renew
1983-87 (.3) 5

CHILTON'S EMISSION CONTROL TUNE-UP

1. Clean or renew P.C.V. valve, hoses and filter.
2. Check fuel tank cap for sealing ability.
3. Check fuel tank and fuel lines for leakage.
4. Check evaporation canister and filter. Replace if necessary.
5. Check engine compression to determine leakage of unburned gases. (Add time for items of interference).
6. Test and clean or renew spark plugs.
7. Check engine oil dipstick for sealing ability.
8. Test exhaust system with analyzer and check system for leakage.
9. Check exhaust manifold heat valve for operation.
10. Adjust ignition timing and carburetor idle speed and mixture.
11. Check automatic choke mechanism for free operation.
12. Inspect air cleaner and element.
13. On models so equipped, test distributor vacuum control switch and transmission control switch.

All models
Four 1.3

(Factory Time) — Chilton Time

(G) Air Cleaner Temperature Sensor, Renew
1983-87 (.2) 3

(Factory Time) — Chilton Time

EXHAUST GAS RECIRCULATION SYSTEM

(G) E.G.R. Valve, Renew
1983-87
Four (.4) 6
V-6 (.6) 8

(G) E.G.R. Thermal Vacuum Switch, Renew
1983-87 (.3) 4

(G) Thermostatic Vacuum Control Switch, Renew
1983-87 (.2) 3

(G) E.G.R. Vacuum Delay Valve, Renew
1983-87 (.2) 3

(G) Thermal Control Valve, Renew
1983-85 (.2) 3

AIR INJECTION REACTOR TYPE

(G) Air Pump, Renew
1983-87 (.6) 1.0
w/P.S. add (.3) 3

(G) A.I.R. Air Cleaner, Renew
1983-87 (.2) 3

(G) A.I.R. Check Valve, Renew
1983-87-one (.3) 4
each adtnl (.1) 1

(G) A.I.R. Centrifugal Fan and/or Filter, Renew
1983-87 (.3) 5

LABOR 3A EMISSION CONTROLS 3A LABOR

(Factory Time)	Chilton Time
(G) Deceleration Valve, Renew	
1983-87 (.2)	.3
(G) Catalytic Converter Air Pipe, Renew	
1983-87	
one piece (.4)	.7
(G) Pair Valve Assembly, Renew	
1983-84 (.6)	.9
(G) Pair Shut Off Valve, Renew	
1983-84 (.3)	.4
THROTTLE BODY INJECTION	
(P) Electronic Control Module, Renew	
1983-87 (.6)	.8
w/A.C. add (.1)	.1
(P) Prom, Renew	
1983-87 (.7)	.9
w/A.C. add (.1)	.1
(P) Coolant Temperature Sensor, Renew	
1983-87 (.4)	.8
(P) Throttle Position Sensor, Adjust	
All models	.6
(P) Back-Up Lamp and Park/Neutral Switch, Renew	
1984-85 (.5)	.7
(P) E.G.R. Vacuum Control Solenoid, Renew	
1984-87 (.5)	.7
(P) Manifold Temperature Sensor, Renew	
1984-87 (.4)	.6
(P) Manifold Absolute Pressure Sensor, Renew	
1983-87 (.5)	.7
(P) Oxygen Sensor, Renew	
1983-87 (.5)	.7
(P) Vehicle Speed Sensor, Renew	
1983-87 (.7)	1.1
(P) Throttle Position Sensor, Renew	
1983-87 (.6)	.9
(P) Air Control/Air Switching Valve, Renew	
1983-87 (1.4)	1.8
(P) Air Switching Valve Solenoid, Renew	
1983-87 (.4)	.6
(P) EFE/EGR Relay, Renew	
1983-87 (.3)	.4
(P) Pulse Air Solenoid, Renew	
1984-85 (.6)	.9
(P) Vacuum Control Purge Solenoid, Renew	
1984-87 (.4)	.6
(P) Power Steering Pressure Idle Speed Module, Renew	
1984-87 (.3)	.4
(P) Calpack Sensor, Renew	
1984-87 (.5)	.9
w/A.C. add (.1)	.1
(P) Tachometer Filter, Renew	
1984-87 (.4)	.6

PARTS 3A EMISSION CONTROLS 3A PARTS

	Part No.	Price
POSITIVE CRANKCASE VENTILATION		
Positive Crankcase Vent. Valve		
1.8L		
1983-87	◆25042116	5.00
1984-85-Turbo	◆25042995	5.50
2.0L		
1983-84	◆8995284	5.00
1985-87	◆25043690	7.00
2.8L		
1985-87	◆25043843	3.25
EVAPORATIVE EMISSION TYPE		
Vapor Canister		
1.8L		
1983-84-wo/Turbo	◆17064625	59.00
1985-87-wo/Turbo	◆17075840	30.00
1984-87-Turbo	◆17075844	40.00
2.0L		
1983-84	◆17075830	67.00
1985-87	◆17063013	39.00
1983-84-Canada	◆17064625	58.75
2.8L		
1985	◆17075854	66.00
CONTROLLED COMBUSTION TYPE		
Air Cleaner Motor		
1983-85	◆25041109	23.25
Air Cleaner Sensor (Temp.)		
1983-87-exc. 2.8L	◆8997787	18.75
2.8L	◆25036751	21.00
EXHAUST GAS RECIRCULATION SYSTEM		
E.G.R. Valve		
Replacement E.G.R. valves must be ordered according to the stamping number on the original valve.		
AIR INJECTOR REACTOR TYPE		
Air Injection Pump		
1983-exc. P.S.	◆7836275	192.00
Power Strg.	◆7835233	135.00
Air Pump Pulley		
1983	◆14081703	4.75
Deceleration Valve		
1983	◆14062774	17.50
COMPUTER COMMAND CONTROL EMISSION SYSTEM		
Calibrator (Prom)		
Order according to the code stamped on the existing calibrator.		
Controller (ECM)		
(Remanufactured)		
1.8L		
1983	◆1226100	110.25
1984-wo/Turbo	◆1226156	110.25
1985-87-wo/Turbo	◆1226864	110.25
1984-85-Turbo	◆1226460	110.25
1986-87	◆1227151	110.00
2.0L		
1983	◆1226026	110.25
1984	◆1226458	110.25
1985	◆1226867	110.00
1986-87-M.T.	◆1227165	110.00
A.T.	◆1226867	110.00
2.8L		
1985	◆1226870	110.00
Oxygen Sensor		
1983-87	◆8990741	28.75
Sensor (Coolant Temp.)		
1983-84	◆25036092	22.00
1985-87	◆25036708	12.75
Throttle Position Sensor		
1.8L		
1983-87	◆17078274	74.75
2.0L		
1983-84	◆17111262	63.00
1985-87	◆17110674	63.00
2.8L		
1985-87	◆17111606	40.25
Fast Idle Solenoid		
1983	◆1977626	N.L.
1984	◆1997688	14.50
Air Control Switching Valve		
1983-M.T.	◆17082701	80.50
A.T.	◆17070619	99.75

LABOR 4 ALTERNATOR & REGULATOR 4 LABOR

(Factory Time)	Chilton Time
(G) Delcotron Circuits, Test	
Includes: Test battery, regulator, Delcotron output.	
All models	.6
(M) Alternator Drive Belt, Renew	
Four	
In Line eng (.2)	.3
w/A.C. add (.5)	.5
OHC eng (.4)	.5
w/A.C. add (.3)	.3
V-6-Serpentine (.3)	.4
w/A.C. add (.3)	.3

LABOR 4 ALTERNATOR AND REGULATOR 4 LABOR

(Factory Time)	Chilton Time
(G) Delcotron Assembly, Renew	
Includes: Transfer fan and pulley.	
1983-87 (.5)	.7
w/Turbo add (.2)	.2
(G) Delcotron, R&R and Recondition	
Includes: Complete disassembly, replacement of parts as required, reassemble.	
1983-87 (1.3)	1.8
w/Turbo add (.2)	.2
(G) Delcotron Front Bearing, Renew	
Includes: R&R Delcotron, separate end frames.	
1983-87 (.6)	1.0
Renew rear brg add	.2
w/Turbo add (.2)	.2
(G) Delcotron Voltage Regulator, Test and Renew	
Includes: R&R, dissassemble and reassemble Delcotron.	
1983-87 (.8)	1.2
w/Turbo add (.2)	.2
(G) Voltmeter, Renew	
1983-87	
Skyhawk (1.1)	2.0
Firenza (.8)	1.5
All other models (.6)	1.1

PARTS 4 ALTERNATOR AND REGULATOR 4 PARTS

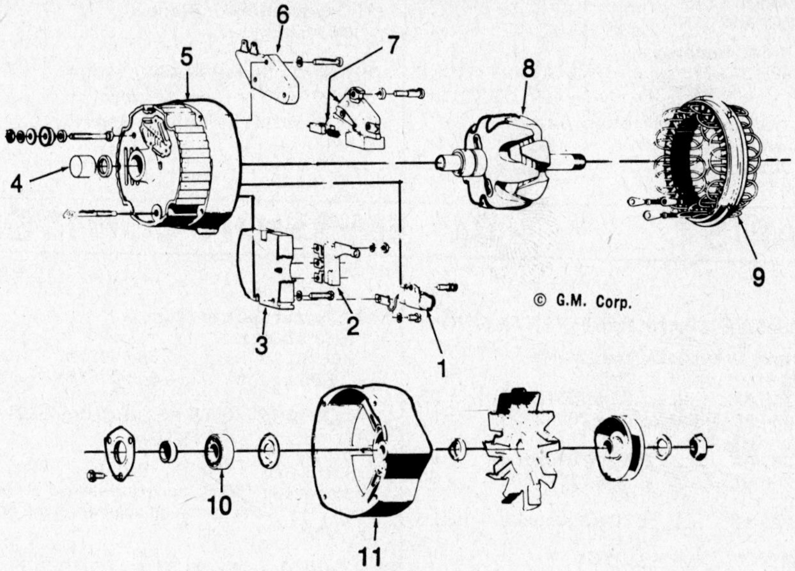

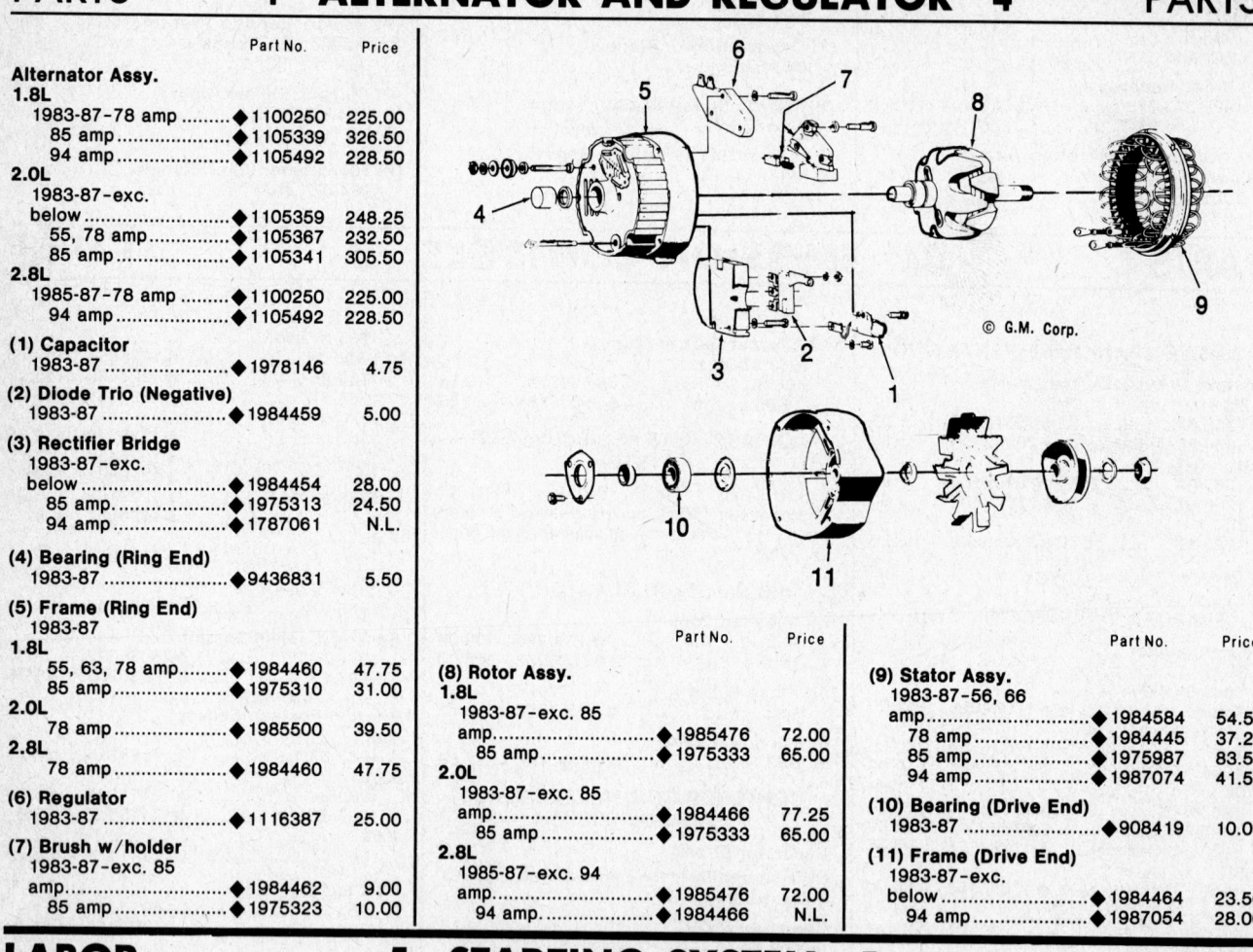

	Part No.	Price
Alternator Assy.		
1.8L		
1983-87-78 amp	◆1100250	225.00
85 amp	◆1105339	326.50
94 amp	◆1105492	228.50
2.0L		
1983-87-exc. below	◆1105359	248.25
55, 78 amp	◆1105367	232.50
85 amp	◆1105341	305.50
2.8L		
1985-87-78 amp	◆1100250	225.00
94 amp	◆1105492	228.50
(1) Capacitor		
1983-87	◆1978146	4.75
(2) Diode Trio (Negative)		
1983-87	◆1984459	5.00
(3) Rectifier Bridge		
1983-87-exc. below	◆1984454	28.00
85 amp.	◆1975313	24.50
94 amp	◆1787061	N.L.
(4) Bearing (Ring End)		
1983-87	◆9436831	5.50
(5) Frame (Ring End)		
1983-87		
1.8L		
55, 63, 78 amp	◆1984460	47.75
85 amp	◆1975310	31.00
2.0L		
78 amp	◆1985500	39.50
2.8L		
78 amp	◆1984460	47.75
(6) Regulator		
1983-87	◆1116387	25.00
(7) Brush w/holder		
1983-87-exc. 85 amp	◆1984462	9.00
85 amp	◆1975323	10.00
(8) Rotor Assy.		
1.8L		
1983-87-exc. 85 amp	◆1985476	72.00
85 amp	◆1975333	65.00
2.0L		
1983-87-exc. 85 amp	◆1984466	77.25
85 amp	◆1975333	65.00
2.8L		
1985-87-exc. 94 amp	◆1985476	72.00
94 amp.	◆1984466	N.L.
(9) Stator Assy.		
1983-87-56, 66 amp	◆1984584	54.50
78 amp	◆1984445	37.25
85 amp	◆1975987	83.50
94 amp	◆1987074	41.50
(10) Bearing (Drive End)		
1983-87	◆908419	10.00
(11) Frame (Drive End)		
1983-87-exc. below	◆1984464	23.50
94 amp	◆1987054	28.00

LABOR 5 STARTING SYSTEM 5 LABOR

(Factory Time)	Chilton Time
(G) Starter Draw Test (On Car)	
All models	.3
(G) Starter Assembly, Renew	
1983-87	
Four	
In Line eng (.6)	.9
OHC eng	
w/M.T. (.8)	1.1
w/A.T. (1.5)	2.2
V-6 (.6)	.9
w/A.C. add (.2)	.2
w/Turbo add (.2)	.2
Add draw test if performed.	
(G) Starter Assy., R&R and Recondition	
Includes: Turn down armature.	
1983-87	
Four	
In Line eng (1.4)	2.0
OHC eng	
w/M.T. (1.6)	2.3
w/A.T. (2.3)	3.3
V-6 (1.4)	2.0
w/A.C. add (.2)	.2
w/Turbo add (.2)	.2
Renew field coils add	.5
Add draw test if performed.	
(G) Starter Drive, Renew	
Includes: R&R starter.	
1983-87	
Four	
In Line eng (.7)	1.0
OHC eng	
w/M.T. (.9)	1.2
w/A.T. (2.0)	2.7
V-6 (.7)	1.0
w/A.C. add (.2)	.2
w/Turbo add (.2)	.2

LABOR 5 STARTING SYSTEM 5 LABOR

	(Factory Time)	Chilton Time
(G) Starter Motor Solenoid, Renew		
1983-87		
Four		
In Line eng	(.3)	.5
OHC eng		
w/M.T.	(.8)	1.2
w/A.T.	(1.5)	2.3
V-6	(.6)	1.0
w/A.C. add	(.2)	.2
w/Turbo add	(.2)	.2
Add draw test if performed.		
(G) Ignition Switch, Renew		
1983-85	(.5)	.9
1986-87	(.8)	1.1
(M) Battery Cables, Renew		
1983-87		
positive	(.4)	.5
negative	(.3)	.3
(M) Battery Terminals, Clean		
All models		.3

PARTS 5 STARTING SYSTEM 5 PARTS

	Part No.	Price
Starter Assy. (New)		
1.8L		
1983'	◆1109551	N.L.
E.F.I.	◆1998447	184.00
1984-87	◆1998529	184.00
2.0L		
1983	◆1109562	186.50
1984	◆1998503	170.25
1985-87	◆1998528	175.50
2.8L		
1985-87	◆1998533	170.25
(1) Frame (Commutator End)		
1983-87	◆1978292	6.50
(2) Brush Holder Kit		
1983-87	◆1893929	11.25
(3) Frame & Fields		
1.8L		
1983-87	◆1984522	75.00
2.0L		
1983-84	◆1985143	71.50
1985-87	◆1987277	71.00
2.8L		
1985-87	◆1985143	71.50
(4) Armature		
1.8L		
1983-85	◆1984504	107.50
1986-87	◆10495958	85.00
2.0L		
1983-85	◆1985138	N.L.
1986-87	◆10495931	71.50
2.8L		
1985-87	◆10495931	71.50

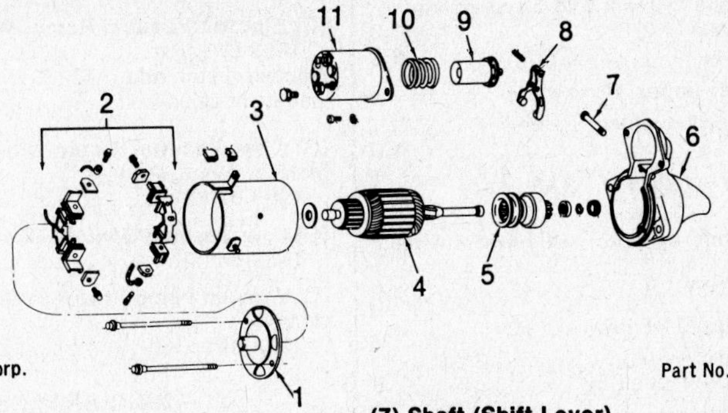

© G.M. Corp.

	Part No.	Price
(5) Drive Assy.		
1.8L		
1983-87	◆1984511	23.50
2.0L		
1983-87	◆1984511	23.50
2.8L		
1985-87	◆1984511	23.50
(6) Housing (Drive)		
1.8L		
1983-87	◆1984528	34.00
2.0L		
1983-87	◆1984734	27.00
2.8L		
1985-87	◆1984734	27.00
(7) Shaft (Shift Lever)		
1983-87	◆1945804	1.50
(8) Shift Lever		
1.8L		
1983-87-E.F.I.	◆1984501	5.00
2.0L		
1983-87	◆1984501	5.00
2.8L		
1985-87	◆1984501	5.00
(9) Plunger		
1983-87	◆1987391	6.75
(10) Spring (Plunger Return)		
1983-87	◆1978281	1.75
(11) Solenoid Switch		
1983-87	◆1114531	N.L.
Battery Cables		
Order by year and model.		

LABOR 6 BRAKE SYSTEM 6 LABOR

	(Factory Time)	Chilton Time
(G) Brake Pedal Free Play, Adjust		
All models		.3
(G) Brakes, Adjust (Minor)		
Includes: R&R wheels and adjust brakes thru access holes in drums. Fill master cylinder.		
two wheels		.4
Remove knock out plugs add, each		.1
(G) Bleed Brakes (Four Wheels)		
Includes: Fill master cylinder.		
All models	(.4)	.5
(G) Free Up or Renew Brake Self-Adjusting Units		
All models-one	(.4)	.6
both	(.6)	1.0
(G) Brake Shoes and/or Pads, Renew		
Includes: Install new or exchange brake shoes or pads, adjust service and hand brake. Bleed system.		
1983-87-front-disc	(.7)	1.1
rear-drum	(.9)	1.5
all four wheels		2.5

COMBINATIONS

Add To Brakes, Renew

See Machine Shop Operations

	(Factory Time)	Chilton Time
(G) RENEW WHEEL CYLINDER		
Each	(.2)	.2
(G) REBUILD WHEEL CYLINDER		
Each	(.2)	.3
(G) REBUILD CALIPER ASSEMBLY		
Each	(.5)	.6
(G) RENEW MASTER CYLINDER		
All models	(.5)	.8
(G) REBUILD MASTER CYLINDER		
All models	(.8)	1.0
(G) RENEW BRAKE HOSE		
Each	(.3)	.3
(G) RENEW BRAKE DRUM		
Each	(.1)	.1
(G) RENEW DISC BRAKE ROTOR		
Each	(.2)	.3

	(Factory Time)	Chilton Time
Resurface disc rotor, add-each		.9
Resurface brake drum, add-each		.5
(G) Brake Drum, Renew		
1983-87-one	(.3)	.4
both	(.5)	.7
(G) Brake Proportioner Valves, Renew		
Includes: Bleed system.		
1983-87-one	(.4)	.7
both	(.5)	1.0

LABOR — 6 BRAKE SYSTEM 6 — LABOR

	(Factory Time)	Chilton Time
(G) Brake System Failure Warning Switch, Renew		
1983-87	(.2)	.3
BRAKE HYDRAULIC SYSTEM		
(G) Wheel Cylinder, Renew		
Includes: Bleed system.		
1983-87-one	(.8)	1.0
both	(1.1)	1.9
(G) Wheel Cylinder, R&R and Rebuild		
Includes: Hone cylinder and bleed system.		
1983-87-one	(1.0)	1.3
both	(1.5)	2.3
(G) Master Cylinder, Renew		
Includes: Bleed complete system.		
1983-87	(.7)	1.0
(G) Master Cylinder, R&R and Rebuild		
Includes: Hone cylinder and bleed complete system.		
1983-87	(1.5)	1.9
(G) Brake Hose, Renew		
Includes: Bleed system.		
1983-87-front-one	(.5)	.8
both	(.6)	1.1
rear-each	(.5)	.7
(G) Brake System, Flush and Refill		
All models		1.2
POWER BRAKES		
(G) Power Brake Cylinder, Renew		
1983-87	(.7)	1.1
(G) Power Brake Cylinder, R&R and Recondition		
1983-87		
single	(1.2)	1.6
tandem	(1.4)	1.8
Recond M/Cyl add	(.8)	.8
(M) Vacuum Check Valve, Renew		
1983-87	(.3)	.5
(G) Electric Vacuum Pump, Renew		
1983-87	(.3)	.4
Recond piston add	(.2)	.2
Renew housing add	(.3)	.3
(G) Low Vacuum Brake Indicator Module Assy., Renew		
1983-87	(.2)	.3
(G) Low Vacuum Switch, Renew		
1983-87	(.2)	.3
(G) Vacuum Pump Pressure Switch, Renew		
1983-87	(.2)	.3
DISC BRAKES		
(G) Disc Brake Pads, Renew		
Includes: Install new disc brake pads only.		
1983-87	(.7)	1.1
(G) Disc Brake Rotor, Renew		
1983-87-one	(.5)	.7
both	(.8)	1.2
(G) Caliper Assembly, Renew		
Includes: Bleed complete system.		
1983-87-one	(.7)	1.0
both	(1.1)	1.5
(G) Caliper Assy., R&R and Recondition		
Includes: Bleed complete system.		
1983-87-one	(1.2)	1.5
both	(2.1)	2.5
PARKING BRAKE		
(G) Parking Brake, Adjust		
All models	(.3)	.4
(G) Parking Brake Lamp Switch, Renew		
1983-87	(.3)	.4
w/Fold down armrest add		.2
(G) Parking Brake Control Assy., Renew		
1983-87	(.6)	.9
(G) Parking Brake Equalizer, Renew		
1983-87	(.3)	.5
(G) Parking Brake Cables, Renew		
1983-87-front	(.9)	1.1
rear-each	(.6)	.9

PARTS — 6 BRAKE SYSTEM 6 — PARTS

	Part No.	Price
Shoe & Lining Kit (Rear)		
1983	◆12300194	34.00
1984	◆12300248	32.00
1985-87	◆12321412	43.00
Rear Wheel Cylinder Assy.		
1983-87	◆18007981	25.00
Rear Wheel Cylinder Repair Kit		
1983-87	◆18008650	7.00
Front Brake Hose		
1983-87-Right	◆9768144	11.00
Left	◆9768127	11.00
Rear Brake Hose		
1983-87	◆9766402	9.25
Master Cylinder Assy.		
1983-87-exc. 2.8L	◆18010087	206.50
1985-87-2.8L	◆18011938	175.00
Master Cylinder Repair Kit		
1983-87	◆18004853	22.50
Brake Drum (Rear)		
1983-87	◆1259649	69.75
POWER BRAKE UNIT		
Power Brake Booster (Vacuum)		
(Single power head)		
1983-87	◆18004550	220.50
(Tandem power head)		
1983	◆18007080	249.75
1984-M.T.	◆18007080	249.75
A.T.	◆18010907	250.25
1985-87	◆18012157	238.75
Power Brake Booster Repair Kit		
1983-84-w/ Tandem Head	◆18007880	51.50
1985-87	◆18013513	51.50
1983-87-w/Sngl. head	◆18010099	40.50
Vacuum Check Valve (Power Brakes)		
1983-87	◆18003614	6.00
PARKING BRAKE		
Parking Brake Lever		
1983-87-w/ Console	◆25513386	25.00
wo/Console	◆25525902	25.00
Front Cable (Parking Brake)		
1983-84	◆25509461	18.00
1985-87	◆25520289	13.75
Rear Cable (Parking Brake)		
1983-84-R.H.	◆25512352	12.75
L.H.	◆25512353	14.00
1985-87-L.H.	◆25520270	14.00
R.H.	◆25520271	14.00
Warning Switch (Master Cylinder)		
1983-87	◆18008614	26.00

PARTS — 6 DISC BRAKES 6 — PARTS

	Part No.	Price
(1) Caliper Assy.		
1983-(w/Non-vented Disc)		
right	◆18008664	139.25
left	◆18008663	139.25
1983-(w/Vented Disc)		
right	◆18008758	124.00
left	◆18011356	131.50
1984-right	◆18011668	163.25
left	◆18011356	131.50
1985-87-right	◆18011668	163.25
left	◆18011667	163.25
(2) Brake Pad Set		
1983-87	◆12321417	N.L.

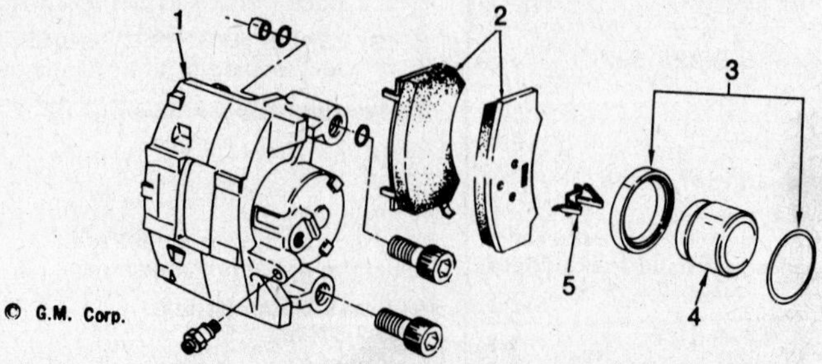

PARTS 6 DISC BRAKES 6 PARTS

	Part No.	Price
(3) Caliper Piston Repair Kit		
1983-84	◆18004873	7.25
1985-87	◆18011670	8.50
(4) Caliper Piston		
1983-87	◆18002866	13.00
(5) Spring (Shoe Retainer)		
1983-87	◆18011280	2.75

LABOR 7 COOLING SYSTEM 7 LABOR

(Factory Time)	Chilton Time
(M) Winterize Cooling System	
Includes: Run engine to check for leaks, tighten all hose connections. Test radiator and pressure cap, drain radiator and engine block. Add anti-freeze and refill system.	
All models	.5
(G) Thermostat, Renew	
1983-87-Four (.6)	.8
V-6 (.4)	.5
(G) Radiator Assembly, R&R or Renew	
Includes: Drain and refill cooling system.	
1983-87 (.7)	1.2
w/A.C. add (.3)	.3
w/A.T. add (.2)	.2
Renew side tank and/or gskt add,	
one (.7)	1.0
both (1.2)	1.7
ADD THESE OPERATIONS TO RADIATOR R&R	
(G) Boil & Repair	1.5
(G) Rod Clean	1.9
(G) Repair Core	1.3
(G) Renew Tank	1.6
(G) Renew Trans. Oil Cooler	1.9
(G) Recore Radiator	1.7
(M) Radiator Hoses, Renew	
1983-87	
upper (.3)	.4
lower (.4)	.5
both (.5)	.7
(M) Drive Belt, Renew	
1983-87-one (.3)	.4
each adtnl (.3)	.3
Serpentine (.3)	.4
(M) Drive Belt, Adjust	
1983-87-one (.2)	.3
each adtnl (.1)	.1
(G) Water Pump and/or Gasket, Renew	
1983-87	
Four	
O.H.C. eng (1.2)	2.0
In Line eng (.7)	1.3
V-6 (.6)	1.1
w/A.C. add (.2)	.2
w/P.S. add (.2)	.2
(G) Engine Coolant Fan and/or Motor, Renew	
1983-85 (.3)	.6

COOLING SYSTEM TUNE-UP

An Annual Cooling System Tune-Up Suggestion List should include (with some exceptions):

1. A visual check of the cooling system for indications of leaks or excessive oil content
2. Pressure check the cooling system for internal and external leaks with filler cap and neck adapter and tester
3. Check crankcase and automatic transmission oil for water content
4. Test coolant thermostat with radiator thermometer
5. Check temperature gauge for accuracy
6. Drain system and flush till clean
7. Clean foreign matter from radiator fins
8. Test radiator pressure cap with cap tester
9. Check fan blades and pulleys for alignment and damage
10. Internal and external inspection of all hoses for cracks and deterioration
11. Check core plugs (where possible) for seepage
12. Refill system with correct coolant and check for air locks
13. Check condition and tension of drive belts with tension gauge

All models 1.5

(Factory Time)	Chilton Time
1986-87	
Four (.4)	.6
V-6 (.5)	.7
(G) Engine Coolant Relay, Renew	
1983-87 (.2)	.3
(G) Coolant Fan Switch, Renew	
1983-87 (.3)	.4
(G) Coolant Fan Pressure Switch, Renew	
1983-87 (.2)	.4
(G) Temperature Gauge (Dash Unit), Renew	
1983-87	
Skyhawk (1.1)	2.0
Firenza (.8)	1.5
Cimarron (.5)	.9
All other models (.3)	.6

(Factory Time)	Chilton Time
(G) Temperature Gauge (Engine Unit), Renew	
1983-87 (.2)	.3
(G) Water Jacket Expansion Plugs, Renew (Side of Block)	
each (.3)	.5
Note: If necessary to R&R any component to gain access to plug, add appropriate time.	
(G) Heater Hoses, Renew	
1983-87-one (.5)	.6
all (.7)	.9
(G) Heater Core, R&R or Renew	
1983-87-wo/A.C. (.5)	.9
w/A.C. (.9)	2.0
ADD THESE OPERATIONS TO HEATER CORE R&R	
(G) Boil & Repair	1.2
(G) Repair Core	.9
(G) Recore	1.2
(G) Blower Motor, Renew	
1983-87-wo/A.C. (.3)	.6
w/A.C. (.3)	.6
(G) Blower Motor Switch, Renew	
1983-84-wo/A.C. (.4)	.6
w/A.C. (.4)	.6
1985-87-w/A.C. (.6)	1.0
wo/A.C. (.6)	1.0
(G) Blower Motor Resistor, Renew	
1983-87 (.2)	.3
(G) Temperature Control Assembly, Renew	
1983-87-wo/A.C. (.6)	1.0
w/A.C. (.6)	1.0
wo/Touch Control (.7)	1.1
w/Touch Control (.3)	.5
(G) Blower Motor Relay, Renew (High Speed)	
1983-87 (.2)	.3

PARTS 7 COOLING SYSTEM 7 PARTS

	Part No.	Price
Radiator Assy.		
Order by year and model.		
Radiator Hoses		
Order by year and model.		
Thermostat		
1.8L		
1983-87	◆3048009	9.50
2.0L		
1983-87	◆3043066	6.75
2.8L		
1985-87	◆3043066	6.75
Water Pump Assy.		
1.8L		
1983-87	◆94636985	95.00
2.0L		
1983-87	◆14089018	N.L.
2.8L		
1985-87	◆14089011	62.25
Engine Coolant Pump Inlet		
1983-87	◆14081794	9.00

PARTS 7 COOLING SYSTEM 7 PARTS

	Part No.	Price
Engine Coolant Motor		
(4 cyl. wo/Turbo)		
1983	◆22035623	77.00
1984-w/A.C.	◆22049801	61.00
1985-87-wo/A.C.	◆22048271	82.00
A.C.	◆22048271	82.00
(4 cyl. w/Turbo)		
1984-87-wo/A.C.	◆22048271	82.00
A.C.	◆22048577	86.75
(V6 engine)		
1985-87-A.C.	◆22048577	86.75
wo/A.C.	◆22048271	82.00
Coolant Motor Relay		
(4 cyl. wo/Turbo)		
1983	◆14073422	6.00
1984-w/1.8 eng.	◆10032082	6.00
w/2.0 eng.	◆14073422	6.00
1985-87	◆10032082	6.00
(4 cyl. Turbo)		
1984-87	◆10030790	21.75
(V6 engine)		
1985-87	◆10032082	6.00
Switch Coolant Temperature (Engine)		
1.8L		
1983-87-w/Gage	◆8993146	19.25
wo/Gage	◆25036373	9.75
2.0L		
1983-87	◆14047196	6.25
2.8L		
1985-87-(Probe)	◆3055285	2.75
Temperature Gauge (Dash)		
Cavalier		
1983-exc.		
Canada	◆8993793	23.50
Canada	◆25034073	25.00
1984-85-exc.		
Canada	◆25034405	24.00
Canada	◆25034407	25.00
Cimarron		
1983-85-exc.		
Canada	◆8993918	23.50
Canada	◆25034111	26.00
J2000 & 2000		
1983-exc. below	◆25034293	24.00
Rally gauges	◆25034290	24.00
Canada	◆25034293	24.00
1984-85-exc.		
Turbo	◆25034392	24.00
Turbo	◆25034417	23.50
Canada	◆25034395	24.00
Firenza		
1983-85-exc.		
Canada	◆25048091	49.00
Canada	◆25034283	44.00
Skyhawk		
1983-87-exc.		
Canada	◆6434401	52.80
Canada	◆6433807	48.25
Fan Belts		
Order by year and model.		
Heater Core		
1983-84 wo/A.C.	◆3047169	54.50
A.C.	◆3047786	59.75
A.C.	◆3058622	61.00
Blower Motor		
(wo/A.C.)		
1983	◆22029799	43.25
1984-87	◆22048574	47.50
(A.C.)		
1983-87	◆22020945	60.00
Resistor (Blower Motor)		
1983-87-wo/A.C.	◆9796480	2.50
A.C.	◆526897	4.50
Heater Control		
Cavalier		
1983	◆16028991	26.75
1984	◆16034571	24.75
1985-87-4 dr.	◆16034571	24.75
2 dr.	◆16030101	32.50
(wo/A.C.)		
1983	◆16028981	35.00
1984	◆16034581	35.25
1985-87	◆16052781	57.50
Cimarron		
1983	◆16027366	33.00
1984-87	◆16030176	119.75
Firenza-Skyhawk		
(wo/A.C.)		
1983	◆16023333	N.L.
1984-87	◆16034560	23.50
(w/A.C.)		
1983	◆16021853	33.00
1984-85	◆16034550	35.00
1986-87-exc.		
2.8L	◆16050180	36.50
2.8L	◆16034550	34.75
J2000 & 2000		
1983	◆16027372	30.25
1984	◆16032872	36.75
1985-87	◆16040692	36.75
Blower Motor Switch		
1983	◆16015256	6.00
1984-87	◆16032480	7.25

LABOR 8 EXHAUST SYSTEM 8 LABOR

(Factory Time)	Chilton Time
(G) Muffler, Renew	
1983-87 (.5)	.8
(G) Front Exhaust Pipe, Renew (To Converter)	
1983-87 (.6)	.9
(G) Rear Exhaust Pipe, Renew	
1983 (.6)	.9
(G) Catalytic Converter, Renew	
1983-87 (.8)	1.0
(G) Tail Pipe, Renew	
1983-87 (.3)	.4
(G) Intermediate Exhaust Pipe, Renew	
1984-87 (.6)	.9
(G) Exhaust Manifold, Renew	
1983-87	
Four	
O.H.C. eng (.5)	*.9
In Line eng (1.2)	1.8
*w/Turbo add (1.4)	1.4
V-6	
right side (1.5)	2.2
left side (.8)	1.2

COMBINATIONS

(G) Muffler, Exhaust and Tail Pipe, Renew	
All models	1.6

PARTS 8 EXHAUST SYSTEM 8 PARTS

	Part No.	Price
Muffler (w/tail pipe)		
Order by year and model.		
Exhaust Pipe (Front)		
1.8L-wo/Turbo		
1983-M.T.	◆10022867	41.75
A.T.	◆10022865	43.50
1984-87-M.T.	◆10029237	25.25
A.T.	◆10029235	25.25
1.8L-Turbo		
1984-87-M.T.	◆10028275	41.00
A.T.	◆10028272	40.00
2.0L		
1983-M.T.		
Note 1	◆14058578	46.00
Note 2	◆14074285	27.25
(Canada)		
1983	◆14040135	46.00
1983-A.T.		
Note 1	◆14058577	46.00
Note 2	◆14069256	27.75
1983-Note 1	◆14040134	46.00
Note 2	◆14069254	46.75
1984-M.T.	◆14074285	27.25
A.T.	◆14069256	27.75
1985-87-M.T.	◆14081494	28.50
A.T.	◆14081495	26.25
(Canada)		
1984-A.T. Note 1	◆14069254	46.75
Note 2	◆14074296	29.75
w/M.T. Note 1	◆14040135	46.00
Note 2	◆14074297	25.75
2.8L		
1985-87-M.T.	◆14081496	20.00
1985-87-A.T.	◆14081497	19.75

Note 1: Uses radial A-C compressor.
Note 2: Uses axial A-C compressor.

	Part No.	Price
Exhaust Pipe (Interm. Rear)		
1.8L-wo/Turbo		
1983-Note 1	◆25515393	31.00
Note 2	◆25516560	31.00
1984	◆25516560	31.00
1985-87-2 dr.	◆10037426	25.50
4 dr.	◆10037427	23.25
1.8L-Turbo		
1984	◆25518480	33.25
1985-87-2 dr.	◆10037424	33.50
4 dr. sedan	◆10037425	33.25

PARTS 8 EXHAUST SYSTEM 8 PARTS

	Part No.	Price
2.0L		
1983	◆14071831	31.00
1984	◆14081147	31.00
1985-2 dr.	◆14101329	26.00
4 dr. sedan	◆14089187	17.75
1986-87	◆14101329	26.00
(Canada)		
1984-Note 1	◆14081146	46.00
Note 2	◆14091364	N.L.
2.8L		
1985-2 dr	◆14089185	20.00
4 dr	◆14089184	20.00
1986-87	◆14101331	21.00

Note 1: muffler has 50MM O.D. outlet.
Note 2: muffler has 44MM O.D. outlet.

	Part No.	Price
Exhaust Manifold (w/Heat stove)		
1.8L		
1983-87	◆10019333	107.00
Turbo	◆10032111	94.25
2.0L engine		
1983-exc. below	◆14062724	111.00
Pulsair	◆14057917	113.00
1984	◆14057917	113.00
1985-87	◆14086036	114.00
2.8L eng.		
1985-L.H.	◆14077829	111.00
R.H.	◆14077836	111.00
1986-87-L.H.	◆10044845	N.L.
R.H.	◆10044850	N.L.

	Part No.	Price
Catalytic Converter		
1.8L		
1983-87	◆25056223	272.25
Turbo	◆25056689	250.25
2.0L		
1983-exc. below	◆8999706	312.25
Pulsair	◆25056301	306.25
1984-87	◆25056301	306.25
(Canada)		
1983-84	◆8999725	223.00
2.8L		
1985-87	◆25056731	320.00

LABOR 9 FRONT SUSPENSION 9 LABOR

(Factory Time) — Chilton Time

NOTE: On all front suspension operations alignment charges must be added if performed. Time given does not include alignment.

(M) Wheel, Renew
one (.5) 5

(G) Wheels, Balance
one 3
each adtnl 2

(M) Wheels, Rotate (All)
All models 5

(G) Check Alignment of Front End
All models 5
NOTE: Deduct if alignment is performed.

(G) Toe-In, Adjust
All models (.6) 8

(G) Caster and Camber, Check
Includes: Check and adjust toe.
All models (.6) 9
Adjust caster and camber
add-each side .... *.5
*Includes time to file struts as needed.

(G) Lower Control Arm Assy., Renew
Add alignment charges.
1983-87-one side (.6) 9
both sides (.9) 1.5

(G) Lower Control Arm Bushings, Renew
Add alignment charges.
1983-87-one side (.9) 1.3
both sides (1.6) 2.5

(G) Lower Ball Joint, Renew
Add alignment charges.
1983-87-one (.6) 1.0
both (1.1) 1.9

(G) Front Coil Springs, Renew
Includes: R&R front strut assy. Add alignment charges if necessary.
1983-87-one (.8) 1.2
both (1.5) 2.3

(G) Front Suspension Assy. Support, Renew
Add alignment charges if necessary.
1983-87-one (.9) 1.3
both (1.5) 2.5

(G) Front Shock Absorber Strut Cartridge, Renew
Includes: R&R front strut assy. Add alignment charges if necessary.
1983-87-one (1.0) 1.4
both (1.7) 2.7

(G) Front Shock Absorber Strut Assy., R&R or Renew
Add alignment charges if necessary.
1983-87-one (.8) 1.1
both (1.5) 2.0
Renew seat or insulator,
add-each (.1) 1

(G) Front Strut Bearing Mount Assy., Renew
Add alignment charges.
1983-87-one (.7) 1.0
both (1.2) 1.9

(G) Steering Knuckle Inner Dust Seal, Renew
1983-87-one (.9) 1.3
both (1.5) 2.4

(G) Front Stabilizer Shaft, Renew
1983-87 (.7) 1.0

(G) Front Stabilizer Shaft Bushing and/or Bracket, Renew
1983-87 (.4) 7

(G) Steering Knuckle and Arm (Integral), Renew
Add alignment charges.
1983-87-one (.9) 1.3
both (1.6) 2.5

(G) Front Wheel Bearing and Hub Assy., Renew
Includes: Renew oil seal.
1983-87-one side (.6) 1.0
both sides (1.1) 1.9
Renew inner dust seal add,
one (.4) 4
both (.6) 6

FRONT DRIVE AXLE

(G) Front Drive Axle, R&R or Renew
1983-87-one (1.2) 1.6
both (1.9) 2.4
Renew shaft add each (.3) 4
Renew C/V Joint add each side (.3) 4
Renew D/O Joint add each side (.3) 4
Renew C/V Joint boots add,
each (.2) 2

(G) Axle Shaft Seal, Renew
Includes: Raise vehicle, R&R caliper, mark cam bolts.
1983-87-one (.6) 1.0
both (1.1) 1.9

PARTS 9 FRONT SUSPENSION 9 PARTS

	Part No.	Price
(1) Front Wheel Hub Bearing		
1983	◆7466917	157.75
1984	◆7470001	N.L.
1985-87	◆7470004	166.00
(2) Steering Knuckle		
1983 (vented whl.)		
right	◆14078588	85.75
left	◆14078587	85.75
1984-right	◆14078588	85.75
left	◆14078587	85.75
1985-87-right	◆14066984	85.75
left	◆14066983	85.75

	Part No.	Price
(3) Front wheel Seal (Inner)		
1983-84	◆14084118	4.50
1985-87	◆14086700	4.50
(4) Front Drive Axle Kit		
(M.T.)		
1983-right	◆7842256	508.00
left	◆7842258	430.00
1984-right	◆7844764	415.00
left	◆7844766	415.00
1985-87-Four speed		
right	◆7845395	N.L.
left	◆7847102	520.00

	Part No.	Price
1985-87-Five Speed		
right	◆7846868	434.00
left	◆7846870	434.00
(A.T.)		
1983-right	◆7842344	430.00
left	◆7842345	430.00
1984-right	◆7844762	435.00
left	◆7844752	483.00
1985-87 (1.8L)		
L.H.	◆7846869	500.00
R.H.	◆7845347	N.L.

PARTS 9 FRONT SUSPENSION 9 PARTS

	Part No.	Price
(2.0L)		
L.H.	◆7846869	500.00
R.H.	◆7847624	434.00
(2.8L)		
L.H.	◆7849409	440.00
(5) Ball Joint (Lower)		
1983-87	◆9767781	52.00
(6) Grommet Kit		
1983-87	◆14039143	4.75
(7) Lower Control Arm		
1983-87-right	◆14026620	93.50
left	◆14026619	93.50
(8) Bushing. (Lower control arm)		
1983-87	◆14026628	7.00
(9) Bracket (support)		
(right)		
1983	◆14059934	77.50
1984-w/M.T.	◆14076632	77.50
w/A.T.	◆14076630	77.50
1985-87-M.T.	◆14076786	74.00
A.T.	◆14076788	74.00
(left)		
1983	◆14046383	77.50
1984	◆14076629	77.50
1985-87	◆14076787	74.00
(10) Stabilizer Shaft (Front)		
1983-84		
22mm dia.	◆14059935	47.50
24mm dia.	◆14059937	47.50
28mm dia.	◆14059936	47.50
1985-87-24mm	◆14076605	47.50
28mm	◆14076607	47.50
(11) Insulator (stabilizer)		
1983		
22mm dia.	◆14026673	1.25
24mm dia.	◆14038791	1.25
28mm dia.	◆14038789	1.25
1984-87		
22mm dia.	◆10030872	1.00
24mm dia.	◆14085145	1.25
28mm dia.	◆14085147	1.25
(12) Strut Mount		
1983-exc. below	◆9769604	48.25
Cimmarron	◆9769668	48.25
1984-exc. below	◆17980538	48.25
Cimarron, Firenza	◆17980539	48.25
Cavalier w/H.D. susp.	◆17980764	48.25
1985-87-exc. below	◆17981435	48.25
Cimarron, Firenza	◆17981437	48.25

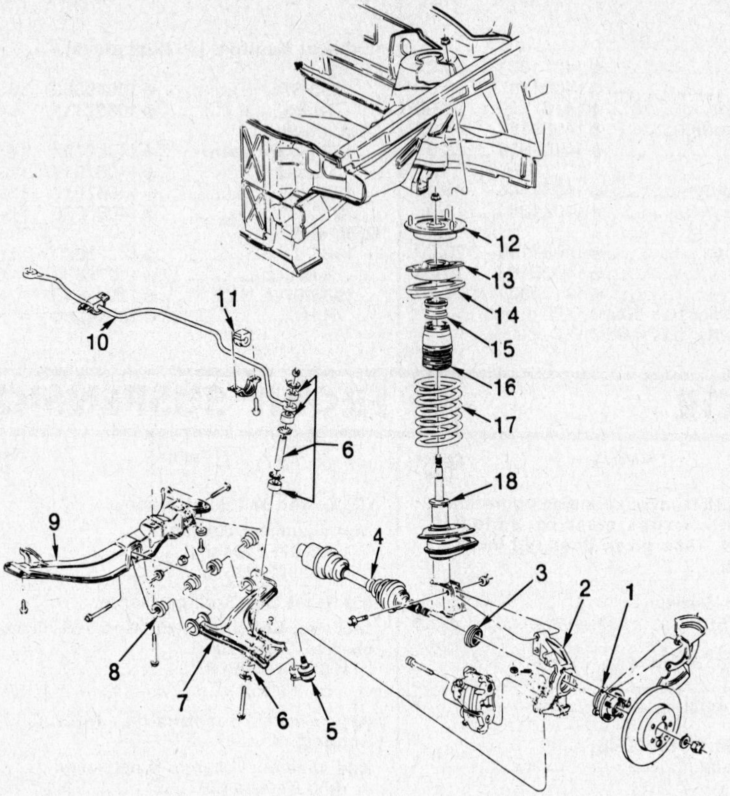

	Part No.	Price
(13) Spring Seat		
1983-87	◆14051008	3.75
(14) Spring Insulator		
1983-87-upper	◆14059999	3.75
lower	◆14060000	3.75
(15) Strut Bumper		
1983	◆90125889	2.75
1984-87	◆14076624	18.50
(16)Strut Shield		
1983	◆14077713	5.25
1984-85	◆14077713	5.25
1986-87	◆14089592	5.50

	Part No.	Price
(17) Coil Spring		
Order by year and model.		
(18) Shock Absorber (w/strut)		
1983-84-right	◆22040430	117.00
left	◆22040429	117.00
1985-87-exc. sta. wag.		
right	◆22047911	114.25
left	◆22047910	114.25
1985-87-sta. wag.		
right	◆22047907	114.25
left	◆22047906	114.25

PARTS 9 FRONT DRIVE AXLE 9 PARTS

TRI-POT DESIGN

	Part No.	Price
(1) Joint Kit		
1983	◆7847467	N.L.
1984-exc. Turbo	◆7845028	200.00
Turbo	◆7845026	175.00
1985-A.T.	◆7846867	N.L.
M.T.	◆7847111	N.L.
1986-87-M.T.	◆26000321	205.00
A.T.	◆7846867	N.L.
(2) Seal Retainer		
1983-87	◆7828314	10.50
(3) Seal Kit		
1983-84-exc. Turbo	◆7845020	45.00
Turbo	◆7845021	34.00

	Part No.	Price
(4) Seal Retaining Clamp		
1983-84	◆7836673	5.00
1985-87	◆7847135	3.75
(5) Axle Shaft		
(M.T.)		
(wo/Turbo)		
1983-84-left	◆7841392	51.00
right	◆7842053	69.00
(Turbo)		
1984-right	◆7843766	90.00
left	◆7843767	70.00
1985-w/four speed (M-17)		
right	◆7845187	74.00
left	◆7846170	62.25

	Part No.	Price
1985-w/four speed (M-19)		
right	◆7846273	62.25
left	◆7846274	47.00
1986-87-right	◆7848751	58.00
left	◆7846170	62.25
(A.T.)		
1983-right	◆7841783	54.00
left	◆7841388	72.00
1984-right	◆7841783	N.L.
left	◆7843976	N.L.
1985-right		
exc. 2.0L	◆7845152	44.00
2.0L	◆7847486	62.25
1985-left	◆7846275	47.00
1985-87-w/2.8L		
left	◆7849226	47.00

PARTS 9 FRONT DRIVE AXLE 9 PARTS

	Part No.	Price
(6) Housing Assy.		
(M.T.)		
1983-85-exc.		
Turbo	◆7842378	111.00
Turbo	◆7843920	136.00
1986-87-exc.		
Turbo	◆7843920	N.L.
Turbo	◆7843920	N.L.
(A.T.)		
1983-85-right	◆7842378	111.00
left	◆7842380	111.00
1986-87	◆7842380	N.L.
(7) Spider Assy.		
1983-84-exc.		
below	◆7845022	71.00
Turbo	◆7845025	92.00
1985-exc. 2.0L	◆7846866	120.00
M.T. (M-17)	◆7847113	120.00
1986-87-A.T.,		
R.H.	◆7846865	110.00
(M.T.)		
right	◆7847114	110.00
left	◆7847113	120.00

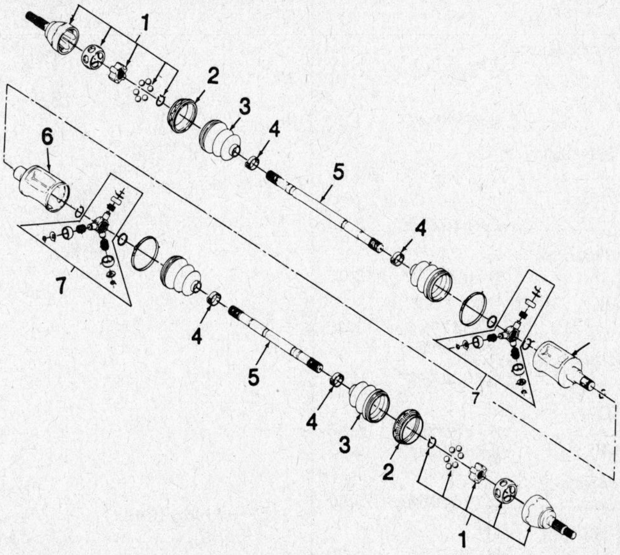

LABOR 11 STEERING GEAR 11 LABOR

(Factory Time) — Chilton Time

STANDARD STEERING

(G) Tie Rod End, Renew

Includes: Reset toe-in.

	Chilton Time
1983-87-one (.7)	.9
both (1.0)	1.2
Renew boot seal add-each	.1

(G) Inner Tie Rod, Renew

Includes: Reset toe-in.

	Chilton Time
1983-85-one (1.1)	1.4
both (1.7)	2.3
1986-87-one (.7)	.9
both (1.0)	1.2

(G) Steering Wheel, Renew

1983-87 (.2)	.3

(G) Horn Contact and Cancelling Cam, Renew

1983-87 (.3)	.5

(G) Multifunction Lever, Renew

All models (.2)	.4
w/Cruise Control add (.5)	.5

(G) Steering Column Lock Actuator Parts, Renew

1983-85	
std colm (.8)	1.4
tilt colm (.9)	1.6
w/Cruise control add (.2)	.2
1986-87	
std colm (1.4)	1.9
tilt colm (.9)	1.6

(G) Steering Column Upper Bearing, Renew

1983-85-std column (.8)	1.4
tilt column (.9)	1.6
w/Cruise control add (.2)	.2
1986-87	
std colm (1.3)	1.8
tilt colm (.5)	.9

(G) Steering Column Lower Bearing, Renew

1983-87 (.9)	1.2

(G) Steering Flexible Coupling, Renew

Includes: R&R gear assy; where required.

1983-85 (2.1)	3.0
1986-87 (1.0)	1.4

(G) Steering Column, R&R

1983-87 (.9)	1.2

(G) Steering Column Assy., R&R and Recondition

1983-85-std column (1.5)	2.1
tilt column (1.6)	2.2
w/Cruise control add (.2)	.2
1986-87	
std colm (2.0)	2.8
tilt colm (2.3)	3.1

(G) Steering Gear Assembly, R&R or Renew

1983-87 (1.6)	3.1

(P) Steering Gear Assy., R&R and Recondition

Includes: Disassemble, renew necessary parts, reassemble and adjust.

1983-87 (2.3)	4.5

POWER STEERING

(G) Trouble Shoot Power Steering

Includes: Test pump and system pressure. Check pounds pull on steering wheel and check for leaks.

All models	.5

(M) Check and Fill Reservoir

All models	.2

(M) Pump Drive Belt, Renew

1983-87 (.3)	.4
w/A.C. add (.5)	.5

(G) Power Steering Gear Assy., R&R or Renew

1983-87 (2.3)	4.0

(G) Power Steering Short Rack Assy., Renew

Includes: Transfer parts as required. Reset toe-in.

All models (2.5)	4.5

(P) Power Steering Gear Assy., R&R and Recondition

1983-87 (3.3)	5.4

(G) Power Steering Pump Shaft Oil Seal, Renew

1983-87 (.7)	1.2
w/Turbo add (.2)	.2

(G) Pump Flow Control Valve, Renew

1983-87 (.4)	.7

(G) Power Steering Pump, Renew

1983-87	
OHC Four (.9)	1.4
In-Line 4 & V-6 (.5)	1.0
w/Turbo add (.2)	.2

(P) Power Steering Pump, R&R and Recondition

1983-87	
OHC Four (1.4)	2.0
In-Line 4 & V-6 (1.0)	1.6
w/Turbo add (.2)	.2

(G) Power Steering Reservoir, Renew

1983-85 (.3)	.5
1986-87 (.5)	.8

(M) Power Steering Hoses, Renew

1983-87-pressure-each (.4)	.6
return-each (.3)	.5

PARTS 11 STEERING GEAR - (STANDARD) 11 PARTS

	Part No.	Price
(1) Damper Kit (Viscous)		
1983-87	◆7838393	47.75
(2) Retaining Ring		
1983-87	◆5684948	1.50
(3) Pinion & Bearing		
1983-87	◆7834430	94.50
(4) Bearing		
1983-87	◆7819358	6.25
(5) Coupling (Flange)		
1983-87	◆7836277	38.00
(6) Seal (Dash)		
1983-87	◆7837994	12.00
(7) Cover (Housing End)		
1983-87	◆7834439	8.75
(8) Grommet		
1983-84-R.H.	◆7834437	5.50
1985-87-R.H.	◆7847007	9.75
(9) Guide (Rack)		
1983-87	◆7841034	15.50
(10) Bearing (Guide)		
1983-87	◆7841034	15.50
(11) Boot Clamp (67mm Dia.)		
1983-87	◆7840234	5.00
(12) Retainer Bushing (Boot)		
1983-87	◆7836972	3.50
(13) Boot Kit		
1983-87	◆7844790	24.25
(14) Boot Clamp (56mm Dia.)		
1983-87	◆7840235	5.00

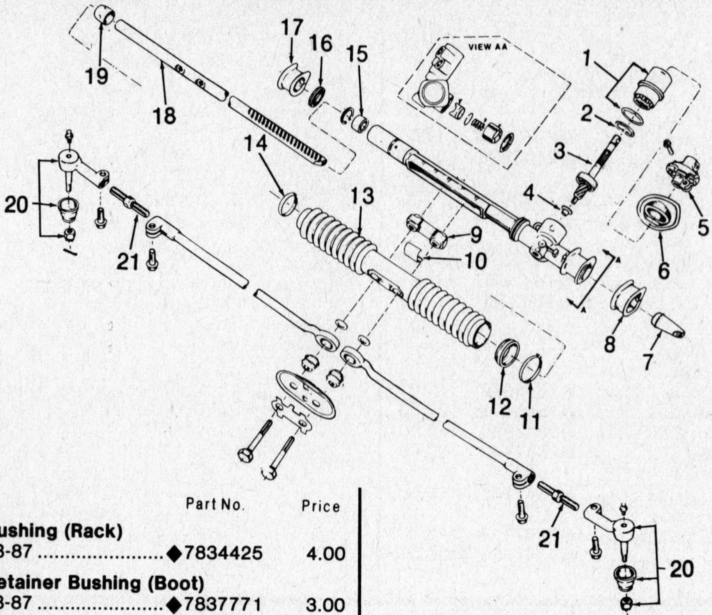

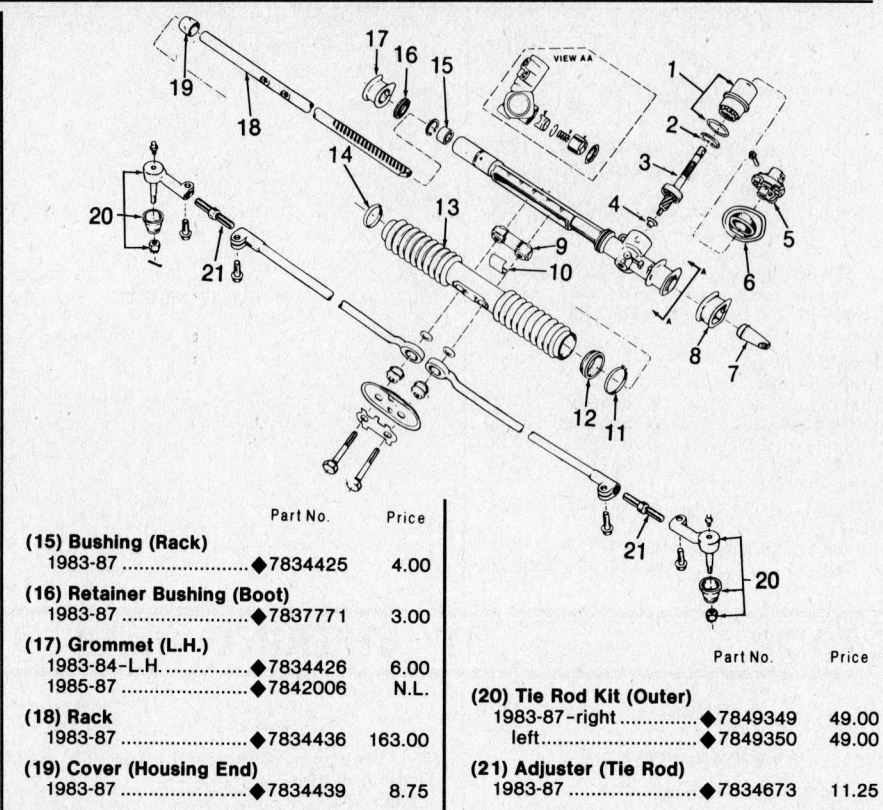

	Part No.	Price
(15) Bushing (Rack)		
1983-87	◆7834425	4.00
(16) Retainer Bushing (Boot)		
1983-87	◆7837771	3.00
(17) Grommet (L.H.)		
1983-84-L.H.	◆7834426	6.00
1985-87	◆7842006	N.L.
(18) Rack		
1983-87	◆7834436	163.00
(19) Cover (Housing End)		
1983-87	◆7834439	8.75

	Part No.	Price
(20) Tie Rod Kit (Outer)		
1983-87-right	◆7849349	49.00
left	◆7849350	49.00
(21) Adjuster (Tie Rod)		
1983-87	◆7834673	11.25

PARTS 11 POWER STEERING GEAR 11 PARTS

	Part No.	Price
Gear Kit (Short Rack Assy)		
Does not include inner and outer tie-rods.		
(exc. 2.8L)		
1983-84	◆7847127	289.00
1985-87	◆7848080	269.00
(2.8L)		
1985-87	◆7849109	269.00
(1) Coupling (Flange)		
1983-87	◆7836230	38.00
(2) Seal (Dash)		
1983-87	◆7837993	12.00
(3) Bearing Kit (Stub Shaft)		
1983-84	◆7829888	19.25
1985-87	◆7838279	19.50
(4) Line Assy Kit (R.H.)		
1983-84	◆7840915	15.75
1985-87	◆7846634	15.75
(5) Line Assy. Kit (L.H.)		
1983-84	◆7840916	15.75
1985-87	◆7846633	15.75
(6) Valve Kit (Pinion)		
1983-84	◆7844630	260.00
1985-87	◆7847236	260.00
1984-87-2.8L	◆7844631	260.00
(7) Rack Bearing		
1983-87	◆7834432	15.00
(8) Spring (Adjuster)		
1983-87	◆7838791	1.50
(9) Plug (Adjuster)		
1983-87	◆7834435	7.75
(10) Grommet (L.H.)		
1983-84	◆7834426	6.00
1985-87	◆7847006	9.75

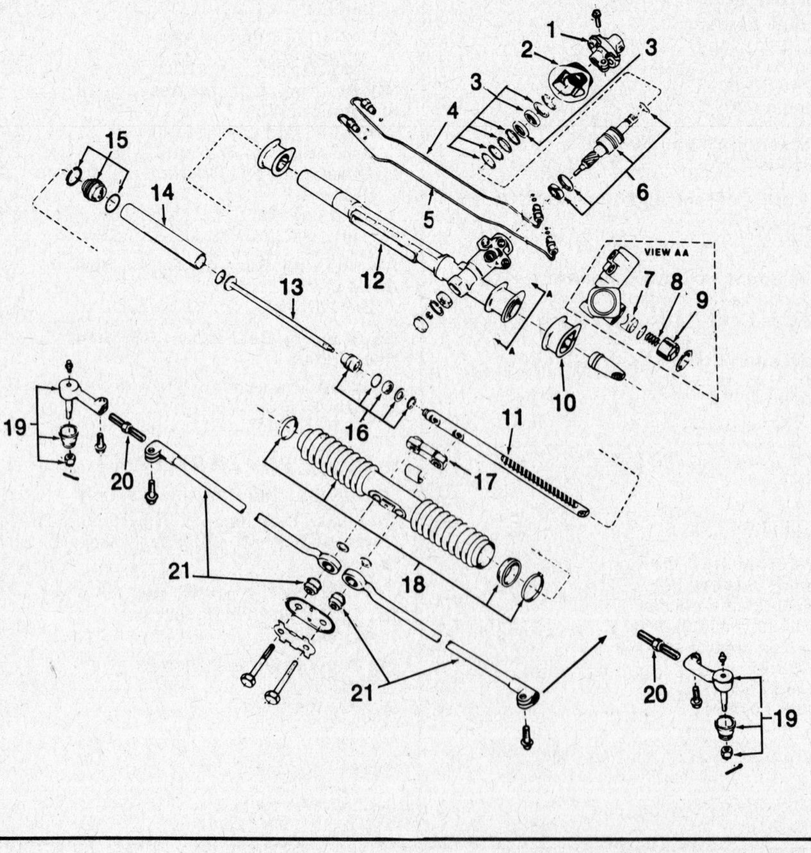

PARTS 11 POWER STEERING GEAR 11 PARTS

	Part No.	Price
(11) Rack		
1983-87-exc. below	◆7833655	163.00
1985-87-2.0L	◆7837719	163.00
(12) Housing Assy. (Rack & Pinion)		
1983	◆7840380	177.00
1984	◆7846636	177.00
1985-87	◆7846635	177.00
(13) Seal Kit		
1983-87	◆7840991	31.50
(14) Tube (Cylinder)		
1983-87	◆7834958	7.25
(15) Bulkhead Kit (Outer)		
1983-87	◆7838285	41.25
(16) Guide Kit		
1983-87	◆7840976	33.25
(17) Guide (Rack)		
1983-87	◆7841034	15.50
(18) Boot Kit		
1983-87 (exc. 2.8 eng.)	◆7844790	24.25
1985-87(2.8L) R.H.	◆7848858	24.25
L.H.	◆7848859	24.25
(19) Tie Rod Kit (Outer)		
1983-87-right	◆7849349	49.00
left	◆7849350	49.00
(20) Adjuster (tie rod)		
1983-87	◆7834673	11.25
(21) Tie Rod Kit (Inner)		
1983-right	◆7837664	49.50
left	◆7837667	49.50
1984-87-right	◆7849351	49.50
left	◆7849353	49.50

PARTS 11 POWER STEERING PUMP 11 PARTS

	Part No.	Price
Power Steering Pressure Hose		
Order by year and model.		
Power Steering Pump		
1.8L-wo/Turbo		
1983-87	◆7842626	199.00
1.8L-Turbo		
1984-87	◆7841344	199.00
2.0L		
1983-84	◆7842628	169.00
1985-87	◆7849438	192.00
2.8L		
1985-station wagon	◆7844910	169.00
exc. station wagon	◆7849700	192.00
1986-87	◆7849700	192.00
(1) Drive Shaft		
1983-84	◆7837321	39.50
1985-87-exc. 1.8L	◆7840633	58.00
1.8L	◆7837321	39.50
(2) Seal Kit		
1983-84	◆7834853	11.00
1985-87-exc. 1.8L	◆7840566	11.00
1.8L	◆7834853	11.00
(3) Pump Housing		
1.8L		
1983-87-exc. Turbo	◆7840525	62.75
Turbo	◆7840157	62.75
2.0L		
1983-84	◆7840517	62.75
1985-87	◆7844818	62.75
2.8L		
1985	◆7845129	100.00
1986-87	◆7849698	100.00
(4) Thrust Plate		
1.8L		
1983-87-wo/turbo	◆7836369	13.75
w/turbo	◆7840139	14.25

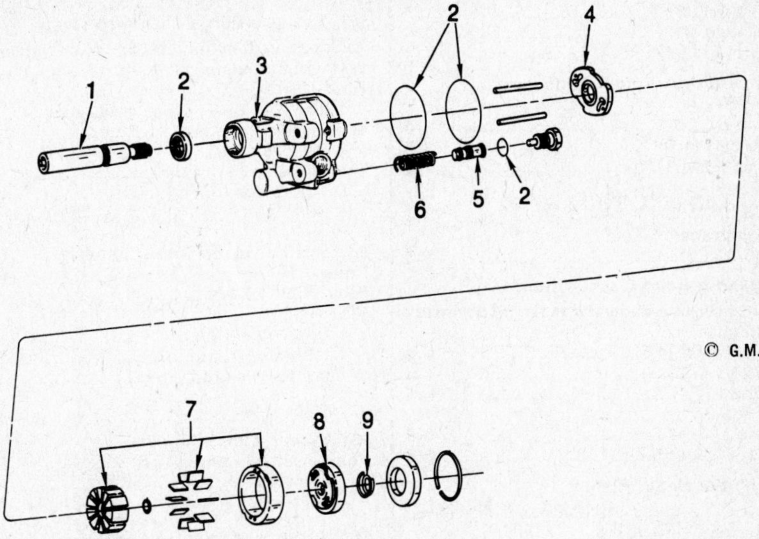

	Part No.	Price
2.0L & 2.8L		
1983-84	◆7836369	13.75
1985-87	◆7840139	14.25
(5) Valve (Control)		
1983-84-exc. Turbo	◆7809229	10.25
Turbo	◆7841851	15.50
1985-87-exc. 1.8L	◆7841851	15.50
1.8L	◆7809229	10.50
(6) Spring (Flow Control)		
1983-87	◆5688037	1.50
(7) Rotor & Vane Kit		
1.8L-wo/Turbo		
1983-87	◆7838790	92.00
1.8L-Turbo		
1984-87	◆7841845	92.00
2.0L		
1983-84	◆7838790	92.00
1985-87	◆7841845	92.00
2.8L		
1985-87-rotor kit	◆7841845	92.00
(8) Plate (Pressure)		
1983-84	◆7839669	14.25
1985-87	◆7840080	14.25
(9) Spring (Pressure Plate)		
1983-84-exc. below	◆7839667	1.00
1985-87-Turbo	◆7839667	1.00
1985-87-2.8L & 2.0L	◆7839989	3.00

LABOR 12 CYLINDER HEAD & VALVE SYSTEM 12 LABOR

(Factory Time) Chilton Time

O. H. C. FOUR

(G) Compression Test

	Chilton Time
1983-87 (.3)	.6

(G) Cylinder Head Gasket, Renew

Includes: Clean carbon and make all necessary adjustments.

	Chilton Time
1983-87 (2.7)	3.8
w/P.S. add (.3)	.3
w/Turbo add (1.3)	1.3

(G) Cylinder Head, Renew

Includes: Transfer all components, reface valves, clean carbon.

	Chilton Time
1983-87 (3.4)	4.7
w/P.S. add (.3)	.3
w/Turbo add (1.3)	1.3

(P) Clean Carbon and Grind Valves

Includes: R&R cylinder head, grind valves and seats. Minor engine tune up.

	Chilton Time
1983-87 (4.4)	6.1
w/P.S. add (.3)	.3
w/Turbo add (1.3)	1.3

LABOR 12 CYLINDER HEAD & VALVE SYSTEM 12 LABOR

(Factory Time)	Chilton Time
(G) Camshaft Housing Cover and/or Gasket, Renew	
1983-87 (.4)	.6
w/Turbo add (.4)	.4
(G) Rocker Arms, Renew	
1983-87	
one cyl (.6)	.8
all cyls (.9)	1.2
w/Turbo add (.1)	.1
(G) Valve Springs, Caps and/or Seals, Renew	
1983-87	
one cyl (2.0)	2.8
each adtnl cyl (.2)	.2
w/Turbo add (.1)	.1
(G) Valve Adjuster, Renew	
1983-87	
one cyl (.6)	.8
all cyls (1.0)	1.4
w/Turbo add (.1)	.1
(G) Rocker Arm Guide, Renew	
1983-87	
one cyl (.6)	.8
all cyls (1.0)	1.4
w/Turbo add (.1)	.1

IN LINE FOUR & V-6

(Factory Time)	Chilton Time
(G) Compression Test	
1983-87 (.3)	.6
(G) Cylinder Head Gasket, Renew	
Includes: Clean carbon and make all necessary adjustments.	
Four–1983-84 (4.5)	6.3
1985-87 (3.2)	4.5
w/P.S. add (.4)	.4
V-6–1985-87	
one side (4.7)	6.8
both sides (5.8)	8.4
(G) Cylinder Head, Renew	
Includes: Transfer all components, reface valves, clean carbon.	
Four–1983-84 (6.7)	9.4
1985-87 (4.9)	6.8
w/P.S. add (.4)	.4
V-6–1985-87	
one side (5.4)	7.8
both sides (7.1)	10.3

COMBINATIONS

Add to Valve Job

See Machine Shop Operations

(Factory Time)	Chilton Time
(G) DRAIN, EVACUATE & RECHARGE AIR CONDITIONING SYSTEM	
All models (.5)	1.0
(G) ROCKER ARM STUD, RENEW	
Each (.2)	.2
(G) HYDRAULIC VALVE LIFTERS, DISASSEMBLE AND CLEAN	
Each (.2)	.2
(G) DISTRIBUTOR, RECONDITION	
All models (.5)	.8
(G) CARBURETOR, RECONDITION	
All models (.9)	1.2
(P) VALVE GUIDES, REAM OVERSIZE	
Each (.2)	.2

(Factory Time)	Chilton Time
(P) Clean Carbon and Grind Valves	
Includes: R&R cylinder head, grind valves and seats. Minor engine tune up.	
Four–1983-84 (6.0)	9.0
1985-87 (4.6)	6.5
w/P.S. add (.4)	.4
V-6–1985-87	
one side (6.0)	8.7
both sides (8.2)	12.0
(G) Rocker Arm Cover Gasket, Renew	
Four–1983-87 (.6)	.8
V-6–1985-87	
right side (1.7)	2.5
left side (.4)	.7
both sides (2.0)	2.9
(G) Rocker Arms, Renew	
Four–1983-87-one cyl (.8)	1.0
all cyls (1.2)	1.6
(G) Rocker Arms and/or Push Rods, Renew	
V-6–1985-87	
one cyl-right side (1.9)	2.8
one cyl-left side (.6)	1.0
one cyl-both sides (2.4)	3.5
each adtnl cyl	.1

(Factory Time)	Chilton Time
(G) Rocker Arm Stud, Renew	
Includes: Drain and refill cooling system.	
Four–1983-87-one (.9)	1.2
each adtnl (.2)	.2
V-6–1985-87	
one-right side (2.0)	2.9
one-left side (.7)	1.1
each adtnl (.3)	.3
(G) Valve Springs and/or Valve Stem Oil Seals, Renew (Head on Car)	
Four–1983-87-one cyl (1.0)	1.5
each adtnl cyl (.4)	.4
V-6–1985-87	
one cyl-right side (2.1)	3.0
one cyl-left side (.8)	1.2
one cyl-each side (2.8)	4.0
each adtnl cyl (.4)	.4
(G) Valve Push Rods and/or Lifters, Renew	
Four–1983-87-one cyl (.7)	1.1
all cyls (1.1)	1.8
(G) Valve Tappets (Lifters), Renew	
Four–1983-87	
one cyl (.8)	1.2
each adtnl cyl (.1)	.2
V-6–1985-87	
one cyl (3.2)	4.6
one cyl-each side (3.3)	4.8
all cyls-both sides (3.8)	5.5

PARTS 12 CYLINDER HEAD & VALVE SYSTEM 12 PARTS

1.8L & 2.0L

	Part No.	Price
(1) Cylinder Head		
1.8L		
1983-87	♦94642734	3.55
2.0L		
1983-87	♦14081798	266.00
(2) Cylinder Head Gasket		
1.8L		
1983-87	♦94627761	13.00
Turbo	♦90200347	13.00
2.0L		
1983-84	♦14058724	13.00
1985-87	♦14086017	13.00
(3) Valve (Intake)		
1.8L		
1983-87	♦90136613	14.50
2.0L		
1983-87	♦14004097	14.50
(4) Valve (Exhaust)		
1.8L		
1983-87	♦90136620	32.25

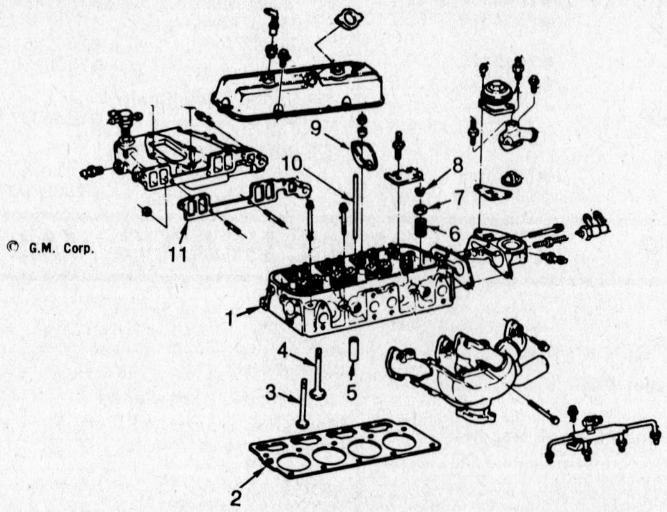

PARTS 12 CYLINDER HEAD & VALVE SYSTEM 12 PARTS

	Part No.	Price
2.0L		
1983-87	◆14004098	17.00
(5) Valve Lifter		
1.8L		
1983-87	◆5233315	11.00
2.0L		
1983-87	◆5233335	9.50
(6) Valve Spring (w/Damper)		
1.8L		
1983-87	◆90118914	3.75
2.0L		
1983-87	◆477292	3.00
(7) Cap (w/Valve Spring)		
1.8L		
1983-87	◆90118784	3.75
2.0L		
1983-87	◆14004099	1.00
(8) Key		
1.8L		
1983-85	◆360505	1.00
2.0L		
1983-87	◆360505	1.00
(9) Rocker Arm (w/Ball)		
1.8L		
1983-87	◆90106142	8.25
2.0L		
1983-87	◆14002446	4.75
(10) Push Rod		
1983-87	◆14018769	3.00
(11) Manifold Gasket (Intake)		
1.8L		
1983	◆10019083	3.00
1984-87	◆10028243	3.50
(Turbo)		
1983	◆10028243	3.50
1984-87	◆10028243	3.50
2.0L		
1983-87	◆14018791	3.50

PARTS 12 CYLINDER HEAD & VALVE SYSTEM 12 PARTS

	Part No.	Price
V6-2.8L		
Engine Overhaul Gasket Kit		
1985	◆14091347	9.00
1986-87	◆14101336	9.25
(1) Cylinder Head		
1985-87	◆14054879	250.00
(2) Cylinder Head Gasket		
1985-87	◆14090561	N.L.
(3) Push Rod		
1985-87	◆476525	5.00
(4) Valve Lifter		
1985-87	◆5234212	N.L.
(5) Intake Valve (Standard)		
1985-87	◆14031328	14.00

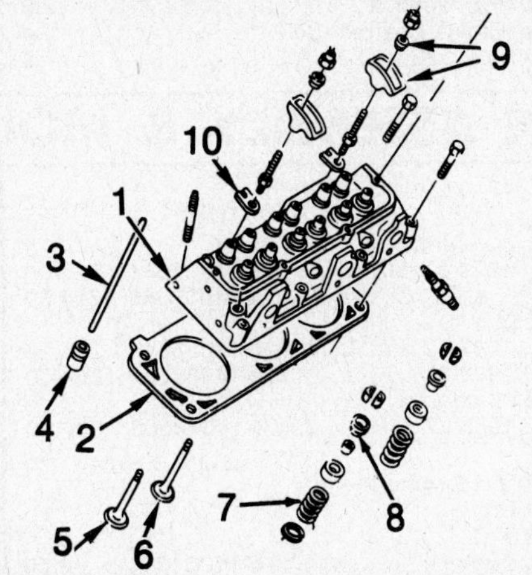

	Part No.	Price
(6) Exhaust Valve (Standard)		
1985-87	◆14031332	15.50
(7) Valve Spring		
1985-87	◆14030029	3.50
(8) Rotator (Cap)		
1985-87	◆14004099	1.00
(9) Rocker Arm		
1985-87	◆14002446	4.75
(10) Guide (Push Rod)		
1985-87	◆476531	1.50
Gasket Kit (Intake Manifold)		
1985-87-center	◆14083328	3.50
side	◆14089022	5.75
plenum	◆14089058	2.25

LABOR 13 ENGINE ASSEMBLY & MOUNTS 13 LABOR

(Factory Time) — Chilton Time

O. H. C. FOUR

(G) Engine Assembly, Remove & Install

Does not include transfer of any parts or equipment.

	Chilton Time
1983-87	5.4
w/A.C. add	.3
w/P.S. add	.2
w/Turbo add	1.3

(G) Engine Assembly, Renew

Includes: R&R engine assembly, transfer all component parts not supplied with replacement engine. Minor tune up.

	Chilton Time
1983-85 (6.0)	9.4
1986-87 (8.1)	11.7
w/A.C. add (.3)	.3
w/P.S. add (.2)	.2
w/Turbo add (1.3)	1.3

(P) Cylinder Block, Renew (w/All Internal Parts Less Cylinder Head and Oil Pan)

Includes: R&R engine assembly, transfer all component parts not supplied with replacement engine. Clean carbon, grind valves. Minor tune up.

	Chilton Time
1983-85 (7.4)	15.5
1986-87 (12.0)	17.4
w/A.C. add (.3)	.3
w/P.S add (.2)	.2
w/Turbo add (1.3)	1.3

(P) Cylinder Block, Renew (w/Pistons, Rings & Bearings)

Includes: R&R engine assembly, transfer all component parts not supplied with replacement engine. Clean carbon, grind valves. Minor tune up.

	Chilton Time
1983-85 (8.5)	16.5
1986-87 (14.9)	21.6
w/A.C. add (.3)	.3
w/P.S. add (.2)	.2
w/Turbo add (1.3)	1.3

(P) Engine Assy., R&R and Recondition

Includes: Rebore block, install new pistons, rings, rod and main bearings. Clean carbon, grind valves. Tune engine.

	Chilton Time
1983-87 (16.7)	23.2
w/A.C. add (.3)	.3
w/P.S. add (.2)	.2
w/Turbo add (1.3)	1.3

(P) Engine Assembly, Recondition (In Car)

Includes: Expand or renew pistons, install new rings, pins, rod and main bearings. Clean carbon, grind valves. Tune engine.

	Chilton Time
1983-87 (12.5)	20.8
w/A.C. add (.3)	.3
w/P.S. add (.2)	.2
w/Turbo add (1.3)	1.3

(G) Engine Mounts, Renew

Front

	Chilton Time
1983-87-each (.6)	.9

IN LINE FOUR & V-6

(G) Engine Assembly, Remove & Install

Does not include transfer of any parts or equipment.

	Chilton Time
Four-1983-87	5.5
V-6-1985-87	4.5
w/A.C. add (.5)	.5
w/P.S. add (.3)	.3
w/Cruise Control add (.1)	.1
w/A.T. add (.4)	.4

(G) Engine Assembly, Renew

Includes: R&R engine assembly, transfer all component parts not supplied with replacement engine. Minor tune up.

	Chilton Time
Four-1983-84 (5.4)	9.5
1985-87 (4.7)	6.8
V-6-1985-87 (5.2)	8.0
w/A.C. add (.8)	.8
w/P.S. add (.3)	.3
w/Cruise Control add (.1)	.1
w/A.T. add (.4)	.4

LABOR 13 ENGINE ASSEMBLY & MOUNTS 13 LABOR

(Factory Time) Chilton Time

(P) Cylinder Block, Renew (w/All Internal Parts Less Cylinder Head and Oil Pan)

Includes: R&R engine assembly, transfer all component parts not supplied with replacement engine. Clean carbon, grind valves. Minor tune up.

Four–1983-84 (10.1)	**15.6**
1985-87 (8.6)	**12.4**
V-6–1985-87 (12.1)	**16.8**
w/A.C. add (.8)	**.8**
w/P.S. add (.3)	**.3**
w/Cruise Control add (.1)	**.1**
w/A.T. add (.4)	**.4**

(P) Cylinder Block, Renew (w/Pistons, Rings and Bearings)

Includes: R&R engine assembly, transfer all component parts. Clean carbon, grind valves. Minor tune up.

Four–1983-84 (11.6)	**18.0**
1985-87 (10.9)	**15.8**
V-6–1985-87 (15.0)	**20.8**
w/A.C. add (.8)	**.8**
w/P.S. add (.3)	**.3**
w/Cruise Control add (.1)	**.1**
w/A.T. add (.4)	**.4**

(P) Engine Assembly, R&R and Recondition

Includes: Rebore block, install new pistons, rings, rod and main bearings. Clean carbon, grind valves. Tune engine.

Four–1983-87 (19.5)	**26.3**
V-6–1985-87 (20.4)	**26.0**
w/A.C. add (.8)	**.8**
w/P.S. add (.3)	**.3**
w/Cruise Control add (.1)	**.1**
w/A.T. add (.4)	**.4**

(P) Engine Assembly, Recondition (In Car)

Includes: Expand or renew pistons, install new rings, pins, rod and main bearings. Clean carbon, grind valves. Tune engine.

Four–1983-87 (14.2)	**21.0**
V-6–1985-87 (15.6)	**21.0**
w/A.C. add (.8)	**.8**
w/P.S. add (.3)	**.3**
w/Cruise Control add (.1)	**.1**
w/A.T. add (.4)	**.4**

(G) Engine Mounts, Renew

Four	
1983-87-rear (.7)	**1.0**
front (.5)	**.9**
both (.9)	**1.5**
V-6	
1985-87-front (.6)	**.9**
rear (.7)	**1.0**
both (.9)	**1.5**

PARTS 13 ENGINE ASSEMBLY & MOUNTS 13 PARTS

	Part No.	Price
Engine Assy. (Partial)		
Includes, crankshaft, crankshaft bearings, pistons and connecting rod bearings.		
1.8L-wo/Turbo		
1983-87-M.T.	◆94622449	1025.25
A.T.	◆94622389	1025.25
1.8L-Turbo		
1984-87-M.T.	◆94637066	1025.25
A.T.	◆94637067	1025.25
2.0L		
1983-84	◆14089032	1061.25
1985-87	◆14089033	1061.00
2.8L		
1985	◆14089007	1230.00
1986-87	◆14101358	1230.00
Cylinder Block		
Includes, crankshaft bearing, piston and rings.		
1.8L-wo/Turbo		
1983-87-M.T.	◆94622387	721.00
A.T.	◆94622388	721.00
1.8L-Turbo		
1984-87-M.T.	◆94637064	721.00
A.T.	◆94637065	721.00
2.0L		
1983	◆14063647	714.25
1985-87	◆14089034	754.00
2.8L engine		
1985-87	◆14089003	942.00
Front Engine Mounts		
1.8L		
A.T.		
1983-84	◆14051034	30.00
1985-87-M.T.	◆14074074	28.00
(wo/Turbo)		
1983-84	◆14051035	30.00
1985-87	◆14074074	28.00
(Turbo)		
1984	◆14074098	30.00
1985-87	◆14074077	28.00
2.0L		
(A.T.)		
1983-84-wo/A.C.	◆14026688	26.25
A.C.	◆14069253	27.50
(M.T.)		
1983-84-wo/A.C.	◆14026689	26.25
A.C.	◆14069252	27.50
1985-87	◆14074074	28.00
2.8L		
1985-87-M.T.	◆14074076	28.50
A.T.	◆14074075	28.00
Rear Engine Mount		
4 Cyl		
1983-87	◆14080987	30.25
V6		
1985-87-M.T.	◆14085064	29.75
A.T.	◆14074092	28.50

LABOR 14 PISTONS, RINGS & BEARINGS 14 LABOR

(Factory Time) Chilton Time

O. H. C. FOUR

(P) Rings, Renew (See Engine Combinations)

Includes: Remove cylinder top ridge, deglaze cylinder walls. Clean piston and ring grooves. Minor tune up.

1983-87-one cyl (4.8)	**6.7**
all cyls (6.9)	**9.6**
w/A.C. add (.3)	**.3**
w/P.S. add (.2)	**.2**
w/Turbo add (1.3)	**1.3**

(P) Pistons or Connecting Rods, Renew

Includes: Remove cylinder top ridge, deglaze cylinder walls. Minor tune up.

1983-87-one cyl (4.8)	**7.0**
all cyls (6.9)	**10.8**
w/A.C. add (.3)	**.3**
w/P.S. add (.2)	**.2**
w/Turbo add (1.3)	**1.3**

(P) Connecting Rod Bearings, Renew

Includes: Plastigauge bearings.

1983-87 (2.1)	**3.0**
w/A.C. add (.2)	**.2**

COMBINATIONS

See Machine Shop Operations

(G) DRAIN, EVACUATE & RECHARGE AIR CONDITIONING SYSTEM	
All models (.5)	**1.0**
(G) ROCKER ARM STUD, RENEW	
Each (.2)	**.2**
(G) HYDRAULIC VALVE LIFTERS, DISASSEMBLE AND CLEAN	
Each (.2)	**.2**
(G) DISTRIBUTOR, RECONDITION	
All models (.5)	**.8**
(G) CARBURETOR, RECONDITION	
All models (.9)	**1.2**
(G) CYLINDER HEADS, R&R (ENGINE REMOVED)	
Four	
OHC eng (1.3)	**1.7**
In-Line eng (1.1)	**1.4**
V-6	
one (3.0)	**3.9**
both (3.5)	**4.5**
(G) CONNECTING ROD, RENEW (ENGINE DISASSEMBLED)	
Four	
OHC eng-each (.4)	**.5**
In-Line eng-each (.3)	**.4**
V-6-each (.3)	**.4**
(P) VALVE GUIDES, REAM OVERSIZE	
Each (.2)	**.2**
(G) DEGLAZE CYLINDER WALLS	
Each (.1)	**.1**
(G) REMOVE CYLINDER TOP RIDGE	
Each (.1)	**.1**
(G) TIMING CHAIN OR GEARS, RENEW (COVER REMOVED)	
All models (.3)	**.5**
(G) MAIN BEARINGS, RENEW (PAN REMOVED)	
All models	**1.5**
(G) PLASTIGAUGE BEARINGS	
Each (.1)	**.1**
(M) OIL FILTER ELEMENT, RENEW	
All models (.3)	**.3**

LABOR 14 PISTONS, RINGS & BEARINGS 14 LABOR

(Factory Time) Chilton Time

IN LINE FOUR & V-6

(P) Rings, Renew (See Engine Combinations)

Includes: Remove cylinder top ridge, deglaze cylinder walls. Clean piston and ring grooves. Minor tune up.

Four–1983-84–one cyl (5.8)	8.1
all cyls (7.0)	9.8
1985-87–one cyl (5.0)	7.0
all cyls (6.4)	8.9
w/A.C. add (.1)	.1
w/P.S. add (.4)	.4
V-6–1985-87	
one cyl (6.1)	8.8
one cyl–each side (7.7)	11.1
all cyls–both sides (9.6)	13.9

(P) Pistons or Connecting Rods, Renew

Includes: Remove cylinder top ridge, deglaze cylinder walls. Minor tune up.

Four–1983-84–one cyl (5.8)	8.4
all cyls (7.0)	11.0
1985-87–one cyl (5.7)	7.7
all cyls (7.7)	11.7
w/A.C. add (.1)	.1
w/P.S. add (.4)	.4
V-6–1985-87	
one cyl (6.1)	9.1
one cyl–each side (7.7)	11.7
all cyls–both sides (10.3)	15.7

(P) Connecting Rod Bearings, Renew

Includes: Plastigauge bearings.

Four–1983-87 (2.6)	3.6
w/A.C. add (.1)	.1
w/A.T. add (.3)	.3
V-6–1985-87 (2.3)	3.6

PARTS 14 PISTONS, RINGS & BEARINGS 14 PARTS

	Part No.	Price
(1) Piston Ring Set (Std.)		
1.8L		
1983-87	◆94622443	16.75
2.0L		
1983-84	◆14059045	17.50
1985-87	◆14089062	17.50
2.8L		
1985-87	◆14089059	17.00

Standard size listed, other sizes available.

	Part No.	Price
(2) Piston Assy. (Std.)		
1.8L		
1983-87	◆94622378	60.25
Turbo	◆94637808	60.75
2.0L		
1983-84	◆14057964	50.25
1985-87	◆14079572	50.25
2.8L		
1985	◆14092910	48.50
1986-87	◆14094104	48.50
(3) Connecting Rod Assy.		
1.8L		
1983-87	◆90136076	43.75

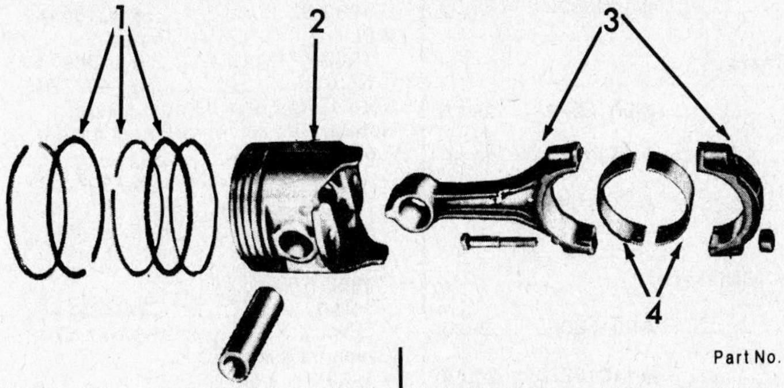

	Part No.	Price
2.0L		
1983-84	◆14049735	44.50
1985-87	◆14079552	44.50
2.8L		
1985-87	◆476521	36.50

	Part No.	Price
(4) Connecting Rod Bearing		
1.8L		
1983-87	◆94642795	6.75
2.0L		
1983-87	◆18009469	7.50
2.8L		
1985-87	◆18008492	N.L.

LABOR 15 CRANKSHAFT & DAMPER 15 LABOR

(Factory Time) Chilton Time

O. H. C. FOUR

(P) Crankshaft and Main Bearings, Renew

Includes: R&R engine, check all bearing clearances.

1983-85 (6.2)	9.6
1986-87 (10.3)	14.9
w/A.C. add (.3)	.3
w/P.S. add (.2)	.2
w/Turbo add (1.3)	1.3

(P) Main Bearings, Renew

Includes: Check all bearing clearances.

1983-87 (2.3)	3.8
w/A.C. add (.2)	.2

(P) Main and Rod Bearings, Renew

Includes: Check all bearing clearances.

1983-87 (2.9)	5.0
w/A.C. add (.2)	.2

(G) Crankshaft Pulley, Renew

1983-87 (.6)	1.0
w/.A.C. add (.3)	.3

(G) Rear Main Bearing Oil Seals, Renew or Repack

Includes: R&R transmission.

1983-87 (3.0)	4.5

IN LINE FOUR & V-6

(P) Crankshaft and Main Bearings, Renew

Includes: R&R engine, check all bearing clearances.

Four–1983-87 (7.2)	12.0
V-6–1985-87 (8.1)	12.0
w/A.C. add (.8)	.8
w/P.S. add (.2)	.2
w/Cruise Control add (.1)	.1
w/A.T. add (.4)	.4

(P) Main Bearings, Renew

Includes: Check all bearing clearances.

Four–1983-87 (2.5)	4.3
V-6–1985-87 (2.1)	3.0
w/A.C. add (.1)	.1
w/A.T. add (.3)	.3

(P) Main and Rod Bearings, Renew

Includes: Check all bearing clearances.

Four–1983-87 (3.1)	5.5
V-6–1985-87 (3.5)	4.8
w/A.C. add (.1)	.1
w/A.T. add (.3)	.3

(G) Crankshaft Pulley, Renew

Four–1983-87 (.5)	1.0
V-6–1985-87 (.5)	1.0
w/A.C. add (.2)	.2
w/P.S. add (.1)	.1

(G) Harmonic Balancer, Renew

Includes: Renew timing cover oil seal.

Four–1983-87 (.7)	1.4
V-6–1985-87 (.6)	1.1
w/A.C. add (.2)	.2
w/P.S. add (.1)	.1

(G) Rear Main Bearing Oil Seals, Renew or Repack

Four–1983–w/M.T. (1.8)	2.6
w/A.T. (2.1)	3.0
w/P.S. add (.1)	.1
1984-87–one piece	
first design (6.2)	*9.2
second design	
w/M.T. (2.5)	4.2
w/A.T. (3.1)	4.8
V-6–1985-87	
w/M.T (2.8)	4.0
w/A.T. (3.4)	4.9
*w/A.C. add (.8)	.8
w/P.S. add (.2)	.2
w/Cruise control add (.1)	.1

PARTS 15 CRANKSHAFT & DAMPER 15 PARTS

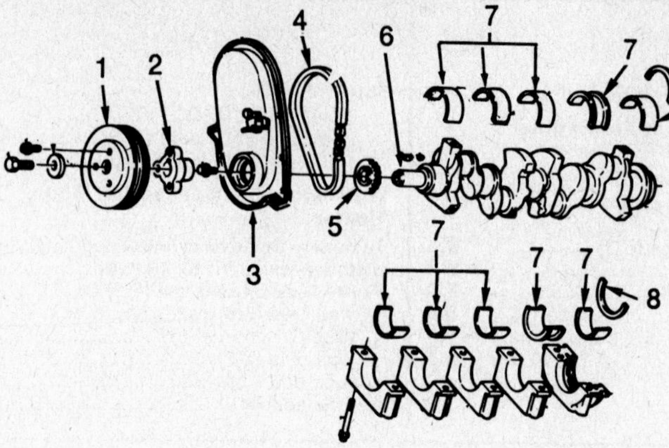

	Part No.	Price
(1) Pulley		
1.8L-wo/Turbo		
1983	◆10022418	33.75
1984	◆10027439	27.00
1985	◆10031363	20.00
1.8L-Turbo		
1984-87	◆10027862	33.75
2.0L		
1983-87	◆14018709	32.50
2.8L		
1985-87	◆14102596	39.75
(2) Hub		
1983-87-4 cyl	◆14018708	28.75
(3) Crankcase Cover		
1.8L		
1983-85	◆10022087	12.00
Turbo	◆10027642	12.00
2.0L		
1983-87	◆14089019	29.00
2.8L		
1985-87	◆14089021	85.00
(4) Timing Chain		
1.8L		
1983-87	◆90122429	28.75
2.0L		
1983-87	◆14062702	30.50
2.8L		
1985	◆14078821	30.75
1986-87		
(5) Sprocket (Crankshaft)		
1.8L		
1983-87	◆90156062	24.25
2.0L		
1983-87	◆14018770	20.25
2.8L		
1985-87	◆14074400	14.25

	Part No.	Price
(6) Crankshaft		
1.8L		
1983-87	◆90156142	291.00
2.0L		
1983-87-Note 1	◆14049740	285.00
Note 2	◆14077243	285.00
Note 1: Has rear oil seal slinger.		
Note 2: Has no rear oil seal slinger.		
2.8L		
1985-87	◆14077817	336.00
(7) Crankshaft Bearings		
1.8L		
(Brown marking)		
1983-87-exc. below	◆94622442	14.25
No. 3	◆94625718	28.25
(Green marking)		
1983-87-exc. below	◆94622445	14.25
No. 3	◆94625719	28.25

	Part No.	Price
2.0L		
1983-87-No. 1, 2, 3	◆18008496	11.50
No. 4	◆14067693	23.75
rear	◆14089137	17.50
2.8L		
1985-87-No. 1, 4	◆18012472	13.25
No. 2	◆18012473	13.25
No. 3	◆18012478	24.75
(8) Rear Seal Kit		
1.8L		
1983-87	◆90122607	34.25
2.0L		
1983-84	◆14081761	14.00
1985-87	◆14085829	14.50
2.8L		
1985-87	◆14085829	14.50

LABOR 16 CAMSHAFT & TIMING GEARS 16 LABOR

(Factory Time)	Chilton Time
O. H. C. FOUR	
(G) Camshaft Drive Belt Cover, R&R or Renew	
1983-87 (.8)	1.2
(G) Camshaft Drive Belt, Adjust	
1983-87 (1.1)	1.5
w/A.C. add (.2)	.2
w/P.S. add (.2)	.2
(G) Camshaft Drive Belt, Renew	
1983-87 (1.4)	1.9
w/A.C. add (.2)	.2
w/P.S. add (.2)	.2
(G) Camshaft Timing Gear, Renew	
1983-87 (.6)	1.0
Renew crank gear add (.8)	.8
Renew cam oil seal add (.2)	.2
w/Turbo add (.1)	.1

(Factory Time)	Chilton Time
(G) Camshaft, Renew	
1983-87 (2.0)	2.8
Renew cam carrier add (.9)	.9
w/Turbo add (.1)	.1
IN LINE FOUR & V-6	
(G) Timing Cover Oil Seal, Renew	
Four-1983-87 (.8)	1.4
V-6-1985-87 (.6)	1.2
w/A.C. add (.2)	.2
w/P.S. add (.1)	.1
(G) Timing Cover or Gasket, Renew	
Four-1983-87 (1.2)	1.9
V-6-1985-87 (2.2)	3.2
w/A.C. add (.2)	.2
w/P.S. add (.1)	.1

(Factory Time)	Chilton Time
(G) Timing Chain or Camshaft Gear, Renew	
Four-1983-87 (1.5)	2.4
V-6-1985-87 (2.3)	3.7
w/A.C. add (.2)	.2
w/P.S. add (.1)	.1
Renew crankshaft gear add (.2)	.2
(G) Camshaft, Renew	
Includes: R&R engine assembly.	
Four-1983-84 (7.3)	10.9
1985-87 (5.5)	7.8
V-6-1985-87 (8.1)	11.7
w/A.C. add (.8)	.8
w/P.S. add (.2)	.2
w/Cruise Control add (.1)	.1
w/A.T. add (.4)	.4

PARTS 16 CAMSHAFT & TIMING GEARS 16 PARTS

	Part No.	Price
(1) Timing Cover		
1.8L-wo/Turbo		
1983-87	◆10022087	12.00
1.8L-Turbo		
1984-85	◆10027642	12.00
2.0L		
1983-87	◆14089019	29.00
2.8L		
1985-87	◆14089021	85.00

	Part No.	Price
(2) Timing Chain		
1.8L		
1983-87	◆90122429	28.75
2.0L		
1983-87	◆14062702	30.50
2.8L		
1985	◆14028821	N.L.
1986-87	◆14102671	28.25

	Part No.	Price
(3) Camshaft Sprocket		
1.8L		
1983-87	◆90106633	32.50
2.0L		
1983-87	◆14018766	21.50
2.8L		
1985-87	◆14074399	18.50

PARTS 16 CAMSHAFT & TIMING GEARS 16 PARTS

	Part No.	Price
Crankshaft Sprocket		
1.8L		
1983-87	◆90156062	24.25
2.0L		
1983-87	◆14018770	20.25
2.8L		
1985-87	◆14074000	N.L.
(4) Thrust Plate		
1983-87	◆14018764	4.25
(5) Camshaft		
1.8L-wo/Turbo		
1983	◆90169203	129.00
1984-87	◆90200003	127.00
1.8L-Turbo		
1984-87	◆90106632	129.00
2.0L		
1983	◆14057996	127.00
1984	◆14079565	127.00
1985-87	◆14058000	127.00
2.8L		
1985-87	◆14031378	122.00

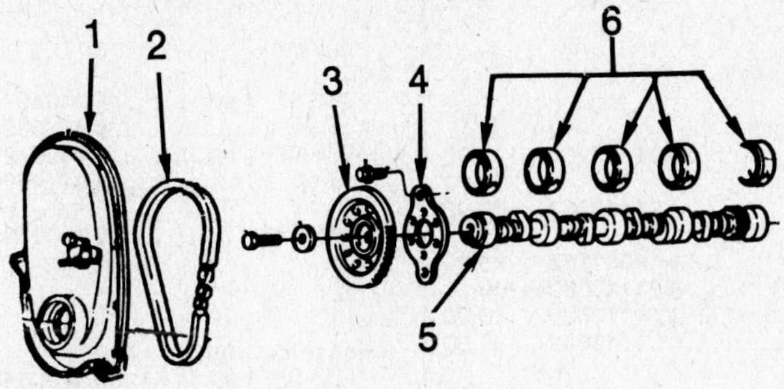

	Part No.	Price
(6) Camshaft Bearings		
4 Cyl		
1983-87-No. 1	◆14095620	6.00
No. 2, rear	◆14002535	14.00
No. 3, 4	◆14002534	14.00
V6		
1985-87-No. 1	◆14033120	13.50
No. 2, 3	◆14002534	14.00
rear	◆14002535	14.00

LABOR 17 ENGINE OILING SYSTEM 17 LABOR

(Factory Time)	Chilton Time
O. H. C. FOUR	
(G) Oil Pan or Gasket, Renew	
1983-87 (1.3)	1.8
w/A.C. add (.2)	.2
(G) Pressure Test Engine Bearings (Pan Off)	
All models	1.0
(G) Oil Pump, Renew	
1983-87 (2.9)	3.9
w/A.C. add (.2)	.2
(M) Oil Filter Element, Renew	
1983-87 (.2)	.3

(Factory Time)	Chilton Time
IN LINE FOUR & V-6	
(G) Oil Pan or Gasket, Renew	
Four-1983-87 (1.3)	1.7
w/A.C. add (.1)	.1
w/A.T. add (.3)	.3
V-6-1985-87 (.8)	1.2
(P) Pressure Test Engine Bearings (Pan Off)	
All models	1.0
(G) Oil Pump, Renew	
Four-1983-87 (1.4)	1.9
w/A.C. add (.1)	.1
w/A.T. add (.3)	.3
V-6-1985-87 (.9)	1.4

(Factory Time)	Chilton Time
(G) Oil Gauge Sending Unit, Renew	
1983-87 (.3)	.4
(G) Oil Gauge (Dash), Renew	
1983-87	
Cavalier (.4)	.6
Cimarron (.4)	.6
Skyhawk (1.1)	2.0
2000 (.4)	.6
Firenza (.8)	1.5
(M) Oil Filter Element, Renew	
1983-87 (.3)	.3

PARTS 17 ENGINE OILING SYSTEM 17 PARTS

	Part No.	Price
Oil Pan Gasket or Seal		
1.8L		
1983-87	◆90106425	6.75
2.0L		
1983-87-rear	◆14018723	2.00
2.8L		
1985-87	◆14077876	2.00
Oil Pump		
1.8L		
1983-87	◆90169113	117.00
2.0L		
1983-87	◆14086060	95.50
2.8L		
1985-87	◆14033227	N.L.

	Part No.	Price
Oil Pump Screen		
1983-87-4 cyl	◆14018726	5.50
1985-87-V6	◆14046491	4.75
Oil Pump Intermediate Shaft		
1983-87-4 cyl	◆14077222	3.25
1985-87-V6	◆14046491	4.65
Oil Pressure Regulator Valve		
1983-87	◆3702366	1.50
Oil Pressure Sender Switch		
1.8L		
1983-87-wo/		
Gauges	◆25036455	9.25
Gauges	◆10030963	20.75
2.0L		
1983-wo/		
Gauges	◆14057554	5.75
Gauges	◆14073454	20.50

	Part No.	Price
1984-87-wo/		
Gauges	◆14014599	5.25
Gauges	◆14040816	18.00
2.8L		
1985-87	◆25036553	7.75
Oil Filter Element		
1.8L		
1983	◆6439929	7.50
1984-87	◆25010792	7.50
2.0L		
1983-87	◆25010908	7.50
2.8L		
1985-87	◆25010792	7.50
Oil Filter By Pass Valve		
1983-87	◆25010497	3.50

LABOR 18 CLUTCH & FLYWHEEL 18 LABOR

(G) Bleed Clutch Hydraulic System
All models (.5) 6

(G) Clutch Master Cylinder, Renew
1985-87 (1.1) 1.5

(G) Clutch Actuator (Slave) Cylinder, Renew
1985-87 (.8) 1.2

(G) Flywheel, Renew
Includes: R&R trans.
1983-87 (2.8) 4.5

(G) Clutch Control Cable, Renew
Includes: Adjust linkage.
1983-87 (.4) 6

(G) Clutch Assembly, Renew
Includes: R&R trans. Renew pressure plate, disc, release bearing and/or fork.
1983-87 (2.6) 4.2

(G) Clutch Release Bearing, Renew
1983-87 (2.4) 4.0

PARTS 18 CLUTCH & FLYWHEEL 18 PARTS

	Part No.	Price
Pressure Plate Assy.		
1.8L		
1983-84 (215mm dia.)	◆94253237	117.00
1984-87 (203mm dia.)	◆94148683	109.00
2.0L		
1983-84-4 sp.	◆14031365	96.00
5 sp.	◆94148662	139.00
1985-87-4 sp.	◆14079598	113.00
5 sp.	◆94148662	139.00
2.8L		
1985-87	◆14091968	113.00
Clutch Driven Plate		
1.8L		
1983-84 (215 mm. dia.)	◆94253238	90.75
1984-85 (203 mm. dia.)	◆94148663	72.25
2.0L		
1983-87-4 sp.	◆14049775	77.00
5 sp.	◆94253238	90.75
1985-87-4 sp.	◆14087237	87.75
5 sp.	◆94148663	72.25
2.8L		
1985-87	◆14087220	89.25
Release Bearing		
1983-87-4 sp.	◆908403	47.25
5 sp.	◆94133417	43.00
Release Lever		
1983-84-4 spd.	◆14024930	71.25
5 spd.	◆94251465	28.25
Bearing (Clutch Fork)		
1983-87	◆474665	3.00
Flywheel		
1.8L		
1983-87-M.T.	◆10018742	141.00
A.T.	◆10018740	59.25
2.0L		
1983-87-M.T.	◆14018711	141.00
A.T.	◆14018713	58.25
2.8L		
1985-87		
M.T.	◆476575	159.00
A.T.	◆14085471	68.75
Ring Gear (Flywheel)		
1983-87	◆359115	21.00

LABOR 21 SHIFT LINKAGE 21 LABOR

(Factory Time)	Chilton Time
STANDARD	
(G) Shift Linkage, Adjust	
1983-87 (.3)	.4
(G) Gearshift Control Assy., R&R or Renew (Floor Shift)	
1983-87 (.6)	1.0
(G) Shift Control Cables, Renew	
1983-87-one (.9)	1.6
both (1.2)	1.9
(G) Shift Lever, Renew	
1983-87 (.3)	.4
AUTOMATIC	
(G) Shift Linkage, Adjust	
All models	
Neutral Safety Switch (.3)	.4
Shift Indicator Needle (.2)	.3
Shift Linkage (.4)	.5
T.V. Cable (.3)	.4
(G) Floor Shift Control Assy., Renew	
1983-87 (.5)	.8
(G) Shift Control Cable, Renew	
1983-87 (.8)	1.3
(G) Shift Indicator Needle and/or Assy., Renew	
1983-87 (.3)	.5
(G) Gear Selector Lever, Renew	
1983-87 (.5)	.7
(G) Park Lock Cable, Renew	
1983-87 (1.0)	1.4

LABOR 26 REAR AXLE AND SUSPENSION 26 LABOR

(Factory Time)	Chilton Time
(G) Rear Coil Springs, Renew	
1983-87-one (.4)	.7
both (.6)	1.0
(G) Lower Control Arm Bushings, Renew	
1983-87-one (.6)	.8
both (.9)	1.3
(G) Rear Shock Absorbers, Renew	
1983-87-one (.3)	.4
both (.4)	.7
(G) Rear Axle Assembly, Renew	
1983-87 (1.3)	2.5
(G) Rear Wheel Bearing and Hub Assy, Clean and Repack or Renew	
1983-87-one (.4)	.6
both (.7)	1.1
(G) Rear Stabilizer Bar, Renew	
1983-87 (.4)	.6

PARTS 26 REAR AXLE AND SUSPENSION 26 PARTS

	Part No.	Price
(1) Shock Absorber		
(exc. Station wagon)		
1983-84-exc. Turbo	◆4993724	24.50
Turbo	◆22046409	24.75
1985	◆22046436	24.50
1986-87	◆22046451	24.50
(Station wagon)		
1983-84	◆4993560	24.50
1985-87	◆22046435	24.50
(2) Coil Spring		
Order by year and model.		
(3) Axle Support		
1983-84	◆10029177	350.00
1985-87	◆10038932	357.50

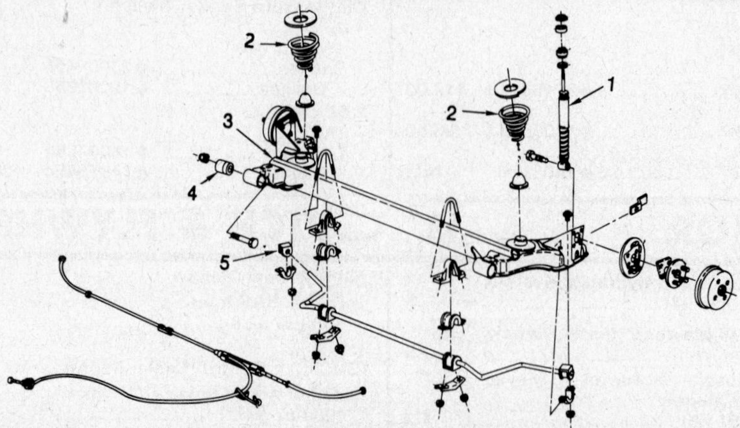

PARTS 26 REAR AXLE AND SUSPENSION 26 PARTS

	Part No.	Price
(4) Bushing (Control Arm)		
Cavalier, J2000, Skyhawk		
1983-87-wo/H.D.		
susp.	◆10018021	8.00
w/H.D. susp.	◆10018450	7.50
Cimarron, Firenza		
1983-87-wo/H.D.		
susp.	◆10018021	8.00
1983-84-w/H.D.		
susp.	◆10019594	7.50
1985-87-w/H.D.		
susp.	◆10018450	7.50
(5) Insulator (Stabilizer)		
1983-87-(shaft dia.)		
19mm	◆10018197	1.00

LABOR 28 AIR CONDITIONING 28 LABOR

(Factory Time) Chilton Time

Note: If more than one item requires replacement where evacuation and discharging the system is already included in the operation, deduct 1.0 hour for each additional item to the times listed.

(G) Drain, Evacuate and Recharge System
All models (.5) 1.0

(G) Leak Test
Includes: Check all lines and connections.
All models 5

(G) Pressure Test System
All models 8

(G) Refrigerant, Add (Partial Charge)
All models 6

(G) Compressor Belt, Renew
1983-87
Four
OHC (.4) 6
In-Line (.4) 6
V-6 (.3) 4

COMPRESSOR 4 CYLINDER RADIAL

(G) Compressor Assembly, Renew
Includes: Transfer all necessary attaching parts. Evacuate and charge system.
1983-87 (1.3) 2.0

(G) Compressor Clutch Plate and Hub Assy., Renew
Includes: R&R hub and drive plate assy. Check air gap.
1983-87 (.5) 8

(G) Compressor Clutch Rotor and/or Bearing, Renew
1983-87 (.6) 1.0

(G) Compressor Clutch Coil and/or Pulley Rim, Renew
1983-87 (.6) 9
Renew pulley and/or bearing add (.1) 1

(G) Compressor Front Seal, Seat and 'O' Ring, Renew
Includes: Evacuate and charge system.
1983-87 (1.1) 2.5
R&R accum add (.2) 3

(G) Compressor Front Head and/or Seal, Renew
Includes: R&R compressor, clutch and pulley assembly and shaft seal assembly. Clean and inspect parts. Evacuate and charge system.
1983-87 (1.5) 2.8

(G) Compressor Discharge Valve Plates, Renew
Includes: R&R compressor, clutch and pulley assembly and shell to internal mechanism. Clean and inspect parts. Evacuate and charge system.
1983-87 (1.9) 2.6

AIR CONDITIONER TUNE-UP

For efficient operation and satisfactory performance in hot weather. The following Air Conditioner tune-up is suggested:
1. Clean intake filter
2. Clean condenser fins
3. Pressure test system
4. Adjust drive belt tension
5. Check anti freeze/coolant
6. Tighten compressor mounts
7. Tighten condenser and evaporator mounts
8. Inspect system for leaks (hoses, couplings, valves, etc.)
9. Partial charge system

All models 1.0
If necessary to evacuate and charge system, add 1.0

(Factory Time) Chilton Time

(G) Compressor Thrust and/or Belleville Washers, Renew
Includes: R&R compressor, clutch and pulley assembly. Clean and inspect parts. Evacuate and charge system.
1983-87 (1.8) 2.8

(G) Compressor Front Main Bearing, Renew
Includes: R&R compressor and clutch and pulley assembly. Clean and inspect parts. Evacuate and charge system.
1983-87 (1.5) 2.8

(G) Compressor Shaft and Cylinder Assy., Renew
Includes: R&R compressor, clutch and pulley assemblies and shaft seal assembly. Remove and transfer front head assembly. R&R compressor shell, 'O' rings and compressor discharge valve plates. R&R pressure relief valve. Clean and inspect parts. Evacuate and charge system.
1983-87 (2.0) 2.9

DA-6 COMPRESSOR

(G) Compressor Assembly, Renew
Includes: Transfer all necessary attaching parts. Evacuate and charge system.
1983-87 (1.3) 2.0

(G) Compressor Clutch Plate and Hub Assy., Renew
Includes: R&R hub and drive plate assy. Check air gap.
1983-87 (1.1) 1.7

(G) Compressor Clutch Rotor and/or Bearing, Renew
Includes: R&R hub and drive plate assy.
1983-87 (1.3) 1.9

(Factory Time) Chilton Time

(G) Compressor Clutch Coil and/or Pulley Rim Assy., Renew
Includes: R&R hub and drive plate assy.
1983-87 (1.3) 1.7
Renew pulley or brg add 2

(G) Compressor Front Seal, Seat and 'O' Ring, Renew
Includes: R&R clutch hub and drive plate assy. Evacuate and charge system.
1983-87 (1.7) 2.5

(G) Compressor Front Head and/or Seal, Renew
Includes: R&R compressor. R&R clutch and pulley assy. R&R shaft seal assy. Clean and inspect parts. Evacuate and charge system.
1983-87 (2.0) 3.1

(G) Compressor Cylinder and Shaft Assy., Renew
Includes: R&R compressor. Transfer all parts as required. Evacuate and charge system.
1983-87 (2.1) 3.2

V-5 COMPRESSOR

(G) Compressor Assembly, Renew
Includes: Transfer all necessary attaching parts. Evacuate and charge system.
1986-87 (1.3) 2.0

(G) Compressor Clutch Plate and Hub Assy., Renew
1986-87 (.8) 1.2

(G) Compressor Rotor and/or Bearing, Renew
1986-87 (1.0) 1.5

(G) Compressor Clutch Coil and/or Pulley Rim, Renew
1986-87 (1.0) 1.5

(G) Compressor Shaft Seal Kit, Renew
Includes: Evacuate and charge system.
1986-87 (1.5) 2.2

(G) Condenser, Renew
Includes: Evacuate and charge system.
1983-87 (1.4) 2.5

(G) Evaporator Core, Renew
Includes: Evacuate and charge system.
1983-87 (1.6) 3.5

(G) Accumulator Assembly, Renew
Includes: Evacuate and charge system.
1983-87 (.7) 1.5

(G) Expansion Tube (Orifice), Renew
Includes: Evacuate and charge system.
1983-87 (.8) 1.5

(G) Pressure Cycling Switch, Renew
1983-87 (.2) 3

LABOR 28 AIR CONDITIONING 28 LABOR

	(Factory Time)	Chilton Time
(G) Blower Motor, Renew		
1983-87	(.4)	.6
(G) Blower Motor Switch, Renew		
1983-87	(.4)	.6
(G) Blower Motor Resistor, Renew		
1983-87	(.2)	.3
(G) Temperature Control Assembly, Renew		
1983-87	(.4)	.7
(G) Air Conditioning Relays, Renew		
1983-87-each	(.2)	.3
(G) Vacuum Selector Valve, Renew		
1983-87	(.4)	.6
(G) Master Electrical Switch, Renew		
1983-87	(.4)	.6
(G) Vacuum Diaphragm Actuator, Renew		
1983-87		
Defroster	(.3)	.6
Upper or lower mode	(.5)	1.0
Recirculation	(.5)	1.0
(G) Air Conditioning Hoses, Renew		
Includes: Evacuate and charge system.		
1983-87-liquid line	(1.3)	1.9
Evaporator to accumulator	(1.0)	1.7
All other hoses-one	(.8)	1.5
each adtnl	(.3)	.3

PARTS 28 AIR CONDITIONING 28 PARTS

	Part No.	Price
Compressor Assy.		
1.8L		
1983	◆12300474	N.L.
1984	◆12321368	N.L.
1985	◆12322334	N.L.
2.0L		
Radial compressor		
1983-A.T.	◆12300849	390.00
M.T.	◆12300474	390.00
DA-6 compressor		
1983-84	◆12309301	410.00
1985-87	◆12322147	N.L.
Clutch Drive		
Radial compressor		
1983	◆6551220	32.50
1984-87	◆6551838	36.00
DA-6 compressor		
1983	◆6551717	38.25
1984-85	◆6551920	40.00
1986-87	◆6551996	41.00
Rotor (w/Bearing)		
1983-87	◆6551216	67.50
Compressor Pulley		
Radial compressor		
1983-87-4.60 dia.	◆6556715	13.00
5.42 dia.	◆6557503	21.50
DA-6 compressor		
1983-87	◆6551888	94.00
Clutch Coil (w/Housing)		
1983-84-Radial comp.	◆6551217	44.00
1983-87-DA-6 comp.	◆6551997	47.50
Shaft Seal Kit		
Radial compressor		
1983-84	◆9956695	13.00
DA-6 compressor		
1983	◆2724280	17.00
1984-87	◆2724319	11.25
Front Head		
Radial compressor		
1983	◆6551142	28.25
1984	◆6551835	41.25
DA-6 compressor		
1983	◆6557376	40.00
1984-87	◆6557800	44.25
Outer Shell Assy.		
1983-87	◆2724158	38.00
Cylinder & Shaft		
Radial compressor		
1983-84	◆2724060	275.00
DA-6 compressor		
1983	◆6551701	281.50
1984-87	◆6551952	307.75
Valve Plate (w/Valve)		
Radial compressor		
1983-84	◆6551141	11.50
DA-6 compressor		
1983-87-front	◆6551700	25.00
rear	◆6551702	25.00
Compressor Drive Belt		
Order by year and model.		
Pressure Relief Valve		
1983-87	◆5914435	13.50
Condenser		
1983-84-exc. DA-6 comp.	◆3053962	176.50
DA-6 comp.	◆3055188	177.75
1985-87-1.8L exc. Turbo	◆3090421	127.25
Turbo	◆3056083	130.25
1985-2.L	◆3057666	146.00
1986-87-2.8L	◆3056277	126.75
Evaporator Core		
1983-87	◆3053166	256.25
Accumulator Dehydrator		
1983-84	◆2724239	80.00
1985-87	◆3059155	80.50
Control Assy (Heater & A.C.)		
Cavalier		
1983	◆16028981	35.00
1984	◆16034581	35.50
1985-87-4 dr.	◆16034581	35.50
2 dr.	◆16052781	57.50
Cimarron		
1983	◆16027366	33.00
1984-87	◆16030176	119.75
Firenza, Skyhawk		
1983	◆16021853	33.25
1984-85	◆16034550	35.00
1986-87-exc. 2.8L	◆16050180	36.50
2.8L	◆16034550	34.75
J2000 & 2000		
1983	◆16027372	30.25
1984	◆16032872	36.75
1985	◆16040692	36.75
1986-87	◆16047082	46.00
Blower Motor		
1983-87	◆22020945	60.00
Blower Motor Resistor		
1983-84	◆526897	4.50
1985	◆10039426	4.50
1986-87	◆22529265	4.50
Blower Motor Switch		
1983	◆16015256	6.00
1984-87	◆16032480	7.50
Relay (Hi Blo)		
1983-87	◆10019535	7.50
Pressure Cut Off Switch		
1983-87	◆3050246	23.00
Selector Valve (Vacuum)		
1983-87	◆16037768	4.50
Time Delay Relay		
1983-87	◆14039681	10.00

AUTOMATIC CLIMATE CONTROL

	Part No.	Price
Programmer		
1983-87	◆25515662	34.50
In Car Sensor		
1983-87	◆25515661	14.25
Ambient Sensor		
1983-87	◆25515658	8.00
Control Assy.		
1983-87	◆25516141	112.00
Compressor & Blower Motor Control Module		
1983-87	◆25515660	76.25

LABOR 29 LOCKS, HINGES & WIND. REGULATORS 29 LABOR

	(Factory Time)	Chilton Time
(G) Hood Latch Assembly, Renew		
1983-87	(.3)	.4
(G) Hood Release Cable, Renew		
1983-87	(.3)	.6
(G) Hood Hinge, Renew (One)		
1983-87	(.5)	.7

LABOR 29 LOCKS, HINGES & WIND. REGULATORS 29 LABOR

(Factory Time)	Chilton Time
(G) Door Lock Cylinder, Renew	
1983-87 (.4)	.7
Recode cyl add (.3)	.3
(G) Door Handle (Outside), Renew	
1983-87-front or rear (.4)	.7
Renew insert add	.1
(G) Lock Striker Plate, Renew	
1983-87 (.2)	.3
(G) Front Door Lock, Renew	
1983-87 (.4)	.7
(G) Door Lock Remote Control, Renew (Front or Rear)	
1983-87 (.4)	.7
(G) Rear Door Lock, Renew	
1983-87 (.7)	1.1
(G) Rear Compartment Lid Lock Cylinder, Renew	
1983-87 (.2)	.3
Recode cyl add (.3)	.3
(G) Tail Gate Hinge, Renew	
Does not include colorcoat.	
1983-87	
Gate side-each (.9)	1.4
Body side-each (1.0)	1.5
(G) Tail Gate Lock Cylinder, Renew	
1983-87 (.3)	.4
Recode cyl add (.3)	.3
(G) Front Door Window Regulator, Renew	
1983-87-manual (.4)	*.8
power (.6)	1.0
*Recond regul add	.2
(G) Rear Door Window Regulator, Renew	
1983-87-manual (.5)	.9
power (.6)	1.0
(G) Rear Compartment Lid Hinge Strap, Renew (One)	
1983-87 (.6)	.9

PARTS 29 LOCKS, HINGES & WIND. REGULATORS 29 PARTS

	Part No.	Price
Hood Latch		
1983-(stamped)		
70	◆14067070	7.00
91	◆14059991	7.00
1984-87	◆14059991	7.00
Hood Hinge		
1983-87-right	◆20538870	18.50
left	◆20538871	18.50
Front Door Lock		
1983-87-right	◆20298852	37.25
left	◆20594023	42.50
Rear Door Lock		
1983-84-right	◆20298866	46.50
left	◆20298867	46.50
1985-87-right	◆20594024	36.50
left	◆20594025	36.50
Door Lock Cylinder Kit		
1983-87	◆9632769	7.75
Door Handle (Outside)		
(exc. Deluxe Door Handle)		
1983-87-right	◆20332644	20.00
left	◆20332645	20.00
(w/Deluxe Door Handle)		
1983-87-right	◆20332646	20.00
left	◆20332647	20.00
Front Window Regulator (Manual)		
Two door		
1983-87-right	◆20162801	33.50
left	◆20446083	32.50
Four door & wagon models		
1983-87-right	◆20446078	32.50
left	◆20446079	32.50
Front Window Regulator (Electric)		
1983-87-right	◆20276320	77.50
left	◆20276321	77.50
(Convertible models)		
1983-87-right	◆20455128	77.50
left	◆20455129	77.50
Rear Window Regulator (Manual)		
(exc. Custom exterior)		
1983-87-right	◆20446084	28.75
left	◆20446085	28.75
(w/Custom exterior)		
1983-87-right	◆20446086	28.75
left	◆20446087	28.75
Electric Window Regulator Motor		
1983-front	◆22021670	75.00
1984-87	◆22020900	N.L.
1983-87-rear	◆22030445	76.50
Rear Compartment Lock		
(Hatchback coupe)		
1983-87	◆20274727	19.00
(Notchback coupe or sedan)		
1983-87	◆20166276	13.75
(Station wagon)		
1983-87	◆20369896	54.00
Trunk Hinges		
(Hatchback coupe)		
1983-87	◆20429150	6.00
(Notchback coupe or sedan)		
1983-87-right	◆20166702	27.75
left	◆20166703	27.75
(Station wagon)		
1983-87-body side	◆20153991	3.25
gate side	◆20166428	1.75

LABOR 30 HEAD AND PARKING LAMPS 30 LABOR

(Factory Time)	Chilton Time
(G) Aim Headlamps	
two	.4
four	.6
(M) Headlamp Sealed Beam Bulb, Renew	
1983-87-one (.2)	.3
each adtnl (.1)	.1
(M) Back-Up Lamp Bulb, Renew	
1983-87 (.2)	.2
(M) License Lamp Bulb, Renew	
1983-87 (.2)	.2
(M) Park and Turn Signal Lamp Bulb, Renew	
1983-87 (.2)	.2
(M) Side Marker Lamp Bulb, Renew	
1983-87 (.2)	.2
(M) Stop and Tail Lamp Bulb, Renew	
1983-87 (.2)	.2
(M) Rear Combination Lamp Assy., Renew	
All models-each (.2)	.3
2 Dr Hatchback add	.2
(M) Park and Turn Signal Lamp Assy., Renew	
All models-each (.2)	.3

PARTS 30 HEAD AND PARKING LAMPS 30 PARTS

	Part No.	Price
Headlamp Seal Beam		
Cavalier		
1983-wo/quartz	◆5968098	22.00
w/quartz	◆5972698	46.50
1984-87-		
outboard	◆5966200	15.00
(inboard)		
wo/quartz	◆5966201	15.00
w/quartz	◆5930567	22.50
Cimarron, Firenza, J2000, Skyhawk		
1983-87-		
Outboard	◆5966200	15.00
(Inboard)		
wo/Quartz	◆5966201	15.00
Quartz	◆5930567	22.50

PARTS 30 HEAD AND PARKING LAMPS 30 PARTS

	Part No.	Price
Parking & Turn Signal Lamp Assy.		
Cavalier		
1983-(exc. 2-door hatchback)		
right	◆915214	22.25
left	◆915213	22.25
1983-(2-door hatchback)		
right	◆915560	18.50
left	◆915559	18.50
1984-87-right	◆918058	23.50
left	◆918057	23.50
Cimarron		
1983-84-right	◆918058	23.50
left	◆918057	23.50
1985-87-right	◆919184	23.50
left	◆919183	23.50
Firenza		
(exc. Special edition)		
1983-86-right	◆917804	19.50
left	◆917803	19.50
1987-right	◆918592	19.50
left	◆918591	19.50
(Special edition)		
1983-87-right	◆918592	19.50
left	◆918591	19.50
J2000		
1983-right	◆915610	18.50
left	◆915609	18.50
1984-87-right	◆915628	18.50
left	◆915627	18.50
Skyhawk		
exc. Amber lens		
1983-87-right	◆916462	19.25
left	◆916461	19.25
Amber lens		
1983-87-right	◆918384	19.25
left	◆918383	19.25
License Plate Lamp Assy.		
Cavalier & Firenza		
1983-87-exc.		
wagon	◆912345	6.25
wagon	◆914752	6.75
Cimarron		
1983-85	◆912366	6.25
1986-87	◆913061	6.25
J-2000 & Skyhawk		
1983-87-exc.		
wagon	◆912116	6.50
wagon	◆914752	6.75
Tail & Stop Lamp Assy.		
Cavalier		
(exc. 2-door hatchback)		
1983 (wo/Custom ext.)		
right	◆914980	62.50
left	◆914979	62.50
1983 (Custom ext.)		
right	◆915456	62.50
left	◆915455	62.50
1984-right	◆914980	62.50
left	◆914979	62.50
1985-87-2 dr		
right	◆919585	108.00
left	◆919586	108.00
1985-87-4 dr		
right	◆914979	62.50
left	◆914980	62.50

	Part No.	Price
(2-door hatchback)		
1983-84-right	◆915314	62.50
left	◆915313	62.50
1985-87-right	◆919579	108.00
left	◆919580	108.00

Cimarron

Only lenses are listed below for Cimarron. Tailamp assy. are not available. Housing and lenses must be ordered separately.

	Part No.	Price
(wo/Deluxe ext. trim)		
1983-right	◆5973618	88.25
left	◆5973617	88.25
1984-85-right	◆16501810	88.25
left	◆16501809	88.25
1986-87-right	◆16504416	102.00
left	◆16504415	102.00
(Deluxe ext. trim)		
1983-right	◆16502382	88.25
left	◆16502381	88.25
1984-85-right	◆16503180	88.25
left	◆16503179	88.25
1986-87-right	◆16504416	102.00
left	◆16504415	102.00
Firenza		
(2-door)		
1983-84-right	◆917732	76.50
left	◆917731	76.50
1985-right	◆919908	73.00
left	◆919907	73.00
1986-87-right	◆5974252	60.50
left	◆5974251	60.50
(4-door)		
1983-84 (wo/Special edition)		
right	◆917738	71.75
left	◆917737	71.75
1985-87-right	◆919922	73.00
left	◆919921	73.00
1984 (Special edition)		
right	◆920006	71.75
left	◆920005	71.75
1985-87-right	◆5974250	73.00
left	◆5974249	73.00
(Station wagon)		
1983-87-right	◆917940	69.50
left	◆917939	69.50

J2000 & 2000

On all models except station wagons the lenses and housing are sold separately and not available as a unit.

	Part No.	Price
(2-door hatchback-lens only)		
(inner)		
1983-right	◆5972428	37.75
left	◆5972427	37.75
1984-87-right	◆16501776	33.25
left	◆16501775	33.25
(outer)		
1983-right	◆5972426	76.75
left	◆5972425	76.75
1984-87-right	◆16501770	76.75
left	◆16501769	76.75
(2 or 4-door notchback-lens only)		
(wo/Custom ext.)		
1983-85-right	◆16501342	78.25
left	◆16501341	78.25
1986-87-right	◆16501976	76.75
left	◆16501975	76.75
(Custom ext.)		
1983-right	◆5972238	81.50
left	◆5972237	81.50
1984-87 (inner)		
right	◆16501776	33.25
left	◆16501775	33.25
1984-87 (outer)		
right	◆16501976	76.75
left	◆16501975	76.75
(station wagon-lamp assy.)		
(wo/Custom ext.)		
1983-85-right	◆918310	67.00
left	◆918309	67.00
1986-87-right	◆5974564	79.25
left	◆5974563	79.25
(Custom ext.)		
1983-87-right	◆918088	69.50
left	◆918087	69.50
Skyhawk		
(exc. Station wagon)		
1983-87-right	◆5973644	70.25
left	◆5973643	70.25
(Station wagon)		
1983-87-right	◆917942	69.50
left	◆917941	69.50
Tail Lamp Housing		
Cimarron		
1983-right	◆5973194	61.50
left	◆5973193	61.50
1984-85-right	◆16501806	61.50
left	◆16501805	61.50
1986-87-right	◆16504412	97.25
left	◆16504411	97.25
J2000		
(exc. 2-door hatchback)		
1983-87 (wo/Custom ext.)		
right	◆16501764	65.75
left	◆16501763	65.75
1984-87 (Custom ext.)		
right	◆16501590	73.25
left	◆16501589	73.25
(2-door hatchback)		
1983-right	◆16501768	73.25
left	◆16501767	73.25
1984-87-right	◆16501590	73.25
left	◆16501589	73.25
Skyhawk		
1983-85-right	◆5973640	45.25
left	◆5973639	45.25
1986-87-right	◆16507666	51.50
left	◆16507665	47.50
Rear High Mount Stop Lamp		
(2-door)		
1986-87	◆5974458	36.00
(3-door Hatchback)		
1986-87-wo/		
Rear splr.	◆918552	39.50
Rear splr.	◆918554	N.L.
(4-door)		
1986-87	◆5974461	36.00
(Station wagon)		
1986-87	◆5974534	35.50

LABOR 31 WINDSHIELD WIPER & SPEEDOMETER 31 LABOR

(Factory Time)	Chilton Time
(G) Windshield Wiper Motor, Renew	
1983-87 (.2)	.4
Recond add (.5)	.5
(G) Rear Window Wiper Motor, Renew	
1983-87 (.4)	.6
Recond add (.5)	.5
(G) Wiper Switch, Renew	
1983-85 (1.0)	1.4
1986-87	
std whl (1.3)	1.7
tilt whl (1.1)	1.5

LABOR 31 WINDSHIELD WIPER & SPEEDOMETER 31 LABOR

(Factory Time) | Chilton Time

(G) Rear Window Wiper Switch, Renew
1983-87 (.3) 4

(G) Pulse Wiper Control Module, Renew
1984-87 (.4) 6

(G) Intermittent Wiper Controller Assy., Renew
1983-87 (.4) 6

(G) Windshield Washer Pump, Renew
1983-87 (.3) 5
Recond add (.3) 3

(G) Wiper Transmission, Renew
Includes: R&R linkage.
1983-87-each (.6) 9

(G) Rear Window Washer Pump, Renew
1983-87 (.3) 5
Recond add (.3) 3

(G) Speedometer Head, R&R or Renew
1983-87
Skyhawk (1.0) 1.9
Firenza (1.0) 1.9
All other models (.5) 9
Reset odometer add 2

(G) Speedometer Cable and Casing, Renew
Skyhawk
1983
upper cable (.4) 7
lower cable (.3) 6
one piece cable (.5) 9
1984-87 (.7) 1.2

Firenza
1983-85
upper cable (.8) 1.4
lower cable (.3) 6
one piece cable (.9) 1.5
1986-87 (.4) 7

All other models
1983-87
upper cable (.3) 6
lower cable (.3) 6
one piece cable (.6) 1.0

(G) Speedometer Cable (Inner), Renew or Lubricate
Skyhawk
1983
upper cable (.4) 7
lower cable (.3) 6
one piece cable (.5) 9
1984-87 (.7) 1.2

Firenza
1983-85
upper cable (.8) 1.4
lower cable (.3) 6
one piece cable (.9) 1.5
1986-87 (.4) 7
All other models
1983-87
upper cable (.3) 6
lower cable (.3) 6
one piece cable (.5) 9

(G) Instrument Panel Cluster Assy., Renew
1984-87 (1.2) 1.8

(G) Speedometer Signal Generator, Renew
1984-87 (.5) 8

(G) Tachometer, R&R or Renew
1983-87
Skyhawk (1.1) 2.0
Firenza (.8) 1.5
All other models (.5) 8

(G) Speedometer Cable Adapter, Renew
1983-87 (.3) 5

(G) Radio, R&R
1983-87 (.6) 9

PARTS 31 WINDSHIELD WIPER & SPEEDOMETER 31 PARTS

	Part No.	Price
Windshield Wiper Motor		
1983	◆22029817	109.25
1984-85-wo/ Pulse wpr.	◆22039727	106.25
Pulse wpr.	◆22039318	144.00
1986-87-wo/ Pulse wpr.	◆22062915	106.75
Pulse wpr.	◆22062913	111.50
Windshield Wiper Transmission		
1983-87-right	◆22039716	23.75
left	◆22039715	26.50
Wiper Module (Pulse Control)		
1983	◆10036435	37.25
Wiper Motor Switch (Pulse)		
1983-wo/Tilt whl.	◆7835512	52.00
Tilt Whl.	◆7837426	52.00
1984-87-wo/Tilt whl.	◆7848195	56.00
Tilt whl.	◆7848196	56.00
Wiper Motor Switch (2 Speed)		
1983-87-wo/Tilt Whl.	◆7835628	41.50
Tilt Whl.	◆7838078	41.50
Windshield Washer Pump		
1983	◆4961623	15.50
1984	◆22039339	17.00
1985-87	◆22054186	18.50

Speedometer Cable (W/Casing)
Order by year and model.

LABOR 32 LIGHT SWITCHES & WIRING 32 LABOR

(Factory Time) | Chilton Time

(G) Headlamp Switch, Renew
1983-87 (.4) 5
Type 10 (.3) 5

(G) Headlamp Dimmer Switch, Renew
1983-87 (.7) 1.0

(G) Back-Up Lamp Switch, Renew
1983-87 (.3) 4

(G) Back-Up Lamp and Park/Neutral Switch, Renew
1983-87 (.4) 5

(G) Parking Brake Lamp Switch, Renew
1983-87 (.3) 4
Type 10 (.5) 8

(G) Stop Light Switch, Renew
1983-87 (.3) 4

(G) Turn Signal and Hazard Warning Switch, Renew
1983-85 (.7) 1.1
1986-87
std whl (.8) 1.2
tilt whl (.9) 1.3

(M) Turn Signal or Hazard Warning Flasher, Renew
1983-87
hazard (.2) 2
turn signal (.3) 4

(G) Horn Relay, Renew
1983-87 (.3) 3

(G) Horn, Renew
1983-87-one (.3) 4
each adtnl (.1) 1

(G) Neutral Start Switch, Renew
1983-87 (.4) 4

PARTS 32 LIGHT SWITCHES & WIRING 32 PARTS

	Part No.	Price
Headlamp Switch		
1983-87-exc. below	◆1972717	16.75
w/twi. sent.	◆1995253	25.00
Headlamp Dimmer Switch (Strg. Col.)		
1983-87	◆7832411	18.50
Stoplight Switch (wo/Cruise cont.)		
1983-84-M.T.	◆1362835	3.00
A.T.	◆25504628	3.75

PARTS 32 LIGHT SWITCHES & WIRING 32 PARTS

	Part No.	Price
1985-M.T.	◆25524844	3.00
A.T.	◆25524846	N.L.
1986-87-M.T.	◆25523466	8.00
A.T.	◆25523464	8.00
(Cruise cont.)		
1983-87	◆9794682	7.75
Turn Signal Switch		
1983-87	◆1997983	30.00
Parking Brake Lamp Switch		
1983-87	◆1264464	1.50
Starter Safety Switch		
M.T.		
1983-84	◆14085143	5.50
1985	◆14080663	18.25
1986	◆14086976	6.75
1987	◆14103396	6.25
1983-87-A.T.	◆1994223	18.00
Back-up Lamp Switch		
M.T.		
1983-87-4 sp.	◆14009262	2.00
5 sp.	◆14047186	17.75
A.T.		
1983-84	◆1994223	18.00
1985-87	◆1994256	13.50
Turn Signal Flasher		
Firenza, J2000, Skyhawk		
(exc. Station wagon)		
1983-84	◆10029240	4.25
1985-87	◆10041073	N.L.
(Station wagon)		
1983-87	◆6450076	4.00
Cavalier, Cimarron		
1983-84	◆6450076	4.00
1985-87	◆10041074	3.75

LABOR 33 GLASS 33 LABOR

(Factory Time)	Chilton Time
(G) Windshield Glass, Renew	
1983-87 (1.3)	1.8
Renew caulk bead add (.4)	.4
(G) Front Door Glass, Renew	
1983-87	
2 dr models (.8)	1.2
4 dr models (1.0)	1.4
(G) Rear Door Glass, Renew	
1983-87	
2 dr models (.5)	.8
4 dr models (.5)	.8
(G) Rear Door Vent Glass, Renew	
1983-87 (.7)	1.2
(G) Quarter Window Movable Glass, Renew	
1983-87 (1.1)	1.7
Renew retainer add (.2)	.2
(G) Quarter Window Stationary Glass, Renew	
1983-87	
2 Dr (1.5)	2.0
wagon (1.0)	1.5
(G) Quarter Window Swing Out Glass, Renew	
1983-87 (.3)	.5
Transfer latch and channel add (.1)	.1
(G) Tailgate Glass, Renew	
1983-87 (1.0)	1.4
w/Elec defogger add (.2)	.2
(G) Back Window Glass, Renew	
1983-87-exc. below (1.3)	2.0
2 Dr Hatchback (1.5)	2.2
w/Elec grid defogger add (.6)	.6
w/Rear wiper add (.2)	.2

LABOR 34 CRUISE CONTROL 34 LABOR

(Factory Time)	Chilton Time
(G) Cruise Control Transducer Assy., Adjust	
1983 (.3)	.4
(G) Cruise Control Transducer Assy., Renew	
1983 (.4)	.6
Adj low spd switch add (.1)	.1
(G) Cruise Control Transducer Filter, Renew	
1983 (.2)	.3
(G) Cruise Control Chain or Cable, Renew	
1983-87 (.3)	.4
(G) Cruise Control Servo Assy., Renew	
1983-87 (.3)	.4
Renew bracket add (.1)	.1
(G) Cruise Control Brake or Clutch Release Switch, Renew	
1983-87 (.3)	.4
(G) Cruise Control Engagement Switch, Renew	
1983-87 (.5)	.7
(G) Cruise Control Vacuum Hoses, Renew	
1983-87-one or all (.2)	.3
(G) Cruise Control Vacuum Control or Check Valve, Renew	
1983-87 (.3)	.4
(G) Cruise Control Module or Controller, Renew	
1984-87 (.3)	.5

PARTS 34 CRUISE CONTROL 34 PARTS

	Part No.	Price
Cruise Control Transducer		
1983	◆25030878	158.00
Vacuum Release Valve		
1983-87-M.T.	◆14046846	2.50
1983-84-A.T.	◆25509432	14.00
1985-87	◆25523376	14.00
Cruise Control Chain (Lever to Servo)		
1983-85	◆25031314	3.25
Cruise Control Servo		
1.8L		
1983	◆25031703	20.75
1984-87	◆25074627	117.00
2.0L		
1983	◆25031983	21.00
1984-87	◆25074627	117.00
Transducer Resume Valve		
1983	◆25030562	26.00
Cruise Control Lever & Switch		
Cavalier, Cimarron, Firenza, Skyhawk		
(wo/Pulse wiper)		
1983	◆25031426	52.25
1984-87	◆25031457	50.00
(Pulse wiper)		
1983	◆25031425	52.25
1984-87	◆25031456	50.00
J2000		
(wo/Pulse wiper)		
1983	◆25031479	50.00
1984-87	◆25031481	50.00
(Pulse wiper)		
1983	◆25031478	50.00
1984-87	◆25031480	50.00

GROUP INDEX

ALPHABETICAL INDEX

General Motors
Front Wheel Drive Cars

CELEBRITY • CENTURY • CIERA • A-6000 • 6000

YEAR IDENTIFICATION

1983 Celebrity

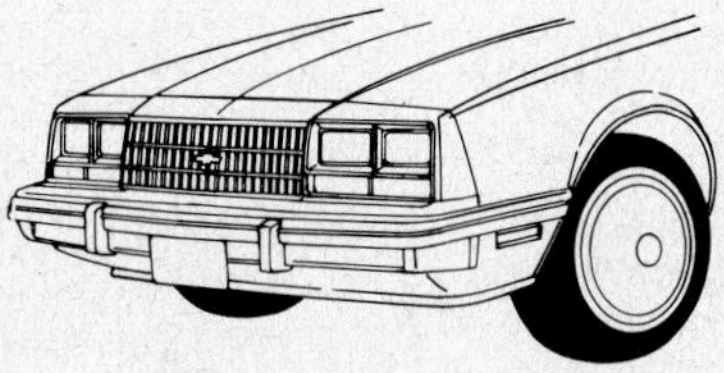

1984–85 Celebrity

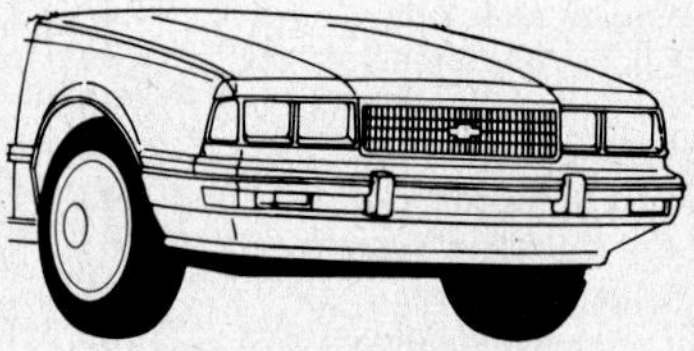

1986–87 Celebrity

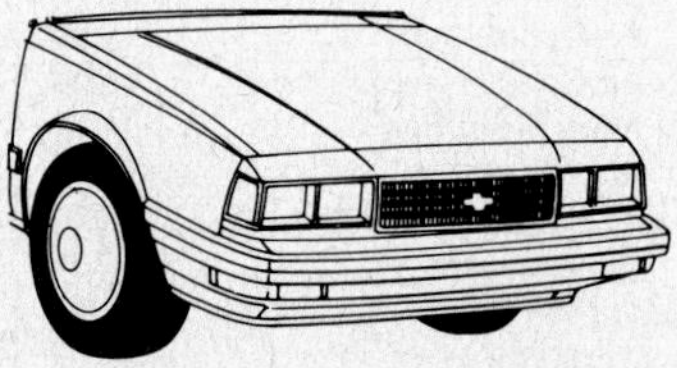

1986–87 Celebrity Eurosport

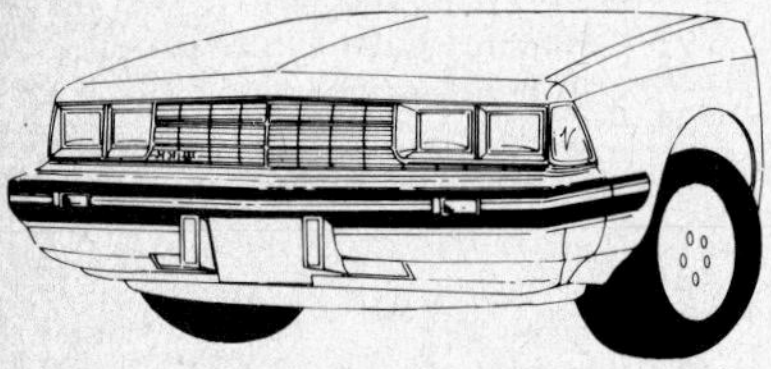

1982–83 Century

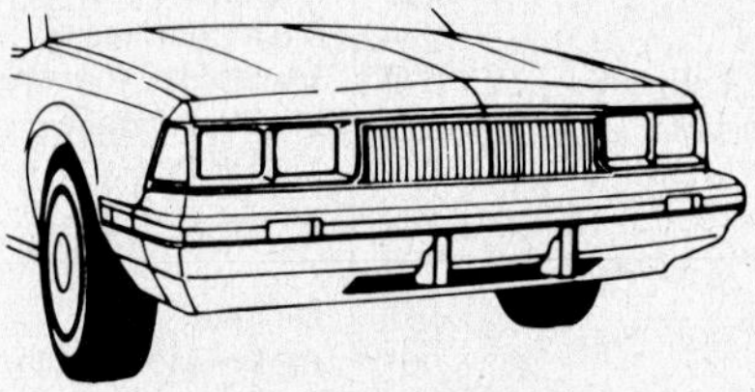

1984–85 Century

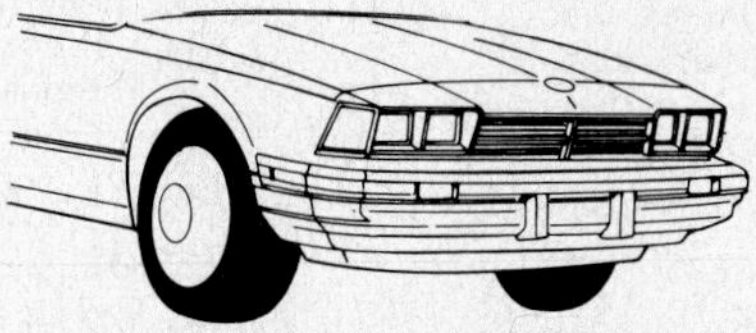

1986–87 Century

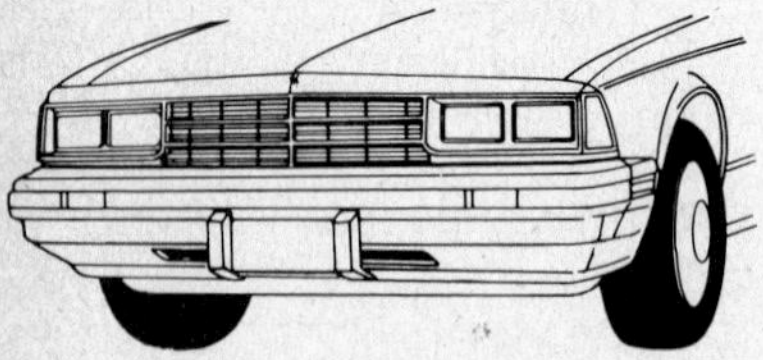

1984 Century T Type

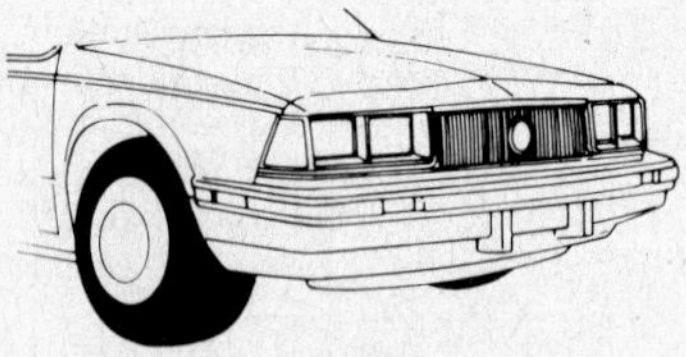

1985 Century T Type

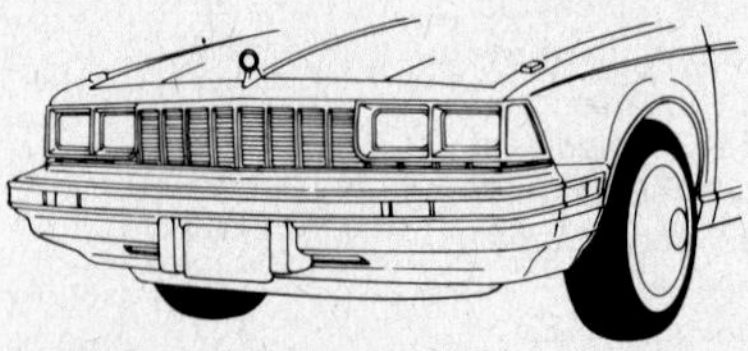

1984 Century Custom, Limited

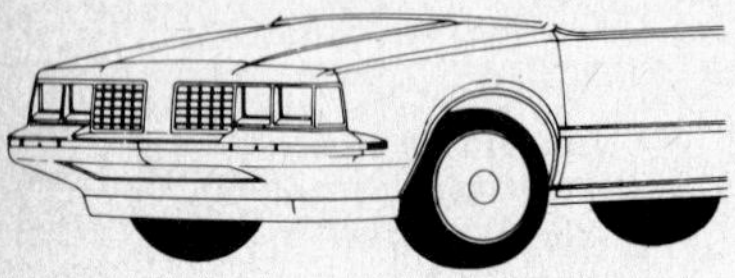

1982–83 Cutlass Ciera

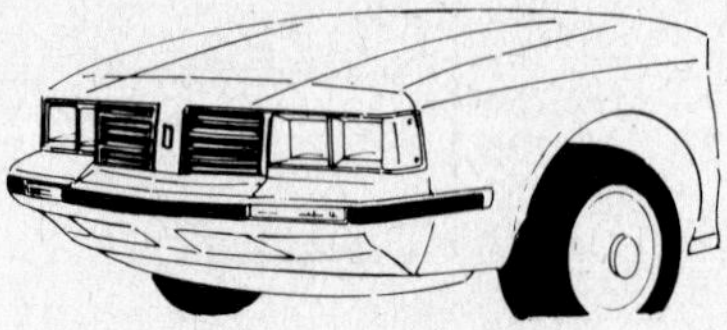

1983 Cutlass Ciera ES

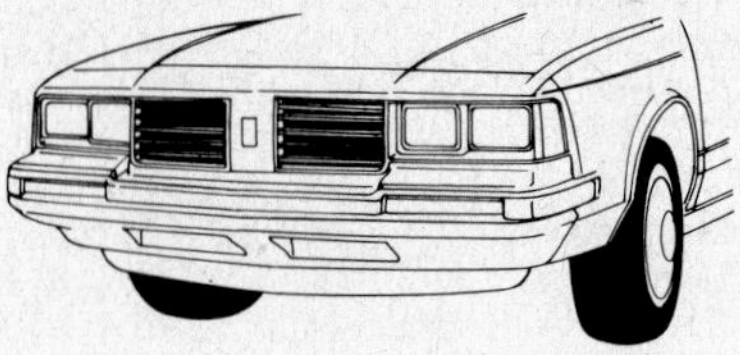

1984 Ciera

YEAR IDENTIFICATION

1985–86 Cutlass Ciera

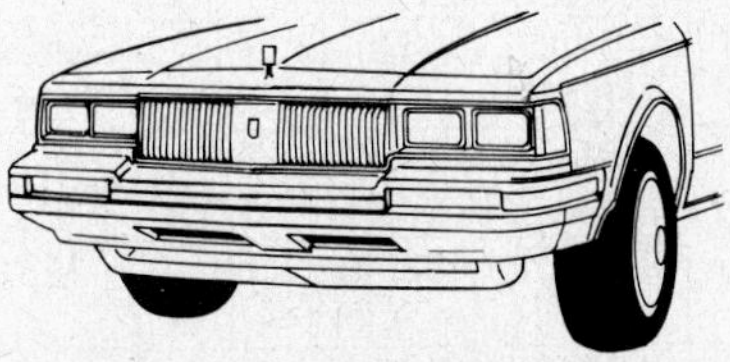

1984–86 Cutlass Cruiser

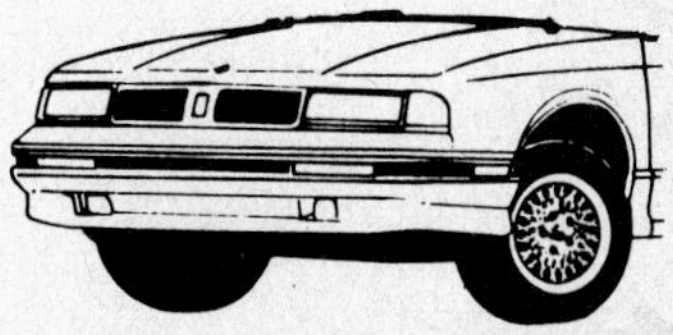

1987 Cutlass Ciera GT

1982–83 6000

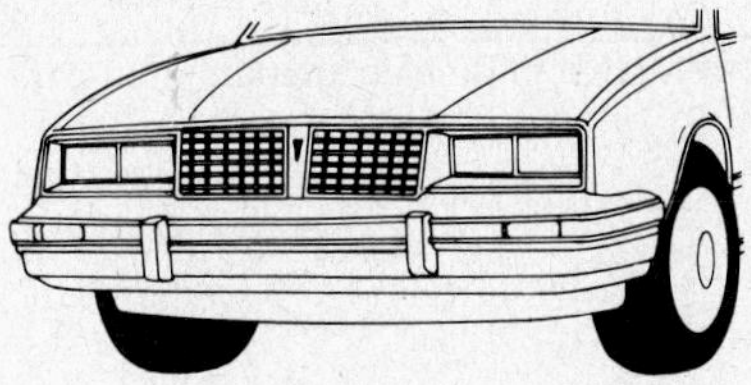

1984 6000, 6000 LE

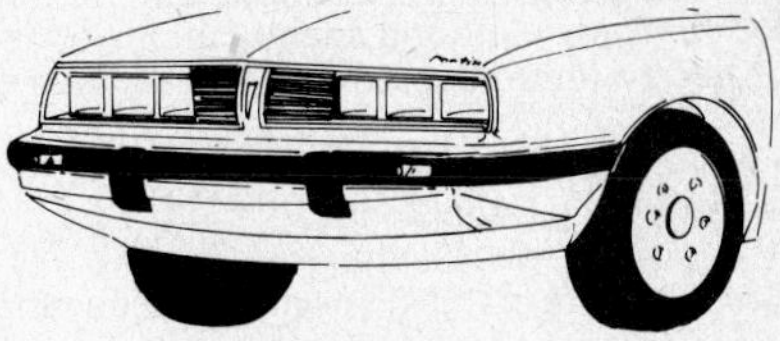

1983–85 6000 STE

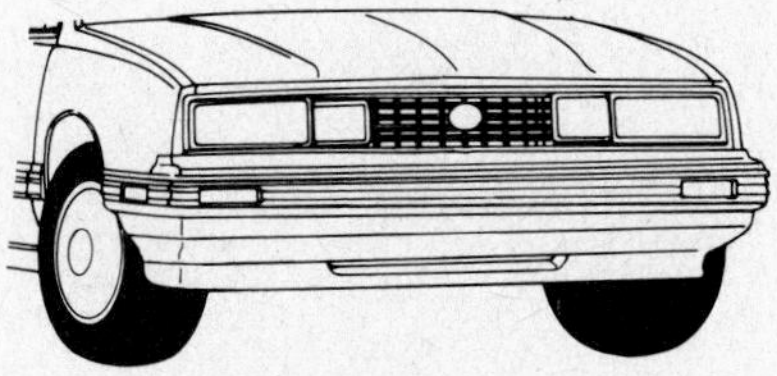

1986 6000 STE

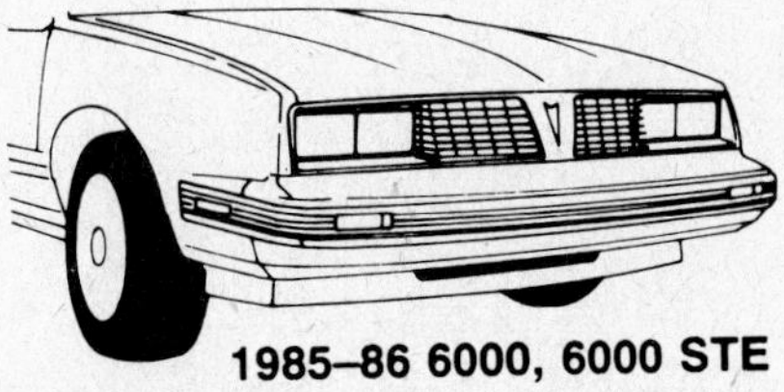

1985–86 6000, 6000 STE

1987 Pontiac 6000 SE

VEHICLE IDENTIFICATION NUMBER (VIN)

It is important for servicing and ordering parts to be certain of the vehicle and engine identification. The VIN (vehicle identification number) is a 13 or 17 digit number visible through the windshield on the driver's side of the dash and contains the vehicle and engine identification codes. It can be interpreted as follows:

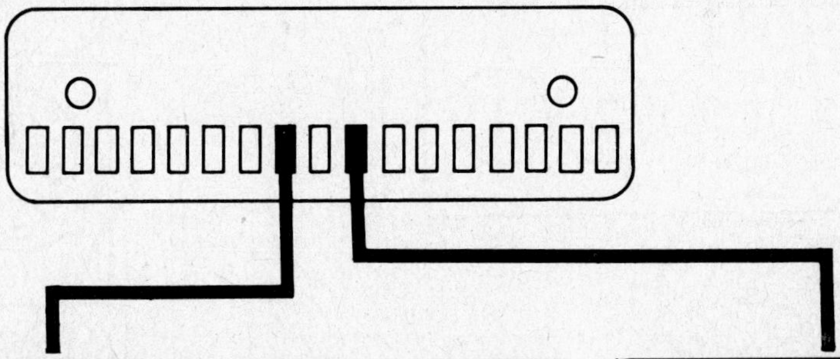

Engine Code

Code	Cu. In.	Liters	Cyl.	Carb.	Eng. Mfg.
5	151	2.5	4	2	Pont.
R	151	2.5	4	TBI	Pont.
X	173	2.8	V6	2	Chev.
Z	173(HO)	2.8	V6	2	Chev.
E	183	3.0	V6	2	Buick
3	231	3.8	V6	MFI	Buick
T	263	4.3	V6	Diesel	Olds

Model Year Code

Code	Year
D	1983
E	1984
F	1985
G	1986
H	1987

The seventeen digit Vehicle Identification Number can be used to determine engine application and model year. The 10th digit indicates the model year and the 8th digit identifies the factory installed engine.
TBI: Throttle Body Injection
MFI: Multi-Point Fuel Injection

TUNE-UP SPECIFICATIONS

When analyzing compression test results, look for uniformity among cylinders rather than specific pressures

Year	VIN Code	Eng. No. Cyl. Displ. Cu. In.	Liters	Eng. Mfg.	hp	Spark Plugs Orig. Type	Spark Plugs Gap (in.)	Ignition Timing (deg) Man. Trans.	Ignition Timing (deg) Auto. Trans.	Intake Valve Opens (deg.)■	Fuel Pump Pressure (psi)	Idle Speed (rpm) Man. Trans.	Idle Speed (rpm) Auto. Trans.
'83–'87	5,R	4-151	2.5	Pont.	90	R-44TSX	0.060	8B	8B	33	6.0–8.0	950 ①	750 ②
	X	6-173	2.8	Chev.	112	R-43CTS	0.045	10B	10B	25	6.0–7.5	800	600
	Z	6-173 HO	2.8	Chev.	135	R-42CTS	0.045	6B	10B	31	6.0–7.5	850 ③	750
	E	6-183	3.0	Buick	110	R-44TS8	0.080	—	15B	16	6.0–8.0	—	see text
	3	6-231	3.8	Buick	125	R-44TS8	0.080	④	④	4.0–6.5	④	④	
	T	6-263	4.3	Olds.	85	④	④	—	6A	N.A.	5.8–8.7	—	650

NOTE: The underhood specifications sticker often reflects tune-up specification changes made in production. Sticker figures must be used if they disagree with those in this chart.

■ All figures Before Top Dead Center
B: Before Top Dead Center
A: After Top Dead Center
Part numbers in this chart are not recommendations by Chilton for any product by brand name.
N.A.: Information not available
① Without air conditioning: 850
② Without air conditioning: 680
③ Calif.: 750
④ See underhood specifications sticker

FIRING ORDERS

NOTE: To avoid confusion, always replace spark plug wires one at a time.

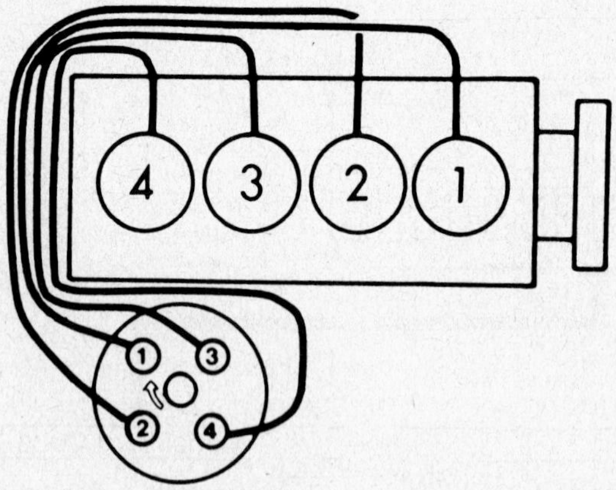

GM (Pontiac) 151–4
Engine firing order: 1–3–4–2
Distributor rotation: clockwise

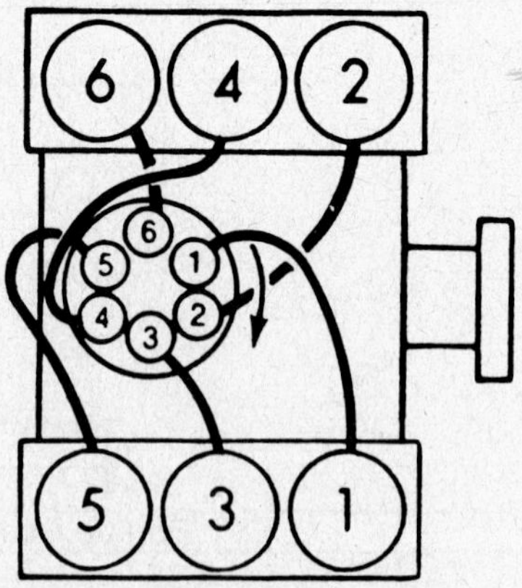

GM (Chevrolet) 173 V6 (2.8L)
Engine firing order: 1–2–3–4–5–6
Distributor rotation: clockwise

FIRING ORDERS

NOTE: To avoid confusion, always replace spark plug wires one at a time.

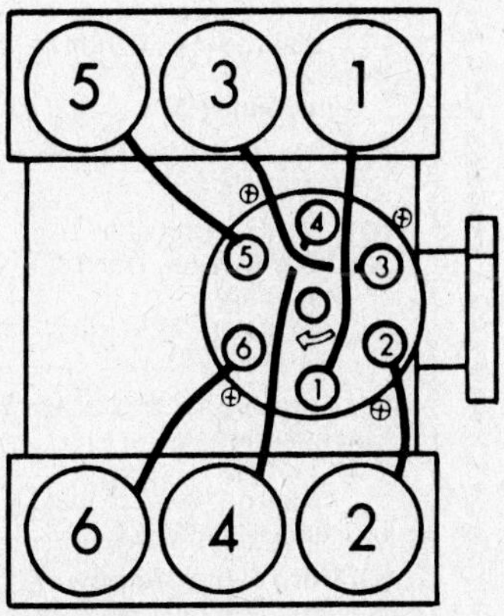

GM (Buick) 183 V8 (3.0L)
Engine firing order: 1–6–5–4–3–2
Distributor rotation: clockwise

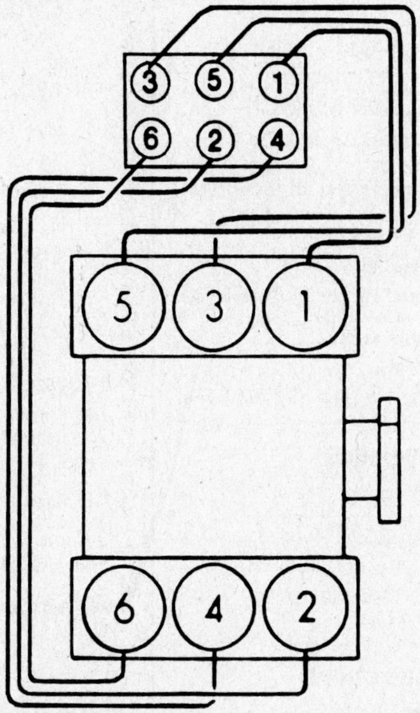

Buick 181 cu. in. V6 (3.0L) C31
Firing order: 1-6-5-4-3-2

WHEEL ALIGNMENT SPECIFICATIONS

		Caster*		Camber			
Year	Model	Range (deg.)	Pref. Setting (deg.)	Range (deg.)	Pref. Setting (deg.)	Toe-In (in.)	Steering Axis (deg.) Inclination
'83–'87	All	0–4P	2P	1/2N-1/2P	0	13/64 out-13/64 in	14.5

*Caster is not adjustable

LABOR — SERVICE BAY OPERATIONS — LABOR

(Factory Time) — Chilton Time

COOLING

(M) Winterize Cooling System

Includes: Run engine to check for leaks, tighten all hose connections. Test radiator and pressure cap, drain radiator and engine block. Add anti-freeze and refill system.

All models 5

(G) Thermostat, Renew

All models
- Four (.2) 4
- V-6 (.4) 5
- Diesel (.6) 8

(M) Drive Belt, Renew

Four–1983-87
- A.C. (.7) 9
- Fan (.6) 8
- P.S. (.5) 6

V-6–1983-87
eng codes X-Z-W
- A.C. (.3) 4
- A.I.R. (.2) 3
- Fan (.2) 3
- P.S. (.3) .... *.4

w/AIR add (.1) 1

*w/A.C. add (.2) 2
eng codes E-3-B
A.C.
- 1983-84 (1.8) 2.5
- 1985-87 (1.1) 1.5
- A.I.R. (.3) 4
- Fan (.5) 7
- P.S. (1.1) 1.5

w/A.C. add (.3) 3

(M) Drive Belt, Adjust

All models-exc below-one (.2) 3
- all (.5) 6

eng codes E-3
- one or all (1.0) 1.4

(M) Serpentine Drive Belt, Renew

All models (.2) 4

(M) Radiator Hoses, Renew

All models-upper (.3) 4
- lower (.4) 5
- both (.5) 7

FUEL

(M) Carburetor Air Cleaner, Service

All models (.2) 3

(G) Carburetor, Adjust (On Car)

All models
- Slow & Fast Idle (.3) 4
- Vacuum Brake-one (.6) 8
- both (.8) 1.0
- Complete (1.3) 1.8

(G) Automatic Choke Diaphragm, Renew

All models-one (.6) 8
- both (.8) 1.0

BRAKES

(G) Brakes, Adjust (Minor)

Includes: R&R wheels and adjust brakes thru access holes in drums. Fill master cylinder.

two wheels 4

Remove knock out plugs, add-each 1

(G) Bleed Brakes (Four Wheels)

Includes: Fill master cylinder.

All models (.4) 5

(G) Brake Pedal Free Play, Adjust

All models 3

LABOR — SERVICE BAY OPERATIONS — LABOR

(Factory Time)	Chilton Time
(M) Parking Brake, Adjust	
All models (.3)	.4

LUBRICATION SERVICE

(M) Lubricate Chassis, Change Oil & Filter	
Includes: Inspect and correct all fluid levels.	
All models	.6
Install grease fittings add	.1
(M) Lubricate Chassis	
Includes: Inspect and correct all fluid levels.	
All models	.4
Install grease fittings add	.1
(M) Engine Oil & Filter, Change	
Includes: Inspect and correct all fluid levels.	
All models	.4

WHEELS

(M) Wheel, Renew	
one (.5)	.5
(M) Wheels, Balance	
one	.3
each adtnl	.2
(M) Wheels, Rotate (All)	
All models	.5

ELECTRICAL

(M) Battery Cables, Renew	
All models-positive (.3)	.4
negative (.3)	.4
(M) Battery Terminals, Clean	
All models	.3
(G) Headlamp Switch, Renew	
All models (.3)	.6

CHILTON'S 10 POINT SAFETY CHECK

CHECK OPERATION & CONDITION OF THE FOLLOWING ITEMS:

1. Legal Registration (serial no.)
2. Tires & Wheels
3. Brake System (R&R all wheels)
4. Light Systems & Signals
5. Accelerator Linkage, Neutral Safety Switch, Shift Indicator Pointer & Seat Position Locks
6. Glass, Mirrors, Door Locks, Seat Belts & Harness
7. Wipers, Washers & Defrosters
8. Frame, Steering, Shocks, Front & Rear Suspension
9. Fuel & Exhaust Systems
10. Road Test Vehicle

All models 1.0
Exhaust Smog Analysis, add 4

(Factory Time)	Chilton Time
(G) Aim Headlamps	
two	.4
four	.6
(M) Headlamp Sealed Beam Bulb, Renew	
All models-one (.2)	.3
each adtnl	.1

(Factory Time)	Chilton Time
(G) Headlamp Dimmer Switch, Renew	
All models (.5)	.7
(G) Stop Light Switch, Renew	
All models (.3)	.4
(G) Turn Signal and Hazard Warning Switch, Renew	
All models	
std colm (.7)	1.1
tilt colm (.9)	1.3
(M) Turn Signal or Hazard Warning Flasher, Renew	
All models	
hazard (.4)	.5
turn signal (.3)	.4
(G) Horn Relay, Renew	
All models (.4)	.4
(G) Horn, Renew	
All models (.3)	.4
(M) Back-Up Lamp Assy., Renew	
All models-each (.3)	.4
(M) Back-Up Lamp Bulb, Renew	
All models-one (.2)	.3
(M) License Lamp Bulb, Renew	
All models-one or all (.2)	.3
(M) Park and Turn Signal Lamp Bulb, Renew	
All models-each	.2
(M) Side Marker Lamp Bulb, Renew	
All models-each	.2
(M) Stop, Tail and Turn Signal Lamp Bulb, Renew	
All models-one	.2
each adtnl	.1

LABOR — 1 TUNE UP 1 — LABOR

(Factory Time)	Chilton Time
(G) Compression Test	
1983-87	
Four (.3)	.5
V-6 (.5)	.8
w/Cruise control add	.3

(G) Engine Tune Up, (Electronic Ignition)

Includes: Test battery and clean connections. Tighten manifold and carburetor mounting bolts. Check engine compression, clean and adjust or renew spark plugs. Test resistance of spark plug cables. Inspect distributor cap and rotor. Adjust air gap. Check vacuum advance operation. Reset ignition timing. Adjust idle mixture and idle speed. Service air cleaner. Inspect and adjust drive belts. Inspect choke operation and adjust or free up. Check operation of EGR valve.

(Factory Time)	Chilton Time
Four–1983-87	1.6
V-6–1983-87	2.0
w/A.C. add	.6
w/Cruise control add	.3
To perform C.C.C. system test add	1.0

LABOR — 2 IGNITION SYSTEM 2 — LABOR

GASOLINE ENGINES

(Factory Time)	Chilton Time
(G) Spark Plugs, Clean and Reset or Renew	
1983-87-Four (.3)	.5
V-6	
eng codes X-Z-W (.5)	.7
eng codes E-3 (1.0)	1.5
w/Cruise control add (.3)	.3
(G) Ignition Timing, Reset	
1983-87 (.4)	.4

(Factory Time)	Chilton Time
(G) Distributor, Renew	
Includes: Reset ignition timing.	
1983-87 (.6)	1.0
(G) Distributor, R&R and Recondition	
Includes: Reset ignition timing.	
1983-87 (.9)	1.6
(G) ESC Module, Renew	
1983-87 (.5)	.7

(Factory Time)	Chilton Time
(G) ESC Knock Sensor, Renew	
1983-85 (.7)	1.0
1986-87 (.3)	.6
(G) Distributor Cap and/or Rotor, Renew	
Includes: R&R coil.	
1983-87 (.3)	.4

LABOR 2 IGNITION SYSTEM 2 LABOR

(Factory Time)	Chilton Time
(G) Ignition Coil, Renew	
Includes: Test coil.	
1983-87	
Four	
dist. mount (.3)	.5
external mount (.6)	1.0
V-6 (.4)	.6
(G) Distributor Module, Renew	
1983-87-Four (.7)	1.0
V-6 (.6)	.9
(G) Distributor Capacitor and/or Module Wiring Harness, Renew	
1983-87	
Four (1.3)	1.8
V-6	
eng codes X-Z-W (.9)	1.3
eng codes E-3 (.4)	.8
Distributor Pick-Up Coil and/or Pole Piece, Renew	
Includes: Reset ignition timing.	
1983-87-Four (1.1)	1.4
V-6	
eng codes X-Z-W (.9)	1.2
eng codes E-3 (.6)	.9
(G) Distributor Hall Effect Switch, Renew	
1983 (1.3)	1.7
(G) Ignition Cables, Renew	
1983-87-Four (.3)	.5
V-6	
eng codes X-Z-W (.4)	.6
eng codes E-3 (.7)	1.0
w/Cruise control add (.3)	.3
(G) Ignition Switch, Renew	
1983-87 (.6)	.9
(G) Ignition Key Warning Switch, Renew	
1983-87 (.6)	.9

DIESEL IGNITION COMPONENTS

(Factory Time)	Chilton Time
(G) Coolant Fast Idle Temperature Switch, Renew	
All models (.2)	.4
(G) Glow Plug Relay, Renew	
All models (.2)	.3
(G) Fast Idle Solenoid, Renew	
All models (.3)	.4
(G) Glow Plugs, Renew	
All models-one bank (.4)	.6
both banks (.6)	1.0
(G) Glow Plug Control Module, Renew (Controller)	
All models (.5)	.7
(G) Glow Plug Control Switch, Renew	
All models (.2)	.4
(G) Control Sensor, Renew	
All models (.2)	.3

PARTS 2 IGNITION SYSTEM 2 PARTS

FOUR CYLINDER

	Part No.	Price
Distributor Assy.		
1983	◆1103513	282.50
1984	◆1103551	236.00
1985	◆1103634	155.75
1986-87	◆1103650	N.L.
(1) Cap		
1983-84	◆1978497	16.00
1985-87	◆10495822	10.75
(2) Rotor		
1983	◆1979703	8.50
1984	◆1988515	8.50
1985-87	◆10495411	3.50
(3) Mainshaft		
1983	◆1979705	40.00
1984	◆1986963	33.25
1985-87	◆1988077	24.75
(4) Terminal Block		
1983	◆1979700	32.75
1984	◆1986972	28.50
(5) Pole Piece & Plate		
1983	◆1979696	36.25
1984	◆1978503	39.25
1985-87	◆1987963	3.50
(6) Module		
1983-84	◆1985342	56.50
1985-87	◆1989747	51.50

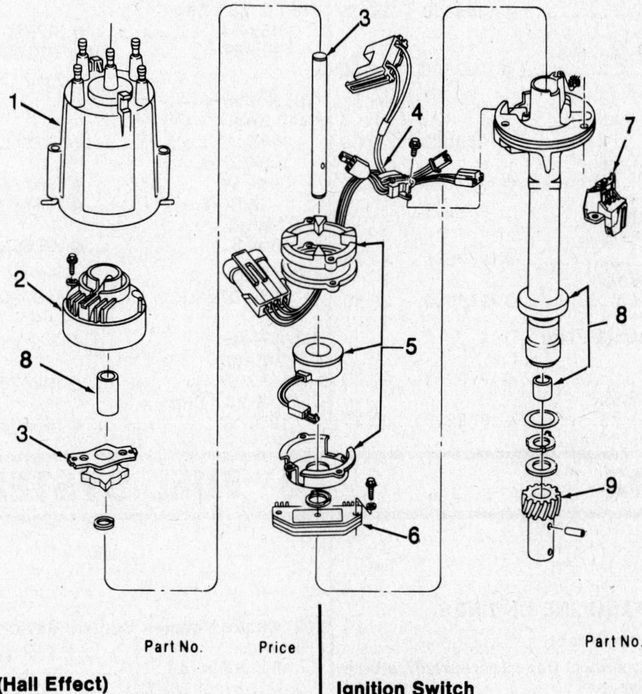

	Part No.	Price
(7) Switch (Hall Effect)		
1983	◆1979711	47.50
(8) Housing		
1983	◆1979701	48.75
1984	◆1988883	40.25
1985-87	◆1988082	26.75
(9) Gear		
1983-87	◆1978509	13.00

	Part No.	Price
Ignition Switch		
wo/tilt wheel		
1983	◆1990109	11.50
1984-85-wo/ Console	◆1990115	11.50
1986-87-w/ console	◆7843497	25.75
(w/tilt wheel)		
1983	◆1990110	11.50
1984-87-exc. below	◆1990116	11.50
w/console	◆7843451	25.75

PARTS 2 IGNITION SYSTEM 2 PARTS

Refer to the "Tune Up" specifications chart for engine code identification.

SIX CYLINDER

	Part No.	Price
Distributor Assy.		
173 Eng.		
1983	◆1103519	243.75
1984	◆1103569	214.00
1985-87		
eng. Code W	◆1103591	176.50
eng. Code X	◆1103643	216.25
181 Eng.		
1983-87	◆1103470	351.25
231 Eng.		
1984-87	◆1103588	289.75
(1) Cover		
1983-87	◆1894209	6.00
(2) Coil		
173 Eng.		
1983-87-exc.		
Code W	◆1115455	58.00
Code W	◆1115315	39.50
181 & 231 Eng.		
1983-87	◆1985474	36.00
(3) Cap		
173 Eng.		
1983-87	◆1979208	20.25
181 Eng.		
1983-87	◆1894979	17.00
231 Eng.		
1984-87	◆1984480	27.25
(4) Brushes		
1983-87	◆1989880	2.50
(5) Rotor		
173 Eng.		
1983-87	◆1978533	9.00
181 & 231 Eng.		
1983-87	◆1977026	6.50
(6) Mainshaft		
173 Eng.		
1983-87	◆1979256	49.75
181 & 231 Eng.		
1983-87	◆1976930	38.50
(7) Pole Piece & Plate		
173 Eng.		
1983-87	◆1979261	33.00
181 & 231 Eng.		
1983-87	◆1976925	30.25

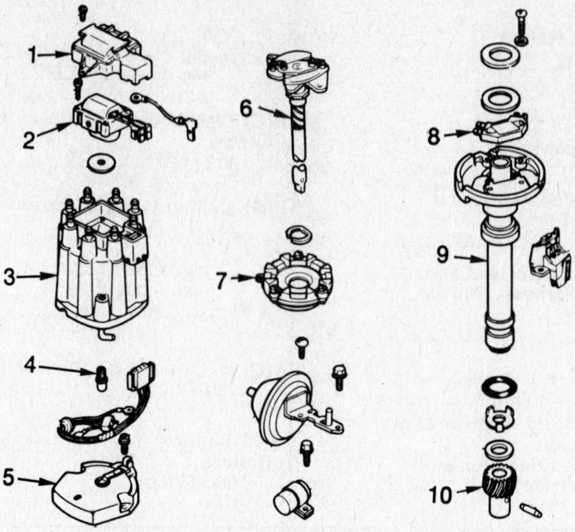

	Part No.	Price
(8) Module		
173 Eng.		
1983-87	◆1979571	58.00
181 & 231 Eng.		
1983-84	◆1976908	60.00
1985-87	◆16022604	66.75
(9) Housing		
173 Eng.		
1983	◆1979254	41.50
1984-87-exc.		
Code W	◆1987841	37.25
Code W	◆1988388	34.25
181 Eng.		
1983-87	◆1976928	36.25
231 Eng.		
1984-87	◆1987900	62.75
(10) Gear		
173 Eng.		
1983-87	◆1985769	22.00
181 & 231 Eng.		
1983-87	◆1892082	15.25

	Part No.	Price
Ignition Switch		
(wo/tilt wheel)		
1983	◆1990109	11.50
1984-87-wo/		
console	◆1990115	11.50
w/console	◆7843497	25.75
(w/tilt wheel)		
1983	◆1990110	11.50
1984-87-wo/		
console	◆1990116	11.50
w/console	◆7843451	25.75

IGNITION SYSTEM (DIESEL)

	Part No.	Price
Glow Plug Module		
1984	◆22520348	91.75
Glow Plug Relay		
1983	◆560580	16.00
Glow Plug Control Switch		
1983	◆22514724	N.L.
Glow Plugs		
1983	◆5613680	19.00
1984-85	◆5613826	16.50

LABOR 3 FUEL SYSTEM 3 LABOR

GASOLINE ENGINES

(Factory Time)	Chilton Time
(G) Fuel Pump, Test	
Includes: Disconnect line at carburetor, attach pressure gauge.	
All models	.2
(M) Carburetor Air Cleaner, Service	
All models (.2)	.3
(G) Carburetor, Adjust (On Car)	
All models	
Slow & Fast Idle (.3)	.4
Vacuum Brake-one (.6)	.8
both (.8)	1.0
Complete (1.3)	1.8
(G) Thermostatic Choke Cover and/or Gasket, Renew	
All models (.6)	1.0
(G) Choke Vacuum Control Switch, Renew	
All models (.2)	.4
(G) Automatic Choke Vacuum Diaphragm, Renew	
All models-one (.6)	.8
both (.8)	1.0
(M) Carburetor Fuel Filter, Renew	
All models (.3)	.4
(G) Electric Choke Relay, Renew	
1983-85 (.2)	.3
1986-87 (.6)	.8
(G) Idle Stop Solenoid, Renew	
1983-84 (.3)	.3
1985-87 (.7)	1.0
(G) Carburetor, Renew	
Includes: All necessary adjustments.	
1983-87 (.6)	1.0
To perform C.C.C. system check, add (.5)	1.0
(G) Carburetor, R&R and Clean or Recondition	
Includes: All necessary adjustments.	
1983-87 (2.3)	3.0
To perform C.C.C. system check, add (.5)	1.0
(G) E.F.E. Heater (Insulator), Renew	
1983-87 (.6)	1.0
(G) Accelerator Pump, Renew	
1983-87 (.9)	1.2

LABOR — 3 FUEL SYSTEM 3 — LABOR

	(Factory Time)	Chilton Time
(G) Carburetor Float and/or Needle Valve and Seat, Renew		
Includes: Adjust float level.		
All models	(.9)	1.5
To perform C.C.C. system check, add	(.5)	1.0
(G) Water In Fuel Detector, Renew (WIF)		
All models	(.9)	1.2
(G) Fuel Pump or Push Rod, Renew		
1983-87	(.5)	.8
Add pump test if performed.		
(G) Fuel Tank, Renew		
Includes: Drain and refill tank, transfer tank gauge unit.		
1983-87	(.7)	1.2
(G) Fuel Gauge (Tank), Renew		
Includes: Drain and refill tank.		
1983-87	(.8)	1.3
Transfer elec. pump add		.1
(G) Fuel Gauge (Dash), Renew		
1983-87		
Celebrity	(.8)	1.4
Century	(.3)	.5
6000	(.5)	.9
Ciera	(.6)	.9
(G) Intake Manifold Gasket, Renew		
1983-87-Four	(2.0)	3.0
V-6		
eng codes X-Z-W	(2.5)	3.4
eng code E	(1.8)	2.5
eng codes 3-B	(2.4)	3.4
w/A.C. add	(.3)	.3
w/A.I.R. add	(.5)	.5
w/Cruise control add	(.2)	.3
w/C.C.C. add	(.3)	.3
Renew manif add	(.3)	.5

E.F.E. SYSTEM

	(Factory Time)	Chilton Time
(G) E.F.E. Valve (Heat Riser), Renew		
1983-85	(.7)	1.1

THROTTLE BODY INJECTION

	(Factory Time)	Chilton Time
(G) Throttle Body and/or Gasket, Renew		
Four-1983-87	(.7)	1.0
Renew meter body add	(.3)	.3
Renew throttle body kit add		.3
(G) Idle Air Control Valve, Renew		
Four-1983-87	(.6)	.9
(G) Throttle Body Injector, Renew		
Four-1983-87-one	(.6)	1.0
(G) Throttle Body Fuel Meter Assy., Renew		
Four-1983-87	(.4)	.6
(G) Fuel Pressure Regulator, Renew		
Four-1983-87	(.7)	1.1
(G) Fuel Pump, Renew (In Tank)		
Four-1983-87	(1.3)	1.7
(G) Fuel Pump Relay, Renew		
Four-1983-87	(.7)	1.0
(G) Minimum Idle Speed, Adjust		
All models	(.5)	.8

PORTED INJECTION

	(Factory Time)	Chilton Time
(G) Throttle Body, R&R		
1985-87	(.6)	1.0
Renew throttle body kit add	(.3)	.3
Renew fuel meter body add	(.3)	.3
(G) Throttle Body Unit, Renew		
1985-87	(.6)	1.0
(G) Throttle Body Fuel Meter Assy; and/or Gasket, Renew		
1985-87	(.4)	.6
(G) Idle Air Control Valve, Renew		
1985-87	(.4)	.6
(G) Minimum Idle Speed, Adjust		
All models	(.4)	.7
(G) Throttle Body Injector and/or Gasket, Renew		
1985-87-one	(.7)	1.1
(G) Fuel Pressure Regulator, Renew		
1985-87	(.3)	.6
Perform balance test add		.4
(G) Fuel Pump, Renew (In Tank)		
1985-87	(1.3)	1.8
(G) Fuel Pump Relay, Renew		
1985-87	(.3)	.4
(G) Cold Start Injector, Renew		
1985-87	(1.0)	1.4
(G) Thermo Start Switch, Renew		
1985-87	(.5)	.7
(G) Fuel Injector, Renew		
1985-87-one		
exc. eng Code W	(.6)	1.1
eng Code W	(1.0)	1.5
each adtnl	(.1)	.1
(G) Fuel Rail, Renew		
1985-87	(.6)	1.0
(G) Mass Air Sensor, Renew		
1985-87	(.3)	.5

DIESEL ENGINE

	(Factory Time)	Chilton Time
(G) Idle Speed, Adjust		
1983-85	(.5)	.6
(G) Air Cleaner, Service		
1983-85	(.2)	.4
(G) Air Intake Crossover, Renew		
1983-85	(.4)	.6
(G) Injection Timing, Check and Adjust		
1983-85	(.7)	.9
(G) Fuel Filter, Renew		
1983-85	(.2)	.4
(G) Fuel Supply Pump, Renew		
1983-85	(.5)	.8
(G) Injection Pump Throttle Shaft Seal, Renew		
1983-85	(.9)	1.3
(G) Injection Pump Adapter and/or Seal, Renew		
1983-85	(1.4)	2.1
(G) Fuel Injection Pump, Renew		
Includes: Pressure and electrical test. Adjust timing.		
1983-85	(2.0)	3.0
(G) High Pressure Fuel Lines, Renew		
1983-85-one	(.9)	1.2
all	(1.3)	2.5
w/A.C. add	(.2)	.2
(G) Injector Nozzle and/or Seal, Renew		
1983-85-one	(1.2)	1.6
all	(2.1)	3.0
Clean nozzle add, each		.2
w/A.C. add	(.2)	.2
(G) Vacuum Pump, Renew		
Includes: Vacuum test.		
1983-85	(.6)	.8
(G) Fuel Solenoid, Renew		
1983-85	(.7)	1.0
(G) Cold Advance Solenoid, Renew		
1983-85	(.8)	1.1
(G) Fuel Injection Head Seal, Renew		
Includes: Renew head and drive shaft seals. Renew governor weight retaining ring.		
1983-85	(2.3)	3.4
(G) Intake Manifold or Gaskets, Renew		
1983-85	(2.8)	3.5
Renew manif add	(.2)	.5

PARTS — 3 FUEL SYSTEM 3 — PARTS

	Part No.	Price
Carburetor Assy. (Rochester)		
173 Eng.		
1983 w/H.O. eng.	◆17079576	802.25
(wo/Hi-output eng.)		
wo/A.C.	◆17079149	786.00
w/A.C.	◆17079167	879.75
1984-87-w/H.O. eng.	◆17110537	777.75
(wo/Hi-output eng.)		
w/Thm 125	◆17110530	771.75
w/Thm 440	◆17110538	771.75
181 Eng.		
1983	◆17079441	904.25
1984-w/Thm 125	◆17110201	856.50
w/Thm 440	◆17110337	912.75
1985-87-w/Thm 125	◆17111182	750.50
w/Thm 440	◆17111188	750.50
Carburetor Gasket Kit		
173 Eng.		
1983	◆17068741	28.25
1984-87	◆17079987	27.25
181 Eng.		
1983-84	◆17068882	31.25
1985-87	◆17111176	32.75
Carburetor Needle & Seat Kit		
173 Eng.		
1983	◆7035156	6.00
1984-87	◆17079792	7.00
181 Eng.		
1983-87	◆7035157	6.00

PARTS 3 FUEL SYSTEM 3 PARTS

	Part No.	Price
Carburetor Power Kit		
173 Eng.		
1983	◆17069019	39.50
1984-87	◆17076122	44.25
181 Eng.		
1983-84	◆17076129	51.00
1985-87	◆17076144	57.75
Fuel Pump		
Four Cyl.		
1983-87-exc. digital cluster	◆6472011	80.00
w/digital cluster	◆6471959	91.50
173 Eng.		
1983-87-exc. Engine Code W	◆6472020	56.25
1985-87 w/eng. Code W	◆6472229	132.50
181 Eng.		
1983-84-exc. digital cluster	◆6471926	N.L.
w/digital cluster	◆6471960	68.00
1985-87	◆6472525	39.75
231 Eng.		
1984-87-exc. digital cluster	◆6472229	132.50
w/digital cluster	◆6472451	75.75
V-6 Diesel		
1983	◆6471952	70.00
1984-exc. fuel filter syst.	◆6472153	59.50
w/fuel filter sys.	◆6442228	59.25
1985-87	◆6442228	59.25
Fuel Tank		
1983-87-exc. diesel	◆22515512	134.00
Diesel	◆22515513	134.00
Fuel Gauge (Tank Unit)		
Four Cyl. Eng.		
1983-87-exc. digital cluster	◆25003275	139.25
1983-84-w/ digital cluster	◆25003646	126.25
1985-87 w/digital cluster	◆25090007	108.75
173 Eng.		
1983-87-exc. digital cluster	◆25003149	72.25
1983-84-w/ digital cluster	◆25004308	79.75
1985-87 w/digital cluster	◆25090066	83.25
181 Eng.		
1983-87-exc. digital cluster	◆25090481	98.50
w/digital cluster	◆25003648	121.00
231 Eng.		
1984-87-exc. digital cluster	◆25003924	112.75
1984-w/digital cluster	◆25003986	123.00
1985-87 w/digital cluster	◆25004999	107.25
V-6, Diesel		
1983-84-wo/in-line fuel filter exc. digital cluster	◆25003150	125.75
w/digital cluster	◆25003645	126.00
1983-84-w/in-line fuel filter exc. digital cluster	◆25004275	106.50
w/digital cluster	◆25004293	107.25
1985-exc. digital cluster	◆25004275	106.50
w/digital cluster	◆25090002	113.00
Fuel Gauge (Dash)		
Celebrity		
(wo/diesel engine)		
1983	◆6433302	22.75
1984-87	◆6433921	24.25
(w/diesel engine)		
1983	◆6433303	22.75
1984-85	◆6433987	24.25
Century		
(wo/gauges)		
1983-87-exc. diesel	◆6433267	23.50
w/diesel	◆6433271	23.25
(w/gauges)		
1983-87	◆25047158	48.50
Ciera		
(wo/gauges)		
1983-84-exc. diesel	◆6433686	28.00
w/diesel	◆6433685	28.00
1985-87	◆6434189	39.75
(w/gauges)		
1983-84-exc. diesel	◆6433688	51.00
w/diesel	◆6433687	52.00
1985-87	◆6434171	53.25
6000		
(wo/gauges)		
1983-exc. diesel	◆6433734	27.25
w/diesel	◆6433717	27.25
1984-exc. diesel	◆6434070	27.75
w/diesel	◆6434081	23.25
1985-87	◆10036465	25.75
(w/gauges)		
1983-exc. diesel	◆6433737	25.25
w/diesel	◆6433716	25.25
1984-exc. diesel	◆6434074	24.00
w/diesel	◆6434084	25.00
1985-87-exc. below	◆10039880	27.50
diesel wo/tach	◆10036465	25.75
Manifold Gasket Set (Intake)		
Four Cyl. Eng.		
1983-87	◆10026023	5.00
173 Eng.		
1983-87	◆14033476	12.50
181 Eng.		
1983-87	◆25505397	15.75
231 Eng.		
1984-87	◆1264924	14.50
V-6 Diesel		
1983-84	◆22514872	16.50
1985	◆22527543	16.50

PARTS 3 FUEL SYSTEM (DIESEL) 3 PARTS

	Part No.	Price
Air Intake Crossover		
1983-84	◆22519924	109.00
1985	◆22524121	80.75
Fuel Filter		
1983-84-exc. in line filter	◆560355	15.00
1984-w/in-line filter	◆22522452	18.50
1985	◆22522452	18.50
Fuel Pump		
1983	◆6471952	70.00
1984-wo/in line filter	◆6472153	59.50
1984-w/in line filter	◆6442228	59.25
1985	◆6442228	59.25
Injection Pump Adapter		
1983-85	◆22516525	52.50
Fuel Injection Pump		
1983-w/A.T.	◆22518692	763.00
w/Hi alt.	◆22520025	763.00
w/Alum. head	◆22520607	763.00
1984 (Federal em.)		
wo/Alum. head	◆22520601	763.00
w/Alum. head	◆22520600	763.00
w/Hi alt.	◆22520604	763.00
1984 (Calif. em.)		
wo/Alum. head	◆22519882	N.L.
w/Alum. head	◆22525402	N.L.
1985-w/A.T. Fed. emis	◆22526624	763.00
Fuel Injector Nozzle		
1983	◆22514509	60.00
1984-85	◆22520376	89.50
Vacuum Pump		
1983-wo/A.C.	◆7844038	115.00
w/A.C.	◆7844039	115.00
1984-85-exc. sta. wag.		
wo/A.C.	◆7844038	115.00
w/A.C.	◆7844039	115.00
1984-85-sta. wag.		
wo/A.C.	◆7846095	119.00
w/A.C.	◆7846096	119.00
Intake Manifold		
1983	◆22510852	312.25
1984	◆22520992	320.00
1985	◆22523860	113.00
Intake Manifold Gasket Kit		
1983-84	◆22514872	16.50
1985	◆22527543	16.50

	Part No.	Price
Four Cyl. Eng.		
Throttle Body Injection		
1983	◆17079592	582.50
1984	◆17110359	582.50
1985-87	◆17110762	498.50
Gasket Kit		
1983-87	◆17068990	24.75
Throttle Body Kit		
1983	◆17079593	266.75
1984	◆17110360	240.00
1985-87	◆17110763	237.25
Idle Air Valve Control Kit		
1983-84	◆17078220	82.00
1985-87	◆17079256	88.75
Fuel Injector Kit		
1983-87	◆17068993	191.75
Fuel Meter Body Kit		
1983-87	◆17078222	109.75
Fuel Meter Kit		
1983-87	◆17068992	425.75

Note: Includes two injectors & Pressure Regulator.

	Part No.	Price
Throttle Position Kit Sensor		
1983-87	◆17078274	74.75
173 Eng.		
(1) Throttle Body Assy.		
1985-M.T.	◆17085023	N.L.
A.T.	◆17085155	N.L.
1986-87-M.T.	◆17085026	N.L.
A.T.	◆17085023	N.L.
(2) Gasket Kit		
1985-87	◆17110827	9.00

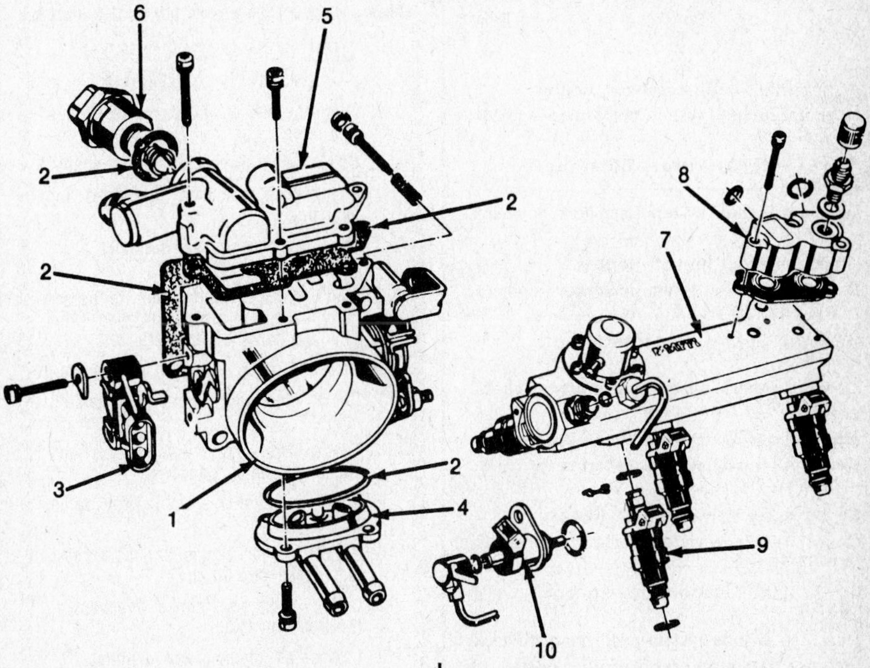

	Part No.	Price
(3) Throttle Position Sensor Kit		
1985-87	◆17110830	46.50
(4) Coolant Cover Kit		
1985-87	◆17110828	39.25
(5) Idle Air Vacuum Housing Kit		
1985-87	◆17110834	30.00
(6) Idle Air Control Valve		
1985-87	◆17111288	58.00

	Part No.	Price
(7) Fuel Rail and Pressure Regulator		
1985-87	◆17110851	162.75
(8) Fuel Inlet/Outlet Block		
1985-87	◆17110853	29.25
(9) Fuel Injector Kit		
1985-87	◆17110855	N.L.
(10) Cold Start Valve		
1985-87	◆17110858	49.50

LABOR 3A EMISSION CONTROLS 3A LABOR

(Factory Time) — Chilton Time

GASOLINE ENGINES

(G) Emission Control Check

Includes: Check and adjust engine idle speed and mixture and ignition timing. Check PCV valve.

All models 6

POSITIVE CRANKCASE VENTILATION

(M) Positive Crankcase Ventilation Valve, Renew
All models (.2) 3

(M) Crankcase Ventilation Filter Assy., Renew
All models (.2) 3

EVAPORATIVE EMISSION TYPE

(G) Charcoal Canister, Renew
All models (.2) 3

(G) Fuel Tank Pressure Control Valve, Renew
All models (.2) 3

CONTROLLED COMBUSTION TYPE

(G) Air Cleaner Vacuum Motor, Renew
All models (.3) 5

(G) Air Cleaner Temperature Sensor, Renew
All models (.2) 3

EXHAUST GAS RECIRCULATION SYSTEM

(G) E.G.R. Valve, Renew
All models-Four (.4) 6
V-6
wo/F.I. (.6) 1.0
w/F.I. (.4) 6

(G) EGR/EFE Thermal Vacuum Switch, Renew
All models (.3) 4

(G) E.G.R. Vacuum Delay Valve, Renew
All models (.3) 4

(G) Thermostatic Vacuum Control Switch, Renew
All models (.2) 3

(G) E.G.R. Thermal Control Valve, Renew
All models (.3) 4

AIR INJECTION REACTION SYSTEM

(G) Air Pump, Renew
1983-87-V-6 (.3) 6

(G) A.I.R. Centrifugal Filter, Renew
All models (.3) 5

(G) A.I.R. Air Cleaner, Renew
All models (.2) 3

(G) Deceleration Valve, Renew
All models (.3) 4

(G) A.I.R. Check Valve, Renew (One)
All models (.2) 3
each adtnl (.2) 2

(G) Air Manifold Pipe, Renew
All models-right (.8) 1.2

(G) Catalytic Converter Air Pipe, Renew
All models
upper (.5) 7
lower (.3) 5
one piece (.6) 9

COMPUTER COMMAND CONTROL SYSTEM (C.C.C.)

(P) Electronic Control Module, Renew
Does not include system performance check.
1983-87 (.8) 1.1

(P) Mixture Control Solenoid, Renew
Does not include system performance check.
1983-87 (.4) 5

(P) Prom, Renew
Does not include system performance check.
Includes: R&R electronic module.
1983-87 (.9) 1.2

(Factory Time) Chilton Time

(P) Throttle Position Sensor, Adjust
Does not include system performance check.
All models 9

(P) EGR/EFE Purge Solenoid, Renew
Does not include system performance check.
1983-87 (.4) 6

(P) Barometric Sensor, Renew
Does not include system performance check.
1983-87 (.5) 7

(P) Idle Speed Control Motor, Renew
Does not include system performance check.
1983-87 (.7) 1.0

(P) Idle Load Compensator, Renew
Does not include system performance check.
1983-87 (.4) 6

(P) Metering Valve Sensor, Renew
Does not include system performance check.
1983-87 (.6) 8

(P) Coolant Temperature Sensor, Renew
Does not include system performance check.
Includes: Drain and refill cooling system.
1983-87 (.5) 7

(P) Manifold Absolute Pressure Sensor, Renew
Does not include system performance check.
1983-87 (.3) 6

(P) Oxygen Sensor, Renew
Does not include system performance check.
1983-87 (.4) 7

(P) Throttle Position Sensor, Renew
Does not include system performance check.
1983-87 (1.1) 1.4

(P) Vehicle Speed Sensor, Renew
Does not include system performance check.
1983-87 (1.1) 1.5
w/Console add (.3) 3

(P) Air Control Valve, Renew
Does not include system performance check.
1983-87 (.4) 6

(P) Air Control/Air Switching Valve, Renew
Does not include system performance check.
1983-87 (.6) 8

(P) Canister Purge Control Valve, Renew
Does not include system performance check.
1983-87 (.4) 6

(P) Manifold Temperature Sensor, Renew
Does not include system performance check.
1983-87 (.4) 6

(P) Calpak, Renew
Does not include system performance check.
1985-87 (.3) 4

(P) Vacuum Control Purge Solenoid, Renew
Does not include system performance check.
1983-87 (.4) 6

CHILTON'S EMISSION CONTROL TUNE-UP

1. Clean or renew P.C.V. valve, hoses and filter.
2. Check fuel tank cap for sealing ability.
3. Check fuel tank and fuel lines for leakage.
4. Check evaporation canister and filter. Replace if necessary.
5. Check engine compression to determine leakage of unburned gases. (Add time for items of interference).
6. Test and clean or renew spark plugs.
7. Check engine oil dipstick for sealing ability.
8. Test exhaust system with analyzer and check system for leakage.
9. Check exhaust manifold heat valve for operation.
10. Adjust ignition timing and carburetor idle speed and mixture.
11. Check automatic choke mechanism for free operation.
12. Inspect air cleaner and element.
13. On models so equipped, test distributor vacuum control switch and transmission control switch.

Four 1.3

For repairs made, charge accordingly.

(Factory Time) Chilton Time

(P) EFE/EGR Relay, Renew
Does not include system performance check.
1983-87 (.3) 5

(P) E.G.R. Vacuum Control Solenoid, Renew
Does not include system performance check.
1983-87 (.3) 5

(P) E.F.E. Vacuum Control Solenoid, Renew
Does not include system performance check.
1983-87 (.4) 6

(P) Back-Up Lamp and Park/Neutral Switch, Renew
Does not include system performance check.
1983-87 (.5) 7

(P) Tachometer Filter, Renew
Does not include system performance check.
1983-87 (.3) 3

(P) Computer Command Control System Performance Check
1983-87 (.5) 1.0

THROTTLE BODY INJECTION

(P) Electronic Control Module, Renew
1983-87 (.7) 9

(P) Throttle Position Sensor, Renew
1983-87 (.9) 1.2

(P) Prom, Renew
1983-87 (.7) 1.0

(Factory Time) Chilton Time

(P) Coolant Temperature Sensor, Renew
1983-87 (.4) 7

(P) Manifold Absolute Pressure Sensor, Renew
1983-87 (.5) 6

(P) Oxygen Sensor, Renew
1983-87 (.5) 7

(P) Vehicle Speed Sensor, Renew
1983-87 (1.1) 1.4

DIESEL ENGINE

(G) Crankcase Depression Regulator Valve, Renew
1983-85 (.2) 3

(G) Crankcase Ventilation Filter, Renew
1983-85 (.2) 3

(G) E.G.R. Valve and/or Gasket, Renew
1983-85 (.4) 7

(G) E.G.R. Control Valve Solenoid, Renew
1983-85 (.2) 4

(G) E.G.R. Control Valve Switch, Renew
1983-85 (.2) 3

(G) E.P.R. Control Valve Solenoid, Renew
1983-85 (.3) 4

(G) E.P.R. Control Valve Switch, Renew
1983-85 (.3) 4

(G) E.P.R. Exhaust Pressure Regulator Valve, Renew
1983-85 (.5) 6

(G) Vacuum Regulator Valve, Renew
1983-85 (.6) 8

(G) Housing Pressure Cold Advance Solenoid, Renew
All models (.5) 7

(G) Altitude Fuel Limiter, Renew
All models (.6) 8

(G) Housing Pressure Altitude Advance Solenoid, Renew
All models (.2) 3

(G) Housing Pressure Altitude Advance Relay, Renew
All models (.4) 6

DIESEL ELECTRONIC EMISSION CONTROLS

(P) Electronic Control Module, Renew
All models (.6) 8

(P) Manifold Absolute Pressure Sensor, Renew
All models (.3) 5

(P) Vehicle Speed Sensor, Renew
All models (.9) 1.4

(P) Coolant Temperature Sensor, Renew
All models (.6) 7

PARTS 3A EMISSION CONTROLS 3A PARTS

	Part No.	Price
POSITIVE CRANKCASE VENTILATION		
Positive Crankcase, Valve		
Four Cyl. Eng.		
1983-84	◆25041498	7.00
1985-87	◆25043669	6.25
173 Eng.		
1983-87	◆8995284	5.00
181 & 231 Eng.		
1983-84	◆6487936	3.50
1985-87	◆25043471	6.75
EVAPORATIVE EMISSION TYPE		
Vapor Canister		
Four Cyl. Eng.		
1983	◆17063013	39.00
1984-87	◆17075840	30.00
173 Eng.		
1983	◆17075831	64.25
1984-w/Z eng	◆17075854	66.00
1985-87-w/W eng	◆17075854	66.00
181 Eng.		
1983-87	◆17064622	39.50
231 Eng.		
1984	◆17075856	60.00
1985-87	◆17085022	48.00
Canister Control Valve		
173 Eng.		
1985-87	◆17072400	23.50
181 Eng.		
1983-w/A.T. 3 port	◆17085929	N.L.
1983-4 port	◆17073535	12.75
1984-87	◆17085928	14.25
Canister Filter		
1983-87	◆7026014	2.50
E.F.E. Valve (w/Actuator)		
1983-w/181 eng.	◆5234110	64.00
Check Valve		
1983-w/181 eng.	◆25510974	3.25
Thermo Purge Switch		
1983-87-w/181 eng.	◆3051170	11.25
Thermo Purge Valve		
1983-Four cyl.	◆10022316	5.75
Purge Solenoid		
173 Eng.		
1983	◆1997616	14.00
1984-87	◆1997662	17.00

	Part No.	Price
CONTROLLED COMBUSTION TYPE		
Vacuum Diaphragm Motor		
Four Cyl. Eng.		
1983-84	◆25041109	23.25
1985-87	◆25042077	60.75
173 Eng.		
1983-87	◆25042360	22.00
181 Eng.		
1983-87	◆8994333	18.75
Air Cleaner Temp. Sensor		
Four Cyl. Eng.		
1983-84	◆8997574	18.75
173 Eng.		
1983-87	◆8997787	18.75
181 Eng.		
1983	◆8997493	18.75
1984-87	◆8997916	18.75
Vacuum Valve Kit		
1983-87	◆8997639	9.75
EXHAUST GAS RECIRCULATION SYSTEM		
E.G.R. Valve		
Note: Replacement E.G.R. valves must be ordered according to the stamping number on the original valve.		
E.G.R. Valve Vacuum Control		
181 Eng.		
1984-87	◆25519958	52.00
231 Eng.		
1984-87	◆25519960	53.75
E.G.R. Vacuum Control Switch		
1984-87-w/181, 231 engs.	◆25522027	11.75
AIR INJECTOR REACTOR TYPE		
Air Injector Reactor Pump		
173 Eng.		
1983-87	◆7842076	141.00
181 Eng.		
1983 (stamped MM, NA)	◆7835233	135.00
1983-85 (stamp. BX)	◆7842853	149.00
Air Injector Pump Fan		
1983-87	◆7835231	5.75
Deceleration Valve		
173 Eng.		
1983-87	◆14056425	17.50

	Part No.	Price
COMPUTER CONTROLLED EMISSION SYSTEM		
Controller (E.C.M.)		
(Remanufactured)		
Four Cyl. Eng.		
1983	◆1226100	110.25
1984	◆1226156	110.25
1985-87	◆1226864	110.25
173 Eng.		
1983	◆1226025	110.25
1984	◆1226455	110.25
1985-87	◆1226865	110.00
181 Eng.		
1983-stamped	◆1226024	110.25
stamped	◆1226153	110.25
1984-87-stamped	◆1226153	110.25
stamped	◆1226519	110.25
231 Eng.		
1984-87	◆1226461	110.25
Calibration Unit (Prom)		
Note: Order according to the code stamped on the existing calibrator.		
Barometric Pressure Sensor		
1983-87	◆16006833	62.25
EMISSION CONTROLS (DIESEL)		
Crankcase Depression Regulator Valve		
1983-84	◆25041551	28.25
1985	◆25043526	23.50
Crankcase Ventilation Filter		
1983	◆22514303	4.00
Vacuum Regulator Valve		
1983	◆17073284	77.00
1984-85	◆17074054	58.00
Diesel Control Module		
1984	◆22518729	190.25
1985	◆22528540	N.L.
E.G.R. Valve Vacuum Control		
1983-exc. Hi alt.	◆22519395	38.00
w/Hi alt.	◆22519396	38.00
1984-w/Fed em.	◆22520665	24.25
w/Calif. em.	◆1997663	32.75
w/Hi alt.	◆22520666	26.75
1985	◆1997663	32.75

LABOR 4 ALTERNATOR AND REGULATOR 4 LABOR

(Factory Time)	Chilton Time
(G) Delcotron Circuits, Test	
Includes: Test battery, regulator, Delcotron output.	
All models	.6
(M) Alternator Drive Belt, Renew	
Four (.5)	.7
V-6	
eng codes X-Z-W (.2)	.3
eng codes E-3-B (.5)	.7
Diesel	
Serpentine (.2)	.4
(G) Delcotron Assembly, Renew	
Four–1983-85 (.7)	1.1
1986-87 (.9)	1.2
V-6–1983 (.4)	.6
1984-87 (.6)	.8
w/70-85 amp gen and A.C. add (.6)	.6
Diesel–1983-85 (.5)	.7

(Factory Time)	Chilton Time
(G) Delcotron, R&R and Recondition	
Includes: Complete disassembly, replacement of parts as required, reassemble.	
Four–1983-85 (1.6)	2.2
1986-87 (1.5)	2.2
V-6–1983 (1.0)	1.7
1984-87 (1.2)	1.8
w/70-85 amp gen and A.C. add (.6)	.6
Diesel–1983-85 (1.3)	1.9
w/Elec. emissions add	.3
(G) Delcotron Front Bearing, Renew	
Includes: R&R Delcotron, separate end frames.	
Four–1983-87 (1.0)	1.4
V-6–1983-87 (.6)	.9
w/70-85 amp gen and A.C. add (.6)	.6

(Factory Time)	Chilton Time
Diesel–1983-85 (.8)	1.2
Renew rear brg add	.2
(G) Delcotron Voltage Regulator, Test and Renew	
Includes: R&R, disassemble and reassemble Delcotron.	
Four–1983-87 (1.0)	1.5
V-6–1983-87 (.7)	1.0
w/70-85 amp gen and A.C. add (.6)	.6
Diesel–1983-85 (.7)	1.1
(G) Voltmeter, Renew	
1983-87	
Celebrity (.8)	1.4
Century (.3)	.5
6000 (.5)	.9
Ciera (.6)	.9

PARTS 4 ALTERNATOR AND REGULATOR 4 PARTS

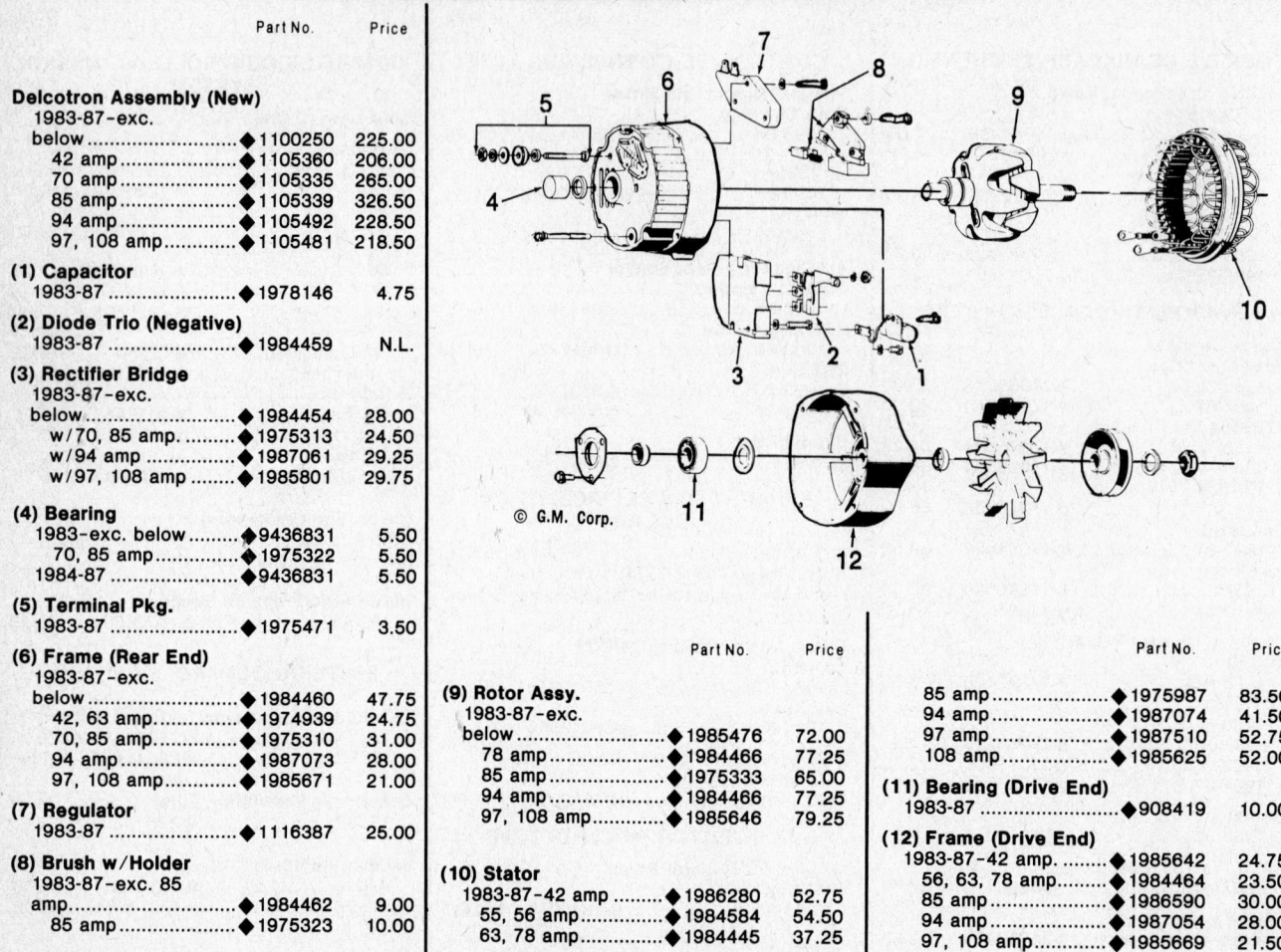

	Part No.	Price
Delcotron Assembly (New)		
1983-87-exc. below	◆1100250	225.00
42 amp	◆1105360	206.00
70 amp	◆1105335	265.00
85 amp	◆1105339	326.50
94 amp	◆1105492	228.50
97, 108 amp	◆1105481	218.50
(1) Capacitor		
1983-87	◆1978146	4.75
(2) Diode Trio (Negative)		
1983-87	◆1984459	N.L.
(3) Rectifier Bridge		
1983-87-exc. below	◆1984454	28.00
w/70, 85 amp.	◆1975313	24.50
w/94 amp	◆1987061	29.25
w/97, 108 amp	◆1985801	29.75
(4) Bearing		
1983-exc. below	◆9436831	5.50
70, 85 amp	◆1975322	5.50
1984-87	◆9436831	5.50
(5) Terminal Pkg.		
1983-87	◆1975471	3.50
(6) Frame (Rear End)		
1983-87-exc. below	◆1984460	47.75
42, 63 amp	◆1974939	24.75
70, 85 amp	◆1975310	31.00
94 amp	◆1987073	28.00
97, 108 amp	◆1985671	21.00
(7) Regulator		
1983-87	◆1116387	25.00
(8) Brush w/Holder		
1983-87-exc. 85 amp	◆1984462	9.00
85 amp	◆1975323	10.00

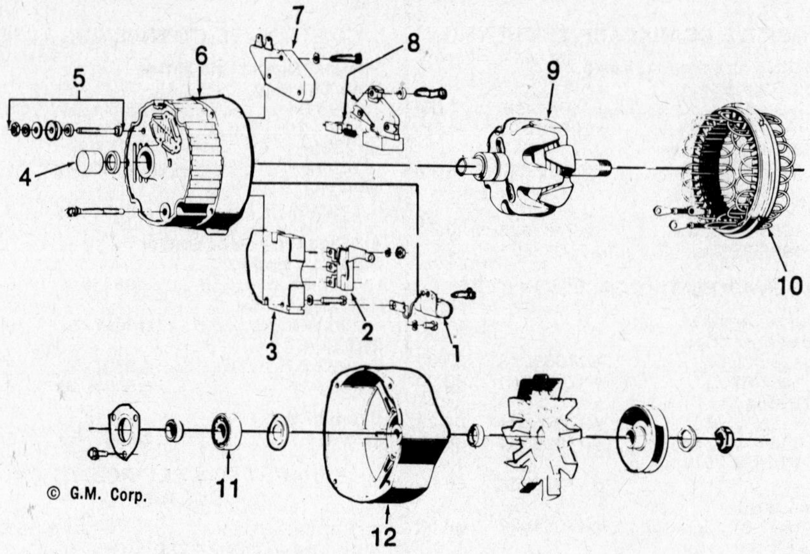

	Part No.	Price
(9) Rotor Assy.		
1983-87-exc. below	◆1985476	72.00
78 amp	◆1984466	77.25
85 amp	◆1975333	65.00
94 amp	◆1984466	77.25
97, 108 amp	◆1985646	79.25
(10) Stator		
1983-87-42 amp	◆1986280	52.75
55, 56 amp	◆1984584	54.50
63, 78 amp	◆1984445	37.25
85 amp	◆1975987	83.50
94 amp	◆1987074	41.50
97 amp	◆1987510	52.75
108 amp	◆1985625	52.00
(11) Bearing (Drive End)		
1983-87	◆908419	10.00
(12) Frame (Drive End)		
1983-87-42 amp.	◆1985642	24.75
56, 63, 78 amp	◆1984464	23.50
85 amp	◆1986590	30.00
94 amp	◆1987054	28.00
97, 108 amp	◆1985669	21.50

LABOR 5 STARTING SYSTEM 5 LABOR

	(Factory Time)	Chilton Time
(G) Starter Draw Test (On Car)		
All models		.3
(G) Starter, Renew		
Four-1983-87	(.4)	.7
V-6-1983-87		
eng codes E-3-B	(.8)	1.1
eng codes X-Z-W	(.5)	.8
Diesel-1983-85	(.8)	1.1
Add draw test if performed.		
(G) Starter, R&R and Recondition		
Includes: Turn down armature.		
Four-1983-87	(1.2)	2.0
V-6-1983-87		
eng codes E-3-B	(1.6)	2.5
eng codes X-Z-W	(1.3)	2.2
Diesel-1983-85	(1.6)	2.5
Renew field coils add	(.2)	.5
Add draw test if performed.		
(G) Starter Drive, Renew		
Includes: R&R starter.		
Four-1983-87	(.6)	1.0
V-6-1983-87		
eng codes E-3-B	(1.1)	1.5
eng codes X-Z-W	(.7)	1.1
Diesel-1983-85	(1.0)	1.4
(G) Starter Motor Solenoid, Renew		
Includes: R&R starter where required.		
Four-1983-87	(.3)	.5
V-6-1983-87		
eng codes E-3-B	(.8)	1.1
eng codes X-Z-W	(.6)	.9
Diesel-1983-85	(.8)	1.1
(G) Neutral Start Switch, Renew		
1983-87		
console mount	(.4)	.5
clutch mount	(.3)	.4
column mount	(.4)	.5
(G) Ignition Switch, Renew		
1983-87	(.6)	.9
(M) Battery Cables, Renew		
1983-87-positive	(.3)	.4
negative	(.3)	.4
(M) Battery Terminals, Clean		
All models		.3

PARTS 5 STARTING SYSTEM 5 PARTS

	Part No.	Price
GASOLINE ENGINES (DELCO-REMY)		
Starter Assy. (New)		
Four Cyl. Eng.		
1983	◆1109556	N.L.
1984-87	◆1998450	186.00
173 Eng.		
1983	◆1109533	214.75
1984-87	◆1109564	165.50
181 Eng.		
1983	◆1998448	191.00
1984-87	◆1998448	191.00
231 Eng.		
1984-87	◆1998445	188.00
(1) Drive Housing		
Four Cyl. Eng.		
1983	◆1984734	27.00
1984-87	◆1985148	25.75
173 Eng.		
1983	◆1978282	32.75
1984-87	◆1984734	27.00
181 & 231 V-6 Eng.		
1983-87	◆1985148	25.75
(2) Drive Assy.		
1983-87	◆1984511	23.50

PARTS 5 STARTING SYSTEM 5 PARTS

	Part No.	Price
(3) Shift Lever		
1983-87	◆1984501	5.00
(4) Plunger		
1983-87	◆1987391	6.75
(5) Plunger Spring		
1983-87	◆1978281	1.75
(6) Solenoid Switch		
1983-87	◆1114531	N.L.
(7) Armature		
1983-Four Cyl.	◆1984504	107.50
173 eng.	◆1978670	83.50
181 eng.	◆1985138	N.L.
1984-87	◆1985138	N.L.
(8) Frame and Field		
1983-Four Cyl.	◆1984522	75.00
173 eng.	◆1978672	78.00
181 eng.	◆1985143	71.50
1984-87-exc.		
231 Eng.	◆1985143	71.50
231 eng.	◆1987277	71.25
(9) Brushes		
1983-87	◆1893296	.50

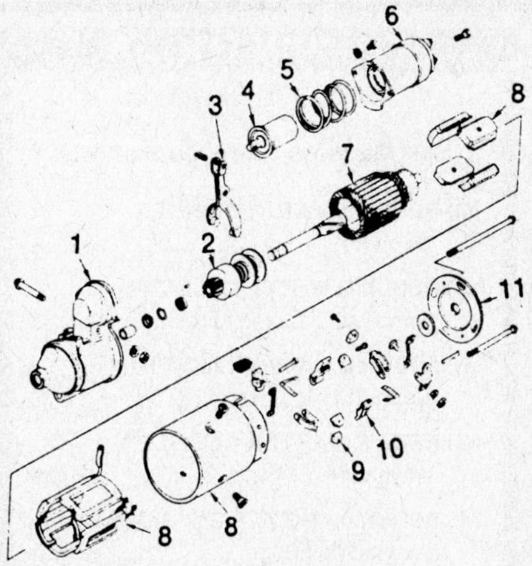

	Part No.	Price
(10) Holder Kit		
1983-87	◆1893929	11.25
(11) Commutator End Frame		
1983-87	◆1978292	6.50

	Part No.	Price
Battery Cables		
Order by year and model.		
Ignition Switch		
(wo/tilt wheel)		
1983	◆1990109	N.L.
1984-87-wo/		
console	◆1990115	11.50
w/console	◆7843497	25.75
(w/tilt wheel)		
1983	◆1990110	N.L.
1984-87-wo/		
console	◆1990116	11.50
w/console	◆7843451	25.75

DIESEL ENGINE (DELCO REMY)

	Part No.	Price
Battery Cables		
Order by year and model.		
Neutral Safety Switch		
(wo/console)		
1983	◆22509632	5.50
1984-85	◆22514861	7.00
(w/console)		
1983-85	◆1994223	18.00

PARTS 5 STARTING SYSTEM 5 PARTS

DIESEL ENGINE (MITSUBISHI)

	Part No.	Price
Starter Assembly (New)		
1983	◆22523207	389.25
1984-85	◆22523207	389.25
(1) Drive Pinion		
1983	◆22516186	8.50
(2) Drive Housing (w/Bushing)		
1983	◆22516190	33.50
1984-85	◆22523730	35.00
(3) Shim Kit		
1983-85	◆22516175	1.50
(4) Solenoid Switch		
1983-85	◆22516196	44.00
(5) Lever Kit		
1983-85	◆22516193	3.25
(6) Drive Pinion Shaft		
1983-85	◆22516183	71.00
(7) Spring w/Holder		
1983-85	◆22516194	2.50
(8) Reduction Gear		
1983-85	◆22516184	9.50
(9) Shim Kit		
1983-85	◆22516175	1.50
(10) Gear Housing		
1983-85	◆22516195	28.50
(11) Pinion Shaft End Cover		
1983-85	◆22516182	2.00
(12) Armature Drive Gear Bearing		
1983-85	◆22516189	9.00

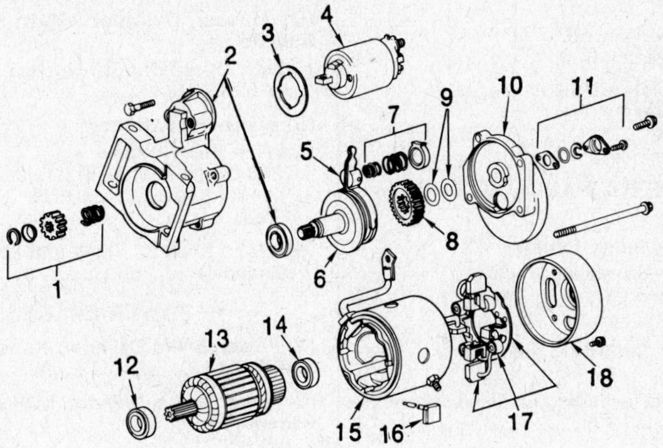

	Part No.	Price
(13) Armature		
1983-85	◆22516197	130.00
(14) Commutator End Bearing		
1983-85	◆22516188	5.50
(15) Field Frame		
1983-85	◆22516181	83.00
(16) Positive Brush		
1983-85	◆22516180	3.25
(17) Negative Brush		
1983-85	◆22516177	3.00

	Part No.	Price
(18) Commutator End Frame		
1983-85	◆22516176	7.50
Ignition Switch		
(wo/tilt wheel)		
1983	◆1990109	N.L.
1984-85-wo/		
console	◆1990115	11.50
w/console	◆7843497	25.75
(w/tilt wheel)		
1983	◆1990110	N.L.
1984-85-wo/		
console	◆1990116	11.50
w/console	◆7843451	25.75
Battery Cables		
Order by year and model.		

LABOR 6 BRAKE SYSTEM 6 LABOR

(Factory Time)	Chilton Time
(G) Brake Pedal Free Play, Adjust	
All models	.3
(G) Brakes, Adjust (Minor)	
Includes: R&R wheels and adjust brakes thru access holes in drums. Fill master cylinder.	
two wheels	.4
Remove knock out plugs, add-each..	.1
(G) Bleed Brakes (Four Wheels)	
Includes: Fill master cylinder.	
All models (.4)	.5
(G) Free Up or Renew Brake Self-Adjusting Units	
All models-one (.4)	.6
each adtnl	.4
(G) Brake Shoes and/or Pads, Renew	
Includes: Install new or exchange shoes or pads, adjust service and hand brake. Bleed system.	
1983-87-front-disc (.7)	1.1
rear-drum (.9)	1.5
all four wheels	2.5
Resurface disc rotor add-each	.9
Resurface brake drum add-each	.5
(G) Brake Drum, Renew (One)	
1983-87 (.4)	.5
(G) Brake Proportioner Valves, Renew	
Includes: Bleed system.	
1983-87-each (.4)	.6
(G) Brake System Failure Warning Switch, Renew	
1983-87 (.2)	.3

BRAKE HYDRAULIC SYSTEM

(G) Wheel Cylinder, Renew	
Includes: Bleed system.	
1983-87-one (.8)	1.0
both (1.1)	1.9
(G) Wheel Cylinder, R&R and Rebuild	
Includes: Hone cylinder and bleed system.	
1983-87-one (1.0)	1.3
both (1.5)	2.1
(G) Master Cylinder, Renew	
Includes: Bleed system.	
1983-87 (.7)	1.0

COMBINATIONS

Add to Brakes, Renew

See Machine Shop Operations

(G) RENEW WHEEL CYLINDER	
Each (.2)	.2
(G) REBUILD WHEEL CYLINDER	
Each (.2)	.3
(G) REBUILD CALIPER ASSEMBLY	
Each (.5)	.6
(G) RENEW MASTER CYLINDER	
All models (.5)	.8
(G) REBUILD MASTER CYLINDER	
All models (.8)	1.0
(G) RENEW BRAKE HOSE	
Each (.3)	.3
(G) RENEW BRAKE DRUM	
Each (.1)	.1
(G) RENEW DISC BRAKE ROTOR	
Each (.2)	.3

(Factory Time)	Chilton Time
(G) Master Cylinder, R&R and Rebuild	
Includes: Bleed complete system.	
1983-87 (1.5)	1.9
(G) Brake Hose, Renew	
Includes: Bleed system.	
1983-87-front-one (.6)	.8
both (.8)	1.1
rear-each (.4)	.6
(G) Brake System, Flush and Refill	
All models	1.2

POWER BRAKES

(G) Power Brake Cylinder, Renew	
1983-87 (.7)	1.1
(G) Power Brake Cylinder, R&R and Recondition	
1983-87 (1.4)	1.8
Recond M/Cyl add (.8)	.8
(M) Vacuum Check Valve, Renew	
1983-87 (.3)	.3

(Factory Time)	Chilton Time
(G) Electric Vacuum Pump, Renew	
1983-87 (.3)	.4
Recond piston add (.2)	.2
Renew housing add (.3)	.3
(G) Vacuum Pump Pressure Switch, Renew	
1983-87 (.2)	.3
(G) Low Vacuum Switch, Renew	
1983-87 (.2)	.3
(G) Low Vacuum Brake Indicator Module, Renew	
1985-87 (.2)	.3

DISC BRAKES

(G) Disc Brake Pads, Renew	
1983-87 (.7)	1.1
(G) Disc Brake Rotor, Renew	
1983-87-one (.4)	.7
both (.8)	1.2
(G) Caliper Assembly, Renew	
Includes: Bleed complete system.	
1983-87-one (.7)	1.0
both (1.0)	1.5
(G) Caliper Assy., R&R and Recondition	
Includes: Bleed complete system.	
1983-87-one (1.2)	1.5
both (2.0)	2.5

PARKING BRAKE

(M) Parking Brake, Adjust	
All models (.3)	.4
(G) Parking Brake Warning Lamp Switch, Renew	
1983-87 (.3)	.4
(G) Parking Brake Control, Renew	
1983-84 (.7)	1.0
1985-87 (1.3)	1.9
(G) Parking Brake Equalizer, Renew	
1983-87 (.3)	.5
(G) Parking Brake Cables, Renew	
1983-87-front (1.1)	1.6
rear-right side (.9)	1.3
left side (.5)	.8
two piece (1.0)	1.5

PARTS 6 BRAKE SYSTEM 6 PARTS

	Part No.	Price
Brake Shoes Set (Rear)		
1983	◆12300249	N.L.
1984-87	◆12321413	43.00
Rear Wheel Cylinder Assy.		
(wo/H.D. brakes)		
1983-87	◆18007981	25.00
(w/H.D. brakes)		
1983-87-exc.		
sta. wag.	◆18010106	27.50
sta. wag. (exc. dies.)	◆18011142	27.25
Wheel Cylinder Repair Kit		
(wo/H.D. brakes)		
1983-87	◆18007982	6.50
(w/H.D. brakes)		
1983-87-exc.		
sta. wag.	◆18010127	7.50
sta. wag. (exc. dies.)	◆18011141	7.75
Front Brake Hose		
(right side)		
1983	◆9767946	15.25
1984-87	◆17980548	18.00
(left side)		
1983-87	◆9767945	15.25
Rear Brake Hose		
(wo/rear disc brakes)		
1983-87	◆9767287	7.50
(w/rear disc brakes)		
1984-87-right	◆10032603	7.50
left	◆10032604	7.50
Master Cylinder Assy.		
(wo/rear disc brakes)		
1983-87-wo/H.D.		
brks.	◆18010087	206.50
w/H.D. brks.	◆18010086	206.50
(w/rear disc brakes)		
1984-87	◆18011235	204.50
Master Cylinder Repair Kit		
1983-87-wo/H.D.		
brks.	◆18004853	22.50
w/H.D. brks.	◆18010085	20.75
Brake Drum (Rear)		
(cast iron)		
1983-87-wo/H.D.		
brks.	◆25516196	72.75
w/H.D. brks.	◆25516194	69.50
sta. wagon	◆25518892	69.50

PARTS 6 BRAKE SYSTEM 6 PARTS

	Part No.	Price
(Aluminum)		
1983 (A6000)		
STE	◆25509919	90.00
fuel ecom. leader	◆25509308	96.50
Oil Seal (Front)		
1983-87-wo/H.D. brks	◆14084120	3.75
w/H.D. brks	◆14084119	3.75
Power Brake Booster (Vacuum)		
1983-87-exc. rear disc brks	◆18006856	213.00
w/rear disc brks	◆18010437	250.25
Power Brake Booster Repair Kit		
1983-87	◆18007897	47.50

PARKING BRAKE

	Part No.	Price
Parking Brake Apply Lever		
1983-87	◆25510994	32.75
Parking Brake Cables (Front)		
1983-87	◆25513279	14.00
Parking Brake Cable (Rear)		
(right side)		
1983-87-exc. STE	◆25516526	19.00
1984-STE	◆10032479	19.25
1985-87-STE	◆10029554	18.50
(left side)		
1983-87-exc. STE	◆25516527	18.50
1984-87-STE	◆10035032	18.25

PARTS 6 DISC BRAKES 6 PARTS

	Part No.	Price
(1) Brake Pads		
(wo/H.D. brakes)		
1983-87	◆12300243	43.50
(w/H.D. brakes)		
1983-87	◆12321410	N.L.
1983-87-STE	◆12300235	43.50
(2) Piston Assy.		
1983-87-wo/H.D. brks	◆18002866	13.00
w/H.D. brks	◆18003155	11.00
(3) Spring Kit (Anti Rattle)		
1983-87-wo/H.D. brks	◆18011280	2.75
1983-w/H.D. brks	◆18006810	3.00
(4) Caliper Repair Kit		
1983-87-wo/H.D. brks	◆18004873	7.25
w/H.D. brks	◆18003724	8.75

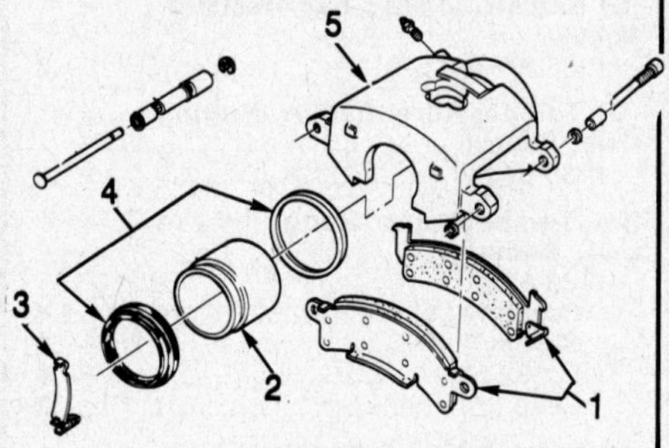

	Part No.	Price
(5) Caliper Assy.		
(Light & Med. Duty)		
1983-R.H.	◆18008758	N.L.
1983-84-L.H.	◆18011356	N.L.
1985-86-Light Duty		
R.H.	◆18011668	163.25
L.H.	◆18011667	163.25
(Heavy & Med. Duty)		
1983-87-right	◆18008319	142.00
left	◆18008318	142.00
Hub and Disc		
(wo/H.D. brakes)		
1983-87	◆14046950	64.50
(w/H.D. brakes)		
1983-87	◆14035588	94.50
Rear Disc		
1984-87	◆10028508	75.00
Brake Pads		
1984-87	◆18011413	N.L.
Caliper Piston		
1984-87-right	◆18008176	68.00
left	◆18008175	66.75
Caliper Repair Kit		
1984-87	◆18011329	20.50
Screw & Locknut Pkg.		
1984-87-right	◆18011416	341.25
left	◆18011415	341.25
Return Spring (Parking Lever)		
1984-87	◆18010465	2.00
Parking Brake Lever		
1984-87-right	◆18010464	7.75
left	◆18010463	7.75

LABOR 7 COOLING SYSTEM 7 LABOR

(Factory Time)	Chilton Time
(M) Winterize Cooling System	
Includes: Run engine to check for leaks, tighten all hose connections. Test radiator and pressure cap, drain radiator and engine block. Add anti-freeze and refill system.	
All models	.5
(G) Thermostat, Renew	
1983-87	
Four (.2)	.4
V-6 (.4)	.5
Diesel (.6)	.8
(G) Radiator Assembly, R&R or Renew	
Includes: Drain and refill cooling system.	
1983-87 (.9)	1.3
Renew side tank and/or gskt add,	
one (.7)	1.0
both (1.2)	1.7
ADD THESE OPERATIONS TO RADIATOR R&R	
(G) Boil & Repair	1.5
(G) Rod Clean	1.9
(G) Repair Core	1.3
(G) Renew Tank	1.6
(G) Renew Trans. Oil Cooler	1.9
(G) Recore Radiator	1.7

COOLING SYSTEM TUNE-UP

An Annual Cooling System Tune-Up Suggestion List should include (with some exceptions):

1. A visual check of the cooling system for indications of leaks or excessive oil content.
2. Pressure check the cooling system for internal and external leaks with filler cap and neck adapter and tester.
3. Check crankcase and automatic transmission oil for water content.
4. Test coolant thermostat with radiator thermometer.
5. Check temperature gauge for accuracy.
6. Drain system and flush till clean.
7. Clean foreign matter from radiator fins.
8. Test radiator pressure cap with cap tester.
9. Check fan blades and pulleys for alignment and damage.
10. Internal and external inspection of all hoses for cracks and deterioration.
11. Check core plugs (where possible) for seepage.
12. Refill system with correct coolant and check for air locks.
13. Check condition and tension of drive belts with tension gauge.

All models 1.5

(Factory Time)	Chilton Time
(M) Radiator Hoses, Renew	
1983-87-upper (.3)	.4
lower (.4)	.5
both (.5)	.7
(M) Thermostat By-Pass Hose or Pipe, Renew	
1983-87-V-6 (.3)	.5

LABOR 7 COOLING SYSTEM 7 LABOR

(Factory Time)	Chilton Time
(M) Drive Belt, Renew	
Four–1983-87	
A.C. (.7)	.9
Fan (.6)	.8
P.S. (.5)	.6
V-6–1983-87	
eng codes X-Z-W	
A.C. (.3)	.4
A.I.R. (.2)	.3
Fan (.2)	.3
P.S. (.3)	*.4
*w/A.C. add (.2)	.2
w/AIR add (.1)	.1
eng codes E-3-B	
A.C.	
1983-84 (1.8)	2.5
1985-87 (1.1)	1.5
A.I.R. (.3)	.4
Fan (.5)	.7
P.S. (1.1)	1.5
w/A.C. add (.3)	.3
(M) Drive Belt, Adjust	
1983-87-exc below-one (.2)	.2
all (.5)	.6
eng codes E-3-B	
one or all (1.0)	1.4
(G) Serpentine Drive Belt, Renew	
1983-87 (.2)	.4
(G) Water Pump and/or Gasket, Renew	
Four–1983-87 (1.3)	2.0
V-6–1983-84	
eng codes X-Z-W (1.3)	2.1
eng codes E-3 (2.3)	3.5
1985-87	
wo/F.I. (1.2)	2.0
w/F.I. (1.4)	2.5

(Factory Time)	Chilton Time
Diesel–1983-85 (2.0)	3.0
w/A.C. add (.3)	.3
w/P.S. add (.4)	.4
(G) Engine Coolant Fan and/or Motor, Renew	
1983-87 (.6)	.8
(G) Engine Coolant Fan Relay, Renew	
1983-87 (.2)	.3
(G) Coolant Fan Switch, Renew	
1983-87 (.2)	.3
(G) Engine Coolant Electronic Control Module, Renew	
1983-87 (.3)	.4
(G) Engine Cooling Fan Resistor, Renew	
1983-87-V-6 (.2)	.3
(G) Temperature Gauge (Engine Unit), Renew	
1983-87 (.2)	.3
(G) Temperature Gauge (Dash Unit), Renew	
1983-87	
Celebrity (.8)	1.4
Century (.3)	.5
6000 (.5)	.9
Ciera (.6)	.9
(G) Water Jacket Expansion Plugs, Renew (Side of Block)	
each (.2)	.5

Note: If necessary to R&R any component to gain access to plug add appropriate time.

(Factory Time)	Chilton Time
(G) Heater Hoses, Renew (wo/A.C.)	
1983-87-one (.2)	.3
both (.4)	.5

(Factory Time)	Chilton Time
(G) Heater Core, R&R or Renew	
1983-87-wo/A.C. (.7)	1.4
w/A.C. (1.4)	2.8
w/Console add (.3)	.3

ADD THESE OPERATIONS TO HEATER CORE R&R

(G) Boil & Repair	1.2
(G) Repair Core	.9
(G) Recore	1.2
(G) Blower Motor, Renew	
1983-87	
Gas	
wo/A.C. (.3)	.5
w/A.C. (.6)	1.0
Diesel	
wo/A.C. (.4)	.6
w/A.C. (1.0)	1.5
(G) Blower Motor Switch, Renew	
Celebrity	
1985-87 (.9)	1.5
All other models	
1983-87-wo/A.C. (.5)	.6
w/A.C. (.5)	.6
(G) Blower Motor Resistor, Renew	
1983-87 (.2)	.3
(G) Temperature Control Assembly, Renew	
Celebrity	
1985-87 (.8)	1.4
All other models	
1983-87-wo/A.C. (.5)	.9
w/A.C. (.5)	.9
(G) Heater Water Control Valve, Renew	
1983-87	
Gas (.4)	.7
Diesel (1.2)	1.6

PARTS 7 COOLING SYSTEM 7 PARTS

Radiator Assy.
Accurate replacement of the radiator can be done only by using the radiator code stamped on a metal tag located on the original radiator. Order by year, model and radiator code no.

Radiator Hoses
Order by year and model.

	Part No.	Price
Water Pump Assy.		
Four Cyl. Eng.		
1983-87-body	◆10013800	49.50
housing	◆10004073	59.75
173 Eng.		
1983-87	◆14033483	61.50
181 & 231 Eng.		
1983-87-exc. 231 eng.	◆25516944	70.00
1984-87-231 eng. 2nd design	◆25525147	78.25

Note: 2nd design pump has additional manifold nipple.

	Part No.	Price
V-6 Diesel		
1983-85	◆22519584	83.00
Thermostat		
(Gasoline engines)		
1983-87-exc. below	◆3051139	5.00
181 eng.	◆1254894	9.00
231 eng.	◆3054228	6.50
173 (Z) eng.	◆3041390	6.00
173 (W) eng.	◆3043066	6.75
(Diesel engine)		
1983	◆3051139	5.00
1984-85	◆3054228	6.50

	Part No.	Price
Temperature Gauge (Engine Unit)		
(w/Gasoline engines)		
(wo/gauges)		
1983-87-exc. 173 Eng.	◆25036371	8.00
173 eng.	◆25036373	9.75
(w/gauges)		
1983-87	◆8993146	19.25
(Diesel engine)		
(wo/gauges)		
1983	◆25036371	8.00
1984-85	◆25036629	9.75
(w/gauges)		
1983	◆8993146	19.25
1984-85	◆25036628	19.75
Engine Air Cooling Motor		
(wo/Air cond.)		
1983-87-exc. 173 (Z) Eng.	◆22035623	77.00
1985-87-w/173 (Z) eng. H.D. cooling exc. A/C	◆22049519	67.00
(w/Air cond.)		
Four Cyl. Eng.		
1983-87	◆22035556	78.50
173 Eng.		
1983	◆22040861	81.75
1984	◆22048577	86.75
1985-87	◆22049519	67.00
181 & 231 Eng.		
1983	◆22035561	186.50
1984	◆22040881	90.25
1985-87	◆22040193	235.75

	Part No.	Price
V-6 Diesel		
1983-85	◆22035570	182.50
Air Cooling Motor Relay		
Four Cyl. Eng.		
1983	◆14078902	12.00
1984-87	◆10032081	5.50
173 Eng.		
1983-87	◆14078902	12.00
181 & 231 Eng.		
1983	◆10026663	5.50
1984-87	◆12034544	8.25
V-6 Diesel		
1983-85	◆22512709	12.00
Air Cooling Motor Switch		
1983-87-exc. Diesel	◆3040674	12.00
diesel eng.	◆3050223	14.00
Heater Core Assy.		
1983-87-wo/A.C.	◆3042073	52.75
w/A.C.	◆3040837	55.00
Blower Motor		
(wo/Air cond.)		
1983	◆22048569	47.50
1984-87	◆22048569	47.50
(w/Air cond.)		
1983-87	◆22020945	60.00
Blower Motor Resistor		
1983-87-wo/A.C.	◆9796480	2.50
w/A.C.	◆526897	4.50

LABOR 8 EXHAUST SYSTEM 8 LABOR

(Factory Time)	Chilton Time
(G) Muffler, Renew	
1983-87 (.6)	.9
(G) Tail Pipe, Renew	
1983 (.5)	.7
1985-87 (.2)	.4
(G) Resonator and Pipe Assy., Renew	
1984-87 (.4)	.6
(G) Front Exhaust Pipe, Renew (To Converter)	
1983-87 (.4)	.8
(G) Exhaust Crossover Pipe, Renew	
1983-87-Gas (.5)	1.0
Diesel (.3)	.6
(G) Intermediate Exhaust Pipe, Renew	
1983-87 (.6)	.8
(G) Catalytic Converter, Renew	
1983-87 (.8)	1.0
(G) Rear Exhaust Pipe, Renew	
1983-right (.6)	.9
(G) E.F.E. Valve (Heat Riser), Renew	
1983-85 (.7)	1.0
(G) Exhaust Manifold or Gasket, Renew	
Four-1983-87 (.6)	1.2
w/A.C. add (.4)	.4
V-6-1983-87	
eng code Z	
right (.7)	1.2
left (.4)	.8
eng codes E-3-B	
right (1.6)	2.5
left (1.1)	1.6
w/A.C. add (.5)	.5
eng code W-X	
wo/Inj	
right (.7)	1.1
left (.7)	1.1
w/Inj	
right (1.2)	1.8
left (.6)	1.0
w/A.C. add (.2)	.2
w/P.S. add (.3)	.3
w/C.C.C. add (.3)	.3
Diesel-1983-85-each (.8)	1.3
w/Cruise control add (.2)	.2

COMBINATIONS

(G) Muffler, Exhaust and Tail Pipe, Renew	
All models	1.6
(G) Muffler and Tail Pipe, Renew	
All models	1.1

PARTS 8 EXHAUST SYSTEM 8 PARTS

	Part No.	Price
Muffler (w/tailpipe)		
Four Cyl. Eng.		
1983	◆10022543	75.00
1984-87-exc.		
sta. wagon	◆10030691	75.00
sta. wagon	◆10029797	63.50
173 Eng.		
1983-84-exc.		
sta. wagon	◆14079443	60.50
1984-sta. wag.	◆14073085	73.25
1985-87-exc.		
STE	◆14089088	76.75
1983-87 (STE)	◆14063936	138.00
181 Eng.		
1983-87-exc.		
sta. wagon	◆25511841	58.00
sta. wagon	◆25514047	N.L.
231 Eng.		
1984-87-exc.		
sporty exh.	◆25520006	75.00
sporty exh.	◆25518518	106.00
sta. wagon	◆25520372	62.00
V-6 Diesel		
1983-85-exc.		
sta. wagon	◆22520392	77.75
sta. wagon	◆22521436	59.75
Front Pipe		
Four Cyl. Eng.		
1983	◆10023182	26.00
1984-87	◆10028746	16.75
173 Eng.		
1983-87	◆14059125	20.25
181 & 231 Eng.		
1983-87	◆25516470	26.00
V-6 Diesel		
1983	◆22517321	16.75
1984-85	◆22523405	19.00
Intermediate Pipe		
Four Cyl. Eng.		
1983-87-exc.		
sta. wagon	◆25513020	26.00
sta. wagon	◆25518960	24.00
173 & 181 Eng.		
1983-87-exc.		
below	◆25511842	42.50
1984-sta. wagon		
(1st design)	◆25519379	23.50
1984-87-sta. wagon		
(2nd design)	◆25522303	24.25

Note: 1st design inter. pipe hanger 500MM rear of pipe inlet. 2nd design is 1000MM.

	Part No.	Price
231 Eng.		
1984-87-exc.		
sta. wagon	◆25518517	43.75
sta. wagon	◆25524622	41.00
V-6 Diesel		
1983-85-exc.		
sta. wagon	◆22520393	42.50
sta. wagon	◆22525042	26.25
Crossover Pipe		
173 Eng.		
1983-87	◆14054541	30.00
181 Eng.		
1983-Note 1	◆25500298	31.00
Note 2	◆25516236	31.00
1984-87	◆25524573	N.L.
231 Eng.		
1984-87	◆25523749	22.50
V-6 Diesel		
1983-84	◆22522768	15.50
1985	◆22530022	46.25

Note 1: heat stove mounted to the exhaust manifold.

Note 2: heat stove mounted to the crossover pipe.

	Part No.	Price
Exhaust Manifold		
Four Cyl. Eng.		
1983-84	◆10023093	94.25
1985-87	◆10032916	48.00
173 Eng.		
1983-87-right	◆14033209	111.00
left	◆14033208	111.00
181 Eng.		
1983-87-right	◆25510098	111.00
left		
Note 1	◆25509259	111.00
Note 2	◆25516237	111.00
231 Eng.		
1984-87-right	◆25515866	71.75
left (1st design)	◆25516029	50.25
left (2nd design)	◆25523099	78.25

Note: 2nd design used on engines with 25522307 stamped on oil level indicator.

	Part No.	Price
V-6 Diesel		
1983-85-right	◆22524574	135.00
left	◆22524575	135.00

Note 1: has a manual E.F.E. system.
Note 2: has an electric E.F.E. system.

	Part No.	Price
Catalytic Converter		
Four Cyl. Eng.		
1983-87	◆25056230	277.25
173 Eng.		
1983-87	◆8999979	302.25
181 Eng.		
1983-84	◆8999981	306.25
1985-87	◆25056910	341.00
231 Eng.		
1984-87	◆25056699	347.25

LABOR 9 FRONT SUSPENSION 9 LABOR

Note: On all front suspension operations alignment charges must be added if performed. Time given does not include alignment.

(Factory Time)	Chilton Time
(M) Wheel, Renew	
one (.5)	.5
(G) Wheels, Balance	
one	.3
each adtnl	.2
(M) Wheels, Rotate (All)	
All models	.5
(G) Check Alignment of Front End	
All models	.5

Note: Deduct if alignment is performed.

(Factory Time)	Chilton Time
(G) Toe-In, Adjust	
All models (.5)	.7
(G) Align Front End	
All models (.8)	1.4
w/A.C. interference add	.5

LABOR 9 FRONT SUSPENSION 9 LABOR

	(Factory Time)	Chilton Time
(G) Lower Control Arm Assy., Renew		
Add alignment charges.		
1983-87-one	(.8)	1.1
both	(1.5)	2.0
(G) Lower Control Arm Bushings, Renew		
Add alignment charges.		
1983-87-one side	(1.1)	1.5
both sides	(2.1)	2.8
(G) Lower Ball Joint, Renew		
Add alignment charges.		
1983-87-one	(.5)	.9
both	(.9)	1.6
(G) Front Shock Absorber Strut Assy., R&R or Renew		
Add alignment charges if necessary.		
1983-87-one	(.9)	1.3
both	(1.6)	2.5
(G) Front Spring, Seat or Insulator, Renew		
Add alignment charges if necessary.		
1983-87-one	(.8)	1.2
both	(1.5)	2.3
(G) Front Strut Bearing Mount Assy., Renew		
Add alignment charges if necessary.		
1983-87-one	(.8)	1.2
both	(1.5)	2.3
(G) Front Stabilizer Shaft, Renew		
1983-87	(.8)	1.0
(G) Front Stabilizer Shaft Bushings, Renew (One or Both)		
1983-87	(.5)	.9
(G) Steering Knuckle and Arm (Integral), Renew		
Add alignment charges.		
1983-87-one	(1.0)	1.4
both	(1.9)	2.7
(G) Steering Knuckle Inner Dust Seal, Renew		
1983-87-one	(.7)	1.2
both	(1.3)	2.3
(G) Front Wheel Bearing and Hub Assy., Renew		
Includes: Renew oil seal.		
1983-87-one side	(.6)	1.0
both sides	(1.1)	1.9
(G) Engine Cradle, Renew		
1983-87-one side	(1.0)	1.9
both sides	(1.6)	2.8
complete	(2.9)	4.0

FRONT DRIVE AXLE

	(Factory Time)	Chilton Time
(G) Front Drive Axle, R&R or Renew		
1983-87-one	(1.1)	1.4
both	(1.6)	2.2
Renew shaft add-each	(.3)	.4
Renew C/V Joint add each side	(.3)	.4
Renew D/O Joint add each side	(.3)	.4
Renew C/V Joint boots add each	(.2)	.2
Renew Tri-Pot Joint add	(.3)	.4
(G) Axle Shaft Seal, Renew		
Includes: Raise vehicle, R&R caliper, mark cam bolts. Drain and refill trans.		
1983-87-w/M.T.-one	(1.1)	1.5
both	(1.5)	2.1
w/A.T.-one	(1.3)	1.7
both	(1.9)	2.7

PARTS 9 FRONT SUSPENSION 9 PARTS

	Part No.	Price
Front Seal Assy.		
1983-87-exc. H.D. brks.	◆14084120	3.75
H.D. brks.	◆14084119	3.75
(1) Strut Mount		
1983-84-right	◆17980090	49.00
left	◆17980089	49.00
1985-87-exc. below		
left	◆17981901	49.00
right	◆17981902	49.00
1985-87-Celebrity Z w/spec. susp.		
left	◆17981597	49.00
right	◆17981598	49.00
(2) Coil Spring		
Note: Order by model and description.		
(3) Shock Absorber		
(wo/H.D. suspension)		
1983-exc. diesel	◆22035659	99.25
diesel eng.	◆22035662	95.00
1984-87-exc. diesel	◆22049969	57.00
diesel eng. (M.T.)	◆22035662	95.00
(w/H.D. suspension)		
1983-exc. diesel	◆22035660	79.00
diesel eng.	◆22035662	95.00
1984-87-exc. diesel	◆22049970	57.00
diesel eng.	◆22049971	74.00
(4) Steering Knuckle		
Light Duty Brk. Sys.		
1983-87-right	◆14076994	86.25
left	◆14076993	86.25
Med. Duty Brk. System.		
1982-84-right	◆14076994	86.25
left	◆14076993	86.25
1985-86-right	◆14079906	160.00
left	◆14079905	160.00
Heavy Duty Brk. System		
1983-right	◆14046978	160.00
left	◆14046977	160.00
1984-87-right	◆14079906	160.00
left	◆14079905	160.00

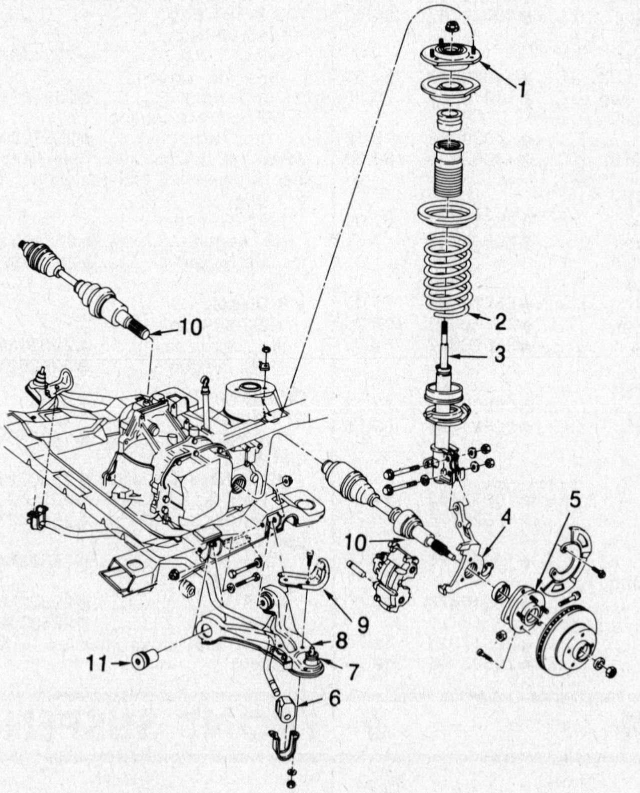

	Part No.	Price
(5) Front Wheel Bearing (Inner)		
Light Duty Brk. System		
1983	◆7466905	160.25
1984-86	◆7420002	N.L.
Med. Duty Brk. System		
1983	◆7466905	160.25
1984	◆7470002	N.L.
1985	◆7466922	173.00
1986-87	◆7470003	184.50

PARTS 9 FRONT SUSPENSION 9 PARTS

	Part No.	Price
Heavy Duty Brk. System		
1983-84	◆7470003	184.50
1985	◆7466922	173.00
1986-87	◆7470003	184.50
(6) Bushing (Shaft to Arm)		
1983-87	◆473525	1.00
(7) Ball Joint Assy. (Lower)		
1983-87	◆17983075	40.25
(8) Lower Control Arm		
1983-87-right	◆14082848	141.00
1983-84-left	◆14082883	141.00
1985-87	◆14082847	141.00
(9) Control Arm Stop		
1983-87-right upper	◆14026942	5.00
left upper	◆14026941	5.00
1983-87-right lower	◆14032232	4.50
left lower	◆14032231	4.50

	Part No.	Price
(10) Axle Kit		
(wo/H.D. suspension)		
1983 (w/Thm 125 trans.)		
right	◆7842346	475.00
left	◆7842347	475.00
1984 (w/Thm 125 trans.)		
right	◆7844750	483.00
left	◆7844752	483.00
1984 (w/Thm 440 trans.)		
right	◆7844758	483.00
left	◆7844760	483.00
1984 (w/manual trans.)		
right	◆7844745	415.00
left	◆7844748	415.00
1985-87 (w/Thm 125 trans.)		
left	◆7848230	425.00
right (4 cyl.)	◆7846871	500.00
right (V-6)	◆7846878	440.00
1985-87 (w/Thm 440 trans.)		
right	◆7846879	500.00
left	◆7846873	500.00
1985-87 (w/manual trans.)		
right	◆7846874	425.00
left	◆7846875	425.00

	Part No.	Price
(w/H.D. suspension)		
1983-84 (w/Thm 125 trans.)		
right	◆7843915	483.00
left	◆7843916	483.00
1984 (w/Thm 440 trans.)		
right	◆7843913	483.00
left	◆7843914	483.00
1984 (w/manual trans.)		
right	◆7843911	475.00
left	◆7843912	483.00
1985-87 (w/Thm 125 trans.)		
right (4 cyl.)	◆7847104	520.00
right (V-6)	◆7847561	520.00
left	◆7847105	520.00
1985-87 (w/Thm 440 trans.)		
right	◆7847560	500.00
left	◆7847107	520.00
1985-87 (w/manual trans.)		
right	◆7847108	500.00
left	◆7847109	520.00
(11) Bushing (Lower Control Arm)		
1983-87	◆14065721	7.00

PARTS 9 FRONT DRIVE AXLE 9 PARTS

	Part No.	Price
(1) Joint Kit		
(wo/H.D. suspension)		
1983	◆7845009	287.25
1984	◆7845028	200.00
1985-87	◆7846867	N.L.
(w/H.D. suspension)		
1983-Note 1	◆7842037	271.00
Note 2	◆7843919	135.00
1984	◆7845024	240.00
1985-87	◆7847112	N.L.

Note 1: Tripot joint housing is cylindrical shaped.
Note 2: Tripot joint housing is "Y" shaped.

	Part No.	Price
(2) Seal Retainer		
1983-87	◆7828314	10.50
(3) Seal Kit (Tripot Joint)		
(wo/H.D. suspension)		
1983 (Note 1)		
right	◆7838298	34.00
left	◆7838299	45.00
1983-84 (Note 2)		
right	◆7843577	53.00
left	◆7843576	31.00
1985-87		
right (4 cyl.)	◆7846800	N.L.
right (V-6)	◆7845350	N.L.
left	◆7845350	N.L.
(w/H.D. suspension)		
1983 (Note 1)		
right	◆7842040	63.50
left	◆7842039	35.00
1983-84 (Note 2)		
right	◆7843917	55.00
left	◆7843924	38.00
1985-87		
right (4 cyl.)	◆7847110	N.L.
right (V-6)	◆7845397	N.L.
left	◆7845397	N.L.

Refer to note with item (1)

	Part No.	Price
Seal Kit (Constant Velocity Joint)		
(wo/H.D. suspension)		
1983	◆7845020	45.00
1984-w/A.T.	◆7845020	45.00
w/M.T.	◆7845015	27.00
1985-87	◆1845351	N.L.
(w/H.D. suspension)		
1983	◆7845021	34.00
1984	◆7845915	N.L.

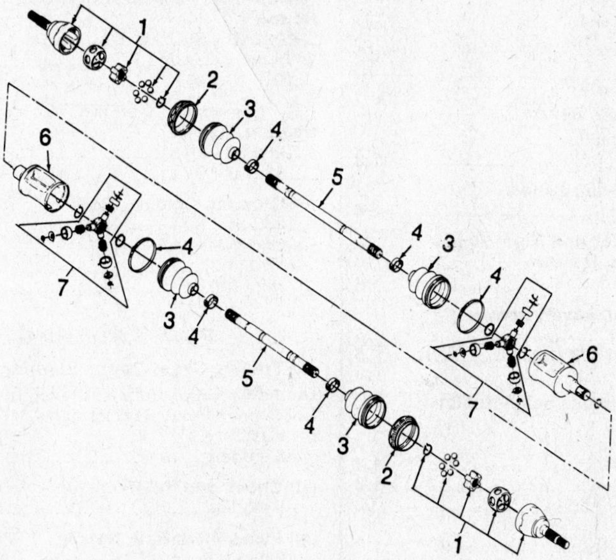

	Part No.	Price
1985-87	◆7845398	N.L.
(4) Seal Retaining Clamp		
1983-87 (31.6mm)	◆7836673	5.00

Note: Smallest size listed, larger sizes available.

	Part No.	Price
(5) Axle Shaft		
(wo/H.D. suspension)		
1983-right	◆7841389	66.50
left (Note 1)	◆7836512	59.00
left (Note 2)	◆7841388	72.00
1984 (w/Thm 125 trans.)		
right	◆7841389	66.50
left	◆7843976	50.00
1985-87 (w/Thm 125 trans.)		
right (4 cyl.)	◆7846269	62.25
right (V-6)	◆7846271	62.25
left	◆7846276	47.00

	Part No.	Price
1984 (w/Thm 440 trans.)		
right	◆7841393	59.00
left	◆7841388	72.00
1985-87 (w/Thm 440 trans.)		
right	◆7846270	49.00
left	◆7846276	47.00
1984 (w/manual trans.)		
right	◆7834181	70.75
left	◆7834179	52.00
1985-87 (w/Manual trans.)		
right	◆7846217	47.00
left	◆7846281	37.00
(w/H.D. suspension)		
1983 (Note 1)		
right	◆7841300	74.00
left (Thm 125)	◆7841303	70.00
left (Thm 440)	◆7841302	N.L.
1983 (Note 2)		
right	◆7843182	70.00
left	◆7843184	46.00

PARTS 9 FRONT DRIVE AXLE 9 PARTS

	Part No.	Price
1984 (w/Thm 125 trans.)		
right	◆7843182	70.00
left	◆7843184	46.00
1985-87 (w/Thm 125 trans.)		
right (4 cyl.)	◆7846164	62.25
right (V-6)	◆7847288	62.25
left	◆7846165	47.00
1984 (w/Thm 440 trans.)		
right	◆7843183	70.00
left	◆7843184	46.00
1985-87 (w/Thm 440 trans.)		
right	◆7847289	58.75
left	◆7846165	47.00
1984 (w/manual trans.)		
right	◆7843185	95.00
left	◆7843186	70.00
1985-87 (w/manual trans.)		
right	◆7846169	62.25
left	◆7846171	95.00

Refer to Note with item (1)

	Part No.	Price
(6) Housing		
(wo/H.D. suspension)		
1983-right	◆7842378	111.00
left (Note 1)	◆7837135	145.00
left (Note 2)	◆7842380	111.00
1984-87-right	◆7842378	111.00
left (Thm 125)	◆7842380	111.00
left (Thm 440)	◆7842379	111.00
(w/H.D. suspension)		
1983 (Note 1)		
right	◆7837071	N.L.
left	◆7840364	N.L.
1983 (Note 2)		
right	◆7843920	136.00
left	◆7843923	170.00
1984-87-right	◆7843920	136.00
left (Thm 125)	◆7843923	170.00
left (Thm 440)	◆7843922	136.00

Refer to Note with item (1)

	Part No.	Price
(7) Spider Assy.		
(wo/H.D. suspension)		
1983-Note 1	◆7842152	110.00
Note 2	◆7845022	71.00
1984	◆7845022	71.00
1985-87 (w/Thm 125 trans.)		
right (4 cyl.)	◆7846865	110.00
right (V-6)	◆7846866	120.00
left	◆7846866	120.00
1985-87 (w/Thm 440 trans.)		
right	◆7846865	110.00
left	◆7846866	120.00
(w/H.D. suspension)		
1983-84-Note 1	◆7842129	85.00
Note 2	◆7845025	92.00
1985-87-exc. below	◆7847113	120.00
w/125 trans (4 cyl.), right	◆7847114	110.00

Refer to Note with item (1)

LABOR 11 STEERING GEAR 11 LABOR

(Factory Time)	Chilton Time
(G) Tie Rod End, Renew	
Includes: Reset toe-in.	
1983-87-one (.7)	.9
both (.9)	1.2
Renew seal add-each	.1
(G) Inner Tie Rod, Renew	
Includes: Reset toe-in.	
1983-87-one (1.8)	2.3
(G) Steering Wheel, Renew	
1983-87 (.3)	.4
(G) Horn Contact and Turn Signal Cancelling Cam, Renew	
1983-87 (.5)	.6
(G) Multifunction Lever, Renew	
All models (.2)	.4
w/Cruise control add (.5)	.5
(G) Steering Column Lock Actuator Parts, Renew	
1983-85	
std colm (.8)	1.4
tilt colm (.9)	1.6
w/Cruise control add (.2)	.2
1986-87	
std colm (1.1)	1.6
tilt colm (.8)	1.3
Renew actuator rod add	.5
(G) Steering Column Upper Bearing, Renew	
1983-85-std column (.8)	1.4
tilt column (.9)	1.6
w/Cruise control add (.2)	.2
1986-87	
std colm (1.1)	1.6
tilt colm (.5)	.9

(Factory Time)	Chilton Time
(G) Intermediate Steering Shaft, Renew	
1983-84 (.6)	1.2
w/Diesel eng add (.2)	.2
1985-87 (.4)	.7
(G) Steering Column Lower Bearing, Renew	
1983-84 (.7)	1.2
1985-87 (.9)	1.4
(G) Steering Column, R&R	
1983-87 (.8)	1.2
Recond colm add	
std (1.0)	1.0
tilt (1.8)	1.8

POWER STEERING

(Factory Time)	Chilton Time
(G) Trouble Shoot Power Steering	
Includes: Test pump and system pressure. Check pounds pull on steering wheel and check for leaks.	
All models	.5
(M) Check and Fill Reservoir	
All models	.2
(M) Pump Drive Belt, Renew	
1983-87-Four (.4)	.6
V-6	
eng Codes X-W (.3)	.4
eng Codes B-3 (1.1)	1.5
w/A.C. add (.3)	.3
(G) Power Steering Gear Assy., R&R or Renew	
1983-87	
w/M.T. (1.4)	3.0
w/A.T. (1.8)	3.3

(Factory Time)	Chilton Time
(G) Power Steering Short Rack Assy., Renew	
Includes: Transfer parts as required. Reset toe-in.	
All models	
w/M.T. (1.9)	3.6
w/A.T. (2.0)	3.9
(P) Power Steering Gear Assy., R&R and Recondition	
1983-87	
w/M.T. (2.8)	5.0
w/A.T. (3.2)	5.5
(G) Power Steering Pump, Renew	
1983-85-Four (1.0)	1.3
V-6-Gas (1.2)	1.7
Diesel (.8)	1.1
w/A.C. add (.2)	.2
1986-87	
Four (1.0)	1.3
V-6	
eng Codes B-3 (.5)	.8
eng Code W (1.1)	1.7
eng Code X (1.5)	2.1
Renew shaft seal add (.1)	.2
Renew reser or 'O' ring add (.2)	.3
Recond pump add (.5)	.7
(G) Power Steering Gear Boot Seals, Renew	
1985-87-one side (1.1)	1.5
both sides (1.4)	1.9
(M) Power Steering Hoses, Renew	
1983-87	
pressure (.4)	.6
return	
Four (.4)	.5
V-6 (.7)	.9

PARTS 11 POWER STEERING GEAR 11 PARTS

	Part No.	Price
Steering Gear Kit (Short Rack Assy.)		
1983-87-exc. below	◆7846792	175.00
Z, STE models	◆7847967	203.00
(1) Tie Rod Assy. (Inner)		
1983-87	◆7839153	49.50

	Part No.	Price
(2) Boot Kit		
1983-87	◆7839156	24.00
(3) Tie Rod Assy. (Outer)		
1983-87	◆7839154	48.50

	Part No.	Price
(4) Rack Assy.		
1983-87-exc. below	◆7846688	123.00
1984-Z, STE models	◆7841803	123.00
1985-87-Z, STE	◆7846689	123.00

PARTS 11 POWER STEERING GEAR 11 PARTS

	Part No.	Price
(5) Steering Gear Seal Kit		
1983-84-1st design	◆7839157	11.75
1984-87-2nd design	◆7847281	11.75
Note: 2nd design has an O-ring between piston ring and piston. 1st design has none.		
(6) Bulkhead Kit		
1983-87	◆7839075	41.50
(7) Steering Gear Bushing		
1983-87	◆22513639	.50
(8) Housing Assy.		
1983-87-exc. below	◆7840216	174.25
1984-Z, STE models	◆7841954	174.25
1985-87-Z, STE	◆7846728	183.00
(9) Valve Assy.		
1983-87-exc. below	◆7842238	263.00
1984-Z, STE models	◆7842504	263.00
1985-87-Z, STE	◆7847866	263.00
(10) Seal Kit		
1983-87	◆7840573	21.25
(11) Bearing Kit (Stub Shaft)		
1983-87-exc. below	◆7829888	19.25
w/Z, ste models	◆7838279	19.50
(12) Adapter (Stub Shaft)		
1983-87	◆7833732	6.75
(13) Cylinder Line Assy. (Right)		
1983-87	◆7840455	15.75
(14) Cylinder Line Assy. (Left)		
1983	◆7840454	14.00
1984-87	◆7843293	14.50

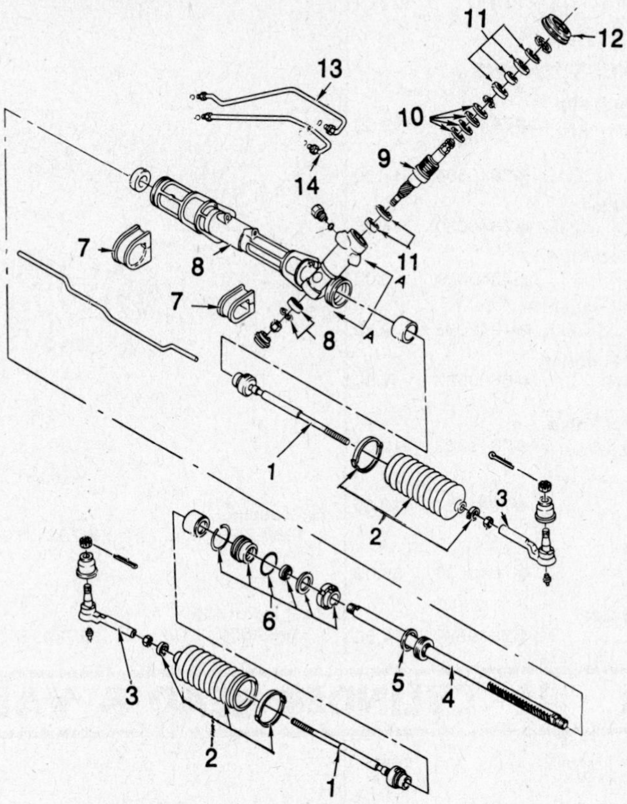

PARTS 11 POWER STEERING PUMP 11 PARTS

	Part No.	Price
GASOLINE ENGINES		
Power Steering Pump		
1983-87-Four cyl.	◆7838471	199.00
173 eng.	◆7838472	199.00
181, 231 engs.	◆7838469	199.00
(1) Drive Shaft		
1983-87	◆7837321	39.50
(2) Seal Kit		
1983-84	◆5688044	10.75
1985-87	◆7848522	N.L.
(3) Pump Housing		
1983-87-four cyl.	◆7830236	62.75
V-6 eng.	◆7830697	62.75
(4) Thrust Plate		
1983-87	◆7839366	25.75
(5) Control Valve		
1983-87	◆7809229	10.25
(6) Flow Control Spring		
1983-87	◆5688037	1.50
(7) Rotor & Vane Kit		
1983-87	◆7838790	92.00
(8) Pressure Plate		
1983-87	◆7839669	14.25
(9) Pressure Plate Spring		
1985-87	◆7839667	1.00

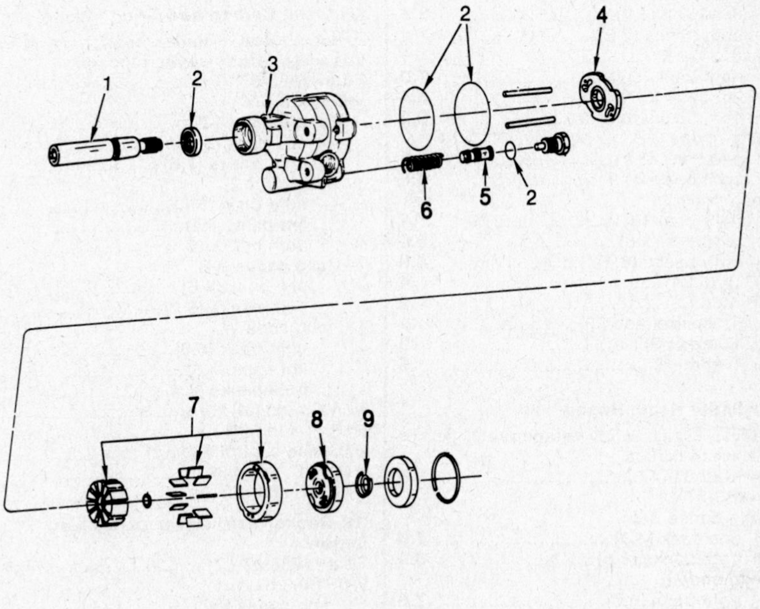

PARTS 11 POWER STEERING PUMP 11 PARTS

	Part No.	Price
DIESEL ENGINE		
Power Steering Pump		
1983-85	◆7841747	199.00
Pump Seal Kit		
1983-85	◆7840566	11.00
(1) Pressure Plate		
1983-85	◆7840080	14.25
(2) Pressure Plate Spring		
1983-85	◆7839989	3.00
(3) Sleeve Kit		
1983-85	◆7842086	9.75
(4) Flow Control Spring		
1983-85	◆5688037	1.50
(5) Flow Control Valve		
1983-85	◆7841853	12.00
(6) Fitting		
1983-85	◆7841467	10.25
(7) Drive Shaft		
1983-85	◆7840633	58.00
(8) Drive Shaft Seal		
1983-85	◆7839589	4.50

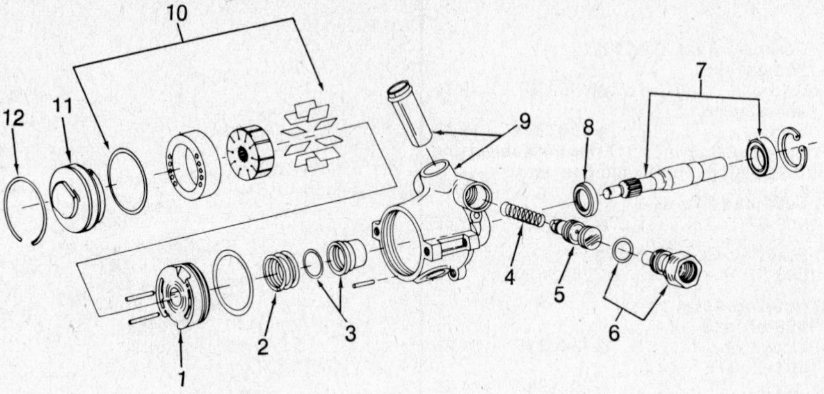

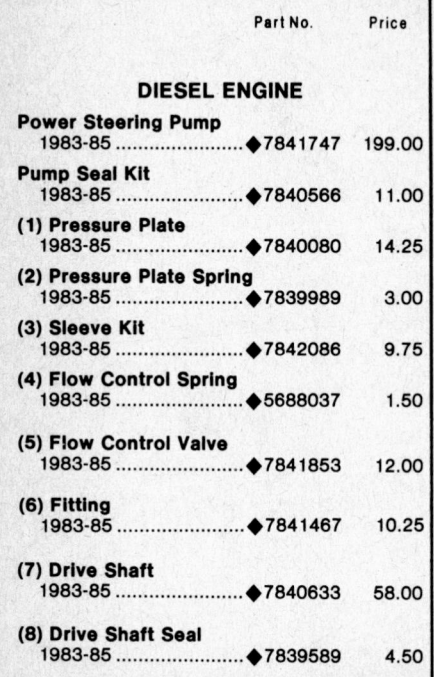

	Part No.	Price
(9) Housing		
1983-85	◆7841770	68.00
(10) Rotor Kit		
1983-85	◆7841845	92.00

	Part No.	Price
Vane Kit		
1983-85	◆7840569	13.50
(11) Thrust Plate		
1983-85	◆7840139	14.25
(12) Retaining Ring		
1983-85	◆7839992	2.00

LABOR 12 CYLINDER HEAD & VALVE SYSTEM 12 LABOR

(Factory Time)	Chilton Time
GASOLINE ENGINES	
(G) Compression Test	
Four–1983-87 (.3)	.5
V-6–1983-87 (.5)	.8
w/Cruise control add	.3
(G) Cylinder Head Gasket, Renew	
Includes: Clean carbon and make all necessary adjustments.	
Four–1983-87 (3.3)	4.5
V-6–1983-87	
eng codes X-Z	
one bank (4.2)	5.8
both banks (5.2)	7.2
eng code E	
right bank (5.1)	7.0
left bank (3.7)	5.1
both banks (6.6)	9.2
eng codes 3-B	
one bank (3.8)	5.2
both banks (4.7)	6.5
eng code W	
right bank (5.1)	7.1
left bank (3.6)	5.0
both banks (6.4)	8.9
w/A.C. add (.4)	.4
w/P.S. add (.2)	.2
w/Cruise control add (.2)	.2
w/C.C.C. add (.3)	.3
w/A.I.R. add (.5)	.5
(G) Cylinder Head, Renew	
Includes: Transfer all components, reface valves, clean carbon.	
Four–1983-87 (4.8)	6.6
V-6–1983-87	
eng codes X-Z	
one bank (4.8)	6.6
both banks (6.5)	8.9
eng code E	
right bank (5.7)	7.8
left bank (4.2)	5.8
both banks (7.7)	10.6

(Factory Time)	Chilton Time
eng codes 3-B	
one bank (4.4)	6.0
both banks (5.9)	8.1
eng code W	
right bank (5.7)	7.9
left bank (4.3)	6.0
both banks (7.4)	10.3
w/A.C. add (.4)	.4
w/P.S. add (.2)	.2
w/Cruise control add (.2)	.2
w/C.C.C. add (.3)	.3
w/A.I.R. add (.5)	.5
(P) Clean Carbon and Grind Valves	
Includes: R&R cylinder head(s), grind valves and seats. Minor engine tune up.	
Four–1983-87 (5.4)	7.4
V-6–1983-87	
eng codes X-Z	
one bank (5.6)	7.7
both banks (7.6)	10.5
eng code E	
right bank (5.8)	8.1
left bank (4.4)	6.1
both banks (8.1)	11.3
eng codes 3-B	
one bank (4.6)	6.4
both banks (6.2)	9.0
eng code W	
right bank (6.3)	8.8
left bank (4.8)	6.7
both banks (8.4)	11.7
w/A.C. add (.4)	.4
w/P.S. add (.2)	.2
w/Cruise control add (.2)	.2
w/C.C.C. add (.3)	.3
w/A.I.R. add (.5)	.5
(G) Rocker Arm Cover or Gasket, Renew	
Four–1983-87 (.7)	1.0
V-6–1983-87	
eng codes X-Z	
one (.7)	1.1
both (1.2)	2.0

(Factory Time)	Chilton Time
eng code E	
right bank (.8)	1.2
left bank (.7)	1.1
both banks (1.3)	2.1
eng codes 3-B	
right bank (.3)	.6
left bank (.6)	.9
both banks (.8)	1.4
eng code W	
right bank (1.2)	1.6
left bank (.9)	1.3
both banks (1.8)	2.6
w/A.C. add (.3)	.3
w/C.C.C. add (.3)	.3
w/Cruise control add (.2)	.2
w/A.I.R. add (.5)	.5
(G) Push Rod Side Cover Gasket, Renew	
Four–1983-87 (2.3)	3.0
(G) Valve Rocker Arms and/or Push Rods, Renew	
Four–1983-87	
one cyl (.8)	1.1
all cyls (1.0)	1.5
V-6–1983-87	
eng codes X-Z	
one cyl (.9)	1.4
all cyls (1.9)	2.8
eng code E	
one bank (1.0)	1.4
both banks (1.9)	2.6
eng codes 3-B	
right bank (.5)	.8
left bank (.8)	1.1
both banks (1.1)	1.7
eng code W	
one cyl (1.5)	2.1
one cyl-each bank (2.1)	2.9
all cyls-both banks (2.5)	3.5
w/A.C. add (.3)	.3
w/Cruise control add (.2)	.2
w/C.C.C. add (.3)	.3
w/A.I.R. add (.5)	.5

LABOR 12 CYLINDER HEAD & VALVE SYSTEM 12 LABOR

	(Factory Time)	Chilton Time
(G) Valve Rocker Arm Stud, Renew (One)		
Includes: Drain and refill cooling system on V-6 engine.		
Four–1983-87	(.8)	1.2
V-6–1983-87		
eng codes X-Z	(1.1)	1.5
eng code W	(1.3)	1.8
each adtnl	(.2)	.2
w/A.C. add	(.3)	.3
w/Cruise control add	(.2)	.2
w/C.C.C. add	(.3)	.3
w/A.I.R. add	(.5)	.5
(G) Valve Springs and/or Valve Stem Oil Seals, Renew (Head on Car)		
Four–1983-87		
one cyl	(.9)	1.4
all cyls	(1.6)	2.3
V-6–1983-87		
eng codes X-Z		
one cyl	(1.1)	1.5
one cyl-each bank	(1.9)	2.5
all cyls-both banks	(3.5)	4.8
eng code E		
one cyl	(1.1)	1.5
one cyl-each bank	(2.1)	2.9
all cyls-both banks	(3.3)	4.6
eng codes 3-B		
right bank-one cyl	(.6)	1.0
left bank-one cyl	(1.0)	1.3
all cyls-both banks	(2.4)	3.3
eng code W		
one cyl-right bank	(1.6)	2.2
one cyl-left bank	(1.3)	1.8
one cyl-each bank	(2.6)	3.6
each adtnl cyl	(.4)	.4
w/A.C. add	(.3)	.3
w/Cruise control add	(.2)	.2
w/C.C.C. add	(.3)	.3
w/A.I.R. add	(.5)	.5
(G) Valve Tappets, Renew (Lifters)		
Four–1983-87		
one cyl	(2.7)	3.6
all cyls	(3.1)	4.0
V-6–1983-87		
eng codes X-Z		
one bank	(3.0)	4.0
both banks	(3.4)	4.5
eng codes E-3-B		
one bank	(2.8)	3.9
both banks	(3.1)	4.3

COMBINATIONS

Add to Valve Job

See Machine Shop Operations

(G) DRAIN, EVACUATE & RECHARGE AIR CONDITIONING SYSTEM		
All models	(.5)	1.0
(G) ROCKER ARM STUD, RENEW		
Each	(.2)	.2
(G) HYDRAULIC VALVE LIFTERS, DISASSEMBLE AND CLEAN		
Each	(.2)	.2
(G) DISTRIBUTOR, RECONDITION		
All models	(.3)	.8
(G) CARBURETOR, RECONDITION		
2 bbl		1.2
(P) VALVE GUIDES, REAM OVERSIZE		
Each	(.2)	.2

	(Factory Time)	Chilton Time
eng code W		
one cyl	(2.9)	4.0
one cyl-each bank	(3.0)	4.2
all cyls-both banks	(3.5)	4.9
w/A.C. add	(.3)	.3
w/Cruise control add	(.2)	.2
w/C.C.C. add	(.3)	.3
w/A.I.R. add	(.5)	.5

DIESEL ENGINE

	(Factory Time)	Chilton Time
(G) Compression Test		
V-6		1.0
(G) Cylinder Head Gasket, Renew		
Includes: R&R injector pump and lines. R&R intake manifold and disconnect exhaust manifolds. Clean gasket surfaces, bleed lifters and adjust timing. Drain and refill cooling system.		
V-6–1983-85		
right side	(6.1)	8.5
left side	(5.1)	7.1
both sides	(7.7)	10.8
w/A.C. add	(.4)	.4
Renew pre-chambers add	(.2)	.2
(G) Cylinder Head, Renew		
Includes: R&R injector pump and lines. R&R intake manifold and disconnect exhaust manifolds. Clean gasket surfaces. Transfer parts, reface valves. Bleed lifters and adjust timing. Drain and refill cooling system.		
V-6–1983-85		
right side	(6.5)	9.1
left side	(5.5)	7.7
both sides	(8.2)	11.5
w/A.C. add	(.4)	.4
(P) Clean Carbon and Grind Valves		
Includes: R&R injector pump and lines. R&R cylinder heads, clean carbon. Recondition valves and seats. Check and adjust valve stem length. Bleed lifters, drain and refill cooling system.		
V-6–1983-85		
right side	(7.0)	9.8
left side	(5.9)	8.2
both sides	(9.4)	13.2
w/A.C. add	(.4)	.4
(G) Rocker Arm Cover and/or Gasket, Renew		
V-6–1983-85		
one	(1.3)	1.8
both	(2.1)	2.9
(G) Rocker Arm, Pivot and/or Push Rod, Renew		
V-6–1983-85		
one cyl	(1.6)	2.2
one cyl-each side	(2.4)	3.3
each adtnl cyl		.1
(G) Valve Springs and/or Valve Stem Oil Seals, Renew (Head on Car)		
V-6–1983-85		
one cyl	(1.7)	2.4
one cyl-each side	(2.6)	3.6
each adtnl cyl	(.3)	.3
(G) Valve Tappets, Renew (Lifters)		
Includes: R&R injector pump and lines, intake manifold and rocker arms. Drain and refill cooling system.		
V-6–1983-85		
one cyl	(3.8)	5.3
one cyl-each side	(4.5)	6.3
each adtnl cyl	(.2)	.2

PARTS 12 CYLINDER HEAD & VALVE SYSTEM 12 PARTS

FOUR CYL. ENGINE

	Part No.	Price
Valve Grind Gasket Set		
1983-84	◆10026815	29.00
1985-87	◆10037280	29.25
(1) Cylinder Head		
1983	◆10020699	290.00
1984	◆10030838	290.00
1985-87	◆10037282	290.00
(2) Cylinder Head Gasket		
1983	◆10018638	11.00
1984	◆10028404	10.50
1985-87	◆10035039	9.75
(3) Valve Cover Gasket		
1983-87	◆10021542	6.25
(4) Rocker Arm and Ball Kit		
1983-87	◆10014819	7.25

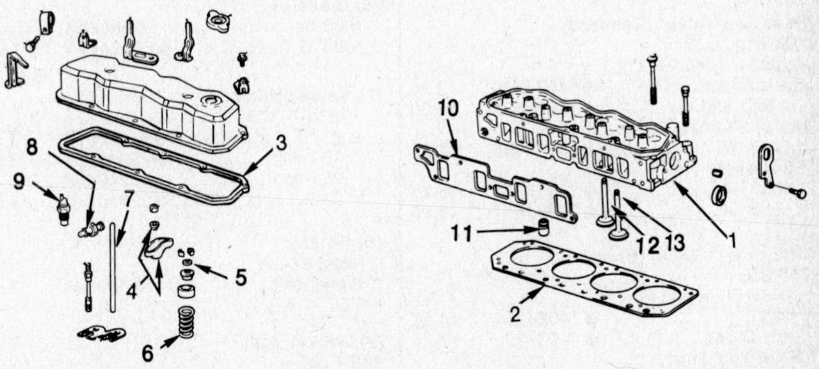

PARTS 12 CYLINDER HEAD & VALVE SYSTEM 12 PARTS

	Part No.	Price
(5) Oil Seal (Valve Stem)		
1983-87	◆3835333	.50
(6) Valve Spring & Damper		
1983-87	◆3735381	3.00
(7) Push Rod		
1983-84	◆10021898	3.00
1985-87	◆10028055	3.25
(8) Switch (Hot Light)		
1983-87	◆25036371	8.00
(9) Switch (Fan Control)		
1983-87	◆3040674	11.00
(10) Manifold Gasket (Intake)		
1983-87	◆10026023	5.00
(11) Valve Lifter		
1983-84	◆5233515	10.50
1985-87	◆5233745	32.50
(12) Intake Valve (Standard)		
1983-87	◆10022882	16.00
(13) Exhaust Valve (Standard)		
1983-84	◆10024039	N.L.
1985-87	◆10034162	16.25

PARTS 12 CYLINDER HEAD & VALVE SYSTEM 12 PARTS

SIX CYL. ENGINE

	Part No.	Price
(1) Cylinder Head		
173 Eng.		
1983-87-wo/H-O eng.	◆14054882	250.00
w/H-O eng.	◆14054879	250.00
181 & 231 Eng.		
1983-87	◆25518679	217.00
V-6 Diesel		
1983-84-cast iron	◆22520040	325.00
1983-84-alum.	◆22522562	357.00
1985	◆22523899	357.00
(2) Cylinder Head Gasket		
173 Eng.		
1983-84	◆476571	4.00
1985-87	◆14085435	4.75
181 Eng.		
1983	◆25500202	8.50
1984-87	◆25524599	8.50
231 Eng.		
1984	◆1261403	8.50
1985-87	◆25524599	8.50
V-6 Diesel		
1983-84	◆22527054	30.50
1985	◆22527030	30.50
(3) Push Rod		
1983-87-173 eng	◆476525	5.00
181, 231 engs.	◆25510025	4.25
diesel eng.	◆22511044	3.25
(4) Valve Lifter		
173 Eng.		
1983-87	◆5234212	N.L.
181 Eng.		
1983-87	◆5234330	N.L.
231 Eng.		
1984-87	◆5234330	N.L.
V-6 Diesel		
1983	◆5234470	38.10
1984-85	◆5234625	N.L.
(5) Intake Valve (Standard)		
173 Eng.		
1983-87-wo/H-O eng.	◆14024249	13.25
H-O eng.	◆14031328	14.00
181 & 231 Eng.		
1983-87	◆25512098	11.25
V-6 Diesel		
1983-84	◆22513937	18.25
1985	◆22524447	18.25
(6) Exhaust Valve (Standard)		
173 Eng.		
1983-87-wo/H-O eng.	◆14024254	14.25
H-O eng.	◆14031322	2.25
181 & 231 Eng.		
1983-87	◆1261380	13.50

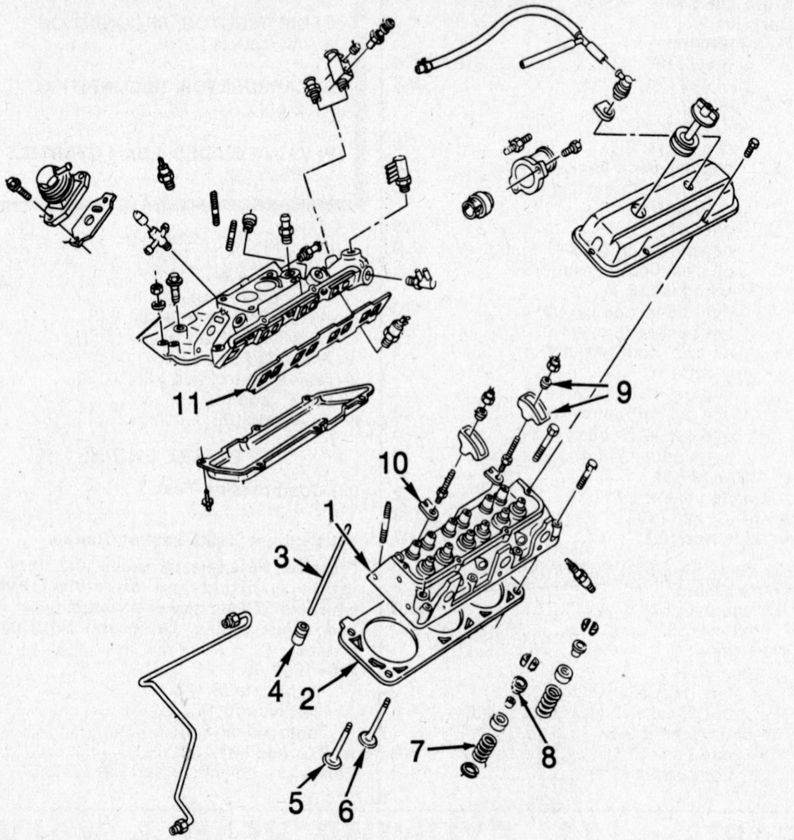

	Part No.	Price
V-6 Diesel		
1983-84	◆558873	13.00
1985	◆22524441	21.00
(7) Valve Spring		
1983-87-173 eng.	◆14030029	3.50
181 eng.	◆25512551	3.00
231 eng.	◆1249267	2.75
Diesel eng.	◆22510372	4.00
(8) Rotator		
1983-87-w/ diesel eng.	◆406996	3.50
(9) Rocker Arm		
173 Eng.		
1983-87	◆14002446	4.75
181 & 231 Eng.		
1983-87-right	◆1241850	4.50
left	◆1241851	4.50
V-6 Diesel		
1983-85	◆22505583	N.L.
(10) Guide (Push Rod)		
1983-87-173 eng.	◆476531	1.50
(11) Gasket Kit (Intake Manifold)		
1983-87-173 eng.	◆14033476	12.50
181 eng.	◆25505397	15.50
1984-87-231 eng.	◆1264924	16.00
1983-84-dies. eng.	◆22514872	16.50
1985-dies. eng.	◆22527543	16.50

PARTS 14 PISTONS, RINGS, PINS & BEARINGS 14 PARTS

	Part No.	Price
(1) Piston Ring Set (Standard)		
Four Cyl. Eng.		
1983	◆10022719	18.00
1984-87	◆10030202	18.00
173 Eng.		
1983-84	◆14034969	15.50
1985-87	◆14089059	17.00
181 Eng.		
1983	◆1261407	N.L.
1983-87	◆25519462	16.50
231 Eng.		
1984-87	◆1240955	15.75
V-6 Diesel		
1983-84	◆22515964	21.00
1985-87	◆22523733	21.00
(2) Piston Assy.		
Four Cyl. Eng.		
1983	◆10027416	50.75
1984-87	◆10027317	53.00
173 Eng.		
1983-84-wo/H-O eng.	◆14033250	48.50
H-O eng.	◆14033251	48.50

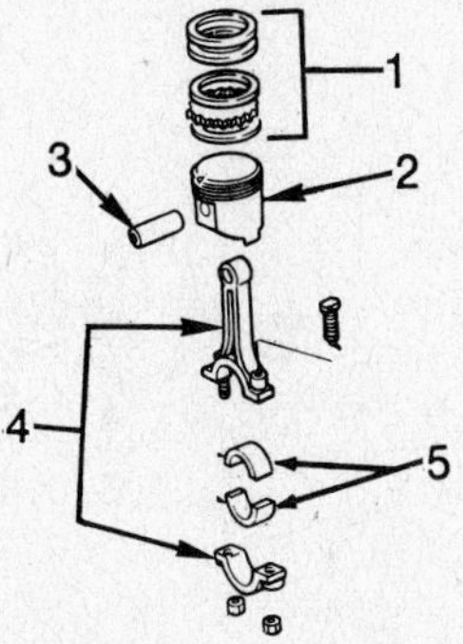

	Part No.	Price
1985-87-Code H.O. eng.	◆14092910	48.50
exc. H.O. eng.	◆14092911	48.50
1985-86-Code X, H.O. Eng.	◆14079779	48.50
exc. H.O. eng.	◆14079778	48.50
181 Eng.		
1983	◆25511557	49.00
1984-87	◆25516698	49.00
231 Eng.		
1984-87	◆25518053	48.25
V-6 Diesel		
1983-85-right	◆22523358	63.75
left	◆22523357	63.75

(3) Piston Pin

Note: Serviced in piston assy. only, except for engines listed below.

	Part No.	Price
1983-87 (151 eng.)		
.001 o.s.	◆500011	5.50
.003 o.s.	◆500012	5.50
(4) Connecting Rod		
1983-87-Four Cyl. Eng.	◆499323	39.50
173 eng.	◆476521	36.50
181 eng.	◆25509405	39.00
231 eng.	◆25506520	39.00
diesel eng.	◆22515315	50.50
(5) Connecting Rod Bearings (Std.)		
1983-87-Four Cyl. Eng.	◆5463932	10.50
173 eng.	◆18008492	N.L.
181, 231 engs.	◆18005399	11.00
diesel eng.	◆18009089	11.75

LABOR 15 CRANKSHAFT & DAMPER 15 LABOR

(Factory Time) — Chilton Time

GASOLINE ENGINES

(P) Crankshaft and Main Bearings, Renew

Includes: R&R engine, check all bearing clearances.

	Chilton Time
Four-1983-87 (7.0)	10.1
w/A.T. add (.4)	.4
V-6-1983-87	
eng codes X-Z-W (8.2)	11.5
eng code E (7.4)	11.4
eng codes 3-B (6.7)	10.5
w/A.C. add (.4)	.4
w/P.S. add (.5)	.5
w/Cruise control add (.2)	.2
w/C.C.C. add (.6)	.6
w/M.T. add (.3)	.3

(P) Main Bearings, Renew

Includes: Check all bearing clearances.

	Chilton Time
Four-1983-87 (3.7)	5.0
V-6-1983-87	
eng codes X-Z-W (2.9)	4.2
eng codes E-3-B (1.7)	2.5

(P) Main and Rod Bearings, Renew

Includes: Check all bearing clearances.

	Chilton Time
Four-1983-87 (4.5)	6.2
V-6-1983-87	
eng codes X-Z-W (4.7)	6.0
eng codes E-3-B (2.9)	4.3

(G) Rear Main Bearing Oil Seal, Renew or Repack

Includes: R&R oil pan and rear main bearing cap on V-6 engines. R&R trans on Four cyl engines.

	Chilton Time
Four-1983 (3.7)	4.5
1984-87	
first design (4.0)	5.8
w/A.T. add (.4)	.4
V-6-1983-87	
eng codes X-Z-W	
full circle type (6.6)	9.2
split lip type (3.9)	5.5
w/A.C. add (.5)	.5
w/P.S. add (.4)	.4
w/C.C.C. add (.6)	.6
w/Cruise control add (.2)	.2
w/M.T. add (.3)	.3
eng codes E-3-B (1.2)	2.2

(G) Crankshaft Pulley or Balancer, Renew

	Chilton Time
Four-1983-87	
pulley (.7)	1.2
balancer (.8)	1.3
V-6-1983-87	
eng codes X-Z-W	
pulley (.8)	1.3
balancer (1.0)	1.5
eng codes E-3-B	
balancer (1.0)	1.5
w/A.C. add (.2)	.2
w/P.S. add (.3)	.3

DIESEL ENGINE

(P) Crankshaft and Main Bearings, Renew

Includes: R&R engine, check all bearing clearances.

	Chilton Time
V-6-1983-85 (8.0)	11.4
w/A.C. add (.4)	.4

(P) Main Bearings, Renew

Includes: Check all bearing clearances.

	Chilton Time
V-6-1983-85 (3.3)	5.2

(P) Main and Rod Bearings, Renew

Includes: Check all bearing clearances.

	Chilton Time
V-6-1983-85 (5.0)	7.0

(G) Rear Main Bearing Oil Seals, R&R and Repack (Upper & Lower)

	Chilton Time
V-6-1983-85	
split lip type (2.4)	4.2
full circle type (7.6)	*10.9
w/A.C. add (.4)	.4

*Includes R&R engine.

(G) Crankshaft Pulley or Balancer, Renew

	Chilton Time
V-6-1983-85	
pulley (.5)	1.1
balancer (.6)	1.2

(G) Crankshaft Front Oil Seal, Renew

	Chilton Time
V-6-1983-85 (.7)	1.4

PARTS 15 CRANKSHAFT & DAMPER 15 PARTS

	Part No.	Price
(1) Crankshaft Assy.		
Four Cyl. Eng.		
1983-85	◆10002685	313.00
1986-87	◆10037018	313.00
173 Eng.		
1983-84	◆14064197	294.25
1985-87-Code W	◆14077817	336.00
1985-87-Code X		
1st design	◆14089826	336.00
2nd design	◆14077817	336.00
181 Eng.		
1983	◆25509404	337.25
1984-87	◆25519733	385.00
231 Eng.		
1984-87	◆25516025	405.00
V-6 Diesel		
1983-85	◆22515610	430.00
(2) Crankshaft Gear		
1983-87-Four Cyl. Eng.	◆10028052	25.75
173 eng.	◆477263	13.25
181, 231 engs.	◆1192916	16.00
diesel eng.	◆22516034	31.50

PARTS 15 CRANKSHAFT & DAMPER 15 PARTS

	Part No.	Price
(3) Crankshaft Pulley		
Four Cyl. Eng.		
1983-87	◆10021360	17.50
173 Eng.		
1983-84	◆14059347	29.50
1985-87	◆14083314	27.25
181 Eng.		
1983	◆25515782	N.L.
1984-87	◆25517706	52.50
231 Eng.		
1984-87	◆25511552	N.L.
V-6 Diesel		
1983-85	◆22518370	78.50
(4) Vibration Damper		
173 Eng.		
1983-87	◆14083394	39.50
Hub		
1983-87-Four Cyl. Eng.	◆10020689	28.50
1984-86	◆10028930	26.75
diesel eng.	◆22514399	31.75
(5) Rear Main Seal		
Four Cyl. Eng.		
1983	◆10018632	9.00
1984-86	◆10036788	N.L.
173 Eng.		
1983-84	◆14081761	14.00
1985-87-Code W	◆14085829	14.50
Code X		
1st design	◆14081761	14.00
2nd design	◆14085829	14.50
Code Z	◆14081761	14.00
181 & 231 Eng.		
1983-87	◆1193151	1.50

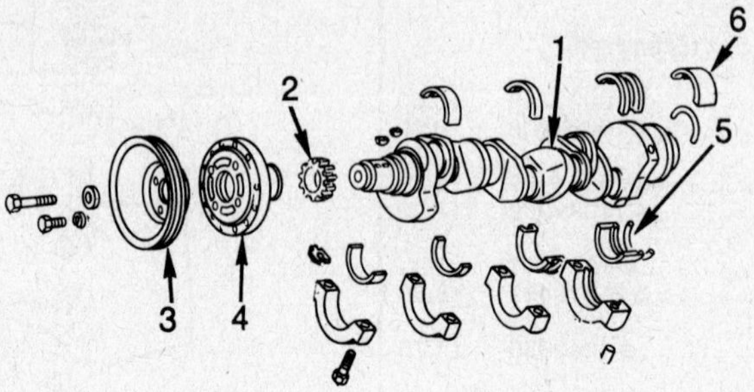

	Part No.	Price
V-6 Diesel		
1983-85 (packing)	◆9772831	1.50
(6) Main Bearing (Std.)		
Four Cyl. Eng.		
1983-87-exc. rear	◆3829061	11.00
rear	◆3829067	14.25
173 Eng.		
1983-87-exc. Code W & X		
No.1	◆18005226	12.75
No.2	◆18005227	12.75
No.3	◆18005225	26.00
rear	◆18005228	24.50
1985-87-Code W		
No. 1	◆18012472	13.25
No. 2	◆18012473	13.25
No. 3	◆18012478	24.75
No. 4	◆18012472	13.25

	Part No.	Price
1985-87-Code X (2nd design)		
No. 1	◆18012472	13.25
No. 2	◆18012473	13.25
No. 3	◆18012478	24.75
No. 4	◆18012472	13.25
181 & 231 Eng.		
1983-87-No.1	◆18009457	12.00
No.2	◆18004602	20.00
No.3	◆18002950	12.50
No.4	◆5468578	13.00
V-6 Diesel		
1983-85-No.1	◆5466312	16.00
No.2	◆5458657	15.00
No.3	◆5463797	26.25
No.4	◆18009091	25.75

LABOR 16 CAMSHAFT & TIMING GEARS 16 LABOR

(Factory Time) — Chilton Time

GASOLINE ENGINES

(G) Timing Cover Oil Seal, Renew

	Chilton Time
Four–1983-87 (.9)	1.4
V-6–1983-87	
eng codes X-Z-W (1.0)	1.6
w/A.C. add (.2)	.2
w/P.S. add (.3)	.3

(G) Timing Cover or Gasket, Renew

	Chilton Time
Four–1983-87 (2.2)	3.0
V-6–1983-87	
eng codes X-Z-W (2.3)	3.2
eng codes E-3-B (3.6)	5.0
Renew cover add (.2)	.4
w/A.C. add (.4)	.4
w/P.S. add (.3)	.3
w/AIR add (.3)	.3

(G) Camshaft Timing Gear, Renew

	Chilton Time
Four–1983-87 (5.7)	8.0
w/A.C. add (.4)	.4
w/P.S. add (.5)	.5
w/A.T. add (.4)	.4

(G) Timing Chain or Camshaft Gear, Renew

	Chilton Time
V-6–1983-87	
eng codes X-Z-W (2.4)	3.7
eng codes E-3-B (3.8)	5.5
Renew crankshaft gear add (.2)	.2
w/A.C. add (.4)	.4
w/P.S. add (.3)	.3

(G) Camshaft, Renew

Includes: R&R engine.

	Chilton Time
Four–1983-87 (5.7)	8.0
w/A.T. add (.4)	.4
V-6–1983-87	
eng codes X-Z (8.1)	11.5
eng code E (7.0)	10.8
eng code 3-B (6.5)	9.1
eng code W (8.4)	12.1
w/A.C. add (.4)	.4
w/P.S. add (.5)	.5
w/Cruise control add (.2)	.2
w/C.C.C. add (.3)	.3

DIESEL ENGINE

(G) Timing Case Cover or Gasket, Renew

Includes: R&R fan blade, crankshaft pulley and balancer. Drain and refill oil and coolant.

	Chilton Time
V-6–1983-85 (1.8)	2.5
w/A.C. add (.4)	.4
Renew cover add (.3)	.4

(G) Timing Chain or Gears, Renew

Includes: R&R fan blade, crankshaft pulley and balancer. Drain and refill oil and coolant.

	Chilton Time
V-6–1983-85 (4.4)	6.3
w/A.C. add (.4)	.4

(G) Camshaft, Renew

Includes: R&R starter, front cover, fuel pump, timing gear and chain. R&R injector pump, intake manifold and lifters. Disconnect exhaust system. Drain and refill oil and coolant. Make all necessary adjustments.

	Chilton Time
V-6–1983-85 (7.6)	10.8
w/A.C. add (.4)	.4
Renew cam brgs add (2.8)	3.8

(G) Camshaft Rear Bearing Plug, Renew

Includes: R&R trans for accessibility.

	Chilton Time
V-6–1983-85 (4.0)	5.7

PARTS 16 CAMSHAFT & TIMING GEARS 16 PARTS

	Part No.	Price
(1) Front Cover Oil Seal		
Four Cyl. & 173 Eng.		
1983-87-exc. 173 Eng.	◆14033199	5.50
1984-87-173 eng.	◆10036286	5.25
181 & 231 Eng.		
1983-87-packing	◆1305044	1.00
shedder	◆1193966	1.50
V-6 Diesel		
1983-85	◆552711	4.25
(2) Timing Case Cover		
Four Cyl. Eng.		
1983-84	◆547797	26.75
1985-87	◆10033836	N.L.
173 Eng.		
1983-87	◆14094526	85.00
181 & 231 Eng.		
1983-84	◆25511672	59.00
1985-87	◆25522653	59.00
V-6 Diesel		
1983	◆22514273	31.75
1984-85	◆22525285	30.75
Timing Case Cover Gasket		
1983-87-Four cyl.	◆3923472	1.00
173 eng.	◆14077849	1.50
181, 231 engs.	◆25512861	3.00
diesel eng.	◆22505997	1.25
(3) Camshaft Gear		
1983-87-Four cyl.	◆10005942	46.75
173 eng.	◆14025558	30.00
diesel eng.	◆22516032	41.00
1983-84-181, 231 engs.	◆1253698	18.50
1985-87-181 & (85) 231 eng.	◆25518767	17.50
1986-87-231 eng.	◆25523115	17.50

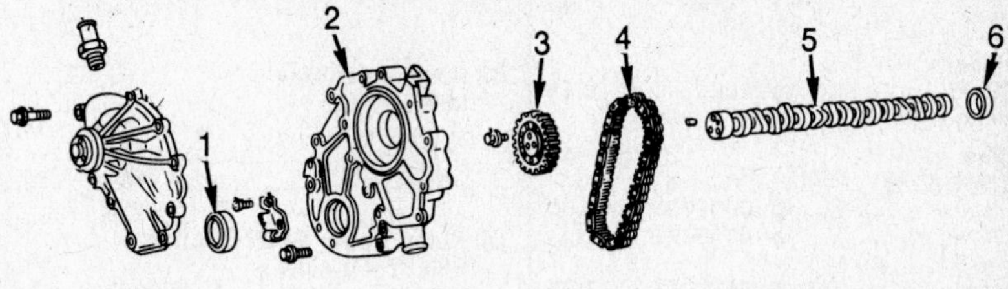

	Part No.	Price
(4) Timing Chain		
1983-87-173 eng.	◆14049741	30.00
181, 231 engs.	◆1257650	26.00

Note: V-6 diesel engs. with Morse type 46 timing chain rollers require that the camshaft sprocket, crankshaft sprocket, & timing chain be replaced as a complete set. Type is stamped on outside master link near vendor ident.

	Part No.	Price
diesel eng.	◆22516033	35.50
(5) Camshaft		
Four Cyl. Eng.		
1983	◆10006745	118.00
1984	◆10029616	118.00
1985-87	◆10029787	118.00
173 Eng.		
1983-87-Code X	◆14024278	113.00
Code W, Z	◆14031378	122.00
181 Eng.		
1983-84	◆25510019	119.00
1985-87	◆25518608	119.00
231 Eng.		
1984 (1st design)	◆1262835	119.00
1984 (2nd design)	◆25510049	119.00
1985	◆25510049	119.00
1986-Code 3	◆25522674	119.00
1986-Code B	◆25523930	124.00
1985-87	◆25518606	119.00

	Part No.	Price
V-6 Diesel		
1983-85	◆22513910	266.00
(6) Camshaft Bearing		
Four Cyl. Eng.		
1983-87	◆14002525	5.50
173 Eng.		
1983-87-No. 1	◆14033120	13.50
No.2,3	◆14002534	14.00
rear	◆14002535	14.00
181 & 231 Eng.		
1983-84-No. 1	◆1234441	7.00
No.2,3,4	◆1231142	7.75
1985-87-No. 1, 4	◆25524301	7.25
No. 2, 3	◆1231142	7.75
V-6 Diesel		
1983-85-No. 1	◆561077	11.50
No.2	◆390300	11.50
No.3	◆390301	11.75
No.4	◆390302	11.50

LABOR 17 ENGINE OILING SYSTEM 17 LABOR

(Factory Time)	Chilton Time
GASOLINE ENGINES	
(G) Oil Pan or Gasket, Renew	
Four-1983-87 (2.6)	3.5
V-6-1983-87	
eng codes X-Z-W (1.6)	2.4
eng codes E-3-B (.9)	1.5
(G) Oil Pump Cover and/or Gears, Renew or Recondition	
V-6-1983-87	
eng codes E-3-B (.8)	1.2
(P) Pressure Test Engine Bearings (Pan Off)	
All models	1.0
(G) Oil Pump, Renew	
Four-1983-87 (2.7)	3.7
V-6-1983-87	
eng codes X-Z-W (1.7)	2.7

(Factory Time)	Chilton Time
(G) Oil Pressure Gauge (Engine), Renew	
1983-87-Four (.4)	.6
V-6 (.6)	.9
(G) Oil Pressure Gauge (Dash), Renew	
1983-87	
Century (.3)	.5
6000 (.5)	.9
Ciera (.6)	.9
(M) Oil Filter Element, Renew	
Four (.3)	.3
V-6 (.3)	.3

DIESEL ENGINE

(G) Oil Pan or Gasket, Renew

Includes: Raise engine, R&R and clean oil pump screen.

(Factory Time)	Chilton Time
V-6-1983-85 (2.1)	3.6
(P) Pressure Test Engine Bearings (Pan Off)	
All models	1.0
(G) Oil Pump, Renew	
Includes: Raise engine, R&R and clean oil pump screen.	
V-6-1983-85 (2.2)	3.8
(G) Oil Pump, R&R and Recondition	
Includes: Raise engine, R&R and clean oil pump screen.	
V-6-1983-85 (2.4)	4.0
(G) Oil Pressure Gauge (Engine), Renew	
1983-85 (.3)	.4
(M) Oil Filter Element, Renew	
1983-85 (.3)	.3

PARTS 17 ENGINE OILING SYSTEM 17 PARTS

	Part No.	Price
Oil Pan Seal		
173 Eng.		
1983-84-Rear	◆476591	1.25
1985-87	◆14077876	2.00

Applications not listed use RTV sealant.

	Part No.	Price
Oil Pan Gasket Kit		
181 Eng.		
1983-84	◆25516877	5.50
1985-86	◆25519254	8.25
231 Eng.		
1984	◆25516877	5.50
1985	◆25519254	8.25
1986-87	◆25526425	7.50

PARTS 17 ENGINE OILING SYSTEM 17 PARTS

	Part No.	Price
V-6 Diesel		
1983-85	◆22520640	8.25
Applications not listed use RTV sealant.		
Oil Pump		
1983-87-Four cyl. eng.	◆10008206	61.00
173 eng.	◆14033227	N.L.
w/181, 231 engs.	◆25525673	7.25
diesel eng.	◆22515464	59.75
Oil Pump Screen		
Note: Oil pump screen for Four cyl. and V-6 engs. not listed are included with oil pump.		
1983-87-173 eng.	◆14046491	4.75
Oil Pump Drive Shaft		
1983-87-Four cyl.	◆1977131	11.75
173 eng.	◆477248	1.50
diesel eng.	◆22512399	11.25
Oil Pump Upper Shaft Bearing		
1983-87-Four cyl.		
upper	◆10008555	1.00
lower	◆10004842	1.50
Oil Pressure Regulator Valve		
1983-87-Four cyl.	◆3829433	1.50
173 eng.	◆3702366	1.50
Oil Pressure Sending Switch		
1983-87-Four cyl. eng.	◆25036378	8.75
173 eng.	◆14014599	5.25
181 eng.	◆25500672	5.50
231 eng.	◆1623576	6.00
diesel eng.	◆3815936	3.50
Oil Filter By Pass Valve		
1983-87 w/151, 173 engs.	◆25010497	3.50
1983-85-V-6 Diesel	◆2511265	N.L.

LABOR 18 CLUTCH & FLYWHEEL 18 LABOR

	(Factory Time)	Chilton Time
(G) Clutch Control Cable, Renew		
1984-87	(.4)	.6
(G) Clutch Release Bearing, Renew		
Includes: R&R trans and make all necessary adjustments.		
1984-87-Four	(2.2)	3.7
V-6	(2.5)	4.0
(G) Clutch Fork Shaft and/or Bushings, Renew		
Includes: R&R trans and make all necessary adjustments.		
1984-87-Four	(2.4)	3.9
V-6	(2.7)	4.2
(G) Clutch Assembly, Renew		
Includes: R&R trans and renew pressure plate, disc and release bearing.		
1984-87-Four	(2.4)	4.0
V-6	(2.7)	4.3
Renew clutch fork and/or bush add	(.3)	.3
(G) Flywheel, Renew		
Includes: R&R transmission.		
1984-87-Four	(2.6)	4.3
V-6	(2.9)	4.6
Renew ring gear add	(.3)	.5

PARTS 18 CLUTCH & FLYWHEEL 18 PARTS

	Part No.	Price
Pressure Plate Assy.		
1984-87-Four cyl.	◆14066979	124.00
Clutch Driven Plate		
1984-Four cyl.	◆476600	89.00
1985-87	◆14087242	83.25
Release Bearing		
1984-87	◆908403	47.25
Release Lever		
1984-87	◆474667	17.00
Bearing (Clutch Fork)		
1984-87	◆474665	3.00
Flywheel		
Four Cyl. Eng.		
1983	◆10031262	70.25
1984-87-w/M.T.	◆10004031	159.00
w/A.T.	◆10031262	70.25
173 Eng.		
1983-87-w/A.T.	◆14085471	68.75
1986-87-w/M.T.	◆476575	159.00
181 Eng.		
1983	◆25512172	67.50
1984-87	◆25517709	67.50
231 Eng.		
1984-87	◆25515222	70.50
V-6 Diesel		
1983-85	◆22520094	75.25

LABOR 21 SHIFT LINKAGE 21 LABOR

	(Factory Time)	Chilton Time
MANUAL		
(G) Gearshift Linkage, Adjust		
All models	(.3)	.3
(G) Gearshift Lever, Renew		
1984-87	(.3)	.4
(G) Gearshift Control Assy., Renew		
Includes: R&R console plate and rear mount. Adjust control cables.		
1984-87	(.6)	1.0
(G) Gearshift Control Opening Seal, Renew		
1984-87	(.3)	.5
(G) Gearshift Control Cables, Renew		
Includes: Raise vehicle and adjust linkage.		
1984-87-one cable	(1.2)	1.6
two cables	(1.4)	1.9
AUTOMATIC		
(G) Shift Linkage, Adjust		
All models		
Neutral Safety Switch	(.3)	.4
Shift Indicator Needle	(.2)	.3
Shift Linkage	(.4)	.5
T.V. Cable	(.3)	.4
(G) Gearshift Selector Lever, Renew		
Includes: Renew pin and lever.		
1983-87		
column mount	(.2)	.4
floor mount	(.5)	.8
w/Cruise control add	(.2)	.2
(G) Shift Control Cable, Renew		
Includes: Necessary adjustments.		
1983-87	(.6)	1.0
(G) Park Lock Cable, Renew		
1983-87		
column shift	(.6)	1.0
floor shift	(1.0)	1.5
(G) Floor Shift Control Assy., Renew		
1983-87	(.6)	.9
(G) Gear Selector Needle and/or Assy., Renew		
1983-87	(.6)	1.0

LABOR 26 REAR AXLE AND SUSPENSION 26 LABOR

(Factory Time) Chilton Time

(G) Rear Coil Spring, Renew
1983-87-one (.4) 6
both (.5) 8

(G) Lower Control Arm Bushings, Renew
1983-87-one (.6) 1.1
both (1.1) 1.9

(G) Rear Axle Tie Rod Assy., Renew
1983-87 (.3) 5
Renew bushings add (.3) 3

(G) Rear Shock Absorbers, Renew
1983-87-one (.3) 4
both (.4) 7

(G) Rear Wheel Bearing and Hub Assy., Clean and Repack or Renew
1983-87-one (.4) 6
both (.7) 1.1

(G) Rear Stabilizer Bar, Renew
1983-87 (.4) 6

(G) Rear Axle Assembly, Renew
1983-87 (1.8) 2.7

(G) Super Lift Shock Absorbers, Renew
1983-87-one (.5) 6
both (.8) 1.0

ELECTRONIC LEVEL CONTROL

(G) Compressor Assembly, Renew
1984-87 (.6) 8

(G) Relay, Renew
1984-87 (.2) 4

(G) Height Sensor, Renew
1984-87 (.4) 6

(G) Height Sensor, Adjust
1984-87 (.4) 5

(G) Electronic Level Control Dryer, Renew
1984-87 (.4) 6

(G) Electronic Level Control Head, Renew
Includes: Renew cover gasket, solenoid and valves.
1984-87 (.5) 9

(G) Electronic Level Control Motor and Cylinder Assy., R&R and Recondition
1984-87 (.8) 1.2

PARTS 26 REAR AXLE AND SUSPENSION 26 PARTS

	Part No.	Price
(1) Coil Spring		
Note: Rear coil springs must be ordered by year and production code taped to spring on vehicle.		
(2) Tie Bar		
1983-87	◆10019317	23.00
(3) Shock Absorber		
1983-87-exc. below	◆4993583	34.00
w/H.D. susp.	◆22046415	25.50
w/sta. wagon	◆22046414	25.50
(4) Bracket (Control Arm)		
1983-right	◆10026571	14.00
left	◆10026572	14.00
1984-87-right	◆10029094	5.50
left	◆10029093	5.50
(5) Support (Rear Axle)		
1983-87	◆10017943	404.25

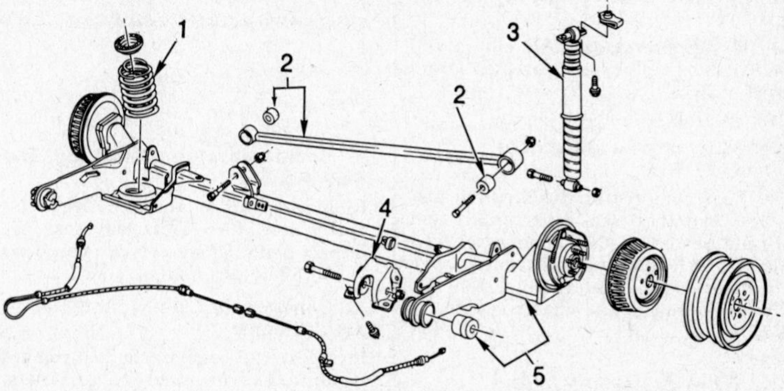

ELECTRONIC LEVEL CONTROL

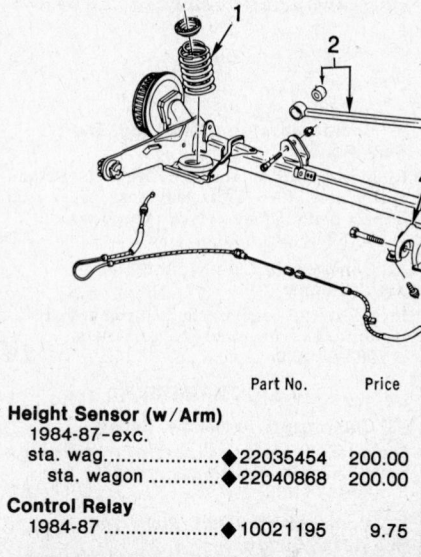

	Part No.	Price
Compressor Assy.		
1984-87	◆22030258	233.00
Height Sensor (w/Arm)		
1984-87-exc. sta. wag.	◆22035454	200.00
sta. wagon	◆22040868	200.00
Control Relay		
1984-87	◆10021195	9.75
Shock Absorber		
(exc. station wagon)		
1984-87-right	◆4993586	79.50
left	◆4993585	79.50
(station wagon)		
1984-87	◆22046414	25.50

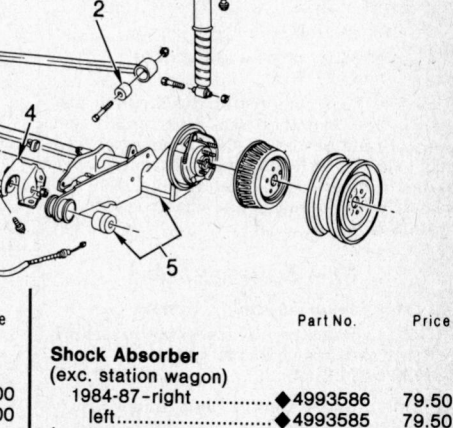

LABOR 28 AIR CONDITIONING 28 LABOR

(Factory Time) Chilton Time

Note: If more than one item requires replacement where evacuation and discharging the system is already included in the operation, deduct 1.0 hour for each additional item to the times listed.

(G) Drain, Evacuate and Recharge System
All models (.5) 1.0

(G) Leak Check
Includes: Check all lines and connections.
All models 5

(G) Refrigerant, Add (Partial Charge)
All models 6

(G) Compressor Belt, Renew
Four (.7) 9
V-6
eng codes X-Z-W (.4) 6
eng codes E-3-B
1983-84 (1.8) 2.5
1985-87 (1.1) 1.5
Diesel
Serpentine (.2) 4

COMPRESSOR 4 CYLINDER RADIAL

(G) Compressor Assembly, Renew
Includes: Transfer all necessary attaching parts. Evacuate and charge system.
1983-87 (1.1) 2.0

(G) Compressor Clutch Plate and Hub Assy., Renew
Includes: R&R hub and drive plate assy. Check air gap.
1983-87 (.3) 6

(G) Compressor Clutch Rotor and/or Bearing, Renew
Includes: R&R hub and drive plate assy.
1983-85 (.6) 9
1986-87 (1.2) 1.8

(G) Compressor Clutch Coil and/or Pulley Rim Assy., Renew
Includes: R&R hub and drive plate assy.
1983-85 (.5) 8
1986-87 (1.2) 1.6
Renew pulley or brg add 2

(G) Compressor Front Seal, Seat and 'O' Ring, Renew
Includes: R&R clutch hub and drive plate assy. Evacuate and charge system.
1983-87 (1.1) 2.1

LABOR 28 AIR CONDITIONING 28 LABOR

(Factory Time) Chilton Time

(G) Compressor Front Head and/or Seal, Renew

Includes: R&R compressor. R&R clutch and pulley assy. R&R shaft seal assy. Clean and inspect parts. Evacuate and charge system.

1983-87 (1.7) 2.8

(G) Compressor Discharge Valve Plates, Renew

Includes: R&R compressor. R&R clutch and pulley assy. R&R shell to internal mechanism. Clean and inspect parts. Evacuate and charge system.

1983-87 (2.0) 3.0

Two or more add (.1) 3

(G) Compressor Thrust and/or Belleville Washers, Renew

Includes: R&R compressor. R&R clutch and pulley assy. R&R shaft seal assy. R&R front head assy. Clean and inspect parts. Evacuate and charge system.

1983-87 (1.7) 2.8

(G) Compressor Main Bearing, Renew

Includes: R&R compressor. R&R clutch and pulley assy. Clean and inspect parts. Evacuate and charge system.

1983-87 (1.7) 2.8

(G) Compressor Shaft and Cylinder Assy., Renew

Includes: R&R compressor, R&R clutch and pulley assy. R&R shaft seal assy, remove and transfer front head assy. R&R compressor shell and 'O' rings. R&R compressor discharge valve plates. R&R pressure relief valve. Clean and inspect parts. Evacuate and charge system.

1983-87 (2.1) 3.1

DA-6 COMPRESSOR

(G) Compressor Assembly, Renew

Includes: Transfer all necessary attaching parts. Evacuate and charge system.

1983-87 (1.3) 2.0

(G) Compressor Clutch Plate and Hub Assy., Renew

Includes: R&R hub and drive plate assy. Check air gap.

1983-87 (.9) 1.3

(G) Compressor Clutch Rotor and/or Bearing, Renew

Includes: R&R hub and drive plate assy.

1983-87 (1.2) 1.7

(G) Compressor Clutch Coil and/or Pulley Rim Assy., Renew

Includes: R&R hub and drive plate assy.

1983-87 (1.2) 1.5

Renew pulley or brg add 2

(G) Compressor Front Seal, Seat and 'O' Ring, Renew

Includes: R&R clutch hub and drive plate assy. Evacuate and charge system.

1983-87 (1.7) 2.5

AIR CONDITIONER TUNE-UP

For efficient operation and satisfactory performance in hot weather. The following air conditioner tune-up is suggested:

1. Clean intake filter
2. Clean condenser fins
3. Pressure test system
4. Adjust drive belt tension
5. Check antifreeze/coolant
6. Tighten compressor mounts
7. Tighten condenser and evaporator mounts
8. Inspect system for leaks (hoses, couplings, valves, etc.)
9. Partial charge system

All models 1.0

If necessary to evacuate and charge system, add 1.0

(Factory Time) Chilton Time

(G) Compressor Front Head and/or Seal, Renew

Includes: R&R compressor. R&R clutch and pulley assy. R&R shaft seal assy. Clean and inspect parts. Evacuate and charge system.

1983-87 (1.9) 2.6

(G) Compressor Cylinder and Shaft Assy., Renew

Includes: R&R compressor. Transfer all parts as required. Evacuate and charge system.

1983-87 (2.0) 2.8

V-5 COMPRESSOR

(G) Compressor Assembly, Renew

Includes: Transfer all necessary attaching parts. Evacuate and charge system.

1986-87 (1.3) 2.0

(G) Compressor Clutch Plate and Hub Assy., Renew

1986-87 (.8) 1.2

(G) Compressor Rotor and/or Bearing, Renew

1986-87 (1.0) 1.5

(G) Compressor Clutch Coil and/or Pulley Rim, Renew

1986-87 (1.0) 1.5

(G) Compressor Shaft Seal Kit, Renew

Includes: Evacuate and charge system.

1986-87 (1.5) 2.2

(G) Condenser, Renew

Includes: Evacuate and charge system.

1983-87 (1.4) 2.4

(Factory Time) Chilton Time

(G) Evaporator Core, Renew

Includes: Evacuate and charge system.

1983-87-Four (2.0) 3.5

V-6 (2.6) 5.0

(G) Accumulator Assembly, Renew

Includes: Evacuate and charge system.

1983-87 (.9) 1.5

(G) Expansion Tube Assy., Clean and Inspect or Renew

Includes: Evacuate and charge system.

1983-87 (.8) 1.4

(G) High Pressure Cut Off Switch, Renew

1983-87 (.2) 3

(G) Pressure Cycling Switch, Renew

1983-87 (.2) 3

(G) Blower Motor and/or Fan, Renew

1983-87

Gas (.4) 6

Diesel (1.0) 1.5

(G) Blower Motor Resistor, Renew

1983-87 (.2) 3

(G) Blower Motor Switch, Renew

Celebrity

1985-87 (.9) 1.5

All other models

1983-87 (.5) 6

(G) Temperature Control Assy., Renew

Celebrity

1985-87 (.8) 1.4

All other models

1983-87 (.5) 9

(G) Vacuum Selector Valve, Renew

Celebrity

1985-87 (.9) 1.4

All other models

1983-87 (.4) 7

(G) Vacuum Diaphragm Actuators, Renew

Defroster diaphragm

Celebrity

1986-87 (3.5) 5.0

All other models

1983-87 (.8) 1.5

Mode door diaphragms

1983-87 (.5) 9

Air inlet diaphragm

1983-87 (.5) 9

(G) Master Electrical Switch, Renew

Celebrity

1985-87 (.9) 1.5

All other models

1983-87 (.5) 7

(G) Air Conditioning Hoses, Renew

Includes: Evacuate and charge system.

1983-87-suction (1.3) 2.0

discharge (1.3) 2.0

liquid line (.8) 1.7

PARTS 28 AIR CONDITIONING 28 PARTS

	Part No.	Price
Compressor Assy.		
(Radial compressor)		
1983-84-Four cyl.	◆12309223	390.00
diesel eng.	◆12309215	390.00
(DA-6 compressor)		
1983-173 eng.	◆12309214	410.00
1985-87-Code W	◆12322322	N.L.
1983-87-Code X & Z	◆12321363	410.00
1983-84-181, 231 engs.	◆12321366	410.00
1985-87-181	◆12322331	N.L.
1985-231 eng.	◆12322330	N.L.
1986-87 (231 B & 3 Eng.)	◆12322327	N.L.

PARTS 28 AIR CONDITIONING 28 PARTS

	Part No.	Price
Clutch Hub & Drive Plate		
(Radial compressor)		
1983-87	◆6551220	32.50
(DA-6 compressor)		
1983-84	◆6551717	38.25
1985-87-173 eng. (Code W)	◆6551996	41.00
1984-Code X	◆6551920	40.00
1984-181, 231 eng	◆6551920	40.00
Rotor (w/Bearing)		
1983-84-Four & 173 eng.	◆6551216	67.50
1983-85-diesel eng	◆6551884	108.50
Compressor Pulley		
1983-84-4.60 dia	◆6556715	13.00
1983-87-4.9 dia.	◆6551713	79.75
5.4 dia.	◆6551888	94.00
Clutch Coil (w/Housing)		
1983-87-radial comp.	◆6551217	44.00
1983-84-DA-6 comp.	◆6551834	41.50
1985-87-DA-6 comp.	◆6551997	47.25
Shaft Seal Kit		
1983-84-radi. comp.	◆9956695	13.00
(DA-6 Compressor)		
1983-84-(OEM 1131419)	◆2724280	17.00
1984-87-(OEM 1131471)	◆2724319	11.25

	Part No.	Price
Front Head		
(radial comp.)		
1983-84	◆6551142	28.25
1985-87	◆6551835	41.25
(DA-6 comp)		
1983-84 (OEM 1131419)	◆6557376	40.00
1984-86-OEM (1131471)	◆6557775	44.25
Outer Shell Assy. (Radial)		
1983-87	◆2724158	38.00
Valve Plate (w/Valve)		
1983-87-Radial comp.	◆6551141	11.50
(DA-6 compressor)		
front	◆6551700	25.00
rear	◆6551702	25.00
Compressor Drive Belt		
Order by year and model.		
Condenser		
1983-84-exc. Diesel	◆3049183	174.00
V-6 Diesel		
exc. A-6000	◆3050155	149.75
A6000	◆3050289	176.00
1985-exc. Diesel	◆3057676	N.L.
1986-87	◆3090818	163.25
Blower Motor Switch		
1983-exc. STE model	◆16017911	4.50
STE model	◆16025293	23.75
1984-87	◆16033615	7.25

	Part No.	Price
Blower Motor Resistor		
1983-84	◆526897	4.50
1985-87	◆10039426	4.50
Evaporator Core		
Four Cyl. Eng.		
1983-84	◆3054167	249.50
1985-87	◆3059160	261.50
173 Eng.		
1983-84	◆3054167	249.50
1985-87	◆3059160	261.50
V-6 (exc. 173)		
1983-87	◆3050133	246.50
Blower Motor		
1983-87	◆22020945	60.00
Accumulator Dehydrator		
Four Cyl. & 173 Eng.		
1983-87	◆2724239	80.00
181 & 231 Engs.		
1983-84	◆2724259	87.00
1985-87-181 eng.	◆2724239	80.00
231 eng.	◆3090492	N.L.
V-6 Diesel		
1983	◆2724259	87.00
1984	◆2724270	80.25
1985	◆3059155	80.50
Expansion Tube (Orifice Assy.)		
1983-87	◆3033879	9.50
Pressure Cutoff Switch		
1983-87	◆3041596	19.00
Blower Motor Relay (Hi Blo)		
1983-87	◆10019535	7.50

LABOR 29 LOCKS, HINGES & WIND. REGULATORS 29 LABOR

(Factory Time)	Chilton Time
(G) Hood Latch Assembly, Renew	
1983-87 (.2)	.4
(G) Hood Release Cable, Renew	
1983-87 (.3)	.6
(G) Hood Hinge, Renew (One)	
1983-87 (1.1)	1.5
(G) Door Lock Assembly, Renew	
1983-87-front (.5)	.8
rear (.4)	.6
(G) Door Lock Cylinder, Renew	
1983-87 (.3)	.4
Recode cyl add (.3)	.3

(Factory Time)	Chilton Time
(G) Door Lock Remote Control, Renew (Front or Rear)	
1983-87 (.3)	.5
(G) Lock Striker Plate, Renew	
1983-87 (.2)	.3
(G) Door Handle (Outside), Renew (Front or Rear)	
1983-87 (.3)	.5
Renew insert add	.1
(G) Door Window Regulator (Manual), Renew (Front or Rear)	
1983-87 (.6)	1.0
(G) Door Window Regulator (Electric), Renew (Front or Rear)	
1983-87 (.8)	1.2

(Factory Time)	Chilton Time
(G) Rear Compartment Lid Lock Assy., Renew	
1983-87 (.2)	.3
(G) Rear Compartment Lid Lock Cylinder, Renew	
1983-87 (.2)	.3
Recode cyl add (.3)	.3
(G) Rear Compartment Lid Hinge Strap, Renew (One)	
1983-87 (.8)	1.2
(G) Tail Gate Hinge, Renew	
1984-87	
Gate side-one (.7)	1.0
Body side-one (1.0)	1.4

PARTS 29 LOCKS, HINGES & WIND. REGULATORS 29 PARTS

	Part No.	Price
Hood Latch		
1983-87-exc. below	◆25519936	9.50
Celebrity	◆14086280	9.50
6000 ('82-'84)	◆10019018	9.50
6000 ('85-'87)	◆10041562	9.50
Hood Hinge		
1983-87-right	◆20538872	15.25
left	◆20538873	15.25
Hood Latch Control		
1983-87	◆20435166	7.25

	Part No.	Price
Front Door Lock		
1983-87-right	◆20298852	37.25
left	◆20298853	38.50
Rear Door Lock		
1983-84-w/non-adjust. rod		
right	◆20298866	46.50
left	◆20298867	46.50
1984-w/adjust. rod		
right	◆20479424	46.50
left	◆20479425	46.50
1985-87-right	◆20594024	36.50
left	◆20594025	36.50

	Part No.	Price
Door Lock Cylinder Unit		
1983-87	◆9632769	7.75
Door Handle (Outside)		
(wo/deluxe door handle)		
1983-87-right	◆20310080	20.00
left	◆20310081	20.00
(w/deluxe door handle)		
1983-87-right	◆20310082	20.00
left	◆20310083	20.00
Front Window Regulator (Electric)		
1983-87-right	◆20041442	79.50
left	◆20041443	79.50

PARTS 29 LOCKS, HINGES & WIND. REGULATORS 29 PARTS

	Part No.	Price
Front Window Regulator (Manual)		
1983-87-right	◆20041428	64.25
left	◆20041429	64.25
Rear Window Regulator (Manual)		
(exc. 6000)		
1983-87-right	◆20315738	59.50
left	◆20315739	59.50
(6000)		
1983-87-right	◆20041430	61.00
left	◆20041431	61.00
Rear Window Regulator (Electric)		
1983-87-right	◆20041434	70.00
left	◆20041435	70.00
Electric Window Regulator Motor		
1983-87-Ft. dr.	◆22029848	72.50
1983-84-R.D.	◆22020900	N.L.
1984-87-R.D.	◆22029848	N.L.
1986-87 (6000)	◆22020900	N.L.
Trunk Lock		
1983-84-exc.		
sta. wag.	◆20166276	13.75
1985-86	◆20513752	11.25
sta. wagon	◆20369896	54.00
Trunk Lock Cylinder		
(exc. 6000)		
1983-87	◆3910570	6.25
(6000)		
1983-87	◆20496705	3.75
Trunk Lid Straps		
1983-87-exc.		
sta. wag.	◆20356018	13.75
1984-86-sta. wagon		
(body side)	◆20298586	2.75
(gate side)	◆20298588	5.00

LABOR 30 HEAD AND PARKING LAMPS 30 LABOR

(Factory Time)	Chilton Time
(G) Aim Headlamps	
two	.4
four	.6
(M) Headlamp Sealed Beam Bulb, Renew	
1983-87-one (.2)	.3
each adtnl	.1
(M) Turn Signal and Parking Lamp Assy., Renew	
1983-87 (.3)	.4
(M) Side Marker Lamp Assy., Renew (Front or Rear)	
1983-87 (.2)	.3
(M) Tail and Stop Lamp Assy., Renew	
1983-87 (.2)	.3
(M) License Lamp Assembly, Renew	
1983-87 (.2)	.3
(M) Back-Up Lamp Assy., Renew	
All models-each (.3)	.4
(M) Back-Up Lamp Bulb, Renew	
All models-one (.2)	.3
(M) License Lamp Bulb, Renew	
All models-one or all (.2)	.3
(M) Park and Turn Signal Lamp Bulb, Renew	
All models-each	.2
(M) Side Marker Lamp Bulb, Renew	
All models-each	.2
(M) Stop, Tail and Turn Signal Lamp Bulb, Renew	
All models-one	.2
each adtnl	.1
(M) High Level Stop Lamp Assy., Renew	
1986-87 (.2)	.4
(M) High Level Stop Lamp Bulb, Renew	
All models (.2)	.3

PARTS 30 HEAD AND PARKING LAMPS 30 PARTS

	Part No.	Price
Headlamp Sealed Beam		
(wo/quartz)		
1983-87-inboard	◆5966201	15.00
outboard	◆5966200	15.00
(w/quartz)		
1983-87-inboard	◆5930567	22.50
outboard (1983)	◆16502327	22.50
outboard (1984-87)	◆16502327	22.50
Parking & Turn Signal Lamp Assy.		
(Celebrity)		
1983-87-right	◆919164	28.50
left	◆919163	28.50
(Century)		
(wo/lamp monitor)		
1983-87-right	◆929844	12.50
left	◆929843	12.50
(w/lamp monitor)		
1983-87-right	◆917938	12.50
left	◆917937	12.50
(Ciera)		
(wo/European styling)		
1983-87-right	◆929350	29.75
left	◆929349	29.75
(w/European styling)		
1983-87-right	◆918734	29.75
left	◆918733	29.75
(6000)		
1983-87-right	◆915604	16.50
left	◆915603	16.50
License Plate Lamp Assy.		
(exc. Century)		
1983-87-exc.		
sta. wag.	◆915086	3.75
sta. wagon	◆915873	8.75
(Century)		
1983	◆915076	7.50
1984-87-exc.		
sta. wag.	◆912368	6.25
sta. wagon	◆915873	8.75
Tail & Stop Lamp Assy.		
(Celebrity)		
(wo/custom exterior)		
1983-right	◆918664	88.50
left	◆918663	88.50
1984-87-exc. sta. wagon		
right	◆918808	88.50
left	◆918807	88.50
1984-87-sta. wagon		
right	◆16503960	34.00
left	◆5973763	48.00
(w/custom exterior)		
1984-87-right	◆919122	88.50
left	◆919121	88.50
(Century)		
(exc. sta. wagon)		
1983-right	◆5973238	69.75
left	◆4973237	N.L.
1984-87-right	◆16501668	69.75
left	◆16501667	69.75
(sta. wagon)		
1984-87-right	◆5973902	N.L.
left	◆5973901	N.L.
(Ciera)		
(exc. sta. wagon)		
1983-right	◆16500930	83.50
left	◆16500929	83.50
1984-87-right	◆16501580	72.50
left	◆16501579	72.50
(sta. wagon)		
1984-87-right	◆5973886	46.25
left	◆5973885	46.25
(6000)		
(wo/custom exterior)		
1983-right	◆16501576	126.00
left	◆16501575	126.00
1984-87-exc. sta. wagon		
right	◆16501702	68.50
left	◆16501701	68.50
1984-87-sta. wagon		
right	◆5973214	42.00
left	◆5973213	42.00
(w/custom exterior)		
1983-right	◆16500328	68.50
left	◆16500327	68.50
1984-87-right	◆16501654	68.50
left	◆16501653	68.50
High Mount Stoplight		
1986-87	◆5974466	36.00

LABOR 31 WINDSHIELD WIPER & SPEEDOMETER 31 LABOR

(Factory Time)	Chilton Time
(G) Windshield Wiper Motor, Renew	
1983-87 (.7)	1.0
(G) Windshield Wiper Motor, R&R and Recondition	
1983-87 (1.2)	1.5
(G) Windshield Wiper Switch, Renew	
1983-85 (1.1)	1.4
1986-87	
std colm (1.3)	1.7
tilt colm (1.1)	1.4
(G) Wiper Transmission, Renew (One)	
Includes: R&R linkage.	
1983-87 (.6)	1.0
(G) Rear Window Wiper Motor, Renew	
1984-87 (.2)	.3
(G) Rear Window Wiper Motor, R&R and Recondition	
1984-87 (.7)	1.0
(G) Rear Window Wiper Switch, Renew	
1984-87 (.2)	.3
(G) Rear Window Washer Pump, Renew	
1984-87 (.3)	.4
(G) Windshield Washer Pump Valve, Renew	
1984-87 (.2)	.3
(G) Intermittent Wiper Controller Assy., Renew	
1983-87 (.3)	.4
(G) Pulse Wiper Control Module, Renew	
1983-87 (.2)	.3
(G) Windshield Washer Pump, Renew	
1983-87 (.2)	.3
Recond pump add (.3)	.3
w/Cruise control add (.1)	.1
w/Pulse wipe add (.1)	.1
(G) Speedometer Head, R&R or Renew	
1983-87	
Celebrity (1.1)	2.0
Century (.6)	1.0
Ciera (.7)	1.2
6000 (.5)	.9
w/Console add (.3)	.3
Reset odometer add	.2
(G) Speedometer Cable and Casing, Renew	
1983-85-upper (.7)	1.1
lower (.3)	.5
both (.9)	1.4
one piece (1.2)	1.7
1986-87-upper (1.2)	1.8
lower (.4)	.6
both (1.3)	2.0
one piece (.9)	1.5
w/Console add (.3)	.3
(G) Speedometer Cable (Inner), Renew or Lubricate	
1983-85-upper (.6)	1.0
lower (.2)	.4
both (.7)	1.3
one piece (1.1)	1.6
1986-87-upper (1.1)	1.7
lower (.3)	.5
both (1.1)	1.9
one piece (.5)	.8
w/Console add (.3)	.3
(G) Tachometer, R&R or Renew	
1983-87	
Celebrity (.8)	1.5
Century (.5)	.9
Ciera (.9)	1.7
6000 (.5)	.9
w/Console add (.3)	.3
(G) Speedometer Driven Gear Adapter, Renew	
1983-87 (.2)	.4
(G) Radio, R&R	
Celebrity	
1985-87 (.9)	1.5
All other models	
1983-87 (.4)	.6
w/Console add (.3)	.3

PARTS 31 WINDSHIELD WIPER & SPEEDOMETER 31 PARTS

	Part No.	Price
Windshield Wiper Motor		
1983-exc. pulse wipers	◆4960974	84.00
pulse wipers	◆4961608	80.00

Note: On 1984-86 models, park switch must be transferred from old pulse wiper motor or purchased new.

	Part No.	Price
1984-87	◆22039687	110.75
Windshield Wiper Transmission		
1983-right	◆22030631	21.75
left	◆22030633	21.50
1984-87-right	◆22039676	22.75
left	◆22039677	22.75
Windshield Wiper Switch		
1983-exc. pulse wiper	◆7835342	22.50
pulse wipers	◆7835340	56.25
1984-87-exc. pulse wiper	◆7842714	44.75
pulse wipers	◆7843683	56.25
Windshield Washer Pump		
1983-exc. pulse wiper	◆22009212	25.00
pulse wipers	◆22021345	38.50
1984-87	◆22039686	16.25

Speedometer Head & Cable Assy.
Order by year and model.

LABOR 32 LIGHT SWITCHES & WIRING 32 LABOR

(Factory Time)	Chilton Time
(G) Headlamp Switch, Renew	
1983-87 (.3)	.6
(G) Headlamp Dimmer Switch, Renew	
1983-87 (.5)	.7
(G) Stop Light Switch, Renew	
1983-87 (.3)	.4
(G) Turn Signal or Hazard Warning Switch, Renew	
1983-85 (.8)	1.1
1986-87	
std colm (.7)	1.1
tilt colm (.9)	1.3
(M) Turn Signal or Hazard Warning Flasher, Renew	
1983-87	
hazard (.4)	.5
turn signal (.3)	.4
(G) Back-Up Lamp Switch, Renew	
1983-87 (.3)	.5
(G) Back-Up Lamp and Park/Neutral Switch, Renew	
1983-87 (.3)	.4
(G) Parking Brake Lamp Switch, Renew	
1983-87 (.3)	.4
(G) Neutral Start Switch, Renew	
1983-87	
console mount (.4)	.5
clutch mount (.3)	.4
column mount (.4)	.5
(G) Horn Relay, Renew	
1983-87 (.4)	.4
(G) Horn, Renew	
1983-87 (.3)	.4

PARTS 32 LIGHT SWITCHES & WIRING 32 PARTS

	Part No.	Price
Headlamp Switch		
(Celebrity)		
1983-87	◆1995217	16.00
(Century)		
(exc. twilight sentinel)		
1983	◆1995260	15.25
1984-87	◆1995285	16.25
(w/twilight sentinel)		
1983	◆16501565	25.25
1984-87	◆16502591	25.25
(Ciera)		
1983-87	◆1972717	17.00
(6000)		
1983-87-exc. STE	◆1995226	16.00
STE model	◆1995264	22.75
Stoplight Switch		
(wo/cruise control)		
1983-84-w/M.T.	◆1362835	3.00
w/A.T.	◆25504628	3.75
1985-87	◆25524846	6.50
(w/cruise control)		
1983-84	◆9794682	7.75
1985-87	◆25524847	6.50
Turn Signal Switch		
1983-84	◆1997983	30.00
1985-87	◆1997988	32.50
Parking Brake Alarm Switch		
1983-87	◆1264464	1.50
Back Up Lamp Switch		
1983-84-exc. console	◆22509632	5.50
1983-84-w/ console	◆1994223	18.00
1984-w/elec. dr. locks	◆22514861	7.00
1984-87-w/man. trans.	◆14009262	2.00

Note: 1985-87 switch for A.T. must be ordered according to type of A.T.

	Part No.	Price
Turn Signal Flasher		
1983-84-3 lamp	◆10029240	4.25
1985-87-3 lamp	◆10041073	N.L.
2 lamp (1983)	◆6450076	4.00

LABOR 33 GLASS 33 LABOR

	(Factory Time)	Chilton Time
(G) Windshield Glass, Renew		
1983-87	(1.3)	1.7
Renew caulk bead add	(.4)	.4
(G) Quarter Window Stationary Glass, Renew		
1983-87		
2 Dr	(1.0)	1.5
4 Dr	(.7)	1.1
Sta Wag	(1.4)	1.8
(G) Front Door Glass, Renew		
1983-87	(.8)	1.2
(G) Rear Door Glass, Renew		
1983-87	(.9)	1.3
(G) Quarter Window Swing Out Glass, Renew		
1983-87	(.3)	.5
Transfer latch and channel add	(.1)	.1
(G) Tail Gate Glass, Renew		
1984-87		
w/Lift glass	(.5)	.8
wo/Lift glass	(1.4)	2.0
(G) Back Window Glass, Renew		
1983-87	(1.0)	1.5
w/Elec grid defogger add	(.4)	.4

LABOR 34 CRUISE CONTROL 34 LABOR

	(Factory Time)	Chilton Time
(G) Regulator Assembly (Transducer), Renew		
1983	(.4)	.7
Adj low spd switch add	(.1)	.1
(G) Brake or Clutch Release Switch, Renew		
1983-85	(.3)	.4
1986-87	(.6)	.8
(G) Cruise Control Servo Assy., Renew		
1983-85	(.3)	.4
1986-87	(.7)	1.0
Renew bracket add	(.1)	.2
(G) Vacuum Hoses, Renew		
1983-87	(.2)	.4
(G) Cruise Control Chain or Cable, Renew		
1983-87	(.2)	.4
(G) Engagement Switch, Renew		
1983-85	(.5)	.9
1986-87	(.7)	1.1
(G) Cruise Control Resume Solenoid, Renew		
1983	(.2)	.3
(G) Cruise Control Module, Renew		
1984-85	(.3)	.5
1986-87	(.5)	.7
(G) Cruise Control Speed Sensor, Renew		
1984	(.6)	.8
(G) Cruise Control Check Valve, Renew		
1984-85	(.3)	.4

PARTS 34 CRUISE CONTROL 34 PARTS

	Part No.	Price
Cruise Control Transducer		
(151, 173, 181 engs.)		
(exc. Century)		
1983	◆25030560	190.25
(Century)		
1983	◆25030878	158.00
V-6 Diesel		
1983	◆25031604	179.25
Vacuum Release Valve		
1983-84	◆25509432	14.00
1985-87	◆25323376	N.L.
Cruise Control Servo		
(151, 231 engines)		
1983	◆25031521	24.00
1984-87	◆25074627	117.00
(173 engine)		
1983	◆25031529	31.75
1984-87-exc. Code W	◆25074624	133.50
1985-87-eng. Code W	◆25074627	117.00
(181 engine)		
1983	◆25030983	19.50
1984-87	◆25074630	116.25
(V-6 Diesel eng.)		
1983	◆25031452	26.75
1984-85	◆25074625	120.00
Cruise Control Lever & Switch		
(wo/pulse wipers)		
1928-83	◆25031426	52.25
1984-87-exc. below	◆25031457	50.00
A6000	◆25031481	50.00
(w/pulse wipers)		
1983	◆25031425	52.25
1984-87-exc. below	◆25031456	50.00
A6000	◆25031480	50.00
Cruise Control Chain (Lever to Servo)		
1983-87	◆25031314	3.25

GROUP INDEX

ALPHABETICAL INDEX

Chevrolet
Nova
Front Wheel Drive Cars

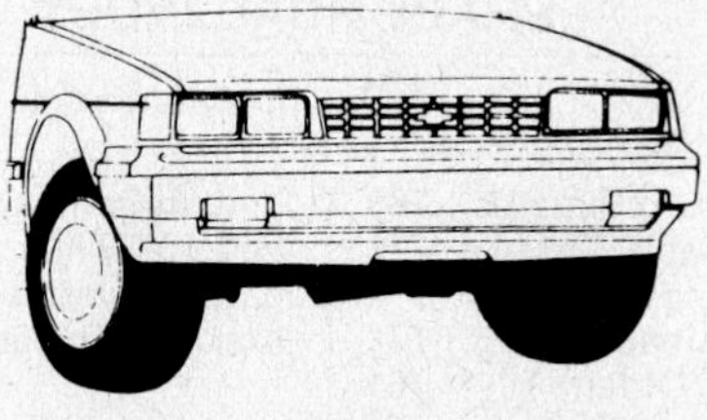

1985–87 Nova

VEHICLE IDENTIFICATION NUMBER (VIN)

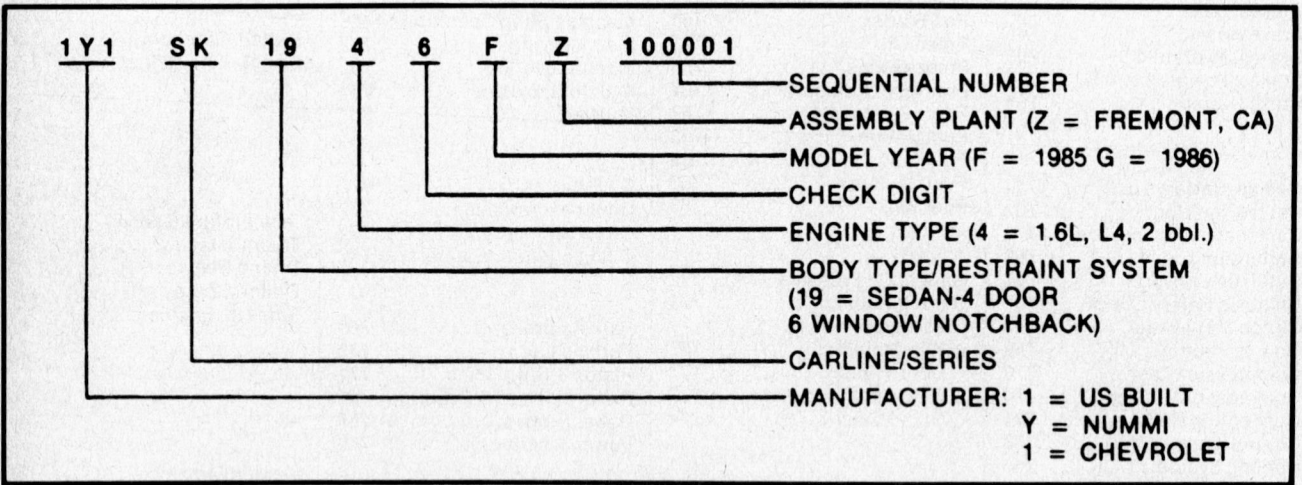

1Y1 SK 19 4 6 F Z 100001

- 100001 — SEQUENTIAL NUMBER
- Z — ASSEMBLY PLANT (Z = FREMONT, CA)
- F — MODEL YEAR (F = 1985 G = 1986)
- 6 — CHECK DIGIT
- 4 — ENGINE TYPE (4 = 1.6L, L4, 2 bbl.)
- 19 — BODY TYPE/RESTRAINT SYSTEM (19 = SEDAN-4 DOOR 6 WINDOW NOTCHBACK)
- SK — CARLINE/SERIES
- 1Y1 — MANUFACTURER: 1 = US BUILT, Y = NUMMI, 1 = CHEVROLET

TUNE-UP SPECIFICATIONS

		Spark Plugs		Distributor		Ignition Timing (deg)			Fuel	Idle Speed (rpm)		Valve Clearance (in)	
Year	Engine Type	Type	Gap (in.)	Point Dwell (deg)	Point Gap (in)	MT	AT	Compression Pressure	Pump Pres.	MT	AT	Intake	Exhaust
'85–'87	4A-LC	BRP5EY11	0.043	Electronic		5B	5B	160	2.5–3.5	650	800	.008	.012

NOTE: If the information given in this chart disagrees with the information on the emission control specification decal located under the hood, use the specifications on the decal.

FIRING ORDER

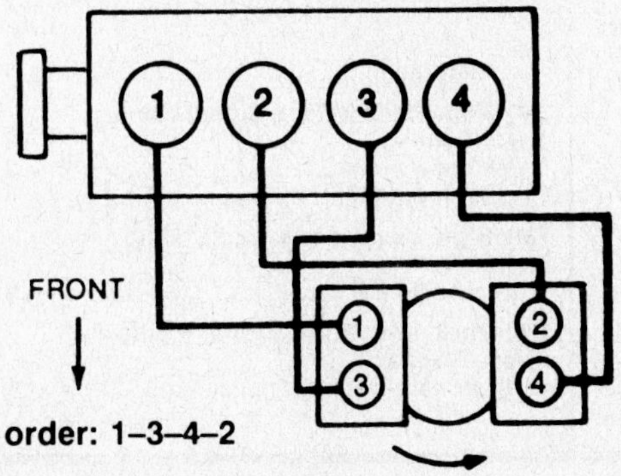

Firing order: 1–3–4–2

WHEEL ALIGNMENT SPECIFICATIONS

	Caster		Camber		Toe-in (mm)	
	Range (deg.)	Pref. (deg.)	Range (deg.)	Pref. (deg.)	Range	Pref.
Front	0°53 ± 45′	0°53 ± 30	-30 ± 45′	-30 ± 30	0 ± 4	0 ± 1
Rear	NA	NA	-31 ± 45′	-31 ± 30	3.8 ± 4	3.8 ± 2

NA Not adjustable

LABOR SERVICE BAY OPERATIONS LABOR

(Factory Time) Chilton Time

COOLING

(M) Winterize Cooling System
Includes: Run engine to check for leaks, tighten all hose connections. Test radiator and pressure cap, drain radiator and engine block. Add anti-freeze and refill system.
All models 5

(M) Thermostat, Renew
1985-87 (.4) 5

(M) Radiator Hoses, Renew
1985-87-upper (.3) 4
lower (.4) 5
both (.4) 6

(M) Drive Belt, Adjust
All models-one (.2) 3
all (.3) 4

(M) Drive Belt, Renew
All models
A.C. (.4) 5
Fan (.3) 4
P.S. (.4) 5

FUEL

(M) Carburetor Air Cleaner, Service
All models 2

(G) Carburetor, Adjust (On Car)
All models
Curb & Fast Idle (.4) 6
Vacuum Brake (.3) 4
Complete (1.3) 1.8

(M) Fuel Filter Element, Renew
All models (.2) 3

(G) Air Cleaner Vacuum Motor, Renew
1985-87 (.2) 3

(G) Air Cleaner Temperature Sensor, Renew
1985-87 (.3) 4

CHILTON'S 10 POINT SAFETY CHECK

CHECK OPERATION & CONDITION OF THE FOLLOWING ITEMS:

1. Legal Registration (serial no.)
2. Tires & Wheels
3. Brake System (R&R all wheels)
4. Light Systems & Signals
5. Accelerator Linkage, Neutral Safety Switch, Shift Indicator Pointer & Seat Position Locks
6. Glass, Mirrors, Door Locks, Seat Belts & Harness
7. Wipers, Washers & Defrosters
8. Frame, Steering, Shocks, Front & Rear Suspension
9. Fuel & Exhaust Systems
10. Road Test Vehicle

All models 1.0
Exhaust Smog Analysis, add 4

(Factory Time) Chilton Time

BRAKES

(G) Brake Pedal Free Play, Adjust
All models (.2) 3

(G) Brakes, Adjust (Minor)
Includes: R&R wheels and adjust brakes thru access holes in drums. Fill master cylinder.
two wheels 4
Remove knock out plugs add, each 1

(G) Bleed Brakes (Four Wheels)
Includes: Fill master cylinder.
All models (.4) 5

(Factory Time) Chilton Time

(M) Parking Brake, Adjust
All models (.3) 4

LUBRICATION SERVICE

(M) Lubricate Chassis, Change Oil & Filter
Includes: Inspect and correct all fluid levels.
All models 6
Install grease fittings add 1

(M) Lubricate Chassis
Includes: Inspect and correct all fluid levels.
All models 4
Install grease fittings add 1

(M) Engine Oil & Filter, Change
Includes: Inspect and correct all fluid levels.
All models 4

WHEELS

(M) Wheel, Renew
one 5

(G) Wheels, Rotate (All)
All models 5

(G) Wheels, Balance
one 3
each adtnl 2

ELECTRICAL

(G) Aim Headlamps
two 4
four 6

(M) Headlamp Sealed Beam Bulb, Renew
All models-one (.2) 3

(M) Battery Cables, Renew
1985-87-positive (.5) 5
negative (.3) 3

(M) Battery Terminals, Clean
All models 3

LABOR — SERVICE BAY OPERATIONS — LABOR

(Factory Time)	Chilton Time
(M) Back-Up Lamp Bulb, Renew	
All models-one	.2
all	.3
(M) Park and Turn Signal Lamp Bulb, Renew	
All models-one	.2
all	.3
(M) License Lamp Bulb, Renew	
All models-one or all	.2
(M) Side Marker Lamp Bulb, Renew	
All models-one	.2
each adtnl	.1
(M) Stop, Tail and Turn Signal Lamp Bulb, Renew	
All models-one	.2
each adtnl	.1
(M) High Level Stop Lamp Bulb, Renew	
All models (.2)	.3
(M) Park and Turn Signal Lamp Assy., Renew	
All models-each	.3
(M) Rear Combination Lamp Assy., Renew	
All models-each	.3
(M) Side Marker Lamp Assy., Renew	
All models-each	.2
(M) High Level Stop Lamp Assy., Renew	
All models (.2)	.3

LABOR — 1 TUNE UP 1 — LABOR

(Factory Time)	Chilton Time
(G) Compression Test	
Four–1985-87	.6

(G) Engine Tune Up (Electronic Ignition)

Includes: Test battery and clean connections. Tighten manifold and carburetor mounting bolts. Check engine compression, clean and adjust or renew spark plugs. Test resistance of spark plug cables. Inspect distributor cap and rotor. Check vacuum advance operation. Reset ignition timing. Adjust idle mixture and idle speed. Service air cleaner. Inspect and adjust drive belts. Inspect choke operation and adjust or free up. Check operation of EGR valve.

(Factory Time)	Chilton Time
Four–1985-87	1.5

LABOR — 2 IGNITION SYSTEM 2 — LABOR

(Factory Time)	Chilton Time
(G) Spark Plugs, Clean and Reset or Renew	
1985-87 (.3)	.5
(G) Distributor, Renew	
Includes: Reset ignition timing.	
1985-87 (.5)	.8
(G) Distributor, R&R and Recondition	
Includes: Reset ignition timing.	
1985-87 (1.2)	1.7
(G) Vacuum Advance Unit, Renew	
Includes: Reset ignition timing.	
1985-87 (.5)	.9
(G) Distributor Cap and/or Rotor, Renew	
1985-87 (.2)	.3
(G) Ignition Coil, Renew	
1985-87 (.6)	.9
(G) Ignition Cables, Renew	
1985-87 (.2)	.3
(G) Distributor Module, Renew	
1985-87 (.6)	.9
(G) Distributor Pick-Up Coil and/or Pole Piece, Renew	
1985-87 (.7)	1.0
(G) Ignition Switch, Renew	
1985-87 (.6)	.9

PARTS — 2 ELECTRONIC IGNITION 2 — PARTS

	Part No.	Price
Distributor Assembly		
1985	94840105	423.00
1986-87	94843955	341.00
(1) Cap		
1985	94840106	20.50
1986-87	◆N.L.	
(2) Rotor		
1985-87	94840108	5.50
(3) Igniter		
1985	94840126	173.00
1986-87	94843911	N.L.
(4) Coil		
1985-87	94840127	52.75
(5) Distributor Signal Rotor		
1985-87	94840121	8.25
(6) Module		
1985-87	94840125	46.75
(7) Shaft		
1985	94842881	27.50
1986-87	94843908	31.75
(8) Vacuum Control		
1985	94840124	41.50
1986-87	94843908	31.75
(9) Wire		
1985-87	94840115	14.75
(10) Gear		
1985-87	94840123	17.75
Ignition Switch		
1985-87	94840334	31.00

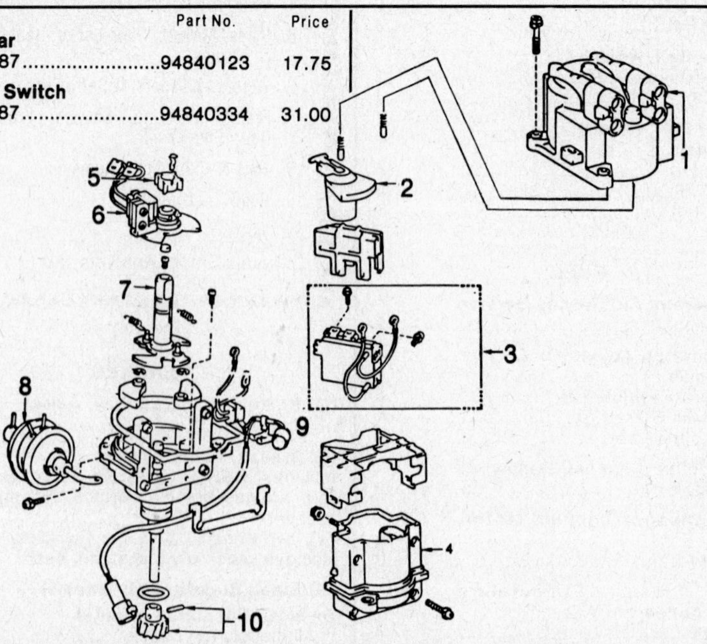

LABOR 3 FUEL SYSTEM 3 LABOR

(Factory Time) Chilton Time

(G) Fuel Pump, Test
Includes: Disconnect line at carburetor, attach pressure gauge.
All models 3

(M) Carburetor Air Cleaner, Service
All models 2

(G) Carburetor, Adjust (On Car)
All models
Curb & Fast Idle (.4) 6
Vacuum Brake (.3) 4
Complete (1.3) 1.8

(M) Fuel Filter Element, Renew
All models (.2) 3

(G) Idle Stop Solenoid, Renew
1985-87-primary (.4) 6
secondary (.4) 6

(G) Carburetor Assy., Renew
Includes: All necessary adjustments.
1985-87 (.9) 1.3

(G) E.F.E. Heater (Insulator), Renew
1985-87 (.8) 1.2

(G) Float or Needle Valve and Seat, Renew
Includes: Set idle speed and mixture.
1985-87 (.7) 1.0

(G) Accelerator Pump, Renew
1985-87 (.7) 1.0

(G) Secondary Throttle Actuator, Renew
1985-87 (.9) 1.2

(G) Fast Idle Actuator, Renew
1985-87-primary (.4) 6
A.C. (.4) 6

(G) Fuel Tank, Renew
Includes: Drain and refill tank, transfer tank gauge unit.
1985-87 (1.3) 1.7

(G) Fuel Gauge (Tank Unit), Renew
1985-87 (.3) 5

(G) Fuel Gauge (Dash Unit), Renew
1985-87 (.7) 1.1

(G) Intake Manifold and/or Gaskets, Renew
1985-87 (1.7) 2.4
Renew manif add (.3) 5

PARTS 3 FUEL SYSTEM 3 PARTS

	Part No.	Price
Carburetor Assy. (Rochester)		
1985-w/M.T.	94840133	375.00
1985-w/A.T.		
Calif.	94840133	375.00
exc. Calif.	94842805	431.00
1986-87	94843888	458.00
Carburetor Gasket Kit		
1985-87	94840613	25.25
Fuel Pump		
1985-87	94840614	45.25
Fuel Tank		
1985-87	94841471	N.L.
Sending Unit (Fuel Tank)		
1985-87	94842997	53.25
Manifold Gasket Set (Intake & Exhaust)		
1985-86	94840104	9.00

LABOR 3A EMISSION CONTROLS 3A LABOR

(Factory Time) Chilton Time

(G) Emission Control Check
Includes. Check and adjust engine idle speed and mixture and ignition timing. Check PCV valve.
All models 6

CRANKCASE EMISSION

(M) Positive Crankcase Ventilation Valve, Renew
All models (.2) 3

EVAPORATIVE EMISSION TYPE

(M) Charcoal Canister, Renew
All models (.3) 4

CONTROLLED COMBUSTION TYPE

(G) Air Cleaner Vacuum Motor, Renew
1985-87 (.2) 3

(G) Air Cleaner Temperature Sensor, Renew
1985-87 (.3) 4

EXHAUST GAS RECIRCULATION SYSTEM

(G) E.G.R. Valve, Renew
1985-87 (.8) 1.1

(G) E.G.R. Modulator, Renew
1985-87 (.3) 4

(G) Thermostatic Vacuum Control Switch, Renew
1985-87 (.3) 4

AIR MANAGEMENT SYSTEM

(G) Pair Valve, Renew
1985-87 (.3) 5

CHILTON'S EMISSION CONTROL TUNE-UP

1. Clean or renew P.C.V. valve, hoses and filter.
2. Check fuel tank cap for sealing ability.
3. Check fuel tank and fuel lines for leakage.
4. Check evaporation canister and filter. Replace if necessary.
5. Check engine compression to determine leakage of unburned gases. (Add time for items of interference).
6. Test and clean or renew spark plugs.
7. Check engine oil dipstick for sealing ability.
8. Test exhaust system with analyzer and check system for leakage.
9. Check exhaust manifold heat valve for operation.
10. Adjust ignition timing and carburetor idle speed and mixture.
11. Check automatic choke mechanism for free operation.
12. Inspect air cleaner and element.
13. On models so equipped, test distributor vacuum control switch and transmission control switch.

Six 1.5

For repairs made, charge accordingly.

(G) Vacuum Delay Valve, Renew
1985-87 (.3) 4

(G) Catalytic Converter Air Pipe, Renew
1985-87-upper (.3) 5
lower (.3) 5

ELECTRONIC EMISSION CONTROLS

(P) Electronic Control Module, Renew
1985-87 (.6) 8

(P) Mixture Control Solenoid, Renew
1985-87 (.3) 4

(P) Barometric Sensor, Renew
1985-87 (.2) 4

(P) Coolant Temperature Sensor, Renew
1985-87 (.3) 5

(P) E.C.M. Relay, Renew
1985-87 (.3) 4

(P) Oxygen Sensor, Renew
1985-87 (.4) 6

(P) Vacuum Switch, Renew
1985-87-one (.2) 3
both (.3) 4

(P) Canister Purge Control Valve, Renew
1985-87 (.3) 5

(P) EGR/EFE Relay, Renew
1985-87 (.2) 3

PARTS 3A EMISSION CONTROLS 3A PARTS

COMPUTER COMMAND CONTROL EMISSION SYSTEM

	Part No.	Price
Controller		
1985-w/Fed	94843661	223.00
1985-w/Calif	94843662	223.00
1986-87		
w/Fed	94843897	223.00
w/Calif	94843898	223.00
Relay (Eng. Compt.)		
1985-87	94840348	36.25

	Part No.	Price
Switch (Exh. Emission Throttle)		
1986-87	94843896	17.00
E.G.R. Valve		
1985-87-w/M.T.	94840209	93.00
w/A.T.	94840210	93.00
E.G.R. Vac. Mod Valve		
1985-87-w/M.T.	94840214	33.00
1985-87-w/A.T.	94840215	33.00

AIR INJECTION REACTOR

	Part No.	Price
Exhaust Check Valve		
1985-87-w/Fed.	94840219	2.75
1985-87-w/Calif.	94840219	2.75
Thermal Vacuum Valve		
1985-87	94840252	56.75
Exhaust Oxygen Sensor		
1985-87	94840346	80.50
Catalytic Converter		
1985-87-w/Calif.	94841559	301.00
1985-87-w/Fed	94841558	329.00

LABOR 4 ALTERNATOR AND REGULATOR 4 LABOR

(Factory Time)	Chilton Time
(G) Generator Circuits, Test	
Includes: Test battery, regulator and generator output.	
All models	.6
(M) Generator Drive Belt, Renew	
1985-87 (.3)	.4
(G) Generator Assembly or Fan Pulley, Renew	
1985-87 (.5)	.7
(G) Generator, R&R and Recondition	
Includes: Test, disassemble, replacement of parts as required, reassemble.	
1985-87 (1.2)	1.7
(G) Generator Front Bearing, Renew	
Includes: R&R generator, separate end frames.	
1985-87 (.7)	.9
Renew rear brg add	.2
(G) Generator Voltage Regulator, Test and Renew	
Includes: R&R generator, disassemble and reassemble.	
1985-87 (.6)	.9

PARTS 4 ALTERNATOR AND REGULATOR 4 PARTS

	Part No.	Price
Alternator Assy.		
1985-87	94840298	389.00
(1) Pulley		
1985-87	94843672	12.50
(2) Drive End Frame		
1985-87	94843673	189.00
(3) Drive End Bearing		
1985-87	94843675	15.75
(4) Rotor		
1985-87	94843678	147.00
(5) Bearing		
1985-87	94840303	12.25

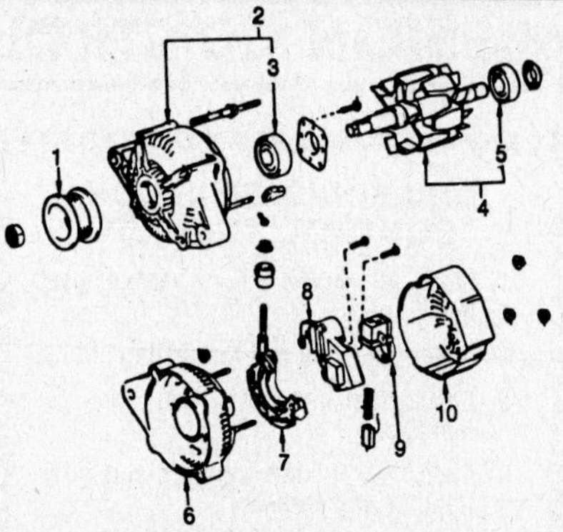

	Part No.	Price
(6) Rectifier End Frame		
1985-87	94842904	23.00
(7) Rectifier		
1985-87	94840306	104.00
(8) Regulator		
1985-87	94840314	57.50
(9) Brush Holder		
1985-87	94843676	18.50
(10) Rear End Cover		
1985-87	94840299	20.50

LABOR 5 STARTING SYSTEM 5 LABOR

(Factory Time)	Chilton Time
(G) Starter Draw Test (On Car)	
All models	.3
(G) Starter Assembly, Renew	
1985-87 (.6)	.8
Add draw test if performed.	
(G) Starter Assy., R&R and Recondition	
Includes: Turn down armature.	
1985-87 (1.5)	2.0
Renew field coils add	.5
Add draw test if performed.	
(G) Starter Drive, Renew	
Includes: R&R starter.	
1985-87 (.8)	1.1
(G) Starter Motor Solenoid, Renew	
Includes: R&R starter.	
1985-87 (.7)	1.0
(G) Neutral Start Switch, Renew	
1985-87 (.3)	.4
(G) Ignition Switch, Renew	
1985-87 (.6)	.9
(M) Battery Cables, Renew	
1985-87-positive (.5)	.5
negative (.3)	.3
(M) Battery Terminals, Clean	
All models	.3

PARTS 5 STARTING SYSTEM 5 PARTS

	Part No.	Price
Starter Assy.		
1985-87	94840315	289.00
(1) Commutator End Frame		
1985-87	94840319	23.00
(2) Brush Holder		
1985-87	94840320	16.75

PARTS 5 STARTING SYSTEM 5 PARTS

	Part No.	Price
(3) Frame & Field		
1985-87	94840318	92.25
(4) Switch		
1985-87	94840322	45.75
(5) Armature		
1985-87	94840323	86.75
(6) Pinion Drive		
1985-87	94840331	11.50
(7) Clutch		
1985-87	94840316	66.25
(8) Drive Housing		
1985-87	94840317	20.00
Battery Cable (Ground)		
1985-87	12022547	17.50

Part No. Price

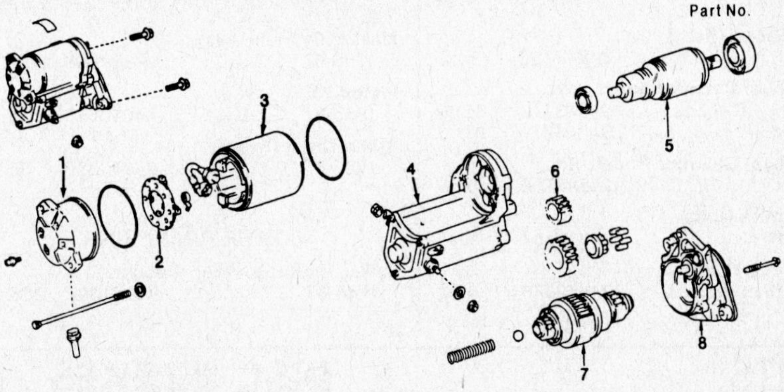

LABOR 6 BRAKE SYSTEM 6 LABOR

(Factory Time) Chilton Time

(G) Brake Pedal Free Play, Adjust
All models (.2) 3

(G) Brakes, Adjust (Minor)
Includes: R&R wheels and adjust brakes thru access holes in drums. Fill master cylinder.
two wheels 4
Remove knock out plugs add, each .. .1

(G) Bleed Brakes (Four Wheels)
Includes: Fill master cylinder.
All models (.4) 5

(G) Free-Up or Renew Brake Self Adjusting Units
one wheel 6
each adtnl 4

(G) Brake Shoes and/or Pads, Renew
Includes: Install new or exchange brake shoes or pads, adjust service and hand brake. Bleed system.
1985-87-front-disc (.5) 9
rear-drum (.9) 1.5
all four wheels 2.3
Resurface disc rotor add-each 6
Resurface brake drum add-each 5

(G) Brake Drums, Renew
1985-87-one (.4) 5
both (.6) 7

(G) Brake Combination Valve, Renew
Includes: Bleed system.
1985-87 (.4) 6

(G) Brake System Failure Warning Switch, Renew
1985-87 (.2) 3

BRAKE HYDRAULIC SYSTEM

(G) Wheel Cylinders, Renew
Includes: Bleed system.
1985-87-one (.6) 9
both (1.0) 1.6

(G) Wheel Cylinders, R&R and Rebuild
Includes: Bleed system.
1985-87-one (.8) 1.2

COMBINATIONS

Add to Brakes, Renew

See Machine Shop Operations

(Factory Time) Chilton Time

(G) RENEW WHEEL CYLINDER
Each (.2) 2

(G) REBUILD WHEEL CYLINDER
Each (.2) 3

(G) REBUILD CALIPER ASSEMBLY
Each (.3) 4

(G) RENEW MASTER CYLINDER
All models 5

(G) REBUILD MASTER CYLINDER
All models (.8) 1.0

(G) RENEW BRAKE HOSE
Each 3

(G) RENEW BRAKE DRUM
Each 2

(G) RENEW DISC BRAKE ROTOR
Each 3

(Factory Time) Chilton Time

both (1.4) 2.2

(G) Brake Hose, Renew (Flex)
Includes: Bleed system.
1985-87-front-each (.4) 6
rear-one (.3) 5
both (.5) 8

(G) Master Cylinder, Renew
Includes: Bleed complete system.
1985-87 (.5) 8

(G) Master Cylinder, R&R and Rebuild
Includes: Bleed complete system.
1985-87 (.8) 1.3

(G) Brake System, Flush and Refill
All models 1.2

(Factory Time) Chilton Time

POWER BRAKES

(G) Power Brake Cylinder, Renew
1985-87 (1.0) 1.4

(G) Power Brake Cylinder, R&R and Recondition
1985-87 (1.4) 1.9

(G) Vacuum Check Valve, Renew
1985-87 (.3) 3

DISC BRAKES

(G) Disc Brake Pads, Renew
Includes: Install new disc brake pads only.
1985-87 (.5) 9

(G) Disc Brake Rotor, Renew
1985-87-one (.5) 7
both (.7) 1.1

(G) Caliper Assembly, Renew
Includes: Bleed complete system.
1985-87-one (.4) 6
both (.6) 1.0

(G) Caliper Assy., R&R and Rebuild
Includes: Bleed complete system.
1985-87-one (.6) 1.0
both (1.0) 1.8

(G) Brake Proportioner Valve, Renew
1985-87 (.5) 7

PARKING BRAKE

(M) Parking Brake, Adjust
All models (.3) 4

(G) Parking Brake Lamp Switch, Renew
1985-87 (.3) 4

(G) Parking Brake Control, Renew
1985-87 (.6) 1.0

(G) Parking Brake Cables, Renew
1985-87-front (.6) 8
rear-one (.6) 8
both (.8) 1.1

PARTS — 6 BRAKE SYSTEM 6 — PARTS

	Part No.	Price
Brake Shoes (Rear)		
1985-87	94843731	15.50
Rear Wheel Cylinder Assy.		
1985-87 (R.H.)	94843772	25.00
1985-87 (L.H.)	94843771	25.00
Rear Wheel Cylinder Repair Kit		
1985-87	94843768	6.50
Front Brake Hose		
1985-87	94840557	16.00
Rear Brake Hose		
1985-87	94842885	14.00

	Part No.	Price
Master Cylinder Assy.		
1985-87	94841098	62.50
Piston Kit		
1985-87	94840666	28.50
Brake Drum (Rear)		
1985-87	94840385	35.75

POWER BRAKE UNIT

	Part No.	Price
Power Brake Booster (Vacuum)		
1985-87	94841097	206.00
Power Brake Booster Repair Kit		
1985-87	94840662	66.00

PARKING BRAKE

	Part No.	Price
Front Cable		
1985-87	94841063	4.00
Rear Cable (R.H.)		
1985-87	94841065	20.75
Rear Cable (L.H.)		
1985-87	94841066	20.75

PARTS — 6 DISC BRAKES 6 — PARTS

	Part No.	Price
(1) Caliper Assy.		
1985-87 (R.H.)	94841068	126.00
(L.H.)	94841070	126.00
(2) Caliper Piston		
1985-87	94841071	25.00
(3) Caliper Mounting Bracket		
1985-87	94841069	85.00
(4) Brake Pads		
1985-87	94840677	19.00
(5) Caliper Repair Kit		
1985-87	94843767	17.25

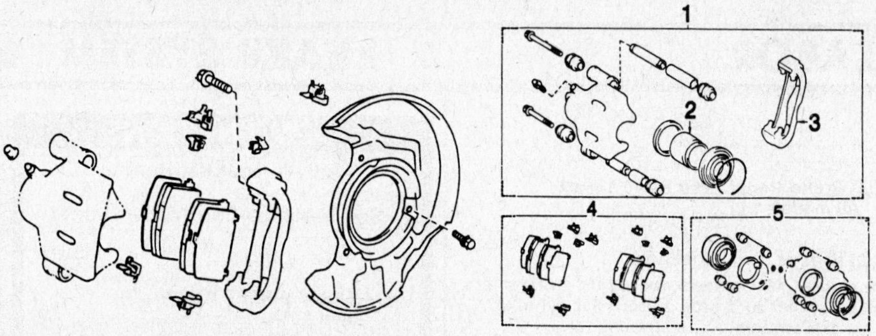

LABOR — 7 COOLING SYSTEM 7 — LABOR

(Factory Time)	Chilton Time
(M) Winterize Cooling System	
Includes: Run engine to check for leaks, tighten all hose connections. Test radiator and pressure cap, drain radiator and engine block. Add anti-freeze and refill system.	
All models	.5
(M) Thermostat, Renew	
1985-87 (.4)	.5
(M) Radiator Assembly, R&R or Renew	
Includes: Drain and refill cooling system.	
1985-87 (.6)	1.0
w/A.C. add (.1)	.1
w/A.T. add (.1)	.1

ADD THESE OPERATIONS TO RADIATOR R&R

(G) Boil & Repair	1.5
(G) Rod Clean	1.9
(G) Repair Core	1.3
(G) Renew Tank	1.6
(G) Renew Trans. Oil Cooler	1.9
(G) Recore Radiator	1.7
(M) Radiator Hoses, Renew	
1985-87-upper (.3)	.4
lower (.4)	.5
both (.4)	.6
(G) Thermostat By-Pass Hose or Pipe, Renew	
1985-87 (2.1)	3.0
w/P.S. add (.3)	.3
(G) Water Pump, Renew	
1985-87 (1.9)	2.8
w/P.S. add (.3)	.3

COOLING SYSTEM TUNE-UP

An Annual Cooling System Tune-Up Suggestion List should include (with some exceptions):

1. A visual check of the cooling system for indications of leaks or excessive oil content.
2. Pressure check the cooling system for internal and external leaks with filler cap and neck adapter and tester.
3. Check crankcase and automatic transmission oil for water content.
4. Test coolant thermostat with radiator thermometer.
5. Check temperature gauge for accuracy.
6. Drain system and flush till clean.
7. Clean foreign matter from radiator fins.
8. Test radiator pressure cap with cap tester.
9. Check fan blades and pulleys for alignment and damage.
10. Internal and external inspection of all hoses for cracks and deterioration.
11. Check core plugs (where possible) for seepage.
12. Refill system with correct coolant and check for air locks.
13. Check condition and tension of drive belts with tension gauge.

All models 1.5

(Factory Time)	Chilton Time
(G) Electric Cooling Fan Blade and/or Motor, Renew	
1985-87 (.3)	.4
(M) Drive Belt, Adjust	
All models-one (.2)	.3
all (.3)	.4
(M) Drive Belt, Renew	
All models	
A.C. (.4)	.5
Fan (.3)	.4
P.S. (.4)	.5
(G) Coolant Fan Switch, Renew	
1985-87 (.3)	.4
(G) Engine Coolant Temperature Switch, Renew	
1985-87 (.4)	.5
(G) Engine Coolant Fan Relay, Renew	
1985-87 (.2)	.3
(G) Temperature Gauge (Dash Unit), Renew	
1985-87 (.6)	1.0
(G) Water Jacket Expansion Plugs, Renew (Side of Block)	
Each	.5
Add time to gain access.	
(G) Heater Blower Motor Switch, Renew	
1985-87 (1.1)	1.5
(G) Master Electrical Switch, Renew (A.C. On-Off)	
1985-87 (.8)	1.2

LABOR 7 COOLING SYSTEM 7 LABOR

	(Factory Time)	Chilton Time
(G) Temperature Control Assembly, Renew		
1985-87	(1.1)	1.5
(G) Heater Blower Motor Resistor, Renew		
1985-87	(.3)	.4
(G) Heater Blower Motor Relay, Renew		
1985-87	(.3)	.4
(G) Heater Blower Motor, Renew		
1985-87	(.6)	.9
(G) Heater Core, R&R or Renew		
1985-87		
wo/A.C.	(1.8)	3.5
w/A.C.	(2.4)	4.7
Add time to evacuate and charge A.C. system if required.		
ADD THESE OPERATIONS TO HEATER CORE R&R		
(G) Boil & Repair		1.2
(G) Repair Core		.9
(G) Recore		1.2
(G) Heater Hoses, Renew		
1985-87		
wo/A.C.-one	(.4)	.6
both	(.8)	1.0
w/A.C.-all	(.8)	1.0

PARTS 7 COOLING SYSTEM 7 PARTS

	Part No.	Price
Radiator Assy.		
1985-87-w/A.T.	3091229	196.00
w/M.T.	3091233	180.00
Upper Radiator Hose		
1985-87	94840244	12.50
Lower Radiator Hose		
1985-87	94840245	7.00
Thermostat		
1985-87	94840251	7.75
Water Pump Assy.		
1985 (Less Cover)	94840082	44.25
1985-87 (Compl.)	94840612	55.50
Engine Cooling Fan		
1985-87	22050877	27.25
Cooling Fan Motor		
1985-87	22061205	N.L.
Engine Temperature Sender		
1985-87	94841819	13.50
Temperature Gauge (Dash)		
1985-87	94841816	21.00
Heater Core		
1985-87	94841683	173.00
Blower Motor		
1985-87	94841680	125.00
Heater Control Switch		
1985-87	94841676	22.50

LABOR 8 EXHAUST SYSTEM 8 LABOR

	(Factory Time)	Chilton Time
(G) Muffler, Renew		
1985-87	(.3)	.5
(G) Catalytic Converter, Renew		
1985-87	(.5)	.8
(G) Front Exhaust Pipe, Renew (To Converter)		
1985-87	(.5)	.7
(G) Exhaust Pipe Seal, Renew		
1985-87-one	(.4)	.6
(G) Intermediate Exhaust Pipe, Renew		
1985-87	(.5)	.8
(G) Exhaust Manifold, Renew		
1985-87	(1.9)	2.6
COMBINATIONS		
(G) Exhaust System, Renew (Complete)		
All models		1.2
(G) Muffler and Tail Pipe, Renew		
All models		.8

PARTS 8 EXHAUST SYSTEM 8 PARTS

	Part No.	Price
Exhaust Manifold		
1985-87	94840098	114.00
Exhaust Pipe (Front)		
1985-87-Calif.	94841554	47.25
Fed.	94841552	47.25
Exhaust Pipe (Intermediate)		
1985-87-Calif.	94841562	50.50
Fed.	94841560	50.50
Tail Pipe & Muffler		
1985	94841563	78.75
1986-87	94843748	15.75
Catalytic Converter		
1985-87-Calif.	94841559	301.00
Fed.	94841558	329.00

LABOR 9 FRONT SUSPENSION 9 LABOR

Note: On all front suspension operations alignment charges must be added if performed. Time given does not include alignment.

	(Factory Time)	Chilton Time
(G) Wheel, Renew		
one		.5
(G) Wheels, Rotate (All)		
All models		.5
(G) Wheels, Balance		
one		.3
each adtnl		.2
(G) Check Alignment Of Front End		
All models		.5
Note: Deduct if alignment is performed.		
(G) Toe-In, Adjust		
All models	(.4)	.6
(G) Front Wheel Bearings, Renew		
Includes: Renew dust seals. Add alignment charges.		
1985-87-one side	(1.1)	1.5
both sides	(1.9)	2.6
(G) Steering Knuckle Assy., Renew		
Includes: Renew dust seals. Add alignment charges.		
1985-87-one side	(1.1)	1.5
both sides	(1.9)	2.6
(G) Steering Knuckle Inner Dust Seals, Renew		
Includes: Renew bearing and hub assy., if necessary. Add alignment charges.		
1985-87-one side	(.8)	1.1
both sides	(1.4)	1.9
(G) Lower Ball Joints and/or Control Arm Assy., Renew		
Add alignment charges.		
1985-87-one side	(.5)	.8
both	(.7)	1.3
(G) Front Coil Springs, Renew		
Add alignment charges.		
1985-87-one	(.9)	1.2

LABOR 9 FRONT SUSPENSION 9 LABOR

(Factory Time)	Chilton Time
both (1.5)	2.0
(G) Lower Control Arm Bushings and/or Shaft, Renew	
Add alignment charges.	
1985-87-one side (.5)	.9
both sides (.7)	1.4
(G) Front Shock Absorber Strut, Renew	
Add alignment charges.	
1985-87-one (.9)	1.2
both (1.5)	2.1
(G) Front Spring Seats and/or Insulators, Renew (Upper or Lower)	
Add alignment charges.	
1985-87-one side (.8)	1.1
both sides (1.5)	2.0
(G) Front Strut Bearing Mounts, Renew	
Includes: Renew bearing assy. Add alignment charges.	
1985-87-one side (.8)	1.1
both sides (1.5)	2.0

FRONT DRIVE AXLE

(Factory Time)	Chilton Time
(G) Drive Axle Assy., R&R or Renew	
1985-87-one (.9)	1.2
both (1.2)	1.7
Renew C.V. Joint Seal (Boot), add-each side (.5)	.5
Renew C.V. (Tri-Pot) Joint, add-each (.3)	.3
(G) Axle Shaft Seals, Renew	
1985-87-one (.6)	.8
both (.7)	1.0

PARTS 9 FRONT SUSPENSION 9 PARTS

	Part No.	Price
(1) Steering Knuckle		
1985-87 (R.H.)	94840412	73.00
(L.H.)	94840411	73.00
(2) Front Strut		
1985-87 (R.H.)	22017867	57.00
(L.H.)	22017866	57.00
(3) Coil Spring		
1985-87-w/A.T. (w/A.C.)	94843597	41.25
w/A.T. (wo/A.C.)	94843596	40.50
w/M.T. (w/A.C.)	94843596	40.50
w/M.T. (wo/A.C.)	94843595	39.75
(4) Upper Insulator		
1985-87	94840565	2.50

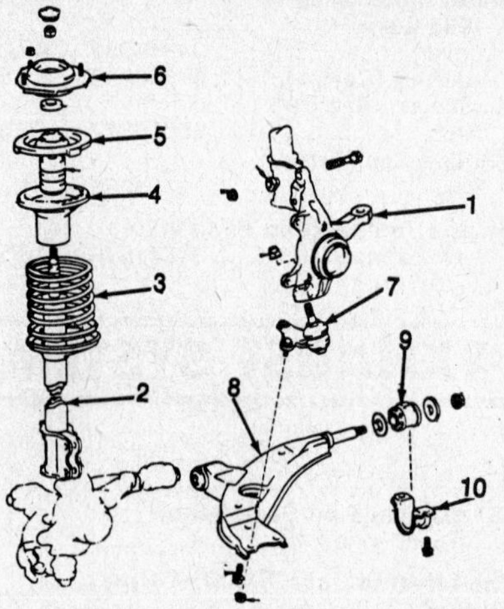

	Part No.	Price
(5) Spring Seat		
1985-87	94841125	4.75
(6) Strut Mount		
1985-87	94843668	46.50
(7) Lower Ball Joint		
1985-87	94843613	32.75
(8) Lower Control Arm		
1985-87 (R.H.)	94840564	75.50
(L.H.)	94840563	75.50
(9) Lower Arm Bushing		
1985-87	94840405	12.50
(10) Lower Arm Bracket		
1985-87	94840406	11.50

PARTS 9 FRONT DRIVE AXLE 9 PARTS

	Part No.	Price
(1) Axle Kit		
1985-87		
(R.H.) Hollow	7846510	301.00
(L.H.) Solid	7846509	279.00
(2) Constant Velocity Joint Kit		
1985-87	7849841	175.00
(3) Boot Kit (Outboard)		
1985-87	7849842	31.50
(4) Shaft		
1985-87		
(R.H.) Hollow	7846776	135.00
(L.H.) Solid	7846771	46.75

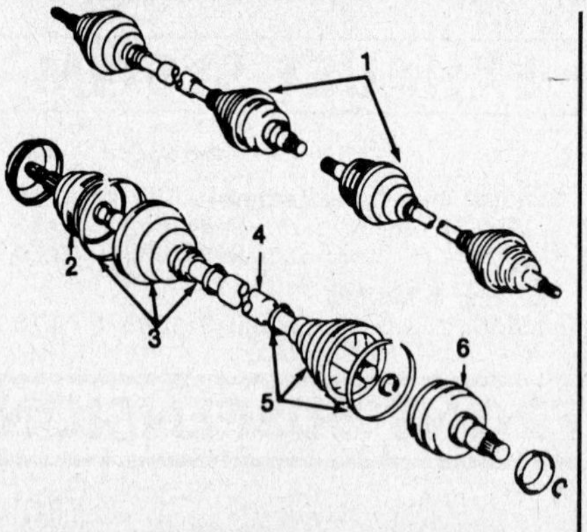

	Part No.	Price
(5) Boot Kit (Inboard)		
1985-87	7849838	27.75
(6) Spider Kit (Inboard)		
1985-87 (L.H.)	7849839	175.00
(R.H.)	7849840	175.00
Hub Disc		
1985-87	94840417	29.00
Oil Seal Kit		
1985-87	94840654	8.00
Hub Bearing		
1985-87	94840410	64.00
Front Axle Hub		
1985-87	94840409	41.75

LABOR 11 STEERING GEAR 11 LABOR

STANDARD STEERING

(Factory Time)	Chilton Time
(G) Tie Rod End and/or Adjusting Sleeve, Renew	
Includes: Reset toe-in.	
1985-87-one side (.7)	1.0
both sides (.9)	1.2
(G) Steering Wheel, Renew	
1985-87 (.2)	.3
(G) Horn Contact and/or Cancelling Cam, Renew	
1985-87 (.3)	.4
(G) Steering Column, R&R or Renew	
1985-87 (.7)	1.0
Recond colm add (.7)	1.0
(G) Steering Intermediate Shaft, Renew	
1985-87 (.2)	.4
(G) Manual Steering Gear, Renew	
Includes: Reset toe-in.	
1985-87 (1.4)	2.0

LABOR 11 STEERING GEAR 11 LABOR

(Factory Time)	Chilton Time
(G) Manual Steering Gear, R&R	
Does not include alignment charges.	
1985-87 (1.2)	1.8
Renew grommets (both) add (1.0)	1.0
Renew rack brg add (.3)	.3
Renew pinion seal add (.3)	.3
Renew pinion shaft assy add (.4)	.4
Renew roller brg add (.4)	.4
Recond complete add (.7)	1.0
(G) Steering Gear Boots, Renew	
1985-87-one side (.5)	.7
both sides (.8)	1.1
POWER STEERING	
(M) Pump Drive Belt, Renew	
1985-87 (.4)	.5
(G) Power Steering Gear Assy., Renew	
1985-87 (1.5)	2.1
(G) Power Steering Short Rack Assy., Renew	
Includes. Transfer parts as required. Reset toe-in.	
1985-87 (1.8)	2.7
(G) Power Steering Gear, R&R	
Add alignment charges.	
1985-87 (1.5)	2.1
Renew grommets add (1.0)	1.0
Renew inner rack seals add (.7)	.7
Renew pinion brg and seal add (.4)	.4
Renew valve and pinion assy add (.4)	.4
Recond rack piston assy add (.5)	.5
Renew housing add (.5)	.5
Bench leak test add (.2)	.2
Recond complete add (.8)	1.2
(G) Power Steering Pump, Renew	
1985-87 (.5)	.8
(G) Pump Shaft Oil Seal, Renew	
1985-87 (.6)	.9
(M) Power Steering Hoses, Renew	
1985-87-pressure (.4)	.5
return (.4)	.5

PARTS 11 STEERING GEAR - (STANDARD) 11 PARTS

	Part No.	Price
Steering Gear		
1985-87	94842977	285.00
(1) Rack Housing		
1985-87	94840498	75.50
(2) Rack Housing Bushing		
1985-87	94840499	12.25
(3) Housing Boot		
1985-87 (L.H.)	94840510	9.50
(R.H.)	94840511	14.25
(4) Pinion		
1985-87	94840501	21.75

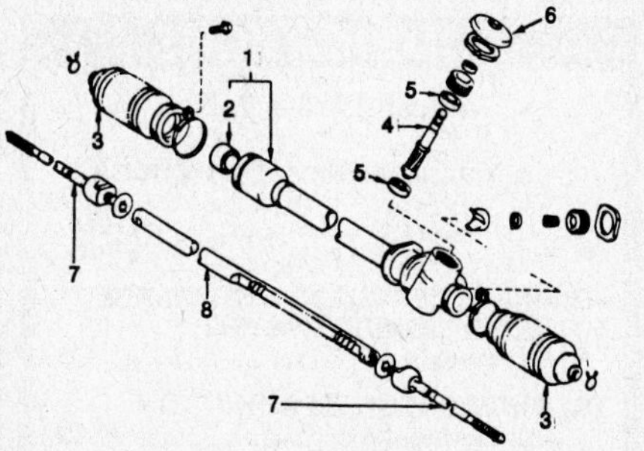

	Part No.	Price
(5) Thrust Bearing		
1985-87-Lower	94840506	15.25
Upper	94840507	18.00
(6) Dust Cover		
1985-87	94840509	2.75
(7) Rack End		
1985-87	94843588	54.75
(8) Steering Rack		
1985-87	94840500	44.75

PARTS 11 POWER STEERING GEAR 11 PARTS

	Part No.	Price
Steering Gear		
1985-87	94842976	552.00
Gasket Kit		
1985-87	94840656	55.75
Control Valve Gasket Kit		
1985-87	94840657	15.50
(11) Housing		
1985-87	94840479	153.00
(2) Control Valve		
1985-87	94840478	170.00
(3) Guide		
1985-87	94840492	3.50
(4) Spring Cap		
1985-87	94840493	4.50
(5) Boot		
1985-87	94840490	7.50
(6) Oil Pressure Pipe		
1985-87 (R. Turn)	94840487	7.25
(L. Turn)	94840488	7.25
(7) Stopper		
1985-87	94840475	3.75
(8) Lower Bearing		
1985-87	94840472	18.25
(9) Cap		
1985-87	94840469	4.75
(10) Steering Rack		
1985-87	94840486	98.00
(11) Rack End		
1985-87	94843589	54.75

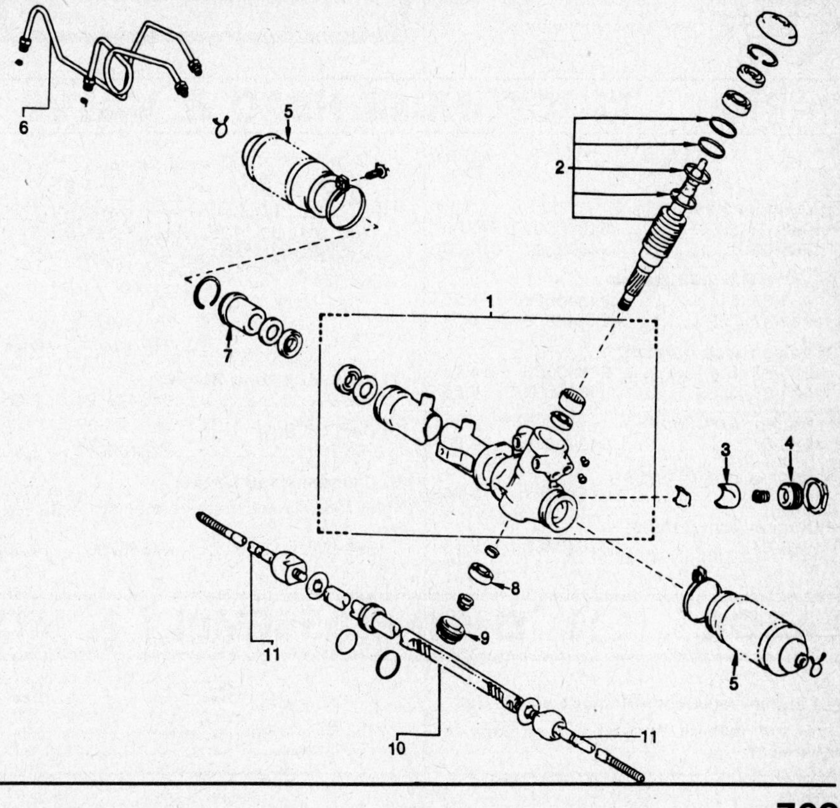

PARTS 11 POWER STEERING PUMP 11 PARTS

	Part No.	Price
Pump		
1985	94840419	275.00
1986-87	◆N.L.	
Gasket Kit		
1985-87	94840658	28.50
(1) Oil Reservoir		
1985-87	94840461	62.50
(2) Shaft		
1985-87	94840437	50.00
(3) Pump Control Valve		
Note: Valve must be ordered by stamped code on valve.		
(4) Front Plate		
1985-87	94840454	46.75
(5) Rotor		
Note: Order by stamped mark on rotor.		

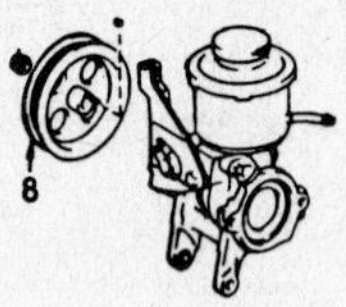

	Part No.	Price
(6) Plate		
1985-87	94840455	46.75
(7) Housing		
1985	94840453	44.00
1986-87	◆N.L.	
(8) Pulley		
1985-87	94840418	57.50

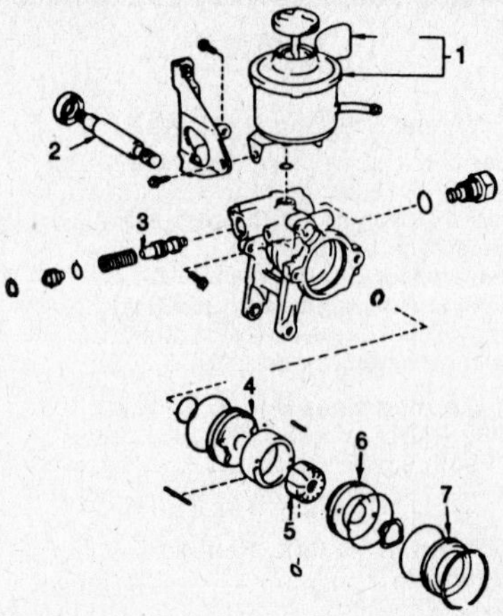

LABOR 12 CYLINDER HEAD & VALVE SYSTEM 12 LABOR

	(Factory Time)	Chilton Time
(G) Compression Test		
1985-87		.6
(G) Cylinder Head Gasket, Renew		
Includes: Clean carbon and make all necessary adjustments.		
1985-87	(3.5)	4.8
w/P.S. add	(.2)	.2
(G) Cylinder Head, Renew		
Includes: Transfer all components, clean carbon. Make all necessary adjustments.		
w/P.S. add	(.2)	.2
(G) Clean Carbon and Grind Valves		
Includes: R&R cylinder head, grind valves and seats. Minor tune up.		
1985-87	(5.9)	8.5
w/P.S. add	(.2)	.2

COMBINATIONS

Add to Valve Job

See Machine Shop Operations

	(Factory Time)	Chilton Time
(G) DRAIN, EVACUATE & RECHARGE AIR CONDITIONING SYSTEM		
All models	(.5)	1.0
(G) DISTRIBUTOR, RECONDITION		
All models	(.5)	.8
(G) CARBURETOR, RECONDITION		
All models	(.9)	1.2
(G) VALVE GUIDES, REAM OVERSIZE		
Each	(.2)	.2

	(Factory Time)	Chilton Time
(G) Rocker Arm Cover or Gasket, Renew		
1985-87	(.4)	.6
(G) Valve Rocker Arms, Renew		
1985-87-one cyl	(.7)	1.0
all cyls	(.9)	1.3
(G) Valve Rocker Shaft, Renew		
1985-87-one or both	(.8)	1.2
(G) Valve Springs and/or Valve Stem Oil Seals, Renew (Head on Car)		
1985-87-one cyl	(.9)	1.3
all cyls	(1.6)	2.2
(G) Valve Adjusters, Renew		
1985-87-one cyl	(.6)	.9
all cyls	(.9)	1.3

PARTS 12 CYLINDER HEAD & VALVE SYSTEM 12 PARTS

	(Factory Time)	Chilton Time
(1) Cylinder Head		
1985	94840001	315.00
1986-87	94843884	315.00
(2) Valve Guide (Exhaust)		
1985-87 (Std.)	94840605	4.25
1985-87 (O.S.)	94840606	4.25
(3) Valve Guide (Intake)		
1985-87 (Std.)	94840603	4.25
1985-87 (O.S.)	94840604	4.25
(4) Rocker Arm Shaft		
1985-87	94840058	25.00
(5) Rocker Arm (Exhaust)		
1985-87	94840057	8.75
(6) Rocker Arm (Intake)		
1985-87	94840056	8.75

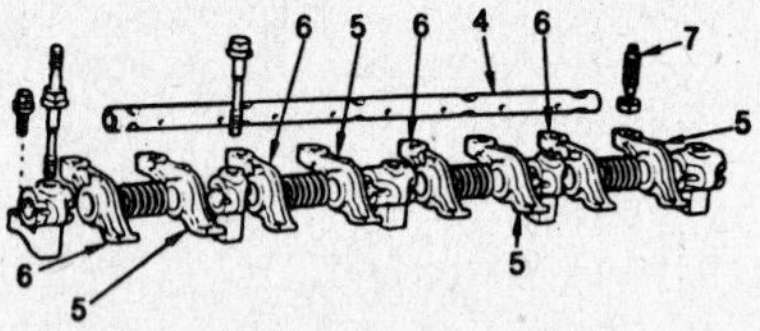

	Part No.	Price
(7) Valve Adjusting Screw		
1985-87	94842819	2.25
(8) Cam Oil Seal		
1985-87	94840006	3.50
(9) Cylinder Head Gasket		
Note: 1985 gasket must be matched with old one.		
1986-87	94843783	14.50

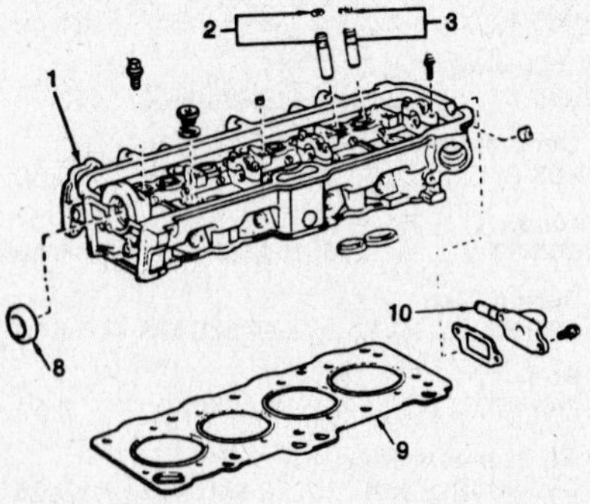

	Part No.	Price
(10) Rear Plate		
1985-87	94840007	8.75

LABOR 13 ENGINE ASSEMBLY & MOUNTS 13 LABOR

	(Factory Time)	Chilton Time
(G) Engine Assembly, Remove and Install		
Does not include transfer of any parts or equipment.		
1985-87		5.1
w/A.C. add		.3
w/P.S. add		.3
w/A.T. add		.4

LABOR 13 ENGINE ASSEMBLY & MOUNTS 13 LABOR

	(Factory Time)	Chilton Time
(G) Engine Assembly, Renew		
Includes: R&R engine assembly, transfer all component parts not supplied with replacement engine. Minor tune up.		
1985-87	(5.9)	8.2
w/A.C. add	(.3)	.3
w/P.S. add	(.3)	.3
w/A.T. add	(.4)	.4
(P) Cylinder Block, Renew (Partial)		
Includes: R&R engine assembly, transfer all component parts not supplied with replacement engine. Minor tune up.		
1985-87	(6.3)	9.0
w/A.C.	(.3)	.3
w/P.S. add	(.3)	.3
w/A.T. add	(.4)	.4
Recond valves add	(2.2)	3.7
(P) Engine Assembly, R&R and Recondition		
Includes: Rebore block, install new pistons, rings, rod and main bearings. Clean carbon, grind valves. Tune engine.		
1985-87	(16.1)	22.5
w/A.C. add	(.3)	.3
w/P.S. add	(.3)	.3
w/A.T. add	(.4)	.4
(P) Engine Assembly, Recondition (In Car)		
Includes: Expand or renew pistons, install new rings, pins, rod and main bearings. Clean carbon, grind valves. Tune engine.		
1985-87	(13.7)	19.1
w/P.S. add	(.2)	.2
(G) Front Engine Mount, Renew		
1985-87	(.6)	.9

PARTS 13 ENGINE ASSEMBLY & MOUNTS 13 PARTS

	Part No.	Price
Engine Assy. (Partial)		
1985-87	94840597	875.00
Engine Mount		
1985-87		
(L.H.) M.T.	94840241	29.50
(L.H.) A.T.	94840242	29.50
(R.H.)	94840238	29.50
Front Engine Mount		
1985-89-M.T.	94840236	19.50
A.T.	94840237	19.50
Rear Engine Mount		
1985-87-M.T.	94840239	22.75
A.T.	94840240	22.75

LABOR 14 PISTONS, RINGS & BEARINGS 14 LABOR

	(Factory Time)	Chilton Time
(P) Rings, Renew (See Engine Combinations)		
Includes: Remove cylinder top ridge, deglaze cylinder walls. Clean ring grooves. Minor tune up.		
1985-87-one cyl	(4.7)	6.5
all cyls	(6.1)	8.5
w/P.S. add	(.2)	.2
(P) Pistons or Connecting Rods, Renew		
Includes: Remove cylinder top ridge, deglaze cylinder walls. Minor tune up.		
1985-87-one cyl	(5.4)	7.2
all cyls	(7.4)	11.3
w/P.S. add	(.2)	.2
(P) Connecting Rod Bearings, Renew		
1985-87	(2.1)	3.0

COMBINATIONS

Add to Engine Work

See Machine Shop Operations

	(Factory Time)	Chilton Time
(G) DRAIN, EVACUATE & RECHARGE AIR CONDITIONING SYSTEM		
All models	(.5)	1.0
(G) DISTRIBUTOR, RECONDITION		
All models	(.5)	.8
(G) CARBURETOR, RECONDITION		
All models		1.2
(G) VALVE GUIDES, REAM OVERSIZE		
Each	(.2)	.2
(G) CYLINDER HEAD, R&R (ENGINE REMOVED)		
All models	(.6)	1.0
(G) CONNECTING ROD, RENEW (ENGINE DISASSEMBLED)		
All models-each	(.3)	.4
(G) DEGLAZE CYLINDER WALLS		
Each	(.1)	.1
(G) REMOVE CYLINDER TOP RIDGE		
Each	(.1)	.1
(G) PLASTIGAUGE BEARINGS		
Each	(.1)	.1
(M) OIL FILTER ELEMENT, RENEW		
All models	(.2)	.3

PARTS 14 PISTONS, RINGS & BEARINGS 14 PARTS

	Part No.	Price
(1) Piston w/Pin		
1985-87	94840037	23.25
(2) Piston Ring Set		
1985-87 (Std.)	94840036	48.50
(3) Connecting Rod		
1985-87	94840610	41.75
(4) Rod Bearing		
1985-87	94840041	6.25

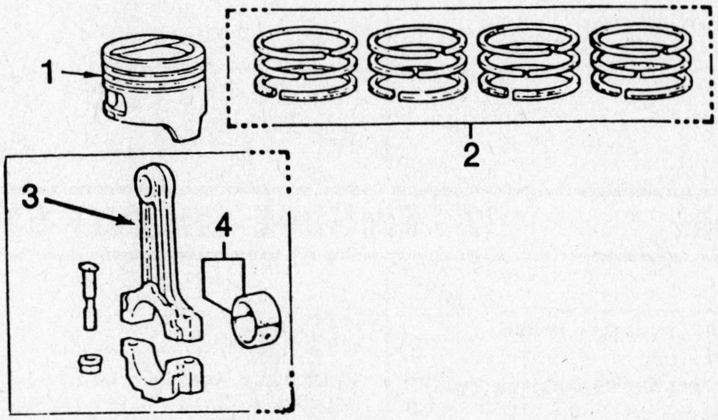

LABOR 15 CRANKSHAFT & DAMPER 15 LABOR

(Factory Time)	Chilton Time
(P) Crankshaft and Main Bearings, Renew	
Includes: R&R engine, check all bearing clearances.	
1985-87 (6.8)	9.5
w/A.C. add (.3)	.3
w/P.S. add (.3)	.3
w/A.T. add (.4)	.4
(P) Main Bearings, Renew	
Includes: Check all bearing clearances.	
1985-87 (2.6)	3.6
w/A.C. add (.2)	.2
(P) Main and Rod Bearings, Renew	
Includes: Check all bearing clearances.	
1985-87 (3.6)	4.8
w/A.C. (.2)	.2
(G) Rear Main Bearing Oil Seal, Renew	
1985-87 (1.9)	2.7
Crankshaft Pulley, Renew	
1985-87 (.7)	1.0
w/A.C. add (.2)	.2

PARTS 15 CRANKSHAFT & DAMPER 15 PARTS

	Part No.	Price
(1) Crankshaft		
1985-87	94840044	237.00
(2) Pulley		
1985-87	94840047	62.00
(3) Timing Pulley		
1985-87	94840050	6.50
(4) Timing Belt Guide		
1985-87	94840052	1.00
(5) Main Bearing Set		
1985-87	94843779	8.00

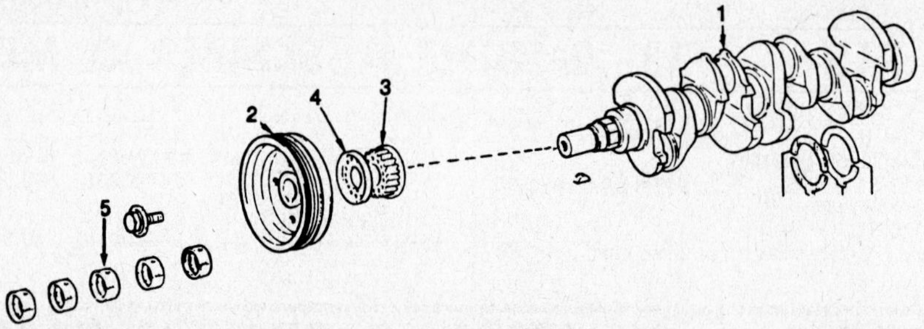

LABOR 16 CAMSHAFT & TIMING GEARS 16 LABOR

(Factory Time)	Chilton Time
(G) Camshaft Drive Belt Cover and/or Gaskets, Renew	
1985-87-upper (1.0)	1.4
middle (1.3)	1.8
lower (.8)	1.2
w/A.C. add (.3)	.3
w/P.S. add (.2)	.2
(G) Camshaft Drive Belt, Renew	
1985-87 (2.3)	3.2
w/A.C. add (.3)	.3
w/P.S. add (.2)	.2
(G) Camshaft Idler Pulley, Renew	
1985-87 (1.6)	2.3
w/A.C. add (.3)	.3
w/P.S. add (.2)	.2
(G) Camshaft Timing Gear, Renew	
1985-87 (1.5)	2.1
w/A.C. add (.3)	.3
w/P.S. add (.2)	.2
Renew cam oil seal add (.1)	.2
* Renew crank gear add (.2)	.2
(G) Camshaft and/or Bearings, Renew	
1985-87 (3.2)	4.5
w/P.S. add (.2)	.2

PARTS 16 CAMSHAFT & TIMING GEARS 16 PARTS

	Part No.	Price
(1) Timing Pulley		
1985-87	94840051	8.75
(2) Camshaft		
1985-87	94840049	118.00
(3) Distributor Drive Gear		
1985-87	94840048	12.50

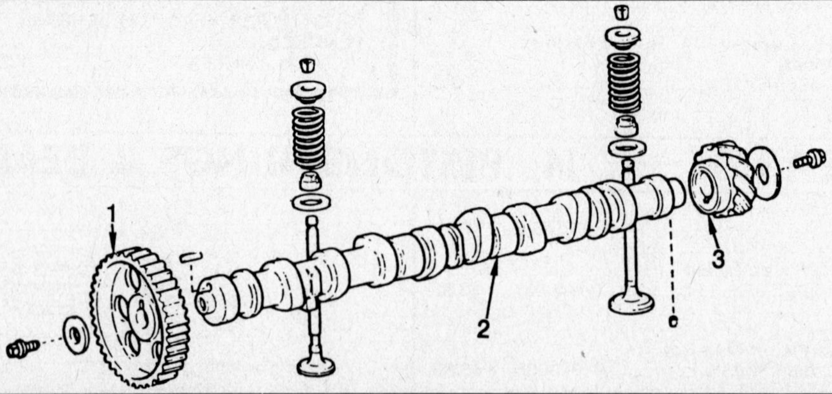

LABOR 17 ENGINE OILING SYSTEM 17 LABOR

(Factory Time)	Chilton Time
(G) Oil Pan and/or Gasket, Renew	
1985-87 (.9)	1.3
(P) Pressure Test Engine Bearings (Pan Off)	
All models	1.0
(G) Oil Pump Seal, Renew	
1985-87 (1.8)	2.5
w/A.C. add (.3)	.3
w/P.S. add (.2)	.2
(G) Oil Pump, Renew	
1985-87 (3.3)	4.6
w/A.C. add (.3)	.3
w/P.S. add (.2)	.2
Recond pump add (.3)	.4
(G) Oil Pressure Gauge (Engine), Renew	
1985-87 (.4)	.5
(M) Oil Filter Element, Renew	
1985-87 (.2)	.3

PARTS 17 ENGINE OILING SYSTEM 17 PARTS

	Part No.	Price
Oil Pump		
1985-87	94840611	68.50
Oil Pump Screen		
1985-87	94840081	19.50
Pressure Regulator Valve		
Note: Must be ordered by stamping cast into pump body.		
Oil Pressure Switch		
1985-87	94841821	10.25
Oil Pan		
1985-87	94840030	37.00
Oil Filter		
1985-87	94840078	5.50

LABOR 18 CLUTCH & FLYWHEEL 18 LABOR

(Factory Time)	Chilton Time
(G) Bleed Clutch Hydraulic System	
All models (.3)	.5
(G) Clutch Master Cylinder, R&R or Renew	
Includes: Bleed system.	
1985-87 (.7)	1.0
Recond cyl add (.4)	.4
(G) Clutch Actuator (Slave) Cylinder, Renew	
Includes: Bleed system.	
1985-87 (.5)	.8
(G) Clutch Release Bearing, Renew	
Includes: R&R trans and adjust linkage.	
1985-87 (1.6)	2.1
(G) Clutch Assembly, Renew	
Includes: R&R trans. Renew clutch disc, pressure plate and release bearing. Adjust linkage.	
1985-87 (1.7)	2.4
Renew clutch fork and/or bushings add (.2)	.2
(G) Flywheel, Renew	
Includes: R&R trans and adjust linkage.	
1985-87 (1.9)	2.7

PARTS 18 CLUTCH & FLYWHEEL 18 PARTS

	Part No.	Price
Pressure Plate		
1985-87	94840846	52.75
Driven Plate		
1985-87	94840847	36.50
Release Bearing		
1985-87	94840697	29.25
Release Fork		
1985-87	94840696	19.50
Clutch Tube		
1985-87 (Rel.Cyl.)	94842515	5.00
(Master Cyl.)	94843641	7.00
Flywheel		
1985-87	94840045	110.00

LABOR 21 SHIFT LINKAGE 21 LABOR

(Factory Time)	Chilton Time
MANUAL	
(G) Shift Linkage, Adjust	
All models (.7)	1.0
(G) Gearshift Control Lever, Renew	
1985-87 (.7)	1.1
(G) Floor Mounted Gearshift Control Assy., Renew	
1985-87 (.5)	.7
(G) Shift Cables, Renew	
1985-87-one (.6)	.9
both (.7)	1.0
AUTOMATIC	
(G) Shift Linkage, Adjust	
All models	
Neutral Safety Switch (.3)	.4
Shift Linkage (.3)	.4
T.V. Cable (.2)	.3
(G) Shift Indicator Needle and/or Assy., Renew	
1985-87 (.3)	.4
(G) Shift Cable, Renew	
1985-87 (.5)	.7
(G) Park Lock Cable, Renew	
1985-87 (.6)	.9
(G) Shift Control Cable, Renew	
1985-87 (.6)	.9
(G) Floor Shift Control Assy., Renew	
1985-87 (.4)	.6

LABOR 26 REAR AXLE AND SUSPENSION 26 LABOR

(Factory Time)	Chilton Time
(G) Rear Toe-In, Adjust	
All models (.3)	.4
(G) Rear Torque Arm, Renew	
1985-87 (.2)	.4
(G) Rear Wheel Bearings, Renew	
1985-87-one side (.6)	.8
both sides (.9)	1.2
(G) Rear Wheel Hub Assy., Renew	
1985-87-one (.6)	.8
both (.9)	1.2
(G) Rear Wheel Spindle, Renew	
1985-87-one (.5)	.7
both (.9)	1.2
(G) Rear Wheel Knuckle Assy., Renew	
1985-87-one (.6)	.8
both (.9)	1.2
(G) Rear Wheel Spindle Control Rod, Renew	
Includes: Reset toe-in.	
1985-87	
right side-one (.5)	.7
left side-one (.5)	.7
each side-one (.6)	.9
(G) Rear Coil Springs, Renew	
1985-87-one (.6)	.8
both (1.0)	1.4
(G) Rear Struts, Renew	
1985-87-one (.6)	.8
both (1.0)	1.4

PARTS 27 REAR SUSPENSION 27 PARTS

	Part No.	Price
(1) Coil Spring		
1985-86 (S19)	94840582	37.75
1986-87 (S68)	94843205	33.50
(2) Shock Absorber		
1985-87 (L.H.)	94840583	96.50
(R.H.)	94840584	96.50
(3) Arm		
1985-87 (Front)	94840585	N.L.
(Rear)	94840586	N.L.
(4) Adjusting Cam		
1985-87	94840593	5.00
(5) Axle Carrier		
1985-87 (L.H.)	94843561	62.75
(R.H.)	94843562	62.75
(6) Strut Rod		
1985-87	94840587	25.25

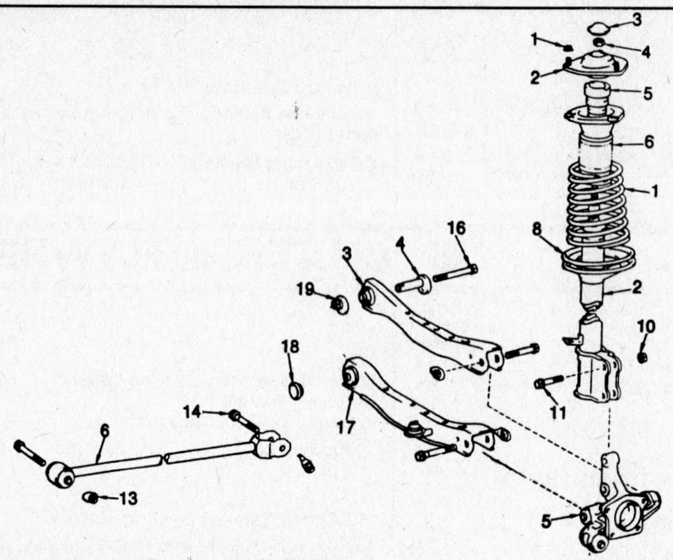

LABOR 28 AIR CONDITIONING 28 LABOR

	(Factory Time)	Chilton Time

Note: If more than one item requires replacement where evacuation and discharging the system is already included in the operation, deduct 1.0 hour for each additional item to the times listed.

(G) Drain, Evacuate and Recharge System
All models (.5) 1.0

(G) Leak Test
Includes: Check all lines and connections.
All models 5

(G) Refrigerant, Add (Partial Charge)
All models 6

(G) Compressor Drive Belt, Renew
All models (.4) 5

(G) Compressor Assembly, Renew
Includes: Transfer all necessary attaching parts. Evacuate and charge system.
1985-87 (1.1) 2.0

(G) Compressor Clutch Plate and Hub Assy., Renew
Includes: R&R hub and drive plate assy.
1985-87 (.7) 1.0

(G) Compressor Clutch Rotor and/or Bearing, Renew
Includes: R&R hub and drive plate assy.
1985-87 (.8) 1.2

(G) Compressor Clutch Coil and/or Pulley Rim Assy., Renew
Includes: R&R hub and drive plate assy.
1985-87 (.8) 1.1

(G) Compressor Front Seal, Seat and 'O' Ring, Renew
Includes: R&R clutch hub and drive plate assy. Evacuate and charge system.
1985-87 (1.3) 2.5

AIR CONDITIONER TUNE-UP

For efficient operation and satisfactory performance in hot weather. The following air conditioner tune-up is suggested:

1. Clean intake filter
2. Clean condenser fins
3. Pressure test system
4. Adjust drive belt tension
5. Check antifreeze/coolant
6. Tighten compressor mounts
7. Tighten condenser and evaporator mounts
8. Inspect system for leaks (hoses, couplings, valves, etc.)
9. Partial charge system

All models 1.0
If necessary to evacuate and charge system, add 1.0

(Factory Time) — Chilton Time

(G) Compressor Front or Rear Head, Reed Assy., and/or Gaskets and Seals, Renew
Includes: R&R compressor. R&R clutch hub and drive plate assy. Evacuate and charge system.
1985-87 (1.8) 2.8

(G) Compressor Shaft and Cylinder Assy., Renew
Includes: R&R compressor. R&R clutch hub and drive plate assy. Clean and inspect all parts. Evacuate and charge system.
1985-87 (1.9) 2.8

(G) Condenser, Renew
Includes: Evacuate and charge system.
1985-87 (1.4) 2.0

(Factory Time) — Chilton Time

(G) Evaporator Core, Renew
Includes: Evacuate and charge system.
1985-87 (1.4) 2.7

(G) Expansion Valve, Renew
Includes: Evacuate and charge system.
1985-87 (1.4) 1.9

(G) In-Line Filter Dryer, Renew
Includes: Evacuate and charge system.
1985-87 (.9) 1.4

(G) Blower Motor and/or Fan, Renew
1985-87 (.6) 8

(G) Blower Motor Resistor, Renew
1985-87 (.3) 4

(G) Blower Motor Relay, Renew
1985-87 (.3) 4

(G) Blower Motor Switch, Renew
1985-87 (1.1) 1.5

(G) Master Electrical Switch, Renew
1985-87 (.8) 1.2

(G) Temperature Control Assy., Renew
1985-87 (1.1) 1.5

(G) A.C. Programmer, Renew
1985-87 (.3) 5

(G) Low Pressure Cut-Off Switch, Renew
1985-87 (.8) 1.1
Add time to recharge A.C. system if required.

(G) High Pressure Cut-Off Switch, Renew
1985-87 (.3) 4
Add time to recharge A.C. system if required.

(G) Air Conditioning Hoses, Renew
Includes: Evacuate and charge system.
1985-87
Expansion Valve Inlet (1.4) 1.9
Comp. Discharge (1.0) 1.7
All other hoses-one (.8) 1.5

PARTS 28 AIR CONDITIONING 28 PARTS

	Part No.	Price
Compressor Assy.		
1985	94841693	265.00
1986-87	94843861	265.00
Cylinder		
1985	94841694	247.00
1986-87	94843862	247.00
Main Shaft		
1985	94841696	64.75
1986-87	94843864	64.00
Actuating Clutch		
1985	94841709	108.00
1986-87	94843866	112.00
Drive Pulley		
1985-87	94841716	36.75
Front & Rear Head		
1985-87 (Frt.)	94841698	57.00
(Rear)	94841699	57.00
Compressor Gasket Kit		
1985-87	94841700	32.50
Condenser		
1985-87	94841731	171.00
Evaporator Core		
1985-87	94841720	116.00
Blower Motor		
1985	94841738	78.75
1986-87	94843877	60.00
Blower Motor Fan		
1985	94841736	13.50
1986-87	94843875	9.75
Expansion Valve		
1985-87	94841721	36.75

LABOR 29 LOCKS, HINGES & WIND. REGULATORS 29 LABOR

(Factory Time)	Chilton Time
(G) Hood Latch, Renew	
1985-87 (.2)	.3
(G) Hood Hinge, Renew	
1985-87-one (.2)	.3
both (.3)	.5
(G) Hood Release Cable, Renew	
1985-87 (.7)	1.1
(G) Door Handle (Outside), Renew (Front or Rear)	
1985-87 (.4)	.6
(G) Front Door Lock Cylinder, Renew	
1985-87 (.4)	.6
Recode cyl add (.3)	.3
(G) Lock Striker Plate, Renew	
1985-87 (.2)	.3
(G) Front Door Lock, Renew	
1985-87 (.5)	.7
(G) Front Door Lock Remote Control, Renew	
1985-87 (.4)	.6
(G) Rear Door Lock, Renew	
1985-87 (.4)	.6
(G) Rear Door Lock Remote Control, Renew	
1985-87 (.3)	.5
(G) Rear Compartment Lid Lock Cylinder, Renew	
1985-87 (.2)	.3
Recode cyl add (.3)	.3
(G) Rear Compartment Lid Release Cable, Renew	
1985-87 (.6)	1.0
(G) Front Door Window Regulator, Renew	
1985-87 (.5)	.8
Recond regul add (.2)	.2
(G) Rear Door Window Regulator, Renew	
1985-87 (.4)	.7

PARTS 29 LOCKS, HINGES & WIND. REGULATORS 29 PARTS

	Part No.	Price
Hood Latch		
1985-87	94841579	16.50
Hood Hinge		
1985-87 (L.H.)	94841149	7.00
(R.H.)	94841150	7.00
Front Door Lock (wo/Power)		
1985-87 (L.H.)	94843513	N.L.
(R.H.)	94843514	N.L.
(w/Power) L.H.	94843517	55.00
(R.H.)	94843518	55.00
Rear Door Lock (wo/Power)		
1985-87 (L.H.)	94843515	N.L.
(R.H.)	94843516	N.L.
(w/Power) (L.H.)	94843519	50.00
(R.H.)	94843520	50.00
Door Handle (Outside)		
Front		
1985-87 (L.H.)	94843565	15.25
(R.H.)	94843566	15.25
Rear		
1985-87 (L.H.)	94843567	15.25
(R.H.)	94843568	15.25
Front Window Regulator		
1985-87 (L.H.)	94841643	40.25
(R.H.)	94841644	40.25
Rear Window Regulator		
1985-87 (L.H.)	94841645	34.25
(R.H.)	94841646	34.25
Rear Compartment Lock		
1986-87	94843337	44.00
Rear Compartment Hinge		
1985-87 (S19)	94841161	17.75
1986-87 (S68)	94842313	1.00

LABOR 30 HEAD AND PARKING LAMPS 30 LABOR

(Factory Time)	Chilton Time
(G) Aim Headlamps	
two	.4
four	.6
(M) Headlamp Sealed Beam Bulb, Renew	
All models-one (.2)	.3
(M) Back-Up Lamp Bulb, Renew	
All models-one	.2
all	.3
(M) Park and Turn Signal Lamp Bulb, Renew	
All models-one	.2
all	.3
(M) License Lamp Bulb, Renew	
All models-one or all	.2
(M) Side Marker Lamp Bulb, Renew	
All models-one	.2
each adtnl	.1
(M) Stop, Tail and Turn Signal Lamp Bulb, Renew	
All models-one	.2
each adtnl	.1
(M) High Level Stop Lamp Bulb, Renew	
All models (.2)	.3
(M) Park and Turn Signal Lamp Assy., Renew	
All models-each	.3
(M) Rear Combination Lamp Assy., Renew	
All models-each	.3
(M) Side Marker Lamp Assy., Renew	
All models-each	.2
(M) High Level Stop Lamp Assy., Renew	
All models (.2)	.4

PARTS 30 HEAD AND PARKING LAMPS 30 PARTS

	Part No.	Price
Headlamp		
1985-87 (wo/Halogen)		
Inboard	94841767	15.00
Outboard	94841768	15.00
1985-87 (w/Halogen)		
Inboard	94841771	23.50
Outboard	94841772	23.50
Parking & Turn Signal Lamps		
1985-87 (L.H.)	94841775	34.25
(R.H.)	94841776	34.25
Parking & Turn Signal Lens		
1985-87 (L.H.)	94841781	3.25
(R.H.)	94841782	3.25
License Plate Lens		
1985-87 (wo/ Cust. Tr.)	94842371	14.75
(w/Cust. Trim)	94841799	14.75
1986-87 (S68)	94843664	2.25
Tail & Stop Lamp Assy.		
1986-87 (S19)	94843755	36.00
1986-87 (S68)	94843756	39.50
Side Marker Lamp		
1985-87 (L.H.)	94841773	38.25
(R.H.)	94841774	38.25
High Mount Stoplight		
1986-87		
Bracket	94843586	6.25
Cover	94843762	19.75

Cover number is representive-order by color.

LABOR 31 WINDSHIELD WIPER & SPEEDOMETER 31 LABOR

(Factory Time)	Chilton Time
(G) Windshield Wiper Motor, Renew	
1985-87 (.4)	.6
(G) Back Window Wiper Motor, Renew	
1985-87 (.4)	.6
(G) Windshield Wiper Switch, Renew	
1985-87 (.7)	1.1
(G) Back Window Wiper Switch, Renew	
1985-87 (.3)	.4
(G) Washer Pump, Renew	
1985-87-front (.4)	.5
rear (.3)	.4
(G) Wiper Transmission, Renew	
1985-87-both (.5)	.8
(G) Speedometer Head, R&R or Renew	
1985-87 (.6)	1.0
Reset odometer add	.2
(G) Speedometer Cable and Casing, Renew	
1985-87	
one piece (.5)	.9
(G) Radio, R&R	
1985-87 (.3)	.5

PARTS 31 WINDSHIELD WIPER & SPEEDOMETER 31 PARTS

	Part No.	Price
Wiper Motor		
1985-87	22057652	107.25
Wiper Blade Arm		
1985-87 (L.H.)	94841827	25.75
(R.H.)	94841830	26.50
Wiper Control Switch		
1985-87		
(wo/Cust. Tr. & Cruise Cont.)	94842626	39.50
(w/Cruise Cont. & wo/Cust. Tr.)	94842628	64.50
(w/Cust. Tr. & wo/Cruise Cont.)	94842625	39.50
(w/Cust. Tr. & Cruise Cont.)	94842627	64.50
Wiper Transmission		
1985-87	94841826	82.75
Washer Pump & Motor		
1985-87	22048173	19.25
Speedometer Head		
1985-87	94842908	112.00

LABOR 32 LIGHT SWITCHES & WIRING 32 LABOR

(Factory Time)	Chilton Time
(G) Headlamp Switch, Renew	
1985-87 (.7)	1.1
(G) Headlamp Dimmer Switch, Renew	
1985-87 (.8)	1.2
(G) Stop Lamp Switch, Renew	
1985-87 (.3)	.4
(G) Back-Up Lamp Switch, Renew	
1985-87 (.3)	.4
(G) Back-Up Lamp and Park/Neutral Switch, Renew	
1985-87 (.3)	.4
(G) Neutral Safety Switch, Renew	
1985-87 (.3)	.4
(G) Parking Brake Lamp Switch, Renew	
1985-87 (.3)	.4
(G) Turn Signal or Hazard Warning Switch, Renew	
1985-87 (.7)	1.1
(M) Turn Signal or Hazard Warning Flasher, Renew	
1985-87	
turn signal (.2)	.3
(G) Horn, Renew	
1985-87 (.3)	.3

PARTS 32 LIGHT SWITCHES & WIRING 32 PARTS

	Part No.	Price
Headlamp Switch		
1985-87	94841824	14.00
Dimmer Switch		
1985-87		
(wo/Cust. Tr.)	94840688	17.75
(w/Cust. Tr.)	94840687	17.75
Stop Lamp Switch		
1985-87		
(wo/Cruise Cont.)	94840335	10.00
(w/Cruise Cont.)	94840336	19.75
Backup Lamp Switch		
1985-87-M.T.	94840339	16.75
Turn Signal Flasher		
1985-87	94841844	25.00
Horn Assy.		
1985-87	94841842	22.25

LABOR 33 GLASS 33 LABOR

	(Factory Time)	Chilton Time
(G) Windshield Glass, Renew		
1985-87	(1.7)	2.3
(G) Front Door Glass, Renew		
1985-87	(.5)	.8
(G) Rear Door Glass, Renew		
1985-87	(.6)	.9
(G) Quarter Window Stationary Glass, Renew		
1985-87	(.5)	.7
(G) Back Window Glass, Renew		
1985-87	(.6)	1.0

LABOR 34 CRUISE CONTROL 34 LABOR

	(Factory Time)	Chilton Time
(G) Cruise Control Chain or Cable, Renew		
1985-87	(.3)	.4
(G) Cruise Control Servo Assy., Renew		
1985-87	(.4)	.6
(G) Brake or Clutch Release Switch, Renew		
1985-87	(.3)	.4
(G) Engagement Switch, Renew		
1985-87	(.7)	1.1
(G) Vacuum Hoses, Renew		
1985-87	(.2)	.3
(G) Cruise Control Module, Renew		
1985-87	(.3)	.4
(G) Cruise Control Dash Switch, Renew (On-Off)		
1985-87	(.2)	.4

PARTS 34 CRUISE CONTROL 34 PARTS

	Part No.	Price
Control Switch		
1985-87-M.T.	94840343	17.50
A.T.	94842795	30.50
Actuator		
1985	94840342	239.00
1986-87	94843746	273.00
Computer		
1985	94840344	467.00
1986-87	94843747	326.00

GROUP INDEX

ALPHABETICAL INDEX

General Motors
Front Wheel Drive Cars

CITATION • OMEGA • PHOENIX • SKYLARK

YEAR IDENTIFICATION

1983 Omega

1984 Omega ES

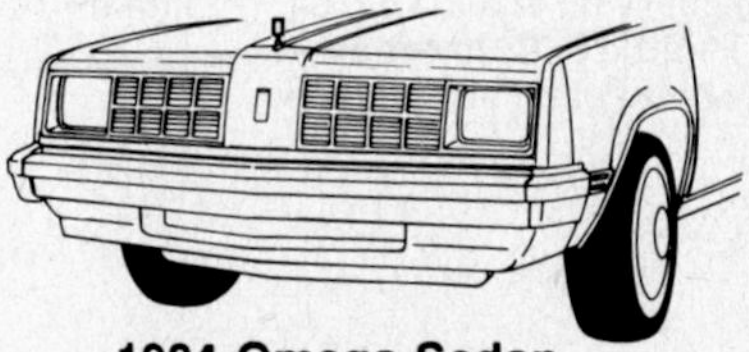

1984 Omega Sedan

1983 Phoenix

1984 Phoenix LE, SE

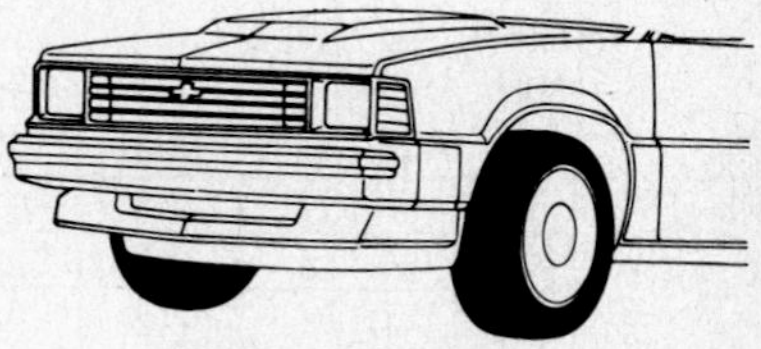

1983–85 Citation

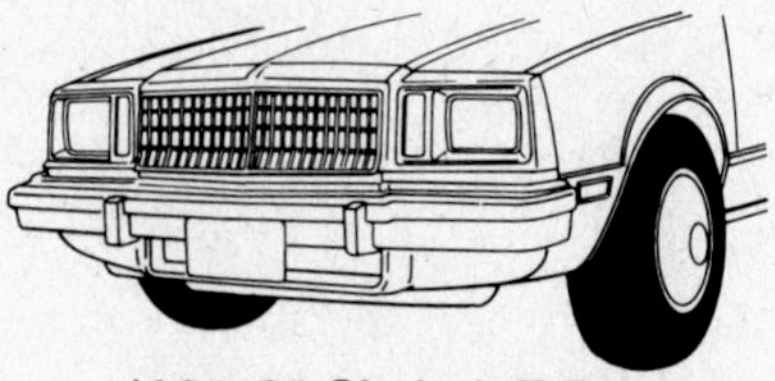

1984–85 Skylark T Type

1981–85 Skylark Sport Coupe

VEHICLE IDENTIFICATION NUMBER (VIN)

It is important for servicing and ordering parts to be certain of the vehicle and engine identification. The VIN (vehicle identification number) is a 13 or 17 digit number visible through the windshield on the driver's side of the dash and contains the vehicle and engine identification codes. It can be interpreted as follows:

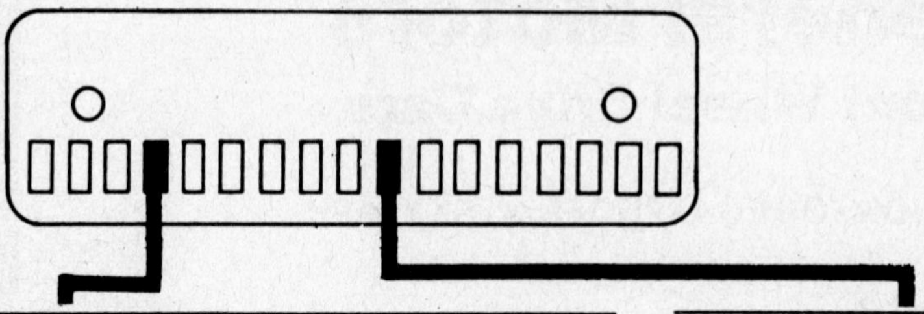

Engine Code

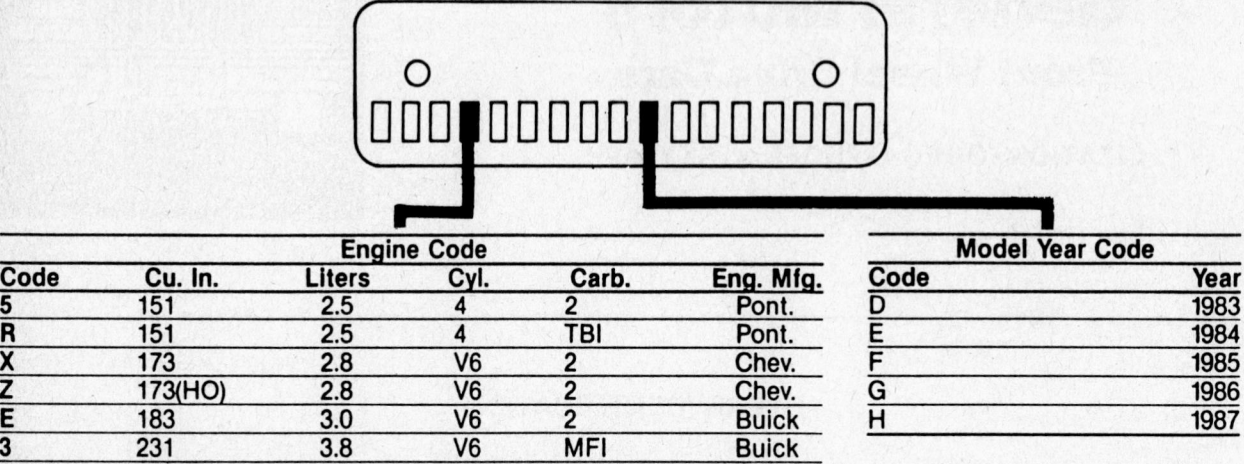

Code	Cu. In.	Liters	Cyl.	Carb.	Eng. Mfg.
5	151	2.5	4	2	Pont.
R	151	2.5	4	TBI	Pont.
X	173	2.8	V6	2	Chev.
Z	173(HO)	2.8	V6	2	Chev.
E	183	3.0	V6	2	Buick
3	231	3.8	V6	MFI	Buick
T	263	4.3	V6	Diesel	Olds

Model Year Code

Code	Year
D	1983
E	1984
F	1985
G	1986
H	1987

The seventeen digit Vehicle Identification Number can be used to determine engine application and model year. The 10th digit indicates the model year and the 8th digit identifies the factory installed engine.

TBI: Throttle Body Injection

MFI: Multi-Point Fuel-Injection

TUNE-UP SPECIFICATIONS

When analyzing compression test results, look for uniformity among cylinders rather than specific pressures

Year	VIN Code	Eng. No. Cyl. Displ. Cu. In.	Liters	Eng. Mfg.	hp	Spark Plugs Orig. Type	Spark Plugs Gap (in.)	Ignition Timing (deg) ▲ Man. Trans.	Ignition Timing (deg) ▲ Auto. Trans.	Intake Valve Opens (deg.)▪	Fuel Pump Pressure (psi)	Idle Speed (rpm) ▲ Man. Trans.	Idle Speed (rpm) ▲ Auto. Trans.
'83–'87	5,R	4-151	2.5	Pont.	90	R-44TSX	0.060	8B	8B	33	6.0–8.0	950 ①	750 ②
	X	6-173	2.8	Chev.	112	R-43CTS	0.045	10B	10B	25	6.0–7.5	800	600
	Z	6-173 HO	2.8	Chev.	135	R-42CTS	0.045	6B	10B	31	6.0–7.5	850 ③	750
	E	6-183	3.0	Buick	110	R-44TS8	0.080	—	15B	16	6.0–8.0	—	see text
	3	6-231	3.8	Buick	125	R-44TS8	0.080	④	④	4.0–6.5	④	④	
	T	6-263	4.3	Olds.	85	④	④	—	6A	N.A.	5.8–8.7	—	650

NOTE: The underhood specifications sticker often reflects tune-up specification changes made in production. Sticker figures must be used if they disagree with those in this chart.

▲ See text for procedure

▪ All figures Before Top Dead Center

B: Before Top Dead Center

A: After Top Dead Center

Part numbers in this chart are not recommendations by Chilton for any product by brand name.

N.A.: Information not available

① Without air conditioning: 850

② Without air conditioning: 680

③ Calif.: 750

④ See underhood specifications sticker

FIRING ORDERS

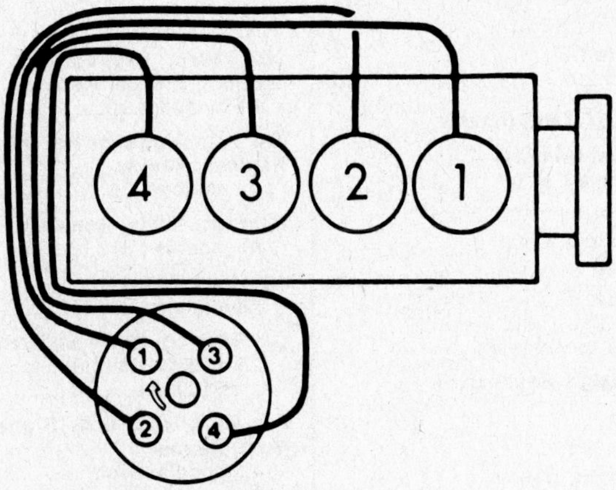

GM (Pontiac) 151-4
Engine firing order: 1-3-4-2
Distributor rotation: clockwise

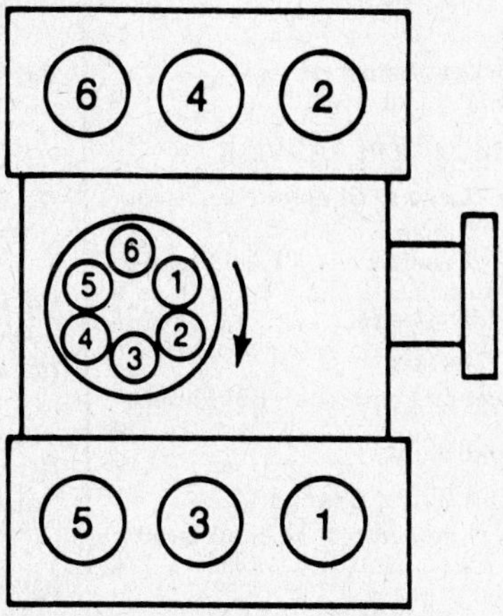

GM (Chevrolet) 173 V6 (2.8 L)
Engine firing order: 1-2-3-4-5-6
Distributor rotation: clockwise

WHEEL ALIGNMENT SPECIFICATIONS

Year	Model	Caster* Range (deg.)	Caster* Pref. Setting (deg.)	Camber Range (deg.)	Camber Pref. Setting (deg.)	Toe-In (in.)	Steering Axis (deg.) Inclination
'83–'87	All	0–4P	2P	1/2N-1/2P	0	13/64 out–13/64 in	14.5

*Caster is not adjustable

LABOR — SERVICE BAY OPERATIONS — LABOR

(Factory Time) Chilton Time

COOLING

(M) Winterize Cooling System

Includes: Run engine to check for leaks, tighten all hose connections. Test radiator and pressure cap, drain radiator and engine block. Add anti-freeze and refill system.

All models.. .5

(G) Thermostat, Renew

All models
Four (.2)... .4
V-6 (.4).. .6

(M) Drive Belt, Renew

All models-one (.2)................................ .3
each adtnl (.2).................................... .2

(M) Drive Belt, Adjust

All models-one (.2)................................ .3
all (.5).. .6

(M) Radiator Hose, Renew

All models-upper (.3).............................. .4
lower (.4).. .5
both (.5)... .7

FUEL

(M) Carburetor Air Cleaner, Service

All models (.2).................................... .3

CHILTON'S 10 POINT SAFETY CHECK

CHECK OPERATION & CONDITION OF THE FOLLOWING ITEMS:

1. Legal Registration (serial no.)
2. Tires & Wheels
3. Brake System (R&R all wheels)
4. Light Systems & Signals
5. Accelerator Linkage, Neutral Safety Switch, Shift Indicator Pointer & Seat Position Locks
6. Glass, Mirrors, Door Locks, Seat Belts & Harness
7. Wipers, Washers & Defrosters
8. Frame, Steering, Shocks, Front & Rear Suspension
9. Fuel & Exhaust Systems
10. Road Test Vehicle

All models 1.0
Exhaust Smog Analysis, add 4

(Factory Time) Chilton Time

(G) Carburetor, Adjust (On Car)

All models
Slow & Fast Idle (.3)............................. .4
Vacuum Brake-one (.6)............................ .8
both (.8).. 1.0
Complete (1.3).................................... 1.8

(G) Thermostatic Choke Cover and/or Gasket, Renew

All models (.6).................................... 1.0

(G) Automatic Choke Vacuum Diaphragm, Renew

All models-one (.6)................................ .8
both (.8).. 1.0

BRAKES

(G) Brakes, Adjust (Minor)

Includes: R&R wheels and adjust brakes thru access holes in drums. Fill master cylinder.

two wheels.. .4
Remove knock out plugs add-each.... .1

(G) Bleed Brakes (Four Wheels)

Includes: Fill master cylinder.

All models (.4).................................... .5

(G) Brake Pedal Free Play, Adjust

All models.. .3

LABOR — SERVICE BAY OPERATIONS — LABOR

(Factory Time) Chilton Time

(M) Parking Brake, Adjust
All models (.3) 4

LUBRICATION SERVICE

(M) Lubricate Chassis, Change Oil & Filter
Includes: Inspect and correct all fluid levels.
All models 6
Install grease fittings add 1

(M) Lubricate Chassis
Includes: Inspect and correct all fluid levels.
All models 4
Install grease fittings add 1

(M) Engine Oil & Filter, Change
Includes: Inspect and correct all fluid levels.
All models 4

WHEELS

(M) Wheel, Renew
one (.5) 5

(G) Wheels, Balance
one 3
each adtnl 2

(M) Wheels, Rotate (All)
All models 5

ELECTRICAL

(M) Battery Cables, Renew
All models-positive (.3) 4
negative (.3) 4

(M) Battery Terminals, Clean
All models 3

(G) Aim Headlamps
two 4
four 6

(M) Headlamp Sealed Beam Bulb, Renew
All models (.3) 3

(G) Headlamp Switch, Renew
All models (.5) 6

(G) Headlamp Dimmer Switch, Renew
All models (.5) 7

(G) Stop Light Switch, Renew
All models (.3) 4

(G) Turn Signal and Hazard Warning Switch, Renew
All models (.9) 1.1

(M) Turn Signal or Hazard Warning Flasher, Renew
All models (.3) 3

(G) Horn Relay, Renew
All models (.3) 4

(G) Horn, Renew
All models (.2) 3

(M) Back-Up Lamp Bulb, Renew
All models-one (.2) 3
all (.3) 5

(M) Park and Turn Signal Lamp Bulb, Renew
All models-each 2

(M) Side Marker Lamp Bulb, Renew
All models-each 2

(M) Stop, Tail and Turn Signal Lamp Bulb, Renew
All models-one 3
each adtnl 1

LABOR — 1 TUNE UP 1 — LABOR

(Factory Time) Chilton Time

(G) Compression Test
1983-85
Four (.3) 5
V-6 (.5) 8
w/Cruise control add 3

(G) Engine Tune Up, (Electronic Ignition)
Includes: Test battery and clean connections. Tighten manifold and carburetor mounting bolts. Check engine compression, clean and adjust or renew spark plugs. Test resistance of spark plug cables. Inspect distributor cap and rotor. Adjust air gap. Check vacuum advance operation. Reset ignition timing. Adjust idle mixture and idle speed. Service air cleaner. Inspect and adjust drive belts. Inspect choke operation and adjust or free up. Check operation of EGR valve.
Four–1983-85 .... 1.6
V-6–1983-85 .... 2.0
w/A.C. add 6
w/Cruise control add 3
To perform C.C.C. system test add 1.0

LABOR — 2 IGNITION SYSTEM 2 — LABOR

(Factory Time) Chilton Time

(G) Spark Plugs, Clean and Reset or Renew
1983-85-Four (.3) 5
V-6 (.5) 7
w/Cruise control add (.3) 3

(G) Ignition Timing, Reset
1983-85 (.4) 4

(G) Distributor, Renew
Includes: Reset ignition timing.
1983-85 (.7) 1.0

(G) Distributor, R&R and Recondition
Includes: Reset ignition timing.
1983-85 (1.1) 1.6

(G) Distributor Cap and/or Rotor, Renew
Includes: R&R coil.
1983-85 (.3) 5

(G) Ignition Coil, Renew
Includes: Test coil.
1983-85 (.4) 5

(G) Distributor Module, Renew
1983-85-Four (.7) 1.0
V-6 (.6) 9

(G) Distributor Capacitor and/or Module Wiring Harness, Renew
1983-85 (.6) 9

(G) Distributor Pick-Up Coil and/or Shaft Assembly, Renew
Includes: Reset ignition timing.
1983-85-Four (1.1) 1.4
V-6 (.9) 1.2

(G) Ignition Cables, Renew
1983-85-Four (.3) 5
V-6 (.4) 6
w/Cruise control add (.3) 3

(G) Distributor Hall Effect Switch, Renew
1983 (1.3) 1.7

(G) Ignition Switch, Renew
1983-84 (.5) 9
1985 (.7) 1.2

PARTS — 2 IGNITION SYSTEM 2 — PARTS

Distributor Assembly
Refer to the "Tune Up specifications chart for engine code identification.

	Part No.	Price
4 cyl.–151 engine		
1983	◆1103513	282.50
1984	◆1103551	236.00
1985	◆1103634	155.75

PARTS 2 IGNITION SYSTEM 2 PARTS

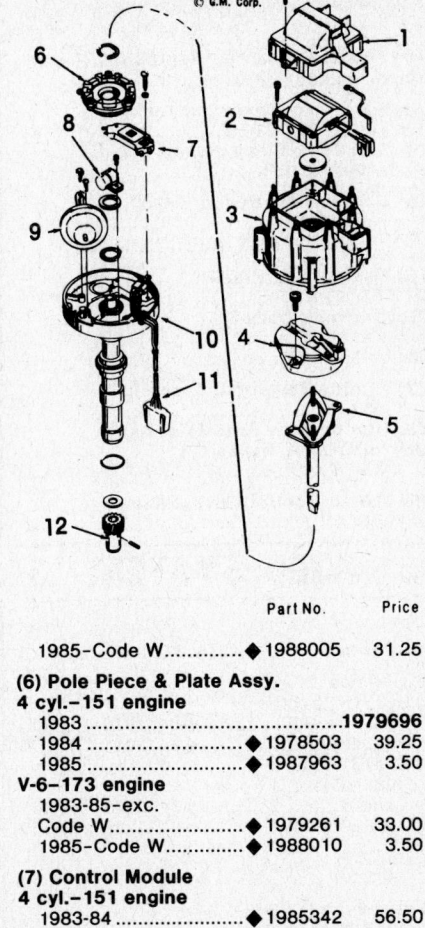

	Part No.	Price
V-6-173 engine		
1983	◆1103519	243.75
1984	◆1103569	214.00
1985-exc. Code X	◆1103591	176.50
Code X	◆1103643	216.25
(1) Cover		
1983-87-151 eng	◆1875960	6.00
V-6 eng	◆1894209	6.00
(2) Coil		
4 cyl-151 engine		
1983-84	◆1115455	58.00
1985	◆1115315	39.50
V-6-173 engine		
1983-84	◆1115455	58.00
1985	◆1115315	39.50
(3) Cap		
4 cyl.-151 engine		
1983-84	◆1978497	16.00
1985	◆1987948	7.00
V-6-173 engine		
1983-85-exc. Code W	◆1979208	20.25
1985-Code W	◆1988001	9.75
(4) Rotor		
4 cyl.-151 engine		
1983	◆1979703	8.50
1984	◆1988515	8.50
1985	◆10495411	3.50
V-6-173 engine		
1983-85-exc. Code W	◆1978533	9.00
1985-Code W	◆10495408	3.50
(5) Mainshaft		
4 cyl.-151 engine		
1983	◆1979705	40.00
1984	◆1986963	33.25
1985	◆1988077	24.75
V-6-173 engine		
1983-85-exc. Code W	◆1979256	49.75

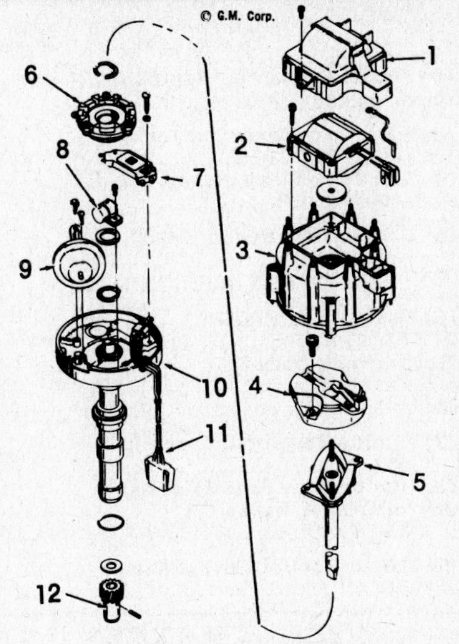

	Part No.	Price
1985-Code W	◆1988005	31.25
(6) Pole Piece & Plate Assy.		
4 cyl.-151 engine		
1983	1979696	
1984	◆1978503	39.25
1985	◆1987963	3.50
V-6-173 engine		
1983-85-exc. Code W	◆1979261	33.00
1985-Code W	◆1988010	3.50
(7) Control Module		
4 cyl.-151 engine		
1983-84	◆1985342	56.50
1985	◆1989747	51.50
V-6-173 engine		
1983-87-exc. Code W	◆1979571	58.00
1985-Code W	◆1987466	46.00
(8) Capacitor		
1983-85	◆1876154	4.50
(10) Housing		
4 cyl.-151 engine		
1983	◆1979701	48.75
1984	◆1988883	40.25
1985	◆1988082	26.75
V-6-173 engine		
1983	◆1979254	41.50
1984-85-exc. Code W	◆1987841	37.25
1985-Code W	◆1988388	34.25
(11) Harness		
4 cyl.-151 engine		
1983	◆1979700	32.75
1984-85	◆1986972	28.50
V-6-173 engine		
1983-84	◆1984219	30.75
1985	◆10495353	29.25
(12) Gear		
4 cyl.-151 engine		
1983-85	◆1978509	13.00
V-6-173 engine		
1983-85	◆1985769	22.00
Ignition Switch		
(wo/tilt wheel)		
1983	◆1990109	11.50
1984-85-wo/console	◆1990115	11.50
w/console	◆7843451	25.75
(w/tilt wheel)		
1983	◆1990110	11.50
1984-85-wo/console	◆1990116	11.50
w/console	◆7843497	25.75

LABOR 3 FUEL SYSTEM 3 LABOR

(Factory Time)	Chilton Time
(G) Fuel Pump, Test	
Includes: Disconnect line at carburetor, attach pressure gauge.	
All models	.2
(M) Carburetor Air Cleaner, Service	
All models (.2)	.3
(G) Carburetor, Adjust (On Car)	
All models	
Slow & Fast Idle (.3)	.4
Vacuum Brake-one (.6)	.8
both (.8)	1.0
Complete (1.3)	1.8
(G) Thermostatic Choke Cover and/or Gasket, Renew	
All models (.6)	1.0
(G) Automatic Choke Vacuum Diaphragm, Renew	
All models-one (.6)	.8
both (.8)	1.0
(M) Carburetor Fuel Filter, Renew	
All models (.3)	.4
(G) Choke Vacuum Control Switch, Renew	
1983-85 (.3)	.3
(G) Electric Choke Relay, Renew	
1983-85 (.2)	.3
(G) Anti-Dieseling or Idle Stop Solenoid, Renew	
1983-85 (.3)	.4
(G) E.F.E. Heater (Insulator), Renew	
1983-85 (.6)	1.0
(G) Carburetor, Renew	
Includes: All necessary adjustments.	
1983-85 (.6)	1.0
To perform C.C.C. system check, add (.5)	1.0
(G) Carburetor, R&R and Clean or Recondition	
Includes: All necessary adjustments.	
1983-85 (2.3)	3.0
To perform C.C.C. system check, add (.5)	1.0
(G) Accelerator Pump, Renew	
1983-85 (.9)	1.2
(G) Float or Needle Valve and Seat, Renew	
1983-85 (.9)	1.2
Perform C.C.C. system test add	1.0
(G) Fast Idle Relay, Renew	
1983-85 (.3)	.4
(G) Fast Idle Actuator, Renew	
1985 (.4)	.5
(G) Fuel Pump or Push Rod, Renew	
1983-85-Four (.6)	.9
V-6 (.5)	1.0
Add pump test if performed.	
(G) Fuel Tank, Renew	
Includes: Drain and refill tank, transfer tank gauge unit.	
1983-85 (.7)	1.2
(G) Fuel Gauge (Tank), Renew	
Includes: Drain and refill tank.	
1983-85 (.8)	1.3
(G) Fuel Gauge (Dash), Renew	
1983-85 (.6)	1.0
(G) Intake Manifold Gasket, Renew	
1983-85-Four (2.0)	3.0
V-6 (2.5)	3.4
w/Port Inj add (.1)	.2
w/A.C. add (.3)	.3
w/A.I.R. add (.5)	.5

LABOR 3 FUEL SYSTEM 3 LABOR

(Factory Time)	Chilton Time
w/Cruise control add (.3)	.3
w/C.C.C. add (.3)	.3
Renew manif add (.3)	.5
(G) Intake Plenum, Renew	
1985 (.5)	.8
(G) Intake Runners, Renew	
1985 (.9)	1.4
E.F.E. SYSTEM	
(G) E.F.E. Valve (Heat Riser), Renew	
1983-84 (.7)	1.1
THROTTLE BODY INJECTION	
(G) Throttle Body and/or Gasket, Renew	
Four–1983-85 (.7)	1.0
Renew meter body add (.3)	.3
(G) Idle Air Control Valve, Renew	
Four–1983-85 (.6)	.9
(G) Throttle Body Injector, Renew	
Four–1983-85 (.7)	1.0
(G) Fuel Pressure Regulator, Renew	
Four–1983-85 (.7)	1.1
(G) Fuel Pump, Renew (In Tank)	
Four–1983-85 (1.3)	1.8
(G) Fuel Pump Relay, Renew	
Four–1983-85 (.7)	1.0
(G) Minimum Idle Speed, Adjust	
All models (.6)	.8
PORTED INJECTION	
(G) Throttle Body, R&R	
1985 (.6)	1.0
Renew throttle body kit add (.3)	.3
Renew fuel meter body add (.3)	.3
(G) Throttle Body Unit, Renew	
1985 (.7)	1.0
(G) Throttle Body Fuel Meter Assy; and/or Gasket, Renew	
1985 (.4)	.6
(G) Idle Air Control Valve, Renew	
1985 (.4)	.6
(G) Minimum Idle Speed, Adjust	
All models (.4)	.7
(G) Throttle Body Injector and/or Gasket, Renew	
1985-one (.7)	1.1
(G) Fuel Pressure Regulator, Renew	
1985 (.7)	.9
(G) Fuel Pump, Renew (In Tank)	
1985 (1.3)	1.8
(G) Fuel Pump Relay, Renew	
1985 (.7)	.9
(G) Cold Start Injector, Renew	
1985 (1.0)	1.4
(G) Thermo Start Switch, Renew	
1985 (.5)	.7
(G) Fuel Injector, Renew	
1985-one (1.2)	1.8
each adtnl (.1)	.1
(G) Fuel Rail, Renew	
1985-87 (.7)	1.2
(G) Mass Air Sensor, Renew	
1985 (.4)	.5

PARTS 3 FUEL SYSTEM 3 PARTS

	Part No.	Price
Carburetor Assy. (Rochester)		
V-6–173X engine		
(Auto. trans.)		
1983-wo/A.C.	◆17079149	786.00
w/A.C.	◆17079167	879.75
1984-85	◆17110530	771.75
(Man. trans.)		
1983-wo/A.C.	◆17079158	889.75
w/A.C.	◆17079170	1014.75
1984-85	◆17110533	777.75
V-6–173Z engine		
(Auto. trans.)		
1983-wo/A.C.	◆17079556	548.00
w/A.C.	◆17079576	802.25
1984	◆17110537	777.75
(Man. trans.)		
1983	◆17079571	811.00
1984	◆17110536	777.75
Carburetor Repair Kit		
V-6–173 engine		
1983	◆17069019	39.50
1984	◆17076122	44.25
1985	◆17076122	44.25
Carburetor Gasket Kit		
V-6–173 engine		
1983	◆17068741	28.25
1984-85	◆17079987	27.25
Fuel Pump		
4 cyl.–151 engine		
1983-wo/E.F.I.	◆6471926	N.L.
1983-85-w/E.F.I.	◆6472011	80.00
V-6–173 engine		
1983-85-exc. Code W	◆6472020	56.25
1985-Code W	◆6472229	132.50
Fuel Tank		
1983-85	◆22515514	94.50
Fuel Gauge (Tank)		
1983-85 (w/151 eng.)		
wo/E.F.I.	◆25090481	98.50
w/E.F.I.	◆25003275	139.25
1983-85 (w/V-6 eng.)		
Code X	◆25003149	72.25
Code W	◆25003924	112.75
Fuel Gauge (Dash)		
Citation		
(wo/gauges)		
1983-84	◆6433476	24.00
1985	◆6434173	27.50
(w/gauges)		
1983-84	◆6433811	25.25
1985	◆6434176	24.50
Omega		
(wo/gauges)		
1983-84	◆6433128	29.00
(w/gauges)		
1983-85	◆6433130	30.00
Phoenix		
(wo/tachometer)		
1983	◆6433769	24.25
1984	◆25058289	24.00
(w/tachometer)		
1983-w/151 eng.	◆25054999	193.00
w/173X eng.	◆25058004	193.00
w/173Z eng.	◆25058036	193.00
1984-w/151 eng.	◆25058281	193.00
w/173X eng.	◆25058276	193.00
w/173Z eng.	◆25058271	193.00
Skylark		
(wo/gauges)		
1983-85	◆6433426	27.25
(w/gauges)		
1983-85	◆6433185	69.75
Manifold Gasket Set (Intake)		
4 cyl.–151 engine		
1983-85	◆10026023	5.00
V-6–173 engine		
1983-85	◆14033476	12.50

PARTS 3 ELECTRONIC FUEL INJECTION 3 PARTS

	Part No.	Price
MULTI-PORT FUEL INJECTION		
V-6–173 eng. (Code W)		
(1) Throttle Body Assy.		
1985-w/A.T.	◆17085023	N.L.
w/M.T.	◆17085173	N.L.
(2) Gasket Kit		
1985	◆17110827	9.00
(3) Throttle Position Sensor Kit		
1985	◆17110830	46.50
(4) Coolant Cover Kit		
1985	◆17110828	39.25
(5) Idle Air Vacuum Housing Kit		
1985	◆17110834	30.00
(6) Idle Air Control Valve		
1985	◆17111288	58.00
(7) Fuel Rail and Pressure Regulator		
1985	◆17110854	19.00

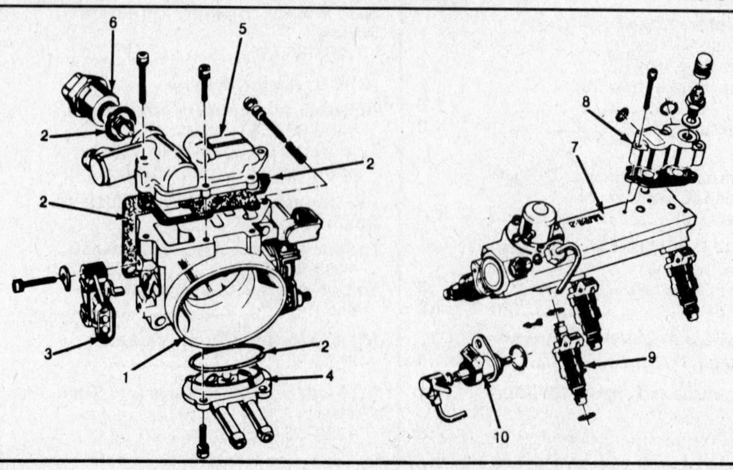

PARTS 3 ELECTRONIC FUEL INJECTION 3 PARTS

(8) Fuel Inlet/Outlet Block
1985 .... ◆17110853 29.25

(9) Fuel Injector Kit
1985 .... ◆17110855 N.L.

(10) Cold Start Valve
1985 .... ◆17110858 49.50

PARTS 3 THROTTLE BODY FUEL INJECTION 3 PARTS

	Part No.	Price
Throttle Body Injection Unit		
1983	◆17079592	582.50
1984	◆17110359	582.50
1985	◆17110762	498.50
(1) Fuel Meter Body Kit		
1983-85	◆17078222	109.75
(2) Fuel Injector Kit		
1983-85	◆17068993	191.75
(3) Gasket Kit		
1983-85	◆17068990	24.75
(4) Sensor Kit (Throttle Position)		
1983-85	◆17078274	74.75
(5) Throttle Body Kit		
1983	◆17079593	266.75
1984	◆17110360	240.00
1985	◆17110763	237.25
(6) Fuel Nut Assortment Kit		
1983-85	◆17078275	5.75
(7) Idle Air Valve Control Kit		
1983-84	◆17078220	82.00
1985	◆17079256	88.75
Fuel Meter Cover Kit		
1983-85	◆17078969	139.75
Screw Assortment Kit		
1983-85	◆17078276	18.25

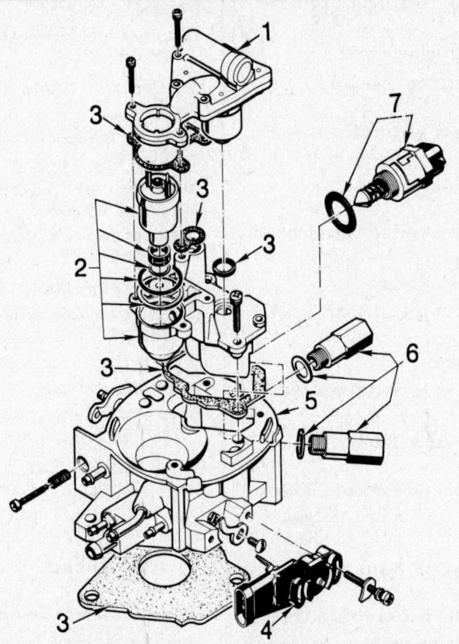

LABOR 3A EMISSION CONTROLS 3A LABOR

(Factory Time) Chilton Time

EMISSION CONTROLS

(G) Emission Control Check
Includes: Check and adjust engine idle speed and mixture and ignition timing. Check PCV valve.
All models 6

(G) Emission Maintenance Reminder Flag, Reset
All models 5

POSITIVE CRANKCASE VENTILATION

(M) Positive Crankcase Ventilation Valve, Renew
All models (.2) 3

(M) Crankcase Ventilation Filter Assy., Renew
All models (.2) 3

EVAPORATIVE EMISSION TYPE

(G) Charcoal Canister, Renew
All models (.3) 5

(G) Fuel Tank Pressure Control Valve, Renew
1983-85 (.2) 3

CONTROLLED COMBUSTION TYPE

(G) Air Cleaner Vacuum Motor, Renew
All models (.3) 5

(G) Air Cleaner Temperature Sensor, Renew
All models (.2) 3

CHILTON'S EMISSION CONTROL TUNE-UP

1. Clean or renew P.C.V. valve, hoses and filter.
2. Check fuel tank cap for sealing ability.
3. Check fuel tank and fuel lines for leakage.
4. Check evaporation canister and filter. Replace if necessary.
5. Check engine compression to determine leakage of unburned gases. (Add time for items of interference).
6. Test and clean or renew spark plugs.
7. Check engine oil dipstick for sealing ability.
8. Test exhaust system with analyzer and check system for leakage.
9. Check exhaust manifold heat valve for operation.
10. Adjust ignition timing and carburetor idle speed and mixture.
11. Check automatic choke mechanism for free operation.
12. Inspect air cleaner and element.
13. On models so equipped, test distributor vacuum control switch and transmission control switch.

Four 1.3
V-6 .... 1.7
For repairs made, charge accordingly.

(Factory Time) Chilton Time

EXHAUST GAS RECIRCULATION SYSTEM

(G) E.G.R. Valve, Renew
All models-Four (.2) 4
V-6 (.6) 1.0

(G) EGR/EFE Thermal Vacuum Switch, Renew
All models (.3) 4

(G) E.G.R. Vacuum Delay Valve, Renew
All models (.2) 4

(G) Thermostatic Vacuum Control Switch, Renew
All models (.2) 3

(G) E.G.R. Thermal Control Valve, Renew
All models (.3) 4

COMPUTER COMMAND CONTROL SYSTEM (C.C.C.)

(P) Electronic Control Module, Renew
Does not include system performance check.
1983-85 (.6) 9

(P) Mixture Control Solenoid, Renew
Does not include system performance check.
1983-85 (.4) 5

LABOR 3A EMISSION CONTROLS 3A LABOR

(Factory Time) — Chilton Time

(P) Prom, Renew
Does not include system performance check.
Includes: R&R electronic module.
1983-85 (.5) ... 1.0

(P) Throttle Position Sensor, Adjust
All models 9
Perform C.C.C. System check add ... 1.0

(P) Manifold Temperature Sensor, Renew
Does not include system performance check.
1983-85 (.4) 6

(P) Manifold Differential Pressure Sensor, Renew
Does not include system performance check.
1983-85 (.5) 7

(P) Barometric Sensor, Renew
Does not include system performance check.
1983-85 (.4) 6

(P) E.G.R. Sensor, Renew
Does not include system performance check.
1985 (.4) 6

(P) Coolant Temperature Sensor, Renew
Does not include system performance check.
Includes: Drain and refill cooling system.
1983-85 (.5) 7

(P) Manifold Pressure Sensor, Renew
Does not include system performance check.
1983-85 (.5) 6

(P) Oxygen Sensor, Renew
Does not include system performance check.
1983-85 (.4) 7

(P) Throttle Position Sensor, Renew
Does not include system performance check.
1983-85 (1.1) ... 1.4

(P) Vehicle Speed Sensor, Renew
Does not include system performance check.
1983-85 (.9) ... 1.5

(P) Air Control Valve, Renew
Does not include system performance check.
1983-85 (.4) 6

(P) Air Control/Air Switching Valve, Renew
Does not include system performance check.
1983-85 (.5) 8

(P) Canister Purge Control Valve, Renew
Does not include system performance check.
1983-85 (.4) 6

(P) Vacuum Control Purge Solenoid, Renew
Does not include system performance check.
1983-85 (.4) 6

(P) EFE/EGR Relay, Renew
Does not include system performance check.
1983-85 (.3) 5

(P) E.G.R. Vacuum Control Solenoid, Renew
Does not include system performance check.
1983-85 (.4) 6

(P) Back-Up Lamp and Park/Neutral Switch, Renew
Does not include system performance check.
1983-85 (.7) ... 1.0

(P) Idle Speed Control Motor, Renew
Does not include system performance check.
1983 (.5) 7

(P) Tachometer Filter, Renew
Does not include system performance check.
1983-85 (.3) 3

(P) Computer Command Control System Performance Check
1983-85 (.5) ... 1.0

PULSE AIR INJECTION REACTION SYSTEM

(G) Pulse A.I.R. Manifold, Renew
All models-right (.8) ... 1.2
left (.4) 7

(G) Pulse A.I.R. Valve Assy., Renew
All models-Four (.4) 7
V-6 (.4) 6

(G) P.A.I.R. Deceleration Valve, Renew
All models (.3) 4

(G) A.I.R. Pump, Renew
All models-Four (.5) 8
V-6 (.4) 7

(G) A.I.R. Check Valve, Renew (One)
All models (.2) 3
each adtnl (.2) 2

(G) A.I.R. Air Cleaner, Renew
All models (.2) 3

(G) A.I.R. Centrifugal Filter, Renew
All models (.3) 5

(G) Air Manifold Pipe, Renew
All models-right (.8) ... 1.2

(G) Catalytic Converter Air Pipe, Renew
All models
upper (.5) 7
lower (.3) 5

THROTTLE BODY INJECTION

(P) Electronic Control Module, Renew
1983-85 (.7) 9

(P) Prom, Renew
1983-85 (.7) ... 1.0

(P) Coolant Temperature Sensor, Renew
1983-85 (.5) 7

(P) Manifold Pressure Sensor, Renew
1983-85 (.5) 6

(P) Oxygen Sensor, Renew
1983-85 (.5) 7

(P) Vehicle Speed Sensor, Renew
1983-85 (1.1) ... 1.5

(P) Throttle Position Sensor, Renew
1983-85 (.9) ... 1.4

PARTS 3A EMISSION CONTROLS 3A PARTS

	Part No.	Price
POSITIVE CRANKCASE VENTILATION		
Positive Crankcase Vent. Valve		
4 cyl.-151 engine		
1983-84	◆25041498	7.00
1985	◆25043669	6.25
V-6-173 engine		
1983-85	◆8995284	5.00
EVAPORATIVE EMISSION TYPE		
Vapor Canister		
4 cyl.-151 engine		
1983	◆17063013	39.00
1984-85	◆17075840	30.00
V-6-173 engine		
1983	◆17075831	64.25
1984	◆17075824	75.50
1985-Code W	◆17075854	66.00
Code X	◆17078849	1616.75
CONTROLLED COMBUSTION TYPE		
Air Cleaner Vacuum Motor		
1983-85-exc. X11	◆25042360	22.00
w/X11	◆8994333	18.75
Air Cleaner Temperature Sensor		
1983-85-exc. 151	◆8997787	18.75
1983-84-151 eng.	◆8997574	18.75

EXHAUST GAS RECIRCULATION SYSTEM

E.G.R. Valve
Replacement E.G.R. valves must be ordered according to the stamping number on the original valve.

	Part No.	Price
E.G.R. Thermal Vacuum Switch		
1983-85-V-6 eng	◆14003932	7.75
E.G.R. Control Valve		
1983-85	◆546895	10.00
AIR INJECTION REACTION SYSTEM		
Air Injection Pump		
V-6-173 engine		
1983-85	◆7842076	141.00
Air Injection Control Valve		
V-6-173 engine		
1983-w/M.T.	◆17073947	112.50
w/A.T.	◆17073948	110.00
1984-85	◆17074977	114.00
Deceleration Valve		
1983-85	◆14056425	17.50
COMPUTER CONTROLLED EMISSION SYSTEM		
Electronic Control Module (ECM)		
4 cyl.-151 engine		
1983	◆1226100	110.25
1984	◆1226156	110.25
1985	◆1226864	110.25
V-6-173 engine		
1983	◆1226025	110.25
1984	◆1226455	110.25
1985-85-Code W	◆1226870	110.00
Code X	◆1226865	110.00

PARTS 3A EMISSION CONTROLS 3A PARTS

	Part No.	Price
Calibration Unit (Prom)		
Note: Order by code stamped on existing calibrator.		
Oxygen Sensor		
1983-85-exc. V-6	◆8990741	28.75
1983-V-6 eng.	◆5613959	29.00
Coolant Temperature Sensor		
1983-85	◆25036092	22.00
Barometric Sensor		
1983-85	◆16006833	62.25
M.A.P. Sensor		
1983-85	◆16017460	N.L.
Manifold Diff. Pressure Sensor		
1983-85	◆16006834	62.25
Vehicle Speed Sensor		
1983	◆25007278	53.50
1984-85	◆25007421	41.50

LABOR 4 ALTERNATOR AND REGULATOR 4 LABOR

(Factory Time)	Chilton Time
(G) Delcotron Circuits, Test	
Includes: Test battery, regulator, Delcotron output.	
All models	.6
(M) Alternator Drive Belt, Renew	
1983-85	
Four (.2)	.3
w/P.S. add (.3)	.3
V-6 (.2)	.3
(G) Delcotron Assembly, Renew	
1983-85-Four (.7)	1.1
V-6 (.4)	.6
w/A.C. add (.4)	.4
w/P.S. add (.3)	.3
(G) Delcotron, R&R and Recondition	
Includes: Complete disassembly, replacement of parts as required, reassemble.	
1983-85-Four (1.5)	2.0
V-6 (1.1)	1.7
w/A.C. add (.4)	.4
w/P.S. add (.3)	.3
(G) Delcotron Front Bearing, Renew	
Includes: R&R Delcotron, separate end frames.	
1983-85-Four (1.0)	1.4
V-6 (.6)	.9
w/A.C. add (.4)	.4
w/P.S. add (.3)	.3
Renew rear brg add	.2
(G) Delcotron Voltage Regulator, Test and Renew	
Includes: R&R, disassemble and reassemble Delcotron.	
1983-85-Four (.9)	1.5
V-6 (.6)	1.0
w/A.C. add (.4)	.4
w/P.S. add (.3)	.3
(G) Voltmeter, Renew	
1983-85 (.6)	1.0

PARTS 4 ALTERNATOR AND REGULATOR 4 PARTS

	Part No.	Price
Delcotron Assembly (New)		
1983-84-42 amp.	◆1105360	206.00
66, 78 amp.	◆1100250	225.00
1985-78 amp.	◆1100250	225.00
94 amp.	◆1105492	228.50
42 amp.	◆1105360	206.00
(1) Capacitor		
1983-85	◆1978146	4.75
(2) Diode Trio (Negative)		
1983-85	◆1984459	5.00
(3) Rectifier Bridge		
1983-85-exc. below	◆1984454	28.00
94 amp.	◆1987061	29.25
(4) Bearing		
1983-85-exc below	◆9436831	5.50
70, 85 amp	◆1975322	5.50
(5) Terminal Pkg.		
1983-85	◆1975471	3.50
(6) Frame (Rear End)		
1983-85-exc. below	◆1984460	47.75
42 amp.	◆1974939	24.75
94 amp.	◆1987073	28.00
(7) Voltage Regulator		
1983-85	◆1116387	25.00
(8) Brush w/Holder		
1983-85	◆1984462	9.00

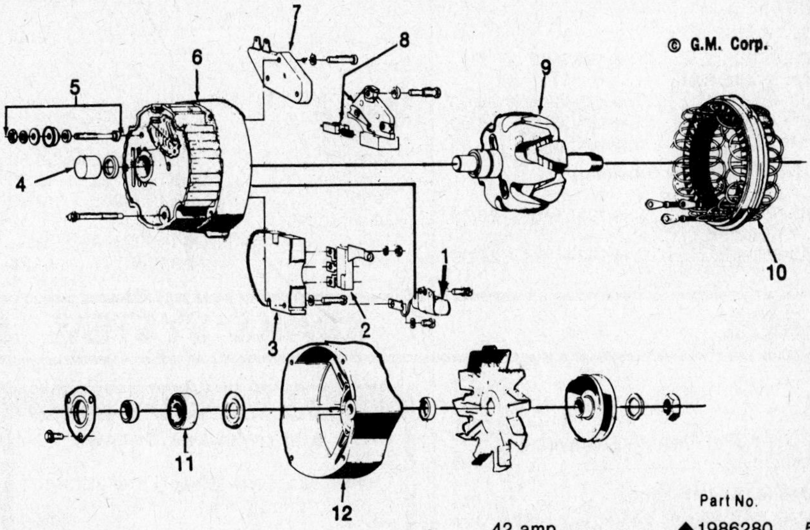

	Part No.	Price
(9) Rotor Assy.		
1983-85-exc. below	◆1985476	72.00
94 amp.	◆1984466	77.25
(10) Stator Assy.		
1983-85-exc. below	◆1984445	37.25
42 amp.	◆1986280	52.75
56 amp.	◆1984584	54.50
94 amp.	◆1987074	41.50
(11) Bearing (Drive End)		
1983-85	◆908419	10.00
(12) Frame (Drive End)		
1983-85-42 amp.	◆1985642	24.75
66, 78 amp.	◆1984464	23.50
94 amp.	◆1987054	28.00

LABOR 5 STARTING SYSTEM 5 LABOR

(Factory Time)	Chilton Time
(G) Starter Draw Test (On Car)	
All models	.3
(G) Starter, Renew	
1983-85-Four (.4)	.7
V-6 (.6)	.9
Add draw test if performed.	
(G) Starter, R&R and Recondition	
Includes: Turn down armature.	
1983-85-Four (1.2)	2.0
V-6 (1.4)	2.2
Renew field coils add (.2)	.5
Add draw test if performed.	
(G) Starter Drive, Renew	
Includes: R&R starter.	
1983-85-Four (.6)	1.0
V-6 (.9)	1.2

LABOR 5 STARTING SYSTEM 5 LABOR

(Factory Time)	Chilton Time
(G) Starter Motor Solenoid, Renew	
Includes: R&R starter on V-6.	
1983-85-Four (.3)	.5
V-6 (.6)	1.0
(G) Starter Safety Switch, Renew	
1983-85-w/M.T. (.2)	.4
w/A.T. (.3)	.5
(G) Voltmeter, Renew	
1983-85 (.6)	1.0
(G) Ignition Switch, Renew	
1983-84 (.5)	.9
1985 (.7)	1.2
(M) Battery Cables, Renew	
1983-85-positive (.3)	.4
negative (.3)	.4
(M) Battery Terminals, Clean	
All models	.3

PARTS 5 STARTING SYSTEM 5 PARTS

	Part No.	Price
(1) Starter Assembly (New)		
4 cyl.–151 engine		
1983	◆1109556	N.L.
1984-85	◆1998450	186.00
V-6–173 engine		
1983	◆1109533	214.75
1984-85	◆1109564	165.50
(2) Solenoid Switch		
1983-85	◆1114531	N.L.
(3) Drive Assy.		
1983-85	◆1984511	23.50
(4) Brushes		
1983-85	◆1893296	.50
(5) Drive End Bushing		
1983-85	◆1932190	.50
(6) Commutator End Plate		
1983-85	◆1978292	6.50
(7) Armature		
1983-85	◆1985138	N.L.
(8) Frame and Field		
1983-Four cyl.	◆1984522	75.00
V-6 eng.	◆1978672	78.00
1984-87	◆1985143	71.50
(9) Drive Housing (w/Bushing)		
4 cyl.–151 engine		
1983-85	◆1985148	25.75
V-6–173 engine		
1983-85	◆1984734	27.00

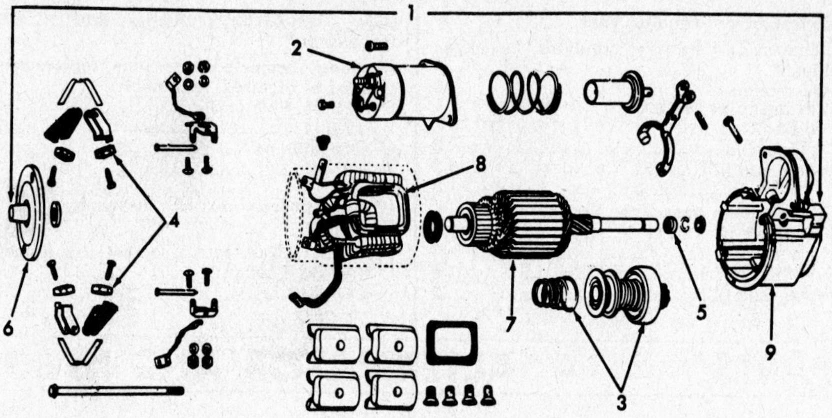

	Part No.	Price
Battery Cables		
Order by year and model.		
Neutral Safety Switch		
(w/auto. trans.)		
1983-84-wo/ console	◆22509632	5.50
w/console	◆1994223	18.00
1985	◆1994255	12.00
(w/man. trans.)		
1983	◆14029519	N.L.
1984-85	◆14080678	4.25
Ignition Switch		
(wo/tilt wheel)		
1983	◆1990109	N.L.
1984-85-wo/ console	◆1990115	11.50
w/console	◆7843451	25.75
(w/tilt wheel)		
1983	◆1990110	N.L.
1984-85-wo/ console	◆1990116	11.50
w/console	◆7843497	25.75

LABOR 6 BRAKE SYSTEM 6 LABOR

(Factory Time)	Chilton Time
(G) Brake Pedal Free Play, Adjust	
All models	.3
(G) Brakes, Adjust (Minor)	
Includes: R&R wheels and adjust brakes thru access holes in drums. Fill master cylinder.	
two wheels	.4
Remove knock out plugs add-each	.1
(G) Bleed Brakes (Four Wheels)	
Includes: Fill master cylinder.	
All models (.4)	.5
(G) Free Up or Renew Rear Brake Self-Adjusting Units	
1983-85-one (.4)	.6
each adtnl	.4
(G) Brake Shoes and/or Pads, Renew	
Includes: Install new or exchange shoes or pads, adjust service and hand brake. Bleed system.	
1983-85-front-disc (.9)	1.1
rear-drum (.9)	1.5
all four wheels	2.5
Resurface disc rotor add-each	.9
Resurface brake drum add-each	.5

COMBINATIONS

Add to Brakes, Renew

See Machine Shop Operations

(Factory Time)	Chilton Time
(G) RENEW WHEEL CYLINDER	
Each (.2)	.2
(G) REBUILD WHEEL CYLINDER	
Each (.2)	.3
(G) REBUILD CALIPER ASSEMBLY	
Each (.5)	.6
(G) RENEW MASTER CYLINDER	
All models (.5)	.8
(G) REBUILD MASTER CYLINDER	
All models (.8)	1.0
(G) RENEW BRAKE HOSE	
Each (.3)	.3
(G) RENEW BRAKE DRUM	
Each (.1)	.1
(G) RENEW DISC BRAKE ROTOR	
Each (.2)	.3

(Factory Time)	Chilton Time
(G) Brake Drum, Renew (One)	
1983-85-rear (.3)	.5
(G) Brake Proportioner Valves, Renew	
Includes: Bleed system.	
1983-85-each (.4)	.6
(G) Brake System Failure Warning Switch, Renew	
1983-85 (.2)	.3

BRAKE HYDRAULIC SYSTEM

(Factory Time)	Chilton Time
(G) Wheel Cylinder, Renew (Rear)	
Includes: Bleed system.	
1983-85-one (.8)	1.0
both (1.1)	1.9
(G) Wheel Cylinder, R&R and Rebuild	
Includes: Hone cylinder and bleed system.	
1983-85-one (1.0)	1.3
both (1.5)	2.1
(G) Master Cylinder, Renew	
Includes: Bleed complete system.	
1983-85 (.7)	1.0

LABOR — 6 BRAKE SYSTEM 6 — LABOR

	(Factory Time)	Chilton Time
(G) Master Cylinder, R&R and Rebuild		
Includes: Hone cylinder and bleed complete system.		
1983-85	(1.5)	1.9
(G) Brake Hose, Renew		
Includes: Bleed system.		
1983-85-front-one	(.6)	.8
both	(.8)	1.1
rear-each	(.4)	.6
(G) Brake System, Flush and Refill		
All models		1.2
POWER BRAKES		
(G) Power Brake Cylinder, Renew		
1983-85	(.7)	1.1
(G) Power Brake Cylinder, R&R and Recondition		
1983-85	(1.4)	1.8
Recond m/Cyl add	(.8)	.8
(M) Vacuum Check Valve, Renew		
1983-85	(.3)	.3
(G) Electric Vacuum Pump, Renew		
1983-85	(.3)	.4
Recond piston add	(.2)	.4
Renew housing add	(.3)	.3
(G) Vacuum Pump Pressure Switch, Renew		
1983-85	(.2)	.3
(G) Low Vacuum Switch, Renew		
1983-85	(.2)	.3
DISC BRAKES		
(G) Disc Brake Pads, Renew		
Includes: Install new disc brake pads only.		
1983-85	(.9)	1.1
(G) Disc Brake Rotor, Renew		
1983-85-one	(.5)	.7
both	(.8)	1.2
(G) Caliper Assembly, Renew		
Includes: Bleed complete system.		
1983-85-one	(.7)	1.0
both	(1.0)	1.5
(G) Caliper Assembly, R&R and Recondition		
Includes: Bleed complete system.		
1983-85-one	(1.2)	1.5
both	(2.0)	2.5
PARKING BRAKE		
(M) Parking Brake, Adjust		
All models	(.3)	.4
(G) Parking Brake Lamp Switch, Renew		
1983-85	(.3)	.4
(G) Parking Brake Control and Ratchet, Renew		
1983-84	(.7)	1.0
1985	(1.7)	2.5
(G) Parking Brake Equalizer, Renew		
1983-85	(.3)	.5
(G) Parking Brake Cables, Renew		
1983-85-front	(.8)	1.1
rear-right side	(.6)	.9
left side	(.5)	.8
both sides	(1.0)	1.5

PARTS — 6 BRAKE SYSTEM 6 — PARTS

	Part No.	Price
Brake Shoe Set (Rear)		
1983	◆12300194	34.00
1984	◆12300248	32.00
1985	◆12321412	43.00
Rear Wheel Cylinder Assy.		
1983-85	◆18007981	25.00
Wheel Cylinder Repair Kit (Rear)		
1983-85	◆18007982	6.50
Front Brake Hose		
(right)		
1983	◆9767946	15.25
1984-85	◆17980548	18.00
(left)		
1983-85	◆9767945	15.25
Rear Brake Hose		
1983-85	◆9767287	7.50
Master Cylinder Assy.		
1983-85-Note 1	◆18010087	206.50
Master Cylinder Repair Kit		
1983-85	◆18004853	22.50
Brake Drum (Rear)		
1983-85	◆25516198	72.25
Oil Seal (Front)		
1983	◆14084120	3.75
1984-85	◆14084120	3.75
Power Brake Booster (Vacuum)		
w/151, 173X engs.		
1983-85	◆18006856	213.00
w/173Z engine		
1983-85	◆18007292	271.25
Power Brake Booster Repair Kit		
1983-85	◆18007897	47.50
Parking Brake Release Handle		
Buick		
1983-85	◆25508854	3.00
Chevrolet		
1983-84	◆14049337	4.75
1985	◆14081966	5.00
Olds.		
1983-84	◆22516036	3.75
Pontiac		
1983-84	◆10018262	3.75
Front Cable (Parking Brake)		
1983-85	◆25516525	14.00
Rear Cable (Parking Brake)		
(right)		
1983-85	◆25516528	19.00
(left)		
1983-85	◆25516529	15.25

PARTS — 6 DISC BRAKES 6 — PARTS

	Part No.	Price
(1) Brake Pads		
(wo/power brakes)		
1983-85	◆12300242	43.50
(w/power brakes)		
1983	◆12300243	43.50
1984-85	◆12300243	43.50
(2) Anti-Rattle Spring		
1983-85	◆18011280	2.75
(3) Caliper Repair Kit		
1983-84	◆18004873	7.25
1985	◆18011670	8.50
(4) Piston Assy.		
1983-85	◆18002866	13.00
(5) Caliper Assy.		
1983-right	◆18008758	124.00
left	◆18011356	131.50
1984-right	◆18011357	131.50
left	◆18011356	131.50

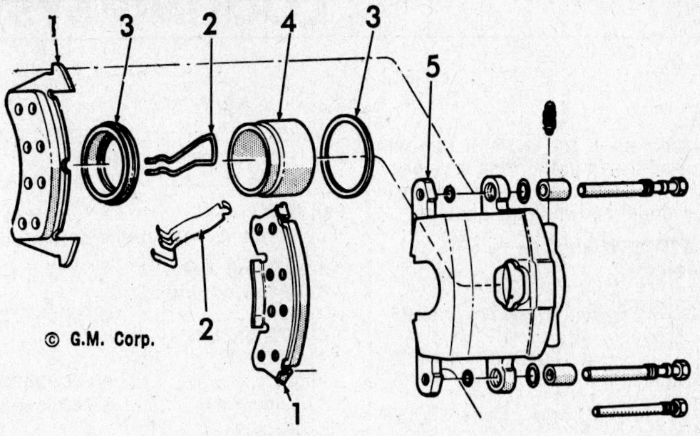

	Part No.	Price
1985-right	◆18011668	163.25
left	◆18011667	163.25

	Part No.	Price
Hub and Disc.		
1983-85	◆14046950	64.50

	(Factory Time)	Chilton Time
(M) Winterize Cooling System		
Includes: Run engine to check for leaks, tighten all hose connections. Test radiator and pressure cap, drain radiator and engine block. Add anti-freeze and refill system.		
All models		.5
(G) Thermostat, Renew		
1983-85		
Four	(.2)	.4
V-6	(.4)	.6
(G) Radiator Assembly, R&R or Renew		
Includes: Drain and refill cooling system.		
1983-85	(.7)	1.1
w/A.T. add	(.2)	.2
ADD THESE OPERATIONS TO RADIATOR R&R		
(G) Boil & Repair		1.5
(G) Rod Clean		1.9
(G) Repair Core		1.3
(G) Renew Tank		1.6
(G) Renew Trans. Oil Cooler		1.9
(G) Recore Radiator		1.7
(M) Radiator Hoses, Renew		
1983-85-upper	(.3)	.4
lower	(.4)	.5
both	(.5)	.7
(M) Drive Belt, Renew		
1983-85-one	(.2)	.3
each adtnl	(.2)	.2
(M) Drive Belt, Adjust		
1983-85-one	(.2)	.2
all	(.5)	.6
(G) Water Pump and/or Gasket, Renew		
1983-85-Four	(.9)	1.3
V-6	(1.3)	1.8
w/P.S. add	(.2)	.2
w/A.C. add		
Four	(.7)	.7
V-6	(.2)	.2
(G) Engine Coolant Fan and/or Motor, Renew		
1983-85	(.4)	.6
(G) Engine Coolant Fan Relay, Renew		
1983-85	(.2)	.3

COOLING SYSTEM TUNE-UP

An Annual Cooling System Tune-Up Suggestion List should include (with some exceptions):

1. A visual check of the cooling system for indications of leaks or excessive oil content.
2. Pressure check the cooling system for internal and external leaks with filler cap and neck adapter and tester.
3. Check crankcase and automatic transmission oil for water content.
4. Test coolant thermostat with radiator thermometer.
5. Check temperature gauge for accuracy.
6. Drain system and flush till clean.
7. Clean foreign matter from radiator fins.
8. Test radiator pressure cap with cap tester.
9. Check fan blades and pulleys for alignment and damage.
10. Internal and external inspection of all hoses for cracks and deterioration.
11. Check core plugs (where possible) for seepage.
12. Refill system with correct coolant and check for air locks.
13. Check condition and tension of drive belts with tension gauge.

All models 1.5

	(Factory Time)	Chilton Time
(G) Coolant Fan Switch, Renew		
1983-85	(.2)	.3
(G) Coolant Fan Pressure Switch, Renew		
1983-85	(.5)	.7
(G) Temperature Gauge (Engine Unit), Renew		
1983-85	(.2)	.3
(G) Temperature Gauge (Dash Unit), Renew		
1983-85	(.6)	1.0
(G) Water Jacket Expansion Plugs, Renew (Side of Block)		
each	(.2)	.5
Note: If necessary to R&R any component to gain access to plug, add appropriate time.		
(G) Heater Hoses, Renew		
1983-85-one	(.2)	.3
all	(.4)	.5
(G) Heater Core, R&R or Renew		
1983-85-wo/A.C.	(.5)	.9
w/A.C.	(1.4)	3.5
ADD THESE OPERATIONS TO HEATER CORE R&R		
(G) Boil & Repair		1.2
(G) Repair Core		.9
(G) Recore		1.2
(G) Blower Motor, Renew		
1983-85-wo/A.C.	(.4)	1.0
w/A.C.	(.4)	1.0
(G) Blower Motor Switch, Renew		
1983-85-wo/A.C.	(.5)	.8
w/A.C.	(.5)	.8
(G) Blower Motor Resistor, Renew		
1983-85	(.2)	.3
(G) Blower Motor Relay, Renew		
1983-85-w/A.C.	(.2)	.3
(G) Temperature Control Assembly, Renew		
1983-85-wo/A.C.	(.5)	1.0
w/A.C.	(.5)	1.0

PARTS 7 COOLING SYSTEM 7 PARTS

Radiator Assy.
Accurate replacement of the radiator can be done only by using the radiator code stamped on a metal tag located on the original radiator. Order by year, model and radiator code no.

	Part No.	Price
Radiator Hose (Upper)		
4 cyl.-151 engine		
(wo/A.C.)		
1983-85	◆10026519	10.25
(w/A.C.)		
1983-85	◆10027287	10.25
V-6-173 engine		
(wo/A.C.)		
1983-85	◆14038539	10.25
(w/A.C.)		
1983-85	◆14038540	10.25
Radiator Hose (Lower)		
4 cyl.-151 engine		
1983-84	◆10020495	14.50
1985	◆10030354	14.00
V-6-173 engine		
1983-85	◆472432	10.25

Fan Belt
Note: Order by model and description.

	Part No.	Price
Water Pump Assy.		
4 cyl.-151 engine		
1983-85	◆10004073	59.75
V-6-173 engine		
1983-85-W, X eng.	◆14033483	61.50
Z eng.	◆14054555	67.50
Thermostat		
4 cyl.-151 engine		
1983-85	◆3048009	9.50
V-6-173 engine		
1983-85-exc. Code W	◆3041390	6.00
1985-Code W	◆3043066	6.75
Temperature Gauge (Engine Unit)		
(wo/gauges)		
1983-85-151 eng.	◆25036371	8.00
173 eng.	◆25036373	9.75
(w/gauges)		
1983-85	◆8993146	19.25
Electric Cooling Fan Motor		
1983-85-wo/A.C.	◆25035623	N.L.
w/A.C.	◆22035556	78.50
Cooling Fan Relay		
4 cyl-151 engine		
1983	◆10033118	5.50
1984-85	◆10032081	5.50
V-6-173 engine		
1983	◆14043278	5.25

PARTS 7 COOLING SYSTEM 7 PARTS

	Part No.	Price
1984-85-exc.		
Code W	◆14078902	12.00
1985-Code W	◆14084351	12.00
Cooling Fan Switch		
1983-85	◆3040674	12.00
Heater Core Assy.		
1983-85-wo/A.C.	◆3042073	52.75
w/A.C.	◆3040837	55.00

	Part No.	Price
Blower Motor		
(wo/A.C.)		
1983	◆22048569	47.50
1984	◆22048569	47.50
1985	◆22020945	60.00
(w/A.C.)		
1983-85	◆22020945	60.00

	Part No.	Price
Blower Motor Resistor		
(wo/A.C.)		
1983-85	◆9796480	2.50
(w/A.C.)		
1983-85-exc.		
below	◆526897	4.50
w/climate cont.	◆1609776	5.50

LABOR 8 EXHAUST SYSTEM 8 LABOR

	(Factory Time)	Chilton Time
(G) Muffler, Renew (Right or Transverse)		
1983-85	(.6)	.9
(G) Tail Pipe, Renew		
1983	(.5)	.7
(G) Front Exhaust Pipe, Renew (To Converter)		
1983-85	(.5)	.8
(G) Exhaust Crossover Pipe, Renew		
1983	(.8)	1.2
1984-85	(.5)	.8
(G) Intermediate Exhaust Pipe, Renew		
1983-85	(.6)	.8
(G) Catalytic Converter, Renew		
1983-85	(.8)	1.0
(G) Rear Exhaust Pipe, Renew		
1983-right	(.6)	.9
(G) E.F.E. Valve (Heat Riser), Renew		
1983-84	(.7)	1.1
(G) Exhaust Manifold or Gasket, Renew		
1983-85-Four	(.6)	1.2
w/A.C. add	(.5)	.5
V-6-wo/Port Inj		
right	(.7)	1.2
left	(.7)	1.2
w/Port Inj		
right	(1.2)	1.8
left	(.6)	1.1
w/P.S. add	(.3)	.3
w/Cruise control add	(.2)	.2
w/C.C.C. add	(.3)	.3

COMBINATIONS

	Chilton Time
(G) Muffler, Exhaust and Tail Pipe, Renew	
All models	1.6
(G) Muffler and Tail Pipe, Renew	
All models	1.1

PARTS 8 EXHAUST SYSTEM 8 PARTS

	Part No.	Price
Muffler (w/Tail Pipe)		
Citation		
(4 cyl.-151 engine)		
1983	◆10022559	84.50
1984-85	◆10030695	112.00
(V-6-173X engine)		
1983-85	◆14079431	84.75
(V-6-173Z engine)		
1983-84	◆14079427	156.00
(V-6-173 W engine)		
1985-exc. X-11	◆14091317	94.50
X-11	◆14091316	94.50
Omega & Skylark		
(4 cyl.-151 engine)		
1983	◆10022558	84.50
1984-85	◆10030694	87.75
(V-6-173X engine)		
1983-85	◆14079432	91.25
(V-6-173Z engine)		
1983-84	◆14079428	108.00
(V-6-173 W engine)		
1985	◆14091312	94.50
Phoenix		
(4 cyl.-151 engine)		
1983	◆10022558	84.50
1984-85-2 dr.	◆10030694	87.75
4 dr.	◆10030695	112.00
(V-6-173X engine)		
1983-84-2 dr.	◆14079432	91.25
4 dr.	◆14079431	84.75
(V-6-173Z engine)		
1983-84-2 dr.	◆14079428	108.00
4 dr.	◆14079429	109.00
Front Pipe		
4 cyl.-151 engine		
1983	◆10023182	26.00
1984-85	◆10028746	16.75
V-6-173 engine		
1983-85-exc.		
Code W	◆14059125	20.25
1985-85-Code W	◆14089518	25.50
Intermediate Pipe		
4 cyl.-151 engine		
1983-85	◆25513019	25.00
V-6-173 engine		
1983-85-w/X		
eng	◆25511840	58.00
1983-84-w/Z		
eng	◆14091403	32.00
1985-w/W eng	◆14091403	32.00
Crossover Pipe		
V-6-173 engine		
1983-85-exc.		
Code W	◆14054541	30.00
1985-Code W	◆14078891	37.00
Exhaust Manifold		
4 cyl.-151 engine		
1983-84	◆10023093	94.25
1985	◆10032916	48.00
V-6-173 engine		
1983-w/eng. X, Z		
right	◆14033209	111.00
left	◆14033208	111.00
1985-w/eng. W		
right	◆14077830	111.00
left	◆14077829	111.00
Catalytic Converter		
4 cyl.-151 engine		
1983-85	◆25056230	277.25
V-6-173 engine		
1983-85-exc.		
Code W	◆8999979	302.25
1985-Code W	◆25056761	295.00

LABOR 9 FRONT SUSPENSION 9 LABOR

Note: On all front suspension operations alignment charges must be added if performed. Time given does not include alignment.

	(Factory Time)	Chilton Time
(M) Wheel, Renew		
one	(.5)	.5
(G) Wheels, Balance		
one		.3
each adtnl		.2
(M) Wheels, Rotate (All)		
All models		.5
(G) Check Alignment of Front End		
All models		.5

Note: Deduct if alignment is performed.

	(Factory Time)	Chilton Time
(G) Toe-In, Adjust		
All models	(.5)	.7
(G) Align Front End		
All models	(.8)	1.4
w/A.C. interference add		.5
(G) Lower Control Arm Assy., Renew		
Add alignment charges.		
1983-85-one side	(.8)	1.1
both sides	(1.4)	2.0

LABOR 9 FRONT SUSPENSION 9 LABOR

	(Factory Time)	Chilton Time
(G) Lower Control Arm Bushings, Renew		
Add alignment charges.		
1983-85-one side	(1.1)	1.5
both sides	(2.1)	2.8
(G) Lower Ball Joint, Renew		
Add alignment charges.		
1983-85-one	(.5)	.9
both	(.9)	1.6
(G) Front Shock Absorber Strut, R&R or Renew		
Add alignment charges if necessary.		
1983-85-one	(.9)	1.3
both	(1.6)	2.5
(G) Front Spring, Seat or Insulator, Renew		
Add alignment charges if necessary.		
1983-85-one	(.8)	1.2
both	(1.5)	2.3
(G) Front Strut Bearing Mount Assy., Renew		
Add alignment charges if necessary.		
1983-85-one	(.8)	1.2
both	(1.5)	2.3
(G) Front Strut Shield and/or Bumper, Renew		
Add alignment charges if necessary.		
1983-85-one	(.8)	1.2
both	(1.5)	2.3
(G) Front Stabilizer Shaft, Renew		
1983-85	(.8)	1.0
(G) Front Stabilizer Shaft Bushings, Renew (One or Both)		
1983-85	(.5)	.9
(G) Steering Knuckle Inner Dust Seal, Renew		
1983-85-one	(.7)	1.2
both	(1.3)	2.3
(G) Steering Knuckle and Arm (Integral), Renew		
Add alignment charges.		
1983-85-one	(1.0)	1.4
both	(1.9)	2.7
(G) Front Wheel Bearing and Hub Assy., Renew		
Includes: Renew oil seal.		
1983-85-one side	(.6)	1.0
both sides	(1.1)	1.9
(G) Engine Cradle, Renew		
1983-85-one side	(1.0)	1.9
both sides	(1.6)	2.8
complete	(2.5)	4.0

FRONT DRIVE AXLE

	(Factory Time)	Chilton Time
(G) Front Drive Axle, R&R or Renew		
1983-85-one	(1.1)	1.4
both	(1.6)	2.2
Renew shaft add-each	(.3)	.4
Renew C/V Joint add each side	(.3)	.4
Renew D/O Joint add each side	(.3)	.4
Renew C/V Joint boots add each	(.2)	.2
(G) Axle Shaft Seal, Renew		
Includes: Raise vehicle, R&R caliper, mark cam bolts. Drain and refill trans.		
1983-85-w/M.T.-one	(1.1)	1.5
both	(1.5)	2.1
w/A.T.-one	(1.3)	1.7
both	(1.9)	2.7

PARTS 9 FRONT SUSPENSION 9 PARTS

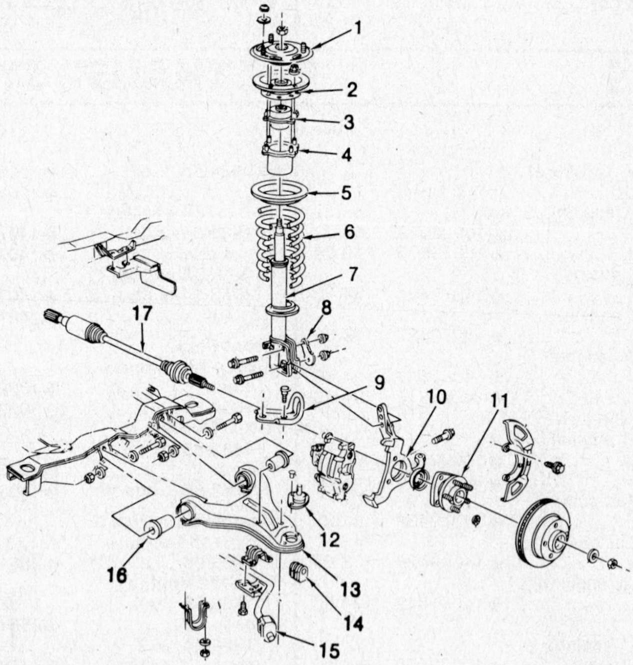

	Part No.	Price
Front Seal Assy.		
1983	◆14084120	3.75
1984-85	◆14084120	3.75
(1) Mount Assy. (Shock Absorber)		
1983-84-right	◆17980090	49.00
left	◆17980089	49.00
1985-w/H.D. susp.		
right	◆17981902	49.00
left	◆17981901	49.00
1985-wo/H.D. susp.		
right	◆17981598	49.00
left	◆17981597	49.00
(2) Seat (Front Spring)		
1983	◆14077769	3.75
1984-85	◆14065776	3.75
(3) Bumper		
1983	◆14036459	2.75
1984-85	◆14065773	2.75
(4) Shield		
1983	◆14034677	5.25
1984-85	◆14077713	5.25
(5) Insulator		
1983	◆14077726	2.00
1984-85	◆14077726	2.00
(6) Coil Spring		
Note: Order by model and description.		
(7) Shock Absorber (Strut)		
(wo/H.D. susp.)		
1983	◆22035660	79.00
1984	◆22049970	57.00
1985	◆22049969	57.00
(w/H.D. susp.)		
1983	◆22035662	95.00
1984-85	◆22049971	74.00
(9) Stop (Lower Cont. Arm)		
1983-right	◆14026942	5.00
left	◆14026941	5.00
1984-85-right	◆14073088	1.00
left	◆14073087	1.00
(10) Steering Knuckle		
1983-right	◆14076994	86.25
left	◆14076993	86.25
1984-85-right	◆14076994	86.25
left	◆14076993	86.25
(11) Bearing Assy.		
1983	◆7466905	160.50
1984-85	◆7470002	132.50
(12) Ball Joint Assy. (Lower)		
1983-85	◆17983075	40.25
(13) Lower Control Arm		
1983-85-right	◆14082884	134.00
left	◆14082883	141.00
(14) Bushing (Stabilizer)		
Order by year and model.		
(15) Bushing (Shaft to Arm)		
1983-85	◆473525	1.00
(16) Bushing (Lower Cont. Arm)		
1983-85	◆14065721	7.00
(17) Drive Axle Kit		
(w/man. trans.)		
1983-right	◆7840073	425.00
left	◆7840074	425.00
1984-right	◆7844745	415.00
left	◆7844748	415.00
1985-w/trans. MY8, M19		
right	◆7846874	425.00
left	◆7846875	425.00
1985-w/trans. MX6		
right	◆7847103	520.00
left	◆7847102	520.00
(w/auto. trans.)		
1983-right	◆7840076	473.00
left	◆7840075	458.00
1984-right	◆7844754	415.00
left	◆7844756	415.00
1985-right	◆7848169	425.00
left	◆7846877	425.00

PARTS 9 FRONT DRIVE AXLE 9 PARTS

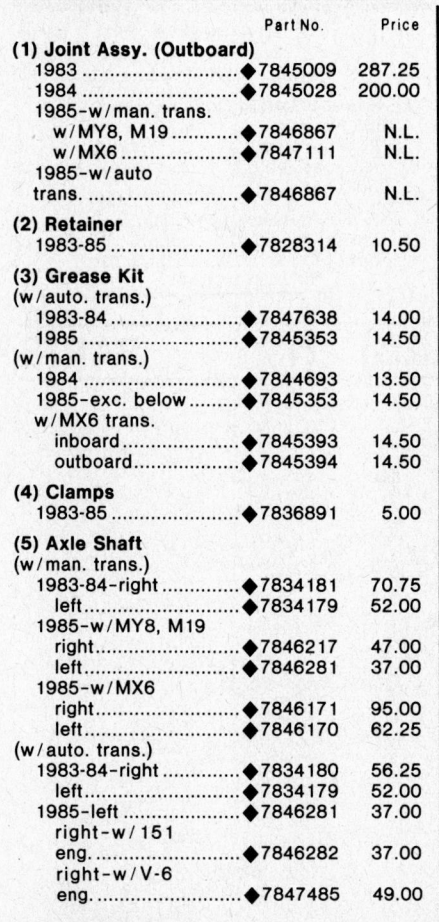

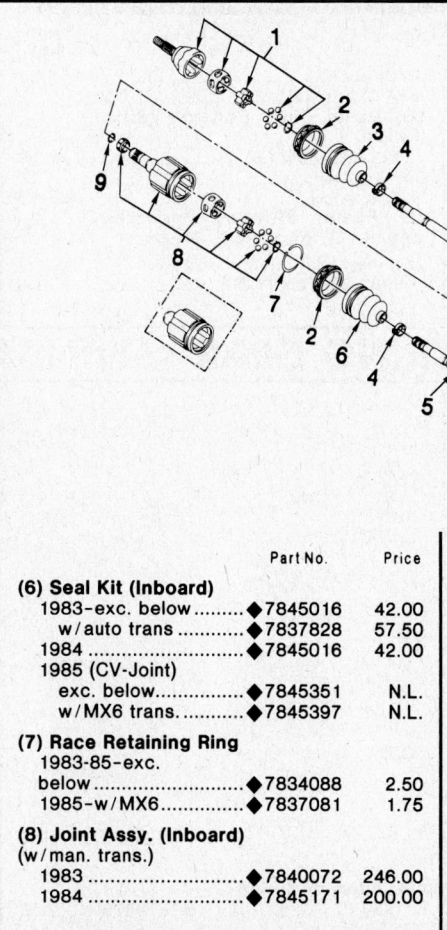

	Part No.	Price
(1) Joint Assy. (Outboard)		
1983	◆7845009	287.25
1984	◆7845028	200.00
1985-w/man. trans.		
w/MY8, M19	◆7846867	N.L.
w/MX6	◆7847111	N.L.
1985-w/auto trans.	◆7846867	N.L.
(2) Retainer		
1983-85	◆7828314	10.50
(3) Grease Kit		
(w/auto. trans.)		
1983-84	◆7847638	14.00
1985	◆7845353	14.50
(w/man. trans.)		
1984	◆7844693	13.50
1985-exc. below	◆7845353	14.50
w/MX6 trans.		
inboard	◆7845393	14.50
outboard	◆7845394	14.50
(4) Clamps		
1983-85	◆7836891	5.00
(5) Axle Shaft		
(w/man. trans.)		
1983-84-right	◆7834181	70.75
left	◆7834179	52.00
1985-w/MY8, M19		
right	◆7846217	47.00
left	◆7846281	37.00
1985-w/MX6		
right	◆7846171	95.00
left	◆7846170	62.25
(w/auto. trans.)		
1983-84-right	◆7834180	56.25
left	◆7834179	52.00
1985-left	◆7846281	37.00
right-w/151 eng.	◆7846282	37.00
right-w/V-6 eng.	◆7847485	49.00

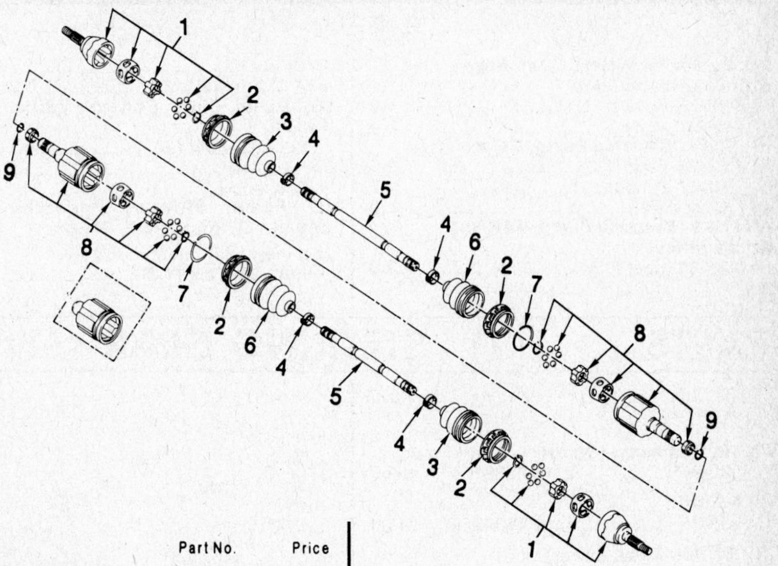

	Part No.	Price
(6) Seal Kit (Inboard)		
1983-exc. below	◆7845016	42.00
w/auto trans	◆7837828	57.50
1984	◆7845016	42.00
1985 (CV-Joint)		
exc. below	◆7845351	N.L.
w/MX6 trans.	◆7845397	N.L.
(7) Race Retaining Ring		
1983-85-exc. below	◆7834088	2.50
1985-w/MX6	◆7837081	1.75
(8) Joint Assy. (Inboard)		
(w/man. trans.)		
1983	◆7840072	246.00
1984	◆7845171	200.00

	Part No.	Price
1985	◆7846861	212.00
(w/auto. trans.)		
1983-right	◆7840071	200.00
left	◆7840070	246.00
1984-right	◆7840071	200.00
left	◆7845019	195.00
1985-w/151 eng.		
right	◆7846860	225.00
left	◆7846862	212.00
1985-w/V-6 eng.	◆7846861	212.00
(9) Ring (Joint Retaining)		
1983-85	◆7829495	1.50

LABOR 11 STEERING GEAR 11 LABOR

(Factory Time)	Chilton Time
STANDARD STEERING	
(G) Tie Rod End, Renew	
Includes: Reset toe-in.	
1983-85-one (.7)	.9
both (.9)	1.2
Renew seal add-each	.1
(G) Inner Tie Rod, Renew	
Includes: Reset toe-in.	
1983-85-w/M.T.-one (1.4)	1.8
w/A.T.-one (2.5)	3.3
(G) Steering Wheel, Renew	
1983-85 (.2)	.3
(G) Horn Contact and Turn Signal Cancelling Cam, Renew	
1983-85 (.3)	.5
(G) Multifunction Lever, Renew	
All models (.2)	.4
w/Cruise control add (.5)	.5
(G) Steering Column Lock Actuator Parts, Renew	
1983-85	
std colm (.8)	1.3
tilt colm (.9)	1.4
w/Cruise control add	.2
(G) Steering Column Upper Bearing, Renew	
1983-85-std column (.8)	1.4
tilt column (.9)	1.6
w/Cruise control add (.2)	.2
(G) Intermediate Steering Shaft, Renew	
1983 (1.0)	1.3
1984-85 (.6)	1.0
(G) Steering Column Lower Bearing, Renew	
1983-85 (.6)	1.2
(G) Steering Column Collar, Bowl or Housing, Renew	
1983-85-std column (1.5)	2.0
tilt column (2.0)	2.5
w/Cruise control add (.2)	.2
(G) Steering Column, R&R	
1983-85 (.6)	.9
(G) Steering Column Assy., R&R and Recondition	
1983-85-std column (1.3)	2.1
tilt column (1.5)	2.2
(G) Steering Gear Assembly, R&R or Renew	
1983-85-w/M.T. (1.3)	1.9
w/A.T. (2.0)	3.0
(P) Steering Gear Assy., R&R and Recondition	
Includes: Disassemble, renew necessary parts, reassemble and adjust.	
1983-85-w/M.T. (2.1)	3.3
w/A.T. (2.8)	4.4
POWER STEERING	
(G) Trouble Shoot Power Steering	
Includes: Test pump and system pressure. Check pounds pull on steering wheel and check for leaks.	
All models	.5
(M) Check and Fill Reservoir	
All models	.2
(M) Pump Drive Belt, Renew	
1983-85 (.5)	.6
(G) Power Steering Gear Assy., Renew	
1983-85-w/M.T. (1.4)	3.1
w/A.T. (1.6)	3.3
(G) Power Steering Short Rack Assy., Renew	
Includes: Transfer parts as required. Reset toe-in.	
All models	
w/M.T. (1.9)	3.6
w/A.T. (2.2)	3.9

LABOR 11 STEERING GEAR 11 LABOR

(Factory Time)	Chilton Time
(P) Power Steering Gear Assy., R&R and Recondition	
1983-85-w/M.T. (2.4)	5.0
w/A.T. (2.6)	5.4
(G) Power Steering Pump, Renew	
1983-85-Four (1.0)	1.3
V-6 (1.2)	1.7
w/A.C. add (.2)	.2
(P) Power Steering Pump, R&R and Recondition	
1983-85-Four (1.5)	2.0
V-6 (1.7)	2.4
w/A.C. add (.2)	.2
(G) Pump Flow Control Valve, Renew	
1983-85-Four (.5)	.8
V-6 (.4)	.7
w/A.C. add (.2)	.2
(G) Power Steering Reservoir and/or 'O' Ring Seals, Renew	
Includes: R&R pump assembly.	
1983-85-Four (1.3)	1.6
V-6 (1.4)	1.9
(M) Power Steering Hoses, Renew	
1983-85-Four	
high pressure (.4)	.6
low pressure (.3)	.5
both (.5)	.9
V-6-high pressure (.7)	.9
low pressure (.7)	.9
both (.8)	1.5

PARTS 11 STEERING GEAR-(STANDARD) 11 PARTS

	Part No.	Price
(1) Tie Rod Assy. (Outer)		
1983-85	◆7839154	48.50
(2) Boot Kit		
1983-85	◆7839278	24.00
(3) Tie Rod Assy. (Inner)		
1983-85	◆7839153	49.50
(4) Housing Assy.		
1983-85	◆7837263	134.00
(5) Rack Assy.		
1983-85	◆7834080	163.00
(6) Bearing		
1983-85	◆7827995	5.00
(7) Bushing		
1983-85	◆22513639	.50
(8) Pinion Bearing Kit		
1983-85	◆7819358	6.25
(9) Seal Kit		
1983-85	◆7829755	4.50
(10) Steering Gear Rack Bearing		
1983-85	◆7827995	5.00
(11) Adjuster Spring		
1983-85	◆7819378	1.50
(12) Adjuster Plug		
1983-85	◆7825181	7.75

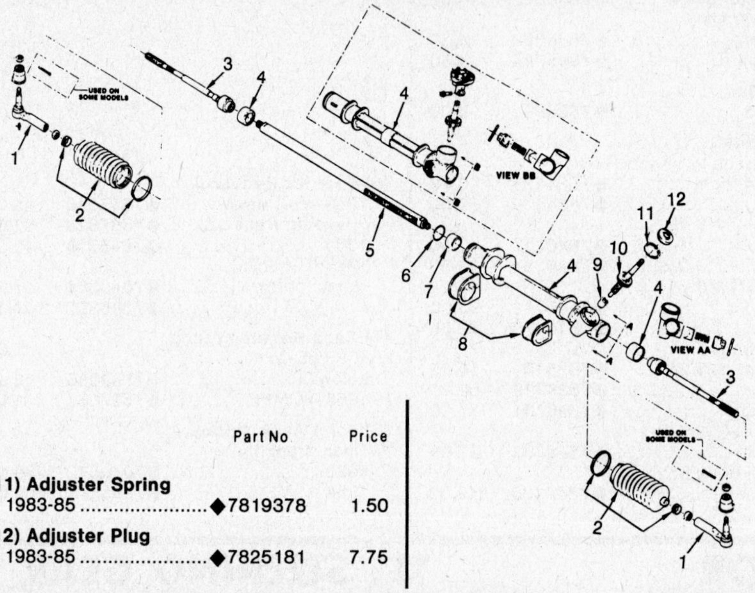

PARTS 11 POWER STEERING GEAR 11 PARTS

	Part No.	Price
Power Steering Gear (Short Rack Assy.)		
1983-85	◆7846792	175.00
(1) Tie Rod Assy. (Inner)		
1983-85	◆7839153	49.50
(2) Boot Clamp (Large)		
1983-85	◆7840235	5.00
(3) Boot Kit		
1983-85	◆7839156	24.00
(4) Boot Clamp (Small)		
1983-85	◆14052374	1.50
(5) Tie Rod Assy. (Outer)		
1983-85	◆7839154	48.50
(6) Tie Rod Dust Seal		
1983-85	◆7828084	4.25
(7) Rack & Pinion Assy.		
1983-84	◆7846688	123.00
(8) Seal Kit (Rack & Pinion)		
1983-84	◆7839157	11.75
1985	◆7847281	11.75
(9) Bulkhead Kit		
1983-85	◆7839075	41.50
(10) Ring (Shock Dampener)		
1983-85	◆7831234	2.00
(11) Breather Tube		
1983-85	◆7837007	8.75

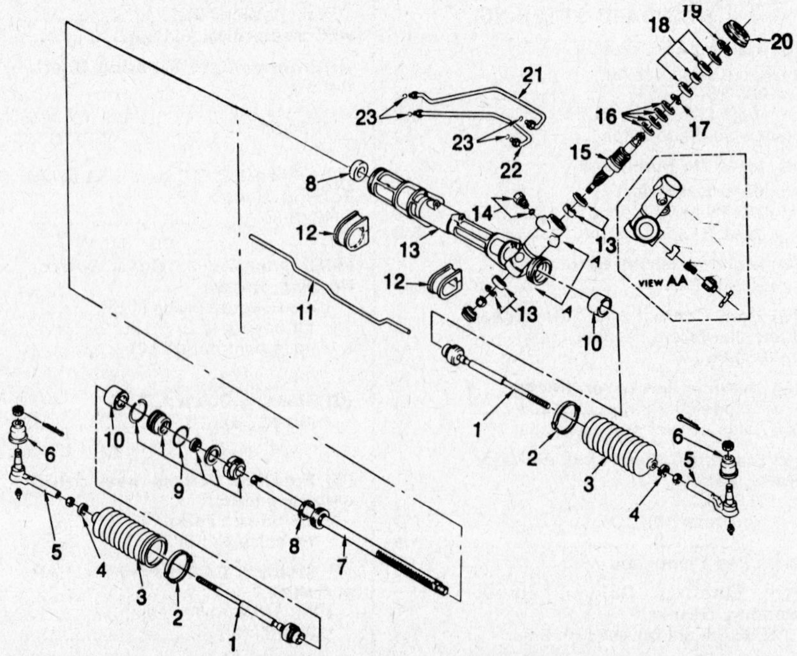

PARTS 11 POWER STEERING GEAR 11 PARTS

	Part No.	Price
(12) Grommet		
1983-85	◆22513639	.50
(13) Housing Assy.		
1983-85	◆7840216	174.25
(14) Fitting (w/Seal)		
1983-85	◆Not serviced.	
(15) Valve Assy.		
1983-85-exc.		
X11	◆7842238	263.00
X11	◆7839507	263.00
(16) Seal Kit		
1983-85	◆7840573	21.25
(17) Retaining Ring		
1983-85	◆7828017	1.50
(18) Bearing Kit (Stub Shaft)		
1983-85	◆7829888	19.25
(19) Retaining Ring (Stub Shaft)		
1983-85	◆7828017	1.50
(20) Adapter (Stub Shaft)		
1983-85	◆7833732	6.75
(21) Cylinder Line Assy. (Right)		
1983-85	◆7840455	15.75
(22) Cylinder Line Assy. (Left)		
1983	◆7840454	14.00
1984-85	◆7843293	14.50
(23) 'O' Ring (Cylinder Line)		
1983-85	◆7828486	1.25

PARTS 11 POWER STEERING PUMP 11 PARTS

	Part No.	Price
Power Steering Pump		
4 cyl.-151 engine		
1983-85	◆7838471	199.00
V-6-173 engine		
1983-85	◆7838472	199.00
Pump Drive Belt		
Order by model and description.		
Oil Pressure Hose		
4 cyl.-151 engine		
1983-85	◆7839955	57.00
V-6-173 engine		
1983-85-w/X, Z eng.		
wo/A.C.	◆7842584	57.00
w/A.C.	◆7842705	57.00
1985-w/W eng.	◆7848525	57.00
(1) Drive Shaft Kit		
1983-85	◆7837321	39.50
(2) Seal Kit		
1983-85	◆5688044	10.75
(3) Pump Housing		
1983-85-w/151		
eng.	◆7830236	62.75
w/173 eng.	◆7830697	62.75
(4) Thrust Plate		
1983-85	◆7836369	13.75

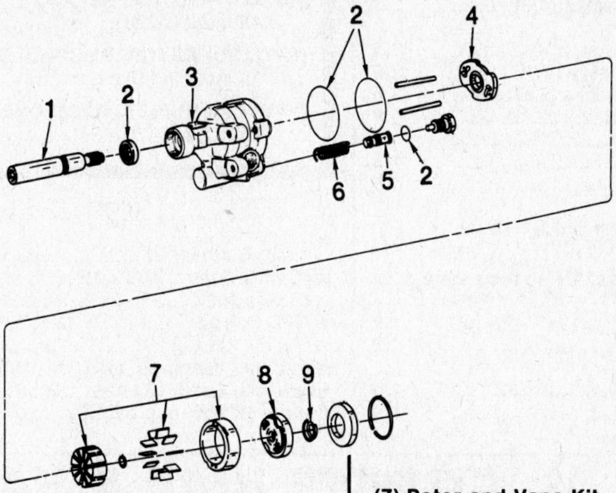

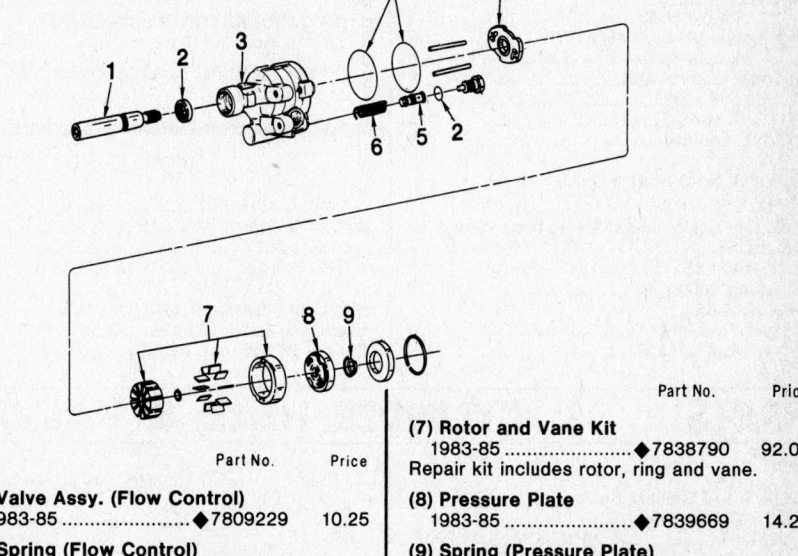

	Part No.	Price
(5) Valve Assy. (Flow Control)		
1983-85	◆7809229	10.25
(6) Spring (Flow Control)		
1983-85	◆5688037	1.50
(7) Rotor and Vane Kit		
1983-85	◆7838790	92.00
Repair kit includes rotor, ring and vane.		
(8) Pressure Plate		
1983-85	◆7839669	14.25
(9) Spring (Pressure Plate)		
1983-85	◆7839667	1.00

LABOR 12 CYLINDER HEAD & VALVE SYSTEM 12 LABOR

(Factory Time)	Chilton Time
(G) Compression Test	
Four-1983-85 (.3)	.5
V-6-1983-85 (.5)	.8
w/Cruise control add	.3
(G) Cylinder Head Gasket, Renew	
Includes: Clean carbon and make all necessary adjustments.	
Four-1983-85 (3.1)	4.3
w/Cruise control add (.2)	.2
w/A.C. add (.5)	.5
w/P.S. add (.2)	.2
V-6-1983-85	
wo/Port Inj	
right (3.8)	5.2
left (4.1)	5.6
both (4.8)	6.6
w/Port Inj	
right (5.1)	7.1
left (3.6)	5.0
both (6.1)	8.5
w/Cruise control add (.2)	.2
w/A.C. add (.4)	.4
w/P.S. add (.3)	.3
w/C.C.C. add (.3)	.3
w/A.I.R. add (.5)	.5
(G) Cylinder Head, Renew	
Includes: Transfer all components, reface valves, clean carbon.	
Four-1983-85 (4.6)	6.4
w/Cruise control add (.2)	.2
w/A.C. add (.5)	.5
w/P.S. add (.2)	.2
V-6-1983-85	
wo/Port Inj	
right (4.4)	6.1
left (4.7)	6.4
both (6.1)	8.4
w/Port Inj	
right (5.7)	7.9
left (4.3)	6.0
both (7.4)	10.3
w/Cruise control add (.2)	.2
w/A.C. add (.4)	.4
w/P.S. add (.3)	.3
w/C.C.C. add (.3)	.3
w/A.I.R. add (.5)	.5
(P) Clean Carbon and Grind Valves	
Includes: R&R cylinder heads, grind valves and seats. Minor engine tune up.	
Four-1983-85 (5.2)	7.2
w/Cruise control add (.2)	.2
w/A.C. add (.5)	.5
w/P.S. add (.2)	.2
V-6-1983-85	
wo/Port Inj (7.2)	9.9
w/Port Inj (8.4)	11.7
w/Cruise control add (.2)	.2
w/A.C. add (.4)	.4
w/P.S. add (.3)	.3
w/C.C.C. add (.3)	.3
w/A.I.R. add (.5)	.5
(G) Rocker Arm Cover or Gasket, Renew	
Four-1983-85 (.7)	1.0
V-6-1983-85	
wo/Port Inj	
right (.7)	1.1
left (.6)	1.0
both (1.1)	2.0
w/Port Inj	
right (1.2)	1.6
left (.9)	1.3
both (1.8)	2.6
w/Cruise control add (.2)	.2
w/A.C. add (.3)	.3

LABOR 12 CYLINDER HEAD & VALVE SYSTEM 12 LABOR

	(Factory Time)	Chilton Time
w/C.C.C. add	(.3)	.3
(G) Push Rod Side Cover Gasket, Renew		
Four–1983-85	(2.3)	3.5
w/Cruise control add	(.2)	.2
(G) Valve Rocker Arms or Push Rods, Renew		
Four–1983-85		
one cyl	(.8)	1.1
all cyls	(1.1)	1.4
V-6–1983-85		
wo/Port Inj		
one cyl	(.9)	1.4
one cyl-each side	(1.4)	2.2
all cyls-both sides	(1.8)	2.8
w/Port Inj		
one cyl	(1.5)	2.1
one cyl-each side	(2.1)	2.9
all cyls-both sides	(2.5)	3.5
w/Cruise control add	(.2)	.2
w/A.C. add	(.3)	.3
w/C.C.C. add	(.3)	.3
w/A.I.R. add	(.5)	.5
(G) Valve Rocker Arm Stud, Renew (One)		
Includes: Drain and refill cooling system on V-6 engine.		
Four–1983-85	(.8)	1.1
each adtnl	(.2)	.2
V-6–1983-85		
wo/Port Inj	(1.0)	1.5
w/Port Inj	(1.3)	1.8

COMBINATIONS

Add to Valve Job

See Machine Shop Operations

	(Factory Time)	Chilton Time
(G) DRAIN, EVACUATE & RECHARGE AIR CONDITIONING SYSTEM		
All models	(.5)	1.0
(G) ROCKER ARM STUD, RENEW		
Each	(.2)	.2
(G) HYDRAULIC VALVE LIFTERS, DISASSEMBLE AND CLEAN		
Each	(.2)	.2
(G) DISTRIBUTOR, RECONDITION		
All models	(.5)	.8
(G) CARBURETOR, RECONDITION		
All models	(.9)	1.2
(P) VALVE GUIDES, REAM OVERSIZE		
Each	(.2)	.2

	(Factory Time)	Chilton Time
each adtnl	(.2)	.2
w/Cruise control add	(.2)	.2
w/A.C. add	(.3)	.3
w/C.C.C. add	(.3)	.3
w/A.I.R. add	(.3)	.3
(G) Valve Springs and/or Valve Stem Oil Seals, Renew (Head on Car)		
Four–1983-85-one cyl	(.9)	1.5

	(Factory Time)	Chilton Time
all cyls	(1.6)	2.4
V-6–1983-85		
wo/Port Inj		
one cyl	(1.1)	1.5
one cyl-each side	(1.9)	2.8
all cyls-both sides	(3.2)	4.4
w/Port Inj		
one cyl-right side	(1.6)	2.2
one cyl-left side	(1.3)	1.8
one cyl-each side	(2.6)	3.6
each adtnl cyl	(.4)	.4
w/Cruise control add	(.2)	.2
w/A.C. add	(.3)	.3
w/C.C.C. add	(.3)	.3
w/A.I.R. add	(.5)	.5
(G) Valve Tappets, Renew (Lifters)		
Includes: R&R intake manifold and make all necessary adjustments.		
Four–1983-85-one cyl	(2.7)	3.6
all cyls	(3.1)	4.2
V-6–1983-85		
wo/Port Inj		
one cyl	(2.7)	3.7
all cyls	(3.4)	4.6
w/Port Inj		
one cyl	(2.9)	4.0
one cyl-each side	(3.0)	4.2
all cyls-both sides	(3.5)	4.9
w/Cruise control add	(.2)	.2
w/A.C. add	(.3)	.3
w/C.C.C. add	(.3)	.3
w/A.I.R. add	(.5)	.5

PARTS 12 CYLINDER HEAD & VALVE SYSTEM 12 PARTS

	Part No.	Price
Valve Grind Gasket Set		
4 cyl.–151 engine		
1983-84	◆10026815	29.00
1985	◆10037280	29.25
V-6–173 engine		
1985-w/W eng.	◆14089075	53.00
(1) Cylinder Head		
4 cyl.–151 engine		
1983	◆10020699	290.00
1984	◆10030838	290.00
1985	◆10037282	290.00
V-6–173 engine		
1983-85-exc. Code X	◆14054879	250.00
Code X	◆14054882	250.00
(2) Cylinder Head Gasket		
4 cyl.–151 engine		
1983	◆10018638	11.00
1984	◆10028404	10.50
1985	◆10035039	9.75
V-6–173 engine		
1983-84	◆476571	4.00
1985	◆14085435	4.75
(3) Valve Cover Gasket		
1983-85-w/151 eng.	◆10007770	6.50
1983-84-w/173 eng.	◆14089252	7.50
1985-w/173 eng.		
W eng.	◆14089253	6.00
X eng.	◆14089252	7.50
(4) Rocker Arm and Ball Kit		
4 cyl.–151 engine		
1983-85	◆10014819	7.25
V-6–173 engine		
1983-85	◆14002446	4.75
(5) Lock (Valve Spring)		
1983-85	◆3947770	.50

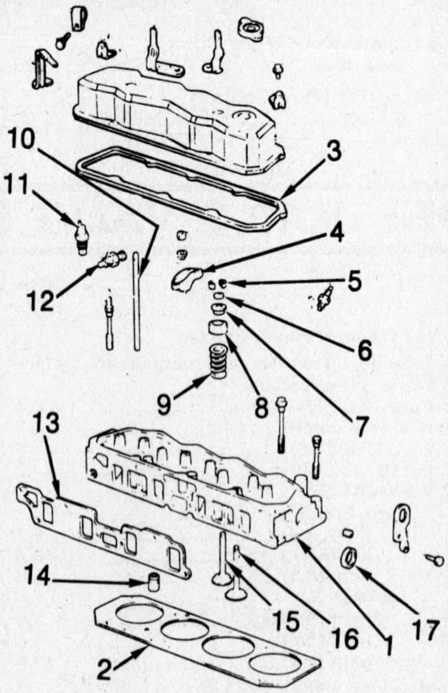

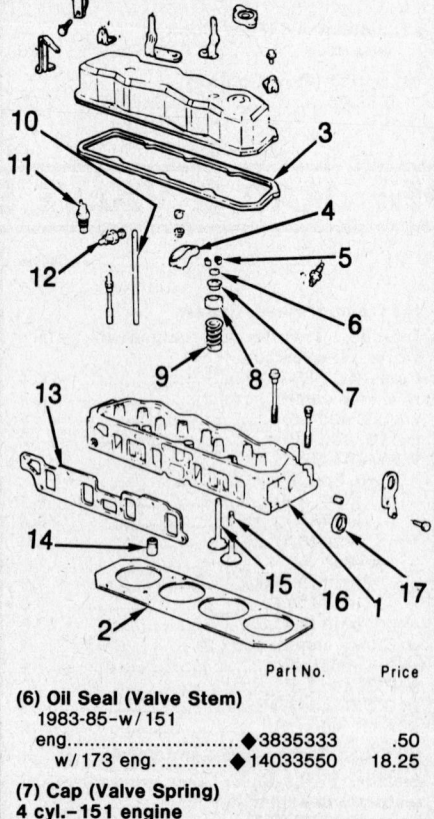

	Part No.	Price
(6) Oil Seal (Valve Stem)		
1983-85-w/151 eng.	◆3835333	.50
w/173 eng.	◆14033550	18.25
(7) Cap (Valve Spring)		
4 cyl.–151 engine		
1983-85	◆3729363	1.00

	Part No.	Price
V-6–173 engine		
1983-85	◆14004099	1.00
(8) Shield (Valve Spring)		
1983-85	◆10007818	.75
(9) Valve Spring & Damper		
4 cyl.–151 engine		
1983-85	◆3735381	3.00
V-6–173 engine		
1983-85	◆14030029	3.50
(10) Push Rod		
4 cyl.–151 engine		
1983-84	◆10021898	3.00
1985	◆10028055	3.25
V-6–173 engine		
1983-85	◆476525	5.00
(11) Switch (Hot Light)		
4 cyl.–151 engine		
1983-85	◆25036371	8.00
V-6–173 engine		
1983-85	◆25036373	10.00
(12) Switch (Fan Control)		
1983-85	◆3040674	11.00
(13) Manifold Gasket (Intake)		
4 cyl.–151 engine		
1983-85	◆10026023	5.00
V-6–173 engine		
1983-85	◆14033476	12.50
(14) Valve Lifter		
4 cyl.–151 engine		
1983-84	◆5233515	10.50
1985	◆5233745	32.50
V-6–173 engine		
1983-85	◆5234212	N.L.

PARTS 12 CYLINDER HEAD & VALVE SYSTEM 12 PARTS

	Part No.	Price
(15) Intake Valve (Std.)		
4 cyl.–151 engine		
1983-85	◆10022882	16.00
V-6–173 engine		
1983-85-exc.		
Code X	◆14031328	14.00
Code X	◆14024249	13.25
(16) Exhaust Valve (Std.)		
4 cyl.–151 engine		
1983-84	◆10024039	N.L.
1985	◆10034162	16.25
V-6–173 engine		
1983-85-exc.		
Code X	◆14031332	15.50
Code X	◆14024254	14.25
(17) Plug (5/8)		
1983-85-151 eng	◆942793	N.L.

LABOR 13 ENGINE ASSEMBLY & MOUNTS 13 LABOR

(Factory Time) Chilton Time

(G) Engine Assembly, Remove and Install

Does not include transfer of any parts or equipment.

	Chilton Time
Four–1983-85–w/M.T.	4.7
w/A.T.	5.1
V-6–1983-85–w/M.T.	6.1
w/A.T.	5.8
w/Cruise control add (.2)	.2
w/A.C. add (.5)	.5
w/P.S. add (.5)	.5
w/C.C.C. add (.6)	.6

(G) Engine Assembly, Renew

Includes: R&R engine assembly, transfer all component parts not supplied with replacement engine. Minor tune up.

	Chilton Time
Four–1983-85–w/M.T. (4.6)	7.0
w/A.T. (5.0)	7.4
V-6–1983-85–w/M.T. (5.5)	8.8
w/A.T. (5.2)	8.5
w/Cruise control add (.2)	.2
w/A.C. add (.5)	.5
w/P.S. add (.5)	.5
w/C.C.C. add (.6)	.6
w/Port Inj add	1.5

(P) Cylinder Block, Renew (w/All Internal Parts Less Cylinder Head(s) and Oil Pan)

Includes: R&R engine assembly, transfer all component parts not supplied with replacement engine. Clean carbon, grind valves. Minor tune up.

	Chilton Time
Four–1983-85–w/M.T. (7.1)	12.4
w/A.T. (7.5)	12.8
V-6–1983-85–w/M.T. (11.4)	17.6
w/A.T. (11.1)	17.3
w/Cruise control add (.2)	.2
w/A.C. add (.5)	.5
w/P.S. add (.5)	.5
w/C.C.C. add (.6)	.6
w/Port Inj add	1.5

(P) Cylinder Block, Renew (w/Pistons, Rings and Bearings)

Includes: R&R engine assembly, transfer all component parts. Clean carbon, grind valves. Minor tune up.

	Chilton Time
Four–1983-85–w/M.T. (8.9)	15.6
w/A.T. (10.3)	16.0
V-6–1983-85–w/M.T. (14.3)	20.3
w/A.T. (14.0)	20.0
w/Cruise control add (.2)	.2
w/A.C. add (.5)	.5
w/P.S. add (.5)	.5
w/C.C.C. add (.6)	.6
w/Port Inj add	1.5

(P) Engine Assembly, R&R and Recondition

Includes: Rebore block, install new pistons, rings, rod and main bearings. Clean carbon, grind valves. Tune engine.

	Chilton Time
Four–1983-85–w/M.T.	21.6
w/A.T.	22.0
V-6–1983-85–w/M.T. (24.7)	34.6
w/A.T. (24.3)	32.5
w/Cruise control add (.2)	.2
w/A.C. add (.5)	.5
w/P.S. add (.5)	.5
w/C.C.C. add (.6)	.6
w/Port Inj add	1.5

(P) Engine Assembly, Recondition (In Car)

Includes: Expand or renew pistons, install new rings, pins, rod and main bearings. Clean carbon, grind valves. Tune engine.

	Chilton Time
Four–1983-85 (9.7)	16.3
V-6–1983-85 (13.3)	18.9
w/Cruise control add (.2)	.2
w/A.C. add (.5)	.5
w/P.S. add (.5)	.5
w/C.C.C. add (.3)	.3
w/Port Inj add	2.0

(G) Front Engine Mount, Renew

	Chilton Time
Four–1983-85-right (1.3)	1.8
V-6–1983-85-right (.6)	.9

PARTS 13 ENGINE ASSEMBLY & MOUNTS 13 PARTS

	Part No.	Price
Engine Overhaul Gasket Set		
4 cyl.–151 engine		
1983-85	◆10026805	20.50
Engine Assy. (Partial)		
Note: Includes block, pistons, connecting rods and crankshaft.		
4 cyl.–151 engine		
1983	◆10022887	1137.25
1984	◆10030773	1128.25
1985	◆10037143	1128.00
V-6–173 engine		
1983-84–w/X eng.	◆14089070	1147.00
w/Z eng.	◆14075315	1223.25
1985–w/W eng.	◆14089007	1230.00
w/X eng.	◆14089008	1176.00
Cylinder Block Assy.		
Note: Includes block and pistons.		
4 cyl.–151 engine		
1983	◆10022888	856.00
1984	◆10030774	856.00
1985	◆10037148	815.00
V-6–173X engine		
1985	◆14089004	891.00
V-6–173Z engine		
Uses RTV sealer for rear oil pan seal, or uses rubber rear oil pan seal, depending on year.		
V-6–173W engine		
1985	◆14089003	942.00
Front Engine Mounts		
1983-84	◆14073097	31.50
1985–w/151 eng.	◆17980976	N.L.
w/173 eng.	◆17980974	N.L.
Rear Engine Mount		
(Front)		
1983-85	◆14034785	21.75
(Rear)		
1983-85	◆14049343	21.50

LABOR 14 PISTONS, RINGS & BEARINGS 14 LABOR

(Factory Time) Chilton Time

(P) Rings, Renew (See Engine Combinations)

Includes: Remove cylinder top ridge, deglaze cylinder walls. Clean piston and ring grooves. Minor tune up.

	Chilton Time
Four–1983-85–one cyl (5.3)	8.3
all cyls (6.2)	9.5
V-6–1983-85	
wo/Port Inj	
one cyl (5.3)	7.8
all cyls (8.1)	11.7
w/Port Inj	
one cyl (7.3)	10.2
one cyl-each side (8.9)	12.4
all cyls-both sides (10.8)	15.1
w/Cruise control add (.2)	.2
w/A.C. add (.5)	.5
w/P.S. add (.3)	.3
w/M.T. add (.2)	.2
w/C.C.C. add (.3)	.3

LABOR 14 PISTONS, RINGS & BEARINGS 14 LABOR

	(Factory Time)	Chilton Time
(P) Piston or Connecting Rod, Renew		
Includes: Remove cylinder top ridge, deglaze cylinder walls. Minor tune up.		
Four–1983-85–one cyl	(5.5)	8.6
all cyls	(6.8)	10.7
V-6–1983-85		
wo/Port Inj		
one cyl	(5.3)	8.1
all cyls	(8.1)	13.5
w/Port Inj		
one cyl	(7.3)	10.5
one cyl-each side	(8.9)	13.0
all cyls-both sides	(11.5)	16.9
w/Cruise control add	(.2)	.2
w/A.C. add	(.5)	.5
w/P.S. add	(.3)	.3
w/M.T. add	(.2)	.2
w/C.C.C. add	(.3)	.3
(P) Connecting Rod Bearings, Renew		
Includes: Plastigauge bearings.		
Four–1983-85–one	(2.8)	3.3
all	(3.6)	4.2
V-6–1983-85–one	(2.0)	2.8
all	(3.2)	4.5
w/A.C. add	(.3)	.3
w/M.T. add	(.2)	.2

COMBINATIONS

See Machine Shop Operations

	(Factory Time)	Chilton Time
(G) DRAIN, EVACUATE & RECHARGE AIR CONDITIONING SYSTEM		
All models	(.5)	1.0
(G) ROCKER ARM STUD, RENEW		
Each	(.2)	.2
(G) HYDRAULIC VALVE LIFTERS, DISASSEMBLE AND CLEAN		
Each	(.2)	.2
(G) DISTRIBUTOR, RECONDITION		
All models	(.5)	.8
(G) CARBURETOR, RECONDITION		
All models	(.9)	1.2
(P) VALVE GUIDES, REAM OVERSIZE		
Each	(.2)	.2
(G) DEGLAZE CYLINDER WALLS		
Each	(.1)	.1
(G) REMOVE CYLINDER TOP RIDGE		
Each	(.1)	.1
(G) PLASTIGAUGE BEARINGS		
Each	(.1)	.1
(M) OIL FILTER ELEMENT, RENEW		
Four	(.2)	.3
V-6	(.3)	.4

PARTS 14 PISTONS, RINGS, PINS & BEARINGS 14 PARTS

	Part No.	Price
Piston Ring Set (Std.)		
4 cyl.–151 engine		
1983	◆10022719	18.00
1984-85	◆10030202	18.00
V-6–173 engine		
1983-84	◆14034969	15.50
1985	◆14089059	17.00
Piston Assy. (Std.)		
4 cyl.–151 engine		
1983	◆10027416	50.75
1984-85	◆10027317	53.00
V-6–173X engine		
1983-84	◆14033250	48.50
1985	◆14079778	48.50
V-6–173Z engine		
1983-85	◆14033129	42.50
V-6–173W engine		
1985	◆14079785	48.50
Piston Pin		
1983-85–151 eng	◆500011	5.50
Connecting Rod		
1983-85–w/151 eng	◆499323	39.50
w/173 eng	◆476521	36.50
Connecting Rod Bearing (Std.)		
1983-85–w/151 eng	◆5463932	10.50
w/173 eng.	◆18008492	N.L.

LABOR 15 CRANKSHAFT & DAMPER 15 LABOR

	(Factory Time)	Chilton Time
(P) Crankshaft and Main Bearings, Renew		
Includes: R&R engine, check all bearing clearances.		
Four–1983-85–w/M.T.	(6.5)	10.1
w/A.T.	(6.9)	10.5
V-6–1983-85		
wo/Port Inj		
w/M.T.	(8.1)	11.8
w/A.T.	(7.8)	11.5
w/Port Inj		
w/M.T.	(8.0)	11.8
w/A.T.	(7.7)	11.5
w/Cruise control add	(.2)	.2
w/A.C. add	(.5)	.5
w/P.S. add	(.5)	.5
w/C.C.C. add	(.6)	.6
(P) Main Bearings, Renew		
Includes: Check all bearing clearances.		
Four–1983-85	(3.7)	5.0
V-6–1983-85	(2.9)	4.2
w/M.T. add	(.2)	.2
(P) Main and Rod Bearings, Renew		
Includes: Check all bearing clearances.		
Four–1983-85	(4.5)	6.2
V-6–1983-85	(4.3)	6.0
w/M.T. add	(.2)	.2
(G) Rear Main Bearing Oil Seal, Renew or Repack		
Includes: R&R trans and flywheel on Four cyl engines. R&R oil pan on V-6 engines with split lip type seal.		
Four–1983-85–w/M.T.	(3.3)	4.5
w/A.T.	(3.7)	5.0
w/P.S. add	(.3)	.3
V-6–1983-85		
full circle	(6.6)	9.2
split lip	(3.9)	5.5
w/A.C. add	(.5)	.5
w/P.S. add	(.4)	.4
w/C.C.C. add	(.6)	.6
w/M.T. add	(.3)	.3
w/Cruise control add	(.2)	.2
(G) Vibration Damper, Renew		
Four–1983-85	(.6)	.9
V-6–1983-85	(.8)	1.2
w/A.C. add	(.2)	.2
w/P.S. add	(.3)	.3
(G) Crankshaft Pulley, Renew		
Four–1983-85	(.5)	.8
V-6–1983-85	(.6)	.9
w/A.C. add	(.2)	.2
w/P.S. add	(.3)	.3

PARTS 15 CRANKSHAFT & DAMPER 15 PARTS

	Part No.	Price
Crankshaft Assy.		
4 cyl.–151 engine		
1983-85	◆10002685	313.00
V-6–173 engine		
1983-84	◆14064197	294.25
1985	◆14077817	336.00
Main Bearings (Std.)		
4 cyl.–151 engine		
1983-85–rear	◆3829067	14.25

PARTS 15 CRANKSHAFT & DAMPER 15 PARTS

	Part No.	Price
1983-84-exc. rear	◆3829061	11.00
1985-exc. rear	◆18012433	11.25
V-6-173 engine		
1983-85-exc. below		
No. 1	◆18005226	12.75
No. 2	◆18005227	12.75
No. 3	◆18005225	26.00
No. 4	◆18005228	24.50
1985-w/X eng. (2nd design)		
No. 1, 4	◆18012472	13.25
No. 2	◆18012473	13.25
No. 3	◆18012478	24.75
1985-w/W eng.		
No. 1, 4	◆18012472	13.25
No. 2	◆18012473	13.25
No. 3	◆18012478	24.75
Rear Main Bearing Oil Seal		
4 cyl.-151 engine		
1983	◆10018632	9.00
1984-85	◆10036788	7.00
V-6-173 engine		
1983	◆14081761	14.00
1984	◆14081761	14.00
1985-w/X eng.		
1st design	◆14081761	14.00
2nd design	◆14085829	14.50
1985-w/W eng.	◆14085829	14.50
Timing Cover Seal		
1983	◆14033199	5.50
1984-85	◆10036286	5.25
Vibration Damper or Pulley		
4 cyl.-151 engine		
1983-85	◆10021360	17.50
V-6-173 engine		
1983	◆14042537	45.50
1984-85	◆14083394	39.50
Crankshaft Gear		
4 cyl.-151 engine		
1983	◆10028052	25.75
1984-85	◆10028052	25.75
V-6-173 engine		
1983-85	◆477263	13.25

LABOR 16 CAMSHAFT & TIMING GEARS 16 LABOR

(Factory Time)	Chilton Time
(G) Timing Cover Oil Seal, Renew	
Four-1983-85 (.7)	1.2
V-6-1983-85 (.8)	1.3
w/A.C. add (.2)	.2
w/P.S. add (.3)	.3
(G) Timing Cover or Gasket, Renew	
Four-1983-85 (2.0)	2.7
V-6-1983-85 (2.3)	3.2
w/A.C. add (.4)	.4
w/P.S. add (.3)	.3
(G) Timing Chain or Camshaft Gear, Renew	
Four-1983-85-w/M.T. (5.2)	9.3
w/A.T. (5.6)	9.5
V-6-1983-85 (2.4)	3.7
Renew crankshaft gear add (.2)	.2
w/A.C. add (.4)	.4
w/P.S. add (.3)	.3
(G) Camshaft, Renew	
Includes: R&R engine assembly.	
Four-1983-85-w/M.T. (5.2)	9.3
w/A.T. (5.6)	9.5
Renew cam brgs add (1.7)	2.5
V-6-1983-85	
wo/Port Inj	
w/M.T. (8.0)	11.8
w/A.T. (7.7)	11.5
w/Port Inj	
w/M.T. (8.4)	12.4
w/A.T. (8.4)	12.1
w/Cruise control add (.2)	.2
w/A.C. add (.5)	.5
w/P.S. add (.5)	.5
w/C.C.C. add (.3)	.3

PARTS 16 CAMSHAFT & TIMING GEARS 16 PARTS

	Part No.	Price
Timing Case Cover		
4 cyl.-151 engine		
1983-84	◆547797	26.75
1985	◆10036836	25.00
V-6-173 engine		
1983-85	◆14033526	85.00
Timing Case Gasket		
1983-85-w/151 eng	◆3923472	1.00
w/173 eng	◆14077849	1.50
Case Cover Oil Seal		
1983-85	◆14033199	5.50
Timing Chain		
1983-85-w/173 eng	◆14049741	30.00
Camshaft Gear		
1983-85-w/151 eng	◆10005942	46.75
w/173 eng	◆14025558	30.00
Camshaft		
4 cyl.-151 engine		
1983	◆10006745	118.00
1984	◆10029616	118.00
1985	◆1002287	N.L.
V-6-173 engine		
1983-87-exc. Code X	◆14031378	122.00
Code X	◆14024278	113.00
Camshaft Bearings		
4 cyl.-151 engine		
1983-85	◆14002525	5.50
V-6-173 engine		
1983-85		
No. 1	◆14033120	13.50
No. 2, 3	◆14002534	14.00
No. 4	◆14002535	14.00

LABOR 17 ENGINE OILING SYSTEM 17 LABOR

(Factory Time)	Chilton Time
(G) Oil Pan or Gasket, Renew	
Four-1983-85 (1.9)	3.0
V-6-1983-85 (1.6)	2.4
w/A.C. add (.3)	.3
w/P.S. add (.7)	.7
w/M.T. add (.2)	.2
(P) Pressure Test Engine Bearings (Pan Off)	
All models	1.0
(G) Oil Pump, Renew	
Four-1983-85 (2.0)	3.3
V-6-1983-85 (1.7)	2.7
w/A.C. add (.3)	.3
w/P.S. add (.7)	.7
w/M.T. add (.2)	.2
(G) Oil Pressure Gauge (Engine), Renew	
1983-85-Four (.6)	.9
V-6 (.3)	.4
(G) Oil Pressure Gauge (Dash), Renew	
1983-85 (.6)	1.0
(M) Oil Filter Element, Renew	
Four (.3)	.3
V-6 (.3)	.3

PARTS 17 ENGINE OILING SYSTEM 17 PARTS

	Part No.	Price
Oil Pan Seal		
V-6-173 engine		
1983-84-rear	◆476591	1.50
1985-rear	◆14077876	2.00
Note: If seal is not listed, use R.T.V. sealer #1052366.		
Oil Pump		
4 cyl.-151 engine		
1983-85	◆10008206	61.00

PARTS 17 ENGINE OILING SYSTEM 17 PARTS

	Part No.	Price
V-6-173 engine		
1983-85	◆14033227	N.L.
Oil Pump Screen		
V-6-173 engine		
1983-85	◆14046491	4.75
Oil Pump Drive Shaft (Upper)		
1983-85-w/151 eng	◆1977131	11.75
w/173 eng	◆477248	1.50
Oil Pump Upper Shaft Bearing		
4 cyl.-151 engine		
1983-85-upper	◆10008555	1.00
lower	◆10004842	1.50
Oil Pressure Regulator Valve		
1983-85-w/151 eng	◆3829433	1.50
w/173 eng	◆3702366	1.50
Oil Pressure Sending Switch		
4 cyl.-151 engine		
(wo/gauges)		
1983-85	◆25036378	8.75
(w/gauges)		
1983-85	◆10030963	20.75
V-6-173 engine		
(wo/gauges)		
1983-85	◆14004902	6.25
(w/gauges)		
1983-85	◆14040816	18.00
Oil Filter Element		
4 cyl.-151 engine		
1983	◆6439929	7.50
1984-85	◆25010792	7.50
V-6-173 engine		
1983	◆25010908	7.50
1984-85	◆25010792	7.50
Oil Filter By-Pass Valve		
1983-85	◆25010497	3.50

LABOR 18 CLUTCH & FLYWHEEL 18 LABOR

	(Factory Time)	Chilton Time
(G) Clutch Control Cable, Renew		
1983-85	(.4)	.7
(G) Clutch Release Bearing, Renew		
Includes: R&R trans and make all necessary adjustments.		
1983-85-Four	(2.2)	3.7
V-6	(2.5)	4.0
(G) Clutch Fork Shaft and/or Bushings, Renew		
Includes: R&R trans and make all necessary adjustments.		
1983-85-Four	(2.4)	3.9
V-6	(2.7)	4.2
(G) Clutch Assembly, Renew		
Includes: R&R trans and make all necessary adjustments.		
1983-85-Four	(2.4)	4.0
V-6	(2.7)	4.3
(G) Flywheel, Renew		
Includes: R&R transmission.		
1983-85-Four	(2.6)	4.3
V-6	(2.9)	4.6
Renew ring gear add	(.3)	.5

PARTS 18 CLUTCH & FLYWHEEL 18 PARTS

	Part No.	Price
Clutch Plate (Driven)		
1983-84	◆476600	89.00
1985-exc. below	◆14087242	83.25
w/173W eng.	◆14087239	78.00
Cover & Pressure Plate		
1983-exc. below	◆14031362	145.25
w/173Z eng	◆14066980	152.00
1984-85-exc. below	◆14066979	124.00
1985-w/173W eng	◆14080210	118.00
Clutch Fork Lever		
1983-85	◆474667	17.00
Clutch Fork Shaft		
1983-85	◆14024930	71.25
Clutch Release Bearing		
1983-85	◆908403	47.25
Clutch Pilot Bearing		
4 cyl.-151 engine		
1983-85-w/M.T.	◆10009785	3.00
w/A.T.	◆10018699	2.75
Flywheel Assy.		
4 cyl.-151 engine		
(w/man. trans.)		
1983-85	◆10004031	159.00
(w/auto. trans.)		
1983	◆10031262	70.25
1984-85	◆10031262	70.25
V-6-173 engine		
(w/man. trans.)		
1983-85	◆476575	159.00
(w/auto. trans.)		
1983-85	◆14033299	N.L.
Flywheel Ring Gear		
1983-85-V-6 eng	◆359115	21.00

LABOR 21 SHIFT LINKAGE 21 LABOR

	(Factory Time)	Chilton Time
MANUAL		
(G) Gearshift Linkage, Adjust		
All models	(.3)	.3
(G) Gearshift Lever, Renew		
1983-85	(.3)	.4
(G) Gearshift Control Assy., Renew		
Includes: R&R console plate and rear mount. Adjust control cables.		
1983-85	(.6)	1.0
(G) Gearshift Control Opening Seal, Renew		
1983-85	(.3)	.5
(G) Gearshift Control Cables, Renew		
Includes: Raise vehicle and adjust linkage.		
1983-85-one cable	(1.2)	1.6
two cables	(1.4)	1.9
AUTOMATIC		
(G) Shift Linkage, Adjust		
Includes: Neutral safety, indicator needle, cable or switch adjustments.		
All models	(.3)	.5
(G) Gearshift Selector Lever, Renew		
Includes: Renew pin and lever.		
1983-85	(.2)	.4
w/Cruise control add	(.2)	.2
(G) Shift Control Cable, Renew		
Includes: Necessary adjustments.		
1983-85	(.6)	1.0
(G) Gear Selector Needle and/or Assy., Renew		
1983-85	(.4)	.7
(G) Floor Shift Control Assy., Renew		
1983-85	(.5)	.9
(G) Park Lock Cable, Renew		
1985	(1.0)	1.5

LABOR 26 REAR AXLE AND SUSPENSION 26 LABOR

	(Factory Time)	Chilton Time
(G) Rear Coil Spring, Renew		
1983-85-one	(.4)	.6
both	(.5)	.9
(G) Lower Control Arm Bushings, Renew		
1983-85-one	(.6)	1.1
both	(1.1)	1.9
(G) Rear Shock Absorbers, Renew		
1983-85-one	(.3)	.5
both	(.4)	.7
(G) Rear Axle Assembly, Renew		
1983-85	(1.8)	2.7
(G) Rear Wheel Bearing and Hub Assy., Clean and Repack or Renew		
1983-85-one	(.4)	.6
both	(.7)	1.1
(G) Rear Axle Tie Rod Assy., Renew		
1983-85	(.3)	.5
Renew bushings add	(.3)	.3
(G) Super Lift Shock Absorbers, Renew		
1983-85-one	(.4)	.6
both	(.5)	1.0
(G) Rear Stabilizer Bar Bushing, Renew		
1983-85	(.3)	.5

PARTS 26 REAR AXLE AND SUSPENSION 26 PARTS

	Part No.	Price
(1) Insulator (Coil Spring)		
1983-85	◆10019319	2.50
(2) Coil Spring		
Note: Order by mnodel and description.		
(3) Tie Bar		
1983-85-exc below	◆10006445	22.25
w/H.D. susp.	◆10006446	22.25
(4) Shock Absorber		
1983-85-exc. below	◆4993583	34.25
w/H.D. susp.	◆4993584	24.75
(5) Bracket (Control Arm)		
1983-85-right	◆10026571	14.25
left	◆10026572	14.25
1984-85-right	◆10029094	5.75
left	◆10029093	5.75

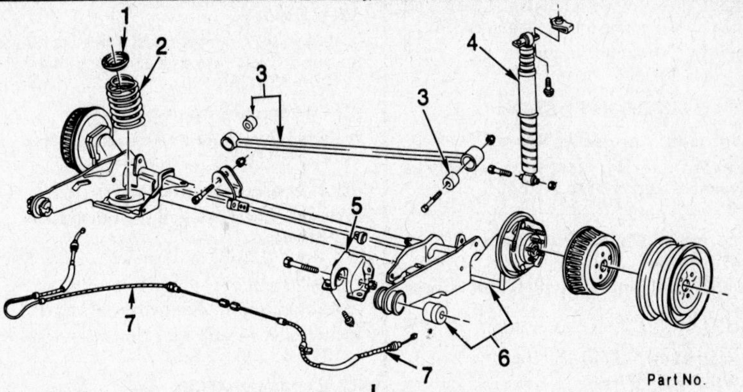

	Part No.	Price
(6) Support (Rear Axle)		
1983-85	◆10025926	394.25
(7) Cable Assy. (Parking Brake)		
1983-85-right	◆25516528	19.00
left	◆25516529	15.25

LABOR 28 AIR CONDITIONING 28 LABOR

Note: If more than one item requires replacement where evacuation and discharging the system is already included in the operation, deduct 1.0 hour for each additional item to the times listed.

	(Factory Time)	Chilton Time
(G) Drain, Evacuate and Recharge System		
All models	(.5)	1.0
(G) Leak Test		
Includes: Check all lines and connections.		
All models		.5
(G) Pressure Test System		
All models		.8
(G) Refrigerant, Add (Partial Charge)		
All models		.6
(G) Compressor Belt, Renew		
1983-85	(.3)	.4
w/P.S. add	(.4)	.4

COMPRESSOR 4 CYLINDER RADIAL

	(Factory Time)	Chilton Time
(G) Compressor Assembly, Renew		
Includes: Transfer all necessary attaching parts. Evacuate and charge system.		
1983-85-Four	(1.0)	2.0
V-6	(1.3)	2.2
(G) Compressor Clutch Plate and Hub Assy., Renew		
Includes: R&R hub and drive plate assy. Check air gap.		
1983-85	(.3)	.6

AIR CONDITIONER TUNE-UP

For efficient operation and satisfactory performance in hot weather. The following air conditioner tune-up is suggested:

1. Clean intake filter
2. Clean condenser fins
3. Pressure test system
4. Adjust drive belt tension
5. Check antifreeze/coolant
6. Tighten compressor mounts
7. Tighten condenser and evaporator mounts
8. Inspect system for leaks (hoses, couplings, valves, etc.)
9. Partial charge system

All models 1.0
If necessary to evacuate and charge system, add 1.0

	(Factory Time)	Chilton Time
(G) Compressor Clutch Rotor and/or Bearing, Renew		
Includes: R&R hub and drive plate assy.		
1983-85	(.6)	1.0
(G) Compressor Clutch Coil and/or Pulley Rim Assy., Renew		
Includes: R&R hub and drive plate assy.		
1983-85	(.5)	.9
Renew pulley or brg add		.1
(G) Compressor Front Seal, Seat and 'O' Ring, Renew		
Includes: R&R clutch hub and drive plate assy. Evacuate and charge system.		
1983-85	(1.0)	2.5
R&R accum add	(.3)	.3
(G) Compressor Front Head and/or Seal, Renew		
Includes: R&R compressor. R&R clutch and pulley assy. R&R shaft seal assy. Clean and inspect parts. Evacuate and charge system.		
1983-85	(1.6)	2.8
(G) Compressor Discharge Valve Plates, Renew		
Includes: R&R compressor. R&R clutch and pulley assy. R&R shell to internal mechanism. Clean and inspect parts. Evacuate and charge system.		
1983-85	(2.0)	2.6
Two or more add	(.1)	.3
(G) Compressor Thrust and/or Belleville Washers, Renew		
Includes: R&R compressor. R&R clutch and pulley assy. R&R shaft seal assy. R&R front head assy. Clean and inspect parts. Evacuate and charge system.		
1983-85	(1.6)	2.8

LABOR 28 AIR CONDITIONING 28 LABOR

(Factory Time)	Chilton Time

(G) Compressor Main Bearing, Renew
Includes: R&R compressor. R&R clutch and pulley assy. Clean and inspect parts. Evacuate and charge system.
1983-85 (1.6) 2.8

(G) Compressor Shaft and Cylinder Assy., Renew
Includes: R&R compressor, R&R clutch and pulley assy. R&R shaft seal assy, remove and transfer front head assy. R&R compressor shell and 'O' rings. R&R compressor discharge valve plates. R&R pressure relief valve. Clean and inspect parts. Evacuate and charge system.
1983-85 (2.1) 2.9

DA-6 COMPRESSOR

(G) Compressor Assembly, Renew
Includes: Transfer all necessary attaching parts. Evacuate and charge system.
1984-85 (.9) 2.0

(G) Compressor Clutch Plate and Hub Assy., Renew
Includes: R&R hub and drive plate assy. Check air gap.
1984-85 (.9) 1.3

(G) Compressor Clutch Rotor and/or Bearing, Renew
Includes: R&R hub and drive plate assy.
1984-85 (.9) 1.3

(G) Compressor Clutch Coil and/or Pulley Rim Assy., Renew
Includes: R&R hub and drive plate assy.
1984-85 (.9) 1.3

(G) Compressor Front Seal, Seat and 'O' Ring, Renew
Includes: R&R clutch hub and drive plate assy. Evacuate and charge system.
1984-85 (1.1) 2.2

(G) Compressor Front Head and/or Seal, Renew
Includes: R&R compressor. R&R clutch and pulley assy. R&R shaft seal assy. Clean and inspect parts. Evacuate and charge system.
1984-85 (1.5) 2.6

(G) Compressor Cylinder and Shaft Assy., Renew
Includes: R&R compressor. Transfer all parts as required. Evacuate and charge system.
1984-85 (1.5) 2.6

(G) Condenser, Renew
Includes: Evacuate and charge system.
1983-85 (1.4) 2.4

(G) Evaporator Core, Renew
Includes: Evacuate and charge system.
1983-85
Four (2.2) 3.5
V-6 (2.6) 5.0

(G) Accumulator Assembly, Renew
Includes: Evacuate and charge system.
1983-85 (.8) 1.5

(G) Expansion Tube Assy., Clean and Inspect or Renew
Includes: Evacuate and charge system.
1983-85 (.8) 1.4

(G) High Pressure Cut Off Switch, Renew
1983-85 (.2) 3

(G) Blower Motor and/or Fan, Renew
1983-85 (.4) 1.0

(G) Blower Motor Resistor, Renew
1983-85 (.2) 3

(G) Blower Motor Relay, Renew
1983-85 (.2) 3

(G) Blower Motor Switch, Renew
1983-85 (.5) 8

(G) Master Electrical Switch, Renew
1983-85 (.5) 8

(G) Temperature Control Assy., Renew
1983-85 (.5) 1.0

(G) Vacuum Diaphragm Actuators, Renew
Defroster door
1983 (2.2) 3.5
1984-85 (1.4) 2.0
Mode door
1983-85 (.5) 9
Air inlet (Recirculation)
1983 (.4) 8
1984-85 (.5) 1.2

(G) Vacuum Selector Valve, Renew
1983-85 (.5) 8

(G) Air Conditioning Hoses, Renew
Includes: Evacuate and charge system.
1983-85-suction (1.3) 2.0
discharge (1.3) 2.0
liquid line-one (1.2) 1.9

PARTS 28 AIR CONDITIONING 28 PARTS

	Part No.	Price
Compressor Assy.		
(Radial compressor)		
1983-exc. below	◆12309223	390.00
w/173Z eng.	◆12300307	390.00
1984-w/151 eng.	◆12309223	390.00
1985	◆12322321	N.L.
(DA-6 compressor)		
1984-85-w/173 eng.	◆12321363	410.00
Clutch Hub & Drive Plate		
(Radial compressor)		
1983-84	◆6551220	32.50
1985	◆6551838	36.00
(DA-6 compressor)		
1984	◆6551920	40.00
1985	◆6551996	41.00
Rotor (w/Bearing)		
1983-85	◆6551216	67.50
Compressor Pulley		
(Radial compressor)		
1983-85 (4.60 dia.)	◆6556715	13.00
w/5.50 dia.	◆6556717	19.50
(DA-6 compressor)		
1983-85 (5.13 dia.)	◆6551713	79.75
Clutch Coil (w/Housing)		
(Radial compressor)		
1983-85	◆6551217	44.00
(DA-6 compressor)		
1984-85-exc. below	◆6551834	41.50
1985-w/151, 173W eng.	◆6551997	47.25
Shaft Seal Kit		
(Radial compressor)		
1983-85	◆9956695	13.00
(DA-6 compressor)		
1984-85	◆2724319	11.25
Front Head		
(Radial compressor)		
1983-84	◆6551142	28.25
1985	◆6551835	41.25
(DA-6 compressor)		
1984-85	◆6557775	44.25
Outer Shell Assy.		
1983-85	◆2724158	38.00
Cylinder & Shaft		
(Radial compressor)		
1983-85	◆2724060	275.00
(DA-6 compressor)		
1984-85	◆6551952	307.75
Valve Plate (w/Valve)		
(Radial compressor)		
1983-85	◆6551141	11.50
(DA-6 compressor)		
1984-85-front	◆6551700	25.00
rear	◆6551702	25.00
Compressor Drive Belt		
Note: Order by model and description.		
Condenser		
1983	◆3039923	160.25
1984-85	◆3055363	152.75
Blower Motor Resistor		
1983-84	◆526897	4.50
1985	◆10039426	4.50
Blower Motor Switch		
1983	◆16015256	6.00
1984	◆16032480	7.50
1985	◆16015450	6.75
Evaporator Core		
1983-84	◆3054167	249.50
1985	◆3059160	261.50
Blower Motor		
1983-85	◆22020945	60.00
Accumulator Dehydrator		
1983-85	◆2724239	80.00
Expansion Tube (Orfice) Assy.		
1983-85	◆3033879	9.50
Pressure Cut Off Switch		
1983-85	◆2724236	19.25
Blower Motor Relay (Hi Blo)		
1983-85	◆10019535	7.50

LABOR 29 LOCKS, HINGES & WIND. REGULATORS 29 LABOR

(Factory Time) — Chilton Time

(G) Hood Latch Assembly, Renew
1983-85 (.3) 4

(G) Hood Release Cable, Renew
1983-85 (.3) 6

(G) Door Lock Assembly, Renew
1983-85-front (.5) 7
rear (.4) 6
w/Elec locks add (.1) 1

(G) Door Lock Cylinder, Renew
1983-85 (.3) 4
Recode cyl add (.3) 3

(G) Door Lock Remote Control, Renew (Front or Rear)
1983-85 (.3) 5

(G) Lock Striker Plate, Renew
1983-85 (.2) 3

(G) Door Handle (Outside), Renew (Front or Rear)
1983-85 (.3) 5
Renew insert add 1

(G) Door Window Regulator (Manual), Renew (Front or Rear)
1983-85 (.6) 1.0

(G) Door Window Regulator (Electric), Renew (Front or Rear)
1983-85 (.8) 1.2

(G) Rear Compartment Lid Strap, Renew
1983-85-one (.8) 1.2

(G) Rear Compartment Lid Lock Assy., Renew
1983-85 (.2) 3

(G) Rear Compartment Lid Lock Cylinder, Renew
1983-85 (.2) 3
Recode cyl add (.3) 3

PARTS 29 LOCKS, HINGES & WIND. REGULATORS 29 PARTS

	Part No.	Price
Hood Catch		
Citation		
1983-85	◆14062135	6.75
Omega, Phoenix, Skylark		
1983-85	◆14070703	16.25
Hood Hinge		
1983-85-right	◆20048554	17.50
left	◆20048555	17.50
Hood Latch Control		
1983-85	◆20373950	8.75
Front Door Lock		
1983-85-right	◆20293612	33.50
left	◆20293613	33.50
Rear Door Lock		
1983-85-right	◆20293642	60.50
left	◆20293643	60.50
Door Lock Cylinder Unit		
1983-85-exc. below	◆9632769	7.75
w/DLX. dr. handle	◆20496703	5.75
Door Handle (Outside)		
(wo/deluxe door handle)		
1983-85-right	◆20111712	26.50
left	◆20111713	26.50
(w/deluxe door handle)		
1983-85-right	◆20260758	25.50
left	◆20260759	25.50
Front Window Regulator (Manual)		
1983-85-right	◆20041428	64.25
left	◆20041429	64.25
Front Window Regulator (Electric)		
1983-85-right	◆20041442	79.50
left	◆20041443	79.50
Rear Window Regulator (Manual)		
1983-85-right	◆20041430	61.00
left	◆20041431	61.00
Rear Window Regulator (Electric)		
1983-85-right	◆20041434	70.00
left	◆20041435	70.00
Electric Window Regulator Motor		
1983-85	◆22029848	72.50
Trunk Lock		
1983-85-w/2 dr.	◆20279741	N.L.
w/4 dr.	◆20279742	18.00
Trunk Lock Cylinder		
1983-85-exc. below	◆3910570	6.25
w/DLX. dr. handle	◆20496705	3.75
Trunk Lid Hinges		
Citation		
1983-85-right	◆20166324	27.00
left	◆20166325	27.00
Omega & Skylark		
1983-right	◆20387102	49.00
left	◆20387103	49.00
1984-85-right	◆20482516	49.00
left	◆20482517	49.00
Phoenix		
(2-door)		
1983-right	◆20387102	49.00
left	◆20387103	49.00
1984-right	◆20482516	49.00
left	◆20482517	49.00
(4 door)		
1983-84-right	◆20166324	27.00
left	◆20166325	27.00

LABOR 30 HEAD AND PARKING LAMPS 30 LABOR

(Factory Time) — Chilton Time

(G) Aim Headlamps
two 4
four 6

(M) Headlamp Sealed Beam Bulb, Renew
1983-85-each (.3) 3

(M) Turn Signal and Parking Lamp Assy., Renew
1983-84 (.2) 3
1985 (.4) 5

(M) Side Marker Lamp Assy., Renew (Front or Rear)
1983-85 (.2) 3

(M) Tail and Stop Lamp Assy., Renew
1983-85 (.2) 3

(M) Tail and Stop Lamp Lens, Renew
1983 (.3) 4
1984-85 (.4) 5

(M) License Lamp Assembly, Renew
1983-85-one (.2) 3

each adtnl 1

(M) Back-Up Lamp Bulb, Renew
All models-one (.2) 3
all (.3) 5

(M) Park and Turn Signal Lamp Bulb, Renew
All models-each 2

(M) Side Marker Lamp Bulb, Renew
All models-each 2

(M) Stop, Tail and Turn Signal Lamp Bulb, Renew
All models-one 3
each adtnl 1

PARTS 30 HEAD AND PARKING LAMPS 30 PARTS

	Part No.	Price
Headlamp Sealed Beam		
1983-85-exc. below	◆5968098	22.00
w/quartz	◆5972698	46.50
Parking and Turn Signal Lamp Assm.		
Citation		
1983-85-right	◆915620	14.75
left	◆915619	14.75
Omega		
(wo/European styling pkg.)		
1983-right	◆918112	20.75
left	◆918111	20.75

PARTS 30 HEAD & PARKING LAMPS 30 PARTS

	Part No.	Price
1984-right	◆918752	20.75
left	◆918751	20.75
(w/European styling pkg.)		
1983-right	◆929336	20.50
left	◆929335	20.50
1984-right	◆918754	20.75
left	◆918753	20.75
Phoenix		
(exc. SJ, SE models)		
1983-84-right	◆918102	25.75
left	◆918101	25.75
(SJ, SE models)		
1983-84-right	◆918330	25.75
left	◆918329	25.75
Skylark		
(wo/amber lens)		
1983-85-right	◆915952	19.50
left	◆915951	19.50
(w/amber lens)		
1983-84-right	◆918340	19.50
left	◆918339	19.50
Tail & Stop Lamp Assy.		
Citation		
(wo/Deluxe trim)		
1983-85-right	◆5969932	61.50
left	◆5969931	61.50
(w/Deluxe trim)		
1983-85-right	◆5971100	52.00
left	◆5971099	52.00
Omega		
(exc. custom exterior)		
1983-84-right	◆16502432	83.50
left	◆16502431	83.50
(w/Custom exterior)		
1983-85-right	◆5973026	83.50
left	◆5973025	83.50
Phoenix		
1983-84-right	◆918194	84.75
left	◆918193	84.75
Skylark		
1983-84-wo/custom exterior		
right	◆5972898	61.50
left	◆5972897	61.50
1983-84-w/custom exterior		
right	◆5970908	61.50
left	◆5970907	61.50
1985-right	◆16502668	61.50
left	◆16502667	61.50
License Plate Lamp Assy.		
Citation		
(wo/Custom exterior)		
1983-85-right	◆5969916	9.75
left	◆5969915	9.75
(w/Custom exterior)		
1983-85-right	◆5970692	9.75
left	◆5970691	9.75
Omega & Skylark		
1983-84	◆913933	4.00
1985	◆912368	6.25
Phoenix		
1983-84-right	◆913986	7.75
left	◆913985	7.75
Side Marker Lamp (Front)		
Citation		
1983-85-right	◆913766	13.00
left	◆913765	13.00
Omega		
1983-84	◆913538	6.50
Phoenix		
1983-84-right	◆915884	10.00
left	◆915883	10.00
Skylark		
1983-85	◆913931	7.00

LABOR 31 WINDSHIELD WIPER & SPEEDOMETER 31 LABOR

(Factory Time)	Chilton Time
(G) Windshield Wiper Motor, Renew	
1983-85 (.6)	1.0
(G) Windshield Wiper Motor, R&R and Recondition	
1983-85 (.9)	1.5
(G) Wiper Switch, Renew	
1983-85 (1.1)	1.4
(G) Pulse Wiper Control Module, Renew	
1984-85 (.3)	.4
(G) Intermittent Wiper Controller Assy., Renew	
1983 (.2)	.3
(G) Wiper Transmission, Renew	
Includes: R&R linkage.	
1983-85 (.7)	1.2
(G) Windshield Washer Pump, Renew	
1983-85 (.3)	.4
(G) Windshield Washer Pump Valve, Renew	
1983 (.2)	.3
(G) Speedometer Head, R&R or Renew	
1983-85 (.6)	1.0
w/Gauge pkg. add	.1
Reset odometer add	.2
(G) Speedometer Cable and Casing, Renew	
Without Cruise Control	
1983-85-one piece or upper (.6)	1.1
lower (.3)	.5
With Cruise Control	
1983-85-upper (.6)	1.1
lower (.3)	.5
both (.8)	1.5
one piece (.6)	1.1
(G) Speedometer Cable (Inner), Renew or Lubricate	
Without Cruise Control	
1983-85-one piece or upper (.5)	1.0
lower (.3)	.5
With Cruise Control	
1983-85-upper (.5)	1.0
lower (.3)	.5
both (.7)	1.3
one piece (.6)	1.1
(G) Tachometer, R&R or Renew	
1983-85 (.6)	1.0
(G) Speedometer Driven Gear Adapter, Renew	
1983-85 (.3)	.5
(G) Radio, R&R	
1983-84 (.5)	.8
1985 (.8)	1.2

PARTS 31 WINDSHIELD WIPER & SPEEDOMETER 31 PARTS

	Part No.	Price
Windshield Wiper Motor		
1983-85	◆22020255	100.50
Windshield Wiper Transmission		
1983-right	◆22010672	18.00
left	◆22039717	18.00
1984-85-right	◆22039718	18.50
left	◆22039717	18.00
Pulse Control Module		
1983-85	◆25506317	47.25
Windshield Washer & Wiper Switch		
(wo/pulse wipers)		
1983-85-wo/tilt whl.	◆7835630	41.50
w/tilt wheel	◆7837281	41.50
(w/pulse wipers)		
1983-wo/tilt whl.	◆7835632	51.50
w/tilt whl.	◆7844954	51.50
1984-85-wo/tilt whl.	◆7844704	56.25
w/tilt wheel	◆7844954	51.50
Windshield Washer Pump		
1983-85-exc. below	◆4961623	15.50
1985-w/173W eng.	◆22039041	18.50
Speedometer Head Assy. & Cable (w/Casing)		
Order by year and model.		

LABOR 32 LIGHT SWITCHES & WIRING 32 LABOR

(Factory Time)	Chilton Time
(G) Headlamp Switch, Renew	
1983-85 (.5)	.6
(G) Headlamp Dimmer Switch, Renew	
1983-85 (.5)	.7
(G) Stop Light Switch, Renew	
1983-85 (.3)	.4

LABOR 32 LIGHT SWITCHES & WIRING 32 LABOR

(Factory Time) — Chilton Time

(G) Turn Signal and Hazard Warning Switch, Renew
1983-85 (.9) 1.1

(M) Turn Signal or Hazard Warning Flasher, Renew
1983-85 (.3) 3

(G) Parking Brake Lamp Switch, Renew
1983-85 (.3) 4

(G) Starter Safety Switch, Renew
1983-85-w/M.T. (.2) 4
w/A.T. (.3) 5

(G) Back-Up Lamp and Park/Neutral Switch, Renew
1983-85 (.3) 4

(G) Back-Up Lamp Switch, Renew
1983-85-w/M.T. (.2) 4
w/A.T. (.3) 5

(G) Horn Relay, Renew
1983-85 (.3) 4

(G) Horn, Renew
1983-85 (.2) 3

PARTS 32 LIGHT SWITCHES & WIRING 32 PARTS

	Part No.	Price
Headlamp Switch		
Citation, Phoenix		
1983-84	◆1995217	16.00
1985	◆1988588	13.75
Omega		
1983-84	◆1972717	17.00
Skylark		
1983-85	◆1995212	28.00
Headlamp Dimmer Switch		
1983	◆1997046	19.25
1984-85	◆7841239	18.50
Stoplight Switch		
(wo/Cruise cont)		
1983-84	◆25504628	3.75
1985-exc. below	◆25524846	6.50
w/151 eng., M.T.	◆25524844	3.00
(w/cruise cont.)		
1983-84	◆9794682	7.75
1985	◆25524847	6.50
Turn Signal Switch		
1983-85	◆1997983	30.00
Parking Brake Lamp Switch		
1983-85	◆1264464	1.50
Starter Safety Switch		
(w/Manual trans.)		
1983-85	◆14080678	4.25
(w/Auto. trans.)		
1983-84-wo/console	◆22509632	5.50
w/console	◆1994223	18.00
1985	◆1994255	11.75
Back-Up Lamp Switch		
(w/man. trans.)		
1983-85	◆14009262	2.00
(w/auto. trans.)		
1983-84-wo/console	◆22509632	5.50
w/console	◆1994223	18.00
1985	◆1994255	11.75
Turn Signal Flasher		
Citation, Omega		
1983	◆491392	N.L.
1984	◆6450076	4.00
1985	◆6450076	4.00
Phoenix, Skylark		
1983-84	◆6450089	3.00
1985	◆10041073	4.25
Hazard Warning Flasher		
1983-85	◆6450089	3.00
Horn Assy.		
1983-85-(A) Note	◆1892164	22.00
(C) Note	◆1892246	27.50
(D) Note	◆1892162	23.50
(F) Note	◆1892163	22.00
Horn Relay		
1983-85	◆25513270	8.50

LABOR 33 GLASS 33 LABOR

(Factory Time) — Chilton Time

(G) Windshield Glass, Renew
1983-85 (1.2) 1.7
Renew caulk bead add (.4) 5

(G) Quarter Window Stationary Glass, Renew
1983-85 (1.0) 1.5

(G) Rear Quarter Swing-Out Glass, Renew
1983-85 (.3) 6
Transfer latch and channel add (.1) 1

(G) Front Door Glass, Renew
1983-85 (.8) 1.2

(G) Rear Door Glass, Renew
1983-85 (.9) 1.3

(G) Back Window Glass, Renew
1983-85-Coupe (1.2) 1.9
Hatchback (.7) 1.2
w/Elec grid defogger add (.2) 3
w/3/4 plug, unpadded add (1.3) 2.0
w/3/4 plug, padded add (2.6) 4.0
w/Full plug, padded add (2.8) 4.4

LABOR 34 CRUISE CONTROL 34 LABOR

(G) Regulator Assembly (Transducer), Renew or Adjust
1983 (.4) 7
Adj low spd switch add (.1) 1

(G) Brake or Clutch Release Switch, Renew
1983-85 (.3) 4

(G) Cruise Control Servo Assy., Renew
1983-85 (.3) 4

Renew bracket add (.1) 2

(G) Vacuum Hoses, Renew
1983-85 (.2) 3

(G) Cruise Control Chain or Cable, Renew
1983-85 (.4) 5

(G) Engagement Switch, Renew
1983-85 (.4) 5

(G) Cruise Control Resume Solenoid, Renew
1983 (.2) 3

(G) Cruise Control Module, Renew
1984-85 (.3) 5

(G) Cruise Control Speed Sensor, Renew
1984 (.6) 8

(G) Cruise Control Check Valve, Renew
1984-85 (.3) 4

PARTS 34 CRUISE CONTROL 34 PARTS

	Part No.	Price
Cruise Control Transducer		
1983	◆25030560	190.25
Cruise Control Servo		
4 cyl.-151 engine		
1983	◆25031521	24.00
1984	◆25074627	117.00
1985	◆25074627	117.00
V-6-173 engine		
1983	◆25031529	31.75
1984	◆25074624	133.50
1985-w/eng. W	◆25074627	117.00
w/eng. X	◆25074624	133.50
Vacuum Release Valve		
1983-84	◆25509432	14.00
1985	◆25523376	14.00
Cruise Control Lever & Switch		
1983-85-exc. below	◆25031426	52.25
w/Pulse wiper	◆25031425	52.25
Cruise Control Chain (Lever to Servo)		
1983-85	◆25031314	3.25
Servo Cable		
1984-w/151 eng.	◆10035893	11.25
1985-w/151 eng.	◆10036106	8.25
w/173Z, X eng.	◆14079963	14.50
w/W eng.	◆14080206	9.00
Cruise Control Module		
4 cyl.-151 engine		
1984-w/M.T.	◆25031946	115.00
w/A.T.	◆25031947	122.00
1985	◆25074704	N.L.
V-6-173 engine		
1984-85	◆25031953	116.00

Buick LeSabre • Electra

GROUP INDEX

ALPHABETICAL INDEX

General Motors
Rear Wheel Drive Cars

BUICK LESABRE • ELECTRA

YEAR IDENTIFICATION

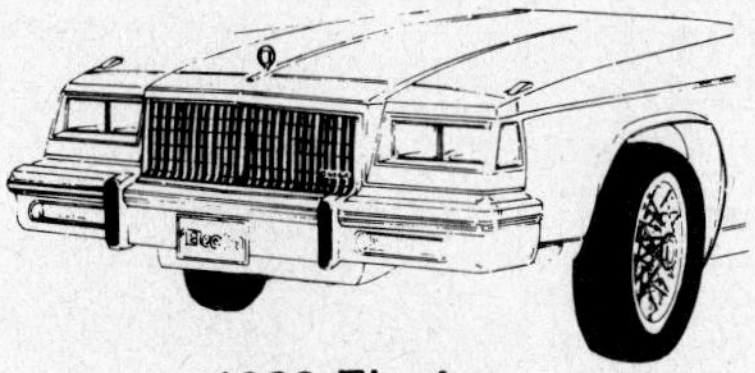

1983 Electra

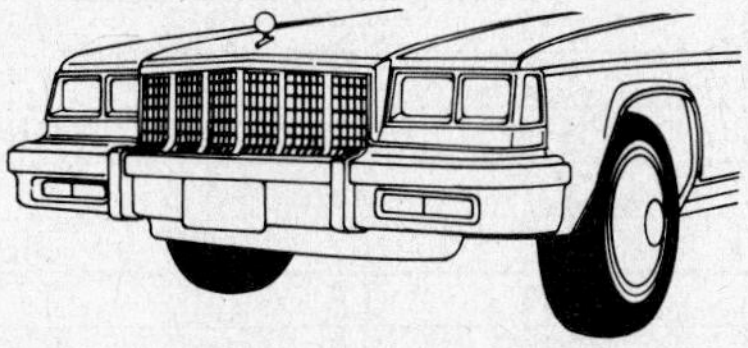

1984 Electra

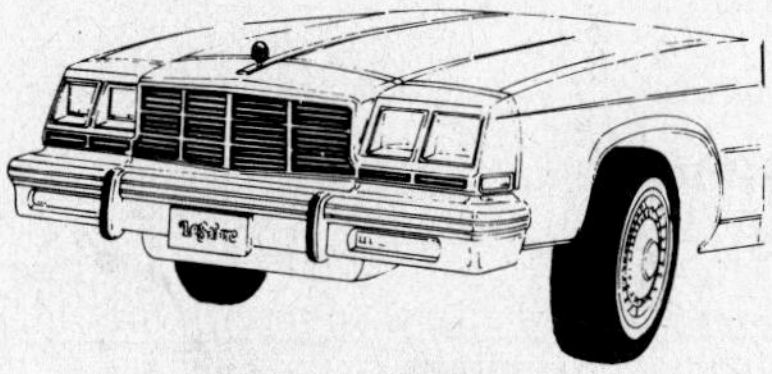

1983 LeSabre

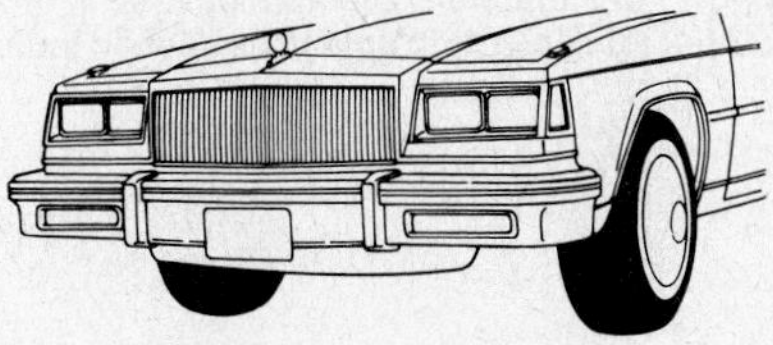

1984–85 LeSabre

TUNE-UP SPECIFICATIONS
Diesel Engines

Year	Engine VIN Code	Engine No. of cyl.-Displacement-Manufacturer	Liters	Fuel Pump Pressure (psi) ③	Injection Nozzle Pressure (psi)	Compression Pressure (psi) ②	Injection Pump Setting (deg)	Intake Valve Opens (°B.T.D.C.)	Idle Speed (rpm)
'83-'85	N	8-350-Olds	5.7	5.5-6.5	1225	275 minimum	④	16	①
'83-'85	V	6-263-Olds	4.3	5.8-8.7	⑤	275 minimum	6ATDC	16	①

NOTE: The underhood specifications sticker often reflects tune-up specification changes made in production. Sticker figures must be used if they disagree with those in this chart.

B.T.D.C.—Before top dead center (No. 1 cylinder)

① See the underhood specifications sticker.

② The lowest cylinder reading must not be less than 70% of the highest cylinder reading.

③ Fuel transfer pump pressure given. Injection pump reading should be 8–12 psi @ 1000 rpm taken at injection pump pressure tap.

④ 4ATDC on 1982 and later models

⑤ Injector opening pressure:
New nozzle (green band/no color)—1000 psi New nozzle (red band)—800 psi
Used nozzle—200 psi less than new

VEHICLE IDENTIFICATION NUMBER (VIN)

The Vehicle Identification Number (VIN) is a seventeen digit number visible through the windshield on the driver's side of the dash and contains the vehicle and engine identification codes. The eight digit identifies the original equipment engine and the tenth digit identifies the model year.

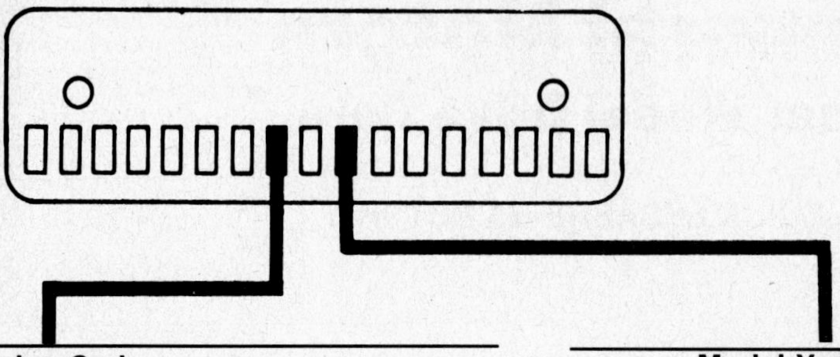

Engine Code

Year	VIN Code	Cu. In.	Liters	Cyl.	Carb. (bbls)	Eng. Mfg.
'83	A	231	3.8	V6	2	Buick
	8	231	3.8	V6	4/Turbo	Buick
	4	252	4.1	V6	4	Buick
	V	263	4.3	V6	Diesel	Olds
	Y	307	5.0	V8	4	Olds
	N	350	5.0	V8	Diesel	Olds
'84	A	231	3.8	V6	2	Buick
	9	231	3.8	V6	SFI/Turbo	Buick
	4	252	4.1	V6	4	Buick
	V	263	4.3	V6	Diesel	Olds
	Y	307	5.0	V8	4	Olds
	N	350	5.7	V8	Diesel	Olds
'85-'87	A	231	3.8	V6	2	Buick
	9	231	3.8	V6	MFI/Turbo	Buick
	V	263	4.3	V6	Diesel	Olds
	Y	307	5.0	V8	4	Olds
	N	350	5.7	V8	Diesel	Olds
	7	231	3.8	V6	SFI	Buick

MFI—Multiport Fuel Injection (Injectors opened in groups)
SFI—Sequential Fuel Injection (Injectors opened individually)

Model Year Code

Code	Year
C	82
D	83
E	84
F	85
G	86
H	87

TUNE-UP SPECIFICATIONS
Gasoline Engines

When analyzing compression test results, look for uniformity among cylinders rather than specific pressures

Year	Engine VIN Code	Engine Type	Liters	Engine Manufacturer	Spark Plugs Type ①	Spark Plugs Gap (in.)	Ignition timing (deg. B.T.D.C.) ② Automatic Transmission ④	Intake Valve Opens (°B.T.D.C.)	Fuel Pump Pressure (psi)	Idle Speed (rmp) Automatic Transmission ④
'83	A	6-231	3.8	Buick	R45TS8	.080	③	16	5½-6½	③
	3	6-231	3.8 ⑤	Buick	R45TSX	.060	③	16	5½-6½	③
	4	6-252	4.1	Buick	R45TS8	.080	③	16	5½-6½	③
	Y	8-307	5.0	Olds	R46SX	.080	③	20	5½-6½	③
'84	A	6-231	3.8	Buick	R45TSX	.060	③	16	5½-6½	③
	9	6-231	3.8 ⑥	Buick	R44TS	.045	③	16	26-51	③
	4	6-252	4.1	Buick	R45TSX	.060	③	16	5½-6½	③
	Y	8-307	5.0	Olds	R46SX	.080	③	20	5½-6½	③
'85-'87	A	6-231	3.8	Buick	R45TSX	.060	③	16	5½-6½	③
	7,9	6-231	3.8 ⑦	Buick	R44TS	.045	③	16	26-51	③
	Y	8-307	5.0	Olds	R45TS	.060	③	20	5½-6½	③

NOTE: The underhood specifications sticker often reflects tune-up specification changes made in production. Sticker figures must be used if they disagree with those in this chart.
B.T.D.C.—Before top dead center
C.I.D.—Cubic inch displacement
Min.—Minimum

TUNE-UP SPECIFICATIONS
Gasoline Engines

Part numbers in this chart are not recommendations by Chilton for any product by brand name.

① All models use electronic ignition systems.
② On some models, the engine must be held at a specific rpm to accurately check and adjust the ignition timing. See the text for specific procedures.
③ On vehicles equipped with computerized emissions systems (which have no distributor vacuum advance unit), the idle speed and ignition timing are controlled by the emissions computer.
④ Manual transmissions not used with 1982 and later Buick rear wheel drive vehicles.
⑤ Turbo
⑥ SFI-Sequential Fuel Injection
⑦ MFI—Multiport Fuel Injection

FIRING ORDERS

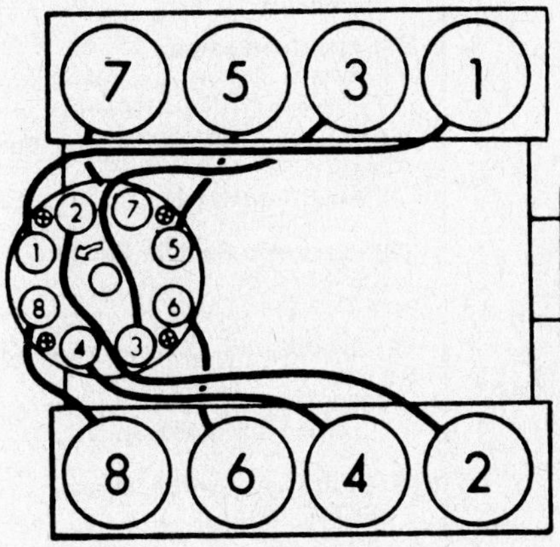

Oldsmobile 307, 350 cu. in. V8 (5.0, 5.7L)
Firing order: 1-8-4-3-6-5-7-2
Distributor rotation: counterclockwise

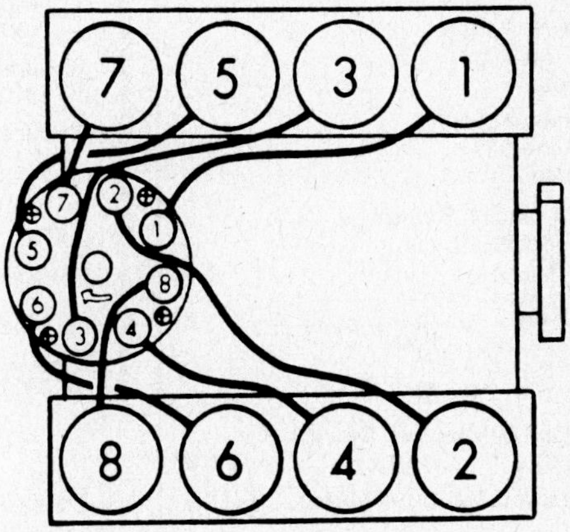

Chevrolet 267, 305 cu. in. V8 (4.3, 5.0L)
Firing order: 1-8-4-3-6-5-7-2
Distributor rotation: clockwise

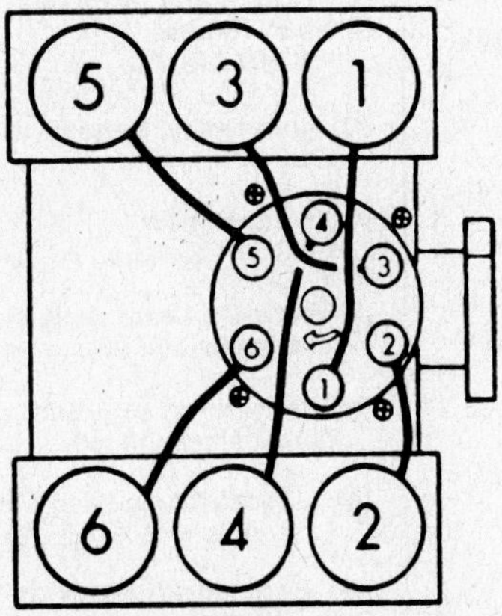

Buick 231, 252 cu. in. V6 (3.8, 4.1L)
Firing order: 1-6-5-4-3-2
Distributor rotation: clockwise

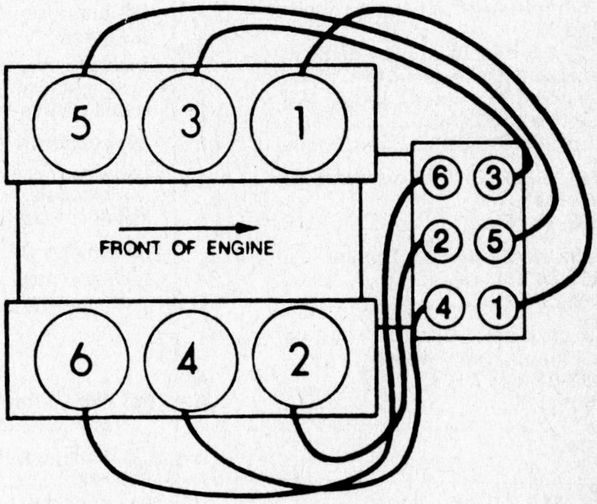

Buick 181 cu. in. V6 (3.0L) C3I
Firing order: 1-6-5-4-3-2

WHEEL ALIGNMENT SPECIFICATIONS

		Caster		Camber		
Year	Model	Range (deg)	Pref Setting (deg)	Range (deg)	Pref Setting (deg)	Toe-in ① Inch (deg)
'83-'87	Regal	2P to 4P	3P	5/16N to 1 5/16P	1/2P	1/16P to 1/4P (1/8P to 1/2P)
'83-'87	All	2P to 4P	3P	0P to 1 5/8P	13/16P	1/16P to 1/4P (1/8P to 1/2P)

LABOR — SERVICE BAY OPERATIONS — LABOR

(Factory Time) — Chilton Time

COOLING

(M) Winterize Cooling System

Includes: Run engine to check for leaks, tighten all hose connections. Test radiator and pressure cap, drain radiator and engine block. Add antifreeze and refill system.

All models 5

(M) Thermostat, Renew

V-6–1983-85 (.7) 8
V-8–1983-87 (.5) 6
Diesel–1983-85 (.5) 6

(M) Drive Belt, Renew

1983-87-one (.3) 4
each adtnl 1

(M) Drive Belt, Adjust

1983-87-one (.2) 3
each adtnl 1

(M) Radiator Hoses, Renew

1983-87-upper (.3) 4
lower (.4) 5
both (.5) 7
by-pass (.5) 6

FUEL

(M) Carburetor Air Cleaner, Service

1983-87 (.2) 3

(G) Air Cleaner Vacuum Motor, Renew

1983-87 (.3) 5

(G) Air Cleaner Temperature Sensor, Renew

1983-87 (.2) 3

(G) Carburetor, Adjust (On Car)

Includes: Adjust vacuum brake, choke coil, fast idle and idle speed, dash pot or solenoid.

1983-87
Slow & Fast Idle (.3) 4
Vacuum Brake-one (.4) 6
both (.6) 8
Choke (.6) 1.0
Complete (1.3) 1.3

(G) Automatic Choke Cover and/or Coil, Renew

1983-87 (.6) 1.0

(G) Idle Stop Solenoid, Renew

1983-84 (.3) 4
1985-87 (.7) 1.0

(G) Automatic Choke Vacuum Brake Diaphragm, Renew

1983-87-one (.4) 6
both (.6) 8

BRAKES

(G) Brakes, Adjust (Minor)

Includes: R&R wheels and adjust brakes thru access holes in drums. Fill master cylinder.

two wheels 4
Remove knock out plugs add, each .. .1

(G) Bleed Brakes (Four Wheels)

Includes: Fill master cylinder.

All models (.3) 5

CHILTON'S 10 POINT SAFETY CHECK

CHECK OPERATION & CONDITION OF THE FOLLOWING ITEMS:

1. Legal Registration (serial no.)
2. Tires & Wheels
3. Brake System (R&R all wheels)
4. Light Systems & Signals
5. Accelerator Linkage, Neutral Safety Switch, Shift Indicator Pointer & Seat Position Locks
6. Glass, Mirrors, Door Locks, Seat Belts & Harness
7. Wipers, Washers & Defrosters
8. Frame, Steering, Shocks, Front & Rear Suspension
9. Fuel & Exhaust Systems
10. Road Test Vehicle

All models 1.0
Exhaust Smog Analysis, add 4

(Factory Time) — Chilton Time

(G) Brake Pedal Free Play, Adjust

All models 3

(M) Parking Brake, Adjust

All models (.3) 4

LUBRICATION SERVICE

(M) Lubricate Chassis, Change Oil & Filter

Includes: Inspect and correct all fluid levels.

All models 6
Install grease fittings add 1

(M) Lubricate Chassis

Includes: Inspect and correct all fluid levels.

All models 4
Install grease fittings add 1

(M) Engine Oil & Filter, Change

Includes: Inspect and correct all fluid levels.

All models 4

WHEELS

(M) Wheel, Renew

one (.5) 5

(G) Wheels, Balance

one 3
each adtnl 2

(G) Front Wheel Bearings, Clean and Repack (Both Wheels)

1983-87 .... 1.6

(G) Front Wheel Bearings and Cups, Renew

1983-87-one side (.7) 9
both sides (1.2) 1.5

(Factory Time) — Chilton Time

(G) Front Wheel Grease Seals, Renew

1983-87-one whl (.7) 8
both whls (1.1) 1.2

ELECTRICAL

(M) Battery Cables, Renew

1983-87-positive (.5) 7
negative (.2) 3
batt to batt (.3) 4

(M) Battery Terminals, Clean

All models 3

(G) Aim Headlamps

two 4
four 6

(M) Headlamp Sealed Beam Bulb, Renew

1983-87-each (.2) 3

(G) Headlamp Switch, Renew

1983-87 (.3) 5
w/A.C. add (.1) 1

(G) Headlamp Dimmer Switch, Renew

1983-87
column mounted (.3) 7

(G) Stop Light Switch, Renew

1983-87 (.3) 4

(G) Turn Signal or Hazard Warning Switch, Renew

w/Cruise control add (.1) 1
1983-87 (.7) 1.1

(G) Back-Up Light Switch, Renew

1983-87 (.3) 4

(M) Turn Signal or Hazard Warning Flasher, Renew

1983-87 (.2) 2

(G) Horn Relay, Renew

1983-87 (.2) 3

(G) Horn, Renew

1983-87 (.2) 3

(M) Back-Up Lamp Bulb, Renew

All models-one (.3) 4

(M) Cornering Lamp Bulb, Renew

All models-each (.2) 3

(M) License Lamp Bulb, Renew

All models-one or all (.2) 3

(M) Park and Turn Signal Lamp Bulb, Renew

All models-each 2

(M) Side Marker Lamp Bulb, Renew

All models-each 2

(M) Stop, Tail and Turn Signal Lamp Bulb, Renew

All models-one 2
each adtnl 1

LABOR 1 TUNE UP 1 LABOR

(Factory Time)	Chilton Time
(G) Compression Test	
V-6–1983-85	.7
V-8–1983-87	.8
w/A.C. add	.3
(G) Engine Tune Up, (Electronic Ignition)	

Includes: Test battery and clean connections. Tighten manifold and carburetor mounting bolts. Check engine compression, clean and adjust or renew spark plugs. Test resistance of spark plug cables. Inspect distributor cap and rotor. Adjust air gap. Check vacuum advance operation. Reset ignition timing. Adjust idle mixture and idle speed. Service air cleaner. Inspect and adjust drive belts. Inspect choke operation and adjust or free up. Check operation of EGR valve.

(Factory Time)	Chilton Time
V-6–1983-85	2.0
V-8–1983-87	2.5
w/A.C. add	.6
To perform C.C.C. system test add	1.0

LABOR 2 IGNITION SYSTEM 2 LABOR

GASOLINE ENGINES

(Factory Time)	Chilton Time
(G) Spark Plugs, Clean and Reset or Renew	
V-6–1983-85 (.5)	.6
V-8–1983-87 (.5)	.7
To clean add	.3
w/A.C. add (.2)	.3
(G) Ignition Timing, Reset	
All models (.3)	.4
(G) Distributor, Renew	
Includes: Reset ignition timing.	
1983-87 (.5)	.8
w/AIR add (.3)	.3
w/Vacuum pump add (.2)	.2
(G) Distributor, R&R and Recondition	
Includes: Reset ignition timing.	
1983-87 (.9)	1.4
w/AIR add (.3)	.3
w/Vacuum pump add (.2)	.2
(G) Distributor Cap and/or Rotor, Renew	
1983-87 (.3)	.5
w/A.I.R. add (.5)	.5
w/Vacuum pump add (.2)	.2
(G) Ignition Coil, Renew	
Includes: Test coil.	
1983-87 (.4)	.5
w/A.I.R. add (.3)	.3
w/Vacuum pump add (.2)	.2
(G) Ignition Cables, Renew	
1983-87–V-6 (1.0)	1.4
V-8 (.3)	.6
(G) Ignition Switch, Renew	
1983-87 (.6)	.9
w/A.C. add (.1)	.1
(G) Ignition Key Warning Switch, Renew	
1983-87 (.5)	.8
(G) Distributor Module, Renew	
Includes: Test.	
1983-87 (.4)	.6
w/A.I.R. add (.3)	.3
w/Vacuum pump add (.2)	.2
(G) Distributor Hall Effect Switch, Renew	
1983 (.5)	.8
(G) ESC Module, Renew	
1983-87 (.5)	.7
(G) ESC Detonation(Knock)Sensor, Renew	
1983-87 (.7)	1.0
(G) Distributor Pick-Up Coil and/or Pole Piece, Renew	
Includes: R&R distributor and reset ignition timing.	
1983-87 (.6)	.9
w/A.I.R. add (.3)	.3
w/Vacuum pump add (.2)	.2
(G) Distributor Capacitor and/or Module Wiring Harness, Renew	
Includes: R&R dist cap and rotor, reset ignition timing.	
1983-87 (.4)	.6
w/A.I.R. add (.3)	.3
w/Vacuum pump add (.2)	.2

DIESEL IGNITION COMPONENTS

(Factory Time)	Chilton Time
(G) Coolant Fast Idle Temperature Switch, Renew	
1983-85 (.2)	.4
(G) Glow Plug Relay, Renew	
1983-85 (.2)	.3
(G) Fast Idle Solenoid, Renew	
1983-85 (.4)	.5
(G) Glow Plugs, Renew	
1983-85-one	.4
one-each bank	.7
all-both banks	1.3
(G) Glow Plug Control Module (Controller), Renew	
1985-85 (.4)	.6
(G) Glow Plug Control Switch, Renew	
1983-85 (.2)	.4
(G) Lamp Control Relay, Renew	
1983-85 (.3)	.4

PARTS 2 ELECTRONIC IGNITION 2 PARTS

Refer to the "Tune-Up" specifications chart for engine code identification.

	Part No.	Price
Distributor Assy.		
V-6-231 engine		
1983-85	◆1103470	351.25
V-6-252 engine		
1983-84	◆1103470	351.25
V-8-307 engine		
1983-84	◆1103457	333.50
1985-87	◆1103602	275.00
(1) Cover		
1983-87-V-8	◆1875960	6.00
V-6	◆1894209	6.00
(2) Coil		
1983-87	◆1985474	36.00
(3) Cap		
V-6 engine		
1983-85	◆1894979	17.00
V-8 engine		
1983-87	◆1974408	17.00
(4) Rotor		
1983-87	◆1977026	6.50

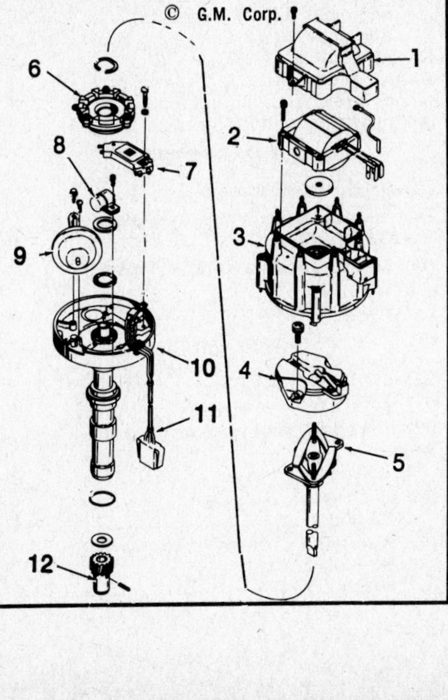

	Part No.	Price
(5) Shaft		
V-6-231 engine		
1983-85	◆1976930	38.50
V-6-252 engine		
1983-84	◆1976930	38.50
V-8-307 engine		
1983-87	◆1979955	42.50
(6) Pole Piece and Plate Assy.		
V-6-231 engine		
1983-85	◆1976925	30.25
V-6-252 engine		
1983-84	◆1976925	30.25
V-8-307 engine		
1983-87	◆1977207	32.00
(7) Module		
1983-87-w/V-6 & 307 engs	◆1976908	60.00
(8) Terminal Block w/Capacitor		
1983-87	◆1892261	N.L.

PARTS 2 ELECTRONIC IGNITION 2 PARTS

	Part No.	Price
(10) Housing		
V-6-231 & 252 engs.		
1983-85	◆1976928	36.25
V-8-307 engine		
1983-85	◆1977208	34.00
(11) Harness		
1983-85	◆1892261	11.00
(12) Gear		
V-6-231 & 252 engs.		
1983-85	◆1892082	15.25
V-8-307 engine		
1983-84	◆1979948	22.25
1985-87	◆1988777	21.50

Spark Plug Wire Set
Note: Spark plug wires are not available as a set. Each wire is sold individually

	Part No.	Price
Ignition Switch		
1983-exc. below	◆1990109	11.50
w/tilt & tele whl	◆1990110	11.50
1984-87-exc. below	◆1990115	11.50
w/tilt & tele whl	◆1990116	11.50

LABOR 3 FUEL SYSTEM 3 LABOR

(Factory Time) — Chilton Time

GASOLINE ENGINES

(G) Fuel Pump, Test
Includes: Disconnect line at carburetor, attach pressure gauge.
All models 3

(M) Carburetor Air Cleaner, Service
1983-87 (.2) 3

(G) Air Cleaner Vacuum Motor, Renew
1983-87 (.3) 5

(G) Air Cleaner Temperature Sensor, Renew
1983-87 (.2) 3

(G) Carburetor, Adjust (On Car)
Includes: Adjust vacuum brake, choke coil, fast idle and idle speed, dash pot or solenoid.
1983-87
Slow & Fast Idle (.3) 4
Vacuum Brake-one (.4) 6
both (.6) 8
Choke (.6) ... 1.0
Complete (1.3) ... 1.8

(G) Automatic Choke Cover and/or Coil, Adjust or Renew
1983-87 (.6) ... 1.0

(G) Idle Stop Solenoid, Renew
1983-84 (.3) 4
1985-87 (.7) ... 1.0

(G) Automatic Choke Vacuum Brake Diaphragm, Renew
1983-87-one (.4) 6
both (.6) 8

(G) Carburetor Needle Valve and Seat, Renew
Includes: Adjust float level.
All models
2 bbl (.9) ... 1.2
4 bbl (.9) ... 1.5
To perform C.C.C. system check, add (.5) ... 1.0

(G) Accelerator Pump, Renew
All models
2 bbl (.7) ... 1.0
4 bbl (.8) ... 1.2

(G) Choke Vacuum Control Switch, Renew
1983-87 (.3) 4

(G) E.F.E. Heater (Insulator), Renew
1983-87 (.6) ... 1.0

(G) Electric Choke Relay, Renew
1983-84 (.2) 3

(G) Carburetor, Renew
Includes: All necessary adjustments.
1983-87 (.6) 9
To perform C.C.C. system check, add (.5) ... 1.0

(G) Carburetor, R&R and Clean or Recondition
Includes: All necessary adjustments.
1983-87-2 bbl (1.8) ... 3.0
4 bbl (2.1) ... 3.2
To perform C.C.C. system check, add (.5) ... 1.0

(G) Carburetor Fuel Filter, Renew
1983-87 (.2) 4

(G) Fuel Pump, Renew
1983-87-V-6 (.4) 8
V-8 (.7) ... 1.0
w/A.C. add (.1) 1
w/P.S. add (.3) 3
w/A.I.R. add (.1) 1
Add pump test if performed.

(G) Fuel Tank, Renew
Includes: Drain and refill tank. Test gauge.
1983-87 (.8) ... 1.0

(G) Fuel Gauge (Tank), Renew
Includes: R&R tank and test gauge.
1983-87 (.8) ... 1.1

(G) Water In Fuel Detector, Renew (WIF)
All models (.9) ... 1.2

(G) Fuel Gauge (Dash), Renew
Includes: Disconnect battery cable.
1983-87 (.3) 5
w/A.C. add (.1) 1

(G) Intake Manifold and/or Gaskets, Renew
Includes: Drain and refill cooling system. Make all necessary adjustments.
V-6-1983-85 (1.8) ... 2.7
V-8-1983-85 (1.7) ... 2.5
1986-87
eng code H (2.0) ... 3.3
eng code Y (2.2) ... 3.2
Renew manif add (.3) 5
w/A.C. add (.1) 1
w/AIR add (.1) 1
w/Cruise control add (.1) 1

E.F.E. SYSTEM

(G) E.F.E. Valve, Renew
Includes: Disconnect crossover pipe.
1983-87 (.5) 8

(G) E.F.E. Vacuum Check Valve, Renew
1983-87 (.2) 4

DIESEL ENGINE

(G) Idle Speed, Adjust
1983-85 (.2) 4

(G) Injection Timing, Check and Adjust
1983-85 (.5) 9

(M) Air Cleaner, Service
1983-85 (.2) 4

(G) Air Intake Crossover, Renew
1983-85
w/Ext EGR (.3) 5
w/Int EGR (.4) 6

(G) Fuel Supply Pump, Renew
1983-85 (.5) 8
w/A.C. add (.2) 2

(G) Fuel Filter, Renew
1983-85 (.2) 4

(G) Fuel Injection Pump, Renew
Includes: Pressure and electrical tests. Adjust timing.
1983-85 (2.1) ... 3.4

(G) Injection Pump Adapter and/or Seal, Renew
1983-85 (1.8) ... 2.5

(G) Fuel Return Lines (At Nozzles), Renew
1983-85-one side (.3) 5
both sides (.4) 7
return hose (.2) 3
w/A.C. add (.2) 2

(G) High Pressure Fuel Lines, Renew
1983-85-one 8
one-each bank ... 1.0
all ... 2.5

(G) Injector Nozzle and/or Seal, Renew
1983-85-one (.4) ... 1.0
one-each bank (.7) ... 1.3
all-both banks (2.0) ... 3.0
Clean nozzles add, each 2
w/A.C. add (.2) 2

(G) Intake Manifold or Gaskets, Renew
1983-85 (2.9) ... 3.5
Renew manif add (.3) 5

(G) Vacuum Pump, Renew
Includes: Vacuum test.
1983-85
gear driven (.4) 6
belt driven (.6) 8

(G) Fuel Injection Pump Throttle Shaft Seal, Renew
1983-85 (.8) ... 1.3

(G) Injection Pump Drive and/or Driven Gears, Renew
1983-85 (4.6) ... 7.0
w/A.C. add (.2) 2

(G) Fuel Solenoid, Renew
1983-85 (.7) 9

(G) Cold Advance Solenoid, Renew
1983-85 (.8) ... 1.0

(G) Fuel Injection Head Seal, Renew
Includes: Renew head and drive shaft seals. Renew governor weight retaining ring.
1983-85 (2.7) ... 3.9

PARTS 3 FUEL SYSTEM 3 PARTS

	Part No.	Price
Carburetor Assy. (Rochester) (New)		
V-6-231 engine–2 bbl		
1983-w/Fed. em.	◆17079438	876.50
w/Calif. em.	◆17079210	666.75
1984	◆17110332	912.75
1985	◆17111175	750.50
V-6-252 engine		
1983		
T.H.200 trans.	◆17079267	767.25
T.H.350 trans.	17079271	767.25
1984	17110447	934.75
V-8-307 engine		
1983	◆17079343	803.00
1984	◆17110609	1079.00
1985	◆17111105	887.00
1986-87	◆17111487	876.00
Carburetor Overhaul Kit (Major)		
V-6-231 engine–2 bbl		
1983-84-w/Fed em.	◆17076129	50.75
w/Calif. em.	◆17076129	51.00
1985-w/Fed. & Calif.	◆17076144	57.75
V-6-252 engine		
1983	17076131	56.25
1984	◆17069095	54.75
V-8-307 engine		
1983	17069050	N.L.
1984	◆17069115	45.50
1985-87	17077141	N.L.
Carburetor Needle & Seat (Rochester)		
V-6-231 engine–2 bbl		
1983-85	◆7035157	6.00
V-6-252 engine		
1983-84	◆7035150	6.50
V-8-307 engine		
1983-87	◆7035134	6.00
Fuel Pump Assy.		
V-6-231 engine		
1983-84-231A eng.	◆6471172	N.L.
1985	◆6471368	32.50
V-6-252 engine		
1983-84-1st. design	◆6471172	N.L.
1984-2nd. design	◆6471368	32.25

	Part No.	Price
V-8-307 engine		
1983-87	◆6471743	35.00
Fuel Tank		
Order by year and model.		
Fuel Gauge (Tank)		
1983-87		
(exc. Station wagon)		
wo/vapor ret.	◆25000599	34.00
w/vapor ret.	◆25000600	35.75
1983-84		
(Station wagon)		
wo/vapor ret.	◆25002211	49.00
w/vapor ret.	◆25002212	52.75
1985-87		
Station wagon	◆25002212	52.75
Fuel Gauge (Dash)		
1983-85 exc. below	25045519	45.75
1984-87-w/anti-theft	25045312	47.00
1983-85-w/low fuel ind.	25045920	97.50
1983-87-w/anti-theft and low fuel ind.	25045520	94.00
Intake Manifold Gaskets		
V-6-231 engine		
1983-84-w/cast iron man.	◆1264924	14.50
1983-85-w/alum. manifold	◆25505397	15.75
V-6-252 engine		
1983-84	◆25505397	15.75
V-8-307 engine		
1983-84	◆557866	20.00
1985-87	◆22527545	31.25

EARLY FUEL EVAPORATION SYSTEM

	Part No.	Price
E.F.E. Valve		
1983-87		
231, 252 engs	◆5233320	64.00
305, 307 engs	◆5233475	52.00

FUEL SYSTEM (DIESEL)

	Part No.	Price
Air Intake Crossover		
1983-84	◆22509735	109.00
1985	◆22526995	109.00
Fuel Pump		
1983-84	◆6471317	N.L.
1985	◆6442228	59.25
Injection Pump Adapter		
1983-84	◆558768	21.75
1985	◆22516525	52.50
Fuel Injection Pump		
1983-w/hi alt.	◆22518689	763.00
(wo/hi altitude)		
exc. sta. wag.	◆22518686	763.00
w/sta. wag.	◆22519990	763.00
1984-w/hi alt.	◆22520999	763.00
(wo/hi altitude)		
exc. sta. wag.	◆22520936	763.00
w/sta. wag.	◆22520937	763.00
1985		
exc. sta. wag.	◆22524421	763.00
sta. wag.	◆22524422	763.00
Fuel Injector Nozzle		
1983	◆22520378	60.00
1984	◆22521207	89.50

Note 1: Identified by a small notch on all six corners of the large hex section.
Note 2: Identified by "cav" stamped on the flat surfaces.

	Part No.	Price
Vacuum Pump		
1983-84	◆7839413	116.00
1985-Lesabre		
w/A.C.	◆7845203	124.00
wo/A.C.	◆7845425	124.00
Intake Manifold Gasket Kit		
1983-84-w/iron manifold	◆22516344	12.00
1983-85-w/alum. manifold	◆22527123	N.L.
Fuel Gauge (Tank)		
1983-84-exc. sta. wagon	◆25003151	99.00
w/sta. wag.	◆25002569	105.50
1985-exc. sta. wagon	◆25004277	86.75
sta. wag.	◆25004280	76.25
Fuel Gauge (Dash)		
1983-84	25045313	47.00

LABOR 3A EMISSION CONTROLS 3A LABOR

(Factory Time) — Chilton Time

GASOLINE ENGINES

(G) Emission Control Check

Includes: Check and adjust engine idle speed and mixture and ignition timing. Check P.C.V. valve.

All models 6

POSITIVE CRANKCASE VENTILATION

(M) Positive Crankcase Ventilation Valve, Renew

All models (.2) 3

(M) Crankcase Ventilation Filter, Renew

All models (.2) 3

EVAPORATIVE EMISSION TYPE

(G) Charcoal Canister, Renew

1983-87 (.2) 3

(G) Relief Valve, Renew

1983-87 (.3) 4

CHILTON'S EMISSION CONTROL TUNE-UP

1. Clean or renew P.C.V. valve, hoses and filter.
2. Check fuel tank cap for sealing ability.
3. Check fuel tank and fuel lines for leakage.
4. Check evaporation canister and filter. Replace if necessary.
5. Check engine compression to determine leakage of unburned gases. (Add time for items of interference).
6. Test and clean or renew spark plugs.
7. Check engine oil dipstick for sealing ability.
8. Test exhaust system with analyzer and check system for leakage.
9. Check exhaust manifold heat valve for operation.
10. Adjust ignition timing and carburetor idle speed and mixture.
11. Check automatic choke mechanism for free operation.
12. Inspect air cleaner and element.
13. On models so equipped, test distributor vacuum control switch and transmission control switch.

V-6 .... **1.7**
V-8 .... **1.8**

For repairs made, charge accordingly.

(Factory Time) Chilton Time

(G) Canister Purge Thermal Vacuum Switch, Renew
1983-87 (.2) 3

CONTROLLED COMBUSTION TYPE

(G) Air Cleaner Vacuum Motor, Renew
1983-87 (.3) 5

(G) Air Cleaner Temperature Sensor, Renew
1983-87 (.2) 3

EXHAUST GAS RECIRCULATION SYSTEM

(G) E.G.R. Valve, Renew
1983-87 (.4) 6

(G) EGR Vacuum Delay Valve, Renew
1983-87 (.2) 3

(G) Thermostatic Vacuum Control Switch, Renew
1983-87 (.3) 4

(G) Thermal Control Valve, Renew
1983-87 (.3) 4

AIR INJECTOR REACTOR TYPE

(G) Air Pump, Renew
1983-87-V-6 (.3) 5
V-8 (.4) 8
w/Vacuum pump add (.2) 2

(G) A.I.R. Air Cleaner, Renew
1983-87 (.2) 3

(G) Check Valve, Renew (One)
1983-87 (.2) 3
each adtnl (.1) 1

(G) A.I.R. Drive Belt, Renew
1983-87 (.2) 3

(G) Air Pump Centrifugal Fan and/or Filter, Renew
All models (.3) 5

(G) Vacuum Delay Valve, Renew
All models (.2) 3

(G) A.I.R. Manifold, Renew
1983-87-V-8-one (.6) 9

(G) Catalytic Converter Air Pipe, Renew
1983-87
one piece (.5) 7

COMPUTER COMMAND CONTROL SYSTEM (C.C.C.)

(P) Throttle Position Sensor, Adjust
All models
2 bbl (.7) 9
4 bbl (.6) 8
Perform C.C.C. system check add 1.0

(P) Electronic Control Module, Renew
Does not include system performance check.
1983-87 (.5) 6

(P) Mixture Control Solenoid, Renew
Does not include system performance check.
1983-87-2 bbl (1.1) 1.4
4 bbl (1.2) 1.5

(P) Prom, Renew
Does not include system performance check. Includes R&R electronic module.
1983-87 (.5) 8

(Factory Time) Chilton Time

(P) Barometric Sensor, Renew
Does not include system performance check.
1983-87 (.4) 7

(P) Coolant Temperature Sensor, Renew
Does not include system performance check. Include drain and refill cooling system.
1983-87 (.6) 7

(P) Manifold Pressure Sensor, Renew
Does not include system performance check.
1983-87 (.5) 6

(P) Oxygen Sensor, Renew
Does not include system performance check.
1983-87 (.6) 7

(P) Throttle Position Sensor, Renew
Does not include system performance check.
1983-87-2 bbl (1.1) 1.4
4 bbl (1.2) 1.5

(P) Back-Up Lamp and Park/Neutral Switch, Renew
Does not include system performance check.
1983-87 (.5) 7

(P) Tachometer Filter, Renew
Does not include system performance check.
1983 (.3) 3

(P) EGR/EFE Purge Solenoid, Renew
Does not include system performance check.
1983-87 (.4) 6

(P) Air Control Valve, Renew
Does not include system performance check.
1983-87 (.4) 6

(P) Air Switching Valve, Renew
Does not include system performance check.
1983-87 (.4) 6

(P) Air Control/Air Switching Valve, Renew
Does not include system performance check.
1983-87 (.5) 7

(P) Canister Purge Control Valve, Renew
Does not include system performance check.
1983-87 (.4) 6

(P) Air Control Valve Solenoid, Renew
Does not include system performance check.
1983-87 (.5) 8

(P) Air Switching Valve Solenoid, Renew
Does not include system performance check.
1983 (.5) 8

(P) E.G.R. Bleed Control Solenoid, Renew
Does not include system performance check.
1983 (.4) 6

(P) Air Control Valve Relay, Renew
Does not include system performance check.
1983 (.4) 6

(P) E.G.R. Bleed Control Relay, Renew
Does not include system performance check.
1983 (.4) 6

(Factory Time) Chilton Time

(P) E.G.R. Vacuum Control Solenoid, Renew
Does not include system performance check.
1983-87 (.3) 4

(P) E.F.E. Vacuum Control Solenoid, Renew
Does not include system performance check.
1983-87 (.3) 4

(P) Vacuum Control Purge Solenoid, Renew
Does not include system performance check.
1983-87 (.3) 5

(P) EFE/EGR Relay, Renew
Does not include system check.
1983-87 (.3) 4

(P) Idle Speed Control Motor, Renew or Adjust
Does not include system performance check.
1983-87 (.6) 7

(P) Idle Load Compensator, Renew
Does not include system performance check.
1983-87 (.4) 6

(P) Vehicle Speed Sensor, Renew
Does not include system performance check.
1983-85 (1.1) 2.0
1986-87 (.6) 1.0

(P) Computer Command Control System Performance Check
1983-87 (.5) 1.0

DIESEL ENGINE

(G) Crankcase Depression Regulator Valve, Renew
1983-85 (.2) 3

(G) Crankcase Ventilation Flow Control Valve, Renew
1983-85 (.2) 3

(G) Crankcase Ventilation Filter, Renew
1983-85 (.2) 3

(G) E.G.R. Valve and/or Gasket, Renew
1983-85 (.5) 7

(G) E.G.R. Control Valve Solenoid, Renew
1983-84 (.2) 3
1985 (.4) 6
Renew ECM add 1

(G) E.G.R. Control Valve Switch, Renew
1983-85 (.2) 3

(G) E.P.R. Control Valve Solenoid, Renew
1983-85 (.3) 4

(G) E.P.R. Control Valve Switch, Renew
1983-85 (.3) 4

(G) E.P.R. Exhaust Pressure Regulator Valve, Renew
1983-84 (.3) 5
1985 (.5) 7

(G) Vacuum Regulator Valve, Renew
1983-85 (.6) 8

PARTS 3A EMISSION CONTROLS 3A PARTS

	Part No.	Price
POSITIVE CRANKCASE VENTILATION		
Ventilation Valve		
1983-85 w/231A, 252 engs.	◆6487534	3.00
1983-87-w/307 eng.	◆8997683	3.50
1983-85-w/diesel	◆25041678	34.50
EVAPORATIVE EMISSION		
Charcoal Canister		
1983-87-w/231 & 307 eng.	◆17064622	N.L.
1983-84-w/252 eng.	◆17064622	39.50
CONTROLLED COMBUSTION TYPE		
Vacuum Motor		
1983-85 w/231, 252 eng.	◆8994262	24.50
w/307 eng.	◆8994333	18.75
Air Cleaner Sensor		
1983-87-w/V-6 eng.	◆8997916	18.75
w/V-8 eng.	◆8997574	18.75
EXHAUST GAS RECIRCULATION SYSTEM		
E.G.R. Valve		
Replacement E.G.R. valves must be ordered according to the stamping number on the original valve.		
E.G.R. Solenoid		
1983-w/307 eng.	◆1997636	13.25
1984-w/307 eng.	◆1997665	43.50
1985-87-w/307 eng.	◆1997126	43.00
Air Pump		
V-6 engine		
1983-84	◆7835397	131.00
V-8 engine		
1983	7842852	N.L.
1984-87	◆7838575	158.00
Manifold Check Valve		
1983-87 w/307 eng.	◆22034702	10.25
w/V6 eng.	◆22034703	12.75
Thermo. Vacuum Switch		
1983-85 w/V-6 eng.	3042272	13.00
1983-87-w/307 eng.	◆3048786	14.50
1984-85	◆3055550	13.75
COMPUTER COMMAND CONTROL EMISSION SYSTEM		
Electronic Control Module (ECM) Remanufactured		
V-6-231 engine		
1983-w/Federal	◆1226024	110.25
w/Calif.	◆1225500	110.25
1984-85	◆1226519	110.25
V-6-252 engine		
1983	◆1225500	110.25
1984	◆1226519	110.25
V-8-307 engine		
1983	◆1225450	110.25
1984	◆1226457	110.25
1985-87-1st. design	◆1226866	110.00
2nd design	◆1227076	110.00
Calibration Unit (PROM)		
V-6-231 engine		
1983-Federal	◆1226271	40.50
Calif.	◆1225707	40.50
1984-Calif.	◆16041526	40.50
Federal	◆16041520	40.50
1985		
Federal	◆16044114	40.50
Calif.	◆16044119	40.50
V-6-252 engine		
1983-84-Federal		
w/TH200 trans.	◆1225909	40.50
w/TH350 trans.	1225546	40.50
1983-84-California		
w/TH200 trans.	◆1225910	40.50
w/TH350 trans.	1225908	40.50
V-8-307 engine		
1983-Sta. wag.		
1st. design	◆1226167	40.50
2nd. design	◆1226435	40.50
w/Calif. em.	◆1226175	40.50
1983-exc. sta. wag. (Calif.)		
w/TH200 trans.	◆1226166	40.50
w/TH250C trans.	◆1226182	40.50
1983-exc. sta. wag. (Federal)		
(w/TH200 trans.)		
w/Code 8182ANN	◆1226183	40.50
w/Code 3365CCU	◆1226434	40.50
(w/TH250C trans.)		
w/Code 8170ANL	◆1226181	40.50
w/Code 3415CDB	◆1226437	40.50
1984		
(200C trans.)		
w/Fed. em.	◆16045639	40.50
Calif. em.	16045644	40.50
(200-4R trans.)		
Calif. em., exc. sta. wag		37.50
1st. design	◆16040790	40.50
2nd. design	16045624	40.50
Fed. em.		
exc. sta. wagon	◆16045609	40.50
sta. wagon	◆16045619	40.50
1985-87		
w/Code 9620DBU	◆16039619	40.50
w/Code 9625DBW	16039624	40.50
w/Code 0269FYU	◆16050268	40.50
w/Code 9615DBS	◆16039614	40.50
Manifold Absolute Pressure (MAP) Sensor		
1983-85 w/V-6 eng.	◆16006835	62.25
Manifold diff. pressure sensor w/307 eng.	◆16006834	62.25
Barometric Sensor		
1983-85-w/231, 252 engs.	◆16006833	62.25
Oxygen Sensor		
1983-84	◆5613959	29.00
1985-87	◆8990741	28.75

LABOR 4 ALTERNATOR AND REGULATOR 4 LABOR

	(Factory Time)	Chilton Time
(G) Delcotron Circuits, Test		
Includes: Test battery, regulator, Delcotron output.		
All models		.6
(M) Alternator Drive Belt, Renew		
1983-87		
V-6	(.2)	.3
w/AIR add	(.1)	.1
V-8	(.2)	.3
Diesel	(.3)	.4
wo/A.C. add	(.1)	.1
(G) Delcotron Assembly, Renew		
Includes: Transfer pulley and fan.		
1983-87	(.4)	.6
Add circuit test if performed.		
(G) Delcotron, R&R and Recondition		
Includes: Complete disassembly, inspect, test, replace parts as required, reassemble.		
1983-87	(1.2)	1.7
w/Diesel eng add	(.1)	.1
(G) Delcotron Front Bearing, Renew		
Includes: R&R Delcotron, separate end frames.		
1983-87	(.8)	1.0
Renew rear brg add		.2
w/Diesel eng add	(.2)	.2
(G) Delcotron Voltage Regulator, Test and Renew		
Includes: R&R, disassemble and reassemble Delcotron.		
1983-87	(.8)	1.2
w/Diesel eng add	(.1)	.1

PARTS 4 ALTERNATOR AND REGULATOR 4 PARTS

	Part No.	Price
Delcotron Assembly		
1983-42 amp	◆1105360	206.00
1983-87-w/66, 78 amp		
V-6 eng.	◆1100250	225.00
V-8 eng.	◆1105369	228.75
70 amp	◆1105335	265.00
85 amp	◆1105339	326.50
(94 amp)		
wo/A.C.	◆1105492	228.50
w/A.C.	◆1105480	232.00

PARTS 4 ALTERNATOR AND REGULATOR 4 PARTS

	Part No.	Price
(1) Capacitor		
1983-87	◆1978146	4.75
(2) Diode		
1983-87	◆1984459	5.00
(3) Rectifier Bridge		
1983-87-exc.		
below	◆1984454	28.00
70, 85 amp	◆1975313	24.50
94 amp	◆1987061	29.25
(4) Bearing		
1983-87-exc.		
below	◆9436831	5.50
70, 85 amp	◆1975322	5.50
(5) Regulator		
1983-87	◆1116387	25.00
(6) Brush Holder		
1983-87-exc.		
below	◆1984462	9.00
70, 85 amp	◆1975323	10.00
(7) Rotor Assy.		
1983-exc below	1876163	55.00
42, 55, 63 amp	◆1985476	72.00
80 amp	1877057	N.L.
70, 85 amp	◆1975333	65.00
1984-87-exc.		
below	◆1984466	77.25
66, 78 amp	◆1985476	72.00
70, 85 amp	◆1975333	65.00

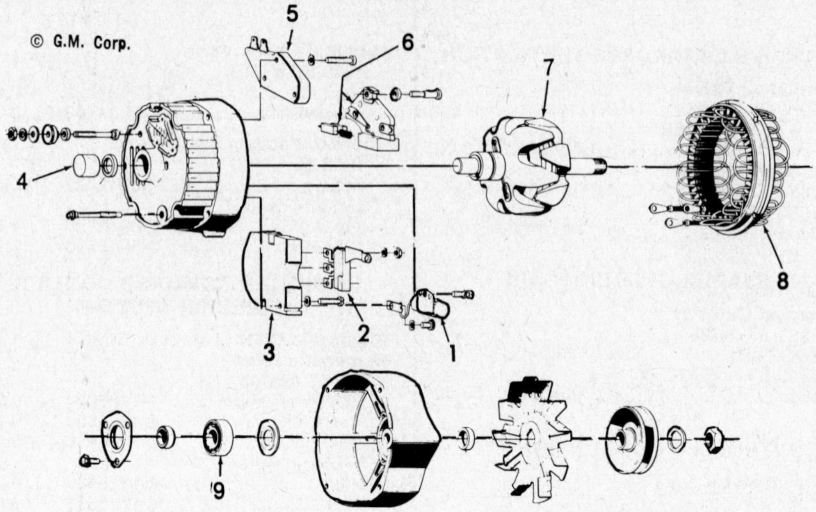

	Part No.	Price
(8) Stator		
1983-87-exc.		
below	◆1971639	41.00
37, 42 amp	◆1986280	52.75
70 amp	◆1975303	48.75
63, 78 amp	◆1984445	37.25
80 amp	◆801818	82.25
85 amp	◆1975987	83.50
94 amp	◆1987074	41.50
(9) Bearing (Front End)		
1983	◆908419	10.00
1984-87	◆908419	10.00

LABOR 5 STARTING SYSTEM 5 LABOR

	(Factory Time)	Chilton Time
(G) Starter Draw Test (On Car)		
All models		.3
(G) Starter, Renew		
V-6–1983-85	(.6)	.9
V-8–1983-85	(.6)	.9
1986-87	(.5)	.8
Diesel–1983-85	(.6)	1.1
(G) Starter, R&R and Recondition		
Includes: Turn down armature.		
V-6–1983-85	(1.4)	1.9
V-8–1983-85	(1.4)	1.9
1986-87	(1.3)	1.9
Diesel–1983-85	(1.8)	2.5
Renew field coils add	(.2)	.5
(G) Starter Drive, Renew		
V-6–1983-85	(.9)	1.1
V-8–1983-85	(.9)	1.1
1986-87	(.6)	1.0
Diesel–1983-85	(1.0)	1.4
(G) Starter Solenoid Switch, Renew		
Includes: R&R starter.		
V-6–1983-85	(.6)	.9
V-8–1983-85	(.6)	.9
1986-87	(.5)	.9
Diesel–1983-85	(.7)	1.1
(G) Ignition Switch, Renew		
1983-87	(.5)	.9
w/A.C. add	(.1)	.1
(M) Battery Cables, Renew		
1983-87-positive	(.5)	.7
negative	(.2)	.3
batt to batt	(.3)	.4
(M) Battery Terminals, Clean		
All models		.3

PARTS 5 STARTING SYSTEM 5 PARTS

	Part No.	Price
(1) Starter Assembly (New)		
V-6–231 engine		
1983-85	◆1998234	220.75
V-6–252 engine		
1983-84	◆1998234	220.75
V-8–307 engine		
1983	◆1109544	209.00
1984-87	◆1998453	180.50
(2) Solenoid Switch		
1983-87	◆1114531	N.L.
(3) Drive Assy.		
1983-87-exc diesel	◆1875687	N.L.
w/diesel	◆1893445	65.00
(4) Brush		
1983-85-exc. 307 eng.	◆1906945	.50
1983-87 w/307 eng.	◆1893296	.50

PARTS 5 STARTING SYSTEM 5 PARTS

	Part No.	Price
(5) Drive End Bushing		
1983-87 exc.		
diesel	◆1932190	.50
diesel	◆1839345	1.00
(6) Armature		
V-6-231 engine		
1983-85	◆1971568	57.00
V-6-252 engine		
1983-84	◆1970548	52.00
V-8-307 engine		
1983	◆1978670	83.50
1984-87	◆1985138	N.L.
(7) Field Coils		
11983-8704,		
1998204	◆1974183	19.25
1108429, 1108789, 1108794, 1109024, 1109026, 1109052, 1109063, 1109067, 1109068, 1109072,		
1998205	◆1877306	26.00
1983	◆1877306	26.00
1984-87-exc.		
below	◆1877306	26.00
w/231 eng.	◆1974183	19.25
(8) Drive Housing and Bushing		
1983-85-exc		
below	◆1876881	20.50

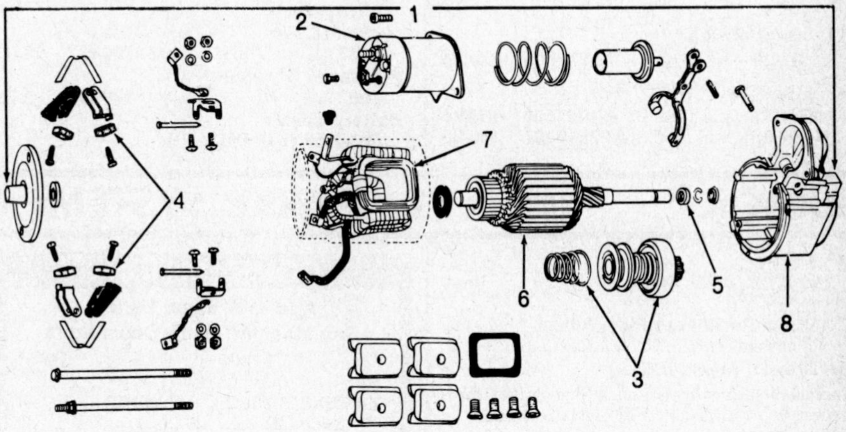

	Part No.	Price
1983-w/307 eng.	◆1893752	19.50
1984-87-w/307		
eng.	◆1987662	25.50
Ignition Switch		
1983-exc. Tilt		
whl.	◆1990109	N.L.

	Part No.	Price
w/Tilt whl.	◆1990110	N.L.
1984-87-exc. Tilt		
whl.	◆1990115	11.50
w/tilt whl.	◆1990116	11.50

Battery Cables
Order by year and model.

PARTS 5 STARTING SYSTEM 5 PARTS

STARTING SYSTEM (DIESEL)

	Part No.	Price
Starter Assy. (New)		
1983	◆1109533	214.50
1984-85	◆22522853	355.00
(1) Solenoid Switch		
1983-85	◆1114531	N.L.
(2) Drive End Bearing		
1983-85	◆9439544	5.00
(3) Starter Drive		
1983-85	◆1893445	65.00
(4) Drive Shaft		
1983-85	◆1972683	29.00
(5) Gear		
1983-85	◆1972685	12.50

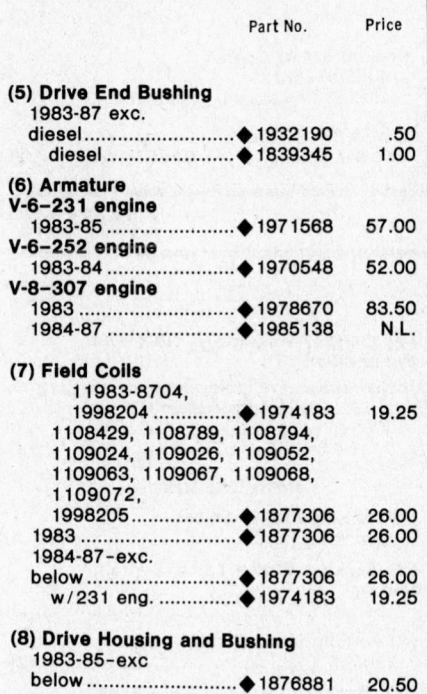

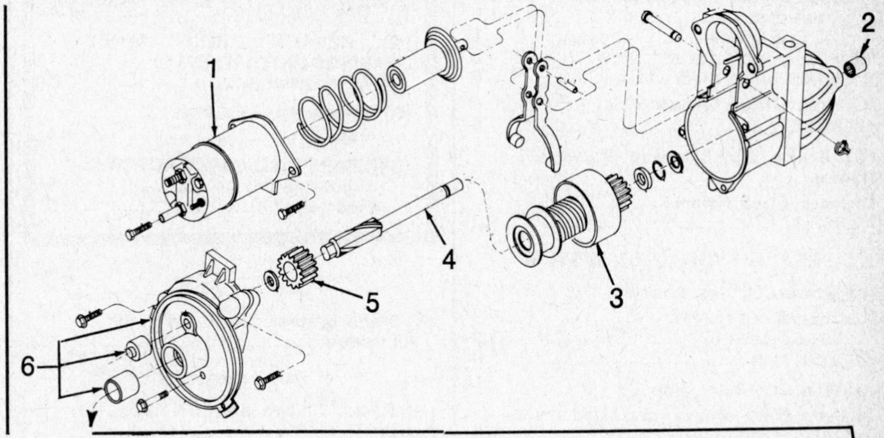

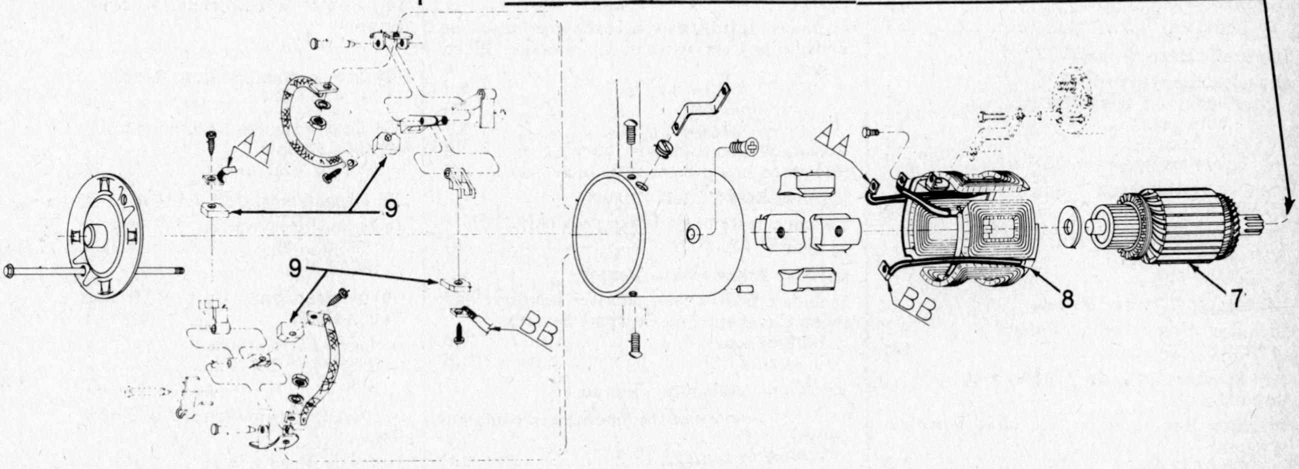

PARTS 5 STARTING SYSTEM 5 PARTS

	Part No.	Price
(6) Gear Housing		
1983-85	◆1972700	29.50
(7) Armature		
1983	◆1987639	139.75
1984-85	◆22516197	130.00
(8) Field Coils		
1983	◆1979982	83.00
(9) Starter Brushes		
1983	◆1852885	2.75
Battery Cables		
Order by year and model.		
Neutral Safety Switch		
1983-87-exc. elec. dr. lks.	◆22509632	5.50
1983-87-w/elec. dr. lks.	◆22514861	7.00

LABOR 6 BRAKE SYSTEM 6 LABOR

	(Factory Time)	Chilton Time
(G) Brake Pedal Free Play, Adjust		
All models		.3
(G) Brakes, Adjust (Minor)		
Includes: R&R wheels and adjust brakes thru access holes in drums. Fill master cylinder.		
two wheels		.4
Remove knock out plugs add, each		.1
(G) Bleed Brakes (Four Wheels)		
Includes: Fill master cylinder.		
All models	(.4)	.5
(G) Free-Up or Renew Brake Self Adjusting Units		
one wheel		.5
each adtnl		.4
(G) Brake Shoes and/or Pads, Renew		
Includes: Install new or exchange shoes or pads, adjust service and hand brake. Bleed system.		
1983-87-front-disc	(.9)	1.1
rear-drum	(.9)	1.5
all four wheels		2.5
Resurface disc rotor add, each		.9
Resurface brake drum add, each		.5
(G) Brake Drum, Renew (One)		
1983-87	(.3)	.5
(G) Brake Combination Valve, Renew		
Includes: Bleed system.		
1983-87	(.7)	1.0

BRAKE HYDRAULIC SYSTEM

	(Factory Time)	Chilton Time
(G) Wheel Cylinder, Renew		
Includes: Bleed system.		
1983-87-one	(.8)	1.0
both	(1.1)	1.9
(G) Wheel Cylinder, Rebuild		
Includes: Hone cylinder and bleed system.		
1983-87-one	(1.0)	1.3
both	(1.5)	2.1
(G) Brake Hose, Renew		
Includes: Bleed system.		
1983-87-front-one	(.5)	.8
both	(.6)	1.1
rear-one	(.5)	.9
power master-each	(.3)	.5
(G) Electro-Hydraulic Pump, Renew		
1985-87	(.4)	.5
(G) Powermaster Pressure Switch, Renew		
1985-87	(.3)	.4
(G) Master Cylinder, Renew		
Includes: Bleed complete system.		
1983-87	(.6)	1.0
(G) Master Cylinder, R&R and Rebuild		
Includes: Hone cylinder and bleed complete system.		
1983-87	(1.4)	1.8
w/Power master cyl	(1.6)	2.2

COMBINATIONS

Add to Brakes, Renew
See Machine Shop Operations

	(Factory Time)	Chilton Time
(G) RENEW WHEEL CYLINDER		
Each	(.2)	.2
(G) REBUILD WHEEL CYLINDER		
Each	(.3)	.3
(G) REBUILD CALIPER ASSEMBLY		
Front-one	(.5)	.6
Rear-one	(.5)	.6
(G) RENEW MASTER CYLINDER		
All models	(.6)	.8
(G) REBUILD MASTER CYLINDER		
All models	(.8)	1.0
(G) RENEW BRAKE HOSE		
Each	(.3)	.3
(G) RENEW REAR WHEEL GREASE SEALS		
One side	(.5)	.5
(G) REPACK FRONT WHEEL BEARINGS (BOTH WHEELS)		
All models	(.6)	.6
(G) RENEW BRAKE DRUM		
Each	(.1)	.1
(G) RENEW DISC BRAKE ROTOR		
Front-one	(.4)	.5
Rear-one	(.4)	.5

	(Factory Time)	Chilton Time
(G) Brake System, Flush and Refill		
All models		1.2

DISC BRAKES

	(Factory Time)	Chilton Time
(G) Brake Shoes and/or Pads, Renew		
Includes: Install new or exchange shoes or pads, adjust service and hand brake. Bleed system.		
1983-87-front-disc	(.9)	1.1
rear-drum	(.9)	1.5
all four wheels		2.5
Resurface disc rotor add, each		.9
Resurface brake drum add, each		.5
(G) Disc Brake Pads, Renew		
Includes: Install new brake pads only.		
1983-87	(.9)	1.1
(G) Disc Brake Rotor, Renew		
Includes: R&R wheel, transfer bearings and races. Clean and repack wheel bearings.		
1983-87-one	(.7)	1.0
both	(1.2)	1.5
(G) Caliper Assembly, Renew		
Includes: Remove brake shoes. Bleed complete system.		
1983-87-one	(.7)	1.0
both	(1.1)	1.5
(G) Caliper Assembly, R&R and Recondition		
Includes: Remove brake shoes, renew parts as required and bleed complete system.		
1983-87-one	(1.2)	1.5
both	(2.1)	2.5

PARKING BRAKE

	(Factory Time)	Chilton Time
(M) Parking Brake, Adjust		
All models	(.3)	.4
(G) Parking Brake Lamp Switch, Renew		
1983-87	(.2)	.3
(G) Parking Brake Control, Renew		
1983-87	(.7)	1.0
(G) Parking Brake Equalizer, Renew		
1983-87	(.3)	.5
(G) Parking Brake Cables, Renew		
Includes: Adjust parking brake.		
Front		
1983-87-one	(.6)	1.0
Rear		
1983-87-each	(.7)	1.1

POWER BRAKES

	(Factory Time)	Chilton Time
(G) Power Brake Cylinder, Renew		
Includes: R&R master cylinder.		
1983-87	(.6)	1.1
(G) Power Brake Cylinder, R&R and Recondition		
Includes: R&R master cylinder.		
1983-87-single cyl	(1.1)	1.8
tandem cyl	(1.3)	2.0
(G) Power Brake Check Valve, Renew		
1983-87	(.3)	.3
(G) Power Brake Vacuum Hose, Renew		
1983-87	(.3)	.3
(G) Low Vacuum Switch, Renew		
1985-87	(.2)	.3
(G) Low Vacuum Brake Indicator Module, Renew		
1985-87	(.2)	.3
(G) Hydra-boost Unit, Renew		
Includes: Bleed system.		
1983-84	(.6)	1.0
1985	(.8)	1.0
(G) Hydra-boost Unit, R&R and Recondition		
Includes: Bleed system.		
1983-84	(1.0)	1.5
1985	(1.2)	1.5
(G) Hydra-boost Pressure Lines, Renew		
Includes: Bleed system.		
1983-85-each	(.3)	.6

PARTS 6 BRAKE SYSTEM 6 PARTS

	Part No.	Price
(1) Brake Shoe Set-Rear (2 wheels)		
(w/9½ x 2 in. brks.)		
1983-87	◆1154580	35.00
(w/11 x 2 in. brks.)		
1984-87	◆1154577	42.50
(2) Wheel Cylinder Assy. (Rear)		
1983-85-w/11″ drums (exc. sta. wag.)	◆18004890	25.75
1983-87-w/9½″ drums	◆18004888	28.50
1983-87-w/Sta. wag.	◆18004793	28.50
Wheel Cylinder Repair Kit (Rear)		
1983-87-w/9½″ drums	◆5466562	7.75
1983-85-w/11″ drums (exc. sta. wag.)	◆5463361	7.50
1983-87-sta. wag.	◆5472328	8.00
Brake Hose Front (Flex)		
1983-87	◆9762809	18.00
Brake Hose Rear (Flex)		
1983-87	◆9757655	15.00
Master Cylinder Assembly		
1983-87-exc 350 diesel	◆18010313	145.75
w/350 diesel	◆25509416	103.00
Master Cylinder Repair Kit		
1983-87-exc diesel	◆18007935	22.50
1983-85-w/ diesel	◆25509843	28.50
Vacuum Power Booster		
1983-85	◆18006566	224.50
1986-87	◆18010313	145.50
Vacuum Power Brake Repair Kit		
1983-85	◆18007935	22.50
Brake Drum (Rear)		
(w/9½″ brakes)		
1983-85-aluminum	◆1255496	90.00

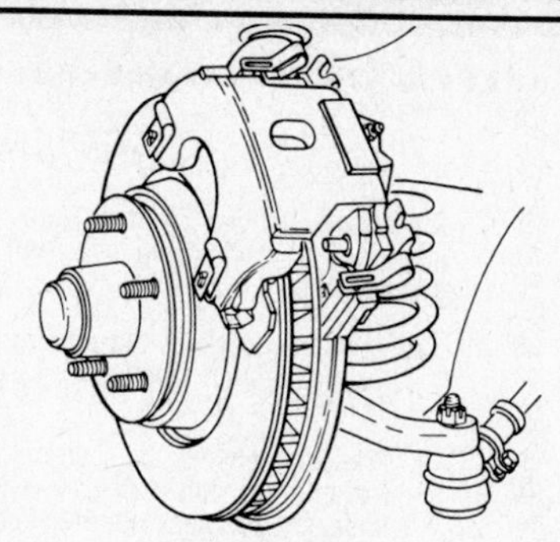

FRONT BRAKE

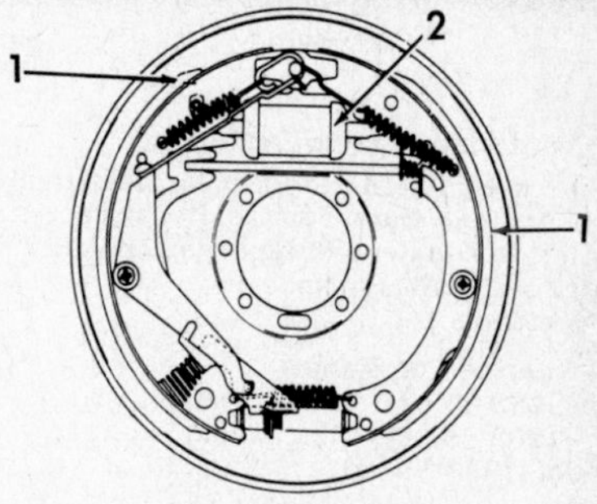

REAR BRAKE

	Part No.	Price
1983-87-cast iron (w/11″ brakes)	◆1249146	73.00
1983-87-(cast iron) w/17 lb.	◆1244835	97.00
1983-84-w/23 lb.	◆1244838	96.25
Front Wheel Oil Seal		
1983-87	◆3965092	3.00

PARKING BRAKE

	Part No.	Price
Parking Brake Lever (Control)		
1983-87	◆25502971	23.50
Parking Brake Cable (Front)		
1983-84-LeSabre	◆25502769	12.00
Electra	◆25502768	13.50
1985-87	◆25520342	12.75
Parking Brake Cable (Rear)		
1983-84 exc. rear disc brks.		
L.H.	◆25502687	22.00
R.H. exc. wag.	◆25502686	22.00
R.H. sta. wag.	◆25502772	22.50
1985-87-L.H.	◆25520337	22.25
R.H. exc. wag.	◆25520338	22.00
R.H. sta. wag.	◆25524602	22.00
left	◆25524603	22.50

HYDRAULIC POWER BRAKES

	Part No.	Price
Power Booster Assembly		
1983-85 w/Diesel eng.	◆1620210	365.00
Cover Repair Kit		
Includes: (1)nut, (1)housing cover, (1)housing seal, (1)piston seal		
1983-85	◆22506436	82.25
Piston Repair Kit		
Includes: (1)housing seal, (1)piston seal.		
1983-85	◆22506438	5.50
Booster Seal Kit		
Includes: (1)boot, (1)housing seal, (1)piston seal, (3)O-rings.		
1983-85	◆22506440	10.75
Piston and Accumulator Kit		
Includes: (1)housing seal, (1)power piston and accumulator assy., (1)piston seal.		
1983-85	◆22506439	128.00
Spool Plug Seal Kit		
Includes: (1)spool plug O-ring, (1)spool plug, (1)spool plug retainer.		
1983-85	◆1612592	3.00

PARTS 6 DISC BRAKES 6 PARTS

FRONT DISC BRAKES

	Part No.	Price
(1) Brake Pads		
1983-85-exc. H.D. brks.	◆1154578	35.00
1983-87-H.D. brks.	◆12300192	47.00
(2) Spring		
1983-87	◆5469497	1.00
(3) Caliper Piston Repair Kit		
1983-87	◆5468767	10.00
(4) Piston		
1983-87	◆2622207	11.00
(5) Caliper		
1983-84-right	◆18007946	124.50
1985-87-right	◆18012309	168.75
1983-87-left	◆18012308	168.75
Hub & Disc		
1983-87-12″	◆14008641	110.00
1983-85-11″	◆14008640	110.00

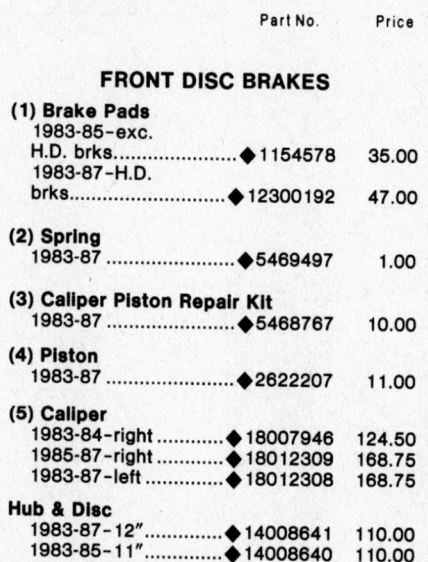

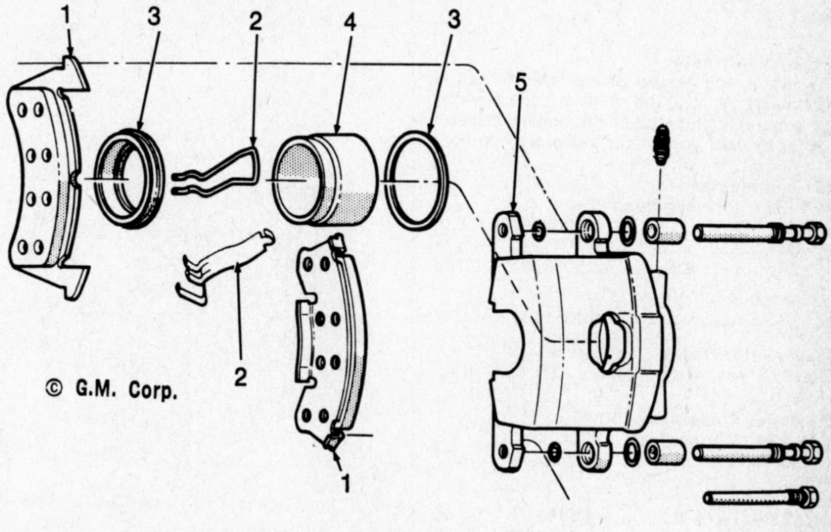

LABOR 7 COOLING SYSTEM 7 LABOR

(Factory Time)	Chilton Time
(M) Winterize Cooling System	
Includes: Run engine to check for leaks, tighten all hose connections. Test radiator and pressure cap, drain radiator and engine block. Add anti-freeze and refill system.	
All models	.5
(M) Thermostat, Renew	
V-6–1983-85 (.7)	.8
V-8–1983-87 (.5)	.6
Diesel–1983-85 (.5)	.6
(M) Radiator Assembly, R&R or Renew	
Includes: Drain and refill cooling system.	
1983-87 (.7)	1.1
ADD THESE OPERATIONS TO RADIATOR R&R	
(G) Boil & Repair	1.5
(G) Rod Clean	1.9
(G) Repair Core	1.3
(G) Renew Tank	1.6
(G) Renew Trans. Oil Cooler	1.9
(G) Recore Radiator	1.7
(M) Radiator Hoses, Renew	
1983-87-upper (.3)	.4
lower (.4)	.5
both (.5)	.7
by-pass (.5)	.6
(M) Drive Belt, Adjust	
1983-87-one (.2)	.3
each adtnl	.1
(M) Drive Belt, Renew	
1983-87-one (.3)	.4
each adtnl	.1
(G) Water Pump, Renew	
Includes: R&R fan and pulleys.	
V-6–1983-85 (.9)	1.7
V-8–1983-87 (1.4)	2.0
Diesel–1983-85 (1.5)	2.3
w/A.C. add (.2)	.2
w/P.S. add (.1)	.1
w/A.I.R. add (.1)	.1

COOLING SYSTEM TUNE-UP

An Annual Cooling System Tune-Up Suggestion List should include (with some exceptions):

1. A visual check of the cooling system for indications of leaks or excessive oil content.
2. Pressure check the cooling system for internal and external leaks with filler cap and neck adapter and tester.
3. Check crankcase and automatic transmission oil for water content.
4. Test coolant thermostat with radiator thermometer.
5. Check temperature gauge for accuracy.
6. Drain system and flush till clean.
7. Clean foreign matter from radiator fins.
8. Test radiator pressure cap with cap tester.
9. Check fan blades and pulleys for alignment and damage.
10. Internal and external inspection of all hoses for cracks and deterioration.
11. Check core plugs (where possible) for seepage.
12. Refill system with correct coolant and check for air locks.
13. Check condition and tension of drive belts with tension gauge.

All models **1.5**

(Factory Time)	Chilton Time
(G) Temperature Gauge (Engine Unit), Renew	
1983-87 (.3)	.4
w/eng Code 4 (.5)	.7
(G) Fan Blades or Clutch Assy., Renew	
1983-87 (.3)	.5
(G) Water Jacket Expansion Plugs, Renew	
1983-87-each (.5)	.5
Note: If necessary to R&R any component to gain access to plug, add appropriate time.	
(G) Heater Hoses, Renew	
1983-87-one (.3)	.5
both (.4)	•.6
•w/A.C. add (.2)	.2
(G) Heater Core, R&R or Renew	
Without Air Conditioning	
1983-85 (1.0)	2.0
1986-87 (.5)	1.0
With Air Conditioning	
1983-87 (1.1)	2.5
ADD THESE OPERATIONS TO HEATER CORE R&R	
(G) Boil & Repair	1.2
(G) Repair Core	.9
(G) Recore	1.2
(G) Heater Control Assembly, Renew	
1983-87-Refer to A.C. group.	
(G) Heater Blower Motor, Renew	
1983-87-Refer to A.C. group.	
(G) Heater Blower Motor Resistor, Renew	
1983-87-Refer to A.C. group.	
(G) Heater Blower Motor Switch, Renew	
1983-87-Refer to A.C. group.	
(G) Heater Water Control Valve, Renew	
1983-87 (.4)	.5

PARTS 7 COOLING SYSTEM 7 PARTS

	Part No.	Price
(1) Radiator Assy.		
Accurate replacement of the radiator can be done only by using the radiator code stamped on a metal tag located on the original radiator. Order by year, model and radiator code no.		
(2) Thermostat		
V-6–231, 252 engines		
1983	◆1254894	9.00
1984	◆3041390	5.00
1985	3090967	N.L.
V-8 engine		
1983-87	◆3051139	5.00
(3) Radiator Hoses		
Order by year and model.		
(4) Water Pump Assy.		
V-6–231, 252 engines		
1983-85	◆1260709	61.75
V-8 engine		
1983-87-w/A.C.	◆556283	95.00
1983-85-wo/A.C.	◆231886	96.50

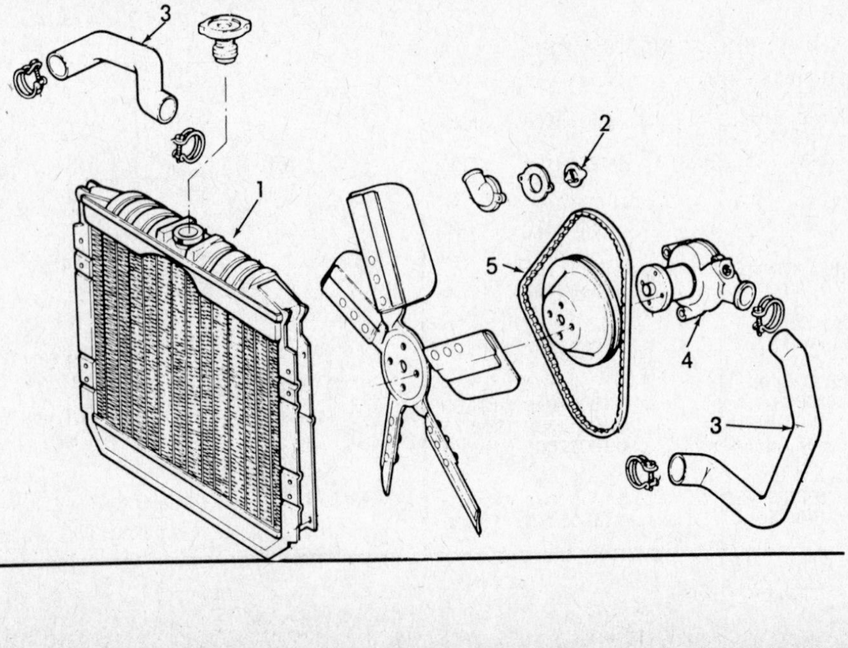

PARTS 7 COOLING SYSTEM 7 PARTS

	Part No.	Price
(5) Fan Belts		
Order by year and model.		
Fan Clutch		
V-6-231, 252 engines		
1983-85 stamped:		
TT or TU	◆22008492	87.50
TS	◆22008490	84.50
V-8-307 engine		
1983-87 stamped:		
OS	◆4974367	84.50
OJ, OL	◆22008668	N.L.
OM	◆561826	122.00
V-8-350 engine		
Engine code N (diesel)		
1983-84-w/A.C.	◆561826	122.00
wo/A.C.	◆22008668	N.L.
Temperature Switch (Engine)		
1983-exc. 307 eng.	◆25036371	8.00
307 eng.	◆25036506	8.75
1984-85-exc. below	◆25036371	8.00
1983-w/307	◆25036506	8.50
1984-87-w/307, 350N engs.	◆25036629	9.75
Temperature Control Valve		
(With Air Conditioning)		
(Except Electronic Temperature Control)		
1983-exc. below	◆22502236	18.00
w/V-6 eng.	◆14032007	22.50
w/diesel eng.	22508956	22.00
1984-87-exc. V-8 engs.	◆14032007	22.50
w/V-8 engs.	◆22502236	18.00
Blower Motor		
(Without Air Conditioning)		
1983-85	◆22048569	47.50
(With Air Conditioning)		
1983-87	◆22020945	60.00
Blower Motor Switch		
1983-exc. climate cont.	◆16015256	6.00
w/climate cont.	3041336	19.00
1984-87	◆16032480	7.25
Heater Core		
1983-85-wo/A.C.	◆3036422	41.25
1984-87-w/A.C.	◆3035420	43.00

LABOR 8 EXHAUST SYSTEM 8 LABOR

	(Factory Time)	Chilton Time
(G) Muffler, Renew		
1983-87	(.5)	.7
(G) Tail Pipe and Resonator Assy., Renew		
1983-87	(.5)	.7
(G) Tail Pipe, Renew		
1983-87		
sdn	(.4)	.6
sta wag	(.2)	.4
(G) Front Exhaust Pipe Seal, Renew		
1983-87	(.4)	.6
(G) Catalytic Converter, Renew		
1983-87	(.8)	1.0
w/AIR add	(.1)	.1
(G) Exhaust Crossover Pipe, Renew		
1983-87-Gas	(.3)	.9
Diesel	(.9)	1.3
(G) Exhaust Intermediate Pipe, Renew		
Includes: Cut at muffler.		
1983-87	(.5)	.7
(G) Front Exhaust Pipe, Renew (To Converter)		
1983-87	(.6)	.9
(G) E.F.E. Valve Assy., With Actuator, Renew		
Includes: Disconnect crossover pipe.		
1983-87	(.5)	.8
(G) Exhaust Manifold, Renew		
V-6-1983-85-each	(.7)	1.1
V-8-1983-85		
right side	(.8)	1.2
left side	(.7)	1.1
1986-87		
305 eng-Code H		
right side	(1.3)	2.1
left side	(1.0)	1.4
w/A.C. add	(.4)	.4
w/C.C.C. add	(.1)	.1
307 eng-Code Y		
right side	(1.1)	1.6
left side	(1.0)	1.5
Diesel-1983		
right side	(.9)	1.3
left side	(.7)	1.1
1984-85		
right side	(1.2)	1.7
left side	(.7)	1.1
w/A.C. add	(.4)	.4
w/P.S. add	(.2)	.2

COMBINATIONS

	(Factory Time)	Chilton Time
(G) Exhaust System, Renew (Complete)		
1983-87-V-6	(.8)	1.3
V-8	(1.0)	1.5

PARTS 8 EXHAUST SYSTEM 8 PARTS

	Part No.	Price
Muffler		
Order by year and model.		
Catalytic Converter		
V-6-231 engine		
1983-84-Federal	◆8999615	312.25
Calif.	◆8999642	271.25
1985	◆25056912	348.00
V-6-252 engine		
1983-84	◆8999615	312.25
V-8-307 engine		
1983	◆25056622	308.25
1984-85-Calif.	◆25056562	313.25
1986-87	◆25100218	323.00
1984-85-Federal	◆25056634	335.00
1986-87	◆25100217	335.00
Resonator		
1983-87 exc. below	25509117	88.75
1983-w/252 eng. (1st. design)	◆25502391	88.75
1983-85-w/252 eng. (2nd. design)	25517126	54.50
307 engine		
1983-85-exc. sta. wgn.	◆22505492	89.25
1983-87-sta. wgn.	◆22506866	58.25
350 diesel		
1983-85-sta. wagon	◆22512354	58.25
Tail Pipe		
1983-w/231 eng. (1st. design)	25504284	51.75
1983-85-w/231 eng. (2nd design)	25502271	48.25
307 eng.		
1983-87 (front of resonater)	◆1251925	
wagon (rear of resonater)	22506867	72.00
350 diesel		
1983-85-exc. wagon	◆25509141	49.25
wagon	◆25512353	14.00
Exhaust Crossover Pipe		
Note: Short pipe between crossover and converter.		
1983-V-6 eng. (1st. design)	◆25506286	31.25
1983-85-V-6 eng. (2nd design)	◆25516456	31.25
1983-87-307 eng.	◆22504709	74.25
1983-85-350 diesel eng.	◆22514728	24.00
Exhaust Front Pipe		
V-6 252 eng.		
1983-84	◆25508302	48.75
V-6 231 eng.		
1983-w/Calif. em.	◆25508302	48.75
1983-85-w/Fed. em.	◆25515214	21.25
V-8 307 eng.		
1983	25510556	N.L.
1984-87	◆22520490	11.00
V-8 350 diesel		
1983-84 LeSabre	◆22512345	53.75
1985 wagon	◆22512346	52.25
exc. wag.	◆22512355	52.25
1983 Electra	◆22512347	52.25

PARTS 8 EXHAUST SYSTEM 8 PARTS

	Part No.	Price
Exhaust Intermediate Pipe		
V-6 252 eng.		
Lesabre		
1983	◆25505629	52.50
1984	25519522	52.50
Electra		
1983	◆25505630	52.50
1984	25519780	31.00
V-6 231 eng.		
1983-85-exc. below	◆25516994	20.00
1983-w/Calif. em.	◆25505629	52.50
V-8 307 eng.		
Lesabre		
1983	◆22512349	51.00
1984-87	◆22524716	51.00
Electra		
1983	◆22512350	51.00
1984	◆22524789	51.00

LABOR 9 FRONT SUSPENSION 9 LABOR

(Factory Time)	Chilton Time
Note: On all front suspension operations alignment charge must be added if performed. Time given does not include alignment.	
(M) Wheel, Renew	
one (.5)	.5
(G) Wheels, Rotate (All)	
All models	.5
(G) Wheels, Balance	
one	.3
each adtnl	.2
(G) Check Alignment of Front End	
All models	.5
Note: Deduct if alignment is performed.	
(G) Toe-in, Adjust	
All models (.4)	.6
(G) Align Front End	
Includes: Adjust front wheel bearings.	
All models (.7)	1.4
w/A.C. interference add	.5
(G) Front Wheel Bearings, Clean and Repack (Both Wheels)	
1983-87 (1.1)	1.6
(G) Front Wheel Bearings and Cups, Renew	
1983-87-one side (.7)	.9
both sides (1.1)	1.5
(G) Front Wheel Grease Seals, Renew	
1983-87-one side (.7)	.8
both sides (1.1)	1.2
(G) Front Shock Absorber, Renew	
1983-87-one (.3)	.4
both (.5)	.7
(G) Rebuild Front Suspension	
Includes: Disassemble, renew necessary parts, reassemble, lubricate and align front end.	
1983-87-one side (3.8)	4.5
both sides (6.0)	7.0
(G) Upper Ball Joint, Renew	
Add alignment charges.	
1983-87-one (.7)	.9
both (1.2)	1.7
(G) Lower Ball Joint, Renew	
Add alignment charges.	
1983-87-one (.6)	.9
both (1.0)	1.7
(G) Steering Knuckle, Renew	
Add alignment charges.	
1983-87-one (1.0)	1.4
both (1.8)	2.5
(G) Upper Control Arm, Renew (One)	
Add alignment charges.	
1983-87 (.7)	1.2
(G) Lower Control Arm, Renew (One)	
Add alignment charges.	
1983-87 (1.0)	1.5
(G) Upper Control Arm Bushings, Renew	
Add alignment charges.	
1983-87-one side (1.0)	1.5
(G) Lower Control Arm Bushings, Renew	
Add alignment charges.	
1983-87-one side (1.2)	1.7
both sides (2.3)	3.3
(G) Front Spring, Renew (One)	
Add alignment charges.	
1983-87 (.8)	1.4
(G) Front Stabilizer Bar and Bushings, Renew	
1983-87 (.5)	.8
(G) Stabilizer Links or Bushings, Renew	
1983-87-one (.3)	.4
both (.4)	.6
(G) Control Arm Bumpers, Renew (Upper or Lower)	
1983-87-one side (.2)	.4

PARTS 9 FRONT SUSPENSION 9 PARTS

	Part No.	Price
(1) Front Wheel Bearing (Outer)		
1983-87	◆7450697	11.00
(2) Front Wheel Bearing (Inner)		
1983-87	◆7450630	11.00
(3) Front Seal Assy.		
1983-87	◆3965092	3.50
(4) Steering Knuckle		
(w/11 in. rotor)		
1983-85-right	◆14012596	116.00
left	◆14012595	116.00
(w/12 in. rotor)		
1983-87-right	◆14012590	144.00
left	◆14012589	144.00
(5) Ball Joint Pkg. (Lower)		
1983-87	◆9767281	31.50
(6) Control Arm (Lower)		
1983-87-L.H.	◆14039015	105.00
R.H.	◆14039016	105.00
(7) Bushing (Rear)		
1983-87	14049624	4.50
(8) Shock Absorber		
1983-84 exc. H.D. susp.	◆4993548	24.50
w/H.D. Susp. (1983-87)	◆4993551	24.50

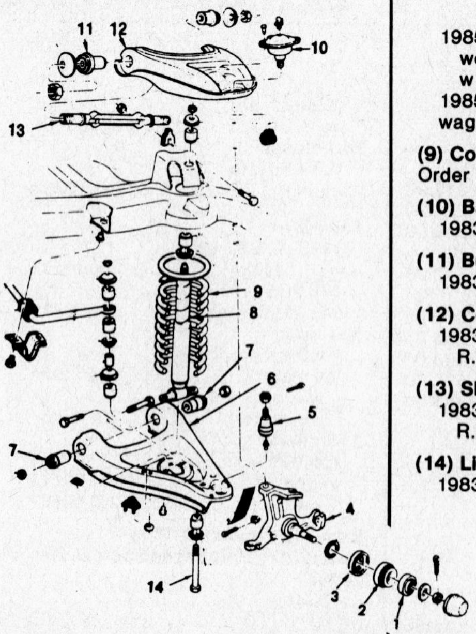

	Part No.	Price
1985-87-exc. sta. wag.		
wo/H.D. susp.	22046423	24.50
w/H.D. susp.	22046424	24.50
1985-87-sta. wag.	22046424	24.50
(9) Coil Spring		
Order by year and model.		
(10) Ball Joint (Upper)		
1983-87	◆9767112	34.75
(11) Bushing (Front)		
1983-87	◆371793	4.25
(12) Control Arm (Upper)		
1983-87-L.H.	◆14039009	109.00
R.H.	◆14039010	109.00
(13) Shaft Pkg. (Upper Control)		
1983-87-L.H.	◆14022171	35.50
R.H.	◆14022172	33.75
(14) Link Pkg.		
1983-87	◆464167	4.25

LABOR 10 STEERING LINKAGE 10 LABOR

	(Factory Time)	Chilton Time
(G) Tie Rods or Tie Rod Ends, Renew		
Includes: Reset toe-in.		
1983-87-one side	(.7)	1.0
both sides	(.9)	1.4
(G) Inner Tie Rods, Renew		
Includes: Reset toe-in.		
1983-87-one side	(.7)	1.0
both sides	(.8)	1.2
(G) Idler Arm, Renew		
Includes: Reset toe-in.		
1983-87	(.7)	1.0
(G) Pitman Arm, Renew		
Note: Does not require toe-in readjustment.		
1983-87	(.3)	.7
(G) Intermediate Rod, Renew		
Includes: Reset toe-in.		
1983-84	(1.0)	1.2
1985-87	(.7)	1.2

PARTS 10 STEERING LINKAGE 10 PARTS

	Part No.	Price
(1) Idler Arm Assy.		
1983-87	◆7837635	51.00
(2) Tie Rod Assy. (Inner)		
1983-87	◆7834224	45.75
(3) Tie Rod End (Outer)		
1983-87	◆12308612	50.50
(4) Tie Rod Sleeve Pkg. (Adjuster)		
1983-87	◆7826714	15.50
(5) Seal Kit (Pitman Arm)		
1983-87	◆7826470	17.00
(6) Pitman Arm Assy.		
1983-87	◆7837645	44.00
w/H.D. susp.	◆7832199	51.50

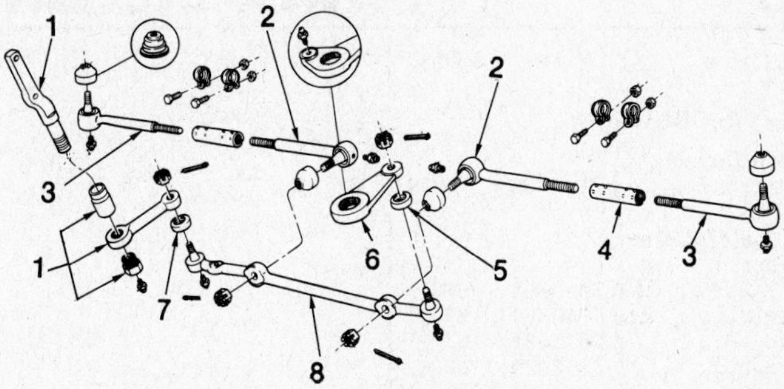

	Part No.	Price
(7) Seal Kit		
1983-87	◆7826470	17.00
(8) Relay Rod Assy.		
1983-87	◆7837639	109.00

LABOR 11 STEERING GEAR 11 LABOR

	(Factory Time)	Chilton Time
(G) Horn Contact or Cancelling Cam, Renew		
1983-87	(.5)	.6
(G) Steering Wheel, Renew		
1983-87	(.3)	.4
(G) Steering Column Shift Bowl, Renew		
Includes: R&R steering wheel and turn signal housing support assy.		
1983-85-std	(1.5)	2.0
tilt	(1.7)	2.3
tilt tel	(1.8)	2.4
1986-87		
std	(1.2)	1.7
tilt	(2.0)	3.0
tilt tel	(2.1)	3.1
(G) Flexible Coupling, Renew		
1983-84	(.5)	.7
(G) Upper Mast Jacket Bearing, Renew		
1983-85		
std colm	(.8)	1.4
tilt colm	(1.1)	1.6
tilt tel colm	(1.2)	1.7
1986-87		
std colm	(1.0)	1.4
tilt colm	(.5)	.9
tilt tel colm	(.6)	1.0
(G) Multifunction Lever, Renew		
All models	(.2)	.4
w/Cruise control add	(.5)	.5
(G) Steering Column Lock Actuator Parts, Renew		
1983-87		
std colm	(1.1)	1.6
tilt colm	(1.3)	1.8
Tilt Tel	(1.3)	1.8

POWER STEERING

	(Factory Time)	Chilton Time
(G) Trouble Shoot Power Steering		
Includes: Test pump and system pressure. Check pounds pull on steering wheel and check system for leaks.		
All models		.5
(M) Pump Drive Belt, Renew		
1983-87	(.4)	.5
w/A.C. add	(.1)	.1
w/A.I.R. add	(.1)	.1
(M) Check Reservoir and Add Fluid		
All models		.2
(G) Power Steering Gear, Adjust		
Includes: R&R gear assy.		
1983-87	(.7)	1.2
(G) Power Steering Gear Assembly, Renew		
1983-87	(1.1)	1.2
(P) Steering Gear Assy., R&R and Recondition		
Includes: Disassemble, renew necessary parts, reassemble and adjust.		
1983-85	(1.7)	2.5
1986-87	(2.1)	3.0
(G) End Cover and/or Seal, Renew		
Includes: R&R gear assy.		
1983-85	(.9)	1.4
1986-87	(1.2)	1.9
(G) Pitman Shaft or Bearing, Renew		
Includes: R&R gear assy.		
1983-85	(1.0)	1.5
1986-87	(1.2)	1.9
(G) Adjustor Plug, R&R and Recondition		
Includes: R&R gear assy.		
1983-85	(1.1)	1.6
1986-87	(1.3)	2.0
(G) Valve Body, Renew or Recondition		
Includes: R&R gear assy.		
1983-85	(1.3)	1.8
1986-87	(1.4)	2.2
(G) Rack Piston and Worm Shaft, Renew		
Includes: R&R gear assy.		
1983-85	(1.5)	2.0
1986-87	(1.5)	2.4
(G) Gear Housing, Renew		
Includes: R&R gear assy.		
1983-85	(1.3)	2.0
1986-87	(1.5)	2.4
(G) Pitman Shaft Seal, Renew		
Does not include R&R gear.		
1983-87	(.5)	1.0

LABOR 11 STEERING GEAR 11 LABOR

	Factory Time	Chilton Time
(G) Power Steering Oil Pump, Renew		
1983-85-V-6	(.5)	.9
V-8	(.9)	1.4
Diesel	(.9)	1.4
1986-87	(.7)	1.4
(P) Power Steering Pump, R&R and Recondition		
Includes: R&R reservoir.		
1983-85-V-6	(1.0)	1.7
V-8	(1.4)	2.2
Diesel	(1.4)	2.2
1986-87	(1.2)	2.2
(G) Power Steering Pump Shaft Oil Seal, Renew		
Includes: R&R pump pulley.		
1983-85		
V-6	(.6)	1.0
V-8	(.9)	1.5
Diesel	(.9)	1.5
1986-87	(.5)	1.5
(G) Pump Flow Control Valve, Renew		
1983-87	(.3)	.7
(M) Power Steering Hoses, Renew		
1983-87-pressure	(.4)	.8
return	(.3)	.5

TILT AND TELESCOPIC COLUMN

	Factory Time	Chilton Time
(G) Tilt Column, R&R and Recondition		
1983-87	(2.5)	3.2
w/Tilt Tel add	(.1)	.2

PARTS 11 POWER STEERING GEAR 11 PARTS

(MODEL 800)

	Part No.	Price
(1) Seal (Side Cover)		
1983-87	◆7817486	9.00
(2) Pitman Shaft (w/Gear)		
1983-87-exc. below	◆7815885	87.50
Sta. wag.	◆7813631	87.50
231 eng.	◆7813631	87.50
w/H.D. susp.	7832020	93.50
(3) Check Valve Kit		
1983-87	◆7834284	5.25
(4) Bearing Kit		
1983-87	◆7826850	11.00
(5) Housing Assy.		
1983-85-exc. H.D. susp.	◆7834139	183.00
H.D. susp.	◆7834141	183.00
(6) Bearing (Pitman Shaft)		
1983-87	◆5697804	15.00
(7) Seal Kit (Pitman Shaft)		
1983-87	◆7826470	17.00
(8) Seal (Adjuster Plug)		
1983-seal	◆5686527	1.50
1983-87-seal kit	◆7832730	8.25
(9) Bearing (Adjuster Plug)		
1983-87	◆7828012	7.25
(10) Plug Assy. (Adjuster)		
1983-87	◆7832731	53.50
(11) Seal Kit		
1983-87	◆5687182	12.50
(12) Valve Assy.		
1983-87-exc. H.D. susp.	◆7832058	212.00
H.D. susp.	◆7832055	202.25
(14) Seal Kit		
1983-87	◆7817485	6.50

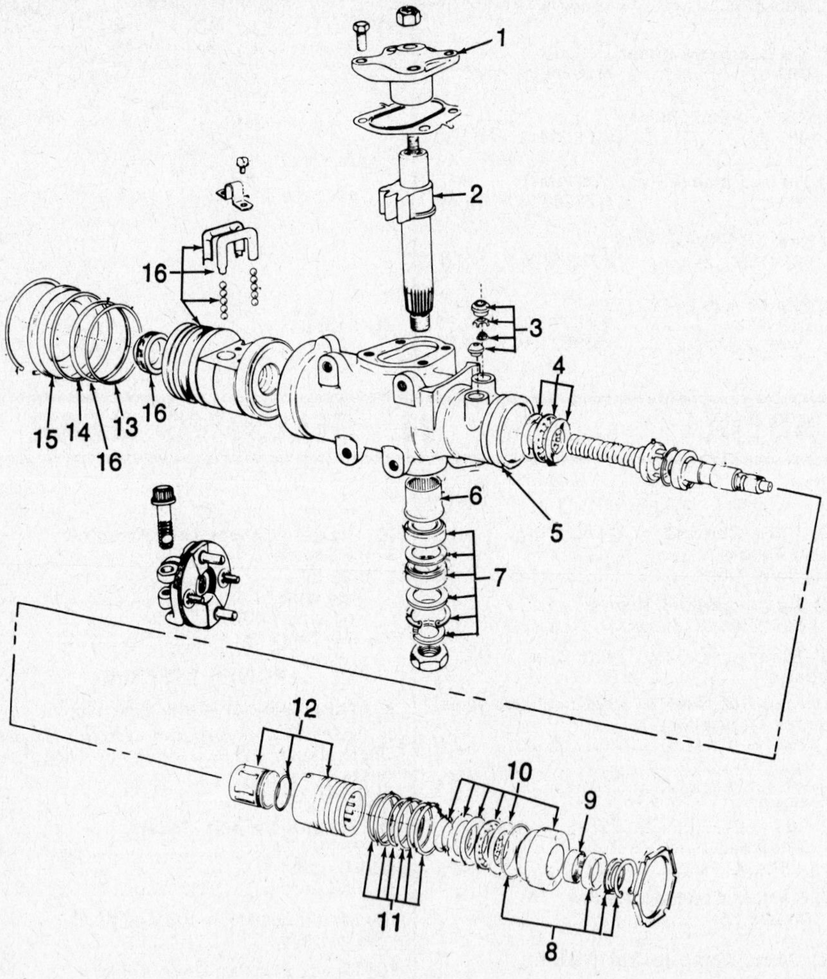

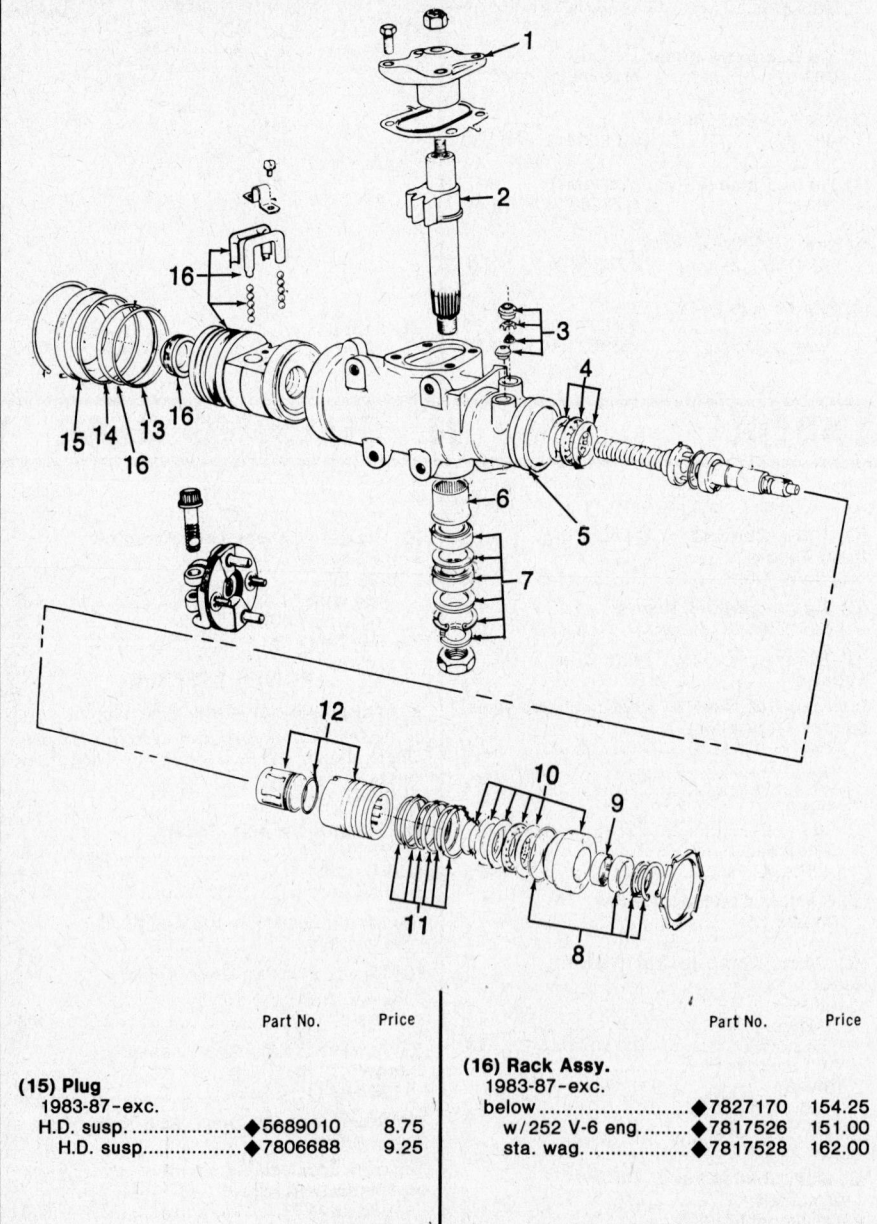

	Part No.	Price
(15) Plug		
1983-87-exc. H.D. susp.	◆5689010	8.75
H.D. susp.	◆7806688	9.25
(16) Rack Assy.		
1983-87-exc. below	◆7827170	154.25
w/252 V-6 eng.	◆7817526	151.00
sta. wag.	◆7817528	162.00

PARTS 11 POWER STEERING PUMP 11 PARTS

	Part No.	Price
Pressure Line Hose		
Note: Order by year and model		
Power Steering Pump Assy.		
1983-85-w/V-6 eng.	◆7839795	199.00
1983-87-w/307 eng.	◆7840244	199.00
1983-84-w/ diesel eng.	◆7839792	213.00
(1) Pressure Plate		
1983-87	◆7839669	14.25
(2) Pressure Plate Spring		
1983-87	◆7839667	1.00
(3) End Plate		
1983-87	◆5689358	3.50
(4) Rotor & Vane Kit		
1983-87	◆7837322	75.00
(5) Pump Thrust Plate		
1983-87	◆7836369	13.75
(6) Valve Assy.		
1983-87	◆7809232	10.75
(7) Flow Control Spring		
1983-87	◆5688037	1.50
(8) Housing		
1983-87	◆7830236	62.75

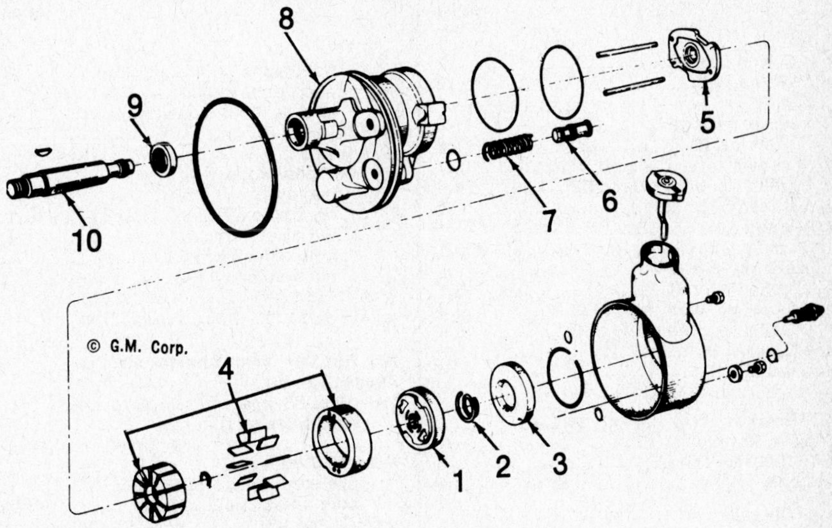

	Part No.	Price
(9) Drive Shaft Seal		
1983-87	◆7808195	4.50
(10) Drive Shaft		
1983-87	◆7837321	39.50

LABOR 12 CYLINDER HEAD & VALVE SYSTEM 12 LABOR

	(Factory Time)	Chilton Time
GASOLINE ENGINES		
(G) Compression Test		
V-6–1983-85		.7
V-8–1983-87		.8
w/A.C. add		.3
(G) Cylinder Head Gasket, Renew		
Includes: Clean gasket surfaces, clean carbon, make all necessary adjustments.		
V-6–1983-85–one	(3.5)	5.8
both	(4.4)	7.6
V-8–1983-85		
one	(4.2)	6.8
both	(5.4)	8.3
w/A.C. add	(.2)	.2
w/A.I.R. add	(.4)	.4
1986-87		
305 eng-Code H		
right side	(5.0)	6.9
left side	(4.6)	6.3
both sides	(7.0)	9.6
w/A.C. add	(.5)	.5
w/P.S. add	(.3)	.3
w/AIR add	(.2)	.2
w/Cruise control add	(.2)	.2
307 eng-Code Y		
right side	(4.0)	5.5
left side	(4.4)	6.0
both sides	(5.8)	8.0
w/A.C. add	(.4)	.4
w/AIR add	(.5)	.5
(G) Cylinder Head, Renew		
Includes: Transfer all parts, reface valves, make all necessary adjustments.		
V-6–1983-85–one	(4.9)	6.6
both	(5.9)	9.1
V-8–1983-85		
one	(4.5)	7.3
both	(6.1)	9.5
w/A.C. add	(.2)	.2
w/A.I.R. add	(.4)	.4

COMBINATIONS
Add to Valve Job
See Machine Shop Operations

	(Factory Time)	Chilton Time
(G) DRAIN, EVACUATE & RECHARGE AIR CONDITIONING SYSTEM		
All models	(.5)	1.0
(G) ROCKER ARM STUD, RENEW		
Each	(.3)	.3
(G) HYDRAULIC VALVE LIFTERS, DISASSEMBLE AND CLEAN		
Each	(.2)	.2
(G) DISTRIBUTOR, RECONDITION		
All models	(.5)	.8
(G) CARBURETOR, RECONDITION		
2 bbl		1.2
4 bbl		1.5
(P) VALVE GUIDES, REAM OVERSIZE		
Each	(.2)	.2
(G) ROCKER ARM SHAFT, RECONDITION		
Each side	(.2)	.3

	(Factory Time)	Chilton Time
1986-87		
305 eng-Code H		
right side	(5.8)	8.0
left side	(5.5)	7.5
both sides	(8.7)	12.0
w/A.C. add	(.5)	.5
w/P.S. add	(.3)	.3
w/AIR add	(.2)	.2
w/Cruise control add	(.2)	.2

	(Factory Time)	Chilton Time
307 eng-Code Y		
right side	(4.2)	5.7
left side	(4.6)	6.3
both sides	(6.2)	8.5
w/A.C. add	(.4)	.4
w/AIR add	(.5)	.5
(P) Clean Carbon and Grind Valves		
Includes: R&R cylinder heads, clean gasket surfaces, clean carbon, reface valves and seats. Minor tune up.		
V-6–1983-85	(8.0)	11.2
V-8–1983-85		
one bank	(5.1)	8.0
both banks	(7.1)	10.8
w/A.C. add	(.2)	.2
w/A.I.R. add	(.4)	.4
1986-87		
305 eng-Code H		
right side	(6.3)	8.6
left side	(5.9)	8.1
both sides	(9.4)	13.0
w/A.C. add	(.5)	.5
w/P.S. add	(.3)	.3
w/AIR add	(.2)	.2
w/Cruise control add	(.2)	.2
307 eng-Code Y		
right side	(5.1)	7.0
left side	(5.6)	7.7
both sides	(8.1)	11.2
w/A.C. add	(.4)	.4
w/AIR add	(.5)	.5
(G) Valve Tappets, Renew (Lifters)		
Includes: Drain and refill cooling system. R&R intake manifold. Make all necessary adjustments.		
V-6–1983-85–one bank	(2.6)	3.4
both banks	(2.9)	4.0
V-8–1983-85		
one cyl	(2.2)	3.7
one cyl-each bank	(2.5)	4.0
each adtnl cyl	(.1)	.1

(Factory Time)	Chilton Time
w/A.C. add (.3)	.3
w/A.I.R. add (.2)	.2
1986-87	
305 eng-Code H	
one cyl (2.5)	3.4
one cyl-each side (2.7)	3.7
all cyls-both sides (3.2)	4.4
w/A.C. add (.5)	.5
w/AIR add (.1)	.1
w/Cruise control add (.1)	.1
307 eng-Code Y	
one cyl (2.7)	3.7
one cyl-each side (3.2)	4.4
all cyls-both sides (5.0)	6.9
w/A.C. add (.2)	.2
w/AIR add (.4)	.4

(G) Rocker Arm Cover and/or Gasket, Renew

V-6-1983-85-one (.5)	.8
both (.8)	1.4
V-8-1983-85	
one (.5)	.9
both (.9)	1.5
w/A.C. add (.3)	.3
w/A.I.R. add (.2)	.2
1986-87	
305 eng-Code H	
right side (.7)	1.0
left side (.5)	.7
both sides (1.1)	1.6
w/A.C. add (.2)	.2
w/C.C.C. add (.2)	.2
w/Cruise control add (.1)	.1
307 eng-Code Y	
right side (.6)	.7
left side (.8)	1.2
both sides (1.4)	1.9
w/A.C. add (.1)	.1
w/AIR add (.3)	.3

(G) Valve Spring and/or Valve Stem Oil Seals, Renew (Head on Car)

V-6-1983-85-one cyl (.8)	1.2
one cyl-each bank (1.4)	2.2
V-8-1983-85	
one cyl (.6)	1.2
one cyl-each bank (1.0)	1.9
Each adtnl cyl-all engines (.3)	.3
w/A.C. add (.3)	.3
w/A.I.R. add (.2)	.2
1986-87	
305 eng-Code H	
one cyl	
right side (1.2)	1.6
left side (.8)	1.1

(Factory Time)	Chilton Time
both sides (1.6)	2.3
each adtnl cyl (.4)	.4
all cyls-both sides (3.3)	4.5
w/A.C. add (.3)	.3
w/AIR add (.1)	.1
307 eng-Code Y	
one cyl	
right side (.7)	1.0
left side (1.1)	1.6
both sides (1.8)	2.4
each adtnl cyl (.4)	.4
w/A.C. add (.1)	.1
w/AIR add (.3)	.3

(G) Rocker Arm Shafts and/or Assys., Renew

V-6-1983-85-one side (.7)	1.1
both sides (1.1)	1.7
V-8-1983-85	
one side (.8)	1.3
both sides (1.4)	2.0
w/A.C. add (.3)	.3
w/A.I.R. add (.2)	.2
Recond each side add (.2)	.3

(G) Valve Rocker Arms and/or Push Rods, Renew

V-6-1983-85	
one side (.7)	1.1
both sides (1.1)	1.7
V-8-1983-85	
one side (.8)	1.3
both sides (1.4)	2.0
w/A.C. add (.3)	.3
w/AIR add (.2)	.2
1986-87	
305 eng-Code H	
one cyl	
right side (.8)	1.2
left side (.6)	.9
both sides (1.3)	2.0
each adtnl cyl (.2)	.2
w/A.C. add (.2)	.2
w/AIR add (.1)	.1
307 eng-Code Y	
one cyl	
right side (.7)	.9
left side (.9)	1.4
both sides (1.5)	2.1
all cyls-both sides (2.0)	2.9
w/A.C. add (.1)	.1
w/AIR add (.3)	.3

DIESEL ENGINE

(G) Compression Test

1983-85	1.3

(Factory Time)	Chilton Time

(G) Cylinder Head Gasket, Renew

Includes: R&R injector pump and lines. R&R intake manifold and disconnect exhaust manifolds. Clean gasket surfaces, bleed lifters and adjust timing. Drain and refill cooling system.

1983-85-left side (5.7)	7.4
right side (6.1)	7.9
both sides (7.6)	9.9
w/A.C. add (.4)	.4

(G) Cylinder Head, Renew

Includes: R&R injector pump and lines. R&R intake manifold and disconnect exhaust manifolds. Clean gasket surfaces. Transfer parts, reface valves. Bleed lifters and adjust timing. Drain and refill cooling system.

1983-85-left side (6.1)	7.9
right side (6.5)	8.4
both sides (8.4)	11.1
w/A.C. add (.4)	.4

(P) Clean Carbon and Grind Valves

Includes: R&R injector pump and lines. R&R cylinder heads, clean carbon. Recondition valves and seats. Check and adjust valve stem length. Bleed lifters, drain and refill cooling system.

1983-85-left side (6.6)	8.5
right side (7.0)	9.1
both sides (9.3)	12.6
w/A.C. add (.4)	.4

(G) Valve Tappets, Renew (Lifters)

Includes: R&R injector pump and lines, intake manifold and rocker arms. Drain and refill cooling system.

1983-85-one cyl (3.5)	4.5
one cyl-each side (3.9)	5.0
each adtnl cyl (.1)	.2

(G) Rocker Arm Cover or Gasket, Renew

Includes: R&R injector pump and lines.

1983-85-one side (1.2)	2.4
both sides (2.0)	2.9

(G) Valve Springs and/or Valve Stem Oil Seals, Renew (Head On Car)

Includes: R&R injector pump and lines.

1983-85-one cyl (1.6)	3.0
one cyl-each bank (2.4)	3.7
each adtnl cyl (.2)	.3
w/A.C. add (.4)	.4

(G) Rocker Arm, Pivot and/or Push Rod, Renew

Includes: R&R injector pump and lines.

1983-85-one cyl (1.5)	2.5
one cyl-each bank (2.3)	3.0
each adtnl cyl. (.1)	.1

PARTS 12 CYLINDER HEAD & VALVE SYSTEM 12 PARTS

	Part No.	Price
Valve Grind Gasket Set		
V-6-231 engine		
1983	◆1264923	38.75
1984		
w/cast iron int. man.	◆25525121	N.L.
w/alum. int. man.	◆25525120	37.00
1985	◆25525120	37.00
V-6-252 engine		
1983-84	◆25518568	N.L.
V-8-307 engine		
1983-84	◆22507725	48.75
1985-87	◆22534926	58.00
V-8-350 engine		
1983-85	◆22522053	94.50
(1) Cylinder Head		
V-6-231 engine		
1983-87	◆25518679	217.00
V-6-252 engine		
1983-84	◆25518679	217.00
V-8-307 engine		
1983-84	◆22511238	247.00
1985-87	◆22530557	247.00
V-8-350 engine		
1983-85	◆22515038	387.00
(2) Cylinder Head Gasket		
V-6-231 engine		
1983-84	◆1261403	8.50
1985	◆25524599	8.50
V-6-252 engine		
1983-84	◆25518453	8.25

PARTS 12 CYLINDER HEAD & VALVE SYSTEM 12 PARTS

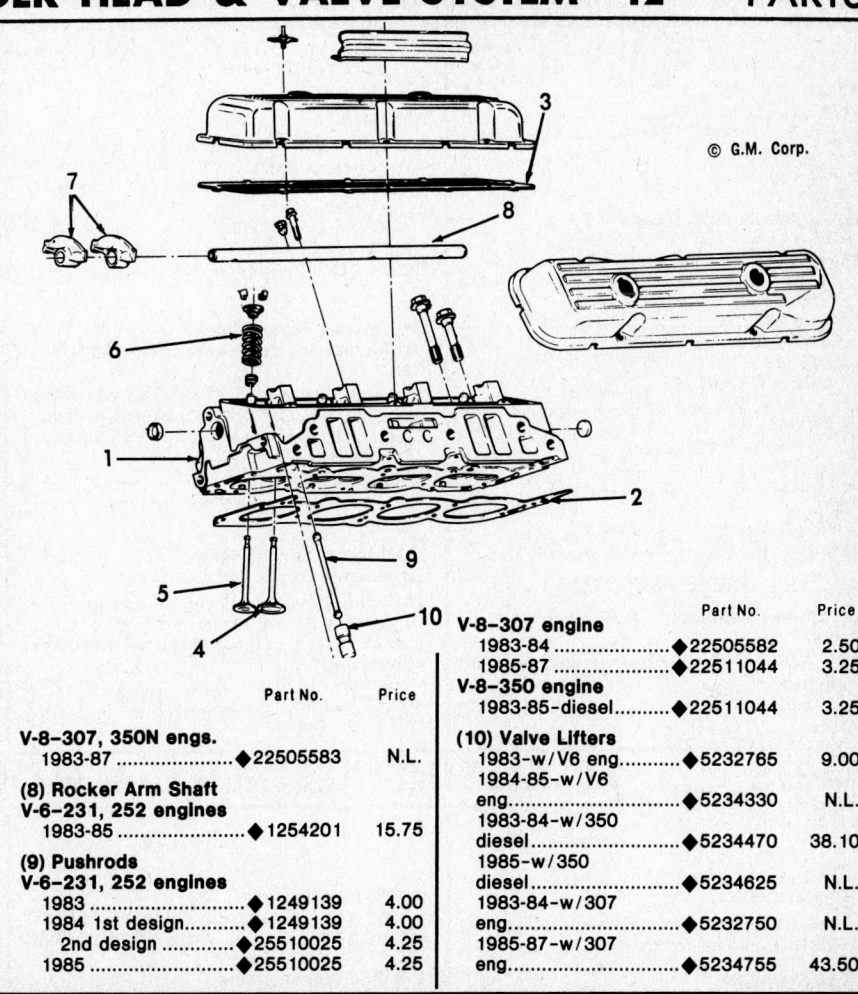

	Part No.	Price
V-8-307 engine		
1983-87	◆22503500	9.25
V-8-350 diesel engine		
1983-85	◆22519416	30.75
(3) Rocker Arm Cover Gaskets		
V-6-231, 252 engines		
1983-85	◆25505889	6.00

Note: On engines not listed use R.T.V. sealer (PN: 1052289) in place of the valve cover gaskets.

	Part No.	Price
(4) Intake Valve		
V-6-231, 252 engines		
1983-87	◆25512098	11.25
V-8-307 engine		
1983-85	◆22503324	11.00
1986-87	◆22530611	20.25
V-8-350 diesel engine		
1983-85	◆22519914	20.00
(5) Exhaust Valve		
V-6-231, 252 engines		
1983-85	◆1261380	13.50
V-8-307 engine		
1983-87	◆555456	13.50
V-8-350 diesel engine		
1983-85	◆558873	13.00
(6) Valve Springs		
V-6-231, 252 engines		
1983-85	◆1249267	2.75
V-8-307 engine		
1983-87	◆411226	4.00
V-8-350 diesel engine		
1983-84	◆22510372	4.00
(7) Rocker Arms		
V-6-231, 252 engines		
1983-85-R.H.	◆1241850	4.50
L.H.	◆1241851	4.50

Important: Rocker arm locations for the V-6 are referred to by right and left sides per cylinder-NOT by right and left sides of the engine.

Note: Arm package includes arm, ball and push rod.

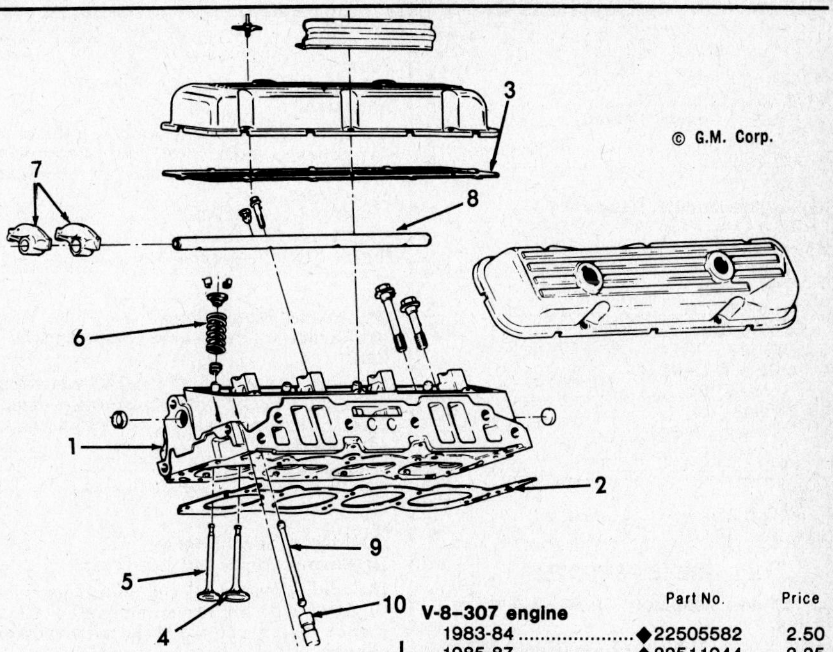

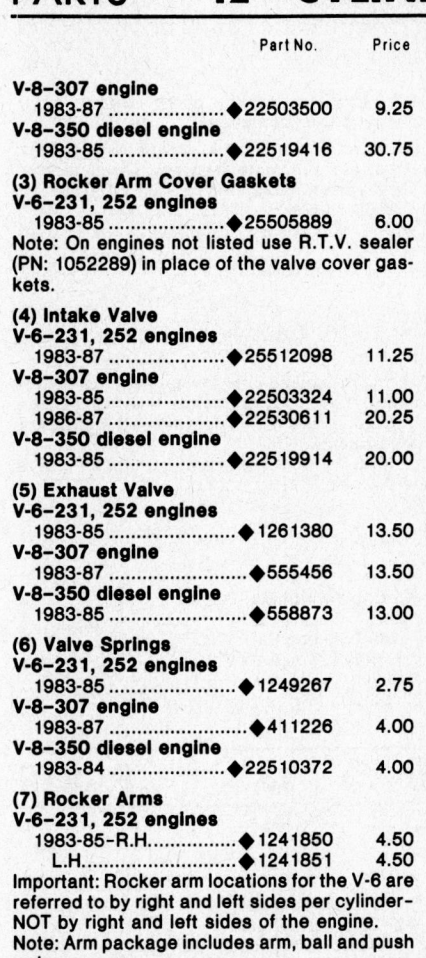

	Part No.	Price
V-8-307, 350N engs.		
1983-87	◆22505583	N.L.
(8) Rocker Arm Shaft		
V-6-231, 252 engines		
1983-85	◆1254201	15.75
(9) Pushrods		
V-6-231, 252 engines		
1983	◆1249139	4.00
1984 1st design	◆1249139	4.00
2nd design	◆25510025	4.25
1985	◆25510025	4.25

	Part No.	Price
V-8-307 engine		
1983-84	◆22505582	2.50
1985-87	◆22511044	3.25
V-8-350 engine		
1983-85-diesel	◆22511044	3.25
(10) Valve Lifters		
1983-w/V6 eng.	◆5232765	9.00
1984-85-w/V6 eng.	◆5234330	N.L.
1983-84-w/350 diesel	◆5234470	38.10
1985-w/350 diesel	◆5234625	N.L.
1983-84-w/307 eng.	◆5232750	N.L.
1985-87-w/307 eng.	◆5234755	43.50

LABOR 13 ENGINE ASSEMBLY & MOUNTS 13 LABOR

(Factory Time)	Chilton Time

GASOLINE ENGINES

(G) Engine Assembly, Remove & Install

Does not include transfer of any parts or equipment.

	Chilton Time
V-6–1983-85	4.0
V-8–1983-87	4.8
w/A.C. add (.4)	.4
w/P.S. add (.3)	.3
w/A.I.R. add (.6)	.6

(G) Engine Assembly, Renew (Universal)

Includes: R&R engine assembly. Transfer all component parts not supplied with replacement engine. Make all necessary adjustments.

	Chilton Time
V-6–1984-85 (7.2)	9.0
w/A.C. add (.3)	.3
w/AIR add (.2)	.2

(G) Engine Assembly, Renew (Partial)

Includes: R&R engine assembly, transfer all component parts not supplied with replacement engine. Minor tune up.

	Chilton Time
V-6–1983-85 (7.0)	11.2
V-8–1983-85 (8.4)	11.7
w/A.C. add (.4)	.4
w/P.S. add (.3)	.3
w/A.I.R. add (.6)	.6
1986-87	
305 eng-Code H (10.1)	14.1
w/A.C. add (.6)	.6
w/AIR add (.4)	.4
307 eng-Code Y (8.4)	11.7
w/A.C. add (.2)	.2
w/AIR add (.4)	.4

(P) Cylinder Block, Renew (w/Pistons, Rings & Brgs)

Includes: R&R engine, transfer all component parts not supplied with replacement engine, clean carbon, grind valves. Minor tune up.

	Chilton Time
V-6–1983-85 (13.2)	18.6
V-8–1983-85 (10.0)	17.2
w/A.C. add (.4)	.4
w/P.S. add (.3)	.3
w/A.I.R. add (.6)	.6
1986-87	
305 eng-Code H (15.5)	21.7
w/A.C. add (.6)	.6
w/AIR add (.4)	.4
307 eng-Code Y (12.6)	17.6
w/A.C. add (.2)	.2
w/AIR add (.4)	.4

(P) Engine Assy., R&R and Recondition (Complete)

Includes: Rebore block, install new pistons, rings, rod and main bearings. Clean carbon, grind valves. Tune engine.

	Chilton Time
V-6–1983-85 (21.4)	25.1
V-8–1983-85 (27.7)	33.4
w/A.C. add (.4)	.4
w/P.S. add (.3)	.3
w/A.I.R. add (.6)	.6
1986-87	
305 eng-Code H (22.4)	30.2
w/A.C. add (.6)	.6
w/AIR add (.4)	.4
307 eng-Code Y (18.6)	26.0
w/A.C. add (.2)	.2
w/AIR add (.4)	.4

(P) Engine Assembly, Recondition (In Car)

Includes: Expand or renew pistons, install new rings, pins, rod and main bearings. Clean carbon, grind valves. Tune engine.

	Chilton Time
V-6–1983-85 (14.9)	18.0
V-8–1983-85 (19.5)	23.7
w/A.C. add (.4)	.4
w/P.S. add (.3)	.3
w/A.I.R. add (.6)	.6
1986-87	
305 eng-Code H (18.8)	26.3

LABOR 13 ENGINE ASSEMBLY & MOUNTS 13 LABOR

	(Factory Time)	Chilton Time
w/A.C. add	(.6)	.6
w/AIR add	(.2)	.2
307 eng-Code Y	(19.4)	27.1
w/A.C. add	(.3)	.3
w/AIR add	(.6)	.6

(G) Engine Mounts, Renew

Front

	(Factory Time)	Chilton Time
V-6-1983-85-one	(.5)	.7
both	(.7)	1.0
V-8-1983-85		
one	(.5)	.8
both	(.6)	1.0
1986-87		
305 eng-Code H		
one	(1.0)	1.4
both	(1.4)	2.1
307 eng-Code Y		
one	(.5)	.8
both	(.6)	1.0
Rear		
V-6-1983-85	(.4)	.6
V-8-1983-87	(.3)	.5

DIESEL ENGINE

(G) Engine Assembly, Remove & Install

Does not include transfer of any parts or equipment.

	(Factory Time)	Chilton Time
1983-85		5.0

(G) Engine Assembly, Renew (Universal)

Includes: R&R engine assembly, transfer all component parts not supplied with replacement engine. Make all necessary adjustments.

	(Factory Time)	Chilton Time
1983-85		20.0
w/A.C. add	(.5)	.5
Renew gov retaining ring add		.7

(P) Cylinder Block, Renew (w/All Internal Parts Less Heads and Oil Pan)

Includes: R&R engine, transfer all component parts not supplied with replacement engine. Clean carbon, grind valves. Make all necessary adjustments.

	(Factory Time)	Chilton Time
1983-85	(13.7)	24.0
w/A.C. add	(.5)	.5

(P) Cylinder Block, Renew (w/Pistons, Rings and Bearings)

Includes: Transfer all component parts not supplied with replacement engine. Clean carbon, grind valves. Make all necessary adjustments.

	(Factory Time)	Chilton Time
1983-85	(16.6)	27.0
w/A.C. add	(.5)	.5

(P) Engine Assy., R&R and Recondition (Complete)

Includes: Rebore block, install new pistons, rings, rod and main bearings. Clean carbon, grind valves. Make all necessary adjustments.

	(Factory Time)	Chilton Time
1983-85	(29.5)	36.0
w/A.C. add	(.5)	.5

(P) Engine Assembly, Recondition (In Car)

Includes: Expand or renew pistons, install new rings, pins, rod and main bearings. Clean carbon, grind valves. Make all necessary adjustments.

	(Factory Time)	Chilton Time
1983-85	(23.2)	27.3
w/A.C. add	(.4)	.4

(G) Engine Mounts, Renew

	(Factory Time)	Chilton Time
Front		
1983-85-one	(.5)	.8
both	(.7)	1.0
Rear		
1983-85	(.3)	.4

PARTS 13 ENGINE ASSEMBLY & MOUNTS 13 PARTS

Cylinder Block

Includes: Block, pistons, rings, connecting rods, crankshaft, and all related bearings.

	Part No.	Price
V-6-231 engine		
1983	◆25519450	950.00
1984	◆25519450	950.00
1985	◆25524288	950.00
V-6-252 engine		
1983-84	◆25516162	971.00
V-8-307 engine		
1983-84	◆22515525	949.00
1985-87	◆22530856	949.00
V-8-350 diesel engine		
1983	◆22518907	1418.00
1984 (see note)	◆22525604	1600.00

Note: Short blocks are not available for the 1984 and later 350 diesel engine. The part number listed above is for an engine assembly.

Front Engine Mount

	Part No.	Price
V-6-231, 252 engines		
1983-85-L.H.	◆25504643	29.00
R.H.	◆1258666	24.00
V-8-307 engine		
1983-87	◆22501573	29.00
V-8-350 diesel engine		
1983-85	◆553915	27.25

LABOR 14 PISTONS, RINGS & BEARINGS 14 LABOR

GASOLINE ENGINES

(P) Rings, Renew (See Engine Combinations)

Includes: Remove cylinder top ridge, deglaze cylinder walls. Minor tune up.

	(Factory Time)	Chilton Time
V-6-1983-85-one cyl	(6.0)	8.4
one cyl-each bank	(7.6)	10.6
all cyls-both banks	(9.5)	13.3
V-8-1983-85	(10.1)	15.4
w/A.C. add	(.5)	.5
w/P.S. add	(.3)	.3
w/A.I.R. add	(.2)	.2
1986-87		
305 eng-Code H		
one cyl	(6.4)	9.2
one cyl-each bank	(8.4)	12.1
all cyls-both banks	(11.2)	16.2
w/A.C. add	(.6)	.6
w/AIR add	(.2)	.2
307 eng-Code Y		
one cyl	(7.6)	11.0
one cyl-each bank	(9.6)	13.9
all cyls-both banks	(11.9)	17.2

COMBINATIONS

Add to Engine Work

See Machine Shop Operations

	(Factory Time)	Chilton Time
(G) DRAIN, EVACUATE & RECHARGE AIR CONDITIONING SYSTEM		
All models	(.5)	1.0
(G) ROCKER ARM STUD, RENEW		
Each	(.3)	.3
(G) HYDRAULIC VALVE LIFTERS, DISASSEMBLE AND CLEAN		
Each	(.2)	.2
(G) DISTRIBUTOR, RECONDITION		
All models	(.5)	.8
(G) CARBURETOR, RECONDITION		
2 bbl		1.2
4 bbl		1.5
(G) CYLINDER HEADS, R&R (ENGINE REMOVED)		
V-6		
eng Codes A-4		
one	(1.1)	1.4
both	(1.8)	2.3
V-8		
eng Code H		
one	(2.4)	3.1
both	(3.7)	4.8
eng Code Y		
one	(1.8)	2.3
both	(2.6)	3.3

LABOR 14 PISTONS, RINGS & BEARINGS 14 LABOR

	(Factory Time)	Chilton Time
w/A.C. add	(.3)	.3
w/AIR add	(.6)	.6

(P) Piston or Connecting Rod, Renew

Includes: Remove cylinder top ridge, deglaze cylinder walls. Minor tune up.

	(Factory Time)	Chilton Time
V-6–1983-85–one cyl	(6.0)	8.7
one cyl-each bank	(7.6)	11.2
all cyls-both banks	(10.2)	15.1
V-8–1983-85	(11.2)	17.8
w/A.C. add	(.5)	.5
w/P.S. add	(.3)	.3
w/A.I.R. add	(.2)	.2
1986-87		
305 eng-Code H		
one cyl	(7.1)	9.9
one cyl-each bank	(9.8)	13.5
all cyls-both banks	(12.3)	18.6
w/A.C. add	(.6)	.6
w/AIR add	(.2)	.2
307 eng-Code Y		
one cyl	(8.2)	11.6
one cyl-each bank	(10.8)	15.1
all cyls-both banks	(13.0)	19.6
w/A.C. add	(.3)	.3
w/AIR add	(.6)	.6

(P) Connecting Rod Bearings, Renew

Includes: R&R oil pan, check all bearing clearances.

	(Factory Time)	Chilton Time
V-6–1983-85	(2.3)	3.4
V-8–1983-85	(3.4)	4.8
1986-87		
305 eng-Code H	(3.7)	5.1
307 eng-Code Y	(4.4)	6.0

COMBINATIONS

Add to Engine Work

See Machine Shop Operations

	(Factory Time)	Chilton Time
(G) CONNECTING ROD, RENEW (ENGINE DISASSEMBLED)		
V-6		
eng Codes A-4		
each	(.5)	.6
V-8		
eng Code H		
each	(.3)	.4
eng Code Y		
each	(.5)	.6
(P) VALVE GUIDES, REAM OVERSIZE		
Each	(.2)	.2
(G) ROCKER ARM SHAFT ASSY., DISASSEMBLE AND CLEAN OR RECONDITION		
Each side	(.2)	.3
(G) DEGLAZE CYLINDER WALLS		
Each	(.1)	.1
(G) REMOVE CYLINDER TOP RIDGE		
Each	(.1)	.1
(G) PLASTIGAUGE BEARINGS		
Each	(.1)	.1
(G) OIL PUMP, RECONDITION		
V-6	(.5)	.8
V-8	(.1)	.3
(M) OIL FILTER ELEMENT, RENEW		
V-6	(.2)	.2
V-8	(.3)	.3

DIESEL ENGINE

(P) Rings, Renew

Includes: Remove cylinder top ridge, deglaze cylinder walls. Clean piston and ring grooves. Make all necessary adjustments.

	(Factory Time)	Chilton Time
1983-85	(12.8)	17.2
w/A.C. add	(.4)	.4

(P) Pistons or Connecting Rods, Renew

Includes: Remove cylinder top ridge, deglaze cylinder walls. Clean piston and ring grooves. Make all necessary adjustments.

	(Factory Time)	Chilton Time
1983-85	(13.3)	19.6
w/A.C. add	(.4)	.4

(P) Connecting Rod Bearings, Renew

Includes: Raise engine and clean oil pump screen.

	(Factory Time)	Chilton Time
1983-85	(4.9)	6.6

PARTS 14 PISTONS, RINGS & BEARINGS 14 PARTS

	Part No.	Price
(1) Piston Ring Set (For One Piston)		
V-6–231 engine		
1983-85	◆1240955	15.75
V-6–252 engine		
1983-84	◆25505382	17.25
V-8–307 engine		
1983-84	◆22506536	16.00
1985-87	◆22529562	18.25
V-8–350 diesel engine		
1983	◆22515964	21.00
1984-85	◆22523733	21.00
(2) Piston Pin (Std.)		
1983-84-w/307	◆398295	4.50
(3) Piston & Pin Assy. (Std.)		
V-6–231 engine		
1983-85	◆25518053	48.25
V-6–252 engine		
1983-84	◆25505374	54.00
V-8–307 engine		
1983-84	◆22506658	48.25
1985-87-L.H.	◆22527479	48.25
R.H.	◆22527480	48.25
V-8–350 diesel engine		
1983-L.H.	22520357	1.00
R.H.	◆22523358	63.75
1984-85-L.H.	◆22523357	63.75
R.H.	◆22523358	63.75

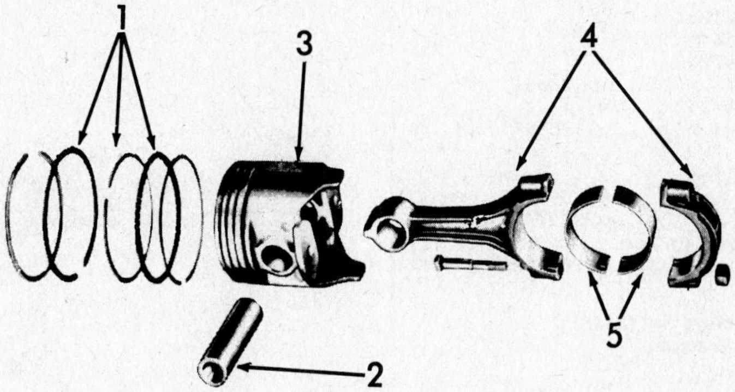

	Part No.	Price
(4) Connecting Rod Assy.		
V-6–231, 252 engines		
1983-85	◆25506520	39.00
V-8–307 engine		
1983-84	◆554976	45.00
1985-87	2257025	N.L.
V-8–350 diesel engine		
1983-85	◆22515313	50.50
(5) Connecting Rod Bearings (Std.)		
V-6–231, 252 engines		
1983-85	◆18005399	11.00
V-8–307 engines		
1983-87	◆18008494	10.50
V-8–350 diesel engine		
1983-85	◆18008494	10.50

LABOR 15 CRANKSHAFT & DAMPER 15 LABOR

	(Factory Time)	Chilton Time
GASOLINE ENGINES		
(P) Crankshaft and Main Bearings, Renew		
Includes: R&R engine, check all bearing clearances.		
V-6–1983-85	(7.1)	10.1
V-8–1983-85	(7.4)	10.9
w/A.C. add	(.4)	.4
w/P.S. add	(.3)	.3
w/A.I.R. add	(.6)	.6
1986-87		
305 eng Code H	(8.4)	11.9
w/A.C. add	(.5)	.5
w/AIR add	(.2)	.2
307 eng Code Y	(7.0)	10.1
w/A.C. add	(.3)	.3
w/AIR add	(.3)	.3
(P) Main Bearings, Renew		
Includes: R&R oil pan and bearing caps. Check all bearing clearances.		
V-6–1983-85	(2.2)	3.6
V-8–1983-85	(2.8)	4.2
1986-87		
305 eng Code H	(3.5)	5.4
w/A.C. add	(.1)	.1
307 eng Code Y	(4.1)	5.7
(P) Main and Rod Bearings, Renew		
Includes: R&R oil pan and bearing caps. Check all bearing clearances.		
V-6–1983-85	(3.4)	5.4
V-8–1983-85	(4.5)	6.6
1986-87		
305 eng Code H	(5.3)	7.8
w/A.C. add	(.1)	.1
307 eng Code Y	(6.3)	8.1
(G) Rear Main Bearing Oil Seal, Renew or Repack		
Includes: R&R oil pan and rear main bearing cap.		
V-6–1983-85	(1.5)	2.2
V-8–1983-85	(2.2)	3.0
1986-87		
305 eng Code H	(2.3)	3.5
w/A.C. add	(.1)	.1
307 eng Code Y	(2.4)	3.6
(G) Crankshaft Pulley and/or Harmonic Balancer, Renew		
V-6–1983-85		
pulley	(.7)	1.2
balancer	(.8)	1.3
V-8–1983-85		
pulley	(.5)	1.1
balancer	(.7)	1.3
1986-87		
305 eng Code H		
pulley	(.6)	1.0
balancer	(.8)	1.2
w/A.C. add	(.2)	.2
307 eng Code Y		
pulley	(.6)	1.0
balancer	(.9)	1.3
w/A.C. add	(.1)	.1
DIESEL ENGINE		
(P) Crankshaft and Main Bearings, Renew		
Includes: R&R engine, check all bearing clearances.		
1983-85	(7.4)	11.2
w/A.C. add	(.4)	.4
(P) Main Bearings, Renew		
Includes: Check all bearing clearances.		
1983-85	(4.1)	5.5
(P) Main and Rod Bearings, Renew		
Includes: Check all bearing clearances.		
1983-85	(6.5)	7.9
(G) Rear Main Bearing Oil Seals, R&R and Repack (Upper & Lower)		
Includes: R&R oil pan and rear main bearing cap.		
1983-85	(2.9)	4.0
(G) Rear Main Bearing Oil Seals, Renew		
Includes: R&R engine assy.		
1983-85	(6.5)	9.1
w/A.C. add	(.4)	.4
(G) Crankshaft Pulley or Balancer, Renew		
1983-85-pulley	(.6)	.8
balancer	(.9)	1.3
w/A.C. add	(.2)	.2
(G) Crankshaft Front Oil Seal, Renew		
1983-85	(.9)	1.5
w/A.C. add	(.2)	.2

PARTS 15 CRANKSHAFT & DAMPER 15 PARTS

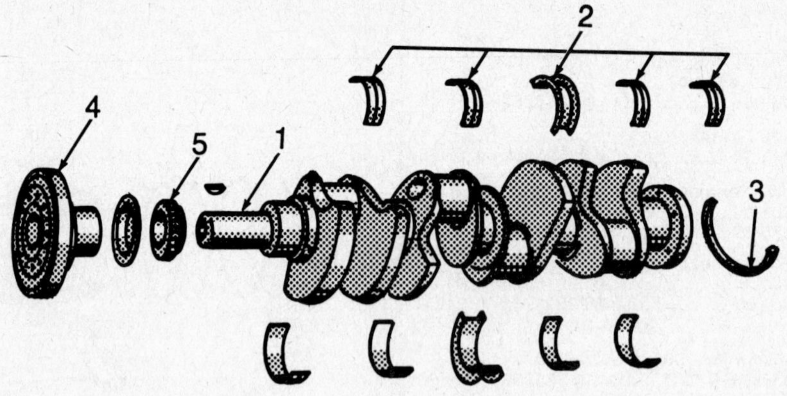

	Part No.	Price
(1) Crankshaft		
V-6–231, 252 engines		
1983-85-w/231 eng.	◆1260877	385.00
1983-84-w/252 eng.	◆1260873	407.00
V-8–307 engine		
1983-84	◆22505615	403.00
1985-87	◆22527438	403.00
V-8–350 diesel engine		
1983-85	◆22511035	439.00
(2) Main Bearing Set (Std.)		
V-6–231, 252 engs.		
1983-85		
No. 1	◆18009457	12.00
No. 2	◆18004602	20.00
No. 3	◆18002950	12.50
No. 4	◆5468578	13.00
V-8–307 eng.		
1983-87-No. 2 & 4	◆5466089	13.00
No. 1	◆5466211	13.00
No. 3	◆5466090	20.00
rear	◆5466091	17.00
V-8–350 diesel eng.		
1983-85		
No. 1	◆5466312	16.00
No. 2, 4	◆5458657	15.00
No. 3	◆5463797	26.25
rear	◆5466314	19.75
(3) Rear Main Bearing Oil Seal		
(Packing)		
1983-87	◆9772831	1.50
(Seal)		
1983-87	◆1193151	1.50
Front Oil Seal (Packing)		
1983-85-V-6	◆1305044	1.00
1983-87-V-8	◆552711	4.25
(4) Crankshaft Balancer		
V-6–231 engine		
1983	◆25506570	42.75
1984-85	◆25523502	41.25
V-6–252 engine		
1983-84	◆25523502	41.25
V-8–307 engine		
1983-87 (hub)	◆22506730	31.75
V-8–350 diesel engine		
1983-85	◆559131	63.25
(5) Crankshaft Sprocket		
V-6–231, 252 engines		
1983-85	◆1192916	16.00
V-8–307 engine		
1983-87	◆382880	16.75
V-8–350 diesel engine		
1983-85	◆558489	44.25

LABOR 16 CAMSHAFT & TIMING GEARS 16 LABOR

(Factory Time) Chilton Time

GASOLINE ENGINES

(G) Timing Cover Oil Seal, Renew

V-8–1983-85 (.8)	1.4
1986-87	
305 eng Code H (.8)	1.4
w/A.C. add (.2)	.2
307 eng Code Y (1.0)	1.5
w/A.C. or AIR add (.1)	.1

(G) Timing Case Cover Gasket, Renew

Includes: R&R fan blade, crankshaft pulley and balancer. Drain and refill oil and coolant.

V-6–1983-85 (2.2)	3.2
V-8–1983-85 (1.3)	2.0
w/A.C. add (.3)	.3
w/P.S. add (.1)	.1
w/A.I.R. add (.2)	.2
Renew cover add (.4)	.6
1986-87	
305 eng Code H (1.8)	2.6
w/A.C. add (.2)	.2
w/AIR add (.2)	.2
307 eng Code Y (1.8)	2.6
w/A.C. add (.3)	.3
w/AIR add (.1)	.1
Renew cover add (.2)	.4
Renew f/pump eccentric add (.1)	.2

(G) Timing Chain or Gears, Renew

Includes: R&R fan blade, crankshaft pulley and balancer, engine front cover. Drain and refill oil and coolant.

V-6–1983-85 (2.4)	3.7
V-8–1983-85 (1.4)	2.5
w/A.C. add (.3)	.3
w/P.S. add (.1)	.1
w/A.I.R. add (.2)	.2
1986-87	
305 eng Code H (2.0)	3.1
w/A.C. add (.2)	.2
w/AIR add (.2)	.2
307 eng Code Y (2.1)	3.1
w/A.C. add (.3)	.3
w/AIR add (.1)	.1

(G) Camshaft, Renew

Includes: R&R pulleys, radiator, harmonic balancer, fuel pump, distributor, timing chain cover, intake manifold, rocker arms, push rods and lifters.

V-6–1983-85 (5.5)	7.0
V-8–1983-85 (4.3)	*7.5
w/A.C. add (.5)	.5
w/P.S. add (.1)	.1
w/A.I.R. add (.4)	.4
*w/A.C. add (1.0)	1.0
1986-87	
305 eng Code H (5.0)	7.0
w/A.C. add (.3)	.3
w/AIR add (.1)	.1
307 eng Code Y (5.7)	*8.1
w/A.C. add (1.0)	1.0
w/AIR add (.4)	.4
*Renew cam brgs add (1.4)	2.0

(G) Camshaft Rear Bearing Plug, Renew

Includes: R&R trans for accessibility.

V-6–1983-85 (2.2)	3.0
V-8–1983-85 (2.1)	3.0
1986-87	
307 eng Code Y (2.2)	3.0

DIESEL ENGINE

(G) Timing Case Cover or Gasket, Renew

Includes: R&R fan blade, crankshaft pulley and balancer. Drain and refill oil and coolant.

1983-85 (2.1)	3.1
Renew cover add (.2)	.4
w/A.C. add (.3)	.3

(G) Timing Chain or Gears, Renew

Includes: R&R fan blade, crankshaft pulley and balancer. Drain and refill oil and coolant.

1983-85 (2.3)	3.5
w/A.C. add (.3)	.3

(G) Camshaft, Renew

Includes: R&R radiator, front cover, fuel pump, timing gear and chain. R&R injector pump, intake manifold and lifters. Disconnect exhaust system. Drain and refill oil and coolant. Make all necessary adjustments.

1983-85 (7.3)	10.0
w/A.C. add (1.0)	1.0
Renew cam brgs add (2.8)	3.8

(G) Camshaft Rear Bearing Plug, Renew

Includes: R&R trans for accessibility.

1983-85 (2.1)	3.0

PARTS 16 CAMSHAFT & TIMING GEARS 16 PARTS

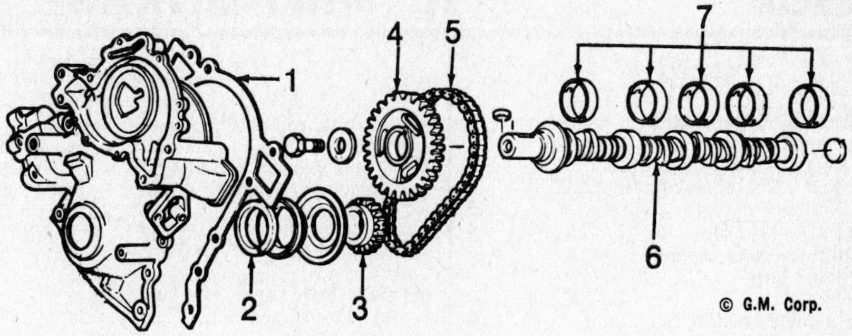

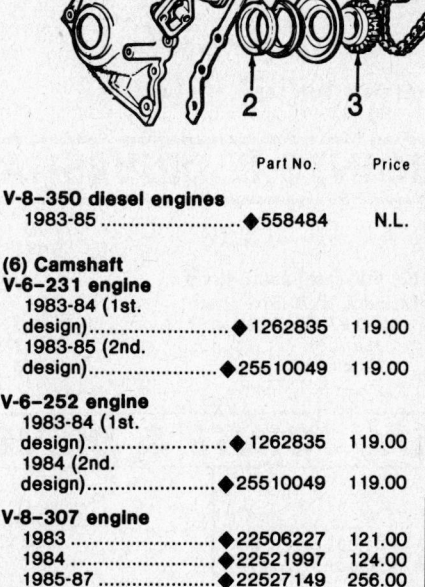

	Part No.	Price
(1) Timing Cover Gasket		
V-6-231, 252 engines		
1983	◆25519461	5.25
1984-85	◆25519461	5.25
V-8-307, 350N engs.		
1983-87	◆22505997	1.25
(2) Oil Shedder Packing		
1983-85	◆1305044	1.00
(3) Timing Gear Sprocket (Crankshaft)		
1983-85-V-6	◆1192916	16.00
1983-87-w/307 eng.	◆382880	16.00
1983-85-w/350 diesel	◆558489	44.25
(4) Timing Gear Sprocket (Camshaft)		
V-6-231, 252 engines		
1983-84	◆1253698	18.50
1985	◆25518767	17.50
V-8-307 engine		
1983-87	◆381263	25.25
V-8-350 diesel engine		
1983-85	◆558767	58.75
(5) Timing Chain		
V-6-231, 252 engs.		
1983-85	◆1257650	26.00
V-8-307 engine		
1983-87	◆401584	31.75
V-8-350 diesel engines		
1983-85	◆558484	N.L.
(6) Camshaft		
V-6-231 engine		
1983-84 (1st. design)	◆1262835	119.00
1983-85 (2nd. design)	◆25510049	119.00
V-6-252 engine		
1983-84 (1st. design)	◆1262835	119.00
1984 (2nd. design)	◆25510049	119.00
V-8-307 engine		
1983	◆22506227	121.00
1984	◆22521997	124.00
1985-87	◆22527149	256.00
V-8-350 diesel engine		
1983-85	◆22510099	266.00
(7) Camshaft Bearings		
V-6-231, 252 engines		
1983-84-No. 1	◆1234441	7.00
1985-No. 1	◆25524301	7.25
1983-85 No. 2, 3, rear	◆1231142	7.75
V-8-307, 350N engs.		
1983-87		
No. 1	◆561077	11.50
No. 2	◆390300	11.50
No. 3	◆390301	11.75
No. 4	◆390302	11.50
No. 5	◆390303	11.50

LABOR 17 ENGINE OILING SYSTEM 17 LABOR

(Factory Time) — Chilton Time

GASOLINE ENGINES

(G) Oil Pan or Gasket, Renew
V-6–1983-85 (1.2) 1.6
V-8–1983-85 (1.7) 2.3
1986-87
305 eng Code H (1.9) 2.7
w/A.C. add (.1) 1
307 eng Code Y (2.1) 2.9

(P) Pressure Test Engine Bearings (Pan Off)
All models 1.0

(G) Oil Pump Cover and/or Gears, R&R and Recondition
Includes: R&R pressure relief valve and inspect. Check pump cover for wear.
V-6–1983-85 (.5) 8

(G) Oil Pump, Renew
V-8–1983-85 (1.8) 2.5
1986-87
305 eng Code H (2.0) 2.9
w/A.C. add (.1) 1
307 eng Code Y (2.2) 3.1

(G) Oil Pump, R&R and Recondition
V-8–1983-85 (1.9) 2.8

(G) Oil Pressure Gauge (Engine), Renew
1983-87 (.3) 4

(M) Oil Filter Element, Renew
V-6–1983-85 (.2) 2
V-8–1983-87 (.3) 3

DIESEL ENGINE

(G) Oil Pan or Gasket, Renew
Includes: Raise engine, R&R and clean oil pump screen.
1983-85 (2.6) 3.4

(P) Pressure Test Engine Bearings (Pan Off)
All models 1.0

(G) Oil Pump, Renew
Includes: Raise engine, R&R and clean oil pump screen.
1983-85 (2.7) 3.6

(G) Oil Pump, R&R and Recondition
Includes: Raise engine, R&R and clean oil pump screen.
1983-85 (2.9) 3.8

(G) Oil Pressure Gauge (Engine), Renew
1983-85 (.3) 4

(M) Oil Filter Element, Renew
1983-85 (.3) 3

PARTS 17 ENGINE OILING SYSTEM 17 PARTS

	Part No.	Price
Oil Pan Gasket		
V-6-231, 252 engines		
1983-84 (1st design)	◆1260771	3.00
1983-85 (2nd design)	◆25521994	8.50
V-8-307 engine		
1983-87	◆22519181	7.00
V-8-350 diesel engine		
1983-84	◆22519181	7.00
Oil Pump Overhaul Kit		
1983-85-w/231 & 252 eng.	◆25523433	39.75
Oil Pump Assembly		
1983-87-w/307 eng.	◆22524583	61.50
1983-85-350 diesel engs.	◆22511732	59.75
Oil Pressure Switch		
V-6-231, 252 engines		
1983-85	◆25500672	5.50
V-8-307 engine		
1983-87	◆3815936	3.50
V-8-350 diesel engine		
1983-85	◆3815936	3.50

LABOR 21 SHIFT LINKAGE 21 LABOR

(Factory Time) — Chilton Time

(G) Shift Linkage, Adjust
All models
Neutral Safety Switch (.3) 4
Shift Indicator Needle (.2) 3
Shift Linkage (.4) 5
T.V. Cable (.3) 4

(G) Shift Linkage, Adjust (w/Diesel Eng)
All models
Fast idle speed (.2) 3
Throttle rod/T.V. cable (.5) 6
Trans vacuum valve (.6) 6
Vacuum regul valve (.6) 8
Complete (1.0) 1.0

(G) Gear Shift Lever, Renew
1983-87 (.3) 5
floor mount (.5) 9

(G) Shift Control Rod, Renew
1983-87 (.4) 5

(G) Shift Indicator Needle, Renew
1983-87 (.3) 5
w/A.C. add (.1) 1

LABOR 25 U-JOINTS & DRIVESHAFT 25 LABOR

(Factory Time) — Chilton Time

(G) Drive Shaft, Renew
1983-87 (.4) 5

(G) Universal Joint, Renew
Includes: R&R drive shaft.
1983-87-front (.6) 8
rear (.5) 7
both (.7) 1.3

(G) Pinion Shaft Flange, Renew
1983-85 (.7) 1.0

PARTS 25 UNIVERSAL JOINTS & DRIVE SHAFT 25 PARTS

	Part No.	Price
Universal Joint Repair Kit		
1983-84-Saginaw	◆7806140	41.00
1983-85-Dana	◆374246	28.50
Pinion Flange		
1983-87-w/8½" ring gr.	◆1256654	35.00
1983-85-w/7½" ring gr	◆7827670	33.75

LABOR 26 REAR AXLE 26 LABOR

(Factory Time)	Chilton Time
(M) Differential, Drain & Refill	
All models	.6
(M) Axle Housing Cover or Gasket, Renew	
1983-87 (.5)	.6
(G) Axle Shaft Assembly, Renew 'C' Lock Type	
1983-87-one (.7)	.9
both (.9)	1.2
(G) Axle Shaft Bearing and/or Seal, Renew 'C' Lock Type	
1983-87-one (.6)	.8
both (.8)	1.1
(G) Pinion Shaft Oil Seal, Renew	
1983-87 (.5)	.8
(G) Axle Housing Assembly, Renew	
Includes: Transfer all parts, bleed and adjust brakes.	
1983-87 (3.4)	5.2
(G) Differential Case, Renew	
Includes: R&R axle shafts and housing cover. Disassemble, inspect and reassemble case. Adjust ring gear backlash and side bearing preload.	
1983-87 (1.8)	2.8
w/Posi-Trac add (.5)	.5
(G) Differential Side Bearings, Renew	
Includes: R&R axle shafts and housing cover and axle case. Adjust ring gear backlash and side bearing preload.	
1983-87 (1.7)	2.5
(P) Ring Gear and Pinion, Renew	
Includes: R&R axle shafts and housing cover. R&R case and rear pinion bearing. Adjust pinion depth and bearing preload, ring gear backlash and side bearing preload.	
1983-87 (2.1)	3.9
Recond complete add	
standard (.3)	.5
limited slip (.7)	1.0
(G) Pinion Bearing and Outer Race, Renew	
Includes: R&R axle shafts and housing cover. Adjust pinion depth and bearing preload, ring gear backlash and side bearing preload.	
1983-87 (2.0)	3.4
Renew side brgs add (.3)	.3
(G) Differential Side Gears and Pinion Shaft, Renew	
Includes: R&R axle shafts and housing cover. Adjust ring gear backlash and side bearing preload.	
1983-87 (.8)	1.8
w/Limited slip add (.5)	.5
(G) Positraction Differential Clutch Plates, Renew	
Includes: R&R axle shafts and housing cover. Adjust ring gear backlash and side bearing preload.	
1983-87 (1.1)	2.0

PARTS 26 REAR AXLE 26 PARTS

Note: To determine rear axle code, refer to 3rd digit (letter) of stamping number located on the forward portion of the right side axle tube.

	Part No.	Price
(1) Axle Shaft		
(w/7½" dia. ring gear)		
1983-85-Type 1	◆22519891	99.50
Type 2	◆22504959	142.25
(w/8½" dia. ring gear)		
1983-85		
w/G-C-K axle (exc. sta. wag.)	◆25501599	114.00
w/light duty brk	◆1255801	114.00
1983-87-sta. wag.	◆14060881	145.25
(w/8¾" dia. ring gear)		
1983 (w/11" x 2" brks.)		
17 lb. brks.	◆526200	135.25
23 lb. brks.	◆526703	139.25
1983 (w/4¾" bolt circle)	◆10020249	127.00

Type 1-Used w/4¾" wheel lug bolt circle diameter.
Type 2-Used w/5" wheel lug bolt circle diameter.

	Part No.	Price
(2) Axle Shaft Seal		
1983-87-exc. Sta. wag.	◆3998519	4.00
Sta. wag.	◆3958078	5.00
(3) Rear Axle Bearing		
1983-87-exc. Sta. wag.	◆7451785	16.00
Sta. wag.	◆7451809	15.00
(4) Pinion Flange		
1983-87-exc below	◆1256654	35.00
w/7 1/2" ring gr.	◆7827670	33.50
(5) Pinion Seal		
1983-w/8¾" ring gr.	◆404294	9.00
1983-87-w/8½" ring gr	◆1243465	7.50
1983-84-w/7½" ring gr	◆552571	8.00
(6) Front Pinion Bearing		
1983-87-exc below	◆7450984	21.00
w/7½" ring gr	◆7451202	16.00

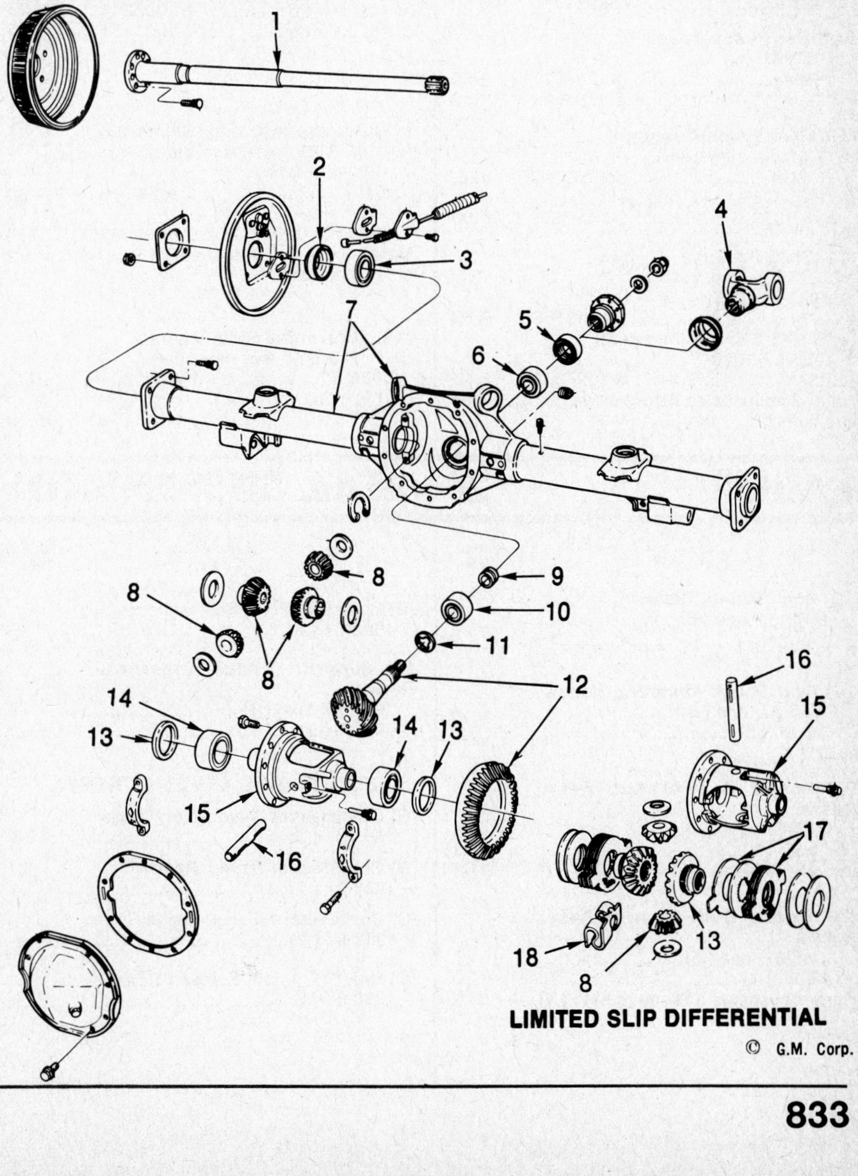

LIMITED SLIP DIFFERENTIAL

© G.M. Corp.

PARTS 26 REAR AXLE 26 PARTS

	Part No.	Price
(7) Axle Housing		
(w/7½" dia. ring gear)		
1983-85	◆22510779	392.25
(w/8½" dia. ring gear)		
1983-87-exc. Sta. wag.	◆14079329	406.25
Sta. wag.	◆14079330	489.75
(w/8¾" dia. ring gear)		
1983-exc. Sta. wag.	◆10004179	603.50
Sta. wag.	◆10004180	610.00
(8) Pinion Gear Package		
(With Limited Slip Differential)		
(w/8¾" dia. ring gear)		
1983	◆547212	173.00
(Without Limited Slip Differential)		
(w/7½" dia. ring gear)		
1983-85	◆22525894	94.50
(w/8½" dia. ring gear)		
1983-87	◆1397647	132.00
(w/8¾" dia. ring gear)		
1983	◆547225	106.00

Note: Gear package contains 2 side gears, 2 pinion gears, thrust washer, pinion shaft.

	Part No.	Price
Side Gears-Sold Separately		
(With Limited Slip Differential)		
(w/8½" dia. ring gear)		
1983-87	◆231075	49.50
(9) Drive Pinion Spacer		
1983-87-exc below	◆1234726	1.50
w/7½" ring gr	◆9785792	1.50
(10) Rear Pinion Bearing		
(w/7½" dia. ring gear)		
1983-85	22510042	N.L.
(w/8½" & 8¾" dia. ring gear)		
1983-87	◆7451155	20.00
(11) Shim Package		
(w/7½" dia. ring gear)		
1983-85 (.020-.024)	◆559755	7.50
(w/8½" & 8¾" dia. ring gear)		
1983-87 (.020-.024)	◆1394892	5.50

Note: Smallest size listed above. Larger sizes available.

	Part No.	Price
(12) Ring and Pinion Gear		
(w/7½" dia. ring gear)		
1983-85		
2.29 ratio	◆560197	259.00
2.41 ratio	◆560198	259.00
2.73 ratio	◆560201	259.00
2.93 ratio	◆560204	261.00
(w/8½" dia. ring gear)		
1983-87		
2.41 ratio	◆1258715	276.00
2.56 ratio	◆1258707	276.00
2.73 ratio	◆1258708	276.00
2.93 ratio	◆1258714	276.00
3.08 ratio	◆1258709	276.00
3.23 ratio	◆1258713	276.00
3.73 ratio	◆1259441	280.00
(w/8¾" dia. ring gear)		
1983		
2.41 ratio	◆10002813	305.25
2.56 ratio	◆10002814	305.25
2.73 ratio	◆10002812	305.25
2.93 ratio	◆10018255	305.25
3.08 ratio	◆10002811	305.25
3.23 ratio	◆10002810	305.25
(13) Bearing Adjusting Shim Pkg.		
(w/7½" & 8½" dia. ring gear)		
1983-87 (.040-.044)	◆3995791	6.50
(w/8¾" dia. ring gear)		
1983 (.040-.044)	◆3996610	6.50

Note: Smallest sizes listed above. Larger sizes available.

	Part No.	Price
(14) Differential Side Bearing		
(w/7½" & 8½" dia. ring gear)		
1983-87	◆9420095	N.L.
(w/8¾" dia. ring gear)		
1983	◆7451140	15.00
(15) Differential Case (Without Limited Slip Differential)		

Note: The following cases do not include the internal gears.

	Part No.	Price
(7½" ring gear)		
1983-85	◆558648	109.00
(8½" ring gear)		
1983-87-exc. below	◆1252981	110.00
w/2.56, 2.93R	◆1252980	110.00
(8¾" ring gear)		
1983-exc. below	◆526205	134.25
w/2.73, 3.08R	◆526207	162.25
w/3.23R	◆527854	162.00
Differential Case (With Limited Slip Differential)		

Note: The internal gears are included in the following cases.

	Part No.	Price
(8½" ring gear)		
1983-87-exc. below	◆14030435	431.25
w/2.41, 2.56R	◆14030434	408.50
(8¾" ring gear)		
1983-P-M axle		
w/2.28, 2.41, 2.56R	527751	286.25
w/2.73, 3.08R	◆527752	428.00
w/3.23R	◆527753	428.00
(16) Pinion Shaft		
(w/7½" dia. ring gear)		
1983-85	◆22507586	11.00
(w/8½" dia. ring gear)		
1983-87	◆14006401	12.50
(w/8¾" dia. ring gear)		
1983	◆9778184	12.75
(17) Friction Disc Kit		
1983-87-exc. below	◆483722	55.75
w/8½" ring gear	◆231127	58.25

Note: Part No. 231127 consist of 8 fixed discs and 6 splined discs. Part No. 483722 consist of 10 eared discs, 8 splined discs and 4 guides.

	Part No.	Price
(18) Preload Spring		
1983-exc. below	◆488332	4.50
1983-87-w/8½" ring gear	◆231260	3.25

LABOR 27 REAR SUSPENSION 27 LABOR

(Factory Time)	Chilton Time
(G) Rear Spring, Renew	
1983-87-one (.6)	.7
both (.7)	.9
(G) Rear Shock Absorber, Renew	
1983-87-one (.3)	.5
both (.5)	.7
(G) Lower Control Arm Assy., Renew	
1983-87-one (.4)	.7
both (.6)	1.0
Renew bushings add-each side (.1)	.3
(G) Upper Control Arm Assy., Renew	
1983-87-one (.5)	.7
both (.7)	1.0
Renew bushings add-each side (.1)	.3
(G) Rear Stabilizer Bar, Renew	
1983-87 (.5)	.7
(G) Superlift Shock Absorbers, Renew	
1983-87-one (.4)	.6
both (.5)	.9

ELECTRONIC LEVEL CONTROL

(Factory Time)	Chilton Time
(G) Compressor Assembly, Renew	
1983-87 (.3)	.5
(G) Compressor Dryer, Renew	
1983-87 (.2)	.4
(G) Compressor Relay, Renew	
1983-87 (.2)	.4
(G) Height Control Sensor, Renew	
1983-87 (.6)	.9
(G) Height Sensor, Adjust	
1983-87 (.3)	.5
(G) Level Control Tubing, Renew	
comp to valve (.6)	.8
valve to shock (.3)	.5
valve to bumper (.3)	.5
(G) Electronic Level Control Head, Renew	

Includes: Renew cover gasket, solenoid and valves.

(Factory Time)	Chilton Time
1983 (.5)	.9
1984-87 (.3)	.9
(G) Electronic Level Control Motor and Cylinder Assy., R&R and Recondition	
1983-87 (.6)	1.2

PARTS 27 REAR SUSPENSION 27 PARTS

	Part No.	Price
(1) Rear Springs		
Order by year and model.		
(2) Rear Shock Absorbers		
(wo/electronic level control)		
1983-84-exc.		
below	◆4993551	24.50
sta. wag.	◆4993554	24.50
1985-exc. sta.		
wag.	◆22046428	24.50
1985-87-sta.		
wag.	◆22046427	24.50
(w/electronic level control)		
1983-84-right	◆4993553	64.00
left	◆4993552	65.00
1985-87-sta. wag.		
right	◆22046426	57.75
left	◆22046425	57.75
1985-exc. sta. wag.		
right	22046443	57.75
left	22046442	57.75
(3) Rear Suspension Upper Control Arm & Bushing		
1983-87		
0 deg.	◆10000887	22.50
2 deg.	◆10000904	30.00
-2 deg.	◆10000910	30.00
(4) Rear Suspension Lower Control Arm & Bushing		
1983-87	◆10000334	32.50

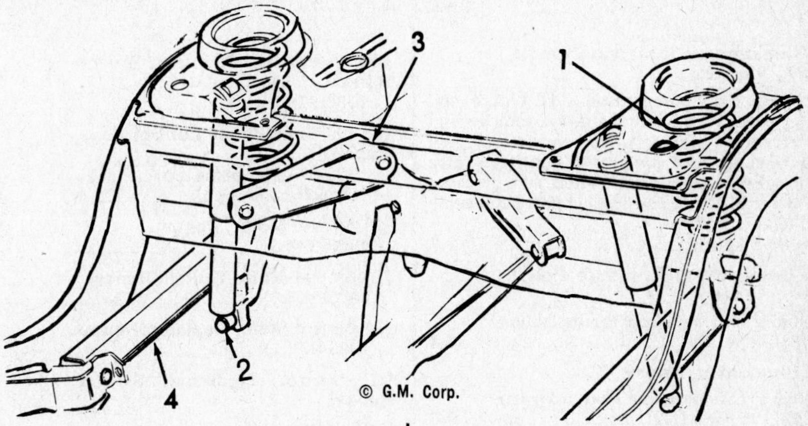

	Part No.	Price
Rear Stabilizer Shaft		
1983-85-w/H.D.		
susp.	370277	43.50

ELECTRONIC LEVEL CONTROL

	Part No.	Price
Compressor Assy.		
1983-84	◆22020538	176.25
1986-87	22062538	233.00
Relay		
1983-87	◆10011579	9.75
Height Sensor		
1983-84-exc.		
wagon	◆22017241	176.25
1983-87-sta.		
wag.	◆22040580	200.00
Compressor Head		
1983-85	◆22020539	68.50
1986-87	◆22062535	68.50
Motor		
1983-85	◆22010692	165.00
1986-87	22062540	152.00

LABOR 28 AIR CONDITIONING 28 LABOR

(Factory Time) Chilton Time

Note: If more than one item requires replacement where evacuation and discharging the system is already included in the operation, deduct 1.0 hour for each additional item to the times listed.

(G) Drain, Evacuate and Recharge System
All models (.5) 1.0

(G) Leak Check
Includes: Check all lines and connections.
All models 5

(G) Refrigerant, Add (Partial Charge)
All models 6

(G) Compressor Belt, Renew
1983-85 (.3) 4
w/A.I.R. add (.1) 2
1986-87
eng Code H (.3) 4
eng Code Y (.4) 5

COMPRESSOR 4 CYLINDER RADIAL

(G) Compressor Assembly, Renew
Includes: Transfer parts as required. Evacuate and charge system.
1983-87 (1.0) 2.0

(G) Compressor Clutch Plate and Hub Assy., Renew
Includes: R&R hub and drive plate assy., check air gap.
1983-87 (.5) 8

(G) Compressor Clutch Rotor and/or Bearing, Renew
Includes: R&R hub and drive plate assy.
1983-87 (.6) 1.2

AIR CONDITIONER TUNE-UP

For efficient operation and satisfactory performance in hot weather. The following air conditioner tune-up is suggested:

1. Clean intake filter
2. Clean condenser fins
3. Pressure test system
4. Adjust drive belt tension
5. Check antifreeze/coolant
6. Tighten compressor mounts
7. Tighten condenser and evaporator mounts
8. Inspect system for leaks (hoses, couplings, valves, etc.)
9. Partial charge system

All models 1.0
If necessary to evacuate and charge system, add 1.0

(Factory Time) Chilton Time

(G) Compressor Clutch Coil and/or Pulley Rim Assembly, Renew
Includes: R&R hub and drive plate assy.
1983-87 (.7) 1.0
Renew pulley or brg add (.1) 2

(G) Compressor Front Seal, Seat and 'O' Ring, Renew
Includes: R&R clutch hub and drive plate assy. Exacuate and charge system.
1983-87 (1.1) 2.5

(Factory Time) Chilton Time

(G) Compressor Front Head and/or Seal, Renew
Includes: R&R compressor, R&R clutch and pulley assy. R&R shaft seal assy. Clean and inspect parts. Evacuate and charge system.
1983-87 (1.3) 2.8

(G) Compressor Discharge Valve Plates, Renew
Includes: R&R compressor. R&R clutch and pulley assy. R&R shell to internal mechanism. Clean and inspect parts. Evacuate and charge system.
1983-87 (1.1) 2.6
two or more add (.1) 2

(G) Compressor Thrust and/or Belleville Washers, Renew
Includes: R&R compressor. R&R clutch and pulley assy. R&R shaft seal assy. R&R front head assy. Clean and inspect parts. Evacuate and charge system.
1983-87 (1.5) 2.8

(G) Compressor Main Bearing, Renew
Includes: R&R compressor. R&R clutch and pulley assy. R&R shaft seal assy. R&R front head assy. Clean and inspect parts. Evacuate and charge system.
1983-87 (1.5) 2.8

(G) Compressor Shell and/or 'O' Rings, Renew
Includes: R&R compressor. R&R clutch and pulley assy. Clean and inspect parts. Evacuate and charge system.
1983-87 (1.5) 2.8

LABOR 28 AIR CONDITIONING 28 LABOR

(Factory Time) Chilton Time

(G) Compressor Shaft and Cylinder Assy., Renew

Includes: R&R compressor. R&R clutch and pulley assy. R&R shaft seal assy., remove and transfer front head assy. R&R compressor shell and 'O' rings. R&R compressor discharge valve plates, R&R super heat switch and pressure relief valve. Clean and inspect parts. Evacuate and charge system.

1983-87 (1.6)........ 2.9

(G) Compressor Pressure Relief Valve, Renew

Includes: Evacuate and charge system.

1983-87 (1.0)........ 1.4

(G) Condenser, Renew

Includes: Evacuate and charge system.

1983-85-Gas (1.2)........ 2.0
Diesel (1.7)........ 2.5
1986-87 (.8)........ 2.0

(G) Evaporator Core, Renew

Includes: Evacuate and charge system.

1983-85 (1.9)........ 3.5
1986-87 (1.5)........ 3.5

(G) Accumulator Assembly, Renew

Includes: Evacuate and charge system.

1983-87 (.8)........ 1.5

(G) Expansion Tube Assembly, Renew

Includes: Evacuate and charge system.

1983-87 (.7)........ 1.4

(G) Thermostatic Control Switch, Renew

1983-87 (.2)........ .4

(G) Pressure Cycling Switch, Renew

1983-87 (.2)........ .3

(G) Air Conditioner Control Assy., Renew

1983-87-exc. below (.6)........ .9
Touch control (.4)........ .6

(G) Blower Motor, Renew

1983-87 (.3)........ .5

(G) Blower Motor Switch, Renew

1983-87 (.3)........ .5

(G) Blower Motor Resistor, Renew

1983-87 (.2)........ .3

(G) Master Electrical Switch, Renew

1983-87 (.4)........ .6

(G) Vacuum Selector Valve, Renew

1983-87 (.4)........ .6
w/Auto. A.C. add (.3)........ .3

(G) Vacuum Actuators, Renew

1983-87
Defroster (1.1)........ 2.0
Upper or Lower Mode (1.4)........ 2.4
Air Inlet (1.4)........ 2.4

(G) Air Conditioning Hoses, Renew

Includes: Evacuate and charge system.

1983-87-one (1.1)........ 1.7
each adtnl (.3)........ .5
Assemble repl. hose add (.3)........ .4

AUTOMATIC CLIMATE CONTROL

(G) Programmer, Renew

1983-87 (.6)........ 1.0

Renew programmer parts add
vacuum valve (.1)........ .2
vacuum motor (.2)........ .3
circuit board (.3)........ .4
transducer (.1)........ .2
amplifier (.3)........ .4
feed back pot (.3)........ .4
out put shaft (.1)........ .4
vacuum relay (.1)........ .2
blower contacts (.2)........ .3
blower switch (.2)........ .3

(G) Control Assembly, Renew

1983-87-exc below (.6)........ .9
Touch control (.4)........ .6

(G) Aspirator Hose, Renew

1983-87 (.2)........ .4

(G) A.C. Aspirator, Renew

1983-87 (.3)........ .5

(G) In-Car Sensor, Renew

1983-87 (.4)........ .5

(G) Ambient Sensor, Renew

1983-87 (.2)........ .5

(G) Electric Actuators, Renew

1983-87
Defroster (.8)........ 1.2
Upper or Lower mode (.9)........ 1.3
Air Inlet (.6)........ 1.0

PARTS 28 AIR CONDITIONING 28 PARTS

	Part No.	Price
COMPRESSOR ASSY.		
Compressor Assembly		
1983-87	◆12300273	390.00
Compressor Clutch		
1983-87	◆6551220	32.50
Compressor Clutch Rotor and Bearing		
1983-87	◆6551216	67.50
Compressor Clutch Coil w/Housing		
1983-87	◆6551217	44.00
Compressor Seal Kit		
1983-87	◆9956695	13.00
Compressor Front Head		
1983-87	◆6551142	28.25
Compressor Discharge Valve Plate		
1983-87	◆6551141	11.50
Compressor Thrust Washer Kit		
1983-87	9956685	4.50

Note: Contains two thrust washers and one belleville washer.

	Part No.	Price
Compressor Main Bearing		
1983-87	◆6556572	4.00
Compressor Shell		
1983-87	◆2724158	38.00
Compressor Shaft and Cylinder		
1983-87	◆2724144	269.00
Compressor Pressure Relief Valve		
1983-87	◆5914435	13.50
Condenser Assembly		
1983-85-w/V-6 eng.	◆3037439	158.25
1983-87-w/V-8 engs.	◆3037438	156.50
Evaporator Core		
1983-84	◆3035240	218.25
1985-87	◆3058130	261.75
Accumulator-Dehydrator		
1983-87	◆2724275	80.25
Expansion Tube Assembly (Orifice)		
1983-87	3034955	15.25
Air Conditioner Control Assembly		
1983	16002900	25.50
1984-87	16034664	37.00
Blower Motor Assembly		
1983-87	◆22020945	60.00
Blower Motor Switch (Fan Control)		
1983	◆16015256	6.00
1984-85	◆16032480	7.50
Blower Motor Resistor		
1983-84	◆526897	4.50
1985-87	◆10039426	4.50
AUTOMATIC CLIMATE CONTROL		
Programmer		
1983-87	25512087	170.00
In Car Sensor		
1983-87	25502278	7.00
Ambient Sensor		
w/Electronic Climate Control 1983-87	25502279	16.75
Automatic Blower Motor Relay		
1983-87	◆10018449	N.L.
Control Assembly (Electronic Climate Control System)		
1983	25509129	112.00
1984-85	25517965	112.00

LABOR 29 LOCKS, HINGES & WIND. REGULATORS 29 LABOR

(Factory Time) Chilton Time

(G) Hood Lock, Renew

1983-87 (.2)........ .5

(G) Hood Hinge, Renew

1983-87-one (.3)........ .4
both (.4)........ .7

(G) Hood Release Cable, Renew

1983-87 (.4)........ .6

LABOR 29 LOCKS, HINGES & WIND. REGULATORS 29 LABOR

	(Factory Time)	Chilton Time
(G) Door Lock, Renew		
Front		
1983-87	(.5)	.8
Rear		
1983-87	(.8)	1.2
(G) Door Lock Remote Control, Renew		
1983-87	(.4)	.7
(G) Door Lock Cylinder, Renew		
1983-87	(.4)	.6
Recode cyl add	(.3)	.3
(G) Door Handle (Outside), Renew (Front or Rear)		
1983-87	(.4)	.6
Renew insert add		.1
(G) Lock Striker Plate, Renew		
1983-87	(.2)	.2
(G) Door Window Regulator (Manual), Renew (Front or Rear)		
1983-87	(.8)	1.1
Recond regul add	(.2)	.2
(G) Door Window Regulator (Electric), Renew (Front or Rear)		
1983-87	(1.0)	1.4
(G) Trunk Lock, Renew		
1983-87	(.3)	.3
(G) Trunk Lock Cylinder, Renew		
1983-87	(.3)	.3
Recode cyl add	(.3)	.3
(G) Rear Compartment Lid Hinge Strap, Renew (One)		
1983-87	(.8)	1.2
(G) Tail Gate Lock Assy., Renew		
1983-87-one	(.5)	.7
(G) Tail Gate Lock Cylinder, Renew		
1983-87	(.3)	.5
Recode cyl add	(.3)	.3
(G) Tail Gate Lock Remote Control, Renew		
1983-87	(.3)	.5
(G) Tail Gate Window Regulator, Renew		
Includes: Transfer motor.		
1983-87	(.7)	1.2

PARTS 29 LOCKS, HINGES & WIND. REGULATORS 29 PARTS

	Part No.	Price
Lower Hood Latch Assm.		
1983-87	◆14070703	16.25
Hood Hinge		
1983-87-right	25502792	28.25
left	25502793	28.25
Front Door Lock		
1983-87-2-door model		
left	◆20293613	33.50
right	◆20293612	33.50
1983-87-4-door model		
left	◆20293605	51.50
right	◆20293604	51.50
Rear Door Lock		
1983-85-right	◆20293624	55.75
left	◆20293625	55.75
Trunk Lid Lock		
1983-85	20616582	21.25
Front Door Outer Handle		
1983-87 (wo/illum entry sys.)		
right	◆20111712	26.50
left	◆20111713	26.50
1983-87 (w/illum entry sys.)		
right	◆20177430	53.75
left	◆20177431	53.75
Rear Door Outer Handle		
1983-87-right	◆20111712	26.50
left	◆20111713	26.50
Front Door Window Regulator Manual		
(2 door)		
1983-85-right	◆20303586	102.00
left	◆20303587	102.00
(4 door)		
1983-87-right	◆20110652	102.00
left	◆20110653	102.00
Rear Door Regulator Manual		
1983-right	◆20147472	88.25
left	◆20147473	88.25
Front Door Window Regulator Electric		
(2 door)		
1983-85-right	◆20303590	108.00
left	◆20303591	108.00
(4 door)		
1983-87-right	◆20192896	114.00
left	◆20192897	114.00
Rear Door Window Regulator Electric		
1983-87-right	◆20192894	114.00
left	◆20192895	114.00

LABOR 30 HEAD AND PARKING LAMPS 30 LABOR

	(Factory Time)	Chilton Time
(G) Aim Headlamps		
two		.4
four		.6
(M) Headlamp Sealed Beam Bulb, Renew		
1983-87-each	(.2)	.3
(M) Back-Up Lamp Assembly, Renew		
1983-87-each	(.3)	.4
(M) Cornering Lamp Assembly, Renew		
1983-87-each	(.3)	.4
(M) Park and Turn Signal Lamp Assy., Renew		
1983-87-each	(.3)	.4
(M) Stop, Tail and Turn Signal Lamp Assy., Renew		
1983-87-each	(.3)	.4
(M) Back-Up Lamp Bulb, Renew		
All models-one	(.2)	.3
(M) Cornering Lamp Bulb, Renew		
All models-each	(.2)	.3
(M) License Lamp Bulb, Renew		
All models-one or all	(.2)	.3
(M) Park and Turn Signal Lamp Bulb, Renew		
All models-each		.2
(M) Side Marker Lamp Bulb, Renew		
All models-each		.2
(M) Stop, Tail and Turn Signal Lamp Bulb, Renew		
All models-one		.2
each adtnl		.1

PARTS 30 HEAD AND PARKING LAMPS 30 PARTS

	Part No.	Price
Headlamp Sealed Beam exc. Quartz Halogen		
1983-87-inner	◆5966200	15.00
outer	◆5966201	15.00
Quartz Halogen		
1983-85-inner	◆5930567	22.50
1983-87-outer	◆16502327	22.50

Parking & Turn Signal Lamp Lens
Note: 1983-87 lens is not sold separately from lamp assy.

PARTS 30 HEAD AND PARKING LAMPS 30 PARTS

	Factory Time	Chilton Time
Parking Lamp Assy. (R.H.)		
1983-87	914099	29.75
License Lamp Assy.		
Electra		
1983-84	914023	3.75
LeSabre		
1983-85-wo/sta. wag.	◆913933	4.00
1983-87-w/sta. wag.	◆912795	7.50
Tail, Stop & Signal Lamp Lens (R.H.)		
LeSabre		
1983-R.H.	5931026	34.00
left	5931025	34.00
1984-85-R.H.	1651960	N.L.
left	1651959	N.L.
Electra		
1983-84-R.H.	5971248	58.00
left	5971247	58.00
High Mount Stoplight		
1986-87	◆918456	39.50

LABOR 31 WINDSHIELD WIPER & SPEEDOMETER 31 LABOR

	Factory Time	Chilton Time
(G) Windshield Wiper Motor, Renew		
1983-87	(.3)	.6
w/Inter wiper add	(.1)	.1
(G) Windshield Wiper Motor, R&R and Recondition		
1983-87	(.8)	1.2
(G) Wiper Transmission, Renew (One)		
1983-87	(.4)	.6
(G) Wiper Switch, Renew		
1983-87-std colm	(.9)	1.4
tilt colm	(.7)	1.3
(G) Wiper Motor Main Drive Gear (Depressed Park), Renew		
1983-87	(.8)	1.3
(G) Wiper Motor Terminal Board and/or Timing Delay Switch, Renew		
1983-87	(.5)	1.0
(G) Windshield Washer Pump, Renew		
1983-87	(.2)	.4
w/Pulse wipe add	(.1)	.1
(G) Windshield Washer Pump, R&R and Recondition		
1983-87	(.5)	.8
(G) Windshield Washer Pump Valve, Renew		
1983-87	(.2)	.4
(G) Speedometer Head, R&R or Renew		
1983-87	(.3)	.7
Reset odometer add		.2
(G) Speedometer Cable and Casing, Renew		
wo/Cruise control		
1983	(.5)	.8
1984-87	(.7)	1.1
w/Cruise control		
1983-upper cable	(.4)	.6
lower cable	(.3)	.5
both	(.6)	1.0
1984-87-one piece	(.7)	1.1
(G) Speedometer Cable (Inner), Renew or Lubricate		
wo/Cruise control		
1983	(.5)	.9
1984-87	(.7)	1.1
w/Cruise control		
1983-upper	(.4)	.6
lower	(.3)	.5
both	(.6)	1.0
1984-87-one piece	(.7)	1.1
(G) Radio, R&R		
1983-87	(.5)	.7

PARTS 31 WINDSHIELD WIPER & SPEEDOMETER 31 PARTS

	Part No.	Price
Windshield Wiper Motor		
(exc. Pulse Wiper System)		
1983-87	◆4960974	84.00
(Pulse Wiper System)		
1983-87	◆4961608	80.00
Windshield Wiper Transmission		
1983-87-L.H.	◆22010449	18.50
R.H.	◆22010448	17.00
Windshield Wiper Motor Control Switch		
(wo/pulse wipers)		
1983	◆7837279	41.50
1984-87	◆7835342	22.50
(w/pulse wipers)		
1983-87-exc. tilt whl.	◆7835340	56.25
w/tilt whl.	◆7837280	53.50
Wiper Motor Main Drive Gear		
1983-87	4919832	7.25
Wiper Motor Terminal Board and Timing Delay Switch		
1983-87-w/Pulse	4961604	10.50
wo/Pulse	4960755	11.00
Speedometer Cable and Casing		
Order by year and model.		

LABOR 32 LIGHT SWITCHES & WIRING 32 LABOR

	Factory Time	Chilton Time
(G) Headlamp Switch, Renew		
1983-87	(.3)	.5
w/A.C. add	(.1)	.1
(G) Headlamp Dimmer Switch, Renew		
1983-87		
column mounted	(.4)	.7
(G) Stop Light Switch, Renew		
1983-87	(.3)	.4
(G) Parking Brake Switch, Renew		
1983-87	(.3)	.4
(G) Neutral Safety and Back-Up Light Switch, Renew		
1983-87	(.3)	.4
(G) Turn Signal or Hazard Warning Switch, Renew		
w/Cruise control add	(.1)	.1
1983-87	(.7)	1.1
(M) Turn Signal or Hazard Warning Flasher, Renew		
1983-87	(.2)	.2
(G) Horn Relay, Renew		
1983-87	(.2)	.3
(G) Horn, Renew		
1983-87	(.2)	.3
(G) Chassis Wiring Harness, Renew		
Headlamp		
1983-87	(.6)	1.1
Engine		
1983-87	(1.2)	1.7
Instrument panel		
1983-87	(1.8)	2.4
Fuse block		
1983-87	(.6)	1.1

PARTS 32 LIGHT SWITCHES & WIRING 32 PARTS

	Part No.	Price
Headlamp Switch		
1983-87-exc below	◆1995226	16.00
w/Auto system	◆1995214	22.75
Headlamp Dimmer Switch		
1983-87	◆7838234	12.50
Stoplight Switch		
1983-84-exc. below	◆25504628	3.75
w/cruise cont.	◆9794682	7.75
1985-exc. below	◆25524846	6.50
w/cruise	◆25524847	6.50
Turn Signal Switch		
1983-87-exc below	◆1997983	30.00
w/Tilt whl.	◆1997984	35.00
Turn Signal Flasher		
1983-84	◆10029240	4.25
1985-87	◆10041073	N.L.
Back-Up Light Switch		
1983-85-exc. below	◆22509632	5.50
1983-87-w/ Elect. door locks	◆22514861	7.00
Chassis Wiring Harness		
Order by year and model.		

LABOR 33 GLASS 33 LABOR

(Factory Time)	Chilton Time
(G) Windshield, Renew	
1983-87 (1.3)	1.8
Renew caulk bead add (.4)	.4
(G) Front Door Glass, Renew	
1983-87 (.9)	1.5
(G) Rear Door Glass, Renew	
1983-87 (.8)	1.4
(G) Quarter Window Stationary Glass, Renew	
1983-87-hdtps (.8)	1.3
1983-87-sta wag (1.0)	1.6
(G) Tail Gate Window Glass, Renew	
1983-87 (.7)	1.0
(G) Back Window Glass, Renew	
1983-87 (1.3)	2.0
w/Elec defogger add (.6)	.6
w/3/4 plug, unpadded add (1.3)	2.0
w/3/4 plug, padded add (2.6)	4.0
w/Full plug, add (2.8)	4.4
(G) Rear Door Vent Glass, Renew	
1983-87 (.7)	1.0

LABOR 34 CRUISE CONTROL 34 LABOR

(Factory Time)	Chilton Time
(G) Cruise Control Transducer Assy., Adjust	
1983 (.3)	.4
(G) Cruise Control Regulator (Transducer), Renew	
1983 (.4)	.6
Adj low spd switch add (.1)	.1
(G) Cruise Control Engagement Switch, Renew	
1983-87 (.5)	.9
(G) Cruise Control Servo, Renew	
Includes: Adjust bead chain.	
1983-85 (.2)	.5
1986-87 (.6)	.8
(G) Cruise Control Vacuum Hoses, Renew	
1983-87-one or all (.2)	.3
(G) Cruise Control Chain or Cable (Servo to Carb), Renew	
1983-87 (.2)	.4
(G) Cruise Control Transducer Filter, Renew	
1983 (.2)	.3
(G) Cruise Control Vacuum Regulator Valve, Renew (w/Diesel Engine)	
1983 (.2)	.4
(G) Cruise Control Resume Solenoid, Renew	
1983 (.2)	.3
(G) Cruise Control Check Valve, Renew	
1983 (.3)	.4
(G) Cruise Control Module, Renew	
1984-87 (.3)	.5
(G) Cruise Control Speed Sensor, Renew	
1984 (.6)	.8

PARTS 34 CRUISE CONTROL 34 PARTS

	Part No.	Price
Cruise Control Power Unit (Servo)		
1983 (w/231, 252 eng.) exc. TH200 trans.	◆25030527	20.50
w/TH200 trans.	◆25031845	26.00
1983 (w/307 engine) exc. below	◆25074220	25.00
w/TH200 trans.	◆25031316	27.00
1983-w/350 diesel	◆25030980	32.75
1984-87-w/V-6 engs.	◆25074630	116.25
w/V-8 engs.	◆25074629	123.50
Cruise Control Lever & Switch		
1983-exc. below	◆25031426	52.25
w/pulse wiper	◆25031425	52.25
1984-87-exc. below	◆25031457	50.00
w/pulse wiper	◆25031456	50.00
Cruise Control Transducer		
1983-w/V-6 eng.	◆25030878	158.00
w/307 eng.	◆25031261	158.00
w/diesel eng.	◆25031604	179.25
Cruise Control Brake Release Switch		
1983-87	◆9794682	8.00
Cruise Control Chain & Ball		
1983 (w/V-6 eng.) exc. TH200 trans.	◆1494424	2.50
w/TH200 trans.	◆25031314	3.25
1984-87-w/V-8 engs.	◆25031314	3.25

Buick Regal

GROUP INDEX

ALPHABETICAL INDEX

General Motors
Rear Wheel Drive Cars

BUICK REGAL

YEAR IDENTIFICATION

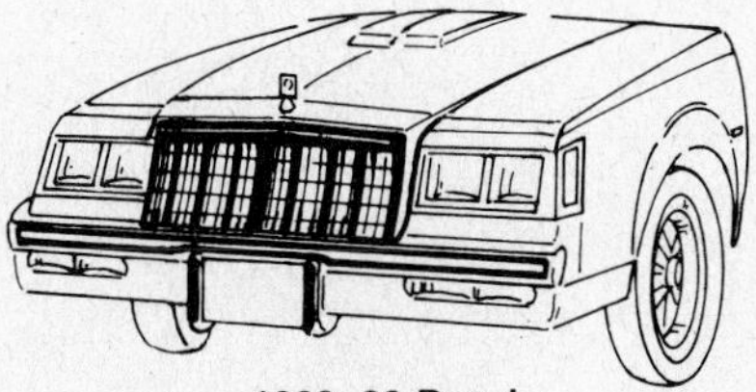

1982–83 Regal

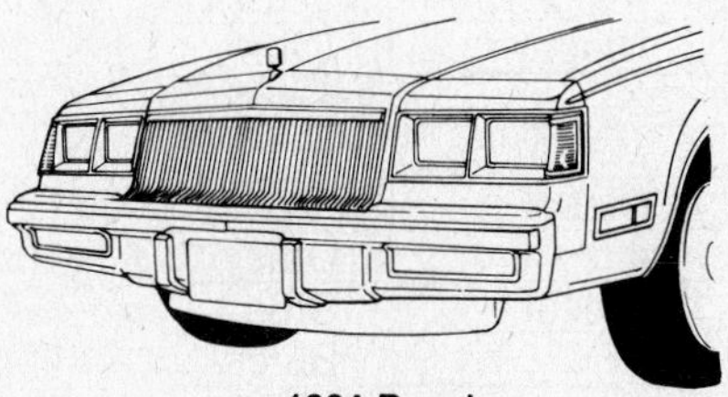

1984 Regal

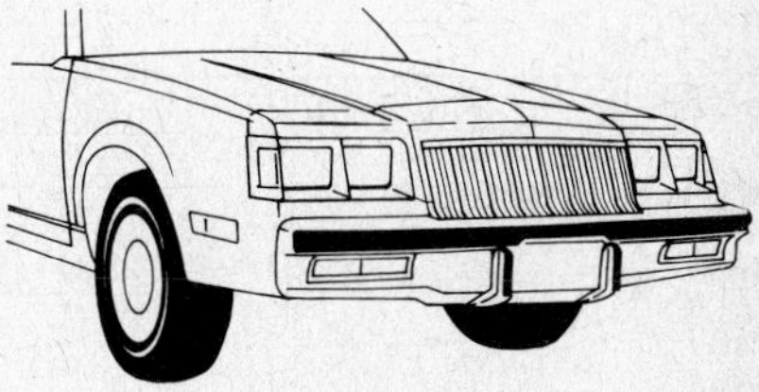

1985–86 Regal

VEHICLE IDENTIFICATION NUMBER (VIN)

The Vehicle Identification Number (VIN) is a seventeen digit number visible through the windshield on the driver's side of the dash and contains the vehicle and engine identification codes. The eight digit identifies the original equipment engine and the tenth digit identifies the model year.

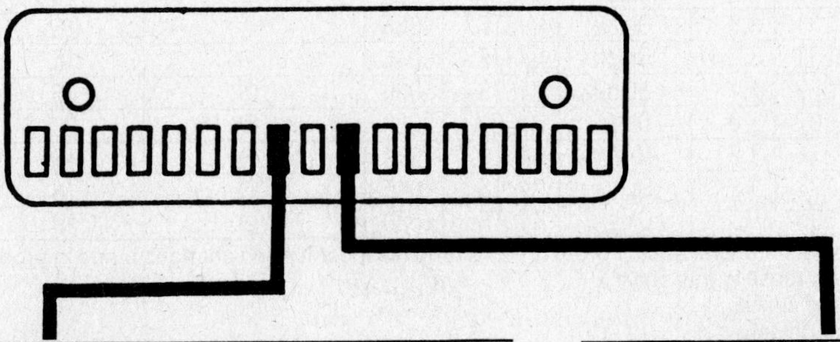

Engine Code

Year	VIN Code	Cu. In.	Liters	Cyl.	Carb. (bbls)	Eng. Mfg.
'83	A	231	3.8	V6	2	Buick
	8	231	3.8	V6	4/Turbo	Buick
	4	252	4.1	V6	4	Buick
	V	263	4.3	V6	Diesel	Olds
	Y	307	5.0	V8	4	Olds

Model Year Code

Code	Year
C	82
D	83
E	84
F	85
G	86

VEHICLE IDENTIFICATION NUMBER (VIN)

The Vehicle Identification Number (VIN) is a seventeen digit number visible through the windshield on the driver's side of the dash and contains the vehicle and engine identification codes. The eight digit identifies the original equipment engine and the tenth digit identifies the model year.

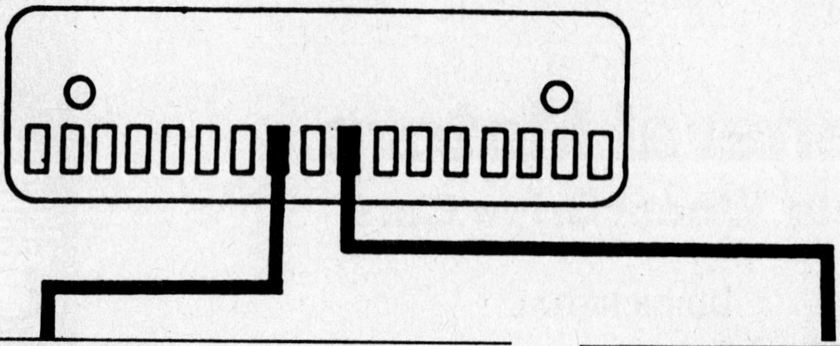

Engine Code

Year	VIN Code	Cu. In.	Liters	Cyl.	Carb. (bbls)	Eng. Mfg.
	N	350	5.0	V8	Diesel	Olds
'84	A	231	3.8	V6	2	Buick
	9	231	3.8	V6	SFI/Turbo	Buick
	4	252	4.1	V6	4	Buick
	V	263	4.3	V6	Diesel	Olds
	Y	307	5.0	V8	4	Olds
	N	350	5.7	V8	Diesel	Olds
'85-'87	A	231	3.8	V6	2	Buick
	9	231	3.8	V6	MFI/Turbo	Buick
	V	263	4.3	V6	Diesel	Olds
	Y	307	5.0	V8	4	Olds
	N	350	5.7	V8	Diesel	Olds
	7	231	3.8	V6	SFI	Buick

MFI—Multiport Fuel Injection (Injectors opened in groups)
SFI—Sequential Fuel Injection (Injectors opened individually)

Model Year Code

Code	Year
H	87

TUNE-UP SPECIFICATIONS
Gasoline Engines

When analyzing compression test results, look for uniformity among cylinders rather than specific pressures

Year	Engine VIN Code	Engine Type	Liters	Engine Manufacturer	Spark Plugs Type ①	Spark Plugs Gap (in.)	Ignition timing (deg. B.T.D.C.) ② Automatic Transmission ④	Intake Valve Opens (°B.T.D.C.)	Fuel Pump Pressure (psi)	Idle Speed (rmp) Automatic Transmission ④
'83	A	6-231	3.8	Buick	R45TS8	.080	③	16	5½-6½	③
	3	6-231	3.8 ⑤	Buick	R45TSX	.060	③	16	5½-6½	③
	4	6-252	4.1	Buick	R45TS8	.080	③	16	5½-6½	③
	Y	8-307	5.0	Olds	R46SX	.080	③	20	5½-6½	③
'84	A	6-231	3.8	Buick	R45TSX	.060	③	16	5½-6½	③
	9	6-231	3.8 ⑥	Buick	R44TS	.045	③	16	26-51	③
	4	6-252	4.1	Buick	R45TSX	.060	③	16	5½-6½	③
	Y	8-307	5.0	Olds	R46SX	.080	③	20	5½-6½	③
'85-'87	A	6-231	3.8	Buick	R45TSX	.060	③	16	5½-6½	③
	9	6-231	3.8 ⑦	Buick	R44TS	.045	③	16	26-51	③
	Y	8-307	5.0	Olds	R45TS	.060	③	20	5½-6½	③

NOTE: The underhood specifications sticker often reflects tune-up specification changes made in production. Sticker figures must be used if they disagree with those in this chart.
B.T.D.C.—Before top dead center
C.I.D.—Cubic inch displacement
Min.—Minimum
Part numbers in this chart are not recommendations by Chilton for any product by brand name.
① All models use electronic ignition systems.
② On some models, the engine must be held at a specific rpm to accurately check and adjust the ignition timing. See the text for specific procedures.
③ On vehicles equipped with computerized emissions systems (which have no distributor vacuum advance unit), the idle speed and ignition timing are controlled by the emissions computer.
④ Manual transmissions not used with 1982 and later Buick rear wheel drive vehicles.
⑤ Turbo
⑥ SFI-Sequential Fuel Injection
⑦ MFI—Multiport Fuel Injection

TUNE-UP SPECIFICATIONS
Diesel Engines

Year	Engine VIN Code	Engine No. of cyl.- Displacement- Manufacturer	Liters	Fuel Pump Pressure (psi) ③	Injection Nozzle Pressure (psi)	Compression Pressure (psi) ②	Injection Pump Setting (deg)	Intake Valve Opens (°B.T.D.C.)	Idle Speed (rpm)
'83-'85	N	8-350-Olds	5.7	5.5-6.5	1225	275 minimum	④	16	①
'83-'85	V	6-263-Olds	4.3	5.8-8.7	⑤	275 minimum	6ATDC	16	①

NOTE: The underhood specifications sticker often reflects tune-up specification changes made in production. Sticker figures must be used if they disagree with those in this chart.

B.T.D.C.—Before top dead center (No. 1 cylinder)

① See the underhood specifications sticker.

② The lowest cylinder reading must not be less than 70% of the highest cylinder reading.

③ Fuel transfer pump pressure given. Injection pump reading should be 8-12 psi @ 1000 rpm taken at injection pump pressure tap.

④ 4ATDC on 1982 and later models

⑤ Injector opening pressure:
New nozzle (green band/no color)—1000 psi
New nozzle (red band)—800 psi
Used nozzle—200 psi less than new

FIRING ORDERS

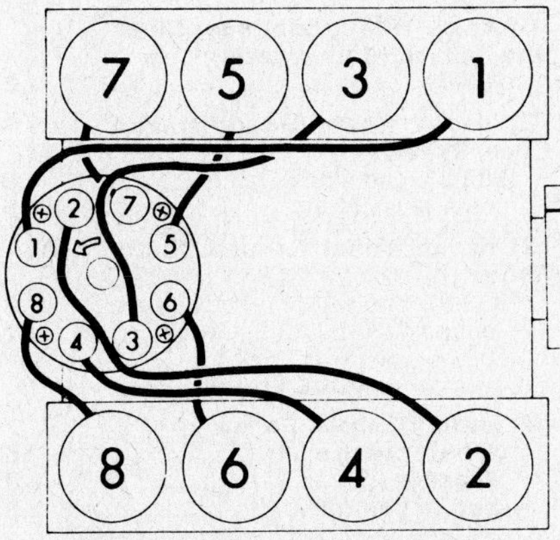

Oldsmobile-manufactured V8 engines
Engine firing order: 1-8-4-3-6-5-7-2
Distributor rotation: counterclockwise

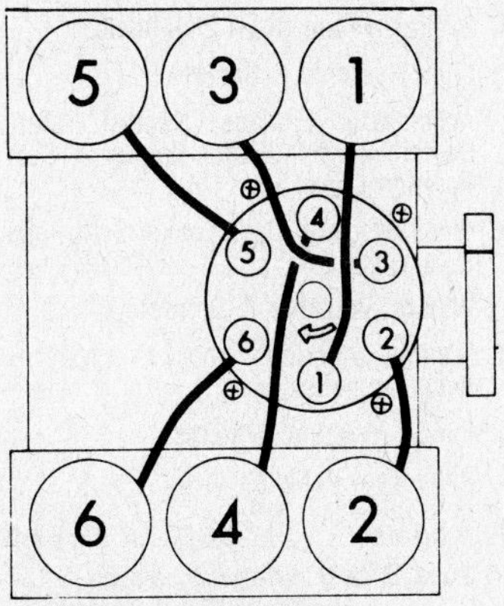

GM (Buick) 231, 252 V6
Engine firing order: 1-6-5-4-3-2
Distributor rotation: clockwise

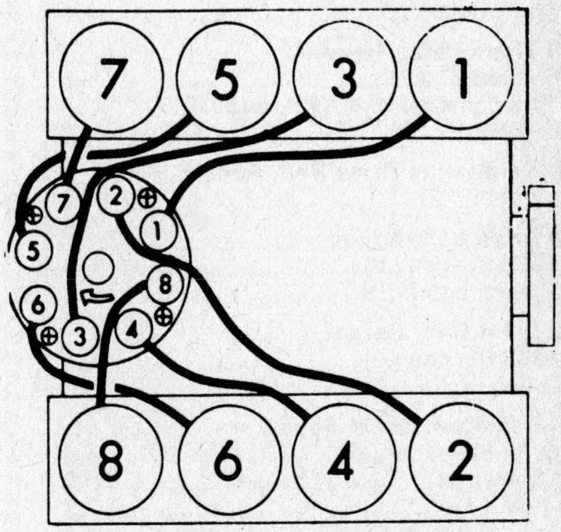

Chevrolet-manufactured V8 engines
Engine firing order: 1-8-4-3-6-5-7-2
Distributor rotation: clockwise

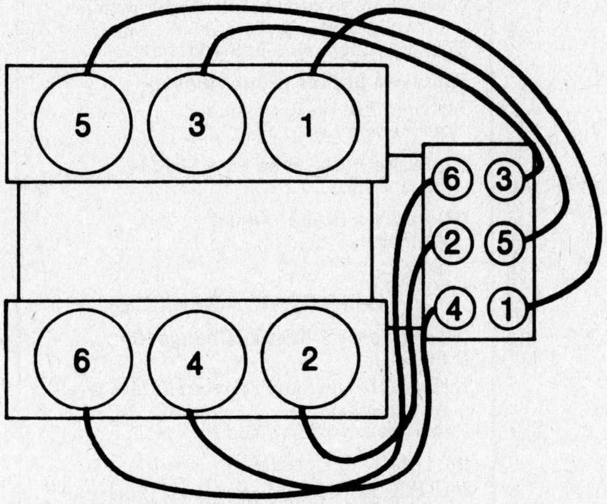

Buick V6 with C3I ignition system
Engine firing order: 1-6-5-4-3-2

WHEEL ALIGNMENT SPECIFICATIONS

Year	Model	Caster Range (deg)	Caster Pref Setting (deg)	Camber Range (deg)	Camber Pref Setting (deg)	Toe-in ① Inch (deg)
'83-'87	Regal	2P to 4P	3P	5/16N to 1 5/16P	1/2P	1/16P to 1/4P (1/8P to 1/2P)
'83-'87	All	2P to 4P	3P	0P to 1 5/8P	13/16P	1/16P to 1/4P (1/8P to 1/2P)

LABOR SERVICE BAY OPERATIONS LABOR

(Factory Time) Chilton Time

COOLING

(M) Winterize Cooling System
Includes: Run engine to check for leaks, tighten all hose connections. Test radiator and pressure cap, drain radiator and engine block. Add anti-freeze and refill system.
All models 5

(M) Thermostat, Renew
V-6–1983-87 (.7) 8
w/Turbocharger and A.I.R. add (.4) 4
V-8–1986-87 (.5) 6

(M) Serpentine Drive Belt, Renew
1983-85 (.2) 4

(M) Drive Belt, Adjust
1983-87-one (.2) 3
each adtnl 1

(M) Drive Belt, Renew
1983-87-one (.3) 4
each adtnl 1

(M) Radiator Hoses, Renew
1983-87-upper (.3) 4
lower (.4) 5
both (.4) 7
by-pass (.6) 8
w/Turbocharger and A.I.R. add (.3) 4

FUEL

(M) Carburetor Air Cleaner, Service
1983-87 (.2) 3

(G) Air Cleaner Vacuum Motor, Renew
1983-87 (.3) 5

(G) Air Cleaner Temperature Sensor, Renew
1983-87 (.2) 3

(G) Carburetor, Adjust (On Car)
Includes: Adjust vacuum brake, choke coil, fast idle and idle speed, dash pot or solenoid.
1983-87
Slow & Fast Idle (.3) 4
Vacuum Brake-one (.4) 6
both (.6) 8
Choke (.6) 1.0
Complete (1.3) 1.8

(G) Automatic Choke Cover and/or Coil, Renew
1983-87 (.6) 1.0

(G) Idle Stop Solenoid, Renew
1983-84 (.3) 4
1985-87 (.7) 1.0

(G) Automatic Choke Vacuum Brake Diaphragm, Renew
1983-87-one (.4) 6
both (.6) 8

CHILTON'S 10 POINT SAFETY CHECK

CHECK OPERATION & CONDITION OF THE FOLLOWING ITEMS:

1. Legal Registration (serial no.)
2. Tires & Wheels
3. Brake System (R&R all wheels)
4. Light Systems & Signals
5. Accelerator Linkage, Neutral Safety Switch, Shift Indicator Pointer & Seat Position Locks
6. Glass, Mirrors, Door Locks, Seat Belts & Harness
7. Wipers, Washers & Defrosters
8. Frame, Steering, Shocks, Front & Rear Suspension
9. Fuel & Exhaust Systems
10. Road Test Vehicle

All models 1.0
Exhaust Smog Analysis, add 4

(Factory Time) Chilton Time

BRAKES

(G) Brakes, Adjust (Minor)
Includes: R&R wheels and adjust brakes thru access holes in drums. Fill master cylinder.
two wheels 4
Remove knock out plugs add, each 1

(G) Bleed Brakes (Four Wheels)
Includes: Fill master cylinder.
All models (.4) 5

(G) Brake Pedal Free Play, Adjust
All models 3

(M) Parking Brake, Adjust
All models (.3) 4

LUBRICATION SERVICE

(M) Lubricate Chassis, Change Oil & Filter
Includes: Inspect and correct all fluid levels.
All models 6
Install grease fittings add 1

(M) Lubricate Chassis
Includes: Inspect and correct all fluid levels.
All models 4
Install grease fittings add 1

(M) Engine Oil & Filter, Change
Includes: Inspect and correct all fluid levels.
All models 4

(Factory Time) Chilton Time

WHEELS

(M) Wheel, Renew
one (.5) 5

(G) Wheels, Balance
one 3
each adtnl 2

(G) Front Wheel Bearings, Clean and Repack (Both Wheels)
1983-87 .... 1.6

(G) Front Wheel Bearings and Cups, Renew
1983-87-one side (.7) 9
both sides (1.1) 1.5

(G) Front Wheel Grease Seals, Renew
1983-87-one whl (.7) 8
both whls (1.1) 1.2

ELECTRICAL

(M) Battery Cables, Renew
1983-87-positive (.4) 6
negative (.2) 3
batt to batt (.2) 3

(M) Battery Terminals, Clean
All models 3

(G) Aim Headlamps
two 4
four 6

(M) Headlamp Sealed Beam Bulb, Renew
1983-87-each (.3) 3

(G) Headlamp Switch, Renew
1983-87 (.3) 5

(G) Headlamp Dimmer Switch, Renew
1983-87
column mounted (.3) 7

(G) Stop Light Switch, Renew
1983-87 (.3) 4

(G) Turn Signal or Hazard Warning Switch, Renew
w/Cruise control add (.1) 1
1983-87 (.7) 1.1

(G) Neutral Safety Switch, Renew
1983-87 (.3) 4

(G) Back-Up Light Switch, Renew
1983-87 (.3) 4

(M) Turn Signal or Hazard Warning Flasher, Renew
1983-87 (.2) 2

(G) Horn Relay, Renew
1983-87 (.2) 3

(G) Horn, Renew
1983-87 (.3) 3

LABOR SERVICE BAY OPERATIONS LABOR

(Factory Time)	Chilton Time
(M) Back-Up Lamp Bulb, Renew	
All models-one (.2)	.3
(M) Cornering Lamp Bulb, Renew	
All models-each (.2)	.3
(M) License Lamp Bulb, Renew	
All models-one or all (.2)	.3
(M) Park and Turn Signal Lamp Bulb, Renew	
All models-each	.2
(M) Side Marker Lamp Bulb, Renew	
All models-each	.2
(M) Stop, Tail and Turn Signal Lamp Bulb, Renew	
All models-one	.2
each adtnl	.1

LABOR 1 TUNE UP 1 LABOR

(Factory Time)	Chilton Time
(G) Compression Test	
V-6–1983-87	*.7
V-8–1986-87	.8
w/A.C. add	.3
*w/Turbocharger add (.4)	.4

(G) Engine Tune Up, (Electronic Ignition)

Includes: Test battery and clean connections. Tighten manifold and carburetor mounting bolts. Check engine compression, clean and adjust or renew spark plugs. Test resistance of spark plug cables. Inspect distributor cap and rotor. Adjust air gap. Check vacuum advance operation. Reset ignition timing. Adjust idle mixture and idle speed. Service air cleaner. Inspect and adjust drive belts. Inspect choke operation and adjust or free up. Check operation of EGR valve.

(Factory Time)	Chilton Time
V-6–1983-87	*2.0
V-8–1986-87	2.5
w/A.C. add	.6
*w/Turbocharger add	1.2
To perform C.C.C. system test add	1.0

LABOR 2 IGNITION SYSTEM 2 LABOR

GASOLINE ENGINES

(Factory Time)	Chilton Time
(G) Spark Plugs, Clean and Reset or Renew	
V-6–1983-87 (.5)	.6
V-8–1986-87 (.5)	.7
To clean add	.3
w/A.C. add (.2)	.3
w/Turbocharger add (.4)	.4
(G) Ignition Timing, Reset	
All models (.4)	.4
(G) Distributor, Renew	
Includes: Reset ignition timing.	
1983-87 (.5)	.8
w/A.I.R. add (.3)	.3
w/Turbocharger add (.3)	.3
(G) Distributor, R&R and Recondition	
Includes: Reset ignition timing.	
1983-87 (.9)	1.4
w/A.I.R. add (.3)	.3
w/Turbocharger add (.3)	.3
(G) Distributor Cap and/or Rotor, Renew	
1983 (.3)	.4
1984-87 (.5)	.7
w/A.I.R. add (.3)	.3
w/Turbocharger add (.2)	.2
(G) Ignition Coil, Renew	
Includes: Test coil.	
1983-87 (.3)	.5
w/A.I.R. add (.3)	.3
w/Turbocharger add (.3)	.3
(G) ESC Knock Sensor, Renew	
1983-87 (.9)	1.3
(G) ESC Module, Renew	
1983-87 (.5)	.7
(G) Ignition Cables, Renew	
1983-87-V-6 (1.0)	1.4
V-8 (.3)	.6
(G) Ignition Switch, Renew	
1983-87 (.4)	.6
w/A.C. add (.1)	.1
(G) Ignition Key Warning Switch, Renew	
1983-87 (.5)	.8
(G) Distributor Module, Renew	
Includes: Test.	
1983-87 (.4)	.6
w/A.I.R. add (.3)	.3
w/Turbocharger add (.3)	.3
(G) Distributor Pick Up Coil and/or Pole Piece, Renew	
Includes: R&R distributor and reset ignition timing.	
1983-87 (.6)	.9
w/A.I.R. add (.3)	.3
w/Turbocharger add (.3)	.3
(G) Distributor Capacitor and/or Module Wiring Harness, Renew	
Includes: R&R dist cap and rotor, reset ignition timing.	
1983-87 (.3)	.6
w/A.I.R. add (.3)	.3
w/Turbocharger add (.3)	.3

DISTRIBUTORLESS IGNITION SYSTEM

(Factory Time)	Chilton Time
(G) Ignition Coil and/or Module, Renew	
1984-87 (.5)	.7
(G) Camshaft Sensor, Renew	
1984-87 (.6)	.9
(G) Crankshaft Sensor, Renew	
1984-87 (.5)	.8

DIESEL IGNITION COMPONENTS

(Factory Time)	Chilton Time
(G) Coolant Fast Idle Temperature Switch, Renew	
All models (.2)	.4
(G) Glow Plug Relay, Renew	
All models (.2)	.3
(G) Fast Idle Solenoid, Renew	
All models (.3)	.4
(G) Glow Plugs, Renew	
All models-one	.4
all-one bank	.7
all-both banks	1.3
(G) Glow Plug Control Module, Renew (Controller)	
All models (.4)	.6
(G) Glow Plug Control Switch, Renew	
All models (.2)	.4
(G) Control Sensor, Renew	
All models (.2)	.3

PARTS 2 IGNITION SYSTEM 2 PARTS

	Part No.	Price
Distributor Assy.		
V-6		
1983-87	◆1103470	351.00
1983-84-Canada	1110766	308.50
1985-87-Canada	◆1103612	262.50
V-8		
1986-87-307	◆1103602	275.00
1983-85-305		
Canada	1103282	308.50
(1) Cover		
V-6		
1983-87	◆1894209	5.75
V-8		
1986-87	◆1875960	5.75
(2) Coil		
1983-87	◆1985474	N.L.
(3) Cap		
V-6		
1983-87	◆1894979	N.L.
V-8		
1986-87	◆1974408	N.L.
(4) Rotor		
1983-87	◆1977026	N.L.
(5) Shaft		
V-6		
1983-87	◆1976930	38.25
V-8		
1986-87	◆1989612	42.25
(6) Pole Piece & Plate Assy.		
V-6		
1983-87	◆1976925	30.00
V-8		
1986-87	◆1977207	31.75
(7) Module		
1983-87	◆1976908	N.L.
(8) Capacitor		
1983-87	◆1876154	4.25
(9) Vacuum Control		
1983-87-		
Canada-V-6	◆1985474	N.L.
V-8	◆1985473	N.L.
(10) Housing		
V-6		
1983-87	◆1976928	36.25
Canada	1876213	43.25
V-8		
1986-87	◆1977208	34.00
Canada-305	1876222	37.00
(11) Harness (Terminal Block)		
1983-87	◆1892261	N.L.
(12) Gear		
V-6		
1983-87	◆1892082	15.25
V-8		
1986-87	◆1988777	21.50
V-6–C31 SYSTEM		
Coil (C31)		
1986-87	◆25526448	109.00
Module (C31)		
1986-87	◆25526449	215.00
Sensor & Drive (Camshaft)		
1986-87	25516915	82.50
Sensor (Crankshaft)		
1986-87	◆25526123	20.25
Spark Plug Wire Set		
Order by year and model.		
Ignition Switch		
(wo/Tilt or tilt/telescopic whl.)		
1983	◆1990109	11.50
1984-87	◆1990115	11.50
(Tilt or tilt/telescopic whl.)		
1983	◆1990110	11.50
1984-87	◆1990116	11.50

LABOR 3 FUEL SYSTEM 3 LABOR

(Factory Time)	Chilton Time
GASOLINE ENGINES	
(G) Fuel Pump, Test	
Includes: Disconnect line at carburetor, attach pressure gauge.	
All models	.2
(M) Carburetor Air Cleaner, Service	
1983-87 (.2)	.3
(G) Air Cleaner Vacuum Motor, Renew	
1983-87 (.3)	.5
(G) Air Cleaner Temperature Sensor, Renew	
1983-87 (.2)	.3
(G) Carburetor, Adjust (On Car)	
Includes: Adjust vacuum brake, choke coil, fast idle and idle speed, dash pot or solenoid.	
1983-87	
Slow & Fast Idle (.3)	.4
Vacuum Brake-one (.4)	.6
both (.6)	.8
Choke (.6)	1.0
Complete (1.3)	1.8
(G) Automatic Choke Cover and/or Coil, Renew	
1983-87 (.6)	1.0
(G) Idle Stop Solenoid, Renew	
1983-84 (.3)	.4
1985-87 (.7)	1.0
(G) Automatic Choke Vacuum Brake Diaphragm, Renew	
1983-87-one (.4)	.6
both (.6)	.8
(G) Carburetor Needle Valve and Seat, Renew	
Includes: Adjust float level.	
All models	
2 bbl (.7)	1.2
4 bbl (.9)	1.5
To perform C.C.C. system check, add (.5)	1.0
(G) Accelerator Pump, Renew	
All models	
2 bbl (.7)	1.0
4 bbl (.8)	1.2
(G) Choke Vacuum Control Switch, Renew	
1983-87 (.3)	.4
(G) Electric Choke Relay, Renew	
1983-84 (.2)	.3
(G) E.F.E. Heater (Insulator), Renew	
1983-87 (.6)	1.0
(G) Carburetor, Renew	
Includes: All necessary adjustments.	
1983-87 (.6)	.9
To perform C.C.C. system check, add (.5)	1.0
(G) Carburetor, R&R and Clean or Recondition	
Includes: All necessary adjustments.	
1983-87-2 bbl (2.3)	3.0
4 bbl (2.5)	3.2
To perform C.C.C. system check, add (.5)	1.0
(G) Carburetor Fuel Filter, Renew	
1983-84-exc. below (.4)	.6
eng code 4 (.6)	.8
1985-87 (.4)	.6
(G) Fuel Pump, Renew	
1983-87	
V-6 (.6)	.8
V-8 (.7)	1.0
w/A.C. add (.2)	.2
w/P.S. add (.2)	.3
w/A.I.R. add (.4)	.4
w/Eng Code Y add (.1)	.1
Add pump test if performed.	
(G) Fuel Tank, Renew	
Includes: Drain and refill tank. Test gauge.	
1983-87 (.7)	1.0
(G) Fuel Gauge (Tank), Renew	
Includes: R&R tank and test gauge.	
1983-87 (.8)	1.1
(G) Water In Fuel Detector, Renew (WIF)	
All models (.9)	1.2
(G) Fuel Gauge (Dash), Renew	
1983-87 (.4)	.7
(G) Intake Manifold and/or Gaskets, Renew	
Includes: Drain and refill cooling system. Make all necessary adjustments.	
V-6–1983 (1.4)	2.4
w/Turbocharger add (1.5)	1.5
1984-87	
eng codes A-4 (1.9)	2.4
eng codes 3-9 (2.2)	3.0
w/A.C. add (.4)	.4
w/A.I.R. add (.1)	.1
V-8–1986-87	
305 eng Code H (2.0)	3.3
307 eng Code Y (2.2)	3.2
w/A.C. add (.1)	.1
w/AIR add (.1)	.1
w/Cruise control add (.2)	.2
Renew manif add	.5

LABOR — 3 FUEL SYSTEM 3 — LABOR

(Factory Time) — Chilton Time

E.F.E. SYSTEM

(G) E.F.E. Valve, Renew
Includes: Disconnect crossover pipe.

1983-87 (.5)	.8

(G) E.F.E. Vacuum Check Valve, Renew

1983-87 (.2)	.4

TURBOCHARGER COMPONENTS

(G) Turbocharger Turbine Housing, Renew
Includes: R&R turbine housing and central housing rotating assembly as a unit. Separate and replace turbine housing.

V-6–1983 (2.4)	3.1
1984-87 (2.2)	3.1

(G) Turbocharger Central Housing Rotating Assembly, Renew
Includes: R&R rotating assy. at compressor housing, transfer turbine housing.

V-6–1983 (2.5)	3.2
1984-87 (2.2)	3.1

(G) Turbocharger Compressor Housing, Renew
Includes: R&R turbine housing and central housing rotating as an assembly.

V-6–1983 (2.4)	3.1
1984-87 (2.1)	3.0

(G) Turbocharger Plenium, Renew
Includes: Drain and refill cooling system. R&R carburetor, transfer E.G.R. manifold and all attaching parts.

V-6–1983 (2.4)	3.1
1984-87 (2.1)	3.0

(G) Turbocharger Outlet Pipe, Renew
Includes: Hoist car, R&R turbocharger inlet pipe.

V-6–1983-87 (.7)	1.3
w/A.C. add (.3)	.3

(G) Turbocharger Inlet Pipe, Renew

V-6–1983-87 (.4)	.6

(G) Turbocharger Carburetor Air Intake Assembly, Renew

V-6–1983-87 (.2)	.4

(G) Turbocharger Vacuum Bleed Valve or Power Enrichment Valve, Renew

V-6–1983 (.5)	.9

(G) Turbocharger Assembly, Renew
Includes: Transfer all necessary parts.

V-6–1983 (2.3)	3.0
1984-87 (1.9)	3.0

(G) Turbocharger Thermo Purge Switch, Renew

V-6–1983 (.4)	.6

(G) Turbocharger Waste Gate Actuator, Renew

V-6–1983-87 (.3)	.5

(G) Turbocharger Waste Gate Elbow, Renew

V-6–1983-87 (.5)	1.0

DIESEL ENGINE

(G) Idle Speed, Adjust

1983-85 (.2)	.4

(G) Air Cleaner, Service

1983-85 (.2)	.4

(G) Air Intake Crossover, Renew

1983-85 (.4)	.6

(G) Injection Timing, Check and Adjust

1983-85 (.7)	.9

(G) Fuel Filter, Renew

1983-85 (.2)	.4

(G) Fuel Supply Pump, Renew

1983-85 (.5)	.8
w/A.C. add (.2)	2

(G) Injection Pump Throttle Shaft Seal, Renew

1983-85 (.8)	1.3

(G) Injection Pump Adapter and/or Seal, Renew

1983-85-V-6 (1.4)	2.1
V-8 (1.8)	2.5

(G) Fuel Injection Pump, Renew
Includes: Pressure and electrical test. Adjust timing.

1983-85-V-6 (1.8)	3.0
V-8 (2.2)	3.4

(G) High Pressure Fuel Lines, Renew

1983-85-one	.8
one-each bank	1.0
all (1.3)	2.5

(G) Injector Nozzle and/or Seal, Renew

1983-85-one (.8)	1.0
one-each side (1.0)	1.3
all-both sides (2.2)	3.0
Clean nozzles add, each	.2

(G) Vacuum Pump, Renew
Includes: Vacuum test.

1983-85	
gear driven (.4)	.6
belt driven (.6)	.8

(G) Fuel Solenoid, Renew

1983-85	
Cav (.3)	.5
V-6 (.6)	.9
V-8 (.5)	.7

(G) Cold Advance Solenoid, Renew

1983-85	
Cav (.6)	.8
V-6 (.7)	1.0
V-8 (.6)	.8

(G) Fuel Injection Head Seal, Renew
Includes: Renew head and drive shaft seals. Renew governor weight retaining ring.

1983-85-V-6 (2.3)	3.5
V-8 (2.7)	3.9

(G) Intake Manifold or Gaskets, Renew

1983-85-V-6 (2.2)	3.0
V-8 (2.9)	3.5
Renew manif add (.2)	.5

FUEL INJECTION

(G) Fuel Injector, Renew

1984-87-one (2.1)	3.1
each adtnl (.1)	.2
Perform balance test add (.4)	.4

(G) Fuel Rail, Renew

1984-87 (2.1)	3.0

(G) Mass Air Sensor, Renew

1984-87 (.2)	.4

(G) Fuel Pressure Regulator, Renew

1984-87 (.3)	.6
Perform balance test add (.4)	.4

(G) Fuel Pump, Renew (In Tank)

1984-87 (.9)	1.2

(G) Idle Air Control Valve, Renew

1984-87 (.2)	.3

(G) Fuel Pump Relay, Renew

1984-87 (.3)	.4

PARTS — 3 FUEL SYSTEM 3 — PARTS

Carburetor Assy. (Rochester)

	Part No.	Price
TWO BARREL CARB		
V-6–231		
1983-Calif.	◆17079205	666.75
Federal	◆17079440	876.50
1984	◆17110332	912.75
1985	17085190	N.L.
1986-87	17086190	N.L.
Canada	17086170	N.L.
FOUR BARREL CARB		
V-6–231		
1983	17079419	997.00
V-6–252		
1983		
THM 200 trans.	17079339	N.L.
THM 350C trans.	17079261	767.25
1984	17110446	934.75
V-8		
1986-87 (307)	17086008	N.L.

Carburetor Minor Repair Kit

	Part No.	Price
V-6–231		
TWO BARREL CARB		
1983-Calif. em.	◆17076129	51.00
Federal em.	◆17076022	28.00
1984	◆17076129	51.00
1985-87	◆17076144	57.75
FOUR BARREL CARBURETOR		
1983	◆17069095	55.00
V-6–252		
1983-84	◆17069095	55.00
V-8		
1986-87 (307)	◆17076141	49.50

Fuel Pump Assy.

	Part No.	Price
V-6–231		
1983-84-231A	◆6471172	N.L.
1985-231A	◆6471368	32.50
231G, 3	◆6471368	32.50
231-9	6472528	133.50
1986-87-231A	◆6472765	37.00
Canada	6472766	33.50

PARTS 3 FUEL SYSTEM 3 PARTS

	Part No.	Price
V-6-252		
1983		
THM 200 trans.	◆6471368	32.50
THM 350C trans.	◆6471172	N.L.
1984	◆6471368	32.50
V-8		
1986-87 (307)	◆6471743	35.00
Canada (305)	◆6470422	24.50
Fuel Tank		
Order by year and model.		
Fuel Gauge		
(Tank Unit)		
1983-85-exc. below	◆25001612	40.00
Sta. wag.	25000758	40.75
1986-87-exc. digital	25001613	40.50
Digital-V-6 (231A)	25091100	87.50
Digital V-8	25090010	51.75
V-6 (231-7) exc. dig.	25090014	116.25
Digital	25090017	116.25
Canada (305)	◆25001612	N.L.
(Instrument Panel Unit)		

Part numbers shown are for pricing reference only. Order by year, engine and gauge style.

	Part No.	Price
1983	6433887	26.25
1984-87 (V-6-231A)		
wo/Console	6433956	50.75
Console	6434106	50.75
1984-87 (V-6-231-9)		
wo/Console	6433953	50.75
Console	6434103	50.75
1984 (V-6-252)		
wo/Console	6433962	50.75
Console	6434106	50.75
Intake Manifold Gasket Kit		
V-6		
1983-87		
Cast iron man.	◆1264924	14.50
Alum. man.	◆25505397	15.75
V-8		
Canada (305)	◆14038088	N.L.
Turbocharger		
1983	25516897	352.25
1984-85	25519874	352.25
1986-87	25527600	385.00
Outlet Pipe		
1983	25513010	83.50
1984-87	25517695	171.00
Inlet Pipe		
1983	25516451	194.00
1984-87	25516238	85.25
Plenum Assy.		
1983	25515253	94.00

	Part No.	Price
Denotation Sensor		
1983-87	◆1997562	37.00
Seal and Bolt Kit (Turbo)		
1983	◆25509647	48.50
(1) Compressor Housing Kit		
1983	25505452	160.00
(2) Center Rotating Housing (Rebuilt)		
1983-87	◆25519876	243.75
1986	25527601	243.75
(3) Housing Kit (Turbo)		
1983	25512719	201.00
(4) Elbow Kit		
1983	25501284	160.00
Elbow Housing Kit (Turbo)		
1984-87	25520377	240.00
(5) Actuator Kit		
1983	25512720	115.00
1984-85	25520375	137.00
1986	25527603	187.00
1986-87	25527603	187.00
Wastegate Solenoid Valve		
1986-87	1997157	13.25
Intercooler		
1986-87	25527604	370.00

PARTS 3 THROTTLE BODY INJECTION 3 PARTS

	Part No.	Price
V-6-231		
Throttle Body Assy.		
1984	22516152	N.L.
1985-87	25519486	186.00
1986-87-Turbo	25525359	180.00
Fuel Pressure Regulator		
1984-87	◆25519368	42.25

	Part No.	Price
Fuel Injector		
1984-87	25519365	85.50
Fuel Rail		
1984-85	25517408	146.00
1986-87	25524302	144.00

	Part No.	Price
Throttle Position Sensor		
1984-87	◆25036658	20.75
Idle Air Control Motor		
1984-87	◆22048225	64.75

PARTS 3 FUEL SYSTEM 3 PARTS

	Part No.	Price
(DIESEL)		
Air Intake Crossover		
V-6-260		
1983	◆22519924	109.00
1984	◆22519924	109.00
Fuel Pump		
V-6-260		
1983	◆6471952	70.00
1984	◆6472153	59.50
V-8-350		
1983	◆6471317	N.L.
Injection Pump Adapter		
V-6-260		
1983-84	◆22516525	52.50
V-8-350		
1983	◆558768	21.75
Fuel Injection Pump		
V-6-260		
1983-wo/Hi alt.	◆22511745	763.00
Hi alt.	◆22518691	763.00
1984-84-exc. below	◆22522524	763.00
Hi alt.	◆22522523	763.00
Calif.	22519881	763.00
V-8-350		
1983-wo/Hi alt.	◆22518686	763.00
Hi alt.	◆22518689	763.00

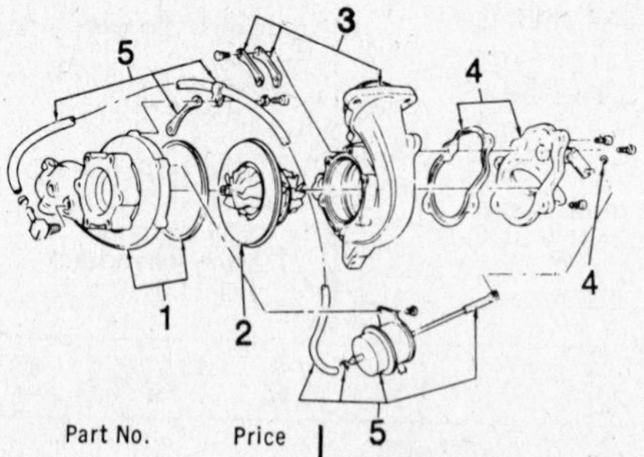

	Part No.	Price
Fuel Injector Nozzle		
V-6-260		
1983	◆22514509	60.00
1984	◆22520376	89.50
V-8-350		
1983	◆22520378	60.00
Vacuum Pump		
V-6-260		
1983-wo/A.C.	◆7844041	115.00
A.C.	◆7844040	115.00
1984-wo/A.C.	◆7844041	115.00
A.C.	◆7844040	115.00
V-8-350		
1983	◆7839413	116.00

	Part No.	Price
Intake Manifold Gaskets		
V-6-260		
1983-84	◆22514872	16.50
V-8-350		
1983	◆22516344	12.00
Fuel Gauge (Tank)		
1983	◆25002566	99.25
Fuel Gauge (Dash)		
1983-wo/ Console	6433391	26.75
Console	6433890	28.25
1984-87-wo/ Console	6433959	50.75
Console	6434109	50.75

(Factory Time) Chilton Time

GASOLINE ENGINES

(G) Emission Control Check

Includes: Check and adjust engine idle speed and mixture and ignition timing. Check P.C.V. valve.

All models 6

POSITIVE CRANKCASE VENTILATION

(M) Positive Crankcase Ventilation Valve, Renew

All models (.2) 3

w/Turbocharger add (.1) 1

(M) Crankcase Ventilation Filter, Renew

All models (.2) 3

EVAPORATIVE EMISSION TYPE

(G) Charcoal Canister, Renew

1983-87 (.2) 3

(G) Canister Purge Thermal Vacuum Switch, Renew

1983-87 (.2) 4

CONTROLLED COMBUSTION TYPE

(G) Air Cleaner Vacuum Motor, Renew

1983-87 (.3) 5

(G) Air Cleaner Temperature Sensor, Renew

1983-87 (.2) 3

EXHAUST GAS RECIRCULATION SYSTEM

(G) E.G.R. Valve, Renew

1983-87

Gas (.4) 6

Diesel (.5) 8

(G) EGR Vacuum Delay Valve, Renew

1983-87 (.2) 3

(G) Thermostatic Vacuum Control Switch, Renew

1983-87 (.3) 4

(G) Thermal Control Valve, Renew

1983-87 (.3) 4

(G) EGR/EFE Thermal Vacuum Switch, Renew

1983-87 (.3) 4

AIR INJECTOR REACTOR TYPE

(G) Air Pump, Renew

1983-87

V-6 (.3) 5

V-8 (.4) 8

(G) A.I.R. Air Cleaner, Renew

1983-87 (.2) 3

(G) Check Valve, Renew (One)

1983-87 (.2) 3

each adtnl 1

(G) Air Pump Centrifugal Fan and/or Filter, Renew

All models (.3) 5

(G) Vacuum Delay Valve, Renew

All models (.2) 3

(G) A.I.R. Drive Belt, Renew

1983-87 (.2) 3

(G) Air Manifold Pipe, Renew

1983-87-each (.6) 9

CHILTON'S EMISSION CONTROL TUNE-UP

1. Clean or renew P.C.V. valve, hoses and filter.
2. Check fuel tank cap for sealing ability.
3. Check fuel tank and fuel lines for leakage.
4. Check evaporation canister and filter. Replace if necessary.
5. Check engine compression to determine leakage of unburned gases. (Add time for items of interference).
6. Test and clean or renew spark plugs.
7. Check engine oil dipstick for sealing ability.
8. Test exhaust system with analyzer and check system for leakage.
9. Check exhaust manifold heat valve for operation.
10. Adjust ignition timing and carburetor idle speed and mixture.
11. Check automatic choke mechanism for free operation.
12. Inspect air cleaner and element.
13. On models so equipped, test distributor vacuum control switch and transmission control switch.

V-6 .... 1.7

V-8 .... 1.8

For repairs made, charge accordingly.

(Factory Time) Chilton Time

(G) Catalytic Converter Air Pipe, Renew

1983-87

one piece (.6) 9

COMPUTER COMMAND CONTROL SYSTEM (C.C.C.)

(P) Throttle Position Sensor, Adjust

All models

2 bbl (.7) 9

4 bbl (.6) 8

Perform C.C.C. system check add 1.0

(P) Electronic Control Module, Renew

Does not include system performance check.

1983-87 (.5) 6

(P) Mixture Control Solenoid, Renew

Does not include system performance check.

1983-87-2 bbl (1.1) 1.4

4 bbl (1.2) 1.5

(P) Prom, Renew

Does not include system performance check. Includes R&R electronic module.

1983-87 (.5) 8

(P) Barometric Sensor, Renew

Does not include system performance check.

1983-87 (.5) 7

(P) Cooling Temperature Sensor, Renew

Does not include system performance check. Include drain and refill cooling system.

1983-87 (.6) 7

(Factory Time) Chilton Time

(P) Manifold Pressure Sensor, Renew

Does not include system performance check.

1983-87 (.5) 6

(P) Oxygen Sensor, Renew

Does not include system performance check.

1983-87 (.6) 7

(P) Throttle Position Sensor, Renew

Does not include system performance check.

1983-87-2 bbl (1.1) 1.4

4 bbl (1.2) 1.5

(P) Back-Up Lamp and Park/Neutral Switch, Renew

Does not include system performance check.

1983-87 (.5) 7

(P) EGR/EFE Purge Solenoid, Renew

Does not include system performance check.

1983-87 (.4) 6

(P) Air Control Valve, Renew

Does not include system performance check.

1983-87 (.4) 6

(P) Air Switching Valve, Renew

Does not include system test.

1983-87 (.4) 6

(P) Air Control/Air Switching Valve, Renew

Does not include system performance check.

1983-87 (.5) 7

(P) Canister Purge Control Valve, Renew

Does not include system performance check.

1983-87 (.4) 6

(P) Air Control Valve Solenoid, Renew

Does not include system performance check.

1983-87 (.5) 8

(P) E.G.R. Vacuum Control Solenoid, Renew

Does not include system performance check.

1983-87 (.3) 5

(P) E.F.E. Vacuum Control Solenoid, Renew

Does not include system performance check.

1983-87 (.3) 4

(P) Vacuum Control Purge Solenoid, Renew

Does not include system performance check.

1983-87 (.3) 5

(P) Idle Speed Control Motor, Renew or Adjust

Does not include system performance check.

1983-87 (.6) 7

(P) Idle Load Compensator, Renew or Adjust

Does not include system performance check.

1983-87 (.4) 6

(P) Vehicle Speed Sensor, Renew

Does not include system performance check.

1983-87 (1.1) 2.0

(P) Tachometer Filter, Renew

Does not include system performance check.

1983 (.3) 3

(P) Computer Command Control System Performance Check

1983-87 (.5) 1.0

LABOR — 3A EMISSION CONTROLS 3A — LABOR

(Factory Time) — Chilton Time

ELECTRONICALLY CONTROLLED EMISSIONS SYSTEM

(P) Electronic Control Module, Renew

1985-87 (.7)	.9

(P) Prom, Renew

1985-87 (.7)	1.0

(P) Coolant Temperature Sensor, Renew

1985-87 (.4)	.7

(P) Manifold Absolute Pressure Sensor, Renew

1985-87 (.5)	.6

(P) Oxygen Sensor, Renew

1985-87 (.5)	.7

(P) Vehicle Speed Sensor, Renew

1985-87 (.7)	1.1

DIESEL ENGINE

(G) Crankcase Depression Regulator Valve, Renew

All models (.2)	.3

(G) Crankcase Ventilation Flow Control Valve, Renew

All models (.2)	.3

(G) Crankcase Ventilation Filter, Renew

All models (.2)	.3

(G) E.G.R. Valve and/or Gasket, Renew

All models (.5)	.8

(G) E.G.R. Control Valve Solenoid, Renew

All models (.2)	.3

(G) E.G.R. Control Valve Switch, Renew

All models (.2)	.3

(G) E.P.R. Control Valve Solenoid, Renew

1983-84 (.3)	.4
1985 (.4)	.6
Renew ECM add	.1

(G) E.P.R. Control Valve Switch, Renew

All models (.3)	.4

(G) E.P.R. Exhaust Pressure Regulator Valve, Renew

1983-84 (.3)	.5
1985 (.5)	.7

(G) Vacuum Regulator Valve, Renew

All models (.6)	.8

PARTS — 3A EMISSION CONTROLS 3A — PARTS

	Part No.	Price

POSITIVE CRANKCASE VENTILATION

Positive Crankcase Valve

	Part No.	Price
V-6		
1983-87	◆6487534	3.00
1986-87-Turbo	25095468	3.75
V-8-350		
1983	◆25041678	34.50
V-8		
1986-87 (307)	◆8997683	N.L.
Canada (305)	◆25040026	N.L.

EVAPORATIVE EMISSION SYSTEM

Canister

	Part No.	Price
V-6		
1983-84-exc. Turbo	◆17064622	39.50
Turbo	17075848	60.00
1985-87-exc. Turbo	◆17064622	39.50
1985-Turbo	17075848	60.00
1986-87-Turbo	◆17085935	44.75
V-8		
1986-87 (307)	◆17064622	N.L.
Canada (305)	17061004	54.50

CONTROLLED COMBUSTION TYPE

Vacuum Motor

	Part No.	Price
1983-85-exc. below	◆8994262	24.50
V-6-260	◆8994333	18.75
V-6-Turbo 231, 252	◆8994333	18.75

Air Cleaner Sensor

	Part No.	Price
1983-84		
V-6-231	◆8997493	18.75
V-6-252	◆8997916	18.75

AIR INJECTOR REACTOR TYPE

Air Pump

	Part No.	Price
V-6		
wo/Turbo		
1983-87	◆7835397	131.00
Turbo		
1983-wo/AC	7836944	192.00
wo/AC	7836179	149.00
V-8		
1986-87-wo/AC	◆7835397	N.L.
AC	◆7838575	N.L.

Manifold Check Valve

	Part No.	Price
1983-85-V-6		
wo/Turbo	◆22040900	N.L.
Turbo	22034706	16.00
1986-Turbo	25525315	7.75
1986-V-8 (307)	◆22040903	13.75

AIR Hoses
Order by model and engine description.

EXHAUST GAS RECIRCULATION (E.G.R.) SYSTEM

EGR Valve
Replacement EGR valves must be ordered according to the stamping number on the original valve.

Thermo-Vacuum Switch (EFE and EGR)

	Part No.	Price
V-6-231		
1983-87	3033795	19.50

COMPUTER CONTROLLED EMISSIONS SYSTEM

The following part numbers are for pricing references only. Order ECM components by the service number displayed on the unit.

Electronic Control Module (ECM)
Remanufactured

	Part No.	Price
V-6-231		
1983-Turbo	◆1226025	110.25
wo/Turbo		
Federal	◆1226024	110.25
Calif.	◆1225500	110.25
1984-87-wo/Turbo	◆1226519	110.25
Turbo	◆1226459	110.25
V-6-252		
1983	◆1225500	110.25
1984	◆1226519	110.25

Calibration Unit (PROM)

	Part No.	Price
V-6-231		
wo/Turbo		
1983-Calif.	◆1226031	40.50
Federal		
Code 0613APK	◆1226297	40.50
Code 3484CDD	◆1226445	40.50
1984-Fed.	◆16041224	40.50
Calif.	◆16041052	40.50
1985-87-Fed.	◆16044104	40.50
Calif.	◆16044109	40.50
Turbo		
1983	1226180	40.50
1984	1227058	40.50
1985-87	16041863	40.50
V-6-252		
1983	1225976	40.50
1984-Fed.	16037649	40.50
Calif.	16037654	40.50

Manifold Pressure Sensor

	Part No.	Price
V-6-231		
1983-87		
Turbo	◆16009886	62.25
wo/Turbo	◆16006835	62.25
V-6-252		
1983-84	◆16006835	62.25
V-8-307		
1986-87	◆16054920	N.L.

Barometric Sensor

	Part No.	Price
1983-87-exc. V-6	16004927	63.75
V-6	◆16006833	62.25

Oxygen Sensor

	Part No.	Price
1983	◆5613959	29.00
1984-87	◆8990741	28.75

Carburetor Mixture Control Solenoid

	Part No.	Price
1983-87	◆17067343	71.00

Coolant Temperature Sensor

	Part No.	Price
1983-84	◆25036092	22.00
1985-87	◆25036708	12.75

Throttle Position Sensor

	Part No.	Price
1983-87	◆17078448	40.50

Air Control Valve

	Part No.	Price
1983-87	◆22034703	12.75

Air Switching Valve

	Part No.	Price
1983-231 Turbo	17071528	47.25

Vehicle Speed Sensor

	Part No.	Price
1983	◆25007227	52.00
1984	◆25007421	41.50
1985-87	◆25007463	44.00

Knock Sensor

	Part No.	Price
1983-87	◆1997562	37.00

LABOR 4 ALTERNATOR AND REGULATOR 4 LABOR

(Factory Time)	Chilton Time
(G) Delcotron Circuits, Test	
Includes: Test battery, regulator, Delcotron output.	
All models	.6
(M) Alternator Drive Belt, Renew	
1983-87	
Gas	
V-6 (.3)	.4
w/AIR add (.1)	.1
V-8	
eng Code H (.2)	.3
w/A.C. add (.2)	.2
eng Code Y (.2)	.3
Diesel	
V-6 (.2)	.4
V-8 (.3)	.4
wo/A.C. add (.1)	.1
(G) Delcotron Assembly, Renew	
Includes: Transfer pulley and fan.	
1983-87 (.4)	.6
w/A.C. and Turbocharger add (.2)	.3
Add circuit test if performed.	
(G) Delcotron, R&R and Recondition	
Includes: Complete disassembly, inspect, test, replace parts as required, reassemble.	
1983-87 (1.2)	1.7
w/A.C. and Turbocharger add (.2)	.3
(G) Delcotron Front Bearing, Renew	
Includes: R&R Delcotron, separate end frames.	
1983-87 (.8)	1.0
w/A.C. and Turbocharger add (.2)	.3
w/Diesel eng add (.1)	.2
Renew rear brg add	.2
(G) Delcotron Voltage Regulator, Test and Renew	
Includes: R&R, disassemble and reassemble Delcotron.	
1983-87 (.8)	1.2
w/A.C. and Turbocharger add (.2)	.3
w/Diesel eng add (.1)	.1
(G) Voltmeter, Renew	
1983-87 (.3)	.5

PARTS 4 ALTERNATOR AND REGULATOR 4 PARTS

	Part No.	Price
Delcotron Assembly		
1983-87 (exc. V-6 Diesel)		
42 amp	◆1105360	206.00
55, 63, 78 amp	◆1100250	225.00
70 amp	◆1105335	265.00
85 amp	◆1105339	326.50
94 amp	◆1105492	228.50
1983-87 (V-6 Diesel)		
42 amp	◆1105357	241.50
63, 78 amp	◆1105369	228.75
94 amp	◆1105480	232.00
(1) Capacitor		
1983-87	◆1978146	4.75
(2) Diode		
1983-87	◆1984459	5.00
(3) Rectifier Bridge		
1983-87-exc. below	◆1984454	28.00
70, 85 amp	◆1975313	24.50
78, 94 amp	◆1987061	29.25
(4) Bearing		
1983-87-exc. below	◆9436831	5.50
70, 85 amp	◆1975322	5.50
(5) Frame, Slip Ring End		
1983-87-exc. below	◆1984460	47.75
70, 85 amp	◆1975310	31.00
94 amp	◆1987073	28.00
(6) Regulator		
1983-87	◆1116387	25.00
(7) Brush Holder & Brush		
1983-87-exc. below	◆1984462	9.00
85 amp	◆1975323	10.00

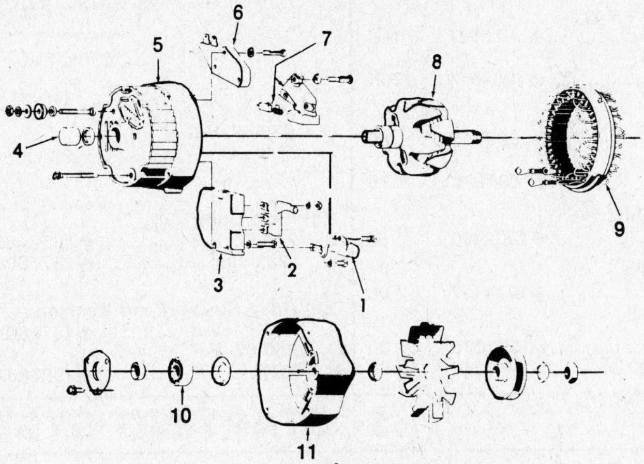

	Part No.	Price
(8) Rotor		
1983-87-exc. below	◆1985476	72.00
70, 80 amp	◆1975333	65.00
78, 94 amp	◆1984466	77.25
(9) Stator		
1983-87-42 amp	◆1986280	52.75
55, 56 amp	◆1984584	54.50
63, 78 amp	◆1984445	37.25
70 amp	◆1975303	48.75
85 amp	◆1975987	83.50
94 amp	◆1987074	41.50
(10) Bearing, Drive End		
1983-87	◆908419	10.00
(11) Frame, Drive End		
1983-exc. below	◆1984464	23.50
42 amp (diesel)	◆1984537	31.50
42 amp (exc. diesel)	◆1985642	24.75
1984-87-70, 85 amp	◆1986590	30.00
78 amp (diesel)	◆1986206	24.00
78 amp (exc. diesel)	◆1984464	23.50
94 amp (diesel)	◆1987997	27.50
94 amp (exc. diesel)	◆1987054	28.00

LABOR 5 STARTING SYSTEM 5 LABOR

(Factory Time)	Chilton Time
(G) Starter Draw Test (On Car)	
All models	.3
(G) Starter, Renew	
V-6–1983-87 (.6)	.9
V-8–1986-87 (.5)	.8
Diesel–1983-85 (.8)	1.1
(G) Starter, R&R and Recondition	
Includes: Turn down armature.	
V-6–1983-87 (1.4)	1.9
V-8–1986-87 (1.3)	1.9
Diesel–1983-85 (1.6)	2.5
Renew field coils add (.2)	.5
(G) Starter Drive, Renew	
Includes: R&R starter.	
V-6–1983-87 (.9)	1.1
V-8–1986-87 (.6)	1.0
Diesel–1983-85 (1.0)	1.4

LABOR 5 STARTING SYSTEM 5 LABOR

	(Factory Time)	Chilton Time
(G) Starter Solenoid Switch, Renew		
Includes: R&R starter.		
V-6–1983-87	(.6)	.9
V-8–1986-87	(.5)	.9
Diesel–1983-85	(.8)	1.1
(G) Neutral Start Switch, Renew		
1983-87	(.3)	.4
(G) Back-Up Lamp and Park/Neutral Switch, Renew		
1983-87	(.3)	.4
(G) Ignition Switch, Renew		
1983-87	(.4)	.6
w/A.C. add	(.1)	.1
(M) Battery Cables, Renew		
1983-87-positive	(.4)	.6
negative	(.2)	.3
batt to batt	(.2)	.3
(M) Battery Terminals, Clean		
All models		.3

PARTS 5 STARTING SYSTEM 5 PARTS

	Part No.	Price
(1) Starter Assy.		
V-6		
1983-84	◆1998234	220.75
1985-87	◆1998516	204.00
V-8–307		
1986-87	◆1998536	180.25
(2) Solenoid Switch		
1983-87	◆1114531	N.L.
(3) Starter Drive Assy.		
1983-87-V-6	◆1875687	N.L.
1986-87-V-8 (307)	◆1984511	23.25
(4) Brush		
1983-87-V-6	◆1906945	.50
1986-87-V-8 (307)	◆1893296	.75
(5) Drive End Bushing		
1983-87	◆1932190	.50
(6) Rear Housing		
1983-87	◆1974157	7.00
(7) Armature		
1983-87-V-6	◆1971568	57.00
252 eng.	◆1970548	52.00

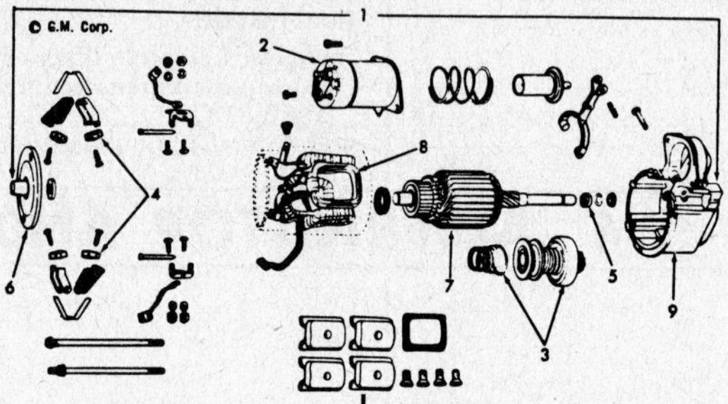

	Part No.	Price
1986-87-V-8 (307)	◆10495931	71.50
(8) Field Coils		
1983-87-V-6	◆1974183	19.25
252 eng.	◆1877306	26.00
(9) Drive Housing and Bushing		
1983-87-V-6	◆1876881	20.50
1986-87-V-8 (307)	◆1987662	25.50

	Part No.	Price
Ignition Switch		
(wo/Tilt or tilt and telescopic strng. whl.)		
1983	◆1990109	N.L.
1984-87	◆1990115	11.50
(Tilt or tilt and telescopic strng. whl.)		
1983	◆1990110	N.L.
1984-87	◆1990116	11.50
Battery Cables		
Order by year and model.		
Starter Neutral Switch		
1983-87	◆22514861	7.00

PARTS 5 STARTING SYSTEM 5 PARTS

STARTING SYSTEM (DIESEL)

	Part No.	Price
Starter Assy.		
1983	◆22522853	355.00
(1) Solenoid Switch		
1983	◆1114531	N.L.
(2) Drive End Bearing		
1983	◆9439544	5.00
(3) Starter Drive		
1983	◆1893445	65.00
(4) Drive Shaft		
1983	◆1972683	29.00
(5) Gear		
1983	◆1972685	12.50
(6) Gear Housing		
1983	◆1972700	29.50
(7) Armature		
1983	◆1987639	139.75
(8) Field Coils		
1983	◆1979982	83.00
(9) Starter Brushes		
1983	◆1852885	2.75
Battery Cables		
Order by year and model.		
Neutral Safety Switch		
1983	◆22514861	7.00

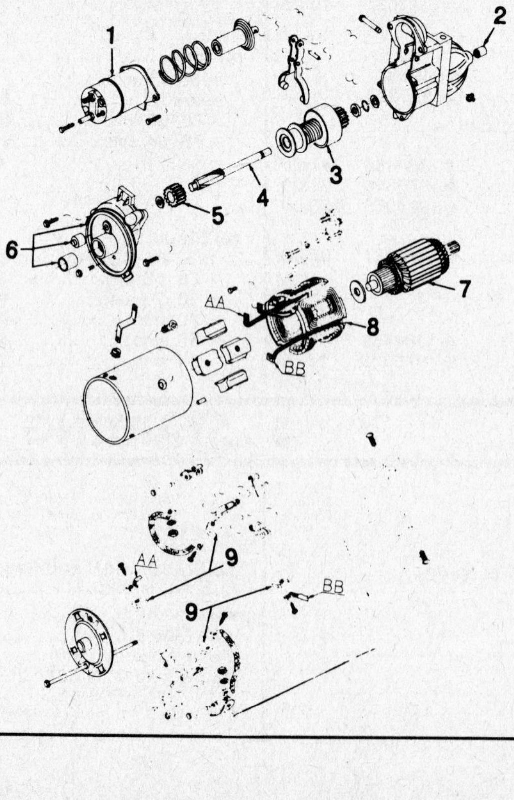

LABOR 6 BRAKE SYSTEM 6 LABOR

(Factory Time) Chilton Time

(G) Brake Pedal Free Play, Adjust
All models 3

(G) Brakes, Adjust (Minor)
Includes: R&R wheels and adjust brakes thru access holes in drums. Fill master cylinder.
two wheels 4
Remove knock out plugs add, each .. .1

(G) Bleed Brakes (Four Wheels)
Includes: Fill master cylinder.
All models (.4) 5

(G) Free-Up or Renew Brake Self Adjusting Units.
one wheel 6
each adtnl 4

(G) Brake Shoes and/or Pads, Renew
Includes: Install new or exchange shoes or pads, adjust service and hand brake. Bleed system.
1983-87-front-disc (.9) 1.1
rear-drum (.9) 1.5
all four wheels 2.5
Resurface disc rotor add, each 9
Resurface brake drum add, each 5

(G) Brake Drum Assembly, Renew (One)
1983-87 (.3) 5

(G) Brake Combination Valve, Renew
Includes: Bleed system.
1983-87 (.7) 1.0

BRAKE HYDRAULIC SYSTEM

(G) Wheel Cylinder, Renew
Includes: Bleed system.
1983-87-one (.8) 1.0
both (1.1) 1.9

(G) Wheel Cylinder, R&R and Rebuild
Includes: Hone cylinder and bleed system.
1983-87-one (1.0) 1.3
both (1.5) 2.1

(G) Brake Hose, Renew
Includes: Bleed system.
1983-87-front-one (.6) 8
both (.8) 1.1
rear-one (.7) 9
powermaster-each (.3) 5

(G) Master Cylinder, Renew
Includes: Bleed complete system.
1983-87 (.6) 1.0

(G) Master Cylinder, R&R and Rebuild
Includes: Hone cylinder and bleed complete system.
1983-87 (1.4) 1.8
w/Powermaster cyl (1.6) 2.2

COMBINATIONS

Add to Brakes, Renew

See Machine Shop Operations

(G) RENEW WHEEL CYLINDER
Each (.2) 2

(G) REBUILD WHEEL CYLINDER
Each (.3) 3

(G) REBUILD CALIPER ASSEMBLY
Each (.5) 6

(G) RENEW MASTER CYLINDER
All models (.6) 8

(G) REBUILD MASTER CYLINDER
All models (.8) 1.0

(G) RENEW BRAKE HOSE
Each (.3) 3

(G) RENEW REAR WHEEL GREASE SEALS
One side (.5) 5

(G) REPACK FRONT WHEEL BEARINGS (BOTH WHEELS)
All models (.6) 6

(G) RENEW BRAKE DRUM
Each (.1) 1

(G) RENEW DISC BRAKE ROTOR
Each (.4) 5

(Factory Time) Chilton Time

(G) Brake System, Flush and Refill
All models 1.2

DISC BRAKES

(G) Brake Shoes and/or Pads, Renew
Includes: Install new or exchange shoes or pads, adjust service and hand brake. Bleed system.
1983-87-front-disc (.9) 1.1
rear-drum (.9) 1.5
all four wheels 2.5
Resurface disc rotor add, each 9
Resurface brake drum add, each 5

(G) Disc Brake Rotor, Renew
Includes: R&R wheel, transfer bearings and races. Clean and repack wheel bearings.
1983-87-one (.7) 1.0
both (1.2) 1.5

(G) Caliper Assembly, Renew
Includes: Remove brake shoes. Bleed complete system.
1983-87-one (.7) 1.0
both (1.1) 1.5

(Factory Time) Chilton Time

(G) Caliper Assembly, R&R and Recondition
Includes: Remove brake shoes, renew parts as required and bleed complete system.
1983-87-one (1.2) 1.5
both (2.1) 2.5

PARKING BRAKE

(M) Parking Brake, Adjust
All models (.3) 4

(G) Parking Brake Warning Lamp Switch, Renew
1983-87 (.3) 4

(G) Parking Brake Control, Renew
1983-87 (.7) 1.0

(G) Parking Brake Equalizer, Renew
1983-87 (.3) 5

(G) Parking Brake Cables, Renew
Includes: Adjust parking brake.
Front
1983-87 (.6) 1.0
Rear
1983-87-one (.8) 1.1

POWER BRAKES

(G) Power Brake Cylinder, Renew
Includes: R&R master cylinder.
1983-87 (.6) 1.1

(G) Power Brake Cylinder, R&R and Recondition
Includes: R&R master cylinder.
1983-87-single cyl (1.1) 1.8
tandem cyl (1.3) 2.0
Recond m/Cyl add (.8) 8

(G) Power Brake Check Valve, Renew
1983-87 (.3) 3

(G) Low Vacuum Switch, Renew
1985-87 (.2) 3

(G) Low Vacuum Brake Indicator Module, Renew
1985-87 (.2) 3

(G) Electro-Hydraulic Pump, Renew
1985-87 (.4) 5

(G) Powermaster Pressure Switch, Renew
1985-87 (.3) 4

(G) Hydraulic Power Brake Cylinder Assy., Renew
Includes: Bleed power steering system.
1983-87 (.6) 1.0
Recond cyl add (.4) 5

PARTS 6 BRAKE SYSTEM 6 PARTS

	Part No.	Price
(1) Brake Shoe Set, Rear		
1983-87-exc. below	◆12300219	41.00
1983-H.D. brks	◆12300214	50.00
(2) Rear Wheel Cyl. Assm.		
1983-87	◆18012303	30.25
Rear Wheel Cyl. Repair Kit		
1983-87	◆18003744	12.75
Front Brake Hose		
1983-87	◆9762810	17.75
Rear Brake Hose		
1983-87	◆9761251	15.00
Master Cyl. Assy.		
1983-exc. below	◆18009816	171.25
Turbo, 350 diesel	◆18009373	134.50
1984-exc. below	◆18009816	171.25
231 Turbo	◆18010591	112.00

PARTS 6 BRAKE SYSTEM 6 PARTS

	Part No.	Price
1985-87-exc.		
below	◆18011916	141.50
350 diesel	◆18009373	134.50
231 Turbo ('85)	◆18010591	111.75
Master Cyl. Repair Kit		
1983-87-exc.		
below	◆18010083	22.75
Turbo, 350 diesel	◆18009375	20.50
Rear Brake Drum		
1983-87-alum.	◆1255496	90.00
cast iron	◆1249146	73.00
Front Wheel Oil Seal		
1983-87	◆3965092	3.00

PARKING BRAKE

	Part No.	Price
Parking Brake Lever/Control		
1983-87	◆25503396	23.25
Parking Brake Cable Front		
1983	◆25502753	11.50
1984-87	◆25520341	11.50
Parking Brake Cable Rear		
1983-R.H.	◆25502794	21.00
L.H.	◆22518169	N.L.
1984-85-R.H.	◆25518168	22.00
L.H.	◆25518169	12.25
1986-87-R.H.	◆25526680	22.00
L.H.	◆25526681	12.25

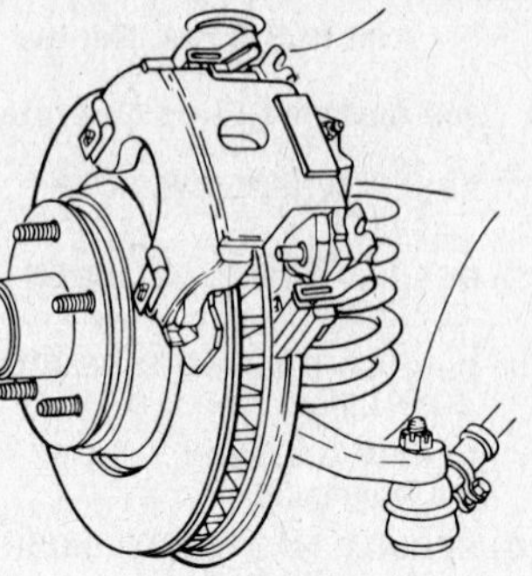

FRONT BRAKE

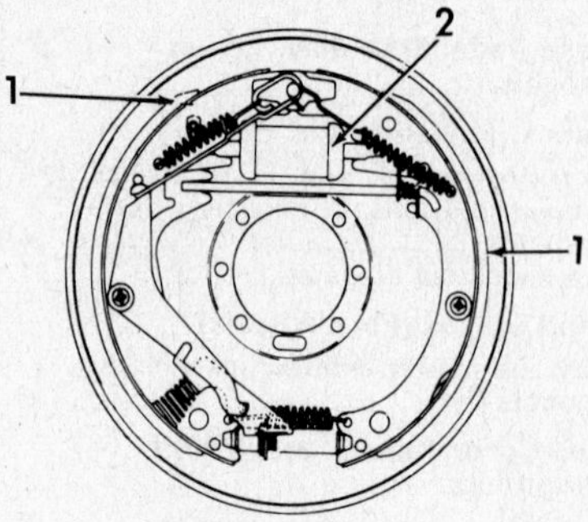

REAR BRAKE

POWER BRAKE UNIT

	Part No.	Price
Power Brake Unit		
1983-87-exc.		
below	◆18010120	271.25
Turbo, 350 diesel	◆25511548	265.00
Power Brake Unit Repair Pkg.		
1983-87-exc.		
below	◆18007897	47.50
Turbo, 350 diesel	◆22506710	16.50

PARTS 6 DISC BRAKES 6 PARTS

	Part No.	Price
(1) Brake Pad Set		
1983-87	◆12300227	43.00
(2) Spring		
1983-87	◆18006810	3.00
(3) Seal Kit		
1983-87	◆18003724	8.75
(4) Piston		
1983-87	◆18003155	11.00
(5) Caliper (R.H.)		
1983-87	◆18010481	148.75
Hub and Disc Assembly (Rotor)		
1983-87	◆14032431	100.25

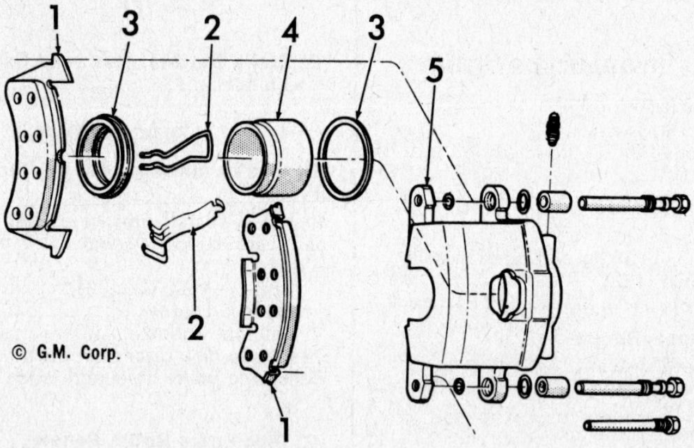

© G.M. Corp.

LABOR 7 COOLING SYSTEM 7 LABOR

	(Factory Time)	Chilton Time
(M) Winterize Cooling System		
Includes: Run engine to check for leaks, tighten all hose connections. Test radiator and pressure cap, drain radiator and engine block. Add anti-freeze and refill system.		
All models		.5
(M) Thermostat, Renew		
V-6–1983-87	(.7)	.8
V-8–1986-87	(.5)	.6
Diesel–1983-85	(.5)	.6
w/Turbocharger and A.I.R. add	(.4)	.4
(M) Radiator Assembly, R&R or Renew		
Includes: Drain and refill cooling system.		
1983-87	(.7)	1.1
w/Diesel eng add	(.2)	.2
w/A.T. add	(.2)	.2
ADD THESE OPERATIONS TO RADIATOR R&R		
(G) Boil & Repair		1.5
(G) Rod Clean		1.9
(G) Repair Core		1.3
(G) Renew Tank		1.6
(G) Renew Trans. Oil Cooler		1.9
(G) Recore Radiator		1.7
(M) Radiator Hoses, Renew		
1983-87-upper	(.3)	.4
lower	(.4)	.5
both	(.4)	.7
by-pass	(.6)	.8
w/Turbocharger and A.I.R. add	(.3)	.4
(M) Drive Belt, Adjust		
1983-87-one	(.2)	.3
each adtnl		.1
(M) Drive Belt, Renew		
1983-87-one	(.3)	.4
each adtnl		.1
(M) Serpentine Drive Belt, Renew		
1983-85	(.2)	.4
(G) Water Pump, Renew		
Includes: R&R fan and pulleys.		
V-6–1983-87	(.9)	1.7
V-8–1986-87	(1.4)	2.0
Diesel–1983-85	(1.7)	2.3
w/A.C. add	(.2)	.2
w/P.S. add	(.1)	.1
w/A.I.R. add	(.1)	.1

LABOR 7 COOLING SYSTEM 7 LABOR

(Factory Time) Chilton Time

(G) Temperature Gauge (Engine Unit), Renew
1983-87-exc. below (.3) .5
eng codes 3-4 (.5) .7

(G) Temperature Gauge (Dash Unit), Renew
1983-87 (.3) .6

(G) Fan Blades or Clutch Assy., Renew
1983-87 (.3) .5

(G) Water Jacket Expansion Plugs, Renew
1983-87-each (.5) .5

Note: If necessary to R&R any component to gain access to plug, add appropriate time.

(G) Heater Hoses, Renew
1983-87-one (.3) .5
both (.4) .7

(G) Heater Core, R&R or Renew
wo/A.C.
1983-87 (.4) .8
w/A.C.
1983-87 (1.3) 2.5

ADD THESE OPERATIONS TO HEATER CORE R&R
(G) Boil & Repair 1.2
(G) Repair Core .9
(G) Recore 1.2

(G) Heater Control Assembly, Renew
1983-87 (.5) .9

(G) Heater Blower Motor, Renew
1983-87 (.3) .5

(G) Heater Blower Motor Resistor, Renew
1983-87 (.2) .3

(G) Heater Blower Motor Switch, Renew
1983-87 (.4) .6

(G) Heater Water Control Valve, Renew
1983-87 (.4) .5
1983-87-Diesel (.6) .8

(G) Heater Blower Motor Relay, Renew
1983-87 (.2) .3

PARTS 7 COOLING SYSTEM 7 PARTS

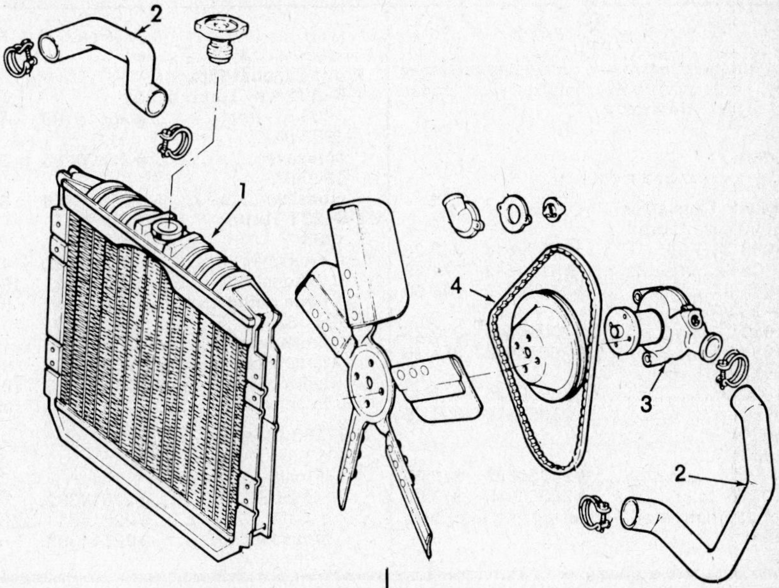

	Part No.	Price
(1) Radiator Assy.		
In order to determine an exact replacement radiator from the manufacturer, it is necessary to obtain the two-letter code from the existing radiator. The radiator code is stamped either on the radiator or on a metal tag attached to the radiator. Order by year, model and radiator code.		
(2) Radiator Hoses		
Order by year and model.		
(3) Water Pump Assembly		
V-6-231, 252		
1983-85	◆1260709	61.75
1986-87	◆25527536	N.L.
V-6-260 Diesel		
1983-87	◆22514839	95.75
V-8-350 Diesel		
1983	◆556283	95.00
V-8-307		
1986-87	◆556283	N.L.
(4) Fan Belts		
Order by year and model.		
Temperature Sending Unit		
1983-87-exc. below	◆25036371	8.00
V-6 diesel	◆25036629	9.75
V-8-307		
1986-87	◆25036629	9.75
Fan Drive Clutch		
V-6-231, 252		
1983-87		
(Code TS)	◆22008490	84.50
(Code TT, TU)	◆22008492	87.50
V-6-260 Diesel		
1983-87-exc. H.D.C.	◆22517701	80.50
H.D.C.	22514197	72.00
V-8-350 Diesel		
1983-exc. H.D.C.	◆22008668	N.L.
V-8-307		
1986-87	◆22049774	N.L.
H.D.C.	◆561826	122.00
Heater Core		
1983-87-wo/A.C.	◆3037852	55.75
A.C.	◆3037689	70.00
Turbo-A.C.	3056515	55.50
Blower Motor		
wo/A.C.		
1984-87	◆22048573	45.75
A.C.		
1983-87	◆22020945	60.00
Heater Water Control Valve		
1983-87-exc. below	370178	20.00
V-6 engs.	◆14032007	22.50
Turbo	25523118	19.25
350 diesel eng.	◆22502236	18.00
Switch, Heater Blower		
1983-87	◆16015256	6.00

LABOR 8 EXHAUST SYSTEM 8 LABOR

(Factory Time) Chilton Time

(G) Muffler, Renew
1983-87 (.4) .7

(G) Tail Pipe or Resonator, Renew
1983-87 (.4) .7

(G) Catalytic Converter, Renew
1983-87 (.8) 1.0
w/AIR add (.1) .1

LABOR 8 EXHAUST SYSTEM 8 LABOR

(Factory Time)	Chilton Time
(G) Exhaust Crossover Pipe, Renew	
1983-87-Gas (.4)	.9
Diesel (1.4)	1.8
(G) Exhaust Intermediate Pipe, Renew	
Includes: Cut at muffler.	
1983-87 (.5)	.7
(G) Front Exhaust Pipe, Renew (To Converter)	
1983-87 (.5)	.8
w/AIR add (.1)	.1
(G) Turbocharger Outlet Pipe, Renew	
1983-87 (.7)	1.3
w/A.C. add (.3)	.3
(G) Turbocharger Inlet Pipe, Renew	
1983-87 (.4)	.6
(G) E.F.E. Valve Assy., With Actuator, Renew	
Includes: Disconnect crossover pipe.	
1983-87 (.5)	.8
(G) Exhaust Manifold, Renew	
V-6–1983-each (.7)	1.1
w/Turbocharger add (.6)	.6
1984-87	
eng codes A-4	
each (1.0)	1.5
eng codes 3-9	
each (1.0)	1.5
V-8–1986-87	
305 eng Code H	
right side (1.3)	2.1
left side (1.0)	1.4
w/A.C. add (.4)	.4
w/C.C.C. add (.1)	.1
307 eng Code Y	
right side (1.1)	1.6
left side (1.0)	1.5
Diesel	
V-6-1983-85	
right side (.9)	1.3
left side (.9)	1.3
V-8	
1983-right (.9)	1.3
left (.7)	1.1
1984-87	
right side (1.2)	1.7
left side (.7)	1.1
w/A.C. add (.4)	.4
w/P.S. add (.2)	.2

COMBINATIONS

(Factory Time)	Chilton Time
(G) Exhaust System, Renew (Complete)	
1983-87-V-6 (.8)	1.3
V-8 (1.0)	1.5
w/AIR add	.1

PARTS 8 EXHAUST SYSTEM 8 PARTS

Part numbers shown are for pricing reference only. Order parts with complete year, engine and model information.

Muffler
Order by year and model.

	Part No.	Price
Catalytic Converter		
V-6-231 wo/Turbo		
1983-84-Fed.	◆8999615	312.25
Calif.	◆8999642	271.25
1985-87	◆25056912	348.00
V-6-231 Turbo		
1983	◆25056345	319.25
1984-87	◆25056546	357.25
V-6-252		
1983	◆8999596	N.L.
1984	25056620	305.25
V-8-307		
1986-87		
Fed.	◆25056632	340.00
Calif.	◆25056345	319.00

Tailpipes not listed above are included with muffler.

	Part No.	Price
Front Exhaust Pipe		
V-6-231 wo/Turbo & 252		
1983-87-front	◆25515198	14.50
1983-84-crossover	◆25506286	31.25
1985-87-crossover	◆25516456	31.25
V-6-231 Turbo		
1983		
crossover	25509232	49.25
turbo inlet	25513011	194.00
turbo outlet	25513010	83.50
1984-87		
crossover	25515323	49.25
turbo inlet	25516238	85.25
turbo outlet	25517695	171.00
to converter	25518391	108.00
V-6-260 Diesel		
1983-84		
(Front)		
Fed.	◆22514392	14.50
Calif.	◆22514311	14.50
crossover	◆22514308	16.75
V-8-350 Diesel		
1983-R.H.	◆563056	41.25
L.H.	◆22504832	19.00
V-8-307		
1986-87		
crossover	◆22504709	74.25
manifold	◆22519894	41.25
Intermediate Exhaust Pipe		
V-6-231 wo/Turbo & 252		
1983	◆25505734	51.50
1984-87	◆25515196	53.00
V-6-231 Turbo		
1983-single exh.	25506725	53.00
dual exh.	◆25509922	N.L.
1984-87-frt.	25518391	108.00
rear R.H.	25520012	27.00
rear L.H.	25520013	27.00
V-6-260 Diesel		
1983-84	◆22515643	42.75
V-8-350 diesel		
1983	◆22505893	58.75
V-8-307		
1986-87	◆22521646	29.00

LABOR 9 FRONT SUSPENSION 9 LABOR

Note: On all front suspension operations alignment charges must be added if performed. Time given does not include alignment.

(Factory Time)	Chilton Time
(M) Wheel, Renew	
one (.5)	.5
(G) Wheels, Rotate (All)	
All models	.5
(G) Wheels, Balance	
one	.3
each adtnl	.2
(G) Check Alignment of Front End	
All models	.5
Note: Deduct if alignment is performed.	
(G) Toe-In, Adjust	
All models (.4)	.6
(G) Align Front End	
Includes: Adjust front wheel bearings.	
All models (.7)	1.4
w/eng code A add	.2
w/A.C. interference add	.5
(G) Front Wheel Bearings, Clean and Repack (Both Wheels)	
1983-87	1.6
(G) Front Wheel Bearings and Cups, Renew	
1983-87-one side (.7)	.9
both sides (1.1)	1.5
(G) Front Wheel Grease Seals, Renew	
1983-87-one whl (.7)	.8
both whls (1.1)	1.2
(G) Front Shock Absorber, Renew	
1983-87-one (.3)	.4
both (.4)	.7
(G) Rebuild Front Suspension	
Includes: Disassemble, renew necessary parts, reassemble, lubricate and align front end.	
1983-87-one side (3.4)	4.0
both sides (5.2)	6.5
(G) Upper Ball Joint, Renew	
Add alignment charges.	
1983-87-one (.7)	.9
both (1.2)	1.7
(G) Lower Ball Joint, Renew	
Add alignment charges.	
1983-87-one (.6)	.9
both (1.0)	1.7

LABOR 9 FRONT SUSPENSION 9 LABOR

(Factory Time) Chilton Time

(G) Steering Knuckle, Renew
Add alignment charges.
1983-87-one (1.0) 1.4
both (1.8) 2.5

(G) Upper Control Arm, Renew (One)
Add alignment charges.
1983-87 (.7) 1.2

(G) Lower Control Arm, Renew (One)
Add alignment charges.
1983-87 (1.0) 1.5

(G) Upper Control Arm Bushings, Renew
Add alignment charges.
1983-87-one side (1.0) 1.5
both sides (1.8) 2.9

(G) Lower Control Arm Bushings, Renew
Add alignment charges.
1983-87-one side (1.2) 1.7
both sides (2.3) 3.3

(G) Front Coil Spring, Renew (One)
Add alignment charges.
1983-87 (.9) 1.4

(G) Front Stabilizer Bar and Bushings, Renew
1983-87 (.7) 8

(G) Stabilizer Links or Bushings, Renew
1983-87-one (.3) 4
both (.4) 6

(G) Control Arm Bumpers, Renew (Upper or Lower)
1983-87-one side (.2) 4

PARTS 9 FRONT SUSPENSION 9 PARTS

	Part No.	Price
(1) Front Wheel Bearing (Outer)		
1983-87	◆14066918	11.75
(2) Front Wheel Bearing (Inner)		
1983-87	◆7450630	11.00
(3) Front Seal Assy.		
1983-87	◆3965092	3.50
(4) Steering Knuckle (R.H.)		
1983-87	◆14012602	117.00
(5) Ball Joint Pkg. (Lower)		
1983	◆9767281	31.50
1984-87	◆9767281	31.50
(6) Control Arm (Lower)		
1983-87-R.H.	◆14045078	92.50
L.H.	◆14075337	96.75
(7) Bushing (Lower Arm)		
1983-87	◆461853	6.25
(8) Shock Absorber		
1983-84	22046439	24.50
1986-87-H.D.	◆22046440	24.50
(9) Coil Spring		
Order by year and model.		
(10) Ball Joint (Upper)		
1983-87	◆9767112	34.75
(11) Bushing (Upper Arm)		
1983-87	◆473786	5.25
(12) Control Arm (Upper)		
1983-87-R.H.	◆14039012	97.75
L.H.	◆14039011	97.75

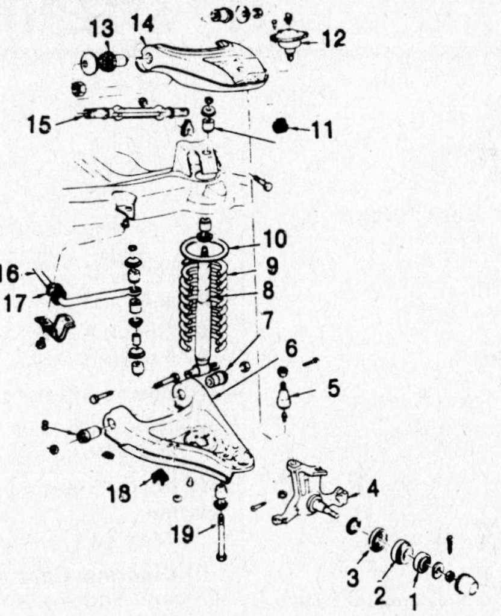

	Part No.	Price
(13) Shaft Pkg. (Upper Control)		
1983-87	◆474001	33.75
(14) Bushing (Stabilizer)		
1983-87		
18mm I.D.	◆392592	1.00
20-23mm I.D. (1983-87)	◆370283	1.00
25mm I.D.	◆371773	1.00
27mm I.D.	◆472117	2.00
30mm I.D.	◆472118	2.00
(15) Link Pkg.		
1983-87	◆470147	4.25

LABOR 10 STEERING LINKAGE 10 LABOR

(Factory Time) Chilton Time

(G) Tie Rods or Tie Rod Ends, Renew
Includes: Reset toe-in.
1983-87-one side (.7) 1.0
both sides (.8) 1.4

(G) Inner Tie Rods, Renew
Includes: Reset toe-in.
1983-87-one side (.7) 1.0
both sides (.8) 1.2

(G) Idler Arm, Renew
Includes: Reset toe-in.
1983-87 (.7) 1.0

(G) Pitman Arm, Renew
Note: Does not require toe-in readjustment.
1983-87 (.4) 7

(G) Intermediate Rod, Renew
Includes: Reset toe-in.
1983-87 (.8) 1.2

PARTS 10 STEERING LINKAGE 10 PARTS

	Part No.	Price
(1) Idler Arm Assy.		
1983-87	◆7837635	51.00
(2) Tie Rod Assy. (Inner)		
1983-87	◆7837183	40.25
(3) Tie Rod End (Outer)		
1983-87	◆7837733	40.00
(4) Tie Rod Sleeve Kit (Adjuster)		
1983-87	◆7829465	15.75
(5) Seal		
1983-87	◆5693125	2.75
(6) Pitman Arm Assy.		
1983-87	◆7837648	44.00
(7) Seal		
1983-87	◆5693125	2.75
(8) Relay Rod Assy.		
1983-87	◆7835787	79.75

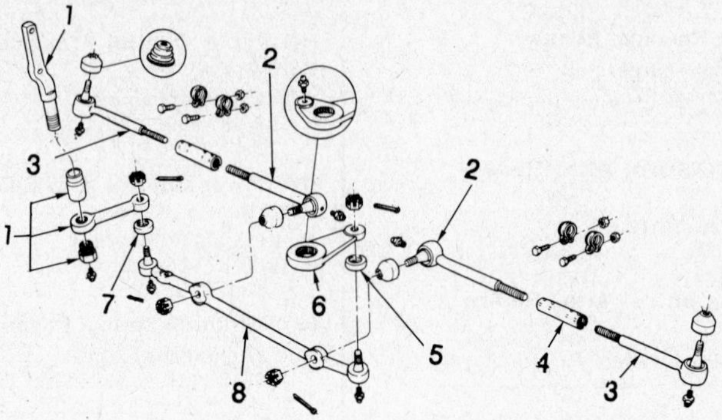

LABOR 11 STEERING GEAR 11 LABOR

(Factory Time)	Chilton Time
(G) Steering Wheel, Renew	
1983-87 (.3)	.4
(G) Horn Contact or Cancelling Cam, Renew	
1983-87 (.5)	.6
(G) Multifunction Lever, Renew	
All models (.2)	.4
w/Cruise control add (.5)	.5
(G) Steering Column Lock Actuator Parts, Renew	
1983-87	
std colm (1.0)	1.5
tilt colm (1.2)	1.7
(G) Steering Column Shift Bowl, Renew	
Includes: R&R steering wheel and turn signal housing support assy.	
1983-85-std column (1.0)	1.6
tilt column (1.7)	2.3
1986-87-std column (1.0)	1.5
tilt column (2.0)	3.0
(G) Flexible Coupling, Renew	
1983-84 (.5)	.7
(G) Upper Mast Jacket Bearing, Renew	
1983-85-std column (.8)	1.4
tilt column (.9)	1.6
1986-87-std column (.8)	1.4
tilt column (.5)	.9

POWER STEERING

(Factory Time)	Chilton Time
(G) Trouble Shoot Power Steering	
Includes: Test pump and system pressure. Check pounds pull on steering wheel and check system for leaks.	
All models	.5
(M) Pump Drive Belt, Renew	
1983-87	
V-6	
Gas (.5)	.6
Diesel (.2)	.4
V-8	
Gas	
eng Code H (.3)	.4
eng Code Y (.4)	.5
Diesel (.3)	.4
w/A.C. add (.3)	.3
w/A.I.R. add (.1)	.1
(M) Check Reservoir and Add Fluid	
All models	.2
(G) Power Steering Gear, Adjust	
Includes: R&R gear assy.	
1983-87	1.2
(G) Power Steering Gear Assembly, Renew	
1983-87 (.7)	1.2
(P) Steering Gear Assy., R&R and Recondition	
Includes: Disassemble, renew necessary parts, reassemble and adjust.	
1983-87 (1.7)	2.5
(G) End Cover and/or Seal, Renew	
Includes: R&R gear assy.	
1983-87 (.8)	1.4
(G) Pitman Shaft or Bearing, Renew	
Includes: R&R gear assy.	
1983-87 (.9)	1.5
(G) Adjustor Plug, R&R and Recondition	
Includes: R&R gear assy.	
1983-87 (.9)	1.6
(G) Valve Body, Renew or Recondition	
Includes: R&R gear assy.	
1983-87 (1.0)	1.8
(G) Rack Piston and Worm Shaft, Renew	
Includes: R&R gear assy.	
1983-87 (1.1)	2.0
(G) Gear Housing, Renew	
Includes: R&R gear assy.	
1983-87 (1.1)	1.8
(G) Pitman Shaft Seal, Renew	
Does not include R&R gear.	
1983-87 (.5)	1.0
(G) Power Steering Oil Pump, Renew	
1983-87-V-6 (.5)	.9
V-8 (.7)	1.4
Diesel (.9)	1.4
w/Turbocharger add (.2)	.2
(P) Power Steering Pump, R&R and Recondition	
Includes: R&R reservoir.	
1983-87-V-6 (1.0)	1.7
V-8 (1.2)	2.2
Diesel (1.4)	2.2
w/Turbocharger add (.2)	.2
(G) Power Steering Pump Seal, Renew	
Includes: R&R pump pulley.	
1983-87-V-6 (.6)	1.0
V-8 (.5)	1.5
Diesel (.9)	1.5
w/A.C. add (.2)	.2
(G) Pump Flow Control Valve, Renew	
1983-87 (.4)	.7
(G) Power Steering Reservoir, Renew	
1983-87 (.3)	.5
(M) Power Steering Hoses, Renew	
1983-87-each (.4)	.6
w/Eng Code A add (.1)	.1
(M) Hydra-Boost Hoses, Renew	
1983-85	
Booster to pump (.6)	1.0
Booster to gear (.3)	.5
Return (.3)	.5

TILT COLUMN

(Factory Time)	Chilton Time
(G) Tilt Column, R&R and Recondition	
1983-87 (2.5)	3.2

PARTS 11 POWER STEERING GEAR 11 PARTS

	Part No.	Price
(1) Seal (Side Cover)		
1983-87	◆7817486	9.00
(2) Pitman Shaft (w/Gear)		
1983-87-Variable	◆7813631	87.50
wo/Variable	◆7815885	87.50
(3) Check Valve Kit		
1983-87	◆7834284	5.25
(4) Bearing Kit		
1983-87	◆7826850	11.00
(5) Housing Assy.		
1983-H.D.	◆7834141	183.00
H.D. susp.	◆7834145	183.00
1984-87	◆7834145	183.00
(6) Bearing (Pitman Shaft)		
1983-87	◆5697804	15.00
(7) Seal Kit (Pitman Shaft)		
1983-87	◆7826470	17.00
(8) Seal (Adjuster Plug)		
1983-87	◆5686527	1.50
(9) Bearing Assy. (Adjuster Plug)		
1983-87	◆7828012	7.25
(10) Plug Assy. (Adjuster)		
1983-87	◆7832731	53.50
Refer to note with item (9)		
(11) Seal Kit		
1983-87	◆5687182	12.50
(12) Valve Assy.		
(wo/H.D. Suspension)		
1983-87	◆7832058	212.00
(H.D. Suspension)		
1983-87	◆7832057	212.00
(14) Seal Kit		
1983-87	◆7817485	6.50
(15) Plug		
1983-V-6 eng.	◆7806688	9.25
V-8 eng.	◆5693463	7.25
1984-87	◆5693463	7.25
(16) Rack Assy.		
1983-87-exc. below	◆7817528	162.00
H.D. susp.	◆7827170	154.25
Touring susp.	◆7839019	162.00

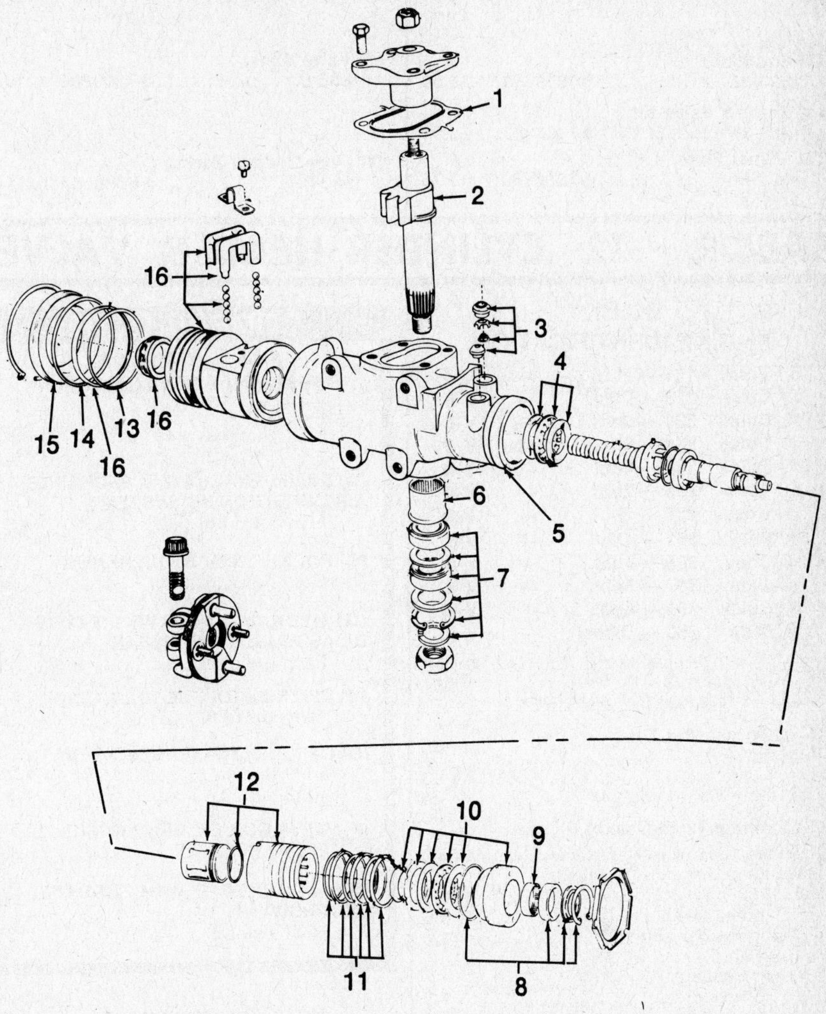

PARTS 11 POWER STEERING PUMP 11 PARTS

POWER STEERING PUMP

	Part No.	Price
Pressure Line Hose		
Order by year and model.		
Power Steering Pump Assy.		
V-6-231 wo/Turbo & 252		
1983-87	◆7839345	199.00
V-6-231 Turbo)		
1983-85-1st design	7841536	199.00
1985-2nd design	◆7839795	199.00
1986-87	26000355	199.00
V-6-260 Diesel		
1983-85	◆7842625	199.00
V-8 350 Diesel		
1983	◆7839997	199.00
V-8-307		
1986-87	◆7840244	199.00
(1) Pressure Plate		
1983-87	◆7839669	14.25
(2) Pressure Plate Spring		
1983-87	◆7839667	1.00

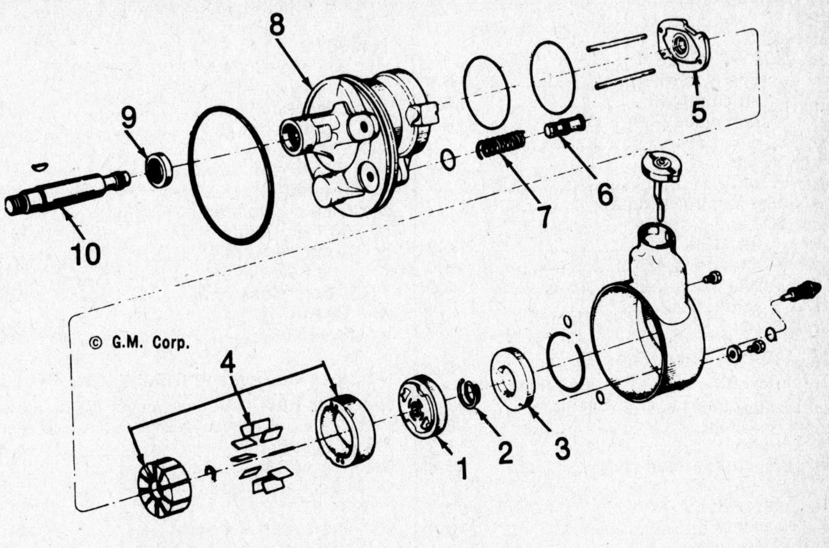

PARTS 11 POWER STEERING PUMP 11 PARTS

	Part No.	Price
(3) End Plate		
1983-87	◆5689358	3.50
(4) Rotor & Valve Kit		
1983-87	◆7837322	75.00
(5) Thrust Plate		
1983-87	◆7836369	13.75
(6) Valve Assy.		
1983-87	◆7809232	10.75
(7) Flow Control Spring		
1983-87	◆5688037	1.50
(8) Pump Assy.		
1983-87	◆7842625	199.00
(9) Drive Shaft Seal		
1983-87	◆7808195	4.50
(10) Drive Shaft		
1983-87	◆7837321	39.50

LABOR 12 CYLINDER HEAD & VALVE SYSTEM 12 LABOR

BUICK ENGINE IDENTIFICATION

5	Pont.	151 — 2bbl	—	L-4
7	Chev.	173 — 2bbl	—	V-6
A	Buick	231 — 2bbl	—	V-6
3	Buick	231 — 4bbl	(turbo)	V-6
4	Buick	252 — 4bbl	—	V-6
S	Pont.	265 — 2bbl	—	V-8
J	Chev.	267 — 2bbl	—	V-8
W	Pont.	301 — 4bbl	—	V-8
H	Chev.	305 — 4bbl	—	V-8
Y	Olds.	307 — 4bbl	—	V-8
B	Buick	350 — 4bbl	—	V-8
N	Olds.	350 — Diesel	—	V-8

(Factory Time) — Chilton Time

GASOLINE ENGINES

(G) Compression Test

V-6–1983-87	*.7
w/A.C. add	.3
*w/Turbocharger add (.4)	.4

(G) Cylinder Head Gasket, Renew

Includes: Clean gasket surfaces, clean carbon, make all necessary adjustments.

V-6–1983-one (3.2)	4.3
both (4.4)	5.9
w/Turbocharger add (1.6)	1.6
1984-87	
eng codes A-4	
one (4.4)	5.8
both (5.3)	7.6
eng codes 3-9-7	
one (4.8)	6.6
both (5.5)	7.5
w/A.C. add (.5)	.5
w/P.S. add (.3)	.3
w/A.I.R. add (.2)	.2
V-8	
1986-87	
305 eng-Code H	
right side (5.0)	6.9
left side (4.6)	6.3
both sides (7.0)	9.6
w/A.C. add (.5)	.5
w/P.S. add (.3)	.3
w/AIR add (.2)	.2
w/Cruise control add (.2)	.2
307 eng-Code Y	
right side (4.0)	5.5
left side (4.4)	6.0
both sides (5.8)	8.0
w/A.C. add (.4)	.4
w/AIR add (.5)	.5

(G) Cylinder Head, Renew

Includes: Transfer all parts, reface valves, make all necessary adjustments.

V-6–1983-one (3.8)	5.1
both (5.5)	7.3
w/Turbocharger add (1.6)	1.6
1984-87	
eng codes A-4	
one (4.9)	6.6
both (5.9)	9.1

COMBINATIONS
Add To Valve Job
See Machine Shop Operations

(Factory Time) — Chilton Time

(G) DRAIN, EVACUATE & RECHARGE AIR CONDITIONING SYSTEM	
All models (.5)	1.0
(G) ROCKER ARM STUD, RENEW	
Each (.3)	.3
(G) HYDRAULIC VALVE LIFTERS, DISASSEMBLE AND CLEAN	
Each (.2)	.2
(G) DISTRIBUTOR, RECONDITION	
All models (.5)	.8
(G) CARBURETOR, RECONDITION	
2 bbl	1.2
4 bbl	1.5
(P) VALVE GUIDES, REAM OVERSIZE	
Each (.2)	.2
(G) ROCKER ARM SHAFT, RECONDITION	
Each side (.2)	.3

(Factory Time) — Chilton Time

eng codes 3-9-7	
one (5.2)	7.1
both (6.8)	9.3
w/A.C. add (.5)	.5
w/P.S. add (.3)	.3
w/A.I.R. add (.2)	.2
V-8	
1986-87	
305 eng-Code H	
right side (5.8)	8.0
left side (5.5)	7.5
both sides (8.7)	12.0
w/A.C. add (.5)	.5
w/P.S. add (.3)	.3
w/AIR add (.2)	.2
w/Cruise control add (.2)	.2
307 eng-Code Y	
right side (4.2)	5.7
left side (4.6)	6.3
both sides (6.2)	8.5
w/A.C. add (.4)	.4
w/AIR add (.5)	.5

(P) Clean Carbon and Grind Valves

Includes: R&R cylinder heads, clean gasket surfaces, clean carbon, reface valves and seats. Minor tune up.

V-6–1983 (5.8)	7.7
w/Turbocharger add (1.6)	1.6
1984-87	
eng codes A-4 (8.0)	11.2
eng codes 3-9-7 (6.0)	8.4

(Factory Time) — Chilton Time

w/A.C. add (.5)	.5
w/P.S. add (.3)	.3
w/A.I.R. add (.2)	.2
V-8	
1986-87	
305 eng-Code H	
right side (6.3)	8.6
left side (5.9)	8.1
both sides (9.4)	13.0
w/A.C. add (.5)	.5
w/P.S. add (.3)	.3
w/AIR add (.2)	.2
w/Cruise control add (.2)	.2
307 eng-Code Y	
right side (5.1)	7.0
left side (5.6)	7.7
both sides (8.1)	11.2
w/A.C. add (.4)	.4
w/AIR add (.5)	.5

(G) Valve Tappets, Renew (Lifters)

Includes: Drain and refill cooling system. R&R intake manifold. Make all necessary adjustments.

V-6–1983-one bank (2.0)	2.7
both banks (2.2)	3.2
w/Turbocharger add (1.5)	1.6
1984-87	
eng codes A-4	
one bank (2.6)	3.4
both banks (2.9)	4.0
eng codes 3-9-7	
one bank (3.1)	4.3
both banks (3.3)	4.6
w/A.C. add (.3)	.3
w/A.I.R. add (.3)	.3
V-8	
1986-87	
305 eng-Code H	
one cyl (2.5)	3.4
one cyl-each side (2.7)	3.7
all cyls-both sides (3.2)	4.4
w/A.C. add (.5)	.5
w/AIR add (.1)	.1
w/Cruise control add (.1)	.1
307 eng-Code Y	
one cyl (2.7)	3.7
one cyl-each side (3.2)	4.4
all cyls-both sides (5.0)	6.9
w/A.C. add (.2)	.2
w/AIR add (.4)	.4

(G) Rocker Arm Cover and/or Gasket, Renew

V-6–1983-one (.5)	.8
both (.7)	1.4
w/Turbocharger add (1.5)	1.5
1984-87	
eng codes A-4	
one (.4)	.7
both (.6)	1.2
eng codes 3-9-7	
right side (.8)	1.2
left side (.3)	.5
both sides (1.1)	1.7
w/A.C. add (.3)	.3
w/A.I.R. add (.3)	.3

LABOR 12 CYLINDER HEAD & VALVE SYSTEM 12 LABOR

(Factory Time) — Chilton Time

V-8
1986-87
305 eng-Code H
right side (.7) ... 1.0
left side (.5) 7
both sides (1.1) ... 1.6
w/A.C. add (.2) 2
w/C.C.C. add (.2) 2
w/Cruise control add (.1) 1
307 eng-Code Y
right side (.6) 7
left side (.8) ... 1.2
both sides (1.4) ... 1.9
w/A.C. add (.1) 1
w/AIR add (.3) 3

(G) Valve Springs and/or Valve Stem Oil Seals, Renew (Head on Car)
V-6–1983-one cyl (.8) ... 1.1
one cyl-each bank (1.4) ... 2.0
w/Turbocharger add (1.5) ... 1.5
1984-87
eng codes A-4
one cyl (.8) ... 1.2
one cyl-each bank (1.4) ... 2.2
eng codes 3-9-7
one cyl (.9) ... 1.5
one cyl-each bank (1.6) ... 2.8
each adtnl cyl-all engs (.3) 4
w/A.C. add (.3) 3
w/A.I.R. add (.3) 3
V-8
1986-87
305 eng-Code H
one cyl'
right side (1.2) ... 1.6
left side (.8) ... 1.1
both sides (1.6) ... 2.3
each adtnl cyl (.4) 4
all cyls-both sides (3.3) ... 4.5
w/A.C. add (.3) 3
w/AIR add (.1) 1
307 eng-Code Y
one cyl'
right side (.7) ... 1.0
left side (1.1) ... 1.6
both sides (1.8) ... 2.4
each adtnl cyl (.4) 4
w/A.C. add (.1) 1
w/AIR add (.3) 3

(G) Rocker Arm Shafts and/or Assy., Renew
V-6–1983-one side (.6) 9
both sides (1.0) ... 1.6
w/Turbocharger add (1.5) ... 1.5
1984-87
eng codes A-4
one side (.8) ... 1.3
both sides (1.3) ... 2.3
eng codes 3-9-7
one side (.8) ... 1.5
both sides (1.4) ... 2.8
w/A.C. add (.3) 3
w/A.I.R. add (.3) 3
Recond each side add (.2) 3

(G) Valve Push Rods, Renew
V-6–1983-one side (.6) 9
both sides (1.0) ... 1.6
w/Turbocharger add (1.5) ... 1.5
1984-87
eng codes A-4
one side (.8) ... 1.4
both sides (1.4) ... 2.4
eng codes 3-9-7
right side (.8) ... 1.3
left side (.5) 7
both sides (1.3) ... 2.0
w/A.C. add (.3) 3
w/A.I.R. add (.3) 3

(G) Valve Rocker Arms and/or Push Rods, Renew
V-8
1986-87
305 eng-Code H
one cyl'
right side (.8) ... 1.2
left side (.6) 9
both sides (1.3) ... 2.0
each adtnl cyl (.2) 2
w/A.C. add (.2) 2
w/AIR add (.1) 1
307 eng-Code Y
one cyl'
right side (.7) 9
left side (.9) ... 1.4
both sides (1.5) ... 2.1
all cyls-both sides (2.0) ... 2.9
w/A.C. add (.1) 1
w/AIR add (.3) 3

DIESEL ENGINE

(G) Compression Test
V-6 ... 1.0
V-8 ... 1.3

(G) Cylinder Head Gasket, Renew
Includes: R&R injector pump and lines. R&R intake manifold and disconnect exhaust manifolds. Clean gasket surfaces, bleed lifters and adjust timing. Drain and refill cooling system.
V-6–1983-85
right side (4.7) ... 6.1
left side (4.9) ... 6.3
both sides (6.3) ... 8.1
V-8–1983-85
right side (6.1) ... 7.9
left side (5.7) ... 7.4
both sides (7.6) ... 9.9
w/A.C. add (.4) 4

(G) Cylinder Head, Renew
Includes: R&R injector pump and lines. R&R intake manifold and disconnect exhaust manifolds. Clean gasket surfaces. Transfer parts, reface valves. Bleed lifters and adjust timing. Drain and refill cooling system.
V-6–1983-85
right side (5.2) ... 6.7
left side (5.3) ... 6.8
both sides (7.6) ... 9.8
V-8–1983-85
right side (6.5) ... 8.4
left side (6.1) ... 7.9
both sides (8.4) ... 11.1
w/A.C. add (.4) 4

(P) Clean Carbon and Grind Valves
Includes: R&R injector pump and lines. R&R cylinder heads, clean carbon. Recondition valves and seats. Check and adjust valve stem length. Bleed lifters, drain and refill cooling system.
V-6–1983-85
right side (5.7) ... 7.4
left side (5.8) ... 7.5
both sides (8.7) ... 11.3
V-8–1983-85
right side (7.0) ... 9.1
left side (6.6) ... 8.5
both sides (9.3) ... 12.6
w/A.C. add (.4) 4

(G) Rocker Arm Cover or Gasket, Renew
V-6–1983-85
one (1.1) ... 1.5
both (1.8) ... 2.4
V-8–1983-85
one (1.2) ... 2.4
both (2.0) ... 2.9

(G) Rocker Arm, Pivot and/or Push Rod, Renew
V-6–1983-85
one cyl (1.2) ... 1.7
one cyl-each side (2.2) ... 3.0
each adtnl cyl 1
V-8–1983-85
one cyl (1.5) ... 2.5
one cyl-each side (2.3) ... 3.0
each adtnl cyl 1

(G) Valve Springs and/or Valve Stem Oil Seals, Renew (Head on Car)
V-6–1983-85
one cyl (1.3) ... 1.8
one cyl-each side (2.2) ... 3.2
each adtnl cyl (.3) 3
V-8–1983-85
one cyl (1.6) ... 3.0
one cyl-each side (2.4) ... 3.7
each adtnl cyl (.3) 3

(G) Valve Tappets, Renew (Lifters)
Includes: R&R injector pump and lines, intake manifold and rocker arms. Drain and refill cooling system.
V-6–1983-85
one cyl (2.6) ... 3.5
one cyl-each side (3.3) ... 4.5
each adtnl cyl (.1) 1
V-8–1983-85
one cyl (3.5) ... 4.5
one cyl-each side (3.9) ... 5.0
each adtnl cyl (.1) 2

PARTS 12 CYLINDER HEAD & VALVE SYSTEM 12 PARTS

	Part No.	Price
Valve Grind Gasket Set		
V-6-231		
1983-1st design	◆25525121	N.L.
2nd design	◆25527307	71.50
1984-85-exc. Turbo.		
Alum. in. man.		
1st des.	◆25525120	37.00
2nd des.	◆25527306	71.50
Cast iron in. man.		
1st des.	◆25525121	N.L.
2nd des.	◆25527307	71.50
1986-87-exc. Turbo	◆25527306	71.50
1984-85-Turbo	◆25525121	N.L.
1986-87-Turbo	25528729	79.50
V-6-252		
1983-84	◆25518568	N.L.
V-6-260 Diesel		
1983-84	22527055	76.25
V-8-350 Diesel		
1983	◆22522053	94.50
V-8-307		
1986-87	◆22534926	58.00

PARTS 12 CYLINDER HEAD & VALVE SYSTEM 12 PARTS

	Part No.	Price
(1) Cylinder Head		
V-6-231 & 252		
1983-87	◆25518679	217.00
V-6-260 Diesel		
1983-84	◆22520040	325.00
V-8-350 Diesel		
1983	◆22515038	387.00
V-8-307		
1986-87	◆22530557	247.00
(2) Cylinder Head Gasket		
V-6-231		
1983-85-1st design	◆1261403	8.50
2nd design	◆25525919	21.25
1985-87-1st design	◆25524599	8.50
2nd design	◆25525919	21.25
1986-87-Turbo	25528486	24.00
V-6-252		
1983-84	◆25518453	8.25
V-6-260 Diesel		
1983-84	◆22527054	30.50
V-8-350 Diesel		
1983	◆22519416	30.75
V-8-307		
1986-87	◆22503500	9.50
(3) Valve Cover Gasket		
V-6		
1983-84	◆25523348	N.L.
1985-87	◆25523348	N.L.
(4) Intake Valve		
V-6-231 & 252		
1983-87	◆25512098	11.25
V-6-260 Diesel		
1983-84	◆22513937	18.25
V-8-350 Diesel		
1983	◆22519914	20.00
V-8-307		
1986-87	◆22530611	20.25
(5) Exhaust Valve		
V-6-231 & 252		
1983-87	◆1261380	13.50
V-6-260 Diesel		
1983-84	◆558873	13.00
V-8-350 Diesel		
1983	◆558873	13.00
V-8-307		
1986-87	◆555456	N.L.

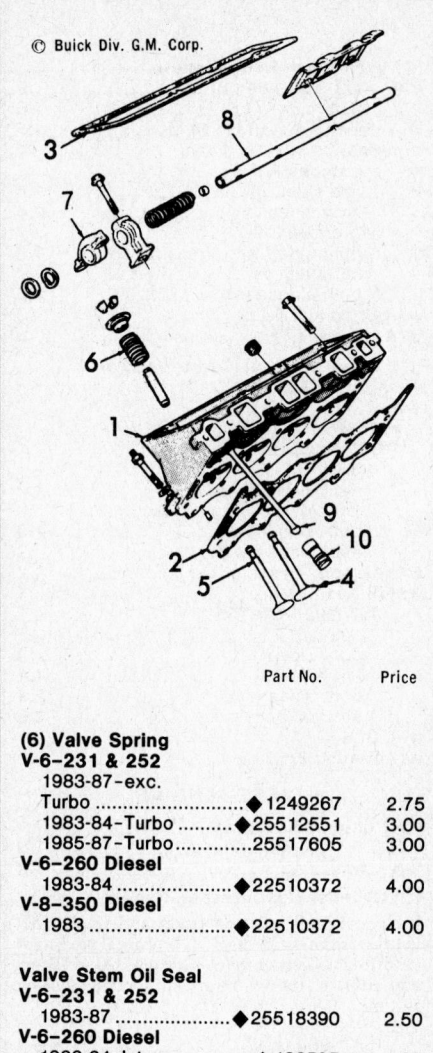

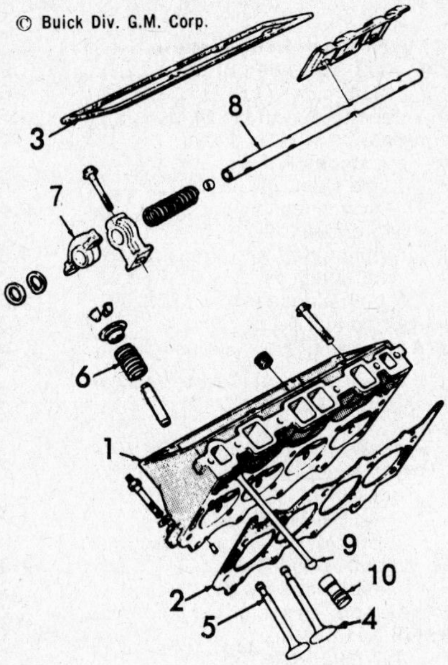

	Part No.	Price
(6) Valve Spring		
V-6-231 & 252		
1983-87-exc. Turbo	◆1249267	2.75
1983-84-Turbo	◆25512551	3.00
1985-87-Turbo	25517605	3.00
V-6-260 Diesel		
1983-84	◆22510372	4.00
V-8-350 Diesel		
1983	◆22510372	4.00
Valve Stem Oil Seal		
V-6-231 & 252		
1983-87	◆25518390	2.50
V-6-260 Diesel		
1983-84-Int.	◆406595	1.00
Exh.	◆401823	1.00

	Part No.	Price
V-8-350 Diesel		
1983-Int.	◆406595	1.00
Exh.	◆401823	1.00
V-8-307		
1986-87		
Int.	◆406595	.75
Exh.	◆401823	.75
(7) Rocker Arm		
V-6-231 & 252		
1983-87-Right	◆1241850	4.50
Left	◆1241851	4.50
V-6-260 Diesel		
1983-84	◆22505583	N.L.
V-8-350 Diesel		
1983	◆22505583	N.L.
V-8-307		
1986-87	◆22505583	N.L.
(8) Rocker Arm Shaft		
V-6-231 & 252		
1983-87	◆1254201	15.75
(9) Valve Push Rods		
V-6-231 & 252		
1983-84-wo/Turbo	◆1249139	4.00
1985-87-wo/Turbo	◆25510025	4.25
1983-87-Turbo	◆25510025	4.25
V-6-260 Diesel		
1983-84	◆22511044	3.25
V-8-350 Diesel		
1983	◆22511044	3.25
V-8-307		
1986-87	◆22533631	3.25
(10) Valve Lifters		
V-6-231 & 252		
1983	◆5232765	9.00
1984-85	◆5234330	N.L.
1986-87-exc. Turbo	◆5234330	N.L.
Turbo	5234485	8.25
V-6-260 Diesel		
1983-84	◆5234470	38.10
V-8-350 Diesel		
1983	5234295	30.50
V-8-307		
1986-87	◆5234755	43.50

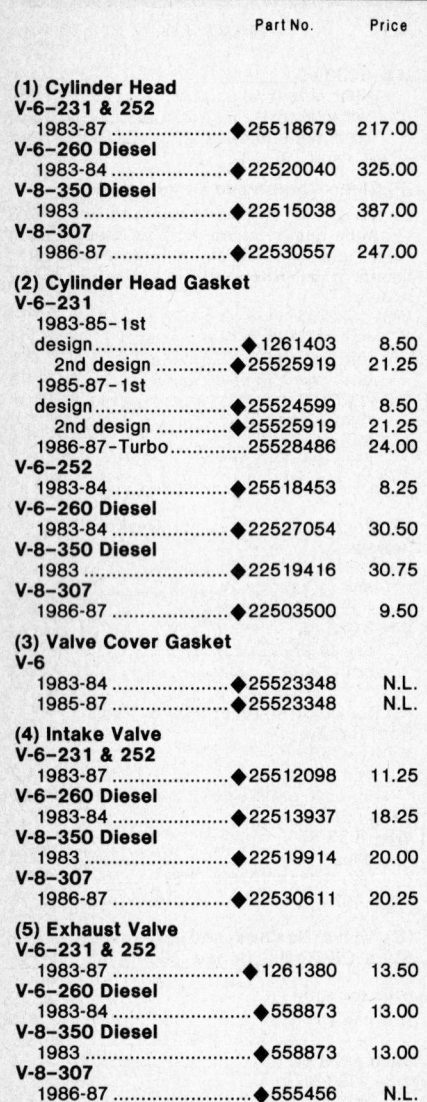

LABOR 13 ENGINE ASSEMBLY & MOUNTS 13 LABOR

(Factory Time) — Chilton Time

GASOLINE ENGINES

(G) Engine Assembly, Remove & Install

Does not include transfer of any parts or equipment.

	Chilton Time
V-6-1983	4.0
w/Turbocharger add	1.6
1984-87	
eng codes A-4	5.5
eng codes 3-9-7	6.0
w/A.C. add (.4)	.4
w/P.S. add (.3)	.3
w/A.I.R. add (.6)	.6
V-8-1986-87	
eng Code Y	5.0
w/A.C. add (.3)	.3

(G) Engine Assembly, Renew

Includes: R&R engine assembly, transfer all component parts not supplied with replacement engine. Minor tune up.

	Chilton Time
V-6-1983 (7.4)	9.9
w/Turbocharger add (1.6)	1.6
1984-85	
eng codes A-4 (7.0)	11.2
eng codes 3-9 (7.2)	11.4
w/A.C. add (.4)	.4
w/P.S. add (.3)	.3
w/A.I.R. add (.6)	.6

(G) Engine Assembly, Renew (Universal)

Includes: R&R engine assy. Transfer all component parts not supplied with replacement engine. Make all necessary adjustments.

	Chilton Time
V-6-1986-87	
eng Codes A-3-7-9- (6.7)	9.7
w/A.C. add (.3)	.3
w/AIR add (.2)	.2

(P) Cylinder Block, Renew (w/All Internal Parts Less Cylinder Heads and Oil Pan)

Includes: R&R engine, transfer all component parts not supplied with replacement engine, clean carbon, grind valves. Minor tune up.

	Chilton Time
V-6-1983 (11.3)	13.5
w/Turbocharger add (1.6)	1.6
1984-87	
eng codes A-4 (13.2)	18.6
eng codes 3-9-7 (12.9)	17.8
w/A.C. add (.4)	.4
w/P.S. add (.3)	.3
w/A.I.R. add (.6)	.6
V-8	
1986-87	
305 eng Code H (9.6)	13.6
w/A.C. add (.4)	.4
w/P.S. add (.3)	.3
w/AIR add (.4)	.4
307 eng Code Y (8.4)	11.7
w/A.C. add (.2)	.2
w/AIR add (.4)	.4

LABOR 13 ENGINE ASSEMBLY & MOUNTS 13 LABOR

(Factory Time) — Chilton Time

(P) Cylinder Block, Renew (w/Pistons, Rings & Bearings)

Includes: R&R engine assy. Transfer all component parts not supplied with replacement engine. Clean carbon, grind valves. Minor tune up.

V-6–1984-87	
eng Codes A-4 (14.1)	**21.0**
eng Codes 3-7-9- (12.9)	**19.8**
w/A.C. add (.3)	**.3**
w/AIR add (.2)	**.2**
V-8–1986-87	
305 eng Code H (15.0)	**21.2**
w/A.C. add (.4)	**.4**
w/P.S. add (.3)	**.3**
w/AIR add (.4)	**.4**
307 eng Code Y (12.6)	**17.6**
w/A.C. add (.2)	**.2**
w/AIR add (.4)	**.4**

(P) Engine Assy., R&R and Recondition (Complete)

Includes: Rebore block, install new pistons, rings, rod and main bearings. Clean carbon, grind valves. Tune engine.

V-6–1983 (26.0)	**31.1**
w/Turbocharger add (1.6)	**1.6**
1984-87	
eng codes A-4 (21.4)	**25.1**
eng codes 3-9-7 (17.1)	**23.0**
w/A.C. add (.4)	**.4**
w/P.S. add (.3)	**.3**
w/A.I.R. add (.6)	**.6**
V-8–1986-87	
305 eng Code H (21.9)	**29.7**
w/A.C. add (.4)	**.4**
w/P.S. add (.3)	**.3**
w/AIR add (.4)	**.4**
307 eng Code Y (18.6)	**26.0**
w/A.C. add (.2)	**.2**
w/AIR add (.4)	**.4**

(P) Engine Assembly, Recondition (In Car)

Includes: Expand or renew pistons, install new rings, pins, rod and main bearings. Clean carbon, grind valves. Tune engine.

V-6–1983 (17.1)	**20.7**
w/Turbocharger add (1.6)	**1.6**
1984-87	
eng codes A-4 (14.9)	**18.0**
eng codes 3-9-7 (14.0)	**17.2**
w/A.C. add (.4)	**.4**
w/P.S. add (.3)	**.3**
w/A.I.R. add (.6)	**.6**
V-8–1986-87	
305 eng Code H (18.6)	**26.1**
w/A.C. add (.5)	**.5**
w/P.S. add (.3)	**.3**
w/AIR add (.2)	**.2**
307 eng Code Y (19.4)	**27.1**
w/A.C. add (.3)	**.3**
w/AIR add (.6)	**.6**

(G) Engine Mounts, Renew

Front	
V-6–1983-87-one (.5)	**.7**
both (.7)	**1.0**
V-8–1986-87	
305 eng Code H	
one (.8)	**1.2**
both (1.4)	**2.0**
307 eng Code Y	
one (.5)	**.8**
both (.6)	**1.0**
Rear	
V-6–1983-87 (.4)	**.6**

DIESEL ENGINE

(G) Engine Assembly, Remove & Install

Does not include transfer of any parts or equipment.

V-6–1983-85	**4.5**
V-8–1983-85	**5.0**
w/A.C. add (.5)	**.5**

(G) Engine Assembly, Renew (Universal)

Includes: R&R engine assembly, transfer all component parts not supplied with replacement engine. Make all necessary adjustments.

V-6–1983-85	**16.5**
V-8–1983-85	**20.0**
w/A.C. add (.5)	**.5**
Renew gov retaining ring add	**.7**

(P) Cylinder Block, Renew (w/All Internal Parts Less Heads and Oil Pan)

Includes: R&R engine, transfer all component parts not supplied with replacement engine. Clean carbon, grind valves. Make all necessary adjustments.

V-6–1983-85 (11.0)	**21.0**
V-8–1983-85 (14.5)	**24.0**
w/A.C. add (.5)	**.5**

(P) Cylinder Block, Renew (w/Pistons, Rings and Bearings)

Includes: R&R engine, transfer all component parts not supplied with replacement engine. Clean carbon, grind valves. Make all necessary adjustments.

V-6–1983-85 (12.2)	**22.0**
V-8–1983-85 (16.6)	**27.0**
w/A.C. add (.5)	**.5**

(P) Engine Assy., R&R and Recondition (Complete)

Includes: Rebore block, install new pistons, rings, rod and main bearings. Clean carbon, grind valves. Make all necessary adjustments.

V-6–1983-85 (17.9)	**27.7**
V-8–1983-85 (29.5)	**36.0**
w/A.C. add (.5)	**.5**

(P) Engine Assembly, Recondition (In Car)

Includes: Expand or renew pistons, install new rings, pins, rod and main bearings. Clean carbon, grind valves. Make all necessary adjustments.

V-6–1983-85 (14.7)	**22.7**
V-8–1983-85 (23.0)	**27.3**
w/A.C. add (.5)	**.5**

(G) Engine Mounts, Renew

Front	
1983-85-one (.5)	**.8**
both (.7)	**1.0**
Rear	
1983 (.4)	**.6**

PARTS 13 ENGINE ASSEMBLY & MOUNTS 13 PARTS

Cylinder Block (Partial)

	Part No.	Price
V-6-231 wo/Turbo		
1983	◆25516156	1263.25
1984	◆25519449	1263.25
1985	◆25524286	1263.00
1986-87	◆25527474	1263.00
V-6-231 Turbo		
1983	◆25516157	1305.25
1984	◆25519451	1305.25
1985	◆25524286	1263.00
1986-87	25527476	1305.00
V-6-252		
1983-84	◆25516158	1319.25
V-6-260 Diesel		
1983	◆22522150	1750.00
1984	◆22522150	1750.00
V-8-350 Diesel		
1983	◆22518906	1950.00
V-8-307		
1986-87	◆22530855	1397.00

Front Engine Mount

	Part No.	Price
V-6-231 & 252		
1983-87 (exc. Station Wagon)		
R.H.	◆1258718	26.25
L.H.	◆25504647	30.75
1983 (Station Wagon)		
R.H.	◆1258666	24.00
L.H.	◆25504643	29.00
V-6-260 Diesel		
1983-84	◆459021	24.00
V-8-350 Diesel		
1983	◆553915	27.25
V-8-307		
1986-87	◆22501573	N.L.

Engine Overhaul Gasket Set

	Part No.	Price
V-6-231 exc. Turbo		
1983-1st design	◆25525119	58.25
2nd design	◆25528727	90.00
1984-Alum int. man.		
1st des.	◆25505370	52.50
2nd des.	◆25527302	89.00
1984-Cast iron man.		
1st des.	◆25525119	58.25
2nd des.	◆25528727	90.00
1985-1st des.	◆25525118	58.25
2nd des.	◆25527302	89.00
1986-87	◆25527302	89.00

1st design-.017 head gasket. 2nd design-.062 head gasket and "XGW" stamped on block near engine date and plant code.

	Part No.	Price
1983-85-Turbo	◆25525119	58.25
1986-87-Turbo	25528728	100.00
V-6-252		
1983-84	◆25518567	53.25
V-6-260 Diesel		
1983-84	22520639	91.50

For complete overhaul, also order a cylinder head gasket package.

	Part No.	Price
V-8-350 Diesel		
1983	22521787	93.50
V-8-307		
1986-87	◆22527539	62.50

LABOR 14 PISTONS, RINGS & BEARINGS 14 LABOR

(Factory Time) Chilton Time

GASOLINE ENGINES

(P) Rings, Renew (See Engine Combinations)

Includes: Remove cylinder top ridge, deglaze cylinder walls. Minor tune up.

	Chilton Time
V-6–1983-one (5.9)	7.8
one-each bank (7.6)	10.1
all-both banks (9.5)	12.1
w/Turbocharger add (1.6)	1.6
1984-87	
eng codes A-4	
one cyl (6.2)	8.9
one cyl-each bank (8.0)	11.6
all cyls-both banks (9.9)	14.3
eng codes 3-9-7	
one cyl (5.6)	8.1
one cyl-each bank (6.5)	9.4
all cyls-both banks (8.4)	12.1
w/A.C. add (.5)	.5
w/P.S. add (.3)	.3
w/A.I.R. add (.2)	.2
V-8	
1986-87	
305 eng-Code H	
one cyl (6.4)	9.2
one cyl-each bank (8.4)	12.1
all cyls-both banks (11.2)	16.2
w/A.C. add (.6)	.6
w/AIR add (.2)	.2
307 eng-Code Y	
one cyl (7.6)	11.0
one cyl-each bank (9.6)	13.9
all cyls-both banks (11.9)	17.2
w/A.C. add (.3)	.3
w/AIR add (.6)	.6

(P) Piston or Connecting Rod, Renew

Includes: Remove cylinder top ridge, deglaze cylinder walls. Minor tune up.

	Chilton Time
V-6–1983-one (6.1)	8.1
one-each bank (8.0)	10.7
all-both banks (10.2)	13.9
w/Turbocharger add (1.6)	1.6
1984-87	
eng codes A-4	
one cyl (6.9)	9.2
one cyl-each bank (9.4)	12.2
all cyls-both banks (10.6)	16.1
eng codes 3-9-7	
one cyl (6.3)	8.4
one cyl-each bank (7.9)	10.0
all cyls-both banks (9.1)	13.9
w/A.C. add (.5)	.5
w/P.S. add (.3)	.3
w/A.I.R. add (.2)	.2
V-8	
1986-87	
305 eng-Code H	
one cyl (7.1)	9.9
one cyl-each bank (9.8)	13.5
all cyls-both banks (12.3)	18.6
w/A.C. add (.6)	.6
w/AIR add (.2)	.2
307 eng-Code Y	
one cyl (8.2)	11.6
one cyl-each bank (10.8)	15.1
all cyls-both banks (13.0)	19.6
w/A.C. add (.3)	.3
w/AIR add (.6)	.6

(P) Connecting Rod Bearings, Renew

Includes: R&R oil pan, check all bearing clearances.

	Chilton Time
V-6–1983 (2.3)	3.0
1984-87 (2.3)	3.0
V-8	
1986-87	
305 eng-Code H (3.9)	5.4
307 eng-Code Y (4.4)	6.0

DIESEL ENGINE

(P) Rings, Renew (See Engine Combinations)

Includes: Remove cylinder top ridge, deglaze cylinder walls. Clean piston and ring grooves. Make all necessary adjustments.

	Chilton Time
V-6–1983-85 (11.9)	16.2
V-8–1983-85 (12.8)	17.2
w/A.C. add (.4)	.4

(P) Pistons or Connecting Rods, Renew

Includes: Remove cylinder top ridge, deglaze cylinder walls. Clean piston and ring grooves. Make all necessary adjustments.

	Chilton Time
V-6–1983-85 (12.6)	18.0
V-8–1983-85 (13.3)	19.6
w/A.C. add (.4)	.4

(P) Connecting Rod Bearings, Renew

Includes: Raise engine and clean oil pump screen.

	Chilton Time
V-6–1983-85 (3.7)	5.4
V-8–1983-85 (4.9)	6.6

COMBINATIONS

Add to Engine Work

See Machine Shop Operations

(Factory Time) Chilton Time

	Chilton Time
(G) DRAIN, EVACUATE & RECHARGE AIR CONDITIONING SYSTEM	
All models (.5)	1.0
(G) ROCKER ARM STUD, RENEW	
Each (.3)	.3
(G) HYDRAULIC VALVE LIFTERS, DISASSEMBLE AND CLEAN	
Each (.2)	.2
(G) DISTRIBUTOR, RECONDITION	
All models (.5)	.8
(G) CARBURETOR, RECONDITION	
2 bbl	1.2
4 bbl	1.5
(G) CYLINDER HEAD, R&R (ENGINE REMOVED)	
V-6	
eng Codes Z-9	
one (2.0)	2.6
both (3.0)	3.9
eng Codes A-4-7	
one (1.1)	1.4
both (1.8)	2.3
V-8	
eng Code H	
one (2.4)	3.1
both (3.7)	4.8
eng Code Y	
one (1.8)	2.3
both (2.6)	3.3
(G) CONNECTING ROD, RENEW (ENGINE DISASSEMBLED)	
V-6	
eng Codes Z-9	
each (.4)	.5
eng Codes A-4-7	
each (.5)	.6
V-8	
eng Code H	
each (.3)	.4
eng Code Y	
each (.5)	.6
(P) VALVE GUIDES, REAM OVERSIZE	
Each (.2)	.2
(G) ROCKER ARM SHAFT ASSY., DISASSEMBLE AND CLEAN OR RECONDITION	
Each side (.2)	.3
(G) DEGLAZE CYLINDER WALLS	
Each (.1)	.1
(G) REMOVE CYLINDER TOP RIDGE	
Each (.1)	.1
(G) PLASTIGAUGE BEARINGS	
Each (.1)	.1
(G) OIL PUMP, RECONDITION	
V-6 (.5)	.8
(M) OIL FILTER ELEMENT, RENEW	
V-6 (.2)	.2
V-8 (.3)	.3

PARTS 14 PISTONS, RINGS & BEARINGS 14 PARTS

2nd design engines use .062 in. head gasket and have the letters "XGW" stamped near engine plant date code on block.

(1) Piston Ring Set (One Piston)

	Part No.	Price
V-6–231 wo/Turbo		
1983-84-1st design	◆1240955	15.75
1983-85-2nd design	◆25526600	17.50
1985-1st design	◆25519462	N.L.
1986-87	◆25526600	17.50
V-6–231 Turbo		
1983-84	◆1240955	15.75
1985	◆25519462	16.50
1986-87	25527543	17.75
V-6–252		
1983-84	◆25505382	17.25
V-6–260 Diesel		
1983-84	◆22515964	21.00
V-8–350 Diesel		
1983	◆22515964	21.00
V-8–307		
1986-87	◆22529562	16.75

PARTS 14 PISTONS, RINGS, PINS & BEARINGS 14 PARTS

	Part No.	Price
(2) Piston Assy. (Standard)		
V-6-231 wo/Turbo		
1983-85	◆25518053	48.25
1986-87	◆25527178	48.25
V-6-231 Turbo		
1983	◆25515840	52.75
1984-85	◆25519444	52.75
1986-87	25528265	51.00
V-6-252		
1983-84	◆25505374	54.00
V-6-260 Diesel		
1983-right	◆22523360	63.75
left	◆22520327	63.75
1984-right	◆22523360	63.75
left	◆22523359	63.75
V-8-350 Diesel		
1983-right	◆22523360	63.75
left	◆22520327	63.75
V-8-307		
1986-87-right	◆22527482	48.25
left	◆22527481	48.25
(3) Connecting Rod Assembly		
V-6-231 & 252		
1983-87	◆25506520	39.00

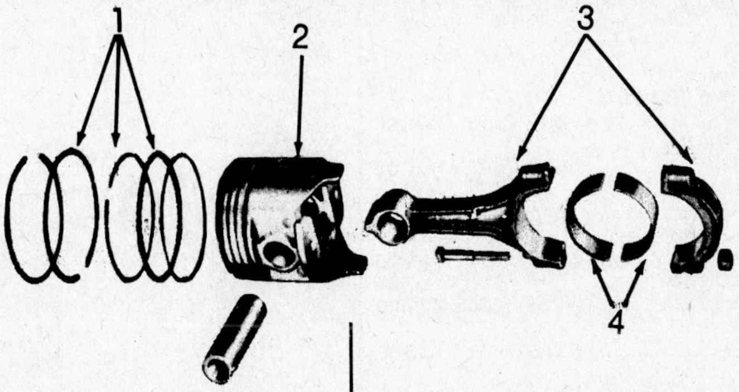

	Part No.	Price
V-6-260 Diesel		
1983-87	◆22515315	50.50
V-8-350 Diesel		
1983	◆22515313	50.50
(4) Connecting Rod Bearing (Std.)		
V-6-231 & 252		
1983-87	◆18005399	11.00

	Part No.	Price
V-6-260 Diesel		
1983-84	◆18009089	11.75
V-8-350 Diesel		
1983	◆18008494	10.50
V-8-307		
1986-87	◆22527025	45.00

LABOR 15 CRANKSHAFT & DAMPER 15 LABOR

(Factory Time) — Chilton Time

GASOLINE ENGINES

(P) Crankshaft and Main Bearings, Renew

Includes: R&R engine, check all bearing clearances.

(Factory Time)	Chilton Time
V-6-1983 (6.9)	10.0
1984-87	
eng codes A-4 (7.1)	10.0
eng codes 3-9-7 (6.2)	9.0
w/A.C. add (.4)	.4
w/P.S. add (.3)	.3
w/A.I.R. add (.6)	.6
V-8	
1986-87	
305 eng Code H (8.4)	11.9
w/A.C. add (.5)	.5
w/AIR add (.2)	.2
307 eng Code Y (7.0)	10.1
w/A.C. add (.3)	.3
w/AIR add (.3)	.3

(P) Main Bearings, Renew

Includes: R&R oil pan and bearing caps. Check all bearing clearances.

(Factory Time)	Chilton Time
V-6-1983 (2.2)	3.6
1984-87	
eng codes A-4 (2.2)	3.6
eng codes 3-9-7 (2.2)	3.6
V-8	
1986-87	
305 eng Code H (3.5)	5.4
w/A.C. add (.1)	.1
307 eng Code Y (4.1)	5.7

(P) Main and Rod Bearings, Renew

Includes: R&R oil pan and bearing caps. Check all bearing clearances.

(Factory Time)	Chilton Time
V-6-1983 (3.4)	5.4
1984-87	
eng codes A-4 (3.4)	5.4
eng codes 3-9-7 (3.4)	5.4
V-8	
1986-87	
305 eng Code H (5.3)	7.8
w/A.C. add (.1)	.1
307 eng Code Y (6.3)	8.1

(G) Rear Main Bearing Oil Seal, Renew or Repack

Includes: R&R oil pan and rear main bearing cap.

(Factory Time)	Chilton Time
V-6-1983 (1.5)	2.2
1984-87	
eng codes	
A-4-3-9-7 (1.5)	2.2
V-8	
1986-87	
305 eng Code H (2.3)	3.5
w/A.C. add (.1)	.1
307 eng Code Y (2.4)	3.6

(G) Crankshaft Pulley and/or Harmonic Balancer, Renew

(Factory Time)	Chilton Time
V-6-1983 (.5)	.8
1984-87	
eng codes	
A-4-3-9-7	
pulley (.7)	1.2
balancer (.8)	1.3
w/A.C. add (.3)	.3
w/P.S. add (.3)	.3
V-8	
1986-87	
305 eng Code H	
pulley (.6)	1.0
balancer (.8)	1.2
w/A.C. add (.2)	.2
307 eng Code Y	
pulley (.6)	1.0
balancer (.9)	1.3
w/A.C. add (.1)	.1

DIESEL ENGINE

(P) Crankshaft and Main Bearings, Renew

Includes: R&R engine, check all bearing clearances.

(Factory Time)	Chilton Time
V-6-1983-85 (8.1)	11.0
V-8-1983-85 (8.3)	11.2
w/A.C. add (.4)	.4

(P) Main Bearings, Renew

Includes: Check all bearing clearances.

(Factory Time)	Chilton Time
V-6-1983-85 (3.4)	4.5
V-8-1983-85 (4.1)	5.5

(P) Main and Rod Bearings, Renew

Includes: Check all bearing clearances.

(Factory Time)	Chilton Time
V-6-1983-85 (5.2)	6.3
V-8-1983-85 (6.5)	7.9

(G) Rear Main Bearing Oil Seals, R&R and Repack (Upper & Lower)

Includes: R&R oil pan and rear main bearing cap.

(Factory Time)	Chilton Time
V-6-1983-85 (2.1)	3.5
V-8-1983-85 (2.9)	4.0

(G) Rear Main Bearing Seals, Renew

Includes: R&R engine assy.

(Factory Time)	Chilton Time
V-6-1983-85 (5.9)	10.5
V-8-1983-85 (7.4)	10.7
w/A.C. add (.4)	.4

(G) Crankshaft Pulley or Balancer, Renew

(Factory Time)	Chilton Time
V-6-1983-85	
pulley (.4)	.6
balancer (.6)	1.2
V-8-1983-85	
pulley (.6)	.8
balancer (.9)	1.3
w/A.C. add (.2)	.2

(G) Crankshaft Front Oil Seal, Renew

(Factory Time)	Chilton Time
V-6-1983-85 (.7)	1.3
V-8-1983-85 (.9)	1.5
w/A.C. add (.2)	.2

PARTS 15 CRANKSHAFT & DAMPER 15 PARTS

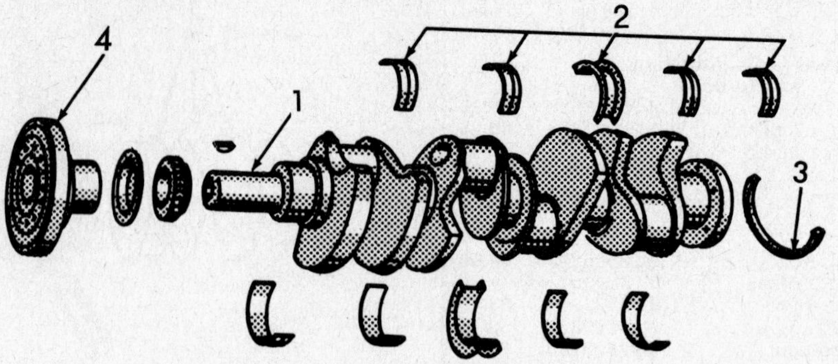

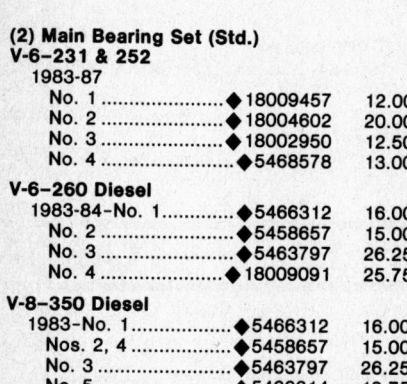

	Part No.	Price
(1) Crankshaft		
V-6-231 wo/Turbo		
1983-87	◆1260877	385.00
V-6-231 Turbo		
1983-87	◆1260873	407.00
V-6-252		
1983-84	◆1260873	407.00
V-6-260 Diesel		
1983-84	◆22515611	430.00
V-8-350 Diesel		
1983	◆22511035	439.00
V-8-307		
1986-87	◆22527438	403.00
(2) Main Bearing Set (Std.)		
V-6-231 & 252		
1983-87		
No. 1	◆18009457	12.00
No. 2	◆18004602	20.00
No. 3	◆18002950	12.50
No. 4	◆5468578	13.00
V-6-260 Diesel		
1983-84-No. 1	◆5466312	16.00
No. 2	◆5458657	15.00
No. 3	◆5463797	26.25
No. 4	◆18009091	25.75
V-8-350 Diesel		
1983-No. 1	◆5466312	16.00
Nos. 2, 4	◆5458657	15.00
No. 3	◆5463797	26.25
No. 5	◆5466314	19.75

	Part No.	Price
V-8-307		
1986-87-No. 1	◆5466211	13.00
Nos. 2, 4	◆5466089	13.00
No. 3	◆5466090	19.75
No. 5	◆5466091	17.00
(3) Rear Main Bearing Oil Seal		
1983-87	◆1193151	1.50
Rear Main Brg. Packing		
1983-87	◆9772831	1.50
Front Oil Seal		
1983-87-exc		
Diesel	◆1305044	1.00
Diesel	◆552711	4.25

	Part No.	Price
(4) Vibration Damper		
V-6-231 wo/Turbo		
1983	◆25506570	42.75
1984-87	◆25523502	41.25
V-6-231 Turbo		
1983	◆25506571	42.75
1984-87	◆25523503	46.25
V-6 252		
1983-84	◆22523502	N.L.
V-6-260 Diesel		
1983-84 (HUB)	◆22514398	33.50
V-8-350 Diesel		
1983	◆559131	63.25
V-8-307		
1986-87	◆22506730	31.75

LABOR 16 CAMSHAFT & TIMING GEARS 16 LABOR

(Factory Time) — Chilton Time

GASOLINE ENGINES

(G) Timing Cover Oil Seal, Renew

	Chilton Time
V-8–1986-87	
305 eng Code H (.8)	1.4
w/A.C. add (.2)	.2
307 eng Code Y (1.0)	1.5
w/A.C. or AIR add (.1)	.1

(G) Timing Case Cover Gasket, Renew

Includes: R&R fan blade, crankshaft pulley and balancer. Drain and refill oil and coolant.

	Chilton Time
V-6–1983 (1.9)	2.5
w/Turbocharger add (.1)	.2
1984-87	
eng codes A-4 (2.2)	3.2
eng codes 3-9-7 (2.8)	4.0
w/A.C. add (.3)	.3
w/P.S. add (.3)	.3
w/A.I.R. add (.3)	.3
Renew cover add (.4)	.4
V-8	
1986-87	
305 eng Code H (1.8)	2.6
w/A.C. add (.2)	.2
w/AIR add (.2)	.2
307 eng Code Y (1.8)	2.6
w/A.C. add (.3)	.3
w/AIR add (.1)	.1
Renew cover add (.2)	.4
Renew f/pump eccentric add (.1)	.2

(G) Timing Chain or Gears, Renew

Includes: R&R fan blade, crankshaft pulley and balancer, engine front cover. Drain and refill oil and coolant.

	Chilton Time
V-6–1983 (2.1)	3.2
w/Turbocharger add (.1)	.2
1984-87	
eng codes A-4 (2.4)	3.7
eng codes 3-9-7 (2.7)	4.5
w/A.C. add (.3)	.3
w/P.S. add (.3)	.3
w/A.I.R. add (.3)	.3
V-8	
1986-87	
305 eng Code H (2.0)	3.1
w/A.C. add (.2)	.2
w/AIR add (.2)	.2
307 eng Code Y (2.1)	3.1
w/A.C. add (.3)	.3
w/AIR add (.1)	.1

(G) Camshaft, Renew

Includes: R&R pulleys, radiator, harmonic balancer, fuel pump, distributor, timing chain cover, intake manifold, rocker arms, push rods and lifters.

	Chilton Time
V-6–1983 (4.2)	6.5
w/Turbocharger add (1.6)	1.6
1984-87	
eng codes A-4 (5.5)	7.0
eng codes 3-9-7 (6.9)	9.6
w/A.C. add (.5)	.5
w/P.S. add (.3)	.3
w/A.I.R. add (.4)	.4
V-8	
1986-87	
305 eng Code H (5.0)	7.0
w/A.C. add (.3)	.3
w/AIR add (.1)	.1
307 eng Code Y (5.7)	*8.1
w/A.C. add (1.0)	1.0
w/AIR add (.4)	.4
*Renew cam brgs add (1.4)	2.0

(G) Camshaft Rear Bearing Plug, Renew

Includes: R&R trans for accessibility.

	Chilton Time
V-6–1983-87 (2.2)	3.1
V-8	
1986-87	
307 eng Code Y (2.2)	3.0

DIESEL ENGINE

(G) Timing Case Cover or Gasket, Renew

Includes: R&R fan blade, crankshaft pulley and balancer. Drain and refill oil and coolant.

	Chilton Time
V-6–1983-85 (1.7)	2.4
V-8–1983-85 (2.1)	3.1
w/A.C. add (.3)	.3

(G) Timing Chain or Gears, Renew

Includes: R&R fan blade, crankshaft pulley and balancer. Drain and refill oil and coolant.

	Chilton Time
V-6–1983-85 (3.6)	5.0
V-8–1983-85 (2.3)	3.5
w/A.C. add (.3)	.3

(G) Camshaft, Renew

Includes: R&R radiator, front cover, fuel pump, timing gear and chain. R&R injector pump, intake manifold and lifters. Disconnect exhaust system. Drain and refill oil and coolant. Make all necessary adjustments.

	Chilton Time
V-6–1983-85 (5.7)	7.5
V-8–1983-85 (7.3)	10.0
w/A.C. add (1.0)	1.0
Renew cam brgs add (2.8)	3.8

(G) Camshaft Rear Bearing Plug, Renew

Includes: R&R trans for accessibility.

	Chilton Time
V-6–1983-85 (2.4)	3.0
V-8–1983-85 (2.1)	3.0

PARTS 16 CAMSHAFT & TIMING GEARS 16 PARTS

	Part No.	Price
(1) Timing Case Cover Gasket		
V-6-231 & 252		
1983-87	◆25519461	5.25
V-6-260 Diesel		
1983-84	◆22505997	1.25
V-8-350 Diesel		
1983	25505997	8.00
V-8-307		
1986-87	◆22505997	1.25
(2) Timing Case Oil Seal		
V-6-231 & 252		
1983-87	◆1305044	1.00
V-6-260 Diesel		
1983-84	◆552711	4.25
V-8-350 Diesel		
1983	◆552711	4.25
V-8-307		
1986-87	◆552711	4.25
(3) Camshaft Gear		
V-6-231 & 252		
1983-84	◆1253698	18.50
1985-87	◆25523115	17.50
V-6-260 Diesel		
1983-84	◆22516032	41.00
V-8-350 Diesel		
1983	◆558767	58.75
V-8-307		
1986-87	◆381263	25.25
(4) Crankshaft Gear		
V-6-231 & 252		
1983-87	◆25519954	14.25
V-6-260 Diesel		
1983-87	◆22516034	31.50
V-8-350 Diesel		
1983	◆558489	44.25
V-8-307		
1986-87	◆382880	16.75

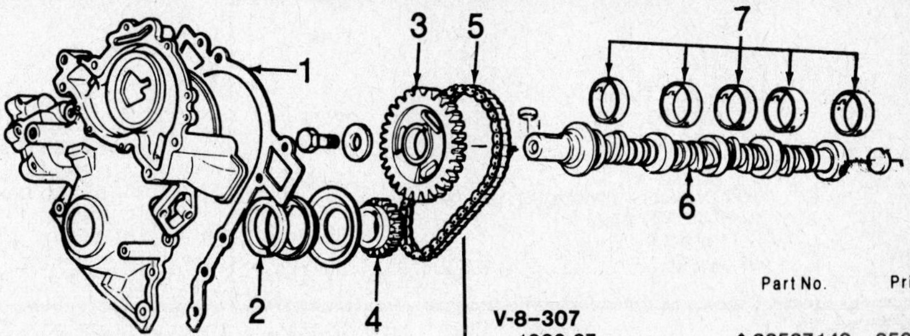

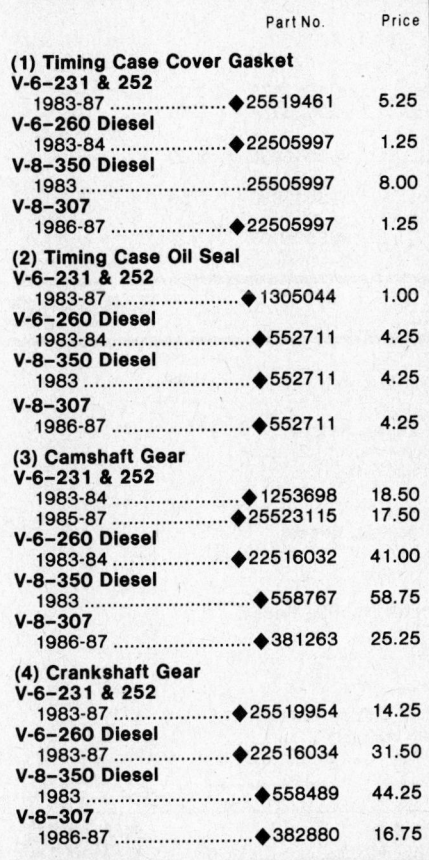

	Part No.	Price
(5) Timing Chain		
V-6-231 & 252		
1983-87	◆1257650	26.00
V-6-260 Diesel		
1983-84	◆22516033	35.50
V-8-350 Diesel		
1983	◆558484	N.L.
V-8-307		
1986-87	◆401584	31.75
(6) Camshaft		
V-6-231 wo/Turbo & 252		
1983-84-1st design	◆1262835	119.00
1983-84-2nd design	◆25510049	119.00
1985	◆25510049	119.00
1986	25517479	134.00
V-6-231 Turbo		
1983	◆25510019	119.00
1984-87	25517479	134.00
V-6-260 Diesel		
1983-84	◆22513910	266.00
V-8-350 Diesel		
1983	◆22510099	266.00

	Part No.	Price
V-8-307		
1986-87	◆22527149	256.00
(7) Camshaft Bearings		
V-6-231 & 252		
1983-84-exc Front	◆1231142	7.75
Front	◆1234441	7.00
1985-87-exc. below	◆25524301	7.25
No. 2, 3	◆1231142	7.75
V-6-260 Diesel		
1983-84-No. 1	◆561077	11.50
No. 2	◆390300	11.50
No. 3	◆390301	11.75
Rear	◆390302	11.50
V-8-350 Diesel		
1983-No. 1	◆561077	11.50
No. 2	◆390300	11.50
No. 3	◆390301	11.75
No. 4	◆390302	11.50
Rear	◆390303	11.50
V-8-307		
1986-87-No. 1	◆561077	11.50
No. 2	◆390300	11.50
No. 3	◆390301	11.75
No. 4	◆390302	11.50
Rear	◆390303	11.50

LABOR 17 ENGINE OILING SYSTEM 17 LABOR

(Factory Time)	Chilton Time
GASOLINE ENGINES	
(G) Oil Pan or Gasket, Renew	
V-6–1983-87 (.9)	1.6
V-8	
1986-87	
305 eng Code H (1.9)	2.7
w/A.C. add (.1)	.1
307 eng Code Y (2.1)	2.9
(P) Pressure Test Engine Bearings (Pan Off)	
All models	1.0
(G) Oil Pump Cover and/or Gears, R&R and Recondition	
Includes: R&R pressure relief valve and inspect. Check pump cover for wear.	
V-6–1983-87 (.5)	.8
O/haul pump add (.1)	.2
(G) Oil Pump, Renew	
V-8	
1986-87	
305 eng Code H (2.0)	2.9
w/A.C. add (.1)	.1
307 eng Code Y (2.2)	3.1
(G) Oil Pressure Gauge (Engine), Renew	
1983-87 (.3)	.4
(M) Oil Filter Element, Renew	
V-6–1983-87 (.2)	.2
V-8–1986-87 (.3)	.3
DIESEL ENGINE	
(G) Oil Pan or Gasket, Renew	
Includes: Raise engine, R&R and clean oil pump screen.	
V-6–1983-85 (1.6)	2.2
V-8–1983-85 (2.6)	3.4
(P) Pressure Test Engine Bearings (Pan Off)	
All models	1.0
(G) Oil Pump, Renew	
Includes: Raise engine, R&R and clean oil pump screen.	
V-6–1983-85 (1.7)	2.4
V-8–1983-85 (2.7)	3.6
(G) Oil Pump, R&R and Recondition	
Includes: Raise engine, R&R and clean oil pump screen.	
V-6–1983-85 (2.0)	2.6
V-8–1983-85 (2.9)	3.8
(G) Oil Pressure Gauge (Engine), Renew	
1983-85 (.3)	.4
(M) Oil Filter Element, Renew	
1983-85 (.2)	.3

PARTS 17 ENGINE OILING SYSTEM 17 PARTS

	Part No.	Price
Oil Pan Gasket		
V-6-231 & 252		
1983-84-14 bolt	◆1260771	3.00
1983-84-20 bolt	◆25521994	8.50
1985-87	◆25521994	8.50
V-6-260 Diesel		
1983-84	◆22520640	8.25
V-8-350 Diesel		
1983	◆22519181	7.00
V-8-307		
1986-87	◆22519181	N.L.
Oil Pump		
V-6-260 Diesel		
1983-84	◆22515464	59.75
V-8-350 Diesel		
1983	◆22525288	61.50
V-8-307		
1986-87	◆22524583	61.50
Oil Pump Overhaul Kit		
V-6-231 wo/Turbo & 252		
1983-87	◆25523433	39.75

PARTS 17 ENGINE OILING SYSTEM 17 PARTS

	Part No.	Price
V-6-231 Turbo		
1983-85	25523434	39.75
1986-87	25527311	39.75
Oil Pressure Switch (Engine Sender)		
V-6-231 & 252		
1983-87-exc. below	◆25500672	5.50
Turbo (1984)	◆1623576	6.00
Turbo (1985-87)	◆25036378	8.75
V-6-260 Diesel		
1983-84	◆3815936	3.50
V-8-350 Diesel		
1983	◆3815936	3.50
V-8-307		
1986-87	◆3815936	N.L.

LABOR 21 SHIFT LINKAGE 21 LABOR

(Factory Time)	Chilton Time
AUTOMATIC	
(G) Shift Linkage, Adjust	
All models	
Neutral Safety Switch (.3)	.4
Shift Indicator Needle (.2)	.3
Shift Linkage (.4)	.5
T.V. Cable (.3)	.4
(G) Shift Linkage, Adjust (w/Diesel eng)	
All models	
Fast idle speed (.2)	.3
Throttle rod T.V. cable (.3)	.6
Trans vacuum valve (.5)	.6
Vacuum regul valve (.6)	.8
Complete (.8)	1.0
(G) Gear Shift Lever, Renew	
1983-87-column mount (.2)	.5
console mount (.4)	.7
(G) Shift Control Rod, Renew	
1983-87 (.4)	.5
(G) Shift Indicator Needle, Renew	
1983 (.6)	.9
1984-87 (.3)	.5
(G) Shift Control Cable, Renew	
1983-87-colm shift (.7)	.9
floor shift (.9)	1.2

PARTS 18 CLUTCH & FLYWHEEL 18 PARTS

	Part No.	Price
Flywheel		
V-6-231 wo/Turbo		
1983-87	◆25512348	72.00
V-6-231 Turbo		
1983-85	25512347	70.50
1986-87	25512350	69.50
V-6-252 engine		
1983-84	◆25512348	72.00
V-6-260 Diesel		
1983-84	◆22512002	75.25
V-8-350 Diesel		
1983	◆22500808	85.50

LABOR 25 U-JOINTS & DRIVESHAFT 25 LABOR

(Factory Time)	Chilton Time
(G) Drive Shaft, Renew	
1983-87 (.4)	.5
(G) Universal Joint, Renew	
Includes: R&R drive shaft.	
1983-87-front (.6)	.8
rear (.5)	.7
both (.7)	1.3
(G) Pinion Shaft Flange, Renew	
1983-87 (.7)	1.0

PARTS 25 UNIVERSAL JOINTS & DRIVE SHAFT 25 PARTS

	Part No.	Price
U/Joint Repair Kit		
1983-87		
Dana shaft	◆374246	28.50
Saginaw shaft	◆7806140	41.00
Yoke, Front		
1983-87	◆7812557	65.25
Rear Pinion Flange		
1983-87		
7½" ring gr.	◆7827670	33.75
8½" ring gr.	◆1256654	35.00

LABOR — 26 REAR AXLE 26 — LABOR

(Factory Time) — Chilton Time

(M) Differential, Drain & Refill
All models.. .6

(M) Axle Housing Cover or Gasket, Renew
1983-87 (.5).................................. .6

(G) Axle Shaft Assembly, Renew
'C' Lock Type
1983-87-one (.7)........................... .9
both (.9).................................. 1.2

(G) Axle Shaft Bearing and/or Seal, Renew
'C' Lock Type
1983-87-one (.6)........................... .8
both (.8).................................. 1.1

(G) Pinion Shaft Oil Seal, Renew
1983-87 (.5).................................. .8

(G) Axle Housing Assembly, Renew
Includes: Transfer all parts, bleed and adjust brakes.
1983-87 (3.4)................................ 5.2

(G) Differential Case, Renew
Includes: R&R axle shafts and housing cover. Disassemble, inspect and reassemble case. Adjust ring gear backlash and side bearing preload.
1983-87 (1.8)................................ 2.8
w/Posi-Trac add (.5)......................... .5

(G) Differential Side Bearings, Renew
Includes: R&R axle shafts and housing cover and axle case. Adjust ring gear backlash and side bearing preload.
1983-87 (1.7)................................ 2.5

(P) Ring Gear and Pinion, Renew
Includes: R&R axle shafts and housing cover. R&R case and rear pinion bearing. Adjust pinion depth and bearing preload, ring gear backlash and side bearing preload.
1983-87 (2.4)................................ 3.9
Recond complete add
std (.3).. .5
limited slip (.7)............................. 1.0

(G) Pinion Bearing and Outer Race, Renew
Includes: R&R axle shafts and housing cover. Adjust pinion depth and bearing preload, ring gear backlash and side bearing preload.
1983-87 (2.0)................................ 3.4

(G) Differential Side Gears and Pinion Shaft, Renew
Includes: R&R axle shafts and housing cover. Adjust ring gear backlash and side bearing preload.
1983-87 (.8).................................. 1.8
w/Limited slip add (.5)..................... .5

(G) Positraction Differential Clutch Plates, Renew
Includes: R&R axle shafts and housing cover. Adjust ring gear backlash and side bearing preload.
1983-87 (1.1)................................ 2.0

PARTS — 26 REAR AXLE 26 — PARTS

Part No. — Price

To obtain correct replacement parts for the rear axle assembly, use the third letter of the rear axle code when ordering parts. The rear axle code is stamped either on the front of the passenger side axle tube or on a metal tag attached to a cover bolt.

(1) Axle Shaft
1983-87
7½" ring gr............◆22519888 104.75
8½" ring gr............◆14075744 100.75

(2) Axle Shaft Seal
1983-87 ....◆3998519 4.00

(3) Axle Bearing
1983-87 ....◆7451785 16.00

(4) Flange
1983-87
7½" ring gr..............◆7827670 33.50
8½" ring gr..............◆1256654 35.00

(5) Pinion Seal
(7½" dia. ring gr.)
1983-87 ....◆552571 8.00
(8½" dia. ring gr.)
1984-87 ....◆1243465 7.50

(6) Front Pinion Bearing
1983-87
7½" ring gr..............◆7451202 16.00
8½" ring gr..............◆7450984 21.00

(7) Axle Housing
1983-87
7½" ring gr...........◆22510780 496.25
8½" ring gr...........◆14079473 406.25

(8) Pinion Gear Package
(7½" dia. ring gr.
1983-87-exc.
below........................◆22514882 105.00
3.42, 3.73
ratios.......................◆22521625 105.00
(8½" dia. ring gr.)
1983-87 ....◆1397647 132.00
Gear packages contain 2 side gears, 2 pinion gears, thrust washers and pinion shaft.

(9) Drive Pinion Spacer
1983-87-7½"
ring gr...........................◆9785792 1.50
8½" ring gr.............◆1234726 1.50

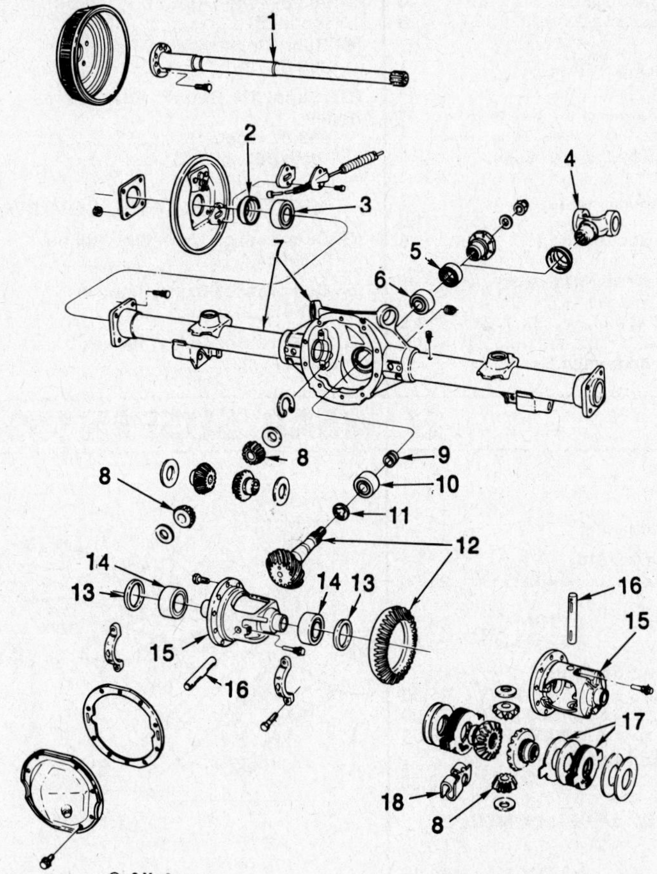

© G.M. Corp.

Part No. — Price

(10) Rear Pinion Bearing
(7½" dia. ring gr.)
1983-87 ....◆7455699 N.L.
(8½" dia. ring gr.)
1983-87 ....◆7451155 20.00

(11) Shim Package
1983-87 (.025-.029)
7½" ring gr................◆553022 5.50
8½" ring gr..............◆1394893 6.50
Various sizes available.

PARTS 26 REAR AXLE 26 PARTS

	Part No.	Price
(12) Ring and Pinion Gear		
(7½" ring gear)		
1983-87		
2.14 ratio	◆563646	255.00
2.29 ratio	◆560197	259.00
2.41 ratio	◆560198	259.00
2.56 ratio	◆560199	259.00
2.73 ratio	◆560201	259.00
2.93 ratio	◆560204	261.00
3.08 ratio	◆560205	N.L.
3.23 ratio	◆560207	259.00
3.42 ratio	◆22521623	276.00
(8½" ring gear)		
1984-87	1258710	276.00
(13) Bearing Adjusting Shim Pkg.		
1983-87	◆3995791	6.50
Smallest sizes listed above. Larger sizes available.		
(14) Differential Side Bearing		
1983-87	◆7451281	15.00
(15) Differential Case		
(Without Limited Slip Differential)		
The following cases do not include the internal gears.		
7½" ring gear		
1983-87-exc. below	◆558648	109.00
3.23, 3.42, 3.73R	◆558649	109.25
8½" ring gear		
1984-87	◆1252981	110.00
(With Limited Slip Differential)		
The internal gears are included in the following cases.		
7½" ring gear		
1983-87-exc. below	◆22514583	278.00
3.23, 3.42, 3.73R	◆22514584	402.00
8½" ring gear		
1984-87	◆14067495	374.25
(16) Pinion Shaft		
(With Limited Slip Differential)		
7½" dia. ring gr.		
1983-87	◆22515972	10.25
8½" dia. ring gr.		
1984-87	◆14006401	12.50
(Without Limited Slip Differential)		
1983-87	◆22507586	11.00
(18) Preload Spring		
1983-87	◆561310	9.50

LABOR 27 REAR SUSPENSION 27 LABOR

(Factory Time)	Chilton Time
(G) Rear Spring, Renew	
1983-87-one (.4)	.6
both (.6)	.8
(G) Rear Axle Bumper, Renew	
1983-87-one (.2)	.3
both (.3)	.4
(G) Lower Control Arm Assy., Renew	
1983-87-one (.4)	.7
both (.5)	1.0
Renew bushings add-each	.3
(G) Upper Control Arm Assy., Renew	
1983-87-one (.4)	.8
both (.6)	1.1
Renew bushings add-each	.3
(G) Rear Shock Absorber, Renew	
1983-87-one (.4)	.5
both (.5)	.7
(G) Rear Stabilizer Bar, Renew	
1983-87 (.5)	.7
(G) Superlift Shock Absorbers, Renew	
1983-87-one (.4)	.6
both (.5)	.9
ELECTRONIC LEVEL CONTROL	
(G) Compressor Assembly, Renew	
1983-87 (.3)	.5
(G) Compressor Dryer, Renew	
1983-87 (.2)	.4
(G) Compressor Relay, Renew	
1983-87 (.2)	.4
(G) Height Sensor, Adjust	
1983-87 (.3)	.5
(G) Height Control Sensor, Renew	
1983-87 (.6)	.9
(G) Level Control Tubing, Renew	
comp to valve (.6)	.8
valve to shock (.3)	.5
valve to bumper (.3)	.5
(G) Electronic Lever Control Head, Renew	
Includes: Renew cover gasket, solenoid and valves.	
1983-87 (.3)	.9
(G) Electronic Level Control Motor and Cylinder Assy., R&R and Recondition	
1983-87 (.6)	1.2

PARTS 27 REAR SUSPENSION 27 PARTS

	Part No.	Price
(1) Rear Spring		
Order by year and model.		
(2) Shock Absorber (Std)		
1983-84	◆4993580	24.50
1985-87-exc. H.D.	◆22046432	24.50
H.D. susp	◆22046440	24.50
(3) Upper Arm and Bushing		
1983-87-0 deg.	◆10000076	15.00
-1½ deg.	◆10001059	30.50
§1½ deg.	◆10001060	15.00
(4) Lower Arm and Bushing		
1983-87	◆10000063	43.25
ELECTRONIC LEVEL CONTROL		
Compressor		
1983-87	◆22020538	176.25

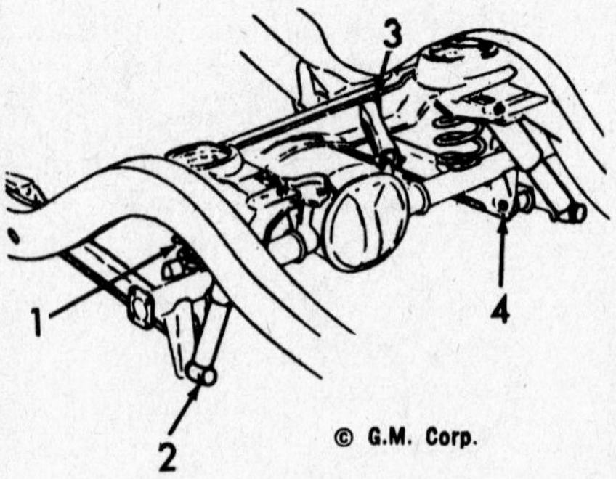

© G.M. Corp.

	Part No.	Price
Height Sensor		
1983-87	22017240	200.00
Control Relay		
1983-87	◆10011579	9.75
Air Dryer Kit		
1983-87	◆22009035	41.50
Shock Absorber		
1983-87-right	◆22012060	58.00
left	◆22012059	58.00
Compressor Head		
1983-87	◆22020539	68.50
Motor (wo/compressor head)		
1983-87	◆22010692	165.00

(Factory Time) Chilton Time

Note: If more than one item requires replacement where evacuation and discharging the system is already included in the operation, deduct 1.0 hour for each additional item to the times listed.

(G) Drain, Evacuate and Recharge System
All models (.5) 1.0

(G) Leak Check
Includes: Check all lines and connections.
All models.................................... .5

(G) Refrigerant, Add (Partial Charge)
All models.................................... .6

(G) Compressor Belt, Renew
1983-87
Gas
V-6 (.5).................................. .6
V-8
eng Code H (.3)................... .4
eng Code Y (.4) 5
Diesel
V-6 (.2).................................. .4
V-8 (.5).................................. .6

COMPRESSOR 4 CYLINDER RADIAL

(G) Compressor Assembly, Renew
Includes: Transfer parts as required. Evacuate and charge system.
1983-87 (1.0).............................. 2.0

(G) Compressor Clutch Plate and Hub Assy., Renew
Includes: R&R hub and drive plate assy., check air gap.
1983-87 (.5)................................ .8

(G) Compressor Clutch Rotor and/or Bearing, Renew
Includes: R&R hub and drive plate assy.
1983-87 (.9)................................ 1.2

(G) Compressor Clutch Coil and/or Pulley Rim Assembly, Renew
Includes: R&R hub and drive plate assy.
1983-87 (.8)................................ 1.0
Renew pulley or brg add.................... .2

(G) Compressor Front Seal, Seat and 'O' Ring, Renew
Includes: R&R clutch hub and drive plate assy. Evacuate and charge system.
1983-87 (1.1).............................. 2.5

(G) Compressor Front Head and/or Seal, Renew
Includes: R&R compressor, R&R clutch and pulley assy. R&R shaft seal assy. Clean and inspect parts. Evacuate and charge system.
1983-87 (1.3).............................. 2.8

(G) Compressor Discharge Valve Plates, Renew
Includes: R&R compressor. R&R clutch and pulley assy. R&R shell to internal mechanism. Clean and inspect parts. Evacuate and charge system.
1983-87 (1.4).............................. 2.6
Two or more add (.1) 2

(G) Compressor Thrust and/or Belleville Washers, Renew
Includes: R&R compressor. R&R clutch and pulley assy. R&R shaft seal assy. R&R front head assy. Clean and inspect parts. Evacuate and charge system.
1983-87 (1.3).............................. 2.8

AIR CONDITIONER TUNE-UP

For efficient operation and satisfactory performance in hot weather. The following air conditioner tune-up is suggested:

1. Clean intake filter
2. Clean condenser fins
3. Pressure test system
4. Adjust drive belt tension
5. Check antifreeze/coolant
6. Tighten compressor mounts
7. Tighten condenser and evaporator mounts
8. Inspect system for leaks (hoses, couplings, valves, etc.)
9. Partial charge system

All models 1.0
If necessary to evacuate and charge system, add 1.0

(Factory Time) Chilton Time

(G) Compressor Main Bearing, Renew
Includes: R&R compressor. R&R clutch and pulley assy. R&R shaft seal assy. R&R front head assy. Clean and inspect parts. Evacuate and charge system.
1983-87 (1.3).............................. 2.8

(G) Compressor Shell and/or 'O' Ring, Renew
Includes: R&R compressor. R&R clutch and pulley assy. Clean and inspect parts. Evacuate and charge system.
1983-87 (1.3).............................. 2.8

(G) Compressor Shaft and Cylinder Assy., Renew
Includes: R&R compressor. R&R clutch and pulley assy. R&R shaft seal assy, remove and transfer front head assy. R&R compressor shell and 'O' rings. R&R compressor discharge valve plates, R&R super heat switch and pressure relief valve. Clean and inspect parts. Evacuate and charge system.
1983-87 (1.6).............................. 2.9

(G) Compressor Pressure Relief Valve, Renew
Includes: Evacuate and charge system.
1983-87 (.9)................................ 1.4
w/Turbo add (.1)............................ .1

(G) Condenser, Renew
Includes: Evacuate and charge system.
1983-87 (1.0).............................. 1.7
w/Diesel eng (1.7)...................... 2.5

(G) Evaporator Core, Renew
Includes: Evacuate and charge system.
1983-87 (2.0).............................. 3.5

(G) Thermostatic Control Switch, Renew
1983-87 (.2)................................ .4

(G) High Pressure Cut-Off Switch, Renew
1983-87 (.2)................................ .3

(G) Pressure Cycling Switch, Renew
1983-87 (.2)................................ .3

(Factory Time) Chilton Time

(G) Expansion Tube (Orifice), Renew
Includes: Evacuate and charge system.
1983-87 (.7)................................ 1.4

(G) Accumulator Assembly, Renew
Includes: Evacuate and charge system.
1983-87 (.8)................................ 1.5

(G) Air Conditioner Control Assy., Renew
1983-87 (.5)................................ .8
Touch control (.4)........................ .6

(G) Blower Motor, Renew
1983-87 (.2)................................ .5

(G) Blower Motor Switch, Renew
1983-87 (.4)................................ .6

(G) Blower Motor Resistor, Renew
1983-87 (.2)................................ .3

(G) Blower Motor Relay, Renew
1983-87 (.2)................................ .3

(G) Master Electrical Switch, Renew
1983-87 (.4)................................ .6

(G) Vacuum Selector Valve, Renew
1983-87 (.5)................................ .6

(G) Vacuum Actuators, Renew
1983-87
Defroster (1.1)........................... 2.0
Upper or Lower mode (1.7)......... 2.7
Air Inlet (.5) 9

(G) Air Conditioning Hoses, Renew
Includes: Evacuate and charge system.
1983-87-one (1.1)........................ 1.7
each adtnl (.3).......................... .5
Assemble repl. hose add (.3)............ .4

AUTOMATIC CLIMATE CONTROL

(G) Programmer, Renew
1983-85 (.4)................................ .6
Renew programmer parts add
vacuum valve (.1)....................... .2
vacuum motor (.2)....................... .3
circuit board (.3)....................... .4
transducer (.1)........................... .2
amplifier (.3)............................. .4
feed back pot (.3)....................... .4
out put shaft (.1)........................ .4
vacuum relay (.1)........................ .2
blower contacts (.2).................... .3
blower switch (.2)....................... .3

(G) In-Car Sensor, Renew
1983-87 (.3)................................ .5

(G) Ambient Sensor, Renew
1983-87 (.2)................................ .5

(G) Potentiometer (Thumb Wheel), Renew
1983 (.5).................................... .8

(G) Aspirator Hose, Renew
1983-87 (.3)................................ .4

(G) A.C. Aspirator, Renew
1983-87 (.3)................................ .5

(G) Electric Actuators, Renew
1983-87
Upper or Lower mode (.5)............ .9
Air Inlet (.5) 9

PARTS 28 AIR CONDITIONING 28 PARTS

	Part No.	Price
COMPRESSOR 4 CYLINDER RADIAL		
Compressor Assembly		
1983-87-exc. below	◆12300273	390.00
V-6 diesel	◆12309216	N.L.
Turbo (1986-87)	12323439	N.L.
1983-87	◆12309216	390.00
Compressor Clutch Plate and Hub Assy.		
1983-87	◆6551220	32.50
Turbo (1986-87)	◆6551838	36.00
Compressor Clutch Rotor w/Bearing		
1983-87-exc. below	◆6551216	67.50
V-6 diesel (1983-84)	◆6551884	108.50
Compressor Clutch Pulley and Rim		
1983-87	◆6556715	13.00
Compressor Shaft Seal Kit		
1983-87	◆9956695	13.00
Turbo (1986-87)	◆2724319	11.25
Compressor Front Head		
1983-87	◆6551142	28.25
Compressor Discharge Valve Plate w/ Valves		
1983-87	◆6551141	11.50

	Part No.	Price
Compressor Thrust Washer Kit		
1983-87	9956685	4.50
Kit contains 2 thrust washers and 1 belleville washer.		
Compressor Main Bearing		
1983-87	◆6556572	4.00
Compressor Shell Assembly		
1983-87	◆2724158	38.00
Compressor Shaft and Cylinder Assembly		
1983-87	◆2724144	269.00
Compressor Pressure Relief Valve		
1983-87	◆5914435	13.50
Condenser		
1983-87	◆3041841	170.00
Evaporator Core		
(exc. Turbo)		
1983-84	◆3037638	201.50
1985-87	◆3058311	275.75
(Turbo)		
1983	3039130	213.50
1984	3056795	200.25
1985-87	3058083	276.50
Accumulator-Dehydrator		
1983	◆2724240	80.00
1984-87-exc. Turbo	◆2724265	87.75
Turbo	3058262	96.50

	Part No.	Price
Control Assembly-Manual A/C		
1983	16002900	25.50
1984-87	16034664	37.00
Blower Motor		
1983-87	◆22020945	60.00
Blower Motor Switch		
1983	◆16015256	6.00
1984-87	◆16032480	7.50
Blower Motor Resistor		
1983-84	◆526897	4.50
1985-87	◆10039426	4.50
AUTOMATIC CLIMATE CONTROL		
Programmer		
1983-87	25512087	170.00
In Car Sensor		
1983-87	25512086	7.75
Ambient Sensor		
1983-87	25502279	16.75
Control Assembly		
1983	25512126	112.00
1984-87	25517962	112.00
Vacuum Selector Valve		
1983-87	◆7897082	3.50

LABOR 29 LOCKS, HINGES & WIND. REGULATORS 29 LABOR

(Factory Time)	Chilton Time
(G) Hood Latch, Renew	
1983-87 (.2)	.5
(G) Hood Hinge, Renew	
1983-87-one (.3)	.4
both (.6)	.7
(G) Hood Release Cable, Renew	
1983-87 (.3)	.6
(G) Door Lock, Renew (One)	
Front	
1983-87 (.5)	.7
Rear	
1983-85 (.6)	.9
(G) Door Lock Remote Control, Renew (Front or Rear)	
1983-87 (.3)	.5
(G) Door Lock Cylinder, Renew	
1983-87 (.3)	.5
Recode cyl add (.3)	.3

(Factory Time)	Chilton Time
(G) Door Handle (Outside), Renew (Front or Rear)	
1983-87 (.4)	.6
Renew insert add	.1
(G) Lock Striker Plate, Renew	
1983-87 (.2)	.2
(G) Door Window Regulator (Manual), Renew	
Front	
1983-87 (.7)	1.0
(G) Door Window Regulator (Electric), Renew	
Front	
1983-87 (.9)	1.3

(Factory Time)	Chilton Time
(G) Trunk Lock, Renew	
1983-87 (.2)	.3
(G) Trunk Lock Cylinder, Renew	
1983-87 (.2)	.3
Recode cyl add (.3)	.3
(G) Rear Compartment Lid Hinge Strap, Renew (One)	
1983-87 (.8)	1.2
(G) Tail Gate Lock Assy., Renew	
1983 (.3)	.5
(G) Tail Gate Lock Cylinder, Renew	
1983 (.3)	.5
Recode cyl add (.3)	.3
(G) Tail Gate Lock Remote Control, Renew	
1983 (.3)	.5

PARTS 29 LOCKS, HINGES & WIND. REGULATORS 29 PARTS

	Part No.	Price
Hood Lock		
1983-87	◆14070703	16.25
Hood Hinge (R.H.)		
1983-87	◆14064326	16.75
Front Door Lock (R.H.)		
1983-84-2 dr.	◆20293612	33.50
4 dr.	◆20293604	51.50
1985-87	◆20298852	37.25
Limited (G47)	◆20293612	33.25
Rear Door Lock (R.H.)		
1983-87	◆20293624	55.75

	Part No.	Price
Front Door Lock Cylinder (w/Keys)		
1983-87 (uncoded)		
2 dr.	◆9632762	5.75
4 dr.	◆9632769	7.75
Trunk Lock		
1983-87	◆20279741	N.L.
Frt. & Rear Outer Door Handle (R.H.)		
1983	◆20099250	24.75
1984-87 (G47)	20454212	23.75
(G69)	◆20099250	24.75
Trunk Hinges (Strap & Link)		
1983-87-2 dr.	◆20343192	24.40
4 dr.	20354294	18.25

	Part No.	Price
Window Regulator-Manual		
(Front R.H.)		
1983-87-2 dr.	◆20094576	64.00
4 dr	◆20244864	59.50
Window Regulator-Electric		
(Front R.H.)		
1983-87-2 dr.	◆20123184	98.00
1983-87-4 dr.	◆20209182	98.00
(Rear R.H.)		
Window Regulator Motor		
1983-87	◆22020900	73.00

LABOR 30 HEAD AND PARKING LAMPS 30 LABOR

(Factory Time) — Chilton Time

(G) Aim Headlamps
two 4
four 6

(M) Headlamp Sealed Beam Bulb, Renew
1983-87-each (.3) 3

(M) License Lamp Assembly, Renew
1983-87 (.2) 3

(M) Back-Up Lamp Assembly, Renew
1983-87-each (.3) 4

(M) Cornering Lamp Assembly, Renew
1983-87-each (.3) 4

(M) Park and Turn Signal Lamp Assy., Renew
1983-87-each (.3) 4

(M) Stop, Tail and Turn Signal Lamp Assy., Renew
1983-87-each (.3) 4

(M) Back-Up Lamp Bulb, Renew
All models-one (.2) 3

(M) Cornering Lamp Bulb, Renew
All models-each (.2) 3

(M) License Lamp Bulb, Renew
All models-one or all (.2) 3

(M) Park and Turn Signal Lamp Bulb, Renew
All models-each 2

(M) Side Marker Lamp Bulb, Renew
All models-each 2

(M) Stop, Tail and Turn Signal Lamp Bulb, Renew
All models-one 2
each adtnl 1

PARTS 30 HEAD AND PARKING LAMPS 30 PARTS

	Part No.	Price
Sealed Beam Unit		
(wo/Quartz)		
1983-87		
Outer	◆5966200	15.00
Inner	◆5966201	15.00
(Quartz)		
1983-87		
Outer (1983)	◆16502327	22.50
Outer (1984-87)	◆16502327	22.50
Inner	◆5930567	22.50
Taillamp Lens (R.H.)		
1983-2 dr.	5971970	63.25
4 dr.	16500866	65.75
1984-87-2 dr.	16501874	53.00
4 dr.	16501604	29.75
High Mount Stoplight		
1985-87	◆5974472	36.00

LABOR 31 WINDSHIELD WIPER & SPEEDOMETER 31 LABOR

(Factory Time) — Chilton Time

(G) Windshield Wiper Motor, Renew
1983-87 (.5) 8
w/Inter wiper add (.1) 1

(G) Windshield Wiper Motor, R&R and Recondition
1983-87 (1.0) 1.4

Wiper Motor Main Drive Gear (Depressed Park), Renew
1983-87 (.7) 1.4

(G) Wiper Motor Terminal Board and/or Timing Delay Switch, Renew
1983-87 (.5) 1.0

(G) Wiper Transmission, Renew (One)
1983-87 (.4) 6

(G) Wiper Switch, Renew
1983-87
std colm (.9) 1.4
tilt colm (.7) 1.3

(G) Windshield Washer Pump, Renew
1983-85 (.2) 4
1986-87 (.6) 8
w/Pulse wipe add 1

(G) Windshield Washer Pump, R&R and Recondition
1983-85 (.5) 8
1986-87 (.9) 1.2

(G) Windshield Washer Pump Valve, Renew
1983-87 (.2) 4

(G) Speedometer Head, R&R or Renew
1983-87 (.4) 8
Reset odometer add 2

(G) Speedometer Cable and Casing, Renew
wo/Cruise control
1983-87 (.7) 1.1
w/Cruise control
1983-87-upper cable (.7) 1.1
lower cable (.3) 5
both (.9) 1.4
one piece (.8) 1.2

(G) Speedometer Cable (Inner), Renew or Lubricate
wo/Cruise control
1983 (.3) 6
1984-87 (.7) 1.1
w/Cruise control
1983-87-upper cable (.4) 6
lower cable (.3) 5
both (.4) 7
one piece (.7) 1.1

(G) Radio, R&R
1983-87 (.4) 7
w/A.C. add (.2) 2

PARTS 31 WINDSHIELD WIPER & SPEEDOMETER 31 PARTS

	Part No.	Price
Wiper Motor		
1983-exc. Pulse	◆4960974	84.00
Pulse wiper	◆4961608	80.00
1984-87	◆22039687	110.75
Wiper Transmission (R.H.)		
1983-87	◆22009387	18.50
Windshield Washer Pump		
1983-exc. Pulse	◆22009212	25.00
Pulse wiper	◆22021345	38.50
1984-87	◆22039686	16.25

Speedometer Head Cable
Order by year and model.

LABOR 32 LIGHT SWITCHES & WIRING 32 LABOR

	(Factory Time)	Chilton Time
(G) Headlamp Switch, Renew		
1983-87	(.3)	.5
(G) Headlamp Dimmer Switch, Renew		
1983-87 column mounted	(.3)	.7
(G) Stop Light Switch, Renew		
1983-87	(.3)	.4
(G) Parking Brake Switch, Renew		
1983-87	(.3)	.4
(G) Neutral Safety and Back-Up Light Switch, Renew		
1983-87	(.3)	.4
(G) Turn Signal or Hazard Warning Switch, Renew		
w/Cruise control add	(.1)	.1
1983-87	(.7)	1.1
(M) Turn Signal or Hazard Warning Flasher, Renew		
1983-87	(.2)	.2
(G) Horn Relay, Renew		
1983-87	(.2)	.3
(G) Horn, Renew		
1983-87	(.3)	.3
(G) Chassis Wiring Harness, Renew		
Headlamp		
1983-87	(.9)	1.4
Engine		
1983-87	(1.0)	1.8
Instrument panel		
1983-87	(2.3)	3.0
Fuse block		
1983-87	(.7)	1.2

PARTS 32 LIGHT SWITCHES & WIRING 32 PARTS

	Part No.	Price
Headlight Switch		
(wo/Twilight sentinel)		
1983	◆1995212	28.00
1984-87	1987380	16.00
(Twilight sentinel)		
1983	◆1995232	41.50
1984-87	1987384	16.75
Headlamp Dimmer Switch		
1983-87	◆7838234	12.50
Stop Light Switch		
(With Power Brakes-exc. Cruise Cont.)		
1983-84	◆25504628	3.75
1985-87	◆25524846	6.50
(With Cruise Control)		
1983-84	◆9794682	7.75
1985-87	◆25524847	6.50
Turn Signal Switch		
1983-87-exc. below	◆1997983	30.00
Cornering lamps	◆1997984	35.00
Turn Signal Flasher		
1983-84	◆10029240	4.25
1985-87	◆10041073	4.25
Back-Up Light Switch		
1983-87	◆22509632	5.50
Chassis Wiring Harness		
Order by year and model.		
Horn		
1983-87-low note	◆1892163	22.00
high note	◆1892164	22.00
Horn Relay		
1983-87	◆25513270	8.50

LABOR 33 GLASS 33 LABOR

	(Factory Time)	Chilton Time
(G) Windshield, Renew		
1983-87	(1.2)	1.8
Renew caulk bead add	(.4)	.4
(G) Front Door Glass, Renew		
1983-87-2 dr	(1.0)	1.6
4 dr	(.8)	1.2
(G) Rear Door Glass, Renew		
1983-85	(.3)	.6
(G) Quarter Window Glass (Stationary), Renew		
1983-87-sdn	(.8)	1.0
sta wag	(1.0)	1.5
2 dr coupe	(.5)	.9
(G) Tail Gate Window Glass, Renew		
1983	(.3)	.4
(G) Rear Door Vent Glass, Renew		
1983-87	(.3)	.5
(G) Back Window Glass, Renew		
1983-87	(1.3)	2.0
w/Elec defogger add	(.6)	.6
w/3/4 plug, unpadded add	(1.3)	2.0
w/3/4 plug, padded add	(2.6)	4.0
w/Full plug, padded add	(2.8)	4.4

LABOR 34 CRUISE CONTROL 34 LABOR

	(Factory Time)	Chilton Time
(G) Cruise Control Transducer Assy., Adjust		
1983	(.3)	.4
(G) Cruise Control Regulator (Transducer), Renew		
1983	(.4)	.6
Adj low spd switch add	(.1)	.1
(G) Cruise Control Engagement Switch, Renew		
1983-87	(.5)	.9
(G) Cruise Control Servo Assy., Renew		
Includes: Adjust bead chain.		
1983-87	(.3)	.5
(G) Cruise Control Vacuum Hoses, Renew		
1983-87-one or all	(.2)	.2
(G) Cruise Control Chain or Cable (Servo. to Carb.), Renew		
1983-87	(.2)	.4
(G) Cruise Control Transducer Filter, Renew		
1983	(.2)	.3
(G) Cruise Control Resume Solenoid, Renew		
1983	(.2)	.3
(G) Cruise Control Vacuum Regulator Valve, Renew		
1983-84	(.2)	.3
(G) Cruise Control Check Valve, Renew		
1983-84	(.2)	.4
(G) Cruise Control Module, Renew		
1984-87	(.3)	.5

	Part No.	Price
Cruise Control Power Unit		
1983		
231-exc. Turbo	◆25030981	19.50
231-Turbo	25031751	33.25
252	◆25030983	19.50
Diesel	◆25030980	32.75
1984-87		
V-6-Exc. Turbo	◆25074630	116.25
V-6-Turbo	◆25074627	117.00
V-6-Diesel	◆25074629	123.50
Cruise Control Lever & Switch		
1983-exc. Pulse	◆25031426	52.25
Pulse wiper	◆25031425	52.25
1984-87-exc.		
Pulse	◆25031457	50.00
Pulse wiper	◆25031456	50.00
Cruise Control Transducer		
1983-exc. below	◆25031261	158.00
non-turbo 231	◆25030878	158.00
Diesel	◆25031604	179.25
Cruise Control Brake Release Switch		
1983-87	◆9794682	8.00
Cruise Control Chain & Ball		
1983-87	◆25031314	3.25

Cadillac Deville • Fleetwood

GROUP INDEX

ALPHABETICAL INDEX

General Motors
Rear Wheel Drive Cars

CADILLAC DEVILLE • FLEETWOOD

1983–87 Cadillac

VEHICLE IDENTIFICATION NUMBER (VIN)

It is important for servicing and ordering parts to be certain of the vehicle and engine identification. The VIN (vehicle identification number) is a 17 digit number visible through the windshield on the driver's side of the dash and contains the vehicle and engine identification codes. It can be interpreted as follows:

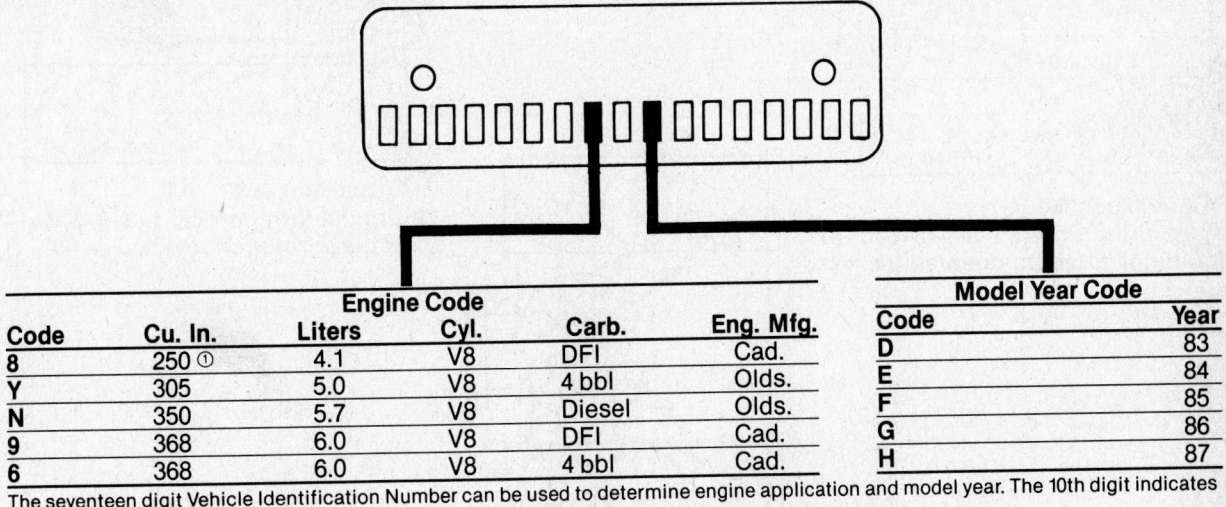

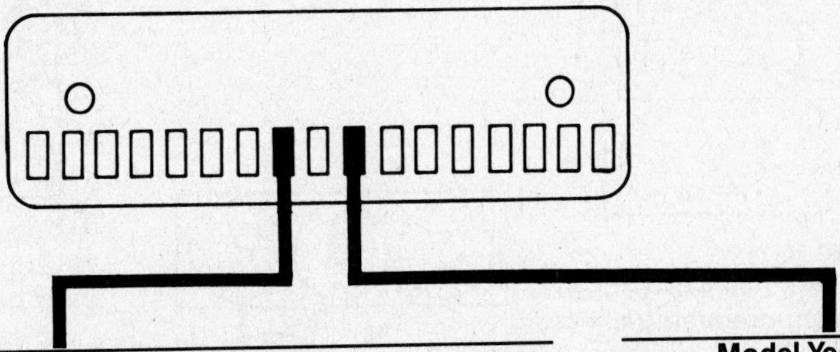

Engine Code

Code	Cu. In.	Liters	Cyl.	Carb.	Eng. Mfg.
8	250 ①	4.1	V8	DFI	Cad.
Y	305	5.0	V8	4 bbl	Olds.
N	350	5.7	V8	Diesel	Olds.
9	368	6.0	V8	DFI	Cad.
6	368	6.0	V8	4 bbl	Cad.

Model Year Code

Code	Year
D	83
E	84
F	85
G	86
H	87

The seventeen digit Vehicle Identification Number can be used to determine engine application and model year. The 10th digit indicates the model year, and the 8th digit identifies the factory installed engine.

① HT4100 engine

TUNE-UP SPECIFICATIONS

When analyzing compression test results, look for uniformity among cylinders rather than specific pressures

Year	VIN Code	Cyl.	Engine Displacement cu. in.	Engine Liters	Mfg.	Fuel Delivery	Spark Plugs Orig. Type	Spark Plugs Gap (in.)	Distributor Point Dwell (deg)	Distributor Point Gap (in.)	Ignition Timing (deg) Auto. Trans.	Valves Intake Opens ▪(deg)	Fuel Pump Pressure (psi)	Idle Speed (rpm) Auto. Trans.
'83	N	V8	350	5.7	Olds.	Diesel	—	—	—		②	16	5.5–6.5	②
	8	V8	250 ①	4.1	Cad.	D.F.I.	R43NTS6	.060	Electronic		10B	20	12–14	450
	9	V8	368	6.0	Cad.	D.F.I.	R45NSX	.060	Electronic		10B	11	12–14	450
	6	V8	368	6.0	Cad.	4 bbl	R45NSX	.060	Electronic		10B	11	5.5–6.5	450
'84	N	V8	350	5.7	Olds.	Diesel	—	—	Electronic		②	16	5.5–6.5	②
	8	V8	250 ①	4.1	Cad.	D.F.I.	R42CLTS6	.060	Electronic		10B	20	12–14	450
	6	V8	368	6.0	Cad.	4 bbl	R45NSX	.060	Electronic		10B	11	5.5–6.5	550/650
'85	N	V8	350	5.7	Olds.	Diesel	—	—	—		②	16	5.5–6.5	②
	8	V8	250 ①	4.1	Cad.	D.F.I.	R44LTS6	.060	Electronic		10B	20	12–14	450
	6	V8	368	6.0	Cad.	4 bbl	R45NSX	.060	Electronic		10B	11	5.5–6.5	550/650
'86–'87	8	V8	250 ①	4.1	Cad.	D.F.I.	R42CLTS6	.060	Electronic		10B	20	12–14	450
	6	V8	368	6.0	Cad.	4 bbl	R45NSX	.060	Electronic		10B	11	5.5–6.5	550/650
	Y	V8	307	5.0	Olds.	4 bbl	FR3LS6	.060	Electronic		20B	N/A	5.5–6.5	425/475

NOTE: The underhood specifications sticker often reflects tune-up specification changes made in production. Sticker figures must be used if they disagree with those in this chart. Part numbers in this chart are not recommendations by Chilton for any product by brand name.

▪ All figures Before Top Dead Center

DFI Digital Fuel Injection
—Not applicable

B Before top dead center
N/A Not available
① HT4100 engine
② See underhood sticker

FIRING ORDERS

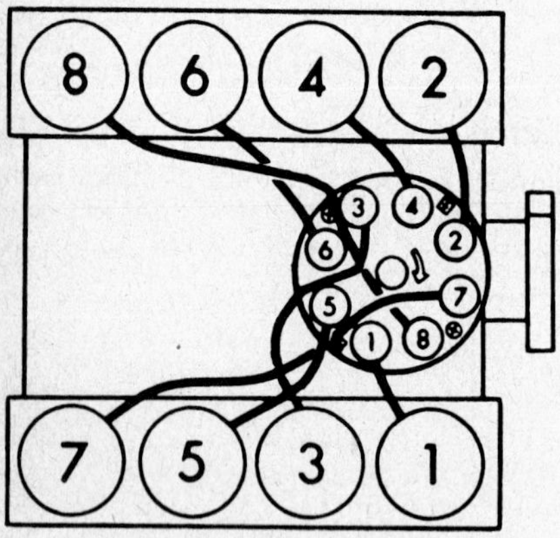

GM (Cadillac) 250 (4.1L) V8
Engine firing order: 1–8–4–3–6–5–7–2
Distributor rotation: counterclockwise

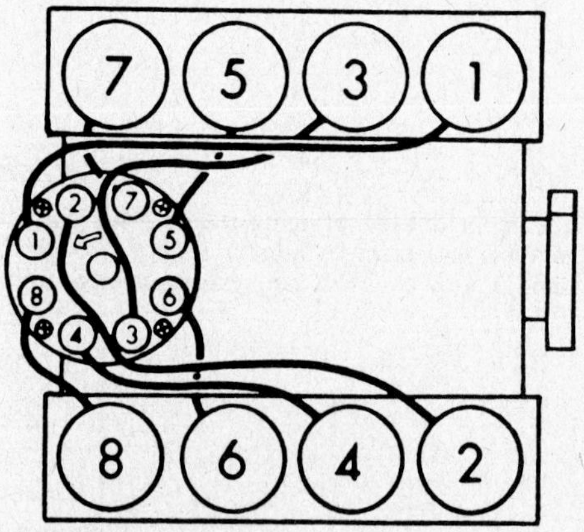

GM (Cadillac) 368
V8 Engine firing order: 1–5–6–3–4–2–7–8
Distributor rotation: clockwise

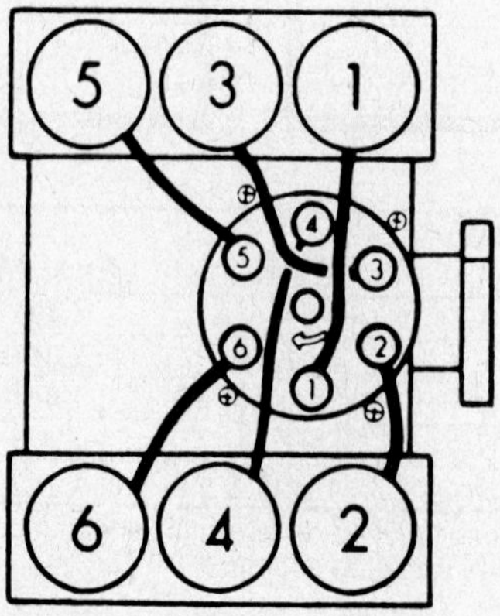

GM (Buick) 252 (4.1L) V6
Engine firing order: 1–6–5–4–3–2
Distributor rotation: clockwise

FIELD SERVICE AND STATIC CHECKING (CURB) * * *				
		TOLERANCES		
ITEM	SET TO SPEC. (1)	(1) CUSTOMER SERVICE SETTING	(2) WARRANTY DIAGNOSIS	(3) PERIODIC INSPECTION
CAMBER	+0.50°	±0.40°	±0.80°	±1.50°
CROSS-CAMBER (LH MINUS RH)	0.0°	±0.50°	± 1.00°**	—
CASTER	+4.00°	±0.50°	±1.00°	±2.00°
CROSS-CASTER (LH MINUS RH)	0.0°	±0.50°	±1.00°**	—
TOE PER WHEEL	0.12°	±0.06°	±0.12°*	±0.38°
SPOKE ANGLE	0.0°	±5.00°	±10.00°	—

** CROSS-CAMBER AND CROSS-CASTER NOT TO EXCEED 1° MAX. PER VEHICLE
* 1/8'' TOE IS EQUIVALENT TO AN ANGLE MEASUREMENT OF .12° PER WHEEL
*** CURB HEIGHT INCLUDES FULL TANK OF FUEL OR EQUIVALENT COMPENSATING WEIGHT.

SUGGESTED SHIM CHANGE TO CORRECT CASTER — CAMBER ALIGNMENT (TOTAL THICKNESS CHANGE IN THOUSANDTHS OF AN INCH)

MEASURED CAMBER READING (CURB) * * *		MEASURED CASTER READING (CURB) * * * +4½°	+4°	+3½°	+3°	+2½°	+2°	+1½°
+1½°	FRONT	+.27	+.24	+.21	+.18	+.15	+.12	+.09
	REAR	+.045	−.09	+.135	+.18	+.225	+.27	+.315
+1°	FRONT	+.18	+.15	+.12	+.09	+.06	+.03	.00
	REAR	−.045	.00	+.045	+.09	+.135	+.18	+.225
+½°	FRONT	+.09	+.06	+.03	.00	−.03	−.06	−.09
	REAR	−.135	−.09	+.045	.00	+.045	+.09	+.135
+0°	FRONT	.00	−.03	−.06	−.09	−.12	−.15	−.18
	REAR	−.225	−.18	−.135	−.09	−.045	.00	+.045
−½°	FRONT	−.09	−.12	−.15	−.18	−.21	−.24	−.27
	REAR	−.315	−.27	−.225	−.18	−.135	−.09	−.045
−1°	FRONT	−.18	−.21	−.24	−.27	−.30	−.33	−.36
	REAR	−.405	−.36	−.315	−.27	−.225	−.18	−.135

(+) = ADD SHIMS AND (−) = REMOVE SHIMS. SHIM USAGE THICKNESS DIFFERENCE BETWEEN FRONT AND REAR ATTACHMENT SHOULD NOT EXCEED .40 IN. MAXIMUM SHIM USAGE IN FRONT AND/OR REAR LOCATION NOT TO EXCEED .60 IN.

Wheel alignment specifications and shim applications for the 1983 and later Brougham

WHEEL ALIGNMENT SPECIFICATIONS

Year	Model	Caster Range (deg)	Caster Pref Setting (deg)	Camber Range (deg)	Camber Pref Setting (deg)	Toe-in (in.)	Steering Axis Inclin. (deg)
'83–'87	Cadillac (RWD)	2P to 4P	3P	5/16N to 1 5/16P	1/2P	1/8	10 19/32

N Negative
P Positive

LABOR — SERVICE BAY OPERATIONS — LABOR

(Factory Time) Chilton Time

COOLING

(M) Winterize Cooling System
Includes: Run engine to check for leaks, tighten all hose connections. Test radiator and pressure cap, drain radiator and engine block. Add anti-freeze and refill system.
All models 5

(G) Thermostat, Renew
1983-87-V-6 (.7) 1.0
V-8 (.3) 5
Diesel (.5) 7

(M) Radiator Hose, Renew
1983-87-upper (.3) 4
lower (.5) 6
both (.6) 8

(M) Fan Belt, Adjust
1983-87-one (.2) 3
each adtnl (.1) 1

(M) Fan Belt, Renew
1983-87 (.3) 4

(M) Drive Belt, Adjust
1983-85
w/Eng Code 8
one or all (.4) 5

(M) Drive Belt, Renew
1983-85
w/Eng Code 8
A.C. (.6) 8
AIR (.5) 7
Alter (.3) 4
Vacuum Pump (.2) 3

FUEL

(M) Carburetor Air Cleaner, Service
All models (.2) 3

(G) Carburetor, Adjust (On Car)
All models
Curb & Fast Idle (.5) 7
Vacuum Break-both (.3) 4
Choke (.7) 1.0
Complete (1.3) 1.8

(G) Choke Cover and/or Gasket, Renew
1986-87 (.6) 1.0

(G) Needle Valve and Seat and/or Float, Renew
1986-87 (.8) 1.2
To perform C.C.C. system check, add (.5) 1.0

(G) Accelerator Pump, Renew
1986-87 (.7) 1.0

CHILTON'S 10 POINT SAFETY CHECK

CHECK OPERATION & CONDITION OF THE FOLLOWING ITEMS:

1. Legal Registration (serial no.)
2. Tires & Wheels
3. Brake System (R&R all wheels)
4. Light Systems & Signals
5. Accelerator Linkage, Neutral Safety Switch, Shift Indicator Pointer & Seat Position Locks
6. Glass, Mirrors, Door Locks, Seat Belts & Harness
7. Wipers, Washers & Defrosters
8. Frame, Steering, Shocks, Front & Rear Suspension
9. Fuel & Exhaust Systems
10. Road Test Vehicle

All models 1.0
Exhaust Smog Analysis, add 4

(Factory Time) Chilton Time

BRAKES

(G) Brakes, Adjust (Minor)
Includes: R&R wheels and adjust brakes thru access holes in drums. Fill master cylinder.
two wheels 4
Remove knock out plugs add, each 1

(G) Bleed Brakes (Four Wheels)
Includes: Fill master cylinder.
All models (.4) 6

(M) Parking Brake, Adjust
All models (.3) 4

LUBRICATION SERVICE

(M) Lubricate Chassis, Change Oil & Filter
Includes: Inspect and correct all fluid levels.
All models 6
Install grease fittings add 1

(M) Lubricate Chassis
Includes: Inspect and correct all fluid levels.
All models 4
Install grease fittings add 1

(M) Engine Oil & Filter, Change
Includes: Inspect and correct all fluid levels.
All models 4

(Factory Time) Chilton Time

WHEELS

(M) Wheel, Renew
one (.5) 5

(G) Wheels, Balance
one 3
each adtnl 2

(G) Wheels, Rotate (All)
All models 5

(G) Front Wheel Bearings, Clean and Repack (Both Wheels)
1983-87 .... 1.6

(G) Front Wheel Grease Seals, Renew
1983-87-one whl (.7) 8
both whls (1.1) 1.5

ELECTRICAL

(M) Battery Cables, Renew
1983-85-positive (.4) 4
ground (.2) 3
batt to batt (.2) 3
1986-87-positive (.5) 6
negative (.2) 3

(M) Battery Terminals, Clean
All models 3

(G) Aim Headlamps
two 4
four 6

(M) Headlamp Sealed Beam Bulb, Renew
1983-87-each (.3) 3

(G) Headlamp Switch, Renew
1983-87 (.3) 7

(G) Headlamp Dimmer Switch, Renew
1983-87
column mount (.5) 7

(G) Stop Light Switch, Renew
1983-87 (.3) 3

(G) Turn Signal Switch, Renew
1983-87-std (.7) 1.1
tilt whl (.9) 1.4

(G) Back-Up Lamp and Park/Neutral Switch, Renew
1983-87 (.3) 4

(M) Turn Signal or Hazard Warning Flasher, Renew
1983-87 (.3) 3

(G) Horn, Renew
1983-87-each (.3) 4

(G) Horn Relay, Renew
1983-87 (.2) 4

LABOR 1 TUNE UP 1 LABOR

	(Factory Time)	Chilton Time
(G) Compression Test		
V-8–1983-87		.8
w/A.I.R. add		.2
w/A.C. add		.3

(G) Engine Tune Up, (Electronic Ignition)

Includes: Test battery and clean connections. Tighten manifold and carburetor mounting bolts. Check engine compression, clean and adjust or renew spark plugs. Test resistance of spark plug cables. Inspect distributor cap and rotor. Adjust air gap. Check vacuum advance operation. Reset ignition timing. Adjust idle mixture and idle speed. Service air cleaner. Inspect and adjust drive belts. Inspect choke operation and adjust or free up. Check operation of EGR valve.

	(Factory Time)	Chilton Time
V-8–1983-87		3.0
To perform C.C.C. system test add		1.0

LABOR 2 IGNITION SYSTEM 2 LABOR

GASOLINE ENGINES

	(Factory Time)	Chilton Time
(G) Spark Plugs, Clean and Reset or Renew		
1983-87	(.5)	.6
To clean add		.2
(G) Ignition Timing, Reset		
1983-87	(.3)	.4
(G) Distributor, Renew		
Includes: Reset ignition timing.		
1983-87	(.6)	.8
(G) Distributor, R&R and Recondition		
Includes: Reset ignition timing.		
1983-87	(.9)	1.5
(G) Distributor Cap and/or Rotor, Renew		
1983-87	(.3)	.4
(G) Vacuum Control Unit, Renew		
Includes: Reset ignition timing.		
1983-87	(.4)	.8
(G) Ignition Coil, Renew		
1983-87	(.3)	.4
(G) Ignition Cables, Renew		
1983-87	(.4)	.8
(G) Ignition Switch, Renew		
1983-87	(.6)	.9
(G) Ignition Key Warning Switch, Renew		
1983-87	(.6)	1.0
(G) Ignition Lock Cylinder, Renew		
1983-87	(.4)	.7
w/Cruise control add	(.1)	.1
w/Tilt Tel add	(.1)	.1
Recode cyl add	(.5)	.5
(G) Distributor Module, Renew		
1983-87	(.3)	.6
(G) Distributor Pick-Up Coil and/or Pole Piece, Renew		
Includes: R&R distributor and main shaft assy.		
1983-87	(.7)	.9
(G) Distributor Capacitor and/or Module Wiring Harness, Renew		
Includes: R&R cap and rotor, check and adjust timing.		
1983-87	(.3)	.6
(G) Distributor Shaft, Renew		
1983-87	(.5)	.9

DIESEL IGNITION COMPONENTS

	(Factory Time)	Chilton Time
(G) Glow Plugs, Renew		
1983-85		
one		.4
one-each bank		.7
all-both banks		1.3
(G) Glow Plug Control Module, Renew (Controller)		
1983-85	(.4)	.6
(G) Coolant Fast Idle Temperature Switch, Renew		
1983-85	(.2)	.4
(G) Fast Idle Solenoid, Renew		
1983-85	(.3)	.4
(G) Glow Plug Relay, Renew		
1983-84	(.3)	.5
(G) Glow Plug Control Switch, Renew		
1983-84	(.3)	.4

PARTS 2 ELECTRONIC IGNITION 2 PARTS

	Part No.	Price
Distributor Assembly		
V-8-250		
1983-84	1103706	306.75
1985-exc.		
Calif.	1103706	306.75
Calif.	1103707	306.75
V-8-368		
1983-84	1103455	347.50
V-8-307		
1986-87	◆1103602	275.00
(1) Distributor Cover		
1983-87	◆1875960	6.00
(2) Coil		
1983-87-exc.		
368	◆1985474	36.00
368	◆1985473	36.00
(3) Cap		
1983-87-exc.		
368	◆1977046	24.50
368	◆1974408	17.00
(4) Rotor		
1983-87	◆1977026	6.50
(5) Shaft		
V-8-250		
1983-85	◆1979556	38.00

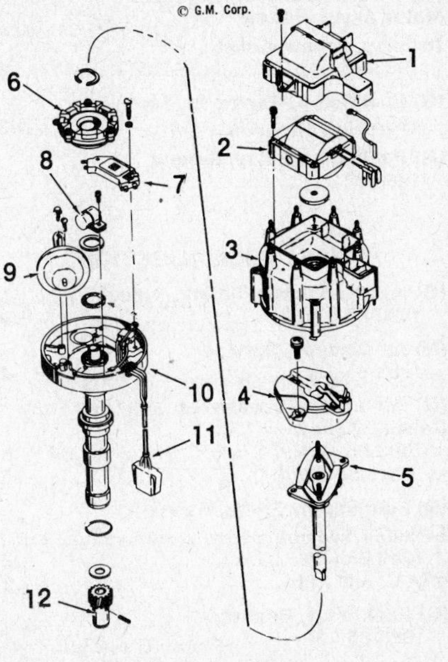

	Part No.	Price
V-8-368		
1983-84	◆1976909	38.50
V-8-307		
1986-87	◆1989612	42.25
(6) Pole Piece and Plate Assy.		
V-8-250		
1983-85	◆1977207	32.00
V-8-368 engine		
1983-84	◆1976897	30.25
V-8-307		
1986-87	◆1977207	31.75
(7) Module		
1983-87-exc.		
C.C.	◆1976908	60.00
Comm. Chassis	1894308	95.00
(8) Capacitor		
1983-87	◆1876154	4.50
(9) Vacuum Control		
1983-87-C.C.	1973719	24.75
(10) Housing		
V-8-250		
1983-84	◆1979554	66.50
1985-exc. Calif.	10497572	66.50
Calif.	◆1988883	40.25

PARTS 2 IGNITION SYSTEM 2 PARTS

	Part No.	Price
V-8–368		
1983-87	1979112	73.25
C.C.	1975338	49.50
V-8–307		
1986-87	◆1977208	34.00
(11) Harness Terminal Block		
1983-87-exc. 368	◆1892261	11.00
(12) Gear		
1983-87-250	◆1979546	37.00
1983-84-368	◆1958599	14.25
Ignition Wires		
Order by year and model.		

DIESEL IGNITION SYSTEM

	Part No.	Price
Glow Plugs		
1983	◆5613680	19.00
1984-85	◆5613826	16.50
Glow Plug Wire		
1983	12017848	66.75
Glow Plug Relay		
1983	◆560580	16.00
Glow Plug Module		
1984	◆22520348	91.75
Glow Plug Controller		
1985	◆22528337	96.00

LABOR 3 FUEL SYSTEM 3 LABOR

(Factory Time)	Chilton Time
(G) Fuel Pump, Test	
Includes: Disconnect line at carburetor, attach pressure gauge.	
All models	.2
(M) Carburetor Air Cleaner, Service	
All models (.2)	.3
(G) Carburetor, Adjust (On Car)	
All models	
Curb & Fast Idle (.5)	.7
Vacuum Break-both (.3)	.4
Choke (.7)	1.0
Complete (1.3)	1.8
(G) Choke Cover and/or Gasket, Renew	
1986-87 (.6)	1.0
(G) Needle Valve and Seat and/or Float, Renew	
1986-87 (.8)	1.2
To perform C.C.C. system check, add (.5)	1.0
(G) Accelerator Pump, Renew	
1986-87 (.7)	1.0
(G) Carburetor Assembly, Renew	
Includes: All necessary adjustments.	
1986-87 (.6)	1.0
To perform C.C.C. system check, add (.5)	1.0
(G) Carburetor, R&R and Clean or Recondition	
Includes: All necessary adjustments.	
1986-87 (2.1)	3.0
To perform C.C.C. system check, add (.5)	1.0
(G) E.F.E. Heater (Insulator), Renew	
1986-87 (.6)	1.0
(M) Fuel Filter Element, Renew	
All models (.3)	.4
(G) Idle Stop Solenoid, Renew	
1986-87 (.6)	1.0
(G) Fuel Pump, Renew	
1986-87 (1.2)	1.6
(G) Fuel Tank, Renew	
Includes: Transfer float if required.	
1983-87 (.7)	1.2
(G) Fuel Gauge (Tank), Renew	
1983-87 (.9)	1.4
(G) Water In Fuel Detector, Renew (WIF)	
All models (.9)	1.2
(G) Fuel Gauge (Dash), Renew	
1983-85 (.3)	.5
1986-87 (.5)	.9
(G) Intake Manifold or Gaskets, Renew	
V-8–1983-85 (1.2)	1.7
1983-85 Eng Code 8 (5.1)	7.1
1986-87 Eng Codes Y-9 (2.6)	3.6
Renew manif add (.3)	.5
w/A.I.R. add (.2)	.2

E.F.E. SYSTEM

(Factory Time)	Chilton Time
(G) E.F.E. Valve, Renew	
1983-87 (.5)	.9
(G) E.F.E. Thermal Vacuum Switch, Renew	
1983-87 (.3)	.4
(G) E.F.E. Vacuum Check Valve, Renew	
1983-87 (.2)	.4

THROTTLE BODY INJECTION (DFI)

(Factory Time)	Chilton Time
(G) Throttle Body and/or Gasket, Renew	
1983-85 (.6)	.9
(G) Throttle Body Injector, Renew	
1983-85-one (.4)	.6
both (.4)	.8
(G) Fuel Pressure Regulator or Meter Assy., Renew	
Includes: Renew gasket.	
1983-85 (.4)	.6
(G) Fuel Pump, Renew (In Tank)	
1983-85 (1.0)	1.3
(G) Fuel Pump Relay, Renew	
1983-85 (.2)	.3

DIESEL FUEL INJECTION

(Factory Time)	Chilton Time
(G) Injection Pump Timing, Adjust	
1983-85 (.7)	.9
(M) Air Cleaner, Service	
1983-85 (.2)	.4
(G) Air Intake Crossover and/or Gasket, Renew	
1983-85-w/Ext E.G.R. (.3)	.5
w/Int E.G.R (.4)	.6
(G) Fuel Supply Pump, Renew	
Includes: Vacuum, pressure, and volume test.	
1983-85 (.5)	.8
w/A.C. add (.2)	.2
(G) Fuel Filter, Renew	
1983-85 (.3)	.4
(G) Vacuum Pump, Renew	
Includes: Vacuum test.	
1983-85 gear driven (.4)	.6
belt driven (.6)	.8
(G) Fuel Solenoid, Renew	
1983-85 (.5)	.9
(G) Cold Advance Solenoid, Renew	
1983-85 (.6)	1.0
(G) Fuel Injection Head Seal, Renew	
Includes: Renew head and drive shaft seals. Renew governor weight retaining ring.	
1983-85 (2.7)	3.9
(G) Fuel Injector Pump, Renew	
Includes: R&R crossover, remove and connect all lines and linkage, and ajdust timing.	
1983-85 (2.2)	3.4
(G) Injection Pump Throttle Shaft Seal, Renew	
1983-85 (.8)	1.3
(G) Injector Pump Adapter and/or Seal, Renew	
Includes: R&R crossover, remove and connect all lines and linkages, and adjust timing.	
1983-85 (1.8)	2.5
Locate timing mark on new adapter, add (.1)	.2
(G) Fuel Return Lines, Renew	
Includes: Check for leaks.	
1983-85-right side (.4)	.6
left side (.3)	.5
both sides (.5)	.7
return hose (.2)	.3
(G) Injector High Pressure Lines, Renew	
Includes: Flush lines and check for leaks.	
1983-85-one (.8)	1.0
all (1.9)	2.5
(G) Injector Nozzles and/or Seals, Renew	
Includes: Check for leaks.	
1983-85-one (.8)	1.0
one-each side (1.0)	1.3
all-both sides (2.4)	3.0
Clean nozzles add, each	.2
(G) Injection Pump Drive and/or Driven Gears, Renew	
1983-85 (4.6)	7.0

LABOR 3 FUEL SYSTEM 3 LABOR

	(Factory Time)	Chilton Time
(G) Intake Manifold or Gasket, Renew		
Includes: R&R oil fill pipe, injection pump and lines. R&R all wires, hoses, and linkage. Drain and refill cooling system.		
1983-85	(2.9)	3.5
Renew manif add	(.2)	.5
(G) Exhaust Manifold, Renew		
1983-right side	(.9)	1.2
left side	(.7)	1.1
1984-85-right side	(1.2)	1.7
left side	(.8)	1.1
V-8-6-4 COMPONENTS		
(G) Electronic Control Module, Renew		
All models	(.5)	.8
(G) Range Module, Renew		
All models	(.4)	.6
(G) Modulated Displacement Driver Assy. (M.D.D.A.), Renew		
All models	(.5)	.9
(G) Valve Selector Solenoid Assy., Renew		
Includes: R&R valve cover.		
All models-one side	(.6)	1.1

PARTS 3 FUEL SYSTEM 3 PARTS

	Part No.	Price
Fuel Pump Assm.		
1983-87-exc.		
307	16472010	N.L.
307	◆6471743	35.00
Fuel Tank		
Order by year and model.		
Fuel Gauge (Tank)		
Part number for pricing reference only.		
1983-87-exc.		
C.C.	25002213	98.25
C.C.	25000614	46.00
Fuel Gauge (Dash)		
1983	6433147	66.50
1984-85	25052085	205.25
1986-87	25024183	215.00
Intake Manifold Gaskets		
1983-85-250	◆3634619	N.L.
1986-87-307	◆22534925	23.50
1983-84-368	3634532	18.75

PARTS 3 FUEL SYSTEM (DIESEL) 3 PARTS

	Part No.	Price
Air Intake Crossover		
1983-84	◆22509735	109.00
1985	◆22526995	109.00
Fuel Pump		
1983-84	◆6471317	N.L.
1985	◆6442228	59.25
Injection Pump Adapter		
1983-84	◆558768	21.75
1985	◆22516525	52.50
Fuel Injection Pump		
1983-exc. Hi Alt.	◆22519990	763.00
Hi Alt.	◆22518689	763.00
1984-exc. Hi Alt.	◆22520937	763.00
Hi Alt.	◆22520999	763.00
1985	◆22524422	763.00
Injector Nozzles		
1983	◆22520378	60.00
1984-85	◆22521207	89.50
Vacuum Pump		
1983-84	◆7839413	116.00
1985	◆7845425	124.00
Intake Manifold Gaskets		
1983-84	◆22516344	12.00
1985	◆22527544	16.50
Fuel Gauge (Tank)		
1983-84	◆25003151	99.00
1985	◆25004277	86.75
Fuel Gauge (Dash)		
1983-85	6433147	66.50

PARTS 3 THROTTLE BODY INJECTION 3 PARTS

	Part No.	Price
(1) Throttle Body Injection Unit		
V-8-250		
1983	17079501	753.75
1984	17110356	879.25
1985	17110665	* 678.00
V-8-368		
1983-84	17067142	983.25
(2) Throttle Body Kit		
V-8-250		
1983	17079502	216.25
1984	17110357	187.25
1985	17110666	185.75
V-8-368		
1983-84	17067977	377.00
(3) Idle Speed Control Kit		
V-8-250		
1983-84	◆17079663	123.50
1985	◆17111169	103.00
V-8-368		
1983-84	17079204	116.40

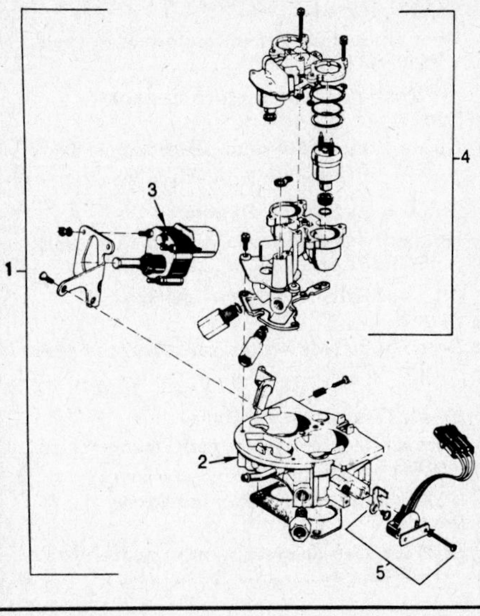

	Part No.	Price
(4) Fuel Meter Kit		
V-8-250		
1983-84	◆17079496	873.75
1985	◆17110657	424.50
V-8-368		
1983-84	17067974	764.50
Two injectors and pressure regulator included.		
(5) Throttle Position Sensor		
V-8-250		
1983	◆17078259	106.00
1984-85	◆17110352	100.50
V-8-368		
1983-84	17067979	101.00
Gasket Kit		
V-8-250		
1983-85	◆17078257	17.75
V-8-368		
1983-84	17067973	23.75
Modulated Displacement Control Module		
1983-84-368	16011846	345.25
Fuel Pump Relay		
1983-85	◆1626239	6.50

(Factory Time) Chilton Time

GASOLINE ENGINES

(G) Emission Control Check

Includes: Check and adjust engine idle speed and mixture and ignition timing. Check P.C.V. valve.

All models 6

POSITIVE CRANKCASE VENTILATION

(M) Positive Crankcase Ventilation Valve, Renew

1983-87 (.2) 3

(M) Crankcase Ventilation Filter Assy., Renew

1983-87 (.2) 3

(G) Canister Purge Thermal Vacuum Switch, Renew

All models (.2) 3

EVAPORATIVE LOSS SYSTEM

(G) Vapor Canister, Renew

1983-87 (.2) 4

(G) E.F.E. Valve, Renew

1983-87 (.5) 9

(G) E.F.E. Vacuum Check Valve, Renew

1983-87 (.2) 4

AIR INJECTOR REACTOR TYPE

(G) Air Injector Pump, Renew

1983-87–V-6 (.3) 5

V-8 (.6) 1.1

(G) Air Pump Belt, Renew

V-8–1983-85 (.5) 6

1986-87 (.2) 3

(G) Check Valve, Renew

1983-87–one (.2) 4

each adtnl 1

(G) Air Pump Centrifugal Filter, Renew

1983-87 (.4) 6

(G) Catalytic Converter Air Pipe, Renew

1983-87

upper (.4) 7

lower (.3) 6

one piece (.4) 7

(G) Air Manifold Pipes, Renew

1986-87

right (.5) 8

left (.4) 7

CONTROLLED COMBUSTION TYPE

(G) Air Cleaner Temperature Sensor, Renew

1983-87 (.2) 3

(G) Air Cleaner Vacuum Motor, Renew

1983-87 (.3) 5

EXHAUST GAS RECIRCULATION TYPE

(G) E.G.R. Valve, Renew

1983-87–Gas (.5) 6

Diesel (.5) 1.0

(G) Thermostatic Vacuum Control Switch, Renew

1983-87 (.2) 4

(G) E.G.R. Thermal Vacuum Switch, Renew

1983-87 (.3) 4

CHILTON'S EMISSION TUNE-UP

1. Clean or renew P.C.V. valve, hoses and filter.
2. Check fuel tank cap for sealing ability.
3. Check fuel tank and fuel lines for leakage.
4. Check evaporation canister and filter. Replace if necessary.
5. Check engine compression to determine leakage of unburned gases. (Add time for items of interference).
6. Test and clean or renew spark plugs.
7. Check engine oil dipstick for sealing ability.
8. Test exhaust system with analyzer and check system for leakage.
9. Check exhaust manifold heat valve for operation.
10. Adjust ignition timing and carburetor idle speed and mixture.
11. Check automatic choke mechanism for free operation.
12. Inspect air cleaner and element.
13. On models so equipped, test distributor vacuum control switch and transmission control switch.

V-6 .... 1.7

V-8 .... 1.8

For repairs made, charge accordingly.

(Factory Time) Chilton Time

COMPUTER COMMAND CONTROL SYSTEM (C.C.C.)

(P) Electronic Control Module, Renew

Does not include system performance check.

1986-87 (.5) 6

(P) Mixture Control Solenoid, Renew

Does not include system performance check.

1986-87 (1.2) 1.5

(P) Prom, Renew

Does not include system performance check.

1986-87 (.5) 8

(P) Barometric Sensor, Renew

Does not include system performance check.

1986-87 (.4) 5

(P) Coolant Temperature Sensor, Renew

Does not include system performance check.

1986-87 (.6) 8

(P) Manifold Differential Pressure Sensor, Renew

Does not include system performance check.

1986-87 (.3) 6

(P) Manifold Absolute Pressure Sensor, Renew

Does not include system performance check.

1986-87 (.5) 7

(P) Manifold Temperature Sensor, Renew

Does not include system performance check.

1986-87 (.3) 4

(P) Oxygen Sensor, Renew

Does not include system performance check.

1986-87 (.5) 7

(P) Throttle Position Sensor, Renew

Does not include system performance check.

1986-87 (.5) 7

(P) Air Control Valve, Renew

Does not include system performance check.

1986-87 (.4) 6

(P) Air Control/Air Switching Valve, Renew

Does not include system performance check.

1986-87 (.4) 6

(Factory Time) Chilton Time

(P) Canister Purge Control Valve, Renew

Does not include system performance check.

1986-87 (.2) 3

(P) Air Control Valve Solenoid, Renew

Does not include system performance check.

1986-87 (.6) 8

(P) E.G.R. Vacuum Control Solenoid, Renew

Does not include system performance check.

1986-87 (.3) 5

(P) Vacuum Control Purge Solenoid, Renew

Does not include system performance check.

1986-87 (.3) 5

(P) Idle Speed Control Motor, Renew or Adjust

Does not include system performance check.

1986-87 (.5) 7

(P) Vehicle Speed Sensor, Renew

Does not include system performance check.

1986-87 (1.1) 1.5

(P) EGR/EFE Relay, Renew

Does not include system performance check.

1986-87 (.2) 3

(P) Idle Load Compensator, Renew

Does not include system performance check.

1986-87 (.3) 4

(P) Throttle Position Sensor, Adjust

Does not include system performance check.

1986-87 (.6) 9

(P) Computer Command Control System Performance Check

1986-87 (.5) 1.0

DIGITAL FUEL INJECTION (DFI)

(P) Electronic Control Module, Renew

1983-85 (.4) 7

(P) Prom, Renew

1983-85 (.4) 8

(P) Barometric Sensor, Renew

1983-85 (.4) 6

(P) Coolant Temperature Sensor, Renew

1983-85 (.3) 4

LABOR 3A EMISSION CONTROLS 3A LABOR

(Factory Time)	Chilton Time
(P) Manifold Pressure Sensor, Renew	
1983-85 (.4)	.5
(P) Manifold Absolute Temperature Sensor, Renew	
1983-85 (.3)	.4
(P) Oxygen Sensor, Renew	
1983-85 (.4)	.6
(P) Vehicle Speed Sensor, Renew	
1983-85 (.6)	1.0
(P) Throttle Position Sensor, Renew	
1983-85 (.5)	.7
(P) Air Control/Air Switching Valve, Renew	
1983-85 (.4)	.6
(P) EGR Vacuum Control Solenoid, Renew	
1983-85 (.3)	.4
(P) Vacuum Control Purge Solenoid, Renew	
1983-85 (.3)	.4
(P) Idle Speed Control Motor, Renew or Adjust	
1983-85 (.5)	.8

DIESEL ENGINE

(Factory Time)	Chilton Time
(G) Crankcase Depression Regulator Valve, Renew	
1983-85 (.2)	.3
(G) E.G.R. Valve and/or Gasket, Renew	
1983-85 (.5)	1.0
(G) E.G.R. Control Valve Switch, Renew	
1983-85 (.2)	.3
(G) Vacuum Regulator Valve, Renew	
1983-85 (.6)	.8

PARTS 3A EMISSION CONTROLS 3A PARTS

	Part No.	Price
Positive Crankcase Ventilation Valve		
1983-84-250	◆6487532	3.00
368	25040622	3.50
1985-87-250	◆6487779	2.50
1986-87-307	◆8997683	N.L.
1983-85-diesel	◆25041678	34.50

EVAPORATIVE LOSS SYSTEM

	Part No.	Price
Vapor Canister		
V-8-250		
1983-85	◆17075825	46.25
V-8-368		
1983-84	17063011	43.00
V-8-307		
1986-87	◆17064622	N.L.
Filter		
1983-87	◆7026014	2.50

AIR INJECTOR REACTOR TYPE

	Part No.	Price
Air Injector Pump		
1983-85	◆7834916	149.00
1986-87	◆7838575	N.L.
Air Injection Check Value		
1983-84-368	◆22034703	12.75
368	22041204	19.75
1985-250	22040902	14.25
1986-87-307	◆22040903	13.75
Air Injection Control Valve		
V-8-250		
1983-85	◆17071106	100.25
V-8-368		
1983-84-exc.		
C.C.	17071540	99.50
Comm. Chassis	17064302	42.75
V-8-307		
1986-87	17086100	66.00

EGR Valve
Replacement E.G.R. valves must be ordered according to the stamping number on the original valve.

EARLY FUEL EVAPORATION SYSTEM

	Part No.	Price
E.F.E. Valve (w/Actuator)		
V-8-250		
1983-85	5234095	64.00
V-8-368		
1983-84	5233636	64.00
E.F.E. Vacuum Switch		
1983-87-2 port	3041857	12.50
3 port	◆3049626	29.25
5 port	◆3049626	29.25

COMPUTER COMMAND CONTROL SYSTEM

The following part numbers are for pricing refrence only. Order with complete model information and unit I.D. number.

	Part No.	Price
Electronic Control Module (E.C.M.)		
V-8-250		
1983-87	◆1226028	110.25
V-8-368		
1983-87	1225120	110.25
Diesel Electronic Control Module		
1985	22529165	300.00
E.F.E./E.G.R. Solenoid Valve		
1983-87	1997499	31.00
Calibrator Unit (PROM)		
V-8-250		
1983-Fed.	1226529	40.50
Calif.	1226530	40.50
hi alt.	1226538	40.50
1984-Fed.	16042063	40.50
Calif.	16042787	40.50
w/3.73R	16042060	40.50
1985-87-Fed.	16043749	40.50
Calif.	16043757	40.50
w/3.73R	16043774	40.50
V-8-368		
1983-87-exc.		
C.C.	1225298	83.25
Comm. Chassis	1224674	40.50
Oxygen Sensor		
1983-84	5613719	29.00
1985-87	◆8990741	28.75
Manifold Absolute Pressure (Map) Sensor		
V-8-Gas		
1983-85	◆16006832	62.25
V-8-Diesel		
1985	◆16017460	N.L.
Barometric Pressure Sensor		
1983-87	◆16006833	62.25
Manifold Air Temperature Sensor		
1983-87	◆25036094	17.25
Coolant Temperature Sensor		
V-8-Gas		
1983-87	◆25036092	22.00
V-8-Diesel		
1985-87	◆25036708	12.75
Throttle Position Sensor		
1983-85-V-8-250	◆17078259	106.00
V-8-368	17067979	94.00
Vehicle Speed Sensor		
1983-87	25007220	29.50

LABOR 4 ALTERNATOR AND REGULATOR 4 LABOR

(G) Delcotron Circuits, Test
Includes: Test battery, regulator, Delcotron output.

(Factory Time)	Chilton Time
All models	.6

(M) Alternator Drive Belt, Renew

(Factory Time)	Chilton Time
All models	
V-8	
eng Code 8 (.3)	.4
eng Codes Y-9 (.2)	.3
Diesel (.2)	.3

(G) Delcotron Assembly, Renew

(Factory Time)	Chilton Time
1983-85 (.5)	.7
1986-87 (.6)	.8

(G) Delcotron, R&R and Recondition
Includes: Complete disassembly, replacement of parts as required.

(Factory Time)	Chilton Time
1983-85 (1.0)	1.7
1986-87 (1.2)	1.7

(G) Delcotron Front Bearing, Renew
Includes: R&R Delcotron, separate end frames.

(Factory Time)	Chilton Time
1983-85 (.8)	1.2
1986-87 (.5)	.9
Renew rear brg add	.2

(G) Delcotron Voltage Regulator, Test and Renew
Includes: R&R, disassemble and reassemble Delcotron.

(Factory Time)	Chilton Time
1983-85 (.7)	1.2
1986-87 (.9)	1.2

PARTS 4 ALTERNATOR & REGULATOR 4 PARTS

	Part No.	Price
Delcotron Assy.		
1983-87-70 amp	◆1101040	257.00
80, 100 amp	◆1101050	536.00
94 amp	◆1105480	232.00
(1) Capacitor		
1983-87	◆1978146	4.75
(2) Diode		
1983-87-70 amp, 94 amp	◆1984459	5.00
80, 100 amp	◆1977064	7.00
(3) Rectifier Bridge		
1983-87-70 amp	◆1975313	24.50
80, 100 amp	◆1875645	42.00
94 amp	◆1987061	29.00
(4) Bearing		
1983-87-exc. 70 amp	◆9436831	5.50
70 amp	◆1975322	5.50
(5) Terminal Pkg.		
1983-87-exc. below	◆1975471	3.50
80, 100 amp	1977747	5.00
(6) Frame (Rear End)		
1983-87-70 amp.	◆1975310	31.00
80, 100 amp	◆1976141	38.50
94 amp	◆1987073	27.75
(7) Regulator		
1983-87	◆1116387	25.00
(8) Brush Holder		
1983-87-exc. 70 amp	◆1984462	9.00
70 amp	◆1975323	10.00

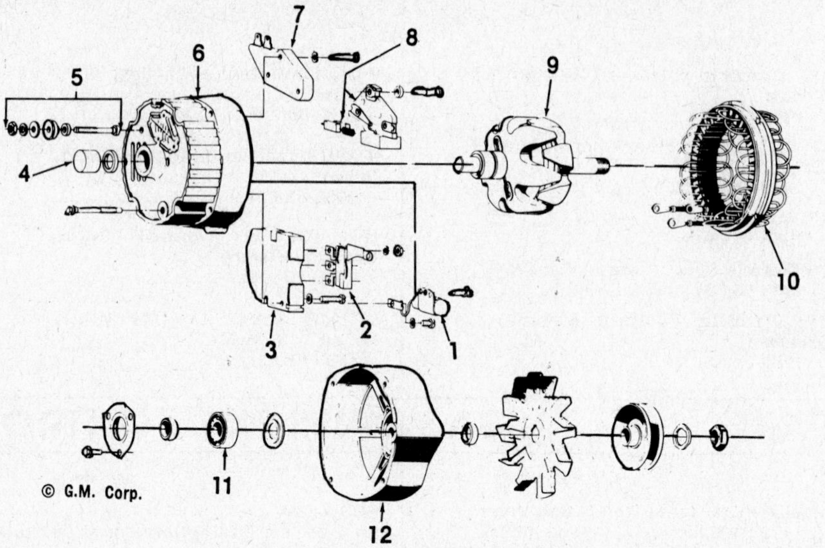

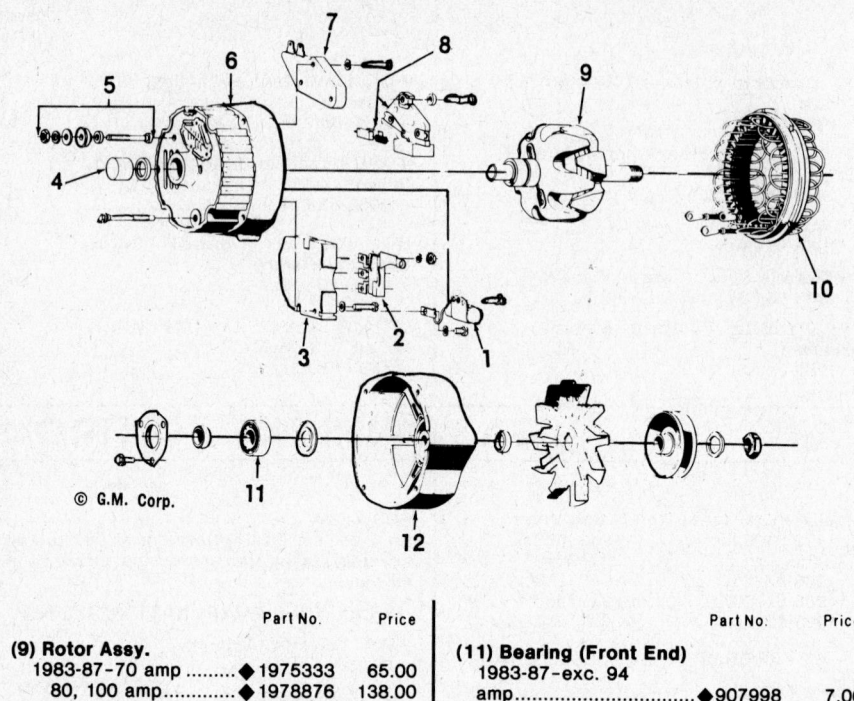

	Part No.	Price
(9) Rotor Assy.		
1983-87-70 amp	◆1975333	65.00
80, 100 amp	◆1978876	138.00
94 amp	◆1984466	N.L.
(10) Stator Assy.		
1983-87-70 amp	◆1975303	48.75
80 amp	◆801818	82.25
94 amp	◆1987074	41.25
100 amp	◆1892941	106.75

	Part No.	Price
(11) Bearing (Front End)		
1983-87-exc. 94 amp	◆907998	7.00
(12) Frame (Drive End)		
94 amp	◆908419	9.75
1983-87-70 amp	◆1986590	30.00
80, 100 amp	◆1976049	30.00
94 amp	◆1987997	27.50

LABOR 5 STARTING SYSTEM 5 LABOR

	(Factory Time)	Chilton Time
(G) Starter Draw Test (On Car)		
All models		.3
(G) Starter, Renew		
1983-85	(.4)	.7
1986-87	(.5)	.7
Add draw test if performed.		
(G) Starter, R&R and Recondition		
Includes: Turn down armature.		
1983-85	(1.3)	1.9
1986-87	(1.2)	1.9
Renew field coils add	(.3)	.5
Add draw test if performed.		

	(Factory Time)	Chilton Time
(G) Starter Drive, Renew		
Includes: R&R starter.		
1983-85	(.6)	1.2
1986-87	(.6)	.9
(G) Starter Solenoid, Renew		
Includes: R&R starter.		
1983-85	(.5)	.9
1986-87	(.5)	.8
(G) Ignition Switch, Renew		
1983-87	(.6)	.9

	(Factory Time)	Chilton Time
(G) Back-Up Lamp and Park/ Neutral Switch, Renew		
1983-87	(.3)	.4
(M) Battery Cables, Renew		
1983-85-positive	(.4)	.4
negative	(.2)	.3
batt to batt	(.3)	.3
1986-87-positive	(.5)	.6
negative	(.2)	.3
(M) Battery Terminals, Clean		
All models		.3

PARTS 5 STARTING SYSTEM 5 PARTS

	Part No.	Price
(1) Starter Assy. (New)		
V-8-250		
1983	1109531	209.00
1984-85	1998434	180.50
V-8-368		
1983-84	1108789	217.25
V-8-307		
1986-87	◆1998536	180.25
(2) Solenoid Unit		
1983-87-exc. below	1114458	27.00
V-8-250, 307	◆1114531	N.L.

	Part No.	Price
(3) Starter Drive		
1983	◆1875687	N.L.
1984-87	◆1984511	23.50
(4) Starter Brushes		
V-8-368		
1983-84	◆1906945	.50
V-8-250		
1983-85	◆1893296	.50
V-8-307		
1986-87	◆1893296	.75

	Part No.	Price
(5) Drive End Bushing		
1983-87	◆1932190	.50
(6) Commutator End Frame		
1983-87-exc. below	◆1974157	7.00
V-8-250, 307	◆1978292	6.50
(7) Armature		
V-8 -368		
1983-84	◆1970548	52.00

PARTS 5 STARTING SYSTEM 5 PARTS

	Part No.	Price
V-8-250		
1983	◆1978670	83.50
1984-85	◆1985138	N.L.
V-8-307		
1986-87	◆10495931	71.50
(8) Field Coils		
V-8-368		
1983-84	◆1877306	26.00
V-8-250		
1983	◆1978672	78.00
1984-85	◆1985143	71.50
V-8-307		
1986-87	◆1985143	71.50
(9) Drive End Housing		
V-8- 368		
1983-84	◆1876881	20.50
V-8-250		
1983	1978675	26.00
1984-85	1987274	25.50
V-8-307		
1986-87	◆1987662	25.50

Battery Cables
Order by year and model.

Ignition Switch
(wo/Tilt wheel)

1983	◆1990109	N.L.
1984-87	◆1990115	11.50

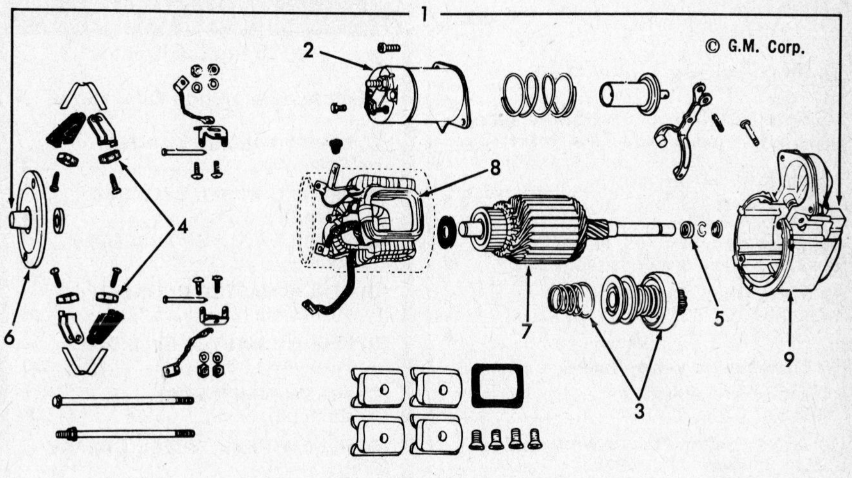

(Tilt wheel)

1983	◆1990110	N.L.
1984-87	◆1990116	11.50

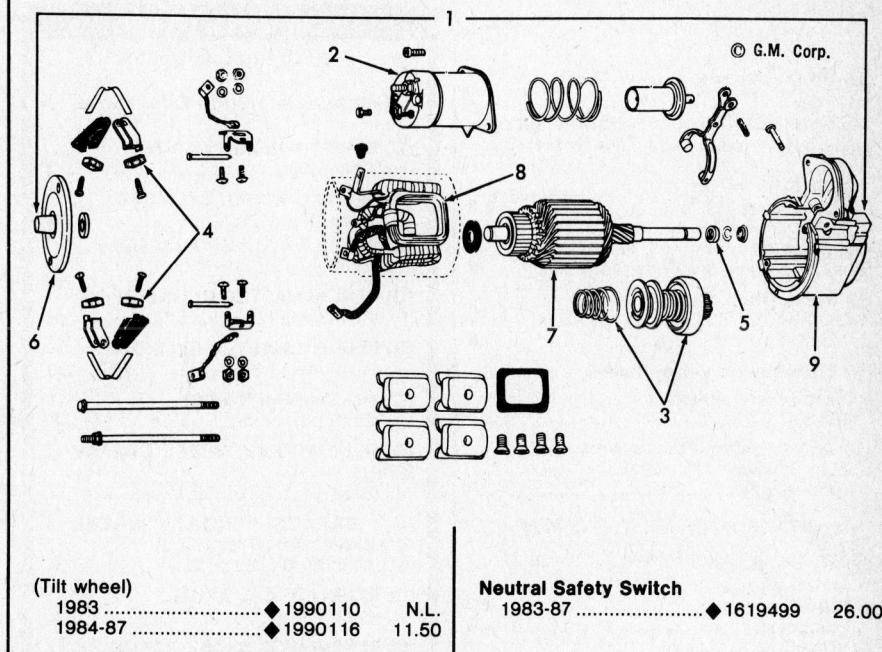

Neutral Safety Switch

1983-87	◆1619499	26.00

PARTS 5 STARTING SYSTEM (DIESEL) 5 PARTS

	Part No.	Price
Starter Assy. (New)		
1983-85	◆22522853	355.00
(1) Solenoid Switch		
1983-85	◆1114531	N.L.
(2) Drive End Bearing		
1983-85	◆22516191	9.00
(3) Starter Drive		
1983-85	◆1893445	65.00
(4) Drive Shaft		
1983-85	◆22516183	71.00
(5) Gear		
1983-85	◆22516184	9.50
(6) Gear Housing		
1983-85	◆22516195	28.50
(7) Armature		
1983	◆1987639	139.75
1984-85	◆22516197	130.00
(8) Field Coils		
1983-85	◆1979982	83.00
(9) Starter Brushes		
1983-85	◆1852885	2.75

Battery Cables
Order by year and model.

Neutral Safety Switch

1983-85	◆1619499	26.00

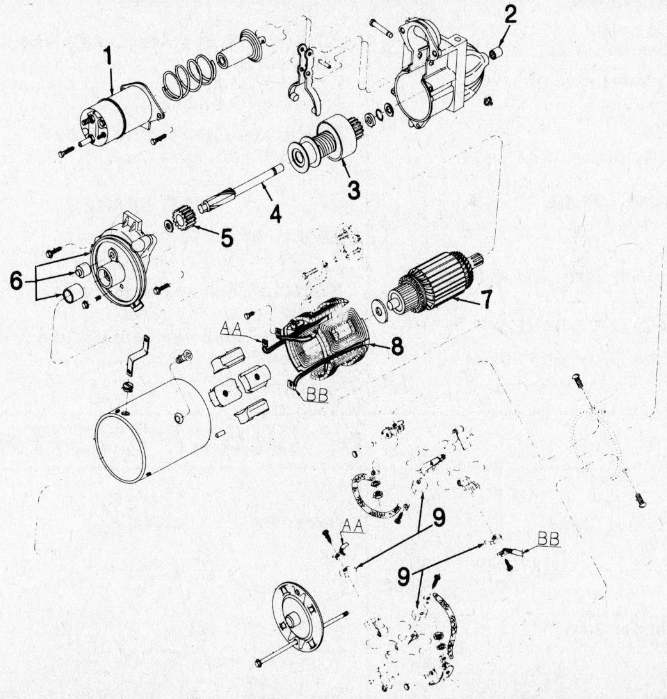

LABOR 6 BRAKE SYSTEM 6 LABOR

(Factory Time) Chilton Time

(G) Brakes, Adjust (Minor)
Includes: R&R wheels and adjust brakes thru access holes in drum. Fill master cylinder.

two wheels	.4
Remove knock out plugs add, each	.1

(G) Bleed Brakes (Four Wheels)
Includes: Fill master cylinder.

All models (.4)	.6

(G) Free-Up or Renew Brake Self Adjusting Units

one wheel	.6
each adtnl	.4

LABOR 6 BRAKE SYSTEM 6 LABOR

	(Factory Time)	Chilton Time
(G) Brake Shoes and/or Pads, Renew		
Includes: Install new or exchange shoes or pads, adjust service and hand brake. Bleed system.		
1983-87-front-disc	(.9)	1.1
rear-drum	(.9)	1.5
all four wheels		2.5
Resurface disc rotor add, each		.9
Resurface brake drum add, each		.5
(G) Brake Drum, Renew		
1983-87-one	(.3)	.4
both	(.5)	.6
(G) Combination Valve, Renew		
Includes: Bleed system.		
1983-87	(.7)	1.1
(G) Brake System Failure Warning Switch, Renew		
1983-87	(.3)	.4

BRAKE HYDRAULIC SYSTEM

	(Factory Time)	Chilton Time
(G) Wheel Cylinder, Renew		
Includes: Bleed system.		
1983-87-one	(.8)	1.0
both	(1.1)	1.9
(G) Wheel Cylinder, Rebuild		
Includes: Hone cylinder and bleed system.		
1983-87-one	(1.0)	1.2
both	(1.5)	2.3
(G) Brake Hose, Renew		
Includes: Bleed system.		
1983-87-each	(.4)	.6
(G) Master Cylinder, Renew		
Includes: Bleed system.		
1983-87	(.6)	1.0
(G) Master Cylinder, R&R and Rebuild		
Includes: Bleed at cylinder.		
1983-87	(1.4)	1.8
Bleed system add	(.4)	.5
(G) Brake System, Flush and Refill		
All models		1.2

POWER BRAKES

	(Factory Time)	Chilton Time
(G) Power Brake Assembly, Renew		
1983-87	(.6)	1.0

COMBINATIONS

Add to Brakes, Renew

See Machine Shop Operations

(G) RENEW WHEEL CYLINDER		
Each	(.3)	.2
(G) REBUILD WHEEL CYLINDER		
Each	(.2)	.3
(G) REBUILD CALIPER ASSEMBLY		
Each	(.5)	.6
(G) RENEW MASTER CYLINDER		
All models	(.3)	.8
(G) REBUILD MASTER CYLINDER		
All models	(.8)	1.0
(G) RENEW BRAKE HOSE		
Each	(.3)	.3
(G) RENEW REAR WHEEL GREASE SEALS		
Each	(.1)	.1
(G) REPACK FRONT WHEEL BEARINGS (BOTH WHEELS)		
All models	(.3)	.6
(G) RENEW BRAKE DRUM		
Each	(.1)	.2
(G) RENEW DISC BRAKE ROTOR		
Each	(.2)	.3

	(Factory Time)	Chilton Time
(G) Power Brake Assy., R&R and Recondition		
1983-87	(1.3)	2.0
Recond m/Cyl add	(.8)	.8
(G) Vacuum Check Valve, Renew		
1983-87	(.3)	.3

DISC BRAKES

	(Factory Time)	Chilton Time
(G) Disc Brake Pads, Renew		
1983-87	(.9)	1.1
(G) Hub, Rotor and Bearing Assy., Renew		
Includes: Install new bearings and seals.		
1983-87-one	(.7)	.9
both	(1.2)	1.4
(G) Caliper Assembly, Renew		
Includes: Bleed system.		
1983-87-one	(.7)	1.0
both	(1.1)	1.5
(G) Caliper Assy., R&R and Recondition		
Includes: Bleed system.		
1983-87-one	(1.2)	1.5
both	(2.1)	2.5

PARKING BRAKE

	(Factory Time)	Chilton Time
(M) Parking Brake, Adjust		
1983-87	(.3)	.4
(G) Parking Brake Switch, Renew		
1983-87	(.3)	.4
(G) Parking Brake Control, Renew		
1983-87	(.7)	1.1
Renew vacuum diaphragm add	(.3)	.3
(G) Parking Brake Cables, Renew		
1983-87-front	(.6)	.7
rear	(.7)	1.0
(G) Parking Brake Equalizer, Renew		
1983-87	(.3)	.5
(G) Power Brake Vacuum Release Valve, Renew		
1986-87	(.3)	.4

HYDRA-BOOST SYSTEM

	(Factory Time)	Chilton Time
(G) Power Brake Booster, Renew		
Includes: Bleed system.		
1983-87	(1.2)	1.8
(G) Power Brake Booster, R&R and Recondition		
Includes: Bleed system.		
1983-87	(1.6)	2.4
(G) Low Vacuum Switch, Renew		
1983-87	(.2)	.3
(G) Low Vacuum Brake Indicator Module Assy., Renew		
1983-87	(.3)	.4

PARTS 6 BRAKE SYSTEM 6 PARTS

	Part No.	Price
(1) Brake Shoe Set (New)		
1983-87-11″ brks.	12300208	35.00
12″ brks.	1154137	42.00
(2) Wheel Cylinder Assy.		
1983-87-11″ brks.	◆18004793	28.50
12″ brks.	◆18004890	25.75
Wheel Cylinder Repair Kit		
1983-87-11″ brks.	◆5472328	8.00
12″ brks.	◆5463361	7.50
Brake Hose, Front (Flex)		
1983-87	◆9762809	18.00
Brake Hose, Rear		
1983-87	◆9757655	15.00

FRONT BRAKE

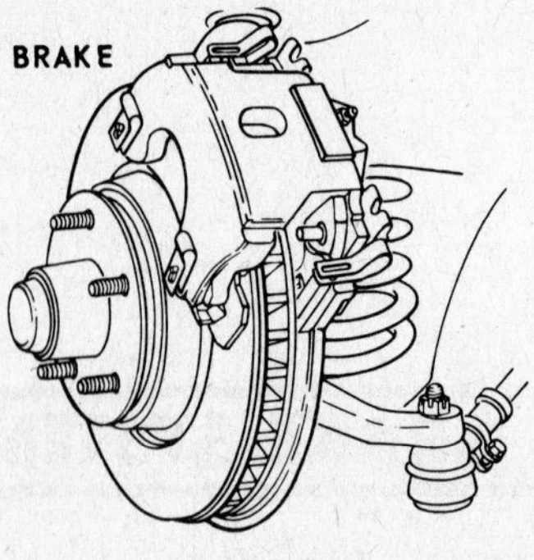

REAR BRAKE

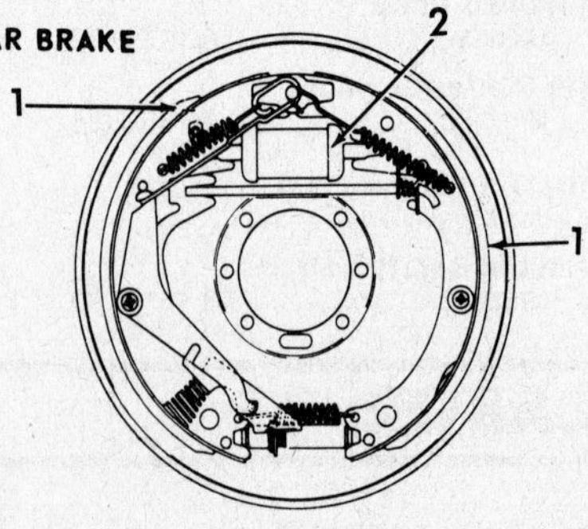

	Part No.	Price
Master Cylinder Assy.		
1983-87-exc. diesel	◆18010313	145.75
diesel	◆25509416	103.00
Master Cylinder Repair Kit		
1983-87-exc. diesel	◆18007935	22.50
diesel	◆25509843	28.50

PARTS 6 BRAKE SYSTEM 6 PARTS

	Part No.	Price
BRAKE BOOSTER ASSEMBLY		
Vacuum Power Brakes		
(V-8-Gas)		
1983-exc. below	◆18006566	224.50
V-8-250	◆18008695	271.25
1984-87-exc.		
C.C.	18006922	250.50
Comm. Chassis	◆18006566	224.50
Hydraulic Power Brakes		
(V-8-Diesel)		
1983-85	◆1620210	365.00
Vacuum Power Booster Repair Kit		
1983-87	◆18007865	47.50
Hydraulic Booster Cover Repair Kit		
Includes: (1) nut, (1) housing cover, (1) housing seal, (1) piston seal.		
1983-85	◆22506436	82.25
Hydraulic Booster Piston Repair Kit		
Includes: (1) housing seal, (1) piston seal.		
1983-85	◆22506438	5.50

	Part No.	Price
Hydraulic Booster Seal Kit		
Includes: (1) boot, (1) housing seal, (1) piston seal, (3) o-rings.		
1983-85	◆22506440	10.75
Hydraulic Booster Piston and Accumulator Kit		
Includes: (1) housing seal, (1) power piston and accumulator assy., (1) piston seal.		
1983-85	◆22506439	128.00
Hydraulic Booster Spool Plug Seal Kit		
Includes: (1) spool plug o-ring, (1) spool plug, (1) spool plug retainer.		
1983-85	◆1612592	3.00
Brake Drum, Rear		
1983-87-11"		
brks.	◆1244835	97.00
12" brks.	1490714	93.00
Oil Seal, Front		
1983-87	◆3965092	3.00

	Part No.	Price
PARKING BRAKE		
Parking Brake Control		
1983-87	1620797	53.75
Parking Brake Cable (Front)		
1983-87-exc.		
below	22503352	6.00
Limo, Comm.		
Chassis	25503351	14.25
Parking Brake Cable (Rear)		
(exc. Limo, Comm. Chassis)		
1983 (2.41 rear axle)		
right	25503688	13.25
left	25503717	13.25
1983-84 (wo/2.41 rear axle)		
right	◆25502686	22.00
left	◆25502687	22.00
1985-87-right	◆25520338	22.00
left	◆25520337	22.25
(Limo, Comm. Chassis)		
1983-87-right	1618191	22.00
left	1618192	22.00

PARTS 6 DISC BRAKES 6 PARTS

	Part No.	Price
FRONT DISC BRAKES		
(1) Brake Pad Set		
1983-87-exc.		
below	12300213	31.00
Limo, Comm.		
Chassis	◆12300192	47.00
(2) Spring		
1983-87	◆5469497	1.00
(3) Repair Kit		
1983-87	◆5468767	10.00
(4) Piston		
1983-87	◆2622207	11.00
(5) Caliper Assy.		
(DeVille, Fleetwood Brougham)		
1983-84-right	◆18007945	124.50
left	◆18007946	124.50
1985-87-right	◆18012309	168.75
left	◆18012308	168.75
(Limo, Comm. Chassis)		
1983-87-right	18007947	161.00
left	18007948	161.00

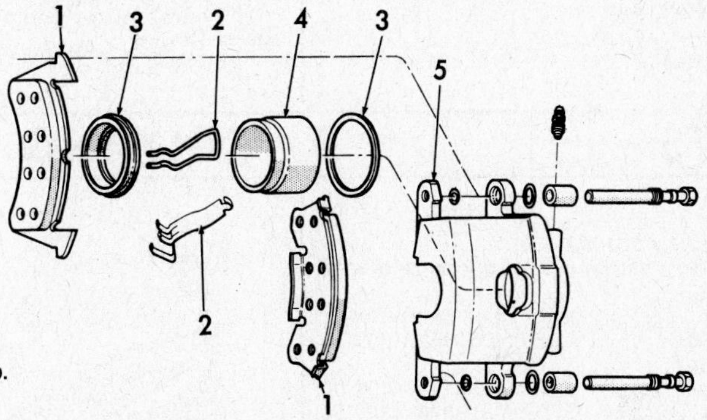

G.M. Corp.

	Part No.	Price
Hub and Disc Assembly		
1983-87-exc.		
below	◆14008641	110.00
Limo, Comm.		
Chassis	6274216	110.00

LABOR 7 COOLING SYSTEM 7 LABOR

	(Factory Time)	Chilton Time
(M) Winterize Cooling System		
Includes: Run engine to check for leaks, tighten all hose connections. Test radiator and pressure cap, drain radiator and engine block. Add anti-freeze and refill system.		
All models		.5
(G) Thermostat, Renew		
1983-87-V-6	(.7)	1.0
V-8	(.3)	.5
Diesel	(.5)	.7
(M) Radiator Assembly, R&R or Renew		
1983-87-V-6	(.6)	1.1
V-8	(.8)	1.4

COOLING SYSTEM TUNE-UP

An Annual Cooling System Tune-Up Suggestion List should include (with some exceptions):

1. A visual check of the cooling system for indications of leaks or excessive oil content.
2. Pressure check the cooling system for internal and external leaks with filler cap and neck adapter and tester.
3. Check crankcase and automatic transmission oil for water content.
4. Test coolant thermostat with radiator thermometer.
5. Check temperature gauge for accuracy.
6. Drain system and flush till clean.
7. Clean foreign matter from radiator fins.
8. Test radiator pressure cap with cap tester.
9. Check fan blades and pulleys for alignment and damage.
10. Internal and external inspection of all hoses for cracks and deterioration.
11. Check core plugs (where possible) for seepage.
12. Refill system with correct coolant and check for air locks.
13. Check condition and tension of drive belts with tension gauge.

All models 1.5

LABOR 7 COOLING SYSTEM 7 LABOR

(Factory Time) Chilton Time

ADD THESE OPERATIONS TO RADIATOR R&R

(G) Boil & Repair	1.5
(G) Rod Clean	1.9
(G) Repair Core	1.3
(G) Renew Tank	1.6
(G) Renew Trans. Oil Cooler	1.9
(G) Recore Radiator	1.7

(G) Thermostat Housing and/or Gasket, Renew

Includes: Partial removal of water pump and renew 'O' rings.

1983-85	
250 eng-Code 8	
w/DFI-lower (2.0)	3.0

(M) Radiator Hoses, Renew

1983-87-upper (.3)	.4
lower (.4)	.6
both (.5)	.8

(G) Water Pump, Renew

1983-87-V-6 (.9)	1.4
V-8 (2.0)	2.7
Diesel (1.8)	2.5
Recond pump add (.3)	.4
w/A.I.R. add (.2)	.2

(M) Fan Belt, Adjust

1983-87-one (.2)	.3
each adtnl (.1)	.1

(M) Fan Belt, Renew

1983-87 (.3)	.4

(M) Drive Belt, Adjust

1983-85	
w/Eng Code 8	
one or all (.4)	.5

(M) Drive Belt, Renew

1983-85	
w/Eng Code 8	
A.C. (.6)	.8
AIR (.5)	.7
Alter (.3)	.4
Vacuum Pump (.2)	.3

(M) Fan Blades or Clutch Assy., Renew

1983-87 (.5)	.7

(G) Thermostat By-Pass Hose or Pipe, Renew

1983-87 (.3)	.6

(G) Water Jacket Expansion Plugs, Renew

1983-87-each (.5)	.5

Note: If necessary to R&R any component to gain accessibility add appropriate time.

(G) Temperature Gauge (Engine Unit), Renew

1983-87 (.2)	.5

(G) Heater Hoses, Renew

1983-87-each (.3)	.5

(G) Heater Core, R&R or Renew

1983-87 (1.1)	2.0

ADD THESE OPERATIONS TO HEATER CORE R&R

(G) Boil & Repair	1.2
(G) Repair Core	.9
(G) Recore	1.2

(G) Heater Control Assembly, Renew

1983-87-Refer to AC group.

(G) Heater Blower Motor, Renew

1983-87-Refer to AC group.

(G) Heater Blower Motor Relay, Renew

1983-87-Refer to AC group.

(G) Heater Blower Motor Switch, Renew

1983-87-Refer to AC group.

(G) Water Control Valve, Renew

1983-87	
Gas (.3)	.4
Diesel (.3)	.5

PARTS 7 COOLING SYSTEM 7 PARTS

	Part No.	Price
(1) Radiator Assembly		
Part numbers shown are for pricing reference only.		
V-8-250		
1983-85	3050452	353.25
V-8-Diesel		
1983-84	3054174	402.00
1985	3058076	328.50
V-8-368		
1983	3043089	310.00
1984-exc. below	3043362	395.00
Comm. Chassis	3043089	310.00
(2) Thermostat		
V-8-Gas		
1983-85-252	1623547	4.50
368	1618063	9.50
307	◆3051139	N.L.
V-8-Diesel		
1983-87	◆3051139	5.00
(3) Radiator Hoses		
Order by year and model.		
(4) Water Pump Assy.		
V-8-250		
1983-87	◆3634580	125.00
V-8-350 Diesel		
1983-87	◆556283	95.00
V-8-368		
1983-87	3634514	115.00
V-8-307		
1986-87	◆556283	N.L.
(5) Fan Belts		
Order by year and model.		
Fan Clutch Assy.		
V-8-Gas		
1983-87-250	22050675	78.75
307	◆22008490	84.50
368	22008520	72.00
V-8-Diesel		
1983-85	22008940	78.00

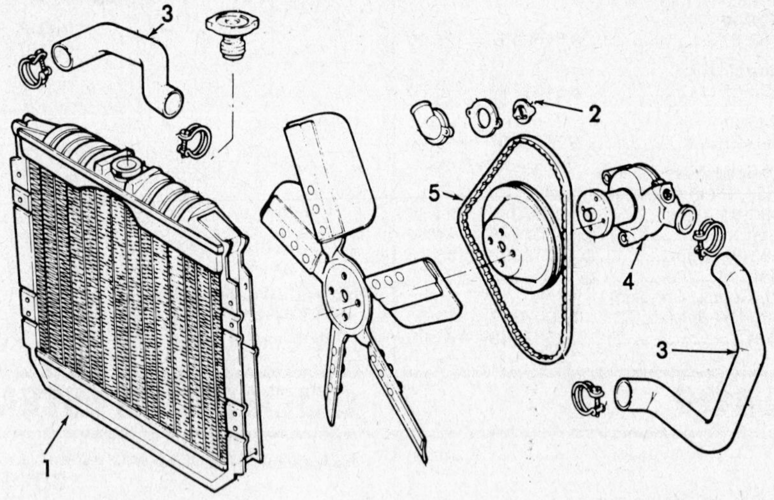

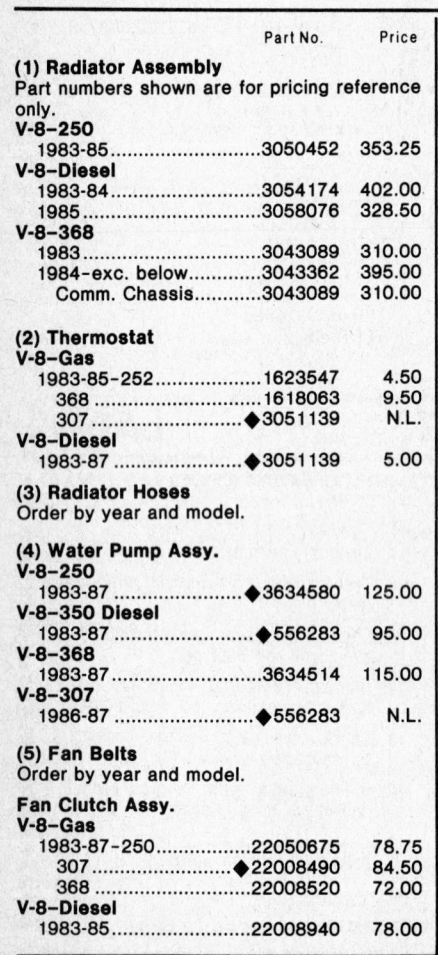

	Part No.	Price
Coolant Temperature Switch/Sensor		
V-8-Gas		
(Switch)		
1983-85-250	◆25036335	21.00
368	1616825	77.25
(Sensor)		
1983-85	◆25036092	19.50
V-8-Diesel		
1983	◆25036371	8.00
1984-85	◆25036629	9.75

	Part No.	Price
Heater Core		
1983-87	◆3035420	43.00
Blower Motor		
1983-87	◆22020945	60.00
Switch, Heater or Defroster (On-Off)		
1983-87 (blower)	7896238	8.25
Heater Water Control Value		
V-8-Gas		
1983-87	500956	17.50
V-8-Diesel		
1983-87	411823	29.00

LABOR 8 EXHAUST SYSTEM 8 LABOR

(Factory Time) Chilton Time

(G) Muffler, Renew
1983-87 (.5) 9

(G) Tail Pipe and Resonator Assy., Renew
1983-87 (.4) 9

(G) Tail Pipe, Renew
1983-87 (.3) 5

(G) Front Exhaust Pipe, Renew (To Converter)
1983-87 (.6) 9

(G) Exhaust Crossover Pipe, Renew
1983-85-V-6 (.4) 7
V-8 (.5) 8
Diesel (.9) 1.4

(G) Catalytic Converter, Renew
1983-85 (.8) 1.0
1986-87 (.9) 1.2

(G) Intermediate Exhaust Pipe, Renew
1983-87 (.4) 7

(G) E.F.E. Valve (Heat Riser), Renew
1983-87 (.5) 9

(G) Exhaust Manifold, Renew
V-8-1983-85-right side (.8) 1.4
left side (.7) 1.3
1983-85-Eng Code 8
right side (.9) 1.4
left side (1.0) 1.5
1986-87-eng Codes Y-9
right side (1.1) 1.6
left side (1.0) 1.5
Diesel-1983
right side (.9) 1.2
left side (.7) 1.1
1984-85
right side (1.2) 1.7
left side (.7) 1.1

COMBINATIONS

(G) Exhaust System, Renew (Complete)
1983-87 .... 1.5

PARTS 8 EXHAUST SYSTEM 8 PARTS

Part numbers are for pricing reference only. Order with complete model, year information.

	Part No.	Price
Muffler		
Order by year and model.		
Resonator		
V-8–Gas		
1983-85-250	1624890	88.75
1986-87-307	◆22505492	89.25
Exhaust Crossover Pipe		
V-8–250		
1983-85	1622032	61.00
V-8–368		
1983-84-exc. C.C.	1619801	159.00
Comm. Chassis	1616693	151.00
V-8–307		
1986-87	◆22504709	74.25
V-8–Diesel		
1983-85	◆22514728	24.00
Exhaust Intermediate Pipe		
V-8–250		
1983	1619674	43.25
1984-85	1627625	35.75
V-8–350		
1985	22512348	52.25
Catalytic Convertor		
V-8–250		
1983	◆25056623	349.25
1984-85	◆25056586	337.25
V-8–368		
1983-87-exc. below	25056619	332.00
Comm. Ch. (1983)	8999106	318.25
Comm. Ch. (1984-87)	25056615	329.25
V-8–307		
1986-87	◆25100217	335.00

LABOR 9 FRONT SUSPENSION 9 LABOR

(Factory Time) Chilton Time

Note: On all front suspension operations alignment charges must be added if performed. Time given does not include alignment.

(M) Wheel, Renew
one (.5) 5

(G) Wheels, Rotate (All)
All models 5

(G) Wheels, Balance
one 3
each adtnl 2

(G) Check Alignment of Front End
All models 5
Note: Deduct if alignment is performed.

(G) Toe-In, Adjust
All models (.4) 6

(G) Align Front End
Includes: Adjust front wheel bearings.
All models (.7) 1.4
w/A.C. interference add 5

(G) Front Wheel Bearings, Clean and Repack (Both Wheels)
1983-87 .... 1.6

(G) Front Wheel Bearings and Cups, Renew
1983-87-one side (.8) 1.0
both sides (1.2) 1.7

(G) Front Wheel Grease Seals, Renew
1983-87-one whl (.8) 8
both whls (1.2) 1.5

(G) Front Shock Absorber, Renew
1983-87-one (.3) 4
both (.5) 7

(G) Rebuild Front Suspension
Includes: Disassemble, renew necessary parts, reassemble, lubricate and align front end.
1983-87-one side 4.6
both sides 8.4

(G) Steering Knuckle, Renew (One)
Includes: Align front end.
1983-87 (1.7) 2.4

(G) Lower Ball Joint, Renew
Add alignment charges.
1983-87-one (.6) 1.0
both (1.0) 1.7

(G) Upper Ball Joint, Renew
Includes: Align front end.
1983-87-one (1.4) 1.8
both (1.9) 2.6

(G) Upper Control Arm, Renew
Includes: Align front end.
1983-87-one side (1.4) 1.8
both sides (1.9) 2.7

(G) Upper Control Arm Inner Pivot Shaft and/or Bushings, Renew
Includes: Align front end.
1983-87-one side (1.7) 2.6
both sides (2.5) 3.9

(G) Lower Control Arm, Renew
Add alignment charges.
1983-87-one (1.0) 1.4
both (1.7) 2.7

(G) Lower Control Arm Bushings, Renew
Add alignment charges.
1983-87-one side (1.2) 1.7
both sides (2.3) 3.3

(G) Front Spring, Renew
Includes: Align front end.
1983-87-one (1.5) 2.3
both (2.1) 3.6

(G) Front Stabilizer Bar, Renew
1983-87 (.5) 8

(G) Stabilizer Links and/or Grommets, Renew
1983-87 (.4) 7

PARTS 9 FRONT SUSPENSION 9 PARTS

	Part No.	Price
(1) Front Wheel Bearing (Outer)		
1983-87	◆7450697	11.00
(2) Front Wheel Bearing (Inner)		
1983-87-exc below	◆7450630	11.00
Limo, Comm. Ch.	7450700	13.00
(3) Front Seal Assy.		
1983-87	◆3965092	3.50
(4) Steering Knuckle		
(DeVille, Fleetwood Brougham)		
1983-87-right	◆14012590	144.00
left	◆14012589	144.00
(Limo, Commercial Chassis)		
1983-87-right	3961262	122.00
left	3961261	122.00
(5) Ball Joint Pkg. (Lower)		
1983-87	◆9767281	31.50
(6) Control Arm (Lower)		
(DeVille, Fleetwood Brougham)		
1983-87-right	◆14039016	105.00
left	◆14039015	105.00
(Limo, Commercial Chassis)		
1983-87-right	343540	96.50
left	343539	96.50
(7) Bushing (Rear)		
1983-87	3993677	7.00
(8) Shock Absorber		
(Standard)		
1983-84	◆4993548	24.50
1985-87	◆4993745	24.50
(9) Coil Spring		
Order by year and model.		
(10) Ball Joint (Upper)		
1983-87	◆9767112	34.75
(11) Bushing (Front)		
1983-87	◆351286	7.00

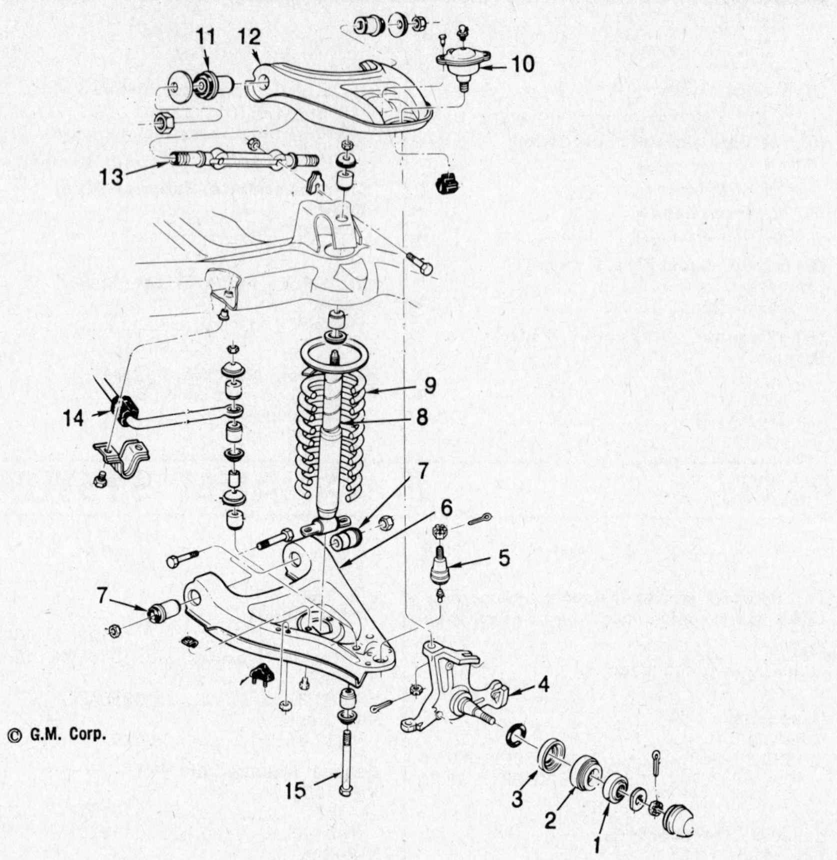

	Part No.	Price
(12) Control Arm (Upper)		
1983-87-right	◆14039010	109.00
left	◆14039009	109.00
(13) Shaft Pkg. (Upper Control)		
1983-87-right	◆14022172	33.75
left	◆14022171	35.50

	Part No.	Price
(14) Bushing (Stabilizer)		
1983-87	◆371773	1.00
(15) Link Pkg.		
1983-87	◆464167	4.25

LABOR 10 STEERING LINKAGE 10 LABOR

	(Factory Time)	Chilton Time
(G) Pitman Arm, Renew		
1983-85	(.5)	.8
1986-87	(.3)	.5
(G) Idler Arm, Renew		
1983-87	(.7)	1.0
(G) Tie Rods or Tie Rod Ends, Renew		
Includes: Adjust toe-in.		
1983-87-one side	(.8)	1.0
both sides	(.9)	1.5
(G) Steering Shock Assembly, Renew		
1983-87	(.3)	.5
(G) Intermediate Rod, Renew		
Includes: Reset toe-in.		
1983-85	(1.0)	1.4
1986-87	(.7)	1.0

PARTS 10 STEERING LINKAGE 10 PARTS

	Part No.	Price
(1) Idler Arm Assy.		
1983-87	◆7837635	51.00
(2) Tie Rod Assembly (Inner)		
(DeVille, Brougham)		
1983-87	◆7834224	45.75
(Limo, Commercial Chassis)		
1983-87	7834292	48.75
(3) Tie Rod Assembly (Outer)		
(DeVille, Brougham)		
1983-87	◆12308612	50.50

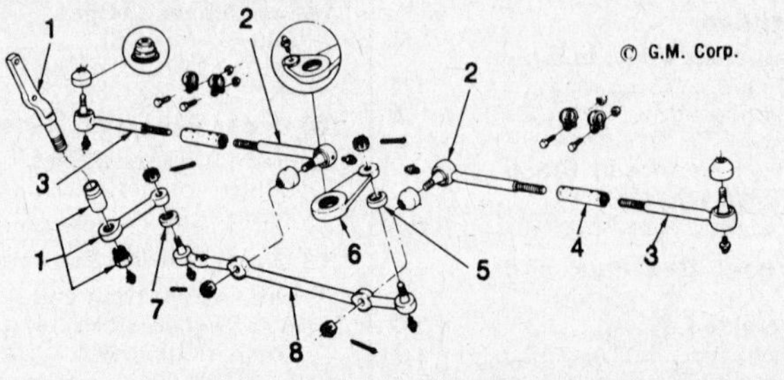

PARTS 10 STEERING LINKAGE 10 PARTS

	Part No.	Price
(Limo, Commercial Chassis)		
1983-87	7834290	51.00
(4) Tie Rod Sleeve Pkg. (Adjuster)		
1983-87	◆7826714	15.50
(5) Seal Kit (Pitman Arm)		
1983-87	◆7826470	17.00
(6) Pitman Arm		
1983-87	7837646	51.25
(7) Seal Kit		
1983-87	◆7826470	17.00
(8) Relay Rod Assy.		
(DeVille, Brougham)		
1983-exc. below	7837640	109.00
Elect. Level Cont.	7837641	119.00
1984-87	7837641	119.00
(Limo, Commercial Chassis)		
1983-87	7837642	119.00
Steering Shock Absorber		
1983-87	4993536	42.50

LABOR 11 STEERING GEAR 11 LABOR

(Factory Time)	Chilton Time
(G) Horn Contacts and/or Cancelling Cam, Renew	
1983-85 (.3)	.6
1986-87 (.5)	.6
w/Tilt-Tel (.4)	.7
(G) Steering Wheel, Renew	
1983-87 (.3)	.5
w/Tilt-Tel (.4)	.6
(G) Steering Column Lock Actuator Parts, Renew	
1983-85	
std colm (1.0)	1.5
tilt colm (.7)	1.2
1986-87	
std colm (1.4)	1.9
tilt tel (1.3)	1.8
(G) Turn Signal Pivot Assy., Renew	
1983-85 (.6)	1.2
w/Tilt-Tel (.9)	1.3
w/Cruise control add (.2)	.2
1986-87 (.6)	1.2
(G) Steering Column Shift Bowl, Renew	
Does not include colorcoat.	
1983-87 (1.5)	2.2
w/Tilt Tel (2.1)	3.1
(G) Upper Mast Jacket Bearing, Renew	
1983-85	
std colm (.8)	1.4
tilt colm (1.1)	1.7
1986-87	
std colm (.8)	1.4
tilt tel (.6)	1.1
(G) Steering Column Lower Bearing, Renew	
1983-87 (.3)	1.0
(G) Steering Shaft Lower Coupling, Renew (Pot Joint)	
1983-85 (.5)	.8
(G) Steering Flex Coupling, Renew (Rag Joint)	
1983-85 (.5)	.8
(G) Pitman Shaft Seal, Renew (On Car)	
1983-87 (.6)	1.0

POWER STEERING

(Factory Time)	Chilton Time
(G) Trouble Shoot Power Steering	
Includes: Test pump and system pressure, check pounds pull on steering wheel and check for fluid leaks.	
All models	.6
(M) Check Reservoir and Add Fluid	
All models (.2)	.3
(M) Pump Drive Belt, Renew or Adjust	
1983-87-renew (.3)	.4
adjust (.2)	.3
(G) Steering Gear, Adjust	
1983-87 (.8)	1.2
(G) Steering Gear Assembly, Renew	
1983-85 (.7)	1.2
1986-87 (1.1)	1.5
(P) Steering Gear Assy., R&R and Recondition	
Includes: Disassemble, renew necessary parts, reassemble and adjust.	
1983-87 (2.1)	2.5
(G) Side Cover 'O' Ring, Renew	
Includes: Adjust gear.	
1983-87 (1.3)	1.4
(G) Adjustor Plug, Recondition	
Includes: R&R gear, renew 'O' ring, oil seal and bearings. Adjust bearing pre-load.	
1983-87 (1.3)	1.6
(G) Valve Body Assy., R&R or Recondition	
Includes: R&R gear and adjust.	
1983-87 (1.4)	1.8
(G) Rack Pinion Assy., R&R or Recondition	
Includes: R&R gear and adjust.	
1983-87 (1.5)	2.0
(G) Pitman Shaft and/or Seal, Renew	
1983-87 (.6)	1.0
(G) Steering Gear Housing, Renew	
Includes: R&R gear, renew pitman shaft seal.	
1983-87 (1.5)	1.8
(G) Pump Flow Control Valve, Renew	
1983-87	
V-8 (.4)	.8
Diesel (.4)	.8
(G) Power Steering Pump Assy., Renew	
Includes: Fill and bleed system.	
1983-87	
V-8 (.9)	1.4
Diesel (1.1)	1.5
(P) Power Steering Pump, R&R and Recondition	
Includes: Fill and bleed system.	
1983-87	
V-8 (1.3)	2.2
Diesel (1.6)	2.3
(G) Power Steering Reservoir, Renew (Remote)	
1983-87 (.3)	.6
(G) Power Steering Pump Shaft Oil Seal, Renew	
1983-85 (.7)	1.1
1986-87 (.9)	1.4
(M) Power Steering Hoses, Renew	
1983-85-each (.4)	.6
1986-87	
pressure (.6)	.8
return (.3)	.5
(M) Hydra-Boost Hoses, Renew	
1983-85-each (.3)	.5

TILT AND TELESCOPE STEERING COLUMN

(Factory Time)	Chilton Time
(G) Steering Column, Renew	
Does not include colorcoat.	
1983-87 (.9)	1.5
w/Cruise control add (.2)	.2
(G) Steering Column, R&R and Recondition	
Includes: Disassemble, inspect and reassemble. Renew parts as required.	
1983-87 (1.6)	2.5
(G) Upper Bearing and Turn Signal Housing, Renew	
1983-85 (1.1)	1.8
Recond housing add (.2)	.4
1986-87 (1.7)	2.5
(G) Steering Shaft and Sphere Assy., Renew	
1983-84 (1.1)	2.2
Renew sphere assy add (.2)	.2
(G) Steering Column Lock Shoes, Renew	
1983-84 (1.3)	2.2
Polish shoes add (.2)	.3

PARTS 11 POWER STEERING GEAR 11 PARTS

	Part No.	Price
(1) Seal (Side Cover)		
1983-87	◆7817486	9.00
(2) Pitman Shaft (w/Gear)		
1983-87-exc. below	◆7813631	87.50
wo/variable P.S.	◆7815885	87.50
(4) Bearing Kit		
1983-87	◆7826850	11.00
(5) Housing Assy.		
1983-87-exc. below	◆7834139	183.00
Limo, Comm. Chassis	7834133	183.00
(6) Bearing (Pitman Shaft)		
1983-87	◆5697804	15.00
(7) Seal Kit (Pitman Shaft)		
1983-87	◆7826470	17.00
(8) Seal (Adjuster Plug)		
1983-87	◆5686527	1.50
(9) Bearing (Adjuster Plug)		
1983-87	◆7828012	7.25
(10) Plug Assy. (Adjuster)		
1983-87	◆7832731	53.50
(11) Seal Kit		
1983-87	◆5687182	12.50
(12) Valve Assy.		
1983-87	◆7832036	212.00
(14) Seal Kit		
1983-87	◆7817485	6.50
(15) Plug		
1983-87-exc. below	◆5689010	8.75
Limo, Comm. Chassis	7805525	10.25
(16) Rack Assy.		
1983-87-exc. below	◆7817528	162.00
Limo, Comm. Chassis	7826560	150.00

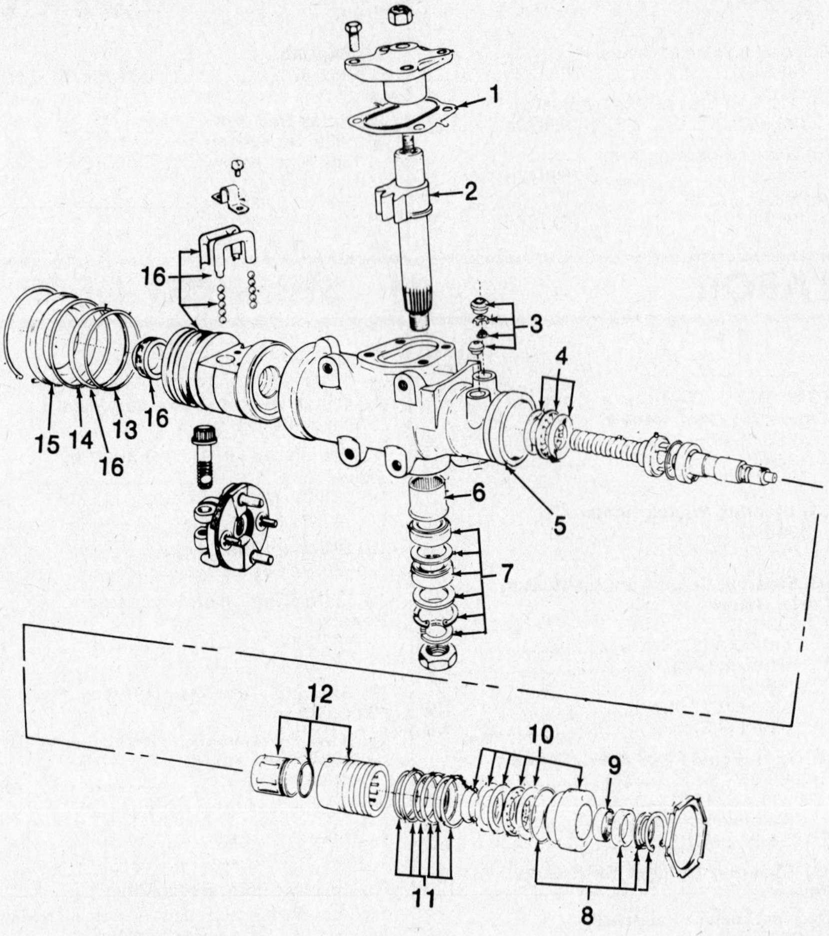

PARTS 11 POWER STEERING PUMP 11 PARTS

	Part No.	Price
Pressure Line Hose		
Order by year and model.		
Power Steering Pump Assy.		
V-8-250		
1983-85	◆7842624	199.00
V-8-350 Diesel		
1983-85	7839789	257.00
V-8-368		
1983-84-Limo	7839821	257.00
Comm. Ch.	7839820	257.00
V-8-307		
1986-87	◆7840244	199.00
(1) Pressure Plate		
1983-87-exc. below	◆7839669	14.25
Limo, Comm. Ch.	7839914	11.00
(2) Pressure Plate Spring		
1983-87-exc. below	◆7839667	1.00
Limo, Comm. Ch.	7839916	1.50
(3) End Plate		
1983-87-exc. below	◆5689358	3.50
Limo, Comm. Ch.	5691489	4.00

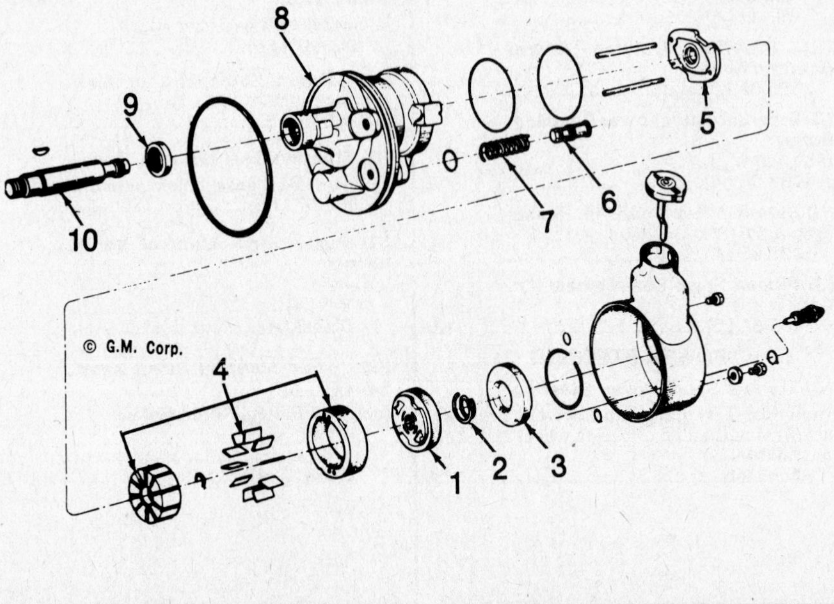

PARTS 11 POWER STEERING PUMP 11 PARTS

	Part No.	Price
(4) Rotor & Vane Kit		
1983-87-exc. below	◆7837322	75.00
Limo, Comm. Ch.	7837324	79.75
(5) Thrust Plate		
1983-87	◆7836369	13.75
(6) Valve Assy.		
1983-87-exc. below	◆7809232	10.75
Limo, Comm. Ch.	7809231	11.75
(7) FLow Control Spring		
1983-87	◆5688037	1.50
(8) Housing Assy.		
(exc. V-8-250)		
1983-84	◆7830236	62.75
(V-8-250)		
1983-85	◆7840520	62.75
(9) Drive Shaft Seal		
1983-87	◆7808195	4.50
(10) Drive Shaft		
1983-87-exc. below	◆7837321	39.50
Limo, Comm. Ch.	7837323	41.00
1986-87	◆411226	4.00

LABOR 12 CYLINDER HEAD & VALVE SYSTEM 12 LABOR

COMBINATIONS
Add to Valve Job

See Machine Shop Operations

	Chilton Time
(G) DRAIN, EVACUATE & RECHARGE AIR CONDITIONING SYSTEM	
All models (.5)	1.0
(G) HYDRAULIC VALVE LIFTERS, DISASSEMBLE AND CLEAN	
Each (.2)	.2
(G) DISTRIBUTOR, RECONDITION	
All models (.6)	.8
(G) CARBURETOR, RECONDITION	
2 bbl	1.2
4 bbl	1.5
(G) ROCKER ARM ASSEMBLY, DISASSEMBLE AND CLEAN	
Each bank (.4)	.5
(P) VALVE GUIDES, REAM OVERSIZE	
Each (.2)	.3

GASOLINE ENGINES

(Factory Time)	Chilton Time
(G) Compression Test	
V-8–1983-87	.8
(G) Cylinder Head Gasket, Renew	
Includes: Clean carbon and make all necessary adjustments.	
V-8–1983-85-one side (3.3)	4.7
both sides (4.5)	5.9
1983-85-Eng Code 8	
one side (6.1)	8.0
both sides (6.8)	9.0
w/A.I.R. add (.3)	.3
1986-87-Eng Codes Y-9	
one side (5.1)	7.0
both sides (6.9)	9.5
(G) Cylinder Head, Renew	
Includes: Transfer all components, reface valves, clean carbon.	
V-8–1983-85-one (4.8)	6.2
both (6.1)	8.4
1983-85-Eng Code 8	
one side (6.5)	8.8
both sides (7.6)	10.6
w/A.I.R. add (.3)	.3
1986-87-Eng Codes Y-9	
one side (5.3)	7.3
both sides (7.3)	10.0
(P) Clean Carbon and Grind Valves	
Includes: R&R cylinder heads, grind valves and seats. Minor tune up.	
V-8–1983-85 (6.0)	9.7
1983-85-Eng Code 8	
one side (6.9)	9.6
both sides (8.4)	12.2
w/A.I.R. add (.3)	.3
1986-87-Eng Codes Y-9	
one side (6.7)	9.2
both sides (9.2)	12.7
(G) Rocker Arm Cover or Gaskets, Renew	
w/A.I.R. add (.3)	.3
V-8–1983-85-each (.5)	.7
1983-85-Eng Code 8	
right side (1.1)	1.5
left side (.7)	1.0
both sides (1.6)	2.3
1986-87-Eng Codes Y-9	
right side (1.0)	1.5
left side (1.2)	1.7
both sides (1.8)	2.8
(G) Valve Tappets, Renew (Lifters)	
Includes: Test and bleed lifter, make all necessary adjustments.	
w/A.I.R. add (.4)	.4
V-8–1983-85-one cyl (1.3)	1.9
one cyl-each side (1.6)	2.4
all cyls-both sides (1.9)	3.0
1983-85-Eng Code 8	
one or all (5.2)	7.3
1986-87-Eng Codes Y-9	
one cyl-right side (3.5)	4.8
one cyl-left side (3.2)	4.4
one cyl-each side (4.0)	5.5
all cyls-both sides (5.8)	8.0
(G) Valve Springs and/or Valve Stem Oil Seals, Renew (Head on Car)	
w/A.I.R. add (.3)	.3
V-8–1983-85-one cyl (.7)	1.1
one cyl-each bank (1.1)	2.0
each adtnl cyl (.2)	.3
1983-85-Eng Code 8	
right side-one cyl (1.6)	2.1
left side-one cyl (1.2)	1.6
each adtnl cyl (.2)	.3
1986-87-Eng Codes Y-9	
one cyl-right side (1.4)	2.0
one cyl-left side (1.8)	2.6
one cyl-each side (2.4)	3.5
all cyls-both sides (4.8)	7.0
(G) Rocker Arm T-Bar Assy., and/or Pivot, Renew	
V-8–1983-85-one cyl (.6)	.9
each adtnl cyl (.1)	.2
1983-85-Eng Code 8	
right side-one cyl (1.4)	1.8
left side-one cyl (1.0)	1.4
both sides-all cyls (2.2)	3.0
1986-87-Eng Codes Y-9	
one cyl-right side (1.1)	1.6
one cyl-left side (1.3)	1.9
one cyl-each side (1.9)	2.8
all cyls-both sides (2.4)	3.5
(G) Valve Push Rods, Renew	
V-8–1983-85-one cyl (.6)	.9
one cyl-each side (.8)	1.5
each adtnl cyl (.1)	.1
1983-85-Eng Code 8	
right side (1.3)	1.7
left side (.9)	1.3
both sides (2.1)	2.8
1986-87-Eng Codes Y-9	
one cyl-right side (1.1)	1.6
one cyl-left side (1.3)	1.9
one cyl-each side (1.9)	2.8
all cyls-both sides (2.4)	3.5
(G) Cylinder Head Gasket, Renew	
Includes: Clean carbon and make all necessary adjustments.	
1983-85-right (6.5)	8.4
left (6.1)	7.9
both (8.0)	10.4
(G) Cylinder Head, Renew	
Includes: Transfer all components, reface valves, clean carbon.	
1983-85-right (6.9)	8.9
left (6.5)	8.4
both (8.8)	11.4
(P) Clean Carbon and Grind Valves	
Includes: R&R cylinder heads, grind valves and seats. Make all necessary adjustments.	
1983-85 (9.7)	12.6
(G) Rocker Arm Cover or Gaskets, Renew	
1983-85-one (1.2)	2.4
both (2.0)	2.9
(G) Valve Tappets, Renew (Lifters)	
Includes: Test and bleed lifters, make all necessary adjustments.	
1983-85-one cyl (3.5)	4.5
one cyl-each bank (3.9)	5.0
each adtnl cyl (.1)	.2

LABOR 12 CYLINDER HEAD & VALVE SYSTEM 12 LABOR

	(Factory Time)	Chilton Time
(G) Valve Springs and/or Valve Stem Oil Seals, Renew (Head on Car)		
1983-85-one cyl	(1.6)	3.0
one cyl-each bank	(2.4)	3.7
each adtnl cyl	(.2)	.3
(G) Rocker Arm T-Bar Assy., and/or Push Rod, Renew		
1983-85-one cyl	(1.5)	2.5
one cyl-each bank	(2.3)	3.0
each adtnl cyl	(.1)	.2
(G) Valve Push Rods, Renew		
1983-85-one cyl	(1.5)	2.5
one cyl-each bank	(2.3)	3.0
each adtnl cyl	(.1)	.1

DIESEL ENGINE

	Chilton Time
(G) Compression Test	
1983-85	1.3

PARTS 12 CYLINDER HEAD & VALVE SYSTEM 12 PARTS

	Part No.	Price
Valve Grind Gasket Set		
V-8-368		
1983-84	3634523	16.75
V-8-Diesel		
1983-84	◆22522053	94.50
1985	◆22527541	N.L.
V-8-307		
1986-87	◆22534926	58.00
(1) Cylinder Head		
V-8-250		
1983	◆1617594	314.00
1984	◆1626693	N.L.
1985-Fed.	◆1628559	296.00
Calif.	◆1628557	296.00
V-8-350-Diesel		
1983-85	◆22515038	387.00
V-8-368		
1983-84-exc. below	3517334	338.00
Fuel Inj.	3517415	420.00
V-8-307		
1986-87	◆22530557	247.00
(2) Rocker Arm Cover Gasket		
V-8-250		
1983-84	1627340	3.00
1985	1630243	8.25
V-8-368		
1983-84	1619840	3.00
(3) Intake Valve		
V-8-250		
1983-85	◆1618837	12.00
V-8-350-Diesel		
1983-85	◆22519914	20.00
V-8-368		
1983-84	1615431	10.75
V-8-307		
1986-87	◆22530611	20.25
(4) Exhaust Valve		
V-8-250		
1983-85	◆1621321	15.25
V-8-350-Diesel		
1983-85	◆558873	13.00
V-8-368		
1983-84	1615436	15.50
V-8-307		
1986-87	◆555456	N.L.
(5) Valve Spring		
V-8-250		
1983-85	◆1622834	4.00
V-8-350-Diesel		
1983-85	◆22510372	4.00

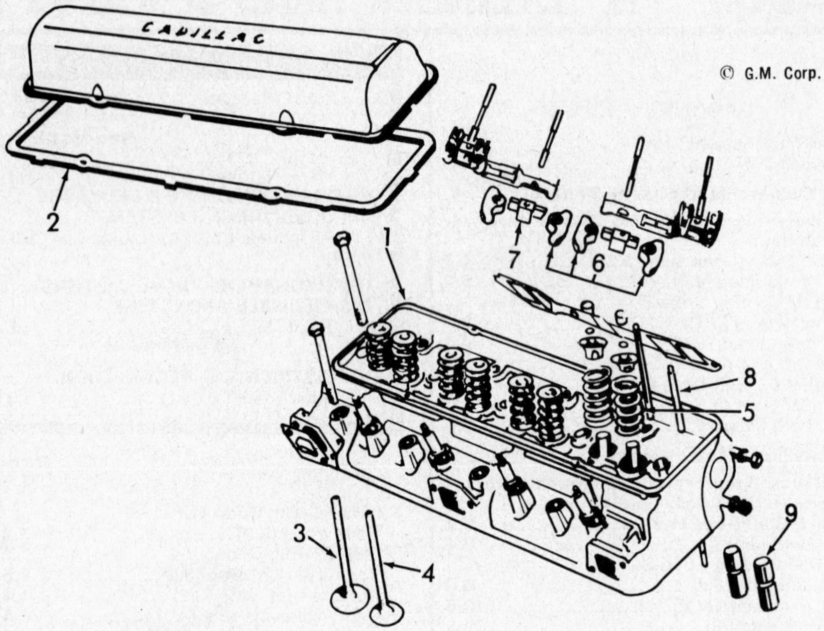

	Part No.	Price
V-8-368		
1983-84	1465408	3.75
V-8-307		
(6) Rocker Arm		
V-8-250		
1983-85	◆1618802	4.75
V-8-350-Diesel		
1983-85	◆22505583	N.L.
V-8-368		
(Limo)		
1983-84	1616818	4.75
(Commercial Chassis)		
1983-84-R.H.	1487269	5.00
L.H.	1487268	5.00
V-8-307		
1986-87	◆22505583	N.L.
(7) Support		
1983-84-368	1487613	6.00

	Part No.	Price
(8) Valve Push Rod		
V-8-250		
1983-85	◆1618805	2.50
V-8-350-Diesel		
1983-85	◆22511044	3.25
V-8-368		
1983-84	1487602	6.00
V-8-307		
1986-87	◆22533631	3.25
(9) Valve Lifter		
V-8-250		
1983-85	◆5234360	8.50
V-8-350-Diesel		
1983-85	◆5234470	38.10
V-8-368		
1983-84	5232510	10.60
V-8-307		
1986-87	◆5234755	43.50

LABOR 13 ENGINE ASSEMBLY & MOUNTS 13 LABOR

(Factory Time) Chilton Time

GASOLINE ENGINES

(G) Engine Assembly, Remove & Install

Does not include transfer of any parts or equipment.

V-8–1983-85 (4.3)	7.0
1983-85	
Eng Code 8	5.5
w/Cruise control add (.1)	.1
w/A.I.R. add (.2)	.2
w/E.F.I. add (.2)	.2
1986-87	
Eng Codes Y-9	5.0

(G) Engine Assembly, Renew

Includes: R&R engine assembly, transfer all component parts not supplied with replacement engine. Minor tune up.

V-8–1983-85 (7.0)	11.6
1983-85	
Eng Code 8 (8.0)	12.0
w/Cruise control add (.1)	.1
w/A.I.R. add (.2)	.2
w/E.F.I. add (.2)	.2
1986-87	
Eng Codes Y-9 (4.6)	8.0

(P) Cylinder Block, Renew (w/All Internal Parts Less Head(s) and Oil Pan)

Includes: Transfer all component parts not supplied with replacement engine, clean carbon, grind valves. Minor tune up.

V-8–1983-85 (11.4)	15.7
1983-85	
Eng Code 8 (14.9)	19.1
w/Cruise control add (.1)	.1
w/A.I.R. add (.2)	.2
w/E.F.I. add (.2)	.2
1986-87	
Eng Codes Y-9 (10.7)	15.5

(P) Cylinder Block, Renew (w/Pistons, Rings and Bearings)

Includes: Transfer all component parts, clean carbon, grind valves. Minor tune up.

V-8–1983-85 (14.1)	18.9
w/Cruise control add (.1)	.1
w/A.I.R. add (.2)	.2
w/E.F.I. add (.2)	.2
1986-87	
Eng Codes Y-9 (13.3)	19.2

(P) Engine Assy., R&R and Recondition (Complete)

Includes: Rebore block, install new pistons, rings, rod and main bearings. Clean carbon, grind valves. Tune engine.

V-8–1983-85 (27.9)	35.9
1983-85	
Eng Code 8 (17.0)	25.1
w/Cruise control add (.1)	.1
w/A.I.R. add (.2)	.2
w/E.F.I. add (.2)	.2
1986-87	
Eng Codes Y-9 (18.3)	26.5

(P) Engine Assembly, Recondition (In Car)

Includes: Expand or renew pistons, install new rings, pins, rod and main bearings. Clean carbon, grind valves. Tune engine.

V-8–1983-85 (20.5)	27.2
1983-85	
Eng Code 8 (14.7)	21.7
w/Cruise control add (.1)	.1
w/A.I.R. add (.2)	.2
w/E.F.I. add (.2)	.2
1986-87	
Eng Codes Y-9 (17.0)	24.6

(G) Engine Mounts, Renew

Front	
V-8	
1983-85-one (.8)	1.1
both (1.0)	1.6
1983-85-Eng Code 8	
one (.7)	1.1
both (1.2)	1.4
1986-87	
Eng Codes Y-9	
one (.8)	1.1
both (1.3)	1.8
Rear	
V-8–1983-87 (.4)	.7

DIESEL ENGINE

(G) Engine Assembly, Remove & Install

Does not include transfer of any parts or equipment.

1983-85	5.7

(G) Engine Assembly, Renew (Universal)

Includes: R&R engine assembly, transfer all component parts not supplied with replacement engine. Make all necessary adjustments.

1983-85 (8.2)	20.0

(P) Cylinder Block, Renew (w/All Internal Parts Less Head(s) and Oil Pan)

Includes: Transfer all component parts not supplied with replacement engine, clean carbon, grind valves. Make all necessary adjustments.

1983-85 (12.6)	24.0

(P) Cylinder Block, Renew (w/Pistons, Rings and Bearings)

Includes: Transfer all component parts, clean carbon, grind valves. Make all necessary adjustments.

1983-85 (17.1)	28.0

(P) Engine Assembly, R&R and Recondition (Complete)

Includes: Rebore block, install new pistons, rings, rod and main bearings. Clean carbon, grind valves. Make all necessary adjustments.

1983-85 (31.5)	36.0

(P) Engine Assembly, Recondition (In Car)

Includes: Expand or renew pistons, install new rings, pins, rod and main bearings. Clean carbon, grind valves. Make all necessary adjustments.

1983-85 (23.1)	27.3

(G) Engine Mounts, Renew

Front	
1983-85-one (.5)	.9
both (.7)	1.1
Rear	
1983-85 (.3)	.6

PARTS 13 ENGINE ASSEMBLY & MOUNTS 13 PARTS

	Part No.	Price
Partial Engine Assembly		
V-8-250		
1983-85	◆1623537	2039.25
V-8-350-Diesel		
1983	22514593	1999.25
1984-85	◆22525604	1600.00
V-8-368		
1983-84-exc. below	3517425	2119.25
Comm. Chassis	3517357	2119.25
V-8-307		
1986-87	◆22530855	1397.00
Front Engine Mounts		
V-8-Gas		
1983-87	1613479	27.00
V-8-Diesel		
1983-85	9764714	27.75
Rear Engine Mounts		
V-8-Gas		
1983-87-exc. below	1623432	14.25
Limo, Comm. Ch.	1613480	25.25
V-8-Diesel		
1983-85	1619088	21.75

LABOR 14 PISTONS, RINGS & BEARINGS 14 LABOR

COMBINATIONS

Add to Engine Work

See Machine Shop Operations

(G) DRAIN, EVACUATE & RECHARGE AIR CONDITIONING SYSTEM
All models (.5) 1.0

(G) HYDRAULIC VALVE LIFTERS, DISASSEMBLE AND CLEAN
Each (.2) 2

(G) DISTRIBUTOR, RECONDITION
All models (.6) 8

(G) CARBURETOR, RECONDITION
2 bbl 1.2
4 bbl 1.5

(G) DEGLAZE CYLINDER WALLS
Each (.1) 1

(P) VALVES, RECONDITION (CYLINDER HEAD REMOVED)
V-8–One head 1.5
Both heads 2.9

(G) REMOVE CYLINDER TOP RIDGE
Each (.1) 1

(G) ROCKER ARM ASSY., DISASSEMBLE AND CLEAN OR RECONDITION
Each bank (.4) 5

(G) MAIN BEARINGS, RENEW (PAN REMOVED)
V-8 (1.0) 1.5

(G) PLASTIGAUGE BEARINGS
Each (.1) 1

(G) CYLINDER LINER, RENEW
Each (.2) 3

(G) OIL PUMP, RECONDITION
V-8 (.3) 5

(M) OIL FILTER ELEMENT, RENEW
All models (.2) 3

(Factory Time) — Chilton Time

GASOLINE ENGINE

(P) Rings, Renew (See Engine Combinations)

Includes: Remove cylinder top ridge, deglaze cylinder walls. Clean piston and ring grooves. Minor tune up.

V-8–1983-85 (8.0) 11.4
1983-85-Eng Code 8
one cyl (7.5) 10.5
one cyl-each side (8.7) 12.1
all cyls-both sides (11.1) 15.5
Renew piston liner add-each (.2) 3
w/A.I.R. add (.3) 3
1986-87
Eng Codes Y-9
one cyl (7.9) 11.4
one cyl-each side (10.5) 15.2
all cyls-both sides (12.8) 18.5

(P) Pistons or Connecting Rods, Renew

Includes: Remove cylinder top ridge, deglaze cylinder walls. Clean piston and ring grooves. Minor tune up.

V-8–1983-85 (8.0) 13.8
1983-85-Eng Code 8
one cyl (7.6) 10.8
one cyl-each side (8.9) 12.7
all cyls-both sides (11.9) 17.9
Renew piston liner add-each (.2) 3
1986-87
Eng Codes Y-9
one cyl (8.5) 12.0
one cyl-each side (11.7) 16.4
all cyls-both sides (13.9) 20.9
w/A.I.R. add (.3) 3

(P) Connecting Rod Bearings, Renew

V-8–1983-85 (3.4) 5.7
1983-85
Eng Code 8 (3.0) 4.0
w/A.I.R. add (.2) 2
1986-87
Eng Codes Y-9 (4.4) 6.0

DIESEL ENGINE

(P) Rings, Renew (See Engine Combinations)

Includes: Remove cylinder top ridge, deglaze cylinder walls. Clean piston and ring grooves. Make all necessary adjustments.

1983-85 (13.2) 17.2

(P) Pistons or Connecting Rods, Renew

Includes: Remove cylinder top ridge, deglaze cylinder walls. Clean piston and ring grooves. Make all necessary adjustments.

1983-85 (13.7) 19.6

(P) Connecting Rod Bearings, Renew

1983-85 (4.9) 6.6

PARTS 14 PISTONS, RINGS & BEARINGS 14 PARTS

	Part No.	Price
(1) Piston Ring Set (Std.)		
V-8-250		
1983-85	◆1623817	20.25
V-8-350-Diesel		
1984-85	◆22523733	21.00
V-8-368		
1983-84	1618669	17.25
V-8-307		
1986-87	◆22529562	16.75
(2) Piston Assembly (Std.)		
V-8-250		
1983-85	◆1623538	107.00
V-8-350-Diesel		
1983-R.H.	◆22523358	63.75
L.H.	◆22523357	63.75
1984-85-R.H.	◆22523358	63.75
L.H.	◆22523357	63.75
V-8-368		
1983-84	1618673	75.50
V-8-307		
1986-87-R.H.	◆22527482	48.25
L.H.	◆22527481	48.25

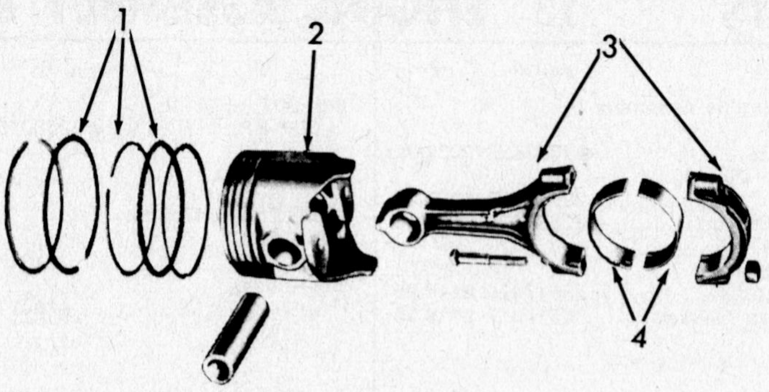

	Part No.	Price
(3) Connecting Rod Assembly		
V-8-250		
1983-85	◆1619145	59.00
V-8-350-Diesel		
1983-85	◆22515313	50.50
V-8-368		
1983-84	1619338	61.50
V-8-307		
1986-87	◆22527025	45.00

PARTS 14 PISTONS, RINGS, PINS & BEARINGS 14 PARTS

	Part No.	Price
(4) Connecting Rod Bearings (Std.)		
V-8-250		
1983-85	◆18009085	11.00
V-8-350-Diesel		
1983-85	◆18008494	10.50
V-8-368		
1983-84	5468609	12.50
V-8-307		
1986-87	◆18008494	N.L.

LABOR 15 CRANKSHAFT & DAMPER 15 LABOR

(Factory Time)	Chilton Time
GASOLINE ENGINE	
(P) Crankshaft and Main Bearings, Renew	
Includes: R&R engine assy., check all bearing clearances.	
V-8–1983-85 (6.8)	9.9
1983-85	
Eng Code 8 (9.5)	13.0
w/Cruise control add (.1)	.1
w/A.I.R. add (.2)	.2
1986-87	
Eng Codes Y-9 (7.6)	11.0
(P) Main Bearings, Renew	
Includes: Check all bearing clearances.	
V-8–1983-85 (2.8)	4.3
1983-85	
Eng Code 8 (2.4)	3.1
1986-87	
Eng Codes Y-9 (4.1)	5.7
(P) Main and Rod Bearings, Renew	
Includes: Check all bearing clearances.	
V-8–1983-85 (4.4)	6.7
1983-85	
Eng Code 8 (4.0)	5.5
1986-87	
Eng Codes Y-9 (6.3)	8.1
(G) Rear Main Bearing Oil Seals, Renew or Repack (Upper & Lower)	
V-8–1983-85 (2.4)	3.9
1983-85	
Eng Code 8 (1.6)	2.5
1986-87	
Eng Codes Y-9 (6.6)	3.5
(G) Crankshaft Pulley or Balancer, Renew	
V-8–1983-85-pulley (.7)	.9
balancer (.8)	1.2
1986-87	
Eng Codes Y-9	
pulley (.7)	1.0
balancer (1.0)	1.4
DIESEL ENGINE	
(P) Crankshaft and Main Bearings, Renew	
Includes: R&R engine assy., check all bearing clearances.	
1983-85 (7.8)	11.6
(P) Main Bearings, Renew	
Includes: Check all bearing clearances.	
1983-85 (4.1)	5.5
(P) Main and Rod Bearings, Renew	
Includes: Check all bearing clearances.	
1983-85 (6.5)	7.9
(G) Rear Main Bearing Oil Seals, R&R and Repack (Upper & Lower)	
1983-85 (2.9)	4.0
(G) Rear Main Bearing Oil Seals, Renew	
Includes: R&R engine assy.	
1983-85 (6.9)	10.7
w/A.C. add (.4)	.4
(G) Crankshaft Front Oil Seal, Renew	
1983-85 (1.1)	1.7
(G) Vibration Damper, Renew	
1983-85 (1.0)	1.5

PARTS 15 CRANKSHAFT & DAMPER 15 PARTS

	Part No.	Price
(1) Crankshaft		
V-8-250		
1983-85	◆1628920	473.00
V-8-350-Diesel		
1983-85	◆22511035	439.00
V-8-368		
1983-84	1621463	611.00
V-8-307		
1986-87	◆22527438	403.00
(2) Main Bearings (Std.)		
V-8-250		
1983-85-No. 1	◆18012316	17.25
Nos. 2, 4	◆18009086	18.75
No. 3	◆18009088	23.75
Rear	◆18009087	16.50
V-8-350-Diesel		
1983-87-No. 1	◆5466312	16.00
No. 2, 4	◆5458657	15.00
No. 3	◆5463797	26.25
No. 5	◆5466314	19.75
V-8-368		
1983-87-No. 1	5468610	20.25
Nos. 2, 4	5468611	18.75
No. 3	5468612	25.25
No. 5	5468613	16.50
V-8-307		
1986-87-No. 1	◆5466211	13.00
Nos. 2, 4	◆5466089	13.00
No. 3	◆5466090	19.75
No.5	◆5466091	17.00

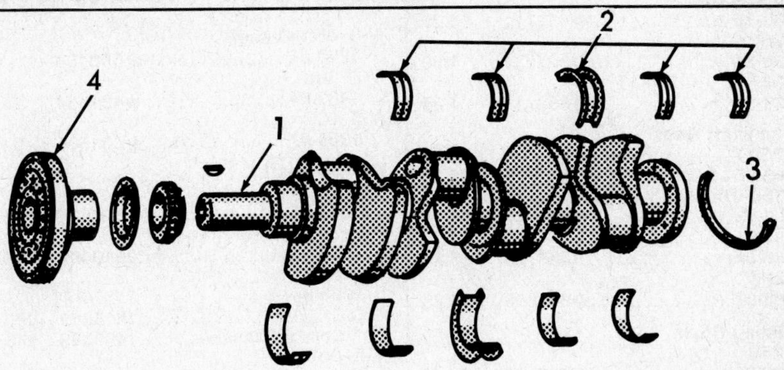

	Part No.	Price
(3) Rear Main Bearing Oil Seal		
V-8-250		
1983-85	◆1627821	7.00
V-8-350-Diesel		
1983-85	◆9772831	1.50
V-8-368		
1983-84	1099399	9.00
V-8-307		
1986-87	◆9772831	1.50
(4) Vibration Damper		
V-8-250		
1983-85	◆3517492	117.00
V-8-350-Diesel		
1983-85	◆559131	63.25
V-8-368		
1983-84-exc.		
C.C.	3517424	116.00
Comm. Chassis	3517348	117.00
V-8-250		
1986-87-hub	◆22506730	31.75

LABOR 16 CAMSHAFT & TIMING GEARS 16 LABOR

(Factory Time)	Chilton Time
GASOLINE ENGINE	
(G) Timing Case Cover Gaskets, Renew	
V-8–1983-85 (2.5)	3.3
1983-85	
Eng Code 8 (2.4)	3.1
Renew oil seal add (.2)	.2
Renew cover add (.4)	.6
w/A.I.R. add (.2)	.2
1986-87	
Eng Codes Y-9 (2.2)	3.0
Renew cover add (.2)	.4
(G) Timing Case Seal, Renew	
V-8–1983-85 (.8)	1.5
1983-85	
Eng Code 8 (1.0)	1.5
1986-87	
Eng Codes Y-9 (1.1)	1.5
(G) Timing Chain and/or Gears, Renew	
V-8–1983-85 (2.8)	3.6
1983-85	
Eng Code 8 (2.5)	3.5
w/A.I.R. add (.2)	.2
1986-87	
Eng Codes Y-9 (2.5)	3.5
(G) Camshaft, Renew	
V-8–1983-85 (5.3)	7.2
1983-85	
Eng Code 8 (7.4)	10.5
w/A.I.R. add (.2)	.2
1986-87	
Eng Codes Y-9 (7.6)	11.0
(G) Camshaft Rear Bearing Plug, Renew	
V-8–1983-87 (2.1)	3.3
Top (1.1)	2.0

(Factory Time)	Chilton Time
DIESEL ENGINE	
(G) Timing Case Seal and Gaskets, Renew	
1983-85 (2.4)	3.4
Renew cover add (.2)	.4
(G) Timing Case Seal, Renew	
1983-85 (1.0)	1.5
(G) Timing Chain, Renew	
1983-85 (2.6)	3.7
(G) Camshaft, Renew	
Includes: R&R engine assembly.	
1983-85 (8.3)	11.4
Renew cam brgs add (2.8)	3.8
(G) Camshaft Rear Bearing Plug, Renew	
1983-85 (2.1)	3.0

PARTS 16 CAMSHAFT & TIMING GEARS 16 PARTS

	Part No.	Price
(1) Timing Case Gasket		
V-8-250		
1983-85	◆1628915	2.75
V-8-350-Diesel		
1983-85	◆22505997	1.25
V-8-368		
1983-84	3634175	4.00
V-8-307		
1986-87	◆22505997	1.25
(2) Timing Case Oil Seal		
V-8-250		
1983-85	◆1627827	4.50
V-8-350-Diesel		
1983-85	◆552711	4.25
V-8-368		
1983-84	1622222	4.50
V-8-307		
1986-87	◆552711	4.25
(3) Camshaft Gear		
V-8-250		
1983-85	◆1617417	32.25
V-8-350-Diesel		
1983-85	◆558767	58.75
V-8-368		
1983-84	1486728	33.25
V-8-307		
1986-87	◆381263	25.25
(4) Timing Chain		
V-8-250		
1983-85	◆1618157	31.75

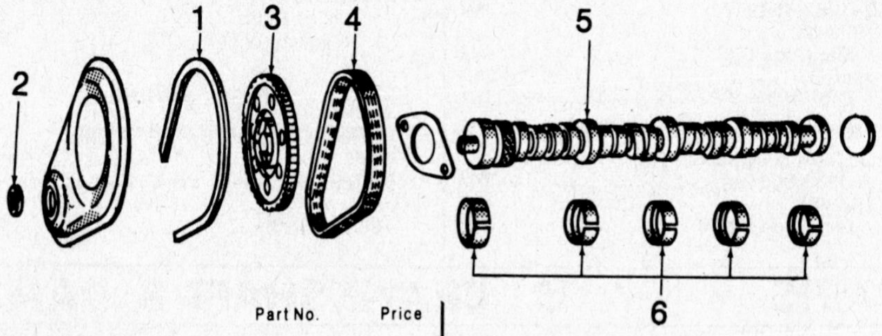

	Part No.	Price
V-8-350-Diesel		
1983-85	◆558484	N.L.
V-8-368		
1983-84	◆401584	31.75
V-8-307		
1986-87	◆401584	31.75
(5) Camshaft		
V-8-250		
1983-85	◆1628822	334.00
V-8-350-Diesel		
1983-85	◆22510099	266.00
V-8-368		
1983-84-exc.		
C.C.	1618652	245.00
Comm. Chassis	1486583	245.00
V-8-307		
1986-87	◆22527149	256.00

	Part No.	Price
(6) Camshaft Bearings		
V-8-350-Diesel		
1983-85-No. 1	◆561077	11.50
No. 2	◆390300	11.50
No. 3	◆390301	11.75
No. 4	◆390302	11.50
No. 5	◆390303	11.50
V-8-368		
1983-84	1479286	6.25
V-8-307		
1986-87-No. 1	◆561077	11.50
No. 2	◆390300	11.50
No. 3	◆390301	11.75
No. 4	◆390302	11.50
No. 5	◆390303	11.50

LABOR 17 ENGINE OILING SYSTEM 17 LABOR

(Factory Time)	Chilton Time
GASOLINE ENGINE	
(G) Oil Pan or Gasket, Renew	
V-8–1983-85 (1.6)	2.8
1983-85	
Eng Code 8 (1.2)	1.6
1986-87	
Eng Codes Y-9 (2.1)	2.9
(P) Pressure Test Engine Bearings (Pan Off)	
All models	1.0
(G) Oil Pump, Renew	
V-8–1983-85 (.5)	1.1
1983-85	
Eng Code 8 (1.3)	1.8
1986-87	
Eng Codes Y-9 (2.2)	3.1
(G) Oil Pump, R&R and Recondition	
V-8–1983-85 (.8)	1.5
1983-85	
Eng Code 8 (1.6)	2.2
(G) Oil Pressure Sending Unit, Renew	
1983-87 (.3)	.4
(G) Oil Pressure Regulator Valve, Renew	
V-8–1983-85 (.5)	.9
1983-85	
Eng Code 8 (1.4)	1.8

LABOR 17 ENGINE OILING SYSTEM 17 LABOR

	(Factory Time)	Chilton Time
(M) Oil Filter Element, Renew		
V-8–1983-87	(.3)	.3
DIESEL ENGINE		
(G) Oil Pan or Gasket, Renew		
1983-85	(2.6)	3.4
(P) Pressure Test Engine Bearings (Pan Off)		
All models		1.0
(G) Oil Pump, Renew		
1983-85	(2.7)	3.6
(G) Oil Pump, R&R and Recondition		
1983-85	(2.9)	3.8
(G) Oil Pressure Sending Unit, Renew		
1983-85	(.3)	.4
(G) Vacuum Pump, Renew		
Includes: Test.		
1983-85		
gear driven	(.4)	.6
belt driven	(.6)	.8
Recond pump add		.3
(M) Oil Filter Element, Renew		
1983-85	(.3)	.3

PARTS 17 ENGINE OILING SYSTEM 17 PARTS

	Part No.	Price
Oil Pan Gasket		
V-8–250		
1983-85	◆1629459	9.75
V-8–350–Diesel		
1983-85	◆22519181	7.00
V-8–368		
1983-84	3633090	9.00
V-8–307		
1986-87	◆22519181	N.L.
Oil Pump		
V-8–250		
1983-85	◆3517509	71.25
V-8–350–Diesel		
1983-85	◆22511732	59.75
V-8–368		
1983-84	3634182	60.75
V-8–307		
1986-87	◆22524583	61.50
Oil Pump Gear Set		
V-8–250		
1983-85	◆1619036	4.75
V-8–350–Diesel		
1983-85	◆585582	4.00
V-8–368		
1983-84	1099297	16.00
V-8–307		
1986-87	◆585582	4.00
Oil Pump Driven Gear Shaft		
V-8–250		
1983-85	◆1619035	3.00
V-8–350–Diesel		
1983-85	◆555737	1.25
V-8–368		
1983-84	3633330	4.00
V-8–307		
1986-87	◆555737	1.25
Oil Pump Screen		
V-8–368		
1983-84	1606989	13.50
Oil Pressure Sending Switch		
V-8–250		
1983-85	◆1623576	6.00
V-8–350–Diesel		
1983-85	◆3815936	3.50
V-8–368		
1983-87-exc. C.C.	1619641	4.00
Comm. Chassis	◆25500672	5.50
V-8–307		
1986-87	◆3815936	N.L.

LABOR 21 SHIFT LINKAGE 21 LABOR

	(Factory Time)	Chilton Time
(G) Shift Linkage, Adjust		
All models		
Neutral Safety Switch	(.3)	.4
Shift Indicator Needle	(.2)	.3
Shift Linkage	(.4)	.5
T.V. Cable	(.3)	.4
(G) Shift Linkage, Adjust (w/Diesel Eng)		
All models		
Fast Idle speed	(.2)	.3
Throttle rod/T.V. cable	(.5)	.6
Trans vacuum valve	(.6)	.6
Vacuum Regul Valve	(.6)	.8
Complete	(.8)	1.0
(G) Gear Shift Lever, Renew		
1983-87	(.2)	.4
(G) Lower Shift Lever, Renew (At Trans)		
1983-87	(.4)	.6
(G) Shift Quadrant Pointer, Renew		
1983-87	(.4)	.6
(G) Steering Column Shift Bowl, Renew		
Does not include colorcoat.		
1983-87	(1.5)	2.2
w/Tilt Tel	(2.1)	3.1

LABOR 25 U-JOINTS & DRIVESHAFT 25 LABOR

	(Factory Time)	Chilton Time
(G) Drive Shaft, Renew		
1983-87	(.4)	.6
(G) Pinion Shaft Flange, Renew		
1983-87	(.7)	1.0
(G) Universal Joints, R&R and Recondition		
Includes: R&R drive shaft.		
1983-87-front	(.6)	.8
rear	(.5)	.7
both	(.7)	1.3
(G) Center Ball Seats, R&R and Recondition		
Includes: R&R drive shaft.		
1983-85-one	(.6)	1.0
both	(.9)	1.4

PARTS 25 U-JOINTS & DRIVESHAFT 25 PARTS

	Part No.	Price
Universal Joint Repair Kit		
1983-87		
Dana	◆374246	28.50
Saginaw	◆7806140	41.00
Flange (On Pinion Shaft)		
1983-87-exc. below	◆7827670	33.75
Limo, Comm. Chassis	7835086	36.50
U/Joint Yoke (Front)		
1983-87-exc. below	◆7812557	65.25
Limo, Comm. Chassis	7801551	80.00

LABOR — 26 REAR AXLE 26 — LABOR

	(Factory Time)	Chilton Time

(M) Differential, Drain & Refill
All models.................................... .6

(G) Axle Shaft, Renew
1983-87-one (.7).................................... .9
both (.9).................................... 1.2

(G) Axle Shaft Oil Seal, Renew
1983-87-one (.6).................................... .8
both (.8).................................... 1.1

(G) Axle Shaft Bearing, Renew
wo/Disc brakes
1983-87-each (.6).................................... 1.1

(G) Pinion Shaft Oil Seal, Renew
1983-87 (.5).................................... .8

(G) Rear Axle Assembly, Remove and Reinstall or Renew
1983-87 (1.7).................................... 3.5

(M) Axle Housing Cover Gasket, Renew
1983-87 (.5).................................... .6

(P) Rear Axle Assembly, R&R and Recondition
Includes: R&R axle shafts, drive shaft, inspection cover. Disassemble pinion gear assembly and differential case. Clean, inspect and replace parts as required. Check gear tooth pattern and backlash, reinstall and fill with lubricant.
1983-87 (2.5).................................... 4.4
w/Limited slip add (.6).................................... .8

(G) Limited Slip Clutch Pack, Renew
Includes: R&R axle shafts, drive shaft, inspection cover. Renew clutch packs and fill with lubricant.
1983-85 (1.1).................................... 2.0

(G) Differential Case, Renew
Includes: R&R axle shafts, drive shaft, inspection cover. Check gear tooth pattern and backlash. Remove, disassemble, assemble and install differential case. Recheck gear tooth pattern and backlash and fill with lubricant.
1983-87 (1.8).................................... 2.8
w/Limited slip add (.5).................................... .8

(G) Pinion Bearings, Renew
Includes: R&R axle shafts, drive shaft, inspection cover. Renew pinion bearings, check gear tooth pattern and backlash and fill with lubricant.
1983-87 (2.0).................................... 3.4

(P) Ring Gear and Pinion, Renew
Includes: R&R axle shafts, drive shaft, inspection cover. Check gear tooth pattern and backlash. Remove pinion assembly, pinion gear, differential case and ring gear. Install new ring gear and pinion. Reinstall case, recheck gear tooth pattern and backlash and fill with lubricant.
1983-87 (2.1).................................... 3.9
Recond diff case add (.3).................................... .5

(G) Differential Case Side Bearings, Renew
Includes: R&R axle shafts, drive shaft, inspection cover. Check gear tooth pattern and backlash. Install new bearings. Recheck gear tooth pattern with new bearings and fill with lubricant.
1983-87 (1.7).................................... 2.5

(G) Differential Pinion and Side Gears, Renew
Includes: R&R axle shafts and axle housing cover gasket. Adjust ring gear backlash and side bearing preload.
1983-87 (.8).................................... 1.8

(P) Ring Gear and Pinion, Adjust
Includes: R&R axle shafts, drive shaft, inspection cover. Check gear tooth pattern and backlash. R&R pinion gear assembly, pinion shims, ring gear shim. Recheck backlash and gear tooth pattern after adjustment. Fill with lubricant.
1983-87 (2.0).................................... 3.2

(G) Rear Axle Housing, Renew
Includes: R&R axle shafts, drive shaft and differential assembly.
1983-87 (3.4).................................... 5.2

PARTS — 26 REAR AXLE 26 — PARTS

	Part No.	Price
(1) Axle Shaft		
(7½" dia. ring gr.)		
1983-87	◆22504959	142.25
(8½" dia. ring gr.)		
1984-87	14086864	142.00
(8¾" dia. ring gr.)		
1983-84-exc. below	◆526200	135.25
Limo, Comm. Chassis	527877	125.00
(2) Seal (Rear Bearing)		
1983-87-exc. below	◆3998519	4.00
Limo, Comm. Chassis	◆3958078	5.00
(3) Bearing Assy. (Rear Axle)		
1983-87-exc. below	◆7451785	16.00
Limo, Comm. Chassis	◆7451809	15.00
(4) Flange (Pinion)		
(7½" dia. ring gr.)		
1983-87	◆7827670	33.50
(8½, 8¾" dia. ring gr.)		
1983-87	7835086	36.50
(5) Seal (Drive Pinion)		
1983-87-7½" dia	◆552571	8.00
8½" dia. ring gr.	◆1243465	7.50
8¾" dia. ring gr.	◆404294	9.00
(6) Front Pinion Bearing		
(7½" dia. ring gr.)		
1983-84	◆7451202	16.00
1985-87	◆9417784	16.25
(8½, 8¾" dia. ring gr.)		
1983-87	◆7450984	21.00

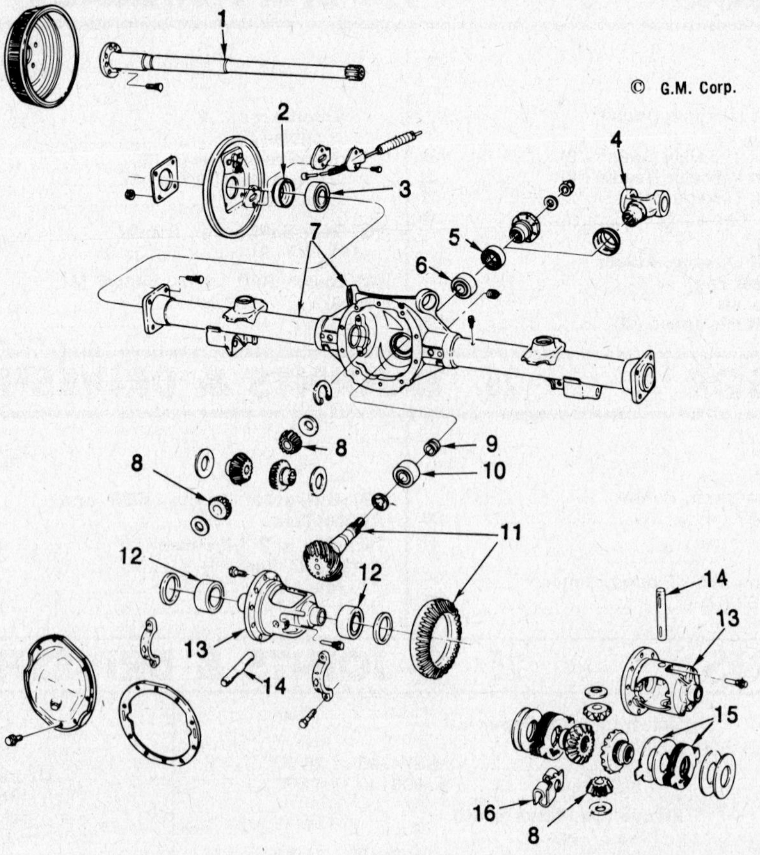

PARTS 26 REAR AXLE 26 PARTS

	Part No.	Price
(7) Housing Assy.		
(7½" dia. ring gr.)		
1983-87	◆22510779	392.25
(8½" dia. ring gr.)		
1984-87	14091342	411.75
(8¾" dia. ring gr.)		
1983-84-exc. below	◆10004179	603.50
Limo, Comm. Chassis	10004178	610.00
(8) Side Gear Pkg.		
(7½" dia. ring gr.)		
1983	◆22514882	105.00
1984-87	◆22525894	94.50
(8½" dia. ring gr.)		
1984-87	◆1397647	132.00
(8¾" dia. ring gr.)		
(wo/Limited slip)		
1983-84-exc. below	◆547225	106.00
Limo, Comm. Chassis	10000058	106.25
(Limited slip)		
1983-84-exc. below	◆547212	173.00
Limo, Comm. Chassis	490778	161.00
(9) Spacer (Front)		
(7½" dia. ring gr.)		
1983-87	◆9785792	1.50
(8½, 8¾" dia. ring gr.)		
1983-87	◆1234726	1.50
(10) Bearing Assy. (Rear)		
(7½" dia. ring gr.)		
1983-87	◆7455699	N.L.
(8½" dia. ring gr.)		
1984-87	◆7451155	20.00
(8¾" dia. ring gr.)		
1983-84-exc. below	◆7451155	20.00
Limo, Comm. Chassis	◆7451409	N.L.
(11) Ring & Pinion Gear Assy.		
(7½" dia. ring gear)		
1983-87-2.93R	◆560204	261.00
3.23R	◆14048436	276.25
3.42R	◆14048378	276.00
3.73R (1983)	◆22521624	276.00
3.73R (1984-87)	14048379	297.00
(8½" dia. ring gr.)		
1984-87-3.08R	◆1258709	276.00
(8¾" dia. ring gear)		
1983-84-2.41R	◆10002813	305.25
2.93R	◆10018255	305.25
3.08R	10006779	178.00
3.23R	◆10002810	305.25
3.42R	527341	305.25
(12) Bearing Assy. (Side)		
(7½, 8½" dia. ring. gr.)		
1983-84	◆7451281	15.00
1985-87	◆9420095	N.L.
(8¾" dia. ring gr.)		
1983-84	◆7451140	15.00
(13) Differential Case		
(7½" dia. ring gr.)		
1983-87-2.93R	◆558648	109.00
3.42, 3.73R	◆558649	109.25
(8½" dia. ring gr.)		
1984-87	◆1252981	110.00
(8¾" dia. ring gr.)		
(exc. Limited slip)		
1983-87		
2.28, 2.41, 2.56R	◆526205	134.25
2.73, 2.93, 3.08R	◆526207	162.25
3.23, 3.42R	◆527854	162.00
(Limited slip)		
1983-87		
2.28, 2.41, 2.56R	◆527751	428.00
2.73, 2.93, 3.08R	◆527752	428.00
3.80R (Limo, comm. chassis)	527755	428.00
3.42R	◆527753	428.00
(14) Pinion Shaft		
(7½" dia. ring gr.)		
1983-87	◆22507586	11.00
(8½" dia. ring gr.)		
1984-87	◆14006401	12.50
(8¾" dia. ring gr.)		
1983-87-exc. below	◆9778184	12.75
limited slip	◆9792718	12.75
(15) Clutch Pkg.		
1983-87	◆483722	55.75
(16) Spring (Preload)		
1983-87	◆488332	4.50

LABOR 27 REAR SUSPENSION 27 LABOR

(Factory Time)	Chilton Time
(G) Rear Spring, Renew	
Note: Axle must be lowered for one or both springs.	
1983-87-one or both (.9)	1.0
(G) Rear Shock Absorber, Renew	
1983-87-one (.3)	.4
both (.5)	.7
(G) Upper Control Arm, Renew	
1983-87-one side (.4)	.8
both sides (.6)	1.2
Renew bushings add, each side (.1)	.2
(G) Lower Control Arm, Renew	
1983-87-one side (.4)	.7
both sides (.6)	1.1
Renew bushings add, each side (.1)	.2
(G) Rear Stabilizer Bar, Renew	
1983-87 (.3)	.5
(G) Rear Stabilizer Bar Bushing, Renew	
1983-87-one (.3)	.5
both (.5)	.8
(G) Frame to Axle Housing Bumper, Renew	
1983-87-each (.2)	.4
ELECTRONIC LEVEL CONTROL	
(G) Compressor Assembly, Renew	
1983-87 (.3)	.7
(G) Height Sensor, Renew	
1983-87 (.6)	.8
(G) Height Sensor, Adjust	
1983-87 (.3)	.6
(G) Compressor Relay, Renew (One or Both)	
1983-87 (.2)	.4
(G) Super Lift Shock Absorbers, Renew	
1983-87-one (.4)	.7
both (.6)	1.1
(G) Level Control Dryer, Renew	
1983-87 (.2)	.4
(G) Level Control Head, Renew	
1983-87 (.3)	.9
(G) Level Control Motor and Cylinder, R&R and Recondition	
1983-87 (.5)	1.2
(G) Level Control Tubing, Renew	
1983-87	
comp to shock (.5)	.7
shock to shock (.3)	.4

PARTS 27 REAR SUSPENSION 27 PARTS

	Part No.	Price
(1) Rear Spring		
Order by year and model.		
(2) Shock Absorber (Standard)		
1983-87	◆4993551	24.50
(3) Upper Control Arm		
1983-87-exc. below	◆10000887	22.50
Limo	10000314	30.50
Comm. Chassis	10003405	30.50
(4) Lower Control Arm		
1983-87-exc. below	◆10000334	32.50
Comm. Chassis	10003404	32.50

PARTS 27 REAR SUSPENSION 27 PARTS

	Part No.	Price
ELECTRONIC LEVEL CONTROL		
Compresser		
1983-87	◆22020538	176.25
Height Sensor		
(DeVille, Brougham)		
1983-84	22017236	172.25
1985-87	22040581	200.00
(Limo, Commercial Chassis)		
1983-87	◆22017243	176.25
Control Relay		
1983-87-exc. below	◆1626239	6.50
Comm. Chassis	12034545	17.75

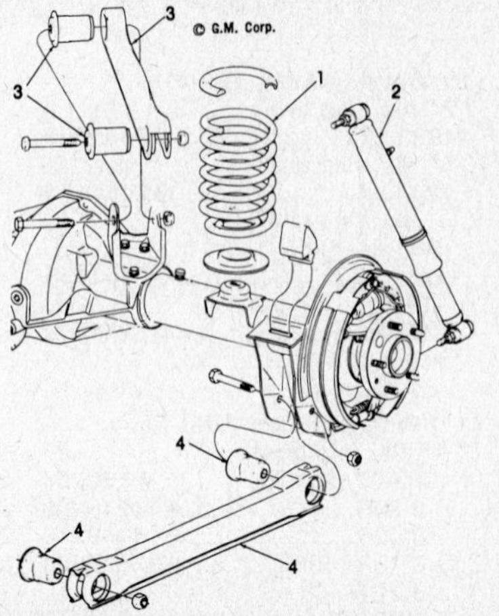

	Part No.	Price
Air Dryer Kit		
1983-87	◆22020540	41.50
Shock Absorber		
1983-84-right	◆4993553	64.00
left	◆4993552	65.00
1985-87-right	4993750	57.75
left	4993749	57.75
Compressor Head		
1983-87	◆22020539	68.50
Motor (wo/compressor head)		
1983-87	◆22010692	165.00

LABOR 28 AIR CONDITIONING 28 LABOR

(Factory Time) Chilton Time

Note: If more than one item requires replacement where evacuation and discharging the system is already included in the operation, deduct 1.0 hour for each additional item to the times listed.

(G) Drain, Evacuate and Recharge System
All models (.5) 1.0

(G) Refrigerant, Add Partial Charge
All models 6

(G) Air Conditioner Drive Belt, Renew
1983-85
V-8 (.6) 8
Diesel (.5) 6
w/A.I.R. add (.2) 2
1986-87 (.4) 5

(G) Compressor R&R, Partial for Engine Work
Note: Hoses remain attached to compressor.
1983-87 (.5) 8

COMPRESSOR 4 CYLINDER RADIAL

(G) Compressor Assembly, Renew
Includes: Transfer parts as required. Evacuate and charge system.
1983-87
Gas (1.2) 2.0
Diesel (.9) 1.8

(G) Compressor Clutch Plate and Hub Assy., Renew
Includes: R&R hub and drive plate assy. Check air gap.
1983-87 (.4) 8

(G) Compressor Rotor and/or Bearing, Renew
Includes: R&R hub and drive plate assy.
1983-87 (.8) 1.2

(G) Compressor Clutch Coil and/or Pulley Rim, Renew
Includes: R&R hub and drive plate assy.
1983-87 (.8) 1.0
Renew pulley or brg add 2

(G) Compressor Shaft Seal, Renew
Includes: R&R compressor. Evacuate and charge system.
1983-87 (1.0) 2.5

AIR CONDITIONER TUNE-UP

For efficient operation and satisfactory performance in hot weather. The following air conditioner tune-up is suggested:

1. Clean intake filter
2. Clean condenser fins
3. Pressure test system
4. Adjust drive belt tension
5. Check antifreeze/coolant
6. Tighten compressor mounts
7. Tighten condenser and evaporator mounts
8. Inspect system for leaks (hoses, couplings, valves, etc.)
9. Partial charge system

All models 1.0
If necessary to evacuate and charge system, add 1.0

(Factory Time) Chilton Time

(G) Compressor Shell and/or 'O' Rings, Renew
Includes: R&R compressor. R&R clutch and pulley assy. Clean and inspect parts. Evacuate and charge system.
1983-87 (2.0) 2.8

(G) Compressor Discharge Valve Plates, Renew
Includes: R&R compressor. R&R clutch and pulley assy. R&R shell to internal mechanism. Clean and inspect parts. Evacuate and charge system.
1983-87 (2.0) 2.6
Two or more add (.1) 2

(G) Compressor Front Head and/or Seal, Renew
Includes: R&R compressor. R&R clutch and pulley assy. R&R shaft seal assy. Clean and inspect parts. Evacuate and charge system.
1983-87 (1.7) 2.8

(Factory Time) Chilton Time

(G) Compressor Thrust and/or Belleville Washer, Renew
Includes: R&R compressor. R&R clutch and pulley assy. R&R shaft seal assy. R&R front head assy. Clean and inspect parts. Evacuate and charge system.
1983-87 (2.0) 2.8

(G) Compressor Main Bearing, Renew
Includes: R&R compressor. R&R clutch and pulley assy. R&R shaft seal assy. R&R front head assy. Clean and inspect parts. Evacuate and charge system.
1983-87 (1.7) 2.8

(G) Compressor Shaft and Cylinder Assy., Renew
Includes: R&R compressor. R&R clutch and pulley assy. R&R shaft seal assy., remove and transfer front head assy. R&R compressor shell and 'O' rings. R&R compressor valve plates, R&R pressure relief valve. Clean and inspect parts. Evacuate and charge system.
1983-87 (2.0) 2.9

(G) Thermostatic Control Switch, Renew
1983-87 (.2) 5

(G) Compressor Low Pressure Switch, Renew
Includes: Evacuate and charge system.
1983-87 (.7) 1.4

(G) Compressor High Pressure Cut-Off Switch, Renew
1983-87 (.2) 3

(G) Condenser, Renew
Includes: Evacuate and charge system.
1983-87 (1.5) 2.6

(G) Accumulator Assembly, Renew
Includes: Evacuate and charge system.
1983-87 (.8) 1.5

(G) Evaporator Core, Renew
Includes: Evacuate and charge system.
1983-87 (1.7) 3.5

(G) Expansion Tube (Orifice), Renew
Includes: Evacuate and charge system.
1983-87 (.7) 1.4

LABOR 28 AIR CONDITIONING 28 LABOR

(Factory Time) — Chilton Time

(G) Power Servo or Programmer, Renew
Includes: Test.
1983-87 (.4) 7
Renew motor add (.2) 3

(G) A.C. Control Assembly, Renew
1983-87 (.3) 6

(G) A.C. Aspirator, Renew
1983-87 (.3) 6

(G) Aspirator Hose, Renew
1983-87 (.3) 6

(G) ECC Power Module, Renew
1983-87 (.3) 5

(G) In-Car Sensor, Renew
1983-87 (.3) 7

(G) Ambient Sensor, Renew
1983-87 (.2) 3

(G) Blower Motor, Renew
1983-87 (.2) 5

(G) Blower Delay Switch, Renew
1983-87 (.2) 5

(G) Vacuum Diaphragm Actuators, Renew
1983-84
Defroster (.4) 7
Upper or lower mode (.8) 1.5
Lower (.4) 7
Air inlet (.3) 6
1985-87
Defroster (.4) 7
Upper or lower mode (.4) 7
Lower (.4) 7
Air inlet (.3) 6

(G) Air Conditioning Hoses, Renew
Includes: Evacuate and charge system.
1983-87-each-exc below (.9) 1.7
receiver to exp valve (1.2) 2.4
cond to evaporator (liquid line) (1.2) 2.4

PARTS 28 AIR CONDITIONING 28 PARTS

	Part No.	Price
Compressor Assembly		
1983-87	◆12300274	390.00
Compressor Drive Clutch		
1983-87	◆6551220	32.50
Compressor Rotor w/Bearing		
1983-87	◆6551216	67.50
Compressor Shell		
1983-87	◆2724158	38.00
Compressor O-Ring Kit		
1983-87	9956746	5.50
Compressor Shaft Seal Kit		
1983-87	◆9956695	13.00
Compressor Pulley (Rim)		
1983-87	◆6556715	13.00
Compressor Discharge Valve Plate		
1983-87	◆6551141	11.50
Compressor Front Head		
1983-87-w/bearing	◆6551142	28.25
Compressor Main Bearing		
1983-87	◆6556572	4.00
Compressor Cylinder w/Shaft		
1983-87	◆2724060	275.00
REFRIGERANT SYSTEM		
Condenser Assembly		
1983-87	3050450	168.75
Accumulator Dehydrator Assembly		
1983-84	12322992	72.25
1985	3059158	83.75
1986-87	◆3059239	80.50
Evaporator Core Assembly		
1983-84	◆3035240	218.25
1985-87	◆3058130	261.75
ELECTRICAL AND CONTROL SYSTEM		
Blower Motor Assembly		
1983-87	◆22020945	60.00
Instrument Panel Control Assembly		
(DeVille, Brougham)		
1983-85 (350 diesel)		
wo/elec. defog.	1225516	88.50
w/elec. defog.	1225514	88.50
1983-85 (V-8-250)		
wo/elec. defog.	1225512	88.50
w/elec. defog.	1225510	88.50
(Fleetwood Limo)		
1983-87-exc. below	16014656	230.25
Elec. defog.	16013926	230.25
(Commercial Chassis)		
1983-87	16019226	117.25
Blower Motor Resistor		
1983-87-exc. below	◆1609776	5.50
Limo, Comm. Ch.	1613555	6.00
Blower Motor Control Switch		
1983-87	7896238	8.00
Programmer		
(DeVille, Brougham)		
1983	1224840	72.50
1984-87	1226527	76.00
(Fleetwood Limo)		
1983-87	16014636	125.25
(Commercial chassis)		
1983-87	7896076	198.00
Module		
1983-87	16022146	137.50

LABOR 29 LOCKS, HINGES & WIND. REGULATORS 29 LABOR

(Factory Time) — Chilton Time

(G) Hood Latch, Renew
1983-87 (.2) 4

(G) Hood Hinge, Renew (One)
1983-87 (.3) 7

(G) Hood Latch Cable, Renew
1983-87 (.4) 7

(G) Door Lock Assembly, Renew
Front
1983-87 (.5) 9
Rear
1983-87 (.8) 1.2

(G) Door Lock Remote Control, Renew (Front or Rear)
1983-87 (.4) 7

(G) Door Lock Cylinder and Keys, Renew
1983-87 (.4) 7
Recode cyl add (.3) 3
w/Illum entry system add 2

(G) Door Handle (Outside), Renew (Front or Rear)
1983-87 (.5) 7
Renew insert add 1

(G) Lock Striker Plate, Renew
1983-87 (.2) 3

(G) Door Window Regulator, Renew (Front or Rear)
1983-87 (1.0) 1.5
Recond manual regul. add 2

(G) Trunk Lock Assembly, Renew
1983-87 (.3) 5

(G) Trunk Lock Cylinder and Key, Renew
1983-87 (.3) 5
Recode cyl add (.3) 3

(G) Rear Compartment Lid Hinge Strap, Renew
Does not include color coat.
1983-87-one (.8) 1.2

PARTS 29 LOCKS, HINGES & WIND. REGULATORS 29 PARTS

	Part No.	Price
Hood Lock		
1983-87-primary	◆14070703	16.25
secondary	1610270	7.75
Hood Hinge		
1983-87-right	1616787	43.50
left	1616786	43.50
Front Door Lock		
(2-door)		
1983-84-right	◆20293612	33.50
left	◆20293613	33.50
1985-87-right	20485476	33.25
left	20485477	33.25
(4-door)		
1983-right	◆20293604	51.50
left	◆20293605	51.50
1985-87-right	20485472	51.50
left	20485473	51.50
Rear Door Lock		
(wo/Limo)		
1983-84-right	20293632	55.75
left	20293633	55.75
1985-87-right	◆20480448	53.25
left	◆20480449	53.25
(Limo)		
1983-87-right	20293634	55.75
left	20293635	55.75
Door Lock Cylinder (Uncoded)		
(wo/Anti-theft or key light)		
1983-87	◆9632769	7.75
(Anti-theft wo/Key light)		
1983-87	9632798	44.75
(Anti-theft w/Key light)		
1983-87	◆9632767	9.50
(Key light wo/Anti-theft)		
1983-87-2 door	◆20496702	7.00
4 door	◆9632766	9.50
Front Door Outer Handle (R.H.)		
1983	◆20273628	23.75
1984-87 (wo/Illuminated entry)		
2 door	◆20479794	28.25
4 door	◆20479416	23.75
1984-87 (Illuminated entry)		
2 door	20507572	53.75
4 door	20480164	23.75
Rear Door Outer Handle		
1983-right	◆20273628	23.75
left	◆20273629	23.75
1984-87-right	◆20479794	28.25
left	◆20479795	28.25
Front Door Window Regulator (Power) (R.H.)		
1983-87-2 dr.	◆20303590	108.00
4 dr.	◆20192896	114.00
Rear Door Window Regulator (Power) (R.H.)		
1983-87-exc.		
Limo	◆20192894	114.00
Limo	20197891	71.25
Window Regulator Electric Motor		
1983-exc. below	◆22029848	72.50
Limo	◆22020900	73.00
1984-87	◆22020900	73.00
Deck Lid Lock		
1983-87	◆20279741	N.L.
Deck Lid Lock Cylinder (Uncoded)		
1983-87	◆3910570	6.25
Deck Lid Hinge Strap w/Links		
(w/Gas supports)		
1983-right	20211764	21.50
left	20211765	21.50
(w/Torque rods)		
1983-87	20434735	15.00

LABOR 30 HEAD AND PARKING LAMPS 30 LABOR

	(Factory Time)	Chilton Time
(G) Aim Headlamps		
two		.4
four		.6
(M) Headlamp Sealed Beam Bulb, Renew		
1983-87-each	(.3)	.3
(M) Park and Turn Signal Lamp Assy., Renew		
1983-87	(.2)	.3
(M) Back-Up Lamp Assembly, Renew		
1983-87	(.3)	.4
(M) Cornering Lamp Assembly, Renew		
1983-87	(.2)	.3
(M) Stop, Tail and Turn Signal Lamp Assy., Renew		
1983-87-each	(.3)	.4
(M) Side Marker Lamp Assy., Renew		
1983-87-each	(.2)	.3
(M) Cornering Lamp Lens, Renew		
1983-87-each	(.2)	.3
(M) Stop, Tail and Turn Signal Lamp Lens, Renew		
1983-87-one	(.3)	.4
all	(.5)	.7

PARTS 30 HEAD & PARKING LAMPS 30 PARTS

	Part No.	Price
Sealed Beam Unit		
(Inner)		
1983-87	◆5930567	22.50
(Outer)		
1983	◆5966200	15.00
1984-87	◆16502327	22.50
Parking Lamp Assm.		
1983-right	917964	38.75
left	917963	38.75
1984-85-right	919120	42.25
left	919119	42.25
1986-87-right	5974788	42.25
left	5974787	42.25
Tail Lamp Assy.		
1983	914945	43.00
1984-87	914880	43.00
High Mount Stoplight		
1985-87	◆5974472	36.00
Back-Up Lamp Assy.		
1983-87	913934	14.25
License Lamp Assy.		
1983-87	◆912345	6.25
Cornering & Side Marker Lamp Assy.		
1983-87-right	914624	43.50
left	914623	43.50

LABOR 31 WINDSHIELD WIPER & SPEEDOMETER 31 LABOR

	(Factory Time)	Chilton Time
(G) Windshield Wiper Motor, Renew		
1983-87	(.3)	.5
w/Intermitt. wiper add		.1
(G) Windshield Wiper Motor, R&R and Recondition		
1983-87	(.8)	1.1
(G) Wiper Transmission, Renew (Complete)		
1983-87	(.4)	.8
(G) Wiper Switch, Renew		
1983-87	(.3)	.5
(G) Windshield Washer Pump, Renew		
1983-87	(.2)	.4
w/Pulse wipe add	(.1)	.1
(G) Windshield Washer Pump, R&R and Recondition		
1983-87	(.5)	.8
w/Pulse wipe add	(.1)	.1
(G) Windshield Washer Pump Valve, Renew		
1983-87	(.2)	.4

LABOR 31 WINDSHIELD WIPER & SPEEDOMETERS 31 LABOR

	(Factory Time)	Chilton Time
(G) Speedometer Head, R&R or Renew		
1983-87	(.5)	1.1
Reset odometer add		.2
(G) Speedometer Cable and Casing, Renew		
1983-87	(.7)	1.0
(G) Speedometer Cable (Inner), Renew or Lubricate		
1983-87	(.5)	.9
(G) Speedometer Driven Pinion or Seal, Renew		
1983-87	(.3)	.4
(G) M.P.G. Sentinel, Renew		
1983-87	(.3)	.6
(G) Radio, R&R		
1983-87	(.4)	.7

PARTS 31 WINDSHIELD WIPER & SPEEDOMETER 31 PARTS

	Part No.	Price
Windshield Wiper Motor		
1983-87-exc		
Pulse	◆4960974	84.00
Pulse wiper	◆4961608	80.00
Wiper Transmission Assembly		
1983-87-L.H.	◆22010449	18.50
R.H.	◆22010448	17.00
Wiper Control Switch, Electric		
1983-84-exc.		
Pulse	1615184	23.50
Pulse wiper	◆1617090	35.00
1985-87	◆1632569	21.75
Windshield Washer Pump		
1983-87-exc.		
Pulse	◆22029665	30.00
Pulse wiper	◆22029601	27.00
Washer Pump Relay		
1983-87	22021347	N.L.
Speedometer Cable & Casing		
1983	25033403	20.75
1984-87	25033572	32.00

LABOR 32 LIGHT SWITCHES & WIRING 32 LABOR

	(Factory Time)	Chilton Time
(G) Headlamp Switch, Renew		
1983-87	(.3)	.7
(G) Headlamp Dimmer Switch, Renew		
1983-87		
column mount	(.5)	.7
(G) Stop Light Switch, Renew		
1983-87	(.3)	.3
(G) Turn Signal Switch, Renew		
1983-87-std	(.7)	1.1
tilt whl	(.9)	1.4
(G) Back-Up Lamp and Park/Neutral Switch, Renew		
1983-87	(.3)	.4
(M) Turn Signal or Hazard Warning Flasher, Renew		
1983-87	(.3)	.3
(G) Horn, Renew		
1983-87-each	(.3)	.4
(G) Horn Relay, Renew		
1983-87	(.2)	.4
(G) Dimmer Switch Pivot Assy., Renew		
1983-87	(.6)	1.2
w/Cruise control add	(.2)	.2

PARTS 32 LIGHT SWITCHES & WIRING 32 PARTS

	Part No.	Price
Headlamp Switch		
1983-87	◆1995225	18.00
Headlamp Dimmer Switch		
(exc. Guidematic)		
1983-87	◆7838234	12.50
(Guidematic)		
1983-87	◆7831354	21.50
Stoplight Switch		
(wo/Cruise control)		
1983-84	◆1362835	3.00
1985-87	◆25524844	3.00
(Cruise control)		
1983-84	◆9794682	7.75
1985-87	◆25524847	6.50
Back-Up Lamp Switch		
1983-87	◆1619499	26.00
Horn Assy.		
1983-87 (marked as such)		
"A" note	◆1892164	22.00
"C" note	◆1892246	27.50
"D" note	◆1892162	23.50
"F" note	◆1892163	22.00
Horn Relay		
1983-87-exc.		
below	◆1626239	6.50
comm. chassis	329820	3.50
Turn Signal Switch		
1983-87	◆1997984	35.00
Turn Signal Flasher		
1983-84	◆10029240	4.25
1985-87	◆10041073	4.25
Emergency Flasher		
1983-87	◆6450089	3.00

LABOR 33 GLASS 33 LABOR

	(Factory Time)	Chilton Time
(G) Windshield, Renew		
1983-87	(1.3)	1.8
Renew caulk bead add	(.4)	.4
(G) Front Door Glass, Renew		
1983-87	(.9)	1.2
(G) Rear Door Glass, Renew		
1983-87	(.8)	1.1
(G) Rear Quarter Stationary Glass, Renew		
1983-87	(.8)	1.2
(G) Rear Door Stationary Vent Glass, Renew		
1983-87	(.7)	1.0
(G) Back Window Glass, Renew		
1983-87	(1.3)	2.0
w/Elec grid defogger add	(.6)	.6
w/3/4 plug, padded add	(2.6)	4.0
w/Full plug, padded add	(2.8)	4.4

LABOR 34 CRUISE CONTROL 34 LABOR

(Factory Time) Chilton Time

(G) Power Unit or Vacuum Servo, Renew
Includes: External adjustments.
1983-87 (.2) 5

(G) Cruise Control On-Off Switch, Renew
1983-87-on inst panel (.3) 5

(G) Cruise Control Module, Renew
Includes: R&R steering column lower cover.
1983-87 (.3) 5
w/DFI (.5) 7

(G) Cruise Control Brake Release Switch, Renew
Includes: Adjust.
1983-87 (.2) 4

(G) Cruise Control Engagement Switch, Renew
Includes: Renew turn signal lever.
1983-87 (.4) 9

(G) Cruise Control Speed Sensor Wiring Harness, Renew
1983-87 (.6) 1.0

(G) Cruise Control Cable or Chain, Renew
1983-87 (.2) 4

(G) Cruise Control Vacuum Control Valve, Renew
1983-85 (.2) 3

(G) Cruise Control Speed Sensor, Renew
1984-85 (.6) 8

(G) Cruise Control Resume Solenoid Valve, Renew
1983-87 (.3) 4

(G) Cruise Control Vacuum Hoses, Renew
1983-87 (.3) 4

PARTS 34 CRUISE CONTROL 34 PARTS

	Part No.	Price
Electronic Controller		
1983-87	1546747	97.25
Cruise Control Switch		
1983-87	1617628	19.00
Cruise Control Vacuum Servo		
(exc. Diesel)		
1983-85	25031516	25.50
1986-87	◆25074629	123.25
(Diesel)		
1983-84	◆25031423	29.00
1985	25074875	N.L.
Cruise Control Wiring Harness		
1983-87	12017343	55.25
Cruise Control Chain (Throttle to Control)		
1983-87	◆25031314	3.25
Cruise Control Solenoid		
1983-85	◆25031699	62.50

GROUP INDEX

ALPHABETICAL INDEX

General Motors
Rear Wheel Drive Cars

CHEVROLET CAMARO • PONTIAC FIREBIRD

YEAR IDENTIFICATION

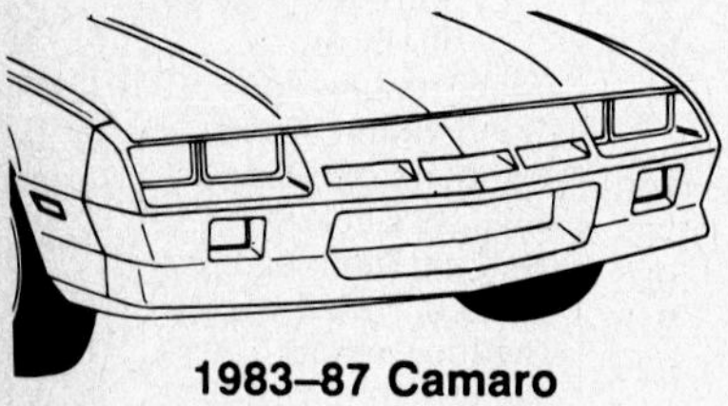

1983–87 Camaro

1983–87 Camaro Z–28

1985–87 Camaro IROC

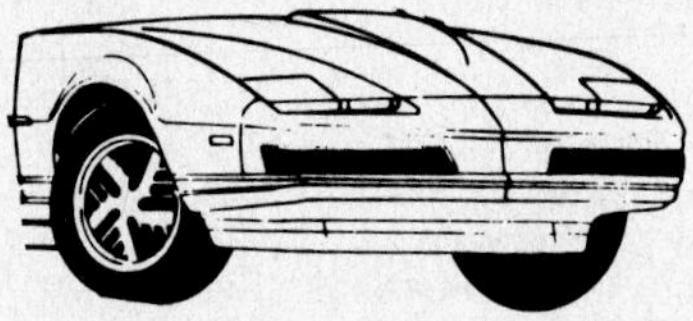

1987 Firebird Formula

1983–87 Firebird

1985–87 Trans Am

VEHICLE IDENTIFICATION NUMBER (VIN)

It is important for servicing and ordering parts to be certain of the vehicle and engine identification. The VIN (vehicle identification number) is a 17 digit number visible through the windshield on the driver's side of the dash and contains the vehicle and engine identification codes. It can be interpreted as follows:

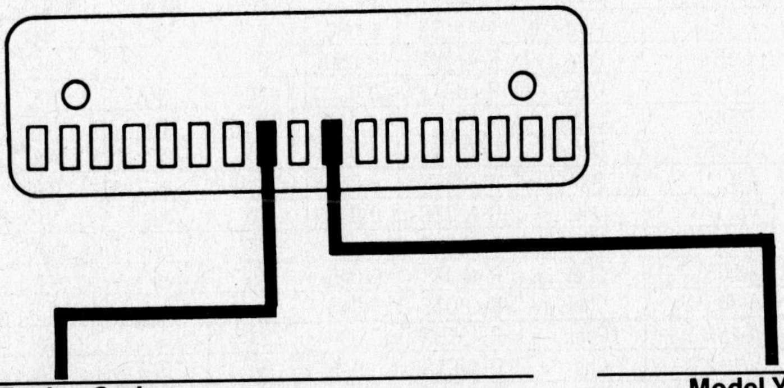

Engine Code					
Code	Cu. In.	Liters	Cyl.	Carb.	Eng. Mfg.
CAMARO					
2	151	2.5	4	T.B.I.	Pont.
F	151	2.5	4	2	Pont.
1	173	2.8	V-6	2	Chev.
L	173	2.8	V-6	2	Chev.
S	173	2.8	V-6	M.F.I.	Chev.
K	229	3.8	6	2	Chev.
A	231	3.8	V-6	2	Buick
J	267	4.4	8	2	Chev.
H	305	5.0	8	4	Chev.
7	305	5.0	8	T.B.I.	Chev.
G	305	5.0	8	4	Chev.
F	305	5.0	8	T.B.I.	Chev.
FIREBIRD					
2	151	2.5	4	T.B.I.	Pont.
F	151	2.5	4	2	Pont.
1	173	2.8	V-6	2	Chev.
L	173	2.8	V-6	2	Chev.
S	173	2.8	V-6	M.F.I.	Chev.
A	231	3.8	V-6	2	Buick
W	301	4.9	8	4	Pont.
T	301 ①	4.9	8	4	Pont.
H	305	5.0	8	4	Chev.
7	305	5.0	8	T.B.I.	Chev.
G	305	5.0	8	4	Chev.
F	305	5.0	8	T.B.I.	Chev.

Model Year Code	
Code	Year
B	1981
C	1982
D	1983
E	1984
F	1985
G	1986
H	1987

The seventeen digit Vehicle Identification Number can be used to determine engine application and model year. The 10th digit indicates the model year, and the 8th digit identifies the factory installed engine.

① Turbocharged engine

T.B.I.—Throttle body (fuel) injection

M.F.I.—Multi-Pont fuel injection

NOTE: Some 1985-and later Camaro and Firebird models are equipped with Tuned Port Injection (TPI).

TUNE-UP SPECIFICATIONS
Camaro

Year	Engine VIN Code	Engine No. of Cyl. Displacement (Cu. In.)	Engine Manufacturer	Spark Plugs Type	Spark Plugs Gap (in.)	Ignition Timing (deg) ①② Man Trans	Ignition Timing (deg) ①② Auto Trans	Intake Valve Opens (deg) ③	Fuel Pump Pressure (psi)	Idle Speed (rpm) ①② Man Trans	Idle Speed (rpm) ①② Auto Trans
'83	2	4-151	Pont.	R-44TSX	0.060	8	8	NA	9–13	750–800	475–525
	F	4-151	Pont.	R-44TSX	0.060	8	8	NA	5½–6½	750–800	475–525
	1	6-173	Chev.	R-43CTS	0.045	10	10	NA	5½–6½	775–1100	600–750
	H	8-305	Chev.	R-45TS	0.045	6	6	NA	5½–6½	700–800	500–650
	7	8-305	Chev.	R-45TS	0.045	6	6	NA	9–13	700–800	500–650
	S	8-305	Chev.	R-45TS	0.045		6	NA	9–13		475

TUNE-UP SPECIFICATIONS
Camaro

Year	Engine VIN Code	Engine No. of Cyl. Displacement (Cu. In.)	Engine Manufacturer	Spark Plugs Type	Spark Plugs Gap (in.)	Ignition Timing (deg) ①② Man Trans	Ignition Timing (deg) ①② Auto Trans	Intake Valve Opens (deg) ③	Fuel Pump Pressure (psi)	Idle Speed (rpm) ①② Man Trans	Idle Speed (rpm) ①② Auto Trans
'84	2	4-151	Pont.	R-44TSX	0.060	8	8	NA	9–13	775	500
	F	4-151	Pont.	R-44TSX	0.060	8	8	NA	5½–6½	775	500
	1	6-173	Chev.	R-43CTS	0.045	10	10	NA	5½–6½	800–1100	600–750
	H	8-305	Chev.	R-45TS	0.045	6	6	NA	5½–6½	700–800	500–650
	G	8-305	Chev.	R-45TS	0.045	6	6	NA	9–13	700–800	500–650
'85	2	4-151	Pont.	R-43TSX	0.060	8	8	NA	9–13	775	500
	S	V6-173	Chev.	R-42CTS	0.045	10	10	NA	6–7.5	④	④
	F	8-305	Chev.	R-43CTS	0.045		6	NA	9–13		500
	G	8-305	Chev.	R-43CTS	0.045	6	6	NA	9–13	700–800	500–650
	H	8-305	Chev.	R-43CTS	0.045	6	6	NA	9–13	700–800	500–650
'86–'87	2	4-151	Pont.	R-43TSX	0.060	④	④	NA	9–13	④	④
	S	V6-173	Chev.	R-42CTS	0.045	④	④	NA	6–7.5	④	④
	F	8-305	Chev.	R-43CTS	0.045	④	④	NA	9–13	④	④
	G	8-305	Chev.	R-43CTS	0.045	④	④	NA	9–13	④	④
	H	8-305	Chev.	R-43CTS	0.045	④	④	NA	9–13	④	④
	6	8-350	Chev.	R-43CTS	0.045	④	④	NA	9–13	④	④

NOTE: The underhood specifications sticker often reflects tune-up specification changes made during the production run. Sticker figures must always be used if they disagree with those in this chart. Part numbers in this chart are not recommendations by Chilton for any product by brand name.
All models use electronic ignition systems.
B Before Top Dead Center
TDC Top Dead Center
—Not applicable
NA—Not available
① See text for procedure
② Figure in parenthesis indicates California engine
③ All figures Before Top Dead Center (B.T.D.C.)
④ These functions are controlled by the emissions computer. In rare instances when adjustment is necessary, refer to the underhood emissions sticker for specifications.

FIRING ORDERS

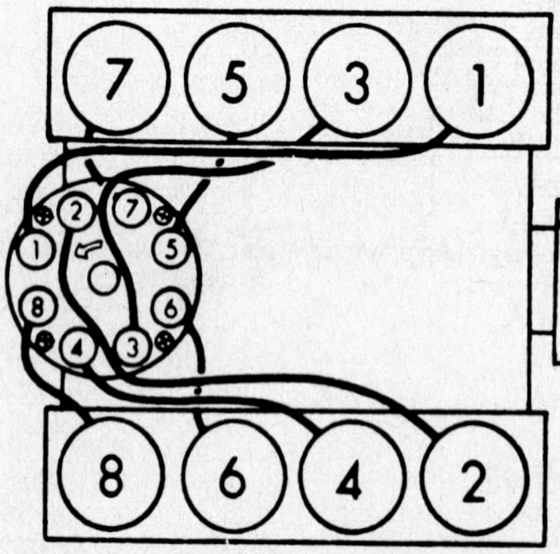

Pontiac-built V8 engines
Engine firing order: 1–8–4–3–6–5–7–2
Distributor rotation: counterclockwise

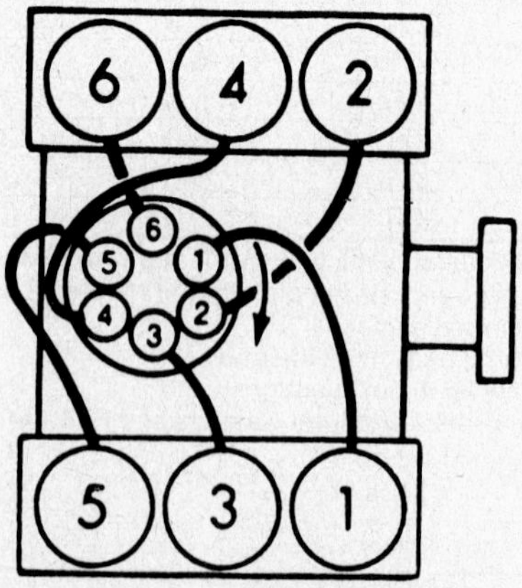

Chevrolet-built 173 V6 engine
Engine firing order: 1–2–3–4–5–6
Distributor rotation: clockwise

FIRING ORDERS

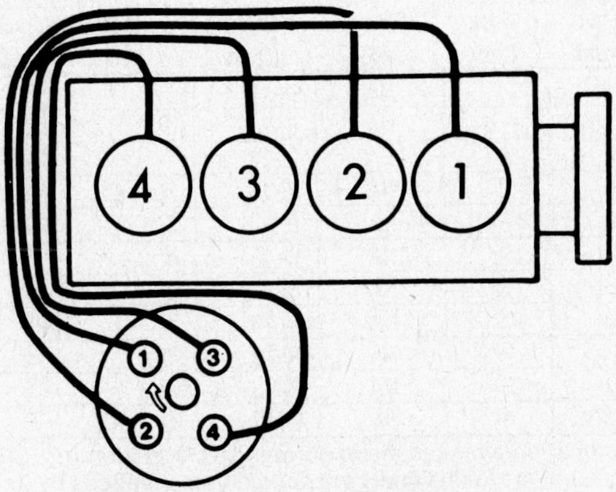

Pontiac-built 151–4 cylinder engine
Engine firing order: 1–3–4–2
Distributor rotation: clockwise

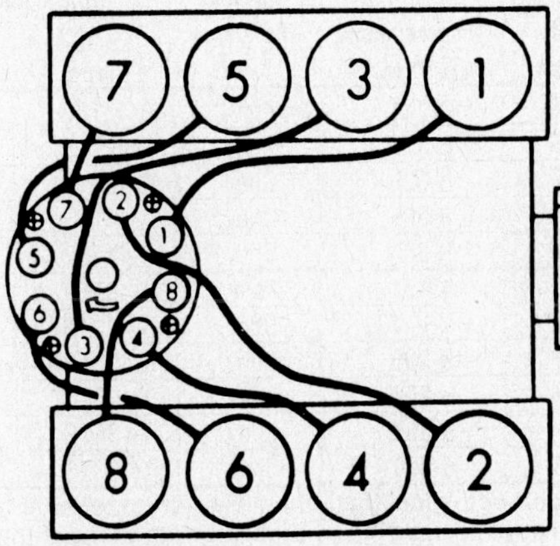

Chevrolet-built V8 engines
Engine firing order: 1–8–4–3–6–5–7–2
Distributor rotation: clockwise

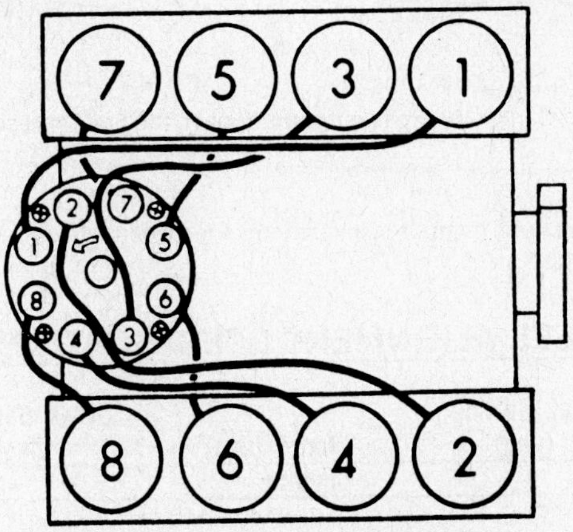

Oldsmobile-built V8 engines
Engine firing order: 1–8–4–3–6–5–7–2
Distributor rotation: counterclockwise

TUNE-UP SPECIFICATIONS
Firebird

Year	Engine VIN Code	Engine No. of Cyl. Displacement (Cu. In.)	Engine Manufac-turer	Spark Plugs Type	Spark Plugs Gap (in.)	Ignition Timing (deg) ①② Man Trans	Ignition Timing (deg) ①② Auto Trans	Intake Valve Opens (deg) ③	Fuel Pump Pressure (psi)	Idle Speed (rpm) ①② Man Trans	Idle Speed (rpm) ①② Auto Trans
'83	2	4-151	Pont.	R-44TSX	0.060	8	8	NA	9-13	750-800	475-525
	F	4-151	Pont.	R-44TS	0.060	8	8	NA	5½-6½	750-800	475-525
	1	6-173	Chev.	R-43CTS	0.045	10	10	NA	5.5-6.5	775-1100	600-750
	L	6-173HO	Chev.	R-42CTS	0.045	10	10	NA	6-7½	800-1100	725-850
	H	8-305	Chev.	R-45TS	0.045	6	6	NA	5.5-6.5	700-800	500-650
	7	8-305	Chev.	R-45TS ⑤	0.045	6	6	NA	9-13	700-800	500-650
	S	8-305	Chev.	R-45TS	0.045		6	NA	9-13		475
'84	2	4-151	Pont.	R-44TSX	0.060	8	8	NA	9-13	775	500
	F	4-151	Pont.	R-44TSX	0.060	8	8	NA	5½-6½	775	500
	X	6-173	Chev.	R-43CTS	0.045	10	10	NA	5½-6½	800-1100	600-750
	Z	6-173	Chev.	R-42CTS	0.045	10	10	NA	6-7½		④
	H	8-305	Chev.	R-45TS	0.045	6	6	NA	5½-6½	700-800	500-650
	G	8-305	Chev.	R-45TS	0.045	6	6	NA	9-13	700-800	500-650

TUNE-UP SPECIFICATIONS
Firebird

Year	Engine VIN Code	Engine No. of Cyl. Displacement (Cu. In.)	Engine Manufacturer	Spark Plugs Type	Spark Plugs Gap (in.)	Ignition Timing (deg) ①② Man Trans	Ignition Timing (deg) ①② Auto Trans	Intake Valve Opens (deg) ③	Fuel Pump Pressure (psi)	Idle Speed (rpm) ①② Man Trans	Idle Speed (rpm) ①② Auto Trans
'85	2	4-151	Pont.	R-43TSX	0.060	8	8	NA	9–13	775	500
	S	6-173	Chev.	R-42CTS	0.045	10	10	NA	6–7½	④	④
	F	8-305	Chev.	R-43CTS	0.045		6	NA	9–13		500
	G	8-305	Chev.	R-44TS	0.045	6	6	NA	9–13	700–800	500–650
	H	8-305	Chev.	R-44TS	0.045	6	6	NA	9–13	700–800	500–650
'86–'87	2	4-151	Pont.	R-43TSX	0.060	④	④	NA	9–13	④	④
	S	V6-173	Chev.	R-42CTS	0.045	④	④	NA	6–7.5	④	④
	F	8-305	Chev.	R-43CTS	0.045	④	④	NA	9–13	④	④
	G	8-305	Chev.	R-43CTS	0.045	④	④	NA	9–13	④	④
	H	8-305	Chev.	R-43CTS	0.045	④	④	NA	9–13	④	④
	8	8-350	Chev.	R-43CTS	0.045	④	④	NA	9–13	④	④

NOTE: The underhood specifications sticker often reflects tune-up specification changes made during the production run. Sticker figures must always be used if they disagree with those in this chart. Part numbers in this chart are not recommendations by Chilton for any product by brand name.
All models use electronic ignition systems.
B Before Top Dead Center
TDC Top Dead Center
—Not applicable
NA—Not available
① See text for procedure
② Figure in parenthesis indicates California engine
③ All figures are in degrees Before Top Dead Center. Where two figures appear, the first represents timing with manual transmission, the second with automatic transmission.
Auto—29
Trans Am—16
④ These functions are controlled by the emissions computer. In rare instances when adjustment is necessary, refer to the underhood emissions sticker for specifications.

WHEEL ALIGNMENT SPECIFICATIONS

Year	Caster Range (deg)	Caster Pref. Setting (deg)	Camber Range (deg)	Camber Pref. Setting (deg)	Toe-in (in.)	Steering Inclin. (deg)
Camaro						
'83-'84	2P to 4P	3P	3/16P to 1 13/16P	1P	3/32 to 5/16	N/A
Z-28	2P to 4P	3P	3/16P to 1 13/16P	1P	1/16 to 1/4	N/A
'85-'87	2 1/2P to 3 1/2P	3P	1/2P to 1 1/2P	1P	1/16 to 1/4	N/A
Z-28	3P to 4P	3 1/2P	1/2P to 1 1/2P	1P	1/16 to 1/4	N/A
Firebird						
'83	2P to 4P	3P	1/8P to 1 13/16P	1P	3/32 to 5/16	N/A
Trans Am	2P to 4P	3P	1/8P to 1 13/16P	1P	1/16 to 1/4	N/A
'84	2P to 4P	3P	3/16P to 1 13/16P	1P	3/32 to 5/16	N/A
Trans Am	2P to 4P	3P	3/16P to 1 13/16P	1P	1/16 to 1/4	N/A
'85	2 5/16P to 3 5/16P	2 13/16P	1/2P to 1 1/2P	1P	1/32 to 1/4	N/A
'86-'87	3P to 4P	3 1/2P	1/2P to 1 1/2P	1P	1/32 to 1/4	N/A

LABOR — SERVICE BAY OPERATIONS — LABOR

(Factory Time) — Chilton Time

COOLING

(M) Winterize Cooling System
Includes: Run engine to check for leaks, tighten all hose connections. Test radiator and pressure cap. Drain radiator and engine block. Add anti-freeze and refill system.
All models.. .5

(M) Thermostat, Renew
1983-87-Four (.5).......................... .6
V-6 (.3).......................... .4
V-8 (.6).......................... .7

(M) Drive Belt, Renew
All models-one (.3).......................... .4
each adtnl.......................... .1

(M) Drive Belt, Adjust
All models-one (.2).......................... .3
each adtnl.......................... .1

(M) Radiator Hoses, Renew
1983-87-upper (.3).......................... .4
lower (.4).......................... .5
both (.5).......................... .7

FUEL

(M) Carburetor Air Cleaner, Service
All models (.2).......................... .3

(G) Carburetor, Adjust (On Car)
1983-87
Slow & Fast Idle (.3).......................... .4
Vacuum Brake-one (.4).......................... .6
both (.6).......................... .8
Choke (.6).......................... 1.0
Complete (1.3).......................... 1.8

LABOR — SERVICE BAY OPERATIONS — LABOR

(Factory Time) — Chilton Time

(G) Fuel Filter, Renew
All models (.3) 4

BRAKES

(G) Brakes, Adjust (Minor)
Includes: R&R wheels and adjust brakes thru access holes in drums. Fill master cylinder.
two wheels 4
Remove knock out plugs add, each .. .1

(G) Bleed Brakes (Four Wheels)
Includes: Fill master cylinder.
All models (.4) 5

(G) Brake Pedal Free Play, Adjust
All models (.2) 3

(M) Parking Brake, Adjust
All models (.3) 5

LUBRICATION SERVICE

(M) Lubricate Chassis, Change Oil & Filter
Includes: Inspect and correct all fluid levels.
All models 6
Install grease fittings add 1

(M) Lubricate Chassis
Includes: Inspect and correct all fluid levels.
All models 4
Install grease fittings add 1

(M) Engine Oil & Filter, Change
Includes: Inspect and correct all fluid levels.
All models 4

WHEELS

(G) Wheel, Renew
one (.5) 5

(G) Wheels, Rotate (All)
All models 5

(G) Wheels, Balance
one 3
each adtnl 2

(G) Front Wheel Bearings, Clean and Repack (Both Wheels)
All models (1.1) 1.6

(G) Front Wheel Grease Seals, Renew
All models–one whl (.7) 8
both whls (1.1) 1.2

CHILTON'S 10 POINT SAFETY CHECK

CHECK OPERATION & CONDITION OF THE FOLLOWING ITEMS:

1. Legal Registration (serial no.)
2. Tires & Wheels
3. Brake System (R&R all wheels)
4. Light Systems & Signals
5. Accelerator Linkage, Neutral Safety Switch, Shift Indicator Pointer & Seat Position Locks
6. Glass, Mirrors, Door Locks, Seat Belts & Harness
7. Wipers, Washers & Defrosters
8. Frame, Steering, Shocks, Front & Rear Suspension
9. Fuel & Exhaust Systems
10. Road Test Vehicle

All models 1.0
Exhaust Smog Analysis, add 4

(Factory Time) — Chilton Time

ELECTRICAL

(M) Battery Cables, Renew
All models–positive (.4) 5
negative (.2) 3

(M) Battery Terminals, Clean
All models 3

(G) Aim Headlamps
two 4
four 6

(M) Headlamp Sealed Beam Bulb, Renew
All models (.2) 3

(G) Headlamp Switch, Renew
1983-87 (.6) 8
w/A.C. add (.2) 2

(G) Headlamp Dimmer Switch, Renew
1983-87 (.5) 9

(Factory Time) — Chilton Time

(G) Headlamp Actuator Switch, Renew
1985-87 (.2) 4

(G) Stop Lamp Switch, Renew
1983-87 (.3) 4

(G) Back-Up Lamp Switch, Renew (w/Manual Trans)
1983-87 (.3) 4

(G) Neutral Start Switch, Renew
1983-87–Camaro (.3) 4
Firebird (.6) 9

(G) Turn Signal or Hazard Warning Switch, Renew
1983-87
std colm (.7) 1.1
tilt colm (.8) 1.2

(M) Turn Signal or Hazard Warning Flasher, Renew
1983-87 (.3) 3

(G) Horn, Renew
1983-87–each (.2) 2

(G) Horn Relay, Renew
1983-87 (.3) 4

(M) Side Marker Lamp Assy., Renew
1983-87–each (.2) 3

(M) Park and Turn Signal Lamp Assy., Renew
1983-87–each (.2) 3

(M) Stop, Tail and Turn Signal Lamp Assy., Renew
1983-87–each (.4) 6

(M) Back-Up Lamp Bulb, Renew
All models–one (.3) 4
all (.5) 7

(M) License Lamp Assembly, Renew
1983-87–one (.2) 3
each adtnl 1

(M) Park and Turn Signal Lamp Bulb, Renew
All models–each 2

(M) Side Marker Lamp Bulb, Renew
All models–each 2

(M) Stop, Tail and Turn Signal Lamp Bulb, Renew
All models–one 3
each adtnl 1

LABOR — 1 TUNE UP 1 — LABOR

(Factory Time) — Chilton Time

(G) Compression Test
Four–1983-87 (.4) 6
V-6–1983-87 (.5) 7
V-8–1983-87 (.6) 8

(G) Engine Tune Up, (Electronic Ignition)
Includes: Test battery and clean connections. Tighten manifold and carburetor mounting bolts. Check engine compression, clean and adjust or renew spark plugs. Test resistance of spark plug cables. Inspect distributor cap and rotor. Adjust air gap. Check vacuum advance operation. Reset ignition timing. Adjust idle mixture and idle speed. Service air cleaner. Inspect and adjust drive belts. Inspect choke operation and adjust or free up. Check operation of EGR valve.
Four–1983-87 .... 1.4
V-6–1983-87 .... 2.0
V-8–1983-87 .... 2.5
To perform C.C.C. system test add... 1.0

LABOR 2 IGNITION SYSTEM 2 LABOR

	(Factory Time)	Chilton Time
(G) Spark Plugs, Clean and Reset or Renew		
Four–1983-87	(.3)	.5
V-6–1983-87	(.4)	.6
V-8–1983-87	(.6)	.8
(G) Ignition Timing, Reset		
All models	(.3)	.4
(G) Distributor, Renew		
Includes: Reset ignition timing.		
Four–1983-87	(.6)	.8
V-6–1983-87	(.5)	.8
V-8–1983-87	(.6)	.8
(G) Distributor, R&R and Recondition		
Includes: Reset ignition timing.		
Four–1983-87	(1.0)	1.4
V-6–1983-87	(.9)	1.4
V-8–1983-87	(1.0)	1.4
(G) Distributor Cap and/or Rotor, Renew		
1983-87	(.4)	.6
(G) Ignition Coil, Renew		
1983-87	(.5)	.6
(G) Ignition Cables, Renew		
Four–1983-87	(.3)	.5
V-6–1983-87	(.6)	.8
V-8–1983-87	(.5)	.7
(G) Distributor Module, Renew		
Four–1983-87	(.6)	.8
V-6–1983-87	(.7)	.9
V-8–1983-87	(.6)	.8
(G) Distributor Pick-Up Coil and/or Pole Piece, Renew		
Four–1983-87	(.8)	1.1
V-6–1983-87	(.6)	1.0
V-8–1983-87	(.8)	1.1
(G) Distributor Capacitor and/or Module Wiring Harness, Renew		
1983-87	(.6)	.9
(G) Distributor Hall Effect Switch, Renew		
1983	(.5)	.8
(G) ESC Detonation Switch, Renew		
1983	(.4)	.6
(G) Ignition Switch, Renew		
1983-87	(.8)	1.2
(G) Ignition Key Warning Switch, Renew		
1983-87	(.6)	.9
(G) E.S.C. Detonation (Knock) Sensor, Renew		
1983-87	(.4)	.6
(G) E.S.C. Module, Renew		
1983-87	(.4)	.6

PARTS 2 IGNITION SYSTEM 2 PARTS

FOUR CYLINDER

	Part No.	Price
Distributor Assy.		
1983	◆1103513	282.50
1984	◆1103551	236.00
1985-87	◆1103634	155.75
(1) Cap		
1983-84	◆1978497	16.00
1985-87	◆1987948	7.00
(2) Rotor		
1983	◆1979703	8.50
1984	◆1988515	8.50
1985-87	◆10495411	3.50
(3) Mainshaft		
1983	◆1979705	40.00
1984	◆1986963	33.25
1985-87	◆1988077	24.75
(4) Terminal Block		
1983-87	◆1979700	32.75
(5) Pole Piece (w/Plate)		
1983	◆1979696	36.25
1984	◆1978503	39.25
1985-87	◆1987963	3.50
(6) Module		
1983-84	◆1985342	56.50
1985-87	◆1989747	51.50
(7) Hall Effect Switch		
1983	◆1979711	47.50
(8) Housing		
1983-84	◆1979701	48.75
1985-87	◆1988082	26.75
(9) Gear		
1983-87	◆1978509	13.00

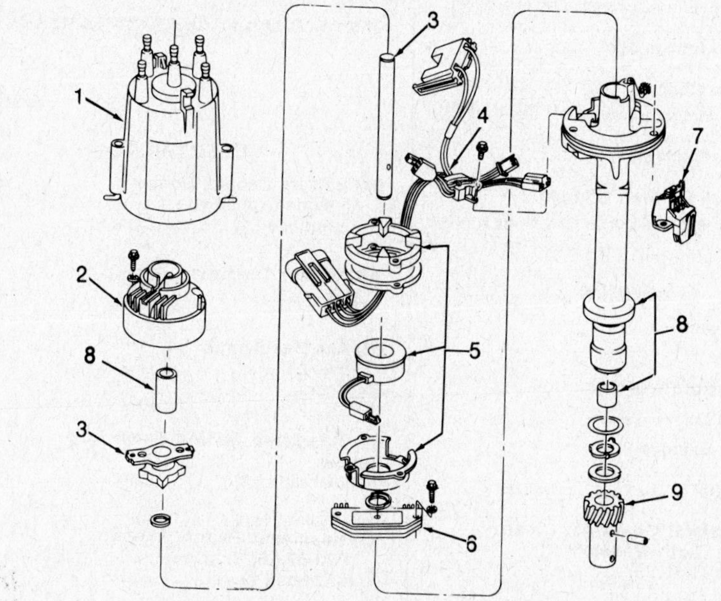

	Part No.	Price
Ignition Switch		
(wo/Tilt wheel)		
1983	◆1990109	11.50
1984-87-M.T.	◆1990115	11.50
A.T.	◆7843497	25.75
(Tilt wheel)		
1983	◆1990110	11.50
1984-87-M.T.	◆1990116	11.50
A.T.	◆7843451	25.75

PARTS 2 ELECTRONIC IGNITION 2 PARTS

Engine codes are identified by the 8th digit or letter of the VIN code.

V-6 & V-8

	Part No.	Price
Distributor Assy.		
V-6		
1983	◆1103519	243.75
1984	◆1103570	214.25
1985	◆1103591	176.50
1986-87	◆1103704	227.50
V-8		
1983 Code S	◆1103539	288.25
1983-84-Code F, 7	◆1103460	333.75
1984-Code G	◆1103598	275.50
1985-87-Code G, H	◆10497135	294.50
1986-87-Code F	◆10497136	272.25
1986-87-350-8	◆10497136	272.25
(1) Cover		
1983-87-V-8	◆1875960	6.00
(2) Coil		
V-6		
1983-84	◆1115455	58.00
1985-87	◆1115315	39.50
V-8		
1983-85-exc. below	◆1985473	36.00
Code G, F	◆1988665	48.75

PARTS 2 ELECTRONIC IGNITION 2 PARTS

	Part No.	Price
1986-87-exc.		
below	◆1985473	N.L.
Code H	◆1875894	N.L.
(3) Cap		
V-6		
1983-84	◆1979208	20.25
1985-87	◆1988001	9.75
V-8		
1983-87-exc.		
below	◆1974408	17.00
Code F	◆1977046	24.50
(4) Brush		
1983-87-V-8	◆1875967	2.50
(5) Rotor		
1983-84-V-6	◆1978533	9.00
1985-V-6	◆10495408	3.50
1986-87-V-6	◆10497452	3.50
1983-87-V-8	◆1977026	6.50
(6) Mainshaft		
1983-84-V-6	◆1979256	49.75
1985-V-6	◆1988005	31.25
1986-87-V-6	◆10497454	27.25
1983-87-V-8	◆1976909	38.50
(7) Pole Piece (w/Plate)		
1983-84-V-6	◆1979261	33.00
1985-87-V-6	◆1988010	3.50
1983-87-V-8	◆1976897	30.25
(8) Module		
V-6		
1983-84	◆1979571	58.00
1985-87	◆1987466	46.00
V-8		
1983-87	◆1976908	60.00
305H-Canada	◆1875990	N.L.
(9) Housing		
V-6		
1983	◆1979254	41.50
1984	◆1987841	37.25
1985	◆1988388	34.25
1986-87	◆10496765	36.25

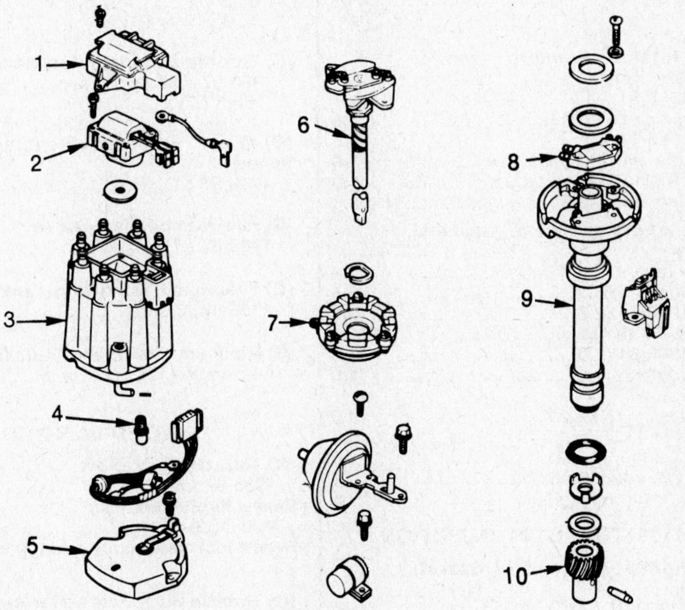

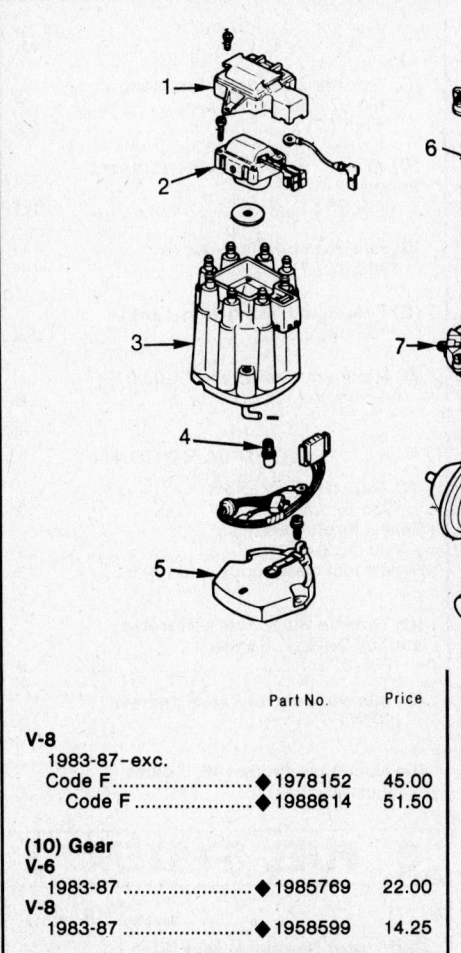

	Part No.	Price
V-8		
1983-87-exc.		
Code F	◆1978152	45.00
Code F	◆1988614	51.50
(10) Gear		
V-6		
1983-87	◆1985769	22.00
V-8		
1983-87	◆1958599	14.25

	Part No.	Price
Ignition Switch		
(wo/Tilt wheel)		
1983	◆1990109	11.50
1984-87-M.T.	◆1990115	11.50
A.T.	◆7843497	25.75
(Tilt wheel)		
1983	◆1990110	11.50
1984-87-M.T.	◆1990116	11.50
A.T.	◆7843451	25.75

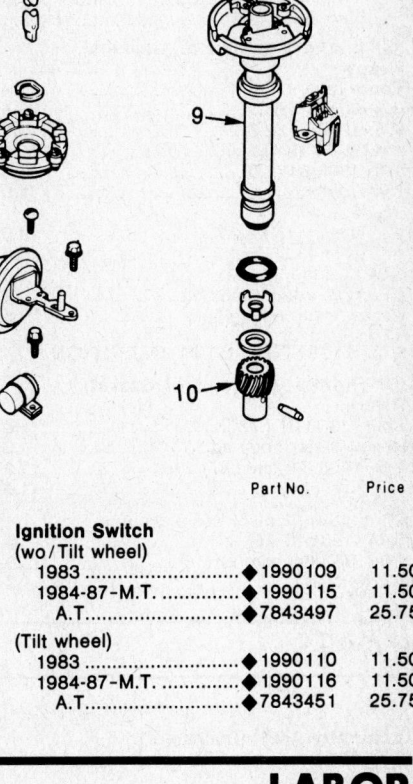

LABOR 3 FUEL SYSTEM 3 LABOR

(Factory Time)	Chilton Time
(G) Fuel Pump, Test	
Includes: Disconnect line at carburetor, attach pressure gauge.	
All models	.3
(M) Carburetor Air Cleaner, Service	
All models (.2)	.3
(G) Carburetor, Adjust (On Car)	
1983-87	
Slow & Fast Idle (.3)	.4
Vacuum Brake-one (.4)	.6
both (.6)	.8
Choke (.6)	1.0
Complete (1.3)	1.8
(G) Choke Vacuum Brake Diaphragm, Renew	
1983-87-one (.4)	.6
both (.6)	.8
(G) Idle Stop Solenoid, Renew	
1983-84 (.3)	.3
1985-87 (.7)	1.0
(G) Electric Choke Relay, Renew	
1983-87 (.2)	.3

(Factory Time)	Chilton Time
(G) Carburetor, Renew	
Includes: All necessary adjustments.	
1983-87 (.6)	1.0
To perform C.C.C. system check, add (.5)	1.0
(G) Carburetor, R&R and Clean or Recondition	
Includes: All necessary adjustments.	
1983-87-2 bbl (2.3)	3.0
4 bbl (2.5)	3.2
To perform C.C.C. system check, add (.5)	1.0
(G) E.F.E. Heater (Insulator), Renew	
1983-87 (.6)	1.0
(G) Float or Needle Valve and Seat, Renew	
Includes: Set idle speed and mixture.	
1983-87-2 bbl (.9)	1.2
4 bbl (.9)	1.5
To perform C.C.C. system check, add (.5)	1.0
(G) Accelerator Pump, Renew	
1983-87-2 bbl (.7)	1.0
4 bbl (.8)	1.2

(Factory Time)	Chilton Time
(G) Fuel Pump or Push Rod, Renew	
V-6-1983-84 (.7)	1.0
1985-87 (.8)	1.1
V-8-1983-84 (1.0)	1.5
1985-87 (.8)	1.1
Add pump test if performed.	
(G) Fuel Tank, Renew	
Includes: Transfer tank gauge unit.	
1983-87 (2.2)	3.0
(G) Fuel Gauge (Tank Unit), Renew	
Includes: Drain and refill tank.	
1983-87 (2.2)	3.0
(G) Fuel Gauge (Dash Unit), Renew	
1983-84 (.3)	.6
1985-87 (.5)	.9
w/Digital cluster add (.3)	.3
(G) Intake Plenum and/or Gaskets, Renew	
V-6-1985-87 (.6)	.9
V-8-1985-87 (1.4)	1.9

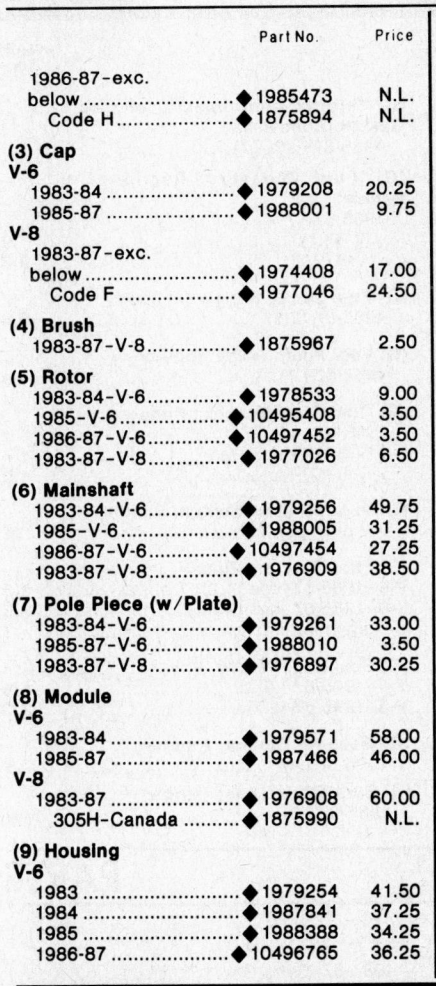

LABOR 3 FUEL SYSTEM 3 LABOR

	(Factory Time)	Chilton Time
(G) Intake Runners and/or Gaskets, Renew		
V-6–1985-87		
one piece	(1.1)	1.5
V-8–1985-87		
right side	(1.3)	1.8
left side	(1.4)	1.9
both sides	(2.3)	3.1
(G) Intake Manifold or Gaskets, Renew		
Four–1983-87	(1.1)	1.8
w/A.C. add	(.5)	.5
V-6–1983-84	(2.7)	3.7
1985-87	(3.4)	4.9
V-8–1983-84	(2.0)	*3.0
*w/T.B.I. add		1.0
1985-87		
wo/Inj	(1.7)	3.0
w/Inj	(3.8)	5.5
w/A.C. add	(.3)	.3
w/C.C.C. add	(.4)	.4
Renew manif add	(.4)	.5

THROTTLE BODY INJECTION

	(Factory Time)	Chilton Time
(G) Throttle Body and/or Gasket, Renew		
Four–1983-87	(.7)	1.0
Renew meter body add	(.3)	.3
V-8–1983-84-one	(.8)	1.2
both	(1.0)	1.5
(G) Idle Air Control Valve, Renew		
Four–1983-87	(.6)	.9
V-8–1983-84-one	(.3)	.5
both	(.4)	.6
(G) Throttle Body Injector, Renew		
1983-87-one	(.6)	1.0
both	(.7)	1.4
(G) Fuel Pressure Regulator, Renew		
1983-87	(.7)	1.1
(G) Fuel Pump Relay, Renew		
1983-87	(.7)	1.0
(G) Fuel Pump, Renew (In Tank)		
1983-87	(2.6)	3.4
(G) Minimum Idle Speed, Adjust		
All models	(.6)	.8

PORTED INJECTION

	(Factory Time)	Chilton Time
(G) Throttle Body, R&R		
1985-87	(.6)	1.0
Renew throttle body kit add	(.3)	.3
Renew fuel meter body add	(.3)	.3
(G) Throttle Body Fuel Meter Assy., and/or Gasket, Renew		
1985-87	(.4)	.6
(G) Idle Air Control Valve, Renew		
1985-87	(.4)	.6
(G) Minimum Idle Speed, Adjust		
All models	(.4)	.7
(G) Throttle Body Injector and/or Gasket, Renew		
1985-87-one	(.7)	1.1
(G) Fuel Pressure Regulator, Renew		
1985-87		
V-6	(.7)	.9
V-8	(2.7)	3.5
(G) Fuel Pump, Renew (In Tank)		
1985-87	(2.6)	3.4
(G) Fuel Pump Relay, Renew		
1985-87	(.7)	.9
(G) Cold Start Injector, Renew		
1985-87		
V-6	(1.0)	1.4
V-8	(.7)	1.0
(G) Thermo Start Switch, Renew		
1985-87	(.5)	.7
(G) Fuel Injector, Renew		
V-6–1985-87-one	(1.2)	1.8
V-8–1985-87-one	(2.5)	3.5
each adtnl	(.1)	.1
(G) Fuel Rail, Renew		
V-6–1985-87	(.9)	1.3
V-8–1985-87	(2.2)	3.0
(G) Mass Air Sensor, Renew		
1985-87	(.4)	.5
(G) Burn Off Module, Renew		
1985-87	(.6)	.8

PARTS 3 FUEL SYSTEM 3 PARTS

	Part No.	Price
Carburetor Assy. (Rochester)		
V-6-173		
(A.T.)		
1983-wo/A.C.	◆17079189	803.00
A.C.	◆17079201	819.25
1984	◆17110012	789.50
(M.T.)		
1983-wo/A.C.	◆17079194	835.50
A.C.	◆17079202	822.00
1984	◆17110024	791.50
V-8-305H		
(A.T.)		
1983	◆17079226	821.25
1984	◆17110449	846.00
1985	◆17110902	887.00
1986-87	◆17111481	876.00
(M.T.)		
1983	◆17110452	846.00
1984	◆17110452	846.00
1985	◆17110903	887.00
1986-87	◆17111482	876.00
V-8-305G		
1984-A.T.	◆17110451	846.00
M.T.	◆17110450	869.50
1985	◆17110901	887.00
1986-87	◆17111486	876.00
Carburetor Power Kit		
V-6		
1983	◆17069030	41.00
1984	◆17076122	44.25
V-8		
1983-84-305H	◆7039467	41.50
305G	◆17076127	48.00
1985-87	◆17076043	33.75
Carburetor Needle & Seat Kit		
V-6		
1983	◆7035156	6.00
1984	◆17079282	19.25
V-8		
1983-84-305H	◆7035134	6.00
305G	◆17079832	7.75
1985-87	◆7035134	6.00
Carburetor Gasket Kit		
V-6		
1983	◆17078047	29.75
1984	◆17110013	29.00
V-8		
1983-87	◆17067999	38.50
Fuel Tank		
(wo/E.F.I.)		
1983-87	◆10028061	126.00
1986-87	◆10042325	N.L.
(E.F.I.)		
1983-85	◆10028060	126.00
1986-87	◆10042327	N.L.
Fuel Pump		
4-151		
1983	◆6471926	N.L.
1984-85	◆6472232	92.00
V-6-173		
1983-84	◆6471930	46.00
1985-87	◆25115429	79.75
V-8		
1983-87-Code H	◆6472366	38.00
1983-Code 7	◆6471252	37.25
1983-Code S	◆6471925	85.25
1984-87-Code G engine	◆6471252	37.25
tank (84)	◆6472395	42.75
tank (85)	◆6472408	43.50
tank (86-87)	◆25115110	57.25
1985-Code F	◆6472393	49.00
1986-87-350-8	◆25115254	87.00
Fuel Gauge (Tank)		
(wo/E.F.I.)		
1983-87-exc. below	◆25003093	115.50
1985-87-w/305 G eng.	◆25004960	164.25
(E.F.I.)		
1983	◆25003095	147.00
1984-87-151	◆25004339	179.50
1985-87-305 F	◆25004387	160.00
173	◆25004383	160.00

Fuel Gauge (Dash)

The following part numbers are for pricing reference only. Order part with complete engine, year and model information.

	Part No.	Price
(Camaro)		
1983-84-wo/ Gauges	◆6433646	28.00
Gauges	◆6433647	23.75
1985-87-wo/ Gauges	◆6434246	26.50
Gauges	◆6434243	25.00
(Firebird)		
1983-wo/ Gauges	◆6433805	27.50
Gauges	◆6433873	56.25
1984-wo/ Gauges	◆6434087	31.50
Gauges	◆25076141	57.75

PARTS 3 FUEL SYSTEM 3 PARTS

	Part No.	Price
1985-87-wo/		
Gauges	◆6434268	31.50
Gauges	◆25078649	37.00
Manifold Gasket Set (Intake)		
4-151		
1983-87	◆10026023	5.00
V-6-173		
1983-84	◆14033476	12.50
1985-87-side	◆10048962	8.00
plenum	◆14089057	2.00

	Part No.	Price
V-8		
1983-85-wo/		
E.F.I.	◆14034821	5.75
1986-87-Code G,		
H	◆14038088	N.L.
1983-E.F.I.	◆14085858	14.75
1985-87-305 Code F		
(complete)	◆14089151	29.00

Silicone Sealer required on 305H eng. for front and rear seals.

	Part No.	Price
E.F.E. SYSTEM		
E.F.E. Valve (w/Actuator)		
1983-87-V-8	◆5233650	64.00
E.F.E. Relay		
1983-V-6	◆14039681	10.00
E.F.E. Control Switch		
1983-87-w/V-8		
eng.	◆3043015	14.50

PARTS 3 ELECTRONIC FUEL INJECTION 3 PARTS

	Part No.	Price
FOUR CYLINDER		
Throttle Body Injection		
1983	◆17079592	582.50
1984	◆17110359	582.50
1985-87	◆17110762	498.50
Throttle Body Kit		
1983	◆17079593	266.75
1984	◆17110360	240.00
1985-87	◆17110763	237.25

	Part No.	Price
Gasket Kit		
1983-87	◆17068990	24.75
Idler Air Valve Control Kit		
1983-84	◆17078220	82.00
1985-87	◆17059256	N.L.
Fuel Injector Kit		
1983-87	◆17068993	191.75

	Part No.	Price
Fuel Meter Body Kit		
1983-87	◆17078222	109.75
Throttle Position Sensor Kit		
1983-87	◆17078274	74.75
Fuel Meter Kit		
1983-87	◆17068992	425.75

Kit includes injector and pressure regulator.

PARTS 3 THROTTLE BODY FUEL INJECTION 3 PARTS

	Part No.	Price
V-8 ENGINE		
Throttle Body Injection		
1983 (complete)	◆17079851	1725.00
Front	◆17079732	404.00
Rear	◆17079730	742.50
Throttle Body Kit		
1983	◆17079716	239.50

	Part No.	Price
Gasket Kit		
1983 (complete)	◆17082054	N.L.
Front & Rear	◆17079729	24.25
Idle Air Valve Control Kit		
1983	◆17078832	80.75
Fuel Injector Kit		
1983-Front	◆17078855	179.75
Rear	◆17078885	179.75

	Part No.	Price
Fuel Meter Body Kit		
1983-Front	◆17079724	59.50
Rear	◆17078833	116.75
Throttle Position Sensor		
1983	◆17111262	63.00
Fuel Meter Kit		
1983-Front	◆17078854	468.00
Rear	◆17079726	470.25

Kit includes injector and pressure regulator.

PARTS 3 ELECTRONIC FUEL INJECTION 3 PARTS

	Part No.	Price
V-6-173		
(1) Throttle Body Assy. (Kit)		
1985-M.T.	◆17110835	191.50
A.T.	◆17111338	193.50
1986-87-M.T.	◆17111336	191.50
A.T.	◆17111338	193.50
(2) Gasket Kit		
1985-87	◆17110827	9.00
(3) Throttle Position Sensor Kit		
1985	◆17110830	46.50
1986-87	◆17111606	40.50
(4) Coolant Cover Kit		
1985-87	◆17110828	39.25
(5) Idle Air Vacuum Housing Kit		
1985-87	◆17110829	31.50
(6) Idle Air Control Valve		
1985-87	◆17111288	58.00
(7) Fuel Rail and Pressure Regulator		
1985-87	◆17110856	162.75
(8) Fuel Inlet/Outlet Block		
1985-87	◆17110853	29.25
(9) Fuel Injector Kit		
1985-87	◆17111297	137.50
(10) Cold Start Valve		
1985-87	◆17110860	49.50

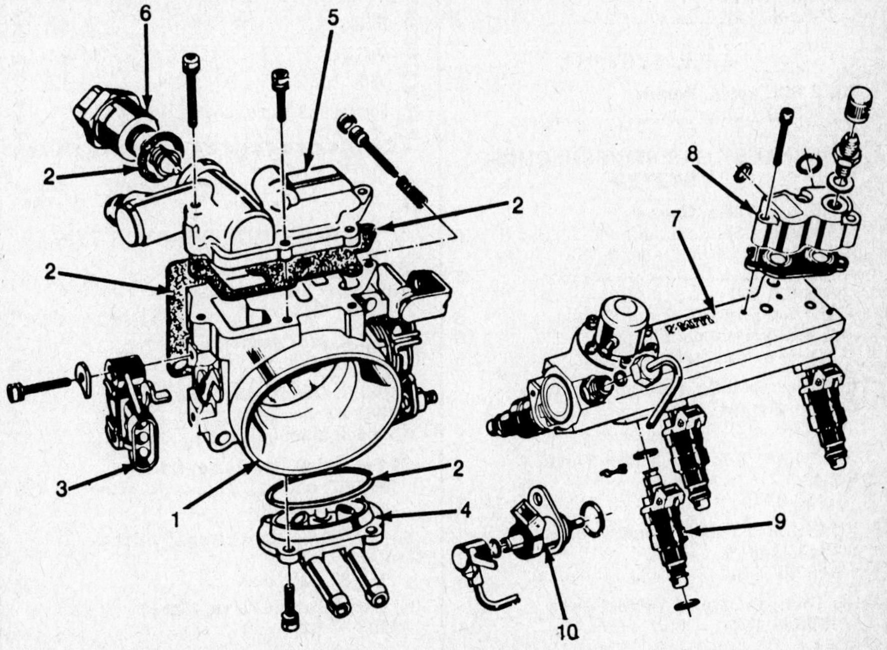

PARTS 3 ELECTRONIC FUEL INJECTION 3 PARTS

	Part No.	Price
V-8-305F		
Throttle Body Assy		
1985-87	◆17110849	232.50
Gasket Kit		
1985-87	◆17110845	8.50
Throttle Position Sensor		
1985-87	◆17110830	46.50
Idle Air Control Valve		
1985-87	◆17111288	58.00
Injector (Fuel)		
1985-87	◆17110872	104.25
Fuel Rail Kit		
1985-87-left	◆17110866	153.25
right	◆17110871	215.50
Regulator (Pressure)		
1985-87	◆17110874	71.25

LABOR 3A EMISSION CONTROLS 3A LABOR

	(Factory Time)	Chilton Time
(G) Emission Control Check		
Includes: Check and adjust engine idle speed and mixture and ignition timing. Check PCV valve.		
All models		.6
CRANKCASE EMISSION		
(M) Positive Crankcase Ventilation Valve, Renew		
All models	(.2)	.3
(M) Crankcase Ventilation Filter Assy., Renew		
All models	(.2)	.3
EVAPORATIVE EMISSION TYPE		
(G) Charcoal Canister, Renew		
All models	(.2)	.3
(G) Canister Purge Thermal Vacuum Switch, Renew		
All models	(.3)	.4
(M) Fuel Tank Pressure Control Switch, Renew		
All models	(.2)	.3
CONTROLLED COMBUSTION TYPE		
(G) Air Cleaner Vacuum Motor, Renew		
1983-87	(.3)	.5
(G) Air Cleaner Temperature Sensor, Renew		
1983-87	(.2)	.3
E.F.E. SYSTEM		
(G) E.F.E. Valve, Renew		
1983-87	(.6)	1.0
EXHAUST GAS RECIRCULATION SYSTEM		
(G) E.G.R. Valve, Renew		
1983-84	(.3)	.5
1985-87		
Four	(.2)	.5
V-6 & V-8		
wo/Port inj	(.4)	.6
V-6-w/Port inj	(.5)	.8
V-8-w/Port inj	(1.9)	2.5
(G) Thermostatic Vacuum Control Switch, Renew		
1983-87	(.3)	.4
(G) E.G.R. Vacuum Delay Valve, Renew		
1983-87	(.2)	.3
(G) E.G.R./E.F.E. Thermal Vacuum Switch, Renew		
1983-87	(.3)	.4
(G) Thermal Control Valve, Renew		
1983-87	(.3)	.4

CHILTON'S EMISSION CONTROL TUNE-UP

1. Clean or renew P.C.V. valve, hoses and filter.
2. Check fuel tank cap for sealing ability.
3. Check fuel tank and fuel lines for leakage.
4. Check evaporation canister and filter. Replace if necessary.
5. Check engine compression to determine leakage of unburned gases. (Add time for items of interference).
6. Test and clean or renew spark plugs.
7. Check engine oil dipstick for sealing ability.
8. Test exhaust system with analyzer and check system for leakage.
9. Check exhaust manifold heat valve for operation.
10. Adjust ignition timing and carburetor idle speed and mixture.
11. Check automatic choke mechanism for free operation.
12. Inspect air cleaner and element.
13. On models so equipped, test distributor vacuum control switch and transmission control switch.

Four	1.3
V-6	1.7
V-8	1.8

For repairs made, charge accordingly.

	(Factory Time)	Chilton Time
AIR INJECTION REACTOR TYPE		
(G) Air Pump, Renew		
1983-87-V-6	(.4)	.7
V-8	(.4)	.8
(G) A.I.R. Air Cleaner, Renew		
1983-87	(.2)	.3
(G) A.I.R. Check Valve, Renew		
1983-87-one	(.2)	.3
each adtnl	(.1)	.1
(G) Vacuum Delay Valve, Renew		
1983-87-one	(.2)	.3
each adtnl	(.1)	.1
(G) Air Pump Centrifugal Filter, Renew		
1983-87	(.3)	.5
(G) Deceleration Valve, Renew		
1983-87	(.2)	.3
(G) A.I.R. Manifold Pipe, Renew		
1983-87-each	(.5)	.8
(G) Catalytic Converter Air Pipe, Renew		
1983-87-one piece	(.5)	.7
COMPUTER COMMAND CONTROL SYSTEM (C.C.C.)		
(P) Electronic Control Module, Renew		
Does not include system performance check.		
1983-87	(.6)	.7
(P) Mixture Control Solenoid, Renew		
Does not include system performance check.		
1983-87-2 bbl	(1.1)	1.4
4 bbl	(1.2)	1.5
(P) Prom, Renew		
Does not include system performance check. Includes: R&R electronic control module.		
1983-87	(.6)	.8
(P) Manifold Absolute Pressure Sensor, Renew		
Does not include system performance check.		
1983-87	(.5)	.6
(P) Throttle Position Sensor, Adjust		
All models		
2 bbl		.9
4 bbl		.8
Perform C.C.C. system check add		1.0
(P) Manifold Temperature Sensor, Renew		
Does not include system performance check.		
1983-87		
V-6	(.4)	.6
V-8	(1.8)	2.6
(P) Manifold Differential Pressure Sensor, Renew		
Does not include system performance check.		
1983-87	(.5)	.7
(P) Barometric Sensor, Renew		
Does not include system performance check.		
1983-87	(.5)	.7
(P) Metering Valve Sensor, Renew		
Does not include system performance check.		
1983-87		
V-6	(.4)	.6
V-8	(1.5)	1.9
(P) Calpak, Renew		
Does not include system performance check.		
1983-87	(.6)	.8
(P) Canister Purge Control Valve, Renew		
Does not include system performance check.		
1983-87	(.4)	.6

LABOR 3A EMISSION CONTROLS 3A LABOR

(Factory Time) Chilton Time

(P) Vacuum Control Purge Solenoid, Renew
Does not include system performance check.
1983-87 (.3) 6

(P) Coolant Temperature Sensor, Renew
Does not include system performance check.
Includes: Drain and refill cooling system.
1983-87 (.5) 6

(P) Oxygen Sensor, Renew
Does not include system performance check.
1983-87 (.5) 7

(P) Throttle Position Sensor, Renew
Does not include system performance check.
1983-87-2 bbl (1.1) 1.4
4 bbl (1.2) 1.5

(P) Air Control Valve, Renew
Does not include system performance check.
1983-87 (.4) 6

(P) Air Control/Air Switching Valve, Renew
Does not include system performance check.
1983-87 (.4) 6

(P) E.G.R. Vacuum Control Solenoid, Renew
Does not include system performance check.
1983-87 (.4) 7

(P) Vehicle Speed Sensor, Renew
Does not include system performance check.
1983-87 (.9) 1.3

(P) E.G.R. Bleed Control Solenoid, Renew
Does not include system performance check.
1983-87 (.4) 6

(P) Air Control Valve Relay, Renew
Does not include system performance check.
1983-87 (.4) 5

(P) Air Switching Valve Relay, Renew
Does not include system performance check.
1983-87 (.3) 4

(P) E.G.R. Bleed Control Relay, Renew
Does not include system performance check.
1983-87 (.4) 5

(P) Back-Up Lamp and Park/Neutral Switch, Renew
Does not include system performance test.
1983-87 (.5) 7

(P) EGR/EFE Relay, Renew
Does not include system performance test.
1983-87 (.3) 4

(P) EGR/EFE Purge Solenoid, Renew
Does not include system performance check.
1983-87 (.4) 6

(P) E.G.R. Sensor, Renew
Does not include system performance check.
1985-87 (1.7) 2.4

(P) Idle Speed Control Motor, Renew or Adjust
Does not include system performance check.
1983-87 (.5) 7

(P) Tachometer Filter, Renew
Does not include system performance check.
1983-87 (.3) 3

(P) Computer Command Control System Performance Check
1983-87 (.5) 1.0

THROTTLE BODY INJECTION

(P) Electronic Control Module, Renew
1983-87 (.7) 9

(P) Prom, Renew
1983-87 (.6) 1.0

(P) Coolant Temperature Sensor, Renew
1983-87 (.4) 7

(P) Manifold Pressure Sensor, Renew
1983-87 (.5) 6

(P) Oxygen Sensor, Renew
1983-87 (.6) 1.0

(P) Vehicle Speed Sensor, Renew
1983-87 (.8) 1.1

(P) Throttle Position Sensor, Renew
1983-87 (.6) 1.4

PARTS 3A EMISSION CONTROLS 3A PARTS

POSITIVE CRANKCASE VENTILATION

	Part No.	Price
Positive Crankcase Vent. Valve		
4-151		
1983-84	◆25041498	7.00
1985-87	◆25043669	6.25
V-6-173		
1983-84	◆8995284	5.00
1985-87	◆25043843	3.25
V-8-305		
1983-87	◆6487779	2.50

EVAPORATIVE EMISSION TYPE

	Part No.	Price
Vapor Canister		
4-151		
1983	◆17063013	39.00
1984-87	◆17075844	40.00
V-6-173		
1983	◆17075831	64.25
1984	◆17075824	75.50
1985-87	◆17075855	66.00
V-8-305		
1983-wo/E.F.I.	◆17075824	75.50
E.F.I.	◆17075825	46.25
1984-87	◆17075849	34.50
Canister w/Solenoid		
1986-87-V-6	◆17075855	66.00
1985-87-V-8-305F	◆17075852	66.00
1986-87-V-8-350	◆17075852	66.00

CONTROLLED COMBUSTION TYPE

	Part No.	Price
Air Cleaner Vacuum Motor		
4-151		
1983-84	◆25041109	23.25
1985-87	◆25042077	60.75
V-6-173		
1983-87	◆25042362	19.75
V-8		
1983-87-wo/E.F.I.	◆8994262	24.50
E.F.I.	◆6488213	24.75
Air Cleaner Temperature Sensor		
1983-87-exc. below	◆8997787	18.75
Four cyl	◆8997574	18.75
1985-87-V-6	◆25036751	21.00

EXHAUST GAS RECIRCULATION SYSTEM

E.G.R. Valve
Replacement E.G.R. valves must be ordered according to the stamping number on the original valve.

	Part No.	Price
E.G.R. Control Valve Relay Solenoid		
1983-84-V-6	◆1997612	16.50
1985-87-V-6	◆14089438	45.00
1983-85-V-8 exc. below	◆1997631	13.75
1985-87-E.F.I.	◆1997111	15.25

AIR INJECTOR REACTOR TYPE

	Part No.	Price
Air Pump		
1983-84-V-6	◆7836061	139.00
1985-87-V-6	◆7834488	140.00
1983-87-V-8	◆7835396	131.00
Air Injection Control Valve		
V-6-173		
1983-M.T.	◆17072581	56.00
A.T.	◆17071231	99.75
1984	◆17074976	104.25
1985-87	◆17085907	76.50
V-8		
1983	◆17070622	144.00
1984-87-exc. below	◆17075122	105.25
Code F	◆17085715	73.50
1986-87-350	◆17085715	73.50
Deceleration Valve		
1983-84-V-6 eng	◆14054880	17.50

COMPUTER CONTROLLED EMISSION SYSTEM

	Part No.	Price
Controller (E.C.M.) Remanufactured		
4-151		
1983	◆1226100	110.25
1984	◆1226156	110.25
1985-87	◆1226864	110.25
V-6-173 & V-8 Codes H, G		
1983	◆1226025	110.25
1984	◆1226455	110.25
1985-87-exc. V-6	◆1226865	110.00
V-6	◆1226870	110.00

PARTS 3A EMISSION CONTROLS 3A PARTS

	Part No.	Price
V-8-305 E.F.I.		
1983	◆1226026	110.25
1985-87	◆1226870	110.00

Calibrator (Prom)
Order according to the code stamped on the existing calibrator.

	Part No.	Price
Manifold Pressure Sensor (M.A.P.)		
1983-87-w/E.F.I.	◆16017460	N.L.
Manifold Differential Pressure Sensor		
1983-87	◆16006834	62.25
Oxygen Sensor		
1983-87-exc. V-6	◆8990741	28.75
1985-87-V-6	◆8990625	29.00
Coolant Temperature Sensor		
1983-84	◆25036092	22.00
1985-87	◆25036708	12.75
Barometric Pressure Sensor		
1984-87	◆16006833	62.25
E.S.C. Knock Sensor		
1983-87	◆1997562	37.00

LABOR 4 ALTERNATOR AND REGULATOR 4 LABOR

(Factory Time) Chilton Time

(G) Delcotron Circuits, Test
Includes: Test battery, regulator, Delcotron output.

	Chilton Time
All models	.6

(M) Alternator Drive Belt, Renew

	Chilton Time
All models (.2)	.3
w/AIR add (.1)	.1

(G) Delcotron Assembly or Fan Pulley, Renew

	Chilton Time
1983-87-Four (.4)	.7
V-6 & V-8 (.5)	.8

(G) Delcotron, R&R and Recondition
Includes: Complete disassembly, replacement of parts as required, reassemble.

	Chilton Time
1983-87-Four (1.0)	1.7
V-6 & V-8 (1.1)	1.8

(G) Delcotron Front Bearing, Renew
Includes: R&R Delcotron, separate end frames.

	Chilton Time
1983-87-Four (.5)	.9
V-6 & V-8 (.4)	1.0
Renew rear brg add	.2

(G) Delcotron Voltage Regulator, Test and Renew
Includes: R&R, disassemble and reassemble Delcotron.

	Chilton Time
1983-87-Four (.5)	1.1
V-6 & V-8 (.6)	1.2

(G) Voltmeter, Renew

	Chilton Time
1983-84 (.3)	.6
1985-87 (.5)	.9
w/Digital cluster add (.3)	.3

PARTS 4 ALTERNATOR AND REGULATOR 4 PARTS

	Part No.	Price
Delcotron Assembly (New)		
1983-87-42 amp	◆1105360	206.00
66 & 78 amp	◆1100250	225.00
85 amp	◆1105339	326.50
94 amp	◆1105492	228.50
97 & 108 amp.	◆1105481	218.50
(1) Capacitor		
1983-87	◆1978146	4.75
(2) Diode Trio (Negative)		
1983-87	◆1984459	5.00
(3) Rectifier Bridge		
1983-87-exc. below	◆1984454	28.00
70, 85 amp	◆1975313	24.50
94 amp	◆1987061	29.25
108 amp.	◆1985801	29.75
(4) Bearing		
1983-87	◆9436831	5.50
(5) Terminal Pkg.		
1983-87	◆1975471	3.50
(6) Frame (Rear End)		
1983-87-exc. below	◆1984460	47.75
42 amp (1984-87)	◆1974939	24.75
70, 85 amp	◆1975310	31.00
94 amp	◆1987073	28.00
108 amp	◆1985671	21.00
(7) Voltage Regulator		
1983-87	◆1116387	25.00
(8) Brush (w/Holder)		
1983-87-exc. below	◆1984462	9.00
70, 85, 108 amp	◆1975323	10.00
(9) Rotor Assy.		
1983-87-exc. below	◆1985476	72.00
70, 85 amp	◆1975333	65.00
78, 94 amp	◆1984466	77.25
108 amp.	◆1985646	79.25

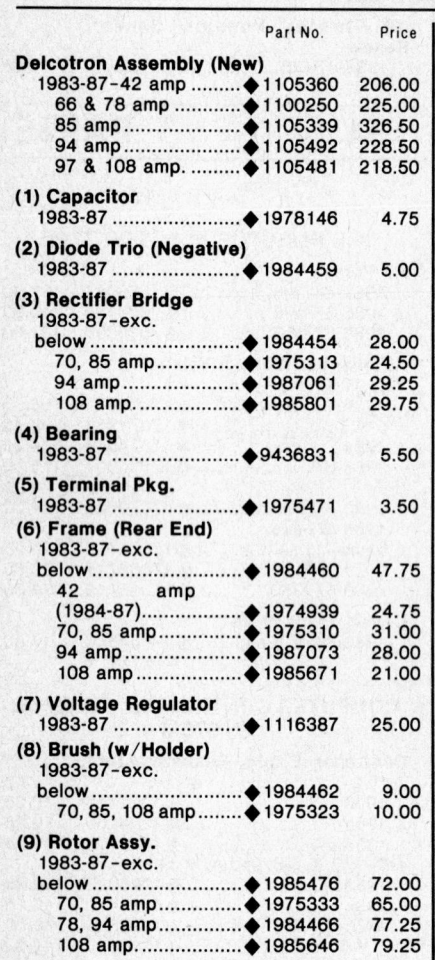

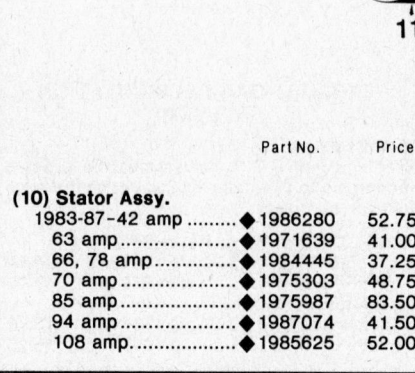

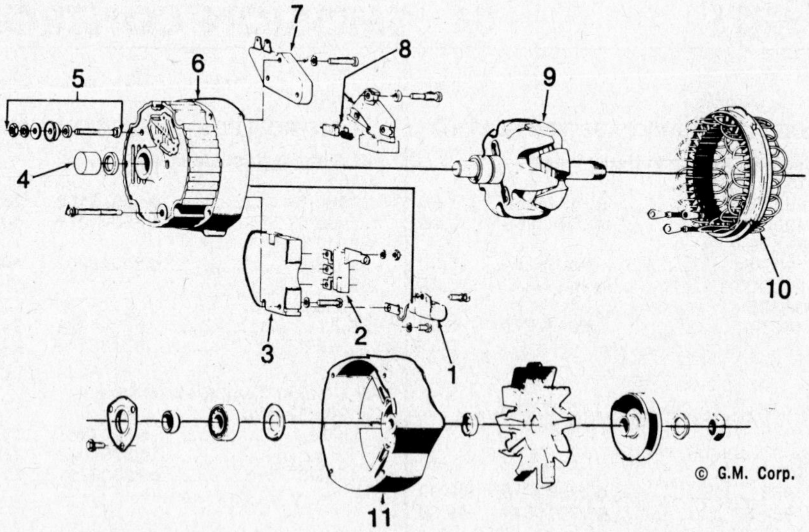

	Part No.	Price
(10) Stator Assy.		
1983-87-42 amp	◆1986280	52.75
63 amp	◆1971639	41.00
66, 78 amp	◆1984445	37.25
70 amp	◆1975303	48.75
85 amp	◆1975987	83.50
94 amp	◆1987074	41.50
108 amp.	◆1985625	52.00
(11) Frame (Drive End)		
1983-87-42 amp	◆1985642	24.75
66, 78 amp	◆1984464	23.50
70, 85 amp	◆1986590	30.00
94 amp	◆1987054	28.00
108 amp.	◆1985669	21.50

LABOR 5 STARTING SYSTEM 5 LABOR

(Factory Time)	Chilton Time
(G) Starter Draw Test (On Car)	
All models	.3
(G) Starter Assy., Renew	
1983-87-Four (.6)	1.1
V-6 & V-8 (.5)	.9
(G) Starter Assy., R&R and Recondition	
Includes: Turn down armature.	
1983-87-Four (1.4)	2.4
V-6 & V-8 (1.5)	1.9
Renew field coils add (.2)	.5
Add draw test if performed.	

(Factory Time)	Chilton Time
(G) Starter Drive, Renew	
Includes: R&R starter.	
1983-87-Four (1.0)	1.3
V-6 & V-8 (.8)	1.1
(G) Starter Solenoid, Renew	
Includes: R&R starter.	
1983-87-Four (.8)	1.2
V-6 & V-8 (.6)	.9
(G) Neutral Safety Switch, Renew	
1983-87-Camaro (.3)	.4
Firebird (.6)	.9

(Factory Time)	Chilton Time
(G) Ignition Switch, Renew	
1983-87 (.8)	1.2
(M) Battery Cables, Renew	
1983-87-positive (.4)	.5
negative (.2)	.3
(M) Battery Terminals, Clean	
All models	.3

PARTS 5 STARTING SYSTEM 5 PARTS

	Part No.	Price
Starter Assembly (New)		
4-151		
1983	◆1109556	N.L.
1984-85	◆1998450	186.00
1986-87	◆1998530	185.75
V-6-173		
1983	◆1109535	209.00
1984-85	◆1998427	185.75
1986-87	◆1998524	187.75
V-8		
1983	◆1109534	219.50
1984-Code H	◆1998430	184.75
Code G	◆1998466	184.75
1985-87-Code H		
M.T.	◆1998466	184.75
A.T.	◆1998435	10.00
1985-87-Code G	◆1998466	184.75
Code G (86-87)	◆1998527	185.75
Code F	◆1998452	212.50
Code F (86-87)	◆1998564	212.50
(1) Drive Housing (w/Bushing)		
4-151		
1983	◆1984734	27.00
1984-87	◆1985148	25.75
V-6-173		
1983	◆1978851	30.25
1984-87	◆1986995	25.00
V-8-305		
1983	◆1978850	27.75
1984-87-exc. below	◆1986096	24.50
1985-87-Code H M.T.	◆1976881	N.L.
1985-87-Code F	◆1976881	N.L.
(2) Drive Assy.		
1983-exc. 4-151	◆1875687	N.L.
4-151	◆1984511	23.50
1984-87-exc. Code H	◆1984511	23.50
Code H	◆1875687	N.L.
(3) Shift Lever		
1983-exc. 4-151	◆1893358	5.50
4-151	◆1984501	5.00
1984	◆1984501	5.00
1985-87	◆1945804	1.50

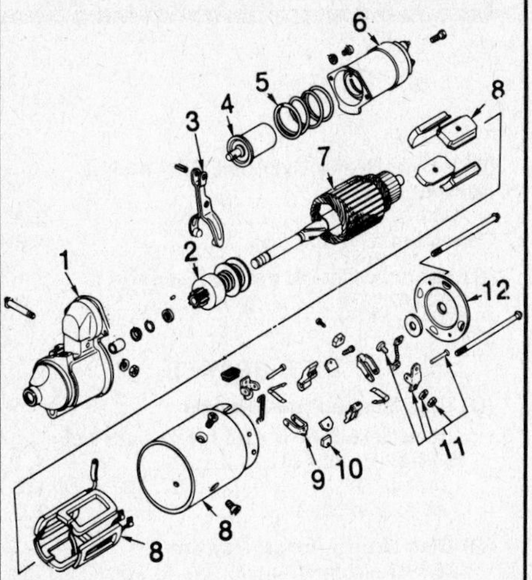

	Part No.	Price
(4) Plunger		
1983-84	◆1987391	6.75
1985-87	◆1987391	6.75
(5) Plunger Spring		
1983-87	◆1978281	1.75
(6) Solenoid Switch		
1983-87	◆1114531	N.L.
(7) Armature		
1983-exc. 4-151	◆1978670	83.50
4-151	◆1984504	107.50
1984-87-exc. below	◆1985138	N.L.
1985-87-Code H A.T.	◆10496043	N.L.
1985-87-Code F	◆1970548	52.00
(8) Frame and Field		
1983-exc. 4-151	◆1978672	78.00
4-151	◆1984522	75.00

	Part No.	Price
1984-exc. Code G	◆1985143	71.50
Code G	◆1987277	71.25
1985-87	◆1987277	71.25
(9) Holder		
1983-87-exc. below	◆1893293	1.25
1984-87-Code H A.T.	◆800091	3.00
1985-Code F	◆1926618	1.50
(10) Brushes		
1983-87-exc. below	◆1893296	.50
1984-87-Code H A.T.	◆1906945	.50
1985-87-Code F	◆1906945	.50
(11) Holder Kit		
1983-87	◆1893929	11.25
(12) Commutator End Frame		
1983-87-exc. below	◆1978292	6.50
1984-87-Code H A.T.	◆1974157	7.00
1985-87-Code F	◆1974157	7.00
Battery Cables (Ground)		
1983-87-25″ long	◆12003646	12.00
30″ Long	◆12011371	15.50
35″ Long	◆12026581	20.75
50″ Long	◆8912120	19.75
Battery Cables (Positive)		
4-151		
1983-87	◆8907031	16.00
V-6 & V-8		
1983-84	◆12007887	14.50
1985-87	◆12026581	20.75
Ignition Switch		
(wo/Tilt wheel)		
1983	◆1990109	N.L.
1984-87-M.T.	◆1990115	11.50
A.T.	◆7843497	25.75
(Tilt wheel)		
1983	◆1990110	N.L.
1984-87-M.T.	◆1990116	11.50
A.T.	◆7843451	25.75

LABOR 6 BRAKE SYSTEM 6 LABOR

(Factory Time)	Chilton Time
(G) Brake Pedal Free Play, Adjust	
All models (.2)	.3

(Factory Time)	Chilton Time
(G) Brakes, Adjust (Minor)	
Includes: R&R wheels and adjust brakes thru access holes in drums. Fill master cylinder.	
two wheels	.4
Remove knock out plugs add, each	.1

(Factory Time)	Chilton Time
(G) Bleed Brakes (Four Wheels)	
Includes: Fill master cylinder.	
All models (.4)	.5

LABOR 6 BRAKE SYSTEM 6 LABOR

(Factory Time) Chilton Time

(G) Free-Up or Renew Brake Self Adjusting Units
one wheel 6
each adtnl 4

(G) Brake Shoes and/or Pads, Renew
Includes: Install new or exchange shoes or pads, adjust service and hand brake. Bleed system.
1983-87-front-disc (.9) 1.1
rear-drum (.9) 1.5
all four wheels 2.5
Resurface disc rotor add-each 9
Resurface brake drum add-each 5

(G) Brake Drum, Renew (One)
1983-87 (.3) 5

(G) Brake Combination Valve, Renew
Includes: Bleed system.
1983-87 (.7) 1.0

BRAKE HYDRAULIC SYSTEM

(G) Wheel Cylinder, Renew
Includes: Bleed system.
1983-87-one (.8) 1.0
both (1.1) 1.9

(G) Wheel Cylinder, R&R and Rebuild
Includes: Hone cylinder and bleed system.
1983-87-one (1.0) 1.3
both (1.5) 2.1

(G) Brake Hose, Renew
Includes: Bleed system.
1983-87-front-one (.4) 6
rear-one (.5) 7

(G) Master Cylinder, Renew
Includes: Bleed complete system.
1983-87 (.6) 8

(G) Master Cylinder, R&R and Rebuild
Includes: Bleed complete system.
1983-87 (1.4) 1.8

(G) Brake System, Flush and Refill
All models 1.2

POWER BRAKES

(G) Power Brake Cylinder, Renew
1983-87 (.8) 1.2

COMBINATIONS

Add to Brakes, Renew
See Machine Shop Operations

(Factory Time) Chilton Time

(G) RENEW WHEEL CYLINDER
Each (.2) 2

(G) REBUILD WHEEL CYLINDER
Each (.3) 3

(G) REBUILD CALIPER ASSEMBLY
Each (.5) 6

(G) RENEW MASTER CYLINDER
All models (.5) 8

(G) REBUILD MASTER CYLINDER
All models (.8) 1.0

(G) RENEW BRAKE HOSE
Each (.3) 3

(G) RENEW REAR AXLE GREASE SEAL
One side 5

(G) REPACK FRONT WHEEL BEARINGS (BOTH WHEELS)
All models 6

(G) RENEW BRAKE DRUM
Each 1

(G) RENEW DISC BRAKE ROTOR
Each 3

(Factory Time) Chilton Time

(G) Power Brake Cylinder, R&R and Recondition
1983-87 (1.5) 2.3
Recond m/Cyl add (.8) 8

(G) Vacuum Check Valve, Renew
1983-87 (.3) 3

DISC BRAKES

(G) Disc Brake Pads, Renew
Includes: Install new disc brake pads only.
1983-87-front (.9) 1.1
rear (1.0) 1.2
all four wheels 2.0

(G) Disc Brake Rotor, Renew
1983-87-front-one (.7) 1.0
both (1.2) 1.5
rear-one (.6) 9
both (.9) 1.4
all four wheels 2.7

(G) Caliper Assembly, Renew
Includes: Bleed complete system.
1983-87-front-one (.7) 1.0
both (1.1) 1.5
rear-one (.7) 1.0
both (1.2) 1.6
all four wheels 2.9

(Factory Time) Chilton Time

(G) Caliper Assy., R&R and Rebuild
Includes: Bleed complete system.
1983-87-front-one (1.2) 1.5
both (2.1) 2.5
rear-one (1.2) 1.6
both (2.2) 2.8
all four wheels 4.9

PARKING BRAKE

(M) Parking Brake, Adjust
All models (.3) 5

(G) Parking Brake Lamp Switch, Renew
1983-87
Camaro (.3) 4
Firebird (.6) 8

(G) Parking Brake Control, Renew
1983-87 (.8) 1.1

(G) Parking Brake Equalizer, Renew
1983-87 (.3) 5

(G) Parking Brake Cables, Renew
1983-87
front (.9) 1.2
rear-each (.5) 7
one piece (.7) 1.1
two piece (.7) 1.1

PARTS 6 BRAKE SYSTEM 6 PARTS

	Part No.	Price
Brake Shoe Set (Rear)		
1983-87-exc. Rr. Disc	◆12300219	41.00
Rr. Disc	◆12300230	43.00
Rear Wheel Cylinder Assy.		
1983-87-exc. below	◆18007980	22.50
1984-87-w/ metric pipe threads	◆18011143	24.25
Wheel Cylinder Repair Kit (Rear)		
1983-87	◆18003744	12.75
Rear Wheel Caliper Assy.		
1983-84	◆18010376	290.50
1985-87	◆18012412	334.00
Rear Wheel Caliper Repair Kit		
1983-87	◆18010453	19.75

	Part No.	Price
Front Brake Hose		
1983-right	◆9767072	18.00
left	◆9767071	18.00
1984-87-right	◆17980324	18.00
left	◆17980323	18.00
Rear Brake Hose		
(wo/Rear disc brakes)		
1983	◆9769738	16.75
1984-87	◆17980325	16.00
(Rear disc brakes)		
1983	◆17980428	16.75
1984-87	◆17980326	10.50
Master Cylinder Assy.		
(wo/Rear disc brakes)		
1983	◆18013414	171.25
1984-87	◆1813427	N.L.

	Part No.	Price
(Rear disc brakes)		
1983	◆18009370	165.00
1984-87	◆18013428	168.50
Master Cylinder Repair Kit		
1983-87-exc. Rr. Disc	◆18009374	21.00
Rr. Disc	◆18009364	20.50
Brake Drum (Rear)		
1983-87-Cast Iron	◆1249146	73.00
Aluminum	◆1255496	90.00
Rear Disc		
1983-87	◆14026865	60.50
Oil Seal (Front)		
1983-87	◆3965092	3.00
Power Brake Booster (Vacuum)		
1983-87	◆18010911	250.25

PARTS 6 BRAKE SYSTEM 6 PARTS

	Part No.	Price
Power Brake Booster Repair Kit		
1983-87	◆18009415	47.50
Parking Brake Apply Lever		
1983-87-exc. Rr. Disc	◆14065767	23.00
w/Rr. Disc	◆14065768	23.00
Front Cable (Parking Brake)		
1983-87	◆14073081	9.75

	Part No.	Price
Rear Cable (Parking Brake)		
(wo/Rear disc brakes)		
1983-left	◆14073078	14.50
right	◆14073077	14.50
1984-85-left	◆14073077	14.50
right	◆14073066	14.50
1986-87-left	◆14094397	14.50
right	◆14094398	14.50
(w/Rear disc brakes)		
1983-87-left	◆14077717	14.50
right	◆14073068	14.50

PARTS 6 DISC BRAKES 6 PARTS

	Part No.	Price
(1) Brake Pad Set		
1983-84	◆12300223	47.00
1985-87	◆12300255	36.00
(2) Piston Assy.		
1983-87	◆18003155	11.00
(3) Anti Rattle Spring Kit		
1983-87	◆18006810	3.00
(4) Caliper Repair Kit		
1983-87	◆18003724	8.75

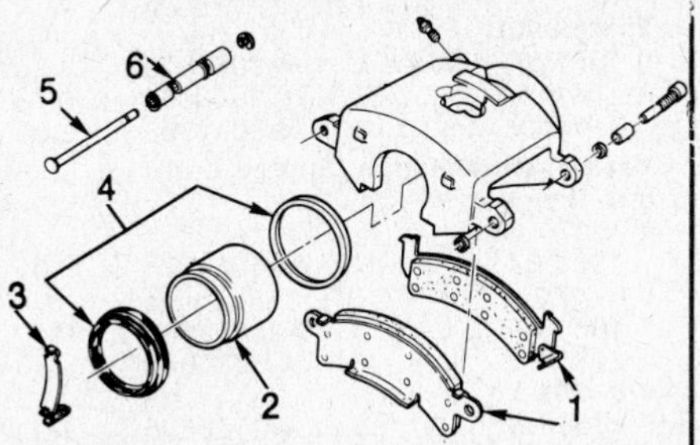

	Part No.	Price
(5) Bolt		
1983-87	◆5468226	9.00
(6) Sleeve		
1983-87	◆18004057	1.50
Caliper Assy.		
1983-87-right	◆18010481	148.75
left	◆18010480	137.00
Rotor (w/Hub)		
1983-87	◆14032431	100.25

LABOR 7 COOLING SYSTEM 7 LABOR

(Factory Time)	Chilton Time
(M) Winterize Cooling System	
Includes: Run engine to check for leaks, tighten all hose connections. Test radiator and pressure cap, drain radiator and engine block. Add anti-freeze and refill system.	
All models	.5
(M) Thermostat, Renew	
1983-87-Four (.5)	.6
V-6 (.3)	.4
V-8 (.6)	.7
(M) Radiator Assembly, R&R or Renew	
Includes: Drain and refill cooling system.	
1983-87 (.4)	.8
w/A.C. add (.2)	.2

ADD THESE OPERATIONS TO RADIATOR R&R

(G) Boil & Repair	1.5
(G) Rod Clean	1.9
(G) Repair Core	1.3
(G) Renew Tank	1.6
(G) Renew Trans. Oil Cooler	1.9
(G) Recore Radiator	1.7
(M) Radiator Hoses, Renew	
1983-87-upper (.3)	.4
lower (.4)	.5
both (.5)	.7
(G) Water Pump, Renew	
1983-87	
Four (1.0)	1.4
w/A.C. add (.5)	.5
V-6-V-8-w/Carb (1.3)	2.0
V-6-w/Fuel inj (.6)	1.0
V-8-w/Fuel inj (1.0)	1.5
w/A.C. add (.3)	.3

COOLING SYSTEM TUNE-UP

An Annual Cooling System Tune-Up Suggestion List should include (with some exceptions):

1. A visual check of the cooling system for indications of leaks or excessive oil content.
2. Pressure check the cooling system for internal and external leaks with filler cap and neck adapter and tester.
3. Check crankcase and automatic transmission oil for water content.
4. Test coolant thermostat with radiator thermometer.
5. Check temperature gauge for accuracy.
6. Drain system and flush till clean.
7. Clean foreign matter from radiator fins.
8. Test radiator pressure cap with cap tester.
9. Check fan blades and pulleys for alignment and damage.
10. Internal and external inspection of all hoses for cracks and deterioration.
11. Check core plugs (where possible) for seepage.
12. Refill system with correct coolant and check for air locks.
13. Check condition and tension of drive belts with tension gauge.

All models 1.5

(Factory Time)	Chilton Time
(M) Drive Belt, Renew	
All models-one (.3)	.4
each adtnl	.1
(M) Drive Belt, Adjust	
All models-one (.2)	.3
each adtnl	.1
(M) Fan Blade or Clutch Fan, Renew	
1983-87 (.3)	.5
(G) Thermostat By-Pass Hose or Pipe, Renew	
1983-87 (.5)	.7
(G) Engine Coolant Fan and/or Motor, Renew	
1983-87 (.5)	.7
(G) Engine Coolant Fan Relay, Renew	
1983-87 (.3)	.4
(G) Coolant Fan Switch, Renew	
1983-87 (.3)	.4
(G) Temperature Gauge (Engine Unit), Renew	
1983-87 (.4)	.5
(G) Temperature Gauge (Dash Unit), Renew	
1983-84 (.3)	.6
1985-87 (.5)	.9
w/Digital cluster add (.3)	.3
(G) Water Jacket Expansion Plugs, Renew (Side of Block)	
All models (.5)	.5
Add time to gain access.	
(G) Heater Blower Motor Switch Assy., Renew	
1983-87 (.4)	.6

LABOR 7 COOLING SYSTEM 7 LABOR

(Factory Time) Chilton Time

(G) Heater Control Assembly, Renew
1983-87 (.3) 6

(G) Heater Blower Motor Resistor, Renew
1983-87 (.2) 3

(G) Heater Blower Motor, Renew
1983-87 (.5) 7

(G) Heater Blower Motor Relay, Renew
1983-87 (.2) 3

(G) Heater Core, R&R or Renew
1983-87-wo/A.C. (.9) 1.7
w/A.C. (.9) 1.7
Add time to recharge A.C. system if required.

ADD THESE OPERATIONS TO HEATER CORE R&R
(G) Boil & Repair 1.2
(G) Repair Core 9
(G) Recore 1.2

(G) Heater Hoses, Renew
1983-87-one (.2) 3
both (.4) 5

PARTS 7 COOLING SYSTEM 7 PARTS

	Part No.	Price
Radiator Assy. Accurate replacement of the radiator can be done only by using the radiator code stamped on a metal tag located on the original radiator. Order by year, model and radiator code no.		
Radiator Hoses Order by year and model.		
Water Pump Assy.		
4-151		
1983-84	◆361054	49.75
1985-87	◆10032022	59.50
V-6-173		
1983-84	◆14054539	N.L.
1985	◆14033483	61.50
1986-87	◆14101304	N.L.
V-8-305		
1983-84	◆474029	72.50
1985-87	◆14085847	75.75
Thermostat		
1983-87-4-151	◆3050922	7.50
V-6	◆3043066	6.75
V-8	◆3041390	5.00
Temperature Gauge (Engine Unit)		
(wo/Gauges)		
4-151		
1983-87	◆25036371	8.00
V-6-173		
1983-84	◆25036535	10.50
1985-87	◆25036647	14.50
V-8-305		
1983-85	◆2503535	N.L.
(Gauges)		
1983-87-exc. V-6	◆8993146	19.25
1985-87-V-6	◆25036649	25.00
Temperature Gauge (Dash Unit)		
(Camaro)		
1983-87-exc. below	◆25034041	25.50
Berlinetta	◆25052905	49.50
(Firebird)		
1983	◆25052819	52.00
1984	◆25076141	57.75
1985-87	◆25078649	37.00
Heater Core Assy.		
1983-87	◆3048945	61.00
Blower Motor		
(wo/A.C.)		
1983-87	◆22048572	47.50
(A.C.)		
1983-87	◆22021790	59.25
Blower Motor Resistor		
(wo/A.C.)		
1983	◆3923052	N.L.
1984-87	◆14052305	2.00
(A.C.)		
1983-84	◆526897	4.50
1985-87	◆10039426	4.50

LABOR 8 EXHAUST SYSTEM 8 LABOR

(Factory Time) Chilton Time

(G) Muffler, Renew
1983-87 (.5) 1.0

(G) Tail Pipe, Renew
1983 (.4) 6

(G) Resonator and Tail Pipe Assy., Renew
1983-87 (.8) 1.2

(G) Catalytic Converter, Renew
1983-87 (.5) 8

(G) Front Exhaust Pipe, Renew (To Converter)
1983-87 (.4) 7

(G) Exhaust Pipe Seal, Renew
1983-87-one (.4) 6

(G) Exhaust Crossover Pipe, Renew
1983-87 (.4) 9

(G) Intermediate Exhaust Pipe, Renew
1983-87 (.4) 7

(G) E.F.E. Valve (Heat Riser), Renew
1983-87 (.6) 1.0

(G) Exhaust Manifold, Renew
Four-1983-87 (.7) 1.2
V-6-1983-84-each (.6) 1.0
1984-87-each (1.0) 1.5
V-8-1983-84
right (1.5) 2.2
left (1.0) 1.6
1985-87
right (1.3) 2.0
left (1.0) *1.6
*w/Port inj add (.2) 2
w/A.C. add (.4) 4
w/C.C.C. add (.4) 4

COMBINATIONS

(G) Muffler, Exhaust and Tail Pipe, Renew
All models 1.2

(G) Muffler and Tail Pipe, Renew
All models 8

PARTS 8 EXHAUST SYSTEM 8 PARTS

Part numbers shown are for pricing reference only. Order part with complete year, model and engine information.

	Part No.	Price
Muffler (w/Tail Pipe) Order by year and model.		
Resonator (w/Tail Pipe)		
V-6-173		
1983	◆10026361	95.25
V-8		
1983-87	◆14042001	225.00
Front Pipe		
4-151		
1983	◆10025690	41.75
1984-87	◆10028726	31.25
Intermediate Pipe		
4-151		
1983-std. exh.	◆14019306	41.75
light wt. exh	◆10021729	41.75
1984-87-std. exh.	◆10030831	38.50
light wt. exh.	◆10030825	75.00
V-6-173		
1983-exc. below	◆14019306	41.75
1983-closed loop	◆14077742	42.00
1984	◆14077742	42.00
1985-87	◆14080788	32.25
V-8-Code H		
1983-87-sngl. exh.	◆14063509	41.75
dual exh.	◆14019311	56.50

PARTS 8 EXHAUST SYSTEM 8 PARTS

	Part No.	Price
V-8 E.F.I.		
1983-sngl. exh.	◆14086840	81.00
dual exh.	◆14019311	56.50
1985-87-Code S	◆14082817	N.L.
V-8–Code G		
1984-87	◆14082817	N.L.
Crossover Pipe		
V-6		
1983-84	◆14041882	89.50
1985-87	◆14080718	95.25
V-8 Code H		
1983-87	◆14059950	83.50
V-8 E.F.I.		
1983	◆14058550	104.00
1985-87-Code F	◆14065746	239.00
V-8 Code G		
1984-87	◆14065746	239.00

	Part No.	Price
Catalytic Converter		
4-151		
1983	◆25056056	263.25
1984-87	◆25056597	276.25
V-6–173		
1983-84	◆25056310	311.25
1985-87	◆25056736	316.00
V-8 Code H		
1983	◆25056381	320.25
1984-87	◆25056382	300.25
V-8 E.F.I.		
1983	◆25056380	311.25
1985-87-Code F	◆25056539	342.00
V-8–Code G		
1984-87	◆25056539	342.00

	Part No.	Price
Exhaust Manifold		
4-151		
1983-84	◆10028204	80.00
1985-87	◆10037596	70.75
V-6–173		
1983-84-R.H.	◆14033087	97.50
L.H. (1983-84)	◆14059321	94.75
1985-87-R.H.	◆14089876	97.50
L.H.	◆14059321	94.75
V-8 Code H, S		
1983-87-R.H.	◆14031361	101.00
L.H.	◆14043373	80.25
V-8 Code G, F & 7		
1984-87-R.H.	◆14071200	101.00
L.H.	◆14075611	97.50

LABOR 9 FRONT SUSPENSION 9 LABOR

Note: On all front suspension operations alignment charges must be added if performed. Time given does not include alignment.

	(Factory Time)	Chilton Time
(G) Wheel, Renew		
one	(.5)	.5
(G) Wheels, Rotate (All)		
All models		.5
(G) Wheels, Balance		
one		.3
each adtnl		.2
(G) Check Alignment of Front End		
All models		.5
Note: Deduct if alignment is performed.		
(G) Toe-In, Adjust		
All models	(.4)	.6
(G) Align Front End		
Includes: Adjust front wheel bearings.		
All models	(.7)	1.4
w/A.C. interference add		.5
(G) Front Wheel Bearings, Clean and Repack (Both Wheels)		
All models	(1.1)	1.6
(G) Front Wheel Bearings and Cups, Renew		
1983-87-one whl	(.7)	.9
both whls	(1.1)	1.5
(G) Front Wheel Grease Seals, Renew		
1983-87-one whl	(.7)	.8
both whls	(1.1)	1.2
(G) Lower Ball Joint, Renew		
Add alignment charges.		
1983-87-one	(.6)	.9
both	(1.0)	1.6
(G) Steering Knuckle Assy., Renew		
Add alignment charges.		
1983-87-one	(1.2)	1.6
both	(2.2)	3.0
(G) Lower Control Arm, Renew		
Add alignment charges.		
1983-87	(1.0)	1.5
both	(1.8)	2.8
(G) Lower Control Arm Shaft or Bushings, Renew		
Add alignment charges.		
1983-87-one	(1.2)	1.8
both	(2.2)	3.4
(G) Front Shock Absorber Strut, R&R or Renew		
Add alignment charges if necessary.		
1983-87-one	(.7)	1.1
both	(1.2)	2.0
(G) Front Spring Seat or Insulator, Renew		
Add alignment charges if necessary.		
1983-87-one	(.8)	1.2
both	(1.4)	2.1
(G) Front Spring, Renew		
Add alignment charges if necessary.		
1983-87-one	(.8)	1.2
both	(1.4)	2.1
(G) Front Strut Bearing Mount Assy., Renew		
Add alignment charges if necessary.		
1983-87-one	(.4)	.6
both	(.7)	1.1
(G) Front Stabilizer Shaft, Renew		
1983-87	(.5)	.8
(G) Stabilizer Link Bushings, Renew		
1983-87	(.4)	.6

PARTS 9 FRONT SUSPENSION 9 PARTS

	Part No.	Price
(1) Front Wheel Bearing (Outer)		
1983-87	◆14045734	N.L.
(2) Front Wheel Bearing (Inner)		
1983-87	◆7450630	11.00
(3) Front Wheel Bearing Seal (Inner)		
1983-87	◆3965092	3.50
(4) Steering Knuckle		
1983-87-right	◆14021196	148.00
left	◆14021195	148.00
(5) Shock Absorber (w/Strut)		
1983-87-exc.		
H.D.	◆22035663	81.00
H.D. susp.	◆22035664	81.00
(6) Mount Assy.		
1983-right	◆14080730	49.25
left	◆14080729	49.25
1984-87-right	◆14080730	49.25
left	◆14080729	49.25

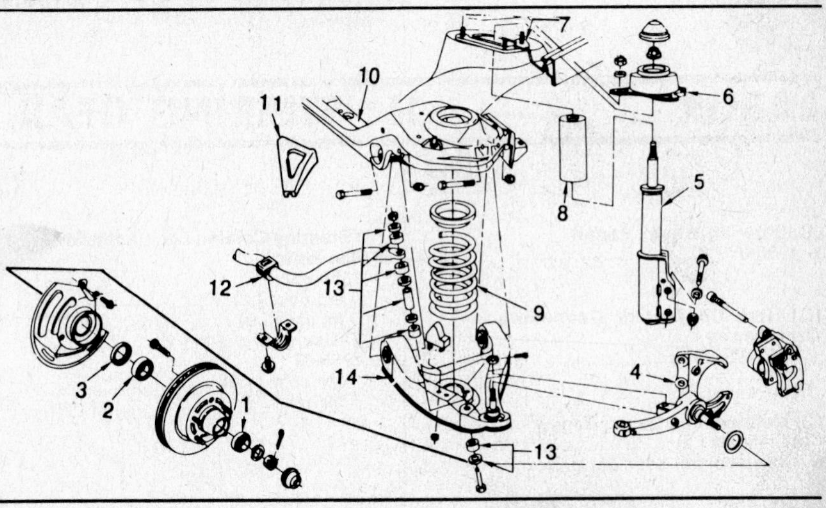

PARTS 9 FRONT SUSPENSION 9 PARTS

	Part No.	Price
(7) Retainer		
1983-87-right	◆14038400	2.50
left	◆14038399	2.50
(8) Shield (Front Strut)		
1983-87	◆14019320	5.25
(9) Coil Spring		
Order by year and model.		
(10) Front Crossmember		
1983-85	◆14082853	545.00
1986-87	◆14089433	545.00
(11) Brace (Front Crossmember)		
1983-87-right	◆14019454	5.50
left	◆14019453	5.50
(12) Insulator (Stabilizer)		
1983-87-exc. below	◆473743	2.00
Z28, Trans-Am	◆14047918	2.00
H.D. susp	◆472117	2.00
(13) Grommet Kit		
1983-87	◆6270704	1.00
(14) Lower Control Arm		
1983-right	◆14083562	105.00
left	◆14083561	105.00
(wo/Touring suspension)		
1984-87-right	◆14083562	105.00
left	◆14083561	105.00
(Touring suspension)		
1985-87-right	◆14091389	105.00
left	◆14091390	105.00

LABOR 10 STEERING LINKAGE 10 LABOR

	(Factory Time)	Chilton Time
(G) Idler Arm, Adjust		
1983-87	(.3)	.5
(G) Idler Arm, Renew		
1983-87	(.6)	.9
(G) Tie Rod or Tie Rod End, Renew		
Includes: Reset toe-in.		
1983-87-one side	(.7)	1.0
both sides	(1.0)	1.4
(G) Inner Tie Rods, Renew		
Includes: Reset toe-in.		
1983-87-one side	(.7)	1.0
both sides	(.8)	1.2
(G) Pitman Arm, Renew		
1983-87	(.4)	.6
(G) Steering Intermediate Rod, Renew		
Includes: Reset toe-in.		
1983-87	(1.0)	1.4

PARTS 10 STEERING LINKAGE 10 PARTS

	Part No.	Price
(1) Tie Rod Assy. (Outer)		
1983-87	◆7837614	33.00
(2) Clamp Kit		
1983-87	◆7829467	6.75
(3) Pitman Arm Kit		
1983-exc. H.D.	◆7837631	48.50
H.D. susp	◆7837632	48.50
1984-87	◆7837632	48.50
(4) Rod Kit (Steering Relay)		
1983-87-exc. H.D.	◆7837597	77.25
H.D. susp	◆7837596	77.25
(5) Idler Arm Kit		
1983-87	◆7837595	49.25

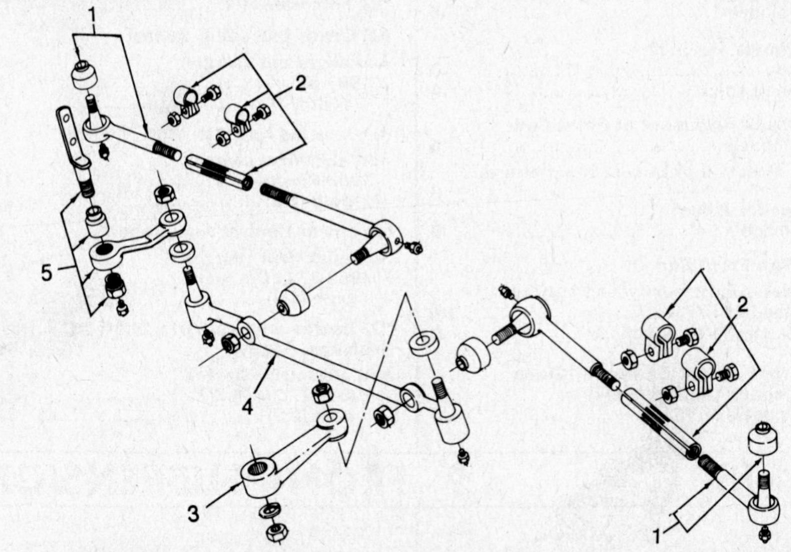

LABOR 11 STEERING GEAR 11 LABOR

	(Factory Time)	Chilton Time
(G) Steering Wheel, Renew		
1983-87	(.3)	.4
(G) Horn Contact or Cancelling Cam, Renew		
1983-87	(.5)	.7
(G) Multifunction Lever, Renew		
All models	(.2)	.4
w/Cruise control add	(.5)	.5
(G) Steering Column Lock Actuator Parts, Renew		
1983-85		
std colm	(.8)	1.3
tilt colm	(.9)	1.4
w/Cruise control add	(.2)	.2
1986-87		
std colm	(1.0)	1.5
tilt colm	(.8)	1.3
(G) Upper Mast Jacket Bearing, Renew		
1983-85-std colm	(.8)	1.4
tilt colm	(.9)	1.6
w/Cruise control add	(.2)	.2
w/Digital cluster add	(.3)	.3
1986-87		
std colm	(.8)	1.4
tilt colm	(.5)	.9
w/Digital cluster add	(.3)	.3
(G) Steering Intermediate Shaft, Renew		
1983-87	(.7)	1.2

LABOR 11 STEERING GEAR 11 LABOR

(Factory Time)	Chilton Time
(G) Steering Lower Coupling Shaft (Pot Joint), Renew	
1983-87 (.7)	1.1
w/Digital cluster add (.3)	.3
(G) Steering Flex Coupling (Rag Joint), Renew	
1983-87 (.7)	.9
(G) Pitman Shaft Oil Seal, Renew	
1983-87 (.6)	1.0

POWER STEERING

(Factory Time)	Chilton Time
(G) Power Steering Gear, Adjust	
All models (.7)	1.2
(M) Pump Drive Belt, Renew	
All models (.3)	.4
w/AIR add (.1)	.1
w/A.C. add (.1)	.1
(G) Power Steering Gear Assy., Renew	
1983-87 (.9)	1.2
(P) Power Steering Gear Assy., R&R and Recondition	
Includes: Disassemble, renew parts as required, reassemble and adjust.	
1983-87 (1.9)	2.5
(G) Valve Body, Recondition	
Includes: R&R gear assy.	
1983-87 (1.2)	1.8
(G) Adjustor Plug Assy., Recondition	
Includes: R&R gear assy.	
1983-87 (1.1)	1.6
(G) Steering Gear Housing, Renew	
Includes: R&R gear assy.	
1983-87 (1.3)	1.8
(G) Side Cover Seal, Renew	
Includes: R&R gear assy.	
1983-87 (1.1)	1.4
(G) End Cover Seal, Renew	
Includes: R&R gear assy.	
1983-87 (1.0)	1.4
(G) Power Steering Pump, Renew	
1983-87 (.6)	1.0
w/A.C. add (.3)	.3
(P) Power Steering Pump, R&R and Recondition	
1983-87 (1.1)	1.8
w/A.C. add (.3)	.3
(G) Pump Reservoir and/or 'O' Ring Seals, Renew	
Includes: R&R pump assy.	
1983-87 (.7)	1.2
w/A.C. add (.3)	.3
(G) Pump Flow Control Valve, Renew	
1983-87 (.4)	.8
(G) Power Steering Pump Shaft Oil Seal, Renew	
1983-87 (.7)	1.2
w/A.C. add (.3)	.3
(M) Power Steering Hoses, Renew	
1983-87-each (.3)	.5
w/A.C. add (.3)	.3

PARTS 11 POWER STEERING GEAR 11 PARTS

	Part No.	Price
(1) Seal Kit (Side Cover)		
1983-87	◆7817486	9.00
(2) Gear Kit (Pitman Shaft)		
1983-87-exc.		
Var.	◆7815885	87.50
Variable	◆7813631	87.50
(3) Check Valve Kit		
1983-87	◆7834284	5.25
(4) Bearing Kit		
1983-87	◆7826850	11.00
(5) Housing Assy.		
1983-87-wo/H.D.		
susp.	◆7834137	183.00
H.D. susp	◆7834143	183.00
(6) Bearing (Pitman Shaft)		
1983-87	◆5697804	15.00
(7) Seal Kit (Pitman Shaft)		
1983-87	◆7826470	17.00
(8) Seal (Adjuster Plug)		
1983-87	◆5686527	1.50
(9) Adjuster Plug Kit		
1983-87	◆7832731	53.50
(10) Seal Kit		
1983-87	◆5687182	12.50
(11) Valve Assy.		
1983-87-wo/H.D.		
susp.	◆7832055	202.25
H.D. susp	◆7832057	212.00
(12) Seal Kit (Steering Gear)		
1983-87	◆7817487	11.75
(13) Seal Kit		
1983-87	◆7817485	6.50
(14) Plug		
1983-87	◆7800715	9.50
(15) Seal Kit (End Plug)		
1983-87	◆7817487	11.75

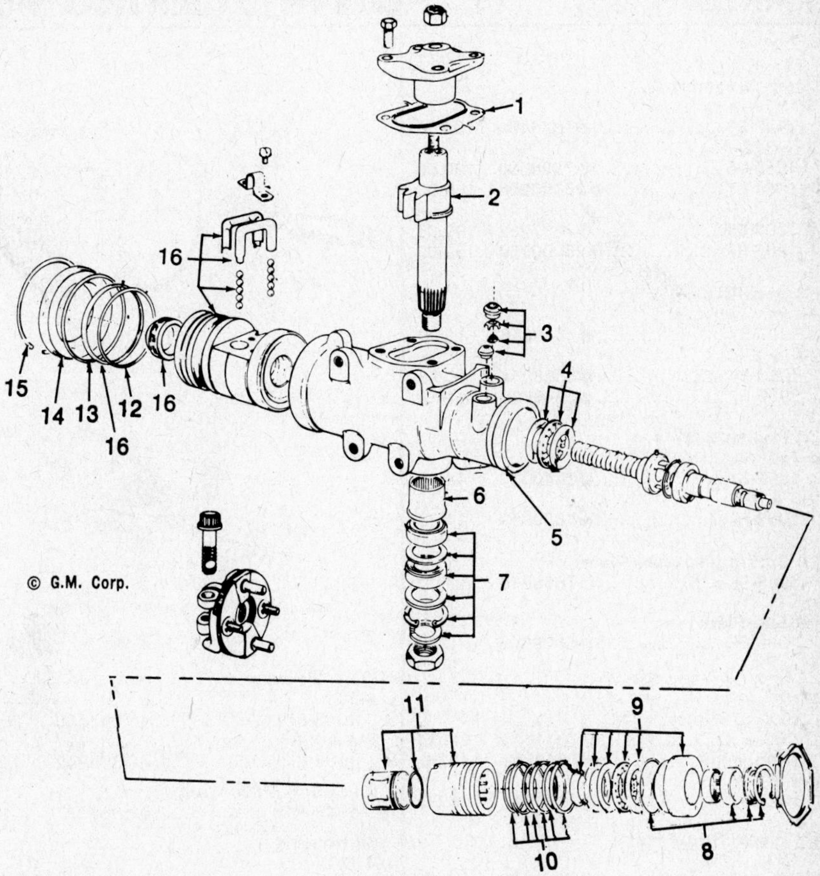

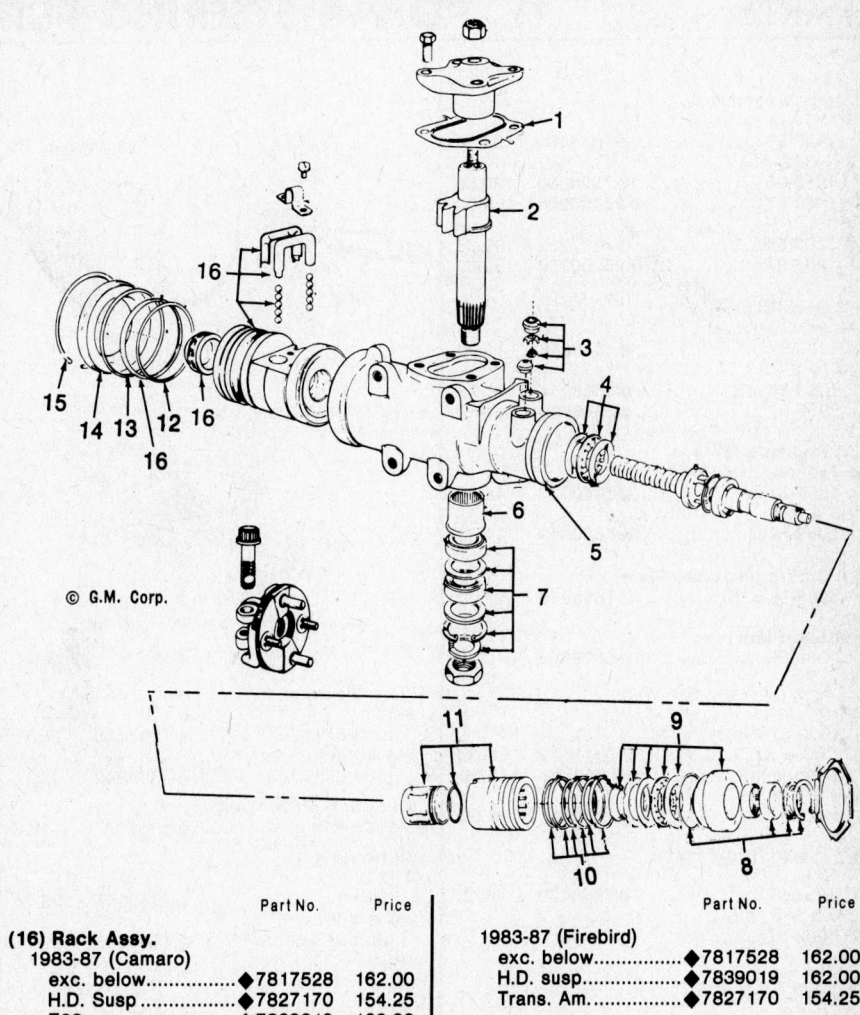

	Part No.	Price
(16) Rack Assy.		
1983-87 (Camaro)		
exc. below	◆7817528	162.00
H.D. Susp	◆7827170	154.25
Z28	◆7839019	162.00
1983-87 (Firebird)		
exc. below	◆7817528	162.00
H.D. susp	◆7839019	162.00
Trans. Am.	◆7827170	154.25

PARTS 11 POWER STEERING GEAR 11 PARTS

The 605 power steering gear is identified by a round side cover held in place by a retaining ring. All others are rectangular and held in place by bolts.

	Part No.	Price
(1) Gear Kit (Pitman Shaft)		
1983	◆7838146	87.50
(2) Seal Kit		
1983	◆7838143	9.25
(3) Connector		
1983	◆7819797	4.50
(4) Housing Assy.		
1983	◆7839238	183.00
(5) Bearing Assy.		
1983	◆7837985	13.50
(6) Bearing Assy. (Pitman Shaft)		
1983	◆7838145	16.25
(7) Seal Kit (Pitman Shaft)		
1983	◆7838143	9.25
(8) Seal Kit (Valve)		
1983	◆7826056	13.50
(9) Valve Assy.		
1983	◆7819796	202.00
(10) Worm Assy.		
1983	◆N.S.	N.S.

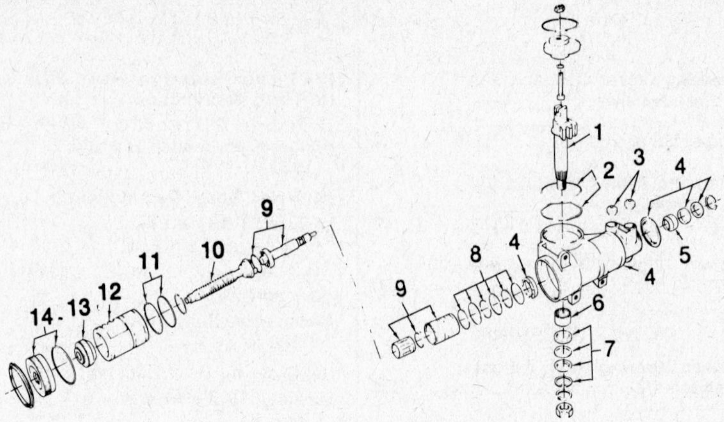

	Part No.	Price
(11) Seal Kit (Rack & Piston)		
1983	◆7819809	5.75
(12) Rack & Piston		
1983	◆7837990	162.00

	Part No.	Price
(13) Bearing Assy. (Lower)		
1983	◆7837985	13.50
(14) Adjuster Plug Kit		
1983	◆7839239	53.50

PARTS 11 POWER STEERING PUMP 11 PARTS

	Part No.	Price
Pump Assembly		
4-151		
1983-87	◆7841464	199.00
V-6–173		
1983-85	◆7838686	199.00
1986-87	◆26000268	199.00
V-8		
1983-85	◆7837232	199.00
1986-87	◆26000269	199.00
(1) Seal Kit		
4-151		
1983-87	◆7840566	11.00
V-6 & V-8		
1983-84	◆5688044	10.75
1985-87	◆7848522	N.L.
(2) Pressure Plate		
4-151		
1983-87	◆7840080	14.25
V-6 & V-8		
1983-87	◆7839669	14.25
(3) Spring (Pressure Plate)		
1983-87	◆7839989	3.00
(4) End Plate		
1983-87	◆5689358	3.50
(5) Rotor & Vane Kit		
4-151		
1983-87 (Rotor kit)	◆7841845	92.00
(Vane kit)	◆7840569	13.50
V-6 & V-8		
1983-87	◆7837322	75.00
(6) Pump Thrust Plate		
4-151		
1983-87	◆7840139	14.25
V-6 & V-8		
1983-87	◆7839366	25.75

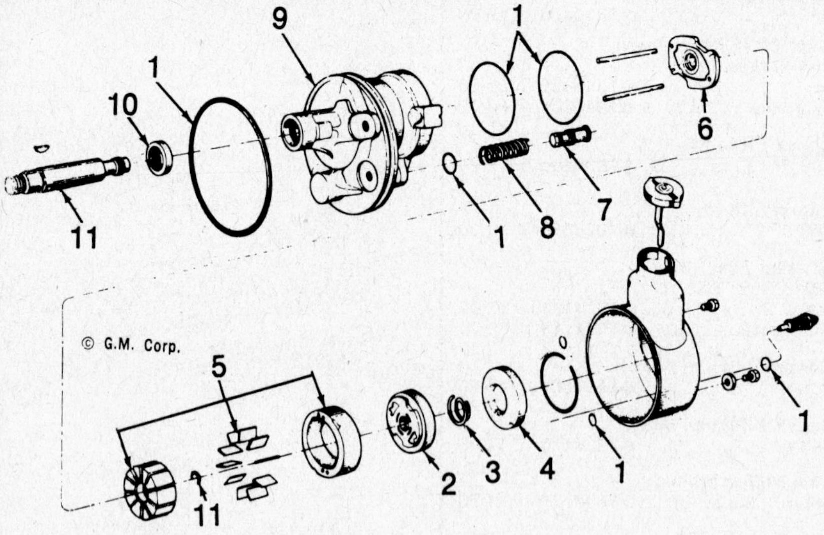

	Part No.	Price
(7) Valve Assy.		
4-151		
1983-87	◆7841855	10.75
V-6 & V-8		
1983-87	◆7809232	10.75
(8) Spring (Flow Control)		
1983-87	◆5688037	1.50
(9) Housing		
4-151		
1983-87	◆7840157	62.75
V-6 & V-8		
1983-87	◆7830236	62.75

	Part No.	Price
(10) Seal (Drive Shaft)		
4-151		
1983-87	◆7839589	4.50
V-6 & V-8		
1983-87	◆7808195	4.50
(11) Drive Shaft		
4-151		
1983-85	◆7840633	58.00
V-6 & V-8		
1983-87	◆7837321	39.50

LABOR 12 CYLINDER HEAD & VALVE SYSTEM 12 LABOR

(Factory Time)	Chilton Time
(G) Compression Test	
Four–1983-87 (.4)	.6
V-6–1983-87 (.5)	.7
V-8–1983-87 (.6)	.8

(G) Cylinder Head Gasket, Renew

Includes: Clean carbon and make all necessary adjustments.

Four–1983-87 (2.2)	3.0
w/A.C. add (.5)	.5
V-6–1983-84	
one side (4.2)	5.9
both sides (5.0)	7.0
1985-87	
one side (5.4)	7.5
both sides (6.4)	8.9
w/A.C. add (.3)	.3
V-8–1983-87	
wo/Port Inj	
right side (5.1)	7.0
left side (3.9)	5.4
both sides (7.3)	10.0
w/Port Inj	
right side (6.9)	9.5
left side (6.2)	8.5
both sides (9.3)	12.8
w/A.C. add (.3)	.3
w/C.C.C. add (.4)	.4

(G) Cylinder Head, Renew

Includes: Transfer all components, reface valves, clean carbon.

Four–1983-87 (3.2)	4.5
w/A.C. add (.5)	.5
V-6–1983-84	
one side (4.9)	6.8
both sides (6.3)	8.8
1985-87	
one side (6.0)	8.3
both sides (7.6)	10.6
w/A.C. add (.3)	.3
V-8–1983-87	
wo/Port Inj	
right side (6.0)	8.3
left side (4.9)	6.8
both sides (9.1)	12.5
w/Port Inj	
right side (7.9)	10.9
left side (7.2)	9.9
both sides (11.1)	15.3
w/A.C. add (.3)	.3
w/C.C.C. add (.4)	.4

(P) Clean Carbon and Grind Valves

Includes: R&R cylinder heads, grind valves and seats. Minor tune up.

Four–1983-87 (3.6)	5.0
w/A.C. add (.5)	.5
V-6–1983-84	
one side (5.6)	7.8
both sides (7.6)	11.0
1985-87	
one side (6.7)	9.3
both sides (8.9)	12.4
w/A.C. add (.3)	.3
V-8–1983-87	
wo/Port Inj	
right side (6.4)	8.8
left side (5.3)	7.3
both sides (9.7)	13.4
w/Port Inj	
right side (8.3)	11.4
left side (7.6)	10.4
both sides (11.7)	16.1
w/A.C. add (.3)	.3
w/C.C.C. add (.4)	.4

COMBINATIONS

Add to Engine Work
See Machine Shop Operations

(Factory Time)	Chilton Time
(G) DRAIN, EVACUATE & RECHARGE AIR CONDITIONING SYSTEM	
All models (.5)	1.0
(G) ROCKER ARM STUD, RENEW	
Each (.1)	.2
(G) HYDRAULIC VALVE LIFTERS, DISASSEMBLE AND CLEAN	
Each (.2)	.2
(G) DISTRIBUTOR, RECONDITION	
All models (.3)	.8
(G) CARBURETOR, RECONDITION	
2 bbl	1.2
4 bbl	1.5
(G) VALVE GUIDES, REAM OVERSIZE	
Each (.1)	.1

(Factory Time)	Chilton Time
(G) Rocker Arm Cover or Gasket, Renew	
Four–1983-87 (.7)	1.0
V-6–1983-84-one (.7)	1.0
both (1.1)	1.7
1985-87-one (1.8)	2.5
both (2.3)	3.2
V-8–1983-84-one (.8)	1.1
both (1.1)	1.6
1985-87	
w/Port inj	
right (.5)	.7
left (.3)	.5
both (.6)	1.0
wo/Port inj	
right side (.9)	1.3
left side (.5)	.8
both sides (1.2)	1.9
w/C.C.C. add (.4)	.4
w/A.C. add (.3)	.3
(G) Valve Rocker Arms or Push Rods, Renew	
Four–1983-87	
one cyl (.8)	1.1
all cyls (1.1)	1.5
V-6–1983-84	
one cyl (.8)	1.2
one cyl-each side (1.5)	2.0
all cyls-both sides (1.9)	2.5
1985-87	
one cyl (2.0)	2.8
one cyl-each side (2.6)	3.6
all cyls-both sides (3.0)	4.1
V-8–1983-84	
one cyl (1.0)	1.5
one cyl-each side (1.4)	2.0
all cyls-both sides (1.9)	2.7
1985-87	
wo/Port inj	
right side (.9)	1.3
left side (.8)	1.2
both sides (1.6)	2.3
w/Port inj	
right side (1.2)	1.7
left side (.9)	1.3
both sides (2.1)	3.0
w/A.C. add (.3)	.3
w/C.C.C. add (.4)	.4
(G) Valve Rocker Arm Stud, Renew	
Four–1983-87	
one (.8)	1.2
each adtnl (.2)	.2

(Factory Time)	Chilton Time
V-6–1983-84	
one (1.0)	1.4
each adtnl (.3)	.3
1985-87	
one (2.1)	2.9
each adtnl (.3)	.3
V-8–1983-84	
one (1.0)	1.5
each adtnl (.3)	.3
1985-87	
w/Port inj	
right side-one (.8)	1.2
left side-one (.7)	1.1
wo/Port inj	
right side-one (1.3)	1.9
left side-one (.8)	1.2
each adtnl (.3)	.3
w/A.C. add (.3)	.3
w/C.C.C. add (.4)	.4
(G) Push Rod Side Cover Gasket, Renew	
Four–1983-87 (1.1)	1.6
(G) Valve Springs and/or Valve Stem Oil Seals, Renew (Head on Car)	
Four–1983-87	
one cyl (.9)	1.2
all cyls (1.6)	2.2
V-6–1983-84	
one cyl (1.1)	1.5
one cyl-each side (2.0)	2.9
all cyls-both sides (3.3)	4.1
1985-87	
one cyl (2.2)	3.0
one cyl-each side (3.2)	4.5
all cyls-both sides (4.5)	6.3
V-8–1983-84	
one cyl (1.3)	1.9
one cyl-each side (2.0)	2.9
all cyls-both sides (3.7)	5.3
1985-87	
w/Port inj	
right side-one cyl (.9)	1.4
left side-one cyl (.8)	1.3
one cyl-each side (1.5)	2.5
all cyls-both sides (3.2)	4.6
wo/Port inj	
right side-one cyl (1.3)	1.9
left side-one cyl (.9)	1.3
one cyl-each side (2.1)	3.0
all cyls-both sides (3.2)	4.4
w/A.C. add (.3)	.3
w/C.C.C. add (.4)	.4

(G) Valve Tappets, Renew (Lifters)

Includes: R&R intake manifold where required. Make all necessary adjustments.

Four–1983-87	
one cyl (1.9)	3.0
each adtnl cyl (.1)	.1
w/A.C. add (.4)	.4
V-6–1983-84	
one cyl (3.0)	4.0
one cyl-each side (3.1)	4.3
all cyls-both sides (3.6)	5.0
1985-87	
one cyl (3.7)	5.1
one cyl-each side (3.8)	5.3
all cyls-both sides (4.3)	6.0
V-8–1983-87	
wo/Port Inj	
one cyl (2.4)	4.0
one cyl-each side (2.9)	4.7
all cyls-both sides (3.5)	5.6
w/Port Inj	
right side-one cyl (4.2)	6.8
left side-one cyl (4.0)	6.4
one cyl-each side (4.5)	7.5
all cyls-both sides (5.1)	8.5
w/A.C. add (.4)	.4
w/C.C.C. add (.4)	.4

PARTS 12 CYLINDER HEAD & VALVE SYSTEM 12 PARTS

FOUR CYLINDER

	Part No.	Price
Valve Grind Gasket Set		
1983-84	◆10026815	29.00
1985-87	◆10037280	29.25
(1) Cylinder Head		
1983	◆10020700	290.00
1984	◆10030839	290.00
1985-87	◆10037283	290.00
(2) Cylinder Head Gasket		
1983	◆10018638	11.00
1984	◆10028404	10.50
1985-87	◆10035039	9.75
(3) Valve Cover Gasket		
1983-87	◆10007770	6.50
(4) Rocker Arm and Ball Kit		
1983-87	◆10014819	7.25
(5) Oil (Valve Stem)		
1983-87	◆3835333	.50
(6) Valve Spring & Damper		
1983-87	◆3735381	3.00
(7) Push Rod		
1983-84	◆10021898	3.00
1985-87	◆10028055	3.25

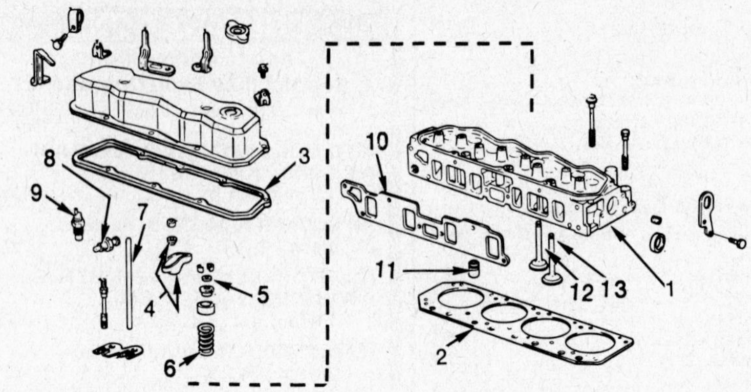

	Part No.	Price
(8) Switch (Hot Light)		
1983-87	◆25036371	8.00
(9) Switch (Fan Control)		
1983-87	◆N.L.	N.L.
(10) Manifold Gasket (Intake)		
1983-87	◆10026023	5.00

	Part No.	Price
(11) Valve Lifter		
1983-84	◆5233515	10.50
1985-87	◆5233745	32.50
(12) Intake Valve (Std.)		
1983-87	◆10022882	16.00
(13) Exhaust Valve (Std.)		
1983-84	◆10024039	N.L.
1985-87	◆10034162	16.25

PARTS 12 CYLINDER HEAD & VALVE SYSTEM 12 PARTS

V-6 & V-8 ENGINES

	Part No.	Price
Valve Grind Gasket Set		
V-6-173		
1985-87	◆14089075	53.00
V-8-305		
1983-87-exc. below	◆14033553	49.25
1983-Code S	◆14085856	53.50
1985-87-Code F	◆14089152	74.25
Code H, G	◆14089154	61.50
1986-87-350	◆10054503	N.L.

Kit requires silicone sealer for intake manifold front and rear.

	Part No.	Price
(1) Cylinder Head		
V-6-173		
1983-84	◆14054877	250.00
1985-87	◆14054879	250.00
V-8		
1983-87-305	◆14034807	247.00
1986-87-350	◆10054503	N.L.
(2) Cylinder Head Gasket		
1983-87-V-6	◆14090561	N.L.
V-8-305	◆462690	6.50
1986-87-350	◆462691	6.50
(3) Intake Valve (Std.)		
V-6-173		
1983-84	◆14024249	13.25
1985-87	◆14031328	14.00
V-8		
1983-87-305	◆14025571	11.75
1986-87-350	◆14025572	N.L.
(4) Exhaust Valve (Std.)		
V-6-173		
1983-84	◆14024254	14.25
1985-87	◆14031332	15.50
V-8		
1983-87	◆14095451	13.50
(5) Valve Lifter		
V-6-173		
1983-87	◆5234212	N.L.
V-8		
1983-87	◆5232720	N.L.

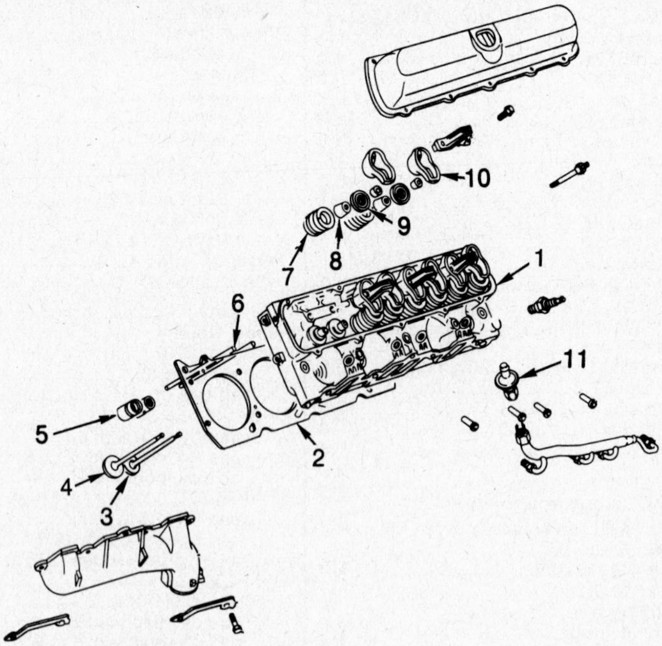

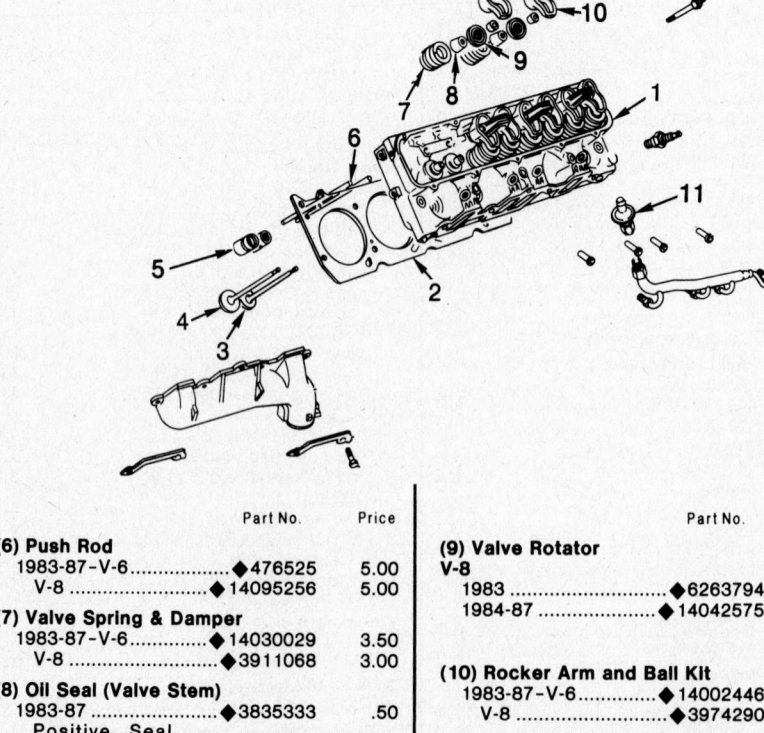

	Part No.	Price
(6) Push Rod		
1983-87-V-6	◆476525	5.00
V-8	◆14095256	5.00
(7) Valve Spring & Damper		
1983-87-V-6	◆14030029	3.50
V-8	◆3911068	3.00
(8) Oil Seal (Valve Stem)		
1983-87	◆3835333	.50
Positive Seal Kit-V-6	◆14033550	18.25
Positive Seal Kit-V-8	◆14033547	33.75

	Part No.	Price
(9) Valve Rotator		
V-8		
1983	◆6263794	5.50
1984-87	◆14042575	4.50
(10) Rocker Arm and Ball Kit		
1983-87-V-6	◆14002446	4.75
V-8	◆3974290	5.50
(11) Check Valve (Air Injection)		
1983-87	◆22040897	13.75

LABOR 13 ENGINE ASSEMBLY & MOUNTS 13 LABOR

(G) Engine Assembly, Remove & Install

Does not include transfer of any parts or equipment.

(Factory Time)	Chilton Time
Four–1983-87	**4.8**
w/A.C. add (.6)	.6
w/P.S. add (.3)	.3
V-6–1983-87	**5.4**
w/A.C. add (.3)	.3
V-8–1983-87	**6.0**
w/A.C. add (.4)	.4
w/C.F.I. add (.3)	.6
w/C.C.C. add (.4)	.4
w/A.T. add (.3)	.3
w/Port Inj add	1.0

(G) Engine Assembly, Renew

Includes: R&R engine assy. Transfer all component parts not supplied with replacement engine. Minor tune up.

(Factory Time)	Chilton Time
Four–1983-87 (4.2)	**7.5**
w/A.C. add (.6)	.6
w/P.S. add (.3)	.3
V-6–1983-87 (5.2)	**9.0**
w/A.C. add (.3)	.3
V-8–1983-87 (5.9)	**9.0**
w/A.C. add (.4)	.4
w/C.F.I. add (.3)	.6
w/C.C.C. add (.4)	.4
w/A.T. add (.3)	.3
w/Port Inj add	1.5

(G) Engine Assembly, Renew (Universal)

Includes: R&R engine assy. Transfer all component parts not supplied with replacement engine. Make all necessary adjustments.

(Factory Time)	Chilton Time
V-8–1983-87 (7.7)	**10.7**
w/A.C. add (.4)	.4
w/C.C.C. add (.4)	.4
w/A.T. add (.3)	.3
w/Port inj add	1.5

(P) Cylinder Block, Renew (w/All Internal Parts Less Head(s) and Oil Pan)

Includes: R&R engine assy. Transfer all component parts not supplied with replacement engine. Clean carbon, grind valves. Minor tune up.

(Factory Time)	Chilton Time
Four–1983-87 (7.1)	**11.0**
w/A.C. add (.6)	.6
w/P.S. add (.3)	.3
V-6–1983-87 (9.7)	**13.5**
w/A.C. add (.3)	.3
V-8–1983-87 (12.8)	**17.0**
w/A.C. add (.4)	.4
w/C.F.I. add (.3)	.6
w/C.C.C. add (.4)	.4
w/A.T. add (.3)	.3
w/Port Inj add	1.5

(P) Cylinder Block, Renew (w/Pistons, Rings and Bearings)

Includes: R&R engine assy. Transfer all component parts. Clean carbon, grind valves. Minor tune up.

(Factory Time)	Chilton Time
Four–1983-87 (8.7)	**12.4**
w/A.C. add (.6)	6
w/P.S. add (.3)	.3
V-6–1983-87 (13.0)	**18.3**
w/A.C. add (.3)	.3
V-8–1983-87 (15.0)	**22.9**
w/A.C. add (.4)	.4
w/C.C.C. add (.4)	.4
w/A.T. add (.3)	.3
w/Port Inj add	1.5

(P) Engine Assy., R&R and Recondition (Complete)

Includes: Rebore block, install new pistons, rings, rod and main bearings. Clean carbon, grind valves. Tune engine.

(Factory Time)	Chilton Time
Four–1983-87 (11.3)	**15.0**
w/A.C. add (.6)	.6
w/P.S. add (.3)	.3
V-6–1983-87 (16.5)	**24.3**
w/A.C. add (.3)	.3
V-8–1983-87 (19.1)	**25.7**
w/A.C. add (.4)	.4
w/C.C.C. add (.4)	.4
w/A.T. add (.3)	.3
w/Port Inj add	1.5

(P) Engine Assembly, Recondition (In Car)

Includes: Expand or renew pistons, install new rings, pins, rod and main bearings. Clean carbon, grind valves. Tune engine.

(Factory Time)	Chilton Time
Four–1983-87 (9.0)	**14.0**
w/A.C. add (.5)	.5
V-6–1983-87 (13.4)	**18.0**
w/A.C. add (.3)	.3
V-8–1983-87 (15.9)	**20.5**
w/A.C. add (.3)	.3
w/C.C.C. add (.4)	.4
w/Port Inj add	2.0

(G) Engine Mounts, Renew

(Factory Time)	Chilton Time
Front	
Four-1983-87-one (.6)	.8
both (.9)	1.3
V-6-1983-87-one (.8)	1.2
both (1.4)	1.9
V-8-1983-87-one (1.0)	1.3
both (1.4)	1.9
Rear	
V-6-1983-87 (.4)	.6
V-8-1983-87 (.4)	.6

PARTS 13 ENGINE ASSEMBLY & MOUNTS 13 PARTS

Engine Overhaul Gasket Kit

	Part No.	Price
4-151		
1983-87	◆10026805	20.50
Head and pan set needed also.		
V-6-173		
1983-85	◆14091347	8.75
1986-87	◆14101336	9.25
1983-87-exc. below	◆14091479	7.95
1986-87-Codes F, G, H & 350	◆14094596	8.00

Engine Assy. (Partial)

Does not include cylinder heads, manifolds, oil pump, oil, fuel and electrical parts.

	Part No.	Price
4-151		
1983-M.T.	◆10022887	1137.25
A.T.	◆10048953	1128.00
1984	◆10030773	1128.25
1985	◆10037142	1128.00
1986-87	◆10042841	1128.00
V-6-173		
1983-84	◆14059035	1176.25
1985-87	◆14089010	1204.00
V-8-305H		
1983-84	◆14019868	1363.00
1985	◆14091328	1300.00
1986-87	◆14101315	1300.00
V-8-305G & E.F.I.		
1985	◆14091328	1300.00
1986-87	◆14101315	1300.00
V-8-350		
1986-87	◆10046307	1910.00

Cylinder Block Assy.

Includes block and pistons.

	Part No.	Price
4-151		
1983	◆10022888	856.00
1984	◆10030774	856.00
1985	◆10037146	815.00
1986-87	◆10042842	856.00
V-6-173		
1983-84	◆14059038	849.25
1985-87	◆14089006	899.00
V-8-305H		
1983-84	◆14019867	949.00
V-8-305G & E.F.I.		
1983-84	◆14048355	949.00

Front Engine Mount

	Part No.	Price
4-151		
1983-87-right	◆10029901	23.50
left	◆10029902	23.50
V-6-173		
1983-right	◆14042098	27.25
left	◆14039405	27.50
1984-right	◆14039405	27.50
left	◆14080731	28.50
1985-87	◆14039405	27.50
V-8-305		
1983-87	◆14039437	27.50

Rear Engine Mount

	Part No.	Price
4-151		
1983	◆17980666	15.25
1984-87	◆17980666	15.25
V-6-173		
(Camaro)		
1983-84	◆9768046	17.75
1985-87	◆17982257	17.75
(Firebird)		
1983	◆10001749	14.00
1984-87	◆10001752	14.00
V-8-305		
(Camaro)		
1983-87	◆17982257	17.75
(Firebird)		
1983-87	◆10001752	14.00

LABOR 14 PISTONS, RINGS & BEARINGS 14 LABOR

	(Factory Time)	Chilton Time
(P) Rings, Renew (See Engine Combinations)		
Includes: Remove cylinder top ridge, deglaze cylinder walls. Clean piston and ring grooves. Minor tune up.		
Four–1983-87		
one cyl	(4.1)	5.7
all cyls	(5.3)	7.5
w/A.C. add	(.5)	.5
V-6–1983-84		
one cyl	(6.3)	8.4
one cyl-each side	(7.4)	10.1
all cyls-both sides	(9.0)	12.3
1985-87		
one cyl	(6.5)	9.5
one cyl-each side	(7.8)	10.8
all cyls-both sides	(9.7)	13.5
w/A.C. add	(.3)	.3
V-8–1983-87		
wo/Port Inj		
one cyl	(7.1)	9.8
one cyl-each side	(9.4)	13.0
all cyls-both sides	(13.0)	18.0
w/Port Inj		
one cyl	(8.9)	12.3
one cyl-each side	(11.9)	15.5
all cyls-both sides	(14.7)	19.4
w/A.C. add	(.4)	.4
w/C.C.C. add	(.4)	.4
w/Cruise control add	(.3)	.3
(P) Pistons or Connecting Rods, Renew		
Includes: Remove cylinder top ridge, deglaze cylinder walls. Minor tune up.		
Four–1983-87		
one cyl	(4.1)	6.0
all cyls	(5.3)	8.7
w/A.C. add	(.5)	.5
V-6–1983-84		
one cyl	(6.3)	8.7
one cyl-each side	(7.4)	10.7
all cyls-both sides	(9.0)	14.1
1985-87		
one cyl	(7.2)	9.8
one cyl-each side	(9.2)	11.4
all cyls-both sides	(10.4)	15.3
w/A.C. add	(.3)	.3
V-8–1983-87		
wo/Port Inj		
one cyl	(7.1)	10.1
one cyl-each side	(9.4)	13.6
all cyls-both sides	(13.0)	20.4
w/Port Inj		
one cyl	(9.6)	12.6
one cyl-each side	(12.6)	16.1
all cyls-both sides	(15.1)	21.8
w/A.C. add	(.4)	.4
w/C.C.C. add	(.4)	.4
w/Cruise control add	(.3)	.3

COMBINATIONS

Add to Engine Work
See Machine Shop Operations

	(Factory Time)	Chilton Time
(G) DRAIN, EVACUATE & RECHARGE AIR CONDITIONING SYSTEM		
All models	(.5)	1.0
(G) ROCKER ARM STUD, RENEW		
Each	(.1)	.2
(G) HYDRAULIC VALVE LIFTERS, DISASSEMBLE AND CLEAN		
Each	(.2)	.2
(G) DISTRIBUTOR, RECONDITION		
All models	(.3)	.8
(G) CARBURETOR, RECONDITION		
2 bbl		1.2
4 bbl		1.5
(G) CYLINDER HEAD, R&R (ENGINE REMOVED)		
Four	(1.2)	1.6
V-6-one	(3.0)	3.9
both	(3.5)	4.5
V-8-one	(2.4)	3.1
both	(3.8)	4.9
(G) CONNECTING ROD, RENEW (ENGINE DISASSEMBLED)		
Four-each	(.4)	.5
V-6-each	(.3)	.4
V-8-each	(.3)	.4
(P) VALVE GUIDES, REAM OVERSIZE		
Each	(.1)	.1
(G) DEGLAZE CYLINDER WALLS		
Each	(.1)	.1
(G) REMOVE CYLINDER TOP RIDGE		
Each	(.1)	.1
(G) PLASTIGAUGE BEARINGS		
Each	(.1)	.1
(M) OIL FILTER ELEMENT, RENEW		
All models	(.3)	.3

	(Factory Time)	Chilton Time
(P) Connecting Rod Bearings, Renew		
Four–1983-87	(2.2)	3.1
V-6–1983-84	(3.5)	4.0
1985-87	(3.6)	4.5
V-8–1983-87	(4.2)	5.9

PARTS 14 PISTONS, RINGS, PINS & BEARINGS 14 PARTS

	Part No.	Price
(1) Piston Ring Set (Std.)		
4-151		
1983	◆10022719	18.00
1984-85	◆10030202	18.00
1986-87	◆10037199	18.00
V-6-173		
1983-84	◆14034969	15.50
1985-87	◆14089059	17.00
V-8-305		
1983-87	◆370409	14.50
(2) Piston Assy. (Std.)		
4-151		
1983	◆10027416	50.75
1984-85	◆10027317	53.00
1986-87	◆10042191	50.75
V-6-173		
1983-84	◆14033250	48.50
1985-87	◆14092910	48.50
V-8-305		
1983-84-Code H	◆364702	43.00
1985-87-Code H	◆14081291	54.50
1983-87-Code G & E.F.I.	◆14081291	54.50
V-8-350		
1986-87	◆14101185	62.50
(3) Piston Pin		
1983-87-4-151	◆500012	5.50
(4) Connecting Rod		
1983-87-4-151	◆499323	39.50
V-6	◆476521	36.50
V-8	◆14031310	39.50
(5) Connecting Rod Bearings (Std.)		
1983-87-4-151	◆5463932	10.50
V-6	◆18008492	N.L.
V-8	◆3910555	7.50

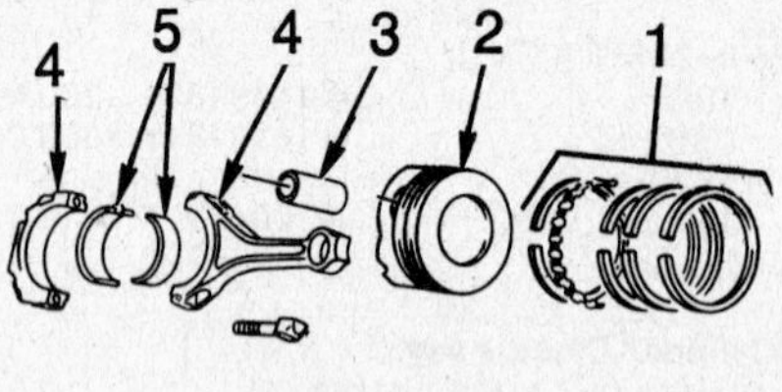

LABOR 15 CRANKSHAFT & DAMPER 15 LABOR

	(Factory Time)	Chilton Time
(P) Crankshaft and Main Bearings, Renew		
Includes: R&R engine, check all bearing clearances.		
Four–1983-87	(4.9)	7.3
w/A.C. add	(.4)	.4
w/P.S. add	(.3)	.3
V-6–1983-84	(7.5)	11.0
1985-87	(7.9)	11.0
w/A.C. add	(.3)	.3
V-8–1983-87	(9.6)	13.3
w/A.C. add	(.4)	.4
w/C.C.C. add	(.4)	.4
w/A.T. add	(.3)	.3

LABOR 15 CRANKSHAFT & DAMPER 15 LABOR

(Factory Time)	Chilton Time
(P) Main Bearings, Renew	
Includes: Check all bearing clearances.	
Four–1983-87 (2.4)	3.5
V-6–1983-84 (3.0)	4.2
1985-87 (2.8)	4.0
V-8–1983-87 (3.0)	5.1
(P) Main and Rod Bearings, Renew	
Includes: Check all bearing clearances.	
Four–1983-87 (3.4)	4.7
V-6–1983-87 (4.8)	6.0
1985-87 (4.2)	5.8
V-8–1983-87 (4.0)	7.5

(Factory Time)	Chilton Time
(G) Rear Main Bearing Oil Seals, Renew or Repack (Upper & Lower)	
Includes: R&R oil pan and rear main bearing cap on V-6 & V-8 engines with split lip type seals. R&R trans on Four cyl. engines.	
Four–1983-87	
w/M.T. (1.9)	3.0
w/A.T. (2.5)	3.8
V-6–1983 (2.1)	3.1
1984-87	
full circle (6.8)	9.5
split lip (1.8)	3.1
w/A.C. add (.3)	.3
w/C.C.C. add (.4)	.4
w/A.T. add (.6)	.6
V-8–1983-87 (2.3)	3.2

(Factory Time)	Chilton Time
(G) Crankshaft Pulley or Balancer, Renew	
Four–1983-87	
pulley (.9)	1.4
balancer (.8)	1.3
w/A.C. add (.1)	.1
w/P.S. add (.2)	.2
V-6–1983-87	
pulley (.4)	.9
balancer (.5)	1.1
w/A.C. add (.2)	.2
V-8–1983-87	
pulley (.5)	1.0
balancer (.7)	1.2
w/A.C. add (.2)	.2

PARTS 15 CRANKSHAFT & DAMPER 15 PARTS

	Part No.	Price
(1) Pulley (Crankshaft)		
4-151		
1983-87	◆10026575	17.50
V-6–173		
1983-84	◆14033107	27.25
1985-87	◆14078841	27.25
V-8–305		
1983-87-exc. Code F		
wo/A.C.	◆14023148	36.25
A.C.	◆14023145	36.25
1985-87-Code F		
A.C.	◆14088683	36.25
wo/A.C.	◆14088682	35.25
Damper		
1983-84-V-6	◆14029033	41.00
1985-87-V-6	◆14085401	39.50
1983-84-V-8 exc. below	◆458653	59.25
Code F	◆6272221	59.25
(2) Hub		
1983-Four Cyl	◆10020689	28.50
1984-87-four cyl.	◆10028930	26.75
(3) Sprocket (Crankshaft)		
1983-87-4-151	◆10028052	25.75
V-6	◆477263	13.25
V-8	◆3896959	16.00
(4) Crankshaft		
1983-85-4-151	◆10002685	313.00
1986-87-4-151	◆10037018	313.00
1983-84-V-6	◆14089826	336.00
1985-87-V-6	◆14077817	336.00
1983-85-V-8	◆361982	407.00
1986-87-V-8-305	◆14088536	407.00
V-8-350	◆14088527	407.00

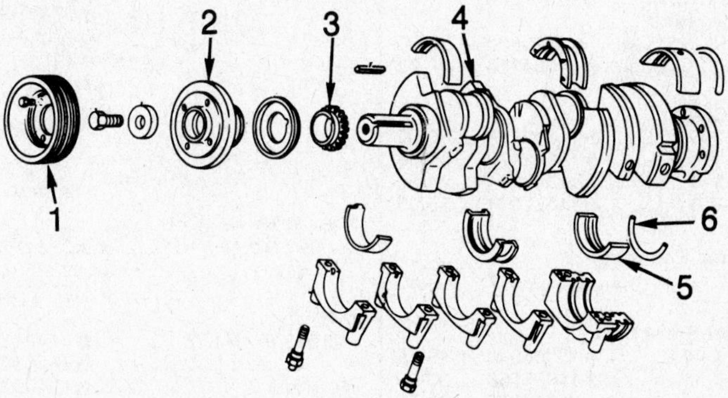

	Part No.	Price
(5) Main Bearing (Std.)		
4-151		
1983-84-rear	◆3829067	14.25
Nos. 1, 2, 3, 4	◆3829061	11.00
1985-87-rear	◆3829067	14.25
Nos. 1, 2, 3, 4	◆18012433	11.25
V-6–173		
1983-84-No. 1	◆18005226	12.75
No. 2	◆18005227	12.75
No. 3	◆18005225	26.00
rear	◆18005228	24.50
1985-87-Nos. 1, 4	◆18012472	13.25
No. 2	◆18012473	13.25
No. 3	◆18012478	24.75

	Part No.	Price
V-8		
1983-87-No. 1		
upper	◆462661	6.50
lower	◆462664	6.50
No. 2, 3, 4	◆3912038	12.50
rear	◆3912030	17.00
(6) Rear Main Bearing Seal		
4-151		
1983	◆10018632	9.00
1984-87	◆10036788	7.00
V-6–173		
1983-84	◆14081761	14.00
1985-87	◆14085829	14.50
V-8		
1983-87	◆473424	9.00

LABOR 16 CAMSHAFT & TIMING GEARS 16 LABOR

(Factory Time)	Chilton Time
(G) Timing Cover Oil Seal, Renew	
Four–1983-87 (.9)	1.5
w/A.C. add (.1)	.1
w/P.S. add (.2)	.2
V-6–1983-84 (.7)	1.3
1985-87 (.5)	1.3
w/A.C. add (.3)	.3
V-8–1983-87 (.8)	1.4
w/A.C. add (.2)	.2

(Factory Time)	Chilton Time
(G) Timing Case Cover and/or Gasket, Renew	
Four–1983-87 (1.3)	1.9
w/A.C. add (.1)	.1
w/P.S. add (.2)	.2
V-6–1983-84 (2.0)	3.0
1985-87 (1.3)	3.0
w/A.C. add (.3)	.3
V-8–1983-87 (2.1)	3.1
w/A.C. add (.3)	.3

(Factory Time)	Chilton Time
(G) Timing Chain or Camshaft Gear, Renew	
V-6–1983-84 (2.2)	3.5
1985-87 (1.3)	3.5
w/A.C. add (.3)	.3
V-8–1983-87 (2.4)	3.6
w/A.C. add (.2)	.2
Renew crank gear add (.2)	.3

LABOR 16 CAMSHAFT & TIMING GEARS 16 LABOR

	(Factory Time)	Chilton Time
(G) Camshaft, Renew		
Four–1983-87	(4.7)	7.0
w/A.C. add	(.4)	.4
w/P.S. add	(.2)	.2
Renew timing gear add		.2
V-6–1983-84	(4.9)	7.5
1985-87	(5.5)	8.0
w/A.C. add	(.3)	.3
w/A.I.R. add	(.4)	.4
V-8–1983-87		
wo/Port Inj	(5.2)	8.0
w/Port Inj	(6.5)	10.0
w/A.C. add	(.3)	.3
w/C.C.C. add	(.4)	.4
(G) Camshaft Rear Bearing Plug, Renew		
Includes: Renew cover and gasket.		
V-6–1983-87	(2.0)	3.0

PARTS 16 CAMSHAFT & TIMING GEARS 16 PARTS

	Part No.	Price
(1) Timing Cover Seal		
1983-87	◆10036286	5.25
(2) Timing Cover Gasket		
1983-87-4-151	◆3923472	1.00
V-6	◆14077849	1.50
V-8 (exc. below)	◆3799620	1.00
(86-87)	◆14094715	.75
(3) Timing Chain		
1983-85-V-6	◆14049741	30.00
1986-87-V-6	◆14102670	30.00
1983-84-V-8	◆346261	24.50
1985-87-V-8	◆14087014	25.25
(4) Fuel Pump Eccentric		
1983-87	◆3704817	5.50
(5) Camshaft Sprocket		
1983-87-4-151	◆10005942	46.75
V-6	◆14025558	30.00
V-8	◆340235	26.25
(6) Camshaft Bearing		
4-151		
1983-87	◆14002525	5.50

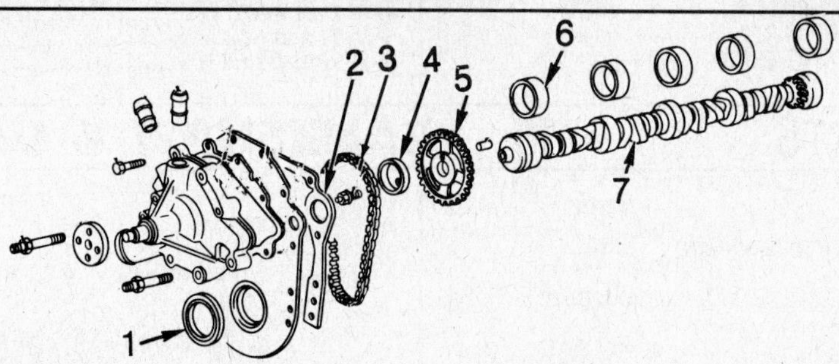

	Part No.	Price
V-6–173		
1983-87-No. 1	◆14033120	13.50
Nos. 2, 3	◆14002534	14.00
Rear	◆14002535	14.00
V-8		
1983-87-No. 1	◆474005	16.75
No. 2	◆474006	12.75
Nos. 3, 4	◆474007	16.75
(7) Camshaft Assy.		
4-151		
1983	◆10006745	118.00
1984	◆10029616	118.00
1985-87	◆10029787	118.00

	Part No.	Price
V-6–173		
1983-84	◆14024278	113.00
1985-87	◆14031378	122.00
V-8–305H		
1983-87	◆14060653	124.00
V-8–305S & 7		
1983-87	◆14060651	137.00
V-8–305G & F		
1984-85	◆14060655	155.00
1986-87-Code F	◆14094097	137.00
V-8–350		
1986-87	◆14060655	155.00

LABOR 17 ENGINE OILING SYSTEM 17 LABOR

	(Factory Time)	Chilton Time
(G) Oil Pan or Gasket, Renew		
Four–1983-87	(1.3)	1.9
V-6–1983-87	(1.6)	2.2
V-8–1983-84	(1.6)	2.2
1985-87	(1.5)	2.5
(P) Pressure Test Engine Bearings (Pan Off)		
All models		1.0
(G) Oil Pump, Renew		
Includes: Transfer screen and drive to pump, if required.		
Four–1983-87	(1.5)	2.2
Recond pump add	(.3)	.5
V-6–1983-87	(1.7)	2.5
V-8–1983-84	(1.7)	2.5
1985-87	(1.7)	2.8
(G) Oil Pressure Gauge (Engine), Renew		
1983-87	(.3)	.4
(G) Oil Pressure Gauge (Dash), Renew		
1983-87	(.5)	.9
(M) Oil Filter Element, Renew		
All models	(.3)	.3

PARTS 17 ENGINE OILING SYSTEM 17 PARTS

	Part No.	Price
Oil Pan Gasket Kit		
V-8		
1983	◆14019828	11.75
1984-85	◆14079398	10.00
1986-87	◆14088505	22.50
Oil Pan Seal		
V-6–173		
1983-84-rear	◆476591	1.50
1985-87	◆14077876	2.00
V-8		
1983-87-front	◆357159	1.50
rear	◆458625	2.00
Oil Pump		
1983-87-4-151	◆10008206	61.00
V-6	◆14033227	N.L.
V-8	◆3764547	49.75
1986-87-V-8-exc. Codes G & H	◆14057041	52.50
Oil Pump Screen		
1983-87-V-6	◆14033077	5.75
V-8	◆3855152	5.50
Oil Pump Driveshaft (upper)		
1983-87-4-151	◆1977131	11.75
Oil Pump Intermediate Shaft		
1983-87-V-6	◆477248	1.50
V-8	◆3998287	6.25

PARTS 17 ENGINE OILING SYSTEM 17 PARTS

	Part No.	Price
Oil Pump Upper Shaft Bearing		
1983-87-4-151		
upper	◆10004842	1.50
lower	◆10008555	1.00
Oil Pressure Regulator Valve		
1983-87-4-151	◆3829433	1.50
V-6 & V-8	◆3702366	1.50
Oil Pressure Sending Switch		
4-151		
(wo/Gauges)		
1983-87	◆25036378	8.75
(Gauges)		
1983	◆10030964	20.75
1984-87	◆10030963	20.75
V-6		
1983-87-wo/		
Gauges	◆14014599	5.25
Gauges	◆14040816	18.00
V-8-305		
(wo/E.F.I.)		
1983-87-wo/		
Gauges	◆3815936	3.50
Gauges	◆14040816	18.00
(E.F.I.)		
1983	◆14039603	23.25
1985-87	◆14004902	6.25
Oil Filter By Pass Valve		
1983-87	◆25010497	3.50

LABOR 18 CLUTCH & FLYWHEEL 18 LABOR

(Factory Time)	Chilton Time
(G) Clutch Pedal Free Play, Adjust	
All models (.3)	.3
(G) Bleed Clutch Hydraulic System	
All models (.5)	.6
(G) Clutch Master Cylinder, Renew	
Includes: Bleed system.	
1984-87 (1.1)	1.6
Recond cyl add	.4
(G) Clutch Assembly, Renew	
Includes: R&R trans and adjust free play.	
1983-87 (2.4)	3.0
Renew pilot brg add (.2)	.2
(G) Clutch Release Bearing or Fork, Renew	
Includes: R&R trans and adjust free play.	
1983-87 (1.8)	2.3
(G) Clutch Cross Shaft Assy., Renew	
1983-87 (.5)	.9
(G) Flywheel, Renew	
Includes: R&R trans.	
1983-87 (1.8)	3.3
Renew ring gear add	.5

PARTS 18 CLUTCH & FLYWHEEL 18 PARTS

	Part No.	Price
Clutch Plate Driven		
4-151		
1983-84-10		
spline	◆14091380	89.25
1983-84-14		
spline	◆14075768	89.25
1985	◆14084166	89.25
1986-87	◆14091980	89.25
V-6-173		
1983-84	◆15550410	89.25
1985	◆14084166	89.25
1986-87	◆14091981	89.25
V-8-305		
1983-85		
10 splines	◆458629	N.L.
26 splines	◆14079940	93.50
Offset spline	◆14088816	93.25
1986-87-Code G	◆14088816	93.25
Code H	◆14088823	85.50
Cover & Pressure Plate		
4-151		
1983	◆14066384	134.25
1984	◆14078520	141.00
1985-87	◆14084165	118.00
V-6-173		
1983-84	◆14089017	N.L.
1985	◆14084165	118.00
1986-87	◆14091979	89.25
V-8-305		
1983	◆14076960	145.25
1984-10" dia.	◆14079939	129.00
10.5" dia.	◆14057043	158.00
1985-87-exc.		
below	◆14088815	129.00
1986-87-Code H	◆14088822	136.00
Clutch Release Fork		
1983	◆14037647	27.50
1984-87-exc.		
below	◆14075718	20.00
V-8	◆14075725	26.50
Clutch Release Bearing		
1983	◆908244	26.00
1984	◆908404	30.75
1985-87	◆15590168	24.00
Clutch Pilot Bearing		
1983-87-exc. V-6	◆3752487	3.00
V-6	◆476574	2.50
Flywheel Assy.		
4-151		
1983-87-M.T.	◆10019119	156.00
A.T.	◆10031262	70.25
V-6-173		
1983-84-M.T.	◆14033180	159.00
1985-87-M.T.	◆14085433	159.00
1983-87-A.T.	◆14085472	67.50
V-8-305		
1983-85-M.T.		
Code H	◆366860	148.00
M.T. Code G	◆14085720	170.00
A.T.	◆471591	55.75
1986-87-M.T.-		
Code G	◆14088646	170.00
M.T.-Code H	◆14088650	152.00
A.T.	◆14088765	55.75
Flywheel Ring Gear		
1983-87-V-6	◆14033090	28.00
V-8	◆3991407	20.00

LABOR 21 SHIFT LINKAGE 21 LABOR

(Factory Time)	Chilton Time
MANUAL	
(G) Shift Linkage, Adjust	
All models (.3)	.4
(G) Gearshift Control Assy., Renew (Floor Mount)	
1983-87 (.9)	1.4
(G) Gearshift Control Rods, Renew	
1983-87-one (.4)	.6
each adtnl	.2
AUTOMATIC	
(G) Shift Linkage, Adjust	
All models	
Neutral Safety Switch (.3)	.4
Shift Indicator Needle (.2)	.3
Shift Linkage (.4)	.5
T.V. Cable (.3)	.4
(G) Floor Shift Control Assy., Renew	
1983-87 (.6)	1.0
(G) Shift Control Cable, Renew	
1983-87 (.5)	.9
(G) Park Lock Cable, Renew	
1983-84 (.5)	.9
1985-87 (.9)	1.3
(G) Gear Selector Needle and/or Assy., Renew	
1983-87 (.3)	.6

LABOR 25 U-JOINTS & DRIVESHAFT 25 LABOR

	(Factory Time)	Chilton Time
(G) Driveshaft, Renew		
1983-87	(.3)	.5
(G) Universal Joints, Renew		
1983-87		
front	(.6)	.9
rear	(.5)	.8
both	(.8)	1.5
(P) Pinion Shaft Flange, Renew		
1983-87	(.8)	1.0

PARTS 25 UNIVERSAL JOINTS & DRIVE SHAFT 25 PARTS

	Part No.	Price
Universal Joint Kit		
1983-87 (Type of driveshaft)		
Saginaw	◆7806140	41.00
Dana	◆374246	28.50
Yoke Assy.		
1983-87	◆7812557	65.25
Propeller Shaft		
Order by year and model.		

LABOR 26 REAR AXLE 26 LABOR

	(Factory Time)	Chilton Time
(M) Differential, Drain & Refill		
All models		.6
(M) Axle Housing Cover or Gasket, Renew		
1983-87	(.4)	.6
(G) Axle Shaft Assembly, Renew		
1983-87-one	(.6)	.9
both	(.7)	1.2
w/Rear disc brks-add		
one side		.5
both sides		.8
(G) Axle Shaft Bearing and/or Seal, Renew		
1983-87-one	(.7)	1.2
both	(.9)	1.7
w/Rear disc brks-add		
one side		.5
both sides		.8
(G) Axle Shaft Wheel Mounting Studs, Renew		
All models-one side		1.0
both sides		1.4
(G) Pinion Shaft Oil Seal, Renew		
1983-87	(.5)	.9
(P) Pinion Shaft and/or Side Pinion Gear, Renew		
Does not include R&R case.		
1983-87	(.8)	1.5
w/Limited slip add	(.5)	.5
w/Rear disc brks add	(.8)	.8
(G) Differential Case Assy., Renew		
1983-87	(1.9)	2.8
w/Limited slip add	(.5)	.5
w/Rear disc brks add	(.8)	.8
(P) Limited Slip Clutch Plates, Renew		
1983-87	(1.1)	2.0
w/Rear disc brks add	(.8)	.8
(P) Differential Side Bearings, Renew (One or Both)		
1983-87	(1.7)	2.5
w/Rear disc brks add	(.8)	.8
(P) Pinion Bearings, Renew (One or Both)		
1983-87	(2.2)	3.4
Renew side brgs add	(.3)	.3
w/Rear disc brks add	(.8)	.8
(P) Ring and Pinion Gears, Renew		
1983-87	(2.4)	3.9
Recond case assy, add		
standard	(.3)	.5
limited slip	(.7)	1.0
w/Rear disc brks add	(.8)	.8
(G) Rear Axle Housing, Renew		
Includes: Transfer all parts as required. Bleed brakes and make all necessary adjustments.		
1983-87	(3.8)	5.2
w/Rear disc brks add	(.8)	.8
(G) Rear Axle Assembly, Renew (Complete)		
1983-87	(2.3)	3.2
w/Rear disc brks add	(.8)	.8

PARTS 26 REAR AXLE 26 PARTS

	Part No.	Price
(1) Axle Shaft		
1983-87-exc. Rr. Disc	◆22515441	124.00
Rr. Disc Brakes	◆22515440	91.00
(2) Retainer (Outer)		
1983-87	◆1255941	4.00
(3) Axle Seal		
1983-87	◆3998519	4.00
(4) Axle Bearing		
1983-87	◆7451785	16.00
(5) Pinion Flange		
1983-87	◆7827670	33.50
(6) Pinion Seal		
1983-87	◆552571	8.00
(7) Front Pinion Bearing		
1983-87	◆7451202	16.00
(8) Axle Housing		
(wo/Rear Disc Brakes)		
1983-84	◆22523878	222.25
1985-87	◆14091324	222.25
(Rear Disc Brakes)		
1983	◆22520081	248.25
1984-87	◆14091323	249.25
(9) Differential Side Gear Kit		
4-151 & V-6		
1983-84	◆22525894	94.50
1985-87	◆14091434	92.25
V-8		
1983-84-M.T.	◆22521625	105.00
A.T.	◆22525894	94.50
1985-87	◆14091434	92.25
Gear package contains 2 side gears, 2 pinion gears, thrust washers and pinion shaft.		
(10) Pinion Shaft Spacer		
1983	◆9785792	1.50
(11) Rear Pinion Bearing		
1983-87	◆7455699	N.L.
(12) Shim Kit (.025-.029)		
1983-87	◆553022	5.50
Smallest size listed, larger sizes available.		
(13) Ring and Pinion Gear Kit		
1983-87		
2.73 ratio	◆560201	259.00
2.93 ratio	◆560204	261.00
3.08 ratio	◆14048380	276.25
3.23 ratio	◆14048436	276.25
3.42 ratio	◆14048378	276.00
(14) Bearing Adjusting Shim Kit (.040, .044)		
1983-87	◆3995791	6.50
Smallest size listed, larger sizes available.		
(15) Differential Side Bearing		
1983-87	◆7451281	15.00

PARTS 26 REAR AXLE AND SUSPENSION 26 PARTS

	Part No.	Price
(16) Differential Case (w/Limited Slip)		
(With Internal Gears)		
1983-84-exc.		
below	◆22514583	278.00
3.23, 3.42,		
3.73R	◆22514584	402.00
1985-87-exc.		
below	◆14084152	417.25
3.08R	◆14084153	417.25
Differential Case (wo/Limited Slip)		
(Without Internal Gears)		
1983-84-exc.		
below	◆558648	109.00
3.23, 3.42,		
3.73R	◆558649	109.25
(17) Pinion Shaft		
1983-87-exc.		
below	◆22507586	11.00
1983-84-Limited		
Slip	◆22515972	10.25
1985-87-Limited		
Slip	◆14048387	11.00
(18) Friction Disc Clutch Kit		
1983-87-left	◆14048385	65.25
right	◆14059084	17.25
(19) Preload Spring		
1983-87	◆561310	9.50

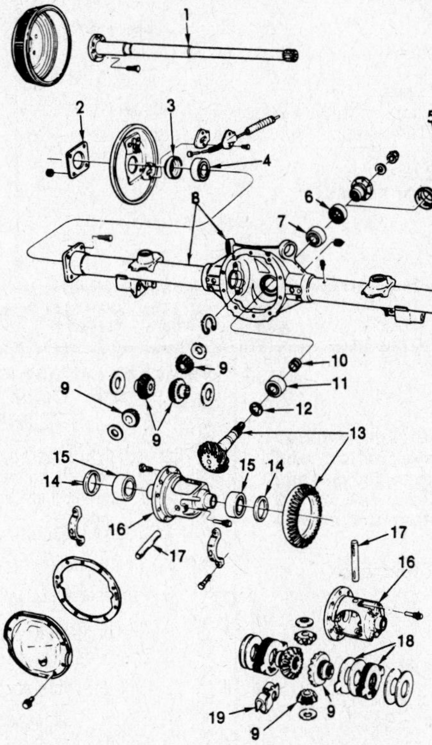

LABOR 27 REAR SUSPENSION 27 LABOR

	(Factory Time)	Chilton Time
(G) Rear Stabilizer Bar, Renew		
1983-87	(.5)	.7
(G) Rear Stabilizer Bar Bushings, Renew		
1983-87-one	(.3)	.5
both	(.4)	.6
(G) Rear Axle Tie Rod Assy., Renew		
1983-87	(.3)	.5
Renew bushings add	(.3)	.3
(G) Rear Torque Arm, Renew		
1983-87	(.6)	1.0
Renew bushing add	(.2)	.2
(G) Rear Coil Springs, Renew		
1983-87-one or both	(.4)	.7
(G) Rear Shock Absorbers, Renew		
1983-87-one	(.6)	.8
both	(1.0)	1.4
(G) Lower Control Arm Assy., Renew		
1983-87-one	(.3)	.5
both	(.4)	.8
Renew bushings add-each		.2

PARTS 27 REAR SUSPENSION 27 PARTS

	Part No.	Price
(1) Torque Arm Insulator (Outer)		
1983-87	◆527690	2.00
(2) Torque Arm		
1983	◆10019492	70.00
1984-87-exc. V-8	◆10030418	54.25
V-8	◆10034255	62.50
(3) Torque Arm Insulator (Inner)		
1983-87-exc.		
THM 700	◆527689	2.75
THM 700 trans.	◆10024068	12.00
(4) Insulator (Stabilizer)		
1983-87-12mm		
dia.	◆10018217	2.00
18mm dia.	◆10018218	2.00
21mm dia.	◆10037104	6.00
25mm dia.	◆10037105	6.00
(5) Lower Control Arm		
1983-87	◆10000063	43.25

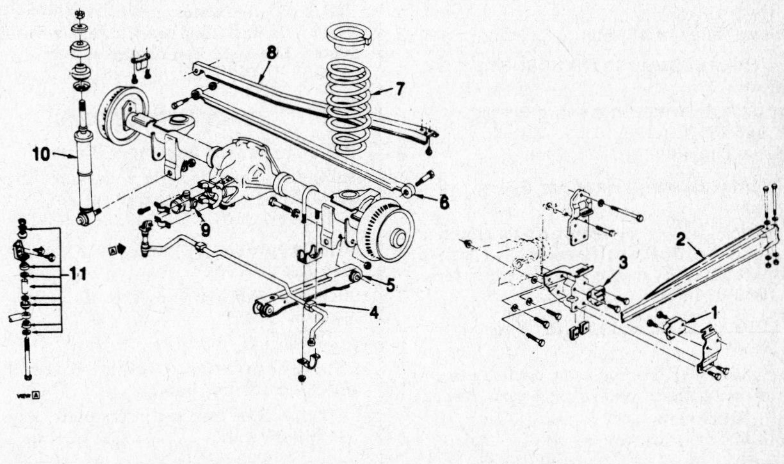

PARTS 27 REAR SUSPENSION 27 PARTS

	Part No.	Price
(6) Tie Rod		
1983-87-exc. below	◆10021047	50.00
Z28, Trans Am	◆10019451	30.50
(7) Coil Spring		
Order by year and model.		
(8) Brace		
1983-87	◆10019526	24.00
(9) Universal Joint Kit		
1983-87 (Type of driveshaft)		
Dana	◆374246	28.50
Saginaw	◆7806140	40.50
(10) Shock Absorber Assy. (Rear)		
1983-84	◆4993566	24.50
1985-87	◆22046438	24.50
(11) Stabilizer Bar Repair Kit		
1983-87	◆10023178	4.25

LABOR 28 AIR CONDITIONING 28 LABOR

(Factory Time) Chilton Time

Note: If more than one item requires replacement where evacuation and discharging the system is already included in the operation, deduct 1.0 hour for each additional item to the times listed.

(G) Drain, Evacuate and Recharge System
All models (.5) 1.0

(G) Leak Test
Includes: Check all lines and connections.
All models 5

(G) Refrigerant, Add (Partial Charge)
All models 6

(G) Compressor Belt, Renew
All models (.3) 4
w/AIR add (.1) 1

COMPRESSOR 4 CYLINDER RADIAL

(G) Compressor Assembly, Renew
Includes: Transfer all attaching parts. Evacuate and charge system.
1983-87 (1.0) 2.0

(G) Clutch Hub and Drive Plate, Renew
Does not include R&R compressor.
1983-87 (.3) 6

(G) Compressor Rotor and/or Bearing, Renew
Add time to recharge A.C. system if required.
1983-87 (.9) 1.2

(G) Compressor Clutch Coil and/or Pulley Rim, Renew
Add time to recharge A.C. system if required.
1983-87 (.9) 1.2
Renew pulley or brg add 1

(G) Compressor Shaft Seal Kit, Renew
Includes: Evacuate and charge system.
1983-87 (1.2) 2.5
R&R accum add (.3) 3

(G) Front Bearing, Head, or Seals, Renew
Includes: R&R compressor, R&R clutch and pulley assy. R&R shaft seal assy. Clean and inspect parts. Evacuate and charge system.
1983-87 (1.5) 2.8

(G) Outer Shell and/or 'O' Rings, Renew
Includes: R&R compressor, R&R clutch and pulley assy. Clean and inspect parts. Evacuate and charge system.
1983-87 (1.7) 2.8

AIR CONDITIONER TUNE-UP

For efficient operation and satisfactory performance in hot weather. The following air conditioner tune-up is suggested:

1. Clean intake filter
2. Clean condenser fins
3. Pressure test system
4. Adjust drive belt tension
5. Check antifreeze/coolant
6. Tighten compressor mounts
7. Tighten condenser and evaporator mounts
8. Inspect system for leaks (hoses, couplings, valves, etc.)
9. Partial charge system

All models 1.0
If necessary to evacuate and charge system, add 1.0

(Factory Time) Chilton Time

(G) Compressor Discharge Valve Plate Assy., Renew
Includes: R&R compressor, R&R clutch and pulley assy. R&R shell to internal mechanism. Clean and inspect parts. Evacuate and charge system.
1983-87 (1.7) 2.8
Renew two or more valves add (.1) 2

(G) Cylinder and Shaft Assy., Renew
Includes: R&R comp assy. Transfer clutch hub and drive plate, rotor, coil and switches. Renew seal kit. Install front head, outer shell and valve plates. Evacuate and charge system.
1983-87 (1.9) 2.9

DA-6 COMPRESSOR

(G) Compressor Assembly, Renew
Includes: Transfer all necessary attaching parts. Evacuate and charge system.
1983-85 (1.0) 2.0

(G) Compressor Clutch Plate and Hub Assy., Renew
Includes: R&R hub and drive plate assy. Check air gap.
1983-85 (.5) 8

(G) Compressor Clutch Rotor and/or Bearing, Renew
Includes: R&R hub and drive plate assy.
1983-85 (.5) 9

(Factory Time) Chilton Time

(G) Compressor Clutch Coil and/or Pulley Rim Assy., Renew
Includes: R&R hub and drive plate assy.
1983-85 (.6) 1.0

(G) Compressor Front Seal, Seat and 'O' Ring, Renew
Includes: R&R clutch hub and drive plate assy. Evacuate and charge system.
1983-85 (1.0) 2.2
R&R accum add (.3) 3

(G) Compressor Front Head and/or Seal, Renew
Includes: R&R compressor. R&R clutch and pulley assy. R&R shaft seal assy. Clean and inspect parts. Evacuate and charge system.
1983-85 (1.6) 2.6

(G) Compressor Cylinder and Shaft Assy., Renew
Includes: R&R compressor. Transfer all parts as required. Evacuate and charge system.
1983-85 (1.6) 2.6

(G) Condenser, Renew
Includes: Evacuate and charge system.
1983-87 (1.0) 2.3

(G) Evaporator Core, Renew
Includes: Evacuate and charge system.
1983-87 (1.2) 2.3

(G) Accumulator Assembly, Renew
Includes: Evacuate and charge system.
1983-87 (.9) 1.5

(G) Expansion Tube Assembly, Renew
Includes: Evacuate and charge system.
1983-87 (.7) 1.4

(G) High Pressure Cut-Off Switch, Renew
1983-87 (.2) 3

(G) Control Assy., Vacuum Selector Valve, Renew
1983-87 (.3) 6

(G) Blower Motor Switch, Renew
1983-87 (.4) 6

(G) High Speed Blower Motor Relay, Renew
1983-87 (.2) 3

(G) A.C. Blower Motor, Renew
1983-87 (.5) 7

(G) Blower Motor Resistor, Renew
1983-87 (.2) 3

(G) Pressure Cycling Switch, Renew
1983-87 (.2) 3

LABOR 28 AIR CONDITIONING 28 LABOR

	(Factory Time)	Chilton Time
(G) Temperature Control Assy., Renew		
1983-87	(.3)	.6
(G) Master Electrical Switch Control Assy., Renew		
1983-87	(.4)	.6
(G) Vacuum Diaphragm Actuators, Renew		
1983-87		
Defroster	(2.3)	3.5
Upper or Lower Mode	(2.3)	3.5
Air inlet	(.2)	.6
(G) Air Conditioning Hoses, Renew		
Includes: Evacuate and charge system.		
1983-87-one	(.8)	1.7
each adtnl	(.3)	.5

PARTS 28 AIR CONDITIONING 28 PARTS

	Part No.	Price
Compressor Assy.		
(Radial compressor)		
1983-87-exc. below	◆12300273	390.00
305G, E.F.I. engs.	◆12300307	390.00
1986-87-Codes G & H	◆12309223	N.L.
(DA-6 compressor)		
1983	◆12309213	410.00
1984-87-4-151	◆12321362	410.00
1985-87-Code G & H		
M.T.	◆12321365	N.L.
A.T.	◆12322349	N.L.
Drive Clutch		
1983-84-exc. DA-6	◆6551220	32.50
DA-6	◆6551717	38.25
1985-87-exc. DA-6	◆6551838	36.00
DA-6	◆6551920	40.00
Rotor (w/Bearing)		
1983-87	◆6551216	67.50
Compressor Pulley		
1983-87-4.60 DIA	◆6556715	13.00
5.13 DIA	◆6551713	79.75
5.50 DIA	◆6556717	19.50
1985-87-Code G DA-6	◆6551933	119.50
Bearing (Pulley)		
1983-87	◆908287	38.00
Relief Valve (Pressure)		
1983-87	◆5914435	13.50
Clutch Coil (w/Housing)		
1983-84-radial comp.	◆6551217	44.00
1983-87-DA-6 comp.	◆6551834	41.50
1985-87-DA-6 comp.	◆6551997	47.25
Shaft Seal Kit		
1983-87-exc. DA-6	◆9956695	13.00
DA-6	◆2724280	17.00
Front Head		
1983-84-exc. DA-6	◆6551142	28.25
DA-6	◆6557376	40.00
1985-87-exc. DA-6	◆6551835	41.25
DA-6	◆6557775	44.25
Outer Shell Assy.		
1983-87-Radial comp.	◆2724158	38.00
Cylinder & Shaft		
(Radial compressor)		
1983-87-exc. below	◆2724144	269.00
305G & E.F.I.	◆2724060	275.00
(DA-6 compressor)		
1983-87	◆6551952	307.75
Valve Plate (w/Valve)		
(Radial compressor)		
1983-87	◆6551141	11.50
(DA-6 compressor)		
1983-87-Front	◆6551700	25.00
rear	◆6551702	25.00
Compressor Drive Belt		
Order by year and model.		
Condenser		
1983-84	◆3050628	160.00
1985-87	◆3057627	149.75
Blower Motor Resistor		
1983-84	◆526897	4.50
1985-87	◆10039426	4.50
Blower Motor Switch		
1983-87	◆16015450	6.75
Evaporator Core		
1983-87	◆3049052	195.50
Blower Motor		
1983-87	◆22021790	59.25
Accumulator Dehydrator		
1983-87	◆2724260	89.50
Expansion Tube (Orifice) Assy.		
1983-87	◆3033879	9.50
Pressure Cut Off Switch		
1983-87	◆14032098	14.00
Blower Motor Relay (Hi Blo)		
1983-87	◆10019535	7.50

LABOR 29 LOCKS, HINGES & WIND. REGULATORS 29 LABOR

	(Factory Time)	Chilton Time
(G) Hood Latch, Renew		
1983-87	(.2)	.4
(G) Hood Hinge, Renew (One)		
1983-87	(.3)	.5
(G) Hood Release Cable, Renew		
1983-87	(.3)	.6
(G) Front Door Handle (Outside), Renew		
1983-87	(.6)	.8
(G) Front Door Lock Cylinder, Renew		
1983-87	(.3)	.6
Recode cyl add	(.3)	.3
(G) Lock Striker Plate, Renew		
1983-87	(.2)	.3
(G) Front Door Lock Remote Control, Renew		
1983-87	(.3)	.5
(G) Rear Compartment Lid Hinge, Renew		
1983-87-one	(.4)	.6
(G) Trunk Lock or Cylinder, Renew		
1983-87	(.2)	.3
Recode cyl add	(.3)	.3
(G) Front Door Window Regulator, Renew		
1983-87		
manual	(.8)	1.2
electric	(1.0)	1.4
Recond regulator add	(.2)	.3

PARTS 29 LOCKS, HINGES & WIND. REGULATORS 29 PARTS

	Part No.	Price
Hood Latch		
1983-87	◆14070703	16.25
Hood Hinge		
1983-87-right	◆14064294	16.75
left	◆14064293	16.75
Hood Latch Control		
1983-87	◆20201245	8.75
Outside Door Lock Cylinder Kit		
(Camaro)		
1983-87	◆20496703	5.75
(Firebird)		
1983-87	◆9632769	7.75
Door Handle (Outside)		
(Black Finish)		
1983-87-right	◆20310082	20.00
left	◆20310083	20.00
(Bright Finish)		
1983-87-right	◆20310080	20.00
left	◆20310081	20.00
Front Window Regulator (Manual)		
1983-87-right	◆20206098	64.25
left	◆20206099	64.25
Front Window Regulator (Power)		
1983-87-right	◆20206720	97.50
left	◆20206721	97.50
Electric Window Regulator Motor		
1983-87	◆22029848	72.50
Lift Gate Lock		
1983	◆20368115	40.25
1984-87	◆20274727	19.00
Lift Gate Lock Cylinder		
(Camaro)		
1983-87	◆3910570	6.25
(Firebird)		
1983-87	◆20496705	3.75
Lift Gate Hinges		
1983-87-right	◆20424524	27.00
left	◆20475847	25.50

LABOR 30 HEAD AND PARKING LAMPS 30 LABOR

(Factory Time)	Chilton Time
(G) Aim Headlamps	
two	.4
four	.6
(M) Headlamp Sealed Beam Bulb, Renew	
All models (.2)	.3
(M) Side Marker Lamp Assy., Renew	
1983-87-each (.2)	.3
(M) Park and Turn Signal Lamp Assy., Renew	
1983-87-each (.2)	.3
(M) Stop, Tail and Turn Signal Lamp Assy., Renew	
1983-87-each (.4)	.6
(M) Back-Up Lamp Bulb, Renew	
All models-one (.3)	.4
all (.5)	.7
(M) License Lamp Assembly, Renew	
1983-87-one (.2)	.3
each adtnl	.1
(M) Park and Turn Signal Lamp Bulb, Renew	
All models-each	.2
(M) Side Marker Lamp Bulb, Renew	
All models-each	.2
(M) Stop, Tail and Turn Signal Lamp Bulb, Renew	
All models-one	.3
each adtnl	.1

PARTS 30 HEAD AND PARKING LAMPS 30 PARTS

	Part No.	Price
Headlamp Sealed Beam		
(Camaro)		
1983-87-outer	◆5966200	15.00
outer quartz	◆16502327	N.L.
(inner)		
wo/Quartz	◆5966201	15.00
Quartz	◆5930567	22.50
(Firebird)		
1983-87	◆5972698	46.50
Tail Lamp Lens		
(Camaro)		
(exc. custom exterior)		
1983-87-right	◆5972990	65.75
left	◆5972989	65.75
(Custom Exterior)		
1983-84-right	◆5973750	104.00
left	◆5973749	104.00
1985-87-right	◆16503488	107.00
left	◆16503487	107.00
(Camaro Berlinetta)		
1983-right	◆16502008	111.00
left	◆16502007	111.00
1984-87-right	◆16502636	111.00
left	◆16502635	111.00
(Firebird)		
(exc. custom exterior)		
1983-87-right	◆5972984	83.75
left	◆5972983	83.75
(Custom exterior)		
1983-84-right	◆5972880	81.25
left	◆5972879	81.25
1985-87 (inner)		
right	◆16502858	35.00
left	◆16502857	35.00
1985-87 (w/reflex)		
right	◆16502860	96.75
left	◆16502859	96.75
High Mount Stoplight		
1986-87	◆918552	39.50
Parking Lamp		
(Camaro)		
1983-84-exc.		
below	◆915545	22.00
Berlinetta	◆915817	24.25
(Z28)		
right	◆915550	33.25
left	◆915549	33.25
1985-87-exc. below		
right	◆919188	23.25
left	◆919187	23.25
1985-87-Berlinetta		
right	◆919302	25.25
left	◆919301	25.25
1985-87-Z-28		
right	◆919186	35.25
left	◆919185	35.25
(Firebird)		
1983-87-right	◆915588	25.50
left	◆915587	25.50
License Plate Lamp Assy.		
(Camaro)		
1983-87-exc. below		
right	◆929936	10.00
left	◆929935	10.00
1985-87-Sp. tail & stop lamp		
left	◆920015	5.00
right	◆920016	5.00
(Firebird)		
1983-87	◆912116	6.50
Side Marker Lamp (Front)		
1983-87-right	◆915590	7.50
left	◆915589	7.50
Side Marker Lamp (Rear)		
1983-87-right	◆915572	10.00
left	◆915571	10.00

LABOR 31 WINDSHIELD WIPER & SPEEDOMETER 31 LABOR

	(Factory Time)	Chilton Time
(G) Windshield Wiper Motor, Renew		
1983-87	(.5)	.6
Recond add	(.5)	.7
(G) Rear Window Wiper Motor, Renew		
1983-87	(.4)	.6
(G) Windshield Wiper Switch, Renew		
1983-85	(1.1)	1.5
1986-87		
std whl	(1.3)	1.7
tilt whl	(1.1)	1.5
(G) Rear Window Wiper Switch, Renew		
1983-87	(.3)	.4
(G) Washer Pump, Renew		
1983-87-front	(.4)	.5
rear	(.3)	.4
Recond pump add	(.3)	.3
w/Cruise control add	(.1)	.1
w/Pulse wipe add	(.1)	.1
(G) Windshield Washer Pump Valve, Renew		
1983-84	(.2)	.3
(G) Wiper Transmission, Renew		
1983-87-each	(.4)	.6
(G) Speedometer Head, R&R or Renew		
1983-87	(.5)	1.1
Reset odometer add		.2
(G) Speedometer Cable and Casing, Renew		
wo/Cruise Control		
1983-87		
one piece	(.7)	1.3
w/Cruise Control		
1983-87		
upper	(.6)	.9
lower	(.3)	.5
both	(.8)	1.3
one piece	(.7)	1.3
(G) Speedometer Cable (Inner), Renew or Lubricate		
wo/Cruise Control		
1983-87		
one piece	(.5)	.9
w/Cruise Control		
1983-87		
upper	(.5)	.8
lower	(.2)	.4
both	(.6)	1.1
one piece	(.5)	.9
(G) Speedometer Driven Gear and/or Oil Seal, Renew (w/Manual Trans)		
1983-87	(.3)	.5
(G) Instrument Panel Cluster Assy., Renew		
1984-87	(1.0)	1.8
(G) Speedometer Signal Generator, Renew		
1984-87	(.5)	.7
(G) Odometer and/or Motor, Renew		
1984-87	(1.0)	1.5
(G) Radio, R&R		
1983-87	(.4)	.6

PARTS 31 WINDSHIELD WIPER & SPEEDOMETER 31 PARTS

	Part No.	Price
Windshield Wiper Motor		
1983-exc. below	◆4960974	84.00
w/Pulse Wipers	◆4961608	80.00
1984-87	◆22039687	110.75
Windshield Wiper Transmission		
1983-right	◆22030627	22.00
left	◆22030629	25.75
1984-right	◆22039678	22.75
left	◆22039679	22.75
1985-87-right	◆22048652	22.00
left	◆22048653	19.25
Windshield Washer & Wiper Switch		
(exc. pulse wiper)		
1983-wo/Tilt whl.	◆7835342	22.50
Tilt wheel	◆7837279	41.50
1984-87-wo/Tilt whl.	◆7842714	44.75
Tilt wheel	◆7843684	44.75
(Pulse wiper)		
1983-wo/Tilt whl.	◆7835340	56.25
Tilt wheel	◆7837280	53.50
1984-87	◆7843683	56.25
Windshield Washer Pump		
1983-wo/Pulse wpr.	◆22029665	30.00
Pulse wipers	◆22029601	27.00
1984-87-exc. below	◆22039686	16.25
Berlinetta	◆22048356	15.75

Speedometer Head & Cable
Order by year and model.

LABOR 32 LIGHT SWITCHES & WIRING 32 LABOR

	(Factory Time)	Chilton Time
(G) Headlamp Switch, Renew		
1983-87	(.6)	.8
w/A.C. add	(.2)	.2
(G) Headlamp Dimmer Switch, Renew		
1983-87	(.5)	.9
(G) Headlamp Actuator Switch, Renew		
1985-87	(.2)	.4
(G) Stop Lamp Switch, Renew		
1983-87	(.3)	.4
(G) Back-Up Lamp Switch, Renew (w/Manual Trans)		
1983-87	(.3)	.4
(G) Neutral Start Switch, Renew		
1983-87-Camaro	(.3)	.4
Firebird	(.6)	.9
(G) Back-Up Lamp and Park/Neutral Switch, Renew		
1983-87	(.5)	.7
(G) Parking Brake Lamp Switch, Renew		
1983-87		
Camaro	(.3)	.4
Firebird	(.6)	.8
(G) Turn Signal or Hazard Warning Switch, Renew		
1983-87		
std colm	(.7)	1.1
tilt colm	(.8)	1.2
(G) Horn, Renew		
1983-87-each	(.2)	.2
(G) Horn Relay, Renew		
1983-87	(.3)	.4
(M) Turn Signal or Hazard Warning Flasher, Renew		
1983-87	(.3)	.3

PARTS 32 LIGHT SWITCHES & WIRING 32 PARTS

	Part No.	Price
Headlamp Switch		
1983-87-exc. below	◆1995226	16.00
Firebird	◆1984371	15.50
Headlamp Dimmer Switch		
1983-87	◆7838234	12.50
Stoplight Switch		
(wo/Cruise control)		
1983-84-M.T.	◆1362835	3.00
A.T.	◆25504628	3.75
1985-87-M.T.	◆25524844	3.00
A.T.	◆25524846	6.50
(Cruise control)		
1983-84	◆9794682	7.75
1985-87	◆25524847	6.50
Turn Signal Switch		
1983-87-exc. below	◆1997983	30.00

PARTS 32 LIGHT SWITCHES & WIRING 32 PARTS

	Part No.	Price
1984-87-Berlinetta	◆1997048	28.50
Parking Brake Lamp Switch		
1983-87	◆14057519	2.00
Starter Safety Switch		
(A.T.)		
1983-87	◆1994223	18.00
(M.T.)		
1983-87	◆14066569	6.00
Back-Up Lamp Switch		
(A.T.)		
1983-87	◆1994223	18.00
(M.T.)		
1983-87	◆14069600	7.00
Turn Signal Flasher		
(Camaro)		
1983	◆491392	N.L.
1984-87	◆6450076	4.00
(Firebird)		
1983-84	◆10029240	4.25
1985-87	◆10041073	4.25
Horn Assy.		
1983-87-Note A	◆1892164	22.00
Note F	◆1892163	22.00
Horn Relay		
1983-87	◆25513270	8.50

LABOR 33 GLASS 33 LABOR

(Factory Time)	Chilton Time
(G) Windshield Glass, Renew	
1983-87 (1.1)	1.5
Renew caulk bead add (.4)	.5
(G) Front Door Glass, Renew	
1983-87 (.9)	1.3
(G) Back Window Glass, Renew	
1983-87 (2.0)	3.0
w/Elec defogger add (.4)	.4
w/Rear wiper add (.3)	.3

LABOR 34 CRUISE CONTROL 34 LABOR

(Factory Time)	Chilton Time
(G) Transducer Assy., Renew or Adjust	
1983 (.4)	.6
Adj low spd switch add (.1)	.1
(G) Cruise Control Resume Solenoid, Renew	
1983 (.2)	.3
(G) Cruise Control Chain or Cable, Renew	
1983-87 (.3)	.4
(G) Cruise Control Servo Assy., Renew	
1983-84 (.3)	.4
1985-87 (.7)	1.0
w/Digital cluster add (.6)	.6
(G) Brake or Clutch Release Switch, Renew	
1983-84 (.3)	.4
1985-87 (.5)	.7
w/Digital cluster add (.6)	.6
(G) Engagement Switch, Renew	
1983-84 (.2)	.3
1985-87 (.6)	1.0
w/Digital cluster add (.6)	.6
(G) Vacuum Hoses, Renew	
1983-87 (.2)	.3
(G) Cruise Control Module, Renew	
1984-87 (.4)	.5
w/Digital cluster add (.5)	.5
(G) Cruise Control Speed Sensor, Renew	
1984 (.6)	.8
(G) Cruise Control Check Valve, Renew	
1984 (.3)	.4
(G) Cruise Control Dash Switch, Renew (On-Off)	
1985-87 (.4)	.6

PARTS 34 CRUISE CONTROL 34 PARTS

	Part No.	Price
Cruise Control Transducer		
1983-exc. V-8	◆25030560	190.25
V-8	◆25031907	162.00
Cruise Control Module		
4-151		
1984	◆25031946	115.00
1985	◆25074704	102.00
V-6-173		
1984-87	◆25074710	102.00
V-8-305		
1984-87	◆25074709	102.00
V-8-350		
1986-87	◆25074704	102.00
Vacuum Release Valve		
1983-87-exc.		
A.T.	◆407437	8.00
A.T.	◆25509432	14.00
Cruise Control Servo		
4-151		
1983	◆25031521	24.00
1984-87	◆25074627	117.00
V-6 & V-8		
1983	◆25031529	31.75
1984-85	◆25074628	133.50
1986	◆25074627	117.00
1987	◆25074625	119.75
Cruise Control Lever & Switch		
(wo/Pulse wipers)		
1983	◆25031479	50.00
1984-87	◆25031481	50.00
(Pulse wipers)		
1983	◆25031478	50.00
1984-87	◆25031480	50.00
Cruise Control Chain		
1983-87	◆25031314	3.25
Cruise Control Cable		
1983-84-4-151	◆10029130	11.75
1985-87-4-151	◆10036107	8.50
1983-84-V-6	◆14046803	14.00
1985-87-V-6	◆14080203	16.50
V-8	◆14046814	14.00

GROUP INDEX

ALPHABETICAL INDEX

General Motors

Rear Wheel Drive Cars

CHEVETTE • PONTIAC T1000-1000

YEAR IDENTIFICATION

1983–87 Chevette

1983 1000

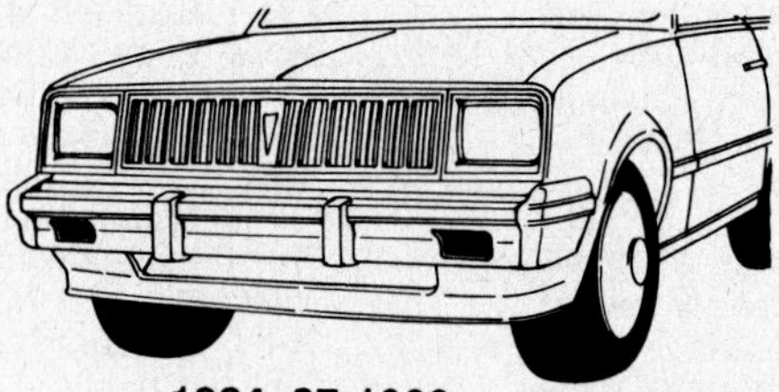

1984–87 1000

VEHICLE IDENTIFICATION NUMBER (VIN)

It is important for servicing and ordering parts to be certain of the vehicle and engine identification. The VIN (vehicle identification number) is a 13 or 17 digit number visible through the windshield on the driver's side of the dash and contains the vehicle and engine identification codes. It can be interpreted as follows:

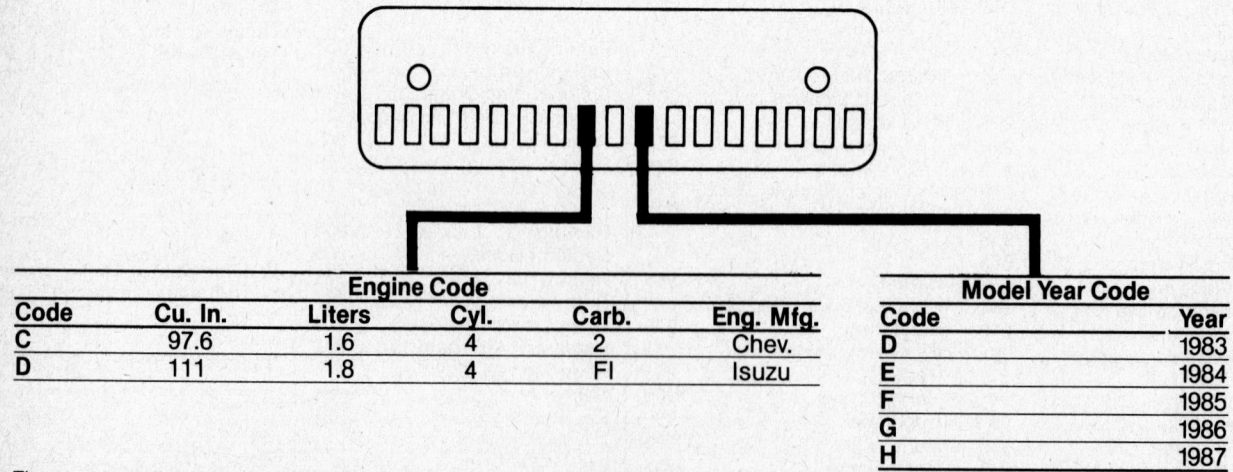

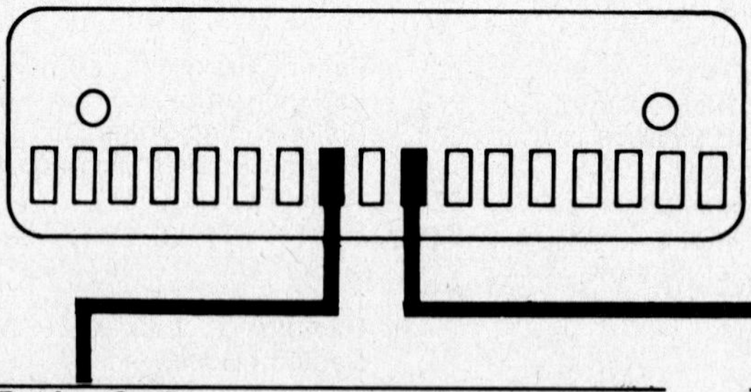

Engine Code					
Code	Cu. In.	Liters	Cyl.	Carb.	Eng. Mfg.
C	97.6	1.6	4	2	Chev.
D	111	1.8	4	FI	Isuzu

Model Year Code	
Code	Year
D	1983
E	1984
F	1985
G	1986
H	1987

The seventeen digit Vehicle Identification Number can be used to determine engine application and model year. The 10th digit indicates the model year, and the 8th digit identifies the factory installed engine.

GASOLINE ENGINE TUNE-UP SPECIFICATIONS

Year	Eng. V.I.N. Code	Engine No. Cyl Displacement (liters)	Mfg.	Spark Plugs Orig. Type	Spark Plugs Gap. (in.)	Distributor	Ignition Timing (deg) Man. Trans.	Ignition Timing (deg) Auto. Trans.	Valves Intake Opens ■ (deg)	Fuel Pump Pressure (psi)	Idle Speed (rpm) Man. Trans.	Idle Speed (rpm) Auto. Trans.
'82-'87		4-1.6	Chev.	R42CTS	.035	Electronic	8B	8B	—	5.5–6.5	800	700

NOTE: The underhood specifications sticker often reflects tune-up specification changes made in production. Sticker figures must be used if they disagree with those in this chart. Product numbers in this chart are not recommendations by Chilton for any product by brand name.

■ All figures Before Top Dead Center

DIESEL ENGINE TUNE-UP SPECIFICATIONS

Year	Engine No. Cyl. Displacement (liters)	Static Injection Timing	Fuel Injection Order	Compression (lbs)	Injection Nozzle Opening Pressure (psi)	Intake Valve Opens (deg)	Idle Speed ▲ (rpm) Man.	Idle Speed ▲ (rpm) Auto.
'83-'87	L-4-1.8	11°B	1-3-4-2	441 ①	1707	32	620	720

NOTE: The underhood specifications sticker often reflects changes made in production. Sticker figures must be used if they disagree with those in the above chart.

▲ See underhood sticker for fast idle speed.

① At 200 rpm

FIRING ORDER

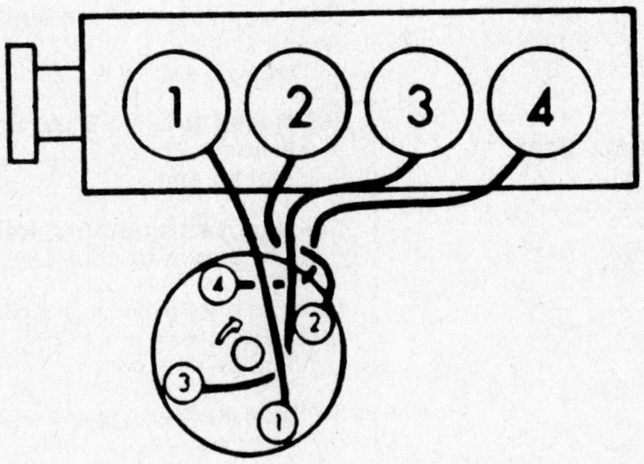

Chevrolet 98 cu. in. (1.6L) 4 cyl.
Engine firing order: 1–3–4–2
Distributor rotation: clockwise

WHEEL ALIGNMENT SPECIFICATIONS

Year	Model	Caster Range (deg)	Caster Pref Setting (deg)	Camber Range (deg)	Camber Pref Setting (deg)	Toe-in (in.)	Steering Axis Inclination (deg)
'83-'87	All	4P-6P	5P	1/4P-1/2P	1/4P	1/16P	—

P Positive

LABOR SERVICE BAY OPERATIONS LABOR

(Factory Time) Chilton Time

COOLING

(M) Winterize Cooling System
Includes: Run engine to check for leaks, tighten all hose connections. Test radiator and pressure cap. Drain radiator and engine block. Add anti-freeze and refill system.
All models 5

(M) Thermostat, Renew
1983-87 (.3) 5
w/Diesel eng add 1

(M) Drive Belt, Renew
1983-87 (.2) 3
w/P.S. add (.3) 3
each adtnl belt (.2) 2

(M) Radiator Hoses, Renew
1983-87-upper (.3) 4
lower (.4) 5
both (.5) 7

FUEL

(G) Carburetor Air Cleaner, Service
1983-87 (.2) 2

(G) Carburetor, Adjust (On Car)
1983-87
Slow & Fast Idle (.3) 4
Vacuum Brake (.4) 6
Complete (.9) 1.3

(G) Thermostatic Choke Cover and/or Gasket, Renew
1983-87 (.6) 1.0

(G) Automatic Choke Vacuum Diaphragm, Renew
1983-87 (.3) 4

BRAKES

(G) Brakes, Adjust (Minor)
Includes: R&R wheels and adjust brakes thru access holes in drums. Fill master cylinder.
two wheels 4

(G) Bleed Brakes (Four Wheels)
Includes: Fill master cylinder.
1983-87 (.4) 5

(G) Brake Pedal Free Play, Adjust
1983-87 (.2) 3

LUBRICATION SERVICE

(M) Lubricate Chassis, Change Oil & Filter
Includes: Inspect and correct all fluid levels.
All models 6
Install grease fittings add 1

(M) Lubricate Chassis
Includes: Inspect and correct all fluid levels.
All models 4
Install grease fittings add 1

CHILTON'S 10 POINT SAFETY CHECK

CHECK OPERATION & CONDITION OF THE FOLLOWING ITEMS:

1. Legal Registration (serial no.)
2. Tires & Wheels
3. Brake System (R&R all wheels)
4. Light Systems & Signals
5. Accelerator Linkage, Neutral Safety Switch, Shift Indicator Pointer & Seat Position Locks
6. Glass, Mirrors, Door Locks, Seat Belts & Harness
7. Wipers, Washers & Defrosters
8. Frame, Steering, Shocks, Front & Rear Suspension
9. Fuel & Exhaust Systems
10. Road Test Vehicle

All models 1.0
Exhaust Smog Analysis, add 4

(Factory Time) Chilton Time

(M) Engine Oil & Filter, Change
Includes: Inspect and correct all fluid levels.
All models 4

WHEELS

(M) Wheel, Renew
one (.3) 5

(G) Wheels, Balance
one 3
each adtnl 2

(G) Wheels, Rotate (All)
1983-87 5

(G) Front Wheel Bearings, Clean and Repack (Both Wheels)
1983-87 (1.1) 1.6

(G) Front Wheel Grease Seals, Renew
1983-87-one whl (.7) 8
both whls (1.1) 1.2

ELECTRICAL

(M) Battery Cables, Renew
1983-87-positive (.5) 6
negative (.2) 3
batt to batt (.3) 4

(M) Battery Terminals, Clean
1983-87 3

(Factory Time) Chilton Time

(G) Aim Headlamps
two 4
four 6

(M) Headlamp Sealed Beam Bulb, Renew
1983-87 (.2) 3

(G) Headlamp Switch, Renew
1983-87 (.3) 4

(G) Headlamp Dimmer Switch, Renew
1983-87 (.4) 6

(G) Stop Light Switch, Renew
1983-87 (.2) 3

(G) Turn Signal and Hazard Warning Switch, Renew
1983-87 (.7) 1.1

(G) Neutral Start or Back Up Light Switch, Renew
1983-87 (.3) 4

(M) Turn Signal or Hazard Warning Flasher, Renew
1983-87 (.2) 2

(G) Horn Relay, Renew
1983-87 (.2) 3

(G) Horns, Renew
1983-87-one (.2) 3
each adtnl 1

(M) Park and Turn Signal Lamp Assy., Renew
1983-87-each (.3) 4

(M) Side Marker Lamp Assy., Renew
1983-87-each (.2) 3

(M) Stop, Tail and Turn Signal Lamp Assy., Renew
1983-87-each (.3) 4

(M) Back-Up Lamp Bulb, Renew
All models-one (.2) 3
each adtnl 1

(M) License Lamp Bulb, Renew
All models-one or all (.2) 3

(M) Park and Turn Signal Lamp Bulb, Renew
All models-each 2

(M) Side Marker Lamp Bulb, Renew
All models-each 2

(M) Stop, Tail and Turn Signal Lamp Bulb, Renew
All models-one 2
each adtnl 1

LABOR 1 TUNE UP 1 LABOR

(Factory Time) Chilton Time

(G) Compression Test
1983-87 6

(G) Engine Tune Up, (Electronic Ignition)
Includes: Test battery and clean connections. Tighten manifold and carburetor mounting bolts. Check engine compression, clean and adjust or renew spark plugs. Test resistance of spark plug cables. Inspect distributor cap and rotor. Adjust air gap. Check vacuum advance operation. Reset ignition timing. Adjust idle mixture and idle speed. Service air cleaner. Inspect and adjust drive belts. Inspect choke operation and adjust or free up. Check operation of EGR valve.
1983-87 .... 2.0
w/A.C. add 6
w/A.C. & P.S. add 1.2
To perform C.C.C. system test add 1.0

LABOR 2 IGNITION SYSTEM 2 LABOR

	(Factory Time)	Chilton Time
GASOLINE ENGINE		
(G) Spark Plugs, Clean and Reset or Renew		
1983-87	(.3)	.4
(G) Ignition Timing, Reset		
1983-87	(.4)	.5
(G) Distributor, Renew		
Includes: Reset ignition timing.		
1983-87	(.8)	1.1
w/A.C. add	(.6)	.6
w/A.C. & P.S. add	(1.2)	1.2
(G) Distributor, R&R and Recondition		
Includes: Reset ignition timing.		
1983-87	(1.3)	1.8
w/A.C. add	(.6)	.6
w/A.C. & P.S. add	(1.2)	1.2
(G) Distributor Cap and/or Rotor, Renew		
1983-87	(.2)	.5
w/A.C. add	(.6)	.6
w/A.C. & P.S. add	(1.2)	1.2
(G) Vacuum Control Unit, Renew		
Includes: Reset ignition timing. Does not include R&R distributor.		
1983-87	(.2)	.5
w/A.C. add	(.6)	.6
(G) Distributor Vacuum Control Solenoid, Renew		
1983-87	(.5)	.7
(G) Ignition Coil, Renew		
1983-87	(.5)	.6
w/A.C. add	(.6)	.6
(G) Ignition Cables, Renew		
1983-87	(.3)	.5
w/A.C. add	(.5)	.5
(G) Ignition Switch, Renew		
1983-87	(.4)	.8
(G) Ignition Key Warning Switch, Renew		
1983-87	(.6)	1.0
(G) Distributor Module, Renew		
1983-87	(.3)	.6
w/A.C. add	(.6)	.6
w/A.C. & P.S. add	(1.2)	1.2
(G) Distributor Capacitor and/or Module Wiring Harness, Renew		
1983-87	(.3)	.4
w/A.C. add	(.6)	.6
w/A.C. & P.S. add	(1.2)	1.2
(G) Distributor Pick-Up Coil and/or Pole Piece, Renew		
Includes: R&R distributor and main shaft.		
1983-87	(1.0)	1.4
w/A.C. add	(.6)	.6
w/A.C. & P.S. add	(1.2)	1.2
DIESEL ENGINE		
(G) Coolant Fast Idle Temperature Switch, Renew		
All models	(.2)	.4
(G) Glow Plug Relay, Renew		
All models	(.2)	.3
(G) Fast Idle Solenoid, Renew		
All models	(.2)	.3
(G) Glow Plugs, Renew		
All models	(.3)	.5
(G) Glow Plug Module, Renew		
All models	(.3)	.4

PARTS 2 ELECTRONIC IGNITION 2 PARTS

	Part No.	Price
Distributor Assy.		
1983-84	◆1103504	252.75
1985-87	◆1103616	212.00
(1) Shield (Coil)		
1983-87	◆1984680	6.00
(2) Cap		
1983-87	◆1880022	14.00
(3) Rotor		
1983-87	◆1893669	8.00
(4) Shaft (Main)		
1983-87	◆1986018	46.50
(5) Retainer (Harness)		
1983-87	◆1984069	2.50
(6) Terminal Block		
1983-87	◆1892262	13.00
(7) Module		
1983-87	◆1875990	33.00
(8) Vacuum Control		
1983-87	◆1973691	11.50
(9) Housing (Dist.)		
1983-84	◆1984048	44.75
1985-87	◆1987988	40.25
(10) Pole Piece (w/Plate)		
1983-87	◆1880020	24.00
(11) Gear (Dist.)		
1983-87	◆1984671	55.25

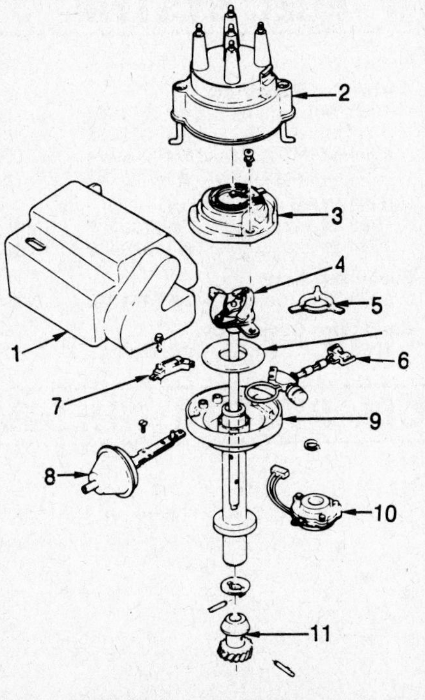

	Part No.	Price
Coil Assy.		
1983-84	◆1115455	58.00
1985-87	◆1115315	39.50
Ignition Switch		
(wo/Tilt wheel)		
1983	◆1990109	11.50
1984-87	◆1990115	11.50
(w/Tilt wheel)		
1983	◆1990110	11.50
1984-87	◆1990116	11.50
DIESEL IGNITION SYSTEM		
Glow Plugs		
1983-87	◆94221719	20.25
Glow Plug Relay		
1983-87	◆94235078	58.75
Glow Plug Controller		
1983-87	◆94223502	117.00
Glow Plug Resistor		
1983-87	◆94235081	39.50
Sensing Resistor		
1983-87	◆94242051	40.00

LABOR 3 FUEL SYSTEM 3 LABOR

	(Factory Time)	Chilton Time
GASOLINE ENGINE		
(G) Fuel Pump, Test		
Includes: Disconnect line at carburetor, attach pressure gauge.		
All models		.3
(M) Carburetor Air Cleaner, Service		
1983-87	(.2)	.2
(G) Carburetor, Adjust (On Car)		
1983-87		
Slow & Fast Idle	(.3)	.4
Vacuum Brake	(.4)	.6
Complete	(.9)	1.3
(G) Thermostatic Choke Cover and/or Gasket, Renew		
1983-87	(.6)	1.0
(G) Automatic Choke Vacuum Diaphragm, Renew		
1983-87	(.3)	.4
(M) Carburetor Fuel Filter, Renew		
1983-87	(.2)	.3

LABOR — 3 FUEL SYSTEM 3 — LABOR

(Factory Time)	Chilton Time
(G) Idle Stop Solenoid, Renew	
Includes: Reset idle speed.	
1983-87 (.3)	.4
(G) E.F.E. Heater (Insulator), Renew	
1983-87 (.5)	.9
(G) Carburetor, Renew	
Includes: Necessary adjustments.	
1983-87 (.7)	1.0
To perform C.C.C. system check, add (.5)	1.0
(G) Carburetor, R&R and Clean or Recondition	
Includes: Necessary adjustments.	
1983-87 (2.3)	3.0
To perform C.C.C. system check, add (.5)	1.0
(G) Float or Needle Valve and Seat, Renew	
Includes: Set idle speed and mixture.	
1983-87 (.6)	.9
To perform C.C.C. system check, add (.5)	1.0
(G) Accelerator Pump, Renew	
1983-87 (.5)	.7
(G) Fuel Pump or Push Rod, Renew	
1983-87 (.6)	1.0
w/A.C. add (.6)	.6
w/A.C. & P.S. add (1.2)	1.2
(G) Water In Fuel Detector, Renew (WIF)	
All models (.3)	.5
(G) Fuel Tank, Renew	
Includes: Transfer tank gauge unit.	
1983-87 (.8)	1.2
(G) Fuel Gauge (Tank), Renew	
Includes: Drain and refill tank.	
1983-87 (.9)	1.3
(G) Fuel Gauge (Dash), Renew	
1983-87 (.5)	.9
(G) Intake Manifold or Gaskets, Renew	
1983 (1.6)	2.5
1984-87 (2.1)	3.1
w/A.C. add (1.0)	1.0
w/P.S. add (.2)	.2
Renew manif add (.3)	.5

DIESEL ENGINE

(Factory Time)	Chilton Time
(G) Air Cleaner, Service	
1983-87 (.2)	.4
(G) Injection Pump Timing, Adjust	
1983-87 (1.6)	2.0
w/P.S. add (.2)	.2
(G) Fuel Injection Pump, Renew	
Includes: Pressure and electrical test. Adjust timing.	
1983-87 (2.3)	3.5
w/P.S. add (.2)	.2
(G) High Pressure Fuel Lines, Renew	
1983-87-one or all (.5)	.9
(G) Injector Nozzle and/or Seal, Renew	
1983-87-one (.5)	.8
all (.7)	1.2
Clean nozzles add-each	.2
(G) Vacuum Pump, Renew	
Includes: Vacuum test.	
1983-87 (.4)	.6
(G) Intake Manifold or Gaskets, Renew	
1983-87 (1.1)	1.8
w/P.S. add (.2)	.2
Renew manif add (.1)	.4

PARTS — 3 FUEL SYSTEM 3 — PARTS

	Part No.	Price
Carburetor Assy. (Holley)		
1983 (M.T.)		
4 sp.	◆14048828	322.00
5 sp.	◆14076321	322.00
1983 (A.T.)		
wo/A.C.	◆14048829	322.00
A.C.	◆14048827	322.00
1984-87 (M.T.)		
4 sp.	◆14068692	322.00
5 sp.	◆14076363	350.00
1984-87 (A.T.)		
wo/A.C.	◆14068691	322.00
A.C.	◆14068692	322.00
Carburetor Repair Kit		
1983-M.T.	◆14071864	40.75
A.T.	◆14039068	60.75
1984-87-M.T.	◆14082794	60.75
A.T.	◆14082793	60.75
Needle Valve & Seat Assy.		
1983	◆6260706	9.25
1984-87	◆14079410	10.00
Fuel Pump Assy.		
1983-87	◆6471542	N.L.
Carburetor Gasket Kit		
1983-87	◆14022278	17.50
Fuel Tank		
1983-87	◆14067581	92.25
Fuel Gauge (Tank Unit)		
1983-87	◆25001583	45.00
Fuel Gauge (Dash Unit)		
1983	◆6433620	26.00
1984-87-T1000	◆6434128	25.75
Chevette	◆6433620	26.00
Intake Manifold Gaskets		
1983-87	◆14023727	3.50

PARTS — 3 FUEL SYSTEM (DIESEL) 3 — PARTS

	Part No.	Price
Fuel Injection Pump		
1983-87-M.T.	◆94243441	763.00
A.T.	◆94243442	763.00
(1) Over Flow Valve		
1983-87	◆94227644	12.75
(2) Pipe (Over Flow)		
1983-87	◆94242276	22.50
(3) Wire (Magnet Valve)		
1983-87	◆94254986	3.50
(4) Magnet Valve		
1983-87	◆94242275	42.25
(5) Micro Switch		
1983-87-A.T.	◆94242294	47.00
(6) Fuel Pipe		
1983-87	◆94242280	15.00
(7) Actuator		
1983-87	◆94242285	33.50
Fuel Injection Nozzle		
1983-87	◆94220084	60.00
Vacuum Pump		
1983-87	◆94237730	162.00

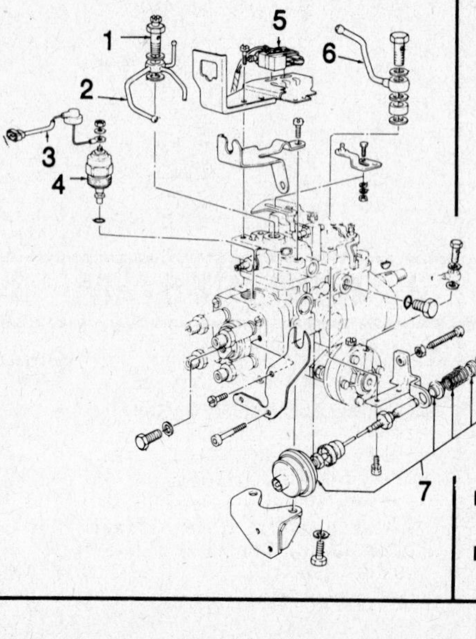

	Part No.	Price
Intake Manifold Gaskets		
1983-87	◆94221022	2.75
Fuel Gauge (Dash)		
1983	◆6433619	26.00
1984-87-T1000	◆6434127	25.75
Chevette	◆6433619	26.00

	Part No.	Price
Fuel Gauge (Tank)		
1983-87	◆25002512	105.25
Fuel Tank		
1983-87	◆14067581	92.25

LABOR 3A EMISSION CONTROLS 3A LABOR

(Factory Time) Chilton Time

EMISSION CONTROLS

(G) Emission Control Check

Includes: Check and adjust engine idle speed and mixture and ignition timing. Check P.C.V. valve.

All models 6

(G) Emission Maintenance Reminder Flag, Reset

All models 5

CRANKCASE EMISSION

(M) Positive Crankcase Ventilation Valve, Renew

1983-87 (.2) 3

EVAPORATIVE EMISSION TYPE

(G) Charcoal Canister, Renew

1983-87 (.2) 4

(G) Fuel Tank Pressure Control Valve, Renew

1983-87 (.2) 3

(G) Canister Purge Thermal Vacuum Switch, Renew

1983-87 (.2) 3

CONTROLLED COMBUSTION TYPE

(G) Air Cleaner Vacuum Motor, Renew

1983-87 (.3) 5

(G) Air Cleaner Temperature Sensor, Renew

1983-87 (.2) 4

EXHAUST GAS RECIRCULATION SYSTEM

(G) Thermostatic Vacuum Control Switch (E.G.R.), Renew

1983-87 (.3) 4

(G) E.G.R. Valve, Renew

1983-87 (.5) 7

(G) E.G.R. Vacuum Delay Valve, Renew

1983-87 (.2) 3

AIR INJECTION SYSTEM

(G) Air Pump, Renew

1983-87 (.6) 8
w/P.S. add (.3) 3

(G) Air Check Valve, Renew

1983-87-one (.3) 4
each adtnl (.3) 3

(G) Air Pump Cleaner, Renew

1983-87 (.2) 3

(G) Air Manifold Pipe, Renew

1983-87 (.5) 9

(G) Air Pump Centrifugal Filter, Renew

1983-87 (.3) 5

(G) Deceleration Valve, Renew

1983-87 (.3) 4

CHILTON'S EMISSION CONTROL TUNE-UP

1. Clean or renew P.C.V. valve, hoses and filter.
2. Check fuel tank cap for sealing ability.
3. Check fuel tank and fuel lines for leakage.
4. Check evaporation canister and filter. Replace if necessary.
5. Check engine compression to determine leakage of unburned gases. (Add time for items of interference).
6. Test and clean or renew spark plugs.
7. Check engine oil dipstick for sealing ability.
8. Test exhaust system with analyzer and check system for leakage.
9. Check exhaust manifold heat valve for operation.
10. Adjust ignition timing and carburetor idle speed and mixture.
11. Check automatic choke mechanism for free operation.
12. Inspect air cleaner and element.
13. On models so equipped, test distributor vacuum control switch and transmission control switch.

Four 1.3

For repairs made, charge accordingly.

(Factory Time) Chilton Time

(G) Catalytic Converter Air Pipe, Renew

1983-87 (.4) 7

COMPUTER COMMAND CONTROL SYSTEM (C.C.C)

(P) Electronic Control Module, Renew

Does not include system performance check.

1983-87 (.5) 6

(P) Throttle Position Sensor, Adjust

All models (.4) 9
Perform C.C.C. system check add 1.0

(P) Idle Speed Control Motor, Adjust

All models (.5) 7
Perform C.C.C. system check add 1.0

(P) Barometric Sensor, Renew

Does not include system performance check.

1985-87 (.5) 7

(P) Mixture Control Solenoid, Renew

Does not include system performance check.

1983-84 (1.1) 1.4

(Factory Time) Chilton Time

1985-87 (.4) 6

(P) Prom, Renew

Does not include system performance check.

Includes: R&R electronic module.

1983-87 (.5) 8

(P) Coolant Temperature Sensor, Renew

Does not include system performance check.

1983-87 (.5) 7

(P) Manifold Pressure Sensor, Renew

Does not include system performance check.

1983-84 (.5) 6

(P) Oxygen Sensor, Renew

Does not include system performance check.

1983-87 (.4) 7
Reset flag add (.2) 2

(P) Throttle Position Sensor, Renew

Does not include system performance check.

1983-87 (.6) 8

(P) Air Control Valve, Renew

Does not include system performance check.

1983-87 (.8) 1.1

(P) E.F.E. Vacuum Control Solenoid, Renew

Does not include system performance check.

1983-87 (.4) 6

(P) E.F.E. Temperature Switch, Renew

Does not include system performance check.

1986-87 (.3) 4

(P) Canister Purge Control Valve, Renew

Does not include system performance check.

1983-84 (.4) 6

(P) Vacuum Control Purge Solenoid, Renew

Does not include system performance check.

1983-87 (.4) 6

(P) Air Control/Air Switching Valve, Renew

Does not include system performance check.

1983-87 (.8) 1.0

(P) Pulse Air Solenoid Valve, Renew

Does not include system performance check.

1983-84 (.4) 6

(P) EFE/EGR Relay, Renew

Does not include system performance check.

1983-87 (.3) 5

(P) Tachometer Filter, Renew

Does not include system performance check.

1983-87 (.3) 3

(P) Computer Command Control System Performance Check

1983-87 (.5) 1.0

PARTS 3A EMISSION CONTROLS 3A PARTS

	Part No.	Price
E.G.R. Valve		
Replacement E.G.R. valves must be ordered according to the stamping number on the original valve.		
Crankcase Ventilation Valve		
1983-87-exc Diesel	◆8995251	3.50
Diesel	◆94220852	30.00
Vapor Canister Assy.		
1983-87	◆17063019	45.00

PARTS 3A EMISSION CONTROLS 3A PARTS

	Part No.	Price
Air Cleaner Element		
1983-87-exc.		
Diesel	◆8996587	10.00
Diesel	◆94217100	48.25
Air Cleaner Thermo Sensor		
1983-87	◆8997574	18.75
Air Cleaner Vacuum Motor		
1983-87	◆8996588	24.75

COMPUTER CONTROLLED EMISSION SYSTEM

	Part No.	Price
Electronic Control Module (ECM)		
1983-87	◆1226020	110.25

Calibration Unit (PROM)

Part numbers listed are for pricing reference only. Order part with complete model information and unit I.D. number.

	Part No.	Price
(A.T.)		
1983-Fed.	◆1226355	40.50
Calif.	◆1226356	40.50
1984-87-Fed.	◆1225587	40.50
Calif.	◆1226663	40.50
(M.T.)		
1983	◆1226357	40.50
1984-87-Fed.	◆1226664	40.50
Calif.	◆1226665	40.50
Oxygen Sensor		
1983-87	◆8990741	28.75

	Part No.	Price
Canister Purge Switch		
1983-87	◆14037782	13.00
Coolant Temperature Sensor		
1983-87	◆25036092	22.00
Barometric Pressure Sensor		
1984-87	◆14073403	23.75
Deceleration Valve		
1983-87	◆14061601	18.25
Air Injection Pump		
1983-87	◆7836061	139.00
Air Injection Control Valve		
1983-87	◆17074393	118.25
Vacuum Switching Valve (Diesel)		
1983	◆94238669	41.50
1984-85	◆94140161	37.50

LABOR 4 ALTERNATOR AND REGULATOR 4 LABOR

	(Factory Time)	Chilton Time
(G) Delcotron Circuits, Test		
Includes: Test battery, regulator, Delcotron output.		
All models		.6
(M) Alternator Drive Belt, Renew		
All models	(.2)	.3
w/P.S. add	(.3)	.3
(G) Delcotron Assembly or Fan Pulley, Renew		
1983-87	(.6)	.8
w/Diesel eng add	(.4)	.4
(G) Delcotron, R&R and Recondition		
Includes: Complete disassembly, replacement of parts as required, reassemble.		
1983-87	(1.2)	1.7
w/Diesel eng add	(.5)	.5
(G) Delcotron Front Bearing, Renew		
Includes: R&R Delcotron, separate end frames.		
1983-87	(.7)	1.0
w/Diesel eng add	(.3)	.3
Renew rear brg add		.2
(G) Delcotron Voltage Regulator, Test and Renew		
Includes: R&R, disassemble and reassemble Delcotron.		
1983-87	(.7)	1.2
w/Diesel eng add	(.5)	.5
(G) Voltmeter, Renew		
1983-87	(.5)	.9

PARTS 4 ALTERNATOR AND REGULATOR 4 PARTS

	Part No.	Price
Delcotron Assy.		
1983-87-42 amp	◆1105356	235.00
63, 66, 78 amp	◆1105368	232.50
(1) Capacitor		
1983-87	◆1978146	4.75
(2) Diode Trio		
1983-87	◆1984459	5.00
(3) Rectifier Bridge		
1983-87	◆1984454	28.00
(4) Bearing		
1983-87	◆9436831	5.50
(5) Terminal Pkg.		
1983-87	◆1975471	3.50
(6) Frame (Rear Unit)		
1983-87	◆1984460	47.75
(7) Regulator		
1983-87	◆1116387	25.00
(8) Brush & Holder		
1983-87	◆1984462	9.00
(9) Rotor Assy.		
1983-87	◆1985476	72.00
(10) Stator Assy.		
1983-87-42 amp	◆1986280	52.75
63, 66, 78 amp	◆1984445	37.25
(11) Bearing (Drive End)		
1983-87	◆908419	10.00
(12) Frame (Drive End)		
1983-87-42 amp	◆1976092	20.25
63, 66, 78 amp	◆1985497	27.00

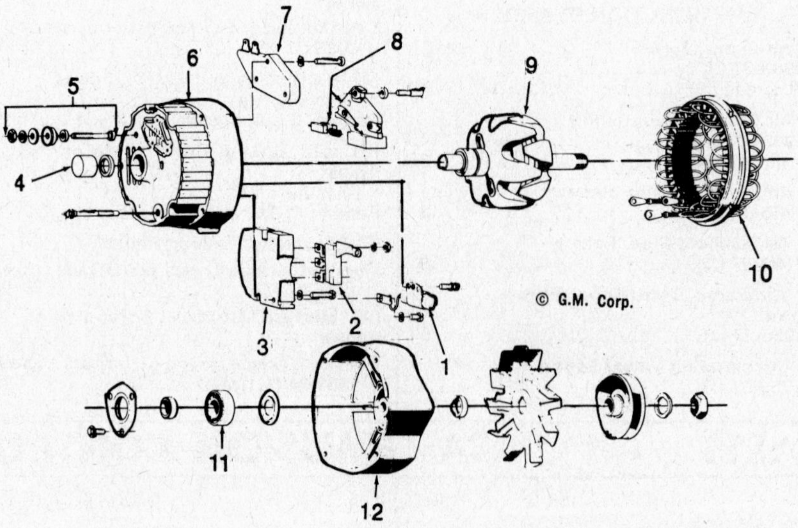

PARTS 4 ALTERNATOR AND REGULATOR 4 PARTS

	Part No.	Price
Delcotron Assy.		
1983-87	◆94234987	369.00
(1) Pulley Assy.		
1983-87	◆94223975	14.50
(2) Rotor Assy.		
1983-87	◆94237722	91.00
(3) Front Cover		
1983-87	◆94223973	34.00
(4) Front Cover Bearing		
1983-87	◆94223979	7.50
(5) Rotor Bearing		
1983-87	◆94223980	7.00
(6) Stator		
1983-87	◆94237723	55.25
(7) Brush Holder		
1983-87	◆94223965	16.00
(8) Brush		
1983-87	◆94223966	4.50
(9) Terminal Block		
1983-87	◆94237726	7.75
(10) Diode		
1983-87	◆94237727	6.00
(11) Regulator		
1983-87	◆94250964	57.00
(12) Lead		
1983-87	◆94117164	7.75

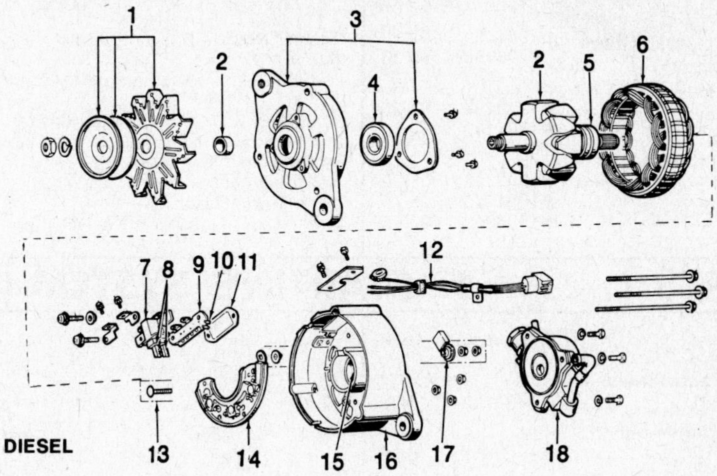

	Part No.	Price
(13) Terminal Bolt		
1983-87	◆94030450	1.75
(14) Diode		
1983-87	◆94237729	56.00
(15) Seal		
1983-87	◆94223981	3.50
(16) Cover		
1983-87	◆94223962	52.50
(17) Condenser		
1983-87	◆94030451	3.75
(18) Vacuum Pump		
1983-87	◆94237730	162.00

LABOR 5 STARTING SYSTEM 5 LABOR

(Factory Time)	Chilton Time
(G) Starter Draw Test (On Car)	
All models	.3
(G) Starter, Renew	
1983-87-Gas (1.0)	1.2
Diesel (.5)	.9
w/P.B. add (.8)	.8
w/A.C. add (.8)	.8
(G) Starter, R&R and Recondition	
Includes: Turn down armature.	
1983-87-Gas (1.8)	2.4
Diesel (1.3)	2.3
w/P.B. add (.8)	.8
w/A.C. add (.8)	.8
Renew field coils add (.2)	.5
(G) Starter Drive, Renew	
Includes: R&R starter.	
1983-87-Gas (1.2)	1.5
Diesel (.6)	1.1
w/P.B. add (.8)	.8
w/A.C. add (.8)	.8
(G) Starter Solenoid Switch, Renew	
Includes: R&R starter.	
1983-87-Gas (1.0)	1.3
Diesel (.5)	1.0
w/P.B. add (.8)	.8
w/A.C. add (.8)	.8
(G) Neutral Start Switch, Renew	
1983-87 (.3)	.4
(G) Ignition Switch, Renew	
1983-87 (.4)	.8
(M) Battery Cables, Renew	
1983-87-positive (.5)	.6
negative (.2)	.3
batt to batt (.3)	.4
(M) Battery Terminals, Clean	
1983-87	.3

PARTS 5 STARTING SYSTEM 5 PARTS

	Part No.	Price
(1) Starter Assy. (New)		
1983	◆1109532	213.00
1984	◆1998428	179.50
1985-87	◆1998525	169.75
(2) Solenoid Switch		
1983-87	◆1114531	N.L.
(3) Drive Assy.		
1983	◆1875687	N.L.
1984-87	◆1984511	23.50
(4) Brushes		
1983-87	◆1893296	.50
(5) Drive End Bushing		
1983-87	◆1932190	.50
(6) Front Plate		
1983-87	◆1978292	6.50
(7) Armature		
1983	◆1978302	83.50

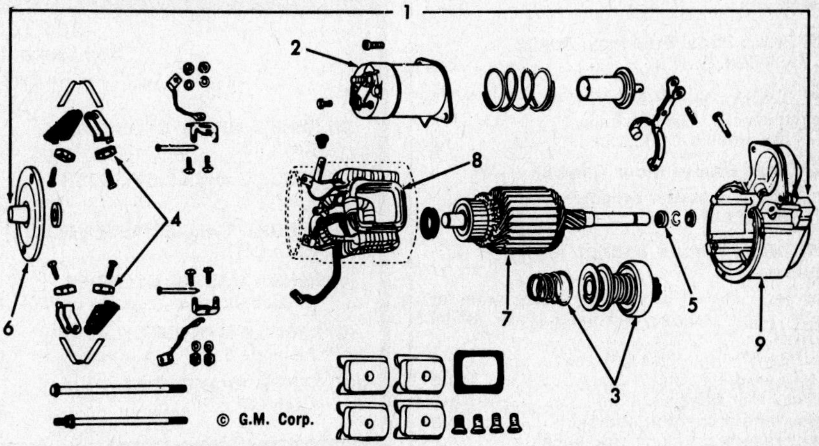

PARTS 5 STARTING SYSTEM 5 PARTS

	Part No.	Price
1984	◆1984504	107.50
1985-87	◆10495958	85.00
(8) Frame & Field		
1983	◆1978284	64.25
1984-87	◆1987100	59.50
(9) Rear Housing		
1983	◆1893332	31.25
1984	◆1985148	25.75
1985-87	◆1986092	27.25

	Part No.	Price
Starter Neutral Safety Switch		
(M.T.)		
1983-87	◆469085	6.00
(A.T.)		
1983-87	◆14052375	6.25
Ignition Switch		
(wo/Tilt wheel)		
1983-wo/Tilt whl.	◆1990109	N.L.

	Part No.	Price
1984-87	◆1990115	11.50
(Tilt wheel)		
1983	◆1990110	N.L.
1984-87	◆1990116	11.50

Battery Cables
Order by year and model.

PARTS 5 STARTING SYSTEM (DIESEL) 5 PARTS

	Part No.	Price
Starter Assy. (New)		
1983-87	◆9438758	N.L.
(1) Bearing Retainer		
1983-87	◆94228456	6.75
(2) Pinion Shaft		
1983-87	◆94242067	28.50
(3) Front Clutch Bearing		
1983-87	◆94228449	8.25
(4) Pinion Clutch		
1983-87	◆94242068	N.L.
(5) Rear Clutch Bearing		
1983-87	◆94228448	11.00
(6) Stop Set		
1983-87	◆94228450	3.50
(7) Gear Case		
1983-87	◆94242069	36.75
(8) Shift Lever Set		
1983-87	◆94228452	3.75
(9) Magnetic Switch		
1983-87	◆94228453	34.50
(10) Front Armature Bearing		
1983-87	◆94228437	10.00
(11) Armature Assy.		
1983-87	◆94242059	220.50
(12) Armature Rear Bearing		
1983-87	◆94228436	10.00
(13) Field Coils		
1983-87	◆94242060	48.00
(14) Brushes		
1983-87	◆94242061	4.00

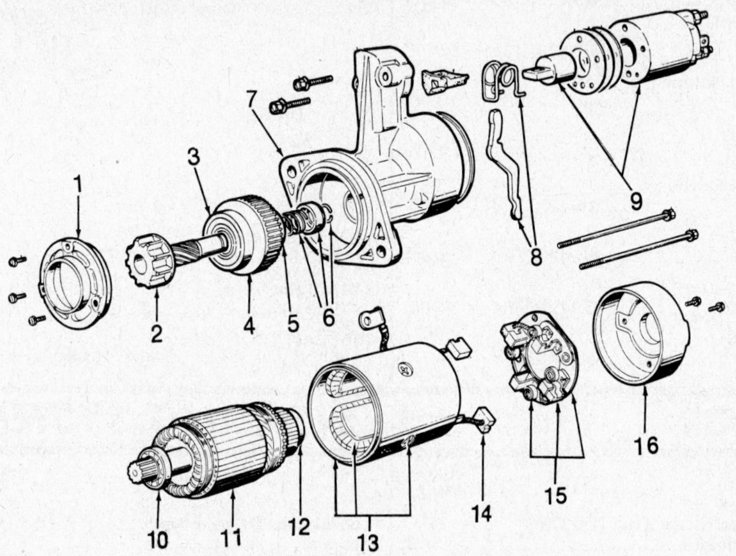

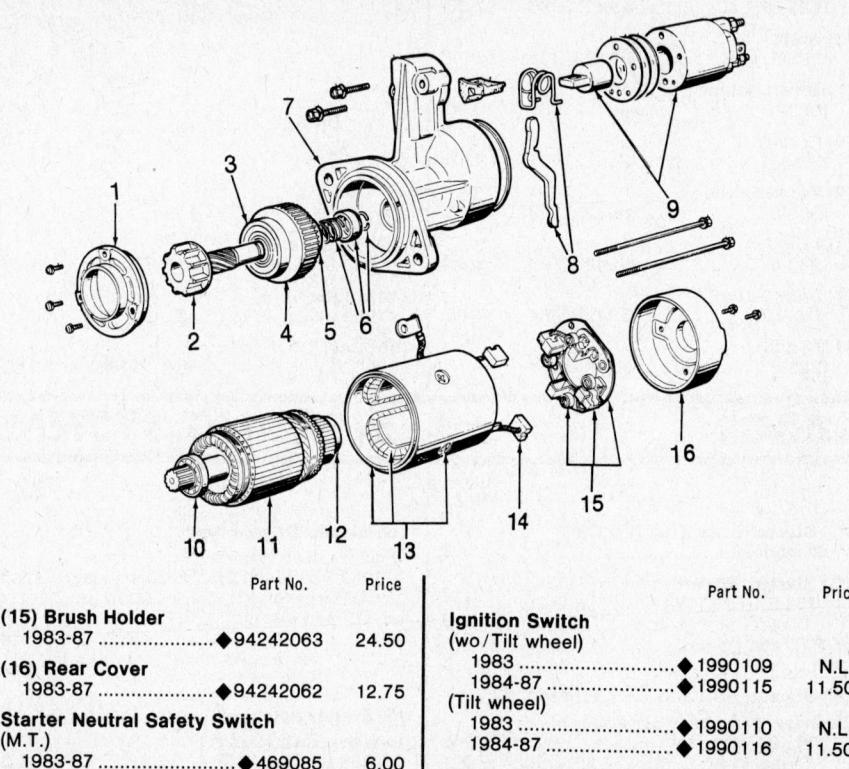

	Part No.	Price
(15) Brush Holder		
1983-87	◆94242063	24.50
(16) Rear Cover		
1983-87	◆94242062	12.75
Starter Neutral Safety Switch		
(M.T.)		
1983-87	◆469085	6.00
(A.T.)		
1983-87	◆14052375	6.25

	Part No.	Price
Ignition Switch		
(wo/Tilt wheel)		
1983	◆1990109	N.L.
1984-87	◆1990115	11.50
(Tilt wheel)		
1983	◆1990110	N.L.
1984-87	◆1990116	11.50

Battery Cables
Order by year and model.

LABOR 6 BRAKE SYSTEM 6 LABOR

(Factory Time)	Chilton Time
(G) Brake Pedal Free Play, Adjust	
1983-87 (.2)	.3
(G) Brakes, Adjust (Minor)	
Includes: Fill master cylinder.	
two wheels	.4
(G) Bleed Brakes (Four Wheels)	
Includes: Fill master cylinder.	
1983-87 (.4)	.5
(G) Brake Shoes and/or Pads, Renew	
Includes: Install new or exchange shoes or pads, adjust service and hand brake. Bleed system.	
1983-87-front-disc (.9)	1.1
rear-drum (.9)	1.5
all four wheels	2.5
Resurface disc rotor, add-each	.9
Resurface brake drum, add-each	.5

COMBINATIONS
Add To Brakes, Renew
See Machine Shop Operations

(Factory Time)	Chilton Time
(G) RENEW WHEEL CYLINDER	
Each (.2)	.2
(G) REBUILD WHEEL CYLINDER	
Each (.3)	.3
(G) REBUILD CALIPER ASSEMBLY	
Each (.5)	.6
(G) RENEW MASTER CYLINDER	
All models (.5)	.8
(G) REBUILD MASTER CYLINDER	
All models (.8)	1.0
(G) RENEW BRAKE HOSE	
Each (.3)	.3

(Factory Time)	Chilton Time
(G) RENEW REAR WHEEL GREASE SEALS	
One side (.5)	.5
(G) REPACK FRONT WHEEL BEARINGS (BOTH WHEELS)	
All models (.6)	.6
(G) RENEW BRAKE DRUM	
Each (.1)	.1
(G) RENEW DISC BRAKE ROTOR	
Each (.3)	.4

LABOR 6 BRAKE SYSTEM 6 LABOR

	(Factory Time)	Chilton Time
(G) Brake Drum, Renew (One)		
1983-87-rear	(.3)	.5
(G) Brake Combination Valve or Switch, Renew		
Includes: Bleed system.		
1983-87	(.7)	1.0
w/A.C. & pwr brakes	(1.0)	1.3

BRAKE HYDRAULIC SYSTEM

	(Factory Time)	Chilton Time
(G) Wheel Cylinder, Renew (Rear)		
Includes: Bleed system.		
1983-87-one	(.8)	1.0
both	(1.1)	1.9
(G) Wheel Cylinder, R&R and Rebuild		
Includes: Hone cylinder and bleed system.		
1983-87-one	(1.0)	1.3
both	(1.5)	2.1
(G) Brake Hose, Renew		
Includes: Bleed system.		
1983-87-front-one	(.5)	.6
rear-one	(.5)	.7
(G) Master Cylinder, Renew		
Includes: Bleed complete system.		
1983-87	(.6)	.8
w/A.C. & P.B.	(.9)	1.6
(G) Master Cylinder, R&R and Rebuild		
Includes: Hone cylinder and bleed complete system.		
1983-87	(1.4)	1.8
w/A.C. & P.B.	(1.7)	2.2
(G) Brake System, Flush and Refill		
1983-87		1.2
(G) Brake Hydraulic System, Recondition (Complete)		
Includes: Renew all rubber parts in brake system and bleed all lines.		
1983-87	(4.5)	6.0

POWER BRAKES

	(Factory Time)	Chilton Time
(G) Power Brake Cylinder, Renew		
1983-87-Gas	(1.2)	1.6
Diesel	(.5)	1.0
(G) Power Brake Cylinder, R&R and Recondition		
1983-87-Gas	(1.7)	2.5
Diesel	(1.0)	1.5
Recond m/Cyl add	(.8)	.8
(G) Vacuum Check Valve, Renew		
1983-87	(.3)	.3

DISC BRAKES

	(Factory Time)	Chilton Time
(G) Disc Brake Pads, Renew		
Includes: Install new disc brake pads only.		
1983-87	(.9)	1.1
(G) Brake Rotor, Renew		
1983-87-one	(.7)	1.0
both	(1.2)	1.5
(G) Caliper Assembly, Renew		
Includes: Bleed complete system.		
1983-87-one	(.7)	1.0
both	(1.1)	1.5
(G) Caliper Assembly, R&R and Recondition		
Includes: Bleed complete system.		
1983-87-one	(1.2)	1.5
both	(2.1)	2.5

PARKING BRAKE

	(Factory Time)	Chilton Time
(M) Parking Brake, Adjust		
1983-87	(.3)	.4
(G) Parking Brake Lamp Switch, Renew		
1983-87		
Chevette	(1.0)	1.4
1000	(.5)	.7
(G) Parking Brake Control, Renew		
1983-87	(1.0)	1.4
(G) Parking Brake Cables, Renew		
1983-87		
two piece		
right	(.6)	.8
left	(.5)	.7
one piece	(.8)	1.2
(G) Parking Brake Equalizer, Renew		
1983-87	(.3)	.5

PARTS 6 BRAKE SYSTEM 6 PARTS

	Part No.	Price
(1) Brake Shoe Set (2 Rear Wheels)		
1983-87	♦12321411	43.00
(2) Rear Wheel Cylinder		
1983-87	♦18007981	25.00
Rear Wheel Cylinder Repair Kit		
1983-87	♦18007982	6.50
Brake Hose (Front)		
1983-87	♦9762812	19.25
Brake Hose (Rear)		
1983-87	♦9759275	18.00
Master Cylinder Assy.		
(wo/Power brakes)		
1983-87	♦18009656	116.75
(Power brakes)		
1983-87	♦18009657	116.75
Master Cylinder Repair Kit		
(wo/Power brakes)		
1983-87	♦18010078	20.00
(Power brakes)		
1983-87	♦18011234	19.25
Power Brake Booster		
1983-87	♦14024422	171.00

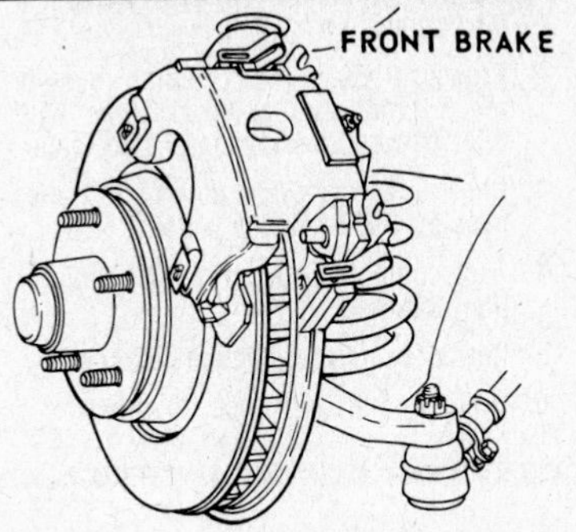

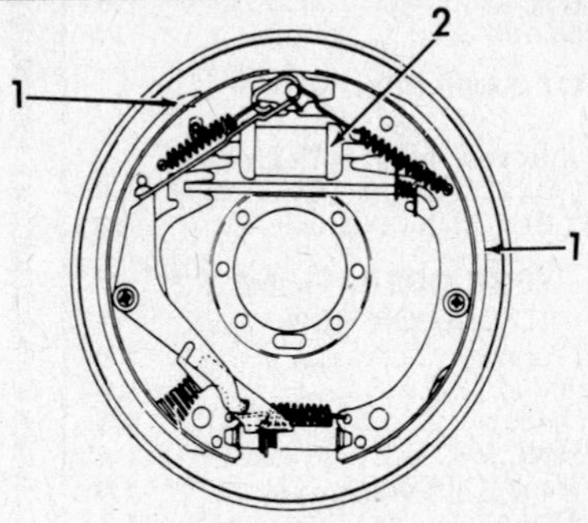

REAR BRAKE

	Part No.	Price
Power Brake Booster Repair Kit		
1983-87	♦14034864	38.75
Brake Drum (Rear)		
1983-87	♦14020936	57.00
Front Wheel Oil Seal		
1983-87	♦361746	3.50
Parking Brake Cable Assy.		
1983-87-right	♦14055484	12.00
left	♦14055483	13.00
Parking Brake Lever		
1983-87-2 dr	♦14011912	26.00
4 dr	♦14011913	26.00

PARTS 6 DISC BRAKES 6 PARTS

	Part No.	Price
Rotor Assy.		
1983-87	♦14041935	110.50
Caliper Repair Kit		
1983-87	♦18008315	8.00
(1) Caliper Assy.		
1983-85-right	♦18008314	139.00
left	♦18008313	139.00
1986-87-right	♦18013452	121.00
left	♦18013451	121.00
(2) Mounting Bracket		
1983-87-right	♦18009692	40.00
left	♦18009691	40.00
(3) Bushing Kit		
1983-87	♦18001032	2.50

PARTS **6 DISC BRAKES 6** PARTS

	Part No.	Price
(4) Bolt Kit (w/Sleeve)		
1983-upper	◆18009689	8.50
lower	◆18009690	8.50
1984-87-upper	◆18011359	6.75
lower	◆18011358	6.00

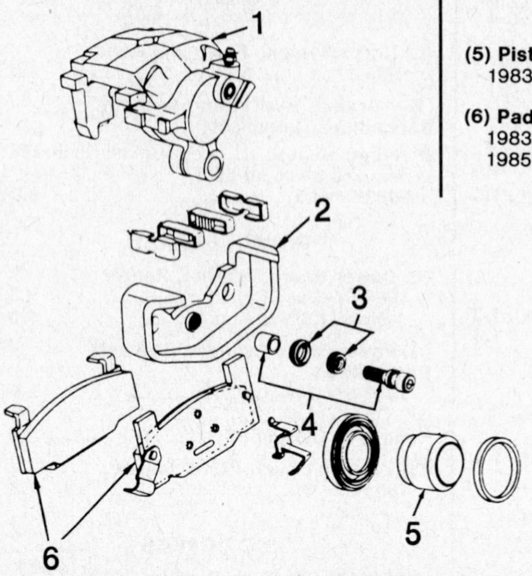

	Part No.	Price
(5) Piston (Caliper)		
1983-87	◆18009682	14.00
(6) Pad Set		
1983-84	◆12300241	43.50
1985-87	◆12321418	N.L.

LABOR 7 COOLING SYSTEM 7 LABOR

(Factory Time)	Chilton Time
(M) Winterize Cooling System	
Includes: Run engine to check for leaks, tighten all hose connections. Test radiator and pressure cap, drain radiator and engine block. Add anti-freeze and refill system.	
All models	.5
(M) Thermostat, Renew	
1983-87 (.3)	.5
w/Diesel eng add	.1
(M) Radiator Assembly, R&R or Renew	
Includes: Drain and refill cooling system.	
1983-87 (.5)	.8
w/A.T. add (.2)	.2
ADD THESE OPERATIONS TO RADIATOR R&R	
(G) Boil and Repair	1.5
(G) Rod Clean	1.9
(G) Repair Core	1.3
(G) Renew Tank	1.6
(G) Renew Trans. Oil Cooler	1.9
(G) Recore Radiator	1.7
(M) Radiator Hoses, Renew	
1983-87-upper (.3)	.4
lower (.4)	.5
both (.5)	.7
(G) Water Pump, Renew	
Gas-1983 (1.2)	1.5
1984-87 (1.5)	2.0
Diesel-1983-87 (.9)	1.4
w/A.C. add (.2)	.2
w/P.S. add (.3)	.3
(M) Drive Belt, Renew	
1983-87-one (.2)	.3
w/P.S. add (.3)	.3
each adtnl belt (.2)	.2
(M) Fan Blades or Clutch Assy., Renew	
1983-87 (.3)	.5
(G) Water Jacket Expansion Plug, Renew (Side of Block)	
each (.3)	.5
Add time to gain accessibility.	

COOLING SYSTEM TUNE-UP

An Annual Cooling System Tune-Up Suggestion List should include (with some exceptions):

1. A visual check of the cooling system for indications of leaks or excessive oil content.
2. Pressure check the cooling system for internal and external leaks with filler cap and neck adapter and tester.
3. Check crankcase and automatic transmission oil for water content.
4. Test coolant thermostat with radiator thermometer.
5. Check temperature gauge for accuracy.
6. Drain system and flush till clean.
7. Clean foreign matter from radiator fins.
8. Test radiator pressure cap with cap tester.
9. Check fan blades and pulleys for alignment and damage.
10. Internal and external inspection of all hoses for cracks and deterioration.
11. Check core plugs (where possible) for seepage.
12. Refill system with correct coolant and check for air locks.
13. Check condition and tension of drive belts with tension gauge.

All models 1.5

(Factory Time)	Chilton Time
(G) Temperature Gauge (Engine Unit), Renew	
1983-87 (.5)	.6
w/A.C. add (.2)	.2
(G) Temperature Gauge (Dash Unit), Renew	
1983-87 (.6)	1.0
(G) Heater Hoses, Renew	
Includes: Drain and refill coolant.	
1983-87 (.4)	.6
w/A.C. add	.2
(G) Heater Core, R&R or Renew	
1983-87-wo/A.C. (.7)	1.3
w/A.C. (.7)	1.3
Diesel (1.9)	3.5
Add time to recharge A.C. system, if required.	

(Factory Time)	Chilton Time
ADD THESE OPERATIONS TO HEATER CORE R&R	
(G) Boil & Repair	1.2
(G) Repair Core	.9
(G) Recore	1.2
(G) Heater Control Assembly, Renew	
1983-87-wo/A.C. (.5)	.9
w/A.C. (.6)	1.0
(G) Heater Blower Motor, Renew	
1983-87 (.3)	.5
w/Diesel eng add (.3)	.3
(G) Heater Blower Motor Resistor, Renew	
1983-87 (.2)	.4
(G) Heater Blower Motor Switch, Renew	
1983-87 (.4)	.5

PARTS 7 COOLING SYSTEM 7 PARTS

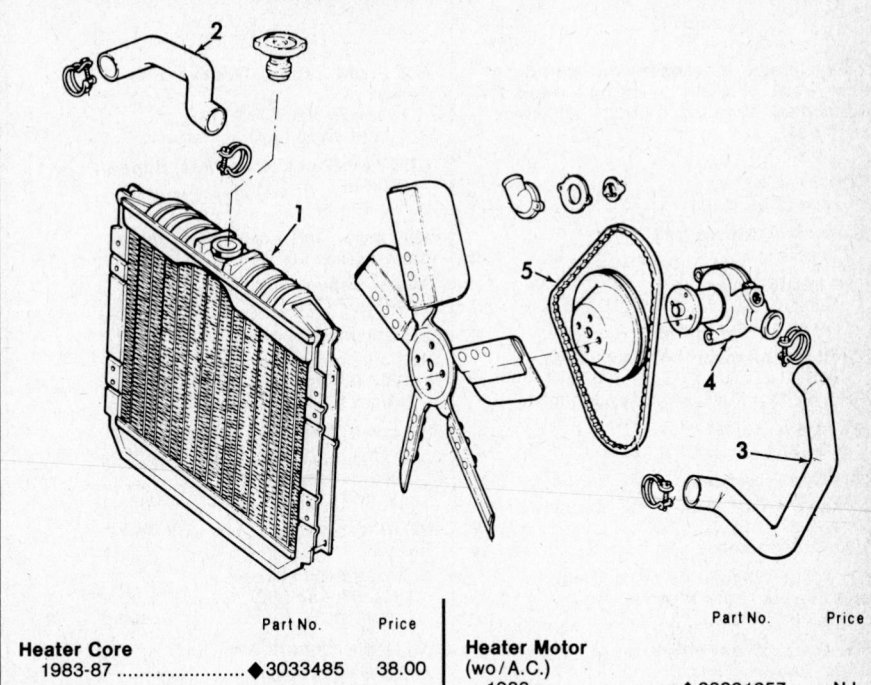

	Part No.	Price
(1) Radiator Assy.		
Accurate replacement of the radiator can be done only by using the radiator code stamped on a metal tag located on the original radiator. Order by year, model and radiator code no.		
(2) Radiator Hose (Upper)		
1.6L		
1983-87-w/H.D.	◆368299	11.00
(wo/H.D. cooling)		
wo/A.C.	◆477410	11.00
A.C.	◆477411	11.00
1.8L Diesel		
1983-87	◆14031637	11.00
(3) Radiator Hose (Lower)		
1983-87-1.6L	◆364812	8.50
Diesel	◆14031638	7.50
Thermostat		
1983-87-1.6L	◆3041415	7.50
Diesel	◆94214962	14.75
(4) Water Pump Assy.		
(1.6L)		
1983-87	◆14071866	71.25
(1.8L Diesel)		
1983-84	◆94240378	80.75
1985-87	◆94118501	97.75
(5) Fan Belt		
Order by model & description.		
Fan Clutch		
1983-87-1.6L	◆14001193	42.75
Diesel	◆94232347	149.00
Heat Indicator Sending Unit		
1983-87	◆25036035	9.75

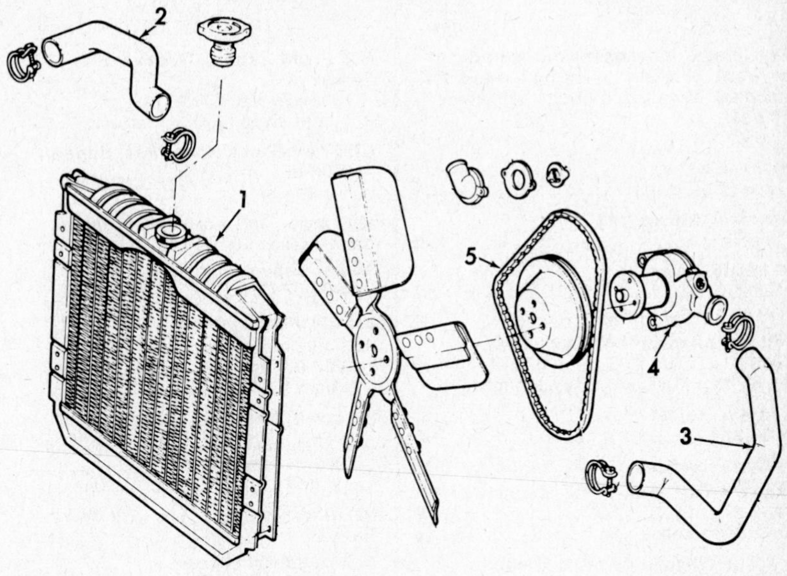

	Part No.	Price
Heater Core		
1983-87	◆3033485	38.00
Heater Switch		
1983-87	◆344883	5.00

	Part No.	Price
Heater Motor		
(wo/A.C.)		
1983	◆22021257	N.L.
1984-87	◆22048573	45.75
(A.C.)		
1983-87	◆22020945	60.00

LABOR 8 EXHAUST SYSTEM 8 LABOR

	(Factory Time)	Chilton Time
(G) Muffler, Renew		
1983	(.7)	.9
1984-87	(.5)	.9
(G) Tail Pipe and Resonator Assy., Renew		
1983	(.6)	.8
1984-87	(.4)	.6
(G) Catalytic Converter, Renew		
1983	(.5)	.8
1984-87	(.8)	1.0
(G) Intermediate Exhaust Pipe, Renew		
1983-87	(.4)	.7

	(Factory Time)	Chilton Time
(G) Tail Pipe, Renew		
1984-87	(.4)	.7
(G) Exhaust Pipe (Rear), Renew		
1983	(.5)	.8
(G) Front Exhaust Pipe, Renew (To Converter)		
1983-87	(.5)	.9
(G) Exhaust Pipe (Front), Renew		
1983-87		
Gas	(.6)	.9
Diesel	(.4)	.7

	(Factory Time)	Chilton Time
(G) Exhaust Manifold, Renew		
Gas-1983	(1.0)	1.5
1984-87	(1.4)	2.0
Diesel-1983-87	(.7)	1.1
w/A.C. add	(.3)	.3

COMBINATIONS

		Chilton Time
(G) Muffler, Exhaust and Tail Pipe, Renew		
1983-87		1.5
(G) Muffler and Tail Pipe, Renew		
1983-87		1.0

PARTS 8 EXHAUST SYSTEM 8 PARTS

	Part No.	Price
Muffler		
1.6L		
1983-87 (2 door)		
Note 1	◆14055093	66.75
Note 2	◆14008949	66.75
(4-door)		
Note 1	◆14055094	66.75
Note 2	◆14008950	74.25
1.8L Diesel		
1983-87-2 dr.	◆14095621	74.25
4 dr	◆14095622	74.25

Note 1: Has duel bed converter.
Note 2: Has single bed converter.

	Part No.	Price
Resonator Assembly (w/Pipe)		
1983-87-Diesel	◆14034719	51.50
Exhaust Pipe		
1.6L		
1983-87	◆14029473	72.25
1.8L Diesel		
1983-87	◆14034713	37.25

	Part No.	Price
Catalytic Converter		
1983-87-w/Air pump	◆25056297	300.25
1983-87-wo/Air pump	◆8999898	232.00
Tail Pipe Assy.		
1983-87	◆14053343	40.75

LABOR 9 FRONT SUSPENSION 9 LABOR

	(Factory Time)	Chilton Time
Note: On all front suspension operations alignment charges must be added if performed. Time given does not include alignment.		
(G) Wheel, Renew		
one	(.3)	.5
(G) Wheels, Rotate (All)		
All models		.5
(G) Wheels, Balance		
one		.3
each adtnl		.2
(G) Check Alignment of Front End		
1983-87		.5
Note: Deduct if alignment is performed.		
(G) Toe-In, Adjust		
1983-87	(.4)	.5
(G) Align Front End		
Includes: Adjust front wheel bearings.		
1983-87	(1.3)	1.9
w/A.C. interference add		.5
(G) Front Wheel Bearings, Clean and Repack (Both Wheels)		
1983-87	(1.1)	1.6
(G) Front Wheel Bearings and Cups, Renew		
1983-87-one side	(.7)	.9
both sides	(1.1)	1.5
(G) Front Wheel Grease Seals, Renew		
1983-87-one side	(.7)	.8
both sides	(1.1)	1.2
(G) Front Shock Absorbers, Renew		
1983-87-one	(.4)	.5
both	(.5)	.7
(G) Upper and Lower Ball Joints, Renew (One Side)		
Add alignment charges.		
1983-87	(1.1)	2.0
(G) Upper Ball Joint, Renew		
Add alignment charges.		
1983-87-one	(.5)	.9
both	(.7)	1.3
(G) Lower Ball Joint, Renew		
Add alignment charges.		
1983-87-one	(.6)	.9
both	(1.0)	1.6
(G) Steering Knuckle and Arm, Renew		
Add alignment charges.		
1983-87-one	(1.0)	1.4
both	(1.8)	2.5
(G) Upper Control Arm, Renew		
Add alignment charges.		
1983-87-one	(.7)	1.0
both	(1.2)	1.8
(G) Lower Control Arm, Renew		
Add alignment charges.		
1983-87-one	(.9)	1.4
both	(1.7)	2.6
(G) Upper Control Arm Inner Pivot Shaft or Bushings, Renew		
Add alignment charges.		
1983-87-one	(.8)	1.1
both	(1.3)	2.1
(G) Lower Control Arm Shaft or Bushings, Renew		
Add alignment charges.		
1983-87-one	(1.2)	1.6
both	(2.2)	3.0
(G) Front Spring, Renew		
Add alignment charges.		
1983-87-one	(.8)	1.0
both	(1.3)	1.8
(G) Front Stabilizer Shaft, Renew		
1983-87	(.6)	.8
(G) Stabilizer Shaft Bushings, Renew (One or Both Sides)		
1983-87	(.4)	.6
(G) Stabilizer Shaft Link or Bushings, Renew (One or Both Sides)		
1983-87	(.4)	.6

PARTS 9 FRONT SUSPENSION 9 PARTS

	Part No.	Price
(1) Front Wheel Bearing (Outer)		
1983-87	◆9415135	10.00
(2) Front Wheel Bearing (Inner)		
1983-87	◆9415132	10.50
(3) Steering Knuckle		
1983-87-right	◆14001236	130.00
left	◆14001235	130.00
(4) Bushing (Stabilizer)		
1983-87	◆363006	1.25
(5) Link Pkg.		
1983-87	◆369123	6.00
(6) Control Arm (Lower)		
1983-right	◆14079440	84.00
left	◆14067681	74.00
1984-87-right	◆14079440	84.00
left	◆14079439	84.00
(7) Ball Joint (Lower)		
1983-87	◆9769592	53.75
(8) Coil Spring		
Order by model and description.		
(9) Bushing (Lower)		
1983-87	◆475305	5.50

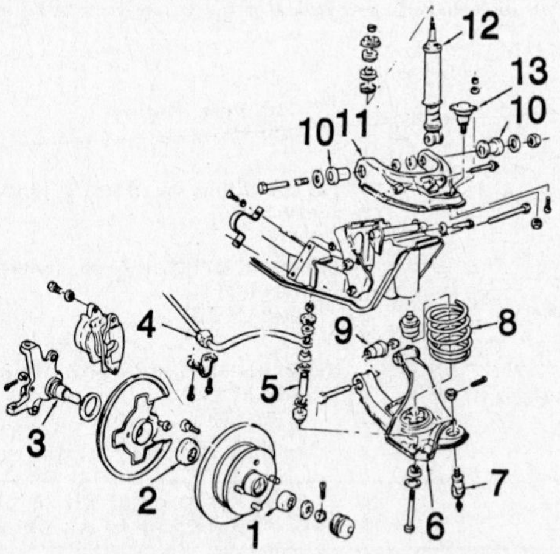

	Part No.	Price
(10) Bushing Pkg. (Upper)		
1983-87	◆474010	19.25
(11) Control Arm (Upper)		
1983-87-right	◆14067684	66.25
left	◆14067683	66.25
(12) Shock Absorber		
1983-87	◆4993581	24.50
(13) Ball Joint (Upper)		
1983	◆9762928	38.50
1984-87	◆9769588	53.75

LABOR 11 STEERING GEAR 11 LABOR

	(Factory Time)	Chilton Time
(G) Tie Rods or Tie Rod Ends, Renew		
Includes: Reset toe-in.		
1983-87-one side	(.7)	.9
both sides	(.8)	1.2
(G) Inner Tie Rod, Renew		
Includes: Reset toe-in.		
1983-87-one side	(.8)	1.2
both sides	(1.2)	1.6
STANDARD STEERING		
(G) Steering Wheel, Renew		
1983-87	(.3)	.4

LABOR 11 STEERING GEAR 11 LABOR

(Factory Time)	Chilton Time
(G) Horn Contact and/or Cancelling Cam, Renew	
1983-87 (.3)	.5
(G) Multifunction Lever, Renew	
All models (.2)	.4
w/Cruise control add (.5)	.5
(G) Steering Column Lock Actuator Parts, Renew	
1983-87	
std colm (1.0)	1.5
tilt colm (.8)	1.3
(G) Steering Coupling (Rag Joint), Renew	
1983-87 (.6)	.8
(G) Steering Column Assembly, R&R or Renew	
Does not include color coat.	
1983-87-std (.8)	1.3
tilt (1.1)	1.6
(G) Steering Gear Assembly, R&R or Renew	
1983-87 (1.0)	1.8
(P) Steering Gear Assy., R&R and Recondition	
Includes: Disassemble, renew necessary parts, reassemble and adjust.	
1983-87 (1.7)	2.6
(G) Upper Mast Jacket Bearing, Renew	
1983-87-std (.8)	1.3
tilt (.5)	.9

POWER STEERING

For operations not listed see Standard Steering

(Factory Time)	Chilton Time
(G) Trouble Shoot Power Steering	
Includes: Check pounds pull on steering wheel, test pump and system pressure and check for leaks.	
All models	.5
(M) Check and Refill Reservoir	
All models	.2
(M) Pump Drive Belt, Renew	
1983-87 (.3)	.4
(G) Power Steering Gear Assy., R&R or Renew	
Includes: Reset toe-in.	
1983-87 (1.1)	1.8
Renew short rack assy, add (.3)	.5
(P) Power Steering Gear Assy., R&R and Recondition	
Includes: Disassemble, renew necessary parts, reassemble and adjust.	
1983-87 (2.0)	3.3
(G) Power Steering Rack Bearing, Renew	
Includes: R&R gear assy and reset toe-in.	
1983-87 (1.3)	2.2
(G) Power Steering Stub Shaft Seals, Renew	
Includes: R&R gear assy and reset toe-in.	
1983-87 (1.5)	2.4
(G) Power Steering Ball Bearing Assy., Renew	
Includes: R&R gear assy and reset toe-in.	
1983-87 (1.6)	2.6
(G) Power Steering Upper Pinion Bushing and Seal, Renew	
Includes: R&R gear assy and reset toe-in.	
1983-87 (1.6)	2.7
(G) Power Steering Valve and Pinion Assy., Renew	
Includes: R&R gear assy and reset toe-in.	
1983-87 (1.5)	2.8
(G) Power Steering Pump Assy., Renew	
1983-87 (1.0)	1.4
(G) Power Steering Pump, R&R and Recondition	
1983-87 (1.5)	2.0
(G) Power Steering Pump Reservoir, Renew	
1983-87 (.3)	.5
(G) Power Steering Pump Shaft Oil Seal, Renew	
1983-87 (1.0)	1.5
(G) Pump Flow Control Valve, Renew	
1983-87 (.4)	.8
(M) Power Steering Hoses, Renew	
1983-87	
pressure-each (.5)	.7
return-each (.4)	.6
reservoir-each (.4)	.6

PARTS 11 STEERING GEAR-(STANDARD) 11 PARTS

	Part No.	Price
(1) Tie Rod Assy. (Outer)		
1983-87	◆7842935	39.75
(2) Tie Rod Assy. (Inner)		
1983-87	◆7836834	47.50
(3) Boot Service Pkg.		
1983-87	◆7835171	25.00
(4) Rack (Steering)		
1983-87	◆7819323	132.00
(5) Adjuster Plug		
1983-87	◆7825181	7.75
(6) Bearing (Steering Rack)		
1983-87	◆7819359	5.50
(7) Grommet		
1983-87	◆7832995	4.25
(8) Housing Assembly		
1983-87	◆7835168	139.00
(9) Bearing Assy. (Pinion Roller)		
1983-87	◆7819358	6.25
(10) Pinion & Bearing Assy.		
1983-87	◆7819353	98.00
(11) Seal (Pinion)		
1983-87	◆7829755	4.50
(12) Flange Assembly		
1983-87	◆7830606	38.00
(13) Bushing		
1983-87	◆7819355	4.50

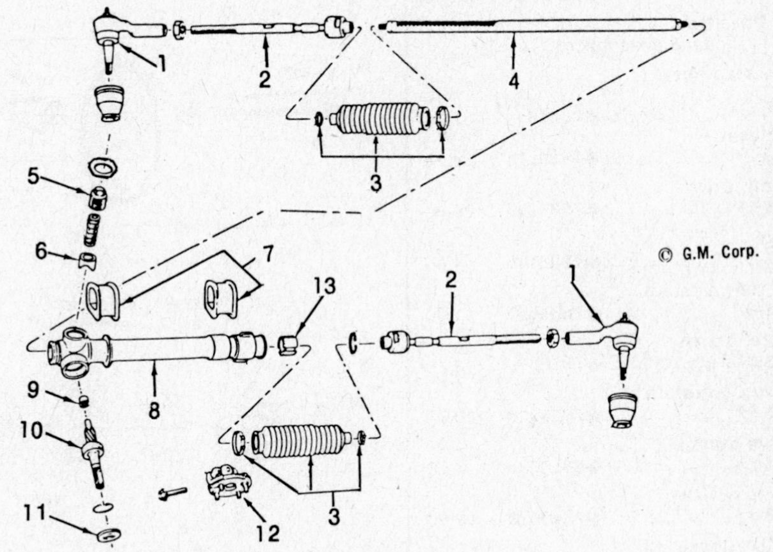

PARTS 11 POWER STEERING GEAR 11 PARTS

	Part No.	Price
(1) Tie Rod Assy. (Inner)		
1983-87	◆7840557	47.50
(2) Boot Clamp (Large)		
1983-87	◆7835312	3.00
(3) Boot Kit		
1983-87	◆7837122	23.00
(4) Boot Clamp (Small)		
1983-87	◆14052374	1.50
(5) Tie Rod Assy. (Outer)		
1983-87	◆7842935	39.75
(6) Rack & Pinion Assy.		
1983-87	◆7835287	132.00
(7) Seal Kit (Rack & Pinion)		
1983	◆7841000	10.50
1984-87	◆7845234	10.25
(8) Bulkhead Kit		
1983-87	◆7840999	41.00
(9) Grommet		
1983-87-right	◆7837127	6.25
left	◆7838415	6.75
(10) Housing Assy.		
1983-87	◆7842091	182.00
(11) Fitting (w/Seal)		
1983-87	◆7830915	6.00
(12) Valve Assy.		
1983-87	◆7837121	260.00
(13) Seal Kit (Valve rings)		
1983-87	◆7840573	21.25
(14) Bearing Kit (Stub shaft)		
1983-87	◆7829888	19.25

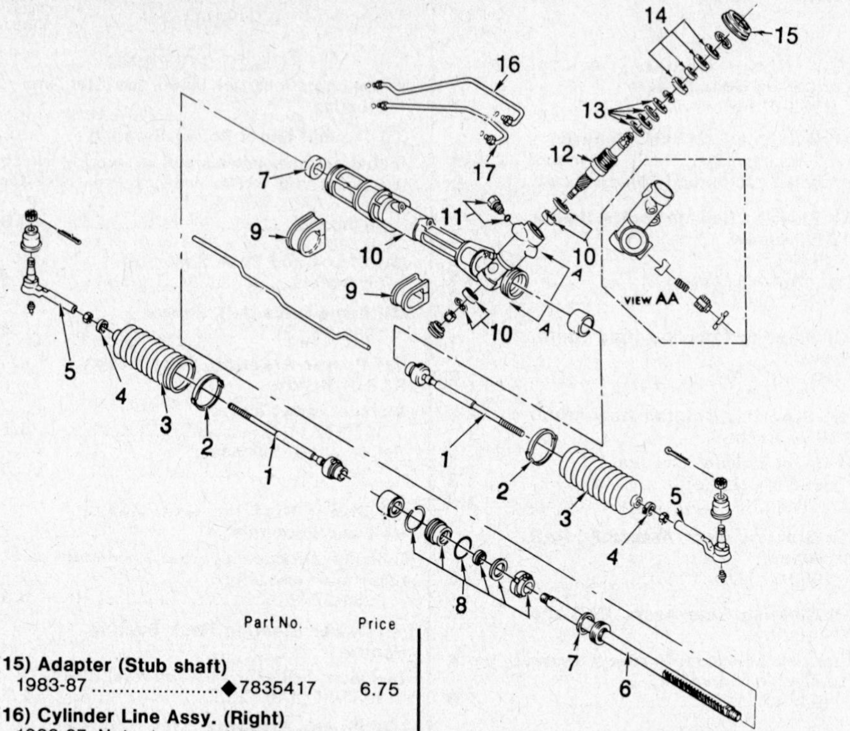

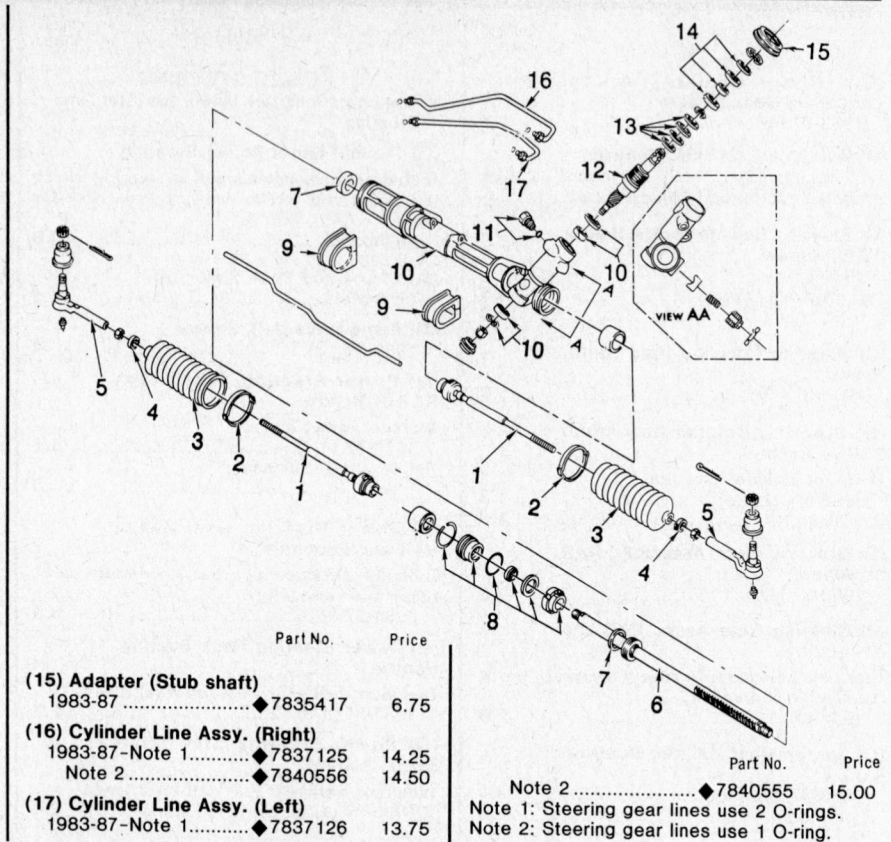

	Part No.	Price
(15) Adapter (Stub shaft)		
1983-87	◆7835417	6.75
(16) Cylinder Line Assy. (Right)		
1983-87-Note 1	◆7837125	14.25
Note 2	◆7840556	14.50
(17) Cylinder Line Assy. (Left)		
1983-87-Note 1	◆7837126	13.75

	Part No.	Price
Note 2	◆7840555	15.00

Note 1: Steering gear lines use 2 O-rings.
Note 2: Steering gear lines use 1 O-ring.

PARTS 11 POWER STEERING PUMP 11 PARTS

	Part No.	Price
Pump Assy.		
1983-87	◆7842630	199.00
Pump Drive Belt		
Order by model & description.		
Oil Pressure Hose		
1.6L		
1983-87	◆7842619	57.00
1.8L Diesel		
1983-87	◆7839871	34.25
(1) Shaft, Drive		
1983-87	◆7837321	39.50
(2) Seal		
1983-87	◆7808195	4.50
(3) 'O' Ring Seal Kit		
1983-87	◆7834853	11.00
(4) Plate, Thrust		
1983-87	◆7836369	13.75
(5) Flow Control Valve		
1983-87	◆7809226	10.75
(6) Valve Spring		
1983-87	◆5688037	1.50
(7) Pump Housing		
1983-87	◆7840523	68.00
(8) Rotor, Repair Kit		
1983-87	◆7837337	91.50
Repair kit includes, rotor, ring & vanes.		
(9) Ring		
1983-87	◆5688014	1.00
(10) Pressure Plate		
1983-87	◆7839669	14.25

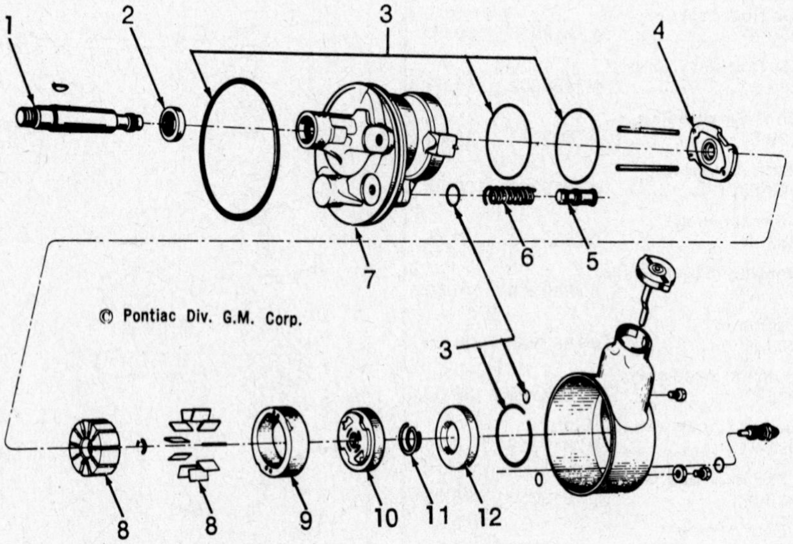

	Part No.	Price
(11) Pressure Plate Spring		
1983-87	◆7839667	1.00
(12) End Plate		
1983-87	◆5689358	3.50

LABOR 12 CYLINDER HEAD & VALVE SYSTEM 12 LABOR

	(Factory Time)	Chilton Time
GASOLINE ENGINE		
(G) Compression Test		
1983-87		.6
(G) Cylinder Head Gasket, Renew		
Includes: Clean carbon and make all necessary adjustments.		
1983	(3.3)	4.5
1984-87	(4.4)	6.0
w/A.C. add	(.3)	.3
w/P.S. add	(2.)	.2
(G) Cylinder Head, Renew		
Includes: Transfer all component parts, reface valves, clean carbon.		
1983	(5.0)	6.7
1984-87	(5.6)	7.6
w/A.C. add	(.3)	.3
w/P.S. add	(.2)	.2
(P) Clean Carbon and Grind Valves		
Includes: R&R cylinder head, grind valves and seats. Minor tune up.		
1983	(4.8)	7.0
1984-87	(5.8)	8.0
w/A.C. add	(.3)	.3
w/P.S. add	(.2)	.2
(G) Valve Rocker Arms, Renew		
1983-87-one cyl	(.7)	1.0
all cyls	(1.0)	1.5
R&R carb add		.5
(G) Valve Rocker Arm Adjusters, Renew		
1983-87-one cyl	(.7)	1.0
all cyls	(1.0)	1.5
R&R carb add		.5

COMBINATIONS

Add to Valve Job

See Machine Shop Operations

	(Factory Time)	Chilton Time
(G) DRAIN, EVACUATE & RECHARGE AIR CONDITIONING SYSTEM		
All models	(.5)	1.0
(G) HYDRAULIC VALVE LIFTERS, DISASSEMBLE AND CLEAN		
Each	(.2)	.2
(G) DISTRIBUTOR, RECONDITION		
All models	(.5)	.8
(G) CARBURETOR, RECONDITION		
All models	(.7)	1.2
(P) VALVE GUIDES, REAM OVERSIZE		
Each	(.2)	.2

	(Factory Time)	Chilton Time
(G) Valve Spring and/or Valve Stem Oil Seals, Renew (Head On Car)		
1983-87-one cyl	(.9)	1.3
all cyls	(1.7)	2.5
R&R carb add		.5
(G) Camshaft Housing Cover or Gasket, Renew		
1983-87-one side	(.4)	.6
both sides	(.6)	1.0
DIESEL ENGINE		
(G) Compression Test		
1983-87		.7
(G) Cylinder Head Gasket, Renew		
Includes: Clean gasket surfaces, bleed lifters and adjust timing. Drain and refill cooling system.		
1983-87	(3.3)	4.5
w/P.S. add	(.2)	.2
(G) Cylinder Head, Renew		
Includes: Clean gasket surfaces, transfer parts. Reface valves. Bleed lifters and adjust timing. Drain and refill cooling system.		
1983-87	(4.3)	5.9
w/P.S. add	(.2)	.2
(P) Clean Carbon and Grind Valves		
Includes: R&R cylinder head, clean carbon. Recondition valves and seats. Check and adjust valve stem length. Bleed lifters, drain and refill cooling system.		
1983-87	(5.1)	7.0
w/P.S. add	(.2)	.2
(G) Rocker Arm Cover or Gasket, Renew		
1983-87	(.5)	.8
(G) Rocker Arm, Renew		
1983-87-one cyl	(.8)	1.1
each adtnl cyl	(.1)	.1
(G) Rocker Arm Shaft, Renew		
1983-87	(.9)	1.2
(G) Valve Clearance, Adjust		
1983-87	(.6)	1.0
(G) Valve Springs and/or Valve Stem Oil Seals, Renew (Head on Car)		
1983-87-one cyl	(.9)	1.3
all cyls	(1.4)	2.0

PARTS 12 CYLINDER HEAD & VALVE SYSTEM 12 PARTS

	Part No.	Price
Valve Grind Gasket Set		
1983-87	◆14033458	38.00
(1) Cylinder Head		
1983-87	◆14083512	282.00
(2) Cylinder Head Gasket		
1983-87	◆359190	8.25
(3) Exhaust Valve (Std.)		
1983-87	◆14032316	23.75
(4) Intake Valve (Std.)		
1983-87	◆14032315	17.50
(5) Temperature Switch		
1983-87	◆25036035	10.50
(6) Valve Spring		
1983-87	◆14032344	2.75

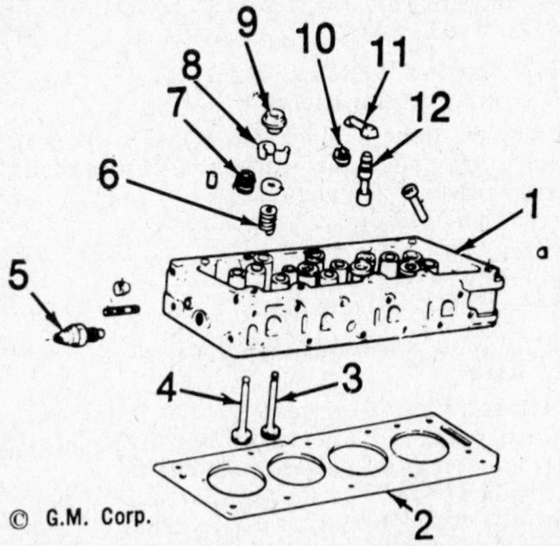

© G.M. Corp.

	Part No.	Price
(7) Valve Stem Seal		
1983-87-Intake	◆470110	4.50
Exhaust	◆470112	4.50
(8) Valve Key		
1983-87	◆360505	1.00
(9) Valve Spring Cap		
1983-87	◆376306	1.00
(10) Guide (Rocker Arm)		
1983-87	◆376308	1.00
(11) Rocker Arm		
1983-87	◆369355	5.50
(12) Adjuster (Valve Lash)		
1983-87	◆5233315	11.00

PARTS 12 CYLINDER HEAD & VALVE SYSTEM 12 PARTS

	Part No.	Price
DIESEL ENGINE		
Overhaul Top Gasket Kit		
1983-87	◆94238643	72.00
Engine Gasket Kit		
1983-84	◆94238642	98.50
1985-87	◆94144592	98.50
(1) Cylinder Head Assy.		
1983-87	◆94257551	378.00
(2) Cylinder Head Gasket		
1983-87	◆94235060	40.50
(3) Valve (Intake)		
1983-87	◆94216589	18.75
(4) Valve (Exhaust)		
1983-87	◆94216590	20.50
(5) End Cap (Valve Stems)		
1983-87	◆94221063	3.50
(6) Inserts (Valve Seats)		
1983-84-Intake	◆94228701	8.00
Exhaust	◆94228702	8.00
1985-Intake	◆94105292	8.10
Exhaust	◆94105293	8.10
(7) Sealing Cup (Cyl. Head)		
1983-87	◆94029588	1.50

PARTS 12 CYLINDER HEAD & VALVE SYSTEM 12 PARTS

	Part No.	Price
(8) Hot Plug Assy.		
1983-87	◆94026504	1.00
(9) Seal Cup (Front & Rear)		
1983-87	◆94029576	4.25
(10) Sealing Cup (Cyl. Head)		
1983-87	◆94030184	2.25
(11) Valve Guides		
1983-87	◆94029594	4.25
(12) Sealing Cup		
1983-87	◆94029604	8.75
(13) Bracket (Rocker Shaft)		
1983-rear	◆94029604	8.75
(14) Spring (Front & Rear)		
1983-87	◆94220054	1.00
(15) Rocker Arm Shaft		
1983-84	◆94029602	35.75
1985-87	◆94139343	27.25
(16) Rocker Arm		
1983-84	◆94221087	12.50
1985-87	◆94139342	12.50
(17) Bracket (Rocker Shaft)		
1983-87-Front	◆94029603	8.75
(18) Valve Key		
1983-87	◆94026380	2.25
(19) Valve Spring Cap (Upper)		
1983-87	◆94029600	3.75
(20) Valve Spring (Outer)		
1983-87	◆94231408	3.00
(21) Valve Spring (Inner)		
1983-87	◆94231409	1.75

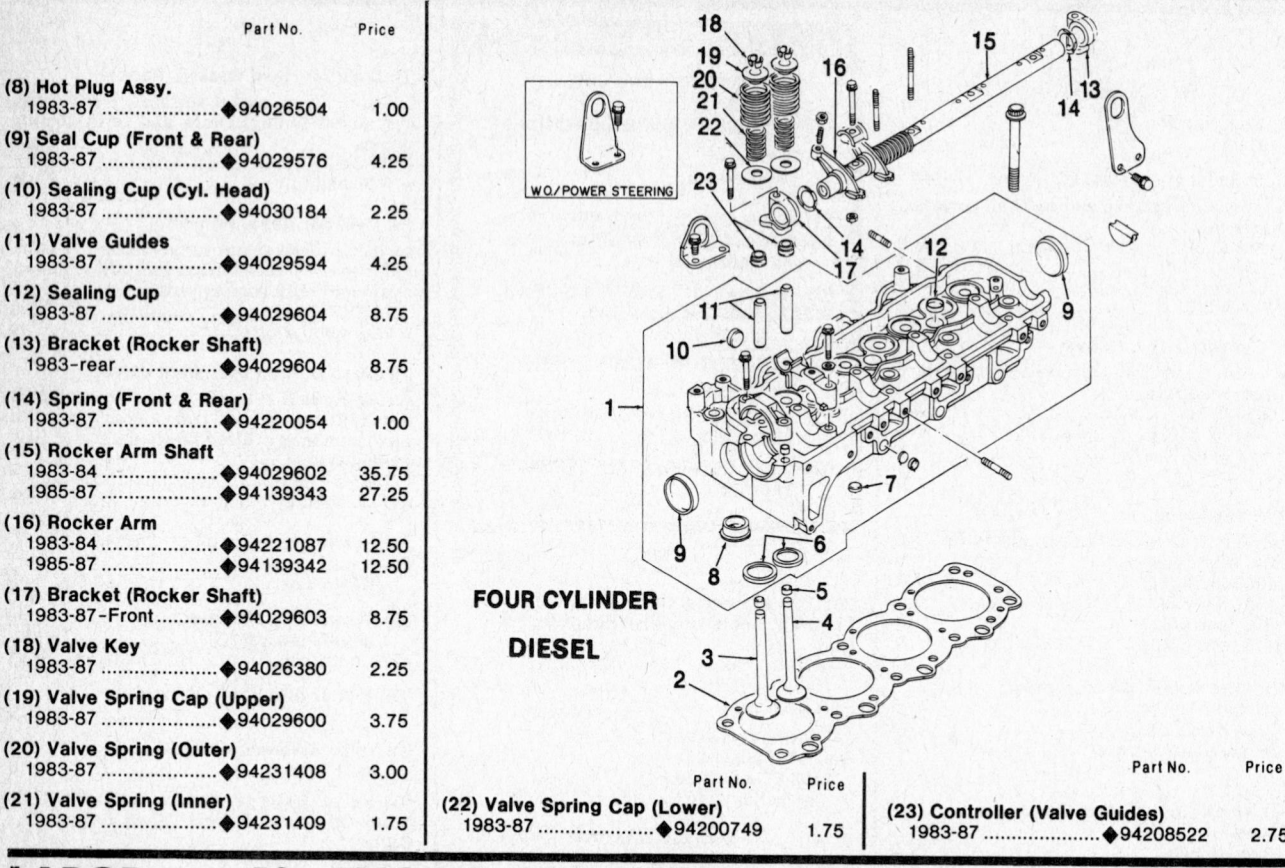

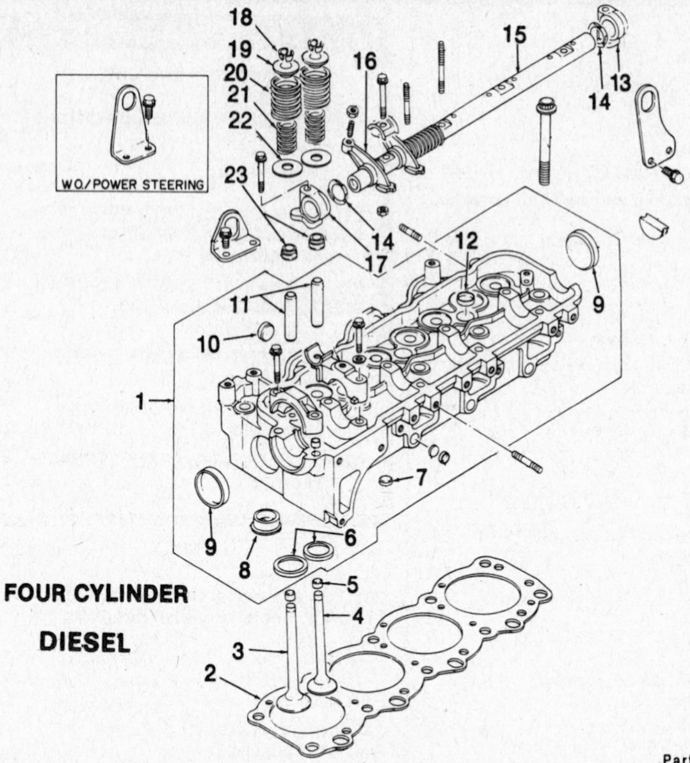

	Part No.	Price
(22) Valve Spring Cap (Lower)		
1983-87	◆94200749	1.75
(23) Controller (Valve Guides)		
1983-87	◆94208522	2.75

LABOR 13 ENGINE ASSEMBLY & MOUNTS 13 LABOR

(Factory Time)	Chilton Time

GASOLINE ENGINE

(G) Engine Assembly, Remove & Install

Does not include transfer of any parts or equipment.

1983-87	5.9
w/A.C. add (.7)	.7
w/P.S. add (.5)	.5
w/A.I.R. add (.4)	.4

(G) Engine Assembly, Renew

Includes: R&R engine and transmission assy. Transfer all component parts not supplied with replacement engine. Minor tune up.

1983-87 (4.8)	7.4
w/A.C. add (.7)	.7
w/P.S. add (.5)	.5
w/A.I.R. add (.4)	.4

(P) Cylinder Block, Renew (w/All Internal Parts Less Head(s) and Oil Pan)

Includes: Transfer all component parts not supplied with replacement engine, clean carbon, grind valves. Minor tune up.

1983-87 (9.8)	13.7
w/A.C. add (.7)	.7
w/P.S. add (.5)	.5
w/A.I.R. add (.4)	.4

(P) Cylinder Block, Renew (w/Pistons, Rings and Bearings)

Includes: R&R engine and transmission assy. Transfer all component parts, clean carbon, grind valves. Minor tune up.

1983-87 (12.3)	17.2
w/A.C. add (.7)	.7
w/P.S. add (.5)	.5
w/A.I.R. add (.4)	.4

(P) Engine Assy., R&R and Recondition (Complete)

Includes: Rebore block, install new pistons, rings, rod and main bearings. Clean carbon, grind valves. Tune engine.

1983-87 (19.8)	27.7
w/A.C. add (.7)	.7
w/P.S. add (.5)	.5
w/A.I.R. add (.4)	.4

(P) Engine Assembly, Recondition (In Car)

Includes: Expand or renew pistons, install new rings, pins, rod and main bearings. Clean carbon and grind valves. Tune engine.

1983-87 (13.2)	16.7
w/A.C. add (.4)	.4
w/P.S. add (.2)	.2
w/A.I.R. add (.4)	.4

(G) Engine Mounts, Renew

1983-87-front-one (.9)	1.1
both (1.1)	1.4
rear (.4)	.5

DIESEL ENGINE

(G) Engine Assembly, Remove & Install

Does not include transfer of any parts or equipment.

1983-87	4.0
w/P.S. add	.2

(G) Engine Assembly, Renew

Includes: R&R engine assembly, transfer all component parts not supplied with replacement engine. Make all necessary adjustments.

1983-87 (3.7)	6.0
w/P.S. add (.2)	.2

(P) Cylinder Block, Renew (w/All Internal Parts Less Head and Oil Pan)

Includes: R&R engine, transfer all component parts not supplied with replacement engine. Clean carbon, grind valves. Make all necessary adjustments.

1983-87 (7.4)	10.7
w/P.S. add (.2)	.2

(P) Engine Assy., R&R and Recondition

Includes: Rebore block, install new pistons, rings, rod and main bearings. Clean carbon, grind valves. Make all necessary adjustments.

1983-87 (12.8)	18.5
w/P.S. add (.2)	.2

(P) Engine Assembly, Recondition (In Car)

Includes: Expand or renew pistons, install new rings, rod and main bearings. Clean carbon, grind valves. Make all necessary adjustments.

1983-87 (10.9)	15.2
w/P.S. add (.2)	.2

(G) Engine Mounts, Renew

Front

1983-87-one (.6)	.9
both (.9)	1.2

Rear

1983-87 (.4)	.6

PARTS 13 ENGINE ASSEMBLY & MOUNTS 13 PARTS

	Part No.	Price
Engine Assembly (Partial)		
1.6L		
1983-87	◆14079004	947.25
1.8L Diesel		
1983-84	◆94239773	1604.25
1985-87	◆94169128	N.L.
Cylinder Block (Fitted)		
1.6L		
1983	◆14033422	631.25
1984-87	◆14079003	663.00
Engine Overhaul Gaskets (Partial)		
1983-87-1.6L	◆14008925	15.00
1983-84-Diesel	◆94238642	98.50
1985-87-Diesel	◆94144592	98.50

For complete overhaul gasket package also order valve grind set.

	Part No.	Price
Engine Mounts		
1983-87-1.6L	◆363406	14.00
Diesel	◆14031507	12.50

LABOR 14 PISTONS, RINGS & BEARINGS 14 LABOR

(Factory Time) Chilton Time

GASOLINE ENGINE

(P) Rings, Renew (See Engine Combinations)

Includes: Remove cylinder top ridge, deglaz cylinder walls. Clean piston and ring grooves. Minor tune up.

	Chilton Time
1983-87-w/200 trans	
one (5.6)	8.1
all (6.8)	9.8
w/M.T. or 180 trans	
one (6.1)	8.4
all (7.3)	10.0
w/A.C. add (.3)	.3
w/P.S. add (.2)	.2
w/A.I.R. add (.2)	.2

(P) Piston or Connecting Rod, Renew

Includes: Remove cylinder top ridge, deglaze cylinder walls, clean piston and ring grooves. Minor tune up.

	Chilton Time
1983-87-w/200 trans	
one (5.6)	8.4
all (6.8)	11.0
w/M.T. or 180 trans	
one (6.1)	8.7
all (7.3)	11.2
w/A.C. add (.3)	.3
w/P.S. add (.2)	.2
w/A.I.R. add (.2)	.2

(P) Connecting Rod Bearings, Renew

	Chilton Time
1983-w/200 trans	
one (1.9)	2.7
all (2.8)	3.7
w/M.T. or 180 trans	
one (2.6)	3.3
all (3.5)	4.3

COMBINATIONS

Add to Engine Work

See Machine Shop Operations

(Factory Time)	Chilton Time
(G) DRAIN, EVACUATE & RECHARGE AIR CONDITIONING SYSTEM	
All models (.5)	1.0
(G) HYDRAULIC VALVE LIFTERS, DISASSEMBLE AND CLEAN	
Each (.2)	.2
(G) DISTRIBUTOR, RECONDITION	
All models (.5)	.8
(G) CARBURETOR, RECONDITION	
All models (.7)	1.2
(G) CYLINDER HEAD R&R (ENGINE REMOVED)	
Four eng Code C (1.5)	2.0
(P) VALVE GUIDES, REAM OVERSIZE	
Each (.2)	.2
(G) CONNECTING ROD, RENEW (ENGINE DISASSEMBLED)	
Four eng Code C-each (.3)	.4
(G) DEGLAZE CYLINDER WALLS	
Each (.1)	.1
(G) REMOVE CYLINDER TOP RIDGE	
Each (.1)	.1
(G) TIMING BELT, RENEW	
All models (.8)	1.4
(G) MAIN BEARINGS, RENEW	
All models (1.5)	2.0
(G) PLASTIGAUGE BEARINGS	
Each (.1)	.1
(M) OIL FILTER ELEMENT, RENEW	
All models (.3)	.3

(Factory Time)	Chilton Time
1984-87-one (3.0)	4.1
all (3.9)	5.4

DIESEL ENGINE

(P) Rings, Renew (See Engine Combinations)

Includes: Remove cylinder top ridge, deglaze cylinder walls. Clean piston and ring grooves. Make all necessary adjustments.

	Chilton Time
1983-87-one cyl (6.5)	9.4
all cyls (7.7)	11.0
w/P.S. add (.2)	.2

(P) Pistons or Connecting Rods, Renew

Includes: Remove cylinder top ridge, deglaze cylinder walls. Make all necessary adjustments.

	Chilton Time
1983-87-one cyl (6.5)	9.7
all cyls (7.7)	12.2
w/P.S. add (.2)	.2

(P) Connecting Rod Bearings, Renew

	Chilton Time
1983-87-one (3.4)	4.4
all (4.3)	5.4
w/P.S. add (.2)	.2

PARTS 14 PISTONS, RINGS & BEARINGS 14 PARTS

	Part No.	Price
(1) Piston Ring Set (1 Piston)		
1.6L		
1983	◆374697	13.50
1984-87	◆14079341	16.50
1.8L Diesel		
1983-87	◆94224221	23.25
(2) Piston Assy. (w/Pin)		
1.6L		
1983	◆14001187	48.50
1984-87	◆14066397	48.50
1.8L Diesel		
1983-87	◆94228886	57.25
(3) Connecting Rod Assy.		
1983-87-1.6L	◆466336	42.25
Diesel	◆94240944	N.L.
(4) Connecting Rod Bearings		
1983-87-1.6L	◆374105	10.00
Diesel	◆94221167	N.L.

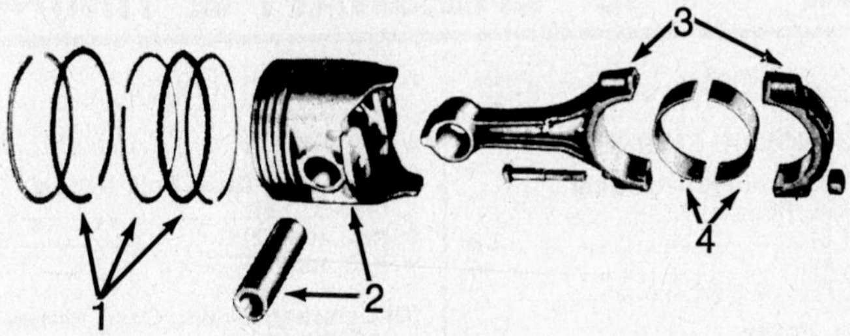

LABOR 15 CRANKSHAFT & DAMPER 15 LABOR

(Factory Time)	Chilton Time
GASOLINE ENGINE	
(P) Crankshaft and Main Bearings, Renew	
Includes: R&R engine, check all bearing clearances.	
1983-87 (7.0)	10.1
w/A.C. add (.5)	.7
w/P.S. add (.4)	.5
(P) Main Bearings, Renew	
Includes: Check all bearing clearances.	
1983-w/200 trans (2.9)	4.0
w/M.T. or 180 trans (3.6)	4.7
1984-87 (4.2)	5.7
(P) Main and Rod Bearings, Renew	
Includes: Check all bearing clearances.	
1983-w/200 trans (4.1)	5.7
w/M.T. or 180 trans (4.8)	6.4
1984-87 (5.4)	6.9
(G) Rear Main Bearing Oil Seal, Renew or Repack	
Includes: R&R engine assy; or trans as required	
1983 (3.8)	6.4
1984-87 (3.0)	4.0
w/A.C. add (.5)	.7
w/P.S. add (.4)	.5
(G) Crankshaft Drive Belt Pulley, Renew	
1983-87 (.3)	.6
w/A.C. add (.2)	.2
w/P.S. add (.3)	.3
DIESEL ENGINE	
(P) Crankshaft and Main Bearings, Renew	
Includes: R&R engine, check all bearing clearances.	
1983-87 (6.6)	9.5
w/P.S. add (.2)	.2
(P) Main Bearings, Renew	
Includes: Check all bearing clearances.	
1983-87 (4.6)	7.0
w/P.S. add (.2)	.2
(P) Main and Rod Bearings, Renew	
Includes: Check all bearing clearances.	
1983-87 (5.2)	8.2
w/P.S. add (.2)	.2
(G) Rear Main Bearing Oil Seal, Renew or Repack	
Includes: R&R trans, oil pan and rear main bearing cap.	
1983-87-w/M.T. (2.0)	3.0
w/A.T. (2.8)	3.8
(G) Crankshaft Pulley, Renew	
1983-87 (.4)	.7
w/P.S. add (.2)	.2
(G) Crankcase Front Cover Seal, Renew	
1983-87 (1.4)	2.0
w/P.S. add (.2)	.2
(G) Crankcase Front Cover and/or Gasket, Renew	
1983-87 (1.5)	2.2
w/P.S. add (.2)	.2

PARTS 15 CRANKSHAFT & DAMPER 15 PARTS

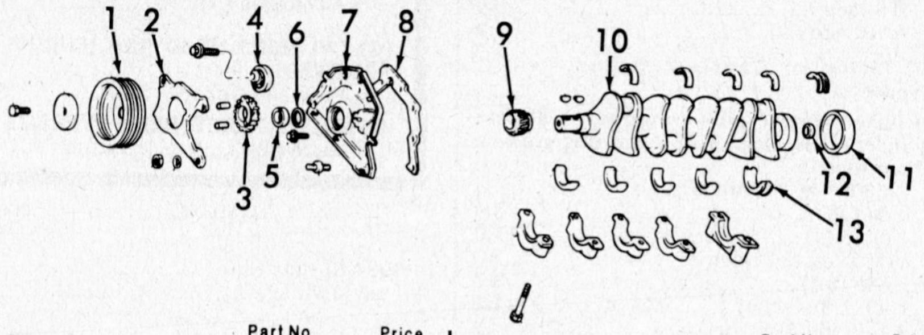

	Part No.	Price
(1) Pulley (Crankshaft)		
1.6L		
1983-87-wo/P.S.	◆14076354	20.50
P.S.	◆14090952	24.25
1.8L Diesel		
1983-87	◆94245136	93.75
(2) Front Cover (Lower)		
1983-87	◆458685	11.00
(3) Crankshaft Gear		
1.6L		
1983-87	◆14076378	N.L.
1.8L Diesel		
1983-87	◆94224637	31.25
(4) Idler Pulley (Timing Belt)		
1983-87-1.6L	◆908252	44.50
Diesel	◆94220901	36.25
(5) Spacer (Crankshaft Gear)		
1983-87-1.6L	◆360567	1.00
Diesel	◆94221742	3.75
(6) Oil Seal (Front)		
1.6L		
1983	◆14033199	5.50
1984-87	◆14076303	4.50
1.8L Diesel		
1983-87	◆94214912	9.50
(7) Crankshaft Cover (Front)		
1983-87	◆14008874	27.00
(8) Cover Gasket (Front)		
1983-87-1.6L	◆359105	3.00
Diesel	◆94217007	2.00
(9) Drive Gear (Distributor)		
1983-87	◆360538	19.50
(10) Crankshaft		
1.6L		
1983-87	◆14023797	298.00
1.8L Diesel		
1983-87	◆94242889	337.00
(11) Rear Main Bearing Oil Seal		
1.6L		
1983-87	◆364800	9.00
1.8L Diesel		
1983-87	◆94214913	17.75
(12) Pilot Bearing		
1.6L		
1983-87	◆476574	2.50
1.8L Diesel		
1983-87	◆900529	9.75
(13) Main Bearing Pkg.		
1.6L		
1983-87-exc. rear	◆374135	N.L.
rear	◆374141	12.75
1.8L Diesel		
1983-84	◆94220838	80.50
1985-87	◆94250262	76.75

LABOR 16 CAMSHAFT & TIMING GEARS 16 LABOR

(Factory Time)	Chilton Time
GASOLINE ENGINE	
(G) Crankcase Front Cover Seal and/or Gasket, Renew	
1983-87 (1.6)	2.8
w/A.C. add (.4)	.4
w/P.S. add (.7)	.7
(G) Camshaft, Renew	
Includes: Raise front of engine. Adjust valves.	
1983-87 (2.5)	3.9
w/A.C. add (.4)	.4
w/P.S. add (.3)	.3
(G) Camshaft Drive Belt, Renew	
1983-87 (.8)	1.4
w/A.C. add (.2)	.2
w/P.S. add (.3)	.3
(G) Camshaft Timing Gear, Renew	
1983-87 (.5)	1.0
Renew oil seal add (.2)	.2
w/A.C. add (.2)	.2
w/P.S. add (.3)	.3
(G) Crankshaft Timing Gear, Renew	
Includes: R&R camshaft drive belt.	
1983-87 (1.3)	2.0
w/A.C. add (.2)	.2
w/P.S. add (.3)	.3
(G) Camshaft Carrier, Renew	
Includes: R&R cylinder head and renew gasket.	
1983 (3.4)	5.1
1984-87 (4.4)	6.0
w/A.C. add (.3)	.3

LABOR 16 CAMSHAFT & TIMING GEARS 16 LABOR

(Factory Time)	Chilton Time
w/P.S. add (.3)	.3
DIESEL ENGINE	
(G) Camshaft Drive Belt Cover and/or Gasket, Renew	
1983-87	
upper (.3)	.5
lower or both (.5)	.8
w/P.S. add (.2)	.2
(G) Camshaft Drive Belt, Renew	
1983-87 (1.6)	2.2
w/P.S. add (.2)	.2
(G) Camshaft Idler Pulley, Renew	
1983-87 (1.7)	2.3
w/P.S. add (.2)	.2
(G) Crankshaft Timing Gear, Renew	
1983-87 (1.9)	2.5
w/P.S. add (.2)	.2
(G) Camshaft Timing Gear, Renew	
1983-87 (1.6)	2.2
Renew oil seal add (.2)	.2
w/P.S. add (.2)	.2
(G) Camshaft, Renew	
1983-87 (2.3)	3.2
w/P.S. add (.2)	.2
(G) Injection Pump Drive Gear, Renew	
1983-87 (1.7)	2.3
w/P.S. add (.2)	.2

PARTS 16 CAMSHAFT & TIMING GEARS 16 PARTS

	Part No.	Price
(1) Timing Belt		
1983-87	◆14001168	22.00
(2) Cover (Upper)		
1983-87	◆376387	11.00
(3) Housing (Camshaft)		
1983-87	◆14001171	202.00
(4) Gasket (Housing Cover)		
1983-87	◆1052366	7.50
(5) Camshaft Gear		
1983-87	◆14001166	31.25
(6) Guide (Camshaft Gear)		
1983-87	◆376405	5.75
(7) Front Oil Seal (Camshaft)		
1983	◆14033199	5.50
1984-87	◆14076303	4.50
(8) Camshaft		
1983-87	◆466334	127.00

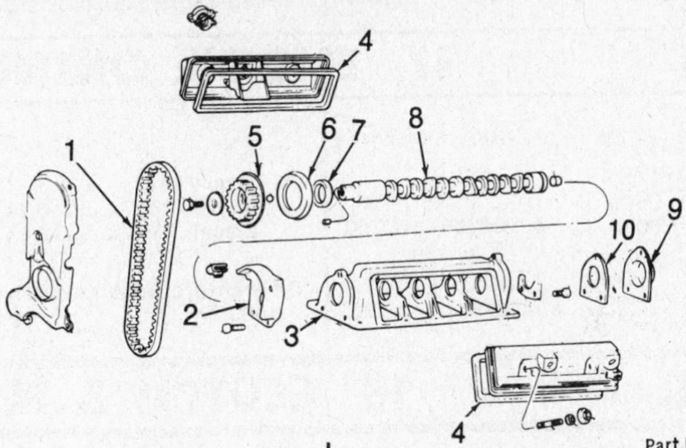

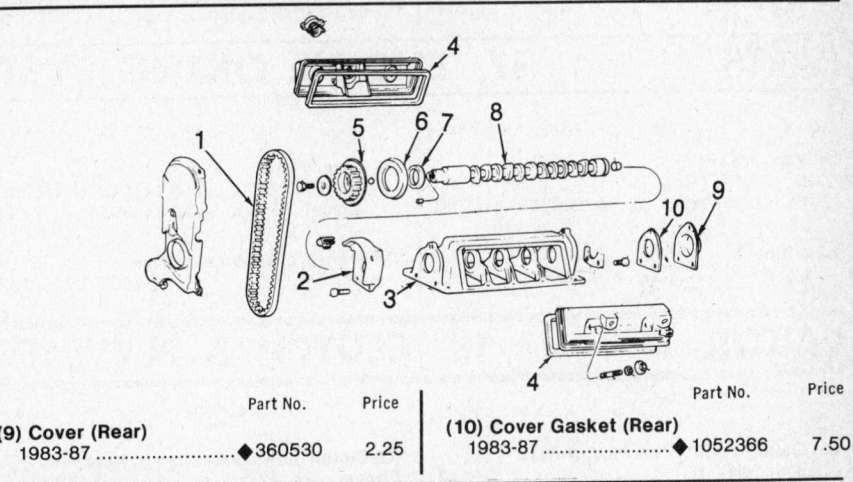

	Part No.	Price
(9) Cover (Rear)		
1983-87	◆360530	2.25
(10) Cover Gasket (Rear)		
1983-87	◆1052366	7.50

PARTS 16 CAMSHAFT & TIMING GEARS 16 PARTS

DIESEL ENGINE

	Part No.	Price
(1) Dust Cover (Upper)		
1983-87	◆94223910	34.25
(2) Gasket (Dustcover)		
1983-87	◆94217019	5.00
(3) Dustcover (Lower)		
1983-87	◆94244595	28.50
(4) Timing Wheel (Oil Pump)		
1983-87	◆94239176	43.25
(5) Timing Pulley (Crankshaft)		
1983-87	◆94224637	31.25
(6) Pulley Flange (Crankshaft)		
1983-87	◆94221742	3.75
(7) Idler		
1983-87	◆94220901	36.25
(8) Pulley Flange (Camshaft)		
1983-87	◆94221333	5.00
(9) Pulley (Tension)		
1983-87	◆94220900	38.75
(10) Plate (Tension Pulley)		
1983-87	◆94223812	17.75
(11) Spring (Tensioner)		
1983-87	◆94223818	1.50
(12) Stopper (Spring Tension)		
1983-87	◆94217011	2.00
(13) Timing Pulley (Injection Pump)		
1983-87	◆94233209	63.50
(14) Pulley Bracket (Injection Pump)		
1983-87	◆94233210	6.00

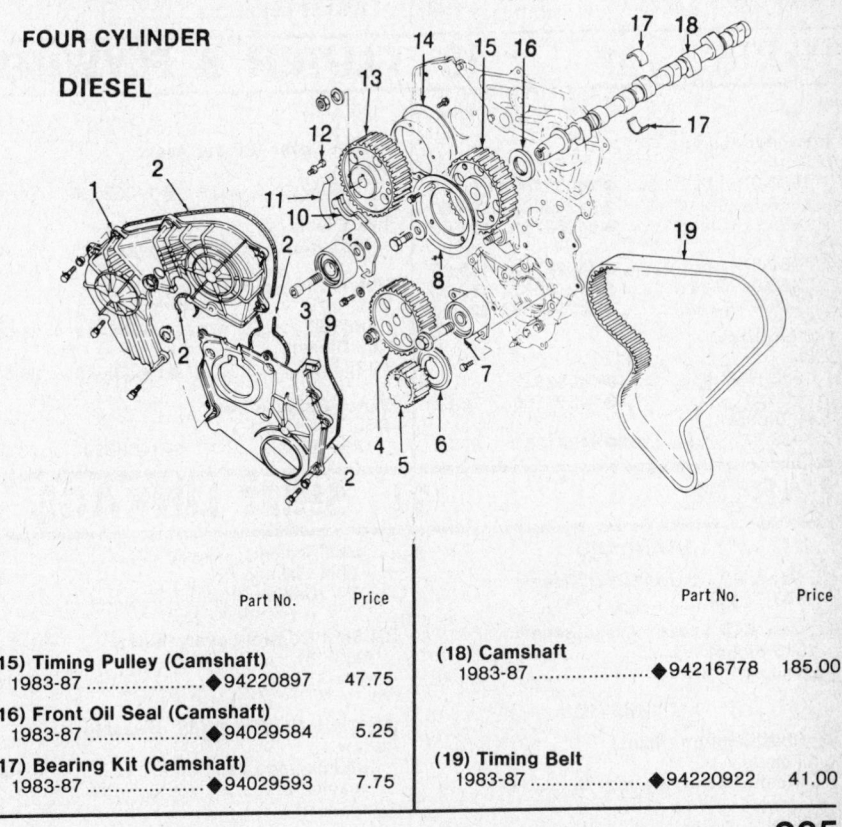

FOUR CYLINDER

DIESEL

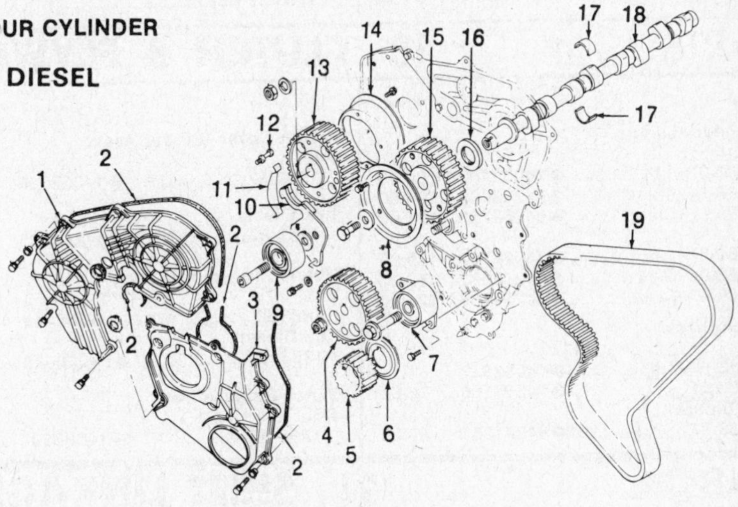

	Part No.	Price
(15) Timing Pulley (Camshaft)		
1983-87	◆94220897	47.75
(16) Front Oil Seal (Camshaft)		
1983-87	◆94029584	5.25
(17) Bearing Kit (Camshaft)		
1983-87	◆94029593	7.75
(18) Camshaft		
1983-87	◆94216778	185.00
(19) Timing Belt		
1983-87	◆94220922	41.00

LABOR 17 ENGINE OILING SYSTEM 17 LABOR

(Factory Time) Chilton Time

GASOLINE ENGINE

(G) Oil Pan or Gasket, Renew
1983-w/200 trans (1.7) 2.5
w/M.T. or 180 trans (2.3) 3.1
w/A.C. add (.2) 5
1984-87 (2.7) 3.6
w/P.S. add (.1) 1

(P) Pressure Test Engine Bearings (Pan Off)
All models 1.0

(G) Oil Pump, Renew
Includes: Transfer screen and drive to pump.
1983-w/200 trans (2.4) 3.4
w/M.T. or 180 trans (3.0) 4.0
w/A.C. add (.5) 5
1984-87 (3.6) 4.8
w/P.S. add (.1) 1

(G) Oil Pressure Gauge (Engine), Renew
1983-87 (.3) 4

(M) Oil Filter By-Pass Valve, Renew
1983-87 (.3) 4

(M) Oil Filter Element, Renew
1983-87 (.3) 4

DIESEL ENGINE

(G) Oil Pan and/or Gasket, Renew
1983-87 (3.6) 4.8
w/P.S. add (.2) 2

(P) Pressure Test Engine Bearings (Pan Off)
All models 1.0

(G) Oil Pump, Renew
1983-87 (1.2) 1.6
w/P.S. add (.2) 2

(M) Oil Filter Element, Renew
1983-87 (.2) 3

PARTS 17 ENGINE OILING SYSTEM 17 PARTS

	Part No.	Price
Oil Pan Gasket		
1.6L		
1983-87 (sealant)	◆1052366	7.50
1.8L Diesel		
1983-87	◆94226564	12.75
Oil Pump Assy.		
1983-87-1.6L	◆14008878	70.00
Diesel	◆94239141	72.25
Oil Pressure Regulator Valve		
1983-87-1.6L	◆360572	1.75
Oil Pump Pipe Assy. (w/Screen)		
1983-87-1.6L	◆376316	11.50
Diesel	◆94217626	34.75
Oil Pressure Switch		
1983-87-1.6L	◆10002798	5.50
Diesel	◆94021127	23.75

LABOR 18 CLUTCH & FLYWHEEL 18 LABOR

(Factory Time) Chilton Time

(G) Clutch Pedal Free Play, Adjust
All models (.3) 3

(G) Clutch Assembly, Renew
Includes: R&R trans and adjust free play.
1983-87 (1.9) 2.8
Renew pilot brg add (.2) 2

(G) Clutch Release Bearing or Fork, Renew
Includes: R&R trans and adjust free play.
1983-87 (1.8) 2.6

(G) Clutch Control Cable, Renew
1983-87 (.5) 8

(G) Flywheel, Renew
Includes: R&R trans assy.
1983-87 (2.1) 3.0
Renew ring gear add (.3) 5

PARTS 18 CLUTCH & FLYWHEEL 18 PARTS

	Part No.	Price
Flywheel Assm.		
(A.T.)		
1983-87-1.6L	◆14001182	60.25
1983-84-Diesel	◆94243383	97.50
1985-87-Diesel	◆94259753	121.00
(M.T.)		
1983-87-1.6L	◆14023782	129.00
1983-84-Diesel	◆94242392	162.00
1985-87-Diesel	◆94259753	121.00
Clutch Disc		
1.6L		
1983-87-4 spd.	◆14032337	N.L.
5 spd.	◆14061506	76.50
1.8L Diesel		
1983-87	◆94241951	89.25
Clutch Cover & Plate Assy.		
1.6L		
1983-87	◆14032336	103.00
1.8L Diesel		
1983-87	◆94245965	123.00
Clutch Throwout Bearing		
1.6L		
1983-87	◆908244	26.00
1.8L Diesel		
1983-87	◆94020016	28.50
Clutch Release Fork		
1.6L		
1983-87	◆14038692	23.50
1.8L Diesel		
1983-84	◆94235755	10.75
1985-87	◆14062647	13.75
Clutch & Flywheel Housing		
1.6L		
1983-87-4 spd.	◆14062665	117.00
5 spd.	◆14053339	109.00
Clutch Control Cable Assy.		
1.6L		
1983	◆14038699	30.00
1984-87	◆14080793	30.75
1.8L Diesel		
1983	◆14038699	30.00
1984-87	◆14080794	30.75

LABOR 21 SHIFT LINKAGE 21 LABOR

STANDARD

(G) Gearshift Control Lever, Renew
1983-87 (.5) 7

(G) Gearshift Control Assy., Renew
1983-87 (.5) 8
Recond add (.3) 4

AUTOMATIC

(G) Shift Linkage, Adjust
All models
Neutral Safety Switch (.3) 4
Shift Indicator Needle (.2) 3
Shift Linkage (.4) 5
T.V. Cable (.3) 4

(G) Shift Control Lever, Renew
1983 (.3) 6
1984-87 (.5) 7

(G) Shift Control Rods or Cable, Renew
1983-84-rod (.3) 5
cable (.9) 1.2

(G) Park Lock Cable, Renew
1983-87 (.6) 9

(G) Gear Selector Indicator Assy. and/or Needle, Renew
Includes: Necessary adjustments.
1983-87 (.4) 8

(G) Floor Shift Control Assy., Renew
1983-87 (.5) 9

LABOR 25 U-JOINTS & DRIVESHAFT 25 LABOR

	(Factory Time)	Chilton Time
(G) Universal Joints, Renew		
Includes: R&R driveshaft.		
1983-87-front	(.6)	.9
rear	(.5)	.9
both	(.8)	1.5
(G) Driveshaft, Renew		
1983-87	(.3)	.5
(G) Pinion Shaft Flange, Renew		
1983-87	(.4)	.7

PARTS 25 UNIVERSAL JOINTS & DRIVE SHAFT 25 PARTS

	Part No.	Price
Universal Joint Assy.		
1983-87	◆7842007	28.75
Yoke Assy.		
1983-87-wo/ Damper	◆7834792	44.00
Damper	◆7834733	150.75

LABOR 26 REAR AXLE 26 LABOR

	(Factory Time)	Chilton Time
(M) Differential, Drain & Refill		
All models		.6
(M) Axle Housing Cover or Gasket, Renew		
1983-87	(.4)	.6
(G) Axle Shaft Oil Seal, Renew		
Includes: R&R bearing.		
1983-87-one	(.6)	1.1
both	(.8)	1.4
(G) Axle Shaft, Renew		
1983-87-one	(.6)	.9
both	(.7)	1.2
(G) Axle Shaft Bearing, Renew		
1983-87-one	(.7)	1.2
both	(.9)	1.5
(G) Axle Shaft Wheel Mounting Studs, Renew		
1983-87-one side		1.0
both sides		1.4
(G) Pinion Shaft Oil Seal, Renew		
1983-87	(.6)	1.0
(G) Differential Case Assy., Renew		
1983-87	(2.0)	3.0
(P) Ring and Pinion Gears, Renew		
1983-87	(2.7)	3.9
Renew pinion brgs add	(.2)	.3
Renew diff side brgs add	(.3)	.4
(P) Pinion Gear Bearings, Renew		
1983-87	(2.5)	3.8
Renew side brgs add	(.3)	.4
(P) Differential Side Bearings, Renew (One or Both)		
1983-87	(1.7)	2.9
(P) Pinion Shaft and/or Side and Pinion Gears, Renew		
Does not include R&R case.		
1983-87	(.9)	1.6
(P) Differential Side and Pinion Gear Bearings, Renew		
1983-87	(2.8)	3.7
(G) Rear Axle Housing, Renew		
1983-87	(3.5)	4.9
(G) Rear Axle Assy., Renew (Complete)		
1983-87	(1.7)	3.4
(G) Rear Axle Extension Assy., Renew		
1983-87	(.5)	.9
Overhaul extension assy. add	(.3)	.5

PARTS 26 REAR AXLE 26 PARTS

	Part No.	Price
(1) Rear Axle Shaft		
1983-87	◆361733	103.50
(2) Seal Assy. (Drive Pinion)		
1983-87	◆367599	8.00
(3) Sleeve (Drive Pinion)		
1983-87	◆359711	16.00
(4) Bearing Assy. (Front)		
1983-87	◆9427851	22.00
(5) Housing (Rear Axle)		
1983-87	◆14069892	385.75
(6) Spacer (Pinion Bearing)		
1983-87	◆14018397	2.25
(7) Bearing Assy. (Rear)		
1983-87	◆9439879	17.00
(8) Shim Pkg. (Pinion Bearing)		
1983-87-.021-.025	◆369131	5.50
.026-.031	◆369132	5.50
.032-.037	◆369133	5.50
.038-.041	◆14079093	1.50
(9) Ring & Pinion Gear Assy.		
1983-87-3.36R	◆14034944	251.25
3.62R	◆14034945	237.25
(10) Pinion Shaft		
1983-87	◆14066905	5.00

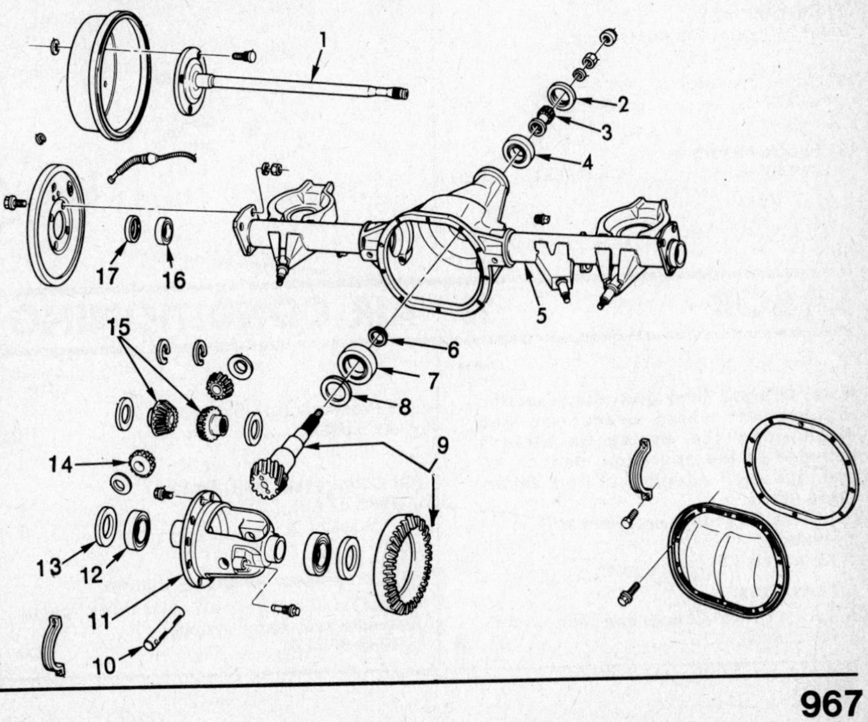

PARTS 26 REAR AXLE 26 PARTS

	Part No.	Price
(11) Differential Case		
1983-87	◆361755	79.00
(12) Side Bearing		
1983-87	◆9427889	21.25
(13) Shim Pkg. (Bearing Adjust)		
1983-87		
.040-.050	◆14024395	7.00
.052-.060	◆462701	11.25
.062-.070	◆462702	11.25
.072-.080	◆462703	11.25
.082-.088	◆462704	9.25
.090-.100	◆14024396	7.00
(14) Pinion Gear		
1983-87	◆14055901	10.75
(15) Side Gear		
1983-87	◆14055902	29.00
(16) Bearing Assy. (Rear Whl.)		
1983-87	◆7451992	17.50
(17) Seal (Rear Wheel Bearing)		
1983-87	◆361750	3.50

LABOR 27 REAR SUSPENSION 27 LABOR

(Factory Time)	Chilton Time
(G) Rear Coil Springs, Renew	
1983-87-one (.4)	.6
both (.5)	.8
(G) Rear Shock Absorbers, Renew	
1983-87-one (.3)	.4
both (.5)	.7
(G) Lower Control Arm Assy., Renew	
1983-87-one (.4)	.6
both (.5)	.9
Renew bushing add-each arm (.3)	.3
(G) Track Rod or Tie Rod Assy., Renew	
1983-87 (.4)	.7
Renew bushings add (.2)	.3
(G) Rear Stabilizer Bar, Renew	
1983-87 (.5)	.7

PARTS 27 REAR SUSPENSION 27 PARTS

	Part No.	Price
(1) Stabilizer Shaft		
(Not available)		
(2) Link Kit		
(Not available)		
(3) Lower Control Arm		
1983-87	◆476899	45.00
(4) Bushing		
1983-87	◆363465	6.25
(5) Axle Tie Rod		
1983-87	◆474794	49.75
(6) Lower Insulator		
1983-87	◆363468	3.50
(7) Rear Spring		
Order by model and description.		
(8) Upper Insulator		
1983-87	◆363467	3.50
(9) Shock Absorber		
1983-87	◆4993582	24.50

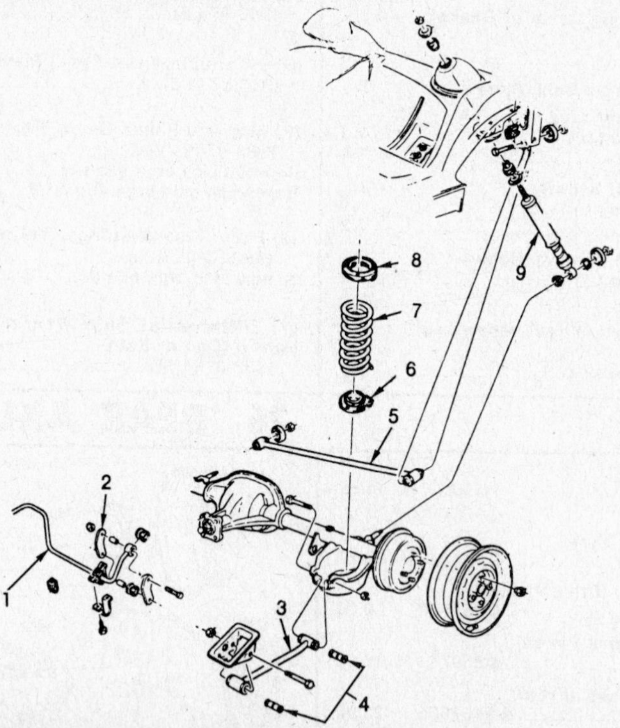

LABOR 28 AIR CONDITIONING 28 LABOR

(Factory Time)	Chilton Time
Note: If more than one item requires replacement where evacuation and discharging the system is already included in the operation, deduct 1.0 hour for each addditional item to the times listed.	
(G) Drain, Evacuate and Recharge System	
All models (.5)	1.0
(G) Leak Test	
Includes: Check all lines and connections.	
All models	.5
(G) Pressure Test System	
All models	1.0
(G) Compressor Belt, Renew	
1983-87 (.3)	.4
w/P.S. add (.3)	.3
(G) Compressor Assembly, Renew	
Includes: Transfer all attaching parts. Evacuate and charge system.	
1983-87 (1.0)	2.0
(G) Clutch Hub and Drive Plate, Renew	
Does not include R&R compressor.	
1983-87 (.5)	.8
(G) Compressor Rotor and/or Bearings, Renew	
1983-87 (.7)	1.0
(G) Compressor Pulley and/or Clutch Coil, Renew	
1983-87 (.7)	1.0
Renew pulley or brg add	.1

LABOR 28 AIR CONDITIONING 28 LABOR

(Factory Time) — Chilton Time

(G) Compressor Shaft Seal Kit, Renew
Includes: Evacuate and charge system.
1983-87 (1.5) 2.5
R&R accum add (.3) 3

(G) Front Bearing, Head or Seals, Renew
Includes: R&R compressor, R&R clutch and pulley assy. R&R shaft seal assy. Clean and inspect parts. Evacuate and charge system.
1983-87 (1.4) 2.8

(G) Outer Shell and/or 'O' Rings, Renew
Includes: R&R compressor, R&R clutch and pulley assy. Clean and inspect parts. Evacuate and charge system.
1983-87 (1.7) 2.8

(G) Valve Plate Assembly, Renew
Includes: R&R compressor, R&R clutch and pulley assy. R&R shell to internal mechanism. Clean and inspect parts. Evacuate and charge system.
1983-87 (1.8) 2.6
Renew two or more valves add (.1) 2

(G) Cylinder and Shaft Assy., Renew
Includes: R&R comp assy. Transfer clutch hub and drive plate, rotor, coil and switches. Renew seal kit. Install front head, outer shell and valve plates. Evacuate and charge system.
1983-87 (2.0) 2.9

(G) Compressor Relief Valve, Renew
Includes: Evacuate and charge system.
1983-87 (1.0) 1.4

(G) Condenser, Renew
Includes: Evacuate and charge system.
1983-87 (1.2) 2.0

AIR CONDITIONER TUNE-UP

For efficient operation and satisfactory performance in hot weather. The following air conditioner tune-up is suggested:

1. Clean intake filter
2. Clean condenser fins
3. Pressure test system
4. Adjust drive belt tension
5. Check antifreeze/coolant
6. Tighten compressor mounts
7. Tighten condenser and evaporator mounts
8. Inspect system for leaks (hoses, couplings, valves, etc.)
9. Partial charge system

All models 1.0
If necessary to evacuate and charge system, add 1.0

(Factory Time) — Chilton Time

(G) Evaporator Core, Renew
Includes: Evacuate and charge system.
1983-87 (1.5) 4.0

(G) Accumulator Assembly, Renew
Includes: Evacuate and charge system.
1983-87 (.8) 1.5

(G) Expansion Tube Assembly, Renew
Includes: Evacuate and charge system.
1983-87 (.7) 1.4

(Factory Time) — Chilton Time

(G) Pressure Cycling Switch, Renew
1983-87 (.2) 3

(G) Time Temperature Relay, Renew (Time Temp)
1983-87 (.3) 4

(G) Temperature Control Head, Renew
1983-87 (.6) 9

(G) Temperature Control Cable, Renew
1983-87-center (.7) 1.0

(G) Vacuum Selector Valve, Renew
1983-87 (.5) 8

(G) Vacuum Door Control Actuators, Renew
1983-87
heater-defroster door (.9) 1.5
outside recirculation door (1.4) 2.0
diverter door (1.1) 1.6
defroster door (2.6) 4.2
upper or lower mode door (2.6) 4.2
air inlet door (1.4) 2.1

(G) Master Electrical Switch, Renew
1983-87 (.5) 8

(G) Blower Motor, Renew
1983-87 (.3) 5

(G) Blower Motor Switch, Renew
1983-87 (.4) 7

(G) Blower Motor Resistor, Renew
1983-87 (.2) 3

(G) Blower Motor Relay, Renew
1983-87 (.2) 3

(G) Air Conditioning Hoses, Renew
Includes: Evacuate and charge system.
1983-87-one (1.0) 1.7
each adtnl (.3) 5

PARTS 28 AIR CONDITIONING 28 PARTS

	Part No.	Price
Compressor Assy.		
1983-87	◆12300273	390.00
Compressor Pulley		
1983-87	◆6556717	19.50
Pulley Bearing		
1983-87	◆908287	38.00
Compressor Clutch Coil (w/Housing)		
1983-87	◆6551217	44.00
Compressor Head		
1983-87	◆6551142	28.25
Compressor Shaft Seal Unit		
1983-87	◆9956695	13.00
Compressor Cylinder and Shaft Assembly		
1983-87	◆2724144	269.00
Compressor Outer Shell		
1983-87	◆2724158	38.00

	Part No.	Price
Compressor Valve Plate Assembly		
1983-87	◆6551141	11.50
Compressor Hub and Drive Plate		
1983-87	◆6551220	32.50
Compressor Pressure Relief Valve		
1983-87	◆5914435	13.50
Condenser Assy.		
1983-87-1st design*	◆3032252	151.50
2nd design**	◆3042357	162.00
Evaporator Core Assy.		
1983-87	◆3046807	290.60
Dehydrator (Accumulator) Assembly		
1983-87	◆2724242	99.50

*1st design used with hose and tube style liquid line.
**2nd design used with metal liquid line.

	Part No.	Price
Air Inlet Valve (Expansion Tube)		
1983-87	◆3033573	13.50
Blower Motor (Cut-Out) Relay		
1983-87	◆14036273	6.50
Compressor (Cut-Out) Relay		
1983-87	◆14004972	33.50
Blower Motor Switch		
1983-87	◆344883	5.00
Blower Motor (Air Cond.)		
1983-87	◆22020945	60.00
Resistor Assy. (Blower Motor)		
1983-87	◆3979727	4.00

LABOR 29 LOCKS, HINGES & WIND. REGULATORS 29 LABOR

(Factory Time) — Chilton Time

(G) Hood Hinge, Renew (One)
1983-87-right (1.1) 1.6
left (1.0) 1.5
both (1.7) 2.5

(G) Hood Latch, Renew
1983-87 (.3) 4

(G) Hood Catch Release Cable, Renew
1983-87 (.3) 6

LABOR 29 LOCKS, HINGES & WIND. REGULATORS 29 LABOR

	(Factory Time)	Chilton Time
(G) Door Lock, Renew		
1983-87	(.4)	.6
(G) Door Lock Remote Control, Renew		
1983-87	(.3)	.5
(G) Door Lock Cylinder, Renew		
1983-87	(.3)	.5
Recode cyl add	(.3)	.3
(G) Door Handle (Outside), Renew (Front or Rear)		
1983-87	(.3)	.5
(G) Lock Striker Plate, Renew		
1983-87	(.2)	.3
(G) Door Window Regulator, Renew		
1983-87	(.5)	.7
Recond add	(.2)	.3
(G) Trunk Lock Cylinder, Renew		
1983-87	(.2)	.4
Recode cyl add	(.3)	.3
(G) Rear Compartment Lid Hinge, Renew		
1983-87		
lid side-one	(1.1)	1.5
both	(1.4)	1.9
body side-each	(1.2)	1.6

PARTS 29 LOCKS, HINGES & WIND. REGULATORS 29 PARTS

	Part No.	Price
Hood Latch Catch		
1983-87	◆474758	4.50
Hood Latch Release Cable		
1983-exc. Diesel	◆14069172	13.50
Diesel	◆14034115	13.50
1984-87	◆14069172	13.50
Hood Hinge		
1983-87-right	◆360800	7.25
left	◆360799	7.25
Front Door Lock		
(2 door)		
1983-87-right	◆1748557	66.50
left	◆1748558	66.50
(4 door)		
1983-87-right	◆20293604	51.50
left	◆20293605	51.50
Rear Door Lock		
1983-87-right	◆20293642	60.50
left	◆20293643	60.50
Door Lock Cylinder Unit		
1983-87-exc.		
Black	◆9632769	7.75
Black	◆20496703	5.75
Trunk Lid Lock		
1983	◆20496705	3.75
1984-87-exc.		
Black	◆20496707	5.50
Black	◆20496710	3.75
Door Handle (Outside) Chevette		
(2 door)		
1983-87-right	◆20338488	27.75
left	◆20338489	27.75
(4 door)		
1983-87-right	◆20260758	25.50
left	◆20260759	25.50
T1000		
(2 door)		
1983-87-right	◆20338488	27.75
left	◆20338489	27.75
(4 door)		
1983-87-right	◆20260758	25.50
left	◆20260759	25.50
Trunk Lid Hinge		
(Lid Side)		
1983-87-right	◆1701524	5.25
left	◆1701523	5.25
(Body side)		
1983-87	◆20346874	15.75
Front Window Regulator (Manual)		
(2 door)		
1983-87-left	◆20041610	54.00
right	◆20041611	54.00
(4 door)		
1983-87-left	◆20046486	54.00
right	◆20046485	54.00
Rear Window Regulator (Manual)		
1983-87-right	◆20036262	52.00
left	◆20036263	52.00

LABOR 30 HEAD AND PARKING LAMPS 30 LABOR

	(Factory Time)	Chilton Time
(G) Aim Headlamps		
two		.4
four		.6
(M) Headlamp Sealed Beam Bulb, Renew		
1983-87	(.2)	.3
(M) Rear Combination Lamp Lens, Renew		
1983-87-each	(.3)	.4
(M) License Lamp Assembly, Renew		
1983-87	(.3)	.4
(M) Side Marker Lamp Assy., Renew		
1983-87	(.2)	.3
(M) Park and Turn Signal Lamp Assy., Renew		
1983-87-each	(.3)	.4
(M) Stop, Tail and Turn Signal Lamp Assy., Renew		
1983-87-each	(.3)	.4
(M) Back-Up Lamp Bulb, Renew		
All models-one	(.2)	.3
each adtnl		.1
(M) License Lamp Bulb, Renew		
All models-one or all	(.2)	.3
(M) Park and Turn Signal Lamp Bulb, Renew		
All models-each		.2
(M) Side Marker Lamp Bulb, Renew		
All models-each		.2
(M) Stop, Tail and Turn Signal Lamp Bulb, Renew		
All models-one		.2
each adtnl		.1

PARTS 30 HEAD AND PARKING LAMPS 30 PARTS

	Part No.	Price
Sealed Beam Bulb		
(wo/Quartz)		
1983-87	◆5968098	22.00
(Quartz)		
1983-87	◆5972698	46.50
Parking Lamp Assy.		
1983-87-right	◆912768	17.50
left	◆912767	17.50
Tail Lamp Lens		
(Chevette)		
1983-87-right	◆5971204	29.75
left	◆5971203	29.75
(T-1000)		
1983-87-right	◆16500602	34.00
left	◆16500601	34.00
Tail Lamp Housing		
(Chevette)		
1983-87-right	◆5971200	58.00
left	◆5971199	58.00
(T-1000)		
1983-87-right	◆16500992	58.00
left	◆16500991	58.00
High Mount Stoplight		
1986-87	◆918959	35.50
License Plate Lamp Assy.		
1983-87	◆912366	6.25
Side Marker Lamp (Front)		
1983-87	◆929564	8.25
Side Marker Lamp (Rear) Chevette		
1983-87-right	◆5971210	13.25
left	◆5971209	13.25
T-1000		
1983-87-right	◆16500608	13.25
left	◆16500607	13.25

LABOR 31 WINDSHIELD WIPER & SPEEDOMETER 31 LABOR

(Factory Time)	Chilton Time
(G) Wiper Motor, Renew (Front or Rear)	
1983-87 (.2)	.6
w/A.C. add (.4)	.4
(G) Wiper Motor, R&R and Recondition (Front or Rear)	
1983-87 (.7)	1.2
w/A.C. add (.4)	.4
(G) Wiper Transmission, Renew	
1983-87-wo/A.C. (.6)	1.0
w/A.C. (1.3)	2.0
(G) Windshield Wiper Switch, Renew	
1983-85 (1.1)	1.5
1986-87	
Chevette	
std colm (1.2)	1.7
tilt colm (1.0)	1.5
1000 (.4)	.6
(G) Washer Pump, Renew (Front or Rear)	
1983-87 (.3)	.4
Recond pump add (.3)	.3
(G) Rear Window Wiper Switch, Renew	
1983-87 (.2)	.3
(G) Speedometer Head, R&R or Renew	
1983-87 (.5)	1.1
Reset odometer add	.2
(G) Speedometer Cable and Casing, Renew	
1983-87 (.5)	.7
(G) Speedometer Cable (Inner), Renew or Lubricate	
1983-87 (.4)	.6
(G) Speedometer Driven Gear, Renew (Manual Transmission)	
1983-87 (.3)	.4
(G) Radio, R&R	
1983-87 (.3)	.7
(G) Windshield Washer Pump Valve, Renew	
1983 (.2)	.3

PARTS 31 WINDSHIELD WIPER & SPEEDOMETER 31 PARTS

	Part No.	Price
Wiper Motor		
1983-87	◆22048242	71.00
Wiper Arm Assy. (Motor Crank)		
1983-87	◆4961736	2.75
Wiper Switch & Pivot		
1983-87-wo/Tilt whl.	◆7832110	31.00
Tilt whl	◆7832332	33.25
Window Washer Pump		
1983-87	◆4961623	15.50
Windshield Wiper Transmission		
1983-87-right	◆4999674	15.00
left	◆4999676	15.25
Speedometer Head		
Chevette		
1983-87	◆25050480	84.00
T1000		
1983	◆25051350	86.75
1984-87	◆25076939	99.00
Speedometer Cable w/Casing		
Order by year and model.		

LABOR 32 LIGHT SWITCHES & WIRING 32 LABOR

(Factory Time)	Chilton Time
(G) Headlamp Switch, Renew	
1983-87 (.3)	.4
(G) Headlamp Dimmer Switch, Renew	
1983-87 (.4)	.6
(G) Back-Up Lamp and Park/Neutral Switch, Renew	
1983-87 (.3)	.4
(G) Parking Brake Lamp Switch, Renew	
1983-87	
Chevette (1.0)	1.4
1000 (.5)	.7
(G) Stop Light Switch, Renew	
1983-87 (.2)	.3
(G) Neutral Start or Back-Up Light Switch, Renew	
1983-87 (.3)	.4
(G) Turn Signal or Hazard Warning Switch, Renew	
1983-87 (.7)	1.1
(M) Turn Signal or Hazard Warning Flasher, Renew	
1983-87 (.2)	.2
(G) Horns, Renew	
1983-87-one (.2)	.3
each adtnl	.1
(G) Horn Relay, Renew	
1983-87 (.2)	.3

PARTS 32 LIGHT SWITCHES & WIRING 32 PARTS

	Part No.	Price
Headlamp Switch		
1983-87	◆1995217	16.00
Headlamp Dimmer Switch		
1983-87	◆7832411	18.50
Stoplight Switch		
1983-87-M.T.	◆1362835	3.00
A.T.	◆25504628	3.75
Turn Signal Switch		
1983-87	◆1997988	32.50
Turn Signal Flasher		
1983	◆491392	N.L.
1984	◆6450076	4.00
1985-87	◆10041074	3.50
Hazard Warning Flasher		
1983-87	◆6450089	3.00
Back-Up Lamp Switch		
(A.T.)		
1983-87	◆14052375	6.00
(M.T.)		
1983-87-4 spd.	◆14014559	7.25
5 sp. (exc. diesel)	◆14069600	7.00
5 sp. (diesel)	◆14034320	7.50
Horn Assy.		
1983-87-Hi note (A)	◆1892164	22.00
Lo note (D)	◆1892162	23.50
Lo note (F)	◆1892163	22.00
Horn Relay		
1983-87	◆25513270	8.50

LABOR 33 GLASS 33 LABOR

	Chilton Time
(G) Windshield Glass, Renew	
1983-87 (.8)	1.2
Renew caulk bead add (.4)	.4
(G) Front Door Glass, Renew	
1983-87 (.7)	1.1
(G) Rear Door Glass, Renew	
1983-87 (.6)	1.0
(G) Quarter Window Stationary Glass, Renew	
1983-87 (.4)	.6
(G) Quarter Window Glass (Movable), Renew	
1983-87 (.3)	.5
Transfer latch and channel add	.2
(G) Back Window Glass, Renew	
1983-87 (.7)	1.1
2 Dr Hatchback add (.2)	.2
w/Elec grid defogger add (.2)	.2

GROUP INDEX

ALPHABETICAL INDEX

General Motors
Rear Wheel Drive Cars

CHEVROLET & CORVETTE

YEAR IDENTIFICATION

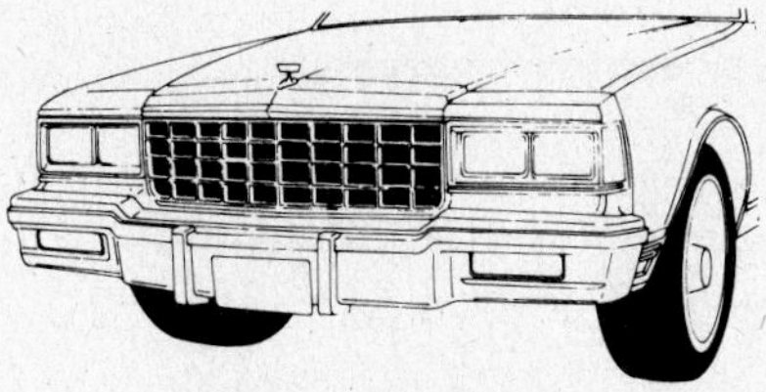

1983–87 Caprice

1983–84 Impala

1984–86 Corvette

TUNE-UP SPECIFICATIONS
All Except Corvette

Year	Engine			Spark Plugs		Distributor	Ignition Timing (deg)▲	Valves	Fuel	Idle Speed (rpm)▲
	Eng. VIN Code	No. Cyl. Displacement	Eng. Mfg.	Orig. Type	Gap. (in.)		Auto. Trans.	Intake Opens ■(deg)	Pump Pressure (psi)	Auto. Trans.
'83	9	6-229	Chev.	R-45TS	.045	Electronic	0B ①	42	4.5–6.0	475/850
	A	6-231	Buick	R-45TS	.045	Electronic	15B ①	16	4.25–5.75	450/900
	H	8-305	Chev.	R-45TS	.045	Electronic	6B ①	44	5.5–7.0	500/650
	N	8-350	Olds.	—	—	—	4A ①	16	5.5–6.5	600/750
	V	6-263	Olds	—	—	—	①	16	5.5–6.5	①

TUNE-UP SPECIFICATIONS
All Except Corvette

Year	Engine: Eng. VIN Code	Engine: No. Cyl. Displacement	Engine: Eng. Mfg.	Spark Plugs: Orig. Type	Spark Plugs: Gap. (in.)	Distributor	Ignition Timing (deg): Auto. Trans.	Valves Intake Opens ■(deg)	Fuel Pump Pressure (psi)	Idle Speed (rpm): Auto. Trans.
'84	9	6-229	Chev.	R-45TS	.045	Electronic	0B ①	42	4.5–6.0	475
	A	6-231	Buick	R-45TS8	.060	Electronic	15B ①	16	4.25–5.75	600/700
	H	8-305	Chev.	R-45TS	.045	Electronic	6B ①	44	5.5–7.0	500/650
	N	8-350	Olds.	—	—	—	4A ①	16	5.5–6.5	600/750
	G	8-305	Chev.	R-45TS	.045	Electronic	6B ①	44	5.5–7.0	①
'85	Z	V6-262	Chev.	R-43CTS	.035	Electronic	6B ①	16	5.5–6.5	450/900
	G	8-305	Chev.	R-45TS	.045	Electronic	6B ①	44	5.5–7.0	500/650
	H	8-305	Chev.	R-45TS	.045	Electronic	6B ①	44	5.5–7.0	500/650
	6	8-350	Chev.	R-45TS	.045	Electronic	6B ①	16	5.5–6.5	475
	N	8-350	Olds.	—	—	—	4A ①	16	5.5–6.5	600/750
'86–'87	Z	V6-262	Chev.	R-43CTS ③	.035	Electronic	6B ①	16	5.5–6.5	450/900
	G	8-305	Chev.	R-45TS ②	.045 ②	Electronic	6B ①	44	5.5–7.0	500/650
	H	8-305	Chev.	R-45TS ②	.045 ②	Electronic	6B ①	44	5.5–7.0	500/650
	6	8-350	Chev.	R-45TS	.045	Electronic	6B ①	16	5.5–6.5	475
	Y	8-307	Olds.	FR3LS6	.060	Electronic	①	—	6.0–7.5	①

NOTE: The underhood specifications sticker often reflects tune-up specification changes made in production. Sticker figures must be used if they disagree with those in this chart.

■ All figures Before Top Dead Center
B Before Top Dead Center
TDC Top Dead Center
—Not applicable
Part numbers in this chart are not recommendations by Chilton for any product by brand name.
① See underhood specifications sticker
② '86 Caprice: R-44TS—.035 gaP
③ '86 Monte Carlo: R-43TS—.035 gaP

TUNE-UP SPECIFICATIONS
Corvette

Year	Engine: No. of Cyl. Displacement (Cu. In.)	Engine: V.I.N. Code	Engine: Option Code	Spark Plugs: Type (A.C.)	Spark Plugs: Gap (in.)	Ignition Timing (deg) ②: Man. Trans.	Ignition Timing (deg) ②: Auto. Trans.	Valves Intake Opens (deg) ③	Fuel Pump Pressure (psi)	Idle Speed (rpm) ②: Man. Trans.	Idle Speed (rpm) ②: Auto. Trans.
'84	8-350	8	L83	R45TS	.045	①	①	32	9–13	①	475
'85	8-350	8	L98	R45TS	.045	①	①	32	9–13	400	450
'86–'87	8-350	8	L98	R45TS	.045	①	①	32	9–13	400	450

NOTE: The underhood specifications sticker often reflects tuneup specification changes made in production. Sticker figures must be used if they disagree with those in this chart. Part numbers in this chart are not recommendations by Chilton for any product by brand name.
B—Before Top Dead Center
① See Underhood Sticker
② See text for procedure
③ All figures Before Top Dead Center

FIRING ORDERS

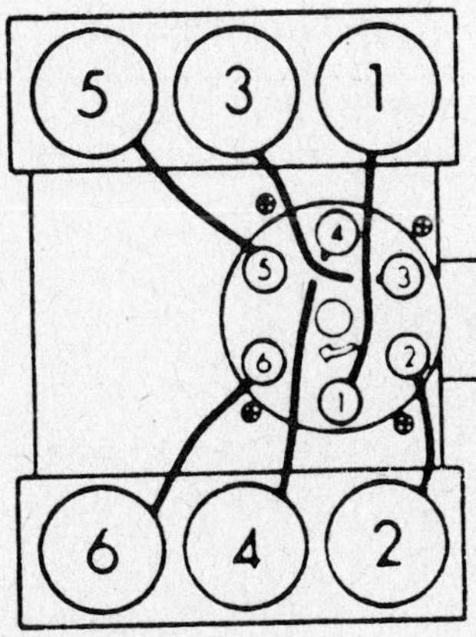

GM (Buick) 231 V6
Engine firing order: 1–6–5–4–3–2
Distributor rotation: clockwise

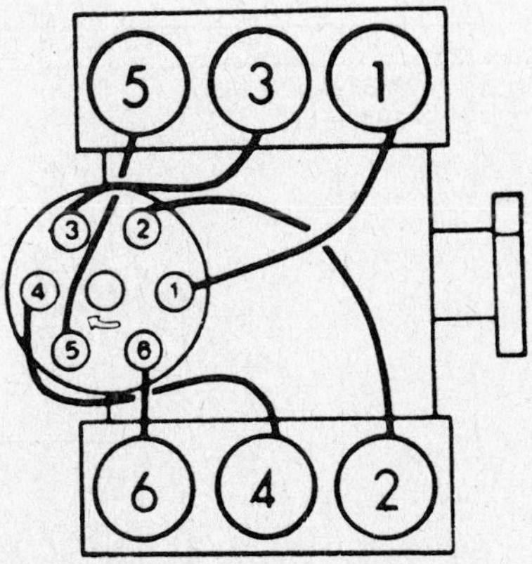

Chevrolet-built V6 engine
Engine firing order: 1–6–5–4–3–2
Distributor rotation: clockwise

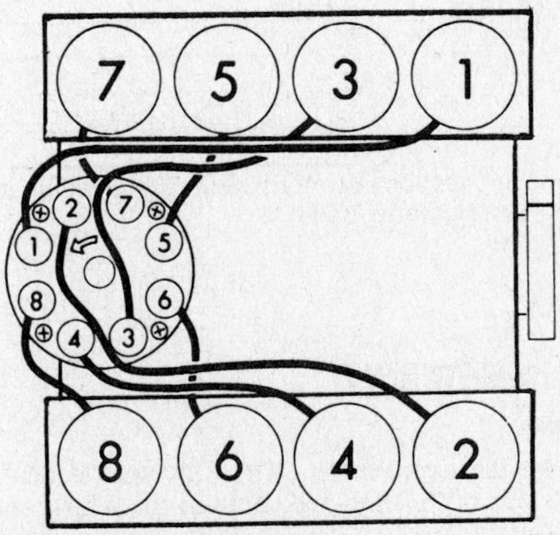

GM (Oldsmobile) 307
Engine firing order: 1–8–4–3–6–5–7–2
Distributor rotation: counterclockwise

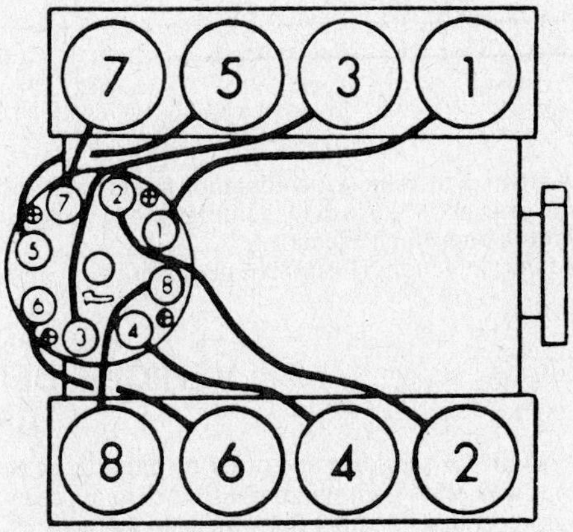

GM (Chevrolet) V8
Engine firing order: 1–8–4–3–6–5–7–2
Distributor rotation: clockwise

WHEEL ALIGNMENT SPECIFICATIONS
Impala, Caprice

		Caster		Camber		
Year	Model	Range (deg)	Pref. Setting (deg)	Range (deg)	Pref. Setting (deg)	Toe-in (in.)
'83-'87	Chevrolet	2P-4P	3P	0-1.6	4/5P	1/16-1/4

N Negative P Positive — Not specified

WHEEL ALIGNMENT SPECIFICATIONS
Corvette

Year	Front Wheel Caster Range	Front Wheel Caster Preferred	Front Wheel Camber Range	Front Wheel Camber Preferred	Rear Wheel Camber Range	Rear Wheel Camber Preferred	Toe-In (in.) Front Wheel	Toe-In (in.) Rear Wheel
'84-'87	2 1/2P-3 1/2P	3P	5/16P-1 5/16P	13/16P	1/32N ± 29/32 ①	13/32 ②	0 – 1/4P	3/32 ± 7/32

N—Negative ① 1984—1/2N-1/2P
P—Positive ② 1984—0

VEHICLE IDENTIFICATION NUMBER (VIN)
Corvette

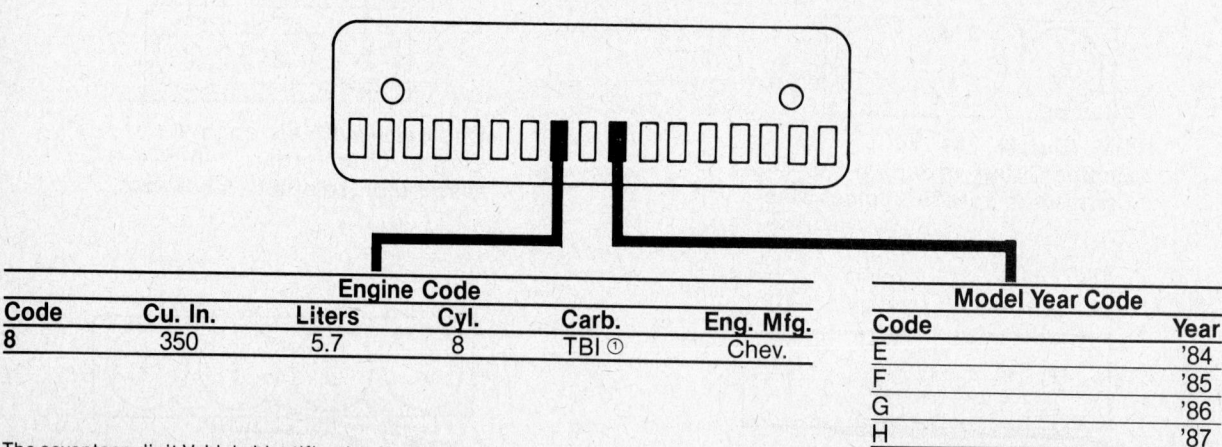

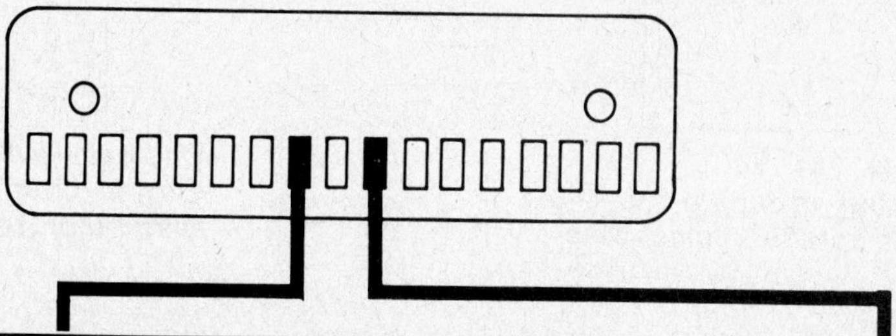

Engine Code

Code	Cu. In.	Liters	Cyl.	Carb.	Eng. Mfg.
8	350	5.7	8	TBI ①	Chev.

Model Year Code

Code	Year
E	'84
F	'85
G	'86
H	'87

The seventeen digit Vehicle Identification Number can be used to determine engine application and model year. The 10th digit indicates the model year, and the 8th digit identifies the factory installed engine. There is no 1983 Corvette model.
TBI—Throttle body (fuel) injection
① Tuned Port Injection (TPI) on 1985 and later.

VEHICLE IDENTIFICATION NUMBER (VIN)
All Except Corvette

It is important for servicing and ordering parts to be certain of the vehicle and engine identification. The VIN (vehicle identification number) is a 13 or 17 digit number visible through the windshield on the driver's side of the dash and contains the vehicle and engine identification codes. It can be interpreted as follows:

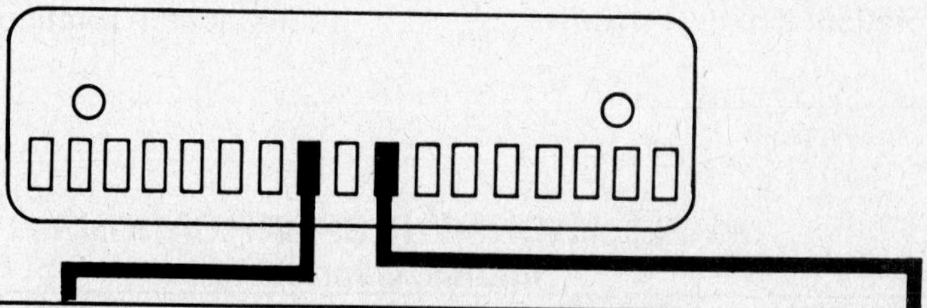

Engine Code

Code	Cu. In.	Liters	Cyl.	Carb.	Eng. Mfg.
Z	262	4.3	6	TBI	Chev.
9	229	3.8	6	2	Chev.
A	231	3.8	6	2	Buick
Y	307	5.0	8	4	Olds.
G	305	5.0	8	4	Chev.
H	305	5.0	8	4	Chev.
6	305	5.7	8	4	Chev.
N	350	5.7	8	Diesel	Chev.

Model Year Code

Code	Year
D	'83
E	'84
F	'85
G	'86
H	'87

(Factory Time) Chilton Time

COOLING

(M) Winterize Cooling System
Includes: Run engine to check for leaks, tighten all hose connections. Test radiator and pressure cap. Drain radiator and engine block. Add anti-freeze and refill system.

All models	.5

(M) Thermostat, Renew

V-6–1983-85	
229 engs (.5)	.6
231 eng (.7)	.8
262 eng (.7)	.9
1986-87 (.3)	.4
V-8–1983-87 (.5)	*.6
*Corvette add	.2
Diesel–1983-85 (.5)	.6

(M) Drive Belt, Renew

1983-87-Chev-V-6	
229 engs (.2)	.3
231 eng (.5)	.7
262 eng (.2)	.3
V-8 engs (.2)	.3
Corvette	
V-8 engs (.7)	.9
Serpentine (.2)	.5

(M) Radiator Hoses, Renew

Chevrolet	
upper (.3)	.4
lower (.4)	.5
both (.5)	.7
Corvette	
upper (.3)	.5
lower (.5)	.6
both (.6)	.8

FUEL

(M) Carburetor Air Cleaner, Service

1983-87 (.2)	.3

(G) Carburetor, Adjust (On Car)

1983-87	
Slow & Fast Idle (.3)	.4
Vacuum Brake-one (.4)	.6
both (.6)	.8
Choke (.6)	1.0
Complete (1.3)	1.8

(G) Thermostatic Choke Cover and/or Gasket, Renew

1983-87 (.6)	1.0

(G) Automatic Choke Vacuum Diaphragm, Renew

Chevrolet	
1983-87-one (.4)	.6
both (.6)	.8

BRAKES

(G) Brakes, Adjust (Minor)
Includes: R&R wheels and adjust brakes thru access holes in drums. Fill master cylinder.

two wheels	.4
Remove knock out plugs add-each	.1

(G) Bleed Brakes (Four Wheels)
Includes: Fill master cylinder.

1983-87 (.4)	.5

CHILTON'S 10 POINT SAFETY CHECK

CHECK OPERATION & CONDITION OF THE FOLLOWING ITEMS:

1. Legal Registration (serial no.)
2. Tires & Wheels
3. Brake System (R&R all wheels)
4. Light Systems & Signals
5. Accelerator Linkage, Neutral Safety Switch, Shift Indicator Pointer & Seat Position Locks
6. Glass, Mirrors, Door Locks, Seat Belts & Harness
7. Wipers, Washers & Defrosters
8. Frame, Steering, Shocks, Front & Rear Suspension
9. Fuel & Exhaust Systems
10. Road Test Vehicle

All models	1.0
Exhaust Smog Analysis, add	.4

(Factory Time) Chilton Time

(G) Brake Pedal Free Play, Adjust

1983-87 (.2)	.3

(M) Parking Brake, Adjust

1983-87-Chev. (.3)	.5
Corv. (.6)	.8

LUBRICATION SERVICE

(M) Lubricate Chassis, Change Oil & Filter
Includes: Inspect and correct all fluid levels.

All models	.6
Install grease fittings add	.1

(M) Lubricate Chassis
Includes: Inspect and correct all fluid levels.

All models	.4
Install grease fittings add	.1

(M) Engine Oil & Filter, Change
Includes: Inspect and correct all fluid levels.

All models	.4

WHEELS

(M) Wheel, Renew

one (.3)	.5

(G) Wheels, Balance

one	.3
each adtnl	.2

(G) Wheels, Rotate (All)

All models	.5

(G) Front Wheel Bearings, Clean and Repack (Both Wheels)

1983-87 (1.1)	1.6

(G) Front Wheel Grease Seals, Renew

1983-87-one whl (.7)	.8
both whls (1.1)	1.2

(Factory Time) Chilton Time

ELECTRICAL

(M) Battery Cables, Renew

Chevrolet	
1983-87-positive (.3)	.4
negative (.2)	.3
Right batt to left batt w/Diesel eng (.3)	.3
Corvette	
1984-87-positive (.6)	.8
negative (.5)	.7

(M) Battery Terminals, Clean

1983-87	.3

(G) Aim Headlamps

two	.4
four	.6

(M) Headlamp Sealed Beam Bulb, Renew

1983-87 (.3)	.3

(G) Headlamp Motor or Actuator, Renew

Corvette	
1984-87-each side (.8)	1.2

(G) Headlamp Switch, Renew

1983-87-Chev. (.4)	.5
Corv. (.7)	.9

(G) Headlamp Dimmer Switch, Renew

1983-87-Chev. (.5)	.7
Corv. (.6)	1.0

(G) Stop Light Switch, Renew

1983-87-Chev. (.2)	.4
Corv. (.3)	.5

(G) Turn Signal and Hazard Warning Switch, Renew

1983-85-exc below (.7)	1.1
w/Tilt wheel (.9)	1.2
w/Tilt-Tel (1.2)	1.5
1986-87-Chev.	
std colm (.6)	1.1
tilt colm (.7)	1.2
Corv. (.9)	1.5

(G) Neutral Start Switch, Renew

Corvette	
1983-87-column mount (.2)	.4
floor mount (1.2)	1.6
clutch mounted (.7)	1.0
console mount (.3)	.4

(M) Turn Signal or Hazard Warning Flasher, Renew

1983 (.2)	.2
1984-87	
Chev. (.2)	.2
Corv.	
turn signal (.4)	.6
hazard warning (.5)	.7

(G) Horn Relay, Renew

1983 (.2)	.3
1984-87-Chev. (.2)	.3
Corv. (.5)	.7

(G) Horn, Renew

1983-87-each (.3)	.3

LABOR 1 TUNE UP 1 LABOR

(Factory Time)	Chilton Time
(G) Compression Test	
Chevrolet	
V-6–1983-87 (.5)	.7
V-8–1983-87 (.7)	.8
Corvette	
1983-87 (1.2)	1.5
w/A.C.-V-8 add	.3

(G) Engine Tune Up, (Electronic Ignition)

Includes: Test battery and clean connections. Tighten manifold and carburetor mounting bolts. Check engine compression, clean and adjust or renew spark plugs. Test resistance of spark plug cables. Inspect distributor cap and rotor. Adjust air gap. Check vacuum advance operation. Reset ignition timing. Adjust idle mixture and idle speed. Service air cleaner. Inspect and adjust drive belts. Inspect choke operation and adjust or free up. Check operation of EGR valve.

(Factory Time)	Chilton Time
Chevrolet	
V-6–1983-87	2.0
V-8–1983-87	2.5
Corvette	
1983-87	3.0
w/A.C. add	.6
To perform C.C.C. system test add	1.0

LABOR 2 IGNITION SYSTEM 2 LABOR

GASOLINE ENGINES

(Factory Time)	Chilton Time
(G) Spark Plugs, Clean and Reset or Renew	
Chevrolet	
V-6–1983-87 (.4)	.6
V-8–1983-87 (.6)	.7
Corvette	
1984-87 (.6)	.8
(G) Ignition Timing, Reset	
1983-87 (.3)	.4
(G) Distributor, Renew	
Includes: Reset ignition timing.	
Chevrolet	
V-6–1983-87 (.6)	.8
V-8–1983-87 (.6)	.8
Corvette	
1983-87 (.6)	.8
(G) Distributor, R&R and Recondition	
Includes: Reset ignition timing.	
Chevrolet	
V-6–1983-87 (.9)	1.4
V-8–1983-87 (.9)	1.4
Corvette	
1983-87 (1.0)	1.5
(G) Distributor Cap and/or Rotor, Renew	
1983-87	
V-6 (.3)	.7
V-8 (.3)	.7
(G) Distributor Hall Effect Switch, Renew	
1983 (.5)	.8
(G) Electronic Module Retard Vacuum Switch (EMR), Renew	
1983-84 (.3)	.5
(G) Ignition Coil, Renew	
1983-87 (.5)	.6
(G) Ignition Cables, Renew	
Chevrolet	
1983-87	
V-6 (1.0)	1.4
V-8 (.6)	.8
Corvette	
1984-87 (.6)	.9
(G) Ignition Switch, Renew	
1983-85-Chev. (.4)	.7
Corv. (.8)	1.3
1986-87-Chev. (.6)	.9
Corv. (.7)	1.3
(G) Ignition Key Warning Switch, Renew	
1983-87-Chev. (.6)	.9
Corv. (.7)	1.3
(G) Distributor Module, Renew	
1983-85-Chev. (.4)	.7
Corv. (.5)	.8
1986-87 (.6)	.8
(G) Distributor Pick-Up Coil and/or Pole Piece, Renew	
Includes: R&R distributor and main shaft.	
1983-87-Chev. (.7)	.9
Corv. (.8)	1.0
(G) Distributor Capacitor and/or Module Wiring Harness, Renew	
1983-85 (.4)	.6
1986-87-Chev. (.5)	.7
Corv. (.6)	.8
(G) ESC Detonation (Knock) Sensor, Renew	
1983-85 (.4)	.6
1986-87 (.6)	.8
(G) ESC Module, Renew	
1983-87 (.5)	.6

DIESEL IGNITION COMPONENTS

(Factory Time)	Chilton Time
(G) Coolant Fast Idle Temperature Switch, Renew	
1983-85 (.2)	.4
(G) Glow Plug Relay, Renew	
1983-85 (.2)	.3
(G) Fast Idle Solenoid, Renew	
1983-85 (.4)	.5
(G) Glow Plugs, Renew	
1983-85-one	.4
all-one bank	.7
all-both banks	1.3
(G) Glow Plug Control Module, Renew (Controller)	
1983-85 (.4)	.6
(G) Glow Plug Control Switch, Renew	
1983-85 (.2)	.4
(G) Fast Idle Relay, Renew	
1983-85 (.3)	.4
(G) Control Sensor, Renew	
1983-85 (.4)	.6

PARTS 2 ELECTRONIC IGNITION 2 PARTS

	Part No.	Price
Distributor Assembly		
(Chevrolet)		
V-6-229		
1983-84	1110584	341.50
V-6-231		
1983-85	◆1103470	351.25
V-6-262		
1985	◆1103574	170.00
1986-87	◆1103655	174.75
V-8-305		
1983-84	◆1103460	333.75
1985-87	◆10497135	294.50
V-8-307Y		
1986-87	◆1103602	275.00
(Corvette)		
V-8-350		
1984-87	10497134	272.25
(1) Cover		
1983-87-V-8	◆1875960	6.00
V-6	◆1894209	6.00
(2) Coil		
1983-84-V-6-229	◆1985473	N.L.
1983-85-V-6-231	◆1985474	N.L.
1985-87-V-6-262	◆1115315	39.50
1983-85-V-8-305	◆1985473	N.L.
1986-87-V-8-305	◆1875894	N.L.
1986-87-V-8-307Y	◆1985474	N.L.
1984-87-V-8-350	10497133	94.50
(3) Cap		
(Chevrolet)		
1983-87-exc below	◆1974408	17.00
229, 231	◆1894979	17.00
262	◆1988001	9.75
(Corvette)		
1984	◆1974408	17.00
1985-87	◆1977046	24.50
(4) Rotor		
1983-87-exc. 262	◆1977026	6.50

PARTS 2 ELECTRONIC IGNITION 2 PARTS

	Part No.	Price
1985-87-262	◆10495408	3.50
(5) Shaft		
(Chevrolet)		
V-6-229		
1983-84	1972735	38.00
V-6-231		
1983-85	◆1976930	38.50
V-6-262		
1985	1988056	33.50
1986-87	10495798	48.75
V-8-305		
1983-87	◆1976909	38.50
V-8-307Y		
1986-87	◆1989612	42.25
(Corvette)		
V-8-350		
1984-87	◆1976909	38.50
(6) Pole Piece & Plate Assy.		
1983-87-exc.		
below	◆1976897	30.25
229	1972729	36.25
231	◆1976925	30.25
262 (85)	◆1988010	3.50
262 (86-87)	◆10495802	4.00
Corvette	◆1977207	32.00
307Y	◆1977207	31.75
(7) Module		
1983-87-exc.		
below	◆1976908	60.00
262	◆10496048	52.75
(8) Capacitor		
1983-87	◆1876154	4.50

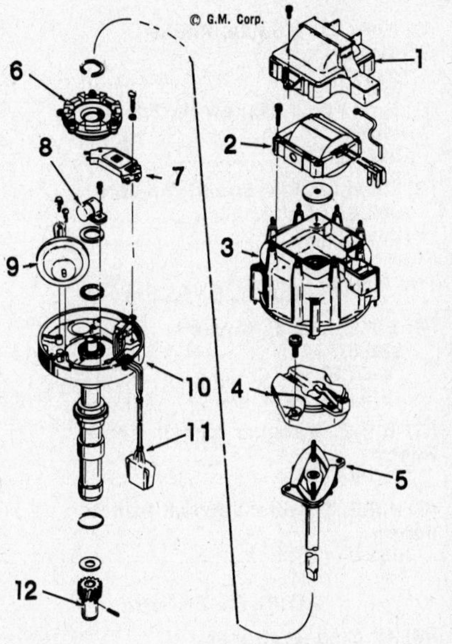

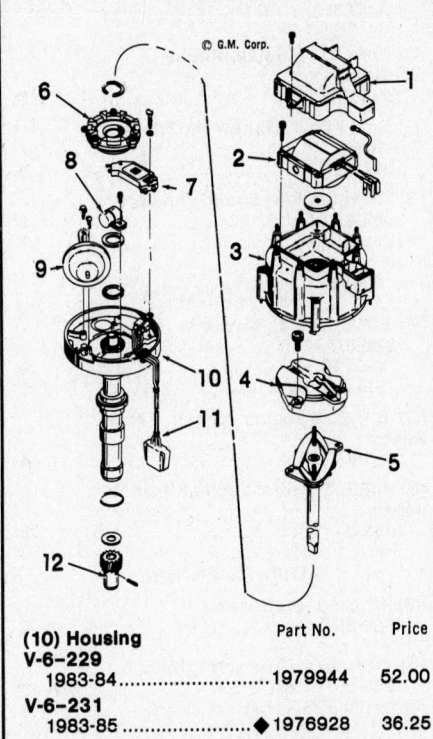

	Part No.	Price
(10) Housing		
V-6-229		
1983-84	1979944	52.00
V-6-231		
1983-85	◆1976928	36.25

	Part No.	Price
V-8-305, 350		
1983-87-exc.		
350	◆1978152	45.00
1986-87-307Y	◆1977208	34.00
1985-87-350	◆1988614	51.50
(12) Gear		
1983-87-exc		
below	◆1958599	14.25
231	◆1892082	15.25
262	◆10495062	20.75
307Y	◆1988777	21.50

Spark Plug Wire Set

Spark plug wires are sold separately for each spark plug and are not available as a set.

	Part No.	Price
Ignition Switch		
(wo/Tilt wheel)		
1983	11990109	N.L.
1984-87	◆1990115	11.50
(Tilt wheel)		
1983	◆1990110	11.50
1984-87	◆1990116	11.50

DIESEL IGNITION SYSTEM

	Part No.	Price
Glow Plugs		
1983	◆5613680	19.00
1984-85	◆5613826	16.50
Glow Plug Relay		
1983	◆560580	16.00
Glow Plug Control Switch		
1983	◆22514724	79.50
Glow Plug Temperature Switch		
1983	25036369	9.75

LABOR 3 FUEL SYSTEM 3 LABOR

	(Factory Time)	Chilton Time
GASOLINE ENGINES		
(G) Fuel Pump, Test		
Includes: Disconnect line at carburetor, attach pressure gauge.		
All models		.3
(M) Carburetor Air Cleaner, Service		
1983-87	(.2)	.3
(G) Carburetor, Adjust (On Car)		
1983-87		
Slow & Fast Idle	(.3)	.4
Vacuum Brake-one	(.4)	.6
both	(.6)	.8
Choke	(.6)	1.0
Complete	(1.3)	1.8
(G) Thermostatic Choke Cover and/or Gasket, Renew		
1983-87	(.6)	1.0
(G) Automatic Choke Vacuum Diaphragm, Renew		
Chevrolet		
1983-87-one	(.4)	.6
both	(.6)	.8
(M) Carburetor Fuel Filter, Renew		
1983-87	(.3)	.3
(G) Choke Vacuum Control Switch, Renew		
1983-87	(.3)	.4
(G) Electric Choke Relay, Renew		
1983-85	(.2)	.3
(G) Idle Stop Solenoid, Renew		
Includes: Reset idle speed.		
1983-84	(.3)	.4
1985-87	(.6)	1.0

	(Factory Time)	Chilton Time
(G) Carburetor, Renew		
Includes: Necessary adjustments.		
1983-87	(.6)	.9
To perform C.C.C. system check, add	(.5)	1.0
(G) Carburetor, R&R and Clean or Recondition		
Includes: Necessary adjustments.		
1983-87-2 bbl	(2.3)	3.0
4 bbl	(2.5)	3.2
To perform C.C.C. system check, add	(.5)	1.0
(G) Float or Needle Valve and Seat, Renew		
Includes: Set idle speed and mixture.		
1983-87-2 bbl	(.7)	1.2
4 bbl	(.9)	1.5
To perform C.C.C. system check, add	(.5)	1.0
(G) Accelerator Pump, Renew		
1983-87-2 bbl	(.7)	1.0
4 bbl	(.8)	1.2
(G) Fuel Pump or Push Rod, Renew		
Chevrolet		
V-6-1983-87-231 eng	(.4)	.7
229 eng	(1.0)	1.4
262 eng	(.8)	1.1
V-8-1983-87	(1.0)	1.4
Add pump test if performed.		
(G) Water In Fuel Detector, Renew (WIF)		
All models	(.9)	1.2
(G) Fuel Tank, Renew		
Includes: Transfer tank gauge unit.		

	(Factory Time)	Chilton Time
Chevrolet		
1983-87-exc below	(.8)	1.0
sta wag	(1.0)	1.5
Corvette		
1983	(1.7)	2.4
1984-87	(5.2)	7.0
(G) Fuel Gauge (Tank), Renew		
Includes: Drain and refill tank.		
Chevrolet		
1983-87-exc below	(.8)	1.1
sta wag	(1.0)	1.3
Corvette		
1983	(.6)	1.0
1984-87	(.7)	1.1
(G) Fuel Gauge (Dash), Renew		
Chevrolet		
1983-85	(.3)	.8
1986-87	(.6)	1.0
(G) Instrument Panel Cluster Assy., Renew		
Corvette		
1984-87	(1.4)	2.5
(G) Intake Plenum and/or Gaskets, Renew		
V-8-1985-87	(1.3)	1.9
(G) Intake Runners and/or Gaskets, Renew		
V-8-1985-87		
right side	(1.3)	1.8
left side	(2.2)	3.1
both sides	(2.2)	3.2

LABOR — 3 FUEL SYSTEM 3 — LABOR

(Factory Time)	Chilton Time
(G) Intake Manifold or Gaskets, Renew	
Chevrolet	
V-6–1983-87	
229 engs (2.0)	3.0
231 eng (1.8)	2.7
262 eng (2.3)	3.0
w/A.C. add (.2)	.2
w/P.S. or A.I.R. add (.5)	.5
w/C.C.C. add (.3)	.3
V-8–1983-87	
eng Code H (2.3)	3.3
eng Code Y (2.2)	3.2
Corvette	
1983-84 (2.6)	3.8
1985-87 (3.8)	5.2
Renew manif add	.5
THROTTLE BODY INJECTION	
(G) Throttle Body and/or Gasket, R&R or Renew	
Corvette	
1983-84-one (.8)	1.2
both (1.0)	1.5
Renew meter body add (.3)	.3
1985-87 (.7)	1.1
Renew throttle body kit add (.3)	.3
(G) Idle Air Control Valve, Renew	
Corvette	
1983-84-one (.5)	.7
both (.6)	.9
1985-87 (.4)	.6
(G) Throttle Body Injector, Renew	
Corvette	
1983-84-one (.7)	1.0
both (.9)	1.2
(G) Fuel Pressure Regulator, Renew	
Corvette	
1983-84 (.7)	1.1
1985-87 (2.6)	3.6
(G) Fuel Pump Relay, Renew	
Corvette	
1983-87 (.3)	.4
(G) Cold Start Injector, Renew	
Corvette	
1985-87 (.7)	1.0
(G) Thermo Start Switch, Renew	
Corvette	
1985-87 (.5)	.7
(G) Fuel Injector, Renew	
Corvette	
1985-87-one (2.5)	3.5
each adtnl (.1)	.1
all (2.7)	4.0
(G) Fuel Rail, Renew	
Corvette	
1985-87 (2.6)	3.6
(G) Mass Air Sensor, Renew	
Corvette	
1985-87 (.4)	.5
(G) Burn Off Module, Renew	
Corvette	
1985-87 (1.4)	2.0
(G) Fuel Pump, Renew (In Tank)	
Corvette	
1983-87 (1.1)	1.5
(G) Minimum Idle Speed, Adjust	
1983-84 (.6)	.8
1985-87 (.4)	.7
E.F.E. SYSTEM	
(G) E.F.E. Valve, Renew	
1983-87	
V-6 (.6)	.9
V-8 (.6)	.9
(G) E.F.E. Vacuum Check Valve, Renew	
1983-84 (.2)	.4
(G) E.F.E. Thermal Vacuum Switch, Renew	
1983-84 (.3)	.5
DIESEL ENGINE	
(M) Air Cleaner, Service	
1983-85 (.2)	.4
(G) Air Intake Crossover, Renew	
1983-85-w/Ext E.G.R. (.3)	.5
w/Int E.G.R. (.4)	.6
(G) Idle Speed, Adjust	
1983-85 (.2)	.4
(G) Injection Timing, Check and Adjust	
1983-85 (.7)	.9
(G) Fuel Supply Pump, Renew	
1983-85 (.5)	.8
w/A.C. add (.2)	.2
(G) Fuel Filter, Renew	
1983-85 (.2)	.4
(G) Fuel Solenoid, Renew	
1983-85 (.5)	.7
(G) Cold Advance Solenoid, Renew	
1983-85 (.6)	1.0
(G) Fuel Injection Pump, Renew	
Includes: Pressure and electrical tests. Adjust timing.	
1983-85 (2.2)	3.4
(G) Injection Pump Adapter and/or Seal, Renew	
1983-85 (1.8)	2.5
(G) Fuel Return Lines (At Nozzles), Renew	
1983-85-one side (.3)	.5
both sides (.4)	.7
return hose (.2)	.3
w/A.C. add (.2)	.2
(G) Injection Pump Drive and/or Driven Gears, Renew	
1983-85 (4.3)	7.5
w/A.C. add (.2)	.2
(G) Injection Pump Throttle Shaft Seal, Renew	
1983-85 (.8)	1.3
(G) High Pressure Fuel Lines, Renew	
1983-85-one	.8
one-each bank	1.0
all	2.5
(G) Injector Nozzle and/or Seal, Renew	
1983-85-one (.8)	1.0
one-each bank (1.0)	1.3
all-both banks (2.2)	3.0
Clean nozzles add, each	.2
(G) Fuel Injection Head Seal, Renew	
Includes: Renew head and drive shaft seals. Renew governor weight retaining ring.	
1983-85 (2.7)	3.9
(G) Intake Manifold or Gaskets, Renew	
1983-85 (2.9)	3.5
Renew manif add (.3)	.5
(G) Vacuum Pump, Renew	
Includes: Vacuum test.	
1983-85	
gear driven (.4)	.6
belt driven (.6)	.8
ELECTRONIC FUEL INJECTION	
(G) Throttle Body, R&R	
V-6–1985-87 (.6)	1.0
Renew throttle body kit, add	.3
Renew fuel meter body add (.3)	.3
(G) Throttle Body Unit, Renew	
V-6–1985-87 (.6)	1.0
(G) Throttle Body Fuel Meter Assy., and/or Gasket, Renew	
V-6–1985-87 (.4)	.6
(G) Idle Air Control Valve, Renew	
V-6–1985-87 (.5)	.8
(G) Minimum Idle Speed, Adjust	
All models (.4)	.7
(G) Throttle Body Injector and/or Gasket, Renew	
V-6–1985-87	
one (.7)	1.1
both (.7)	1.2
(G) Fuel Pressure Regulator, Renew	
V6–1985-87 (.6)	1.0
(G) Fuel Pump, Renew (In Tank)	
1985-87 (1.3)	1.8
(G) Fuel Pump Relay, Renew	
1985-87 (.5)	.7

PARTS — 3 FUEL SYSTEM 3 — PARTS

	Part No.	Price
Air Cleaner Element (Paper Type)		
(Chevrolet)		
V-6–229		
1983-84	25040929	10.00
V-6–231		
1983-85	◆6419892	8.00
V-6–262		
1985-87	6483645	N.L.
V-8–305 & 307Y		
1983-87	◆6484235	10.00
Corvette		
V-8–350		
1984	25042383	27.50
1985-87	25042562	21.75

PARTS 3 FUEL SYSTEM 3 PARTS

	Part No.	Price
Choke Vacuum Control Assembly		
V-6-229		
1983-84	17067497	27.25
V-6-231		
1983-85-main	17067466	8.25
auxiliary	17068802	41.75
V-8-305		
1983-87	17067800	28.75
Carburetor Assembly		
(Chevrolet)		
V-6-229		
1983-84-exc.		
A/C	17068494	696.00
A/C	17068495	696.00
V-6-231		
1983	◆17079210	666.75
1984-85	◆17110332	912.75
V-8-305		
1983	◆17079226	821.25
1984	◆17110449	846.00
1985	◆17110902	887.00
1986-87	◆17111481	876.00
V-8-307Y		
1986-87	◆17111487	876.00
Carburetor Minor Repair Kit (Rochester)		
V-6-229		
1983-84	7039492	43.50
V-6-231		
1983	◆17076129	51.00
1984-85	◆17076129	51.00
V-8-305		
1983-84	◆7039467	41.50
1985-87	◆17076043	33.75
V-8-307Y		
1986-87	◆17076141	49.50

	Part No.	Price
Fuel Pump Assy. (A.C.)		
(Chevrolet)		
V-6-229		
1983-84	6471588	25.50
V-6-231		
1983-85	◆6471172	N.L.
V-6-262		
1985	◆6472370	57.00
V-8-305		
1983-87	◆6470422	24.75
V-8-307Y		
1986-87	◆6471743	35.00
(Corvette)		
1984	6472120	91.25
1985	6472490	81.75
1986-87	6472987	75.75
Fuel Tank		
Order by year and model.		
Fuel Tank Gauge (Tank Unit)		
(Chevrolet-exc. Sta. wagon)		
1983-87	◆25000599	34.00
(Corvette)		
1984	25003533	188.00
1985-87	25004793	224.25
(Station Wagon)		
1983-87	◆25002211	49.00
Fuel Gauge (Dash Unit)		
(Chevrolet)		
(wo/Gauges)		
1983-84	6432786	24.00
1985-87	6434143	27.75
(Gauges)		
1983-84-exc.		
below	6432791	25.50

	Part No.	Price
THM2004R	◆6433460	28.25
THM700R4	6434163	34.25
1985-87	6434136	32.00
Intake Manifold Gaskets		
V-6-229		
1983-84	14033549	7.25
V-6-231		
1983-85 (type of int. man.)		
cast iron	◆1264924	14.50
alum.	◆25505397	15.75
V-6-262		
1985	◆14089020	2.50
1986	14101306	7.50
1987	◆14089020	2.50
V-8-305		
1983-87	◆14034821	5.75
V-8-307Y		
1986-87	◆22534925	23.50
V-8-350		
1984	◆14085858	15.50
1985	◆14089151	29.00
1986-87-Alum.		
head	14094583	29.00
Cast iron hd.	10046309	29.00

EARLY FUEL EVAPORATION SYSTEM

	Part No.	Price
E.F.E. Actuator Switch		
1983-87	◆3043015	14.50
Valve & Actuator		
V-6-229		
1983-87	◆5233475	52.00
V-6-231		
1983-85	◆5233320	64.00
V-8-305		
1983-87	◆5233650	64.00

PARTS 3 FUEL SYSTEM (DIESEL) 3 PARTS

	Part No.	Price
Air Cleaner Element (Paper Type)		
1983-85	◆8997189	18.50
Air Intake Crossover		
1983-85	◆22509735	109.00
Fuel Pump		
1983-85	◆6471317	N.L.
Injection Pump Adapter		
1983-85	◆558768	21.75
Fuel Injection Pump		
1983-Hi alt.	◆22518689	763.00
(wo/Hi altitude)		
exc. sta. wag.	◆22518686	763.00
Sta. wag.	◆22519990	763.00

	Part No.	Price
1984-85-exc.		
Sta. wag.	◆22520936	763.00
Sta. wag.	◆22520937	763.00
Fuel Injection Nozzles		
1983	◆22520378	60.00
1984-85	◆22521207	89.50
Vacuum Pump		
1983-85	◆7839413	116.00
Intake Manifold Gaskets		
1983-84-Iron int.		
man.	◆22516344	12.00
Alum. int. man.	◆22527123	N.L.
1985	◆22527544	16.50

	Part No.	Price
Fuel Gauge (Tank)		
(exc. Station Wagon)		
1983-84	◆25003151	99.00
1985	◆25004277	86.75
(w/Station Wagon)		
1983-84	◆25002569	105.50
1985	◆25004280	76.25
Fuel Gauge (Dash)		
(wo/Gauges)		
1983-84	◆6432935	24.25
1985	6434143	27.75
(Gauges)		
1983-84	◆6433229	25.50
1985	6434138	25.50
Water Detector Kit		
1983-85	◆25002621	97.50

PARTS 3 ELECTRONIC FUEL INJECTION 3 PARTS

	Part No.	Price
Throttle Body Injection (Complete)		
1984-A.T.	17079853	1725.00
M.T. (complete)	17110601	1643.25
Throttle Body Injection		
1984-front	17079738	404.00
rear	17079736	742.50
Gasket Kit		
1984	◆17079729	24.25
Throttle Body Kit		
1984-front	◆17079716	239.50
rear	17079718	286.25
Idle Air Valve Control Kit		
1984	◆17078832	80.75

	Part No.	Price
Manifold Inlet Cover Kit		
1984	17079728	172.50
Fuel Injector Kit		
1984-front	17078846	179.75
rear	17078827	179.75
Fuel Meter Body Kit		
1984-front	17078842	109.75
rear	◆17078833	116.75
Fuel Meter Kit (One Inj. & Pressure Reg. Incl.)		
1984-front	17078845	468.00
rear	17079734	474.75

	Part No.	Price
Fuel Nut Assortment Kit		
1984-front	17078847	11.50
rear	17078830	12.50
Screw Assortment Kit		
1984-front	17078848	13.25
rear	17078831	16.00
Throttle Position Sensor Kit		
1984	◆17111262	63.00
Fuel Tube Kit		
1984	17073087	26.00

PARTS 3 ELECTRONIC FUEL INJECTION 3 PARTS

	Part No.	Price
Throttle Body Kit		
1985-87	17110843	232.00
Gasket Kit		
1985-87	◆17110845	8.50
Throttle Position Sensor Kit		
1985-87	◆17110830	46.50
Idle Air Control Valve Kit		
1985-87	◆17111288	58.00
Port Fuel Injector		
1985-87	17110870	104.25
Fuel Rail and Plug		
1985-87-L.H.	◆17110866	153.25
R.H.	17110865	215.50
Pressure Regulator		
1985-87	17110868	67.00

PARTS 3 ELECTRONIC FUEL INJECTION 3 PARTS

V-6-262

	Part No.	Price
Throttle Body Injection Unit		
1985	◆17111155	655.50
(1) Fuel Meter Body Kit		
1985-87	◆17078262	128.75
(2) Fuel Injector Kit		
1985	◆17111159	179.50
1986-87	◆17111468	179.50
(3) Gasket Kit		
1985-87	◆17111156	39.25
(4) Throttle Position Sensor Kit		
1985	◆17111162	62.75
1986-87	◆17111471	47.75
(5) Throttle Body Kit		
1985	◆17111160	185.75
1986-87	◆17111469	185.75
(6) Fuel Nut Assortment Kit		
1985-87	◆17078261	15.50
(7) Idle Air Valve Control Kit		
1985-87	◆17079256	88.75
Fuel Meter Kit Includes injector & pressure regulator.		
1985	◆17111157	350.00
1986-87	17111466	296.75

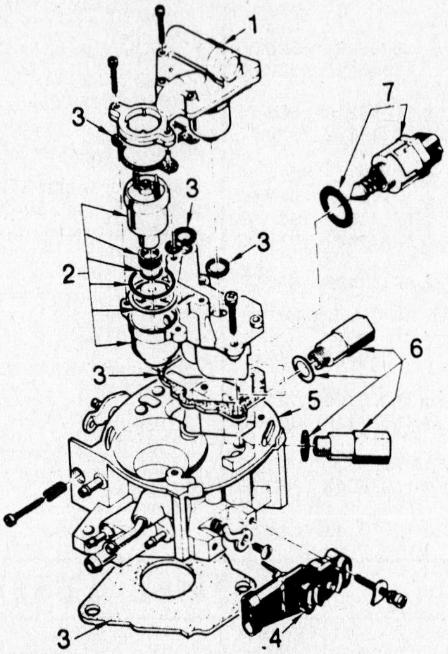

LABOR 3A EMISSION CONTROLS 3A LABOR

	(Factory Time)	Chilton Time
EMISSION CONTROLS		
GASOLINE ENGINES		
(G) Emission Control Check Includes: Check and adjust engine idle speed and mixture and ignition timing. Check PCV valve.		
All models		.6
CRANKCASE EMISSION		
(M) Positive Crankcase Ventilation Valve, Renew		
1983-87	(.2)	.3
(M) Crankcase Ventilation Filter, Renew		
All models	(.2)	.3
EVAPORATIVE EMISSION TYPE		
(G) Charcoal Canister, Renew		
Chevrolet		
1983-87	(.2)	.3
Corvette		
1984-87	(.2)	.3
(G) Canister Purge Thermal Vacuum Switch, Renew		
1983-87	(.2)	.3
(G) Fuel Tank Pressure Control Valve, Renew		
1983-87	(.3)	.3
CONTROLLED COMBUSTION TYPE		
(G) Air Cleaner Vacuum Motor, Renew		
1983-87	(.3)	.5
(G) Air Cleaner Temperature Sensor, Renew		
1983-87	(.2)	.3
EXHAUST GAS RECIRCULATION SYSTEM		
(G) E.G.R. Valve, Renew		
1983-84-Gas	(.3)	.5
Diesel	(.5)	.8
1985-87-Chev.	(.6)	.8
Corv.	(1.7)	2.5
(G) Thermostatic Vacuum Control Switch, Renew		
1983-87	(.3)	.4
(G) E.G.R. Vacuum Delay Valve, Renew		
1983-87	(.2)	.3
(G) E.G.R. Thermal Vacuum Switch, Renew		
1983-87	(.3)	.4
AIR INJECTOR REACTOR TYPE		
(G) Air Pump, Renew		
1983-84-Chev.-V-6	(.4)	.6
V-8	(.6)	.8
Corv.	(.4)	.7
1985-87	(.5)	.8
(G) A.I.R. Air Cleaner, Renew		
1983-87	(.2)	.3
(G) Vacuum Delay Valve, Renew		
1983-87-one	(.2)	.3
(G) Check Valve, Renew		
1983-87-one	(.2)	.3
each adtnl	(.1)	.1
(G) Air Pump Centrifugal Filter, Renew		
1983-87	(.3)	.5
(G) Catalytic Converter Air Pipe, Renew		
1983-87		
one piece	(.4)	.7
(G) A.I.R. Manifold Pipe, Renew		
1983-87		
V-6-one	(.4)	.6
both	(.7)	1.0
V-8-one	(.4)	.6
both	(.7)	1.0
w/A.C. add	(.2)	.2

(Factory Time) Chilton Time

COMPUTER COMMAND CONTROL SYSTEM (C.C.C.)

(P) Electronic Control Module, Renew
Does not include system performance check.
1983-87 (.5) 6

(P) Mixture Control Solenoid, Renew
Does not include system performance check.
1983-87-2 bbl (1.1) 1.4
4 bbl (1.2) 1.5

(P) Prom, Renew
Does not include system performance check.
Includes: R&R electronic module.
1983-87 (.5) 8

(P) Barometric Sensor, Renew
Does not include system performance check.
1983-87 (.4) 7

(P) Coolant Temperature Sensor, Renew
Does not include system performance check.
Include: Drain and refill cooling system.
1983-87 (.5) 7

(P) Manifold Differential Pressure Sensor, Renew
Does not include system performance check.
1983-87 (.5) 6

(P) Manifold Absolute Pressure Sensor, Renew
Does not include system performance check.
1983-87 (.5) 7

(P) Oxygen Sensor, Renew
Does not include system performance check.
1983-87 (.4) 7

(P) Throttle Position Sensor, Renew
Does not include system performance check.
1983-87-2 bbl (1.1) 1.4
4 bbl (1.2) 1.5

(P) Throttle Position Sensor, Adjust
All models
2 bbl (.4) 9
Perform C.C.C. system check add 1.0

(P) Vacuum Control Purge Solenoid, Renew
Does not include system test.
1983-87 (.4) 6

(P) Calpak, Renew
Does not include system test.
1984-87 (.5) 7

(P) EGR Sensor, Renew
Does not include system test.
1983-87 (.4) 6

(P) Canister Purge Control Valve, Renew
Does not include system performance check.
1983-87 (.4) 6

(P) EGR/EFE Purge Solenoid, Renew
Does not include system performance check.
1983-85 (.4) 6

(P) Air Control Valve, Renew
Does not include system performance check.
1983-87 (.4) 6

(P) Air Control/Air Switching Valve, Renew
Does not include system performance check.

CHILTON'S EMISSION CONTROL TUNE-UP

1. Clean or renew P.C.V. valve, hoses and filter.
2. Check fuel tank cap for sealing ability.
3. Check fuel tank and fuel lines for leakage.
4. Check evaporation canister and filter. Replace if necessary.
5. Check engine compression to determine leakage of unburned gases. (Add time for items of interference).
6. Test and clean or renew spark plugs.
7. Check engine oil dipstick for sealing ability.
8. Test exhaust system with analyzer and check system for leakage.
9. Check exhaust manifold heat valve for operation.
10. Adjust ignition timing and carburetor idle speed and mixture.
11. Check automatic choke mechanism for free operation.
12. Inspect air cleaner and element.
13. On models so equipped, test distributor vacuum control switch and transmission control switch.

Six 1.5
V-6 .... 1.7
V-8 .... 1.8

For repairs made, charge accordingly.

(Factory Time) Chilton Time

1983-87 (.5) 6
w/229 Eng (.7) 9

(P) Air Control Valve Solenoid, Renew
Does not include system performance check.
1983-85 (.4) 6

(P) E.G.R. Vacuum Control Solenoid, Renew
Does not include system performance check.
1983-87 (.5) 7

(P) Idle Speed Control Motor, Renew
Does not include system performance check.
1983-85 (.5) 7
Recond motor add (.3) 3

(P) Vehicle Speed Sensor, Renew
Does not include system performance check.
1983-87 (.8) 2.0

(P) E.G.R. Bleed Control Solenoid, Renew
Does not include system performance check.
1983-87 (.4) 6

(P) Air Control Valve Relay, Renew
Does not include system performance check.
1983-85 (.4) 5

(P) Air Switching Valve Relay, Renew
Does not include system performance check.
1983-85 (.3) 4

(Factory Time) Chilton Time

(P) E.G.R. Bleed Control Relay, Renew
Does not include system performance check.
1983-85 (.4) 5

(P) Back-Up Lamp and Park/Neutral Switch, Renew
Does not include system performance check.
1983-87 (.5) 7

(P) Tach Signal Conditioner, Renew
Does not include system performance check.
1983-85 (.4) 6

(P) Tachometer Filter, Renew
Does not include system performance check.
1983-85 (.3) 3

(P) Computer Command Control System Performance Check
1983-87 (.5) 1.0

THROTTLE BODY INJECTION

(P) Electronic Control Module, Renew
1985-87 (.5) 7

(P) Prom, Renew
1985-87 (.5) 8

(P) Coolant Temperature Sensor, Renew
1985-87 (.5) 7

(P) Manifold Pressure Sensor, Renew
1985-87 (.5) 6

(P) Oxygen Sensor, Renew
1985-87 (.6) 1.0

(P) Vehicle Speed Sensor, Renew
1985-87 (.8) 1.1

(P) Throttle Position Sensor, Renew
1985-87 (.6) 8

ELECTRONIC EMISSION CONTROLS

(P) Electronic Control Module, Renew
1983-87-Corv. (.5) 6

(P) Prom, Renew
1983-87-Corv. (.6) 8

(P) Coolant Temperature Sensor, Renew
1983-87-Corv. (.5) 6

(P) Manifold Pressure Sensor, Renew
1983-85-Corv. (.4) 6

(P) Oxygen Sensor, Renew
1983-87-Corv. (.7) 1.2

(P) Vehicle Speed Sensor, Renew
1983-87-Corv. (.6) 1.1

(P) Throttle Position Sensor, Renew
1983-87-Corv. (.5) 7

(P) Manifold Temperature Sensor, Renew
1985-87-Corv. (1.6) 2.6

(P) E.G.R. Sensor, Renew
1985-87-Corv. (1.6) 2.6

(P) Tachometer Filter, Renew
1985-87-Corv. (.3) 4

(P) Metering Valve Sensor, Renew
1984-85-Corv. (1.5) 2.0

(P) Calpak, Renew
1984-87-Corv. (.6) 8

LABOR 3A EMISSION CONTROLS 3A LABOR

(Factory Time) Chilton Time

(P) Air Control Valve, Renew
1983-87-Corv. (.4) .6

(P) EGR Vacuum Control Solenoid, Renew
1983-87-Corv. (.4) .5

(P) Park/Neutral Relay, Renew
1984-85-Corv. (.5) .7

DIESEL ENGINE

(G) Crankcase Depression Regulator Valve, Renew
1983-85 (.2) .3

(G) Crankcase Ventilation Flow Control Valve, Renew
1983-85 (.2) .3

(G) Crankcase Ventilation Filter, Renew
1983-85 (.2) .3

(G) E.G.R. Valve and/or Gasket, Renew
1983-85 (.5) 1.0

(G) E.G.R. Control Valve Solenoid, Renew
1983-85 (.2) .3

(G) E.G.R. Control Valve Switch, Renew
1983-85 (.2) .3

(G) E.P.R. Control Valve Solenoid, Renew
1983-85 (.3) .4

(G) E.P.R. Control Valve Switch, Renew
1983-85 (.3) .4

(G) E.P.R. Exhaust Pressure Regulator Valve, Renew
1983-85 (.5) .7

(G) Vacuum Regulator Valve, Renew
1983-85 (.6) .8

(G) Altitude Fuel Limiter, Renew
All models (.6) .8

(G) Housing Pressure Altitude Advance Solenoid, Renew
All models (.2) .3

(G) Housing Pressure Altitude Advance Relay, Renew
All models (.4) .6

DIESEL ELECTRONIC EMISSION CONTROLS

(P) Electronic Control Module, Renew
1985-85 (.6) .8

(P) Manifold Absolute Pressure Sensor, Renew
1985-85 (.3) .5

(P) Vehicle Speed Sensor, Renew
1985 (.9) 1.4

(P) Coolant Temperature Sensor, Renew
1985 (.6) .7

PARTS 3A EMISSION CONTROLS 3A PARTS

	Part No.	Price
Air Pump		
Chevrolet		
V-6-229		
1983-84	◆7834916	149.00
V-6-231		
1983-85	◆7835397	131.00
V-6-262		
1985-87	◆7834916	149.00
V-8-305		
1983-87	◆7834916	149.00
V-8-307Y		
1986-87-exc A.C.	◆7835397	N.L.
A.C.	◆7838575	N.L.
(Corvette)		
1984	7845380	192.00
1985	7846432	149.00
1986-87	7834915	N.L.

E.G.R. Valve

Replacement E.G.R. valves must be ordered according to the stamping number on the original valve.

	Part No.	Price
P.C.V. Valve		
(Chevrolet)		
V-6-229		
1983-84	◆8995284	5.00
V-6-231		
1983-85	◆6487534	3.00
V-6-262		
1985-87	◆8995284	5.00
V-8-305		
1983-87	◆6487779	2.50
V-8-307Y		
1986-87	◆8997683	N.L.
V-8-Diesel		
1983-85	◆25041678	34.50
(Corvette)		
1983-84	◆25040026	5.00
1985-87	◆6487779	2.50
Idle Stop Solenoid		
Diesel		
1983	22511974	30.75
1984-85	22521781	14.75

EVAPORATIVE EMISSION

	Part No.	Price
Canister		
(Chevrolet)		
1983	◆17075824	75.50
1984-85-exc. 262	◆17075849	34.50
262	◆17075859	66.00
1986-87-262	◆17086095	51.75
305	◆17075849	34.25
307Y	◆17064622	N.L.
(Corvette)		
1984	17075835	45.50
1985	17085909	43.00
1986-87	17086076	41.50
Air Cleaner Sensor		
V-6-229 & V-8-305, 350		
1983-87	◆8997787	18.75
V-6-231		
1983-85	◆8997916	18.75
V-6-262		
1985-87	◆8997574	18.75
Air Cleaner Motor		
(Chevrolet)		
1983-87-exc. below	◆8994262	24.50
229, 267	◆8994333	18.75
(Corvette)		
1984-87	◆8994333	18.75

COMPUTER CONTROLLED EMISSIONS SYSTEM

Part numbers are for pricing reference only. Order part with complete year, model, engine and unit I.D. number.

	Part No.	Price
Controller-remanufactured (E.C.M.)		
(Chevrolet)		
V-6-229		
1983	◆1226024	110.25
1984	1226454	110.25
V-6-231		
1983	◆1225500	110.25
1984-85	◆1226519	110.25
V-8-305		
1983	◆1226025	110.25
1984	◆1226455	110.25
1985-87	◆1226865	110.00
V-6-262		
1985-87	◆1226868	110.00
(Corvette)		
V-8-350		
1984-A.T.	◆1226026	110.25
M.T.	1226430	110.25
1985-87	◆1226870	110.00
Calibration Unit (PROM)		
(Chevrolet)		
V-6-229		
1983	1226309	40.50
1984	16037390	40.50
V-6-231		
1983	◆1225707	40.50
1984-85	◆16041526	40.50
V-6-262		
1985-87 (Code no.)		
8252DSK	◆16048249	40.50
0694HDZ	◆16050693	40.50
8256DSL	◆16048255	40.50
0699HFA	◆16050698	40.50
V-8-305		
1983 (Code no.)		
8659BKD	1226327	40.50
8670BKH	1226353	40.50
8693BKM	◆1226329	40.50
1984 (Code no.)		
7815BDS	◆16037814	40.50
7820BDT	◆16037819	40.50
7825BDU	◆16037824	40.50
7830BDW	16037829	40.50
0345DDH	◆16040344	40.50
0350DDJ	◆16040349	40.50
1985-87 (Code no.)		
6506DWD	◆16046505	40.50
6512DWU	◆16046511	40.50
6517DWS	◆16046516	40.50
6522DWR	◆16046521	40.50
6527DWT	◆16046526	40.50
6532DWP	◆16046531	40.50
Corvette		
(A.T.)		
1984	1226466	40.50
(M.T.)		
1984-Fed.	1225429	40.50
Calif.	1225428	40.50
1985-87 (Code no.)		
9732FUN	16049730	40.50
9573FTW	16049572	40.50
Manifold (ABS) Pressure Sensor		
(Chevrolet)		
(exc. V-6-231)		
1983-87	◆16017460	N.L.
(V-6-231)		
1983-85	◆16006835	62.25

PARTS 3A EMISSION CONTROLS 3A PARTS

	Part No.	Price
(Corvette)		
1983-87	◆16017460	N.L.
Manifold Diff. Sensor		
1985-87	◆16006834	62.25
Barometric Sensor		
1983-87	◆16006833	62.25
Oxygen Sensor		
1983-87-exc.		
262	◆8990741	28.75
262	14082487	28.75
Coolant Temperature Sensor		
1983-87	◆25036092	22.00
Vehicle Speed Sensor		
1983	◆25007278	53.50
1984-87	◆25007463	44.00

LABOR 4 ALTERNATOR & REGULATOR 4 LABOR

(Factory Time)	Chilton Time
(G) Delcotron Circuits, Test	
Includes: Test battery, regulator, Delcotron output.	
All models	.6
(M) Alternator Drive Belt, Renew	
1983-87	
V-6 (.2)	.3
w/AIR add (.1)	.1
V-8 (.2)	.3
Diesel (.3)	.4
*wo/A.C. add (.1)	.1
(G) Delcotron Assembly or Fan Pulley, Renew	
1983-87	
V-6 (.5)	.7
V-8 (.5)	.8
Diesel (.6)	.8
(G) Delcotron, R&R and Recondition	
Includes: Complete disassembly, replacement of parts as required, reassemble.	
1983-87	
V-6 (1.1)	1.7
V-8 (1.1)	1.8
Diesel (1.7)	2.3
(G) Delcotron Front Bearing, Renew	
Includes: R&R Delcotron, separate end frames.	
1983-87 (.5)	1.0
w/Diesel eng add (.2)	.2
Renew rear bearing add	.2
(G) Delcotron Voltage Regulator, Test and Renew	
Includes: R&R, disassemble and reassemble Delcotron.	
1983-87 (.6)	1.2
w/Diesel eng add (.2)	.2
(G) Voltmeter, Renew	
1984-Chev. (.3)	.5
1985 (.6)	1.0

PARTS 4 ALTERNATOR AND REGULATOR 4 PARTS

	Part No.	Price
Delcotron Assy. (New)		
1983-87-37, 42 amp	◆1105360	206.00
55, 63, 78 amp	◆1100250	225.00
70 amp	◆1105335	265.00
78 amp	◆1105369	228.75
85, 97 amp	◆1105481	218.50
94 amp	◆1105492	228.50
105 amp	1105678	N.L.
120 amp	1105585	228.25
(1) Capacitor		
1983-87	◆1978146	4.75
(2) Diode Trio		
1983-87-exc.		
105, 120 amp.	◆1984459	5.00
120 amp	1988985	10.75
(3) Rectifier Bridge		
1983-87-exc.		
below	◆1984454	28.00
85, 97 amp	◆1985801	29.75
105 amp	1989658	N.L.
120 amp	1988976	33.75
(4) Bearing		
1983-87-exc		
below	◆9436831	5.50
70, 85 amp	◆1975322	5.50
(5) Terminal Pkg.		
1983-87	◆1975471	3.50
(6) Frame (Rear End)		
1983-87-exc.		
below	◆1984460	47.75
85 amp	◆1985671	21.00
94 amp	◆1987073	27.75
120 amp	1988991	31.50
(7) Regulator		
1983-87-exc.		
105, 120 amp.	◆1116387	25.00

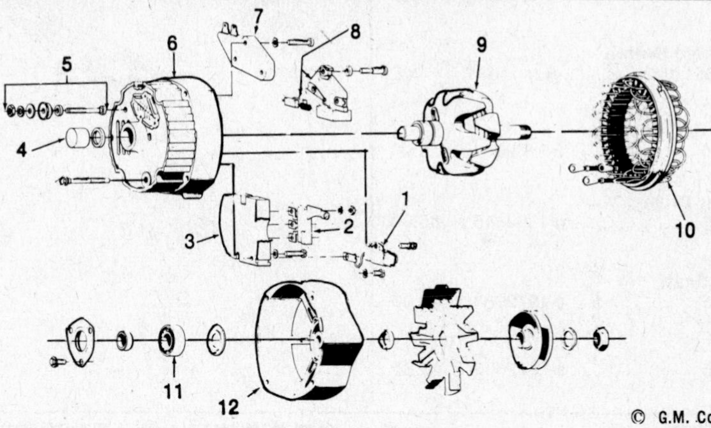

© G.M. Corp.

	Part No.	Price
105 amp	1116408	N.L.
120 amp	1988988	26.75
(8) Brush & Holder		
1983-87-exc.		
below	◆1984462	9.00
85, 97 amp	◆1975323	10.00
120 amp	1988986	7.25
(9) Rotor Assy.		
1983-87-exc.		
below	◆1985476	72.00
70 amp	◆1975333	65.00
78, 94 amp	◆1984466	77.25
85, 97 amp	◆1985646	79.25
105 amp	1989632	N.L.
120 amp	1988967	78.25
(10) Stator Assy.		
1983-87-37, 42 amp	◆1986280	52.75
56, 66 amp	◆1984584	54.50
63, 78 amp	◆1984445	37.25
70 amp	◆1975303	48.75
85, 97 amp	◆1987510	52.75
94 amp	◆1987074	41.50
105 amp	10495350	N.L.
120 amp	1988989	52.75
(11) Bearing		
1983-87	◆908419	10.00
(12) Frame (Drive End)		
1983-87-exc.		
below	◆1984464	23.50
37, 42 amp	◆1985642	24.75
85 amp	◆1985669	21.50
94 amp	◆1987054	28.00
97 amp	◆1985669	21.50
105 amp	10496671	N.L.
120 amp	◆1988983	22.25

LABOR 5 STARTING SYSTEM 5 LABOR

	(Factory Time)	Chilton Time
(G) Starter Draw Test (On Car)		
All models		.3
(G) Starter, Renew		
V-6–1983-87	(.8)	.9
V-8–1983-87	(.8)	.9
Diesel–1983-85	(.8)	1.1
(G) Starter, R&R and Recondition		
Includes: Turn down armature.		
V-6–1983-87	(1.6)	1.9
V-8–1983-87	(1.6)	1.9
Diesel–1983-85	(1.8)	2.5
Renew field coils add	(.2)	.5
(G) Starter Drive, Renew		
Includes: R&R starter.		
V-6–1983-87	(1.0)	1.1
V-8–1983-87	(1.0)	1.1
Diesel–1983-85	(1.0)	1.4
(G) Starter Solenoid Switch, Renew		
Includes: R&R starter.		
V-6–1983-87	(.8)	.9
V-8–1983-87	(.8)	.9
Diesel–1983-85	(.8)	1.1
(G) Back-Up Lamp and Park/Neutral Switch, Renew		
1983-87-Chev.	(.3)	.5
Corv.-column mount	(.2)	.4
floor mount	(1.2)	1.6
clutch mount	(.4)	.6
console mount	(.3)	.4
(G) Ignition Switch, Renew		
1983-85-Chev.	(.4)	.7
Corv.	(.8)	1.3
1986-87-Chev.	(.6)	.9
Corv.	(.7)	1.3
(M) Battery Cables, Renew		
Chevrolet		
1983-87-positive	(.3)	.4
negative	(.2)	.3
Right batt to left batt w/Diesel eng	(.3)	.3
Corvette		
1984-87-positive	(.6)	.8
negative	(.5)	.7
(M) Battery Terminals, Clean		
All models		.3

Battery Cables
Order by year and model.

PARTS 5 STARTING SYSTEM (DIESEL) 5 PARTS

	Part No.	Price
DIESEL ENGINE		
Starter Assy. (New)		
1983	◆22522853	355.00
1984-85	◆22522853	355.00
(1) Solenoid Switch		
1983-85	◆1114531	N.L.
(2) Drive End Bearing		
1983-85	◆9439544	5.00
(3) Starter Drive		
1983-85	◆1893445	65.00
(4) Drive Shaft		
1983-85	◆1972683	29.00
(5) Gear		
1983-85	◆1972685	12.50

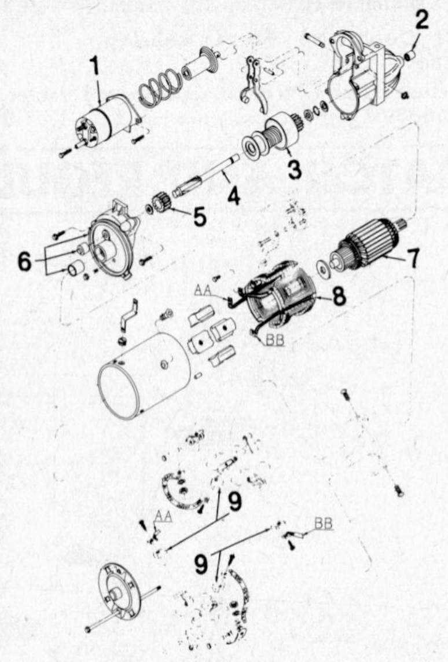

	Part No.	Price
(6) Gear Housing		
1983-85	◆1972700	29.50
(7) Armature		
1983-85	◆1979966	135.00
1983-85	◆1987639	139.75
(8) Field Coils		
1983-85	◆1979982	83.00
(9) Starter Brushes		
1983-85	◆1852885	2.75

Battery Cables
Order by year and model.

	Part No.	Price
Neutral Safety Switch		
1983-87	◆22514861	7.00

PARTS 5 STARTING SYSTEM 5 PARTS

	Part No.	Price
(1) Starter Assembly (New)		
GASOLINE ENGINES		
(Chevrolet)		
V-6-229		
1983	◆1109534	219.50
1984	◆1998452	212.50
V-8-231		
1983-85	◆1998234	220.75
V-6-262		
1985	◆1998435	10.00
1986-87	◆1998557	201.75
V-8		
1983	◆1109534	219.50
1984	◆1998430	184.75
1985-305	◆1998435	10.00
1986-87-305	◆1998557	201.75
(Corvette)		
1984	1998400	206.50
1985-87	◆1998435	10.00
1986-87	◆1998557	201.75
(2) Solenoid Switch		
1983-87	◆1114531	N.L.

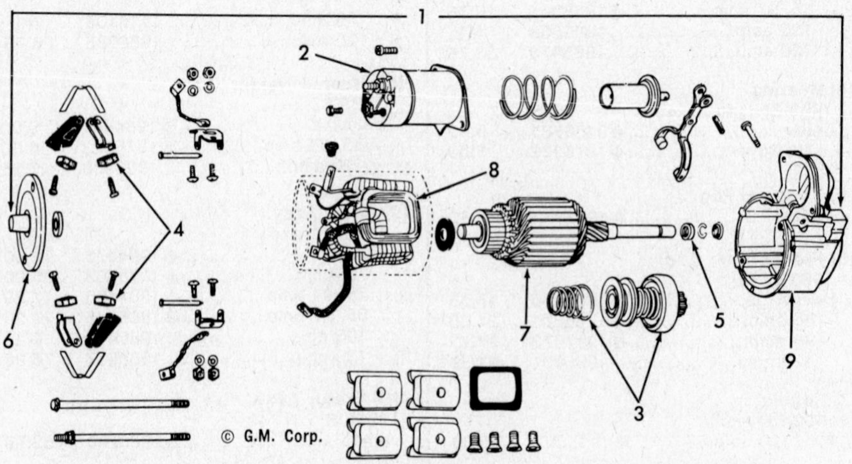

PARTS 5 STARTING SYSTEM 5 PARTS

	Part No.	Price
(3) Drive Assembly		
1983-87-exc.		
below	◆1875687	N.L.
305 (1984)	◆1984511	23.50
307Y	◆1984511	23.25
(4) Brushes		
exc. V-6-231 & V-8-307Y		
1983	◆1893296	.50
1984-87	◆1906945	.50
V-6-231		
1983-85	◆1906945	.50
V-8-307Y		
1986-87	◆1893296	.75
(5) Drive End Bushing		
1983-87	◆1932190	.50
(6) Front Plate		
exc. V-6-231 & V-8-307Y		
1983	◆1978292	6.50
1984-87	◆1974157	7.00
V-6-231		
1983-85	◆1974157	7.00
V-8-307Y		
1986-87	◆1978292	6.50
(7) Armature		
Order by starters stamping number.		
(8) Field Coils		
exc. V-6-231 & V-8-307Y		
1983	◆1978672	78.00
1984-87	◆1877306	26.00
V-6-231		
1983-85	◆1974183	19.25
(9) Housing		
(Chevrolet)		
V-6		
1983-87	◆1876881	20.50
V-8		
1983	◆1978850	27.75
1984-87	◆1876881	20.50
(Corvette)		
1984-87	◆1876881	20.50
Starter Neutral Switch		
(Chevrolet)		
1983-87	◆22514861	7.00
(Corvette)		
(M.T.)		
1984-87	14047136	14.50
(A.T.)		
1984-87	1994242	17.00

LABOR 6 BRAKE SYSTEM 6 LABOR

(Factory Time)	Chilton Time
(G) Brake Pedal Free Play, Adjust	
All models (.2)	.3
(G) Brakes, Adjust (Minor)	
Includes: R&R wheels and adjust brakes thru access holes in drums. Fill master cylinder.	
two wheels	.4
Remove knock out plugs add, each	.1
(G) Bleed Brakes (Four Wheels)	
Includes: Fill master cylinder.	
All models (.4)	.5
(G) Free-Up or Renew Brake Self Adjusting Units.	
one wheel	.6
each adtnl	.4
(G) Brake Shoes and/or Pads, Renew	
Includes: Install new or exchange shoes or pads, adjust service and hand brake. Bleed system.	
Chevrolet	
1983-87-front-disc (.9)	1.1
rear-drum (.9)	1.5
all four wheels	2.5
Corvette	
1983-87-front-disc (.6)	1.2
rear-disc (.6)	1.2
all four wheels	2.0
Resurface disc rotor, add-each	.9
Resurface brake drum, add-each	.5
(G) Brake Drum, Renew (One)	
1983-87 (.3)	.5
(G) Brake Combination Valve or Switch, Renew	
Includes: Bleed system.	
1983-87 (.7)	1.0

BRAKE HYDRAULIC SYSTEM

(Factory Time)	Chilton Time
(G) Wheel Cylinder, Renew	
Includes: Bleed system.	
1983-87-one (.8)	1.0
both (1.1)	1.9
(G) Wheel Cylinder, R&R and Rebuild	
Includes: Hone cylinder and bleed system.	
1983-87-one (1.0)	1.3
both (1.5)	2.1
(G) Brake Hose, Renew	
Includes: Bleed system.	
Front	
1983-87-one (.5)	.6

COMBINATIONS

Add to Brakes, Renew
See Machine Shop Operations

(Factory Time)	Chilton Time
(G) RENEW WHEEL CYLINDER	
Each (.2)	.2
(G) REBUILD WHEEL CYLINDER	
Each (.3)	.3
(G) REBUILD CALIPER ASSEMBLY	
Front-one (.5)	.6
Rear-one (.5)	.6
(G) RENEW MASTER CYLINDER	
All models (.5)	.8
(G) REBUILD MASTER CYLINDER	
All models (.8)	1.0
(G) RENEW BRAKE HOSE	
Each (.3)	.3
(G) RENEW REAR AXLE GREASE SEALS	
Chev.-one side (.5)	.5
(G) REPACK FRONT WHEEL BEARINGS (BOTH WHEELS)	
All models (.6)	.6
(G) RENEW BRAKE DRUM	
Each (.1)	.1
(G) RENEW DISC BRAKE ROTOR	
Front-one (.3)	.5
Rear	
1984-87-one (.2)	.3

(Factory Time)	Chilton Time
Rear	
1983-87-one (.5)	.7
(G) Electro-Hydraulic Pump, Renew	
1985-87 (.4)	.5
(G) Powermaster Pressure Switch, Renew	
1985-87 (.3)	.4
(G) Brake System Failure Warning Switch, Renew	
1984-87-Corv. (.2)	.3
(G) Brake Proportioner Valve, Renew	
1984-87-Corv. (.8)	1.2
(G) Master Cylinder, Renew	
Includes: Bleed complete system.	
1983 (.6)	.8
1984-87-Chev. (.6)	1.0
Corv. (.7)	1.0
(G) Master Cylinder, R&R and Rebuild	
Includes: Hone cylinder and bleed complete system.	
1983 (1.4)	1.8
1984-87-Chev. (1.4)	1.8
Corv. (1.2)	1.6
w/Powermaster cyl (1.6)	2.2
(G) Brake System, Flush and Refill	
All models	1.2
(G) Brake Hydraulic System, Recondition (Complete)	
Includes: Renew all rubber parts in brake system and bleed all lines.	
1983-87 (4.4)	6.0

POWER BRAKES

(Factory Time)	Chilton Time
(G) Power Brake Cylinder, Renew	
1983-Chev. (.6)	.9
Corv. (1.0)	1.5
1984-87-Chev. (.6)	1.0
Corv. (.5)	.9
(G) Power Brake Cylinder, R&R and Recondition	
1983-Chev. (1.4)	1.9
1984-87-Chev.	
single (1.1)	1.8
tandem (1.3)	2.0
Corv. (1.1)	1.8
Recond m/Cyl add (.8)	.8
(G) Vacuum Check Valve, Renew	
1983-87 (.3)	.3
(G) Hydra-boost Unit, Renew	
Includes: Bleed system.	
1983-85 (.6)	1.0
(G) Hydra-boost Unit, R&R and Recondition	
Includes: Bleed system.	
1983-85 (1.0)	1.5
(G) Hydra-boost Pressure Lines, Renew	
Includes: Bleed system.	
1983-85-each (.3)	.6

LABOR 6 BRAKE SYSTEM 6 LABOR

(Factory Time)	Chilton Time
DISC BRAKES	
(G) Disc Brake Pads, Renew	
Chevrolet	
1983-87 (.9)	1.1
Corvette	
1983-87-front (.6)	1.2
rear (.6)	1.2
all four wheels	2.0
(G) Disc Brake Rotor, Renew	
Chevrolet	
1983-87-one (.7)	1.0
both (1.2)	1.5
Corvette	
1984-87	
Front or Rear	
one (.5)	.7
two (.7)	1.1
all four wheels	2.0
(G) Caliper Assembly, Renew	
Includes: Bleed complete system.	
Chevrolet	
1983-87-one (.7)	1.0
both (1.1)	1.5
Corvette	
1984-87	
Front or Rear	
one (.7)	1.0
two (1.0)	1.6
all four wheels (2.0)	3.0
(G) Caliper Assembly, R&R and Recondition	
Includes: Bleed complete system.	
Chevrolet	
1983-87-one (1.2)	1.5
both (2.0)	2.5
Corvette	
1984-87	
Front or Rear	
one (1.0)	1.4
two (1.6)	2.4
all four wheels (3.2)	4.6
PARKING BRAKE	
(M) Parking Brake, Adjust	
1983-87-Chev. (.3)	.4
Corv. (.6)	.8
(G) Parking Brake Warning Lamp Switch, Renew	
1983-Chev. (.2)	.4
1984-87-Chev. (.2)	.4
Corv. (.4)	.6
(G) Parking Brake Control, Renew	
1983-Chev. (.7)	.9
Corv. (.9)	1.1
1984-87-Chev. (.7)	1.0
Corv. (1.2)	1.6
(G) Parking Brake Equalizer, Renew	
1983 (.3)	.5
1984-87-Chev. (.3)	.5
Corv. (.7)	1.0
(G) Parking Brake Cables, Renew	
Front	
1983-Chev. (.6)	.7
Corv. (.9)	1.0
1984-87-Chev. (.6)	1.0
Corv. (1.4)	1.9
Rear	
1983-87-one (.7)	1.1
both (1.1)	1.4
two piece (1.1)	1.5
Note: If necessary to drill out rivets, add appropriate time.	
(G) Parking Brake Shoes, Renew	
Corvette	
1983-one side (1.4)	*1.8
both sides (2.3)	*2.8
1984-87	
both sides (1.4)	2.0
*Not necessary to R&R hub assy.	
ANTI-SKID BRAKE SYSTEM (ABS)	
(G) Wheel Speed Sensors, Renew (Front or Rear)	
1986-87-one (.3)	.5
both (.5)	.9
Renew brkt add (.2)	.2
(G) Brake Controller, Renew	
1986-87 (.5)	.7
(G) Modulator, R&R or Renew	
1986-87 (1.0)	1.5
(G) Relay, Renew	
1986-87 (.4)	.5
(G) Lateral Accelerometer, Renew	
1986-87 (.8)	1.1

PARTS 6 BRAKE SYSTEM 6 PARTS

	Part No.	Price
(1) Rear Brake Shoe Set		
1983-87-9½" x 2" brk.	◆1154580	35.00
11" x 2" brk	◆1154577	42.50
(2) Rear Wheel Cylinder Assy.		
(9½" x 2" brks.)		
1983-87	◆18004888	28.50
(11" x 2" brks.)		
1983-87-exc. Sta. wag.	◆18004890	25.75
Sta. wag.	◆18004793	28.50
Rear Wheel Cylinder Repair Kit		
(9½" x 2" brks.)		
1983-87	◆5466562	7.75
(11" x 2" brks.)		
1983-87-exc. Sta. wag.	◆5463361	7.50
Sta. wag.	◆5472328	8.00
Brake Hose, Front Flex		
(Chevrolet)		
1983-87	◆9762809	18.00
(Corvette)		
1984	14050079	16.75
1985-87	14076178	16.50
Brake Hose, Rear Flex		
(Chevrolet)		
1983-87	◆9757655	15.00
(Corvette)		
1984	14076124	13.00
1985	14076179	18.50
1986-87	14091293	18.75
Master Cylinder Assy.		
(Chevrolet)		
1983-87-exc. diesel	◆18010313	145.75
Diesel	◆25509416	103.00

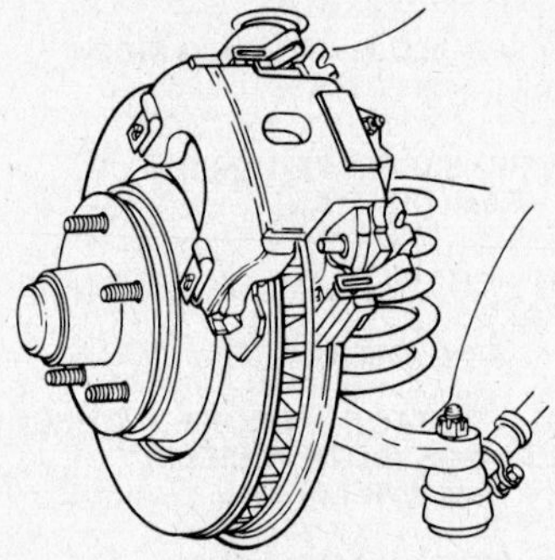

FRONT BRAKE

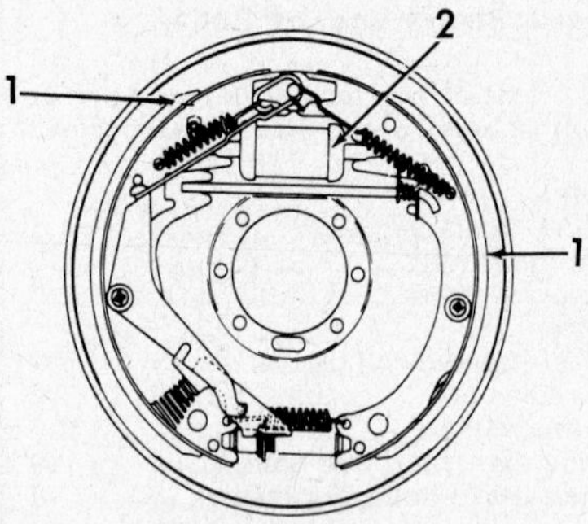

REAR BRAKE

	Part No.	Price
(Corvette)		
1984	14046850	106.50
1985	14080223	125.00
1986-87	14087634	158.00
Power Brake Cylinder Assy. (Vacuum)		
(Chevrolet)		
(exc. Diesel)		
1983-87	◆18006566	224.50
(Diesel)		
1983-85	◆1620210	365.00
(Corvette)		
1984	14046849	186.50
1985-87	14080222	186.00
Master Cylinder Repair Kit		
(Chevrolet)		
1983-87-exc. diesel	◆18007935	22.50
Diesel	◆25509843	28.50
(Corvette)		
1984	14067548	46.50
1985	14085883	40.50
1986-87	14105963	48.00
Vacuum Power Brake Cylinder Repair Kit		
(Chevrolet)		
1983-87	◆18007865	47.50
Brake Drum, Rear		
(9½" x 2" brks.)		
1983-87-Cast	◆1249146	73.00
Alum.	◆1255496	90.00
(11" x 2" brks.)		
1983-87-1716. drum	◆1244835	97.00
2316. drum	◆1244838	96.25

PARTS 6 BRAKE SYSTEM 6 PARTS

POWER BRAKE BOOSTER (DIESEL)

	Part No.	Price
Booster Assy. (Hydraulic)		
1983-85	◆1620210	365.00
Cover Kit (Input Seal)		
1983-85	◆22506436	82.25
Piston Kit (w/housing)		
1983-85	◆22506438	5.50
Piston Kit (w/accumulator)		
1983-85	◆22506439	128.00
Seal Kit (Spool Plug)		
1983-85	◆1612592	3.00
Seal Kit (Booster)		
1983-85	◆22506440	10.75

PARKING BRAKE

	Part No.	Price
Brake Cable (Front)		
(Chevrolet)		
1983-84	◆25502769	12.00
1985-87	◆25520342	12.75
(Corvette)		
1984-87	14048980	16.75
Brake Cable (Rear)		
(Chevrolet)		
1983-84-L.H.	◆25502687	22.00
R.H. (exc. Wag)	◆25502686	22.00
R.H. (Sta wag)	◆25502772	22.50

	Part No.	Price
1985-87-L.H. (exc. Wag.)	◆25520337	22.25
L.H. (Sta. wag.)	◆25524603	22.50
R.H. (exc. Wag.)	◆25520338	22.00
R.H. (Sta. wag.)	◆25524602	22.00
(Corvette)		
1984-87-L.H.	14048981	15.75
R.H.	14048982	15.75
Parking Brake Apply Lever		
(Chevrolet)		
1983-87	◆25502971	23.50
(Corvette)		
1984-87	14050061	54.75

PARTS 6 DISC BRAKES 6 PARTS

CORVETTE

	Part No.	Price
Disc Rotor		
1984-87-front	14084142	67.00
rear	14084143	67.00
Caliper Repair Kit		
1984-87-front	14067584	6.75
rear	14067585	5.50
(1) Caliper Assy.		
(Front)		
1984-87-right	14067554	66.75
left	14067553	66.75
(Rear)		
1984-87-right	14067556	62.25
left	14067555	62.25
(2) Brake Pad Set		
1984-87-front	14091367	50.00
rear	14091368	44.50
1984-Parking	14067571	49.00
1985-87-Parking	14085890	49.00
(3) Boot		
1984-87-front	14067565	2.75
rear	14067566	2.75

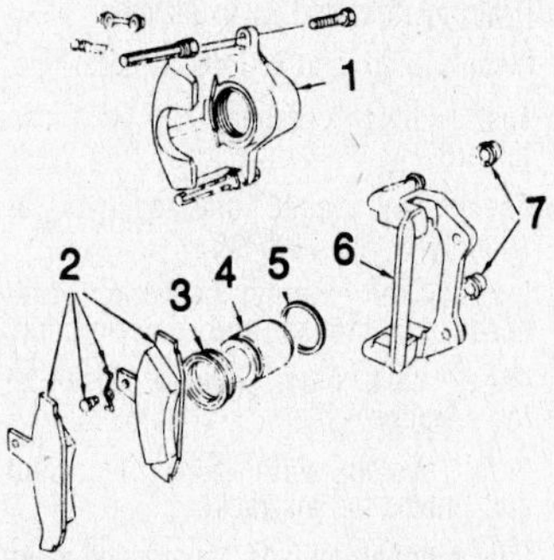

	Part No.	Price
(4) Piston		
1984-87-front	14067563	9.75
rear	14067564	8.50
(5) Seal		
1984-87-front	14067561	2.50
rear	14067562	2.50
(6) Mounting Plate (Caliper)		
1984-87-front	14067557	35.50
rear	14067558	35.50

	Part No.	Price
(7) Guide Pin Boot		
1984-87	14067552	1.00

ANTI-SKID BRAKE SYSTEM (ABS)

CORVETTE

	Part No.	Price
Wheel Sensors		
1986-87-Front		
L.H.	14084077	61.75
R.H.	14084078	61.75
1986-87-Rear		
L.H.	14084079	61.75
R.H.	14084080	61.75
Modulator Valve		
1986-87	14105966	825.00
Relay (Valve Pump Motor)		
1986-87	14105968	30.50
Relay (Modulator Valve Solenoid)		
1986-87	14105967	28.25
Switch (Lateral Accelerometer)		
1986-87	14093144	78.00
Module (Control)		
1986-87	14103343	724.00

PARTS 6 DISC BRAKES 6 PARTS

CHEVROLET

	Part No.	Price
Disc Rotor		
(11″ rotor)		
1983-87	◆14008640	110.00
(12″ rotor)		
1983-87	◆14008641	110.00
(1) Brake Pad Set		
1983-87-exc. H.D.	◆1154578	35.00
H.D. brks.	◆12300192	47.00
(2) Spring		
1983-87	◆5469497	1.00
(3) Caliper Repair Kit		
1983-87	◆5468767	10.00

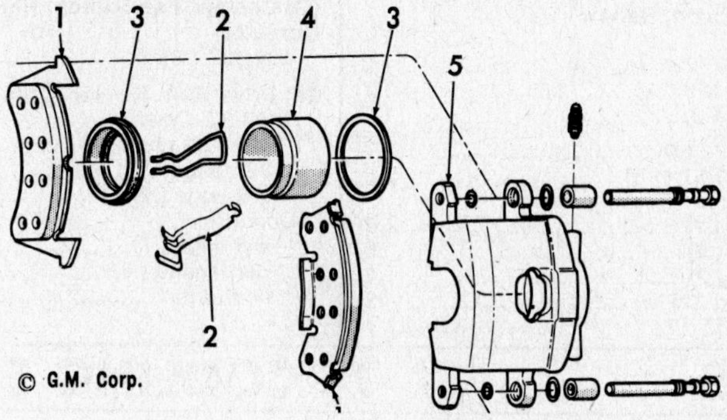

	Part No.	Price
(4) Piston		
1983-87	◆2622207	11.00

	Part No.	Price
(5) Caliper Assy.		
1983-87-right	◆18012309	168.75
left	◆18012308	168.75

LABOR 7 COOLING SYSTEM 7 LABOR

(Factory Time) Chilton Time

(M) Winterize Cooling System
Includes: Run engine to check for leaks, tighten all hose connections. Test radiator and pressure cap, drain radiator and engine block. Add anti-freeze and refill system.
All models 5

(M) Thermostat, Renew
V-6–1983-85
229 engs (.5) 6
231 eng (.7) 8
262 eng (.7) 9
1986-87 (.3) 4
V-8–1983-87 (.5) .... *.6
Diesel–1983-85 (.5) 6
*Corvette add 2

(M) Radiator Assembly, R&R or Renew
Includes: Drain and refill cooling system.
Chevrolet
Gasoline Engines
1983-87 (.5) 1.1
Diesel Engines
1983-85 (.7) 1.0
Corvette
1983-87 (.9) 1.4
w/A.C. add 3
w/A.T. add 2

ADD THESE OPERATIONS TO RADIATOR R&R
(G) Boil & Repair 1.5
(G) Rod Clean 1.9
(G) Repair Core 1.3
(G) Renew Tank 1.6
(G) Renew Trans. Oil Cooler 1.9
(G) Recore Radiator 1.7

(M) Radiator Hoses, Renew
Chevrolet
upper (.3) 4
lower (.4) 5
both (.5) 7
Corvette
upper (.3) 5
lower (.5) 6
both (.6) 8

(G) Thermostat By-Pass Hose, Renew
1983-84 (.5) 6

(G) Water Pump, Renew
Chevrolet
V-6–1983-87-231 eng (.9) 1.3
229 eng (1.3) 1.7
262 eng (1.3) 1.7
V-8–1983-87 (1.0) 1.7
Diesel–1983-87 (1.5) 2.5
Corvette
1984-87 (1.7) 2.4
w/A.C. add (.5) 5
w/P.S. add (.2) 2
w/Air inj add (.2) 2

COOLING SYSTEM TUNE-UP

An Annual Cooling System Tune-Up Suggestion List should include (with some exceptions):

1. A visual check of the cooling system for indications of leaks or excessive oil content.
2. Pressure check the cooling system for internal and external leaks with filler cap and neck adapter and tester.
3. Check crankcase and automatic transmission oil for water content.
4. Test coolant thermostat with radiator thermometer.
5. Check temperature gauge for accuracy.
6. Drain system and flush till clean.
7. Clean foreign matter from radiator fins.
8. Test radiator pressure cap with cap tester.
9. Check fan blades and pulleys for alignment and damage.
10. Internal and external inspection of all hoses for cracks and deterioration.
11. Check core plugs (where possible) for seepage.
12. Refill system with correct coolant and check for air locks.
13. Check condition and tension of drive belts with tension gauge.

All models 1.5

(Factory Time) Chilton Time

(G) Electric Cooling Fan and/or Motor, Renew
Corvette
1983-87 (.5) 8

(G) Engine Coolant Fan Electronic Control Module Assy., Renew
Corvette
1984-87 (.2) 3

(G) Coolant Fan Switch, Renew
Corvette
1984-87 (.3) 5

(M) Drive Belt, Renew (One)
1983-87-Chev.
229-262 engs (.2) 3
231 eng (.5) 7
V-8 engs (.2) 3
Corvette
V-8 engs (.7) 9
Serpentine (.2) 5
each adtnl 1

(Factory Time) Chilton Time

(M) Clutch Fan, Renew
Chevrolet
1983-87 (.3) 5

(G) Temperature Gauge (Engine Unit), Renew
1983-87-Chev. (.3) 4
Corv. (.4) 6

(G) Temperature Gauge (Dash Unit), Renew
Chevrolet
1983-84 (.3) 7
1985-87 (.6) 1.0

(G) Instrument Panel Cluster Assy., Renew
1984-87-Corv. (1.4) 2.5

(G) Water Jacket Expansion Plug, Renew (Side of Block)
All models (.5) 5
Add time to gain accessibility.

(G) Heater Hoses, Renew
Includes: Drain and refill coolant.
1983-87 (.4) 7

(G) Heater Core, R&R or Renew
Chevrolet–Without Air Conditioning
1983-87 (.5) 1.0
Chevrolet–With Air Conditioning
1983-87 (1.2) 1.8
Corvette–With Air Conditioning
1984-87 (1.9) 3.7

ADD THESE OPERATIONS TO HEATER CORE R&R
(G) Boil & Repair 1.2
(G) Repair Core 9
(G) Recore 1.2

(G) Heater Control Assembly, Renew
1983-85 (.5) 9
1986-87 (.7) 1.0

(G) Heater Blower Motor, Renew
1983 (.2) 5
1984-87-Chev. (.2) 5

(G) Heater Blower Motor Resistor, Renew
1983-87 (.2) 3

(G) Heater Blower Motor Switch, Renew
1983 (.3) 6
1984-87-Chev. (.6) 9

(G) Hot Water Shut Off Valve, Renew
1983-87-Chev. (.3) 5
Corv. (.4) 6
Diesel (.6) 8

PARTS 7 COOLING SYSTEM 7 PARTS

	Part No.	Price
(1) Radiator Assembly		
Accurate replacement of the radiator can be done only by using the radiator code stamped on a metal tag located on the original radiator. Order by year, model and radiator code no.		
Thermostat		
1983-87-exc.		
below	◆3051139	5.00
231	◆1254894	9.00
305	◆3041390	5.00
(2) Radiator Hoses		
Order by year and model.		
(3) Water Pump Assembly		
(Chevrolet)		
V-6–229		
1983-84	◆474029	72.50
V-6–231		
1983-85	◆1260709	61.75
V-6–262		
1985-87	◆14085847	75.75
V-8–305		
1983-84	◆474029	72.50
1985-87	◆14085847	75.75
V-8–307Y		
1986-87	◆556283	N.L.
V-8 Diesel		
1983-85	◆556283	95.00

PARTS 7 COOLING SYSTEM 7 PARTS

	Part No.	Price
(Corvette)		
1984-87	14094538	92.25

(4) Fan Belt
Order by year and model.

Fan Clutch Assembly

Part numbers are for pricing reference only. Order part with complete year, model and unit I.D. code.

	Part No.	Price
1983-87 (Code stamped on clutch)		
AB	14044660	143.00
AD	◆22007636	73.50
AK	342754	67.25
AS	◆22008426	84.50
CB	460798	84.50
CY	22008434	74.50
FB	22007562	84.50
OJ (diesel)	◆22008668	N.L.
OM (diesel)	◆561826	122.00
TS	◆22008490	84.50
TT, TU	◆22008492	87.50
CM, FC, KC	14077971	104.00

Heat Indicator, Sending Unit

	Part No.	Price
(Chevrolet)		
(wo/Gauges)		
(exc. V-6-231 & Diesel)		
1983-87	◆25036136	11.75
(V-6-231)		
1983-85	◆25036371	8.00
(Diesel)		
1983	◆25036371	8.00
1984-85	◆25036629	9.75
(Gauges)		
1983-87	◆8993146	19.25
(Corvette)		
1983-87	25036135	11.00

Heat Indicator, Dash Unit

	Part No.	Price
(Chevrolet)		
1983-84	8993590	25.50
1985-87	25034454	29.75

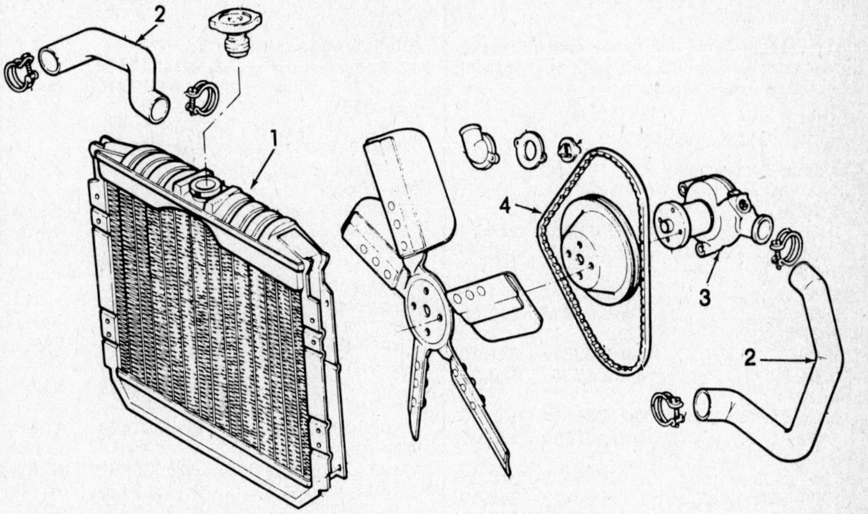

Heater Core

	Part No.	Price
(Chevrolet)		
1983-87-wo/A.C.	◆3036422	41.25
A.C.	◆3035420	43.00
(Corvette)		
1984-87	3052870	85.75

Heater Blower Switch

	Part No.	Price
(Chevrolet)		
(wo/A.C.)		
1983-84	6273329	3.75
1985-87	◆16015450	6.75
(A.C.)		
1983	◆16015256	6.00
1984	◆16032480	7.25
1985-87	◆16015450	6.75
(Corvette)		
1984-87	16022463	7.00

Heater Blower Motor

	Part No.	Price
(Chevrolet)		
(wo/A.C.)		
1983-87	◆22048569	47.50
(A.C.)		
1983-87	◆22020945	60.00
(Corvette)		
1984-87	22029164	60.00

LABOR 8 EXHAUST SYSTEM 8 LABOR

(Factory Time)	Chilton Time
(G) Muffler, Renew (One)	
1983-87-Chev. (.5)	.7
Corv. (.5)	.8
(G) Tail Pipe, Renew	
1983-87 (.4)	.6
(G) Resonator Assy., Renew	
1983-87 (.4)	.6
(G) Catalytic Converter, Renew	
1983-Chev. (.5)	.8
Corv. (.5)	1.0
1984-87-Chev. (.8)	1.0
Corv. (.9)	1.2
w/AIR add (.1)	.1
(G) Exhaust Pipe Flange Gasket or Seal, Renew	
1983-87-each (.4)	.6
(G) Exhaust Crossover Pipe, Renew	
1983-Chev. (.6)	1.2
Corv. (.6)	1.0
Diesel (.9)	1.3
1984-87-Chev. (.4)	.7
Corv. (.8)	1.2
Diesel (.9)	1.3
(G) Intermediate Exhaust Pipe, Renew	
1983-Chev. (.5)	.7
Corv. (.6)	1.0
1984-87-Chev. (.4)	.7
Corv. (1.0)	1.4
(G) Exhaust Pipe (Front), Renew	
Diesel-1983-85 (.4)	.7
(G) E.F.E. Valve (Heat Riser), Renew	
1983-87 (.6)	.9
(G) E.F.E. Vacuum Check Valve, Renew	
1983-84 (.2)	.4
(G) Exhaust Manifold, Renew	
V-6-1983-87	
229 engs	
right (1.0)	1.4
left (.8)	1.2
231 eng	
right (.7)	1.1
left (.6)	1.0
262 eng-right (1.2)	1.9
left (.7)	1.2
w/A.C. add (.5)	.5
w/P.S. add (.2)	.2
w/C.C.C. add (.2)	.2
V-8-1983-right (1.5)	2.2
left (1.2)	1.7
1984-87-Chev.	
305 eng Code H	
right side (1.3)	2.1
left side (1.0)	1.4
307 eng Code Y	
right side (1.1)	1.6
left side (1.0)	1.5
1984-Corv.-right (2.0)	2.7
left (1.1)	1.5
1985-87-right (2.8)	3.8
left (1.1)	1.5
w/C.C.C. add (.2)	.2
w/A.C. add (.6)	.6
w/Air inj add (.2)	.2
Diesel-1983-right (.9)	1.3
left (.7)	1.1
1984-85-right (1.2)	1.7
left (.7)	1.1

COMBINATIONS

(Factory Time)	Chilton Time
(G) Muffler, Exhaust and Tail Pipe, Renew	
All models	1.8
w/Crossover pipe add	.4
(G) Muffler and Tail Pipe, Renew	
All models	1.0

PARTS 8 EXHAUST SYSTEM 8 PARTS

Part numbers listed are for pricing reference only. Order parts with complete year, model and engine information.

	Part No.	Price
Muffler		
Order by year and model.		
Catalytic Converter		
(Chevrolet)		
V-6-229		
1983	25056364	274.25
1984	◆25056381	320.25
V-6-231		
1983	◆8999642	271.25
1984-85	◆8999615	312.25
V-8-305		
1983	◆8999642	271.25
1984-87	◆25056382	300.25
V-8-307Y		
1986-87-Fed.	◆25056634	335.00
Calif.	◆25100218	323.00
(Corvette)		
1984	25056438	348.25
1985-87	25056723	345.00
1986-87	25058000	309.00
Resonator Assembly (w/Pipes)		
Order by year and model.		
Tail Pipe		
V-6-229, 231		
1983-87	◆14011207	46.25
V-6-262		
1985-87	◆14089453	48.25
V-8-305		
(exc. Station wagon)		
1983-87-exc.		
below	◆14011207	46.25
3.08, 3.23R	14011208	49.25
(Station wagon)		
1983-87-2.56R	◆14011209	54.50
3.08R	14011210	69.50
V-8-307Y		
1986-87-exc.		
Wagon	◆1251925	
Wagon	◆22505492	89.25
V-8-Diesel		
1983-87-wagon	◆22512353	55.75
Wagon	◆25509141	49.25
Intermediate Pipe		
(Chevrolet)		
V-6-229		
1983-84	14070202	N.L.
V-6-231		
1983-85	◆25505629	52.50
V-6-262		
1985-87	◆14091439	31.50
V-8-305		
1983	25505632	46.00
1984	◆14089120	23.00
1985-87	◆14089130	46.00
V-8-307Y		
1986-87	◆22524716	51.00
V-8-Diesel		
1983-85	◆22512345	53.75
Manifold Pipe		
(Corvette)		
1984-85	14060182	134.00
1986-87	14087659	121.00
(Chevrolet)		
1983-231A	◆25508302	48.75
1984-231A		
(Calif.)	◆25515214	21.25
1983-84-Diesel	25512345	N.L.
1985-Diesel		
exc. wagon	◆22512355	52.25
wagon	◆22512346	52.25
V-8-307Y		
1986-87	◆22520490	11.00
Crossover Pipe		
(Chevrolet)		
V-6-229		
1983-84	14059194	52.50
V-6-231		
1983	◆25506286	31.25
1984-85	◆25516456	31.25
V-6-262		
1985-87	◆14082873	59.50
V-8-305		
1983-84-exc.		
below	14025046	87.50
Dual bed conv.	◆14059196	46.00
1985-87	◆14059196	46.00
V-8-307Y		
1986-87	◆22504709	74.25
V-8-Diesel		
1983-85	◆22514728	24.00
(Corvette)		
1984	14060154	77.75
1985-1st design	14076185	51.75
2nd design	14087616	59.00

2nd design is used on vehicles with integral welded heat shields.

LABOR 9 FRONT SUSPENSION 9 LABOR

(Factory Time) — Chilton Time

Note: On all front suspension operations alignment charges must be added if performed. Time given does not include alignment.

	Chilton Time
(G) Wheel, Renew	
one (.5)	.5
(G) Wheels, Rotate (All)	
All models	.5
(G) Wheels, Balance	
one	.3
each adtnl	.2
(G) Check Alignment of Front End	
All models	.5
Note: Deduct if alignment is performed.	
(G) Toe-In, Adjust	
All models (.4)	.6
(G) Align Front End	
Includes: Adjust front wheel bearings.	
Chevrolet-all models (.7)	1.4
Corvette	
1984-87 (.6)	1.0
w/A.C. interference add	.5
(G) Front Wheel Bearing and Hub Assy., Renew	
Corvette	
1984-87-one side (.6)	.8
both sides (.9)	1.3
(G) Front Wheel Bearings, Clean and Repack (Both Wheels)	
1983-87 (1.1)	1.6
(G) Front Wheel Bearings and Cups, Renew	
1983-87-one side (.7)	.9
both sides (1.1)	1.5
(G) Front Wheel Grease Seals, Renew	
1983-87-one side (.7)	.8
both sides (1.1)	1.2
(G) Front Shock Absorbers, Renew	
1983-85-one (.3)	.4
both (.5)	.7
1986-87-Chev.-one (.3)	.4
both (.5)	.7
Corv.-one (.6)	.9
both (1.0)	1.6
(G) Rebuild Front Suspension	
Includes: Disassemble, renew necessary parts, reassemble, lubricate and align front end.	
Chevrolet	
1983-87-one side (4.8)	5.9
both sides (7.8)	9.5
(G) Upper and Lower Ball Joints, Renew (One Side)	
Add alignment charges.	
1983-87-Chev. (1.1)	1.8
(G) Upper Ball Joint, Renew (One)	
Add alignment charges.	
1983-87-Chev. (.7)	.9
Corv. (.6)	1.0
(G) Lower Ball Joint, Renew (One)	
Add alignment charges.	
1983-87-Chev. (.6)	.9
Corv. (.9)	1.3
(G) Steering Knuckle, Renew (One)	
Add alignment charges.	
Corvette	
1984-87 (.9)	1.5
(G) Steering Knuckle and Arm, Renew (One)	
Add alignment charges.	
Chevrolet	
1983-87 (1.0)	1.4
(G) Upper Control Arm, Renew (One)	
Add alignment charges.	
Chevrolet	
1983-87 (.7)	1.2
Corvette	
1984-87 (.8)	1.2
(G) Lower Control Arm, Renew (One)	
Add alignment charges.	
Chevrolet	
1983-87 (1.0)	1.5
Corvette	
1984-87 (.7)	1.1
(G) Upper Control Arm Inner Pivot Shaft or Bushings, Renew (One Side)	
Add alignment charges.	
1983-87-Chev. (1.0)	1.5
(G) Lower Control Arm Shaft or Bushings, Renew (One Side)	
Add alignment charges.	
Chevrolet	
1983-87 (1.2)	1.7

LABOR 9 FRONT SUSPENSION 9 LABOR

	(Factory Time)	Chilton Time
(G) Front Spring, Renew (One)		
Add alignment charges.		
Chevrolet		
1983-87	(.8)	1.4
(G) Front Transverse Spring, Renew		
Corvette		
1984-87	(1.4)	1.8
(G) Front Stabilizer Bar and Bushings, Renew		
1983-87-Chev.	(.5)	.8
Corv.	(.7)	1.0
(G) Stabilizer Links or Grommets, Renew		
1983-87-one	(.3)	.4
both	(.4)	.6

PARTS 9 FRONT SUSPENSION 9 PARTS

CHEVROLET

	Part No.	Price
(1) Front Wheel Bearing (Outer)		
1983-87	◆7450697	11.00
(2) Front Wheel Bearing (Inner)		
1983-87	◆7450630	11.00
(3) Front Seal Assy.		
1983-87	◆3965092	3.50
(4) Steering Knuckle		
(11″ rotor)		
1983-87-right	◆14012596	116.00
left	◆14012595	116.00
(12″ rotor)		
1983-87-right	◆14012590	144.00
left	◆14012589	144.00
(5) Ball Joint Pkg. (Lower)		
1983	◆9767281	31.50
1984-87	◆9767281	31.50
(6) Control Arm (Lower)		
1983-87-right	◆14039016	105.00
left	◆14039015	105.00

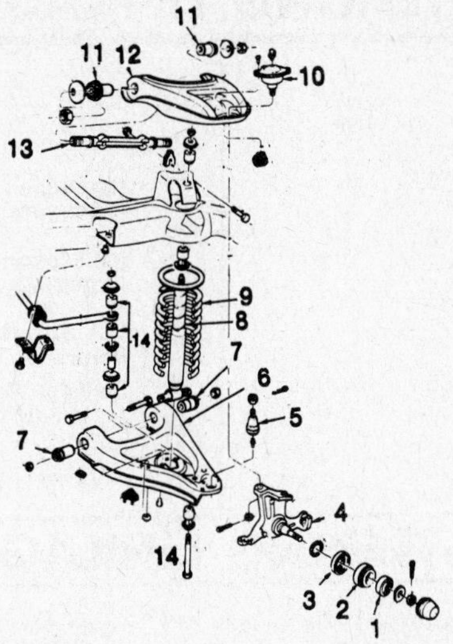

	Part No.	Price
(7) Bushing		
1983-87-front	◆351286	7.00
rear	3933677	N.L.
(8) Shock Absorber		
1983-std	◆4993548	24.50
H.D. & wagon	◆4993548	24.50
1984-87	◆4993745	24.50
(9) Coil Spring		
Order by year and model.		
(10) Ball Joint (Upper)		
1983-87	◆9767112	34.75
(11) Bushing		
1983-87-front	◆371793	4.25
rear	14020223	5.50
(12) Control Arm (Upper)		
1983-87-right	◆14039010	109.00
left	◆14039009	109.00
(13) Shaft Pkg. (Upper Control)		
1983-87-right	◆14022172	33.75
left	◆14022171	35.50
(14) Stabilizer Link Pkg.		
1983-87	◆464167	4.25

PARTS 9 FRONT SUSPENSION 9 PARTS

CORVETTE

	Part No.	Price
(1) Control Arm (Lower)		
1984-87-right	14067624	294.00
left	14067623	294.00
(2) Ball Joint (Lower)		
1984-87	9769599	66.00
(3) Hub		
1984-85	7466923	213.50
1986-87	7466931	225.00
(4) Steering Knuckle Assy.		
1984-right	14035700	192.00
left	14035699	192.00
1985-87-right	14084048	192.00
left	14084047	192.00
(5) Ball Joint (Upper)		
1984-87	9769596	75.25
(6) Control Arm (Upper)		
1984-87-right	14042228	N.L.
left	14042227	N.L.
(7) Shock Absorber		
1984-87-exc. H.D. susp.	4993594	25.50
H.D. susp.	4993596	25.50
1985-87-wo/gas shock wo/H.D. susp.	22046416	25.25
(8) Retainer		
1984-87	14044559	1.00
(9) Insulator (Lower)		
1984-87	14044561	1.00

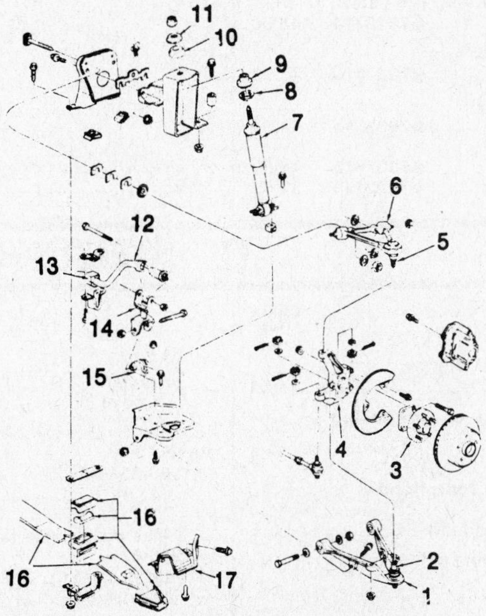

PARTS 9 FRONT SUSPENSION 9 PARTS

	Part No.	Price
(10) Insulator (Upper)		
1984-87	14044560	1.00
(11) Retainer		
1984-87	14044559	1.00
(12) Stabilizer Shaft		
1984-exc. H.D. susp.	14060132	81.50
H.D. susp.	14048992	85.00
1985-87-wo/H.D. susp.	14076196	81.50
H.D. susp.	14084067	85.00
(13) Stabilizer Bushing		
1984-87-exc. below	14060134	
1985-87-H.D. susp.	14048983	2.00
(14) Stabilizer Link Kit		
1984	14048977	3.25
1985-87	14087645	3.25
(15) Insulator		
1984	14048975	5.00
1985-87	14084098	5.25
(16) Front Spring		
1984-exc. H.D. susp.	14045781	301.00
H.D. susp.	14045782	301.00
1985-87-wo/H.D. susp.	14065897	301.00
H.D. susp.	14080186	301.00
(17) Spring Protector		
1984-87	14048914	15.00

LABOR 10 STEERING LINKAGE 10 LABOR

	(Factory Time)	Chilton Time
(G) Inner Tie Rods, Renew		
Includes: Reset toe-in.		
1983-87-one side	(.7)	1.0
both sides	(.8)	1.2
(G) Tie Rod or Tie Rod End, Renew (One Side)		
Includes: Reset toe-in.		
1983-87-Chev.	(.7)	1.0
Corv.	(.6)	.9
(G) Pitman Arm, Renew		
1983-87	(.3)	.7
(G) Steering Idler Arm, Renew		
1983-87-Chev.	(.7)	1.0
(G) Steering Intermediate Rod, Renew		
Includes: Reset toe-in.		
1983-87	(.7)	1.2

PARTS 10 STEERING LINKAGE 10 PARTS

	Part No.	Price
(1) Idler Arm Assy.		
1983-87	◆7837635	51.00
(2) Tie Rod Assy. (Inner)		
1983-87	◆7834224	45.75
(3) Tie Rod End (Outer)		
1983-87	◆12308612	50.50
(4) Tie Rod Sleeve Pkg. (Adjuster)		
1983-87	◆7826714	15.50
(5) Seal Kit (Pitman Arm)		
1983-87	◆7826470	17.00
(6) Pitman Arm Assy.		
1983-84	◆7837645	44.00
1985-87-wo/H.D. susp.	◆7837645	44.00
H.D. susp.	◆7832199	51.50

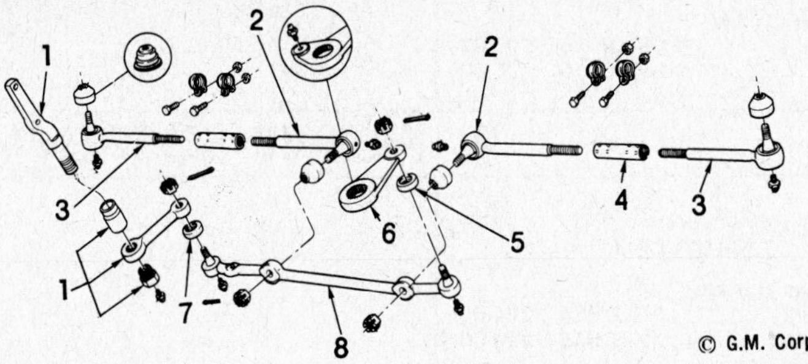

© G.M. Corp.

	Part No.	Price
(7) Seal Kit		
1983	◆5693125	2.75
(8) Relay Rod Assy.		
1983-87	◆7837639	109.00

LABOR 11 STEERING GEAR 11 LABOR

	(Factory Time)	Chilton Time
(G) Steering Wheel, Renew		
1983-87	(.3)	.4
(G) Horn Contact or Cancelling Cam, Renew		
1983-87	(.5)	.6
(G) Multifunction Lever, Renew		
All models	(.2)	.4
w/Cruise control add	(.5)	.5
(G) Steering Column Lock Actuator Parts, Renew		
1983-85		
std colm	(.8)	1.3
tilt colm	(.9)	1.4
w/Cruise control add	(.2)	.2
1986-87		
std colm	(1.1)	1.6
tilt colm	(1.3)	1.8
(G) Upper Mast Jacket Bearing, Renew		
1983-85-std	(.8)	1.4
tilt	(.9)	1.6
Tilt-Tel	(1.1)	1.7
w/Cruise control add	(.2)	.2
1986-87		
std colm	(1.0)	1.4
tilt colm	(.5)	.9
(G) Steering Intermediate Shaft, Renew		
1983-87	(.4)	.9
(G) Steering Lower Coupling Shaft (Pot Joint), Renew		
1983-85	(.5)	.8
(G) Steering Coupling (Rag Joint), Renew		
1983-85	(.5)	.8
(G) Steering Pitman Shaft Seal, Renew		
1983-87	(.6)	1.0

POWER STEERING

GEAR TYPE

For operations not listed see Standard Steering

LABOR 11 STEERING GEAR 11 LABOR

(Factory Time) — Chilton Time

(G) Steering Gear, Adjust
1983-87 (.7)... 1.2

(M) Pump Drive Belt, Renew
V-6–1983-87
229 engs (.3)... .4
231 eng (.6)... .8
262 eng (.4)... .5
w/A.C. add (.1)... .1
V-8–1983-87 (.3)... .4
w/AIR add (.1)... .1
w/A.C. add (.2)... .2

(G) Power Steering Gear Assy., Renew
1983-87 (.7)... 1.2

(P) Power Steering Gear Assy., R&R and Recondition
1983-85 (1.7)... 2.5
1986-87 (2.1)... 3.0

(G) Valve Body, Recondition
Includes: R&R gear assy.
1983-85 (1.0)... 1.8
1986-87 (1.4)... 2.2

(G) Adjustor Plug Assy., Recondition
Includes: R&R gear assy.
1983-85 (.9)... 1.6
1986-87 (1.3)... 2.0

(G) Steering Gear Housing, Renew
Includes: R&R gear assy.
1983-85 (1.1)... 1.8
1986-87 (1.5)... 2.4

(G) Side Cover Seal, Renew
1983-87 (.9)... 1.4

(G) End Cover Seal, Renew
1983-87 (.4)... .6

(G) Pitman Shaft Seal, Renew
1983-87 (.6)... 1.0

(G) Power Steering Pump, Renew
1983-87
V-6 (.5)... .9
V-8 (.9)... 1.4
Diesel (.9)... 1.4
w/A.C. add (.2)... .2
w/Hydra Boost add (.1)... .1

(P) Power Steering Pump, R&R and Recondition
1983-87
V-6 (1.0)... 1.7
V-8 (1.4)... 2.2
Diesel (1.4)... 2.2
w/A.C. add (.2)... .2
w/Hydra Boost add (.1)... .1

(G) Pump Reservoir or 'O' Ring Seals, Renew
Includes: R&R pump assy.
1983-87
V-6 (.6)... 1.0
V-8 (1.0)... 1.5
Diesel (1.0)... 1.5
w/A.C. add (.2)... .2
w/Hydra Boost add (.1)... .1

(G) Pump Flow Control Valve, Renew
V-6–1983-87 (.4)... .7
V-8–1983-87 (.3)... .9
w/A.C. add (.2)... .2

(G) Power Steering Pump Shaft Oil Seal, Renew
1983-87
V-6 (.6)... 1.0
V-8 (.9)... 1.5
Diesel (.9)... 1.5
w/A.C. add (.2)... .2

(M) Power Steering Hoses, Renew
1983-87-pressure (.6)... .8
return (.3)... .4

(M) Hydra-boost Hoses, Renew
1983-85-each (.3)... .5

RACK AND PINION TYPE

(G) Inner Tie Rod Assy., Renew
Includes: R&R rack and pinion assy; and reset toe-in.
1984-87-one (1.5)... 2.2
both (1.6)... 2.4

(G) Tie Rod End, Renew
Includes: Reset toe-in.
1984-87-one (.6)... .9
both (.8)... 1.1

(G) Power Steering Pump Shaft Oil Seal, Renew
1984-87 (.4)... .7

(G) Pump Flow Control Valve, Renew
1984-87 (.5)... .8

(G) Power Steering Pump, Renew
1984-87 (.5)... .7

(G) Power Steering Pump, R&R and Recondition
1984-87 (.9)... 1.5

(G) Power Steering Pump Reservoir, Renew
1984-87 (.5)... .7

(G) Power Rack and Pinion Assy., R&R or Renew
Includes: Reset toe-in.
1984-87 (1.4)... 2.0
Renew cyl line, add-each (.2)... .2
Renew rack brg, add (.2)... .3
Renew stub shaft seals, add (.3)... .4
Renew breather tube, add (.2)... .3
Renew ball brg assy, add (.3)... .4
Renew upper bush & seal, add (.4)... .5
Renew valve & pinion assy., add (.4)... .5

(G) Power Steering Short Rack Assy., Renew
Includes: R&R assembly, transfer parts as required. Add alignment charges.
1984-87 (1.7)... 2.5

(M) Power Steering Hoses, Renew
1984-87-each (.3)... .5

PARTS 11 POWER STEERING GEAR 11 PARTS

CORVETTE (Rack & Pinion)

	Part No.	Price
(1) Tie Rod Kit (Outer)		
1984-85	26000001	84.50
1986-87	7849266	84.50
(2) Boot Kit		
1984-87	7841628	39.00
(3) Tie Rod Kit (Inner)		
1984-87	7841627	60.50
(4) Ring		
1984-85	7841291	4.50
1986-87	7849530	4.50
(5) Bulkhead Kit		
1984-85	7841624	48.25
1986-87	7849269	307.00
(6) Seal Kit		
1984-87	7841622	15.50

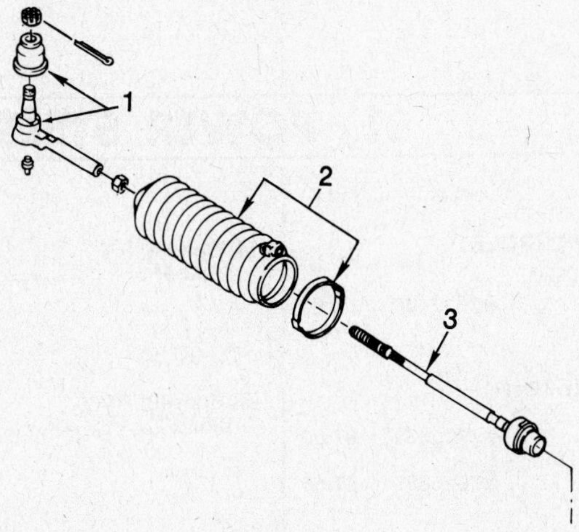

PARTS 11 POWER STEERING GEAR 11 PARTS

	Part No.	Price
(7) Rack Assy. (w/Piston)		
1984-85-exc.		
H.D. susp.	7840286	197.00
H.D. susp.	7841042	197.00
1986-87	7849007	197.00
(8) Cylinder Line Kit (R.H.)		
1984-87	7841626	17.00
(9) Cylinder Line Kit (L.H.)		
1984-87	7841625	17.00
(10) Bearing Kit (Stub Shaft)		
1984-87	◆7838279	19.50
(11) Valve Assy.		
1984-87-exc.		
H.D. susp.	7841620	265.00
H.D. susp.	7841621	265.00
(12) Rack Bearing		
1984-87	◆7827995	5.00
(13) Adjuster Spring		
1984-87	◆7838791	1.50
(14) Adjuster Plug		
1984-87	7841283	6.25
(15) Ring		
1984-87	7841291	4.50
(16) Bearing Kit (Pinion)		
1984-87	7838278	53.50
(17) Bushing Kit		
1984-87	7841634	15.00
(18) Housing Assy.		
1984-85	7841632	208.00
1986-87	7849267	208.00
(19) Grommet		
1984-87	7840293	6.25
(20) Seal Kit		
1984-87	7841622	15.50

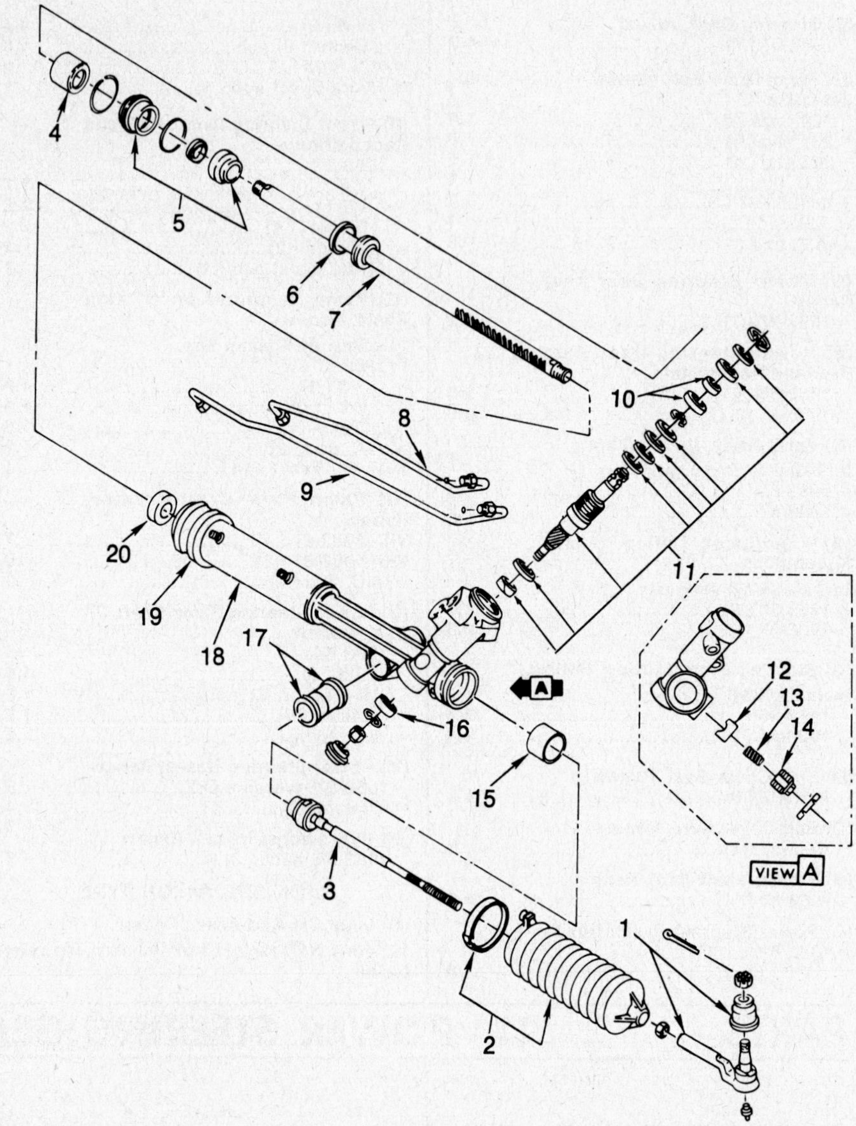

PARTS 11 POWER STEERING GEAR 11 PARTS

CHEVROLET

	Part No.	Price
(1) Seal (Side Cover)		
1983-87	◆7817486	9.00
(2) Pitman Shaft (w/Gear)		
1983-87-exc.		
below	◆7813631	87.50
Non variable strg.	◆7815885	87.50
(3) Check Valve Kit		
1983-87	◆7834284	5.25
(4) Bearing Kit		
1983-87	◆7826850	11.00
(5) Housing Assy.		
1983-87	◆7834139	183.00
(6) Bearing (Pitman Shaft)		
1983-87	◆5697804	15.00
(7) Seal Kit (Pitman Shaft)		
1983-87	◆7826470	17.00
(8) Seal (Adjuster Plug)		
1983-87	◆5686527	1.50
(9) Bearing (Adjuster Plug)		
1983-87	◆7828012	7.25

PARTS 11 POWER STEERING GEAR 11 PARTS

	Part No.	Price
(10) Plug Assy. (Adjuster)		
1983-87	◆7832731	53.50
(11) Seal Kit		
1983-87	◆5687182	12.50
(12) Valve Assy.		
1983-87	◆7832058	212.00
(14) Seal Kit		
1983-87	◆7817485	6.50
(15) Plug		
1983-87	◆5689010	8.75
(16) Rack Assy.		
(exc. Sta. wagon)		
1983-84-exc. below	◆7827170	154.25
229, 231	◆7817528	162.00
1985-87-exc. below	◆7817526	151.00
262	◆7817528	162.00
(Sta. wagon)		
1983-85	◆7817528	162.00

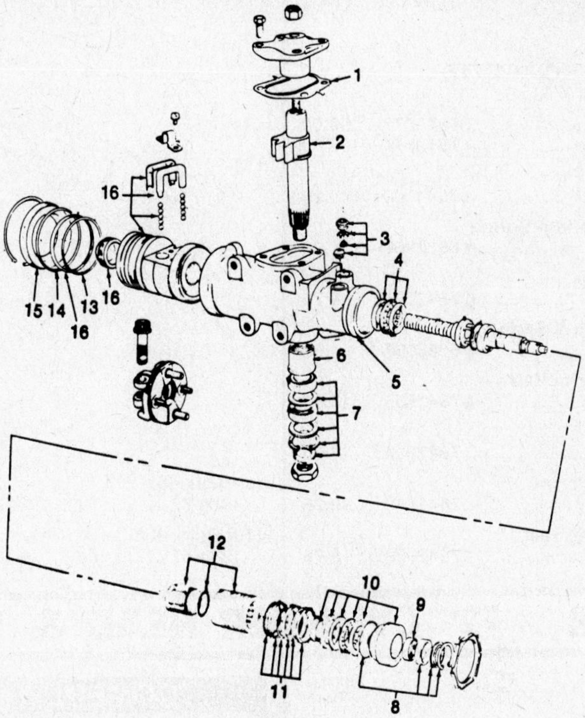

PARTS 11 POWER STEERING PUMP 11 PARTS

	Part No.	Price
Pressure Line Hose		
Order by year and model.		
Power Steering Pump Assy.		
(Chevrolet)		
V-6-229		
1983-84	◆7843087	199.00
V-6-231		
1983-85	◆7839795	199.00
V-6-262		
1985-87	◆7843087	199.00
V-8-305		
1983-87-wo/A.C.	◆7839788	199.00
A.C.	◆7839787	199.00
V-8-307Y		
1986-87	◆7840244	199.00
V-8-Diesel		
1983-87	◆7839792	213.00
(1) Pressure Plate		
1983-87	◆7839669	14.25
(2) Pressure Plate Spring		
1983-87	◆7839667	1.00
(3) End Plate		
1983-87	◆5689358	3.50
(4) Rotor & Vane Kit		
1983-87	◆7837322	75.00

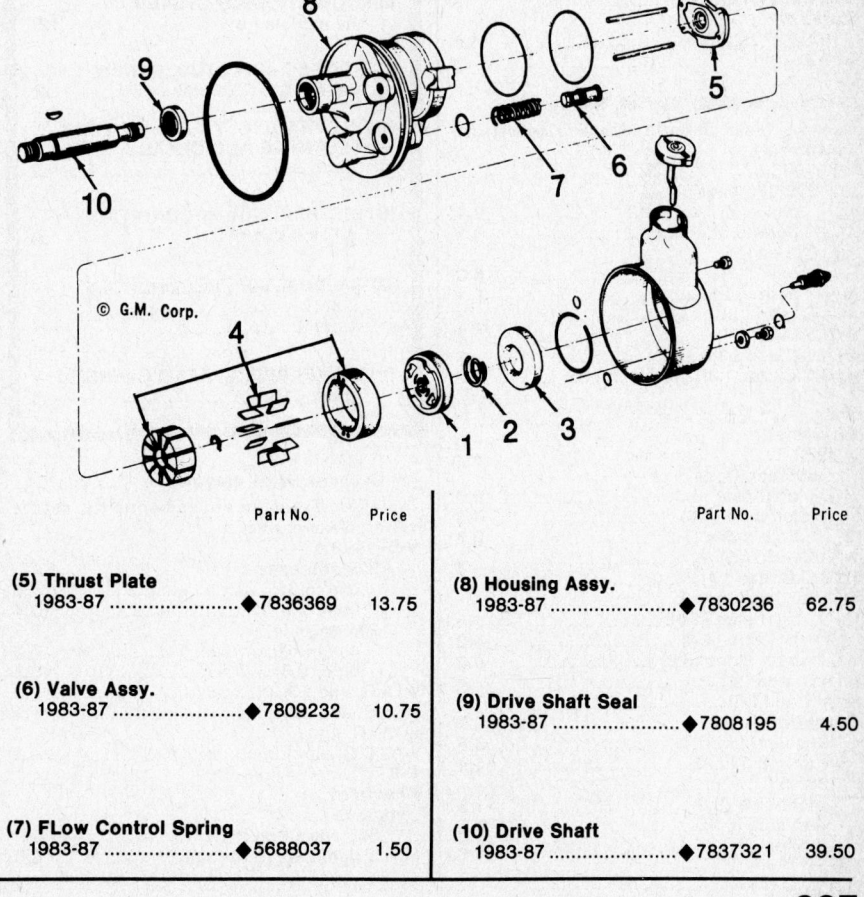

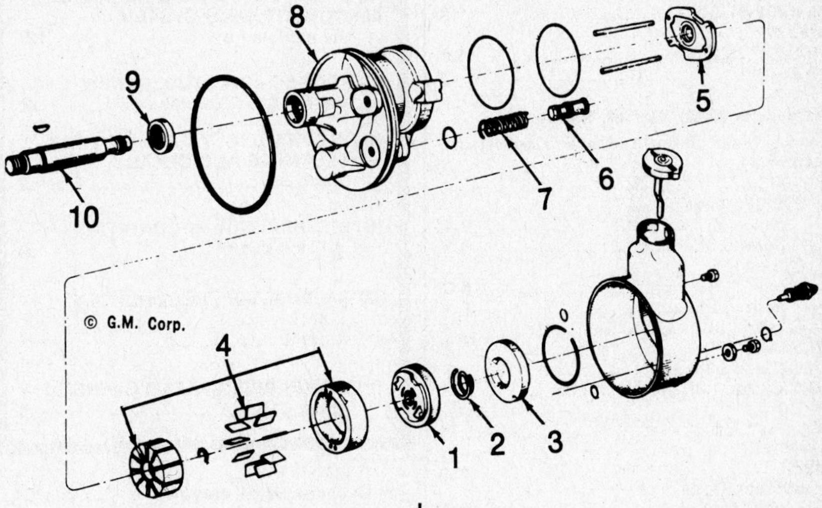

	Part No.	Price
(5) Thrust Plate		
1983-87	◆7836369	13.75
(6) Valve Assy.		
1983-87	◆7809232	10.75
(7) FLow Control Spring		
1983-87	◆5688037	1.50

	Part No.	Price
(8) Housing Assy.		
1983-87	◆7830236	62.75
(9) Drive Shaft Seal		
1983-87	◆7808195	4.50
(10) Drive Shaft		
1983-87	◆7837321	39.50

PARTS 11 POWER STEERING PUMP 11 PARTS

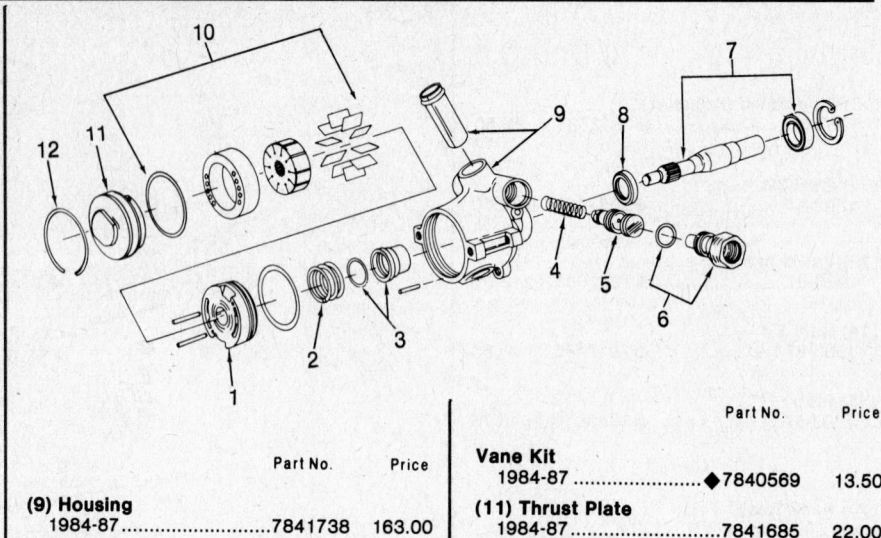

	Part No.	Price
CORVETTE		
Pump Assy.		
1984-86	7842277	199.00
1987	7849814	199.00
(1) Pressure Plate		
1984-87	7841700	15.25
(2) Pressure Plate Spring		
1984-87	◆7839989	3.00
(3) Sleeve Kit		
1984-87	◆7842086	9.75
(4) Flow Control Spring		
1984-87	◆5688037	1.50
(5) Flow Control Valve		
1984-87	◆7841851	15.50
(6) Fitting		
1984-87	7842600	13.00
(7) Drive Shaft		
1984-87	7841740	92.25
(8) Drive Shaft Seal		
1984-87	7841739	5.75

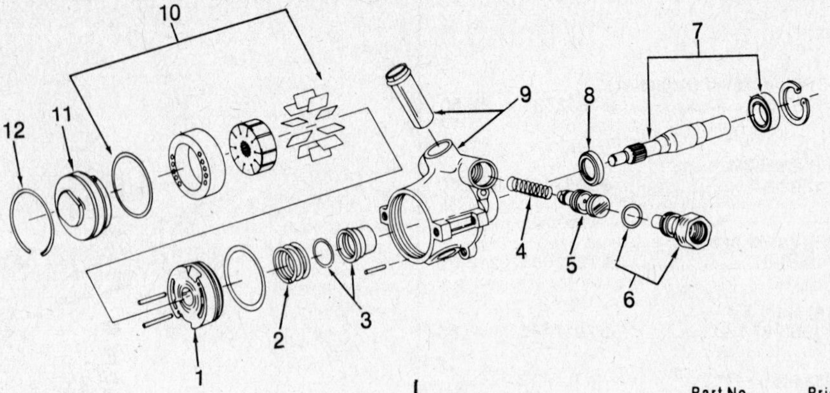

	Part No.	Price
(9) Housing		
1984-87	7841738	163.00
(10) Rotor Kit		
1984-87	◆7841845	92.00

	Part No.	Price
Vane Kit		
1984-87	◆7840569	13.50
(11) Thrust Plate		
1984-87	7841685	22.00
(12) Retaining Ring		
1984-87	◆7839992	2.00

LABOR 12 CYLINDER HEAD & VALVE SYSTEM 12 LABOR

(Factory Time)	Chilton Time
GASOLINE ENGINES	
(G) Compression Test	
Chevrolet	
V-6–1983-87 (.5)	.7
V-8–1983-87 (.7)	.8
Corvette	
1983-87 (1.2)	1.5
w/A.C. add	.3
(G) Cylinder Head Gasket, Renew	
Includes: Clean carbon and make all necessary adjustments.	
V-6–1983-87	
229-262 engs	
one (4.7)	6.4
both (6.5)	8.9
231 eng	
one (3.9)	5.3
both (5.2)	7.1
w/A.C. add (.3)	.3
w/P.S. add (.2)	.2
w/A.I.R. add (.3)	.3
w/C.C.C. add (.3)	.3
V-8	
Chevrolet	
1983-87	
305 eng Code H	
right side (5.0)	6.9
left side (4.6)	6.3
both sides (7.0)	9.6
w/A.C. add (.5)	.5
w/C.C.C. add (.4)	.4
307 eng Code Y	
right side (4.0)	5.5
left side (4.4)	6.0
both sides (5.8)	8.0
w/A.C. add (.4)	.4
w/AIR add (.5)	.5
Corvette	
1984-one (6.3)	8.6
both (8.3)	11.4
1985-87	
right side (8.3)	11.6
left side (6.8)	9.5
both sides (11.1)	15.5

COMBINATIONS

Add to Valve Job

See Machine Shop Operations

(G) DRAIN, EVACUATE & RECHARGE AIR CONDITIONING SYSTEM	
All models (.5)	1.0
(G) ROCKER ARM STUD, RENEW	
Each (.1)	.2
(G) HYDRAULIC VALVE LIFTERS, DISASSEMBLE AND CLEAN	
Each	.2
(G) DISTRIBUTOR, RECONDITION	
All models (.5)	.8
(G) CARBURETOR, RECONDITION	
2 bbl	1.2
4 bbl	1.5
(P) VALVE GUIDES, REAM OVERSIZE	
Each (.1)	.1

(Factory Time)	Chilton Time
(G) Cylinder Head, Renew	
Includes: Transfer all components, reface valves, clean carbon.	
V-6–1983-87	
229-262 engs	
one (5.3)	7.3
both (7.6)	10.4
231 eng	
one (4.5)	6.2
both (6.3)	8.6
w/A.C. add (.3)	.3
w/P.S. add (.2)	.2
w/A.I.R. add (.3)	.3
w/C.C.C. add (.3)	.3
V-8	
Chevrolet	
1983-87	
305 eng Code H	
right side (5.8)	8.0
left side (5.5)	7.5
both sides (8.7)	12.0
w/A.C. add (.5)	.5
w/C.C.C add (.4)	.4
307 eng Code Y	
right side (4.2)	5.7
left side (4.6)	6.3
both sides (6.2)	8.5
w/A.C. add (.4)	.4
w/AIR add (.5)	.5
Corvette	
1984-one (7.1)	9.7
both (9.9)	13.6
1985-87	
right side (9.2)	12.8
left side (7.8)	10.9
both sides (12.7)	17.7
(P) Clean Carbon and Grind Valves	
Includes: R&R cylinder heads, grind valves and seats. Minor tune up.	
V-6–1983-87	
229-262 engs	
one side (5.7)	7.8
both sides (8.5)	11.7
231 eng	
one side (4.6)	6.3
both sides (6.7)	9.2
w/A.C. add (.3)	.3
w/P.S. add (.2)	.2
w/A.I.R. add (.3)	.3
w/C.C.C. add (.3)	.3
V-8	
Chevrolet	
1983-87	
305 eng Code H	
right side (6.3)	8.6
left side (5.9)	8.1
both sides (9.4)	13.0
w/A.C. add (.5)	.5
w/C.C.C. add (.4)	.4
307 eng Code Y	
right side (5.1)	7.0
left side (5.6)	7.7
both sides (8.1)	11.2
w/A.C. add (.4)	.4
w/AIR add (.5)	.5

(Factory Time)	Chilton Time
Corvette	
1984-one side (7.6)	10.4
both sides (10.7)	14.7
1985-87	
right side (9.7)	13.5
left side (8.2)	11.4
both sides (13.5)	18.9

(G) Rocker Arm Cover or Gasket, Renew

(Factory Time)	Chilton Time
V-6–1983-87	
229 eng	
one (.7)	1.0
both (1.2)	1.8
231 eng	
one (.6)	.8
both (.9)	1.2
262 eng	
right (.6)	.9
left (.3)	.5
both (.8)	1.3
w/A.C. add (.2)	.2
w/A.I.R. add (.3)	.3
w/Cruise control add (.2)	.2
w/C.C.C. add (.3)	.3
V-8	
Chevrolet	
1983-87	
305 eng-Code H	
right side (.7)	1.0
left side (.5)	.7
both sides (1.1)	1.6
w/A.C. add (.2)	.2
w/C.C.C. add (.2)	.2
307 eng-Code Y	
right side (.6)	.7
left side (.8)	1.2
both sides (1.4)	1.9
w/A.C. add (.1)	.1
w/AIR add (.3)	.3
Corvette	
1984-one (1.0)	1.4
both (1.7)	2.3
1985-87	
right (3.0)	4.2
left (.6)	.9
both (3.6)	5.0

(G) Valve Tappets, Renew (Lifters)

Includes: R&R intake manifold where required. Make all necessary adjustments.

(Factory Time)	Chilton Time
V-6–1983-87	
229 eng	
one cyl (2.6)	3.4
one cyl-each bank (3.1)	4.0
all cyls-both banks (3.6)	4.5
231 eng	
one bank (2.4)	3.2
both banks (2.8)	3.8
262 eng	
right side-one cyl (2.8)	3.9
left side-one cyl (2.6)	3.6
each side-one cyl (3.0)	4.2
both sides-all cyls (3.5)	5.0
w/A.C. add (.2)	.2
w/A.I.R. add (.3)	.3
w/Cruise control add (.2)	.2
w/C.C.C. add (.3)	.3
V-8	
Chevrolet	
1983-87	
305 eng Code H	
one cyl (2.5)	3.4
one cyl-each side (3.1)	3.7
all cyls-both sides (3.7)	4.4
w/A.C. add (.3)	.3
w/C.C.C. add (.2)	.2
307 eng Code Y	
one cyl (2.7)	3.7
one cyl-each side (3.2)	4.4
all cyls-both sides (5.0)	6.9
w/A.C. add (.2)	.2
w/AIR add (.4)	.4
Corvette	
1984-one cyl (3.5)	4.9
one cyl-each side (4.1)	5.7
all cyls-both sides (4.7)	6.5
1985-87	
right side-one cyl (6.7)	9.3
left side-one cyl (4.0)	5.6
each side-one cyl (7.4)	10.3
both sides-all cyls (8.0)	11.2

(G) Valve Springs and/or Valve Stem Oil Seals, Renew (Head on Car)

(Factory Time)	Chilton Time
V-6–1983-87	
229 eng	
one cyl (1.2)	1.6
one cyl-each bank (2.0)	2.5
all cyls-both banks (3.3)	4.2
231 eng	
one cyl (.8)	1.1
one cyl-each bank (1.4)	1.9
all cyls-both banks (2.6)	3.5
262 eng	
one cyl-right side (1.0)	1.5
one cyl-left side (.7)	1.1
one cyl-each side (1.5)	2.2
all cyls-both sides (2.7)	4.0
w/A.C. add (.2)	.2
w/A.I.R. add (.3)	.3
w/Cruise control add (.2)	.2
w/C.C.C. add (.3)	.3
V-8	
Chevrolet	
1983-87	
305 eng Code H	
one cyl'	
right side (1.2)	1.6
left side (1.0)	1.1
both sides (2.0)	2.3
each adtnl cyl (.4)	.4
all cyls-both sides (3.7)	4.5
w/A.C. add (.2)	.2
w/C.C.C. add (.1)	.1
307 eng Code Y	
one cyl'	
right side (.7)	1.0
left side (1.1)	1.6
both sides (2.0)	2.4
each adtnl cyl (.4)	.4
w/A.C. add (.1)	.1
w/AIR add (.3)	.3
Corvette	
1984-one cyl (1.5)	2.1
one cyl-each side (2.6)	3.6
all cyls-both sides (4.6)	6.4
1985-87	
right side-one cyl (3.5)	4.9
left side-one cyl (1.1)	1.6
each side-one cyl (4.3)	6.0
both sides-all cyls (6.0)	8.4

(G) Valve Rocker Arms or Push Rods, Renew

(Factory Time)	Chilton Time
V-6–1983-87	
229-262 engs	
one cyl (.9)	1.2
one cyl-each bank (1.5)	1.9
all cyls-both banks (1.9)	2.1
231 eng	
one bank (.7)	.9
both banks (1.1)	1.4
Recond shaft add-each	.2
w/A.C. add (.2)	.2
w/A.I.R. add (.3)	.3
w/Cruise control add (.2)	.2
w/C.C.C. add (.3)	.3
V-8	
Chevrolet	
1983-87	
305 eng Code H	
one cyl'	
right side (.9)	1.2
left side (.6)	.9
both sides (1.2)	2.0
each adtnl cyl (.2)	.2
w/A.C. add (.2)	.2
w/C.C.C. add (.2)	.2
307 eng Code Y	
one cyl'	
right side (.7)	.9
left side (.9)	1.4
both sides (1.5)	2.1
all cyls-both sides (2.0)	2.9
w/A.C. add (.1)	.1
w/AIR add (.3)	.3
Corvette	
1984-one cyl (1.2)	1.7
one cyl-each side (2.0)	2.8
all cyls-both sides (2.5)	3.5
1985-87	
right side-one cyl (3.2)	4.4
left side-one cyl (.8)	1.2
each side-one cyl (4.0)	5.6
both sides-all cyls (4.5)	6.3

(G) Rocker Arm Stud, Renew

(Factory Time)	Chilton Time
V-6–1983-87	
229 eng	
one (1.1)	1.4
262 eng	
right side-one (1.0)	1.5
left side-one (.7)	1.1
w/C.C.C. add (.3)	.3
V-8	
Chevrolet	
1983-87	
305 eng Code H	
right side-one (1.1)	1.5
left side-one (.9)	1.2
Corvette	
1984	
right side-one (1.4)	2.0
left side-one (1.2)	1.7
1985-87	
right side-one (3.4)	4.7
left side-one (1.0)	1.5
each adtnl stud	
All engs (.3)	.3
w/A.C. add (.3)	.3
w/C.C.C. add (.3)	.3

(G) Valve Tappets, Adjust

(Factory Time)	Chilton Time
V-6–1983-87	1.5
V-8	
Chevrolet	
1983-85	2.0
1986-87	2.5
Corvette	
1984	2.6
1985-87	5.6
w/A.C. add	.3
w/C.C.C. add	.3

DIESEL ENGINE

(G) Compression Test

(Factory Time)	Chilton Time
1983-85	1.3

(G) Cylinder Head Gasket, Renew

Includes: R&R injector pump and lines. R&R intake manifold and disconnect exhaust manifolds. Clean gasket surfaces, bleed lifters and adjust timing. Drain and refill cooling system.

(Factory Time)	Chilton Time
1983-85-left side (5.7)	7.4
right side (6.1)	7.9
both sides (7.6)	9.9
w/A.C. add (.4)	.4

LABOR 12 CYLINDER HEAD & VALVE SYSTEM 12 LABOR

	(Factory Time)	Chilton Time
(G) Cylinder Head, Renew		
Includes: R&R injector pump and lines. R&R intake manifold and disconnect exhaust manifolds. Clean gasket surfaces. Transfer parts, reface valves. Bleed lifters and adjust timing. Drain and refill cooling system.		
1983-85-left side	(6.1)	7.9
right side	(6.5)	8.4
both sides	(8.4)	11.1
w/A.C. add	(.4)	.4
(P) Clean Carbon and Grind Valves		
Includes: R&R injector pump and lines. R&R cylinder heads, clean carbon. Recondition valves and seats. Check and adjust valve stem length. Bleed lifters, drain and refill cooling system.		
1983-85-left side	(6.6)	8.5
right side	(7.0)	9.1
both sides	(9.3)	12.6
w/A.C. add	(.4)	.4
(G) Valve Tappets, Renew (Lifters)		
Includes: R&R injector pump and lines, intake manifold and rocker arms. Drain and refill cooling system.		
1983-85-one cyl	(3.5)	4.5
one cyl-each side	(3.9)	5.0
each adtnl cyl	(.1)	.2
(G) Rocker Arm Cover or Gasket, Renew		
Includes: R&R injector pump and lines.		
1983-85-one side	(1.2)	2.4
both sides	(2.0)	2.9
(G) Valve Spring and/or Valve Stem Oil Seals, Renew (Head on Car)		
Includes: R&R injector pump and lines.		
1983-85-one cyl	(1.6)	3.0
one cyl-each bank	(2.4)	3.7
each adtnl cyl	(.3)	.3
w/A.C. add	(.3)	.3
(G) Rocker Arm, Pivot and/or Push Rod, Renew		
Includes: R&R injector pump and lines.		
1983-85-one cyl	(1.5)	2.5
one cyl-each bank	(2.3)	3.0
each adtnl cyl	(.1)	.1

PARTS 12 CYLINDER HEAD & VALVE SYSTEM 12 PARTS

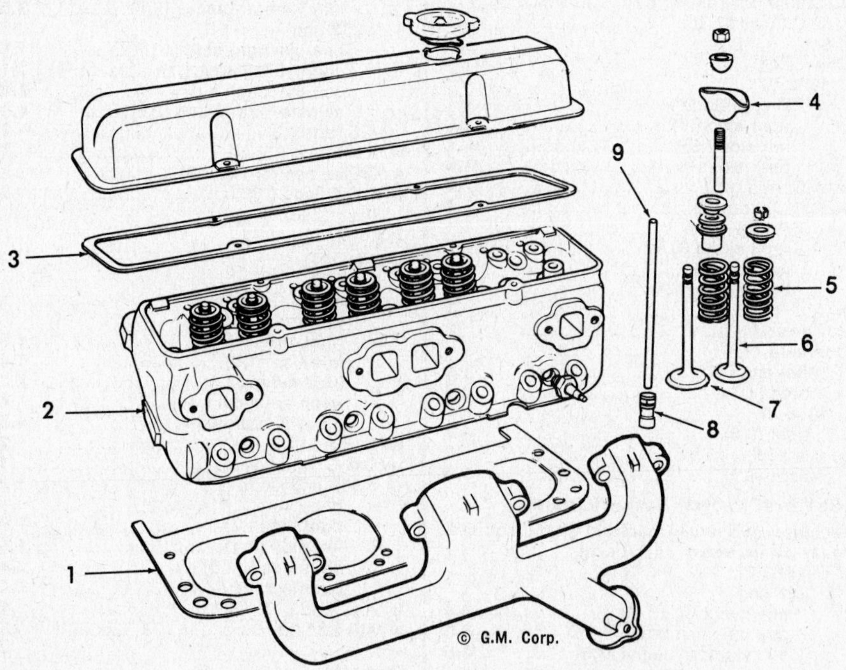

	Part No.	Price
Valve Grind Gasket Set		
V-6-229		
1983-84	14033548	43.50
V-6-231		
1st design: .017 in. thick head gasket. 2nd design: .062 in. thick head gasket.		
1983-1st design	◆25525121	N.L.
2nd design	◆25527307	71.50
1984-Cast man.		
1st design	◆25525121	N.L.
2nd design	◆25527307	71.50
1984-Alum man.		
1st design	◆25525120	37.00
2nd design	◆25527306	71.50
V-6-262		
1985	◆14091326	53.00
1986	14101305	58.25
V-8-305		
1983-84	◆14033553	49.25
1985-87	◆14089154	61.50
V-8-307Y		
1986-87	◆22534926	58.00
V-8-350		
1984	14085857	54.00
1985	14089153	58.00
1986-87-Cast hd.	10046308	115.00
Aluminum hd	14094584	8.25
V-8-Diesel		
1983-84	◆22522053	94.50
1985	◆22527541	N.L.
(1) Cylinder Head Gasket		
V-6-229		
1983-84	471593	8.00
V-6-231		
1st design: .017 in. thick. 2nd design: .062 in. thick.		
1983-85-1st design	◆1261403	8.50
2nd design	◆25525919	21.25
V-6-262		
1985-87	◆14075646	7.00
V-8-305		
1983-87	◆462690	6.50
V-8-307Y		
1986-87	◆22503500	9.50
V-8-350		
1984-85	◆462691	6.50
1986-87-Aluminum hd.	14088948	14.00
Cast hd.	14085905	N.L.
V-8-350 Diesel		
1983-85	◆22519416	30.75
(2) Cylinder Head		
V-6-229		
1983-84	14029985	237.00
V-6-231		
1983	◆25518679	217.00
1984-85	◆25518679	217.00
V-6-262		
1985-87	◆14085869	242.00
V-8-305		
1983-87	◆14034807	247.00
V-8-307Y		
1986-87	◆22530557	247.00
V-8-Diesel		
1983-85	◆22515038	387.00
V-8-350		
1983-85	14034808	288.00
1986-87-Aluminum hd.	14101127	295.00
Cast hd.	14034808	288.00
(3) Valve Rocker Cover Gasket		
V-6-229		
1984	14082319	7.50
V-6-231		
1983-85	◆25505889	6.00
V-6-262		
1985-87	◆14081257	7.25
V-8-305		
1984-87	◆14082322	8.75
V-8-350		
1984-85	14101065	9.75
1986-87-Alum hd.	14088564	8.00
Cast hd.	14101065	9.75
Use R.T.V. sealer (# 1052366) in place of gaskets not listed.		
(4) Rocker Arm		
V-6-229		
1983-84	◆3974290	5.50

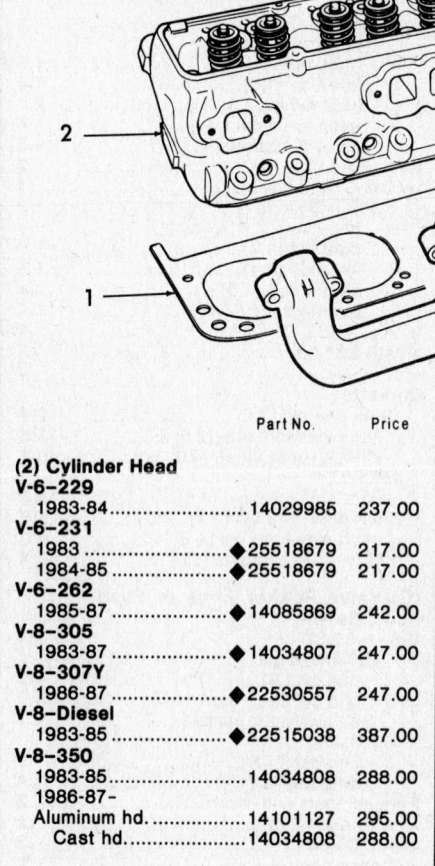

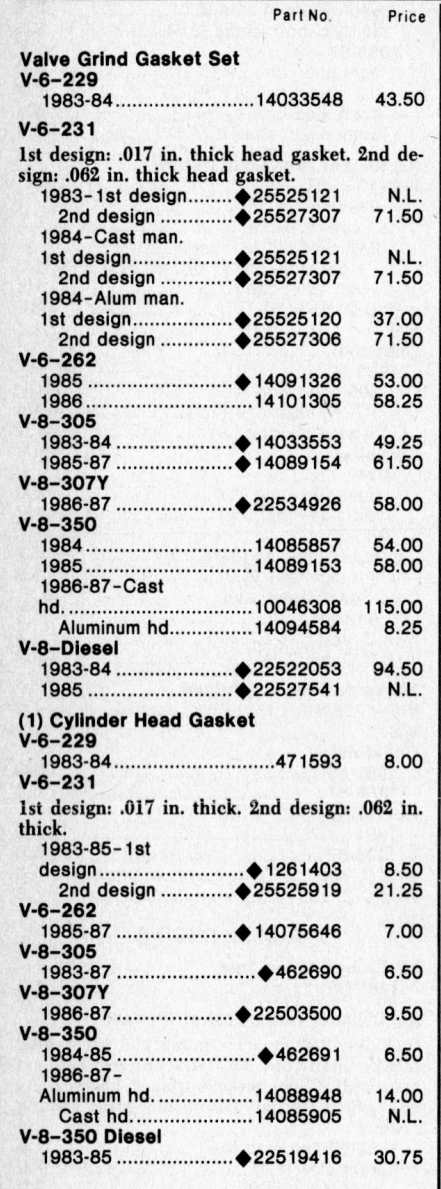

PARTS 12 CYLINDER HEAD & VALVE SYSTEM 12 PARTS

	Part No.	Price
V-6-231		
1983-85-right	◆1241850	4.50
left	◆1241851	4.50
V-6-262		
1985-87	◆3974290	5.50
V-8-Gas		
1983-87	◆3974290	5.50
V-8-Diesel		
1983-85	◆22505583	N.L.
(5) Valve Spring		
V-6-229		
1983-84	◆3911068	3.00
V-6-231		
1983-85	◆1249267	2.75
V-6-262		
1985-87	◆3911068	3.00
V-8-Gas		
1983-87-int & exh.	◆3911068	3.00
V-8-Diesel		
1983-85	◆22510372	4.00
(6) Intake Valve		
V-6-229		
1983-84	◆14025571	11.75
V-6-262		
1985-87	◆14075641	14.00
V-6-231		
1983-85	◆25512098	11.25
V-8-305		
1983-87	◆14025571	11.75
V-8-350		
1983-87-Cast hd.	◆14025572	11.50
1986-87-Alum. hd.	14025573	12.25
V-8-Diesel		
1983-85	◆22519914	20.00
(7) Exhaust Valve		
V-6-229		
1983-84	◆14095451	13.50
V-6-231		
1983-85	◆1261380	13.50
V-6-262		
1985-87	◆14095451	13.50
V-8-305 & 350		
1983	◆14095451	13.50
1984-87	◆14095451	13.50
V-8-Diesel		
1983-87	◆558873	13.00
(8) Valve Lifter		
V-6-229		
1983-84	◆5232720	N.L.
V-6-231		
1983-85	◆5232765	9.00
V-6-262		
1985-87	◆5232720	N.L.
V-8-Gas		
1983-87	◆5232720	N.L.
V-8-Diesel		
1983-85	◆5234470	38.10
(9) Push Rods		
V-6-229		
1983-84	◆14095256	5.00
V-6-262		
1985-87	◆14095256	5.00
V-6-231		
1983-85	◆1249139	4.00
V-8-Gas		
1983-87	◆14095256	5.00
V-8-Diesel		
1983-87	◆22511044	3.25

LABOR 13 ENGINE ASSEMBLY & MOUNTS 13 LABOR

(Factory Time) — Chilton Time

GASOLINE ENGINES

(G) Engine Assembly, Remove & Install

Does not include transfer of any parts or equipment.

	Chilton Time
V-6-1983-87	
229 engs	4.8
231 eng	4.0
262 eng	6.5
w/A.C. add (.3)	.3
w/P.S. add (.3)	.3
w/A.I.R. add (.2)	.2
w/C.C.C. add (.3)	.3
V-8	
Chevrolet	
1983-87	6.0
Corvette	
1984	7.6
1985-87	8.0

(G) Engine Assembly, Renew

Includes: R&R engine and transmission assy. Transfer all component parts not supplied with replacement engine. Minor tune up.

	Chilton Time
V-6-1983-87	
229 engs (6.3)	10.7
262 eng (5.7)	9.1
w/A.C. add (.3)	.3
w/P.S. add (.3)	.3
w/A.I.R. add (.2)	.2
w/C.C.C. add (.3)	.3
V-8	
Chevrolet	
1983-87 (5.8)	9.0
Corvette	
1984 (8.3)	12.4
1985-87 (7.5)	12.0

(G) Engine Assembly, Renew (Partial/Basic)

Includes: R&R engine assy. Transfer all component parts not supplied with replacement engine. Make all necessary adjustments.

	Chilton Time
V-6-1983-87	
231 eng (10.6)	14.8
w/A.C. (.3)	.3
w/AIR add (.2)	.2
Recond valves add (1.2)	1.2
262 eng (9.3)	13.0
w/A.C. add (.4)	.42
Recond valves add (2.0)	2.0
V-8	
Chevrolet	
1983-87	
305 Eng Code H (9.9)	13.8
w/A.C. add (.4)	.4
w/C.C.C. add (.4)	.4
Recond valves add (2.7)	2.7
307 eng Code Y (8.4)	11.7
w/A.C. add (.3)	.3
w/AIR add (.4)	.4
Recond valves add (1.6)	1.6
Corvette	
1984 (15.1)	20.4
1985-87 (14.3)	20.0

(P) Cylinder Block, Renew (w/Pistons, Rings and Bearings)

Includes: R&R engine and transmission assy. Transfer all component parts, clean carbon, grind valves. Minor tune up.

	Chilton Time
V-6-1983-87	
229 engs (15.5)	21.7
231 eng (15.0)	21.0
262 eng (13.5)	18.7
w/A.C. add (.3)	.3
w/P.S. add (.3)	.3
w/A.I.R. add (.2)	.2
w/C.C.C. add (.3)	.3
V-8	
Chevrolet	
1983-87	
305 eng Code H (16.3)	21.7
w/A.C. add (.4)	.4
w/C.C.C. add (.4)	.4
307 eng Code Y (12.6)	17.6
w/A.C. add (.3)	.3
w/AIR add (.4)	.4
Corvette	
1984 (18.7)	25.2
1985-87 (18.0)	25.0

(P) Engine Assy., R&R and Recondition (Complete)

Includes: Rebore block, install new pistons, rings, rod and main bearings. Clean carbon, grind valves. Tune engine.

	Chilton Time
V-6-1983-87	
229 engs (24.7)	28.9
231 eng (20.2)	25.1
262 eng (17.8)	24.9
w/A.C. add (.3)	.3
w/P.S. add (.3)	.3
w/A.I.R. add (.2)	.2
w/C.C.C. add (.3)	.3
V-8	
Chevrolet	
1983-87	
305 eng Code H (23.9)	30.2
w/A.C. add (.4)	.4
w/C.C.C. add (.3)	.3
307 eng Code Y (18.6)	26.0
w/A.C. add (.3)	.3
w/AIR add (.4)	.4
Corvette	
1984 (31.1)	39.8
1985-87 (29.8)	39.0

(P) Engine Assembly, Recondition (In Car)

Includes: Expand or renew pistons, install new rings, pins, rod and main bearings. Clean carbon and grind valves. Tune engine.

	Chilton Time
V-6-1983-87	
229 engs (17.8)	21.4
231 eng (14.1)	18.0
262 eng (15.6)	20.3
w/A.C. add (.3)	.3
w/P.S. add (.3)	.3
w/A.I.R. add (.2)	.2
w/C.C.C. add (.3)	.3
V-8	
Chevrolet	
1983-87	
305 eng Code H (21.1)	26.3
w/A.C. add (.4)	.4
w/C.C.C. add (.3)	.3
307 eng Code Y (19.4)	27.1

LABOR 13 ENGINE ASSEMBLY & MOUNTS 13 LABOR

(Factory Time)	Chilton Time
w/A.C. add (.3)	.3
w/AIR add (.6)	.6
Corvette	
1984	
1985-87 (23.1)	30.0
w/A.C. add (.6)	.6
w/P.S. add (.3)	.3
w/A.I.R. add (.3)	.3
w/C.C.C. add (.3)	.3

(G) Engine Mounts, Renew
Front

(Factory Time)	Chilton Time
V-6–1983-87	
229 engs	
one (1.0)	1.4
both (1.6)	2.1
231 eng	
one (.5)	.7
both (.7)	1.0
262 eng-one (.7)	1.1
both (1.0)	1.6
V-8	
Chevrolet	
1983-87	
305 eng Code H	
one (1.0)	1.4
both (1.5)	2.1
307 eng Code Y	
one (.8)	1.2
both (1.3)	2.0
Corvette	
1984-87-right (.8)	1.1
left (.6)	.8
both (1.1)	1.5
Rear	
1983-87 (.4)	.6

DIESEL ENGINE

(G) Engine Assembly, Remove & Install

Does not include transfer of any parts or equipment.

(Factory Time)	Chilton Time
1983-85	5.0

(G) Engine Assembly, Renew (Universal)

Includes: R&R engine assembly, transfer all component parts not supplied with replacement engine. Make all necessary adjustments.

(Factory Time)	Chilton Time
1983-85	20.0
w/A.C. add (.5)	.5

(P) Cylinder Block, Renew (w/All Internal Parts Less Heads and Oil Pan)

Includes: R&R engine, transfer all component parts not supplied with replacement engine. Clean carbon, grind valves. Make all necessary adjustments.

(Factory Time)	Chilton Time
1983-85 (14.5)	24.0
w/A.C. add (.5)	.5

(P) Engine Assy., R&R and Recondition (Complete)

Includes: Rebore block, install new pistons, rings, rod and main bearings. Clean carbon, grind valves. Make all necessary adjustments.

(Factory Time)	Chilton Time
1983-85 (29.5)	36.0
w/A.C. add (.5)	.5

(P) Engine Assembly, Recondition (In Car)

Includes: Expand or renew pistons, install new rings, pins, rod and main bearings. Clean carbon, grind valves. Make all necessary adjustments.

(Factory Time)	Chilton Time
1983-85 (23.2)	27.3
w/A.C. add (.5)	.5

(G) Engine Mounts, Renew

(Factory Time)	Chilton Time
Front	
1983-85-one (.5)	.8
both (.7)	1.0
Rear	
1983-85 (.3)	.6

PARTS 13 ENGINE ASSEMBLY & MOUNTS 13 PARTS

Partial Engine Assembly

Includes: Block, crankshaft, pistons, rings, connecting rods and bearings.

	Part No.	Price
V-6–229		
1983-84	14019896	1232.25
V-6–231		
1983	◆25516156	1263.25
1984-85	◆25519449	1263.25
V-6–262		
1985	◆14085899	1307.00
1986-87	◆14094574	1307.00
V-8–305		
1983-84	◆14019868	1363.00
1985	◆14091328	1300.00
V-8–307Y		
1986-87	◆22530855	1397.00
V-8–350		
1984-85	14083505	1910.25
1986-87-Cast hds.	◆10046307	1910.00
Alum. hds.	14101310	1910.00
V-8–Diesel		
1983	◆22518906	1950.00

Cylinder Block (Fitted)

Includes: Pistons, rings, main bearings.

	Part No.	Price
V-6–229		
1983-84	14019895	889.25
V-6–231		
1983	◆25516160	905.25
1984-85	◆25519450	950.00
V-6–262		
1985	◆14085898	969.00
V-8–305		
1983-84-Code H	◆14019867	949.00
1984-Code G	◆14048355	949.00
V-8–Diesel		
1983	◆22518907	1418.00

Engine Mounts, Front

	Part No.	Price
(Chevrolet)		
V-6–229		
1983-84-right	14020242	22.50
left	14020241	22.50
V-6–231		
1983-85-right	◆1258666	24.00
left	◆25504643	29.00
V-6–262		
1985-87-L.H.	17981701	27.25
R.H.	◆17981702	27.25
V-8–Gas		
1983-87	◆459021	24.00
V-8–Diesel		
1983-85	◆553915	27.25
(Corvette)		
1984-85	17980387	32.50
1986-87	17984499	32.50

Engine Mounts, Rear

Order by model & description.

Engine Overhaul Gasket Kit

	Part No.	Price
V-6–229		
1983-84	14050645	10.25

V-6–231

1st design: .017 in. thick head gasket. 2nd design: .062 in. thick head gasket.

	Part No.	Price
1983-1st design	◆25525119	58.25
2nd design	◆25528727	90.00
1984-Cast man.		
1st design	◆25525119	58.25
2nd design	◆25528727	90.00
1984-Alum. man.		
1st design	◆25505370	52.50
2nd design	◆25527302	89.00
V-6–262		
1985	◆14091479	7.95
1986-87	◆14094596	8.00
V-8–305		
1983-85	◆14091479	N.L.
1986-87	140994596	N.L.
V-8–307Y		
1986-87	◆22527539	62.50
V-8–350		
1984-85	◆14091479	N.L.
1986-87	◆14094596	8.00
V-8–Diesel		
1983-85	◆22521786	90.00

LABOR 14 PISTONS, RINGS & BEARINGS 14 LABOR

GASOLINE ENGINES

(P) Rings, Renew (See Engine Combinations)

Includes: Remove cylinder top ridge, deglaze cylinder walls. Clean piston and ring grooves. Minor tune up.

(Factory Time)	Chilton Time
V-6–1983-87	
229-262 engs	
one cyl (6.8)	9.5
all cyls (10.6)	15.1
231 eng	
one cyl (6.4)	8.8
all cyls (11.2)	15.5
w/A.C. add (.3)	.3
w/P.S. add (.2)	.2
w/A.I.R. add (.3)	.3
w/C.C.C. add (.3)	.3

LABOR 14 PISTONS, RINGS & BEARINGS 14 LABOR

	(Factory Time)	Chilton Time
V-8		
Chevrolet		
1983-87		
305 eng-Code H		
one cyl	(6.4)	9.2
one cyl-each bank	(8.4)	12.1
all cyls-both banks	(11.2)	16.2
w/A.C. add	(.6)	.6
w/AIR add	(.2)	.2
307 eng-Code Y		
one cyl	(7.6)	11.0
one cyl-each bank	(9.6)	13.9
all cyls-both banks	(11.9)	17.2
w/A.C. add	(.3)	.3
w/AIR add	(.6)	.6
Corvette		
1984-one cyl	(7.8)	10.4
one cyl-each side	(10.2)	13.8
all cyls-both sides	(13.8)	19.0
1985-87		
one cyl-right side	(8.9)	12.9
one cyl-left side	(7.9)	11.4
one cyl-each side	(11.7)	16.9
all cyls-both sides	(14.5)	21.0

(P) Piston or Connecting Rod, Renew

Includes: Remove cylinder top ridge, deglaze cylinder walls, clean piston and ring grooves. Minor tune up.

	(Factory Time)	Chilton Time
V-6-1983-87		
229-262 engs		
one cyl	(6.8)	9.8
all cyls	(10.6)	16.9
231 eng		
one cyl	(6.4)	9.1
all cyls	(11.2)	17.3
w/A.C. add	(.3)	.3
w/P.S. add	(.2)	.2
w/A.I.R. add	(.3)	.3
w/C.C.C. add	(.3)	.3
V-8		
Chevrolet		
1983-87		
305 eng-Code H		
one cyl	(7.1)	9.9
one cyl-each bank	(9.8)	13.5
all cyls-both banks	(12.3)	18.6
w/A.C. add	(.6)	.6
w/AIR add	(.2)	.2
307 eng-Code Y		
one cyl	(8.2)	11.6
one cyl-each bank	(10.8)	15.1
all cyls-both banks	(13.0)	19.6
w/A.C. add	(.3)	.3
w/AIR add	(.6)	.6

COMBINATIONS

Add to Engine Work

See Machine Shop Operations

(G) DRAIN, EVACUATE & RECHARGE AIR CONDITIONING SYSTEM	
All models (.5)	1.0
(G) ROCKER ARM STUD, RENEW	
Each (.1)	.2
(G) HYDRAULIC VALVE LIFTERS, DISASSEMBLE AND CLEAN	
Each	.2
(G) DISTRIBUTOR, RECONDITION	
All models (.5)	.8
(G) CARBURETOR, RECONDITION	
2 bbl	1.2
4 bbl	1.5
(G) CYLINDER HEAD, R&R (ENGINE REMOVED)	
V-6	
262 eng-Code Z	
one (2.0)	2.6
both (3.0)	3.9
V-8	
305 eng-Code H	
one (2.4)	3.1
both (3.6)	4.8
307 eng-Code Y	
one (1.8)	2.3
both (2.6)	3.3
(G) CONNECTING ROD, RENEW (ENGINE DISASSEMBLED)	
V-6	
262 eng-Code Z	
each (.4)	.5
V-8	
305 eng-Code H	
each (.3)	.4
307 eng-Code Y	
each (.5)	.6
(P) VALVE GUIDES, REAM OVERSIZE	
Each (.1)	.1
(G) DEGLAZE CYLINDER WALLS	
Each (.1)	.1
(G) REMOVE CYLINDER TOP RIDGE	
Each (.1)	.1
(G) PLASTIGAUGE BEARINGS	
Each (.1)	.1
(G) OIL PUMP, RECONDITION	
All models	.6
(M) OIL FILTER ELEMENT, RENEW	
All models (.3)	.3

	(Factory Time)	Chilton Time
Corvette		
1984-one cyl	(7.8)	10.7
one cyl-each side	(10.2)	14.4
all cyls-both sides	(13.8)	21.4
1985-87		
one cyl-right side	(9.6)	13.9
one cyl-left side	(8.6)	12.4
one cyl-each side	(13.1)	18.9
all cyls-both sides	(18.4)	26.6

(P) Connecting Rod Bearings, Renew

	(Factory Time)	Chilton Time
V-6-1983-87		
229-262 engs		
one	(2.3)	3.2
all	(3.8)	4.7
231 eng		
one	(1.3)	1.9
all	(2.3)	3.4
w/C.C.C. add	(.2)	.2
V-8		
Chevrolet		
1983-87		
305 eng-Code H	(4.3)	5.1
307 eng-Code Y	(4.4)	6.0
Corvette		
1984	(3.7)	5.1
1985-87	(3.6)	5.1

DIESEL ENGINES

(P) Rings, Renew (See Engine Combinations)

Includes: Remove cylinder top ridge, deglaze cylinder walls. Clean piston and ring grooves. Make all necessary adjustments.

1983-85	(12.8)	17.2
w/A.C. add	(.4)	.4

(P) Piston or Connecting Rod, Renew

Includes: Remove cylinder top ridge, deglaze cylinder walls. Clean piston and ring grooves. Make all necessary adjustments.

1983-85	(13.3)	19.6
w/A.C. add	(.4)	.4

(P) Connecting Rod Bearings, Renew

Includes: Raise engine and clean oil pump screen.

1983-85	(4.9)	6.6

PARTS 14 PISTONS, RINGS & BEARINGS 14 PARTS

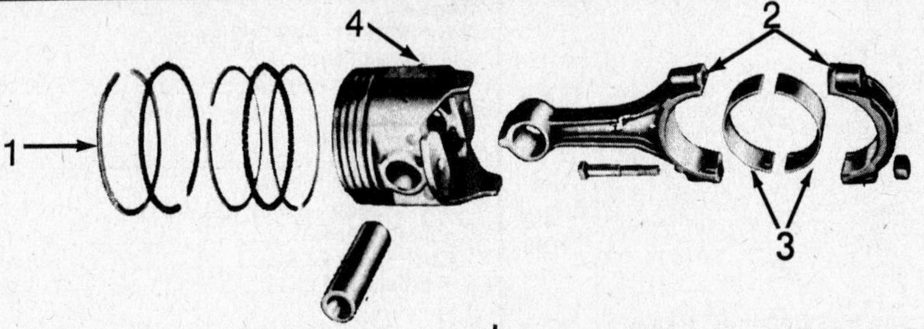

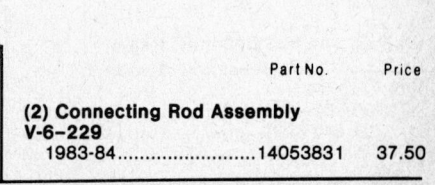

	Part No.	Price
(1) Piston Ring Set (Std.-One Piston)		
V-6-229		
1983-84	◆370409	14.50
V-6-231		
1983-85	◆1240955	15.75
V-6-262		
1985-87	◆14089025	18.00
V-8-305		
1983-87	◆370409	14.50
V-8-307Y		
1986-87	◆22529562	16.75
V-8-350		
1983-84	328506	15.50
1985	14089027	N.L.
1986-87	14094555	16.50
V-8-Diesel		
1983	◆22515964	21.00
1984-85	◆22523733	21.00

	Part No.	Price
(2) Connecting Rod Assembly		
V-6-229		
1983-84	14053831	37.50

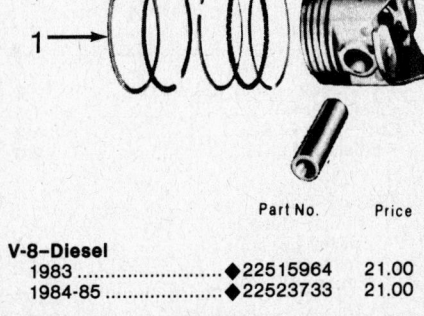

PARTS 14 PISTONS, RINGS & BEARINGS 14 PARTS

	Part No.	Price
V-6-231		
1983-85	◆25506520	39.00
V-6-262		
1985-87	◆14077944	42.25
V-8-305		
1983-87	◆14031310	39.50
V-8-307Y		
1986-87	◆22527025	45.00
V-8-350		
1983-87	◆14031310	39.50
V-8-Diesel		
1983-85	◆22515313	50.50
(3) Connecting Rod Bearings		
V-6-229		
1983-84	474095	8.00
V-6-262		
1985-87	◆18012481	10.00
V-6-231		
1983-85	◆18005399	11.00
V-8-exc. 307Y		
1983-87	◆3910555	7.50
V-8-307Y		
1986-87	◆18008494	N.L.
V-8-Diesel		
1983-87	◆18008494	10.50
(4) Piston Assembly (Std.)		
V-6-229		
1983-84	14019883	48.25
V-6-231		
1983	◆25518053	48.25
1984-85	◆25518053	48.25
V-6-262		
1985-87	◆14077948	48.25
V-8-305		
1983-84	◆364702	43.00
1985-87	◆14081292	54.50
V-8-307Y		
1986-87-L.H.	◆22527481	48.25
R.H.	◆22527482	48.25
V-8-350		
1984-85	474190	77.75
1986-87-Cast hd.		
Alum. hd.	14093695	66.00
V-8-Diesel		
1983-right	◆22523358	63.75
left	◆22523357	63.75
1984-85-right	◆22523358	63.75
left	◆22523357	63.75

LABOR 15 CRANKSHAFT & DAMPER 15 LABOR

(Factory Time) — Chilton Time

GASOLINE ENGINES

(P) Crankshaft and Main Bearings, Renew

Includes: R&R engine, check all bearing clearances.

	Chilton Time
V-6-1983-87	
229-262 engs (8.9)	12.0
231 eng (7.1)	10.0
w/A.C. add (.3)	.3
w/P.S. add (.2)	.2
w/A.I.R. add (.2)	.2
w/C.C.C. add (.3)	.3
V-8	
Chevrolet	
1983-87	
305 eng-Code H (8.5)	11.9
w/A.C. add (.4)	.4
w/C.C.C. add (.3)	.3
307 eng-Code Y (7.0)	10.1
w/A.C. add (.3)	.3
w/AIR add (.3)	.3
Corvette	
1984 (12.0)	16.8
1985-87 (10.7)	15.0

(P) Main Bearings, Renew

Includes: Check all bearing clearances.

	Chilton Time
V-6-1983-87	
229-262 engs (3.7)	4.6
231 eng (2.1)	3.6
w/C.C.C. add (.3)	.3
V-8	
Chevrolet	
1983-87	
305 eng-Code H (3.4)	5.4
307 eng-Code Y (4.1)	5.7
Corvette	
1984 (2.9)	4.0
1985-87 (2.6)	3.6

(P) Main and Rod Bearings, Renew

Includes: Check all bearing clearances.

	Chilton Time
V-6-1983-87	
229-262 engs (5.5)	6.4
231 eng (3.3)	5.4
w/C.C.C. add (.3)	.3
V-8	
Chevrolet	
1983-87	
305 eng-Code H (5.7)	7.8
307 eng-Code Y (6.3)	8.1
Corvette	
1984 (5.3)	6.4
1985-87 (4.9)	6.0

(G) Rear Main Bearing Oil Seals, Renew or Repack (Upper & Lower)

Includes: R&R oil pan and rear main bearing cap.

	Chilton Time
V-6-1983-87	
229-262 engs (2.3)	3.0
231 eng (1.5)	2.2
w/C.C.C. add (.3)	.3
V-8	
Chevrolet	
1983-87	
305 eng-Code H (2.0)	3.5
307 eng-Code Y (6.0)	3.6
Corvette	
1984 (1.5)	2.1
1985-87	
w/M.T. (2.8)	4.0
w/A.T. (2.2)	3.2

(G) Crankshaft Pulley or Balancer, Renew

	Chilton Time
V-6-1983-87-229-262 engs	
pulley (.6)	.8
balancer (.8)	1.0
231 eng	
pulley (.7)	1.1
balancer (.8)	1.2
1983-Chev.-pulley (.6)	.8
balancer (.8)	1.1
Corv.-pulley (.8)	1.2
balancer (1.5)	2.0
1984-87-Chev.	
305 Eng-Code H	
pulley (.6)	1.0
balancer (.8)	1.2
w/A.C. add (.2)	.2
307 eng-Code Y	
pulley (.6)	1.0
balancer (.9)	1.3
w/A.C. add (.1)	.1
Corv.-pulley (.3)	.6
balancer (.6)	1.0
w/A.C. add (.2)	.2

DIESEL ENGINE

(P) Crankshaft and Main Bearings, Renew

Includes: R&R engine, check all bearing clearances.

	Chilton Time
1983-85 (7.4)	11.2
w/A.C. add (.4)	.4

(P) Main Bearings, Renew

Includes: Check all bearing clearances.

	Chilton Time
1983-85 (4.1)	5.5

(P) Main and Rod Bearings, Renew

Includes: Check all bearing clearances.

	Chilton Time
1983-85 (6.5)	7.9

(G) Rear Main Bearing Oil Seals, Renew

Includes: R&R engine assy.

	Chilton Time
1983-85 (7.4)	10.7
w/A.C. add (.4)	.4

(G) Rear Main Bearing Oil Seals, R&R and Repack (Upper & Lower)

Includes: R&R oil pan and rear main bearing cap.

	Chilton Time
1983-85 (2.9)	4.0

(G) Crankshaft Pulley or Balancer, Renew

	Chilton Time
1983-85-pulley (.6)	.8
balancer (.9)	1.3
w/A.C. add (.2)	.2

(G) Crankshaft Front Oil Seal, Renew

	Chilton Time
1983-85 (.9)	1.5
w/A.C. add (.2)	.2

PARTS 15 CRANKSHAFT & DAMPER 15 PARTS

	Part No.	Price
(1) Crankshaft		
V-6-229		
1983-84	14006726	383.00
V-6-231		
1983-85	◆1260877	385.00
V-6-262		
1985	◆14071174	383.00
1986-87	◆14088639	383.00
V-8-305		
1983-85	◆361982	407.00
1986-87	◆14088536	407.00
V-8-307Y		
1986-87	◆22527438	403.00
V-8-350		
1984-85	3932444	407.00
1986-87	◆14088527	407.00
V-8-Diesel		
1983-85	◆22511035	439.00
(2) Main Bearing (Std.)		
V-6-229 & 262		
1983-87		
No. 1 upper	◆462661	6.50
No. 1 lower	◆462664	6.50
Nos. 2, 3	◆3912038	12.50
No. 4	◆3912030	17.00
V-6-231		
1983-85-No. 1	◆18009457	12.00
No. 2	◆18004602	20.00
No. 3	◆18002950	12.50
No. 4	◆5468578	13.00
V-8-305 & 350		
1983-87		
No. 1 upper	◆462661	6.50
No. 1 lower	◆462664	6.50
Nos. 2, 3, 4	◆3912038	12.50
No. 5	◆3912030	17.00
V-8-307Y		
1986-87-No. 1	◆5466211	13.00
Nos. 2, 4	◆5466089	13.00

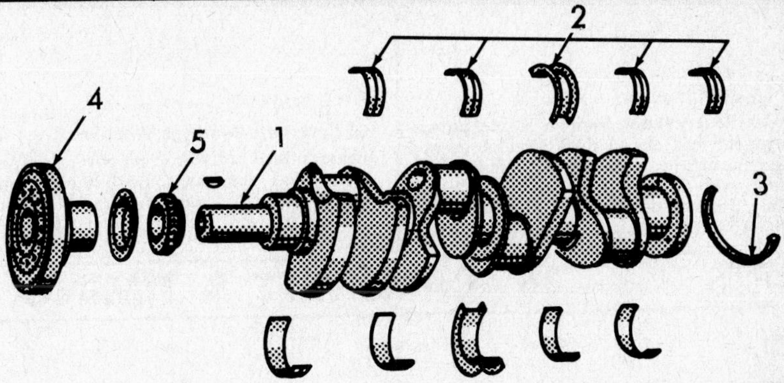

	Part No.	Price
No. 3	◆5466090	19.75
No. 5	◆5466091	17.00
V-8-Diesel		
1983-85-No. 1	◆5466312	16.00
Nos. 2, 4	◆5458657	15.00
No. 3	◆5463797	26.25
No. 5	◆5466314	19.75
(3) Main Bearing Oil Seals		
exc. V-6-231 & Diesel		
1983-87	◆473424	9.00
V-6-231, Diesel		
1983-87	◆9772831	1.50
(4) Vibration Damper		
(Chevrolet)		
V-6-229		
1983-84	◆14082324	41.00
V-6-231		
1983	◆25506570	42.75
1984-85	◆22523502	N.L.

	Part No.	Price
V-6-262		
1985-87	◆14082324	41.00
V-8-305		
1983-87	◆458653	59.25
V-8-Diesel		
1983-87	◆559131	63.25
(5) Crankshaft Timing Gear		
V-6-229		
1983-84	◆464617	29.50
V-6-231		
1983-85	◆25519954	14.50
V-6-262		
1985-87	◆464617	29.50
V-8-305		
1983-87	◆3896959	16.00
V-8-307Y		
1986-87	◆382880	16.75
V-8-Diesel		
1983-87	◆558489	44.25

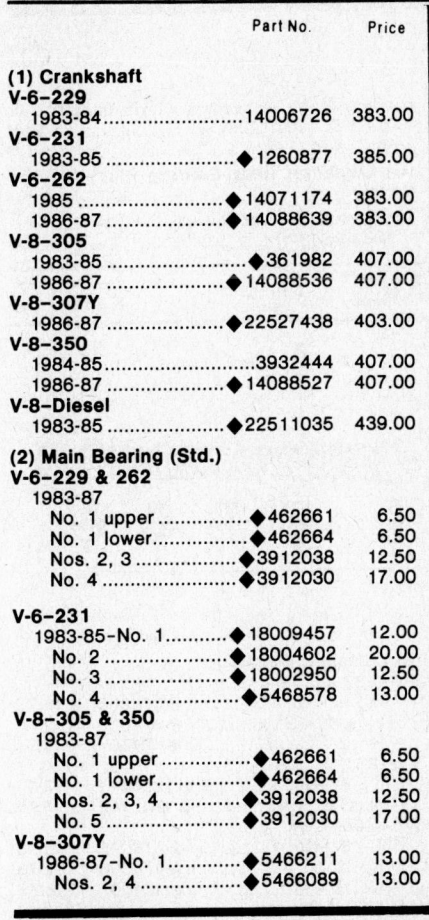

LABOR 16 CAMSHAFT & TIMING GEARS 16 LABOR

(Factory Time)	Chilton Time
GASOLINE ENGINES	
(G) Timing Cover Oil Seal, Renew	
V-6-1983-87	
229-262 engs (.8)	1.2
V-8	
Chevrolet	
1983-87	
305 eng-Code H (.8)	1.4
w/A.C. add (.2)	.2
307 eng-Code Y (1.0)	1.5
w/A.C. or AIR add (.1)	.1
Corvette	
1984-87 (.6)	1.2
(G) Timing Case Cover or Gasket, Renew	
V-6-1983-87	
229-262 engs (2.1)	2.7
231 eng (2.2)	3.2
w/A.C. add (.2)	.2
w/P.S. add (.2)	.2
w/A.I.R. add (.2)	.2
Renew cover add (.4)	.6
V-8	
Chevrolet	
1983-87	
305 eng-Code H (1.8)	2.6
w/A.C. add (.2)	.2
w/AIR add (.2)	.2
307 eng-Code Y (1.8)	2.6
w/A.C. add (.3)	.3
w/AIR add (.1)	.1
Renew cover add (.2)	.4

(Factory Time)	Chilton Time
Renew f/pump eccentric add (.1)	.2
Corvette	
1984-87 (2.3)	3.2
(G) Timing Chain or Camshaft Gear, Renew	
Includes: R&R engine front cover.	
V-6-1983-87	
229-262 engs (2.4)	3.2
231 eng (2.4)	3.7
w/A.C. add (.2)	.2
w/P.S. add (.2)	.2
w/A.I.R. add (.2)	.2
V-8	
Chevrolet	
1983-87	
305 eng-Code H (2.0)	3.1
w/A.C. add (.2)	.2
w/AIR add (.2)	.2
307 eng-Code Y (2.1)	3.1
w/A.C. add (.3)	.3
w/AIR add (.1)	.1
Corvette	
1984-87 (2.4)	3.7
Renew crank gear add (.3)	.4
(G) Camshaft, Renew	
Includes: R&R engine and oil pan, where required.	
V-6-1983-87	
229-262 engs (5.8)	8.0
231 eng (4.6)	7.0
w/A.C. add (.2)	.2

(Factory Time)	Chilton Time
w/P.S. add (.2)	.2
w/A.I.R. add (.4)	.4
w/C.C.C. add (.3)	.3
V-8	
Chevrolet	
1983-87	
305 eng-Code H (5.0)	7.0
w/A.C. add (.9)	.9
w/C.C.C. add (.1)	.1
307 eng-Code Y (5.7)	*8.1
w/A.C. add (1.0)	1.0
w/AIR add (.4)	.4
*Renew cam brgs add (1.4)	2.0
Corvette	
1984 (6.9)	9.7
1985-87 (10.4)	14.5
DIESEL ENGINE	
(G) Timing Case Cover or Gasket, Renew	
Includes: R&R fan blade, crankshaft pulley and balancer. Drain and refill oil and coolant.	
1983-85 (2.1)	3.1
Renew cover add (.2)	.3
w/A.C. add (.3)	.3
(G) Timing Chain or Gears, Renew	
Includes: R&R fan blade, crankshaft pulley and balancer. Drain and refill oil and coolant.	
1983-85 (2.3)	3.5
w/A.C. add (.3)	.3

LABOR 16 CAMSHAFT & TIMING GEARS 16 LABOR

(Factory Time) Chilton Time

(G) Camshaft, Renew
Includes: R&R radiator, front cover, fuel pump, timing gear and chain. R&R injector pump, intake manifold and lifters. Disconnect exhaust system. Drain and refill oil and coolant. Make all necessary adjustments.
1983-85 (7.3) 10.0
w/A.C. add (1.0) 1.0

(G) Camshaft Bearings, Renew
Includes: R&R radiator, front cover, fuel pump, timing gear and chain. R&R injector pump, intake manifold and lifters. Disconnect exhaust system. Drain and refill oil and coolant. Make all necessary adjustments.
1983-85 (10.1) 13.8
w/A.C. add (1.0) 1.0

(G) Camshaft Rear Bearing Plug, Renew
Includes: R&R trans for accessibility.
1983-85 (2.1) 3.0

PARTS 16 CAMSHAFT & TIMING GEARS 16 PARTS

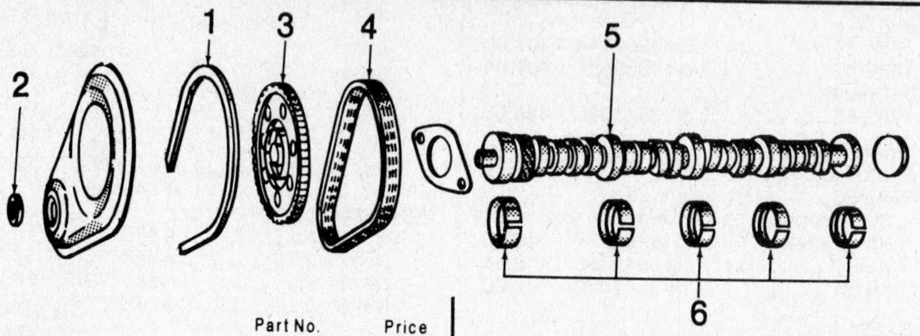

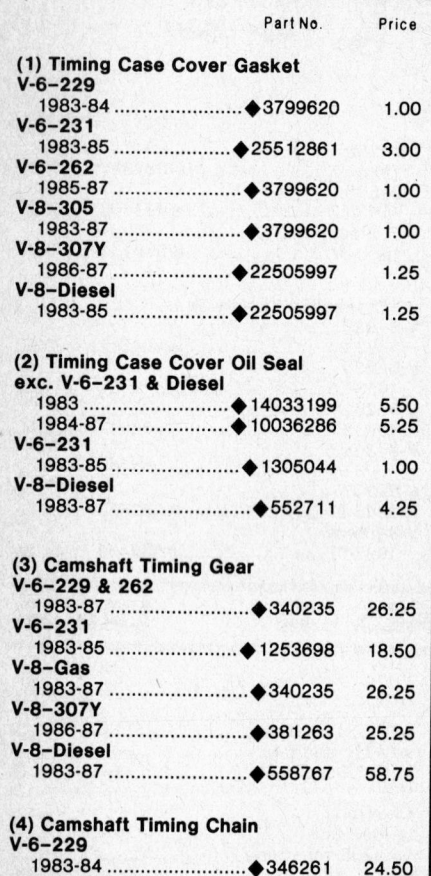

	Part No.	Price
(1) Timing Case Cover Gasket		
V-6-229		
1983-84	◆3799620	1.00
V-6-231		
1983-85	◆25512861	3.00
V-6-262		
1985-87	◆3799620	1.00
V-8-305		
1983-87	◆3799620	1.00
V-8-307Y		
1986-87	◆22505997	1.25
V-8-Diesel		
1983-85	◆22505997	1.25
(2) Timing Case Cover Oil Seal exc. V-6-231 & Diesel		
1983	◆14033199	5.50
1984-87	◆10036286	5.25
V-6-231		
1983-85	◆1305044	1.00
V-8-Diesel		
1983-87	◆552711	4.25
(3) Camshaft Timing Gear		
V-6-229 & 262		
1983-87	◆340235	26.25
V-6-231		
1983-85	◆1253698	18.50
V-8-Gas		
1983-87	◆340235	26.25
V-8-307Y		
1986-87	◆381263	25.25
V-8-Diesel		
1983-87	◆558767	58.75
(4) Camshaft Timing Chain		
V-6-229		
1983-84	◆346261	24.50
V-6-231		
1983-87	◆1257650	26.00
V-6-262		
1985-87	◆14087014	25.25
V-8-Gas		
1983-84	◆346261	24.50
1985-87	◆14087014	25.25
V-8-307Y		
1986-87	◆401584	31.75
V-8-Diesel		
1983-87	◆558484	N.L.
(5) Camshaft		
V-6-229		
1983-84	14060649	118.00
V-6-262		
1985-87	◆14077973	120.00
V-6-231		
1983-85	◆1262835	119.00
V-8-305		
1983-87	◆14060653	124.00
V-8-307Y		
1986-87	◆22527149	256.00
V-8-350		
1984-87	◆14060655	155.00
V-8-Diesel		
1983-87	◆22510099	266.00
(6) Camshaft Bearings		
V-6-229 & 262		
1983-87-No. 1	◆474005	16.75
Nos. 2, 4	◆474006	12.75
No. 3	◆474007	16.75
V-6-231		
1983-87-No. 1	◆1234441	7.00
Nos. 2, 3, 4	◆1231142	7.75
V-8-Gas		
1983-87-No. 1	◆474005	16.75
No. 2, 5	◆474006	12.75
No. 3, 4	◆474007	16.75
V-8-307 & Diesel		
1983-87-No. 1	◆561077	11.50
No. 2	◆390300	11.50
No. 3	◆390301	11.75
No. 4	◆390302	11.50
No. 5	◆390303	11.50
Camshaft Thrust Button V-6-231 & Diesel		
1983-85	◆1250948	2.50
Camshaft Thrust Button Spring		
V-6-231		
1983-85	◆1254199	1.00
Diesel		
1983-85	22514206	1.25

LABOR 17 ENGINE OILING SYSTEM 17 LABOR

(Factory Time) Chilton Time

GASOLINE ENGINES

(G) Oil Pan or Gasket, Renew
V-6-1983-87
229-262 engs (1.8) 2.4
231 eng (1.1) 1.6
w/C.C.C. add (.2) 2
V-8
Chevrolet
1983-87
305 eng-Code H (1.8) 2.9
307 eng-Code Y (2.1) 2.9
Corvette
1984-87 (1.1) 1.5
w/C.C.C. add (.2) 2

(P) Pressure Test Engine Bearings (Pan Off)
All models 1.0

(G) Oil Pump, Renew
Includes: Transfer screen and drive to pump.
V-6-1983-87
229-262 engs (1.9) 2.6
231 eng (.5) 8
w/C.C.C. add (.2) 2
V-8
Chevrolet
1983-87
305 eng-Code H (1.9) 3.1
307 eng-Code Y (2.2) 3.1
Corvette
1984-87 (1.2) 1.7
w/C.C.C. add (.2) 2

(G) Oil Pressure Gauge (Engine), Renew
1983 (.3) 4
1984-87-Chev. (.3) 4
Corv. (.6) 1.0

(M) Oil Filter Element, Renew
1983-87
V-6 (.3) 4
V-8 (.3) 4

(M) Oil Filter By-Pass Valve, Renew
V-6-1983-87
229-262 engs (2.1) 3.0
V-8-1983-87 (.3) 4

DIESEL ENGINE

(G) Oil Pan or Gasket, Renew
Includes: Raise engine, R&R and clean oil pump screen.
1983-85 (2.6) 3.4

LABOR 17 ENGINE OILING SYSTEM 17 LABOR

	(Factory Time)	Chilton Time
(P) Pressure Test Engine Bearings (Pan Off)		
All models		1.0
(G) Oil Pump, Renew		
Includes: Raise engine, R&R and clean oil pump screen.		
1983-85	(2.7)	3.6
(G) Oil Pump, R&R and Recondition		
Includes: Raise engine, R&R and clean oil pump screen.		
1983-85	(2.9)	3.8
(G) Oil Pressure Gauge (Engine), Renew		
1983-85	(.3)	.4
(M) Oil Filter Element, Renew		
1983-85	(.3)	.3

PARTS 17 ENGINE OILING SYSTEM 17 PARTS

	Part No.	Price
Oil Pan Gasket Set		
V-6-229		
1983-84	471830	10.75
V-6-262		
1985	◆14079397	N.L.
1986-87	◆14088514	29.25
V-6-231		
1983-85-14 bolts	◆1260771	3.00
20 bolts	◆25521994	8.50
V-8-Gas		
1983	◆14019828	11.75
1984-85	◆14079398	10.00
1986-87	◆14088505	22.50
V-8-307Y		
1986-87	◆22519181	N.L.
V-8-Diesel		
1983-85	◆22519181	7.00
Oil Pump Assm.		
V-6-229		
1983-84	◆3764547	49.75
V-6-231		
1983	◆25519448	38.00
1984-85	◆25519448	38.00
V-6-262		
1985-87	◆3764547	49.75
V-8-Gas		
1983-87	◆3764547	49.75
V-8-307Y		
1986-87	◆22524583	61.50
V-8-Diesel		
1983-87	◆22511732	59.75
Oil Pump Screen		
V-6-229 & 262		
1983-87	◆3855152	5.50
V-8-Gas		
1983-87-exc. 307Y	◆3855152	5.50
Oil Pump Cover		
V-6-229 & 262		
1983-87	3836980	12.50
V-6-231		
1983-85	966093	N.L.
V-8-Gas		
1983-85	3836980	12.50
V-8-Diesel		
1983-87	397933	1.50
Oil Pressure Switch (Engine)		
(Chevrolet)		
V-6-229		
1983-84	◆10002798	5.50
V-6-262		
1985-87	◆14014599	5.25
V-6-231		
1983-85	◆25500672	5.50
V-8-Gas		
1983-87	14034354	12.00
V-8-Diesel		
1983-87	◆3815936	3.50
(Corvette)		
1983-87	◆14073454	20.50

LABOR 18 CLUTCH & FLYWHEEL 18 LABOR

	(Factory Time)	Chilton Time
(G) Clutch Pedal Free Play, Adjust		
All models		.3
(G) Bleed Clutch Hydraulic System		
All models		.5
(G) Clutch Assembly, Renew		
Includes: R&R trans and adjust free play.		
Corvette		
1984-87	(2.6)	3.7
Renew pilot brg add	(.2)	.2
(G) Clutch Release Bearing, Renew		
Includes: R&R trans and adjust free play.		
Corvette		
1984-87	(2.1)	3.0
(G) Flywheel, Renew		
Includes: R&R trans assy.		
Corvette		
1984-87	(2.7)	3.9
Renew ring gear add	(.3)	.5
(G) Clutch Master Cylinder, Renew		
Includes: Bleed system.		
1984-87-Corv.	(.8)	1.1
Recond cyl add	(.4)	.4
(G) Clutch Slave Cylinder, Renew		
Includes: Bleed system.		
1984-87-Corv.	(.6)	.9
Recond cyl add	(.4)	.4

PARTS 18 CLUTCH & FLYWHEEL 18 PARTS

	Part No.	Price
Clutch Disc		
1984	14055162	106.00
1985-87	14084177	106.00
Clutch Pressure Plate		
1984	14060624	143.00
1985-87	14084176	147.00
Clutch Master Cylinder		
1984-87	14047679	113.00
Clutch Slave Cylinder		
1984-87	14047671	102.00
Clutch Throwout Bearing		
1984-87	◆908404	30.75
Clucth Release Fork		
1984-87	14048868	19.50
Flywheel (w/Ring Gear)		
(M.T.)		
1984-87	3991406	162.25
(A.T.)		
V-6-229 & 262		
1983-87	◆471591	55.75
V-6-231		
1983	◆25512346	70.50
1984-85	◆25512348	72.00
V-8 305		
1983-87	◆471591	55.75
V-8-307Y		
1986-87	◆22500807	85.50
V-8-350		
1984-87	◆471591	55.75
V-8-Diesel		
1983-87	◆22500808	85.50

LABOR 21 SHIFT LINKAGE 21 LABOR

(Factory Time) — Chilton Time

STANDARD

(G) Shift Linkage, Adjust
1984-87-Corv. (.9) 1.2

(G) Gearshift Control Rods, Renew
Includes: Adjust linkage.
1984-87-Corv.-one (1.0) 1.4
each adtnl add (.1) 1

(G) Floor Mounted Gearshift Control Assy., Renew
Corvette
1984-87 (1.3) 1.7

(G) Floor Shift Back Drive Rod or Cable, Renew
Corvette
1984-87 (.6) 9

AUTOMATIC

(G) Shift Linkage, Adjust
All models
Neutral Safety Switch (.3) 4
Shift Indicator Needle (.2) 3
Shift Linkage (.4) 5
T.V. Cable (.3) 4

(G) Shift Linkage, Adjust (w/Diesel Eng)
All models
Fast idle speed (.2) 3
Throttle rod/T.V. cable (.5) 6
Trans vacuum valve (.5) 6
Vacuum regul valve (.6) 8
Complete (.8) 1.0

(G) Gear Selector, Indicator Needle and/or Assembly, Renew
Chevrolet
1983-87 (.3) 5
Corvette
1984-87 (.4) 7

(G) Park Lock Cable, Renew
Corvette
1984-87 (.8) 1.3

(G) Shift Control Cable, Renew
Corvette
1984-87 (1.3) 1.8

(G) Gear Selector Lever, Renew
1983-87-column (.2) 5
floor (.9) 1.2

(G) Shift Control Rods or Cable, Renew
1983-87-Chev. (.4) 5
Corv. (.6) 8

(G) Steering Column Gearshift Tube and/or Bowl, Renew
Chevrolet
Does not include colorcoat.
1983-87-std (1.2) 2.4
tilt (2.0) 3.0
w/Cruise control add (.2) 2

(G) Floorshift Control Assembly, Renew
Includes: R&R console plate and adjust control rods.
Corvette
1984-87 (.6) 9
Recond assy add (.3) 5

LABOR 25 U-JOINTS & DRIVESHAFT 25 LABOR

(Factory Time) — Chilton Time

(G) Universal Joints, Renew
Includes: R&R drive shaft.
Chevrolet
1983-87-front (.6) 8
rear (.5) 7
both (.7) 1.3
Corvette
1984-87-one (1.3) 2.0
both (1.5) 2.4

(G) Driveshaft, Renew
Chevrolet
1983-87 (.4) 5
Corvette
1984-87 (1.1) 1.7

(G) Pinion Shaft Flange, Renew
1983-87-Chev. (.7) 1.0

PARTS 25 UNIVERSAL JOINTS & DRIVE SHAFT 25 PARTS

	Part No.	Price
Universal Joint Repair Kit		
(Chevrolet)		
1983-87 (type of driveshaft)		
Dana	◆374246	28.50
Saginaw	◆7806140	41.00
(Corvette)		
1984-87	14067678	26.00

LABOR 26 REAR AXLE 26 LABOR

(Factory Time) — Chilton Time

(M) Differential, Drain & Refill
All models 6

(M) Axle Housing Cover or Gasket, Renew
Chevrolet
1983-87 (.5) 6
Corvette
1984-87 (2.5) 3.5

(G) Axle Shaft Assembly, Renew
Includes: R&R bearing.
Chevrolet
'C' Lock Type
1983-87-one (.7) 9
both (.9) 1.2

(G) Axle Shaft Bearing and/or Seal, Renew
Chevrolet
'C' Lock Type
1983-87-one (.6) 8
both (.8) 1.1

(G) Axle Drive Shaft, Renew
Corvette
1984-87-one (1.1) 1.4
both (1.7) 2.2
Recond U-Joint add (.3) 3

(G) Axle Shaft Wheel Mounting Studs, Renew (One Side)
Chevrolet
1983-87 .... 1.0

(G) Pinion Shaft Oil Seal, Renew
Chevrolet
1983-87 (.5) 8
Corvette
1984-87 (2.7) 3.6

SERVICES REQUIRING R&R

CHEVROLET

(G) Differential Case Assy., Renew
1983-87 (1.9) 2.8
w/Positraction add (.5) 5

(P) Ring and Pinion Gears, Renew
1983-87 (2.4) 3.9

LABOR — 26 REAR AXLE 26 — LABOR

(Factory Time)	Chilton Time
Recond diff case add	
std (.3)	.5
limited slip (.7)	1.0
(P) Pinion Gear Bearings, Renew	
1983-87 (2.2)	3.4
Renew side brgs add (.3)	.3
(P) Differential Side Bearings, Renew (One or Both)	
1983-87 (1.7)	2.5
(P) Pinion Shaft and/or Side and Pinion Gears, Renew	
Does not include R&R case.	
1983-87 (.8)	1.8
w/Limited slip add (.5)	.5
(P) Limited Slip Clutch Plates, Renew	
1983-87 (1.1)	2.0

(Factory Time)	Chilton Time
(G) Rear Axle Housing, Renew	
1983-87 (3.4)	5.2
(G) Rear Axle Assy., Renew (Complete)	
1983-87 (1.7)	3.2

SERVICES REQUIRING R&R

CORVETTE

(Factory Time)	Chilton Time
(G) Differential Carrier, R&R or Renew	
1984-87 (2.9)	3.8
Recond comp add (2.6)	3.6
(P) Differential Case, Renew	
1984-87 (4.1)	5.4
(P) Pinion Shaft and/or Side Gears, Renew	
Includes: R&R clutch pack.	
1984-87 (3.7)	5.2

(Factory Time)	Chilton Time
(P) Ring Gear and Pinion, Renew	
1984-87 (5.0)	6.6
(P) Differential Pinion Bearings, Renew	
1984-87 (4.5)	6.0
(P) Differential Side Bearings, Renew	
1984-87 (3.5)	5.0
(P) Pinion Bearings and Diff. Side Bearings, Renew	
1984-87 (4.7)	6.2
(G) Yoke Bearings and Oil Seals, Renew (Both Sides)	
1983-87 (3.5)	5.0

PARTS — 26 REAR AXLE 26 — PARTS

CORVETTE

	Part No.	Price
(1) Yoke (w/Deflector)		
1984-87-exc. below	14071738	25.00
1985-87-M.T.	14091396	26.50
(2) Oil Seal (Pinion)		
1984-87-exc. below	14079450	5.25
1985-87-M.T.	14079089	4.50
(3) Preload Bearing (Outer)		
1983-87	9436127	22.00
(4) Carrier (w/Cap)		
1984-87-exc. below	14079445	192.25
1985-87-M.T.	14091393	244.00
(5) Shim Kit (Preload Adj.)		
1984-87	14079448	39.75
(6) Pinion Bearing (Inner)		
1983-87	9417781	36.50
(7) Ring & Pinion Gear Set		
1984-3.07R	14079446	N.L.
3.31R	14089043	255.00
1985-87-3.07R		
A.T.	14085885	248.00
M.T.	14091394	303.00
1985-87-2.73R	14091462	287.00
(8) Cover (Diff. Carrier)		
(wo/H.D. susp.)		
1985-87-M.T.	14087653	367.00
A.T.	14079976	345.00
(H.D. susp.)		
1984-87-M.T.	14084008	367.00
A.T.	14079977	345.00
(10) Case Assy. (w/Internal Gears)		
1984-87-exc. below	14091437	136.00
1985-87-M.T.	14091424	311.00

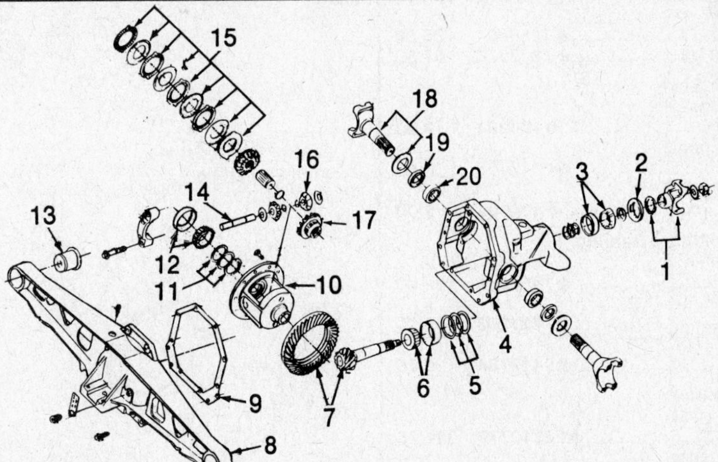

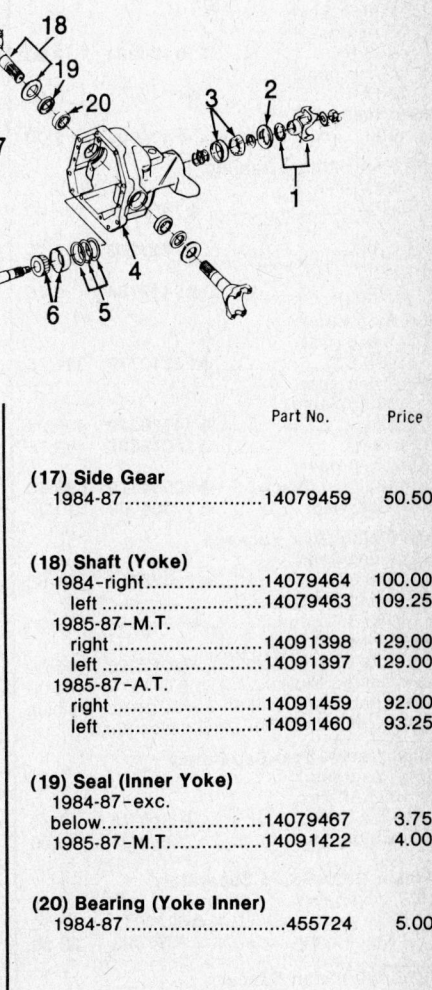

	Part No.	Price
(11) Shim Kit (Brg. Preload)		
1984-87	14079455	4.75
(12) Side Bearing		
1984-87	7451226	17.00
(13) Bushing (Carrier Cover)		
1984-87-wo/H.D. susp.	14075762	9.25
H.D. susp.	14066929	9.00
(14) Pinion Shaft		
1984-87	14091436	6.75
(15) Plate Kit (w/Disc)		
1984-87-exc. below	14079461	95.50
1985-87-M.T.	14091400	99.25
(16) Pinion Gear		
1984-87	14079457	10.50

	Part No.	Price
(17) Side Gear		
1984-87	14079459	50.50
(18) Shaft (Yoke)		
1984-right	14079464	100.00
left	14079463	109.25
1985-87-M.T.		
right	14091398	129.00
left	14091397	129.00
1985-87-A.T.		
right	14091459	92.00
left	14091460	93.25
(19) Seal (Inner Yoke)		
1984-87-exc. below	14079467	3.75
1985-87-M.T.	14091422	4.00
(20) Bearing (Yoke Inner)		
1984-87	455724	5.00

CHEVROLET

To obtain correct replacement parts for the rear axle assembly, use the third letter of the rear axle code when ordering parts. The rear axle code is stamped either on the front of the passenger side axle tube or on a metal tag attached to a cover bolt.

(1) Axle Shaft
1983-87-7½″ r. gr. ....◆22519891 99.50
(8½″ ring gear)
wo/Sta. wag. ....◆1255801 114.00
Sta. wag. ....◆14060881 145.25
(8¾″ ring gear)
1716. drum ....◆10020249 127.25
2316. drum ....◆526703 139.25

(2) Axle Seal
1983-87-exc. below ....◆3998519 4.00
Sta. wag. ....◆3958078 5.00
11″ x 2″ brks. ....◆3958078 5.00

(3) Axle Bearing
1983-87-exc. below ....◆7451785 16.00
Sta. wag. ....◆7451809 15.00

(4) Pinion Flange
1983-87-exc below ....◆1256654 35.00
7½″ r. gr. ....◆7827670 33.50

(5) Pinion Seal
(7½″ ring gear)
1983-87 ....◆404294 9.00
(8½″ ring gear)
1983-87 ....◆1243465 7.50
(8¾″ ring gear)
1983 ....◆404294 9.00

(6) Front Pinion Bearing
1983-87-exc below ....◆7450984 21.00
7½″ r. gr. ('82-'84) ....◆7451202 16.00
7½″ r. gr. ('85-'86) ....◆9417784 16.25

(7) Axle Housing
(7½″ ring gear)
1983-87 ....◆22510779 392.25
(8½″ ring gear)
1983-87-exc. below ....◆14079329 406.25
Sta. wag. ....◆14079330 489.75
(8¾″ ring gear)
1983-exc. below ....◆10004179 603.50
Sta. wag. ....◆10004180 610.00

(8) Pinion Gear Package
(7½″ ring gear)
1983-87 ....◆22525894 94.50
(8½″ ring gear)
1983-87 ....◆1397647 132.00
(8¾″ ring gear)
1983-exc. below ....◆547225 106.00
limited slip ....◆547212 173.00
Gear packages contain 2 side gears, 2 pinion gears, thrust washers and pinion shaft.

Side Gears–Sold Separately
(8½″ ring gear)
1983-87-exc. below ....◆231075 49.50
Eaton type 3995894 51.00

Pinion Gears–Sold Separately
(8½″ ring gear)
1983-exc. below ....◆6270977 17.50
Eaton type 3995895 22.50

(9) Drive Pinion Spacer
1983-87-exc below ....◆1234726 1.50
7½″ ring gr. ....◆9785792 1.50

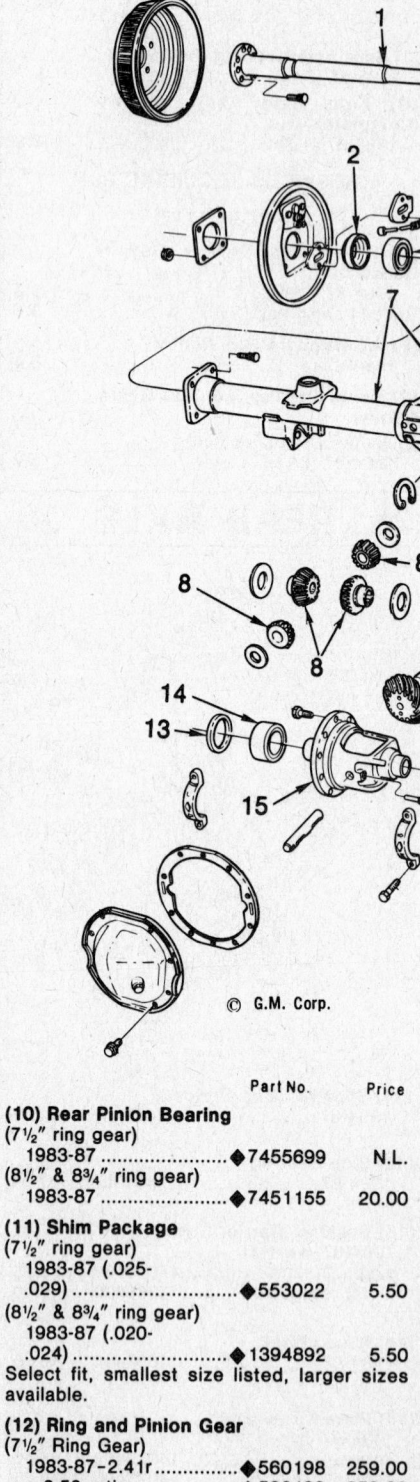

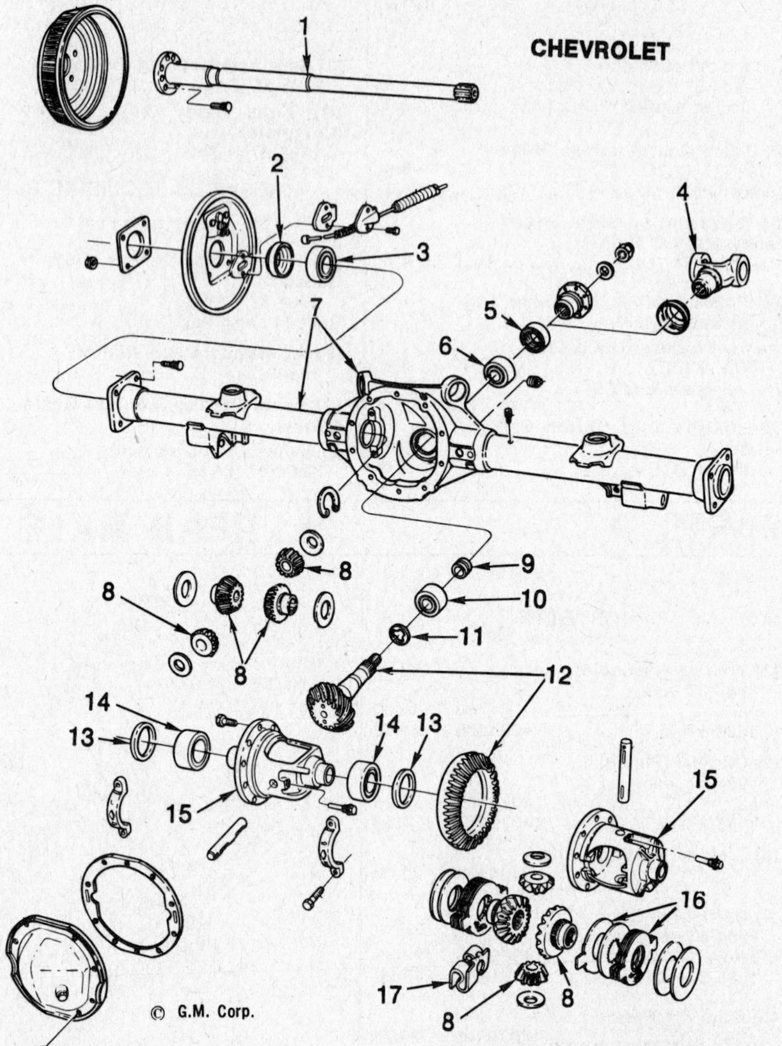

LIMITED SLIP DIFFERENTIAL

Part No. Price

(10) Rear Pinion Bearing
(7½″ ring gear)
1983-87 ....◆7455699 N.L.
(8½″ & 8¾″ ring gear)
1983-87 ....◆7451155 20.00

(11) Shim Package
(7½″ ring gear)
1983-87 (.025-.029) ....◆553022 5.50
(8½″ & 8¾″ ring gear)
1983-87 (.020-.024) ....◆1394892 5.50
Select fit, smallest size listed, larger sizes available.

(12) Ring and Pinion Gear
(7½″ Ring Gear)
1983-87-2.41r ....◆560198 259.00
2.56 ratio ....◆560199 259.00
2.73 ratio ....◆560201 259.00
2.93 ratio ....◆560204 261.00
(8½″ Ring Gear)
1983-87-2.41r ....◆1258715 276.00
2.56 ratio ....◆1258707 276.00
2.73 ratio ....◆1258708 276.00
2.93 ratio ....◆1258714 276.00
3.08 ratio ....◆1258709 276.00
3.23 ratio ....◆1258713 276.00

Part No. Price

(8¾″ Ring Gear)
1983-2.41r ....◆10002813 305.25
2.56 ratio ....◆10002814 305.25
2.73 ratio ....◆10002812 305.25
2.93 ratio ....◆10018255 305.25
3.08 ratio ....◆10002811 305.25
3.23 ratio ....◆10002810 305.25

(13) Bearing Adjusting Shim Pkg.
(7½″ & 8½″ ring gear)
1983-87 (.040-.044) ....◆3995791 6.50
(8¾″ ring gear)
1983 (.040-.046) ....◆3996610 6.50
Select fit, smallest size listed, larger sizes available.

(14) Differential Side Bearing
1983-84-exc below ....◆7451281 15.00
8¾″ ring gr. ....◆7451140 15.00
1985-87 ....◆9420095 N.L.

(15) Differential Case
(wo/Limited Slip Differential)
(7½″ ring gear)
1983-87 ....◆558648 109.00

PARTS 26 REAR AXLE 26 PARTS

	Part No.	Price
(8½″ ring gear)		
1983-87-exc.		
below	◆1252981	110.00
2.56, 2.93R	◆1252980	110.00
(8¾″ ring gear)		
1983-3.23R	◆527854	162.00
2.41, 2.56R	◆526205	134.25
2.73, 3.08R	◆526207	162.25

	Part No.	Price
(Limited Slip Differential)		
(8½″ ring gear)		
1983-87-exc.		
below	◆14030435	431.25
2.41, 2.56R	◆14030434	408.50
(8¾″ ring gear)		
1983-3.23R	◆527753	428.00
2.41, 2.56R	◆527751	428.00
2.73, 3.08R	◆527752	428.00

	Part No.	Price
(16) Friction Disc Kit		
1983-87-8½″		
ring gr.	◆231127	58.25
8¾″ ring gr.	◆483722	55.75
(17) Preload Spring		
1983-87-w/8½″		
ring gr.	◆231260	3.25
8¾″ ring. gr.	◆488332	4.50

LABOR 27 REAR SUSPENSION 27 LABOR

(Factory Time)	Chilton Time
(G) Rear Suspension Toe-in, Adjust	
Corvette	
1984-87 (.3)	.5
(G) Rear Suspension, Align (Complete)	
Corvette	
1984-87 (.4)	.6
(G) Rear Spring, Renew	
Chevrolet	
1983-87-coil spring-one (.6)	.8
Corvette	
1984-87 (.7)	1.2
(G) Rear Shock Absorbers, Renew	
1983-87-one (.3)	.4
both (.4)	.7
(G) Lower Control Arm Assy., Renew	
Chevrolet	
1983-87-one (.4)	.7
both (.5)	1.0
Renew bushing add-each arm (.3)	.3
(G) Upper Control Arm Assy., Renew	
Chevrolet	
1983-87-one (.4)	.8
both (.6)	1.1
Renew bushing add-each arm (.3)	.3
(G) Rear Wheel Spindle, Renew	
Includes: R&R spindle bearings.	
Corvette	
1984-87-one (1.0)	1.5
(G) Rear Wheel Spindle Control Rods, Renew	
1984-87-one (.4)	.6
both (.6)	1.0
Renew brkt add-each	.2
(G) Rear Axle Tie Rod Assy., Renew	
Includes: Alignment.	
1984-87 (.9)	1.4
(G) Rear Stabilizer Bar, Renew	
1983 (.5)	.7
1984-87-Chev. (.5)	.7
Corv. (.7)	1.0
(G) Superlift Shock Absorbers, Renew	
1983-87-one (.4)	.6
both (.5)	.9
(G) Rear Wheel Knuckle Support Arms, Renew	
Corvette	
1984-one (.4)	.6
both (.6)	1.0
(G) Rear Wheel Knuckle Assy., Renew	
Corvette	
1984-87-one (1.5)	2.1
both (2.6)	3.9
(G) Rear Wheel Hub and Bearing Assy., Renew	
Corvette	
1984-87-one (1.2)	1.6
both (2.0)	2.8
(G) Rear Torque Arm, Renew	
Corvette	
1984-87 (1.4)	1.9
(G) Rear Tie Rod Ends, Renew	
Includes: Alignment.	
Corvette	
1984-87-one (.6)	.9
both (.8)	1.3
(G) Rear Wheel Spindle Control Rods, Renew	
Corvette	
1984-87-one (.4)	.6
both (.6)	1.0
(G) Rear Wheel Spindle Rods, Renew	
Includes: Alignment.	
Corvette	
1984-87-one (.6)	.8
both (.8)	1.2

PARTS 27 REAR SUSPENSION 27 PARTS

CHEVROLET

	Part No.	Price
(1) Rear Control Arm (Lower)		
1983-87	◆10000334	32.50
(2) Spring Assy.		
Order by model and description.		
(3) Shock Absorber		
(wo/Superlift)		
(wo/Sta. wagon)		
1983-84	◆4993551	24.50
1985-87	◆22046428	24.50
(Sta. wagon)		
1983-84	◆4993554	24.50
1985-87	◆22046427	24.50
(Superlift)		
(Sta. wagon)		
1983-84-right	◆4993553	64.00
left	◆4993552	65.00
1985-87-right	◆22046426	57.75
left	◆22046425	57.75
(4) Rear Control Arm (Upper)		
1983-87-Code		
YC	◆10000887	22.50
Code YGK	◆10000904	30.00
Code YGS	◆10000910	30.00

© G.M. Corp.

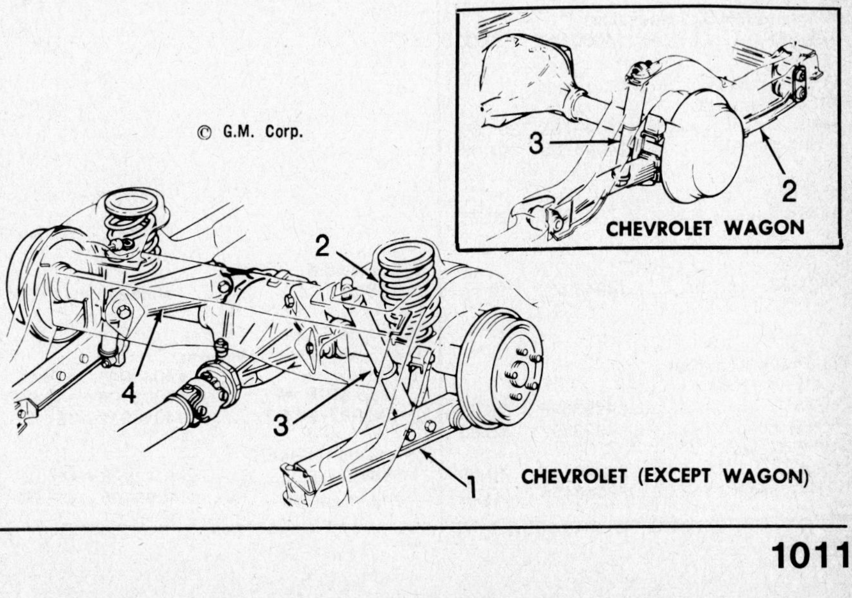

CHEVROLET WAGON

CHEVROLET (EXCEPT WAGON)

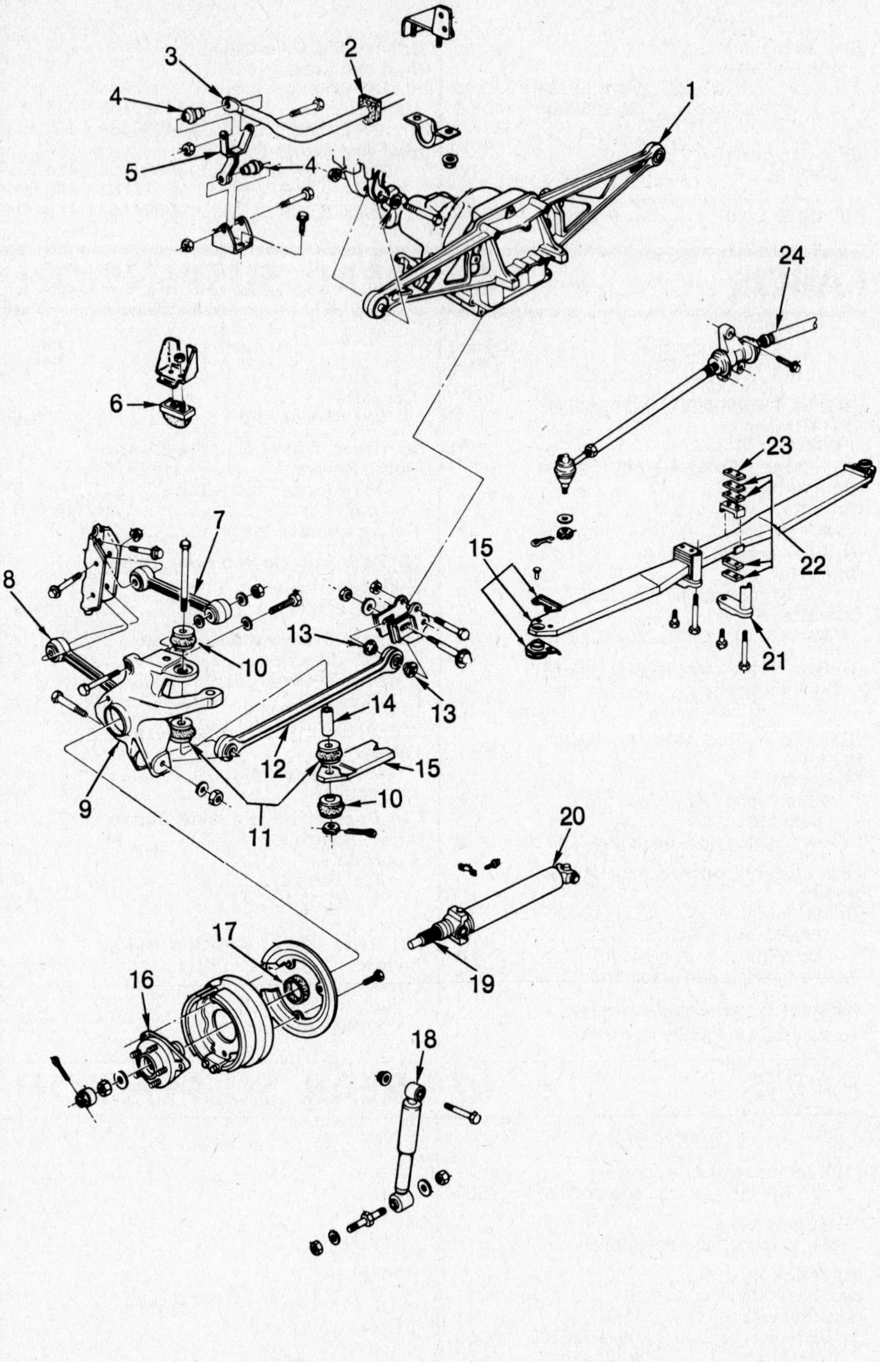

	Part No.	Price
CORVETTE		
(1) Carrier, (Differential)		
Order by year and model.		
(2) Stabilizer Bushing		
1984-87-wo/H.D. susp.	14060111	2.00
1984-H.D. susp.	14060112	2.00
1985-87-H.D. susp.	14084065	2.00
(3) Stabilizer Shaft		
1984-87-wo/H.D. susp.	14060109	43.75
1984-H.D. susp.	14060110	43.75
1985-87-H.D. susp.	14084066	43.75
(4) Insulator		
1984-87	14060114	2.00
(5) Link		
1984-87	14060113	3.25
(6) Bumper		
1984-87	14044577	3.00
(7) Rod (Upper)		
1984-87	14048930	37.50
(8) Rod (Lower)		
1984-87	14048931	34.00
(9) Knuckle		
1984-87-right	14041902	267.00
left	14041901	267.00
(10) Insulator		
1984-87	14044580	2.50
(11) Insulator		
Use only with H.D. suspension.		
1984-87	14044580	2.50
(12) Rod (Spindle)		
1984-87-right	14048948	38.00
left	14048947	38.00
(13) Bushing		
1984-87	14060166	2.00
(14) Spacer		
Use only with H.D. suspension.		
1984-87	14060140	2.00
(15) Spring Assy.		
1984-87-wo/H.D. susp.	14045785	301.00
H.D. susp.	14045786	301.00
(16) Hub		
1984-87	7466924	220.75
(17) Seal		
1984-87	14046941	3.25
(18) Shock Absorber		
1984-wo/H.D. susp.	4993595	25.50
H.D. susp.	4993597	40.50
1985-87-wo/H.D. susp.	22046417	40.50
H.D. susp.	22046450	90.00

	Part No.	Price
(19) Spindle		
1984-87	14055941	148.00
(20) Axle Shaft		
(wo/6-way power seat)		
1984-w/M.T.	14041925	114.00
1985-87-w/M.T.	14093105	114.00
1984-87-w/A.T.	14046912	154.00
(6-way power seat)		
1984	14041925	114.00
1985-87	14093105	114.00

	Part No.	Price
(21) Anchor Plate		
1984-87	14048993	2.75
(22) Spacer		
1984-87-wo/H.D. susp.	14048950	1.00
H.D. susp.	14044572	1.00
(23) Insulator		
1984-87	14044575	8.00
(24) Tie Rod		
1984-87	14091320	98.75

(Factory Time) Chilton Time

Note: If more than one item requires replacement where evacuation and discharging the system is already included in the operation, deduct 1.0 hour for each additional item to the time listed.

(G) Drain, Evacuate and Recharge System
All models (.5)........ 1.0

(G) Leak Test
Includes: Check all lines and connections.
All models........ .5

(G) Compressor Belt, Renew
1983-87
V-6-229 engs (.4)........ .6
V-6-231 eng (.5)........ .7
V-6-262 eng (.3)........ .4
V-8 engs (.3)........ *.4
Diesel (.4)........ .6
Serpentine (.2)........ .5
*Corv.-add (.3)........ .3
w/eng Code Y add (.1)........ .1

COMPRESSOR 4 CYLINDER RADIAL

(G) Compressor Assembly, Renew
Includes: Transfer all attaching parts. Evacuate and charge system.
Chevrolet
1983-87 (.9)........ 2.0
Corvette
1984-87 (1.4)........ 2.7

(G) Clutch Hub and Drive Plate, Renew
Does not include R&R compressor.
1983-87 (.3)........ .8

(G) Rotor and/or Bearings, Renew
1983-87 (.6)........ 1.2

(G) Compressor Pulley and/or Clutch Coil, Renew
1983-87 (.5)........ 1.0
Renew pulley or brg add........ .2

(G) Compressor Shaft Seal Kit, Renew
Includes: Evacuate and charge system.
1983-87 (1.2)........ 2.5

(G) Front Bearing, Head, or Seals, Renew
Includes: R&R compressor, R&R clutch and pulley assy. R&R shaft seal assy. Clean and inspect parts. Evacuate and charge system.
1983-87 (1.7)........ 2.8

(G) Outer Shell and/or 'O' Rings, Renew
Includes: R&R compressor, R&R clutch and pulley assy. Clean and inspect parts. Evacuate and charge system.
1983-87 (1.9)........ 2.8

(G) Valve Plate Assembly, Renew
Includes: R&R compressor, R&R clutch and pulley assy. R&R shell to internal mechanism. Clean and inspect parts. Evacuate and charge system.
1983-87 (2.0)........ 2.6
Renew two or more valves add (.1)... .2

AIR CONDITIONER TUNE-UP

For efficient operation and satisfactory performance in hot weather. The following air conditioner tune-up is suggested:

1. Clean intake filter
2. Clean condenser fins
3. Pressure test system
4. Adjust drive belt tension
5. Check antifreeze/coolant
6. Tighten compressor mounts
7. Tighten condenser and evaporator mounts
8. Inspect system for leaks (hoses, couplings, valves, etc.)
9. Partial charge system

All models 1.0
If necessary to evacuate and charge system, add 1.0

(Factory Time) Chilton Time

(G) Cylinder and Shaft Assy., Renew
Includes: R&R comp assy. Transfer clutch hub and drive plate, rotor, coil and switches. Renew seal kit. Install front head, outer shell and valve plates. Evacuate and charge system.
1983-87 (2.1)........ 2.9

(G) Compressor Relief Valve, Renew
Includes: Evacuate and charge system.
1983-87 (.9)........ 1.4

(G) Condenser, Renew
Includes: Evacuate and charge system.
Chevrolet
1983-87-Gas (.9)........ 1.7
Diesel (1.5)........ 2.5
Corvette
1984-87 (1.3)........ 2.5

(G) Evaporator Core, Renew
Includes: Evacuate and charge system.
Chevrolet
1983-87 (1.5)........ 3.5
Corvette
1984-87 (2.1)........ 4.9

(G) Accumulator Assembly, Renew
Includes: Evacuate and charge system.
Chevrolet
1983-87 (.7)........ 1.5
Corvette
1984-87 (.8)........ 1.5

(G) Expansion Tube Assembly, Renew
Includes: Evacuate and charge system.
1983-87 (.9)........ 1.4

(G) Temperature Control Head, Renew
Chevrolet
1983-87 (.7)........ .9

(Factory Time) Chilton Time

Corvette
1984-87 (.6)........ 1.0
Touch Control (.4)........ .6

(G) Temperature Control Cable, Renew
Chevrolet
1983-87 (.6)........ .7
Corvette
1984-87 (.8)........ 1.2

(G) Master Electrical Switch, Renew
1983-84-Chev. (.3)........ .6
Corv. (.5)........ .8
1985-87 (.6)........ .9

(G) Vacuum Selector Valve, Renew
1983-87 (.6)........ .7

(G) Vacuum Door Control Actuators, Renew
Chevrolet
Defroster door
1983-87 (.4)........ 1.0
Heat-A/C mode door
1983-87 (2.3)........ 3.0
Outside recirculation door
1983-87 (.3)........ .7
Corvette
Defroster door
1984-87 (1.9)........ 3.0
Heat-A/C mode door
1984-87 (7.2)........ 10.0
Air Inlet (Recirculation)
1984-87 (.6)........ 1.0

(G) Blower Motor, Renew
Chevrolet
1983-87 (.3)........ .5
Corvette
1984-87 (.5)........ .8

(G) Blower Motor Switch, Renew
Chevrolet
1983-87 (.6)........ .7
Corvette
1984-87 (.6)........ .9

(G) Blower Motor Resistor, Renew
1983-87 (.2)........ .3

(G) Blower Motor Relay, Renew
1983-87 (.2)........ .3

(G) Air Conditioning Hoses, Renew
Includes: Evacuate and charge system.
Chevrolet
1983-87-one (1.1)........ 1.7
each adtnl (.3)........ .5
Corvette
1984-87
Liquid line (.8)........ 1.7
Evap to accum (1.0)........ 1.9
suction & discharge (.8)........ 1.7

AUTOMATIC TEMPERATURE CONTROL

(G) A.C. Programmer, R&R or Renew
1984-87-Corv. (.3)........ .5

(G) In-Car Sensor, Renew
1984-87-Corv. (.3)........ .5

(G) Electric Actuators, Renew
1984-87-Corv.
Temp Door (.5)........ .8

PARTS 28 AIR CONDITIONING 28 PARTS

	Part No.	Price
Compressor Assembly		
(Chevrolet)		
1983-84	◆12300273	390.00
1985-exc. below	◆12321365	N.L.
1985-262	◆12322349	N.L.
1986-87	◆12326201	N.L.
(Corvette)		
1984	12309211	390.00
1985-87	12322324	N.L.
Clutch Hub and Drive Plate		
1983-87-exc. below	◆6551220	32.50
1985-87-262	◆6551838	36.00
1984-87 Corvette	◆6551838	36.00
Rotor and Bearing Assy.		
1983-87	◆6551216	67.50
Compressor Pulley		
1983-87-exc. below	◆6556715	13.00
1984-Corvette	6551719	97.50
1985-87-Corvette	6551971	120.75
Compressor Clutch Coil		
1983-87-exc. below	◆6551217	44.00
1985-87-262, Diesel	◆6551997	47.25
1984-Corvette	◆6551834	41.50
1985-87-Corvette	◆6551997	47.25
Compressor Shaft Seal Kit		
1983-84	◆9956695	13.00
1985-87	◆2724319	11.25
Front Head Main Bearing		
1983-87	◆6556572	4.00
Compressor Front Head		
1983-87-exc. below	◆6551142	28.25
1984-87 Corvette	◆6551835	41.25
Compressor Outer Shell		
1983-87	◆2724158	38.00
Rear Discharge Valve Plate w/Valves		
1983-87	◆6551141	11.50
Cylinder and Shaft Assy.		
1983-87-exc. below	◆2724144	269.00
1984-Corvette	◆2724060	275.00
Compressor Pressure Relief Valve		
1983-87	◆5914435	13.50
Condenser		
(Chevrolet)		
1983-87-exc. diesel & 307Y	◆3037439	158.25
Diesel	◆3037438	156.50
1986-87-307Y	◆3037438	N.L.
(Corvette)		
1984-87	3050981	168.00
Evaporator Core Assembly		
(Chevrolet)		
1983-84	◆3035240	218.25
1985-87	◆3058130	261.75
(Corvette)		
1984	3052790	247.50
1985-87	3057733	287.00
Accumulator Dehydrator		
(Chevrolet)		
1983	◆2724275	80.25
1984-87	◆2724275	80.25
(Corvette)		
1984-87	2724288	75.50
Blower Motor Relay		
(wo/Auto temp control)		
1983-87-exc. below	◆10018449	N.L.
1984-87 Corvette	◆10019535	7.50
Blower Switch		
(Corvette)		
1984-87	16022463	6.50
(Chevrolet)		
1983	◆16015256	6.00
1984	◆16032480	7.50
1985-87	◆16015450	6.75
Evaporator Blower Motor		
1983-87-exc. below	◆22020945	60.00
1984-87 Corvette	22029164	58.00

LABOR 29 LOCKS, HINGES & WIND. REGULATORS 29 LABOR

(Factory Time)	Chilton Time
(G) Hood Latch, Renew	
Chevrolet	
1983-87 (.2)	.3
Corvette	
1984-87-(.3)	.4
(G) Hood Hinge, Renew (One)	
1983-Chev. (.3)	.4
Corv. (.3)	.5
1984-87-Chev. (.3)	.4
Corv. (.5)	.7
(G) Hood Release Cable, Renew	
1983 (.4)	.6
1984-87-Chev. (.4)	.6
Corv. (.6)	1.0
(G) Door Lock, Renew	
Chevrolet	
Front	
1983-87 (.5)	.8
w/Electric lock add (.1)	.1
Rear	
1983-87 (.8)	1.2
Corvette	
1984-87 (1.0)	1.5
(G) Door Lock Remote Control, Renew	
1983 (.4)	.7
1984-87-Chev. (.4)	.7
Corv. (.7)	1.0
(G) Door Lock Cylinder, Renew	
1983-Chev. (.4)	.6
Corv. (.8)	1.1
1984-87-Chev. (.4)	.6
Corv. (1.2)	1.7
Recode cyl add (.3)	.3
(G) Door Handle (Outside), Renew (Front or Rear)	
1983-Chev. (.4)	.7
Corv. (.6)	.9
1984-87-Chev. (.4)	.6
Corv. (1.2)	1.5
Renew insert add	.1
(G) Lock Striker Plate, Renew	
1983-87 (.2)	.3
(G) Door Window Regulator (Manual), Renew	
Chevrolet	
1983-87 (.8)	1.2
(G) Door Window Regulator (Electric), Renew	
Includes: Transfer motor.	
1983-Chev. (1.0)	1.4
Corv. (1.1)	1.5
1984-87-Chev. (1.0)	1.4
Corv. (1.5)	2.0
(G) Trunk Lock and Cylinder, Renew	
1983-87 (.2)	.3
Recode cyl add (.3)	.3
(G) Trunk Hinge or Strap, Renew (One)	
1983-87-Chev. (.8)	1.2
Corv.	
lid side (.9)	1.3
body side-each (.6)	.9
(G) Tailgate Lock Cylinder, Renew	
1983-87 (.3)	.5
Recode cyl add	.3
(G) Tailgate Handle (Outer), Renew	
1983-87 (.3)	.5
(G) Tailgate Hinge, Renew	
1983-87-lower (.7)	1.1
upper (.3)	.7
(G) Tailgate Window Regulator, Renew	
1983-87 (.7)	1.3

PARTS 29 LOCKS, HINGES & WIND. REGULATORS 29 PARTS

	Part No.	Price
Hood Lock (Upper Plate Assy.)		
(Chevrolet)		
1983-87	◆14070703	16.25
(Corvette)		
1984-87-right	14043006	5.75
left	14043005	5.75
Hood Catch		
(Chevrolet)		
1983-87	14032197	6.50
Hood Hinge		
(Chevrolet)		
1983-87-right	◆14015976	29.00
left	◆14015975	29.00

PARTS 29 LOCKS, HINGES & WIND. REGULATORS 29 PARTS

	Part No.	Price
(Corvette)		
1984-right	14043012	16.50
left	14043011	16.50
1985-87-right	14089640	17.50
left	14089639	17.50
Front Door Lock (Left Side)		
(Chevrolet)		
1983-87-2 dr.	◆20293613	33.50
4 dr.	◆20293605	51.50
(Corvette)		
1984	◆20298853	38.50
1985-87	◆20594023	N.L.
Rear Door Lock (Left Side)		
1983-87	◆20293625	55.75
Door Lock Cylinder Unit		
(Chevrolet)		
1983-87	◆9632769	7.75
(Corvette)		
1984-87	14075360	6.50
Trunk Lid Lock		
(Chevrolet)		
(wo/Station wagon)		
1983-87	◆20279741	N.L.
(Station wagon)		
1983-upper	◆20452016	72.50
lower	◆20452014	137.00
1984-87-upper	◆20452016	72.50
lower	◆20452014	137.00
Trunk Lock Cylinder & Keys		
(Chevrolet)		
(wo/Station wagon)		
1983-87	◆3910570	6.25
(Station wagon)		
1983-87	◆9632769	7.75
Door Handle Outside, Front & Rear (R.H.)		
(Chevrolet)		
1983-87	◆20111712	26.50
(Corvette)		
1984-87	14075358	15.50
Trunk Lid Hinge Strap (R.H.)		
(Chevrolet)		
1983	◆20287998	24.50
1984-87	◆20434734	13.50
Front Window Regulator (Manual) - Left		
(Chevrolet)		
(2 door)		
1983-87	◆20303587	102.00
(4 door)		
1983-87	◆20110653	102.00
Rear Window Regulator (Manual) - Left		
1983-87	◆20147473	88.25
Front Window Regulator (Electric) - Left		
(Chevrolet)		
(2 door)		
1983-87	◆20303591	108.00
(4 door)		
1983-87	◆20192897	114.00
(Corvette)		
1984-87	14046661	118.00
Rear Window Regulator (Electric) - Left		
1983-87	◆20192895	114.00
Door Window Regulator Motor		
(Chevrolet)		
1983-87	◆22020900	N.L.
(Corvette)		
1984-87	22039707	80.00

LABOR 30 HEAD AND PARKING LAMPS 30 LABOR

(Factory Time)	Chilton Time
(G) Aim Headlamps	
two	.4
four	.6
(M) Headlamp Sealed Beam Bulb, Renew	
1983-87 (.3)	.3
(G) Headlamp Motor or Actuator, Renew	
1984-87-one side (.8)	1.2
(M) Tail and Stop Light Lamp Lens, Renew	
1983-87-exc below (.7)	1.0
sta wag (.2)	.3
(M) License Lamp Assembly, Renew	
1983-87 (.2)	.3
(M) Side Marker Lamp Assy., Renew	
1983-87 (.2)	.3
(M) High Level Stop Lamp Assy., Renew	
1986-87-Chev. (.3)	.5
Corv. (.5)	.7
(M) High Level Stop Lamp Bulb, Renew	
All models (.3)	.4

PARTS 30 HEAD & PARKING LAMPS 30 PARTS

	Part No.	Price
Sealed Beam Bulb		
(Chevrolet)		
(wo/Quartz)		
1983-87-inner	◆5966201	15.00
outer	◆5966200	15.00
(Quartz)		
1983-87-inner	◆5930567	22.50
outer	◆16502327	22.50
(Corvette)		
1984-87	◆5972698	46.50
Parking Lamp Assy.		
(Chevrolet)		
1983-87-right	◆914550	23.50
left	914549	23.50
(Corvette)		
1984-87-right	16500702	72.00
left	16500701	72.00
Cornering Lamp Assy.		
(Chevrolet)		
1983-87-right	◆914554	25.50
left	◆914553	25.50
(Corvette)		
1984-87-right	917886	29.50
left	917885	29.50
Tail Lamp Assy.		
(Chevrolet Impala)		
(wo/Sta. wagon)		
1983-87-right	◆5971188	53.50
left	5971187	53.50
(Chevrolet Caprice)		
(wo/Sta. wagon)		
1983-87-right	5971604	64.00
left	5971603	64.00
(Sta. wag.)		
1983-87-right	5931038	50.50
left	5931037	50.50
(Corvette)		
1984-87	915787	25.50
High Mount Stoplight		
1986-87	◆5974457	36.00
Sta. wag.	◆918456	39.50
License Plate Lamp Assy.		
(Chevrolet-exc. Sta. wag.)		
1983-87	◆914000	3.75
(Chevrolet Station wagon)		
1983-87	◆912795	7.50
(Corvette)		
1983-87	◆912116	6.50

LABOR 31 WINDSHIELD WIPER & SPEEDOMETER 31 LABOR

(Factory Time) Chilton Time

(G) Windshield Wiper Motor, Renew
1983-87-Chev. (.3) .5
Corv. (.6) 1.0

(G) Windshield Wiper Motor, R&R and Recondition
Chevrolet
1983-87 (.8) 1.5
Corvette
1983-87 (.8) 1.6

(G) Wiper Transmission, Renew (One)
Chevrolet
1983-87 (.4) .7
Corvette
1984-87-one side (.4) .7

(G) Windshield Wiper Switch, Renew
Chevrolet
1983-84 (.3) .4
1985 (1.0) 1.4
1986-87
std colm (1.2) 1.6
tilt colm (1.0) 1.4
Corvette
1984-87
dash mount (.4) .7

(G) Windshield Washer Pump, Renew
Chevrolet
1983-87 (.2) .4
Corvette
1984-85 (.9) 1.4
1986-87 (.6) 1.0

(G) Windshield Washer Pump, R&R and Recondition
Chevrolet
1983-87 (.5) .7

(G) Windshield Washer Pump Valve, Renew
1983-87 (.2) .4

(G) Instrument Panel Cluster Assy., R&R or Renew
Corvette
1984-87 (1.4) 2.5

(G) Speedometer Signal Generator, Renew
Corvette
1984-87 (.5) .9

(G) Odometer and/or Motor, Renew
Corvette
1984-87 (1.2) 1.5

(G) Speedometer Head, R&R or Renew
Chevrolet
1983-84 (.3) .5
1985-87 (.7) 1.2
Reset odometer add .2

(G) Speedometer Cable and Casing, Renew
Chevrolet
1983-87-upper (.5) .8
lower (.4) .7
one piece (.7) 1.1

(G) Speedometer Cable (Inner), Renew or Lubricate
Chevrolet
1983-87-upper (.3) .6
lower (.3) .6
one piece (.7) 1.1

(G) Radio, R&R
Chevrolet
1983-84 (.4) .8
1985-87 (.8) 1.2
Corvette
1983-87 (.6) 1.0

PARTS 31 WINDSHIELD WIPER & SPEEDOMETER 31 PARTS

	Part No.	Price
Wiper Motor		
(Chevrolet)		
1983-87-exc		
Pulse	◆4960974	84.00
Pulse wiper	◆4961608	80.00
(Corvette)		
1984-87	22038790	178.75
Wiper Transmission		
(Chevrolet)		
1983-87-right	◆22010448	17.00
left	◆22010449	18.50
(Corvette)		
1984-87-right	22038692	32.50
left	22038693	36.00
Wiper Switch		
(Chevrolet)		
(wo/Pulse wiper)		
1983	◆1994232	26.50
1984-87	◆7835342	22.50
(Pulse wiper)		
1983	◆14029586	27.25
1984-87-exc.		
below	◆7835340	56.25
w/tilt wheel	◆7837280	53.50
(Corvette)		
1984	14047170	29.25
1985-87	14080668	30.50

Speedometer Head & Cable Assy.
Order by year and model.

LABOR 32 LIGHT SWITCHES & WIRING 32 LABOR

(Factory Time) Chilton Time

(G) Headlamp Switch, Renew
1983-87-Chev. (.4) .5
Corv. (.7) .9

(G) Headlamp Dimmer Switch, Renew
1983-87-Chev. (.5) .7
Corv. (.6) 1.0

(G) Stop Light Switch, Renew
1983-87-Chev. (.3) .4
Corv. (.3) .5

(G) Back-Up Lamp and Park/Neutral Switch, Renew
1983-87 (.3) .4

(G) Parking Brake Lamp Switch, Renew
1983 (.2) .4
1984-87-Chev. (.2) .4
Corv. (.4) .6

(G) Back-Up Lamp Switch, Renew
1983-Chev. (.3) .4
Corv. (.6) .9
1984-87-Corv. (.3) .4

(G) Turn Signal or Hazard Warning Switch, Renew
1983-85-exc below (.7) 1.1
w/Tilt wheel (.9) 1.2
w/Tilt-Tel (1.2) 1.5
1986-87-Chev.
std colm (.6) 1.1
tilt colm (.7) 1.2
Corv. (.9) 1.5

(M) Turn Signal or Hazard Warning Flasher, Renew
1983 (.2) .2
1984-87
Chev. (.2) .2
Corv.
turn signal (.4) .6
hazard warning (.5) .7

(G) Horns, Renew
1983-87-each (.3) .3

(G) Horn Relay, Renew
1983 (.2) .3
1984-87-Chev. (.2) .3
Corv. (.5) .7

PARTS 32 LIGHT SWITCHES & WIRING 32 PARTS

	Part No.	Price
Headlamp Switch		
(Chevrolet)		
1983-84	◆1995217	16.00
1985-87	1995248	16.00
(Corvette)		
1984-87	1995257	24.00
Headlamp Dimmer Switch		
(Chevrolet)		
1983-87	◆7838234	12.50

PARTS 32 LIGHT SWITCHES & WIRING 32 PARTS

	Part No.	Price
(Corvette)		
1983-87	◆7832411	18.50
Stoplight Switch		
(Chevrolet)		
(wo/Cruise control)		
1983-84	◆25504628	3.75
1985-87	◆25524846	6.50
(Cruise control)		
1983-84	◆9794682	7.75
1985-87	◆25524847	6.50
(Corvette)		
(wo/Cruise control)		
1984-M.T.	◆1362835	3.00
A.T.	◆25504628	3.75
1985-87-M.T.	◆25524844	3.00
A.T.	◆25524846	6.50
(Cruise control)		
1983-84	◆9794682	7.75
1985-87	◆25524847	6.50
Turn Signal Flasher		
1983-84	◆10029240	4.25
1985-87	◆10041073	4.25
Hazard Lamp Flasher		
1983-87	◆6450089	3.00
Turn Signal Switch		
(Chevrolet)		
1983-87-exc below	◆1997983	30.00
Corn lamps	◆1997984	35.00
(Corvette)		
1983-87	◆1997984	35.00
Back-Up Lamp Switch		
(Chevrolet)		
1983-87	◆22509632	5.50
(Corvette)		
(M.T.)		
1984-87	1994242	16.75
(A.T.)		
1984-87	1994242	16.75
Horn		
(Chevrolet)		
1983-87-Note A	◆1892164	22.00
Note C	◆1892246	27.50
Note D	◆1892162	23.50
Note F	◆1892163	22.00
(Corvette)		
1984-87-Note A	1999729	22.00
Note C	1999730	22.00
Horn Relay		
1983-87	◆25513270	8.50

LABOR 33 GLASS 33 LABOR

	(Factory Time)	Chilton Time
(G) Windshield Glass, Renew		
Chevrolet		
1983-87	(1.3)	1.8
Corvette		
1984-87	(2.4)	3.3
Renew caulk bead add	(.4)	.4
(G) Front Door Glass, Renew		
Chevrolet		
1983-87	(.9)	1.2
Corvette		
1983-87	(.9)	1.5
(G) Rear Door Glass, Renew		
1983-87	(.8)	1.1
(G) Rear Door Vent Glass, Renew		
1983-87	(.7)	1.1
(G) Quarter Window Stationary Glass, Renew		
1983-87-htp	(.8)	1.2
sta wag	(1.0)	1.5
(G) Tail Gate Glass, Renew		
1983-87	(.6)	1.0
(G) Rear Window Glass, Renew		
Chevrolet		
1983-87	(1.3)	2.0
w/3/4 plug unpadded, add	(1.3)	2.0
w/3/4 plug padded, add	(2.6)	4.0
w/Elec defogger add	(.6)	.6
Corvette		
1983	(.9)	1.9
1984-87	(.5)	.9
w/Elec grid defogger add	(.2)	.3

LABOR 34 CRUISE CONTROL 34 LABOR

	(Factory Time)	Chilton Time
(G) Regulator Assembly (Transducer), Renew or Adjust		
1983	(.4)	.7
(G) Engagement Switch, Renew		
1983	(.4)	.6
1984-85-Chev.	(.4)	.9
Corv.	(.6)	1.0
1986-87-Chev.	(.4)	.9
Corv.	(1.3)	1.7
(G) Brake or Clutch Release Switch, Renew		
1983-85	(.3)	.4
1986-87-Chev.	(.5)	.7
Corv.	(1.1)	1.5
(G) Vacuum Servo, Renew		
1983-85	(.3)	.5
1986-87-Chev.	(.3)	.5
Corv.	(1.1)	1.5
Renew bracket add	(.1)	.2
(G) Vacuum Hoses, Renew		
1983-87	(.2)	.3
(G) Chain or Cable, Servo to Carburetor, Renew		
1983-87	(.3)	.4
(G) Cruise Control Vacuum Regulator Valve, Renew (w/Diesel engine)		
1983-84	(.2)	.3
(G) Cruise Control Resume Solenoid, Renew		
1983	(.2)	.3
(G) Cruise Control Power Unit Solenoid, Renew		
1984-Corv.	(.3)	.4
(G) Cruise Control Module, Renew		
1984-87	(.3)	.5
(G) Cruise Control Speed Sensor, Renew		
1984	(.6)	.8
(G) Cruise Control Check Valve, Renew		
1984-87	(.3)	.4

	Part No.	Price
CRUISE CONTROL–PARTS		
Cruise Control Transducer Assy.		
(Chevrolet)		
(exc. Diesel)		
1983	◆25030878	158.00
(Diesel)		
1983	◆25031683	169.50
(Corvette)		
Cruise Control Engagement Switch		
1983-84	◆9794682	8.00
1985-87	◆25524847	6.50
Cruise Control Vacuum Servo		
(Chevrolet)		
(exc. V-6-231 & Diesel)		
1983	◆25030983	19.50
1984-87	◆25074628	133.50
(V-6-231)		
1983	◆25030527	20.50
1984-87	◆25074630	116.25
(Diesel)		
1983-exc. below	◆25030980	32.75
w/THM 2004R	◆25031726	33.75
1984-85	◆25074629	123.50
(Corvette)		
1984	25074659	127.75
1985-87	25074811	140.00
Cruise Control Chain		
1983-87	◆25031314	3.25
Vacuum Regulator (Diesel)		
1983	6466910	13.50
Cruise Control Module		
1984-85-231	◆25031964	115.00
229, 262, 305	◆25031953	116.00
Diesel	◆25031948	116.00
1986-87		
262	◆25074704	102.00
305	◆25074710	102.00
307Y	25074716	102.00
Vacuum Release Valve		
1983-84	◆25509432	14.00
1985-87	◆25523376	14.00

GROUP INDEX

ALPHABETICAL INDEX

General Motors

Rear Wheel Drive Cars

CHEVROLET MONTE CARLO • MALIBU

YEAR IDENTIFICATION

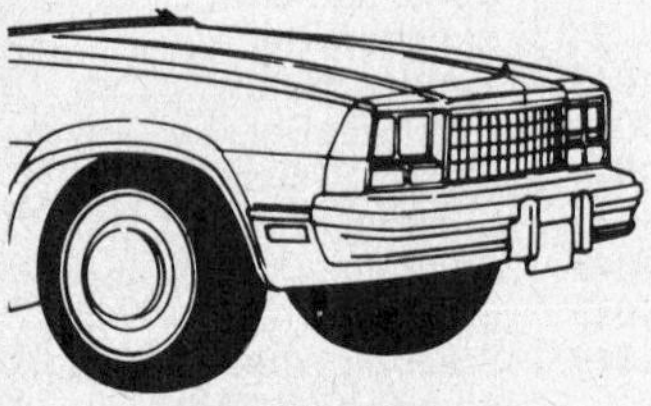

1983 Malibu

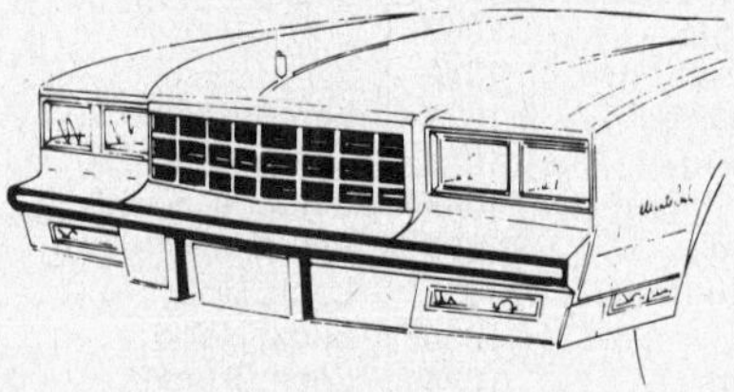

1983–86 Monte Carlo

1984–87 Monte Carlo SS

VEHICLE IDENTIFICATION NUMBER (VIN)
All Except Corvette

It is important for servicing and ordering parts to be certain of the vehicle and engine identification. The VIN (vehicle identification number) is a 13 or 17 digit number visible through the windshield on the driver's side of the dash and contains the vehicle and engine identification codes. It can be interpreted as follows:

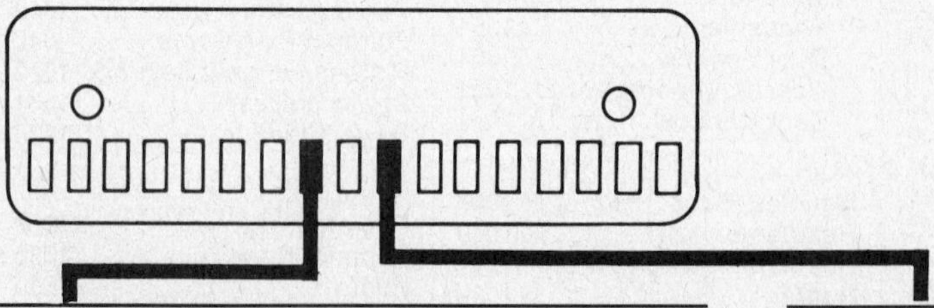

Engine Code

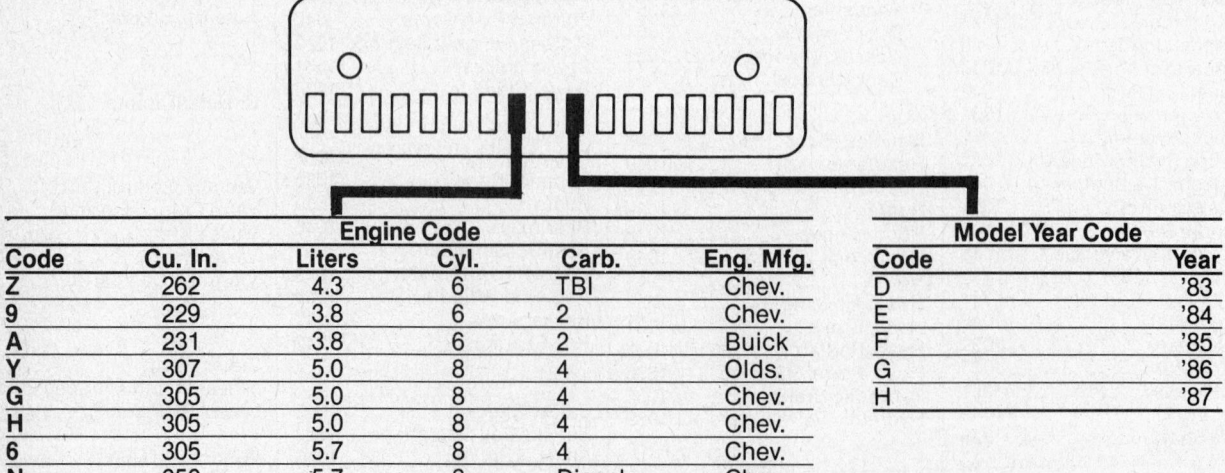

Code	Cu. In.	Liters	Cyl.	Carb.	Eng. Mfg.
Z	262	4.3	6	TBI	Chev.
9	229	3.8	6	2	Chev.
A	231	3.8	6	2	Buick
Y	307	5.0	8	4	Olds.
G	305	5.0	8	4	Chev.
H	305	5.0	8	4	Chev.
6	305	5.7	8	4	Chev.
N	350	5.7	8	Diesel	Chev.

Model Year Code

Code	Year
D	'83
E	'84
F	'85
G	'86
H	'87

TUNE-UP SPECIFICATIONS
All Except Corvette

Year	Engine: Eng. VIN Code	Engine: No. Cyl. Displacement	Engine: Eng. Mfg.	Spark Plugs: Orig. Type	Spark Plugs: Gap. (in.)	Distributor	Ignition Timing (deg)▲ Auto. Trans.	Valves Intake Opens ▪(deg)	Fuel Pump Pressure (psi)	Idle Speed (rpm)▲ Auto. Trans.
'83	9	6-229	Chev.	R-45TS	.045	Electronic	0B ①	42	4.5–6.0	475/850
	A	6-231	Buick	R-45TS	.045	Electronic	15B ①	16	4.25–5.75	450/900
	H	8-305	Chev.	R-45TS	.045	Electronic	6B ①	44	5.5–7.0	500/650
	N	8-350	Olds.	—	—	—	4A ①	16	5.5–6.5	600/750
	V	6-263	Olds	—	—	—	①	16	5.5–6.5	①
'84	9	6-229	Chev.	R-45TS	.045	Electronic	0B ①	42	4.5–6.0	475
	A	6-231	Buick	R-45TS8	.060	Electronic	15B ①	16	4.25–5.75	600/700
	H	8-305	Chev.	R-45TS	.045	Electronic	6B ①	44	5.5–7.0	500/650
	N	8-350	Olds.	—	—	—	4A ①	16	5.5–6.5	600/750
	G	8-305	Chev.	R-45TS	.045	Electronic	6B ①	44	5.5–7.0	①
'85	Z	V6-262	Chev.	R-43CTS	.035	Electronic	6B ①	16	5.5–6.5	450/900
	G	8-305	Chev.	R-45TS	.045	Electronic	6B ①	44	5.5–7.0	500/650
	H	8-305	Chev.	R-45TS	.045	Electronic	6B ①	44	5.5–7.0	500/650
	6	8-350	Chev.	R-45TS	.045	Electronic	6B ①	16	5.5–6.5	475
	N	8-350	Olds.	—	—	—	4A ①	16	5.5–6.5	600/750
'86–'87	Z	V6-262	Chev.	R-43CTS ③	.035	Electronic	6B ①	16	5.5–6.5	450/900
	G	8-305	Chev.	R-45TS ②	.045 ②	Electronic	6B ①	44	5.5–7.0	500/650
	H	8-305	Chev.	R-45TS ②	.045 ②	Electronic	6B ①	44	5.5–7.0	500/650
	6	8-350	Chev.	R-45TS	.045	Electronic	6B ①	16	5.5–6.5	475
	Y	8-307	Olds.	FR3LS6	.060	Electronic	①	—	6.0–7.5	①

NOTE: The underhood specifications sticker often reflects tune-up specification changes made in production. Sticker figures must be used if they disagree with those in this chart.

▲ See text for procedure
▪ All figures Before Top Dead Center
B Before Top Dead Center
TDC Top Dead Center
—Not applicable
Part numbers in this chart are not recommendations by Chilton for any product by brand name.
① See underhood specifications sticker
② '86 Caprice: R-44TS—.035 gaP
③ '86 Monte Carlo: R-43TS—.035 gaP

FIRING ORDERS

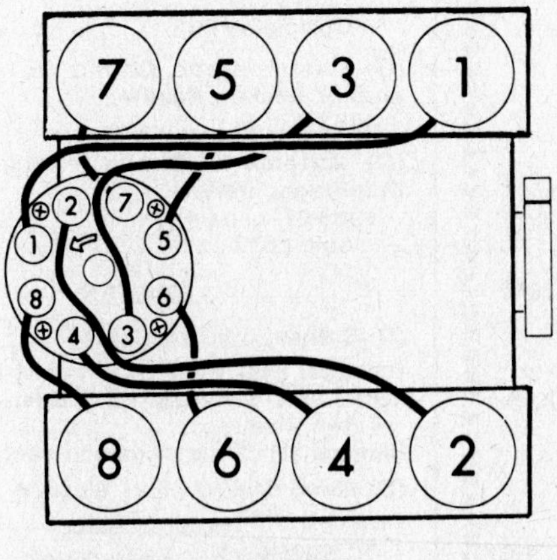

GM (Oldsmobile) 307
Engine firing order: 1–8–4–3–6–5–7–2
Distributor rotation: counterclockwise

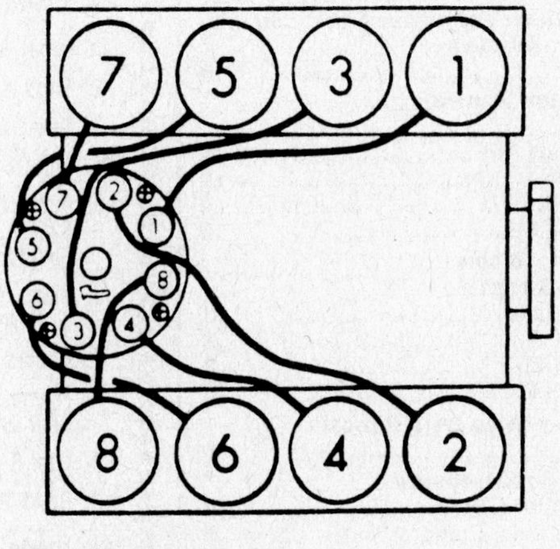

GM (Chevrolet) V8
Engine firing order: 1–8–4–3–6–5–7–2
Distributor rotation: clockwise

FIRING ORDERS

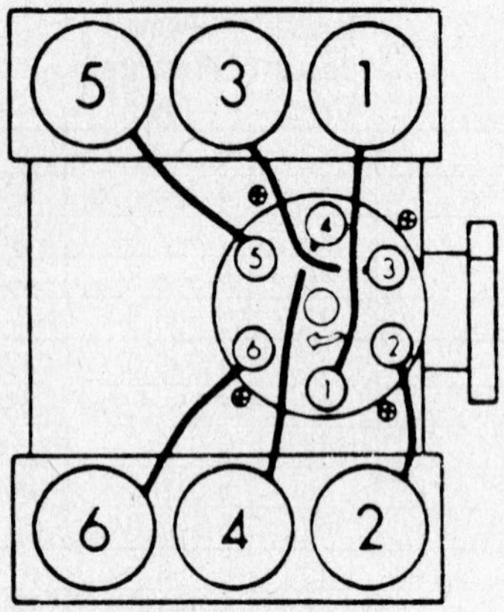

GM (Buick) 231 V6
Engine firing order: 1–6–5–4–3–2
Distributor rotation: clockwise

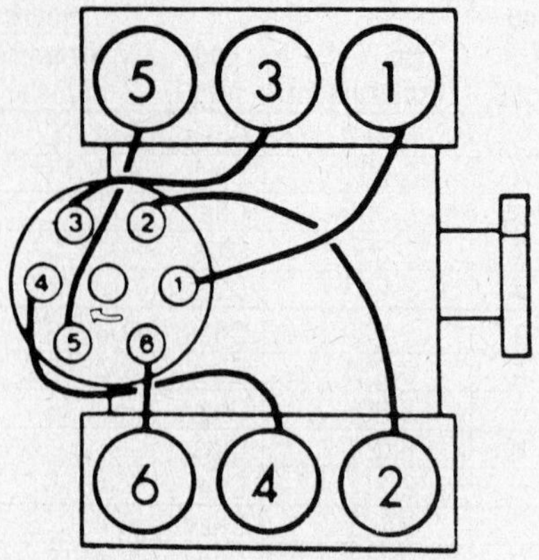

Chevrolet-built V6 engine
Engine firing order: 1–6–5–4–3–2
Distributor rotation: clockwise

WHEEL ALIGNMENT SPECIFICATIONS
Malibu, Monte Carlo

Year	Model	Caster Range (deg)	Caster Pref. Setting (deg)	Camber Range (deg)	Camber Pref. Setting (deg)	Toe-In (in.)	Steering Axis (deg) Inclination
'83-'87	Monte Carlo, Manual Steer.	0 to 2P	1P	3/10N to 1 3/10P	1/2P	1/16 to 1/4	7 7/8
	Monte Carlo, Pow. Steer.	2P to 4P	3P	3/10N to 1 3/10P	1/2P	1/16 to 1/4	7 7/8

N Negative P Positive

LABOR SERVICE BAY OPERATIONS LABOR

(Factory Time) Chilton Time

COOLING

(M) Winterize Cooling System
Includes: Run engine to check for leaks, tighten all hose connections. Test radiator and pressure cap, drain radiator and engine block. Add anti-freeze and refill system.
All models 5

(M) Thermostat, Renew
V-6–1983-87
200-229 engs (.5) 6
231 eng (.7) 8
262 Eng (.7) 9
V-8–1983-87 (.5) 6

(M) Drive Belt, Renew
1983-87-V-6 engs
200-229 engs (.2) 3
231 eng (.5) 7
262 Eng (.2) 3
V-8 engs (.2) 3

(M) Serpentine Drive Belt, Renew
1983 (.2) 4

(M) Radiator Hoses, Renew
1983-87-upper (.3) 4
lower (.4) 5
both (.5) 7

FUEL

(M) Carburetor Air Cleaner, Service
All models (.2) 3

CHILTON'S 10 POINT SAFETY CHECK

CHECK OPERATION & CONDITION OF THE FOLLOWING ITEMS:

1. Legal Registration (serial no.)
2. Tires & Wheels
3. Brake System (R&R all wheels)
4. Light Systems & Signals
5. Accelerator Linkage, Neutral Safety Switch, Shift Indicator Pointer & Seat Position Locks
6. Glass, Mirrors, Door Locks, Seat Belts & Harness
7. Wipers, Washers & Defrosters
8. Frame, Steering, Shocks, Front & Rear Suspension
9. Fuel & Exhaust Systems
10. Road Test Vehicle

All models 1.0
Exhaust Smog Analysis, add 4

(Factory Time) Chilton Time

(G) Carburetor, Adjust (On Car)
1983-87
Slow & Fast Idle (.3) 4
Vacuum Brake-one (.4) 6
both (.6) 8
Choke (.6) 1.0
Complete (1.3) 1.8

(G) Thermostatic Choke Cover and/or Gasket, Renew
1983-87 (.6) 1.0

(G) Automatic Choke Vacuum Diaphragm, Renew
1983-87-one (.4) 6
both (.6) 8

BRAKES

(G) Brakes, Adjust (Minor)
Includes: R&R wheels and adjust brakes thru access holes in drums. Fill master cylinder.
two wheels 4
Remove knock out plugs add-each.... .1

(G) Bleed Brakes (Four Wheels)
Includes: Fill master cylinder.
All models (.4) 5

(G) Brake Pedal Free Play, Adjust
All models (.2) 3

(M) Parking Brake, Adjust
All models (.3) 4

LABOR — SERVICE BAY OPERATIONS — LABOR

(Factory Time) Chilton Time

LUBRICATION SERVICE

(M) Lubricate Chassis, Change Oil & Filter
Includes: Inspect and correct all fluid levels.
All models 6
Install grease fittings add 1

(M) Lubricate Chassis
Includes: Inspect and correct all fluid levels.
All models 4
Install grease fittings add 1

(M) Engine Oil & Filter, Change
Includes: Inspect and correct all fluid levels.
All models 4

WHEELS

(M) Wheel, Renew
one (.3) 5

(G) Wheels, Balance
one 3
each adtnl 2

(M) Wheels, Rotate (All)
All models 5

(G) Front Wheel Bearings, Clean and Repack (Both Wheels)
All models (1.1) 1.6

(G) Front Wheel Grease Seals, Renew
All models
one wheel (.7) 8
both wheels (1.1) 1.2

ELECTRICAL

(M) Battery Cables, Renew
1983-87-positive
V-6 (.4) 4
V-8 (.4) 4
negative (.2) 3
batt to batt (.2) 3

(M) Battery Terminals, Clean
All models 3

(G) Aim Headlamps
two 4
four 6

(M) Headlamp Sealed Beam Bulb, Renew
All models (.2) 3

(G) Headlamp Switch, Renew
1983-87 (.4) 5

(G) Headlamp Dimmer Switch, Renew
1983-87 (.5) 7

(G) Stop Light Switch, Renew
1983-87 (.3) 4

(G) Turn Signal and Hazard Warning Switch, Renew
1983-85 (.7) 1.1
1986-87
std colm (.7) 1.1
tilt colm (.8) 1.2

(G) Back-Up Lamp and Park/Neutral Switch, Renew
1983-87 (.3) 5

(M) Turn Signal or Hazard Warning Flasher, Renew
1983-87 (.3) 3

(G) Horn, Renew
1983-87 (.3) 3

(G) Horn Relay, Renew
1983-87 (.3) 3

(M) Back-Up Lamp Assembly, Renew
1983-85-each (.3) 4

(M) Cornering Lamp Assembly, Renew
1983-87-each (.3) 4

(M) Park and Turn Signal Lamp Assy., Renew
1983-87-each (.3) 4

(M) Stop, Tail and Turn Signal Lamp Assy., Renew
1983-85-each (.3) 4

LABOR — 1 TUNE UP 1 — LABOR

(Factory Time) Chilton Time

(G) Compression Test
V-6–1983-87 (.5) 7
V-8–1983-87 (.8) 8
w/A.C. add 3

(G) Engine Tune Up, (Electronic Ignition)
Includes: Test battery and clean connections. Tighten manifold and carburetor mounting bolts. Check engine compression, clean and adjust or renew spark plugs. Test resistance of spark plug cables. Inspect distributor cap and rotor. Adjust air gap. Check vacuum advance operation. Reset ignition timing. Adjust idle mixture and idle speed. Service air cleaner. Inspect and adjust drive belts. Inspect choke operation and adjust or free up. Check operation of EGR valve.
V-6–1983-87 .... 2.0
V-8–1983-87 .... 2.5
w/A.C. add 6
To perform C.C.C. system test add 1.0

LABOR — 2 IGNITION SYSTEM 2 — LABOR

(Factory Time) Chilton Time

GASOLINE ENGINES

(G) Spark Plugs, Clean and Reset or Renew
V-6–1983-87 (.4) 6
V-8–1983-87 (.5) 7
w/A.C. V-8 add 3

(G) Ignition Timing, Reset
1983-87 (.3) 4

(G) Distributor, Renew
Includes: Reset ignition timing.
1983-87 (.4) 8

(G) Distributor, R&R and Recondition
Includes: Reset ignition timing.
1983-87 (.7) 1.4

(G) Distributor Cap and/or Rotor, Renew
1983-87 (.3) 7

(G) Vacuum Control Unit, Renew
Includes: Reset ignition timing. Does not include R&R distributor.
V-6–1983-84 (.4) 6

(G) Ignition Coil, Renew
1983-87 (.4) 5

(G) Electronic Module Retard Vacuum Switch (EMR), Renew
1983-84 (.3) 5

(G) Ignition Cables, Renew
1983-87
V-6 (1.0) 1.4
V-8 (.5) 7

(G) Ignition Switch, Renew
1983-87 (.6) 9

(G) Ignition Key Warning Switch, Renew
1983-87 (.5) 8

(G) Distributor Module, Renew
1983-87 (.4) 6

(G) Distributor Pick-Up Coil and/or Pole Piece, Renew
Includes: R&R distributor and main shaft.
1983-87 (.6) 9

(G) Distributor Capacitor and/or Module Wiring Harness, Renew
Includes: R&R cap and rotor, check and adjust timing.
1983-87 (.4) 6

LABOR 2 IGNITION SYSTEM 2 LABOR

(Factory Time)	Chilton Time
(G) Distributor Hall Effect Switch, Renew	
1983 (.5)	.8
DIESEL IGNITION COMPONENTS	
(G) Coolant Fast Idle Temperature Switch, Renew	
All models (.2)	.4
(G) Glow Plug Relay, Renew	
All models (.2)	.3
(G) Fast Idle Solenoid, Renew	
All models (.3)	.4
(G) Glow Plugs, Renew	
All models-one	.4
all-one bank	.7
all-both banks	1.3
(G) Glow Plug Module, Renew	
All models (.3)	.5
(G) Glow Plug Control Switch, Renew	
All models (.2)	.4
(G) Control Sensor, Renew	
All models (.2)	.3

PARTS 2 ELECTRONIC IGNITION 2 PARTS

	Part No.	Price
Distributor Assy.		
V-6-229		
1983-84	1110584	341.50
V-6-231		
1983-84	◆1103470	351.25
1985-87-Canada	◆1103612	262.50
V-6-262		
1985	◆1103574	170.00
1986-87	◆1103655	174.75
V-8-305		
1983-85-Code H	◆1103460	333.75
1984-85-Code G	◆1103598	275.50
1986-87	◆10497135	294.50
(1) Cover		
1983-87-V-6	◆1894209	6.00
V-8	◆1875960	6.00
(2) Coil		
1983-87-exc. below	◆1985473	36.00
231	◆1985474	36.00
305G (83-85)	◆1988665	48.75
1986-87-V-8	◆1875894	N.L.
(3) Cap		
1983-87-229 & 231	◆1894979	17.00
262	◆1988001	9.75
V-8	◆1974408	17.00
(4) Rotor		
1983-87-exc. 262	◆1977026	6.50
262	◆10495408	3.50
(5) Shaft		
V-6-229		
1983-84	1972735	38.00
V-6-231		
1983-84	◆1976930	38.50
V-6-262		
1985	1988056	33.50
1986-87	10495798	48.75

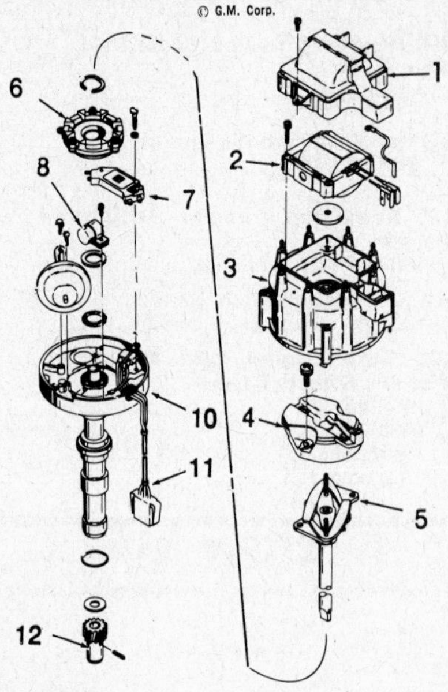

	Part No.	Price
V-8-305		
1983-87	◆1976909	38.50
(6) Pole Piece & Plate Assy.		
V-6-229		
1983-84	1972729	36.25
V-6-231		
1983-84	◆1976925	30.25
V-6-262		
1985	◆1988010	3.50
V-8-305		
1983-87	◆1976897	30.25

	Part No.	Price
(7) Control Module		
1983-87-exc. below	◆1976908	60.00
1985-87-305H	16022621	114.75
305G	1988500	53.00
262 (85)	◆1987466	46.00
262 (86-87)	◆10496048	52.75
(8) Capacitor		
1983-87	◆1876154	4.50
(10) Housing		
V-6-229		
1983-84	1979944	52.00
V-6-231		
1983-84	◆1976928	36.25
V-6-262		
1985	◆1989808	57.00
1986-87	◆10495860	43.75
V-8		
1983-87	◆1978152	45.00
(11) Harness		
1983-87	◆1892261	11.00
(12) Gear		
1983-87-exc. below	◆1958599	14.25
231	◆1892082	15.25
262 (85)	◆10495062	20.75
262 (86-87)	◆10495062	20.75
DIESEL IGNITION SYSTEM		
Glow Plugs		
1983	◆5613680	19.00
1984-85	◆5613826	16.50
Glow Plug Relay		
1983	◆560580	16.00
1984-85	◆22520348	91.75
Glow Plug Control Sensor		
1983	◆12015288	58.50

LABOR 3 FUEL SYSTEM 3 LABOR

(Factory Time)	Chilton Time
GASOLINE ENGINES	
(G) Fuel Pump, Test	
Includes: Disconnect line at carburetor, attach pressure gauge.	
All models	.3
(M) Carburetor Air Cleaner, Service	
All models (.2)	.3
(G) Carburetor, Adjust (On Car)	
1983-87	
Slow & Fast Idle (.3)	.4
Vacuum brake-one (.4)	.6
both (.6)	.8
Choke (.6)	1.0
Complete (1.3)	1.8
(G) Thermostatic Choke Cover and/or Gasket, Renew	
1983-87 (.6)	1.0
(G) Automatic Choke Vacuum Diaphragm, Renew	
1983-87-one (.4)	.6
both (.6)	.8
(M) Carburetor Fuel Filter, Renew	
1983-87 (.3)	.3
(G) Choke Vacuum Control Switch, Renew	
1983-87 (.3)	.4
(G) Electric Choke Relay, Renew	
1983-85 (.3)	.4
(G) Idle Stop Solenoid, Renew	
Includes: Reset idle speed.	
1983-84 (.3)	.4
1985-87 (.7)	1.0
(G) Carburetor, Renew	
Includes: Necessary adjustments.	
1983-87 (.6)	.9
To perform C.C.C. system check, add (.5)	1.0
(G) Carburetor, R&R and Clean or Recondition	
Includes: Necessary adjustments.	
1983-87-2 bbl (2.3)	3.0
4 bbl (2.5)	3.2

LABOR — 3 FUEL SYSTEM 3 — LABOR

(Factory Time)	Chilton Time
To perform C.C.C. system check, add (.5)	1.0
(G) Float or Needle Valve and Seat, Renew	
Includes: Set idle speed and mixture.	
1983-87	
2 bbl (.9)	1.2
4 bbl (.8)	1.5
To perform C.C.C. system check, add (.5)	1.0
(G) Accelerator Pump, Renew	
1983-87	
2 bbl (.7)	1.0
4 bbl (.8)	1.2
(G) Fuel Pump or Push Rod, Renew	
V-6–1983-87–231 eng (.4)	.6
200-229 engs (1.0)	1.4
262 eng (.8)	1.1
V-8–1983-87 (1.0)	1.4
w/P.S. add (.2)	.2
w/A.I.R. add (.5)	.5
Add pump test if performed.	
(G) Water In Fuel Detector, Renew (WIF)	
All models (.9)	1.2
(G) Fuel Tank, Renew	
Includes: Transfer tank gauge unit.	
1983-87 (.7)	1.0
(G) Fuel Gauge (Tank), Renew	
Includes: Drain and refill tank.	
1983-87 (.8)	1.1
(G) Fuel Gauge (Dash), Renew	
Monte Carlo, Malibu	
1983-87 (.6)	1.0
(G) Intake Manifold or Gaskets, Renew	
V-6–1983-87	
200, 229 engs (2.0)	3.0
231 eng (1.8)	2.7
262 eng (2.2)	3.0
V-8–1983-87 (2.0)	3.3
w/P.S. add (.3)	.3
w/A.C. add (.2)	.2
w/A.I.R. add (.1)	.1
w/C.C.C. add (.3)	.3
Renew manif add (.2)	.5

ELECTRONIC FUEL INJECTION

(Factory Time)	Chilton Time
(G) Throttle Body, R&R	
V-6–1985-87 (.6)	1.0
Renew throttle body kit add (.3)	.3
Renew fuel meter body add (.3)	.3
(G) Throttle Body Unit, Renew	
V-6–1985-87 (.6)	1.0
(G) Throttle Body Fuel Meter Assy., and/or Gasket, Renew	
V-6–1985-87 (.4)	.6
(G) Idle Air Control Valve, Renew	
V-6–1985-87 (.5)	.8
(G) Minimum Idle Speed, Adjust	
All models (.4)	.7
(G) Throttle Body Injector and/or Gasket, Renew	
V-6–1985-87	
one (.7)	1.1
both (.7)	1.2
(G) Fuel Pressure Regulator, Renew	
V-6–1985-87 (.6)	1.0
(G) Fuel Pump, Renew (In Tank)	
1985-87 (1.3)	1.8
(G) Fuel Pump Relay, Renew	
1985-87 (.5)	.7

E.F.E. SYSTEM

(Factory Time)	Chilton Time
(G) E.F.E. Valve, Renew	
1983-87	
V-6 (.6)	.9
V-8 (.6)	.9
(G) E.F.E. Vacuum Check Valve, Renew	
1983-85 (.2)	.4
(G) E.F.E. Thermal Vacuum Switch, Renew	
1983-87 (.3)	.5

DIESEL ENGINE

(Factory Time)	Chilton Time
(G) Idle Speed, Adjust	
1983-84 (.2)	.4
(G) Air Cleaner, Service	
1983-84 (.2)	.4
(G) Air Intake Crossover, Renew	
1983-84 (.4)	.6
(G) Injection Timing, Check and Adjust	
1983-84 (.5)	.9
(G) Fuel Filter, Renew	
1983-84 (.2)	.4
(G) Fuel Supply Pump, Renew	
1983-84 (.5)	.8
w/A.C. add (.2)	.2
(G) Injection Pump Throttle Shaft Seal, Renew	
1983-84 (.9)	1.3
(G) Injection Pump Adapter and/or Seal, Renew	
1983-84–V-6 (1.4)	2.1
V-8 (1.8)	2.5
(G) Fuel Injection Pump, Renew	
Includes: Pressure and electrical test. Adjust timing.	
1983-84–V-6 (1.8)	3.0
V-8 (2.2)	3.4
(G) High Pressure Fuel Lines, Renew	
1983-84–one (.9)	1.0
all (1.3)	2.5
(G) Injector Nozzle and/or Seal, Renew	
1983-84–one (.8)	1.0
one-each bank (1.0)	1.3
all-both banks (2.2)	3.0
Clean nozzles add, each	.2
(G) Vacuum Pump, Renew	
Includes: Vacuum test.	
1983-84 (.4)	.6
(G) Fuel Solenoid, Renew	
1983-84	
Cav (.3)	.5
V-6 (.6)	.9
V-8 (.5)	.7
(G) Cold Advance Solenoid, Renew	
1983-84 (.6)	.8
(G) Fuel Injection Head Seal, Renew	
Includes: Renew head and drive shaft seals. Renew governor weight retaining ring.	
1983-84–V-6 (2.3)	3.5
V-8 (2.7)	3.9
(G) Intake Manifold or Gaskets, Renew	
1983-84–V-6 (2.0)	3.0
V-8 (2.9)	3.5
Renew manif add (.2)	.5

PARTS — 3 FUEL SYSTEM 3 — PARTS

	Part No.	Price
Carburetor Assembly (Rochester)		
V-6-229		
(wo/A.C.)		
1983-84	17068494	696.00
(A.C.)		
1983-84	17068495	696.00
V-6-231		
1983	◆17079205	666.75
1984	◆17110332	912.75
V-8-305		
(4 bbl)		
1983	◆17079226	821.25
1984-Code H	◆17110449	846.00
Code G	◆17110451	846.00
1985-Code H	◆17110902	887.00
Code G	17110898	887.00
1986-87-Code H	◆17111481	876.00
Code G	17111478	876.00
Carburetor Power Kit		
V-6-229		
1983-84	7039492	43.50
V-6-231		
1983	◆17076129	51.00
1984	◆17076129	51.00
V-8-305		
1983-84-Code H	◆7039467	41.50
Code G	◆17076127	48.00
1985-87	◆17076043	33.75
Fuel Pump Assy.		
V-6-229		
1983-84	6471588	25.50
V-6-231		
1983-84	◆6471172	N.L.
V-6-262		
1985-87	◆6472011	80.00
El Camino	◆6472421	57.00
V-8-305		
1983-87	◆6470422	24.75
Fuel Tank		
Order by year and model.		
Fuel Gauge (Tank)		
(Malibu)		
1983-exc Sta. wag.	◆25001612	40.00
Sta. wagon	25000757	38.75
(Monte Carlo)		
1983-87	◆25001612	40.00
Fuel Gauge (Dash)		
1983-87	6432821	23.50
Intake Manifold Gaskets		
V-6-229		
1983-84	14033549	7.25

PARTS 3 FUEL SYSTEM 3 PARTS

	Part No.	Price
V-6-231		
1983-84-exc		
Alum.	◆1264924	14.50
Alum. man.	◆25505397	15.75

	Part No.	Price
V-6-262		
1985-87-side	◆14089020	2.50

	Part No.	Price
V-8-305		
1983-85	◆14034821	5.75
1986-87	◆14038088	N.L.

PARTS 3 THROTTLE BODY INJECTION 3 PARTS

	Part No.	Price
V-6-262		
Throttle Body Injection Unit		
1985	◆17111155	655.50
1986-87	17111465	650.00
(1) Fuel Meter Body Kit		
1985-87	◆17078262	128.75
(2) Fuel Injector Kit		
1985	◆17111159	179.50
1986-87	◆17111468	179.50
(3) Gasket Kit		
1985-87	◆17111156	39.25
(4) Throttle Position Sensor Kit		
1985	◆17111162	62.75
1986-87	◆17111471	47.75
(5) Throttle Body Kit		
1985	◆17111160	185.75
1986-87	◆17111469	185.75
(6) Fuel Nut Assortment Kit		
1985-87	◆17078261	15.50
(7) Idle Air Valve Control Kit		
1985-87	◆17079256	88.75
Fuel Meter Kit		
Includes injector & pressure regulator.		
1985	◆17111157	350.00

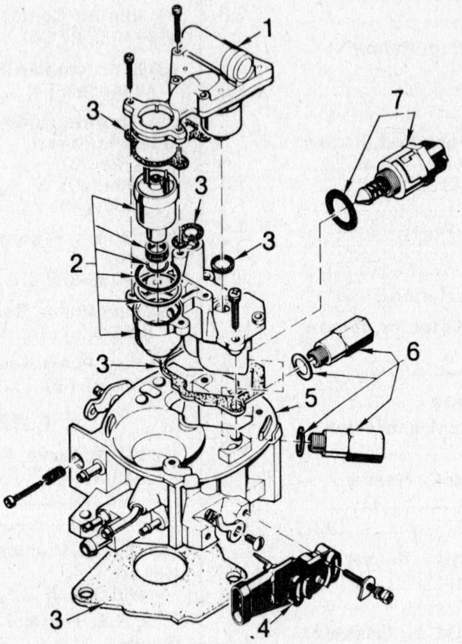

PARTS 3 FUEL SYSTEM 3 PARTS

	Part No.	Price
DIESEL FUEL SYSTEM		
Air Intake Crossover		
1983-84	◆22509735	109.00
Fuel Pump		
1983-84	◆6471317	N.L.
Injection Pump Adapter		
1983-84	◆558768	21.75

	Part No.	Price
Fuel Injection Pump		
1983-wo/Hi alt.	◆22518686	763.00
Hi alt.	◆22518689	763.00
1984-wo/Hi alt.	◆22520936	763.00
Hi alt.	◆22520999	763.00
Fuel Injection Nozzles		
1983	◆22520378	60.00
1984	◆22521207	89.50

	Part No.	Price
Vacuum Pump		
1983-84	◆7839413	116.00
Intake Manifold Gaskets		
1983-84	◆22516344	12.00
Fuel Gauge (Tank)		
1983-84	◆25002567	104.50
Fuel Gauge (Dash)		
1983-84	6433450	22.25

LABOR 3A EMISSION CONTROLS 3A LABOR

	(Factory Time)	Chilton Time
GASOLINE ENGINES		
EMISSION CONTROLS		
(G) Emission Control Check		
Includes: Check and adjust engine idle speed and mixture and ignition timing. Check PCV valve.		
All models		.6

	(Factory Time)	Chilton Time
POSITIVE CRANKCASE VENTILATION		
(M) Positive Crankcase Ventilation Valve, Renew		
All models	(.2)	.3
(M) Crankcase Ventilation Filter Assy., Renew		
All models	(.2)	.3

	(Factory Time)	Chilton Time
EVAPORATIVE EMISSION TYPE		
(G) Charcoal Canister, Renew		
1983-87	(.2)	.3
(G) Canister Purge Thermal Vacuum Switch, Renew		
1983-87	(.3)	.3

(Factory Time) Chilton Time

(G) Fuel Tank Pressure Control Valve, Renew
1983-87 (.2) .3

CONTROLLED COMBUSTION TYPE

(G) Air Cleaner Vacuum Motor, Renew
1983-87 (.3) .5

(G) Air Cleaner Temperature Sensor, Renew
1983-87 (.2) .3

EXHAUST GAS RECIRCULATION SYSTEM

(G) E.G.R. Valve, Renew
1983-84-Gas (.3) .5
Diesel (.5) 1.0
1985-87 (.6) .8

(G) E.G.R. Vacuum Delay Valve, Renew
1983-87 (.2) .3

(G) Thermostatic Vacuum Control Switch, Renew
1983-87 (.3) .4

(G) E.G.R./E.F.E. Thermal Vacuum Switch, Renew
1983-87 (.3) .4

AIR INJECTOR REACTOR TYPE

(G) Air Pump, Renew
1983-87
V-6 (.5) .8
V-8 (.6) 1.0

(G) A.I.R. Air Cleaner, Renew
1983-87 (.2) .3

(G) Check Valve, Renew
1983-87-one (.2) .3
each adtnl (.1) .1

(G) Air Pump Centrifugal Fan and/or Filter, Renew
All models (.3) .5

(G) A.I.R. Manifold Pipe Renew
1983-87
V-6-one (.4) .7
both (.6) .9
V-8-one (.4) .7
both (.6) .9
w/A.C. add (.2) .2

(G) Catalytic Converter Air Pipe, Renew
1983-87-one piece (.4) .7

(G) Vacuum Delay Valve, Renew
1983-87-one (.2) .3

(G) Air By-Pass Valve, Renew
All models (.2) .3

COMPUTER COMMAND CONTROL SYSTEM (C.C.C.)

(P) Electronic Control Module, Renew
Does not include system performance check.
1983-87 (.5) .6

(P) Mixture Control Solenoid, Renew
Does not include system performance check.
1983-87-2 bbl (1.1) 1.4
4 bbl (1.2) 1.5

(P) Prom, Renew
Does not include system performance check.
Includes: R&R electronic module.
1983-87 (.5) .8

CHILTON'S EMISSION CONTROL TUNE-UP

1. Clean or renew P.C.V. valve, hoses and filter.
2. Check fuel tank cap for sealing ability.
3. Check fuel tank and fuel lines for leakage.
4. Check evaporation canister and filter. Replace if necessary.
5. Check engine compression to determine leakage of unburned gases. (Add time for items of interference).
6. Test and clean or renew spark plugs.
7. Check engine oil dipstick for sealing ability.
8. Test exhaust system with analyzer and check system for leakage.
9. Check exhaust manifold heat valve for operation.
10. Adjust ignition timing and carburetor idle speed and mixture.
11. Check automatic choke mechanism for free operation.
12. Inspect air cleaner and element.
13. On models so equipped, test distributor vacuum control switch and transmission control switch.

Six 1.5
V-6 1.7
V-8 1.8

For repairs made, charge accordingly.

(Factory Time) Chilton Time

(P) Barometric Sensor, Renew
Does not include system performance check.
1983-87 (.4) .7

(P) Coolant Temperature Sensor, Renew
Does not include system performance check.
Includes: Drain and refill cooling system.
1983-87 (.5) .7

(P) Manifold Differential Pressure Sensor, Renew
Does not include system performance check.
1983-87 (.5) .6

(P) Manifold Aboslute Pressure Sensor, Renew
Does not include system performance check.
1983-87 (.5) .6

(P) Oxygen Sensor, Renew
Does not include system performance check.
1983-87 (.4) .7

(P) Throttle Position Sensor, Renew
Does not include system performance check.
1983-87-2 bbl (1.1) 1.4
4 bbl (1.2) 1.5

(P) Throttle Position Sensor, Adjust
All models
2 bbl (.4) .9
Perform C.C.C. system check add 1.0

(P) Vacuum Control Purge Solenoid, Renew
Does not include system test.
1983-87 (.4) .6

(Factory Time) Chilton Time

(P) Calpak, Renew
Does not include system test.
1984-87 (.5) .7

(P) EGR Sensor, Renew
Does not include system test.
1983-87 (.4) .6

(P) Canister Purge Control Valve, Renew
Does not include system performance check.
1983-87 (.4) .6

(P) EGR/EFE Purge Solenoid, Renew
Does not include system performance check.
1983-84 (.4) .6

(P) Air Control Valve, Renew
Does not include system performance check.
1983-87 (.4) .6

(P) Air Control/Air Switching Valve, Renew
Does not include system performance check.
1983-87 (.5) .7
w/229 Eng (.7) .9

(P) E.G.R. Vacuum Control Solenoid, Renew
Does not include system performance check.
1983-87 (.5) .7

(P) Idle Speed Control Motor, Renew
Does not include system performance check.
1983-84 (.5) .7
Recond motor add (.3) .3

(P) Vehicle Speed Sensor, Renew
Does not include system performance check.
1983-87 (1.1) 2.0

(P) E.G.R. Bleed Control Solenoid, Renew
Does not include system performance check.
1983-87 (.4) .6

(P) Air Control Valve Relay, Renew
Does not include system performance check.
1983-85 (.4) .5

(P) Air Switching Valve Relay, Renew
Does not include system performance check.
1983-85 (.3) .4

(P) E.G.R. Bleed Control Relay, Renew
Does not include system performance check.
1983-85 (.4) .5

(P) Back-Up Lamp and Park/Neutral Switch, Renew
Does not include system performance check.
1983-87 (.5) .7

(P) Tach Signal Conditioner, Renew
Does not include system performance check.
1983-85 (.4) .6

(P) Tachometer Filter, Renew
Does not include system performance check.
1983-87 (.3) .3

(P) Computer Command Control Performance Check
1983-87 (.5) 1.0

ELECTRONICALLY CONTROLLED EMISSIONS SYSTEM

(P) Electronic Control Module, Renew
1985-87 (.5) .9

LABOR 3A EMISSION CONTROLS 3A LABOR

(Factory Time)	Chilton Time
(P) Throttle Position Sensor, Renew	
1985-87 (1.1)	1.4
(P) Prom, Renew	
1985-87 (.5)	1.0
(P) Coolant Temperature Sensor, Renew	
1985-87 (.5)	.7
(P) Manifold Absolute Pressure Sensor, Renew	
1985-87 (.5)	.6
(P) Oxygen Sensor, Renew	
1985-87 (.6)	.8
(P) Vehicle Speed Sensor, Renew	
1985-87 (1.1)	1.5

DIESEL ENGINE

(Factory Time)	Chilton Time
(G) Crankcase Depression Regulator Valve, Renew	
All models (.2)	.3
(G) Crankcase Ventilation Flow Control Valve, Renew	
All models (.2)	.3
(G) Crankcase Ventilation Filter, Renew	
All models (.2)	.3
(G) E.G.R. Valve and/or Gasket, Renew	
All models (.5)	1.0
(G) E.G.R. Control Valve Solenoid, Renew	
All models (.2)	.3
(G) E.G.R. Control Valve Switch, Renew	
All models (.2)	.3
(G) E.P.R. Control Valve Solenoid, Renew	
All models (.3)	.4
(G) E.P.R. Control Valve Switch, Renew	
All models (.3)	.4
(G) E.P.R. Exhaust Pressure Regulator Valve, Renew	
All models (.3)	.4
(G) Vacuum Regulator Valve, Renew	
All models (.6)	.8

PARTS 3A EMISSION CONTROLS 3A PARTS

	Part No.	Price
Crankcase Ventilator Valve (PCV)		
Order by engine model & stamped number.		
(CV-590)	6421934	4.25
(CV-609C)	6421971	3.00
(CV-722C)	6422717	3.00
(CV-723C)	6422718	3.00
(CV-726C)	6422721	4.75
(CV-736C)	6423695	3.00
(CV-746C)	6484525	3.00
(CV-770C)	◆6487534	3.00
(CV-774C)	◆6487779	2.50
(CV-781C)	◆6487936	3.50
(CV-789C)	◆8995284	5.00
(CV-853C)	◆25040026	5.00
(CV-866)	◆25041678	34.50

EVAPORATIVE EMISSION

	Part No.	Price
Vapor Canister		
1983-229, 305	◆17075824	75.50
1984-87-exc. below	◆17075849	34.50
1983-84-231	◆17064622	39.50
1985-262	◆17075859	66.00
1986-87-262	◆17086095	51.75

CONTROLLED COMBUSTION TYPE

	Part No.	Price
Bow Tie Breather		
1983-87-exc below	6484966	3.00
231-2 bbl.	8996724	5.00
Air Cleaner Sensor		
1983-87-exc. below	◆8997787	18.75
231	◆8997916	18.75
262	◆8997574	18.75

AIR INJECTOR REACTOR TYPE

	Part No.	Price
Air Pump		
V-6-229		
1983-87	◆7834916	149.00
V-6-231		
1983-87	◆7835397	131.00
V-6-262		
1985-87	◆7834916	149.00
V-8		
1983-87	◆7834916	149.00
Air Injection Control Valve		
V-6-229		
1983	17074085	44.25
1984	17075123	108.00
V-6-262		
1983	◆17071711	35.00
1984	◆17072997	73.75
1986-87	17085718	N.L.
V-8-305		
1984-87	17075123	107.75

E.G.R. Valve
Replacement E.G.R. valves must be ordered according to the stamping number on the original valve.

COMPUTER CONTROLLED EMISSIONS SYSTEM

Part numbers are for pricing reference only. Order with complete year, engine and unit I.D. number.

	Part No.	Price
Controller (ECM)		
V-6		
1983-Fed.	◆1226024	110.25
Calif.	◆1225500	110.25
1984-87-229	1226454	110.25
231	◆1226519	110.25
262	◆1226868	110.00
V-8		
1983	◆1226025	110.25
1984	◆1226455	110.25
1985-87	◆1226865	110.00

Calibration Unit (PROM)
Order according to the code stamped on the existing calibrator.

	Part No.	Price
Barometric Sensor		
1983-87	◆16006833	62.25
Manifold Absolute Pressure Sensor (M.A.P.)		
V-6-231		
1983-84	◆16006835	62.25
Manifold Differential Pressure Sensor		
1983-84-231	◆16006834	62.25
1985-87-diesel, 262	◆16017460	N.L.
Oxygen Sensor		
1983-87-exc. 262	◆8990741	28.75
262	14082487	28.75
Coolant Temperature Sensor		
1983-84	◆25036092	22.00
1985-87	◆25036708	12.75
ESC Knock Sensor		
1983-87-exc. 262	◆1997562	37.00
1985-87-262	◆1997699	28.75
Throttle Position Sensor		
1983-87	◆17078448	40.50
E.G.R. Control Valve Solenoid		
1983-87	◆1997631	13.75
E.G.R. Valve Vacuum Control		
V-6-231		
1984-87	22517809	6.00
V-8-Diesel		
1983	22514746	38.00
1984	◆22520665	24.25
Idle Speed Control Motor		
1983-84-exc. 231	17079129	116.75
231	17079132	116.75

LABOR 4 ALTERNATOR AND REGULATOR 4 LABOR

(Factory Time)	Chilton Time
(G) Delcotron Circuits, Test	
Includes: Test battery, regulator, Delcotron output.	
All models	.6
(M) Alternator Drive Belt, Renew	
All models (.2)	.3
w/A.C. add (.2)	.2
(G) Delcotron Assembly or Fan Pulley, Renew	
1983-87 (.5)	.6

LABOR 4 ALTERNATOR AND REGULATOR 4 LABOR

	(Factory Time)	Chilton Time
(G) Delcotron, R&R and Recondition		
Includes: Complete disassembly, replacement of parts as required, reassemble.		
1983-87	(1.1)	1.7
w/Diesel eng add	(.2)	.2
(G) Delcotron Front Bearing, Renew		
Includes: R&R Delcotron, separate end frames.		
1983-87	(.5)	1.0
Renew rear brg add		.2
w/Diesel eng add	(.1)	.2
(G) Delcotron Voltage Regulator, Test and Renew		
Includes: R&R, disassemble and reassemble Delcotron.		
1983-87	(.6)	1.2
w/Diesel eng add	(.1)	.1
(G) Ammeter and/or Voltmeter, Renew		
1983-87	(.6)	1.0

PARTS 4 ALTERNATOR AND REGULATOR 4 PARTS

	Part No.	Price
Delcotron Assembly (New)		
1983-87-wo/Diesel		
37, 42 amp	◆1105360	206.00
56, 63, 78 amp	◆1100250	225.00
94 amp	◆1105492	228.50
1983-84-Diesel	◆1105360	206.00
42 amp	◆1105357	241.50
56, 66, 78 amp	◆1105369	228.75
(1) Capacitor		
1983-87-exc. 94 amp	◆1978146	4.75
94 amp	◆1988873	4.00
(2) Diode		
1983-87	◆1984459	5.00
(3) Rectifier Bridge		
1983-87	◆1984454	28.00
(4) Bearing (Rear)		
1983-87-exc 70 amp	◆9436831	5.50
70 amp	◆1975322	5.50
(5) Terminal Pkg.		
1983-87	◆1975471	3.50
(6) Frame (Rear End)		
1983-87-exc. 94 amp	◆1984460	47.75
94 amp	◆1987073	28.00
(7) Regulator		
1983-87	◆1116387	25.00
(8) Brush Holder		
1983-87	◆1984462	9.00
(9) Rotor		
1983-87-exc. below	◆1985476	72.00
78, 94 amp	◆1984466	77.25

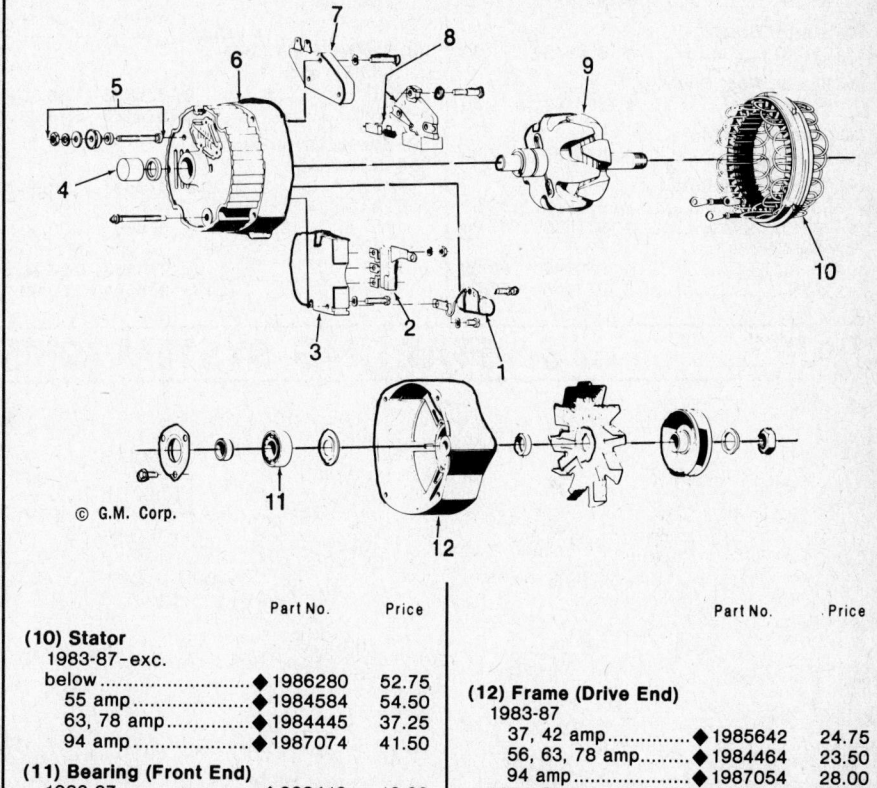

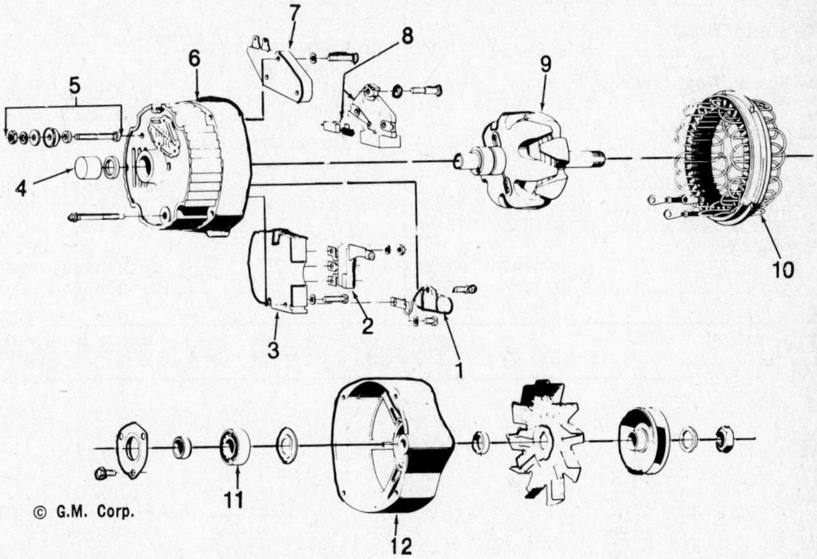

© G.M. Corp.

	Part No.	Price
(10) Stator		
1983-87-exc. below	◆1986280	52.75
55 amp	◆1984584	54.50
63, 78 amp	◆1984445	37.25
94 amp	◆1987074	41.50
(11) Bearing (Front End)		
1983-87	◆908419	10.00
(12) Frame (Drive End)		
1983-87		
37, 42 amp	◆1985642	24.75
56, 63, 78 amp	◆1984464	23.50
94 amp	◆1987054	28.00
1984-Diesel	◆1986206	24.00

LABOR 5 STARTING SYSTEM 5 LABOR

	(Factory Time)	Chilton Time
(G) Starter Draw Test (On Car)		
All models		.3
(G) Starter, Renew		
V-6–1983-87	(.8)	.9
V-8–1983-87	(.6)	.9
Diesel–1983-84	(.8)	1.1
(G) Starter, R&R and Recondition		
Includes: Turn down armature.		
V-6–1983-87	(1.6)	1.9
V-8–1983-87	(1.4)	1.9
Diesel–1983-84	(1.6)	2.5
Renew field coils add	(.2)	.5
Add draw test if performed.		
(G) Starter Drive, Renew		
Includes: R&R starter.		
V-6–1983-87	(1.0)	1.1
V-8–1983-87	(.9)	1.1
Diesel–1983-84	(1.0)	1.4
(G) Starter Solenoid Switch, Renew		
Includes: R&R starter.		
V-6–1983-87	(.8)	.9
V-8–1983-87	(.7)	.9
Diesel–1983-84	(.8)	1.1
(G) Back-Up Lamp and Park/Neutral Switch, Renew		
1983-87-floor shift	(.3)	.5
column shift	(.3)	.5
(G) Ignition Switch, Renew		
1983-87	(.6)	.9
(M) Battery Cables, Renew		
1983-87-positive		
V-6	(.4)	.4
V-8	(.4)	.4
negative	(.2)	.3
batt to batt	(.2)	.3
(M) Battery Terminals, Clean		
All models		.3

PARTS 5 STARTING SYSTEM 5 PARTS

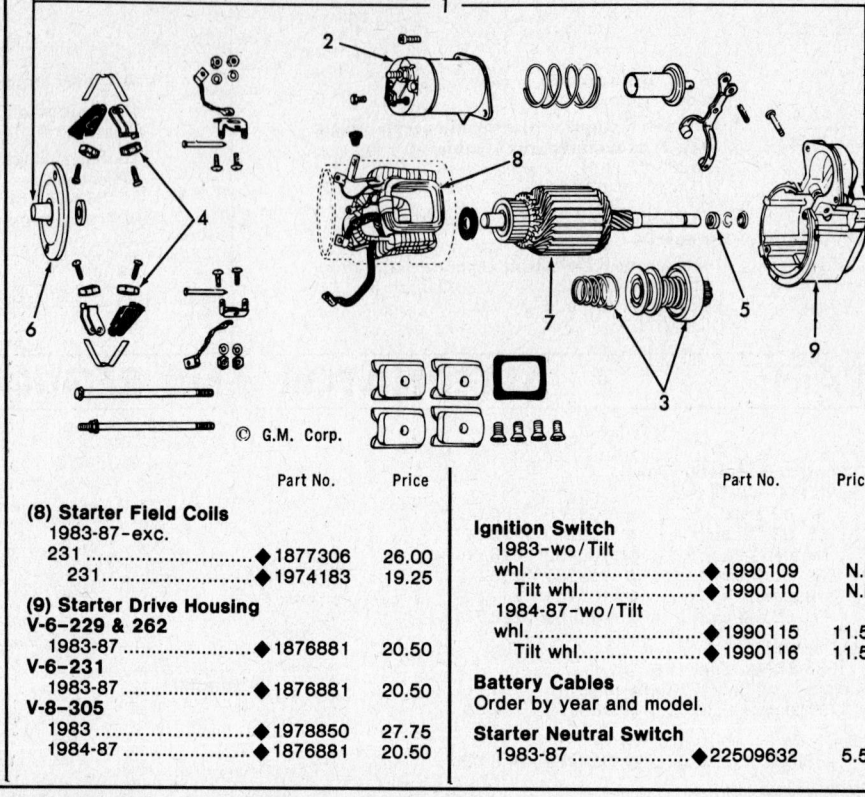

	Part No.	Price
(1) Starter Assembly		
V-6-229		
1983	◆1109534	219.50
1984	◆1998452	212.50
V-6-231		
1983-84	◆1998234	220.75
V-6-262		
1985	◆1998435	10.00
1986-87	◆1998557	201.75
V-8-305H		
1983	◆1109534	219.50
1984-85	◆1998435	10.00
1986-87	◆1998557	201.75
V-8-305G		
1984-85	◆1998452	212.50
1986-87	◆1998564	212.50
(2) Starter Solenoid Switch		
1983-87	◆1114531	N.L.
(3) Starter Drive Assy.		
1983-87	◆1875687	N.L.
(4) Starter Brush		
1983-87	◆1906945	.50
(5) Starter Rear Bushing		
1983-87	◆1932190	.50
(6) Starter End Plate		
1983-87	◆1974157	7.00
(7) Starter Armature		
1983-exc. 231	◆1978670	83.50
231	◆1971568	57.00
1984-87-exc. 231	◆1970548	52.00
231	◆1971568	57.00

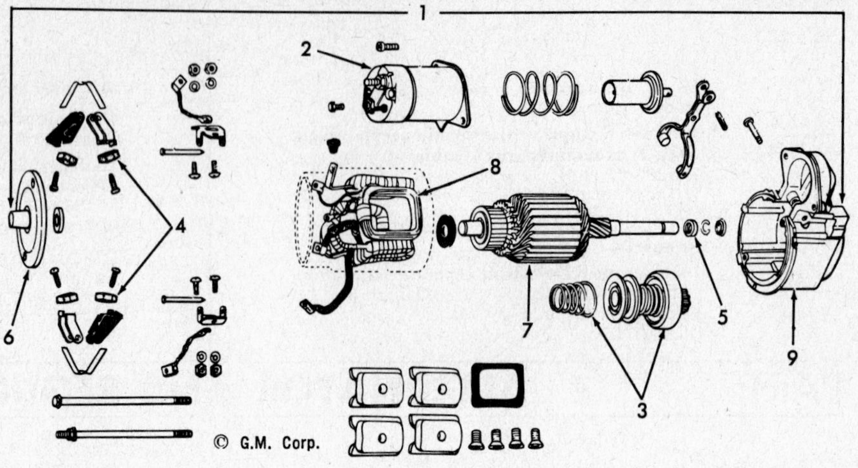

	Part No.	Price
(8) Starter Field Coils		
1983-87-exc. 231	◆1877306	26.00
231	◆1974183	19.25
(9) Starter Drive Housing		
V-6-229 & 262		
1983-87	◆1876881	20.50
V-6-231		
1983-87	◆1876881	20.50
V-8-305		
1983	◆1978850	27.75
1984-87	◆1876881	20.50

	Part No.	Price
Ignition Switch		
1983-wo/Tilt whl.	◆1990109	N.L.
Tilt whl.	◆1990110	N.L.
1984-87-wo/Tilt whl.	◆1990115	11.50
Tilt whl.	◆1990116	11.50
Battery Cables		
Order by year and model.		
Starter Neutral Switch		
1983-87	◆22509632	5.50

PARTS 5 STARTING SYSTEM (DIESEL) 5 PARTS

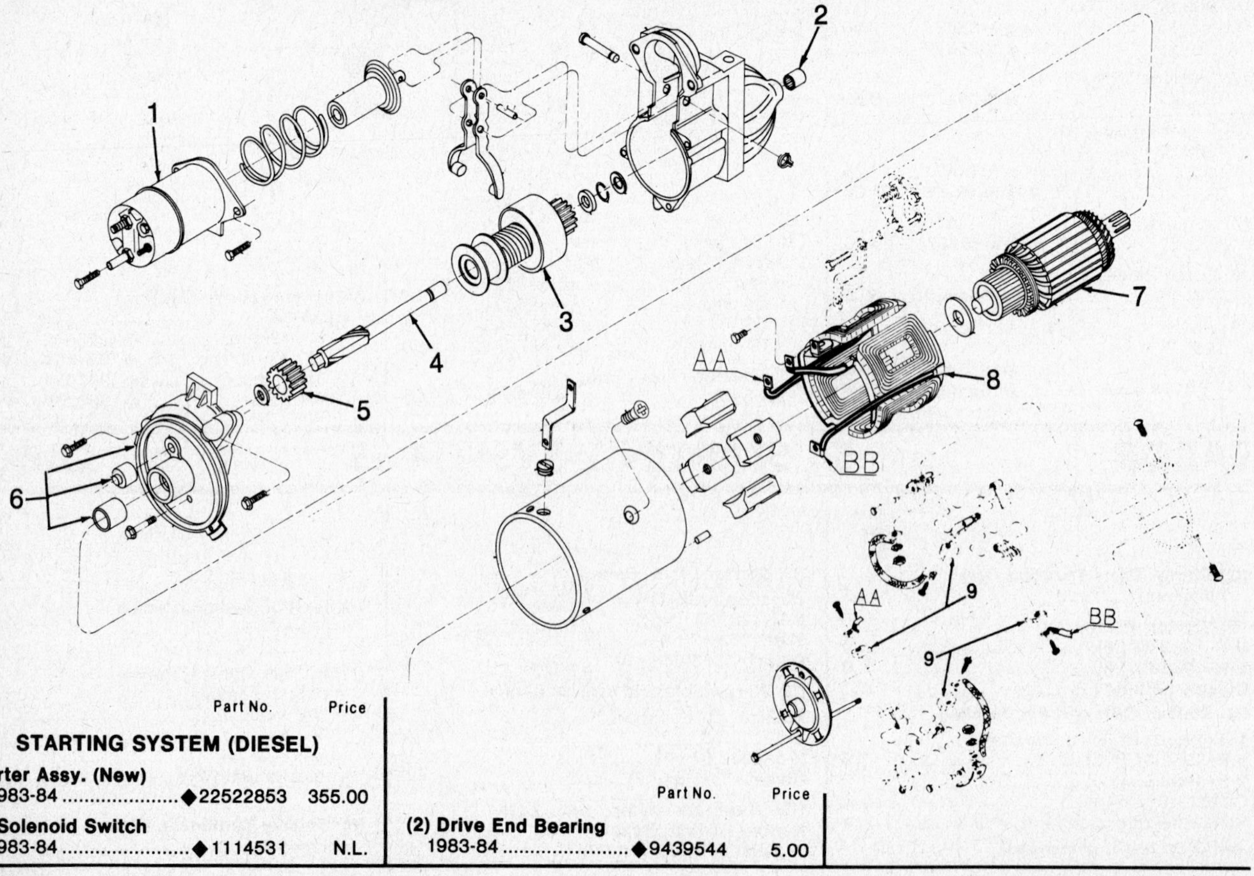

	Part No.	Price
STARTING SYSTEM (DIESEL)		
Starter Assy. (New)		
1983-84	◆22522853	355.00
(1) Solenoid Switch		
1983-84	◆1114531	N.L.

	Part No.	Price
(2) Drive End Bearing		
1983-84	◆9439544	5.00

PARTS 5 STARTING SYSTEM 5 PARTS

	Part No.	Price
(3) Starter Drive		
1983-84	◆1893445	65.00
(4) Drive Shaft		
1983-84	◆1972683	29.00
(5) Gear		
1983-84	◆1972685	12.50
(6) Gear Housing		
1983-84	◆1972700	29.50
(7) Armature		
1983-84	◆1987639	139.75
(8) Field Coils		
1983-84	◆1979982	83.00
(9) Starter Brushes		
1983-84	◆1852885	2.75
Battery Cables		
Order by year and model.		
Neutral Safety Switch		
1983-84	◆22509632	5.50

LABOR 6 BRAKE SYSTEM 6 LABOR

(Factory Time) — Chilton Time

(G) Brake Pedal Free Play, Adjust
All models (.2) 3

(G) Brakes, Adjust (Minor)
Includes: R&R wheels and adjust brakes thru access holes in drums. Fill master cylinder.
two wheels 4
Remove knock out plugs add, each .. .1

(G) Bleed Brakes (Four Wheels)
Includes: Fill master cylinder.
All models (.4) 5

(G) Free-Up or Renew Brake Self Adjusting Units
one wheel 6
each adtnl 4

(G) Brake Shoes and/or Pads, Renew
Includes: Install new or exchange shoes or pads, adjust service and hand brake. Bleed system.
1983-87-front-disc (.9) 1.1
rear-drum (.9) 1.5
all four wheels 2.5
Resurface disc rotor, add-each 9
Resurface brake drum, add-each 5

(G) Brake Drum, Renew (One)
1983-87 (.3) 5

(G) Brake Combination Valve or Switch, Renew
Includes: Bleed system.
1983-87 (.7) 1.0

BRAKE HYDRAULIC SYSTEM

(G) Wheel Cylinder, Renew
Includes: Bleed system.
1983-87-one (.8) 1.0
both (1.1) 1.9

(G) Wheel Cylinder, R&R and Rebuild
Includes: Hone cylinder and bleed system.
1983-87-one (1.0) 1.3
both (1.5) 2.1

(G) Brake Hose, Renew
Includes: Bleed system.
1983-87-front-one (.4) 6
rear-one (.5) 7
each adtnl (.2) 3

(G) Master Cylinder, Renew
Includes: Bleed complete system.
1983-87 (.6) 1.0

COMBINATIONS

Add to Brakes, Renew

See Machine Shop Operations

(G) RENEW WHEEL CYLINDER
Each (.2) 2

(G) REBUILD WHEEL CYLINDER
Each (.3) 3

(G) REBUILD CALIPER ASSEMBLY
Each (.5) 6

(G) RENEW MASTER CYLINDER
All models (.5) 8

(G) REBUILD MASTER CYLINDER
All models (.8) 1.0

(G) RENEW BRAKE HOSE
Each (.3) 3

(G) RENEW REAR AXLE GREASE SEALS
One side (.5) 5

(G) REPACK FRONT WHEEL BEARINGS (BOTH WHEELS)
All models (.6) 6

(G) RENEW BRAKE DRUM
Each (.1) 1

(G) RENEW DISC BRAKE ROTOR
Each (.3) 5

(Factory Time) — Chilton Time

(G) Master Cylinder, R&R and Rebuild
Includes: Hone cylinder and bleed complete system.
1983-87 (1.4) 1.8
w/Powermaster (1.6) 2.2

(G) Brake System, Flush and Refill
All models 1.2

POWER BRAKES

(G) Power Brake Cylinder, Renew
1983-87 (.6) 1.0

(G) Power Brake Cylinder, R&R and Recondition
1983-87
Single (1.1) 1.8
Tandem (1.3) 2.0
Recond M/Cyl add (.8) 8

(Factory Time) — Chilton Time

(G) Vacuum Check Valve, Renew
1983-87 (.3) 3

(G) Hydraulic Power Brake Cylinder Assy., Renew
Includes: Bleed power steering system.
1983-84 (.6) 9
Recond cyl add (.4) 6

DISC BRAKES

(G) Brake Shoes and/or Pads, Renew
Includes: Install new or exchange shoes or pads, adjust service and hand brake. Bleed system.
1983-87-front-disc (.9) 1.1
rear-drum (.9) 1.5
all four wheels 2.5
Resurface disc rotor, add-each 9
Resurface brake drum, add-each 5

(G) Disc Brake Rotor, Renew
1983-87-one (.7) 1.0
both (1.2) 1.5

(G) Caliper Assembly, Renew
Includes: Bleed complete system.
1983-87-one (.7) 1.0
both (1.1) 1.5

(G) Caliper Assembly, R&R and Recondition
Includes: Bleed complete system.
1983-87-one (1.2) 1.5
both (2.1) 2.5

PARKING BRAKE

(M) Parking Brake, Adjust
All models (.3) 4

(G) Parking Brake Warning Lamp Switch, Renew
1983-87 (.4) 4

(G) Parking Brake Control, Renew
1983-87 (.7) 1.0

(G) Parking Brake Cables, Renew
Front
1983-87 (.6) 1.0
Rear
1983-87-each (.8) 1.1

(G) Parking Brake Equalizer, Renew
1983-87 (.3) 5

PARTS 6 BRAKE SYSTEM 6 PARTS

	Part No.	Price
(1) Brake Shoe Set (2 Rear wheels)		
1983-87-exc. H.D.	◆12300219	41.00
1983-H.D.	◆12300214	50.00
(2) Wheel Cylinder Assy., Rear		
1983-84	◆18007980	22.50
1985-87	◆18012303	30.25
Wheel Cylinder Repair Kit, Rear		
1983-87	◆18003744	12.75
Brake, Hose, Front (Flex)		
1983-87	◆9762810	17.75

PARTS 6 BRAKE SYSTEM 6 PARTS

	Part No.	Price
Brake Hose, Rear (Flex)		
1983-87	◆9761251	15.00
Master Cylinder Assy.		
exc. Diesel		
1983-84	◆18009816	171.25
1985-87	◆18011916	141.50
Diesel		
1983-84	◆18009373	134.50
Master Cylinder Repair Kit		
exc. Diesel		
1983-87	◆18010083	22.75
Diesel		
1983-84	◆18009375	20.50

POWER BRAKE BOOSTER

	Part No.	Price
Power Cylinder Assy.		
exc. Diesel		
1983-87-sngl. diaph.	18010113	188.00
Dual diaphragm	◆18010120	271.25
Diesel		
1983-84	◆25511548	265.00
Brake Booster Repair Kit		
exc. Diesel		
1983-87-sngl. diaph.	18007855	41.25
dual diaph.	◆18007897	47.50

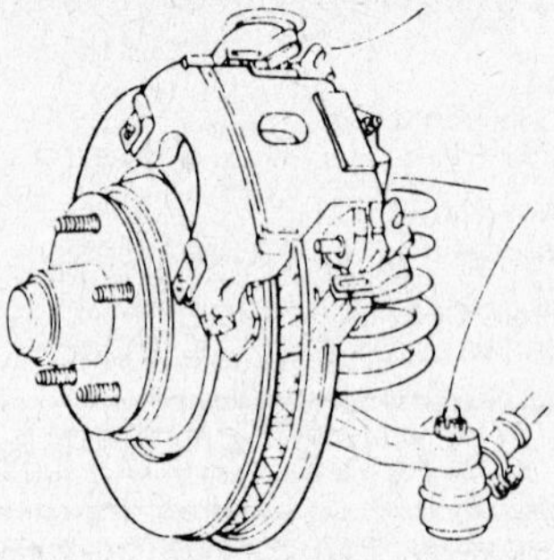

FRONT BRAKE

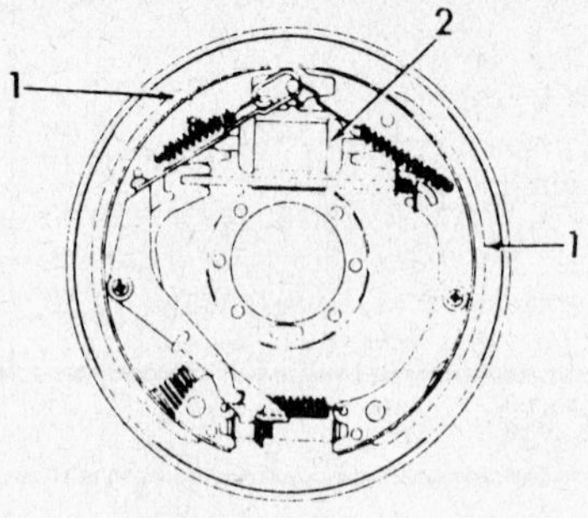

REAR BRAKE

	Part No.	Price
Diesel		
1983-84	◆22506710	16.50
Brake Drum, Rear		
1983-87	◆1249146	73.00
Oil Seal, Front		
1983-87	◆3965092	3.00

PARKING BRAKE

	Part No.	Price
Front Cable		
1983	◆25502753	11.50
1984-87	◆25520341	11.50

	Part No.	Price
Rear Cable		
1983-R.H.	◆25502794	21.00
L.H.	◆22518169	N.L.
1984-85-R.H.	◆25518168	22.00
L.H.	◆25518169	12.25
1986-87-R.H.	◆25526680	22.00
L.H.	◆25526681	12.25
Parking Brake Control/Handle		
(Control)		
1983-87	◆25503396	23.25
(Handle)		
1983-87	468861	4.75

PARTS 6 DISC BRAKES 6 PARTS

	Part No.	Price
Front Hub and Rotor		
1983-87	◆14032431	100.25
Caliper Repair Kit		
1983-87	◆18003724	8.75
(1) Shoe Unit		
1983-87	◆12300227	43.00
(2) Spring		
1983-87	◆18006810	3.00
(3) Piston		
1983-87	◆18003155	11.00
(4) Caliper Assy. (L.H.)		
1983-87	◆18010480	137.00

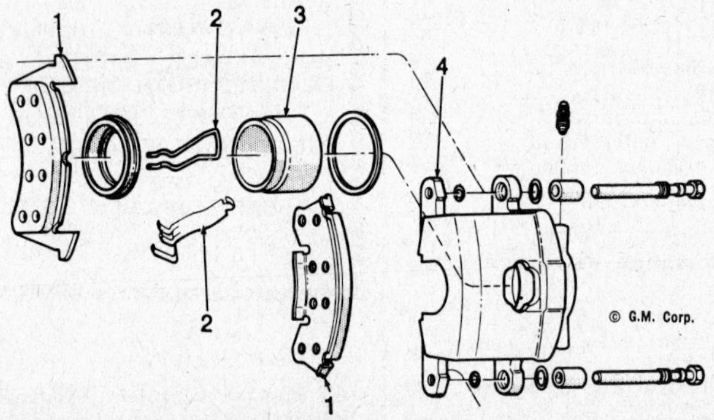

LABOR 7 COOLING SYSTEM 7 LABOR

	(Factory Time)	Chilton Time
(M) Winterize Cooling System		
Includes: Run engine to check for leaks, tighten all hose connections. Test radiator and pressure cap, drain radiator and engine block. Add anti-freeze and refill system.		
All models		.5
(M) Thermostat, Renew		
V-6–1983-87		
200-229 engs	(.5)	.6
231 eng	(.6)	.7
262 eng	(.5)	.9
V-8–1983-87	(.5)	.6
Diesel–1983-84	(.5)	.6
(M) Radiator Assembly, R&R or Renew		
Includes: Drain and refill cooling system.		
1983-87	(.7)	1.1
w/A.T. add	(.2)	.2

COOLING SYSTEM TUNE-UP

An Annual Cooling System Tune-Up Suggestion List should include (with some exceptions):

1. A visual check of the cooling system for indications of leaks or excessive oil content.
2. Pressure check the cooling system for internal and external leaks with filler cap and neck adapter and tester.
3. Check crankcase and automatic transmission oil for water content.
4. Test coolant thermostat with radiator thermometer.
5. Check temperature gauge for accuracy.
6. Drain system and flush till clean.
7. Clean foreign matter from radiator fins.
8. Test radiator pressure cap with cap tester.
9. Check fan blades and pulleys for alignment and damage.
10. Internal and external inspection of all hoses for cracks and deterioration.
11. Check core plugs (where possible) for seepage.
12. Refill system with correct coolant and check for air locks.
13. Check condition and tension of drive belts with tension gauge.

All models **1.5**

LABOR 7 COOLING SYSTEM 7 LABOR

(Factory Time)	Chilton Time
ADD THESE OPERATIONS TO RADIATOR R&R	
(G) Boil & Repair	1.5
(G) Rod Clean	1.9
(G) Repair Core	1.3
(G) Renew Tank	1.6
(G) Renew Trans. Oil Cooler	1.9
(G) Recore Radiator	1.7
(M) Radiator Hoses, Renew	
1983-87-upper (.3)	.4
lower (.4)	.5
both (.5)	.7
(G) Thermostat By-Pass Hose or Pipe, Renew	
1983-84 (.6)	.8
(G) Water Pump, Renew	
1983-87	
V-6-200-229 engs (1.3)	1.7
231 eng (.9)	1.3
262 eng (1.2)	1.7
V-8 engs (1.3)	1.7
Diesel (1.7)	2.5
w/A.C. add (.3)	.3
(M) Drive Belt, Renew	
1983-87-V-6 engs	
200-229 engs (.2)	.3
231 eng (.5)	.7
262 eng (.2)	.3
V-8 engs (.2)	.3
each adtnl	.2

(Factory Time)	Chilton Time
(M) Serpentine Drive Belt, Renew	
1983 (.2)	.4
(M) Clutch Fan, Renew	
1983-87 (.3)	.5
(M) Fan Blades, Renew	
1983-87 (.3)	.5
(G) Temperature Gauge (Engine Unit), Renew	
1983-87 (.4)	.4
(G) Temperature Gauge (Dash Unit), Renew	
1983-87 (.6)	1.0
(G) Water Jacket Expansion Plug, Renew (Side of Block)	
All models (.5)	.5
Add time to gain accessibility.	
(G) Heater Hoses, Renew	
Includes: Drain and refill coolant.	
wo/A.C.	
1983-87 (.4)	.6
w/A.C.	
1983-87 (.4)	.7
(G) Heater Core, R&R or Renew	
wo/A.C.	
1983-87 (.5)	1.1
w/A.C.	
1983-84 (1.3)	2.5
1985-87 (1.6)	2.5

(Factory Time)	Chilton Time
ADD THESE OPERATIONS TO HEATER CORE R&R	
(G) Boil & Repair	1.2
(G) Repair Core	.9
(G) Recore	1.2
(G) Heater Control Assembly, Renew	
wo/A.C.	
1983-87 (.4)	.7
w/A.C.	
1983-87 (.4)	.7
(G) Heater Blower Motor, Renew	
1983-87-Gas (.3)	.5
Diesel (.4)	.6
(G) Heater Blower Motor Resistor, Renew	
1983-87 (.2)	.3
(G) Heater Blower Motor Relay, Renew	
1983-87 (.2)	.3
(G) Heater Blower Motor Switch, Renew	
1983-87 (.5)	.6
(G) Hot Water Shut Off Valve, Renew	
1983-87-Gas (.3)	.5
Diesel (.6)	.8

PARTS 7 COOLING SYSTEM 7 PARTS

	Part No.	Price
(1) Radiator Assy.		
Accurate replacement of the radiator can be done only by using the radiator code stamped on a metal tag located on the original radiator. Order by year, model and radiator code no.		
(2) Radiator Hoses		
Order by year and model.		
(3) Water Pump Assembly		
V-6-229		
1983-84	◆474029	72.50
V-6-231		
1983-87	◆1260709	61.75
V-6-262		
1985-87	◆14085847	75.75
V-8-305		
1983-84	◆474029	72.50
1985-87	◆14085847	75.75
V-8-Diesel		
1983-84	◆556283	95.00
(4) Fan Belt		
Order by year and model.		
Water Temperature Sender		
(Gauge package)		
1983-87	◆8993146	19.25
Water Temperature Switch		
(wo/Gauge package)		
(exc. 231 & Diesel)		
1983-87	◆25036136	11.75
(231)		
1983-84	◆25036371	8.00
(Diesel)		
1983	◆25036371	8.00
1984	◆25036629	9.75
Temperature Gauge-Dash Unit		
1983-84	8993605	24.50
1985-87	25034419	27.00

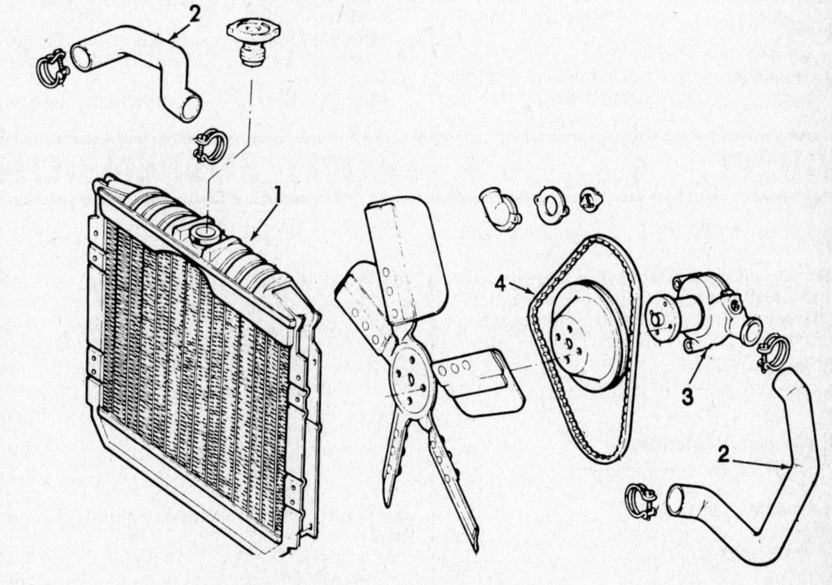

	Part No.	Price
Heater Core		
1983-87-wo/A.C.	◆3037852	55.75
A.C.	◆3037689	70.00
Heater Blower Motor		
(Without Air Conditioning)		
1983-exc. diesel	◆22021257	N.L.
Diesel	◆22048569	47.50

	Part No.	Price
1984-87-exc. diesel	◆22048573	45.75
Diesel	◆22048569	47.50
(With Air Conditioning)		
1983-87	◆22020945	60.00
Heater Blower Switch		
1983-87	◆16015256	6.00

LABOR 8 EXHAUST SYSTEM 8 LABOR

(Factory Time) — Chilton Time

(G) Muffler, Renew (One)
1983-87 (.4) 7

(G) Tail Pipe, Renew (One)
1983 (.4) 7

(G) Resonator Assy., Renew
1983-87 (.4) 7

(G) Catalytic Converter, Renew
1983-87 (.8) 1.0
w/AIR add (.1) 1

(G) Exhaust Pipe Flange Gasket or Seal, Renew
1983-87 (.4) 6

(G) Intermediate Exhaust Pipe, Renew
1983-87 (.5) 7

(G) Exhaust Crossover Pipe, Renew
1983-87-Gas (.4) 9
Diesel (1.4) 1.8

(G) Exhaust Pipe (Rear), Renew
1983 (.5) 8

(G) Exhaust Pipe (Front), Renew
1983-84
V-6 (.6) 9
V-8 (.6) 9
Diesel (.4) 7

(G) E.F.E. Valve (Heat Riser), Renew
1983-87
V-6 (.6) 9
V-8 (.6) 9

(G) Exhaust Manifold, Renew
V-6–1983-87
200, 229 engs-right (1.0) 1.4
left (.8) 1.2
231 eng-right (.7) 1.1
left (.6) 1.0
262 eng-right (1.4) 1.9
left (.8) 1.2
w/A.C. add (.5) 5
w/C.C.C. add (.2) 2
V-8
1983-87-right (1.5) 2.0
left (1.0) 1.5
w/A.C. add (.4) 4
w/C.C.C. add (.2) 2
Diesel
1983-right (.9) 1.3
left (.7) 1.1
1984-right (1.2) 1.7
left (.7) 1.1

COMBINATIONS

(G) Muffler, Exhaust and Tail Pipe, Renew
All models 1.8
w/Crossover pipe add 4

(G) Muffler and Tail Pipe, Renew
All models 1.0

PARTS 8 EXHAUST SYSTEM 8 PARTS

Part number listed are for pricing reference only. Order part with complete year, model and engine information.
Tail pipes are included with muffler assm.

	Part No.	Price
Exhaust Pipe		
V-6-229		
(crossover)		
1983-84	14063921	94.75
(intermediate)		
1983-84	14063926	51.50
V-6-231		
1983-84		
crossover	◆25506286	31.25
front	◆25506875	14.00
intermed. (1983-87)	◆25515196	53.00
V-6-262		
1985-87		
front	14082868	54.50
intermed.	14082867	32.25
V-8-305H		
1983-87-interm.	◆14063928	53.00
crossover	◆14063922	95.00
V-8-305G		
1984-87-Front	14065781	224.00
interm.	14073082	216.00
V-8-Diesel		
1983-84-front	◆563056	41.25
intermed.	14063930	58.75
crossover	◆22514728	24.00
Catalytic Convertor		
V-6-229		
1983-84	25036381	N.L.
V-6-231		
1983	◆8999642	271.25
1984	◆8999615	312.25
V-6-262		
1985-87	◆25056790	335.00
V-8-305		
1983	◆8999642	271.25
1984-87-Code H	◆25056382	300.25
Code G	◆25056539	342.00

LABOR 9 FRONT SUSPENSION 9 LABOR

(Factory Time) — Chilton Time

Note: On all front suspension operations alignment charges must be added if performed. Time given does not include alignment.

(G) Wheel, Renew
one (.3) 5

(G) Wheels, Rotate (All)
All models 5

(G) Wheels, Balance
one 3
each adtnl 2

(G) Check Alignment of Front End
All models 5
Note: Deduct if alignment is performed.

(G) Toe-In, Adjust
All models (.4) 6

(G) Align Front End
Includes: Adjust front wheel bearings.
All models (.7) 1.4
w/A.C. interference add 5

(G) Front Wheel Bearings, Clean and Repack (Both Wheels)
All models (1.1) 1.6

(G) Front Wheel Bearings and Cups, Renew
All models
one whl (.7) 9
both whls (1.1) 1.5

(G) Front Wheel Grease Seals, Renew
All models
one whl (.7) 8
both whls (1.1) 1.2

(G) Front Shock Absorbers, Renew
1983-87-one (.3) 4
both (.5) 7

(G) Rebuild Front Suspension
Includes: Disassemble, renew necessary parts, reassemble, lubricate and align front end.
1983-87-one side 5.1
both sides 9.0

(G) Upper and Lower Ball Joints, Renew (One Side)
Add alignment charges.
1983-87 (1.3) 1.8

(G) Upper Ball Joint, Renew
Add alignment charges.
1983-87-one (.7) 9
both (1.2) 1.7

(G) Lower Ball Joint, Renew
Add alignment charges.
1983-87-one (.6) 9
both (1.0) 1.7

(G) Steering Knuckle and Arm, Renew
Add alignment charges.
1983-87-one (1.0) 1.4
both (1.8) 2.5

(G) Upper Control Arm, Renew (One)
Add alignment charges.
1983-87 (.7) 1.2

LABOR 9 FRONT SUSPENSION 9 LABOR

(Factory Time)	Chilton Time
(G) Lower Control Arm, Renew	
Add alignment charges.	
1983-87-one (1.0)	1.5
both (1.7)	2.6
(G) Upper Control Arm Inner Pivot Shaft or Bushings, Renew (One Side)	
Add alignment charges.	
1983-87 (1.0)	1.5
(G) Lower Control Arm Shaft or Bushings, Renew (One Side)	
Add alignment charges.	
1983-87 (1.2)	1.7
(G) Front Spring, Renew	
Add alignment charges.	
1983-87-one (.8)	1.4
both (1.4)	2.5
(G) Front Stabilizer Bar and Bushings, Renew	
1983-87 (.5)	.8
(G) Stabilizer Links or Grommets, Renew	
1983-87-one (.3)	.4
both (.4)	.6

PARTS 9 FRONT SUSPENSION 9 PARTS

	Part No.	Price
(1) Front Wheel Bearing (Outer)		
1983-87	◆14045734	N.L.
(2) Front Wheel Bearing (Inner)		
1983-87	◆7450630	11.00
(3) Front Seal Assy.		
1983-87	◆3965092	3.50
(4) Steering Knuckle (R.H.)		
1983-87	◆14012602	117.00
(5) Ball Joint Pkg. (Lower)		
1983	◆9767281	31.50
1984-87	◆9767281	31.50
(6) Control Arm (Lower)		
1983-87-R.H.	◆14045078	92.50
L.H.	◆14075337	96.75
(7) Bushing (Rear)		
1983-87	◆461853	6.25
(8) Shock Absorber		
1983-87	◆4993579	24.50
(9) Coil Spring		
Order by year and model.		
(10) Ball Joint (Upper)		
1983-87	◆9767112	34.75
(11) Bushing		
1983-87	◆473786	5.25
(12) Control Arm (Upper)		
1983-87-R.H.	◆14039012	97.75
L.H.	◆14039011	97.75
(13) Shaft Pkg. (Upper Control)		
1983-87	338387	34.25

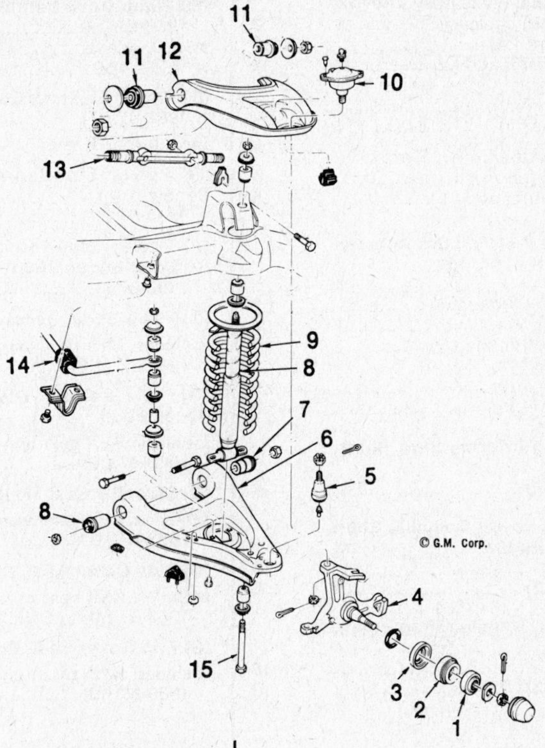

	Part No.	Price
(14) Bushing (Stabilizer)		
1983-87		
.75″ hole	◆392592	1.00
.87″ hole	◆388294	1.00
1.0″ hole	◆371773	1.00
1.08″ hole	◆472117	2.00
1.18″ hole	◆472118	2.00
(15) Link Pkg.		
1983-87	◆470147	4.25

LABOR 10 STEERING LINKAGE 10 LABOR

(Factory Time)	Chilton Time
(G) Tie Rods or Tie Rod Ends, Renew	
Includes: Reset toe-in.	
1983-87-one side (.7)	1.0
both sides (.9)	1.4
(G) Inner Tie Rods, Renew	
Includes: Reset toe-in.	
1983-87-one side (.7)	1.0
both sides (.8)	1.2
(G) Pitman Arm, Renew	
1983-87 (.4)	.7
(G) Steering Idler Arm, Renew	
1983-87 (.7)	1.0
(G) Steering Intermediate Rod, Renew	
Includes: Reset toe-in.	
1983-87 (.9)	1.2

LABOR 11 STEERING GEAR 11 LABOR

(Factory Time)	Chilton Time

(G) Steering Wheel, Renew
1983-87 (.3) 4

(G) Horn Contact or Cancelling Cam, Renew
1983-87 (.5) 6

(G) Upper Mast Jacket Bearing, Renew
1983-85-std (.8) 1.4
tilt (.9) 1.6
w/Cruise control add (.2) 2
1986-87
std colm (.8) 1.4
tilt colm (.5) 9

(G) Turn Signal Pivot Assy., Renew
1983-85-std column (.8) 1.2
tilt column (.6) 1.1
w/Cruise control add (.2) 2
1986-87
std colm (1.2) 1.7
tilt colm (1.1) 1.6

(G) Multifunction Lever, Renew
All models (.2) 4
w/Cruise control add (.5) 5

(G) Steering Column Lock Actuator Parts, Renew
1983-85
std colm (.8) 1.3
tilt colm (.9) 1.4
w/Cruise control add (.2) 2
1986-87
std colm (1.0) 1.5
tilt colm (1.2) 1.7

(G) Steering Intermediate Shaft, Renew
1983-87 (.4) 9

(G) Steering Lower Coupling Shaft (Pot Joint), Renew
1983 (.5) 8
1984-85 (.3) 8

(G) Steering Coupling (Rag Joint), Renew
1983 (.5) 8
1984-85 (.3) 8

(Factory Time)	Chilton Time

(G) Steering Pitman Shaft Seal, Renew
1983-87 (.6) 1.0

POWER STEERING

(G) Trouble Shoot Power Steering
Includes: Check pounds pull on steering wheel, test pump and system pressure and check for external leaks.
All models 5

(M) Check and Fill Reservoir
All models 2

(M) Pump Drive Belt, Renew
1983-87 (.3) 4
w/A.C. add 1
w/A.I.R. add 1

(G) Power Steering Gear, Adjust
1983-87 (.7) 1.2
Includes: R&R gear.

(G) Power Steering Gear Assy., Renew
1983-87 (.7) 1.2

(P) Power Steering Gear Assy., R&R and Recondition
1983-87 (1.7) 2.5

(G) Valve Body, Recondition
Includes: R&R gear assy.
1983-87 (1.0) 1.8

(G) Adjustor Plug Assy., Recondition
Includes: R&R gear assy.
1983-87 (.9) 1.6

(G) Steering Gear Housing, Renew
Includes: R&R gear assy.
1983-87 (1.1) 1.8

(G) Side Cover Seal, Renew
Includes: R&R gear assy.
1983-87 (.9) 1.4

(G) End Cover Seal, Renew
Includes: R&R gear assy.
1983-87 (.8) 1.4

(Factory Time)	Chilton Time

(G) Pitman Shaft Seal, Renew
1983-87 (.6) *1.0
*Does not require R&R gear assy.

(G) Power Steering Pump, Renew
1983-87-V-6 (.5) 9
V-8 (.9) 1.4
Diesel (.9) 1.4
w/A.C. add (.2) 2
w/Hydro-Boost add (.1) 1
Renew reservoir add (.1) 2

(P) Power Steering Pump, R&R and Recondition
1983-87-V-6 (1.0) 1.7
V-8 (1.4) 2.2
Diesel (1.4) 2.2
w/A.C. add (.2) 2

(G) Pump Flow Control Valve, Renew
V-6-1983-87 (.4) 7
V-8-1983-87 (.4) 7
w/A.C. add (.2) 2

(G) Power Steering Reservoir, Renew (Remote)
1983-87 (.3) 5

(M) Power Steering Hoses, Renew
1983-87-one (.4) 6
both (.6) 8
w/A.C. add (.2) 2

(G) Power Steering Pump Shaft Seal, Renew
1983-87
V-6 (.6) 1.0
V-8 (.9) 1.5
Diesel (.9) 1.5
w/A.C. add (.2) 2

(M) Hydro-Boost Hoses, Renew
1983-84
Booster to pump (.6) 1.0
Booster to gear (.3) 5
Return (.3) 5

TILT COLUMN

(G) Tilt Column, R&R and Recondition
1983-87 (2.4) 3.0

PARTS 10 STEERING LINKAGE 10 PARTS

	Part No.	Price
(1) Idler Lever Assy.		
1983-87	◆7837635	51.00
(2) Inner Tie Rod Assy.		
1983-87	◆7837183	40.25
(3) Outer Tie Rod End Assy.		
1983-87	◆7837733	40.00
(4) Adjuster Sleeve Pkg.		
1983-87	◆7829465	15.75
(5) Pitman Arm Assy.		
1983-87-800" gear	◆7837648	44.00
1983-V-6-605" gear	7837644	44.00
1983-V-8-605" gear	◆7837649	44.00

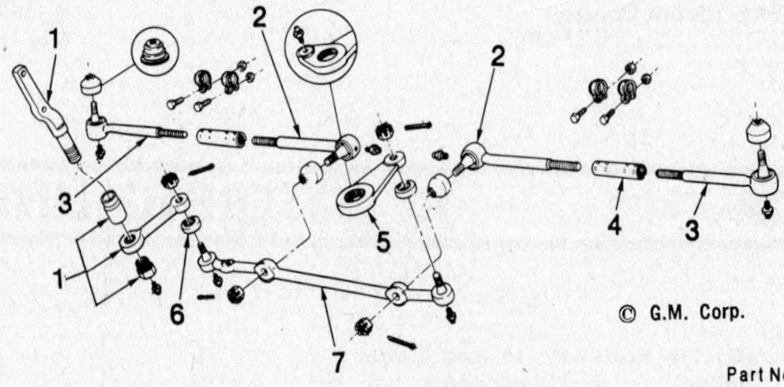

Part No. Price

The model 605" steering gearbox uses a round cover retained by a ring, the model 800" steering gearbox uses a rectangular cover retained by bolts.

	Part No.	Price
(6) Ball Stud Seal		
1983-87	◆5693125	2.75
(7) Relay Rod		
1983-87-exc. H.D.	◆7835787	79.75
H.D. susp.	7837638	79.75

PARTS 11 POWER STEERING GEAR 11 PARTS

	Part No.	Price
(1) Seal (Side Cover)		
1983-87	◆7817486	9.00
(2) Pitman Shaft (w/Gear)		
1983-87-exc. below	◆7813631	87.50
Non-variable strg.	◆7815885	87.50
(4) Bearing Kit		
1983-87	◆7826850	11.00
(5) Housing Assy.		
1983-87	◆7834145	183.00
(6) Bearing (Pitman Shaft)		
1983-87	◆5697804	15.00
(7) Seal Kit (Pitman Shaft)		
1983-87	◆7826470	17.00
(8) Seal (Adjuster Plug)		
1983-87	◆5686527	1.50
(9) Bearing (Adjuster Plug)		
1983-87	◆7828012	7.25
(10) Plug Assy. (Adjuster)		
1983-87	◆7832731	53.50
(11) Seal Kit		
1983-87	◆5687182	12.50
(12) Valve Assy.		
1983-87-exc. below	◆7832058	212.00
H.D. susp.	◆7832055	202.25
SS pkg.	◆7832057	212.00
(14) Seal Kit		
1983-87	◆7817485	6.50
(15) Plug		
1983-87	◆5693463	7.25
(16) Rack Assy.		
1983-87-exc. below	◆7817528	162.00
1983-84-H.D. susp.	◆7827170	154.25
1985-87-H.D. susp.	◆7817526	151.00
1983-87-SS pkg.	◆7839019	162.00

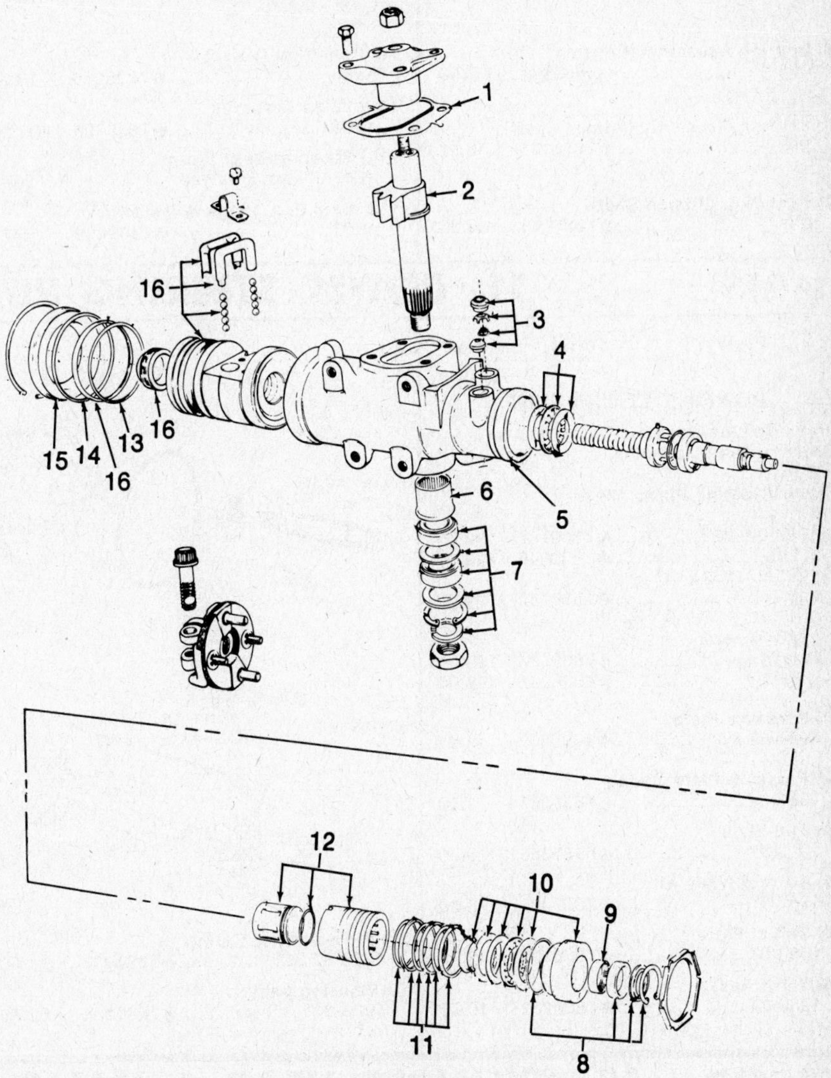

PARTS 11 POWER STEERING GEAR 11 PARTS

MODEL 605 STEERING GEAR

The 605 type gear is identified by a round side cover retained by a retaining ring, all others have a rectangular cover retained by bolts.

	Part No.	Price
(1) Cover		
1983	◆7819790	26.75
(2) Pitman Shaft Gear		
1983	◆7838146	87.50
(3) Seal Pkg.		
1983	◆7819809	5.75
(4) Connector		
1983	◆7819797	4.50
(5) Housing Assembly		
V-6		
1983	◆7832279	181.00
V-8		
1983	◆7834920	183.00

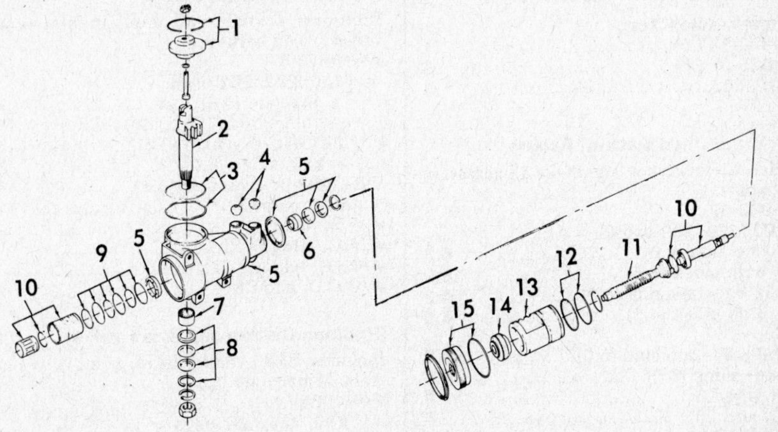

PARTS 11 POWER STEERING GEAR 11 PARTS

	Part No.	Price
(6) Bearing Assembly (Housing)		
1983	5683229	7.50
(7) Bearing Assembly (Pitman Shaft)		
1983	◆7838145	16.25
(8) Seal Pkg. (Pitman Shaft)		
1983	◆7838143	9.25
(9) Seal Pkg. (Valve)		
1983	◆7826056	13.50
(10) Valve Assembly		
1983	◆7819796	202.00
(11) Steering Gear Worm		
1983-87-Not serviced.		
(12) Seal Pkg. (Rack & Piston)		
1983	◆7819809	5.75
(13) Rack and Piston		
1983	◆7837990	162.00
(14) Bearing Assembly (Lower)		
1983	◆7837985	13.50
(15) Adjuster Plug		
1983-V-6 eng.	◆7819792	52.25
V-8 engine	◆7828584	59.25

PARTS 11 POWER STEERING PUMP 11 PARTS

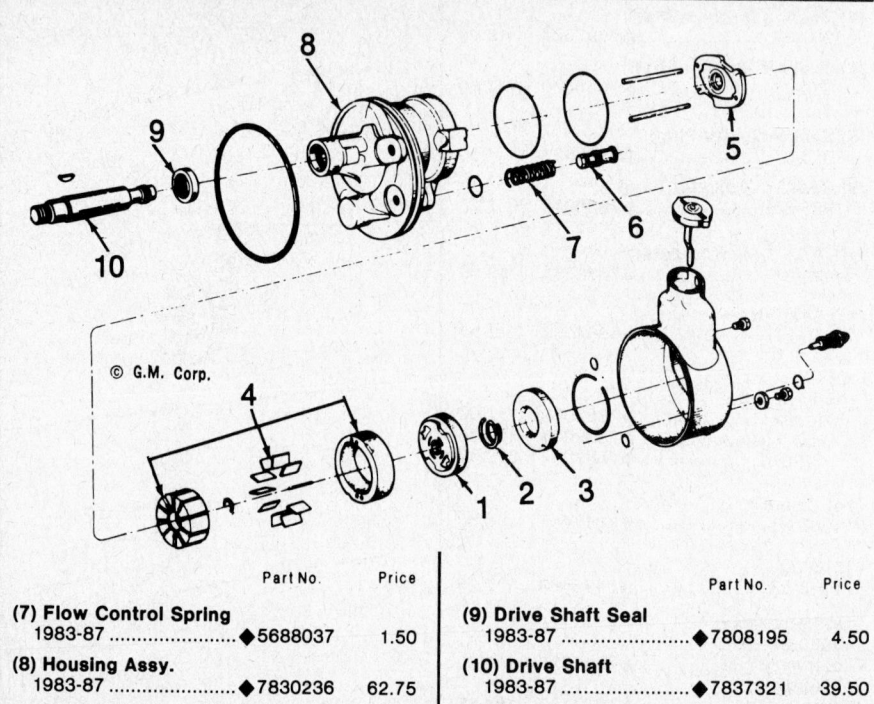

	Part No.	Price
POWER STEERING PUMP		
Pressure Line Hose		
Order by year and model.		
Power Steering Pump Assy.		
V-6		
1983-84-229	◆7839787	199.00
231	◆7839345	199.00
1985-87-262 eng.	◆7839787	199.00
V-8		
1983-87-exc. diesel	◆7839787	199.00
Diesel	◆7839997	199.00
(1) Pressure Plate		
1983-87	◆7839669	14.25
(2) Pressure Plate Spring		
1983-87	◆7839667	1.00
(3) End Plate		
1983-87	◆5689358	3.50
(4) Rotor & Vane Kit		
1983-87	◆7837322	75.00
(5) Thrust Plate		
1983-87	◆7836369	13.75
(6) Valve Assy.		
1983-87	◆7809232	10.75

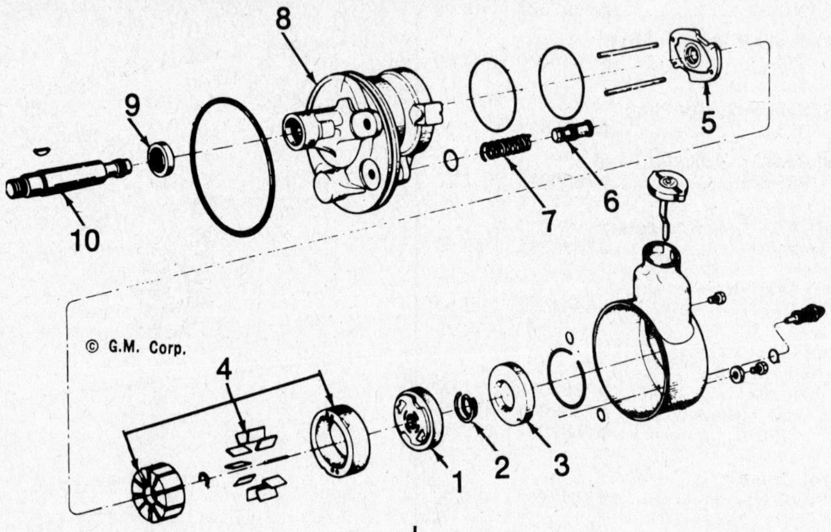

	Part No.	Price
(7) Flow Control Spring		
1983-87	◆5688037	1.50
(8) Housing Assy.		
1983-87	◆7830236	62.75
(9) Drive Shaft Seal		
1983-87	◆7808195	4.50
(10) Drive Shaft		
1983-87	◆7837321	39.50

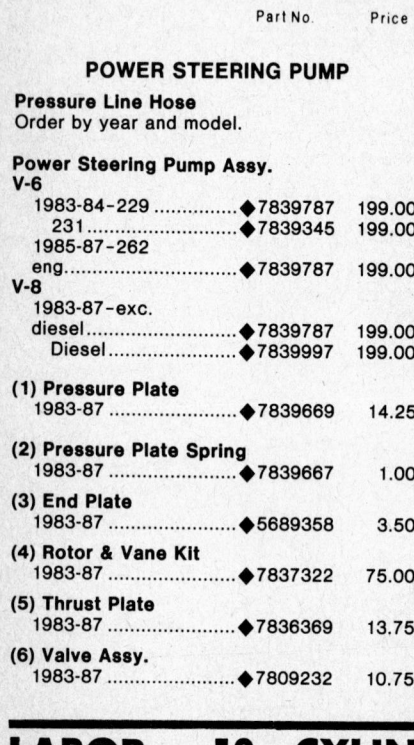

LABOR 12 CYLINDER HEAD & VALVE SYSTEM 12 LABOR

(Factory Time)	Chilton Time
GASOLINE ENGINES	
(G) Compression Test	
V-6–1983-87 (.5)	.7
V-8–1983-87 (.6)	.8
w/A.C. add	.3
(G) Cylinder Head Gasket, Renew	
Includes: Clean carbon and make all necessary adjustments.	
V-6–1983-87	
200, 229, 262 engs	
one side (4.6)	6.3
both sides (6.5)	8.9
231 eng-one side (3.2)	4.3
both sides (4.9)	6.6
V-8–1983-87-one side (5.0)	6.6
both sides (7.0)	9.3
w/P.S. add (.3)	.3
w/A.C. add (.5)	.5
w/A.I.R. add (.2)	.2
w/C.C.C. add (.3)	.3
(G) Cylinder Head, Renew	
Includes: Transfer all components, reface valves, clean carbon.	
V-6–1983-87	
200, 229, 262 engs.	
one side (5.3)	7.3
both sides (7.6)	10.4
231 eng-one side (3.8)	5.1
both sides (6.0)	8.1
V-8–1983-87-one side (5.8)	7.8
both sides (8.7)	11.6
w/P.S. add (.3)	.3
w/A.C. add (.5)	.5
w/A.I.R. add (.2)	.2
w/C.C.C. add (.3)	.3
(P) Clean Carbon and Grind Valves	
Includes: R&R cylinder head, grind valves and seats. Minor tune up.	
V-6–1983-87	
200, 229, 262 engs	
one side (5.7)	7.8
both sides (8.5)	11.7
231 eng-one side (4.4)	6.0
both sides (6.7)	9.2
V-8–1983-87-one side (6.3)	8.3
both sides (9.4)	12.5
w/P.S. add (.3)	.3
w/A.C. add (.5)	.5
w/A.I.R. add (.2)	.2
w/C.C.C. add (.3)	.3
(G) Valve Tappets, Adjust	
V-6–1983-87	1.5
V-8–1983-87	2.0
w/A.C. add	.3
w/C.C.C. add	.3
(G) Rocker Arm Cover or Gasket, Renew	
V-6–1983-87	
200, 229 engs	
one side (.7)	1.0
both sides (1.2)	1.8
231 eng-one side (.5)	.7
both (.7)	1.1
262 eng	
right side (.6)	.9

(Factory Time) Chilton Time

left side (.3) .5
both sides (.8) 1.3
V-8–1983-87
right side (.7) 1.0
left side (.5) .7
both sides (1.1) 1.6
w/A.C. add (.2) .2
w/A.I.R. add (.3) .3
w/C.C.C. add (.3) .3

(G) Valve Tappets, Renew (Lifters)

Includes: R&R intake manifold on V-6 & V-8 engines. Make all necessary adjustments.

V-6–1983-87
200, 229 engs
one (2.7) 3.5
all (3.0) 4.2
231 eng-one bank (2.0) 2.7
both banks (2.2) 3.3
262 eng
one cyl (2.7) 3.9
one cyl-each bank (3.0) 4.3
all-both banks (3.5) 5.0

V-8–1983-87
one cyl (2.8) 3.9
one cyl-each bank (3.1) 4.3
all cyls-both banks (3.7) 5.2
w/A.C. add (.2) .2
w/A.I.R. add (.1) .1
w/C.C.C. add (.3) .3

(G) Valve Springs and/or Valve Stem Oil Seals, Renew (Head on Car)

V-6–1983-87
200, 229 engs
one (1.2) 1.6
all (3.3) 4.2
231 eng-one cyl (.8) 1.1
all cyls (2.6) 3.5
262 eng
one cyl-right bank (1.0) 1.5
one cyl-left bank (.7) 1.1
one cyl-each bank (1.5) 2.2
all cyls-both banks (2.7) 4.0

V-8–1983-87
one cyl (1.2) 1.7
one cyl-each bank (2.0) 2.8
all cyls-both banks (3.7) 5.2
w/A.C. add (.2) .2
w/A.I.R. add (.1) .1
w/C.C.C. add (.3) .3

(G) Valve Rocker Arms or Push Rods, Renew

V-6–1983-87
200, 229, 262 engs
one (.8) 1.2
all (1.5) 2.1
231 eng-one (.6) .9
all (1.0) 1.4

V-8–1983-87
right bank-one cyl (.9) 1.3
left bank-one cyl (.6) .9
one cyl-each bank (1.2) 1.7
all cyls-both banks (1.7) 2.4
w/A.C. add (.2) .2
w/A.I.R. add (.1) .1
w/C.C.C. add (.3) .3

COMBINATIONS
Add to Valve Job

See Machine Shop Operations

(G) CARBURETOR, RECONDITION
2 BBL (.9) 1.2
4 BBL (1.2) 1.5

(P) VALVE GUIDES, REAM OVERSIZE
Each (.1) .1

(G) DRAIN, EVACUATE & RECHARGE AIR CONDITIONING SYSTEM
All models (.5) 1.0

(G) ROCKER ARM STUD, RENEW
Each (.1) .2

(G) HYDRAULIC VALVE LIFTERS, DISASSEMBLE AND CLEAN
Each .2

(G) DISTRIBUTOR, RECONDITION
V-6 (.5) .8
V-8 (.5) .8

(Factory Time) Chilton Time

(G) Rocker Arm Stud, Renew

V-6–1983-84
200, 229 engs-one (1.1) 1.4
262 eng
right bank-one (1.0) 1.5
left bank-one (.7) 1.1
V-8–1983-87
right bank-one (1.1) 1.5
left bank-one (.9) 1.3
All engines, each adtnl-add (.3) .4
w/A.C. add (.2) .2
w/A.I.R. add (.1) .1
w/C.C.C. add (.3) .3

(G) Rocker Arm Shaft Assy., Renew

V-6–1983-85
231 eng-one side (.6) .9
both sides (1.1) 1.6
w/A.C. add (.5) .5
w/A.I.R. add (.3) .3
w/C.C.C. add (.3) .3
Recond assy add-each .2

DIESEL ENGINE

(G) Compression Test

V-6 1.0
V-8 1.3

(G) Cylinder Head Gasket, Renew

Includes: R&R injector pump and lines. R&R intake manifold and disconnect exhaust manifolds. Clean gasket surfaces, bleed lifters and adjust timing. Drain and refill cooling system.

V-6–1983
right side (4.4) 6.1
left side (3.8) 6.3
both sides (6.1) 8.1

V-8–1983-84
right side (6.1) 7.9
left side (5.7) 7.4
both sides (7.6) 9.9
w/A.C. add (.4) .4

(Factory Time) Chilton Time

(G) Cylinder Head, Renew

Includes: R&R injector pump and lines. R&R intake manifold and disconnect exhaust manifolds. Clean gasket surfaces. Transfer parts, reface valves. Bleed lifters and adjust timing. Drain and refill cooling system.

V-6–1983
right side (4.9) 6.7
left side (4.3) 6.8
both sides (6.9) 9.8
V-8–1983-84
right side (6.5) 8.4
left side (6.1) 7.9
both sides (8.4) 11.1
w/A.C. add (.4) .4

(P) Clean Carbon and Grind Valves

Includes: R&R injector pump and lines. R&R cylinder heads, clean carbon. Recondition valves and seats. Check and adjust valve stem length. Bleed lifters, drain and refill cooling system.

V-6–1983
right side (5.4) 7.4
left side (4.8) 7.5
both sides (8.0) 11.3
V-8–1983-84
right side (7.0) 9.1
left side (6.6) 8.5
both sides (9.3) 12.6
w/A.C. add (.4) .4

(G) Rocker Arm Cover or Gasket, Renew

V-6–1983
one (.8) 1.5
both (1.3) 2.4
V-8–1983-84
one (1.2) 2.4
both (2.0) 2.9

(G) Rocker Arm, Pivot and/or Push Rod, Renew

V-6–1983
one cyl (1.0) 1.7
one cyl-each side (1.5) 3.0
each adtnl cyl .1
V-8–1983-84
one cyl (1.5) 2.5
one cyl-each side (2.3) 3.0
each adtnl cyl .1

(G) Valve Springs and/or Valve Stem Oil Seals, Renew (Head on Car)

V-6–1983
one cyl (1.1) 1.8
one cyl-each side (1.7) 3.2
each adtnl cyl (.3) .3
V-8–1983-84
one cyl (1.6) 3.0
one cyl-each side (2.4) 3.7
each adtnl cyl (.3) .3

(G) Valve Tappets, Renew (Lifters)

Includes: R&R injector pump and lines, intake manifold and rocker arms. Drain and refill cooling system.

V-6–1983
one cyl (2.4) 3.5
one cyl-each side (2.8) 4.0
each adtnl cyl (.2) .2
V-8–1983-84
one cyl (3.5) 4.5
one cyl-each side (3.9) 5.0
each adtnl cyl (.1) .2

PARTS 12 CYLINDER HEAD & VALVE SYSTEM 12 PARTS

	Part No.	Price
Valve Grind Gasket Set		
Includes: Gaskets required to R&R cylinder heads.		
1983-84	14033548	43.50
V-6-231		
1983-84 (Type of int. manifold)		
aluminum	◆25505372	N.L.
cast iron	◆1264923	38.75
V-6-262		
1985-87	◆14091326	53.00
V-8-305		
1983-84	◆14033553	49.25
1985-87	◆14089154	61.50
V-8-Diesel		
1983-84	◆22522053	94.50
(1) Cylinder Head Gasket		
V-6-229		
1983-84	471593	8.00
V-6-231		
1983-84	◆1261403	8.50
V-6-262		
1985-87	◆14075646	7.00
V-8-305		
1983-87	◆462690	6.50
V-8-Diesel		
1983-84	◆22519416	30.75
(2) Cylinder Head		
V-6-229		
1983-84	14029985	237.00
V-6-231		
1983	◆25518679	217.00
1984	◆25518679	217.00
V-6-262		
1985-87	◆14085869	242.00
V-8-305		
1983-87	◆14034807	247.00
V-8-Diesel		
1983-84	◆22515038	387.00
(3) Valve Cover Gasket		
V-6-229		
1984	14082319	7.50
V-6-231		
1983-87	◆25505889	6.00
V-8-305		
1984-87	◆14082322	8.75
Use #1052289 R.T.V. sealer for applications not listed.		
(4) Rocker Arm		
V-6-229		
1983-84	◆3974290	5.50
V-6-231		
1983-84-right	◆1241850	4.50
left	◆1241851	4.50
V-6-262		
1985-87	◆14081257	7.25
V-8-305 & Diesel		
1983-87-exc. diesel	◆3974290	5.50
Diesel	◆22505583	N.L.
Valve Rotator		
V-8-exc. Diesel		
1983	◆6263794	5.50
1984-87	◆14042575	4.50

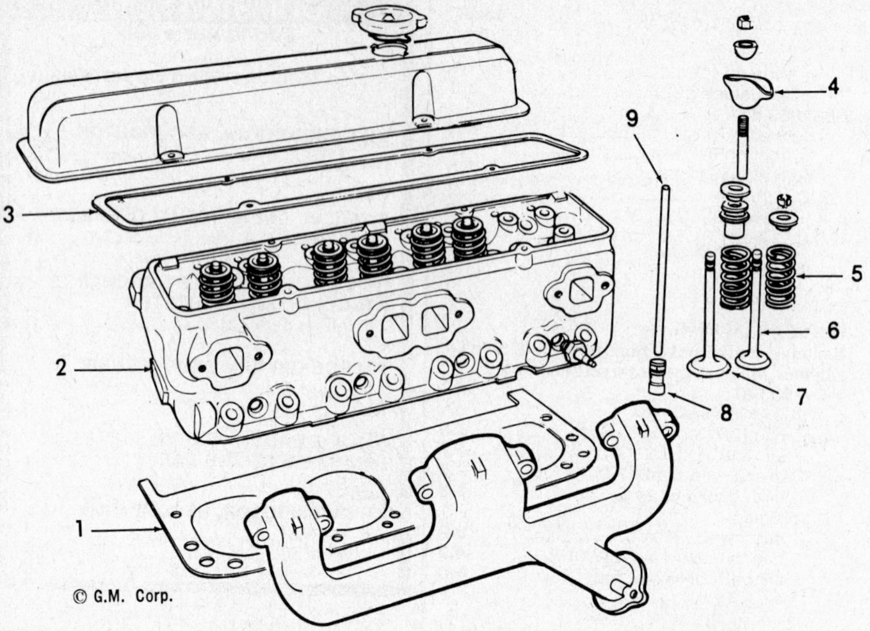

© G.M. Corp.

	Part No.	Price
Diesel		
1983-84	◆406996	3.50
(5) Valve Spring		
V-6-229 & 262		
1983-87	◆3911068	3.00
V-6-231		
1983-84	◆1249267	2.75
V-8-305		
1983-87	◆3911068	3.00
V-8-Diesel		
1983-84	◆22510372	4.00
(6) Intake Valve		
V-6-229		
1983-84	◆14025571	11.75
V-6-231		
1983-87	◆25512098	11.25
V-6-262		
1985-87	◆14075641	14.00
V-8-305		
1983-87	◆14025571	11.75
V-8-Diesel		
1983-84	◆22519914	20.00
(7) Exhaust Valve		
V-6-229		
1983-84	◆14095451	13.50
V-6-231		
1983-84	◆1261380	13.50
V-6-262		
1985-87	◆14095451	13.50
V-8-305		
1983	◆14095451	13.50
1984-87	◆14095451	13.50

	Part No.	Price
V-8-Diesel		
1983-84	◆558873	13.00
(8) Valve Lifters		
V-6-229 & 262		
1983-87	◆5232720	N.L.
V-6-231		
1983-84	◆5232765	9.00
V-8-305		
1983-87	◆5232720	N.L.
V-8-Diesel		
1983-84	◆5234470	38.10
(9) Push Rods		
V-6-229		
1983-84	◆14095256	5.00
V-6-231		
1983-87	◆1249139	4.00
V-6-262		
1985-87	◆14095256	5.00
V-8-305		
1983-87	◆14095256	5.00
V-8-Diesel		
1983-84	◆22511044	3.25
(10) Valve Stem Oil Seal exc. V-6-231 & Diesel		
1983-87	◆3835333	.50
V-6-231		
1983	◆25519324	2.25
1984	◆25518390	2.50
Diesel		
1983-84-intake	◆406595	1.00
exhaust	◆401823	1.00

LABOR 13 ENGINE ASSEMBLY & MOUNTS 13 LABOR

(Factory Time)	Chilton Time
GASOLINE ENGINES	
(G) Engine Assembly, Remove & Install	
Does not include transfer of any parts or equipment.	
V-6-1983-87	
200, 229 engs	5.4
231 eng	5.0
262 eng	6.5
V-8-1983-87	6.5
w/P.S. add (.3)	.3
w/A.C. add (.4)	.4
w/A.I.R. add (.4)	.4
w/C.C.C. add (.3)	.3
(G) Engine Assembly, Renew	
Includes: R&R engine and transmission assy. Transfer all component parts not supplied with replacement engine. Minor tune up.	
V-6-1983-87	
200, 229 engs (7.1)	10.7
262 eng (5.7)	9.1

LABOR 13 ENGINE ASSEMBLY & MOUNTS 13 LABOR

(Factory Time)	Chilton Time
V-8–1983-87 (6.3)	9.5
w/P.S. add (.3)	.3
w/A.C. add (.4)	.4
w/A.I.R. add (.4)	.4
w/C.C.C. add (.3)	.3

(G) Engine Assembly, Renew (Universal)

Includes: R&R engine assy. Transfer all component parts not supplied with replacement engine. Make all necessary adjustments.

V-8–1983-87 (8.4)	11.7
w/A.C. add (.5)	.5
w/C.C.C. add (.4)	.4
w/Cruise control add (.1)	.1

(P) Cylinder Block, Renew (w/All Internal Parts Less Head(s) and Oil Pan)

Includes: R&R engine and transmission assy. Transfer all component parts not supplied with replacement engine, clean carbon, grind valves. Minor tune up.

V-6–1983-84	
200, 229 engs (13.3)	18.6
231 eng (12.1)	15.8
262 eng (11.5)	15.2
V-8–1983-84 (14.0)	18.1
w/P.S. add (.3)	.3
w/A.C. add (.4)	.4
w/A.I.R. add (.4)	.4
w/C.C.C. add (.3)	.3

(P) Cylinder Block, Renew (w/Pistons, Rings and Bearings)

Includes: Transfer all component parts, clean carbon grind valves. Minor tune up.

V-6–1983-87	
200, 229 engs (15.5)	21.7
231 eng (15.0)	21.0
262 eng (13.5)	18.7
V-8–1983-87 (16.7)	24.2
w/P.S. add (.3)	.3
w/A.C. add (.4)	.4
w/A.I.R. add (.4)	.4

(G) Engine Assembly, Renew (Universal)

Includes: R&R engine assembly, transfer all component parts not supplied with replacement engine. Make all necessary adjustments.

V-6–1983	16.5
V-8–1983-84	20.0
w/A.C. add (.5)	.5

(P) Cylinder Block, Renew (w/All Internal Parts Less Heads and Oil Pan)

Includes: R&R engine, transfer all component parts not supplied with replacement engine. Clean carbon, grind valves. Make all necessary adjustments.

V-6–1983 (9.7)	21.0
V-8–1983-84 (14.5)	24.0
w/A.C. add (.5)	.5

(P) Engine Assembly, Renew (Partial/Basic)

Includes: R&R engine assy. Transfer all component parts not supplied with replacement engine. Make all necessary adjustments.

V-6–1985-87	
262 eng (9.5)	13.3
w/A.C. add (.4)	.4
Recond valves add (2.0)	2.0
V-8–1985-87 (11.2)	15.6
w/A.C. add (.5)	.5
w/C.C.C. add (.3)	.3
Recond valves add (2.7)	2.7

(P) Engine Assy., R&R and Recondition (Complete)

Includes: Rebore block, install new pistons, rings, rod and main bearings. Clean carbon, grind valves. Tune engine.

V-6–1983-87	
200, 229 engs (24.7)	28.9
231 eng (20.2)	25.1
262 eng (17.8)	24.9
V-8–1983-87 (20.6)	27.8
w/P.S. add (.3)	.3
w/A.C. add (.4)	.4
w/A.I.R. add (.4)	.4
w/C.C.C. add (.3)	.3

(P) Engine Assembly, Recondition (In Car)

Includes: Expand or renew pistons, install new rings, pins, rod and main bearings. Clean carbon and grind valves. Tune engine.

V-6–1983-87	
200, 229 engs (17.8)	21.4
231 eng (14.1)	18.0
262 eng (15.6)	20.3
V-8–1983-87 (16.9)	23.6
w/P.S. add (.3)	.3
w/A.C. add (.4)	.4
w/A.I.R. add (.4)	.4
w/C.C.C. add (.3)	.3

(G) Engine Mounts, Renew

Front	
V-6–1983-87	
200, 229 engs-one (1.0)	1.4
both (1.5)	2.1
231 eng-one (.5)	.7
both (.7)	1.0
262 eng-one (.7)	1.1
both (1.0)	1.6
V-8–1983-87	
one (1.0)	1.4
both (1.5)	2.1
Rear	
1983-87 (.4)	.6

DIESEL ENGINE

(G) Engine Assembly, Remove & Install

Does not include transfer of any parts or equipment.

V-6–1983	4.5
V-8–1983-84	5.0
w/A.C. add (.5)	.5

(P) Cylinder Block, Renew (w/Pistons, Rings and Bearings)

Includes: R&R engine, transfer all component parts not supplied with replacement engine. Clean carbon, grind valves. Make all necessary adjustments.

V-6–1983 (10.8)	22.0
V-8–1983-84 (16.6)	27.0
w/A.C. add (.5)	.5

(P) Engine Assy., R&R and Recondition (Complete)

Includes: Rebore block, install new pistons, rings, rod and main bearings. Clean carbon, grind valves. Make all necessary adjustments.

V-6–1983 (17.9)	27.7
V-8–1983-84 (29.5)	36.0
w/A.C. add (.5)	.5

(P) Engine Assembly, Recondition (In Car)

Includes: Expand or renew pistons, install new rings, pins, rod and main bearings. Clean carbon, grind valves. Make all necessary adjustments.

V-6–1983 (14.7)	22.7
V-8–1983-84 (23.0)	27.3
w/A.C. add (.5)	.5

(G) Engine Mounts, Renew

Front	
1983-84-one (.5)	.8
both (.7)	1.0
Rear	
1983-84 (.3)	.6

PARTS 13 ENGINE ASSEMBLY & MOUNTS 13 PARTS

Short Block (Partial Engine w/Crankshaft, Timing Gears, Pistons and Connecting Rods.)

	Part No.	Price
V-6–229		
1983-84	14019896	1232.25
V-6–231		
1983	◆25516156	1263.25
1984	◆25519449	1263.25
V-6–262		
1985	◆14085899	1307.00
1986-87	◆14094574	1307.00
V-8–305		
1983-84-Code H	◆14019868	1363.00
Code G	◆14091328	1300.00
1985	◆14091328	1300.00
1986-87	◆14101315	1300.00
V-8–Diesel		
1983	◆22518906	1950.00
1984	◆22525604	1600.00

Cylinder Block (w/Pistons, Rings and Bearings)

	Part No.	Price
V-6–229		
1983-84	14019895	889.25
V-6–231		
1983	◆25516160	905.25
1984	◆25519450	950.00
V-6–262		
1985	◆14085898	969.00
V-8–305		
1983-84-Code H	◆14019867	949.00
Code G	◆14048355	949.00
1985	14091327	904.00
V-8–Diesel		
1983	◆22518907	1418.00
1984	◆22525604	1600.00

PARTS 13 ENGINE ASSEMBLY & MOUNTS 13 PARTS

	Part No.	Price
Engine Overhaul Gasket Set		
V-6–229		
1983-84	14050645	10.25
V-6–231		
1983	25505751	41.50
1984-alum. man.	◆25505370	52.50
cast iron man.	◆25519460	48.00
V-6–262		
1985	◆14091479	7.95
1986-87	◆14094596	8.00
V-8–305		
1983-84	14050645	10.25
1985	◆14091479	7.95
1986-87	◆14094596	8.00
V-8–Diesel		
1983-84	◆22521786	90.00
Engine Mounts, Front		
V-6–229		
1983-84-right	14020242	22.50
left	14020241	22.50
V-6–231		
1983-left	◆25504643	29.00
right	◆1258666	24.00
1984-right	◆1258718	26.25
left	◆25504647	30.75
V-6–262		
1985-87-right	17981699	27.25
left	17981700	27.25
V-8–305 & Diesel		
1983-87-exc. diesel	◆459021	24.00
Diesel	◆553915	27.25

LABOR 14 PISTONS, RINGS & BEARINGS 14 LABOR

(Factory Time) — Chilton Time

GASOLINE ENGINES

(P) Rings, Renew (See Engine Combinations)

Includes: Remove cylinder top ridge, deglaze cylinder walls. Clean piston and ring grooves. Minor tune up.

	Chilton Time
V-6–1983-87	
200, 229, 262 engs	
one (6.8)	9.5
all (10.6)	15.1
231 eng-one (6.2)	8.5
all (11.3)	15.5
V-8–1983-87-one cyl (7.7)	10.6
all cyls (12.5)	17.9
w/P.S. add (.3)	.3
w/A.C. add (.5)	.5
w/A.I.R. add (.2)	.2
w/C.C.C. add (.3)	.3

(P) Piston or Connecting Rod, Renew

Includes: Remove cylinder top ridge, deglaze cylinder walls, clean piston and ring grooves. Minor tune up.

	Chilton Time
V-6–1983-87	
200, 229, 262 engs	
one (6.8)	9.8
all (10.6)	16.9
231 eng-one (6.2)	8.8
all (11.3)	17.3
V-8–1983-87-one cyl (7.7)	10.9
all cyls (12.5)	19.7
w/P.S. add (.3)	.3
w/A.C. add (.5)	.5
w/A.I.R. add (.2)	.2
w/C.C.C. add (.3)	.3

(P) Connecting Rod Bearings, Renew

	Chilton Time
V-6–1983-87	
200, 229, 262 engs	
one (2.3)	3.2
all (3.8)	4.7
w/C.C.C. add (.2)	.2
231 eng-one (1.3)	1.9
all (2.3)	3.4

COMBINATIONS

Add to Engine Work
See Machine Shop Operations

(Factory Time)	Chilton Time
(G) DRAIN, EVACUATE & RECHARGE AIR CONDITIONING SYSTEM	
All models (.5)	1.0
(G) ROCKER ARM STUD, RENEW	
Each (.1)	.2
(G) HYDRAULIC VALVE LIFTERS, DISASSEMBLE AND CLEAN	
Each	.2
(G) DISTRIBUTOR, RECONDITION	
V-6 (.5)	.8
V-8 (.5)	.8
(G) CARBURETOR, RECONDITION	
2 BBL (.9)	1.2
4 BBL (1.2)	1.5
(G) CYLINDER HEAD, R&R (ENGINE REMOVED)	
V-6	
262 eng	
one (2.0)	2.6
both (3.0)	3.9
V-8	
305 eng	
one (2.3)	.3.0
both (3.7)	4.8
(G) CONNECTING ROD, RENEW (ENGINE DISASSEMBLED)	
V-6	
262 eng	
each (.3)	.4
V-8	
305 eng	
each (.3)	.4
(P) VALVE GUIDES, REAM OVERSIZE	
Each (.1)	.1
(G) DEGLAZE CYLINDER WALLS	
Each (.1)	.1
(G) REMOVE CYLINDER TOP RIDGE	
Each (.1)	.1
(G) PLASTIGAUGE BEARINGS	
Each (.1)	.1
(G) OIL PUMP, RECONDITION	
V-6-231 eng (.5)	.8
(M) OIL FILTER ELEMENT, RENEW	
V-6 (.3)	.3
V-8 (.3)	.3

(Factory Time)	Chilton Time
V-8–1983-87-one (2.6)	3.6
all (4.7)	6.3

DIESEL ENGINE

(P) Rings, Renew (See Engine Combinations)

Includes: Remove cylinder top ridge, deglaze cylinder walls. Clean piston and ring grooves. Make all necessary adjustments.

	Chilton Time
V-6–1983 (11.2)	16.2
V-8–1983-84 (12.8)	17.2
w/A.C. add (.4)	.4

(P) Pistons or Connecting Rods, Renew

Includes: Remove cylinder top ridge, deglaze cylinder walls. Clean piston and ring grooves. Make all necessary adjustments.

	Chilton Time
V-6–1983 (11.2)	18.0
V-8–1983-84 (13.3)	19.6
w/A.C. add (.4)	.4

(P) Connecting Rod Bearings, Renew

Includes: Raise engine and clean oil pump screen.

	Chilton Time
V-6–1983 (3.6)	5.4
V-8–1983-84 (4.3)	6.6

PARTS 14 PISTONS, RINGS & BEARINGS 14 PARTS

	Part No.	Price
(1) Piston Ring Set (Std.)		
V-6–229		
1983-84	◆370409	14.50
V-6–231		
1983-84	◆1240955	15.75
V-6–262		
1985-87	◆14089025	18.00

PARTS 14 PISTONS, RINGS & BEARINGS 14 PARTS

	Part No.	Price
V-8-305		
1983-87	◆370409	14.50
V-8-Diesel		
1983	◆22515964	21.00
1984	◆22523733	21.00
(2) Piston Assy. (Std.)		
V-6-229		
1983-84	14019833	102.00
V-6-231		
1983	◆25518053	48.25
1984	◆25518053	48.25
V-6-262		
1985-87	◆14077948	48.25
V-8-305		
1983-87-Code H		
(83-84)	◆364702	43.00
Code H (85-87)	◆14081291	54.50
Code G	◆14081291	54.50
V-8-Diesel		
1983-right	◆22523360	63.75
left	◆22520327	63.75
1984-right	◆22523358	63.75
left	◆22523357	63.75
(3) Connecting Rod Assembly		
V-6-229		
1983-84	14053831	37.50
V-6-231		
1983-84	◆25506520	39.00

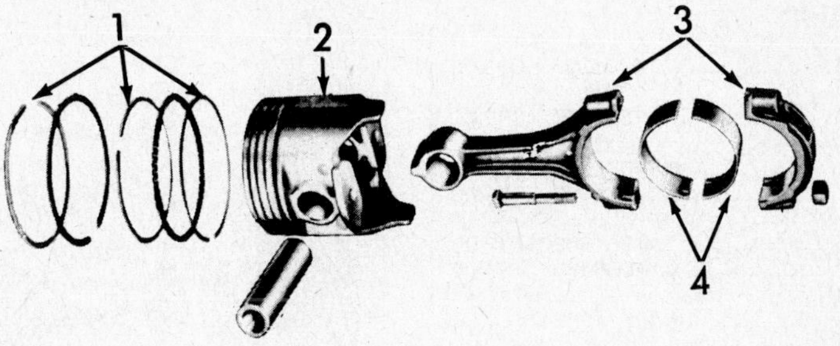

	Part No.	Price
V-6-262		
1985-87	◆14077944	42.25
V-8-305		
1983-87	◆14031310	39.50
V-8-Diesel		
1983-84	◆22515313	50.50
(4) Connecting Rod Bearings		
V-6-229		
1983-84	474095	8.00

	Part No.	Price
V-6-231		
1983-84	◆18005399	11.00
V-6-262		
1985-87	◆18012481	10.00
V-8-305		
1983-87	◆3910555	7.50
V-8-Diesel		
1983-84	◆18008494	10.50

LABOR 15 CRANKSHAFT & DAMPER 15 LABOR

(Factory Time) — Chilton Time

GASOLINE ENGINES

(P) Crankshaft and Main Bearings, Renew

Includes: R&R engine, check all bearing clearances.

(Factory Time)	Chilton Time
V-6-1983-87	
200, 229 engs (9.1)	12.7
231 eng (7.1)	9.9
262 eng (8.6)	12.0
V-8-1983-87 (9.5)	13.3
w/P.S. add (.3)	.3
w/A.C. add (.4)	.4
w/A.I.R. add (.4)	.4
w/C.C.C. add (.6)	.6

(P) Main Bearings, Renew

Includes: Check all bearing clearances.

V-6-1983-87	
200, 229 engs (3.7)	4.6
w/C.C.C. add (.2)	.2
231 eng (2.4)	3.6
262 eng (2.7)	4.6
V-8-1983-87 (3.4)	5.2

(P) Main and Rod Bearings, Renew

Includes: Check all bearing clearances.

V-6-1983-87	
200, 229 engs (5.5)	6.4
w/C.C.C. add (.2)	.2
231 eng (3.6)	5.4
262 eng (4.1)	6.4
V-8-1983-87 (5.7)	7.6

(G) Rear Main Bearing Oil Seals, Renew or Repack (Upper & Lower)

Includes: R&R oil pan and rear main bearing cap.

(Factory Time)	Chilton Time
V-6-1983-87	
200, 229 engs (2.3)	3.0
262 eng (2.1)	3.0
w/C.C.C. add (.2)	.2
231 eng (1.5)	2.2
V-8-1983-87 (2.0)	3.5

(G) Vibration Damper, Renew

V-6-1983-87 (.6)	1.0
V-8-1983-87 (.8)	1.2
w/P.S. add (.1)	.1
w/A.C. add (.3)	.3
w/A.I.R. add (.3)	.3

(G) Crankshaft Drive Belt Pulley, Renew

V-6-1983-87 (.5)	.8
w/A.C. add (.2)	.2
V-8-1983-87 (.6)	1.0
w/A.C. add (.2)	.2

DIESEL ENGINE

(P) Crankshaft and Main Bearings, Renew

Includes: R&R engine, check all bearing clearances.

V-6-1983 (4.1)	11.0
V-8-1983-84 (8.3)	11.2
w/A.C. add (.4)	.4

(P) Main Bearings, Renew

Includes: Check all bearing clearances.

V-6-1983 (3.6)	4.5
V-8-1983-84 (4.1)	5.5

(P) Main and Rod Bearings, Renew

Includes: Check all bearing clearances.

(Factory Time)	Chilton Time
V-6-1983 (4.8)	6.3
V-8-1983-84 (6.5)	7.9

(G) Rear Main Bearing Oil Seals, Renew

Includes: R&R engine assy.

V-6-1983 (5.9)	10.5
V-8-1983-84 (7.4)	10.7
w/A.C. add (.4)	.4

(G) Rear Main Bearing Oil Seals, Renew or Repack (Upper & Lower)

Includes: R&R oil pan and rear main bearing cap.

V-6-1983 (2.8)	3.5
V-8-1983-84 (2.9)	4.0

(G) Crankshaft Pulley or Balancer, Renew

V-6-1983	
pulley (.3)	.6
balancer (.3)	1.2
V-8-1983-84	
pulley (.6)	.8
balancer (.9)	1.3
w/A.C. add (.2)	.2

(G) Crankshaft Front Oil Seal, Renew

V-6-1983 (.5)	1.3
V-8-1983-84 (.9)	1.5
w/A.C. add (.2)	.2

PARTS 15 CRANKSHAFT & DAMPER 15 PARTS

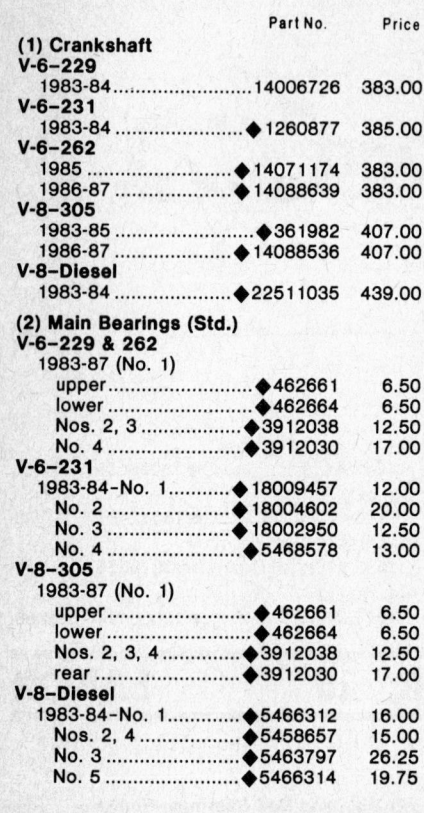

	Part No.	Price
(1) Crankshaft		
V-6–229		
1983-84	14006726	383.00
V-6–231		
1983-84	◆1260877	385.00
V-6–262		
1985	◆14071174	383.00
1986-87	◆14088639	383.00
V-8–305		
1983-85	◆361982	407.00
1986-87	◆14088536	407.00
V-8–Diesel		
1983-84	◆22511035	439.00
(2) Main Bearings (Std.)		
V-6–229 & 262		
1983-87 (No. 1)		
upper	◆462661	6.50
lower	◆462664	6.50
Nos. 2, 3	◆3912038	12.50
No. 4	◆3912030	17.00
V-6–231		
1983-84–No. 1	◆18009457	12.00
No. 2	◆18004602	20.00
No. 3	◆18002950	12.50
No. 4	◆5468578	13.00
V-8–305		
1983-87 (No. 1)		
upper	◆462661	6.50
lower	◆462664	6.50
Nos. 2, 3, 4	◆3912038	12.50
rear	◆3912030	17.00
V-8–Diesel		
1983-84–No. 1	◆5466312	16.00
Nos. 2, 4	◆5458657	15.00
No. 3	◆5463797	26.25
No. 5	◆5466314	19.75

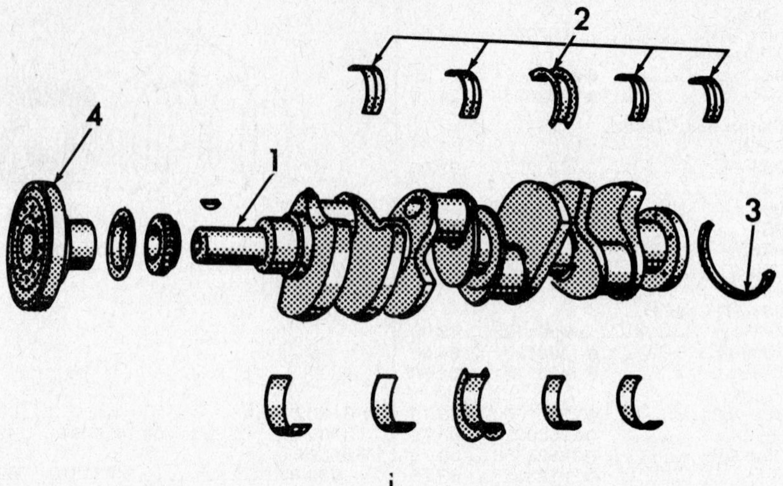

	Part No.	Price
(3) Main Bearing Oil Seal (Rear)		
V-6–229 & 262		
1983-87	◆473424	9.00
V-6–231		
1983-84	◆1193151	1.50
V-8–305		
1983-87	◆473424	9.00
V-8–Diesel		
1983-84	◆9772831	1.50

	Part No.	Price
(4) Vibration Damper		
V-6–229 & 262		
1983-87	◆14082324	41.00
V-6–231		
1983	◆25506570	42.75
1984	◆22523502	N.L.
V-8–305		
1983-87	◆458653	59.25
V-8–Diesel		
1983-84	◆559131	63.25

LABOR 16 CAMSHAFT & TIMING GEARS 16 LABOR

(Factory Time)	Chilton Time
GASOLINE ENGINES	
(G) Timing Cover Oil Seal, Renew	
V-6–1983-87 (.6)	1.2
V-8–1983-87 (.8)	1.4
w/A.C. add (.1)	.1
(G) Timing Case Cover and Gasket, Renew	
V-6–1983-87	
200, 229 engs (2.2)	2.7
231 eng (2.2)	3.2
262 eng (1.8)	2.7
V-8–1983-87 (2.0)	3.0
w/P.S. add (.1)	.1
w/A.C. add (.2)	.2
w/A.I.R. add (.2)	.2
(G) Timing Chain or Camshaft Gear, Renew	
Includes: R&R engine front cover.	
V-6–1983-87	
200, 229 engs (2.4)	3.2
231 eng (2.4)	3.7
262 eng (1.9)	3.2
V-8–1983-87 (2.3)	3.5
w/P.S. add (.1)	.1
w/A.C. add (.2)	.2
w/A.I.R. add (.2)	.2
Renew crank gear add (.2)	.2
(G) Camshaft, Renew	
Includes: R&R engine and oil pan.	
V-6–1983-87	
200, 229 engs (6.0)	8.0
231 eng (4.7)	7.0
262 eng (4.6)	8.0
w/A.C. add (2.2)	2.5
V-8–1983-87 (6.2)	8.6
w/P.S. add (.1)	.1
w/A.C. add (.3)	.3
w/A.I.R. add (.2)	.2
w/C.C.C. add (.3)	.3
DIESEL ENGINE	
(G) Timing Case Cover or Gasket, Renew	
Includes: R&R fan blade, crankshaft pulley and balancer. Drain and refill oil and coolant.	
V-6–1983 (1.1)	2.4
V-8–1983-84 (2.1)	3.1
w/A.C. add (.3)	.3
(G) Timing Chain or Gears, Renew	
Includes: R&R fan blade, crankshaft pulley and balancer. Drain and refill oil and coolant.	
V-6–1983 (3.6)	5.0
V-8–1983-84 (2.3)	3.5
w/A.C. add (.3)	.3
(G) Camshaft, Renew	
Includes: R&R radiator, front cover, fuel pump, timing gear and chain. R&R injector pump, intake manifold and lifters. Disconnect exhaust system. Drain and refill oil and coolant. Make all necessary adjustments.	
V-6–1983 (4.0)	7.0
V-8–1983-84 (7.3)	10.0
w/A.C. add (1.0)	1.0
Renew cam brgs add	3.8
(G) Camshaft Rear Bearing Plug, Renew	
Includes: R&R trans for accessibility.	
V-6–1983 (2.1)	3.0
V-8–1983-84 (2.1)	3.0

PARTS 16 CAMSHAFT & TIMING GEARS 16 PARTS

	Part No.	Price
(1) Timing Case Gasket		
V-6–229 & 262		
1983-87	◆3799620	1.00
V-6–231		
1983-84	◆25512861	3.00
V-8–305		
1983-87	◆3799620	1.00
V-8–Diesel		
1983-84	◆22505997	1.25
(2) Timing Case Oil Seal		
exc. V-6–231 & Diesel		
1983	◆14033199	5.50
1985-87	◆10036286	5.25

PARTS 16 CAMSHAFT & TIMING GEARS 16 PARTS

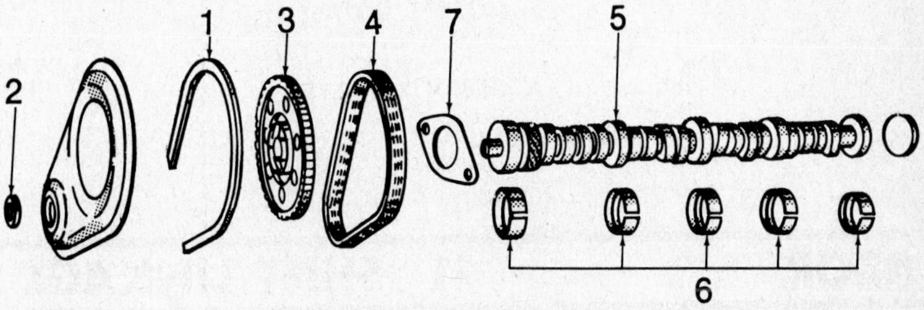

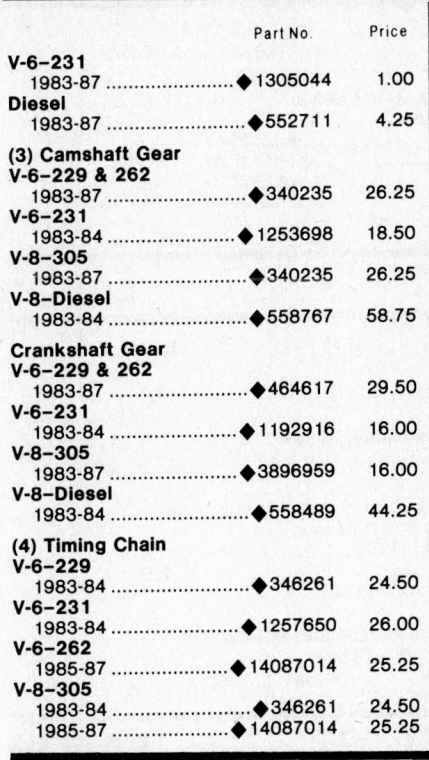

	Part No.	Price
V-6-231		
1983-87	◆1305044	1.00
Diesel		
1983-87	◆552711	4.25
(3) Camshaft Gear		
V-6-229 & 262		
1983-87	◆340235	26.25
V-6-231		
1983-84	◆1253698	18.50
V-8-305		
1983-87	◆340235	26.25
V-8-Diesel		
1983-84	◆558767	58.75
Crankshaft Gear		
V-6-229 & 262		
1983-87	◆464617	29.50
V-6-231		
1983-84	◆1192916	16.00
V-8-305		
1983-87	◆3896959	16.00
V-8-Diesel		
1983-84	◆558489	44.25
(4) Timing Chain		
V-6-229		
1983-84	◆346261	24.50
V-6-231		
1983-84	◆1257650	26.00
V-6-262		
1985-87	◆14087014	25.25
V-8-305		
1983-84	◆346261	24.50
1985-87	◆14087014	25.25

	Part No.	Price
V-8-Diesel		
1983-84	◆558484	N.L.
(5) Camshaft		
V-6-229		
1983-84	14060649	118.00
V-6-231		
1983-84	◆1262835	119.00
V-6-262		
1985-87	◆14077973	120.00
V-8-305		
1983-87-Code H	◆14060653	124.00
Code G	◆14060655	155.00
V-8-Diesel		
1983-84	◆22510099	266.00
(6) Camshaft Bearings		
V-6-229 & 262		
1983-87-No. 1	◆474005	16.75

	Part No.	Price
No. 2 & rear	◆474006	12.75
No. 3	◆474007	16.75
V-6-231		
1983-84-exc. frt.	◆1231142	7.75
front	◆1234441	7.00
V-8-305		
1983-87-No. 1	◆474005	16.75
Nos. 2, 5	◆474006	12.75
Nos. 3, 4	◆474007	16.75
V-8-Diesel		
1983-84-No. 1	◆561077	11.50
No. 2	◆390300	11.50
No. 3	◆390301	11.75
No. 4	◆390302	11.50
rear	◆390303	11.50
(7) Camshaft Thrust Button		
V-6-231		
1983-84	◆1250948	2.50

LABOR 17 ENGINE OILING SYSTEM 17 LABOR

(Factory Time)	Chilton Time
GASOLINE ENGINES	
(G) Oil Pan or Gasket, Renew	
V-6-1983-87	
200, 229 engs (1.8)	2.4
w/C.C.C. add (.2)	.2
231 eng (1.1)	1.6
262 eng (1.4)	2.4
V-8-1983-87 (1.8)	3.0
(P) Pressure Test Engine Bearings (Pan Off)	
All models	1.0
(G) Oil Pump, Renew	
Includes: Transfer screen and drive to pump.	
V-6-1983-87	
200, 229 engs (1.9)	2.6
w/C.C.C. add (.2)	.2
262 eng (1.5)	2.6
V-8-1983-87 (2.0)	3.2
(G) Oil Pressure Gauge (Engine), Renew	
1983-87 (.3)	.4

(Factory Time)	Chilton Time
(G) Oil Pressure Gauge (Dash), Renew	
1983-87 (.6)	1.0
(G) Oil Pump, R&R and Recondition	
V-6-1983-84-231 eng (.5)	.8
(M) Oil Filter By-Pass Valve, Renew	
V-6-1983-87	
200, 229 engs (2.1)	3.0
w/C.C.C. add (.2)	.2
262 eng (1.6)	3.0
V-8-1983-87 (.3)	.4
(M) Oil Filter Element, Renew	
1983-87	
V-6 (.3)	.4
V-8 (.3)	.4
DIESEL ENGINE	
(G) Oil Pan or Gasket, Renew	
Includes: Raise engine, R&R and clean oil pump screen.	
V-6-1983 (2.1)	2.2

(Factory Time)	Chilton Time
V-8-1983-84 (2.6)	3.4
(P) Pressure Test Engine Bearings (Pan Off)	
All models	1.0
(G) Oil Pump, Renew	
Includes: Raise engine, R&R and clean oil pump screen.	
V-6-1983 (2.2)	2.4
V-8-1983-84 (2.7)	3.6
(G) Oil Pump, R&R and Recondition	
Includes: Raise engine, R&R and clean oil pump screen.	
V-6-1983 (2.4)	2.6
V-8-1983-84 (2.9)	3.8
(G) Oil Pressure Gauge (Engine), Renew	
1983-87 (.3)	.4
(M) Oil Filter Element, Renew	
1983-87 (.3)	.3

PARTS 17 ENGINE OILING SYSTEM 17 PARTS

	Part No.	Price
Oil Pan Gasket		
V-6-229 & 262		
1983	471830	10.75
1984-85	◆14079397	N.L.
1986-87	◆14088514	29.25
V-6-231		
1983-87	◆1260771	3.00
V-8-305		
1983	◆14019828	11.75
1984-85	◆14079398	10.00
1986-87	◆14088505	22.50

	Part No.	Price
V-8-Diesel		
1983-84	◆22519181	7.00
Oil Pump		
V-6-229 & 262		
1983-87	◆3764547	49.75
V-6-231		
1983	◆25519448	38.00
1984	◆25519448	38.00
V-8-305		
1983-87	◆3764547	49.75

	Part No.	Price
V-8-Diesel		
1983-84	◆22511732	59.75
Oil Pressure Gauge (Engine Unit)		
(wo/Gauges)		
1983-87-exc.		
below	◆10002798	5.50
231	◆25500672	5.50
Diesel	◆3815936	3.50
262	◆14014599	5.25

PARTS 17 ENGINE OILING SYSTEM 17 PARTS

	Part No.	Price
(gauges)		
1983-87	◆459417	17.75
Oil Pressure Gauge (Dash Unit)		
1983-87	25025579	25.00
Oil Pressure Relief Valve		
1983-87-exc.		
below	◆3702366	1.50
231	◆25515390	1.25
Diesel	◆557238	2.00

LABOR 21 SHIFT LINKAGE 21 LABOR

(Factory Time)	Chilton Time
AUTOMATIC	
(G) Shift Linkage, Adjust	
All models	
Neutral Safety Switch (.3)	.4
Shift Indicator Needle (.2)	.3
Shift Linkage (.4)	.5
T.V. Cable (.3)	.4
(G) Gear Selector Lever, Renew	
1983-87-colm shift (.2)	.5
floor shift (.8)	1.3
(G) Shift Control Rods or Cable, Renew	
1983-87-Rods-each (.4)	.5
Cable (.9)	1.3
(G) Park Lock Cable, Renew	
1985-87 (1.0)	1.5
(G) Steering Column Gearshift Tube and/or Bowl, Renew	
1983-87-std (1.0)	2.4
tilt (2.0)	3.0
w/Cruise control add (.2)	.2
(G) Gear Selector, Indicator Needle and/or Assembly, Renew	
1983-87 (.4)	.5

LABOR 25 U-JOINTS & DRIVESHAFT 25 LABOR

(Factory Time)	Chilton Time
(G) Universal Joints, Renew (One)	
Includes: R&R driveshaft.	
1983-87-front (.6)	.8
rear (.5)	.7
both (.7)	1.3
(G) Driveshaft, Renew	
1983-87 (.4)	.5
(G) Pinion Shaft Flange, Renew	
1983-87 (.8)	1.0

PARTS 25 UNIVERSAL JOINTS & DRIVE SHAFT 25 PARTS

	Part No.	Price
Universal Joint Repair Kit		
1983-87 (Type of driveshaft)		
Dana	◆374246	28.50
Saginaw	◆7806140	41.00

LABOR 26 REAR AXLE 26 LABOR

(Factory Time)	Chilton Time
(M) Differential, Drain & Refill	
All models	.6
(M) Axle Housing Cover or Gasket, Renew	
1983-87 (.5)	.6
(G) Axle Shaft Assembly, Renew	
Includes: R&R bearing.	
'C' Lock Type	
1983-87-one (.7)	.9
both (.9)	1.2
(G) Axle Shaft Bearing and/or Seal, Renew	
'C' Lock Type	
1983-87-one (.6)	.8
both (.8)	1.1
(G) Axle Shaft Wheel Mounting Studs, Renew	
1983-87-one side	1.0
both sides	1.4
(G) Pinion Shaft Oil Seal, Renew	
1983-87 (.5)	.8
(G) Differential Case Assy., Renew	
1983-87 (1.9)	2.8
w/Positraction add (.5)	.5
(P) Ring and Pinion Gears, Renew	
1983-87 (2.4)	3.9
Recond complete add	
std (.3)	.5
limited slip (.7)	1.0
(P) Pinion Bearings, Renew	
1983-87 (2.2)	3.4
Renew side brgs add (.3)	.3
(P) Differential Side Bearings, Renew (One or Both)	
1983-87 (1.7)	2.5
(P) Pinion Shaft and/or Side and Pinion Gears, Renew	
Does not include R&R case.	
1983-87 (.8)	1.8
w/Limited slip add (.5)	.5
(P) Limited Slip Clutch Plates, Renew	
1983-87 (1.1)	2.0
(G) Rear Axle Housing, Renew	
1983-87 (3.4)	5.2
(G) Rear Axle Assembly, Renew (Complete)	
1983-87 (1.7)	3.2

PARTS — 26 REAR AXLE 26 — PARTS

Part No. Pr

For positive identification of the rear axle, obtain the rear axle code which is stamped on the front portion of the passenger side axle tube. The manufacturer identity code (3rd letter of the rear axle code) must be used in some cases when ordering parts.

(1) Axle Shaft
1983-87 ....◆22519888 104.75

(2) Axle Seal
1983-87 ....◆3998519 4.00

(3) Axle Bearing
1983-87 ....◆7451785 16.00

(4) Pinion Flange
1983-87 ....◆7827670 33.50

(5) Pinion Seal
1983-87 ....◆552571 8.00

(6) Front Pinion Bearing
1983-84 ....◆7451202 16.00
1985-87 ....◆9417784 16.25

(7) Axle Housing
1983-87 ....◆22510780 496.25

Pinion and Side Gear Package
1983-85-7½" ring gear
wo/3.42, 3.73R......◆22525894 94.50
3.42, 3.73R ....◆22521625 105.00
Gear Packages contain 2 side gears, 2 pinion gears, thrust washers and pinion shaft.

(9) Drive Pinion Spacer
1983-87 ....◆9785792 1.50

(10) Rear Pinion Bearing
1983-87 ....◆7455699 N.L.

(11) Shim Package
(7½" dia. ring gear)
1983-87 (.025-0.29) ....◆553022 5.50

(12) Ring and Pinion Gear
(7½" ring gear)
(2.29 ratio)
1983-87 ....◆560197 259.00
(2.41 ratio)
1983-87 ....◆560198 259.00
(2.56 ratio)
(2.73 ratio)
1983-87 ....◆560201 259.00
(2.93 ratio)
(3.08 ratio)
1983-87 ....◆14048380 276.25
(3.23 ratio)
1983-87 ....◆560207 259.00
(3.42 ratio)
1983-84 ....◆22521623 276.00
(3.73 ratio)
1984 ....◆22521624 276.00
1985-87..............................14089179 276.00

(13) Bearing Adjusting Shim Pkg.
1983-87 (7½" ring gear)
(.040-.044)................◆3995791 6.50
Select fit, smallest size listed, larger sizes available.

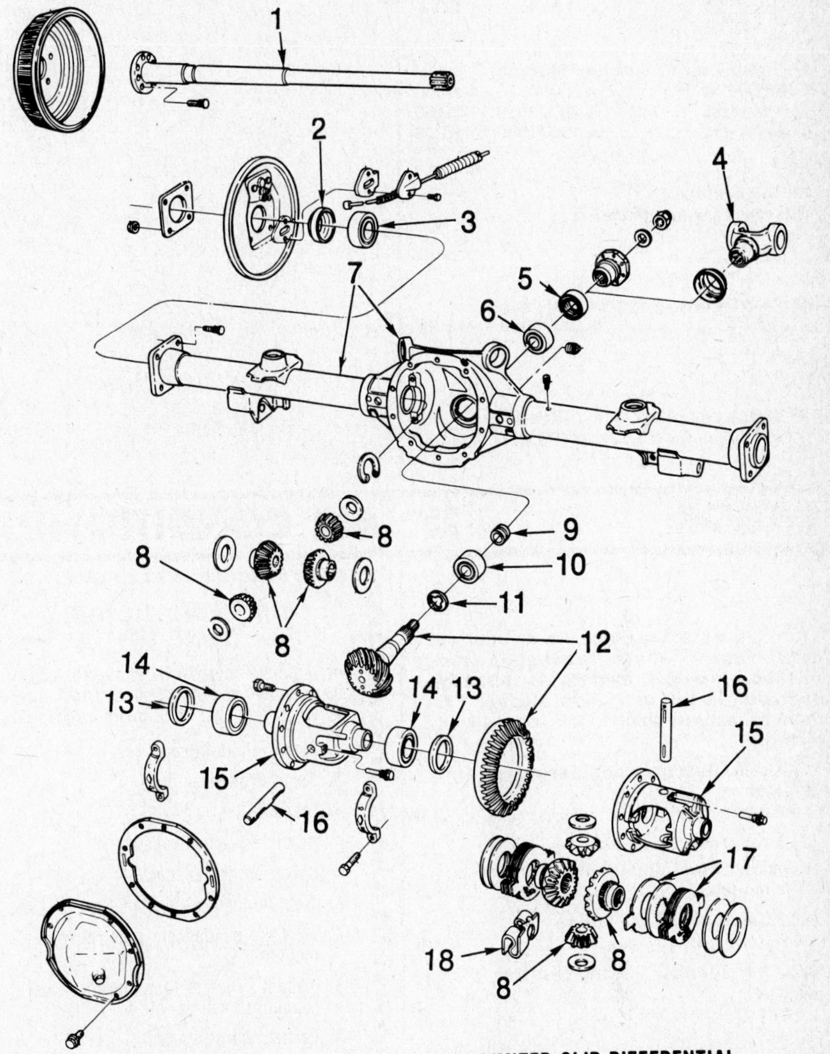

LIMITED SLIP DIFFERENTIAL

Part No. Price

(14) Differential Side Bearing
1983-87 ....◆7451281 15.00

(15) Differential Case
(Without Limited Slip Differential)
(7½" dia. ring gear)
1983-87-exc.
below ....◆558648 109.00
3.23, 3.42,
3.73R.............................◆558649 109.25
(With Limited Slip Differential)
(7½" dia. ring gear)
1983-87-exc.
below ....◆22514583 278.00
3.23, 3.42,
3.73R.......................◆22514584 402.00

(16) Pinion Shaft
(Without Limited Slip Differential)
(7½" dia. ring gear)
1983-87 ....◆22507586 11.00
(With Limited Slip Differential)
1983-87-exc.
below.........................◆22515972 10.25
1985-87-3.73R.........◆14048387 11.00

(18) Preload Spring
1983-87 ....◆561310 9.50

LABOR — 27 REAR SUSPENSION 27 — LABOR

(Factory Time) Chilton Time

(G) Rear Coil Spring, Renew
1983-87-one (.4)..................................... .6
both (.5) 8

(G) Rear Shock Absorbers, Renew
1983-87-one (.3)..................................... .4
both (.4) 7

(G) Lower Control Arm Assy., Renew
1983-87-one (.4)........................... .7
both (.5) 1.0
Renew bushings add-each arm (.3) 3

(G) Upper Control Arm Assy., Renew
1983-87-one (.4)........................... .8
both (.6) 1.1
Renew bushings add-each arm (.3) 3

(G) Rear Stabilizer Bar, Renew
1983-87 (.5)....................................... .7

PARTS 27 REAR SUSPENSION 27 PARTS

	Part No.	Price
(1) Upper Control Arm (w/Bushing)		
1983-87-0 deg.	◆10000076	15.00
-1½ deg.	◆10001059	30.50
1½ deg.	◆10001060	15.00
(2) Coil Spring		
Order by year and model.		
(3) Lower Control Arm (w/Bushing)		
1983-87	◆10000063	43.25
(4) Shock Absorber Assy. (Rear)		
1983-87	◆4993580	24.50

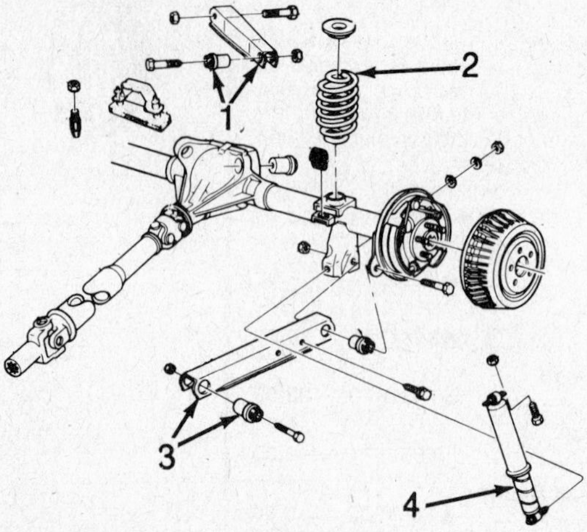

© G.M. Corp.

LABOR 28 AIR CONDITIONING 28 LABOR

(Factory Time) — Chilton Time

Note: If more than one item requires replacement where evacuation and discharging the system is already included in the operation, deduct 1.0 hour for each additional item to the times listed.

(G) Drain, Evacuate and Recharge System
All models (.5) 1.0

(G) Leak Test
Includes: Check all lines and connections.
All models 5

(G) Compressor Belt, Renew
1983-87 (.4) 6

(G) Refrigerant, Add (Partial Charge)
All models 6

COMPRESSOR 4 CYLINDER RADIAL

(G) Compressor Assembly, Renew
Includes: Transfer all attaching parts. Evacuate and charge system.
1983-87 (1.0) 2.0

(G) Clutch Plate and Hub Assy., Renew
1983-87 (.6) 8

(G) Rotor and/or Bearings, Renew
1983-87 (.9) 1.2
Add time to recharge A.C. system if required.

(G) Compressor Shaft Seal Kit, Renew
Includes: Evacuate and charge system.
1983-87 (1.0) 2.5

(G) Front Bearing, Head, or Seals, Renew
Includes: R&R compressor, R&R clutch and pulley assy. R&R shaft seal assy. Clean and inspect parts. Evacuate and charge system.
1983-87 (1.5) 2.8

(G) Outer Shell and/or 'O' Rings, Renew
Includes: R&R compressor, R&R clutch and pulley assy. Clean and inspect parts. Evacuate and charge system.
1983-87 (1.7) 2.8

AIR CONDITIONER TUNE-UP

For efficient operation and satisfactory performance in hot weather. The following air conditioner tune-up is suggested:

1. Clean intake filter
2. Clean condenser fins
3. Pressure test system
4. Adjust drive belt tension
5. Check antifreeze/coolant
6. Tighten compressor mounts
7. Tighten condenser and evaporator mounts
8. Inspect system for leaks (hoses, couplings, valves, etc.)
9. Partial charge system

All models 1.0
If necessary to evacuate and charge system, add 1.0

(Factory Time) — Chilton Time

(G) Valve Plate Assembly, Renew
Includes: R&R compressor, R&R clutch and pulley assy. R&R shell to internal mechanism. Clean and inspect parts. Evacuate and charge system.
1983-87 (1.8) 2.6
Renew two or more valves add (.1) 2

(G) Cylinder and Shaft Assy., Renew
Includes: R&R comp assy. Transfer clutch hub and drive plate, rotor, coil and switches. Renew seal kit. Install front head, outer shell and valve plates. Evacuate and charge system.
1983-87 (1.9) 2.9

(G) Compressor Relief Valve, Renew
Includes: Evacuate and charge system.
1983-87 (.9) 1.4

(G) Condenser, Renew
Includes: Evacuate and charge system.
1983-87-Gas (.8) 1.7
Diesel (1.5) 2.5

(Factory Time) — Chilton Time

(G) Evaporator Core, Renew
Includes: Evacuate and charge system.
1983-87 (2.0) 3.5

(G) Accumulator Assembly, Renew
Includes: Evacuate and charge system.
1983-87 (.8) 1.5

(G) Expansion Tube Assembly, Renew
Includes: Evacuate and charge system.
1983-87 (.7) 1.4

(G) Pressure Cycling Switch, Renew
1983-87 (.2) 3

(G) Vacuum Door Control Actuators, Renew
Defroster Door
1983-85 (3.4) 5.0
1986-87 (1.3) 2.0
Heat A/C Mode Door
1983 (3.4) 5.0
1984-87 (1.7) 2.4
Outside Recirculation Door
1983-87 (.4) 7

(G) Temperature Control Cable, Renew
1983-87 (.6) 1.0

(G) Vacuum Selector Valve, Renew
1983-87 (.5) 6

(G) Master Electrical Switch, Renew
1983-87 (.5) 6

(G) Blower Motor, Renew
1983-87-Gas (.2) 5
Diesel (.4) 6

(G) Blower Motor Switch, Renew
1983-87 (.5) 6

(G) Blower Motor Resistor, Renew
1983-87 (.2) 3

(G) Blower Motor Relay, Renew
1983-87 (.2) 3

(G) Temperature Control Head, Renew
1983-87 (.4) 6

(G) Air Conditioning Hoses, Renew
Includes: Evacuate and charge system.
1983-87-one (.8) 1.7
each adtnl (.3) 5

PARTS 28 AIR CONDITIONING 28 PARTS

	Part No.	Price
Compressor Assy.		
1983-84	◆12300273	390.00
1985	◆12321365	N.L.
1986-87	◆12326201	N.L.
Clutch Hub and Drive Plate		
1983-84	◆6551220	32.50
Rotor and Bearing		
1983-87	◆6551216	67.50
Compressor Shaft Seal Kit		
1983-84	◆9956695	13.00
1985-87	◆2724319	11.25
Front Head		
1983-87	◆6551142	28.25
Front Head Main Bearing		
1983-87	◆6556572	4.00
Outer Shell Assy.		
1983-87	◆2724158	38.00
Valve Plate Assy.		
1983-87	◆6551141	11.50
Cylinder and Shaft Assy.		
1983-87	◆2724144	269.00
Condenser Assembly		
(exc. V-6-231 & Diesel)		
1983-87	3040935	183.00
(V-6-231 & Diesel)		
1983-84	◆3041841	170.00
Evaporator Core Assembly		
1983-87	◆3037638	201.50
Accumulator		
1983	◆2724240	80.00
1984-87	◆2724265	87.75
Blower Motor		
(With Air Conditioning)		
1983-87	◆22020945	60.00
(Without Air Conditioning)		
1983-exc. diesel	◆22021257	N.L.
Diesel	◆22048569	47.50
1984-87-exc. diesel	◆22048573	41.00
Diesel	◆22048569	47.50
Blower Control Switch		
1983-87-exc. A.C.	◆16015256	6.00
1984-87-A.C.	◆16032480	7.50
Blower Motor Relay		
1983-87	◆10018449	N.L.
Blower Motor Resistor		
1983-84	◆526897	4.50
1985-87	◆10039426	4.50

LABOR 29 LOCKS, HINGES & WIND. REGULATORS 29 LABOR

	(Factory Time)	Chilton Time
(G) Hood Latch, Renew		
1983-87	(.2)	.5
(G) Hood Hinge, Renew (One)		
1983-87	(.3)	.4
(G) Hood Release Cable, Renew		
1983-87	(.3)	.6
(G) Door Lock, Renew (One)		
1983-87	(.5)	.8
w/Electric lock add	(.1)	.1
(G) Door Lock Remote Control, Renew		
1983-87	(.3)	.6
(G) Door Lock Cylinder, Renew		
1983-87	(.3)	.5
Recode cyl add	(.3)	.3
(G) Door Handle (Outside), Renew (Front or Rear)		
1983-87	(.4)	.6
Renew insert add		.1
(G) Lock Striker Plate, Renew		
1983-87	(.2)	.3
(G) Door Window Regulator (Manual), Renew		
1983-87	(.7)	1.0
Recond add	(.2)	.3
(G) Window Regulator (Electric), Renew		
1983-87	(.9)	1.3
(G) Trunk Lock and Cylinder, Renew		
1983-87	(.2)	.3
Recode cyl add	(.3)	.3
(G) Trunk Hinge or Strap, Renew (One)		
1983-87	(.8)	1.2
(G) Tailgate Lock Cylinder, Renew		
1983	(.3)	.5
Recode cyl add	(.3)	.3

PARTS 29 LOCKS, HINGES & WIND. REGULATORS 29 PARTS

	Part No.	Price
Hood Lock		
1983-87	◆14070703	16.25
Hood Hinge		
Malibu		
1983-right	◆14064326	16.75
left	◆14064325	16.75
Monte Carlo		
1983-87-right	14086422	16.25
left	14018481	16.25
Door Lock–Front (L.H.)		
1983-Malibu	◆20293605	51.50
1983-87-Monte Carlo	◆20293613	33.50
Door Lock–Rear (L.H.)		
Malibu		
1983	◆20293625	55.75
Door Lock Cylinder		
1983-87-exc. below	◆9632762	5.75
Deluxe dr. handle	20497701	5.25
Malibu	◆9632769	7.75
Door Handle (Outside) (L.H.)		
1983-87-exc. below	◆20099251	24.75
Deluxe dr. handle	20454213	23.75
Trunk Lock Cylinder & Keys		
1983-87-exc. below	◆3910570	6.25
Sta. wagon	◆9632765	7.25
Deluxe dr. handle	◆20496705	3.75
Window Regulator–Manual (R.H.)		
Malibu		
1983-Malibu	◆20009424	59.50
Malibu classic	◆20244864	59.50
Monte Carlo		
1983-87	2009422	131.00
Window Regulator–Electric (R.H.)		
(2 door)		
1983-87	◆20123184	98.00
(4 door)		
1983	◆20209182	98.00
Window Regulator Motor		
1983-87	◆22020900	73.00

LABOR 30 HEAD AND PARKING LAMPS 30 LABOR

	(Factory Time)	Chilton Time
(G) Aim Headlamps		
two		.4
four		.6
(M) Headlamp Sealed Beam Bulb, Renew		
All models	(.2)	.3
(M) License Lamp Assembly, Renew		
1983-87	(.2)	.3
(M) Back-Up Lamp Assembly, Renew		
1983-85-each	(.3)	.4
(M) Cornering Lamp Assembly, Renew		
1983-87-each	(.3)	.4
(M) Park and Turn Signal Lamp Assy., Renew		
1983-87-each	(.3)	.4

LABOR 30 HEAD AND PARKING LAMPS 30 LABOR

	(Factory Time)	Chilton Time
(M) High Level Stop Lamp Assy., Renew		
1986-87	(.2)	.4
(M) Stop, Tail and Turn Signal Lamp Assy., Renew		
1983-85-each	(.3)	.4
(M) Back-Up Lamp Bulb, Renew		
All models-one	(.2)	.3
(M) Cornering Lamp Bulb, Renew		
All models-each	(.2)	.3
(M) License Lamp Bulb, Renew		
All models-one or all	(.2)	.3
(M) Park and Turn Signal Lamp Bulb, Renew		
All models-each		.2
(M) Side Marker Lamp Bulb, Renew		
All models-each		.2
(M) Stop, Tail and Turn Signal Lamp Bulb, Renew		
All models-one		.2
each adtnl		.1
(M) High Level Stop Lamp Bulb, Renew		
All models	(.2)	.3

PARTS 30 HEAD AND PARKING LAMPS 30 PARTS

	Part No.	Price
Seated Beam Unit		
(wo/Quartz)		
1983-87-inner	◆5966201	15.00
outer	◆5966200	15.00
(Quartz)		
1983-87-inner	◆5930567	22.50
outer	◆16502327	N.L.
Tail & Stop Lamp Assy. (L.H.)		
Malibu		
1983	5971815	75.00
Monte Carlo		
1983-87-exc. below	5971993	57.00
Custom ext.	16502139	57.00
High Mount Stoplight		
1986-87	◆5974464	36.00
License Lamp Assy.		
Malibu		
1983	◆913204	6.25
Monte Carlo		
(wo/Custom ext.)		
1983-87-right	914104	7.50
left	914103	7.50
(Custom ext.)		
1983-87-right	919056	7.50
left	919055	7.50
Parking Lamp Assy.		
Malibu		
1983-right	914120	26.25
left	914119	26.25
Monte Carlo		
(wo/SS package)		
1983-87-right	915220	24.50
left	915219	24.50
(SS package)		
1983-87-right	919026	24.25
left	919025	24.25
Side Marker Lamp (Front)		
Malibu		
1983-right	929986	8.75
left	929985	8.75
Monte Carlo		
1983-87-right	915228	9.75
left	915227	9.75

LABOR 31 WINDSHIELD WIPER & SPEEDOMETER 31 LABOR

	(Factory Time)	Chilton Time
(G) Windshield Wiper Motor, Renew		
1983	(.5)	.6
1984-87	(.4)	.8
(G) Windshield Wiper Motor, R&R and Recondition		
1983	(1.0)	1.3
1984-87	(.9)	1.4
(G) Wiper Transmission, Renew (One)		
1983-87	(.4)	.6
(G) Wiper Switch, Renew		
1983-85	(.9)	1.4
1986-87		
std colm	(1.2)	1.7
tilt colm	(1.1)	1.6
(G) Windshield Washer Pump, Renew		
1983	(.2)	.4
1984	(.6)	.8
1985-87	(.3)	.4
(G) Windshield Washer Pump, R&R and Recondition		
1983		
non-depressed type	(.5)	.8
depressed type	(.7)	1.0
1984	(.9)	1.2
(G) Windshield Washer Pump Valve, Renew		
1983-85	(.2)	.4
(G) Speedometer Head, R&R or Renew		
1983-87	(.6)	1.0
Reset odometer add		.2
(G) Speedometer Cable and Casing, Renew		
wo/Cruise Control		
1983-87	(.6)	1.1
w/Cruise Control		
1983-87-upper	(.7)	1.1
lower	(.5)	.7
both	(.7)	1.5
one piece	(.7)	1.1
(G) Speedometer Cable (Inner), Renew or Lubricate		
wo/Cruise Control		
1983-87	(.7)	1.1
w/Cruise Control		
1983-87-upper	(.6)	1.0
lower	(.3)	.5
both	(.6)	1.3
one piece	(.6)	1.1
(G) Radio, R&R		
1983-87	(.4)	.7
w/A.C. add	(.1)	.1
w/Floor console add	(.3)	.3

PARTS 31 WINDSHIELD WIPER & SPEEDOMETER 31 PARTS

	Part No.	Price
Wiper Motor		
1983-exc Pulse	◆4960974	84.00
Pulse wiper	◆4961608	80.00
1984-87	◆22039687	110.75
Wiper Transmission		
Malibu		
1983-right	◆22009387	18.50
left	◆22009389	18.00
Monte Carlo		
1983-87-right	◆22009387	18.50
left	◆22009388	18.00
Wiper Switch		
(wo/Pulse wiper)		
1983-wo/Tilt whl.	◆7835342	22.50
Tilt wheel	◆7837279	41.50
1984-87-wo/Tilt whl.	◆7842714	44.75
Tilt wheel	◆7843684	44.75
(Pulse wiper)		
1983-wo/Tilt whl.	◆7835340	56.25
Tilt wheel	◆7837280	53.50
1984-87	◆7843683	56.25
Windshield Washer Pump		
1983-exc. pulse wpr.	◆22009212	25.00
Pulse wipers	◆22021345	38.50
1984-87	◆22039686	16.25

Speedometer Cable & Head Assy.
Order by year and model.

LABOR 32 LIGHT SWITCHES & WIRING 32 LABOR

	(Factory Time)	Chilton Time
(G) Headlamp Switch, Renew		
1983-87	(.4)	.5
(G) Headlamp Dimmer Switch, Renew		
1983-87	(.5)	.7
(G) Stop Light Switch, Renew		
1983-87	(.3)	.4
(G) Back-Up Lamp and Park/Neutral Switch, Renew		
1983-87	(.3)	.5
(G) Parking Brake Lamp Switch, Renew		
1983-87	(.4)	.4
(G) Turn Signal or Hazard Warning Switch, Renew		
1983-85	(.7)	1.1
1986-87		
std colm	(.7)	1.1
tilt colm	(.8)	1.2
(G) Turn Signal Pivot Assy., Renew		
1983-87-std column	(.8)	1.2
tilt column	(.6)	1.1
w/Cruise control add	(.2)	.2
(M) Turn Signal or Hazard Warning Flasher, Renew		
1983-87	(.3)	.3
(G) Horns, Renew		
1983-87-each	(.3)	.3
(G) Horn Relay, Renew		
1983-87	(.2)	.3

PARTS 32 LIGHT SWITCHES & WIRING 32 PARTS

	Part No.	Price
Headlamp Switch		
1983-87	◆1995217	16.00
Dimmer Switch		
1983-87	◆7838234	12.50
Stop Light Switch		
(wo/Cruise cont.)		
1983-84	◆25504628	3.75
1985-87	◆25524846	6.50
(Cruise cont.)		
1983-84	◆9794682	7.75
1985-87	◆25524847	6.50
Directional Signal Switch		
1983-87-exc below	◆1997983	30.00
w/corn. lamps	◆1997984	35.00
Back-Up Lamp Switch		
1983-87	◆22509632	5.50
Turn Signal Flasher		
1983-84-2 lamp	◆491392	N.L.
3 lamp	◆10029240	4.25
1985-87	◆10041073	4.25
Hazard Lamp Flasher		
1983-87	◆6450089	3.00
Horn Assy.		
1983-87-'D" note	◆1892162	23.50
'F" note	◆1892163	22.00
'A" note	◆1892164	22.00
Horn Relay		
1983-87	◆25513270	8.50

LABOR 33 GLASS 33 LABOR

	(Factory Time)	Chilton Time
(G) Windshield, Renew		
1983-87	(1.2)	1.8
Renew caulk bead add	(.4)	.4
(G) Front Door Glass, Renew		
1983-87-4 Dr	(.8)	1.2
2 Dr	(1.0)	1.5
(G) Rear Door Glass, Renew		
1983	(.3)	.6
(G) Quarter Window Stationary Glass, Renew		
1983-87-hdtp	(.5)	.9
sta wag	(1.0)	1.5
(G) Tail Gate Glass, Renew		
1983	(.3)	.6
(G) Rear Window Glass, Renew		
1983-87	(1.3)	2.0
w/Electric grid defogger add	(.6)	.6
w/3/4 plug, unpadded add	(1.3)	2.0
w/3/4 plug, padded add	(2.6)	4.0

LABOR 34 CRUISE CONTROL 34 LABOR

	(Factory Time)	Chilton Time
(G) Regulator Assembly (Transducer), Renew or Adjust		
1983	(.4)	.6
Adj low spd switch add	(.1)	.1
(G) Engagement Switch, Renew		
1983-87	(.5)	.9
(G) Brake Release Switch, Renew		
1983-87	(.4)	.4
(G) Vacuum Servo, Renew		
1983-85	(.3)	.5
1986-87	(.6)	.8
Renew bracket add	(.1)	.2
(G) Vacuum Hoses, Renew		
1983-87	(.2)	.3
(G) Chain or Cable, Servo to Carburetor, Renew		
1983-87	(.3)	.4
(G) Cruise Control Resume Solenoid, Renew		
1983	(.2)	.3
(G) Cruise Control Vacuum Regulator Valve, Renew		
1983	(.2)	.3
(G) Cruise Control Module, Renew		
1984-87	(.3)	.5
(G) Cruise Control Speed Sensor, Renew		
1984	(.6)	.8
(G) Cruise Control Check Valve, Renew		
1984-87	(.2)	.4

	Part No.	Price
Brake Release Switch		
1983-87	◆9794682	8.00
Cruise Control Transducer		
1983-exc. diesel	◆25030560	190.25
Diesel eng.	◆25031604	179.25
Cruise Control Module		
1984-87-231	◆25031964	115.00
229, 262, 305	◆25031953	116.00
Diesel	◆25031948	116.00
Cruise Control Vacuum Servo		
V-6-229 & V-8-305		
1983	◆25030983	19.50
1984	◆25074632	116.75
1985-87	◆25074632	116.75
V-6-231		
1983	◆25030981	19.50
1984	◆25074630	116.25
V-6-262		
1985-87	◆25074627	117.00
Diesel		
1983	◆25030980	32.75
1984	◆25074629	123.50
Vacuum Release Valve		
1983-84	◆25509432	14.00
1985-87	◆25523376	14.00

GROUP INDEX

ALPHABETICAL INDEX

General Motors
Rear Wheel Drive Cars

OLDSMOBILE CUTLASS

YEAR IDENTIFICATION

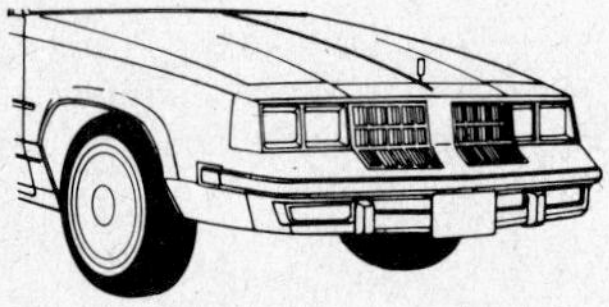

1983 Cutlass Supreme

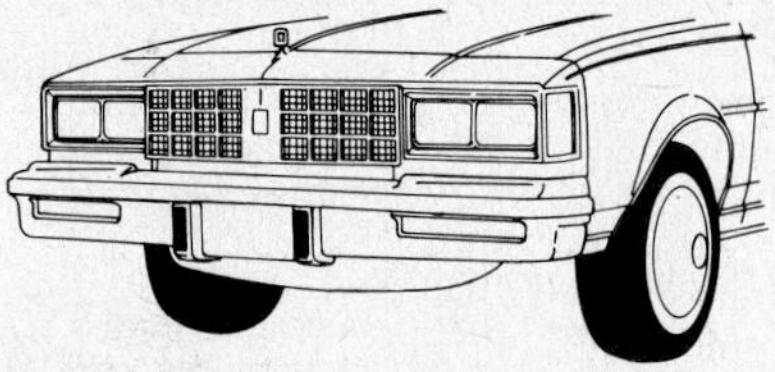

1984 Cutlass Supreme Sedan

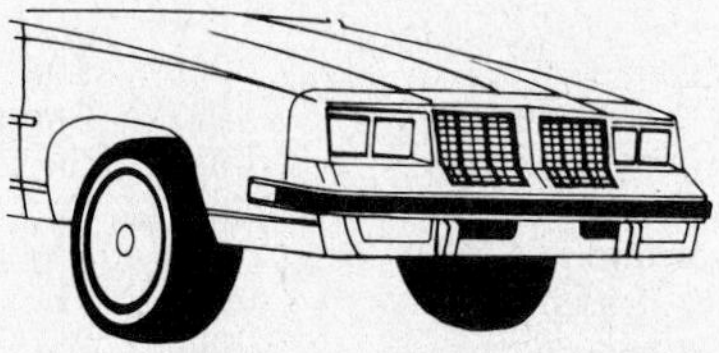

1985–87 Cutlass Supreme

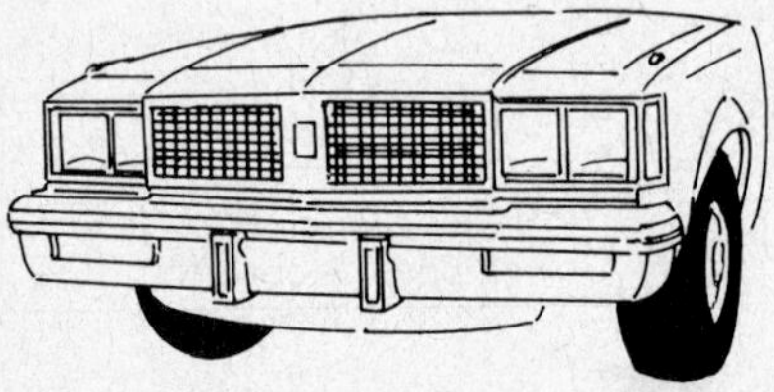

1983 Cutlass Supreme Brougham Sedan

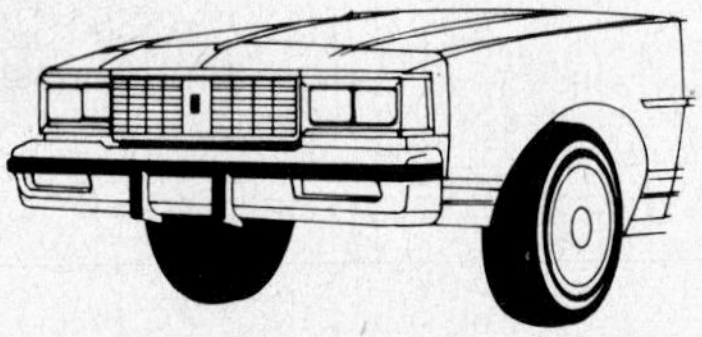

1985–87 Cutlass Supreme Brougham

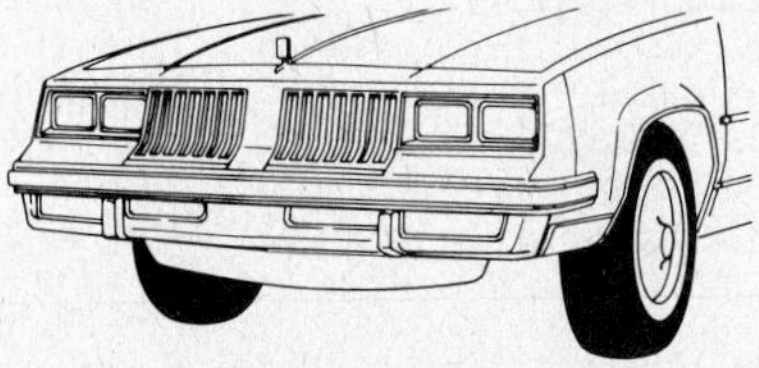

1984 Cutlass Supreme Coupe

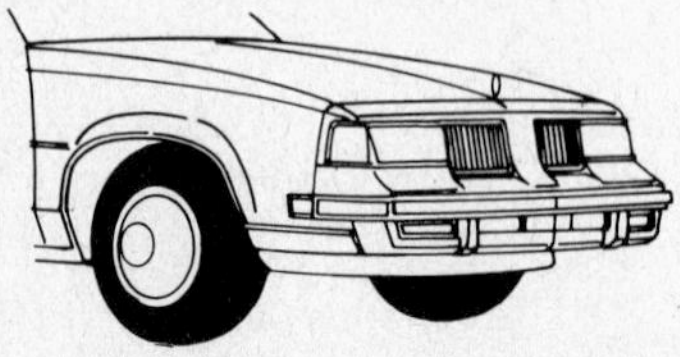

1986 Cutlass Salon

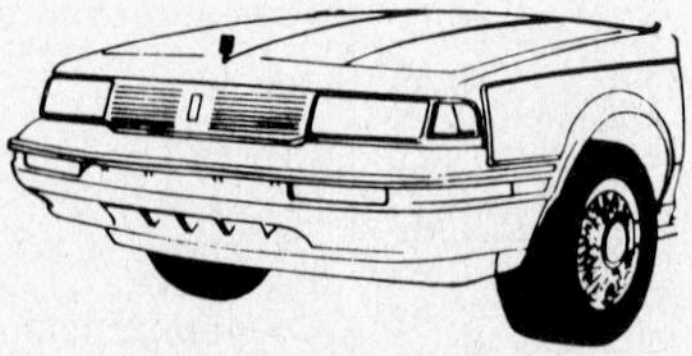

1987 Cutlass Cruiser

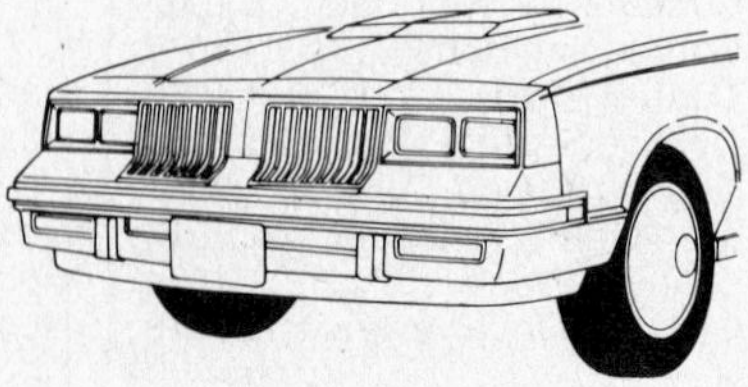

1984–87 Hurst Olds

VEHICLE IDENTIFICATION NUMBER (VIN)

It is important for servicing and ordering parts to be certain of the vehicle and engine identification. The VIN (vehicle identification number) is a 13 or 17 digit number visible through the windshield on the driver's side of the dash and contains the vehicle and engine identification codes. It can be interpreted as follows:

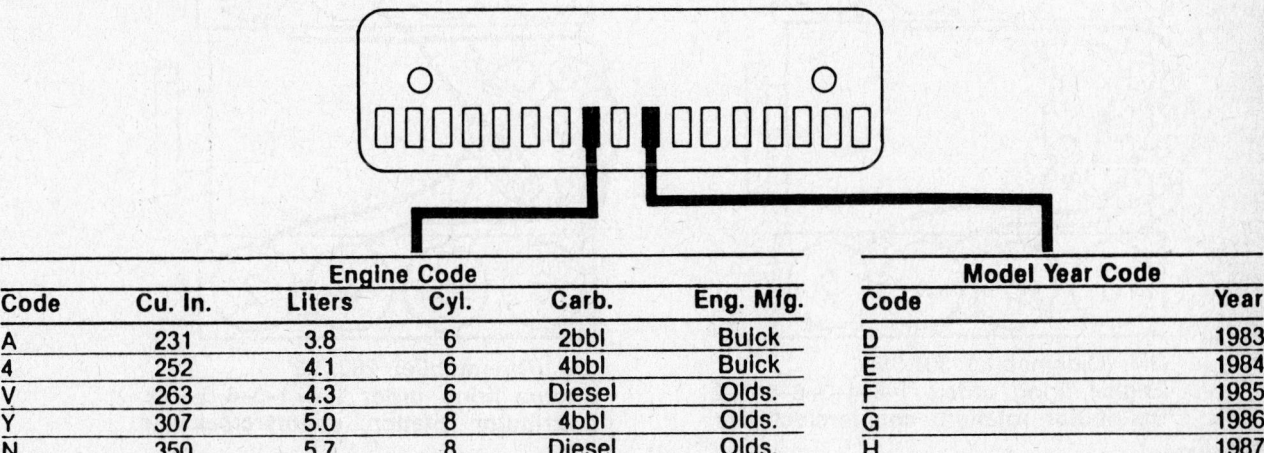

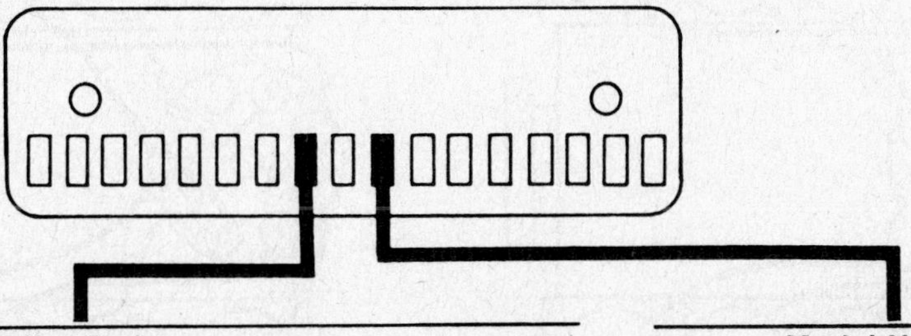

Engine Code					
Code	Cu. In.	Liters	Cyl.	Carb.	Eng. Mfg.
A	231	3.8	6	2bbl	Buick
4	252	4.1	6	4bbl	Buick
V	263	4.3	6	Diesel	Olds.
Y	307	5.0	8	4bbl	Olds.
N	350	5.7	8	Diesel	Olds.

Model Year Code	
Code	Year
D	1983
E	1984
F	1985
G	1986
H	1987

The seventeen digit Vehicle Identification Number can be used to determine engine application and model year. The 10th digit indicates the model year and the 8th digit identifies the factory installed engine.

TUNE-UP SPECIFICATIONS
Gasoline Engines

When analyzing compression test results, look for uniformity among cylinders rather than specific pressures

Year	Engine: Eng. VIN Code	Engine: No. Cyl. Displacement (cu. in.)	Liter	Eng. Mfg.	Spark Plugs: Orig. Type	Spark Plugs: Gap (in.)	Distributor: Point Dwell (Deg.)	Distributor: Point Gap (in.)	Ignition Timing (deg.) Auto. Trans.	Fuel Pump Pressure (psi)	Idle Speed (rpm) Auto. Trans.
'83	A	6-231	3.8	Buick	R-45TS8	.080	Electronic		①	5.6–6.5	①
	4	6-252	4.1	Buick	R-45TS8	.080	Electronic		①	5.6–6.5	①
	Y	8-307	5.0	Olds.	R-46SX	.080	Electronic		①	5.6–6.5	①
	9 ②	8-307	5.0	Olds.	R-46SX	.080	Electronic		①	5.5–6.5	①
'84	A	6-231	3.8	Buick	R45TSX	0.060	Electronic		①	5.5–6.5	①
	4	6-252	4.1	Buick	R45TSX	0.060	Electronic		①	5.5–6.5	①
	9	8-307	5.0	Olds.	R46SX ④	0.080	Electronic		①	5.5–6.5	①
	Y	8-307	5.0	Olds.	R46SX ④	0.080	Electronic		①	5.5–6.5	①
'85	A	6-231	3.8	Buick	R45TSX	0.060	Electronic		①	5.5–6.5	①
	9	8-307	5.0	Olds.	R46SZ	0.060	Electronic		①	5.5–6.5	①
	Y	8-307	5.0	Olds.	FR3LS6	0.060	Electronic		①	5.5–6.5	①
'86	A	6-231	3.8	Buick	R45TSX	0.060	Electronic		①	5.5–6.5	①
	Y	8-307	5.0	Olds.	FR3LS6 ⑤	0.060	Electronic		①	6.0–7.5	①
	9	8-307	5.0	Olds.	FR3LS6 ⑤	0.060	Electronic		①	6.0–7.5	①
'87	Refer to the Underhood Emission Label and/or Owner's Manual General Specifications										

NOTE: The underhood specifications sticker often reflects tuneup specification changes made in production. Sticker figures must be used if they disagree with those in this chart. Part numbers in this chart are not recommendations by Chilton for any product by brand name.

▪ All figures are in degrees Before Top Dead Center
① See Underhood Emission Label
② Hurst/Olds Package
③ Type of driving mode may necessitate a change of heat range application and reference number of the spark plugs as listed in the above specifications
④ Or R46SZ
⑤ Or FR3CLS6

FIRING ORDERS

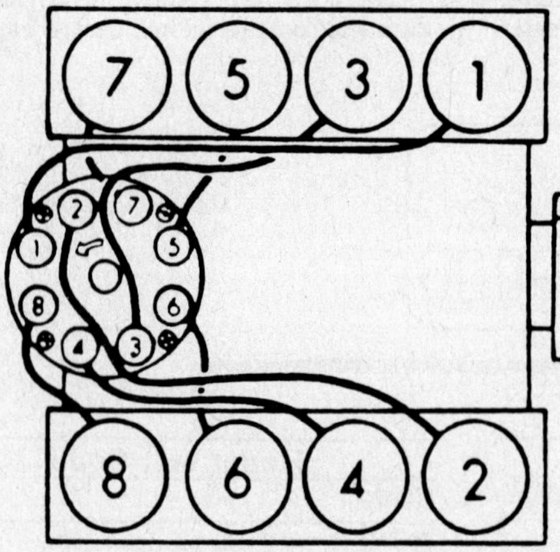

GM (Oldsmobile) 307,350
Engine firing order: 1–8–4–3–6–5–7–2
Distributor rotation: counterclockwise

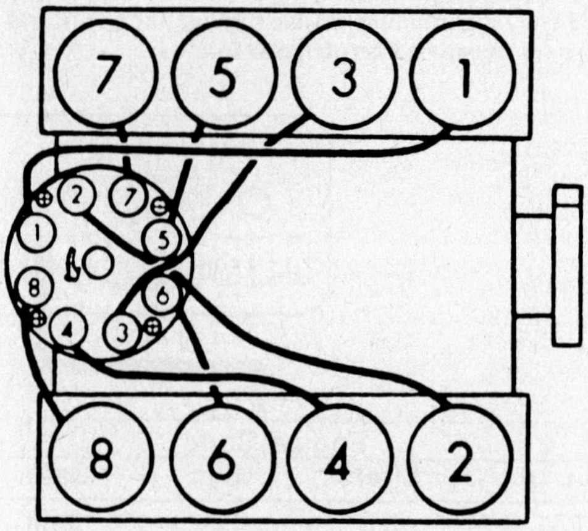

GM (Oldsmobile) 260 V8
Engine firing order 1–8–4–3–6–5–7–2
Distributor rotation: counterclockwise

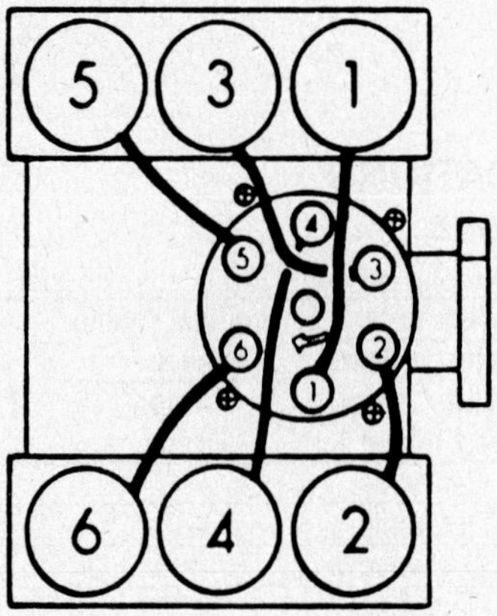

GM (Buick) 231,252 V6
3.8L, 4.1L)
Engine firing order: 1–6–5–4–3–2
Distributor rotation: clockwise

V6 harmonic balancers have two timing marks: one is 1/8 in. wide, and one is 1/16 in. wide. Use the 1/16 in. mark for timing with a hand held light. The 1/8 in. mark is used only with a magnetic timing pick-up probe

WHEEL ALIGNMENT

		Caster		Camber				Wheel Pivot Ratio (deg.)	
Year	Model	Range (deg.)	Pref Setting (deg.)	Range (deg.)	Pref. Setting (deg.)	Toe (in.)	Steering Axis Inclin. (deg.)	Inner Wheel	Outer Wheel
'83	Cutlass w/Power Steering	2P to 4P	3P	5/16N to 15/16P	1/2P	1/16 to 1/4	7	NA	NA
	w/Manual Steering	0 to 2P	1P	5/16N to 15/16P	1/2P	1/16 to 1/4	7	NA	NA
'84–'85	Cutlass	2P to 4P	3P	5/16N to 15/16P	1/2P	1/16 to 1/4	7	NA	NA
'86	Cutlass	1 13/16P to 3 13/16P	2 13/16P	0 to 15/8P	13/16P	1/16 to 1/4	NA	NA	NA
'83–'85	88–98 Series	2P to 4P	3P	0 to 15/8P	3/16P	1/16 to 1/4	10 9/16	NA	NA

NA Not Available
N Negative
P Positive

LABOR SERVICE BAY OPERATIONS LABOR

(Factory Time) Chilton Time

COOLING

(M) Winterize Cooling System

Includes: Run engine to check for leaks, tighten all hose connections. Test radiator and pressure cap, drain radiator and engine block. Add anti-freeze and refill system.

All models... .5

(M) Thermostat, Renew

Includes: Test thermostat.

V-6–1983-87 (.7)... .8
V-8–1983-87 (.4)... .6
Diesel–1983-85 (.5)... .6

(M) Drive Belt, Adjust

1983-87-one (.2)... .3
each adtnl... .1

(M) Drive Belt, Renew

1983-87 (.3)... .4
each adtnl... .1

(M) Serpentine Drive Belt, Renew

1983-85 (.2)... .4

(M) Radiator Hoses, Renew

1983-87-one (.3)... .4
both (.5)... .7
by-pass-V-6 (.6)... .8
V-8 (.5)... .7

FUEL

(M) Carburetor Air Cleaner, Service

All models (.2)... .3

(G) Air Cleaner Vacuum Motor, Renew

1983-87 (.3)... .5

(G) Air Cleaner Temperature Sensor, Renew

1983-87 (.2)... .3

(G) Carburetor, Adjust (On Car)

Includes: Adjust pump rod, idle vent, air valve, fast idle, choke rod, vacuum break, unloader, secondary lockout, idle speed and mixture.

1983-87
Slow & Fast Idle (.3)... .4
Vacuum Brake-one (.4)... .6
both (.6)... .8
Choke (.6)... 1.0
Complete (1.3)... 1.8

(G) Automatic Choke Cover and/or Coil, Renew

1983-87 (.6)... 1.0

(G) Automatic Choke Vacuum Brake Diaphragm, Renew or Adjust

1983-87-one (.4)... .6
both (.6)... .8

(G) Idle Stop Solenoid, Renew

Includes: Adjust.

1983-84 (.3)... .4
1985-87 (.6)... 1.0

BRAKES

(G) Brakes, Adjust (Minor)

Includes: R&R wheels and adjust brakes thru access holes in drums. Fill master cylinder.

two wheels... .4
Remove knock out plugs add, each .. .1

(G) Bleed Brakes (Four Wheels)

Includes: Fill master cylinder.

All models (.4)... .5

CHILTON'S 10 POINT SAFETY CHECK

CHECK OPERATION & CONDITION OF THE FOLLOWING ITEMS:

1. Legal Registration (serial no.)
2. Tires & Wheels
3. Brake System (R&R all wheels)
4. Light Systems & Signals
5. Accelerator Linkage, Neutral Safety Switch, Shift Indicator Pointer & Seat Position Locks
6. Glass, Mirrors, Door Locks, Seat Belts & Harness
7. Wipers, Washers & Defrosters
8. Frame, Steering, Shocks, Front & Rear Suspension
9. Fuel & Exhaust Systems
10. Road Test Vehicle

All models ... 1.0
Exhaust Smog Analysis, add 4

(Factory Time) Chilton Time

(G) Brake Pedal Free Play, Adjust

All models... .3

(M) Parking Brake, Adjust

All models (.3)... .4

LUBRICATION SERVICE

(M) Lubricate Chassis, Change Oil & Filter

Includes: Inspect and correct all fluid levels.

All models... .6
Install grease fittings add... .1

(M) Lubricate Chassis

Includes: Inspect and correct all fluid levels.

All models... .4
Install grease fittings add... .1

(M) Engine Oil & Filter, Change

Includes: Inspect and correct all fluid levels.

All models... .4

WHEELS

(M) Wheel, Renew

one (.3)... .5

(G) Wheels, Balance

one... .3
each adtnl... .2

(G) Wheels, Rotate (All)

All models... .5

(G) Front Wheel Bearings, Clean and Repack (Both Wheels)

All models (1.1)... 1.6

(G) Front Wheel Bearings and Cups, Renew

All models
one side (.7)... .9
both sides (1.1)... 1.5

(Factory Time) Chilton Time

(G) Front Wheel Grease Seals, Renew

All models
one whl (.7)... .8
both whls (1.1)... 1.2

ELECTRICAL

(M) Battery Cables, Renew

1983-87-negative (.2)... .3
positive-V-6 (.4)... .5
V-8 (.5)... .6
right batt to left batt
w/Diesel eng (.3)... .3

(M) Battery Terminals, Clean

All models... .3

(G) Aim Headlamps

two... .4
four... .6

(G) Headlamp Sealed Beam Bulb, Renew

1983-87-each (.3)... .3

(G) Headlamp Switch, Renew

1983-87 (.3)... .5

(G) Headlamp Dimmer Switch, Renew

1983-87-column mounted (.5)... .7

(G) Stop Light Switch, Renew

1983-87 (.2)... .3

(G) Turn Signal Switch, Renew

1983-87 (.6)... 1.1

(G) Back-Up Lamp and Park/Neutral Switch, Renew

1983-87
wo/Console (.2)... .3
w/Console (.5)... .7

(M) Turn Signal or Hazard Warning Flasher, Renew

All models (.2)... .2

(G) Horn Relay, Renew

1983-87 (.2)... .3

(G) Horn, Renew

1983-85-one (.4)... .5
1986-87-one (.2)... .3
each adtnl... .1

(M) Back-Up Lamp Bulb, Renew

All models-one (.2)... .3

(M) Cornering Lamp Bulb, Renew

All models-each (.2)... .3

(M) License Lamp Bulb, Renew

All models-one or all (.2)... .3

(M) Park and Turn Signal Lamp Bulb, Renew

All models-each... .2

(M) Side Marker Lamp Bulb, Renew

All models-each... .2

(M) Stop, Tail and Turn Signal Lamp Bulb, Renew

All models-one... .2
each adtnl... .1

LABOR 1 TUNE UP 1 LABOR

(Factory Time) Chilton Time

(G) Compression Test
V-6–1983-87 (.5)........ .7
V-8–1983-87 (.6)........ .8
w/A.C. add 3

(G) Engine Tune Up, (Electronic Ignition)

Includes: Test battery and clean connections. Tighten manifold and carburetor mounting bolts. Check engine compression, clean and adjust or renew spark plugs. Test resistance of spark plug cables. Inspect distributor cap and rotor. Adjust air gap. Check vacuum advance operation. Reset ignition timing. Adjust idle mixture and idle speed. Service air cleaner. Inspect and adjust drive belts. Inspect choke operation and adjust or free up. Check operation of EGR valve.
V-6–1983-87 .... 2.0
V-8–1983-87 .... 2.5
w/A.C. add 6
To perform C.C.C. system test add... 1.0

LABOR 2 IGNITION SYSTEM 2 LABOR

(Factory Time) Chilton Time

GASOLINE ENGINES

(G) Spark Plugs, Clean and Reset or Renew
V-6–1983-87 (.4)........ .6
V-8–1983-87 (.5)........ .7
To clean add (.2)........ .2
w/A.C. add (.2)........ .2

(G) Ignition Timing, Reset
1983-87 (.3)........ .4

(G) Distributor, Renew
Includes: Reset ignition timing.
1983-87 (.5)........ .8
w/A.I.R. add (.3)........ .3

(G) Distributor, R&R and Recondition
Includes: Reset ignition timing.
1983-87 (.9)........ 1.4
w/A.I.R. add (.3)........ .3

(G) Distributor Cap and/or Rotor, Renew
1983-87
V-6 (.5)........ .7
V-8 (.3)........ .5
w/A.I.R. add (.5)........ .5

(G) Ignition Coil, Renew
1983-87 (.3)........ .4
Test add (.2)........ .2
w/A.I.R. add (.3)........ .3

(G) Ignition Cables, Renew
V-6–1983-85 (1.0)........ 1.4
1986-87 (.5)........ 1.4
V-8–1983-87 (.3)........ .6

(G) Ignition Switch, Renew
1983-87 (.4)........ .6

(G) Ignition Lock Cylinder, Renew
1983-87 (.6)........ .7

(G) Ignition Key Warning Switch, Renew
1983-87 (.5)........ .9

(G) Distributor Module, Renew
1983-87 (.3)........ .6
To perform C.C.C. system test add (.5)........ 1.0
w/A.I.R. add (.3)........ .3

(G) Distributor Hall Effect Switch, Renew
1983 (.5)........ .8

(G) Distributor Capacitor and/or Module Wiring Harness, Renew
1983-87 (.3)........ .6
w/A.I.R. add (.3)........ .3

(G) Distributor Pick-Up Coil and/or Pole Piece, Renew
Includes: R&R distributor and reset ignition timing.
1983-87 (.6)........ .9
w/A.I.R. add (.3)........ .3

(G) ESC Knock Sensor, Renew
1983-87 (.7)........ 1.0

(G) ESC Module, Renew
1983-87 (.5)........ .7

DIESEL IGNITION COMPONENTS

(G) Glow Plugs, Renew
1983-85
one........ .4
all-one bank........ .7
all-both banks........ 1.3

(G) Glow Plug Module (Controller), Renew
1983-85 (.6)........ .8

(G) Coolant Fast Idle Temperature Switch, Renew
1983-85 (.2)........ .4

(G) Fast Idle Solenoid, Renew
1983-85 (.4)........ .5

(G) Fast Idle Relay, Renew
1983-85 (.3)........ .4

(G) Glow Plug Relay, Renew
1983 (.2)........ .4
1984-85 (.4)........ .6

(G) Control Sensor, Renew
1983-85 (.4)........ .6

(G) Glow Plug Control Switch, Renew
1983-85 (.2)........ .4

PARTS 2 ELECTRONIC IGNITION 2 PARTS

	Part No.	Price
Distributor Assembly		
V-6–231		
1983-87	◆1103470	351.25
V-8–307		
1983-85	◆1103457	333.50
1986-87	◆1103602	275.00
(1) Cover		
1983-87-V-6	◆1894209	6.00
V-8	◆1875960	6.00
(2) Lead Assy.		
1983-87	1894868	1.50
(3) Coil		
1983-87	◆1985474	36.00
(4) Seal		
1983-87	1875962	3.50
(5) Cap		
1983-87-V-6	◆1894979	17.00
V-8	◆1974408	17.00
(6) Rotor		
1983-87	◆1977026	6.50
(7) Shaft		
V-6–231		
1983-87	◆1976930	38.50
V-8–307		
1983-85	◆1979955	42.50
1986-87	◆1989612	42.25
(8) Retainer		
1983-87	830446	.50
(9) Pole Piece & Plate Assy.		
V-6–231		
1983-87	◆1976925	30.25
V-8–307		
1983-87	◆1977207	32.00
(10) Module		
1983-87	◆1976908	60.00
(11) Capacitor		
1983-87	◆1876154	4.50
(13) Seal		
1983-87	1950569	1.75

PARTS 2 ELECTRONIC IGNITION 2 PARTS

	Part No.	Price
(14) Housing		
V-6-231		
1983-87	◆1976928	36.25
V-8-307		
1983-87	◆1977208	34.00
(15) Harness		
1983-87-V-6	1979733	22.00
V-8	◆1892261	11.00
(16) Washer (Thrust)		
1983-87	1984361	.50
(17) Washer		
1983-87	1837617	.50
(18) Gear		
V-6-231		
1983-87	◆1892082	15.25
V-8-307		
1983-85	◆1979948	22.25
1986-87	◆1988777	21.50

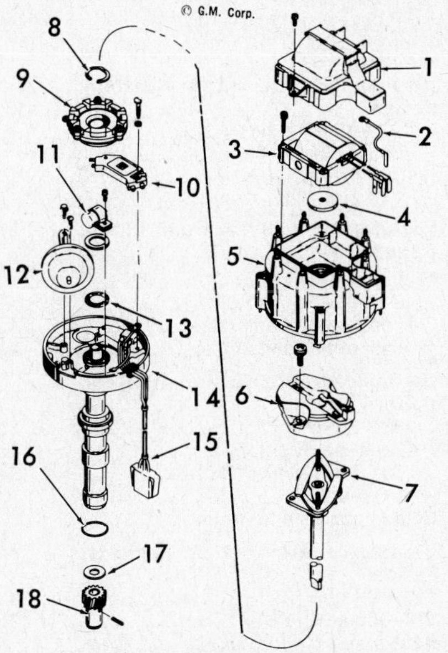

	Part No.	Price
Ignition Switch		
(wo/Tilt wheel)		
1983-87	◆1990115	11.50
(Tilt wheel)		
1983-87	◆1990116	11.50

DIESEL IGNITION SYSTEM

	Part No.	Price
Glow Plugs		
1983	◆5613680	19.00
1984-85	◆5613826	16.50
Glow Plug Relay		
1983	◆560580	16.00
Glow Plug Control Sensor		
1983	◆12015288	58.50
Glow Plug Module		
1984	◆22520348	91.75
Glow Plug Controller		
1985	◆22528337	96.00

LABOR 3 FUEL SYSTEM 3 LABOR

(Factory Time) — Chilton Time

GASOLINE ENGINES

(G) Fuel Pump, Test

Includes: Disconnect line at carburetor, attach pressure gauge.

All models	.2

(M) Carburetor Air Cleaner, Service

1983-87 (.2)	.3

(G) Carburetor, Adjust (On Car)

Includes: Adjust pump rod, idle vent, air valve, fast idle, choke rod, vacuum break, unloader, secondary lockout, idle speed and mixture.

1983-87	
Slow & Fast Idle (.3)	.4
Vacuum Brake-one (.4)	.6
both (.6)	.8
Choke (.6)	1.0
Complete (1.3)	1.8

(P) Throttle Position Sensor, Adjust

All models	
2 bbl (.7)	.9
4 bbl (.6)	.8
Perform C.C.C. system check add	1.0

(G) Automatic Choke Cover and/or Coil, Renew

1983-87 (.6)	1.0

(G) Automatic Choke Vacuum Brake Diaphragm, Renew or Adjust

1983-87-one (.4)	.6
both (.6)	.8

(G) Idle Stop Solenoid, Renew

Includes: Adjust.

1983-84 (.3)	.4
1985-87 (.6)	1.0

(G) Choke Vacuum Control Switch, Renew

1983-85 (.3)	.4

(G) Electric Choke Relay, Renew

1983-87 (.2)	.3

(G) Carburetor, Renew

Includes: Transfer parts, make all necessary adjustments.

1983-87 (.6)	.9
To perform C.C.C. system check, add (.5)	1.0

(G) Carburetor, R&R and Clean or Recondition

Includes: All necessary adjustments.

1983-87-2 bbl (1.8)	3.0
4 bbl (2.1)	3.2
To perform C.C.C. system check, add (.5)	1.0

(G) Accelerator Pump, Renew

All models	
2 bbl (.7)	1.0
4 bbl (.8)	1.2

(G) E.F.E. Heater (Insulator), Renew

All models (.6)	1.0

(G) Float or Needle Valve and Seat, Renew

Includes: All necessary adjustments.

1983-87	
2 bbl (.9)	1.2
4 bbl (.9)	1.5
To perform C.C.C. system check, add (.5)	1.0

(G) Flexible Fuel Line, Renew

1983-87-each (.3)	.4

(G) Fuel Pump, Renew

V-6-1983-87 (.6)	.8
V-8-1983-85 (.7)	1.0
1986-87 (.5)	.8
w/A.C. and A.I.R. add (.4)	.4

Add pump test if performed.

(G) Fuel Tank, Renew

Includes: Drain and refill tank. Test gauge.

1983-87 (.7)	1.0

(G) Water In Fuel Detector, Renew (WIF)

All models (.9)	1.2

(G) Fuel Gauge (Tank), Renew

Includes: Drain and refill tank.

1983-87 (.8)	1.1

(G) Fuel Gauge (Dash), Renew

1983-85 (.4)	.8
1986-87 (.7)	1.2

(G) Intake Manifold or Gaskets, Renew

Includes: Adjust carburetor and linkage as necessary. Drain and refill radiator. Adjust timing.

V-6-1983-87 (1.4)	2.4
V-8-1983-85 (1.7)	2.5
1986-87 (2.2)	3.2
Renew manif add (.3)	.5
w/A.C. add (.4)	.4
w/A.I.R. add (.1)	.1
w/Cruise control add (.2)	.2

E.F.E. SYSTEM

(G) E.F.E. Valve, Renew

Includes: Hoist car.

1983-84 (.5)	.8
1985-87 (.3)	.8

(G) E.F.E. Thermal Vacuum Switch, Renew

1983-87 (.2)	.4

(G) E.F.E. Vacuum Check Valve, Renew

1983-84 (.2)	.4
1985 (.4)	.4

DIESEL ENGINE

(G) Idle Speed, Adjust

1983-85 (.2)	.4

(G) Injection Timing, Check and Adjust

1983-85 (.7)	.9

(M) Air Cleaner, Service

1983-85 (.2)	.4

LABOR — 3 FUEL SYSTEM 3 — LABOR

(Factory Time)	Chilton Time
(G) Air Intake Crossover, Renew	
1983-85-w/Ext EGR (.3)	.5
w/Int EGR (.4)	.6
(G) Fuel Supply Pump, Renew	
1983-85 (.5)	.8
w/A.C. add (.2)	.2
(G) Fuel Filter, Renew	
1983-85 (.2)	.4
(G) Vacuum Pump, Renew	
Includes: Vacuum test.	
1983-85	
gear driven (.4)	.6
belt driven (.6)	.8
(G) Fuel Injection Pump, Renew	
Includes: Pressure and electrical tests. Adjust timing.	
V-6–1983-85 (2.0)	3.0
V-8–1983-85 (2.1)	3.4
(G) Injector Pump Adapter and/or Seal, Renew	
V-6–1983-85 (1.3)	2.1
V-8–1983-85 (1.8)	2.5
(G) Fuel Return Lines (At Nozzles), Renew	
1983-85-one side (.3)	.5
both sides (.4)	.7
return hose (.2)	.3
w/A.C. add (.2)	.2
(G) High Pressure Fuel Lines, Renew	
Includes: Flush lines.	
1983-85-one (.8)	.8
one-each bank (.9)	1.0
all-both banks (1.1)	2.5
(G) Injector Nozzle and/or Seal, Renew	
1983-85-one (.4)	1.0
one-each bank (.7)	1.3
all-both banks (2.0)	3.0
w/A.C. add (.2)	.2
Clean nozzles add-each	.2
(G) Intake Manifold or Gaskets, Renew	
V-6–1983-85 (2.2)	3.2
V-8–1983-85 (2.9)	3.5
Renew manif add (.3)	.5
(G) Fast Idle Relay, Renew	
1983-85 (.3)	.4
(G) Fuel Injection Pump Throttle Shaft Seal, Renew	
V-6–1983-85 (.9)	1.3
V-8–1983-85 (.8)	1.3
(G) Fuel Solenoid, Renew	
1983-85	
Cav (.3)	.5
V-6 (.6)	.9
V-8 (.5)	.7
(G) Cold Advance Solenoid, Renew	
V-6–1983-85 (.7)	.9
V-8–1983-85 (.6)	.8
(G) Fuel Injection Head Seal, Renew	
Includes: Renew head and drive shaft seals. Renew governor weight retaining ring.	
V-6–1983-85 (2.3)	3.5
V-8–1983-85 (2.7)	3.9

PARTS — 3 FUEL SYSTEM 3 — PARTS

	Part No.	Price
Air Cleaner Element		
1983-87-V-6	◆6419892	8.00
V-8	◆6484235	10.00
Carburetor Assy. (Rochester)		
V-6-231		
1983-Fed.	◆17079440	876.50
Calif.	◆17079205	666.75
1984	◆17110332	912.75
1985	◆17111175	750.50
1986-87	◆17111526	743.25
V-8-307		
1983-exc. below	◆17079343	803.00
Hurst-Olds	17079354	812.00
1984-exc. below	17110445	1079.00
Hurst-Olds	17110443	901.00
1985-exc. below	◆17111105	887.00
Hurst-Olds	17111239	827.75
1986-87	1711487	N.L.
Rebuilding Kit (Rochester)		
V-6-231		
1983-84-Fed.	◆17076022	28.00
Calif.	◆17076129	51.00
1985	◆17076144	57.75
V-8-307		
1983-84	◆17076044	32.00
1985-87	◆17076141	49.50
Fuel Pump Assy.		
V-6-231		
1983-84	◆6471172	N.L.
1985	◆6471368	32.50
1986-87	◆6472765	37.00
V-8-307		
1983-87	◆6471743	35.00
Fuel Tank Assy.		
Order by year and model.		
Fuel Gauge (Dash)		
(wo/Gauges)		
1983-87	6433112	25.00
(Gauges)		
1983-87	6433115	43.00
Fuel Gauge (Tank)		
Order by year and model.		
Intake Manifold Gasket		
V-6-231		
1983	◆1264924	14.50
1984-87-Alum.	◆25505397	15.75
Cast iron	◆1264924	14.50
V-8-307		
1983-84	◆557866	20.00
1985	◆22527545	

EARLY FUEL EVAPORATION SYSTEM

	Part No.	Price
E.F.E. Valve (w/Actuator)		
V-6-231		
1983-87	◆5233320	64.00
V-8-307		
1983-87	◆5233475	52.00
V-8-350 Diesel		
1985	5234623	111.75
E.F.E. Control Switch		
1983	◆3048786	14.75
E.F.E. Check Valve		
1983-87	◆25510974	3.25

PARTS — 3 FUEL SYSTEM 3 — PARTS

	Part No.	Price
Air Intake Crossover		
V-6-260		
1983-84	◆22519924	109.00
V-8-350		
1983-84	◆22509735	109.00
1985	◆22526995	109.00
Fuel Pump		
V-6-260		
1983	◆6471952	70.00
1984	◆6472153	59.50
V-8-350		
1983-84	◆6471317	N.L.
1985	◆6442228	59.25
Injection Pump Adapter		
1983-84-V-6	◆22516525	52.50
V-8	◆558768	21.75
1985	◆22516525	52.50
Fuel Injection Pump		
V-6-260		
(wo/Hi altitude)		
1983	◆22511745	763.00
1984	◆22522524	763.00
(Hi altitude)		
1983	◆22518691	763.00
1984	◆22522523	763.00
V-8-350		
1983-exc. below	◆22518686	763.00
Sta. wag.	◆22519990	763.00
Hi alt.	◆22518689	763.00
1984-exc. below	◆22520936	763.00
Sta. wag.	◆22520937	763.00
Hi alt.	◆22520999	763.00
1985	◆22524421	763.00
Fuel Injection Nozzles		
V-6-260		
1983	◆22514509	60.00
1984	◆22520376	89.50
V-8-350		
1983	◆22520378	60.00
1984-85	◆22521207	89.50
Vacuum Pump		
V-6-260		
1983-wo/A.C.	◆7844041	115.00
A.C.	◆7844040	115.00
1984-wo/A.C.	7846098	119.00
A.C.	7846097	119.00
V-8-350		
1983-84	◆7839413	116.00
1985-wo/A.C.	◆7845203	124.00
A.C.	◆7845425	124.00

PARTS 3 FUEL SYSTEM 3 PARTS

	Part No.	Price
Intake Manifold Gaskets		
V-6-260		
1983-84	◆22514872	16.50
V-8-350		
1983-84-Alum.	◆22527123	N.L.
Cast iron	◆22516344	12.00
1985	◆22527544	16.50

	Part No.	Price
Fuel Gauge (Tank)		
1983-84-wo/Sta. wag.	◆25002566	99.25
Sta. wag.	◆25002567	104.50
1985	25004276	79.75

	Part No.	Price
Fuel Gauge (Dash)		
(wo/Gauges)		
1983-85	6433112	25.00
(Gauges)		
1983-85	6433117	43.50
Water Detector Kit		
1983-85	25003964	81.50

LABOR 3A EMISSION CONTROLS 3A LABOR

(Factory Time) — Chilton Time

GASOLINE ENGINES

(G) Emission Control Check
Includes: Check and adjust engine idle speed and mixture and ignition timing. Check P.C.V. valve.
All models 6

POSITIVE CRANKCASE VENTILATION

(M) Positive Crankcase Ventilation Valve, Renew
All models (.2) 3

(M) Crankcase Ventilation Filter, Renew
All models (.2) 3

EVAPORATIVE EMISSION TYPE

(G) Charcoal Canister, Renew
1983-87 (.2) 3

(G) Canister Purge Thermal Vacuum Switch, Renew
1983-87 (.3) 3

CONTROLLED COMBUSTION TYPE

(G) Air Cleaner Vacuum Motor, Renew
1983-87 (.3) 5

(G) Air Cleaner Temperature Sensor, Renew
1983-87 (.2) 3

EXHAUST GAS RECIRCULATION SYSTEM

(G) E.G.R. Valve, Renew
1983-87 (.4) 7

(G) Thermal Control Valve, Renew
1983-85 (.3) 3

(G) E.G.R. Vacuum Relay, Renew
1983 (.3) 4

(G) Vacuum Delay Valve, Renew
1983-87 (.2) 3

(G) Control Valve Cover, Renew
1983-85 (.2) 3

(G) Thermal Vacuum Switch, Renew
1983-87 (.3) 4

(G) Thermostatic Vacuum Control Switch, Renew
1983-85 (.3) 4

AIR INJECTOR REACTOR TYPE

(G) Air Pump, Renew
V-6-1983-87 (.3) 5
V-8-1983-87 (.5) 8

(G) A.I.R. Air Cleaner, Renew
1983-85 (.2) 3

(G) Check Valve, Renew
1983-87-one (.2) 3
each adtnl (.1) 1

CHILTON'S EMISSION CONTROL TUNE-UP

1. Clean or renew P.C.V. valve, hoses and filter.
2. Check fuel tank cap for sealing ability.
3. Check fuel tank and fuel lines for leakage.
4. Check evaporation canister and filter. Replace if necessary.
5. Check engine compression to determine leakage of unburned gases. (Add time for items of interference).
6. Test and clean or renew spark plugs.
7. Check engine oil dipstick for sealing ability.
8. Test exhaust system with analyzer and check system for leakage.
9. Check exhaust manifold heat valve for operation.
10. Adjust ignition timing and carburetor idle speed and mixture.
11. Check automatic choke mechanism for free operation.
12. Inspect air cleaner and element.
13. On models so equipped, test distributor vacuum control switch and transmission control switch.

V-6 .... **1.7**
V-8 .... **1.8**

For repairs made, charge accordingly.

(Factory Time) — Chilton Time

(G) Catalytic Converter Air Pipe, Renew
1983-87-one piece (.6) 8

(G) A.I.R. Manifolds, Renew
V-8-1983-87-each (.6) 9

(G) A.I.R. Drive Belt, Renew
1983-87 (.2) 3
w/A.C. add (.3) 3

(G) Air Pump Centrifugal Fan and/or Filter, Renew
All models (.3) 5

(G) Vacuum Delay Valve, Renew
All models (.2) 3

COMPUTER COMMAND CONTROL SYSTEM (C.C.C.)

(P) Throttle Position Sensor, Adjust
Does not include system performance check.
All models
2 bbl (.7) 9
4 bbl (.5) 8

(Factory Time) — Chilton Time

(P) Manifold Differential Pressure Sensor, Renew
Does not include system performance check.
1986-87 (.3) 6

(P) EGR/EFE Relay, Renew
Does not include system performance check.
1986-87 (.2) 3

(P) Electronic Control Module, Renew
Does not include system performance check.
1983-87 (.6) 6

(P) Mixture Control Solenoid, Renew
Does not include system performance check.
1983-87-2 bbl (1.1) 1.4
4 bbl (.8) 1.5

(P) Prom, Renew
Includes: R&R electronic module.
Does not include system performance check.
1983-87 (.6) 8

(P) Barometric Sensor, Renew
Does not include system performance check.
1983-87 (.3) 7

(P) Coolant Temperature Sensor, Renew
Includes: Drain and refill cooling system.
Does not include system performance check.
1983-87 (.4) 7

(P) Manifold Absolute Pressure Sensor, Renew
Does not include performance check.
1983-87 (.3) 6

(P) Oxygen Sensor, Renew
Does not include system performance check.
1983-87 (.5) 7

(P) Throttle Position Sensor, Renew
Does not include system performance check.
1983-85-2 bbl (1.1) 1.4
4 bbl (1.2) 1.5
1986-87 (.9) 1.4

(P) Back-Up Lamp and Park/Neutral Switch, Renew
Does not include system performance check.
1983-87 (.3) 7

(P) EGR/EFE Purge Solenoid, Renew
Does not include system performance check.
1983-85 (.4) 6

(P) Metering Valve Sensor, Renew
Does not include system test.
1985 (.6) 8

(P) Air Control Valve Solenoid, Renew
Does not include system test.
1983-85 (.5) 8

LABOR 3A EMISSION CONTROLS 3A LABOR

(Factory Time) Chilton Time

(P) Air Switching Valve, Renew
Does not include system test.
1983-87 (.4) .6

(P) Air Control Valve, Renew
Does not include system performance check.
1983-87 (.4) .6

(P) Air Control/Air Switching Valve, Renew
Does not include system performance check.
1983-87 (.5) .6

(P) Canister Purge Control Valve, Renew
Does not include system performance check.
1983-87 (.2) .6

(P) E.G.R. Vacuum Control Solenoid, Renew
Does not include system performance check.
1983-87 (.3) .4

(P) E.F.E. Vacuum Control Solenoid, Renew
Does not include system performance check.
1983-85 (.3) .4

(P) Vacuum Control Purge Solenoid, Renew
Does not include system performance check.
1983-85 (.3) .5

(P) Idle Speed Control Motor, Renew
Does not include system performance check.
1983 (.6) .8
Recond motor add (.3) .4

(G) Idle Load Compensator, Renew
Does not include system performance check.
1983-87 (.4) .6

(G) Vehicle Speed Sensor, Renew
Does not include system performance check.
1983-87 (.8) 1.0

(P) Tachometer Filter, Renew
Does not include system performance check.
1983 (.3) .3

(P) Computer Command Control System Performance Check
1983-87 (.5) 1.0

DIESEL ENGINE

(G) Crankcase Depression Regulator Valve, Renew
1983-85 (.2) .3

(G) Crankcase Ventilation Flow Control Valve, Renew
1983-85 (.2) .3

(G) Crankcase Ventilation Filter, Renew
1983-85 (.2) .3

(G) E.G.R. Valve and/or Gasket, Renew
1983-85 (.5) .7

(G) E.G.R. Control Valve Solenoid, Renew
1983-84 (.2) .3
1985 (.4) .6
Renew ECM add .1

(G) E.G.R. Control Valve Switch, Renew
1983-85 (.2) .3

(G) E.P.R. Control Valve Solenoid, Renew
1983-85 (.3) .4

(G) E.P.R. Control Valve Switch, Renew
1983-85 (.3) .4

(G) E.P.R. Exhaust Pressure Regulator Valve, Renew
1983-84 (.3) .4
1985 (.5) .7

(G) Vacuum Regulator Valve, Renew
1983-85 (.6) .8

DIESEL ELECTRONIC EMISSION CONTROLS

(P) Electronic Control Module, Renew
1985 (.6) .8

(P) Manifold Absolute Pressure Sensor, Renew
1985 (.3) .5

(P) Vehicle Speed Sensor, Renew
1985 (.9) 1.4

(P) Coolant Temperature Sensor, Renew
1985 (.6) .7

PARTS 3A EMISSION CONTROLS 3A PARTS

	Part No.	Price
Vapor Canister		
1983-87	◆17064622	39.50
Positive Crankcase Vent Valve		
V-6-231		
1983-87	◆6487534	3.00
V-8-307		
1983-87	◆8997683	3.50
V-8-350 Diesel		
1983-85	◆25041678	34.50
Vapor Canister Filter		
1983-87	◆7026014	2.50
Air Cleaner Sensor		
V-6-231		
1983-87	◆8997916	18.75
V-8-307		
1983-87	◆8997574	18.75

E.G.R. Valve
Replacement E.G.R. valves must be ordered according to the stamping number on the original valve.

AIR INJECTOR REACTOR TYPE

	Part No.	Price
Air Pump Assm.		
V-6-231		
1983-87	◆7835397	131.00
V-8		
1983-87-wo/A.C.	◆7835397	131.00
A.C.	◆7838575	158.00
Check Valve		
V-6-231		
1983	◆22040900	N.L.
1984-87	22048579	14.25
V-8		
1983-87	◆22034702	10.25
Pulley		
1983-87-		
stamped 'AU'	14062717	N.L.
stamped 'DB'	14023171	4.75
stamped 'KP'	410627	11.75
stamped "KQ"	412335	8.00
stamped "LF"	22506549	8.75
stamped "TL"	25503831	4.75
stamped "TR"	25511026	5.00

COMPUTER CONTROLLED EMISSIONS SYSTEMS

Part numbers shown are for pricing reference only. Order part with complete year, engine and component I.D. information.

	Part No.	Price
Electronic Control Module (ECM)		
(Remanufactured)		
V-6-231		
1983-Fed.	◆1226024	110.25
Calif.	◆1225500	110.25
1984-87	◆1226519	110.25
V-8-307		
1983	◆1225450	110.25
1984	◆1226457	110.25
1985-87-		
stamped	◆1226866	110.00
stamped	◆1227076	110.00
stamped	◆1226457	110.25
Calibration Unit (PROM)		
V-6-231		
1983-Calif.	◆1226031	40.50
(Federal em.)		
Code 0613APK	◆1226297	40.50
Code 3484CDD	◆1226445	40.50
1984-Calif.	◆16041052	40.50
(Federal em.)		
Code 7635CFH	◆16041224	40.50
Code 1225DFW	◆16041224	40.50
1985-87-Fed.	◆16044104	40.50
Calif.	◆16044109	40.50
V-8-307		
(Federal em.)		
1983-THM200	1226360	40.50
(THM250C trans.)		
Code 8170ANL	◆1226181	40.50
Code 3415CDB	◆1226437	40.50
1984-THM200C	◆16045639	40.50
(THM2004R trans.)		
Code 0230BRU	◆16045609	40.50
Code 5165CJK	16040809	40.50
1985-87 (stamped)		
Code 9630DBX	16039629	40.50
Code 0097FPB	16050096	40.50
Code 7987FCH	16047986	40.50
(California em.)		
1983-THM200	1226361	40.50
THM250C	◆1226182	40.50
1984-THM200C	16040828	40.50
(THM2004R trans.)		
Code 0246BRW	16045614	40.50
Code 5170CJL	16035169	40.50
1985-87 (stamped)		
Code 9635DBY	16039634	40.50
Code 0103FPC	16050102	40.50
Manifold Pressure Sensor		
V-6-231		
1983-87	◆16006835	62.25
Barometric Sensor		
1983-87	◆16006833	62.25

PARTS 3A EMISSION CONTROLS 3A PARTS

	Part No.	Price
Oxygen Sensor		
1983	◆5613959	29.00
1984-87	◆8990741	28.75
Vehicle Speed Sensor		
1983	◆25007227	52.00
1984	◆25007421	41.50
1985-87	◆25007463	44.00
Coolant Temperature Sensor		
1983-84	◆25036092	22.00
1985-87	◆25036708	12.75
ESC Knock Sensor		
1983-87	◆1997562	37.00

LABOR 4 ALTERNATOR AND REGULATOR 4 LABOR

(Factory Time) Chilton Time

(G) Delcotron Circuits, Test
Includes: Test battery, regulator, Delcotron output.

	Chilton Time
All models	.6

(M) Alternator Drive Belt, Renew

	Chilton Time
All models	
V-6 (.3)	.4
V-8 (.2)	.3
wo/A.C. add (.1)	.1
Diesel (.2)	.3
wo/A.C. add (.1)	.1

(G) Delcotron Assembly or Fan Pulley, Renew

	Chilton Time
V-6–1983-87 (.4)	.7
V-8–1983-87 (.5)	.8
Diesel–1983-85 (.6)	.8

(G) Delcotron, R&R and Recondition
Includes: Complete disassembly, replacement of parts as required. Reassemble.

	Chilton Time
1983-87	
V-6 (1.3)	1.7
V-8 (1.4)	1.8
Diesel (1.7)	2.3

(G) Delcotron Front Bearing, Renew
Includes: R&R Delcotron, separate end frames.

	Chilton Time
1983-87 (.8)	1.0
w/Diesel eng add (.2)	.2
Renew rear brg add	.2

(G) Delcotron Voltage Regulator, Test and Renew
Includes: R&R, disassemble and reassemble Delcotron.

	Chilton Time
1983-87 (.9)	1.2
w/Diesel eng add (.1)	.2

(G) Voltmeter, Renew

	Chilton Time
1983-85 (.4)	.8
1986-87 (.7)	1.2

PARTS 4 ALTERNATOR AND REGULATOR 4 PARTS

	Part No.	Price
Delcotron Assembly (New)		
(Gas engines)		
1983-87-exc. below	◆1100250	225.00
42 amp	◆1105360	206.00
70 amp	◆1105335	265.00
85 amp	◆1105339	326.50
(Diesel engines)		
1983-87-42 amp	◆1105357	241.50
63, 66, 78 amp	◆1105369	228.75
94 amp	◆1105480	232.00
(1) Capacitor		
1983-87	◆1978146	4.75
(2) Diode Trio		
1983-87	◆1984459	5.00
(3) Rectifier Bridge		
1983-87-exc. below	◆1984454	28.00
70, 85 amp	◆1975313	24.50
94 amp	◆1987061	29.25
(4) Bearing		
1983-87-exc below	◆9436831	5.50
70, 85 amp	◆1975322	5.50
(5) Terminal Pkg.		
1983-87	◆1975471	3.50
(6) Frame (Rear End)		
1983-87-exc. below	◆1984460	47.75
70, 85 amp	◆1975310	31.00
94 amp	◆1987073	28.00
(7) Regulator		
1983-87	◆1116387	25.00
(8) Brush Pkg.		
1983-87-exc below	◆1984462	9.00
70, 85 amp	◆1975323	10.00
(9) Rotor		
1983-87-exc. below	◆1985476	72.00

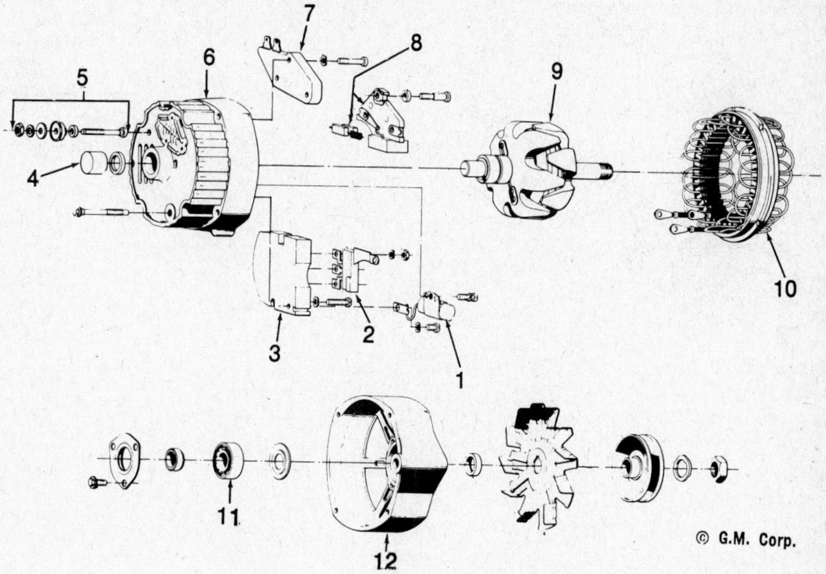

	Part No.	Price
70, 85 amp	◆1975333	65.00
78 amp	◆1984466	77.25
(10) Stator		
1983-87-42 amp.	◆1986280	52.75
55 amp	◆1984584	54.50
63, 78 amp	◆1984445	37.25
70 amp	◆1975303	48.75
85 amp	◆1975987	83.50
94 amp	◆1987074	41.50
(11) Bearing		
1983-87	◆908419	10.00
(12) Frame (Drive End)		
(exc. V-6 Diesel)		
1983-42 amp	◆1985642	24.75
63, 78 amp	◆1984464	23.50
70, 85 amp	◆1986590	30.00
1984-87-exc. below	◆1984464	23.50
66 amp	◆1986206	24.00
70, 85 amp	◆1986590	30.00
(V-6 Diesel)		
1983-exc. below	◆1984537	31.50
70, 85 amp.	1984426	34.75
1984-87-78 amp	◆1986206	24.00
94 amp	◆1987997	27.50

LABOR 5 STARTING SYSTEM 5 LABOR

(Factory Time)	Chilton Time
(G) Starter Draw Test	
All models	.3
(G) Starter, Renew	
Includes: R&R solenoid.	
V-6–1983-87 (.6)	.9
V-8–1983-87 (.5)	.9
Diesel–1983-85 (.5)	1.1
Add draw test if performed.	
(G) Starter, R&R and Recondition	
Includes: Turn down armature.	
V-6–1983-87 (1.2)	1.9
V-8–1983-87 (1.1)	1.9
Diesel–1983-85 (1.1)	2.5
Renew field coils add (.2)	.5
Add draw test if performed.	
(G) Starter Motor Solenoid, Renew	
Includes: R&R starter.	
V-6–1983-87 (.6)	.9
V-8–1983-87 (.5)	.9
Diesel–1983-85 (.6)	1.1
(G) Starter Drive, Renew	
Includes: R&R starter and solenoid.	
V-6–1983-87 (.9)	1.1
V-8–1983-87 (.6)	1.1
Diesel–1983-85 (.6)	1.4
(G) Back-Up Lamp and Park/ Neutral Switch, Renew	
1983-87 (.2)	.3
w/Console (.5)	.7
(G) Ignition Switch, Renew	
1983-87 (.4)	.6
(M) Battery Cables, Renew	
1983-87-negative (.2)	.3
positive-V-6 (.4)	.5
V-8 (.5)	.6
right batt to left batt w/Diesel eng (.3)	.3
(M) Battery Terminals, Clean	
All models	.3

PARTS 5 STARTING SYSTEM (DIESEL) 5 PARTS

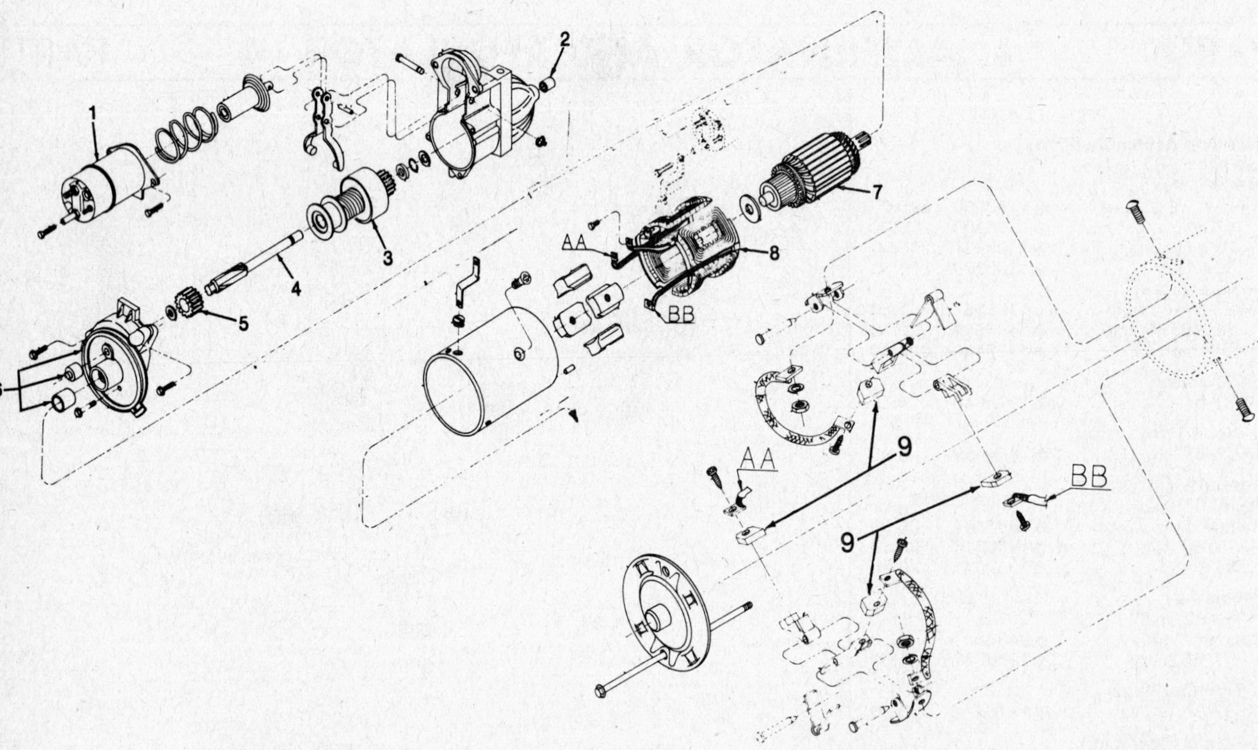

	Part No.	Price
Starter Assy. (New)		
1983-85	◆22522853	355.00
(1) Solenoid Switch		
1983-85	◆1114531	N.L.
(2) Drive End Bearing		
1983-85	◆22516191	9.00
(3) Starter Drive		
1983-85	◆1893445	65.00
(4) Drive Shaft		
1983-85	◆22516183	71.00
(5) Gear		
1983-85	◆22516184	9.50
(6) Gear Housing		
1983-85	◆22516195	28.50
(7) Armature		
1983-84	◆1987639	139.75
1985	◆22516197	130.00
(8) Field Coils		
1983-85	◆1979982	83.00
(9) Starter Brushes		
1983-85	◆1852885	2.75
Battery Cables		
Order by year and model.		
Neutral Safety Switch		
1983-87-exc. below	◆22509632	5.50
Elec. comp. lid	◆22514861	7.00

PARTS 5 STARTING SYSTEM 5 PARTS

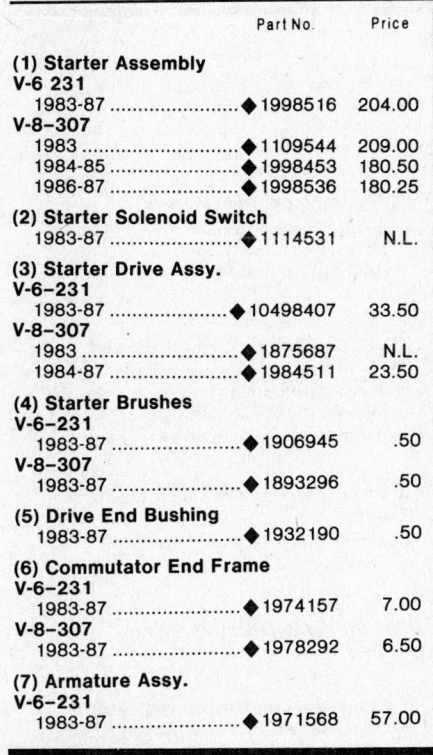

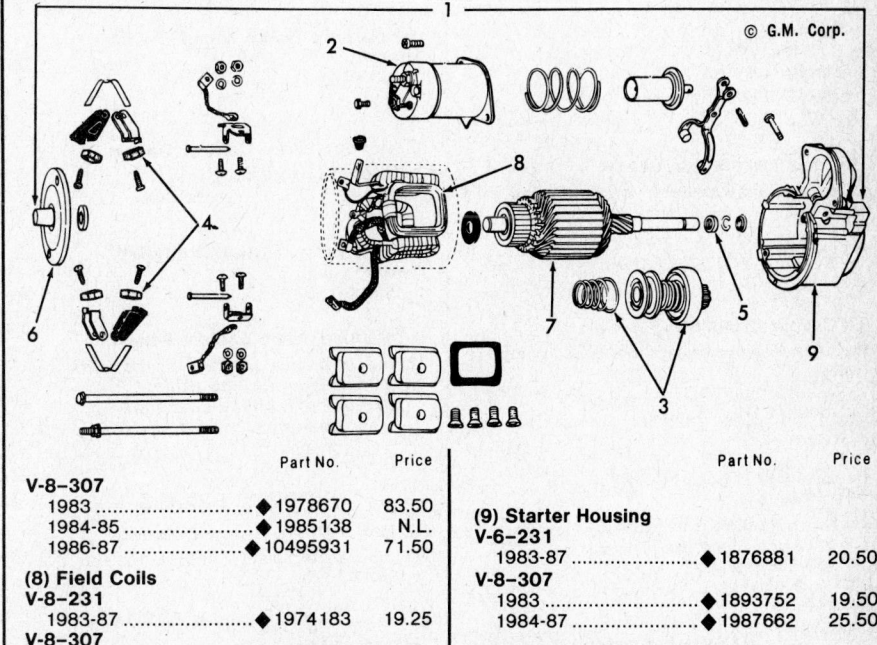

	Part No.	Price
(1) Starter Assembly		
V-6 231		
1983-87	◆1998516	204.00
V-8-307		
1983	◆1109544	209.00
1984-85	◆1998453	180.50
1986-87	◆1998536	180.25
(2) Starter Solenoid Switch		
1983-87	◆1114531	N.L.
(3) Starter Drive Assy.		
V-6-231		
1983-87	◆10498407	33.50
V-8-307		
1983	◆1875687	N.L.
1984-87	◆1984511	23.50
(4) Starter Brushes		
V-6-231		
1983-87	◆1906945	.50
V-8-307		
1983-87	◆1893296	.50
(5) Drive End Bushing		
1983-87	◆1932190	.50
(6) Commutator End Frame		
V-6-231		
1983-87	◆1974157	7.00
V-8-307		
1983-87	◆1978292	6.50
(7) Armature Assy.		
V-6-231		
1983-87	◆1971568	57.00

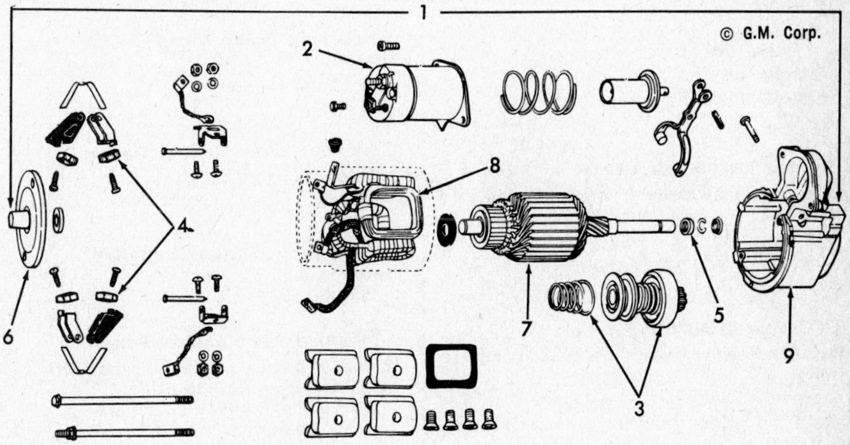

	Part No.	Price
V-8-307		
1983	◆1978670	83.50
1984-85	◆1985138	N.L.
1986-87	◆10495931	71.50
(8) Field Coils		
V-8-231		
1983-87	◆1974183	19.25
V-8-307		
1983	◆1978672	78.00
1984-87	◆1985138	N.L.

	Part No.	Price
(9) Starter Housing		
V-6-231		
1983-87	◆1876881	20.50
V-8-307		
1983	◆1893752	19.50
1984-87	◆1987662	25.50

Battery Cables
Order by year and model.

LABOR 6 BRAKE SYSTEM 6 LABOR

(Factory Time) Chilton Time

(G) Brake Pedal Free Play, Adjust
All models 3

(G) Brakes, Adjust (Minor)
Includes: R&R wheels and adjust brakes thru access holes in drums. Fill master cylinder.
two wheels 4
Remove knock out plugs add, each .. .1

(G) Bleed Brakes (Four Wheels)
Includes: Fill master cylinder.
All models 5

(G) Free-Up or Renew Brake Self Adjusting Units
one wheel 6
each adtnl 4

(G) Brake Shoes and/or Pads, Renew
Includes: Install new or exchange shoes or pads, adjust service and hand brake. Bleed system.
1983-87-front-disc (.6) 1.1
rear-drum (.6) 1.5
all four wheels 2.5
Resurface disc rotor add, each 9
Resurface brake drum add, each 5

(G) Brake Drum, Renew (One)
1983-87 (.3) 5

(G) Brake Combination Valve, Renew
Includes: Bleed system.
1983-87 (.7) 1.0

BRAKE HYDRAULIC SYSTEM

(G) Wheel Cylinder, Renew
Includes: Bleed system.
1983-87-one (.8) 1.0
both (1.1) 1.9

COMBINATIONS

Add to Brakes, Renew

See Machine Shop Operations

(Factory Time) Chilton Time

(G) RENEW WHEEL CYLINDER
Each 2

(G) REBUILD WHEEL CYLINDER
Each (.3) 3

(G) REBUILD CALIPER ASSEMBLY
Each (.3) 6

(G) RENEW MASTER CYLINDER
All models (.6) 8

(G) REBUILD MASTER CYLINDER
All models (.8) 1.0

(G) RENEW BRAKE HOSE
Each (.3) 3

(G) RENEW REAR WHEEL GREASE SEALS
One side (.4) 5

(G) REPACK FRONT WHEEL BEARINGS (BOTH WHEELS)
All models (.6) 6

(G) RENEW BRAKE DRUM
Each (.1) 1

(G) RENEW DISC BRAKE ROTOR
Each (.3) 5

(Factory Time) Chilton Time

(G) Wheel Cylinder, Rebuild
Includes: Hone cylinder and bleed system.
1983-87-one (1.0) 1.3
both (1.5) 2.1

(G) Brake Hose, Renew
Includes: Bleed system.
1983-87-each (.6) 8

(G) Electro-Hydraulic Pump, Renew
1985-87 (.4) 5

(G) Powermaster Pressure Switch, Renew
1985-87 (.3) 4

(G) Master Cylinder, Renew
Includes: Bleed system.
1983-87 (.6) 8

(G) Master Cylinder, R&R and Rebuild
Includes: Hone cylinder and bleed system.
1983-87 (1.4) 1.8
w/Powermaster cyl (1.6) 2.2

(G) Brake System, Flush and Refill
All models 1.2

(G) Brake Hydraulic System, Recondition (Complete)
Includes: Renew all rubber parts in brake system and bleed all lines.
1983-87 (4.2) 5.3

DISC BRAKES

(G) Brake Shoes and/or Pads, Renew
Includes: Install new or exchange shoes or pads, adjust service and hand brake. Bleed system.
1983-87-front-disc (.6) 1.1

LABOR 6 BRAKE SYSTEM 6 LABOR

(Factory Time)	Chilton Time
rear-drum (.6)	1.5
all four wheels	2.5
Resurface disc rotor add, each	.9
Resurface brake drum add, each	.5

(G) Disc Brake Rotor, Renew
Includes: R&R wheel, brake shoes and bearings.

1983-87-one (.7)	1.0
both (1.2)	1.5

(G) Caliper Assembly, Renew
Includes: Remove brake shoes. Bleed complete system.

1983-87-one (.7)	1.0
both (1.1)	1.5

(G) Caliper Assembly, R&R and Recondition
Includes: Remove brake shoes, renew parts as required and bleed complete system.

1983-87-one (1.2)	1.5
both (2.1)	2.5

PARKING BRAKE

(M) Parking Brake, Adjust

All models (.3)	.4

(Factory Time)	Chilton Time

(G) Parking Brake Lamp Switch, Renew

1983-87 (.2)	.3

(G) Parking Brake Control, Renew
Includes: Adjust parking brake.

1983-87 (.7)	1.0

(G) Parking Brake Equalizer, Renew

1983-87 (.3)	.5

(G) Parking Brake Cables, Renew
Includes: Adjust parking brake, R&R rear wheel and drum for rear cable.

1983-87-front (.6)	.8
rear-one (.8)	1.1

POWER BRAKES

(G) Power Brake Cylinder, Renew
Includes: R&R master cylinder.

1983-87 (.6)	1.0

(G) Power Brake Cylinder, R&R and Recondition
Includes: R&R master cylinder.

1983-87 (1.3)	1.7
Recond m/Cyl add (.8)	.8

(Factory Time)	Chilton Time

(G) Power Brake Check Valve, Renew

1983-87 (.3)	.3

(G) Hydra-boost Unit, Renew
Includes: Bleed system.

1983-84 (.6)	1.0
1985 (.8)	1.0

(G) Hydra-boost Unit, R&R and Recondition
Includes: Bleed system.

1983-84 (1.0)	1.5
1985 (1.2)	1.5

(G) Hydra-boost Pressure Lines, Renew
Includes: Bleed system.

1983-85-each (.3)	.6

(G) Low Vacuum Switch, Renew

1985-87 (.2)	.3

(G) Low Vacuum Brake Indicator Module, Renew

1985-87 (.2)	.3

PARTS 6 BRAKE SYSTEM 6 PARTS

	Part No.	Price
(1) Shoe and Lining Set (Drum)		
(exc. H.D. brakes)		
1983-87	◆12300219	41.00
(H.D. brakes)		
1983-87	◆12300214	50.00
(2) Wheel Cylinder Assy.		
1983-87	◆18007980	22.50
1985-87	◆18012303	30.25
Wheel Cylinder Repair Kit		
1983-87	◆18003744	12.75
Front Brake Hose		
1983-87	◆9762810	17.75
Rear Brake Hose		
1983-87	◆9761251	15.00
Master Cylinder Assy.		
(exc. Diesel)		
1983-84	◆18009816	171.25
1985-87	◆18011916	141.50
(Diesel)		
1983-85	◆18009373	134.50
Rear Drum		
1983-87-alum	◆1255496	90.00
cast iron	◆1249146	73.00
Front Hub Oil Seal		
1983-87	◆3965092	3.00

PARKING BRAKE

Parking Brake Front Cable		
1983	◆25502753	11.50
1984-87	◆25520341	11.50

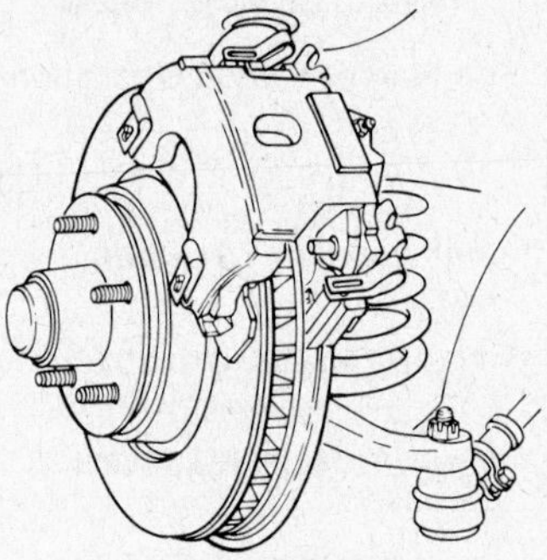

FRONT BRAKE

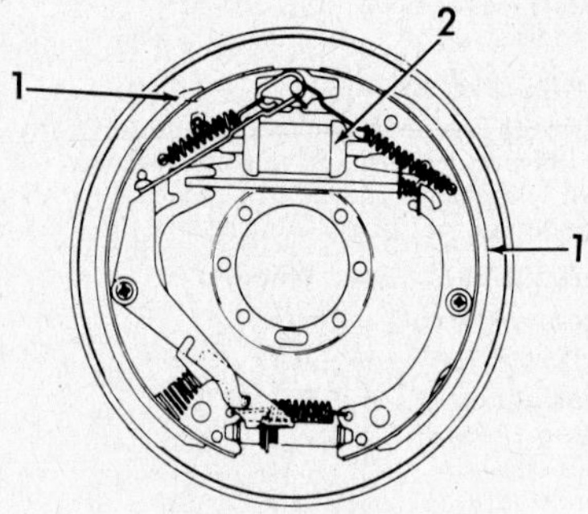

REAR BRAKE

	Part No.	Price
Rear Brake Cable		
1983-right	◆25502794	21.00
left	◆22518169	N.L.
1984-85-right	◆25518168	22.00
left	◆25518169	12.25
1986-87-right	◆25526680	22.00
left	◆25526681	12.25
Parking Brake Lever		
1983-87	◆25503396	23.25

POWER BRAKE CYLINDER

Power Brake Cylinder Assy.		
(exc. Diesel)		
1983-87	◆18010120	271.25

	Part No.	Price
(Diesel)		
1983-85	◆25511548	265.00
Power Brake Cyl. Repair Kit		
(exc. Diesel)		
1983-87	◆18007897	47.50
(Diesel)		
1983-85	◆22506710	16.50
Master Cylinder Repair Kit		
(exc. Diesel)		
1983-87	◆18010083	22.75
(Diesel)		
1983-85	◆18009375	20.50

PARTS — 6 DISC BRAKES 6 — PARTS

	Part No.	Price
Front Hub & Disc Assy.		
1983-87	◆14032431	100.25
(1) Brake Pad Set		
1983-87	◆12300227	43.00
(2) Spring		
1983-87	◆18006810	3.00
(3) Boot		
Included in repair kit.		
(4) Piston Assy.		
1983-87	◆18003155	11.00

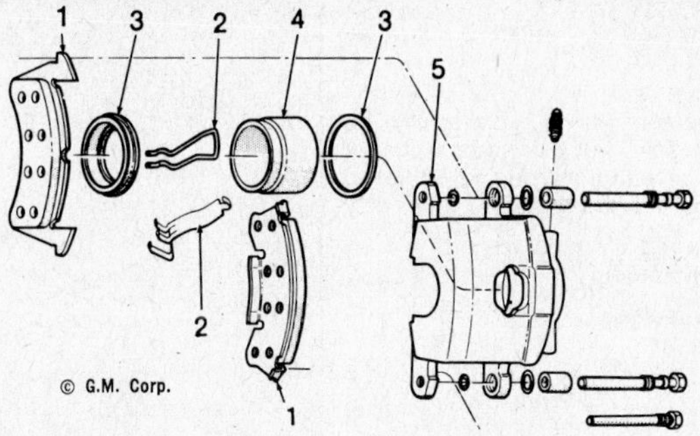

	Part No.	Price
(5) Caliper Assy.		
1983-87-right	◆18010481	148.75
left	◆18010480	137.00

	Part No.	Price
Caliper Repair Kit		
1983-87	◆18003724	8.75

LABOR — 7 COOLING SYSTEM 7 — LABOR

(Factory Time) — Chilton Time

(M) Winterize Cooling System

Includes: Run engine to check for leaks, tighten all hose connections. Test radiator and pressure cap, drain radiator and engine block. Add anti-freeze and refill system.

All models	.5

(M) Thermostat, Renew

Includes: Test thermostat.

V-6–1983-87 (.7)	.8
V-8–1983-87 (.4)	.6
Diesel–1983-85 (.5)	.6

(M) Radiator Assembly, R&R or Renew

Includes: Drain and refill cooling system.

1983-87	
V-6 (.7)	1.1
V-8 (.5)	.9
Diesel (.7)	1.0
w/A.T. add (.1)	.2
Renew lower insulators add (.1)	.1

ADD THESE OPERATIONS TO RADIATOR R&R

(G) Boil & Repair	1.5
(G) Rod Clean	1.9
(G) Repair Core	1.3
(G) Renew Tank	1.6
(G) Renew Trans. Oil Cooler	1.9
(G) Recore Radiator	1.7

(M) Radiator Hoses, Renew

1983-87-one (.3)	.4
both (.5)	.7
by-pass-V-6 (.6)	.8
V-8 (.5)	.7

(G) Water Pump, Renew

Includes: R&R fan blade and pulley. Drain and refill radiator. Adjust belts.

V-6–1983-87 (1.0)	1.7
V-8–1983-87 (1.2)	2.0
Diesel–1983-85 (1.7)	2.5
w/A.C. add (.1)	.1
w/P.S. add (.3)	.3
w/A.I.R. add (.1)	.1

(M) Drive Belt, Adjust

1983-87-one (.2)	.3
each adtnl	.1

(M) Drive Belt, Renew

1983-87-one (.3)	.4
each adtnl	.1

COOLING SYSTEM TUNE-UP

An Annual Cooling System Tune-Up Suggestion List should include (with some exceptions):

1. A visual check of the cooling system for indications of leaks or excessive oil content.
2. Pressure check the cooling system for internal and external leaks with filler cap and neck adapter and tester.
3. Check crankcase and automatic transmission oil for water content.
4. Test coolant thermostat with radiator thermometer.
5. Check temperature gauge for accuracy.
6. Drain system and flush till clean.
7. Clean foreign matter from radiator fins.
8. Test radiator pressure cap with cap tester.
9. Check fan blades and pulleys for alignment and damage.
10. Internal and external inspection of all hoses for cracks and deterioration.
11. Check core plugs (where possible) for seepage.
12. Refill system with correct coolant and check for air locks.
13. Check condition and tension of drive belts with tension gauge.

All models 1.5

(Factory Time) — Chilton Time

(M) Serpentine Drive Belt, Renew

1983-85 (.2)	.4

(G) Temperature Gauge (Engine Unit), Renew

1983-87 (.3)	.4

(G) Temperature Gauge (Dash Unit), Renew

1983-85 (.4)	.8
1986-87 (.7)	1.2

(G) Water Jacket Expansion Plugs, Renew (Side of Block)

1983-87-each (.5)	.5

(Factory Time) — Chilton Time

Note: If necessary to R&R any component to gain access to plug, add appropriate time.

(G) Heater Hoses, Renew

Includes: Drain and refill coolant.

1983-87-one (.2)	.4
both (.4)	.6

(G) Heater Core, R&R or Renew

wo/A.C.	
1983-87 (.3)	1.1
w/A.C.	
1983-87 (1.1)	2.5

ADD THESE OPERATIONS TO HEATER CORE R&R

(G) Boil & Repair	1.2
(G) Repair Core	.9
(G) Recore	1.2

(G) Heater Control Assembly, Renew

1983-87 (.3)	.7

(G) Heater Blower Motor, Renew

1983-87-Gas (.3)	.5
Diesel (.4)	.6

(G) Heater Blower Motor Resistor, Renew

1983-87 (.2)	.3

(G) Heater Blower Motor Relay, Renew

1983-87 (.2)	.3

(G) Heater Blower Motor Switch, Renew

1983-87 (.3)	.7

(G) Fan Blades, Clutch Assy., and/or Pulley, Renew

V-6–1983-87 (.3)	.4
V-8–1983-87 (.4)	.6
Diesel–1983-85 (.4)	.6
w/A.C. add (.1)	.1

(G) Heater Water Control Valve, Renew

1983-87-Gas (.4)	.5
Diesel (.6)	.8

PARTS 7 COOLING SYSTEM 7 PARTS

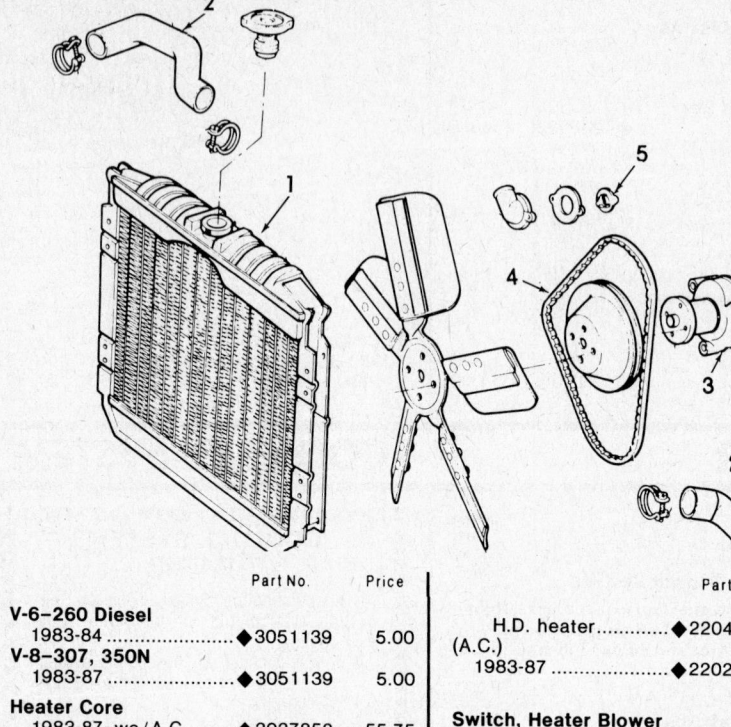

	Part No.	Price
(1) Radiator Assy.		
Accurate replacement of the radiator can be done only by using the radiator code stamped on a metal tag located on the original radiator. Order by year, model and radiator code no.		
(2) Radiator Hoses		
Order by year and model.		
(3) Water Pump Assy.		
V-6-231		
1983-85	◆1260709	61.75
1986-87	◆25527536	N.L.
V-6-260 Diesel		
1983-84	◆22514839	95.75
V-8-307, 350N		
1983-87-wo/A.C.	◆231886	96.50
A.C.	◆556283	95.00
Fan Clutch Assy.		
Part numbers shown are for pricing reference only. Order by code number and year.		
1983-87(code stamped on existing unit)		
'AD'	◆22007636	73.50
'AS'	◆22008426	84.50
'LF'	◆22517701	80.50
'OM'	◆561826	122.00
'OJ', 'OL'	◆22008668	N.L.
'OS'	◆4974367	84.50
'TS'	◆22008490	84.50
'TT'	◆22008492	87.50
'TU'	◆22008492	87.50
(4) Fan Belt		
Order by model and description.		
(5) Thermostat		
V-6-231		
1983	◆1254894	9.00
1984-87	◆3041390	6.00

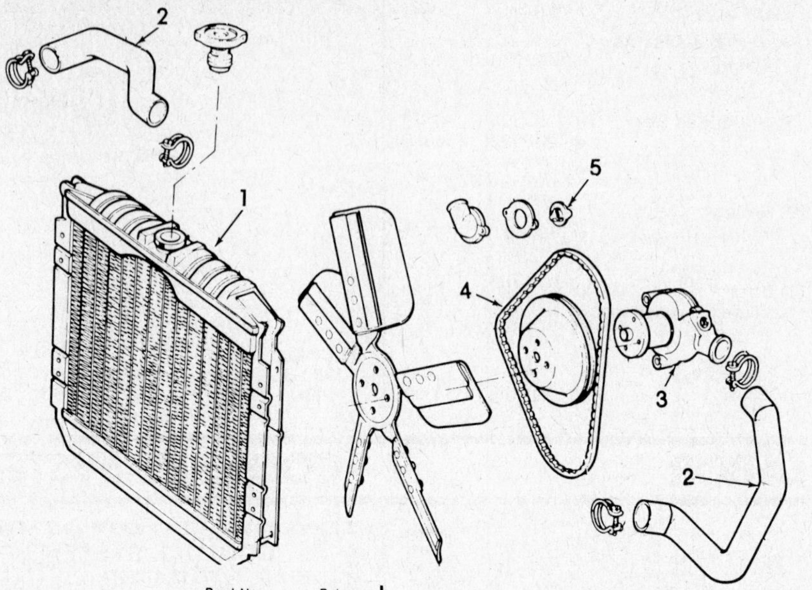

	Part No.	Price
V-6-260 Diesel		
1983-84	◆3051139	5.00
V-8-307, 350N		
1983-87	◆3051139	5.00
Heater Core		
1983-87-wo/A.C.	◆3037852	55.75
A.C.	◆3037689	70.00
Blower Motor		
(wo/A.C.)		
1983-87-exc. below	◆22048573	45.75

	Part No.	Price
H.D. heater	◆22048569	47.50
(A.C.)		
1983-87	◆22020945	60.00
Switch, Heater Blower		
1983	◆16015256	6.00
1984-87	◆16032480	7.25
Resistor, Heater Blower		
1983-87	14093318	1.75

LABOR 8 EXHAUST SYSTEM 8 LABOR

(Factory Time)	Chilton Time
(G) Muffler, Renew	
1983-87-single (.5)	.7
dual-each (.4)	.7
(G) Resonator Assy., Renew	
1983-87 (.4)	.7
(G) Catalytic Converter, Renew	
1983-87 (.8)	1.0
(G) Exhaust Pipe Flange Gasket or Seal, Renew	
1983-87 (.4)	.6
(G) Front Exhaust Pipe, Renew (To Converter)	
1983-87 (.6)	.9
(G) Intermediate Exhaust Pipe, Renew	
1983-87-single (.5)	.7
dual (.6)	.9

(Factory Time)	Chilton Time
(G) Exhaust Crossover Pipe, Renew	
Gas-1983-87 (.3)	.9
Diesel-1983-85 (1.4)	1.8
(G) E.F.E. Valve (Heat Riser), Renew	
1983-84 (.5)	.9
1985-87 (.3)	.8
(G) E.F.E. Thermal Vacuum Switch, Renew	
1983 (.2)	.4
(G) E.F.E. Vacuum Check Valve, Renew	
1983-84 (.2)	.4
1985-87 (.4)	.4
(G) Exhaust Manifold, Renew	
V-6-1983-87-right side (1.0)	1.5
left side (.7)	1.1
w/A.C. add (.2)	.2

(Factory Time)	Chilton Time
V-8-1983-85	
right side (.8)	1.2
left side (.7)	1.1
1986-87	
right side (1.1)	1.6
left side (1.0)	1.5
Diesel	
V-6-1983-85	
each (.9)	1.3
V-8-1983	
right side (.9)	1.3
left side (.7)	1.1
1984-85	
right side (1.2)	1.7
left side (.7)	1.1
w/A.C. add (.5)	.5
w/A.I.R. add (.2)	.2

COMBINATIONS

(G) Exhaust Pipe, Muffler and Tail Pipe, Renew	
V-6-1983-87 (.8)	1.3
V-8-1983-87 (1.0)	1.5
Diesel-1983-85 (1.0)	1.5

PARTS 8 EXHAUST SYSTEM 8 PARTS

	Part No.	Price

Part numbers shown are for pricing reference only. Order with complete year, model and engine information.

	Part No.	Price
Muffler (w/tailpipe)		
V-6-231		
1983-87-Federal	25515884	59.50
Calif.	25513398	59.00
V-6-260 Diesel		
1983-84	22515612	87.75
V-8-307		
(wo/Dual exhaust)		
1983-87	22505920	76.75
(Dual exhaust)		
1983-87-right	22526204	86.00
left	22526205	86.00
V-8-350 Diesel		
1983	22505891	115.25
1984-85	22524190	81.75
Exhaust Pipe (Crossover)		
V-6-231		
1983-87-Fed.	◆25516456	31.25
Calif.	◆25506286	31.25
V-6-260 Diesel		
1983-84	◆22514308	16.75
V-8-307		
1983-87	◆22504709	74.25
V-8-350 Diesel		
1983-87	◆22514728	24.00
Intermediate Exhaust Pipe		
V-6-231		
1983-87-Fed.	◆25515196	53.00
Calif.	◆25505734	51.50
V-6-260 Diesel		
1983-84	◆22515643	42.75
V-8-307		
1983-exc. below	25504476	53.00
Hurst Olds.	◆25509922	N.L.
1984-87-exc. below	◆22521646	29.00
Hurst Olds.	25516189	53.50
V-8-350 Diesel		
1983-85	◆22505893	58.75
Front Exhaust Pipe		
V-6-231		
1983	◆25506875	14.00
1984-87	◆25515198	14.50
V-6-260 Diesel		
1983-84-Fed.	◆22514392	14.50
Calif.	◆22514311	14.50
V-8-307		
1983-87-exc. below	22510552	29.75
Hurst Olds.	◆22519894	41.25
V-8-350 Diesel		
1983-85	◆563056	41.25
Catalytic Converter		
V-6-231		
1983-84	◆8999615	312.25
1985-87	◆25056912	348.00
V-8-307		
1983	◆25056622	308.25
1984-87-Fed.	◆25056632	340.00
Calif.	◆25056345	319.25

LABOR 9 FRONT SUSPENSION 9 LABOR

(Factory Time) — Chilton Time

Note: On all front suspension operations alignment charges must be added if performed. Time given does not include alignment.

	Chilton Time
(M) Wheel, Renew	
one (.3)	.5
(G) Wheels, Rotate (All)	
All models	.5
(G) Wheels, Balance	
one	.3
each adtnl	.2
(G) Check Alignment of Front End	
All models	.5
Note: Deduct if alignment is performed.	
(G) Toe-In, Adjust	
All models (.4)	.6
(G) Align Front End	
Includes: Adjust front wheel bearings.	
All models (.7)	1.4
w/A.C. interference add	.5
(G) Front Wheel Bearings, Clean and Repack (Both Wheels)	
All models (1.1)	1.6
(G) Front Wheel Bearings and Cups, Renew	
All models	
one side (.7)	.9
both sides (1.1)	1.5
(G) Front Wheel Grease Seals, Renew	
All models	
one whl (.7)	.8
both whls (1.1)	1.2
(G) Front Shock Absorber, Renew	
1983-87-one (.3)	.4
both (.5)	.7
(G) Rebuild Front Suspension	
Includes: Disassemble, renew necessary parts, reassemble, lubricate and align front end.	
1983-87-one side (3.2)	4.0
both sides (4.6)	5.4
(G) Upper and Lower Ball Joints, Renew (One Side)	
Add alignment charges.	
1983-87 (1.3)	1.8
(G) Upper Ball Joint, Renew	
Add alignment charges.	
1983-87-one (.7)	.9
both (1.2)	1.7
(G) Lower Ball Joint, Renew	
Add alignment charges.	
1983-87-one (.6)	.9
both (1.0)	1.7
(G) Steering Knuckle, Renew	
Add alignment charges.	
1983-87-one (1.0)	1.4
both (1.8)	2.5
(G) Upper Control Arm, Renew	
Add alignment charges.	
1983-87-one (.7)	1.2
both (1.3)	2.3
(G) Lower Control Arm, Renew	
Add alignment charges.	
1983-87-one (1.0)	1.5
both (1.7)	2.6
(G) Upper Control Arm Inner Pivot Shaft or Bushings, Renew	
Add alignment charges.	
1983-87-one side (1.0)	1.5
both sides (1.9)	2.9
(G) Lower Control Arm Shaft or Bushings, Renew	
Add alignment charges.	
1983-87-one side (1.2)	1.7
both sides (2.3)	3.3
(G) Front Spring, Renew	
Includes: R&R wheel and shock. Disconnect stabilizer link and control arm pivot bolts.	
Add alignment charges.	
1983-87-one (.9)	1.4
both (1.6)	2.5
(G) Front Stabilizer Bar and Bushings, Renew	
1983-87 (.5)	.8
(G) Stabilizer Links or Grommets, Renew	
1983-87-one (.3)	.4
both (.4)	.6
(G) Control Arm Bumpers, Renew (Upper or Lower)	
1983-87-one side (.2)	.4

PARTS 9 FRONT SUSPENSION 9 PARTS

	Part No.	Price
(1) Front Wheel Bearing (Outer)		
1983-87	◆14045734	N.L.
(2) Front Wheel Bearing (Inner)		
1983-87	◆7450630	11.00
(3) Front Seal Assy.		
1983-87	◆3965092	3.50
(4) Steering Knuckle		
1983-87-right	◆14012602	117.00
left	14012601	117.00
(5) Ball Joint Pkg. (Lower)		
1983-87	◆9767281	31.50
(6) Control Arm (Lower)		
1983-87-right	◆14045078	92.50
left	◆14075337	96.75
(7) Bushing (Rear)		
1983-87	◆461853	6.25
(8) Shock Absorber		
1983-87	◆4993579	24.50
(9) Coil Spring		
Order by model and description.		
(10) Ball Joint (Upper)		
1983-87	◆9767112	34.75
(11) Bushing (Front)		
1983-87	◆473786	5.25
(12) Control Arm (Upper)		
1983-87-right	◆14039012	97.75
left	◆14039011	97.75
(13) Shaft Pkg. (Upper Control)		
1983-87	◆474001	33.75

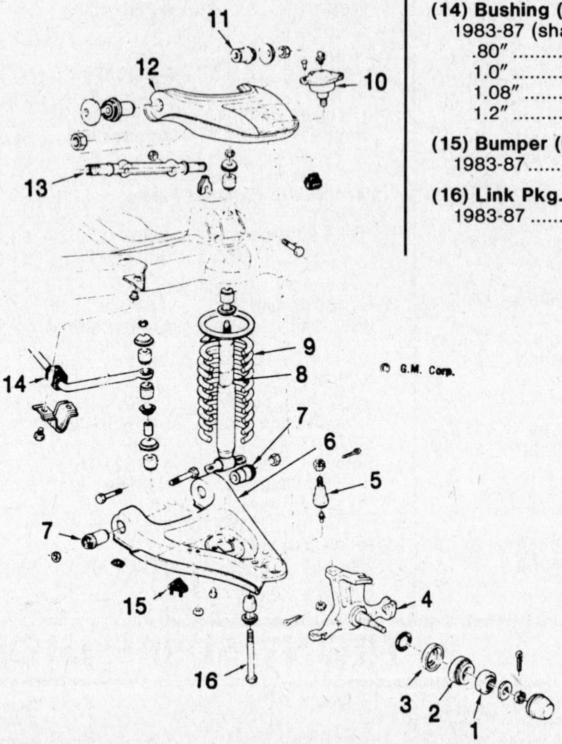

	Part No.	Price
(14) Bushing (Stabilizer)		
1983-87 (shaft dia.)		
.80"	◆370283	1.00
1.0"	◆371773	1.00
1.08"	◆472117	2.00
1.2"	◆472118	2.00
(15) Bumper (Lower)		
1983-87	459023	3.00
(16) Link Pkg.		
1983-87	◆470147	4.25

LABOR 10 STEERING LINKAGE 10 LABOR

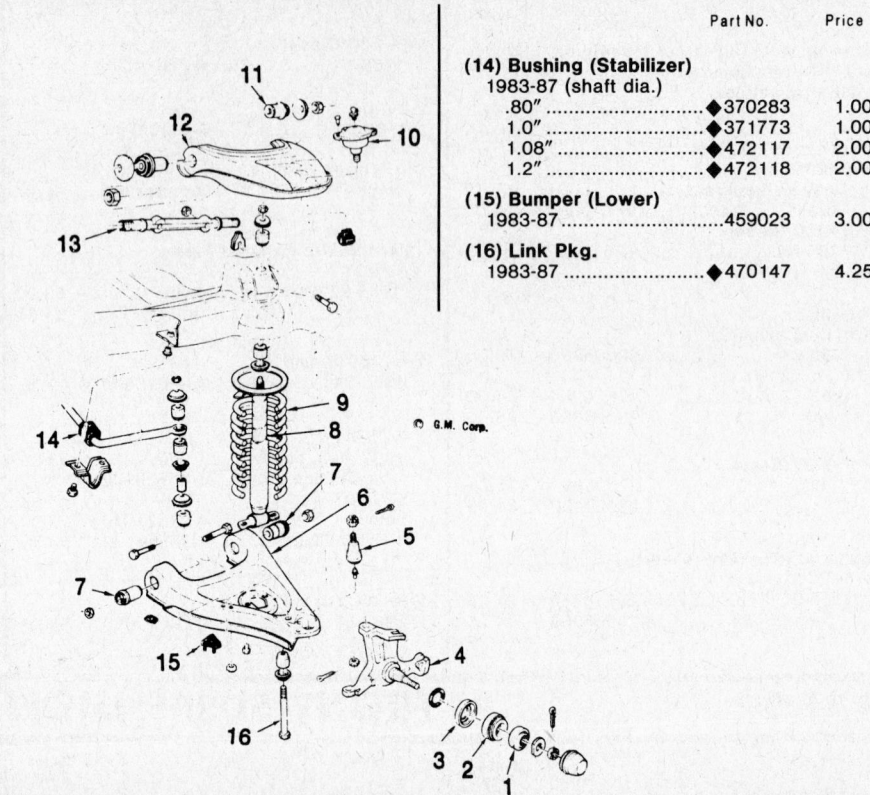

(Factory Time) — Chilton Time

(G) Tie Rods or Tie Rod Ends, Renew
Includes: Adjust toe-in and spoke alignment.
- 1983-87-one side (.7) 1.0
- both sides (.9) 1.4

(G) Inner Tie Rods, Renew
Includes: Reset toe-in.
- 1983-87-one side (.7) 1.0
- both sides (.8) 1.2

(G) Idler Arm, Renew
Includes: Adjust toe-in and spoke alignment.
- 1983-87 (.8) 1.0

(G) Intermediate Rod, Renew
Includes: Adjust toe-in and spoke alignment.
- 1983-87 (.9) 1.2

(G) Pitman Arm, Renew
Includes: Adjust toe-in and spoke alignment.
- 1983-87 (.5) 7

PARTS 10 STEERING LINKAGE 10 PARTS

	Part No.	Price
(1) Idler Arm Assy.		
1983-87	◆7837635	51.00
(2) Tie Rod Assy. (Inner)		
1983-87	◆7837183	40.25
(3) Tie Rod End (Outer)		
1983-87	◆7837733	40.00
(4) Tie Rod Sleeve Pkg. (Adjuster)		
1983-87	◆7829465	15.75
(5) Seal Kit (Pitman Arm)		
(605 gear)		
1983	◆7838143	9.25
(800 gear)		
1983-87	◆7826470	17.00
(6) Pitman Arm Assy.		
(605 gear)		
1983	◆7837649	44.00
(800 gear)		
1983-87	◆7837648	44.00

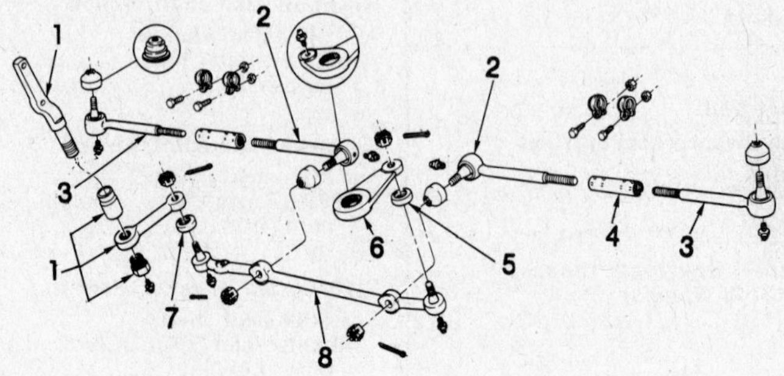

	Part No.	Price
(7) Seal Kit		
Serviced with No. 5.		

	Part No.	Price
(8) Relay Rod Assy.		
1983-87	◆7835787	79.75

LABOR 11 STEERING GEAR 11 LABOR

(Factory Time) — Chilton Time

(G) Horn Contact or Cancelling Cam, Renew

	Chilton Time
1983-87 (.5)	.6

(G) Steering Wheel, Renew

	Chilton Time
1983-87 (.3)	.4

(G) Upper Mast Jacket Bearing, Renew

	Chilton Time
1983-85-std column (.8)	1.4
tilt column (.9)	1.6
1986-87	
std colm (.8)	1.4
tilt colm (.5)	.9

(G) Steering Column Lock Actuator Parts, Renew

	Chilton Time
1983-85	
std colm (1.0)	1.5
tilt colm (.9)	1.4
1986-87	
std colm (1.0)	1.5
tilt colm (1.2)	1.7

(G) Steering Column Shift Bowl, Renew

Does not include colorcoat.

	Chilton Time
1983-85	
std colm (1.0)	1.6
tilt colm (1.7)	2.3
1986-87	
std colm (1.0)	1.6
tilt colm (2.0)	3.0

(G) Multifunction Lever, Renew

	Chilton Time
All models (.2)	.4
w/Cruise control add (.5)	.5

(G) Dimmer Switch Pivot Assy., Renew

	Chilton Time
1983-87-std colm (.9)	1.4
tilt colm (.8)	1.3
w/Cruise control add (.2)	.2

(G) Flexible Coupling, Renew

	Chilton Time
1983-84 (.3)	.5

(G) Intermediate Shaft Assembly, Renew

	Chilton Time
1983-87 (.4)	.9

(G) Universal Joint (Pot Joint), Renew

	Chilton Time
1983-84 (.3)	.8

(G) Pitman Shaft Seal, Renew

	Chilton Time
1983-87 (.6)	1.0

POWER STEERING

(G) Trouble Shoot Power Steering

Includes: Test pump and system pressure. Check pounds pull on steering wheel and check system for leaks.

	Chilton Time
All models	.5

(M) Pump Drive Belt, Renew

	Chilton Time
1983-87	
V-6 (.5)	.6
V-8 (.4)	.5
w/A.C. add (.3)	.3
w/AIR add (.1)	.1

(M) Check Reservoir and Add Fluid

	Chilton Time
All models	.2

(G) Steering Gear, Adjust

Includes: R&R gear assy., make all necessary adjustments.

	Chilton Time
1983-87 (.7)	1.2

(G) Steering Gear Assembly, Renew

	Chilton Time
1983-87 (.7)	1.2

(P) Steering Gear Assy., R&R and Recondition

Includes: Disassemble, renew necessary parts, reassemble and adjust.

	Chilton Time
1983-87 (1.7)	2.5

(G) Valve Body, Renew

Includes: R&R gear assy.

	Chilton Time
1983-87 (1.0)	1.8

(G) Steering Gear Housing, Renew

Includes: R&R gear assy.

	Chilton Time
1983-87 (1.1)	1.8

(G) Pitman Shaft Oil Seal, Renew

Does not require R&R gear assy.

	Chilton Time
1983-87 (.6)	1.0

(G) Power Steering Oil Pump, Renew

	Chilton Time
V-6–1983-87 (.6)	.9
V-8–1983-87 (.9)	1.4
Diesel–1983-85 (.9)	1.4
w/Hydra Boost add (.1)	.1

(P) Power Steering Pump, R&R and Recondition

	Chilton Time
V-6–1983-87 (.9)	1.7
V-8–1983-87 (1.4)	2.2
Diesel–1983-85 (1.4)	2.2
w/Hydra Boost add (.1)	.1

(G) Pump Shaft Oil Seal, Renew

	Chilton Time
V-6–1983-87 (.7)	1.0
V-8–1983-87 (.9)	1.5
Diesel–1983-85 (.9)	1.5
w/Hydra-Boost add (.1)	.1

(M) Hydra-Boost Hoses, Renew

	Chilton Time
1983-85	
Booster to pump (.6)	1.0
Booster to gear (.3)	.6
Return (.3)	.5

(G) Pump Flow Control Valve, Renew

	Chilton Time
1983-87 (.4)	.8

(M) Power Steering Hoses, Renew

	Chilton Time
1983-87-one (.4)	.6

TILT COLUMN

(G) Tilt Column Steering Shaft, Renew

	Chilton Time
1983-87 (1.5)	2.0
w/Cruise control add (.2)	.2

(G) Tilt Column, R&R and Recondition

	Chilton Time
1983-87 (2.4)	3.0

PARTS 11 POWER STEERING GEAR 11 PARTS

MODEL 605

	Part No.	Price
(1) Cover Assy.		
1983	◆7819790	26.75
(2) Pitman Shaft Assembly		
1983	◆7838146	87.50
(3) Seal Kit		
1983	7827371	8.25
(4) Connector		
1983	◆7819797	4.50
(5) Housing Assembly		
1983-V-6	◆7832279	181.00
V-8	◆7834920	183.00
(6) Bearing Assembly (Housing)		
1983	◆7828012	7.25
(7) Bearing Assembly (Pitman Shaft)		
1983	◆7838145	16.25
(8) Seal Kit (Pitman Shaft)		
1983	◆7838143	9.25
(9) Seal Kit (Valve)		
1983	◆7826056	13.50

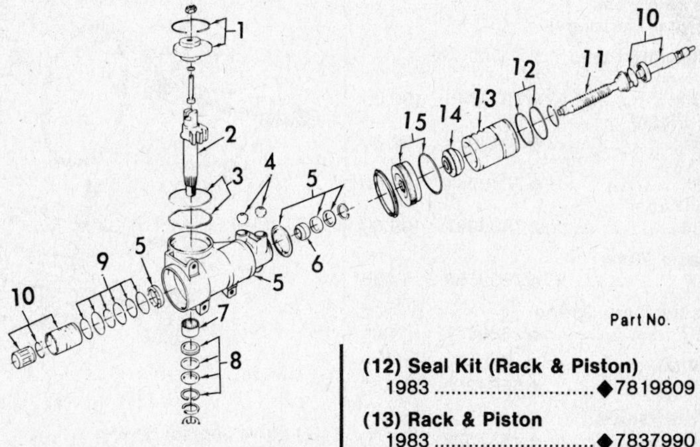

	Part No.	Price
(10) Valve Assembly		
1983	◆7819796	202.00
(11) Worm Assembly		
Not serviced Sep.		

	Part No.	Price
(12) Seal Kit (Rack & Piston)		
1983	◆7819809	5.75
(13) Rack & Piston		
1983	◆7837990	162.00
(14) Bearing Assembly (Lower)		
1983	◆7837985	13.50
(15) Adjuster Plug		
1983-V-6	◆7819792	52.25
V-8	◆7828584	59.25

PARTS 11 POWER STEERING GEAR 11 PARTS

	Part No.	Price
MODEL 800		
(1) Seal (Side Cover)		
1983-87	◆7817486	9.00
(2) Pitman Shaft (w/Gear)		
1983-87-exc.		
below	◆7815885	87.50
Var. strg.	◆7813631	87.50
(3) Check Valve Kit		
1983-87	◆7834284	5.25
(4) Bearing Kit		
1983-87	◆7826850	11.00
(5) Housing Assy.		
1983-87	◆7834145	183.00
(6) Bearing (Pitman Shaft)		
1983-87	◆5697804	15.00
(7) Seal Kit (Pitman Shaft)		
1983-87	◆7826470	17.00
(8) Seal (Adjuster Plug)		
1983-87	◆5686527	1.50
(9) Bearing (Adjuster Plug)		
1983-87	◆7828012	7.25
(10) Plug Assy. (Adjuster)		
1983-87	◆7832731	53.50
(14) Seal Kit		
1983-87	◆5687182	12.50
(12) Valve Assy.		
1983-87-exc.		
below	◆7832058	212.00
H.D. susp.	◆7832055	202.25
Hurst Olds.	◆7832057	212.00
(14) Seal Kit		
1983-87	◆7817485	6.50
(15) Plug		
1983-87	◆5693463	7.25
(16) Rack Assy.		
1983-87-exc.		
below	◆7817528	162.00
H.D. susp.	◆7827170	154.25
Hurst Olds.	◆7839019	162.00

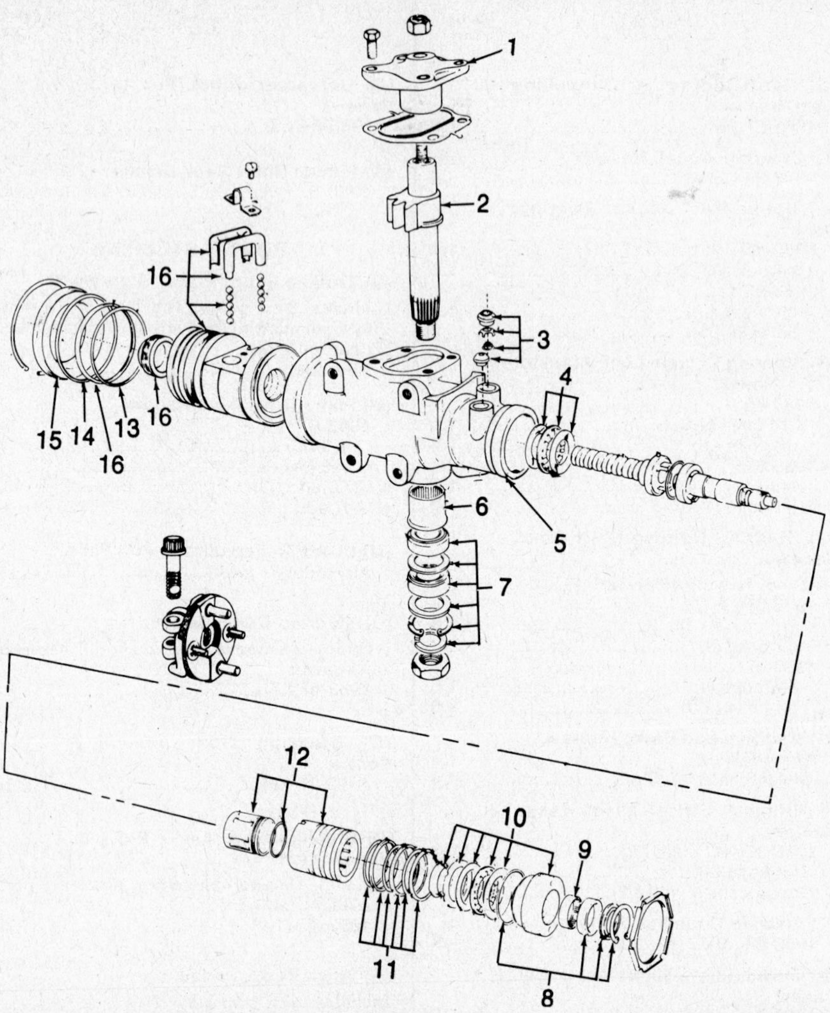

PARTS 11 POWER STEERING PUMP 11 PARTS

	Part No.	Price
Pressure Line Hose		
Order by year and model.		
Power Steering Pump		
V-6-231		
1983-87	◆7839345	199.00
V-6-260 Diesel		
1983-84	◆7842625	199.00
V-8-307		
1983-87	◆7840244	199.00
V-8-350 Diesel		
1983-85	◆7839997	199.00
(1) Pressure Plate		
1983-87	◆7839669	14.25
(2) Pressure Plate Spring		
1983-87	◆7839667	1.00
(3) End Plate		
1983-87	◆5689358	3.50
(4) Rotor & Vane Kit		
1983-87	◆7837322	75.00
(5) Thrust Plate		
1983-87	◆7839366	25.75
(6) Valve Assy.		
1983-87	◆7809232	10.75

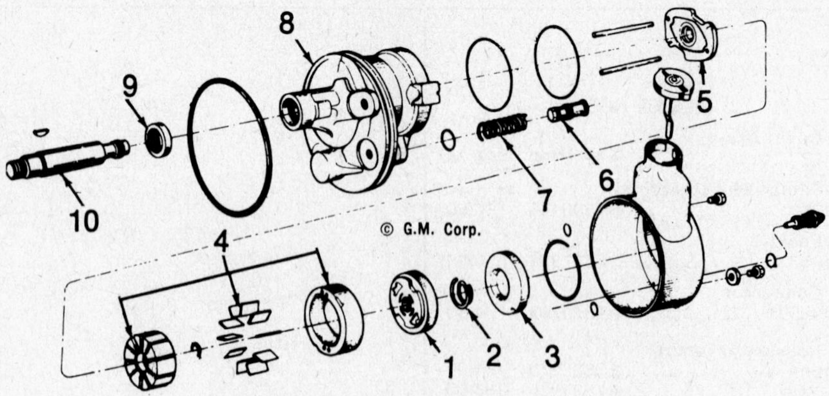

	Part No.	Price
(7) Flow Control Spring		
1983-87	◆5688037	1.50
(8) Housing Assy.		
1983-87-exc.		
below	◆7830236	62.75
V-6 Diesel	7840514	62.75

	Part No.	Price
(9) Drive Shaft Seal		
1983-87	◆7808195	4.50
(10) Drive Shaft		
1983-87	◆7837321	39.50

LABOR 12 CYLINDER HEAD & VALVE SYSTEM 12 LABOR

(Factory Time) Chilton Time

GASOLINE ENGINES

(G) Compression Test

V-6–1983-87 (.5)	.7
V-8–1983-87 (.6)	.8
w/A.C. add	.3

(G) Cylinder Head Gasket, Renew

Includes: Drain and refill cooling system. Clean gasket surfaces. Make all necessary adjustments including carburetor and timing.

V-6–1983-87-one (4.4)	5.8
both (5.3)	7.6
V-8–1983-85-one (4.2)	5.7
both (5.4)	7.4
1986-87	
right side (4.0)	5.5
left side (4.4)	6.0
both sides (5.8)	8.0
w/A.C. add (.6)	.6
w/A.I.R. add (.4)	.4

(G) Cylinder Head, Renew

Includes: Drain and refill cooling system. Clean gasket surfaces, transfer parts, reface valves. Minor engine tune up.

V-6–1983-87-one (4.9)	6.6
both (5.9)	9.1
V-8–1983-85-one (4.5)	6.2
both (6.1)	8.4
1986-87	
right side (4.2)	5.7
left side (4.6)	6.3
both sides (6.2)	8.5
w/A.C. add (.6)	.6
w/A.I.R. add (.4)	.4

(P) Clean Carbon and Grind Valves

Includes: Drain and refill cooling system. R&R cylinder heads. Recondition valve seats, adjust valve stem length. Minor engine tune up.

V-6–1983-87-one bank (5.4)	7.5
both banks (8.0)	11.2
V-8–1983-85-one bank (5.1)	7.0
both banks (7.1)	9.7
1986-87	
right bank (5.1)	7.0
left bank (5.6)	7.7
both banks (8.1)	11.2
w/A.C. add (.6)	.6
w/A.I.R. add (.4)	.4

(G) Valve Tappets, Renew (Lifters)

Includes: Drain and refill cooling system. R&R intake manifold. Make all necessary adjustments.

V-6–1983-87-one bank (2.6)	3.4
both banks (2.9)	4.0
V-8–1983-85-one bank (2.5)	3.4
both banks (3.1)	4.2
1986-87	
one cyl (2.7)	3.7
one cyl-each side (3.2)	4.4
all cyls-both sides (5.0)	6.9
w/A.C. add (.3)	.3
w/A.I.R. add (.2)	.2

(G) Rocker Arm Cover or Gasket, Renew

V-6–1983-87-one (.4)	.7
both (.6)	1.1
V-8–1983-85-one (.5)	.7
both (.9)	1.6
1986-87	
right side (.6)	.7
left side (.8)	1.2
both sides (1.4)	1.9
w/A.C. add (.3)	.3
w/AIR add (.2)	.2

COMBINATIONS

Add to Valve Job

See Machine Shop Operations

(Factory Time) Chilton Time

(G) DRAIN, EVACUATE & RECHARGE AIR CONDITIONING SYSTEM	
All models (.5)	1.0
(G) ROCKER ARM STUD, RENEW	
Each (.3)	.3
(G) HYDRAULIC VALVE LIFTERS, DISASSEMBLE AND CLEAN	
Each (.2)	.2
(G) DISTRIBUTOR, RECONDITION	
All models (.5)	.8
(G) CARBURETOR, RECONDITION	
2 BBL	1.2
4 BBL	1.5
(P) VALVE GUIDES, REAM OVERSIZE	
Each (.1)	.1
(G) Rocker Arm Shaft, Recondition	
Each side (.2)	.3

(Factory Time) Chilton Time

(G) Valve Spring and/or Valve Stem Oil Seal, Renew (Head on Car)

V-6–1983-87-one cyl (.8)	1.2
one cyl-each bank (1.4)	2.0
V-8–1983-85-one cyl (.6)	1.0
one cyl-each bank (1.0)	1.8
1986-87	
one cyl'	
right side (.7)	1.0
left side (1.1)	1.6
both sides (1.8)	2.4
each adtnl cyl-all engs (.2)	.3
w/A.C. add (.3)	.3
w/AIR add (.2)	.2

(G) Rocker Arm, Pivot and/or Push Rod, Renew

V-6–1983-87-one side (.8)	1.1
both sides (1.3)	1.7
Recond assy add-each side	.3
V-8–1983-85-one side (.9)	1.3
both sides (1.4)	2.0
1986-87	
one cyl'	
right side (.7)	.9
left side (.9)	1.4
both sides (1.5)	2.1
all cyls-both sides (2.0)	2.9
w/A.C. add (.3)	.3
w/AIR add (.2)	.2

(G) Valves, Adjust

V-6–1983-87	1.5
V-8–1983-85	2.0
1986-87	2.5

DIESEL ENGINE

(G) Compression Test

V-6	1.0
V-8	1.3

(G) Cylinder Head Gasket, Renew

Includes: R&R injector pump and lines. R&R intake manifold and disconnect exhaust manifolds. Clean gasket surfaces, bleed lifters and adjust timing. Drain and refill cooling system.

V-6–1983-85	
right side (4.7)	6.3
left side (4.9)	6.6
both sides (6.3)	8.5
V-8–1983-85	
left side (5.7)	7.4
right side (6.1)	7.9
both sides (7.6)	9.9
w/A.C. add (.4)	.4

(G) Cylinder Head, Renew

Includes: R&R injector pump and lines. R&R intake manifold and disconnect exhaust manifolds. Clean gasket surfaces. Transfer parts, reface valves. Bleed lifters and adjust timing. Drain and refill cooling system.

V-6–1983-85	
right side (5.2)	7.0
left side (5.3)	7.1
both sides (7.6)	10.2
V-8–1983-85	
left side (6.1)	7.9
right side (6.5)	8.4
both sides (8.4)	11.1
w/A.C. add (.4)	.4

(P) Clean Carbon and Grind Valves

Includes: R&R injector pump and lines. R&R cylinder heads, clean carbon. Recondition valves and valve seats. Check and adjust valve stem length. Bleed lifters, drain and refill cooling system.

V-6–1983-85	
right side (5.7)	7.6
left side (5.8)	7.8
both sides (8.7)	11.7
V-8–1983-85	
left side (6.6)	8.5
right side (7.0)	9.1
both sides (9.3)	12.6
w/A.C. add (.4)	.4

(G) Valve Tappets, Renew (Lifters)

Includes: R&R injector pump and lines, intake manifold and rocker arms. Drain and refill cooling system.

V-6–1983-85	
one cyl (2.7)	3.6
one cyl-each side (3.3)	4.5
each adtnl cyl (.2)	.2
V-8–1983-85	
one cyl (3.5)	4.5
one cyl-each side (3.9)	5.0
each adtnl cyl (.1)	.1

(G) Rocker Arm Cover or Gasket, Renew

V-6–1983-85	
one (1.1)	1.5
both (1.8)	2.5
V-8–1983-85	
one side (1.2)	2.4
both sides (2.0)	2.9

(G) Valve Spring or Valve Stem Oil Seals, Renew (Head On Car)

V-6–1983-85	
one cyl (1.3)	1.8
one cyl-each side (2.2)	3.0
each adtnl cyl (.3)	.3
V-8–1983-85	
one cyl (1.6)	3.0
one cyl-each bank (2.4)	3.7
each adtnl cyl (.3)	.3

(G) Rocker Arm, Pivot and/or Push Rod, Renew

V-6–1983-85	
one cyl (1.2)	1.6
one cyl-each side (2.2)	3.0
each adtnl cyl	.1
V-8–1983-85	
one cyl (1.5)	2.5
one cyl-each bank (2.3)	3.0
each adtnl cyl (.1)	.1

PARTS 12 CYLINDER HEAD & VALVE SYSTEM 12 PARTS

	Part No.	Price
Valve Grind Gasket Set		
V-6-231		
1st design: .017 in. thick head gasket. 2nd design: .062 in. thick head gasket.		
1983-1st design	◆25525121	N.L.
2nd design	◆25527307	71.50
1984-Alum. man.		
1st design	◆25525120	37.00
2nd design	◆25527306	71.50
1984-Cast iron man.		
1st design	◆25525121	N.L.
2nd design	◆25527307	71.50
1985-1st design	◆25525120	37.00
2nd design	◆25527306	71.50
1986-87	◆25527306	71.50
V-6 260 Diesel		
1983-84	◆22528684	79.50
V-8-307		
1983-84	◆22507725	48.75
1985-87	◆22534926	58.00
V-8-350 Diesel		
1983-84	◆22522053	94.50
1985	◆22527541	N.L.
(1) Pivot		
1983-87	22524396	2.00
(2) Rocker Arm		
V-6-231		
1983-87-right	◆1241850	4.50
left	◆1241851	4.50
V-6-260 Diesel		
1983-84	◆22505583	N.L.
V-8-307, 350N		
1983-87	◆22505583	N.L.
(3) Valve Key		
1983-87	◆3947770	.50
(4) Valve Spring Retainer		
V-6		
1983-87	◆1254900	1.50
(5) Valve Stem Seals		
V-6-231		
1983-87	◆25518390	2.50
V-6-260 Diesel		
1983-84-intake	◆406595	1.00
exhaust	◆401823	1.00
V-8-307, 350N		
1983-87-intake	◆406595	1.00
exhaust	◆401823	1.00

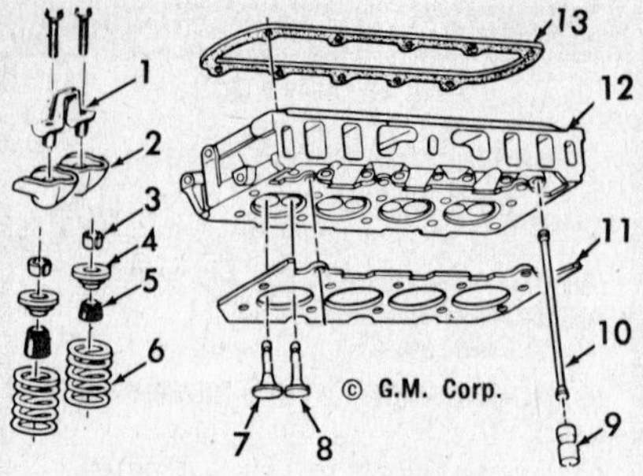

	Part No.	Price
(6) Valve Spring		
V-6-231		
1983-87	◆1249267	2.75
V-6 & V-8 Diesel		
1983-85	◆22510372	4.00
V-8-307		
1983-87	◆411226	4.00
(7) Intake Valve		
V-6-231		
1983-87	◆25512098	11.25
V-6-260 Diesel		
1983-84	◆22513937	18.25
V-8-307		
1983-85	◆22503324	11.00
1986-87	◆22530611	20.25
V-8-350 Diesel		
1983-85	◆22519914	20.00
(8) Exhaust Valve		
V-6-231		
1983-87	◆1261380	13.50
V-6 & V-8 Diesel		
1983-85	◆558873	13.00
V-8-307		
1983-87	◆555456	13.50
(9) Valve Lifter Assy.		
V-6-231		
1983	◆5232765	9.00
1984-87	◆5234330	N.L.
V-6 & V-8 Diesel		
1983-85	◆5234470	38.10
V-8-307		
1983-84	◆5232750	N.L.
1985-87	◆5234755	43.50

	Part No.	Price
(10) Valve Push Rod		
V-6-231		
1983-84	◆1249139	4.00
1985-87	◆25510025	4.25
V-6 & V-8 Diesel		
1983-85	◆22511044	3.25
V-8-307		
1983-84	◆22505582	2.50
1985-87	◆22533631	3.25
(11) Cylinder Head Gasket		
V-6-231		
1st design: .017 in. thick. 2nd design: .062 in. thick.		
1983-84-1st design		
2nd design	◆25525919	21.25
1985-1st design	◆25524599	8.50
2nd design	◆25525919	21.25
1986-87	◆25525919	21.25
V-6-260 Diesel		
1983-84	◆22527054	30.50
V-8-307		
1983-87	◆22503500	9.25
V-8-350 Diesel		
1983-85	◆22519416	30.75
(12) Cylinder Head		
V-6-231		
1983-87	◆25518679	217.00
V-6-260 Diesel		
1983-84	◆22520040	325.00
V-8-307		
1983-84	◆22511238	247.00
1985-87	◆22530557	247.00
V-8-350 Diesel		
1983-85	◆22515038	387.00
(13) Valve Cover Gasket		
V-6-231		
1983-84	◆25523348	N.L.
1985-87	◆25523348	N.L.
V-8		
For valve cover gaskets not listed, use R.T.V. sealant.		

LABOR 13 ENGINE ASSEMBLY & MOUNTS 13 LABOR

GASOLINE ENGINES

(Factory Time)	Chilton Time
(G) Engine Assembly, Remove & Install	
Does not include transfer of any parts or equipment.	
V-6-1983-87	5.0
V-8-1983-87	4.8
w/A.C. add (.6)	.6
w/P.S. add (.3)	.3
w/A.I.R. add (.4)	.4
(G) Engine Assembly, Renew (Universal)	
Includes: R&R engine assembly. Transfer all component parts not supplied with replacement engine. Make all necessary adjustments.	
V-6-1984-87 (5.5)	9.0
w/A.C. add (.3)	.3
w/AIR add (.2)	.2

(Factory Time)	Chilton Time
(G) Engine Assembly, Renew (Partial)	
Includes: R&R engine assembly, transfer all component parts not supplied with replacement engine. Minor tune up.	
V-6-1983-87 (7.0)	11.2
Recond valves add (1.2)	1.2
V-8-1983-87 (8.4)	11.7
w/A.C. add (.6)	.6
w/P.S. add (.3)	.3
w/A.I.R. add (.4)	.4
Recond valves add (1.6)	1.6
(P) Cylinder Block, Renew (w/All Internal Parts Less Head(s) and Oil Pan)	
Includes: R&R engine, transfer all component parts not supplied with replacement engine, clean carbon, grind valves. Minor tune up.	
V-6-1983-87 (13.2)	18.6
V-8-1983-87 (12.6)	17.6
w/A.C. add (.6)	.6
w/P.S. add (.3)	.3
w/A.I.R. add (.4)	.4

(Factory Time)	Chilton Time
(P) Engine Assy., R&R and Recondition (Complete)	
Includes: Rebore block, install new pistons, rings, rod and main bearings. Clean carbon, grind valves. Tune engine.	
V-6-1983-87 (21.4)	25.1
V-8-1983-87 (18.6)	26.0
w/A.C. add (.6)	.6
w/P.S. add (.3)	.3
w/A.I.R. add (.4)	.4
(P) Engine Assembly, Recondition (In Car)	
Includes: Expand or renew pistons, install new rings, pins, rod and main bearings. Clean carbon, grind valves. Tune engine.	
V-6-1983-87 (14.9)	18.0
V-8-1983-87 (19.4)	27.1
w/A.C. add (.6)	.6
w/P.S. add (.3)	.3
w/A.I.R. add (.4)	.4

LABOR 13 ENGINE ASSEMBLY & MOUNTS 13 LABOR

	(Factory Time)	Chilton Time
(G) Engine Mounts, Renew		
Front		
V-6–1983-87-one	(.5)	.7
both	(.7)	1.0
V-8–1983-87-one	(.5)	.8
both	(.6)	1.0
Rear		
1983-87	(.3)	.6

DIESEL ENGINE

(G) Engine Assembly, Remove & Install

Does not include transfer of any parts or equipment.

	(Factory Time)	Chilton Time
V-6–1983-85		4.5
V-8–1983-85		5.0
w/A.C. add	(.4)	.5

(G) Engine Assembly, Renew (Universal)

Includes: R&R engine assembly, transfer all component parts not supplied with replacement engine. Make all necessary adjustments.

	(Factory Time)	Chilton Time
V-6–1983-85		16.5
V-8–1983-85		20.0
w/A.C. add	(.4)	.5
Renew gov retaining ring add		.7

(P) Cylinder Block, Renew (w/Pistons, Rings and Bearings)

Includes: Transfer all component parts not supplied with replacement engine, clean carbon, grind valves. Make all necessary adjustments.

	(Factory Time)	Chilton Time
V-6–1983-85	(11.6)	22.0
V-8–1983-85	(16.6)	27.0
w/A.C. add	(.4)	.5

(P) Cylinder Block, Renew (w/All Internal Parts Less Heads and Oil Pan)

Includes: R&R engine, transfer all component parts not supplied with replacement engine, clean carbon, grind valves. Make all necessary adjustments.

	(Factory Time)	Chilton Time
V-6–1983-85	(10.8)	21.0
V-8–1983-85	(13.8)	24.0
w/A.C. add	(.5)	.5

(P) Engine Assy., R&R and Recondition (Complete)

Includes: Rebore block, install new pistons, rings, pins, rod and main bearings. Clean carbon, grind valves. Make all necessary adjustments.

	(Factory Time)	Chilton Time
V-6–1983-85	(19.1)	27.7
V-8–1983-85	(29.5)	36.0
w/A.C. add	(.4)	.5

(P) Engine Assembly, Recondition (In Car)

Includes: Expand or renew pistons, install new rings, pins, rod and main bearings. Clean carbon, grind valves. Make all necessary adjustments.

	(Factory Time)	Chilton Time
V-6–1983-85	(15.0)	22.7
V-8–1983-85	(23.0)	27.3
w/A.C. add	(.4)	.5

	(Factory Time)	Chilton Time
(G) Engine Mounts, Renew		
Front		
1983-85-one	(.5)	.8
both	(.7)	1.0
Rear		
1983-85	(.3)	.4

PARTS 13 ENGINE ASSEMBLY & MOUNTS 13 PARTS

Cylinder Block Assy.
Includes: Pistons, rings & bearings.

	Part No.	Price
V-6-231		
1983-84	◆25519450	950.00
1985	◆25524288	950.00
1986-87	◆25527475	950.00
V-6-260 Diesel		
1983	22518904	1421.00
V-8-307		
(wo/Hurst-Olds)		
1983-84	◆22515525	949.00
1985-87	◆22530856	949.00
(Hurst-Olds)		
1983-85	22530082	949.00
V-8-350 Diesel		
1983	◆22518907	1418.00
1984-85	◆22525604	1600.00

Partial Engine Assy.
Includes: Crankshaft, pistons, connecting rods, bearings, and rear seal.

	Part No.	Price
V-6-231		
1983	◆25516156	1263.25
1984	◆25519449	1263.25
1985	◆25524286	1263.00
1986-87	◆25527474	1263.00
V-6-260 Diesel		
1983-84	◆22522150	1750.00
V-8-307		
(wo/Hurst-Olds.)		
1983-84	◆22504938	1397.00
1985-87	◆22530855	1397.00
(Hurst-Olds.)		
1983-85	22530083	1397.00
V-8-350 Diesel		
1983	◆22518906	1950.00
1984-85	◆22525604	1600.00

Engine Front Mount

	Part No.	Price
V-6-231		
1983-87-right	◆1258666	24.00
left	◆25504643	29.00
V-6-260 Diesel		
1983-84	◆459021	24.00
V-8-307		
1983-87	◆22501573	29.00
V-8-350 Diesel		
1983-85	◆553915	27.25

Engine Gasket Set
For complete overhaul cylinder head gasket set must also be used.

V-6-231
1st design: .017 in. thick head gasket. 2nd design: .062 in. thick head gasket.

	Part No.	Price
1983-1st design	◆25525119	58.25
2nd design	◆25528727	90.00
1984-Alum. man.		
1st design	◆25505370	52.50
2nd design	◆25527302	89.00
1984-Cast iron man.		
1st design	◆25525119	58.25
2nd design	◆25528727	90.00
1985-1st design	◆25525118	58.25
1986-87	◆25527302	89.00
V-6-260 Diesel		
1983-84	◆22528685	97.50
V-8-307		
1983-84	◆22506498	58.75
1985-87	◆22527539	62.50
V-8-350 Diesel		
1983-84	◆22521786	90.00
1985	◆22527538	N.L.

LABOR 14 PISTONS, RINGS & BEARINGS 14 LABOR

COMBINATIONS
Add to Engine Work
See Machine Shop Operations

(G) DRAIN, EVACUATE & RECHARGE AIR CONDITIONING SYSTEM		
All models	(.5)	1.0
(G) ROCKER ARM STUD, RENEW		
Each	(.3)	.3
(G) HYDRAULIC VALVE LIFTERS, DISASSEMBLE AND CLEAN		
Each	(.2)	.2
(G) DISTRIBUTOR, RECONDITION		
All models	(.5)	.8
(G) CARBURETOR, RECONDITION		
2 BBL		1.2
4 BBL		1.5
(G) CYLINDER HEAD, R&R (ENGINE REMOVED)		
V-6		
eng Codes A-4		
one	(1.1)	1.4
both	(1.8)	2.3
V-8		
eng Code Y		
one	(1.8)	2.3
both	(2.6)	3.3
(G) CONNECTING ROD, RENEW (ENGINE DISASSEMBLED)		
V-6		
eng Codes A-4		
each	(.5)	.6
V-8		
eng Code Y		
each	(.5)	.6

LABOR 14 PISTONS, RINGS & BEARINGS 14 LABOR

(Factory Time)	Chilton Time

GASOLINE ENGINES

(P) Rings, Renew (See Engine Combinations)

Includes: Remove cylinder top ridge, deglaze cylinder walls. Clean piston and ring grooves. Minor tune up.

V-6–1983-87 (9.5)	13.3
V-8–1983-85 (10.1)	14.6
1986-87	
one cyl (7.6)	11.0
one cyl–each bank (9.6)	13.9
all cyls–both banks (11.9)	17.2
w/A.C. add (.3)	.3
w/P.S. add (.3)	.3
w/A.I.R. add (.2)	.2

(P) Pistons or Connecting Rods, Renew

Includes: Remove cylinder top ridge, deglaze cylinder walls, clean piston and ring grooves. Minor tune up.

V-6–1983-87 (10.2)	15.1
V-8–1983-85 (11.2)	17.0
1986-87	
one cyl (8.2)	11.6
one cyl–each bank (10.8)	15.1
all cyls–both banks (13.0)	19.6

COMBINATIONS

Add to Engine Work
See Machine Shop Operations

(Factory Time)	Chilton Time
(P) VALVE GUIDES, REAM OVERSIZE	
Each (.1)	.1
(G) DEGLAZE CYLINDER WALLS	
Each (.1)	.1
(G) REMOVE CYLINDER TOP RIDGE	
Each (.1)	.1
(G) ROCKER ARM SHAFT ASSY., DISASSEMBLE AND CLEAN OR RECONDITION	
V-6-one side (.2)	.3
(G) PLASTIGAUGE BEARINGS	
Each (.1)	.1
(G) OIL PUMP, RECONDITION	
All models (.2)	.4
(M) OIL FILTER ELEMENT, RENEW	
All models (.3)	.3

(Factory Time)	Chilton Time
w/A.C. add (.3)	.3
w/P.S. add (.3)	.3
w/A.I.R. add (.2)	.2

(P) Connecting Rod Bearings, Renew

(Factory Time)	Chilton Time
V-6–1983-87 (2.3)	3.4
V-8–1983-85 (3.4)	4.8
1986-87 (4.4)	6.0

DIESEL ENGINE

(P) Rings, Renew (See Engine Combinations)

Includes: Remove cylinder top ridge, deglaze cylinder walls. Clean piston and ring grooves. Make all necessary adjustments.

V-6–1983-85 (11.6)	16.2
V-8–1983-85 (12.8)	17.2
w/A.C. add (.4)	.4

(P) Piston or Connecting Rod, Renew

Includes: Remove cylinder top ridge, deglaze cylinder walls, clean piston and ring grooves. Make all necessary adjustments.

V-6–1983-85 (12.3)	18.0
V-8–1983-85 (13.3)	19.6
w/A.C. add (.4)	.4

(P) Connecting Rod Bearings, Renew

Includes: Raise engine and clean oil pump screen.

V-6–1983-85 (3.9)	5.4
V-8–1983-85 (4.9)	6.6

PARTS 14 PISTONS, RINGS, PINS & BEARINGS 14 PARTS

(1) Ring Set (1 Piston)

1st design: .017 in. thick head gasket. 2nd design: .062 in. thick head gasket.

	Part No.	Price
V-6–231		
1983-84-1st design	◆1240955	15.75
2nd design	◆25526600	17.50
1985-1st design	◆25519462	N.L.
2nd design	◆25526600	17.50
1986-87	◆25526600	17.50
V-6–260 Diesel		
1983-84	◆22515964	21.00
V-8–307		
1983-87	◆22529562	18.25
V-8–350 Diesel		
1983	◆22515964	21.00
1984-85	◆22523733	21.00

(2) Piston Pin

Serviced with No. 3.

(3) Piston Assy. (Std.)

	Part No.	Price
V-6–231		
1983-85	◆25518053	48.25
1986-87	◆25527178	48.25

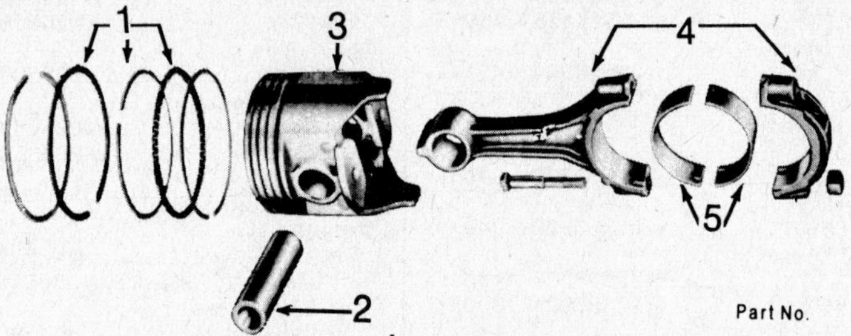

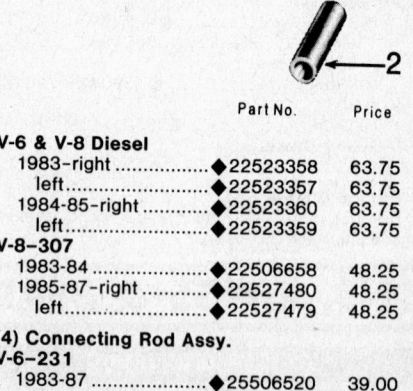

	Part No.	Price
V-6 & V-8 Diesel		
1983-right	◆22523358	63.75
left	◆22523357	63.75
1984-85-right	◆22523360	63.75
left	◆22523359	63.75
V-8–307		
1983-84	◆22506658	48.25
1985-87-right	◆22527480	48.25
left	◆22527479	48.25

(4) Connecting Rod Assy.

	Part No.	Price
V-6–231		
1983-87	◆25506520	39.00
V-6–260 Diesel		
1983-84	◆22515315	50.50
V-8–307		
1983-84	◆554976	45.00
1985-87	◆22527025	45.00
V-8–350 Diesel		
1983-85	◆22515313	50.50

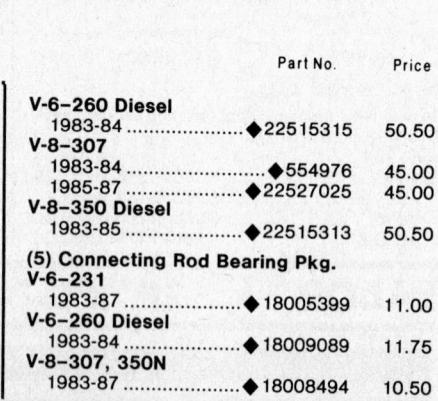

(5) Connecting Rod Bearing Pkg.

	Part No.	Price
V-6–231		
1983-87	◆18005399	11.00
V-6–260 Diesel		
1983-84	◆18009089	11.75
V-8–307, 350N		
1983-87	◆18008494	10.50

LABOR 15 CRANKSHAFT & DAMPER 15 LABOR

(Factory Time)	Chilton Time

GASOLINE ENGINES

(P) Crankshaft and Main Bearings, Renew

Includes: R&R engine, check all bearing clearances.

V-6–1983-87 (7.1)	10.0
V-8–1983-85 (7.4)	10.5
1986-87 (7.0)	10.1
w/A.C. add (.4)	.4
w/P.S. add (.3)	.3
w/A.I.R. add (.2)	.2

(P) Main Bearings, Renew

Includes: Check all bearing clearances.

(Factory Time)	Chilton Time
V-6–1983-87 (2.2)	3.6
V-8–1983-85 (2.8)	4.2
1986-87 (4.1)	5.7

LABOR 15 CRANKSHAFT & DAMPER 15 LABOR

(Factory Time) Chilton Time

(P) Main and Rod Bearings, Renew
Includes: Check all bearing clearances.
V-6–1983-87 (3.4) 5.4
V-8–1983-85 (4.5) 6.6
1986-87 (6.3) 8.1

(G) Rear Main Bearing Oil Seals, Renew or Repack (Upper & Lower)
Includes: R&R oil pan and rear main bearing cap.
V-6–1983-87 (1.5) 2.2
V-8–1983-85 (2.2) 3.0
1986-87 (6.0) 3.6

(G) Crankshaft Pulley or Balancer, Renew
V-6–1983-87–pulley (.7) 1.2
balancer (.8) 1.3
V-8–1983-85–pulley (.5) 7
balancer (.7) 1.2
1986-87–pulley (.6) 1.0
balancer (.9) 1.3
w/A.C. add (.2) 2
w/A.I.R. add (.2) 2
w/P.S. add (.1) 1

(Factory Time) Chilton Time

(G) Crankshaft Front Oil Seal, Renew
V-6–1983-87 (2.3) *3.2
V-8–1983-85 (.8) 1.4
1986-87 (1.0) 1.5
w/A.C. add (.2) 2
w/AIR add (.1) 1
*Includes R&R front cover.

DIESEL ENGINE

(P) Crankshaft and Main Bearings, Renew
Includes: R&R engine, check all bearing clearances.
V-6–1983-85 (8.0) 11.0
V-8–1983-85 (8.3) 11.2
w/A.C. add (.4) 4

(P) Main Bearings, Renew
Includes: Check all bearing clearances.
V-6–1983-85 (3.2) 4.5
V-8–1983-85 (4.1) 5.5

(P) Main and Rod Bearings, Renew
Includes: Check all bearing clearances.
V-6–1983-85 (5.0) 6.3
V-8–1983-85 (6.5) 7.9

(Factory Time) Chilton Time

(G) Rear Main Bearing Oil Seals, R&R and Repack
Includes: R&R oil pan and rear main bearing cap.
V-6–1983-85 (2.1) 3.5
V-8–1983-85 (2.9) 4.0

(G) Rear Main Bearing Oil Seals, Renew
Includes: R&R engine assy.
V-6–1983-85 (7.3) 10.5
V-8–1983-85 (7.4) 10.7
w/A.C. add (.4) 4

(G) Crankshaft Pulley or Balancer, Renew
V-6–1983-85
pulley (.4) 6
balancer (.6) 8
V-8–1983-85–pulley (.6) 8
balancer (.9) 1.3
w/A.C. add (.2) 2

(G) Crankshaft Front Oil Seal, Renew
V-6–1983-85 (.7) 1.3
V-8–1983-85 (.9) 1.5
w/A.C. add (.2) 2

PARTS 15 CRANKSHAFT & DAMPER 15 PARTS

	Part No.	Price
(1) Crankshaft		
V-6-231		
1983-87	◆1260877	385.00
V-6-260 Diesel		
1983-84	◆22515611	430.00
V-8-307		
1983-84	◆22505615	403.00
1985-87	◆22527438	403.00
V-8-350 Diesel		
1983-85	◆22511035	439.00
(2) Main Bearing (Std.)		
V-6-231		
1983-87-No. 1	◆18009457	12.00
No. 2	◆18004602	20.00
No. 3	◆18002950	12.50
No. 4	◆5468578	13.00
V-6-260 Diesel		
1983-84-No. 1	◆5466312	16.00
No. 2	◆5458657	15.00
No. 3	◆5463797	26.25
No. 4	◆18009091	25.75
V-8-307		
1983-87-No. 1	◆5466211	13.00
No. 2, 4	◆5466089	13.00
No. 3	◆5466090	20.00
No. 5	◆5466091	17.00
V-8-350 Diesel		
1983-85-No. 1	◆5466312	16.00
No. 2, 4	◆5458657	15.00
No. 3	◆5463797	26.25
No. 5	◆5466314	19.75

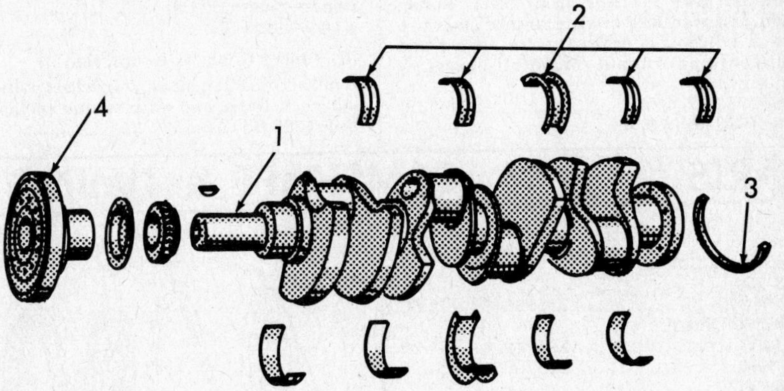

	Part No.	Price
(3) Rear Main Oil Seal		
1983-87-packing	◆9772831	1.50
1983-87-V-6		
Seal	◆1193151	1.50
Timing Cover Seal		
V-6-231		
1983-87-packing	◆1305044	1.00
oil shedder	◆1193966	1.50
V-6 & V-8 Diesel		
1983-85	◆552711	4.25
V-8-307		
1983-87	◆552711	4.25
(4) Vibration Damper		
V-6-231		
1983	◆25506570	42.75
1984-87	◆25523502	41.25
V-6-260 Diesel		
1983-84	◆22514398	33.50

	Part No.	Price
V-8-307		
1983-87	◆22506730	31.75
V-8-350 Diesel		
1983-85	◆559131	63.25
Flywheel Assy.		
V-6-231		
1983	◆25512346	70.50
1984-87	◆25512348	72.00
V-6-260 Diesel		
1983-84	◆22512002	75.25
V-8-307		
1983-87	◆22500807	85.50
V-8-350 Diesel		
1983-85	◆22500808	85.50

LABOR 16 CAMSHAFT & TIMING GEARS 16 LABOR

(Factory Time) — Chilton Time

GASOLINE ENGINES

(G) Timing Cover Oil Seal, Renew

V-8–1983-85 (.8) 1.4
1986-87 (1.0) 1.5
w/A.C. add (.1) 1

(G) Timing Case Cover or Gasket, Renew

Includes: R&R fan blade, crankshaft pulley and balancer. Drain and refill oil and coolant.

V-6–1983-87 (2.2) 3.2
V-8–1983-85 (1.3) 2.0
1986-87 (1.8) 2.6
w/A.C. add (.3) 3
w/P.S. add (.1) 1
w/A.I.R. add (.2) 2
Renew cover add (.4) 4
Renew f/pump eccentric add (.1) 2

(G) Timing Chain or Gears, Renew

Includes: R&R fan blade, crankshaft pulley and balancer. Drain and refill oil and coolant.

V-6–1983-87 (2.4) 3.7
V-8–1983-85 (1.4) 2.5
1986-87 (2.1) 3.1
w/A.C. add (.3) 3
w/P.S. add (.1) 1
w/A.I.R. add (.2) 2

(G) Camshaft, Renew

Includes: R&R radiator, front cover, timing chain and gear, R&R intake manifold and valve lifters. Disconnect exhaust system. Drain and refill oil and coolant. Make all necessary adjustments.

V-6–1983-87 (5.6) 7.0
V-8–1983-85 (4.3) 7.2
1986-87 (5.7) 8.1
w/A.C. add (1.3) 1.3
w/P.S. add (.1) 1
w/A.I.R. add (.4) 4

(G) Camshaft Bearings, Renew

Includes: R&R radiator, front cover, timing chain and gear. R&R intake manifold and valve lifters. Disconnect exhaust system. Drain and refill oil and coolant. Make all necessary adjustments.

V-6–1983-87 (6.8) 8.7
V-8–1983-85 (5.7) 8.8
1986-87 (7.1) 10.1
w/A.C. add (1.3) 1.3
w/P.S. add (.1) 1
w/A.I.R. add (.4) 4

(G) Camshaft Rear Bearing Plug, Renew

Includes: R&R trans for accessibility.

1983-87 (2.1) 3.0

DIESEL ENGINE

(G) Timing Case Cover or Gasket, Renew

Includes: R&R fan blade, crankshaft pulley and balancer. Drain and refill oil and coolant.

V-6–1983-85 (1.7) 2.4
V-8–1983-85 (2.1) 3.1
Renew cover add (.2) 4
w/A.C. add (.3) 3

(G) Timing Chain or Gears, Renew

Includes: R&R fan blade, crankshaft pulley and balancer. Drain and refill oil and coolant.

V-6–1983-85 (3.6) 5.0
V-8–1983-85 (2.3) 3.5
w/A.C. add (.3) 3

(G) Injector Pump Drive Gear, Renew

Includes: R&R timing gear and chain. R&R intake manifold and lifters. Drain and refill oil and coolant.

V-6–1983-85 (4.1) 5.9
V-8–1983-85 (4.3) 7.0
Renew driven gear add (.1) 1
w/A.C. add (.3) 3

(G) Camshaft, Renew

Includes: R&R radiator, front cover, fuel pump, timing gear and chain. R&R injector pump, intake manifold and lifters. Disconnect exhaust system. Drain and refill oil and coolant. Make all necessary adjustments.

V-6–1983-85 (5.4) 7.5
V-8–1983-85 (7.3) 10.0
w/A.C. add (1.0) 1.0

(G) Camshaft Bearings, Renew

Includes: R&R radiator, front cover, fuel pump, timing gear and chain. R&R injector pump, intake manifold and lifters. Disconnect exhaust system. Drain and refill oil and coolant. Make all necessary adjustments.

V-6–1983-85 (8.2) 11.8
V-8–1983-85 (10.1) 13.6
w/A.C. add (1.0) 1.0

(G) Camshaft Rear Bearing Plug, Renew

Includes: R&R trans for accessibility.

V-6–1983-85 (2.1) 3.0
V-8–1983-85 (2.1) 3.0

PARTS 16 CAMSHAFT & TIMING GEARS 16 PARTS

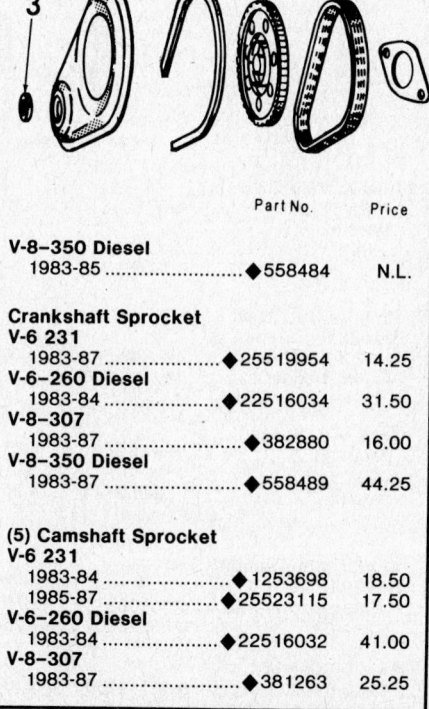

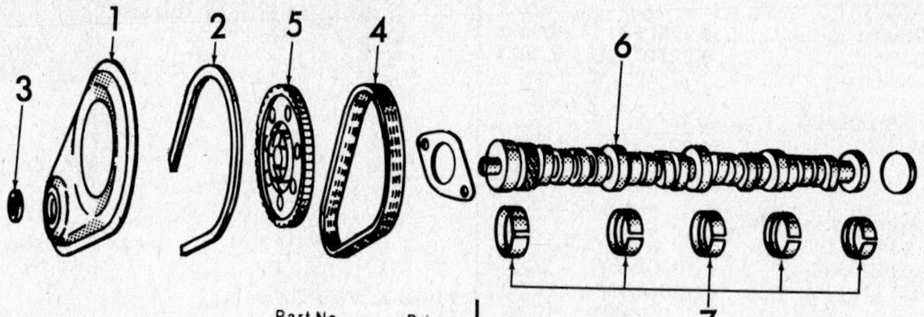

Part No. — Price

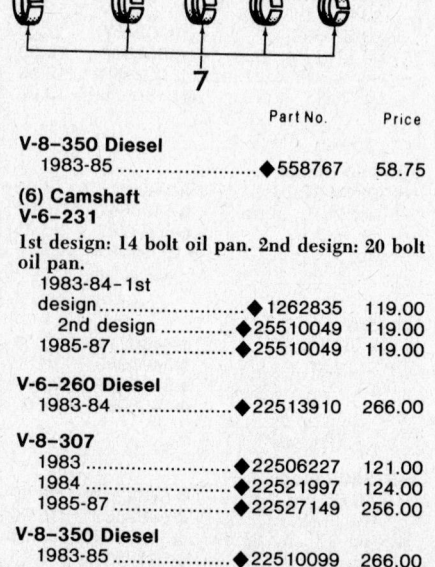

(1) Timing Cover Assy.

V-6 231
1983-87 .... 25522648 .... 108.00
V-6 260 Diesel
1983 .... 22514274 .... 31.75
1984 .... 22525284 .... 30.75
V-8-307
1983 .... 382926 .... N.L.
1984-87 .... 22525282 .... 23.00
V-8-350 Diesel
1983 .... 558989 .... 31.75
1984-85 .... 22525283 .... 30.75

(2) Timing Cover Gasket

V-6 231
1983-87 .... ◆25519461 .... 5.25
V-6 & V-8 Diesel
1983-85 .... ◆22505997 .... 1.25
V-8-307
1983-87 .... ◆22505997 .... 1.25

(3) Timing Cover Seal

V-6-231
1983-87-packing .... ◆1305044 .... 1.00
oil shedder .... ◆1193966 .... 1.50
V-6 & V-8 Diesel
1983-87 .... ◆552711 .... 4.25
V-8-307
1983-87 .... ◆552711 .... 4.25

(4) Timing Chain

V-6–231
1983-87 .... ◆1257650 .... 26.00
V-6–260 Diesel
1983-84 .... ◆22516033 .... 35.50
V-8-307
1983-87 .... ◆401584 .... 31.75
V-8–350 Diesel
1983-85 .... ◆558484 .... N.L.

Crankshaft Sprocket

V-6 231
1983-87 .... ◆25519954 .... 14.25
V-6–260 Diesel
1983-84 .... ◆22516034 .... 31.50
V-8–307
1983-87 .... ◆382880 .... 16.00
V-8–350 Diesel
1983-87 .... ◆558489 .... 44.25

(5) Camshaft Sprocket

V-6 231
1983-84 .... ◆1253698 .... 18.50
1985-87 .... ◆25523115 .... 17.50
V-6–260 Diesel
1983-84 .... ◆22516032 .... 41.00
V-8–307
1983-87 .... ◆381263 .... 25.25
V-8–350 Diesel
1983-85 .... ◆558767 .... 58.75

(6) Camshaft

V-6–231

1st design: 14 bolt oil pan. 2nd design: 20 bolt oil pan.

1983-84–1st design .... ◆1262835 .... 119.00
2nd design .... ◆25510049 .... 119.00
1985-87 .... ◆25510049 .... 119.00

V-6–260 Diesel
1983-84 .... ◆22513910 .... 266.00

V-8–307
1983 .... ◆22506227 .... 121.00
1984 .... ◆22521997 .... 124.00
1985-87 .... ◆22527149 .... 256.00

V-8–350 Diesel
1983-85 .... ◆22510099 .... 266.00

PARTS 16 CAMSHAFT & TIMING GEARS 16 PARTS

	Part No.	Price
(7) Camshaft Bearings		
V-6–231		
(Nos. 1, 4)		
1983-84	◆1234441	7.00
1985-87	◆25524301	7.25
(No. 2, 3, 5)		
1983-87	◆1231142	7.75
V-6 & V-8 Diesel		
1983-87-No. 1	◆561077	11.50
No. 2	◆390300	11.50
No. 3	◆390301	11.75
No. 4	◆390302	11.50
No. 5	◆390303	11.50
V-8–307		
1983-87-No. 1	◆561077	11.50
No. 2	◆390300	11.50
No. 3	◆390301	11.75
No. 4	◆390302	11.50
No. 5	◆390303	11.50

LABOR 17 ENGINE OILING SYSTEM 17 LABOR

(Factory Time)	Chilton Time
GASOLINE ENGINE	
(G) Oil Pan or Gasket, Renew	
Includes: Raise engine, R&R and clean oil pump screen.	
V-6–1983-87 (1.2)	1.6
V-8–1983-85 (1.7)	2.3
1986-87 (2.1)	2.9
(P) Pressure Test Engine Bearings (Pan Off)	
All models	1.0
(G) Oil Pump, Renew (V-8)	
Includes: Raise engine, R&R and clean oil pump screen.	
V-8–1983-85 (1.8)	2.5
1986-87 (2.2)	3.1
To overhaul pump add (.2)	.3
(G) Oil Filter and Pump Cover, Renew (V-6)	
V-6–1983-87 (.5)	.8
To overhaul pump add (.1)	.2
(G) Oil Pressure Relief Valve, Renew	
V-6–1983-87	1.1
(G) Oil Pressure Gauge (Engine), Renew	
1983-87 (.3)	.4
(G) Oil Pressure Gauge (Dash), Renew	
1983-85 (.4)	.8
1986-87 (.7)	1.2
(M) Oil Filter Element, Renew	
1983-87 (.3)	.3
DIESEL ENGINE	
(G) Oil Pan or Gasket, Renew	
Includes: Raise engine, R&R and clean oil pump screen.	
V-6–1983-85 (1.6)	2.2
V-8–1983-85 (2.6)	3.4
(P) Pressure Test Engine Bearings (Pan Off)	
All models	1.0
(G) Oil Pump, Renew	
Includes: Raise engine, R&R and clean oil pump screen.	
V-6–1983-85 (1.7)	2.4
V-8–1983-85 (2.7)	3.6
(G) Oil Pump, R&R and Recondition	
Includes: Raise engine, R&R and clean oil pump screen.	
V-6–1983-85 (1.9)	2.6
V-8–1983-85 (2.9)	3.8
(G) Oil Pressure Gauge (Engine), Renew	
1983-85 (.3)	.4
(M) Oil Filter Element, Renew	
1983-85 (.3)	.3

PARTS 17 ENGINE OILING SYSTEM 17 PARTS

	Part No.	Price
Oil Pan Gasket		
V-6 231		
1983-84-14 blt.	◆1260771	3.00
1985-87-20 blt.	◆25521994	8.50
V-6 260 Diesel		
1983-84	◆22520640	8.25
V-8–307, 350N		
1983-87	◆22519181	7.00
Oil Pump Assy.		
V-6–231		
1983-87-kit	◆25523433	39.75
V-6–260 Diesel		
1983-84	◆22515464	59.75
V-8–307		
1983-87	◆22524583	61.50
V-8–350 Diesel		
1983-85	◆22511732	59.75
Driven Gear		
1983-87-V-8	◆585582	4.00
Engine Oil Pressure Switch		
(wo/Gauges)		
1983-87-exc.		
231	◆3815936	3.50
231	◆25500672	5.50
(Gauges)		
1983-87	◆459417	17.75

LABOR 21 SHIFT LINKAGE 21 LABOR

(Factory Time)	Chilton Time
AUTOMATIC	
(G) Shift Linkage, Adjust	
All models	
Neutral Safety Switch (.3)	.4
Shift Indicator Needle (.2)	.3
Shift Linkage (.4)	.5
T.V. Cable (.3)	.4
(G) Shift Linkage, Adjust (w/Diesel Eng)	
All models	
Fast idle speed (.2)	.3
Throttle rod/T.V. cable (.5)	.6
Trans vacuum valve (.5)	.6
Vacuum regul valve (.6)	.8
Complete (1.0)	1.0
(G) Gear Selector Lever, Renew	
Column shift	
1983-87 (.2)	.4
Floor shift	
1983-87 (.5)	.8
(G) Shift Lever Seal, Renew	
In console	
1983 (.3)	.5
Under console	
1983 (.5)	.8
(G) Shift Control Cable, Renew	
1983-87	
colm shift (.7)	1.0
floor shift (.9)	1.4
(G) Gear Selector Indicator Needle, Renew	
1983 (.6)	1.0
1984-87 (.3)	.6
(G) Steering Column Shift Bowl, Renew	
Does not include colorcoat.	
1983-87	
Std colm (1.4)	2.1
Tilt colm (2.0)	3.0
w/Cruise control add (.2)	.2
(G) Shift Control Rods, Renew	
Includes: Adjust.	
1983-87 (.4)	.6
(G) Floor Shift Control Assy., Renew	
1983 (.5)	.9
1984-85 (.8)	1.2
1986-87 (.5)	.9
(G) Shift Control Lever, Renew (At Trans)	
Includes: Adjust.	
1983-87 (.3)	.5

LABOR 25 U-JOINTS & DRIVESHAFT 25 LABOR

(Factory Time) Chilton Time

(G) Universal Joints, R&R and Recondition
Includes: R&R drive shaft.
1983-87-front (.6) 9
rear (.5) 7
both (.7) 1.3

(G) Drive Shaft, Renew
1983-87 (.4) 5

(G) Pinion Shaft Flange, Renew
1983-87 (.7) 1.0

PARTS 25 UNIVERSAL JOINTS & DRIVE SHAFT 25 PARTS

	Part No.	Price
U/Joint Repair Kit		
1983-87-Saginaw	◆7806140	41.00
Dana	◆374246	28.50
Pinion Flange		
1983-87-exc. below	◆7827670	33.75
w/8½″ ring gr.	◆1256654	35.00

LABOR 26 REAR AXLE 26 LABOR

(Factory Time) Chilton Time

(M) Differential, Drain & Refill
All Models 6

(M) Differential Cover or Gasket, Renew
1983-87 (.5) 6

(G) Axle Shaft Assembly, Renew 'C' Lock Type
1983-87-one (.7) 9
both (.9) 1.2

(G) Axle Shaft Bearing and/or Seal, Renew 'C' Lock Type
1983-87-one (.6) 8
both (.8) 1.1

(G) Axle Shaft Wheel Mounting Studs, Renew
All models-one side (.6) 1.0
both sides (1.0) 1.5

(G) Pinion Shaft Oil Seal, Renew
1983-87 (.5) 8

(G) Differential Case, Remove & Reinstall
1983-87 (1.8) 2.8
w/Limited slip add (.5) 5

(G) Limited Slip Clutch Plates, Renew
1983-87 (1.1) 2.0

(G) Side Carrier Bearings, Renew
1983-87 (1.7) 2.5

(G) Pinion Bearings, Renew
1983-87 (2.0) 3.4

(P) Ring Gear and Pinion, Renew
1983-87 (2.1) 3.9
Recond diff case add
std (.3) 5
limited slip (.7) 1.0

(G) Side Carrier Gears, Renew
1983-87 (.8) 1.8
w/Limited slip add (.5) 5

(P) Rear Axle Housing, Renew
Includes: R&R housing, install new ring and pinion gear and side bearings. Adjust pre-load and backlash.
1983-87 (3.4) 5.2

PARTS 26 REAR AXLE 26 PARTS

	Part No.	Price
(1) Axle Shaft		
1983-87-exc. below	◆22519888	104.75
8½″ ring gr.	◆14075744	100.75
(2) Grease Seal		
1983-87	◆3998519	4.00
(3) Rear Axle Bearing		
1983-87	◆7451785	16.00
(4) Pinion Flange		
1983-87-exc. below	◆7827670	33.50
8½″ ring gr.	◆1256654	35.00
(5) Pinion Seal		
1983-87-exc. below	◆552571	8.00
8½″ ring gr.	◆1243465	7.50
(6) Front Pinion Bearing		
(7½″ dia. ring gr.)		
1983-87	◆7451202	16.00
(8½″ dia. ring gr.)		
1984-87	◆7450984	21.00
(7) Axle Housing		
1983-87-exc. below	◆22510780	496.25
8½″ ring gr.	◆14079473	406.25
(8) Pinion Gear Package		
(Without Limited Slip Differential)		
7½″ dia. ring gr.		
1983-87-exc. below	◆22525894	94.50
3.42, 3.73 ratios	◆22521625	105.00
8½″ dia. ring gr.		
1984-87	◆1397647	132.00

Gear packages contain 2 side gears, 2 pinion gears, thrust washers and pinion shaft.

	Part No.	Price
Pinion Gears-Sold Separately		
(Limited slip diff.)		
1984-87	◆6270977	17.50
Side Gears-Sold Separately		
(Limited slip diff.)		
1984-87-right	15599620	50.25
left	15599619	73.50
(9) Drive Pinion Spacer		
1983-87-exc below	◆9785792	1.50
8½″ ring gr.	◆1234726	1.50
(10) Rear Pinion Bearing		
7½″ dia. ring gr.		
1983-87	◆7455699	N.L.
8½″ dia. ring gr.		
1984-87	◆7451155	20.00
(11) Shim Package		
1983-87 (.025-.029)		
7½″ ring gr.	◆553022	5.50
8½″ ring gr.	◆1394893	6.50

Select fit, various sizes available.

	Part No.	Price
(12) Ring and Pinion Gear		
7½″ dia. ring gr.		
1983-87-2.14 to 1	◆563646	255.00
2.29 to 1	◆560197	259.00
2.41 to 1	◆560198	259.00
2.56 to 1	◆560199	259.00
2.93 to 1	◆560204	261.00

PARTS 26 REAR AXLE 26 PARTS

	Part No.	Price
3.08 to 1	◆14048380	276.25
3.23 to 1	◆560207	259.00
3.73 to 1	◆22521624	276.00
8½″ dia. ring gr.		
1984-87-3.73r	◆1259441	280.00
(13) Bearing Adjusting Shim Pkg.		
1983-87 (.040-.044)	◆3995791	6.50
Smallest size listed, larger sizes available.		
(14) Differential Side Bearing		
1983-87	◆9420095	N.L.
(15) Differential Case		
(wo/Limited slip diff.)		
7½″ ring gear		
1983-87-w/3.23, 3.42	◆558649	109.25
exc 3.23, 3.42	◆558648	109.00
8½″ ring gear		
1984-87	1252891	N.L.
(Limited slip diff.)		
7½″ ring gear		
1983-87-exc. below	◆22514583	278.00
3.23, 3.42	◆22514584	402.00
8½″ ring gear		
1984-87	◆14067495	374.25
(16) Pinion Shaft		
(wo/Limited slip diff.)		
1983-87-exc. below	◆22507586	11.00
8½″ ring gr.	◆14006401	12.50
(Limited slip diff.)		
1983-87-exc. below	◆22515972	10.25
8½″ ring gr.	14048412	23.25

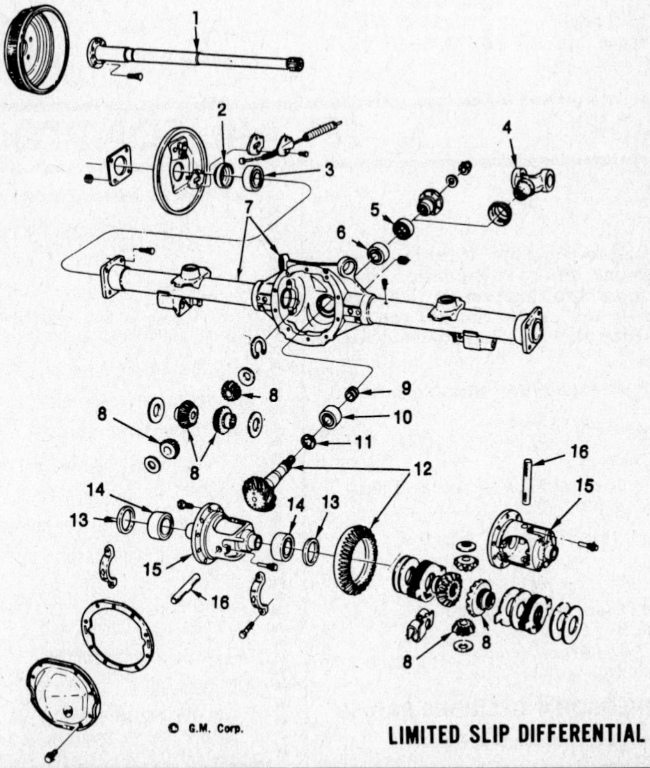

LABOR 27 REAR SUSPENSION 27 LABOR

	(Factory Time)	Chilton Time
(G) Rear Spring, Renew		
1983-87-one	(.4)	.6
both	(.4)	.8
(G) Rear Shock Absorber, Renew		
1983-87-one	(.3)	.4
both	(.5)	.7
(G) Upper Control Arm, Renew		
1983-87-one	(.5)	.7
both	(.8)	1.0
Renew bushings add, each side	(.2)	.3
(G) Lower Control Arm, Renew		
1983-87-one	(.4)	.7
both	(.5)	1.0
Renew bushings add, each side	(.2)	.3
(G) Rear Stabilizer Bar, Renew		
1983-87	(.5)	.7

PARTS 27 REAR SUSPENSION 27 PARTS

	Part No.	Price
(1) Upper Control Arm (w/Bushing)		
1983-87-0 deg.	◆10000076	15.00
+1½ deg.	◆10001060	15.00
-1½ deg.	◆10001059	30.50
(2) Insulator (Spring)		
1983-87	◆10004110	2.25
(3) Coil Spring		
Order by model and description.		
(4) Bumper (Axle)		
1983-87	10000812	2.00
(5) Bushing (Axle Housing)		
1983-87-exc. below	◆10000068	6.50
8½″ ring gr.	22526178	6.50
(6) Lower Control Arm (w/Bushing)		
1983-87	◆10000063	43.25

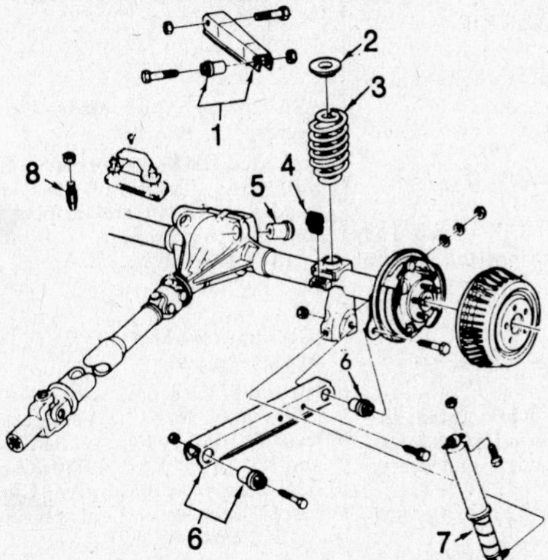

PARTS 27 REAR SUSPENSION 27 PARTS

	Part No.	Price
(7) Shock Absorber Assy. (Rear)		
(wo/Hurst Olds.)		
1983	◆4993580	24.50
1984-exc. below	◆4993579	24.50
H.D. susp	◆4993580	24.50
1985-87-exc.		
below	◆22046432	24.50
H.D. susp	◆22046440	24.50
(Hurst Olds.)		
1983-87-right	◆22012060	58.00
left	◆22012059	58.00
(8) Bumper (Pinion)		
1983-87	10000811	3.00

LABOR 28 AIR CONDITIONING 28 LABOR

(Factory Time) — Chilton Time

Note: If more than one item requires replacement where evacuation and discharging the system is already included in the operation, deduct 1.0 hour for each additional item to the times listed.

(G) Drain, Evacuate and Recharge System
All models (.5) 1.0

(G) Leak Check
Includes: Check all lines and connections.
All models (.3) 5

(G) Refrigerant, Add (Partial Charge)
All models 6

(G) Compressor Belt, Renew
V-6–1983-87 (.5) 7
V-8–1983-87 (.4) 5
w/AIR add (.1) 1

COMPRESSOR 4 CYLINDER RADIAL

(G) Compressor Assembly, Renew
Includes: Transfer parts as required. Evacuate and charge system.
1983-87 (.9) 2.0

(G) Compressor Clutch Plate and Hub Assy., Renew
Includes: R&R hub and drive plate assy. Check air gap.
1983-87 (.5) 8

(G) Compressor Rotor and/or Bearing, Renew
Includes: R&R hub and drive plate assy.
1983-87 (.8) 1.2

(G) Compressor Clutch Coil and/or Pulley Rim, Renew
Includes: R&R hub and drive plate assy.
1983-87 (.7) 1.0
Renew pulley or brg add (.1) 2

(G) Compressor Shaft Seal Kit, Renew
Includes: R&R compressor. Evacuate and charge system.
1983-87 (1.1) 2.5

(G) Compressor Shell and/or 'O' Rings, Renew
Includes: R&R compressor. R&R clutch and pulley assy. Clean and inspect parts. Evacuate and charge system.
1983-87 (1.3) 2.8

(G) Compressor Discharge Valve Plates, Renew
Includes: R&R compressor. R&R clutch and pulley assy. R&R shell to internal mechanism. Clean and inspect parts. Evacuate and charge system.
1983-87 (1.4) 2.6
Two or more add (.1) 2

AIR CONDITIONER TUNE-UP

For efficient operation and satisfactory performance in hot weather. The following air conditioner tune-up is suggested:

1. Clean intake filter
2. Clean condenser fins
3. Pressure test system
4. Adjust drive belt tension
5. Check antifreeze/coolant
6. Tighten compressor mounts
7. Tighten condenser and evaporator mounts
8. Inspect system for leaks (hoses, couplings, valves, etc.)
9. Partial charge system

All models 1.0
If necessary to evacuate and charge system, add 1.0

(Factory Time) — Chilton Time

(G) Compressor Front Head and/or Seal, Renew
Includes: R&R compressor. R&R clutch and pulley assy. R&R shaft seal assy. Clean and inspect parts. Evacuate and charge system.
1983-87 (1.3) 2.8

(G) Compressor Thrust and/or Belleville Washers, Renew
Includes: R&R compressor. R&R clutch and pulley assy. R&R shaft seal assy. R&R front head assy. Clean and inspect parts. Evacuate and charge system.
1983-87 (1.3) 2.8

(G) Compressor Main Bearing, Renew
Includes: R&R compressor. R&R clutch and pulley assy. R&R shaft seal assy. R&R front head assy. Clean and inspect parts. Evacuate and charge system.
1983-87 (1.3) 2.8

(G) Compressor Shaft and Cylinder Assy., Renew
Includes: R&R compressor. R&R clutch and pulley assy. R&R shaft seal assy., remove and transfer front head assy. R&R compressor shell and 'O' rings. R&R compressor valve plates. R&R pressure relief valve. Clean and inspect parts. Evacuate and charge system.
1983-87 (1.6) 2.9

(Factory Time) — Chilton Time

(G) Condenser, Renew
Includes: Evacuate and charge system.
1983-87 (1.0) 2.5
w/Diesel eng (1.5) 2.9

(G) Evaporator Core, Renew
Includes: Evacuate and charge system.
1983-87 (2.0) 3.5

(G) Accumulator, Renew
Includes: Evacuate and charge system.
1983-87 (.8) 1.5

(G) Expansion Tube (Orifice), Renew
1983-87 (.7) 1.4

(G) Pressure Cycling Switch, Renew
1983-87 (.2) 3

(G) Compressor Cut-Off Switch, Renew
1983-87 (.2) 3
Add time to evacuate and charge system if required.

(G) Blower Motor, Renew
1983-87 (.2) 5

(G) Blower Motor Switch, Renew
1983-87 (.3) 6

(G) Blower Motor Resistor, Renew
1983-87 (.2) 3

(G) Temperature Control Assembly, Renew
1983 (.4) 7
1984-87
Custom Air (.3) 6

(G) Vacuum Selector Valve, Renew
1983-87 (.3) 6

(G) Master Electrical Switch, Renew
1983-87 (.3) 6

(G) Blower Motor Relay, Renew
1983-87 (.2) 3

(G) Vacuum Actuators, Renew
1983
Defroster (.4) 7
Upper or Lower mode (.5) 9
Air Inlet (.4) 7
1984-85
Defroster (1.1) 2.0
Upper mode (1.1) 2.0
Lower mode (1.5) 2.4
Air Inlet (.2) 4
1986-87
Defroster (1.1) 2.0
Upper or Lower mode (2.9) 4.5
Air Inlet (2.3) 4.0

(G) Air Conditioning Hoses, Renew
Includes: Evacuate and charge system.
1983-87-one (1.1) 1.7
each adtnl (.3) 5

PARTS 28 AIR CONDITIONING 28 PARTS

	Part No.	Price
AUTOMATIC TEMPERATURE CONTROL		
(G) Temperature Control Units, Renew		
aspirator hose (.2)		.4
sensor and ambient switch (under hood) (.2)		.3
aspirator (.8)		1.2
in car sensor (.3)		.6
(G) Programmer and/or Actuating Link, Renew		
1983 (.3)		.8
Bench test programmer add (.7)		1.0
Renew vacuum modulator add		.1
Renew power spring add		.1
Renew output shaft add		.2
Renew vacuum motor add		.2
Renew vacuum relay add		.1
Renew compensator add		.1

PARTS 28 AIR CONDITIONING 28 PARTS

	Part No.	Price
Compressor Assembly exc. V-6 Diesel		
1983-87	◆12300273	390.00
V-6 Diesel		
1983-84	◆12309216	390.00
Cylinder and Shaft Assembly		
1983-87	◆2724144	269.00
Clutch Plate w/Hub		
1983-87	◆6551220	32.50
Rotor and Bearing exc. V-6 Diesel		
1983-87	◆6551216	67.50
V-6 Diesel		
1983-84	◆6551884	108.50
Clutch Holding Coil		
1983-87	◆6551217	44.00
Compressor Front Seal Kit		
1983-87	◆9956695	13.00
Compressor Shell Assy.		
1983-87	◆2724158	38.00
Compressor Pulley		
1983-87	◆6556715	13.00
Compressor Relief Valve		
1983-87	◆5914435	13.50
Condenser Assembly		
1983-87	◆3041841	170.00
Accumulator-Dehydrator		
1983-84	◆2724265	87.75
1985-87	◆3059315	85.25
Evaporator Assembly		
1983-87	◆3037638	201.50
Dash Control Unit		
1983	16027273	33.75
1984-87	16034743	38.50
Blower Motor		
1983-87	◆22020945	60.00
Blower Switch		
1983	◆16015256	6.00
1984-87	◆16032480	7.50

LABOR 29 LOCKS, HINGES & WIND. REGULATORS 29 LABOR

	(Factory Time)	Chilton Time
(G) Hood Release Cable, Renew		
1983-87 (.3)		.6
(G) Hood Lock, Renew		
1983-87 (.2)		.3
(G) Hood Hinge, Renew		
1983-87-one (.3)		.4
both (.5)		.7
(G) Door Lock, Renew		
Front		
1983-87 (.5)		.8
Rear		
1983-87 (.6)		.9
(G) Door Lock Remote Control, Renew		
1983-87 (.3)		.6
(G) Door Lock Cylinder, Renew		
1983-87 (.3)		.5
Recode cyl add (.3)		.3
(G) Door Handle (Outside), Renew		
Front		
1983-87 (.4)		.6
Rear		
1983-87 (.3)		.5
Renew insert add (.1)		.1
(G) Lock Striker Plate, Renew		
1983-87 (.2)		.2
(G) Door Window Regulator (Manual), Renew (Front or Rear)		
1983-87 (.7)		1.0
Recond add (.2)		.3
(G) Door Window Regulator (Electric), Renew (Front or Rear)		
1983-87 (.9)		1.5
(G) Trunk Lock and Cylinder, Renew		
1983-87 (.2)		.4
Recode cyl add (.3)		.3
(G) Trunk Hinge or Strap, Renew (One)		
1983-87 (.8)		1.2
(G) Tailgate Lock Cylinder, Renew		
Includes: Recode cylinder.		
1983 (.6)		.8
(G) Tailgate Hinge, Renew		
1983 (.5)		.7

PARTS 29 LOCKS, HINGES & WIND. REGULATORS 29 PARTS

	Part No.	Price
Hood Latch		
1983-87	◆14070703	16.25
Hood Hinge		
1983-87-right	◆14064326	16.75
left	◆14064325	16.75
Front Door Lock		
(2-door)		
1983-87-right	◆20293612	33.50
left	◆20293613	33.50
(4-door)		
1983-87-right	◆20293604	51.50
left	◆20293605	51.50
Rear Door Lock		
1983-87-right	◆20293624	55.75
left	◆20293625	55.75
Door Lock Cylinder and Key		
1983-87-2 dr.	◆9632762	5.75
4 dr.	◆9632769	7.75
Door Lock Striker		
1983-87	◆20151275	5.50
Outer Door Handle		
1983-87-right	◆20099250	24.75
left	◆20099251	24.75
Trunk Lock		
1983-87	◆20279741	N.L.
Trunk Lock Pkg. (Uncoded)		
1983-87	◆3910570	6.25
Tailgate Lock		
1983-L.H.	◆20012859	N.L.
R.H.	◆20367776	58.50
window-center	◆20367780	42.75
Tailgate Lock Cylinder and Key		
1983	◆9632765	7.25
Manual Window Regulators		
(2-door)		
1983-87 (wo/Custom ext.)		
right	20337706	59.50
left	20337707	59.50
1983-87 (Custom ext.)		
right	◆20094576	64.00
left	20094577	64.00
(4-door)		
1983-87-right	◆20244864	59.50
left	20244865	59.50
Electric Window Regulators		
(2-door)		
1983-87-right	◆20123184	98.00
left	20123185	98.00
(4-door)		
1983-87-right	◆20209182	98.00
left	20209183	98.00
Electric Window Motor		
1983-87	◆22020900	73.00

LABOR 30 HEAD AND PARKING LAMPS 30 LABOR

	(Factory Time)	Chilton Time
(G) Aim Headlamps		
two		.4
four		.6
(M) Headlamp Sealed Beam Bulb, Renew		
1983-87-each	(.3)	.3
(M) Tail and Stop Light Lamp Lens, Renew		
1983-87	(.3)	.5
(M) License Lamp Assembly, Renew		
1983-87	(.2)	.3
(M) Side Marker Lamp Assy., Renew		
1983-87-each	(.2)	.4
(M) Back-Up Lamp Assembly, Renew		
1983-87-each	(.3)	.4
(M) High Level Stop Lamp Assy., Renew		
1986-87	(.2)	.4
(M) Cornering Lamp Assembly, Renew		
1983-87-each	(.2)	.3
(M) Park and Turn Signal Lamp Assy., Renew		
1983-87-each	(.3)	.4
(M) Stop, Tail and Turn Signal Lamp Assy., Renew		
1983-87-each	(.3)	.4
(M) Back-Up Lamp Bulb, Renew		
All models-one	(.2)	.3
(M) Cornering Lamp Bulb, Renew		
All models-each	(.2)	.3
(M) License Lamp Bulb, Renew		
All models-one or all	(.2)	.3
(M) Park and Turn Signal Lamp Bulb, Renew		
All models-each		.2
(M) Side Marker Lamp Bulb, Renew		
All models-each		.2
(M) Stop, Tail and Turn Signal Lamp Bulb, Renew		
All models-one		.2
each adtnl		.1
(M) High Level Stop Lamp Bulb, Renew		
All models	(.2)	.3

PARTS 30 HEAD AND PARKING LAMPS 30 PARTS

	Part No.	Price
Sealed Beam Bulb		
(wo/Quartz)		
1983-87-inner	◆5966201	15.00
outer	◆5966200	15.00
(Quartz)		
1983-87	◆5930567	22.50
Tail Lamp Lens		
(4-door)		
1983-right	5971834	32.75
left	5971833	32.75
1984-87-right	16501922	27.75
left	16501921	27.75
Tail Lamp Assy.		
(2 door)		
1983-right	5972034	50.50
left	5972033	50.50
1984-87-right	16502484	50.50
left	16502483	50.50
(4 door)		
1983-right	5971854	39.25
left	5971853	39.25
1984-87-right	16502282	39.25
left	16502281	39.25
(Sta. wagon)		
1983-right	◆915930	35.00
left	915929	35.00
High Mount Stoplight		
1986-87-G47	◆5974464	36.00
G69	5974460	36.00
License Plate Lamp Assy.		
(2 door)		
1983-exc. below	915156	61.75
Cust. ext.	918762	61.75
1984-87-exc. below	918366	53.25
Cust. ext.	920022	53.25
(4 door)		
1983-87-right	912822	6.25
left	912821	6.25
(Sta. wagon)		
1983	◆913204	6.25
Side Marker Lamp (Front)		
(2 door)		
1983-87-right	915316	8.25
left	915315	8.25
(4 door)		
1983-87-right	915552	11.00
left	915551	11.00
Side Marker Lamp (Rear)		
(2 door)		
1983-87-right	915164	8.25
left	915163	8.25
(4 door)		
1983-87	915001	10.75
(Sta. wagon)		
1983	913417	10.50

LABOR 31 WINDSHIELD WIPER & SPEEDOMETER 31 LABOR

	(Factory Time)	Chilton Time
(G) Windshield Wiper Motor, Renew		
1983-87	(.6)	.8
(G) Windshield Wiper Motor, R&R and Recondition		
1983-87-round motor	(.8)	1.2
rectangular motor	(1.1)	1.4
(G) Wiper Transmission, Renew (One)		
1983-87	(.4)	.6
(G) Wiper Switch, Renew		
1983-87		
std colm	(.9)	1.4
tilt colm	(.8)	1.3
(G) Windshield Washer Pump, Renew		
1983-87	(.6)	.9
w/Pulse wipe add	(.1)	.1
(G) Windshield Washer Pump, R&R and Recondition		
1983-87	(.9)	1.3
w/Pulse wipe add	(.1)	.1
(G) Windshield Washer Pump Valve, Renew		
1983-87	(.2)	.4
(G) Speedometer Head, R&R or Renew		
1983-87	(.6)	.9
Reset odometer add		.2
(G) Speedometer Cable and Casing, Renew		
1983-87		
one piece	(.9)	1.4
upper cable	(.4)	.7
lower cable	(.3)	.6
(G) Speedometer Cable (Inner), Renew or Lubricate		
1983-87		
one piece	(.9)	1.4
upper cable	(.4)	.6
lower cable	(.2)	.5
(G) Radio, R&R		
1983-87	(.4)	.6

PARTS 31 WINDSHIELD WIPER & SPEEDOMETER 31 PARTS

	Part No.	Price
Wiper Motor		
1983-exc Pulse	◆4960974	84.00
Pulse wiper	◆4961608	80.00
1984-87	◆22039687	110.75
Wiper Transmission		
1983-87-right	◆22009387	18.50
(left)		
2 dr.	◆22009388	18.00
4 dr.	◆22009389	18.00

	Part No.	Price
Wiper Control Switch		
(wo/Pulse wipers)		
1983-exc. Tilt	◆7835342	22.50
Tilt wheel	◆7837279	41.50
1984-87-exc. Tilt	◆7842714	44.75
Tilt wheel	◆7843684	44.75
(Pulse wipers)		
1983	◆7837280	53.50
1984-87	◆7843683	56.25

	Part No.	Price
Windshield Washer Pump		
1983-exc. Pulse	◆22009212	25.00
Pulse wpr.	◆22021345	38.50
1984-87	◆22039686	16.25

Speedometer Head & Cable (w/Casing)
Order by year and model.

LABOR 32 LIGHT SWITCHES & WIRING 32 LABOR

(Factory Time)	Chilton Time
(G) Headlamp Switch, Renew	
1983-87 (.3)	.5
(G) Headlamp Dimmer Switch, Renew	
1983-87-column mounted (.5)	.7
(G) Stop Light Switch, Renew	
1983-87 (.2)	.3
(G) Back-Up Lamp and Park/Neutral Switch, Renew	
1983-87	
wo/Console (.2)	.3
w/Console (.5)	.7

(Factory Time)	Chilton Time
(G) Parking Brake Lamp Switch, Renew	
1983-87 (.2)	.3
(G) Multifunction Lever, Renew	
All models (.2)	.4
w/Cruise control add (.5)	.5
(G) Dimmer Switch Pivot Assy., Renew	
1983-87-std column (.9)	1.4
tilt column (.8)	1.3
w/Cruise control add (.2)	.2
(G) Turn Signal Switch, Renew	
1983-87 (.6)	1.0

(Factory Time)	Chilton Time
(M) Turn Signal or Hazard Warning Flasher, Renew	
1983-87 (.2)	.2
(G) Horns, Renew	
1983-85-one (.4)	.5
1986-87-one (.2)	.3
each adtnl	.1
(G) Horn Relay, Renew	
1983-87 (.2)	.3
(G) Chassis Wiring Harness, Renew	
Headlamp harness	
1983-87 (.9)	1.4
Instrument panel	
1983-87 (1.8)	2.4
Engine harness - V-8	
1983-87 (.8)	1.4

PARTS 32 LIGHT SWITCHES & WIRING 32 PARTS

	Part No.	Price
Headlight Switch		
1983-87-exc.		
below	◆1972717	17.00
TWI sent	◆1995232	41.50
Headlamp Dimmer Switch		
1983-87	◆7838234	12.50
Stop Light Switch		
(wo/Cruise control)		
1983-84	◆25504628	3.75
1985-87	◆25524846	6.50
(Cruise control)		
1983-84	◆9794682	7.75
1985-87	◆25524847	6.50

	Part No.	Price
Turn Signal Switch		
1983-87-exc.		
cornering	◆1997983	30.00
Cor. lamp	◆1997984	35.00
Turn Signal Flasher		
1983-3 lamp	◆10029240	4.25
2 lamp	◆491392	N.L.
1984	◆6450076	4.00
1985-87-2 dr.	◆10041073	4.25
4 dr.	◆10041074	3.50
Back-Up Lamp Switch		
1983-87-exc.		
below	◆22509632	5.50

	Part No.	Price
Elect. trunk lid	◆22514861	7.00
Emergency Flasher		
1983-87	◆6450089	3.00
Horn Assy.		
1983-87-Note (A)	◆1892164	22.00
Note (C)	◆1892246	27.50
Note (D)	◆1892162	23.50
Note (F)	◆1892163	22.00
Horn Relay		
1983-87	◆25513270	8.50

LABOR 33 GLASS 33 LABOR

(Factory Time)	Chilton Time
(G) Windshield Glass, Renew	
1983-87 (1.2)	1.8
Renew caulk bead add (.4)	.4
(G) Front Door Glass, Renew	
1983-87-2 dr (1.0)	1.5
4 dr (.8)	1.1
(G) Rear Door Glass, Renew	
1983-87 (.3)	.6
(G) Quarter Window Stationary Glass, Renew	
1983-87-exc below (.5)	.9
sta wag (1.0)	1.7

(Factory Time)	Chilton Time
(G) Tail Gate Glass, Renew	
1983 (.3)	.5
w/Elec defogger add (.1)	.2
(G) Rear Window Glass, Renew	
1983-87 (1.3)	2.0
w/Elec defogger add (.6)	.6
w/3/4 plug padded add (2.6)	4.0
(G) Rear Door Stationary Vent Glass, Renew	
1983-87 (.3)	.6

LABOR 34 CRUISE CONTROL 34 LABOR

(Factory Time) Chilton Time

(G) Cruise Control External Adjustments

Includes: Adjust electric and vacuum brake switches and centering spring.

1983 (.2)	.5

(G) Cruise Control Regulator (Transducer), Renew

Includes: R&R cover and external adjustments.

1983 (.4)	.6
Adjust low speed switch add (.1)	.1
Overhaul vacuum regulator add (.4)	.6

(G) Cruise Control Chain or Cable, Renew

1983-87 (.2)	.4

(G) Cruise Control Wiring Harness, Renew

1983-87 (.5)	.8

(G) Cruise Control Engagement Switch, Renew

1983-87 (.5)	.9

(G) Cruise Control Brake Release Switch, Renew

1983 (.3)	.5

(G) Cruise Control Vacuum Servo, Renew

1983-87 (.4)	.5

(G) Cruise Control Vacuum Hoses, Renew

1983-85-one or all (.2)	.3
1986-87	
to source (.2)	.3
servo to b/switch (.5)	.6

(G) Cruise Control Vacuum Regulator Valve, Renew (w/Diesel engine)

1983 (.2)	.3

(G) Cruise Control Resume Solenoid, Renew

1983 (.2)	.3

(G) Cruise Control Module, Renew

1984-87 (.4)	.5

PARTS 34 CRUISE CONTROL 34 PARTS

	Part No.	Price
Cruise Control Servo		
V-6-231		
1983	◆25030981	19.50
1984-87	◆25074630	116.25
V-6 & V-8 Diesel		
1983	◆25030980	32.75
1984-85	◆25074629	123.50
V-8-307		
1983	◆25074220	25.00
1984-87	◆25074629	123.50
Cruise Control Transducer		
V-6-231		
1983	◆25030881	160.00
V-6 & V-8 Diesel		
1983	◆25031683	169.50
V-8–Gas		
1983	◆25030882	158.00
Cruise Control Module		
1984-87-231	◆25031964	115.00
307	25031985	116.25
Diesel	◆25031948	116.00
Cruise Control Lever & Switch		
1983-exc. Pulse	◆25031426	52.25
Pulse wpr.	◆25031425	52.25
1984-87-exc.		
Pulse	◆25031457	50.00
Pulse wpr.	◆25031456	50.00
Cruise Control Chain		
1983	◆1494424	2.50
1984-87	◆25031314	3.25
Vacuum Release Valve		
1983-84	◆25509432	14.00
1985-87	◆25523376	14.00
Cruise Control Release Switch		
1983-84	◆9794682	8.00
1985-87	◆25524847	6.50

GROUP INDEX

ALPHABETICAL INDEX

General Motors
Rear Wheel Drive Cars

OLDSMOBILE 88•98

YEAR IDENTIFICATION

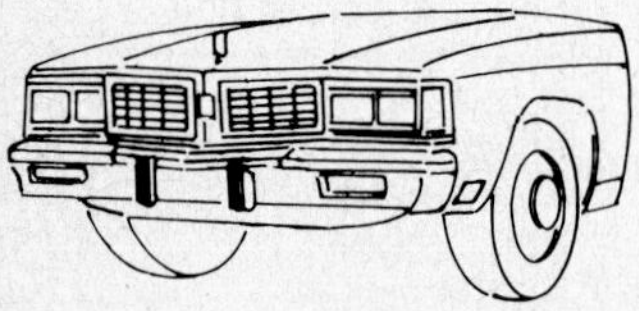

1983–84 Delta 88

1985 Delta 88 Royale Coupe

1985 Delta 88 Royale Brougham LS Sedan

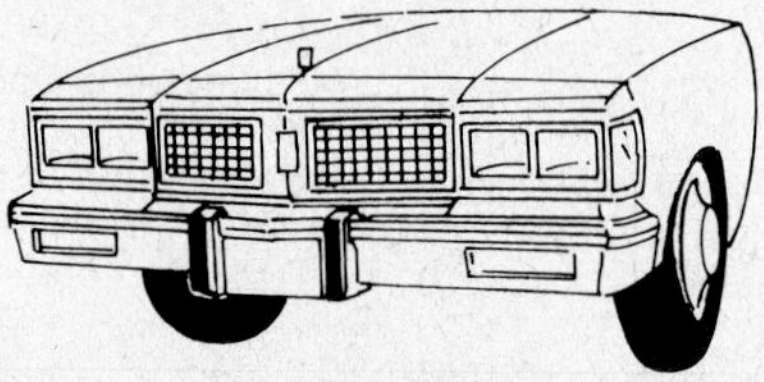

1983–84 98

VEHICLE IDENTIFICATION NUMBER (VIN)

It is important for servicing and ordering parts to be certain of the vehicle and engine identification. The VIN (vehicle identification number) is a 13 or 17 digit number visible through the windshield on the driver's side of the dash and contains the vehicle and engine identification codes. It can be interpreted as follows:

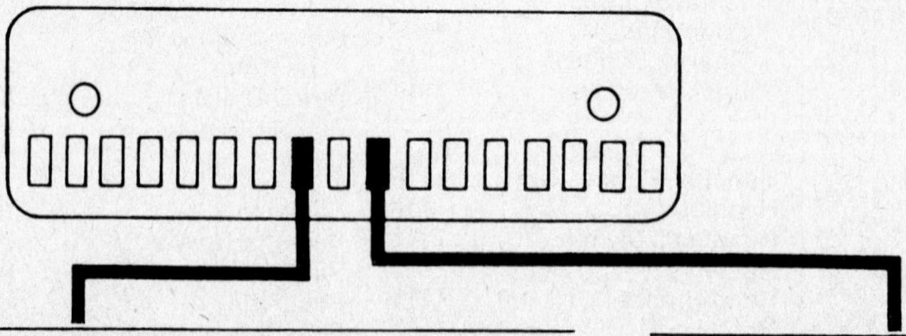

Engine Code

Code	Cu. In.	Liters	Cyl.	Carb.	Eng. Mfg.
A	231	3.8	6	2bbl	Buick
4	252	4.1	6	4bbl	Buick
V	263	4.3	6	Diesel	Olds.
Y	307	5.0	8	4bbl	Olds.
N	350	5.7	8	Diesel	Olds.

Model Year Code

Code	Year
D	1983
E	1984
F	1985
G	1986
H	1987

The seventeen digit Vehicle Identification Number can be used to determine engine application and model year. The 10th digit indicates the model year and the 8th digit identifies the factory installed engine.

TUNE-UP SPECIFICATIONS
Gasoline Engines

When analyzing compression test results, look for uniformity among cylinders rather than specific pressures

Year	Engine: Eng. VIN Code	Engine: No. Cyl. Displacement (cu. in.)	Engine: Liter	Eng. Mfg.	Spark Plugs: Orig. Type	Spark Plugs: Gap (in.)	Distributor: Point Dwell (Deg.)	Distributor: Point Gap (in.)	Ignition Timing (deg.) Auto. Trans.	Fuel Pump Pressure (psi)	Idle Speed (rpm) Auto. Trans.
'83	A	6-231	3.8	Buick	R-45TS8	.080	Electronic		①	5.6–6.5	①
	4	6-252	4.1	Buick	R-45TS8	.080	Electronic		①	5.6–6.5	①
	Y	8-307	5.0	Olds.	R-46SX	.080	Electronic		①	5.6–6.5	①
	9 ②	8-307	5.0	Olds.	R-46SX	.080	Electronic		①	5.5–6.5	①
'84	A	6-231	3.8	Buick	R45TSX	0.060	Electronic		①	5.5–6.5	①
	4	6-252	4.1	Buick	R45TSX	0.060	Electronic		①	5.5–6.5	①
	9	8-307	5.0	Olds.	R46SX ④	0.080	Electronic		①	5.5–6.5	①
	Y	8-307	5.0	Olds.	R46SX ④	0.080	Electronic		①	5.5–6.5	①
'85	A	6-231	3.8	Buick	R45TSX	0.060	Electronic		①	5.5–6.5	①
	9	8-307	5.0	Olds.	R46SZ	0.060	Electronic		①	5.5–6.5	①
	Y	8-307	5.0	Olds.	FR3LS6	0.060	Electronic		①	5.5–6.5	①
'86	A	6-231	3.8	Buick	R45TSX	0.060	Electronic		①	5.5–6.5	①
	Y	8-307	5.0	Olds.	FR3LS6 ⑤	0.060	Electronic		①	6.0–7.5	①
	9	8-307	5.0	Olds.	FR3LS6 ⑤	0.060	Electronic		①	6.0–7.5	①
'87	Refer to the Underhood Emission Label and/or Owner's Manual General Specifications										

NOTE: The underhood specifications sticker often reflects tuneup specification changes made in production. Sticker figures must be used if they disagree with those in this chart. Part numbers in this chart are not recommendations by Chilton for any product by brand name.

- All figures are in degrees Before Top Dead Center

① See Underhood Emission Label
② Hurst/Olds Package
③ Type of driving mode may necessitate a change of heat range application and reference number of the spark plugs as listed in the above specifications
④ Or R46SZ
⑤ Or FR3CLS6

FIRING ORDERS

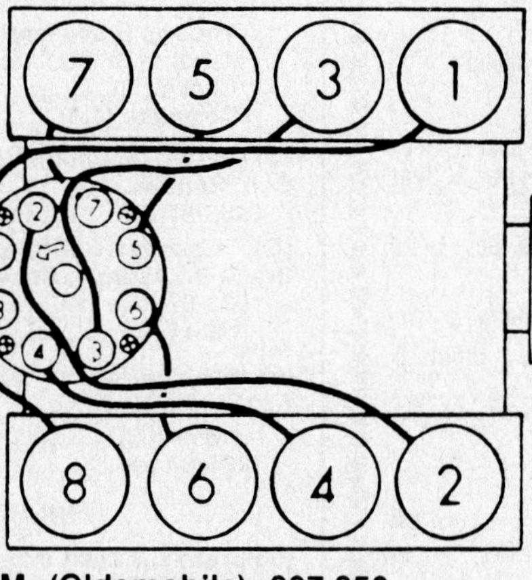

GM (Oldsmobile) 307,350
Engine firing order: 1–8–4–3–6–5–7–2
Distributor rotation: counterclockwise

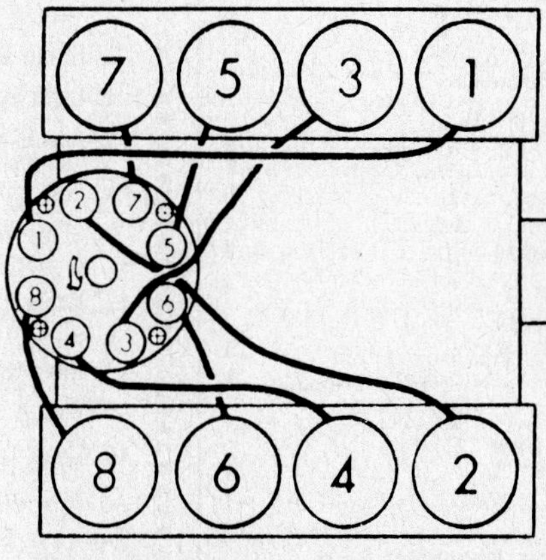

GM (Oldsmobile) 260 V8
Engien firing order 1–8–4–3–6–5–7–2
Distributor rotation: counterclockwise

FIRING ORDERS

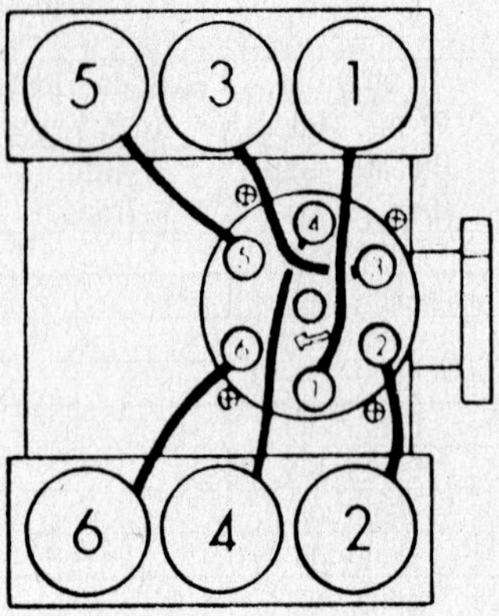

GM (Buick) 231,252 V6
3.8L, 4.1L)
Engine firing order: 1–6–5–4–3–2
Distributor rotation: clockwise

V6 harmonic balancers have two timing marks: one is $^1/_8$ in. wide, and one is $^1/_{16}$ in. wide. Use the $^1/_{16}$ in. mark for timing with a hand held light. The $^1/_8$ in. mark is used only with a magnetic timing pick-up probe

WHEEL ALIGNMENT

Year	Model	Caster Range (deg.)	Caster Pref Setting (deg.)	Camber Range (deg.)	Camber Pref. Setting (deg.)	Toe (in.)	Steering Axis Inclin. (deg.)	Wheel Pivot Ratio (deg.) Inner Wheel	Wheel Pivot Ratio (deg.) Outer Wheel
'83–'85	88-98 Series	2P to 4P	3P	0 to 1⁵⁄₈P	³⁄₁₆P	¹⁄₁₆ to ¹⁄₄	10⁹⁄₁₆	NA	NA

NA Not Available
N Negative
P Positive

LABOR — SERVICE BAY OPERATIONS — LABOR

(Factory Time) Chilton Time

COOLING

(M) Winterize Cooling System
Includes: Run engine to check for leaks, tighten all hose connections. Test radiator and pressure cap, drain radiator and engine block. Add anti-freeze and refill system.
All models 5

(M) Thermostat, Renew
Includes: Test thermostat.
1983-87-V-6 (.7) .... *.8
V-8 (.4) 6
Diesel (.5) 6
*w/A.C. add (.1) 1
w/Cruise control add (.1) 1

(M) Drive Belt, Adjust
1983-87-one (.2) 3
each adtnl 1

(M) Drive Belt, Renew
1983-87-one (.3) 4
each adtnl 1

(M) Radiator Hoses, Renew
1983-87-one (.3) 4
both (.4) 7
by-pass (.5) 6
w/A.C. add (.1) 1

FUEL

(M) Carburetor Air Cleaner, Service
1983-87 (.2) 3

CHILTON'S 10 POINT SAFETY CHECK

CHECK OPERATION & CONDITION OF THE FOLLOWING ITEMS:

1. Legal Registration (serial no.)
2. Tires & Wheels
3. Brake System (R&R all wheels)
4. Light Systems & Signals
5. Accelerator Linkage, Neutral Safety Switch, Shift Indicator Pointer & Seat Position Locks
6. Glass, Mirrors, Door Locks, Seat Belts & Harness
7. Wipers, Washers & Defrosters
8. Frame, Steering, Shocks, Front & Rear Suspension
9. Fuel & Exhaust Systems
10. Road Test Vehicle

All models 1.0
Exhaust Smog Analysis, add 4

(Factory Time) Chilton Time

(G) Air Cleaner Vacuum Motor, Renew
1983-87 (.3) 5

(G) Air Cleaner Temperature Sensor, Renew
1983-87 (.2) 3

(Factory Time) Chilton Time

(G) Carburetor, Adjust (On Car)
Includes: Adjust pump rod, idle vent, air valve, fast idle, choke rod, vacuum brake, unloader, secondary lockout, idle speed and mixture.
1983-87
Slow & Fast Idle (.3) 4
Vacuum Brake-one (.4) 6
both (.6) 8
Choke (.6) 1.0
Complete (1.3) 1.8

(G) Automatic Choke Cover and/or Coil, Renew
1983-87 (.6) 1.0

(G) Automatic Choke Vacuum Brake Diaphragm, Renew or Adjust
1983-87-one (.4) 6
both (.6) 8

(G) Idle Stop Solenoid, Renew
Includes: Adjust.
1983-84 (.3) 4
1985-87 (.6) 1.0

BRAKES

(G) Brakes, Adjust (Minor)
Includes: R&R wheels and adjust brakes thru access holes in drums. Fill master cylinder.
two wheels 4
Remove knock out plugs add, each .. .1

(G) Bleed Brakes (Four Wheels)
Includes: Fill master cylinder.
All models 5

(G) Brake Pedal Free Play, Adjust
All models 3

LABOR SERVICE BAY OPERATIONS LABOR

(Factory Time) Chilton Time

(M) Parking Brake, Adjust
All models (.3) 4

LUBRICATION SERVICE

(M) Lubricate Chassis, Change Oil & Filter
Includes: Inspect and correct all fluid levels.
All models 6
Install grease fittings add 1

(M) Lubricate Chassis
Includes: Inspect and correct all fluid levels.
All models 4
Install grease fittings add 1

(M) Engine Oil & Filter, Change
Includes: Inspect and correct all fluid levels.
All models 4

WHEELS

(M) Wheel, Renew
one (.3) 5

(G) Wheels, Balance
one 3
each adtnl 2

(G) Wheels, Rotate (All)
All models 5

(G) Front Wheel Bearings, Clean and Repack (Both Wheels)
1983-87 (1.1) 1.6

(G) Front Wheel Bearings and Cups, Renew
1983-87-one side (.7) 9
both sides (1.1) 1.5

(G) Front Wheel Grease Seals, Renew
1983-87-one whl (.7) 8
both whls (1.1) 1.2

ELECTRICAL

(M) Battery Cables, Renew
1983-87-negative (.2) 2
positive (.5) 5
Right batt to left batt w/Diesel eng (.3) 3

(M) Battery Terminals, Clean
All models 3

(G) Aim Headlamps
two 4
four 6

(G) Headlamp Sealed Beam Bulb, Renew
1983-87-each (.3) 3

(G) Headlamp Switch, Renew
1983-87 (.3) 5

(G) Headlamp Dimmer Switch, Renew
1983-87-column mounted (.5) 7

(G) Stop Light Switch, Renew
1983-87 (.2) 3

(G) Turn Signal Switch, Renew
1983-87
std colm (.6) 1.1
tilt colm (.7) 1.2

(G) Back-Up Lamp and Park/Neutral Switch, Renew
1983-87 (.2) 4

(M) Turn Signal or Hazard Warning Flasher, Renew
All models (.2) 2

(G) Horn Relay, Renew
1983-87 (.2) 3

(G) Horn, Renew
1983-87 (.2) 3

(M) Back-Up Lamp Bulb, Renew
All models-one (.2) 3
both (.3) 4

(M) Cornering Lamp Bulb, Renew
All models-each (.2) 3

(M) License Lamp Bulb, Renew
All models-one or all (.2) 3

(M) Park and Turn Signal Lamp Bulb, Renew
All models-each 2

(M) Side Marker Lamp Bulb, Renew
All models-each 2

(M) Stop, Tail and Turn Signal Lamp Bulb, Renew
All models-one 2
each adtnl 1

LABOR 1 TUNE UP 1 LABOR

(Factory Time) Chilton Time

(G) Compression Test
V-6–1983-85 (.5) 7
V-8–1983-87 (.6) 8
w/A.C. add (.3) 3

(G) Engine Tune Up, (Electronic Ignition)
Includes: Test battery and clean connections. Tighten manifold and carburetor mounting bolts. Check engine compression, clean and adjust or renew spark plugs. Test resistance of spark plug cables. Inspect distributor cap and rotor. Adjust air gap. Check vacuum advance operation. Reset ignition timing. Adjust idle mixture and idle speed. Service air cleaner. Inspect and adjust drive belts. Inspect choke operation and adjust or free up. Check operation of EGR valve.
V-6–1983-85 .... 2.0
V-8–1983-87 .... 2.5
w/A.C. add 6
To perform C.C.C. system test add 1.0

LABOR 2 IGNITION SYSTEM 2 LABOR

(Factory Time) Chilton Time

GASOLINE ENGINES

(G) Spark Plugs, Clean and Reset or Renew
1983-87-V-6 (.4) 6
V-8 (.5) 7
To clean add (.2) 2

(G) Ignition Timing, Reset
1983-87 (.3) 4

(G) Distributor, Renew
Includes: Reset ignition timing.
1983-87 (.5) 8
w/Vacuum pump add (.2) 2
w/AIR add (.3) 3

(G) Distributor, R&R and Recondition
Includes: Reset ignition timing.
1983-87 (.8) 1.4
w/Vacuum pump add (.2) 2
w/AIR add (.3) 3

(G) Distributor Cap and/or Rotor, Renew
1983-87
V-6 (.5) 7
V-8 (.3) 5
w/AIR add (.3) 3

(G) Ignition Coil, Renew
1983-87 (.3) 4
w/AIR add (.3) 3
Test add (.2) 2

(G) Ignition Cables, Renew
1983-87-V-6 (1.0) 1.4
V-8 (.4) 6

(G) Ignition Switch, Renew
1983-87 (.5) 9

(G) Ignition Key Warning Switch, Renew
1983-87 (.4) 7

(G) Distributor Module, Renew
1983-87 (.3) 6
w/AIR add (.3) 3

LABOR 2 IGNITION SYSTEM 2 LABOR

(Factory Time)	Chilton Time
w/Vacuum pump add (.2)	.2
To perform C.C.C. system test add	1.0

(G) Distributor Capacitor and/or Module Wiring Harness, Renew

1983-87 (.3)	.6
w/AIR add (.3)	.3
w/Vacuum pump add (.2)	.2

(G) Distributor Pick-Up Coil and/or Pole Piece, Renew

Includes: R&R distributor and reset ignition timing.

1983-87 (.6)	.9
w/AIR add (.3)	.3
w/Vacuum pump add (.2)	.2

(G) Distributor Hall Effect Switch, Renew

1983 (.5)	.8

(G) ESC Knock Sensor, Renew

1983-85 (.7)	1.0

(G) ESC Module, Renew

1983-85 (.5)	.7

DIESEL IGNITION COMPONENTS

(G) Coolant Fast Idle Temperature Switch, Renew

All models (.2)	.4

(G) Glow Plugs, Renew

All models-one	.4
all-one bank	.7
all-both banks	1.3

(G) Glow Plug Control Switch, Renew

All models (.4)	.6

(G) Fast Idle Solenoid, Renew

All models (.4)	.5

(G) Fast Idle Relay, Renew

All models (.3)	.4

(G) Glow Plug Relay, Renew

1983 (.2)	.3
1984-85 (.4)	.6

(G) Glow Plug Control Module (Controller), Renew

All models (.4)	.6

PARTS 2 ELECTRONIC IGNITION 2 PARTS

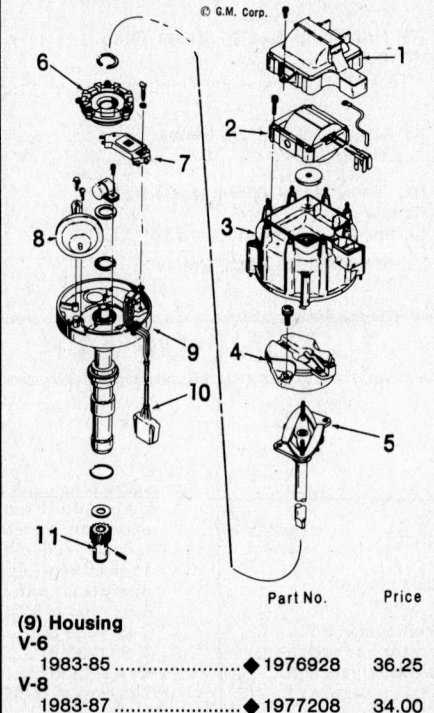

	Part No.	Price
Distributor Assembly		
V-6-231, 252		
1983-85	◆1103470	351.25
V-8-307		
1983-84	◆1103457	333.50
1985-87	◆1103602	275.00
(1) Cover		
1983-87-V-6	◆1894209	6.00
V-8	◆1875960	6.00
(2) Coil		
1983-87	◆1985474	36.00
(3) Cap		
1983-87-V-6	◆1894979	17.00
V-8	◆1974408	17.00
(4) Rotor		
1983-87	◆1977026	6.50
(5) Shaft		
V-6-231, 252		
1983-85	◆1976930	38.50
V-8-307		
1983-84	◆1979955	42.50
1985-87	◆1989612	42.50
(6) Pole Piece and Plate Assy.		
1983-87-V-6	◆1976925	30.25
V-8	◆1977207	32.00
(7) Module		
1983-87	◆1976908	60.00

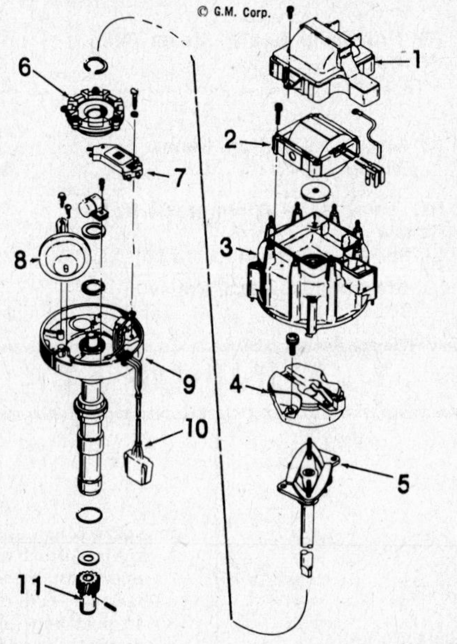

	Part No.	Price
(9) Housing		
V-6		
1983-85	◆1976928	36.25
V-8		
1983-87	◆1977208	34.00
(11) Gear		
V-6		
1983-85	◆1892082	15.25
V-8		
1983-84	◆1979948	22.25
1985-87	◆1988777	21.50

Ignition Wires

Spark plug wires are sold separately for each spark plug and are not available as a set.

	Part No.	Price
Ignition Switch		
(wo/Tilt wheel)		
1983-87	◆1990115	11.50
(Tilt wheel)		
1983-87	◆1990116	11.50

DIESEL IGNITION SYSTEM

	Part No.	Price
Glow Plugs		
1983	◆5613680	19.00
1984-85	◆5613826	16.50
Glow Plug Relay		
1983	◆560580	16.00
Glow Plug Control Switch		
1983	◆22514724	79.50
Glow Plug Module		
1984	◆22520348	91.75
Glow Plug Controller		
1985	◆22528337	96.00

LABOR 3 FUEL SYSTEM 3 LABOR

GASOLINE ENGINES

(G) Fuel Pump, Test

Includes: Disconnect line at carburetor, attach pressure gauge.

(Factory Time)	Chilton Time
All models	.2

(M) Carburetor Air Cleaner, Service

1983-87 (.2)	.3

(G) Carburetor, Adjust (On Car)

Includes: Adjust pump rod, idle vent, air valve, fast idle, choke rod, vacuum brake, unloader, secondary lockout, idle speed and mixture.

1983-87	
Slow & Fast idle (.3)	.4
Vacuum Brake-one (.4)	.6
both (.6)	.8
Choke (.6)	1.0
Complete (1.3)	1.8

(P) Throttle Position Sensor, Adjust

All models	
2 bbl (.7)	.9
4 bbl (.6)	.8
Perform C.C.C. system check add	1.0

(G) Automatic Choke Cover and/or Coil, Renew

1983-87 (.6)	1.0

(G) Automatic Choke Vacuum Brake Diaphragm, Renew or Adjust

1983-87-one (.4)	.6
both (.6)	.8

(G) Idle Stop Solenoid, Renew

Includes: Adjust.

1983-84 (.3)	.4
1985-87 (.6)	1.0

(G) Choke Vacuum Control Switch, Renew

1983-85 (.3)	.4

(G) Electric Choke Relay, Renew

1983-84 (.2)	.3

(G) Carburetor, Renew

Includes: Transfer parts, make all necessary adjustments.

1983-87 (.6)	.9
To perform C.C.C. system check, add (.5)	1.0

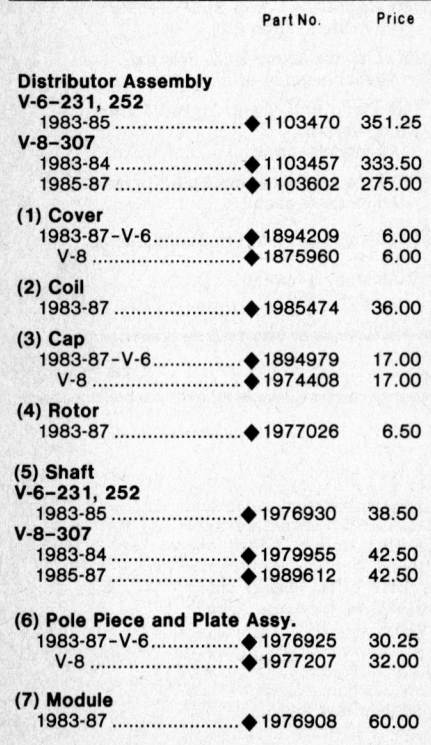

LABOR 3 FUEL SYSTEM 3 LABOR

(Factory Time) Chilton Time

(G) Carburetor, R&R and Clean or Recondition
Includes: All necessary adjustments.
1983-87-2 bbl (1.8) 3.0
4 bbl (2.1) 3.2
To perform C.C.C. system check, add (.5) 1.0

(G) Float or Needle Valve and Seat, Renew
Includes: All necessary adjustments.
1983-87
2 bbl (.9) 1.2
4 bbl (.9) 1.5
To perform C.C.C. system check, add (.5) 1.0

(G) Accelerator Pump, Renew
All models
2 bbl (.7) 1.0
4 bbl (.8) 1.2

(G) E.F.E. Heater (Insulator), Renew
All models (.6) 1.0

(G) Fuel Pump, Renew
1983-87-V-6 (.6) 8
V-8 (.8) 1.0
wo/A.C. add (.1) 1
w/A.C. and A.I.R. add (.4) 4
Add pump test if performed.

(G) Fuel Tank, Renew
Includes: Drain and refill tank. Test gauge.
1983-87 (.8) 1.0

(G) Fuel Gauge (Tank), Renew
Includes: Drain and refill tank.
1983-87 (.8) 1.1

(G) Water In Fuel Detector, Renew (WIF)
All models (.9) 1.2

(G) Fuel Gauge (Dash), Renew
1983-85 (.3) 5
1986-87 (.5) 9

(G) Intake Manifold or Gaskets, Renew
Includes: Adjust carburetor and linkage as necessary. Drain and refill radiator. Adjust timing.
V-6-1983-85 (1.8) 2.7
V-8-1983-85 (1.7) 2.5
1986-87 (2.3) 3.2
Renew manif add (.3) 5
w/A.C. add (.4) 4
w/A.I.R. add (.1) 1
w/Cruise control add (.2) 2

E.F.E. SYSTEM

(G) E.F.E. Valve, Renew
Includes: Hoist car.
1983-87 (.5) 8

(G) E.F.E. Thermal Vacuum Switch, Renew
1983 (.3) 4

(G) E.F.E. Vacuum Check Valve, Renew
1983-84 (.2) 4
1985 (.4) 4

DIESEL ENGINE

(G) Idle Speed, Adjust
1983-85 (.2) 4

(G) Injection Timing, Check and Adjust
1983-85 (.7) 9

(M) Air Cleaner, Service
1983-85 (.2) 4

(G) Air Intake Crossover, Renew
1983-85-w/Ext EGR (.3) 5
w/Int EGR (.4) 6

(G) Fuel Supply Pump, Renew
1983-85 (.5) 8
w/A.C. add (.2) 2

(G) Fuel Filter, Renew
1983-85 (.2) 4

(G) Fuel Solenoid, Renew
1983-85 (.5) 7

(G) Cold Advance Solenoid, Renew
1983-85 (.6) 8

(G) Fuel Injection Head Seal, Renew
Includes: Renew head and drive shaft seals. Renew governor weight retaining ring.
1983-85 (2.7) 3.9

(G) Fast Idle Relay, Renew
1983-85 (.3) 4

(G) Vacuum Pump, Renew
Includes: Vacuum test.
1983-85
gear driven (.4) 6
belt driven (.6) 8

(G) Fuel Injection Pump, Renew
Includes: Pressure and electrical tests. Adjust timing.
1983-85 (2.1) 3.4

(G) Injector Pump Adapter and/or Seal, Renew
1983-85 (1.8) 2.5

(G) Fuel Return Lines (At Nozzles), Renew
1983-85-one side (.3) 5
both sides (.4) 7
return hose (.2) 3
w/A.C. add (.2) 2

(G) High Pressure Fuel Lines, Renew
Includes: Flush lines.
1983-85-one (.8) 8
one-each bank (.9) 1.0
all-both banks (2.0) 2.5

(G) Injector Nozzle and/or Seal, Renew
1983-85-one (.8) 1.0
one-each bank (1.0) 1.3
all-both banks (2.4) 3.0
Clean nozzles add-each 2
w/A.C. add (.2) 2

(G) Intake Manifold or Gaskets, Renew
1983-85 (2.9) 3.5
Renew manif add (.3) 5

(G) Fuel Injection Pump Throttle Shaft Seal, Renew
1983-85 (.8) 1.3

PARTS 3 FUEL SYSTEM 3 PARTS

	Part No.	Price
Air Cleaner Element		
V-6-231, 252		
1983-85	◆6419892	8.00
V-8-307		
1983-87	◆6484235	10.00
Carburetor Assy. (Rochester)		
V-6-231		
1983-Fed.	◆17079438	876.50
Calif.	◆17079210	666.75
1984	◆17110332	912.75
1985	◆17111175	750.50
V-6-252		
1983	◆17079267	767.25
V-8-307		
1983	◆17079343	802.75
1984	◆17110609	1079.00
1985	1711105	N.L.
1986-87	◆17111487	876.00
Rebuilding Kit (Rochester)		
V-6-231		
1983-84-Fed.	◆17076022	28.00
Calif.	◆17076129	51.00
1985	◆17076144	57.75
V-6-252		
1983	◆17069095	55.00
V-8-307		
1983	◆17076044	32.00
1984	◆17069115	45.50
1985-87	◆17076141	49.50
Carb. Needle & Seat Assy.		
V-6-231		
1983-85	◆7035157	6.00
V-6-252		
1983	◆7035150	6.50
V-8-307		
1983-87	◆7035134	6.00
Fuel Pump Assy.		
V-6-231, 252		
1983-84	◆6471172	N.L.
1985	◆6471368	32.50
V-8-307		
1983-87	◆6471743	35.00
Fuel Tank		
Order by year and model.		
Fuel Gauge (Tank)		
(exc. station wagons)		
1983-87		
96 litre, 2 lines	◆25000599	34.00
96 litre, 3 lines	◆25000600	35.75
(Station wagons)		
1983-87		
82 litre, 2 lines	◆25002211	49.00
83 litre, 3 lines	◆25002212	52.75
Fuel Gauge (Dash)		
1983-87	6433124	24.75

PARTS 3 FUEL SYSTEM 3 PARTS

	Part No.	Price
Intake Manifold Gaskets		
V-6-231		
1983-85-exc. below	◆1264924	14.50
Alum.	◆25505397	15.75
V-6-252		
1983	◆25505397	15.75
V-8-307		
1983-84	◆557866	20.00
1985	◆22527545	31.25
1986-87	◆22534925	23.50

DIESEL FUEL SYSTEM

	Part No.	Price
Air Cleaner Element		
1983-85	◆8997189	18.50
Air Intake Crossover		
1983-84	◆22509735	109.00
1985	◆22526995	109.00
Fuel Pump		
1983-84	◆6471317	N.L.
1985	◆6442228	59.25
Injection Pump Adapter		
1983-84	◆558768	21.75
1985	◆22516525	52.50
Fuel Injection Pump		
1983-exc. below	◆22518686	763.00
Sta. wag.	◆22519990	763.00
Hi alt.	◆22518689	763.00
1984-exc. below	◆22520936	763.00
Sta. wag.	◆22520937	763.00
Hi alt.	◆22520999	763.00
1985-exc. Sta. wag.	◆22524421	763.00
Sta. wag.	◆22524422	763.00
Fuel Injection Nozzles		
1983	◆22520378	60.00
1984-85	◆22521207	89.50
Vacuum Pump		
1983-84	◆7839413	116.00
1985-wo/A.C.	◆7845203	124.00
A.C.	◆7845425	124.00
Intake Manifold Gaskets		
1983-84	◆22516344	12.00
1985	◆22527544	16.50
Fuel Gauge (Tank)		
(wo/Station wagon)		
1983-84	◆25003151	99.00
1985	◆25004277	86.75
(Station wagon)		
1983-84	◆25002569	105.50
1985	◆25004280	76.25
Water Detector Kit		
1983-85	◆25002621	97.50
Fuel Gauge (Dash)		
1983-85	6433124	24.75

LABOR 3A EMISSION CONTROLS 3A LABOR

(Factory Time) Chilton Time

GASOLINE ENGINES

(G) Emission Control Check
Includes: Check and adjust engine idle speed and mixture and ignition timing. Check P.C.V. valve.
All models 6

POSITIVE CRANKCASE VENTILATION

(M) Positive Crankcase Ventilation Valve, Renew
1983-87 (.2) 3

(M) Crankcase Ventilation Filter, Renew
All models (.2) 3

EVAPORATIVE EMISSION TYPE

(G) Charcoal Canister, Renew
1983-87 (.2) 3

(G) Canister Purge Thermal Vacuum Switch, Renew
1983-87 (.2) 3

CONTROLLED COMBUSTION TYPE

(G) Air Cleaner Vacuum Motor, Renew
1983-87 (.3) 5

(G) Air Cleaner Temperature Sensor, Renew
1983-87 (.2) 3

EXHAUST GAS RECIRCULATION SYSTEM

(G) E.G.R. Valve, Renew
1983-87 (.3) 6

(G) EGR/EFE Thermal Vacuum Switch, Renew
1983-87 (.3) 4

(G) E.G.R. Valve Relay, Renew
1983 (.3) 4

(G) Check Valve, Renew
1983-87-one (.2) 3
each adtnl 1

(G) Vacuum Delay Valve, Renew
1983-87 (.2) 3

(G) Control Valve Cover, Renew
1983-85 (.2) 3

CHILTON'S EMISSION CONTROL TUNE-UP

1. Clean or renew P.C.V. valve, hoses and filter.
2. Check fuel tank cap for sealing ability.
3. Check fuel tank and fuel lines for leakage.
4. Check evaporation canister and filter. Replace if necessary.
5. Check engine compression to determine leakage of unburned gases. (Add time for items of interference).
6. Test and clean or renew spark plugs.
7. Check engine oil dipstick for sealing ability.
8. Test exhaust system with analyzer and check system for leakage.
9. Check exhaust manifold heat valve for operation.
10. Adjust ignition timing and carburetor idle speed and mixture.
11. Check automatic choke mechanism for free operation.
12. Inspect air cleaner and element.
13. On models so equipped, test distributor vacuum control switch and transmission control switch.

V-6 .... 1.7
V-8 .... 1.8

For repairs made, charge accordingly.

(Factory Time) Chilton Time

(G) Thermostatic Vacuum Control Switch, Renew
1983-87 (.3) 4

AIR INJECTOR REACTOR TYPE

(G) Air Pump, Renew
1983-87-V-6 (.3) 5
V-8 (.5) 8
w/Vacuum pump add (.2) 2

(G) Air Pump Filter, Renew
1983-87 (.3) 4

(G) A.I.R. Air Cleaner, Renew
1983-85 (.2) 3

(G) Check Valve, Renew
1983-87-one (.2) 3
each adtnl 1

(G) A.I.R. Manifold Pipe, Renew
1983-87-V-6-right (.4) 7
left (.3) 6
V-8-each (.6) 9

(G) Catalytic Converter Air Pipe, Renew
1983-87
one piece (.4) 7

(G) A.I.R. Drive Belt, Renew
1983-87 (.2) 3
w/A.C. add (.3) 3

COMPUTER COMMAND CONTROL SYSTEM (C.C.C.)

(P) Electronic Control Module, Renew
Does not include system performance check.
1983-87 (.6) 6

(P) Mixture Control Solenoid, Renew
Does not include system performance check.
1983-87-2 bbl (1.1) 1.4
4 bbl (1.2) 1.5

(P) Prom, Renew
Does not include system performance check.
Includes R&R electronic module.
1983-87 (.6) 8

(P) Barometric Sensor, Renew
Does not include system performance check.
1983-87 (.3) 7

(P) Coolant Temperature Sensor, Renew
Does not include system performance check.
Includes drain and refill cooling system.
1983-87 (.4) 7

(P) Manifold Absolute Pressure Sensor, Renew
Does not include system performance check.
1983-87 (.5) 6

LABOR 3A EMISSION CONTROLS 3A LABOR

(Factory Time) Chilton Time

(P) Oxygen Sensor, Renew
Does not include system performance check.
1983-87 (.5) 7

(P) Throttle Position Sensor, Renew
Does not include system performance check.
1983-85-2 bbl (1.1) 1.4
4 bbl (1.2) 1.5
1986-87 (.9) 1.4

(P) Metering Valve Sensor, Renew
Does not include system performance check.
1985 (.6) 8

(P) EGR/EFE Purge Solenoid, Renew
Does not include system performance check.
1983-85 (.4) 6

(P) Air Control Valve, Renew
Does not include system performance check.
1983-87 (.4) 6

(P) Air Switching Valve, Renew
Does not include system performance check.
1983-87 (.4) 6

(P) Canister Purge Control Valve, Renew
Does not include system performance check.
1983-87 (.2) 6

(P) Back-Up Lamp and Park/Neutral Switch, Renew
Does not include system performance check.
1983-87 (.3) 7

(P) Air Control/Air Switching Valve, Renew
Does not include system performance check.
1983-87 (.5) 7

(P) Air Control Valve Solenoid, Renew
Does not include system performance check.
1983-85 (.5) 8

(P) Air Switching Valve Solenoid, Renew
Does not include system performance check.
1983 (.5) 8

(P) E.G.R. Bleed Control Solenoid, Renew
Does not include system performance check.
1983 (.4) 6

(P) Air Control Valve Relay, Renew
Does not include system performance check.
1983 (.4) 6

(P) E.G.R. Bleed Control Relay, Renew
Does not include system performance check.
1983 (.4) 6

(P) E.G.R. Vacuum Control Solenoid, Renew
Does not include system performance check.
1983-87 (.3) 4

(P) E.F.E. Vacuum Control Solenoid, Renew
Does not include system performance check.
1983-87 (.3) 4

(P) Vacuum Control Purge Solenoid, Renew
Does not include system performance check.
1983-85 (.3) 5

(P) Idle Speed Control Motor, Renew
Does not include system performance check.
1983 (.6) 8
Recond motor add (.3) 4

(P) Idle Load Compensator, Renew
Does not include system performance check.
1983-87 (.3) 6

(P) Vehicle Speed Sensor, Renew
Does not include system performance check.
1983-87 (1.1) 2.0

(P) Tachometer Filter, Renew
Does not include system performance check.
1983 (.3) 3

(P) Computer Command Control System Performance Check
1983-87 (.5) 1.0

DIESEL ENGINE

(G) Crankcase Depression Regulator Valve, Renew
1983-85 (.2) 3

(G) Crankcase Ventilation Flow Control Valve, Renew
1983-85 (.2) 3

(G) Crankcase Ventilation Filter, Renew
1983-85 (.2) 3

(G) E.G.R. Valve and/or Gasket, Renew
1983-85 (.5) 7

(G) E.G.R. Control Valve Solenoid, Renew
1983-84 (.2) 3
1985 (.4) 6
Renew ECM add 1

(G) E.G.R. Control Valve Switch, Renew
1983-85 (.2) 3

(G) E.P.R. Control Valve Solenoid, Renew
1983-85 (.3) 4

(G) E.P.R. Control Valve Switch, Renew
1983-85 (.3) 4

(G) E.P.R. Exhaust Pressure Regulator Valve, Renew
1983-84 (.3) 5
1985 (.5) 7

(G) Vacuum Regulator Valve, Renew
1983-85 (.6) 8

DIESEL ELECTRONIC EMISSION CONTROLS

(P) Electronic Control Module, Renew
1985-85 (.6) 8

(P) Manifold Absolute Pressure Sensor, Renew
1985-85 (.3) 5

(P) Vehicle Speed Sensor, Renew
1985-85 (.9) 1.4

(P) Coolant Temperature Sensor, Renew
1985-85 (.6) 7

PARTS 3A EMISSION CONTROLS 3A PARTS

	Part No.	Price
Positive Crankcase Vent. Valve		
V-6		
1983-85	◆6487534	3.00
V-8-307		
1983-87	◆8997683	3.50
V-8-350 Diesel		
1983-85	◆25041678	34.50

EVAPORATIVE EMISSION TYPE

	Part No.	Price
Charcoal Canister		
1983-87	◆17064622	39.50

CONTROLLED COMBUSTION TYPE

	Part No.	Price
Air Cleaner Motor		
(exc. 231, 260 engs.)		
1983-85	◆8994333	18.75
(231, 260 engs)		
1983-85	◆8994262	24.50
Air Cleaner Sensor		
V-6-231		
1983-85	◆8997916	18.75
V-6-252		
1983	6484244	12.50
V-8		
1983-87	◆8997574	18.75

E.G.R. Valve
Replacement E.G.R. valves must be ordered according to the stamping number on the original valve.

AIR INJECTOR REACTOR TYPE

	Part No.	Price
Air Pump		
V-6		
1983-85	◆7835397	131.00
V-8		
1983-87-wo/A.C.	◆7835397	131.00
A.C.	◆7838575	158.00
Air Injection Control Valve		
V-6-231		
1983-Fed.	17072906	100.50
Calif.	◆17071711	35.00
1984-85	◆17072997	73.75
V-6-252		
1983	17072906	100.50
V-8		
1983-wo/A.C.	17064869	51.50
A.C.	◆17064379	51.50
1984-87-wo/A.C.	17075082	64.00
A.C.	17075080	59.00

COMPUTER CONTROLLED EMISSION SYSTEM

Part numbers listed are for pricing reference only. Order part with complete model, year, engine and unit I.D. information.

PARTS 3A EMISSION CONTROLS 3A PARTS

	Part No.	Price
Electronic Control Module (ECM)		
Remanufactured		
V-6-231		
1983-Fed.	◆1226024	110.25
Calif.	◆1225500	110.25
1984-85	◆1226519	110.25
V-6-252		
1983	◆1225500	110.25
V-8-260, 307		
1983	◆1225450	110.25
1984	◆1226457	110.25
1985-87-		
stamped	◆1226866	110.00
stamped	◆1227076	110.00
Calibration Unit (PROM)		
V-6-231		
1983-Fed.	◆1226271	40.50
Calif.	◆1225707	40.50
1984-Fed.	◆16041520	40.50
Calif.	◆16041526	40.50
1985-Fed.	◆16044114	40.50
Calif.	◆16044119	40.50
V-6-252		
1983-Fed.	◆1225909	40.50
Calif.	◆1225910	40.50
V-8-307		
1983 (Federal)		
Code 0028ANP	◆1226167	40.50
Code 3370CCW	◆1226435	40.50
Code 8182ANN	◆1226183	40.50
Code 3365CCU	◆1226434	40.50
Code 8170ANL	◆1226181	40.50
Code 3415CDB	◆1226437	40.50
1983 (California)		
Code 8176ANM	◆1226182	40.50
Code 8187ANO	◆1226166	40.50
Code 8198ANR	◆1226175	40.50
1984 (Federal)		
Code 0238CJN	◆16045639	40.50
Code 0226BRZ	◆16045619	40.50
Code 0230BRU	◆16045609	40.50
1984 (California)		
Code 7164BSA	◆16040790	40.50
Code 0250CJP	16040828	40.50
1985-87 (Federal)		
Code 9630DBX	16039629	40.50
Code 0097FPB	16050096	40.50
Code 9620DBU	◆16039619	40.50
Code 0086FNZ	16050085	40.50
Code 9615DBS	◆16039614	40.50
Code 0074FNX	16050073	40.50
1985-87 (California)		
Code 9635DBY	16039634	40.50
Code 0103FPC	16050102	40.50
Code 0269FYU	◆16050268	40.50
Code 0092FPA	16050090	40.50
Code 9610DCD	16039609	40.50
Code 0080FNY	16050079	40.50
Manifold Pressure Sensor		
V-6-231, 252		
1983-85	◆16006835	62.25
V-8-307		
1983-87	◆16006834	62.25
Barometric Sensor		
1983-87	◆16006833	62.25
Oxygen Sensor		
1983	◆5613959	29.00
1984-87	◆8990741	28.75
Coolant Temperature Sensor		
1983-84	◆25036092	22.00
1985-87	◆25036708	12.75
ESC Knock Sensor		
(V-6)		
1983-85	◆1997562	37.00
Vehicle Speed Sensor		
1983	◆25007227	52.00
1984	◆25007421	41.50
1985-87	◆25007463	44.00

LABOR 4 ALTERNATOR AND REGULATOR 4 LABOR

(Factory Time) — Chilton Time

(G) Delcotron Circuits, Test

Includes: Test battery, regulator, Delcotron output.

	Chilton Time
All models	.6

(M) Alternator Drive Belt, Renew

	Chilton Time
All models	
V-6 (.3)	.4
V-8 (.2)	.3
wo/A.C. add (.1)	.1
Diesel (.2)	.3
wo/A.C. add (.1)	.1

(G) Delcotron Assembly or Fan Pulley, Renew

	Chilton Time
1983-87	
V-6 (.5)	.7
V-8 (.6)	.8
Diesel (.6)	.8

(G) Delcotron, R&R and Recondition

Includes: Complete disassembly, replacement of parts as required.

	Chilton Time
1983-87	
V-6 (1.3)	1.7
V-8 (1.4)	1.8
Diesel (1.7)	2.3

(G) Delcotron Front Bearing, Renew

Includes: R&R Delcotron, separate end frames.

	Chilton Time
1983-87 (.5)	1.0
w/Diesel eng add (.2)	.2
Renew rear brg add	.2

(G) Delcotron Voltage Regulator, Test and Renew

Includes: R&R, disassemble and reassemble Delcotron.

	Chilton Time
1983-87 (.9)	1.2
w/Diesel eng add (.1)	.1

(G) Voltmeter, Renew

	Chilton Time
1983-87 (.3)	.5

PARTS 4 ALTERNATOR AND REGULATOR 4 PARTS

	Part No.	Price
Delcotron Assembly		
1983-84-42 amp.	◆1105360	206.00
56, 78 amp.	◆1100250	225.00
66 amp	◆1105369	228.75
70 amp.	◆1105335	265.00
85 amp.	◆1105339	326.50
1985-87-V-6 (78 amp)	◆1100250	225.00
V-8 (78 amp)	◆1105369	228.75
(1) Capacitor		
1983-87	◆1978146	4.75
(2) Diode		
1983-87	◆1984459	5.00
(3) Rectifier Bridge		
1983-87-exc. below	◆1984454	28.00
70, 85 amp.	◆1975313	24.50

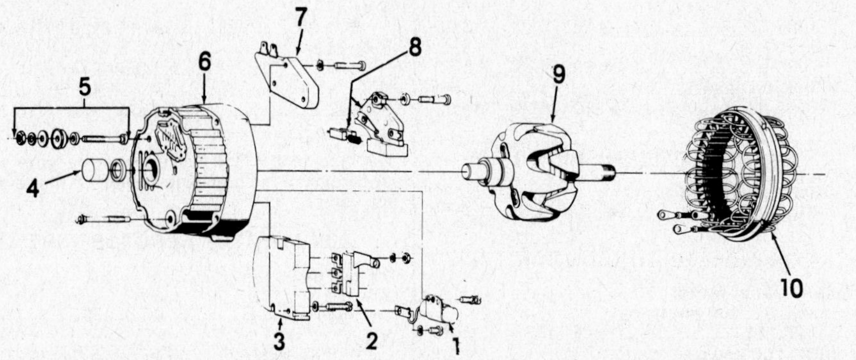

PARTS 4 ALTERNATOR AND REGULATOR 4 PARTS

	Part No.	Price
(4) Bearing		
1983-87-exc.		
below	◆9436831	5.50
70 amp.	◆1975322	5.50
(5) Terminal Pkg.		
1983-87	◆1975471	3.50
(6) Frame (Rear End)		
1983-87-exc.		
below	◆1984460	47.75
70, 85 amp.	◆1975310	31.00
(7) Regulator		
1983-87	◆1116387	25.00
(8) Brush Holder		
1983-87-exc.		
below	◆1984462	9.00
70, 85 amp.	◆1975323	10.00
(9) Rotor		
1983-87-exc.		

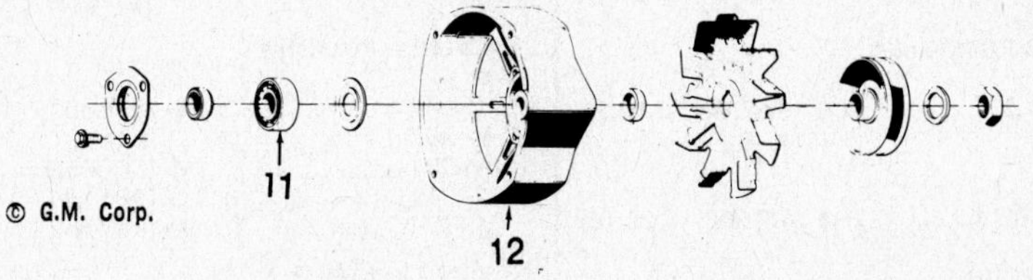

	Part No.	Price
below	◆1985476	72.00
70, 85 amp.	◆1975333	65.00
78 amp.	◆1984466	77.25
(10) Stator		
1983-87-37, 42		
amp.	◆1986280	52.75
56 amp	◆1984584	54.50
66, 78 amp.	◆1984445	37.25
70 amp.	◆1975303	48.75

	Part No.	Price
85 amp.	◆1975987	83.50
(11) Bearing (Front End)		
1983-87	◆908419	10.00
(12) Frame (Drive End)		
1983-87-42 amp.	◆1985642	24.75
55, 63, 78 amp.	◆1984464	23.50
66 amp	◆1986206	24.00
70, 85 amp.	◆1986590	30.00

LABOR 5 STARTING SYSTEM 5 LABOR

(Factory Time)	Chilton Time
(G) Starter Draw Test	
All models	.3
(G) Starter, Renew	
1983-87	
V-6 (.6)	.9
V-8 (.5)	.9
Diesel (.5)	1.1
Add draw test if performed.	
(G) Starter, R&R and Recondition	
Includes: Turn down armature.	
1983-87	
V-6 (1.2)	1.9
V-8 (1.0)	1.9

(Factory Time)	Chilton Time
Diesel (.9)	2.5
Renew field coils add (.2)	.5
Add draw test if performed.	
(G) Starter Drive, Renew	
Includes: R&R starter and solenoid.	
1983-87	
V-6 (.9)	1.1
V-8 (.6)	1.1
Diesel (.6)	1.4
(G) Starter Motor Solenoid, Renew	
Includes: R&R starter.	
1983-87	
V-6 (.6)	.9
V-8 (.5)	.9
Diesel (.6)	1.1

(Factory Time)	Chilton Time
(G) Back-Up Lamp and Park/Neutral Switch, Renew	
1983-87 (.3)	.4
(G) Ignition Switch, Renew	
1983-87 (.5)	.9
(M) Battery Cables, Renew	
1983-87-negative (.2)	.2
positive (.5)	.5
Right batt to left batt w/Diesel eng (.3)	.3
(M) Battery Terminals, Clean	
All models	.3

PARTS 5 STARTING SYSTEM 5 PARTS

	Part No.	Price
(1) Starter Assembly (New)		
V-6-231, 252		
1983-85	◆1998234	220.75
V-8-307		
1983	◆1109544	209.00
1984	◆1998450	186.00
1985-87	198536	N.L.
(2) Starter Solenoid Switch		
1983-87	◆1114531	N.L.
(3) Starter Drive Assembly		
V-6		
1983-85	◆1875687	N.L.
V-8		
1983	◆1875687	N.L.
1984-87	◆1984511	23.50
(4) Starter Brush		
1983-87-V-6	◆1906945	.50
V-8	◆1893296	.50
(5) Starter Drive End Bushing		
1983-87	◆1932190	.50
(6) Starter Front Plate		
1983-87-V-6	◆1974157	7.00
V-8	◆1978292	6.50

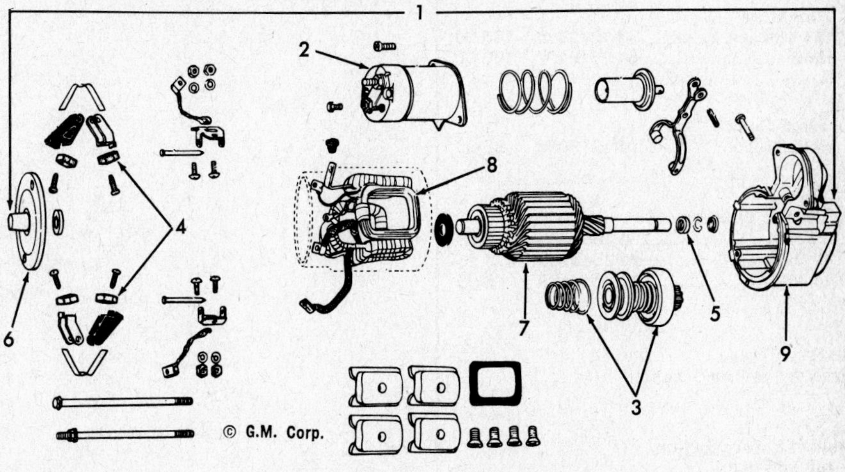

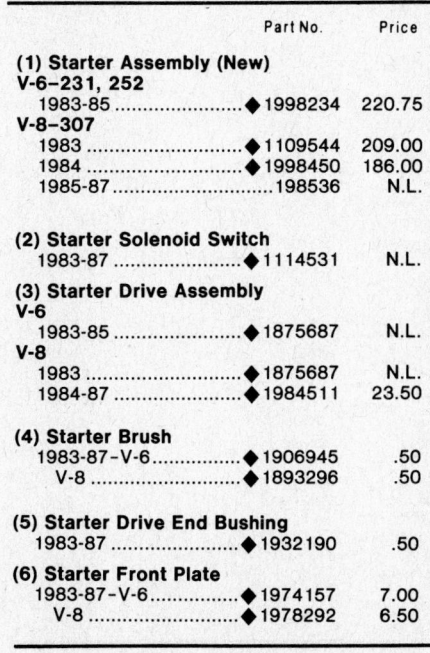

	Part No.	Price
(7) Starter Armature		
V-6-231		
1983-85	◆1971568	57.00
V-6-252		
1983	◆1970548	52.00

	Part No.	Price
V-8-307		
1983	◆1978670	83.50
1984-87	◆1985138	N.L.

PARTS 5 STARTING SYSTEM 5 PARTS

	Part No.	Price
(8) Starter Field Coils		
V-6–231		
1983-85	◆1974183	19.25
V-6–252		
1983	◆1877306	26.00
V-8–307		
1983	◆1978672	78.00
1984-87	◆1985143	71.50
(9) Starter Housing		
V-6		
1983-85	◆1876881	20.50
V-8–307		
1983	◆1893752	19.50
1984	◆1985148	25.75
1985-87	◆1987662	25.50
Ignition Switch		
(wo/Tilt wheel)		
1983	◆1990109	N.L.
1984-87	◆1990115	11.50
(Tilt wheel)		
1983	◆1990110	N.L.
1984-87	◆1990116	11.50
Neutral Safety Switch		
1983-87-exc. below	◆22509632	5.50
Elect. door lks.	◆22514861	7.00
Battery Cables		
Order by year and model.		

PARTS 5 STARTING SYSTEM (DIESEL) 5 PARTS

	Part No.	Price
Starter Assy. (New)		
1983-85	◆22522853	355.00
(1) Solenoid Switch		
1983-85	◆1114531	N.L.
(2) Drive End Bearing		
1983-84	◆9439544	5.00
1985	◆22516191	9.00
(3) Starter Drive		
1983-85	◆1893445	65.00
(4) Drive Shaft		
1983-84	◆1972683	29.00
1985	◆22516183	71.00
(5) Gear		
1983-84	◆1972685	12.50
1985	◆22516184	9.50
(6) Gear Housing		
1983-84	◆1972700	29.50
1985	◆22516195	28.50
(7) Armature		
1983-84	◆1979966	135.00
1985	◆22516197	130.00
(8) Field Coils		
1983-85	◆1979982	83.00
(9) Starter Brushes		
1983-84	◆1852885	2.75
1985-pos.	◆22516180	3.25
negative	◆22516177	3.00
Battery Cables		
Order by year and model.		
Neutral Safety Switch		
1983-85-exc. below	◆22509632	5.50
Elec. dr. lks.	◆22514861	7.00

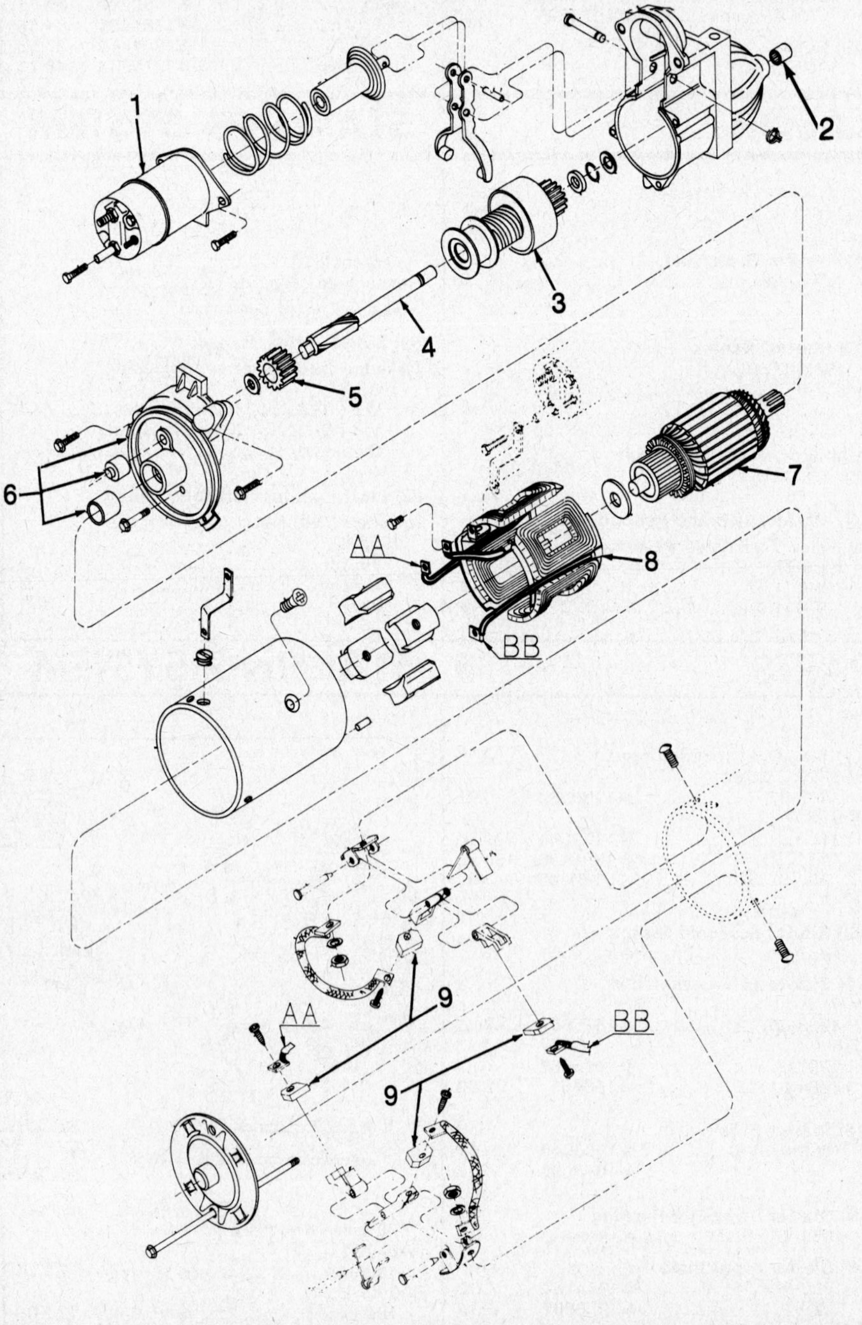

LABOR 6 BRAKE SYSTEM 6 LABOR

(Factory Time) Chilton Time

(G) Brake Pedal Free Play, Adjust
All models 3

(G) Brakes, Adjust (Minor)
Includes: R&R wheels and adjust brakes thru access holes in drums. Fill master cylinder.
two wheels 4
Remove knock out plugs add, each .. .1

(G) Bleed Brakes (Four Wheels)
Includes: Fill master cylinder.
All models 5

(G) Free-Up or Renew Brake Self Adjusting Units
one wheel 6
each adtnl 4

(G) Brake Shoes and/or Pads, Renew
Includes: Install new or exchange shoes or pads, adjust service and hand brake. Bleed system.
1983-87-front-disc (.9) 1.1
rear-drum (.9) 1.5
all four wheels 2.5
Resurface disc rotor add, each 9
Resurface brake drum add, each 5

(G) Brake Drum, Renew (One)
1983-87 (.3) 5

(G) Brake Combination Valve, Renew
Includes: Bleed system.
1983-87 (.7) 1.0

BRAKE HYDRAULIC SYSTEM

(G) Wheel Cylinder, Renew
Includes: Bleed system.
1983-87-one (.8) 1.0
both (1.1) 1.9

(G) Wheel Cylinder, Rebuild
Includes: Hone cylinder and bleed system.
1983-87-one (1.0) 1.3
both (1.5) 2.1

(G) Brake Hose, Renew
Includes: Bleed system.
1983-87-each (.6) 8

(G) Electro-Hydraulic Pump, Renew
1985-87 (.4) 5

(G) Powermaster Pressure Switch, Renew
1985-87 (.3) 4

(G) Master Cylinder, Renew
Includes: Bleed complete system.
1983-87 (.6) 1.0

(G) Master Cylinder, R&R and Rebuild
Includes: Hone cylinder and bleed complete system.
1983-87 (1.4) 1.8
w/Powermaster cyl (1.6) 2.2

COMBINATIONS

Add to Brakes, Renew

See Machine Shop Operations

(G) RENEW WHEEL CYLINDER
Each 2

(G) REBUILD WHEEL CYLINDER
Each (.3) 3

(G) REBUILD CALIPER ASSEMBLY
Each (.3) 6

(G) RENEW MASTER CYLINDER
All models (.6) 8

(G) REBUILD MASTER CYLINDER
All models (.8) 1.0

(G) RENEW BRAKE HOSE
Each (.3) 3

(G) RENEW REAR WHEEL GREASE SEALS
One side (.4) 5

(G) REPACK FRONT WHEEL BEARINGS (BOTH WHEELS)
All models (.6) 6

(G) RENEW BRAKE DRUM
Each (.1) 1

(G) RENEW DISC BRAKE ROTOR
Each (.3) 5

(Factory Time) Chilton Time

(G) Brake System, Flush and Refill
All models 1.2

(G) Brake Hydraulic System, Recondition (Complete)
Includes: Renew all rubber parts in brake system and bleed all lines.
1983-87-Bendix type (5.1) 6.9
Moraine type (5.4) 7.2

DISC BRAKES

(G) Brake Shoes and/or Pads, Renew
Includes: Install new or exchange shoes or pads, adjust service and hand brake. Bleed system.
1983-87-front-disc (.9) 1.1
rear-drum (.9) 1.5
all four wheels 2.5
Resurface disc rotor add, each 9
Resurface brake drum add, each 5

(G) Disc Brake Rotor, Renew
Includes: R&R wheel, brake shoes and bearings.
1983-87-one (.7) 1.0
both (1.2) 1.5

(Factory Time) Chilton Time

(G) Caliper Assembly, Renew
Includes: Remove brake shoes. Bleed complete system.
1983-87-one (.7) 1.0
both (1.1) 1.5

(G) Caliper Assembly, R&R and Recondition
Includes: Remove brake shoes, renew parts as required and bleed complete system.
1983-87-one (1.2) 1.5
both (2.1) 2.5

PARKING BRAKE

(M) Parking Brake, Adjust
All models (.3) 4

(G) Parking Brake Lamp Switch, Renew
1983-87 (.3) 4

(G) Parking Brake Control, Renew
Includes: Adjust parking brake.
1983-87 (.7) 9

(G) Parking Brake Cables, Renew
Includes: Adjust parking brake, R&R rear wheel and drum for rear cable.
1983-87-front (.6) 8
rear-one (.7) 9
two piece (1.1) 1.6

(G) Parking Brake Equalizer, Renew
1983-87 (.3) 5

POWER BRAKES

(G) Power Brake Cylinder, Renew
Includes: R&R master cylinder.
1983-87 (.6) 1.0

(G) Power Brake Cylinder, R&R and Recondition
Includes: R&R master cylinder.
1983-87 (1.3) 1.8
Recond m/Cyl add (.8) 8

(G) Power Brake Check Valve, Renew
1983-87 (.3) 3

(G) Hydra-boost Unit, Renew
Includes: Bleed system.
1983-84 (.6) 1.0
1985 (.8) 1.0

(G) Hydra-boost Unit, R&R and Recondition
Includes: Bleed system.
1983-84 (1.0) 1.5
1985 (1.2) 1.5

(G) Hydra-boost Pressure Lines, Renew
Includes: Bleed system.
1983-85-each (.3) 6

(G) Low Vacuum Switch, Renew
1985-87 (.2) 3

(G) Low Vacuum Brake Indicator Module, Renew
1985-87 (.2) 3

PARTS 6 BRAKE SYSTEM 6 PARTS

	Part No.	Price
(1) Brake Shoe & Lining Set		
9½" x 2" brks.		
1983-87	◆1154580	35.00
11" x 2" brks.		
1983-87	◆1154577	42.50
(2) Wheel Cylinder Assy.		
9½" x 2" brks.		
1983-87	◆18004888	28.50
11" x 2" brks.		
1983-87-wo/Sta.		
wag.	◆18004890	25.75
Sta. wag.	◆18004793	28.50
Wheel Cylinder Repair Kit		
9½" x 2" brks.		
1983-87	◆5466562	7.75

PARTS 6 BRAKE SYSTEM 6 PARTS

	Part No.	Price
11″ x 2″ brks.		
1983-87-wo/Sta. wag.	◆5463361	7.50
Sta. wag.	◆5472328	8.00
Front Brake Hose		
1983-87	◆9762809	18.00
Rear Brake Hose		
1983-87	◆9757655	15.00

POWER BRAKES

	Part No.	Price
Master Cylinder Assembly		
1983-85-exc. diesel	◆18010313	145.75
Diesel	◆25509416	103.00
1986-87	1803682	N.L.
Master Cylinder Repair Kit		
1983-85-exc. diesel	◆18007935	22.50
Diesel	◆25509843	28.50
Power Brake Booster (Vacuum)		
1983-exc. below	◆18006566	224.50
THM 2004R	◆18008695	271.25
1984-87	◆18006566	224.50
Power Brake Booster (Hydraulic)		
1983-85	◆1620210	365.00
Power Brake Booster Repair Kit (Vacuum)		
1983-87	◆18007865	47.50
Power Brake Booster, Seal Kit (Hydraulic)		
1983-85	◆22506440	10.75
Rear Brake Drum		
9½″ x 2″ brks.		
1983-87-alum.	◆1255496	90.00

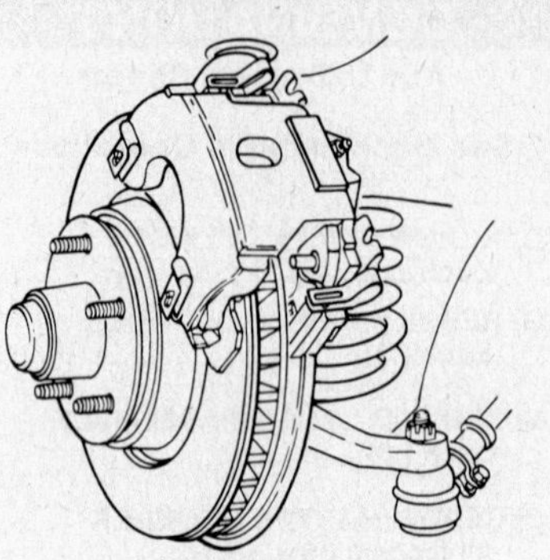

FRONT BRAKE

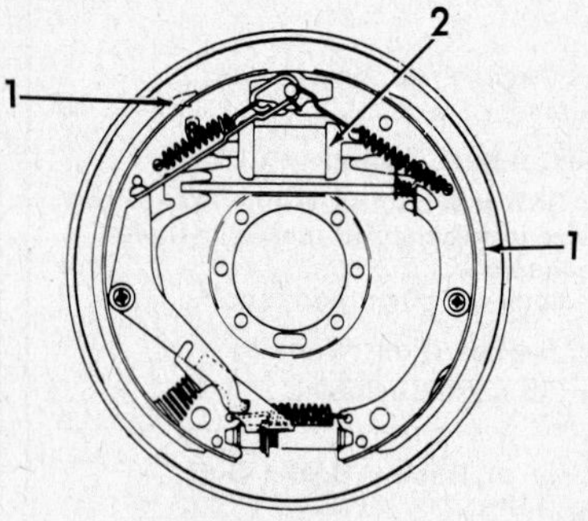

REAR BRAKE

	Part No.	Price
cast iron	◆1249146	73.00
11″ x 2″ brks.		
1983-87-17 lb. drum	◆1244835	97.00
23 lb. drum	◆1244838	96.25
Front Hub Oil Seal		
1983-87	◆3965092	3.00

PARKING BRAKES

	Part No.	Price
Parking Brake Front Cable		
1983-84-Delta 88	◆25502769	12.00
Olds. 98	◆25502768	13.50
1985-87	◆25520342	12.75

	Part No.	Price
Parking Brake Rear Cable		
(Right)		
1983-84-exc. S.W.	◆25502686	22.00
Sta. wag.	◆25502772	22.50
1985-87-exc. S.W.	◆25520338	22.00
Sta. wag.	◆25524602	22.00
(Left)		
1983-84	◆25502687	22.00
1985-87-exc. S.W.	◆25520337	22.25
Sta. wag.	◆25524603	22.50
Parking Brake Lever		
1983-87	◆25502971	23.50

PARTS 6 DISC BRAKES 6 PARTS

	Part No.	Price
(1) Brake Pad Set		
1983-87-wo/H.D. brks.	◆1154578	35.00
H.D. brks.	◆12300192	47.00
(2) Spring		
1983-87	◆5469497	1.00
(3) Seal		
1983-87-Included in Repair Kit		
(4) Piston		
1983-87	◆2622207	11.00
(5) Caliper		
1983-84-right	◆18007946	124.50
left	◆18007945	124.50

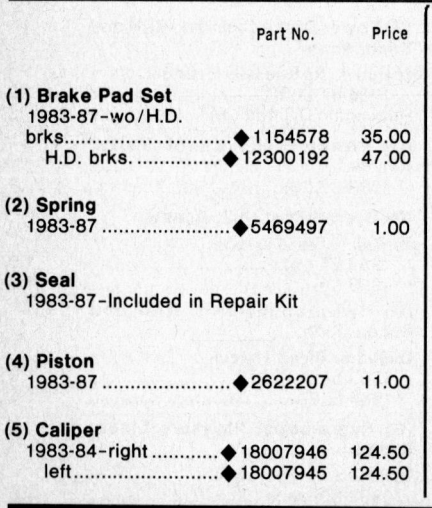

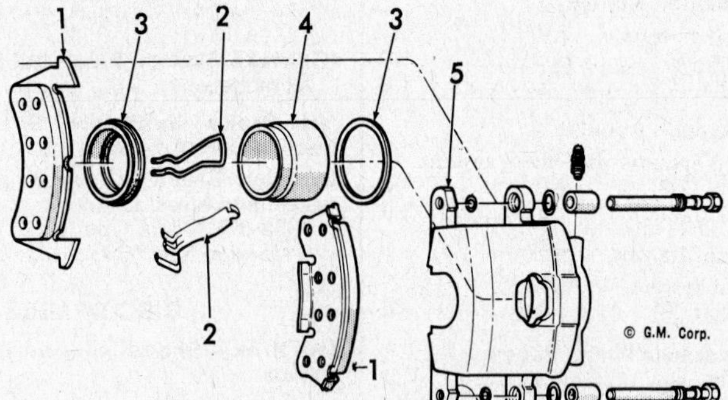

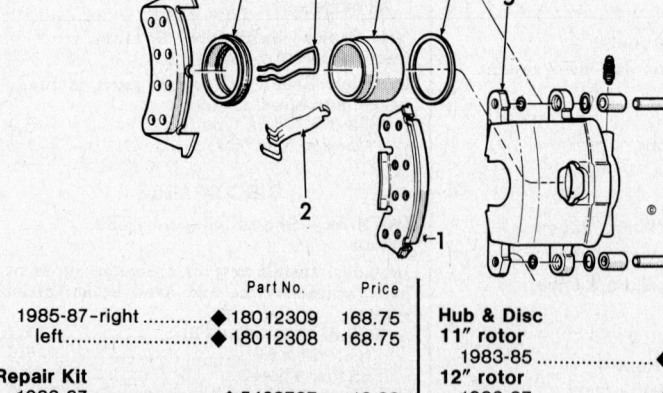

	Part No.	Price
1985-87-right	◆18012309	168.75
left	◆18012308	168.75
Repair Kit		
1983-87	◆5468767	10.00

	Part No.	Price
Hub & Disc		
11″ rotor		
1983-85	◆14008640	110.00
12″ rotor		
1983-87	◆14008641	110.00

LABOR 7 COOLING SYSTEM 7 LABOR

(Factory Time)	Chilton Time
(M) Winterize Cooling System	
Includes: Run engine to check for leaks, tighten all hose connections. Test radiator and pressure cap, drain radiator and engine block. Add anti-freeze and refill system.	
All models	.5
(M) Thermostat, Renew	
Includes: Test thermostat.	
1983-87-V-6 (.7)	•.8
V-8 (.5)	.6
Diesel (.5)	.6
•w/A.C. add (.1)	.1
w/Cruise control add (.1)	.1
(M) Radiator Assembly, R&R or Renew	
Includes: Drain and refill cooling system.	
1983-87-V-6 (.7)	1.1
V-8 (.6)	.9
Diesel (.7)	1.0
Renew lower insulators add (.1)	.1

ADD THESE OPERATIONS TO RADIATOR R&R

(G) Boil & Repair	1.5
(G) Rod Clean	1.9
(G) Repair Core	1.3
(G) Renew Tank	1.6
(G) Renew Trans. Oil Cooler	1.9
(G) Recore Radiator	1.7

LABOR 7 COOLING SYSTEM 7 LABOR

(Factory Time) Chilton Time

(M) Radiator Hoses, Renew
1983-87-one (.3) 4
both (.4) 7
by-pass (.5) 6
w/A.C. add (.1) 1

(G) Fan Blades or Clutch Assy., Renew
1983-87 (.3) 5

(G) Water Pump, Renew
Includes: R&R fan blade and pulley. Drain and refill radiator. Adjust belts.
1983-87-V-6 (1.0) 1.7
V-8 (1.6) 2.0
Diesel (1.5) 2.3
w/A.C. add (.1) 1
w/A.I.R. add (.1) 1

(M) Drive Belt, Renew
1983-87-one (.3) 4
each adtnl 1

(M) Drive Belt, Adjust
1983-87-one (.2) 3
each adtnl 1

(G) Temperature Gauge (Dash Unit), Renew
1983-87 (.4) 7

(G) Temperature Gauge (Engine Unit), Renew
1983-87 (.3) 4

(G) Water Jacket Expansion Plugs, Renew (Side of Block)
1983-87-each (.5) 5
Note: If necessary to R&R any component to gain access to plug, add appropriate time.

(G) Heater Hoses, Renew
Includes: Drain and refill coolant.
1983-87-one (.3) 5

COOLING SYSTEM TUNE-UP

An Annual Cooling System Tune-Up Suggestion List should include (with some exceptions):

1. A visual check of the cooling system for indications of leaks or excessive oil content.
2. Pressure check the cooling system for internal and external leaks with filler cap and neck adapter and tester.
3. Check crankcase and automatic transmission oil for water content.
4. Test coolant thermostat with radiator thermometer.
5. Check temperature gauge for accuracy.
6. Drain system and flush till clean.
7. Clean foreign matter from radiator fins.
8. Test radiator pressure cap with cap tester.
9. Check fan blades and pulleys for alignment and damage.
10. Internal and external inspection of all hoses for cracks and deterioration.
11. Check core plugs (where possible) for seepage.
12. Refill system with correct coolant and check for air locks.
13. Check condition and tension of drive belts with tension gauge.

All models **1.5**

(Factory Time) Chilton Time

both (.4) .... *.6
*w/A.C. add (.2) 2

(G) Heater Core, R&R or Renew
Without Air Conditioning
1983-84 (.5) 1.1
With Air Conditioning
1983 (1.3) 2.5
1984-87 (.9) 2.5

ADD THESE OPERATIONS TO HEATER CORE R&R
(G) Boil & Repair 1.2
(G) Repair Core 9
(G) Recore 1.2

(G) Heater Control Assembly, Renew
1983-84 (.5) 7
1985-87 Refer to A.C. group.

(Factory Time) Chilton Time

(G) Heater Blower Motor, Renew
1983-84 (.2) 5
1985-87 Refer to A.C. group.

(G) Heater Blower Motor Resistor, Renew
1983-84 (.2) 3
1985-87 Refer to A.C. group.

(G) Heater Blower Motor Switch, Renew
1983-84 (.3) 5
1985-87 Refer to A.C. group.

(G) Heater Water Control Valve, Renew
1983-87 (.4) 5

PARTS 7 COOLING SYSTEM 7 PARTS

Part No. Price

(1) Radiator Assy.
Accurate replacement of the radiator can be done only by using the radiator code stamped on a metal tag located on the original radiator. Order by year, model and radiator code no.

(2) Radiator Hose, Upper
V-6
1983-85 .... 25502037 7.00
V-8
1983-87 .... 22505268 12.00

(3) Radiator Hose, Lower
V-6
1983-85 .... 1264041 15.75
V-8
1983-exc. below 22510762 12.00
w/diesel eng. 22515684 12.00
1984-87 .... 22522723 12.00

(4) Water Pump Assembly
V-6
1983-85 .... ◆1260709 61.75
V-8
1983-85-wo/A.C. .... ◆231886 96.50
A.C. .... ◆556283 95.00
1986-87 .... ◆556283 N.L.

Fan Clutch Assy.
V-6
1983-87-Code (TT, TU) .... ◆22008492 87.50
Code (TS) .... ◆22008490 84.50

Part No. Price

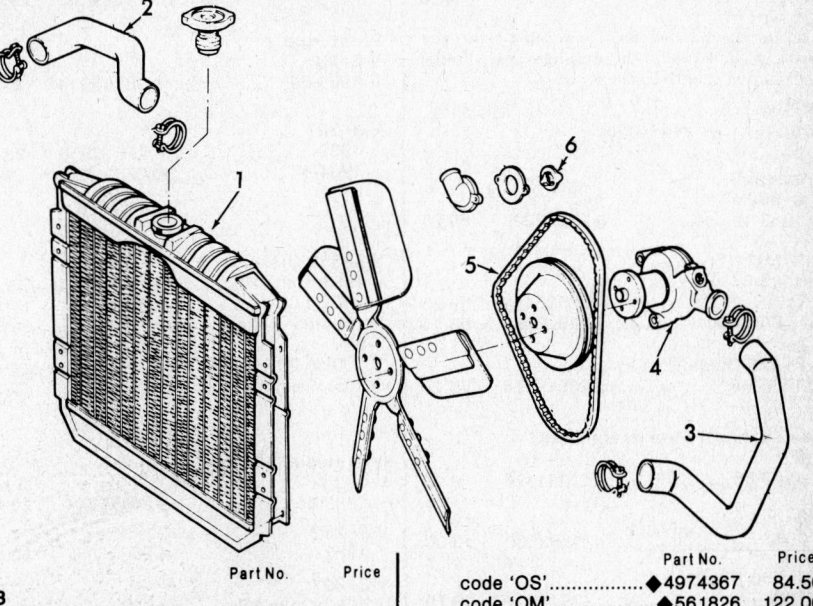

V-8
1983-87 (code stamped on unit)
code 'OH' 22007979 84.50
code 'OJ', 'OL' .... ◆22049774 N.L.

Part No. Price

code 'OS' .... ◆4974367 84.50
code 'OM' .... ◆561826 122.00

(5) Fan Belt
Order by model & description.

PARTS 7 COOLING SYSTEM 7 PARTS

	Part No.	Price
Temperature Gauge (Block Unit)		
V-6		
1983-85	◆25036371	8.00
V-8		
(wo/Gauges)		
1983	◆25036506	8.75
1984-87	◆25036629	9.75
(Gauges)		
1983	8993106	12.50
1984-87	◆25036628	19.75
V-8 Diesel		
1983	◆8993146	19.25
1984-85-wo/		
Gauges	◆25036629	9.75
Gauges	◆25036628	19.75
(6) Thermostat		
V-6		
1983	◆1254894	9.00
1984-85	◆3041390	6.00
V-8		
1983-87	◆3051139	5.00
Heater Core		
1983-87-wo/A.C.	◆3036422	41.25
A.C.	◆3035420	43.00
Blower Motor		
(wo/A.C.)		
1983-87	◆22048569	47.50
(A.C.)		
1983-87	◆22020945	60.00
Heater Temperature Control Valve		
1983-87	3036444	6.50
Switch, Heater Blower		
1983-87	◆16015256	6.00
Resistor, Heater Blower		
1983-87	◆9796480	2.50

LABOR 8 EXHAUST SYSTEM 8 LABOR

(Factory Time)	Chilton Time
(G) Muffler, Renew	
1983-87 (.5)	.7
(G) Tail Pipe and Resonator Assy., Renew	
1983-87 (.5)	.7
(G) Catalytic Converter, Renew	
1983-87 (.8)	1.0
(G) Exhaust Pipe Flange Gasket or Seal, Renew	
1983-87 (.4)	.6
(G) Front Exhaust Pipe (To Converter), Renew	
1983-87 (.6)	.9
(G) Intermediate Exhaust Pipe, Renew	
1983-87 (.5)	.7
(G) Exhaust Crossover Pipe, Renew	
1983-87-Gas (.3)	.9
Diesel (.9)	1.3
(G) E.F.E. Valve (Heat Riser), Renew	
1983-84 (.5)	.8
1985-87 (.3)	.8
(G) E.F.E. Thermal Vacuum Switch, Renew	
1983 (.3)	.4
(G) E.F.E. Vacuum Check Valve, Renew	
1983-84 (.2)	.4
1985 (.4)	.4
(G) Exhaust Manifold, Renew	
V-6–1983-85	
right side (.7)	1.1
left side (.7)	1.1
w/A.C. add (.3)	.3
V-8–1983-85	
right side (.8)	1.2
left side (.7)	1.1
1986-87	
right side (1.1)	1.6
left side (1.0)	1.5
Diesel–1983	
right side (.9)	1.3
left side (.7)	1.1
1984-85	
right side (1.2)	1.7
left side (.7)	1.1
w/A.C. add (.5)	.5
w/A.I.R. add (.2)	.2

COMBINATIONS

(Factory Time)	Chilton Time
(G) Exhaust Pipe, Muffler, Resonator and Tail Pipe, Renew	
1983-87-one side (1.0)	1.5

PARTS 8 EXHAUST SYSTEM 8 PARTS

Part numbers listed are for pricing reference only. Order parts with complete year, model and engine identification.

Muffler
Order by year and model.

	Part No.	Price
Resonator		
V-6-252		
1983	◆25502391	88.75
V-8-307		
1983-87-wo/Sta. wag.	◆22505492	89.25
Sta. wag.	◆22506866	58.25
V-8-350 Diesel		
1983-85	◆22512354	58.25
Seal–Exhaust Pipe to Manifold		
V-6		
1983-85	1261476	6.25
V-8		
1983-87	1262500	13.00
V-8-350 Diesel		
1983-84	22511912	10.75
1985	22511910	10.75
Front Pipe		
V-6-231		
1983-85	◆25515214	21.25
V-8-307		
1983	22510556	28.50
1984-87	◆22520490	11.00
V-8-350 Diesel		
1983-Delta 88	◆22512345	53.75
Olds 98	◆22512347	52.25
1984-85-Delta 88	◆22512355	52.25
Olds 98	◆22512347	52.25
Sta. wag.	◆22512346	52.25
Intermediate Pipe		
V-6-231		
1983-85	◆25516994	20.00
V-8-252		
1983	◆25505630	52.50
V-8-307		
1983-Delta 88	◆22512349	51.00
Olds. 98	◆22512350	51.00
1984-85-Delta 88	◆22524716	51.00
Olds. 98	◆22524789	51.00
Crossover Pipe		
V-6		
1983-87	◆25516456	31.25
V-8-307		
1983-87	◆22504709	74.25
V-8-350 Diesel		
1983-87	◆22514728	24.00
Catalytic Converter		
V-6-231		
1983-84	◆8999615	312.25
1985	◆25056912	348.00
V-6-252		
1983	◆8999596	N.L.
V-8-307		
1983	◆25056622	308.25
1984-85-Fed.	◆25056634	335.00
Calif.	◆25056562	313.25
1986-87-Fed.	22521622	8.25
Calif.	◆25100217	335.00

LABOR 9 FRONT SUSPENSION 9 LABOR

(Factory Time) Chilton Time

Note: On all front suspension operations alignment charges must be added if performed. Time given does not include alignment.

(M) Wheel, Renew
one (.3) 5

(G) Wheels, Rotate (All)
All models 5

(G) Wheels, Balance
one 3
each adtnl 2

(G) Check Alignment of Front End
All models 5
Note: Deduct if alignment is performed.

(G) Toe-In, Adjust
All models (.4) 6

(G) Align Front End
Includes: Adjust front wheel bearings.
All models (.7) 1.4
w/A.C. interference add 5

(G) Front Wheel Bearings, Clean and Repack (Both Wheels)
1983-87 (1.1) 1.6

(G) Front Wheel Bearings and Cups, Renew
1983-87-one side (.7) 9
both sides (1.1) 1.5

(G) Front Wheel Grease Seals, Renew
1983-87-one whl (.7) 8
both whls (1.1) 1.2

(G) Front Shock Absorber, Renew
1983-87-one (.3) 4
both (.5) 7

(G) Rebuild Front Suspension
Includes: Disassemble, renew necessary parts, reassemble, lubricate and align front end.
1983-87-one side (4.1) 4.6
both sides (7.5) 8.4

(G) Upper and Lower Ball Joints, Renew (One Side)
Add alignment charges.
1983-87 (1.1) 1.8

(G) Upper Ball Joint, Renew (One)
Add alignment charges.
1983-87 (.7) 9

(G) Lower Ball Joint, Renew (One)
Add alignment charges.
1983-87 (.6) 9

(G) Steering Knuckle, Renew (One)
Add alignment charges.
1983-87 (1.0) 1.4

(G) Upper Control Arm, Renew (One)
Add alignment charges.
1983-87 (.7) 1.2

(G) Lower Control Arm, Renew (One)
Add alignment charges.
1983-87 (1.0) 1.5

(G) Upper Control Arm Inner Pivot Shaft or Bushings, Renew (One Side)
Add alignment charges.
1983-87 (1.0) 1.5

(G) Lower Control Arm Shaft or Bushings, Renew (One Side)
Add alignment charges.
1983-87 (1.2) 1.7

(G) Front Spring, Renew (One)
Includes: R&R wheel and shock. Disconnect stabilizer link and control arm pivots bolts. Add alignment charges.
1983-87 (.9) 1.4

(G) Front Stabilizer Bar and Bushings, Renew
1983-87 (.5) 8

(G) Stabilizer Links or Grommets, Renew
1983-87-one (.3) 4
both (.4) 6

PARTS 9 FRONT SUSPENSION 9 PARTS

	Part No.	Price
(1) Front Wheel Bearing (Outer)		
1983-87	◆7450697	11.00
(2) Front Wheel Bearing (Inner)		
1983-87	◆7450630	11.00
(3) Front Seal Assy.		
1983-87	◆3965092	3.50
(4) Steering Knuckle		
11″ rotor		
1983-87-right	◆14012596	116.00
left	◆14012595	116.00
12″ rotor		
1983-87-right	◆14012590	144.00
left	◆14012589	144.00
(5) Ball Joint Pkg. (Lower)		
1983	◆9767281	31.50
1984-87	◆9767281	31.50
(6) Control Arm (Lower)		
1983-87-right	◆14039016	105.00
left	◆14039015	105.00
(7) Bushing (Rear)		
1983-87	14041609	4.50
(8) Shock Absorber		
1983-87	◆4993548	24.50
(9) Coil Spring		
Order by model and description.		
(10) Ball Joint (Upper)		
1983-87	◆9767112	34.75
(11) Bushing (Front)		
1983-87	◆351286	7.00
(12) Control Arm (Upper)		
1983-87-right	◆14039010	109.00
left	◆14039009	109.00
(13) Shaft Pkg. (Upper Control)		
1983-87-right	◆14022172	33.75
left	◆14022171	35.50

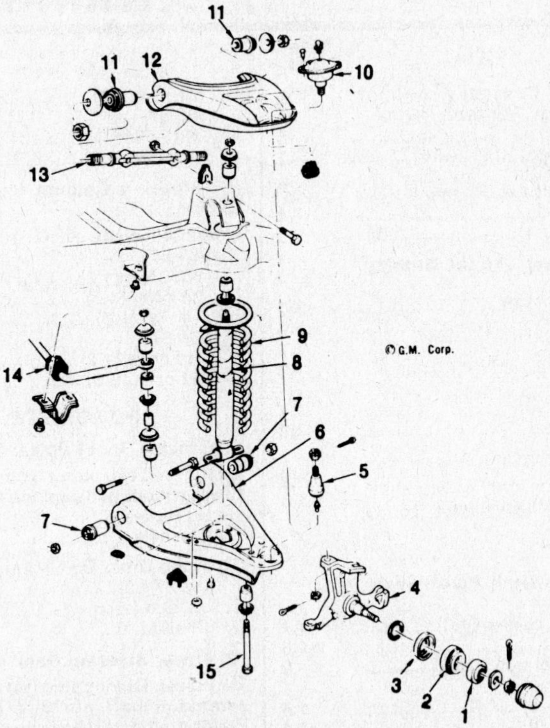

	Part No.	Price
(14) Bushing (Stabilizer)		
1983-87-1″ I.D.	◆371773	1.00
1.08″ I.D.	◆472117	2.00
.80″ I.D.	◆370283	1.00
27mm	◆473743	2.00
(orange)	14011249	1.50
(15) Link Pkg.		
1983-87	◆464167	4.25

LABOR 10 STEERING LINKAGE 10 LABOR

(Factory Time) Chilton Time

(G) Tie Rods or Tie Rod Ends, Renew
Includes: Adjust toe-in and spoke alignment.
1983-87-one side (.7) 1.0
both sides (.9) 1.4

(G) Inner Tie Rods, Renew
Includes: Reset toe-in.
1983-87-one side (.7) 1.0
both sides (.8) 1.2

(G) Idler Arm, Renew
Includes: Adjust toe-in and spoke alignment.
1983-87 (.8) 1.0

(G) Intermediate Rod, Renew
Includes: Adjust toe-in and spoke alignment.
1983-84 (1.0) 1.2
1985-87 (.9) 1.2

(G) Pitman Arm, Renew
Includes: Adjust toe-in and spoke alignment.
1983-87 (.5) 7

PARTS 10 STEERING LINKAGE 10 PARTS

	Part No.	Price
(1) Idler Arm Assy.		
1983-87	◆7837635	51.00
(2) Tie Rod Assy. (Inner)		
1983-87	◆7834224	45.75
(3) Tie Rod End (Outer)		
1983-87	◆12308612	50.50
(4) Tie Rod Sleeve Pkg. (Adjuster)		
1983-87	◆7826714	15.50
(5) Seal Kit (Pitman Arm)		
1983-87	◆7826470	17.00
(6) Pitman Arm Assy.		
1983-87	◆7837645	44.00

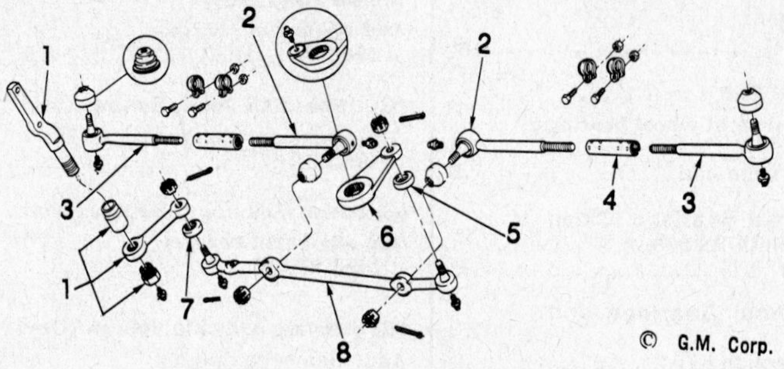

	Part No.	Price
(7) Seal Kit		
1983-87	◆7826470	17.00
(8) Relay Rod Assy.		
1983-87	◆7837639	109.00

LABOR 11 STEERING GEAR 11 LABOR

(Factory Time) Chilton Time

(G) Horn Contact and/or Cancelling Cam, Renew
1983-87 (.5) 6
w/Tilt Tel add (.1) 1

(G) Steering Wheel, Renew
1983-87 (.3) 4
w/Tilt Tel add (.1) 1

(G) Upper Mast Jacket Bearing, Renew
1983-85-std (1.0) 1.4
tilt (1.1) 1.6
Tilt Tel (1.2) 1.7
w/Cruise control add (.2) 2
1986-87
std colm (1.0) 1.4
tilt colm (.5) 9

(G) Flexible Coupling, Renew
1983-84 (.5) 7

(G) Universal Joint (Pot Joint), Renew
1983-84 (.5) 8

(G) Dimmer Switch Pivot Assy., Renew
1983-85-std column (1.0) 1.4
tilt column (.7) 1.3
w/Cruise control add (.2) 2
1986-87
std colm (1.0) 1.4
tilt colm (1.0) 1.4

(G) Steering Column Lock Actuator Parts, Renew
1983-85
std colm (1.1) 1.5
tilt colm (1.1) 1.5
Tilt Tel (1.5) 2.0
1986-87
std colm (1.1) 1.5
tilt colm (1.3) 1.8

(G) Steering Column Shift Bowl, Renew
Does not include colorcoat.
1983-85
std colm (1.2) 1.6
tilt colm (1.3) 1.7
Tilt Tel (1.8) 2.4
1986-87
std colm (1.2) 1.6
tilt colm (2.0) 3.0

POWER STEERING

(G) Trouble Shoot Power Steering
Includes: Test pump and system pressure. Check pounds pull on steering wheel and check system for leaks.
All models 5

(M) Pump Drive Belt, Renew
1983-87 (.3) 4
w/A.C. add (.3) 3
w/AIR add (.1) 1

(G) Power Steering Gear, Adjust
Includes: Disconnect pitman arm. Check combined ball nut and bearing preload. Perform pitman shaft overcenter adjustment.
1983-87 (.8) *1.2
*Includes R&R gear assy.

(G) Steering Gear Assembly, Renew
1983-87 (.7) 1.2

(P) Steering Gear Assy., R&R and Recondition
Includes: Disassemble, renew necessary parts, reassemble and adjust.
1983-85 (1.7) 2.5
1986-87 (2.1) 3.0

(G) Valve Body, Renew
Includes: R&R gear assy.
1983-85 (1.0) 1.5
1986-87 (1.4) 2.2

(G) Steering Gear Housing, Renew
Includes: R&R gear assy.
1983-85 (1.1) 1.6
1986-87 (1.5) 2.4

(G) Pitman Shaft Oil Seal, Renew
Does not require R&R gear assy.
1983-87 (.5) 1.0

(G) Power Steering Oil Pump, Renew
1983-87
V-6 (.5) 9
V-8 (.9) 1.4
Diesel (.9) 1.4
w/Hydra Boost add (.1) 1

(P) Power Steering Pump, R&R and Recondition
1983-87
V-6 (1.0) 1.7
V-8 (1.4) 2.2
Diesel (1.4) 2.2
w/Hydra Boost add (.1) 1

LABOR 11 STEERING GEAR 11 LABOR

	(Factory Time)	Chilton Time
(G) Pump Shaft Oil Seal, Renew		
1983-87		
V-6	(.6)	1.0
V-8	(.5)	1.5
Diesel	(.9)	1.5
(G) Pump Flow Control Valve, Renew		
1983-87	(.3)	.7
(M) Power Steering Hoses, Renew		
1983-87		
pressure	(.4)	.8
return	(.3)	.5
(M) Hydra-boost Hoses, Renew		
1983-85-each	(.4)	.6
TILT COLUMN		
(G) Tilt Column Steering Shaft, Renew		
1983-85	(1.2)	1.9
w/Cruise control add	(.2)	.2
w/Tilt Tel add	(.4)	.4
1986-87	(1.6)	2.3
(G) Tilt Column, R&R and Recondition		
1983-85	(2.1)	2.7
w/Cruise control add	(.2)	.2
1986-87	(2.5)	3.2

PARTS 11 POWER STEERING GEAR 11 PARTS

	Part No.	Price
(1) Cover Seal Kit		
1983-87	◆7817486	9.00
(2) Pitman Shaft (w/Gear)		
1983-87-Var. P.S.	◆7813631	87.50
Non-Var. P.S.	◆7815885	87.50
(3) Check Valve Kit		
1983-87	◆7834284	5.25
(4) Bearing Kit		
1983-87	◆7826850	11.00
(5) Housing Assy.		
1983-87	◆7834139	183.00
(6) Bearing (Pitman Shaft)		
1983-87	◆5697804	15.00
(7) Seal Kit (Pitman Shaft)		
1983-87	◆7826470	17.00
(8) Seal (Adjuster Plug)		
1983-84	◆5686527	1.50
1985-87	◆7832730	8.25
(9) Bearing (Adjuster Plug)		
1983-87	◆7828012	7.25
(10) Plug Assy. (Adjuster)		
1983-87	◆7832731	53.50
(11) Seal Kit		
1983-87	◆5687182	12.50
(12) Valve Assy.		
1983-87	◆7832058	212.00
(14) Seal Kit		
1983-87	◆7817485	6.50
(15) Plug		
1983-87	◆5689010	8.75
(16) Rack Assy.		
1983-87-exc. below	◆7827170	154.25
V-6 & Sta. wag.	◆7817528	162.00

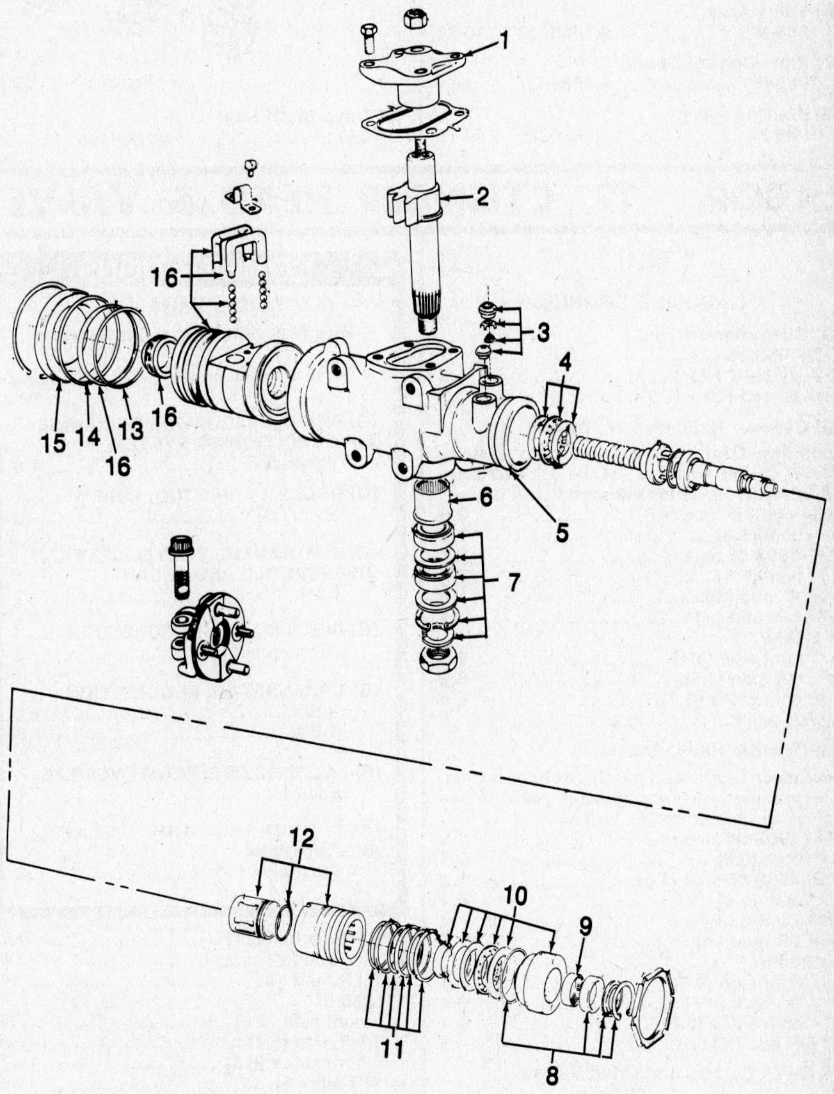

PARTS 11 POWER STEERING PUMP 11 PARTS

	Part No.	Price
Pressure Line Hose		
Order by year and model.		
Power Steering Pump		
V-6		
1983-85	◆7839795	199.00
V-8		
1983-87	◆7840244	199.00
V-8-350 Diesel		
1983-87	◆7839792	213.00
(1) Pressure Plate		
1983-87	◆7839669	14.25
(2) Pressure Plate Spring		
1983-87	◆7839667	1.00
(3) End Plate		
1983-87	◆5689358	3.50
(4) Rotor & Vane Kit		
1983-87	◆7837322	75.00
(5) Thrust Plate		
1983-87	◆7836369	13.75
(6) Valve Assy.		
1983-87	◆7809232	10.75
(7) Flow Control Spring		
1983-87	◆5688037	1.50
(8) Housing Assy.		
1983-87	◆7830236	62.75

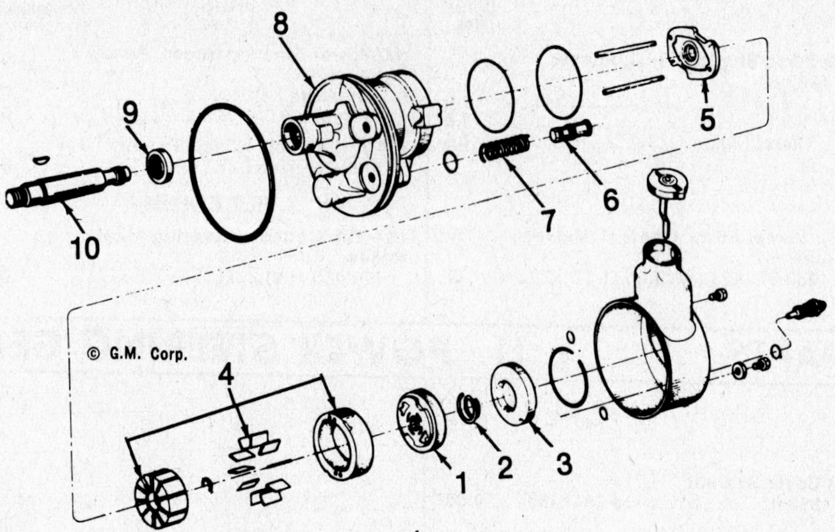

	Part No.	Price
(9) Drive Shaft Seal		
1983-87	◆7808195	4.50

	Part No.	Price
(10) Drive Shaft		
1983-87	◆7837321	39.50

LABOR 12 CYLINDER HEAD & VALVE SYSTEM 12 LABOR

(Factory Time)	Chilton Time
GASOLINE ENGINES	
(G) Compression Test	
V-6–1983-85 (.5)	.7
V-8–1983-87 (.6)	.8
w/A.C. add (.3)	.3
(G) Cylinder Head Gasket, Renew	
Includes: Drain and refill cooling system. Clean gasket surfaces. Make all necessary adjustments including carburetor and timing.	
V-6–1983-85-one (4.4)	5.8
both (5.3)	7.6
V-8–1983-85-one (4.2)	5.7
both (5.4)	7.4
w/A.C. add (.6)	.6
w/A.I.R. add (.4)	.4
1986-87	
right side (4.4)	6.0
left side (4.5)	6.2
both sides (6.2)	8.5
w/AIR add (.5)	.5
(G) Cylinder Head, Renew	
Includes: Drain and refill cooling system. Clean gasket surfaces, transfer parts, reface valves and minor engine tune up.	
V-6–1983-85-one (4.9)	6.6
both (5.9)	9.1
V-8–1983-85-one (4.5)	6.2
both (6.1)	8.4
w/A.C. add (.6)	.6
w/A.I.R. add (.4)	.4
1986-87	
right side (4.6)	6.3
left side (4.7)	6.4
both sides (6.6)	9.1
w/AIR add (.5)	.5
(P) Clean Carbon and Grind Valves	
Includes: Drain and refill cooling system. R&R cylinder heads. Recondition valve seats, adjust valve stem length. Minor engine tune up.	
V-6–1983-85-one bank (5.4)	7.5
both banks (8.0)	11.2
V-8–1983-85	
one bank (5.1)	7.0
both banks (7.1)	9.7
w/A.C. add (.6)	.6
w/A.I.R. add (.4)	.4
1986-87	
right side (5.5)	7.5
left side (5.7)	7.8
both sides (8.5)	11.7
w/AIR add (.5)	.5

COMBINATIONS

Add to Valve Job
See Machine Shop Operations

(Factory Time)	Chilton Time
(G) DRAIN, EVACUATE & RECHARGE AIR CONDITIONING SYSTEM	
All models (.5)	1.0
(G) ROCKER ARM STUD, RENEW	
Each (.3)	.3
(G) HYDRAULIC VALVE LIFTERS, DISASSEMBLE AND CLEAN	
Each (.2)	.2
(G) DISTRIBUTOR, RECONDITION	
All models (.5)	.8
(G) CARBURETOR, RECONDITION	
2 BBL	1.2
4 BBL	1.5
(P) VALVE GUIDES, REAM OVERSIZE	
Each (.1)	.1
(G) ROCKER ARM SHAFT, RECONDITION	
Each side (.2)	.3

(Factory Time)	Chilton Time
(G) Valve Tappets, Renew (Lifters)	
Includes: Drain and refill cooling system. R&R intake manifold. Make all necessary adjustments.	
V-6–1983-85-one bank (2.5)	3.4
both banks (2.9)	4.0
V-8–1983-85-one cyl (2.5)	3.4
one cyl-each bank (3.1)	4.2
each adtnl cyl (.1)	.1
w/A.C. add (.3)	.3
w/A.I.R. add (.2)	.2
1986-87	
one cyl (2.9)	4.0
one cyl-each side (3.4)	4.6
all cyls-both sides (5.2)	7.1
w/AIR add (.4)	.4
(G) Rocker Arm Cover or Gasket, Renew	
V-6–1983-85-one (.5)	.8
both (.8)	1.4
V-8–1983-85-one (.5)	.7
both (.9)	1.6
w/A.C. add (.3)	.3
w/AIR add (.2)	.2
1986-87	
right side (.7)	.9
left side (.8)	1.2
both sides (1.5)	2.1
w/AIR add (.3)	.3
(G) Valve Spring and/or Valve Stem Oil Seal, Renew (Head on Car)	
V-6–1983-85-one cyl (.8)	1.2
one cyl-each bank (1.4)	2.2
V-8–1983-85-one cyl (.6)	1.0
one cyl-each bank (1.0)	1.8
each adtnl cyl (.3)	.4
w/A.C. add (.3)	.3
1986-87	
one cyl	
right side (.8)	1.2
left side (1.1)	1.6
both sides (2.1)	2.5
each adtnl cyl (.4)	.4
w/AIR add (.3)	.3
(G) Rocker Arm, Pivot and/or Push Rod, Renew	
V-6–1983-85-one side (.7)	1.1
both sides (1.1)	1.7
Recond assy add-each side	.3
V-8–1983-85-one side (.9)	1.3

LABOR 12 CYLINDER HEAD & VALVE SYSTEM 12 LABOR

(Factory Time)	Chilton Time
both sides (1.4)	2.0
w/A.C. add (.3)	.3
w/AIR add (.2)	.2
1986-87	
one cyl	
right side (.8)	1.0
left side (.9)	1.4
both sides (1.6)	2.2
all cyls-both sides (2.1)	3.0
w/AIR add (.3)	.3

(G) Valves, Adjust

V-6-1983-85	1.5
V-8-1983-85	2.0
1986-87	2.5
w/AIR add	.3

DIESEL ENGINE

(G) Compression Test

1983-85 (.9)	1.3

(G) Cylinder Head Gasket, Renew

Includes: R&R injector pump and lines. R&R intake manifold and disconnect exhaust manifolds. Clean gasket surfaces, bleed lifters and adjust timing. Drain and refill cooling system.

(Factory Time)	Chilton Time
1983-85-left side (5.7)	7.4
right side (6.1)	7.9
both sides (7.6)	9.9
w/A.C. add (.4)	.4

(G) Cylinder Head, Renew

Includes: R&R injector pump and lines. R&R intake manifold and disconnect exhaust manifolds. Clean gasket surfaces. Transfer parts, reface valves. Bleed lifters and adjust timing. Drain and refill cooling system.

1983-85-left side (6.1)	7.9
right side (6.5)	8.4
both sides (8.4)	11.1
w/A.C. add (.4)	.4

(P) Clean Carbon and Grind Valves

Includes: R&R injector pump and lines. R&R cylinder heads, clean carbon. Recondition valves and valve seats. Check and adjust valve stem length. Bleed lifters, drain and refill cooling system.

1983-85-left side (6.6)	8.5
right side (7.0)	9.1
both sides (9.3)	12.6
w/A.C. add (.4)	.4

(G) Valve Tappets, Renew (Lifters)

Includes: R&R injector pump and lines, intake manifold and rocker arms. Drain and refill cooling system.

(Factory Time)	Chilton Time
1983-85-one cyl (3.5)	4.5
one cyl-each side (3.9)	5.0
each adtnl cyl (.1)	.1

(G) Rocker Arm Cover or Gasket, Renew

Includes: R&R injector pump and lines.

1983-85-one side (1.2)	2.4
both sides (2.0)	2.9

(G) Valve Springs or Valve Stem Oil Seals, Renew (Head on Car)

Includes: R&R injector pump and lines.

1983-85-one cyl (1.6)	3.0
one cyl-each bank (2.4)	3.7
each adtnl cyl (.3)	.3
w/A.C. add (.3)	.3

(G) Rocker Arm, Pivot and/or Push Rod, Renew

Includes: R&R injector pump and lines.

1983-85-one cyl (1.5)	2.5
one cyl-each bank (2.3)	3.0
each adtnl cyl (.1)	.1

PARTS 12 CYLINDER HEAD & VALVE SYSTEM 12 PARTS

	Part No.	Price
Valve Grind Gasket Set		
V-6-231		
1983	◆1264923	38.75
1984-exc. below	◆25525121	N.L.
alum. intake	◆25505372	N.L.
1985	◆25525120	37.00
V-6-252		
1983	◆25518568	N.L.
V-8-307		
1983-84	◆22507725	48.75
1985-87	◆22534926	58.00
V-8-350 Diesel		
1983-84	◆22522053	94.50
1985	◆22527541	N.L.

	Part No.	Price
(1) Rocker Arm		
V-6		
1983-85-right	◆1241850	4.50
left	◆1241851	4.50
V-8		
1983-87	◆22505583	N.L.
(2) Valve Spring Retainer		
1983-85-V-6	1254371	.50
(3) Valve Oil Seal		
V-6		
1983-85-Note 1	◆25519324	2.25
Note 2	◆25518390	2.50
V-8		
1983-87-intake	◆406595	1.00
exhaust	◆401823	1.00

Note 1: has .605" dia. intake guides.
Note 2: has .552" dia. intake guides.

	Part No.	Price
(4) Valve Spring		
V-6		
1983-85	◆1249267	2.75
V-8		
1983-87	◆411226	4.00
V-8-Diesel		
1983-85	◆22510372	4.00

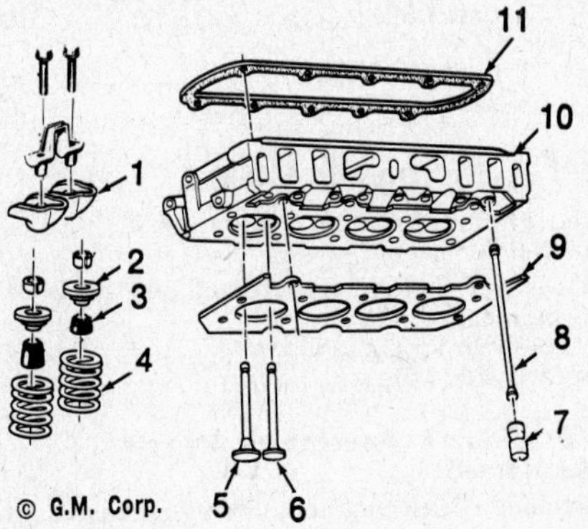

© G.M. Corp.

	Part No.	Price
(5) Intake Valve		
V-6-231, 252		
1983-85	◆25512098	11.25
V-8-307		
1983-85	◆22503324	11.00
1986-87	◆22530611	20.25
V-8-350 Diesel		
1983-85	◆22519914	20.00
(6) Exhaust Valve		
V-6-231, 252		
1983-85	◆1261380	13.50
V-8-307		
1983-87	◆555456	13.50
V-8-350 Diesel		
1983-85	◆558873	13.00
(7) Valve Lifter		
V-6		
1983	◆5232765	9.00
1984-85	◆5234330	N.L.
V-8-307		
1983-84	◆5232750	N.L.
1985-87	◆5234755	43.50
V-8-350 Diesel		
1983-87	◆5234625	N.L.

	Part No.	Price
(8) Valve Push Rod		
V-6		
1983-84	◆1249139	4.00
1985	◆25510025	4.25
V-8-307		
1983-84	22500582	N.L.
1985-87	◆22533631	3.25
V-8-350 Diesel		
1983-85	◆22511044	3.25
(9) Cylinder Head Gasket		
V-6-231		
1983-84	◆1261403	8.50
1985	◆25524599	8.50
V-6-252		
1983	◆25518453	8.25
V-8-307		
1983-87	◆22503500	9.25
V-8-350 Diesel		
1983-85	◆22519416	30.75
(10) Cylinder Head		
V-6-231		
1983-85	◆25518679	217.00
V-6-252		
1983	◆25518679	217.00
V-8-307		
1983-84	◆22511238	247.00
1985-87	◆22530557	247.00
V-8-350 Diesel		
1983-85	◆22515038	387.00
Prechamber		
V-8-350 Diesel		
1983-85	22515655	28.25
(11) Valve Cover Gasket		
V-6		
1983-85	◆25505889	6.00

For applications not listed, use R.T.V. sealer No. 1052289.

LABOR 13 ENGINE ASSEMBLY & MOUNTS 13 LABOR

(Factory Time) Chilton Time

GASOLINE ENGINES

(G) Engine Assembly, Remove & Install

Does not include transfer of any parts or equipment.

	Chilton Time
V-6–1983-85	5.0
V-8–1983-87	5.1
w/A.C. add (.6)	.6
w/P.S. add (.2)	.2
w/A.I.R. add (.4)	.4

(G) Engine Assembly, Renew (Universal)

Includes: R&R engine assembly. Transfer all component parts not supplied with replacement engine. Make all necessary adjustments.

	Chilton Time
V-6–1984-85 (5.5)	9.0
w/A.C. add (.3)	.3
w/AIR add (.2)	.2

(G) Engine Assembly, Renew (Partial)

Includes: R&R engine assembly, transfer all component parts not supplied with replacement engine. Minor tune up.

	Chilton Time
V-6–1983-85 (7.0)	11.2
Recond valves add (1.2)	1.2
V-8–1983-85 (8.4)	11.7
w/A.C. add (.6)	.6
w/P.S. add (.2)	.2
w/A.I.R. add (.4)	.4
1986-87 (8.7)	11.7
w/AIR add (.4)	.4
Recond valves add (1.6)	1.6

(P) Cylinder Block, Renew (w/All Internal Parts Less Head(s) and Oil Pan)

Includes: R&R engine, transfer all component parts not supplied with replacement engine, clean carbon, grind valves. Minor tune up.

	Chilton Time
V-6–1983-85 (13.2)	18.6
V-8–1983-85 (10.0)	17.6
w/A.C. add (.6)	.6
w/P.S. add (.2)	.2
w/A.I.R. add (.4)	.4
1986-87 (12.9)	17.6
w/AIR add (.4)	.4

(P) Engine Assy., R&R and Recondition (Complete)

Includes: Rebore block, install new pistons, rings, rod and main bearings. Clean carbon, grind valves. Tune engine.

	Chilton Time
V-6–1983-85 (21.4)	25.1
V-8–1983-85 (18.6)	26.0
w/A.C. add (.6)	.6
w/P.S. add (.2)	.2
w/A.I.R. add (.4)	.4
1986-87 (18.9)	26.0
w/AIR add (.6)	.6

(P) Engine Assembly, Recondition (In Car)

Includes: Expand or renew pistons, install new rings, pins, rod and main bearings. Clean carbon, grind valves. Tune engine.

	Chilton Time
V-6–1983-85 (14.9)	18.0
V-8–1983-85 (19.5)	27.1
w/A.C. add (.6)	.6
w/P.S. add (.2)	.2
w/A.I.R. add (.4)	.4
1986-87 (19.7)	27.1
w/AIR add (.6)	.6

(G) Engine Mounts, Renew

	Chilton Time
Front	
V-6–1983-85-one (.5)	.7
both (.7)	1.0
V-8–1983-87-one (.5)	.8
both (.6)	1.0
Rear	
V-6-1983-85 (.4)	.6
V-8-1983-87 (.3)	.5

DIESEL ENGINE

(G) Engine Assembly, Remove & Install

Does not include transfer of any parts or equipment.

	Chilton Time
1983-85	5.0
w/A.C. add (.5)	.5

(G) Engine Assembly, Renew (Universal)

Includes: R&R engine assembly, transfer all component parts not supplied with replacement engine. Make all necessary adjustments.

	Chilton Time
1983-85	20.0
w/A.C. add (.5)	.5
Renew gov. ring add	.7

(P) Cylinder Block, Renew (w/All Internal Parts Less Head(s) and Oil Pan)

Includes: R&R engine, transfer all component parts not supplied with replacement engine, clean carbon, grind valves. Make all necessary adjustments.

	Chilton Time
1983-85 (13.8)	24.0
w/A.C. add (.5)	.5

(P) Cylinder Block, Renew (w/Pistons, Rings and Bearings)

Includes: R&R engine assy. Transfer all component parts not supplied with replacement engine. Clean carbon, grind valves. Make all necessary adjustments.

	Chilton Time
1983-85 (16.6)	27.0
w/A.C. add (.5)	.5

(P) Engine Assy., R&R and Recondition (Complete)

Includes: Rebore block, install new pistons, rings, pins, rod and main bearings. Clean carbon, grind valves. Make all necessary adjustments.

	Chilton Time
1983-85 (29.5)	36.0
w/A.C. add (.5)	.5

(P) Engine Assembly, Recondition (In Car)

Includes: Expand or renew pistons, install new rings, pins, rod and main bearings. Clean carbon, grind valves. Make all necessary adjustments.

	Chilton Time
1983-85 (23.2)	27.3
w/A.C. add (.5)	.5

(G) Engine Mounts, Renew

	Chilton Time
Front	
1983-85-one (.5)	.8
both (.7)	1.0
Rear	
1983-85 (.3)	.4

PARTS 13 ENGINE ASSEMBLY & MOUNTS 13 PARTS

Cylinder Block (Fitted)

Includes: pistons, rings, main bearings.

	Part No.	Price
V-6-231		
1983	◆25516160	905.25
1984	◆25519450	950.00
1985	◆25524288	950.00
V-6-252		
1983	◆25516162	971.00
V-8-307		
1983-84	◆22515525	949.00
1985-87	◆22530856	949.00
V-8-350 Diesel		
1983	◆22518907	1418.00
1984-85	◆22525604	1600.00

Partial Engine Assm.

Includes block, pistons, connecting rods, and crankshaft.

	Part No.	Price
V-6-231		
1983	◆25516156	1263.25
1984	◆25519449	1263.25
1985	◆25524286	1263.00
V-6-252		
1983	◆25516158	1319.25
V-8-307		
1983-84	◆22504938	1397.00
1985-87	◆22530855	1397.00
V-8-350 Diesel		
1983	◆22518906	1950.00
1984-85	◆22525604	1600.00

Gasket Kit, Engine Overhaul

	Part No.	Price
V-6-231		
1983	◆25519460	48.00
1984	◆25505370	52.50
1985	◆25525118	58.25
V-6-252		
1983	◆25518567	53.25
V-8-307		
1983-84	◆22506498	58.75
1985-87	◆22527539	62.50
V-8-350 Diesel		
1983-84	◆22521786	90.00
1985	◆22527538	N.L.

Engine Mount Front

	Part No.	Price
V-6		
1983-85-right	◆1258666	24.00
left	◆25504643	29.00
V-8-307		
1983-87	◆22501573	29.00
V-8-350 Diesel		
1983-85	◆553915	27.25

Engine Mount Rear (Trans.)

	Part No.	Price
V-6-231		
1983-85	◆1257692	14.50
V-6-252		
1983	1259456	13.50
V-8		
1983-87	◆472143	14.00

LABOR 14 PISTONS, RINGS & BEARINGS 14 LABOR

COMBINATIONS

Add to Engine Work

See Machine Shop Operations

(Factory Time)	Chilton Time
(G) DRAIN, EVLACUATE & RECHARGE AIR CONDITIONING SYSTEM	
All models (.5)	1.0
(G) ROCKER ARM STUD, RENEW	
Each (.3)	.3
(G) HYDRAULIC VALVE LIFTERS, DISASSEMBLE AND CLEAN	
Each (.2)	.2
(G) DISTRIBUTOR, RECONDITION	
All models (.5)	.8
(G) CARBURETOR, RECONDITION	
2 BBL	1.2
4 BBL	1.5
(G) CYLINDER HEAD, R&R (ENGINE REMOVED)	
V-6	
eng Codes A-4	
one (1.1)	1.4
both (1.8)	2.3
V-8	
eng Code Y	
one (1.8)	2.3
both (2.6)	3.3
(G) CONNECTING ROD, RENEW (ENGINE DISASSEMBLED)	
V-6	
eng Codes A-4	
each (.5)	.6
V-8	
eng Code Y	
each (.5)	.6
(P) VALVE GUIDES, REAM OVERSIZE	
Each (.1)	.1
(G) DEGLAZE CYLINDER WALLS	
Each (.1)	.1
(G) REMOVE CYLINDER TOP RIDGE	
Each (.1)	.1
(G) ROCKER ARM SHAFT ASSY., DISASSEMBLE AND CLEAN OR RECONDITION	
V-6-each side (.2)	.3
(G) PLASTIGAUGE BEARINGS	
Each (.1)	.1
(G) OIL PUMP, RECONDITION	
All models (.2)	.4
(M) OIL FILTER ELEMENT, RENEW	
All models (.3)	.3

GASOLINE ENGINES

(P) Rings, Renew (See Engine Combinations)

Includes: Remove cylinder top ridge, deglaze cylinder walls. Clean piston and ring grooves. Minor tune up.

V-6–1983-85 (9.4)	13.3
V-8–1983-85 (10.1)	14.6
w/A.C. add (.3)	.3
w/A.I.R. add (.2)	.2
1986-87	
one cyl (7.7)	11.0
one cyl-each bank (9.9)	13.9
all cyls-both banks (12.2)	17.2
w/AIR add (.6)	.6

(P) Pistons or Connecting Rods, Renew

Includes: Remove cylinder top ridge, deglaze cylinder walls, clean piston and ring grooves. Minor tune up.

V-6–1983-85 (10.1)	15.1
V-8–1983-85 (11.2)	17.0
w/A.C. add (.3)	.3
w/A.I.R. add (.2)	.2
1986-87	
one cyl (8.3)	11.6
one cyl-each bank (11.1)	15.1
all cyls-both banks (13.3)	19.6
w/AIR add (.6)	.6

(P) Connecting Rod Bearings, Renew

Includes: Raise engine, clean oil pump screen.

V-6–1983-85 (2.3)	3.4
V-8–1983-85 (3.4)	4.8
1986-87 (4.4)	6.0

DIESEL ENGINE

(P) Rings, Renew (See Engine Combinations)

Includes: Remove cylinder top ridge, deglaze cylinder walls. Clean piston and ring grooves. Make all necessary adjustments.

1983-85 (12.8)	17.2
w/A.C. add (.4)	.4

(P) Pistons or Connecting Rods, Renew

Includes: Remove cylinder top ridge, deglaze cylinder walls, clean piston and ring grooves. Make all necessary adjustments.

1983-85 (13.3)	19.6
w/A.C. add (.4)	.4

(P) Connecting Rod Bearings, Renew

Includes: Raise engine and clean oil pump screen.

1983-85 (4.9)	6.6

PARTS 14 PISTONS, RINGS & BEARINGS 14 PARTS

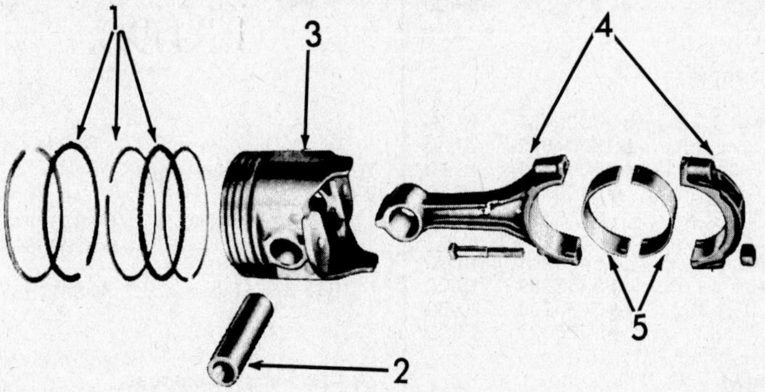

	Part No.	Price
(1) Ring Set Std. (1 Piston)		
V-6–231		
1983-85	◆1240955	15.75
V-6–252		
1983	◆25505382	17.25
V-8–307		
1983-84	◆22506536	16.00
1985-87	◆22529562	18.25
V-8–350 Diesel		
1983	◆22515964	21.00
1984-85	◆22523733	21.00
(2) Piston Pin		
left	◆22527479	48.25
Serviced with piston assy.		
(3) Piston (Std.)		
V-6–231		
1983	◆25518053	48.25
1984-85	◆25518053	48.25
V-6–252		
1983	◆25505374	54.00
V-8–307		
1983-84	◆22506658	48.25
1985-87-right	◆22527480	48.25
V-8–350 Diesel		
1983-84-right	◆22523358	63.75
left	◆22523357	63.75
(4) Connecting Rod Assy.		
V-6–231, 252		
1983-85	◆25506520	39.00
V-8–307		
1983-84	◆554976	45.00
1985-87	◆22527025	45.00
V-8–350 Diesel		
1983-85	◆22515313	50.50
(5) Connecting Rod Bearing (Std.)		
V-6–231, 252		
1983-85	◆18005399	11.00
V-8		
1983-87	◆18008494	10.50

LABOR 15 CRANKSHAFT & DAMPER 15 LABOR

	(Factory Time)	Chilton Time
GASOLINE ENGINES		
(P) Crankshaft and Main Bearings, Renew		
Includes: R&R engine, check all bearing clearances.		
V-6–1983-85	(7.1)	10.1
V-8–1983-85	(7.4)	10.9
w/A.C. add	(.4)	.4
w/A.I.R. add	(.2)	.2
1986-87	(7.3)	10.4
w/AIR add	(.3)	.3
(P) Main Bearings, Renew		
Includes: Check all bearing clearances.		
V-6–1983-85	(2.2)	3.6
V-8–1983-85	(2.8)	4.2
1986-87	(4.1)	5.7
(P) Main and Rod Bearings, Renew		
Includes: Check all bearing clearances.		
V-6–1983-85	(3.4)	5.4
V-8–1983-85	(4.2)	6.6
1986-87	(6.3)	8.1
(G) Rear Main Bearing Oil Seals, Renew or Repack (Upper & Lower)		
Includes: R&R oil pan and rear main bearing cap.		
V-6–1983-85	(1.5)	2.2
V-8–1983-85	(2.2)	3.0
1986-87	(6.3)	3.6

	(Factory Time)	Chilton Time
(P) Main Bearings, Renew		
Includes: Check all bearing clearances.		
1983-85	(4.1)	5.5
(G) Crankshaft Pulley or Balancer, Renew		
V-6–1983-85-pulley	(.7)	1.2
balancer	(.8)	1.3
V-8–1983-85-pulley	(.5)	.7
balancer	(.7)	1.2
w/A.C. add	(.2)	.2
w/A.I.R. add	(.1)	.1
1986-87-pulley	(.7)	1.1
balancer	(1.0)	1.5
(G) Crankshaft Front Oil Seal, Renew		
V-6–1983-85	(2.3)	*3.2
V-8–1983-85	(.8)	1.4
w/A.C. add	(.2)	.2
w/A.I.R. add	(.1)	.1
1986-87	(1.1)	1.6

*Includes R&R front cover.

	(Factory Time)	Chilton Time
DIESEL ENGINE		
(P) Crankshaft and Main Bearings, Renew		
Includes: R&R engine, check all bearing clearances.		
1983-85	(8.0)	11.2
w/A.C. add	(.4)	.4
(P) Main and Rod Bearings, Renew		
Includes: Check all bearing clearances.		
1983-85	(6.5)	7.9
(G) Rear Main Bearing Oil Seals, R&R and Repack		
Includes: R&R oil pan and rear main bearing cap.		
1983-85	(2.9)	4.0
(G) Crankshaft Rear Main Bearing Seals, Renew		
Includes: R&R engine assy.		
1983-85	(6.5)	9.1
w/A.C. add	(.4)	.4
(G) Crankshaft Pulley or Balancer, Renew		
1983-85-pulley	(.6)	.8
balancer	(.9)	1.3
w/A.C. add	(.2)	.2
(G) Crankshaft Front Oil Seal, Renew		
1983-85	(.9)	1.5
w/A.C. add	(.2)	.2

PARTS 15 CRANKSHAFT & DAMPER 15 PARTS

	Part No.	Price
(1) Crankshaft		
V-6-231		
1983-85	◆1260877	385.00
V-6-252		
1983	◆1260873	407.00
V-8-307		
1983-84	◆22505615	403.00
1985-87	◆22527438	403.00
V-8-350 Diesel		
1983-85	◆22511035	439.00
(2) Main Bearings		
V-6		
1983-87-No. 1	◆18009457	12.00
No. 2	◆18004602	20.00
No. 3	◆18002950	12.50
No. 4	◆5468578	13.00
V-8-307		
1983-87-No. 1	◆5466211	13.00
No. 2, 4	◆5466089	13.00
No. 3	◆5466090	20.00
rear	◆5466091	17.00
V-8-350 Diesel		
1983-85-No. 1	◆5466312	16.00
Nos. 2, 4	◆5458657	15.00
No. 3	◆5463797	26.25
No. 5	◆5466314	19.75
(3) Main Brg. Oil Seals, Rear		
1983-87	◆9772831	1.50

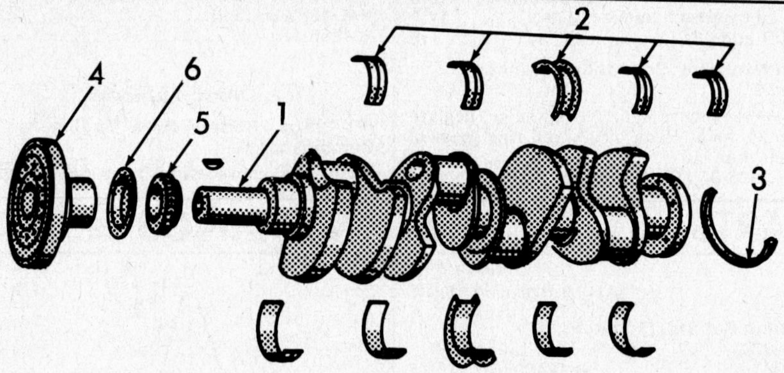

	Part No.	Price
Timing Cover Oil Seal		
V-6		
1983-85-packing	◆1305044	1.00
shedder	◆1193966	1.50
V-8-307		
1983-87	◆552711	4.25
(4) Crankshaft Balancer		
V-6-231		
1983	◆25506570	42.75
1984-85	◆25523502	41.25
V-6-252		
1983	◆25523502	41.25
V-8-307		
1983-87-hub	◆22506730	31.75

	Part No.	Price
V-8-350 Diesel		
1983-87	◆559131	63.25
(5) Crankshaft Sprocket Gear		
V-6		
1983-85	◆1192916	16.00
V-8-307		
1983-87	◆382880	16.75
V-8-350 Diesel		
1983-85	◆558489	44.25
(6) Crankshaft Oil Slinger		
V-6		
1983-85	◆1193967	1.00
V-8		
1983-87	◆382572	.75
V-8-350 Diesel		
1983-85	◆22513590	2.00

LABOR 16 CAMSHAFT & TIMING GEARS 16 LABOR

(Factory Time) Chilton Time

GASOLINE ENGINES

(G) Timing Cover Oil Seal, Renew

V-8–1983-85 (.8)	1.4
1986-87 (1.1)	1.6

(G) Timing Case Cover or Gasket, Renew

Includes: R&R fan blade, crankshaft pulley and balancer. Drain and refill oil and coolant.

V-6–1983-85 (2.2)	3.2
V-8–1983-85 (1.3)	2.5
w/A.C. add (.3)	.3
w/P.S. add (.1)	.1
w/A.I.R. add (.2)	.2
Renew cover add (.4)	.4
1986-87 (2.1)	2.9
w/AIR add (.1)	.2
Renew cover add (.2)	.4
Renew f/pump eccentric add (.1)	.2

(G) Timing Chain or Gears, Renew

Includes: R&R fan blade, crankshaft pulley and balancer. Drain and refill oil and coolant.

V-6–1983-85 (2.4)	3.7
V-8–1983-85 (1.4)	3.0
w/A.C. add (.3)	.3
w/P.S. add (.1)	.1
w/A.I.R. add (.2)	.2
1986-87 (2.4)	3.4
w/AIR add (.1)	.2

(G) Camshaft, Renew

Includes: R&R radiator, front cover, timing chain and gear, R&R intake manifold and valve lifters. Disconnect exhaust system. Drain and refill oil and coolant. Make all necessary adjustments.

V-6–1983-85 (5.5)	7.0
V-8–1983-85 (4.3)	7.5
w/A.C. add (1.3)	1.3
w/P.S. add (.1)	.1
w/A.I.R. add (.4)	.4
1986-87 (6.7)	9.1
w/AIR add (.4)	.4

(G) Camshaft Bearings, Renew

Includes: R&R radiator, front cover, timing chain and gear. R&R intake manifold and valve lifters. Disconnect exhaust system. Drain and refill oil and coolant. Make all necessary adjustments.

V-6–1983-87 (6.8)	8.7
V-8–1983-85 (5.7)	8.8
w/A.C. add (1.3)	1.3
w/P.S. add (.1)	.1
w/A.I.R. add (.4)	.4
1986-87 (8.1)	10.5
w/AIR add (.4)	.4

(G) Camshaft Rear Bearing Plug, Renew

Includes: R&R trans for accessibility.

1983-87 (2.2)	3.0

DIESEL ENGINE

(G) Timing Case Cover or Gasket, Renew

Includes: R&R fan blade, crankshaft pulley and balancer. Drain and refill oil and coolant.

1983-85 (2.1)	3.1
Renew cover add (.2)	.4
w/A.C. add (.3)	.3

(G) Timing Chain or Gears, Renew

Includes: R&R fan blade, crankshaft pulley and balancer. Drain and refill oil and coolant.

1983-85 (2.3)	3.5
w/A.C. add (.3)	.3

(G) Injector Pump Drive Gear, Renew

Includes: R&R timing gear and chain. R&R intake manifold and lifters. Drain and refill oil and coolant.

1983-85 (4.3)	7.1
Renew driven gear add (.1)	.1
w/A.C. add (.3)	.3

(G) Camshaft, Renew

Includes: R&R radiator, front cover, fuel pump, timing gear and chain. R&R injector pump, intake manifold and lifters. Disconnect exhaust system. Drain and refill oil and coolant. Make all necessary adjustments.

1983-85 (7.3)	10.0
w/A.C. add (1.0)	1.0

(G) Camshaft Bearings, Renew

Includes: R&R radiator, front cover, fuel pump, timing gear and chain. R&R injector pump, intake manifold and lifters. Disconnect exhaust system. Drain and refill oil and coolant. Make all necessary adjustments.

1983-85 (10.1)	13.6
w/A.C. add (1.0)	1.0

(G) Camshaft Rear Bearing Plug, Renew

Includes: R&R trans for accessibility.

1983-85 (2.1)	3.0

PARTS 16 CAMSHAFT & TIMING GEARS 16 PARTS

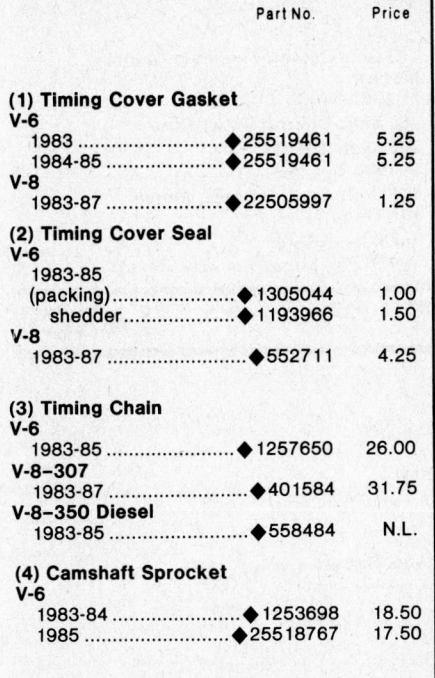

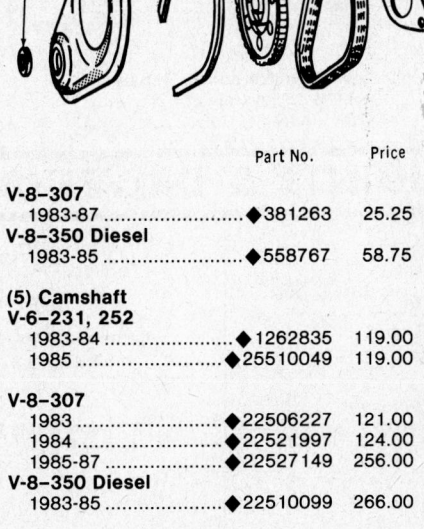

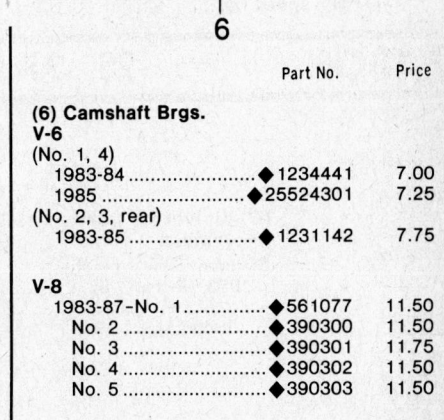

	Part No.	Price
(1) Timing Cover Gasket		
V-6		
1983	◆25519461	5.25
1984-85	◆25519461	5.25
V-8		
1983-87	◆22505997	1.25
(2) Timing Cover Seal		
V-6		
1983-85		
(packing)	◆1305044	1.00
shedder	◆1193966	1.50
V-8		
1983-87	◆552711	4.25
(3) Timing Chain		
V-6		
1983-85	◆1257650	26.00
V-8-307		
1983-87	◆401584	31.75
V-8-350 Diesel		
1983-85	◆558484	N.L.
(4) Camshaft Sprocket		
V-6		
1983-84	◆1253698	18.50
1985	◆25518767	17.50

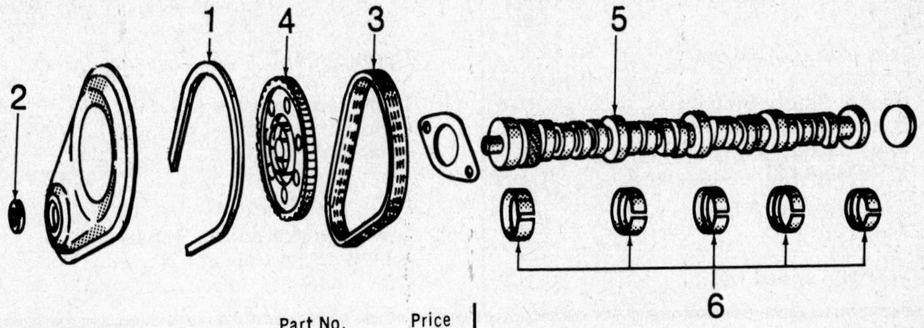

	Part No.	Price
V-8-307		
1983-87	◆381263	25.25
V-8-350 Diesel		
1983-85	◆558767	58.75
(5) Camshaft		
V-6-231, 252		
1983-84	◆1262835	119.00
1985	◆25510049	119.00
V-8-307		
1983	◆22506227	121.00
1984	◆22521997	124.00
1985-87	◆22527149	256.00
V-8-350 Diesel		
1983-85	◆22510099	266.00

	Part No.	Price
(6) Camshaft Brgs.		
V-6		
(No. 1, 4)		
1983-84	◆1234441	7.00
1985	◆25524301	7.25
(No. 2, 3, rear)		
1983-85	◆1231142	7.75
V-8		
1983-87-No. 1	◆561077	11.50
No. 2	◆390300	11.50
No. 3	◆390301	11.75
No. 4	◆390302	11.50
No. 5	◆390303	11.50

LABOR 17 ENGINE OILING SYSTEM 17 LABOR

(Factory Time) — Chilton Time

GASOLINE ENGINES

(G) Oil Pan or Gasket, Renew
Includes: Raise engine, R&R and clean oil pump screen.
V-6–1983-85 (1.2) 1.6
V-8–1983-85 (1.7) 2.3
1986-87 (2.1) 2.9

(P) Pressure Test Engine Bearings (Pan Off)
All models 1.0

(G) Oil Pump, Renew (V-8)
Includes: Raise engine, R&R and clean oil pump screen.
1983-85 (1.8) 2.5
1986-87 (2.2) 3.1
To overhaul pump add (.2) 3

(G) Oil Filter and Pump Cover, Renew (V-6)
1983-85 (.5) 8
To overhaul pump add (.1) 2

(G) Oil Pressure Relief Valve, Renew
V-6–1983-85 .... 1.1
V-8–1983-85 .... *2.9
*Includes R&R oil pan and pump.

(G) Oil Pressure Gauge (Engine), Renew
1983-87 (.2) 4

(G) Oil Pressure Gauge (Dash), Renew
1983-85 (.3) 5
1986-87 (.4) 7

(M) Oil Filter Element, Renew
1983-87 (.3) 3

DIESEL ENGINE

(G) Oil Pan or Gasket, Renew
Includes: Raise engine, R&R and clean oil pump screen.
1983-85 (2.6) 3.4

(P) Pressure Test Engine Bearings (Pan Off)
All models 1.0

(G) Oil Pump, Renew
Includes: Raise engine, R&R and clean oil pump screen.
1983-85 (2.7) 3.6

(G) Oil Pump, R&R and Recondition
Includes: Raise engine, R&R and clean oil pump screen.
1983-85 (2.9) 3.8

(G) Oil Pressure Gauge (Engine), Renew
1983-85 (.3) 4

(M) Oil Filter Element, Renew
1983-85 (.3) 3

PARTS 17 ENGINE OILING SYSTEM 17 PARTS

	Part No.	Price
Oil Pan Gasket		
V-6		
1983-84	◆1260771	3.00
1985	◆25521994	8.50
V-8		
1983-87	◆22519181	7.00
Oil Pump		
V-6		
1983	◆25519448	38.00
1984-85	◆25519448	38.00
V-8–307		
1983-87	◆22524583	61.50
V-8–350 Diesel		
1983-85	◆22511732	59.75
Oil Pump Gear Set		
1983-87-V-8	◆585582	4.00
Oil Pump Relief Valve		
1983-87-V-8	◆557238	2.00
Oil Pump Relief Spring		
1983-87-V-8	401366	1.00
Oil Pump Drive Shaft		
V-8		
1983-87	559127	4.00
Oil Pump Driven Shaft		
1983-87-V-8	◆555737	1.25
Oil Pressure Switch		
(wo/Gauges)		
1983-87-exc. V-6	◆3815936	3.50
V-6	◆25500672	5.50
(Gauges)		
1983-87	◆459417	17.75

LABOR 21 SHIFT LINKAGE 21 LABOR

(Factory Time) — Chilton Time

(G) Shift Linkage, Adjust
All models
Neutral Safety Switch (.3) 4
Shift Indicator Needle (.2) 3
Shift Linkage (.4) 5
T.V. Cable (.3) 4

(G) Shift Linkage, Adjust (w/Diesel Eng)
All models
Fast idle speed (.2) 3
Throttle rod/T.V. cable (.5) 6
Trans vacuum valve (.5) 6
Vacuum regul valve (.6) 8
Complete (1.0) 1.0

(G) Gear Selector Lever, Renew
1983-87-column mount (.2) 5
floor mount (.5) 7

(G) Gear Selector Indicator Needle, Renew
1983-87 (.3) 6

(G) Shift Control Rods, Renew
Includes: Adjust.
1983-87 (.4) 6

(G) Shift Control Lever, Renew (At Trans)
Includes: Adjust.
1983-87 (.3) 5

LABOR 25 U-JOINTS & DRIVESHAFT 25 LABOR

(Factory Time) — Chilton Time

(G) Universal Joints, R&R and Recondition
Includes: R&R drive shaft.
1983-87-front (.6) 8
rear (.5) 7
both (.7) 1.3

(G) Drive Shaft, Renew
1983-87 (.3) 5

(G) Pinion Shaft Flange, Renew
1983-87 (.7) 1.0

PARTS 25 UNIVERSAL JOINTS & DRIVE SHAFT 25 PARTS

	Part No.	Price
Universal Joint Kit, (Front & Rear)		
1983-87-Saginaw	◆7806140	41.00
Dana	◆374246	28.50
Slip Yoke		
1983-87	◆7812557	65.25

LABOR 26 REAR AXLE 26 LABOR

(Factory Time)	Chilton Time
(M) Differential, Drain & Refill	
All models	.6
(M) Differential Cover or Gasket, Renew	
1983-87 (.5)	.6
(G) Axle Shaft Assembly, Renew 'C' Lock Type	
1983-87-one (.7)	.9
both (.9)	1.2
(G) Axle Shaft Bearing and/or Seal, Renew 'C' Lock Type	
1983-87-one (.6)	.8
both (.8)	1.1
(G) Axle Shaft Wheel Mounting Studs, Renew	
All models-one side (.6)	1.0
both sides (1.0)	1.5
(G) Pinion Shaft Oil Seal, Renew	
1983-87 (.5)	.8
(G) Differential Case, Remove & Reinstall	
1983-87 (1.8)	2.8
w/Limited slip add (.5)	.5
(G) Limited Slip Clutch Plates, Renew	
1983-87 (1.1)	2.0
(G) Side Carrier Bearings, Renew	
1983-87 (1.7)	2.5
(G) Pinion Bearings, Renew	
1983-87 (2.0)	3.4
Renew side brgs add (.3)	.3
(P) Ring Gear and Pinion, Renew	
1983-87 (2.1)	3.9
Recond diff case add	
std (.3)	.5
limited slip (.7)	1.0
(G) Side Carrier Gears, Renew	
1983-87 (.8)	1.8
w/Limited slip add (.5)	.5
(P) Rear Axle Housing, Renew	
Includes: R&R housing, install new ring and pinion gear and side bearings. Adjust pre-load and backlash.	
1983-87 (3.4)	5.2

PARTS 26 REAR AXLE 26 PARTS

To obtain correct replacement parts for the rear axle assembly, use the third letter of the rear axle code when ordering parts. The rear axle code is stamped either on the front of the passenger side axle tube or on a metal tab attached to a cover bolt.

	Part No.	Price
(1) Axle Shaft		
7½" dia. ring gr. (w/4¾" flange)		
1983-87	◆22519891	99.50
(w/5" flange)		
1983-87	◆22504959	142.25
8½" dia. ring gr.		
1983-87-exc. below	◆1255801	114.00
C-G-K type	◆25501599	114.00
Sta. wag.	◆14060881	145.25
8¾" dia. ring gr.		
1983-17 lb. drum	◆526200	135.25
23 lb. drum	◆526703	139.25
(2) Axle Shaft Seal		
1983-87-wo/Sta. wag.	◆3998519	4.00
Sta. wag.	◆3958078	5.00
(3) Rear Axle Bearing		
1983-87-wo/Sta. wag.	◆7451785	16.00
Sta. wag.	◆7451809	15.00
(4) Pinion Flange		
1983-87-exc. below	◆1256654	35.00
7½" ring gr.	◆7827670	33.50
(5) Pinion Seal		
7½" dia. ring gr.		
1983-87	◆552571	8.00
8½" dia. ring gr.		
1983-87	◆1243465	7.50
8¾" dia. ring gr.		
1983	◆404294	9.00

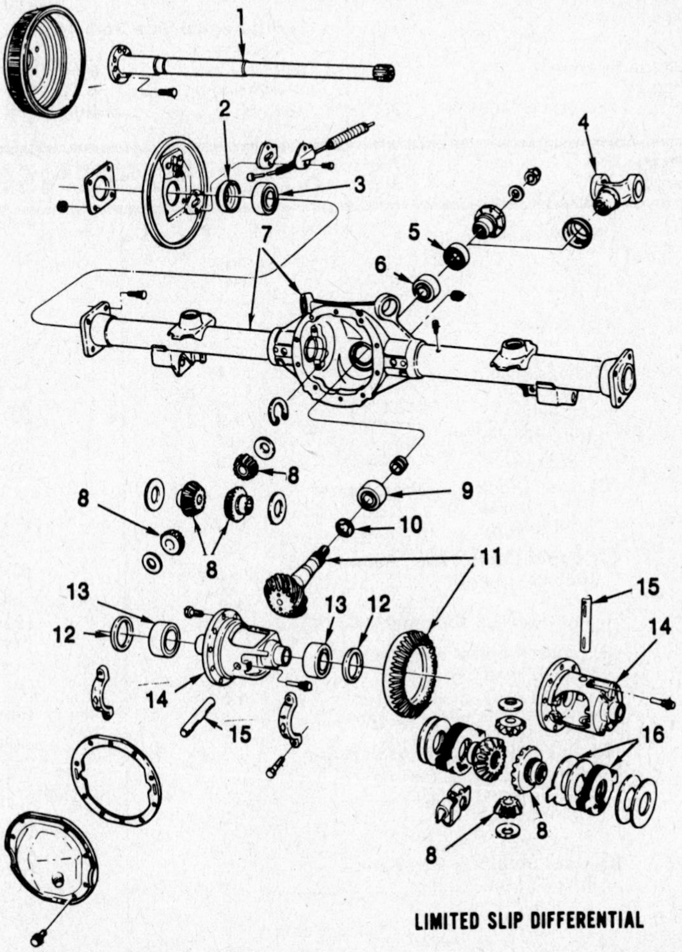

LIMITED SLIP DIFFERENTIAL

PARTS 26 REAR AXLE 26 PARTS

	Part No.	Price
(6) Front Pinion Bearing		
7½" dia. ring gr.		
1983-84	◆7451202	16.00
1985-87	◆9417784	16.25
8½", 8¾" dia. ring gr.		
1983-87	◆7450984	21.00
(7) Axle Housing		
7½" dia. ring gr.		
1983-87	◆22510779	392.25
8½" dia. ring gr.		
1983-87-wo/Sta. wag.	◆14079329	406.25
Sta. wag.	◆14079330	489.75
8¾" dia. ring gr.		
1983-wo/Sta. wag.	◆10004179	603.50
Sta. wag.	◆10004180	610.00
(8) Pinion Gear Package		
7½" dia. ring gr.		
1983-87	◆22525894	94.50
8½" dia. ring gr.		
1983-87	◆1397647	132.00
8¾" dia. ring gr.		
1983-exc. below	◆547225	106.00
Limited slip	◆547212	173.00

Gear packages contain 2 side gears, 2 pinion gears, thrust washers and pinion shaft.

	Part No.	Price
Side Gears-Sold Separately		
8½" dia. ring gr. (Limited slip)		
1983-87	◆231075	49.50
Pinion Gears-Sold Separately		
8½" dia. ring gr. (Limited slip)		
1983-87	◆6270977	17.50
(9) Rear Pinion Bearing		
7½" dia. ring gr.		
1983-87	◆7455699	N.L.
8½" & 8¾" dia. ring gr.		
1983-87	◆7451155	20.00
(10) Shim Package		
1983-87 (.020-.024)		
exc below	◆1394892	5.50
7½" ring gr.	◆559755	7.50
(11) Ring and Pinion Gear		
7½" dia. ring gr.		
1983-87-2.41R	◆560198	259.00
2.56R	◆560199	259.00
2.73R	◆560201	259.00
2.93R	◆560204	261.00
8½" dia. ring gr.		
1983-87-2.41R	◆1258715	276.00
2.56R	◆1258707	276.00
2.73R	◆1258708	276.00
2.93R	◆1258714	276.00
3.08R	◆1258709	276.00
3.23R	◆1258713	276.00
3.73R	◆1259441	280.00
8¾" dia. ring gr.		
1983-2.41R	◆10002813	305.25
2.56R	◆10002814	305.25
2.73R	◆10002812	305.25
2.93R	◆10018255	305.25
3.08R	◆10002811	305.25
3.23R	◆10002810	305.25
(12) Bearing Adjusting Shim Pkg.		
1983-87 (.040-.046)		
exc. below	◆3996610	6.50
7½" ring gr.	◆3995791	6.50
(13) Differential Side Bearing		
1983-84-exc. below	◆7451281	15.00
8¾" ring gr.	◆7451140	15.00
1985-87	◆9420095	N.L.
(14) Differential Case		
(wo/Limited slip)		
7½" dia. ring gr.		
1983-87-exc. below	◆558648	109.00
3.23, 3.42R	◆558649	109.25
8½" dia. ring gr.		
1983-87-exc. below	◆1252981	110.00
2.56, 2.73R	◆1252980	110.00
8¾" dia. ring gr.		
1983-2.41, 2.56R	◆526205	134.25
2.73, 3.08R	◆526207	162.25
3.23R	◆527854	162.00
(Limited slip)		
8½" dia. ring gr.		
1983-87-exc. below	◆14030435	431.25
2.41, 2.56R	◆14030434	408.50
8¾" dia. ring gr.		
1983-2.41, 2.56R	◆527751	428.00
2.73, 3.08R	◆527752	428.00
3.23R	◆527753	428.00
(15) Pinion Shaft		
7½" dia. ring gr.		
1983-87	◆22507586	11.00
8½" dia. ring gr.		
1983-87	◆14006401	12.50
8¾" dia. ring gr.		
1983-exc. below	◆9778184	12.75
Limited slip	◆9792718	12.75
(16) Friction Disc Kit		
1983-87-exc. below	◆483722	55.75
8½" ring gr.	◆231127	58.25

LABOR 27 REAR SUSPENSION 27 LABOR

(Factory Time)	Chilton Time
(G) Rear Spring, Renew	
1983-one (.4)	.7
both (.6)	.8
1984-87-one (.6)	.7
both (.7)	.8
(G) Rear Shock Absorber, Renew	
1983-87-one (.3)	.4
both (.5)	.7
(G) Upper Control Arm, Renew	
1983-87-one (.5)	.7
both (.7)	1.0
Renew bushings add, each side (.2)	.3
(G) Lower Control Arm, Renew	
1983-87-one (.4)	.6
both (.6)	1.0
Renew bushings add-each arm	.3
(G) Superlift Shock Absorbers, Renew	
1983-87-one (.4)	.6
both (.6)	.9
(G) Rear Stabilizer Bar, Renew	
1983-87 (.5)	.7

ELECTRONIC LEVEL CONTROL

(Factory Time)	Chilton Time
(G) Compressor Assembly, Renew	
1983-87 (.5)	.6
(G) Relay, Renew	
1983-87 (.3)	.4
(G) Height Sensor, Renew	
1983-87 (.4)	.6
(G) Height Sensor, Adjust	
1983-87 (.4)	.5
(G) Electronic Level Control Dryer, Renew	
1983-87 (.3)	.4
(G) Electronic Level Control Head, Renew	
Includes: Renew cover gasket, solenoid and valves.	
1983 (.5)	.9
1984-87 (.4)	.9
(G) Electronic Level Control Motor and Cylinder Assy., R&R and Recondition	
1983-87 (.6)	1.2

PARTS 27 REAR SUSPENSION 27 PARTS

	Part No.	Price
(1) Upper Control Arm (w/Bushing)		
1983-87 (O deg.)	◆10000887	22.50
(+2 deg)	◆10000904	30.00
(-2 deg)	◆10000910	30.00
(2) Insulator (Spring)		
1983-87	◆10004110	2.25
(3) Coil Spring		
Order by year and model.		
(4) Bumper (Axle)		
1983-87	10000812	2.00
(5) Bushing (Axle Housing)		
1983-87-lt. grn	◆10000953	6.50
orange	◆10000952	6.50
(6) Lower Control Arm (w/Bushing)		
1983-87	◆10000334	32.50
(7) Shock Absorber Assy. (Rear)		
1983-84-exc. H.D.	◆4993551	24.50
H.D. susp.	◆4993554	24.50
1985-87-exc. Sta. wag.	◆22046428	24.50
Sta. wag.	◆22046427	24.50
(8) Bumper (Pinion)		
1983-87	486136	3.00

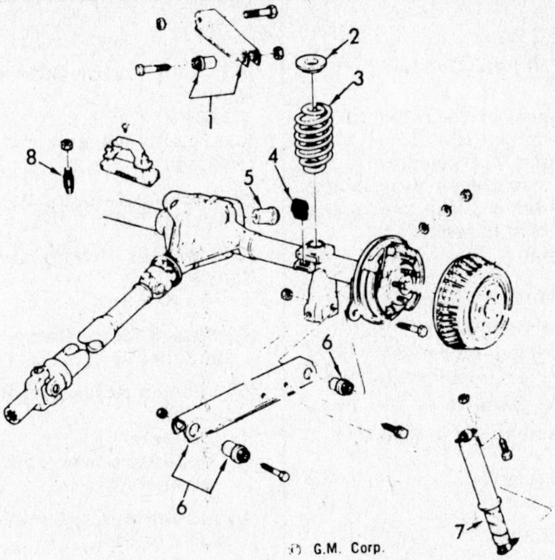

AUTOMATIC LEVEL CONTROL

	Part No.	Price
Compressor Assembly		
1983-87	◆22020538	176.25
Sta. wag.	◆22040580	200.00
Relay		
1983-87	◆10011579	9.75
Height Sensor		
1983-84-exc. below	◆22017241	176.25
Sta. wag.	22017242	N.L.
Delta "88"	◆22017243	176.25
1985-87-exc. Sta. wag.	22040578	200.00
Compressor Head		
1983-87	◆22020539	68.50
Motor		
1983-87	◆22010692	165.00
Cover and Solenoid Assm.		
1983	22010695	43.00

LABOR 28 AIR CONDITIONING 28 LABOR

	(Factory Time)	Chilton Time

Note: If more than one item requires replacement where evacuation and discharging the system is already included in the operation, deduct 1.0 hour for each additional item to the time listed.

(G) Drain, Evacuate and Recharge System
All models (.5) 1.0

(G) Leak Check
Includes: Check all lines and connections.
All models (.3) 5

(G) Refrigerant, Add (Partial Charge)
All models 6

(G) Compressor Belt, Renew
V-6–1983-87 (.4) 5
w/AIR add (.1) 1
V-8–1983-87 (.4) 5
Diesel–1983-87 (.5) 6

COMPRESSOR 4 CYLINDER RADIAL

(G) Compressor Assembly, Renew
Includes: Transfer parts as required. Evacuate and charge system.
1983-87 (1.0) 2.0

(G) Compressor Clutch Plate and Hub Assy., Renew
Includes: R&R hub and drive plate assy. Check air gap.
1983-87 (.5) 8

(G) Compressor Rotor and/or Bearing, Renew
Includes: R&R hub and drive plate assy.
1983-87 (.8) 1.2

AIR CONDITIONER TUNE-UP

For efficient operation and satisfactory performance in hot weather. The following air conditioner tune-up is suggested:

1. Clean intake filter
2. Clean condenser fins
3. Pressure test system
4. Adjust drive belt tension
5. Check antifreeze/coolant
6. Tighten compressor mounts
7. Tighten condenser and evaporator mounts
8. Inspect system for leaks (hoses, couplings, valves, etc.)
9. Partial charge system

All models 1.0
If necessary to evacuate and charge system, add 1.0

	(Factory Time)	Chilton Time

(G) Compressor Clutch Coil and/or Pulley Rim, Renew
Includes: R&R hub and drive plate assy.
1983-87 (.7) 1.0
Renew pulley or brg add (.1) 2

(G) Compressor Shaft Seal Kit, Renew
Includes: R&R compressor. Evacuate and charge system.
1983-87 (1.0) 2.5

	(Factory Time)	Chilton Time

(G) Compressor Shell and/or 'O' Rings, Renew
Includes: R&R compressor. R&R clutch and pulley assy. Clean and inspect parts. Evacuate and charge system.
1983-87 (1.4) 2.8

(G) Compressor Discharge Valve Plates, Renew
Includes: R&R compressor. R&R clutch and pulley assy. R&R shell to internal mechanism. Clean and inspect parts. Evacuate and charge system.
1983-87 (1.1) 2.6
Two or more add (.1) 2

(G) Compressor Front Head and/or Seal, Renew
Includes: R&R compressor. R&R clutch and pulley assy. R&R shaft seal assy. Clean and inspect parts. Evacuate and charge system.
1983-87 (1.3) 2.8

(G) Compressor Thrust and/or Belleville Washers, Renew
Includes: R&R compressor. R&R clutch and pulley assy. R&R shaft seal assy. R&R front head assy. Clean and inspect parts. Evacuate and charge system.
1983-87 (1.5) 2.8

(G) Compressor Main Bearing, Renew
Includes: R&R compressor. R&R clutch and pulley assy. R&R shaft seal assy. R&R front head assy. Clean and inspect parts. Evacuate and charge system.
1983-87 (1.5) 2.8

LABOR 28 AIR CONDITIONING 28 LABOR

(Factory Time) Chilton Time

(G) Compressor Shaft and Cylinder Assy., Renew

Includes: R&R compressor. R&R clutch and pulley assy. R&R shaft seal assy., remove and transfer front head assy. R&R compressor shell and 'O' rings. R&R compressor valve plates. R&R pressure relief valve. Clean and inspect parts. Evacuate and charge system.

1983-87 (1.6)........ 2.9

(G) Condenser, Renew

Includes: Evacuate and charge system.

1983-87 (.9)........ 1.7
w/Diesel eng (1.3)........ 2.5

(G) Evaporator Core, Renew

Includes: Evacuate and charge system.

1983-87
Gas (1.5)........ 3.5
Diesel (1.4)........ 3.4

(G) Accumulator, Renew

Includes: Evacuate and charge system.

1983-87 (.8)........ 1.5

(G) Expansion Tube (Orifice), Renew

Includes: Evacuate and charge system.

1983-87 (.7)........ 1.4

(G) Pressure Cycling Switch, Renew

1983-87 (.2)........ .3

(G) Compressor Cut-Off Switch, Renew

1983-87 (.2)........ .3
Add time to evacuate and charge system if required.

(G) Vacuum Selector Valve, Renew

1983-87 (.4)........ .6

(G) Master Electrical Switch, Renew

1983-87 (.3)........ .6

(G) Blower Motor Relay, Renew

1983-87 (.2)........ .3

(G) Vacuum Actuators, Renew

1983-87
Defroster (.3)........ .6
Upper or Lower mode (.7)........ 1.2
Air Inlet (.4)........ .7

(G) Blower Motor, Renew

1983-87 (.3)........ .5

(G) Blower Motor Switch, Renew

1983-87 (.4)........ .5
1985-87 (.3)........ .5

(G) Blower Motor Resistor, Renew

1983-87 (.2)........ .3

(G) Temperature Control Assembly, Renew

1983-87 (.5)........ .7
1984-87
Custom Air (.3)........ .6
Tempmatic (.3)........ .6

(G) Air Conditioning Hoses, Renew

Includes: Evacuate and charge system.

1983-87-one (1.1)........ 1.7
each adtnl (.3)........ .5

AUTOMATIC TEMPERATURE CONTROL

(G) Temperature Control Units, Renew

aspirator hose (.2)........ .4
sensor and ambient switch (under hood) (.2)........ .3
aspirator (.8)........ 1.2
in car sensor (.3)........ .6

(G) Programmer and/or Actuating Link, Renew

1983-87 (.6)........ .8
Bench test programmer add (.7)........ 1.0
Renew vacuum modulator add........ .1
Renew vacuum checking valve add........ .1
Renew power spring add........ .1
Renew output shaft add........ .2
Renew vacuum motor add........ .2
Renew vacuum relay add........ .1
Renew compensator add........ .1

PARTS 28 AIR CONDITIONING 28 PARTS

	Part No.	Price
Compressor Assembly		
1983-87	◆12300273	390.00
Cylinder w/Shaft Assy.		
1983-87	◆2724144	269.00
Compressor Clutch Drive		
1983-87	◆6551220	32.50
Rotor and Bearing Assy.		
1983-87	◆6551216	67.50
Clutch Coil w/Housing		
1983-87	◆6551217	44.00
Compressor Seal Kit		
1983-87	◆9956695	13.00
Condenser Assembly		
1983-87-V-6	◆3037439	158.25
V-8	◆3037438	156.50
Compressor Relief Valve		
1983-87	◆5914435	13.50
Accumulator-Dehydrator		
1983-87	◆2724275	80.25
Evaporator Core		
1983-84	◆3035240	218.25
1985-87	◆3058130	261.75
Blower Motor		
1983-87	◆22020945	60.00
Blower Switch		
1983	◆16015256	6.00
1984-87	◆16032480	7.50

AUTOMATIC TEMPERATURE CONTROL

	Part No.	Price
Control Assy.		
1983	16027233	33.75
1984-87	16034683	35.75
Programmer		
1983-87	16016473	87.00

LABOR 29 LOCKS, HINGES & WIND. REGULATORS 29 LABOR

(Factory Time) Chilton Time

(G) Hood Release Cable, Renew

1983-84 (.3)........ .6
1985-87 (.5)........ .6

(G) Hood Lock, Renew

1983-87 (.2)........ .3

(G) Hood Hinge, Renew (One)

1983-87 (.4)........ .5

(G) Door Lock, Renew

Front
1983-87 (.5)........ .8
Rear
1983-87 (.8)........ 1.1
w/Electric locks add (.1)........ .1

(G) Door Lock Remote Control, Renew

1983-87 (.4)........ .6

(G) Door Lock Cylinder, Renew

1983-87 (.4)........ .7
Recode cyl add (.3)........ .3
w/Ill entry sys add (.2)........ .2

(G) Door Handle (Outside), Renew (Front or Rear)

1983-87 (.4)........ .6
Renew insert add (.1)........ .1

(G) Lock Striker Plate, Renew

1983-87 (.2)........ .2

(G) Door Window Regulator (Manual), Renew (Front or Rear)

1983-87 (.8)........ 1.2
Recond regul add (.2)........ .2

(G) Door Window Regulator (Electric), Renew (Front or Rear)

1983-87 (1.0)........ 1.4
Transfer motor add (.2)........ .3

(G) Trunk Lock and Cylinder, Renew

1983-85 (.3)........ .5
Recode cyl add (.3)........ .3

(G) Trunk Hinge or Strap, Renew (One)

1983-85 (.8)........ 1.2

(G) Tailgate Lock Cylinder, Renew

1983-87 (.3)........ .5
Recode cyl add (.3)........ .3

(G) Tailgate Handle (Inner), Renew

1983-87 (.2)........ .3

(G) Tailgate Hinge, Renew

Does not include color coat.

1983-87-upper (.3)........ .6
lower (.7)........ 1.0

(G) Tailgate Window Regulator, Renew

1983-87 (.7)........ 1.1

PARTS 29 LOCKS, HINGES & WIND. REGULATORS 29 PARTS

	Part No.	Price
Hood Latch		
1983-87	◆14070703	16.25
Hood Hinge		
(Aluminum hood)		
1983-87-right	555712	33.75
left	555713	33.75
(Steel hood)		
1983-87-right	◆14015976	29.00
left	◆14015975	29.00
Front Door Lock		
(2-door)		
1983-87-right	◆20293612	33.50
left	◆20293613	33.50
(4-door)		
1983-87-right	◆20293604	51.50
left	◆20293605	51.50
Rear Door Lock		
1983-87-right	◆20293624	55.75
left	◆20293625	55.75
Lock Cylinder & Keys		
1983-87	◆9632769	7.75
1985-87	◆9632766	9.50
Striker		
1983-87	◆20151275	5.50
Door Outer Handle		
(wo/Illum. entry)		
1983-87-right	◆20111712	26.50
left	◆20111713	26.50
(Illum. entry)		
1983-87-right	◆20177430	53.75
left	◆20177431	53.75
Trunk Lock Cylinder		
(wo/Station wagon)		
1983-85	◆3910570	6.25
(Station wagon)		
1983-87	◆9632769	7.75
Trunk Hinge Strap		
1983-right	◆20287998	24.50
left	20287999	24.50
1984-87	◆20434734	13.50
Front Window Regulator		
(Manual)		
(2-door)		
1983-87-right	◆20303586	102.00
left	◆20303587	102.00
(4-door)		
4 dr.	◆20192896	114.00
1983-87-right	◆20110652	102.00
left	◆20110653	102.00
(Electric)		
(2-door)		
1983-87-right	◆20303590	108.00
left	◆20303591	108.00
(4-door)		
1983-87-right	◆20192896	114.00
left	◆20192897	114.00
Rear Window Regulator		
(Manual)		
1983-87-right	◆20147472	88.25
left	◆20147473	88.25
(Electric)		
1983-87-right	◆20192894	114.00
left	◆20192895	114.00
Electric Window Regulator Motor		
1983-87	◆22029848	72.50

LABOR 30 HEAD AND PARKING LAMPS 30 LABOR

(Factory Time)	Chilton Time
(G) Aim Headlamps	
two	.4
four	.6
(M) Headlamp Sealed Beam Bulb, Renew	
1983-87-each (.3)	.3
(M) Back-Up Lamp Assembly, Renew	
1983-87-each (.4)	.5
(M) Corning Lamp Assembly, Renew	
1983-87-each (.2)	.3
(M) Park and Turn Signal Lamp Assy., Renew	
1983-87-each (.2)	.3
(M) Rear Combination Lamp Assy., Renew	
1983-87-each (.3)	.4
(M) License Lamp Assembly, Renew	
1983-87 (.2)	.2
(M) Side Marker Lamp Assy., Renew	
1983-87-each (.3)	.4
(M) Back-Up Lamp Bulb, Renew	
All models-one (.2)	.3
both (.3)	.4
(M) Cornering Lamp Bulb, Renew	
All models-each (.2)	.3
(M) License Lamp Bulb, Renew	
All models-one or all (.2)	.3
(M) Park and Turn Signal Lamp Bulb, Renew	
All models-each	.2
(M) Side Marker Lamp Bulb, Renew	
All models-each	.2
(M) Stop, Tail and Turn Signal Lamp Bulb, Renew	
All models-one	.2
each adtnl	.1

PARTS 30 HEAD AND PARKING LAMPS 30 PARTS

	Part No.	Price
Sealed Beam Bulb		
(wo/Quartz)		
1983-87-inner	◆5966201	15.00
outer	◆5966200	15.00
(Quartz)		
1983-87	◆5930567	22.50
Tail Lamp Lens		
(Olds. 98)		
1983-84-right	5971954	31.75
left	5971953	31.75
Lenses not shown above are available as a lamp unit only.		
Tail Lamp Assy.		
(88 & Custom Cruiser)		
(wo/Station wagon)		
(exc. special tail lamp)		
1983-right	5934198	49.00
left	5934197	49.00
1984-85-right	16502020	90.75
left	16502019	90.75
(Special tail lamp)		
1984-85-right	16502934	90.75
left	16502935	N.L.
(Station wagon)		
1983-87-right	5971652	59.50
left	5971651	59.50
High Mount Stoplight		
1986-87	◆918456	39.50
(Olds. "98")		
1983-84-right	5936622	32.25
left	5936621	32.25
Parking Lamp Assy.		
(wo/Station wagon)		
1983-85-right	914870	26.25
left	914869	26.25
(Station wagon)		
1983-87-right	914836	27.50
left	914835	27.50
License Plate Lamp Assy.		
(wo/Station wagon)		
1983-85	◆913061	6.25
(Station wagon)		
1983-87	◆912795	7.50
Front Side Marker Lamp		
(Olds. 98)		
1983-right	914648	12.75
left	914647	12.75
1984-right	920046	12.75
left	920045	12.75
(88 & Custom Cruiser)		
1983-87-right	914648	12.75
left	914647	12.75

LABOR 31 WINDSHIELD WIPER & SPEEDOMETER 31 LABOR

(Factory Time)	Chilton Time
(G) Windshield Wiper Motor, Renew	
1983-87 (.4)	.6
(G) Windshield Wiper Motor, R&R and Recondition	
1983-87-round motor (.8)	1.2
rectangular motor (1.0)	1.4
(G) Wiper Transmission, Renew (One)	
1983-87 (.3)	.6
(G) Wiper Switch, Renew	
1983-85-std colm (1.0)	1.4
tilt colm (.7)	1.3
1986-87	
std colm (1.0)	1.4
tilt colm (1.0)	1.4
(G) Windshield Washer Pump, Renew	
1983-87 (.3)	.4
w/Pulse wipe add (.1)	.1
(G) Windshield Washer Pump, R&R and Recondition	
1983-87 (.6)	.8
(G) Windshield Washer Pump Valve, Renew	
1983-87 (.2)	.4
(G) Speedometer Head, R&R or Renew	
1983-87 (.5)	.8
Reset odometer add	.2
(G) Speedometer Cable and Casing, Renew	
1983-87	
one piece (.7)	1.1
upper cable (.4)	.7
lower cable (.3)	.6
(G) Speedometer Cable (Inner), Renew or Lubricate	
1983-87	
one piece (.5)	.9
upper cable (.3)	.6
lower cable (.2)	.5
(G) Radio, R&R	
1983-87 (.4)	.7

PARTS 31 WINDSHIELD WIPER & SPEEDOMETER 31 PARTS

	Part No.	Price
Windshield Wiper Motor		
1983-87-exc.		
Pulse	◆4960974	84.00
Pulse wiper	◆4961608	80.00
Wiper Transmission		
1983-87-right	◆22010448	17.00
left	◆22010449	18.50
Wiper Switch		
(wo/Pulse wiper)		
1983-wo/Tilt		
whl.	◆7835342	22.50
Tilt wheel	◆7837279	41.50
1984-87-wo/Tilt		
whl.	◆7835342	22.50
Tilt whl.	◆7837279	41.50
(Pulse wipers)		
1983-87-wo/Tilt		
whl.	◆7835340	56.25
Tilt wheel	◆7837280	53.50
Windshield Washer Pump		
(wo/Pulse wiper)		
1983-87	◆22029665	30.00
(Pulse wipers)		
1983-87	◆22029601	27.00
Speedometer Cable (w/Casing)		
(wo/Cruise control)		
1983	25032644	15.25
1984-87	25033590	29.00
(Cruise control)		
1983-upper	25032594	15.50
lower	6480250	13.00
1984-87	25033590	29.00
Speedometer Head Assy.		
Order by year and model.		

LABOR 32 LIGHT SWITCHES & WIRING 32 LABOR

(Factory Time)	Chilton Time
(G) Headlamp Switch, Renew	
1983-87 (.3)	.5
(G) Headlamp Dimmer Switch, Renew	
1983-87-column mounted (.5)	.7
(G) Stop Light Switch, Renew	
1983-87 (.2)	.3
(G) Back-Up Lamp and Park/Neutral Switch, Renew	
1983-87 (.2)	.4
(G) Parking Brake Lamp Switch, Renew	
1983-87 (.3)	.4
(G) Turn Signal Switch, Renew	
1983-87	
std colm (.6)	1.1
tilt colm (.7)	1.2
(M) Turn Signal or Hazard Warning Flasher, Renew	
1983-87 (.2)	.2
(G) Dimmer Switch Pivot Assy., Renew	
1983-85-std (1.0)	1.4
tilt (.7)	1.3
w/Cruise control add (.2)	.2
1986-87	
std colm (1.0)	1.4
tilt colm (1.0)	1.4
(G) Multifunction Lever, Renew	
All models (.2)	.4
w/Cruise control add (.5)	.5
(G) Horns, Renew	
1983-87 (.2)	.3
(G) Horn Relay, Renew	
1983-87 (.2)	.3
(G) Chassis Wiring Harness, Renew	
Fusible Link	
1983-87 (.4)	.6
Headlamp Harness	
1983-87 (.8)	1.4
Instrument Panel	
1983-87 (1.8)	2.4
Engine Harness	
1983-87 (1.0)	1.6

PARTS 32 LIGHT SWITCHES & WIRING 32 PARTS

	Part No.	Price
Turn Signal Switch		
1983-87-exc		
cornering	◆1997983	30.00
Corn lamps	◆1997984	35.00
Turn Signal Flasher		
1983-87-2 lamp	◆6450076	4.00
3 lamp	◆10029240	4.25
6 lamp	◆6450089	3.00
Headlamp Switch		
1983-exc. below	◆1995226	16.00
Twi. sent	◆1995214	22.75
1984-87	1995222	14.00
Headlamp Dimmer Switch		
1983-87	◆7838234	12.50
Stoplight Switch		
(wo/Cruise control)		
1983-84	◆25504628	3.75
1985-87	◆25524846	6.50
(Cruise control)		
1983-84	◆9794682	7.75
1985-87	◆25524847	6.50
Horn Assy.		
1983-87-Note (A)	◆1892164	22.00
Note (C)	◆1892246	27.50
Note (D)	◆1892162	23.50
Note (F)	◆1892163	22.00
Horn Relay		
1983-87	◆25513270	8.50

LABOR 33 GLASS 33 LABOR

(Factory Time)	Chilton Time
(G) Windshield Glass, Renew	
1983-87 (1.3)	1.8
Renew caulk bead add (.4)	.4
(G) Front Door Glass, Renew	
1983-87 (.9)	1.5
(G) Rear Door Glass, Renew	
1983-87 (.8)	1.4
(G) Rear Door Stationary Vent Glass, Renew	
1983-87 (.7)	1.0
(G) Quarter Window Stationary Glass, Renew	
1983-87-exc below (.8)	1.4
sta wag (1.0)	1.6
(G) Tail Gate Glass, Renew	
1983-87 (.6)	1.0
(G) Rear Window Glass, Renew	
1983-85 (1.3)	2.0
w/Elec defogger add (.6)	.6
w/3/4 plug unpadded, add (1.3)	2.0
w/3/4 plug padded, add (2.6)	4.0

LABOR 34 CRUISE CONTROL 34 LABOR

(Factory Time)	Chilton Time
(G) Cruise Control External Adjustments	
Includes: Adjust electric and vacuum brake switches and centering spring.	
1983 (.3)	.5
(G) Cruise Control Regulator (Transducer), Renew	
Includes: R&R cover and external adjustments.	
1983 (.4)	.6
Adjust low speed switch add (.1)	.1
(G) Cruise Control Chain or Cable, Renew	
1983-87 (.2)	.4
(G) Cruise Control Wiring Harness, Renew	
1983-87 (.5)	.8
(G) Cruise Control Engagement Switch, Renew	
1983-87 (.5)	.9
(G) Cruise Control Brake Release Switch, Renew	
1983 (.2)	.4
(G) Cruise Control Servo Assy., Renew	
1983-85 (.2)	.5
1986-87 (.6)	.8
(G) Cruise Control Vacuum Hoses, Renew	
1983-87-one or all (.3)	.4
(G) Cruise Control Vacuum Regulator Valve, Renew (w/Diesel Engine)	
1983 (.2)	.3
(G) Cruise Control Resume Solenoid, Renew	
1983 (.2)	.3
(G) Cruise Control Module, Renew	
1984-87 (.4)	.5

PARTS 34 CRUISE CONTROL 34 PARTS

	Part No.	Price
Cruise Control Servo		
V-6-231		
1983	◆25030527	20.50
1984-85	◆25074630	116.25
V-6-252 engine		
1983	◆25031845	26.00
V-8-307		
1983-exc. below	◆25074220	25.00
THM 200 4R	◆25031316	27.00
1984-87	◆25074629	123.50
V-8-350 Diesel		
1983-exc. below	◆25030980	32.75
w/THM 200 4R	◆25031726	33.75
1984-85	◆25074629	123.50
Cruise Control Transducer		
V-6		
1983	◆25030878	158.00
V-8		
1983	◆25030882	158.00
V-8-350 Diesel		
1983	◆25031604	179.25
Cruise Control Module		
1984-87-231	◆25031964	115.00
307	25031985	116.25
Diesel	◆25031948	116.00
Cruise Control Release Switch		
1983-84	◆9794682	8.00
1985-87	◆25524847	6.50
Cruise Control Chain		
1983	◆1494424	2.50
1984-87	◆25031314	3.25
Cruise Control Lever & Switch Assy.		
1983-exc. below	◆25031426	52.25
Pulse wpr.	◆25031425	52.25
1984-87-exc. below	◆25031457	50.00
Pulse wpr.	◆25031456	50.00

GROUP INDEX

ALPHABETICAL INDEX

General Motors
Rear Wheel Drive Cars

PONTIAC BONNEVILLE • PARISIENNE • GRAND PRIX

YEAR IDENTIFICATION

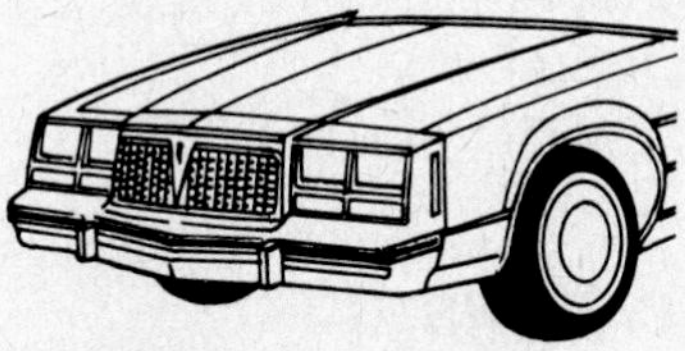

1983–84 Bonneville

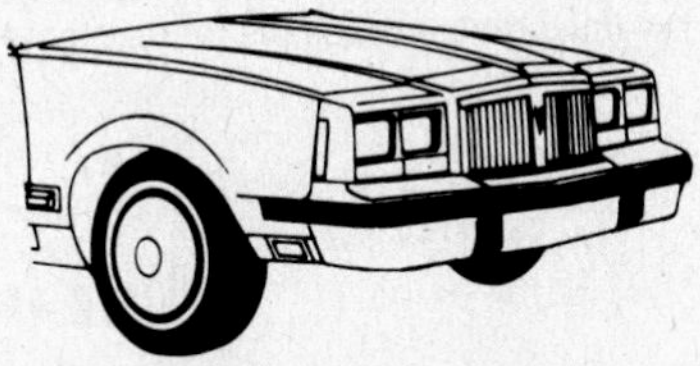

1985–87 Bonneville

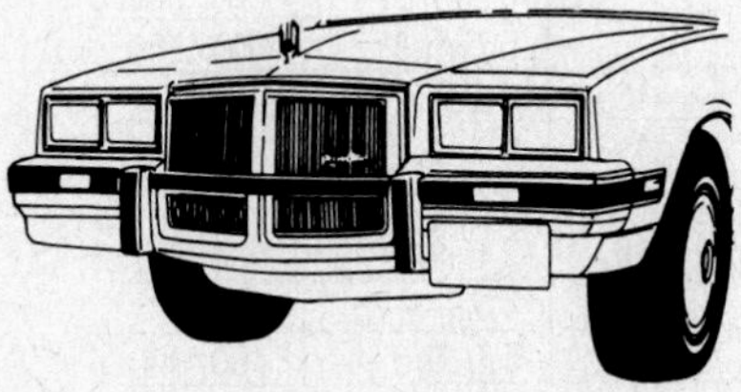

1983–84 Grand Prix

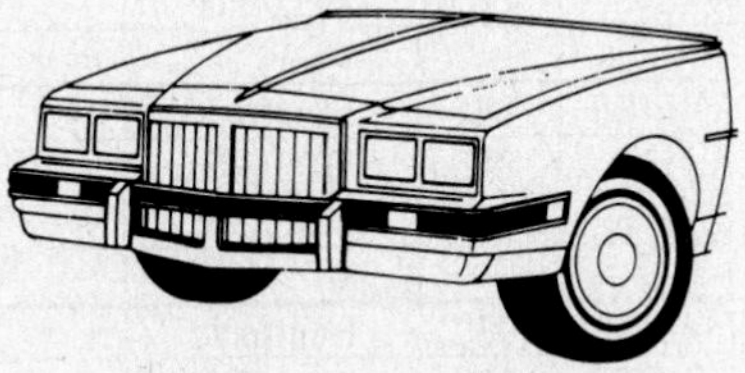

1985–86 Grand Prix

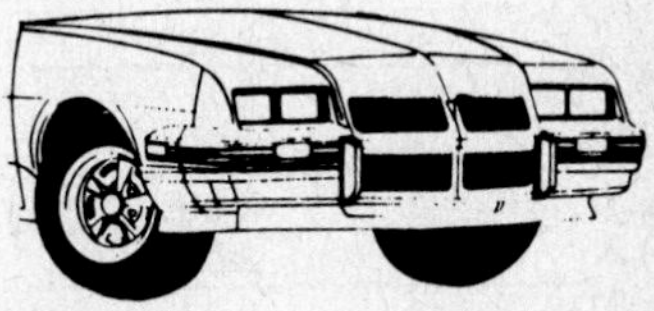

1987 Grand Prix

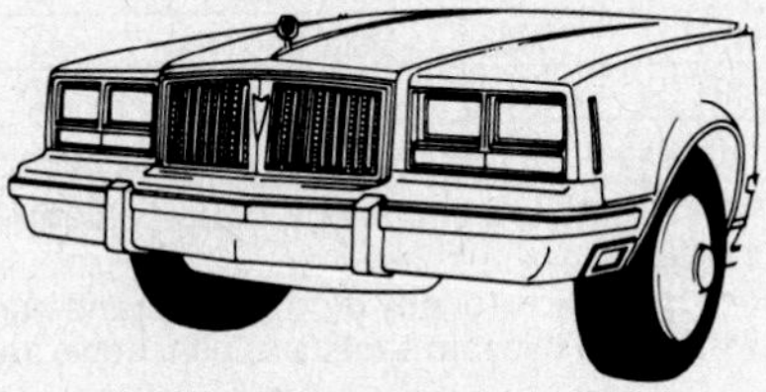

1984–87 Parisienne

VEHICLE IDENTIFICATION NUMBER (VIN)

It is important for servicing and ordering parts to be certain of the vehicle and engine identification. The VIN (vehicle identification number) is a 17 digit number visible through the windshield on the driver's side of the dash and contains the vehicle and engine identification codes. It can be interpreted as follows:

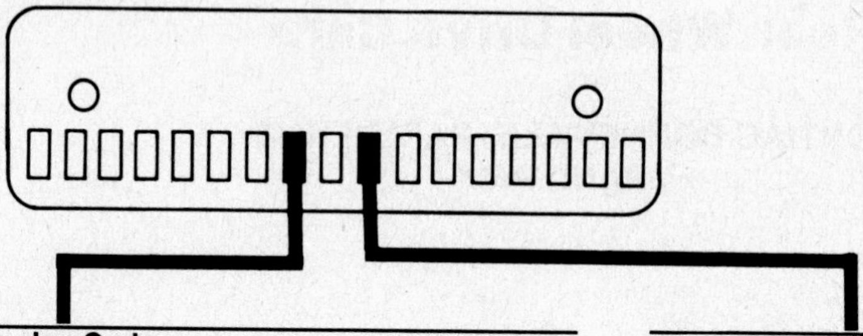

Engine Code

Code	Cu. In.	Liters	Cyl.	Carb.	Eng. Mfg.
A	231	3.8	6	2	Buick
Z	262	4.3	6	Fuel Injection	Chev.
6	350	5.7	8	4	Chev.
G	305	5.0	8	4	Chev.
H	305	5.0	8	4	Chev.
N	350	5.7	8	Diesel	Olds.

Model Year Code

Code	Year
D	83
E	84
F	85
G	86
H	87

The seventeen digit Vehicle Identification Number can be used to determine engine application and model year. The 10th digit indicates the model year, and the 8th digit identifies the factory installed engine.

TUNE-UP SPECIFICATIONS

When analyzing compression test results, look for uniformity among cylinders rather than specific pressures.

Year	Eng. VIN Code	Engine No. Cyl. Displacement Cu. In.	Liter	Eng. Mfg.	Spark Plugs Orig. Type•	Spark Plugs Gap (in.)	Distributor Point Dwell (deg)	Distributor Point Gap (in.)	Ignition Timing (deg)▲ Auto. Trans.	Intake Valve Opens ■(deg)	Fuel Pump Pressure (psi)	Idle Speed• (rpm) Auto. Trans.
'83	A	6-231	3.8	Buick	R-45TS8	.080	Electronic		15B	16	4.25–5.75	500
	H	8-305	5.0	Chev.	R-45TS	.045	Electronic		6B	—	5.5–7.0	500/650
	N	8-350	5.7	Olds.	—	—	—		4A	16	5.5–6.5	600/750
'84	A	6-231	3.8	Buick	R-45TS8	.080	Electronic		15B	16	4.25–5.75	500
	H	8-305	5.0	Chev.	R-45TS	.045	Electronic		6B	44	5.5–7.0	500/650
	G	8-305	5.0	Chev.	R-45TS	.045	Electronic		6B	44	5.5–7.0	500/650
	N	8-350	5.7	Olds.	—	—	—		4A	16	5.5–6.5	600-750
'85	A	6-231	3.8	Buick	R-45TS8	.080	Electronic		15B	16	4.25–5.75	500
	Z	6-262	4.3	Chev.	R-43CTS	.035	Electronic		6B	16	5.5–6.5	450/900
	H	8-305	5.0	Chev.	R-45TS	.045	Electronic		6B	44	5.5–7.0	500/650
	G	8-305	5.0	Chev.	R-45TS	.045	Electronic		6B	44	5.5–7.0	500/650
	6	8-350	5.7	Chev.	R-45TS	.045	Electronic		6B	16	5.5–6.5	475
	N	8-350	5.7	Olds.	—	—	—		4A	16	5.5–6.5	600-750
'86	A	6-231	3.8	Buick	R-45TS8	.080	Electronic		①	16	5.5–6.5	①
	G	8-305	5.0	Chev.	R45TS	.045	Electronic		①	44	5.5–7.0	①
	H	8-305	5.0	Chev.	R45TS	.045	Electronic		①	44	5.5–7.0	①
	Z	6-262	4.3	Chev.	R43CTS	.035	Electronic		①	16	5.5–6.5	①
'87	Refer to Underhood Emission Information Decal											

NOTE: The underhood specifications sticker often reflects tune-up specification changes made in production. Sticker figures must be used if they disagree with those in this chart.

Part numbers in this chart are not recommendations by Chilton for any product by brand name.

• Figure in parentheses indicates California engine. Where two idle speeds appear separately by a slash, the second is with the solenoid disconnected.

■ All figures are in degrees Before Top Dead Center.

① Refer to Underhood Emission Information Decal

FIRING ORDERS

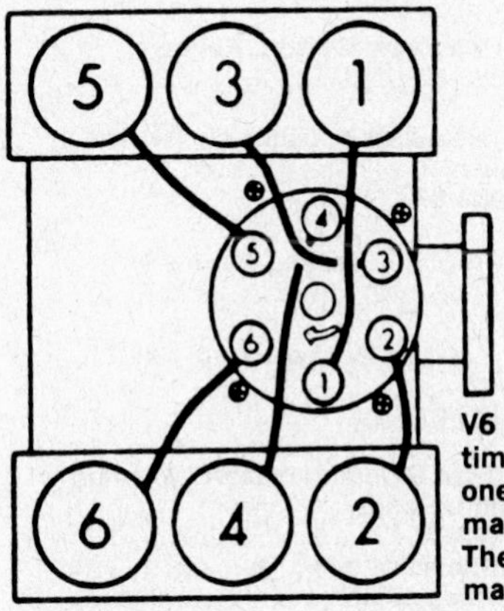

V6 harmonic balancers have two timing marks: one is 1/8 in. wide, and one is 1/16 in. wide. Use the 1/16 in. mark for timing with a hand held light. The 1/8 in. mark is used only with a magnetic timing pick-up probe.

GM (Buick) 231 V6 engine
GM (Chevrolet) 262 V6 engine
Firing order: 1–6–5–4–3–2
Distributor rotation: clockwise

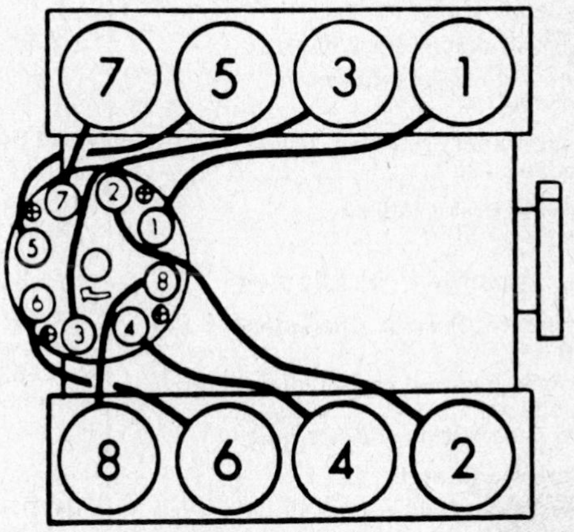

GM (Chevrolet) 305, 350 V8 engines
Firing order: 1–8–4–3–6–5–7–2
Distributor rotation: clockwise

WHEEL ALIGNMENT SPECIFICATIONS

Year	Model	Caster Range (deg)	Caster Pref. Setting (deg)	Camber Range (deg)	Camber Pref. Setting (deg)	Toe-in (in.)	Steering Axis inclin. (deg.)
'83	Gran Prix and Bonneville	2P-4P	3P	5/16N-15/16P	1/2P	1/8	8
'84	Gran Prix and Bonneville	3P-4P	3 1/2P	5/16N-15/16P	1/2P	1/8	8
'85-'87	Gran Prix and Bonneville	2P-4P	3P	5/16N-15/16P	1/2P	1/8	8
'84-'87	Parisenne	2P-4P	3P	0-1 5/8P	13/16P	1/8	9 3/4

P Positive
N Negative

LABOR — SERVICE BAY OPERATIONS — LABOR

(Factory Time) Chilton Time

COOLING

(M) Winterize Cooling System
Includes: Run engine to check for leaks, tighten all hose connections. Test radiator and pressure cap, drain radiator and engine block. Add anti-freeze and refill system.
All models 5

(G) Thermostat, Renew
1983-85
V-6
229 eng (.7) 8
231 eng (.6) 7
V-8 (.5) 6
Diesel (.5) 6
1986-87
V-6
Pontiac (.7) 9
Grand Prix (.3) 4
V-8 (.5) 6

(M) Drive Belt, Renew
1983-87-one (.3) 4
each adtnl 1

(M) Drive Belt, Adjust
1983-87-one (.3) 3
each adtnl 1

(M) Radiator Hoses, Renew
1983-87-upper (.3) 4
lower (.4) 5
both (.5) 7
by-pass (.6) 8

CHILTON'S 10 POINT SAFETY CHECK

CHECK OPERATION & CONDITION OF THE FOLLOWING ITEMS:

1. Legal Registration (serial no.)
2. Tires & Wheels
3. Brake System (R&R all wheels)
4. Light Systems & Signals
5. Accelerator Linkage, Neutral Safety Switch, Shift Indicator Pointer & Seat Position Locks
6. Glass, Mirrors, Door Locks, Seat Belts & Harness
7. Wipers, Washers & Defrosters
8. Frame, Steering, Shocks, Front & Rear Suspension
9. Fuel & Exhaust Systems
10. Road Test Vehicle

All models 1.0
Exhaust Smog Analysis, add 4

(Factory Time) Chilton Time

FUEL

(M) Carburetor Air Cleaner, Service
1983-87 (.2) 3

(G) Air Cleaner Vacuum Motor, Renew
1983-87 (.3) 5

(G) Air Cleaner Temperature Sensor, Renew
1983-87 (.2) 5

(G) Carburetor, Adjust (On Car)
Includes: Adjust vacuum brake, choke coil, fast idle and idle speed, dash pot or solenoid.
1983-87
Slow & Fast Idle (.3) 4
Vacuum Brake-one (.4) 6
both (.6) 8
Choke (.6) 1.0
Complete (1.3) 1.8

(G) Fuel Filter, Renew
All models (.2) 3

BRAKES

(G) Brakes, Adjust (Minor)
Includes: R&R wheels and adjust brakes thru access holes in drums. Fill master cylinder.
two wheels 4
Remove knock out plugs add, each .. .1

LABOR SERVICE BAY OPERATIONS LABOR

	(Factory Time)	Chilton Time
(G) Bleed Brakes (Four Wheels)		
Includes: Fill master cylinder.		
All models	(.4)	.5
(G) Brake Pedal Free Play, Adjust		
All models		.3
(M) Parking Brake, Adjust		
All models	(.3)	.4

LUBRICATION SERVICE

	(Factory Time)	Chilton Time
(M) Lubricate Chassis, Change Oil & Filter		
Includes: Inspect and correct all fluid levels.		
All models		.6
Install grease fittings add		.1
(M) Lubricate Chassis		
Includes: Inspect and correct all fluid levels.		
All models		.4
Install grease fittings add		.1
(M) Engine Oil & Filter, Change		
Includes: Inspect and correct all fluid levels.		
All models		.4

WHEELS

	(Factory Time)	Chilton Time
(M) Wheel, Renew		
one	(.4)	.5
(G) Wheels, Balance		
one		.3
each adtnl		.2
(G) Wheels, Rotate (All)		
All models		.5
(G) Front Wheel Bearings, Clean and Repack (Both Wheels)		
All models	(1.1)	1.6
(G) Front Wheel Bearings and Cups, Renew		
1983-87-one side	(.7)	.9
both sides	(1.1)	1.5
(G) Front Wheel Grease Seals, Renew		
1983-87-one	(.7)	.8
both	(1.1)	1.2

ELECTRICAL

	(Factory Time)	Chilton Time
(M) Battery Cables, Renew		
1983-87-positive	(.3)	.4
negative	(.2)	.3
batt to batt	(.2)	.3
(M) Battery Terminals, Clean		
All models		.3
(G) Aim Headlamps		
two		.4
four		.6
(M) Headlamp Sealed Beam Bulb, Renew		
1983-87-each	(.3)	.3
(G) Headlamp Switch, Renew		
1983-87	(.3)	.5
(G) Headlamp Dimmer Switch, Renew		
1983-87	(.3)	.6
(G) Stoplight Switch, Renew		
1983-87	(.2)	.3
(G) Parking Brake Lamp Switch, Renew		
1983-87	(.2)	.3
(G) Turn Signal or Hazard Warning Switch, Renew		
1983-87	(.7)	1.1
w/Tilt column add	(.1)	.1
w/Cruise control add	(.2)	.2
(G) Neutral Safety or Back-Up Lamp Switch, Renew		
1983-87	(.3)	.4
(M) Turn Signal or Hazard Warning Flasher, Renew		
1983-87	(.2)	.2
(G) Horn Relay, Renew		
1983-87	(.2)	.3
(G) Horn, Renew		
1983-87-each	(.2)	.3

LABOR 1 TUNE UP 1 LABOR

	(Factory Time)	Chilton Time
(G) Compression Test		
V-6-1983-87	(.5)	.7
V-8-1983-87	(.6)	.8
w/A.C. add		.3
(G) Engine Tune Up, (Electronic Ignition)		

Includes: Test battery and clean connections. Tighten manifold and carburetor mounting bolts. Check engine compression, clean and adjust or renew spark plugs. Test resistance of spark plug cables. Inspect distributor cap and rotor. Adjust air gap. Check vacuum advance operation. Reset ignition timing. Adjust idle mixture and idle speed. Service air cleaner. Inspect and adjust drive belts. Inspect choke operation and adjust or free up. Check operation of EGR valve.

	(Factory Time)	Chilton Time
V-6-1983-87		2.0
V-8-1983-87		2.5
w/A.C. add		.6
To perform C.C.C. system test add		1.0

LABOR 2 IGNITION SYSTEM 2 LABOR

GASOLINE ENGINES

	(Factory Time)	Chilton Time
(G) Spark Plugs, Clean and Reset or Renew		
V-6-1983-87	(.4)	.6
V-8-1983-87	(.6)	.7
To clean add		.3
w/A.C. add		.3
(G) Ignition Timing, Reset		
1983-87	(.3)	.4
(G) Distributor, Renew		
Includes: Reset ignition timing.		
V-6-1983-87	(.6)	.9
V-8-1983-87	(.6)	.9
(G) Distributor, R&R and Recondition		
Includes: Reset ignition timing.		
V-6-1983-87	(.9)	1.4
V-8-1983-87	(.9)	1.4
(G) Distributor Cap and/or Rotor, Renew		
1983-87		
V-6	(.5)	.7
V-8	(.3)	.5
(G) Electronic Module Retard Vacuum Switch (EMR), Renew		
V-6-1983	(.3)	.5
(G) ESC Detonation (Knock) Sensor, Renew		
V-6-1983-87	(.4)	1.0
(G) ESC Module, Renew		
V-6-1983-87	(.4)	.7
(G) Ignition Coil, Renew		
1983-87	(.3)	.4
(G) Ignition Cables, Renew		
V-6-1983-87	(.3)	1.4
V-8-1983-87	(.5)	.6
(G) Ignition Switch, Renew		
1983-85	(.5)	.9
1986-87		
Pontiac	(.4)	.7
Grand Prix	(.6)	.9
(G) Ignition Key Warning Switch, Renew		
1983-87	(.6)	1.0
(G) Distributor Module, Renew		
1983-87	(.3)	.6
(G) Distributor Pick-Up Coil and/or Pole Piece, Renew		
Includes: R&R distributor and reset ignition timing.		
1983-87	(.6)	.9
(G) Distributor Capacitor and/or Module Wiring Harness, Renew		
1983-87	(.4)	.6

LABOR 2 IGNITION SYSTEM 2 LABOR

	(Factory Time)	Chilton Time
DIESEL IGNITION COMPONENTS		
(G) Glow Plugs, Renew		
1983-85		
one		.4
all-one bank		.7
all-both banks		1.3
(G) Glow Plug Control Module, Renew (Controller)		
1983-85	(.4)	.6
(G) Glow Plug Relay, Renew		
1983-85	(.2)	.3
(G) Coolant Fast Idle Temperature Switch, Renew		
1983-85	(.2)	.4
(G) Fast Idle Solenoid, Renew		
1983-85	(.4)	.5

PARTS 2 IGNITION SYSTEM 2 PARTS

	Part No.	Price
Distributor Assy.		
V-6-231		
1983-87	◆1103470	351.25
V-6-262		
1985	◆1103574	170.00
1986-87	◆1103655	174.75
V-8-305		
1983-84	◆1103460	333.75
1986-87	◆10497135	294.50
V-8-307		
1986-87	◆1103602	275.00
(1) Cover		
1983-87-V-6	◆1894209	6.00
V-8	◆1875960	6.00
(2) Coil		
1983-87-V-6	◆1985474	36.00
V-8	◆1985473	36.00
(3) Cap		
V-6-231		
1983-87	◆1894979	17.00
V-6-262		
1985-87	◆1988001	9.75
V-8-305		
1983-87	◆1974408	17.00
V-8-307		
1986-87	◆1974408	N.L.
(4) Rotor		
exc. V-6-262		
1983-87	◆1977026	6.50
V-6-262		
1985-87	◆10495408	3.50
(5) Shaft		
V-6-231		
1983-87	◆1976930	38.50
V-8-305		
1983-87	◆1976909	38.50
V-8-307		
1986-87	◆1989612	42.25
(6) Pole Piece & Plate Assy.		
V-6-231		
1983-87	◆1976925	30.25
V-6-262		
1985	◆1988010	3.50
1986-87	◆10495802	4.00

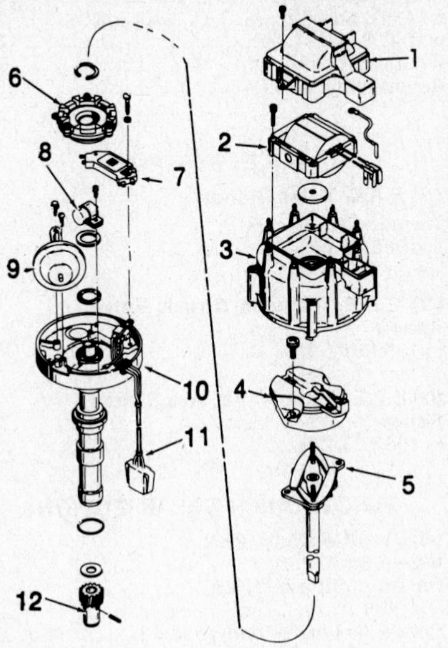

	Part No.	Price
V-8-305		
1983-87	◆1976897	30.25
V-8-307		
1986-87	◆1976897	30.00
(7) Module		
V-6-231		
1983-87	◆1976908	60.00
V-6-262		
1985	◆1987466	46.00
1986-87	◆10496048	52.75
V-8-305		
1983-85	◆1875990	33.00
1986-87	◆1976908	N.L.
V-8-307		
1986-87	◆1976908	N.L.
V-8-305		
1983-87	◆1978152	45.00

	Part No.	Price
V-8-307		
1986-87	◆1977208	34.00
(8) Capacitor		
1983-87	1978617	69.50
(10) Housing		
V-6-231		
1983-87	◆1976928	36.25
V-6-262		
1983-85	◆1989808	57.00
1986-87	◆10495860	43.75
(11) Harness		
1983-87	◆1892261	11.00
(12) Gear		
1983-87-exc.		
below	◆1892082	15.25
V-6-262	◆10495062	20.75
V-8-305	◆1958599	14.25
V-8-307	◆1988777	21.50

Ignition Wires
Spark plug wires are sold separately for each spark plug and are not available as a set.

	Part No.	Price
Ignition Switch		
(wo/Tilt wheel)		
1983	◆1990109	11.50
1984-87	◆1990115	11.50
(Tilt wheel)		
1983	◆1990110	11.50
1984-87	◆1990116	11.50
DIESEL IGNITION SYSTEM		
Glow Plugs		
1983	◆5613680	19.00
1984-85	◆5613826	16.50
Glow Plug Relay		
1983	◆560580	16.00
Glow Plug Module		
1984	◆22520348	91.75
Glow Plug Control Switch		
1983	◆22514724	79.50
Glow Plug Controller		
1985	◆22528337	96.00

LABOR 3 FUEL SYSTEM 3 LABOR

	(Factory Time)	Chilton Time
GASOLINE ENGINES		
(G) Fuel Pump, Test		
Includes: Disconnect line at carburetor, attach pressure gauge.		
All models		.3
(M) Carburetor Air Cleaner, Service		
1983-87	(.2)	.3
(G) Air Cleaner Vacuum Motor, Renew		
1983-87	(.3)	.5
(G) Air Cleaner Temperature Sensor, Renew		
1983-87	(.2)	.3
(G) Carburetor, Adjust (On Car)		
Includes: Adjust vacuum brake, choke coil, fast idle and idle speed, dash pot or solenoid.		
1983-87		
Slow & Fast Idle	(.3)	.4
Vacuum Brake-one	(.4)	.6
both	(.6)	.8
Choke	(.6)	1.0
Complete	(1.3)	1.8
(G) Fuel Filter, Renew		
All models		
in carb	(.3)	.4
in line	(.4)	.5
(G) Choke Vacuum Control Switch, Renew		
1983-87	(.3)	.4
(G) Electric Choke Relay, Renew		
1983-87	(.2)	.3
(G) E.F.E. Heater (Insulator), Renew		
1983-87	(.6)	1.0

(Factory Time) Chilton Time

(G) Carburetor Needle Valve and Seat, Renew
Includes: Adjust float level.
All models
2 bbl (.9) 1.2
4 bbl (.9) 1.5
To perform C.C.C. system check, add (.5) 1.0

(G) Accelerator Pump, Renew
All models
2 bbl (.7) 1.0
4 bbl (.8) 1.2

(G) Water In Fuel Detector, Renew (WIF)
All models (.9) 1.2

(G) Carburetor, Renew
Includes: All necessary adjustments.
V-6–1983-87 (.6) 9
V-8–1983-87 (.6) 9
To perform C.C.C. system check, add (.5) 1.0

(G) Carburetor, R&R and Clean or Recondition
Includes: All necessary adjustments.
V-6–1983-87 .... 3.0
V-8–1983-87–2 bbl 3.0
4 bbl 3.2
To perform C.C.C. system check, add (.5) 1.0

(G) Idle Stop Solenoid, Renew
Includes: Adjust.
1983-84 (.3) 4
1985-87 (.7) 1.0

(G) Vacuum Brake Diaphragm, Renew
1983-87–one (.4) 6
both (.6) 8

(G) Fuel Pump, Renew
1983-84
Pontiac
V-6 (1.0) 1.4
V-8 (1.0) 1.4
w/A.C. add (.2) 2
Grand Prix
V-6 (.4) 7
V-8 (.5) 9
1985-87
V-6 (.4) 7
V-8 (1.0) 1.4
w/A.C. add (.2) 2
w/P.S. add (.2) 2
Add pump test if performed.

(G) Fuel Tank, Renew
Includes: Drain and refill tank.
1983-87 (.7) 1.0

(G) Fuel Gauge (Tank), Renew
Includes: R&R tank and test gauge.
1983-87 (.8) 1.1

(G) Fuel Gauge (Dash), Renew
Includes: Disconnect battery cable.
1983-87 (.3) 6

(G) Intake Manifold or Gaskets, Renew
V-6–1983-87
229 eng (2.0) 2.6
231 eng (1.4) 2.7
262 eng (2.0) 3.0
V-8–1983-87
305 eng–Code H (2.3) 3.3
307 eng–Code Y (2.2) 3.2
w/A.C. add (.4) 4
w/A.I.R. add (.2) 2
w/C.C.C. add (.3) 3
w/Cruise control add (.2) 2
Renew manif add (.4) 5

E.F.E. SYSTEM

(G) E.F.E. Valve, Renew
Includes: Hoist car.
1983-87 (.6) 8

(G) E.F.E. Vacuum Check Valve, Renew
1983-87 (.2) 4

(G) E.F.E. Thermal Vacuum Switch, Renew
1983-87 (.3) 4

ELECTRONIC FUEL INJECTION

(G) Throttle Body, R&R
V-6–1985-87 (.6) 1.0
Renew throttle body kit, add 3
Renew fuel meter body add (.3) 3

(G) Throttle Body Unit, Renew
V-6–1985-87 (.6) 1.0

(G) Throttle Body Fuel Meter Assy., and/or Gasket, Renew
V-6–1985-87 (.4) 6

(G) Idle Air Control Valve, Renew
V-6–1985-87 (.6) 8

(G) Minimum Idle Speed, Adjust
All models (.4) 7

(G) Throttle Body Injector and/or Gasket, Renew
V-6–1985-87
one (.7) 1.1
both (.7) 1.2

(G) Fuel Pressure Regulator, Renew
V-6–1985-87 (.7) 1.0

(G) Fuel Pump, Renew (In Tank)
1985-87 (1.3) 1.8

(G) Fuel Pump Relay, Renew
1985-87 (.7) 9

DIESEL ENGINES

(M) Air Cleaner, Service
1983-85 (.2) 4

(G) Air Intake Crossover, Renew
1983-85–w/Ext EGR (.3) 5
w/Int EGR (.4) 6

(G) Injection Timing, Check and Adjust
1983-85 (.7) 9

(G) Fuel Supply Pump, Renew
1983-85 (.5) 8
w/A.C. add 2

(G) Fuel Filter, Renew
1983-85 (.2) 4

(G) Fuel Injection Pump Throttle Shaft Seal, Renew
1983-85 (.8) 1.3

(G) Injection Pump Adapter and/or Seal, Renew
1983-85–Cav (1.4) 2.1
Rem (1.8) 2.5

(G) Fuel Solenoid, Renew
1983-85
Cav (.3) 5
Rem (.5) 7

(G) Cold Advance Solenoid, Renew
1983-85 (.6) 1.0

(G) Fuel Injection Head Seal, Renew
Includes: Renew head and drive shaft seals. Renew governor weight retaining ring.
1983-85 (2.7) 3.9

(G) Fuel Injection Pump, Renew
Includes: Pressure and electrical tests. Adjust timing.
1983-85
Cav (1.8) 3.0
Rem (2.2) 3.4

(G) Fuel Return Lines (at Nozzles), Renew
1983-85–one side (.3) 5
both sides (.4) 7
return hose (.2) 3
w/A.C. add (.2) 2

(G) High Pressure Fuel Lines, Renew
1983-85–one 8
one-each bank 1.0
all (1.9) 2.5
w/A.C. add (.2) 2

(G) Injector Nozzle and/or Seal, Renew
1983-85–one (.6) 1.0
one-each bank (.7) 1.3
all-both banks (2.0) 3.0
w/A.C. add (.2) 2
Clean nozzles add, each 2

(G) Intake Manifold or Gaskets, Renew
1983-85 (2.9) 3.5
Renew manif add (.3) 5

(G) Vacuum Pump, Renew
Includes: Vacuum test.
1983-85
gear driven (.4) 6
belt driven (.6) 8

PARTS 3 FUEL SYSTEM 3 PARTS

	Part No.	Price
V-6-262 ENGINE		
Throttle Body Injection Unit		
1985	◆17111155	655.50
1986-87	◆17111156	39.25
(1) Fuel Meter Body Kit		
1985-87	◆17078262	128.75
(2) Fuel Injector Kit		
1985	◆17111159	179.50
1986-87	◆17111468	179.50
(3) Gasket Kit		
1985-87	◆17111156	39.25
(4) Throttle Position Sensor Kit		
1985	◆17111162	62.75
1986-87	◆17111471	47.75
(5) Throttle Body Kit		
1985	◆17111160	185.75
1986-87	◆17111469	185.75
(6) Fuel Nut Assortment Kit		
1985-87	◆17078261	15.50
(7) Idle Air Valve Control Kit		
1985-87	◆17079256	88.75
Fuel Meter Kit		
Includes injector & pressure regulator.		
1985	◆17111157	350.00
1986-87	◆17078262	128.75

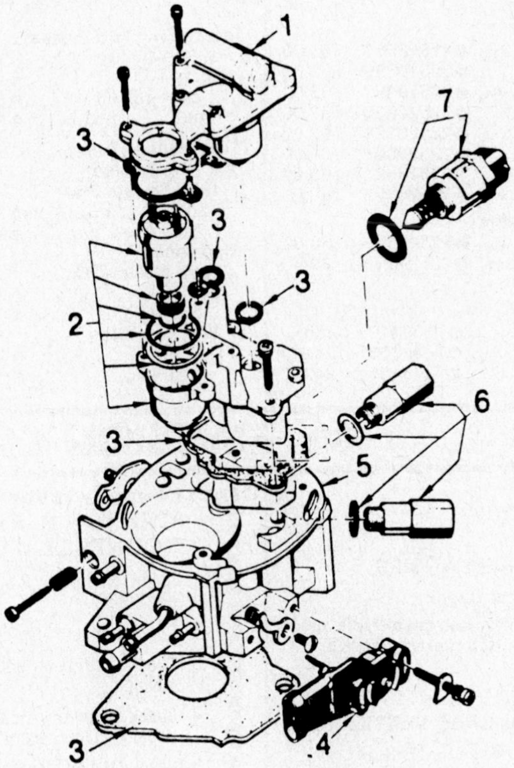

PARTS 3 FUEL SYSTEM 3 PARTS

	Part No.	Price
Carburetor Assy.		
V-6-231		
1983-Fed.	◆17079440	876.50
Calif.	◆17079205	666.75
1984	◆17110332	912.75
1985	◆17111175	750.50
1986-87	◆17111526	743.25
V-8-305		
1983	◆17079226	821.25
1984	◆17110449	846.00
1985	◆17110902	887.00
1986-87	◆17111481	876.00
V-8-307		
1986-87	◆17111487	876.00
Carburetor Power Kit		
V-6-231		
1983-Fed.	◆17076022	28.00
Calif.	◆17076129	51.00
1984	17068868	32.75
1985-87	◆17076144	57.75
V-8-305		
1983-84	◆7039467	41.50
1985-87	◆17076043	33.75
V-8-307		
1986-87	◆17076141	49.50
Fuel Pump Assy.		
V-6-231		
1983-84	◆6471172	N.L.
1985-87	◆6471368	32.50
V-6-262		
1985-exc. Sta. wag.	◆6472370	57.00
Sta. wag.	◆6472421	57.00
1986-87	◆6472011	N.L.
V-8-305		
1983-87	6470442	N.L.
V-8-307		
1986-87	◆6471743	35.00
Fuel Tank		
Order by year and model.		
Fuel Gauge (Dash)		
Part numbers listed are for pricing reference only. Order with complete model and optional equipment identification.		
(exc. Parisienne)		
1983	6432928	30.00
1984-87	6433933	24.25
(Parisienne)		
1983-exc. below	6433191	25.50
THM 700 trans.	◆6433460	28.25
1984-87-exc. below	6434216	29.00
THM 700 trans.	6434196	29.00
Fuel Gauge (Tank)		
Order by year and model.		
Manifold Gasket Set		
V-6-231		
1983-87-Alum.	◆25505397	15.75
Cast iron	◆1264924	14.50
V-6-262		
1985-87	◆14089020	2.50
V-8-305		
1983-85	◆14034821	5.75
1986-87	◆14038088	N.L.
V-8-307		
1986-87	◆22534925	23.50

PARTS 3 FUEL SYSTEM 3 PARTS

	Part No.	Price
Air Intake Crossover		
1983-84	◆22509735	109.00
1985	◆22526995	109.00
DIESEL FUEL SYSTEM		
Fuel Pump		
1983-84	◆6471317	N.L.
1985	◆6442228	59.25
Injection Pump Adapter		
1983-84	◆558768	21.75
1985	◆22516525	52.50

PARTS — 3 FUEL SYSTEM 3 — PARTS

	Part No.	Price
Fuel Injection Pump		
1983-exc. below	◆22518686	763.00
Hi alt	◆22518689	763.00
Sta. wag	◆22519990	763.00
1984-exc. below	◆22520936	763.00
Hi alt	◆22520999	763.00
Sta. wag	◆22520937	763.00
1985-exc. below	◆22524421	763.00
Sta. wag	◆22524422	763.00
Fuel Injection Nozzles		
1983	◆22520378	60.00
1984-85	◆22521207	89.50
Vacuum Pump		
1983-84	◆7839413	116.00
1985-wo/A.C.	◆7845203	124.00
A.C.	◆7845425	124.00

	Part No.	Price
Intake Manifold Gaskets		
1983-84-alum. int	◆22527123	N.L.
cast iron int	◆22516344	12.00
1985	◆22527544	16.50
Fuel Gauge (Tank)		
(exc. Parisienne)		
1983-84-wo/Sta. wag	◆25002566	99.25
Sta. wag	◆25002567	104.50
(Parisienne)		
1983-84-wo/Sta. wag	◆25003151	99.00
Sta. wag	◆25002569	105.50
1985-wo/Sta. wag	◆25004277	86.75
Sta. wag	◆25004280	76.25

	Part No.	Price
Fuel Gauge (Dash)		
(exc. Parisienne)		
1983	6433320	23.50
1984-85	6433935	24.25
(Parisienne)		
1983-wo/Gauges	◆6432935	24.25
(Gauges) exc. below	◆6433229	25.50
THM 700 trans.	6433702	28.50
1984-85-exc. below	6434204	26.50
THM 250C	6434208	29.00
Water Detector Kit		
1983-85	◆25002621	97.50

LABOR — 3A EMISSION CONTROLS 3A — LABOR

(Factory Time) — Chilton Time

GASOLINE ENGINES

(G) Emission Control Check
Includes: Check and adjust engine idle speed and mixture and ignition timing. Check P.C.V. valve.
All models 6

POSITIVE CRANKCASE VENTILATION

(M) Positive Crankcase Ventilation Valve, Renew
All models (.2) 3

(M) Crankcase Ventilation Filter Assy., Renew
All models (.2) 3

EVAPORATIVE EMISSION TYPE

(G) Charcoal Canister, Renew
1983-87 (.2) 3

(G) Canister Purge Thermal Vacuum Switch, Renew
1983-87 (.2) 3

(G) Fuel Tank Pressure Control Valve, Renew
1983-87 (.2) 3

CONTROLLED COMBUSTION TYPE

(G) Air Cleaner Vacuum Motor, Renew
All models (.3) 5

(G) Air Cleaner Temperature Sensor, Renew
All models (.2) 3

(G) Thermal Vacuum Switch, Renew
All models (.3) 4

EXHAUST GAS RECIRCULATION SYSTEM

(G) E.G.R. Valve, Renew
All models (.3) 4

(G) E.G.R. Valve, Clean
All models (.4) 5

(G) E.G.R. Vacuum Delay Valve, Renew
All models (.2) 3

(G) Thermostatic Vacuum Control Switch, Renew
All models (.3) 4

CHILTON'S EMISSION CONTROL TUNE-UP

1. Clean or renew P.C.V. valve, hoses and filter.
2. Check fuel tank cap for sealing ability.
3. Check fuel tank and fuel lines for leakage.
4. Check evaporation canister and filter. Replace if necessary.
5. Check engine compression to determine leakage of unburned gases. (Add time for items of interference).
6. Test and clean or renew spark plugs.
7. Check engine oil dipstick for sealing ability.
8. Test exhaust system with analyzer and check system for leakage.
9. Check exhaust manifold heat valve for operation.
10. Adjust ignition timing and carburetor idle speed and mixture.
11. Check automatic choke mechanism for free operation.
12. Inspect air cleaner and element.
13. On models so equipped, test distributor vacuum control switch and transmission control switch.

V-6 .... 1.7
V-8 .... 1.8

For repairs made, charge accordingly.

(Factory Time) — Chilton Time

(G) EGR/EFE Thermal Vacuum Switch, Renew
All models (.3) 4

(G) Thermal Control Valve, Renew
All models (.3) 4

AIR INJECTOR REACTOR TYPE

(G) A.I.R. Pump, Renew
1983-87-V-6 (.4) 6
V-8 (.6) 8

(G) A.I.R. Pump Drive Belt, Renew
1983-87 (.2) 3

(Factory Time) — Chilton Time

(G) Check Valve, Renew
1983-87-one (.2) 3
each adtnl (.1) 1

(G) A.I.R. Air Cleaner, Renew
1983-87 (.2) 3

(G) Air Pump Centrifugal Filter, Renew
1983-87 (.3) 5

(G) A.I.R. Manifold Pipe, Renew
1983-87
V-6-each (.4) 6
V-8-each (.6) 9
w/A.C. add (.2) 2

(G) Catalytic Converter Air Pipe, Renew
1983-87
one piece (.4) 7

COMPUTER COMMAND CONTROL SYSTEM (C.C.C.)

(P) Throttle Position Sensor, Adjust
All models
2 bbl 9
4 bbl 8
Perform C.C.C. system check add 1.0

(P) Idle Speed Control Motor, Adjust
All models 7

(P) Electronic Control Module, Renew
Does not include system performance check.
1983-87 (.5) 6

(P) Mixture Control Solenoid, Renew
Does not include system performance check.
1983-87
2 bbl (1.1) 1.4
4 bbl (1.2) 1.5

(P) Prom, Renew
Does not include system performance check.
Includes: R&R electronic module.
1983-87 (.5) 8

(P) Barometric Sensor, Renew
Does not include system performance check.
1983-87 (.5) 7

(Factory Time) Chilton Time

(P) Coolant Temperature Sensor, Renew
Does not include system performance check.
Includes: Drain and refill cooling system.
1983-87 (.5) 7

(P) Manifold Pressure Sensor, Renew
Does not include system performance check.
1983-87 (.5) 6

(P) Oxygen Sensor, Renew
Does not include system performance check.
1983-87 (.5) 7

(P) Throttle Position Sensor, Renew
Does not include system performance check.
1983-87
2 bbl (1.0) 1.4
4 bbl (1.2) 1.5

(P) Back-Up Lamp and Park/Neutral Switch, Renew
Does not include system performance check.
1983-87 (.5) 7

(P) Air Control Valve, Renew
Does not include system performance check.
1983-87 (.4) 6

(P) Air Control/Air Switching Valve, Renew
Does not include system performance check.
1983-87 (.4) 6
w/229 Eng (.7) 9
w/262 Eng (.7) 9

(P) Canister Purge Control Valve, Renew
Does not include system performance check.
1983-87 (.4) 6

(P) Air Control Valve Solenoid, Renew
Does not include system performance check.
1983-87 (.5) 6

(P) Air Switching Valve, Renew
Does not include system performance check.
1983-87 (.4) 6

(P) E.G.R. Vacuum Control Solenoid, Renew
Does not include system performance check.
1983-87 (.5) 7

(P) E.F.E. Vacuum Control Solenoid, Renew
Does not include system performance check.
1983-87 (.3) 5

(P) Vacuum Control Purge Solenoid, Renew
Does not include system performance check.
1983-87 (.3) 5

(P) EGR Bleed Control Solenoid, Renew
Does not include system performance check.
1983-87 (.4) 6

(P) Air Control Valve Relay, Renew
Does not include system performance check.
1983-87 (.4) 5

(P) Air Switching Valve Relay, Renew
Does not include system performance check.
1983-87 (.3) 4

(P) EGR Bleed Control Relay, Renew
Does not include system performance check.
1983-87 (.4) 5

(P) EFE/EGR Relay, Renew
Does not include system performance check.
1983-87 (.3) 5

(P) EGR/EFE Purge Solenoid, Renew
Does not include system check.
1983-85 (.4) 6

(P) Idle Speed Control Motor, Renew or Adjust
1983-87 (.5) 7

(P) Idle Load Compensator, Renew
1983-84 (.4) 6

(P) Vehicle Speed Sensor, Renew
1983-87 (.8) 1.5

(P) Tachometer Filter, Renew
Does not include system performance check.
1983-87 (.3) 3

(P) Computer Command Control System Performance Check
1983-87 (.5) 1.0

EMISSION CONTROLS THROTTLE BODY INJECTION

(P) Electronic Control Module, Renew
1985-87 (.6) 9

(P) Prom, Renew
1985-87 (.5) 1.0

(P) Coolant Temperature Sensor, Renew
1985-87 (.5) 7

(P) Manifold Pressure Sensor, Renew
1985-87 (.5) 6

(P) Oxygen Sensor, Renew
1985-87 (.5) 7

(Factory Time) Chilton Time

(P) Vehicle Speed Sensor, Renew
1985-87 (.8) 1.5

(P) Throttle Position Sensor, Renew
1985-87 (.9) 1.4

DIESEL ENGINE

(G) Crankcase Depression Regulator Valve, Renew
1983-85 (.2) 3

(G) Crankcase Ventilation Flow Control Valve, Renew
1983-85 (.2) 3

(G) Crankcase Ventilation Filter, Renew
1983-85 (.2) 3

(G) E.G.R. Valve and/or Gasket, Renew
1983-85 (.5) 1.0

(G) E.G.R. Control Valve Solenoid, Renew
1983-85 (.2) 3

(G) E.G.R. Control Valve Switch, Renew
1983-85 (.2) 3

(G) E.P.R. Control Valve Solenoid, Renew
1983-85 (.3) 4

(G) E.P.R. Control Valve Switch, Renew
1983-85 (.3) 4

(G) E.P.R. Exhaust Pressure Regulator Valve, Renew
1983-85 (.3) 4

(G) Vacuum Regulator Valve, Renew
1983-85 (.6) 8

DIESEL ELECTRONIC EMISSION CONTROLS

(P) Electronic Control Module, Renew
1985 (.6) 8

(P) Manifold Absolute Pressure Sensor, Renew
1985 (.3) 5

(P) Vehicle Speed Sensor, Renew
1985 (.9) 1.4

(P) Coolant Temperature Sensor, Renew
1985 (.6) 7

PARTS 3A EMISSION CONTROLS 3A PARTS

	Part No.	Price
Canister		
V-6-231		
1983-87	◆17064622	39.50
V-6-262		
1985	◆17075859	66.00
1986-87	◆17086095	51.75
V-8-305		
1983	◆17075824	75.50
1984-87	◆17075849	34.50
V-8-307		
1986-87	◆17064622	N.L.
Element (Canister Filter)		
1983-87	◆7026014	2.50
Positive Crankcase Vent Valve		
V-6-231		
1983-87	◆6487534	3.00
V-6-262		
1985-87	◆8995284	5.00
V-8-305		
1983-87	◆6487779	2.50
V-8-307		
1986-87	◆8997683	N.L.
V-8-350 diesel		
1983-85	◆25041678	34.50

E.G.R. Valve

Replacement E.G.R. valve must be ordered according to the stamping number on the original valve.

AIR INJECTOR REACTOR TYPE

	Part No.	Price
Air Pump Assy.		
V-6-231		
1983-87	◆7835397	131.00
V-6-262		
1983-87	◆7834916	149.00
V-8-305		
1983-87	◆7834916	149.00
V-8-307		
1986-87-exc. A.C.	◆7835397	N.L.
A.C.	◆7838575	N.L.
Check Valve		
1983-87-V-6-231	22048209	10.25
V-6-262, V-8-305	22036195	11.50

COMPUTER CONTROLLED EMISSION SYSTEM

Part numbers shown are for pricing reference only. Order with complete year, model and component I.D. information.

	Part No.	Price
Electronic Control Module (ECM)		
Remanufactured		
V-6-231		
1983-Fed.	◆1226024	110.25
Calif.	◆1225500	110.25
1984-87	◆1226519	110.25
V-6-262		
1985-87	◆1226868	110.00
V-8-305, 350		
1983	◆1226025	110.25
1984	◆1226455	110.25
1985-87	◆1226865	110.00
Calibration Unit (PROM)		
V-6-231		
1983-Calif. em.	◆1226031	40.50
(Federal em.)		
Code 0613AKP	◆1226297	40.50
Code 3484CDD	◆1226445	40.50
1984 (Calif. em.)		
Code 7619CFI	◆16041526	40.50
Code 1053DFS	◆16041052	40.50
1984 (Fed. em.)		
Code 7645CFK	◆16041520	40.50
Code 7635CFH	◆16041224	40.50
Code 1225DFW	◆16041224	40.50
1985-87-Fed.	◆16044104	40.50
Calif.	◆16044109	40.50
V-6-262		
1985-87 (Fed. em.)		
Code 8252DSK	◆16048249	40.50
Code 0694HDZ	◆16050693	40.50
Code 0682HDZ	16050680	40.50
1985-87 (Calif. em.)		
Code 8256DSL	◆16048255	40.50
Code 0699HFA	◆16050698	40.50
Code 4010CRT	16048286	40.50
Code 0687HD6	16050686	40.50
V-8-305		
1983 (Calif. em.)		
Code 8693BKM	◆1226329	40.50
Code 7637BLU	1226354	40.50
1983 (Fed. em.)		
Code 8665BKF	1226328	40.50
Code 0658BPK	1226331	40.50
Code 7626 BLS	1226330	40.50
1984 (Calif. em.)		
Code 0350DDJ	◆16040349	40.50
Code 7825BDU	◆16037824	40.50
Code 1880DKZ	16041879	40.50
Code 5798CJS	16035797	40.50
1984 (Fed. em.)		
Code 7820BDT	◆16037819	40.50
Code 0345DDH	◆16040344	40.50
Code 7815BDS	◆16037814	40.50
Code 7835BDX	16037834	40.50
Code 7845BCZ	16039921	40.50
Code 9922DCS	16039921	40.50
Code 7840BDY	16037839	40.50
1985-87 (Fed. em.)		
Code 6517DWS	◆16046516	40.50
Code 6522DWR	◆16046521	40.50
Code 6532DWF	◆16046531	40.50
Code 4240CPN	16044239	40.50
Code 4245CPP	16044244	40.50
Code 6500 DXR	16046499	40.50
1985-87 (Calif. em.)		
Code 6506DWW	◆16046505	40.50
Code 6512DWU	◆16046511	40.50
Code 6527DWT	◆16046526	40.50
Code 4255CPS	16044254	40.50
Code 6475DYJ	16046474	40.50
Code 6490DYD	16046489	40.50
Manifold Pressure Sensor		
V-6-231		
1983-87	◆16006835	62.25
V-6-262		
1985-87	◆16017460	N.L.
V-8-305, 307		
1983-87	◆16054920	N.L.
Barometric Sensor		
1983-87	◆16006833	62.25
Oxygen Sensor		
1983	◆5613959	29.00
1984-87	◆8990741	28.75
Coolant Temperature Sensor		
1983-84	◆25036092	22.00
1985-87	◆25036708	12.75
ESC Knock Sensor		
1983-87-exc. V-6-262	◆1997562	37.00
V-6-262	◆1997699	28.75
Vehicle Speed Sensor		
(Bonneville, Grand Prix)		
1983	◆25007227	52.00
1984	◆25007421	41.50
1985-87	◆25007463	44.00
(Parisienne)		
1983	◆25007278	53.50
1984-87	◆25007463	44.00

LABOR 4 ALTERNATOR AND REGULATOR 4 LABOR

	(Factory Time)	Chilton Time
(G) Delcotron Circuits, Test		
Includes: Test battery, regulator, Delcotron output.		
All models		.6
(G) Delcotron Assembly, Renew		
Includes: Transfer pulley and fan.		
1983-87		
V-6	(.4)	.7
V-8	(.4)	.8
Diesel	(.4)	.8
Add circuit test if performed.		
(G) Delcotron, R&R and Recondition		
Includes: Complete disassembly, inspect, test, replace parts as required. Reassemble.		
1983-87		
V-6	(1.1)	1.7
V-8	(1.1)	1.8
Diesel	(1.3)	2.3
w/Diesel eng add	(.1)	.1
(G) Delcotron Front Bearing, Renew		
Includes: R&R Delcotron, separate end frames.		
1983-87-one	(.6)	1.0
Renew rear brg add		.2
w/Diesel eng add	(.2)	.2
(G) Delcotron Voltage Regulator, Renew		
Includes: R&R, disassemble and reassemble Delcotron.		
1983-87	(.6)	1.2
w/Diesel eng add	(.2)	.2
Add circuit test if performed.		
(G) Voltmeter, Renew		
1983-87	(.3)	.5

PARTS 4 ALTERNATOR AND REGULATOR 4 PARTS

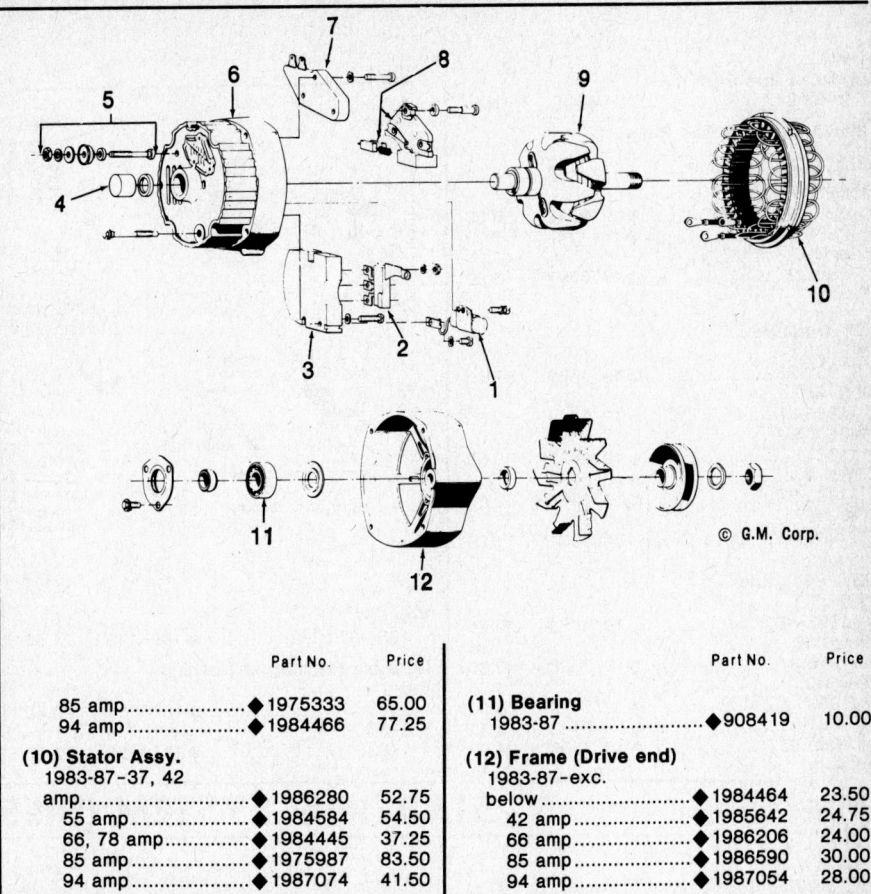

	Part No.	Price
Delcotron Assembly (New)		
1983-87-42 amp	◆1105360	206.00
56, 63, 78 amp	◆1100250	225.00
66 amp	◆1105369	228.75
85 amp	◆1105339	326.50
94 amp	◆1105492	228.50
(1) Capacitor		
1983-87	◆1978146	4.75
(2) Diode Trio		
1983-87	◆1984459	5.00
(3) Rectifier Bridge		
1983-87-exc. below	◆1984454	28.00
85 amp	◆1975313	24.50
(4) Bearing		
1983-87-exc below	◆9436831	5.50
70, 85 amp	◆1975322	5.50
(5) Terminal Pkg.		
1983-87	◆1975471	3.50
(6) Frame (Rear End)		
1983-87-exc. below	◆1984460	47.75
85 amp	◆1975310	31.00
94 amp	◆1987073	28.00
(7) Regulator		
1983-87	◆1116387	25.00
(8) Brush Pkg.		
1983-87-exc. below	◆1984462	9.00
85 amp	◆1975323	10.00
(9) Rotor Assy.		
1983-87-exc. below	◆1985476	72.00

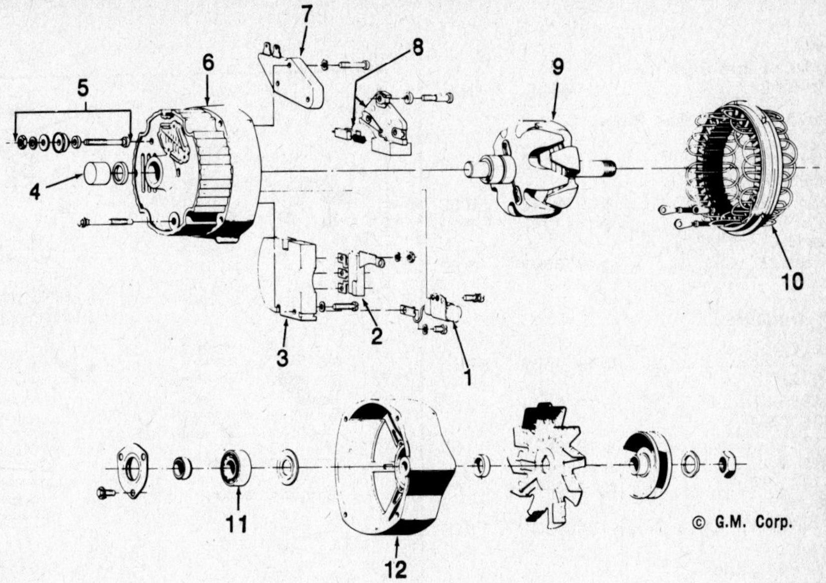

	Part No.	Price
85 amp	◆1975333	65.00
94 amp	◆1984466	77.25
(10) Stator Assy.		
1983-87-37, 42 amp	◆1986280	52.75
55 amp	◆1984584	54.50
66, 78 amp	◆1984445	37.25
85 amp	◆1975987	83.50
94 amp	◆1987074	41.50

	Part No.	Price
(11) Bearing		
1983-87	◆908419	10.00
(12) Frame (Drive end)		
1983-87-exc. below	◆1984464	23.50
42 amp	◆1985642	24.75
66 amp	◆1986206	24.00
85 amp	◆1986590	30.00
94 amp	◆1987054	28.00

LABOR 5 STARTING SYSTEM 5 LABOR

(Factory Time)	Chilton Time
(G) Starter Draw Test (On Car)	
All models	.3
(G) Starter, Renew	
Includes: Separate solenoid, clean and inspect plunger and spring.	
V-6–1983-87 (.8)	.9
V-8–1983-87 (.8)	.9
Diesel–1983-85 (.8)	1.1
Add draw test if performed.	
(G) Starter, R&R and Recondition	
Includes: Turn down armature.	
V-6–1983-87 (1.6)	1.9
V-8–1983-87 (1.6)	1.9
Diesel–1983-85 (1.8)	2.5
Renew field coils add (.2)	.5

(Factory Time)	Chilton Time
(G) Starter Drive, Renew	
Includes: R&R starter.	
V-6–1983-87 (1.0)	1.1
V-8–1983-87 (1.0)	1.1
Diesel–1983-85 (1.0)	1.4
(G) Starter Solenoid, Renew	
Includes: R&R starter.	
V-6–1983-87 (.8)	.9
V-8–1983-87 (.8)	.9
Diesel–1983-85 (.8)	1.1
(G) Neutral Start Switch, Renew	
1983-87 (.3)	.4

(Factory Time)	Chilton Time
(G) Back-Up Lamp and Park/Neutral Switch, Renew	
1983-87 (.3)	.5
(G) Ignition Switch, Renew	
1983-85 (.5)	.9
1986-87	
Pontiac (.4)	.7
Grand Prix (.6)	.9
(M) Battery Cables, Renew	
1983-87-positive (.3)	.4
negative (.2)	.3
batt to batt (.2)	.3
(M) Battery Terminals, Clean	
All models	.3

PARTS 5 STARTING SYSTEM 5 PARTS

	Part No.	Price
(1) Starter Assy. (New)		
V-6-231		
1983-87	◆1998516	204.00
V-6-262		
1985-87	◆1998557	202.00
V-8-305		
1983	◆1109534	219.50
1984	◆1998430	184.75
1985-87	◆1998557	202.00

	Part No.	Price
V-8-307		
1986-87	◆1998536	180.25
(2) Solenoid Switch		
1983-87	◆1114531	N.L.
(3) Drive Assy.		
1983-87	◆1875687	N.L.

	Part No.	Price
(4) Brushes		
V-6-231		
1983-87	◆1906945	.50
V-8-305		
1983-84	◆1893296	.50
1985-87	◆1906945	.50
V-8-307		
1986-87	◆1893296	.75

PARTS 5 STARTING SYSTEM 5 PARTS

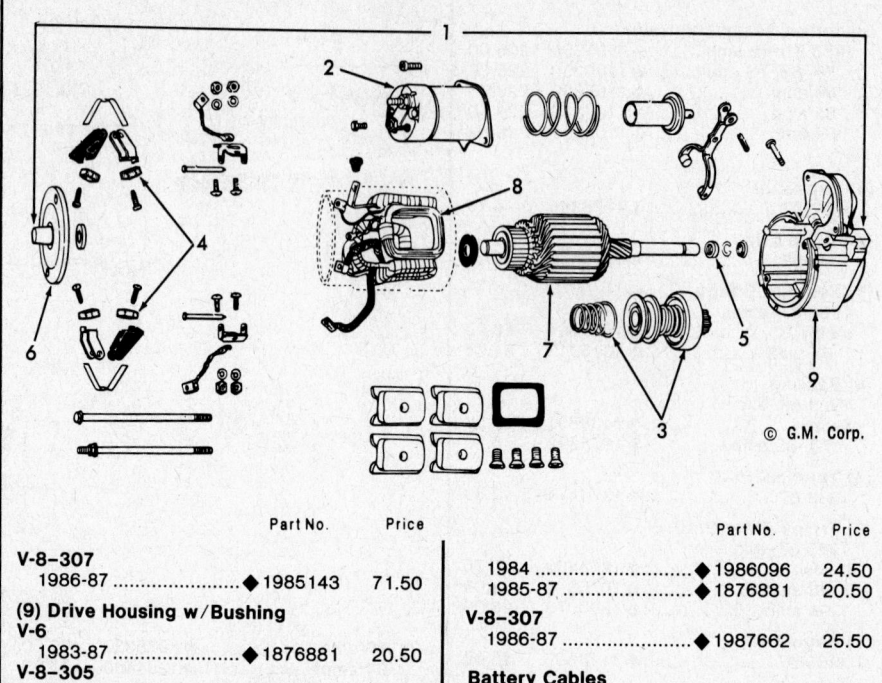

	Part No.	Price
(5) Drive End Bushing		
1983-87	◆N.S.	N.S.
(6) Commutator End Plate		
V-6		
1983-87	◆1974157	7.00
V-8-305		
1983-84	◆1978292	6.50
1985-87	◆1974157	7.00
V-8-307		
1986-87	◆1978292	6.50
(7) Armature		
V-6-231		
1983-87	◆1971568	57.00
V-6-262		
1985-87	◆1970548	52.00
V-8-305		
1983	◆1978670	83.50
1984	◆1985138	N.L.
1985-87	◆1970548	52.00
V-8-307		
1986-87	◆10495931	71.50
(8) Field Coils		
V-6-231		
1983-87	◆1974183	19.25
V-6-262		
1985-87	◆1877306	26.00
V-8-305		
1983	◆1978672	78.00
1984	◆1985143	71.50
1985-87	◆1877306	26.00

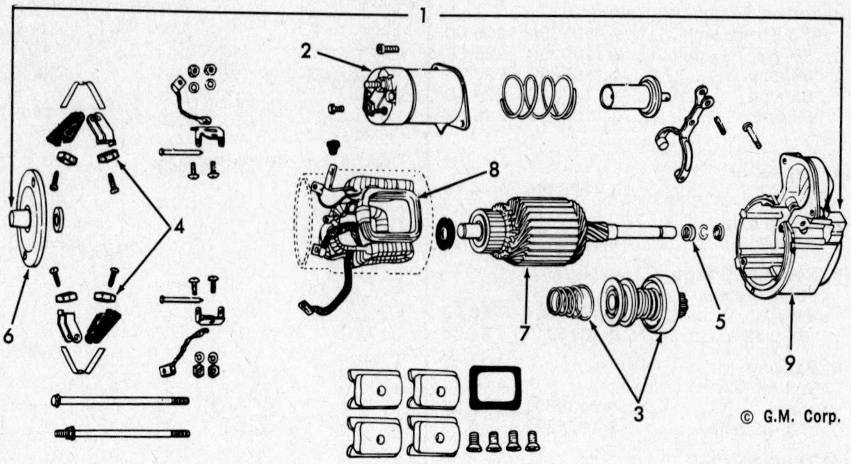

	Part No.	Price
V-8-307		
1986-87	◆1985143	71.50
(9) Drive Housing w/Bushing		
V-6		
1983-87	◆1876881	20.50
V-8-305		
1983	◆1978850	27.75
1984	◆1986096	24.50
1985-87	◆1876881	20.50
V-8-307		
1986-87	◆1987662	25.50

Battery Cables
Order by year and model.

PARTS 5 STARTING SYSTEM (DIESEL) 5 PARTS

	Part No.	Price
Starter Assy. (New)		
1983-85	◆22522853	355.00
(1) Solenoid Switch		
1983-85	◆1114531	N.L.
(2) Drive End Bearing		
1983-85	◆9439544	5.00
(3) Starter Drive		
1983-85	◆1893445	65.00
(4) Drive Shaft		
1983-85	◆1972683	29.00
(5) Gear		
1983-85	◆1972685	12.50
(6) Gear Housing		
1983-85	◆1972700	29.50
(7) Armature		
1983-85	◆1987639	139.75
(8) Field Coils		
1983-85	◆1979982	83.00
(9) Starter Brushes		
1983-85	◆1852885	2.75

Battery Cables
Order by year and model.

	Part No.	Price
Neutral Safety Switch		
1983-85	◆22509632	5.50

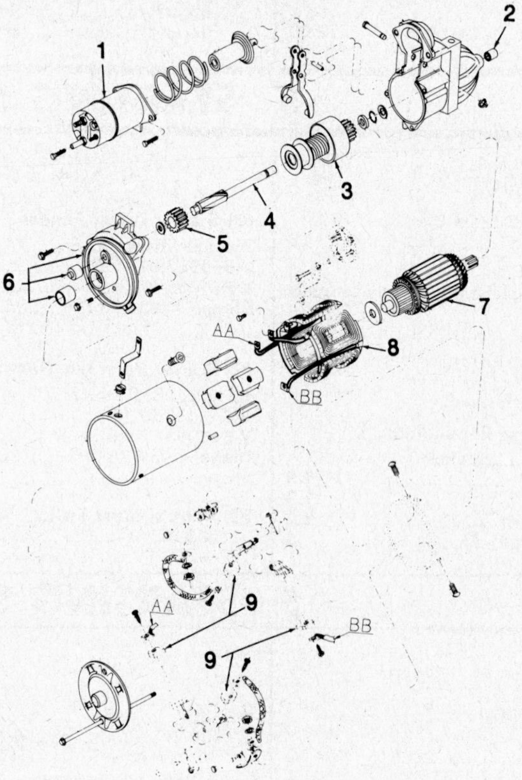

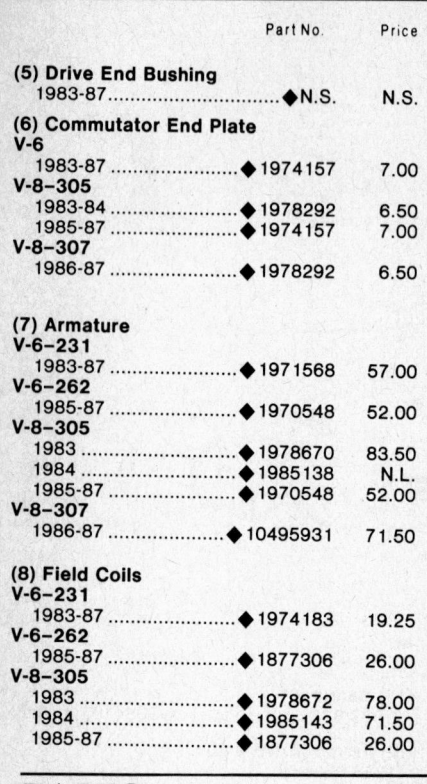

(Factory Time) Chilton Time

(G) Brake Pedal Free Play, Adjust
All models 3

(G) Brakes, Adjust (Minor)
Includes: R&R wheels and adjust brakes thru access holes in drums. Fill master cylinder.
two wheels 4
Remove knock out plugs add, each .. .1

(G) Bleed Brakes (Four Wheels)
Includes: Fill master cylinder.
All models (.4) 5

(G) Free-Up or Renew Brake Self Adjusting Units.
one wheel 6
each adtnl 4

(G) Brake Shoes and/or Pads, Renew
Includes: Install new or exchange shoes or pads, adjust service and hand brake. Bleed system.
1983-87-front-disc (.9) 1.1
rear-drum (.9) 1.5
all four wheels 2.5
Resurface disc rotor add, each 9
Resurface brake drum add, each 5

(G) Brake Drum, Renew
1983-87-each (.3) 5

(G) Brake Combination Valve, Renew
Includes: Bleed system.
1983-87 (.7) 1.0

BRAKE HYDRAULIC SYSTEM

(G) Wheel Cylinder, Renew
Includes: Bleed system.
1983-87-one (.8) 1.0
both (1.1) 1.9

(G) Wheel Cylinder, R&R and Rebuild
Includes: Hone cylinder, bleed system.
1983-87-one (1.0) 1.3
both (1.5) 2.1

(G) Brake Hose, Renew
Includes: Bleed system.
1983-87-one (.4) 6

(G) Electro-Hydraulic Pump, Renew
1985-87 (.4) 5

(G) Powermaster Pressure Switch, Renew
1985-87 (.3) 4

(G) Master Cylinder, Renew
Includes: Bleed cylinder.
1983-87 (.6) 1.0

(G) Master Cylinder, R&R and Rebuild
Includes: Bleed cylinder.
1983-87 (1.4) 1.8
w/Powermaster cyl (1.6) 2.2

(G) Brake Hydraulic System, Recondition
Includes: Renew all rubber parts and bleed system.
1983-87 (5.0) 6.4

(G) Brake System, Flush and Refill
All models 1.2

COMBINATIONS

Add to Brakes, Renew
See Machine Shop Operations

(Factory Time) Chilton Time

(G) RENEW WHEEL CYLINDER
Each (.2) 2

(G) REBUILD WHEEL CYLINDER
Each (.2) 3

(G) REBUILD CALIPER ASSEMBLY
Each (.5) 6

(G) RENEW MASTER CYLINDER
All models (.4) 8

(G) REBUILD MASTER CYLINDER
All models (.8) 1.0

(G) RENEW BRAKE HOSE
Each (.3) 3

(G) RENEW REAR WHEEL GREASE SEALS
One side (.4) 5

(G) REPACK FRONT WHEEL BEARINGS (BOTH WHEELS)
All models (.6) 6

(G) RENEW BRAKE DRUM
Each (.1) 1

(G) RENEW DISC BRAKE ROTOR
Each (.3) 5

(Factory Time) Chilton Time

DISC BRAKES

(G) Brake Shoes and/or Pads, Renew
Includes: Install new or exchange shoes or pads, adjust service and hand brake. Bleed system.
1983-87-front-disc (.9) 1.1
rear-drum (.9) 1.5
all four wheels 2.5
Resurface disc rotor add, each 9
Resurface brake drum add, each 5

(G) Disc Brake Rotor, Renew
1983-87-one (.7) 1.0
both (1.2) 1.5

(G) Caliper Assembly, Renew
Includes: Remove brake shoes, bleed system.
1983-87-one (.7) 1.0
both (1.1) 1.5

(G) Caliper Assembly, R&R and Recondition
Includes: Remove brake shoes, renew parts as required and bleed system.
1983-87-one (1.2) 1.5
both (2.1) 2.5

PARKING BRAKE

(M) Parking Brake, Adjust
All models (.3) 4

(G) Parking Brake Control, Renew
1983-87 (.7) 1.0

(G) Parking Brake Switch, Renew
1983-87 (.2) 3

(G) Parking Brake Cables, Renew
Includes: Adjust parking brake.
1983-87-front (.6) 8
intermediate (.3) 5
rear-each (.8) 1.1
two piece (1.0) 1.4

(Factory Time) Chilton Time

(G) Parking Brake Equalizer, Renew
1983-87 (.3) 5

POWER BRAKES

(G) Power Brake Cylinder, Renew
1983-87 (.6) 1.1

(G) Power Brake Cylinder, R&R and Recondition
1983-87 (1.3) 1.8
Recond m/Cyl add (.8) 8

(G) Low Vacuum Switch, Renew
1985-87 (.2) 3

(G) Low Vacuum Brake Indicator Module, Renew
1985 (.2) 3

(G) Electric Vacuum Pump, Renew
1983-85 (.3) 4
Recond piston add (.2) 2
Renew housing add (.3) 3

(G) Vacuum Pump Pressure Switch, Renew
1983-87 (.2) 3

(G) Power Brake Vacuum Check Valve, Renew
1983-87 (.3) 3

(G) Hydra-boost Unit, Renew
Includes: Bleed system.
1983-85 (.6) 9

(G) Hydra-boost Unit, R&R and Recondition
Includes: Bleed system.
1983-85 (1.0) 1.5

(G) Hydra-boost Pressure Lines, Renew
Includes: Bleed system.
1983-85-each (.3) 6

PARTS 6 BRAKE SYSTEM 6 PARTS

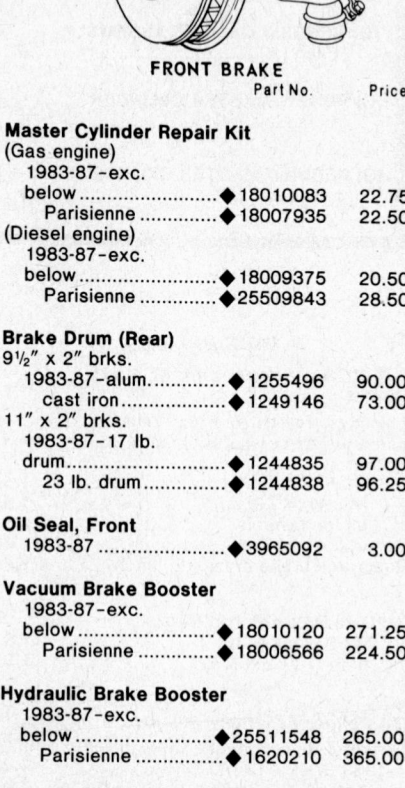

	Part No.	Price
(1) Brake Shoe Set, Rear		
9½" x 2" brks.		
(exc. Parisienne)		
1983-87-exc.		
H.D.	◆12300219	41.00
1983-H.D. brks.	◆12300214	50.00
(Parisienne)		
1983-87	◆1154580	35.00
11" x 2" brks.		
1983-87	◆1154577	42.50
(2) Rear Wheel Cylinder Assy.		
9½" x 2" brks.		
1983-87-exc.		
Grand Prix	◆18004888	28.50
Grand Prix	◆18012303	30.25
11" x 2" brks.		
1983-87-exc.		
Sta. wag.	◆18004890	25.75
Sta. wag.	◆18004793	28.50
Wheel Cylinder Repair Kit		
9½" x 2" brks.		
1983-87-exc.		
Grand Prix	5466563	7.75
Grand Prix	◆18003744	12.75
11" x 2" brks.		
1983-87	◆5472328	8.00
Front Brake Hose		
exc. Parisienne		
1983-87	◆9762810	17.75
(Parisienne)		
1983-87	◆9762809	18.00
Rear Brake Hose		
(exc. Parisienne)		
1983-87	◆9761251	15.00
(Parisienne)		
1983-87	◆9757655	15.00
Master Cylinder Assy.		
(Gas engine)		
1983-84-exc.		
below	◆18009816	171.25
Parisienne	◆18010313	145.75
1985-87-exc.		
below	◆18011916	141.50
Parisienne	◆18010313	145.75
(Diesel engine)		
1983-85	◆25509416	103.00

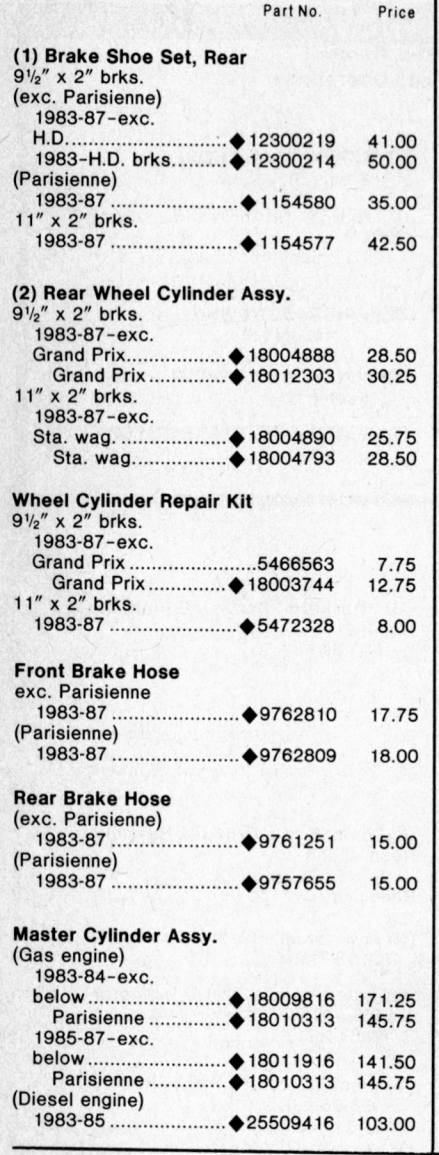

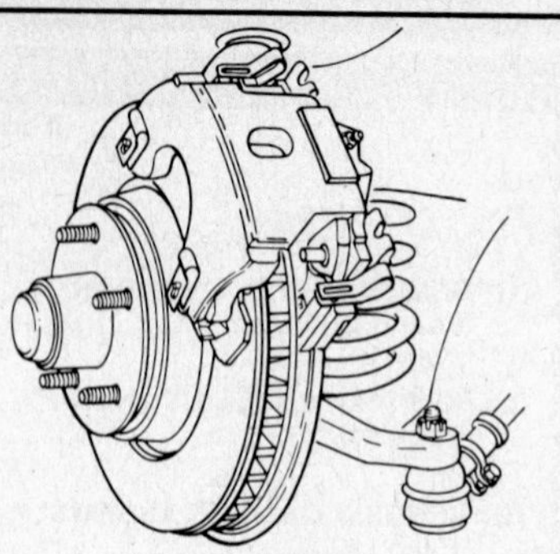

FRONT BRAKE

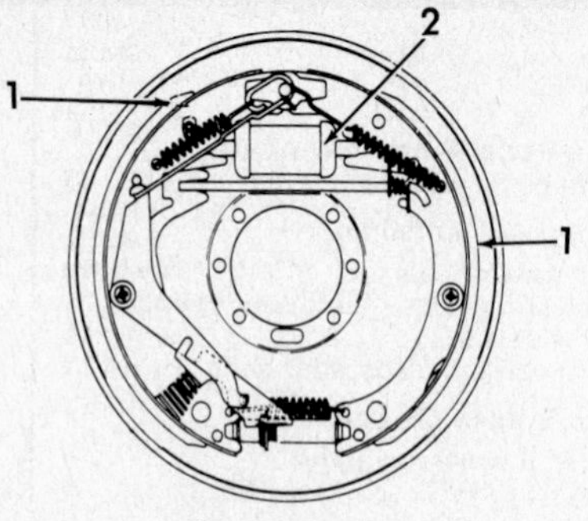

REAR BRAKE

	Part No.	Price
Master Cylinder Repair Kit		
(Gas engine)		
1983-87-exc.		
below	◆18010083	22.75
Parisienne	◆18007935	22.50
(Diesel engine)		
1983-87-exc.		
below	◆18009375	20.50
Parisienne	◆25509843	28.50
Brake Drum (Rear)		
9½" x 2" brks.		
1983-87-alum.	◆1255496	90.00
cast iron	◆1249146	73.00
11" x 2" brks.		
1983-87-17 lb.		
drum	◆1244835	97.00
23 lb. drum	◆1244838	96.25
Oil Seal, Front		
1983-87	◆3965092	3.00
Vacuum Brake Booster		
1983-87-exc.		
below	◆18010120	271.25
Parisienne	◆18006566	224.50
Hydraulic Brake Booster		
1983-87-exc.		
below	◆25511548	265.00
Parisienne	◆1620210	365.00
Vacuum Booster Repair Kit		
1983-87-exc.		
below	◆18007897	47.50
Parisienne	◆18007865	47.50

	Part No.	Price
Hydraulic Booster Seal Kit		
1983-87-exc.		
below	◆22506710	16.50
Parisienne	◆22506440	10.75
Parking Brake		
Front Cable		
1983-87	◆25502753	11.50
(Bonneville, Grand Prix)		
1983	◆25502753	11.50
1984-87	◆25520341	11.50
(Parisienne)		
1983-84	◆25502769	12.00
1985-87	◆25520342	12.75
Rear Cable		
(Bonneville, Grand Prix)		
1983-R.H.	◆25502794	21.00
L.H.	◆22518169	N.L.
1984-85-R.H.	◆25518168	22.00
L.H.	◆25518169	12.25
1986-87-R.H.	◆25526680	22.00
L.H.	◆25526681	12.25
(Parisienne)		
1983-84-L.H.	◆25502687	22.00
R.H. (exc. wag.)	◆25502686	22.00
R.H. (sta. wag.)	◆25502772	22.50
1985-87-L.H.	◆25520337	22.25
L.H. (sta. wag.)	◆25524603	22.50
R.H.	◆25520338	22.00
R.H. (sta. wag.)	◆25524602	22.00
Parking Brake Control		
(Bonneville, Grand Prix)		
1983-87	◆25503396	23.25
(Parisienne)		
1983-87	◆25502971	23.50

PARTS 6 DISC BRAKES 6 PARTS

	Part No.	Price
(1) Brake Pads		
(Bonneville, Grand Prix)		
1983-87	◆12300227	43.00
(Parisienne)		
1983-87-exc.		
H.D.	◆1154578	35.00
H.D. brks.	◆12300192	47.00
(2) Anti-Rattle Spring		
(Bonneville, Grand Prix)		
1983-87	◆18006810	3.00
(Parisienne)		
1983-87	◆5469497	1.00
(3) Repair Kit		
(Bonneville, Grand Prix)		
1983-87	◆18003724	8.75
(Parisienne)		
1983-87	◆5468767	10.00

Consists of 1 seal, 1 boot & 1 'O' ring.

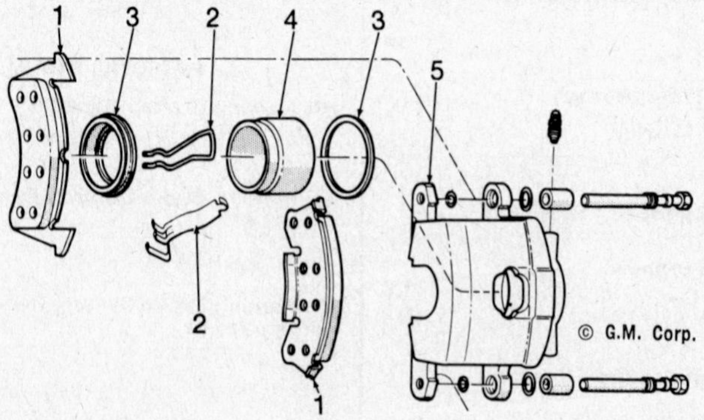

	Part No.	Price
(4) Piston Assy.		
(Bonneville, Grand Prix)		
1983-87	◆18003155	11.00
(Parisienne)		
1983-87	◆2622207	11.00

PARTS **6 DISC BRAKES 6** PARTS

	Part No.	Price
(5) Caliper Assy.		
(Bonneville, Grand Prix)		
1983-87-R.H.	◆18010481	148.75
L.H.	◆18010480	137.00
(Parisienne)		
1983-87-R.H.	◆18012309	168.75
L.H.	◆18012308	168.75
Hub & Disc		
(Bonneville, Grand Prix)		
1983-87	◆14032431	100.25
(Parisienne)		
1983-87-11" rotor	◆14008640	110.00
12" rotor	◆14008641	110.00

LABOR **7 COOLING SYSTEM 7** LABOR

(Factory Time) Chilton Time

(M) Winterize Cooling System

Includes: Run engine to check for leaks, tighten all hose connections. Test radiator and pressure cap, drain radiator and engine block. Add anti-freeze and refill system.

All models 5

(G) Thermostat, Renew

1983-85	
V-6	
229 eng (.7)	.8
231 eng (.6)	.7
262 eng (.7)	.9
V-8 (.5)	.6
Diesel (.5)	.6
1986-87	
V-6	
Pontiac (.7)	.9
Grand Prix (.3)	.4
V-8 (.5)	.6

(M) Radiator, R&R or Renew

Includes: Drain and refill cooling system.

1983-87 (.7)	1.1
w/A.C. add (.2)	.2
w/Diesel eng add (.1)	.1

ADD THESE OPERATIONS TO RADIATOR R&R

(G) Boil & Repair	1.5
(G) Rod Clean	1.9
(G) Repair Core	1.3
(G) Renew Tank	1.6
(G) Renew Trans., Oil Cooler	1.9
(G) Recore Radiator	1.7

(M) Radiator Hoses, Renew

1983-87-upper (.3)	.4
lower (.4)	.5
both (.5)	.7
by-pass (.6)	.8

(M) Drive Belt, Adjust

1983-87-one (.3)	.3
each adtnl	.1

(M) Fan Belt, Renew

1983-87-one (.3)	.4
each adtnl	.1

(G) Water Pump, Renew

V-6-1983-87-231 eng (.9)	1.3
229 eng (1.3)	1.7
262 eng (.9)	1.4
V-8-1983-87 (1.3)	1.7
Diesel-1983-85 (1.7)	2.5

COOLING SYSTEM TUNE-UP

An Annual Cooling System Tune-Up Suggestion List should include (with some exceptions):

1. A visual check of the cooling system for indications of leaks or excessive oil content.
2. Pressure check the cooling system for internal and external leaks with filler cap and neck adapter and tester.
3. Check crankcase and automatic transmission oil for water content.
4. Test coolant thermostat with radiator thermometer.
5. Check temperature gauge for accuracy.
6. Drain system and flush till clean.
7. Clean foreign matter from radiator fins.
8. Test radiator pressure cap with cap tester.
9. Check fan blades and pulleys for alignment and damage.
10. Internal and external inspection of all hoses for cracks and deterioration.
11. Check core plugs (where possible) for seepage.
12. Refill system with correct coolant and check for air locks.
13. Check condition and tension of drive belts with tension gauge.

All models 1.5

(Factory Time) Chilton Time

w/A.C. add (.2)	.2
w/P.S. add (.1)	.1

(G) Temperature Gauge (Engine Unit), Renew

1983-87 (.3) 4

(G) Temperature Gauge (Dash Unit), Renew

1983-87 (.3) 5

(G) Fan Blades, Renew

1983-87 (.3)	.5
w/Thermo fan clutch add (.1)	.1
w/A.C. add (.2)	.2
w/P.S. add (.1)	.1

(G) Water Jacket Expansion Plugs, Renew (Side of Block)

1983-87-each (.5) 5

Note: If necessary to R&R any component to gain access to plug, add appropriate time.

(G) Heater Hoses, Renew

1983-87-one (.2)	.4
both (.4)	.5
all (.4)	.6

(G) Heater Core, R&R or Renew Without Air Conditioning

1983-87-Grand Prix (.4)	.9
Pontiac (.5)	1.0

With Air Conditioning

1983-87-Grand Prix (1.1)	2.3
Pontiac (1.2)	2.5

(Factory Time) Chilton Time

ADD THESE OPERATIONS TO HEATER CORE R&R

(G) Boil & Repair	1.2
(G) Repair Core	.9
(G) Recore	1.2

(G) Heater Control Assembly, Renew

1983-85-Grand Prix (.4)	.7
Pontiac (.5)	.9
1986-87-Grand Prix (.4)	.7
Pontiac (.7)	1.0

(G) Heater Blower Motor, Renew

1983-87 (.3) 5

(G) Heater Blower Motor Resistor, Renew

1983-87 (.2) 3

(G) Heater Blower Motor Switch, Renew

1983-85-Grand Prix (.4)	.6
Pontiac (.3)	.6
1986-87	
Grand Prix (.4)	.7
Pontiac (.6)	.9

(G) Water Control Valve, Renew (w/A.T.C.)

1983-85	
Grand Prix	
Gas (.5)	.8
Diesel (.6)	.8
Pontiac (.3)	.5
1986-87-Grand Prix (.5)	.8
Pontiac (.3)	.5

PARTS — 7 COOLING SYSTEM 7 — PARTS

	Part No.	Price
(1) Radiator Assy.		
Accurate replacement of the radiator can be done only by using the radiator code stamped on a metal tag located on the original radiator. Order by year, model and radiator code no.		
(2) Radiator Upper Hose		
Order by year and model.		
(3) Fan Belt		
Order by model & description.		
(4) Water Pump Assy.		
V-6-231		
1983-85	◆1260709	61.75
1986-87	◆25527536	N.L.
V-6-262		
1985-87	◆14085847	75.75
V-8-305		
1983-84	◆474029	72.50
1985-87	◆14085847	75.75
V-8-307		
1986-87	◆556283	N.L.
V-8-350 Diesel		
1983-85	◆556283	95.00
(5) Radiator Lower Hose		
Order by year and model.		
(6) Thermostat		
V-6		
1983	◆1254894	9.00
1984-87	◆3041390	6.00
V-8-305		
1983-87	◆3041390	6.00
V-8-307		
1986-87	◆3051139	N.L.
V-8-350 Diesel		
1983-87	◆3051139	5.00
Temperature Gauge (Engine Unit)		
(Gas engine)		
(wo/gauges)		
1983-87	◆25036136	11.75
(w/gauges)		
1983-87	◆8993146	19.25

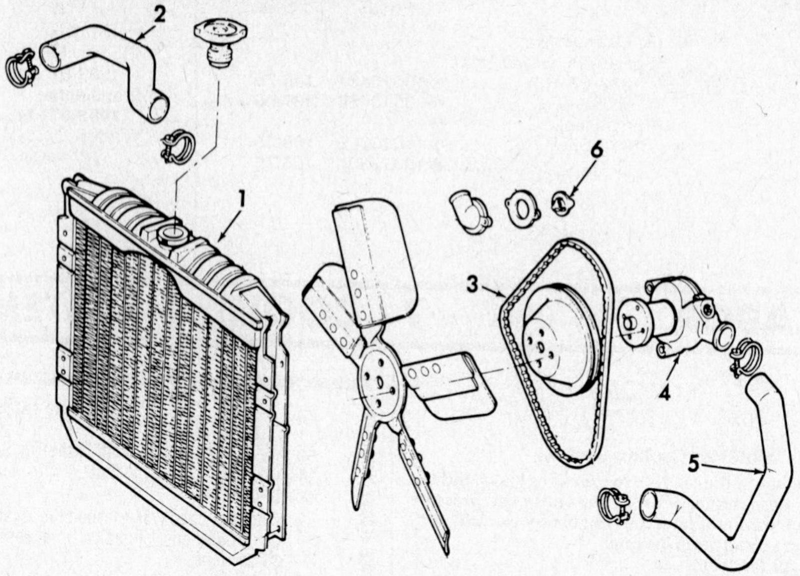

	Part No.	Price
(Diesel engine)		
(wo/gauges)		
1983	◆25036371	8.00
1984-87	◆25036629	9.75
(w/gauges)		
1983	◆8993146	19.25
1984	◆25036628	19.75
1985-87	◆8993146	19.25
Heater Core Assembly		
(Bonneville, Grand Prix)		
1983-87-wo/A.C.	◆3037852	55.75
A.C.	◆3037689	70.00

	Part No.	Price
(Parisienne)		
1983-87-wo/A.C.	◆3036422	41.25
A.C.	◆3035420	43.00
Blower Motor (wo/A.C.)		
(wo/H.D. heater)		
1983	◆22021257	N.L.
1984-87	◆22048573	45.75
(H.D. heater)		
1983	◆22048569	47.50
1984-87	◆22048569	47.50
Switch, Heater Control		
1983	◆16015256	6.00
1984-87	◆16032480	7.25

LABOR — 8 EXHAUST SYSTEM 8 — LABOR

(Factory Time)	Chilton Time
(G) Muffler, Renew	
1983-87-each (.5)	.7
If welded add	.2
(G) Tail Pipe, Renew	
1983-87 (.5)	.6
(G) Resonator Assy., Renew	
1983-87 (.4)	.6
If welded add	.2
(G) Catalytic Converter, Renew	
1983-87 (.8)	1.0
(G) Front Exhaust Pipe, Renew (To Converter)	
1983-87 (.5)	1.0
(G) Exhaust Crossover Pipe, Renew	
1983-87-Grand Prix	
Gas (.4)	.8
Diesel (1.4)	2.2
Pontiac	
Gas (.4)	.8
Diesel (.9)	1.3
(G) Intermediate Exhaust Pipe, Renew	
1983-87 (.5)	.8

(Factory Time)	Chilton Time
(G) E.F.E. Valve (Heat Riser), Renew	
Includes: Hoist car.	
1983-87 (.5)	.8
(G) Exhaust Manifold or Gasket, Renew	
Pontiac	
V-6-1983-87	
229 eng	
right (1.0)	1.4
left (.8)	1.2
231 eng	
right (.7)	1.1
left (.7)	1.1
w/A.C. add (.3)	.3
262 eng	
right side (1.0)	1.5
left side (.8)	1.2
w/A.C. add (.5)	.5
w/C.C.C. add (.2)	.2
V-81983-87	
305 eng-Code H	
right side (1.3)	2.1
left side (1.0)	1.4
307 eng-Code Y	
right side (1.1)	1.6
left side (1.0)	1.5

(Factory Time)	Chilton Time
Diesel-1983	
right side (.9)	1.3
left side (.7)	1.1
1984-85-right side (1.2)	1.7
left side (.7)	1.1
Grand Prix	
V-6-1983-87	
right side (.7)	1.1
left side (.7)	1.1
w/A.C. add (.3)	.3
V-8-1983-87	
right side (1.3)	2.1
left side (1.0)	1.4
w/A.C. add (.4)	.4
w/C.C.C. add (.2)	.2
Diesel	
1983-right side (.9)	1.3
left side (.7)	1.1
1984-85-right side (1.2)	1.7
left side (.7)	1.1
w/A.C. add (.5)	.5

COMBINATIONS

(Factory Time)	Chilton Time
(G) Muffler, Exhaust and Tail Pipe, Renew	
1983-87-V-6 (.7)	1.3
V-8 (.9)	1.5

PARTS 8 EXHAUST SYSTEM 8 PARTS

	Part No.	Price
Part numbers shown are for pricing reference only. Order parts with complete year, model and engine identification.		
Resonator		
V-6-305 eng.		
1985-87-Sedan		
rear exit pipe	14080800	61.75
side exit pipe	14089452	64.75
1985-87-Sta. wag.	14082801	71.50
V-8-350 Diesel		
1983-87-sta. wag.	◆22512354	58.25
Muffler		
Order by year and model.		
Tailpipe Assm.		
Pipes not listed are included with muffler assm.		
Parisienne		
V-6-231		
1984	◆14011207	46.25
V-6-262		
1985-87	1409453	N.L.
V-8-305		
1983-84-exc. Sta. wag.	◆14011207	46.25
Sta. wag.	◆14011209	54.50
1985-87	◆14089453	48.25
V-8-307		
exc. Sta. wag.	9251925	N.L.
Sta. wag.	◆22505492	89.25
V-8-350 Diesel		
1983-87-4 dr. sedan	◆25509141	49.25
1983-87-sta. wag.	◆22512353	55.75

	Part No.	Price
Front Pipe		
V-6-231		
Bonneville, Grand Prix		
1983-Fed.	◆25515198	14.50
Calif.	◆25506875	14.00
1984-87	◆25515198	14.50
Parisienne		
1983	◆25508302	48.75
1984	◆25515214	21.25
V-8-307		
1986-87	◆22520490	11.00
V-8-350 Diesel		
Bonneville, Grand Prix		
1983-84	◆563056	41.25
Parisienne		
1983-84	◆22512345	53.75
1985-87-sedan	◆22512355	52.25
sta. wag.	◆22512346	52.25
Intermediate Pipe		
V-6-231		
1983-87-exc. below	◆25515196	53.00
1984-Parisienne	◆25516994	20.00
V-6-262		
1985-87	◆14091439	31.50
V-8-305		
1983-87-exc. below	◆14063928	53.00
1983-84-Parisienne	◆14089120	23.00
1985-87-Parisienne	◆14089130	46.00
V-8-307		
1986-87	◆22524716	51.00

	Part No.	Price
V-8-350 Diesel		
exc. Parisienne		
1983-84	◆22505893	58.75
Crossover Pipe		
V-6-231		
1983	◆25506286	31.25
1984-87	◆25516456	31.25
V-6-262		
1985-87	◆14082873	59.50
V-8-305		
exc. Parisienne		
1983-87	◆14063922	95.00
Parisienne		
1983-87	◆14059196	46.00
V-8-307		
1986-87	◆22504709	74.25
V-8-350 Diesel		
1983-87-Parisienne	◆22514728	24.00
Catalytic Converter		
V-6-231		
1983	◆8999642	271.25
1984	◆8999615	312.25
1985-87	◆25056912	348.00
V-6-262		
1985-87	◆25056790	335.00
V-8-305		
1983	◆25056381	320.25
1984-87	◆25056382	300.25
V-8-307		
1986-87-exc. Calif.	◆25056634	335.00
Calif.	◆25100218	323.00

LABOR 9 FRONT SUSPENSION 9 LABOR

(Factory Time)	Chilton Time
Note: On all front suspension operations alignment charges must be added if performed. Time given does not include alignment.	
(M) Wheel, Renew	
one (.4)	.5
(G) Wheels, Rotate (All)	
All models	.5
(G) Wheels, Balance	
one	.3
each adtnl	.2
(G) Check Alignment of Front End	
All models	.5
Note: Deduct if alignment is performed.	
(G) Toe-In, Adjust	
All models (.4)	.6
(G) Align Front End	
Includes: Adjust front wheel bearings.	
All models (.7)	1.4
w/A.C. interference add	.5
(G) Front Wheel Bearings, Clean and Repack (Both Wheels)	
1983-87 (1.1)	1.6
(G) Front Wheel Bearings and Cups, Renew	
1983-87-one side (.7)	.9
both sides (1.1)	1.5

(Factory Time)	Chilton Time
(G) Front Wheel Grease Seals, Renew	
1983-87-one (.7)	.8
both (1.1)	1.2
(G) Front Shock Absorbers, Renew	
1983-87-one (.3)	.4
both (.5)	.7
(G) Rebuild Front Suspension	
Includes: Disassemble, renew necessary parts, reassemble, lubricate and align front end.	
1983-87-one side (4.8)	5.8
both sides (7.8)	9.5
(G) Upper and Lower Ball Joints, Renew (One Side)	
Add alignment charges.	
1983-87 (1.3)	1.7
(G) Upper Ball Joint, Renew (One)	
Add alignment charges.	
1983-87 (.7)	.9
(G) Lower Ball Joint, Renew (One)	
Add alignment charges.	
1983-87 (.6)	.9
(G) Steering Knuckle, Renew (One)	
Add alignment charges.	
1983-87 (1.0)	1.4

(Factory Time)	Chilton Time
(G) Upper Control Arm, Renew (One)	
Includes: Align front end.	
1983-87 (1.4)	2.6
(G) Lower Control Arm, Renew (One)	
Add alignment charges.	
1983-87 (1.0)	1.5
(G) Upper Control Arm Shaft and/or Bushings, Renew (One Side)	
Add alignment charges.	
1983-87 (1.0)	1.7
(G) Lower Control Arm Bushings, Renew (One Side)	
Add alignment charges.	
1983-87 (1.2)	1.5
(G) Front Spring, Renew (One)	
Add alignment charges.	
1983-87 (.8)	1.4
(G) Front Stabilizer Bar, Renew	
1983-87 (.5)	.8
(G) Stabilizer Bar Link or Link Bushings, Renew	
1983-87-one side (.3)	.4
both sides (.4)	.6

PARTS 9 FRONT SUSPENSION 9 PARTS

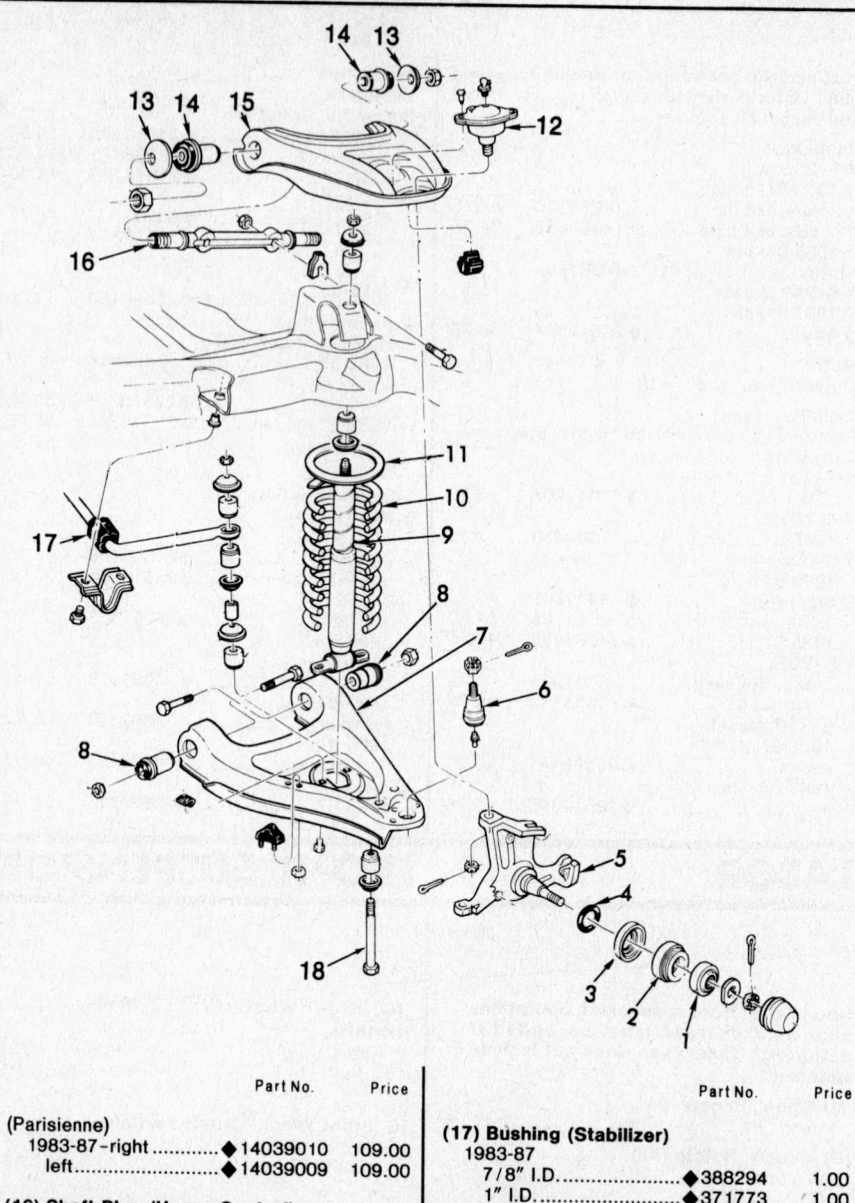

	Part No.	Price
(1) Front Wheel Bearing (Outer)		
(exc. Parisienne)		
1983-87	◆14066918	11.50
(Parisienne)		
1983-87	◆7450697	11.00
(2) Front Wheel Bearing (Inner)		
1983-87	◆7450630	11.00
(3) Front Seal Assy.		
1983-87	◆3965092	3.50
(4) Gasket (Splash Shield)		
1983-87	3966202	.50
(5) Steering Knuckle (R. H.)		
(Bonneville, Grand Prix)		
1983-87	◆14012602	117.00
(Parisienne)		
1983-87-11″ rotor	◆14012596	116.00
12″ rotor	◆14012590	144.00
(6) Ball Joint Pkg. (Lower)		
1983-87	◆9767281	31.50
(7) Control Arm (Lower)		
(Bonneville, Grand Prix)		
1983-87-right	14075338	96.75
left	◆14075337	96.75
(Parisienne)		
1983-87-right	◆14039016	105.00
left	◆14039015	105.00
(8) Bushing (Rear)		
1983-87	◆461853	6.25
(9) Shock Absorber		
(Bonneville, Grand Prix)		
1983-87	◆4993579	24.50
(Parisienne)		
1983-84	◆4993548	24.50
1985-87	◆4993745	24.50
(10) Coil Spring		
Order by model and description.		
(11) Spring Insulator		
1983-87	15597425	2.00
(12) Ball Joint (Upper)		
1983-87	◆9767112	34.75
(13) Retainer		
1983-87	351212	1.00
(14) Bushing (Front)		
(Bonneville, Grand Prix)		
1983-87	14039483	7.25
(Parisienne)		
1983-87	◆351286	7.00
(15) Control Arm (Upper)		
(Bonneville, Grand Prix)		
1983-87-right	◆14039012	97.75
left	◆14039011	97.75

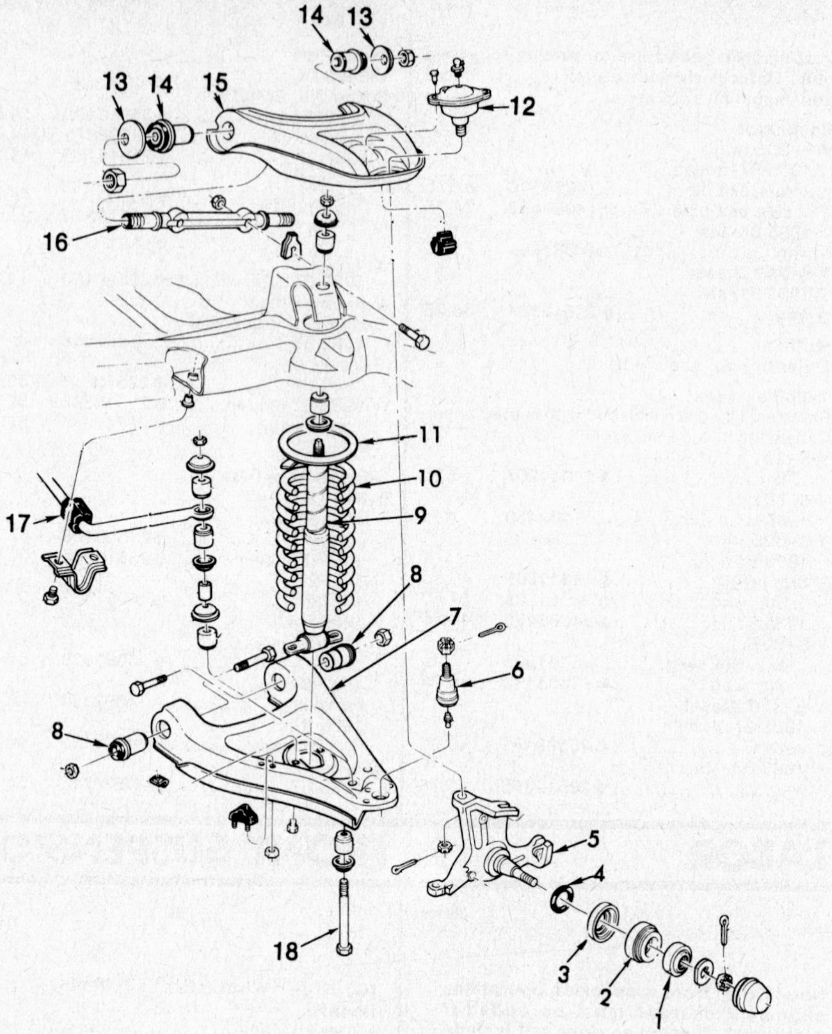

	Part No.	Price
(Parisienne)		
1983-87-right	◆14039010	109.00
left	◆14039009	109.00
(16) Shaft Pkg. (Upper Control)		
(Bonneville, Grand Prix)		
1983-87	◆474001	33.75
(Parisienne)		
1983-87-right	◆14022172	33.75
left	◆14022171	35.50

	Part No.	Price
(17) Bushing (Stabilizer)		
1983-87		
7/8″ I.D.	◆388294	1.00
1″ I.D.	◆371773	1.00
1.08 I.D.	◆472117	2.00
(18) Link Pkg.		
(Bonneville, Grand Prix)		
1983-87	◆470147	4.25
(Parisienne)		
1983-87	◆464167	4.25

LABOR 10 STEERING LINKAGE 10 LABOR

	(Factory Time)	Chilton Time
(G) Tie Rods or Tie Rod Ends, Renew		
Includes: Reset toe-in.		
1983-87-one side	(.7)	1.0
both sides	(.9)	1.4
(G) Inner Tie Rods, Renew		
Includes: Reset toe-in.		
1983-87-one side	(.7)	1.0
both sides	(.8)	1.2

	(Factory Time)	Chilton Time
(G) Idler Arm, Renew		
Includes: Reset toe-in.		
1983-87	(.7)	1.0
(G) Pitman Arm, Renew		
1983-87	(.4)	.7
(G) Intermediate Rod, Renew		
Includes: Reset toe-in.		
1983-87-Grand Prix	(.8)	1.2
Pontiac	(1.0)	1.4

PARTS 10 STEERING LINKAGE 10 PARTS

	Part No.	Price
(1) Idler Arm Assy.		
1983-87	◆7837635	51.00
(2) Tie Rod Assy. (Inner)		
(Bonneville, Grand Prix)		
1983-87	◆7837183	40.25
(Parisienne)		
1983-87	◆7834224	45.75
(3) Tie Rod End (Outer)		
(Bonneville, Grand Prix)		
1983-87	◆7837733	40.00
(Parisienne)		
1983-87	◆12308612	50.50
(4) Tie Rod Sleeve Pkg. (Adjuster)		
(Bonneville, Grand Prix)		
1983-87	◆7829465	15.75
(Parisienne)		
1983-87	◆7826714	15.50
(5) Seal Kit (Pitman Arm)		
1983-87	◆7826470	17.00

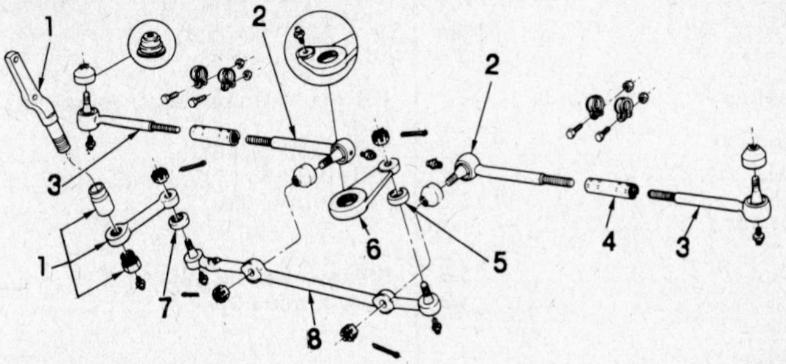

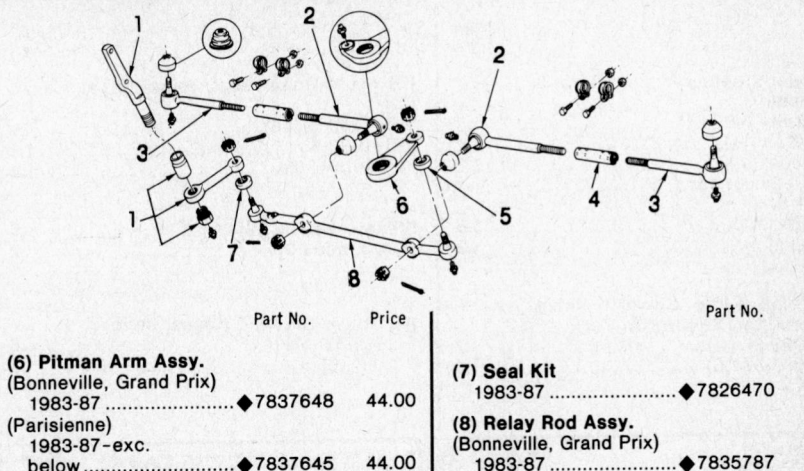

	Part No.	Price
(6) Pitman Arm Assy.		
(Bonneville, Grand Prix)		
1983-87	◆7837648	44.00
(Parisienne)		
1983-87-exc. below	◆7837645	44.00
1985-87-H.D. susp	783499	N.L.

	Part No.	Price
(7) Seal Kit		
1983-87	◆7826470	17.00
(8) Relay Rod Assy.		
(Bonneville, Grand Prix)		
1983-87	◆7835787	79.75
(Parisienne)		
1983-87	◆7837639	109.00

LABOR 11 STEERING GEAR 11 LABOR

(Factory Time) Chilton Time

STANDARD STEERING

	Chilton Time
(G) Horn Contact or Cancelling Cam, Renew	
1983-87 (.5)	.6
(G) Steering Wheel, Renew	
1983-87 (.3)	.4
(G) Upper Mast Jacket Bearing, Renew	
1983-85 (.8)	1.4
tilt colm (.9)	1.6
w/Cruise control add (.2)	.2
1986-87	
std colm (1.0)	1.4
tilt colm (.5)	.9
(G) Dimmer Switch Pivot Assy., Renew	
1983-85	
std column (.8)	1.4
tilt column (.6)	1.2
w/Cruise control add (.2)	.2
(G) Multifunction Lever, Renew	
All models (.2)	.4
w/Cruise control add (.5)	.5
(G) Steering Column Lock Actuator Parts, Renew	
1983-85	
std colm (.8)	1.2
tilt colm (.9)	1.3
w/Cruise control add (.2)	.2
1986-87	
std colm (1.1)	1.6
tilt colm (1.3)	1.8
(G) Steering Intermediate Shaft, Renew	
1983-85 (.3)	.7
(G) Lower Pot Joint, Renew	
1983-85 (.5)	.8
(G) Steering Column Shift Bowl, Renew	
Includes: R&R steering column.	
Does not include colorcoat.	
1983-85-std column (1.5)	2.1
w/Cruise control add (.2)	.2
1986-87 (1.2)	1.7

	Chilton Time
(G) Flexible Coupling (Rag Joint), Renew	
1983-85 (.5)	.8

POWER STEERING

	Chilton Time
(G) Trouble Shoot Power Steering	
Includes: Test pump and system pressure. Check pounds pull on steering wheel and check system for leaks.	
All models	.5
(M) Pump Drive Belt, Renew or Adjust	
1983-87	
V-6-renew (.4)	.5
adjust (.3)	.4
V-8-renew (.3)	.4
adjust	.3
(M) Check Reservoir and Add Fluid	
All models	.2
(G) Power Steering Gear, Adjust	
1983-87 (.7)	1.2
(G) Power Steering Gear Assembly, Renew	
Includes: Fill and bleed.	
1983-87 (.7)	1.2
(P) Steering Gear Assy., R&R and Recondition	
Includes: Disassemble, renew necessary parts, reassemble, fill, bleed and adjust.	
1983-85 (1.7)	2.5
1986-87	
Pontiac (2.1)	3.0
Grand Prix (1.7)	2.5
(G) Adjustor Plug Assembly, Recondition	
Includes: R&R gear assy.	
1983-85 (.9)	1.6
1986-87	
Pontiac (1.3)	2.0
Grand Prix (.9)	1.6

	Chilton Time
(G) Pitman Shaft Bearing and/or Housing, Renew	
Includes: R&R gear assy.	
1983-85 (.9)	1.5
1986-87	
Pontiac (1.2)	1.9
Grand Prix (.9)	1.5
(G) Rack Piston and Worm Shaft, Recondition	
Includes: R&R gear assy.	
1983-85 (1.1)	2.0
1986-87	
Pontiac (1.5)	2.4
Grand Prix (1.1)	2.0
(G) Valve Body, Recondition	
Includes: R&R gear assy.	
1983-85 (1.0)	1.8
1986-87	
Pontiac (1.4)	2.2
Grand Prix (1.0)	1.8
(G) End Housing Plug and/or Seal, Renew	
Does not require gear R&R.	
1983-87 (.4)	.6
(G) Pitman Shaft Seal, Renew	
Does not require gear R&R.	
1983-87 (.6)	1.0
(G) Side Cover 'O' Ring, Renew	
Does not require gear R&R.	
1983-87 (.4)	.6
(G) Power Steering Pump, Renew	
1983-85-V-6 (.9)	1.3
V-8 (.9)	1.4
Diesel (.9)	1.4
w/Hydra boost add (.1)	.1
1986-87	
V-6 (.5)	.8
V-8 (.9)	1.4

LABOR 11 STEEERING GEAR 11 LABOR

	(Factory Time)	Chilton Time
(P) Power Steering Pump, R&R and Recondition		
1983-85-V-6	(1.1)	1.8
V-8	(1.4)	2.2
Diesel	(1.4)	2.2
w/Hydra boost add	(.1)	.1
1986-87		
V-6	(1.0)	1.5
V-8	(1.4)	2.2
(G) Pump Flow Control Valve and/or Filter, Renew (On Car)		
V-6-1983-87	(.4)	.7
V-8-1983-87	(.6)	.9
(G) Front Pump Seal, Renew (On Car)		
V-6-1983-87	(.6)	.9
V-8-1983-85	(.7)	1.5
1986-87	(.9)	1.5
Diesel-1983-85	(.9)	1.5
w/A.C. add	(.2)	.2
(M) Power Steering Hoses, Renew		
1983-87-one	(.4)	.6
all	(.6)	.9

TILT COLUMN

	(Factory Time)	Chilton Time
(G) Steering Column Shift Bowl, Renew		
Includes: R&R steering column.		
Does not include colorcoat.		
1983-85	(1.7)	2.8
w/Cruise control add	(.2)	.2
1986-87	(2.0)	3.0
(G) Tilt Column Assy., R&R and Recondition		
1983-85	(2.1)	3.0
w/Cruise control add	(.2)	.2
1986-87	(2.5)	3.2

PARTS 11 POWER STEERING GEAR 11 PARTS

	Part No.	Price
(1) Cover Seal Kit		
1983-87	◆7817486	9.00
(2) Pitman Shaft (w/Gear)		
1983-87-exc. H.D.	◆7813631	87.50
H.D. susp.	◆7815885	87.50
(3) Check Valve Kit		
1983-87	◆7834284	5.25
(4) Bearing Kit		
1983-87	◆7826850	11.00
(5) Housing Assy.		
(Bonneville, Grand Prix)		
1983-87-V-6	◆7834141	183.00
V-8	◆7834145	183.00
(Parisienne)		
1983-87	◆7834139	183.00
(6) Bearing (Pitman Shaft)		
1983-87	◆5697804	15.00
(7) Seal Kit (Pitman Shaft)		
1983-87	◆7826470	17.00
(8) Seal (Adjuster Plug)		
1983-87	◆5686527	1.50
(9) Bearing (Adjuster Plug)		
1983-87	◆7828012	7.25
(10) Plug Assy. (Adjuster)		
1983-87	◆7832731	53.50

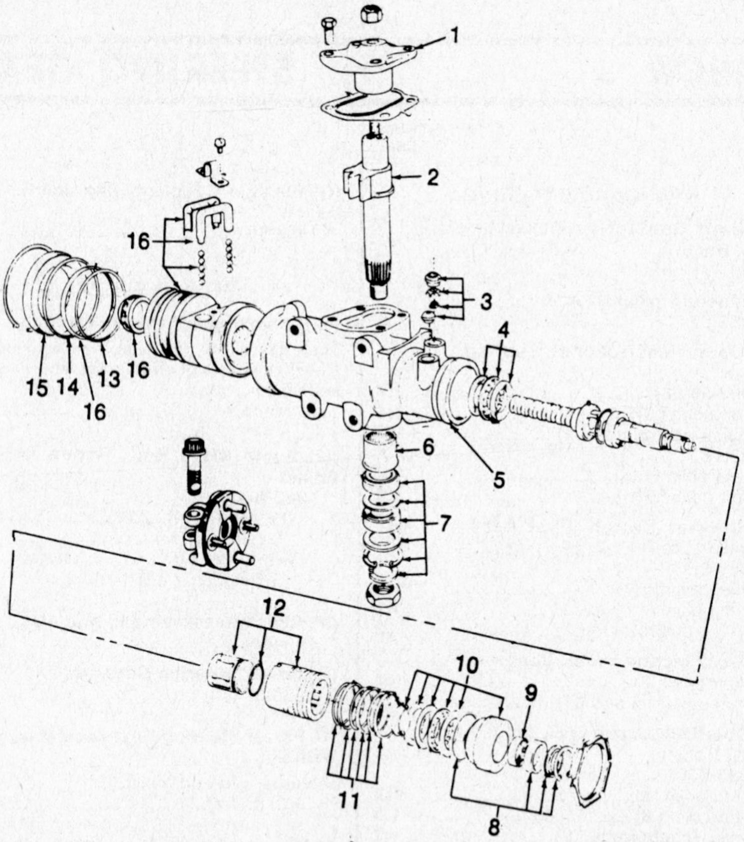

	Part No.	Price
(11) Seal Kit		
1983-87	◆5687182	12.50
(12) Valve Assy.		
1983-87-V-6	◆7832055	202.25
V-8	◆7832058	212.00
H.D. susp.	◆7832057	212.00
(14) Seal Kit		
1983-87	◆7817485	6.50

	Part No.	Price
(15) Plug		
(Bonneville, Grand Prix)		
1983-87-V-6	◆7806688	9.25
V-8	◆5693463	7.25
(Parisienne)		
1983-87	◆5689010	8.75
(16) Rack Assy.		
1983-87-exc. below	◆7817528	162.00
1983-87-Bonneville, Grand Prix H.D. susp.	◆7827170	154.25

PARTS 11 POWER STEERING PUMP 11 PARTS

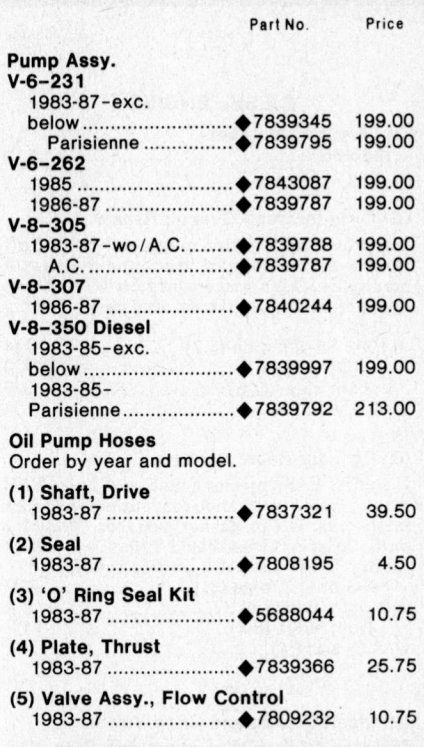

	Part No.	Price
Pump Assy.		
V-6-231		
1983-87-exc. below	◆7839345	199.00
Parisienne	◆7839795	199.00
V-6-262		
1985	◆7843087	199.00
1986-87	◆7839787	199.00
V-8-305		
1983-87-wo/A.C.	◆7839788	199.00
A.C.	◆7839787	199.00
V-8-307		
1986-87	◆7840244	199.00
V-8-350 Diesel		
1983-85-exc. below	◆7839997	199.00
1983-85-Parisienne	◆7839792	213.00

Oil Pump Hoses
Order by year and model.

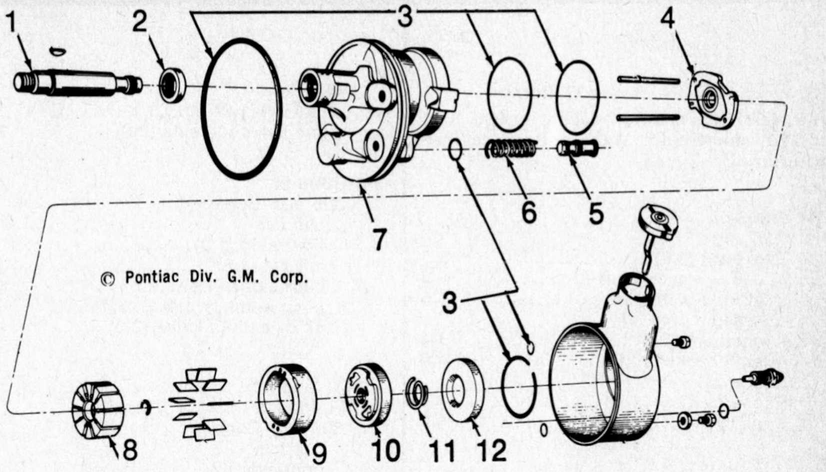

	Part No.	Price
(1) Shaft, Drive		
1983-87	◆7837321	39.50
(2) Seal		
1983-87	◆7808195	4.50
(3) 'O' Ring Seal Kit		
1983-87	◆5688044	10.75
(4) Plate, Thrust		
1983-87	◆7839366	25.75
(5) Valve Assy., Flow Control		
1983-87	◆7809232	10.75
(6) Valve Spring		
1983-87	◆5688037	1.50
(7) Pump Housing		
1983-87	◆7830236	62.75
(8) Rotor & Vane Repair Kit		
1983-87	◆7837322	75.00

Repair kit includes, rotor, ring & vanes.

	Part No.	Price
(9) Ring		
1983-87	See item No. 8	
(10) Plate, Pressure		
1983-87	◆7839669	14.25
(11) Spring, Pressure Plate		
1983-87	◆7839667	1.00
(12) Plate, End		
1983-87	◆5689358	3.50

LABOR 12 CYLINDER HEAD & VALVE SYSTEM 12 LABOR

(Factory Time)	Chilton Time
GASOLINE ENGINES	
(G) Compression Test	
V-6-1983-87 (.5)	.7
V-8-1983-87 (.6)	.8
w/A.C. add	.3

(G) Cylinder Head Gasket, Renew

Includes: R&R cylinder head, clean carbon, make all necessary adjustments.

V-6-1983-87	
229 eng	
one (4.2)	6.4
both (6.1)	8.9
231 eng	
one (4.4)	5.8
both (5.3)	7.6
262 eng	
one (4.7)	6.4
both (6.5)	8.9
V-8-1983-87	
305 eng-Code H	
right side (5.0)	6.9
left side (4.6)	6.3
both sides (7.0)	9.6
w/A.C. add (.5)	.5
w/P.S. add (.3)	.3
w/AIR add (.2)	.2
w/Cruise control add (.2)	.2
307 eng-Code Y	
right side (4.0)	5.5
left side (4.4)	6.0
both sides (5.8)	8.0
w/A.C. add (.4)	.4
w/AIR add (.5)	.5

(G) Cylinder Head, Renew

Includes: Clean gasket surfaces, clean carbon. Transfer all parts, reface valves. Make all necessary adjustments.

V-6-1983-87	
229 eng	
one (4.9)	7.3
both (7.2)	10.4
231 eng	
one (4.9)	6.6
both (5.9)	9.1
262 eng	
one	7.3
both	10.4
V-8-1983-87	
305 eng-Code H	
right side (5.8)	8.0
left side (5.5)	7.5
both sides (8.7)	12.0
w/A.C. add (.5)	.5
w/P.S. add (.3)	.3
w/AIR add (.2)	.2
w/Cruise control add (.2)	.2
307 eng-Code Y	
right side (4.2)	5.7
left side (4.6)	6.3
both sides (6.2)	8.5
w/A.C. add (.4)	.4
w/AIR add (.5)	.5

COMBINATIONS
Add to Valve Job
See Machine Shop Operations

(Factory Time)	Chilton Time
(G) DRAIN, EVACUATE & RECHARGE AIR CONDITIONING SYSTEM	
All models (.5)	1.0
(G) ROCKER ARM STUD, RENEW	
Each (.3)	.3
(G) HYDRAULIC VALVE LIFTERS, DISASSEMBLE AND CLEAN	
Each (.2)	.2
(G) DISTRIBUTOR, RECONDITION	
All models (.5)	.8
(G) CARBURETOR, RECONDITION	
2 bbl	1.2
4 bbl	1.5
(P) VALVE GUIDES, REAM OVERSIZE	
Each (.2)	.2
(G) ROCKER ARM SHAFT, RECONDITION	
Each side (.2)	.3

(P) Clean Carbon and Grind Valves

Includes: R&R cylinder heads, reface valves and seats. Minor tune up.

V-6-1983-87	
229 eng (8.1)	11.7
231 eng (8.0)	11.2
262 eng	11.7
V-8-1983-87	
305 eng-Code H	
right side (6.3)	8.6
left side (5.9)	8.1
both sides (9.4)	13.0
w/A.C. add (.5)	.5
w/P.S. add (.3)	.3
w/AIR add (.2)	.2
w/Cruise control add (.2)	.2
307 eng-Code Y	
right side (5.1)	7.0
left side (5.6)	7.7
both sides (8.1)	11.2
w/A.C. add (.4)	.4
w/AIR add (.5)	.5

(Factory Time) Chilton Time

(G) Valve Tappets, Renew (Lifters)
Includes: Drain and refill cooling system. R&R intake manifold. Make all necessary adjustments.

V-6–1983-87
229 eng
one cyl (2.6) ... 3.5
one cyl-each bank (3.1) ... 4.2
all cyls-both banks (3.6) ... 4.5
231 eng
one bank (2.6) ... 3.4
both banks (2.9) ... 4.0
262 eng
one cyl (2.6) ... 3.5
all cyls (3.1) ... 4.2

V-8–1983-87
305 eng-Code H
one cyl (2.5) ... 3.4
one cyl-each side (2.7) ... 3.7
all cyls-both sides (3.2) ... 4.4
w/A.C. add (.5) 5
w/AIR add (.1) 1
w/Cruise control add (.1) 1
307 eng-Code Y
one cyl (2.7) ... 3.7
one cyl-each side (3.2) ... 4.4
all cyls-both sides (5.0) ... 6.9
w/A.C. add (.2) 2
w/AIR add (.4) 4

(G) Rocker Arm Cover and/or Gasket, Renew
V-6–1983-87
229 eng
one (.7) ... 1.0
both (1.2) ... 1.8
231 eng
one (.5) 8
both (.8) ... 1.4
262 eng
one (.7) ... 1.0
both (1.2) ... 1.8

V-8–1983-87
305 eng-Code H
right side (.7) ... 1.0
left side (.5) 7
both sides (1.1) ... 1.6
w/A.C. add (.2) 2
w/C.C.C. add (.2) 2
w/Cruise control add (.1) 1
307 eng-Code Y
right side (.6) 7
left side (.8) ... 1.2
both sides (1.4) ... 1.9
w/A.C. add (.1) 1
w/AIR add (.3) 3

(G) Valve Spring and/or Valve Stem Oil Seals, Renew (Head on Car)
V-6–1983-87
229 eng
one cyl (1.2) ... 1.6
one cyl-each side (2.0) ... 2.8
all cyls-both sides (3.3) ... 4.2
231 eng
one cyl (.8) ... 1.2
one cyl-each side (1.4) ... 2.2
all cyls-both sides (2.6) ... 3.5
262 eng
one cyl (1.2) ... 1.6
one cyl-each side (2.0) ... 2.8

V-8–1983-87
305 eng-Code H
one cyl
right side (1.2) ... 1.6
left side (.8) ... 1.1
both sides (1.6) ... 2.3
each adtnl cyl (.4) 4
all cyls-both sides (3.3) ... 4.5

w/A.C. add (.3) 3
w/AIR add (.1) 1
307 eng-Code Y
one cyl
right side (.7) ... 1.0
left side (1.1) ... 1.6
both sides (1.8) ... 2.4
each adtnl cyl (.4) 4
w/A.C. add (.1) 1
w/AIR add (.3) 3

(G) Rocker Arm Shafts and/or Assy's., Renew
V-6–1983-87-each (.6) ... 1.1
Recond shaft add-each 3
w/A.C. add (.3) 3
w/A.I.R. add (.3) 3

(G) Rocker Arm and/or Push Rod, Renew
V-6–1983-87
229 eng
one cyl (.9) ... 1.2
one cyl-each side (1.5) ... 2.1
231 eng
one side (.6) ... 1.1
both sides (1.4) ... 1.7
262 eng
one cyl (.9) ... 1.2
one cyl-each side (1.5) ... 2.1

V-8–1983-85
one side (.8) ... 1.3
both sides (1.4) ... 2.0
w/A.C add (.3) 3
w/AIR add (.2) 2

1986-87
305 eng-Code H
one cyl
right side (.8) ... 1.2
left side (.6) 9
both sides (1.3) ... 2.0
each adtnl cyl (.2) 2
w/A.C. add (.2) 2
w/AIR add (.1) 1
307 eng-Code Y
one cyl
right side (.7) 9
left side (.9) ... 1.4
both sides (1.5) ... 2.1
all cyls-both sides (2.0) ... 2.9
w/A.C. add (.1) 1
w/AIR add (.3) 3

(G) Valves, Adjust
V-6–1983-87 ... 1.5
V-8–1983-87 ... 2.0
w/A.C. add 3
w/C.C.C. add 3

DIESEL ENGINE

(G) Compression Test
1983-85 ... 1.3

(G) Cylinder Head Gasket, Renew
Includes: R&R injector pump and lines. R&R intake manifold and disconnect exhaust manifolds. Clean gasket surfaces, bleed lifters and adjust timing. Drain and refill cooling system.
1983-85-left side (5.7) ... 7.4
right side (6.1) ... 7.9
both sides (7.6) ... 9.9
w/A.C. add (.4) 4

(G) Cylinder Head, Renew
Includes: R&R injector pump and lines. R&R intake manifold and disconnect exhaust manifolds. Clean gasket surfaces. Transfer parts, reface valves. Bleed lifters and adjust timing. Drain and refill cooling system.
1983-85-left side (6.1) ... 7.9
right side (6.5) ... 8.4
both sides (8.4) ... 11.1
w/A.C. add (.4) 4

(P) Clean Carbon and Grind Valves
Includes: R&R injector pump and lines. R&R cylinder heads, clean carbon. Recondition valves and seats. Check and adjust valve stem length. Bleed lifters, drain and refill cooling system.
1983-85-left side (6.6) ... 8.5
right side (7.0) ... 9.1
both sides (9.3) ... 12.6
w/A.C. add (.4) 4

(G) Valve Tappets, Renew (Lifters)
Includes: R&R injector pump and lines, intake manifold and rocker arms. Drain and refill cooling system.
1983-85-one cyl (3.5) ... 4.5
one cyl-each side (3.9) ... 5.0
each adtnl cyl (.1) 1

(G) Rocker Arm Cover or Gasket, Renew
Includes: R&R injector pump and lines.
1983-85-one side (1.2) ... 2.4
both sides (2.0) ... 2.9

(G) Valve Springs and/or Valve Stem Oil Seals, Renew (Head on Car)
Includes: R&R injector pump and lines.
1983-85-one cyl (1.6) ... 3.0
one cyl-each bank (2.4) ... 3.7
each adntl cyl (.3) 3
w/A.C. add (.3) 3

(G) Rocker Arm, Pivot and/or Push Rod, Renew
Includes: R&R injector pump and lines.
1983-85-one cyl (1.5) ... 2.5
one cyl-each bank (2.3) ... 3.0
each adtnl cyl (.1) 1

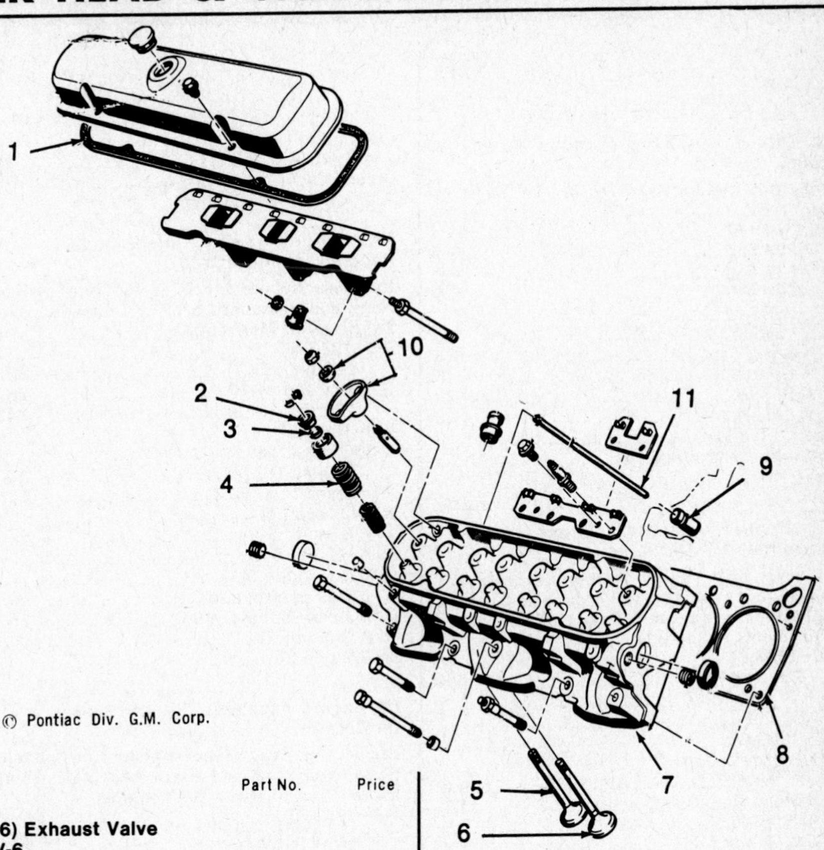

© Pontiac Div. G.M. Corp.

	Part No.	Price
Valve Grind Gasket Set		
1st design: .017 in. thick head gasket. 2nd design: .062 in. thick head gasket.		
V-6-231		
1983-1st design	◆25525121	N.L.
2nd design	◆25527307	71.50
1984-Alum. man.		
1st design	◆25525120	37.00
2nd design	◆25527306	71.50
1984-Cast iron man.		
1st design	◆25525121	N.L.
2nd design	◆25527307	71.50
1985-1st design	◆25525120	37.00
2nd design	◆25527306	71.50
1986-87	◆25527306	71.50
1984-87		
V-6-262 eng.		
1985-87	◆14091326	53.00
V-8-305		
1983-87	◆14089154	61.50
V-8-350 Diesel		
1983-85	◆22527541	N.L.
V-8-307		
1986-87	◆22534926	58.00
(1) Cover Gasket		
V-6		
1983-87-231	◆25523348	N.L.
1985-87-262	◆14081257	7.25
V-8-305		
1984-87	◆14082322	8.75

If gasket for your application is not listed, use R.T.V. sealer No. 1052366.

	Part No.	Price
(2) Cap, Valve Spring		
V-6		
1983-87-231	◆1254900	1.50
262	14003974	1.00
V-8-305		
1983-87	14003974	1.00
V-8-307		
1986-87	◆406996	3.25
V-8-350 Diesel		
1983-85	◆406996	3.50
(3) Seal, Valve Guide		
V-6		
1983	◆25519324	2.25
1984-87-exc.		
262	◆25518390	2.50
262	◆3835333	N.L.
V-8-305		
1983-87	◆3835333	.50
V-8-307		
1986-87-intake	◆406595	.75
exhaust	◆401823	.75
V-8-350 Diesel		
1983-85-intake	◆406595	1.00
exhaust	◆401823	1.00
(4) Valve Spring Assy.		
V-6		
1983-87-exc.		
262	◆1249267	2.75
262	◆3911068	3.00
V-8-305		
1983-87	◆3911068	3.00
V-8-307		
1986-87	◆411226	4.00
V-8-350 Diesel		
1983-87	◆22510372	4.00
(5) Intake Valve (Std.)		
V-6		
1983-87-exc.		
262	◆25512098	11.25
262	◆14075641	14.00
V-8-305		
1983-87	◆14025571	11.75
V-8-307		
1986-87	◆22530611	20.25
V-8-350 Diesel		
1983-85	◆22519914	20.00

	Part No.	Price
(6) Exhaust Valve		
V-6		
1983-87-exc.		
262	◆1261380	13.50
262	◆14095451	13.50
V-8-305		
1983-87	◆14095451	13.50
V-8-307		
1986-87	◆555456	N.L.
V-8-350 Diesel		
1983-85	◆558873	13.00
(7) Cylinder Head		
V-6-231		
1983-87	◆25518679	217.00
V-6-262		
1985-87	◆14085869	242.00
V-8-305		
1983-87	◆14034807	247.00
V-8-307		
1986-87	◆22530557	247.00
V-8-350 Diesel		
1983-85	◆22515038	387.00
(8) Cylinder Head Gasket		
1st design: .017 in. thick. 2nd design: .067 in. thick.		
V-6-231		
1983-84-1st design	◆1261403	8.50
2nd design	◆25525919	21.25
1985-1st design	◆25524599	8.50
2nd design	◆25525919	21.25
1986-87	◆25525919	21.25
V-6-262		
1985-87	◆14075646	7.00
V-8-305		
1983-87	◆462690	6.50
V-8-307		
1986-87	◆22503500	9.50
V-8-350 Diesel		
1983-85	◆22519416	30.75

	Part No.	Price
(9) Valve Lifter		
V-6-231		
1983	◆5232765	9.00
1984-87	◆5234330	N.L.
V-6-262		
1985-87	◆5232720	N.L.
V-8-305		
1983-87	◆5232720	N.L.
V-8-307		
1986-87	◆5234755	43.50
V-8-350 Diesel		
1983-85	◆5234625	N.L.
(10) Rocker Arm		
V-6-231		
1983-87-right	◆1241850	4.50
left	◆1241851	4.50
V-6-262		
1985-87	◆3974290	5.50
V-8-305		
1983-87	◆3974290	5.50
V-8-307		
1986-87	◆22505583	N.L.
V-8-350 Diesel		
1983-85	◆22505583	N.L.
(11) Valve Push Rod		
V-6-231		
1983-84	◆1249139	4.00
1985-87	◆25510025	4.25
V-6-262		
1985-87	◆14095256	5.00
V-8-305		
1983-87	◆14095256	5.00
V-8-307		
1986-87	◆22533631	3.25
V-8-350 Diesel		
1983-85	◆22511044	3.25

LABOR 13 ENGINE ASSEMBLY & MOUNTS 13 LABOR

	(Factory Time)	Chilton Time
GASOLINE ENGINES		
(G) Engine Assembly, Remove & Install		
Does not include transfer of any parts or equipment.		
V-6–1983-87		
229 eng		4.8
231 eng		4.0
262 eng		6.5
V-8–1983-87		
Pontiac		6.0
Grand Prix		6.5
w/A.C. add		.5
w/P.S. add		.3
w/A.I.R. add		.6
w/C.C.C. add		.3
w/Cruise control add	(.3)	.3
(G) Engine Assembly, Renew (Universal)		
Includes: R&R engine assembly, transfer all component parts not supplied with replacement engine. Make all necessary adjustments.		
V-6–1983-87		
231 eng	(6.7)	9.4
w/A.C. add	(.8)	.8
w/AIR add	(.2)	.2
V-8–1983-87		
305 eng-Code H		
Pontiac	(7.1)	9.5
Grand Prix	(8.4)	11.7
w/A.C. add	(.5)	.5
w/C.C.C. add	(.4)	.4
w/Cruise control add	(.1)	.1
(G) Engine Assembly, Renew (Partial/Basic)		
Includes: R&R engine assy. Transfer all component parts not supplied with replacement engine. Make all necessary adjusments.		
V-6–1983-87		
231 eng	(10.6)	14.8
w/A.C. add	(.3)	.3
w/AIR add	(.2)	.2
Recond valves add	(1.2)	1.2
262 eng	(9.3)	13.0
w/A.C. add	(.2)	.2
Recond valves add	(2.0)	2.0
V-8–1983-87		
305 eng-Code H		
Pontiac	(9.9)	13.8
Grand Prix	(11.2)	15.6
w/A.C. add	(.5)	.5
w/C.C.C. add	(.4)	.4
Recond valves add	(2.7)	2.7
307 eng-Code Y	(8.4)	11.7
w/A.C. add	(.2)	.2
w/AIR add	(.4)	.4
Recond valves add	(1.6)	1.6
(P) Engine Assy., R&R and Recondition (Complete)		
Includes: Rebore block, install new pistons, rings, rod and main bearings. Clean carbon, grind valves. Tune engine.		
V-6–1983-87		
229 eng	(24.7)	28.9
231 eng	(21.4)	25.1
262 eng	(17.8)	24.9
V-8–1983-87		
305 eng-Code H		
Pontiac	(19.5)	26.3
Grand Prix	(20.6)	27.8
w/A.C. add	(.5)	.5
w/P.S. add	(.3)	.3
w/A.I.R. add	(.6)	.6
w/C.C.C. add	(.3)	.3
w/Cruise control add	(.3)	.3
307 eng-Code Y	(18.6)	26.0
w/A.C. add	(.2)	.2
w/AIR add	(.4)	.4
(P) Engine Assembly, Recondition (In Car)		
Includes: Expand or renew pistons, install new rings, pins, rod and main bearings. Clean carbon, grind valves. Tune engine.		
V-6–1983-87		
229 eng	(17.8)	21.4
231 eng	(14.9)	18.0
262 eng	(15.6)	20.3
V-8–1983-87		
305 eng-Code H		
Pontiac	(16.5)	23.1
Grand Prix	(16.9)	23.6
w/A.C. add	(.5)	.5
w/P.S. add	(.3)	.3
w/A.I.R. add	(.6)	.6
w/C.C.C. add	(.3)	.3
w/Cruise control add	(.2)	.2
307 eng-Code Y	(19.4)	27.1
w/A.C. add	(.3)	.3
w/AIR add	(.6)	.6
(G) Engine Mounts, Renew		
Front		
V-6–1983-87		
229-262 engs		
one	(1.0)	1.4
both	(1.6)	2.1
231 eng		
one	(.5)	.7
both	(.7)	1.0
V-8–1983-87		
305 eng-Code H		
one	(1.0)	1.4
both	(1.5)	2.1
307 eng-Code Y		
one	(.8)	1.1
both	(1.3)	1.8
Rear		
V-6–1983-87	(.4)	.6
V-8–1983-87	(.4)	.6
DIESEL ENGINE		
(G) Engine Assembly, Remove & Install		
Does not include transfer of any parts or equipment.		
1983-85		5.0
w/A.C. add		.5
(G) Engine Assembly, Renew (Universal)		
Includes: R&R engine assembly, transfer all component parts not supplied with replacement engine. Make all necessary adjustments.		
1983-85		20.0
w/A.C. add	(.5)	.5
(P) Cylinder Block, Renew (w/All Internal Parts Less Heads and Oil Pan)		
Includes: R&R engine, transfer all component parts not supplied with replacement engine. Clean carbon, grind valves. Make all necessary adjustments.		
1983-85	(14.5)	24.0
w/A.C. add	(.5)	.5
(P) Engine Assy., R&R and Recondition (Complete)		
Includes: Rebore block, install new pistons, rings, rod and main bearings. Clean carbon, grind valves. Make all necessary adjustments.		
1983-85	(29.5)	36.0
w/A.C. add	(.5)	.5
(P) Engine Assembly, Recondition (In Car)		
Includes: Expand or renew pistons, install new rings, pins, rod and main bearings. Clean carbon, grind valves. Make all necessary adjustments.		
1983-85	(23.2)	27.3
w/A.C. add	(.5)	.5
(G) Engine Mounts, Renew		
Front		
1983-85-one	(.5)	.8
both	(.7)	1.0
Rear		
1983-85	(.3)	.4

PARTS 13 ENGINE ASSEMBLY & MOUNTS 13 PARTS

	Part No.	Price
Engine Overhaul Gasket Set		
1st design: .017 in. thick head gasket. 2nd design: .067 in. thick head gasket.		
V-6-231		
1983-1st design	◆25525119	58.25
2nd design	◆25528727	90.00
1984-Alum. man.		
1st design	◆25505370	52.50
2nd design	◆25527302	89.00
1984-Cast iron man.		
1st design	◆25525119	58.25
2nd design	◆25528727	90.00
1985-1st design	◆25525118	58.25
2nd design	◆25527302	89.00
1986-87	◆25527302	89.00
V-6-262		
1985	◆14091479	7.95
1986-87	◆14094596	8.00
V-8-305		
1983-84	◆14091479	N.L.
1985-87-14094596		
V-8-307		
1986-87		
V-8-350 Diesel		
1983-84	◆22521786	90.00
1985	◆22527538	N.L.
For complete overhaul, also use valve grind gasket set.		
Front Engine Mounts (R.H.)		
V-6-231		
1983-87-exc. below	◆1258718	26.25
Parisienne	◆1258666	24.00

PARTS 13 ENGINE ASSEMBLY & MOUNTS 13 PARTS

	Part No.	Price
V-6-262		
1985-87-exc.		
below	◆1258718	26.25
Parisienne	◆17981702	27.25
V-8-305		
1983-87-R.H.	10001133	26.25
V-8-307		
1986-87	◆22501573	N.L.
V-8-350 Diesel		
1983-85	◆553915	27.25
Rear Engine Mounts		
V-6-231		
1983-87	◆1257692	14.50
V-6-262		
1985-87	1258457	13.50
V-8-305		
1983-87-exc.		
below	◆10001749	14.00
Parisienne	14073052	13.75

	Part No.	Price
V-8-307		
1986-87	14025017	59.50
V-8-350 Diesel		
1983-85	◆472143	14.00
Partial Engine Assy.		
V-6-231		
1983	◆25516156	1263.25
1984	◆25519449	1263.25
1985	◆25524286	1263.00
1986-87	◆25527474	1263.00
V-6-262		
1985	◆14085899	1307.00
1986-87	◆14094574	1307.00
V-8-305		
1983-84	◆14019868	1363.00
1985	◆14091328	1300.00
1986-87	◆14101315	1300.00

	Part No.	Price
V-8-307		
1986-87	◆22530855	1397.00
V-8-350 Diesel		
1983	◆22518906	1950.00
Cylinder Block (Fitted)		
Includes: pistons, rings, main bearings.		
V-6-231		
1983-84	◆25519450	950.00
1985	◆25524288	950.00
1986-87	◆25527475	950.00
V-6-262		
1985	◆14085898	969.00
V-8-305		
1983-84	◆14019867	949.00
V-8-307		
1986-87	◆22530856	949.00
V-8-350 Diesel		
1983	◆22518907	1418.00

LABOR 14 PISTONS, RINGS & BEARINGS 14 LABOR

(Factory Time) — Chilton Time

GASOLINE ENGINES

(P) Rings, Renew (See Engine Combinations)

Includes: Remove cylinder top ridge, deglaze cylinder walls. Minor tune up.

	Chilton Time
V-6-1983-87	
229-262 engs	
one cyl (6.9)	9.5
one cyl-each side (9.0)	12.4
all cyls-both sides (11.0)	15.1
231 eng	
one cyl (5.8)	8.4
one cyl-each side (7.6)	10.6
all cyls-both sides (9.5)	13.3
V-8-1983-87	
305 eng-Code H	
one cyl (6.4)	9.2
one cyl-each bank (8.4)	12.1
all cyls-both banks (11.2)	16.2
w/A.C. add (.6)	.6
w/AIR add (.2)	.2
307 eng-Code Y	
one cyl (7.6)	11.0
one cyl-each bank (9.6)	13.9
all cyls-both banks (11.9)	17.2
w/A.C. add (.3)	.3
w/AIR add (.6)	.6

(P) Piston or Connecting Rod, Renew

Includes: Remove cylinder top ridge, deglaze cylinder walls. Minor tune up.

	Chilton Time
V-6-1983-87	
229-262 engs	
one cyl (7.6)	9.8
one cyl-each side (10.4)	13.0
all cyls-both sides (11.7)	16.9
231 eng	
one cyl (6.3)	8.7
one cyl-each side (8.6)	11.2
all cyls-both sides (10.2)	15.1
V-8-1983-87	
305 eng-Code H	
one cyl-each side (7.1)	9.9
one cyl-each bank (9.8)	13.5
all cyls-both banks (12.3)	18.6
w/A.C. add (.6)	.6
w/AIR add (.2)	.2
307 eng-Code Y	
one cyl (8.2)	11.6
one cyl-each bank (10.8)	15.1
all cyls-both banks (13.0)	19.6
w/A.C. add (.3)	.3
w/AIR add (.6)	.6

COMBINATIONS

Add to Engine Work

See Machine Shop Operations

(Factory Time)	Chilton Time
(G) DRAIN, EVACUATE & RECHARGE AIR CONDITIONING SYSTEM	
All models (.5)	1.0
(G) ROCKER ARM STUD, RENEW	
Each (.3)	.3
(G) HYDRAULIC VALVE LIFTERS DISASSEMBLE AND CLEAN	
Each (.2)	.2
(G) DISTRIBUTOR, RECONDITION	
All models (.5)	.8
(G) CARBURETOR, RECONDITION	
2 bbl	1.2
4 bbl	1.5
(G) CYLINDER HEAD, R&R (ENGINE REMOVED)	
V-6	
eng Codes Z-9	
one (2.0)	2.6
both (3.0)	3.9
eng Code A	
one (1.1)	1.4
both (1.8)	2.3
V-8	
eng Code H	
one (2.4)	3.1
both (3.7)	4.8
eng Code Y	
one (1.8)	2.3
both (2.6)	3.3
(G) CONNECTING ROD, RENEW (ENGINE DISASSEMBLED)	
V-6	
eng Codes Z-9	
each (.4)	.5
eng Code A	
each (.5)	.6
V-8	
eng Code H	
each (.3)	.4
eng Code Y	
each (.5)	.6
(P) VALVE GUIDES, REAM OVERSIZE	
Each (.2)	.2
(G) ROCKER ARM SHAFT ASSY., DISASSEMBLE AND CLEAN OR RECONDITION	
Each side (.2)	.3
(G) DEGLAZE CYLINDER WALLS	
Each (.1)	.1
(G) REMOVE CYLINDER TOP RIDGE	
Each (.1)	.1
(G) TIMING CHAIN, RENEW (COVER REMOVED)	
All models (.3)	.5
(G) MAIN BEARINGS, RENEW (PAN REMOVED)	
V-6 (1.2)	1.8
V-8 (1.0)	1.5
one cyl (7.1)	9.9
Each (.1)	.1
(G) OIL PUMP, RECONDITION	
V-6 (.5)	.8
V-8	.3
(M) OIL FILTER ELEMENT, RENEW	
All models (.2)	.3

(P) Connecting Rod Bearings, Renew

Includes: R&R oil pan, check all bearing clearances.

(Factory Time)	Chilton Time
V-6-1983-87	
229-262 engs(3.5)	4.7
231 eng (2.3)	3.4
V-8-1983-87	
305 eng-Code H (3.7)	5.1
307 eng-Code Y (4.4)	6.0

LABOR 14 PISTONS, RINGS & BEARINGS 14 LABOR

(Factory Time) Chilton Time

DIESEL ENGINE

(P) Rings, Renew

Includes: Remove cylinder top ridge, deglaze cylinder walls. Clean piston and ring grooves. Make all necessary adjustments.

	Chilton Time
1983-85 (12.8)	17.2
w/A.C. add (.4)	.4

(P) Pistons or Connecting Rods, Renew

Includes: Remove cylinder top ridge, deglaze cylinder walls. Clean piston and ring grooves. Make all necessary adjustments.

	Chilton Time
1983-85 (13.3)	19.6
w/A.C. add (.4)	.4

(P) Connecting Rod Bearings, Renew

Includes: Raise engine and clean oil pump screen.

	Chilton Time
1983-85 (4.9)	6.6

PARTS 14 PISTONS, RINGS & BEARINGS 14 PARTS

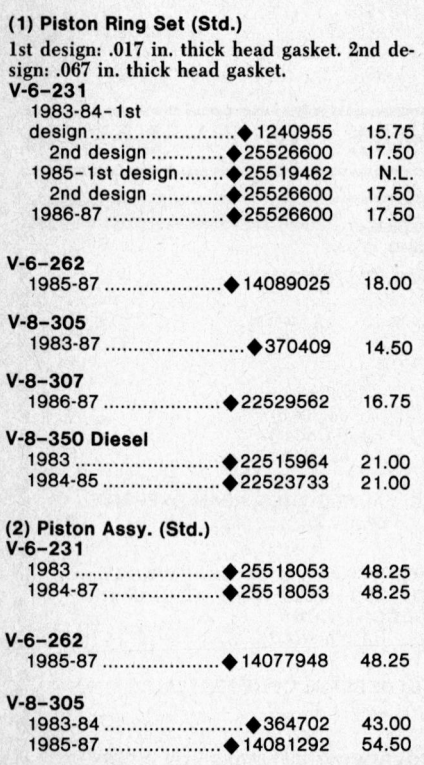

(1) Piston Ring Set (Std.)

1st design: .017 in. thick head gasket. 2nd design: .067 in. thick head gasket.

	Part No.	Price
V-6-231		
1983-84-1st design	◆1240955	15.75
2nd design	◆25526600	17.50
1985-1st design	◆25519462	N.L.
2nd design	◆25526600	17.50
1986-87	◆25526600	17.50
V-6-262		
1985-87	◆14089025	18.00
V-8-305		
1983-87	◆370409	14.50
V-8-307		
1986-87	◆22529562	16.75
V-8-350 Diesel		
1983	◆22515964	21.00
1984-85	◆22523733	21.00

(2) Piston Assy. (Std.)

	Part No.	Price
V-6-231		
1983	◆25518053	48.25
1984-87	◆25518053	48.25
V-6-262		
1985-87	◆14077948	48.25
V-8-305		
1983-84	◆364702	43.00
1985-87	◆14081292	54.50

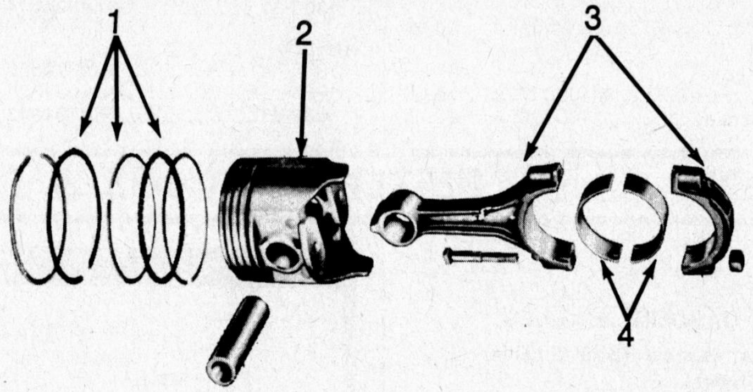

	Part No.	Price
V-8-307		
1986-87-L.H.	◆22527479	48.25
R.H.	◆22527480	48.25
V-8-350 Diesel		
1983-L.H.	◆22523357	63.75
R.H.	◆22523358	63.75
1984-87-L.H.	◆22523357	63.75
R.H.	◆22523358	63.75

(3) Connecting Rod

	Part No.	Price
V-6-231		
1983-87	22506520	N.L.
V-6-262		
1985-87	◆14077944	42.25
V-8-305		
1983-87	◆14031310	39.50
V-8-307		
1986-87	◆22527025	45.00
V-8-350 Diesel		
1983-85	◆22515313	50.50

(4) Connecting Rod Bearing (Std.)

	Part No.	Price
V-6-231		
1983-87	◆18005399	11.00
V-6-262		
1985-87	◆18012481	10.00
V-8-305		
1983-87	◆3910555	7.50
V-8-307		
1986-87	◆18008494	N.L.
V-8-350 Diesel		
1983-85	◆18008494	10.50

LABOR 15 CRANKSHAFT & DAMPER 15 LABOR

(Factory Time) Chilton Time

GASOLINE ENGINES

(P) Crankshaft and Main Bearings, Renew

Includes: R&R engine assy., drain and refill crankcase and radiator, separate engine at transmission and make all necessary adjustments.

	Chilton Time
V-6-1983-87	
229-262 engs (8.9)	12.0
231 eng (6.9)	10.1
V-8-1983-87	
305 eng-Code H	
Pontiac (8.5)	11.9
Grand Prix (9.5)	13.3
w/A.C. add (.5)	.5
w/P.S. add (.3)	.3
w/A.I.R. add (.6)	.6
w/C.C.C. add (.3)	.3
w/Cruise control add (.3)	3
307 eng-Code Y (7.0)	10.1
w/A.C. add (.3)	.3
w/AIR add (.3)	.3

(P) Main Bearings, Renew

Includes: R&R oil pan and baffle, clean baffle and screen.

	Chilton Time
V-6-1983-87	
229-262 engs (3.7)	4.6
231 eng (2.1)	3.6
V-8-1983-87	
305 eng-Code H (3.5)	5.4
w/A.C. add (.1)	.1
307 eng-Code Y (4.1)	5.7

(P) Main and Rod Bearings, Renew

Includes: R&R oil pan and baffle, clean baffle and screen.

	Chilton Time
V-6-1983-87	
229-262 engs (5.5)	6.4
231 eng (3.3)	5.4
V-8-1983-87	
305 eng-Code H (5.3)	7.8
w/A.C. add (.1)	.1
307 eng-Code Y (6.3)	8.1

(G) Rear Main Bearing Oil Seal, Renew or Repack

Includes: R&R oil pan and rear main bearing cap.

	Chilton Time
V-6-1983-87	
229 eng (2.3)	3.0
231 eng (1.5)	2.2
262 eng (1.8)	3.0
V-8-1983-87	
305 eng-Code H (2.3)	3.5
w/A.C. add (.1)	.1
307 eng-Code Y (6.0)	3.6

(G) Crankshaft Pulley and/or Harmonic Balancer, Renew

	Chilton Time
V-6-1983-87	
229-262 engs	
pulley (.6)	.8
balancer (.8)	1.0

LABOR 15 CRANKSHAFT & DAMPER 15 LABOR

	(Factory Time)	Chilton Time
231 eng		
pulley	(.7)	1.2
balancer	(.8)	1.3
V-8-1983-87		
305 eng-Code H		
pulley	(.6)	1.0
balancer	(.8)	1.2
w/A.C. add	(.2)	.2
307 eng-Code Y		
pulley	(.6)	1.0
balancer	(.9)	1.3
w/A.C. add	(.1)	.1

DIESEL ENGINES

(P) Crankshaft and Main Bearings, Renew

Includes: R&R engine, check all bearing clearances.

	(Factory Time)	Chilton Time
1983-85	(8.3)	11.2
w/A.C. add	(.4)	.4

(P) Main Bearings, Renew

Includes: Check all bearing clearances.

	(Factory Time)	Chilton Time
1983-85	(4.1)	5.5

(P) Main and Rod Bearings, Renew

Includes: Check all bearing clearances.

	(Factory Time)	Chilton Time
1983-85	(6.5)	7.9

(G) Rear Main Bearing Oil Seals, R&R and Repack (Upper & Lower)

Includes: R&R oil pan and rear main bearing cap.

	(Factory Time)	Chilton Time
1983-85	(2.9)	4.0

(G) Rear Main Bearing Oil Seals, Renew

Includes: R&R engine assy.

	(Factory Time)	Chilton Time
1983-85	(6.5)	9.1
w/A.C. add	(.4)	.4

(G) Crankshaft Pulley or Balancer, Renew

	(Factory Time)	Chilton Time
1983-85-pulley	(.6)	.8
balancer	(.9)	1.3
w/A.C. add	(.2)	.2

(G) Crankshaft Front Oil Seal, Renew

	(Factory Time)	Chilton Time
1983-85	(.9)	1.5
w/A.C. add	(.2)	.2

PARTS 15 CRANKSHAFT & DAMPER 15 PARTS

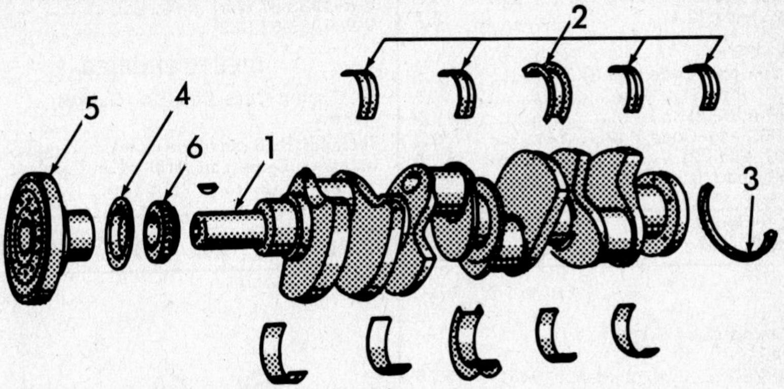

	Part No.	Price
(1) Crankshaft Assy.		
V-6-231		
1983-87	◆1260877	385.00
V-6-262		
1985	◆14071174	383.00
1986-87	◆14088639	383.00
V-8-305		
1983-87	◆361982	407.00
V-8-307		
1986-87	◆22527438	403.00
V-8-350 Diesel		
1983-85	◆22511035	439.00
(2) Main Bearings (Std.)		
V-6-231		
1983-87-No. 1	◆18009457	12.00
No. 2	◆18004602	20.00
No. 3	◆18002950	12.50
rear	◆5468578	13.00
V-6-262		
1985-87 (No. 1)		
upper	◆462661	6.50
lower	◆462664	6.50
Nos. 2, 3, 4	◆3912038	12.50
rear	◆3912030	17.00
V-8-305		
1983-87 (No. 1)		
upper	◆462661	6.50
lower	◆462664	6.50
Nos. 2, 3, 4	◆3912038	12.50
rear	◆3912030	17.00
V-8-307		
1986-87-No. 1	◆5466211	13.00
Nos. 2, 4	◆5466089	13.00
No. 3	◆5466090	19.75
rear	◆5466091	17.00
V-8-350 Diesel		
1983-87-No. 1	◆5466312	16.00
Nos. 2, 4	◆5458657	15.00
No. 3	◆5463797	26.25
No. 5	◆5466314	19.75

	Part No.	Price
(3) Rear Main Bearing Oil Seal		
V-6-231		
1983-87-seal	◆1193151	1.50
packing	◆9772831	1.50
V-6-262		
1985-87	◆473424	9.00
V-8-305		
1983-87	◆473424	9.00
V-8-307		
1986-87	◆9772831	1.50
V-8-350 Diesel		
1983-85	◆9772831	1.50
(4) Timing Cover Seal		
V-6-231		
1983-87-shedder	◆1193966	1.50
packing	◆1305044	1.00
V-6-262		
1985-87	◆10036286	5.25
V-8-305		
1983-87	◆10036286	5.25
V-8-307		
1986-87	◆552711	4.25
V-8-350 Diesel		
1983-87	◆552711	4.25

	Part No.	Price
(5) Vibration Damper		
V-6-231		
1983	◆25506570	42.75
1984-87	◆25523502	41.25
V-6-262		
1985-87	◆14082324	41.00
V-8-305		
1983-87	◆458653	59.25
V-8-307		
1986-87	◆458653	59.25
V-8-350 Diesel		
1983-87	◆559131	63.25
(6) Crankshaft Gear		
V-6-231		
1983-87	◆25519954	14.50
V-6-262		
1985-87	◆464617	29.50
V-8-305		
1983-87	◆3896959	16.00
V-8-307		
1986-87	◆382880	16.75
V-8-350 Diesel		
1983-87	◆558489	44.25

LABOR 16 CAMSHAFT & TIMING GEARS 16 LABOR

GASOLINE ENGINES

(G) Timing Cover Oil Seal, Renew

	(Factory Time)	Chilton Time
V-6-1983		
229-262 engs	(.8)	1.2
V-8-1983-87		
305 eng-Code H	(.8)	1.4
w/A.C. add	(.2)	.2
307 eng-Code Y	(1.0)	1.5
w/A.C. or AIR add	(.1)	.1

LABOR 16 CAMSHAFT & TIMING GEARS 16 LABOR

(Factory Time) Chilton Time

(G) Timing Case Cover Gasket, Renew
Includes: R&R fan blade, crankshaft pulley and balancer.
V-6–1983-87
229-262 engs (2.1) 2.7
231 eng (2.2) 3.2

V-8–1983-87
305 eng-Code H (2.0) 3.0
w/A.C. add (.2) 2
w/AIR add (.2) 2
307 eng-Code Y (1.8) 2.6
w/A.C. add (.3) 3
w/AIR add (.1) 1
Renew cover add (.2) 4
Renew f/pump eccentric
add (.1) 2

(G) Timing Chain or Gears, Renew
Includes: R&R fan blade, crankshaft pulley and balancer.
V-6–1983-87
229-262 engs (2.4) 3.2
231 eng (2.4) 3.7

V-8–1983-87
305 eng-Code H (2.3) 3.5
w/A.C. add (.2) 2
w/AIR add (.2) 2
307 eng-Code Y (2.1) 3.1
w/A.C. add (.3) 3
w/AIR add (.1) 1

(G) Camshaft, Renew
Includes: R&R radiator, intake manifold, rocker arms, push rods, lifters and timing chain cover.
V-6–1983-87
229-262 engs (5.8) 8.0
231 eng (5.5) 7.0
V-8–1983-87
305 eng-Code H
Pontiac (5.5) .... &77.7
Grand Prix (6.2) 8.6
w/A.C. add (.4) 4
w/P.S. add (.2) 2
w/A.I.R. add (.4) 4
†w/A.C. add (.9) 9
w/C.C.C. add (.3) 3
w/Cruise control add (.2) 2
307 eng-Code Y (5.7) *8.1
w/A.C. add (1.0) 1.0
w/AIR add (.4) 4
*Renew cam brgs add (1.4) 2.0

(G) Camshaft Rear Bearing Plug, Renew
Includes: R&R trans for accessibility.
V-6–1983-87 (2.2) 3.0
V-8–1983-87 (2.2) 3.0

DIESEL ENGINES

(G) Timing Case Cover or Gasket, Renew
Includes: R&R fan blade, crankshaft pulley and balancer. Drain and refill oil and coolant.
1983-85 (2.1) 3.1
Renew cover add (.2) 4
w/A.C. add (.3) 3

(G) Timing Chain or Gears, Renew
Includes: R&R fan blade, crankshaft pulley and balancer. Drain and refill oil and coolant.
1983-85 (2.3) 3.5
w/A.C. add (.3) 3

(G) Camshaft, Renew
Includes: R&R radiator, front cover, fuel pump, timing gear and chain. R&R injector pump, intake manifold and lifters. Disconnect exhaust system. Drain and refill oil and coolant. Make all necessary adjustments.
1983-85 (7.3) 10.0
w/A.C. add (1.0) 1.0

(G) Camshaft Bearings, Renew
Includes: R&R radiator, front cover, fuel pump, timing gear and chain. R&R injector pump, intake manifold and lifters. Disconnect exhaust system. Drain and refill oil and coolant. Make all necessary adjustments.
1983-85 (10.1) 13.8
w/A.C. add (1.0) 1.0

(G) Camshaft Rear Bearing Plug, Renew
Includes: R&R trans for accessibility.
1983-85 (2.1) 3.0

PARTS 16 CAMSHAFT & TIMING GEARS 16 PARTS

Part No. Price

(1) Timing Case Gasket
V-6–231
1983-87 .... ◆25519461 5.25
V-6–262
1985-87 .... ◆3799620 1.00
V-8–305
1983-87 .... ◆3799620 1.00
V-8–307
1986-87 .... ◆22505997 1.25
V-8–350 Diesel
1983-87 .... ◆22505997 1.25

(2) Case Cover Oil Seal
V-6–231
1983-87-shedder .... ◆1193966 1.50
packing .... ◆1305044 1.00
V-6–262
1985-87 .... ◆10036286 5.25
V-8–305
1983-87 .... ◆10036286 5.25
V-8–307
1986-87 .... ◆552711 4.25
V-8–350 Diesel
1983-87 .... ◆552711 4.25

(3) Timing Chain
V-6–231
1983-87 .... ◆1257650 26.00
V-6–262
1985-87 .... ◆14087014 25.25
V-8–305
1983-84 .... ◆346261 24.50
1985-87 .... ◆14087014 25.25
V-8–307
1986-87 .... ◆401584 31.75
V-8–350 Diesel
1983-85 .... ◆558484 N.L.

(4) Camshaft Sprocket
V-6–231
1983-84 .... ◆1253698 18.50
1985-87 .... ◆25523115 17.50

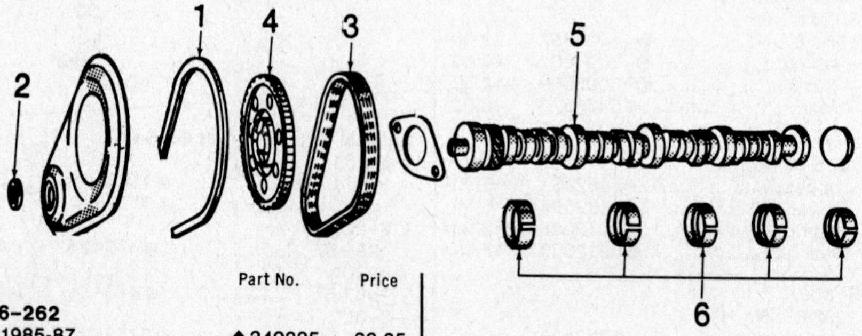

Part No. Price

V-6–262
1985-87 .... ◆340235 26.25
V-8–305
1983-87 .... ◆3896959 N.L.
V-8–307
1986-87 .... ◆382880 16.75
V-8–350 Diesel
1983-85 .... ◆558489 44.25

(5) Camshaft
V-6–231
1983-84-1st
design .... ◆1262835 119.00
2nd design .... ◆25510049 119.00
1985-87 .... ◆25510049 119.00
V-6–262
1985-87 .... ◆14077973 120.00
V-8–305
1983-87 .... ◆14060653 124.00
V-8–307
1986-87 .... ◆22527149 256.00
V-8–350 Diesel
1983-87 .... ◆22510099 266.00

(6) Camshaft Bearings
V-6–231
1983-84-exc. frt. .... ◆1231142 7.75
frt. .... ◆1234441 7.00

Part No. Price

1985-87-exc.
below .... ◆1231142 7.75
No. 1, 4 .... ◆25524301 7.25
V-6–262
1985-87-No. 1 .... ◆474005 16.75
No. 2, 5 .... ◆474006 12.75
No. 3, 4 .... ◆474007 16.75
V-8–305
1983-87-No. 1 .... ◆474005 16.75
No. 2, 5 .... ◆474006 12.75
No. 3, 4 .... ◆474007 16.75
V-8–307
1986-87-No. 1 .... ◆561077 11.50
No. 2 .... ◆390300 11.50
No. 3 .... ◆390301 11.75
No. 4 .... ◆390302 11.50
No. 5 .... ◆390303 11.50
V-8–350 Diesel
1983-87-No. 1 .... ◆561077 11.50
No. 2 .... ◆390300 11.50
No. 3 .... ◆390301 11.75
No. 4 .... ◆390302 11.50
No. 5 .... ◆390303 11.50

LABOR 17 ENGINE OILING SYSTEM 17 LABOR

(Factory Time) — Chilton Time

GASOLINE ENGINES

(G) Oil Pan or Gasket, Renew
V-6–1983-87
229-262 engs (1.8) 2.4
231 eng (1.2) 1.6
w/C.C.C. add (.2) 2
V-8–1983-87
305 eng-Code H (1.9) 2.7
w/A.C. add (.1) 1
307 eng-Code Y (2.1) 2.9

(P) Pressure Test Engine Bearings (Pan Off)
All models 1.0

(G) Oil Pump, Renew
V-6–1983-87
229-262 engs (1.9) 2.6
231 eng (.5) 8
w/C.C.C. add (.2) 2
V-8–1983-87
305 eng-Code H (2.0) 2.9
w/A.C. add (.1) 1
307 eng-Code Y (2.2) 3.1

(G) Oil Pump, R&R and Recondition
V-6–1983-87
231 eng (.5) 8

(G) Oil Pressure Gauge (Engine), Renew
1983-87 (.3) 4
w/A.I.R. add (.3) 3

(G) Oil Pressure Gauge (Dash), Renew
1983-87-Grand Prix (.3) 5

(M) Oil Filter Element, Renew
1983-87 (.3) 3

DIESEL ENGINES

(G) Oil Pan or Gasket, Renew
Includes: Raise engine, R&R and clean oil pump screen.
1983-85 (2.6) 3.4

(P) Pressure Test Engine Bearings (Pan Off)
All models 1.0

(G) Oil Pump, Renew
Includes: Raise engine, R&R and clean oil pump screen.
1983-85 (2.7) 3.6

(G) Oil Pump, R&R and Recondition
Includes: Raise engine, R&R and clean oil pump screen.
1983-85 (2.9) 3.8

(G) Oil Pressure Gauge (Engine), Renew
1983-85 (.3) 4

(M) Oil Filter Element, Renew
1983-85 (.3) 3

PARTS 17 ENGINE OILING SYSTEM 17 PARTS

	Part No.	Price
Oil Pan Gasket Set		
V-6-231		
1983-84-1st design (14 blt.)	◆1260771	3.00
2nd design (20 blt.)	◆25521994	8.50
1985-86	◆25521994	8.50
V-6-262		
1985	◆14079397	N.L.
1986-87	◆14088514	29.25
V-8-305		
1983	◆14019828	11.75
1984-87	◆14079398	10.00
V-8-307		
1986-87	◆22519181	N.L.
V-8-350 Diesel		
1983-85	◆22519181	7.00
Oil Pump		
V-6-231		
1983-87-kit	◆25523433	39.75
V-6-262		
1985-87	◆3764547	N.L.
V-8-305		
1983-87	◆3764547	49.75
V-8-307		
1986-87	◆22524583	61.50
V-8-350 Diesel		
1983-85	◆22511732	59.75
Oil Pump Shaft		
V-8-307		
1986-87-drive	22525286	7.75
driven	◆555737	1.25
V-8-350 Diesel		
1983-87-drive	22511730	N.L.
driven	◆555737	1.25
Oil Pressure Gauge (Engine Unit)		
V-6-231		
(wo/Gauges)		
1983-87	◆25500672	5.50
(Gauges)		
1983-87	14039612	17.00
V-8-305		
(wo/Gauges)		
1983-87	◆10002798	5.50
(Gauges)		
1983-87	14039612	17.00
V-8-307		
1986-87	38515936	N.L.
V-8-350 Diesel		
(wo/Gauges)		
1983-87	◆3815936	3.50
(Gauges)		
1983-87	◆459417	17.75

PARTS 18 CLUTCH & FLYWHEEL 18 PARTS

	Part No.	Price
Flywheel Assy.		
V-6-231		
1983	◆25512346	70.50
1984-87	◆25512348	72.00
V-6-262		
1985	◆471591	55.75
1986-87	◆14088765	55.75
V-8-305		
1983-87	◆471591	55.75
V-8-307		
1986-87	◆22500807	85.50
V-8-350 Diesel		
1983-85	◆22500808	85.50

LABOR 21 SHIFT LINKAGE 21 LABOR

(Factory Time) — Chilton Time

AUTOMATIC

(G) Shift Linkage, Adjust
All models
Neutral Safety Switch (.3) 4
Shift Indicator Needle (.2) 3
Shift Linkage (.4) 5
T.V. Cable (.3) 4

(G) Shift Linkage, Adjust (w/Diesel Eng)
All models
Fast idle speed (.2) 3
Throttle rod/T.V. cable (.5) 6
Vacuum regul valve (.6) 8
Trans vacuum valve (.5) 6
Complete (.8) 1.0

(G) Gearshift Lever, Renew
1983-87-column mount (.3) 5
floor mount (.5) 9

(G) Shift Control Cable, Renew
1983-87 (.7) 1.0

(G) Shift Control Rod and/or Swivel, Renew
1983-87 (.4) 5

(G) Gearshift Indicator Assembly, Renew
1983-87
Grand Prix
column mount (.6) 1.0
floor mount (.2) 4
Pontiac (.4) 6

LABOR 25 U-JOINTS & DRIVESHAFT 25 LABOR

(Factory Time)	Chilton Time
(G) Drive Shaft, Renew	
1983-87 (.4)	.5
(G) Universal Joint, Renew	
Includes: R&R drive shaft.	
1983-87-front (.6)	.8
rear (.5)	.7
both (.7)	1.3
double Cardan (1.1)	1.6
(G) Front Slip Yoke, Renew	
1983-87 (.6)	.8
(G) Rear Companion Flange, Renew	
1983-87 (.7)	1.0

PARTS 25 UNIVERSAL JOINTS & DRIVE SHAFT 25 PARTS

	Part No.	Price
Front Universal Yoke		
1983-87	◆7812557	65.25
U/Joint Repair Kit		
1983-87-Dana	◆374246	28.50
Saginaw	◆7806140	41.00

LABOR 26 REAR AXLE 26 LABOR

(Factory Time)	Chilton Time
(M) Differential, Drain & Refill	
All models	.6
(M) Differential Cover and/or Gasket, Renew	
1983-87 (.5)	.6
(G) Axle Shaft, Renew	
Includes: R&R axle shaft bearing.	
'C' Lock Type	
1983-87-one (.7)	.9
both (.9)	1.2
(G) Axle Shaft Bearing and/or Oil Seal, Renew	
'C' Lock Type	
1983-87-one (.6)	.8
both (.8)	1.1
(G) Pinion Shaft Oil Seal, Renew	
1983-87 (.5)	.8
(G) Differential Case Assy., Remove and Reinstall	
Includes: R&R rear wheels and axle shafts. Check and adjust backlash and side bearing preload.	
1983-87 (1.8)	2.8
w/Limited slip add (.5)	.5
(G) Differential Side Bearings, Renew	
1983-87 (1.7)	2.5
(G) Limited Slip Clutch Plates, Renew	
1983-87 (1.1)	2.0
(G) Differential Pinion Bearings, Renew	
Includes: R&R drive shaft and pinion. Check and renew outer races if required.	
1983-87 (2.0)	3.4
Renew side brgs add (.3)	.3
(P) Ring Gear and Pinion, Renew	
Includes: Transfer or renew pinion bearings.	
1983-87 (2.1)	3.9
Recond diff case add	
std (.3)	.5
limited slip (.7)	1.0
(G) Pinion Shaft and/or Side Pinion Gears, Renew	
1983-87 (.8)	1.8
w/Limited slip add (.5)	.5
(G) Rear Axle Housing, Renew	
Includes: Transfer differential case assy. and all attaching parts. Bleed and adjust brakes.	
1983-87 (3.4)	5.2

PARTS 26 REAR AXLE 26 PARTS

	Part No.	Price
(1) Axle Shaft		
7½" dia. ring gr.		
(Bonneville, Grand Prix)		
1983-87	◆22519888	104.75
(Parisienne)		
7½" dia. ring gr.		
1983-87	◆22519891	99.50
8½" dia. ring gr.		
1983-87-wo/Sta. wag.	◆1255801	114.00
Sta. wag.	◆14060881	145.25
(3) Axle Shaft Seal		
1983-87-wo/Sta. wag.	◆3998519	4.00
Sta. wag.	◆3958078	5.00
(4) Rear Axle Bearing		
1983-87-wo/Sta. wag.	◆7451785	16.00
Sta. wag.	◆7451809	15.00
(5) Pinion Flange		
1983-87-exc below	◆1256654	35.00
7½" ring gr.	◆7827670	33.50
(6) Pinion Seal		
7½" dia. ring gr.		
1983-87	◆552571	8.00
8½" dia. ring gr.		
1938-87	◆1243465	7.50
8¾" dia. ring gr.		
(7) Front Pinion Bearing		
1983-87-exc below	◆7450984	21.00
7½" ring gr.	◆7451202	16.00
(8) Axle Housing		
(Bonneville, Grand Prix)		
1983-87	22510780	496.25
(Parisienne)		
7½" ring gr.		
1983-87	22510779	392.25
8½" dia. ring gr.		
1983-87-wo/Sta. wag.	14079329	406.25
Sta. wag.	14079330	489.75
(9) Pinion Gear Package		
7½ T dia. ring gr.		
1983-87-exc. below	22525894	94.50
3.42, 3.73R	22521625	105.00
8½" dia. ring gr.		
1983-87	1397647	132.00
Gear packages contain 2 side gears, 2 pinion gears, thrust washers and pinion shaft.		
Side Gears-Sold Separately		
(w/Limited slip)		
1983-87-8½" ring gr.	231075	49.50
Pinion Gears-Sold Separately		
(w/limited slip)		
1983-87-8½" ring gr.	6270977	17.50
(10) Drive Pinion Spacer		
1983-87-exc. below	1234726	1.50
7½" ring gr.	9785792	1.50
(11) Rear Pinion Bearing		
7½" dia. ring gr.		
1983-87	7455699	N.L.
8½", 8¾" dia. ring gr.		
1983-87	7451155	20.00
(12) Shim Package		
1983-87 (.025-.029)		
exc. below	1394893	6.50
7½" ring gr.	553022	5.50
(13) Ring and Pinion Gear		
7½" dia. ring gr.		
1983-87-2.29R	560197	259.00
2.41R	560198	259.00
2.56R	560199	259.00
2.73R	560201	259.00
2.93R	560204	261.00
3.08R	560205	N.L.
3.23R	560207	259.00

PARTS 26 REAR AXLE 26 PARTS

	Part No.	Price
8½" dia. ring gr.		
1983-87-2.41R	1258715	276.00
2.56R	1258707	276.00
2.73R	1258708	276.00
3.08R	1258709	276.00
3.23R	1258713	276.00
(14) Bearing Adjusting Shim Pkg.		
1983-87 (.040-.044)		
exc. below	3995791	6.50
8¾" ring gr.	3996610	6.50
(15) Differential Side Bearing		
1983-87-exc below	7451281	15.00
8¾" ring gr.	7451140	15.00
(16) Differential Case		
7½" dia. ring gr.		
(wo/Limited slip)		
1983-87-exc. below	558648	109.00
3.23, 3.42, 3.73R	558649	109.25
(Limited slip)		
1983-87-exc. below	22514583	278.00
3.23, 3.42, 3.73R	22514584	402.00
8½" dia. ring gr.		
(wo/Limited slip)		
1983-87-exc. below	1252981	110.00
2.41, 2.56, 2.93	1252980	110.00
(Limited slip)		
1983-87-exc. below	14030435	431.25
2.41, 2.56R	14030434	408.50
(17) Pinion Shaft		
7½" dia. ring gr.		
(wo/Limited slip)		
1983-87	22507586	11.00
(Limited slip)		
1983-87	22515972	10.25
8½" dia. ring gr.		
1983-87	14006401	12.50
(18) Friction Disc Kit		
1983-87-exc. below	231127	58.25
Eaton	483722	55.75

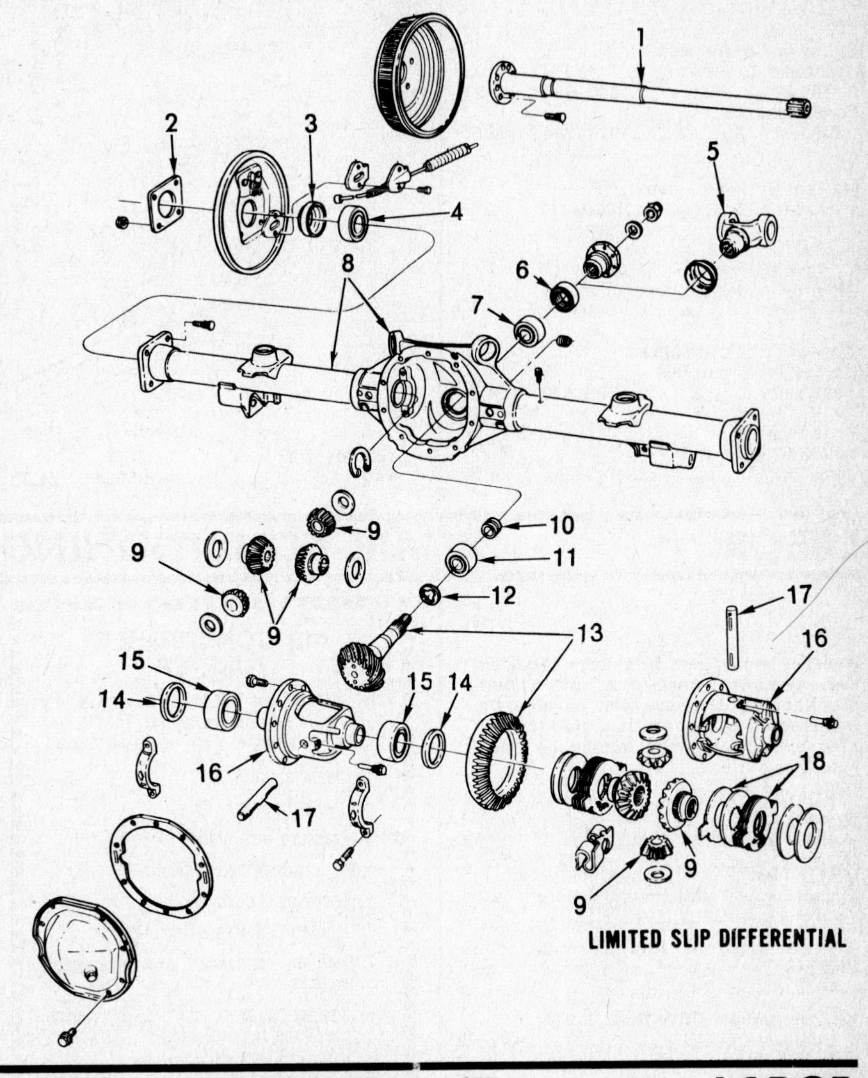

LABOR 27 REAR SUSPENSION 27 LABOR

(Factory Time)	Chilton Time
(G) Rear Spring, Renew	
1983-87-Grand Prix-one (.4)	.7
both (.5)	.9
Pontiac-one (.6)	.8
both (.7)	1.1
(G) Lower Control Arm Assy., Renew	
1983-87-one (.4)	.7
both (.6)	1.0
Renew bushings add-each side (.1)	.3
(G) Upper Control Arm Assy., Renew	
Pontiac	
1983-87-one (.5)	.8
both (.7)	1.2
Grand Prix	
1983-87-one (.5)	.8
both (.8)	1.2
Renew bushings add-each side (.1)	.3
(G) Rear Shock Absorber, Renew	
1983-87-one (.3)	.4
both (.5)	.7
(G) Rear Stabilizer Bar, Renew	
1983-87 (.5)	.7
(G) Airlift Shock Absorbers, Renew	
1983-87-one (.4)	.7
both (.5)	1.1

PARTS 27 REAR SUSPENSION 27 PARTS

	Part No.	Price
(1) Upper Control Arm		
(Bonneville, Grand Prix)		
1983-87-"0" deg.	10000076	15.00
"+1½" deg.	10001060	15.00
"-1½" deg.	10001059	30.50
(Parisienne)		
1983-87-"0" deg.	10000887	22.50
"+2" deg.	10000904	30.00
"-2" deg.	10000910	30.00
(2) Control Arm Bushing		
(Bonneville, Grand Prix)		
1983-87-upper	10000068	6.50
lower	10000072	4.50
(Parisienne)		
1983-87-orange	10000952	6.50
lt. green	10000953	6.50

PARTS 27 REAR SUSPENSION 27 PARTS

	Part No.	Price
(3) Lower Control Arm		
(Bonneville, Grand Prix)		
1983-87	10000063	43.25
(Parisienne)		
1983-87	10000334	32.50
(4) Rear Spring Insulator		
1983-87	10004110	2.25
(5) Rear Spring		
Order by model and description.		
(6) Rear Shock Absorber		
(Bonneville, Grand Prix)		
1983-87	4993580	24.50
(Parisienne)		
1983-87-wo/Sta. wag.	4993551	24.50

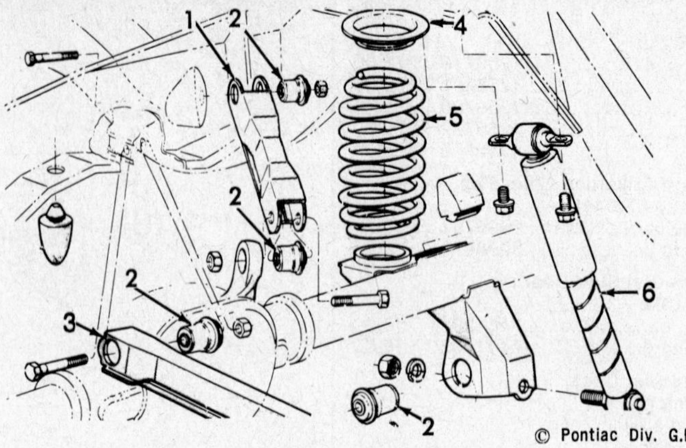

© Pontiac Div. G.M. Corp.

	Part No.	Price
1983-84-Sta. wag.	4993554	24.50
1985-87-Sta. wag.	22046427	24.50

LABOR 28 AIR CONDITIONING 28 LABOR

	(Factory Time)	Chilton Time

Note: If more than one item requires replacement where evacuation and discharging the system is already included in the operation, deduct 1.0 hour for each additional item to the times listed.

(G) Drain, Evacuate and Charge System
All models (.5) 1.0

(G) Leak Check
Includes: Check all lines and connections.
All models 5

(G) Referigerant Add (Partial Charge)
All models 6

(G) Compressor Drive Belt, Renew
1983-87-V-6 (.4) 5
V-8 (.3) 4
Diesel (.5) 6
w/AIR add (.1) 1

(G) Vacuum Selector Valve, Renew
1983-87 (.4) 6

(G) Master Electrical Switch, Renew
1983-85 (.4) 6
1986-87-Pontiac (.6) 8
Grand Prix (.4) 6

(G) Air Conditioning Control Assy., Renew
1983-85 (.4) 6
1986-87-Pontiac (.7) 9
Grand Prix (.4) 6

(G) Blower Motor, Renew
1983-87 (.3) 5

(G) Blower Motor Resistor, Renew
1983-87 (.2) 3

(G) Blower Motor Switch, Renew
1983-85 (.4) 5
1986-87-Pontiac (.6) 8
Grand Prix (.4) 6

(G) High Blower Relay, Renew
1983-87 (.2) 4

AIR CONDITIONER TUNE-UP

For efficient operation and satisfactory performance in hot weather. The following air conditioner tune-up is suggested:

1. Clean intake filter
2. Clean condenser fins
3. Pressure test system
4. Adjust drive belt tension
5. Check antifreeze/coolant
6. Tighten compressor mounts
7. Tighten condenser and evaporator mounts
8. Inspect system for leaks (hoses, couplings, valves, etc.)
9. Partial charge system

All models 1.0
If necessary to evacuate and charge system, add 1.0

	(Factory Time)	Chilton Time

(G) Vacuum Control Diaphragm, Renew
Pontiac
Defroster diaphragm
1983-87 (.4) 8
Upper or lower mode
1983-87 (2.3) 3.0
Air inlet diaphragm
1983-87 (.3) 7
Grand Prix
Defroster diaphragm
1983-84 (3.4) 5.0
1985-87 (1.3) 2.1
Upper or lower mode
1985-87 (1.7) 3.0
Air inlet diaphragm
1983-84 (3.4) 5.0
1985-87 (.4) 7

(G) Air Conditioning Hoses, Renew
Includes: Evacuate and charge system.
1983-87-one (1.0) 1.7
each adtnl (.3) 5

	(Factory Time)	Chilton Time

COMPRESSOR 4 CYLINDER RADIAL

(G) Compressor Assembly, Renew
Includes: Transfer parts as required. Evacuate and charge system.
1983-87 (1.0) 2.0

(G) Compressor Clutch Plate and Hub Assy., Renew
1983-85 (.3) 6
1986-87-Pontiac (.3) 6
Grand Prix (.5) 8

(G) Compressor Clutch Coil and/or Pulley Rim, Renew
1983-85 (.5) 9
1986-87-Pontiac (.5) 9
Grand Prix (.9) 1.2
Renew pulley or brg add (.1) 1

(G) Compressor Rotor and/or Bearing, Renew
1983-85 (.6) 1.0
1986-87-Pontiac (.6) 1.0
Grand Prix (.9) 1.2

(G) Compressor Shaft Seal Kit, Renew
Includes: Evacuate and charge system.
Does not include R&R compressor.
1983-85 (1.0) 2.5
1986-87-Pontiac (1.0) 2.5
Grand Prix (1.4) 2.5

(G) Compressor Front Head, 'O' Ring Seal, Main Bearing and/or Thrust/Belleville Washers, Renew
Includes: R&R compressor. R&R rotor and bearing assy., clutch coil and pulley rim as an assembly. Evacuate and charge system.
1983-87 (1.5) 2.8

(G) Compressor Shell and/or 'O' Rings, Renew
Includes: R&R compressor. R&R clutch and pulley assy. Clean and inspect parts. Evacuate and charge system.
1983-87 (1.7) 2.8

(G) Compressor Discharge Valve Plates, Renew
Includes: R&R compressor. R&R clutch and pulley assy. R&R shell to internal mechanism.

LABOR 28 AIR CONDITIONING 28 LABOR

(Factory Time) Chilton Time

Clean and inspect parts. Evacuate and charge system.

1983-87 (1.8)	2.6
Two or more add (.1)	.2

(G) Compressor Shaft and Cylinder Assy., Renew

Includes: R&R compressor. R&R clutch and pulley assy. R&R shaft seal assy., remove and transfer front head assy. R&R compressor shell and 'O' rings. R&R compressor discharge valve plates, R&R superheat switch and pressure relief valve. Clean and inspect parts. Evacuate and charge system.

1983-87 (1.9)	2.9

(G) Evaporator Core, Renew

Includes: Evacuate and charge system.

Pontiac	
1983-87 (1.5)	3.5
Grand Prix	
1983-87 (2.0)	3.9

(G) Condenser and Seals, Renew

Includes: Evacuate and charge system.

Pontiac	
1983-87 (.9)	2.0
w/Diesel eng	2.5
Grand Prix	
1983-87 (1.1)	2.2
w/Diesel eng	2.5

(G) Accumulator Assembly, Renew

Includes: Evacuate and charge system.

1983-87 (.7)	1.5

(G) Expansion Tube Assy., Renew

Includes: Evacuate and carge system.

1983-87 (.7)	1.4

(G) Pressure Cycling Switch, Renew

1983-87 (.2)	.3

PARTS 28 AIR CONDITIONING 28 PARTS

	Part No.	Price
Compressor Assembly		
1983-87	12300273	390.00
5.4 in. dia	12326201	N.L.
Clutch Hub and Drive Plate		
1983-87	6551220	32.50
5.4 in. dia	6551838	36.00
Rotor and Bearing Assy.		
1983-87	6551216	67.50
Compressor Pulley		
1983-87	6556715	13.00
Compressor Clutch Coil		
1983-87	6551217	44.00
Compressor Shaft Seal Kit		
1983-87	9956695	13.00
Front Head Main Bearing		
1983-87	6556572	4.00
Compressor Front Head		
1983-87	6551142	28.25
Compressor Outer Shell		
1983-87	2724158	38.00
Valve Plate		
1983-87	6551141	11.50
Cylinder and Shaft Assy.		
1983-87	2724144	269.00
Compressor Pressure Relief Valve		
1983-87	5914435	13.50
Condenser		
(Bonneville, Grand Prix)		
1983-87	3041841	170.00
(Parisienne)		
1983-87-exc.		
Diesel	3037439	158.25
Diesel	3037438	156.50
Evaporator Core Assembly		
(Bonneville, Grand Prix)		
1983-84	3037638	201.50
1985-87	3058311	275.75
(Parisienne)		
1983-84	3035240	218.25
1985-87	3058130	261.75
Accumulator Dehydrator		
(Bonneville, Grand Prix)		
1983	2724240	80.00
1984	2724265	87.75
1985-87	3059315	85.25
(Parisienne)		
1983	2724275	80.25
1984-87	2724275	80.25
Blower Motor Relay		
1983-87	10018449	N.L.
Blower Motor Switch		
1983	16015256	6.00
1984-87	16032480	7.50
Evaporator Blower Motor		
1983-87	22020945	60.00

PROGRAMMER ASSY. & PARTS

	Part No.	Price
Vacuum Valve		
1983-87-exc.		
below	7896861	3.75
Gr. Prix	7897082	3.50

LABOR 29 LOCKS, HINGES & WIND. REGULATORS 29 LABOR

(Factory Time) Chilton Time

(G) Hood Release Cable, Renew

1983-87 (.3)	.6

(G) Hood Latch, Renew

1983-87 (.2)	.3

(G) Hood Hinge, Renew (One)

1983-87 (.3)	.5

(G) Door Lock, Renew

Front	
1983-87 (.5)	.8
Rear	
1983-87-Grand Prix (.6)	1.0
Pontiac (.8)	1.2
w/Electric locks add (.1)	.1

(G) Door Lock Remote Control, Renew (Front or Rear)

1983-87 (.4)	.7

(G) Door Lock Cylinder, Renew

1983-87 (.3)	.6
Recode cyl add (.3)	.3

(G) Door Handle (Outside), Renew (Front or Rear)

1983-87 (.4)	.6
Renew insert add	.1

(G) Lock Striker Plate, Renew

1983-87 (.2)	.2

(G) Door Window Regulator (Manual), Renew (Front or Rear)

1983-87 (.8)	1.1
Recond add (.2)	.3

(G) Door Window Regulator (Electric), Renew (Front or Rear)

1983-87 (1.0)	1.4

(G) Trunk Lock, Renew

1983-87 (.3)	.4

(G) Trunk Lock Cylinder, Renew

1983-87 (.3)	.4
Recode cyl add (.3)	.3

(G) Trunk Hinge or Strap, Renew (One)

1983-87 (.8)	1.2

(G) Tailgate Window Regulator, Renew

1983-87 (.7)	1.2

(G) Tailgate Lock Cylinder, Renew

1983-87 (.3)	.5
Recode cyl add (.3)	.3

PARTS 29 LOCKS, HINGES & WIND. REGULATORS 29 PARTS

	Part No.	Price
Hood Lock		
1983-87	14070703	16.25
Hood Hinge		
(Bonneville, Grand Prix)		
1983-87-right	10020566	21.50
left	10020567	21.50
(Parisienne)		
1983-87-right	14015976	29.00
left	14015975	29.00
Front Door Lock (R.H.)		
1983-87-2 dr.	20293612	33.50
4 dr.	20293604	51.50
Door Lock, Rear		
1983-87-right	20293624	55.75
left	20293625	55.75
Door Lock Cylinder & Keys		
1983-87-2 dr.	9632762	5.75
4 dr.	9632769	7.75
Striker		
1983-87	20151275	5.50
Trunk Lid Hinge Strap		
(Bonneville, Grand Prix)		
1983-87-2 dr.	20343192	24.40
4 dr.	20313446	22.75
sta. wag.	20055238	8.75
(Parisienne)		
1983-87	20434734	13.50
Front Window Regulator, Manual (R.H.)		
(Bonneville, Grand Prix)		
1983-87-2 dr.	20009422	64.00
4 dr.	20009424	59.50
(Parisienne)		
1983-87	20110652	102.00
Rear Window Regulator, Manual (R.H.)		
1983-87	20147472	88.25
Front Window Regulator, Electric (R.H.)		
(Bonneville, Grand Prix)		
1983-87-2 dr.	20123184	98.00
4 dr.	20209182	98.00
(Parisienne)		
1983-87	20192896	114.00
Rear Window Regulator, Electric (R.H.)		
1983-87	20192894	114.00
Trunk Lock		
(wo/Sta. wagon)		
1983-87	20279741	N.L.
(Sta. wagon)		
1983-exc.		
Parisienne	20367780	42.75
1983-Parisienne		
L.H.	20012859	N.L.
R.H.	20367776	58.50
end gate	20367780	42.75
1984-87-Parisienne		
L.H.	20210034	58.50
R.H. (upper)	20452014	137.00
R.H. (lower)	20452016	72.50
Door Handle, Outside (R.H.)		
(Bonneville, Grand Prix)		
1983-87	20099250	24.75
(Parisienne)		
1983-87	20111712	26.50
Power Window Motor		
(Bonneville, Grand Prix)		
1983-87	22020900	73.00
(Parisienne)		
1983	22029848	72.50
1984-86	22020900	N.L.

LABOR 30 HEAD AND PARKING LAMPS 30 LABOR

	(Factory Time)	Chilton Time
(G) Aim Headlamps		
two		.4
four		.6
(M) Headlamp Sealed Beam Bulb, Renew		
1983-87-each	(.3)	.3
(M) Back-Up Lamp Assembly, Renew		
1983-87-each	(.3)	.4
(M) High Level Stop Lamp Assy., Renew		
1986-87	(.2)	.4
(M) Cornering Lamp Assembly, Renew		
1983-87-each	(.3)	.4
(M) Park and Turn Signal Lamp Assy., Renew		
1983-87-each	(.3)	.4
(M) Stop, Tail and Turn Signal Lamp Assy., Renew		
Pontiac		
sdn-each	(.7)	1.0
wag-each	(.3)	.4
Grand Prix-each	(.3)	.4
(M) Back-Up Lamp Bulb, Renew		
All models-one	(.2)	.3
(M) Cornering Lamp Bulb, Renew		
All models-each	(.2)	.3
(M) License Lamp Bulb, Renew		
All models-one or all	(.2)	.3
(M) Park and Turn Signal Lamp Bulb, Renew		
All models-each		.2
(M) Side Marker Lamp Bulb, Renew		
All models-each		.2
(M) Stop, Tail and Turn Signal Lamp Bulb, Renew		
All models-one		.2
each adtnl		.1
(M) High Level Stop Lamp Bulb, Renew		
All models	(.2)	.3

PARTS 30 HEAD AND PARKING LAMPS 30 PARTS

	Part No.	Price
Headlamp Sealed Beam		
(wo/Quartz)		
1983-87-inner	5966201	15.00
outer	5966200	15.00
(Quartz)		
1983-87-inner	5930567	22.50
outer	16502327	22.50
Parking Lamp Assy. (R.H.)		
(Bonneville)		
1983-87	929908	39.75
(Grand Prix)		
1983-87	914756	12.50
(Parisienne)		
1983-87	914550	23.50

Tail & Stop Lamp Lens (R.H.)

Part numbers shown are for pricing reference only. Order part with complete model information.

	Part No.	Price
(Bonneville, Grand Prix)		
1983-84-2 dr.	5971904	83.50
4 dr.	5972058	73.50
Sta. wag.	915930	35.00
1985-87	16503248	83.50
(Parisienne)		
1983-84-exc. wag.	5971188	53.50
1985-87-exc. wag.	5971978	69.75
1983-87-Sta. wag.	5931902	59.50
High Mount Stoplight		
1986-87		
Bonn., GP	5974464	36.00
Paris.	5974457	36.00
License Plate Lamp Assy.		
(Bonneville, Grand Prix)		
1983-87-2 dr	912345	6.25
4 dr.	913061	6.25
Sta. wag.	913204	6.25
(Parisienne)		
1983-87-exc. below	914000	3.75
Sta. wag.	912795	7.50
Cornering Lamp Assy.		
(Bonneville, Grand Prix)		
1983-87-right	915192	25.50
left	915191	25.50
(Parisienne)		
1983-87-right	914554	25.50
left	914553	25.50

LABOR 31 WINDSHIELD WIPER & SPEEDOMETER 31 LABOR

(Factory Time)	Chilton Time
(G) Windshield Wiper Motor, Renew	
1983-87-Pontiac (.3)	*.6
Grand Prix (.6)	.8
*w/Cruise control add (.1)	1
(G) Windshield Wiper Motor, R&R and Recondition	
1983-87-Pontiac (.8)	1.2
Grand Prix (1.1)	1.4
(G) Wiper Transmission, Renew (One)	
1983-87 (.4)	.6
(G) Wiper Switch, Renew	
1983-85-Grand Prix (1.0)	1.4
Pontiac (.3)	.5
1986-87 (.9)	1.4
(G) Windshield Washer Pump, Renew	
1983 (.2)	.4
1984-87-Grand Prix (.6)	.8
Pontiac (.2)	*.4
Recond pump add	.3
w/Pulse wipe add (.1)	.1
*w/Cruise control add (.1)	.1
(G) Windshield Washer Pump Valve, Renew	
1983-87 (.2)	.4
(G) Speedometer Head, R&R or Renew	
1983-87-Grand Prix (.5)	.9
Pontiac (.3)	.5
Reset odometer add	.2
(G) Speedometer Cable and Casing, Renew	
wo/Cruise control	
1983-87-upper (.6)	1.0
lower (.3)	.5
one piece (.7)	1.1
w/Cruise control	
1983-87-upper cable (.6)	1.0
lower cable (.3)	.6
one piece (.7)	1.1
(G) Speedometer Cable (Inner), Renew or Lubricate	
wo/Cruise control	
1983-87-upper (.4)	.7
lower (.3)	.4
one piece (.7)	1.0
w/Cruise control	
1983-87-upper cable (.3)	.6
lower cable (.3)	.5
one piece (.6)	1.0
(G) Radio, R&R	
1983-87 (.5)	.8
w/A.C. add (.2)	.2

PARTS 31 WINDSHIELD WIPER & SPEEDOMETER 31 PARTS

	Part No.	Price
Wiper Motor		
(Parisienne)		
1983-87-exc. pulse	4960974	84.00
Pulse	4961608	80.00
(Bonneville, Grand Prix)		
1983-exc. pulse	4960974	84.00
Pulse	4961608	80.00
1984-87	22039687	110.75
Wiper Transmission (R.H.)		
(Bonneville, Grand Prix)		
1983-87	22009387	18.50
(Parisienne)		
1983-87	22010448	17.00
Wiper Switch		
(exc. Parisienne)		
(wo/Pulse wiper)		
1983-exc. tilt	7835342	22.50
Tilt whl.	7837279	41.50
1984-87-exc. tilt	7842714	44.75
Tilt whl.	7843684	44.75
(Pulse wiper)		
1983	7837280	53.50
1984-87	7843683	56.25
(Parisienne)		
1983-exc. pulse	1994232	26.50
Pulse wpr.	14029586	27.25
1984-87-exc. tilt	7835340	56.25
Tilt whl.	7837280	53.50
Washer Pump		
1983-exc. pulse	22009212	25.00
pulse wpr.	22021345	38.50
1984-87	22039686	16.25
Speedometer Head & Cable		
Order by year and model.		

LABOR 32 LIGHT SWITCHES & WIRING 32 LABOR

(Factory Time)	Chilton Time
(G) Headlamp Switch, Renew	
1983-87 (.3)	.5
(G) Headlamp Dimmer Switch, Renew	
1983-87 (.3)	.7
(G) Stop Light Switch, Renew	
1983-87 (.2)	.3
(G) Parking Brake Lamp Switch, Renew	
1983-87 (.2)	.3
(G) Back-Up Lamp and Park/Neutral Switch, Renew	
1983-87 (.3)	.4
(G) Dimmer Switch Pivot Assy., Renew	
1983-85	
std column (.8)	1.4
tilt column (.6)	1.2
w/Cruise control add (.2)	.2
1986-87 (.9)	1.4
(G) Turn Signal or Hazard Warning Switch, Renew	
1983-87 (.7)	1.1
w/Tilt column add (.1)	.1
w/Cruise control add (.2)	.2
(M) Turn Signal or Hazard Warning Flasher, Renew	
1983-87 (.2)	.2
(G) Horn Relay, Renew	
1983-87 (.2)	.3
(G) Horn, Renew	
1983-87-each (.2)	.3
(G) Wiring Harness, Renew	
Front end harness-Pontiac	
1983-87 (1.0)	1.5
Grand Prix	
1983-87 (1.0)	1.5
Instrument panel-Pontiac	
1983-87 (2.0)	3.1
Grand Prix	
1983-87 (2.0)	3.1
Engine harness-Pontiac	
1983-87-V-6 (.7)	1.2
V-8 (.9)	1.7
Grand Prix	
1983-87-V-6 (.7)	1.2
V-8 (.9)	1.7

PARTS 32 LIGHT SWITCHES & WIRING 32 PARTS

	Part No.	Price
Headlamp Switch		
(Bonneville, Grand Prix)		
1983-87	1995226	16.00
(Parisienne)		
1983-87	1995217	16.00
Headlamp Dimmer Switch		
1983-87	7838234	12.50
Stoplight Switch		
(wo/Cruise control)		
1983-84	25504628	3.75
1985-87	25524846	6.50
(Cruise control)		
1983-84	9794682	7.75
1985-87	25524847	6.50
Turn Signal Switch		
1983-87-exc cornering	1997983	30.00
Corn lamps	1997984	35.00
Turn Signal Flasher		
1983-87-2 lamps	491392	N.L.
3 lamps	10041073	4.25
6 lamps	6450089	3.00

PARTS 32 LIGHT SWITCHES & WIRING 32 PARTS

	Part No.	Price
Back-Up Lamp Switch		
1983-87	22509632	5.50
Horn Assy.		
1983-87-Note (A)	1892164	22.00
Note (C)	1892246	27.50
Note (D)	1892162	23.50
Note (F)	1892163	22.00
Horn Relay		
1983-87	25513270	8.50

LABOR 33 GLASS 33 LABOR

	(Factory Time)	Chilton Time
(G) Windshield Glass, Renew		
Pontiac		
1983-87	(1.3)	1.8
Grand Prix		
1983-87	(1.2)	1.8
Renew caulk bead add	(.4)	.4
(G) Front Door Glass, Renew		
1983-87		
2 Dr.	(1.0)	1.5
4 Dr	(.8)	1.2
Wag	(1.0)	1.5
(G) Rear Door Glass, Renew		
1983-87-Grand Prix	(.3)	.6
Pontiac	(.8)	1.4
(G) Quarter Window Stationary Glass, Renew		
Pontiac		
1983-87-exc below	(.5)	.8
sta wag	(1.0)	1.6
Grand Prix		
1983-87	(.5)	.8
(G) Tail Gate Window Glass, Renew		
1983	(.3)	.5
1984-87	(.6)	1.0
w/Elec defogger add	(.1)	.2
(G) Rear Door Vent Glass, Renew		
1983-87		
Pontiac	(.7)	1.0
Grand Prix	(.3)	.6
(G) Back Window Glass, Renew		
1983-87	(1.3)	2.0
w/Elec defogger add	(.6)	.6
w/3/4 plug, unpadded add	(1.3)	2.0
w/3/4 plug, padded add	(2.6)	4.0
w/Full plug, padded add	(2.8)	4.4

LABOR 34 CRUISE CONTROL 34 LABOR

	(Factory Time)	Chilton Time
(G) Cruise Control Regulator (Transducer), Renew or Adjust		
1983	(.4)	.6
(G) Cruise Control Engagement Switch, Renew		
1983-84-Grand Prix	(.2)	.4
Pontiac	(.4)	.9
1985-87	(.4)	.9
(G) Cruise Control Wire Harness, Renew		
1983-87	(.5)	.9
w/A.C. add	(.1)	.1
(G) Cruise Control Brake Release Switch, Renew		
1983-87	(.3)	.4
(G) Cruise Control Servo, Renew		
1983-85	(.3)	.5
1986-87-Pontiac	(.6)	.8
Grand Prix	(.3)	.5
(G) Cruise Control Transducer Filter, Renew		
1983	(.2)	.3
(G) Cruise Control Vacuum Hoses, Renew		
1983-87	(.2)	.3
(G) Cruise Control Chain or Cable, Renew		
1983-87	(.2)	.4
(G) Cruise Control Vacuum Regulator Valve, Renew (In Line)		
1983-85	(.2)	.3
(G) Cruise Control Resume Solenoid, Renew		
1983	(.2)	.3
(G) Cruise Control Controller (Module), Renew		
1984-87	(.3)	.5
(G) Cruise Control Check Valve, Renew		
1984-87	(.3)	.4

PARTS 34 CRUISE CONTROL 34 PARTS

	Part No.	Price
Cruise Control Servo		
V-6-231		
1983	25030981	19.50
1984-87	25074630	116.25
V-6-262		
1985-87	25074627	117.00
Parisienne (85)	25074628	133.50
V-8-305		
1983	25030983	19.50
1984-87-exc. below	25074632	116.75
Parisienne	25074628	133.50
V-8-307		
1986-87	25074629	123.25
V-8-350 Diesel		
1983	25030980	32.75
1984-87	25074629	123.50
Cruise Control Transducer		
1983-exc. diesel	25030878	158.00
Diesel	25031604	179.25
Cruise Control Module		
1984-87-231	25074715	102.00
305	25074704	102.00
Diesel	25031948	116.00
262	25074704	N.L.
Cruise Control Lever & Switch		
1983-exc. pulse	25031426	52.25
Pulse wiper	25031425	52.25
1984-87-exc. pulse	25031457	50.00
Pulse wpr.	25031456	50.00
Cruise Control Release Switch		
1983-87	9794682	8.00
Vacuum Release Valve		
1983-84	25509432	14.00
1985-87	25523376	14.00

GROUP INDEX

ALPHABETICAL INDEX

General Motors

Rear Wheel Drive Cars

PONTIAC FIERO

YEAR IDENTIFICATION

1984–85 Fiero

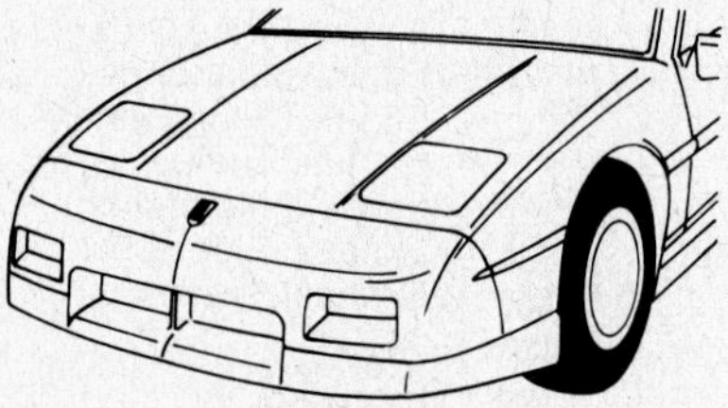

1986 Fiero

VEHICLE IDENTIFICATION NUMBER (VIN)

It is important for servicing and ordering parts to be certain of the vehicle and engine identification. The VIN (vehicle identification number) is a 17 digit number visible through the windshield on the driver's side of the dash and contains the vehicle and engine identification codes. It can be interpreted as follows:

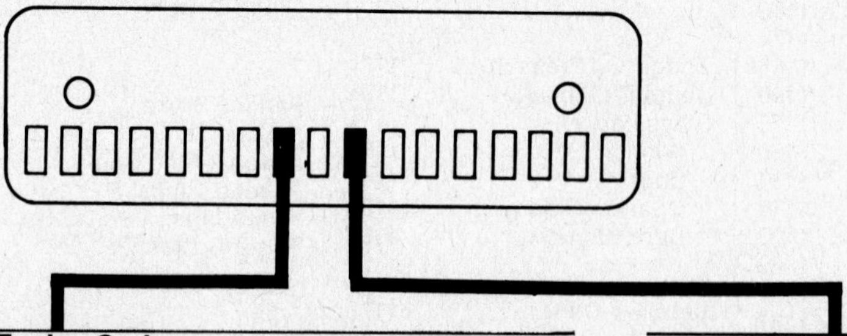

Engine Code					
Code	**Cu. In.**	**Liters**	**Cyl.**	**Carb.**	**Eng. Mfg.**
R	151	2.5	4	TBI	Pontiac
9	173	2.8	6	MFI	Chev.

Model Year Code	
Code	**Year**
E	1984
F	1985
G	1986
H	1987

The seventeen digit Vehicle Identification Number can be used to determine engine application and model year. The 10th digit indicates the model year, and the 8th digit identifies the factory installed engine.
TBI (Throttle body injection)

TUNE-UP SPECIFICATIONS

Year	VIN Code	Eng. No. Cyl. Displ. Cu. In.	Eng. Mfg.	hp	Spark Plugs Orig Type	Spark Plugs Gap (in.)	Ignition Timing (deg)▲ Man. Trans.	Ignition Timing (deg)▲ Auto. Trans.	Intake Valve Opens (deg)■	Fuel Pump Pressure (psi)	Idle Speed (rpm)▲ Man. Trans.	Idle Speed (rpm)▲ Auto. Trans.
'84–'85	R	151	Pont	90	R43CTS	.060	①	①	33	6–8	①	①
'86–'87	R	151	Pont	92	R43CTS6	.060	①	①	33	6–8	①	①
'85–'87	9	173	Chev	130	R42CTS	.045	①	①	25	6–8	①	①

FIRING ORDER

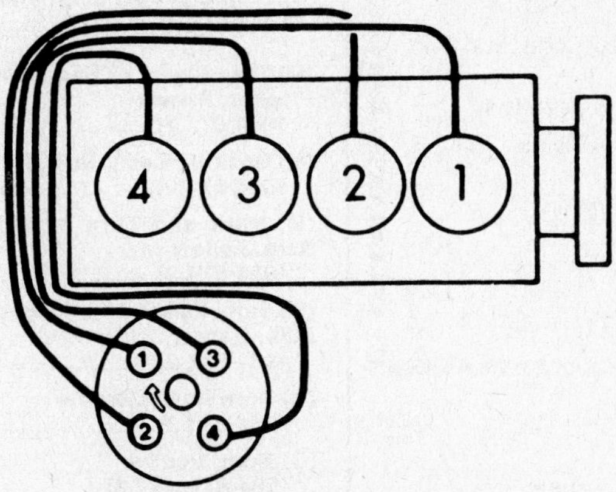

GM (Pontiac) 151–4
Engine firing order: 1–3–4–2
Distributor rotation: clockwise

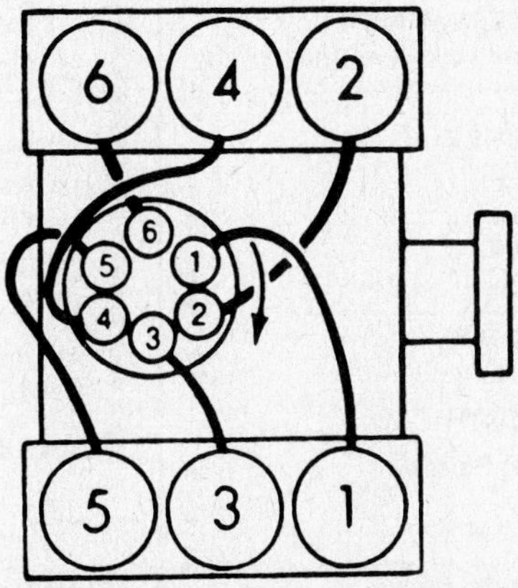

GM (Chevrolet) 173 V6 (2.8L)
Engine firing order: 1–2–3–4–5–6
Distributor rotation: clockwise

WHEEL ALIGNMENT SPECIFICATIONS

Year	Model	Caster Range (deg)	Caster Pref. Setting (deg)	Camber Range (deg)	Camber Pref. Setting (deg)	Toe-in (in.)	Steering Axis (deg) Inclination
'84–'87	All	3P–7P	5P	5/16N–1 5/16P	1/2P	1/16 ± 1/32	—

LABOR — SERVICE BAY OPERATIONS — LABOR

(Factory Time) — Chilton Time

COOLING

(M) Winterize Cooling System

Includes: Run engine to check for leaks, tighten all hose connections. Test radiator and pressure cap, drain radiator and engine block. Add anti-freeze and refill system.

All models 5

(M) Drive Belt, Renew

1984-87-Four-one (.3) 4
each adtnl (.2) 2

V-6
A.C. (.5) 7
Fan/Generator (.3) 4

(M) Drive Belt, Adjust

1984-87-one (.2) 2
all (.3) 4

(M) Radiator Hoses, Renew

1984-87
upper or lower
rad to pipe (.4) 5
thermo to pipe (.6) 7

both
front (.6) 8
rear (1.0) 1.3
by-pass (.4) 6

(G) Thermostat, Renew

1984-87-Four (.2) 4

FUEL

(M) Air Cleaner, Service

All models (.2) 3

(G) Minimum Idle Speed, Adjust

All models (.4) 6

(G) Fuel Filter Element, Renew

All models (.2) 3

BRAKES

(G) Bleed Brakes (Four Wheels)

Includes: Fill master cylinder.

All models (.4) 5

(M) Parking Brake, Adjust

All models (.3) 4

LABOR SERVICE BAY OPERATIONS LABOR

	(Factory Time)	Chilton Time
LUBRICATION SERVICE		
(M) Lubricate Chassis, Change Oil & Filter		
Includes: Inspect and correct all fluid levels.		
All models		.6
Install grease fittings add		.1
(M) Lubricate Chassis		
Includes: Inspect and correct all fluid levels.		
All models		.4
Install grease fittings add		.1
(M) Engine Oil & Filter, Change		
Includes: Inspect and correct all fluid levels.		
All models		.4
WHEELS		
(M) Wheel, Renew		
one	(.5)	.5
(M) Wheels, Balance		
one		.3
each adtnl		.2
(M) Wheels, Rotate (All)		
All models		.5
ELECTRICAL		
(M) Battery Cables, Renew		
1984-87		
positive	(.4)	.5
negative	(.2)	.3
(M) Battery Terminals, Clean		
All models		.3

CHILTON'S 10 POINT SAFETY CHECK

CHECK OPERATION & CONDITION OF THE FOLLOWING ITEMS:

1. Legal Registration (serial no.)
2. Tires & Wheels
3. Brake System (R&R all wheels)
4. Light Systems & Signals
5. Accelerator Linkage, Neutral Safety Switch, Shift Indicator Pointer & Seat Position Locks
6. Glass, Mirrors, Door Locks, Seat Belts & Harness
7. Wipers, Washers & Defrosters
8. Frame, Steering, Shocks, Front & Rear Suspension
9. Fuel & Exhaust Systems
10. Road Test Vehicle

All models 1.0
Exhaust Smog Analysis, add 4

	(Factory Time)	Chilton Time
(G) Headlamp Switch, Renew		
1984-87	(.2)	.4
(G) Headlamp Dimmer Switch, Renew		
1984	(.5)	.7
1985-87	(.2)	.4
(G) Aim Headlamps		
two		.4
four		.6
(M) Headlamp Sealed Beam Bulb, Renew		
1984-87	(.2)	.3
(G) Stop Light Switch, Renew		
1984-87	(.2)	.3
(M) Turn Signal or Hazard Warning Flasher, Renew		
1984-87	(.2)	.2
(M) Back-Up Lamp Bulb, Renew		
1984-87	(.2)	.3
(M) Park and Turn Signal Lamp Bulb, Renew		
1984-87	(.2)	.3
(M) Stop, Tail and Turn Signal Lamp Bulb, Renew		
1984-87	(.2)	.3
(G) Horn Relay, Renew		
1984-87	(.2)	.3
(G) Horn, Renew		
1984-87-one	(.3)	.4
each adtnl		.1

LABOR 1 TUNE UP 1 LABOR

	(Factory Time)	Chilton Time
(G) Compression Test		
Four-1984-87		.5
V-6-1985-87		1.4

(G) Engine Tune Up, (Electronic Ignition)

Includes: Test battery and clean connections. Tighten manifold mounting bolts, check engine compression, clean and adjust or renew spark plugs. Test resistance of spark plug cables. Inspect distributor cap and rotor. Adjust air gap. Reset ignition timing. Adjust minimum idle speed. Service air cleaner. Inspect and adjust drive belts. Check operation of EGR valve.

	(Factory Time)	Chilton Time
Four-1984-87		1.4
V-6-1985-87		2.5

LABOR 2 IGNITION SYSTEM 2 LABOR

	(Factory Time)	Chilton Time
(G) Spark Plugs, Clean and Reset or Renew		
1984-87-Four	(.3)	.5
V-6	(.8)	1.2
(G) Ignition Timing, Reset		
1984-87	(.3)	.4
(G) Distributor, Renew		
Includes: Reset ignition timing.		
1984-87	(.6)	1.0
(G) Distributor, R&R and Recondition		
Includes: Reset ignition timing.		
1984-87	(1.0)	1.6
(G) Distributor Cap and/or Rotor, Renew		
Includes: R&R coil.		
1984-87	(.3)	.4
(G) Ignition Coil, Renew		
Includes: Test coil.		
1984-87-Four	(.3)	.5
V-6	(.3)	.5
(G) Distributor Module, Renew		
1984-87-Four	(.5)	.7
V-6	(.5)	.7
(G) Distributor Capacitor and/or Module Wiring Harness, Renew		
1984-87-Four	(.3)	.5
(G) Distributor Pick-Up Coil and/or Pole Piece, Renew		
Includes: Reset ignition timing.		
1984-87-Four	(.9)	1.4
V-6	(.9)	1.4
(G) Distributor Hall Effect Switch, Renew		
1984	(.3)	.6
(G) Ignition Cables, Renew		
1984-87-Four	(.3)	.5
V-6	(.4)	.6
(G) Ignition Switch, Renew		
1984-87	(.5)	.7
(G) Ignition Lock Cylinder, Renew		
1984-87	(.4)	.7
w/Tilt whl add	(.1)	.1
Recode cyl add	(.3)	.3

PARTS 2 IGNITION SYSTEM 2 PARTS

FOUR CYLINDER

	Part No.	Price
Distributor Assy.		
1984	1103551	236.00
1985-87	1103632	157.00
(1) Dist. Cap		
1984	1978497	16.00
1985-87	1989767	12.00
(2) Rotor		
1984	1988515	8.50
1985-87	10495411	3.50
(3) Dist. Housing		
1984	1988883	40.25
1985-87	1988082	26.75
(4) Main Shaft		
1984	1986963	33.25
1985-87	1988077	24.75
(5) Retainer (Pole Piece & Plate)		
1984	1977947	.50
1985-87 (pick-up)	1989282	.75
(6) Terminal Block		
1984-87	1986972	28.50
(7) Pole Piece (w/Plate)		
1984	1978503	39.25
1985-87 (stationary)	1987963	3.50
(8) Seal (Housing)		
1984	1977957	.50
(9) Module		
1984	1985342	56.50
1985-87	1989747	51.50

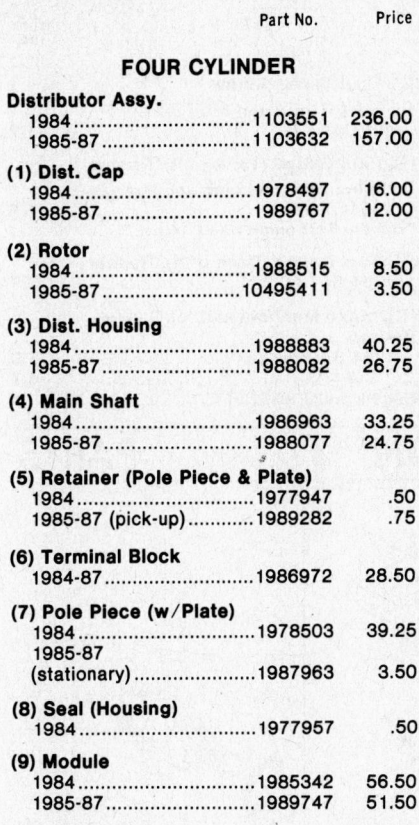

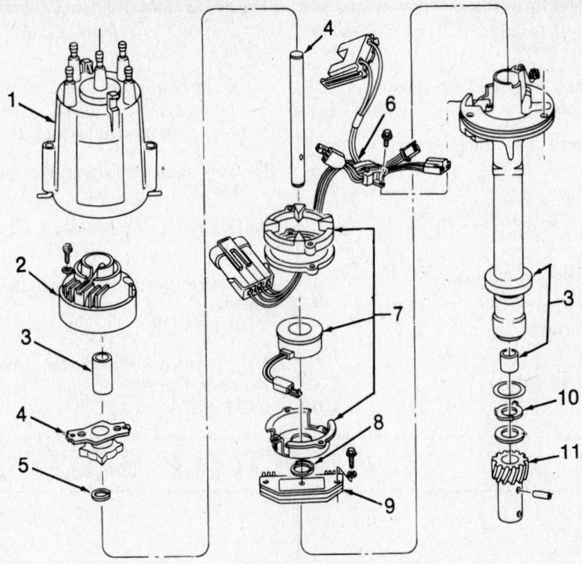

	Part No.	Price
(10) Tang Washer		
1984	1978512	.50
1985-87	1988075	1.50
(11) Dist. Gear		
1984-87	1978509	13.00
Ignition Coil		
1984	1115455	58.00
1985-87	1115315	39.50

	Part No.	Price
Spark Plug Wire Set		
Spark plug wires are sold individually from the manufacture and are not available as a set.		
Ignition Switch		
1984-87-exc. below	1990115	11.50
(w/Tilt whl.)		
M.T.	1990116	11.50
A.T.	7843451	25.75

PARTS 2 IGNITION SYSTEM 2 PARTS

SIX CYLINDER

	Part No.	Price
Distributor Assy		
1985	1103633	179.00
1986-87	1103705	234.75
(1) Cover		
1985-87 (not used)		
(2) Coil		
1985-87	1115315	39.50
(3) Cap		
1985-87	1989797	10.25
(4) Resistor Brush		
1985-87 (not used)		
(5) Rotor		
1985-87	10495408	3.50
(6) Mainshaft		
1985-87	1988005	31.25
(7) Pole Piece (stationary)		
1985-87	1988010	3.50
(8) Module		
1985-87	1987466	46.00

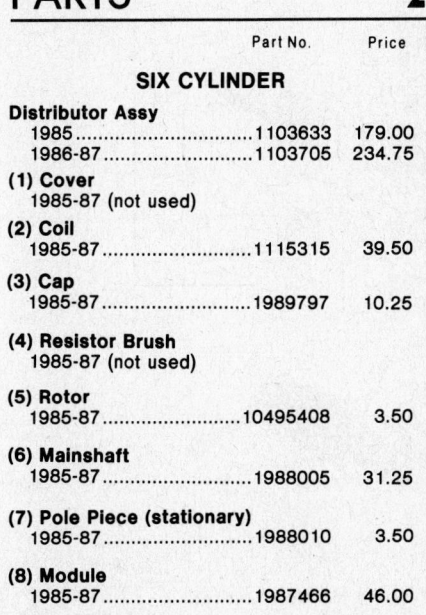

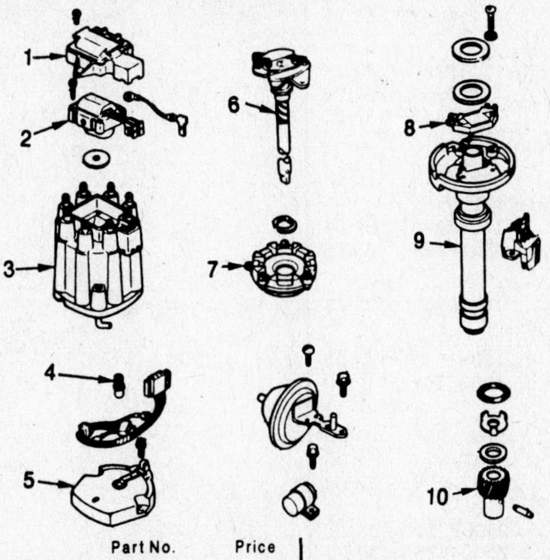

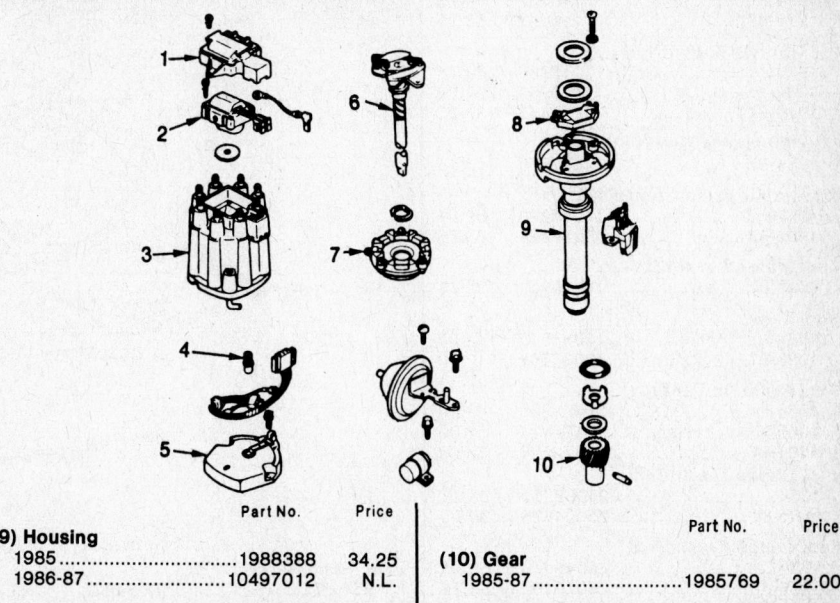

	Part No.	Price
(9) Housing		
1985	1988388	34.25
1986-87	10497012	N.L.

	Part No.	Price
(10) Gear		
1985-87	1985769	22.00

LABOR 3 FUEL SYSTEM 3 LABOR

(Factory Time)	Chilton Time
(G) Minimum Idle Speed, Adjust	
1984-87 (.4)	.6
(G) Fuel Filter Element, Renew	
1984-87 (.2)	.3
(G) Throttle Body and/or Gasket, Renew	
1984-87 (.3)	.6

LABOR 3 FUEL SYSTEM 3 LABOR

(Factory Time)	Chilton Time
(G) Throttle Body Injector, Renew	
1984-87 (.6)	1.0
(G) Fuel Pressure Regulator, Renew	
1984-87 (.7)	1.1
(G) Fuel Pump, Renew (In Tank)	
1984-87 (.7)	1.1
(G) Fuel Pump Relay, Renew	
1984-87 (.7)	.9
(G) Fuel Rail, Renew	
1984-87 (.7)	1.2
(G) Fuel Injectors, Renew	
1984-87-one (1.2)	1.8
each adtnl (.1)	.1
all (1.4)	2.2
Perform balance test add (.4)	.4
(G) Cold Start Injector, Renew	
1984-87 (1.0)	1.4
(G) Idle Air Control Valve, Renew	
1984-87 (.6)	.9
(G) Intake Plenum and/or Gaskets, Renew	
1984-87 (.5)	.8
(G) Intake Runners and/or Gaskets, Renew	
1984-87 (.9)	1.4
(G) Fuel Tank, Renew	
Includes: Drain and refill tank.	
1984-87 (.7)	1.2
(G) Fuel Gauge (Tank Unit), Renew	
Includes: R&R fuel tank and test gauge.	
1984-87 (.7)	1.1
Transfer fuel pump add (.1)	.1
(G) Fuel Gauge (Dash Unit), Renew	
1984-87 (.4)	.7
(G) Intake Manifold and/or Gasket, Renew	
1984-87-Four (2.0)	3.0
V-6 (3.3)	4.7
Renew manif add (.2)	.5

PARTS 3 THROTTLE BODY INJECTION 3 PARTS

	Part No.	Price
FOUR CYLINDER		
1984	17110647	588.25
1985	17110768	513.50
1986-87	17111449	522.25
(1) Fuel Meter Kit		
1984-87	17068992	425.75
Includes one injecter and pressure regulater.		
(2) Fuel Meter Body Kit		
1984-87	17078222	109.75
(3) Fuel Injector Kit		
1984-87	17068993	191.75
(4) Gasket Kit		
1984-87	17068990	24.75
(5) Sensor Kit (Throttle Position)		
1984	17110632	94.75
1985-87	17110648	68.75
(6) Throttle Body Kit		
1984	17110366	269.75
1985	17110769	237.25
1986-87	17111450	237.25
(7) Fuel Inlet & Outlet Kit		
1984-87	17078275	5.75
(8) Idle Air Valve Control Kit		
1984	17078220	82.00
1985-87	17079256	88.75
Fuel Meter Cover Kit		
1984-87	17078969	139.75
Fuel Tank		
1984	10031918	112.00
1985-87	10037262	112.00
Fuel Pump (In Tank)		
1984	6471959	91.50
1985	6472421	57.00
1986-87	6472526	57.00
Fuel Gauge (Tank Unit)		
1984	25003251	133.25
1985-87	25004825	130.00
Fuel Gauge (Dash Unit)		
1984	25048178	50.75
1985-87	25079162	51.75

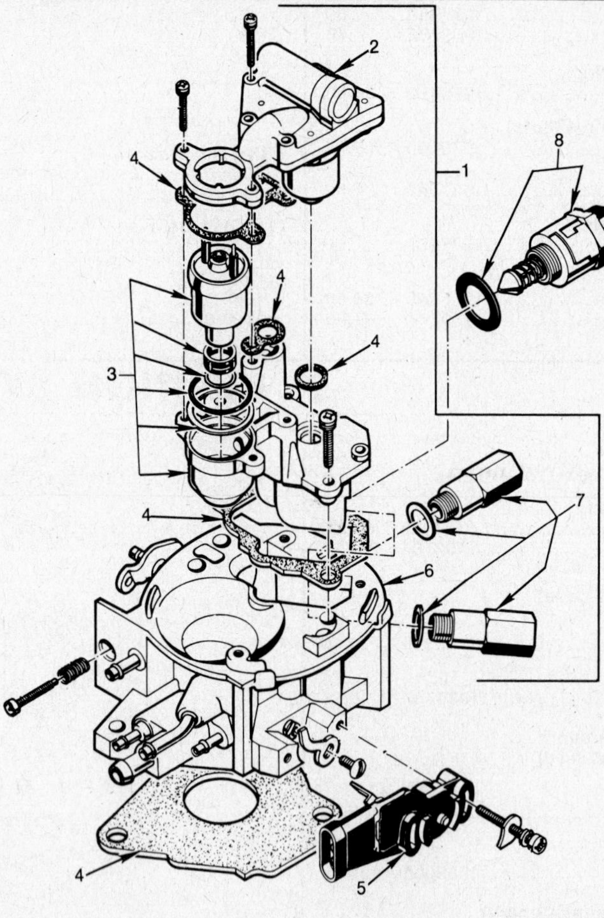

	Part No.	Price
Fuel Pump Relay		
1984-87	10034222	N.L.
Intake Manifold Gasket		
1984-87	10026023	5.00

PARTS 3 FUEL INJECTION 3 PARTS

	Part No.	Price
MULTI PORT FUEL INJECTION		
SIX CYLINDER		
(1) Throttle Body Assy.		
1985-87	10031441	163.00
(2) Sensor Kit		
1985-87	10031271	60.50
(3) Idle Control Kit		
1985-87	17111288	58.00

PARTS 3 FUEL INJECTION 3 PARTS

	Part No.	Price
(4) Fuel Rail and Pressure Regulator		
1985-87	17110851	162.75
(5) Fuel Inlet/Outlet Block		
1985-87	17110853	29.25
(6) Fuel Injector Kit		
1985-87	17111297	137.50
(7) Cold Start Valve		
1985-87	17110860	49.50
Fuel Tank		
1985-87	10037262	112.00
Fuel Pump (In Tank)		
1985	25115429	79.75
1986	25115190	89.50
1987	25115429	79.75
Fuel Gauge (Tank Unit)		
1985-87	25004825	130.00
Fuel Gauge (Dash Unit)		
1985-87	25078495	51.75
Fuel Pump Relay		
1985-87	10034222	N.L.
Intake Manifold Gasket		
1985-87-center	14083328	3.50
side	10048962	8.00
plenum	14089057	2.00

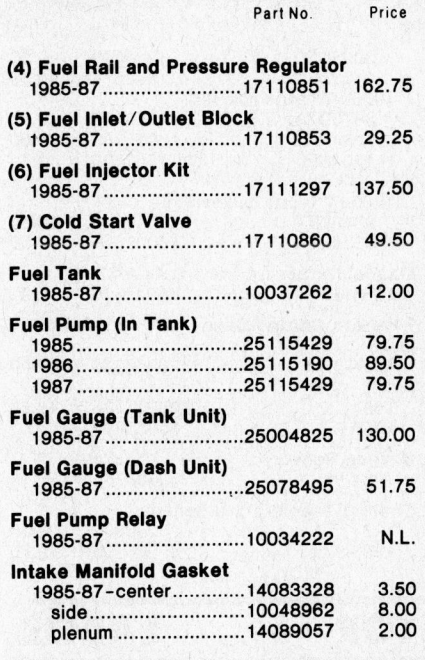

LABOR 3A EMISSION CONTROLS 3A LABOR

	(Factory Time)	Chilton Time
(G) Emission Control Check Includes: Check and adjust engine speed and ignition timing. Check PCV valve.		
All models		.6

POSITIVE CRANKCASE VENTILATION

(M) Positive Crankcase Ventilation Valve, Renew		
1984-87 (.2)		.3
(M) Crankcase Ventilation Filter Assy., Renew		
1984-87 (.2)		.3

CONTROLLED COMBUSTION TYPE

(G) Air Cleaner Vacuum Motor, Renew		
1984-87 (.3)		.5
(G) Air Cleaner Temperature Sensor, Renew		
1984-87 (.2)		.3

EXHAUST GAS RECIRCULATION SYSTEM

(G) E.G.R. Valve, Renew		
1984-87-Four (.2)		.4
V-6 (.3)		.5

ELECTRONIC EMISSION CONTROLS

(P) Throttle Position Sensor, Adjust		
1984-87 (.4)		.9
(P) Electronic Control Module, Renew		
1984-87 (.6)		.9

CHILTON'S EMISSION CONTROL TUNE-UP

1. Clean or renew P.C.V. valve, hoses and filter.
2. Check fuel tank cap for sealing ability.
3. Check fuel tank and fuel lines for leakage.
4. Check evaporation canister and filter. Replace if necessary.
5. Check engine compression to determine leakage of unburned gases. (Add time for items of interference).
6. Test and clean or renew spark plugs.
7. Check engine oil dipstick for sealing ability.
8. Test exhaust system with analyzer and check system for leakage.
9. Check exhaust manifold heat valve for operation.
10. Adjust ignition timing and carburetor idle speed and mixture.
11. Check automatic choke mechanism for free operation.
12. Inspect air cleaner and element.
13. On models so equipped, test distributor vacuum control switch and transmission control switch.

Four 1.3
V-6 .... 1.7

For repairs made, charge accordingly.

	(Factory Time)	Chilton Time
(P) Throttle Position Sensor, Renew		
1984-87 (.9)		1.2
(P) Prom, Renew		
1984-87 (.6)		1.0
(P) Coolant Temperature Sensor, Renew		
1984-87 (.4)		.7
(P) Manifold Pressure Sensor, Renew		
1984-87 (.5)		.6
(P) E.G.R. Vacuum Control Solenoid, Renew		
1985-87 (.3)		.5
(P) Tachometer Filter, Renew		
1984-87 (.3)		.7
(P) Manifold Temperature Sensor, Renew		
1985-87-V-6 (.4)		.6
(P) Oxygen Sensor, Renew		
1984-87 (.5)		.7
(P) Vehicle Speed Sensor, Renew		
1984-87 (.7)		1.0
(P) Back-Up Lamp and Park/Neutral Switch, Renew		
1984-87 (.3)		.4

PARTS 3A EMISSION CONTROLS 3A PARTS

	Part No.	Price
CRANKCASE EMISSION		
Positive Crankcase Valve		
4-151		
1984	25041498	7.00
1985-87	25043669	6.25
V-6 173		
1985-87	8995284	5.00
EVAPORATIVE EMISSION TYPE		
Vapor Canister		
1984-87	17075840	30.00
Canister Filter (Air Inlet)		
1984-87	7021743	1.75
CONTROLLED COMBUSTION TYPE		
Air Cleaner Vacuum Motor		
1984-4 cyl.	25041109	23.25
1985-87-4 cyl.	25042077	60.75
Air Cleaner Temperature Sensor		
1984-4 cyl.	8997574	18.75
1985-87-4 cyl.	8997787	18.75

	Part No.	Price
EXHAUST GAS RECIRCULATION SYSTEM		
E.G.R. Valve		
1984-87-4 cyl.	17110478	63.50
1985-87-V-6	17110813	53.00

COMPUTER COMMAND CONTROL SYSTEM (C.C.C.)

Parts number listed are for pricing reference only. Order with complete year, engine and unit I.D. number.

	Part No.	Price
Controller (E.C.M.)		
4-151		
1984	1226156	110.25
1985-87	1226864	110.25
V-6-173		
1985-87	1226869	110.00
Calibration (Prom)		
4-151		
1984 (code number)		
1888DYK	1226907	40.50
0203DDB	1226699	40.50
1438DJC	1226874	40.50
1985-87 (code number)		
6875DZA	16046873	40.50
1384HHZ	16051388	40.50
1104HFL	1651108	N.L.
V-6-173		
1985-87 (code number)		
9349FTX	16049348	40.50
9355FTY	16049354	40.50
Manifold Pressure Sensor (M.A.P.)		
1984-87	16017460	N.L.
Emission Control Sensor (Vehicle Speed)		
(A.T.)		
1984-87	25007335	44.00
(M.T.)		
1984	25007336	42.25
1985-87	25036929	47.50
Oxygen Sensor		
1984-87	8990741	28.75
Coolant Temperature Sensor		
1984	25036092	22.00
1985-87	25036708	12.75

LABOR 4 ALTERNATOR AND REGULATOR 4 LABOR

	(Factory Time)	Chilton Time
(G) Delcotron Circuits, Test		
Includes: Test battery, regulator, Delcotron output.		
All models		.6
(M) Alternator Drive Belt, Renew		
1984-87	(.3)	.4
(G) Delcotron Assembly, Renew		
1984-87-Four	(.6)	.8
V-6	(.7)	1.0
(G) Delcotron, R&R and Recondition		
Includes: Complete disassembly, replacement of parts as required, reassemble.		
1984-87-Four	(1.4)	1.9
V-6	(1.5)	2.0
(G) Delcotron Front Bearing, Renew		
Includes: R&R Delcotron, separate end frames.		
1984-87-Four	(1.0)	1.4
V-6	(.5)	1.0
Renew rear brg add		.2
(G) Delcotron Voltage Regulator, Test and Renew		
Includes: R&R, disassemble and reassemble Delcotron.		
1984-87	(.9)	1.3

PARTS 4 ALTERNATOR AND REGULATOR 4 PARTS

	Part No.	Price
Alternator Assy. (New)		
1984-87-78 amp	1100250	225.00
94 amp	1105492	228.50
(1) Capacitor		
1984-87	1978146	4.75
(2) Diode Trio (Negative)		
1984-87	1984459	5.00
(3) Rectifier Bridge		
1984-87-94 amp	1987061	29.25
78 amp	1984454	28.00
(4) Bearing (Slip Ring End)		
1984-87	9436831	5.50
(5) Voltage Regulator		
1984-87	1116387	25.00
(6) Brush (w/Holder)		
1984-87	1984462	9.00
(7) Rotor Assy.		
1984-87-94 amp	1984466	77.25
78 amp	1985476	72.00
(8) Stator Assy.		
1984-87-94 amp	1987074	41.50
78 amp	1984445	37.25
(9) Bearing (Drive End)		
1984-87	908419	10.00

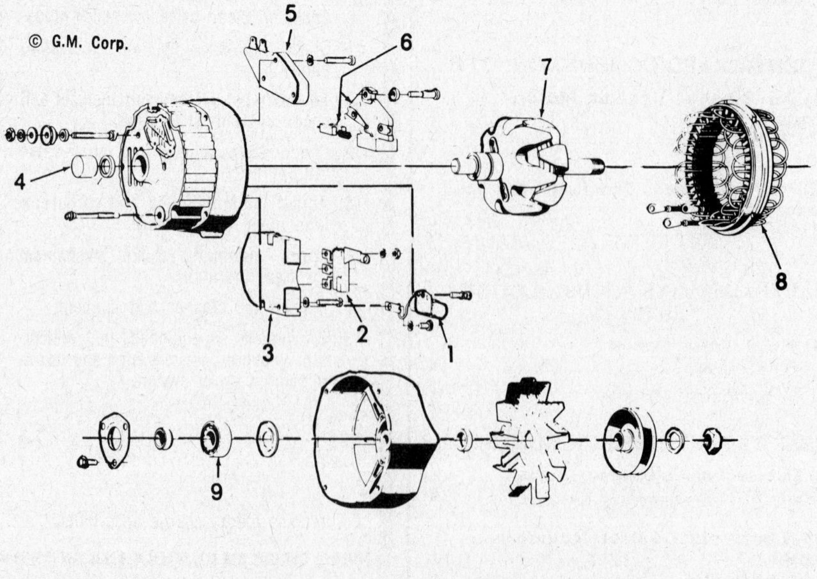

LABOR 5 STARTING SYSTEM 5 LABOR

	(Factory Time)	Chilton Time
(G) Starter Draw Test (On Car)		
All models		.3
(G) Starter Assy., Renew		
Includes: Transfer starter solenoid.		
1984-87	(.4)	.6
(G) Starter, R&R and Recondition		
Includes: Turn down armature.		
1984-87	(1.2)	1.9
Renew field coils add		.5
Add draw test if performed.		
(G) Starter Drive, Renew		
Includes: R&R starter.		
1984-87	(.7)	1.0
(G) Starter Motor Solenoid, Renew		
Does not require starter R&R on Four cyl. engine.		
1984-87-Four	(.3)	.5
V-6	(.6)	.9
(M) Battery Cables, Renew		
1984-87		
positive	(.4)	.5
negative	(.2)	.3
(M) Battery Terminals, Clean		
All models		.3

PARTS 5 STARTING SYSTEM 5 PARTS

	Part No.	Price
Starter Assy. (New)		
1984	1998503	170.25
1985-87	1998533	170.25
(1) Solenoid Switch		
1984	1114531	N.L.
1985-87	1114566	33.50
(2) Spring (Plunger)		
1984-87	1978281	1.75
(3) Plunger (Sol. Switch)		
1984-87	1987391	6.75
(4) Shift Lever		
1984-87	1984501	5.00
(5) Armature		
1984-87	1985138	N.L.
(6) Drive Assy.		
1984-87	1984511	23.50
(7) Grommet (Field Frame)		
1984-87	1984527	1.00
(8) Frame (w/Field)		
1984-87	1985143	71.50
(9) Brush Holder Kit		
1984-87	1893929	11.25
(10) Brushes		
1984-87	1893296	.50
(11) Insulators (Brush Holder)		
1984-87	1893293	1.25

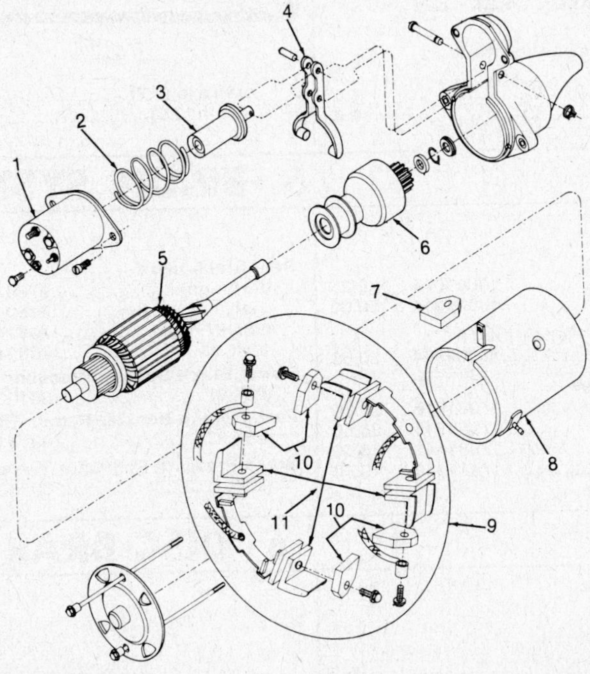

LABOR 6 BRAKE SYSTEM 6 LABOR

	(Factory Time)	Chilton Time
(G) Bleed Brakes (Four Wheels)		
Includes: Fill master cylinder.		
All models	(.4)	.5
(G) Disc Brake Pads, Renew		
Includes: Install new disc brake pads only.		
1984-87		
front	(.9)	1.1
rear	(1.0)	1.3
all four wheels		2.3
Resurface disc rotor add-each		.9
(G) Brake System Failure Warning Switch, Renew		
1984-87	(.2)	.3

BRAKE HYDRAULIC SYSTEM

	(Factory Time)	Chilton Time
(G) Master Cylinder, Renew		
Includes: Bleed system.		
1984-87	(.6)	.9
(G) Master Cylinder, R&R and Rebuild		
Includes: Bleed complete system.		
1984-87	(1.4)	1.8
(G) Brake Hose, Renew		
Includes: Bleed system.		
1984-87-front-one	(.5)	.7
rear-one	(.6)	.8
(G) Brake Combination Valve, Renew		
Includes: Bleed system.		
1984-87	(.7)	1.0
(G) Brake System, Flush and Refill		
All models		1.2

POWER BRAKES

	(Factory Time)	Chilton Time
(G) Power Brake Cylinder, Renew		
1984-87	(.5)	.8
(G) Power Brake Cylinder, R&R and Recondition		
1984-87	(1.2)	1.8
Recond m/Cyl add	(.8)	.8

LABOR — 6 BRAKE SYSTEM 6 — LABOR

(Factory Time) — Chilton Time

(M) Vacuum Check Valve, Renew
1984-87 (.3) 3

DISC BRAKES

(G) Disc Brake Pads, Renew
Includes: Install new disc brake pads only.
1984-87
front (.9) 1.1
rear (1.0) 1.3
all four wheels 2.3
Resurface disc rotor add-each 9

(G) Caliper Assembly, Renew
Includes: Bleed complete system.
1984-87
front-one (.7) 1.0
both (1.1) 1.6
rear-one (.7) 1.0
both (1.0) 1.5

(G) Caliper Assy., R&R and Recondition
Includes: Bleed complete system.
1984-87
front-one (1.2) 1.5
both (2.1) 2.6

COMBINATIONS
Add To Brakes, Renew
See Machine Shop Operations

(G) REBUILD CALIPER ASSEMBLY
Each (.5) 5

(G) RENEW MASTER CYLINDER
All models (.5) 6

(G) REBUILD MASTER CYLINDER
All models (.8) 1.0

(G) Renew Brake Hose
Each 3

(G) RENEW DISC BRAKE ROTOR
Each (.2) 3

(G) FRONT WHEEL BEARINGS, CLEAN AND REPACK (BOTH WHEELS)
All models 6

(Factory Time) — Chilton Time

rear-one (1.2) 1.5
both (2.0) 2.5

(Factory Time) — Chilton Time

(G) Disc Brake Rotor, Renew
Includes: Transfer or renew bearings, races and seals.
1984-87
front-one (.7) 9
both (1.2) 1.6
rear-one (.5) 7
both (.8) 1.2

PARKING BRAKE

(G) Parking Brake, Adjust
All models (.3) 4

(G) Parking Brake Lamp Switch, Renew
1984-87 (.3) 4

(G) Parking Brake Control, Renew
1984-87 (.5) 7

(G) Parking Brake Equalizer, Renew
1984-87 (.3) 5

(G) Parking Brake Cables, Renew
1984-87-front (.8) 1.1
rear-each (.5) 7
two piece (.8) 1.2

PARTS — 6 BRAKE SYSTEM 6 — PARTS

	Part No.	Price
Master Cylinder		
1984	18009044	189.25
1985-87	18011914	150.00
Master Cylinder Repair Kit		
1984-87	18009364	20.50
Front Brake Hose		
1984-right	17981515	25.50
left	17981515	25.50
1985-87-right	17981448	18.00
left	17981449	19.50
Rear Brake Hose		
1984-right	9769480	15.00
left	9769481	15.00
1985-87-right	17982498	12.50
left	17982499	12.50
Power Brake Booster (Vacuum)		
1984-87	18010390	250.25
Power Brake Booster Repair Kit		
1984-87	18011119	47.75
Brake Pressure Regulator Valve		
1984	10026021	31.50
1985-87	10036563	31.50
PARKING BRAKE		
Parking Brake Apply Lever		
1984-87	10032454	32.50
Parking Brake Cable (Front)		
1984-87	10036833	22.50
Parking Brake Cable (Rear)		
1984-87-right	10040814	11.25
left	10040815	11.25

PARTS — 6 DISC BRAKES 6 — PARTS

	Part No.	Price
Brake Pad Set		
1984-87	12300237	43.50
Caliper Piston		
1984-87	18010264	12.50
Caliper Repair Kit		
1984-87	18011295	8.50
(1) Grease Cap		
1984-87	14012617	1.75
(2) Front Wheel Bearing (Outer)		
1984-87	9415135	9.50
(3) Rotor & Hub Assy		
1984-87	10039013	58.25
(4) Bearing (Inner)		
1984-87	9415132	10.00
(5) Splash Shield		
1984-87	10022522	N.L.
(6) Steering Knuckle		
1984-87-right	14001236	130.00
left	14001235	130.00
(7) Bracket		
1984-87-right	18012302	39.75
left	18012301	39.75

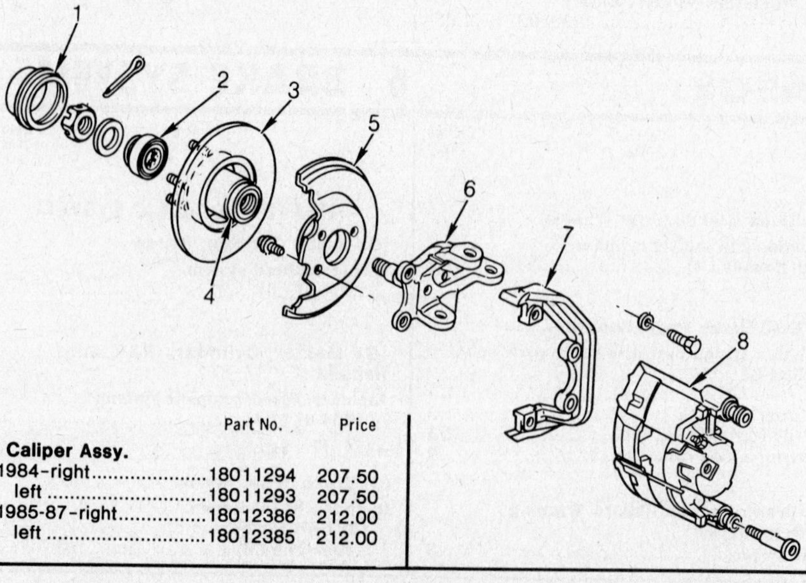

	Part No.	Price
(8) Caliper Assy.		
1984-right	18011294	207.50
left	18011293	207.50
1985-87-right	18012386	212.00
left	18012385	212.00

PARTS — 6 DISC BRAKES 6 — PARTS

	Part No.	Price
Brake Pad Set		
1984-87	12300238	N.L.
Caliper Repair Kit		
1984-87	18011329	20.50
(1) Rotor Assy.		
1984-87	10022442	49.50
(2) Splash Shield		
1984-87	10031892	1.75
(3) Bearing (Suspension)		
1984-87	7470002	130.00
(4) Knuckle		
1984-87-right	14076994	86.50
left	14076993	86.50
(5) Seal (Knuckle)		
1984-87	14076995	N.L.
(6) Caliper Bolt		
1984-87	18011243	6.50
(7) Bushing		
1984-87	18001032	2.50

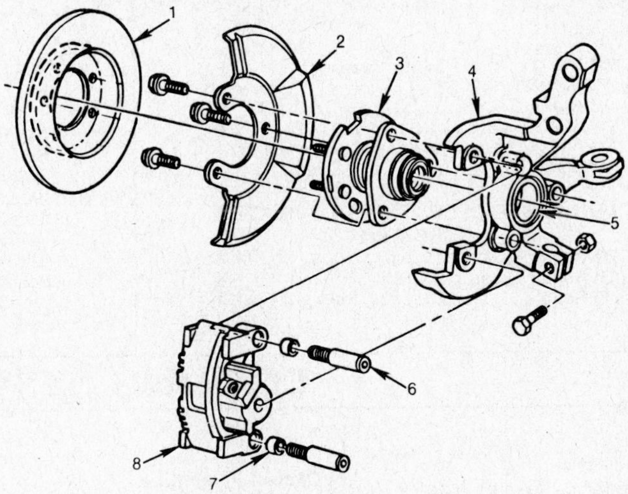

	Part No.	Price
(8) Caliper Assy.		
1984-right	18011332	303.75
left	18011331	307.50
1985-87-right	18012388	348.75
left	18012387	348.75

LABOR — 7 COOLING SYSTEM 7 — LABOR

(Factory Time) — Chilton Time

(M) Winterize Cooling System
Includes: Run engine to check for leaks, tighten all hose connections. Test radiator and pressure cap, drain radiator and engine block. Add anti-freeze and refill system.

	Chilton Time
All models	.5

(G) Thermostat, Renew

1984-87-Four (.2)	.4

(G) Radiator Assembly, R&R or Renew
Includes: Drain and refill cooling system.

1984-87 (.8)	1.2
w/A.T. add (.2)	.2

ADD THESE OPERATIONS TO RADIATOR R&R

(G) Boil & Repair	1.5
(G) Rod Clean	1.9
(G) Repair Core	1.3
(G) Renew Tank	1.6
(G) Renew Trans. Oil Cooler	1.9
(G) Recore Radiator	1.7

(M) Radiator Hoses, Renew

1984-87	
upper or lower	
rad to pipe (.4)	.5
thermo to pipe (.6)	.7
both	
front (.6)	.8
rear (1.0)	1.3
by-pass (.4)	.6

(M) Drive Belt, Renew

1984-87-Four-one (.3)	.4
each adtnl (.2)	.2
V-6	
A.C. (.5)	.7
Fan/Generator (.3)	.4

(M) Drive Belt, Adjust

1984-87-one (.2)	.2
all (.3)	.3

COOLING SYSTEM TUNE-UP

An Annual Cooling System Tune-Up Suggestion List should include (with some exceptions):

1. A visual check of the cooling system for indications of leaks or excessive oil content.
2. Pressure check the cooling system for internal and external leaks with filler cap and neck adapter and tester.
3. Check crankcase and automatic transmission oil for water content.
4. Test coolant thermostat with radiator thermometer.
5. Check temperature gauge for accuracy.
6. Drain system and flush till clean.
7. Clean foreign matter from radiator fins.
8. Test radiator pressure cap with cap tester.
9. Check fan blades and pulleys for alignment and damage.
10. Internal and external inspection of all hoses for cracks and deterioration.
11. Check core plugs (where possible) for seepage.
12. Refill system with correct coolant and check for air locks.
13. Check condition and tension of drive belts with tension gauge.

All models 1.5

(Factory Time) — Chilton Time

(G) Water Pump and/or Gasket, Renew

1984-87-Four (1.3)	2.0
V-6 (1.4)	2.2

(G) Electric Coolant Fan and/or Motor, Renew

1984-87 (.6)	.8

(G) Coolant Fan Switch, Renew

1984-87 (.3)	.4

(G) Engine Coolant Fan Relay, Renew

1984-87 (.3)	.4

(G) Blower Motor Relay, Renew

1984-87 (.2)	.3

(G) Engine Blower Fan Relay, Renew

1984-87 (.3)	.4

(G) Engine Cooling Fan Resistor, Renew

1984-87 (.2)	.3

(G) Engine Blower Fan, Renew

1984-87 (.3)	.4

(G) Temperature Gauge (Engine Unit), Renew

1984-87 (.3)	.4

(G) Temperature Gauge (Dash Unit), Renew

1984-87 (.4)	.7

(G) Water Jacket Expansion Plugs, Renew (Side of Block)

each (.5)	.7

Note: Add time to gain access to plug.

(G) Heater Hoses, Renew

1984-87	
heater pipe to core	
one or both (.8)	1.1
All other hoses	
each (.4)	.5

LABOR 7 COOLING SYSTEM 7 LABOR

	(Factory Time)	Chilton Time
(G) Heater Core, R&R or Renew		
1984-87		
wo/A.C.	(.4)	.7
w/A.C.	(.5)	.9
Add time to recharge A.C. system if required.		
ADD THESE OPERATIONS TO HEATER CORE R&R		
(G) Boil & Repair		1.2
(G) Repair Core		.9
(G) Recore		1.2
(G) Heater or A.C. Blower Motor, Renew		
1984-87	(.2)	.4
(G) Heater or A.C. Blower Motor Resistor, Renew		
1984-87	(.2)	.3
(G) Heater or A.C. Blower Motor Switch, Renew		
1984-87	(.3)	.5
(G) Heater or A.C. Control Assy., Renew		
1984-87	(.3)	.6

PARTS 7 COOLING SYSTEM 7 PARTS

Radiator Assy.
Replacement radiators must be ordered according to the two-letter code stamped on a metal tag attached to the original radiator.

	Part No.	Price
Radiator Inlet Hose (Upper)		
4-151		
1984-87-front	10024723	5.00
1984-rear	10027046	6.25
1985-87-rear	10033683	8.25
V-6-173		
1985-87-frt.	10024723	5.00
rear	10032771	8.25
inner	10041086	8.00
Radiator Outlet Hose (Lower)		
4-151		
1984-87-front	10024909	3.50
1984-rear	10026966	6.25
1985-87-rear	10036255	9.00
V-6-173		
1985-87-frt.	10024909	3.50
rear	10036860	6.50
Thermostat		
1984-87	3048009	9.50
Coolant Pump Body		
1984-87	10013800	49.50
Coolant Pump Inlet		
4-151		
1984-87	10022997	5.00
Coolant Pump Housing		
4-151		
1984-87	10004073	59.75
Includes shaft, bearing, seal and turbine.		
Coolant Pump Kit		
V-6-173		
1985	14033483	61.50
1986-87	14101304	N.L.
Electric Cooling Motor		
1984-A.C.	22062546	236.00
wo/A.C.	22035556	78.50
1985-87-A.C.	22049519	67.00
wo/A.C.	22048271	82.00
A.C. & H.D.	22062546	236.00
Electric Cooling Resistor		
1984-A.C.	22040855	27.00
1985-87-A.C.	22049799	27.25
Electric Cooling Fan Relay		
(wo/A.C.)		
1984	14078902	12.00
1985-87	10038311	5.50
(A.C.)		
1984	10032629	13.50
1985-87	10038311	5.50
H.D.-2 stage	10040131	20.00
Switch (Temperature Fan)		
1984-87-A.C.	3050223	14.00
wo/A.C.	3040674	12.00
Temperature Sending Unit (Eng.)		
1984-87 (hot light)	25036809	17.75
Temperature Gauge (Dash)		
1984	25048178	50.75
1985-87-4 cyl.	25079162	51.75
V-6	25078495	51.75
Heater (Eng. Block)		
1984-87-4 cyl.	52351033	20.00
1985-87-V-6	52350510	20.00
Heater Cord (Eng. Block)		
4-151		
1984-85	52353027	12.75
1986-87	52354643	14.50
V-6-173		
1985-87	52353631	12.75
Air Baffle (Radiator)		
1984-87-right	10021372	2.00
(left side)		
wo/A.C.	10027191	2.00
A.C.	10021479	2.00
Heater Core Assy.		
1984-87-wo/A.C.	3052181	66.50
A.C.	3052427	47.50
Blower Motor		
1984-87	22020947	55.25
Heater Relay		
1984-87	10026663	5.50
Blower Motor Resistor		
1984-87-wo/A.C.	10024378	3.75
Heater Control		
1984	16018312	50.25
1985-87	16040672	47.75
Water Flow Control Valve		
1984-87	10026905	8.50

LABOR 8 EXHAUST SYSTEM 8 LABOR

	(Factory Time)	Chilton Time
(G) Muffler, Renew		
1984-87	(.7)	1.0
(G) Front Exhaust Pipe, Renew (To Converter)		
1984-87	(.7)	1.0
(G) Intermediate Exhaust Pipe, Renew		
1984-87	(.8)	1.1
(G) Crossover Exhaust Pipe, Renew		
1985-87	(1.1)	1.5
(G) Front Exhaust Pipe Seal, Renew		
1984-87	(.4)	.7
(G) Tail Pipe, Renew		
1985-87-one	(.2)	.4
both	(.3)	.6
(G) Catalytic Converter, Renew		
1984-87	(.8)	1.0
(G) Exhaust Manifold or Gasket, Renew		
1984-87-Four	(.6)	1.2
V-6-left side	(1.4)	2.0
COMBINATIONS		
(G) Exhaust System, Renew (Complete)		
1984-87		
Four		1.6
V-6		1.2

PARTS 8 EXHAUST SYSTEM 8 PARTS

	Part No.	Price
Part numbers listed are for pricing reference only. Order with complete engine and model information.		
Muffler (w/Pipes)		
1984-85-4 cyl.	10030386	91.25
1986-87-4 cyl.	10044148	121.00
1985-87-V-6	14105910	215.00
Exhaust Manifold Pipe (Front)		
1984-87-4 cyl.	10032754	56.50
Exhaust Crossover Pipe		
1985-87-V-6	10034315	83.50
Tail Pipe & Extension		
1984-87-4 cyl.	10038302	83.50
Shield (Tail Pipe)		
1984-87	10035379	13.75
Catalytic Converter		
4-151		
1984-87	25056349	258.25
V-6-173		
1985-87	25056776	321.00
Exhaust Manifold		
4-151		
1984	10023093	94.25
1985-87	10034347	48.75
V-6-173		
1985-87-right	10034570	39.25
left	10034571	39.25

LABOR 9 FRONT SUSPENSION 9 LABOR

(Factory Time)	Chilton Time
Note: On all front suspension operations alignment charges must be added if performed. Time given does not include alignment.	
(G) Wheel, Renew	
one (.3)	.5
(G) Wheels, Rotate (All)	
All models	.5
(G) Wheels, Balance	
one	.3
each adtnl	.2
(G) Check Alignment of Front End	
All models	.5
Note: Deduct if alignment is performed.	
(G) Toe-In, Adjust	
All models (.4)	.5
(G) Align Front End	
Includes: Adjust front wheel bearings.	
All models (1.3)	1.9
w/A.C. interference add	.5
(G) Front Wheel Bearings, Clean and Repack (Both Wheels)	
All models (1.1)	1.6
(G) Front Wheel Bearings and Cups, Renew	
1984-87-one side (.7)	.9
both sides (1.1)	1.5
(G) Front Wheel Grease Seals, Renew	
1984-87-one side (.7)	.8
both sides (1.1)	1.2
(G) Front Shock Absorbers, Renew	
1984-87-one (.3)	.5
both (.4)	.7
(G) Upper and Lower Ball Joints, Renew (One Side)	
Add alignment charges.	
1984-87 (1.1)	2.0
(G) Upper Ball Joint, Renew	
Add alignment charges.	
1984-87-one (.5)	.9
both (.7)	1.3
(G) Lower Ball Joint, Renew	
Add alignment charges.	
1984-87-one (.6)	.9
both (1.0)	1.6
(G) Steering Knuckle and Arm, Renew	
Add alignment charges.	
1984-87-one (1.0)	1.4
both (1.8)	2.5
(G) Upper Control Arm, Renew	
Add alignment charges.	
1984-87-one (.7)	1.0
both (1.2)	1.8
(G) Lower Control Arm, Renew	
Add alignment charges.	
1984-87-one (.9)	1.4
both (1.7)	2.6
(G) Upper Control Arm Inner Pivot Shaft or Bushings, Renew	
Add alignment charges.	
1984-87-one (.8)	1.1
both (1.3)	2.1
(G) Lower Control Arm Shaft or Bushings, Renew	
Add alignment charges.	
1984-87-one (1.2)	1.6
both (2.2)	3.0
(G) Front Spring, Renew	
Add alignment charges.	
1984-87-one (.8)	1.0
both (1.3)	1.8
(G) Front Stabilizer Shaft, Renew	
1984-87 (.6)	.8
(G) Stabilizer Shaft Link or Bushings, Renew (One or Both Sides)	
1984-87 (.4)	.6
(G) Engine Cradle, Renew	
Add alignment charges.	
1984-87 (1.5)	2.5
(P) Front Suspension Cross Member, Renew	
Add alignment charges.	
1984-87 (7.0)	10.0

PARTS 9 FRONT SUSPENSION 9 PARTS

	Part No.	Price
(1) Front Crossmember		
1984	10031894	114.25
1985-87	10040357	130.00
(2) Steering Knuckle		
1984-87-R.H.	14001236	130.00
L.H.	14001235	130.00
(3) Shock Absorber		
1984-87	22046407	24.50
(4) Insulator (Stabilizer)		
1984-87	363006	1.25
(5) Stabilizer Shaft		
1984-87	10023227	27.00
(6) Link Kit (Stabilizer)		
1984-87	10030987	4.25
(7) Upper Control Arm		
1984-87-R.H.	10023747	47.50
L.H.	10023748	47.50
(8) Ball Joint Kit (Upper)		
1984-87	9769588	53.75

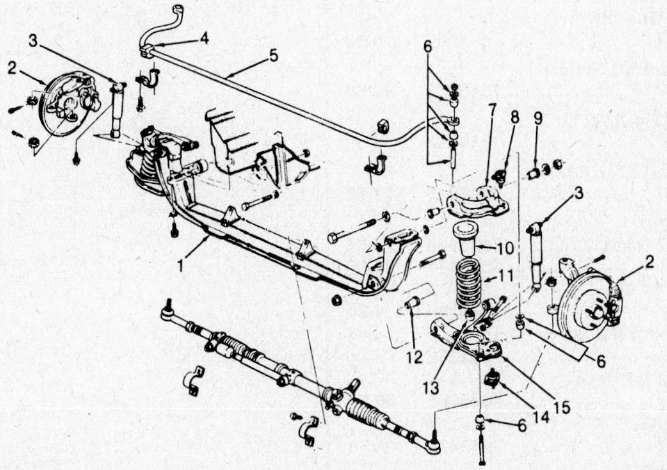

PARTS 9 FRONT SUSPENSION 9 PARTS

	Part No.	Price
(9) Bushing (Upper Cont. Arm)		
1984-87	10027598	2.75
(10) Insulator (Spring)		
1984-87	14036460	2.00
(11) Coil Spring		
Order by year and model.		
(12) Bushing (Lower Cont. Arm)		
1984-87	10026261	5.25
(13) Bumper (Lower)		
1984-87	10027536	1.00
(14) Ball Joint (Lower)		
Part of lower control arm.		
(15) Lower Control Arm		
1984-R.H.	10032527	206.00
L.H.	10032528	206.00
1985-87-R.H.	10042392	114.00
L.H.	10042391	114.00

LABOR 11 STEERING GEAR 11 LABOR

(Factory Time)	Chilton Time
(G) Tie Rods or Tie Rod Ends, Renew	
Includes: Reset toe-in.	
1984-87-one side (.7)	.9
both sides (.8)	1.2
(G) Inner Tie Rod, Renew	
Includes: Reset toe-in.	
1984-87-one side (.8)	1.2
both sides (1.2)	1.6

STANDARD STEERING

(Factory Time)	Chilton Time
(G) Steering Wheel, Renew	
1984-87 (.2)	.4
(G) Horn Contact or Cancelling Cam, Renew	
1984-87 (.3)	.5
(G) Multifunction Lever, Renew	
1984-87 (.2)	.4
w/Cruise control add (.5)	.5
(G) Steering Column Lock Actuator Parts, Renew	
1984-87	
std colm (1.0)	1.5
tilt colm (.9)	1.4
(G) Upper Mast Jacket Bearing, Renew	
1984-87-std colm (.8)	1.4
tilt colm (.5)	.9
(G) Steering Coupling (Rag Joint), Renew	
1984-87 (.7)	1.0
(G) Steering Column Assembly, R&R or Renew	
1984-87-std colm (.8)	1.5
tilt colm (1.1)	1.9
Recond colm add (.8)	1.0
(G) Steering Gear Assembly, R&R or Renew	
1984-87 (1.2)	1.8
(G) Steering Gear Assy., R&R and Recondition	
1984-87 (1.7)	2.6
(G) Steering Damper, Renew	
1984-87 (.3)	.5

PARTS 11 POWER STEERING GEAR 11 PARTS

	Part No.	Price
Steering Gear Complete		
1984-exc. Perf.	7846406	346.00
Performance	7847087	346.00
1985	7847087	346.00
1986-87-P37	7846406	346.00
P97	7847087	346.00
(1) Steering Gear Housing		
1984-87	7838090	89.50
(2) Pinion (w/Bearing)		
1984-87	7838288	49.25
(3) Adjusting Plug		
1984-87-exc. below	7825181	7.75
w/WS6	7844230	4.75
(4) Spring (Ajd. Plug)		
1984-87	7819378	1.50
(5) Rack Bearing		
1984-87	7819359	5.50
(6) Tie Rod Kit (Inner)		
1984-87	7840738	40.00
(7) Seal (Tie Rod)		
1984-87	7819398	5.50
(8) Tie Rod Kit (Outer)		
1984-87	7847818	47.75
(9) Boot Kit		
1984-87-right	7840718	20.75
left	7835171	25.00
(10) Grommet		
1984-87	7832995	4.25
(11) Bushing (Rack)		
1984-87	7819355	4.50
(12) Steering Rack		
1984-87	7838086	80.00
(13) Adapter		
1984-87	7842475	6.75
(14) Damper		
1984-87	22025400	N.L.

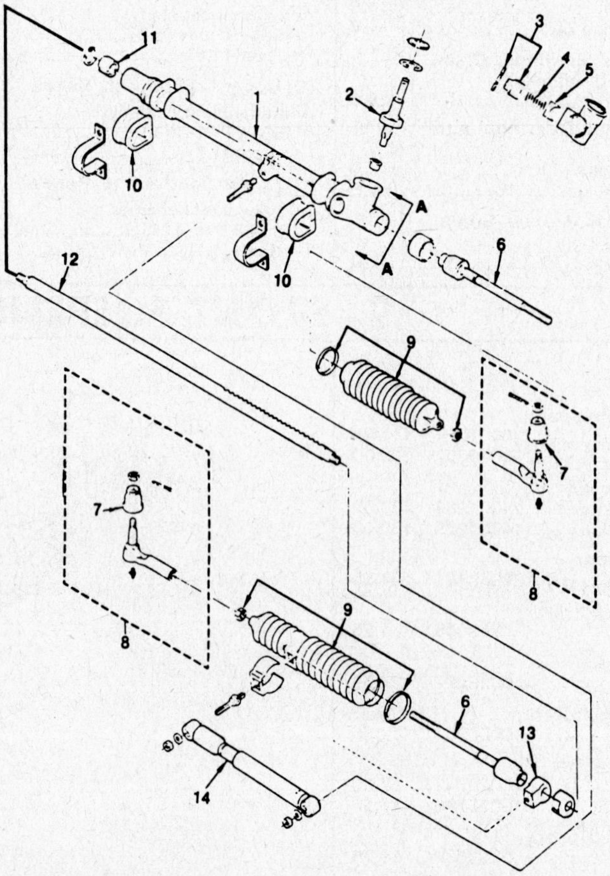

LABOR 12 CYLINDER HEAD & VALVE SYSTEM 12 LABOR

	(Factory Time)	Chilton Time
(G) Compression Test		
Four–1984-87	(.3)	.5
V-6–1985-87		1.4
(G) Cylinder Head Gasket, Renew		
Includes: Clean carbon and make all necessary adjustments.		
Four–1984-87	(3.1)	4.5
V-6–1985-87-one	(5.5)	7.8
both	(6.7)	9.5
(G) Cylinder Head, Renew		
Includes: Transfer all components, reface valves, clean carbon.		
Four–1984-87	(4.6)	6.6
V-6–1985-87-one	(6.0)	8.5
both	(7.8)	11.1
(P) Clean Carbon and Grind Valves		
Includes: R&R cylinder head, grind valves and seats. Minor engine tune up.		
Four–1984-87	(5.2)	7.4
V-6–1985-87-one	(6.7)	9.5
both	(9.1)	12.9
(G) Rocker Arm Cover or Gasket, Renew		
Four–1984-87	(.7)	1.0
V-6–1985-87		
right side	(.7)	1.0
left side	(1.2)	1.7
both sides	(1.7)	2.4

COMBINATIONS

Add To Valve Job

See Machine Shop Operations

(G) DRAIN, EVACUATE & RECHARGE AIR CONDITIONING SYSTEM		
All models	(.5)	1.0
(G) ROCKER ARM STUD, RENEW		
Each	(.2)	.2
(G) HYDRAULIC VALVE LIFTERS, DISASSEMBLE AND CLEAN		
Each	(.2)	.2
(G) DISTRIBUTOR, RECONDITION		
All models	(.5)	.8
(G) VALVE GUIDES, REAM OVERSIZE		
Each	(.2)	.2

	(Factory Time)	Chilton Time
(G) Push Rod Side Cover Gasket, Renew		
Four–1984-87	(2.3)	3.0
(G) Valve Rocker Arms and/or Push Rods, Renew		
Four–1984-87		
one cyl	(.8)	1.1
all cyls	(1.0)	1.5
V-6–1985-87		
one cyl-right side	(.9)	1.3
one cyl-left side	(1.4)	2.0
all cyls-both sides	(2.3)	3.3
(G) Valve Rocker Arm Stud, Renew (One)		
Four–1984-87	(.8)	1.2
each adtnl		.2
V-6–1985-87		
right side-one	(1.0)	1.4
left side-one	(1.5)	2.1
each adtnl	(.3)	.3
(G) Valve Springs and/or Valve Stem Oil Seals, Renew (Head on Car)		
Four–1984-87		
one cyl	(1.0)	1.4
all cyls	(1.7)	2.3
V-6–1985-87		
one cyl-right side	(1.1)	1.6
one cyl-left side	(1.6)	2.3
one cyl-each side	(2.4)	3.4
all cyls-both sides	(3.7)	5.3
(G) Valve Tappets, Renew (Lifters)		
Four–1984-87		
one cyl	(2.7)	3.6
all cyls	(2.9)	4.0
V-6–1985-87		
one side	(3.9)	5.5
both sides	(4.2)	6.0

PARTS 12 CYLINDER HEAD & VALVE SYSTEM 12 PARTS

FOUR CYLINDER

	Part No.	Price
Valve Grind Gasket Set		
1984-87	10037280	29.25
(1) Cylinder Head		
1984	10038231	290.00
1985-87	10037282	290.00
(2) Cylinder Head Gasket		
1985-87	10035039	9.75
(3) Valve Cover Gasket		
1984-87	10007770	6.50
(4) Rocker Arm and Ball Kit		
1984-87	10014819	7.25
(5) Lock (Valve Spring)		
1984-87	3947770	.50
(6) Oil Seal (Valve stem)		
1984-87	3835333	.50
(7) Cap (Valve Spring)		
1984-87	3729363	1.00
(8) Shield (Valve Spring)		
1984-87	10007818	.75

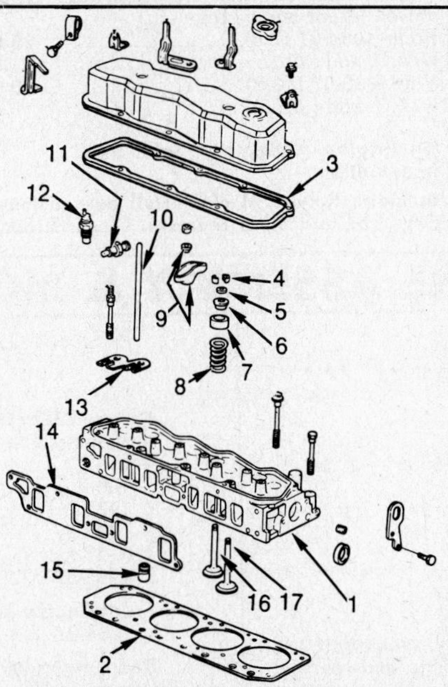

	Part No.	Price
(9) Valve Spring & Damper		
1984-87	3735381	3.00
(10) Push Rod		
1984	10021898	3.00
1985-87	10028055	3.25
(11) Switch (Fan Control)		
1984-87-A.C.	3050223	14.00
wo/A.C.	3040674	11.00
(12) Switch (Temperature)		
1984-87 (hot light)	25036809	17.75
(13) Manifold Gasket (Intake)		
1984-87	10026023	5.00
(14) Valve Lifter		
1984	5233515	10.50
1985-87	5233745	32.50
(15) Intake Valve (Std.)		
1984-87	10022882	16.00
(16) Exhaust Valve (Std.)		
1984-87	10034162	16.25
(17) Plug		
1984-87	3994255	1.00

PARTS 12 CYLINDER HEAD & VALVE SYSTEM 12 PARTS

SIX CYLINDER

	Part No.	Price
(1) Cylinder Head Assy.		
1985-87	14054879	250.00
(2) Cylinder Head Gasket		
1985-87	14085435	4.75
Cylinder Head Gasket Kit		
1985-87	14089077	52.00

PARTS 12 CYLINDER HEAD & VALVE SYSTEM 12 PARTS

	Part No.	Price
(3) Push Rod		
1985-87	476525	5.00
(4) Valve Lifter		
1985-87	5234212	N.L.
(5) Intake Valve		
1985-87	14031328	14.00
(6) Exhaust Valve		
1985-87	14031332	15.50

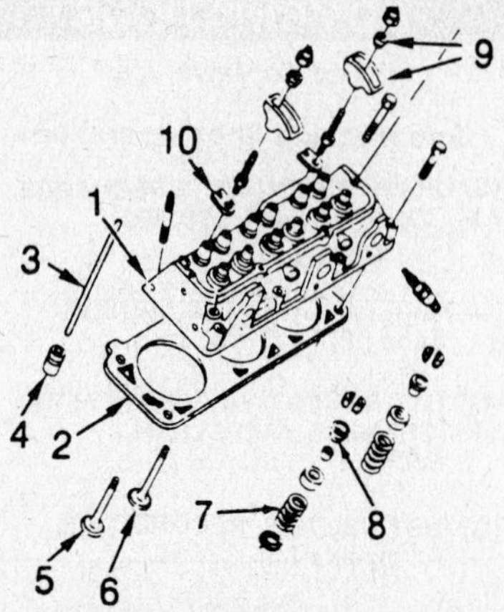

	Part No.	Price
(7) Valve Spring		
1985-87	14030029	3.50
(8) Valve Spring Cap		
1985-87	14004099	1.00
(9) Rocker Arm w/Ball		
1985-87	14002446	4.75
(10) Push Rod Guide		
1985-87	476531	1.50

LABOR 13 ENGINE ASSEMBLY & MOUNTS 13 LABOR

(Factory Time) Chilton Time

(G) Engine Assembly, Remove & Install

Does not include transfer of any parts or equipment.

	Chilton Time
Four–1984-87	4.7
w/A.C. add	.8
V-6–1985-87	4.4
w/A.C. add	.5

(G) Engine Assembly, Renew

Includes: R&R engine assembly, transfer all component parts nor supplied with replacement engine. Minor tune up.

	Chilton Time
Four–1984-87 (4.1)	7.0
w/A.C. add (.8)	.8
V-6–1985-87 (4.4)	7.4
w/A.C. add (.5)	.5

(P) Cylinder Block, Renew (w/All Internal Parts Less Cylinder Head and Oil Pan)

Includes: R&R engine assembly, transfer all component parts not supplied with replacement engine. Clean carbon, grind valves. Minor engine tune up.

	Chilton Time
Four–1984-87 (6.3)	12.4
w/A.C. add (.8)	.8
V-6–1985-87 (10.9)	15.8
w/A.C. add (.5)	.5

(P) Cylinder Block, Renew (w/Pistons, Rings and Bearings)

Includes: R&R engine assembly, transfer all component parts not supplied with replacement engine. Clean carbon, grind valves. Minor engine tune up.

	Chilton Time
Four–1984-87 (7.8)	15.6
w/A.C. add (.8)	.8
V-6–1985-87 (13.8)	20.0
w/A.C. add (.5)	.5

(P) Engine Assembly, R&R and Recondition

Includes: Rebore block, install new pistons, rings, rod and main bearings. Clean carbon, grind valves. Tune engine.

	Chilton Time
Four–1984-87 (13.8)	21.6
w/A.C. add (.8)	.8
V-6–1985-87 (20.2)	29.2
w/A.C. add (.5)	.5

(P) Engine Assembly, Recondition (In Car)

Includes: Expand or renew pistons, install new rings, pins, rod and main bearings. Clean carbon, grind valves. Tune engine.

	Chilton Time
Four–1984-87 (13.7)	16.3
w/A.C. add (.4)	.4
V-6–1985-87 (18.7)	27.0

(G) Front Engine Mount, Renew

	Chilton Time
1984-87-right (1.3)	1.8

PARTS 13 ENGINE ASSEMBLY & MOUNTS 13 PARTS

	Part No.	Price
Engine Overhaul Gasket Kit		
4-151		
1984-87	10026805	20.50
V-6–173		
1985	14091347	8.75
1986-87	14101336	9.25
Engine Assy. (Partial) Includes block, piston, rod assy, crankshaft, crankshaft bearings, rod bearings and rear seal.		
4-151		
1984	10030773	1128.25
1985	10037143	1128.00
1986	10042843	1128.00
1987	10049067	N.L.
V-6–173		
1985-87	14101358	1230.00

	Part No.	Price
Cylinder Block Assy. Includes piston and pin assembly.		
4-151		
1984	10030774	856.00
1985	10037148	815.00
1986-87	10042846	856.00
V-6–173		
1985-87	14101357	935.00
Front Engine Mount (R.H.)		
1984-87	14073097	31.50
Rear Engine Mount		
(four speed)		
1984	14034785	21.75
1985-87	10036062	N.L.
(five speed)		
1985-87	10036062	N.L.
(A.T.)		
1984	10027799	16.50
1985-87	10036062	N.L.

LABOR 14 PISTONS, RINGS & BEARINGS 14 LABOR

	(Factory Time)	Chilton Time
(P) Rings, Renew (See Engine Combinations)		
Includes: Remove cylinder top ridge, deglaze cylinder walls. Clean piston and ring grooves. Minor tune up.		
Four–1984-87		
one cyl	(5.6)	7.5
all cyls	(6.5)	8.8
w/A.C. add	(.4)	.4
V-6–1985-87		
one cyl	(7.5)	10.8
one cyl-each side	(9.0)	13.0
all cyls-both sides	(10.9)	15.8
(P) Pistons or Connecting Rods, Renew		
Includes: Remove cylinder top ridge, deglaze cylinder walls. Minor tune up.		
Four–1984-87		
one cyl	(5.6)	7.8
all cyls	(6.5)	10.0
w/A.C. add	(.4)	.4
V-6–1985-86		
one cyl	(8.2)	11.5
one cyl-each side	(10.4)	14.4
all cyls-both sides	(11.6)	20.0

COMBINATIONS

Engine Combinations
See Machine Shop Operations

	(Factory Time)	Chilton Time
(G) DRAIN, EVACUATE & RECHARGE AIR CONDITIONING SYSTEM		
All models	(.5)	1.0
(G) ROCKER ARM STUD, RENEW		
Each	(.2)	.2
(G) HYDRAULIC VALVE LIFTERS, DISASSEMBLE AND CLEAN		
Each	(.2)	.2
(G) DISTRIBUTOR, RECONDITION		
All models	(.5)	.8
(G) CYLINDER HEAD, R&R (ENGINE REMOVED)		
Four	(1.2)	1.6
V-6-one	(3.2)	4.2
both	(5.0)	6.5
(G) CONNECTING ROD, RENEW (ENGINE DISASSEMBLED)		
Four-each	(.3)	.4
V-6-each	(.3)	.4
(G) VALVE GUIDES, REAM OVERSIZE		
Each	(.2)	.2
(G) DEGLAZE CYLINDER WALLS		
Each	(.1)	.1
(G) REMOVE CYLINDER TOP RIDGE		
Each	(.1)	.1
(G) MAIN BEARINGS, RENEW (PAN REMOVED)		
Four		1.2
V-6		1.8
(G) PLASTIGAUGE BEARINGS		
Each	(.1)	.1
(M) OIL FILTER ELEMENT, RENEW		
All models	(.3)	.3

	(Factory Time)	Chilton Time
(P) Connecting Rod Bearings, Renew		
Includes: Plastigauge bearings.		
Four–1984-87	(2.6)	4.4
V-6–1985-87	(3.0)	4.3

PARTS 14 PISTONS, RINGS, PINS & BEARINGS 14 PARTS

	Part No.	Price
(1) Piston Ring Set (Std.)		
4-151		
1984-85	10030202	18.00
1986-87	10037199	18.00
V-6–173		
1985-87	14089059	17.00
(2) Piston Assy. (Std.)		
4-151		
1984-85	10027317	53.00
1986-87	10042191	50.75
V-6–173		
1985-87	14094101	48.50
(3) Piston Pin		
1984-87-151	500012	5.50

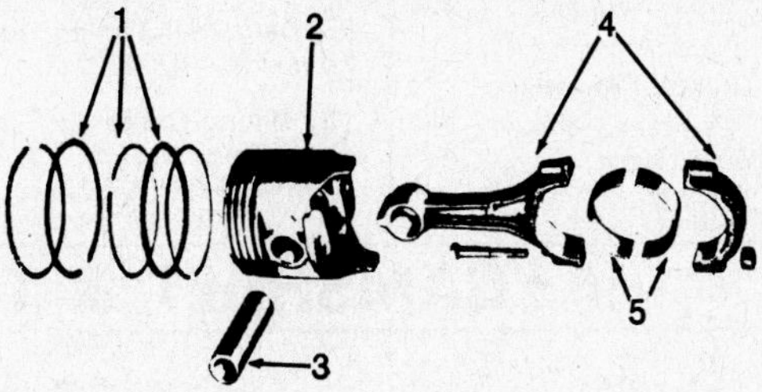

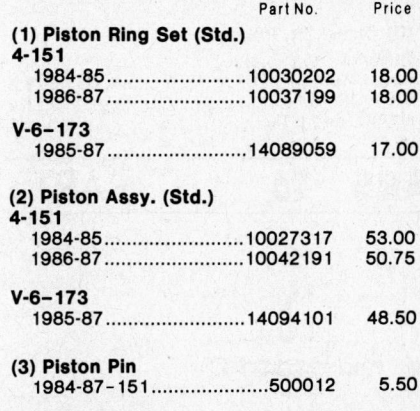

	Part No.	Price
(4) Connecting Rod		
4-151		
1984-87	499323	39.50
V-6-173		
1985-87	476521	36.50
(5) Connecting Rod Bearings (Std.)		
4-151		
1984-87	5463932	10.50
V-6-173		
1985-87	18008492	N.L.

LABOR 15 CRANKSHAFT & DAMPER 15 LABOR

	(Factory Time)	Chilton Time
(P) Crankshaft and Main Bearings, Renew		
Includes: R&R engine, check all bearing clearances.		
Four–1984-87	(4.9)	9.0
w/A.C. add	(.6)	.6
V-6–1985-87	(7.4)	10.7
w/A.C. add	(.5)	.5
(P) Main Bearings, Renew		
Includes: Check all bearing clearances.		
Four–1984-87	(2.9)	4.9
V-6–1985-87	(2.4)	3.5
(P) Main and Rod Bearings, Renew		
Includes: Check all bearing clearances.		
Four–1984-87	(3.5)	6.1
V-6–1985-87	(4.2)	5.3
(G) Rear Main Bearing Oil Seals, Renew or Repack		
Four–1984-87	(3.3)	5.0
w/A.T. add	(.4)	.4
V-6–1985-87		
w/A.T.	(5.9)	8.5
(G) Crankshaft Pulley or Balancer, Renew		
Four–1984-87		
pulley	(.5)	.9
balancer	(.6)	1.0
V-6–1985-87		
pulley	(.6)	1.0
balancer	(.8)	1.2
w/A.C. add	(.3)	.3

PARTS 15 CRANKSHAFT & DAMPER 15 PARTS

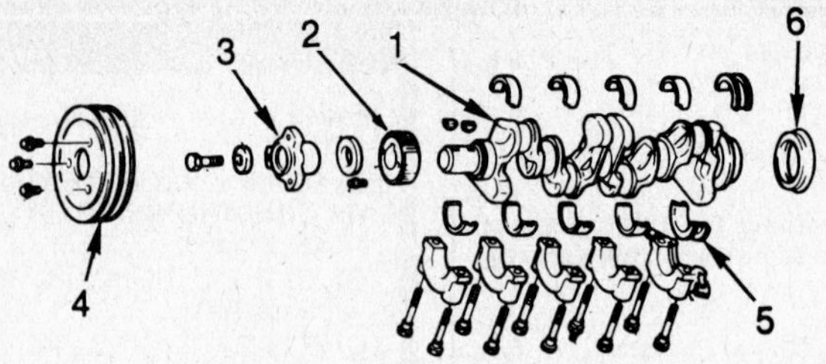

	Part No.	Price
(1) Crankshaft		
4-151		
1984-85	10002685	313.00
1986-87	10037018	313.00
V-6-173		
1985-87	14077817	336.00
(2) Crankshaft Gear		
4-151		
1984-87	10028052	25.75
V-6-173		
1985-87	477263	13.25
(3) Hub (Crank. Pulley)		
4-151		
1984-87	10028930	26.75
Damper		
V-6-173		
1985-87	10032616	41.00
(4) Pulley (Crankshaft)		
4-151		
1984-87	10021630	4.50
V-6-173		
1985-87	10041616	17.50
(5) Bearing Kit		
4-151		
1984-exc. rear	3829061	11.00
rear	3829067	14.25
1985-87-rear	18012433	11.25
rear	3829067	14.25
V-6-173		
1985-87-No. 1, 4	18012472	13.25
No. 2	18012473	13.25
No. 3	18012478	24.75
(6) Rear Main Bearing Oil Seal		
4-151		
1984-87	10036788	7.00
V-6-173		
1985-87	14085829	14.50

LABOR 16 CAMSHAFT & TIMING GEARS 16 LABOR

(Factory Time)	Chilton Time
(G) Timing Cover Oil Seal, Renew	
Four-1984-87 (.7)	1.4
V-6-1985-87 (.8)	1.4
w/A.C. add (.3)	.3
(G) Timing Cover or Gasket, Renew	
Four-1984-87 (2.0)	3.0
V-6-1985-87 (2.6)	3.8
w/A.C. add (.3)	.3
(G) Crankshaft Timing Gear, Renew	
Four-1984-87 (2.3)	3.5
(G) Camshaft Timing Gear, Renew	
Four-1984-87 (5.2)	8.0
(G) Timing Chain and/or Camshaft Gear, Renew	
V-6-1985-87 (2.7)	4.3
w/A.C. add (.3)	.3
Renew crank gear add (.2)	.2
(G) Camshaft, Renew	
Includes: R&R engine.	
Four-1984-87 (5.6)	8.5
V-6-1985-87 (7.7)	11.2
w/A.C. add (.3)	.3

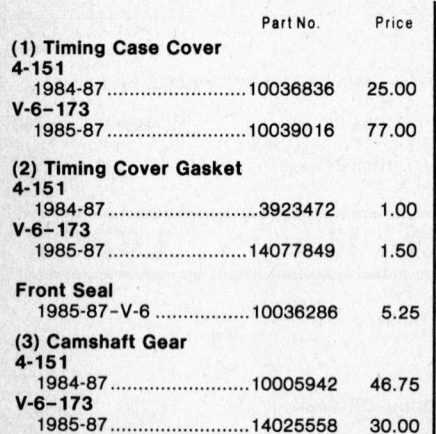

PARTS 16 CAMSHAFT & TIMING GEARS 16 PARTS

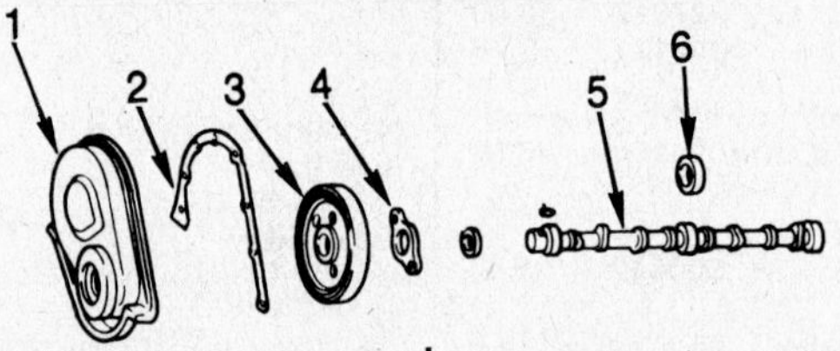

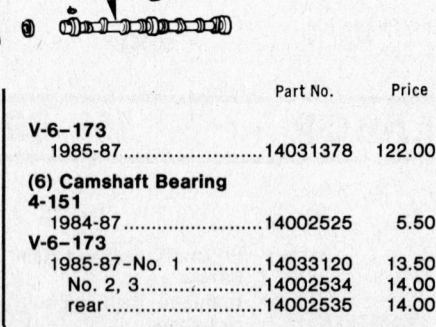

	Part No.	Price
(1) Timing Case Cover		
4-151		
1984-87	10036836	25.00
V-6-173		
1985-87	10039016	77.00
(2) Timing Cover Gasket		
4-151		
1984-87	3923472	1.00
V-6-173		
1985-87	14077849	1.50
Front Seal		
1985-87-V-6	10036286	5.25
(3) Camshaft Gear		
4-151		
1984-87	10005942	46.75
V-6-173		
1985-87	14025558	30.00
(4) Bearing Camshaft Sprocket		
4-151		
1984-87	10000568	4.25
(5) Camshaft		
4-151		
1984	10029616	118.00
1985-87	10029787	118.00
V-6-173		
1985-87	14031378	122.00
(6) Camshaft Bearing		
4-151		
1984-87	14002525	5.50
V-6-173		
1985-87-No. 1	14033120	13.50
No. 2, 3	14002534	14.00
rear	14002535	14.00

LABOR 17 ENGINE OILING SYSTEM 17 LABOR

(Factory Time)	Chilton Time
(G) Oil Pan or Gasket, Renew	
Four-1984-87 (2.2)	3.2
V-6-1985-87 (1.1)	1.6
(P) Pressure Test Engine Bearings (Pan Off)	
All models	1.0
(G) Oil Pump, Renew	
Four-1984-87 (2.3)	3.4
V-6-1985-87 (1.2)	1.8
(G) Oil Pump Drive and/or Gasket, Renew	
Four-1984-87 (.5)	.7
(G) Oil Pressure Gauge (Engine), Renew	
1984-87 (.3)	.4
(G) Oil Pressure Gauge (Dash), Renew	
1984-87 (.4)	.7
(M) Oil Filter Element, Renew	
1984-87 (.3)	.3

PARTS 17 ENGINE OILING SYSTEM 17 PARTS

	Part No.	Price
Oil Pump Assy.		
4-151		
1984-87	10008206	61.00
V-6-173		
1985-87	14033227	N.L
Oil Pump Upper Drive Shaft		
4-151		
1984-87	1977131	11.75
Oil Pump Intermediate Shaft		
V-6-173		
1985-87	477248	1.50
Oil Pump Shaft Bearing		
4-151		
1984-87-upper	10008555	1.00
lower	10004842	1.50
Oil Pressure Regulator Valve		
4-151		
1984-87	3829433	1.50
V-6-173		
1985-87	3702366	1.50
Oil Pressure Sending Switch		
1984	25036378	8.75
1985-87	10030963	20.75
Oil Filter Element		
1984-87	25010792	7.50
Oil Filter By Pass Valve		
1984-87	25010497	3.50

LABOR 18 CLUTCH & FLYWHEEL 18 LABOR

(Factory Time)	Chilton Time
(G) Clutch Master Cylinder, Renew	
Includes: Bleed system.	
1984-87 (.8)	1.2
Recond cyl add (.2)	.3
(G) Clutch Actuator Cylinder, Renew	
Includes: Bleed system.	
1984-87 (.4)	.6
Recond cyl add (.2)	.3
(G) Clutch Release Fork and/or Ball Stud, Renew	
Includes: R&R trans.	
1984-87-Four (3.4)	6.3
V-6 (2.5)	3.7
(G) Clutch Release Bearing, Renew	
Includes: R&R trans.	
1984-87-Four (3.4)	6.3
V-6 (2.5)	3.7
(G) Clutch Assembly, Renew	
Includes: R&R trans.	
1984-87-Four (3.6)	6.5
V-6 (5.6)	8.3
Renew forkshaft and bushings add (.3)	.3
(G) Flywheel, Renew	
Includes: R&R trans.	
1984-87-Four (3.8)	6.8
V-6 (5.8)	8.5

PARTS 18 CLUTCH & FLYWHEEL 18 PARTS

	Part No.	Price
Clutch Plate (Driven)		
4-151		
1984	14085591	89.25
1985-87	14091962	85.75
V-6-173		
1985-87	14087220	89.25
Cover & Pressure Plate		
4-151		
1984	14085590	135.00
1985-87	14091961	114.00
V-6-173		
1985-87	14087221	114.00
Clutch Fork Lever		
4-151		
1984	10037448	N.L.
1985-87	10034202	16.75
V-6-173		
1985-87	10039912	16.75
Clutch Fork Shaft		
4-151		
1984	14024930	71.25
1985-87	94251465	28.25
V-6-173		
1985-87	14024430	66.75
Clutch Release Bearing		
4-151		
1984	908403	47.25
1985-87	94133417	43.00
V-6-173		
1985-87	908403	47.25
Flywheel Assy.		
4-151		
1984-87-M.T.	10004031	159.00
A.T.	10031262	70.25
V-6-173		
1985-87-M.T.	476575	159.00
A.T.	14085471	68.25

LABOR 21 SHIFT LINKAGE 21 LABOR

(Factory Time)	Chilton Time
MANUAL	
(G) Gearshift Linkage, Adjust	
All models (.3)	.3
(G) Floor Mounted Gearshift Control Assy., Renew	
1984-87 (1.4)	1.9
(G) Gearshift Control Cables, Renew	
Includes: Adjust cables.	
1984-87-one (1.7)	2.3
both (1.8)	2.5
(G) Floor Shift Back Drive Rod or Cable, Renew	
1984-87 (.8)	1.1
AUTOMATIC	
(G) Shift Linkage, Adjust	
All models	
Neutral Safety Switch (.3)	.4
Shift Indicator Needle (.2)	.3
Shift Linkage (.4)	.5
T.V. Cable (.3)	.4
(G) Floor Mounted Shift Lever, Renew	
1984-87 (1.7)	2.4
(G) Park Lock Cable, Renew	
1984-87 (.8)	1.1
(G) Shift Control Cable, Renew	
1984-87 (1.8)	2.6
(G) Gear Shift Indicator Needle and/or Assembly, Renew	
1984-87 (.2)	.4

LABOR 26 REAR AXLE AND SUSPENSION 26 LABOR

(Factory Time)	Chilton Time
(G) Rear Suspension Toe-In, Adjust	
1984-87 (.5)	.7
(G) Rear Suspension, Align	
Includes: Adjust toe-in.	
1984-87 (.8)	1.2
(G) Rear Tie Rod Ends, Renew	
Includes: Reset toe-in.	
1984-87-one side (.8)	1.1
both sides (1.0)	1.3

PARTS 26 REAR AXLE AND SUSPENSION 26 PARTS

	(Factory Time)	Chilton Time
(G) Rear Tie Rods, Renew		
Includes: Reset toe-in.		
1984-87-one side	(.9)	1.2
both	(1.2)	1.5
(G) Rear Wheel Bearing and Hub Assy., Clean and Repack or Renew		
1984-87-one side	(.7)	1.0
both sides	(1.2)	1.8
(G) Rear Wheel Knuckle Assy., Renew		
1984-87-one	(.9)	1.2
both	(1.7)	2.3
(G) Rear Coil Springs, Renew		
1984-87-one	(.8)	1.1
both	(1.4)	2.0
(G) Control Arm Ball Joint, Renew		
1984-87-each	(.5)	.9
(G) Lower Control Arm Bushings, Renew		
1984-87-one side	(1.1)	1.5
both sides	(2.2)	3.0
(G) Lower Control Arm Assy., Renew		
1984-87-one side	(.8)	1.1
both sides	(1.5)	2.1
(G) Rear Shock Absorber Strut Cartridge, Renew		
1984-87-one side	(.8)	1.1
both sides	(1.3)	1.9
(G) Rear Strut Bearing Mount, Renew		
1984-87-one side	(.8)	1.2
both sides	(1.4)	2.0

DRIVE AXLE

	(Factory Time)	Chilton Time
(G) Front Drive Axle, R&R or Renew		
1984-87-one	(1.1)	1.4
both	(1.6)	2.2
Renew shaft add-each	(.3)	.4
Renew C/J Joint add each side	(.3)	.4
Renew D/O Joint add each side	(.3)	.4
Renew C/V Joint boots add each	(.2)	.2
(G) Axle Shaft Seal, Renew		
1984-87-one	(1.1)	1.5
both	(1.5)	2.1

PARTS 26 REAR AXLE AND SUSPENSION 26 PARTS

	Part No.	Price
(1) Frame		
4-151		
1984-87-wo/H.D.	10033671	173.00
H.D. susp.	10033670	173.00
V-6-173		
1985-wo/H.D.	10033671	173.00
H.D. susp.	10033670	173.00
1986-87	10033670	173.00
(2) Axle Kit		
1984 (M.T.)		
right	7844541	431.00
left	7844671	504.00
1985-87 (M.T.)		
right	7847103	520.00
left	7847102	520.00
1984 (A.T.)		
right	7842351	431.00
left	7844804	431.00
1985-87 (A.T.)		
right	7846878	440.00
left	7848230	425.00
(3) Rear Wheel Spindle Rod		
1984-87	7845327	43.50
(4) Knuckle (Rear Wheel)		
1984-87-right	14076994	86.25
left	14076993	86.25
(5) Control Arm (Lower)		
1984-87-right	10034335	58.00
left	10034336	69.50
(6) Insulator (Lower)		
1984-87	14036460	2.00
(7) Strut		
1984-87	22049973	68.50
(8) Coil Spring		
Order by model and description.		
(9) Dust Shield (Shock Absorber)		
1984-87	10026674	2.75
(10) Bumper (Axle Jounce)		
1984-87	10026720	3.75
(11) Insulator (Spring)		
1984-87	10026618	2.25
(12) Spring Seat		
1984-87	10026721	3.75
(13) Strut Mount		
1984-87	10031286	11.00

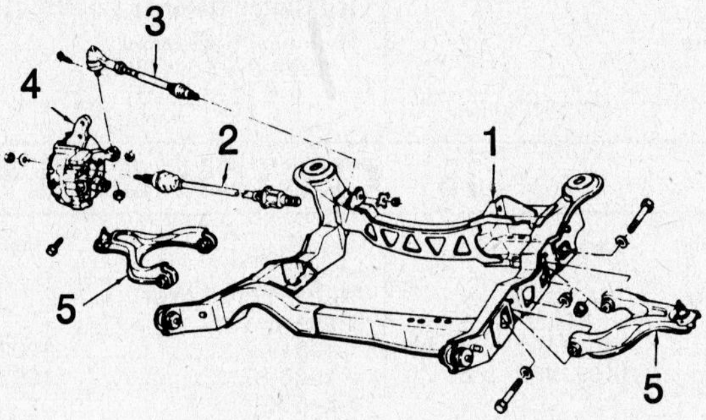

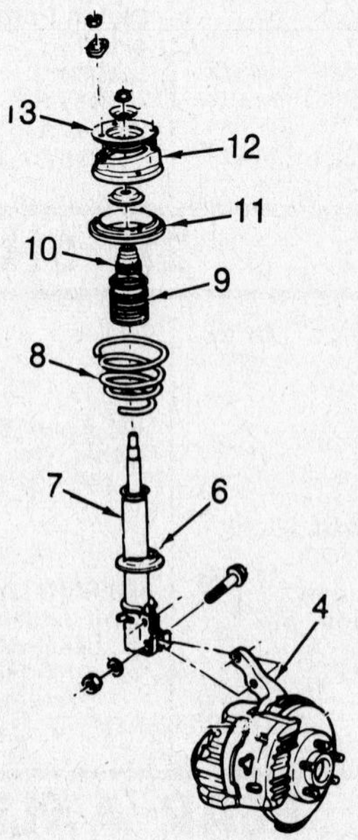

LABOR 28 AIR CONDITIONING 28 LABOR

(Factory Time) Chilton Time

Note: If more than one item requires replacement where evacuation and discharging the system is already included in the operation, deduct 1.0 hour for each additional item to the times listed.

(G) Drain, Evacuate and Recharge System
All models (.5) 1.0

(G) Leak Check
Includes: Check all lines and connections.
All models 5

(G) Pressure Test System
All models 8

(G) Refrigerant, Add (Partial Charge)
All models 6

(G) Compressor Belt, Renew
1984-87-Four (.2) 4
V-6 (.5) 7

DA-6 COMPRESSOR

(G) Compressor Assembly, Renew
Includes: Transfer all necessary attaching parts. Evacuate and charge system.
1984-87 (1.6) 2.5

(G) Compressor Clutch Plate and Hub Assy., Renew
Includes: R&R hub and drive plate assy. Check air gap. Evacuate and charge system.
1984-87 (1.7) 2.6

(G) Compressor Clutch Rotor and/or Bearing, Renew
Includes: R&R hub and drive plate assy. Evacuate and charge system.
1984-87 (1.8) 2.7

(G) Compressor Clutch Coil and/or Pulley Rim Assy., Renew
Includes: Evacuate and charge system.
1984-87 (1.9) 3.0
Renew pulley or brg add 1

AIR CONDITIONER TUNE-UP

For efficient operation and satisfactory performance in hot weather. The following air conditioner tune-up is suggested:

1. Clean intake filter
2. Clean condenser fins
3. Pressure test system
4. Adjust drive belt tension
5. Check antifreeze/coolant
6. Tighten compressor mounts
7. Tighten condenser and evaporator mounts
8. Inspect system for leaks (hoses, couplings, valves, etc.)
9. Partial charge system

All models 1.0
If necessary to evacuate and charge system, add 1.0

(Factory Time) Chilton Time

(G) Compressor Front Seal, Seat and 'O' Ring, Renew
Includes: R&R clutch hub and drive plate assy. Evacuate and charge system.
1984-87 (2.0) 3.0

(G) Compressor Front Head and/or Seal, Renew
Includes: R&R compressor. R&R clutch and pulley assy. R&R shaft seal assy. Clean and inspect parts. Evacuate and charge system.
1984-87 (2.1) 3.2

(G) Compressor Cylinder and Shaft Assy., Renew
Includes: R&R compressor. Transfer all parts as required. Evacuate and charge system.
1984-87 (2.3) 3.4

(Factory Time) Chilton Time

(G) High Pressure Cut-Off Switch, Renew
1984-87 (.3) 4

(G) Electric Actuators, Renew
1984-87
air inlet (recirculation) (.6) 1.0
upper or lower mode (.6) 1.0

(G) Condenser Assembly, Renew
Includes: Evacuate and charge system.
1984-87 (.9) 2.0

(G) Expansion Tube (Orifice), Renew
Includes: Evacuate and charge system.
1984-87 (.9) 1.5

(G) Accumulator Assembly, Renew
Includes: Evacuate and charge system.
1984-87 (.7) 1.4

(G) Evaporator Core, Renew
Includes: Evacuate and charge system.
1984-87 (1.2) 2.5

(G) Pressure Cycling Switch, Renew
1984-87 (.2) 4

(G) Blower Motor Switch, Renew
1984-87 (.3) 5

(G) Temperature Control Assy., Renew
1984-87 (.3) 6

(G) Blower Motor Resistor, Renew
1984-87 (.2) 3

(G) Blower Motor, Renew
1984-87 (.2) 4

(G) Air Conditioning Hoses, Renew
Includes: Evacuate and charge system.
1984-87
suction (.8) 1.7
discharge (.8) 1.7
cond inlet (1.3) 2.0
liquid line (.7) 1.7
suction & discharge assy. (.9) 1.7

PARTS 28 AIR CONDITIONING 28 PARTS

	Part No.	Price
Compressor Assy.		
1984-87		
4.9″ pulley	12321361	N.L.
5.7″ pulley	12322333	N.L.
Clutch Hub & Drive Plate		
1984 (OEM 1131413)	6551717	38.25
(OEM 1131469)	6551920	40.00
1985-87	6551996	41.00
Compressor Pulley		
1984-87	6551713	79.75
Clutch Coil (w/Housing)		
1984	6551834	41.50
1985-87	6551997	47.25
Shaft Seal Kit		
1984-87 (OEM 1131413)	2724280	17.00
(OEM 1131469)	2724319	11.25
Front Head		
1984-87 (OEM 1131413)	6557376	40.00
(OEM 1131469)	6557775	44.25
Cylinder & Shaft		
1984-87 (OEM 1131413)	6551701	281.50
(OEM 1131469)	6551952	307.75
Valve Plate		
1984-87-front	6551700	25.00
rear	6551702	25.00
Condenser		
1984-87	3050988	165.50
Blower Motor Resistor		
1984	10030701	3.50
1985-87	10039031	3.50
Blower Motor Switch		
1984-87	16023827	7.00
Evaporator Core		
1984-87	3054185	359.50
Blower Motor		
1984-87	22020947	55.50
Accumulator Dehydrator		
1984	2724312	86.00
1985-87	3059313	85.25
Expansion Tube Assy. (Orifice)		
1984-87	3033879	9.50
Pressure Cut-Off Switch		
1984-87	3041596	19.00

LABOR 29 LOCKS, HINGES & WIND. REGULATORS 29 LABOR

(Factory Time) Chilton Time

(G) Hood Latch Assembly, Renew
1984-87 (.2) 4

(G) Hood Release Cable, Renew
1984-87 (.4) 6

(G) Hood Hinge, Renew
1984-87-one (.2) 3
both (.3) 5

(G) Front Door Lock Assy., Renew
1984-87 (.5) 8

(G) Front Door Lock Cylinder, Renew
1984-87 (.5) 8
Recode cyl add (.3) 3

(G) Front Door Lock Remote Control, Renew
1984-87 (.2) 5

(G) Lock Striker Plate, Renew
1984-87 (.2) 3

(G) Front Door Handle (Outside), Renew
1984-87 (.5) 8

(G) Front Door Window Regulator, Renew
1984-87-manual (.8) 1.2
electric (.8) 1.4

(G) Rear Compartment Lid Torque Rod, Renew
1984-87 (.6) 8

(G) Rear Compartment Lid Lock, Renew
1984-87 (.2) 3

(G) Rear Compartment Lid Hinge, Renew
1984-87-one (.4) 6
both (.8) 1.2

(G) Rear Compartment Lid Lock Cylinder, R&R or Renew
1984-87 (.2) 3
Recode cyl add (.3) 3

PARTS 29 LOCKS, HINGES & WIND. REGULATORS 29 PARTS

	Part No.	Price
Hood Lock		
1984-87	20369893	49.75
Hood Hinge		
1984-87-right	20594604	6.00
left	20301249	6.00
Hood Striker		
1984-87	20484234	5.75
Front Door Lock		
1984-87-right	20488070	34.00
left	20488071	34.00
Door Lock Cylinder		
1984-87	20498261	5.75
Door Handle (Outside)		
1984-87-right	20364124	34.25
left	20364125	34.25
Window Regulator (Manual)		
1984-87-right	20302330	59.75
left	20302331	59.75
Window Regulator (Power)		
1984-87-right	20311752	80.00
left	20311753	80.00
Window Regulator Motor		
1984-87	22029848	72.50
Trunk Lock		
1984-87	20166276	13.75
Trunk Lock Cylinder		
1984-87	20496710	3.75
Trunk Lid Hinge		
1984-87-right	20484240	42.50
left	20484241	42.50

LABOR 30 HEAD AND PARKING LAMPS 30 LABOR

(Factory Time) Chilton Time

(G) Aim Headlamps
two 4
four 6

(M) Headlamp Sealed Beam Bulb, Renew
1984-87 (.2) 3

(M) Back-Up Lamp Assy., Renew
1984-87 (.2) 3

(M) License Lamp Assembly, Renew
1984-87 (.2) 3

(M) Park and Turn Signal Lamp Assy., Renew
1984-87 (.2) 3

(M) Side Marker Lamp Assy., Renew
1984-87 (.2) 3

(M) Stop, Tail and Turn Signal Lamp Assy., Renew
1984-87 (.2) 3

PARTS 30 HEAD AND PARKING LAMPS 30 PARTS

	Part No.	Price
Headlamps Seal Beam		
1984-87	5972698	46.50
Side Marker Lamp (Front)		
1984-87-right	920058	11.50
left	920057	11.50
Side Marker Lamps (Rear)		
1984-87-right	920060	11.50
left	920059	11.50
Parking & Turn Signal Lamp Assy.		
1984-87-right	917328	15.00
left	917327	15.00
Tail Lamp Housing		
1984-87-right	16500454	73.25
left	16500453	73.25
Tail Lamp Lens		
1985-87-outer		
left	16500461	57.25
right	16500462	57.25
1985-87-inner		
left	16500457	29.75
inner	16500458	29.75
1986-87-PG		
left	16504929	90.75
right	16504930	90.75
High Mount Stoplight		
1986-87	918421	35.50
License Plate Lamp Assy.		
1984-87	912116	6.50

LABOR 31 WINDSHIELD WIPER & SPEEDOMETER 31 LABOR

(Factory Time) Chilton Time

(G) Windshield Wiper Motor, Renew
1984-87 (.5) 7

(G) Windshield Wiper Motor, R&R and Recondition
1984-87 (1.0) 1.4

(G) Windshield Wiper Switch, Renew
1984-87 (1.0) 1.4

PARTS 31 WINDSHIELD WIPER & SPEEDOMETER 31 PARTS

	(Factory Time)	Chilton Time
(G) Wiper Transmission, Renew (One)		
1984-87	(.6)	1.0
(G) Windshield Washer Pump, Renew		
1984-87	(.2)	.3
(G) Windshield Washer Pump Valve, Renew		
1984-87	(.2)	.3
(G) Pulse Wiper Control Module, Renew		
1984-87	(.3)	.4
(G) Intermittent Wiper Controller, Renew		
1984	(.3)	.4
(G) Speedometer Head, R&R or Renew		
1984-87	(.4)	.7
(G) Speedometer Signal Generator, Renew		
1984-87	(.6)	1.0
(G) Odometer and/or Motor, Renew		
1984-87	(.6)	1.0
(G) Speedometer Driven Gear, Renew		
1984-87	(.3)	.4
(G) Radio, R&R		
1984-87	(.3)	.6

PARTS 31 WINDSHIELD WIPER & SPEEDOMETER 31 PARTS

	Part No.	Price
Windshield Wiper Motor		
1984	22030809	105.00
1985-87-Pulse	22049813	132.75
wo/Pulse	22030809	105.00
1986-87-PM wo/ Pulse	22062915	106.75
Windshield Wiper Transmission		
1984-87-right	22039336	20.75
left	22039337	20.75
Windshield Wiper Switch		
1984-87 (wo/Pulse wiper)		
wo/Tilt whl.	7841050	44.75
Tilt whl.	7841051	46.75
1984-87 (Pulse wiper)		
wo/Tilt whl.	7841052	56.00
Tilt whl.	7841053	56.00
Windshield Washer Pump		
1984-87	22039339	17.00
Speedometer Head Assy.		
1984-exc. below	25054495	268.25
w/cruise cont.	25048173	368.00
1985-87-151	25054495	268.25
V-6	25078487	326.50

LABOR 32 LIGHT SWITCHES & WIRING 32 LABOR

	(Factory Time)	Chilton Time
(G) Headlamp Actuator Switch, Renew		
1985-87	(.2)	.4
(G) Headlamp Switch, Renew		
1984-87	(.3)	.4
(G) Headlamp Dimmer Switch, Renew		
1984	(.5)	.7
1985-87	(.2)	.4
(G) Stop Light Switch, Renew		
1984-87	(.2)	.3
(G) Turn Signal and Hazard Warning Switch, Renew		
1984-87	(.7)	1.1
(G) Back-Up Lamp and Park/Neutral Switch, Renew		
1984-87	(.3)	.5
(G) Parking Brake Lamp Switch, Renew		
1984-87	(.3)	.4
(M) Turn Signal or Hazard Warning Flasher, Renew		
1984-87	(.2)	.2
(G) Horn Relay, Renew		
1984-87	(.2)	.3
(G) Horn, Renew		
1984-87	(.3)	.4
each adtnl		.1

PARTS 32 LIGHT SWITCHES & WIRING 32 PARTS

	Part No.	Price
Head Lamp Switch		
1984	1972717	17.00
1985-87	1995294	13.50
Head Lamp Dimmer Switch		
1984-87	7832411	18.50
Stop Light Switch		
1984-wo/Cruise cont.		
M.T.	1362835	3.00
A.T.	25504628	3.75
1984-Cruise cont.	9794682	7.75
1985-87-wo/Cruise cont.		
M.T.	25524844	3.00
A.T.	25524846	6.50
1985-87-Cruise cont.	25524847	6.50
Turn Signal Switch		
1984-87	1997983	30.00
Turn Signal Flasher		
1984-87	10029240	4.25
Hazard Warning Flasher		
1984-87	6450089	3.00
Back-Up Lamp Switch		
(M.T.)		
1984	14009262	2.00
1985-MT2	10035929	13.25
M17	14009262	2.00
1986-87	10035929	13.25
(A.T.)		
1984-87	1994255	11.75
Horn Assy.		
1984-87		
"A" note	10024319	13.75
"F" note	10034318	N.L.
Horn Relay		
1984-87	25513270	8.50

LABOR 33 GLASS 33 LABOR

	Part No.	Price
(G) Windshield Glass, Renew		
1984-87 (.8)		**1.2**
Renew caulk bead add (.4)		**.4**
(G) Front Door Glass, Renew		
1984-87 (.5)		**.9**
(G) Back Window Glass, Renew		
1984-87 (2.9)		**4.0**
w/Elec grid defogger add (.1)		**.1**

LABOR 34 CRUISE CONTROL 34 LABOR

(Factory Time)	Chilton Time
(G) Cruise Control Servo Assy., Renew	
1984-87 (.3)	**.4**
(G) Cruise Control Chain or Cable, Renew	
1984-87 (.3)	**.4**
(G) Brake or Clutch Release Switch, Renew	
1984-87 (.2)	**.3**
(G) Engagement Switch, Renew	
1984-87 (.2)	**.4**
(G) Cruise Control Vacuum Hoses, Renew	
1984-87 (.2)	**.3**
(G) Cruise Control Module, Renew	
1986-87 (.3)	**.5**
(G) Cruise Control Check Valve, Renew	
1985-87 (.3)	**.4**

PARTS 34 CRUISE CONTROL 34 PARTS

	Part No.	Price
Cruise Control Servo		
1984	25074627	117.00
1985-87	25074627	117.00
Vacuum Release Switch		
1984-87	10024217	4.25
Cruise Control Servo Cable		
1984	10035893	11.25
1985-87-151	10035748	10.50
V-6	10042227	10.00
Cruise Control (Lever & Switch)		
1984-87-exc.		
Pulse	15031481	N.L.
Pulse wiper	25031480	50.00

Code following part numbers indicate interchangeability of this part with other Chrysler Corporation cars.
C—Chrysler I—Imperial D—Dodge P—Plymouth

153199	C I D P
153200	C I D P
153201	C I D P
153440	C I D P
153481	C I D P
153590	C I D P
153775	C D P
153784	C D P
432344	C D
1327319	C I D P
1632526	C I D P
1637657	C I D P
1671465	C I D P
1673324	D P
1733625	I D P
1733790	I D P
1739534	C I D P
1790541	C I D P
1822150	I D P
1822156	C I D P
1822157	I D P
1822158	C I D P
1822380	C I D P
1822390	C I D P
1822406	I D P
1823151	I D P
1856292	C I D P
1937770	C I D P
1937771	C I D P
1947225	I D P
1947554	C I D P
1947623	C I D P
2070316	C I D P
2070317	C I D P
2070318	C I D P
2070319	C I D P
2084384	C I D P
2084653	I D P
2098478	C I D P
2120764	I D P
2121727	C I D P
2128912	C I D P
2129012	C I D P
2203353	D P
2258404	C D P
2258413	C D P
2269127	I D P
2298534	C I D P
2402473	D P
2421305	C I D P
2427237	C I D P
2448294	C I D P
2448295	C I D P
2463385	C I D P
2465335	C I D P
2468849	C I D P
2532149	C I D P
2537796	C I D P
2537820	C I D P
2537823	C D P
2537828	C D P
2537833	C I D P
2537838	C I D P
2537899	C D P
2658878	I D P
2780999	C I D P
2800484	C I D P
2800485	C I D P
2806270	C I D P
2806945	C I D P
2808550	C I D P
2808553	C I D P
2808868	C I D P
2808869	C I D P
2843208	I D P
2843610	C I D P
2881041	C I D P
2881423	C I D P
2891460	C I D P
2891695	C D P
2891741	D P
2899556	C I D P
2926275	C I D P
2931875	C I D P
2932814	C I D P
2932877	C I D P
2948855	C I D P
3079736	D P
3402540	I D P
3402640	C I D P
3402641	C I D P
3420154	C I D P
3420155	C I D P
3420973	C I D P
3432435	C I D P
3438159	I D P
3438721	C I D P
3438729	D P
3488432	C I D P
3507575	C I D P
3507876	C I D P
3514151	C I D P
3514182	C I D P
3514187	C I D P
3514866	C I D P
3548955	C I D P
3549957	C I D P
3577586	C I D P
3580723	C I D P
3580824	I D P
3580888	C D P
3620790	C I D P
3620793	C I D P
3621939	C I D P
3642818	C I D P
3642821	C I D P
3643129	C I D P
3643173	C I D P
3643280	C I D P
3643301	I D P
3643302	C I D P
3643315	C I D P
3643317	I D P
3643321	I D P
3643360	C D P
3643423	C D P
3643424	C D P
3643425	C D P
3643453	C D P
3643469	C D P
3643470	C D P
3643471	C D P
3643989	C I D P
3656017	C I D P
3656444	C I D P
3656862	C I D P
3671076	C I D P
3683801	C I D P
3683947	C I D P
3683974	D P
3683975	C I D P
3685751	C I D P
3722614	I D P
3723020	C I D P
3723251	C I D P
3723569	C I D P
3723620	C I D P
3723672	C I D P
3723967	C I D P
3723982	C I D P
3744495	C I D P
3744889	D P
3744933	D P
3746813	C I D P
3747298	C I D P
3747529	C I D P
3747653	C I D P
3747654	C I D
3747881	C D P
3747882	C D P
3747895	C D P
3747914	C D P
3747993	C D P
3747995	C D P
3751015	C I D P
3751741	C I D P
3751831	C I D P
3755114	C I D P
3755184	C I D P
3755261	I D P
3755474	C I D P
3755627	C I D P
3755711	I D P
3755727	I D P
3755773	I D P
3755951	C I D P
3766292	C I D P
3766435	C D P
3766448	C I D P
3766498	C D P
3769261	C I D P
3780075	C I D P
3780250	C I D P
3780515	C I D P
3780525	C I D P
3780537	C I D P
3799087	C D P
3799090	C D P
3799324	C D P
3799462	C I D P
3799479	C I D P
3799595	C D P
3799597	C D P
3799600	C D P
3799684	C D P
3799713	C D P
3799791	D P
3799795	C D P
3799814	D P
3799837	D P
3799858	C D P
3815207	I D P
3815210	I D P
3815669	I D P
3815688	C I D P
3815704	I D P
3815712	C I D P
3815713	C I D P
3815727	C I D P
3815777	C I D P
3815811	C D P
3815816	C D P
3815839	D P
3815840	C D
3815841	D P
3815854	C I D
3815861	C D P
3815862	C D P
3815865	C D P
3815866	C D P
3815868	C D P
3815870	C D P
3815871	C D P
3815872	C D P
3815873	C D P
3815874	C D P
3815875	C D P
3815876	C D P
3815878	C D P
3815879	C D P
3815880	C D P
3815881	C D P
3815882	C D P
3815883	C D P
3815884	C D P
3815914	C I D P
3815947	C D P
3815956	C D P
3815961	C I D P
3815962	C I D P

Chrysler Corporation Part Number Interchange

Code following part numbers indicate interchangeability of this part with other Chrysler Corporation cars.
C—Chrysler   I—Imperial   D—Dodge   P—Plymouth

3815964	C D P	3848217	C D P	3880072	C I D P	4026048	C I D P
3815965	C D P	3848236	C D P	3880074	C I D P	4026082	C D P
3815966	C I D P	3848307	C D P	3880075	C I D P	4026083	C D P
3815967	C I D P	3848374	C I D P	3880277	C D P	4026303	C I D P
3815971	C I D P	3848455	C I D P	3880289	C I D P	4026648	C I D P
3815980	D P	3848460	C D P	3880348	C I D P	4026825	C I D P
3815982	D P	3848530	C D P	3880349	D P	4027798	C I D P
3815983	C D P	3848563	C D	3880408	C D P	4041733	C I D P
3815987	D P	3848564	C D	3880409	C D P	4041737	C I D P
3815991	C I D P	3848645	D P	3880410	C D	4041966	C I D P
3817237	C I D P	3848654	D P	3880426	C D P	4041994	C I D P
3817295	C I D P	3848673	C I D P	3880427	D P	4047534	C I D
3830108	C I D P	3848674	C I D P	3880483	D P	4047537	C I D
3830109	C I D P	3848689	C D P	3880685	C I D P	4047724	I D P
3830603	C I D P	3848789	C D	3882274	C I D P	4049198	I D P
3837087	C I D P	3848807	C D P	3882275	C I D P	4049208	C I D P
3837161	C I D P	3848840	C D P	3882290	C I D P	4049242	C I D P
3837162	C I D P	3848854	D P	3882291	C I D P	4049249	C I D P
3837334	C I D P	3848859	C D	3882350	C I D P	4049256	C I D P
3837337	C I D P	3848969	C I D P	3882351	C I D P	4049264	C I D P
3837340	I D P	3848981	C I D P	3882621	I D P	4049265	C I D P
3837579	C I D P	3848982	C D P	3882648	C I D	4049276	C I D P
3837580	C I D P	3848983	C D P	3882649	C I D	4049277	C I D P
3837581	C I D P	3848995	D P	3882742	C I D	4049287	C I D P
3837582	C I D	3848996	C I D P	3882743	C I D	4049338	C I D P
3837605	C I D P	3848999	D P	3882800	C I D P	4049661	C I D P
3837622	C I D P	3849032	C D P	3882801	I D P	4049682	C I D P
3837641	C I D P	3849075	C D P	3882805	C I D	4049699	C I D P
3837644	C I D P	3849139	C D P	3882808	I D P	4049797	C I D P
3837648	C I D P	3849140	C D P	3882809	I D P	4051140	I D P
3838078	C I D P	3849142	C D	4001801	C I D P	4051141	I D P
3838079	C I D P	3849150	C D	4001861	C I D	4051348	C I D P
3846845	C I D P	3849160	C D P	4012595	I D P	4051388	C I D P
3846895	I D P	3849199	C D P	4014004	C I D P	4051389	C I D P
3846898	I D P	3849235	C D P	4014005	C I D P	4051398	C I D P
3847178	C I D P	3849240	C D P	4014033	I D P	4051399	C I D
3847179	C I D P	3849266	C D P	4014050	I D P	4051415	C I D
3847256	C I D P	3849335	C D P	4014085	C I D P	4051454	D P
3847291	C I D P	3861819	C I D P	4014089	C I D P	4051455	D P
3847296	C I D P	3870088	C I D P	4014100	C I D P	4051479	C D P
3847435	C I D P	3871274	C I D	4014126	I D P	4051480	C D P
3847475	C I D	3871275	C I D	4014142	C I D P	4051541	C D P
3847512	D P	3874074	C I D P	4014143	C I D P	4051542	C D P
3847576	C I D P	3874345	C I D P	4014239	C D P	4051565	C D P
3847589	C I D P	3874401	C I D P	4014323	C D P	4051583	C I D
3847600	C I D P	3874817	C I D P	4014325	D P	4051602	D P
3847742	C I D P	3874818	C I D P	4014330	C D P	4051614	D P
3847764	C D P	3874878	C I D P	4014362	C D P	4051640	C D
3847766	C I D P	3874995	I D P	4014368	C I D P	4051663	C D P
3847789	C I D P	3879281	C I D	4014369	C I D P	4051674	C I D
3847830	C I D P	3879401	C I D P	4014418	C D P	4051682	C D P
3847910	C I D P	3879707	C D P	4014432	C D	4051684	C D P
3847916	C D P	3879736	C I D P	4014433	C D	4051687	C D P
3847940	C I D P	3879919	I D P	4014436	C D P	4051720	D P
3847943	C D P	3879920	I D P	4014441	C D P	4051734	D P
3847997	C I D	3879921	C I D P	4014469	C D P	4051737	D P
3848015	C D P	3879924	C I D P	4019369	C I D P	4051744	D P
3848114	D P	3879925	C D P	4019750	C D P	4051745	D P
3848136	D P	3879932	C I D P	4019851	C I D	4051772	C D P
3848195	C D P	3880038	C I D P	4026046	C I D P	4051786	C D P

Code following part numbers indicate interchangeability of this part with other Chrysler Corporation cars.
C—Chrysler I—Imperial D—Dodge P—Plymouth

4051793	C D P
4051804	D P
4051805	D P
4051831	C D P
4051833	D P
4051849	C D P
4051866	C D
4051867	C I D P
4051869	C D P
4051882	D P
4051885	D P
4051895	C D P
4052125	I D P
4052509	C D P
4052522	C D P
4052541	C D P
4052544	C D P
4052545	C D
4052549	C D
4052580	C D P
4052581	C D P
4052583	C D P
4052613	C D P
4052634	C D P
4052635	C D P
4052646	C D P
4052647	D P
4052671	C D P
4052672	C D P
4052680	D P
4052684	C D P
4052819	C D P
4052822	C D P
4052824	C D P
4052825	C D P
4052838	C D P
4052839	C D P
4052844	D P
4052845	D P
4052850	C D P
4052861	C D P
4052862	C D P
4052931	D P
4052996	D P
4054081	C D
4054805	C I D P
4054825	C I D P
4054962	C I D P
4057085	I D P
4057094	C I D P
4057750	C I D P
4057928	C I D P
4057933	D P
4057940	C I D P
4057981	D P
4057983	D P
4071006	C I D P
4075445	C D P
4076566	I D P
4076567	I D P
4076570	I D P
4076571	I D P
4076688	I D P
4076689	I D P
4076704	C I D
4076705	C I D
4076714	C I D
4076715	C I D
4076808	C I D
4076812	I D P
4076850	C I D
4076892	C I D
4076893	C I D
4076988	C I D
4076989	C I D
4091142	C I D P
4091147	C I D P
4091383	C I D
4091398	D P
4091460	C I D P
4091471	C I D P
4091515	C I D P
4091517	C I D P
4091533	I D P
4091534	I D P
4091565	C I D P
4091667	I D P
4091719	C D P
4091914	C I D P
4091994	I D P
4094060	C I D P
4094070	I D P
4094071	I D P
4094810	D P
4094818	D P
4094827	D P
4094874	D P
4095071	C I D P
4095088	C I D P
4095107	C I D
4095227	I D P
4095231	C I D P
4095260	I D P
4095291	C I D P
4095330	C I D P
4095337	C I D P
4095338	C I D P
4095527	C I D P
4095708	C I D P
4095709	C I D P
4095776	C I D P
4095784	C I D P
4095984	C I D P
4100387	C I D P
4100397	C I D P
4100405	C I D P
4100632	C I D P
4100646	C I D P
4100696	C I D P
4100754	C I D P
4100755	C I D P
4100756	C I D P
4100774	C I D P
4100775	C I D P
4103194	C D P
4103216	D P
4103217	D P
4103428	C I D P
4103429	I D P
4103760	C D P
4103761	C D P
4103904	C I D
4104330	C I D P
4104331	C I D P
4105275	C I D P
4105293	C D P
4105395	C D P
4105399	C D P
4105409	C D P
4105421	D P
4105436	D P
4105442	C D P
4105443	C D P
4105461	C D P
4105465	C D P
4105468	C D P
4105475	C D P
4105486	C D P
4105498	C D P
4105714	C D P
4105715	C D P
4105716	C D P
4105719	C D P
4105745	C D P
4105755	C D P
4105768	C D P
4105783	C D P
4105793	C D P
4105794	C D P
4105800	C D P
4105979	C I D P
4105987	C I D P
4105989	C I D P
4106009	C I D P
4106028	C I D P
4106048	C I D P
4106092	C I D P
4106140	C D P
4106161	I D P
4106180	C D P
4106195	C I D P
4111179	I D P
4111180	I D P
4111481	C I D P
4111482	C I D P
4111630	C I D P
4111640	C I D P
4111747	C I D
4111850	C I D P
4111935	I D P
4111959	I D P
4111971	C I D P
4111990	C I D P
4126502	C I D P
4126737	C D P
4126842	C I D P
4126843	C I D P
4126886	C I D
4126947	C D P
4129638	C I D
4129804	I D P
4129805	I D P
4131062	D P
4131116	C D P
4131121	C D P
4131141	C I D P
4131147	D P
4131166	D P
4131202	D P
4131203	C I D P
4131240	C I D P
4131243	C I D P
4131251	C I D P
4131348	C D P
4131349	C D P
4131367	C I D P
4131373	C I D P
4131522	I D P
4131525	C I D P
4132000	D P
4134518	C I D P
4134519	I D P
4137013	C I D P
4137051	C I D P
4137426	C I D P
4137452	C I D P
4137621	C I D P
4137623	C I D P
4140380	C I D P
4140381	C I D P
4140382	C I D P
4140383	C I D P
4140394	C I D P
4140547	D P
4140569	C D P
4140574	C D P
4140576	C D P
4145049	C I D
4145061	C I D
4145070	C I D
4145202	C I D P
4145210	C I D
4145239	C I D P
4145348	D P
4145360	C I D P
4145613	C I D
4145716	C D P
4145752	C I D P
4145754	C I D P
4145955	C I D P

Chrysler Corporation Part Number Interchange

Code following part numbers indicate interchangeability of this part with other Chrysler Corporation cars.

C—Chrysler I—Imperial D—Dodge P—Plymouth

4145978	C I D P
4147000	D P
4147009	C D P
4147079	D P
4147080	C D P
4147081	C D P
4147082	D P
4147083	C D P
4147085	C D P
4147086	D P
4147087	C D P
4147088	D P
4147089	C D P
4147090	C D P
4147091	C D P
4147092	C D P
4147093	C D P
4147094	D P
4147095	C D P
4147096	C D P
4147098	C D P
4147133	D P
4147136	C D P
4147139	C D P
4147140	C D P
4147224	D P
4147225	D P
4147228	D P
4147230	D P
4147231	C D P
4147280	C D P
4147289	D P
4147303	C D P
4147306	C D P
4147307	C D P
4147353	C D P
4147356	C D P
4147415	C D P
4147420	C D P
4147421	C D P
4147451	C D P
4147472	C D P
4147708	C D P
4147747	C D P
4147752	C D P
4147759	C D P
4147813	C D P
4147814	C D P
4147816	C D P
4147817	C D P
4147848	C D P
4147849	C D P
4147852	C D P
4147857	C D P
4147903	C D P
4147904	C D P
4147912	D P
4147951	C D P
4150170	C I D P
4150186	C I D P
4150280	I D P
4150324	C I D P
4150330	C I D P
4150342	C I D P
4150425	I D P
4150438	D P
4150439	D P
4150462	C I D
4150524	C I D P
4150553	C I D
4150624	D P
4150625	D P
4150715	C I D P
4150718	C I D P
4150722	C I D
4150744	C I D P
4150772	C D
4150783	C D P
4150784	C D P
4150792	D P
4150793	D P
4150796	C D P
4150809	C D
4150823	D P
4150833	D P
4150847	C D P
4150965	D P
4150989	D P
4167046	C I D P
4172305	C I D
4172348	C I D
4172663	C I D
4172826	C I D
4173390	C D P
4173433	D P
4173443	C I D P
4173482	C I D P
4173703	D P
4173739	D P
4173751	D P
4173752	D P
4173753	D P
4173754	D P
4173755	D P
4173756	D P
4173757	D P
4173758	D P
4173775	D P
4173909	C I D P
4174002	C D P
4174003	C D P
4174008	C I D
4174009	C I D P
4174042	C I D
4174046	C D P
4174047	C D P
4174070	C I D
4174071	C I D
4174080	C D P
4174081	C D P
4174096	C D P
4174097	C D P
4174118	C D P
4174119	C D P
4174200	C D P
4174201	C D P
4174206	C D
4174207	C D
4174214	C D P
4174215	C D P
4174224	C D P
4174311	C D P
4174364	C I D
4174365	C I D
4174422	C D P
4174423	C D P
4174500	C D
4174501	C D
4174502	C D
4174503	C D
4174510	D P
4174511	D P
4174560	D P
4174744	C D P
4174745	C D P
4174762	C D
4174763	C D
4174768	C D
4174769	C D
4174790	C D P
4174791	C D P
4174796	C D P
4174797	C D P
4174804	C D P
4174805	C D P
4174808	C D P
4174809	C D P
4174814	D P
4174815	D P
4174832	C D
4174833	C D
4174837	D P
4174842	D P
4174843	D P
4176004	C I D P
4176006	C I D P
4176007	C I D P
4176009	C I D P
4176059	C I D P
4176560	C D P
4176754	C I D P
4176778	C I D P
4176794	C I D P
4176999	C I D P
4179128	C I D P
4179130	C I D
4179177	C I D P
4179306	C D P
4179719	C I D P
4179776	C I D P
4179777	C I D P
4179778	C I D P
4179848	C D P
4179849	C D P
4179893	C I D P
4184018	C D P
4184019	C D P
4184060	C D P
4184061	C D P
4184156	C D P
4184228	C D P
4184316	C D P
4184317	C D P
4184548	C D P
4184549	C D P
4184566	C D P
4184567	C D P
4184616	C D P
4184617	C D P
4184620	C D P
4184623	C D P
4184624	C D P
4184625	C D P
4184710	C I D P
4184711	C I D P
4184747	D P
4184748	D P
4184750	D P
4184753	D P
4184776	D P
4184777	D P
4185414	D P
4186118	C I D P
4186175	C I D P
4186180	C I D P
4186182	C I D P
4186183	C I D P
4186194	C I D P
4186209	D P
4186220	D P
4186268	D P
4186275	D P
4186331	D P
4186348	C I D P
4186352	C I D
4186867	D P
4186868	D P
4186956	C I D
4186957	C I D P
4186969	C I D P
4186989	C I D P
4186990	C I D P
4188672	D P
4188832	C D P
4188856	D P
4191891	C D P
4191970	C D P
4191988	C D P
4196430	C I D P
4201200	C I D P

Code following part numbers indicate interchangeability of this part with other Chrysler Corporation cars.

C—Chrysler I—Imperial D—Dodge P—Plymouth

4201385	D P
4201459	C D P
4201464	C D P
4201755	D P
4201761	D P
4201974	C D P
4201991	D P
4201992	C D P
4202378	C D P
4202927	D P
4203540	D P
4203652	D P
4203774	D P
4205830	D P
4205838	C D P
4205845	D P
4205864	D P
4205865	D P
4205888	C I D P
4205921	C I D
4205951	C I D P
4205982	C D P
4205984	C D P
4205985	C D P
4205995	C D P
4210760	D P
4213582	D P
4213597	D P
4220107	D P
4220740	D P
4220741	D P
4220742	C D P
4220744	C D
4220745	C D P
4220748	C D P
4220892	D P
4221042	C I D P
4221051	C I D
4221071	C D P
4221080	C D P
4221125	C D P
4221135	D P
4221180	D P
4221198	C D P
4221200	C D P
4221201	C D P
4221205	C I D P
4221206	C I D P
4221218	D P
4221223	C I D P
4221231	C D
4221232	C D P
4221233	C D P
4221248	C I D P
4221279	C D P
4221282	D P
4221303	C D P
4221304	C I D P
4221305	C I D P
4221309	D P
4221337	C I D P
4221338	C I D P
4221339	D P
4221396	C D P
4221405	C D P
4221407	C D P
4221415	D P
4221416	D P
4221438	C I D P
4221455	C D P
4221456	D P
4221462	C D P
4221482	C D P
4221485	C I D P
4221486	C I D P
4221497	D P
4221498	I D P
4221500	C I D P
4221542	D P
4221549	D P
4221576	D P
4221587	C D P
4221615	D P
4221651	C D P
4221670	C D P
4221677	C D P
4221680	C D P
4221681	C I D P
4221682	C I D
4221696	D P
4221697	C D P
4221779	D P
4221780	D P
4221899	C D P
4221902	C D P
4221949	D P
4221954	D P
4221955	D P
4221956	D P
4221976	C D P
4221980	D P
4222060	C I D P
4222288	C D P
4222447	C I D
4227251	C I D P
4227337	I D P
4227361	D P
4227362	D P
4227365	C D P
4227368	D P
4227369	D P
4227370	D P
4227371	D P
4227372	C D P
4227374	C D P
4227375	C D P
4227377	D P
4227378	D P
4227379	D P
4227382	C D P
4227383	C D P
4227384	C D P
4227385	C D P
4227386	D P
4227387	D P
4227388	D P
4227389	D P
4227390	D P
4227391	D P
4227670	C I D P
4227672	C I D P
4227879	C I D P
4227880	C I D P
4227894	C I D P
4227948	C I D P
4227973	C D P
4228083	D P
4228096	C D P
4228098	D P
4228099	D P
4228117	C D P
4228123	C D P
4228159	C D P
4228251	C D P
4228256	C D P
4228260	C D P
4228261	C D P
4228310	D P
4228312	C D P
4228313	C D P
4228324	D P
4228330	D P
4228333	D P
4228334	D P
4228335	C D P
4228336	C D P
4228337	D P
4228377	C D P
4228396	D P
4228401	D P
4228410	C I D P
4228411	C I D P
4228413	C I D P
4228414	C I D P
4228440	C D P
4228450	D P
4228452	D P
4228453	D P
4228454	C D P
4228455	C D P
4228501	C D P
4228502	D P
4228503	C D P
4228504	C D P
4228505	D P
4228516	D P
4228530	C D P
4228536	C D P
4228537	C D P
4228538	C D P
4228539	C D P
4228540	C D P
4228541	C D P
4228562	D P
4228563	D P
4228671	C D P
4228672	C D P
4228673	C D P
4228675	C D P
4238531	C D P
4238538	C D P
4238551	C D P
4238567	C D P
4238570	C D P
4238588	C D P
4238676	D P
4238677	D P
4238683	C D P
4238692	D P
4238693	D P
4238697	D P
4238698	C D P
4238701	C D P
4238706	C D P
4238710	C D P
4238711	C D P
4238712	C D P
4238786	C D P
4238788	C D P
4238826	C D P
4238827	C D P
4240007	C D P
4240008	C D P
4240013	C D P
4240019	C D P
4240025	C D P
4240044	C I D P
4240049	D P
4240062	C I D P
4240083	C I D P
4240098	C D P
4240102	C D P
4240137	C D P
4240141	D P
4240147	C I D
4240149	C I D
4240150	C I D P
4240153	C I D P
4240199	C D P
4240405	C D P
4240413	C I D P
4240414	C I D P
4240415	C I D
4240416	C I D
4240417	C D P
4240422	C D P
4240425	C I D P
4240426	C D P
4240432	D P
4240433	I D P

Chrysler Corporation Part Number Interchange

Code following part numbers indicate interchangeability of this part with other Chrysler Corporation cars.

C—Chrysler I—Imperial D—Dodge P—Plymouth

4240435	C D P
4240446	C D P
4240448	D P
4240470	C D P
4240471	C D P
4240472	C D P
4240484	C D P
4240488	C I D P
4240492	D P
4240493	C D P
4240494	C D P
4240495	C D
4240508	C I D P
4240509	C I D P
4240511	C D P
4240512	C D P
4240519	C I D P
4240520	C I D P
4240528	C I D
4240629	D P
4240746	C D
4240747	C D
4241150	D P
4241249	C I D P
4241438	C I D P
4241551	C I D P
4241575	D P
4241645	C I D P
4241773	C D P
4241774	C D P
4241831	C D P
4241836	C D P
4241837	C D P
4241838	C I D P
4241839	C I D
4241841	I D P
4241842	C I D
4241995	C I D P
4246296	D P
4246299	C D
4246328	D P
4246360	C D P
4246500	D P
4246517	D P
4246563	C D
4246564	C D
4246596	C D P
4246597	C D P
4246610	C D
4246611	C D
4246627	C D
4246628	C D
4246630	D P
4246646	D P
4246675	D P
4246701	D P
4246774	D P
4246775	D P
4246776	D P
4246782	D P
4246798	D P
4246799	D P
4246800	D P
4246801	D P
4246827	D P
4246837	C D P
4246940	D P
4246984	C D
4266033	C I D P
4266038	C I D P
4266069	C D P
4266074	C D P
4266138	C D P
4266196	C D P
4266255	C D P
4266260	C D P
4266262	D P
4266271	D P
4266281	D P
4266282	C D P
4266285	D P
4266293	C D P
4266294	D P
4266298	D P
4266345	D P
4266346	D P
4266348	C D P
4266349	C D P
4266350	D P
4266378	D P
4266482	C D P
4266692	C D P
4266696	C D P
4266697	C D P
4266721	C D P
4266723	D P
4266729	C D P
4266739	D P
4266762	C D P
4266763	C D P
4266952	C D P
4266954	C D P
4267126	C I D
4267128	C I D
4267133	C I D P
4267155	I D P
4267174	C D P
4267177	C D P
4267187	C I D P
4267197	D P
4267205	C D
4267206	C D
4267209	C D P
4267222	D P
4267225	D P
4267227	C D P
4267228	D P
4267245	C I D P
4267281	C D P
4267310	C I D
4267328	I D P
4267329	D P
4267330	D P
4267331	C D P
4267344	I D P
4267850	C I D P
4268416	D P
4268801	C D P
4268804	D P
4268924	D P
4268961	C I D P
4268963	C I D P
4269277	D P
4269279	D P
4269308	C D P
4269309	C D P
4269354	D P
4270091	D P
4270773	C D P
4270976	C D P
4270978	C D P
4270980	C D P
4270997	C D P
4271370	C D P
4271382	C D P
4271388	C D P
4271389	C D P
4271868	C I D
4271875	C D P
4271882	C D P
4271891	D P
4271892	C D P
4271893	C I D P
4271894	C I D P
4271910	C D P
4271926	C D P
4271927	C D P
4271929	C D P
4271931	D P
4271945	I D P
4271946	D P
4271956	C I D P
4271962	C I D P
4271980	D P
4271982	C I D P
4271994	C D P
4271995	D P
4273129	C I D P
4273145	C D P
4273184	C D P
4273238	C D P
4273241	C D P
4273243	C D P
4273260	C D P
4273269	C D P
4273270	C D P
4273271	C D P
4273322	C I D P
4273486	C D P
4273488	C D P
4273515	D P
4273519	D P
4273530	D P
4273535	D P
4273536	D P
4273551	D P
4273561	D P
4273587	D P
4273590	D P
4273601	D P
4273603	D P
4273608	D P
4273621	D P
4273635	D P
4273645	D P
4273651	D P
4273657	D P
4273660	D P
4273663	D P
4273676	D P
4273677	D P
4273678	D P
4273679	D P
4273686	D P
4273722	D P
4273725	C D P
4273761	D P
4273768	D P
4273787	D P
4273793	D P
4273802	D P
4273803	D P
4273842	D P
4273847	D P
4273874	D P
4273879	D P
4273883	D P
4273884	D P
4274272	C D P
4274273	C D P
4274814	D P
4274886	C D P
4274887	C D P
4274975	C D P
4275053	C D P
4275301	C D P
4275312	C D P
4275313	C D P
4275531	C D P
4275555	C D P
4275594	D P
4275617	C D P
4275651	D P
4275985	C D P
4279296	C D P
4279485	C D P
4279499	D P
4279599	C D P
4279603	C D P
4279605	C D P

Code following part numbers indicate interchangeability of this part with other Chrysler Corporation cars.

C—Chrysler I—Imperial D—Dodge P—Plymouth

4279653	C D P
4279657	C D P
4279661	D P
4279896	D P
4279898	D P
4279911	C D P
4279917	C D P
4279949	D P
4279950	C D P
4279951	C D P
4279987	C D P
4280432	C D P
4280433	C D P
4280436	C D P
4280437	C D P
4280640	C D P
4280641	C D P
4287023	C I D P
4287051	C I D P
4287073	C I D P
4287087	C D P
4287089	C I D P
4287093	C D P
4287316	C D P
4287320	C D P
4287324	C D P
4287704	C D P
4287712	C D P
4287714	C D P
4287730	C D P
4287743	C D P
4288009	D P
4288054	D P
4288055	C D P
4288057	C D P
4288058	D P
4288059	C D P
4288088	D P
4288276	C D P
4288277	D P
4288414	D P
4288425	C D P
4288428	C D P
4288433	D P
4288436	D P
4288437	D P
4288438	D P
4288439	D P
4288440	C D P
4288441	C D P
4288444	C D P
4288445	C D P
4288450	D P
4288451	D P
4288482	C D P
4288483	C D P
4288484	D P
4288521	D P
4288576	C I D P
4288578	C I D P
4288581	C I D P
4289087	C I D P
4293110	C I D P
4293111	C I D
4293164	C D P
4293168	D P
4293179	D P
4293185	D P
4293195	C D P
4293196	C D P
4293200	C D P
4293310	C I D
4293725	C D P
4293726	D P
4293767	D P
4293773	C I D P
4293776	C D P
4293799	C D P
4293801	D P
4293802	C D P
4293803	C I D P
4293815	C D P
4293817	C D P
4293819	C D P
4293824	C D P
4293830	C D P
4293838	C D P
4293839	D P
4293850	C D P
4293851	D P
4293853	D P
4293854	C D P
4293856	C D P
4293879	C D P
4293888	C D P
4293895	C I D P
4293898	C D P
4294049	D P
4294051	D P
4294069	C D
4294136	C D P
4294139	C D
4294172	D P
4294212	C D P
4294268	C D P
4294411	D P
4294412	D P
4294445	C D P
4294495	C D P
4294515	C D P
4295006	C D P
4295007	C D P
4295018	C D P
4295173	D P
4295198	C D P
4295237	C D P
4295255	C D P
4295257	C D P
4295260	C D P
4295265	C D P
4295266	C D P
4295426	C D P
4295428	C D P
4295459	C I D P
4295584	C D P
4295596	C D P
4296448	C D
4296449	C D
4296593	D P
4296976	D P
4296977	D P
4297681	C D
4298125	C D P
4298137	C D P
4298142	C D P
4300011	C I D P
4300012	C I D P
4300017	D P
4300018	D P
4300252	C D P
4300253	D P
4300254	C D P
4300257	C D P
4300263	C D P
4300264	C D P
4300265	C D P
4300266	C D P
4300376	C I D P
4300381	D P
4300382	C D P
4300383	D P
4301037	C D P
4301070	C D P
4301087	D P
4301088	D P
4301091	D P
4301100	C I D
4301175	C I D P
4301193	C D
4301220	D P
4301221	D P
4301223	D P
4301224	D P
4301225	C D
4301226	C D
4301227	C D P
4301229	D P
4301230	D P
4301231	C D P
4301232	C D P
4301233	C D
4301240	C D P
4301242	D P
4301247	C D P
4301254	C D P
4301262	D P
4301263	C D P
4301265	D P
4301266	C D P
4301291	D P
4301294	C D
4301303	C D P
4301305	C D
4301315	C D P
4301324	D P
4301339	C I D P
4301341	I D P
4301346	C D P
4301375	C I D P
4301394	D P
4301395	D P
4301396	D P
4301406	D P
4301425	D P
4301426	C D P
4301427	C D
4301428	C D P
4301429	C D P
4301438	D P
4301441	D P
4301448	C D P
4301453	D P
4301460	D P
4301467	D P
4301468	D P
4301470	D P
4301473	C D P
4301492	D P
4301494	C D P
4301502	C D P
4301503	C D
4301506	C D P
4301507	C D P
4301512	C D
4301513	C D
4301518	D P
4301530	C D P
4301534	I D P
4301538	C D P
4301539	C D
4301547	C D P
4301551	C D
4301558	D P
4301560	D P
4301572	C D P
4301576	C D P
4301578	C D P
4301583	C D P
4301591	D P
4301630	C D P
4301653	D P
4301655	D P
4301657	D P
4301658	D P
4301659	C D P
4301660	C D P
4301661	C D P
4301662	C D P
4301663	C D P
4301664	D P

Code following part numbers indicate interchangeability of this part with other Chrysler Corporation cars.
C—Chrysler I—Imperial D—Dodge P—Plymouth

4301665	D P
4301666	C D P
4304473	C D P
4304555	C D P
4304678	D P
4306024	C D P
4306113	D P
4306202	C D P
4306411	C I D P
4306433	C I D P
4306923	C D P
4307221	C D P
4307255	C D P
4307257	D P
4307565	C D P
4310014	C D P
4310015	C D P
4310017	C D P
4310018	C D P
4310206	C D P
4310526	C I D P
4310529	C I D P
4310532	C I D P
4310533	C I D P
4310642	C D P
4310643	C D P
4310688	C D P
4310689	C D P
4310739	C D P
4310938	C D P
4310939	C D P
4310940	D P
4310941	D P
4312002	C D
4312032	D P
4312035	D P
4312186	C I D P
4312327	D P
4312328	D P
4312331	C D
4312332	C D P
4312334	C D P
4312816	C D P
4313029	C D P
4313040	C D P
4313054	C D P
4313236	D P
4313237	D P
4313238	C D P
4313239	D P
4313266	D P
4313429	C D P
4313591	D P
4313592	C D P
4313593	C D P
4313633	C D P
4313634	C D P
4313635	C D P
4313642	C D P
4313758	C D P
4313772	D P
4313773	D P
4313962	C D P
4313963	C D P
4314194	C D
4314195	C D
4315408	D P
4315409	D P
4317001	C D P
4317030	C D P
4317031	C D P
4318114	C D P
4318115	C D P
4318117	C D P
4318118	C D P
4318707	D P
4318708	C D P
4318709	C D P
4318717	D P
4318721	C D P
4318723	C D P
4318726	D P
4318794	C D P
4318795	C D P
4318818	C I D P
4318819	C I D P
4318829	C I D P
4319707	D P
4321062	C D P
4321063	C D P
4321068	C D P
4321069	C D P
4321072	C D P
4321074	C D P
4321116	D P
4321117	D P
4321514	D P
4321515	D P
4321516	D P
4321517	D P
4321526	C D
4321527	C D
4321528	C D
4321529	C D
4321530	C D
4321531	C D
4321578	C D P
4321579	C D P
4321643	D P
4321649	C D
4321650	C D
4321716	C D P
4321717	C D P
4321740	C D P
4321741	C D P
4321992	C D
4322014	C D P
4322017	C D P
4322028	C D
4322046	C D P
4322059	C D P
4322099	C D
4322154	C D P
4322155	C D P
4322158	C D P
4322159	C D P
4322249	C D P
4322250	C D P
4322271	D P
4322276	C D
4322277	C D
4322285	C D P
4322298	C D P
4322601	D P
4322610	D P
4322628	C D P
4322641	C D P
4322678	D P
4322679	C D P
4322701	C D P
4322704	C D P
4322705	C D P
4322733	C D P
4322734	C D P
4322735	C D P
4322736	D P
4322745	D P
4322751	C D P
4322756	D P
4322757	D P
4322760	C D P
4322820	D P
4322881	C D P
4323026	C D P
4323028	C D P
4323030	D P
4323038	C D P
4323039	C D P
4323041	C D P
4323043	C D P
4323099	C D P
4323100	C D P
4323205	C I D P
4323225	C D P
4323235	C I D P
4323239	C I D P
4323244	C D P
4323249	C D P
4323288	C D P
4323327	C D P
4323346	C I D P
4323423	C I D P
4323444	C D P
4323619	C I D P
4323621	C I D P
4324608	D P
4324610	D P
4324612	D P
4324647	C I D P
4324669	D P
4324670	D P
4328690	D P
4328691	D P
4328698	D P
4329177	C D P
4329588	C D P
4330251	C D P
4331481	C D P
4331482	C D P
4331519	C D P
4333062	C I D P
4333098	C D P
4333100	C D P
4333101	D P
4333103	C D P
4333104	C D P
4333122	C D P
4333123	C D P
4333124	D P
4333125	D P
4333130	C D P
4333147	C D P
4333148	C D P
4333149	D P
4333275	C D P
4333340	D P
4333434	C D P
4333449	C D P
4333450	C D P
4333451	C D P
4334131	C D P
4334132	C D P
4334190	D P
4334562	C D P
4334564	C D P
4334569	C D P
4336149	C D P
4336150	C D P
4336192	D P
4336193	D P
4336196	D P
4336197	D P
4336377	C D P
4336378	C D P
4336380	C D P
4336381	C D P
4336394	D P
4336395	D P
4336444	D P
4336445	D P
4336542	C D P
4336543	C D P
4336544	C D P
4336545	C D P
4336600	C D
4336601	C D
4336604	C D
4336605	C D
4336766	D P
4336767	D P

Code following part numbers indicate interchangeability of this part with other Chrysler Corporation cars.
C—Chrysler I—Imperial D—Dodge P—Plymouth

4336782	D P
4336783	D P
4337402	C D
4337403	C D
4338872	C D P
4338874	C D P
4339401	C I D P
4339411	D P
4339422	D P
4339423	C D P
4339432	C D P
4339438	C I D P
4339440	C D P
4339449	C I D P
4339450	C D P
4339455	C D P
4339456	C D P
4339472	C D P
4339704	C D P
4339705	C D P
4340035	C D P
4341462	D P
4341952	D P
4342154	C D P
4342203	C I D
4342207	C D P
4342209	C I D P
4342707	D P
4342709	C D P
4342716	C I D
4342751	C D P
4342765	D P
4342772	C I D P
4342800	D P
4342801	D P
4342805	C I D P
4342808	C I D P
4342812	C I D P
4342819	C I D P
4342832	C I D P
4342860	C I D P
4342872	C D P
4342876	C D P
4342882	C D P
4342890	C D P
4342934	C I D P
4342940	C D P
4342948	C D P
4343198	C D P
4343405	C D P
4343407	C D P
4343428	C D P
4343436	C D P
4343521	C D P
4343588	C D P
4343590	C D P
4343627	C D P
4343639	C D P
4343725	C D P
4343766	C D P
4343783	C D P
4343785	C D P
4343820	C D P
4343821	C D P
4343824	C D P
4343871	C D P
4343873	D P
4343874	D P
4343946	C D P
4348312	C D P
4348314	C D P
4348327	C D P
4352613	D P
4364485	C D P
4364773	C D P
4364778	C D P
4364779	C D P
4364782	C D P
4364785	C D P
4364786	C I D P
4365062	D P
4365063	D P
4365414	D P
4365415	D P
4365464	C D P
4365465	C D P
4365474	C D P
4365475	C D P
4365928	C D P
4365929	C D P
4368366	C D P
4368367	C D P
4371930	C D
4371931	C D
4372064	D P
4372065	D P
4375008	D P
4375010	C D P
4375032	D P
4375034	D P
4375064	D P
4375081	C D P
4375085	C D P
4375099	D P
4375130	D P
4377449	D P
4377458	C D P
4377769	C D P
4377771	D P
4378038	D P
4378039	D P
4378053	C D
4378171	C D
4378172	C D
4379100	C D P
4386384	D P
4386385	D P
4386556	D P
4386557	D P
4387201	C D P
4387202	C D P
4387203	D P
4387319	C D P
4387614	D P
4396015	C D P
4396016	C D P
4396017	D P
4396208	D P
4396209	D P
4396402	C D
4396403	C D
4396737	D P
4397498	D P
4397632	C D P
4397634	C D P
4397636	C D P
4397642	C I D P
4397643	C I D P
4397657	D P
4397666	D P
4397680	C D P
4397681	C D P
4397827	C D P
4399100	C I D P
4415410	D P
4415411	D P
4419012	D P
4419013	D P
4419014	D P
4419015	D P
4419315	C D P
4419316	C D P
4501663	D P
5200722	D P
5200723	D P
5201084	D P
5201085	D P
5202975	D P
5203322	D P
5203324	C D P
5203325	C D P
5203384	C D P
5203401	C D P
5203415	C D P
5203432	C D P
5203469	C D P
5203491	C D P
5203575	C D P
5203585	C D P
5203590	C D P
5203778	C D P
5203780	C D P
5203800	D P
5204069	D P
5204080	D P
5204111	D P
5204120	D P
5204149	C I D P
5204255	D P
5204260	D P
5204261	D P
5204264	D P
5204534	C D P
5204535	C D P
5204537	D P
5204538	C D P
5204595	C D P
5204608	C D P
5204610	C D P
5204615	D P
5204622	C D P
5204734	D P
5204932	D P
5204937	D P
5204939	D P
5204969	D P
5205032	D P
5205038	D P
5205097	D P
5205114	C D P
5205142	D P
5205149	D P
5205154	D P
5205174	D P
5205182	D P
5205185	D P
5205186	D P
5205189	D P
5205191	D P
5205194	D P
5205195	D P
5205225	C D P
5205226	C D P
5205227	C D P
5205267	C D P
5205278	C D P
5205280	C D P
5205282	C D P
5205284	C D P
5205286	C D P
5205287	C D P
5205293	C D P
5205295	C D P
5205299	C D P
5205313	C D P
5205328	C D P
5205336	C D P
5206246	D P
5206255	D P
5206265	D P
5206359	D P
5206360	D P
5206421	C D P
5206422	C D P
5206564	D P
5206601	D P
5206602	D P
5206603	D P
5206604	D P
5206605	C D P

Chrysler Corporation Part Number Interchange

Code following part numbers indicate interchangeability of this part with other Chrysler Corporation cars.

C—Chrysler I—Imperial D—Dodge P—Plymouth

5206606	C D P
5206607	C D P
5206608	D P
5206609	D P
5206610	D P
5206612	D P
5206622	D P
5206623	D P
5206624	D P
5206625	D P
5206626	D P
5206627	D P
5206630	D P
5206631	C D P
5206632	D P
5206634	C D P
5206637	D P
5206638	D P
5206641	D P
5206647	D P
5206648	D P
5206649	D P
5206650	D P
5206945	D P
5207088	D P
5207203	D P
5207340	D P
5207341	D P
5207345	D P
5207383	D P
5207386	C D P
5207516	D P
5207568	D P
5207569	D P
5207648	D P
5207649	D P
5207656	D P
5207657	D P
5207674	D P
5207675	D P
5207686	D P
5207687	D P
5207722	D P
5207723	D P
5207736	D P
5207737	D P
5207766	D P
5207767	D P
5207786	D P
5207787	D P
5207788	D P
5207789	D P
5209694	D P
5209863	D P
5209875	D P
5209891	D P
5209928	D P
5209994	C I D P
5210365	D P
5210377	C I D P
5210384	C D P
5210420	D P
5210438	D P
5211003	D P
5211004	D P
5211008	D P
5211009	D P
5211084	D P
5211087	D P
5211115	C D P
5211383	D P
5211437	D P
5211439	D P
5211772	C D P
5211931	D P
5212521	D P
5212535	D P
5212545	D P
5212547	C D P
5212559	D P
5212770	D P
5212980	D P
5213045	C D P
5213053	C D P
5213079	C D P
5213092	C D P
5213295	D P
5213301	D P
5213309	C D P
5213310	C D P
5213311	C D P
5213312	C D P
5213313	C D
5213315	D P
5213348	C D P
5213352	D P
5213353	D P
5213361	D P
5213363	D P
5213372	D P
5213373	D P
5213382	C D P
5213383	C D P
5213384	C D P
5213385	C D P
5213387	D P
5213395	D P
5213450	C D P
5213463	C D
5213522	C D P
5213524	C D P
5213525	C D P
5213540	C D P
5213541	C D P
5213542	D P
5213548	D P
5213549	D P
5213574	C D P
5213575	D P
5213581	C D P
5213629	C I D P
5213641	D P
5213679	D P
5213728	C D P
5213737	D P
5213749	D P
5213753	D P
5213760	D P
5213762	C D P
5213763	C D P
5213764	D P
5213774	D P
5213776	D P
5213780	D P
5213785	D P
5213788	D P
5213794	D P
5213831	D P
5213834	C D P
5213836	C D P
5213838	C D P
5213840	C D P
5213847	C D P
5213850	D P
5213852	C D P
5213854	C D P
5213858	C D P
5213868	D P
5213872	D P
5213873	D P
5213875	D P
5213898	C D P
5213903	C D P
5213907	C D P
5213921	C D P
5213957	C D P
5213964	D P
5213974	D P
5213980	C D P
5213982	D P
5213984	D P
5213986	D P
5213987	D P
5213988	D P
5213991	D P
5213993	D P
5213994	D P
5213997	D P
5214198	D P
5214336	D P
5214339	C I D
5214342	D P
5214479	C D P
5214486	D P
5214490	D P
5214513	D P
5214518	C D P
5214521	I D P
5214609	C D P
5214737	C D P
5214861	C D P
5214866	C D P
5214870	C D P
5214895	C D P
5214959	C D P
5214968	C D P
5214969	C D P
5217088	D P
5217136	D P
5222707	C D
5222708	C D
5222972	D P
5226019	D P
5226020	D P
5226084	D P
5226096	D P
5226106	D P
5226156	D P
5226164	D P
5226223	C D P
5226224	C D P
5226272	C D P
5226284	C D P
5226286	C D P
5226315	C D P
5226324	D P
5226347	C D P
5226352	C D P
5226355	C D
5226356	D P
5226359	C D P
5226361	C D
5226374	C D P
5226411	D P
5226429	D P
5226432	C D P
5226439	C D P
5226444	C D P
5226449	D P
5226451	C D P
5226455	C D P
5226505	C D P
5226507	D P
5226509	C D P
5226525	D P
5226527	C D P
5226535	C D P
5226572	D P
5226575	C D P
5226608	D P
5226611	C D P
5226616	C D P
5226617	C D P
5226648	C D P
5226741	C D P
5226765	C D P
5226766	C D P
5226785	D P
5226786	D P
5226794	C D P

Code following part numbers indicate interchangeability of this part with other Chrysler Corporation cars.

C—Chrysler I—Imperial D—Dodge P—Plymouth

5226840	C D P
5226841	C D P
5226845	C D P
5226846	D P
5226848	D P
5226856	D P
5227114	C D P
5227115	C D P
5227119	C D P
5227125	C D P
5227131	C D P
5227160	C D P
5227169	C D P
5227255	C D P
5227306	C D P
5227309	C D P
5227315	C D P
5227318	C D P
5227321	C D P
5227328	C D P
5227331	C D P
5227371	C D P
5227400	C D P
5227449	C D P
5227452	C D P
5227455	C D P
5227458	C D P
5227461	C D P
5227607	C D P
5231046	D P
5231047	D P
5231650	D P
5231651	D P
5231742	D P
5231743	D P
5232057	C D P
5232101	D P
5240156	D P
5240311	D P
5240346	D P
5240369	D P
5240370	D P
5240405	D P
5240416	D P
5240417	D P
5240427	D P
5240431	D P
5240433	D P
5240440	D P
5240441	D P
5240442	D P
5240449	D P
5240468	D P
5240469	D P
5240503	D P
5240504	D P
5240505	D P
5240507	D P
5240508	D P
5240510	D P
5240511	D P
5240515	D P
5240522	D P
5240524	D P
5240594	D P
5240607	D P
5240700	D P
5240793	D P
5240794	D P
5240918	D P
5240923	D P
5240924	D P
5240925	D P
5240946	D P
5240967	D P
5240985	D P
5240986	D P
5240988	D P
5240996	D P
5240998	D P
5266572	C D P
5313441	D P
6027513	D P
6032473	C I D P
6100750	D P
6101277	D P
6500150	D P
6500415	C D P
6501297	C D
8349266	C D P
H201EK1	C I D P
X135EX8	D P
MD000508	C D P
MD005131	C D P
MD005371	C D
MD009440	C D P
MD013789	C D P
MD013791	C D P
MD013793	C D P
MD015531	C D P
MD017066	C D P
MD017307	C D P
MD020308	C D P
MD020551	C D P
MD020561	C D P
MD020843	C D P
MD020855	C D P
MD020897	C D P
MD021045	C D P
MD021155	C D P
MD021170	C D P
MD021172	C D P
MD021230	C D P
MD021233	C D P
MD021246	C D P
MD021247	C D P
MD022557	C D P
MD022558	C D P
MD022591	C D P
MD023196	C D P
MD023198	C D P
MD023225	C D
MD023226	C D P
MD024505	C D P
MD024518	C D P
MD024519	C D P
MD024548	C D P
MD024628	C D P
MD024682	C D P
MD024777	C D P
MD024845	C D P
MD024846	C D P
MD024893	C D P
MD025190	C D P
MD025199	C D P
MD025215	C D P
MD025223	C D P
MD025235	C D P
MD025263	C D P
MD025264	C D
MD025273	C D P
MD025274	C D P
MD025534	C D P
MD025587	C D
MD025684	C D P
MD025703	C D P
MD025787	C D P
MD026200	C D P
MD026408	C D P
MD026430	C D P
MD026510	C D P
MD026581	C D P
MD026591	C D P
MD026613	C D P
MD026654	C D P
MD026706	C D
MD026708	C D P
MD026725	C D P
MD026730	C D P
MD026815	C D P
MD026835	C D P
MD026921	C D P
MD027723	C D P
MD027766	C D P
MD031805	C D P
MD050604	C D P
MD060517	C D P
MD061258	C D P
MD061313	C D P
MD061314	C D P
MD062006	C D P
MD062007	C D P
MD067134	C D P
MD068740	C D P
MD068743	C D P
MD069867	C D P
MD070897	C D
MD071172	C D P
MD071430	C D
MD071769	C D P
MD072033	C D P
MD072035	C D P
MD073036	C D
MD073096	C D P
MD073398	C D P
MD073500	C D
MD073978	C D P
MD074096	C D P
MD075460	C D P
MD076139	C D
MD076310	C D P
MD076311	C D
MD076312	C D P
MD080152	C D P
MD081509	C D P
MD082058	C D P
MD082758	C D P
MD083848	C D P
MD083851	C D P
MD084289	C D P
MD085766	C D P
MD088137	C D P
MD088537	C D
MD602412	C D P
MD602789	C D P
MD604317	C D P
MD604318	C D P
MD604319	C D P
MD604320	C D P
MD604321	C D P
MD604322	C D P
MD604324	C D P
MD604332	C D P
MD606849	C D P
MD606946	C D P
MD607226	C D P
MD607359	C D P
MD607372	C D P
MD607405	C D P
MD607425	C D P
MD607426	C D P
MD607428	C D P
MD607429	C D P
MD607430	C D P
MD607466	C D P
MD607468	C D P
MD607470	C D P
MD607474	C D P
MD607475	C D P
MD607477	C D P
MD607478	C D P
MD607734	C D P
MD607770	C D P
MD607779	C D P
MD607885	C D P
MD607886	C D P
MD608571	C D P
MD608643	C D P
MD608797	C D P
MD612215	C D P

Code following part numbers indicate interchangeability of this part with other Chrysler Corporation cars.
C—Chrysler I—Imperial D—Dodge P—Plymouth

MD612217 .... C D P
MD997021 .... C D P
MD997050 .... C D P
MM502264 .... C D P

Code following part numbers indicate interchangeability of this part with other General Motors cars.

1—Buick 2—Oldsmobile 3—Pontiac 5—Chevrolet 9—Cadillac

231075	1 2 3 5
231127	1 2 3 5
231260	1 5
231886	1 2 9
340235	3 5
344883	3 5
346261	3 5
351286	2 3 5 9
357159	3 5
359105	3 5
359115	1 2 3 5 9
359190	3 5
359711	3 5
360505	1 2 3 5 9
360530	3 5
360538	3 5
360567	3 5
360572	3 5
360799	3 5
360800	3 5
361054	3 5
361733	3 5
361746	3 5
361750	3 5
361755	3 5
361982	3 5
363006	3 5
363406	3 5
363465	3 5
363467	3 5
363468	3 5
364702	3 5
364800	3 5
364812	3 5
366860	3 5
367599	3 5
368299	3 5
369123	3 5
369131	3 5
369132	3 5
369133	3 5
369355	3 5
370283	1 2 9
370409	3 5
371773	1 2 3 5 9
371793	1 5
374105	3 5
374135	3 5
374141	3 5
374246	1 2 3 5 9
374697	3 5
376306	3 5
376308	3 5
376316	3 5
376387	3 5
376405	3 5
381263	1 2 5 9
382572	1 2 9
382880	1 2 3 5 9
388294	3 5
390300	1 2 3 5 9
390301	1 2 3 5 9
390302	1 2 3 5 9
390303	1 2 3 5 9
391095	1 2
392592	1 5
398295	1 2 9
401584	1 2 3 5 9
401823	1 2 3 5 9
404294	1 2 5 9
406595	1 2 3 5 9
406996	1 2 3 5 9
407437	1 2 3 5 9
411226	1 2 3 9
411283	1 2 9
458483	1 2 9
458484	1 2 9
458625	3 5
458629	3 5
458653	3 5
458685	3 5
459021	1 2 5
459417	2 3 5
461853	1 2 3 5
462661	3 5
462664	3 5
462690	3 5
462691	3 5
462701	3 5
462702	3 5
462703	3 5
462704	3 5
464167	1 2 3 5 9
464617	3 5
466334	3 5
466336	3 5
469085	3 5
470110	3 5
470112	3 5
470147	1 2 3 5
471591	3 5
472117	1 2 3 5
472118	1 2 5
472143	2 3
472432	1 2 3 5
473424	3 5
473525	1 2 3 5
473743	2 3 5
473786	1 2 5
474001	1 2 3
474005	3 5
474006	3 5
474007	3 5
474010	3 5
474029	3 5
474665	1 2 3 5 9
474667	1 2 3 5
474758	3 5
474794	3 5
475305	3 5
476521	1 2 3 5 9
476525	1 2 3 5 9
476531	1 2 3 5 9
476571	1 2 3 5
476574	3 5
476575	1 2 3 5 9
476591	1 2 3 5
476600	1 2 3 5
476899	3 5
477248	1 2 3 5
477263	1 2 3 5
477292	1 2 3 5 9
477410	3 5
477411	3 5
483722	1 2 3 5 9
484365	1 2 9
484366	1 2 9
488332	1 5 9
491160	1 2 3
491392	1 2 3 5
499323	1 2 3 5
500011	1 2 3 5
500012	1 2 3 5
526200	1 2 9
526205	1 2 5 9
526207	1 2 5 9
526703	1 2 5
526897	1 2 3 5 9
527689	3 5
527690	3 5
527751	2 5 9
527752	1 2 5 9
527753	1 2 5 9
527854	1 2 5 9
546895	1 2 3 5
547212	1 2 5 9
547225	1 2 5 9
547797	1 2 3 5
552571	1 2 3 5 9
552711	1 2 3 5 9
553022	1 2 3 5
553915	1 2 3 5
554976	1 2 9
555456	1 2 3 9
555737	2 3 9
556283	1 2 3 5 9
557238	2 5
557866	1 2 9
558484	1 2 3 5 9
558489	1 2 3 5 9
558648	1 2 3 5 9
558649	1 2 3 5 9
558767	1 2 5 9
558768	1 2 3 5 9
558873	1 2 3 5 9
559131	1 2 3 5 9
559255	1 2 9
559256	1 2 9
559697	1 2 9
559755	1 2
560197	1 2 3 5
560198	1 2 3 5
560199	1 2 3 5
560201	1 2 3 5
560204	1 2 3 5 9
560205	1 3
560207	1 2 3 5
560355	1 2 3 5
560580	1 2 3 5 9
560680	1 2 9
561077	1 2 3 5 9
561310	1 3 5
561756	1 2 9
561826	1 2 5 9
561891	1 2 9
562088	1 2 9
562089	1 2 9
562090	1 2 9
562091	1 2 9
562092	1 2 9
562093	1 2 9
562094	1 2 9
562095	1 2 9
562354	1 2 9
562355	1 2 9
562374	1 2 9
562622	1 2 9
563056	1 2 3 5
563432	1 2 9
563634	1 2 9
563646	1 2
585582	1 2 9
800091	3 5
801818	1 2 9
900529	3 5
907998	1 2 9
908244	3 5
908252	3 5
908287	3 5
908403	1 2 3 5 9
908404	3 5
908419	1 2 3 5 9
912116	1 2 3 5 9
912345	1 2 3 5 9
912366	1 2 3 5 9
912368	1 2 3 5
912767	3 5
912768	3 5
912795	1 2 3 5
913061	1 2 3 5 9
913204	2 3 5
913538	1 2 3 5
913578	1 2 9
913584	1 2 9
913765	1 2 3 5
913766	1 2 3 5
913781	1 2 9
913782	1 2 9
913807	1 2 9
913808	1 2 9

Code following part numbers indicate interchangeability of this part with other General Motors cars.

1—Buick 2—Oldsmobile 3—Pontiac 5—Chevrolet 9—Cadillac

Part No.	Code
913907	1 2 9
913931	1 2 3 5
913933	1 2 3 5
913935	1 2 9
913936	1 2 9
913937	1 2 9
913938	1 2 9
913941	1 2 9
913942	1 2 9
913957	1 2 9
913958	1 2 9
913963	1 2 9
913964	1 2 9
913979	1 2 9
913980	1 2 9
913985	1 2 3 5
913986	1 2 3 5
914000	3 5
914317	1 2 9
914327	1 2 9
914328	1 2 9
914333	1 2 9
914334	1 2 9
914550	3 5
914553	3 5
914554	3 5
914691	1 2 9
914692	1 2 9
914752	1 2 3 5 9
914979	1 2 3 5 9
914980	1 2 3 5 9
915027	1 2 9
915028	1 2 9
915076	1 2 3 5
915086	1 2 3 5
915213	1 2 3 5 9
915214	1 2 3 5 9
915313	1 2 3 5 9
915314	1 2 3 5 9
915455	1 2 3 5 9
915456	1 2 3 5 9
915493	1 2 9
915494	1 2 9
915545	3 5
915549	3 5
915550	3 5
915559	1 2 3 5 9
915560	1 2 3 5 9
915571	3 5
915572	3 5
915587	3 5
915588	3 5
915589	3 5
915590	3 5
915603	1 2 3 5
915604	1 2 3 5
915609	1 2 3 5 9
915610	1 2 3 5 9
915619	1 2 3 5
915620	1 2 3 5
915627	1 2 3 5 9
915628	1 2 3 5 9
915817	3 5
915873	1 2 3 5
915883	1 2 3 5
915884	1 2 3 5
915930	2 3
915951	1 2 3 5
915952	1 2 3 5
916461	1 2 3 5 9
916462	1 2 3 5 9
917307	1 2 9
917308	1 2 9
917731	1 2 3 5 9
917732	1 2 3 5 9
917737	1 2 3 5 9
917738	1 2 3 5 9
917755	1 2 9
917803	1 2 3 5 9
917804	1 2 3 5 9
917881	1 2 9
917882	1 2 9
917935	1 2 9
917936	1 2 9
917937	1 2 3 5
917938	1 2 3 5
917939	1 2 3 5 9
917940	1 2 3 5 9
917941	1 2 3 5 9
917942	1 2 3 5 9
917984	1 2
917985	1 2
918057	1 2 3 5 9
918058	1 2 3 5 9
918065	1 2
918066	1 2
918067	1 2 9
918068	1 2 9
918087	1 2 3 5 9
918088	1 2 3 5 9
918101	1 2 3 5
918102	1 2 3 5
918111	1 2 3 5
918112	1 2 3 5
918181	1 2 9
918182	1 2 9
918193	1 2 3 5
918194	1 2 3 5
918235	1 2 9
918236	1 2 9
918304	1 2
918307	1 2
918308	1 2
918309	1 2 3 5 9
918310	1 2 3 5 9
918329	1 2 3 5
918330	1 2 3 5
918339	1 2 3 5
918340	1 2 3 5
918346	1 2 3
918351	1 2 3
918352	1 2 3
918383	1 2 3 5 9
918384	1 2 3 5 9
918409	1 2 3
918410	1 2 3
918456	1 2 5
918552	1 2 3 5 9
918554	1 2 3 5 9
918563	1 2 3
918564	1 2 3
918591	1 2 3 5 9
918592	1 2 3 5 9
918616	1 2 3
918663	1 2 3 5
918664	1 2 3 5
918669	1 2 3
918670	1 2 3
918671	1 2 3
918672	1 2 3
918733	1 2 3 5
918734	1 2 3 5
918751	1 2 3 5
918752	1 2 3 5
918753	1 2 3 5
918754	1 2 3 5
918807	1 2 3 5
918808	1 2 3 5
918949	1 2 3
918950	1 2 3
918959	3 5
919081	1 2 3
919082	1 2 3
919083	1 2 3
919084	1 2 3
919121	1 2 3 5
919122	1 2 3 5
919163	1 2 3 5
919164	1 2 3 5
919183	1 2 3 5 9
919184	1 2 3 5 9
919185	3 5
919186	3 5
919187	3 5
919188	3 5
919301	3 5
919302	3 5
919417	1 2 9
919418	1 2 9
919579	1 2 3 5 9
919580	1 2 3 5 9
919585	1 2 3 5 9
919586	1 2 3 5 9
919623	1 2 3
919624	1 2 3
919687	1 2 3
919688	1 2 3
919803	1 2 9
919804	1 2 9
919889	1 2 9
919890	1 2 9
919907	1 2 3 5 9
919908	1 2 3 5 9
919921	1 2 3 5 9
919922	1 2 3 5 9
919989	1 2
919995	1 2 9
919996	1 2 9
920005	1 2 3 5 9
920006	1 2 3 5 9
920015	3 5
920016	3 5
920027	1 2 9
920028	1 2 9
920116	1 2
920135	1 2
920136	1 2
929335	1 2 3 5
929336	1 2 3 5
929349	1 2 3 5
929350	1 2 3 5
929475	1 2 9
929564	3 5
929843	1 2 3 5
929844	1 2 3 5
929935	3 5
929936	3 5
942793	1 2 3 5
966464	1 2 9
966520	1 2
966534	1 2
966535	1 2
1002287	1 2 3 5
1052366	3 5
1100250	1 2 3 5 9
1101040	1 2 9
1101050	1 2 9
1101225	1 2 9
1103038	1 2 9
1103457	1 2 9
1103460	3 5
1103470	1 2 3 5 9
1103504	3 5
1103513	1 2 3 5
1103515	1 2 3 5 9
1103519	1 2 3 5
1103535	1 2 3 5 9
1103539	3 5
1103541	1 2 9
1103548	1 2 3 5 9
1103551	1 2 3 5
1103561	1 2 3 5 9
1103567	1 2 3 5 9
1103569	1 2 3 5
1103570	3 5
1103574	3 5
1103585	1 2 3 5 9
1103588	1 2 3 5 9
1103589	1 2 3 5 9
1103591	1 2 3 5 9

Code following part numbers indicate interchangeability of this part with other General Motors cars.
1—Buick 2—Oldsmobile 3—Pontiac 5—Chevrolet 9—Cadillac

1103598	3 5
1103602	1 2 3 5 9
1103608	1 2 9
1103609	1 2 3 5 9
1103610	1 2 3 5 9
1103612	1 5
1103616	3 5
1103634	1 2 3 5
1103643	1 2 3 5
1103650	1 2 3 5
1103653	1 2 3 5 9
1103655	3 5
1103683	1 2 9
1103691	1 2 9
1103704	1 2 3 5 9
1103730	1 2 9
1105335	1 2 3 5 9
1105339	1 2 3 5 9
1105341	1 2 3 5 9
1105356	3 5
1105357	1 2 5
1105359	1 2 3 5 9
1105360	1 2 3 5 9
1105367	1 2 3 5 9
1105368	3 5
1105369	1 2 3 5 9
1105402	1 2 9
1105480	1 2 9
1105481	1 2 3 5 9
1105492	1 2 3 5 9
1109495	1 2 9
1109532	3 5
1109533	1 2 3 5
1109534	3 5
1109535	3 5
1109544	1 2
1109551	1 2 3 5 9
1109556	1 2 3 5
1109562	1 2 3 5 9
1109564	1 2 3 5
1114531	1 2 3 5 9
1114557	1 2 9
1115315	1 2 3 5 9
1115455	1 2 3 5 9
1116387	1 2 3 5 9
1154577	1 2 3 5
1154578	1 2 3 5
1154580	1 2 3 5
1192916	1 2 3 5 9
1193151	1 2 3 5 9
1193966	1 2 3 5
1193967	1 2 9
1225450	1 2 9
1225500	1 2 3 5 9
1225587	3 5
1225707	1 2 5
1225909	1 2
1225910	1 2
1225977	1 2 9
1226020	3 5
1226024	1 2 3 5
1226025	1 2 3 5 9
1226026	1 2 3 5 9
1226028	1 2 9
1226031	1 2 3
1226100	1 2 3 5 9
1226153	1 2 3 5
1226156	1 2 3 5 9
1226159	1 2 9
1226166	1 2
1226167	1 2
1226175	1 2
1226181	1 2
1226182	1 2
1226183	1 2
1226271	1 2
1226286	1 2 9
1226297	1 2 3
1226329	3 5
1226355	3 5
1226356	3 5
1226357	3 5
1226434	1 2
1226435	1 2
1226436	1 2 9
1226437	1 2
1226445	1 2 3
1226455	1 2 3 5
1226457	1 2 9
1226458	1 2 3 5 9
1226459	1 2 9
1226460	1 2 3 5 9
1226461	1 2 3 5 9
1226462	1 2 9
1226509	1 2 9
1226519	1 2 3 5 9
1226532	1 2 9
1226533	1 2 9
1226535	1 2 9
1226536	1 2 9
1226539	1 2 9
1226540	1 2 9
1226662	1 2 9
1226663	3 5
1226664	3 5
1226665	3 5
1226864	1 2 3 5 9
1226865	1 2 3 5
1226866	1 2 9
1226867	1 2 3 5 9
1226868	3 5
1226870	1 2 3 5 9
1226930	1 2 9
1226948	1 2 3 9
1227056	1 2 9
1227057	1 2 9
1227076	1 2
1227148	1 2 9
1227151	1 2 3 5 9
1227153	1 2 3
1227165	1 2 3 5 9
1231141	1 2 9
1231142	1 2 3 5 9
1234441	1 2 3 5 9
1234726	1 2 3 5 9
1240955	1 2 3 5
1241850	1 2 3 5 9
1241851	1 2 3 5 9
1243465	1 2 3 5 9
1244835	1 2 3 5 9
1244838	1 2 3 5
1249139	1 2 3 5 9
1249146	1 2 3 5 9
1249267	1 2 3 5 9
1250948	1 2 5 9
1251925	1 5
1252980	1 2 3 5
1252981	1 2 3 5 9
1253698	1 2 3 5 9
1254199	1 2 5 9
1254201	1 2 9
1254894	1 2 3 5 9
1254900	2 3
1255496	1 2 3 5 9
1255801	1 2 3 5
1255941	3 5
1256654	1 2 3 5
1257650	1 2 3 5 9
1257692	2 3
1258666	1 2 3 5
1258707	1 2 3 5
1258708	1 2 3 5
1258709	1 2 3 5 9
1258713	1 2 3 5
1258714	1 2 5
1258715	1 2 3 5
1258718	1 3 5
1259441	1 2
1259649	1 2 3 5 9
1260709	1 2 3 5 9
1260771	1 2 3 5 9
1260873	1 2 9
1260877	1 2 3 5 9
1261380	1 2 3 5 9
1261403	1 2 3 5 9
1261407	1 2 3 5 9
1261535	1 2 9
1261559	1 2 9
1261596	1 2 3
1261850	1 2 9
1262835	1 2 3 5 9
1263020	1 2 9
1264464	1 2 3 5 9
1264923	1 2 5
1264924	1 2 3 5 9
1305044	1 2 3 5 9
1356634	1 2
1358909	1 2
1362835	1 2 3 5 9
1394892	1 2 5
1394893	1 2 3
1397647	1 2 3 5 9
1494424	1 2
1607317	1 2 9
1609776	1 2 3 5 9
1612337	1 2 9
1612338	1 2 9
1612360	1 2 9
1612376	1 2 9
1612377	1 2 9
1612592	1 5 9
1613288	1 2 9
1613620	1 2 9
1613714	1 2 9
1614067	1 2 9
1614068	1 2 9
1614499	1 2 9
1614578	1 2 9
1614579	1 2 9
1615116	1 2 9
1615321	1 2 9
1615530	1 2 9
1615577	1 2 9
1615578	1 2 9
1615579	1 2 9
1616589	1 2 9
1617090	1 2 9
1617417	1 2 9
1617591	1 2 9
1617594	1 2 9
1618157	1 2 9
1618159	1 2 9
1618323	1 2 9
1618692	1 2 9
1618802	1 2 9
1618805	1 2 9
1618837	1 2 9
1619035	1 2 9
1619036	1 2 9
1619040	1 2 9
1619145	1 2 9
1619361	1 2 9
1619499	1 2 9
1619814	1 2 9
1620158	1 2 9
1620210	1 2 3 5 9
1620998	1 2 9
1621280	1 2 9
1621293	1 2 9
1621294	1 2 9
1621295	1 2 9
1621296	1 2 9
1621297	1 2 9
1621298	1 2 9
1621321	1 2 9
1621460	1 2 9
1621731	1 2 9
1622005	1 2 9
1622006	1 2 9
1622125	1 2 9

Code following part numbers indicate interchangeability of this part with other General Motors cars.

1—Buick 2—Oldsmobile 3—Pontiac 5—Chevrolet 9—Cadillac

1622249	1 2 9
1622622	1 2 9
1622623	1 2 9
1622630	1 2 9
1622802	1 2 9
1622834	1 2 9
1623384	1 2 9
1623537	1 2 9
1623538	1 2 9
1623576	1 2 3 5 9
1623817	1 2 9
1623928	1 2 9
1623970	1 2 9
1625161	1 2 9
1625764	1 2 9
1625959	1 2 9
1626038	1 2 9
1626087	1 2 9
1626192	1 2 9
1626239	1 2 9
1626372	1 2 9
1626516	1 2 9
1626693	1 2 9
1626705	1 2 9
1626753	1 2 9
1626754	1 2 9
1626790	1 2 9
1627287	1 2 9
1627298	1 2 9
1627299	1 2 9
1627641	1 2 9
1627642	1 2 9
1627643	1 2 9
1627644	1 2 9
1627755	1 2 9
1627772	1 2 9
1627781	1 2 9
1627806	1 2 9
1627821	1 2 9
1627827	1 2 9
1628539	1 2 9
1628557	1 2 9
1628559	1 2 9
1628806	1 2 9
1628813	1 2 9
1628822	1 2 9
1628915	1 2 9
1628920	1 2 9
1629205	1 2 9
1629249	1 2 9
1629251	1 2 9
1629458	1 2 9
1629459	1 2 9
1629870	1 2 9
1630283	1 2 9
1630692	1 2 9
1631190	1 2 9
1631192	1 2 9
1631193	1 2 9
1631383	1 2 9
1631384	1 2 9
1631399	1 2 9
1631926	1 2 9
1632107	1 2 9
1632135	1 2 9
1632195	1 2 9
1632207	1 2 9
1632333	1 2 9
1632569	1 2 9
1632576	1 2 9
1632640	1 2 9
1632837	1 2 9
1632838	1 2 9
1632883	1 2 9
1632884	1 2 9
1632916	1 2 9
1633128	1 2 9
1633804	1 2 9
1633808	1 2 9
1633850	1 2 9
1634058	1 2 9
1634059	1 2 9
1634218	1 2 9
1634312	1 2 9
1634313	1 2 9
1634359	1 2 9
1635539	1 2 9
1636120	1 2 9
1636132	1 2 9
1636204	1 2 9
1636275	1 2 9
1636949	1 2 9
1636950	1 2 9
1637471	1 2 9
1638239	1 2 9
1638555	1 2 9
1638574	1 2 9
1638595	1 2 9
1638785	1 2 9
1638786	1 2 9
1638787	1 2 9
1650327	1 2 9
1701523	3 5
1701524	3 5
1748557	3 5
1748558	3 5
1787061	1 2 3 5 9
1813427	3 5
1839345	1 2 9
1845351	1 2 3 5
1852880	1 2 9
1852885	1 2 3 5 9
1875645	1 2 9
1875687	1 2 3 5 9
1875894	3 5
1875960	1 2 3 5 9
1875967	3 5
1875987	1 2 9
1875990	3 5
1876154	1 2 3 5 9
1876881	1 2 3 5 9
1877306	1 2 3 5 9
1880020	3 5
1880022	3 5
1892082	1 2 3 5 9
1892162	1 2 3 5 9
1892163	1 2 3 5 9
1892164	1 2 3 5 9
1892246	1 2 3 5 9
1892261	1 2 3 5 9
1892262	3 5
1892941	1 2 9
1893293	1 2 3 5 9
1893296	1 2 3 5 9
1893332	3 5
1893358	3 5
1893445	1 2 3 5 9
1893669	3 5
1893752	1 2
1893929	1 2 3 5 9
1894209	1 2 3 5 9
1894979	1 2 3 5 9
1906945	1 2 3 5 9
1926618	3 5
1932190	1 2 3 5 9
1945804	1 2 3 5 9
1958599	3 5 9
1970548	1 2 3 5 9
1971568	1 2 3 5 9
1971639	1 2 3 5 9
1971986	1 2 9
1972683	1 2 3 5
1972685	1 2 3 5
1972700	1 2 3 5
1972717	1 2 3 5 9
1973691	3 5
1974123	1 2 9
1974157	1 2 3 5 9
1974183	1 2 3 5
1974408	1 2 3 5 9
1974786	1 2 9
1974897	1 2 9
1974939	1 2 3 5
1975303	1 2 3 5 9
1975310	1 2 3 5 9
1975313	1 2 3 5 9
1975322	1 2 3 5 9
1975323	1 2 3 5 9
1975333	1 2 3 5 9
1975336	1 2 9
1975471	1 2 3 5 9
1975987	1 2 3 5 9
1976049	1 2 9
1976092	3 5
1976141	1 2 9
1976881	3 5
1976897	1 2 3 5 9
1976908	1 2 3 5 9
1976909	3 5 9
1976925	1 2 3 5 9
1976928	1 2 3 5 9
1976930	1 2 3 5 9
1977026	1 2 3 5 9
1977046	1 2 3 5 9
1977064	1 2 9
1977131	1 2 3 5
1977207	1 2 5 9
1977208	1 2 3 5 9
1977626	1 2 3 5 9
1977936	1 2 3 5 9
1978123	1 2 9
1978137	1 2 9
1978146	1 2 3 5 9
1978152	3 5
1978281	1 2 3 5 9
1978282	1 2 3 5
1978284	3 5
1978292	1 2 3 5 9
1978302	3 5
1978497	1 2 3 5 9
1978503	1 2 3 5 9
1978509	1 2 3 5
1978533	1 2 3 5 9
1978631	1 2 3 5 9
1978670	1 2 3 5 9
1978672	1 2 3 5 9
1978776	1 2 3 5 9
1978778	1 2 3 5 9
1978850	3 5
1978851	3 5
1978876	1 2 9
1979107	1 2 3 5 9
1979208	1 2 3 5
1979254	1 2 3 5
1979256	1 2 3 5
1979261	1 2 3 5
1979511	1 2 3 5 9
1979546	1 2 9
1979554	1 2 9
1979556	1 2 9
1979571	1 2 3 5
1979696	1 2 3 5
1979700	1 2 3 5
1979701	1 2 3 5
1979703	1 2 3 5
1979705	1 2 3 5
1979711	1 2 3 5
1979948	1 2 9
1979955	1 2 9
1979966	2 5
1979982	1 2 3 5 9
1984048	3 5
1984069	3 5
1984148	1 2 3 5 9
1984219	1 2 3 5
1984371	3 5
1984445	1 2 3 5 9
1984454	1 2 3 5 9
1984459	1 2 3 5 9
1984460	1 2 3 5 9

Code following part numbers indicate interchangeability of this part with other General Motors cars.
1—Buick 2—Oldsmobile 3—Pontiac 5—Chevrolet 9—Cadillac

Part No.	Interchange
1984462	1 2 3 5 9
1984464	1 2 3 5 9
1984466	1 2 3 5 9
1984480	1 2 3 5 9
1984501	1 2 3 5 9
1984504	1 2 3 5 9
1984511	1 2 3 5 9
1984522	1 2 3 5 9
1984527	1 2 3 9
1984528	1 2 3 5 9
1984537	1 2
1984584	1 2 3 5 9
1984671	3 5
1984680	3 5
1984734	1 2 3 5 9
1985138	1 2 3 5 9
1985143	1 2 3 5 9
1985148	1 2 3 5
1985219	1 2 9
1985342	1 2 3 5 9
1985348	1 2 9
1985473	1 2 3 5 9
1985474	1 2 3 5 9
1985476	1 2 3 5 9
1985497	3 5
1985500	1 2 3 5 9
1985625	1 2 3 5 9
1985642	1 2 3 5
1985646	1 2 3 5 9
1985669	1 2 3 5 9
1985671	1 2 3 5 9
1985749	1 2 3 5 9
1985769	1 2 3 5
1985771	1 2 3 5 9
1985774	1 2 3 5 9
1985801	1 2 3 5 9
1986018	3 5
1986092	3 5
1986096	3 5
1986102	1 2 3 5 9
1986139	1 2 3 5 9
1986206	1 2 3 5 9
1986280	1 2 3 5
1986590	1 2 3 5 9
1986951	1 2 3 5 9
1986963	1 2 3 5
1986972	1 2 3 5
1986995	3 5
1987007	1 2 3 5 9
1987054	1 2 3 5 9
1987061	1 2 3 5 9
1987073	1 2 3 5 9
1987074	1 2 3 5 9
1987095	1 2 3 5 9
1987100	3 5
1987277	1 2 3 5 9
1987334	1 2 3 5 9
1987391	1 2 3 5 9
1987465	1 2 3 5 9
1987466	1 2 3 5 9
1987510	1 2 3 5 9
1987639	1 2 3 5 9
1987662	1 2 3 9
1987744	1 2 9
1987841	1 2 3 5
1987900	1 2 3 5 9
1987937	1 2 3 5 9
1987940	1 2 3 5 9
1987948	1 2 3 5
1987958	1 2 3 5 9
1987963	1 2 3 5 9
1987964	1 2 3
1987968	1 2 3 5 9
1987988	3 5
1987997	1 2 9
1988001	1 2 3 5 9
1988005	1 2 3 5 9
1988010	1 2 3 5 9
1988077	1 2 3 5
1988082	1 2 3 5
1988388	1 2 3 5 9
1988465	1 2 3 5 9
1988515	1 2 3 5 9
1988588	1 2 3 5
1988614	3 5
1988665	3 5
1988777	1 2 3 5
1988873	1 2 3 5
1988883	1 2 3 5 9
1988983	1 2 5 9
1989284	1 2 3 5 9
1989286	1 2 3 5 9
1989612	1 2 3 5 9
1989747	1 2 3 5
1989808	3 5
1989880	1 2 3 5 9
1990109	1 2 3 5 9
1990110	1 2 3 5 9
1990115	1 2 3 5 9
1990116	1 2 3 5 9
1990118	1 2 9
1990120	1 2 9
1994223	1 2 3 5 9
1994232	3 5
1994245	1 2 9
1994253	1 2 9
1994255	1 2 3 5
1994256	1 2 3 5 9
1994258	1 2
1994267	1 2 9
1995212	1 2 3 5 9
1995214	1 2
1995217	1 2 3 5
1995225	1 2 9
1995226	1 2 3 5
1995230	1 2 9
1995232	1 2 9
1995238	1 2 9
1995241	1 2 9
1995253	1 2 3 5 9
1995260	1 2 3 5
1995264	1 2 3 5
1995283	1 2 9
1995284	1 2 9
1995285	1 2 3 5
1997046	1 2 3 5
1997048	3 5
1997052	1 2 9
1997054	1 2 9
1997111	3 5
1997126	1 2 9
1997156	1 2 9
1997562	1 2 3 5 9
1997612	3 5
1997616	1 2 3 5
1997631	3 5
1997636	1 2 9
1997652	1 2 3 5 9
1997662	1 2 3 5
1997663	1 2 3 5 9
1997665	1 2 9
1997675	1 2 9
1997688	1 2 3 5 9
1997699	3 5
1997983	1 2 3 5 9
1997984	1 2 3 5 9
1997988	1 2 3 5
1998234	1 2 5
1998237	1 2 9
1998427	3 5
1998428	3 5
1998430	3 5
1998435	3 5
1998445	1 2 3 5 9
1998447	1 2 3 5 9
1998448	1 2 3 5 9
1998450	1 2 3 5
1998452	3 5
1998453	1 2
1998466	3 5
1998476	1 2 9
1998503	1 2 3 5 9
1998509	1 2 9
1998516	1 2 3
1998521	1 2
1998524	3 5
1998525	3 5
1998526	1 2 3
1998527	3 5
1998528	1 2 3 5 9
1998529	1 2 3 5 9
1998530	3 5
1998531	1 2 3
1998533	1 2 3 5 9
1998534	1 2 9
1998536	1 2 3 9
1998544	1 2
1998545	1 2 9
1998557	3 5
1998564	3 5
2098912	1 2 9
2503535	3 5
2511265	1 2 3 5
2552718	1 2 9
2622207	1 2 3 5 9
2724060	1 2 3 5 9
2724144	1 2 3 5 9
2724158	1 2 3 5 9
2724236	1 2 3 5
2724239	1 2 3 5 9
2724240	1 3 5
2724242	3 5
2724259	1 2 3 5 9
2724260	1 2 3 5 9
2724261	1 2 9
2724265	1 2 3 5
2724270	1 2 3 5
2724272	1 2 9
2724275	1 2 3 5
2724280	1 2 3 5 9
2724319	1 2 3 5 9
2724325	1 2 3 9
2724333	1 2
3032252	3 5
3033485	3 5
3033573	3 5
3033879	1 2 3 5
3035240	1 2 3 5 9
3035420	1 2 3 5 9
3036422	1 2 3 5
3037438	1 2 3 5
3037439	1 2 3 5
3037638	1 2 3 5
3037689	1 2 3 5
3037747	1 2 3 9
3037852	1 2 3 5
3039923	1 2 3 5
3040531	1 2 9
3040548	1 2 9
3040674	1 2 3 5 9
3040690	1 2 9
3040837	1 2 3 5
3041390	1 2 3 5 9
3041415	3 5
3041596	1 2 3 5
3041841	1 2 3 5
3042073	1 2 3 5
3042357	3 5
3042897	1 2 9
3043015	3 5
3043066	1 2 3 5 9
3046807	3 5
3047169	1 2 3 5 9
3047786	1 2 3 5 9
3048009	1 2 3 5 9
3048786	1 2 9
3048945	3 5
3049052	3 5
3049183	1 2 3 5
3049626	1 2 9

Code following part numbers indicate interchangeability of this part with other General Motors cars.

1—Buick 2—Oldsmobile 3—Pontiac 5—Chevrolet 9—Cadillac

3050133	1 2 3 5
3050155	1 2 3 5
3050223	1 2 3 5 9
3050246	1 2 3 5 9
3050289	1 2 3 5
3050628	3 5
3050653	1 2 9
3050922	3 5
3051139	1 2 3 5 9
3051170	1 2 3 5
3053166	1 2 3 5 9
3053427	1 2 9
3053428	1 2 9
3053452	1 2 9
3053464	1 2 9
3053654	1 2 9
3053962	1 2 3 5 9
3054167	1 2 3 5
3054228	1 2 3 5 9
3055188	1 2 3 5 9
3055285	1 2 3 5 9
3055363	1 2 3 5
3055550	1 2 9
3055576	1 2 3
3055672	1 2 9
3056083	1 2 3 5 9
3056277	1 2 3 5 9
3057067	1 2 9
3057627	3 5
3057666	1 2 3 5 9
3057676	1 2 3 5
3058130	1 2 3 5 9
3058311	1 3
3058622	1 2 3 5 9
3058630	1 2 9
3058661	1 2 9
3058662	1 2 9
3058764	1 2 9
3059131	1 2 3
3059155	1 2 3 5 9
3059160	1 2 3 5
3059239	1 2 9
3059315	2 3
3059793	1 2 3
3059973	1 2 3
3090421	1 2 3 5 9
3090492	1 2 3 5
3090818	1 2 3 5
3091128	1 2 9
3092035	1 2
3092084	1 2 9
3092683	1 2 9
3092972	1 2 9
3093683	1 2
3517442	1 2 9
3517492	1 2 9
3517509	1 2 9
3517546	1 2 9
3517549	1 2 9
3517635	1 2 9
3517640	1 2 9
3634475	1 2 9
3634580	1 2 9
3634606	1 2 9
3634619	1 2 9
3634639	1 2 9
3634655	1 2 9
3634656	1 2 9
3702366	1 2 3 5 9
3704817	3 5
3729363	1 2 3 5
3735381	1 2 3 5
3752487	3 5
3764547	3 5
3792507	1 2 3
3799620	3 5
3815936	1 2 3 5 9
3829061	1 2 3 5
3829067	1 2 3 5
3829433	1 2 3 5
3835333	1 2 3 5
3853759	1 2 9
3853760	1 2 9
3853761	1 2 9
3853762	1 2 9
3853912	1 2 9
3855152	3 5
3896959	3 5
3907088	1 2 9
3907089	1 2 9
3910555	3 5
3910570	1 2 3 5 9
3911068	3 5
3912030	3 5
3912038	3 5
3915936	1 2 9
3923052	3 5
3923472	1 2 3 5
3947770	1 2 3 5
3958078	1 2 3 5 9
3965092	1 2 3 5 9
3974290	3 5
3979727	3 5
3991407	3 5
3995791	1 2 3 5 9
3995792	1 2 9
3996610	1 2 3 5
3998287	3 5
3998519	1 2 3 5 9
4941130	1 2 9
4960974	1 2 3 5 9
4961608	1 2 3 5 9
4961623	1 2 3 5 9
4961736	3 5
4973237	1 2 3 5
4974367	1 2 9
4993543	1 2 9
4993548	1 2 3 5 9
4993551	1 2 3 5 9
4993552	1 5 9
4993553	1 5 9
4993554	1 2 3 5
4993560	1 2 3 5 9
4993566	3 5
4993579	2 3 5
4993580	1 2 3 5
4993581	3 5
4993582	3 5
4993583	1 2 3 5
4993584	1 2 3 5
4993585	1 2 3 5
4993586	1 2 3 5
4993587	1 2 9
4993724	1 2 3 5 9
4993745	3 5 9
4999674	3 5
4999676	3 5
5232720	3 5
5232750	1 2 9
5232765	1 2 3 5 9
5233155	1 2 9
5233315	1 2 3 5 9
5233320	1 2 5
5233335	1 2 3 5 9
5233475	1 2 5 9
5233515	1 2 3 5
5233650	3 5
5233745	1 2 3 5
5234104	1 2 9
5234110	1 2 3 5
5234212	1 2 3 5 9
5234330	1 2 3 5 9
5234360	1 2 9
5234470	1 2 3 5 9
5234580	1 2 9
5234625	1 2 3 5 9
5234755	1 2 3 9
5324485	1 2 3
5458657	1 2 3 5 9
5463361	1 2 5 9
5463797	1 2 3 5 9
5463932	1 2 3 5
5466089	1 2 3 5 9
5466090	1 2 3 5 9
5466091	1 2 3 5 9
5466211	1 2 3 5 9
5466312	1 2 3 5 9
5466314	1 2 3 5 9
5466562	1 2 5
5468226	3 5
5468578	1 2 3 5 9
5468767	1 2 3 5 9
5469497	1 2 3 5 9
5472328	1 2 3 5 9
5613611	1 2
5613680	1 2 3 5 9
5613695	1 2 9
5613826	1 2 3 5 9
5613959	1 2 3 5 9
5684948	1 2 3 5 9
5686527	1 2 3 5 9
5687182	1 2 3 5 9
5688014	3 5
5688037	1 2 3 5 9
5688044	1 2 3 5 9
5689010	1 2 3 5 9
5689358	1 2 3 5 9
5693125	1 5
5693463	1 2 3 5
5697804	1 2 3 5 9
5914435	1 2 3 5 9
5930567	1 2 3 5 9
5966200	1 2 3 5 9
5966201	1 2 3 5 9
5968098	1 2 3 5 9
5969915	1 2 3 5
5969916	1 2 3 5
5969931	1 2 3 5
5969932	1 2 3 5
5970111	1 2 9
5970112	1 2 9
5970535	1 2 9
5970536	1 2 9
5970553	1 2 9
5970554	1 2 9
5970691	1 2 3 5
5970692	1 2 3 5
5970907	1 2 3 5
5970908	1 2 3 5
5971099	1 2 3 5
5971100	1 2 3 5
5971188	3 5
5971199	3 5
5971200	3 5
5971203	3 5
5971204	3 5
5971209	3 5
5971210	3 5
5972237	1 2 3 5 9
5972238	1 2 3 5 9
5972425	1 2 3 5 9
5972426	1 2 3 5 9
5972427	1 2 3 5 9
5972428	1 2 3 5 9
5972461	1 2 9
5972462	1 2 9
5972698	1 2 3 5 9
5972879	3 5
5972880	3 5
5972897	1 2 3 5
5972898	1 2 3 5
5972983	3 5
5972984	3 5
5972989	3 5
5972990	3 5
5973025	1 2 3 5
5973026	1 2 3 5
5973193	1 2 3 5 9
5973194	1 2 3 5 9
5973213	1 2 3 5

Code following part numbers indicate interchangeability of this part with other General Motors cars.

1—Buick 2—Oldsmobile 3—Pontiac 5—Chevrolet 9—Cadillac

5973214	1 2 3 5
5973238	1 2 3 5
5973563	1 2 9
5973617	1 2 3 5 9
5973618	1 2 3 5 9
5973639	1 2 3 5 9
5973640	1 2 3 5 9
5973643	1 2 3 5 9
5973644	1 2 3 5 9
5973749	3 5
5973750	3 5
5973763	1 2 3 5
5973885	1 2 3 5
5973886	1 2 3 5
5973901	1 2 3 5
5973902	1 2 3 5
5974199	1 2 3
5974249	1 2 3 5 9
5974250	1 2 3 5 9
5974251	1 2 3 5 9
5974252	1 2 3 5 9
5974397	1 2
5974398	1 2
5974457	3 5
5974458	1 2 3 5 9
5974461	1 2 3 5 9
5974462	1 2 9
5974464	2 3 5
5974465	1 2
5974466	1 2 3 5
5974467	1 2 9
5974468	1 2
5974469	1 2 3
5974472	1 9
5974473	1 2 9
5974534	1 2 3 5 9
5974539	1 2
5974540	1 2
5974563	1 2 3 5 9
5974564	1 2 3 5 9
5974659	1 2 9
5974660	1 2 9
5974765	1 2 9
5974766	1 2 9
5974767	1 2 9
5974768	1 2 9
6260706	3 5
6263794	3 5
6270704	1 2 3 5 9
6270977	2 3 5
6272221	3 5
6419892	2 5
6432935	3 5
6433030	1 2 3 5 9
6433050	1 2 9
6433052	1 2 9
6433062	1 2 9
6433063	1 2 9
6433064	1 2 9
6433065	1 2 9
6433128	1 2 3 5
6433130	1 2 3 5
6433185	1 2 3 5
6433229	3 5
6433267	1 2 3 5
6433271	1 2 3 5
6433302	1 2 3 5
6433303	1 2 3 5
6433323	1 2 9
6433326	1 2 9
6433329	1 2 9
6433339	1 2 3 5 9
6433385	1 2 3 5 9
6433426	1 2 3 5
6433447	1 2 9
6433460	3 5
6433476	1 2 3 5
6433597	1 2 9
6433619	3 5
6433620	3 5
6433646	3 5
6433647	3 5
6433680	1 2 3 5 9
6433685	1 2 3 5
6433686	1 2 3 5
6433687	1 2 3 5
6433688	1 2 3 5
6433706	1 2 3 5 9
6433716	1 2 3 5
6433717	1 2 3 5
6433734	1 2 3 5
6433737	1 2 3 5
6433769	1 2 3 5
6433805	3 5
6433807	1 2 3 5 9
6433811	1 2 3 5
6433817	1 2 3 5 9
6433821	1 2 3 5 9
6433828	1 2 3 5 9
6433873	3 5
6433874	1 2 3 5 9
6433896	1 2 3 5 9
6433897	1 2 3 5 9
6433898	1 2 3 5 9
6433921	1 2 3 5
6433987	1 2 3 5
6434009	1 2 9
6434053	1 2 3 5 9
6434070	1 2 3 5
6434074	1 2 3 5
6434081	1 2 3 5
6434084	1 2 3 5
6434087	3 5
6434118	1 2 3 5 9
6434120	1 2 3 5 9
6434127	3 5
6434128	3 5
6434171	1 2 3 5
6434173	1 2 3 5
6434176	1 2 3 5
6434189	1 2 3 5
6434222	1 2 3 5 9
6434243	3 5
6434246	3 5
6434268	3 5
6434345	1 2 3 5 9
6434401	1 2 3 5 9
6434421	1 2 3 5 9
6434423	1 2 3 5 9
6434427	1 2 3 5 9
6439929	1 2 3 5 9
6442223	1 2 9
6442228	1 2 3 5 9
6450076	1 2 3 5 9
6450089	1 2 3 5 9
6470422	1 5
6471172	1 2 3 5
6471252	3 5
6471317	1 2 3 5 9
6471368	1 2 3
6471542	3 5
6471554	1 2 9
6471743	1 2 3 5 9
6471925	3 5
6471926	1 2 3 5
6471930	3 5
6471952	1 2 3 5
6471959	1 2 3 5
6471960	1 2 3 5
6472009	1 2 9
6472011	1 2 3 5 9
6472020	1 2 3 5
6472026	1 2 9
6472143	1 2 3 5 9
6472153	1 2 3 5 9
6472229	1 2 3 5
6472230	1 2 9
6472232	3 5
6472248	1 2 9
6472311	1 2 3 5 9
6472358	1 2 9
6472366	3 5
6472370	3 5
6472375	1 2 3 5 9
6472393	3 5
6472395	3 5
6472408	3 5
6472421	3 5
6472451	1 2 3 5
6472524	1 2 3 5 9
6472525	1 2 3 5
6472526	1 2 3 5 9
6472527	1 2 9
6472529	1 2 9
6472531	1 2 9
6472765	1 2
6472998	1 2 9
6484235	2 5
6487532	1 2 9
6487534	1 2 3 5 9
6487779	1 2 3 5 9
6487936	1 2 3 5 9
6488213	3 5
6551141	1 2 3 5 9
6551142	1 2 3 5 9
6551216	1 2 3 5 9
6551217	1 2 3 5 9
6551220	1 2 3 5 9
6551700	1 2 3 5 9
6551701	1 2 3 5 9
6551702	1 2 3 5 9
6551713	1 2 3 5 9
6551717	1 2 3 5 9
6551834	1 2 3 5
6551835	1 2 3 5 9
6551838	1 2 3 5 9
6551884	1 2 3 5 9
6551888	1 2 3 5 9
6551920	1 2 3 5 9
6551933	3 5
6551952	1 2 3 5 9
6551983	1 2 3 9
6551996	1 2 3 5 9
6551997	1 2 3 5 9
6556572	1 2 3 5 9
6556715	1 2 3 5 9
6556717	1 2 3 5
6557376	1 2 3 5 9
6557377	1 2 3 9
6557378	1 2 3
6557503	1 2 3 5 9
6557580	1 2 9
6557775	1 2 3 5 9
6557800	1 2 3 5 9
6558046	1 2 9
7021743	1 2 3
7026014	1 2 3 5 9
7035134	1 2 3 5 9
7035150	1 2 9
7035156	1 2 3 5
7035157	1 2 3 5 9
7039467	3 5
7420002	1 2 3 5
7450630	1 2 3 5 9
7450697	1 2 3 5 9
7450984	1 2 3 5 9
7451140	1 2 3 5 9
7451155	1 2 3 5 9
7451202	1 2 3 5 9
7451281	1 2 3 5 9
7451409	1 2 9
7451785	1 2 3 5 9
7451809	1 2 3 5 9
7451992	3 5
7455699	1 2 3 5 9
7466902	1 2 9
7466903	1 2 9
7466905	1 2 3 5
7466907	1 2 9
7466917	1 2 3 5 9

Code following part numbers indicate interchangeability of this part with other General Motors cars.

1—Buick 2—Oldsmobile 3—Pontiac 5—Chevrolet 9—Cadillac

Part Number	Codes
7466922	1 2 3 5 9
7466926	1 2 9
7466929	1 2 9
7470001	1 2 3 5 9
7470002	1 2 3 5
7470003	1 2 3 5 9
7470004	1 2 3 5 9
7800715	3 5
7804414	1 2 9
7805168	1 2 9
7806140	1 2 3 5 9
7806688	1 3
7808195	1 2 3 5 9
7809226	3 5
7809229	1 2 3 5 9
7809232	1 2 3 5 9
7811092	1 2 9
7812557	1 2 3 5 9
7813631	1 2 3 5 9
7815885	1 2 3 5 9
7817485	1 2 3 5 9
7817486	1 2 3 5 9
7817487	3 5
7817526	1 2 5 9
7817528	1 2 3 5 9
7819323	3 5
7819353	3 5
7819355	3 5
7819358	1 2 3 5 9
7819359	3 5
7819367	1 2 9
7819378	1 2 3 5
7819790	2 5
7819792	2 5
7819796	2 3 5
7819797	2 3 5
7819809	2 3 5
7825181	1 2 3 5 9
7826056	2 3 5
7826470	1 2 3 5 9
7826714	1 2 3 5 9
7826850	1 2 3 5 9
7827170	1 2 3 5 9
7827670	1 2 3 5 9
7827995	1 2 3 5 9
7828012	1 2 3 5 9
7828017	1 2 3 5 9
7828084	1 2 3 5
7828314	1 2 3 5 9
7828486	1 2 3 5 9
7828584	2 5
7829465	1 2 3 5
7829467	3 5
7829495	1 2 3 5
7829755	1 2 3 5
7829884	1 2 9
7829888	1 2 3 5 9
7830112	1 2 9
7830137	1 2 9
7830236	1 2 3 5 9
7830606	3 5
7830666	1 2 9
7830667	1 2 9
7830697	1 2 3 5 9
7830915	3 5
7831234	1 2 3 5
7831354	1 2 9
7831535	1 2 9
7832036	1 2 9
7832055	1 2 3 5
7832057	1 2 3 5
7832058	1 2 3 5
7832110	3 5
7832199	1 5
7832279	2 5
7832332	3 5
7832411	1 2 3 5 9
7832730	1 2 9
7832731	1 2 3 5 9
7832945	1 2 9
7832995	3 5
7833039	1 2 9
7833122	1 2 9
7833193	1 2 9
7833360	1 2 9
7833361	1 2 9
7833362	1 2 9
7833655	1 2 3 5 9
7833732	1 2 3 5 9
7834080	1 2 3 5
7834082	1 2 9
7834088	1 2 3 5
7834135	1 2 9
7834137	3 5
7834139	1 2 3 5 9
7834141	1 3
7834143	3 5
7834145	1 2 3 5
7834179	1 2 3 5
7834180	1 2 3 5
7834181	1 2 3 5
7834224	1 2 3 5 9
7834238	1 2 9
7834239	1 2 9
7834241	1 2 9
7834244	1 2 9
7834245	1 2 9
7834284	1 2 3 5 9
7834425	1 2 3 5 9
7834426	1 2 3 5 9
7834430	1 2 3 5 9
7834432	1 2 3 5 9
7834435	1 2 3 5 9
7834436	1 2 3 5 9
7834437	1 2 3 5 9
7834439	1 2 3 5 9
7834488	3 5
7834621	1 2 9
7834673	1 2 3 5 9
7834733	3 5
7834792	3 5
7834853	1 2 3 5 9
7834916	3 5 9
7834919	1 2 9
7834920	2 5
7834958	1 2 3 5 9
7835070	1 2 9
7835168	3 5
7835171	3 5
7835231	1 2 3 5 9
7835233	1 2 3 5 9
7835287	3 5
7835312	3 5
7835314	1 2 9
7835340	1 2 3 5
7835342	1 2 3 5
7835396	3 5
7835397	1 2 3 5 9
7835417	3 5
7835512	1 2 3 5 9
7835628	1 2 3 5 9
7835630	1 2 3 5
7835632	1 2 3 5
7835787	1 2 3 5
7836061	3 5
7836230	1 2 3 5 9
7836275	1 2 3 5 9
7836277	1 2 3 5 9
7836369	1 2 3 5 9
7836512	1 2 3 5
7836673	1 2 3 5 9
7836834	3 5
7836891	1 2 3 5
7836972	1 2 3 5 9
7837007	1 2 3 5
7837071	1 2 3 5
7837081	1 2 3 5
7837084	1 2 9
7837121	3 5
7837122	3 5
7837125	3 5
7837126	3 5
7837127	3 5
7837135	1 2 3 5
7837182	1 2 9
7837183	1 2 3 5
7837232	3 5
7837263	1 2 3 5
7837279	1 2 3 5 9
7837280	1 2 3 5 9
7837281	1 2 3 5
7837321	1 2 3 5 9
7837322	1 2 3 5 9
7837337	3 5
7837426	1 2 3 5 9
7837595	3 5
7837596	3 5
7837597	3 5
7837614	3 5
7837631	3 5
7837632	3 5
7837635	1 2 3 5 9
7837639	1 2 3 5
7837645	1 2 3 5
7837648	1 2 3 5
7837649	2 5
7837664	1 2 3 5 9
7837667	1 2 3 5 9
7837719	1 2 3 5 9
7837733	1 2 3 5
7837771	1 2 3 5 9
7837828	1 2 3 5
7837985	2 3 5
7837990	2 3 5
7837993	1 2 3 5 9
7837994	1 2 3 5 9
7838078	1 2 3 5 9
7838143	2 3 5
7838145	2 3 5
7838146	2 3 5
7838234	1 2 3 5 9
7838279	1 2 3 5 9
7838285	1 2 3 5 9
7838298	1 2 3 5
7838299	1 2 3 5
7838393	1 2 3 5 9
7838415	3 5
7838469	1 2 3 5 9
7838471	1 2 3 5
7838472	1 2 3 5
7838575	1 2 3 5 9
7838686	3 5
7838790	1 2 3 5 9
7838791	1 2 3 5 9
7839019	1 2 3 5
7839075	1 2 3 5 9
7839153	1 2 3 5 9
7839154	1 2 3 5
7839156	1 2 3 5
7839157	1 2 3 5 9
7839238	3 5
7839239	3 5
7839278	1 2 3 5
7839345	1 2 3 5
7839366	1 2 3 5 9
7839413	1 2 3 5 9
7839507	1 2 3 5
7839589	1 2 3 5 9
7839667	1 2 3 5 9
7839669	1 2 3 5 9
7839718	1 2 9
7839787	3 5
7839788	3 5
7839790	1 2 9
7839792	1 2 3 5
7839794	1 2 9
7839795	1 2 3 5
7839796	1 2 9
7839871	3 5
7839955	1 2 3 5

Code following part numbers indicate interchangeability of this part with other General Motors cars.
1—Buick 2—Oldsmobile 3—Pontiac 5—Chevrolet 9—Cadillac

Part No.	Code
7839989	1 2 3 5 9
7839992	1 2 3 5 9
7839997	1 2 3 5
7840070	1 2 3 5
7840071	1 2 3 5
7840072	1 2 3 5
7840073	1 2 3 5
7840074	1 2 3 5
7840075	1 2 3 5
7840076	1 2 3 5
7840080	1 2 3 5 9
7840139	1 2 3 5 9
7840157	1 2 3 5 9
7840216	1 2 3 5
7840234	1 2 3 5 9
7840235	1 2 3 5 9
7840244	1 2 3 5 9
7840364	1 2 3 5
7840380	1 2 3 5 9
7840454	1 2 3 5
7840455	1 2 3 5
7840517	1 2 3 5 9
7840520	1 2 9
7840523	3 5
7840525	1 2 3 5 9
7840555	3 5
7840556	3 5
7840557	3 5
7840566	1 2 3 5 9
7840567	1 2 9
7840569	1 2 3 5 9
7840573	1 2 3 5 9
7840633	1 2 3 5 9
7840807	1 2 9
7840915	1 2 3 5 9
7840916	1 2 3 5 9
7840976	1 2 3 5 9
7840991	1 2 3 5 9
7840999	3 5
7841000	3 5
7841034	1 2 3 5 9
7841079	1 2 9
7841238	1 2 9
7841239	1 2 3 5
7841300	1 2 3 5
7841302	1 2 3 5
7841303	1 2 3 5
7841344	1 2 3 5 9
7841388	1 2 3 5 9
7841389	1 2 3 5
7841392	1 2 3 5 9
7841393	1 2 3 5
7841463	1 2 9
7841464	3 5
7841467	1 2 3 5 9
7841515	1 2 9
7841747	1 2 3 5 9
7841770	1 2 3 5 9
7841783	1 2 3 5 9
7841803	1 2 3 5
7841845	1 2 3 5 9
7841851	1 2 3 5 9
7841853	1 2 3 5 9
7841855	1 2 3 5 9
7841954	1 2 3 5
7842006	1 2 3 5 9
7842007	3 5
7842037	1 2 3 5
7842039	1 2 3 5
7842040	1 2 3 5
7842053	1 2 3 5 9
7842076	1 2 3 5
7842086	1 2 3 5 9
7842091	3 5
7842129	1 2 3 5
7842145	1 2 9
7842146	1 2
7842152	1 2 3 5
7842238	1 2 3 5
7842256	1 2 3 5 9
7842258	1 2 3 5 9
7842344	1 2 3 5 9
7842345	1 2 3 5 9
7842346	1 2 3 5
7842347	1 2 3 5
7842378	1 2 3 5 9
7842379	1 2 3 5
7842380	1 2 3 5 9
7842504	1 2 3 5
7842584	1 2 3 5
7842619	3 5
7842624	1 2 9
7842625	1 2
7842626	1 2 3 5 9
7842628	1 2 3 5 9
7842630	3 5
7842638	1 2 9
7842705	1 2 3 5
7842714	1 2 3 5 9
7842853	1 2 3 5 9
7842935	3 5
7843087	3 5
7843182	1 2 3 5
7843183	1 2 3 5
7843184	1 2 3 5
7843185	1 2 3 5
7843186	1 2 3 5
7843187	1 2 9
7843188	1 2 9
7843189	1 2 9
7843190	1 2 9
7843191	1 2 9
7843293	1 2 3 5
7843451	1 2 3 5 9
7843497	1 2 3 5 9
7843576	1 2 3 5
7843577	1 2 3 5
7843683	1 2 3 5 9
7843684	2 3 5
7843737	1 2 9
7843739	1 2 9
7843742	1 2 3
7843744	1 2 9
7843766	1 2 3 5 9
7843767	1 2 3 5 9
7843875	1 2 9
7843911	1 2 3 5
7843912	1 2 3 5
7843913	1 2 3 5
7843914	1 2 3 5
7843915	1 2 3 5
7843916	1 2 3 5
7843917	1 2 3 5
7843919	1 2 3 5
7843920	1 2 3 5 9
7843922	1 2 3 5 9
7843923	1 2 3 5
7843924	1 2 3 5
7843976	1 2 3 5 9
7844038	1 2 3 5
7844039	1 2 3 5
7844040	1 2
7844041	1 2
7844064	1 2 9
7844065	1 2 9
7844066	1 2 9
7844067	1 2 9
7844531	1 2 9
7844630	1 2 3 5 9
7844631	1 2 3 5 9
7844693	1 2 3 5
7844704	1 2 3 5
7844745	1 2 3 5
7844748	1 2 3 5
7844750	1 2 3 5
7844752	1 2 3 5 9
7844754	1 2 3 5
7844756	1 2 3 5
7844758	1 2 3 5
7844760	1 2 3 5
7844762	1 2 3 5 9
7844764	1 2 3 5 9
7844766	1 2 3 5 9
7844790	1 2 3 5 9
7844812	1 2
7844813	1 2
7844818	1 2 3 5 9
7844910	1 2 3 5 9
7844954	1 2 3 5
7844994	1 2 9
7845009	1 2 3 5
7845012	1 2 9
7845013	1 2 9
7845014	1 2 9
7845015	1 2 3 5
7845016	1 2 3 5
7845019	1 2 3 5
7845020	1 2 3 5 9
7845021	1 2 3 5 9
7845022	1 2 3 5 9
7845023	1 2 9
7845024	1 2 3 5
7845025	1 2 3 5 9
7845026	1 2 3 5 9
7845028	1 2 3 5 9
7845129	1 2 3 5 9
7845152	1 2 3 5 9
7845153	1 2 3
7845161	1 2 3
7845165	1 2
7845171	1 2 3 5
7845187	1 2 3 5 9
7845188	1 2 3
7845203	1 2 3
7845234	3 5
7845286	1 2 9
7845347	1 2 3 5 9
7845348	1 2 3
7845350	1 2 3 5
7845351	1 2 3 5
7845353	1 2 3 5
7845378	1 2
7845393	1 2 3 5
7845394	1 2 3 5
7845395	1 2 3 5 9
7845396	1 2 3
7845397	1 2 3 5
7845398	1 2 3 5 9
7845409	1 2 3
7845425	1 2 3 9
7845426	1 2 9
7845561	1 2 9
7845577	1 2 3
7845915	1 2 3 5
7846095	1 2 3 5
7846096	1 2 3 5 9
7846161	1 2 9
7846164	1 2 3 5
7846165	1 2 3 5
7846169	1 2 3 5
7846170	1 2 3 5 9
7846171	1 2 3 5
7846210	1 2 9
7846217	1 2 3 5
7846269	1 2 3 5
7846270	1 2 3 5
7846271	1 2 3 5
7846273	1 2 3 5 9
7846274	1 2 3 5 9
7846275	1 2 3 5 9
7846276	1 2 3 5
7846281	1 2 3 5
7846282	1 2 3 5
7846340	1 2 9
7846610	1 2 9
7846633	1 2 3 5 9
7846634	1 2 3 5 9
7846635	1 2 3 5 9
7846636	1 2 3 5 9
7846688	1 2 3 5

General Motors Part Number Interchange

Code following part numbers indicate interchangeability of this part with other General Motors cars.

1—Buick 2—Oldsmobile 3—Pontiac 5—Chevrolet 9—Cadillac

Part Number	Interchange
7846689	1 2 3 5
7846690	1 2 9
7846691	1 2 9
7846712	1 2 9
7846728	1 2 3 5
7846729	1 2 9
7846792	1 2 3 5
7846800	1 2 3 5
7846860	1 2 3 5
7846861	1 2 3 5
7846862	1 2 3 5
7846865	1 2 3 5 9
7846866	1 2 3 5 9
7846867	1 2 3 5 9
7846868	1 2 3 5 9
7846869	1 2 3 5 9
7846870	1 2 3 5 9
7846871	1 2 3 5
7846873	1 2 3 5
7846874	1 2 3 5
7846875	1 2 3 5
7846877	1 2 3 5
7846878	1 2 3 5
7846879	1 2 3 5
7846884	1 2
7846953	1 2 3
7847006	1 2 3 5 9
7847007	1 2 3 5 9
7847100	1 2 9
7847102	1 2 3 5 9
7847103	1 2 3 5
7847104	1 2 3 5
7847105	1 2 3 5
7847107	1 2 3 5
7847108	1 2 3 5
7847109	1 2 3 5
7847110	1 2 3 5
7847111	1 2 3 5 9
7847112	1 2 3 5 9
7847113	1 2 3 5 9
7847114	1 2 3 5 9
7847127	1 2 3 5 9
7847135	1 2 3 5 9
7847236	1 2 3 5 9
7847281	1 2 3 5 9
7847288	1 2 3 5
7847289	1 2 3 5
7847368	1 2 9
7847369	1 2 9
7847407	1 2 9
7847408	1 2 9
7847467	1 2 3 5 9
7847485	1 2 3 5
7847486	1 2 3 5 9
7847560	1 2 3 5
7847561	1 2 3 5
7847624	1 2 3 5 9
7847638	1 2 3 5
7847866	1 2 3 5
7847967	1 2 3 5
7848080	1 2 3 5 9
7848082	1 2 3
7848110	1 2
7848115	1 2 9
7848148	1 2 9
7848169	1 2 3 5
7848195	1 2 3 5 9
7848196	1 2 3 5 9
7848230	1 2 3 5
7848444	1 2 9
7848522	1 2 3 5 9
7848525	1 2 3 5
7848751	1 2 3 5 9
7848858	1 2 3 5 9
7848859	1 2 3 5 9
7848880	1 2 9
7849037	1 2 9
7849050	1 2 9
7849109	1 2 3 5 9
7849226	1 2 3 5 9
7849244	1 2
7849349	1 2 3 5 9
7849350	1 2 3 5 9
7849351	1 2 3 5 9
7849353	1 2 3 5 9
7849409	1 2 3 5 9
7849438	1 2 3 5 9
7849440	1 2 3
7849698	1 2 3 5 9
7849700	1 2 3 5 9
7849750	1 2 3
7897082	1 3
8907031	3 5
8907035	1 2 3
8912120	3 5
8990625	3 5
8990741	1 2 3 5 9
8993146	1 2 3 5 9
8993793	1 2 3 5 9
8993918	1 2 3 5 9
8994262	1 2 3 5
8994333	1 2 3 5 9
8995251	3 5
8995284	1 2 3 5 9
8996587	3 5
8996588	3 5
8996990	1 2 9
8997189	2 5
8997493	1 2 3 5 9
8997574	1 2 3 5 9
8997639	1 2 3 5 9
8997683	1 2 3 5 9
8997787	1 2 3 5 9
8997916	1 2 3 5 9
8999596	1 2 9
8999615	1 2 3 5 9
8999642	1 3 5
8999706	1 2 3 5 9
8999725	1 2 3 5 9
8999898	3 5
8999979	1 2 3 5
8999981	1 2 3 5
9415132	3 5
9415135	3 5
9417784	2 5 9
9418356	1 2 9
9420095	1 2 5 9
9427851	3 5
9427889	3 5
9436831	1 2 3 5 9
9438758	3 5
9439544	1 2 3 5
9439879	3 5
9441607	1 2
9632728	1 2 9
9632762	1 2 3 5
9632765	2 5
9632766	1 2 9
9632767	1 2 9
9632769	1 2 3 5 9
9757655	1 2 3 5 9
9759275	3 5
9761251	1 2 3 5
9762702	1 2 9
9762703	1 2 9
9762809	1 2 3 5 9
9762810	1 2 3 5
9762812	3 5
9762928	3 5
9766402	1 2 3 5 9
9767071	3 5
9767072	3 5
9767112	1 2 3 5 9
9767281	1 2 3 5 9
9767287	1 2 3 5
9767781	1 2 3 5 9
9767945	1 2 3 5
9767946	1 2 3 5
9768046	3 5
9768127	1 2 3 5 9
9768144	1 2 3 5 9
9769365	1 2 9
9769366	1 2 9
9769588	3 5
9769592	3 5
9769604	1 2 3 5 9
9769668	1 2 3 5 9
9769738	3 5
9772831	1 2 3 5 9
9778184	1 2 9
9785792	1 2 3 5 9
9792718	2 9
9794682	1 2 3 5 9
9796480	1 2 3 5 9
9956695	1 2 3 5 9
10000063	1 2 3 5
10000068	2 3
10000076	1 2 3 5
10000334	1 2 3 5 9
10000887	1 2 3 5 9
10000904	1 2 3 5
10000910	1 2 3 5
10000952	2 3
10000953	2 3
10001059	1 2 3 5
10001060	1 2 3 5
10001749	3 5
10001752	3 5
10002685	1 2 3 5
10002798	3 5
10002810	1 2 5 9
10002811	1 2 5
10002812	1 2 5
10002813	1 2 5 9
10002814	1 2 5
10004031	1 2 3 5
10004073	1 2 3 5
10004110	2 3
10004179	1 2 5 9
10004180	1 2 5
10004842	1 2 3 5
10005354	1 2 9
10005942	1 2 3 5
10006445	1 2 3 5
10006446	1 2 3 5
10006745	1 2 3 5
10007770	1 2 3 5
10007818	1 2 3 5
10008206	1 2 3 5
10008555	1 2 3 5
10009785	1 2 3 5
10011579	1 2
10013800	1 2 3 5
10014819	1 2 3 5
10017875	1 2 3
10017943	1 2 3 5
10018021	1 2 3 5 9
10018197	1 2 3 5 9
10018217	3 5
10018218	3 5
10018255	1 2 5 9
10018262	1 2 3 5
10018449	1 2 3 5 9
10018450	1 2 3 5 9
10018632	1 2 3 5
10018638	1 2 3 5
10018699	1 2 3 5
10018740	1 2 3 5 9
10018742	1 2 3 5 9
10019018	1 2 3 5
10019083	1 2 3 5 9
10019119	3 5
10019317	1 2 3 5
10019319	1 2 3 5
10019333	1 2 3 5 9
10019451	3 5
10019492	3 5
10019526	3 5
10019535	1 2 3 5 9
10019594	1 2 3 5 9

Code following part numbers indicate interchangeability of this part with other General Motors cars.
1—Buick 2—Oldsmobile 3—Pontiac 5—Chevrolet 9—Cadillac

Part Number	Code
10020249	1 5
10020495	1 2 3 5
10020689	1 2 3 5
10020699	1 2 3 5
10020700	3 5
10021047	3 5
10021195	1 2 3 5
10021360	1 2 3 5
10021542	1 2 3 5
10021729	3 5
10021898	1 2 3 5
10022087	1 2 3 5 9
10022316	1 2 3 5
10022418	1 2 3 5 9
10022543	1 2 3 5
10022558	1 2 3 5
10022559	1 2 3 5
10022719	1 2 3 5
10022865	1 2 3 5 9
10022867	1 2 3 5 9
10022882	1 2 3 5
10022887	1 2 3 5
10022888	1 2 3 5
10023093	1 2 3 5
10023178	3 5
10023182	1 2 3 5
10023355	1 2 3
10024039	1 2 3 5
10024068	3 5
10024378	1 2 3
10025690	3 5
10025926	1 2 3 5
10026023	1 2 3 5
10026361	3 5
10026519	1 2 3 5
10026571	1 2 3 5
10026572	1 2 3 5
10026575	3 5
10026578	1 2 9
10026663	1 2 3 5 9
10026678	1 2
10026724	1 2 3 5 9
10026772	1 2 9
10026773	1 2 9
10026805	1 2 3 5
10026815	1 2 3 5
10027004	1 2 9
10027029	1 2 9
10027268	1 2 9
10027287	1 2 3 5
10027317	1 2 3 5
10027416	1 2 3 5
10027439	1 2 3 5 9
10027595	1 2 3
10027642	1 2 3 5 9
10027719	1 2 3
10027766	1 2 3
10027772	1 2 3
10027862	1 2 3 5 9
10028052	1 2 3 5
10028055	1 2 3 5
10028060	3 5
10028061	3 5
10028204	3 5
10028219	1 2 3
10028243	1 2 3 5 9
10028272	1 2 3 5 9
10028275	1 2 3 5 9
10028404	1 2 3 5
10028508	1 2 3 5
10028726	3 5
10028746	1 2 3 5
10028860	1 2 9
10028930	1 2 3 5
10029093	1 2 3 5
10029094	1 2 3 5
10029130	3 5
10029177	1 2 3 5 9
10029235	1 2 3 5 9
10029237	1 2 3 5 9
10029240	1 2 3 5 9
10029554	1 2 3 5
10029616	1 2 3 5
10029787	1 2 3 5
10029797	1 2 3 5
10029829	1 2 9
10029901	3 5
10029902	3 5
10030011	1 2 3
10030202	1 2 3 5
10030354	1 2 3 5
10030418	3 5
10030691	1 2 3 5
10030694	1 2 3 5
10030695	1 2 3 5
10030773	1 2 3 5
10030774	1 2 3 5
10030790	1 2 3 5 9
10030825	3 5
10030831	3 5
10030838	1 2 3 5
10030839	3 5
10030872	1 2 3 5 9
10030873	1 2 3
10030963	1 2 3 5 9
10030964	3 5
10031027	1 2 3 5 9
10031028	1 2 3 5 9
10031208	1 2 3 5 9
10031262	1 2 3 5
10031268	1 2 3 5 9
10031271	1 2 3 5 9
10031363	1 2 3 5 9
10031423	1 2 3
10032022	3 5
10032079	1 2 3 5 9
10032081	1 2 3 5
10032082	1 2 3 5 9
10032111	1 2 3 5 9
10032479	1 2 3 5
10032603	1 2 3 5
10032604	1 2 3 5
10032916	1 2 3 5
10033118	1 2 3 5
10033836	1 2 3 5
10034162	1 2 3 5
10034216	1 2 3
10034222	1 2 3
10034255	3 5
10034268	1 2 3
10035032	1 2 3 5
10035038	1 2 3
10035039	1 2 3 5
10035893	1 2 3 5
10036062	1 2 3 5
10036106	1 2 3 5
10036107	3 5
10036285	1 2 3
10036286	1 2 3 5
10036435	1 2 3 5 9
10036465	1 2 3 5
10036788	1 2 3 5
10036836	1 2 3 5
10036837	1 2 3
10036939	1 2 3
10036983	1 2 3
10037018	1 2 3 5
10037104	3 5
10037105	3 5
10037142	3 5
10037143	1 2 3 5
10037144	1 2 3
10037146	3 5
10037147	1 2 3
10037148	1 2 3 5
10037199	3 5
10037279	1 2 3
10037280	1 2 3 5
10037281	1 2 3
10037282	1 2 3 5
10037283	3 5
10037309	1 2 3
10037424	1 2 3 5 9
10037425	1 2 3 5 9
10037426	1 2 3 5 9
10037427	1 2 3 5 9
10037596	3 5
10038311	1 2 3
10038490	1 2 3
10038601	1 2 9
10038932	1 2 3 5 9
10039426	1 2 3 5 9
10039880	1 2 3 5
10040095	1 2 3 5 9
10040131	1 2 3
10041073	1 2 3 5 9
10041074	1 2 3 5 9
10041215	1 2 3
10041562	1 2 3 5
10042008	1 2 3 5 9
10042191	3 5
10042325	3 5
10042327	3 5
10042841	3 5
10042842	3 5
10042843	1 2 3 5
10042846	1 2 3 5
10044245	1 2 3
10044845	1 2 3 5 9
10044850	1 2 3 5 9
10046307	3 5
10048953	3 5
10048962	3 5
10049070	1 2 3
10054503	3 5
10054506	1 2 3
10456319	1 2 9
10495062	3 5
10495253	1 2 9
10495353	1 2 3 5
10495408	1 2 3 5 9
10495411	1 2 3 5 9
10495788	1 2 3 5 9
10495801	1 2 3 5 9
10495802	3 5
10495822	1 2 3 5 9
10495845	1 2 3 5 9
10495860	3 5
10495877	1 2
10495881	1 2 9
10495885	1 2 9
10495931	1 2 3 5 9
10495958	1 2 3 5 9
10496043	3 5
10496048	3 5
10496330	1 2
10496541	1 2 3 5 9
10496765	1 2 3 5 9
10497046	1 2 3
10497108	1 2 9
10497110	1 2
10497111	1 2 9
10497118	1 2 3
10497119	1 2 3
10497120	1 2 3
10497121	1 2 3
10497135	3 5
10497136	3 5
10497180	1 2 3 9
10497452	1 2 3 5 9
10497454	1 2 3 5 9
10497570	1 2 9
10497771	1 2 3
10498407	1 2 3 9
10499163	1 2 9
12003646	1 2 3 5
12007887	3 5
12011371	3 5
12013431	1 2 3
12015288	2 5

General Motors Part Number Interchange

Code following part numbers indicate interchangeability of this part with other General Motors cars.

1—Buick 2—Oldsmobile 3—Pontiac 5—Chevrolet 9—Cadillac

12026581	1 2 3 5
12028276	1 2 3 5 9
12034544	1 2 3 5 9
12042315	1 2
12046243	1 2
12300192	1 2 3 5 9
12300194	1 2 3 5 9
12300210	1 2 9
12300214	1 2 3 5
12300219	1 2 3 5 9
12300220	1 2 9
12300221	1 2 9
12300223	3 5
12300227	1 2 3 5
12300228	1 2 9
12300230	3 5
12300235	1 2 3 5
12300241	3 5
12300242	1 2 3 5
12300243	1 2 3 5
12300248	1 2 3 5 9
12300249	1 2 3 5
12300255	3 5
12300273	1 2 3 5 9
12300274	1 2 9
12300307	1 2 3 5
12300474	1 2 3 5 9
12300849	1 2 3 5 9
12308612	1 2 3 5 9
12309213	3 5
12309214	1 2 3 5
12309215	1 2 3 5
12309216	1 2
12309223	1 2 3 5
12309301	1 2 3 5 9
12321358	1 2 9
12321360	1 2 9
12321362	3 5
12321363	1 2 3 5
12321365	3 5
12321366	1 2 3 5
12321368	1 2 3 5 9
12321410	1 2 3 5 9
12321411	3 5
12321412	1 2 3 5 9
12321413	1 2 3 5
12321414	1 2 9
12321415	1 2 9
12321416	1 2 9
12321417	1 2 3 5 9
12321418	3 5
12321420	1 2 9
12322146	1 2 3
12322147	1 2 3 5 9
12322321	1 2 3 5
12322322	1 2 3 5
12322327	1 2 3 5
12322330	1 2 3 5
12322331	1 2 3 5
12322334	1 2 3 5 9
12322336	1 2 9
12322348	1 2 9
12322349	3 5
12323602	1 2 9
12323603	1 2 9
12323604	1 2 9
12326201	3 5
14001166	3 5
14001168	3 5
14001171	3 5
14001182	3 5
14001187	3 5
14001193	3 5
14001235	3 5
14001236	3 5
14002446	1 2 3 5 9
14002525	1 2 3 5
14002534	1 2 3 5 9
14002535	1 2 3 5 9
14003932	1 2 3 5
14004097	1 2 3 5 9
14004098	1 2 3 5 9
14004099	1 2 3 5 9
14004902	1 2 3 5
14004972	3 5
14006401	1 2 3 9
14008640	1 2 3 5
14008641	1 2 3 5 9
14008874	3 5
14008878	3 5
14008925	3 5
14008949	3 5
14008950	3 5
14009262	1 2 3 5 9
14011207	3 5
14011209	3 5
14011912	3 5
14011913	3 5
14012589	1 2 5 9
14012590	1 2 3 5 9
14012595	1 2 5
14012596	1 2 3 5
14012602	1 2 3 5
14014559	3 5
14014599	1 2 3 5 9
14015975	2 3 5
14015976	2 3 5
14018397	3 5
14018708	1 2 3 5 9
14018709	1 2 3 5 9
14018711	1 2 3 5 9
14018713	1 2 3 5 9
14018723	1 2 3 5 9
14018726	1 2 3 5 9
14018764	1 2 3 5 9
14018766	1 2 3 5 9
14018769	1 2 3 5 9
14018770	1 2 3 5 9
14018791	1 2 3 5 9
14019306	3 5
14019311	3 5
14019320	3 5
14019453	3 5
14019454	3 5
14019828	3 5
14019867	3 5
14019868	3 5
14020936	3 5
14021195	3 5
14021196	3 5
14022171	1 2 3 5 9
14022172	1 2 3 5 9
14022278	3 5
14023145	3 5
14023148	3 5
14023727	3 5
14023782	3 5
14023797	3 5
14024249	1 2 3 5
14024254	1 2 3 5
14024278	1 2 3 5
14024395	3 5
14024396	3 5
14024422	3 5
14024930	1 2 3 5 9
14025558	1 2 3 5
14025571	3 5
14025572	3 5
14026610	1 2 3
14026619	1 2 3 5 9
14026620	1 2 3 5 9
14026628	1 2 3 5 9
14026673	1 2 3 5 9
14026688	1 2 3 5 9
14026689	1 2 3 5 9
14026865	3 5
14026941	1 2 3 5
14026942	1 2 3 5
14028821	1 2 3 5 9
14029033	3 5
14029473	3 5
14029519	1 2 3 5
14029586	3 5
14030029	1 2 3 5 9
14030434	1 2 3 5
14030435	1 2 3 5
14031310	3 5
14031322	1 2 3 5
14031328	1 2 3 5 9
14031332	1 2 3 5 9
14031361	3 5
14031362	1 2 3 5
14031365	1 2 3 5 9
14031378	1 2 3 5 9
14031507	3 5
14031637	3 5
14031638	3 5
14032007	1 2 9
14032098	3 5
14032231	1 2 3 5
14032232	1 2 3 5
14032315	3 5
14032316	3 5
14032336	3 5
14032337	3 5
14032344	3 5
14032431	1 2 3 5
14033077	3 5
14033087	3 5
14033090	3 5
14033107	3 5
14033120	1 2 3 5 9
14033129	1 2 3 5
14033180	3 5
14033199	1 2 3 5
14033208	1 2 3 5
14033209	1 2 3 5
14033227	1 2 3 5 9
14033250	1 2 3 5
14033251	1 2 3 5
14033299	1 2 3 5
14033422	3 5
14033458	3 5
14033476	1 2 3 5
14033483	1 2 3 5
14033526	1 2 3 5
14033547	3 5
14033550	1 2 3 5
14033553	3 5
14034115	3 5
14034320	3 5
14034677	1 2 3 5
14034713	3 5
14034719	3 5
14034785	1 2 3 5
14034807	3 5
14034821	3 5
14034864	3 5
14034944	3 5
14034945	3 5
14034969	1 2 3 5
14035588	1 2 3 5 9
14036273	3 5
14036459	1 2 3 5
14037647	3 5
14037782	3 5
14038088	1 3 5
14038192	1 2 9
14038194	1 2 9
14038399	3 5
14038400	3 5
14038539	1 2 3 5
14038540	1 2 3 5
14038692	3 5
14038699	3 5
14038789	1 2 3 5 9
14038791	1 2 3 5 9
14039009	1 2 3 5 9
14039010	1 2 3 5 9
14039011	1 2 3 5

Code following part numbers indicate interchangeability of this part with other General Motors cars.
1—Buick 2—Oldsmobile 3—Pontiac 5—Chevrolet 9—Cadillac

Part Number	Code
14039012	1 2 3 5
14039015	1 2 3 5 9
14039016	1 2 3 5 9
14039068	3 5
14039143	1 2 3 5 9
14039219	1 2 9
14039220	1 2 9
14039229	1 2 9
14039230	1 2 9
14039405	3 5
14039437	3 5
14039603	3 5
14039681	1 2 3 5 9
14040134	1 2 3 5 9
14040135	1 2 3 5 9
14040816	1 2 3 5 9
14041882	3 5
14041893	1 2 9
14041935	3 5
14042001	3 5
14042098	3 5
14042537	1 2 3 5
14042575	3 5
14043278	1 2 3 5
14043373	3 5
14045078	1 2 5
14045734	2 3 5
14046383	1 2 3 5 9
14046491	1 2 3 5 9
14046803	3 5
14046814	3 5
14046846	1 2 3 5 9
14046950	1 2 3 5
14046977	1 2 3 5
14046978	1 2 3 5
14047186	1 2 3 5 9
14047196	1 2 3 5 9
14047918	3 5
14048355	3 5
14048378	3 5 9
14048380	2 3 5
14048385	3 5
14048387	3 5
14048436	3 5 9
14048827	3 5
14048828	3 5
14048829	3 5
14049337	1 2 3 5
14049343	1 2 3 5
14049735	1 2 3 5 9
14049740	1 2 3 5 9
14049741	1 2 3 5
14049775	1 2 3 5 9
14051008	1 2 3 5 9
14051034	1 2 3 5 9
14051035	1 2 3 5 9
14052305	3 5
14052374	1 2 3 5
14052375	3 5
14053339	3 5
14053343	3 5
14054539	3 5
14054541	1 2 3 5
14054555	1 2 3 5
14054877	3 5
14054879	1 2 3 5 9
14054880	3 5
14054882	1 2 3 5
14055093	3 5
14055094	3 5
14055483	3 5
14055484	3 5
14055901	3 5
14055902	3 5
14056179	1 2 9
14056425	1 2 3 5
14056648	1 2
14057041	3 5
14057043	3 5
14057519	3 5
14057554	1 2 3 5 9
14057917	1 2 3 5 9
14057964	1 2 3 5 9
14057996	1 2 3 5 9
14058000	1 2 3 5 9
14058550	3 5
14058577	1 2 3 5 9
14058578	1 2 3 5 9
14058724	1 2 3 5 9
14059035	3 5
14059038	3 5
14059045	1 2 3 5 9
14059084	3 5
14059125	1 2 3 5
14059196	3 5
14059321	3 5
14059347	1 2 3 5
14059934	1 2 3 5 9
14059935	1 2 3 5 9
14059936	1 2 3 5 9
14059937	1 2 3 5 9
14059950	3 5
14059991	1 2 3 5 9
14059999	1 2 3 5 9
14060000	1 2 3 5 9
14060651	3 5
14060653	3 5
14060655	3 5
14060881	1 2 3 5
14061506	3 5
14061601	3 5
14062135	1 2 3 5
14062647	3 5
14062665	3 5
14062702	1 2 3 5 9
14062724	1 2 3 5 9
14062774	1 2 3 5 9
14063507	1 2 9
14063509	3 5
14063647	1 2 3 5 9
14063922	3 5
14063928	3 5
14063936	1 2 3 5
14064197	1 2 3 5
14064293	3 5
14064294	3 5
14064325	2 5
14064326	1 2 5
14065721	1 2 3 5
14065746	3 5
14065767	3 5
14065768	3 5
14065773	1 2 3 5
14065776	1 2 3 5
14066384	3 5
14066397	3 5
14066569	3 5
14066905	3 5
14066918	1 3
14066979	1 2 3 5
14066980	1 2 3 5
14066983	1 2 3 5 9
14066984	1 2 3 5 9
14067070	1 2 3 5 9
14067495	1 2
14067581	3 5
14067681	3 5
14067683	3 5
14067684	3 5
14067693	1 2 3 5 9
14068691	3 5
14068692	3 5
14069172	3 5
14069227	1 2 9
14069252	1 2 3 5 9
14069253	1 2 3 5 9
14069254	1 2 3 5 9
14069256	1 2 3 5 9
14069600	3 5
14069892	3 5
14070703	1 2 3 5 9
14071174	3 5
14071200	3 5
14071831	1 2 3 5 9
14071864	3 5
14071866	3 5
14073066	3 5
14073068	3 5
14073077	3 5
14073078	3 5
14073081	3 5
14073085	1 2 3 5
14073087	1 2 3 5
14073088	1 2 3 5
14073097	1 2 3 5
14073403	3 5
14073422	1 2 3 5 9
14073454	1 2 3 5 9
14074000	1 2 3 5 9
14074042	1 2 9
14074053	1 2 3
14074054	1 2 3
14074074	1 2 3 5 9
14074075	1 2 3 5 9
14074076	1 2 3 5 9
14074077	1 2 3 5 9
14074092	1 2 3 5 9
14074093	1 2 3
14074098	1 2 3 5 9
14074285	1 2 3 5 9
14074296	1 2 3 5 9
14074297	1 2 3 5 9
14074399	1 2 3 5 9
14074400	1 2 3 5 9
14075315	1 2 3 5
14075337	1 2 3 5
14075611	3 5
14075641	3 5
14075646	3 5
14075718	3 5
14075725	3 5
14075744	1 2
14075768	3 5
14076303	3 5
14076321	3 5
14076354	3 5
14076363	3 5
14076378	3 5
14076605	1 2 3 5 9
14076607	1 2 3 5 9
14076612	1 2 3
14076613	1 2 3
14076624	1 2 3 5 9
14076627	1 2 9
14076629	1 2 3 5 9
14076630	1 2 3 5 9
14076632	1 2 3 5 9
14076647	1 2 9
14076786	1 2 3 5 9
14076787	1 2 3 5 9
14076788	1 2 3 5 9
14076960	3 5
14076993	1 2 3 5
14076994	1 2 3 5
14077222	1 2 3 5 9
14077243	1 2 3 5 9
14077713	1 2 3 5 9
14077717	3 5
14077726	1 2 3 5
14077742	3 5
14077769	1 2 3 5
14077798	1 2 3 5
14077817	1 2 3 5 9
14077829	1 2 3 5 9
14077830	1 2 3 5
14077836	1 2 3 5 9
14077849	1 2 3 5
14077876	1 2 3 5 9
14077944	3 5
14077948	3 5

General Motors Part Number Interchange

Code following part numbers indicate interchangeability of this part with other General Motors cars.

1—Buick 2—Oldsmobile 3—Pontiac 5—Chevrolet 9—Cadillac

14077973	3 5
14078520	3 5
14078587	1 2 3 5 9
14078588	1 2 3 5 9
14078821	1 2 3 5 9
14078841	3 5
14078891	1 2 3 5
14078902	1 2 3 5
14078922	1 2 3
14079003	3 5
14079004	3 5
14079093	3 5
14079329	1 2 3 5
14079330	1 2 3 5
14079341	3 5
14079397	3 5
14079398	3 5
14079410	3 5
14079427	1 2 3 5
14079428	1 2 3 5
14079429	1 2 3 5
14079431	1 2 3 5
14079432	1 2 3 5
14079439	3 5
14079440	3 5
14079443	1 2 3 5
14079473	1 2
14079552	1 2 3 5 9
14079565	1 2 3 5 9
14079572	1 2 3 5 9
14079598	1 2 3 5 9
14079778	1 2 3 5
14079779	1 2 3 5
14079785	1 2 3 5
14079905	1 2 3 5
14079906	1 2 3 5
14079939	3 5
14079940	3 5
14079963	1 2 3 5
14080203	3 5
14080206	1 2 3 5
14080210	1 2 3 5
14080212	1 2 3
14080232	1 2 3
14080264	1 2 9
14080265	1 2 9
14080266	1 2 9
14080663	1 2 3 5 9
14080678	1 2 3 5
14080718	3 5
14080729	3 5
14080730	3 5
14080731	3 5
14080780	1 2 3 5
14080788	3 5
14080793	3 5
14080794	3 5
14080987	1 2 3 5 9
14081146	1 2 3 5 9
14081147	1 2 3 5 9
14081257	3 5
14081291	3 5
14081292	3 5
14081407	1 2 9
14081408	1 2 9
14081409	1 2 9
14081410	1 2 9
14081414	1 2 9
14081415	1 2 9
14081493	1 2
14081494	1 2 3 5 9
14081495	1 2 3 5 9
14081496	1 2 3 5 9
14081497	1 2 3 5 9
14081609	1 2
14081620	1 2
14081703	1 2 3 5 9
14081761	1 2 3 5 9
14081794	1 2 3 5 9
14081798	1 2 3 5 9
14081966	1 2 3 5
14082322	3 5
14082324	3 5
14082793	3 5
14082794	3 5
14082814	1 2 9
14082817	3 5
14082847	1 2 3 5
14082848	1 2 3 5
14082853	3 5
14082873	3 5
14082883	1 2 3 5
14082884	1 2 3 5
14082893	1 2 9
14082894	1 2 9
14083314	1 2 3 5
14083328	1 2 3 5 9
14083394	1 2 3 5
14083512	3 5
14083559	1 2 9
14083561	3 5
14083562	3 5
14084118	1 2 3 5 9
14084119	1 2 3 5 9
14084120	1 2 3 5
14084152	3 5
14084153	3 5
14084165	3 5
14084166	3 5
14084351	1 2 3 5
14085064	1 2 3 5 9
14085142	1 2 3
14085143	1 2 3 5 9
14085145	1 2 3 5 9
14085147	1 2 3 5 9
14085152	1 2 3
14085156	1 2 3
14085392	1 2 9
14085397	1 2 9
14085401	3 5
14085433	3 5
14085435	1 2 3 5
14085471	1 2 3 5 9
14085472	3 5
14085720	3 5
14085829	1 2 3 5 9
14085847	3 5
14085856	3 5
14085858	3 5
14085869	3 5
14085898	3 5
14085899	3 5
14086017	1 2 3 5 9
14086036	1 2 3 5 9
14086060	1 2 3 5 9
14086280	1 2 3 5
14086601	1 2 3
14086602	1 2 3
14086605	1 2 3
14086606	1 2 3
14086700	1 2 3 5 9
14086832	1 2 9
14086840	3 5
14086860	1 2
14086877	1 2 9
14086958	1 2 3
14086976	1 2 3 5 9
14087014	3 5
14087220	1 2 3 5 9
14087237	1 2 3 5 9
14087239	1 2 3 5
14087241	1 2 3
14087242	1 2 3 5
14088505	3 5
14088514	3 5
14088527	3 5
14088536	3 5
14088639	3 5
14088646	3 5
14088650	3 5
14088682	3 5
14088683	3 5
14088765	3 5
14088815	3 5
14088816	3 5
14088822	3 5
14088823	3 5
14089003	1 2 3 5 9
14089004	1 2 3 5
14089006	3 5
14089007	1 2 3 5 9
14089008	1 2 3 5
14089010	3 5
14089011	1 2 3 5 9
14089017	3 5
14089018	1 2 3 5 9
14089019	1 2 3 5 9
14089020	3 5
14089021	1 2 3 5 9
14089022	1 2 3 5 9
14089025	3 5
14089032	1 2 3 5 9
14089033	1 2 3 5 9
14089034	1 2 3 5 9
14089057	3 5
14089058	1 2 3 5 9
14089059	1 2 3 5 9
14089062	1 2 3 5 9
14089070	1 2 3 5
14089075	1 2 3 5
14089088	1 2 3 5
14089117	1 2 9
14089118	1 2 9
14089120	3 5
14089130	3 5
14089137	1 2 3 5 9
14089151	3 5
14089152	3 5
14089154	3 5
14089184	1 2 3 5 9
14089185	1 2 3 5 9
14089187	1 2 3 5 9
14089252	1 2 3 5
14089253	1 2 3 5
14089433	3 5
14089438	3 5
14089453	3 5
14089518	1 2 3 5
14089592	1 2 3 5 9
14089826	1 2 3 5
14089876	3 5
14090561	1 2 3 5 9
14090952	3 5
14091312	1 2 3 5
14091316	1 2 3 5
14091317	1 2 3 5
14091323	3 5
14091324	3 5
14091326	3 5
14091328	3 5
14091347	1 2 3 5 9
14091364	1 2 3 5 9
14091380	3 5
14091389	3 5
14091390	3 5
14091403	1 2 3 5
14091434	3 5
14091439	3 5
14091479	3 5
14091757	1 2 3
14091759	1 2 3
14091968	1 2 3 5 9
14091979	3 5
14091980	3 5
14091981	3 5
14092910	1 2 3 5 9
14092911	1 2 3 5
14094097	3 5
14094104	1 2 3 5 9
14094397	3 5

Code following part numbers indicate interchangeability of this part with other General Motors cars.
1—Buick 2—Oldsmobile 3—Pontiac 5—Chevrolet 9—Cadillac

14094398	3 5
14094526	1 2 3 5
14094574	3 5
14094596	3 5
14094715	3 5
14095256	3 5
14095451	3 5
14095620	1 2 3 5 9
14095621	3 5
14095622	3 5
14101185	3 5
14101304	3 5
14101315	3 5
14101329	1 2 3 5 9
14101331	1 2 3 5 9
14101336	1 2 3 5 9
14101358	1 2 3 5 9
14102596	1 2 3 5 9
14102670	3 5
14102671	1 2 3 5 9
14103396	1 2 3 5 9
14105927	1 2 3
14105928	1 2 3
15550410	3 5
15590168	3 5
16003736	1 2 9
16004018	1 2 9
16004273	1 2 9
16006832	1 2 9
16006833	1 2 3 5 9
16006834	1 2 3 5 9
16006835	1 2 3 5 9
16009886	1 2 9
16010356	1 2 9
16012468	1 2 9
16015256	1 2 3 5 9
16015450	1 2 3 5 9
16015606	1 2 9
16017460	1 2 3 5 9
16017911	1 2 3 5
16018196	1 2 9
16021853	1 2 3 5 9
16022134	1 2
16022604	1 2 3 5
16022614	1 2 9
16022654	1 2 3
16023256	1 2 9
16023333	1 2 3 5 9
16023856	1 2 9
16025293	1 2 3 5
16025803	1 2
16027366	1 2 3 5 9
16027372	1 2 3 5 9
16028093	1 2 9
16028106	1 2 9
16028981	1 2 3 5 9
16028991	1 2 3 5 9
16029953	1 2 9
16030101	1 2 3 5 9
16030176	1 2 3 5 9
16030474	1 2 9
16032480	1 2 3 5 9
16032872	1 2 3 5 9
16033615	1 2 3 5
16033806	1 2 9
16034550	1 2 3 5 9
16034560	1 2 3 5 9
16034571	1 2 3 5 9
16034581	1 2 3 5 9
16035382	1 2 3
16035383	1 2 3
16035392	1 2 3
16035393	1 2 3
16035412	1 2 3
16036494	1 2
16037553	1 2 9
16037674	1 2 9
16037745	1 2 9
16037768	1 2 3 5 9
16037814	3 5
16037819	3 5
16037824	3 5
16037849	1 2 9
16038094	1 2 9
16038634	1 2 3
16038644	1 2 3
16039614	1 2
16039619	1 2
16039649	1 2 9
16040344	3 5
16040349	3 5
16040692	1 2 3 5 9
16040790	1 2
16040802	1 2 9
16041052	1 2 3
16041224	1 2 3
16041520	1 2 3
16041526	1 2 3 5
16041589	1 2 9
16041935	1 2 9
16042000	1 2 9
16042010	1 2 9
16042014	1 2 9
16042017	1 2 9
16042020	1 2 9
16042024	1 2 9
16042042	1 2 9
16042045	1 2 9
16042066	1 2 9
16042069	1 2 9
16043718	1 2 9
16043785	1 2 9
16043792	1 2 9
16043798	1 2 9
16043804	1 2 9
16043810	1 2 9
16043816	1 2 9
16043882	1 2 9
16044104	1 2 3
16044109	1 2 3
16044114	1 2
16044119	1 2
16045609	1 2
16045619	1 2
16045629	1 2 9
16045639	1 2
16045931	1 2 9
16046505	3 5
16046511	3 5
16046516	3 5
16046521	3 5
16046526	3 5
16046531	3 5
16047082	1 2 3 5 9
16047215	1 2 9
16047237	1 2 9
16047428	1 2 3
16047526	1 2 9
16047800	1 2 9
16048138	1 2 9
16048249	3 5
16048255	3 5
16048879	1 2 9
16049206	1 2 9
16049534	1 2 9
16049998	1 2 3
16050180	1 2 3 5 9
16050268	1 2
16050672	1 2 9
16050693	3 5
16050698	3 5
16050729	1 2 9
16051108	1 2 3
16051333	1 2 3
16051685	1 2 9
16052184	1 2 9
16052276	1 2 9
16052282	1 2 9
16052614	1 2 9
16052781	1 2 3 5 9
16052959	1 2 3
16053017	1 2 9
16053048	1 2 9
16053643	1 2 9
16054434	1 2 9
16054464	1 2 9
16054466	1 2 9
16054920	1 3
16055132	1 2
16055155	1 2 9
16055169	1 2 9
16055821	1 2
16055825	1 2
16057846	1 2
16059158	1 2 9
16059163	1 2 9
16059913	1 2 9
16059958	1 2 3
16060264	1 2 9
16060423	1 2 9
16060587	1 2 9
16060592	1 2 9
16060865	1 2 3
16346489	1 2 9
16500327	1 2 3 5
16500328	1 2 3 5
16500488	1 2 9
16500533	1 2 9
16500534	1 2 9
16500601	3 5
16500602	3 5
16500607	3 5
16500608	3 5
16500679	1 2 9
16500680	1 2 9
16500791	1 2 9
16500929	1 2 3 5
16500930	1 2 3 5
16500959	1 2 9
16500960	1 2 9
16500991	3 5
16500992	3 5
16501053	1 2 9
16501054	1 2 9
16501334	1 2 9
16501335	1 2 9
16501341	1 2 3 5 9
16501342	1 2 3 5 9
16501565	1 2 3 5
16501575	1 2 3 5
16501576	1 2 3 5
16501579	1 2 3 5
16501580	1 2 3 5
16501589	1 2 3 5 9
16501590	1 2 3 5 9
16501653	1 2 3 5
16501654	1 2 3 5
16501667	1 2 3 5
16501668	1 2 3 5
16501701	1 2 3 5
16501702	1 2 3 5
16501725	1 2 9
16501726	1 2 9
16501763	1 2 3 5 9
16501764	1 2 3 5 9
16501767	1 2 3 5 9
16501768	1 2 3 5 9
16501769	1 2 3 5 9
16501770	1 2 3 5 9
16501775	1 2 3 5 9
16501776	1 2 3 5 9
16501805	1 2 3 5 9
16501806	1 2 3 5 9
16501809	1 2 3 5 9
16501810	1 2 3 5 9
16501819	1 2 3
16501820	1 2 3
16501837	1 2 3
16501839	1 2 3
16501840	1 2 3

General Motors Part Number Interchange

Code following part numbers indicate interchangeability of this part with other General Motors cars.

1—Buick 2—Oldsmobile 3—Pontiac 5—Chevrolet 9—Cadillac

Part Number	Code
16501843	1 2 3
16501844	1 2 3
16501895	1 2 9
16501896	1 2 9
16501975	1 2 3 5 9
16501976	1 2 3 5 9
16502007	3 5
16502008	3 5
16502327	1 2 3 5 9
16502381	1 2 3 5 9
16502382	1 2 3 5 9
16502415	1 2 9
16502416	1 2 9
16502431	1 2 3 5
16502432	1 2 3 5
16502591	1 2 3 5 9
16502635	3 5
16502636	3 5
16502644	1 2 3
16502667	1 2 3 5
16502668	1 2 3 5
16502681	1 2 9
16502682	1 2 9
16502857	3 5
16502858	3 5
16502859	3 5
16502860	3 5
16503179	1 2 3 5 9
16503180	1 2 3 5 9
16503277	1 2 9
16503278	1 2 9
16503377	1 2 3
16503435	1 2 9
16503436	1 2 9
16503487	3 5
16503488	3 5
16503835	1 2
16503951	1 2
16503960	1 2 3 5
16504015	1 2 9
16504411	1 2 3 5 9
16504412	1 2 3 5 9
16504415	1 2 3 5 9
16504416	1 2 3 5 9
16504685	1 2 9
16504686	1 2 9
16504687	1 2 9
16504688	1 2 9
16506895	1 2 3
16507665	1 2 3 5 9
16507666	1 2 3 5 9
17059256	3 5
17063013	1 2 3 5 9
17063019	3 5
17064379	1 2 9
17064622	1 2 3 5 9
17064625	1 2 3 5 9
17064880	1 2 9
17066983	1 2 3
17066984	1 2 3
17067277	1 2 9
17067343	1 2 9
17067999	3 5
17068741	1 2 3 5
17068871	1 2 9
17068882	1 2 3 5 9
17068938	1 2 9
17068941	1 2 9
17068990	1 2 3 5 9
17068992	1 2 3 5
17068993	1 2 3 5
17069019	1 2 3 5
17069030	3 5
17069095	1 2 9
17069115	1 2 9
17070619	1 2 3 5 9
17070622	3 5
17071106	1 2 9
17071231	3 5
17071525	1 2 9
17071711	2 5
17071991	1 2 9
17072400	1 2 3 5
17072581	3 5
17072786	1 2 9
17072997	1 2 5 9
17073284	1 2 3 5
17073535	1 2 3 5
17073947	1 2 3 5
17073948	1 2 3 5
17074054	1 2 3 5
17074370	1 2 9
17074393	3 5
17074976	3 5
17074977	1 2 3 5
17075081	1 2 9
17075122	3 5
17075280	1 2 9
17075824	1 2 3 5
17075825	1 2 3 5 9
17075830	1 2 3 5 9
17075831	1 2 3 5
17075834	1 2 9
17075840	1 2 3 5 9
17075844	1 2 3 5 9
17075849	3 5
17075852	3 5
17075854	1 2 3 5 9
17075855	3 5
17075856	1 2 3 5
17075859	3 5
17076022	1 2 3
17076043	3 5
17076044	1 2 9
17076122	1 2 3 5
17076127	3 5
17076129	1 2 3 5 9
17076141	1 2 3 5 9
17076144	1 2 3 5 9
17078047	3 5
17078220	1 2 3 5
17078222	1 2 3 5 9
17078257	1 2 9
17078259	1 2 9
17078261	3 5
17078262	3 5
17078270	1 2 3 5 9
17078272	1 2 3 5 9
17078273	1 2 3 5 9
17078274	1 2 3 5 9
17078275	1 2 3 5
17078276	1 2 3 5 9
17078448	1 2 5 9
17078832	3 5
17078833	3 5
17078849	1 2 3 5
17078854	3 5
17078855	3 5
17078885	3 5
17078969	1 2 3 5
17079035	1 2 9
17079149	1 2 3 5
17079158	1 2 3 5
17079167	1 2 3 5
17079170	1 2 3 5
17079189	3 5
17079194	3 5
17079201	3 5
17079202	3 5
17079205	1 2 3 5
17079210	1 2 5
17079226	3 5
17079255	1 2 3 5 9
17079256	1 2 3 5 9
17079266	1 2 9
17079267	1 2
17079282	3 5
17079343	1 2
17079412	1 2 9
17079438	1 2
17079440	1 2 3
17079441	1 2 3 5
17079495	1 2 9
17079496	1 2 9
17079498	1 2 9
17079500	1 2 9
17079556	1 2 3 5
17079571	1 2 3 5
17079576	1 2 3 5
17079592	1 2 3 5
17079593	1 2 3 5
17079596	1 2 3 5 9
17079597	1 2 3 5 9
17079599	1 2 3 5 9
17079607	1 2 3 5 9
17079608	1 2 3 5 9
17079609	1 2 3 5 9
17079663	1 2 9
17079672	1 2 9
17079694	1 2 3 5 9
17079716	3 5
17079724	3 5
17079726	3 5
17079729	3 5
17079730	3 5
17079732	3 5
17079792	1 2 3 5
17079832	3 5
17079837	1 2 3 5 9
17079841	1 2 3 5 9
17079851	3 5
17079987	1 2 3 5
17082054	3 5
17082701	1 2 3 5 9
17083702	1 2 9
17085022	1 2 3 5 9
17085023	1 2 3 5
17085026	1 2 3 5
17085027	1 2 9
17085155	1 2 3 5
17085173	1 2 3 5
17085715	3 5
17085907	3 5
17085928	1 2 3 5 9
17085929	1 2 3 5
17085935	1 2 9
17086041	1 2
17086095	3 5
17110012	3 5
17110013	3 5
17110024	3 5
17110201	1 2 3 5
17110332	1 2 3 5
17110337	1 2 3 5 9
17110352	1 2 9
17110353	1 2 9
17110354	1 2 9
17110359	1 2 3 5
17110360	1 2 3 5
17110362	1 2 3 5 9
17110363	1 2 3 5 9
17110368	1 2 3 5 9
17110369	1 2 3 5 9
17110370	1 2 3 5 9
17110371	1 2 3 5 9
17110372	1 2 3 5 9
17110376	1 2 3 5 9
17110377	1 2 3 5 9
17110444	1 2 9
17110448	1 2 9
17110449	3 5
17110450	3 5
17110451	3 5
17110452	3 5
17110461	1 2 9
17110463	1 2 9
17110478	1 2 3
17110487	1 2 9
17110530	1 2 3 5
17110533	1 2 3 5

Code following part numbers indicate interchangeability of this part with other General Motors cars.
1—Buick 2—Oldsmobile 3—Pontiac 5—Chevrolet 9—Cadillac

Part Number	Code
17110536	1 2 3 5
17110537	1 2 3 5
17110538	1 2 3 5
17110599	1 2 9
17110609	1 2
17110635	1 2 9
17110636	1 2 9
17110646	1 2 9
17110656	1 2 9
17110657	1 2 9
17110659	1 2 9
17110662	1 2 9
17110663	1 2 9
17110671	1 2 3 5 9
17110672	1 2 3 5 9
17110674	1 2 3 5 9
17110675	1 2 3 5 9
17110676	1 2 3 5 9
17110759	1 2 3 5 9
17110760	1 2 3 5 9
17110762	1 2 3 5
17110763	1 2 3 5
17110816	1 2 3
17110819	1 2 3
17110820	1 2 3
17110821	1 2 3
17110827	1 2 3 5 9
17110828	1 2 3 5 9
17110829	3 5
17110830	1 2 3 5
17110832	1 2 3 5 9
17110834	1 2 3 5 9
17110835	3 5
17110837	1 2 3 5 9
17110845	3 5
17110849	3 5
17110851	1 2 3 5 9
17110853	1 2 3 5 9
17110854	1 2 3 5
17110855	1 2 3 5
17110856	3 5
17110858	1 2 3 5
17110860	1 2 3 5 9
17110866	3 5
17110871	3 5
17110872	3 5
17110874	3 5
17110901	3 5
17110902	3 5
17110903	3 5
17111092	1 2 9
17111105	1 2 9
17111155	3 5
17111156	3 5
17111157	3 5
17111159	3 5
17111160	3 5
17111162	3 5
17111169	1 2 9
17111170	1 2 9
17111175	1 2 3
17111176	1 2 3 5 9
17111182	1 2 3 5
17111188	1 2 3 5 9
17111245	1 2 3
17111262	1 2 3 5 9
17111277	1 2 9
17111286	1 2 3
17111288	1 2 3 5 9
17111290	1 2 9
17111292	1 2 9
17111293	1 2 3
17111297	1 2 3 5 9
17111336	3 5
17111338	3 5
17111388	1 2 3
17111389	1 2 3
17111468	3 5
17111469	3 5
17111471	3 5
17111481	3 5
17111482	3 5
17111486	3 5
17111487	1 2 3 5
17111500	1 2 9
17111501	1 2 9
17111503	1 2 9
17111526	2 3
17111571	1 2
17111583	1 2 9
17111584	1 2 9
17111590	1 2
17111606	1 2 3 5 9
17980089	1 2 3 5
17980090	1 2 3 5
17980323	3 5
17980324	3 5
17980325	3 5
17980326	3 5
17980428	3 5
17980538	1 2 3 5 9
17980539	1 2 3 5 9
17980548	1 2 3 5
17980666	3 5
17980764	1 2 3 5 9
17980900	1 2 9
17980973	1 2 3 5
17980974	1 2 3 5
17980976	1 2 3 5
17981435	1 2 3 5 9
17981437	1 2 3 5 9
17981597	1 2 3 5
17981598	1 2 3 5
17981674	1 2 9
17981675	1 2 9
17981702	3 5
17981778	1 2 9
17981840	1 2 9
17981901	1 2 3 5
17981902	1 2 3 5
17982002	1 2 9
17982257	3 5
17982337	1 2 9
17982338	1 2 9
17983075	1 2 3 5
17983307	1 2 9
17983482	1 2 9
17983797	1 2 9
17983799	1 2
17984350	1 2 9
17985050	1 2 9
17985060	1 2 9
17985122	1 2 9
17985370	1 2 9
17985579	1 2 9
17985580	1 2 9
17985868	1 2 9
17986404	1 2
17986405	1 2
18001032	3 5
18002866	1 2 3 5 9
18002950	1 2 3 5 9
18003044	1 2 9
18003045	1 2 9
18003155	1 2 3 5 9
18003479	1 2 9
18003614	1 2 3 5 9
18003724	1 2 3 5 9
18003744	1 2 3 5
18003905	1 2 9
18004057	3 5
18004550	1 2 3 5 9
18004602	1 2 3 5 9
18004702	1 2
18004793	1 2 3 5 9
18004853	1 2 3 5 9
18004873	1 2 3 5 9
18004888	1 2 3 5
18004890	1 2 3 5 9
18005225	1 2 3 5
18005226	1 2 3 5
18005227	1 2 3 5
18005228	1 2 3 5
18005281	1 2 9
18005296	1 2 9
18005297	1 2 9
18005311	1 2 9
18005312	1 2 9
18005399	1 2 3 5 9
18006566	1 2 3 5 9
18006810	1 2 3 5 9
18006856	1 2 3 5
18007080	1 2 3 5 9
18007280	1 2 9
18007292	1 2 3 5
18007627	1 2 9
18007696	1 2 9
18007865	1 2 3 5 9
18007877	1 2 9
18007880	1 2 3 5 9
18007897	1 2 3 5 9
18007935	1 2 3 5 9
18007945	2 9
18007946	1 2 9
18007980	2 3 5
18007981	1 2 3 5 9
18007982	1 2 3 5
18008175	1 2 3 5
18008176	1 2 3 5
18008313	3 5
18008314	3 5
18008315	3 5
18008318	1 2 3 5 9
18008319	1 2 3 5 9
18008492	1 2 3 5 9
18008494	1 2 3 5 9
18008496	1 2 3 5 9
18008614	1 2 3 5 9
18008649	1 2 3
18008650	1 2 3 5 9
18008663	1 2 3 5 9
18008664	1 2 3 5 9
18008673	1 2 9
18008695	2 9
18008736	1 2 9
18008743	1 2 9
18008758	1 2 3 5 9
18008777	1 2 9
18008784	1 2 9
18008845	1 2 9
18008846	1 2 9
18008847	1 2 9
18008848	1 2 9
18009085	1 2 9
18009086	1 2 9
18009087	1 2 9
18009088	1 2 9
18009089	1 2 3 5 9
18009091	1 2 3 5 9
18009166	1 2 9
18009167	1 2 9
18009364	1 2 3 5 9
18009369	1 2 9
18009370	3 5
18009373	1 2 5 9
18009374	3 5
18009375	1 2 3 5 9
18009415	3 5
18009419	1 2 9
18009457	1 2 3 5 9
18009469	1 2 3 5 9
18009656	3 5
18009657	3 5
18009682	3 5
18009689	3 5
18009690	3 5
18009691	3 5
18009692	3 5
18009816	1 2 3 5 9
18010078	3 5

General Motors Part Number Interchange

Code following part numbers indicate interchangeability of this part with other General Motors cars.
1—Buick 2—Oldsmobile 3—Pontiac 5—Chevrolet 9—Cadillac

18010083	1 2 3 5 9
18010085	1 2 3 5 9
18010086	1 2 3 5
18010087	1 2 3 5 9
18010099	1 2 3 5 9
18010106	1 2 3 5 9
18010120	1 2 3 5
18010127	1 2 3 5 9
18010249	1 2 9
18010263	1 2 9
18010278	1 2 9
18010313	1 2 3 5 9
18010376	3 5
18010437	1 2 3 5
18010453	3 5
18010463	1 2 3 5
18010464	1 2 3 5
18010465	1 2 3 5
18010480	2 3 5
18010481	1 2 3 5
18010591	1 2 9
18010907	1 2 3 5 9
18010911	3 5
18011141	1 2 3 5
18011142	1 2 3 5
18011143	3 5
18011234	3 5
18011235	1 2 3 5
18011243	1 2 3
18011280	1 2 3 5 9
18011329	1 2 3 5
18011356	1 2 3 5 9
18011357	1 2 3 5
18011358	3 5
18011359	3 5
18011413	1 2 3 5
18011415	1 2 3 5
18011416	1 2 3 5
18011608	1 2 9
18011667	1 2 3 5 9
18011668	1 2 3 5 9
18011670	1 2 3 5 9
18011749	1 2 9
18011750	1 2 9
18011916	1 2 3 5
18011938	1 2 3 5 9
18012129	1 2 9
18012130	1 2 9
18012132	1 2 9
18012157	1 2 3 5 9
18012303	1 2 3 5
18012308	1 2 3 5 9
18012309	1 2 3 5 9
18012316	1 2 9
18012412	3 5
18012422	1 2 3
18012423	1 2 3
18012433	1 2 3 5
18012435	1 2 3
18012472	1 2 3 5 9
18012473	1 2 3 5 9
18012478	1 2 3 5 9
18012481	3 5
18012582	1 2 9
18012657	1 2 9
18012679	1 2 9
18012689	1 2 9
18012690	1 2 9
18012691	1 2 9
18012692	1 2 9
18012693	1 2 9
18012702	1 2 9
18012703	1 2 9
18013409	1 2 9
18013414	3 5
18013423	1 2 9
18013425	1 2 9
18013428	3 5
18013442	1 2 9
18013451	3 5
18013452	3 5
18013489	1 2
18013495	1 2 9
18013501	1 2
18013513	1 2 3 5 9
18013564	1 2 9
18013677	1 2 9
18013824	1 2 9
18013882	1 2 9
18013996	1 2 9
18013998	1 2 9
18013999	1 2 9
18014006	1 2 9
20009424	3 5
20012859	2 3
20036262	3 5
20036263	3 5
20041428	1 2 3 5
20041429	1 2 3 5
20041430	1 2 3 5
20041431	1 2 3 5
20041434	1 2 3 5
20041435	1 2 3 5
20041442	1 2 3 5
20041443	1 2 3 5
20041610	3 5
20041611	3 5
20046485	3 5
20046486	3 5
20048554	1 2 3 5
20048555	1 2 3 5
20094576	1 2
20099250	1 2 3
20099251	2 5
20099256	1 2 9
20099257	1 2 9
20101210	1 2 9
20101211	1 2 9
20110652	1 2 3
20110653	1 2 5
20111712	1 2 3 5
20111713	1 2 3 5
20123184	1 2 3 5
20147472	1 2 3
20147473	1 2 5
20151038	1 2 9
20151039	1 2 9
20151275	2 3
20153991	1 2 3 5 9
20162801	1 2 3 5 9
20166276	1 2 3 5 9
20166324	1 2 3 5
20166325	1 2 3 5
20166428	1 2 3 5 9
20166702	1 2 3 5 9
20166703	1 2 3 5 9
20177430	1 2
20177431	1 2
20192894	1 2 3 9
20192895	1 2 5
20192896	1 2 3 9
20192897	1 2 5
20201245	3 5
20206098	3 5
20206099	3 5
20206720	3 5
20206721	3 5
20209182	1 2 3 5
20216520	1 2 9
20216521	1 2 9
20244864	1 2 5
20260758	1 2 3 5
20260759	1 2 3 5
20273628	1 2 9
20273629	1 2 9
20274727	1 2 3 5 9
20276320	1 2 3 5 9
20276321	1 2 3 5 9
20279741	1 2 3 5 9
20279742	1 2 3 5
20287998	2 5
20293604	1 2 3 5 9
20293605	1 2 3 5 9
20293612	1 2 3 5 9
20293613	1 2 3 5 9
20293620	1 2 9
20293621	1 2 9
20293624	1 2 3
20293625	1 2 3 5
20293642	1 2 3 5
20293643	1 2 3 5
20298586	1 2 3 5
20298588	1 2 3 5
20298852	1 2 3 5 9
20298853	1 2 3 5 9
20298866	1 2 3 5 9
20298867	1 2 3 5 9
20303046	1 2 9
20303047	1 2 9
20303586	1 2
20303587	1 2 5
20303590	1 2 9
20303591	1 2 5
20304754	1 2 9
20304755	1 2 9
20304758	1 2 9
20304759	1 2 9
20310080	1 2 3 5
20310081	1 2 3 5
20310082	1 2 3 5
20310083	1 2 3 5
20315738	1 2 3 5
20315739	1 2 3 5
20332644	1 2 3 5 9
20332645	1 2 3 5 9
20332646	1 2 3 5 9
20332647	1 2 3 5 9
20338488	3 5
20338489	3 5
20343192	1 3
20346874	3 5
20356018	1 2 3 5
20361484	1 2 3
20361485	1 2 3
20361488	1 2 3
20361489	1 2 3
20361962	1 2 3
20361963	1 2 3
20367776	2 3
20367780	2 3
20368115	3 5
20369896	1 2 3 5 9
20373950	1 2 3 5
20375834	1 2 9
20375835	1 2 9
20377438	1 2 9
20377439	1 2 9
20377440	1 2 9
20377441	1 2 9
20387102	1 2 3 5
20387103	1 2 3 5
20424524	3 5
20429150	1 2 3 5 9
20434734	2 3 5
20434752	1 2 9
20434753	1 2 9
20435166	1 2 3 5
20445878	1 2 3
20445879	1 2 3
20445880	1 2 3
20445881	1 2 3
20446078	1 2 3 5 9
20446079	1 2 3 5 9
20446083	1 2 3 5 9
20446084	1 2 3 5 9
20446085	1 2 3 5 9
20446086	1 2 3 5 9
20446087	1 2 3 5 9
20452014	3 5
20452016	3 5

Code following part numbers indicate interchangeability of this part with other General Motors cars.
1—Buick 2—Oldsmobile 3—Pontiac 5—Chevrolet 9—Cadillac

Part Number	Code
20453912	1 2
20453913	1 2
20453916	1 2
20453917	1 2
20455128	1 2 3 5 9
20455129	1 2 3 5 9
20455140	1 2 9
20455141	1 2 9
20455506	1 2 9
20455507	1 2 9
20457822	1 2
20457823	1 2
20470537	1 2 9
20470542	1 2 9
20470543	1 2 9
20471222	1 2 9
20471223	1 2 9
20472584	1 2 9
20475162	1 2 9
20475163	1 2 9
20475164	1 2 9
20475165	1 2 9
20475847	3 5
20479416	1 2 9
20479417	1 2 9
20479424	1 2 3 5
20479425	1 2 3 5
20479756	1 2 9
20479757	1 2 9
20479794	1 2 9
20479795	1 2 9
20480172	1 2 9
20480173	1 2 9
20480174	1 2 9
20480175	1 2 9
20480448	1 2 9
20480449	1 2 9
20480596	1 2
20480597	1 2
20482494	1 2
20482495	1 2
20482516	1 2 3 5
20482517	1 2 3 5
20484246	1 2 3
20484247	1 2 3
20489074	1 2 3
20489075	1 2 3
20496702	1 2 9
20496703	1 2 3 5
20496705	1 2 3 5
20496707	3 5
20496710	3 5
20513752	1 2 3 5
20513755	1 2 3 9
20530266	1 2 9
20530267	1 2 9
20531542	1 2 3
20531543	1 2 3
20538870	1 2 3 5 9
20538871	1 2 3 5 9
20538872	1 2 3 5
20538873	1 2 3 5
20566380	1 2 9
20566381	1 2 9
20594023	1 2 3 5 9
20594024	1 2 3 5 9
20594025	1 2 3 5 9
20611636	1 2
20611637	1 2
20611642	1 2
20611643	1 2
20611674	1 2
20611675	1 2
20618096	1 2 3
20618097	1 2 3
20618098	1 2 3
20618099	1 2 3
20634672	1 2
20634673	1 2
20643060	1 2
20643061	1 2
20643062	1 2
20643063	1 2
20661424	1 2 9
20661425	1 2 9
22007636	2 5
22008426	2 5
22008464	1 2 9
22008490	1 2 5 9
22008492	1 2 5 9
22008668	1 2 5 9
22009035	1 2 9
22009212	1 2 3 5
22009387	1 2 3 5
22009388	2 5
22009389	2 5
22010448	1 2 3 5 9
22010449	1 2 5 9
22010672	1 2 3 5
22010688	1 2 9
22010690	1 2 9
22010692	1 2 9
22012059	1 2
22012060	1 2
22012063	1 2 9
22012064	1 2 9
22016688	1 2 9
22017155	1 2 9
22017162	1 2 9
22017241	1 2
22017243	2 9
22017481	1 2 9
22020255	1 2 3 5
22020538	1 2 9
22020539	1 2 9
22020540	1 2 9
22020900	1 2 3 5 9
22020945	1 2 3 5 9
22020947	1 2 3 9
22021257	3 5
22021345	1 2 3 5
22021670	1 2 3 5 9
22021790	3 5
22029597	1 2 9
22029601	1 2 3 5 9
22029665	1 2 3 5 9
22029799	1 2 3 5 9
22029817	1 2 3 5 9
22029848	1 2 3 5 9
22030258	1 2 3 5
22030445	1 2 3 5 9
22030627	3 5
22030629	3 5
22030631	1 2 3 5
22030633	1 2 3 5
22034702	1 2 9
22034703	1 2 9
22034704	1 2 9
22035454	1 2 3 5
22035556	1 2 3 5
22035561	1 2 3 5
22035570	1 2 3 5
22035623	1 2 3 5 9
22035659	1 2 3 5
22035660	1 2 3 5
22035662	1 2 3 5
22035663	3 5
22035664	3 5
22036292	1 2 9
22036293	1 2
22038796	1 2 3 9
22039041	1 2 3 5 9
22039318	1 2 3 5 9
22039321	1 2 9
22039328	1 2 9
22039330	1 2 9
22039331	1 2 9
22039339	1 2 3 5 9
22039676	1 2 3 5
22039677	1 2 3 5
22039678	3 5
22039679	3 5
22039686	1 2 3 5
22039687	1 2 3 5
22039693	1 2 3
22039715	1 2 3 5 9
22039716	1 2 3 5 9
22039717	1 2 3 5
22039718	1 2 3 5
22039727	1 2 3 5 9
22040193	1 2 3 5
22040429	1 2 3 5 9
22040430	1 2 3 5 9
22040573	1 2 9
22040574	1 2 9
22040580	1 2
22040861	1 2 3 5
22040868	1 2 3 5
22040881	1 2 3 5
22040897	3 5
22040899	1 2 9
22040900	1 2
22040903	1 9
22041011	1 2 9
22046409	1 2 3 5 9
22046414	1 2 3 5
22046415	1 2 3 5
22046425	1 5
22046426	1 5
22046427	1 2 3 5
22046428	1 2 5
22046432	1 2
22046435	1 2 3 5 9
22046436	1 2 3 5 9
22046438	3 5
22046440	1 2
22046451	1 2 3 5 9
22047906	1 2 3 5 9
22047907	1 2 3 5 9
22047910	1 2 3 5 9
22047911	1 2 3 5 9
22047914	1 2 9
22047916	1 2 3
22047917	1 2 3
22047918	1 2 3
22047919	1 2 3
22047938	1 2 9
22047939	1 2 9
22047940	1 2 9
22047941	1 2 9
22047948	1 2 9
22047949	1 2 9
22047954	1 2
22047955	1 2
22048210	1 2 9
22048225	1 2 9
22048226	1 2 3 5 9
22048242	3 5
22048271	1 2 3 5 9
22048356	3 5
22048569	1 2 3 5
22048572	3 5
22048573	1 2 3 5
22048574	1 2 3 5 9
22048577	1 2 3 5 9
22048620	1 2 3
22048625	1 2 9
22048627	1 2 9
22048652	3 5
22048653	3 5
22049373	1 2 3 9
22049519	1 2 3 5 9
22049520	1 2 9
22049526	1 2 9
22049769	1 2 9
22049774	1 2
22049801	1 2 3 5 9
22049806	1 2 9
22049807	1 2 9
22049808	1 2 9

General Motors Part Number Interchange

Code following part numbers indicate interchangeability of this part with other General Motors cars.

1—Buick 2—Oldsmobile 3—Pontiac 5—Chevrolet 9—Cadillac

22049969	1 2 3 5
22049970	1 2 3 5
22049971	1 2 3 5
22054186	1 2 3 5 9
22054198	1 2 3 9
22054216	1 2 9
22054217	1 2 9
22054218	1 2 9
22054220	1 2 9
22054222	1 2 9
22054238	1 2 9
22054244	1 2 9
22062398	1 2 3
22062528	1 2 9
22062531	1 2 9
22062535	1 2 9
22062567	1 2
22062568	1 2 9
22062913	1 2 3 5 9
22062915	1 2 3 5 9
22063201	1 2 9
22500606	1 2 9
22500607	1 2 9
22500630	1 2 9
22500807	2 3 5
22500808	1 2 3 5
22500910	1 2 9
22501022	1 2 9
22501573	1 2 3
22502236	1 2 9
22503324	1 2 9
22503500	1 2 3 5 9
22504368	1 2 9
22504369	1 2 9
22504709	1 2 3 5 9
22504832	1 2 9
22504938	1 2 9
22504959	1 2 9
22505220	1 2 9
22505492	1 2 3 5 9
22505582	1 2 9
22505583	1 2 3 5 9
22505615	1 2 9
22505893	1 2 3
22505997	1 2 3 5 9
22506227	1 2 9
22506436	1 5 9
22506438	1 2 5 9
22506439	1 2 5 9
22506440	1 2 3 5 9
22506498	1 2 9
22506536	1 2 9
22506658	1 2 9
22506710	1 2 3 5 9
22506730	1 2 9
22506866	1 2
22507586	1 2 3 5 9
22507725	1 2 9
22507974	1 2 9
22509632	1 2 3 5 9
22509735	1 2 3 5 9
22510099	1 2 3 5 9
22510143	1 2 9
22510372	1 2 3 5 9
22510562	1 2 9
22510564	1 2 9
22510779	1 2 3 5 9
22510780	1 2 3 5
22510852	1 2 3 5
22511035	1 2 3 5 9
22511044	1 2 3 5 9
22511238	1 2 9
22511564	1 2 9
22511565	1 2 9
22511732	1 2 3 5 9
22511745	1 2
22512002	1 2
22512345	1 2 3 5
22512346	1 2 3 5
22512347	1 2
22512349	1 2
22512350	1 2
22512351	1 2 9
22512352	1 2 9
22512353	3 5
22512354	1 2 3
22512355	1 2 3 5
22512399	1 2 3 5 9
22512709	1 2 3 5 9
22513590	1 2 9
22513639	1 2 3 5 9
22513910	1 2 3 5 9
22513937	1 2 3 5 9
22514246	1 2 9
22514273	1 2 3 5
22514303	1 2 3 5 9
22514308	1 2
22514311	1 2
22514382	1 2 9
22514383	1 2 9
22514392	1 2
22514398	1 2
22514399	1 2 3 5 9
22514509	1 2 3 5
22514583	1 2 3 5
22514584	1 2 3 5
22514724	1 2 3 5
22514725	1 2 9
22514728	1 2 3 5 9
22514732	1 2 9
22514733	1 2 9
22514839	1 2
22514861	1 2 3 5 9
22514872	1 2 3 5 9
22514882	1 9
22515038	1 2 3 5 9
22515313	1 2 3 5 9
22515315	1 2 3 5 9
22515440	3 5
22515441	3 5
22515464	1 2 3 5 9
22515512	1 2 3 5
22515513	1 2 3 5
22515514	1 2 3 5
22515525	1 2
22515610	1 2 3 5 9
22515611	1 2
22515643	1 2
22515964	1 2 3 5 9
22515972	1 2 3 5
22516032	1 2 3 5 9
22516033	1 2 3 5 9
22516034	1 2 3 5 9
22516036	1 2 3 5
22516175	1 2 3 5 9
22516176	1 2 3 5 9
22516177	1 2 3 5 9
22516180	1 2 3 5 9
22516181	1 2 3 5
22516182	1 2 3 5 9
22516183	1 2 3 5 9
22516184	1 2 3 5 9
22516186	1 2 3 5 9
22516188	1 2 3 5 9
22516189	1 2 3 5 9
22516190	1 2 3 5
22516191	2 9
22516193	1 2 3 5 9
22516194	1 2 3 5 9
22516195	1 2 3 5 9
22516196	1 2 3 5 9
22516197	1 2 3 5 9
22516344	1 2 3 5 9
22516525	1 2 3 5 9
22517321	1 2 3 5
22517701	1 2
22517897	1 2 9
22517996	1 2 9
22518169	1 2 3 5
22518370	1 2 3 5 9
22518686	1 2 3 5
22518688	1 2 9
22518689	1 2 3 5 9
22518691	1 2
22518692	1 2 3 5
22518729	1 2 3 5
22518791	1 2 3 5 9
22518903	1 2 3 5
22518906	1 2 3 5 9
22518907	1 2 3 5
22519181	1 2 3 5 9
22519395	1 2 3 5
22519396	1 2 3 5
22519416	1 2 3 5 9
22519584	1 2 3 5 9
22519882	1 2 3 5
22519888	1 2 3 5
22519891	1 2 3 5
22519894	1 2
22519914	1 2 3 5 9
22519924	1 2 3 5 9
22519945	1 2 3
22519990	1 2 3 5 9
22520025	1 2 3 5
22520040	1 2 3 5
22520081	3 5
22520094	1 2 3 5
22520327	1 5
22520348	1 2 3 5 9
22520376	1 2 3 5 9
22520378	1 2 3 5 9
22520392	1 2 3 5
22520393	1 2 3 5
22520490	1 2 3 5
22520600	1 2 3 5
22520601	1 2 3 5
22520604	1 2 3 5
22520607	1 2 3 5
22520640	1 2 3 5 9
22520659	1 2 9
22520665	1 2 3 5
22520666	1 2 3 5
22520936	1 2 3 5
22520937	1 2 3 5 9
22520938	1 2 9
22520992	1 2 3 5
22520999	1 2 3 5 9
22521207	1 2 3 5 9
22521436	1 2 3 5
22521623	1 5
22521624	2 5 9
22521625	1 2 3 5
22521646	1 2
22521739	1 2 9
22521786	1 2 3 5 9
22521799	1 2 9
22521988	1 2 9
22521997	1 2 9
22522053	1 2 5 9
22522087	1 2 9
22522150	1 2
22522151	1 2 3 5
22522452	1 2 3 5
22522523	1 2
22522524	1 2
22522562	1 2 3 5 9
22522768	1 2 3 5 9
22522801	1 2 9
22522853	1 2 3 5 9
22522937	1 2 9
22522938	1 2 9
22523207	1 2 3 5 9
22523357	1 2 3 5 9
22523358	1 2 3 5 9
22523359	1 2 9
22523360	1 2 5 9
22523405	1 2 3 5
22523502	1 5
22523601	1 2 9
22523727	1 2 3 5 9

Code following part numbers indicate interchangeability of this part with other General Motors cars.
1—Buick 2—Oldsmobile 3—Pontiac 5—Chevrolet 9—Cadillac

22523730	1 2 3 5 9
22523733	1 2 3 5 9
22523860	1 2 3 5
22523878	3 5
22523899	1 2 3 5 9
22524121	1 2 3 5
22524391	1 2 9
22524419	1 2 9
22524421	1 2 3
22524422	1 2 3 9
22524423	1 2 9
22524441	1 2 3 5
22524447	1 2 3 5 9
22524543	1 2 9
22524574	1 2 3 5 9
22524575	1 2 3 5 9
22524583	1 2 3 5 9
22524715	1 2 9
22524716	1 2 3 5
22524789	1 2
22525042	1 2 3 5
22525280	1 2 9
22525285	1 2 3 5 9
22525288	1 2 9
22525351	1 2 9
22525402	1 2 3 5
22525604	1 2 5 9
22525606	1 2 9
22525894	1 2 3 5 9
22526504	1 2 9
22526624	1 2 3 5
22526891	1 2 9
22526995	1 2 3 9
22527025	1 2 3 5 9
22527030	1 2 3 5 9
22527054	1 2 3 5 9
22527083	1 2 3 5 9
22527123	1 2 3 5
22527149	1 2 3 5 9
22527438	1 2 3 5 9
22527449	1 2 9
22527465	1 2 9
22527479	1 2 3 9
22527480	1 2 3 9
22527481	1 5 9
22527482	1 5 9
22527537	1 2 3 5 9
22527538	1 2 3 9
22527539	1 2 5 9
22527541	1 2 3 5 9
22527542	1 2 9
22527543	1 2 3 5
22527544	1 2 3 5 9
22527545	1 2 9
22527549	1 2 9
22527729	1 2 9
22527791	1 2 9
22527792	1 2 9
22527858	1 2 9
22527859	1 2 9
22527863	1 2 9
22527910	1 2 9
22528027	1 2 9
22528083	1 2 9
22528086	1 2 9
22528089	1 2 9
22528091	1 2 9
22528337	1 2 3 9
22528540	1 2 3 5
22528562	1 2 9
22528563	1 2 9
22528684	1 2 9
22528685	1 2 3 5 9
22528793	1 2 9
22528799	1 2 9
22528801	1 2 9
22529161	1 2 9
22529265	1 2 3 5 9
22529266	1 2 3
22529562	1 2 3 5 9
22529763	1 2
22530022	1 2 3 5 9
22530557	1 2 3 5 9
22530611	1 2 3 9
22530855	1 2 3 5 9
22530856	1 2 3
22530936	1 2 9
22533631	1 2 3 9
22534925	2 3 5 9
22534926	1 2 3 5 9
25000599	1 2 5
25000600	1 2
25001583	3 5
25001612	1 5
25002211	1 2 5
25002212	1 2
25002474	1 2 9
25002512	3 5
25002566	1 2 3
25002567	2 3 5
25002569	1 2 3 5
25002573	1 2 9
25002621	2 3 5
25003093	3 5
25003095	3 5
25003149	1 2 3 5
25003150	1 2 3 5
25003151	1 2 3 5 9
25003272	1 2 9
25003273	1 2 9
25003275	1 2 3 5
25003645	1 2 3 5
25003646	1 2 3 5
25003648	1 2 3 5
25003684	1 2 9
25003686	1 2 9
25003699	1 2 9
25003923	1 2 9
25003924	1 2 3 5
25003986	1 2 3 5
25003990	1 2 3 5 9
25004275	1 2 3 5
25004277	1 2 3 5 9
25004278	1 2 9
25004279	1 2 9
25004280	1 2 3 5
25004293	1 2 3 5
25004300	1 2 3 5 9
25004308	1 2 3 5
25004339	3 5
25004383	3 5
25004387	3 5
25004390	1 2 3 5 9
25004392	1 2 3 5 9
25004960	3 5
25004981	1 2 9
25004989	1 2 3 5 9
25004992	1 2 3
25004999	1 2 3 5
25007227	1 2 3
25007278	1 2 3 5
25007335	1 2 3 9
25007336	1 2 3
25007421	1 2 3 5
25007463	1 2 3 5 9
25007540	1 2 9
25007653	1 2 9
25010324	1 2 9
25010497	1 2 3 5 9
25010792	1 2 3 5 9
25010908	1 2 3 5 9
25011523	1 2 3
25012305	1 2 3
25026385	1 2
25030527	1 2 5
25030560	1 2 3 5
25030562	1 2 3 5 9
25030878	1 2 3 5 9
25030881	1 2 9
25030882	1 2 9
25030980	1 2 3 5 9
25030981	1 2 3 5
25030983	1 2 3 5
25031261	1 2 9
25031314	1 2 3 5 9
25031316	1 2 9
25031423	1 2 9
25031425	1 2 3 5 9
25031426	1 2 3 5 9
25031452	1 2 3 5
25031456	1 2 3 5 9
25031457	1 2 3 5 9
25031478	1 2 3 5 9
25031479	1 2 3 5 9
25031480	1 2 3 5 9
25031481	1 2 3 5 9
25031521	1 2 3 5
25031529	1 2 3 5
25031604	1 2 3 5 9
25031683	1 2 5 9
25031699	1 2 9
25031703	1 2 3 5 9
25031713	1 2 9
25031726	2 5
25031845	1 2
25031846	1 2 9
25031907	3 5
25031915	1 2 9
25031943	1 2 9
25031946	1 2 3 5
25031947	1 2 3 5
25031948	2 3 5
25031953	1 2 3 5
25031964	2 5
25031983	1 2 3 5 9
25031999	1 2 9
25034041	3 5
25034073	1 2 3 5 9
25034111	1 2 3 5 9
25034283	1 2 3 5 9
25034290	1 2 3 5 9
25034293	1 2 3 5 9
25034392	1 2 3 5 9
25034395	1 2 3 5 9
25034405	1 2 3 5 9
25034407	1 2 3 5 9
25034417	1 2 3 5 9
25035623	1 2 3 5
25036035	3 5
25036092	1 2 3 5 9
25036094	1 2 9
25036136	3 5
25036335	1 2 9
25036371	1 2 3 5 9
25036373	1 2 3 5 9
25036378	1 2 3 5 9
25036390	1 2 9
25036391	1 2 9
25036455	1 2 3 5 9
25036506	1 2 9
25036535	3 5
25036553	1 2 3 5 9
25036581	1 2 9
25036588	1 2 9
25036612	1 2 9
25036628	1 2 3 5 9
25036629	1 2 3 5 9
25036647	3 5
25036649	3 5
25036658	1 2 9
25036663	1 2 9
25036708	1 2 3 5 9
25036751	1 2 3 5 9
25036925	1 2 9
25037034	1 2 3
25040026	1 5
25041109	1 2 3 5 9
25041498	1 2 3 5
25041551	1 2 3 5 9
25041678	1 2 3 5 9

Code following part numbers indicate interchangeability of this part with other General Motors cars.
1—Buick 2—Oldsmobile 3—Pontiac 5—Chevrolet 9—Cadillac

Part Number	Code
25041743	1 2 9
25042077	1 2 3 5
25042116	1 2 3 5 9
25042360	1 2 3 5
25042362	3 5
25042995	1 2 3 5 9
25043244	1 2 9
25043452	1 2 9
25043471	1 2 3 5 9
25043526	1 2 3 5
25043669	1 2 3 5
25043690	1 2 3 5 9
25043843	1 2 3 5 9
25043852	1 2 9
25047158	1 2 3 5
25048091	1 2 3 5 9
25050480	3 5
25051350	3 5
25052819	3 5
25052905	3 5
25054999	1 2 3 5
25056056	3 5
25056223	1 2 3 5 9
25056230	1 2 3 5
25056297	3 5
25056301	1 2 3 5 9
25056310	3 5
25056343	1 2 9
25056345	1 2 9
25056380	3 5
25056381	3 5
25056382	3 5
25056539	3 5
25056546	1 2 9
25056562	1 2 9
25056586	1 2 9
25056597	3 5
25056622	1 2 9
25056623	1 2 9
25056632	1 2
25056634	1 2 3 5 9
25056689	1 2 3 5 9
25056699	1 2 3 5 9
25056700	1 2 9
25056706	1 2 3
25056731	1 2 3 5 9
25056736	3 5
25056761	1 2 3 5
25056790	3 5
25056910	1 2 3 5
25056912	1 2 3
25056944	1 2 9
25057868	1 2 9
25057897	1 2 3
25057926	1 2 9
25058004	1 2 3 5
25058036	1 2 3 5
25058271	1 2 3 5
25058276	1 2 3 5
25058281	1 2 3 5
25058289	1 2 3 5
25059071	1 2 3 5 9
25061381	1 2 3 5 9
25061382	1 2 3 5 9
25061402	1 2 3 5 9
25061403	1 2 3 5 9
25074202	1 2 9
25074220	1 2
25074223	1 2 3
25074624	1 2 3 5
25074625	1 2 3 5 9
25074627	1 2 3 5 9
25074628	3 5
25074629	1 2 3 5 9
25074630	1 2 3 5 9
25074632	3 5
25074704	1 2 3 5
25074708	1 2 9
25074709	3 5
25074710	3 5
25074717	1 2 3
25074736	1 2 9
25074738	1 2
25074786	1 2 9
25074874	1 2 9
25076141	3 5
25076939	3 5
25077732	1 2 3
25078266	1 2 3
25078394	1 2 3
25078649	3 5
25090002	1 2 3 5
25090007	1 2 3 5
25090030	1 2 9
25090034	1 2 9
25090066	1 2 3 5
25090481	1 2 3 5
25090490	1 2 9
25090493	1 2 9
25090544	1 2 9
25091211	1 2 9
25091299	1 2 3
25091303	1 2 3
25091315	1 2 3
25091319	1 2 3
25091491	1 2 9
25092103	1 2 9
25092116	1 2 9
25092119	1 2 9
25094278	1 2 9
25095333	1 2 9
25095452	1 2 3
25095481	1 2 9
25100217	1 2 9
25100218	1 3 5
25101076	1 2 3
25101078	1 2 9
25101933	1 2 9
25115110	3 5
25115190	1 2 3
25115254	3 5
25115334	1 2 9
25115429	1 2 3 5 9
25323376	1 2 3 5
25500202	1 2 3 5
25500296	1 2 3
25500297	1 2 3
25500298	1 2 3 5
25500672	1 2 3 5 9
25501289	1 2 9
25501290	1 2 9
25501599	1 2
25502391	1 2
25502686	1 2 3 5 9
25502687	1 2 3 5 9
25502753	1 2 3 5
25502768	1 2
25502769	1 2 3 5
25502772	1 2 3 5
25502794	1 2 3 5
25502971	1 2 3 5
25503141	1 2 9
25503372	1 2 9
25503396	1 2 3 5
25504628	1 2 3 5 9
25504643	1 2 5
25504647	1 5
25505370	1 2 3 5 9
25505372	2 5
25505374	1 2 9
25505382	1 2 9
25505397	1 2 3 5 9
25505451	1 2 9
25505629	1 5
25505630	1 2
25505734	1 2
25505889	1 2 5 9
25505905	1 2 9
25506254	1 2 9
25506256	1 2 9
25506286	1 2 3 5
25506317	1 2 3 5
25506520	1 2 3 5 9
25506570	1 2 3 5
25506571	1 2 9
25506875	2 3 5
25507677	1 2 9
25508195	1 2 9
25508196	1 2 9
25508293	1 2 9
25508302	1 3 5
25508667	1 2 9
25508854	1 2 3 5
25508956	1 2 9
25508960	1 2 9
25509141	1 3 5
25509259	1 2 3 5
25509308	1 2 3 5
25509404	1 2 3 5
25509405	1 2 3 5 9
25509416	1 2 3 5 9
25509432	1 2 3 5 9
25509461	1 2 3 5 9
25509647	1 2 9
25509843	1 2 3 5 9
25509919	1 2 3 5 9
25509922	1 2
25510019	1 2 3 5 9
25510025	1 2 3 5 9
25510049	1 2 3 5 9
25510098	1 2 3 5 9
25510974	1 2 3 5
25510994	1 2 3 5
25511547	1 2 9
25511548	1 2 3 5
25511552	1 2 3 5
25511557	1 2 3 5
25511568	1 2 9
25511570	1 2 9
25511669	1 2 9
25511672	1 2 3 5 9
25511840	1 2 3 5
25511841	1 2 3 5
25511842	1 2 3 5
25512098	1 2 3 5 9
25512172	1 2 3 5
25512346	2 3 5
25512348	1 2 3 5
25512352	1 2 3 5 9
25512353	1 2 3 5 9
25512551	1 2 3 5 9
25512716	1 2 9
25512717	1 2 9
25512861	1 2 3 5 9
25513019	1 2 3 5
25513020	1 2 3 5
25513237	1 2 9
25513257	1 2 9
25513270	1 2 3 5 9
25513279	1 2 3 5
25513386	1 2 3 5 9
25514047	1 2 3 5
25514708	1 2 9
25514979	1 2 9
25515026	1 2 9
25515136	1 2 9
25515196	1 2 3 5
25515198	1 2 3
25515214	1 2 3 5
25515222	1 2 3 5
25515308	1 2 9
25515310	1 2 9
25515390	1 2 3 5
25515393	1 2 3 5 9
25515658	1 2 3 5 9
25515660	1 2 3 5 9
25515661	1 2 3 5 9
25515662	1 2 3 5 9
25515782	1 2 3 5
25515793	1 2 9

Code following part numbers indicate interchangeability of this part with other General Motors cars.

1—Buick 2—Oldsmobile 3—Pontiac 5—Chevrolet 9—Cadillac

Part No.	Code
25515840	1 2 9
25515866	1 2 3 5
25516025	1 2 3 5 9
25516029	1 2 3 5 9
25516141	1 2 3 5 9
25516155	1 2 3 5
25516156	1 2 3 5
25516157	1 2 9
25516158	1 2 9
25516159	1 2 3 5
25516160	2 5
25516162	1 2
25516194	1 2 3 5
25516196	1 2 3 5
25516198	1 2 3 5
25516236	1 2 3 5 9
25516237	1 2 3 5 9
25516456	1 2 3 5
25516470	1 2 3 5
25516525	1 2 3 5
25516526	1 2 3 5
25516527	1 2 3 5
25516528	1 2 3 5
25516529	1 2 3 5
25516560	1 2 3 5 9
25516613	1 2 9
25516653	1 2 9
25516668	1 2 9
25516698	1 2 3 5 9
25516701	1 2 3 5 9
25516702	1 2 3 5 9
25516877	1 2 3 5 9
25516899	1 2 9
25516944	1 2 3 5 9
25516994	1 2 3
25517008	1 2 9
25517514	1 2 9
25517516	1 2 9
25517517	1 2 9
25517518	1 2 9
25517519	1 2 9
25517535	1 2 9
25517697	1 2 3 5
25517706	1 2 3 5
25517709	1 2 3 5
25517726	1 2 9
25518053	1 2 3 5 9
25518168	1 2 3 5
25518169	1 2 3 5
25518390	1 2 3 5 9
25518453	1 2 9
25518462	1 2 3
25518480	1 2 3 5 9
25518487	1 2 9
25518488	1 2 9
25518490	1 2 9
25518491	1 2 9
25518517	1 2 3 5
25518518	1 2 3 5
25518526	1 2
25518546	1 2
25518567	1 2 9
25518568	1 2 9
25518606	1 2 3 5
25518608	1 2 3 5
25518609	1 2 9
25518679	1 2 3 5 9
25518725	1 2 3
25518766	1 2 3
25518767	1 2 3 5 9
25518771	1 2
25518779	1 2 3
25518826	1 2
25518827	1 2
25518850	1 2 3
25518881	1 2 9
25518882	1 2 9
25518889	1 2 9
25518892	1 2 3 5
25518960	1 2 3 5
25519254	1 2 3 5 9
25519324	2 3 5
25519359	1 2 3
25519366	1 2 9
25519368	1 2 9
25519379	1 2 3 5
25519444	1 2 9
25519447	1 2 9
25519448	1 2 5 9
25519449	1 2 3 5
25519450	1 2 3 5
25519451	1 2 9
25519453	1 2 3 5 9
25519454	1 2 3 5 9
25519460	2 5
25519461	1 2 3
25519462	1 2 3 5 9
25519576	1 2 3
25519733	1 2 3 5 9
25519860	1 2
25519875	1 2 9
25519876	1 2 9
25519936	1 2 3 5
25519954	1 2 3 5 9
25519956	1 2 9
25519958	1 2 3 5 9
25519960	1 2 3 5 9
25519994	1 2 9
25520006	1 2 3 5
25520078	1 2 9
25520198	1 2 9
25520270	1 2 3 5 9
25520271	1 2 3 5 9
25520289	1 2 3 5 9
25520316	1 2
25520337	1 2 3 5 9
25520338	1 2 3 5 9
25520341	1 2 3 5
25520342	1 2 3 5
25520372	1 2 3 5
25520376	1 2 9
25520378	1 2 9
25521323	1 2 3
25521417	1 2 9
25521841	1 2 3 9
25521935	1 2 3 9
25521994	1 2 3 5 9
25522027	1 2 3 5
25522041	1 2
25522149	1 2
25522194	1 2
25522287	1 2 9
25522298	1 2 3
25522303	1 2 3 5
25522339	1 2 9
25522515	1 2 9
25522528	1 2
25522584	1 2 3
25522611	1 2 3
25522653	1 2 3 5 9
25522674	1 2 3 5
25522717	1 2 3 9
25522740	1 2
25522748	1 2 9
25522837	1 2
25522880	1 2 9
25522881	1 2 9
25522896	1 2 9
25523078	1 2 3
25523099	1 2 3 5 9
25523115	1 2 3 5 9
25523196	1 2 9
25523220	1 2 3
25523221	1 2 3
25523227	1 2 9
25523228	1 2 9
25523281	1 2
25523327	1 2 9
25523344	1 2 3
25523348	1 2 3
25523376	1 2 3 5 9
25523377	1 2
25523380	1 2 9
25523381	1 2 9
25523433	1 2 3
25523435	1 2 9
25523462	1 2 3 9
25523464	1 2 3 5 9
25523466	1 2 3 5 9
25523502	1 2 3 9
25523503	1 2 9
25523510	1 2 3
25523523	1 2 3
25523688	1 2 3
25523695	1 2 9
25523703	1 2 3
25523720	1 2 3
25523721	1 2 3
25523722	1 2 3
25523723	1 2 9
25523724	1 2 9
25523739	1 2 9
25523749	1 2 3 5 9
25523768	1 2 3
25523769	1 2 3
25523770	1 2 3 9
25523801	1 2 3
25523930	1 2 3 5 9
25523934	1 2 3
25523976	1 2 9
25523994	1 2 9
25523995	1 2 9
25524286	1 2 3 9
25524288	1 2 3
25524292	1 2 3
25524295	1 2 3 5 9
25524296	1 2 3 5 9
25524297	1 2 3 5 9
25524298	1 2 3 5 9
25524301	1 2 3 5 9
25524317	1 2 9
25524335	1 2 3
25524543	1 2 3 9
25524565	1 2 9
25524573	1 2 3 5
25524597	1 2 9
25524599	1 2 3 5 9
25524602	1 2 3 5
25524603	1 2 3 5
25524622	1 2 3 5
25524844	1 2 3 5 9
25524846	1 2 3 5 9
25524847	1 2 3 5 9
25525116	1 2 3 5 9
25525118	1 2 3
25525119	1 2 3 5 9
25525120	1 2 3 5
25525121	1 2 3 5 9
25525147	1 2 3 5 9
25525159	1 2 3 9
25525644	1 2 9
25525645	1 2 9
25525666	1 2 3
25525673	1 2 3 5
25525690	1 2 3
25525711	1 2 3
25525796	1 2
25525797	1 2
25525799	1 2
25525862	1 2 9
25525863	1 2 9
25525902	1 2 3 5 9
25525919	1 2 3 5 9
25525963	1 2 3
25525965	1 2 3 9
25526123	1 2
25526124	1 2 3
25526153	1 2 9
25526230	1 2 9
25526379	1 2 3 9

Code following part numbers indicate interchangeability of this part with other General Motors cars.

1—Buick 2—Oldsmobile 3—Pontiac 5—Chevrolet 9—Cadillac

25526425	1 2 3 5 9
25526448	1 2 3 9
25526449	1 2 3 9
25526600	1 2 3
25526641	1 2 9
25526680	1 2 3 5
25526681	1 2 3 5
25526727	1 2 9
25526849	1 2 3
25526889	1 2
25526890	1 2
25526902	1 2 9
25526949	1 2 9
25526955	1 2 9
25526957	1 2
25526969	1 2
25527009	1 2 9
25527077	1 2 9
25527098	1 2 9
25527101	1 2 9
25527105	1 2
25527106	1 2
25527144	1 2 9
25527150	1 2
25527178	1 2 9
25527181	1 2 3
25527186	1 2 9
25527302	1 2 3 5
25527305	1 2
25527306	1 2 3 5
25527307	1 2 3 5
25527308	1 2 9
25527472	1 2 3
25527473	1 2 3
25527474	1 2 3
25527475	2 3
25527478	1 2 9
25527479	1 2 9
25527480	1 2
25527481	1 2
25527496	1 2 9
25527536	1 2 3
25527537	1 2 3 9
25527546	1 2 3 5 9
25527547	1 2
25527594	1 2
25527786	1 2 9
25527787	1 2 9
25528308	1 2 9
25528628	1 2 9
25528692	1 2 9
25528695	1 2 9
25528696	1 2 9
25528697	1 2
25528727	1 2 3 5
25528757	1 2 9
25528758	1 2
25528759	1 2 9
25528822	1 2 9
25529592	1 2
25529593	1 2
25529860	1 2 9
25529968	1 2 9
25530151	1 2 3
25530152	1 2 9
25530153	1 2 9
26000072	1 2
26000076	1 2 9
26000077	1 2 9
26000098	1 2
26000117	1 2 9
26000268	3 5
26000269	3 5
26000317	1 2 9
26000318	1 2 9
26000321	1 2 3 5 9
26000322	1 2 9
26000326	1 2 9
26000329	1 2 9
26000332	1 2 9
26000375	1 2 9
26000384	1 2 9
26000407	1 2 9
26000944	1 2 3
26001375	1 2 3 9
26001376	1 2 3
26001378	1 2
26001530	1 2 9
26001531	1 2 9
26001767	1 2 9
26001938	1 2
26001939	1 2 9
26002397	1 2 9
26002694	1 2 9
26003284	1 2 9
26003285	1 2 9
90106142	1 2 3 5 9
90106425	1 2 3 5 9
90106632	1 2 3 5 9
90106633	1 2 3 5 9
90118784	1 2 3 5 9
90118914	1 2 3 5 9
90122429	1 2 3 5 9
90122607	1 2 3 5 9
90125889	1 2 3 5 9
90136076	1 2 3 5 9
90136613	1 2 3 5 9
90136620	1 2 3 5 9
90156062	1 2 3 5 9
90156142	1 2 3 5 9
90169113	1 2 3 5 9
90169203	1 2 3 5 9
90200003	1 2 3 5 9
90200347	1 2 3 5 9
94020016	3 5
94021127	3 5
94026380	3 5
94026504	3 5
94029576	3 5
94029584	3 5
94029588	3 5
94029593	3 5
94029594	3 5
94029600	3 5
94029602	3 5
94029603	3 5
94029604	3 5
94030184	3 5
94030450	3 5
94030451	3 5
94105292	3 5
94105293	3 5
94117164	3 5
94118501	3 5
94133417	1 2 3 5 9
94139342	3 5
94139343	3 5
94140161	3 5
94144592	3 5
94148662	1 2 3 5 9
94148663	1 2 3 5 9
94148683	1 2 3 5 9
94169128	3 5
94200749	3 5
94208522	3 5
94214912	3 5
94214913	3 5
94214962	3 5
94216589	3 5
94216590	3 5
94216778	3 5
94217007	3 5
94217011	3 5
94217019	3 5
94217100	3 5
94217626	3 5
94220054	3 5
94220084	3 5
94220838	3 5
94220852	3 5
94220897	3 5
94220900	3 5
94220901	3 5
94220922	3 5
94221022	3 5
94221063	3 5
94221087	3 5
94221167	3 5
94221333	3 5
94221719	3 5
94221742	3 5
94223502	3 5
94223812	3 5
94223818	3 5
94223910	3 5
94223962	3 5
94223965	3 5
94223966	3 5
94223973	3 5
94223975	3 5
94223979	3 5
94223980	3 5
94223981	3 5
94224221	3 5
94224637	3 5
94226564	3 5
94227644	3 5
94228436	3 5
94228437	3 5
94228448	3 5
94228449	3 5
94228450	3 5
94228452	3 5
94228453	3 5
94228456	3 5
94228701	3 5
94228702	3 5
94228886	3 5
94231408	3 5
94231409	3 5
94232347	3 5
94233209	3 5
94233210	3 5
94234987	3 5
94235060	3 5
94235078	3 5
94235081	3 5
94235755	3 5
94237722	3 5
94237723	3 5
94237726	3 5
94237727	3 5
94237729	3 5
94237730	3 5
94238642	3 5
94238643	3 5
94238669	3 5
94239141	3 5
94239176	3 5
94239773	3 5
94240378	3 5
94240944	3 5
94241951	3 5
94242051	3 5
94242059	3 5
94242060	3 5
94242061	3 5
94242062	3 5
94242063	3 5
94242067	3 5
94242068	3 5
94242069	3 5
94242275	3 5
94242276	3 5
94242280	3 5
94242285	3 5
94242294	3 5
94242392	3 5
94242889	3 5
94243383	3 5

Code following part numbers indicate interchangeability of this part with other General Motors cars.
1—Buick 2—Oldsmobile 3—Pontiac 5—Chevrolet 9—Cadillac

94243441........................3 5
94243442........................3 5
94244595........................3 5
94245136........................3 5
94245965........................3 5
94250262........................3 5
94250964........................3 5
94251465...........1 2 3 5 9
94253237...........1 2 3 5 9
94253238...........1 2 3 5 9
94254986........................3 5
94257551........................3 5
94259753........................3 5
94622378...........1 2 3 5 9
94622387...........1 2 3 5 9
94622388...........1 2 3 5 9
94622389...........1 2 3 5 9
94622442...........1 2 3 5 9
94622443...........1 2 3 5 9
94622445...........1 2 3 5 9
94622449...........1 2 3 5 9
94625718...........1 2 3 5 9
94625719...........1 2 3 5 9
94627761...........1 2 3 5 9
94636985...........1 2 3 5 9
94637064...........1 2 3 5 9
94637065...........1 2 3 5 9
94637066...........1 2 3 5 9
94637067...........1 2 3 5 9
94637808...........1 2 3 5 9
94642734...........1 2 3 5 9
94642795...........1 2 3 5 9
250002276.................1 2 9
N.L..............................3 5
N.S. 3 5
Not serviced..........1 2 3 5

Manual Transmissions / Transaxles

INDEX

AMERICAN MOTORS

AMC/JEEP

CHRYSLER CORPORATION

FORD MOTOR COMPANY

GENERAL MOTORS CORPORATION

LABOR 19 STANDARD TRANSMISSION 19 LABOR

(Factory Time) Chilton Time

AMERICAN MOTORS

(G) Transmission Assy., Remove & Install

Includes: R&R exhaust pipes on V-8's.

4 Speed
Model HR-1
Model SR-4 & T-4
1983-87-exc below (1.3)............... 1.9
Eagle-Four (1.4)........................ 2.0
Six (1.9)................................ 2.7
5 Speed
Model T-5
1983-87-exc below (1.3)............... 1.9
Eagle-Four (1.4)........................ 2.0
Six (1.9)................................ 2.7
Renew assy add 3

(G) Transmission, R&R and Recondition

Includes: Complete disassembly, clean and inspect or renew all parts. Install new gaskets and seals.

4 Speed
Model HR-1
Model SR-4 & T-4
1983-87-exc below (3.4)............... 4.9
Eagle-Four (3.7)........................ 5.7
Six (4.2)................................ 6.0
5 Speed
Model T-5
1983-87-exc below (3.6)............... 5.2
Eagle-Four (3.7)........................ 5.7
Six (4.5)................................ 6.5

(G) Transmission, Recondition (Off Car)

4 Speed
1983-87
Model HR-1 (1.7)........................ 3.0
Model SR-4 (2.3)........................ 3.3
Model T-4 (2.3)......................... 3.0
5 Speed
1983-87
Model T-5 (2.6)......................... 4.0

(G) Transmission Front Oil Seal, Renew

Includes: R&R transmission.

4 Speed
Model HR-1
Model SR-4 & T-4
1983-87-exc below (1.5)............... 2.1
Eagle-Four (1.6)........................ 2.2
Six (2.1)................................ 2.9
5 Speed
Model T-5
1983-87-exc below (1.5)............... 2.1
Eagle-Four (1.6)........................ 2.2
Six (2.1)................................ 2.9

(G) Transmission Rear Oil Seal, Renew

All models
wo/Trans case (.5)....................... .8
w/Trans case (1.7)....................... 2.5

(G) Speedometer Driven Gear, Renew

1983-87 (.4)................................ .5

TRANSFER CASE

(G) Transfer Case Vacuum Harness, Renew

Eagle
1983-87 (.2)................................ .5

(G) Transfer Case Vacuum Motor Assy., Renew

Eagle
1983-87 (.3)................................ .6
Renew boot add (.1)........................ .1

(G) Vacuum Check Valve, Renew

Eagle
1983-87 (.3)................................ .4

(G) Front Output Shaft Companion Flange, R&R or Renew

Includes: Refill gear oil as required.

Eagle
1983-87 (.7)................................ 1.0
Renew oil seal add (.3).................... .4

(G) Rear Output Shaft Companion Flange, R&R or Renew

Eagle
1983-87 (.7)................................ 1.0
Renew oil seal add (.3).................... .4

(G) Speedometer Driven Gear, Renew

Eagle
1983-87 (.3)................................ .5

(G) Speedometer Drive Gear, Renew

Eagle
1983-87 (.9)................................ 1.3

(G) Transfer Case Assy., R&R or Renew

Eagle
1983-87-w/M.T. (1.1)..................... 2.0
w/A.T. (1.0)............................. 1.9
Renew assy add (.3)........................ .5

(G) Transfer Case Assy., R&R and Recondition

Includes: Disassemble, clean and inspect all parts. Renew all parts as required. Reassemble with all new seals and gaskets. Make all necessary adjustments. Road test.

Eagle
1983-87-w/M.T. (4.1)..................... 5.6
w/A.T. (4.0)............................. 5.5

PARTS 19 STANDARD TRANS. (4 Speed) 19 PARTS

Part No. Price

MODEL T4

Transmission Assy.
1983-exc. 4W.D. 3240236 1132.75
4W.D............................3240237 1132.75
1984-87-exc. 150.....8933001698 1132.75
Four-150 ....8933001450 1150.50

(1) Front Bearing Retainer
1983-87..........................8134013 56.25

(2) Oil Seal (Input Shaft)
1983-87..........................8132779 4.00

(3) Shim Set
1983-87..........................8134016 10.00

(4) Cup
Note: Serviced in No. 5.

(5) Bearing (Input Shaft)
1983-87..........................8134015 28.25

(6) Input Shaft
1983..............................8134014 232.50
1984-87-exc. 150.....8983500975 231.00
Four-150 ....8983500968 231.00

(7) Case Assy.
1983-87..........................8134009 200.00

(8) Back-Up Light Switch
1983-87..........................3229472 10.50

(9) Relay Lever (Reverse)
1983-87..........................8134042 44.50

(10) Bushing (Reverse)
1983-87..........................8134336 3.00

(11) Reverse Idler Gear (w/Bushing)
1983-87..........................8134038 147.75

(12) Reverse Idler Shaft
1983-87..........................8134039 33.50

(13) Breather
1983-87..........................912375 1.50

(14) Oil Seal (Adapter)
1983-87..........................8132672 3.50

(15) Housing (Adapter)
1983-87..........................8134011 259.50

(16) Detent Ball
1983-87..........................G453593 1.00

(17) Detent Spring
1983-87..........................8134057 1.00

(18) Shift Lever (Offset)
1983-87-exc.
4W.D. 8134054 35.00
4W.D...........................8134055 45.00

(19) Damper Sleeve
1983-87..........................8134056 1.50

(20) Thrust Bearing
1983-87..........................8134034 4.25

(21) Rear Bearing (Cluster Gear)
1983-87..........................8134036 18.75

(22) Spacer
1983-87..........................8134035 9.25

(23) Cluster Gear
1983..............................8134031 529.50
1984-87....................8983500970 476.25

(24) Thrust Washer
1983-87..........................8134032 4.50

(25) Front Bearing (Cluster Gear)
1983-87..........................8134033 25.50

(26) Pilot Roller (Mainshaft)
1983-87..........................8127397 .50

(27) Thrust Bearing (Needle)
1983-87..........................8134018 5.50

(28) Synchro. Rings
1983-87
1st & 2nd.....................8127403 45.50
3rd & 4th.....................8134058 47.00

(29) Clutch Assy. (3rd & 4th)
1983.........................8983510191 128.50
1984-87....................8983510192 134.00

(30) 3rd Speed Gear
1983.........................8983500285 178.25
1984-87....................8983500380 169.00

(31) Thrust Washer (2nd Speed)
1983-87..........................8134025 4.00

(32) 2nd Speed Gear
1983-87..........................8134024 165.25

PARTS 19 STANDARD TRANS. (4 Speed) 19 PARTS

	Part No.	Price
(33) Mainshaft (w/1st & 2nd Synchro.)		
1983-exc. 4W.D.	8983501165	515.00
4W.D.	8983501166	554.75
1984-87	8983501944	515.00
(34) Synchro Plate (1st & 2nd)		
1983-87	8127401	.75
(35) Spring (Synchro.)		
1983-87	8134021	1.00
(36) 1st Speed Gear		
1983	8983501103	183.25
1984-87	8983500965	143.75
(37) Bearing (Rear)		
1983-87	8134030	37.00
(38) Shift Fork (3rd & 4th)		
1983-87	8134048	42.00
(39) Selector Arm Assy.		
1983-87	8127487	32.25
(40) Shift Plate		
1983-87	8134050	22.00
(41) Shift Fork (1st & 2nd)		
1983-87	8134049	42.00
(42) Shifter Shaft		
1983-exc. 4W.D.	8134052	64.00
4W.D.	8134091	52.25
1984-87-exc. 150	8134091	52.25
Four-150	8983510072	45.25
(43) Case Cover		
1983-87	8134045	91.00

MODEL T-4

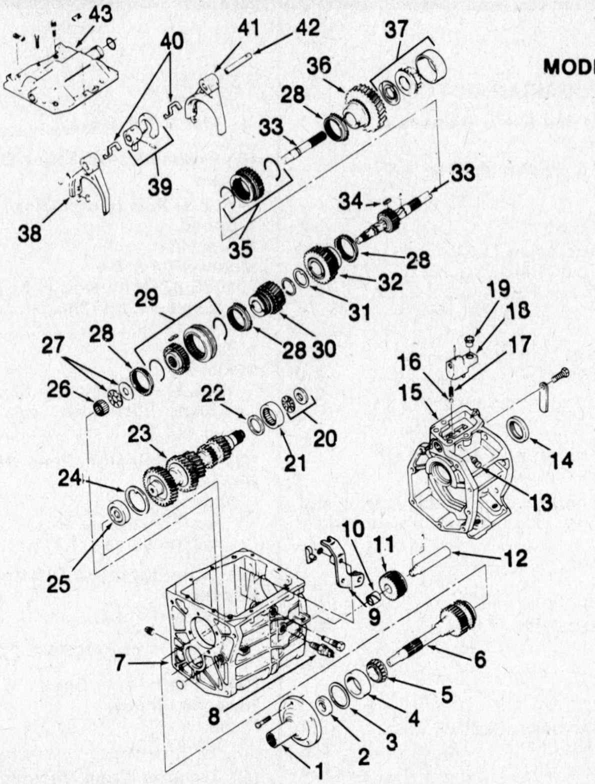

PARTS 19 STANDARD TRANS. (5 Speed) 19 PARTS

MODEL T5

	Part No.	Price
Transmission Assy.		
1983 (wo/4W.D.)		
Four	3242157	1293.75
Six	3242156	N.L.
1983 (w/4W.D.)		
Four	8933002355	1257.25
Six	3242152	N.L.
1984-87-exc. 150	8933001700	N.L.
Four-150	8933002355	1257.25
(1) Front Bearing Retainer		
1983-87	8134013	56.25
(2) Oil Seal (Input Shaft)		
1983-87	8132779	4.00
(3) Bearing & Cup (Input Shaft)		
1983-87	8134015	28.25
(4) Input Shaft		
1983	8134014	232.50
1984-87-exc. 150	8983500975	231.00
Four-150	8983500968	231.00
(5) Case Assy.		
1983-87	8134093	200.00
(6) Back-Up Light Switch		
1983-87	3229472	10.50
(7) Reverse Idler Gear (w/Bushing)		
1983-87	8134038	147.75
(8) Reverse Idler Shaft		
1983-87	8134039	33.50
(9) Housing (Adapter)		
1983-87	8134028	207.00
(10) Oil Seal (Adapter)		
1983-87	8132672	3.50

	Part No.	Price
(11) Spring (Detent)		
1983-87	8134057	1.00
(12) Shift Lever (Offset)		
1983-87-exc.		
4W.D.	8134054	35.00
4W.D.	8134055	45.00

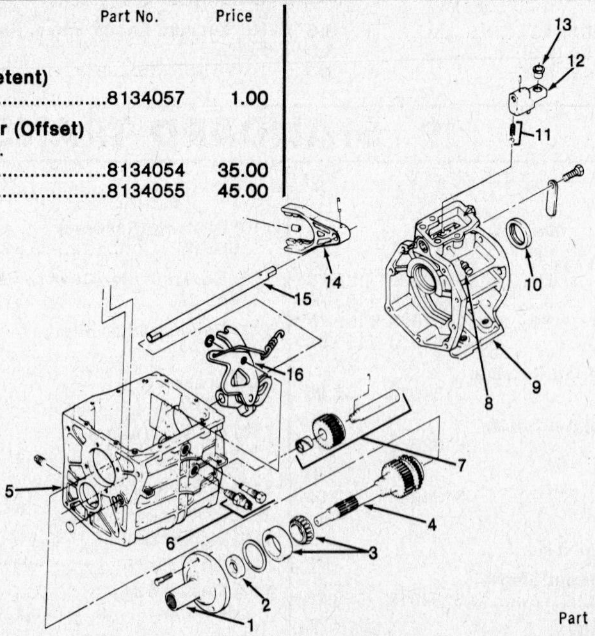

	Part No.	Price
(13) Damper Sleeve		
1983-87	8134056	1.50
(14) Shift Fork (5th Speed)		
1983-87	8134085	41.00
(15) Rail Assy. (w/Pin & Roller)		
1983-87	8134079	39.25
(16) Lock Plate (Reverse)		
1983-87	8134078	7.50

	Part No.	Price
(17) Front Bearing (Cluster Gear)		
1983-87	8134071	39.75
(18) Cluster Gear		
1983	8134069	535.50
1984-87	8983500967	431.50
(19) Rear Bearing (Cluster Gear)		
1983-87	8134036	18.75
(20) Spacer		
1983-87	8134072	4.75

PARTS 19 STANDARD TRANS. (5 Speed) 19 PARTS

	Part No.	Price
(21) Drive Gear (5th Speed)		
1983-87		
Four	8134084	181.50
Six	8134083	220.25
(22) Clutch Assy. (5th Speed)		
1983-87	8134086	143.75
(23) Blocking Ring (5th Speed)		
1983-87	8127414	N.L.
(24) Retainer (Strut)		
1983-87	8134087	1.50
(25) Thrust Bearing (Needle)		
1983-87	8134034	4.25
(26) Race (Thrust)		
1983-87	8134037	2.25
(27) Funnel		
1983-87	8134090	1.50
(28) Pilot Roller (Mainshaft)		
1983-87	8127397	.50
(29) Thrust Bearing (Needle)		
1983-87	8134018	5.50
(30) Blocking Ring (3rd & 4th)		
1983-87	8134058	47.00
(31) Clutch Assy. (3rd & 4th)		
1983	8983510191	128.50
1984-87	8983510192	134.00
(32) 3rd Speed Gear		
1983	8983500285	178.25
1984-87	8983500380	169.00
(33) 2nd Speed Gear		
1983-87	8134024	165.25
(34) Synchronizer Plate (1st & 2nd)		
1983-87	8127401	.75
(35) Mainshaft (w/1st & 2nd Synchro.)		
1983-exc. 4W.D.	8983501165	515.00
4W.D.	8983501166	554.75
1984-87	8983501944	515.00

MODEL T-5

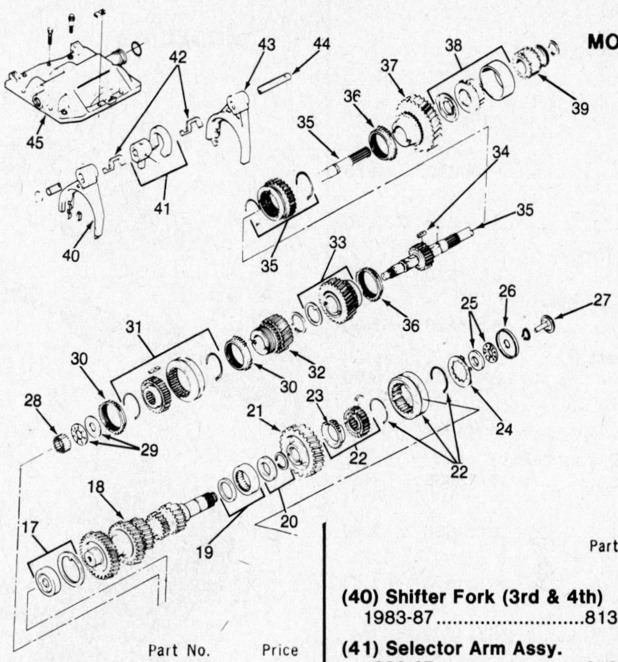

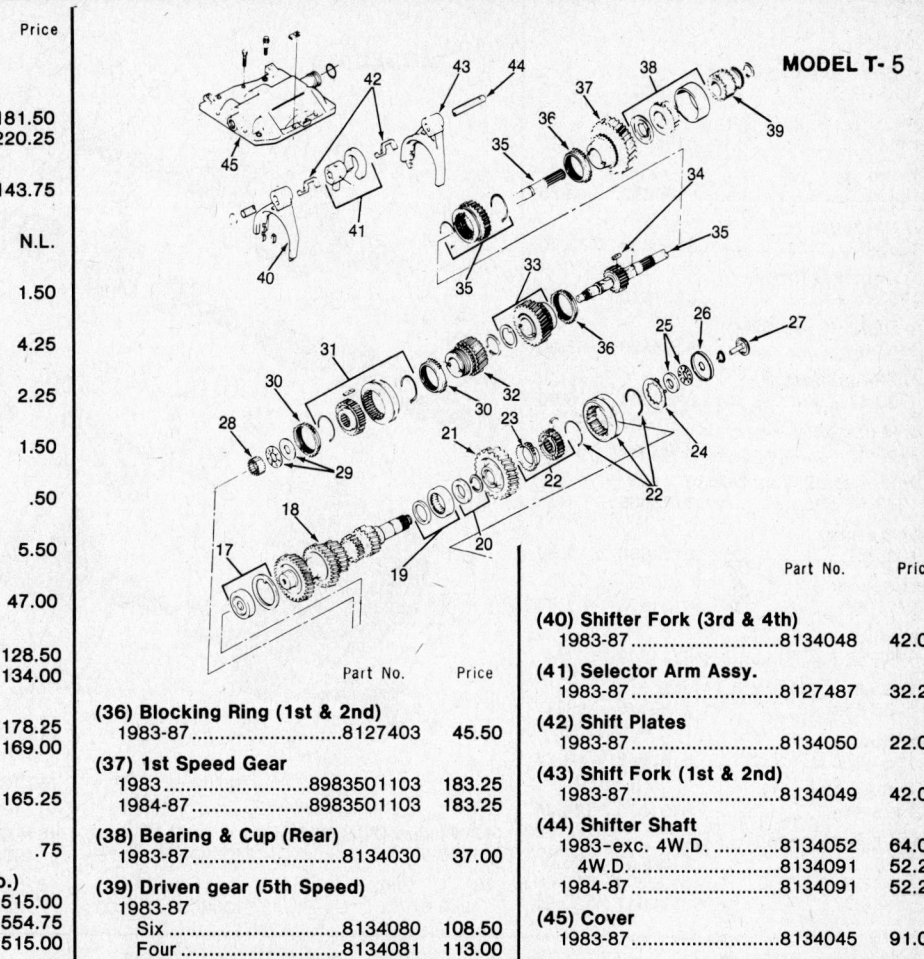

	Part No.	Price
(36) Blocking Ring (1st & 2nd)		
1983-87	8127403	45.50
(37) 1st Speed Gear		
1983	8983501103	183.25
1984-87	8983501103	183.25
(38) Bearing & Cup (Rear)		
1983-87	8134030	37.00
(39) Driven gear (5th Speed)		
1983-87		
Six	8134080	108.50
Four	8134081	113.00

	Part No.	Price
(40) Shifter Fork (3rd & 4th)		
1983-87	8134048	42.00
(41) Selector Arm Assy.		
1983-87	8127487	32.25
(42) Shift Plates		
1983-87	8134050	22.00
(43) Shift Fork (1st & 2nd)		
1983-87	8134049	42.00
(44) Shifter Shaft		
1983-exc. 4W.D.	8134052	64.00
4W.D.	8134091	52.25
1984-87	8134091	52.25
(45) Cover		
1983-87	8134045	91.00

PARTS 19 TRANSFER CASE 19 PARTS

MODEL 129

	Part No.	Price
Transfer Case		
1983-85		
M.T.	8933001100	1439.25
A.T.	8933001099	N.L.
1986-87		
M.T.	8933002769	1284.00
A.T.	8933002769	1284.00

Needs additional part 8953000502 for installation on M.T. models.

	Part No.	Price
(1) Front Yoke (Output)		
1983-87	8131621	55.25
(2) Spring		
1983-87	8133679	1.50
(3) Ball		
1983-87	8983501349	1.50
(4) Oil Seal (Input Shaft)		
1983-87	5359457	2.75
(5) Bearing (Input Shaft)		
1983-87	8130868	19.75
(6) Seal (Vent Chamber)		
1983	8133743	1.50
1984-87	8133743	1.50
(7) Case (Front Half)		
1983-87	8133650	N.L.
(8) Bearing (Input Shaft)		
1983-87	8130868	19.75
(9) Rail Shaft		
1983-87	8133637	27.50
(10) Shift Fork		
1983-87	8133636	49.25
(11) Selector Mode		
1983-87	8133638	33.75
(12) Rear Output Bearing (Inner)		
1983	8130835	30.25
1984-87	8133644	36.50
(13) Washer (Inner)		
1983-87	8130834	1.00
(14) Output Bearing (Front)		
1983-87	8130869	13.50
(15) Output Bearing Assy. (Front)		
1983-87	8130819	13.25
(16) Output Shaft (Front)		
1983-87	8130850	92.50
(17) Sprocket (Driven)		
1983-87	8130849	100.00
(18) Chain		
1983-87	8130831	223.00
(19) Output Bearing Assy. (Front)		
1983-87	8130819	13.25
(20) Magnet		
1983-87	8130823	2.00
(21) Front Output Bearing (Rear)		
1983-87	8130836	13.25
(22) Case (Rear Half)		
1983-87	8133642	114.00
(23) Output Bearing (Outer)		
1983-87	8136626	27.75
(24) Seal (Vent Chamber)		
1983	8133743	1.50
1984-87	8133743	1.50
(25) Retainer (Rear)		
1983-87	8131618	N.L.
(26) Seal (Rear Output)		
1983	8133432	6.25
1984-85	8983502508	4.50
1986-87	8983502798	9.00
(27) Yoke (Rear)		
1983-87	8130817	57.25
(28) Spacer		
1983-87	8130847	6.50
(29) Side Gear Rollers (Kit of 85)		
1983-87	8130846	N.L.
(30) Spacer		
1983-87	8130848	3.75

	Part No.	Price
(31) Gear (Viscous Clutch)		
1983-87	8130801	22.75
(32) Carrier Rollers (Kit of 120)		
1983-87	8131611	19.25
(33) Spacer		
1983-87	8131612	3.75
(34) Carrier		
1983-87	8133632	83.50
(35) Sprocket (Drive)		
1983-87	8131610	100.00
(36) Clutch Gear (Side)		
1983-87	8133633	53.00
(37) Thrust Washer		
1983-87	8130844	6.00
(38) Mainshaft		
1983-87	8133634	188.75
(39) Sleeve (Sliding Clutch)		
1983-87	8133635	N.L.
(40) Washer		
1983-87	8131606	1.50
(41) Spacer		
1983-87	8131603	1.75
(42) Input Gear		
1983-87	8131602	N.L.
(43) Bearing Kit (Input Thrust)		
1983-87	8130875	N.L.
(44) Spacer		
1983-87	8130848	3.75
(45) Side Gears		
1983-87	8131608	125.25
(46) Viscous Coupling Assy.		
1983	8130800	586.00
1984-85	8130800	586.00
1986-87	8983502517	130.00

MODEL 119

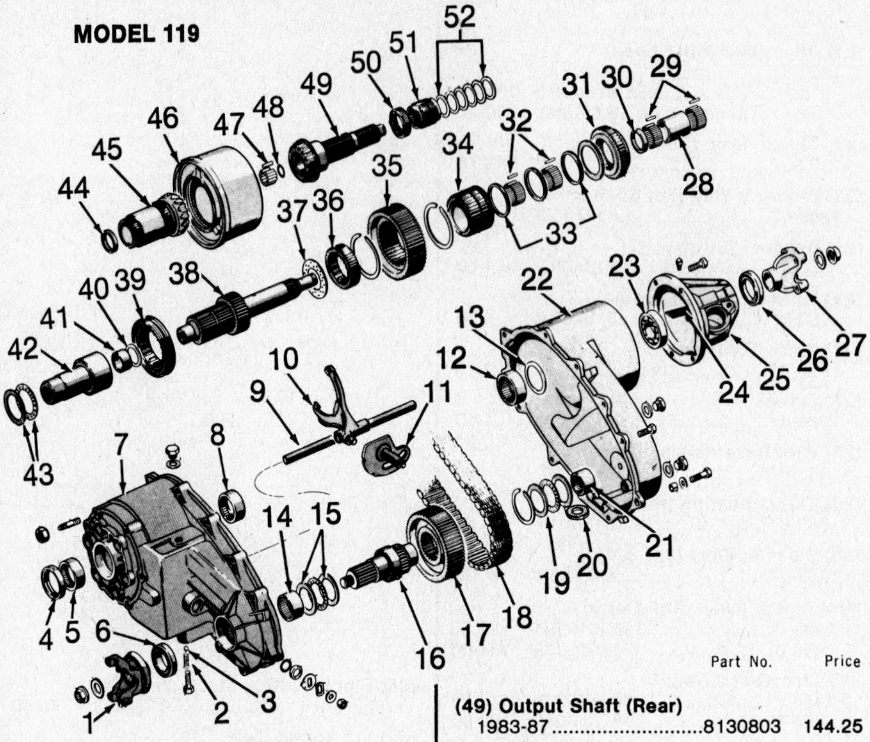

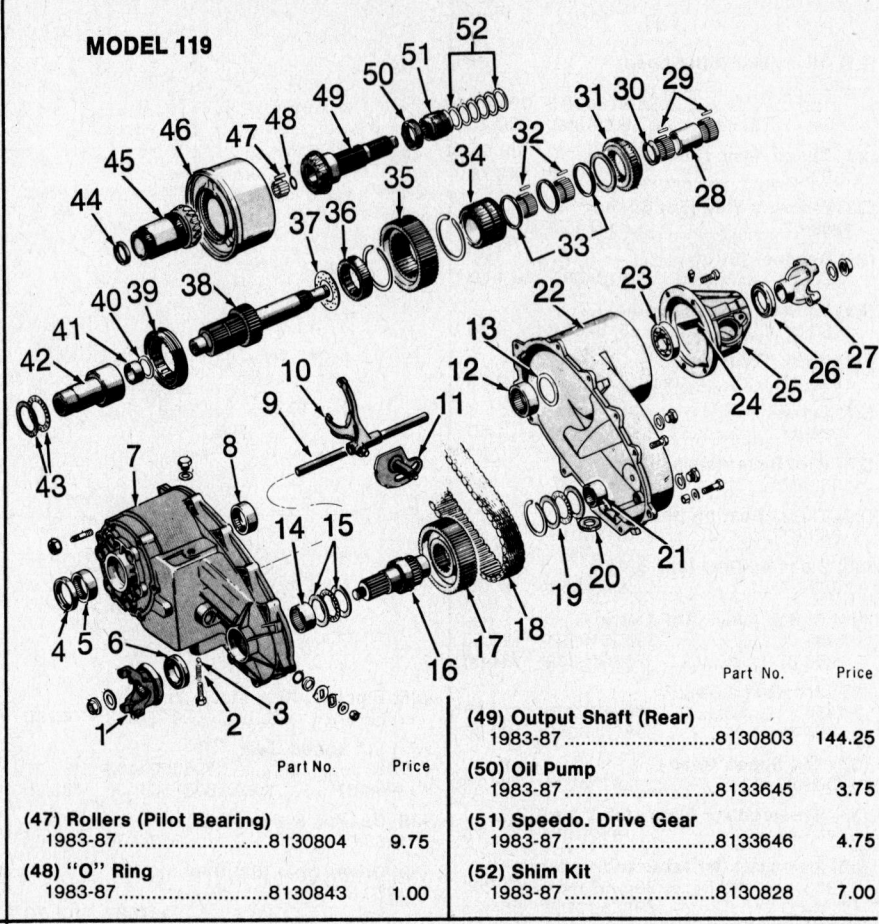

	Part No.	Price
(47) Rollers (Pilot Bearing)		
1983-87	8130804	9.75
(48) "O" Ring		
1983-87	8130843	1.00

	Part No.	Price
(49) Output Shaft (Rear)		
1983-87	8130803	144.25
(50) Oil Pump		
1983-87	8133645	3.75
(51) Speedo. Drive Gear		
1983-87	8133646	4.75
(52) Shim Kit		
1983-87	8130828	7.00

LABOR 19 STANDARD TRANSMISSION 19 LABOR

JEEP

(G) Transmission and Transfer Case, Remove & Reinstall (As A Unit)

CJ/Scrambler (2.7)	3.4
Cherokee/Grand Wagoneer/ Truck (3.4)	4.3
Cke/Wag/Comanche	
2 WD (1.9)	2.3
4 WD (2.9)	3.7
Diesel (3.0)	3.9
Renew front seal add	.2

(G) Transmission Assy., Recondition (Off Truck)

Note: Add this time to removal and installation operation to obtain R&R and Recondition.

4 Speed	
T-4 (2.3)	3.2
AX-4 (1.9)	2.6
T-18A, T-176 (2.3)	3.2
5 Speed	
T-5 (2.6)	3.6
AX-5 (2.1)	2.9

(G) Transmission Cover Gasket, Renew

CJ/Scrambler	
T-176 (.8)	1.2
Cherokee/Grand Wagoneer	
T-176 (1.0)	1.5
Truck	
T-176 (1.1)	1.6

(G) Transmission Rear Oil Seal, Renew

Includes: R&R transfer case if required.

CJ/Scrambler (1.6)	2.2
Cherokee/Grand Wagoneer (1.9)	2.6
Truck	
Six (1.9)	2.6
V-8 (1.5)	2.0
Cke/Wag/Comanche	
w/Command-Trac (1.3)	1.7
w/Selec-Trac (1.6)	2.2
w/2 WD (.4)	.7

(G) Speedometer Driven Gear and/or Seal, Renew

All models (.3)	.5

(G) Transmission Mounts, Renew

CJ/Scrambler (.5)	.7
Cherokee/Grand Wagoneer	
Rear Support	
Six (.8)	1.1
V-8 (.4)	.6
Cke/Wag/Comanche (.6)	.9

TRANSFER CASE

(G) Transfer Case Assy., Remove & Reinstall

CJ/Scrambler (1.1)	1.9
Cherokee/Grand Wagoneer/ Truck	
Six (1.4)	2.1
V-8 (1.0)	1.7
Selec-Trac 229 (1.8)	2.5
Cke/Wag/Comanche	
Command Trac (1.1)	1.9
Selec-Trac (1.4)	2.1
Renew assy add (.3)	.5

(G) Transfer Case Assy., Recondition (Off Truck)

Note: Add this time to removal and installation operation to obtain R&R and Recondition.

CJ/Scrambler (2.6)	3.5
Cherokee/Grand Wagoneer/ Truck	
wo/Selec-Trac 229 (2.7)	3.6
w/Selec-Trac 229 (2.8)	3.7
Cke/Wag/Comanche	
Command Trac (1.7)	2.2
Selec-Trac 229 (2.8)	3.7

(G) Output Shaft Flange, R&R or Renew (Front or Rear)

All models (.6)	.8
Renew shaft seal add (.1)	.2

(G) Rear Bearing Retainer, Renew

All models (1.0)	1.4

(G) Transfer Case Bottom Cover and/or Gasket, Renew

CJ/Scrambler (.8)	1.1

(G) Front Axle Shift Switch, Renew

All models (.3)	.5

(G) Transfer Case Shift Lever, Renew

CJ/Scrambler (1.0)	1.4
Cke/Wag/Comanche	
w/M.T. (1.1)	1.5
w/A.T. (.6)	.9
Recond lever add (.5)	.5

(G) Vacuum Tube Assembly, Renew

All models (1.4)	2.0

PARTS 19 STANDARD TRANS. (4 Speed) 19 PARTS

MODEL T-176, T-177

	Part No.	Price
Transmission Assy.		
1983-Model T-176	5362086	1343.75
Model T-177	5359386	494.25
(1) Blocking Ring (3rd & 4th)		
1983	8132378	N.L.
(2) Clutch Assy. (3rd & 4th)		
1983	8132376	141.50
(3) Third Speed Gear		
1983-T-176	8132379	157.50
T-177	8132429	177.25
(4) Second Speed Gear		
1983-T-176	8132382	156.75
T-177	8132384	157.75
(5) Blocking Ring		
1983	8132378	N.L.
(6) Clutch Assy. (1st & 2nd)		
1983	8132386	221.00
(7) Plate Assy. (1st & 2nd)		
1983	8132387	7.00
(8) Low Gear		
1983	8132389	122.50
(9) Oil Seal (Front Bearing)		
1983	8124881	N.L.
(10) Gasket (Front Bearing Cap)		
1983	8132423	1.75
(11) Ball Bearing (Front)		
1983	8132426	62.50

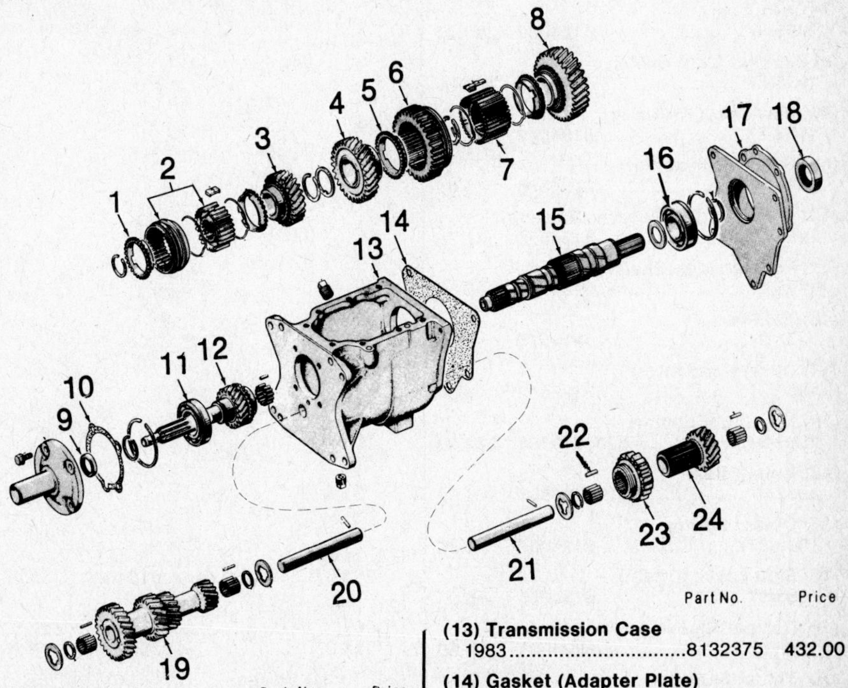

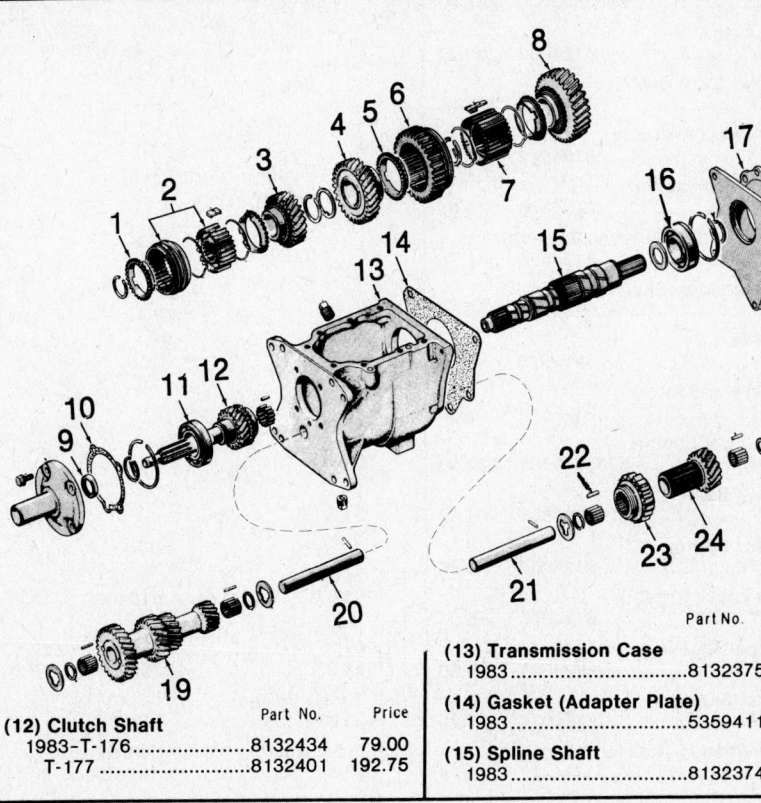

	Part No.	Price
(12) Clutch Shaft		
1983-T-176	8132434	79.00
T-177	8132401	192.75

	Part No.	Price
(13) Transmission Case		
1983	8132375	432.00
(14) Gasket (Adapter Plate)		
1983	5359411	1.75
(15) Spline Shaft		
1983	8132374	149.75

PARTS 19 STANDARD TRANS. (4 Speed) 19 PARTS

	Part No.	Price
(16) Ball Bearing (Rear)		
1983	8136623	68.00
(17) Adapter Plate (To Transfer Case)		
1983	5359381	61.75
(18) Seal (Adapter Plate)		
1983	5359457	2.75
(19) Countershaft Gear		
1983-T-176	8132391	334.00
T-177	8132393	454.25
(20) Countershaft		
1983	8132397	42.00
(21) Idler Gear Shaft		
1983	8132398	19.50
(22) Roller Bearing (Reverse Idler Gear)		
1983	8132403	.75
(23) Sliding Gear (Reverse Idler)		
1983	8132402	95.75
(24) Idler Gear (Reverse)		
1983	8132399	117.75

PARTS 19 STANDARD TRANS. (4 Speed) 19 PARTS

MODEL T4

T4 transmissions may have been substituted for the AX4 in some Series 70 vehicles. Use the following parts list for price reference only on Series 70.

	Part No.	Price
Transmission Assy.		
1983-Four-151	8953001940	1072.25
150	8953001097	N.L.
Six	8953001940	1072.25
1984-87		
Four	8953001941	1090.25
Six	8953001940	1072.25
(1) Front Bearing Retainer		
1983-87	8134013	56.25
(2) Oil Seal (Input Shaft)		
1983-87	8132779	4.00
(3) Shim Set		
1983-87	8134016	10.00
(4) Cup		
Note: Included with No. 5		
(5) Bearing (Input Shaft)		
1983-87	8134015	28.25
(6) Input Shaft		
1983	8134014	232.50
1984-87-Four	8983500968	231.00
Six	8983500975	231.00
(7) Case Assy.		
1983-87	8134009	200.00
(8) Back-Up Light Switch		
1983-87	3229472	10.50
(9) Relay Lever (Reverse)		
1983-87	8134042	44.50
(10) Bushing (Reverse)		
1983-87	8134336	3.00
(11) Reverse Idler Gear (w/Bushing)		
1983-87	8134038	147.75
(12) Reverse Idler Shaft		
1983-87	8134039	33.50
(13) Breather		
1983-87	912375	1.50
(14) Oil Seal (Adapter)		
1983-87	8132672	3.50
(15) Housing (Adapter)		
1983-87	8983510185	232.00
(16) Detent Ball		
1983-87	G453593	1.00
(17) Detent Spring		
1983-87	8134057	1.00
(18) Shift Lever (Offset)		
1983-87	8134055	45.00
(19) Damper Sleeve		
1983-87	8134056	1.50
(20) Thrust Bearing		
1983-87	8134034	4.25
(21) Rear Bearing (Cluster Gear)		
1983-87	8134036	18.75

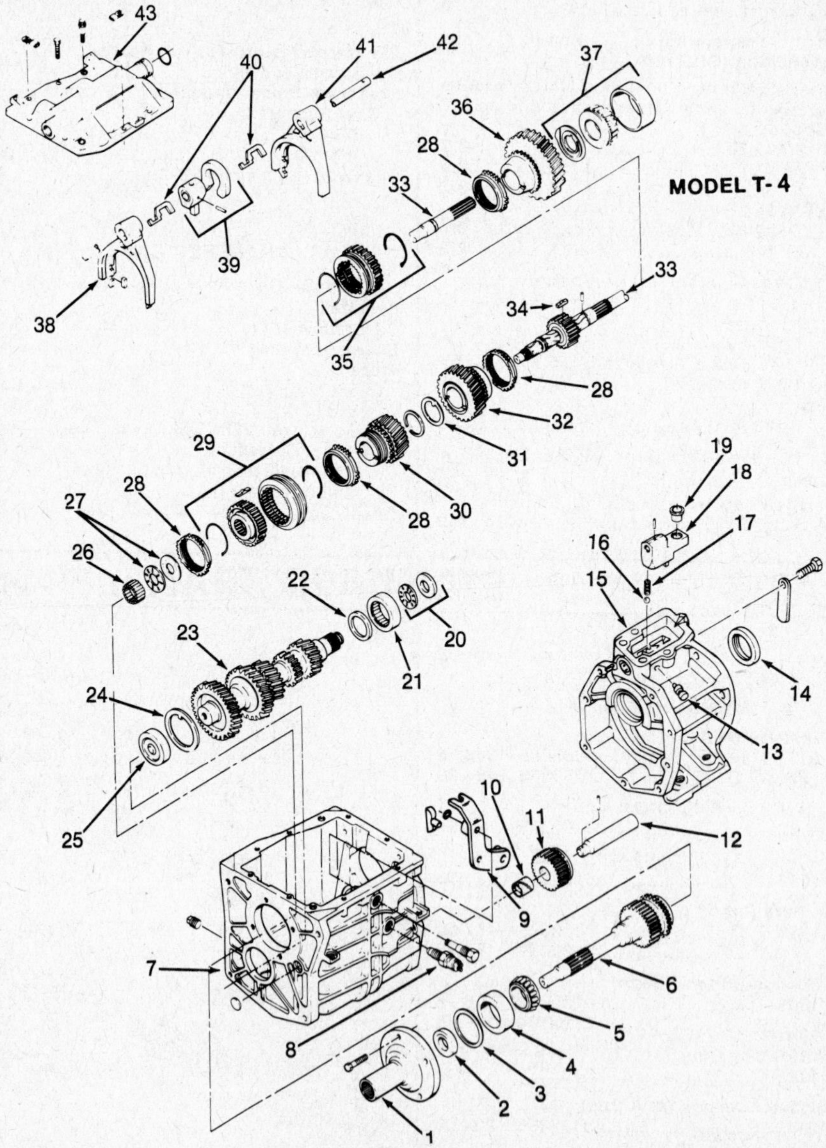

	Part No.	Price
(22) Spacer		
1983-87	8134034	4.25
(23) Cluster Gear		
1983	8134031	529.50
1984-87	8983500970	476.25
(24) Thrust Washer		
1983-87	8134032	4.50
(25) Front Bearing (Cluster Gear)		
1983-87	8134033	25.50
(26) Pilot Roller (Mainshaft)		
1983-87	8134034	4.25
(27) Thrust Bearing (Needle)		
1983-87	8134018	5.50
(28) Synchro. Ring		
1983-87		
1st & 2nd	8127403	45.50
3rd & 4th	8134058	47.00

PARTS 19 STANDARD TRANS. (4 Speed) 19 PARTS

	Part No.	Price
(29) Clutch Assy. (3rd & 4th)		
1983	8983510191	128.50
1984-87	8983510192	134.00
(30) 3rd Speed Gear		
1983-151 & Six	8983500285	178.25
1983-150	8983500285	178.25
1984-87	8983500380	169.00
(31) Thrust Washer (2nd Speed)		
1983-87	8134025	4.00
(32) 2nd Speed Gear		
1983-87	8134024	165.25
(33) Mainshaft (w/1st & 2nd Synchro.)		
1983-87	8983501166	554.75
(34) Synchro. Plate (1st & 2nd)		
1983-87	8127401	.75
(35) Spring (Synchro.)		
1983-87	8134021	1.00
(36) 1st Speed Gear		
1983-87	8983501103	183.25
(37) Bearing (Rear)		
1983-87	8134030	37.00
(38) Shift Fork (3rd & 4th)		
1983-87	8134048	42.00
(39) Selector Arm Assy.		
1983-87	8127487	32.25
(40) Shift Plate		
1983-87	8134050	22.00
(41) Shift Fork (1st & 2nd)		
1983-87	8134049	42.00
(42) Shifter Shaft		
151 & Six	8134091	52.25
1984-87-Four	8983510072	45.25
Six	8134091	52.25
(43) Case Cover		
1983-151 & Six	8134045	91.00
1984-87-Four	8983500977	102.00
Six	8134045	91.00

PARTS 19 STANDARD TRANSMISSION 19 PARTS

MODEL AX4 & AX5

The AX4 & AX5 trans. can be identified by the gray cast iron intermediate plate located between the transfer case and adapter housing.

	Part No.	Price
Transmission Assy.		
1984-85-2W.D.		
AX4	8953001670	931.25
AX5	8953001671	1010.25
1986-87-2W.D.		
AX4	8953004250	917.00
AX5	8953003386	1022.25
1984-85-4W.D.		
AX4	8953001565	1000.75
AX5	8953001566	1069.50
1986-87-4W.D.		
AX4	8953004249	956.75
AX5	8953003385	908.50
(1) Output Shaft		
1984-87-2 W.D.	8983502117	177.50
4 W.D.	8983500559	223.75
(2) Snap Ring		
1984-87	8983500613	3.50
(3) Snap Ring		
1984-87 (2.67 MM)	8983500587	1.00
(4) 5th Gear		
1984-87	8983500971	97.50
(5) Bearing Retainer		
1984-87	8134087	1.50
(6) 4th Gear Synchronizer Ring		
1984-87	8983500566	20.50
(7) Input Shaft		
1984-85-Gas eng	8983500554	247.50
Diesel eng	8983501409	231.00
1986-87-Gas eng	8983502682	183.75
Diesel eng	8983502683	204.00
(8) Oil Slinger		
1984-87		
(9) Counter Gear Rear Bearing Snap Ring		
1984-87	8134073	1.25
(10) Counter Gear Rear Bearing		
1984-87	8134036	18.75
(11) Counter Gear (Cluster)		
1984-87	8983500557	401.25
(12) Counter Gear (Cluster)		
1984-87	8983500557	401.25
(13) Counter Gear Rear Bearing		
1984-87	8983500580	26.75
(14) Snap Ring		
1984-87	8983500581	1.25
(15) Washer		
1984-87	8983500640	5.00

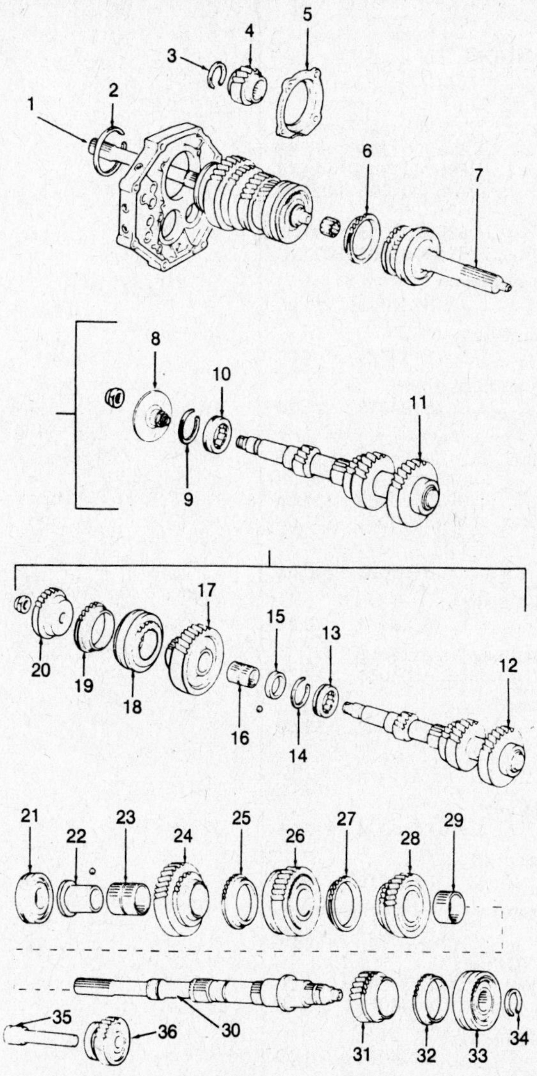

	Part No.	Price
(16) 5th Gear Roller Bearing		
1984-87	8983500644	68.25
(17) Counter 5th Gear		
1984-87	8983500553	147.75
(18) Synchronizer Sleeve		
1984-87	8983500642	55.50
(19) 5th Gear Synchronizer Ring		
1984-87	8983500566	20.50
(20) 5th Gear		
1984-87	8983500639	60.75
(21) Rear Bearing		
1984-87	8983500575	50.25

PARTS 19 STANDARD TRANSMISSION 19 PARTS

	Part No.	Price
(22) Inner Race		
1984-87	8983500560	20.00
(23) Bearing (1st Gear Roller)		
1984-87	8983500578	60.25
(24) 1st Gear		
1984-87	8983500550	176.50
(25) 1st Gear Synchronizer Ring		
1984-87	8983500567	19.00
(26) Synchronizer Sleeve		
1984-87	8983500563	45.75
(27) 2nd Gear Synchronizer Ring		
1984-87	8983500567	19.00
(28) 2nd Gear		
1984-87	8983500551	132.25
(29) 2nd Gear Roller Bearing		
1984-87	8983500577	44.00
(30) Output Shaft		
1984-87-2 W.D.	8983502117	177.50
4 W.D.	8983500559	223.75
(31) 3rd Gear		
1984-87	8983500552	115.75
(32) 3rd Gear Synchronizer Ring		
1984-87	8983500566	20.50
(33) Synchronizer Sleeve		
1984-87	8983500563	45.75
(34) Snap Ring		
1984-87	8983500598	1.00
(35) Reverse Idler Shaft		
1984-87	8983500570	34.50
(36) Reverse Idler Gear		
1984-87	8983500556	90.75
Transmission Overhaul Gasket Set		
1984-87	8983500632	9.75

PARTS 19 STANDARD TRANS. (5 Speed) 19 PARTS

MODEL T5

	Part No.	Price
Transmission Assy.		
1983-151		
3.54 axle	3241886	1257.50
4.09 axle	8953001945	1442.75
1983-Six	8953001945	1442.75
1983-150	8953001098	1400.75
1984-87		
Four	8953001508	1400.75
Six	8953001507	1400.75
(1) Front Bearing Retainer		
1983-87	8134013	56.25
(2) Oil Seal (Input Shaft)		
1983-87	8132779	4.00
(3) Bearing & Cup (Input Shaft)		
1983-87	8134015	28.25
(4) Input Shaft		
1983-exc. 150	8134014	232.50
1983-150	8983500286	240.25
1984-87-Four	8983500968	231.00
Six	8983500975	231.00
(5) Case Assy.		
1983-87	8134093	200.00
(6) Back-Up Light Switch		
1983-87	3229472	10.50
(7) Reverse Idler Gear (w/Bushing)		
1983-87	8134038	147.75
Reverse Idler Shaft		
1983-87	8134039	33.50
(8) Breather		
1983-87	912375	1.50
(9) Housing (Adapter)		
1983-87	8134095	210.75
(10) Oil Seal (Adapter)		
1983-87	8132672	3.50
(11) Spring (Detent)		
1983-87	8134057	1.00
(12) Shift Lever (Offset)		
1983-exc. below	8134054	35.00
1983-87	8134055	45.00
(13) Damper Sleeve		
1983-87	8134056	1.50
(14) Shift Fork (5th Speed)		
1983-87	8134085	41.00
(15) Rail Assy. (w/Pin & Roller)		
1983-87	8134079	39.25
(16) Lock Plate (Reverse)		
1983-87	8134078	7.50
(17) Front Bearing (Cluster Gear)		
1983-87	8134071	39.75

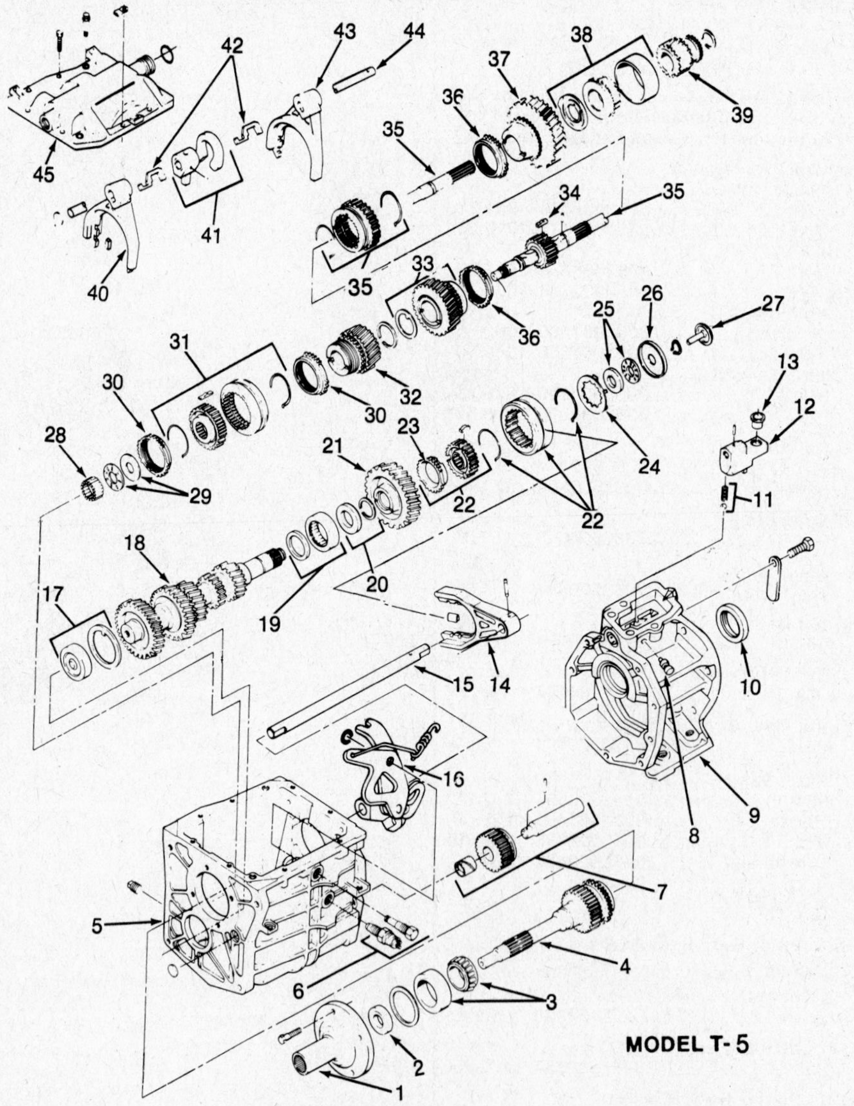

MODEL T-5

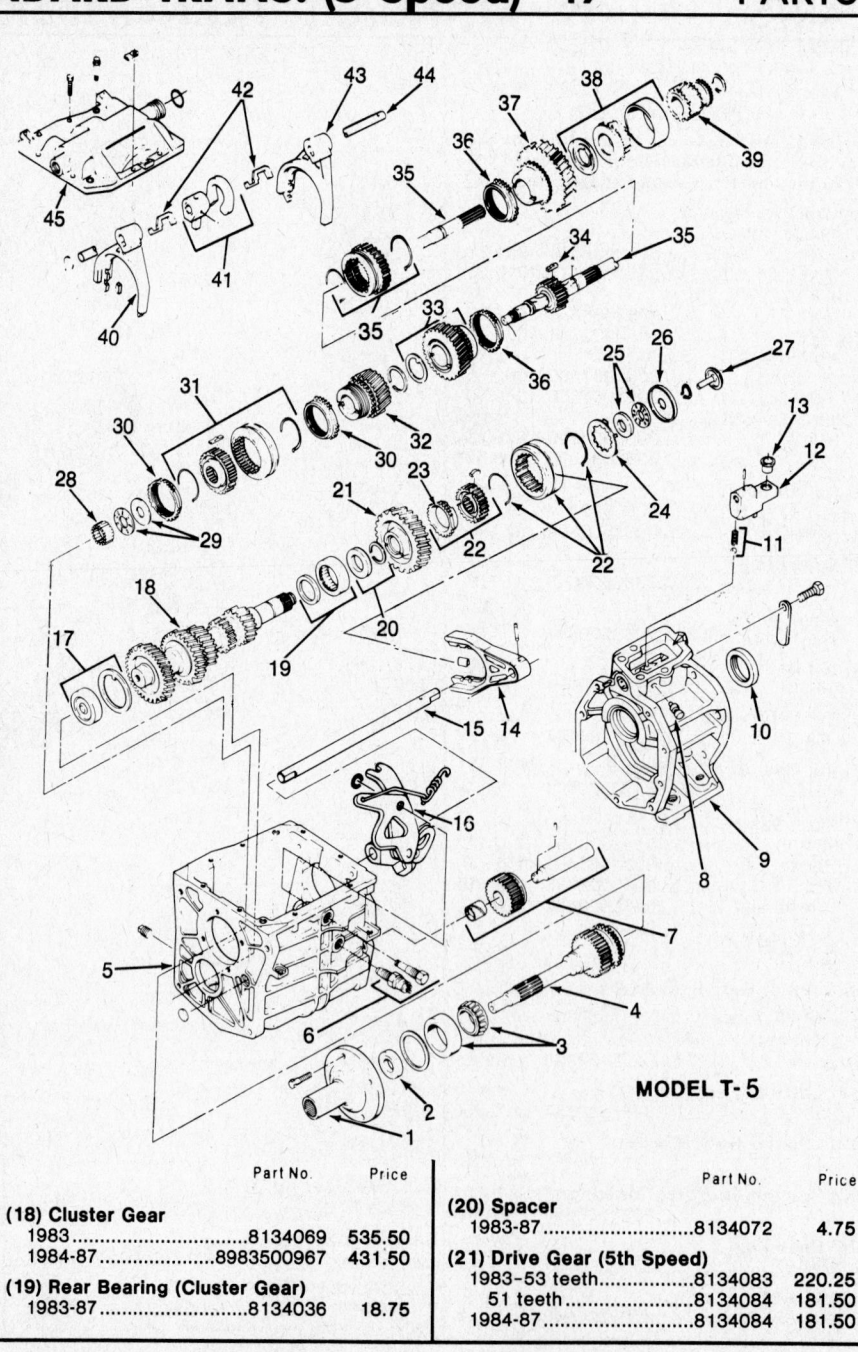

	Part No.	Price
(18) Cluster Gear		
1983	8134069	535.50
1984-87	8983500967	431.50
(19) Rear Bearing (Cluster Gear)		
1983-87	8134036	18.75
(20) Spacer		
1983-87	8134072	4.75
(21) Drive Gear (5th Speed)		
1983-53 teeth	8134083	220.25
51 teeth	8134084	181.50
1984-87	8134084	181.50

PARTS 19 STANDARD TRANS. (5 Speed) 19 PARTS

	Part No.	Price
(22) Clutch Assy. (5th Speed)		
1983-87	8134086	143.75
(23) Blocking Ring (5th Speed)		
1983-87	8127414	N.L.
(24) Retainer (Strut)		
1983-87	8134087	1.50
(25) Thrust Bearing (Needle)		
1983-87	8134034	4.25
(26) Race Thrust		
1983-87	8134037	2.25
(27) Funnel		
1983-87	8134090	1.50
(28) Pilot Roller (Mainshaft)		
1983-87	8127397	.50
(29) Thrust Bearing (Needle)		
1983-87	8134018	5.50
(30) Blocking Ring (3rd & 4th)		
1983-87	8134058	47.00
(31) Clutch Assy. (3rd & 4th)		
1983	8983510191	128.50
1984-87	8983510192	134.00
(32) 3rd Speed Gear		
1983	8983500285	178.25
1984-87	8983500380	169.00
(33) Second Speed Gear		
1983-87	8134024	165.25
(34) Synchro. Plate		
1983-87	8127401	.75
(35) Mainshaft (w/1st & 2nd Synchro.)		
1983-87	8983501166	554.75
(36) Blocking Ring (1st & 2nd)		
1983-87	8127403	45.50
(37) 1st Speed Gear		
1983-87	8983501103	183.25
(38) Bearing (Rear)		
1983-87	8134030	37.00
(39) Driven Gear (5th Speed)		
1983-23 teeth	8134080	108.50
25 teeth	8134081	113.00
1984-87-Four	8134081	113.00
Six	8134080	108.50
(40) Shift Fork (3rd & 4th)		
1983-87	8134048	42.00
(41) Selector Arm Assy.		
1983-87	8127487	32.25
(42) Shift Plates		
1983-87	8134050	22.00
(43) Shift Fork (1st & 2nd)		
1983-87	8134049	42.00
(44) Shifter Shaft		
1983-87	8134091	52.25
(45) Cover		
1983-87	8134045	91.00

PARTS 19 TRANSFER CASE 19 PARTS

MODEL 207 JEEP

	Part No.	Price
Transfer Case		
1984-87 (Tag No. Listed Below)		
No. 154, 421	8953000154	1101.50
No. 221, 224	8953000224	228.50
No. 390, 738	8953003738	780.75
No. 520	8953000520	N.L.
No. 521	8953000521	205.00
No. 559, 735	8953003735	780.75
Case (Front Half)		
1984-87-M.T.	8983500953	147.00
A.T.	8134443	118.75
Vacuum Switch		
1984-87	8953001101	9.75
Lockout Plate (Low Range)		
1984-87	8130873	47.00
Main Drive Shaft		
1984-87	8134467	145.25
Oil Pump		
1984-87	8133645	3.75
1984-87	8134493	6.50
Oil Seal		
1984-87	8130982	2.50
Housing Oil Pump		
1984-87	8134486	8.00
Bearing		
1984-87	8134445	18.75
Bearing		
1984-87	8134450	15.50
Annulus Gear		
1984-87	8134452	121.00
Planetary Gear		
1984-87	8134455	201.00
Thrust Ring (2)		
1984-87	8134456	1.50
Synchronizer Strut (3)		
1984-87	8983500990	1.25
Synchronizer (Mode Shift)		
1984-87	8134480	93.00
Sprocket (Drive)		
1984-87	8134468	83.25
Bearing (2)		
1984-87	8134469	17.50
Thrust Washer		
1984-87	8134470	5.25
Bearing		
1984-87	8134484	10.50
Chain (Drive)		
1984-87	8134471	170.25
Output Shaft		
1984-87	8134482	125.00
Bearing		
1984-87	8134445	18.75
Flange w/Slinger		
1984-87-exc. 390, 559	8953000906	118.00
No. 390, 559	8983502644	41.50
Bearing Kit		
1984-87	8134451	4.75
Bearing (2)		
1984-87	8134444	20.50
Input Gear		
1984-87-A.T.	8983500951	123.50
M.T.	8134495	134.25
Case (Rear Half)		
1984-87	8983501192	116.50
Sensor (Oil Level)		
1984-87	8953000376	23.25
Extension Case		
1984-87	8134489	58.75
Fork (Range Shift)		
1984-87	8134459	16.50
Shift Rail		
1984-87	8134466	13.50
Fork (Mode Shift)		
1984-87	8134461	17.25
Sector Shaft		
1984-87	8134457	29.00

PARTS 19 TRANSFER CASE 19 PARTS

MODEL 208 JEEP

	Part No.	Price
Transfer Case Assy.		
1983-87		
Assy. No.	8933001383	1283.75
Assy. No.	8933001384	1283.75
Assy. No.	8933001385	1283.75
Assy. No.	8933001386	1246.50
(1) Bearing (Roller)		
1983-87	8130972	38.50
(2) Spacer		
1983-87	8130971	1.50
(3) Thrust Washer		
1983-87	8134130	9.75
(4) Pump (Oil)		
1983-87	8130826	2.50
(5) Speedo. Gear (Drive)		
1983-87	8130827	3.75
(6) Bearing Kit (Input)		
1983-87	8130875	N.L.
(7) Input Gear Assy. (w/Bearing)		
1983-87-5 sp. trans.	8130877	130.25
exc. 5 spd. trans.	8132818	130.25
(8) Bearing (Input)		
1983-87	8130878	10.25
(9) Planetary Gear Assy.		
1983-87	8130862	273.25
(10) Thrust Washer		
1983-87	8130863	5.50
(11) Annulus Gear Assy.		
1983-87	8983500259	153.75
(12) Thrust Bearing (Main Shaft)		
1983-87	8130879	5.50

PARTS 19 TRANSFER CASE 19 PARTS

	Part No.	Price
(13) Mainshaft		
1983-87	8983510093	196.25
(14) Thrust Washer		
1983-87	8130967	2.50
(15) Clutch Gear (Mode)		
1983-87	8983510094	49.50
(16) Spring (Mode Shift)		
1983-87	8134545	N.L.
(17) Ring (Sprocket Stop)		
1983-87	8130970	1.75
(18) Sprocket (Drive)		
1983-87	8130968	83.75
(19) Fork (Range)		
1983-87	8983500260	38.50
(20) Spring (Mode Fork)		
1983-87	8130876	1.00
(21) Fork (Mode)		
1983-87	8130851	15.00
(22) Bracket (Mode)		
1983-87	8130821	16.00
(23) Sector (Range)		
1983-87	8130820	43.00
(24) Rear Output Bearing (Inner)		
1983-87	8130835	30.25
(25) Washer		
1983-87	8130834	1.00
(26) Case (Rear Half)		
1983-87	8130978	86.50
(27) Pump Housing		
1983-87	8130981	5.25
(28) Bearing Retainer (Rear)		
1983-87	8130983	52.00
(29) Vent		
1983-87	8130985	5.25
(30) Yoke (Rear)		
1983-87	8130817	57.25
(31) Oil Seal (Output)		
1983-87	8133432	6.25
(32) Seal (Pump Housing)		
1983-87	8130982	2.50
(33) Front Output Shaft Bearing (Rear)		
1983-87	8130836	13.25
(34) Magnet		
1983-87	8130823	2.00

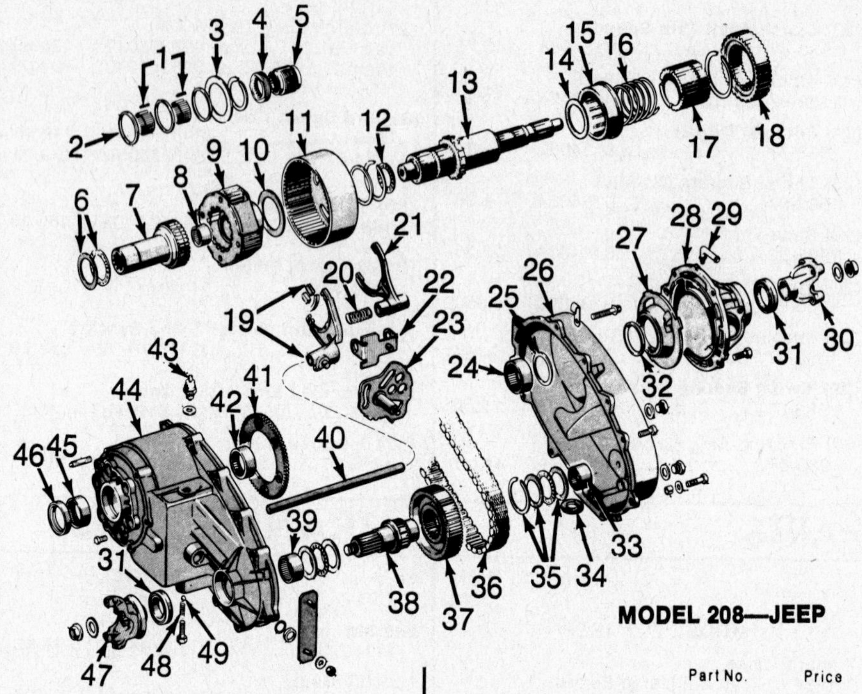

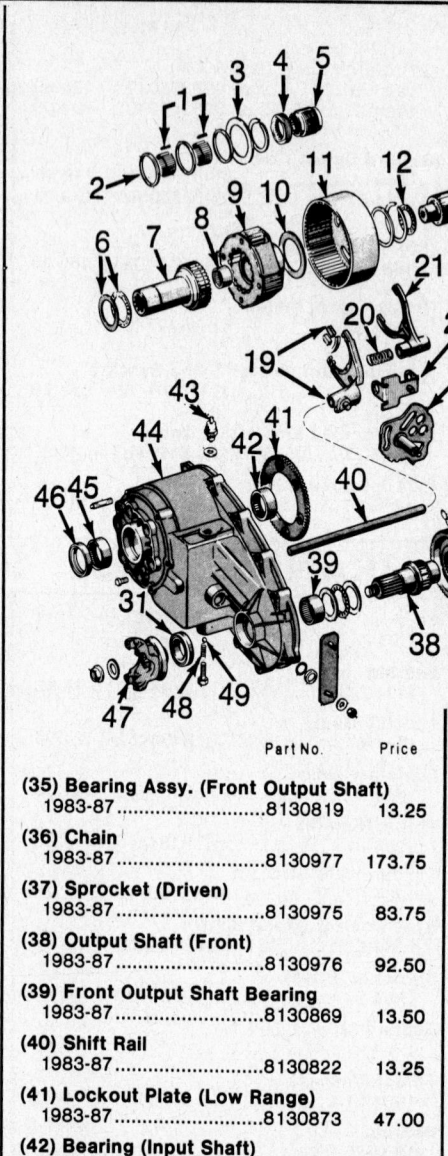

MODEL 208—JEEP

	Part No.	Price
(35) Bearing Assy. (Front Output Shaft)		
1983-87	8130819	13.25
(36) Chain		
1983-87	8130977	173.75
(37) Sprocket (Driven)		
1983-87	8130975	83.75
(38) Output Shaft (Front)		
1983-87	8130976	92.50
(39) Front Output Shaft Bearing		
1983-87	8130869	13.50
(40) Shift Rail		
1983-87	8130822	13.25
(41) Lockout Plate (Low Range)		
1983-87	8130873	47.00
(42) Bearing (Input Shaft)		
1983-87	8130868	19.75

	Part No.	Price
(43) Switch (Lockout)		
1983-87	8130829	10.25
(44) Case (Front Half)		
1983-87	8130867	136.00
(45) Bearing (Input Shaft)		
1983-87	8130868	19.75
(46) Oil Seal (Input Shaft)		
1983-87	5359457	2.75
(47) Yoke (Front Output)		
1983-87	8130818	66.75
(48) Spring		
1983-87	8130856	N.L.
(49) Ball		
1983-87	8983501349	1.50
left	7846210	N.L.

PARTS 19 TRANSFER CASE 19 PARTS

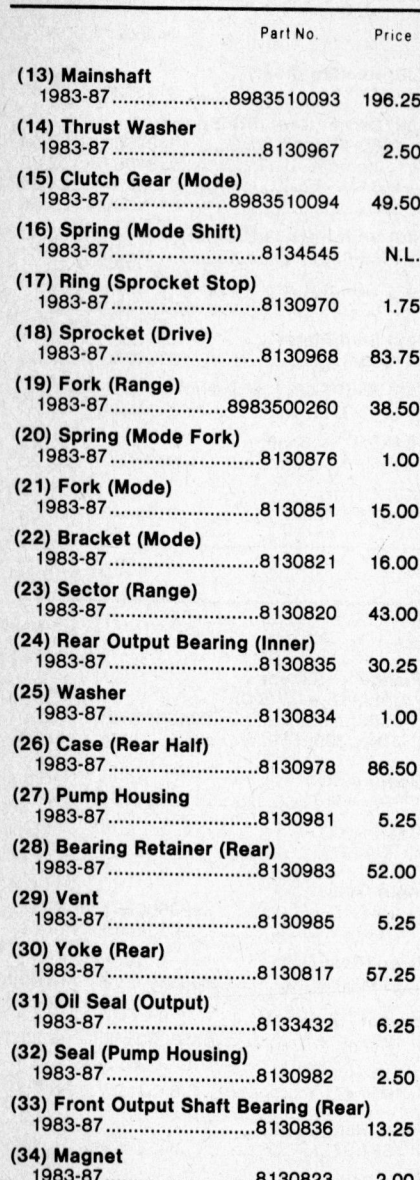

MODEL 228 and 229 JEEP

	Part No.	Price
Transfer Case Assy.		
1983-85-229	5363353	1594.00
1986-87-228	8953003970	N.L.
(1) Spacer		
1983-87	8130848	3.75
(2) Side Gear		
1983-87	8131608	125.25
(3) Viscous Coupling Assy.		
1983-85-229	8130800	586.00
1986-87-228	8983502517	130.00
(4) Pilot Bearing (Roller)		
1983-87	8130804	9.75
(5) Output Shaft (Rear)		
1983-87	8130803	144.25
(6) Oil Pump		
1983-87	8133645	3.75

	Part No.	Price
(7) Speedo. Gear (Drive)		
1983-87	8133646	4.75
(8) Shim Kit		
1983-87	8130828	7.00
(9) Thrust Bearing (Input)		
1983-87	8130868	19.75
(10) Input Race		
1983-87	N.L.	
(11) Input Shaft		
1983-87	8983500492	128.75
(12) Input Bearing		
1983-87	8130878	10.25
(13) Planetary Gear Assy.		
1983-87	8983500383	239.00
(14) Annulus Gear		
1983-87	8130864	204.00

	Part No.	Price
(15) Bushing (Annulus)		
1983-87	8133677	5.25
(16) Thrust Bearing		
1983-87	8130879	5.50
(17) Sliding Clutch Sleeve (Hi Range)		
1983-85-229	8134273	N.L.
1986-87-228	8983502611	31.75
(18) Sliding Clutch Sleeve (Mode)		
1983-85-229	8133635	N.L.
1986-87-228	8983502516	41.75
(19) Mainshaft		
1983-87	8134274	196.25
(20) Thrust Washer (Mainshaft)		
1983-87	8130844	6.00
(21) Side Gear (Clutch)		
1983-87	8133633	53.00

PARTS 19 TRANSFER CASE 19 PARTS

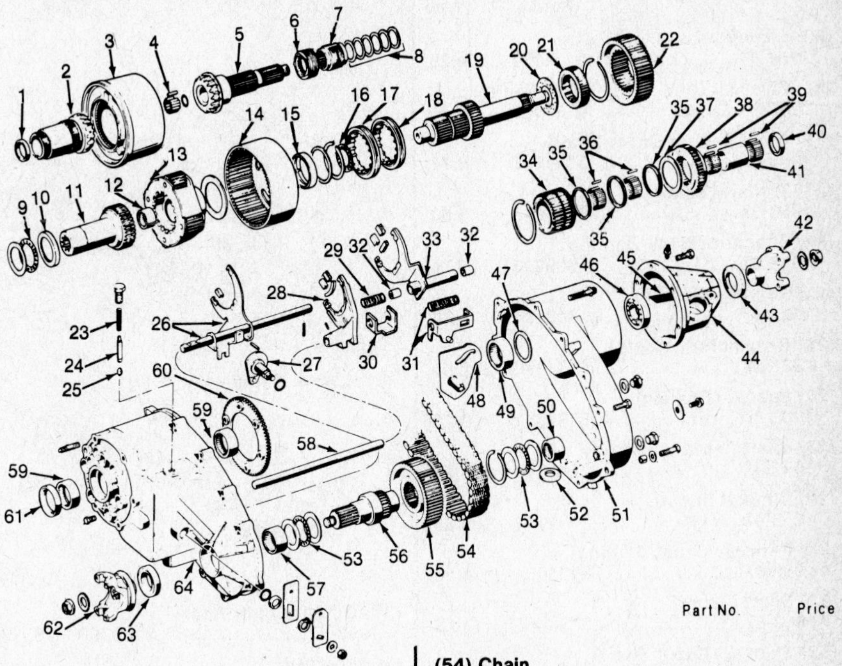

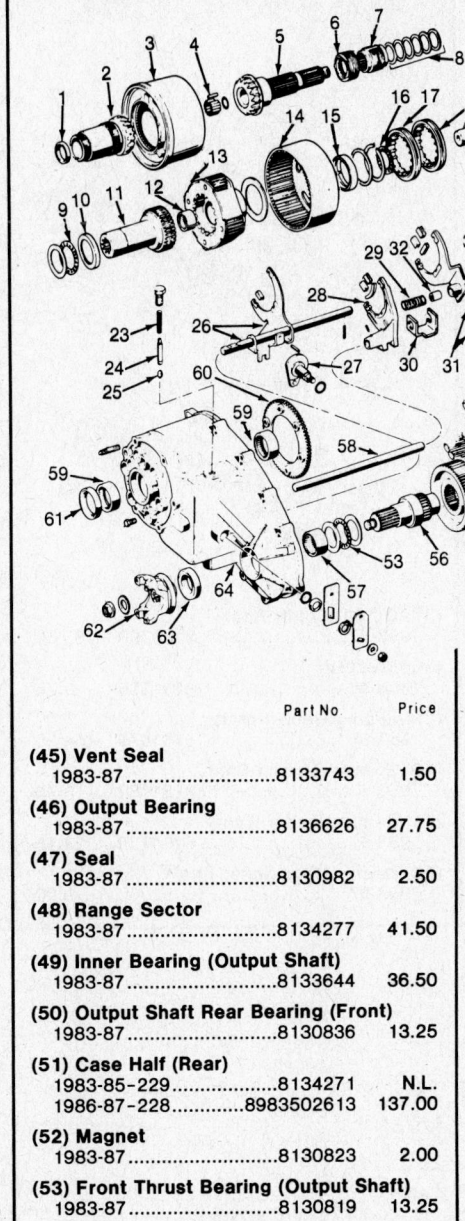

	Part No.	Price
(22) Sprocket 1983-87	8131610	100.00
(23) Spring (Plunger) 1983-87	8134289	3.75
(24) Plunger 1983-87	8134282	2.00
(25) Ball 1983-87	8983501349	1.50
(26) Mode Fork Assy. 1983-87	8134275	37.50
(27) Sector (Mode) 1983-87	8134288	37.25
(28) Fork (Range) 1983-87	8134276	61.75
(29) Spring (Inner) 1983-87	8134284	2.50
(30) Range Bracket (Inner) 1983-87	8134298	3.75
(31) Range Bracket (Outer) 1983-87	8134407	17.75
(32) Bushing (Locking Fork) 1983-87	8134291	1.50
(33) Locking Fork 1983-87	8134287	33.75
(34) Carrier 1983-87	8133632	83.50
(35) Spacer 1983-87	8131612	3.75
(36) Roller (Kit of 120) 1983-87	8131611	19.25
(37) Thrust Washer (Sprocket) 1983-87	8131613	6.50
(38) Gear (Viscous Clutch) 1983-85-229	8130801	22.75
(39) Side Gear Roller (Kit of 82) 1983-87	8130846	N.L.
(40) Spacer (Short) 1983-87	8130848	3.75
(41) Spacer (Long) 1983-87	8130847	6.50
(42) Yoke (Rear) 1983-87	8130817	57.25
(43) Seal 1983-87	8133432	6.25
(44) Retainer (Rear) 1983-87	8130806	52.00
(45) Vent Seal 1983-87	8133743	1.50
(46) Output Bearing 1983-87	8136626	27.75
(47) Seal 1983-87	8130982	2.50
(48) Range Sector 1983-87	8134277	41.50
(49) Inner Bearing (Output Shaft) 1983-87	8133644	36.50
(50) Output Shaft Rear Bearing (Front) 1983-87	8130836	13.25
(51) Case Half (Rear) 1983-85-229	8134271	N.L.
1986-87-228	8983502613	137.00
(52) Magnet 1983-87	8130823	2.00
(53) Front Thrust Bearing (Output Shaft) 1983-87	8130819	13.25
(54) Chain 1983-87	8130831	223.00
(55) Sprocket (Driven) 1983-87	8983500491	N.L.
(56) Output Shaft (Front) 1983-87	8130850	92.50
(57) Output Bearing (Front) 1983-87	8130869	13.50
(58) Range Rail 1983-87	8134280	36.50
(59) Bearing (Input Shaft) 1983-87	8130868	19.75
(60) Lockout Plate (Low Range) 1983-87	8130873	47.00
(61) Oil Seal (Input Shaft) 1983-87	5359457	2.75
(62) Output Yoke (Front) 1983-87	8134272	83.25
(63) Seal 1983-87	8133432	6.25
(64) Case Half (Front) 1983-87	8134278	148.50

PARTS 19 TRANSFER CASE 19 PARTS

MODEL 300 JEEP

	Part No.	Price
Transfer Case Assy. 1983-87	5364854	1317.75
(1) Shift Rod (Front) 1983-87	8131673	49.75
(2) Shift Rod (Rear) 1983-87	8131672	49.75
(3) Shift Fork (Front) 1983-87	8131665	27.00
(4) Shift Fork (Rear) 1983-87	8131666	38.50
(5) Clip (Shift Fork) 1983-87	8131670	1.50
(6) Poppet Spring (Rear) 1983-87	8131675	.75
(7) Poppet Ball 1983-87	G453593	1.00
(8) Poppet Spring (Front) 1983-87	8131676	.75
(9) Oil Seal (Shift Rod) 1983-87	8131674	4.75
(10) Yoke Assy. (Front & Rear) 1983-87	8131656	51.75
(11) Oil Seal 1983-87	8131669	2.50
(12) Front Cap (Output Bearing) 1983-87	8131671	202.50
(13) Bearing Cup (Front) 1983-87	3156062	5.50
(14) Cone & Bearing (Front) 1983-87	3156063	13.25
(15) Output Gear (Front) 1983-87	8131680	117.75
(16) Output Shaft (Front) 1983-87	8131660	117.75
(17) Case (Transfer) 1983-87	8133466	217.50
(18) Thimble (Shift Rod) 1983-87	934281	2.50
(19) Collar (Clutch) 1983-87	8131667	55.75

PARTS 19 TRANSFER CASE 19 PARTS

	Part No.	Price
(20) Sliding Gear (Drive)		
1983-87	8131679	154.25
(21) Shim Kit (003, 010, 030–2 Each)		
1983-87	8131668	3.25
(22) Front Output Cover (Rear)		
1983-87	8131657	8.75
(23) Thrust Washer		
1983-87	8121813	5.50
(24) Spacer (Interm. Bearing)		
1983-87	809295	1.75
(25) Bearing (Needle)		
1983-87	809294	.25
(26) Gear (Intermediate)		
1983-87	8131678	232.50
(27) Spacer (Bearing)		
1983-87	8131661	3.25
(28) Shaft (Intermediate)		
1983-87	942115	21.25
(29) Oil Seal (Input)		
1983-87	8131684	3.25
(30) Retainer (Input Bearing)		
1983-87	8131681	35.50
(31) Shaft (Input)		
1983-87	8131687	111.25
(32) Shim Kit (Input Shaft)		
1983-87	8131689	2.00
(33) Bearing (Input)		
1983-87	8131682	52.75
(34) Snap Ring (Bearing)		
1983-87	8131683	1.50
(35) Gear (Input)		
1983-87	8131685	124.50
(36) Case Cover		
1983-87	8131663	14.50

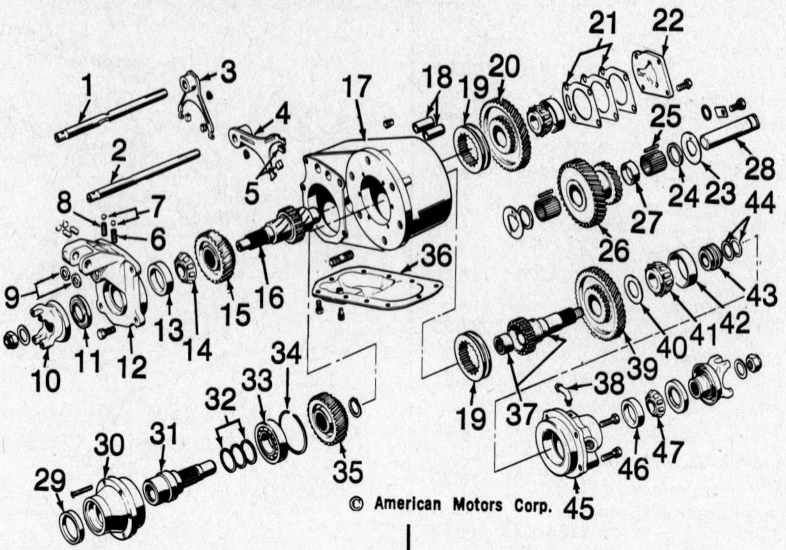

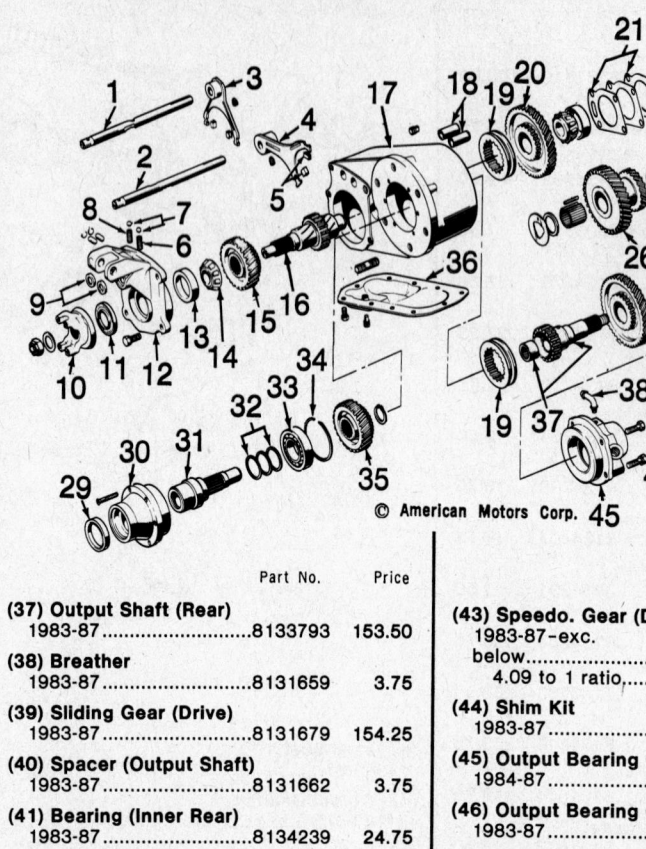

© American Motors Corp.

	Part No.	Price
(37) Output Shaft (Rear)		
1983-87	8133793	153.50
(38) Breather		
1983-87	8131659	3.75
(39) Sliding Gear (Drive)		
1983-87	8131679	154.25
(40) Spacer (Output Shaft)		
1983-87	8131662	3.75
(41) Bearing (Inner Rear)		
1983-87	8134239	24.75
(42) Bearing Cup (Inner Rear)		
1983-87	52800	9.00

	Part No.	Price
(43) Speedo. Gear (Drive)		
1983-87-exc. below	931381	20.25
4.09 to 1 ratio	5352816	39.00
(44) Shim Kit		
1983-87	933743	2.00
(45) Output Bearing Cap (Rear)		
1984-87	8983500445	130.25
(46) Output Bearing Cup (Rear Outer)		
1983-87	8124570	N.L.
(47) Output Bearing (Rear Outer)		
1983-87	933737	11.00

LABOR 19 TRANSAXLE 19 LABOR

(Factory Time) Chilton Time

MANUAL TRANS/AXLE

CHRYSLER CORP. A-412

(G) Drive Shaft Boot, Renew
Includes: Clean and lubricate C/V joint.
Horizon-Omni-TC3-024
1983
one-inner or outer (.8) 1.2
both-one side (1.0)................... 1.5

(G) Drive Shaft C/V Joint, Renew
Horizon-Omni-TC2-024
1983
one-inner or outer (.8) 1.2
both-one side (1.0)................... 1.5

(G) Front Wheel Drive Shaft Assy., Renew
Horizon-Omni-TC3-024
1983-each (.9) 1.3
Renew shaft seal
add-each (.2)............................ .3

(G) Drive Shaft Flange, Renew
Includes: Renew oil seal.
Horizon-Omni-TC3-024
1983-one (.9) 1.3

(G) Manual Trans/Axle Assy., Remove & Install
Horizon-Omni-TC3-024
1983 (2.5)....................................... 3.5
Renew assy add (.4) 5

(G) Manual Trans/Axle Assy., R&R and Recondition (Complete)
Horizon-Omni-TC3-024
1983 (7.2)....................................... 11.0
Renew ring gear and pinion add (.7).. 1.5
Renew clutch assy add (.2) 3

(G) Manual Trans/Axle Ring Gear and Pinion Assy., Renew
Includes: R&R trans/axle.
Horizon-Omni-TC3-024
1983 (6.5)....................................... 9.5

(G) Manual Trans/Axle Assy., Recondition (Off Car)
Horizon-Omni-TC3-024
1983 (4.7)....................................... 6.2

A-460 A-465 A-525

(G) Drive Shaft Boot, Renew
Includes: Clean and lubricate C/V joint.
All models
1983-87
one-inner or outer (.7) 1.0
both-one side (1.0)................... 1.4
Renew shaft seal, add
right side (.1) 1
left side (.3)............................... .3

(G) Drive Shaft C/V Joint, Renew
All models
1983-87
one-inner or outer (.7) 1.0
both-one side (1.0)................... 1.4
inter shaft U-joint (.6)................. 1.0
Renew shaft seal, add
right side (.1) 1
left side (.3)............................... .3

(G) Front Wheel Drive Shaft Assy., Renew
All models
1983-87
inter spline yoke (.6) 1.0
inter stub shaft (.6) 1.0
all others-each (1.0)................... 1.4
Renew shaft seal, add
right side (.1) 1
left side (.3)............................... .3

(G) Intermediate Shaft Support Bearing, Renew
1984-87-each (.6) 1.0

(G) Drive Shaft Oil Seal, Renew
Horizon-Omni-TC3-024
1983-87-right (.5)........................ .8
left (.8) 1.1
All other models
1983-87-right (.5)........................ .8
left (.7) 1.1

(G) Extension Housing 'O' Ring Seal, Renew
1983-87
All models (.5)............................ .7

(G) Transaxle Selector Shaft, Renew
1983-87
All models (1.3)........................... 1.7

(G) Differential Gear Cover, Renew or Reseal
1983-87
All models (1.0)............................ 1.3

(G) Extension Housing and/or Bearing Retainer, Renew
All models (3.0) 4.0
Renew R/inner C.V.
joint, add (.2)................................ .2

(G) End Cover, Renew or Reseal
All models
A460 (.8) 1.1
A465-A525 (1.2)............................ 1.6
Renew syncro assy.,
add (1.6) 1.6

(G) Manual Trans/Axle Assembly, Remove & Install
Does not include transfer of any parts.
w/1.6L eng
1983-87 (2.1)................................. 2.9
w/1.7L eng
1983 (2.7)...................................... 3.7
w/2.2L & 2.5L eng
1983-87
Horizon-Omni (3.1)...................... 4.3
All other models (2.7) 3.7
Renew assy add (.4) 6
w/Cruise control add (.2)................ .2

(G) Manual Trans/Axle Assy., R&R and Recondition (Complete)
w/1.6L eng
1983-87 (4.9)................................. 6.9
w/1.7L eng
1983 (5.2)...................................... 7.5
w/2.2L & 2.5L eng
1983-87
Horizon-Omni (5.9)...................... 8.4
All other models (5.5) 8.0
Renew ring gear and pinion add (.7).. 1.5
Renew clutch assy add (.2) 2
w/Cruise control add (.2)................ .2

(G) Manual Trans/Axle Assy., Recondition (Off Car)
1983-87
A460 (2.5) 3.9
A465-A525 (2.8)............................ 4.2

PARTS 19 TRANSAXLE (4 SPEED) 19 PARTS

Part No. Price

A-412

(Differential Carrier and Clutch Housing)

	Part No.	Price
Transmission Assy.		
1983	5240048	1503.25
Seal & Gasket Repair Pkg.		
1983	4186097	42.75
(1) Seal (Lip)		
1983	4094829	6.00
(2) Transmission Case (Partial)		
1983	5240088	100.00
(3) Slinger		
1983	5240111	1.00
(4) Spring (Shift)		
1983	5240110	N.L.
(5) Housing (Shift Shaft)		
1983	5240113	7.25

TRANSAXLE A-412

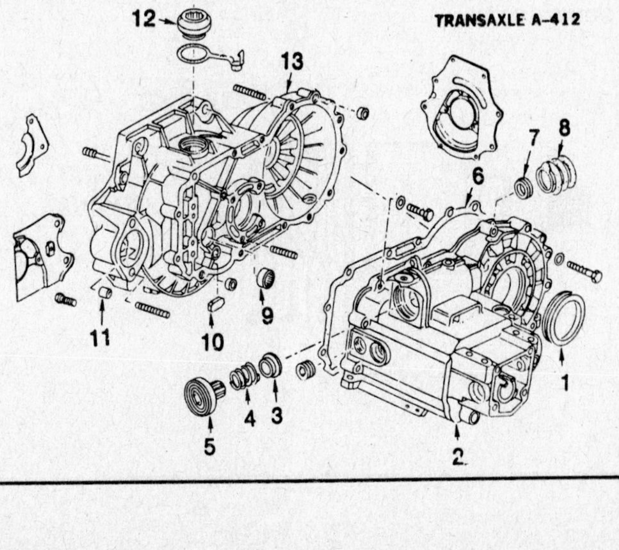

SHAFT IDENTIFICATION, DRIVE

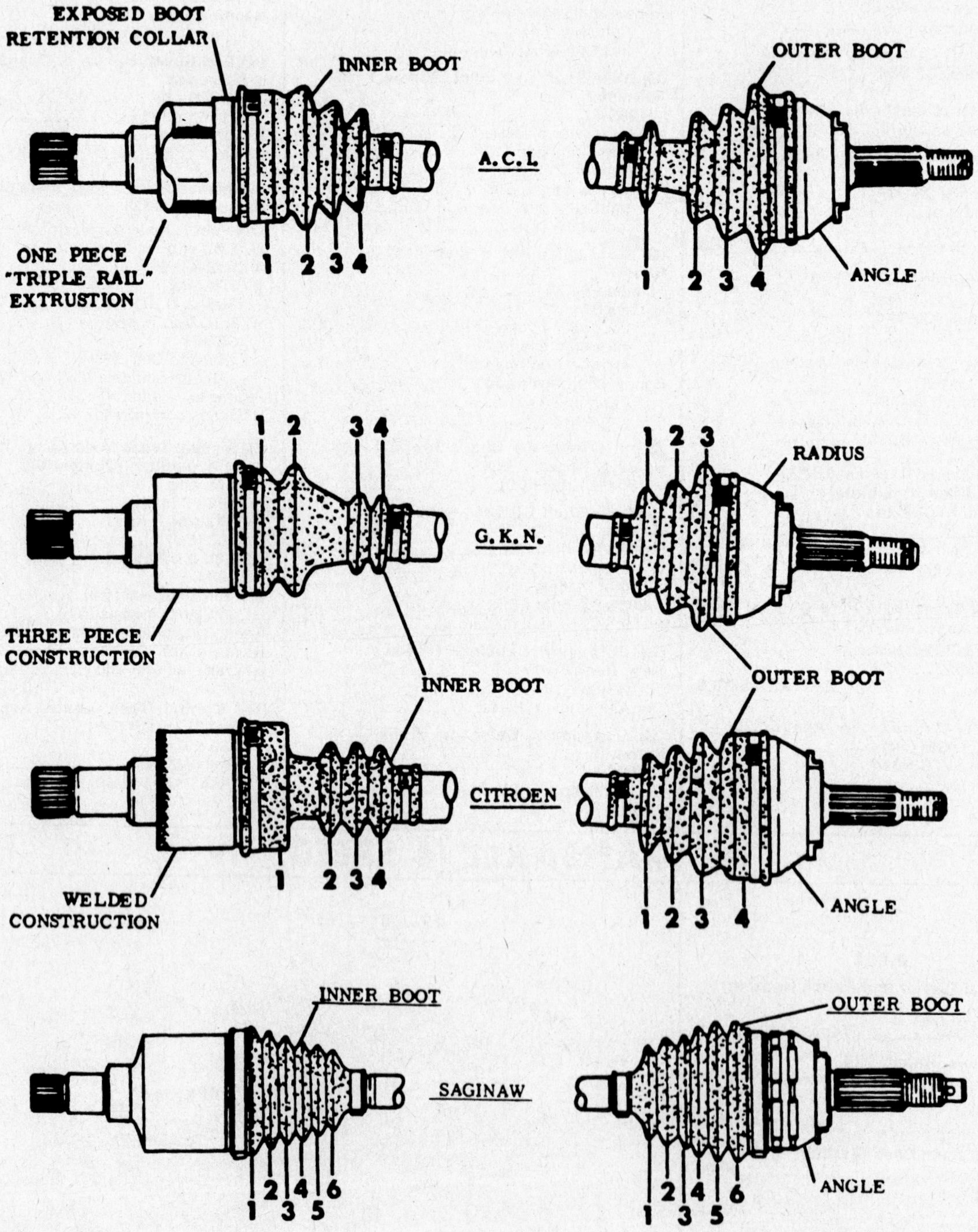

PARTS 19 TRANSAXLE (4 SPEED) 19 PARTS

	Part No.	Price
(6) Gasket		
1983	5240106	2.25
(7) Shift Shaft Seal (Inner)		
1983	4094830	2.50
(8) Seal or Boot (Outer)		
1983	5240127	3.00
(9) Needle Bearing (Drive Shaft)		
1983	5240150	6.50
(10) Magnet (Chip Collector)		
1983	5240099	2.00
(11) Bushing (Starter Pilot)		
1983	5240101	2.25
(12) Retainer (Probe)		
1983	5240163	2.00
(13) Housing (Diff. Carrier & Clutch)		
1983	5240092	318.00

PARTS 19 TRANSAXLE GEAR TRAIN (4 SPEED) 19 PARTS

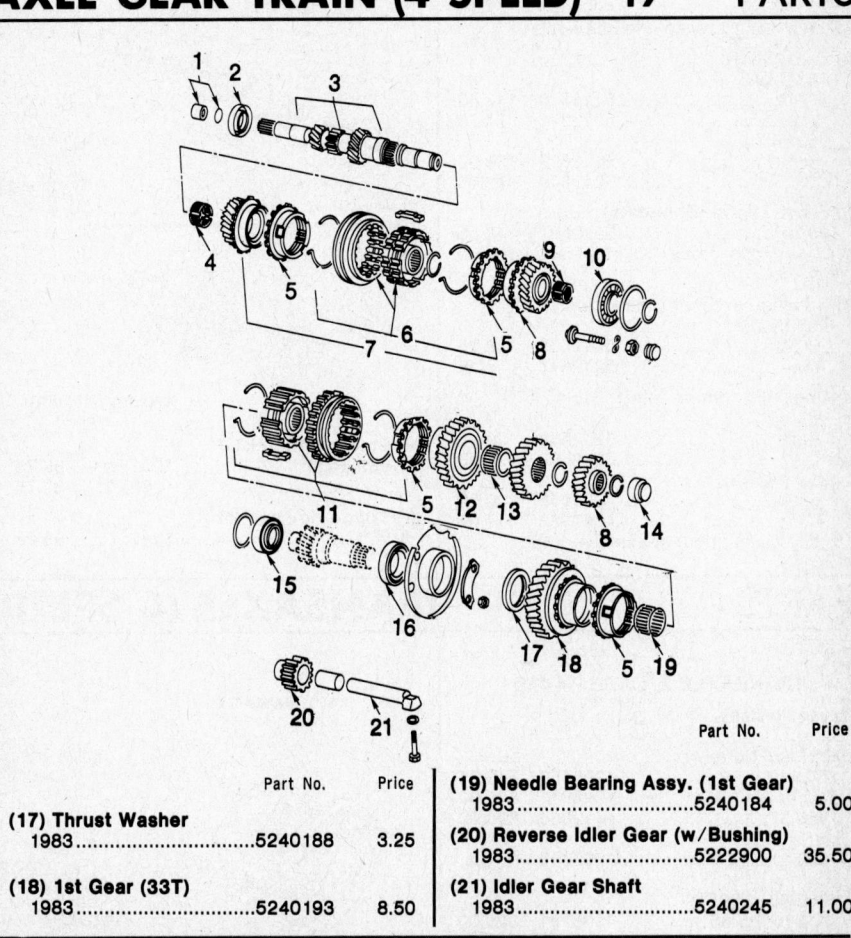

	Part No.	Price
A-412		
(1) Clutch Bushing (w/Seal)		
1983	4186099	6.25
(2) Seal Assy. (Input Shaft Lip)		
1983	4094831	4.75
(3) Input Shaft Assy.		
1983	4202770	124.00
(4) Needle Bearing		
1983	5240213	4.25
(5) Synchronizer Ring (2nd, 3rd & 4th)		
1983	5240199	15.00
(6) Synchronizer Assy. (3rd & 4th)		
1983	5240202	62.00
(7) Gear Set (3rd)		
1983	5240195	25.00
(8) Gear Set (4th Speed)		
1983	5240218	108.75
(9) Needle Bearing		
1983	4094832	5.00
(10) Input Shaft Bearing (Rear)		
1983	4186095	22.75
(11) Clutch Gear (1st & 2nd)		
1983	5240191	16.75
(12) 2nd Gear (35T)		
1983	5240194	55.50
(13) Needle Bearing Assy. (2nd Gear)		
1983	5240190	11.00
(14) Bearing Assy. (Needle)		
1983	4202546	4.75
(15) Race (Inner)		
1983	5240260	10.75
(16) Bearing Assy.		
1983	5222801	26.00

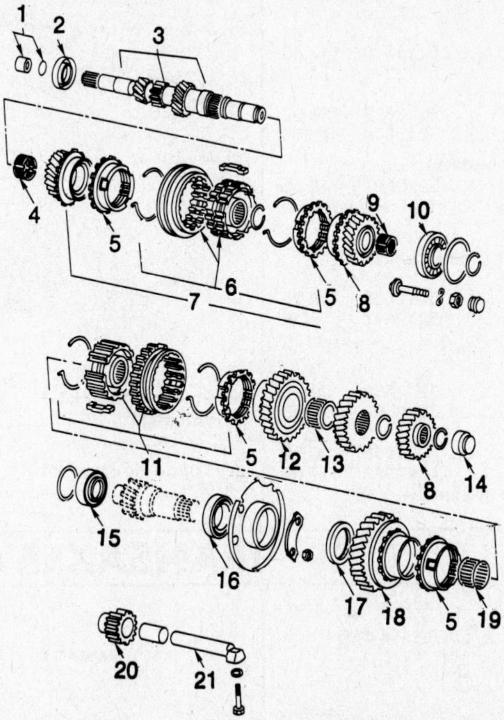

	Part No.	Price
(17) Thrust Washer		
1983	5240188	3.25
(18) 1st Gear (33T)		
1983	5240193	8.50
(19) Needle Bearing Assy. (1st Gear)		
1983	5240184	5.00
(20) Reverse Idler Gear (w/Bushing)		
1983	5222900	35.50
(21) Idler Gear Shaft		
1983	5240245	11.00

PARTS 19 TRANSAXLE DIFFERENTIAL (4 SPEED) 19 PARTS

	Part No.	Price
A-412		
(1) Pinion & Cross Shaft Pkg.		
1983	4094835	8.50
(2) Flange Seal		
1983	4094834	2.00
(3) Flange (w/Slinger)		
1983	4202773	27.75
(4) Output Shaft		
1983	5240290	25.75
(5) Race Assy.		
1983-Inner	5222819	9.25
Outer	5222823	15.50
(6) Differential Housing		
1983	5240271	95.50
(7) Ring & Pinion Gear		
1983	4057394	240.50

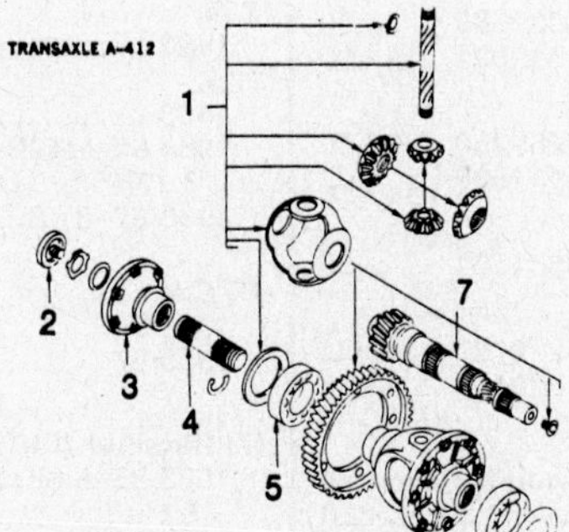

PARTS 19 TRANSAXLE DRIVESHAFT 19 PARTS

Part No. Price

A-412

(1) Oil Slinger (Outer Joint)
1983 ....5212526 N.L.

(2) Outer Joint (Complete)
1983 ....4186890 192.75
Includes cage, ball, cross and housing.

(3) Boot Pkg. (Outer Joint)
1983 ....4205853 17.75
Includes clamps, snap ring and boot.

(4) Drive Shaft
1983 (M.T.)
Right 5212570 143.50
Left 5212571 77.75
1983 (A.T.)
Right 5212629 138.00
Left 5212579 70.75

(5) Front Tripod (Complete)
1983 ....5212567 48.75
Includes circlip, cross, "O" ring, retainer, race and needle.

(6) Housing w/Shaft (Joint Inner)
1983 (A.T.)
Right 5212576 136.25
Left ....5212577 N.L.

(7) Boot Pkg. (Inner Joint)
1983 (M.T.)
Right 5212568 29.25
Left 5212569 29.25
1983 (A.T.)
Right 4205852 29.50
Left 4057033 17.50
Includes clamp, boot and seal.

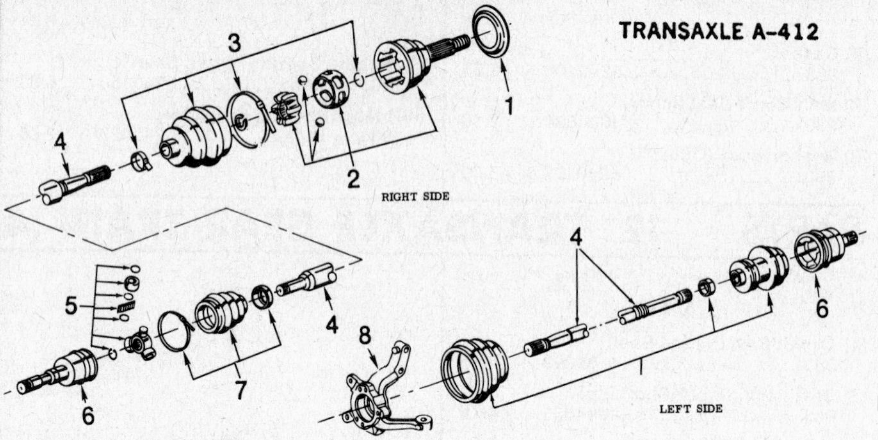

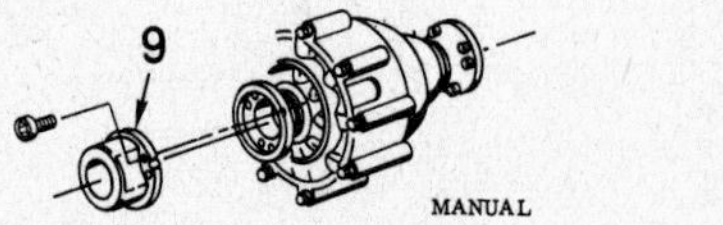

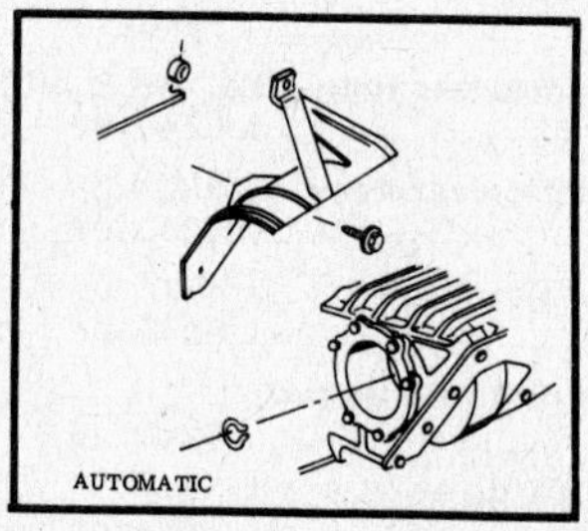

Part No. Price

(8) Steering Knuckle
1983-Right 4052580 89.75
Left 4052581 89.75

(9) Tripod Housing (M.T.)
1983 ....5212572 95.25

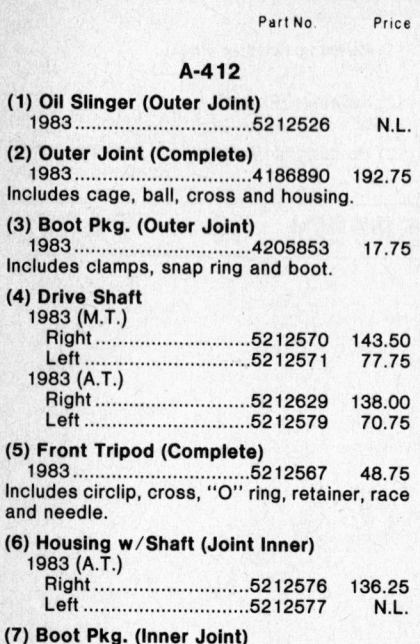

PARTS 19 TRANSAXLE (4 SPEED) 19 PARTS

Part No. Price

TRANSAXLE & CASE - A460

Transaxle Assy.
1.6L
1983-85-Up to 4-17-85 ....4295753 849.75
After 4-17-85 ....4329611 825.00
1986-87 ....4412030 825.00
1.7L
1983 ....4295733 N.L.
2.2L
1983-85-2.69R
Up to 6-5-85 ....4295751 825.00
After 6-5-85 ....4329612 825.00
1983-85-3.13R
Up to 5-31-85 ....4295752 825.00
After 5-31-85 ....4329617 825.00
1986-87-3.13R 4377757 825.00

(1) Plate (Bearing Retainer)
1983-85 ....4329580 54.50
1986-87 ....4340091 54.00

(2) Cover (Rear)
1983-85 ....4269258 13.00
1986-87 ....4411969 N.L.

(3) Magnet (Chip Collector)
1983-87 ....3681601 2.50

(4) Oil Pan
1983 ....5222787 N.L.
1984-87 ....4329464 11.75

(5) Transaxle Case
Order case by transaxle I.D. number stamped on a tag that is attached to the end cover. Part numbers shown here are for pricing reference only.
1.6L
1983 ....4269129 284.00
1984-87 ....4295666 269.00

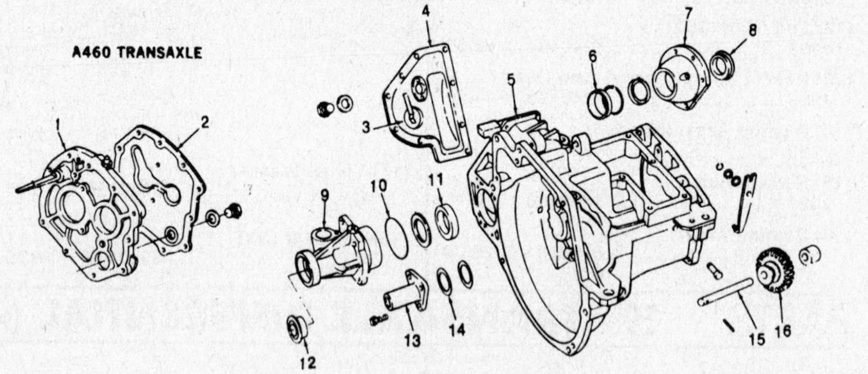

Part No. Price

1.7L
1983 ....4269128 271.00
2.2L
1983 ....4269021 N.L.
1984-85-2.69R 4295664 269.00
3.13R 4329545 284.00
1986-87-3.13R 4377710 269.00

(6) Cup
1983-84 ....5222259 6.00
1985-87 ....4269676 5.50

(7) Retainer (Diff. Bearing)
1983-85-5 blts. 5222781 58.25
8 blts. 4329549 58.25
1986-87-8 blts. ....4377730 N.L.

(8) Seal (Bearing Retainer)
1983-87 ....4295904 3.50

Part No. Price

(9) Extension
1983-87 ....4269961 29.50

(10) "O" Ring Extension
1983-87 ....6500111 2.25

(11) Cup (Diff. Retainer)
1983-84 ....5222259 6.00
1985-87 ....4269676 5.50

(12) Seal (Extension)
1983-87 ....4295904 3.50

(13) Retainer (Bearing Pilot & Seal)
1983-87 ....4295175 13.50

(14) Seal (Input Shaft)
1983-87 ....5222721 2.50

(15) Shaft (Reverse Idler)
1983-87 ....5222654 13.25

(16) Gear (Reverse Idler)
1983-87 ....5222651 70.50

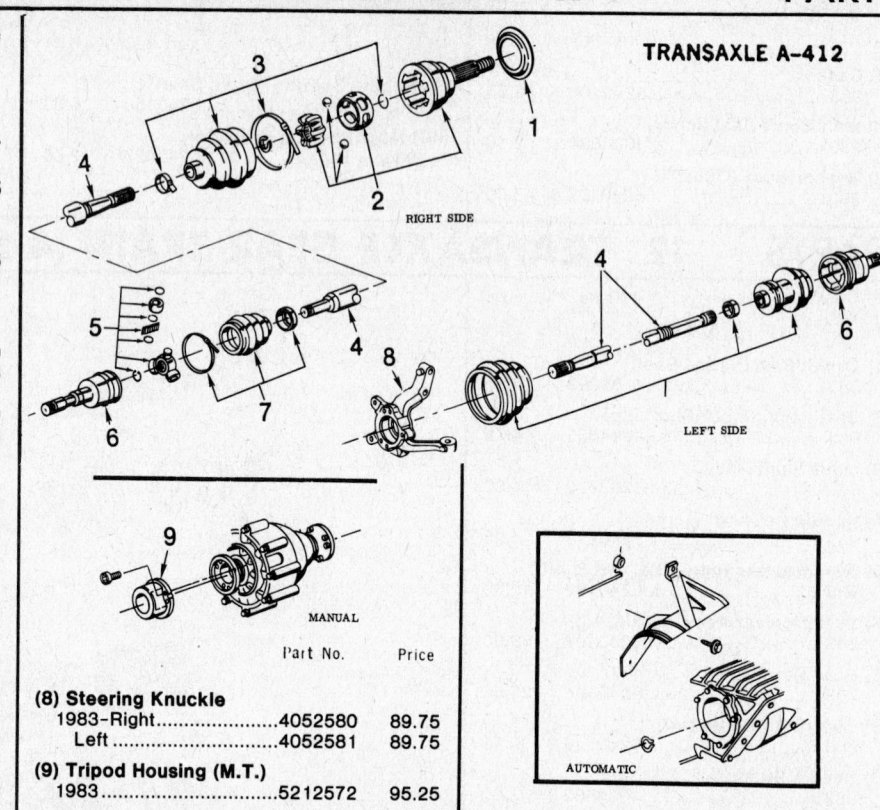

PARTS 19 TRANSAXLE GEAR TRAIN (4 SPEED) 19 PARTS

	Part No.	Price
(1) Third Gear		
1983-87	4269065	74.25
(2) Stop Ring (4th Speed)		
1983-87	4295799	13.75
(3) Synchronizer (3rd & 4th)		
1983-87	4269388	92.75
(4) Fourth Gear		
1983-87	4269066	80.25
(5) Rear Bearing (Inter. Shaft)		
1983-85	4202524	23.50
1986-87	4348270	24.25
(6) Synchronizer (1st & 2nd)		
1983	4269386	100.75
1984-87	4295725	100.75
(7) Second Gear		
1983	4269064	88.00
1984-87-36-51T	4269065	74.25
39-53T	4295728	87.50
(8) Roller Bearing (Inter. Shaft)		
1983-87	4202590	9.00
(9) Intermediate Shaft		
1983-87-2.69R	4202110	139.50
3.13R	4207945	139.25
(10) First Gear		
1983	4269063	91.75
1984-87	4295714	91.00
(11) Front Cup (Input Shaft Bearing)		
1983-87	5205564	4.50
(12) Front Bearing (Input Shaft)		
1983-87	5205565	10.00
(13) Input Shaft		
1983	4269139	169.00
1984-87	4269349	167.50
(14) Rear Bearing (Input Shaft)		
1983-87	5205568	11.25
(15) Rear Bearing Cup (Input Shaft)		
1983-87	5205567	5.50

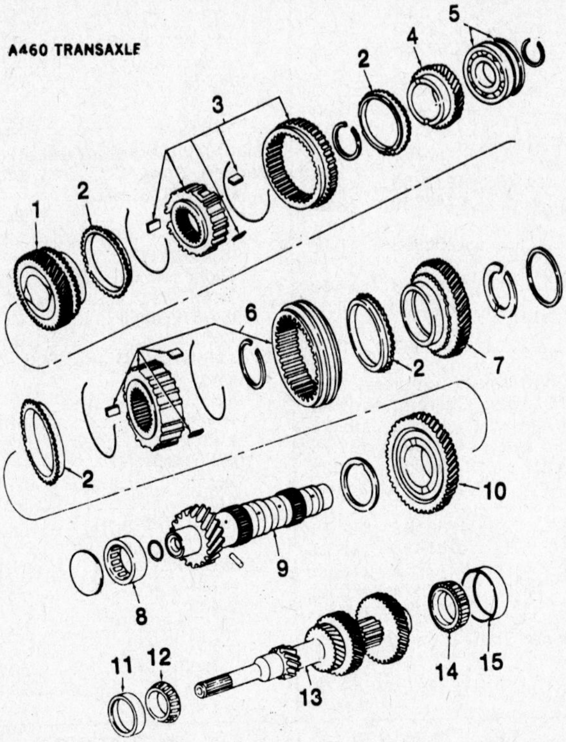

PARTS 19 TRANSAXLE DRIVESHAFT 19 PARTS

A-460

TRANSAXLE DRIVE SHAFT

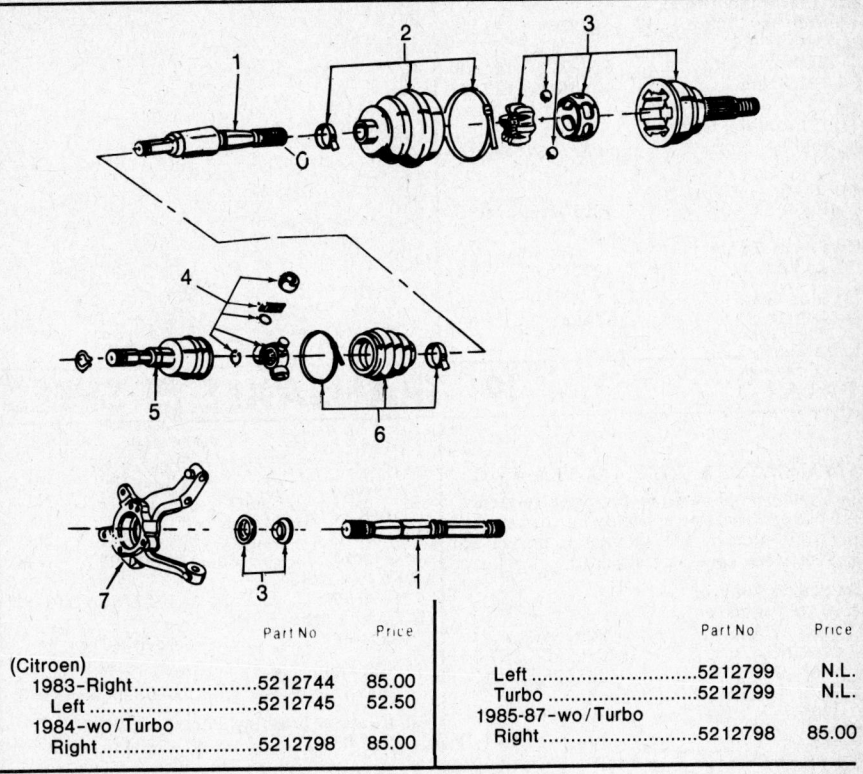

	Part No.	Price
(1) Drive Shaft		
1.6L		
1983-Right	5212676	137.50
Left	5212677	76.00
1984-87-Right	5212862	137.50
Left	5212863	76.00
1.7L		
1983-Right	5212646	137.50
Left	5212647	72.50
2.2L & 2.6L		
Horizon, Omni, TC3, 024, Turismo, Charger		
(GKN)		
1983-Right	5212660	137.50
Left	5212661	76.00
1984-87-Right	5212862	137.50
Left-Up to 8-6-86	5212863	76.00
After 8-6-84	5212933	76.00
(Citroen)		
1985-87-wo/Turbo		
Right	5212766	85.00
Left-Up to 1-28-85	5212765	52.25
After 1-28-85	5212935	52.25
Turbo	5212935	52.25
Exc. Horizon, Omni, TC3, 024, Turismo, Charger		
(GKN)		
1983-Right	5212662	137.50
Left	5212663	76.00
1984-87-Right	5212872	123.00
Left	5212913	76.00
(Citroen)		
1983-Right	5212744	85.00
Left	5212745	52.50
1984-wo/Turbo		
Right	5212798	85.00
Left	5212799	N.L.
Turbo	5212799	N.L.
1985-87-wo/Turbo		
Right	5212798	85.00

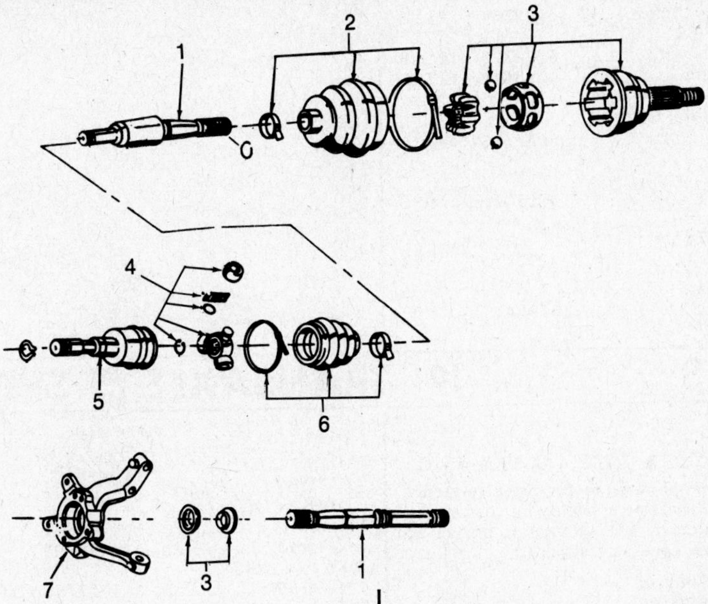

PARTS 19 TRANSAXLE DRIVESHAFT 19 PARTS

	Part No.	Price
Left	5212763	52.25
Turbo	5212763	52.25
(A.C.I.)		
1984-87-Right	5212826	123.00
Left	5212827	76.00
(2) Boot Pkg. (Outer)		
(Citroen)		
1983	5212713	19.00
1984-87	5212738	19.00
(GKN)		
1983	4205853	17.75
1984-87-wo/ Turbo	5212858	17.50
Turbo	4205853	17.75
(A.C.I.)		
1985-87	5212809	17.50
(3) Outer Drive Shaft Joint (Complete)		
Horizon, Omni, TC3, 024, Charger, Turismo		
1983-exc. 2.2L	4186890	192.75
2.2L	4186891	192.75
1984-87	5212856	170.25
Exc. Horizon, Omni, TC3, 024, Charger, Turismo		
1983-Citroen	4186892	192.75
GKN	4186891	192.75
1984-87-Citroen	5212789	170.25
GKN	5212869	170.25
A.C.I.	5212830	170.25
(4) Tripod Pkg. Inner Shaft (Complete)		
(Citroen)		
1983-87	5212711	48.75
(G.K.N.)		
1983-exc. 2.2L	5212567	48.75
2.2L	5212608	48.75
1984-87	5212859	48.75
(A.C.I.)		
1984-87	5212812	48.75
(5) Housing W/Shaft (Inner)		
Horizon, Omni, TC3, 024, Charger, Turismo		
1983-1.6L & 1.7L		
Right	5212896	139.50
Left	5212897	104.25
1983-2.2L		
Right	5212898	146.00
Left	5212899	146.00
1984-87-Right	5212896	139.50
Left	5212897	104.25
Exc. Horizon, Omni, TC3, 024, Charger, Turismo		
1983 (Citroen)		
Right	5212746	85.00
Left	5212747	72.25
1983 (GKN)		
Right	5212898	146.00
Left	5212899	146.00
1984-87 (Citroen)		
(wo/Turbo)		
Right	5212746	85.00
Left	5212747	72.25
(Turbo)		
Right & Left	5212747	72.25
1984-87 (GKN)		
Right	5212896	139.50
Left	5212897	104.25
1984-87 (A.C.I.)		
Right	5212824	139.25
Left	5212825	139.25
(6) Boot Pkg. (Inner)		
(G.K.N.)		
1983-1.6L & 1.7L		
Right	4205852	29.50
Left	4057033	17.50
1983-2.2L		
Right	5212612	31.50
Left	5212613	31.50
1984-87-Right	4205852	29.50
Left	4057033	17.50
(Citroen)		
1983-87-wo/Turbo		
right	5212716	19.00
left	5212717	19.00
Turbo	5212717	19.00
(A.C.I.)		
1984-87-Right	5212810	17.50
Left	5212811	17.50
(7) Steering Knuckle		
1983-Right	4052580	89.75
Left	4052581	89.75
1984-87 (Horizon, Omni, TC3 & 024)		
Right	4052844	89.75
Left	4052845	89.75
1984-87 (exc. Horizon, Omni, TC3 & 024)		
Right	4052838	89.75
Left	4052839	89.75

PARTS 19 TRANSAXLE DIFFERENTIAL (4 SPEED) 19 PARTS

A-460

	Part No.	Price
(1) Differential Bearing		
1983-84	5224301	11.00
1985-87	4269677	11.00
(2) Gear (Final Drive)		
1983-exc. below	5222774	121.25
1983-87-58 Teeth	5222772	121.25
57 Teeth	4295417	120.25
(3) Differential Case		
1983-87	5222775	99.75
(4) Shaft		
1983-87	4207073	4.75
(5) Pinion Gears		
1983-87	4295416	8.25
(6) Side Gear		
1983-87	4295415	12.00

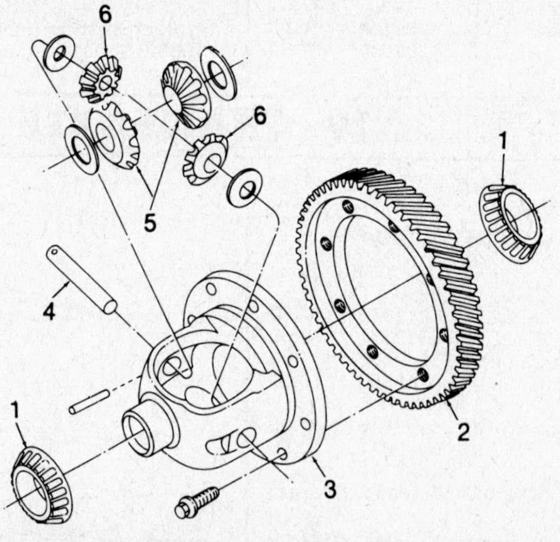

PARTS 19 TRANSAXLE (5 SPEED) 19 PARTS

TRANSAXLE & CASE - A465 & A525

Part numbers shown are for price reference only. Order transaxle assembly by year, model and I.D. number. I.D. number is on tag attached to end cover of transaxle.

	Part No.	Price
Transaxle Assy.		
2.20 to 1 ratio		
1983	4269224	N.L.
1984-85	4295755	937.50
1986-87	4377678	910.00
2.57 to 1 ratio		
1983	4269226	N.L.
1984-85-wo/ Turbo	4329151	N.L.
Turbo	4295754	N.L.
1986-87-wo/ Turbo	4412981	N.L.
Turbo	4412982	N.L.
2.77 to 1 ratio		
1986-87	4377758	910.00
2.78 to 1 ratio		
1984-85	4329521	N.L.
(1) Extension Seal		
1983-87	4295904	3.50
(2) Retainer (Bearing Pilot & Seal)		
1983-87	4295175	13.50
(3) Input Shaft Seal		
1983-87	5222721	2.50
(4) "O" Ring Extension		
1983-87	6500111	2.25
(5) Cup (Retainer Diff.)		
1983-84	5222259	6.00
1985-87	4269676	5.50
(6) Magnet (Chip Collector)		
1983-87	3681601	2.50
(7) Oil Scoop (Rear Bearing)		
1983-84	4202842	1.75
1985-87	4329583	2.00

PARTS 19 TRANSAXLE (5 SPEED) 19 PARTS

	Part No.	Price
(8) Plate (Bearing Retainer)		
1983-85	4329582	N.L.
1986-87	4340091	54.00
(9) Plate (Bearing Back-Up)		
1983-85	5222758	6.25
1986-87	4348281	6.00
(10) Cup		
1983-84	5222259	6.00
1985-87	4269676	5.50
(11) Oil Feed Baffle		
1983-87	5222256	1.25
(12) Seal (Bearing Retainer)		
1983-87	4295904	3.50
(13) Gear (Reverse Idler)		
1983-87	5222651	70.50
(14) Shaft (Reverse Idler)		
1983-87	5222654	13.25

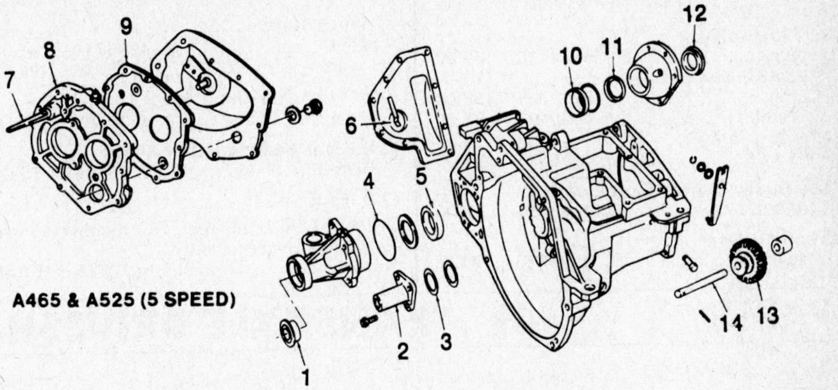

PARTS 19 TRANSAXLE GEAR TRAIN (5 SPEED) 19 PARTS

A465 & A525 (5 SPEED)

	Part No.	Price
(1) Fifth Gear		
Order by I.D. tag number. Part numbers shown for pricing reference only.		
1983-85-exc. below	4269138	N.L.
2.78R, Turbo	4329355	76.75
1986-87	4329372	76.75
(2) Stop Ring (5th Speed)		
1983-87	4295799	13.75
(3) Synchronizer (5th Speed)		
1983-87	5222760	92.25
Spring (5th Speed Synchro.)		
1983-87	4202124	1.00
(4) Retainer Plate (5th Speed Synchro.)		
1983-87	5222762	1.25
(5) Third Gear		
1983-87-36-51T	4269065	74.25
36-55T	4295659	74.50
(6) Stop Ring (4th Speed)		
1983-87	4295799	13.75
(7) Synchronizer (3rd & 4th)		
1983-87	4269388	92.75
(8) Fourth Gear		
1983	4269066	80.25
1984-87	4295660	74.50
(9) Rear Bearing (Inter. Shaft)		
1983-87	4269136	15.50
(10) Stop Ring (1st & 2nd)		
1983	4295799	13.75
1984-87	4329142	13.75
(11) Synchronizer (1st & 2nd)		
1983	4269386	100.75
1984-87	4295725	100.75
Spring (1st & 2nd Speed Synchro.)		
1983	4202124	1.00
1984-87	4269350	1.00
(12) Second Gear		
1983	4269064	88.00
1984-87-2 oil grooves	4295719	87.50
3 oil grooves	4295721	87.50
(13) Thrust Washer (Split)		
1983-87	4202533	2.50
(14) Retaining Ring		
1983-87	5222749	.50
(15) Feeder (Inter. Shaft Inner Oil)		
1983-87	5222957	1.00

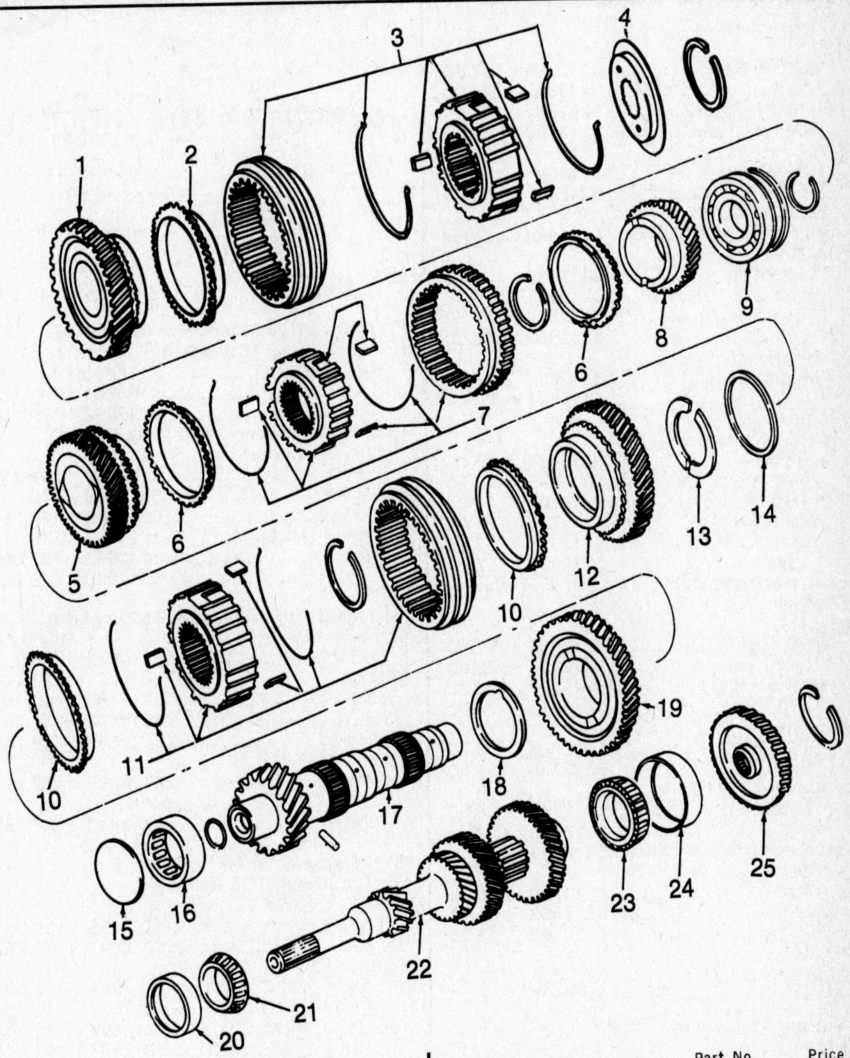

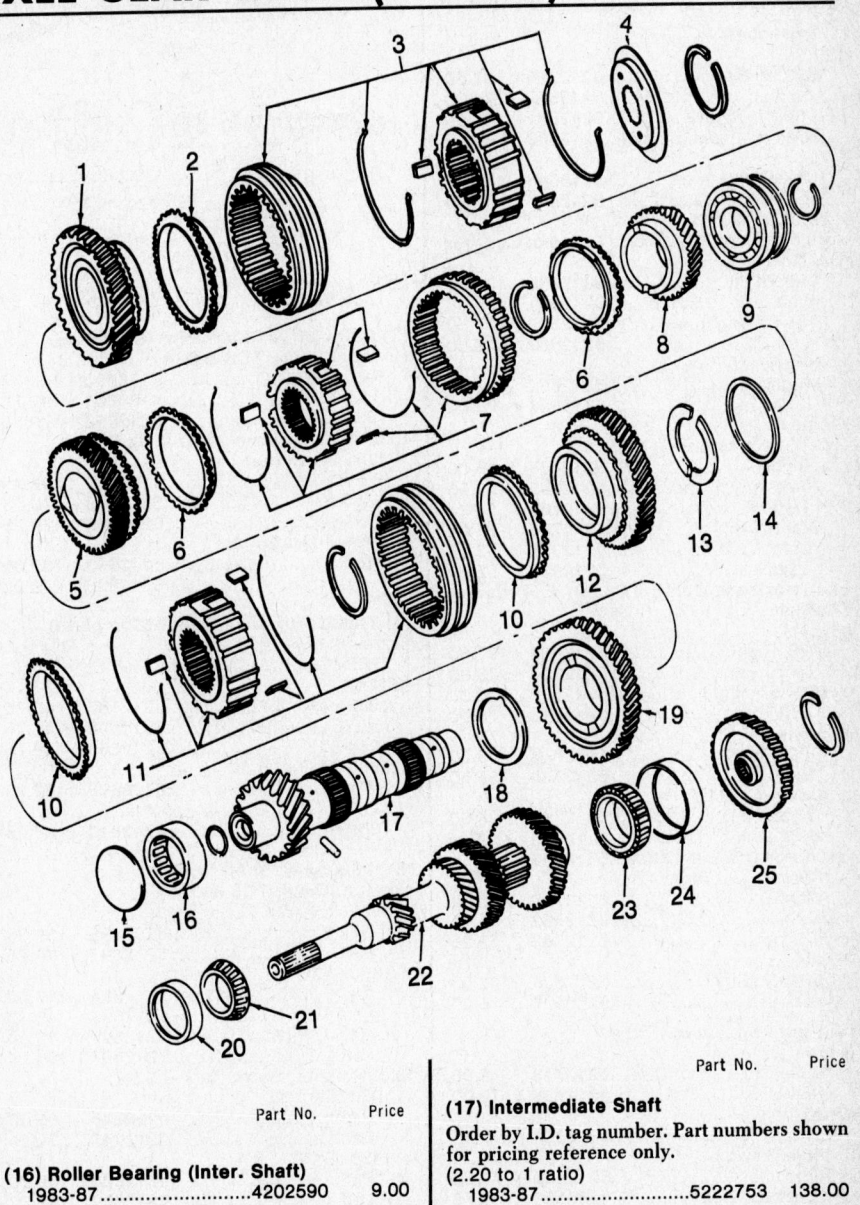

	Part No.	Price
(16) Roller Bearing (Inter. Shaft)		
1983-87	4202590	9.00

	Part No.	Price
(17) Intermediate Shaft		
Order by I.D. tag number. Part numbers shown for pricing reference only.		
(2.20 to 1 ratio)		
1983-87	5222753	138.00

PARTS 19 TRANSAXLE GEAR TRAIN (5 SPEED) 19 PARTS

	Part No.	Price
(2.57 to 1 ratio)		
1983	5222755	138.00
1984-87-wo/ Turbo	5222755	138.00
Turbo	4295420	138.00
(2.78 to 1 ratio)		
1984-87	4295525	138.00
(18) Thrust Washer (Low Gear)		
1983-87	4202534	3.00
(19) First Gear		
1983	4269063	91.75
1984-87-exc. below	4295714	91.00
Turbo	4295716	91.00
(20) Front Cup (Input Shaft Bearing)		
1983-87	5205564	4.50
(21) Front Bearing (Input Shaft)		
1983-87	5205565	10.00
(22) Input Shaft		
Order by I.D. tag number. Part numbers shown for pricing reference only.		
1983	5222725	167.50
1984-87	4295657	167.50
(23) Rear Bearing (Input Shaft)		
1983-87	5205568	11.25
(24) Rear Bearing Cup (Input Shaft)		
1983-87	5205567	5.50
(25) Fifth Gear (Input Shaft)		
1983	5222659	76.75
1984-85	4295548	76.75
1986-87	4329367	N.L.

PARTS 19 TRANSAXLE DRIVESHAFT 19 PARTS

A465 & A525 (5 SPEED)

Part numbers shown are for pricing reference only. Order by year model and type.

	Part No	Price
(1) Driveshaft		
1.6L		
1983-Right	5212676	137.50
Left	5212677	76.00
1984-87-Right	5212862	137.50
Left	5212863	76.00
1.7L		
1983-Right	5212646	137.50
Left	5212647	72.50
2.2L, 2.5L & 2.6L		
Horizon, Omni, 024, TC3, Turismo, Charger		
(G.K.N.)		
1983-Right	5212660	137.50
Left	5212661	76.00
1984-87-Right	5212862	137.50
Left	5212863	76.00
1986-87-H/P Right	5212862	137.50
Left	5212933	76.00
(Citroen)		
1985-wo/Turbo Right	5212766	85.00
Left	5212765	52.25
Turbo	5212765	52.25
1986-87-Right	5212766	85:00
Left	5212935	52.25
Turbo	5212935	52.25
Exc. Horizon, Omni, TC3, 024, Turismo, Charger		
(G.K.N.)		
1983-Right	5212662	137.50
Left	5212663	76.00
1984-87-Right	5212872	123.00
Left	5212913	76.00
(Citroen)		
1983-Right	5212744	85.00
Left	5212745	52.50
1984-wo/Turbo right	5212798	85.00
left	5212799	N.L.
Turbo	5212799	N.L.
1985-87-wo/Turbo Right	5212798	85.00
Left	5212763	52.25
Turbo	5212763	52.25
(A.C.I.)		
1984-87-Right	5212826	123.00
Left	5212827	76.00
(2) Boot Pkg. (Outer)		
(Citroen)		
1983	5212713	19.00
1984-87	5212738	19.00
(GKN)		
1983	4205853	17.75
1984-87-wo/ Turbo	5212858	17.50
Turbo & 2.5L	4205853	17.75

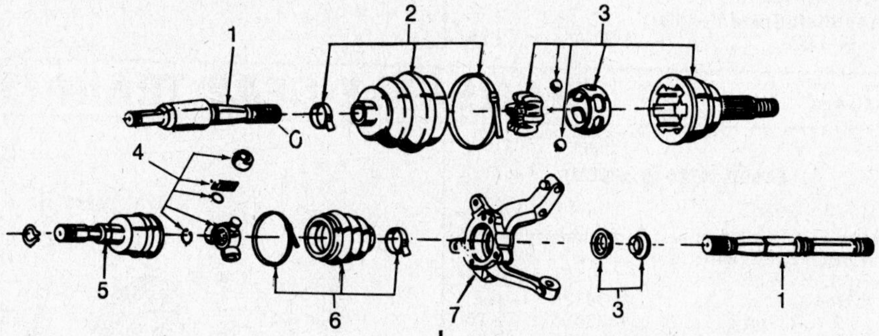

	Part No.	Price
(A.C.I.)		
1985-87	5212809	17.50
(3) Outer Drive Shaft Joint (Complete)		
Horizon, Omni, TC3 & 024		
1983-exc. 2.2L	4186890	192.75
2.2L	4186891	192.75
1984-87	5212856	170.25
Exc. Horizon, Omni, TC3 & 024)		
1983-87-Citroen (83-85)	4186892	192.75
(86-87)	5212789	170.25
GKN	5212869	170.25
GKN (Turbo & 2.5L)	5212696	162.00
A.C.I.	5212830	170.25
(4) Tripod Pkg. Inner Shaft (Complete)		
(Citroen)		
1983-87	5212711	48.75
(G.N.K.)		
1983- exc. 2.2L	5212567	48.75
2.2L	5212608	48.75
1984-87	5212859	48.75
1986-87-Turbo & 2.5L	5212608	52.25
(A.C.I.)		
1984-87	5212812	48.75
(5) Housing W/Shaft (Inner)		
Horizon, Omni, TC3 & 024		
1983-1.6L & 1.7L Right	5212896	139.50
Left	5212897	104.25
1983-2.2L Right	5212898	146.00
Left	5212899	146.00
1984-87-Right	5212896	139.50
Left	5212897	104.25
Exc. Horizon, Omni, TC3 & 024		
1983 (Citroen) Right	5212746	85.00
Left	5212747	72.25
1983 (GKN) Right	5212898	146.00
Left	5212899	146.00
1984-87 (Citroen) (wo/Turbo) Right	5212746	85.00
Left	5212747	72.25
(Turbo) Right & Left	5212747	72.25
1984-87 (GKN) Right	5212896	139.50
Left	5212897	104.25
1986-87 2.5L-Right	5212898	146.00
Left	5212899	146.00
Turbo	5212899	146.00
1984-87 (A.C.I.) Right	5212824	139.25
Left	5212825	139.25
(6) Boot Pkg. (Inner)		
(G.K.N.)		
1983-1.6L & 1.7L Right	4205852	29.50
Left	4057033	17.50
1983-2.2L Right	5212612	31.50
Left	5212613	31.50
1984-87-Right	4205852	29.50
Left	4057033	17.50
Turbo	5212613	31.50
(Citroen)		
1983-87-wo/Turbo Right	5212716	19.00
Left	5212717	19.00
Turbo	5212717	19.00
(A.C.I.)		
1984-87-Right	5212810	17.50
Left	5212811	17.50
(7) Steering Knuckle		
1983-Right	4052580	89.75
Left	4052581	89.75
1984-87 (Horizon, Omni, TC3 & 024) Right	4052844	89.75
Left	4052845	89.75
1984-87 (exc. Horizon, Omni, TC3 & 024) Right	4052838	89.75
Left	4052839	89.75

PARTS 19 TRANSAXLE DIFFERENTIAL (5 SPEED) 19 PARTS

	Part No.	Price
A465 & A525 (5 SPEED)		
(1) Differential Bearing		
1983-84	5224301	11.00
1985-87	4269677	11.00
(2) Gear (Final Drive)		
Order by transaxle I.D. number. Part numbers shown for pricing reference only.		
(2.20 to 1 ratio)		
1983-87	5222772	121.25
(2.57 to 1 ratio)		
1983	5222774	121.25
1984-87-wo/ Turbo	5222774	121.25
Turbo	4295417	120.25
(2.78 to 1 ratio)		
1983-87	4295523	120.25
(3) Differential Case		
1983-87	5222775	99.75
(4) Roll Pin		
1983-87	6101284	.75
(5) Shaft		
1983-87	4207073	4.75
(6) Washer (Pinion)		
1983-87	5212211	1.50
(7) Pinion Gears		
1983-87	4295416	8.25

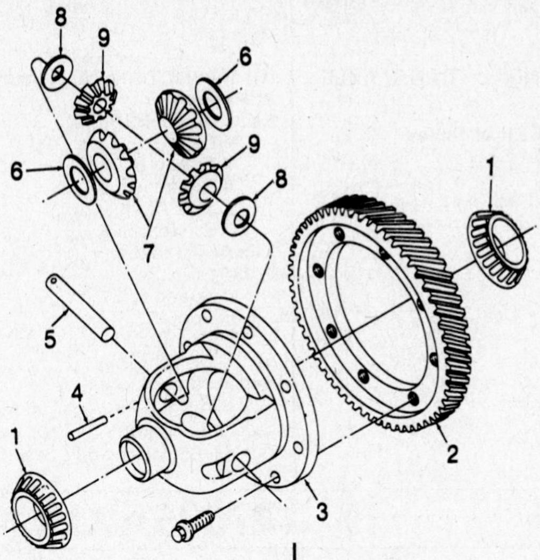

	Part No.	Price
(8) Washer (Side Gear)		
1983-87	5212212	1.50

	Part No.	Price
(9) Side Gear		
Order by transaxle I.D. number. Part number shown is for pricing reference only.		
1983-87	4295415	12.00

LABOR 19 TRANSAXLE 19 LABOR

	(Factory Time)	Chilton Time
4 & 5 SPEED MANUAL TRANS/AXLE		
(G) Halfshaft Assy., R&R or Renew		
Escort-Lynx-EXP-LN7		
1983-87		
one	(.9)	1.2
both	(1.7)	2.2
Tempo-Topaz		
1984-87		
one	(.9)	1.2
both	(1.7)	2.2
Renew C.V. joint add-each	(.2)	.3
Renew diff oil seal add-each	(.2)	.3
(G) Manual Trans/Axle Assy., R&R or Renew		
Escort-Lynx-EXP-LN7		
1983-87		
4 Speed	(2.0)	3.5
5 Speed		
Gas	(2.0)	3.5
Diesel	(3.9)	5.6
Tempo-Topaz		
1984-87		
4 Speed	(2.3)	3.8
5 Speed		
Gas	(2.3)	3.5
Diesel	(3.9)	5.6
Separate and reseal case add	(.3)	.6
Renew case add	(.2)	.4
O/Haul diff case add	(.6)	1.0
Recond trans complete add	(1.7)	2.5
(G) Differential Case, R&R and Recondition (w/Manual Trans/Axle)		
Escort-Lynx-EXP-LN7		
1983-87		
4 Speed	(3.5)	5.0
5 Speed		
Gas	(3.3)	4.7
Diesel	(5.5)	8.0
Tempo-Topaz		
1984-87		
4 Speed	(3.9)	5.6
5 Speed		
Gas	(3.9)	5.6
Diesel	(5.5)	8.0

PARTS 19 TRANSAXLE (4 SPEED) 19 PARTS

	Part No.	Price
MODEL (RGT, RJS)		
Transaxle Assy. Serviced in detail only.		
(1) Second Gear (Trans. Ident.)		
1983-85-exc. below	E1FZ-7102A	49.00
1983-84-RGT-AL, AP	E3FZ-7102B	49.00
1984-85-RGT-AR, AV	E43Z-7102A	49.00
1985-87-RJS	E5FZ-7102A	49.00
(2) Blocking Ring		
1983-85	E1FZ-7107A	15.25
1986-87	E5FZ-7107A	15.25
(3) Spring		
1983-85	E1FZ-7109A	1.25
1986-87	E5FZ-7109A	2.00
(4) Synchronizer Assy.		
1983-85-1st & 2nd	E1FZ-7124A	96.00
3rd & 4th	E1FZ-7124B	80.25
1986-87-1st. & 2nd.	E5FZ-7124B	96.00
3rd. & 4th.	E5FZ-7124C	80.25
(5) Hub Insert (Synchronizer)		
1983-87-1st & 2nd	E1FZ-7A044A	1.50
3rd & 4th	E1FZ-7A044B	1.50
(6) Shim (Input Shaft)		
1983-87	E1FZ-7L172B	6.75
(7) Bearing Assy. (Front & Rear)		
1983-85	E1FZ-7025A	15.75
1986-87	E3FZ-7025A	17.50
(8) Input Shaft (Trans. Ident.)		
1983-85-exc. below	E1FZ-7017A	137.25
1983-84-RGT-AG, AH, AN	E2FZ-7017A	151.75
RGT-AL, AP	E3FZ-7017B	151.75
1984-85-RGT-AR, AV	E43Z-7017A	151.75
1986-87-RJS	E5FZ-7017A	151.75
(9) Seal (Input Shaft)		
1983-85	E1FZ-7A011A	4.25
1986-87	E3FZ-7A011A	4.25
(10) Shaft (Input Shift)		
1983-85	E1FZ-7L267A	13.25
1986-87	E3FZ-7L267A	13.25

4-SPEED

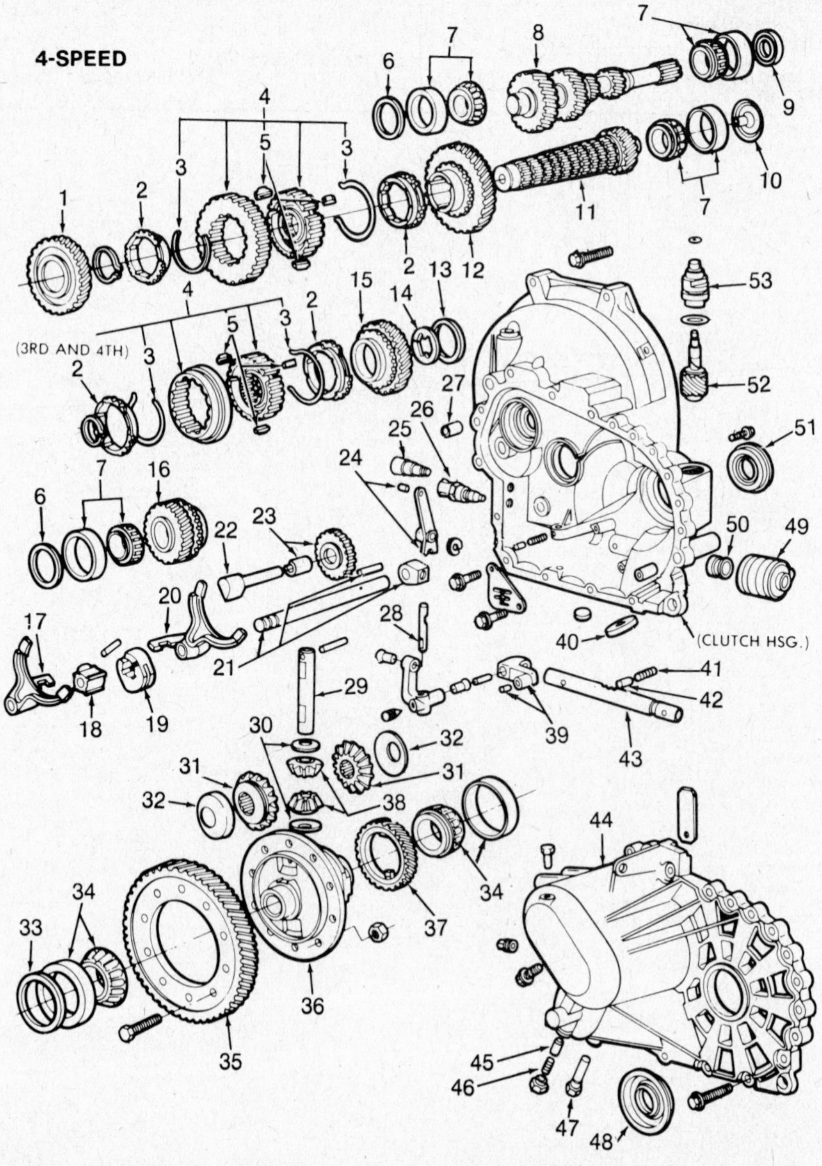

PARTS 19 TRANSAXLE (4 SPEED) 19 PARTS

	Part No	Price
(11) Output Shaft		
(Trans. Ident.)		
1983-exc. below	E1FZ-7061A	111.50
1983-RGT-AL	E3FZ-7061E	111.50
1984-85-RGT-AM, AN, AS	E4FZ-7061C	111.50
RGT-AP, AR, AV	E43Z-7061C	111.50
1985-87-RJS-AB	E5FZ-7061A	111.50
(12) First Gear		
(Trans. Ident.)		
1983-85-exc. below	E1FZ-7100A	62.75
1983-84-RGT-AL, AP	E43Z-7100A	‡62.75
1984-85-RGT-AR	E43Z-7100A	62.75
1985-87-RJS-AB	E5FZ-7100A	62.75
(13) Thrust Washer Retaining Ring		
1983-87	E1FZ-7A046A	2.75
(14) Thrust Washer (2nd & 3rd)		
1983-85	E1FZ-7A385A	4.75
1986-87	E43Z-7A385A	4.75
(15) Third Gear		
(Trans. Ident.)		
1983-85-exc. below	E3FZ-7B340B	46.75
RGT-AG	E2FZ-7B340A	46.75
1983-84-RGT-AH, AN	E3FZ-7B340C	46.75
1985-87-RJS-AB	E5FZ-7B340A	46.75
(16) Fourth Gear		
(Trans. Ident.)		
1983-85-exc. below	E1FZ-7112A	43.50
1983-84-RGT-AG, AH, AN	E2FZ-7112A	43.50
1985-87-RJS-AB	E5FZ-7112A	43.50
(17) Shifter Fork (1st & 2nd)		
1983-85	E1FZ-7230A	35.75
1986-87	E5FZ-7230A	35.75
(18) Selector Arm		
1983-85	E1FZ-7346A	15.25
1986-87	E5FZ-7346A	14.25
(19) Interlock Sleeve (Selector)		
1983-84	E1FZ-7K201A	12.25
1985	E5FZ-7K201B	11.25
1986-87	E5FZ-7K201A	11.25

	Part No	Price
(20) Shifter Fork (3rd & 4th)		
1983-85	E1FZ-7230B	35.75
1986-87	E5FZ-7230B	35.75
(21) Shift Control Shaft Assy.		
1983-84	E1FZ-7358A	18.75
1985	E5FZ-7358B	17.50
1986-87	E5FZ-7358A	23.50
(22) Idler Gear Shaft (Reverse)		
1983-85	E1FZ-7140A	16.25
1986-87	E5FZ-7140A	18.75
(23) Reverse Idler Gear		
1983-85	E1FZ-7141A	40.00
1986-87	E5FZ-7141B	42.50
(24) Reverse Lever Assy.		
1983-84	E1FZ-7K002A	13.25
1985	E5FZ-7K002B	13.25
1986-87	E5FZ-7K077C	N.L.
(25) Relay Lever Pivot Pin (Reverse)		
1983-85	E1FZ-7F111A	7.00
1986-87	E3FZ-7F111A	7.00
(26) Back-Up Switch		
1983-84	E5FZ-15520B	21.50
1985-87	E5FZ-15520B	21.50
(27) Dowel (Case To Clutch Housing)		
1983-85-1.6L eng.	E1FZ-6397A	2.00
2.3L eng.	E43Z-6397A	2.00
(28) Shift Lever Shaft		
1983-84	E1FZ-7C355A	10.75
1985	E5FZ-7C355B	10.75
1986-87	E5FZ-7C355C	29.25
(29) Pinion Shaft		
Escort, Lynx, Exp & LN7		
1983-85	E1FZ-4211A	13.75
1986-87	E6FZ-4211A	13.75
Tempo & Topaz		
1984-85	E43Z-4211B	13.75
1986-87	E6FZ-4211A	13.75
(30) Pinion Thrust Washer		
1983-87	E3FZ-4230A	1.50
(31) Side Gear Kit		
1983-85	E1FZ-4236A	40.00
1986-87	E5FZ-4236A	40.00
(32) Thrust Washer (Side Gear)		
1983-87	E1FZ-4228A	2.75
(33) Shim (.30mm)		
1983-87	E1FZ-4067Y	3.25

Other sizes available from .30mm up to 1.25mm.

	Part No	Price
(34) Bearing Assy. (Differential)		
1983-87	E1FZ-4221B	15.75
(35) Output Gear (Final Drive)		
1983-85-exc. below	E1FZ-7F343A	127.25
RGT-AL, AP, AR	E3FZ-7F343C	117.50
1985-87-RJS-AB, AE	E5FZ-7F343A	1.25
(36) Case Assy. (Transaxle)		
1983-87	E1FZ-4204B	136.50
(37) Speedo. Drive Gear		
1983-87	E1FZ-17285A	13.75
(38) Pinion Gear (Differential)		
1983-87	E3FZ-4215A	25.75
(39) Input Shift Arm Assy.		
1983-85	E1FZ-7F477A	20.00
1986-87	E5FZ-7D477A	N.L.
(40) Magnet (Case)		
1983-87	E1FZ-7L027A	6.75
(41) Spring (Meshlock)		
1983-85	E1FZ-7234B	.75
1986-87	E3FZ-7234A	.75
(42) Plunger (Meshlock)		
1983-87	E1FZ-7233A	2.25
(43) Funnel (Output Shaft)		
1983-85	E1FZ-7L276A	4.25
1986-87	E3FZ-7L276A	4.25
(44) Case (Trans. Half)		
1983	E5FZ-7005E	353.25
1984	E5EZ-7005E	353.25
1985	E5FZ-7005E	353.25
1986-87	E6FZ-7005B	300.75
(45) Plunger (Meshlock)		
1983-85	E1FZ-7233B	2.25
1986-87	E1FZ-7233A	2.25
(46) Spring (Meshlock)		
1983-85	E1FZ-7234B	.75
1986-87	E3FZ-7234A	.75
(47) Pin (Interlock)		
1983-85	E1FZ-7F488A	4.00
1986-87	E3FZ-7F488A	9.25
(48) Rear Bearing Oil Seal (Inner)		
1983-87	E1FZ-1177A	10.75

PARTS 19 TRANSAXLE & DRIVE SHAFT 19 PARTS

	Part No.	Price
(1) Joint Assy. (Outer)		
1983-84	E5FZ-3B413A	219.75
1985-87	E5FZ-3B413A	219.75

Includes 1 nut, 1 washer, 1 retaining ring and 1 pkg. of grease.

	Part No.	Price
(2) Boot (Outer)		
1983-85	E1FZ-3A331A	17.00
1986-87	E53Z-3A331C	21.25

Includes 2 clamps, 1 retaining ring and 3 pkgs. of grease.

	Part No.	Price
(3) Front Axle Shaft		
1983-84-right	E4FZ-3A329A	98.25
left	E3FZ-3A329G	37.75
1985-87-right	E4FZ-3A329A	98.25
left	E3FZ-3A329G	37.75

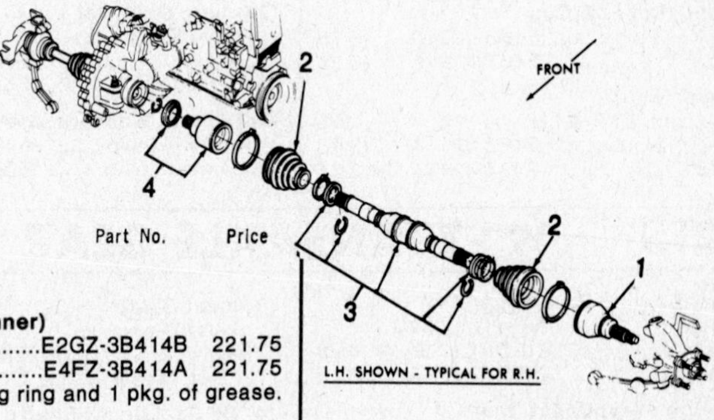

	Part No.	Price
(4) Joint Assy. (Inner)		
1983-84	E2GZ-3B414B	221.75
1985-87	E4FZ-3B414A	221.75

Includes 1 retaining ring and 1 pkg. of grease.

PARTS 19 TRANSAXLE (5 SPEED) 19 PARTS

Part No. Price

MODEL RWB

Transaxle Assy.
Serviced in detail only.

(1) Fork Control Shaft (5th Spd.)
1983-84 .... E3FZ-7241A 18.75
1985-87 .... E5FZ-7241A 23.25

(2) Reverse Idler Gear Shaft
1983-84 .... E3FZ-7140A 18.75
1985-87 .... E5FZ-7140A 18.75

(3) Relay Lever Assy. (5th Spd.)
1983-84 .... E3FZ-7G043A 20.75
1985-87 .... E5FZ-7G043A 20.75

(4) Reverse Idler Gear
1983-84 .... E3FZ-7141A 42.50
1985-87 .... E5FZ-7141A 42.50

(5) Back-Up Lamp Switch
1983-84 .... E5FZ-15520B 21.50
1985-87 .... E5FZ-15520A 21.50

(6) Driven Gear Bearing (Speedo.)
1983-87 .... E1FZ-17K288A 4.00

(7) Driven Gear (Speedo.)
1983-87 .... E3FZ-17271A 7.25

(8) Wheel Bearing Oil Seal (Inner)
1983-87 .... E1FZ-1177A 10.75

(9) Boot
1983-87 .... E3FZ-7F110A 9.00

(10) Seal (Shifter Shaft)
1983-87 .... E43Z-7288A 3.50

(11) Input Shaft
1983-87 .... E3FZ-7L267A 13.25

(12) Arm Assy. (Selector Plate)
1983-84 .... E3FZ-7F477A 17.25
1985-87 .... E5FZ-7F477A 20.00

(13) Shaft (Shifter Lever)
1983-87 .... E5FZ-7C355A 29.25

(14) Ring (Output Shaft)
1983-87 .... E1FZ-7A046A 2.75

(15) Selector Lever (Shift Fork)
1983-84 .... E4FZ-7F116A 17.75
1985-87 .... E5FZ-7F116A 17.75

(16) Magnet (Case)
1983-87 .... E1FZ-7L027A 6.75

(17) Shaft Assy. (Shift Control)
1983-84 .... E3FZ-7358A 25.25
1985-87 .... E5FZ-7358A 23.50

(18) Case Assy.
Order by year and model.

(19) Shim (30mm)
1983-87-w/2 pin E1FZ-4067Y 3.25
4 pin E43Z-4067A 3.00
Other sizes available from .30mm up to 1.30mm.

(20) Cone, Roller & Cup
1983-87-2 pin E1FZ-4221B 15.75
4 pin E43Z-4221A 20.25

(21) Pinion Shaft
Escort, Lynx, EXP & LN7
1983-87-2 pin E1FZ-4211A 13.75
4 pin E43Z-4211A 13.75

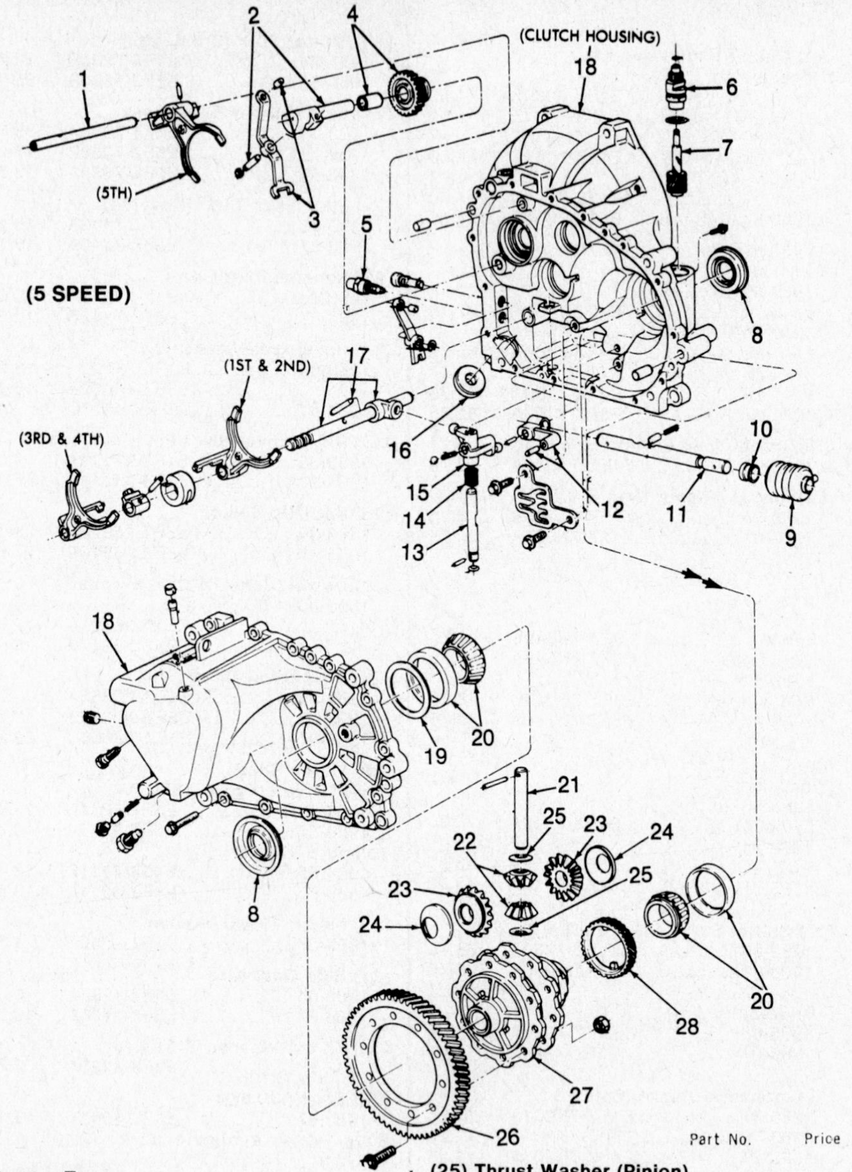

Tempo, Topaz
1984-87-2 pin E43Z-4211B 13.75
4 pin E43Z-4211A 13.75
Taurus, Sable
1986-87 .... E6FZ-4211A 13.75

(22) Pinion
1983-87 .... E3FZ-4215A 25.75

(23) Side Gear Set
1983-85-2 pin E1FZ-4236A 40.00
4 pin E3FZ-4236A 40.00
1986-87-2 pin E5FZ-4236A 40.00

(24) Thrust Washer (Side Gear)
1983-87-2 pin E1FZ-4228A 2.75
4 pin E3FZ-4228A 2.50

Part No. Price

(25) Thrust Washer (Pinion)
1983-87 .... E3FZ-4230A 1.50

(26) Output Gear (Final Drive)
Escort, Lynx, EXP & LN7
1983-87-1.6L E3FZ-7F343B 117.50
2.0L Diesel E4FZ-7F343A 117.50
Tempo, Topaz
1984-87-exc.
Diesel E43Z-7F343A 117.50
2.0L Diesel E3FZ-7F343B 117.50

(27) Case Assy.
1983-87-2 pin E3FZ-4204A 124.50
4 pin E43Z-4204A 125.00

(28) Drive Gear (Speedo.)
1983-87 .... E3FZ-17285A 13.00

PARTS 19 TRANSAXLE GEAR TRAIN (5 SPEED) 19 PARTS

(1) Shim (Bearing Preload)
1983-87-exc.
below E1FZ-7L172B 6.75
5th gear E3FZ-7L172A 6.75

(2) Bearing Assy. (Input Shaft)
1983-87 .... E3FZ-7025A 17.50

(3) Input Shaft
1983-87-exc.
below E3FZ-7017A 137.25
2.0L Diesel E4FZ-7017A 151.75

(4) Oil Seal (Input Shaft)
1983-87 .... E3FZ-7A011A 4.25

(5) Bearing Assy. (5th Gear Shaft)
1983-87 .... E3FZ-7F431A 15.25

(6) Fifth Speed Gear
1983-87-exc.
below E3FZ-7K316A 43.50
2.0L Diesel E4FZ-7K316A 43.50

PARTS 19 TRANSAXLE GEAR TRAIN (5 SPEED) 19 PARTS

	Part No.	Price
(7) Blocking Ring (Synchro.)		
1983-87		
1st & 2nd	E1FZ-7107A	15.25
3rd & 4th	E3FZ-7107A	15.25
5th spd.	E3FZ-7107B	15.25
(8) Synchronizer (5th Spd.)		
1983-84	E3FZ-7124C	80.25
1985-86	E5FZ-7124A	80.25
(9) Fifth Gear (Drive)		
1983-87		
30 teeth	E3FZ-7061D	89.25
31 teeth	E4FZ-7061B	89.25
32 teeth	E43Z-7061B	89.25
(10) Funnel (Output & 5th Spd. Shaft)		
1983-87-output	E1FZ-7L276A	4.25
5th spd.	E3FZ-7L276A	4.25
(11) Synchronizer (1st & 2nd)		
1983-87	E3FZ-7124A	96.00
(12) First Speed Gear		
1983-87-exc. below	E3FZ-7100A	62.75
2.0L Diesel	E4FZ-7100A	62.75
(13) Output Shaft		
Escort, Lynx, EXP, LN7		
1983	E3FZ-7061B	111.50
1984-87-1.6L eng.	E4FZ-7061D	111.50
2.0L Diesel	E4FZ-7061A	111.50
Tempo & Topaz		
1984-87-exc. below	E43Z-7061A	111.50
2.0L Diesel	E4FZ-7061D	111.50
Taurus, Sable		
1986-87	E4FZ-7061D	111.50
(14) Bearing Assy. (Output Shaft)		
1983-87	E1FZ-7025A	15.75
(15) Fourth Speed Gear		
1983-87-exc. below	E3FZ-7112A	43.50
2.0L Diesel	E4FZ-7112A	43.50
(16) Synchronizer (3rd & 4th)		
1983-87	E3FZ-7124B	80.25
(17) Third Speed Gear		
1983-87	E3FZ-7B340A	46.75
(18) Retaining Ring		
1983-87	E1FZ-7A046A	2.75
(19) Second Speed Gear		
1983-87	E3FZ-7102A	49.00

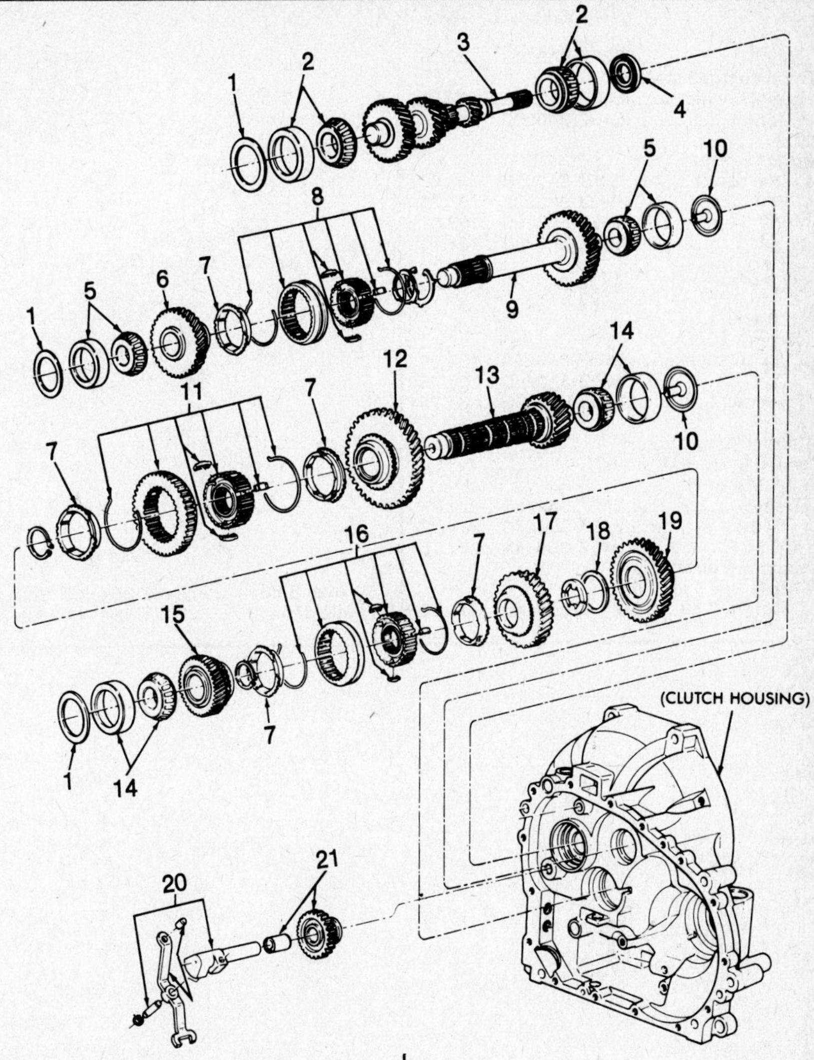

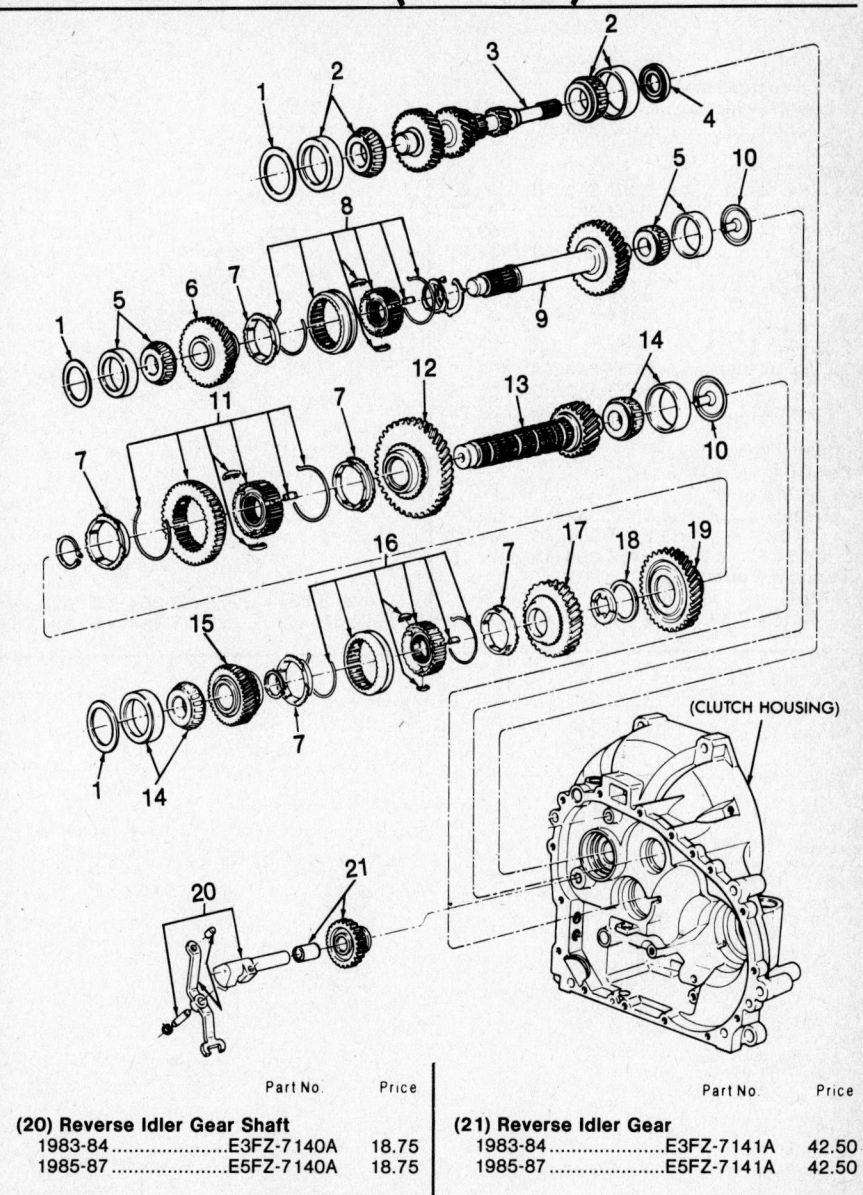

	Part No.	Price
(20) Reverse Idler Gear Shaft		
1983-84	E3FZ-7140A	18.75
1985-87	E5FZ-7140A	18.75

	Part No.	Price
(21) Reverse Idler Gear		
1983-84	E3FZ-7141A	42.50
1985-87	E5FZ-7141A	42.50

PARTS 19 TRANSAXLE DRIVESHAFT 19 PARTS

	Part No.	Price
(1) Joint Assy. (Outer)		
Escort, Lynx, EXP & LN7		
1983-84-exc. Turbo	E5FZ-3B413A	219.75
Turbo	E43Z-3B413B	214.25
1985-87	E5FZ-3B413A	219.75
Tempo & Topaz		
1984-exc. Diesel	E43Z-3B413B	214.25
2.0L Diesel	E5FZ-3B413A	219.75
1985-87-exc. H.O.	E5FZ-3B413A	219.75
(2.3L H.O.)		
right	E43Z-3B413B	214.25
left	E5FZ-3B413A	219.75
Taurus, Sable		
1986-87	E6DZ-3B413B	212.50
(2) Boot (Outer)		
Escort, Lynx, EXP & LN7		
1983-87	E1FZ-3A331A	17.00

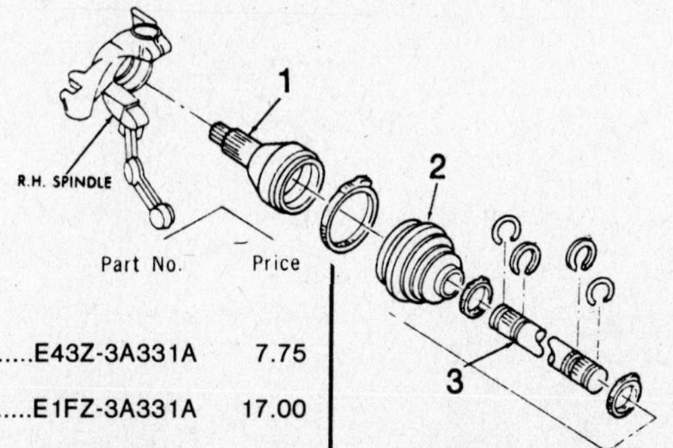

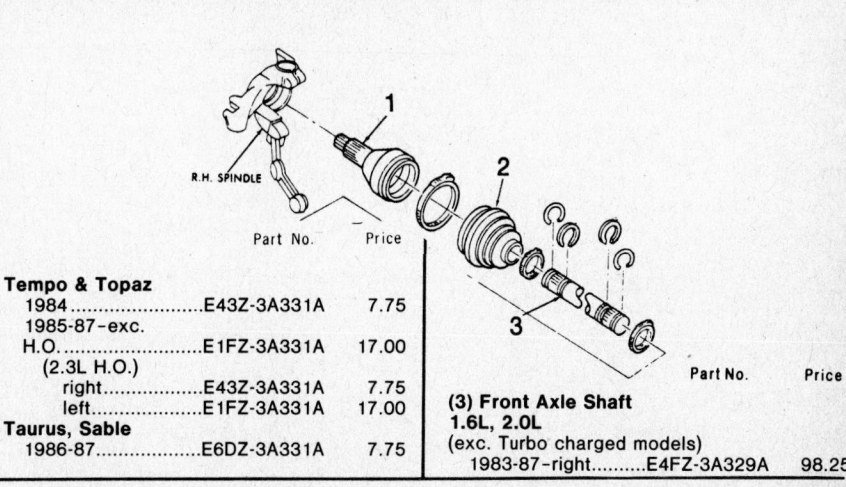

	Part No.	Price
Tempo & Topaz		
1984	E43Z-3A331A	7.75
1985-87-exc. H.O.	E1FZ-3A331A	17.00
(2.3L H.O.)		
right	E43Z-3A331A	7.75
left	E1FZ-3A331A	17.00
Taurus, Sable		
1986-87	E6DZ-3A331A	7.75

	Part No.	Price
(3) Front Axle Shaft		
1.6L, 2.0L		
(exc. Turbo charged models)		
1983-87-right	E4FZ-3A329A	98.25

	Part No.	Price
left	E3FZ-3A329G	37.75
(Turbo charged models)		
1984-87-right	E4GZ-3A329A	98.25
left	E4GZ-3A329B	37.75
2.3L		
(wo/H.O. eng.)		
1984-right	E43Z-3A329B	133.00
left	E43Z-3A329A	37.75
1985-87-right	E43Z-3A329C	133.00
left	E3FZ-3A329G	37.75
(H.O. eng.)		
1985-87-right	E43Z-3A329B	133.00
left	E3FZ-3A329E	37.75
2.5L		
1986-87-right	E6DZ-3A329A	133.00
left	E6DZ-3A329C	37.75
center	E6DZ-3A329G	37.75

(4) Joint Assy. (Inner)
Escort, Lynx, EXP & LN7

	Part No.	Price
1983-84-exc. Turbo	E2GZ-3B414B	221.75
Turbo	E43Z-3B414C	214.25
1985-87	E4FZ-3B414A	221.75
Tempo & Topaz		
1984		
before 8-83	E43Z-3B414B	214.25
from 8-83	E43Z-3B414C	214.25
1985-87	E4FZ-3B414A	221.75

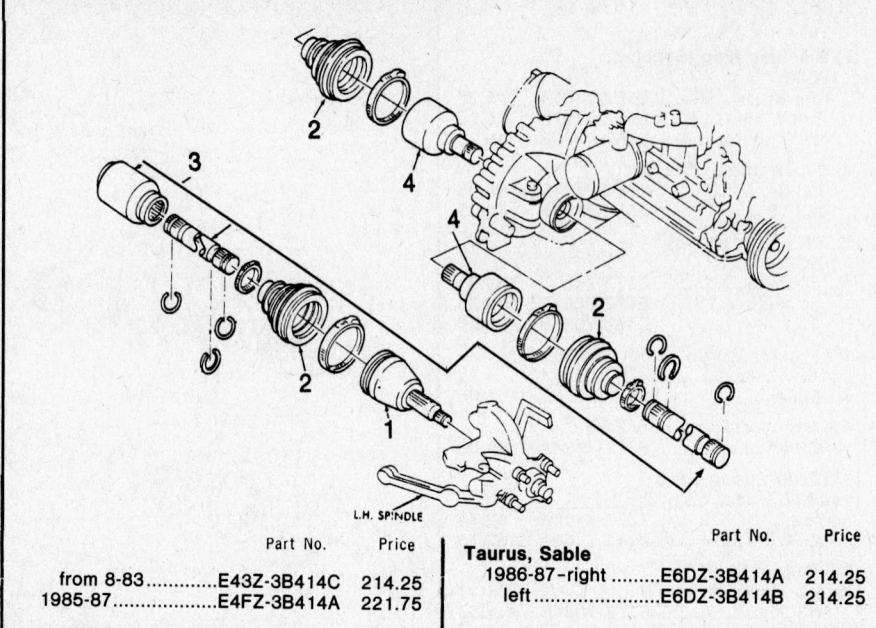

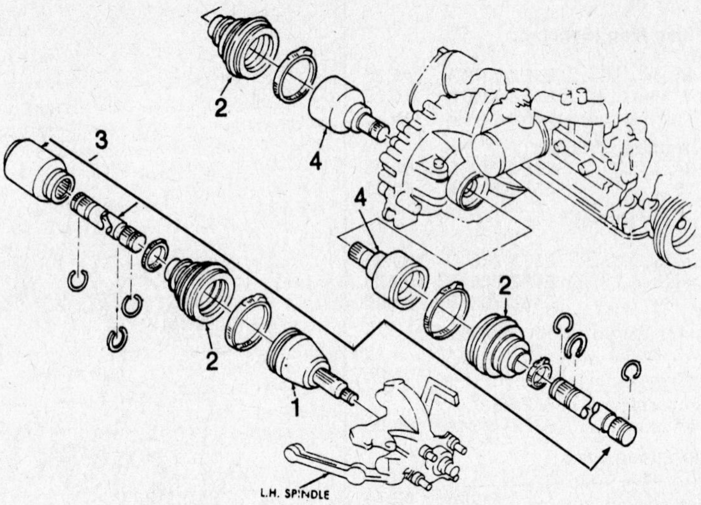

Taurus, Sable

	Part No.	Price
1986-87-right	E6DZ-3B414A	214.25
left	E6DZ-3B414B	214.25

LABOR 19 STANDARD TRANSMISSION 19 LABOR

(Factory Time) Chilton Time

FORD MOTOR CORPORATION

4 SPEED (GERMAN) E T

(G) Transmission Assy., Remove & Install

Mustang-Capri
1983-87 (1.5) 2.1

Fairmont-Zephyr
1983 (1.5) 2.1

LTD-Marquis
1983-84 (1.5) 2.1

Renew front seal add (.1) 2

(G) Transmission Assy., R&R and Reconditíon

Includes: Completely disassemble trans, clean and inspect or renew all parts. Install all new gaskets and seals.

Mustang-Capri
1983-87 (3.7) 5.0

Fairmont-Zephyr
1983 (3.7) 5.0

LTD-Marquis
1983-84 (3.7) 5.0

(G) Transmission, Recondition (Off Car)
All models (2.2) 3.0

(G) Transmission Rear Oil Seal and/or Bushing, Renew
All models (.5) 8

(G) Speedometer Driven Gear, Renew
All models (.3) 5

4 SPEED (SROD) RUG

(G) Transmission Assy., Remove & Install

Mustang-Capri
1983 (1.4) 1.9

Renew front seal add (.1) 2

(G) Transmission Assy., R&R and Recondition

Includes: Completely disassemble trans, clean and inspect or renew all parts. Install all new gaskets and seals.

Mustang-Capri
1983 (3.4) 4.7

(G) Transmission, Recondition (Off Car)
All models (2.0) 2.8

(G) Transmission Rear Oil Seal and/or Bushing, Renew
All models (.5) 8

(G) Speedometer Driven Gear, Renew
All models (.3) 5

5 SPEED (M5OD) RAP

(G) Transmission Assy., Remove & Install

Mustang-Capri
1983 (2.0) 2.7

Renew front seal add (.1) 2

(G) Transmission Assy., R&R and Recondition

Includes: Completely disassemble trans, clean and inspect or renew all parts. Install all new gaskets and seals.

Mustang-Capri
1983 (3.6) 5.1

(G) Transmission, Recondition (Off Car)
All models (1.6) 2.4

(G) Transmission Rear Oil Seal and/or Bushing, Renew
All models (.5) 8

(G) Speedometer Driven Gear, Renew
All models (.3) 5

5 SPEED BORG WARNER (REP)

(G) Transmission Assy., Remove & Install

Mustang-Capri
1983-87
Four (1.5) 2.0
V-8 (1.6) 2.1

Thunderbird-Cougar
1983-87 (1.5) 2.0

Renew front seal add (.1) 2

(G) Transmission Assy., R&R and Recondition

Includes: Completely disassemble trans, clean and inspect or renew all parts. Install all new gaskets and seals.

Mustang-Capri
1983-87
Four (3.7) 5.0
V-8 (3.8) 5.1

Thunderbird-Cougar
1983-87 (3.7) 5.0

(G) Transmission, Recondition (Off Car)
All models (2.2) 3.0

(G) Transmission Rear Oil Seal and/or Bushing, Renew
All models (.5) 8

(G) Speedometer Driven Gear, Renew
All models (.3) 5

5 SPEED (WARNER) T5OD

(G) Transmission Assy., Remove & Install

Mustang-Capri
1983-87 (1.6) 2.1

Renew front seal add (.1) 2

(G) Transmission Assy., R&R and Recondition

Includes: Completely disassemble trans, clean and inspect or renew all parts. Install all new gaskets and seals.

Mustang-Capri
1983-87 .... 5.1

(G) Transmission, Recondition (Off Car)
All models 3.0

(G) Transmission Rear Oil Seal and/or Bushing, Renew
All models (.5) 8

(G) Speedometer Driven Gear, Renew
All models (.3) 5

PARTS 19 STANDARD TRANS. (4 Speed) 19 PARTS

	Part No.	Price
(GERMAN TYPE)		
Transmission Assy. Serviced in detail only.		
Transmission Gasket & Seal Pkg.		
1983-87	D1FZ-7153A	3.75
Small Parts Repair Kit		
1983	D3RY-7B331B	28.50
Repair kit includes snap rings, washers, pins, balls & rings.		
(1) Bearing Retainer		
Capri & Mustang		
1983	D8BZ-7050B	30.25
1984-87	E0BZ-7050A	30.25
Exc. Capri & Mustang		
1983	E0BZ-7050A	30.25
(2) Oil Seal (Retainer)		
1983-87	D1FZ-7051A	1.00
(3) Rear Oil Seal (Input Shaft)		
1983-87	E0ZZ-7A283A	7.25
(4) Plate (Interlock)		
1983-87	D1FZ-7K201A	10.25
(5) Fork (Gear Shifter)		
(1st & 2nd spd.)		
1983-87	E1ZZ-7230A	27.75
(3rd & 4th spd.)		
1983	D1FZ-7230D	21.25
1984-87	E5ZZ-7230A	19.75
(Reverse)		
1983-87	D4FZ-7231A	8.75
(6) Shaft (Gear Shift)		
1983-87	D8BZ-7358A	52.50
(7) Bushing (Ext. Housing)		
1983-87	D1FZ-7341A	3.00
(8) Bushing (Gear Shift Shaft)		
1983-87	D2FZ-7K453A	4.00
(9) Oil Seal (Extension)		
1983-87	E0ZZ-7052A	10.75
(10) Bushing (Extension)		
1983-87	D1FZ-7034C	3.75
(11) Extension Housing		
1983-87	D8BZ-7A039C	100.75
(12) Spring (Meshlock)		
1983-87	D2FZ-7234A	.50
(13) Plunger (Meshlock)		
1983	E0BZ-7233A	2.25
(14) Case Assy.		
1983-87	E3ZZ-7005A	138.00
(15) Pilot Bearing		
1983-87	D4ZZ-7600A	5.25
(16) Bearing Assy. (Drive Gear)		
1983-87	D1FZ-7025A	15.75
(17) Input Shaft		
1983	D8BZ-7017B	97.75
1984-87	E5ZZ-7017D	97.75
(18) Pilot Bearing (Input Shaft)		
1983	D1FZ-7120B	6.50
1984-87	E5RY-7600A	13.50

PARTS 19 STANDARD TRANS. (4 Speed) 19 PARTS

	Part No.	Price
(19) Spring		
(1st & 2nd spd.)		
1983-87	D1FZ-7109A	1.00
(3rd & 4th spd.)		
1983	D1FZ-7109B	1.00
1984-87	E0RZ-7109A	1.75
(20) Insert (Synchronizer Hub)		
(1st & 2nd spd.)		
1983-87	D1FZ-7A044A	.50
(3rd & 4th spd.)		
1983	D1FZ-7A044B	.50
1984-87	E4ZZ-7A044B	1.50
(21) Output Shaft Assy.		
1983	D4FZ-7061A	253.75
1984-87	E5ZZ-7061B	253.75
(22) Blocking Ring		
(1st & 2nd spd.)		
1983-87	E5RY-7107A	24.00
(3rd & 4th spd.)		
1983	D1FZ-7107A	18.50
1984-87	D8RZ-7107B	19.00
(23) First Gear		
1983-87	D4FZ-7100A	86.25
(24) Third Gear		
1983	D7FZ-7B340A	63.50
1984-87	E5ZZ-7B340C	63.50
(25) Second Gear		
1983	D6RY-7102A	70.00
1984-87	E5RY-7102A	49.00
(26) Synchronizer Assy. (3rd & 4th)		
1983	D1FZ-7124A	87.25
1984-87	E5RY-7124B	87.25
(27) Countershaft Gear		
1983	D7FZ-7113A	164.25
1984-87	E5ZZ-7113D	164.25
(28) Reverse Idler Gear		
1983-87	D4FZ-7141A	58.50
(29) Idler Gear Shaft		
1983-87	D1FZ-7140A	19.75

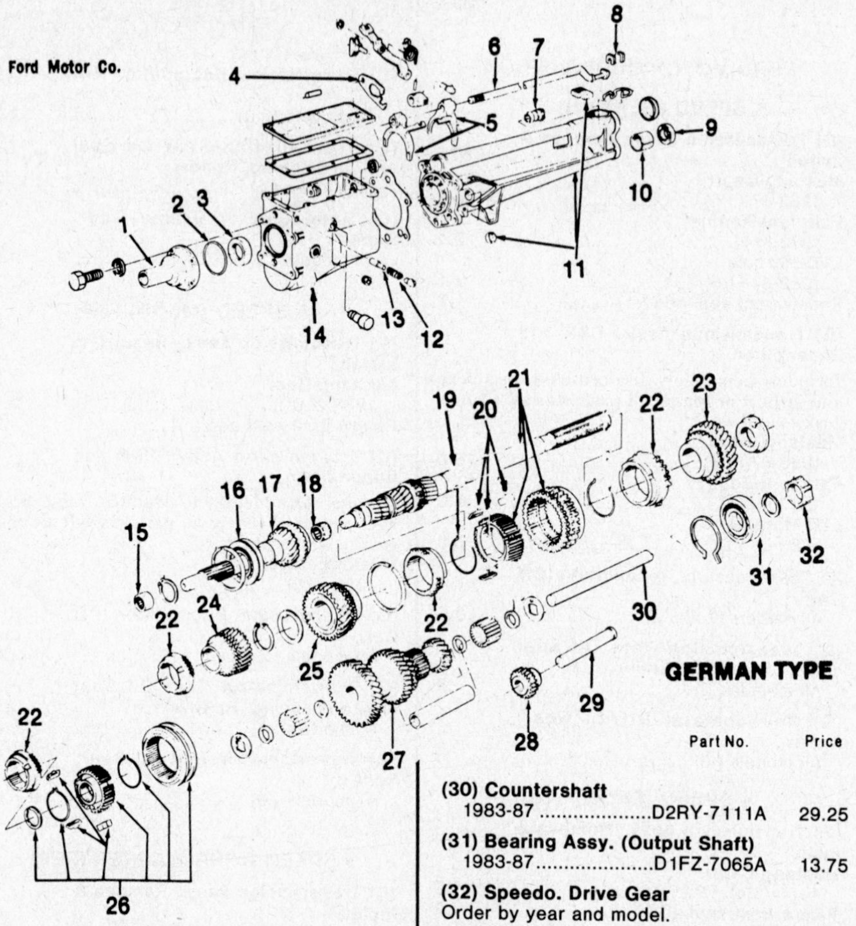

GERMAN TYPE

	Part No.	Price
(30) Countershaft		
1983-87	D2RY-7111A	29.25
(31) Bearing Assy. (Output Shaft)		
1983-87	D1FZ-7065A	13.75
(32) Speedo. Drive Gear		
Order by year and model.		

PARTS 19 STD. TRANS. (4 SPEED) WITH OVERDRIVE 19 PARTS

(MODEL RUG)

	Part No.	Price
Transmission Assy.		
Serviced in detail only.		
Transmission Gasket & Seal Kit		
1983	E2ZZ-7153A	5.50
Small Parts Repair Kit		
1983	C4MY-7B331B	22.00
Repair Kit includes snap rings, washers, pins, balls and rings.		
(1) Bearing Retainer		
1983	D9BZ-7050A	45.50
(2) Oil Seal (Input Shaft)		
1983	D8UZ-7A283B	3.75
(3) Case Assy.		
1983	D9BZ-7005A	343.00
(4) Extension Housing Gasket		
1983	E0BZ-7086A	1.00
(5) Extension Housing		
1983	D9BZ-7A039A	143.25
(6) Bushing (Extension)		
1983	B3TZ-7A034B	2.25
(7) Oil Seal (Extension)		
1983	D9BZ-7052A	11.25
(8) Shaft Sleeve (Gear Shift)		
1983-4 63/64" long	D9BZ-7K424B	3.50

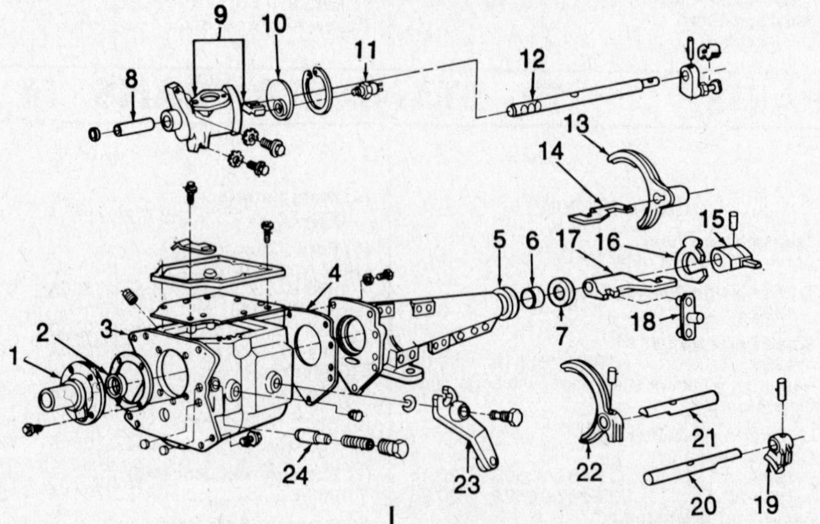

	Part No.	Price
(9) Turret Assy. (Shifter)		
1983	D9BZ-7F305A	66.50
(10) Cover Assy. (Turret Shifter)		
1983	E0BZ-7F307A	N.L.

	Part No.	Price
(11) Switch Assy. (Back-Up Lamp)		
1983	D8BZ-15520A	N.L.
(12) Shaft (Gear Shift)		
1983-1 29/64" long	D9DZ-7358C	77.75

PARTS 19 STD. TRANS. (4 SPEED) WITH OVERDRIVE 19 PARTS

Part No. Price

(13) Shifter Fork (1st & 2nd)
1983 .... E1TZ-7230A 46.75

(14) Plate (Selector Arm)
Selector arm plate not required on 1983 models.

(15) Selector Arm Assy.
1983 .... E1TZ-7230A 46.75

(16) Plate (Selector Interlock)
1983 .... D9BZ-7K201A 8.50

(17) Pawl (Overdrive Shift)
1983 .... D9BZ-7F304A 28.00

(18) Control Link Assy. (Overdrive)
1983 .... E1ZZ-7F310A 13.50

(19) Shifter Fork (Reverse)
1983 .... D9BZ-7231A 31.00

(20) Shifter rail (Reverse)
1983 .... D9BZ-7442A N.L.

(21) Shifter Rail (3rd & 4th)
1983 .... D9BZ-7241A 12.75

(22) Shifter Fork (3rd & 4th)
1983 .... E1ZZ-7230B 47.25

(23) Lever Assy. (Reverse)
1983 .... D9BZ-7K002A 30.00

(24) Plunger (Meshlock)
1983 .... E0BZ-7233A 2.25

(25) Countershaft
1983 .... C4AZ-7111A 18.25

(26) Reverse Idler Gear (w/Bushing)
1983 .... D7DZ-7141A 131.75

(27) Idler Sliding Gear (Reverse)
1983 .... D9BZ-7D223A 112.25

(28) Idler Gear Shaft (Reverse)
1983 .... C4AZ-7140A 16.25

(29) Bearing Assy. (Input Shaft)
1983 .... E1ZZ-7025A 22.25

(30) Input Shaft
1983 .... D9BZ-7017B 139.75

(31) Blocking Ring
1983 .... D9BZ-7107A 29.00

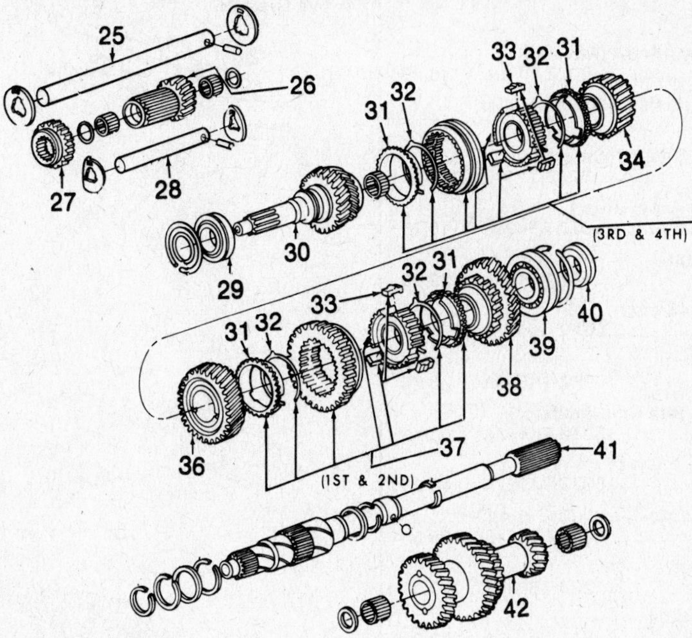

Part No. Price

(32) Snap Ring (Hub Insert)
1983 .... C3AZ-7109D 1.25

(33) Hub Insert (Synchronizer)
1983
1st & 2nd C4AZ-7A044B 1.25
3rd & 4th C3AZ-7A044C 1.25

(34) Third Speed Or Overdrive Gear
1983 .... D9BZ-7B340B 100.50

(35) Synchronizer Assy. (3rd & 4th)
1983 .... D9BZ-7124B 179.25

(36) Second Speed Gear
1983 .... E4TZ-7102D N.L.

Part No. Price

(37) Synchronizer Assy. (1st & 2nd)
1983 .... D9BZ-7124A 192.50

(38) First Gear
1983 .... D9BZ-7A029B 81.50

(39) Bearing Assy. (Output Shaft)
1983 .... E1ZZ-7065A 22.25

(40) Speedo. Drive Gear
Order by year and model.

(41) Output Shaft
1983 .... D9BZ-7061A 181.75

(42) Countershaft Gear
1983 .... D9BZ-7113B 224.00

PARTS 19 STD. TRANS. (5 SPEED) WITH OVERDRIVE 19 PARTS

Part No. Price

(MODEL RAP)

Transmission Assy.
Serviced in detail only.

Transmission Gasket & Seal Kit
1983 .... E0ZZ-7153A 8.25

Small Parts Repair Kit
1983 .... E0AZ-7B331A 30.25
Repair Kit includes snap rings, washers, pins, balls and rings.

(1) Shaft Assy. (Gear shift)
1983 .... E0ZZ-7358A 72.25

(2) Interlock Sleeve (Gear Selector)
1983-exc. below..... E0ZZ-7K201A 40.25
5th speed E0ZZ-7K201B 25.00

(3) Shifter Fork
1983
3rd & 4th E0ZZ-7230B 45.50
5th spd. E3ZZ-7230A 38.50

Part No. Price

(4) Shifter Fork (1st & 2nd)
1983 .... E0ZZ-7230A 38.50

(5) Return Spring (Shift Lever)
1983 .... E0ZZ-7K205A 1.75

(6) Shifter Fork (Reverse)
1983 .... E2ZZ-7231A 29.75

(7) Shift Lever (Reverse)
1983 .... D9BZ-7K003A 6.75

(8) Bearing Retainer
1983
$4\frac{1}{4}$″ long E0ZZ-7050A 48.75
$4\frac{13}{16}$″ long E0ZZ-7050B 48.75

(9) Oil Seal (Input Shaft)
1983 .... E0ZZ-7A283A 7.25

(10) Shim Kit
1983 .... E0ZZ-7051A 20.00

Part No. Price

(11) Seal (Bearing Retainer)
1983 .... E0ZZ-7A248A 2.50

(12) Bearing Assy. (Input Shaft)
1983 .... E0ZZ-7025A 14.25

(13) Input Shaft
1983 (Trans. ident.)
RAP-AB, AH,
AP E0ZZ-7017B 150.00
RAP-AG, AM,
AR E1ZZ-7017B 136.50

(14) Case Assy.
1983 .... E0ZZ-7005A 422.50

(15) Output Shaft
1983 .... E0ZZ-7061B 213.75

(16) Shim Kit (Front Bearing)
1983 .... E0ZZ-7L172A 23.25

(17) Bearing Assy. (Front)
1983 .... E0ZZ-7F431A 8.75

PARTS 19 STD. TRANS. (5 SPEED) WITH OVERDRIVE 19 PARTS

	Part No.	Price
(18) Idler Gear Shaft (Reverse)		
1983	E0ZZ-7140A	16.25
(19) Gear & Bushing (Reverse Idler)		
1983	E0ZZ-7141A	92.00
(20) Cluster Gear (Countershaft)		
1983	E0ZZ-7113B	202.25
(21) Bearing Assy. (Rear)		
1983	E0ZZ-7F431B	15.75
(22) Fifth Gear		
1983	E0ZZ-7144A	89.00
(23) Back-Up Switch		
1983	D3FZ-15520A	6.00
(24) Lever Stop		
1983	D9BZ-7K003A	6.75
(25) Plunger (5th Spd. Inhibitor)		
1983	E0ZZ-7K457A	58.75
(26) Housing Assy. (Extension)		
1983	E3ZZ-7A039A	143.25
(27) Synchronizer Assy. (3rd & 4th)		
1983	E0ZZ-7124B	135.00
(28) Third Gear		
1983	E2ZZ-7B340A	149.00
(29) Second Gear		
1983	E0ZZ-7102A	130.00
(30) Synchronizer Assy. (1st & 2nd)		
1983	E0ZZ-7061B	213.75
(31) First Gear		
1983	E0ZZ-7100A	79.25
(32) Bearing Assy. (Output Shaft)		
1983	E0ZZ-7025A	14.25
(33) Synchronizer Assy. (5th Speed)		
1983	E0ZZ-7124B	135.00
(34) Spacer		
1983	E0ZZ-7L049A	11.25
(35) Speedo. Gear (Drive)		
Order by year and model.		

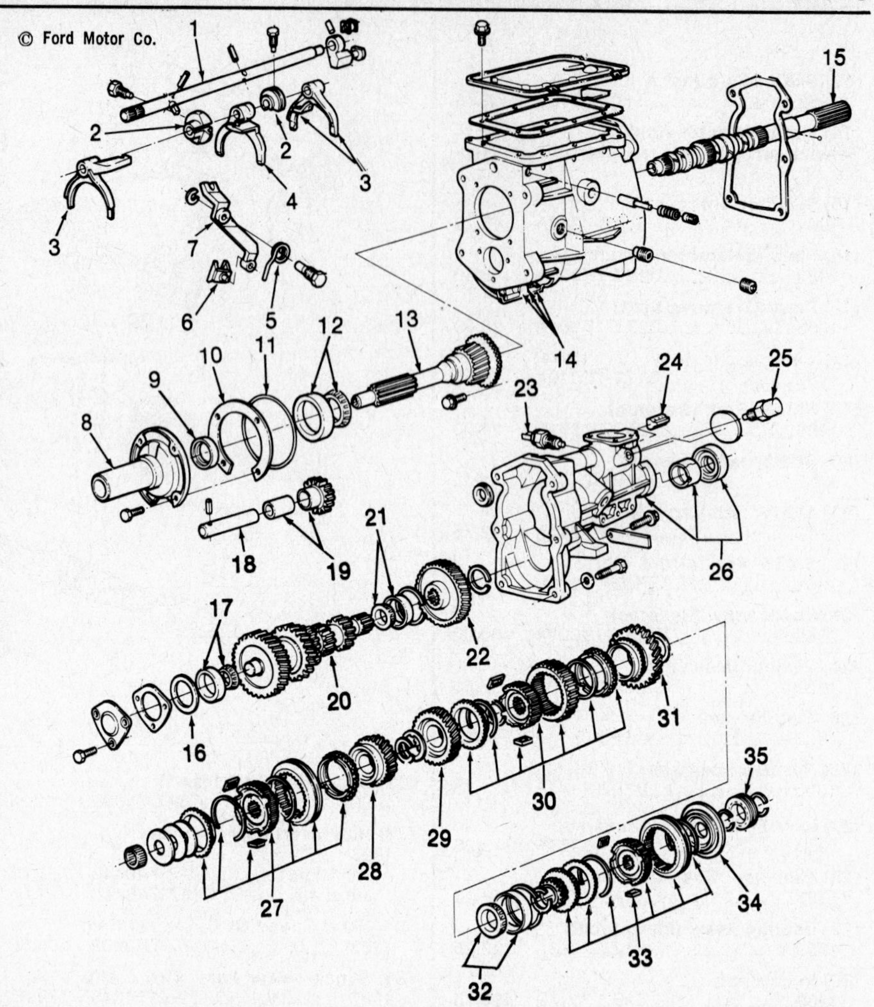

PARTS 19 STANDARD TRANS. (5 Speed) 19 PARTS

	Part No.	Price
WARNER (MODEL REP)		
Transmission Assy.		
Serviced in detail only.		
(1) Seal Assy. (Input Shaft)		
1983-87	C5TZ-7052A	5.75
(2) Bearing Assy. (Input Shaft)		
1983-87	E0ZZ-7025A	14.25
(3) Input Shaft		
Capri, Mustang		
1983-84-4 cyl.	E3ZZ-7017B	248.25
V-8 eng.	E3ZZ-7017A	265.00
1985-87-4 cyl.	E5ZZ-7017C	207.00
V-8 eng.	E5ZZ-7017B	207.00
Cougar, Thunderbird		
1983-84	E3ZZ-7017B	248.25
1985-87	E5ZZ-7017A	192.50
(4) Reverse Idler Gear (w/Bushing)		
1983-87	E3ZZ-7141A	86.75
(5) Reverse Idler Gear Shaft		
1983-87	E3ZZ-7140A	20.50
(6) Extension Housing		
1983-84	E3ZZ-7A039B	169.00
1985-87	E5ZZ-7A039A	224.50
(7) Bushing (Extension)		
1983-87	B3TZ-7A034B	2.25
(8) Seal Assy. (Extension)		
1983-87	D9BZ-7052A	11.25
(9) Lever Assy. (Reverse)		
1983-87	E3ZZ-7K002A	26.00
(10) Fork (Reverse)		
1983-87	E3ZZ-7231A	138.75
(11) Spring (Lever Return)		
1983-87	E3ZZ-7K205A	5.75
(12) Rail Assy. (Reverse)		
1983-84	E3ZZ-7240A	51.50
1985-87	E5ZZ-7240A	51.50
(13) Fork (5th Gear)		
1983-87	E3ZZ-7230D	25.25
(14) Bearing Assy. (Front)		
1983-84	E3ZZ-7F431A	11.50
1985-87	E5ZZ-7F431A	29.25
(15) Cluster Gear		
Capri, Mustang		
1983-84-4 cyl.	E3ZZ-7113C	466.00
V-8 eng.	E3ZZ-7113A	466.00
1985-87-4 cyl.	E5ZZ-7113A	402.25
V-8 eng.	E5ZZ-7113C	425.50
Cougar, Thunderbird		
1983-84	E3ZZ-7113C	466.00
1985-87	E5ZZ-7113B	396.50
(16) Bearing Assy. (Rear)		
1983-84	E3ZZ-7F431A	11.50
1985-87	E5ZZ-7F431A	29.25
(17) Fifth Speed Gear (Drive)		
Capri, Mustang		
1983-4 cyl.	E3ZZ-7144B	158.00
V-8 eng.	E3ZZ-7144A	192.25
1984	E3ZZ-7144B	158.00
1985-87-4 cyl.	E5ZZ-7144A	192.25
V-8 eng.	E5ZZ-7144B	192.25
Cougar, Thunderbird		
1983-84	E3ZZ-7144B	158.00
1985-87	E5ZZ-7144B	192.25
(18) Blocking Ring		
(1st & 2nd spd.)		
1983-84	D4ZZ-7107A	24.00
1985-87	E5ZZ-7107A	17.25
(3rd & 4th spd.)		
1983-84	E3ZZ-7107B	18.50
1985-87	E5ZZ-7107C	17.25
(5th spd.)		
1983-87	D4ZZ-7107B	18.50
(19) Synchronizer Assy. (5th Speed)		
1983-84	E3ZZ-7124B	135.00
1985-87	E5ZZ-7124B	125.75
(20) Thrust Bearing Race (Front)		
1983-84	E3ZZ-7E487A	6.00

	Part No.	Price
(21) Thrust Bearing (Rear)		
1983-87	D4ZZ-3571A	6.50
(22) Thrust Bearing Race (Rear)		
1983-84	E3ZZ-7D236A	3.25
(23) Funnel (Countershaft)		
1983-84	E3ZZ-7L276A	2.00
1985-87	E5ZZ-7L276A	2.00
(24) Pilot Bearing (Input Shaft)		
1983-87	C3AZ-7118A	.50
(25) Thrust Bearing Assy. (Input Shaft)		
1983-87	E3ZZ-7D234A	4.75
Thrust Bearing Race (Input Shaft)		
1983-87	E3ZZ-7D235A	3.25
(27) Synchronizer Assy. (3rd & 4th)		
1983-84	E4ZZ-7124A	186.50
1985-87	E5ZZ-7124A	173.50
(28) Third Speed Gear		
Capri, Mustang		
1983-84-4 cyl.	E3ZZ-7B340D	149.00
V-8 eng.	E3ZZ-7B340B	149.00
1985-87	E5ZZ-7B340A	138.50
Cougar, Thunderbird		
1983-84	E3ZZ-7B340D	149.00
1985-87	E5ZZ-7B340B	138.50
(29) Second Speed Gear		
Capri, Mustang		
1983-84-4 cyl.	E3ZZ-7102B	156.00
V-8 eng.	E3ZZ-7102B	156.00
1985-87-4 cyl.	E5ZZ-7102A	91.25
V-8 eng.	E5ZZ-7102B	101.00
Cougar, Thunderbird		
1983-84	E3ZZ-7102B	156.00
1985-87	E5ZZ-7102A	91.25
(30) Output Shaft Assy.		
1983-84	E3ZZ-7061A	294.25
1985-87	E5ZZ-7061A	291.75
Includes 1st & 2nd synchronizer assembly.		
(31) First Speed Gear		
Capri, Mustang		
1983-84	E3ZZ-7100A	135.50
1985-87-4 cyl.	E5ZZ-7100B	96.75
V-8 eng.	E5ZZ-7100A	89.50
Cougar, Thunderbird		
1983-84	E3ZZ-7100A	135.50
1985-87	E5SZ-7100A	96.75
(32) Bearing Assy. (Rear)		
1983-87	C3TZ-1216B	12.75
(33) Cup (Rear Bearing)		
1983-87	C6TZ-7169A	6.25

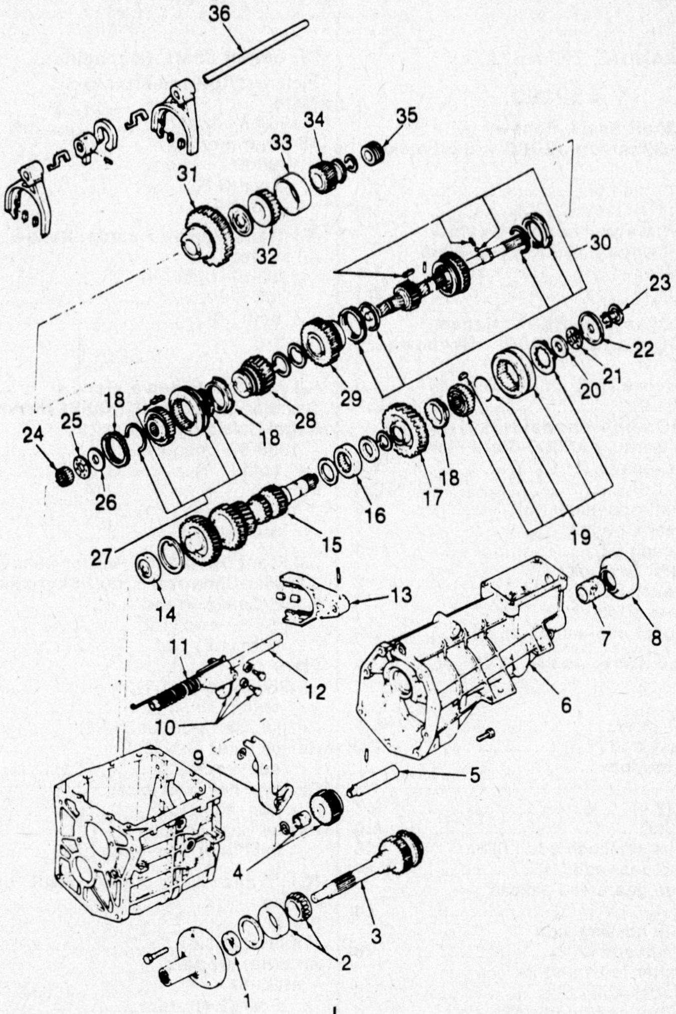

(34) Fifth Speed Gear (Driven)		
Capri, Mustang		
1983-4 cyl.	E3ZZ-7K316B	89.25
V-8 eng.	E3ZZ-7K316A	112.75
1984	E3ZZ-7K316B	89.25
1985-87-4 cyl.	E3ZZ-7K316B	89.25
V-8 eng.	E5ZZ-7K316A	58.00
Cougar, Thunderbird		
1983-84	E3ZZ-7K316B	89.25
1985-87	E5ZZ-7K316A	58.00

(35) Speedo. Drive Gear
Order by year and model.

(36) Shaft (Gear Shift)		
Capri, Mustang		
1983-84	E3ZZ-7358A	68.00
1985-87-4 cyl.	E5ZZ-7358A	63.25
V-8 eng.	E5ZZ-7358B	63.25
Cougar, Thunderbird		
1983-84	E3ZZ-7358A	68.00
1985-87	E5ZZ-7358A	63.25

(Factory Time) Chilton Time

MANUAL TRANS/AXLES

4 SPEED

(G) Axle Shaft Seals, Renew
Cavalier-Cimarron-J2000 Skyhawk-Firenza
1983-87-one (.6) 1.0
both (1.1) 1.9
Citation-Omega-Phoenix-Skylark Celebrity-Century-A6000-Ciera-Fiero
1983-87-one (1.1) 1.4
both (1.5) 2.1

(G) Front Drive Axle, R&R or Renew
Cavalier-Cimarron-J2000 Skyhawk-Firenza
1983-87-one (1.2) 1.6
both (1.9) 2.7
Citation-Omega-Phoenix-Skylark Celebrity-Century-A6000-Ciera-Fiero
1983-87-one (1.1) 1.5
both (1.6) 2.4
Renew shaft add-each (.3) 4
Renew outer C/V joint add-each (.3) 4
Renew outer D/O joint add-each (.3) 4
Renew inner or outer joint boot add-each (.2) 2

(G) Trans/Axle Assy., R&R or Renew
Fiero
1984-87 (3.6) 5.1
Renew assy add (1.8) 2.0
All other models
1983-87
Four (2.4) 3.7
V-6 (2.6) 4.0
Check shim selection add (.6) 6
Renew ring gear add (.4) 4
Renew side gears and pinions add (.4) 4
Renew axle housing side bearings add (.8) 8
Renew shifter forks and/or interlocks add (.5) 5
Renew shifter shaft add (.4) 4
Renew input shaft seal add (.3) 3
Renew shaft seal bearing and retainer 'O' ring add (.4) 4
Renew speedo drive gear add (.4) 4

(P) Trans/Axle Assy., R&R and Recondition
Includes: Disassemble, clean and inspect all parts. Renew all trans and differential parts as required. Install all new gaskets and seals.
Fiero
1984-87 (6.6) 9.4
All other models
1983-87
Four (5.4) 7.5
V-6 (5.6) 7.8

(G) Axle Case Half, Renew
Includes: R&R trans/axle assy.
Fiero
1984-87 (4.7) 6.7
All other models
1983-87
Four (3.5) 4.9
V-6 (3.7) 5.2

(G) Input Shaft, Recondition
Includes: R&R trans/axle assy.
Fiero
1984-87 (4.7) 6.7
All other models
1983-87
Four (3.5) 4.9
V-6 (3.7) 5.2

(Factory Time) Chilton Time

(G) Output Shaft, Recondition
Includes: R&R trans/axle assy.
Fiero
1984-87 (4.9) 7.0
All other models
1983-87
Four (3.7) 5.2
V-6 (3.9) 5.5

(G) Transmission Mounts, Renew
All models
1983-87-right (.4) 6
left (.4) 6
both (.6) 9

5 SPEED

(G) Axle Shaft Seals, Renew
Cavalier-Cimarron-J2000-Skyhawk-Firenza Regal-Calais-Grand Am
1983-87-one (.6) 1.0
both (1.1) 1.9
Fiero
1986-87-one (1.1) 1.4
both (1.5) 2.1

(G) Front Drive Axle, R&R or Renew
Cavalier-Cimarron-J2000-Skyhawk-Firenza Regal-Calais-Grand Am
1983-87-one (1.2) 1.6
both (1.9) 2.7
Fiero
1986-87-one (1.1) 1.4
both (1.6) 2.2
Renew shaft add-each (.3) 4
Renew outer C/V joint add-each (.3) 4
Renew outer D/O joint add-each (.3) 4
Renew inner or outer joint boot add-each (.2) 2

(G) Trans/Axle Assy., R&R or Renew
Fiero
1986-87 (3.6) 5.1
All other models
1983-87
Four (2.4) 3.7
V-6 (2.6) 4.0
Check shim selection add (.6) 6
Renew ring gear add (1.9) 1.9
Renew side gears and pinions, add (2.0) 2.0
Renew axle housing side bearings add (.8) 8
Renew shifter forks and/or interlocks add (.5) 5
Renew shifter shaft add (.4) 4
Renew shaft seal bearing and retainer 'O' ring add (.4) 4
Renew speedo drive gear add (.4) 4

(P) Trans/Axle Assy., R&R and Recondition
Includes: Disassemble, clean and inspect all parts. Renew all trans and differential parts as required. Install all new seals and gaskets.
Fiero
1986-87 (7.1) 10.3
All other models
1983-87
Four (5.9) 8.2
V-6 (6.1) 8.5

(G) Axle Case Half, Renew
Includes: R&R trans/axle assy.
Fiero
1986-87 (5.3) 7.6
All other models
1983-87
Four (4.1) 5.7
V-6 (4.3) 6.0

(Factory Time) Chilton Time

(G) Input Shaft, Recondition
Includes: R&R trans/axle assy.
Fiero
1986-87 (5.2) 7.5
All other models
1983-87
Four (4.0) 5.6
V-6 (4.2) 5.9

(G) Output Shaft, Recondition
Includes: R&R trans/axle assy.
Fiero
1986-87 (5.2) 7.5
All other models
1983-87
Four (4.0) 5.6
V-6 (4.2) 5.9

(G) Trans/Axle Rear Cover, R&R or Renew
1983-87 (.5) 8
Recond 5th gear synco assy add (.3) 4
Renew counter shaft add (.3) 4
Renew input shaft add (.2) 3
Renew 5th gear shift fork add (.2) 3
Recond 5th gear assy add (.4) 5

(G) Transmission Mounts, Renew
All models
1983-87-right (.4) 6
left (.4) 6
both (.6) 9

5 SPEED MM-5

CHEVROLET NOVA

1985-87

(G) Drive Axle Assy., R&R or Renew
1985-87-one (.9) 1.2
both (1.2) 1.7
Renew C.V. Joint Seal (Boot), add-each side (.5) 5
Renew C.V. (Tri-Pot) Joint, add-each (.3) 3

(G) Axle Shaft Seals, Renew
1985-87-one (.6) 8
both (.7) 1.0

(G) Trans/Axle Rear Cover, R&R or Renew
1985-87 (.9) 1.3
Recond 5th syncro add (.3) 4
Renew 5th gear counter shaft add (.3) 4
Renew 5th gear input shaft add (.3) 4
Renew 5th gear shift fork add (.3) 3
Recond 5th gear assy add (.3) 4

(P) Trans/Axle Assy., R&R or Renew
1985-87 (1.8) 2.5
Renew ring gear add (1.4) 1.4
Renew side gears and pinions add (1.6) 1.6
Renew axle housing side bearings add (1.8) 1.8
Renew right side axle case half add (1.0) 1.0
Renew left side axle case half add (1.6) 1.6
Renew speedo drive gear add (1.4) 1.4
Renew input shaft seal add (.3) 3
Recond output shaft add (1.4) 1.4
Recond complete add (2.3) 3.0

LABOR 19 TRANSAXLE 19 LABOR

	(Factory Time)	Chilton Time
(G) Speedometer Driven Gear and/or Seal, Renew		
1985-87	(.3)	.5
(G) Transmission Shift Cover and/or Gasket, Renew		
1985-87	(1.8)	2.4
Recond shaft add	(.3)	.4
(G) Transmission Mount, Renew		
1985-87-left	(.6)	.8

PARTS 19 TRANSAXLE (4 SPEED) 19 PARTS

Pontiac Models: Phoenix, 2000, 6000, Fiero

Oldsmobile Models: Omega, Firenza, Ciera

Buick Models: Skylark, Skyhawk, Century

Chevrolet Models: Citation, Cavalier, Celebrity

	Part No.	Price
(1) Trans/Axle Case Assy.		
1983-84	14071749	156.00
1985-87	14101340	156.00
(2) Seal Assy. (Axle Shaft)		
1983-87	8631156	3.50
(3) Bearing Assy. (Case)		
1983-84	9437771	16.50
1985-87	14091909	N.L.
(4) 4th Speed Gear (Input)		
M-19-Trans.		
1983-87-exc.		
Calif.	14066955	95.75
1987-Calif.	14092852	95.00
MX-6-Trans.		
1985-87	14092852	95.00
(5) Blocking Ring		
1983	464835	10.75
1984-87	14079923	9.00
(6) Synchronizer Assy. (3rd & 4th)		
1983	14062631	97.50
1984-85	14084173	112.00
1986-87	14085537	127.00
(7) 3rd Speed Gear (Input)		
M-19-Trans.		
1983-87-exc.		
Calif.	14066960	85.00
1987-Calif.	14092851	95.00
MX-6-Trans.		
1985-87	14092851	95.00
(8) Input Cluster Gear		
1983-84	14020899	220.00
M-19-Trans.		
1985-87-exc.		
Calif.	14085557	145.00
Calif.	14085556	155.00
MX-6-Trans.		
1985-87	14085556	155.00
(9) Bearing Assy. (Input Gear)		
1983-87	9415132	N.L.
(10) Seal Assy. (Input Gear)		
1983-87	476793	1.50
(11) Retainer Assy. (Input Gear)		
1983-87	14020834	36.00
(12) Bearing Assy. (Clutch Release)		
1983-87	908403	47.25
(13) Reverse Idler Shaft		
1983-87	476724	43.25
(14) Reverse Idler Gear		
1983	14009179	89.50
1984-87	14079925	65.00
(15) Spring Seat (Reverse Inhibitor)		
1983-87	464866	2.75

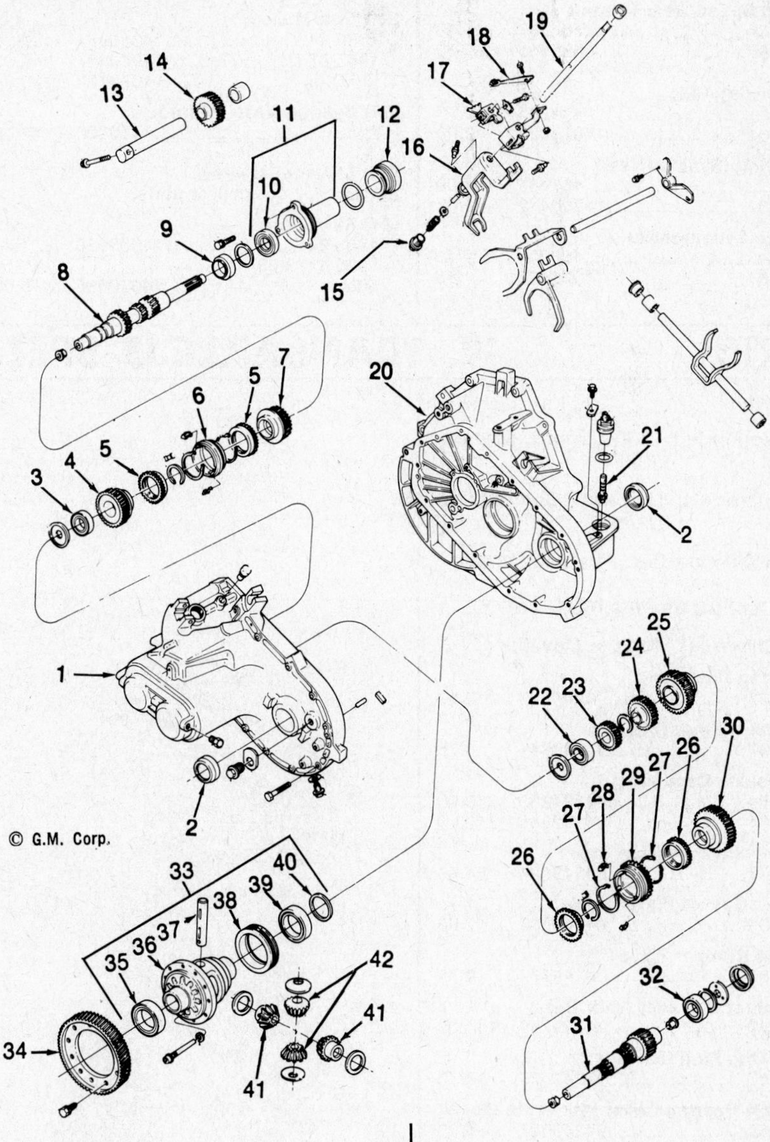

	Part No.	Price
(16) Lever (Reverse Shaft)		
1983-87	14008271	59.50
(17) Lever Assy. (Detent)		
1983-85	14079907	23.00
1986-87	14101494	19.50
(18) Spring (Detent)		
1983-87	465436	1.00
(19) Shift Shaft		
1983-87	463091	23.00
(20) Housing Assy. (Clutch & Diff.)		
1983-84	14071748	173.00
1985	14101397	173.00
1986-87	12324900	165.00

	Part No.	Price
(21) Speedo. Gear (Driven)		
1983-87	464848	1.25
(22) Bearing Assy. (Case)		
1983-84	9437771	16.50
1985-87	14091909	N.L.
(23) 4th Speed Gear (Output)		
M-19-Trans.		
1983-87-exc.		
Calif.	14066956	40.50
1987-Calif.	14073783	144.00
MX-6-Trans.		
1985-87	14073787	N.L.

PARTS 19 TRANSAXLE (4 SPEED) 19 PARTS

	Part No.	Price
(24) 3rd Speed Gear (Output)		
M-19-Trans.		
1983-87-exc. Calif.	14066961	58.75
1987-Calif.	14073783	144.00
MX-6-Trans.		
1985-87	14073783	144.00
(25) 2nd Speed Gear (Output)		
1983-84	464837	101.00
1985-87	14085555	80.00
(26) Blocking Ring		
1983	464835	10.75
1984-87	14079923	9.00
(27) Spring (Synchronizer)		
1983	465431	1.00
1984-87	14066412	1.25
(28) Key (Synchronizer)		
1983	468334	N.L.
1984-87	14066424	.50
(29) Synchronizer Assy. (1st & 2nd)		
1983	14062629	103.00
1984-85	14084172	156.00
1986-87	14085536	146.00
(30) 1st Speed Gear (Output)		
1983-87 (M-19)	14085553	88.00
(MX-6)	14085554	88.00
(31) Output Gear		
1983-84	14066957	189.00
1985-87 (M-19)	14020884	244.00
(MX-6)	14073781	220.00
(32) Bearing Assy. (Output)		
1983-87	7450700	12.00
(33) Differential Assy.		
Serviced by component parts.		
(34) Ring Gear		
1983-84	14066958	N.L.
1985-87-3.65 ratio	14020885	176.00
1986-87-3.32 ratio	14078563	119.25
(35) Bearing Assy.		
1983-87	9437733	N.L.
(36) Case Assy. (wo/Gear)		
1983-87	14047636	70.50
(37) Pinion Shaft		
1983-87	463062	7.00
(38) Speedo. Gear (Drive)		
1983-87	14047637	7.75
(39) Bearing Assy.		
1983-87	9437733	N.L.
(40) Shim		
Shims must be ordered by thickness.		
(41) Side Gear		
1983-84	14040530	24.50
1985-87	14076988	22.25
(42) Pinion Gear		
1983-87	463060	16.00

PARTS 19 TRANSAXLE (5 SPEED) 19 PARTS

Pontiac Models: 2000, Fiero, Grand AM

Buick Models: Skyhawk, Somerset Regal

Oldsmobile Models: Firenza, Omega

Cadillac Models: Cimarron

Chevrolet Models: Cavalier

	Part No.	Price
(1) Bearing Retainer		
1983-87	94249526	12.50
(2) Thrust Washer (5th Gear)		
1983-87	94249744	4.75
(3) Transaxle Case Assy.		
1983-84	94121233	210.00
1985-87	94152585	210.00
(4) Transaxle Extension Cover		
1983-87	94249527	84.00
(5) Cover Gasket (Extension)		
1983-87	94249530	2.00
(6) Insert Stopper Plate		
1983-87	94249752	2.75
(7) Synchronizer Assy. (5th Gear)		
1983-87	94249749	141.00
(8) Blocking Ring (5th Gear)		
1983-87	94249580	26.50
(9) Needle Bearing Collar (4th & 5th Gear)		
1983-87	94249587	6.75
(10) Needle Bearing (3rd, 4th, 5th Gear)		
1983-87	94249586	14.25
(11) 5th Speed Gear (Output)		
1983-87	94139578	84.00
(12) 5th Speed Gear (Input)		
1983-87	94249612	90.25
(13) Shim		
1983-87	94249660	3.00
Smallest size listed larger sizes available.		
(14) Rear Bearing (Output)		
1983-87	94249643	14.75
(15) 3rd & 4th Speed Gear (Output)		
1983-87-exc. 2.0L	94249639	95.25
2.0L	94249640	116.00

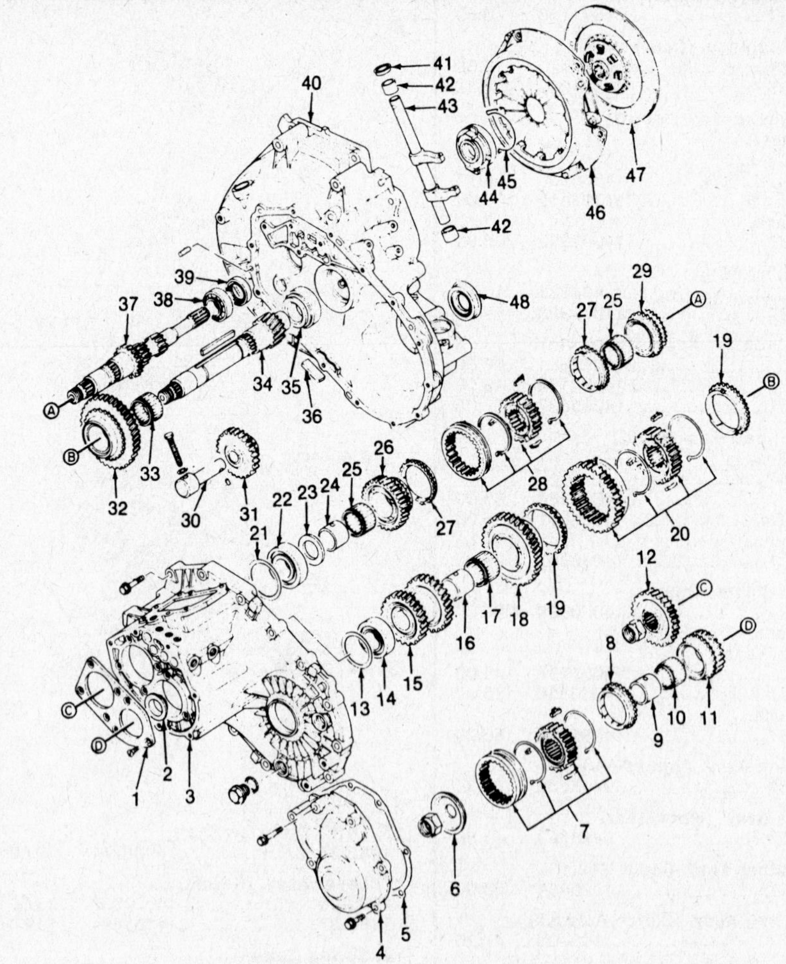

	Part No.	Price
(16) Needle Bearing Collar (2nd Gear)		
1983-87	94249638	11.00
(17) Bearing (1st & 2nd Gear)		
1983-87	94249637	10.25
(18) 2nd Speed Gear (Output)		
1983-84	94249633	103.00
1985-87	94152550	82.25
Grand AM, Omega	94152551	84.00

PARTS 19 TRANSAXLE (5 SPEED) 19 PARTS

	Part No.	Price
(19) Blocking Ring (1st & 2nd Gear)		
1983-84	94249631	28.50
1985-87	94151510	24.75
(20) Synchronizer Assy. (1st & 2nd Gear)		
1983-84	94249624	144.00
1985-87	94152554	116.00
(21) Shim		
1983-87	94115571	3.50
Smallest size listed larger sizes available.		
(22) Rear Bearing (Input)		
1983-87	94249610	15.50
(23) Thrust Washer (4th Gear)		
1983-87	94249588	4.25
(24) Needle Bearing Collar (4th Gear)		
1983-87	94249587	6.75
(25) Needle Bearing (3rd & 4th Gear)		
1983-87	94249586	14.25
(26) 4th Speed Gear (Input)		
(exc. Grand AM, Omega)		
1983-87-1.8L	94139575	84.00
2.0L	94139576	84.00
(Grand AM, Omega)		
1985-87	94139575	84.00
(27) Blocking Ring (3rd & 4th Gear)		
1983-87	94249580	26.50
(28) Synchronizer Assy. (3rd & 4th Gear)		
1983-87	94249573	141.00
(29) 3rd Speed Gear (Input)		
1983-1.8L	94139573	77.75
1984-87	94149668	62.25
1983-87-2.0L	94139574	77.75
(30) Reverse Idler Shaft		
1983	94100543	11.75
1984-87	94153350	11.75
(31) Reverse Idler Gear		
1983	94249753	84.00
1984-87	94160949	71.50
(32) 1st Speed Gear (Output)		
(exc. Grand AM, Omega)		
1983-84	94249620	96.75
1985-87	94152547	96.75
(Grand Am, Omega)		
1985-87	94152548	96.75
(33) Bearing (1st & 2nd Gear)		
1983-87	94249637	10.25
(34) Output Shaft		
3.45 Ratio		
1983-84	94123715	162.00
1985-87	94146821	105.00
3.83 Ratio		
1983-84	94123714	113.00
1985-87	94146819	105.00
3.35 Ratio		
1985-87	94146822	105.00
(35) Front Bearing (Output Shaft)		
1983-87	94249619	19.50
(36) Magnet (Chip Collector)		
1983-87	465474	1.00
(37) Input Shaft		
(exc. Grand AM, Omega)		
1983-84	94123712	171.00
1985-87	94160942	171.00
(Grand AM, Omega)		
1985-87	94160944	171.00
(38) Front Bearing (Input Shaft)		
1983-87	94249564	27.50
(39) Oil Seal (Input Shaft)		
1983-87	94249521	4.50
(40) Housing Assy. (Clutch Diff.)		
1.8L		
1983-84	94248718	226.00
1985-87	94152591	226.00
2.0L		
1983-84	94241733	226.00
2.5L		
1985-87	94152589	226.00
(41) Seal (Clutch Shaft)		
1983-87	474679	2.00
(42) Bushing (Clutch Shaft)		
1983-87	474665	2.75
(43) Shaft (Clutch Fork)		
1983-87	94251465	28.25
(44) Bearing (Clutch Release)		
1983-87	94133417	43.00
(45) Spring (Release Bearing)		
1983-87	94251599	1.50
(46) Pressure Plate Assy.		
1983-84-1.8L	94253237	117.00
1985-87	94148683	109.00
1983-84-2.0L	94253236	139.00
1985-87-2.5L	14080212	147.00
1985-87-2.8L	14091968	113.00
(47) Clutch Driven Plate		
1.8L & 2.0L		
1983-84	94253238	90.75
1985	94148663	72.25
2.5L		
1985-87	14087241	89.25
2.8L		
1985-87	14087220	89.25

PARTS 19 TRANSAXLE DIFFERENTIAL (5 SPEED) 19 PARTS

	Part No.	Price
(1) Shim		
1983-87	94249544	3.25
Smallest size listed, larger sizes available.		
(2) Bearing Assy. (Diff.)		
1983-87	94249542	30.25
(3) Ring Gear		
1983-87		
3.45 ratio	94145127	109.25
3.83 ratio	94249540	88.25
(4) Case Assy.		
1983-87	94244546	65.00
(5) Speedo. Drive Gear		
1983-87	94408341	4.00
(6) Thrust Washer (Side Gear)		
1983-87	14040531	1.00
(7) Side Gear		
1983-84	14040530	24.50
1985-87	14076988	22.25
(8) Pinion Shaft		
1983-87	463062	7.00

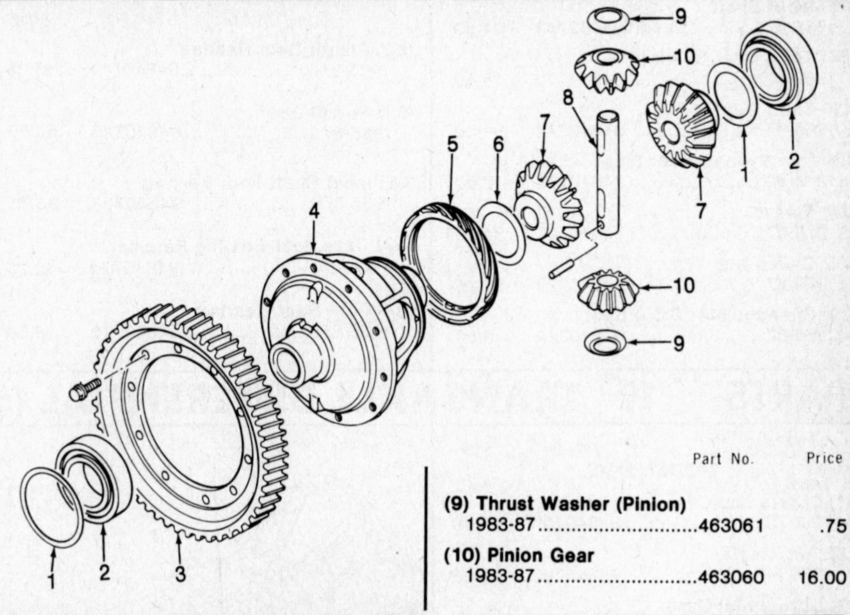

	Part No.	Price
(9) Thrust Washer (Pinion)		
1983-87	463061	.75
(10) Pinion Gear		
1983-87	463060	16.00

PARTS 19 TRANSAXLE (5 SPEED) 19 PARTS

	Part No.	Price
MODEL MM5		
(1) Transmission Case		
1985-87	94840720	196.00
(2) Case Cover		
1985-87	94840725	51.25
(3) Clutch Housing		
1985-87	94840714	232.00
(4) Output Shaft Cover		
1985-87	94840718	1.50
(5) Output Shaft Front Bearing		
1985-87	94840704	38.75

PARTS 19 TRANSAXLE (5 SPEED) 19 PARTS

	Part No.	Price
(6) Output Shaft		
1985-87	94840789	67.25
(7) Bearing Lock Plate		
1985-87	94840716	.75
(8) First Gear Bearing		
1985-87	94840708	22.25
(9) Thrust Washer		
1985-87	94840736	9.00
(10) First Gear		
1985-87	94840742	62.50
(11) Synchronizer Ring		
1985-87	94840734	10.50
(12) Reverse Gear		
1985-87	94840731	53.50
(13) Clutch Hub		
1985-87	9480732	N.L.
(14) Second Gear Bearing Spacer		
1985-87	94840738	1.25
(15) Second Gear Bearing		
1985-87	94840709	20.00
(16) Second Gear		
1985-87	94840743	64.00
(17) Output Gear Spacer		
1985-87	94840737	9.00
(18) Fourth Gear		
1985-87	9480747	N.L.
(19) Output Shaft Rear Bearing		
1985-87	94840705	44.00
(20) Fifth Gear		
1985-87	94840749	37.75
(21) Case Oil Receiver		
1985-87	94840717	11.00
(22) Input Shaft Front Bearing		
1985-87	94840702	31.50
(23) Input Shaft		
1985-87	94840741	94.50
(24) Third Gear Bearing		
1985-87	94840710	18.50
(25) Third Gear		
1985-87	94840744	51.50
(26) Hub Synchronizer Ring		
1985-87	94840729	10.50
(27) Sleeve		
1985-87	94840727	34.75
(28) Clutch Hub		
1985-87	94840726	27.25
(29) Speedometer Drive Gear		
1985-87	94840822	3.50

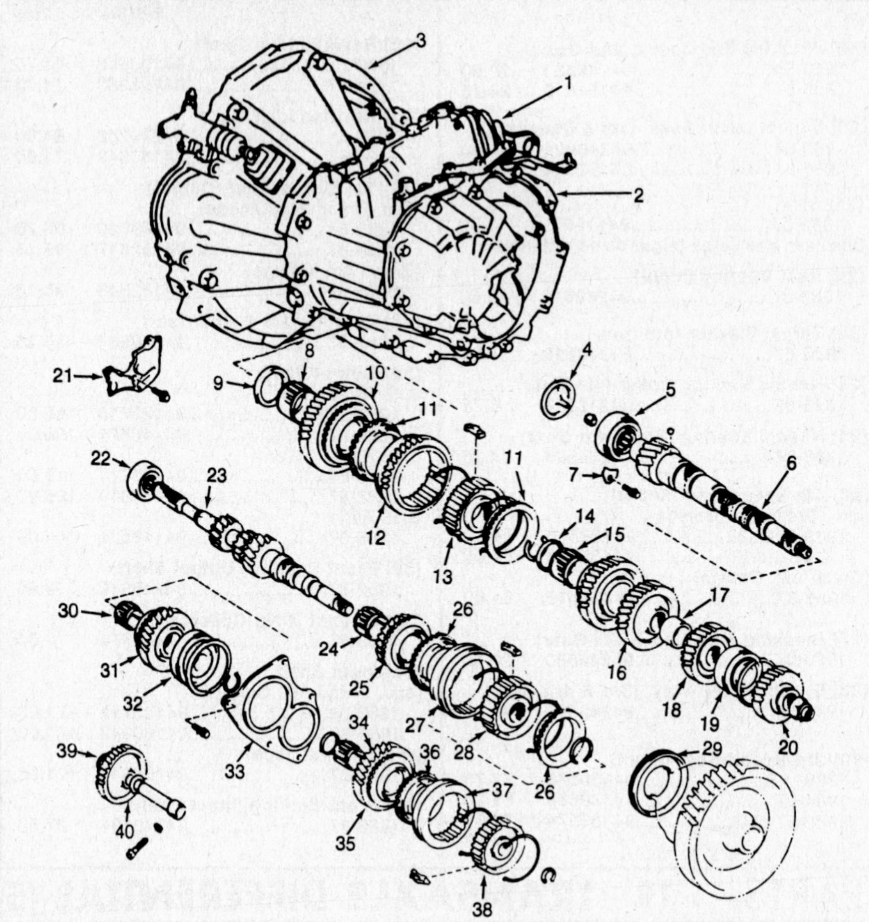

	Part No.	Price
(30) Fourth Gear Bearing		
1985-87	94840711	15.25
(31) Fourth Gear		
1985-87	94840746	53.50
(32) Input Shaft Rear Bearing		
1985-87	94840703	35.75
(33) Case Rear Bearing Retainer		
1985-87	94840723	12.25
(34) Fifth Gear Bearing		
1985-87	94840712	16.50

	Part No.	Price
(35) Fifth Gear		
1985-87	94840748	72.50
(36) Synchronizer Ring		
1985-87	94840753	8.50
(37) Clutch Hub Sleeve		
1985-87	94840751	32.50
(38) Clutch Hub		
1985-87	94840750	25.25
(39) Reverse Idler Gear		
1985-87	94843000	31.50
(40) Reverse Idler Gear Shaft		
1985-87	94843201	11.75

PARTS 19 TRANSAXLE DIFFERENTIAL (5 SPEED) 19 PARTS

	Part No.	Price
MODEL MM5		
(1) Differential Case Rear Bearing		
1985-87	94840707	27.50
(2) Ring Gear		
1985-87	94840790	82.25
(3) Differential Case		
1985-87	94840791	159.00
(4) Side Gear		
1985-87	94840792	23.75
(5) Gear Shaft		
1985-87	94840794	9.50
(6) Washer		
1985-87	94840796	1.75

Smallest size listed other sizes available.

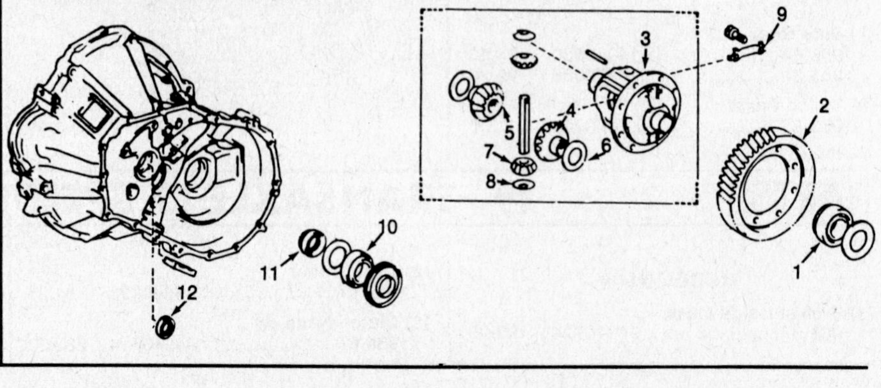

PARTS 19 TRANSAXLE DIFFERENTIAL (5 SPEED) 19 PARTS

	Part No.	Price
(7) Pinion Gear		
1985-87	94843822	17.50
(8) Thrust Washer		
1985-87	94840795	1.25
(9) Ring Gear Bolt Lock Plate		
1985-87	94840802	.75
(10) Differential Case Front Bearing		
1985-87	94840706	16.00
(11) Drive Shaft Seal		
1985-87	94840624	4.25
(12) Input Shaft Seal		
1985-87	94840623	2.00

LABOR 19 STANDARD TRANSMISSION 19 LABOR

(Factory Time) — Chilton Time

GENERAL MOTORS CORP

4 SPEED WARNER (M24-M26)

(G) Transmission Assy., Remove & Reinstall

Does not include transfer of any attaching parts.

Camaro-Firebird

1983-87 (1.4)	2.0
Renew main drive brg, retainer or gskt add (.3)	.3
Renew speedo drive gear add (.6)	.6

(G) Transmission Assy., R&R and Recondition

Includes: Complete disassembly, clean and inspect or renew all parts. Install all new gaskets and seals.

Camaro-Firebird

1983-87 (3.7)	5.5

(G) Transmission, Recondition (Off Car)

All models (2.3)	3.5

(G) Transmission Shift Cover, Renew or Recondition

Does not require R&R of trans.

All models (.6)	1.0
Recond cover add (.4)	.4

(G) Transmission Rear Oil Seal, Renew

All models (.6)	.8
Renew bushing add (.1)	.1

(G) Speedometer Driven Gear, Renew

All models (.3)	.5

4 SPEED (70MM)

(G) Transmission Assy., Remove & Reinstall

Does not include transfer of any attaching parts.

Chevette-T1000

1983-87 (1.8)	2.3
Renew speedo drive gear add (.3)	.4

(G) Transmission Assy., R&R and Recondition

Includes: Complete disassembly, clean and inspect or renew all parts. Install all new gaskets and seals.

Chevette-T1000

1983-87 (3.4)	5.3

(G) Transmission, Recondition (Off Car)

All models (1.6)	3.0

(G) Transmission Rear Oil Seal, Renew

All models (.4)	.7
Renew bushing add (.1)	.1

(G) Transmission Shift Cover and/or Gasket, Renew

All models (.5)	.9

(G) Speedometer Driven Gear, Renew

All models (.3)	.5

4 SPEED DOUG NASH (83MM)

(G) Transmission Assy., Remove & Reinstall

Does not include transfer of any attaching parts.

Corvette

1984-87 (2.2)	3.2
Renew main drive brg, retainer and/or gskt add (.3)	.3
Renew speedo drive gear add (1.6)	1.6

(G) Transmission Assy., R&R and Recondition

Includes: Complete disassembly of the transmission only. Clean and inspect or renew all parts. Install all new gaskets and seals.

Corvette

1984-87 (4.5)	6.5

(G) Transmission and Overdrive, Recondition

Includes: R&R complete unit, disassemble trans and overdrive units completely. Clean and inspect all parts. Install all new gaskets and seals.

Corvette

1984-87 (7.0)	9.5

(G) Overdrive Pan and/or Gasket, Renew

Corvette

1984-87 (.5)	.7

(G) Overdrive Valve Body, R&R or Renew

Corvette

1984-87 (.6)	1.0
Recond valve body add (.4)	.4
Renew O/Drive solenoid add (.1)	.1
Renew O/Drive switch add (.1)	.1

(G) Overdrive Unit, R&R or Renew

Includes: R&R trans and overdrive unit. Separate units when removed from vehicle.

Corvette

1984-87 (2.5)	3.5
Renew assy add (.2)	.2
Renew adapter and/or seal add (.5)	.5
Recond piston and accumulator add (.6)	.6
Recond planetary carrier gear set add (1.0)	1.0
Recond direct and O/Drive clutch add (1.2)	1.2
Renew output shaft add (1.5)	1.5
Renew speedo drive gear add (1.2)	1.2
Recond oil pump add (1.5)	1.5
Recond complete add (2.3)	3.0

(G) Transmission and Overdrive, Recondition (Off Car)

All models (4.8)	6.9

(G) Transmission Shift Cover and/or Gasket, Renew

All models (1.0)	1.5
Recond cover add (.6)	.6

(G) Speedometer Driven Gear, Renew

All models (.3)	.5

5 SPEED ISUZU (M75)

(G) Transmission Assy., Remove & Reinstall

Does not include transfer of any attaching parts.

Chevette

1983-87 (1.8)	2.6
Renew main drive brg, retainer and/or gskt add (.3)	.3
Renew speedo drive gear add (.3)	.3

(G) Transmission Assy., R&R and Recondition

Includes: Complete disassembly, clean and inspect or renew all parts. Install all new gaskets and seals.

Chevette

1983-87 (3.5)	5.1

(G) Transmission, Recondition (Off Car)

All models (1.7)	2.5

(G) Transmission Shift Cover and/or Gasket, Renew

All models (.5)	.9
Recond cover add (.4)	.4

(G) Transmission Rear Oil Seal, Renew

All models (.4)	.7
Renew bushing add (.1)	.1

(G) Speedometer Driven Gear, Renew

All models (.3)	.5

5 SPEED WARNER (77MM)

MODELS MB4 - MK4 - MK5 - MK6 - ML3 - ML8 - MB1 - M39

(G) Transmission Assy., Remove & Reinstall

Does not include transfer of any attaching parts.

Chevette-T1000

1983 (1.6)	2.3

Camaro-Firebird

1983-87 (1.8)	2.5
Renew main drive brg, retainer and/or gskt add (.3)	.3
Renew speedo drive gear add (.3)	.3

(G) Transmission Assy., R&R and Recondition

Includes: Complete disassembly, clean and inspect or renew all parts. Install all new gaskets and seals.

Chevette-T1000

1983 (3.6)	5.3

LABOR 19 STANDARD TRANSMISSION 19 LABOR

	(Factory Time)	Chilton Time
Camero-Firebird		
1983-87 (3.8)		5.5
(G) Transmission, Recondition (Off Car)		
All models	(2.0)	3.0
(G) Transmission Shift Cover and/or Gasket, Renew		
All models	(.8)	1.2
Recond cover add	(.3)	.3
(G) Transmission Rear Oil Seal, Renew		
All models	(.4)	.7
Renew bushing add	(.1)	.1
(G) Speedometer Driven Gear, Renew		
All models	(.3)	.5

PARTS 19 STANDARD TRANS. (4 Speed) 19 PARTS

	Part No.	Price
Transmission Assy. (Warner) (M26) Camaro & Firebird		
1983-84	14030872	N.L.
(1) Bearing Retainer		
1983-84	3859032	16.50
(2) Main Drive Gear Bearing		
1983-84	907929	N.L.
(3) Case Assy.		
1983-84	3925654	109.00
(4) Main Drive Gear		
1983-84	340621	135.00
(5) Synchronizer Unit (3rd & 4th)		
1983-84	14078543	79.00
(6) Synchronizer Ring		
1983-84	3859027	N.L.
(7) Third Speed Gear		
1983-84	3859986	41.25
(8) Mainshaft		
1983-84	468253	78.50
(9) Second Speed Gear		
1983-84	352239	49.25
(10) Synchronizer Unit (1st & 2nd)		
1983-84	368051	74.75
(11) First Speed Gear		
1983-84	468253	78.50
(12) Mainshaft Bearing (Rear)		
1983-84	907763	N.L.
(13) Speedometer Drive Gear		
Order by year and model.		
(14) Reverse Idler Gear (Front)		
1983-84	3915037	37.50
(15) Reverse Idler Shaft		
1983-84	3915039	7.25
(16) Extension Assy.		
1983-84	14030873	174.00
(17) Extension Seal		
1983-84	14053338	4.75

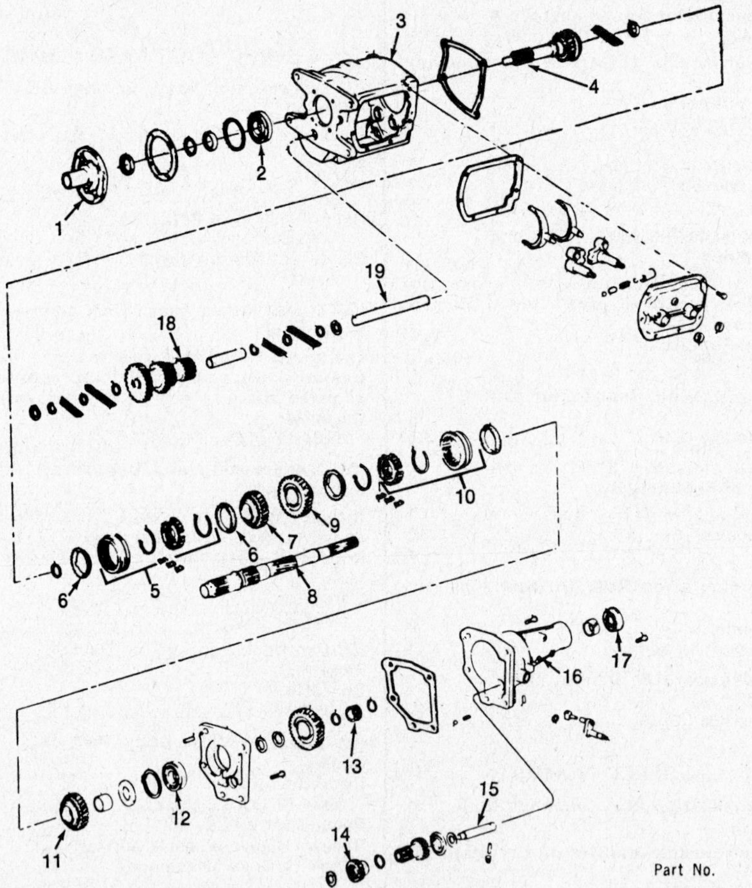

	Part No.	Price
(18) Countershaft Gear		
1983-87	14004878	171.00
(19) Shaft		
1983-87	3859005	17.00

PARTS 19 STANDARD TRANS. (4 Speed) 19 PARTS

	Part No.	Price
Transmission Assy. (70MM)		
1983-87-exc. below	14038688	962.00
Chev. Scooter	14038687	962.00
Gasket Set (Overhaul)		
Use sealing compound.		
(1) Main Drive Gear Bearing Retainer		
1983-87	14038689	36.50
(2) Seal		
1983-87	361648	3.50
(3) Gasket		
1983-87	368088	.50
(4) Clutch Housing		
1983-87	14062665	6.25
(5) Gasket		
1983-87	7316456	2.00
(6) Case Assy.		
1983-87	458498	109.00
(7) Gasket		
1983-87	7316448	2.50
(8) Back-Up Lamp Switch		
1983-87	14014559	7.25
(9) Main Drive Gear (Clutch)		
1983-87	14024970	158.00
(10) Countershaft Gear Bearing (Front)		
1983-87	9436880	3.25
(11) Clutch Gear Bearing		
1983-87	907258	20.00
(12) Extension Assy.		
1983-84-exc. below	14000353	78.25
w/sport shift	14000351	62.75
1985-87	14000351	62.75
(13) Housing Gasket		
1983-87	8967474	1.75

PARTS 19 STANDARD TRANS. (4 Speed) 19 PARTS

	Part No.	Price
(14) Rear Seal (Extension)		
1983-87	3932255	6.00
(15) Synchronizer (1st & 2nd)		
1983-87	14076940	66.00
(16) Blocking Ring		
1983-87	361638	15.00
(17) Synchronizer Spring		
1983-87	368087	1.50
(18) Synchronizer Key		
1983-87	376277	1.50
(19) 2nd Speed Gear		
1983-87	361633	54.00
(20) Mainshaft		
1983-84-exc. below	358439	81.00
w/sport shifter	358451	81.00
1985-87	358451	81.00
(21) 3rd Speed Gear		
1983-87	376254	50.00
(22) Synchronizer (3rd & 4th)		
1983-87	14076941	77.25
(23) Countershaft Gear		
1983	14068705	144.00
1984-87	14068705	144.00
(24) Rear Bearing Assy.		
1983-87	7451998	51.25
(25) Reverse Countershaft Gear		
1983-87	361636	29.00

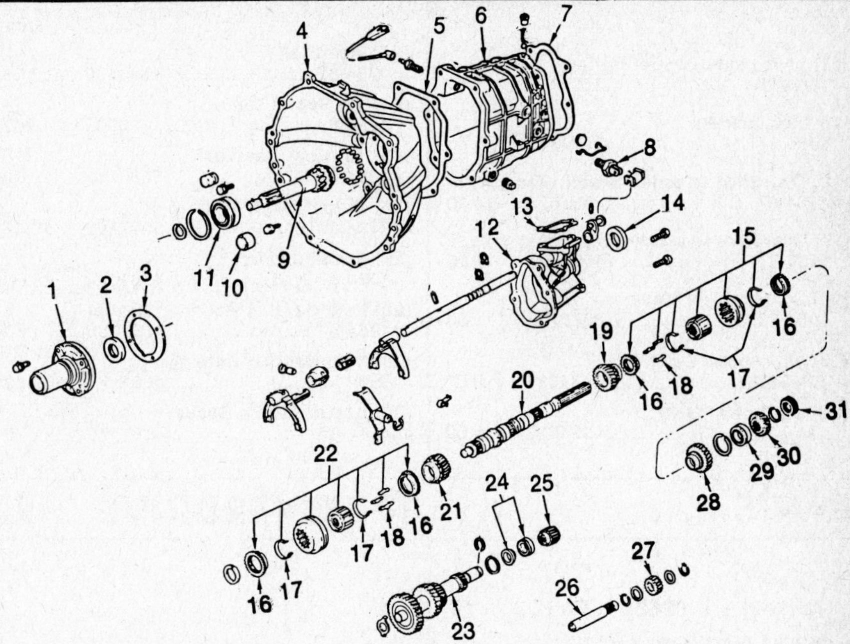

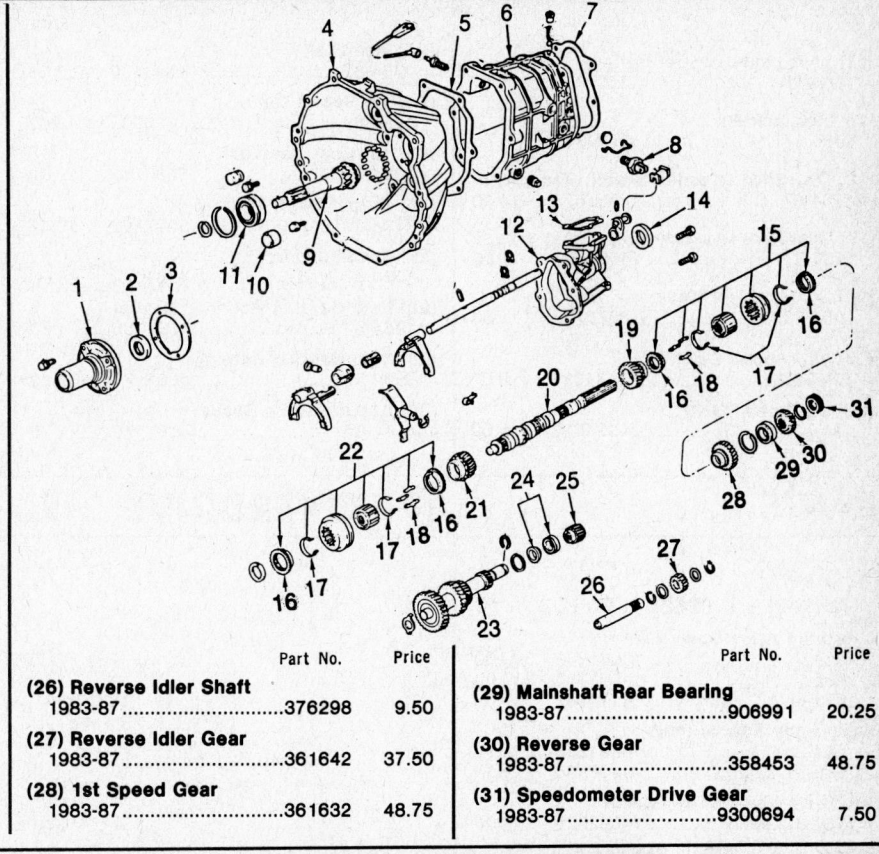

	Part No.	Price
(26) Reverse Idler Shaft		
1983-87	376298	9.50
(27) Reverse Idler Gear		
1983-87	361642	37.50
(28) 1st Speed Gear		
1983-87	361632	48.75

	Part No.	Price
(29) Mainshaft Rear Bearing		
1983-87	906991	20.25
(30) Reverse Gear		
1983-87	358453	48.75
(31) Speedometer Drive Gear		
1983-87	9300694	7.50

PARTS 19 STD. TRANS. (4 Speed) WITH OVERDRIVE 19 PARTS

DOUG NASH (MK2)

1984-87 CORVETTE

	Part No.	Price
(1) Retainer		
1984-87	360806	31.75
(2) Seal		
1984-87	3987936	3.50
(3) Gasket		
1984-87	1359473	.50
(4) Spacer		
1984-87	3709350	1.00
(5) Bearing		
1984-87	908216	38.50
(6) Main Drive Gear		
1984-87	14024318	122.00
(7) Mainshaft Roller Bearing		
1984-87	7451735	.50
(8) Countershaft Roller Bearing		
1984-87	435847	.50
(9) Synchronizer Assy. (3rd & 4th)		
1984-87	360100	97.75
(10) Countershaft Gear		
1984-87	14024317	217.00
(11) Spacer		
1984-87	474036	3.00
(12) Countergear Shaft		
1984-87	6260711	17.00
(13) Synchronizer Assy. (1st & 2nd)		
1984-87	360801	90.50

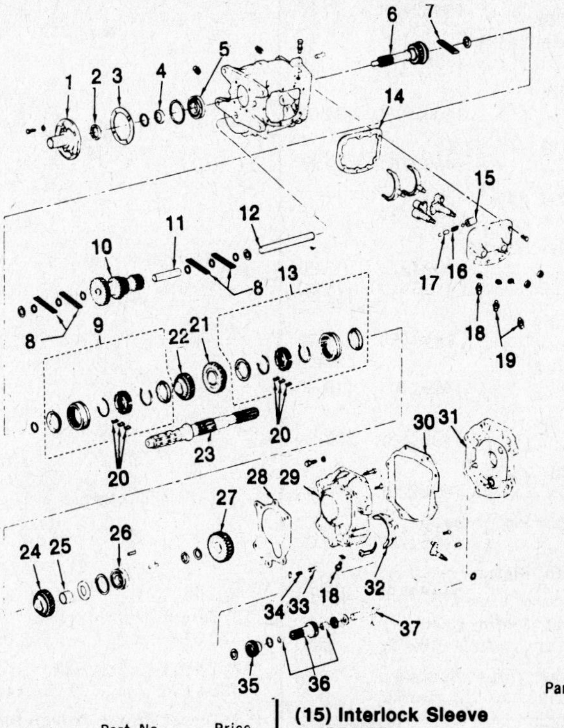

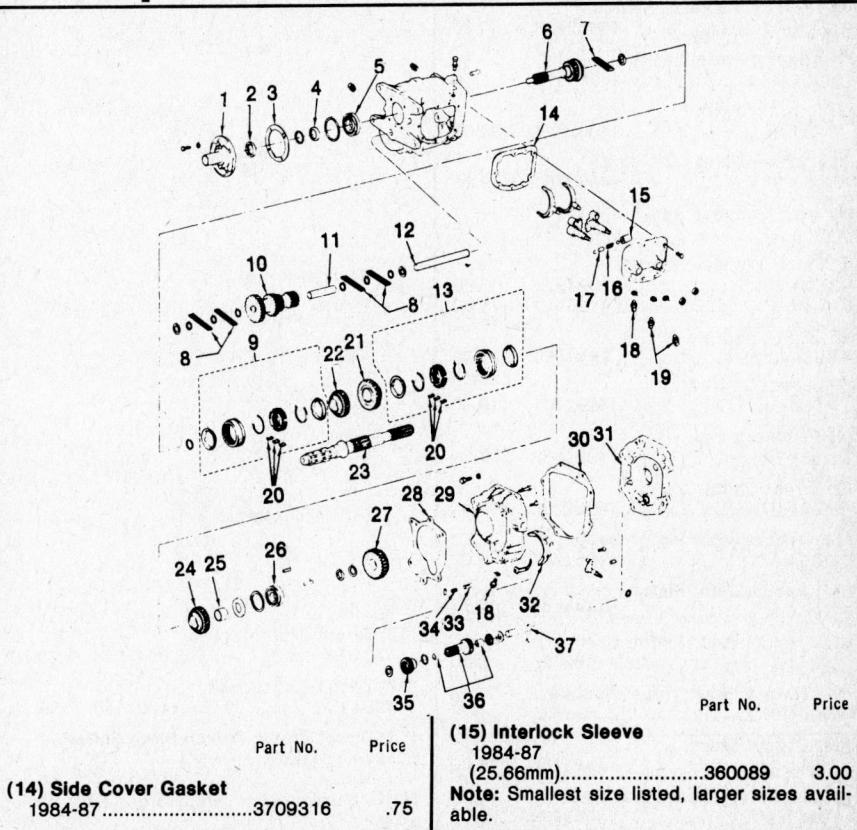

	Part No.	Price
(14) Side Cover Gasket		
1984-87	3709316	.75

	Part No.	Price
(15) Interlock Sleeve		
1984-87 (25.66mm)	360089	3.00

Note: Smallest size listed, larger sizes available.

PARTS 19 STD. TRANS. (4 Speed) WITH OVERDRIVE 19 PARTS

	Part No.	Price
(16) Shift Lever Poppet Spring		
1984-87	3709310	.50
(17) Interlock Pin		
1984-87	3709315	.75
(18) Overdrive Override Switch (3rd & 4th)		
1984-87	14057528	14.00
(19) Overdrive Override Switch (1st & 2nd)		
1984-87	14057529	9.00
(20) Synchronizer Keys		
1984-87	3870793	1.50
(21) 2nd Speed Gear		
1984-87	474035	119.00
(22) 3rd Speed Gear		
1984-87	14024322	125.00

	Part No.	Price
(23) Mainshaft		
1984-87	14081170	190.00
(24) 1st Speed Gear		
1984-87	360803	113.00
(25) 1st Gear Sleeve		
1984-87	6260712	20.50
(26) Output Shaft Bearing		
1984-87	907458	52.25
(26) Reverse Gear		
1984-87	14081174	86.00
(28) Rear Bearing Retainer Gasket		
1984-87	14081165	1.50
(29) Rear Bearing Retainer		
1984-87	14081177	153.00
(30) Adapter Plate Gasket		
1984-87	14081178	1.10

	Part No.	Price
(31) Overdrive Adapter Plate		
1984-87	14082724	83.00
(32) Reverse Shift Fork		
1984-87	14081173	94.00
(33) Reverse Detent Pin		
1984-87	14081176	11.50
(34) Reverse Detent Poppet Spring		
1984-87	14082799	1.00
(35) Reverse Idler Gear (Front)		
1984-87	14024315	122.00
(36) Reverse Idler Gear (Rear)		
1984-87	14081171	122.00
(37) Reverse Idler Shaft		
1984-87	3746277	13.00

PARTS 19 OVERDRIVE 19 PARTS

MK2 - (4 SPEED) - PART II

	Part No.	Price
Overdrive Valve Body Assy.		
1984	14091332	330.00
1985	14091355	330.00
1986-87	14105937	N.L.
Valve Body Spacer Plate		
1984-85	14091350	4.75
1986-87	14105936	N.L.
Overdrive Valve Body Gasket		
1984-87	14082726	1.00
Overdrive Valve Body Solenoid		
1984-87	14082729	81.75
Valve Body Pressure Switch		
1984-87	14082730	50.25
(1) Adapter Plate Gasket		
1984-87	14081178	1.10
(2) Adapter Plate		
1984-87	14082724	83.00
(3) Adapter Plate "O" Ring		
1984-87	14082751	9.25
(4) Input Sungear Seal		
1984-87	14082784	4.75
(5) Planetary Gear Carrier		
1984-85	14094571	160.00
1986-87	14105940	315.00
(6) Thrust Bearing		
1984-87	9440400	6.00
(7) Input Sun Gear		
1984-87	14082711	116.00
(8) Planetary Gear		
1984-87	14091329	305.00
(9) Direct Clutch Drum		
1984-87	14082702	168.00
(10) Accumulator Piston Seal		
1984-87	14082757	8.00
(11) Accumulator Piston		
1984-87	14082722	96.75
(12) Accumulator Piston Seal		
1984-87	14082756	3.50
(13) Output Shaft Thrust Bearing		
1984-87	N.L.	
(14) Output Shaft		
1984-87	14081185	275.00
(15) Planetary Gearthrust Plate		
1984-87	14082708	23.00

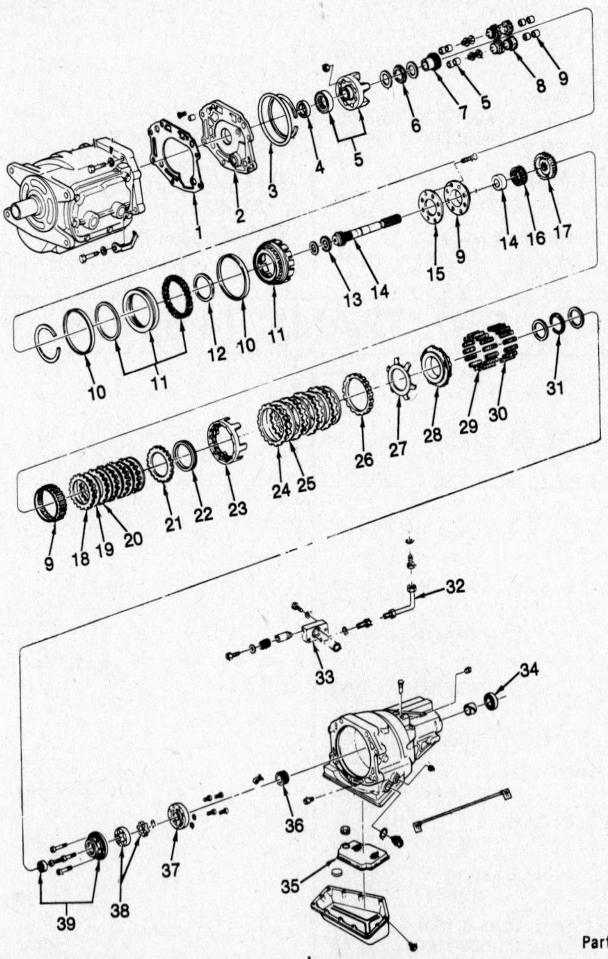

	Part No.	Price
(16) Direct Clutch Sprag		
1984-87	8647084	23.00
(17) Direct Clutch Hub		
1984-87	14081186	135.00
(18) Direct Clutch Driven Plate (Inner)		
1984-87 (.080-.084)	14081195	7.75

Note: Smallest size listed, larger sizes available.

	Part No.	Price
(19) Direct Clutch Plate		
1984-87	14081192	9.25
(20) Direct Clutch Driven Plate		
1984-87	14081193	6.00
(21) Direct Clutch Pressure Plate		
1984-87	14081191	30.50
(22) Direct Clutch Bearing		
1984-87	N.L.	

PARTS 19 OVERDRIVE 19 PARTS

	Part No.	Price
(23) Overdrive Clutch Piston		
1984-87	14082707	30.00
(24) Overdrive Clutch Driven Plate		
1984-87	14082706	10.50
(25) Overdrive Clutch Plate		
1984-87	14082705	10.75
(26) Overdrive Clutch Pressure Plate		
1984-87	14082704	44.00
(27) Direct Clutch Thrust Washer		
1984-87	14091496	30.00
(28) Direct Clutch Piston		
1984-87	14081184	36.00
(29) Direct Clutch Spring (Outer)		
1984-87	14081182	1.00
(30) Direct Clutch Spring (Inner)		
1984-87	14081183	.50
(31) Hub Thrust Bearing		
1984-87	N.L.	
(32) Oil Cooler Tube		
1984-87	14082740	11.50
(33) Oil Cooler Valve		
1984-87	14082738	67.50
(34) Output Shaft Seal		
1984-87	3932255	6.00
(35) Overdrive Oil Screen		
1984-87	14082735	11.25
(36) Speedometer Drive Gear		
1984-87	8640517	2.75
(37) Pump Spool		
1984-87	14091349	79.00
(38) Overdrive Oil Pump		
1984-87	14081188	39.00
(39) Pump Housing w/Bearing		
1984-87	14081187	43.50

PARTS 19 STANDARD TRANS. (5 Speed) 19 PARTS

(M-75 Diesel)

CHEVROLET CHEVETTE

PONTIAC T-1000

	Part No.	Price
1983-87	94162763	1307.00
Transmission Repair Kit		
1983-87	94029664	11.75
(1) Front Cover		
1983-87	94225282	24.75
(2) Front Cover Gasket		
1983-87	94029258	2.75
(3) Spring (Top Gear Shaft)		
1983-87	94022587	N.L.
(4) Seal (Front Cover)		
1983-87	94024633	4.25
(5) Bearing (4th Gear Shaft)		
1983-87	94223058	17.25
(6) Top Gear Shaft (w/Synchro. Cone)		
1983-87	94024660	76.25
(7) Needle Bearing (Mainshaft)		
1983-87	94020017	11.00
(8) Mainshaft		
1983-87	94236680	113.00
(9) Blocking Ring		
1983-87	94020566	37.50
(10) 5th Speed Gear		
1983-87	94237882	126.00
(11) Needle Bearing (5th Gear)		
1983-87	94238097	8.00
(12) Bearing (Mainshaft End)		
1983-87	94238106	13.75
(13) Drive Gear (Speedo.)		
1983-87	9300694	7.50
(14) Blocking Ring		
1983-87	94020566	37.50
(15) Synchronizer (3rd & 4th Gear)		
1983-87	94026994	99.00
(16) 3rd Gear Assy.		
1983-87	94223030	52.00
(17) 2nd Gear Assy.		
1983-87	94024663	49.25
(18) Blocking Ring (1st & 2nd)		
1983-87	94238647	31.75
(19) Synchronizer (1st & 2nd)		
1983-87	94026995	90.75
(20) 1st Gear Assy.		
1983-87	94024968	85.00
(21) Needle Bearing		
1983-87	94024620	11.00

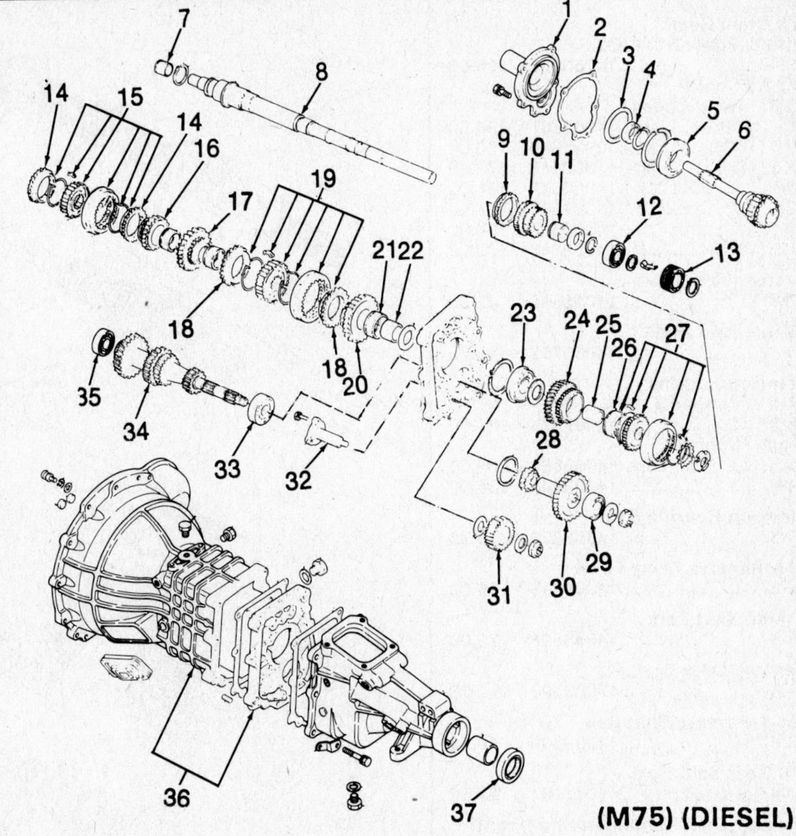

	Part No.	Price
(22) Needle Bearing Collar		
1983-87	94248620	10.00
(23) Bearing (Mainshaft)		
1983-87	94205102	16.75
(24) Reverse Gear Assy.		
1983-87	94025573	57.25
(25) Needle Bearing Collar		
1983-87	94248620	10.00
(26) Needle Bearing (1st & Rev.)		
1983-87	94024620	11.00
(27) Synchronizer Assy. (Rev. & 5th Gear)		
1983-87	94026996	103.00
(28) Counter Gear (Reverse)		
1983-87	94223042	44.00
(29) Bearing (Counter End)		
1983-87	94025559	7.00

(M75) (DIESEL)

	Part No.	Price
(30) Counter Gear (5th)		
1983-87	94029613	91.75
(31) Reverse Idler Gear		
1983-87	94029547	63.50
(32) Reverse Idler Shaft		
1983-87	94026293	13.50
(33) Bearing (Cluster Gear)		
1983-87	94223040	19.25
(34) Cluster Gear Assy.		
1983-87	94030206	149.00
(35) Bearing (Counter)		
1983-87	94225283	N.L.
(36) Case (w/Plate)		
1983-87	94244870	210.00
(37) Oil Seal (Rear Cover)		
1983-87	94238096	4.75

	Part No.	Price
MODEL MB4, MK4, MK5, MK6, ML3, ML8, MB1 & M39		
CHEVROLET MODELS: CHEVETTE, CAMARO		
PONTIAC MODELS: T-1000, FIREBIRD		
Transmission Assy. (77mm)		
Chevette & Pontiac T-1000		
1983-87	14040550	1260.00
Camaro & Firebird		
Transmission assy. must be ordered by code letters.		
(1) Oil Seal Main Drive Gear		
1983-87	3987936	3.50
(2) Main Drive Gear Bearing		
1983-87	7450700	12.00
(3) Main Drive Gear		
Chevette & Pontiac T-1000		
1983-87	14050777	196.00
Camaro & Firebird		
1983-87-Trans. codes:		
MK4, MK6	14069867	194.00
MK6 (1983)	14083546	172.00
MK6 (1984)	14083546	172.00
ML3	14083542	165.00
ML8	14069867	194.00
MB1	14069867	194.00
MK6 (1985)	14083546	172.00
(4) Reverse Idler Gear		
1983-87	14085848	62.50
(5) Reverse Idler Shaft		
1983-87	14050753	18.25
(6) Extension Housing		
Chevette & Pontiac T-1000		
1983-87	14069828	147.00
Camaro & Firebird		
1983	14069831	135.00
1984-87	14083545	135.00
(7) Extension Housing Seal		
1983-87	14053338	4.75
(8) 5th & Reverse Relay Lever		
1983-87	14069816	36.00
(9) Reverse Shift Fork		
1983-87	14053306	72.00
(10) Reverse Lock Spring		
1983-87	14053308	2.25
(11) 5th & Reverse Shift Rail		
1983-87	14053309	19.75
(12) 5th Gear Shift Fork		
1983-87	14071734	27.00
(13) Counter Gear Thrust Bearing (Front)		
1983-87	9439886	10.50
(14) Counter Gear		
Chevette & Pontiac T-1000		
1983-87	14050800	316.00
Camaro & Firebird		
1983-87-Trans codes:		
MK4, MK5 (31th)	14079434	290.00
MK4, MK5 (34th)	14069888	290.00
MK6	14071730	N.L.
ML3	14083536	290.00
ML8	14079434	290.00
MB1	14091373	290.00
M39	14071730	N.L.
(15) Counter Gear Thrust Bearing (Rear)		
1983-87	7451785	14.00
(16) 5th Gear (Drive)		
Chevette & Pontiac T-1000		
1983-87	14053314	126.00

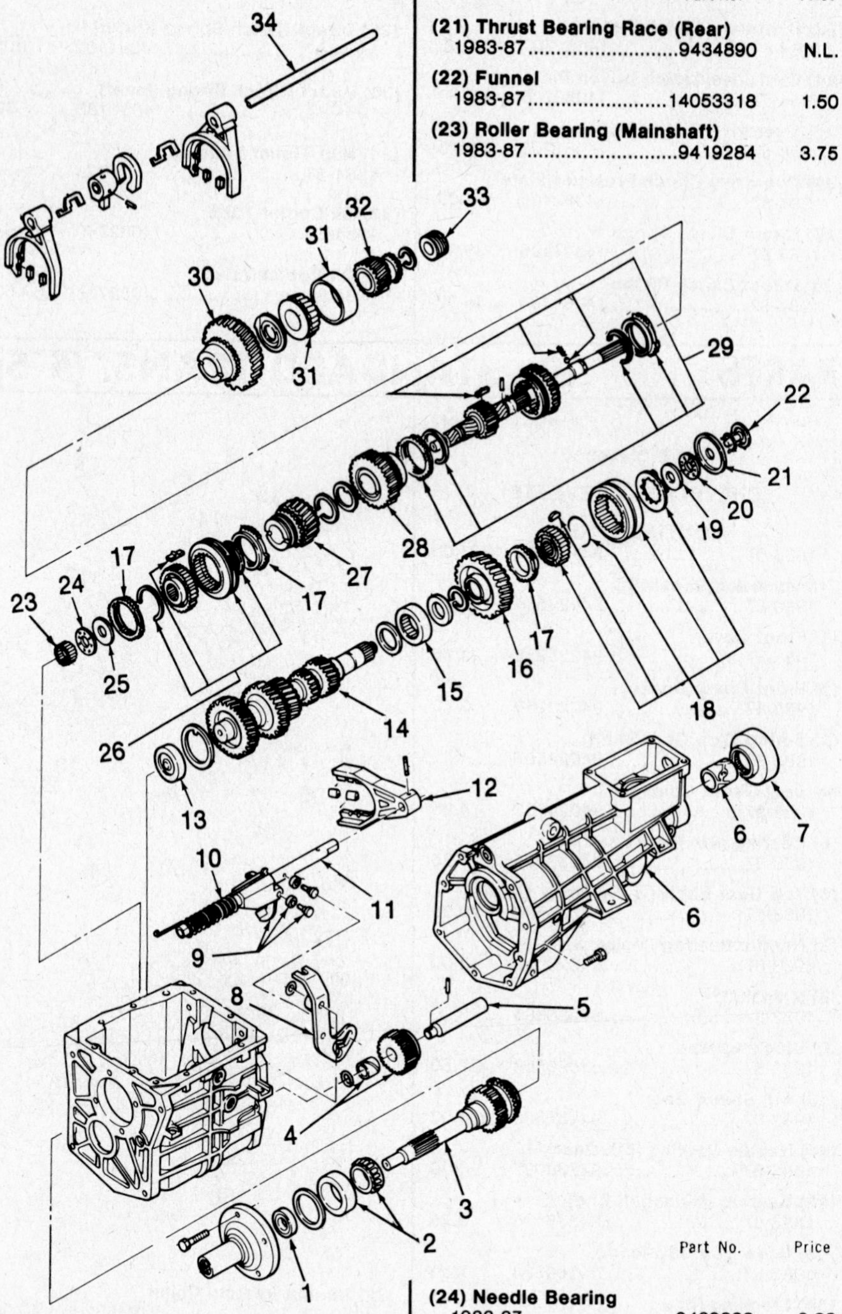

	Part No.	Price
Camaro & Firebird		
1983-87-Trans. codes:		
MK4	14071844	107.00
MK5, ML8, MB1, M39	14053314	126.00
MK6	14071733	N.L.
ML3	14083544	120.00
(17) Blocking Ring (3rd & 4th)		
1983-87	14050746	18.00
(18) Synchronizer Assy. (5th Gear)		
1983-87	14053316	113.00
(19) Thrust Bearing Race (Front)		
1983-87	9439889	4.50
(20) Needle Bearing Race		
1983-87	9424090	8.00

	Part No.	Price
(21) Thrust Bearing Race (Rear)		
1983-87	9434890	N.L.
(22) Funnel		
1983-87	14053318	1.50
(23) Roller Bearing (Mainshaft)		
1983-87	9419284	3.75

	Part No.	Price
(24) Needle Bearing		
1983-87	9439888	3.00
(25) Thrust Bearing Race		
1983-87	9439887	3.75
(26) Synchronizer Assy. (3rd & 4th)		
1983-87	14089014	N.L.
(27) 3rd Gear		
Chevette & Pontiac T-1000		
1983-87	14050798	91.25
Camaro & Firebird		
1983-87-Trans. codes:		
MK4, MK5 (27th)	14079419	113.00
MK4, MK5 (29th)	14071741	92.00
MK6, M39	14071729	N.L.
ML3	14083540	92.00
ML8	14079419	113.00

	Part No.	Price
(28) 2nd Gear		
Chevette & Pontiac T-1000		
1983-87	14050795	64.25
Camaro & Firebird		
1983-87-Trans. codes:		
MK4, MK5	14050794	64.25
MK6, M39	14085853	115.00
ML3	14050795	64.25
ML8	14050794	64.25
MB1	14091375	111.00
(29) Output Shaft		
Chevette & Pontiac T-1000		
1983-87	14083550	275.00
Camaro & Firebird		
1983-87	14085849	290.00

Note: Includes 1st & 2nd gear synchronizer assy.

	Part No.	Price
(30) 1st Gear		
Chevette & Pontiac T-1000		
1983-87	14050793	99.75
Camaro & Firebird		
1983-87-Trans codes:		
MK4, MK5, ML8	14083551	110.00
MK6 (1983)	14085850	105.00
MK6 (1984)	14085850	105.00
ML3	14050793	99.75
MB1, M39	14085850	105.00
(31) Output Shaft Bearing (Rear)		
1983-87	9431708	19.00
(32) 5th Gear (Driven)		
Chevette & Pontiac T-1000		
1983-87	14053313	126.00
Camaro & Firebird		
1983-87-Trans codes:		
MK4	14071843	107.00
MK5, ML3	14053313	126.00
MK6	14071732	102.00
ML3 (1985-87)	14091341	51.00
MB1	14083538	126.00
M39	14091374	58.00
(33) Speedo. Gear		
1983-87	94249541	N.L.
(34) Shift Shaft		
1983-87	14071735	53.00

Automatic Transmissions

INDEX

(Factory Time) Chilton Time

JEEP—MODEL 727

ON CAR SERVICES

(G) Drain & Refill Unit
All models.......... .8

(G) Oil Pressure Check
All models.......... .6

(G) Check Unit For Oil Leaks
Includes: Clean and dry outside of case and run unit to determine point of leak.
All models.......... .9

(G) Neutral Safety Switch, Renew
1983 (.3).......... .5

(G) Oil Cooler Lines, Renew
1983-one (.4).......... .6
both (.5).......... .8

(G) Extension Housing, R&R or Renew
CJ Series
1983 (1.1).......... 1.6
WAG-CKE-TRK
1983-Six (1.4).......... 1.9
V-8 (1.0).......... 1.5
Renew output shaft brg add (.1).......... .2

(G) Oil Pan Gasket, Renew
1983 (.5).......... .8

(G) Oil Filter, Renew
1983 (.6).......... .9

(G) Valve Body Assembly, Renew
Includes: R&R oil pan.
1983 (.7).......... 1.2

(P) Valve Body, R&R and Recondition
Includes: R&R oil pan and filter. Disassemble, clean, inspect, free all valves. Replace parts as required.
1983 (1.7).......... 2.8

(G) Low and Reverse Band, Adjust
Includes: R&R oil pan.
1983 (.6).......... 1.0

(G) Throttle Valve Lever Shaft Seal, Renew
Includes: R&R oil pan.
1983 (.6).......... .9

(G) Kickdown Servo, Renew or Recondition
Includes: R&R oil pan.
1983 (.9).......... 1.5

(G) Accumulator Piston, Renew or Recondition
Includes: R&R oil pan.
1983 (.6).......... 1.1

(G) Low and Reverse Servo, Renew or Recondition
Includes: R&R oil pan.
1983 (.8).......... 1.4

(G) Throttle and Regulator Valves, Adjust
Includes: R&R oil pan.
1983 (.6).......... 1.0

(G) Throttle Valve Linkage, Adjust
Includes: R&R oil pan.
1983 (.6).......... 1.0

(G) Kickdown Band, Adjust
Includes: R&R oil pan.
1983 (.6).......... 1.0

CHILTON'S AUTOMATIC TRANSMISSION TUNE-UP

1. Check engine performance
2. Check condition of transmission oil
3. Check transmission, oil cooler and oil cooler lines for external leaks
4. Remove oil pan, clean or renew screen or filter
5. Torque valve body
6. Adjust bands
7. Clean oil pan and install pan with new gasket
8. Check modulator and hose
9. Install new transmission oil to proper level
10. Adjust manual and throttle linkage
11. Road test

All models 1.5
Charge for parts used

(Factory Time) Chilton Time

SERVICES REQUIRING R&R

(G) Transmission and Transfer Case, R&R or Renew
1983-Six (2.4).......... 3.9
V-8 (2.0).......... 3.5
Renew trans add (.2).......... .5

(P) Transmission and Converter, R&R and Recondition
Includes: Disassemble trans completely, including valve body. Clean and inspect all parts. Renew parts as required. Reassemble and test.
1983-Six (8.6).......... 11.9
V-8 (8.2).......... 11.5
Clean and pressure test converter, add .7

(G) Transmission Assembly, Reseal
Includes: R&R trans and renew all seals and gaskets.
1983-Six.......... 5.9
V-8.......... 5.5

(G) Torque Converter, Renew
Includes: R&R trans and transfer case.
1983-Six (2.6).......... 4.1
V-8 (2.2).......... 3.7

(G) Converter Drive Plate, Renew
Includes: R&R trans and transfer case.
1983-Six (2.6).......... 4.2
V-8 (2.2).......... 3.8

(G) Front Pump Assembly, Renew or Recondition
Includes: R&R trans and transfer case.
1983-Six (2.7).......... 4.5
V-8 (2.3).......... 4.1

(G) Front Pump Oil Seal, Renew
Includes: R&R trans and transfer case.
1983-Six (2.6).......... 4.2
V-8 (2.2).......... 3.8

JEEP—MODEL 904 & 999

ON CAR SERVICES

(G) Drain & Refill Unit
All models.......... .8

(Factory Time) Chilton Time

(G) Oil Pressure Check
All models.......... .6

(G) Check Unit For Oil Leaks
Includes: Clean and dry outside of case and run unit to determine point of leak.
All models.......... .9

(G) Neutral Safety Switch, Renew
1983-87 (.3).......... .5

(G) Oil Cooler Lines, Renew
1983-87-one (.4).......... .6
both (.5).......... .8

(G) Auxiliary Oil Cooler Assy., Renew
All models (.6).......... 1.0

(G) Oil Pan Gasket, Renew
1983-87 (.6).......... .8

(G) Oil Filter, Renew
1983-87 (.7).......... .9

(G) Valve Body Assembly, Renew
Includes: R&R oil pan.
1983-87 (.9).......... 1.2

(P) Valve Body, R&R and Recondition
Includes: R&R oil pan and filter. Disassemble, clean, inspect, free all valves. Replace parts as required.
1983-87 (1.9).......... 2.8

(G) Throttle Valve Linkage, Adjust
1983-87 (.2).......... .3

SERVICES REQUIRING R&R

(G) Transmission Assembly, Remove & Install
CJ/Scrambler (2.1).......... 2.8
Cherokee/Grand Wagoneer/
Truck (3.9).......... 5.3
Cke/Wag/Comanche
2 WD (1.6).......... 2.2
4 WD
Four (2.2).......... 3.0
V-6 (2.8).......... 3.8
Diesel (3.2).......... 4.4
Renew assy add (.5).......... .5

(P) Transmission and Converter, R&R and Recondition
Includes: Disassemble trans completely, including valve body. Clean and inspect all parts. Renew all parts as required.
CJ/Scrambler (6.9).......... 9.6
Cherokee/Grand Wagoneer/
Truck (8.7).......... 12.1
Cke/Wag/Comanche
2 WD (6.4).......... 8.9
4 WD
Four (7.0).......... 9.8
V-6 (7.6).......... 10.6
Diesel (8.0).......... 11.2
Clean and test conv add.......... .5

(G) Transmission Assembly, Reseal
Includes: R&R trans and renew all gaskets and seals.
CJ/Scrambler.......... 5.8
Cherokee/Grand Wagoneer/
Truck.......... 8.3
Cke/Wag/Comanche
2 WD.......... 5.2
4 WD
Four.......... 6.0
V-6.......... 6.8
Diesel.......... 7.4

LABOR 23 AUTOMATIC TRANSMISSION 23 LABOR

(Factory Time) Chilton Time

(G) Front Pump Oil Seal, Renew
Includes: R&R trans.
CJ/Scrambler (2.7) 3.7
Cherokee/Grand Wagoneer/Truck (3.9) 5.4
Cke/Wag/Comanche
2 WD (2.2) 3.0
4 WD (2.8) 3.9
Diesel (3.8) 5.3

AMC–MODEL 904 & 998

ON CAR SERVICES

(G) Drain & Refill Unit
All models 8

(G) Oil Pressure Check
All models 6

(G) Check Unit For Oil Leaks
Includes: Clean and dry outside of case and run unit to determine point of leak.
All models 9

(G) Neutral Safety Switch, Renew
1983-87-exc below (.3) 5
1983-87-Eagle (.6) 1.0

(G) Oil Cooler Lines, Renew
1983-87-one (.4) 6
both (.5) 8

(G) Transmission Auxiliary Oil Cooler, Renew
1983-87 (.6) 1.0

(G) Extension Housing, R&R or Renew
1983-87-exc below (.8) 1.6
1983-87-Eagle (1.3) 2.0
Renew output shaft brg add (.1) 1
Renew oil seal add (.1) 1
Renew bushing add (.1) 1

(G) Extension Housing Oil Seal, Renew
1983-87-exc below (.4) 7
1983-87-Eagle (1.2) 1.7

(G) Governor, R&R and Recondition
Includes: R&R extension housing.
1983-87-exc below (1.2) 2.0
1983-87-Eagle (1.6) 2.4

(G) Oil Pan Gasket, Renew
1983-87 (.6) 8

(G) Oil Filter, Renew
1983-87 (.7) 9

(G) Valve Body Assembly, Renew
Includes: R&R oil pan.
1983-87 (.9) 1.2

(P) Valve Body, R&R and Recondition
Includes: R&R oil pan and filter. Disassemble, clean, inspect, free all valves. Replace parts as required.
1983-87 (1.9) 2.8

(G) Low and Reverse Band, Adjust
Includes: R&R oil pan.
1983-87 (.6) 1.0

(G) Throttle Valve Lever Shaft Seal, Renew
Includes: R&R oil pan.
1983-87 (.6) 9

(G) Kickdown Servo, Renew or Recondition
Includes: R&R oil pan.
1983-87 (.9) 1.5

(G) Accumulator Piston, Renew or Recondition
Includes: R&R oil pan.
1983-87 (.6) 1.1

(G) Low and Reverse Servo, Renew or Recondition
Includes: R&R oil pan.
1983-87 (.8) 1.4

(G) Torque Converter, Renew
Includes: R&R trans.
CJ/Scrambler (2.3) 3.1
Cherokee/Grand Wagoneer/Truck (4.1) 5.6
Cke/Wag/Comanche
2 WD (1.8) 2.5
4 WD (2.4) 3.3
Diesel (3.4) 4.7
Renew drive plate add (.2) 3

(G) Parking Brake Sprag, Renew
Includes: R&R extension housing.
1983-87-exc below (.9) 1.7
1983-87-Eagle (1.3) 2.2

(G) Throttle and Regulator Valves, Adjust
Includes: R&R oil pan.
1983-87 (.6) 1.0

(G) Throttle Valve Linkage, Adjust
Includes: R&R oil pan.
1983-87 (.6) 1.0

(G) Kickdown Band, Adjust
Includes: R&R oil pan.
1983-87 (.6) 1.0

SERVICES REQUIRING R&R

(G) Transmission, R&R or Renew
Four–1983-87-exc below (1.4) 3.0
Eagle (2.8) 4.0
Six–1983-87-exc below (1.9) 3.5
1983-87-Eagle (3.0) 4.2
Renew trans add (.2) 3

(G) Transmission Assembly, Reseal
Includes: R&R trans and renew all seals and gaskets.
Four–1983-87-exc below 5.3
Eagle 6.5
Six–1983-87-exc below 5.1
1983-87-Eagle 5.2

(P) Transmission and Converter, R&R and Recondition
Four–1983-87-exc below (8.0) 12.0
Eagle (7.6) 11.8
Six–1983-87-exc below (7.7) 11.9
1983-87-Eagle (7.8) 12.0
Clean and pressure check converter add (.5) 7

(G) Converter Drive Plate, Renew
Includes: R&R transmission.
Four–1983-87-exc below (1.6) 3.4
Eagle (3.2) 4.4
Six–1983-87-exc below (2.1) 3.7
1983-87-Eagle (3.4) 4.6

(G) Torque Converter, Renew
Includes: R&R transmission.
Four–1983-87-exc below (1.6) 3.5
Eagle (3.0) 4.5
Six–1983-87-exc. below (2.1) 3.7
1983-87-Eagle (3.2) 4.7

(G) Front Pump Oil Seal, Renew
Includes: R&R transmission.
Four–1983-87-exc below (1.6) 3.5
Eagle (3.5) 4.7
Six–1983-87-exc. below (2.1) 3.7
1983-87-Eagle (3.7) 4.9

(G) Front Oil Pump, Renew or Recondition
Includes: R&R transmission.
Four–1983-87-exc below (1.7) 3.8
Eagle (3.1) 4.8
Six–1983-87-exc. below (2.2) 4.0
1983-87-Eagle (3.3) 5.0

(G) Front Clutch, Recondition
Includes: R&R transmission. Disassemble, clean, inspect and reassemble.
Four–1983-87-exc below (3.5) 6.0
Eagle (4.9) 7.0
Six–1983-87-exc. below (4.0) 6.2
1983-87-Eagle (5.1) 7.2

(G) Rear Clutch, Recondition
Includes: R&R transmission. Disassemble, clean, inspect and reassemble.
Four–1983-87-exc below (3.2) 5.4
Eagle (4.6) 6.4
Six–1983-87-exc. below (3.7) 5.6
1983-87-Eagle (4.8) 6.6

(G) Overrunning Clutch, Recondition
Includes: R&R transmission. Disassemble, clean, inspect and reassemble.
Four–1983-87-exc below (3.3) 5.5
Eagle (4.7) 6.5
Six–1983-87-exc below (3.8) 5.7
1983-87-Eagle (4.9) 6.7

(G) Planetary Gear Set, Recondition
Includes: R&R transmission. Disassemble, clean, inspect and reassemble.
Four–1983-87-exc below (3.4) 6.0
Eagle (4.8) 7.0
Six–1983-87-exc. below (3.9) 6.2
1983-87-Eagle (5.0) 7.2

(G) Front or Rear Servo, Recondition
Includes: R&R transmission. Disassemble, clean, inspect and reassemble.
Four–1983-87-exc below (3.3) 5.5
Eagle (4.7) 6.5
Six–1983-87-exc. below (3.8) 5.7
1983-87-Eagle (4.9) 6.7

PARTS 23 TORQUE COMMAND—CASE & PARTS 23 PARTS

	Part No.	Price
Transmission Assembly		
American Motors		
1983-Four-151		
Concord, Spirit	8933000863	N.L.
Eagle, SX4	8933000864	1063.25
1983-Four-150		
Eagle	8933001416	1226.25
1983-Six-258		
Concord, Spirit	3240229	1301.00
Eagle, SX4	8933000916	1062.75

PARTS 23 TORQUE COMMAND–CASE AND PARTS 23 PARTS

	Part No.	Price
1984-87		
Eagle		
w/Lock-up	8933000916	1063.00
wo/Lock-up	8933002366	1036.75
AMC-Jeep		
1984-85-904 Trans.		
Series 70		
2W.D.		
Gas	8953002430	1226.25
Diesel	8953001975	N.L.
4W.D.		
Gas	8953001141	1179.00
Diesel	8953001334	79.75
1986-87-904 Trans.		
Series 70		
2W.D.	8953001672	1165.25
4W.D.	8953002097	1147.75
1983-87-999 Trans.		
Six-258	8933000913	1263.00
1983-87-727 Trans.		
2.73 ratio	8933000915	1263.00
3.31 & 3.73	8933000914	1263.00
non-lockup	8953001836	1370.50
Gasket & Seal Kit		
1983-87 (AMC)		
wo/4W.D.	8130350	59.00
w/4W.D.	8134681	77.25
1983-87 (Jeep)		
727 trans.	8134763	54.75
904, 999 trans.	8134681	77.25
Filter Screen		
1983-87		
999 trans.	8123042	2.50
727 trans.	8123042	2.50
70 Series	8123042	2.50
Valve Body Assy.		
American Motors		
1983-151	8130337	290.50
150	8983500427	N.L.
1983-84		
w/4W.D.	8133860	301.00
wo/4W.D.	8133859	310.00
1984-87		
wo/Lockup	8133859	310.00
w/Lockup	8133860	301.00
AMC Jeep–exc. 70 series		
1983-87 (wo/Lock-up converter)		
727 trans.	8133783	305.25
999 trans.	8133860	301.00
1983-87 (727 w/Lock-up)		
2.73 axle ratio	8133403	305.25
3.31 axle ratio	8133404	305.25
AMC Jeep–70 Series		
1984-87-Gas	8983500427	N.L.
Diesel	8983501951	312.75
(1) Clutch Rollers		
1983-87-exc. 727	8120847	1.50
727 trans.	3213743	10.75
(2) Clutch Spring		
1983-87-exc. 727	8120845	.50
727 trans.	8120846	.50
(3) Overrunning Clutch Race		
1983-87-exc. 727	8120849	45.50
727 trans.	8120850	43.75
(4) Overrunning Clutch (Kit)		
1983-87-exc. 727	8124585	122.75
727 trans.	8122438	59.50
(5) Gasket (Extension)		
1983-87	8120979	2.00
(6) Bushing (Extension)		
1983-87	8121152	8.25
(7) Seal (Extension)		
1983-87-exc.		
4W.D.	8122739	7.50
4W.D.	8134680	9.00

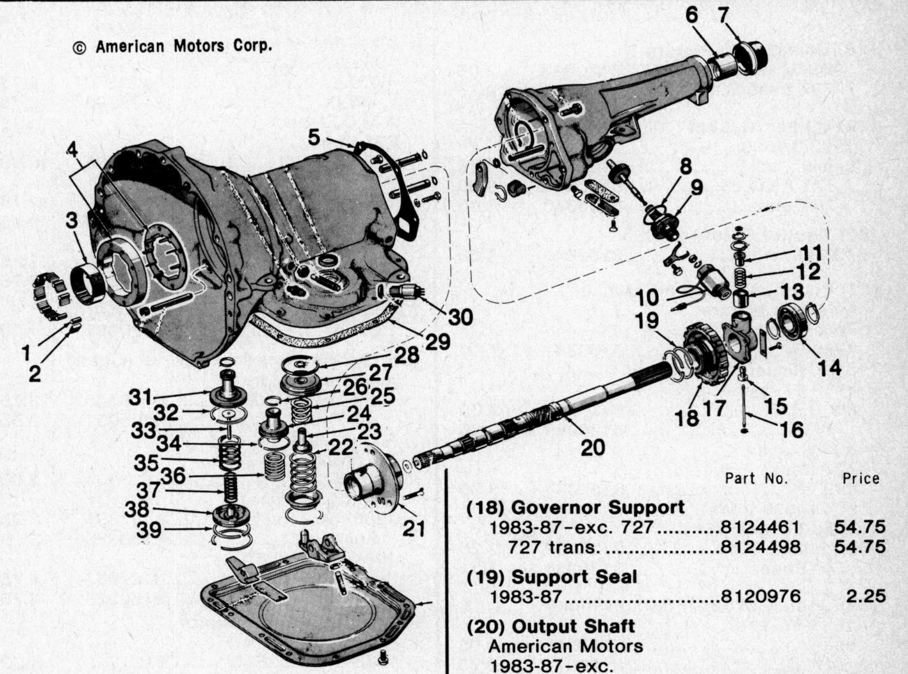

	Part No.	Price
(8) "O" Ring Seal		
1983-87	8136628	1.50
(9) Adapter		
1983-87 (Jeep)		
1 position	3212707	3.75
2 position	3212893	5.25
1983-87 (American Motors)		
1 position	3241421	3.75
2 position	3237440	3.75
(10) T.C.S. Switch		
1983-87	3219327	11.00
(11) Weight (Inner)		
1983-87-exc. 150		
eng.	8121130	3.75
150 eng.	8983500954	2.50
(12) Weight Spring		
1983-87-exc. 150		
eng.	8132498	1.50
150 eng.	8983500426	1.25
(13) Weight (Outer)		
1983-87-exc. 150		
eng.	8132497	3.75
150 eng.	8983500425	3.75
(14) Bearing (Output Shaft)		
American Motors		
1983-87-exc.		
4W.D.	8121077	14.75
4W.D.	8132499	33.25
AMC Jeep		
727 Trans.		
1983	8133580	21.75
1984-87-exc.		
below	8121078	21.25
w/locking conv.	8133580	21.75
904 & 999 Trans.		
1983-87	8132499	33.25
(15) Governor Valve		
1983-87	8121149	6.75
(16) Valve Shaft		
1983-87	8121150	5.25
(17) Governor Body		
1983-87-exc. 727	8132495	18.00
727 trans.	8132496	18.00

	Part No.	Price
(18) Governor Support		
1983-87-exc. 727	8124461	54.75
727 trans.	8124498	54.75
(19) Support Seal		
1983-87	8120976	2.25
(20) Output Shaft		
American Motors		
1983-87-exc.		
4W.D.	8130343	160.25
4W.D.	8132490	160.25
A.M.C. Jeep-exc. 70 Series		
1983-87		
727 trans.	8132491	160.25
999 trans.	8132490	160.25
AMC Jeep-70 series		
1984-87-4W.D.		
Diesel eng.	8983501949	150.25
Gas eng.	8132490	160.25
1984-87-2W.D.	8130343	160.25
(21) Output Shaft Support		
1983-87-exc. 727	8120841	54.00
727 trans.	8120842	58.75
(22) Spring (Servo Piston)		
1983-87-exc. 727	8121172	2.75
727 trans.	8121173	2.75
(23) Plug (Reverse Servo)		
American Motors		
1983-84-Four cyl.	8125824	3.75
Six cyl.	8124497	7.75
A.M.C. Jeep		
1983-exc. Four	8124497	7.75
Four cyl.	8125824	3.75
1984-87-exc. 70		
Ser.	8124497	7.75
70 Series	3125824	N.L.
(24) Piston (Accumulator)		
1983-87	8121054	11.25
(25) Spring (Servo Cushion)		
American Motors		
1983-87-exc.		
4W.D.	8124581	2.75
4W.D.	8130603	3.50
A.M.C. Jeep		
727 trans		
1983-87	8124581	2.75
904 & 999 Trans		
1983-87-exc. 70		
Ser.	8130603	3.50
w/70 Ser.	8124581	2.75
(26) Seal, Accumulator Piston (Small)		
1983-87	8120981	N.L.
(27) Piston (Reverse Servo)		
1983-87-exc. 727	8121180	7.00
727 trans.	8121181	10.00

PARTS 23 TORQUE COMMAND—CASE & PARTS 23 PARTS

	Part No.	Price
(28) Seal (Servo Piston)		
1983-87-exc. 727	8120992	2.00
727 trans.	8129044	2.75
(29) Oil Pan Gasket		
1983-87-exc.		
below	8136640	3.25
727 trans.	8120984	3.00
70 Series	8136640	3.00
(30) Neutral Safety Switch		
1983-87	3232844	9.50
(31) Piston, Kickdown Servo		
American Motors		
Four Cylinder		
1983-84	8130331	7.00
Six Cylinder		
1983-87-exc.		
4W.D.	8130331	7.00
4W.D.	8128989	12.25
A.M.C. Jeep		
727 trans		
1983-87	8121094	15.75
904 & 999 trans.		
1983-87-exc. 70		
Ser.	8128989	12.25
70 Series	3130331	N.L.
(32) Seal, Kickdown Servo (Small)		
1983-87-exc.		
below	8120968	2.00
4W.D.	8120971	3.75
727 trans.	8120987	3.75
70 Series	8120969	2.50
(33) Rod (Kickdown Servo)		
American Motors		
Four Cylinder		
1983-84	8130332	9.75
Six Cylinder		
1983-87-exc.		
4W.D.	8130332	9.75
4W.D.	8128990	12.75
A.M.C. Jeep		
727 trans.		
1983-87	8121095	16.00
904 & 999 trans.		
1983-exc. Four	8128990	12.75
Four cyl.	8130332	9.75
1984-87-exc. 70		
Ser.	8128990	12.75
70 Series	8130332	9.75
(34) Seal, Accumulator Piston (Large)		
1983-87	8120982	1.50
(35) Spring, Kickdown Servo (Outer)		
American Motors		
1983-exc. 4W.D.	8130333	3.75
4W.D.	8128991	2.50
A.M.C. Jeep		
727 trans		
1983-87	8121101	3.00
904 & 999 trans.		
1983-exc. Four	8127837	3.75
Four cyl.	8130333	3.75
1984-87-exc. 70		
Ser.	8127837	3.75
70 Series	8130333	3.75
(36) Spring, Accumulator		
American Motors		
1983-87-exc. Four	8121141	3.00
Four Cylinder		
150 eng.	8983500428	3.00
151 eng.	8127837	3.75
A.M.C. Jeep		
1983-727 trans.	8121141	3.00
904 & 999 trans		
exc. Four	8132508	2.50
Four cyl.	8127837	3.75
1984-87-727 trans.		
exc. Lock-up	8132508	2.50
w/Locking conv.	8121141	3.00
1984-87-Six cyl.		
999 trans.	8121141	3.00
1984-87-70 Series		
Gas eng.	8983500428	3.00
Diesel eng.	8127837	3.75
(37) Spring, Kickdown Servo (Inner)		
1983-87-exc. 727	8121099	2.50
727 trans.	8121096	1.00
(38) Guide, Kickdown Servo		
American Motors		
1983-87-exc.		
below	8121105	7.75
4W.D.	8121106	7.75
727 trans.	8121107	9.50
A.M.C. Jeep		
727 trans.		
1983-87	8121107	9.50
904 & 999 trans.		
1983-exc. Four	8121106	7.75
Four cyl.	8121105	7.75
1984-87-exc. 70		
Ser.	8121106	7.75
70 Series	8121105	7.75
(39) Seal, Kickdown Servo Guide		
American Motors		
1983-87-exc.		
4W.D.	8120969	2.50
4W.D.	8120972	3.75
A.M.C. Jeep		
1983-87		
727 trans.	8120988	3.75
999 trans.	8120972	3.75
70 Series	8120969	2.50

PARTS 23 CONVERTER, PUMP & CLUTCH 23 PARTS

	Part No.	Price
(1) Drive Plate (Flex Plate)		
American Motors		
Four Cylinder		
1983-84-151 eng.	3251290	70.50
150 eng.	8953001184	57.00
Six Cylinder		
1983-87	3232138	74.50
A.M.C. Jeep		
727 trans.		
1983-87	3232139	74.50
904 & 999 trans.		
1983-exc. Four	3232138	74.50
Four cyl.	3251290	70.50
1984-87-exc.		
below	3232138	74.50
1984-87-70 series		
4 cyl. (Gas)	8953001184	57.00
4 cyl. (Diesel)	8953001926	55.00
Six cyl.	8953001255	37.75
(2) Reinforcement Plate		
Four Cylinder		
1983-87-151 eng.	3251288	1.50
150 eng.	8953001186	4.00
1984-87-70 Series		
4 cyl. (Gas)	8953001186	3.75
4 cyl. (Diesel)	7700623834	N.L.
Six engine		
1983-87-exc. 70		
Ser.	3214094	1.00
1984-87-70 Series	8953001401	3.75
(3) Torque Converter		
American Motors		
Four Cylinder		
1983-87-exc.		
4W.D.	8933000862	425.25
4W.D.		
151 eng.	8933000862	425.25
150 eng.	8982775082	190.00
Six Cylinder		
1983-87	8132569	554.25
A.M.C. Jeep		
727 trans.		
Six		
w/Lockup	8982775037	‡138.75
wo/Lockup	8982775036	‡92.25
V-8		
w/Lockup	8982775038	138.75
wo/Lockup	8982775036	‡92.25
904 & 999 trans.		
1983-87-exc. 70		
Ser.	8132569	554.25
Four cyl.	3234274	546.00
1984-87-70 Series		
4 cyl. (Gas)	8982775082	190.00
4 cyl. (Diesel)	8953001333	282.00
Six cyl.	8982775040	40.00
1986-87-Rebuilt	8982775082	10.00
(4) Seal, Oil Pump Impeller Hub		
1983-87-exc. 727	8134675	8.00
727 trans.	8126792	3.75
(5) Oil Pump		
1983-87-exc. 727	8130353	147.50
727 trans.	8132482	140.25
1984-87-70 Series		
Gas eng.	8130353	147.50
Diesel eng.	8983501958	132.25
(6) "O" Ring Seal, Pump Housing		
1983-87-exc. 727	8120858	N.L.
727 trans.	8120859	2.00
(7) Bushing, Pump Housing		
1983-87-exc. 727	8120854	6.50
727 trans.	8120855	23.00
(8) Rotor, Oil Pump (Inner & Outer)		
1983-87-exc. 727	8127834	41.00
727 trans.	8124495	51.00
(9) Reaction Shaft & Bushing		
American Motors		
Four Cylinder		
1983-87-151 eng.	8128972	142.50
150 eng.	8130336	142.50
Six Cylinder		
1983-87	8130336	142.50
A.M.C. Jeep		
727 trans.		
1983-87	8133386	143.00
904 & 999 trans.		
1983-87-exc. 70 Ser.		
Six cyl.	8130336	142.50
Four cyl.	8128972	142.50
1984-87-70 Series		
Gas eng.	8130336	142.50
Diesel eng.	8983501959	218.00
(10) Gasket, Pump Housing		
1983-87-exc. 727	8126903	2.50
727 trans.	8126898	2.50
(11) Bushing, Reaction Shaft		
1983-87-exc. 727	8128974	6.75
727 trans.	8120865	6.25
(12) Seal, Reaction Shaft		
1983-87-exc. 727	8120866	1.75
727 trans.	8120867	4.00
(13) Kickdown Band		
1983-87-exc. 727	8132494	34.75
727 trans.	8123297	32.00

PARTS 23 CONVERTER, PUMP & CLUTCH 23 PARTS

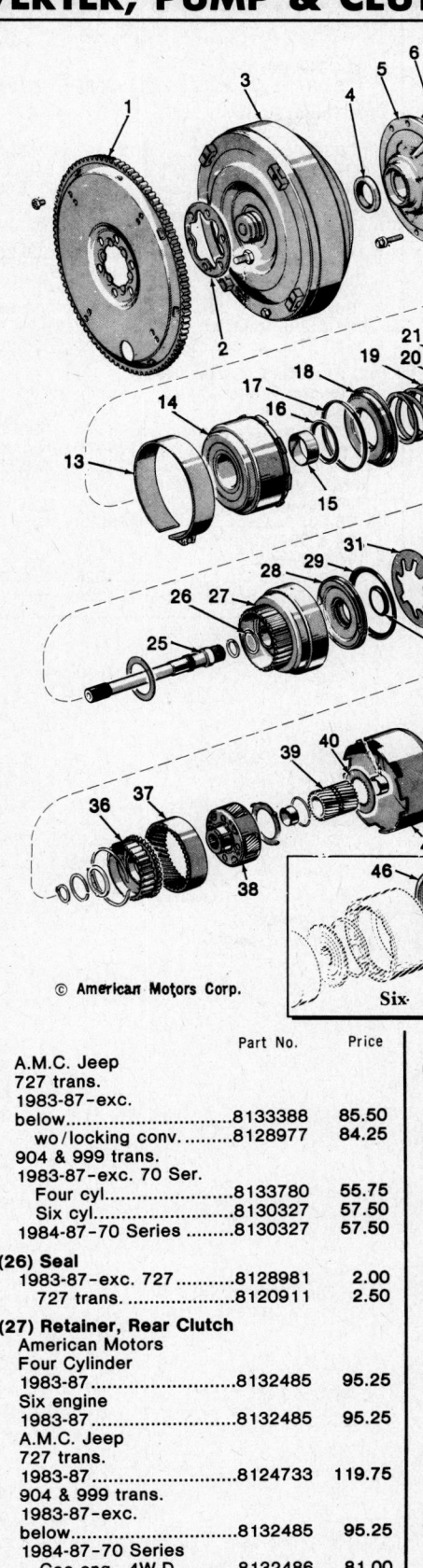

	Part No.	Price
(14) Retainer, Front Clutch		
American Motors		
1983-87-exc.		
below	8120843	113.50
Four cyl	8120943	107.25
727 trans.	8128968	126.50
A.M.C. Jeep		
727 trans.		
1983-87-exc.		
below	8128969	126.50
wo/locking conv.	8128968	126.50
904 & 999 trans.		
1983-87-exc. 70		
Ser.	8132483	119.00
Six cyl.	8132483	119.00
1984-87-70 series		
Gas eng.	8120843	113.50
Diesel eng	8120943	107.25
Four cyl	8120943	107.25
(15) Bushing, Front Clutch		
1983-87-exc. 727	8120896	9.25
727 trans.	8128970	29.75
(16) Seal, Front Clutch (Inner)		
1983-87-exc. 727	8120881	2.50
727 trans.	8120882	2.50
(17) Seal, Front Clutch (Outer)		
1983-87-exc. 727	8132510	5.25
727 trans.	8120884	2.50
(18) Piston, Front Clutch		
American Motors		
1983-87	8123447	26.50
A.M.C. Jeep		
727 trans.		
1983-87	8120880	41.25
904 & 999 trans.		
1983-87-exc. 70 Ser.		
Four cyl	8123447	26.50
Six cyl.	8132484	26.25
1984-87-70 Series	8123447	26.50
(19) Spring, Front Clutch		
American Motors		
Four Cylinder		
1983-87-exc.		
4W.D.	8133387	5.25
4W.D.	8126888	4.25
Six Cylinder		
1983-87-exc.		
4W.D.	8120967	5.25
4W.D.	8126888	4.25
A.M.C. Jeep		
727 trans		
1983-87	8120966	.75
904 & 999 trans.		
1983-87	8126888	4.25
(20) Retainer		
1983-87-exc. 727	8120885	2.50
727 trans.	8120886	3.75
(21) Ring, Inner		
1983-87-exc. 727	8120887	1.50
727 trans.	8120888	1.50
(22) Plates, Front Clutch Drive		
1983-87-exc. 727	8120890	4.00
727 trans.	8136611	3.75
(23) Disc Assy., Front Clutch		
1983-87-exc. 727	8120879	4.75
727 trans.	8120889	4.25
(24) Pressure Plate, Front Clutch		
1983-87-exc. 727	8120932	12.50
727 trans.	8120933	15.75
(25) Input Shaft		
American Motors		
Four Cylinder		
1983-87-exc. 150	8133780	55.75
150 eng.	8130327	57.50
Six Cylinder		
1983-87	8130327	57.50

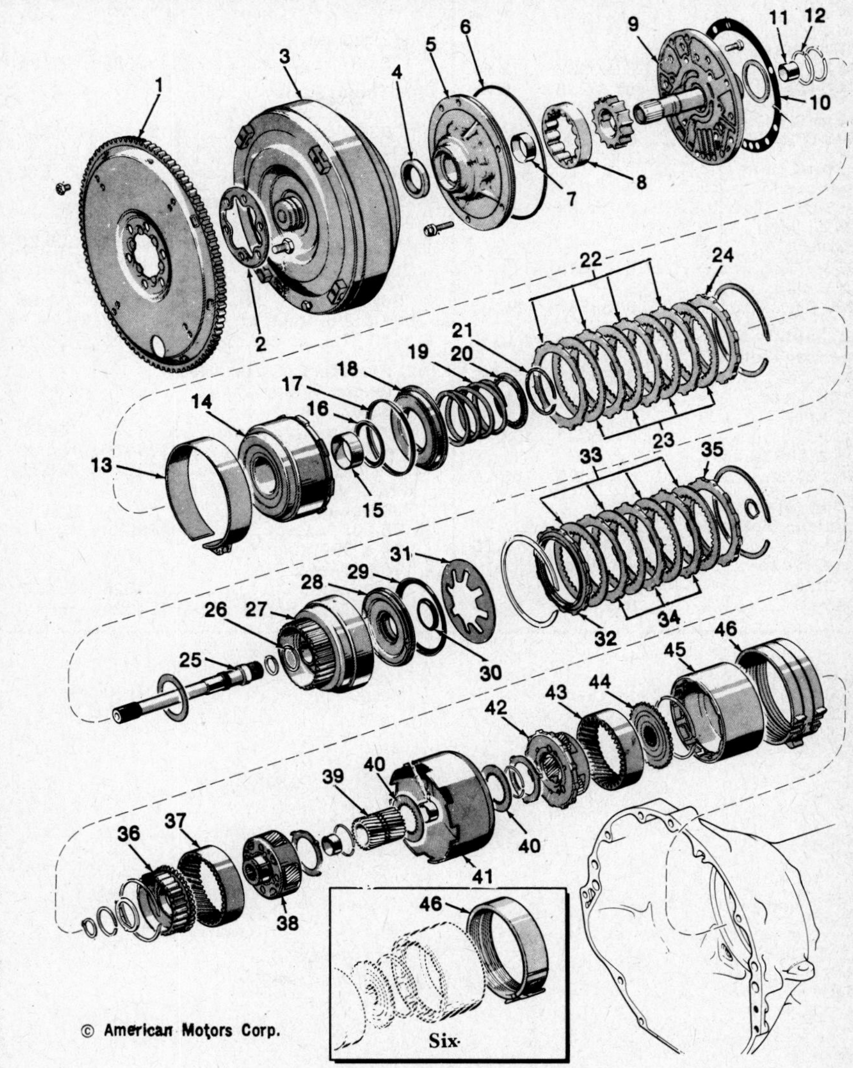

© American Motors Corp.

	Part No.	Price
A.M.C. Jeep		
727 trans.		
1983-87-exc.		
below	8133388	85.50
wo/locking conv.	8128977	84.25
904 & 999 trans.		
1983-87-exc. 70 Ser.		
Four cyl	8133780	55.75
Six cyl	8130327	57.50
1984-87-70 Series	8130327	57.50
(26) Seal		
1983-87-exc. 727	8128981	2.00
727 trans.	8120911	2.50
(27) Retainer, Rear Clutch		
American Motors		
Four Cylinder		
1983-87	8132485	95.25
Six engine		
1983-87	8132485	95.25
A.M.C. Jeep		
727 trans.		
1983-87	8124733	119.75
904 & 999 trans.		
1983-87-exc.		
below	8132485	95.25
1984-87-70 Series		
Gas eng., 4W.D.	8132486	81.00

	Part No.	Price
(28) Piston, Rear Clutch		
1983-87-exc. 727	8120912	29.25
727 trans.	8124732	30.00
(29) Seal, Rear Clutch Piston (Outer)		
1983-87-exc. 727	8120917	2.50
727 trans.	8120918	2.50
(30) Seal, Rear Clutch Piston (Inner)		
1983-87-exc. 727	8120915	2.00
727 trans.	8120916	2.00
(31) Spring, Rear Clutch		
727 trans.		
1983-87	8124734	8.25
904 & 999 trans.		
1983-87	8120919	5.75
(32) Pressure Plate, Front		
1983-87-exc. 727	8120926	13.50
727 trans.	8120927	12.75
(33) Disc Assy. Rear Clutch		
1983-87-exc. 727	8120928	5.00
727 trans.	8120929	4.75
(34) Plates, Rear		
1983-87-exc. 727	8120890	4.00
727 trans.	8136611	3.75

PARTS 23 CONVERTER, PUMP & CLUTCH 23 PARTS

	Part No.	Price
(35) Pressure Plate, Rear		
1983-87-exc. 727	8120932	12.50
727 trans.	8120933	15.75
(36) Front Gear Support		
1983-87	8133396	72.25
(37) Front Gear		
American Motors		
1983-87	8133393	85.00
A.M.C. Jeep		
727 trans.		
1983-87	8121015	111.75
904 & 999 trans.		
1983-87	8133393	85.00
(38) Planetary Carrier (Front)		
American Motors		
1983-87	8133395	156.25
A.M.C. Jeep		
727 trans.		
1983-87	8126582	168.75
904 & 999 trans.		
1983-87	8133395	156.25
(39) Sun Gear		
American Motors		
1983-87	8133389	73.25
A.M.C. Jeep		
727 trans.		
1983-87	8121285	81.00
904 & 999 trans.		
1983-87	8133389	73.25
(40) Thrust Plate		
727 trans.		
1983-87	8121027	2.50
904 & 999 trans.		
1983-87	8133391	3.75
(41) Shell, Sun Gear Driving		
American Motors		
1983-87	8133390	25.25
A.M.C. Jeep		
727 trans.		
1983-87	8121026	38.25
904 & 999 trans.		
1983-87	8133390	25.25
(42) Planetary Carrier (Rear)		
American Motors		
1983-87-exc.		
below	8124324	154.00
4W.D.	8124325	154.00
727 trans.	8121070	168.75
A.M.C. Jeep		
727 trans.		
1983-87	8121070	168.75
904 & 999 trans.		
1983-87-exc. 70		
Ser	8124325	154.00
1984-87-70 Series	8124324	154.00
(43) Rear Gear		
American Motors		
1983-87	8124159	85.00
A.M.C. Jeep		
727 trans.		
1983-87	8121075	123.50
904 & 999 trans.		
1983-87	8124159	85.00
(44) Rear Gear Support		
1983-87	8121074	64.00
(45) Reverse Drum		
1983-87-exc. 727	8132492	91.25
727 trans.	8121080	91.25
(46) Reverse Band		
American Motors		
1983-87-exc.		
below	8132493	38.50
4W.D.	8132812	59.00
727 trans.	8121119	54.25
A.M.C. Jeep		
727 trans.		
1983-87	8121119	54.25
904 & 999 trans.		
1983-87-exc 70		
Ser	8132812	59.00
1984-87-70 Series	8132493	38.50

(Factory Time) Chilton Time

CHRYSLER TORQUE FLITE - A404 - A413 - A470

ON CAR SERVICES

(G) Drain & Refill Unit
All models.................................... .6

(G) Oil Pressure Check
All models.................................... .8

(M) Check Unit For Oil Leaks
Includes: Clean and dry outside of case and run unit to determine point of leak.
All models.................................... .9

(G) Neutral Safety Switch, Renew
All models (.3) 4

(G) Transmission Auxiliary Oil Cooler, Renew
1983-87
Ramvan-Caravan-Voyager (.5) 9
All other models (.3) 6

(G) Oil Cooler Lines, Renew
Includes: Cut and form to size.
1983-87 (.4)................................ .6

(G) Throttle Linkage, Adjust
1983-87 (.2)................................ .4

(G) Kickdown Band, Adjust
1983-87 (.2)................................ .4

(G) Throttle Lever Control Cable, Renew
Includes: Adjust cable.
1983-87 (.3)................................ .6

(G) Extension Housing 'O' Ring Seal, Renew
1983-87 (.5)................................ .7

(G) Extension Housing and/or Bearing Retainer, Renew
1983-87 (2.4)............................... 3.3
Renew inner C.V. Joint,
add (.2)....................................... .2

(G) Throttle Valve Lever Shaft Seal, Renew
1983-87 (.5)................................ .8

(G) Valve Body Manual Lever Shaft Seal, Renew
1983-87 (.3)................................ .6

(G) Differential Gear Cover, Renew or Reseal
1983-87 (.8)................................ 1.2

(G) Drive Shaft Boot, Renew
Includes: Clean and lubricate C/V joint.
All models
1983-87
one-inner or outer (.7) 1.0
both-one side (1.0)..................... 1.4
Renew shaft seal, add
right side (.1) 1
left side (.3)............................... .3

(G) Drive Shaft C/V Joint, Renew
All models
1983-87
one-inner or outer (.7) 1.0
both-one side (1.0)..................... 1.4
inter shaft U-joint (.6)................ 1.0
Renew shaft seal, add
right side (.1) 1
left side (.3)............................... .3

(G) Front Wheel Drive Shaft Assy., Renew
All models
1983-87
inter spline yoke (.6)................. 1.0
inter stub shaft (.6) 1.0

CHILTON'S AUTOMATIC TRANSMISSION TUNE-UP

1. Check engine performance
2. Check condition of transmission oil
3. Check transmission, oil cooler and oil cooler lines for external leaks
4. Remove oil pan, clean or renew screen or filter
5. Torque valve body
6. Adjust bands
7. Clean oil pan and install pan with new gasket
8. Check modulator and hose
9. Install new transmission oil to proper level
10. Adjust manual and throttle linkage
11. Road test

All models 1.5
Charge for parts used

(Factory Time) Chilton Time

all others-each (1.0).................. 1.4
Renew shaft seal, add
right side (.1) 1
left side (.3)............................... .3

(G) Intermediate Shaft Support Bearing, Renew
1984-87-each (.6)........................ 1.0

(G) Drive Shaft Seal, Renew
1983-87
right side (.5) 8
left side (.8)............................... 1.1

(G) Transfer Gear Cover, Renew or Reseal
1983-87 (.5)................................ .7

(G) Transfer Gear Set, Renew
Includes: R&R cover, renew bearing.
1983-87 (1.0)............................... 1.3

(G) Governor Assy., Renew or Recondition
Includes: R&R oil pan.
1983-87 (1.3)............................... 2.4

(G) Governor Support and Parking Gear, Renew
Includes: R&R oil pan.
1983-87 (1.9)............................... 2.9

(G) Oil Pan and/or Gasket, Renew
1983-87 (.6)................................ 1.2

(G) Oil Filter, Renew
Includes: R&R oil pan.
1983-87 (.7)................................ 1.4

(G) Parking Lock Sprag, Renew
Includes: R&R oil pan.
1983-87 (1.5)............................... 2.6

(G) Accumulator Piston, Renew or Recondition
Includes: R&R oil pan.
1983-87 (1.1)............................... 2.2

(G) Kickdown Servo, Renew
Includes: R&R oil pan.
1983-87 (1.4)............................... 2.5

(Factory Time) Chilton Time

(G) Reverse Servo, Renew or Recondition
Includes: R&R oil pan.
1983-87 (1.2)............................... 2.2

(G) Valve Body, Renew
Includes: R&R oil pan and renew filter.
1983-87 (1.0)............................... 2.1

(P) Valve Body, R&R and Recondition
Includes: R&R oil pan and renew filter.
1983-87 (1.7)............................... 3.2

SERVICES REQUIRING R&R

(G) Trans/Axle Assy., Remove & Install
Omni & Horizon
1983-87
1.6-1.7L engs (2.7)..................... 3.7
2.2L eng (3.1)............................ 4.2
w/Cruise control add (.2)................ .2
All other models
1983-87
2.2L eng (3.4)............................ 3.7
2.6L eng (3.6)............................ 4.1

(G) Trans/Axle Assembly, Reseal
Includes: R&R trans axle and renew all seals and gaskets.
Omni & Horizon
1983-87
1.6-1.7L engs............................ 7.0
2.2L eng.................................... 7.5
w/Cruise control add (.2)................ .2
All other models
1983-87
2.2L eng (5.4)............................ 7.0
2.6L eng (5.6)............................ 7.4

(G) Trans/Axle Assembly, Renew
Includes: Remove and reinstall all necessary interfering parts. Transfer any parts not supplied with replacement unit. Road test.
Omni & Horizon
1983-87
1.6-1.7L engs (3.1)..................... 4.3
2.2L eng (3.5)............................ 4.8
w/Cruise control add (.2)................ .2
All other models
1983-87
2.2L eng (4.3)............................ 4.3
2.6L eng (4.0)............................ 4.7

(P) Trans/Axle Assy., R&R and Recondition
Includes: Disassemble complete, clean, inspect and replace parts as required.
Omni & Horizon
1983-87
1.6-1.7L engs (9.1)..................... 12.5
2.2L eng (9.5)............................ 13.0
w/Cruise control add (.2)................ .2
All other models
1983-87
2.2L eng (9.4)............................ 12.5
2.6L eng (9.6)............................ 12.9
Flush converter and cooler lines
add (.5)....................................... .5

(G) Kickdown Band, Renew
Omni & Horizon
1983-87
1.6-1.7L engs (3.6)..................... 4.9
2.2L eng (4.0)............................ 5.4
w/Cruise control add (.2)................ .2
All other models
1983-87
2.2L eng (4.3)............................ 4.9
2.6L eng (4.5)............................ 5.3

LABOR 23 AUTOMATIC TRANSAXLE 23 LABOR

(Factory Time) Chilton Time

(G) Reverse Band, Renew
Omni & Horizon
1983-87
1.6-1.7L engs (3.8) 5.2
2.2L eng (4.2) 5.7
w/Cruise control add (.2) 2

All other models
1983-87
2.2L eng (4.5) 5.2
2.6L eng (4.7) 5.6

(G) Trans/Axle Case, Renew
Omni & Horizon
1983-87
1.6-1.7L engs (7.3) 10.0
2.2L eng (7.7) 10.5
w/Cruise control add (.2) 2
All other models
1983-87
2.2L eng (8.0) 10.0
2.6L eng (8.2) 10.4

(G) Front and Rear Clutch Seals, Renew
Omni & Horizon
1983-87
1.6-1.7L engs (3.8) 5.2
2.2L eng (4.2) 5.7
w/Cruise control add (.2) 2

All other models
1983-87
2.2L eng (4.5) 5.2
2.6L eng (4.7) 5.6

(Factory Time) Chilton Time

(G) Torque Converter, Renew
Omni & Horizon
1983-87
1.6-1.7L eng (2.9) 4.0
2.2L eng (3.3) 4.5
w/Cruise control add (.2) 2

All other models
1983-87
2.2L eng (3.6) 4.0
2.6L eng (3.8) 4.4

(G) Torque Converter Drive Plate, Renew
(Flywheel)
Omni & Horizon
1983-87
1.6-1.7L engs (2.9) 4.0
2.2L eng (3.3) 4.5
w/Cruise control add (.2) 2

All other models
1983-87
2.2L eng (3.6) 4.0
2.6L eng (3.8) 4.4

(G) Front Oil Pump, Renew
Omni & Horizon
1983-87
1.6-1.7L engs (3.3) 4.5
2.2L eng (3.7) 5.0
w/Cruise control add (.2) 2
All other models
1983-87
2.2L eng (4.0) 4.5
2.6L eng (4.2) 4.9

(Factory Time) Chilton Time

(G) Front Pump Oil Seal, Renew
Omni & Horizon
1983-87
1.6-1.7L engs (2.9) 4.0
2.2L eng (3.3) 4.5
w/Cruise control add (.2) 2
All other models
1983-87
2.2L eng (3.6) 4.0
2.6L eng (3.8) 4.4

(G) Reaction Shaft and/or Bushing, Renew
Includes: Renew front pump if necessary.
Omni & Horizon
1983-87
1.6-1.7L engs (3.3) 4.5
2.2L eng (3.7) 5.0
w/Cruise control add (.2) 2
All other models
1983-87
2.2L eng (4.0) 4.5
2.6L eng (4.2) 4.9

(P) Trans Axle Differential Assy., Recondition
Includes: R&R trans axle, completely recondition differential assembly only.
Omni & Horizon
1983-87
1.6-1.7L engs (6.6) 9.0
2.2L eng (7.0) 9.5
w/Cruise control add (.2) 2
All other models
1983-87
2.2L eng (6.6) 9.0
2.6L eng (6.9) 9.4

PARTS 23 CASE AND PARTS 23 PARTS

Part No. Price

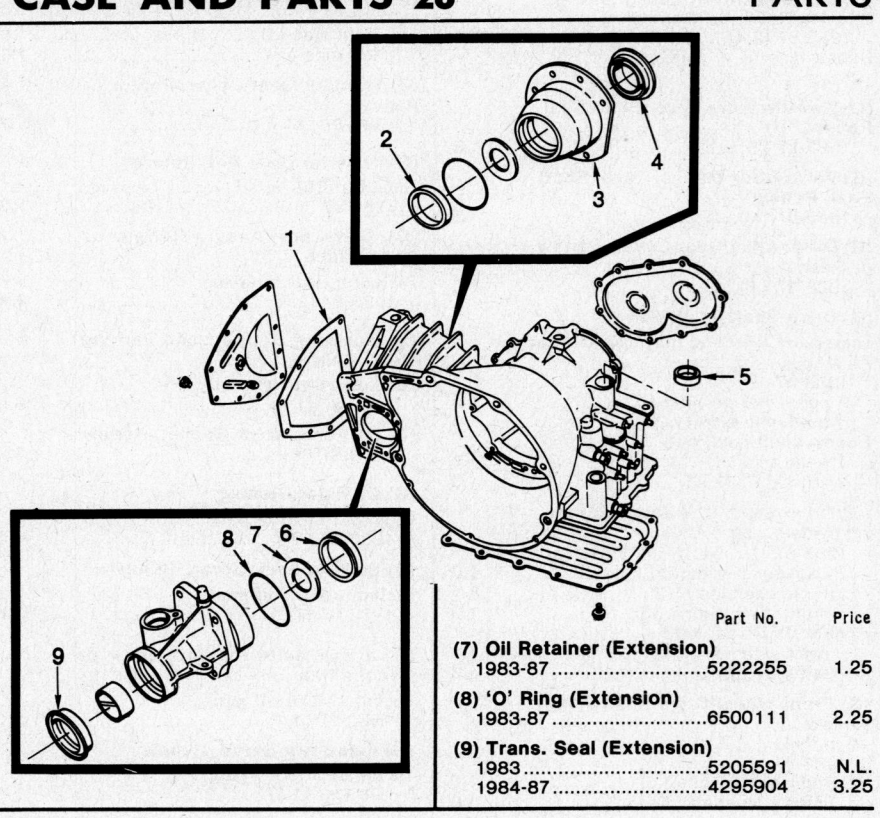

CASE, EXTENSION AND RETAINER

Transaxle Assembly (New)
Order by year and model.

Neutral Starter & Back-up Switch
1983-87 .... 4057750 8.75

Valve Body
1983-87-exc. below 4269716 246.00
4329538, 4377907, 955 trans. 4269929 246.00

Filter Screen
1983-87 .... 4269649 6.00

(1) Oil Pan Gasket
1983-87-Use R.T.V. Sealer

(2) Differential Cup
1983-84 .... 5222259 5.50
1985-87 .... 4269676 5.50

(3) Bearing Retainer
1983-87 .... 4205855 43.00

(4) Seal
1983 .... 5205591 N.L.
1984-87 .... 4295904 3.25

Gasket, Rear Cover
Gasket is not serviced; use R.T.V. sealer.

(5) Seal (Manual Lever)
1983-87 .... 3878447 2.25

(6) Cup (Extension)
1983-84 .... 5222259 5.50
1985-87 .... 4269676 5.50

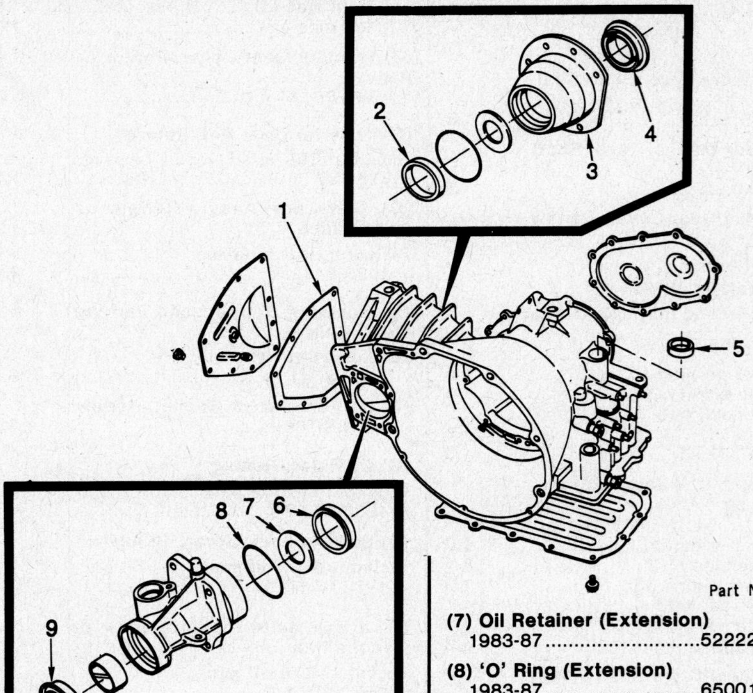

Part No. Price

(7) Oil Retainer (Extension)
1983-87 .... 5222255 1.25

(8) 'O' Ring (Extension)
1983-87 .... 6500111 2.25

(9) Trans. Seal (Extension)
1983 .... 5205591 N.L.
1984-87 .... 4295904 3.25

PARTS 23 OIL PUMP & REACTION SHAFTS 23 PARTS

	Part No.	Price
(1) Seal		
1983-87	5212305	2.00
(2) Reaction Shaft (w/Support)		
1983-85	5222412	76.50
1986-87	4377120	75.00
(3) Oil Pump Housing (w/Bushing & Rotor)		
1983-85	4207217	120.75
1986-87	4377996	121.00
(4) Gasket (Pump Housing)		
1983-87	4269661	1.00
(5) Seal (Pump Housing)		
1983-87	5205660	2.00
(6) Impeller Hub Seal (Torque Conv.)		
1983-87	4269057	7.00

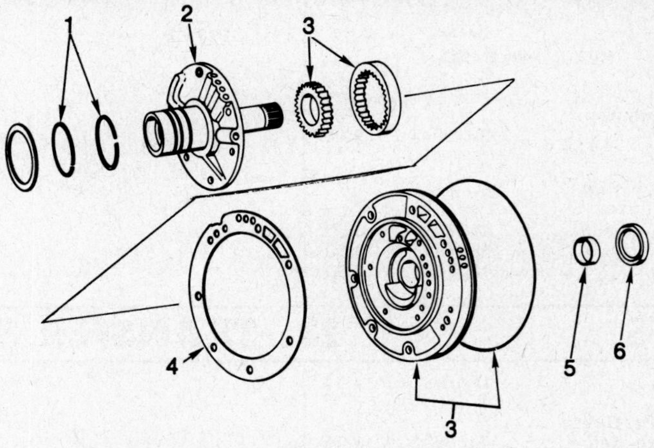

PARTS 23 FRONT & REAR SERVO 23 PARTS

	Part No.	Price
(1) Guide Ring (Kickdown Servo)		
1983-87	6031545	1.25
(2) Guide (Kickdown Servo)		
1983-87	5224344	7.00
(3) Piston Spring (Kickdown Servo)		
1983-87-exc. below	4207229	1.25
4329538, 4377907, 955 trans	4207205	1.25
(4) Piston Rod (Kickdown Servo)		
1983-87	4058943	8.25
(5) Piston (Kickdown Servo)		
1983-87	4269524	7.50
(6) Piston (Accumulator)		
1983-87	3410908	10.75
(7) Spring (Accumulator)		
1983-87-exc. below	4207211	2.25
4329538, 4377907, 955 trans	4329807	2.25
(8) Plate (Accumulator)		
1983-87	4205857	4.75
(9) Plate Ring (Accumulator)		
1983-87	6031545	1.25
(10) Spring Retainer (Reverse Servo)		
1983-87	4205854	15.25
(11) Piston Spring (Reverse Servo)		
1983-87	3681434	2.50
(12) Plug (Reverse Servo)		
1983-87	4269707	7.00

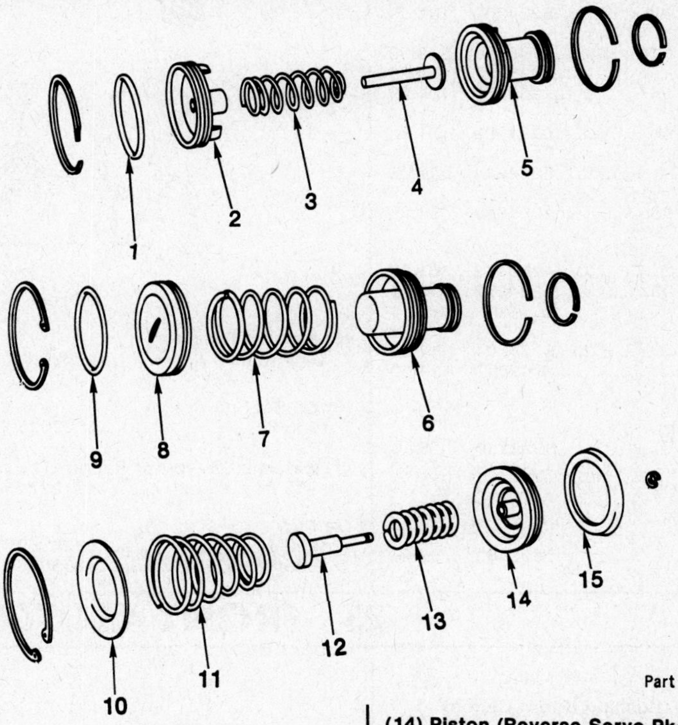

	Part No.	Price
(13) Spring (Rev. Servo Cushion)		
1983-87	4205854	15.25

	Part No.	Price
(14) Piston (Reverse Servo Pkg.)		
1983-87	3743898	10.75
(15) Piston Seal (Reverse Servo)		
1983-87	4269736	2.00

PARTS 23 REVERSE BAND & LINKAGE 23 PARTS

	Part No.	Price
(1) Lever (w/Pin and Stem)		
1983-87	5224203	6.50
(2) Strut		
1983-87	5224264	2.75
(3) Reverse Band		
1983-87	5205765	28.00
(4) Anchor		
1983-87	5212344	3.75
(5) Lever Shaft		
1983-87	5222090	3.00

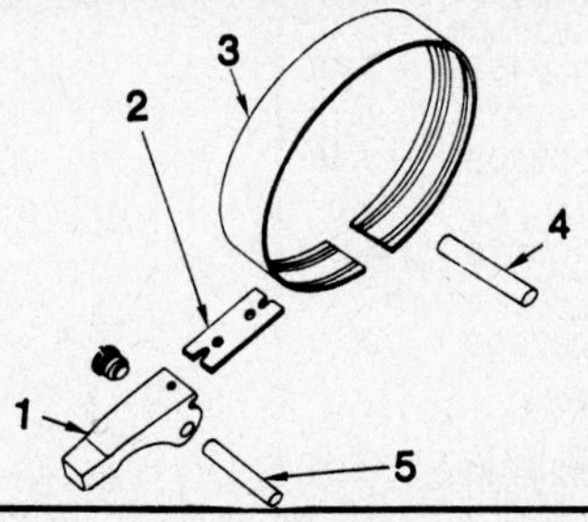

PARTS 23 BAND & LINKAGE 23 PARTS

	Part No.	Price
KICKDOWN BAND		
(1) Lever Shaft		
1983-87	5212047	2.25
(2) Lever (w/Pin)		
1983-87-exc. below	4207009	6.50
1.7 L	4207091	6.50
1.6 L	4207091	6.50

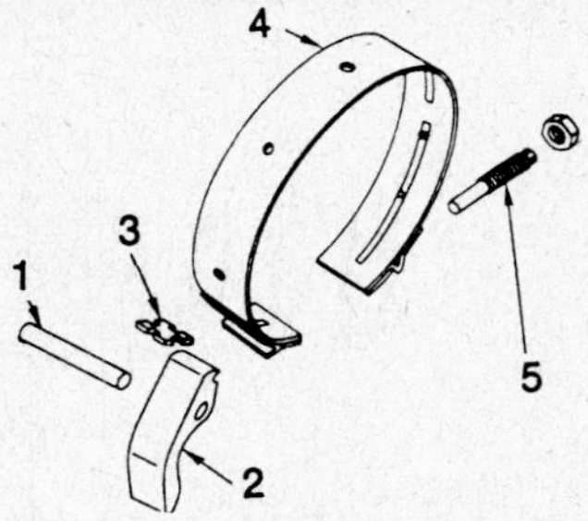

	Part No.	Price
(3) Strut		
1983-87	5212343	2.50
(4) Kickdown Band		
1983-87	4269663	14.00
(5) Adjusting Screw		
1983-87	5212255	2.25

PARTS 23 TRANSFER SHAFT 23 PARTS

	Part No.	Price
(1) Shaft (w/Gear)		
1983-exc. below	4186873	213.00
(Trans. I.D.)		
4295383	4293069	N.L.
4269687	4205889	N.L.
4269684, 791	4186872	N.L.
1984-exc. below	5224209	101.50
(Trans. I.D.)		
4295512, 514	4186873	213.00
4329827	4295842	101.25
4229555, 557	4269172	101.25
1985-87-exc. below	5224209	101.50
(Trans. I.D.)		
4207905	5224211	99.75
4329538, 564, 4377907, 955	4295842	101.25
4329546, 565, 4377903, 911, 952, 958	4269172	101.25
4377902, 951	5224209	99.75
(2) Bearing		
1983-84	5224301	11.00
1985-87	4269677	11.00
(3) Bearing Cup		
1983-84	5222259	5.50
1985-87	4269676	5.50
(4) "O" Ring		
1983-87	6500169	2.25

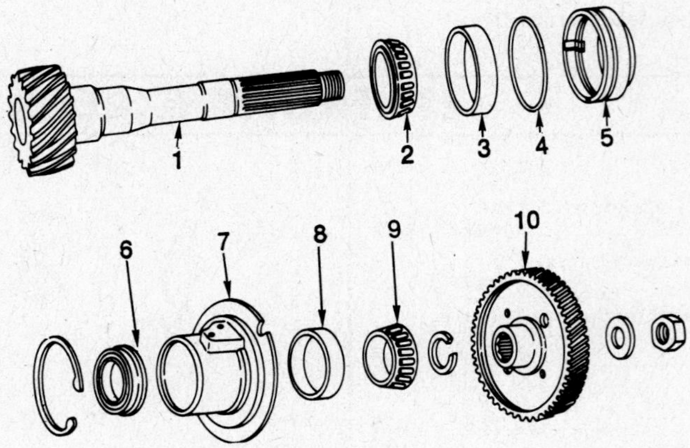

	Part No.	Price
(5) Bearing Retainer		
1983-87	4269688	13.50
(6) Oil Seal		
1983-87	5222015	6.00
(7) Retainer (Governor Support)		
1983-87	5212371	35.25
(8) Cup		
1983-84	5222259	5.50
1985-87	4269676	5.50

	Part No.	Price
(9) Bearing		
1983-84	5224301	11.00
1985-87	4269677	11.00
(10) Gear Set		
1983-87-exc. below	4205871	173.25
(Trans. I.D.)		
4269683, 686, 687, 4295896, 4295512, 4207905, 4377906, 954	4186871	173.25

PARTS 23 FRONT CLUTCH 23 PARTS

	Part No.	Price
(1) Retainer w/Bushing (Front Clutch)		
1983-87-exc. below	5224316	70.00
1.7 L	5224169	70.00
(2) Front Clutch Piston Seal (Inner)		
1983-87	5205670	2.00
(3) Piston (Front Clutch)		
1983-87	5224171	12.50
(4) Front Clutch Piston Seal (Outer)		
1983-87	4058487	3.75
(5) Plate (Front Clutch)		
1983-87	4207208	3.50
(6) Disc (Front Clutch)		
1983-87	5205675	4.25
(7) Reaction Plate (Front Clutch)		
1983-87	4207209	9.50
(8) Piston Spring (Front Clutch)		
1983-87-exc. below	5224144	4.50

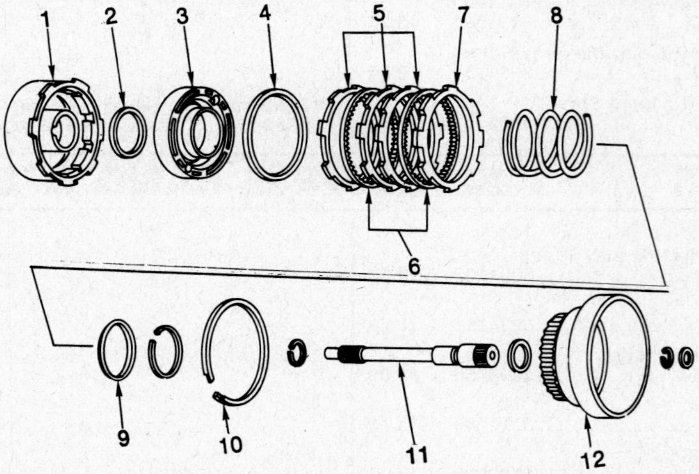

PARTS 23 FRONT CLUTCH 23 PARTS

	Part No.	Price
w/4329538 trans	4207227	4.50
(9) Retainer (Front Clutch)		
1983-87	5205673	2.25
(10) Seal Ring (Input Shaft)		
1983-85	1401221	1.75
1986-87	4377047	1.00
(11) Input Shaft		
1983-85	5222400	40.75
1986-87	4377106	39.75
(12) Retainer (Rear Clutch)		
1983-87-exc. below	4269624	68.00
(Trans. I.D.) 4295514, 4329555, 4329557, 827, 4329538, 546, 4329564, 565, 4377903, 907, 911, 952, 955, 958	4269616	69.25

PARTS 23 REAR CLUTCH 23 PARTS

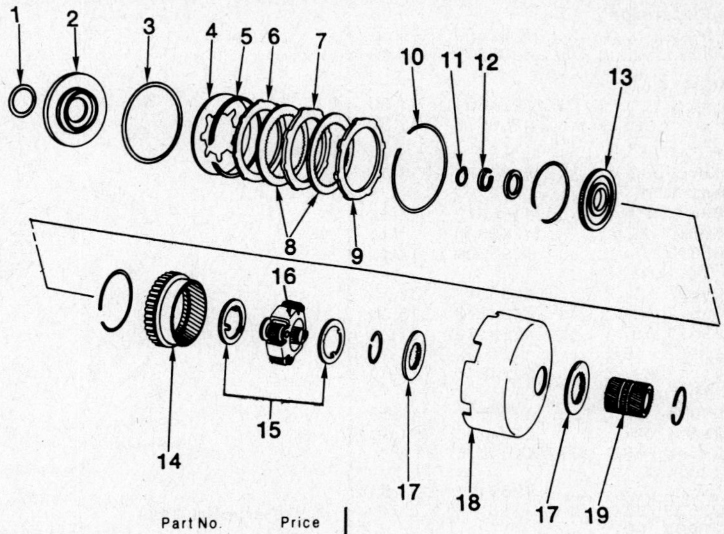

	Part No.	Price
(1) Rear Clutch Piston Seal (Inner)		
1983-87	5212373	2.00
(2) Piston (Rear Clutch)		
1983-87	4207202	20.50
(3) Rear Clutch Piston Seal (Outer)		
1983-87	5205701	2.50
(4) Piston Spring (Rear Clutch)		
1983-87-exc. below	4207246	5.25
(Trans. I.D.) 4295514, 4329555, 4329557, 827, 4329538, 546, 4329564, 565, 4377903, 907, 911, 952, 955, 958	4269623	5.25
(5) Rear Clutch Spring (Wave)		
1983-87	4207265	2.75
(6) Reaction Plate (Rear Clutch)		
1983	5224072	9.75
1984-87	4269619	10.00
(7) Plate (Rear Clutch)		
1983-87	5224073	3.50
(8) Disc (Rear Clutch)		
1983-87	5224084	4.00
(9) Pressure Plate (Rear Clutch)		
1983	4207181	9.75
1984-87	4269618	10.00
(10) Snap Ring (Rear Clutch)		
1983-87	4130775	2.00
(11) Snap Ring (Input Shaft)		
1983-87	5205691	.50
(12) Seal Ring (Rear Clutch)		
1983-87	5205697	2.00
(13) Support w/Bushing (Frt. Annulus)		
1983-87	5224070	51.00
(14) Front Annulus Gear		
1983	5224310	N.L.
1984-87	4269620	68.75
(15) Thrust Washer (Frt. Planet Carrier)		
1983-87	5224066	1.75
(16) Front Planet Pinion Carrier		
1983	4269941	110.00
1984-87	4269941	110.00
Includes hub, cup, plate, pinion, shaft, rollers and washers.		
(17) Thrust Plate (Sun Gear Shell)		
1983-87	5205737	2.00
(18) Sun Gear Driving Shell		
1983-87	4207195	19.50
(19) Sun Gear (w/Bushing)		
1983-87	5224192	57.50

PARTS 23 REAR CARRIER & SHAFT 23 PARTS

	Part No.	Price
(1) Output Shaft		
1983-84	4269599	N.L.
1985-87	4329822	28.00
(2) Washer (Rear Planet Carrier)		
1983-87	5205724	2.00
(3) Rear Planet Pinion Carrier		
1983	5205740	16.75
1984-87	4269942	110.00
Includes pinion, plate, shaft, rollers and washers.		
(4) Rear Annulus Gear		
1983-87	5222047	67.50
(5) Drum, w/Cam (Low and Reverse)		
1983-87	4207117	72.00
Bushing (Low and Reverse)		
1983-87	5222137	5.00

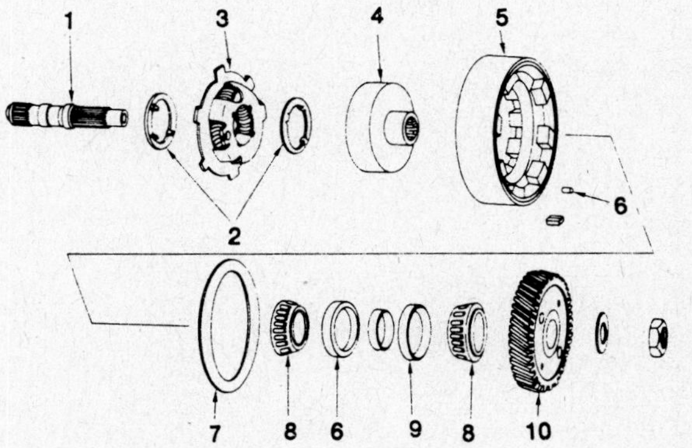

PARTS 23 REAR CARRIER & SHAFT 23 PARTS

	Part No.	Price
(6) Spring & Roller Pkg. (Overrun. Clutch)		
1983-87	4186886	4.25
(7) Thrust Washer (Overrun, Clutch)		
1983-87	5205772	2.25
(8) Bearing (Output Shaft)		
1983-87	5224300	10.75
(9) Cup Pkg.		
1983-87	5224299	5.00
(10) Gear Set (Output Shaft)		
1983-exc. below	4186889	173.25
wo/Hi alt.	4186871	173.25
Hi alt.	4205871	173.25
1984-87-exc. below	4205871	173.25
(Trans. I.D.) 4295512, 4207905, 4337906, 954	4186871	173.25

PARTS 23 DIFFERENTIAL 23 PARTS

	Part No.	Price
(1) Cup (Extension)		
1983-84	5222259	5.50
1985-87	4269676	5.50
(2) Bearing		
1983-84	5224301	11.00
1985-87	4269677	11.00
(3) Gear Set		
1983-exc. below	4186873	213.00
(Trans. I.D.)		
4269684, 791	4186872	N.L.
4269687	4205889	N.L.
4295838	4293069	N.L.
1984 (Trans. I.D.)		
4329827	4295841	131.50
4295512, 514	4186873	213.00
4329555, 557	4269172	101.25
4329551, 552, 554	5224210	131.50
1985-87 (Trans. I.D.)		
4207905	4186873	213.00
4329506, 547	5224210	131.50
4329546, 565, 4377903, 906, 911, 952, 954, 958	4269171	131.50
4329538, 564, 4377902, 907, 951, 955	4295841	131.50

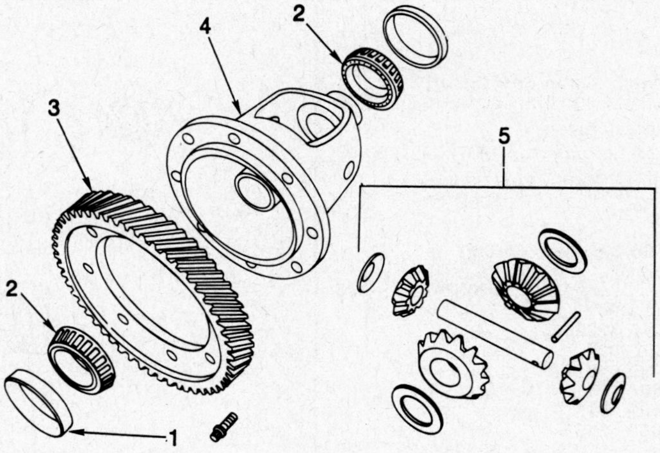

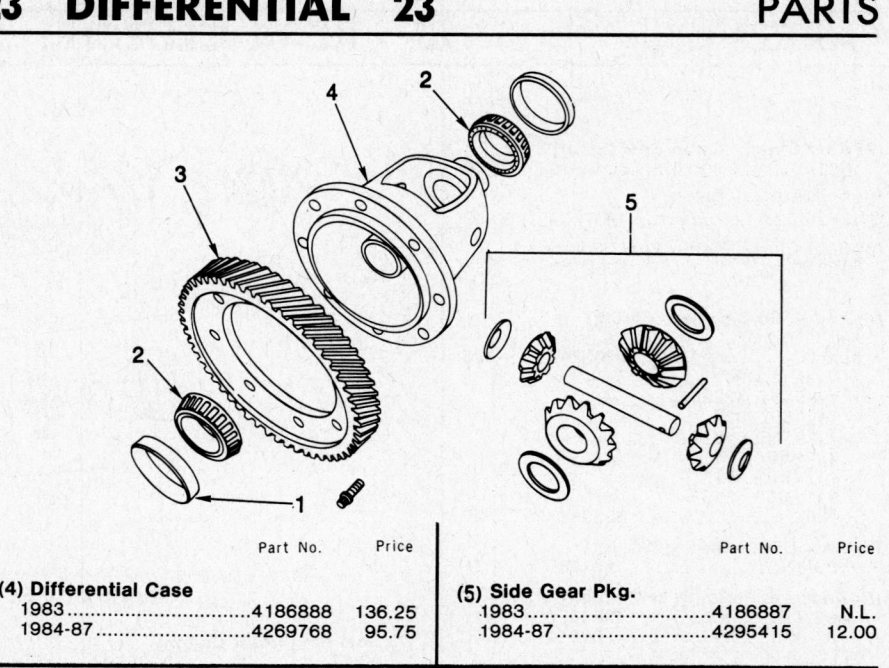

	Part No.	Price
(4) Differential Case		
1983	4186888	136.25
1984-87	4269768	95.75
(5) Side Gear Pkg.		
1983	4186887	N.L.
1984-87	4295415	12.00

(Factory Time) Chilton Time

ON CAR SERVICES

(G) Drain & Refill Unit
All models 7

(G) Oil Pressure Check
All models (.6) 9

(M) Check Unit For Oil Leaks
Includes: Clean and dry outside of case and run unit to determine point of leak.
All models 9

(G) Neutral Safety Switch, Renew
All models (.3) 4

(G) Oil Cooler Lines, Renew
Includes: Cut and form to size.
1983-one (.5) 1.0

(G) Transmission Auxiliary Oil Cooler, Renew
1983
Mirada-Cordoba
Imperial (.6) 9
All other models (.3) 9

(G) Throttle Linkage, Adjust
All models (.3) 6

(G) Bands, Adjust
Includes: R&R oil pan.
All models
kickdown (.7) 1.4
reverse (.7) 1.4

(G) Throttle Valve Lever Shaft Seal, Renew
1983 (.3) 6

(G) Valve Body Manual Lever Shaft Seal, Renew
1983 (.7) 1.0

(G) Extension Housing Oil Seal, Renew
1983 (.4) 1.1

(G) Oil Pan Gasket, Renew
1983 (.6) 1.0

(G) Oil Filter, Renew
1983 (.7) 1.1

(G) Valve Body Assembly, Renew
Includes: R&R oil pan.
1983 (1.1) 1.6

(P) Valve Body Assy., R&R and Recondition
Includes: R&R oil pan and replace filter. Disassemble, clean, inspect, free all valves. Replace parts as required.
1983 (2.0) 2.3

(G) Parking Lock Sprag Control Rod, Renew
Includes: R&R oil pan and remove valve body.
1983 (1.0) 1.8

(G) Accumulator Piston, Renew or Recondition
Includes: R&R oil pan and adjust band.
1983 (1.2) 1.6

(G) Servos, Renew or Recondition
Includes: R&R oil pan and adjust band.
1983-kickdown (.9) 1.8
reverse (.9) 1.8

(G) Extension Housing and/or Gasket, Renew
Gran Fury
1983 (1.4) 2.0
Chrysler - Imperial
1983 (1.4) 2.0
Cordoba - Mirada
1983 (1.4) 2.0

CHILTON'S AUTOMATIC TRANSMISSION TUNE-UP

1. Check engine performance
2. Check condition of transmission oil
3. Check transmission, oil cooler and oil cooler lines for external leaks
4. Remove oil pan, clean or renew screen or filter
5. Torque valve body
6. Adjust bands
7. Clean oil pan and install pan with new gasket
8. Check modulator and hose
9. Install new transmission oil to proper level
10. Adjust manual and throttle linkage
11. Road test

All models 1.5
Charge for parts used

(G) Governor Assembly, Renew or Recondition
Includes: R&R extension housing.
Diplomat - Gran Fury
1983 (1.5) 2.5
Chrysler - Imperial
1983 (1.5) 2.5
Cordoba - Mirada
1983 (1.5) 2.5

SERVICES REQUIRING R&R

(G) Transmission Assembly, R&R
Diplomat - Gran Fury
1983 (2.2) 3.0
Chrysler - Imperial
1983 (2.2) 3.0
Cordoba - Mirada
1983 (2.2) 3.0

(G) Transmission Assembly, Renew (w/Remanufactured Unit)
Includes: R&R trans, remove and install all necessary interfering parts. Transfer any parts not supplied with replacement unit. Road test.
Diplomat - Gran Fury
1983 (2.5) 3.5
Chrysler - Imperial
1983 (2.5) 3.5
Cordoba - Mirada
1983 (2.5) 3.5

(G) Transmission Assembly, Reseal
Includes: R&R trans and renew all seals and gaskets.
Diplomat - Gran Fury
1983 (4.0) 6.2
Chrysler - Imperial
1983 (4.0) 6.2
Cordoba - Mirada
1983 (4.0) 6.2
Flush cooler lines and converter
add (.5) 7

(P) Transmission and Converter, R&R and Recondition
Includes: Disassemble trans including valve body, clean, inspect and replace parts as required.

(Factory Time) Chilton Time

Diplomat - Gran Fury
1983 (6.9) 11.7
Chrysler - Imperial
1983 (6.9) 11.7
Cordoba - Mirada
1983 (6.9) 11.7

(G) Torque Converter Drive Plate, Renew (Flywheel)
Includes: R&R transmission.
Diplomat - Gran Fury
1983 (2.4) 3.3
Chrysler - Imperial
1983 (2.4) 3.3
Cordoba - Mirada
1983 (2.4) 3.3

(G) Torque Converter, Renew
Includes: R&R transmission.
Diplomat - Gran Fury
1983 (2.4) 3.3
Chrysler - Imperial
1983 (2.4) 3.3
Cordoba - Mirada
1983 (2.4) 3.3

(G) Front Pump Oil Seal, Renew
Includes: R&R transmission.
Diplomat - Gran Fury
1983 (2.4) 3.3
Chrysler - Imperial
1983 (2.4) 3.3
Cordoba - Mirada
1983 (2.4) 3.3

(G) Front Oil Pump, Renew or Recondition
Includes: R&R transmission, replace reaction shaft if necessary.
Diplomat - Gran Fury
1983 (2.8) 3.9
Chrysler - Imperial
1983 (2.8) 3.9
Cordoba - Mirada
1983 (2.8) 3.9

(G) Transmission Case, Renew
Includes: R&R transmission.
Diplomat - Gran Fury
1983 (4.1) 5.7
Chrysler - Imperial
1983 (4.1) 5.7
Cordoba - Mirada
1983 (4.1) 5.7

(G) Kickdown Band, Renew
Includes: R&R transmission.
Diplomat - Gran Fury
1983 (2.9) 4.0
Chrysler - Imperial
1983 (2.9) 4.0
Cordoba - Mirada
1983 (2.9) 4.0

(G) Reverse Band, Renew
Includes: R&R transmission.
Diplomat - Gran Fury
1983 (3.3) 4.6
Chrysler - Imperial
1983 (3.3) 4.6
Cordoba - Mirada
1983 (3.3) 4.6

(G) Front and Rear Clutch Seals, Renew
Includes: R&R transmission.
Diplomat - Gran Fury
1983 (3.3) 4.6
Chrysler - Imperial
1983 (3.3) 4.6
Cordoba - Mirada
1983 (3.3) 4.6

PARTS 23 CASE & PARTS 23 PARTS

	Part No.	Price
Transmission Assembly		
Chrysler Corporation supplies remanufactured transmissions as well as remanufactured torque converter units. Check Chrysler dealer for availability and prices.		
Drive Plate (Flex Plate)		
1983	4058429	17.25
Transmission Seal and Gasket Kit		
1983	4186864	65.50
(1) Gasket		
1983	2466954	3.75
(2) Support (Output Shaft)		
1983	2466882	50.50
(3) Governor Weight Pkg.		
1983	4130892	6.25
(4) Bearing (Output Shaft)		
1983	2466224	19.25
(5) Valve Shaft (Governor)		
1983	1556082	2.50
(6) Valve (Governor)		
1983	3515479	6.00
(7) Governor Repair Pkg.		
1983	4106587	5.00
(8) Support (Governor)		
1983	3743517	47.75
(9) Shaft (Output)		
1983	4106594	150.00
(10) Switch (Neutral & Back-Up)		
1983	4057750	8.75
(11) Seal		
1983	3878447	2.25
(12) Piston (Kickdown)		
1983-exc below	3410440	14.75
w/Inner rod	3410445	14.75
(13) Piston (Accumulator)		
1983	3410908	10.75
(14) Spring		
1983	3410444	1.00
(15) Spring		
1983	3410518	2.50
(16) Spring (Accumulator Piston)		
1983	3515079	2.50
(17) Valve Body & Plate		
1983	4202578	299.75
(18) Filter		
1983	3515996	6.00
(19) Gasket (Pan)		
1983	2464324	3.00
(20) Link w/Anchor (Reverse Band)		
1983	2204820	18.75

	Part No.	Price
(21) Lever w/Stem (Reverse Band)		
1983	1942137	22.25
(22) Retainer (Reverse Servo)		
1983	1942150	2.00

	Part No.	Price
(23) Spring (Reverse Servo Piston)		
1983	2801241	2.50
(24) Plug (Reverse Servo)		
1983	3743353	7.00

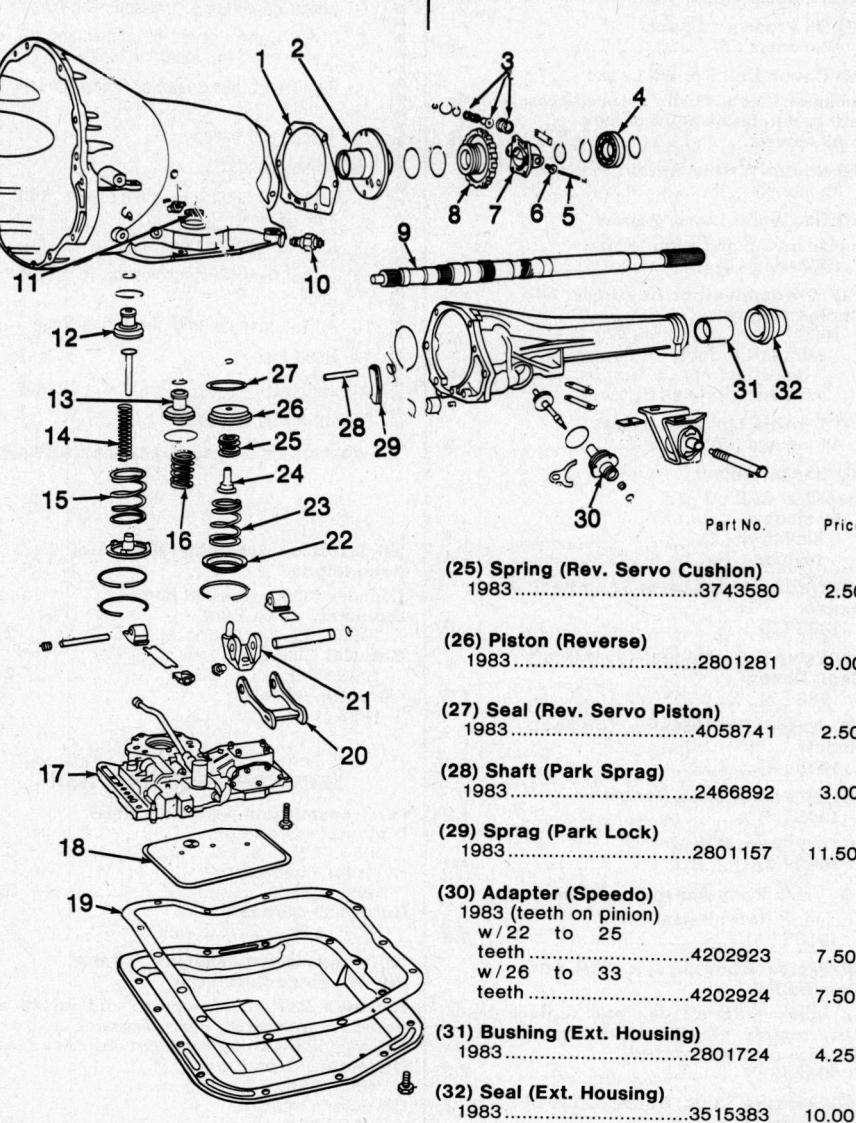

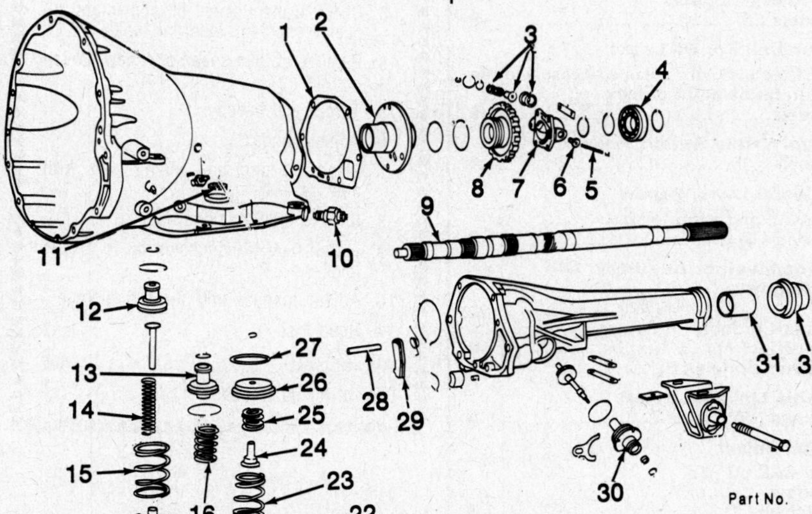
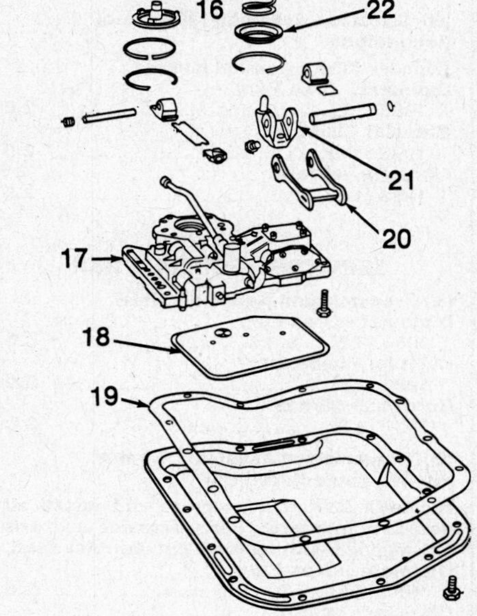

	Part No.	Price
(25) Spring (Rev. Servo Cushion)		
1983	3743580	2.50
(26) Piston (Reverse)		
1983	2801281	9.00
(27) Seal (Rev. Servo Piston)		
1983	4058741	2.50
(28) Shaft (Park Sprag)		
1983	2466892	3.00
(29) Sprag (Park Lock)		
1983	2801157	11.50
(30) Adapter (Speedo)		
1983 (teeth on pinion)		
w/22 to 25 teeth	4202923	7.50
w/26 to 33 teeth	4202924	7.50
(31) Bushing (Ext. Housing)		
1983	2801724	4.25
(32) Seal (Ext. Housing)		
1983	3515383	10.00

PARTS 23 GEAR TRAIN 23 PARTS

	Part No.	Price
(1) Oil Seal		
1983	3515137	6.75
(2) Bushing (Pump Housing)		
1983	2466324	4.50
(3) 'O' Ring		
1983	1942021	1.75
(4) Oil Pump Housing		
1983	4130193	120.25
(5) Gasket (Oil Pump)		
1983	4028377	1.00

	Part No.	Price
(6) Rotor Pkg. (Oil Pump)		
1983	3780239	40.75
(7) Shaft w/Support (Reaction)		
1983	4028273	111.25
(8) Baffle		
1983	3420087	2.50
(9) Seal Rings		
1983	3743689	4.25
(10) Band (Kickdown)		
1983	3621491	27.75

	Part No.	Price
(11) Retainer (Front Clutch)		
1983	4058648	98.75
(12) Inner Seal		
1983	3410226	2.00
(13) Outer Seal		
1983	4058484	3.75
(14) Piston (Front Clutch)		
1983	2464651	36.50
(15) Spring (Front)		
1983	2801243	.50

(16) Retainer
1983..............................2801949 2.25

(17) Plates (Front Clutch)
1983..............................2124826 3.75

(18) Disc (Front Clutch)
1983..............................2801167 4.00

(19) Pressure Plate (Front Clutch)
1983..............................2801961 11.00

(20) Outer Ring (Front Clutch)
1983..............................3410570 2.25

(21) Retainer (Rear Clutch)
1983..............................3743622 98.75

(22) Input Shaft
1983-wo/L.T.C. 4058665 72.25
L.T.C. 4058035 72.25

(23) Retainer (Rear Piston)
1983..............................4028299 62.00

(24) Seal (Outer)
1983..............................2124835 2.50

(25) Piston (Rear Clutch)
1983..............................3743624 29.50

(26) Seal (Inner)
1983..............................1942054 2.00

(27) Spring (Rear)
1983..............................3743621 5.25

(28) Spring (Wave)
1983..............................2466806 4.25

(29) Clutch Pressure Plate (Front)
1983..............................2466803 11.00

(30) Clutch Plate (Rear)
1983..............................2124826 3.75

(31) Clutch Disc (Rear)
1983..............................2801992 4.00

(32) Clutch Pressure Plate (Rear)
1983..............................2801961 11.00

(33) Pinion Carrier (Front)
1983-exc below.............4028120 120.00
(Trans. I.D.)
4202064.................4028110 120.00

(34) Annulus Gear (Front)
1983..............................2892656 94.00

(35) Lock Ring (Sun Gear)
1983..............................1736521 .75

(36) Shell (Sun Gear)
1983..............................2400662 36.00

(37) Driving Plate (Sun Gear)
1983..............................1942080 1.75

(38) Lock Ring
1983..............................1736521 .75

(39) Sun Gear
1983..............................2801311 75.25

(40) Pinion Carrier (Rear)
1983..............................2466539 120.00

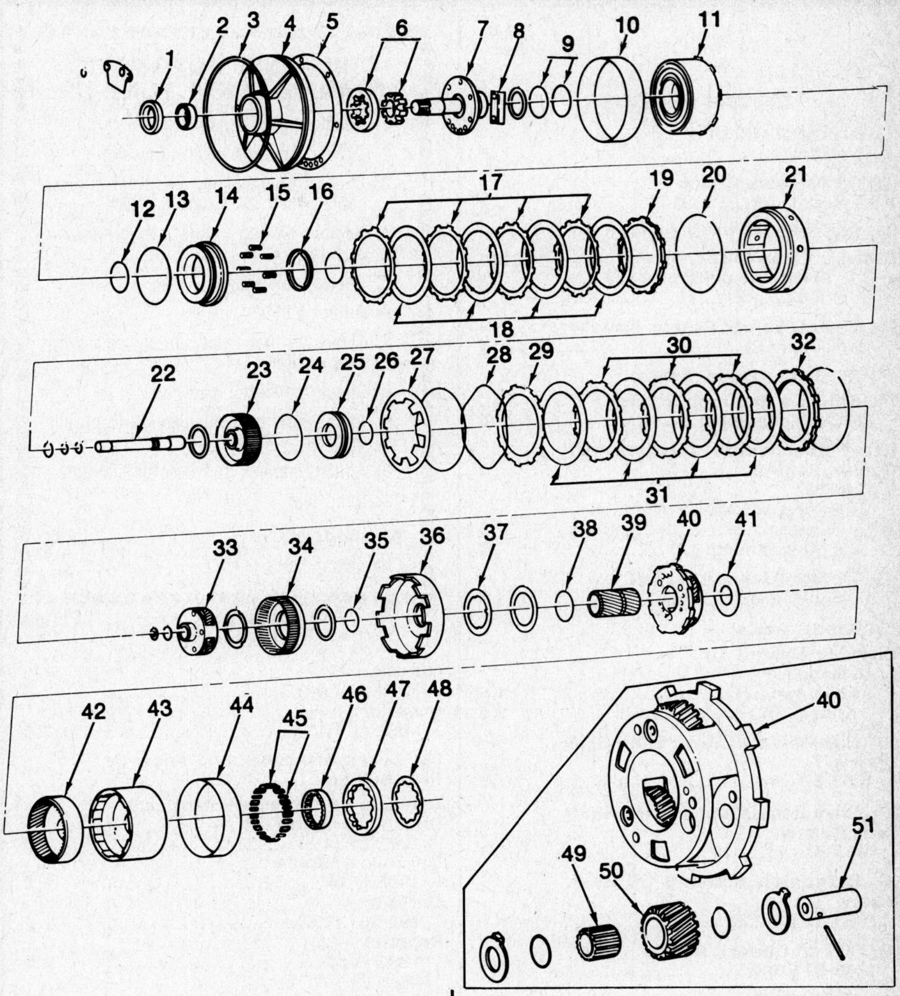

(41) Thrust Plate
1983..............................2400580 1.75

(42) Annulus Gear (Rear)
1983..............................2538185 104.75

(43) Drum (Reverse)
1983..............................3515451 72.00

(44) Band (Reverse)
1983..............................1942133 39.00

(45) Roller & Spring Pkg.
1983..............................2808673 5.25

(46) Race
1983..............................3420100 35.50

(47) Clutch Cam
1983..............................1942095 58.25

(48) Spring Retainer
1983..............................2801426 4.25

(49) Roller
1983..............................2204647 .50

(50) Pinion Gear
1983..............................2400667 8.00

(51) Shaft
1983..............................2464178 1.75

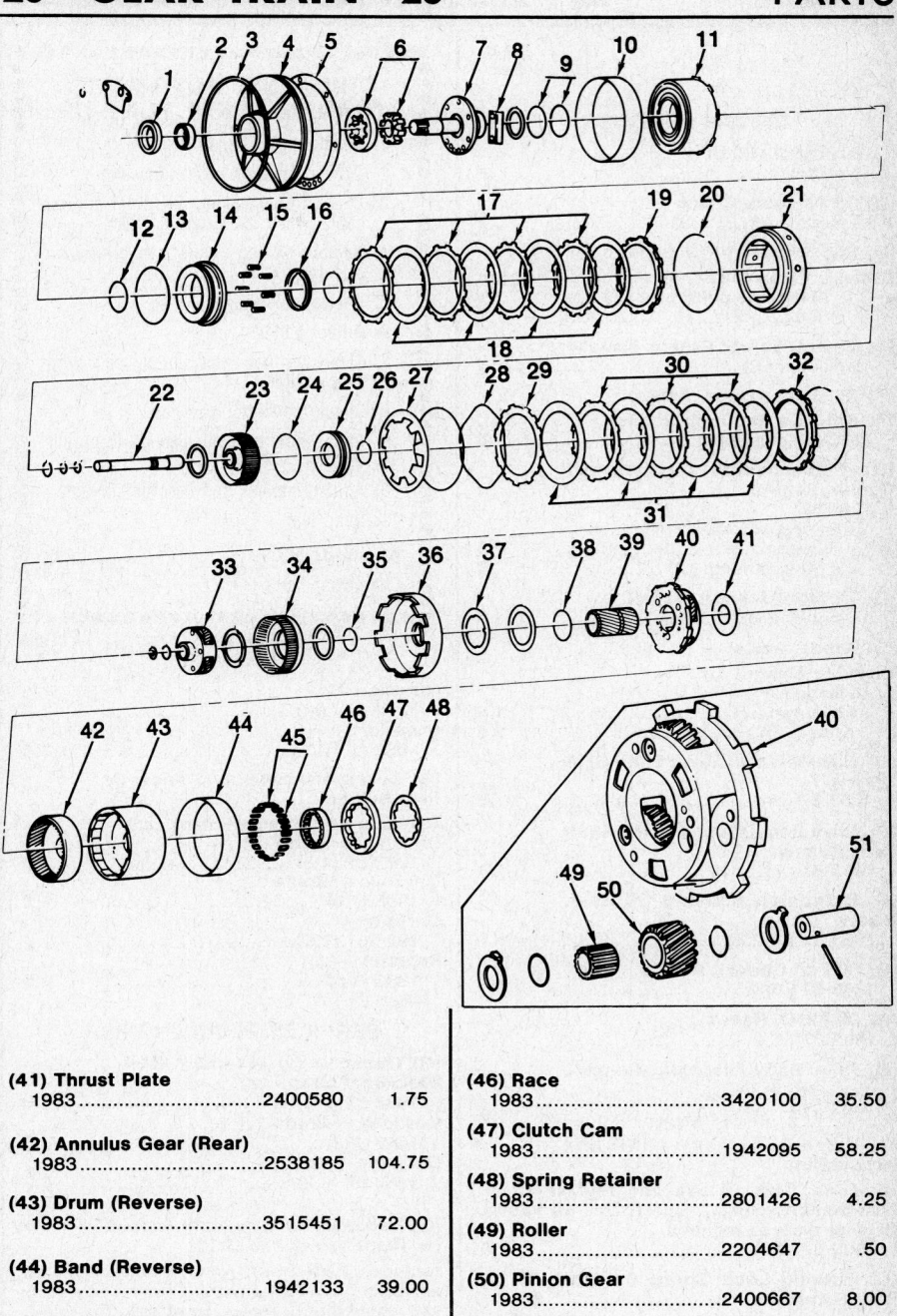

LABOR 23 AUTOMATIC TRANSMISSION 23 LABOR

(Factory Time) Chilton Time

ON CAR SERVICES

(G) Drain & Refill Unit
All models 7

(G) Oil Pressure Check
All models (.6) 9

(M) Check Unit For Oil Leaks
Includes: Clean and dry outside of case and run unit to determine point of leak.
All models 9

(G) Neutral Safety Switch, Renew
All models (.3) 4

(G) Oil Cooler Lines, Renew
Includes: Cut and form to size.
1983-87-one (.5) ... 1.0

(G) Transmission Auxiliary Oil Cooler, Renew
1983-87
Mirada-Cordoba
Imperial (.6) 9
All other models (.3) 9

(G) Throttle Linkage, Adjust
All models (.3) 6

(G) Bands, Adjust
Includes: R&R oil pan.
All models
kickdown (.7) ... 1.4
reverse (.7) ... 1.4

(G) Throttle Valve Lever Shaft Seal, Renew
1983-87 (.3) 6

(G) Valve Body Manual Lever Shaft Seal, Renew
1983-87 (.7) ... 1.0

(G) Extension Housing Oil Seal, Renew
1983-87 (.4) ... 1.1

(G) Oil Pan Gasket, Renew
1983-87 (.6) ... 1.0

(G) Oil Filter, Renew
1983-87 (.7) ... 1.1

(G) Valve Body Assembly, Renew
Includes: R&R oil pan.
1983-87 (1.1) ... 1.6

(P) Valve Body Assy., R&R and Recondition
Includes: R&R oil pan and replace filter. Disassemble, clean, inspect, free all valves. Replace parts as required.
1983-87 (2.0) ... 2.3

(G) Parking Lock Sprag Control Rod, Renew
Includes: R&R oil pan and remove valve body.
1983-87 (1.0) ... 1.8

(G) Accumulator Piston, Renew or Recondition
Includes: R&R oil pan and adjust band.
1983-87 (1.2) ... 1.6

(G) Servos, Renew or Recondition
Includes: R&R oil pan and adjust band.
1983-87-kickdown (.9) ... 1.8
reverse-A904 (.9) ... 1.8
A904LA (1.7) ... 3.0

(G) Extension Housing and/or Gasket, Renew
Diplomat - Gran Fury
1983-87 (1.4) ... 2.0
Cordoba - Mirada
1983 (1.4) ... 2.0

CHILTON'S AUTOMATIC TRANSMISSION TUNE-UP

1. Check engine performance
2. Check condition of transmission oil
3. Check transmission, oil cooler and oil cooler lines for external leaks
4. Remove oil pan, clean or renew screen or filter
5. Torque valve body
6. Adjust bands
7. Clean oil pan and install pan with new gasket
8. Check modulator and hose
9. Install new transmission oil to proper level
10. Adjust manual and throttle linkage
11. Road test

All models ... 1.5
Charge for parts used

(Factory Time) Chilton Time

Chrysler
1983-87 (1.4) ... 2.0
Imperial
1983 (1.4) ... 2.0

(G) Governor Assembly, Renew or Recondition
Includes: R&R extension housing.
Diplomat - Gran Fury
1983-87 (1.5) ... 2.5
Cordoba - Mirada
1983 (1.5) ... 2.5
Chrysler
1983-87 (1.5) ... 2.5
Imperial
1983 (1.5) ... 2.5

SERVICES REQUIRING R&R

(G) Transmission Assembly, R&R
Diplomat - Gran Fury
1983-87 (2.2) ... 3.0
Cordoba - Mirada
1983 (2.2) ... 3.0
Chrysler - Imperial
1983-87 (2.2) ... 3.0

(G) Transmission Assembly, Renew (w/Remanufactured Unit)
Includes: R&R trans, remove and install all necessary interfering parts. Transfer any parts not supplied with replacement unit. Road test.
Diplomat - Gran Fury
1983-87 (2.5) ... 3.5
Chrysler - Imperial
1983-87 (2.5) ... 3.5
Cordoba - Mirada
1983 (2.5) ... 3.5

(G) Transmission Assembly, Reseal
Includes: R&R trans and renew all seals and gaskets.
Diplomat - Gran Fury
1983-87 (4.0) ... 6.2
Cordoba - Mirada
1983 (4.0) ... 6.2
Chrysler - Imperial
1983-87 (4.0) ... 6.2
Flush cooler lines and converter
add (.5) 7

(Factory Time) Chilton Time

(P) Transmission and Converter, R&R and Recondition
Includes: Disassemble trans including valve body, clean, inspect and replace parts as required.
Diplomat - Gran Fury
1983-87 (6.9) ... 11.7
Cordoba - Mirada
1983 (6.9) ... 11.7
Chrysler - Imperial
1983-87 (6.9) ... 11.7

(G) Torque Converter Drive Plate, Renew (Flywheel)
Includes: R&R transmission.
Diplomat - Gran Fury
1983-87 (2.4) ... 3.3
Cordoba - Mirada
1983 (2.4) ... 3.3
Chrysler - Imperial
1983-87 (2.4) ... 3.3

(G) Torque Converter, Renew
Includes: R&R transmission.
Diplomat - Gran Fury
1983-87 (2.4) ... 3.3
Cordoba - Mirada
1983 (2.4) ... 3.3
Chrysler - Imperial
1983-87 (2.4) ... 3.3

(G) Front Pump Oil Seal, Renew
Includes: R&R transmission.
Diplomat - Gran Fury
1983-87 (2.4) ... 3.3
Cordoba - Mirada
1983 (2.4) ... 3.3
Chrysler - Imperial
1983-87 (2.4) ... 3.3

(G) Front Oil Pump, Renew or Recondition
Includes: R&R transmission, replace reaction shaft if necessary.
Diplomat - Gran Fury
1983-87 (2.8) ... 3.9
Cordoba - Mirada
1983 (2.8) ... 3.9
Chrysler - Imperial
1983-87 (2.8) ... 3.9

(G) Transmission Case, Renew
Includes: R&R transmission.
Diplomat - Gran Fury
1983-87 (4.1) ... 5.7
Cordoba - Mirada
1983 (4.1) ... 5.7
Chrysler - Imperial
1983-87 (4.1) ... 5.7

(G) Kickdown Band, Renew
Includes: R&R transmission.
Diplomat - Gran Fury
1983-87 (2.9) ... 4.0
Cordoba - Mirada
1983 (2.9) ... 4.0
Chrysler - Imperial
1983-87 (2.9) ... 4.0

(G) Reverse Band, Renew
(G) Front and Rear Clutch Seals, Renew
Includes: R&R transmission.
Diplomat - Gran Fury
1983-87 (3.3) ... 4.6
Cordoba - Mirada
1983 (3.3) ... 4.6
Chrysler - Imperial
1983-87 (3.3) ... 4.6

PARTS 23 CASE & PARTS 23 PARTS

	Part No.	Price
Transmission Assembly		
Chrysler Corporation supplies remanufactured transmission assemblies as well as remanufactured torque converter units. Check Chrysler dealer for availabilty and prices.		
Drive Plate (Flex Plate)		
Six-225		
1983	4058428	14.50
V-8-318		
1983-87	4058429	17.25
Transmission Seal and Gasket Kit		
1983-87	4186862	67.00
(1) Gasket		
1983-87	2466954	3.75
(2) Support		
1983-87	2466881	47.50
(3) Governor Weight Pkg.		
1983-87	4202658	6.25
(4) Bearing (Output Shaft)		
1983-87	3410465	13.50
(5) Shaft (Governor Valve)		
1983-87	1556082	2.50
(6) Valve (Governor)		
1983-87	3515479	6.00
(8) Support (Governor)		
1983-87	3743518	47.75
(9) Shaft (Output)		
1983-87	4186093	131.25
(10) Switch (Neutral & Back-Up)		
1983-87	4057750	8.75
(11) Seal		
1983-87	3878447	2.25
(12) Piston (Kickdown Servo)		
1983-87-Six	4058942	6.25
V-8	4058777	10.75
(13) Rod (Kickdown Piston)		
1983-87-Six	4058943	8.25
V-8	4058780	11.75
(14) Piston (Accumulator)		
1983-87	3410908	10.75
(15) Spring (Kickdown Piston)		
1983-87	3410444	1.00
(16) Spring (Servo Piston)		
1983-87-Six	4058945	2.00
V-8	4058885	2.00
(17) Spring (Accumulator Piston)		
1983-87	3515079	2.50
(18) Guide (Kickdown Servo)		
1983-87-Six	1942485	7.00
V-8	3410332	7.00
(19) Valve Body and Plate		
1983-87 (Trans. I.D.)		
4202662 trans.	4202637	276.50
4202663 trans.	4202781	287.00
4202675 trans.	4202635	286.75
4058383 trans.	4202636	286.75
4058398 trans.	4202634	286.75
4202664 trans.	4202637	276.50

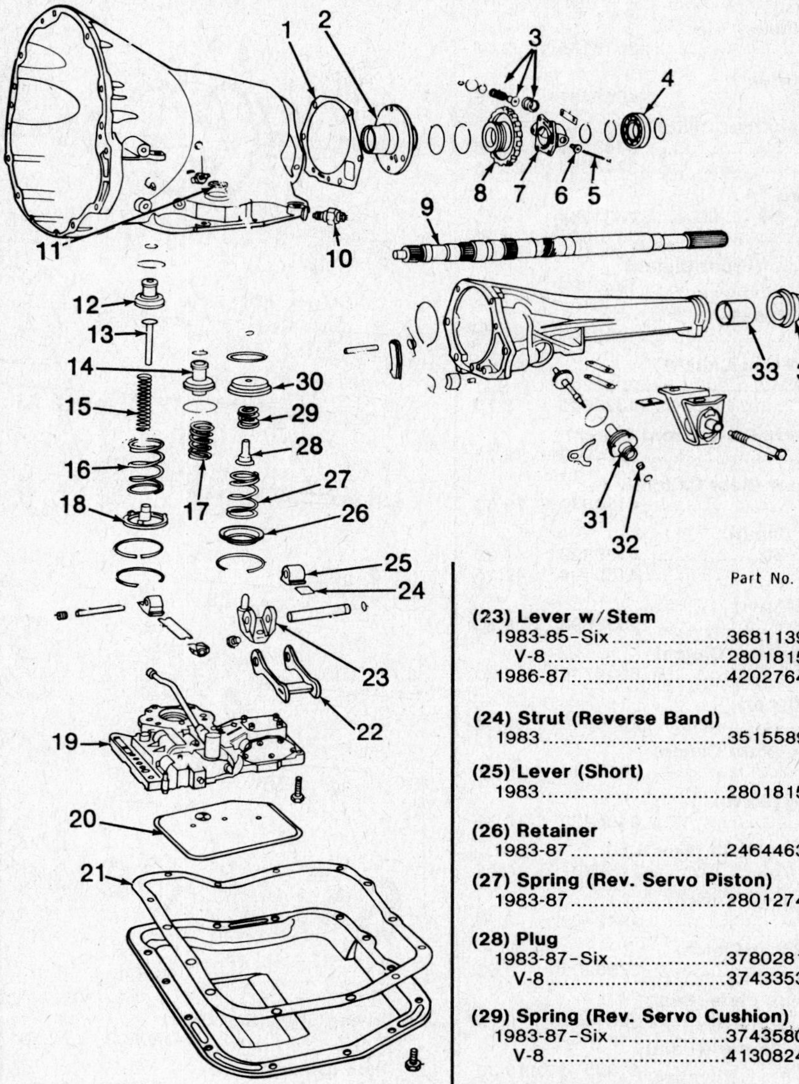

	Part No.	Price
4295887,		
4329436 trans.	4295888	286.75
4348703 trans.	4348759	278.75
4412001,002		
trans.	4412488	N.L.
(20) Filter		
1983-87	3515996	6.00
(21) Gasket (Oil Pan)		
1983	2205299	3.00
1984-87	4295875	3.00
(22) Link w/Anchor		
1983-87	2464439	17.25

	Part No.	Price
(23) Lever w/Stem		
1983-85-Six	3681139	16.25
V-8	2801815	22.25
1986-87	4202764	7.75
(24) Strut (Reverse Band)		
1983	3515589	2.50
(25) Lever (Short)		
1983	2801815	22.25
(26) Retainer		
1983-87	2464463	2.25
(27) Spring (Rev. Servo Piston)		
1983-87	2801274	2.50
(28) Plug		
1983-87-Six	3780281	N.L.
V-8	3743353	7.00
(29) Spring (Rev. Servo Cushion)		
1983-87-Six	3743580	2.50
V-8	4130824	3.00
(30) Piston (Reverse Servo)		
1983-87	2801271	7.00
(31) Adapter		
1983-87 (teeth on pinion)		
22 to 25 teeth	4202923	7.50
26 to 33 teeth	4202924	7.50
(32) Adaptor Seal Kit		
1983-87	4057046	4.00
(33) Bushing (Ext. Housing)		
1983-87	2801726	4.25
(34) Seal (Ext. Housing)		
1983-87	4058047	8.25

PARTS 23 GEAR TRAIN 23 PARTS

	Part No.	Price
(1) Seal & Gasket Pkg. (Ft. Pump)		
1983-87	4131042	13.75
(2) Bushing (Front Pump)		
1983-87	2466796	4.00
(3) Seal (Front Pump)		
1983-87	2204709	1.75
(4) Front Pump Housing		
1983-87	4130192	120.75
(5) Gasket		
1983-87	4028364	1.00
(6) Reaction Shaft		
1983-87-Six	4058941	111.25
V-8	4058413	111.25
(7) Seal Rings		
1983-87	1942389	1.75
(8) Band (Kickdown)		
1983-87	4058863	23.50
(9) Retainer (Front Clutch)		
1983-87-Six	3621476	98.75
V-8	3743382	94.00

23 GEAR TRAIN 23

	Part No.	Price
(10) Seal (Inner)		
1983-87	3515176	2.00
(11) Seal (Outer)		
1983-87	4058487	3.75
(12) Piston (Front Clutch)		
1983-87-Six	3743090	23.25
V-8	3743384	23.25
(13) Springs		
1983-87-Six	2801844	4.50
V-8	3515054	4.50
(14) Retainer (Front Clutch)		
1983-87	1942399	2.00
(15) Plate (Front)		
1983-87	1942403	3.50
(16) Disc (Front Clutch)		
1983-84	2205203	N.L.
1985-87	4329805	3.75
(17) Pressure Plate (Front Clutch)		
1983-87	2801969	9.75
(18) Retainer (Rear Clutch)		
1983-87	4186879	79.50
(19) Shaft (Input)		
1983-87-Six	4130399	49.25
V-8	4130194	49.25
(20) Seal (Outer)		
1983-87	2538695	2.50
(21) Piston (Rear Clutch)		
1983-87	3515716	27.50
(22) Seal (Inner)		
1983-87	2538510	2.00
(23) Spring (Rear Clutch)		
1983-87	1942414	5.25
(24) Spring (Wave)		
1983-87	2466283	3.75
(25) Pressure Plate (Front)		
1983-87	2466281	10.25
(26) Plate (Rear Clutch)		
1983-87	1942403	3.50
(27) Disc (Rear Clutch)		
1983-87	3780285	3.50
(28) Pressure Plate (Rear)		
1983-87	2801969	9.75
(29) Pinion Carrier (Front)		
1983-87	4130514	110.00
(30) Annulus Gear (Front)		
1983-87-Six	3743184	72.00
V-8	4130512	72.00

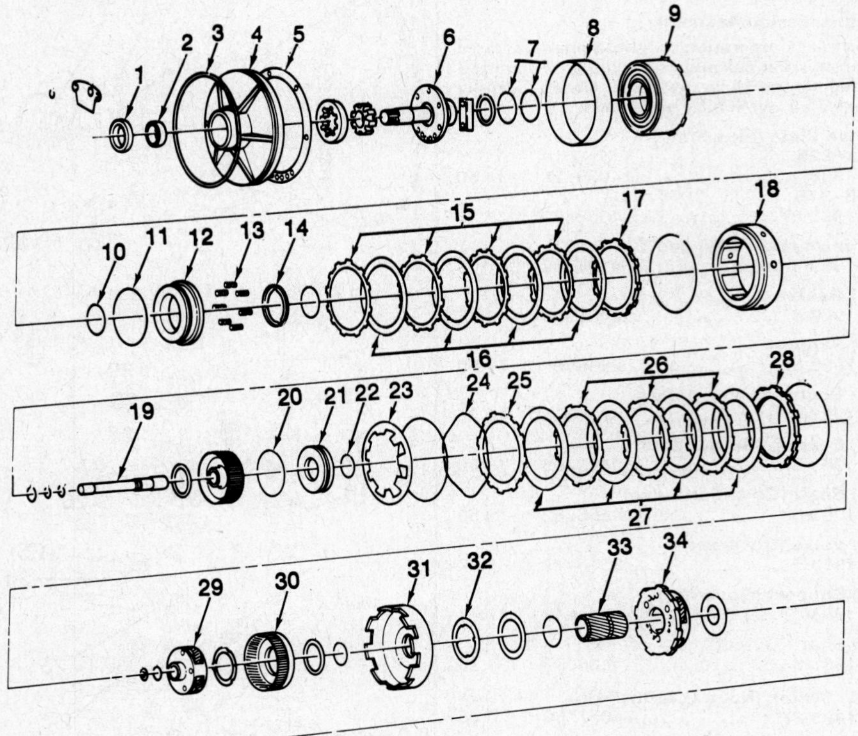

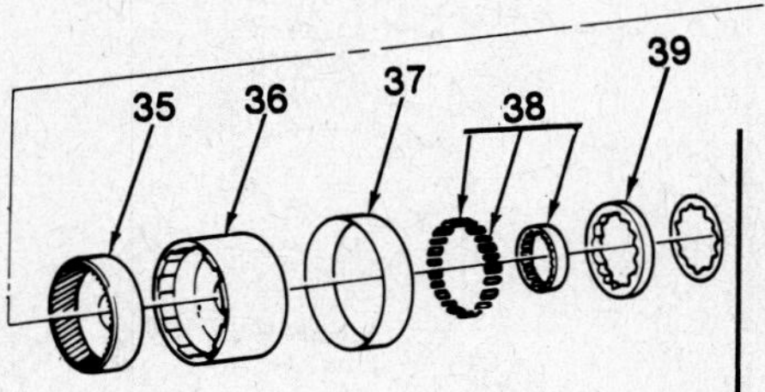

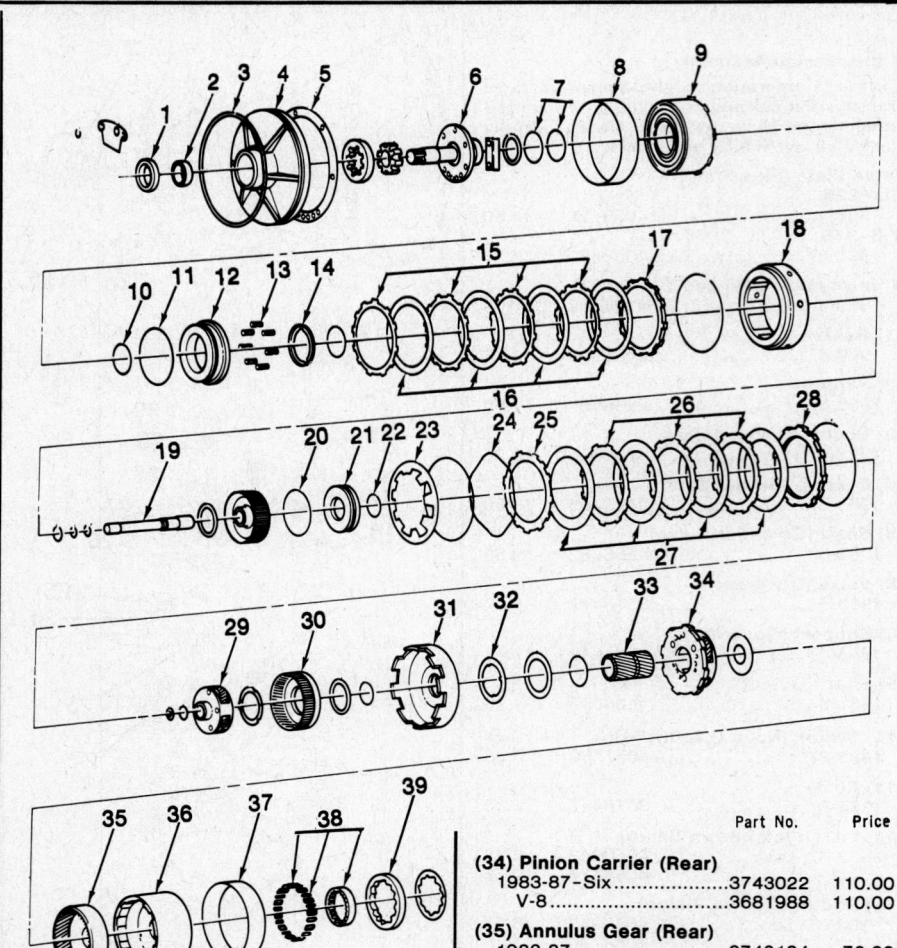

	Part No.	Price
(31) Driving Shell (Sun Gear)		
1983-87	4130509	22.50
(32) Plate (Driving Shell)		
1983-87	4130600	1.75
(33) Sun Gear		
1983-87	4130685	64.00

	Part No.	Price
(34) Pinion Carrier (Rear)		
1983-87-Six	3743022	110.00
V-8	3681988	110.00
(35) Annulus Gear (Rear)		
1983-87	3743184	72.00
(36) Drum (Reverse)		
1983-87	4130867	72.00
(37) Band (Reverse)		
1983-87-Six	4202040	28.00
V-8	4130981	49.50
(38) Race, Roller & Spring Pkg.		
1983-87	3420023	34.00
(39) Retainer & Cam		
1983-87	3780221	99.50

LABOR 23 AUTOMATIC TRANSMISSION 23 LABOR

(Factory Time) Chilton Time

ON CAR SERVICES

(G) Drain & Refill Unit
All models 7

(G) Oil Pressure Check
All models 5

(M) Check Unit For Oil Leaks
Includes: Clean and dry outside of case and run unit to determine point of leak.
All models 9

(G) Neutral Safety Switch, Renew
All models (.3) 4

(G) Linkage, Adjust
manual (.3) 4
throttle (.3) 5
manual & throttle (.6) 9
kickdown (.3) 5

(G) Selector Indicator, Renew
1985-87
column shift (.8) 1.2
floor shift (.3) 4

(G) Front Band, Adjust
All models (.2) 5

(G) Extension Housing Oil Seal and/or Bushing, Renew
All models (.5) 8

(G) Vacuum Modulator, Renew
All models (.5) 7

(G) Front Servo, Recondition
Includes: Adjust band.
All models (.4) 1.3

(G) Rear Servo, Recondition
Includes: R&R oil pan.
All models (1.0) 1.4

(G) Governor Assembly, Renew
All models (1.6) 2.5
Clean and polish gov. add (.1) 2

(G) Throttle and Manual Seals and/or Levers, Renew
Includes: R&R oil pan and valve body.
All models (1.2) 1.9

(G) Extension Housing and/or Gasket, Renew
T-Bird-Cougar (1.3) 1.8
All other models (1.1) 1.5

(G) Parking Pawl, Renew
Includes: R&R extension housing.
All models (1.4) 2.0

(G) Oil Pan Gasket, Renew
All models (.7) 1.0

(G) Valve Body Assembly, Renew
Includes: R&R oil pan.
All models (1.0) 1.7

(P) Valve Body Assy., R&R and Recondition
Includes: R&R oil pan and replace filter. Disassemble, clean, inspect, free all valves. Replace parts as required.
All models (1.5) 2.7

CHILTON'S AUTOMATIC TRANSMISSION TUNE-UP

1. Check engine performance
2. Check condition of transmission oil
3. Check transmission, oil cooler and oil cooler lines for external leaks
4. Remove oil pan, clean or renew screen or filter
5. Torque valve body
6. Adjust bands
7. Clean oil pan and install pan with new gasket
8. Check modulator and hose
9. Install new transmission oil to proper level
10. Adjust manual and throttle linkage
11. Road test

All models 1.5
Charge for parts used

(Factory Time) Chilton Time

SERVICES REQUIRING R&R

(G) Transmission Assembly, R&R or Renew
Includes: R&R trans and converter assembly. Drain and refill unit. Adjust linkage.
T-Bird-Cougar
1983-87 (2.2) 3.0
Fairmont & Zephyr
1983 (2.4) 3.2
Capri - Mustang
1983-87 (2.2) 3.0
LTD-Marquis
1983-87 (2.2) 3.0

(P) Transmission and Converter, R&R and Recondition
Includes: Disassemble trans, including valve body, inspect and replace parts as required.
T-Bird-Cougar
1983-87 (5.9) 11.1
Fairmont & Zephyr
1983 (6.4) 11.4
Capri - Mustang
1983-87 (6.2) 11.1
LTD-Marquis
1983-87 (5.9) 11.1
Clean and check converter add (.5) 5
Flush oil cooler and lines add (.2) 2

(G) Transmission Assembly, Reseal
Includes: R&R trans and renew all seals and gaskets.
T-Bird-Cougar
1983-87 (3.3) 5.5
Fairmont & Zephyr
1983 (3.5) 5.8

(Factory Time) Chilton Time

Capri - Mustang
1983-87 (3.3) 5.5
LTD-Marquis
1983-87 (3.3) 5.5

(P) Transmission, Recondition (Off Car)
1983-87 (3.7) 6.7

(G) Flywheel and Ring Gear Assy., Renew
Includes: R&R trans.
T-Bird-Cougar
1983-87 (2.5) 3.5
Fairmont & Zephyr
1983 (2.7) 3.7
Capri - Mustang
1983-87 (2.5) 3.5
LTD-Marquis
1983-87 (2.5) 3.5

(G) Torque Converter, Renew
Includes: R&R trans.
T-Bird-Cougar
1983-87 (2.1) 3.2
Fairmont & Zephyr
1983 (1.9) 4.0
Capri - Mustang
1983-87 (2.7) 3.2
LTD-Marquis
1983-87 (1.9) 3.2

(G) Front Pump Oil Seal, Renew
Includes: R&R trans.
T-Bird-Cougar
1983-87 (2.3) 3.2
Fairmont & Zephyr
1983 (2.5) 4.0
Capri - Mustang
1983-87 (2.3) 3.2
LTD-Marquis
1983-87 (2.3) 3.2

(G) Front Oil Pump, Renew or Recondition
Includes: R&R trans.
T-Bird-Cougar
1983-87 (2.8) 3.9
Fairmont & Zephyr
1983 (3.0) 4.2
Capri - Mustang
1983-87 (2.8) 3.9
LTD-Marquis
1983-87 (2.8) 3.9

(G) Bands, Renew (One or Both)
Includes: R&R trans.
T-Bird-Cougar
1983-87 (3.7) 5.2
Fairmont & Zephyr
1983 (3.9) 5.4
Capri - Mustang
1983-87 (3.7) 5.2
LTD-Marquis
1983-87 (3.7) 5.2

PARTS 23 CASE AND PARTS 23 PARTS

	Part No.	Price
Flywheel (Flex Plate)		
1983-87-4 cyl.	D5FZ-6375A	81.75
1983-200 eng.	E1BZ-6375B	79.00
Transmission Seal & Gasket Kit		
1983-87	D7ZZ-7153A	46.75
(1) Converter		
1983-87-4 cyl.	E1ZZ-7902B	555.50
1983-200 eng.	E1ZZ-7902A	555.50
(2) Shaft (Input)		
1983-87	D4ZZ-7017C	190.00

PARTS 23 CASE AND PARTS 23 PARTS

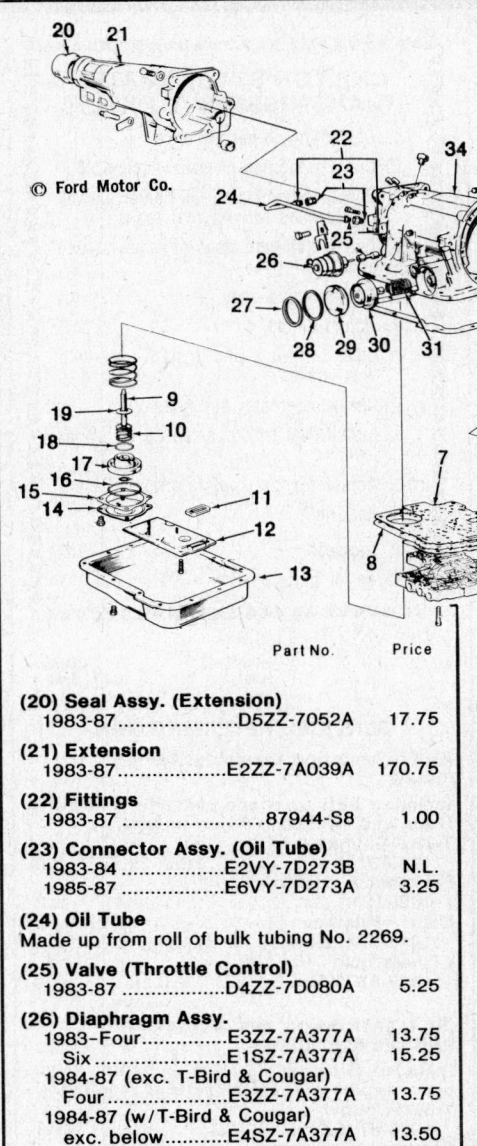

	Part No.	Price
(3) Seal Assy. (Front Pump)		
1983-87	E5TZ-7A248A	9.25
(4) Housing Assy. (Converter)		
1983-87-4 cyl.	D4ZZ-7976C	170.25
1983-200 eng.	D8BZ-7976A	200.75
(5) Control Valve Assy.		
Four-140		
1983-87-(Stamped on body)		
DRA, DRB	E3ZZ-7A100B	300.75
EBA, EBB	E4ZZ-7A100A	281.25
ECA, ECB,		
EMA	E4SZ-7A100A	281.25
EDA, EDB	E4ZZ-7A100B	281.25
ENA	E6SZ-7A100B	281.25
Six-200		
1983	E2ZZ-7A100C	300.75
(6) Gasket (Lower)		
1983-87	D4ZZ-7D100A	1.25
(7) Gasket (Upper)		
1983-87	D4ZZ-7D100B	1.50
(8) Plate (Separator)		
1983	D9BZ-7A008A	DISC.
(9) Piston & Rod (Reverse Band Servo.)		
1983-87		
no grooves	D7ZZ-7D189B	11.50
1 groove	D7ZZ-7D189C	11.50
2 grooves	D7ZZ-7D189A	11.50
(10) Spring (Accumulator)		
1983-87	D4ZZ-7E207A	2.25
(11) Gasket (Pan Screen)		
1983-87	D4ZZ-7E062A	1.75
(12) Screen Assy.		
1983-87	D4ZZ-7A098B	16.50
(13) Oil Pan		
1983-87	D4ZZ-7A194A	19.00
(14) Cover (Servo)		
1983-87	D4ZZ-7D036A	6.25
(15) Gasket		
1983-87	D4ZZ-7L173A	.75
(16) Seal (Large)		
1983-87	D4ZZ-7423A	1.25
(17) Piston (Servo)		
Reverse Band Servo. Piston & Rod are one assembly.		
(18) Seal (Small)		
1983-87	D4ZZ-7423B	1.00
(19) Spacer		
1983-87	D4ZZ-7D300A	1.25

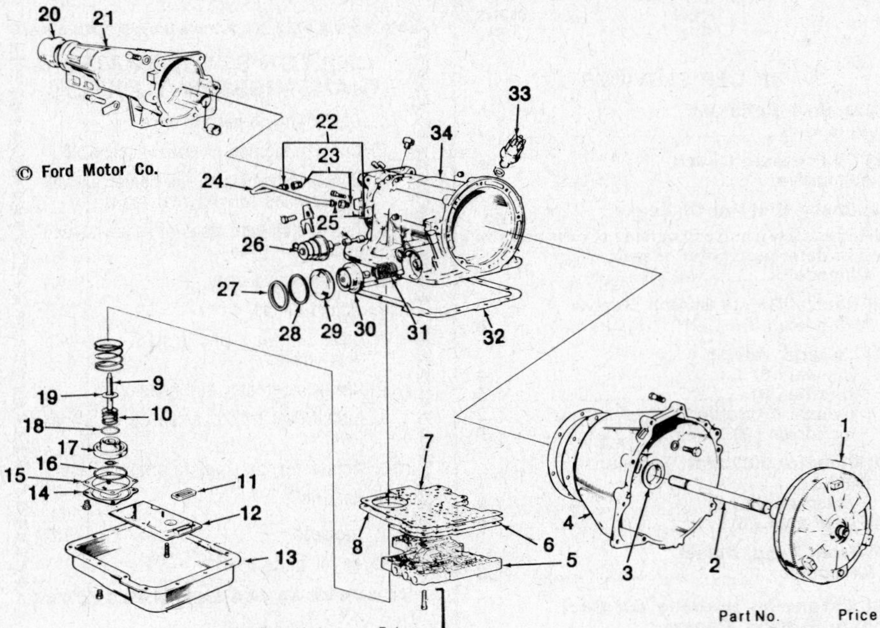

	Part No.	Price
(20) Seal Assy. (Extension)		
1983-87	D5ZZ-7052A	17.75
(21) Extension		
1983-87	E2ZZ-7A039A	170.75
(22) Fittings		
1983-87	87944-S8	1.00
(23) Connector Assy. (Oil Tube)		
1983-84	E2VY-7D273B	N.L.
1985-87	E6VY-7D273A	3.25
(24) Oil Tube		
Made up from roll of bulk tubing No. 2269.		
(25) Valve (Throttle Control)		
1983-87	D4ZZ-7D080A	5.25
(26) Diaphragm Assy.		
1983-Four	E3ZZ-7A377A	13.75
Six	E1SZ-7A377A	15.25
1984-87 (exc. T-Bird & Cougar)		
Four	E3ZZ-7A377A	13.75
1984-87 (w/T-Bird & Cougar)		
exc. below	E4SZ-7A377A	13.50
w/Hi alt.	E4SZ-7A377B	13.50

	Part No.	Price
(27) Retainer		
1983-87	E860106-S	1.00
(28) Seal (Servo Cover)		
1983-87	D4ZZ-7D040A	.50
(29) Cover		
1983-87-Four	E5TZ-7D027B	14.75
1983-Six	D5FZ-7D027A	14.75
(30) Piston and Rod Assy.		
1983-87-Four	E3ZZ-7D021A	8.25
1983-Six	D8DZ-7D021A	8.25
(31) Spring		
1983-87	EOBZ-7D028A	2.50
(32) Gasket (Oil Pan)		
1983-87	D5ZZ-7A191B	5.00
(33) Neutral Switch Assy.		
1983-87	D6RY-7A247B	33.25
(34) Case Assy.		
1983-87	E3ZZ-7005C	420.00

PARTS 23 GEAR TRAIN 23 PARTS

	Part No.	Price
(1) Housing Assy. (Converter)		
1983-87-Four	D4ZZ-7976C	170.25
1983-Six	D8BZ-7976A	200.75
(2) Plate (Pump Adaptor)		
1983-87	D4ZZ-7B472A	27.50
(3) Gasket (Oil Pump)		
1983-84	D4ZZ-7A136A	1.75
1985-87	E5TZ-7A136B	1.50
(4) Support & Gear Assy.		
1983-87	D6ZZ-7A103A	192.50
(5) Washer (Thrust)		
1983-84	D4ZZ-7D014A	1.75
1985-87	E5TZ-7D014A	1.75
(6) Seal Assy. (Front Pump)		
1983-87	D5ZZ-7A248A	2.50

	Part No.	Price
(7) Lever (Inter. Band)		
Four-140		
1983-87-exc.		
below	E0BZ-7330A	4.75
T-Bird, Cougar	D4ZZ-7330B	N.L.
Six-200		
1983	D6ZZ-7330A	4.75
(8) Strut		
1983-87	D4ZZ-7D029A	2.25
(9) Band Assy. (Inter. Servo)		
1983-87	E6TZ-7D034A	39.50
(10) Adjusting Screw		
1983-87	D4ZZ-7C492A	2.50
(11) Strut (Anchor)		
1983-87	E5TZ-7D430A	3.25
(12) Drum Assy.		
1983-84-4 cyl.	D8ZZ-7D044A	63.00

	Part No.	Price
1985	E5TZ-7D044G	61.25
1986-87	E5TZ-7D044F	61.25
(13) Seal (Piston Inner)		
1983-87	D7ZZ-7D404A	.75
(14) Seal (Piston Outer)		
1983-87	D4ZZ-7A548A	1.00
(15) Piston (Front)		
1983-87	E0ZZ-7A262A	10.25
(16) Springs (Piston)		
1983-87	D4ZZ-7A480B	.50
(17) Retainer (High)		
1983-87	E5TZ-7A527A	2.75
(18) Washer (Thrust)		
1983-84	D4ZZ-7C096A	3.25
1985-87	E5TZ-7C096A	3.25

	Part No.	Price
(19) Plate Assy. (External Spline)		
1983-87-high	D8ZZ-7B442B	2.25
forward	D8ZZ-7B442A	2.25
(20) Plate Assy. (Internal Spline)		
(Forward)		
1983-87	E3ZZ-7B164A	3.00
(high)		
1983-87	E3ZZ-7B164B	3.00
(21) Plate (Pressure)		
1983-87-19 teeth	D4ZZ-7B066A	4.00
20 teeth	D4ZZ-7B066B	4.00
(22) Seal (Outer)		
1983-87	D4ZZ-7D019A	1.50
(23) Cylinder Assy.		
1983-84	D8ZZ-7A360C	DISC.
1985-87	E5TZ-7A360A	47.50
(24) Seal (Inner)		
1983-87	D4ZZ-7A548B	1.00
(25) Piston Assy. (Forward)		
1983-87	D8ZZ-7A262A	11.75
(26) Spring (Piston)		
1983-87	D4ZZ-7A480A	2.75
(27) Retainer (Forward)		
1983-87	D4ZZ-7A527A	2.75
(28) Spring (Cushion)		
1983-87	D8ZZ-7B070A	3.00
(29) Washer (Thrust)		
1983-87	D4ZZ-7D090B	2.50
(30) Hub (Forward)		
1983-84	D4ZZ-7B067A	20.75
1985-87	E5TZ-7B067A	20.75
(31) Ring Gear (Forward)		
1983-87	D4ZZ-7D392A	62.50
(32) Washer (Thrust)		
1983-84	D4ZZ-7A166A	2.25
1985-87	E1FZ-7F374A	3.00
(33) Planet Assy. (Forward)		
1983-87	D4ZZ-7A398A	100.75
(34) Bearing Race (Thrust)		
1983-87	D5ZZ-7D235A	1.50
(35) Sun Gear Assy.		
1983-87	D4ZZ-7D063A	30.00
(36) Shell (Input)		
1983-84	D4ZZ-7D064A	18.00
1985-87	E5TZ-7D064A	N.L.
(37) Washer (Thrust)		
1983-87	D4ZZ-7D066A	4.00

© Ford Motor Co.

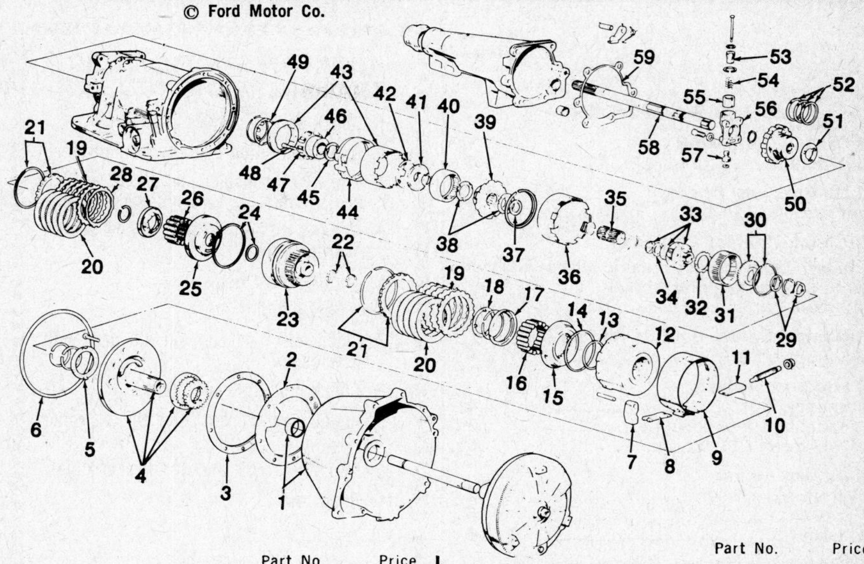

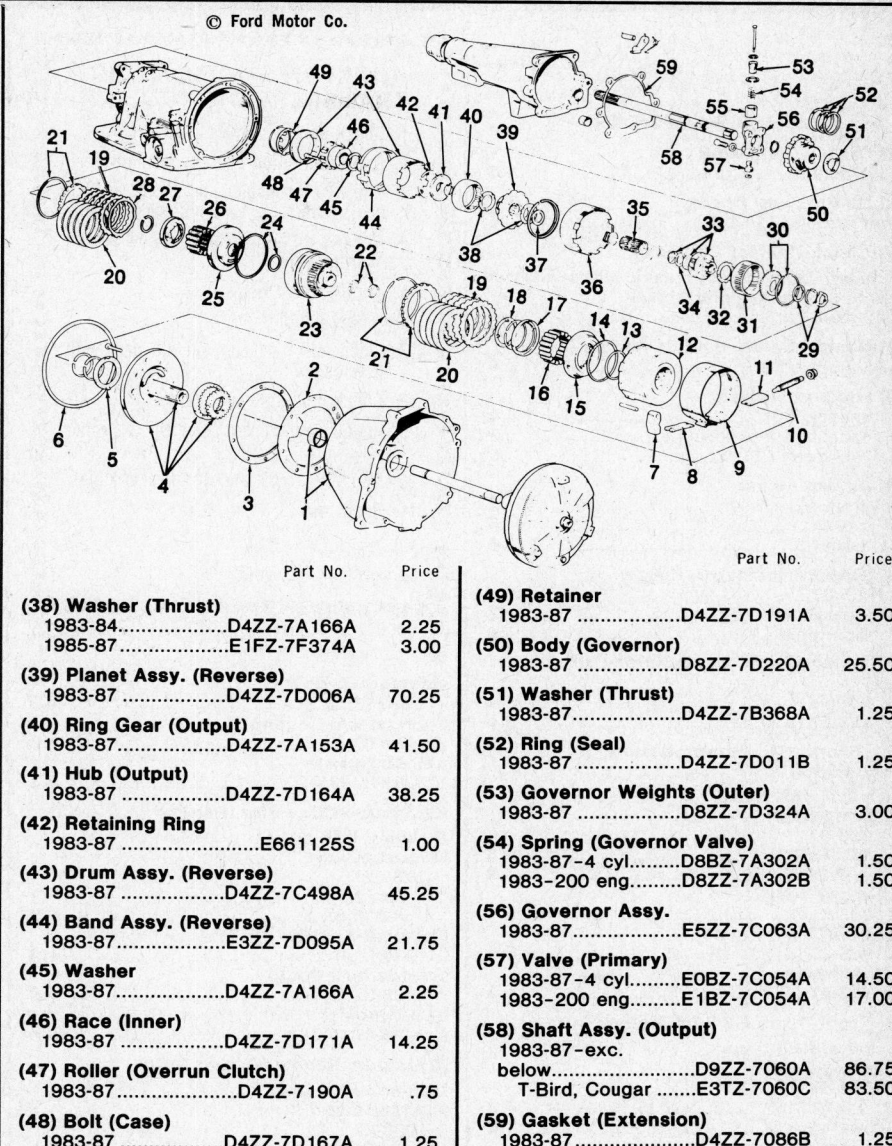

	Part No.	Price
(38) Washer (Thrust)		
1983-84	D4ZZ-7A166A	2.25
1985-87	E1FZ-7F374A	3.00
(39) Planet Assy. (Reverse)		
1983-87	D4ZZ-7D006A	70.25
(40) Ring Gear (Output)		
1983-87	D4ZZ-7A153A	41.50
(41) Hub (Output)		
1983-87	D4ZZ-7D164A	38.25
(42) Retaining Ring		
1983-87	E661125S	1.00
(43) Drum Assy. (Reverse)		
1983-87	D4ZZ-7C498A	45.25
(44) Band Assy. (Reverse)		
1983-87	E3ZZ-7D095A	21.75
(45) Washer		
1983-87	D4ZZ-7A166A	2.25
(46) Race (Inner)		
1983-87	D4ZZ-7D171A	14.25
(47) Roller (Overrun Clutch)		
1983-87	D4ZZ-7190A	.75
(48) Bolt (Case)		
1983-87	D4ZZ-7D167A	1.25

	Part No.	Price
(49) Retainer		
1983-87	D4ZZ-7D191A	3.50
(50) Body (Governor)		
1983-87	D8ZZ-7D220A	25.50
(51) Washer (Thrust)		
1983-87	D4ZZ-7B368A	1.25
(52) Ring (Seal)		
1983-87	D4ZZ-7D011B	1.25
(53) Governor Weights (Outer)		
1983-87	D8ZZ-7D324A	3.00
(54) Spring (Governor Valve)		
1983-87-4 cyl.	D8BZ-7A302A	1.50
1983-200 eng.	D8ZZ-7A302B	1.50
(56) Governor Assy.		
1983-87	E5ZZ-7C063A	30.25
(57) Valve (Primary)		
1983-87-4 cyl.	E0BZ-7C054A	14.50
1983-200 eng.	E1BZ-7C054A	17.00
(58) Shaft Assy. (Output)		
1983-87-exc.		
below	D9ZZ-7060A	86.75
T-Bird, Cougar	E3TZ-7060C	83.50
(59) Gasket (Extension)		
1983-87	D4ZZ-7086B	1.25

(Factory Time) — Chilton Time

ON CAR SERVICES

(G) Drain & Refill Unit
All models 1.0

(G) Oil Pressure Check
All models 5

(M) Check Unit for Oil Leaks
Includes: Clean and dry outside of case and run unit to determine point of leak.
All models 9

(G) Neutral Safety Switch, Renew
All models (.3) 4

(G) Linkage, Adjust
manual (.3) 4
manual & kickdown (.6) 9
kickdown (.3) 5

(G) Bands, Adjust
front (.2) 5
rear (.2) 5
both (.3) 8

(G) Selector Indicator, Renew
1985-87
column shift (.8) 1.2
floor shift (.3) 4

(P) Transmission, Recondition (Off Car)
All models
1983-87 (3.8) 6.5

(G) Front Oil Pump, Renew or Recondition
Includes: R&R trans.
Mustang-Capri
1983-87
Six (3.2) 5.3
V-6 (4.0) 5.9
Fairmont-Zephyr
1983 (3.1) 5.3
Thunderbird-Cougar
1983-87 (4.1) 5.9
LTD-Marquis
1983-87 (4.0) 5.9

(G) Front Pump Oil Seal, Renew
Includes: R&R trans.
Mustang-Capri
1983-87
Six (2.6) 4.3
V-6 (3.4) 4.9
Fairmont-Zephyr
1983 (2.5) 4.3
Thunderbird-Cougar
1983-87 (3.5) 4.9
LTD-Marquis
1983-87 (3.4) 4.9

(G) Parking Pawl, Renew
Includes: R&R trans.
Mustang-Capri
1983-87
Six (3.9) 5.6
V-6 (4.7) 6.2
Fairmont-Zephyr
1983 (2.7) 5.6
Thunderbird-Cougar
1983-87 (4.8) 6.2
LTD-Marquis
1983-87 (4.7) 6.2

(G) Flywheel and Ring Gear Assy., Renew
Includes: R&R trans.
Mustang-Capri
1983-87
Six (2.8) 4.7
V-6 (3.6) 5.3

CHILTON'S AUTOMATIC TRANSMISSION TUNE-UP

1. Check engine performance
2. Check condition of transmission oil
3. Check transmission, oil cooler and oil cooler lines for external leaks
4. Remove oil pan, clean or renew screen or filter
5. Torque valve body
6. Adjust bands
7. Clean oil pan and install pan with new gasket
8. Check modulator and hose
9. Install new transmission oil to proper level
10. Adjust manual and throttle linkage
11. Road test

All models 1.5
Charge for parts used

(Factory Time) — Chilton Time

Fairmont-Zephyr
1983 (2.7) 4.7
Thunderbird-Cougar
1983-87 (3.7) 5.3
LTD-Marquis
1983-87 (3.6) 5.3

(G) Torque Converter, Renew
Includes: R&R trans.
Mustang-Capri
1983-87
Six (2.5) 4.2
V-6 (3.3) 4.8
Fairmont-Zephyr
1983 (2.4) 4.2
Thunderbird-Cougar
1983-87 (3.4) 4.8
LTD-Marquis
1983-87 (3.3) 4.8

(G) Bands, Renew (One or Both)
Includes: R&R trans.
Mustang-Capri
1983-87
Six (3.8) 5.5
V-6 (4.6) 6.1
Fairmont-Zephyr
1983 (3.7) 5.5
Thunderbird-Cougar
1983-87 (4.7) 6.1
LTD-Marquis
1983-87 (4.6) 6.1

(G) Extension Housing Bushing, Renew
Includes: Renew seal.
All models (.5) 8

(G) Governor Assembly, Renew
All models (1.3) 2.0
Clean and polish gov. add (.1) 2

(G) Vacuum Modulator, Renew
All models (.5) 7

(G) Front Servo, Recondition (External)
Includes: Adjust band.
All models (.9) 1.5

(G) Oil Pan Gasket, Renew
All models (.7) 1.0

(Factory Time) — Chilton Time

(G) Rear Servo, Recondition (External)
Includes: Adjust band.
All models (.7) 1.3

(G) Extension Housing and/or Gasket, Renew
All models (1.3) 2.2

(G) Valve Body Assembly, Renew
Includes: R&R oil pan.
All models (1.0) 1.5

(P) Valve Body Assy., R&R and Recondition
Includes: R&R oil pan and replace filter. Disassemble, clean, inspect, free all valves. Replace parts as required.
All models (1.7) 2.8

(G) Throttle and Manual Seals and/or Levers, Renew
Includes: R&R oil pan and valve body.
All models (1.0) 1.7

SERVICES REQUIRING R&R

(G) Transmission Assembly, R&R or Renew
Includes: R&R trans and converter assembly. Drain and refill unit. Adjust linkage.
Mustang-Capri
1983-87
Six (2.5) 4.0
V-6 (3.3) 4.6
Fairmont-Zephyr
1983 (2.4) 4.0
Thunderbird-XR7
1983-87 (3.4) 4.7
LTD-Marquis
1983-87 (3.3) 4.6

(P) Transmission and Converter, R&R and Recondition
Includes: Disassemble trans, including valve body. Clean, inspect and replace parts as required.
Mustang-Capri
1983-87
Six (6.3) 10.5
V-6 (7.1) 11.1
Fairmont-Zephyr
1983 (6.5) 10.5
Thunderbird-Cougar
1983-87 (7.2) 11.5
LTD-Marquis
1983-87 (7.1) 11.1
Clean and check converter add (.5) 5
Flush oil cooler and lines add (.2) 2

(G) Transmission Assembly, Reseal
Includes: R&R trans and renew all seals and gaskets.
Mustang-Capri
1983-87
Six (4.1) 6.4
V-6 (4.9) 7.0
Fairmont-Zephyr
1983 (4.0) 6.4
Thunderbird-Cougar
1983-87 (5.0) 7.0
LTD-Marquis
1983-87 (4.9) 7.0

PARTS 23 CASE AND PARTS 23 PARTS

	Part No.	Price
Transmission Assy.		
Capri & Mustang		
V-6		
1983 (Trans. ident.)		
PEP-B1	E3ZP-7000AA	N.S.S.
PEP-R	E3ZP-7000BA	N.S.S.
1984	E4ZP-7000CA	N.S.S.
1985-87	E5ZP-7000AA	1299.75
Cougar & Thunderbird		
V-6		
1983 (Trans. ident.)		
PEP-V	E3SP-7000CA	N.S.S.
PEP-W	E3AP-7000GA	N.S.S.
1984 (Trans. ident.)		
PEP-AD	E4SP-7000BA	N.S.S.
PEP-AE	E4DP-7000LA	N.S.S.
1985-87 (Trans. ident.)		
PEP-AD1, AN	E5SP-7000CA	1299.75
PEP-AE1	E5DP-7000HA	1299.75
PEP-AP	E5SP-7000HA	1299.75
Fairmont & Zephyr		
200 engine		
1983 (Trans. ident.)		
PEN-G1	E3BP-7000AA	N.S.S.
PEN-P1	E3BP-7000BA	N.S.S.
PEN-AA	E3BP-7000CA	N.S.S.
PEN-AB	E3BP-7000DA	N.S.S.
PEN-BA	E3BP-7000EA	N.S.S.
PEN-CA	E3BP-7000FA	N.S.S.
LTD & Marquis		
200 engine		
1983 (Trans. ident.)		
PEN-S1	E3SP-7000AA	N.S.S.
PEN-U	E3DP-7000BA	N.S.S.
PEN-Y	E3DP-7000CA	N.S.S.
PEN-Z	E3DP-7000DA	N.S.S.
V-6		
1983 (Trans. ident.)		
PEP-R	E3ZP-7000BA	N.S.S.
PEP-V	E3SP-7000CA	N.L.
PEP-W	E3AP-7000GA	N.S.S.
1984 (Trans. ident.)		
PEP-AC	E4DP-7000GA	N.S.S.
PEP-AE	E4DP-7000LA	N.S.S.
PEP-Z	E4DP-7000DA	N.S.S.
PEK-AK	E4DP-7000RA	N.L.
1985-87 (Trans. ident.)		
PEP-Z1, AM	E5DP-7000FA	1299.75
PEP-AC1, AL	E5DP-7000GA	1299.75
PEP-AE1	E5DP-7000HA	1299.75
Transmission Seal & Gasket Set		
1983-87	E2BZ-7153A	40.25
Neutral Safety Switch		
1983-87	E2DZ-7A247A	38.50
Flywheel Assy.		
200 engine		
1983	E2SZ-6375B	94.75
V-6		
1983-87-exc. below	E3SZ-6375B	89.50
Capri, Mustang	E3DZ-6375B	94.75
(1) Torque Converter		
1983-87-200 eng.	E2DZ-7902A	809.75
V-6	E2DZ-7902B	809.75

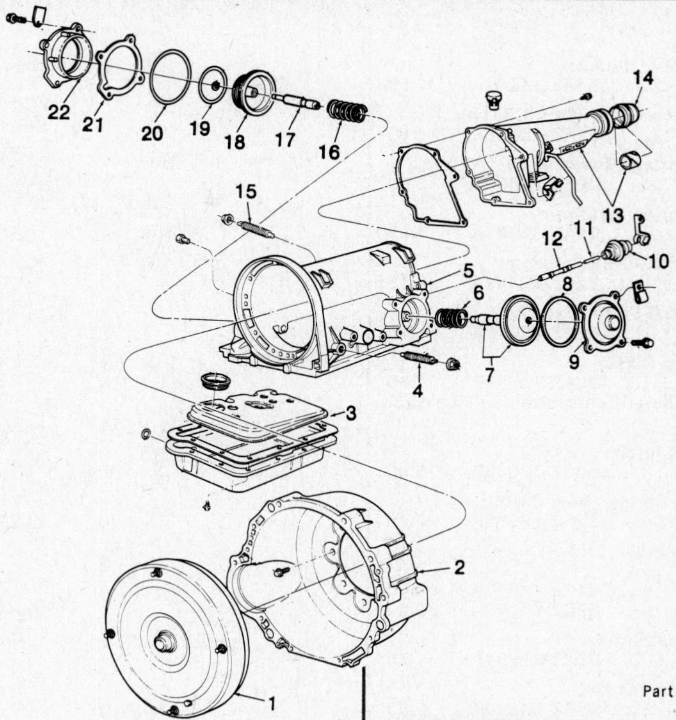

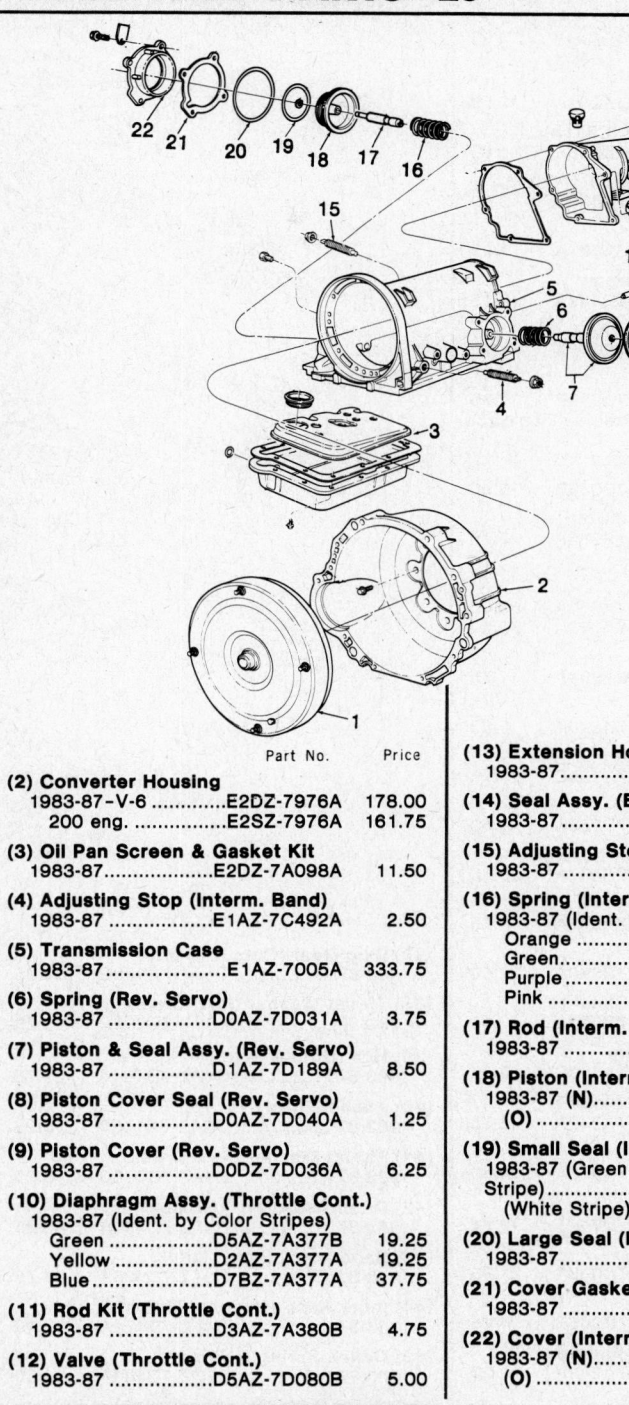

	Part No.	Price
(2) Converter Housing		
1983-87-V-6	E2DZ-7976A	178.00
200 eng.	E2SZ-7976A	161.75
(3) Oil Pan Screen & Gasket Kit		
1983-87	E2DZ-7A098A	11.50
(4) Adjusting Stop (Interm. Band)		
1983-87	E1AZ-7C492A	2.50
(5) Transmission Case		
1983-87	E1AZ-7005A	333.75
(6) Spring (Rev. Servo)		
1983-87	D0AZ-7D031A	3.75
(7) Piston & Seal Assy. (Rev. Servo)		
1983-87	D1AZ-7D189A	8.50
(8) Piston Cover Seal (Rev. Servo)		
1983-87	D0AZ-7D040A	1.25
(9) Piston Cover (Rev. Servo)		
1983-87	D0DZ-7D036A	6.25
(10) Diaphragm Assy. (Throttle Cont.)		
1983-87 (Ident. by Color Stripes)		
Green	D5AZ-7A377B	19.25
Yellow	D2AZ-7A377A	19.25
Blue	D7BZ-7A377A	37.75
(11) Rod Kit (Throttle Cont.)		
1983-87	D3AZ-7A380B	4.75
(12) Valve (Throttle Cont.)		
1983-87	D5AZ-7D080B	5.00

	Part No.	Price
(13) Extension Housing		
1983-87	E2SZ-7A039B	101.75
(14) Seal Assy. (Extension)		
1983-87	E2DZ-7052A	11.25
(15) Adjusting Stop (Rev. Band)		
1983-87	C4AZ-7C492B	2.25
(16) Spring (Interm. Servo)		
1983-87 (Ident. by Color Code)		
Orange	E2SZ-7D028A	7.25
Green	E1SZ-7D028A	5.00
Purple	E1AZ-7D028A	5.00
Pink	E2BZ-7D028A	8.25
(17) Rod (Interm. Servo)		
1983-87	D3AZ-7D023A	3.50
(18) Piston (Interm. Servo)		
1983-87 (N)	E2DZ-7D022A	10.75
(O)	E2SZ-7D022A	10.75
(19) Small Seal (Interm. Servo)		
1983-87 (Green Stripe)	E2DZ-7D025A	2.00
(White Stripe)	E2SZ-7D025A	.75
(20) Large Seal (Interm. Servo)		
1983-87	E1AZ-7D024A	1.00
(21) Cover Gasket (Interm. Servo)		
1983-87	C4AZ-7D026C	.50
(22) Cover (Interm. Servo)		
1983-87 (N)	E2DZ-7D027A	14.75
(O)	E2SZ-7D027A	14.75

PARTS 23 GEAR TRAIN 23 PARTS

	Part No.	Price
(1) Input Shaft		
1983-87	D1AZ-7017A	34.50
(2) Pump Assy. (Front)		
1983-87	E2SZ-7A103A	174.00
(3) Support Assy. (Front Pump)		
1983-87	E2SZ-7A108A	82.00
(4) Thrust Washer (.055)		
1983-87	D0AZ-7D014E	1.75

Smallest size listed other sizes available for selective fit.

	Part No.	Price
(5) Thrust Washer (Clutch Hub)		
1983-87 (Selective fit)		
.033 thick	D0AZ-7D091F	2.75
.057 thick	D0AZ-7D091B	1.00
.074 thick	D0AZ-7D091C	1.25
(6) Anchor Strut (Interm. Band)		
1983-87	D3AZ-7D029B	2.25

	Part No.	Price
(7) Intermediate Band		
1983-87	D9AZ-7D034C	15.50
(8) Actuating Strut (Interm. Band)		
1983-87	C4AZ-7D029A	2.25
(9) Drum Assy. (Interm. Brake)		
1983-87	E2SZ-7D044A	80.00
(10) Inner Piston Seal (Rev. Clutch)		
1983-87	D0AZ-7D404A	.50

23 GEAR TRAIN 23

Part No. Price

(11) Piston (Rev. Clutch)
1983-87..................E1AZ-7A262A 12.50

(12) Outer Piston Seal (Rev. Clutch)
1983-87..................E1AZ-7A548A 1.00

(13) Piston Spring (Rev. Clutch)
1983-87 ....D0AZ-7A480B 3.00

(14) Piston Spring Retainer
1983-87 ....D2AZ-7A527A 1.25

(15) Rear Clutch Plate (Internal)
1983-87..................E2SZ-7B164A 2.25

(16) Rear Clutch Plate (External)
1983-87..................E2SZ-7B442A 1.75

(17) Snap Ring (.052)
1983-87 ....D0AZ-7A577B 1.75
Smallest size listed other sizes available for selective fit.

(18) Reverse Clutch
1983-87..................E2SZ-7B066B 6.50

(19) Pressure Spring (Rev. Clutch)
1983-87..................E2SZ-7E085A 2.75

(20) Cylinder (Front Clutch)
1983-87
1 groove.............E1AZ-7A360A 59.00
2 grooves............E2DZ-7A360A 60.50

(21) Piston Seal (Inner)
1983-87 ....D0AZ-7A294A .75

(22) Piston Seal (Outer)
1983-87.................D8OZ-7A548A 1.00

(23) Piston (Forward Clutch)
1983-87 ....E0AZ-7A262C 15.75

(24) Ring (Forward Clutch)
1983-87 ....C4AZ-7D256A 1.50

(25) Piston Disc Spring (Front Clutch)
1983-87..................E1AZ-7B067A 20.50

(26) Ring (Wave Type)
1983-87..................E1AZ-7A577A 2.75

(27) Thrust Washer
1983-87 ....D0AZ-7D090A 2.50

(28) Hub & Bushing (Front Clutch)
1983-87..................E1AZ-7B067A 20.50

(29) Ring Gear (Front Clutch)
1983-87 ....C4AZ-7A153C 39.25

(30) Thrust Washer (Planet Pinion)
1983-87 ....C4AZ-7A242A 2.75

(31) Planet Assy.
1983-87 ....D1AZ-7A398A 114.50

(32) Input Shell
1983-87.................D2OZ-7D064A 16.75

(33) Sun Gear Assy.
1983-87..................E1AZ-7D063A 21.75

(34) Thrust Washer
1983-87..................C4AZ-7D066B 4.25

(35) Thrust Washer (Planet Pinion)
1983-87.................D2OZ-7A242A 2.25

(36) Planet Assy. (Reverse)
1983-87 ....D74Y-7D006A 70.25

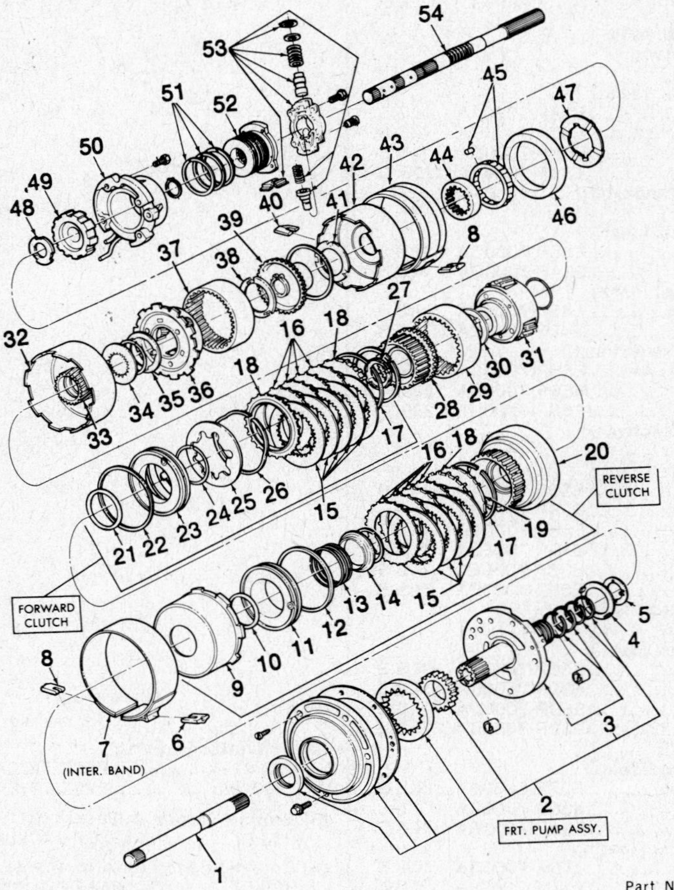

Part No. Price

(37) Ring Gear (Output Shaft)
1983-87 ....C4AZ-7A153C 39.25

(38) Thrust Washer (Rev. Drum)
1983-87 ....E0AZ-7C096C 3.25

(39) Hub (Output Shaft)
1983-87 ....C4AZ-7D164A 29.75

(40) Anchor Strut
1983-87 ....D0AZ-7A175A 3.25

(41) Thrust Washer (Rev. Drum)
1983-87 ....E0AZ-7C096C 3.25

(42) Drum Assy. (Rev. Brake)
1983-87 ....D4FZ-7C498A 45.25

(43) Band Assy. (Rev. Clutch)
1983-87 ....D0AZ-7D095A 25.75

(44) Inner Race (Overrun Clutch)
1983-87 ....D4FZ-7D171A 15.25

(45) Clutch Spring Retainer
1983-87..................D8OZ-7D191A 3.50

(46) Outer Race (Overrun Clutch)
1983-87..................D4FZ-7B456A 31.00

Part No. Price

(47) Washer
1983-87..................E0AZ-7D072A 2.50

(48) Rear Washer (Output Shaft)
1983-87 ....C4AZ-7B368A 1.00

(49) Parking Gear (Output Shaft)
1983 ....C4AZ-7A233A 22.75
1984-87..................E3DZ-7A233A 22.75

(50) Sleeve (Oil Distributor)
1983-87 ....D0AZ-7C232A 19.75

(51) Seal Ring (Gover. Housing)
1983-87 ....C4AZ-7D011A 1.50

(52) Oil Collector Body
1983-87 ....C4AZ-7D220B 24.50

(53) Body Assy. (Governor)
1983-87 ....E2DZ-7C063A 29.75

(54) Output Shaft
(wo/Snap ring groove)
1983-87-7 tooth E4SZ-7060A 117.50
8 tooth..................E3SZ-7060A 118.25
(w/Snap ring groove)
1983-8 tooth............E2DZ-7060A 127.50

(Factory Time) Chilton Time

ON CAR SERVICES

(G) Drain & Refill Unit
All models.......... 1.1

(G) Oil Pressure Check
All models.......... .8

(M) Check Unit For Oil Leaks
Includes: Clean and dry outside of case and run unit to determine point of leak.
All models.......... .9

(G) Neutral Safety Switch, Renew
All models (.4).......... .6

(G) Linkage, Adjust
manual (.3).......... .6
throttle (.3).......... .5

(G) Halfshaft Assy., R&R or Renew
1983-87
right (1.1).......... 1.4
left (1.0).......... 1.3
both (1.7).......... 2.3
Renew C.V. Joint
add-each (.2).......... .3
Renew diff oil seal
add-each (.2).......... .3

(M) Selector Indicator, Renew
All models
floor shift (.3).......... .4

(G) Governor Driven Gear, Renew
All models (.6).......... .9

(G) Oil Pan Gasket, Renew
All models (.7).......... 1.1

(G) Main Control Valve Body Assembly, Renew
Includes: R&R oil pan.
All models (1.2).......... 1.8
w/Cruise control add (.2).......... .2

(P) Valve Body Assy., R&R and Recondition
Includes: Disassemble, clean, inspect, free all valves. Replace parts as required.
All models (2.1).......... 2.8
w/Cruise control add (.2).......... .2

(G) Throttle and Manual Seals and/or Levers, Renew
Includes: R&R oil pan and valve body.
All models (1.2).......... 2.0

(G) Governor and Counterweight Assy., Renew
Includes: Road test.
All models (.7).......... 1.0

SERVICES REQUIRING R&R

(G) Automatic Trans/Axle Assy., R&R or Renew
Includes: R&R trans and converter assembly. Drain and refill unit. Adjust linkage.

CHILTON'S AUTOMATIC TRANSMISSION TUNE-UP

1. Check engine performance
2. Check condition of transmission oil
3. Check transmission, oil cooler and oil cooler lines for external leaks
4. Remove oil pan, clean or renew screen or filter
5. Torque valve body
6. Adjust bands
7. Clean oil pan and install pan with new gasket
8. Check modulator and hose
9. Install new transmission oil to proper level
10. Adjust manual and throttle linkage
11. Road test

All models.......... 1.5
Charge for parts used

(Factory Time) Chilton Time

Escort-Lynx
EXP-LN7
1983-87 (3.1).......... 4.9
Tempo-Topaz
1984-87 (5.5).......... 7.0
w/A.C. add (.8).......... .8

(P) Automatic Transmission, R&R and Recondition (Complete)
Includes: Recondition automatic transmission only.
Escort-Lynx
EXP-LN7
1983-87 (7.0).......... 11.0
Tempo-Topaz
1984-87 (9.1).......... 12.5
w/A.C. add (.8).......... .8
Clean and check converter add (.5).......... .5
Flush oil cooler and lines add (.2).......... .2

(P) Automatic Trans/Axle Assy., R&R and Recondition (Complete)
Includes: Recondition automatic transmission and differential assemblies.
Escort-Lynx
EXP-LN7
1983-87 (8.8).......... 13.5
Tempo-Topaz
1984-87 (9.6).......... 14.4
w/A.C. add (.8).......... .8

(Factory Time) Chilton Time

(G) Front Pump Oil Seal, Renew
Includes: R&R transmission.
Escort-Lynx
EXP-LN7
1983-87 (3.2).......... 5.1
Tempo-Topaz
1984-87 (5.6).......... 7.2
w/A.C. add (.8).......... .8

(G) Front Oil Pump, Renew or Recondition
Includes: R&R transmission.
Escort-Lynx
EXP-LN7
1983-87 (3.6).......... 5.8
Tempo-Topaz
1984-87 (6.0).......... 7.8
w/A.C. add (.8).......... .8

(G) Converter Assembly, Renew
Includes: R&R transmission.
Escort-Lynx
EXP-LN7
1983-87 (3.1).......... 5.0
Tempo-Topaz
1984-87 (5.0).......... 7.0
w/A.C. add (.8).......... .8

(G) Parking Pawl, Renew
Includes: R&R transmission.
Escort-Lynx
EXP-LN7
1983-87 (4.7).......... 6.9
Tempo-Topaz
1984-87 (6.8).......... 9.2
w/A.C. add (.8).......... .8

(G) Flywheel and Ring Gear Assy., Renew
Includes: R&R transmission.
Escort-Lynx
EXP-LN7
1983-87 (3.4).......... 5.3
Tempo-Topaz
1984-87 (5.8).......... 7.5
w/A.C. add (.8).......... .8

(G) Front or Rear Bands, Renew
Includes: R&R transmission.
Escort-Lynx
EXP-LN7
1983-87 (4.7).......... 6.9
Tempo-Topaz
1984-87 (7.1).......... 9.9
w/A.C. add (.8).......... .8

(P) Differential Case, Recondition (w/ATX)
Includes: R&R trans/axle and recondition differential assy; only.
Escort-Lynx
EXP-LN7
1983-87 (4.4).......... 6.9
Tempo-Topaz
1984-87 (6.5).......... 9.0
w/A.C. add (.8).......... .8

	Part No.	Price
Automatic Trans/Axle (wo/Converter)		
1.6L		
1983 (Trans. ident.)		
PMA-K3, 4	E3EP-7002BA	N.S.S.
PMA-P, P1	E3EP-7002AB	N.S.S.
PMA-R1, 2	E3GP-7002AA	N.S.S.
PMA-T	E3EP-7002EC	N.S.S.
PMA-U	E3EP-7002FD	N.S.S.
PMA-V	E3EP-7002GC	N.S.S.
PMA-Y, Y1	E3EP-7002MA	N.L.
PMA-2	E3EP-7002NB	N.L.
1984-wo/H.O.	E4EP-7002AA	1816.75
H.O.	E4EP-7002BA	1816.75
Canada	E4EP-7002CA	N.L.
1985 (Trans. ident.)		
PMA-U4	E5EP-7002GA	NA
PMA-U5, 6	E5EP-7002GB	1816.75
PMA-V5	E5EP-7002HA	NA
PMA-V6, 7	E5EP-7002HB	1816.75
PMA-Z6	E5EP-7002JA	N.L.
PMA-Z7, 8	E5EP-7002JB	1816.75
1.9L		
1986-87 (Trans. ident.)		
PMA-AD	E6EP-7002AA	N.L.
PMA-AM	E6EP-7002CA	N.L.
PMA-AP	E6EP-7002GA	N.L.
2.3L		
1984 (Trans. ident.)		
PMA-N, N1	E33P-7002AB	N.S.S.
PMA-N2, N3	E43P-7002DB	N.S.S.
PMA-AA	E33P-7002BA	N.L.

PARTS 23 CASE AND PARTS 23 PARTS

	Part No.	Price
PMA-AA2, AA3	E43P-7002EB	1816.75
PMA-AE	E43P-7002GA	1816.75
1985 (Trans. ident.)		
PMA-N5	E53P-7002DA	NA
PMA-N6, 7	E53P-7002DB	1816.75
PMA-AD	E53P-7002EB	NA
PMA-AS	E53P-7002GA	NA
PMA-AA6, 7	E53P-7002EA	1816.75
1986-87 (Trans. ident.)		
PMA-N8, 9	E63P-7002DA	N.L.
PMA-AA8, 9	E63P-7002EA	N.L.
2.5L		
1986-87	E6DP-7002AA	N.L.
(1) Cover Gasket (Main Control)		
1983-87	E1FZ-7F396A	2.50
(2) Oil Screen (Governor)		
1983-87	E1FZ-7E242A	1.75
(3) Case Assy.		
1983-84	E3FZ-7005D	575.00
1985	E5FZ-7005F	575.00
1985-87	E5FZ-7005G	575.00
(4) Support Assy. (Conv. Stator)		
1983-87	E1FZ-7A108A	82.00
(5) Seal Assy. (Impeller Hub)		
1983-87	E3FZ-7F401A	4.25
(6) Converter Assy.		
1.6L		
1983-85	E6FZ-7902A	555.50
1.9L		
1986-87-wo/ E.F.I.	E6FZ-7902A	555.50
E.F.I.	E6FZ-7902B	555.50

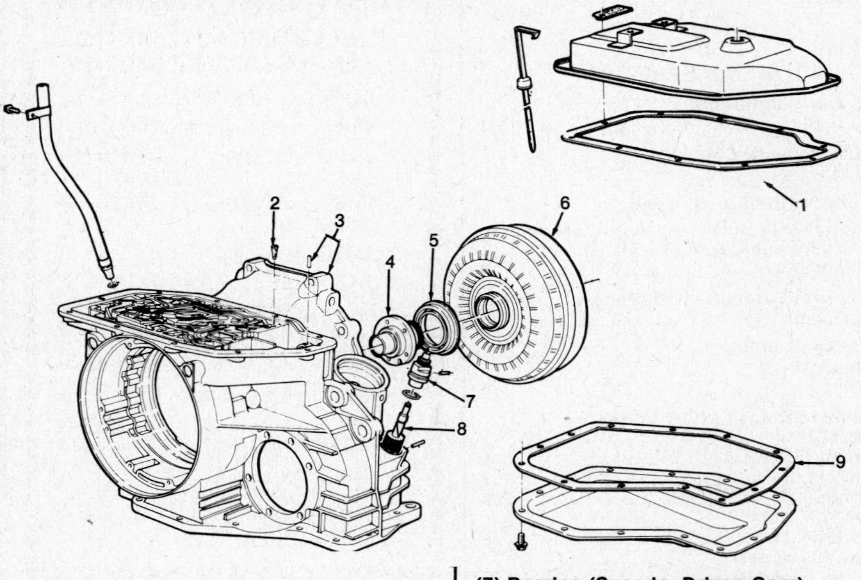

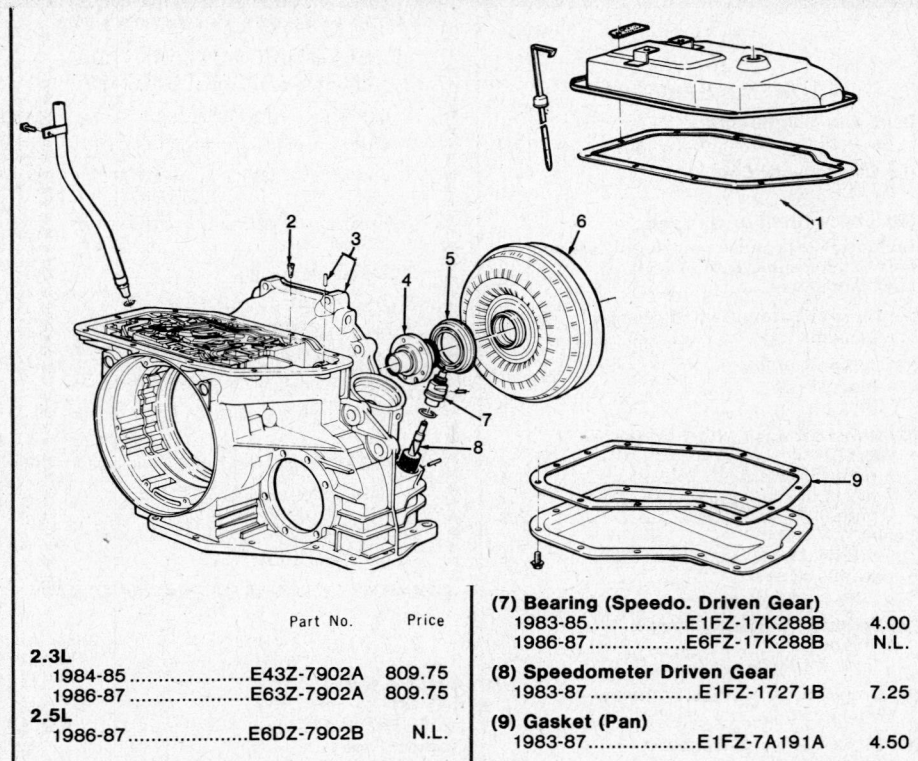

	Part No.	Price
2.3L		
1984-85	E43Z-7902A	809.75
1986-87	E63Z-7902A	809.75
2.5L		
1986-87	E6DZ-7902B	N.L.

(7) Bearing (Speedo. Driven Gear)		
1983-85	E1FZ-17K288B	4.00
1986-87	E6FZ-17K288B	N.L.
(8) Speedometer Driven Gear		
1983-87	E1FZ-17271B	7.25
(9) Gasket (Pan)		
1983-87	E1FZ-7A191A	4.50

PARTS 23 GEAR TRAIN 23 PARTS

	Part No.	Price
(1) Oil Pump Assy.		
1983-87	E1FZ-7A103A	180.50
(2) Drive Shaft (Oil Pump)		
1983-87	E1FZ-7B328A	15.25
(3) Seal (Oil Pump)		
1983-87	E1FZ-7A248A	3.25
(4) Inner Seal (Interm. Clutch)		
1983-87	E1FZ-7D019A	.75
(5) Thrust Washer (Oil Pump)		
1983-87-.060	E1FZ-7D014A	3.25
Other sizes available for selective fit.		
(6) Thrust Bearing (Interm. Clutch)		
1983-87	E1FZ-7F374A	3.00
(7) Gasket (Oil Pump)		
1983-87	E1FZ-7A136A	1.25
(8) Cylinder Assy. (Interm Clutch)		
(4 plate pkg.)		
1983	E1FZ-7D044A	87.75
(6 plate pkg.)		
1983	E2FZ-7D044A	87.75
1984-87	E3FZ-7D044A	85.50
(9) Inner Piston Seal (Interm. Clutch)		
1983-87	E1FZ-7F225A	3.25
(10) Outer Piston Seal (Interm. Clutch)		
1983-87	E1FZ-7F224A	3.25
(11) Piston (Interm. Clutch)		
1983-87	E3FZ-7E005A	15.50
(12) Retainer & Spring Assy. (Interm. Clutch)		
1983-87	E3FZ-7F222A	9.25
(13) Direct Clutch (External)		
1983-87	E1FZ-7B442A	2.50

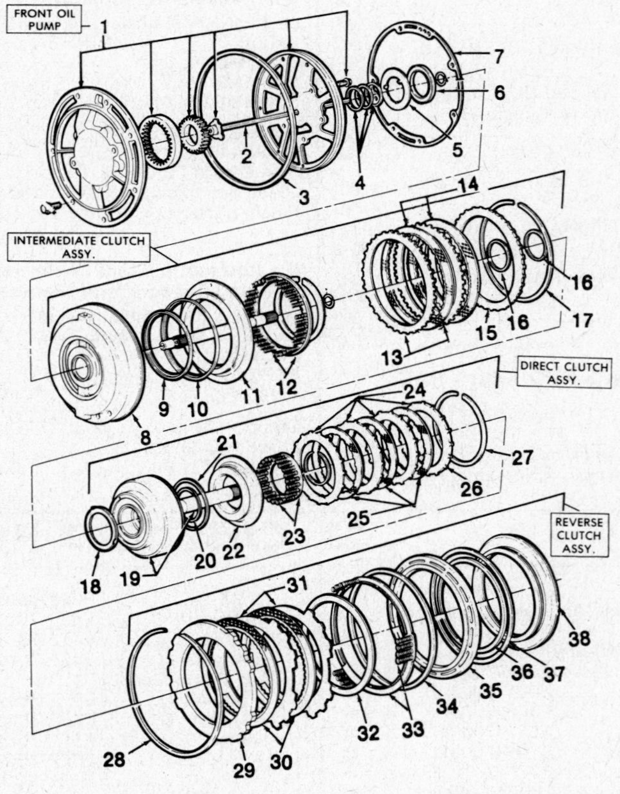

	Part No.	Price
(14) Direct Clutch (Internal)		
1983-87	E1FZ-7B164A	5.00
(15) Pressure Plate (Interm. Clutch)		
1983-87	E1FZ-7B066B	11.00
(16) Outer Seal (Interim Clutch)		
1983-87	E1FZ-7D020A	1.50
(17) Snap Ring (.050 Thick)		
1983-87	E1FZ-7D483D	3.00
Other sizes available for selective fit.		
(18) Thrust Bearing Assy.		
1983-87	E1FZ-7F373A	11.75
(19) Cylinder Assy. (Direct Clutch)		
Escort, EXP		
1983-87	E4FZ-7F283A	140.00
Tempo, Topaz		
1984		
before 6-25-84	E3FZ-7F283D	N.L.
1984-87		
from 6-25-84	E4FZ-7F283B	145.25
(20) Inner Seal (Direct Clutch)		
1983-87	E5FZ-7C099A	1.00
(21) Outer Seal (Direct Clutch)		
1983-87	E5FZ-7A548A	2.25
(22) Piston (Direct Clutch)		
1983-87	E3FZ-7A262A	15.75
(23) Retainer & Spring Assy. (Direct Clutch)		
1983-87	E3FZ-7F235A	6.00
(24) Direct Clutch (External)		
1983-87	E1FZ-7B442A	2.50
(25) Direct Clutch (Internal)		
1983-87	E1FZ-7B164A	5.00
(26) Pressure Plate (Direct Clutch)		
1983-87	E1FZ-7B066A	6.00
(27) Snap Ring (.052″ Thick)		
1983-87	E1FZ-7D483A	2.75
Other sizes available for selective fit.		
(28) Snap Ring (.076″ Thick)		
1983-85	E1FZ-7D483G	3.25
1986-87	E6FZ-7D483A	2.75
Other sizes available for selective fit.		
(29) Pressure Plate (Reverse Clutch)		
1983-87	E1FZ-7B066C	11.00
(30) Reverse Clutch (Internal)		
1983-87	E1FZ-7B164B	4.00
(31) Reverse Clutch (External)		
1983-87	E1FZ-7B442C	5.25
(32) Pressure Spring (Reverse Clutch)		
1983-85	E3FZ-7E085A	5.75
1986-87	E6FZ-7E085A	7.75
(33) Retainer & Spring Assy. (Reverse Clutch)		
1983-87	E1FZ-7D406A	9.00
(34) Cylinder Seal (Reverse Clutch)		
1983-87	E1FZ-7A548A	2.25
(35) Piston (Reverse Clutch)		
1983-87 (Trans. ident.)		
exc. below	E2GZ-7D402A	51.50
PMA-A, K, T	E1FZ-7D402A	14.75
(36) Inner Piston Seal (Reverse Clutch)		
1983-87	E1FZ-7D404A	1.50
(37) Outer Piston Seal (Reverse Clutch)		
1983-87	E1FZ-7D403A	1.75
(38) Cylinder (Reverse Clutch)		
1983-87	E1FZ-7F341A	15.50
(39) Bearing (Overrunning Clutch)		
1983-87	E1FZ-7A623A	6.25
(40) Clutch Assy. (Overrunning)		
1983-87	E1FZ-7A089A	9.25

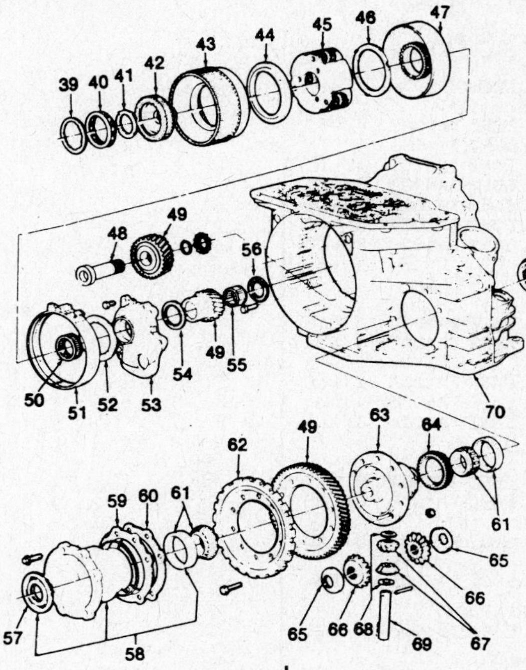

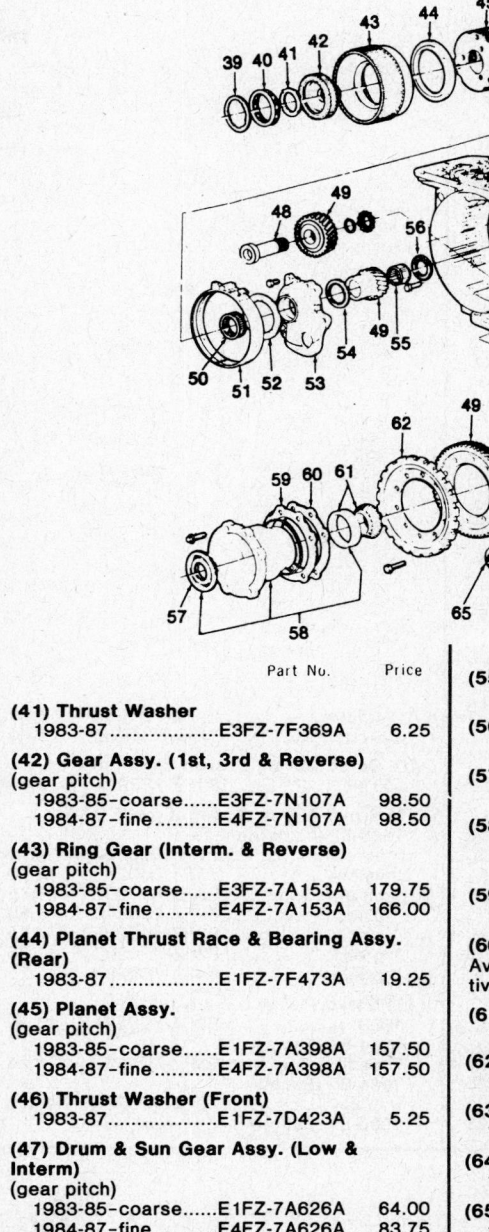

	Part No.	Price
(41) Thrust Washer		
1983-87	E3FZ-7F369A	6.25
(42) Gear Assy. (1st, 3rd & Reverse)		
(gear pitch)		
1983-85-coarse	E3FZ-7N107A	98.50
1984-87-fine	E4FZ-7N107A	98.50
(43) Ring Gear (Interm. & Reverse)		
(gear pitch)		
1983-85-coarse	E3FZ-7A153A	179.75
1984-87-fine	E4FZ-7A153A	166.00
(44) Planet Thrust Race & Bearing Assy. (Rear)		
1983-87	E1FZ-7F473A	19.25
(45) Planet Assy.		
(gear pitch)		
1983-85-coarse	E1FZ-7A398A	157.50
1984-87-fine	E4FZ-7A398A	157.50
(46) Thrust Washer (Front)		
1983-87	E1FZ-7D423A	5.25
(47) Drum & Sun Gear Assy. (Low & Interm)		
(gear pitch)		
1983-85-coarse	E1FZ-7A626A	64.00
1984-87-fine	E4FZ-7A626A	83.75
(48) Idler Gear Shaft		
1983-85	E1FZ-7F358A	10.75
1985-87	E5FZ-7F358A	10.75
(49) Matched Gear Set (Final Drive)		
1983-85	E43Z-7F475A	118.50
1985-87	E3FZ-7F475A	118.50
(50) Bearing Assy. (Transfer Housing)		
1983-87	E1FZ-7F380A	19.25
(51) Band Assy. (Low & Interm.)		
1983-85	E1FZ-7D034B	35.00
1986-87	E6FZ-7D034A	35.00
(52) Thrust Washer (Interm. Sun Gear)		
1983-87	E1FZ-7F368A	6.25
(53) Only serviced in case assembly.		
(54) Thrust Bearing Assy. (Rear)		
1983-87	E1FZ-7F405A	9.25

	Part No.	Price
(55) Bearing Assy. (Input Gear)		
1983-87	E3FZ-7F403A	11.75
(56) Inner Piston Seal (Reverse Clutch)		
1983-87	E1FZ-7D404A	1.50
(57) Inner Wheel Bearing Seal (Rear Whl.)		
1983-87	E1FZ-1177A	10.75
(58) Retainer Assy. (Diff. Bearing)		
1983-84	E3FZ-7F447A	66.50
1985-87	E5FZ-7F447A	66.50
(59) Shim (Bearing Retainer)		
1983-copper	E1FZ-7K084A	5.25
(60) Shims (Diff. Bearing)		
Available from .30 mm up to 1.30 mm for selective fit.		
(61) Axle Bearing Assy.		
1983-87	E3FZ-4221B	20.50
(62) Parking Gear (Output Shaft)		
1983-87	E1FZ-7A233A	57.75
(63) Case Assy. (Trans/Axle)		
1983-87	E3FZ-4204B	124.50
(64) Speedometer Drive Gear		
1983-87	E1FZ-17285B	13.75
(65) Thrust Washer (Side Gear)		
1983-87	E1FZ-4228A	2.75
(66) Side Gear Kit		
1983-85	E1FZ-4236A	40.00
1986-87	E6FZ-4236A	40.00
(67) Pinion Kit		
1983-87	E3FZ-4215A	25.75
(68) Thrust Washer (Pinion)		
1983-87	E3FZ-4230A	1.50
(69) Pinion Shaft		
1983-85-exc.		
Tempo	E1FZ-4211A	13.75
Tempo	E43Z-4211B	13.75
1986-87-exc.		
3.23 ratio	E43Z-4211B	13.75
3.23 ratio	E6FZ-4211A	13.75
(70) Case Assy. (Trans/Axle)		
1983-84	E3FZ-7005D	575.00
1985-87	E5FZ-7005G	575.00

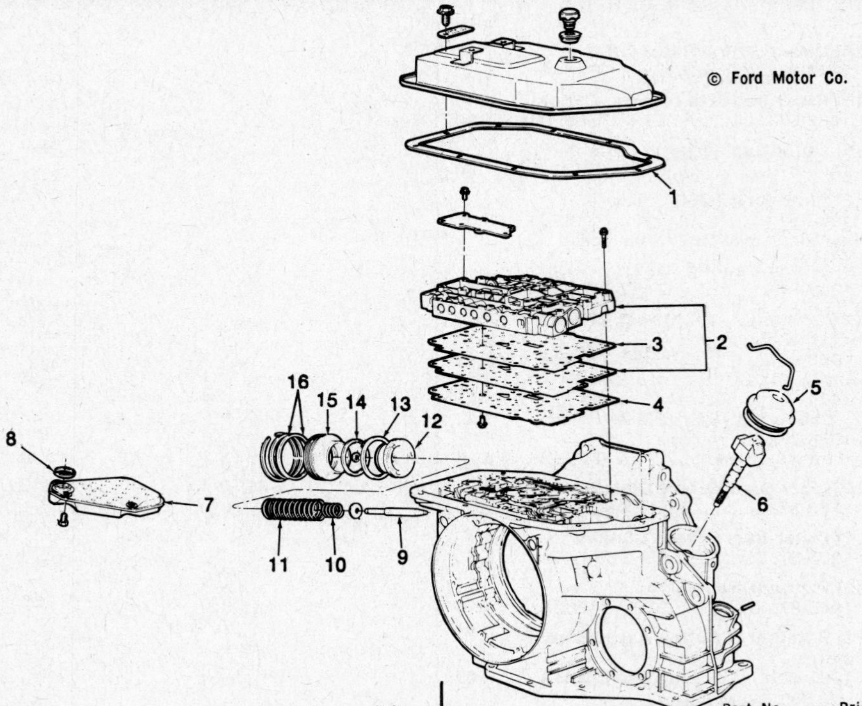

	Part No.	Price
(1) Cover Gasket (Main Cont.)		
1983-87	E1FZ-7F396A	2.50
(2) Valve Body Assy. (Main Cont.) exc. Tempo & Topaz		
1983-exc. below	E3FZ-7A100S	421.50
w/H.O.	E3FZ-7A100R	421.50
w/E.F.I.	E3FZ-7A100T	421.50
1984-wo/H.O.	E5FZ-7A100A	394.00
w/H.O.	E5FZ-7A100B	394.00
1985-wo/H.O.	E5FZ-7A100A	394.00
w/H.O.	E5FZ-7A100B	394.00
Tempo & Topaz		
1984 (Trans. ident.)		
E33 (exc. Canada)	E3FZ-7A100U	357.75
(Canada)	E3FZ-7A100V	N.L.
E43 (exc. Canada)	E43Z-7A100A	334.50
(Canada)	E43Z-7A100B	N.L.
1985	E63Z-7A100A	311.00
Escort, Lynx		
1986-87-exc. E.F.I.	E6FZ-7A100A	332.75
w/E.F.I.	E6FZ-7A100B	357.75
Tempo, Topaz		
1986-87	E63Z-7A100A	311.00
Taurus, Sable		
1986-87	E6DZ-7A100E	N.L.
(3) Gasket (Valve Body Plate)		
1983-87	E1FZ-7D100A	1.25
(4) Gasket (Valve Body)		
1983-87	E3FZ-7C155A	2.00
(5) Cover (Governor)		
1983-87	E1FZ-7A301A	10.25
(6) Governor Assy.		
1.6L		
1983-85	E3FZ-7C053A	71.50
1.9L		
2.3L		
1984	E43Z-7C053A	70.00
1985-87	E43Z-7C053B	60.50
2.5L		
1986-87	E6DZ-70053B	N.L.
(7) Screen & Gasket Kit (Oil Pan)		
1983-87	E1FZ-7A098A	17.50
(8) Gasket (Oil Pan Screen)		
1983-87	E1FZ-7E062A	1.75
(9) Servo Piston Rod (Low & Interm.)		
1983-87 (number of notches on rod)		
No notch	E1FZ-7D190G	7.75
1 notch	E1FZ-7D190H	7.25
2 notches	E1FZ-7D190J	7.25
3 notches	E1FZ-7D190K	7.25
4 notches	E1FZ-7D190L	7.25
5 notches	E1FZ-7D190M	5.00
(10) Servo Spring (Piston Cushion)		
1983-87	E1FZ-7F390A	3.50
(11) Servo Piston Spring (Low & Interm.)		
1983-87 (color ident.)		
no color	E1FZ-7D028A	11.75
yellow	E3FZ-7D028A	11.75
purple	E3FZ-7D028C	11.75
pink	E3FZ-7D028D	5.50
black	E3FZ-7D028E	7.25
green	E3FZ-7D028C	11.75
orange	E43Z-7D028A	5.75
(12) Servo Piston (Low & Interm.)		
1983	E3FZ-7D022A	11.25
1984-87 (Tempo, Topaz)	E3FZ-7D022C	11.25
1984-85 (Escort-w/1.6)	E3FZ-7D022C	11.25
1985-87 (Escort-w/1.9)	E5FZ-7D022A	11.25
1986-87 (Taurus, Sable)	E6DZ-7D022B	N.L.
(13) Large Piston Seal (Low & Interm.)		
1983-87	E1FZ-7D024A	1.75
(14) Small Piston Seal (Low & Interm.)		
1983	E3FZ-7D025A	.75
1984-87 (Tempo, Topaz)	E4FZ-7D025B	.75
1984-85 (Escort-w/1.6)	E4FZ-7D025B	.75
1985-87 (Escort-w/1.9)	E5FZ-7D025A	.75
1986-87 (Taurus, Sable)	E6DZ-7D025B	N.L.
(15) Piston Cover (Low & Interm.)		
1983	E3FZ-7D027A	21.00
1984-87	E4FZ-7D027D	21.00
(16) Piston Cover Seal (Low & Interm.)		
1983-87	E1FZ-7D026A	2.25

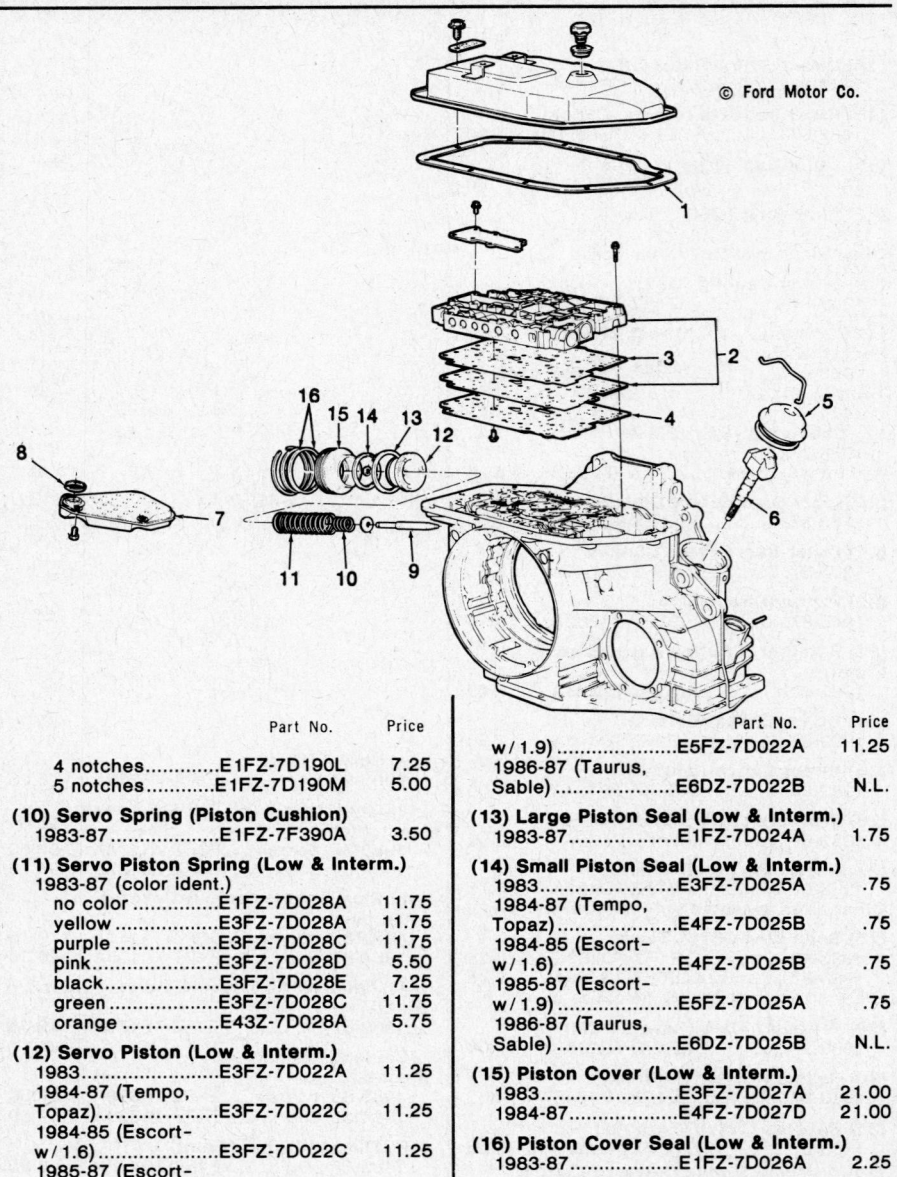

LABOR 23 AUTOMATIC TRANSMISSION 23 LABOR

(Factory Time) Chilton Time

ON CAR SERVICES

(G) Drain & Refill Unit
All models.. 1.0

(G) Oil Pressure Check
All models.. .5

(M) Check Unit for Oil Leaks
Includes: Clean and dry outside of case and run unit to determine point of leak.
All models.. .9

(G) Neutral Safety Switch, Renew
All models (.3).. .4

(G) Shift Linkage, Adjust
manual (.3).. .4
throttle valve (.4).. .5

(G) Selector Indicator, Renew
All models
column shift (.7).. 1.1

(G) Governor Assembly, Renew
All models (.3).. .5

(G) Oil Pan and/or Gasket, Renew
All models (.7).. 1.0

(G) Parking Pawl, Renew
All models (.7).. 1.1

(G) Halfshaft Assembly, R&R or Renew
All models
one side (1.0).. 1.3
both sides (1.8).. 2.4
Renew C.V. joint
add-each (.2).. .3
Renew diff oil seal
add-each (.1).. .2

SERVICES REQUIRING R&R

(G) Automatic Trans/Axle Assy., R&R or Renew
Includes: R&R trans and converter assembly. Drain and refill unit.
Sable-Taurus
1986-87 (5.4).. 7.5

(P) Automatic Transmission, R&R and Recondition (Complete)
Includes: Recondition automatic transmission only.
Sable-Taurus
1986-87 (10.2).. 14.0
Clean and check converter
add (.5).. .5

(P) Differential Case, Recondition (w/AXOD)
Includes: R&R trans/axle and recondition differential assy. only.
Sable-Taurus
1986-87 (10.9).. 15.0

(G) Front or Rear Bands, Renew
Includes: R&R trans/axle.
Sable-Taurus
1986-87 (7.3).. 10.0

(G) Converter Assembly, Renew
Includes: R&R trans/axle.
Sable-Taurus
1986-87 (5.1).. 7.5

(G) Converter Impeller Hub Oil Seal, Renew
Includes: R&R trans/axle.
Sable-Taurus
1986-87 (5.5).. 7.7

(G) Flywheel and Ring Gear Assy., Renew
Includes: R&R trans/axle.
Sable-Taurus
1986-87 (5.7).. 8.0

PARTS 23 CASE AND PARTS 23 PARTS

	Part No.	Price
Automatic Trans./Axle (wo/Converter) 3.0L		
1986-87	E6DP-7002BA	N.L.
(1) Case Assy.		
1986-87	E6DZ-7005A	575.00
(2) Oil Filler Tube Grommet		
1986-87	E2FZ-7N243A	2.75
(3) Oil Filler Tube		
1986-87	E6DZ-7A228A	5.50
(4) Governor Assy.		
1986-87	E6DZ-7C053A	71.50
(5) Speedometer Drive Gear		
1986-87	E6DZ-17285A	5.00
(6) Governor Cover		
1986-87	E6DZ-7A301A	1.75
(7) Governor Thrust Bearing Assy.		
1986-87	E6DZ-7G173A	3.75
(8) Converter Assy.		
1986-87	E6DZ-7902A	753.25
(9) Impeller Hub Seal Assy.		
1986-87	E6DZ-7F401A	4.25
(10) Converter Housing Cover		
1986-87	E6DZ-7986A	N.L.
(11) Oil Transfer Tube Seal		
1986-87	E6DZ-7G085A	6.25
(12) Oil Pan Gasket		
1986-87	E6DZ-7A191A	3.75
(13) Oil Pan		
1986-87	E6DZ-7A194A	20.25
(14) Oil Pan Screen & Gasket		
1986-87	E6DZ-7A098A	29.25

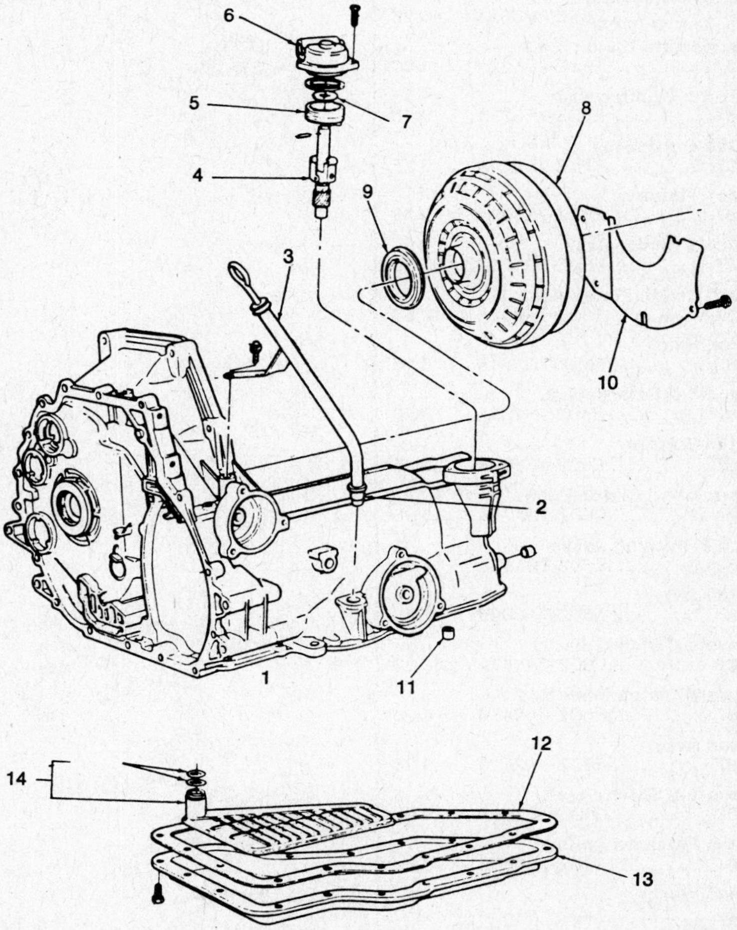

	Part No.	Price
(1) Snap Ring (Pressure Plate Retainer) Reverse Clutch		
1986-87 .062	E6DZ-7D483R	2.75
(2) Reverse Clutch Plate		
1986-87	E6DZ-7B066D	10.00
(3) Reverse Clutch Internal Plate		
1986-87	E6DZ-7B164C	4.00
(4) Reverse Clutch External Plate		
1986-87	E6DZ-7B442C	3.00
(5) Pressure Spring		
1986-87	E6DZ-7E085A	1.00
(6) Reverse Clutch Support & Spring Assy.		
1986-87	E6DZ-7G335A	5.75
(7) Output Shaft		
1986-87	E6DZ-7060A	52.25
(8) Reverse Clutch Piston		
1986-87	E6DZ-7D402A	7.00
(9) Piston Outer Seal		
1986-87	E6DZ-7D403A	1.75
(10) Piston Inner Seal		
1986-87	E6DZ-7D404A	1.25
(11) Reverse Clutch Cylinder		
1986-87	E6DZ-7F341A	64.00
(12) Front Sun Shell Assy.		
1986-87	E6DZ-7D064A	16.75
(13) Thrust Bearing & Race Assy.		
1986-87	E6DZ-7C096A	2.50
(14) Intermediate Clutch Hub		
1986-87	E6DZ-7B067A	46.25
(15) Intermediate Clutch Ring		
1986-87	E6DZ-7C122A	1.00
(16) Support & Spring Assy.		
1986-87	E6DZ-7F222A	9.25
(17) Clutch Outer Seal		
1986-87	E6DZ-7F224A	3.25
(18) Clutch Piston		
1986-87	E6DZ-7E005A	6.75
(19) Clutch Cylinder Assy.		
1986-87	E6DZ-7G120A	157.00
(20) Direct Clutch Piston Assy.		
1986-87	E6DZ-7A262A	10.50
(21) Piston Ring		
1986-87	E6DZ-7G341A	6.25
(22) Support & Spring Assy.		
1986-87	E6DZ-7F235A	6.00
(23) Thrust Washer		
1986-87	E6DZ-7F369A	6.25
(24) Overrunning Clutch Race		
1986-87	E6DZ-7D171A	15.25
(25) Race & Bushing Assy.		
1986-87	E6DZ-7G156A	5.00
(26) Clutch Assy.		
1986-87	E6DZ-7A089B	N.L.
(27) Forward Clutch Cylinder		
1986-87	E6DZ-7A360A	60.50
(28) Forward Clutch Inner Seal		
1986-87	E6DZ-7A548B	4.00
(29) Piston Assy.		
1986-87	E6DZ-7A262B	8.25
(30) Support & Spring Assy.		
1986-87	E6DZ-7G299A	9.25
(31) Clutch Pressure Spring		
1986-87	E6DZ-7E085B	8.00
(32) Thrust Washer		
1986-87	E6DZ-7A166A	1.50

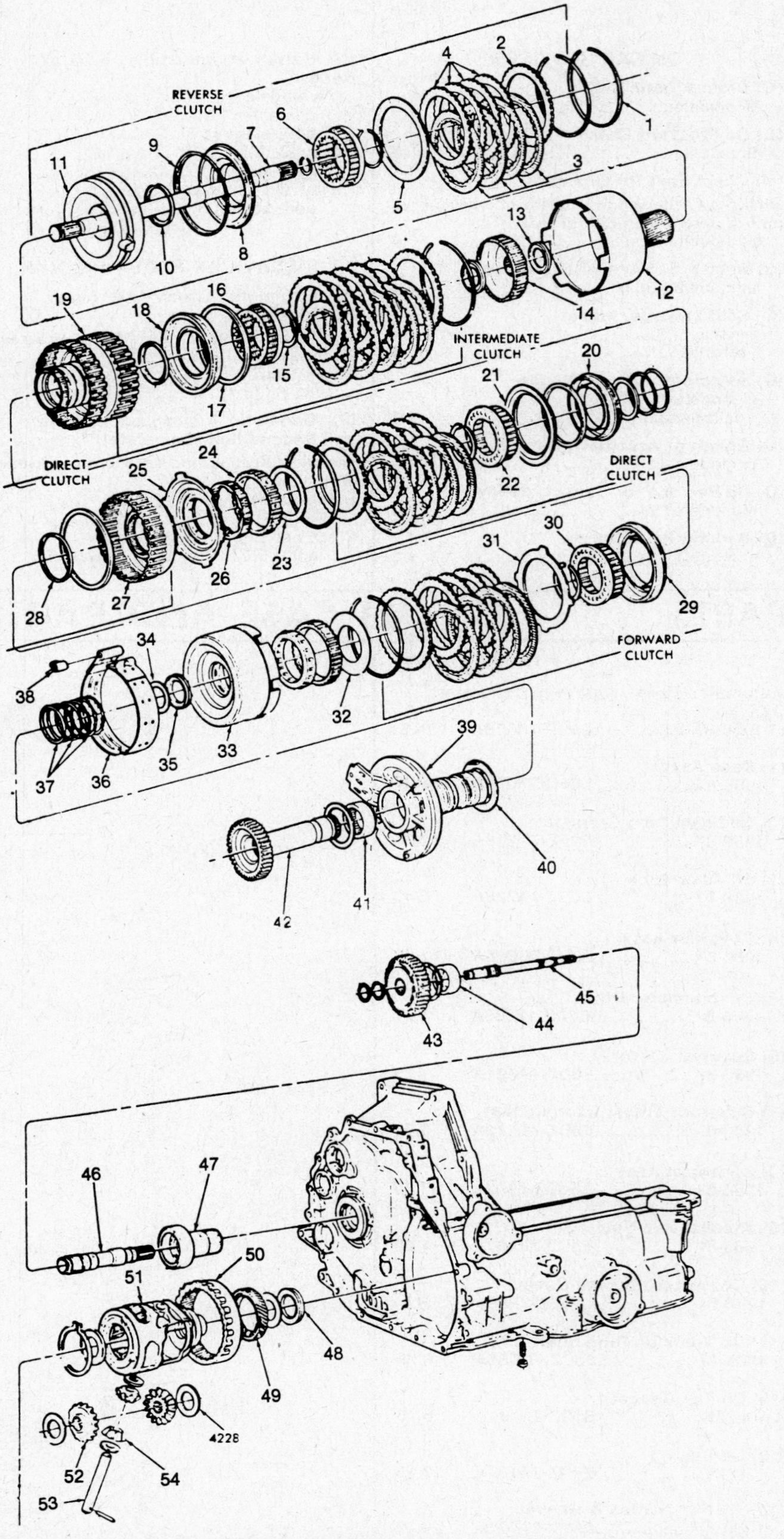

PARTS 23 GEAR TRAIN 23 PARTS

	Part No.	Price
(33) Overdrive Drum Assy.		
1986-87	E6DZ-7L669A	99.00
(34) Driven Sprocket Support Washer		
1986-87 (Natural)	E6DZ-7G273A	2.25
Other sizes available for selective fit.		
(35) Bearing & Race Assy.		
1986-87	E6DZ-7F240A	7.50
(36) Overdrive Band Assy.		
1986-87	E6DZ-7F196A	15.50
(37) Clutch Cylinder Seal		
1986-87	E6DZ-7D019A	.75
(38) Band Anchor Strut		
1986-87	E6DZ-7D430A	3.25
(39) Support Assy.		
1986-87	E6DZ-7G166A	13.00
(40) Thrust Washer		
1986-87 .088	E6DZ-7D014A	1.50
Other sizes available for selective fit.		
(41) Bearing Assy.		
1986-87	E6DZ-7G247A	6.50
(42) Driven Sprocket Assy.		
1986-87	E6DZ-7G132A	32.50
(43) Drive Sprocket Assy.		
1986-87	E6DZ-7G129A	35.50
(44) Bearing Assy.		
1986-87	E6DZ-7G233A	3.00
(45) Oil Pump Drive Shaft Assy.		
1986-87	E6DZ-7G328A	N.L.

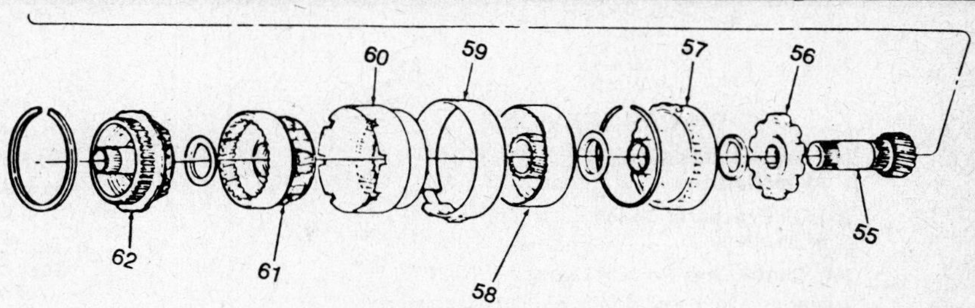

	Part No.	Price
(46) Turbine Shaft		
1986-87	E6DZ-7F213A	13.50
(47) Stator Support		
1986-87	E6DZ-7A108A	31.50
(48) Carrier Bearing & Race Assy.		
1986-87	E6DZ-7G112A	7.75
(49) Governor Drive Gear		
1986-87	E6DZ-7G237A	2.75
(50) Final Drive Ring Gear		
1986-87	E6DZ-7F343A	62.25
(51) Planet & Carrier Assy.		
1986-87	E6DZ-7F465A	N.L.
(52) Differential Side Gear Kit		
1986-87	E6DZ-4236A	40.00
(53) Pinion Shaft		
1986-87	E6DZ-4211A	13.75

	Part No.	Price
(54) Differential Pinion		
1986-87	E6DZ-4215A	20.00
(55) Final Drive Sun Gear Assy.		
1986-87	E6DZ-7F342A	91.25
(56) Park Gear		
1986-87	E6DZ-7A233A	11.00
(57) Rear Planet Support Assy.		
1986-87	E6DZ-7A130A	75.00
(58) Gear & Drum Assy.		
1986-87	E6DZ-7A626A	83.75
(59) Band Assy.		
1986-87	E6DZ-7D034AZ	N.L.
(60) Rear Ring Gear		
1986-87	E6DZ-7A153A	98.50
(62) Front Planet Assy.		
1986-87	E6DZ-7A398A	157.50

PARTS 23 SERVOS & CONTROL VALVE BODY 23 PARTS

	Part No.	Price
(1) Main Control Cover Gasket		
1986-87	E6DZ-7F396A	2.50
(2) Front Oil Pump Assy.		
1986-87	E6DZ-7A103A	180.50
(3) Separator Plate Gasket		
1986-87	E6DZ-7G331A	1.50
(4) Oil Pump Gasket		
1986-87	E6DZ-7A136A	1.75
(5) Valve Body Assy.		
1986-87	E6DZ-7A100A	357.75
(6) Gasket		
1986-87	E6DZ-7D100A	1.25
(7) Screen Assy.		
1986-87	E6DZ-7G308A	2.25
(8) By-pass Clutch Solenoid		
1986-87	E6DZ-7G136A	10.50
(9) Oil Pressure Switch Assy.		
1986-87	E6DZ-7E440B	10.00
(10) Valve Body Separator Plate		
1986-87	E6DZ-7G348A	4.75
(11) Valve Body Gasket		
1986-87	E6DZ-7C155A	
(12) Chain Cover Assy.		
1986-87	E6DZ-7G188A	182.25
(13) Wiring Bulkhead Assy.		
1986-87	E6DZ-7G276A	15.00
(14) Overdrive Servo		
1986-87	E6DZ-7D027B	9.00
(15) Low & Intermediate Servo.		
1986-87	E6DZ-7D027A	11.00

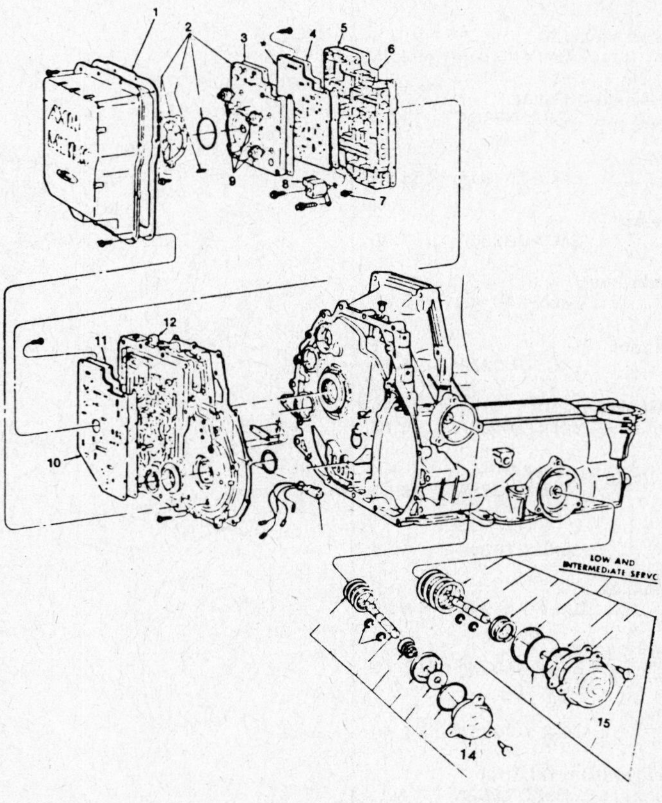

LABOR 23 AUTOMATIC TRANSMISSION 23 LABOR

(Factory Time) Chilton Time

ON CAR SERVICES

(G) Drain & Refill Unit
All models.................................... 1.0

(G) Oil Pressure Check
All models.................................... .5

(M) Check Unit For Oil Leaks
Includes: Clean and dry outside of case and run unit to determine point of leak.
All models.................................... .9

(G) Selector Indicator, Renew
All models
column shift (.9)......................... 1.2
floor shift (.5)............................ .7

(G) Throttle Valve Control Linkage, Renew
All models
cable (.3).................................... .4

(G) Neutral Safety Switch, Renew
All models (.6)............................... .8

(G) Extension Housing Oil Seal and/or Bushing, Renew
All models (.5)............................... .8

(Factory Time) Chilton Time

(G) Parking Pawl, Renew
Includes: R&R extension housing.
All models (1.8)............................. 2.4

(G) Extension Housing and/or Gasket, Renew
All models (1.9)............................. 2.5

(G) Governor Assembly, Renew
Includes: R&R extension hosuing.
Clean and polish gov add (.1)........... .2

(G) Oil Gasket, Renew
All models (.8)............................... 1.0

(G) Valve Body Assembly, Renew
Includes: R&R oil pan.
All models (1.1)............................. 1.5

(G) Transmission Assy., R&R or Renew
Continental-Mark VII
1984-85 (3.2)................................ 4.6
Renew assy add.............................. .4
Note: Internal repairs cannot be performed on this unit.

PARTS 23 CASE & PARTS 23 PARTS

	Part No.	Price
Transmission Assy.		
1984-85	E4LY-7000A	1403.00
Flywheel Assy.		
1984-85	E45Y-6375A	229.25
(1) Converter Housing		
1984-85	E4LY-7976A	499.25
(2) Converter Housing Cover		
1984-85	E4LY-7986A	8.00
(3) Oil Pan Assy.		
1984-85	E4LY-7A194A	158.25
(4) Oil Pan Clamp		
1984-85	E4LY-7B085A	3.50
(5) Oil Pan Drain Plug		
1984-85	E4LY-7A010A	5.00
(6) Oil Pan Magnet		
1984-85	E4LY-7L027A	4.75
(7) Oil Pump Gasket		
1984-85	E4LY-7A136A	3.75
(8) Extension Housing Gasket		
1984-85	E4LY-7086A	2.50
(9) Vent Assy.		
1984-85	E4LY-7034A	5.50
(10) Oil Pan Gasket		
1984-85	E4LY-7A191A	5.25
(11) Extension Housing		
1984-85	E4LY-7A039A	537.75
(12) Vent Cap		
1984-85	E4LY-7036A	2.50
(13) Extension Housing Oil Seal		
1984-85	E3ZZ-7052A	N.L.

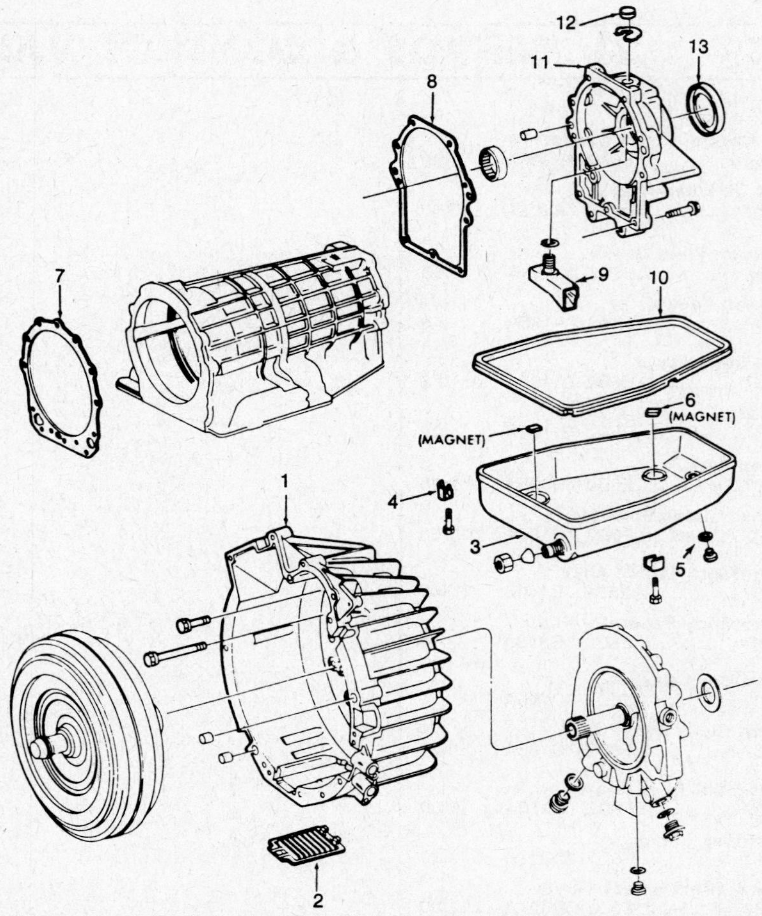

(Factory Time) Chilton Time

ON CAR SERVICES

(G) Drain & Refill Unit
1983-87
T-Bird-Cougar 1.9
1985-87
Cont-Mark VII 1.9
All other models 1.0

(G) Oil Pressure Check
All models 5

(M) Check Unit For Oil Leaks
Includes: Clean and dry outside of case and run unit to determine point of leak.
All models 9

(G) Neutral Safety Switch, Renew
All models (.4) 6

(G) Linkage, Adjust
manual (.3) 4
throttle (.3) 5
manual & throttle (.4) 7
throttle valve control (.4) 6

(G) Selector Indicator, Renew
1985-87
column shift (.9) 1.4
floor shift
Mustang-Capri (.3) 4
Mark VII (.5) 7

(G) Extension Housing Oil Seal, Renew
All models (.5) 8

(G) Governor Assembly, Renew
1983-87
T-Bird-Cougar (2.2) 3.0
1985-87
Cont-Mark VII (1.6) 2.2
All other models (1.3) 2.0
Clean and polish gov. add (.1) 2

(G) Oil Pan or Gasket, Renew
Includes: Drain and refill unit.
1983-87
T-Bird-Cougar (1.4) 1.9
1985-87
Cont-Mark VII (1.4) 1.9
All other models (.7) 1.0

(G) Valve Body Assembly, Renew
Includes: R&R oil pan.
1983-87
T-Bird-Cougar (1.7) 2.4
1985-87
Cont-Mark VII (1.7) 2.4
All other models (1.0) 1.9

(P) Valve Body Assy., R&R and Recondition
Includes: R&R oil pan and replace filter. Disassemble, clean, inspect, free all valves. Replace parts as required.
1983-87
T-Bird-Cougar (2.6) 3.5
1985-87
Cont-Mark VII (2.6) 3.5
All other models (1.9) 3.0

(G) Throttle and Manual Seals and/or Levers, Renew
Includes: R&R oil pan and valve body.
1983-87
T-Bird-Cougar (1.7) 2.5
1985-87
Cont-Mark VII (1.7) 2.5
All other models (1.0) 1.7

(G) Parking Pawl, Renew
Includes: R&R oil pan.
1983-87
T-Bird-Cougar (2.3) 3.0

CHILTON'S AUTOMATIC TRANSMISSION TUNE-UP

1. Check engine performance
2. Check condition of transmission oil
3. Check transmission, oil cooler and oil cooler lines for external leaks
4. Remove oil pan, clean or renew screen or filter
5. Torque valve body
6. Adjust bands
7. Clean oil pan and install pan with new gasket
8. Check modulator and hose
9. Install new transmission oil to proper level
10. Adjust manual and throttle linkage
11. Road test

All models 1.5
Charge for parts used

(Factory Time) Chilton Time

1985-87
Cont-Mark VII (2.3) 3.0
All other models (1.7) 2.5

(G) Front Servo, Recondition
Includes: R&R oil pan, adjust band.
1983-87
T-Bird-Cougar (1.8) 2.6
1985-87
Cont-Mark VII (1.8) 2.6
All other models (1.1) 1.5

(G) Rear Servo, Recondition
Includes: R&R oil pan, adjust band.
1983-87
T-Bird-Cougar (1.8) 2.6
1985-87
Cont-Mark VII (1.8) 2.6
All other models (1.1) 1.5

SERVICES REQUIRING R&R

(G) Transmission Assembly, R&R or Renew
Includes: R&R trans. and converter assembly. Drain and refill unit. Adjust linkage.
Ford-Mercury
1983-87 (2.6) 4.0
Thunderbird-Cougar-Mark VII
1983-87 (3.2) 4.6
Lincoln-Mark VI
1983-87 (2.6) 4.0
Continental
1983-87 (3.2) 4.6
LTD-Marquis
Mustang-Capri
1983-87 (3.3) 4.6

(P) Transmission and Converter, R&R and Recondition
Includes: Disassemble trans., including valve body, clean, inspect and replace parts as required.
Ford-Mercury
1983-87 (7.5) 11.7
Thunderbird-Cougar-Mark VII
1983-87 (8.1) 12.3
Lincoln-Mark VI
1983-87 (7.5) 11.7
Continental
1983-87 (8.1) 12.3

(Factory Time) Chilton Time

LTD-Marquis
Mustang-Capri
1983-87 (8.4) 12.3
Clean and check converter add (.5) 5
Flush oil cooler and lines add (.2) 2

(G) Transmission Assembly, Reseal
Includes: R&R trans. and renew all seals and gaskets.
All models 7.0

(G) Front Oil Pump, Renew or Recondition
Includes: R&R transmission.
Ford-Mercury
1983-87 (3.2) 4.9
Thunderbird-Cougar-Mark VII
1983-87 (3.8) 5.5
Lincoln-Mark VI
1983-87 (3.2) 4.9
Continental
1983-87 (3.8) 5.5
LTD-Marquis
Mustang-Capri
1983-87 (3.9) 5.5

(G) Front Pump Oil Seal, Renew
Includes: R&R transmission.
Ford-Mercury
1983-87 (2.7) 4.2
Thunderbird-Cougar-Mark VII
1983-87 (3.3) 4.8
Lincoln-Mark VI
1983-87 (2.7) 4.2
Continental
1983-87 (3.3) 4.8
LTD-Marquis
Mustang-Capri
1983-87 (3.4) 4.8

(G) Flywheel and Ring Gear Assembly, Renew
Includes: R&R transmission.
Ford-Mercury
1983-87 (2.9) 4.4
Thunderbird-Cougar-Mark VII
1983-87 (3.5) 5.0
Lincoln-Mark VI
1983-87 (2.9) 4.4
Continental
1983-87 (3.5) 5.0
LTD-Marquis
Mustang-Capri
1983-87 (3.6) 5.0

(G) Front or Rear Bands, Renew
Includes: R&R transmission.
Ford-Mercury
1983-87 (4.2) 5.9
Thunderbird-Cougar-Mark VII
1983-87 (4.8) 6.5
Lincoln-Mark VI
1983-87 (4.2) 5.9
Continental
1983-87 (4.8) 6.5
LTD-Marquis
Mustang-Capri
1983-87 (4.9) 6.5

(G) Transmission Case, Renew
Includes: R&R trans., transfer all parts, make all necessary adjustments. Road test.
Ford-Mercury
1983-87 (5.5) 8.3
Thunderbird-Cougar-Mark VII
1983-87 (6.1) 8.9
Lincoln-Mark VI
1983-87 (5.5) 8.3
Continental
1983-87 (6.1) 8.9
LTD-Marquis
Mustang-Capri
1983-87 (6.2) 8.9

PARTS 23 CASE AND PARTS 23 PARTS

	Part No.	Price
Transmission Seal & Gasket Kit		
1983-87	E0AZ-7153A	54.50
Overhaul Kit		
1983-87	E4AZ-7C391A	197.25
Oil Pan Screen		
1983-87	E1AZ-7A098A	12.75
(1) Flywheel Assy.		
V-6–232 eng.		
(Capri, Mustang, Cougar, T-Bird)		
1983-84	E3SZ-6375A	94.75
1985-87	E5SZ-6375A	94.75
(LTD & Marquis)		
1983-84	E3DZ-6375A	94.75
1985	E3DZ-6375B	94.75
V-8–302 eng.		
1983-87	E2AZ-6375A	94.75
V-8–351 eng.		
1983-87	E0AZ-6375A	94.75
(2) Torque Converter		
V-6–232 eng.		
1983-84	E25Y-7902A	586.75
1985-87	E5DZ-7902A	586.75
V-8–302 eng.		
(Crown Victoria, T-Bird, Cougar)		
1983-84	E5SZ-7902A	607.25
1985	E5SZ-7902A	607.25
1986-87	E6AZ-7902A	607.25
(Mustang, Capri, LTD, Marquis)		
1984-85	E5DZ-7902A	586.75
1986-87	E6AZ-7902A	607.25
V-8–351 eng.		
1983-84	E5AZ-7902A	607.25
1985-87	E5AZ-7902A	607.25
(3) Gasket (Oil Pan)		
1983-87	E0AZ-7A191B	3.75
(4) Transmission Case Assy.		
1983-87	E4AZ-7005A	115.00
(5) Oil Seal (Manual Control)		
1983-87	D5AZ-7B498A	6.00
(6) Neutral Safety Switch		
1983-87	D6RY-7A247B	33.25

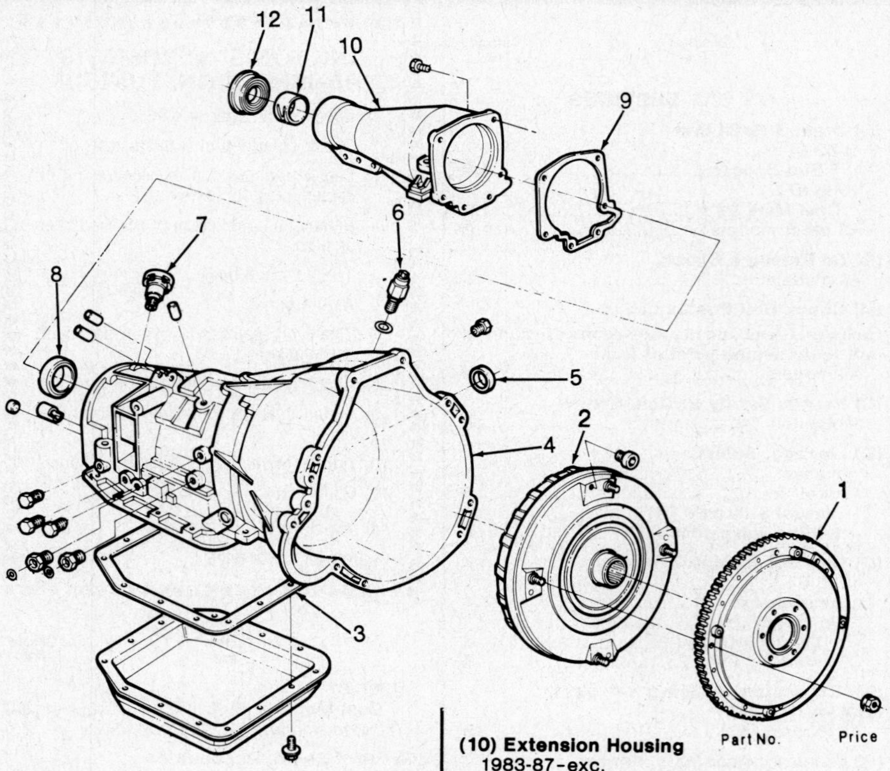

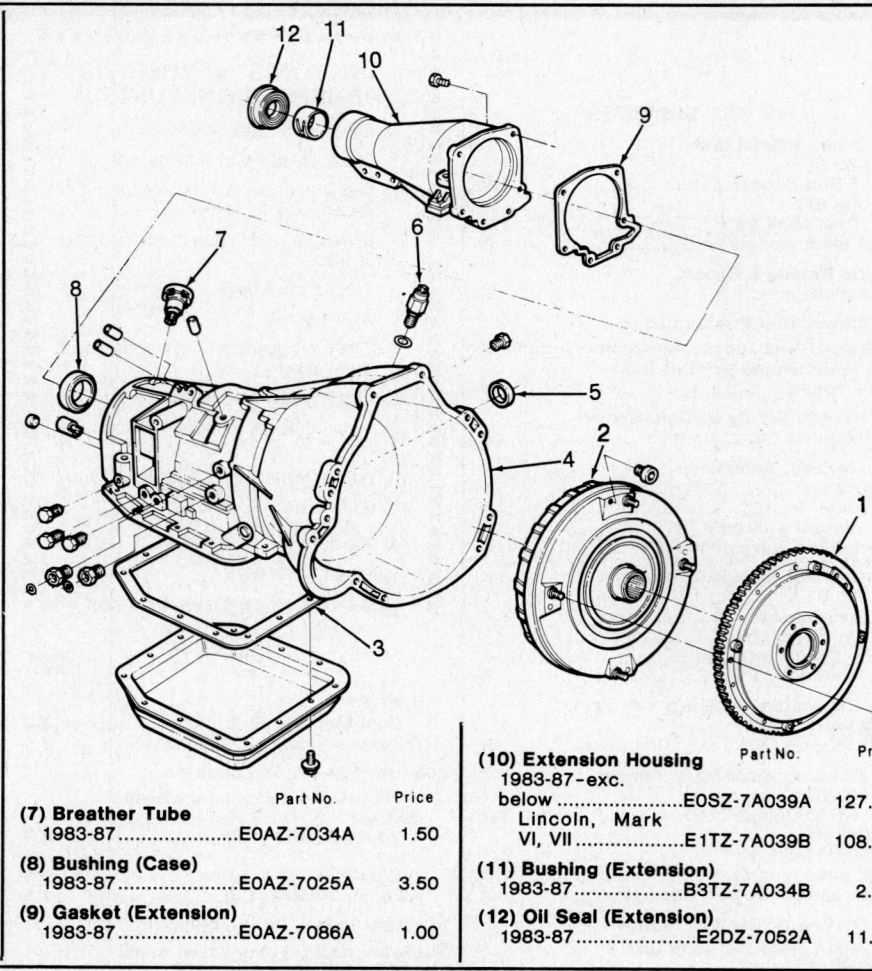

	Part No.	Price
(7) Breather Tube		
1983-87	E0AZ-7034A	1.50
(8) Bushing (Case)		
1983-87	E0AZ-7025A	3.50
(9) Gasket (Extension)		
1983-87	E0AZ-7086A	1.00

	Part No.	Price
(10) Extension Housing		
1983-87-exc. below	E0SZ-7A039A	127.75
Lincoln, Mark VI, VII	E1TZ-7A039B	108.25
(11) Bushing (Extension)		
1983-87	B3TZ-7A034B	2.50
(12) Oil Seal (Extension)		
1983-87	E2DZ-7052A	11.25

PARTS 23 GEAR TRAIN 23 PARTS

	Part No.	Price
(1) Shaft (Direct Drive)		
1983-87	E0AZ-7F208A	18.25
(2) Oil Pump Assy. (Front)		
1983-87	E0AZ-7A103A	288.75
(3) Thrust Washer (Pump Support)		
1983-87	E0AZ-7D014A	1.00
(4) Cylinder Seal (Forward Clutch)		
1983-87	E0AZ-7D019A	1.50
(5) Piston (Interm. Clutch)		
1983-87	E0AZ-7E005A	16.50
(6) Piston Seal (Outer)		
1983-87	E0AZ-7F224A	4.00
(7) Piston Seal (Inner)		
1983-87	E0AZ-7F225A	2.75
(8) Retainer & Spring Assy. (Interm. Clutch)		
1983-87	E0AZ-7F222A	9.75
(9) Front Gasket (Oil Pump to Case)		
1983-87	E3SZ-7A136A	1.75
(10) Intermediate Clutch (External)		
1983-87	E0AZ-7B442B	34.75
(11) Intermediate Clutch (Internal)		
1983-87	E0AZ-7B164D	4.25

	Part No.	Price
(12) Clutch Plate (Pressure)		
1983-87-V-8	E0AZ-7B066D	11.75
V-6	E2SZ-7B066A	7.75
(13) Retainer (Overrun Clutch)		
1983-87	E0AZ-7D191B	2.25
(14) Clutch Assy. (Overrunning)		
1983-87-		
Intermediate	E0AZ-7A089A	17.00
Plantary	C3AZ-7A089A	9.25
(15) Hub (Interm. Clutch)		
1983-87	E0AZ-7F221A	39.00
(16) Band Assy. (Overdrive)		
1983-87	E0AZ-7F196A	23.25
(17) Drum Assy. (Reverse Clutch)		
1983-87-exc.		
351 eng.	E2AZ-7D044B	128.75
351 eng.	E2AZ-7D044A	128.75
(18) Thrust Washer (Forward Clutch)		
1983-87	E0AZ-7A166A	6.00
(19) Piston Assy. (Reverse Clutch)		
1983-87	E0AZ-7D402A	12.50
(20) Piston Seal (Outer)		
1983-87	E0AZ-7D403A	1.25
(21) Piston Seal (Inner)		
1983-87	E0AZ-7D404A	1.50

	Part No.	Price
(22) Piston Spring (Reverse Clutch)		
1983-87	E0AZ-7B070A	7.25
(23) Pressure Plate (Front)		
1983-87	E0AZ-7B066B	11.00
(24) Reverse Clutch (Internal)		
1983-87		
before 7-19-83	E0AZ-7B164B	3.25
from 7-19-83	E0AZ-7B164A	4.25
(25) Reverse Clutch (External)		
1983-87	C8AZ-7B442A	1.75
(26) Pressure Plate (Rear)		
1983-87	E0AZ-7B066C	6.25
(27) Cylinder & Shaft Assy. (Forward Clutch)		
1983-87-exc.		
351 eng.	E4AZ-7F207B	97.25
351 eng.	E4AZ7F207A	90.75
(28) Piston Seal (Outer)		
1983-87	E0AZ-7A548A	2.75
(29) Piston Assy. (Forward Clutch)		
1983-87	E0AZ-7A262A	16.75
(30) Seal (Clutch Cylinder)		
1983-87	E0AZ-7C099A	2.00
(31) Return Spring (Forward Clutch)		
1983-87	E0AZ-7A480A	8.25

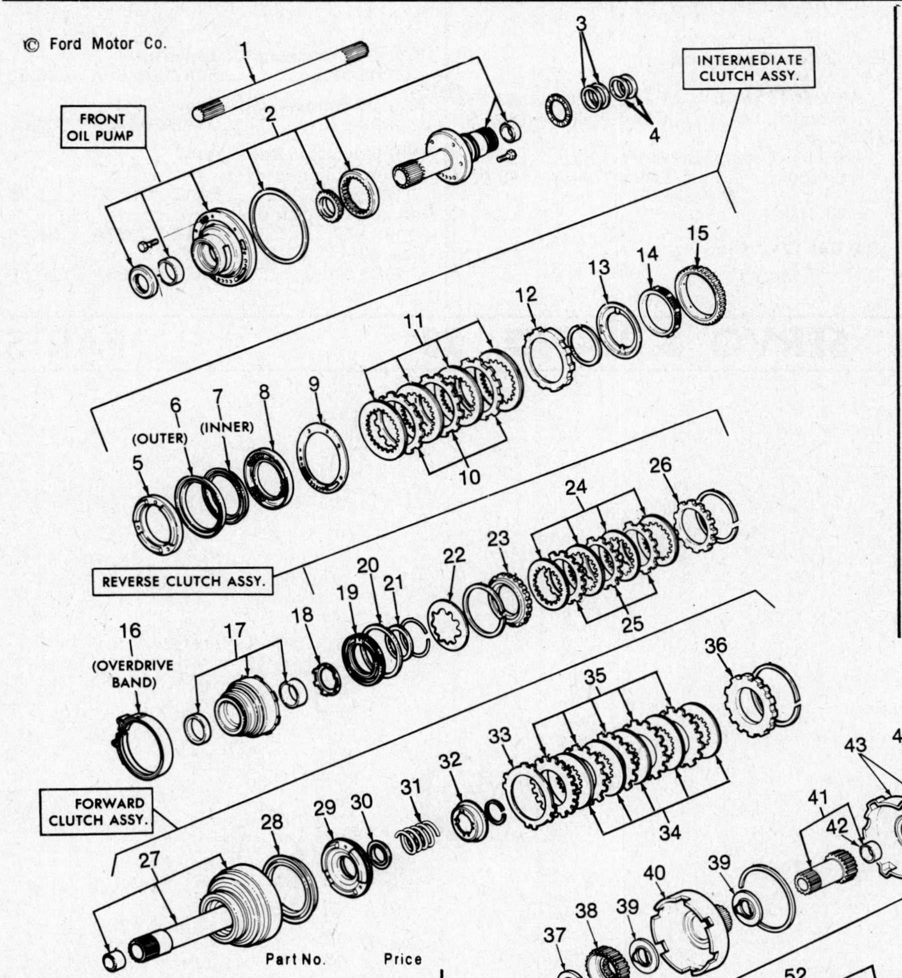

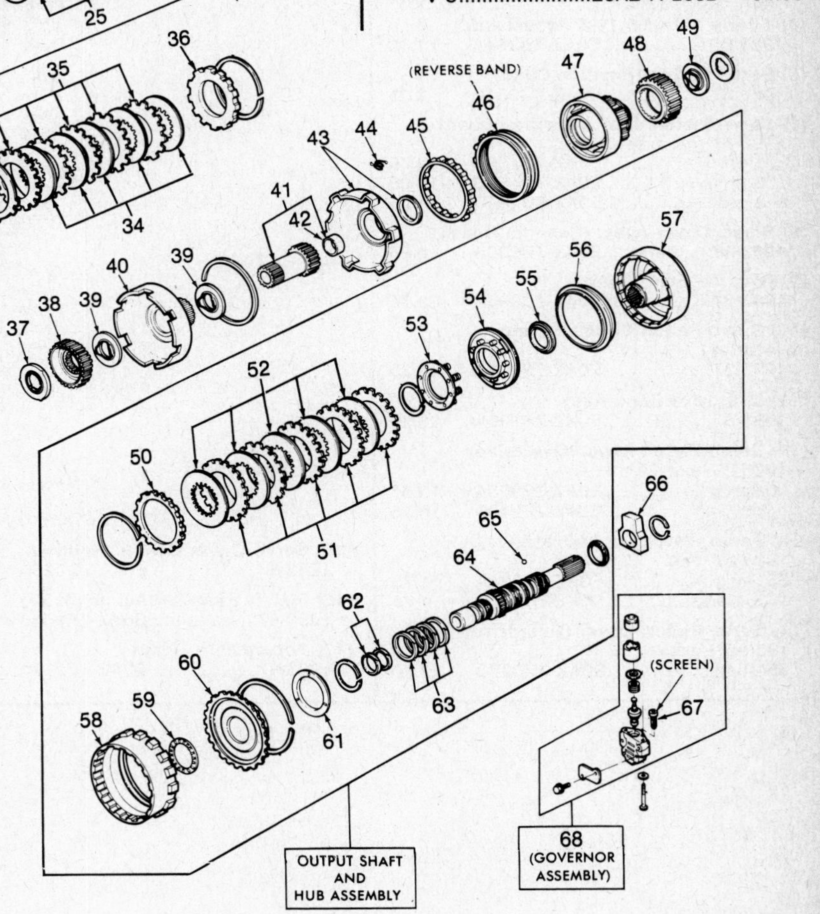

	Part No.	Price
(32) Retainer (Piston Spring)		
1983-87	E0AZ-7A527A	5.50
(33) Spring (Clutch Pressure)		
1983-87	D0AZ-7E085A	3.75
(34) Forward Clutch (Internal)		
1983-87	E0AZ-7B164A	4.25
(35) Forward Clutch (External)		
1983-87	C8AZ-7B442A	1.75
(36) Pressure Plate		
1983-87		
before 7-19-83	E0AZ-7B066A	6.25
from 7-19-83	E0AZ-7B066C	6.25
(37) Clutch Hub Bearing Assy. (Front)		
1983-87	E0AZ-7F231A	8.25
(38) Forward Clutch Hub		
1983-87	E0AZ-7B067A	20.75
(39) Thrust Bearing Assy.		
1983-87	E0AZ-7C096A	8.50
(40) Gear & Shell Assy. (Reverse Clutch)		
1983-87	E0AZ-7A019A	80.50
(41) Sun Gear Assy. (Forward Clutch)		
1983-87	E0AZ-7A399A	144.00
(42) Piston Assy.		
1983-87	E0AZ-7A262A	16.75
(43) Planetary Support Assy.		
1983-87	E0AZ-7A130A	78.50
(44) Spring (Case to Planet Support)		
1983-87	E0AZ-7F277A	2.00

	Part No.	Price
(45) Clutch Assy. (Overrunning)		
1983-87	C3AZ-7A089A	9.25
(46) Reverse Band Assy.		
1983-87	E0AZ-7D095A	33.75

	Part No.	Price
(47) Planet Assy.		
1983-85	E6AZ-7A398A	215.50
1986-87	E6AZ-7A398A	215.50
(48) Hub (Direct Clutch)		
1983-87	E0AZ-7F236B	10.25
(49) Inner Bearing Assy. (Direct Clutch)		
1983-87	E0AZ-7F243A	6.25
(50) Pressure Plate (Direct Clutch)		
1983-87	E0AZ-7B066E	6.25
(51) Direct Clutch (Internal)		
1983-87	E0AZ-7B164C	4.25
(52) Direct Clutch (External)		
1983-87	E0AZ-7B442A	2.50
(53) Retainer & Spring Assy.		
1983-87	E5AZ-7F235A	6.00
(54) Piston Assy. (Direct Clutch)		
1983-87	E0AZ-7A262B	16.75
(55) Seal (Clutch Cylinder)		
1983-87	E0AZ-7C099B	2.00
(56) Piston Seal (Outer)		
1983-87	E0AZ-7A548B	2.50
(57) Cylinder Assy. (Direct Clutch)		
1983-87-V-6	E2SZ-7F283A	86.50
V-8	E0AZ-7F283B	94.50

	Part No.	Price
(58) Ring Gear (Output Shaft)		
1983-87	E0AZ-7A153A	117.50
(59) Outer Bearing Assy. (Direct Clutch)		
1983-87	E0AZ-7F240A	7.50

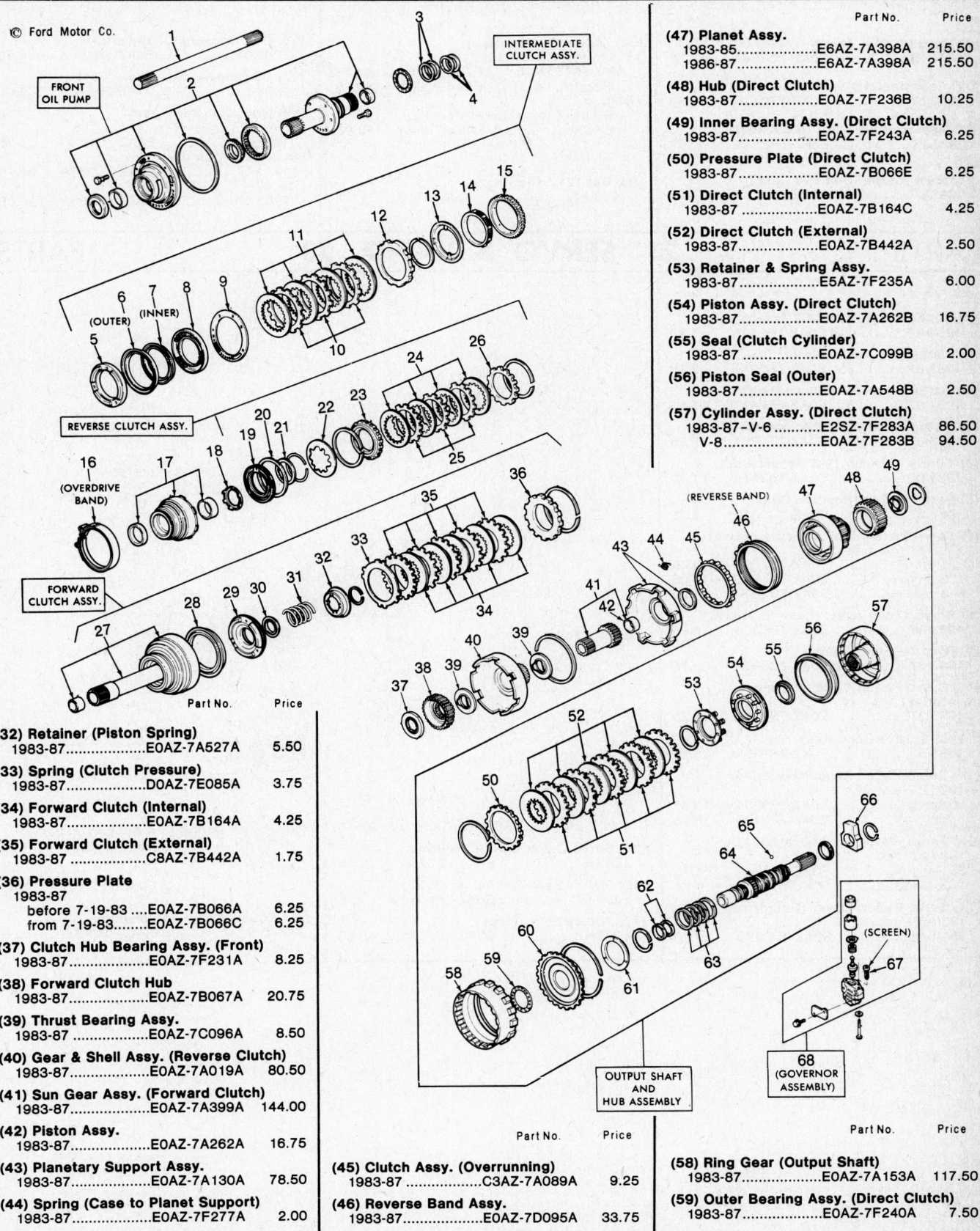

PARTS 23 GEAR TRAIN 23 PARTS

	Part No.	Price
(60) Hub (Output Shaft)		
1983-87	E0AZ-7D164A	87.75
(61) Rear Bearing Assy. (Case)		
1983-87	E0AZ-7F242A	8.00
(62) Seal (Output Shaft to Cylinder)		
1983-87	E3AZ-7F274A	2.25
(63) Seal (Output Shaft to Case)		
1983-87	E6AZ-7F273A	N.L.
(64) Output Shaft Assy.		
15″ long		
1983-87-7 teeth	E2AZ-7060A	193.75
8 teeth	E0AZ-7060A	180.75
16″ long		
1983-87-7 teeth	E2VY-7060A	165.50
8 teeth	E0VY-7060A	165.00
(65) Ball (7¼″ Dia.)		
1983-87	353351S	.25
(66) Counterweight (Governor)		
1983-87	E0AZ-7A189A	10.50
(67) Oil Screen (Governor)		
1983-87	D1AZ-7E242A	5.00
(68) Governor Body Assy.		
(yellow or purple dye)		
1983-87	E2AZ-7C063B	25.25
(no color or pink dye)		
1983-87	E2AZ-7C063A	26.75
(Tan dye)		
1986-87	E6ZZ-7C063A	28.00

PARTS 23 SERVO & BAND 23 PARTS

	Part No.	Price
(1) Upper Piston Seal (2-3 Accumulator)		
1983-87	E0AZ-7F250A	1.50
(2) Piston (2-3 Accumulator)		
1983-87	E0AZ-7F251A	3.75
(3) Piston Seal (2-3 Accumulator)		
1983-87	E0AZ-7F249A	1.50
(4) Piston Spring (2-3 Accumulator)		
1983-87	E0AZ-7F285A	13.25
(5) Spring Retainer (2-3 Accumulator)		
1983-87	E0AZ-7B264A	1.00
(6) Servo Spring (Reverse Band)		
1983-87	E0AZ-7D031B	3.25
(7) Servo Piston Assy. (Reverse Band)		
1983-87 (grooves on rod)		
1 groove	E0AZ-7D189A	9.75
2 grooves	E0AZ-7D189B	11.00
3 grooves	E0AZ-7D189C	10.25
(8) Servo Cover Assy. (Reverse Band)		
1983-87	E0AZ-7D036A	6.25
(9) Reverse Band Assy.		
1983-87	E0AZ-7D095A	33.75
(10) Servo Piston Return Spring (Overdrive)		
1983-87	E0AZ-7F201A	11.25
(11) Overdrive Band Assy.		
1983-87	E0AZ-7F196A	23.25
(12) Servo Piston Assy. (Overdrive)		
1983-87-exc.		
351 eng.	E0AZ-7F200A	15.75
351 eng	E0AZ-7F200B	15.75
(13) Servo Piston Seal (Overdrive)		
1983-87-exc.		
351 eng.	E0AZ-7D024A	1.75
351 eng	E0AZ-7D024B	1.75
(14) Servo Piston Cover (Overdrive)		
1983-87-exc.		
351 eng.	E0AZ-7D027C	22.50

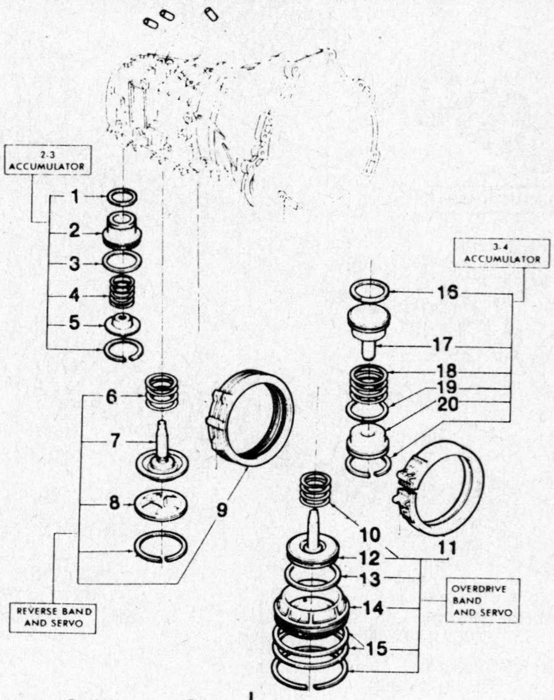

	Part No.	Price
351 eng.	E0AZ-7D027D	22.50
(15) Servo Cover Seal (Overdrive)		
1983-87	E0AZ-7D026A	2.25
(16) Piston Seal (3-4 Accumulator)		
1983-87	E0AZ-7F248A	1.25
(17) Accumulator Piston		
1983-87	E2AZ-7F287A	10.50
(18) Piston Spring (3-4 Accumulator)		
1983-87	E0AZ-7F288A	1.75
(19) Seal		
1983-87	E0AZ-7F294A	1.50
(20) Retainer (3-4 Accumulator)		
1983-87	E2AZ-7F247A	5.25

LABOR 23 AUTOMATIC TRANSMISSION 23 LABOR

(Factory Time) Chilton Time

MODEL A131L (MX-1)

ON CAR SERVICES

(G) Drain and Refill Unit
All models 9

(G) Oil Pressure Check
All models 5

(M) Check Unit for Oil Leaks
Includes: Clean and dry outside of case and run unit to determine point of leak.
All models 9

(G) Neutral Safety Switch, Renew
All models (.3) 4

(G) Shift Linkage, Adjust
All models
Neutral Safety Switch (.3) 4
Shift Linkage (.3) 4
T.V. Cable (.2) 3

(G) Oil Cooler Lines, Renew
All models-upper (.4) 6
lower (.4) 6
both (.4) 9

(G) Throttle Valve Control Cable and/or 'O' Ring, Renew
All models (.7) 1.0

(G) Speedometer Driven Gear and/or Seal, Renew
All models (.3) 4

(G) Governor Cover and/or Seal, Renew
All models (.5) 7

(G) Governor Assembly, Renew
All models (.6) 9
Recond gov or renew gear add (.2) 2

(G) Oil Pan and/or Gasket, Renew
All models (.5) 8

(G) Valve Body Assembly, Renew
Includes: R&R oil pan.
All models (.7) 1.1

(P) Valve Body Assy., R&R and Recondition
Includes: R&R oil pan. Disassemble, clean, inspect all valves. Replace parts as required.
All models (1.3) 2.0

(G) Intermediate Servo Assy., R&R or Renew
All models (.6) 1.0
Recond servo add (.2) 2

(G) Accumulator Piston and/or Spring, Renew
All models (.7) 1.1

(G) Transmission Mount or Bracket, Renew
All models
left (.3) 5
front (.4) 6
rear (.4) 6

CHILTON'S AUTOMATIC TRANSMISSION TUNE-UP

1. Check engine performance
2. Check condition of transmission oil
3. Check transmission, oil cooler and oil cooler lines for external leaks
4. Remove oil pan, clean or renew screen or filter
5. Torque valve body
6. Adjust bands
7. Clean oil pan and install pan with new gasket
8. Check modulator and hose
9. Install new transmission oil to proper level
10. Adjust manual and throttle linkage
11. Road test

All models 1.5
Charge for parts used

(Factory Time) Chilton Time

(G) Trans/Axle Shaft Oil Seals, Renew
All models-one (.5) 7
both (.6) 9

(G) Transmission Rear Cover and/or Gasket, Renew
All models (.7) 1.1

(G) Differential Side Cover and/or Gasket, Renew
All models (.6) 1.0

SERVICES REQUIRING R&R

(G) Trans/Axle Assy., R&R or Renew
Nova
1985-87 (2.1) 3.1

(P) Trans/Axle Assy., R&R and Recondition
Includes: Recondition automatic transmission only.
Nova
1985-87 (7.5) 11.2
Recond diff assy add 8

(G) Torque Converter, Renew
Includes: R&R trans/axle.
Nova
1985-87 (2.0) 3.0

(G) Flywheel (Flexplate), Renew
Includes: R&R trans/axle.
Nova
1985-87 (2.3) 3.4

(Factory Time) Chilton Time

(G) Torque Converter Seal, Renew
Includes: R&R trans/axle.
Nova
1985-87 (2.0) 3.0
Leak check conv add (.2) 2
Renew bushing add (.1) 1

(G) Oil Pump and/or Gasket, Renew
Includes: R&R trans/axle.
Nova
1985-87 (2.2) 3.3
Recond pump add (.3) 5

(G) Parking Pawl, Shaft, Rod or Spring, Renew
Includes: R&R trans/axle.
Nova
1985-87 (2.6) 3.9

(G) Intermediate Band, Direct and Forward Clutches, Renew
Includes: R&R trans/axle.
Nova
1985-87 (2.8) 4.2
Recond valve body add (.7) 9
Recond oil pump add (.3) 5
Recond servo add (.2) 3
Recond direct clutch add (.4) 5
Recond forward clutch add (.4) 5
Renew bushings add, each (.1) 1

(G) Input Gear and Drum, Internal Gear and Carrier Assy., Renew
Includes: R&R trans/axle.
Nova
1985-87 (3.0) 4.5
Recond valve body add (.7) 9
Recond oil pump add (.3) 5
Recond servo add (.2) 3
Recond direct clutch add (.4) 5
Recond forward clutch add (.4) 5
Renew bushings add (.1) 1

(G) Low and Reverse Clutches, Renew
Includes: R&R trans/axle.
Nova
1985-87 (3.4) 5.1
Recond valve body add (.7) 9
Recond oil pump add (.3) 5
Recond servo add (.2) 3
Recond gov add (.2) 3
Recond low and reverse clutches add (.4) 5
Renew bushings add, each (.1) 1

(G) Differential and Final Drive Assy., R&R or Renew
Nova
1985-87 (2.6) 3.9
Renew side gears, pinion shafts, and pinion gears add (.2) 4
Renew diff carrier add (.2) 4

PARTS 23 CASE & PARTS 23 PARTS

	Part No.	Price
Automatic Transaxle Assy.		
1985-87	94840857	1950.00
Overhaul Gasket Kit		
1985-87	94840620	134.00
(1) Case Protector		
1985-87	94843512	5.00
(2) Breather Plug		
1985-87	94842856	2.25
(3) Drive Pin Cap.		
1985-87	94840870	4.25
(4) Cap O-Ring		
1985-87	94843017	1.00
(5) Oil Level Indicator		
1985-87	94840865	3.50
(6) Case Cap		
1985-87	94841015	3.50
(7) Wiring Harness Cap.		
1985-87	94841014	4.75
(8) Oil Filler Tube		
1985-87	94840864	10.75
(9) Oil Pan		
1985-87	94843612	37.75
(10) Oil Pan Gasket		
1985-87	94840634	4.25

PARTS 23 CASE AND PARTS 23 PARTS

	Part No.	Price
(11) Rear Cover		
1985-87	94840934	113.00
(12) Governor Oil Strainer		
1985-87	94840636	1.50
(13) Gasket (Rear Cover)		
1985-87	94840631	3.75
(14) Transmission Case		
1985-87	94840867	561.00
(15) Differential Case Seal		
1985-87	94841023	4.50
(16) Speedometer Shaft Sleeve		
1985-87	94840862	10.25
(17) Speedometer Driven Gear		
1985-87	94840630	9.50
(18) Governor Cover Bracket		
1985-87	94840943	11.75
(19) Governor Cover		
1985-87	94840939	2.25
(20) Governor Body		
1985-87	9483637	N.L.
(21) Body Adapter		
1985-87	94840940	7.00
(22) Press Adapter		
1985-87	94843617	11.75

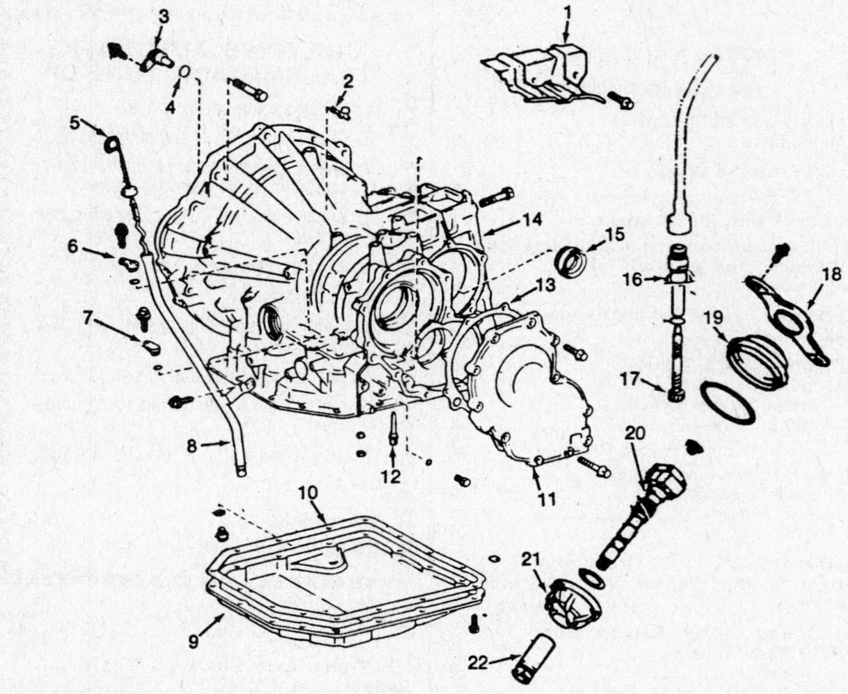

PARTS 23 GEAR TRAIN 23 PARTS

	Part No.	Price
(1) Sun Gear Thrust Bearing		
1985-87	94840932	6.50
(2) Planetary Sun Gear		
1985-87	94843621	60.50
(3) Thrust Bearing Race		
1985-87	94842762	3.50
(4) Input Drum		
1985-87	94840924	23.25
(5) Brake Cylinder (2nd)		
1985-87	94840901	23.25
(6) Brake Piston (2nd)		
1985-87	94840900	16.75
(7) Brake Piston Retaining Spring		
1985-87	94840902	6.00
(8) Clutch Plate (No. 3)		
1985-87	94840903	8.50
(9) Clutch Disc (No. 3)		
1985-87	94840905	9.75
(10) Second Brake Flange (No. 1)		
1985-87	94840904	19.25
(11) Second Brake Clutch		
1985-87	94840906	156.00
(12) Front Planetary Gear Thrust Bearing		
1985-87	94840931	8.00
(13) Ring Gear Flange		
1985-87	94840920	19.75
(14) Ring Gear		
1985-87	94840921	61.50
(15) Front Planetary Gear		
1985-87	94840922	42.25
(16) Thrust Washer		
1985-87	94840647	5.25
(17) First & Reverse Brake Clutch Race		
1985-87	94840919	33.50

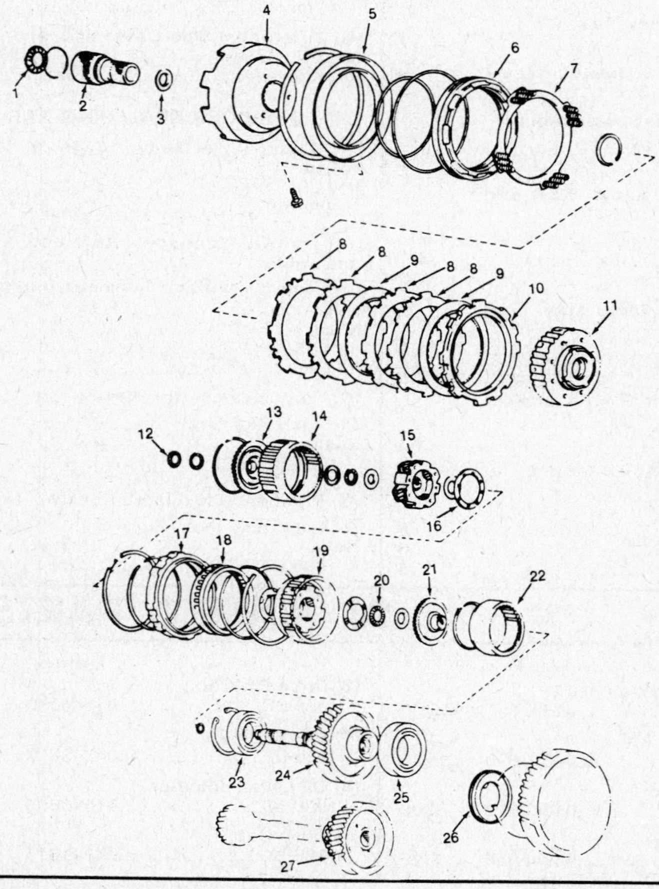

PARTS 23 GEAR TRAIN 23 PARTS

	Part No.	Price
(18) First & Reverse Brake Clutch		
1985-87	94840918	69.25
(19) Rear Planetary Gear		
1985-87	94840925	132.00
(20) Thrust Bearing		
1985-87	94840933	5.25
(21) Planetary Ring Gear Flange		
1985-87	94840927	21.00
(22) Rear Planetary Ring Gear		
1985-87	94840926	33.50
(23) Mainshaft Front Bearing		
1985-87	94840935	20.75
(24) Intermediate Shaft		
1985-87	94842998	57.75
(25) Main Shaft Rear Bearing		
1985-87	94840936	16.50
(26) Speedometer Drive Gear		
1985-87	94841020	5.25
(27) Center Driven Gear		
1985-87	94841016	96.25

PARTS 23 GEAR TRAIN 23 PARTS

	Part No.	Price
(1) Second Coast Brake Cover Ring		
1985-87	94843475°	
(2) Second Coast Brake Cover		
1985-87	94840913	4.75
(3) Brake Piston		
1985-87	94840908	5.75
(4) Brake Piston Rod		
1985-87	94840909	3.75
(5) Brake Band		
1985-87	94840907	37.75
(6) Direct Clutch Drum		
1985-87	94840896	60.50
(7) Direct Clutch Piston		
1985-87	94840897	13.50
(8) Spring Seat		
1985-87	94840898	1.25
(9) Forward Direct Clutch Plate		
1985-87	94840893	8.50
(10) Forward Direct Clutch Disc		
1985-87	94840892	9.50
(11) Direct Clutch Flange		
1985-87	94840894	17.75
(12) Input Shaft Thrust Bearing		
1985-87	94840930	8.25
(13) Thrust Bearing Race		
1985-87	94842755	3.25
(14) Clutch Input Shaft		
1985-87	94840888	123.00
(15) Forward Clutch Piston		
1985-87	94840889	13.50
(16) Spring Seat		
1985-87	94840890	1.00
(17) First & Reverse Brake Flange		
1985-87	94840904	19.25
(18) First & Reverse Clutch Disc		
1985-87	94840917	9.75
(19) Brake Clutch Plate		
1985-87	94840916	8.75
(20) Brake Retaining Spring		
1985-87	94840914	9.25
(21) Brake Piston		
1985-87	94840915	17.00

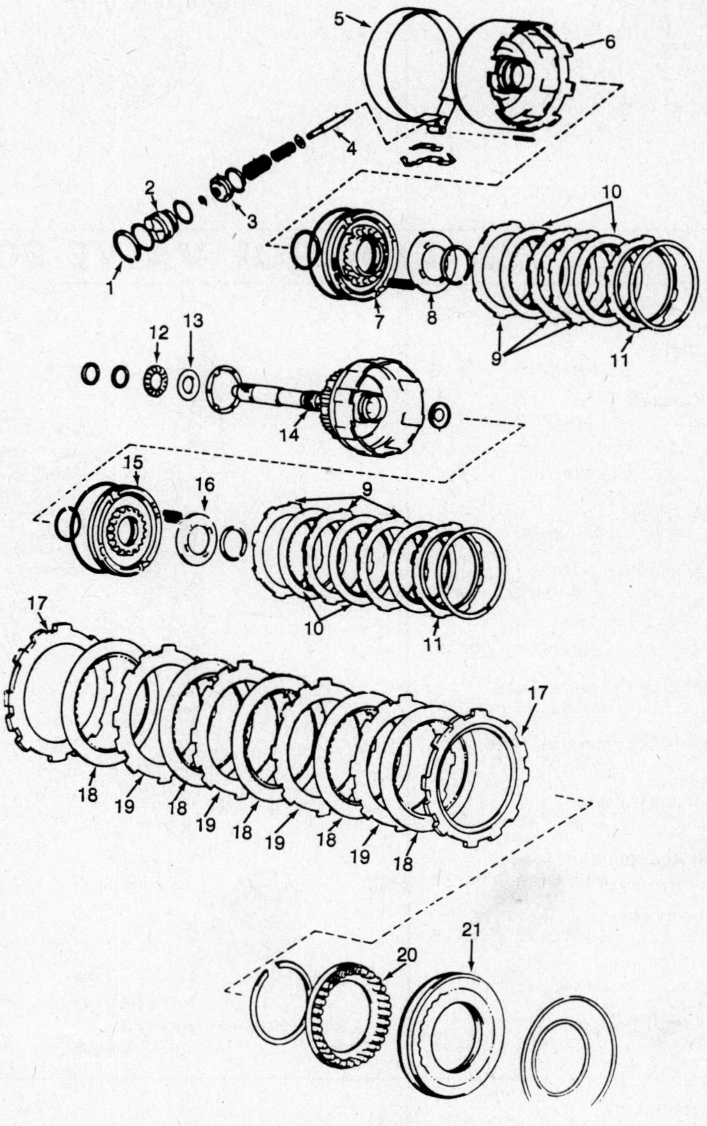

PARTS 23 CONVERTER & OIL PUMP 23 PARTS

	Part No.	Price
(1) Front Spacer		
1985-87	94841053	4.50
(2) Rear Spacer		
1985-87	94841054	3.00
(3) Flywheel		
1985-87	94841052	56.75
(4) Torque Converter		
1985-87	94840861	520.00
(5) Front Oil Pump Seal		
1985-87	94843031	11.25

PARTS 23 CONVERTER & OIL PUMP 23 PARTS

	Part No.	Price
(6) Body		
1985 (Note 1)	94842978	106.00
(Note 2)	94844047	118.00
1986-87 (wo/Gears)		
Note 1	94842978	106.00
Note 2	94844047	118.00
1986-87 (w/Gears)		
Note 1	94844097	118.00
Note 2	94844047	118.00

Note 1: Has no notches on ridge that runs around outer edge of part.
Note 2: Has six notches.

(7) Driven Gear
Must be ordered by letter stamped on gear.

	Part No.	Price
(8) Shaft		
1985-87	94843524	1.25

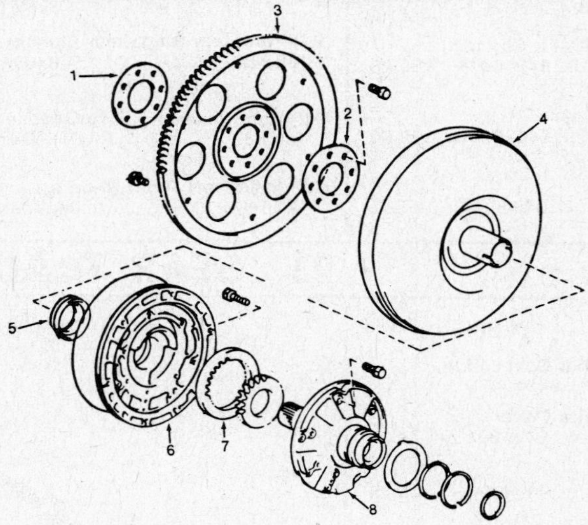

PARTS 23 CONTROL VALVE BODY 23 PARTS

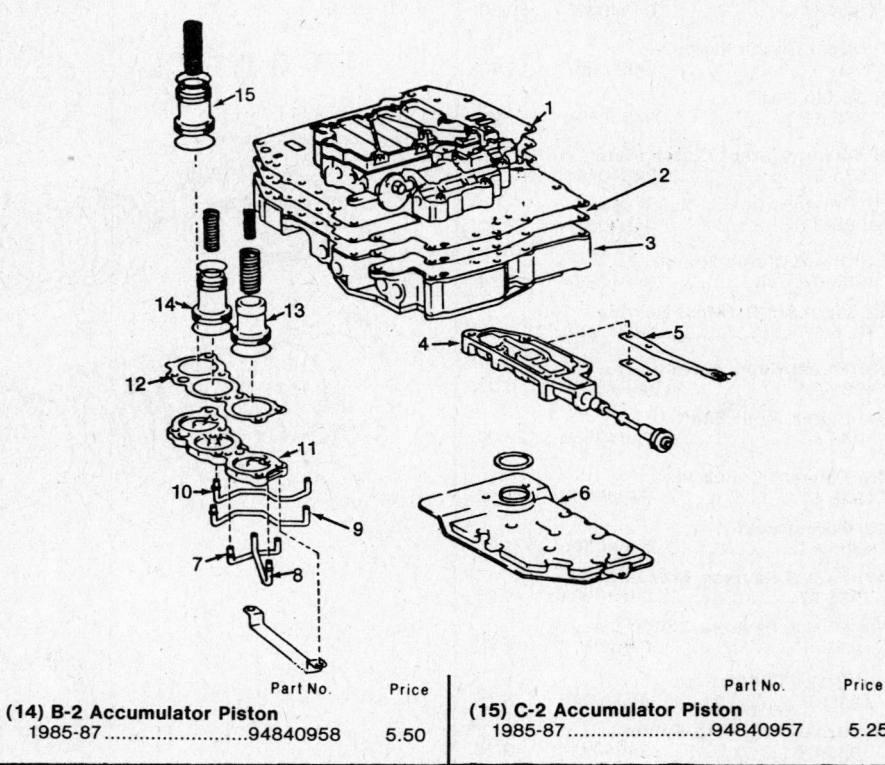

	Part No.	Price
(1) Valve Body Plate		
1985-87	94840949	11.25
(2) Valve Body Gasket		
1985-87	94840638	2.50
(3) Valve Body		
1985-87	94840945	488.00
(4) Manual Valve Body		
1985-87	94840954	31.00
(5) Manual Detent Spring		
1985-87	94840953	3.00
(6) Oil Strainer		
1985-87	94840966	21.00
(7) Accumulator Back Pressure Tube		
1985-87	94843713	3.00
(8) Forward Clutch Accumulator Tube		
1985-87	94843716	2.25
(9) Brake Accumulator Tube		
1985-87	94843715	3.75
(10) Rear Clutch Accumulator Tube		
1985-87	94843714	3.75
(11) Accumulator Cover		
1985-87	94840960	11.75
(12) Gasket		
1985-87	94840642	.75
(13) C-1 Accumulator Piston		
1985-87	94840959	5.50

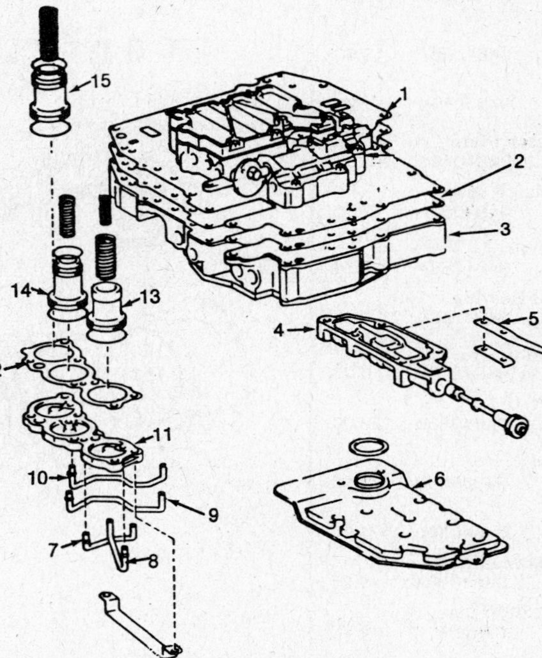

	Part No.	Price
(14) B-2 Accumulator Piston		
1985-87	94840958	5.50
(15) C-2 Accumulator Piston		
1985-87	94840957	5.25

(Factory Time) Chilton Time

ON CAR SERVICES

(G) Drain and Refill Unit
All models .7

(G) Oil Pressure Check
All models .5

(M) Check Unit For Oil Leaks
Includes: Clean and dry outside of case and run unit to determine point of leak.
All models .9

(G) Neutral Safety Switch, Renew
All models (.3) .5

(G) Shift Linkage, Adjust
All models
Neutral Safety Switch (.3) .4
Shift Indicator Needle (.2) .3
Shift Linkage (.4) .5
T.V. Cable (.3) .4

(G) Shift Linkage, Adjust (w/Diesel Eng)
All models
Throttle cable (.3) .4
Vacuum regulator valve (.6) .8
Complete (.8) 1.0

(G) Torque Converter Clutch Delay Module, Renew
All models
w/Diesel eng (.3) .4

(G) Speedometer Driven Gear, Renew
All models (.3) .5

(G) Torque Converter Clutch Brake Switch, Renew
All models (.2) .3

(G) Torque Converter Clutch Thermal Vacuum Switch, Renew
All models (.3) .4

(G) Engine Metal Temperature Indicator Switch, Renew
All models (.3) .4

(G) Torque Converter Clutch Vacuum Delay Valve, Renew
All models (.2) .3

(G) Engine Low Vacuum Switch, Renew
All models (.2) .4

(G) High Vacuum Switch, Renew
All models (.3) .5

(G) Vacuum Relay, Renew
All models (.2) .3

(G) Governor Assy., R&R or Renew
Includes: Renew cover and gasket.
All models (.3) .8
Recond gov or renew gear
add (.5) .6

(G) Oil Pan Gasket, Renew
All models (.6) .9

(G) Manual Shaft Seal and/or Lever, Renew
Includes: R&R oil pan.
All models (.7) 1.1

(G) Intermediate Servo Assy., Renew
Includes: R&R oil pan.
All models (.7) 1.0
Recond servo add (.2) .3

(G) Throttle Valve Lever Assy., Renew
Includes: R&R valve body cover gasket.
All models (.7) 1.3

CHILTON'S AUTOMATIC TRANSMISSION TUNE-UP

1. Check engine performance
2. Check condition of transmission oil
3. Check transmission, oil cooler and oil cooler lines for external leaks
4. Remove oil pan, clean or renew screen or filter
5. Torque valve body
6. Adjust bands
7. Clean oil pan and install pan with new gasket
8. Check modulator and hose
9. Install new transmission oil to proper level
10. Adjust manual and throttle linkage
11. Road test

All models 1.5
Charge for parts used

(Factory Time) Chilton Time

(G) Governor Pressure Switch, Renew
Includes: R&R valve body cover and renew gasket.
All models (.7) 1.1

(G) Converter Clutch Solenoid Assy., Renew
Includes: R&R valve body cover and renew gasket.
All models (.8) 1.2

(G) Valve Body Cover and/or Gasket, Renew
All models (.7) 1.0
'A'-Body-w/L-4 eng
add (.7) .7

(G) Valve Body and Oil Pump, Renew
Includes: R&R oil pan.
All models (1.1) 1.6
'A'-Body-w/L-4 eng
add (.7) .7

(P) Valve Body and Oil Pump, R&R and Recondition
Includes: R&R oil pan, recondition valve body and pump as required.
All models (2.2) 3.0
'A'-Body-w/L-4 eng
add (.7) .7

(G) Auxiliary Valve Body Cover and/or Gasket, Renew
All models (.9) 1.3
'A'-Body-w/L-4 eng
add (.7) .7

(G) Auxiliary Valve Body, Renew
All models (1.2) 1.7
'A'-Body-w/L-4 eng
add (.7) .7

(G) Parking Pawl, Shaft and Spring, Renew
Includes: R&R oil pan.
All models (.7) 1.0

(Factory Time) Chilton Time

(G) Transmission Output Shaft, Renew
Includes: R&R axle shaft and oil pan. Drain and refill unit.
All models (1.1) 1.5

(G) Transmission Axle Shaft Oil Seal, Renew
Citation-Omega-Phoenix-Skylark-Celebrity-Century-Ciera-A6000-Fiero
1983-87
one side (1.3) 1.7
both sides (1.9) 2.7
All other models
1983-87
one side (.6) 1.0
both sides (1.1) 1.9

(G) Transmission Mounts, Renew
Citation-Omega-Phoenix-Skylark-Celebrity-Century-Ciera-A600-Fiero
1983-87
front (.6) .9
rear (.8) 1.1
both (1.1) 1.5
All other models
1983-87
front (.6) .9
rear (.4) .6
both (.8) 1.3

SERVICES REQUIRING R&R

(G) Transmission Assy., R&R or Renew
Includes: Drain and refill unit.
Citation - Omega - Phoenix - Skylark
1983-85 (3.5) 4.7
Cavalier - Cimarron - J-2000 Skyhawk - Firenza
1983-87 (3.3) 4.7
Celebrity-Century-Ciera-A6000-Fiero
1983-87 (3.5) 4.7
Regal-Calais-Grand Am
1985-87 (3.3) 4.7
w/P.S. add (.3) .3
w/Diesel eng add (.5) .5
Drain and leak check converter
add (.2) .3

(P) Transmission and Converter Assy., R&R and Recondition
Includes: Disassemble trans, inspect and replace parts as required. Make all necessary adjustments. Road test.
Citation - Omega - Phoenix - Skylark
1983-85 (9.8) 13.2
Cavalier - Cimarron - J-2000 Skyhawk - Firenza
1983-87 (9.6) 13.2
Celebrity-Century-Ciera-A6000-Fiero
1983-87 (9.8) 13.2
Regal-Calais-Grand Am
1985-87 (9.6) 13.2
Recond diff assy add (.8) 1.5
w/P.S. add (.3) .3
w/Diesel eng add (.5) .5

(G) Torque Converter, Renew
Includes: R&R transmission, check pressure and end play of converter.
Citation - Omega - Phoenix - Skylark
1983-85 (3.5) 4.7
Cavalier - Cimarron - J-2000 Skyhawk - Firenza
1983-87 (3.3) 4.7
Celebrity-Century-Ciera-A6000-Fiero
1983-87 (3.5) 4.7
Regal-Calais-Grand Am
1985-87 (3.3) 4.7
w/P.S. add (.3) .3
w/Diesel eng add (.5) .5

LABOR 23 AUTOMATIC TRANSAXLE 23 LABOR

(Factory Time) Chilton Time

(G) Flywheel (Flexplate), Renew

Includes: R&R transmission and converter.

Citation - Omega - Phoenix - Skylark		
1983-85	(3.7)	4.9
Cavalier - Cimarron - J-2000 Skyhawk - Firenza		
1983-87	(3.5)	4.9
Celebrity-Century-Ciera-A6000-Fiero		
1983-87	(3.7)	4.9
Regal-Calais-Grand Am		
1985-87	(3.5)	4.9
w/P.S. add	(.3)	.3
w/Diesel eng add	(.5)	.5

(G) Converter Seal, Renew

Includes: R&R transmission and converter.

Citation - Omega - Phoenix - Skylark		
1983-85	(3.5)	4.7
Cavalier - Cimarron - J-2000 Skyhawk - Firenza		
1983-87	(3.2)	4.7
Celebrity-Century-Ciera-A6000-Fiero		
1983-87	(3.5)	4.7
Regal-Calais-Grand Am		
1985-87	(3.2)	4.7
w/P.S. add	(.3)	.3
w/Diesel eng add	(.5)	.5

(G) Transmission Case Cover Gaskets, Renew

Includes: R&R transmission and converter. R&R valve body and pump assemblies.

Citation - Omega - Phoenix - Skylark		
1983-85	(4.4)	5.9
Cavalier - Cimarron - J-2000 Skyhawk - Firenza		
1983-87	(4.2)	5.9
Celebrity-Century-Ciera-A6000-Fiero		
1983-87	(4.4)	5.9
Regal-Calais-Grand Am		
1985-87	(4.2)	5.9
w/P.S. add	(.3)	.3
w/Diesel eng add	(.5)	.5

(G) Transmission Drive Link Assy., and Sprocket Support, Renew

Includes: R&R transmission and converter. R&R valve body and case cover.

Citation - Omega - Phoenix - Skylark		
1983-85	(4.4)	6.0
Cavalier - Cimarron - J-2000 Skyhawk - Firenza		
1983-87	(4.2)	6.0
Celebrity-Century-Ciera-A6000-Fiero		
1983-87	(4.4)	6.0
Regal-Calais-Grand Am		
1985-87	(4.2)	6.0
w/P.S. add	(.3)	.3
w/Diesel eng add	(.5)	.5
Renew drive sprocket support add	(.1)	.2
Renew driven sprocket support add	(.3)	.5
Renew support bearings add	(.3)	.5

(G) Transmission Reaction Gear Set, R&R

Includes: R&R transmission and converter. R&R clutches and input unit parts. Make all necessary adjustments.

Citation - Omega - Phoenix - Skylark		
1983-85	(5.0)	6.7
Cavalier - Cimarron - J-2000 Skyhawk - Firenza		
1983-87	(4.8)	6.7
Celebrity-Century-Ciera-A6000-Fiero		
1983-87	(5.0)	6.7
Regal-Calais-Grand Am		
1985-87	(4.8)	6.7
w/P.S. add	(.3)	.3
w/Diesel eng add	(.5)	.5
Recond reactor gear set add	(.2)	.4
Recond input unit parts add	(.2)	.4

(G) Direct, Forward, Low and Reverse Clutches and Intermediate Band, Renew

Includes: R&R transmission and converter. R&R oil pan, servo, case cover, drive link, sprockets and manual shaft. Make all necessary adjustments.

Citation - Omega - Phoenix - Skylark		
1983-85	(4.9)	6.8
Cavalier - Cimarron - J-2000 Skyhawk - Firenza		
1983-87	(4.7)	6.8
Celebrity-Century-Ciera-A6000-Fiero		
1983-87	(4.9)	6.8
Regal-Calais-Grand Am		
1985-87	(4.7)	6.8
w/P.S. add	(.3)	.3
w/Diesel eng add	(.5)	.5
Recond forward clutch add	(.3)	.5
Recond direct clutch add	(.3)	.5
Recond low and reverse clutches add	(.3)	.5

(G) Transmission Differential and Final Drive Assembly, R&R

Includes: R&R transmission and converter.

Citation - Omega - Phoenix - Skylark		
1983-85	(5.2)	7.0
Cavalier - Cimarron - J-2000 Skyhawk - Firenza		
1983-87	(5.0)	7.0
Celebrity-Century-Ciera-A6000-Fiero		
1983-87	(5.2)	7.0
Regal-Calais-Grand Am		
1985-87	(5.0)	7.0
w/P.S. add	(.3)	.3
w/Diesel eng add	(.5)	.5

(P) Transmission Differential and Final Drive Assy., R&R and Recondition

Includes: R&R transmission and converter. R&R clutches, input and reaction gear sets. Recondition differential and final drive only. Make all necessary adjustments. Road test.

Citation - Omega - Phoenix - Skylark		
1983-85	(6.3)	8.5
Cavalier - Cimarron - J-2000 Skyhawk - Firenza		
1983-87	(6.1)	8.5
Celebrity-Century-Ciera-A6000-Fiero		
1983-87	(6.3)	8.5
Regal-Calais-Grand Am		
1985-87	(6.1)	8.5
w/P.S. add	(.3)	.3
w/Diesel eng add	(.5)	.5

(P) Transmission Differential Carrier, Renew

Includes: R&R transmission and converter. R&R differential and final drive assy. Transfer all parts and make all necessary adjustments. Road test.

Citation - Omega - Phoenix - Skylark		
1983-85	(6.1)	8.2
Cavalier - Cimarron - J-2000 Skyhawk - Firenza		
1983-87	(5.9)	8.2
Celebrity-Century-Ciera-A6000-Fiero		
1983-87	(6.1)	8.2
Regal-Calais-Grand Am		
1985-87	(5.9)	8.2
w/P.S. add	(.3)	.3
w/Diesel eng add	(.5)	.5

(G) Transmission Governor Drive Gear, Renew

Includes: R&R transmission and converter. R&R differential and final drive. Make all necessary adjustments. Road test.

Citation - Omega - Phoenix - Skylark		
1983-85	(5.3)	7.1
Cavalier - Cimarron - J-2000 Skyhawk - Firenza		
1983-87	(5.1)	7.1
Celebrity-Century-Ciera-A6000-Fiero		
1983-87	(5.3)	7.1
Regal-Calais-Grand Am		
1985-87	(5.1)	7.1
w/P.S. add	(.3)	.3
w/Diesel eng add	(.5)	.5

PARTS 23 CASE & DRIVE LINK 23 PARTS

Parts numbers shown are for pricing reference only. Order unit with complete year, engine, model and unit I.D. number.

Transaxle Assy. (New)

	Part No.	Price
Citation, Omega, Phoenix, Skylark		
1983		
Code PW	8643185	1950.00
Code PD	8643193	1950.00
Code CE	8643519	1950.00
Code CL	8643463	N.L.
Code CT	8643229	1950.00
1984-87		
Code CE	8643519	1950.00
Code CT	8643533	1950.00
Code PD	8643464	1950.00
Code PW	8643649	1950.00
Code CC	8643533	1950.00
Cavalier, Cimarron, Firenza, J2000, Skyhawk		
1983		
Code PG	8643240	1950.00
Code P3	8643184	1950.00
Code CA	8643241	1950.00
Code CB	8643467	N.L.
Code CF	8637861	1950.00
Code CJ	8637157	1950.00
1984		
Code CA	8643469	1950.00
Code CB	8643467	N.L.
Code CF	8643468	N.L.
Code PE	8643534	1950.00
Code PG	8643530	1950.00
Code PJ	8643535	1950.00
1985-87		
Code CB	8643666	1950.00
Code CA	8643667	1950.00
Code CI	8652373	1950.00
Code CC	8652374	1950.00
Code CJ	8643571	1950.00
Celebrity, Century, Cutlass Ciera, 6000		
1983		
Code PW	8643185	1950.00
Code PD	8643193	1950.00
Code BF	8643528	N.L.
Code BL	8643245	1950.00
Code OP	8643279	1950.00
Code CL	8643463	N.L.
Code CT	8643229	1950.00
Code CC	8643327	N.L.

PARTS 23 CASE & DRIVE LINK 23 PARTS

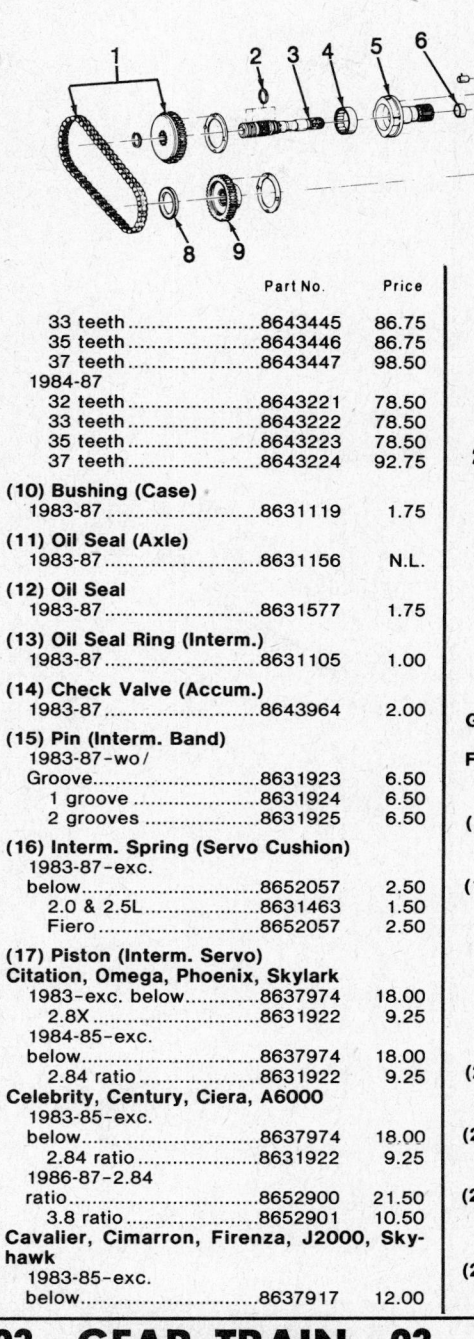

	Part No.	Price
1984-87		
Code BL	8643657	1950.00
Code BF	8643528	N.L.
Code CC	8643533	1950.00
Code CL	8643463	N.L.
Code OP	8643529	1950.00
Code PD	8643464	1950.00
Code PW	8643649	1950.00
Code PD	8643650	1950.00
Code CX	8643647	1950.00
Code CT	8652634	N.L.
Code CP	8656611	N.L.
Code CL	8643648	N.L.
Code CW	8656113	N.L.
Code OP	8643660	1950.00
Code PW	8643649	1950.00
Code BL	8643657	1950.00
Code BA	8656119	N.L.
Code BF	8643658	1950.00
Grand AM, Omega, Somerset Regal		
1985-87-3.0L	8643672	1950.00
2.5L	8643671	1950.00
Fiero		
1984-87		
Code 4PF	8643536	1950.00
Code 5PF	8643669	1950.00
Code 5CD	8643670	1950.00
Overhaul Gasket & Seal Kit		
1983-87	8631914	N.L.
(1) Sprocket Kit (w/Drive Link)		
1983		
33 teeth	8631197	78.50
35 teeth	8631740	78.50
37 teeth	8631741	74.00
38 teeth	8637172	70.00
1984-87		
33 teeth	8643209	92.75
32 teeth	8643221	78.50
35 teeth	8643210	78.50
37 teeth	8643211	78.50
38 teeth	8643212	78.50
(2) Snap Ring Kit		
1983-87	8631948	2.25
(3) Turbine Shaft (w/Sleeve)		
1983-84	8637166	71.50
1985-87	8652382	36.00
(4) Bearing (Drive Sprocket)		
1983-87	8631186	8.25
(5) Support (Drive Sprocket)		
1983-87	8637185	70.00
(6) Bushing		
1983-87	8628915	5.50
(7) Seal (Helix)		
1983-87	8637906	4.50
(8) Roller Bearing		
1983-87	9436851	5.25
(9) Sprocket (Driven)		
1983		
32 teeth	8643444	74.00

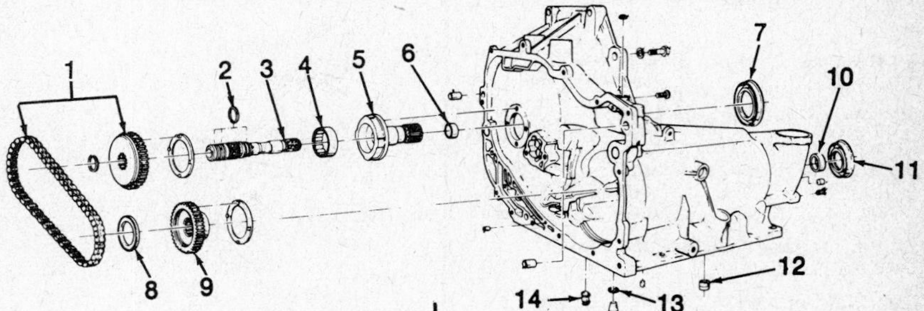

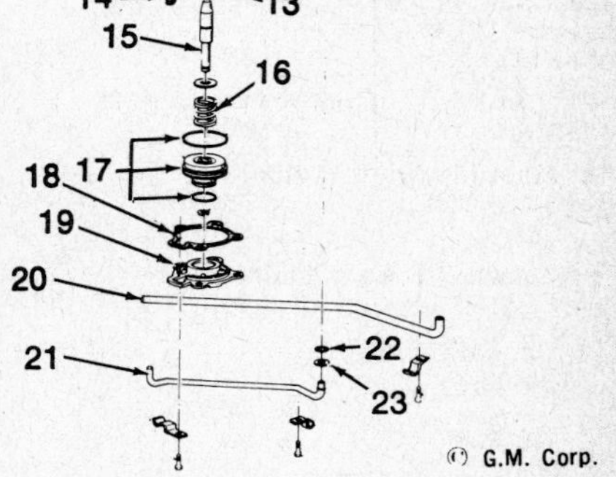

	Part No.	Price
33 teeth	8643445	86.75
35 teeth	8643446	86.75
37 teeth	8643447	98.50
1984-87		
32 teeth	8643221	78.50
33 teeth	8643222	78.50
35 teeth	8643223	78.50
37 teeth	8643224	92.75
(10) Bushing (Case)		
1983-87	8631119	1.75
(11) Oil Seal (Axle)		
1983-87	8631156	N.L.
(12) Oil Seal		
1983-87	8631577	1.75
(13) Oil Seal Ring (Interm.)		
1983-87	8631105	1.00
(14) Check Valve (Accum.)		
1983-87	8643964	2.00
(15) Pin (Interm. Band)		
1983-87-wo/		
Groove	8631923	6.50
1 groove	8631924	6.50
2 grooves	8631925	6.50
(16) Interm. Spring (Servo Cushion)		
1983-87-exc.		
below	8652057	2.50
2.0 & 2.5L	8631463	1.50
Fiero	8652057	2.50
(17) Piston (Interm. Servo)		
Citation, Omega, Phoenix, Skylark		
1983-exc. below	8637974	18.00
2.8X	8631922	9.25
1984-85-exc.		
below	8637974	18.00
2.84 ratio	8631922	9.25
Celebrity, Century, Ciera, A6000		
1983-85-exc.		
below	8637974	18.00
2.84 ratio	8631922	9.25
1986-87-2.84		
ratio	8652900	21.50
3.8 ratio	8652901	10.50
Cavalier, Cimarron, Firenza, J2000, Skyhawk		
1983-85-exc.		
below	8637917	12.00

	Part No.	Price
2.0L	8637974	18.00
1.8J, 2.8W	8631922	9.25
1986-87	8652900	21.50
Grand AM, Omega, Somerset Regal		
1985-87	8631922	9.25
Fiero		
1984-87	8631922	9.25
(18) Gasket (Servo Cover)		
1983-87	8631698	1.00
(19) Cover (Interm. Servo)		
1983-exc. below	8631703	15.00
2.8W	8631702	15.50
1984-87-exc.		
below	8631703	15.00
2.84 ratio	8631702	15.50
1.8J	8631702	15.50
Fiero	8631702	15.50
(20) Oil Pipe (Governor)		
1983-87	8631335	4.50
(21) Oil Pipe (Reverse)		
1983-87	8631330	4.25
(22) Seal (Reverse Pipe)		
1983-87	8631331	1.00
(23) Seal Kit (Reverse)		
1983-87	8631944	1.75

PARTS 23 GEAR TRAIN 23 PARTS

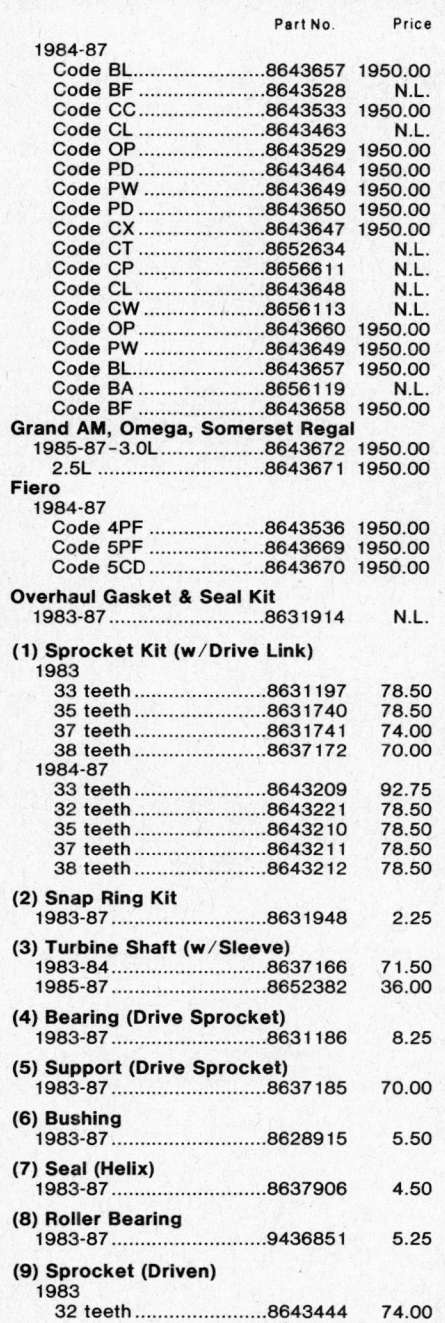

	Part No.	Price
(1) Support (Driven Sprocket)		
1983-87	8652564	131.00
(2) Bushing		
1983-87	8631900	2.00
(3) Support Ring		
1983-84	8631195	1.50
1986-87	8652535	1.50
(4) Band (Interm.)		
1983-84 (Kit)	8643941	140.00
1986-87	8653982	140.00

	Part No.	Price
(5) Front Bushing (Direct Clutch)		
1983-87	8631902	2.75
(6) Housing w/Drum (Direct Clutch)		
1983-84	8637976	100.00
1985-87	8653971	95.00
(7) Piston Seal Kit (Direct Clutch)		
1983-87	8631911	N.L.
(8) Piston (Direct Clutch)		
1983-84	8631009	14.75
1985-87	8652062	14.75

	Part No.	Price
(9) Ring (Direct Clutch)		
1983-85	8631017	13.75
1986-87	8652067	13.50
(10) Plate (Forward & Direct Clutch)		
1983-84	8631025	3.75
1985-87	8643741	3.50
2.3L (86-87)		
Flat	8631026	N.L.
(11) Backing Plate		
1983-84	8631764	N.L.
1985-87	8652562	7.25

	Part No.	Price
(12) Retainer (Check Valve w/Ball)		
1983-87	8628732	.50
(13) Oil Seal Ring (Input Shaft)		
1983-87	8631048	1.00
(14) Housing (Forward Clutch)		
1983-87	8637645	N.L.
1985-87	8652579	185.00
(15) Piston Seal Kit (Forward Clutch)		
1983-87	8637973	7.00
(16) Piston (Forward Clutch)		
1983-87 (inc. seals)	8637973	7.00
(17) Guide & Spring (Forward Clutch)		
1983-87	8631927	6.50
(18) Plate (Forward Clutch)		
1983-87-flat	8631379	3.50
wave	8652126	5.50
Plate Assy. (Forward Clutch)		
1983-87 (Faced)	8631025	3.75
(19) Backing Plate		
1983-87		
"J"	8652562	7.25
"A & N" (4.64 mm)	8637882	14.50
(5.34 mm)	8637881	14.50
(6.03 mm)	8637883	14.25
(20) Internal Gear w/Bushing		
1983-87	8631049	62.50
(21) Retainer (Check Valve w/Ball)		
1983-87	8628064	N.L.
(22) Input Carrier (Complete)		
1983-87	8631681	N.L.
(23) Sun Gear (Input)		
1983-87	8631061	22.75
(24) Input Drum		
1983-87-exc. ratio below	8643191	50.50
2.39, 2.53, 2.84R	8637511	14.50
1984-Fiero	8637511	14.50
(25) Bushing		
1983-87	8631906	2.50
(26) Sun Gear (Reaction)		
1983-87	8631845	46.25
(27) Low and Reverse Clutch Housing		
1983	8653915	70.00
1984	8643007	50.75
1985-87	8652780	69.25
(28) Seal Kit (Lo & Rev. Clutch)		
1983-87	8631913	4.00
(29) Piston (Lo & Rev. Clutch)		
1983	8653916	24.00
1984	8652024	24.00
1985-87	8643798	24.00
(30) Ring (Lo & Rev. Clutch)		
1983-87	8631231	5.75
(31) Spring (Lo & Rev. Clutch)		
1983-87	8628222	2.00
(32) Retainer		
1983-87	8631075	1.75
(33) Plate (Lo & Rev. Clutch)		
1983	8631079	3.00
1984-87	8652027	4.50
Plate Assy. (Lo & Rev. Clutch)		
1983	8631080	4.50
1984-87	8652028	6.00
(34) Backing Plate (Lo & Rev. Clutch)		
1983-87	8631091	10.25

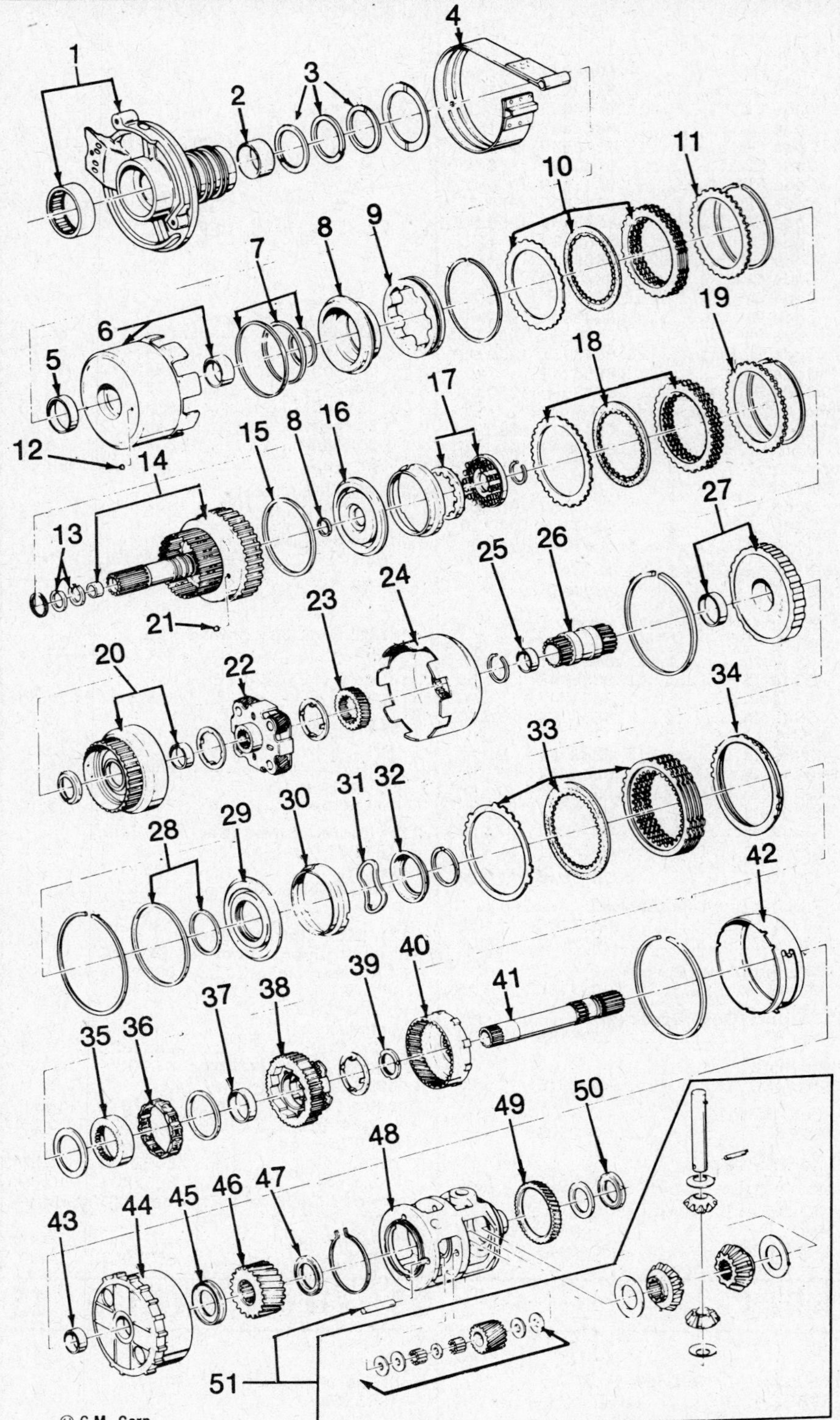

© G.M. Corp.

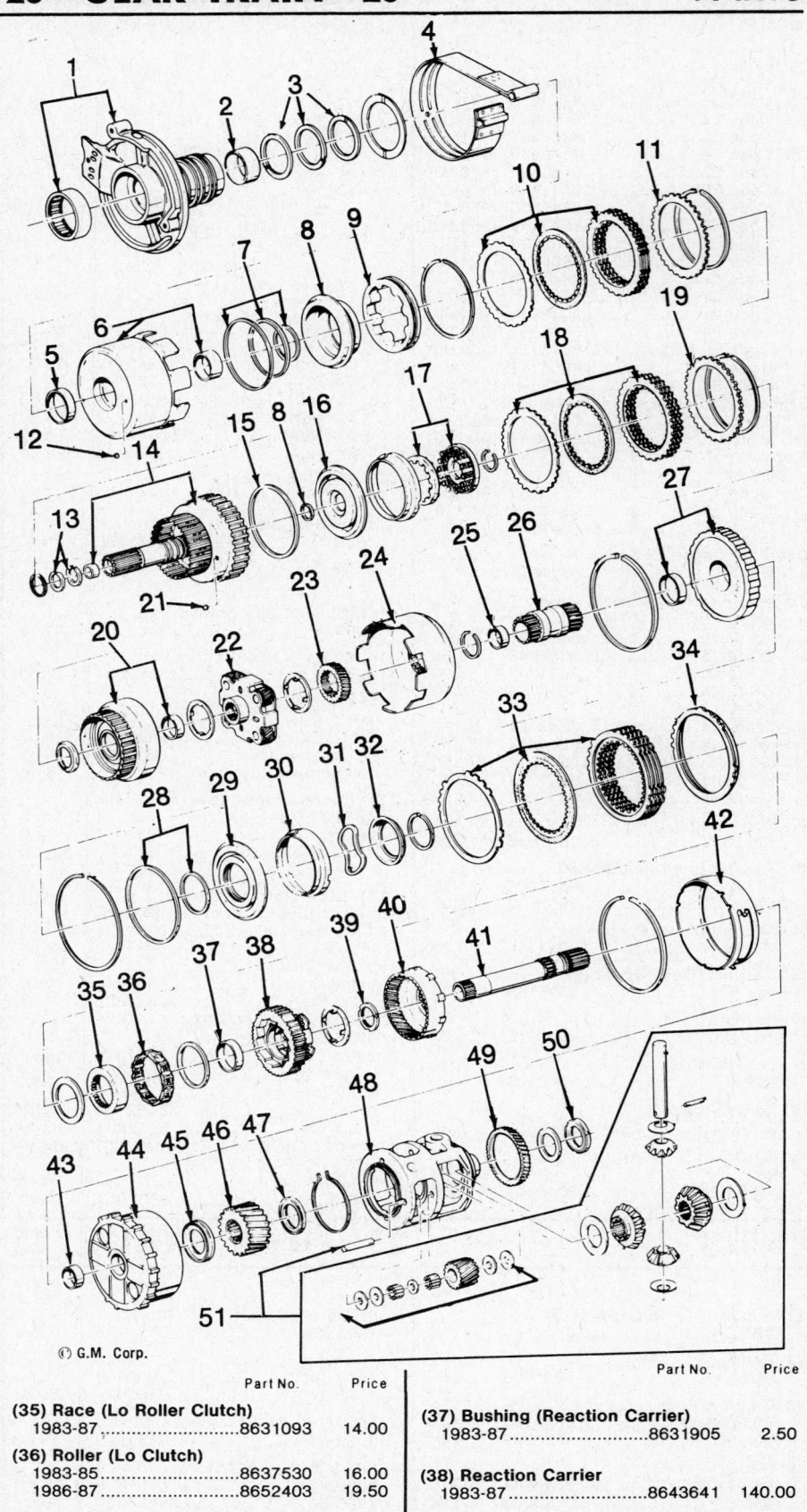

	Part No.	Price
(35) Race (Lo Roller Clutch)		
1983-87	8631093	14.00
(36) Roller (Lo Clutch)		
1983-85	8637530	16.00
1986-87	8652403	19.50

	Part No.	Price
(37) Bushing (Reaction Carrier)		
1983-87	8631905	2.50
(38) Reaction Carrier		
1983-87	8643641	140.00

PARTS 23 GEAR TRAIN 23 PARTS

	Part No.	Price
(39) Bearing		
1983-87	8628962	4.50
(40) Internal Gear (Reaction)		
1983-87	8652236	62.50
(41) Sun Gear Shaft (Final Drive)		
1983-87	8652388	70.00
(42) Spacer (Final Drive)		
1983	8637015	8.75
1984-87	8652022	9.00
(43) Case Bushing (Final Drive)		
1983-87	8631119	1.75
(44) Internal Gear (w/Bushing)		
1983-87	8631117	71.75
(45) Bearing		
1983-87	8631116	4.50
(46) Sun Gear (Final Drive)		
1983-87-exc. ratio below	8631155	35.25
2.97, 3.73, 3.74R.	8631115	N.L.
3.06, 3.43R	8644237	77.25
(47) Bearing		
1983-87	8628962	4.50
(48) Carrier (wo/Gears)		
1983-87-exc. below	8637972	140.00
3.06, 3.43R	8643990	189.00
2.97, 3.33, 3.73R	8643963	218.00
1984-87-exc. below	8653941	205.00
3.06, 3.43R	8643990	189.00
2.97, 3.33, 3.73R	8643963	218.00
(49) Gear (Governor Drive)		
1983-87	8631571	14.00
(50) Bearing		
1983-87	8631362	6.50
(51) Diff. Gear & Pinion Kit		
1983-87	8637919	N.L.

PARTS 23 CASE & PARTS 23 PARTS

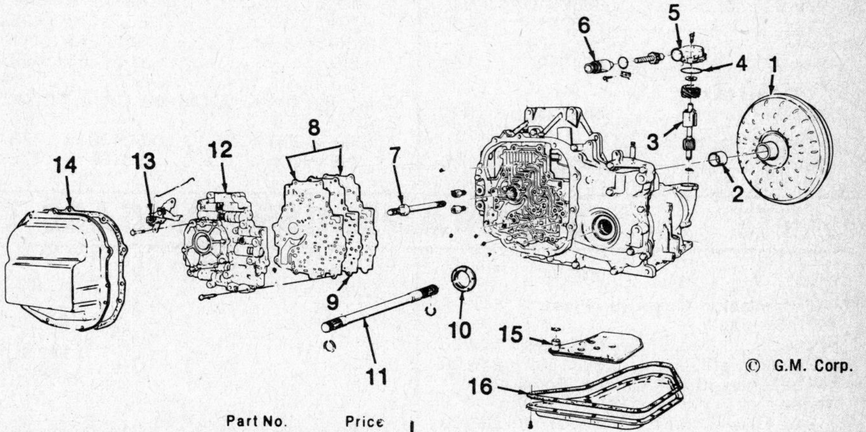

Part numbers shown are for pricing reference only. Order with complete engine, model, year and unit I.D. number.

	Part No.	Price
(1) Torque Converter (Rebuilt)		
Citation, Omega, Phoenix, Skylark		
1983-85 (2.5L) (Trans. code)		
PD, PW	8643902	340.00
PI, PK, PL	8637909	340.00
1983 (2.8L)		
MD9 trans.	8637909	340.00
M34 trans.	8637913	169.00
1984-85 (2.8L)		
Code X	8637909	340.00
Code Z	8643902	340.00
Cavalier, Cimarron, Firenza, J2000, Skyhawk		
1983-87-1.80	8643900	340.00
1.8J	8653932	340.00
2.0L	8643901	340.00
Celebrity, Century, Cutlass Ciera, 6000		
2.5L		
1983-trans. code		
PD, PW	8643902	340.00
PI, PK, PL	8637909	340.00
1984-87	8653937	324.00
2.8L		
1983-87-exc. below	8637909	340.00
Codw W	8653954	340.00
3.0L		
1983	8643903	340.00
1984-87-exc. below	8653939	340.00
3.33R	8644936	340.00
4.3L		
1983-87	8643936	N.L.
Grand AM, Omega, Somerset Regal		
1985-87-2.5L	8653940	340.00
3.0L	8653954	340.00
Fiero		
1984-87-exc. below	8653937	324.00
3.06R	8653954	340.00
(2) Bushing (Conv. Pump)		
1983-87	8631119	1.75
(3) Governor Kit (w/Seals)		
Citation, Omega, Phoenix, Skylark		
1983-85 (2.5L)		
2.39 ratio	8637947	51.25
2.84 ratio	8643992	52.00
1983-85 (2.8X)		
2.53 ratio	8637949	51.25
2.84 ratio	8631932	45.25
1983-85 (2.8Z)		
2.97 ratio	8637990	51.50
3.06 ratio	8643969	54.50
(Cavalier, Cimarron, Firenza, J2000, Skyhawk)		
1983-87 (1.8L)		
2.84 ratio	8637948	51.25
3.18 ratio	8637953	45.25
3.18 ratio (Fuel inj.)	8643906	57.50
3.33 ratio (1983)	8643908	57.50
3.33 ratio (1984-87)	8643994	70.75
3.43 ratio	8653919	61.50
3.73 ratio	8643907	57.50
1983-87 (2.0L)		
3.18 ratio	8643993	64.75
3.43 ratio	8643908	57.50
3.73 ratio	8643910	54.25
1985-87 (2.8L)		
3.18 ratio	8653929	62.00
Celebrity, Century, Cutlass Ciera, 6000		
1983-87 (2.5L)		
2.39 ratio	8637947	51.25
2.84 ratio	8643992	52.00
1983-87 (2.8X)		
2.84 ratio	8631932	45.25
1983-87 (2.8Z)		
3.06 ratio	8643969	54.50
3.33 ratio	8643991	55.00
1983-87 (3.0L)		
2.53 ratio	8637951	52.00
2.97 ratio (1983-87)	3643968	N.L.
3.03 ratio	3644954	N.L.
3.33 ratio	3644958	N.L.
1983-87 (4.3L)		
2.39 ratio	8637952	50.00
Grand AM, Omega, Somerset Regal		
1985-87-2.5L	8643992	52.00
3.0L	8653921	59.25
Fiero		
1984-87-exc. below	8653920	61.50
3.06R	8653922	59.25
(4) 'O' Ring (Gov. Cover)		
1983-87	8649382	1.25
(5) Cover Kit (w/Gov. Seals)		
1983-87	8643984	22.50
(6) Speedo. Sleeve (Driven Gear)		
1983	25519848	6.50
1984-87-exc. below	25519848	6.50
Fiero	25007336	42.25
(7) Pump Drive Shaft		
1983-85	8643627	63.00
1986-87	8643764	48.00
(8) Gasket (Spacer Plate)		
1983-87	8643051	2.75
(9) Spacer (Valve Body)		
Citation, Omega, Phoenix, Skylark		
1983 (2.5L)		
MD9 trans. (1983)	8643030	6.50
M34 trans.	8637122	5.50
1983 (2.8L)		
X eng.	8643943	9.25
Z eng. (1983)	8643043	N.L.
1984-85-2.5L	8643497	9.50
2.8X	8643036	7.00
2.8Z	8643047	9.25
Cavalier, Cimarron, Firenza, J2000 Skyhawk		
1.8L		
1983	8643044	6.75

PARTS 23 CASE & PARTS 23 PARTS

	Part No.	Price
1984-87-exc.		
below	8643498	10.75
Code J	8643497	9.50
2.0L		
1983-exc. below	8643960	N.L.
3.18, 3.43R	8643040	7.00
1984-87	8643048	10.75
Celebrity, Century, Cutlass Ciera, 6000		
2.5L		
1983	8643944	10.25
1984-87	8643497	9.50
2.8L		
1983	8643043	N.L.
1984-87-Code X	8643036	7.00
Code Z	8643047	9.25
3.0L		
1983-87	8643040	7.00
4.3L		
1983-87	8643041	7.00
Grand AM, Omega, Somerset Regal		
1985-87-2.5L	8652510	N.L.
3.0L	8652525	10.50
Fiero		
1984-87	8643497	9.50
(10) Oil Seal (Axle)		
1983-87	8631156	N.L.
(11) Output Shaft		
1983-87	8631640	82.00

	Part No.	Price
(12) Oil Pump (w/Cont. Valve)		
Citation, Omega, Phoenix, Skylark		
1983-85 (2.5)		
2.39 ratio	8643919	473.00
2.84 ratio (1983)	8643918	475.00
2.84 ratio (1984-85)	8652183	475.00
1983-85 (2.8X)		
2.84 ratio (1983-85)	8643920	473.00
2.53 ratio	8637928	446.00
1983-85 (2.8Z)		
2.97 ratio	8637980	446.00
3.06 ratio	8652181	433.00
Cavalier, Cimarron, Firenza, J2000, Skyhawk		
(Fuel Injected)		
1983-84-1.8	8652172	493.00
1.8J	8652270	540.00
2.0	8652173	493.00
1985-87-1.8J	8652271	N.L.
2.0	8652255	493.00
2.8	8652272	N.L.
Celebrity, Century, Cutlass Ciera, 6000		
2.5L		
1983-2.39R	8643919	473.00
2.84 ratio	8643918	475.00

	Part No.	Price
1984-87-exc.		
below	8643919	473.00
2.84 ratio	8653583	N.L.
2.8L		
1983-87-Code X	8643920	473.00
Code Z	8652181	433.00
3.0L		
1983-87	8637927	433.00
4.3L		
1983-87	8652170	433.00
Grand AM, Omega, Somerset Regal		
1985-87-2.5L	8652275	478.00
3.0L	8652480	420.00
Fiero		
1984-87-exc.		
below	8652268	N.L.
3.06R	8652273	N.L.
(13) Throttle Lever		
1983-87	8631694	19.50
(14) Gasket (Valve Body Cover)		
1983	8631340	N.L.
1984-87	8643573	N.L.
(15) Oil Strainer		
1983-85	8631951	N.L.
1986-87	8652910	16.25
(16) Gasket (Oil Pan)		
1983-87	8631338	3.75

PARTS 23 TRANSMISSION CASE COVER 23 PARTS

	Part No.	Price
(1) Transmission Cover (w/Pins)		
1983-87-exc.		
below	8631996	212.00
Cavalier, etc.	8631997	212.00
1985-87-Grand AM, Omega, Somerset Regal		
2.5L	8653968	238.00
3.0L	8653970	250.00
(2) Valve Assy. (Manual)		
1983-84	8643316	15.00
1985-87	8652132	14.75
(3) Plug (Manual Valve Bore)		
1983-87	8637863	1.50
(4) Pin (Spring Thermo. Element)		
1983-87	8631687	.75
(5) Pin (Thermo. Element)		
1983-87	8631654	.75
(6) Plate (Thermo. Element)		
1983-87	8631719	1.25

© G.M. Corp.

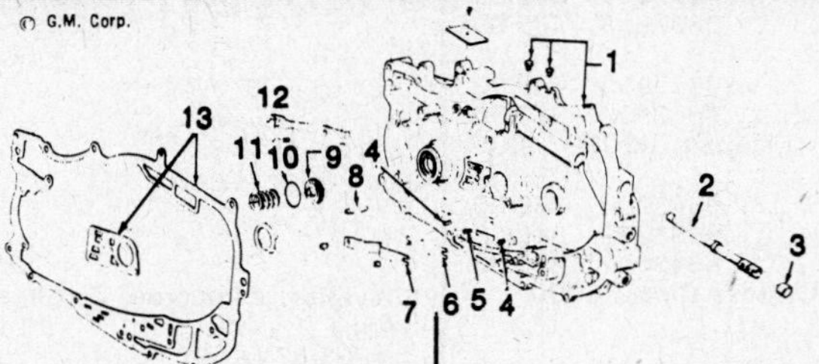

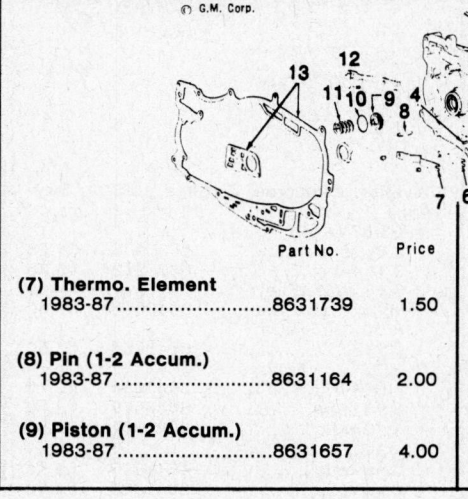

	Part No.	Price
(7) Thermo. Element		
1983-87	8631739	1.50
(8) Pin (1-2 Accum.)		
1983-87	8631164	2.00
(9) Piston (1-2 Accum.)		
1983-87	8631657	4.00

	Part No.	Price
(10) Ring (Oil Seal)		
1983-87	8631895	.75
(11) Spring (1-2 Accum.)		
1983-87	8631168	1.75
(12) Spring (Manual Detent)		
1983-87	8631748	3.25
(13) Gasket (Case to Cover)		
1983-87	8631979	3.75

(Factory Time) Chilton Time

ON CAR SERVICES

(G) Drain & Refill Unit
All models 7

(G) Oil Pressure Check
All models 5

(M) Check Unit For Oil Leaks
Includes: Clean and dry outside of case and run unit to determine point of leak.
All models 9

(G) Neutral Safety Switch, Renew
All models (.3) 5

(G) Shift Linkage, Adjust
All models
Neutral Safety Switch (.3) 4
Shift Indicator Needle (.2) 3
Shift Linkage (.4) 5
T.V. Cable (.3) 4

(G) Vacuum Modulator, Renew
All models (.4) 5

(G) Speedometer Driven Gear, Renew
All models (.3) 6

(G) Speedometer Drive Gear, Renew
All models (1.0) 1.7

(G) Torque Converter Clutch Switches, Renew
All models
Brake switch (.2) 4
Thermal vacuum (.3) 5
Engine temp (.3) 5

(G) Detent Cable, Adjust
All models (.2) 4

(G) Detent Cable, Renew
All models (.5) 9

(G) Detent Valve, Renew
Includes: R&R oil pan and valve body, servo cover and reinforcement plate.
All models (1.6) 2.2

(G) Extension Housing or Gasket, Renew
Chevrolet
1983-87-Chevette (1.1) 1.6
Pontiac
1983-87-T1000 (1.1) 1.6

(G) Extension Housing Rear Seal, Renew
All models (.4) 7

(G) Extension Housing Bushing, Renew
Includes: R&R extension housing.
Chevrolet
1983-87-Chevette (1.3) 2.1
Pontiac
1983-87-T1000 (1.3) 2.1

(G) Governor Assembly, Renew
Includes: R&R drive shaft and extension housing.
Chevrolet
1983-87-Chevette (1.0) 1.6
Pontiac
1983-87-T1000 (1.0) 1.6
Recondition governor hub add (.1) 3

(G) Oil Pan Gasket, Renew
All models (.6) 1.0

(G) Governor Pressure Switch and/or Electrical Connector, Renew
Includes: R&R oil pan.
Chevrolet
1983-87-Chevette (.6) 1.1

CHILTON'S AUTOMATIC TRANSMISSION TUNE-UP

1. Check engine performance
2. Check condition of transmission oil
3. Check transmission, oil cooler and oil cooler lines for external leaks
4. Remove oil pan, clean or renew screen or filter
5. Torque valve body
6. Adjust bands
7. Clean oil pan and install pan with new gasket
8. Check modulator and hose
9. Install new transmission oil to proper level
10. Adjust manual and throttle linkage
11. Road test

All models 1.5
Charge for parts used

(Factory Time) Chilton Time

Pontiac
1983-87-T1000 (.6) 1.1

(G) Converter Clutch Solenoid Assy., Renew
Includes: R&R oil pan.
Chevrolet
1983-87-Chevette (.7) 1.2
Pontiac
1983-87-T1000 (.7) 1.2

(G) Low Band Servo, Renew
Includes: R&R oil pan, reinforcement plate, servo cover and valve body. Adjust servo.
All models (1.1) 1.6
Recon servo add (.1) 3

(G) Valve Body Assembly, Renew
Includes: R&R oil pan, reinforcement plate, screen and servo cover.
All models (1.0) 1.5

(P) Valve Body Assy., R&R and Recondition
Includes: R&R oil pan, reinforcement plate, screen and servo cover. Disassemble, clean, inspect all valves. Replace parts as required.
All models (1.6) 2.2

(G) Parking Pawl, Renew
Includes: R&R oil pan and extension housing.
Chevrolet
1983-87-Chevette (1.1) 1.9
Pontiac
1983-87-T1000 (1.1) 1.9

(G) Transmission Mount, Renew
1983-87
rear (.4) 6

SERVICES REQURING R&R

(G) Transmission Assy., R&R or Renew
Includes: R&R converter and front pump seal.
Chevrolet
1983-87-Chevette (2.4) 4.0
Pontiac
1983-87-T1000 (2.4) 4.0
Renew trans. add (.3) 5

(Factory Time) Chilton Time

(P) Transmission and Converter Assy., R&R and Recondition
Includes: Disassemble trans, inspect and replace parts as required. Make all necessary adjustments. Road test.
Chevrolet
1983-87-Chevette (8.1) 11.3
Pontiac
1983-87-T1000 (8.1) 11.3

(G) Transmission Assembly, Reseal
Includes: R&R transmission and install all new gaskets and seals.
Chevrolet
1983-87-Chevette 6.5
Pontiac
1983-87-T1000 .... 6.5

(P) Transmission Assembly, Recondition (Off Car)
All models (4.2) 6.0

(G) Front Oil Pump Seal, Renew
Includes: R&R converter and seal.
Chevrolet
1983-87-Chevette (2.4) 3.8
Pontiac
1983-87-T1000 (2.4) 3.8

(G) Torque Converter, Renew
Chevrolet
1983-87-Chevette (2.4) 4.2
Pontiac
1983-87-T1000 (2.4) 4.2

(G) Flywheel (Flex Plate), Renew
Chevrolet
1983-87-Chevette (2.5) 3.9
Pontiac
1983-87-T1000 (2.5) 3.9

(G) Front Oil Pump, Renew
Chevrolet
1983-87-Chevette (3.3) 5.0
Pontiac
1983-87-T1000 (3.3) 5.0
Renew pump bushing add (.3) 3
Renew converter housing bushing add (.2) 2

(G) Front Oil Pump, R&R and Recondition
Chevrolet
1983-87-Chevette (3.9) 5.7
Pontiac
1983-87-T1000 (3.9) 5.7
Renew pump bushing add (.3) 3
Renew converter housing bushing add (.2) 2

(G) Apply and Actuator Valve and/or Bushing, Renew
Includes: R&R trans, converter and oil pump.
Chevrolet
1983-87-Chevette (2.9) 4.7
Pontiac
1983-87-T1000 (2.9) 4.7

(P) Second and Third Clutch Assemblies, Renew
Includes: R&R trans and converter, housing and pump reverse clutch assy., second clutch bushing.
Chevrolet
1983-87-Chevette (3.6) 5.5
Pontiac
1983-87-T1000 (3.6) 5.5
Overhaul second clutch add (.5) 5
Overhaul third clutch add (.4) 4
R&R planetary carrier and reaction sun gear add (.6) 6
Renew sun gear drum bushing add (.3) 3

LABOR 23 AUTOMATIC TRANSMISSION 23 LABOR

(Factory Time) — Chilton Time

(P) Low Band, Renew

Includes: R&R trans and converter housing, pump valve body and servo. Remove second and third clutch assys., extension housing and speedometer drive and driven gears. Remove governor body and hub sun gear, planetary carrier and modulator.

Chevrolet

	Chilton Time
1983-87-Chevette (3.7)	5.6

Pontiac

	Chilton Time
1983-87-T1000 (3.7)	5.6
Overhaul second clutch add (.5)	.6
Overhaul third clutch add (.4)	.5
Overhaul reverse clutch add (1.3)	1.4
Renew pump bushing add (.3)	.4
Renew converter housing bushing add (.2)	.3
Leak check converter add (.2)	.3
Overhaul valve body add (.6)	.7
Renew converter housing seal add (.1)	.1
Renew extension housing seal add (.1)	.1
Overhaul low servo add (.1)	.2
Overhaul governor and hub add (.1)	.2
Renew parking pawl rod add (.1)	.2
Renew selector shaft seal add (.1)	.2
Renew reaction sun gear and drum bushing add (.3)	.4
Renew case bushing add (.1)	.1

PARTS 23 CONVERTER, PUMP & CLUTCH 23 PARTS

	Part No.	Price
Flywheel (Flex Plate)		
1983-87	14001182	60.25
Transmission Assy.		
1983-84	96013579	1670.00
1985-87	96013691	1670.00
(1) Converter Assy. (Rebuilt)		
1983-87	14095663	340.00
(2) Seal (Converter Housing)		
1983-87	8626916	N.L.
(3) Gasket (Oil Pump Assy.)		
1983-87	96013211	4.00
(4) Bushing (Oil Pump Body)		
1983-87	8958621	9.00
(5) Plate (Oil Pump Wear)		
1983-87	96013212	18.25
(6) Oil Pump Assy.		
1983-87	96040245	222.00
(7) Sleeve (Oil Pump Valve)		
1983-87	90064150	27.00
(8) Valve (Oil Pump Boost.)		
1983-87	90064151	12.50
(9) Seat (Pressure Regulator)		
1983-87	5258219	.50
(10) Spring (Pressure Regulator)		
1983-87	5259631	2.00
(11) Valve (Oil Pump)		
1983-87	5258140	8.25
(12) Seal (Oil Pump Body)		
1983-87	5258119	3.25
(13) Bushing (Oil Pump Body)		
1983-87	8958621	9.00
(14) Screen (Governor Valve)		
1983-87	5258383	3.50
(15) Seal (Inner)		
1983-87	5258005	.75
(16) Seal (Outer)		
1983-87	5258004	1.50
(17) Piston (Reverse Clutch)		
1983-87	5258971	28.00
(18) Spring		
1983-87	8958719	.50

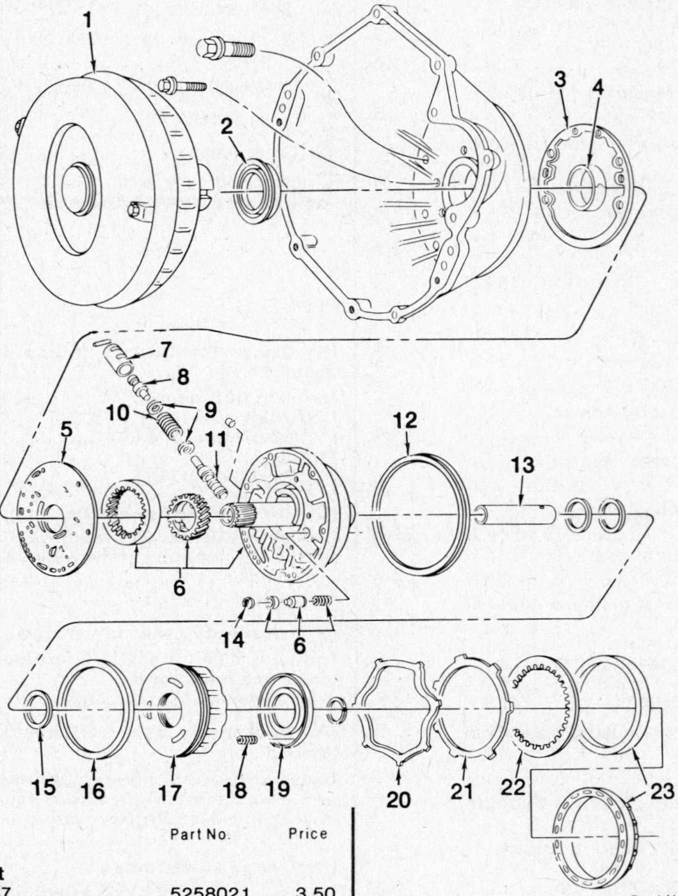

	Part No.	Price
(19) Seat		
1983-87	5258021	3.50
(20) Plate (Reverse Clutch)		
1983-87	5258989	8.50
(21) Plate (Reverse Gear)		
1983-87	5258957	8.00
(22) Plate (Reverse Drive)		
1983-87	90064284	N.L.
(23) Plate (Reverse Pressure)		
1983-87	8958733	9.50

PARTS 23 GEAR TRAIN 23 PARTS

	Part No.	Price
(1) Bushing (2nd Spd. Clutch Hub)		
1983-87	5258128	5.75
(2) Drum (2nd Spd. Clutch)		
1983-87	8958745	130.00
(3) Piston Seal (Inner)		
1983-87	5258043	1.75
(4) Piston Seal (Outer)		
1983-87	5258041	2.50
(5) Piston Assy. (2nd Spd. Clutch)		
1983-87	5258109	35.00
(6) Spring		
1983-87	8958719	.50
(7) Seat (2nd Spd. Clutch)		
1983-87	5258038	3.25
(8) Plate (2nd Spd. Clutch)		
1983-87	5258990	8.50
(9) Plate Assy. (2nd Spd. Clutch Drive)		
1983-87	90064283	7.50

PARTS 23 GEAR TRAIN 23 PARTS

	Part No.	Price
(10) Plate (2nd Spd. Clutch Driven)		
1983-87	5258956	6.25
(11) Plate (2nd Spd. Clutch Spacer)		
1983-87	5258965	15.00
(12) Ring Gear		
1983-87	8958696	56.25
(13) Shaft (3rd Clutch Drum & Input)		
1983-87	96013224	130.00
(14) Piston Seal (Outer)		
1983-87	5258042	2.75
(15) Piston Seal (Inner)		
1983-87	5258543	1.25
(16) Piston Assy. (3rd Clutch)		
1983-87	8958601	35.00
(17) Spring		
1983-87	8958719	.50
(18) Seat (3rd Clutch)		
1983-87	5258039	2.25
(19) Retaining Ring		
1983-87	5258094	.75
(20) Seal Ring (Governor Hub)		
1983-87	5258837	3.50
(21) Governor Assy.		
1983-87	96013408	56.50
(22) Sun Gear Assy. (Reaction)		
1983-87	8958865	82.50
(23) Bushing (Reaction)		
1983-87	5258075	5.00
(24) Plate Assy. (3rd Clutch Drive)		
1983-87	90064281	7.50
(25) Plate Assy. (3rd Clutch Driven)		
1983-87	5258955	6.25
(26) Cushion (3rd Spd. Piston)		
1983-87	8958678	8.00
(27) Bearing (Reaction Sun Gr.)		
1983-87	5686837	4.00
(28) Bearing Assy. (Front)		
1983-87	8958606	7.75

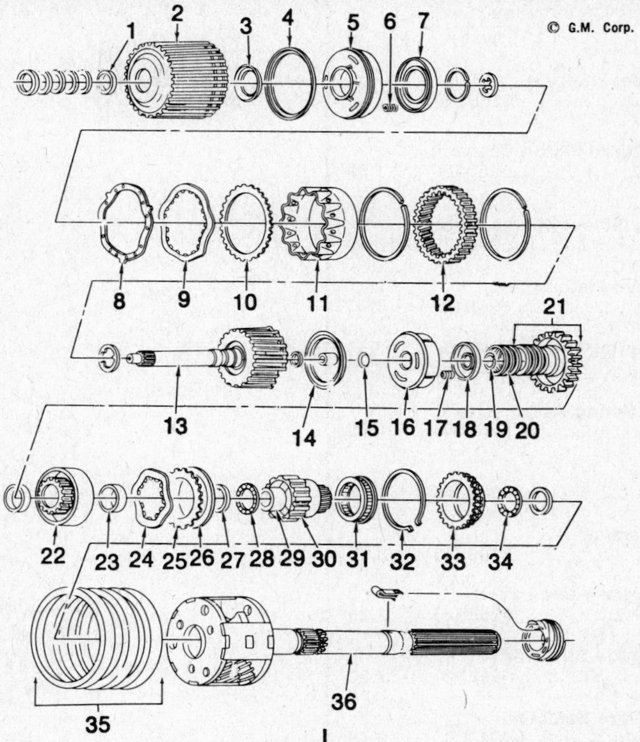

	Part No.	Price
(29) Sleeve (Reaction Sun Drum Brg.)		
1983-87	5258158	10.00
(30) Sun Gear Assy. (Input)		
1983-87	8958866	91.00
(31) Sprag Assy. (Complete)		
1983-87	5258546	41.25
(32) Retaining Ring (3rd Clutch)		
1983-87	8958684	1.50
(33) Race & Retainer Assy. (Input Sprag)		
1983-87	5258351	32.50
(34) Bearing Assy. (Rear)		
1983-87	8958607	N.L.
(35) Band Assy.		
1983-87	8958960	N.L.
(36) Planetary Carrier Assy.		
1983-87	8958851	250.25

PARTS 23 CASE & PARTS 23 PARTS

	Part No.	Price
(1) Ring (Input Sprag. Retainer)		
1983-87	8958661	24.00
(2) Breather		
1983-87	8640496	1.25
(3) Oil Seal (Detent Valve)		
1983-87	5258338	.75
(4) Sleeve (Detent Valve)		
1983-87	5258337	22.00
(5) Valve (Kickdown)		
1983-87	90064021	9.00
(6) Seat (Detent Valve)		
1983-87	5258231	.50
(7) Spring (Kickdown Valve)		
1983-87	90064020	.75
(8) Modulator Assy.		
1983-87	96013169	16.00
(9) Seal		
1983-87	11078101	.50
(10) Plunger (Modulator)		
1983-87	5258244	.50
(11) Valve (Modulator)		
1983-87	5258920	11.00
(12) Sleeve (Modulator)		
1983-87	5258921	14.00
(13) Ball (Valve Body)		
1983-87	11066201	.50
(14) Bushing (Trans. Case)		
1983-87	5258191	5.00
(15) Gasket (Extension)		
1983-87	5258199	2.25
(16) Bushing (Extension)		
1983-87	96013309	2.00
(17) Oil Seal (Extension)		
1983-87	3932255	N.L.
(18) Ball (Valve Body)		
1983-87		
9/32″ diameter	11066201	.50
1/8″ diameter	11052399	.25
(19) Gasket (Plate to Case)		
1983-87	5258155	3.00
(20) Plate (Transfer)		
1983-87	90064114	14.00
(21) Gasket (Valve Body)		
1983-87	5258443	2.00
(22) Piston Assy. (Accumulator)		
1983-87	8958522	N.L.
(23) Ring (Oil Seal)		
1983-87	8623653	1.00
(24) Spring (Accum. Piston)		
1983-87	5258862	N.L.
(25) Valve Body Assy.		
1983-87	96040048	298.00
(26) Screen Assy. (Oil Pump)		
1983-87	14024456	N.L.
(27) Gasket (Oil Pump Screen)		
1983-87	5258245	.50
(28) Gasket (Oil Pan)		
1983-87	14050668	4.50
(29) Reinforcement (Trans. Plate)		
1983-87	5258318	6.00
(30) Cover (Servo Piston)		
1983-87	5258153	7.50
(31) Gasket (Servo Cover)		
1983-87	5258339	2.00
(32) Ring (Servo Piston)		
1983-87	5258159	4.75

PARTS 23 CASE & PARTS 23 PARTS

	Part No.	Price
(33) Piston Assy. (Servo)		
1983-87	5258569	32.50
(34) Spring (Servo Piston Cushion)		
1983-87	5258565	1.50
(35) Adjusting Sleeve (Servo Piston)		
1983-87	5258523	17.50
(36) Rod (Servo Piston)		
1983-87	5258182	1.00
(37) Return Spring (Servo Piston)		
1983-87	5259662	7.25
(38) Roller & Spring Assy.		
1983-87	5258991	2.00
(39) Seal Assy.		
1983-87	8623056	1.25
(40) Valve (Manual)		
1983-87	5258145	13.50
(41) Link (Manual Valve Lever)		
1983-87	5258243	2.25
(42) Lever (Range Selector)		
1983-87	8958721	7.50
(43) Shaft (Range Selector)		
1983	96040093	9.75
1984-87	96040093	9.75
(44) Actuator Assy.		
1983-87	90064258	9.25

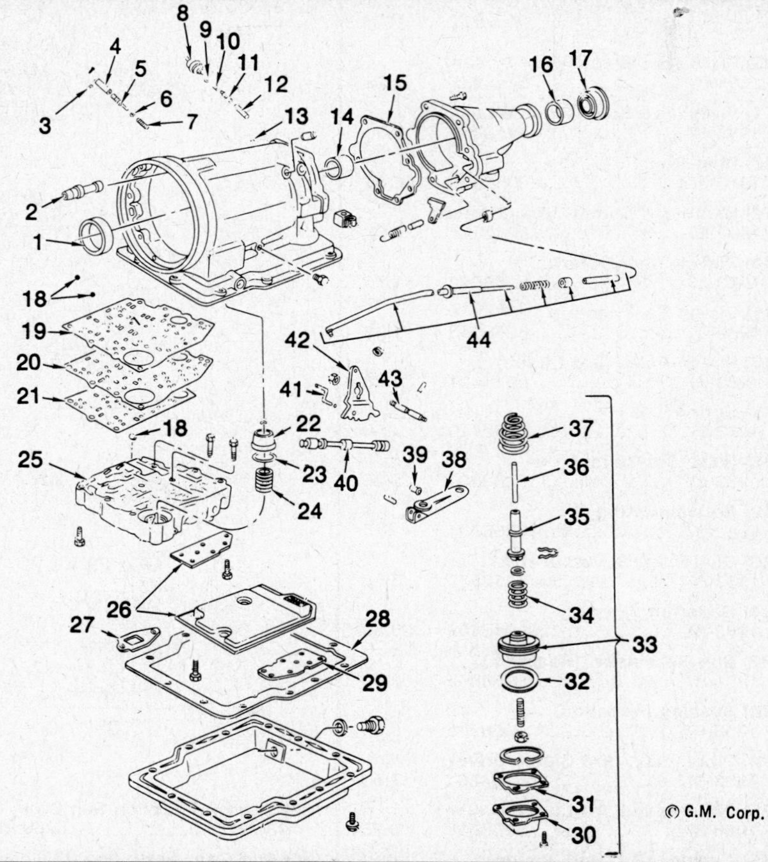

PARTS 23 REACTION CARRIERS & SHAFTS 23 PARTS

	Part No.	Price
(1) Bearing		
1983-87	5686837	4.00
(2) Sun Gear Assy. (Reaction)		
1983-87	8958865	82.50
(3) Band Assy.		
1983-87	8958960	N.L.
(4) Bushing		
1983-87	5258075	5.00
(5) Seal Ring (Governor Hub)		
1983-87	5258837	3.50
(6) Screen (Governor Valve)		
1983-87	5258383	3.50
(7) Governor Assy.		
1983-87	96013408	56.50

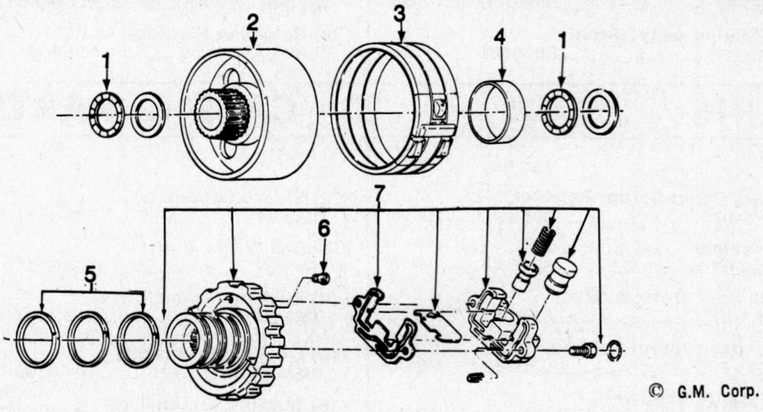

(Factory Time)	Chilton Time

ON CAR SERVICES

(G) Drain & Refill Unit
All models (.5) 7

(G) Oil Pressure Check
All models (.5) 5

(M) Check Unit for Oil Leaks
Includes: Clean and dry outside of case and run unit to determine point of leak.
All models (.7) 9

(G) Back-Up Lamp and Park/Neutral Switch, Renew
All models
wo/Console (.2) 3
w/Console (.5) 7

(G) Shift Linkage, Adjust
All models
Neutral Safety Switch (.3) 4
Shift Indicator Needle (.2) 3
Shift Linkage (.4) 5
T.V. Cable (.3) 4

(G) Shift Linkage, Adjust (w/Diesel Eng)
All models
Throttle Rod/T.V. cable (.5) 6
Vacuum Regulator Valve (.6) 8
Complete (.8) 1.0

(G) Torque Converter Clutch Brake Switch, Renew
All models (.2) 4

(G) Torque Converter Clutch Thermal Vacuum Switch, Renew
All models (.3) 5

(G) Engine Low Vacuum Switch, Renew
All models (.4) 6

(G) Engine High Vacuum Switch, Renew
All models (.5) 7

(G) Torque Converter Clutch Vacuum Delay Valve, Renew
All models (.2) 3

(G) Relay Valve, Renew
All models (.2) 3

(G) Engine Metal Temperature Indicator Switch, Renew
All models (.2) 5

(G) Speedometer Driven Gear and/or Seal, Renew
All models (.3) 4

(G) Governor Cover and/or Seal, Renew
All models (.3) 4

(G) Manual Lever Shaft Seal, Detent Lever and/or Park Actuator Rod, Renew
Includes: R&R oil pan.
All models (.7) 1.0

(G) Transmission Mount, Renew
All models (.4) 6

(G) Oil Pan Gasket, Renew
All models (.6) 9

(G) Oil Control Valve Body, Renew
Includes: R&R oil pan.
All models (.9) 1.5

(P) Oil Control Valve Body R&R, Disassemble and Clean
Includes: R&R oil pan.
All models (1.6) 2.3

CHILTON'S AUTOMATIC TRANSMISSION TUNE-UP

1. Check engine performance
2. Check condition of transmission oil
3. Check transmission, oil cooler and oil cooler lines for external leaks
4. Remove oil pan, clean or renew screen or filter
5. Torque valve body
6. Adjust bands
7. Clean oil pan and install pan with new gasket
8. Check modulator and hose
9. Install new transmission oil to proper level
10. Adjust manual and throttle linkage
11. Road test

All models 1.5
Charge for parts used

(Factory Time)	Chilton Time

(G) Governor Pressure Switch and/or Electrical Connector, Renew
Includes: R&R oil pan.
All models (.6) 1.1

(G) Servos, R&R or Renew (Intermediate)
Includes: R&R oil pan and valve body.
Buick Models
1983-87 (.5) 8
Chevrolet Models
1983-84-exc below (.4) 8
Chevette (.5) 9
1985-87 (.5) 8
Oldsmobile Models
1983-87 (.5) 8
Pontiac Models
1983-87 (.5) 8
Recond servo add (.2) 2

(G) Throttle Valve Control Cable, Renew
Buick Models
1983-87 (.5) 8
Chevrolet Models
1983-87 (.5) 8
Oldsmobile Models
1983-87 (.5) 8
Pontiac Models
1983-87 (.5) 8

(G) Pressure Regulator Valve, Renew
Includes: R&R oil pan.
All models (.7) 1.1

(G) Governor Assembly, Renew
Buick Models
1983-87 (.4) 7
Chevrolet Models
1983-84-exc. below (.4) 7
Chevette (.6) 1.0
1985-87 (.4) 7
Oldsmobile Models
1983-87 (.4) 7
Pontiac Models
1983-87 (.4) 7
Recond gov or renew gear add (.2) 4

(Factory Time)	Chilton Time

(G) Transmission Rear Oil Seal, Renew
Includes: R&R propeller shaft.
All models (.4) 7

(G) 1-2 Accumulator Spring or Piston, Renew
Includes: R&R oil pan, valve body, and detent cable bracket.
Buick Models
1983-87 (.9) 1.3
Chevrolet Models
1983-87 (.9) 1.3
Oldsmobile Models
1983-87 (.9) 1.3
Pontiac Models
1983-87 (.9) 1.3
Overhaul accumulator add (.2) 3

(G) Parking Pawl Shaft, Rod Spring, Renew
Includes: R&R oil pan and valve body.
Buick Models
1983-87 (1.1) 1.7
Chevrolet Models
1983-84-exc below (1.2) 1.9
Chevrolet (1.1) 1.7
Monte Carlo (1.1) 1.7
1985-87 (1.1) 1.7
Oldsmobile Models
1983-87 (1.1) 1.7
Pontiac Models
1983-87 (1.1) 1.7

SERVICES REQUIRING R&R

(G) Transmission Assembly, R&R or Renew
Buick Models
1983-87 (2.1) 3.5
Chevrolet Models
1983-84-exc below (2.1) 3.5
Chevette (2.4) 3.8
1985-87 (1.8) 3.5
Oldsmobile Models
1983-87 (2.1) 3.5
Pontiac Models
1983-87 (1.8) 3.5
Replace transmission add (.3) 5

(G) Flywheel (Flex Plate), Renew
Buick Models
1983-87 (2.3) 3.7
Chevrolet Models
1983-84-exc below (2.3) 3.7
Chevette (2.9) 4.3
1985-87 (2.0) 3.7
Oldsmobile Models
1983-87 (2.3) 3.7
Pontiac Models
1983-87 (2.0) 3.7

(G) Transmission and Converter Assy., R&R and Recondition
Includes: Drain and pressure test converter, recondition pump, clutch assemblies, shaft assemblies, carrier assembly, governor, servo valve body, and adjust cable and linkage.
Buick Models
1983-87 (6.0) 10.5
Chevrolet Models
1983-84-exc below (7.1) 10.5
Chevette (5.9) 11.0
1985-87 (7.1) 10.5
Oldsmobile Models
1983-87 (7.0) 10.5
Pontiac Models
1983-87 (5.9) 10.5

LABOR 23 AUTOMATIC TRANSMISSION 23 LABOR

(Factory Time)	Chilton Time
(G) Transmission Assembly, Reseal	
Includes: R&R transmission and renew all gaskets and seals.	
Buick models	
1983-87	6.0
Chevrolet models	
1983-84-exc below	6.0
Chevette	6.5
1985-87	6.0
Oldsmobile models	
1983-87	6.0
Pontiac models	
1983-87	6.0
(G) Torque Converter, Renew	
Includes: Pressure test converter and check end play.	
Buick Models	
1983-87 (2.1)	3.6
Chevrolet Models	
1983-84-exc below (2.2)	3.6
Chevette (2.4)	3.9
1985-87 (1.8)	3.6
Oldsmobile Models	
1983-87 (2.1)	3.6
Pontiac Models	
1983-87 (1.8)	3.6
(G) Converter Clutch Solenoid Assy., Renew	
Includes: R&R transmission, converter and oil pump.	
All models	
1983-87 (3.1)	4.0
(G) Apply and Actuator Valves and/or Bushing, Renew	
Includes: R&R transmission, converter and oil pump.	
All models	
1983-87 (2.6)	4.1
(G) Front Oil Pump, Renew	
Includes: R&R transmission, pump seal and check front unit end play.	
Buick Models	
1983-87 (2.3)	4.0
Chevrolet Models	
1983-84-exc below (2.4)	4.0
Chevette (2.7)	4.3
1985-87 (2.0)	4.0
Oldsmobile Models	
1983-87 (2.3)	4.0
Pontiac Models	
1983-87 (2.6)	4.0
Overhaul front pump add (.5)	.7
Renew pump bushing add	.1
w/Torque conv clutch add	.2
(G) Transmission Direct Clutch, Forward Clutch and Intermediate Band, Renew	
Includes: R&R transmission, converter, pump and seal, oil pan, valve body, and servo.	
Buick Models	
1983-87 (3.2)	4.9
Chevrolet Models	
1983-84-exc. below (3.3)	4.9
Chevette (3.5)	5.1
1985-87 (2.6)	4.9
Oldsmobile Models	
1983-87 (3.2)	4.9
Pontiac Models	
1983-87 (2.6)	4.9
Overhaul oil pump add (.5)	.6
Overhaul valve body add (.7)	.8
Overhaul direct clutch add (.3)	.4
Overhaul forward clutch add (.4)	.5
Overhaul servo add (.2)	.3
(G) Transmisssion Output Carrier, Sun Gear and Drive Shell, R&R	
Includes: R&R transmission, converter, pump and seal, oil pan, valve body, direct and forward clutches, and intermediate band and servo.	
Buick Models	
1983-87 (3.5)	5.2
Chevrolet Models	
1983-84-exc. below (3.7)	5.2
Chevette (3.8)	5.5
1985-87 (2.8)	5.2
Oldsmobile Models	
1983-87 (3.5)	5.2
Pontiac Models	
1983-87 (2.8)	5.2
Overhaul direct clutch add (.3)	.4
Overhaul forward clutch add (.4)	.5
Overhaul oil pump add (.5)	.6
Overhaul valve body add (.7)	.8
Overhaul servo add (.2)	.3
Overhaul sun gear and drum add (.2)	.3
(G) Low and Reverse Clutch Housing and Output Shaft Assembly, R&R	
Includes: R&R transmission, converter, front pump and seal, oil pan, valve body, direct and forward clutches, intermediate band, servo, output carrier, sun gear, drive shell, input drum, rear sun gear, roller clutch, and speedometer drive gear.	
Buick Models	
1983-87 (3.9)	5.5
Chevrolet Models	
1983-84-exc below (3.9)	5.5
Chevette (4.1)	6.0
1985-87 (3.4)	5.5
Oldsmobile Models	
1983-87 (3.9)	5.5
Pontiac Models	
1983-87 (3.4)	5.5
Overhaul direct clutch add (.3)	.4
Overhaul forward clutch add (.4)	.5
Overhaul valve body add (.7)	.8
Overhaul oil pump add (.5)	.6
Overhaul low & reverse clutches add (.3)	.4
Overhaul servo add (.2)	.3
Overhaul sun gear and drum add (.2)	.3
Overhaul roller clutch add (.2)	.3
(G) Speedometer Drive Gear, Renew	
Includes: R&R transmission, converter, oil pump and seal, oil pan, valve body, direct and forward clutches, intermediate band, servo, output carrier, sun gear, drive shell, low and reverse clutch housing, input drum, rear sun gear, roller clutch and output shaft.	
Buick Models	
1983-87 (3.9)	5.5
Chevrolet Models	
1983-84-exc below (3.9)	5.5
Chevette (4.1)	6.0
1985-87 (3.9)	5.5
Oldsmobile Models	
1983-87 (3.9)	5.5
Pontiac Models	
1983-87 (3.9)	5.5

PARTS 23 CASE & PARTS 23 PARTS

Part numbers shown are for pricing reference only. Order unit with complete year, model, engine and unit I.D. number.

	Part No.	Price
Transmission Assy.		
Buick		
1983-V-6 Diesel	8633885	1703.00
350 Diesel	8648092	N.L.
1984-231	8648117	1703.00
350 Diesel	8648101	1703.00
1985-87-231	8648169	1703.00
350 Diesel	8648172	1703.00
Chevrolet		
1983-Caprice, Impala, Malibu, Monte Carlo		
V-6 Diesel	8633885	1703.00
V-8 Diesel	8648092	N.L.
1983-Camaro		
2.5L	8633883	1703.00
(2.8L)		
Code CN	8633886	N.L.
Code CS	8648104	1703.00
305	8633881	DISC.
1983-Chevette	8648114	1703.00
1984-231	8648117	1703.00
1.8L Diesel	8648114	1703.00
350 Diesel	8648101	1703.00
1985-87-231	8648195	1703.00
305	8648175	1703.00
Oldsmobile		
1983-V-6 Diesel	8633885	1703.00
350 Diesel	8648092	N.L.
1984-231	8648117	1703.00
V-6 Diesel	8648115	1703.00
307	8648105	1703.00
350 Diesel	8648101	1703.00
1985-87-231	8648169	1703.00
(307)		
Code OG	8639582	2135.00
Code OI	8648171	1703.00
Code OJ	8639588	2135.00
305	8648196	1703.00
350 Diesel	8648172	1703.00
Pontiac		
1983-Grand Prix		
350 Diesel	8648092	N.L.
1983-Firebird		
2.5L	8633883	1703.00
(2.8L)		
Code CN	8633886	N.L.
Code CS	8648104	1703.00
305	8633868	1703.00
1983-T1000	8648114	1703.00
1984-231	8648117	1703.00
1.8L	8648114	1703.00
350 Diesel	8648101	1703.00
1985-87-4.3L	8648174	1703.00
231	8648169	1703.00
305	8648175	1703.00
350 Diesel	8648172	1703.00
Gasket & Seal Pkg. (Overhaul)		
1983-87	8638919	N.L.
Snap Ring Pkg.		
1983-87	8628942	3.25
(1) Torque Converter Assy.		
Chevrolet		
1983-Camaro		
2.5, 2.8	8633972	340.00
305-4 bbl.	8642934	340.00
305-E.F.I.	8633974	340.00
1983-Malibu, Monte Carlo & El Camino		
V-6 Diesel	8638926	340.00
1983-84-		

	Part No.	Price
Chevette	8633949	340.00
1983-84-350		
Diesel	8638927	326.00
1984-87-231	8633954	340.00
1985-87-4.3L	8642934	340.00
305	8642934	340.00
350 Diesel	8638927	326.00
Buick		
1983-84-Regal		
V-6 Diesel	8638926	340.00
1983-87-231	8633954	340.00
1983-84-307	8633955	340.00
350 Diesel	8638927	326.00
1985-87-305	8642934	340.00
350 Diesel	8638927	326.00
Oldsmobile		
1983-Cutlass		
V-6 Diesel	8638926	340.00
1983-87-231	8633954	340.00
1983-84-307	8633955	340.00
350 Diesel	8638927	326.00
1985-87-307	8638947	340.00
350 Diesel	8638927	326.00
Pontiac		
1983-Firebird		
2.5 & 2.8L	8633972	340.00
305	8642934	340.00
1983-84-exc. Firebird		
231	8633954	340.00
1.8L Diesel	8633949	340.00
350 Diesel	8638927	326.00
305	8642934	340.00
4.3L	8642934	340.00

(2) Seal Assy. (Pump)

1983-87	8630921	4.25

(3) Bushing (Pump Body)

1983-87	8628913	4.75

(4) Bushing (Pump Front Cover)

1983-87	8628915	5.50

(5) Pump Assy.

Not serviced separately. Serviced by components only.

(6) Bushing (Pump Rear Cover)

1983-87	8628916	5.75
1983-87	8626281	.50

(7) Oil Seal Ring (Pump Cover)

1983-87	8628055	1.00

(8) Seal Assy. (Pump to Case)

1983-87	8628052	1.25

(9) Gasket (Pump to Case)

1983-87	8633899	2.25

(10) Cover Pkg. (Servo)

Buick		
1983-87-exc.		
below	8632904	11.25
1984-231	8632927	11.25
V-6 Diesel eng.	8632927	11.25
Chevrolet		
1983-87-exc.		
below	8632904	11.25
V-6 eng. (1983)	8632927	11.25
4.3L	8632927	11.25
1983-87-		
Chevette	8632927	11.25
1983-Camaro		
2.5L	8632927	11.25
2.8L	8632904	11.25
305	8632903	11.25
Oldsmobile		
1983-87-exc.		
below	8632904	11.25
1984-V-6	8632927	11.25
Pontiac		
1983-87-exc.		
below	8632904	11.25
1.6L	8632927	11.25

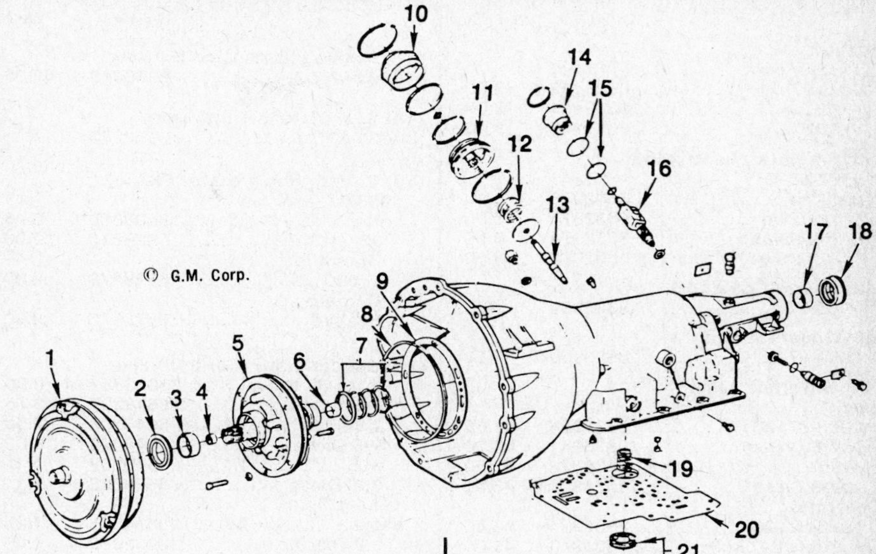

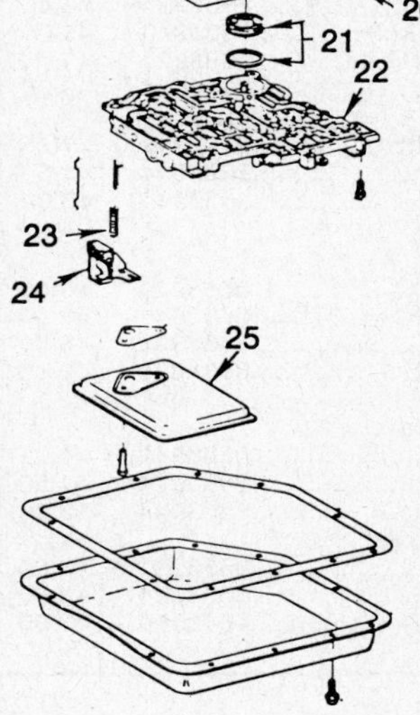

	Part No.	Price
4.3L	8632927	11.25

(11) Servo Piston (Intermediate)

Chevrolet		
1983-87-Impala & Caprice		
inner	8632979	8.00
outer-exc.		
below	8638937	15.75
1985-87-231		
outer	8638935	15.50
1983-87-Chevette		
inner	8632980	8.00
outer	8638938	14.25
1983-Camaro		
2.5L-inner	8632980	8.00
2.5L	8638938	14.25
2.8L	8632979	8.00
2.8L-outer	8638937	15.75
305-inner	8632978	8.00
305-outer	8638936	15.75
1983-84-Malibu, Monte Carlo & El Camino		
inner	8632979	8.00
outer	8638937	15.75
1983-V-6 Diesel		
inner	8632980	8.00
outer	8638938	14.25
Pontiac		
1983-87-Four cyl.		
inner	8632980	8.00
outer	8638938	14.25
1983-87-231, 2.8L & 350 Diesel		
inner	8632979	8.00
outer	8638937	15.75
1983-87-305		
inner	8632979	8.00
outer	8632980	8.00
Buick		
1983-87 (exc. 231A & 307)		
inner	8632979	8.00
outer	8638937	15.75
1983 (231A)		
inner	8632980	8.00
outer	8638938	14.25
1984-87 (231A)		
inner	8632979	8.00
outer	8638935	15.50
1983-V-6 Diesel eng.		
inner	8632980	8.00
outer	8638938	14.25
1984 (307)		
inner	8632979	8.00
outer	8638937	15.75

	Part No.	Price
Oldsmobile		
1983-87 (exc. 231A & 307)		
inner	8632979	8.00
outer	8638937	15.75
1983 (231A)		
inner	8632980	8.00
outer	8638938	14.25
1983-87-V-6 Diesel		
inner	8632980	8.00
outer	8638938	14.25
1984-87 (231A)		
inner	8632979	8.00
outer	8638935	15.50
1984 (307)		
inner	8632979	8.00
outer	8638937	15.75

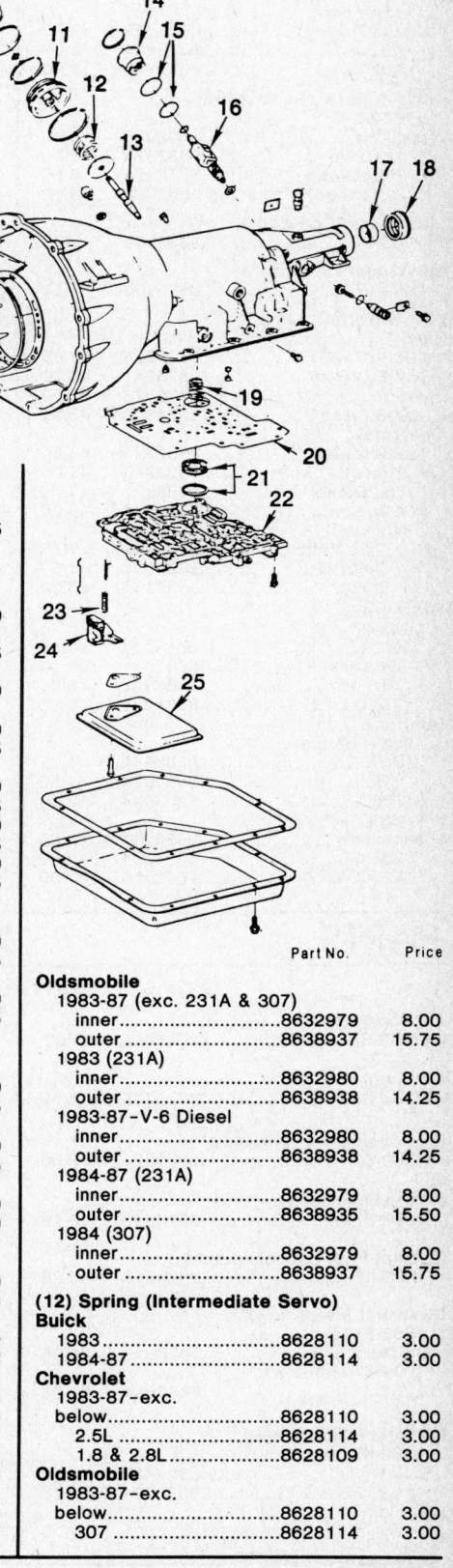

(12) Spring (Intermediate Servo)

Buick		
1983	8628110	3.00
1984-87	8628114	3.00
Chevrolet		
1983-87-exc.		
below	8628110	3.00
2.5L	8628114	3.00
1.8 & 2.8L	8628109	3.00
Oldsmobile		
1983-87-exc.		
below	8628110	3.00
307	8628114	3.00

PARTS 23 CASE AND PARTS 23 PARTS

	Part No.	Price
Pontiac		
1983-87-exc. below	8628109	3.00
2.5L	8628114	3.00
2.8L	8628110	3.00
(13) Pin (Inter. Band Apply)		
1983-85-0 grooves	8632976	8.50
1 groove	8632973	8.50
2 grooves	8632974	8.50
3 grooves	8632975	8.50
(14) Cover (Governor)		
1983-87	8628933	N.L.
(15) Governor Seal		
1983-87	8628955	1.50
(16) Governor Assy.		
Buick		
1983-87-231	8638924	43.50
V-6 Diesel	8633941	43.00
307	8638933	43.50
V-8 Diesel	8638921	43.50
Chevrolet		
1983-87-231	8638924	43.50
Chevette	8633940	43.00
350 Diesel	8638921	43.50
4.3L	8638921	43.50
(Camaro)		
2.5L	8633942	N.L.
2.8L	8633914	41.50
305	8633941	43.00
Oldsmobile		
1983-87-231 & 305	8638924	43.50
V-6 Diesel	8633941	43.00
307	8638933	43.50
V-8 Diesel	8638921	43.50
Pontiac		
1983-Firebird		
2.5L	8633942	N.L.
2.8L	8633914	41.50
305	8633941	43.00
1983-87-exc.below	8638921	43.50
231	8638924	43.50
T1000	8633940	43.00

	Part No.	Price
(17) Bushing (Extension Housing)		
1983-87	6260048	2.00
(18) Seal (Extension Housing)		
1983-87	3932255	N.L.
(19) Spring (Accumulator Piston)		
1983-87-exc. below	8630885	2.75
231 & 307	8628276	2.00
Chevette, T1000	8628276	2.00
Camaro, Firebird	8628276	2.00
(20) Spacer Plate (Control Valve)		
1983-1.8L Diesel	8633689	6.00
2.5L	8648327	6.75
2.8L	8648303	7.50
V-6 Diesel	8648022	6.00
305	8648302	N.L.
350 Diesel	8648023	N.L.
1984-87-exc. below	8648335	N.L.
1.8 Diesel	8633689	6.00
350 Diesel	8648022	6.00
1985-87-231	8648330	N.L.
4.3L	8630712	N.L.
305	8648336	N.L.
(21) Accumulator Piston		
1983-87	8628318	6.25
(22) Control Valve Assy.		
Buick		
1983-V-6 Diesel	8648030	235.00
V-8 Diesel	8648095	255.00
1984-87-231	8648128	235.00
307	8638932	223.00
1984-350 Diesel	8648132	235.00
1985-87-350 Diesel	8648373	255.00
Chevrolet		
1983-exc. Camaro & Chevette (V-6 Diesel)		
1983-85	8648030	235.00
350 Diesel	8648095	255.00

	Part No.	Price
1983-Camaro		
2.5L		
1983-87	8648020	235.00
2.8L	8648100	235.00
305	8633841	222.00
1984-exc. Chevette		
231	8648128	235.00
307	8638932	223.00
350 Diesel	8648132	235.00
1.6L	8633643	222.00
1985-87-231	8648369	255.00
4.3L	8648371	255.00
305	8648370	255.00
350 Diesel	8648373	255.00
Oldsmobile		
1983-V-6 Diesel	8648030	235.00
V-8 Diesel	8648095	255.00
1984-231	8648128	235.00
307	8638932	223.00
350 Diesel	8648132	235.00
1985-87-231	8648128	235.00
305	8648368	255.00
307	8648376	255.00
350	8648373	255.00
Pontiac		
1983-Firebird		
2.5L		
1983	8648020	235.00
2.8L	8648100	235.00
305	8633841	222.00
1983-exc. below	8648095	255.00
T1000	8633643	222.00
1984-231	8648128	235.00
1.8L Diesel	8633643	222.00
307	8638932	223.00
350 Diesel	8648132	235.00
1985-87-231	8648128	235.00
305	8648370	255.00
4.3L	8648371	255.00
350 Diesel	8648373	255.00
(23) Spring (Throttle Valve Lifter)		
1983-87	8628834	.75
(24) Lever & Bracket Assy. (Throttle)		
1983-87	8634301	16.00
(25) Oil Screen Assy.		
1983-87	8638930	14.50

PARTS 23 GEAR TRAIN 23 PARTS

	Part No.	Price
(1) Band Assy.		
1983-87	8628098	N.L.
(2) Bushing (Front)		
1983-87	8628918	6.50
(3) Housing & Drum Assy.		
1983-87	8630922	132.00
(4) Bushing (Rear)		
1983-87	8628917	6.75
(5) Seal Pkg. (Direct Clutch)		
1983-87	8628919	5.25
(6) Direct Piston Assy.		
1983-87-exc below	8630913	22.00
1983-87-1.8, 2.5 & 2.8L	8630914	22.00
(7) Direct Clutch Ring		
1983-87-exc. below	8628459	4.00
1.8, 2.5 & 2.8L	8628461	4.00

	Part No.	Price
(8) Guide (Release Spring)		
1983-87	8630195	2.75
(9) Retainer & Spring Assy.		
1983-87-exc. below	8630096	9.00
1.8, 2.5 & 2.8L	8630211	9.00
(10) Plate (Direct Clutch)		
1983-87	8628484	3.00
(11) Plate Backing		
1983-87	8628088	7.75
(12) Housing Assy. (Forward Clutch)		
1983-87-exc. below	8638944	160.00
1.8, 2.5 & 2.8L	8633948	118.25
(13) Seal Pkg. (Forward Clutch)		
1983-87	8628924	3.25
(14) Piston Assy. (Forward Clutch)		
1983-87-exc below	8628971	15.00
1.8, 2.5 & 2.8L	8628970	15.00

	Part No.	Price
(15) Ring (Forward Clutch)		
1983-87-exc below	8628458	3.00
1.8, 2.5 & 2.8L	8628460	2.75
(16) Retainer & Spring Assy. (Forward)		
1983-87	8628492	9.00
(17) Plate (Forward Clutch)		
1983-87	8630214	N.L.
(18) Plate (Backing)		
1983-87	8628088	7.75
(19) Gear & Bushing Assy. (Front Internal)		
1983-87	8630909	66.50
(20) Bushing (Front)		
1983-87	8630990	6.75
(21) Bearing Assy. (Gear to Carrier)		
1983-87	8628202	5.50
(22) Carrier Assy. (Front)		
1983-87	8628174	N.L.

PARTS 23 GEAR TRAIN 23 PARTS

	Part No.	Price
(23) Bearing Assy. (Sun to Internal Gear)		
1983-87	8628487	N.L.
(24) Sun Gear (Front)		
1983-87	8628190	28.50
(25) Drum (Input)		
1983-87	8628203	N.L.
(26) Bushing (Rear Sun Gear)		
1983-87	8628928	5.75
(27) Sun Gear Assy. (Rear)		
1983-87	8628206	N.L.
(28) Clutch Housing (Low & Rev.)		
1983-87	8628212	51.00
(29) Spacer (Housing to Case)		
1983-87	8628221	1.25
(30) Seal Pkg. (Low & Rev. Piston)		
1983-87	8628930	4.25
(31) Piston Assy. (Low & Rev.)		
1983-87-exc. below	8633934	20.00
1.8, 2.5 & 2.8L	8633936	20.00
(32) Ring (Clutch Apply Direct)		
1983-87-exc. below	8628459	4.00
1.8, 2.5 & 2.8L	8628461	4.00
(33) Spring (Reverse Clutch Release)		
1983-87	8628222	2.00
(34) Retainer (Low & Rev. Spring)		
1983-87	8628223	1.75
(35) Plate (Low & Rev. Clutch)		
1983-87-steel	8628224	3.25
fibre	8628804	N.L.
(36) Race (Low Clutch Roller)		
1983-87	8628184	16.50
(37) Roller Assy. (Low Clutch)		
1983-87	8628183	16.50
(38) Bushing (Rear Carrier)		
1983-87	8628947	6.25
(39) Carrier Assy. (Rear)		
1983-87	8628194	121.00
(40) Bearing Assy.		
1983-87	8628962	4.50
(41) Gear (Rear Internal)		
1983-87	8628195	62.00
(42) Output Shaft		
1983-87	8630720	77.50

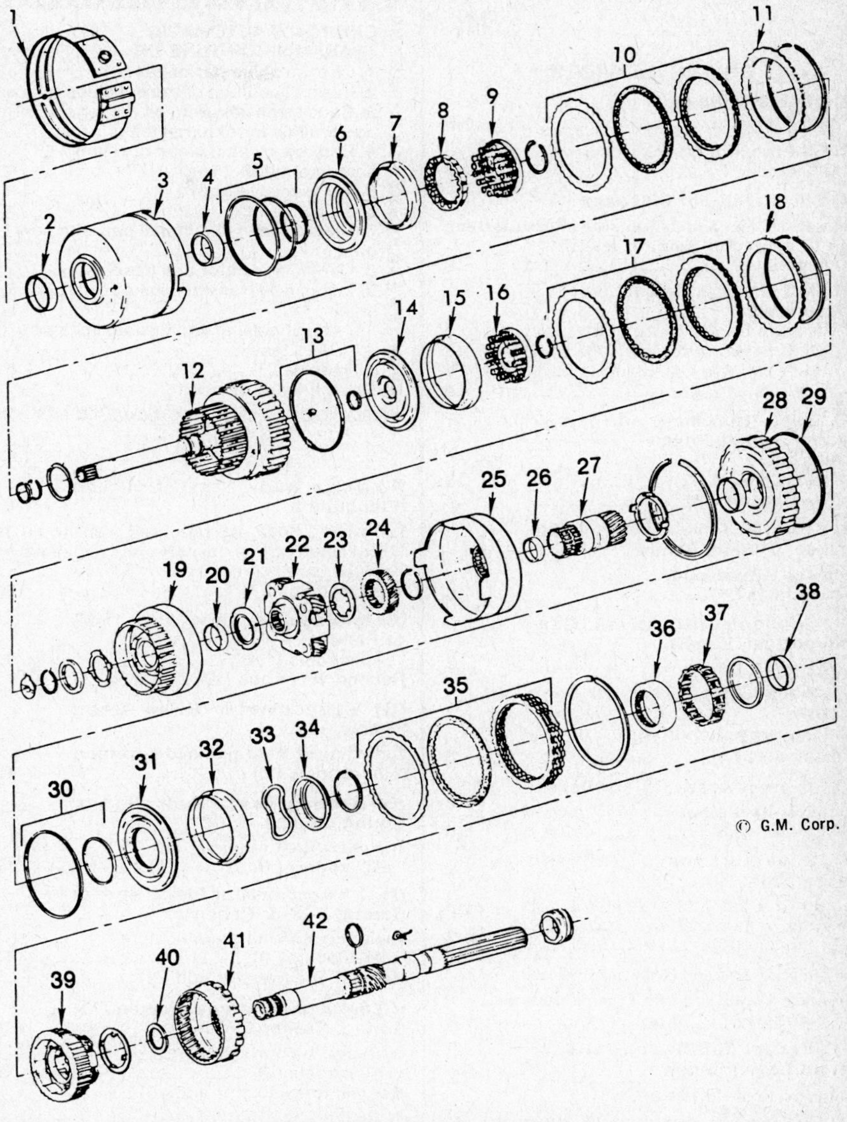

PARTS 23 CONVERTER & OIL PUMP 23 PARTS

	Part No	Price
Pump Body Assy.		
1983-84	8632944	N.L.
1985-87	8638922	98.50
Pump Cover Assy.		
1983-84-exc. below	8633957	174.25
Chevette, T1000	8633956	174.25
Camaro, Firebird	8633958	174.25
1985-87	8633958	174.25
Spring (Pressure Regulator)		
1983-84-exc. below	8632551	1.25
Chevette, T1000	8630345	1.50
Camaro, Firebird	8630093	1.50
1985-87-exc. 350 diesel	8630093	1.50
Valve (Pressure Regulator)		
1983-87	8630094	4.75
Plug (Valve Bore)		
1983-87	8628048	1.25

Locking Torque Converter System-Parts

	Part No.	Price
Clutch Brake Switch		
1983-87-exc. below	25504628	3.75
Cruise Cont.	9794682	7.75
Clutch Solenoid Assy.		
1983-87-exc. below	8633945	22.50
1983-84-350 Diesel	8633947	22.50
1.8L	8633946	22.50
Clutch Apply Valve		
1983-87	8633877	3.50
Clutch Actuator Valve		
1983-87	8633439	N.L.

(Factory Time) Chilton Time

ON CAR SERVICES

(G) Drain & Refill Unit
All models .9

(G) Oil Pressure Check
All models (.5) .7

(M) Check Unit For Oil Leaks
Includes: Clean and dry outside of case and run unit to determine point of leak.
All models .9

(G) Shift Linkage, Adjust
All models
Neutral Safety Switch (.3) .4
Shift Indicator Needle (.2) .3
Shift Linkage (.4) .5
T.V. Cable (.3) .4

(G) Back-Up Lamp and Park/Neutral Switch, Renew
All models
wo/Console (.2) .3
w/Console (.5) .7

(G) Throttle Valve Control Cable and/or 'O' Ring, Renew
Includes: Adjust cable.
All models (.6) .8

(G) Speedometer Driven Gear and/or Seal, Renew
All models (.3) .5

(G) Transmission Rear Oil Seal, Renew
Includes: R&R driveshaft.
All models (.4) .8

(G) Governor Assy., R&R or Renew
Includes: R&R oil pan, renew governor seal.
All models (.6) 1.0

(G) Governor Assy., R&R and Recondition
Includes: R&R oil pan, clean and inspect governor, renew seal and gear.
All models (.8) 1.5

(G) Oil Pan and/or Gasket, Renew
Includes: Clean pan and service screen.
All models (.5) .9

(G) Manual Shaft Seal and/or Detent Lever, Renew
Includes: R&R oil pan.
All models (.6) 1.1

(G) Converter Clutch Solenoid Assy., Renew
Includes: R&R oil pan.
All models (.4) 1.1

(G) Governor Pressure Switch and/or Electrical Connector, Renew
Includes: R&R oil pan.
All models
w/Diesel eng (.6) 1.1

(G) 4-3 Pressure Switch, Renew
Includes: R&R oil pan.
All models (.5) 1.0

(G) 4th Clutch Pressure Switch, Renew
Includes: R&R oil pan.
All models (.5) 1.0

(G) Valve Body Assembly, Renew
Includes: R&R oil pan and renew filter.
All models (.9) 1.5

(G) Transmission Mount, Renew
All models (.4) .5

CHILTON'S AUTOMATIC TRANSMISSION TUNE-UP
1. Check engine performance
2. Check condition of transmission oil
3. Check transmission, oil cooler and oil cooler lines for external leaks
4. Remove oil pan, clean or renew screen or filter
5. Torque valve body
6. Adjust bands
7. Clean oil pan and install pan with new gasket
8. Check modulator and hose
9. Install new transmission oil to proper level
10. Adjust manual and throttle linkage
11. Road test
All models 1.5
Charge for parts used

(Factory Time) Chilton Time

(P) Valve Body Assy., R&R and Recondition
Includes: R&R oil pan and renew filter. Disassemble, clean, inspect and free all valves. Replace parts as required.
All models (1.7) 2.8

(G) Intermediate Servo Assy., R&R or Renew
All models (1.4) 2.0
Recond servo add (.2) .2

(G) Speedometer Drive Gear, Renew
Includes: R&R oil pan and governor.
All models (.6) 1.1

(G) Parking Pawl, Shaft, Rod or Spring, Renew
Includes: R&R oil pan.
All models (.6) 1.2

(G) 1-2 Accumulator Piston and/or Spring, R&R or Renew
Includes: R&R oil pan.
All models (.9) 1.4
Recond accumulator add (.2) .3

(G) 3-4 Accumulator Piston and/or Spring, R&R or Renew
Includes: R&R oil pan.
All models (.9) 1.4
Recond accumulator add (.2) .3

SERVICES REQUIRING R&R

(G) Transmission Assembly, R&R or Renew
All models
1983-87 (2.2) 3.7

(G) Flywheel (Flexplate), Renew
Includes: R&R transmission.
All models
1983-87 (2.4) 3.9

(P) Transmission and Converter, R&R and Recondition
Includes: Disassemble transmission completely, including valve body and overdrive unit. Clean and inspect all parts. Renew all parts as required. Make all necessary adjustments. Road test.
All models
1983-87 (8.0) 11.5

(G) Transmission Assy., R&R and Reseal
Includes: Install all new gaskets and seals.
All models
1983-87 6.5

(Factory Time) Chilton Time

(G) Torque Converter, Renew
Includes: R&R transmission.
All models
1983-87 (2.2) 3.9

(G) Front Pump Oil Seal, Renew
Includes: R&R transmission.
All models
1983-87 (2.2) 4.0

(G) Front Pump Assy., Renew or Recondition
Includes: R&R transmission, oil pan, converter clutch solenoid, filter and pipe. Check overdrive unit end play.
All models
1983-87 (2.6) 4.2
Recond front pump add (.6) .8
Renew bushing add (.1) .1

(G) 4th Clutch Pack and Overdrive Unit, R&R or Recondition
Includes: R&R transmission.
All models
1983-87 (2.7) 4.3
Recond front pump add (.6) .8
Recond servo add (.2) .2
Recond overdrive unit add (.6) 1.0

(G) Direct, Forward Clutches and Intermediate Band, Renew
Includes: R&R transmission. Check overdrive unit end play.
All models
1983-87 (3.8) 5.4
Recond valve body add (.8) 1.0
Recond oil pump add (.6) .8
Recond servo add (.2) .2
Recond direct clutch add (.3) .4
Recond forward clutch add (.4) .5
Renew bushings add-each (.1) .1

(G) Input Drum and Sun Gear, Renew
Includes: R&R transmission.
All models
1983-87 (4.0) 5.6
Recond valve body add (.8) 1.0
Recond oil pump add (.6) .8
Recond servo add (.2) .2
Recond direct clutch add (.3) .4
Recond forward clutch add (.4) .5
Recond overdrive unit add (.6) 1.0
Recond center support add (.2) .3
Renew bushings add-each (.1) .1
Renew rear clutch pack add (.1) .2
Renew bushing add-each (.1) .1

(G) Low and Reverse Clutch Housing, Rear Gear and Clutch Pack, Renew
Includes: R&R transmission.
All models
1983-87 (4.1) 6.0
Recond valve body add (.8) 1.0
Recond oil pump add (.6) .8
Recond servo add (.2) .2
Recond direct clutch add (.3) .4
Recond forward clutch add (.4) .5
Recond low and reverse
clutches add (.3) .4
Recond O/Drive unit add (.6) 1.0
Recond center support add (.2) .2
R&R internal gear and/or
roller brg add (.1) .1
R&R rear carrier and
roller clutch add (.2) .2
Renew bushings add-each (.1) .1

PARTS 23 TURBO HYDRA-MATIC CASE & PARTS 23 PARTS

Part numbers shown are for pricing reference only. Order unit with complete year, model, engine and unit I.D. number.

	Part No.	Price
Transmission Assy.		
1983 (Trans. Codes)		
Code AA	8639184	2135.00
Code AP	8639046	2135.00
Code BQ	8639223	N.L.
Code BR	8639044	2135.00
Code BT	8639223	N.L.
Code BY	8639187	2135.00
Code OG	8639042	2135.00
Code OM	8639183	2135.00
Code OZ	8639191	2135.00
1984 (Trans. Codes)		
Code AA	8639184	2135.00
Code AP	8639185	2135.00
Code BQ	8639188	2135.00
Code BT	8639189	2135.00
Code BY	8639187	2135.00
Code CH	8639170	2135.00
Code CR	8639192	2135.00
Code HG	8639181	2135.00
Code OF	8639261	2135.00
Code OG	8639186	2135.00
Code OJ	8639263	2135.00
Code OM	8639183	2135.00
Code OZ	8639191	2135.00
1985-87 (Trans. Codes)		
Code CH	8639272	2135.00
Code CR	8639557	2135.00
Code CQ	8639273	2135.00
Code OB	8639588	2135.00
Code OG	8639582	2135.00
Code OM	8639583	2135.00
Code OZ	8657028	2135.00
Code HG	8639585	2135.00
Code 6KC	8657179	2135.00
Code 6KJ	8657180	2135.00
Code 6BR	8657306	2135.00
Code 6KA	8648432	1703.00
Code 6KB	8648480	1622.00
Trans. Gasket Kit		
1983	8634957	N.L.
1984-87	8634988	N.L.
Consists of Gaskets and Seals.		
Trans. Overhaul Kit		
1983	8634989	N.L.
1984-87	8634989	N.L.
Consists of Gaskets, Seals and Plates.		
Snap Ring Kit		
1983-87	8634910	7.25
(1) Torque Converter (Rebuilt)		
V-6-4.3L		
1985-87	8642934	340.00
V-6-231		
1983-87-exc. below	8633954	340.00
Turbo	8635928	340.00
Fuel Inj.	8634993	340.00
V-6-252		
1983-84-exc. below	8633954	340.00
3.73 ratio	8633955	340.00
V-6-260 Diesel		
1983-84	8632926	N.L.
V-8-305		
1983-87-exc. below	8633955	340.00
Code G	8635928	340.00
V-8-307		
1983-84-exc. below	8633955	340.00
Hurst Olds.	8634993	340.00
1985-86	8638947	340.00
2.73R (86)	8656902	340.00
V-8-350 Diesel		
1983-85	8638927	326.00

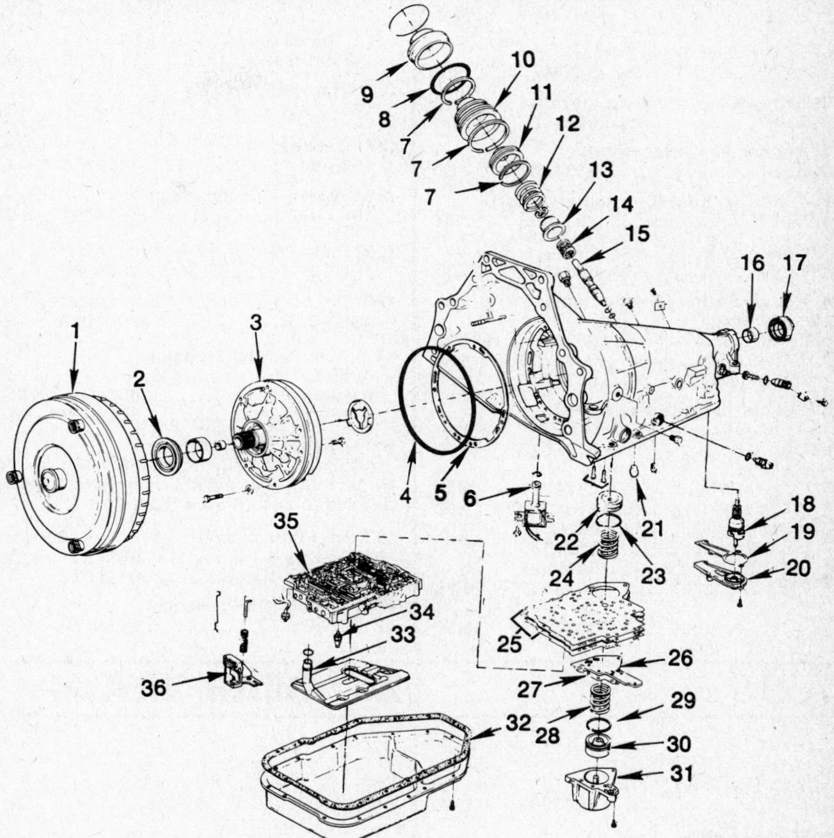

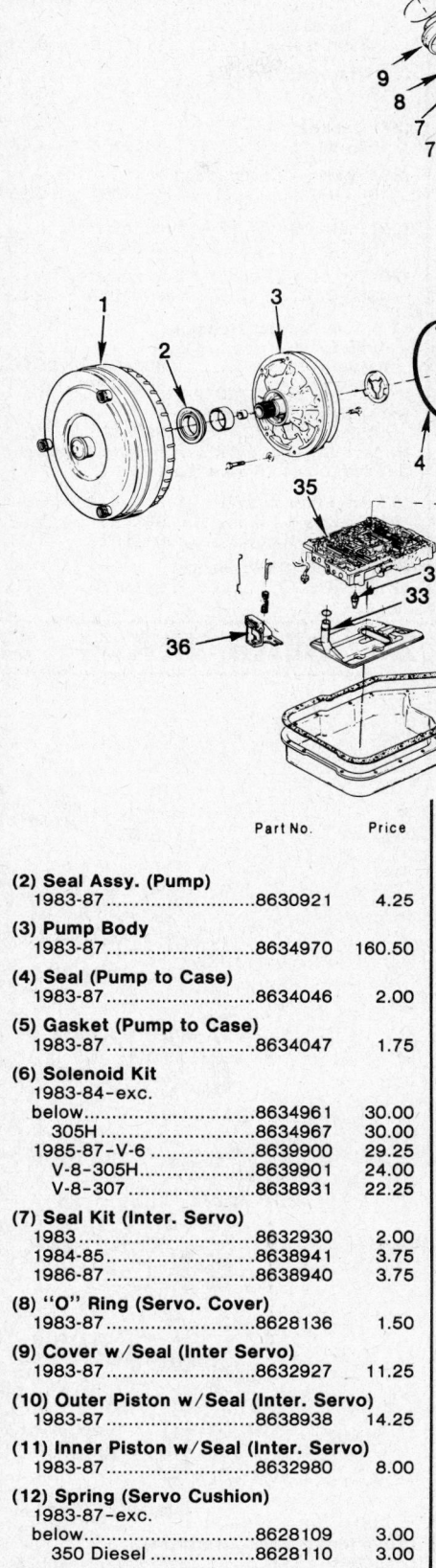

	Part No.	Price
(2) Seal Assy. (Pump)		
1983-87	8630921	4.25
(3) Pump Body		
1983-87	8634970	160.50
(4) Seal (Pump to Case)		
1983-87	8634046	2.00
(5) Gasket (Pump to Case)		
1983-87	8634047	1.75
(6) Solenoid Kit		
1983-84-exc. below	8634961	30.00
305H	8634967	30.00
1985-87-V-6	8639900	29.25
V-8-305H	8639901	24.00
V-8-307	8638931	22.25
(7) Seal Kit (Inter. Servo)		
1983	8632930	2.00
1984-85	8638941	3.75
1986-87	8638940	3.75
(8) "O" Ring (Servo. Cover)		
1983-87	8628136	1.50
(9) Cover w/Seal (Inter Servo)		
1983-87	8632927	11.25
(10) Outer Piston w/Seal (Inter. Servo)		
1983-87	8638938	14.25
(11) Inner Piston w/Seal (Inter. Servo)		
1983-87	8632980	8.00
(12) Spring (Servo Cushion)		
1983-87-exc. below	8628109	3.00
350 Diesel	8628110	3.00

	Part No.	Price
(13) Retainer (Servo Spring)		
1983-87	8632146	1.25
(14) Inner Spring (Inter. Servo)		
1983-87	8632661	1.50
(15) Inter. Band Pin (w/Seal)		
1983-87		
No Grooves	8632976	8.50
1 Groove	8632973	8.50
2 Grooves	8632974	8.50
3 Grooves	8632975	8.50
(16) Rear Bushing (Case)		
1983-87	6260048	2.00
(17) Rear Oil Seal (Case)		
1983-87	3932255	N.L.
(18) Governor Kit (w/Seal)		
V-6-231		
1983	8634971	51.75
1984-87	8634992	56.25
Turbo 1983-87	8639928	56.75
V-6-252		
1983-84	8634928	46.75
3.73R (84)	8634986	49.00
Regal	8634986	49.00
V-6 Diesel (1983)	8634982	51.75
V-6 Diesel (1984)	8634959	51.25
V-8-250		
exc. Hi alt.	8634928	47.00
Hi alt.	8634964	54.00
V-8-305		
1983	8634933	46.75
1984-87	8634927	46.75
V-8-307		
1983-84	8634927	46.75
1985-87	8634959	51.25

PARTS 23 TURBO HYDRA-MATIC CASE & PARTS 23 PARTS

	Part No.	Price
(19) Cover Gasket (Governor)		
1983-87	8634477	1.25
(20) Cover Kit w/Seal (Governor)		
1983-87	8634929	47.00
(21) Anchor Pin (Inter Band)		
1983-87	8634159	2.50
(22) Piston w/Seal (3-4 Accumulator)		
1983-87	8634956	12.75
(23) Seal		
1983-87	8634161	1.25
(24) Piston Spring (3-4 Accumulator)		
1983-87-exc. below	8639074	1.75
252	8634703	1.50
350 Diesel	8634703	1.50
(25) Spacer Plate (Valve Body)		
1983-87-exc. below	8657026	7.50
V-6-231		
Code BQ	8639235	N.L.
Code BR	8657026	7.50
Fuel inj.	8639277	6.00
V-6 Diesel	8639330	6.00
252	8639027	N.L.
305	8634842	6.25
V-8-307		
exc. below	8639026	6.00
Hurst Olds	8639174	6.00
350 Diesel	8639139	6.00
(26) Plate (w/Gasket)		
1983-87	8634924	3.75
(27) Gasket		
1983-87	8634166	1.25
(28) Spring (1-2 Accumulator)		
1983-87	8634391	2.25
(29) Piston Seal (1-2 Accumulator)		
1983-87	8634390	1.25
(30) Piston w/Seal (1-2 Accumulator)		
1983-87	8634923	3.50
(31) Accumulator Housing		
1983-87-exc. below	8634310	28.00
350 Diesel	8634858	39.75
(32) Gasket (Oil Pan)		
1983-87	8634198	N.L.

Gasket used on raised rib oil pans. Pans with flat surface use RTV sealant.

	Part No.	Price
(33) Oil Filter Assy.		
1983-84	8634931	26.25
1985-87	8639921	N.L.
(34) Switch (Oil Pressure)		
1983-87	8634475	12.00
(35) Valve Assy. (Control)		

Part numbers shown are for pricing reference only. Order with complete year, model, engine and unit I.D. number.

	Part No.	Price
1983-exc. below	8939133	N.L.
V-6-231		
Code BQ	8639130	N.L.
Code BR	8639129	443.50
250	8639342	443.50
307	8639218	443.50
350 diesel	8639474	245.25
1984-87-231		
(1984)	8639363	N.L.
231 (1985)	8639365	443.50
252	8639371	N.L.
V-6 Diesel	8639326	443.50
V-8-305		
1984	8639430	443.50
1985-87	8639129	443.50
V-8-307		
exc. below	8638932	223.00
Closed loop	8639452	245.25
Hurst Olds.	8639918	424.25
350 Diesel	8639474	245.25
1985-87		
2.73R	8639252	N.L.
328, 308R	8639462	N.L.
(36) Lever (w/Throttle Bracket)		
1983-87	8634301	16.00

PARTS 23 GEAR TRAIN 23 PARTS

	Part No.	Price
(1) Shaft (Turbine)		
1983-87	8639283	75.75
(2) Oil Seal Rings		
1983-87	8628090	1.00
(3) Retaining Ring (4th Clutch)		
1983-87	8634158	2.25
(4) Backing Plate (4th Clutch)		
1983-87	8634866	6.75
(5) Plate (4th Clutch)		
1983-87 (Faced)	8634691	5.25
(Steel)	8634026	3.50
(6) Housing (Overrun Clutch)		
1983-87	8634107	89.00
(7) Piston (Overrun Clutch)		
1983-87	8634110	13.50
(8) Seal Kit (Overrun Clutch)		
1983-87	8634909	3.25
(9) Plate (Overrun Clutch)		
1983-87 (Faced)	8634051	3.75
(Steel)	8634050	2.75
(10) Backing Plate (Overrun Clutch)		
1983-87	8634864	6.50
(11) Release Spring (Waved)		
1983-87	8634116	2.50
(12) Retainer, Overrun Clutch Spr.		
1983-87	8634061	1.50
(13) Roller Assy. (Overdrive Clutch)		
1983-87	8634049	15.00
(14) Roller Cam (Overdrive Clutch)		
1983-87	8634038	23.00
(15) Sun Gear (Overdrive)		
1983-87	8634033	7.75
(16) Carrier Complete (Overdrive)		
1983-87	8634117	204.00
(17) Bearing (Carrier to Int. Gear)		
1983-87	8634035	4.50

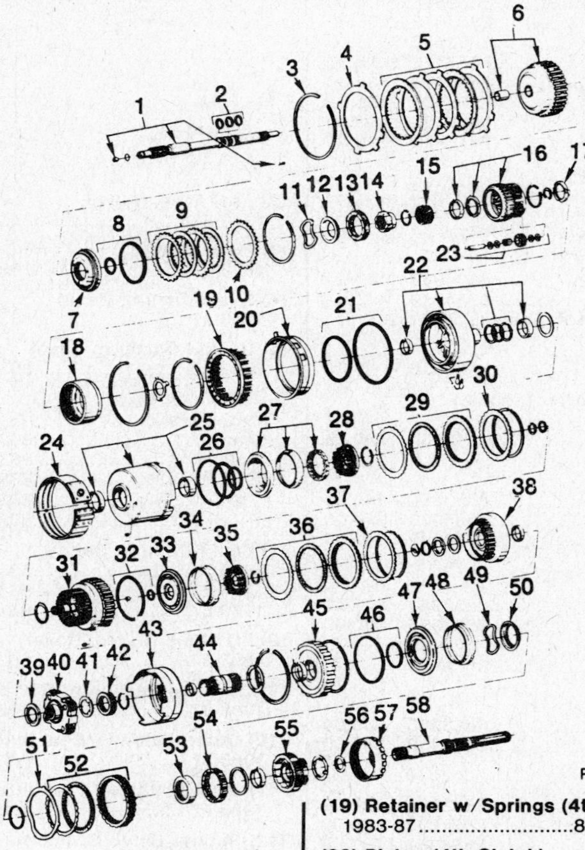

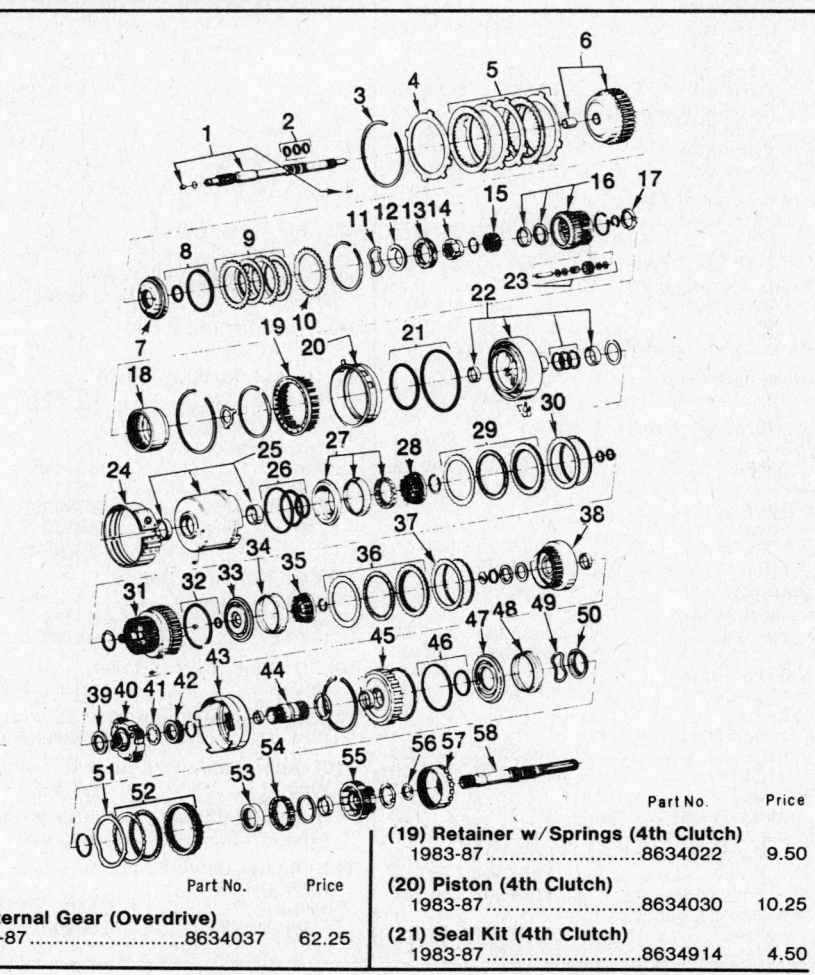

	Part No.	Price
(18) Internal Gear (Overdrive)		
1983-87	8634037	62.25
(19) Retainer w/Springs (4th Clutch)		
1983-87	8634022	9.50
(20) Piston (4th Clutch)		
1983-87	8634030	10.25
(21) Seal Kit (4th Clutch)		
1983-87	8634914	4.50

PARTS 23 GEAR TRAIN 23 PARTS

	Part No.	Price
(22) Support (Center)		
1983-87	8634140	139.50
(23) Pinion (Overdrive Carrier)		
1983-87	8634920	40.00
(24) Band Assy. (Intermediate)		
1983-87	8628098	N.L.
(25) Housing w/Valve (Direct Clutch)		
1983-87	8634916	113.75
(26) Piston Seal Kit (Direct Clutch)		
1983-87	8628919	5.25
(27) Piston Kit (Direct Clutch)		
1983-87	8630913	22.00
(28) Retainer w/Springs (Direct Clutch)		
1983-87	8630096	9.00
(29) Plate (Direct Clutch)		
1983-87 (Faced)	8630214	N.L.
(Flat)	8628484	3.00
(30) Backing Plate (Direct Clutch)		
1983-87	8632570	10.50
(31) Housing Kit (Forward Clutch)		
1983-87	8634926	105.75
(32) Piston Seal Kit (Forward Clutch)		
1983-87	8628924	3.25
(33) Piston (Forward Clutch)		
1983-87	8628971	15.00
(34) Ring (Forward Clutch Apply)		
1983-87	8628458	3.00
(35) Retainer w/Springs (Forward Clutch)		
1983-87	8628492	9.00
(36) Plate (Forward Clutch)		
1983-87 (Flat)	8628086	3.00
(Faced)	8630214	N.L.
(37) Backing Plate (Forward Clutch)		
1983-87	8628088	7.75
(38) Front Internal Gear (w/Bushing)		
1983-87	8630909	66.50
(39) Bearing (Int. Gear to Carrier)		
1983-87	8628202	5.50
(40) Front Carrier (Complete)		
1983-87	8628174	N.L.
(41) Front Carrier Bearing (w/Race)		
1983-87	8628487	N.L.
(42) Front Sun Gear		
1983-87	8628190	28.50
(43) Drum (Input)		
1983-87	8628203	N.L.
(44) Rear Sun Gear (w/Bushing)		
1983-87	8628206	N.L.
(45) Housing (Lo & Rev. Clutch)		
1983-87	8628212	51.00
(46) Seal Kit (Lo & Rev. Piston)		
1983-87	8628930	4.25
(47) Piston Kit (Lo & Rev. Clutch)		
1983-87	8633934	20.00
(48) Ring Kit (Lo & Rev. Clutch)		
1983-87	8633937	10.25
(49) Release Spring (Rev. Clutch)		
1983-87	8628222	2.00
(50) Retainer (Lo & Rev. Clutch)		
1983-87	8628223	1.75
(51) Plate (Lo & Rev. Clutch)		
1983-87	8633371	4.00
(52) Plate (Lo & Rev. Clutch)		
1983-87 (Flat)	8628224	3.25
(53) Roller Race (Lo Clutch)		
1983-87	8628184	16.50
(54) Roller (Lo Clutch)		
1983-87	8628183	16.50
(55) Rear Carrier (Complete)		
1983-87	8628194	121.00
(56) Bearing (Sun Gear to Int. Gear)		
1983-87	8628962	4.50
(57) Internal Gear (Rear)		
1983-87-exc. below	8628195	62.00
1984-85-Diesel	8639016	161.50
(58) Output Shaft		
1983-87-exc. below	8634021	84.50
1984-85-Diesel	8639016	161.50

PARTS 23 OIL PUMP 23 PARTS

	Part No.	Price
Gasket (Oil Pump)		
1983-87	8634047	1.75
(1) Seal Assy.		
1983-87	8630921	4.25
(2) Body Assy. (Oil Pump)		
1983-87	8634970	160.50
Turbo	8639916	155.00
(3) Spring (pump slide)		
1983-87	8634078	.50
(4) Vane Kit (Oil Pump)		
1983-87	8634904	21.75
(5) Bushing (TV Boost)		
1983-87-Only serviced with No. 6		
(6) Valve (TV Boost)		
1983-87-exc. below	8634941	6.25
231 (1984-87)	8634940	6.25
Diesel	8634955	6.25
(7) Bushing (Rev. Boost Valve)		
1983-87-Only serviced with No. 8		
(8) Valve (Reverse Boost)		
1983-87	8634939	6.25
(9) Valve Spring (Pressure Regulator)		
1983-87-exc. below	8634490	1.00
229, 231 & 305G	8639002	1.00
252	8639171	1.00
Hurst Olds	8639164	6.50
(10) Valve (Pressure Regulator)		
1983-87	8637546	8.50

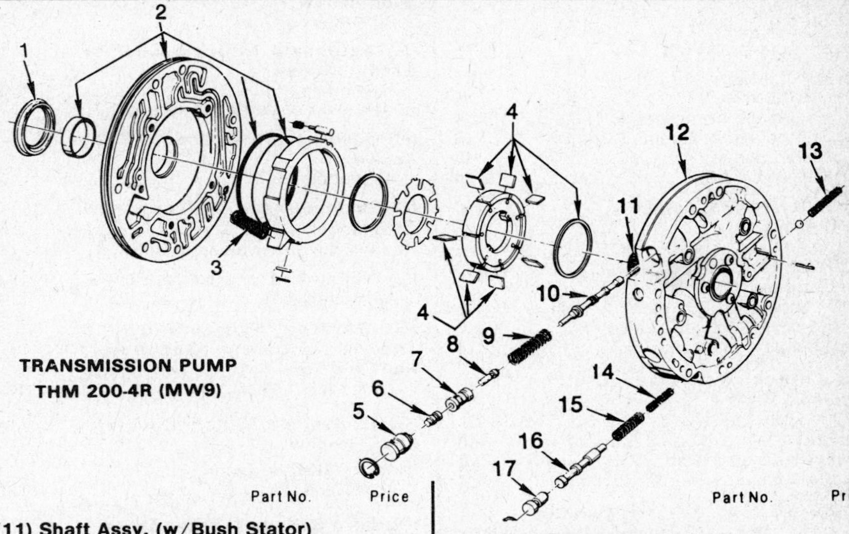

TRANSMISSION PUMP THM 200-4R (MW9)

	Part No.	Price
(11) Shaft Assy. (w/Bush Stator)		
1983-87-Only serviced with No. 12		
(12) Cover (Oil pump)		
1983-87-exc. below	8639083	386.50
229, 231	8639102	386.50
231 (1984-87)	8639279	386.50
252	8639176	386.50
Diesel (1983)	8639136	386.50
Diesel (1984-87)	8639335	386.50
Hurst Olds	8639199	386.50
(13) Spring (Pressure Relief)		
1983-87	8634106	1.25
(14) Clutch Spring (Inner)		
1983-87	8634378	1.00
(15) Clutch Spring (Outer)		
1983-87	8634399	1.00
(16) Valve (Converter Clutch)		
1983-87	8634031	4.50
(17) Stop Valve (Conv. Clutch)		
1983-87	8634705	1.00

TURBO HYDRA-MATIC 250-250C-350-350C

APPLICATION

1983-84

BUICK
LeSabre-Electra-Regal

CADILLAC
DeVille

CHEVROLET
Caprice-Impala-Monte Carlo-Malibu

OLDSMOBILE
88-98-Cutlass

PONTIAC
Parisienne-Bonneville-Grand Prix

(Factory Time) — Chilton Time

ON CAR SERVICES

(G) Drain and Refill Unit
All models 9

(G) Oil Pressure Check
All models (.6) 8

(M) Check Unit For Oil Leaks
Includes: Clean and dry outside of case and run unit to determine point of leak.
All models 9

(G) Back-Up Lamp and Park/Neutral Switch, Renew
All models
colm mount (.2) 3
console mount (.5) 7

(G) Shift Linkage, Adjust
All models
Neutral Safety Switch (.3) 4
Shift Indicator Needle (.2) 3
Shift Linkage (.4) 5
T.V. Cable (.3) 4

(G) Shift Linkage, Adjust (w/Diesel Eng)
All models
Fast Idle Speed (.2) 3
Throttle Rod/T.V. cable (.5) 6
Vacuum Regulator Valve (.6) 8
Complete (1.0) 1.4

(G) Torque Converter Clutch Switches, Renew
All models
Brake (.4) 5
Engine metal temp. (.2) 3
Thermal vacuum (.3) 4

(G) Engine Low Vacuum Switch, Renew
All models (.4) 6

(G) Engine High Vacuum Switch, Renew
All models (.5) 7

(G) Vacuum Relay, Renew
All models (.2) 3

(G) Intermediate Band, Adjust
All models (.3) 5

(G) Vacuum Modulator and/or Seal, Renew
All models (.3) 5

(G) Detent Valve Control Cable and/or Seal, Renew
All models (.5) 7

CHILTON'S AUTOMATIC TRANSMISSION TUNE-UP

1. Check engine performance
2. Check condition of transmission oil
3. Check transmission, oil cooler and oil cooler lines for external leaks
4. Remove oil pan, clean or renew screen or filter
5. Torque valve body
6. Adjust bands
7. Clean oil pan and install pan with new gasket
8. Check modulator and hose
9. Install new transmission oil to proper level
10. Adjust manual and throttle linkage
11. Road test

All models 1.5
Charge for parts used

(Factory Time) — Chilton Time

(G) Speedometer Driven Gear and/or Seal, Renew
All models (.3) 4

(G) Extension Housing Rear Oil Seal, Renew
All models (.4) 7

(G) Extension Housing Seal or Gasket, Renew
All models (.6) 1.0
Renew ext housing bushing add 1

(G) Governor Cover and/or Seal, Renew
All models (.3) 5

(G) Governor Assy., R&R or Renew
All models (.4) 6
Recond gov or renew gear add (.2) 2

(G) Oil Pan and/or Gasket, Renew
All models (.5) 8

(G) Governor Pressure Switch and/or Electrical Connector, Renew
All models (.6) 1.0

(G) Converter Clutch Solenoid Assy., Renew
Includes: R&R oil pan.
All models (.6) 1.0

(G) Valve Body Assembly, Renew
Includes: R&R oil pan.
All models (.9) 1.3
Renew selector shaft seal add 1

(G) Valve Body Assy., R&R and Recondition
Includes: R&R oil pan. Disassemble, clean, inspect, free all valves. Replace parts as required.
All models
250C (1.3) 2.0
350C (1.4) 2.2

(G) Auxiliary Valve Body and/or Apply Valve, Renew
Includes: R&R oil pan.
All models (.9) 1.3

(Factory Time) — Chilton Time

(G) Parking Pawl, Shaft, Rod or Spring, Renew
Includes: R&R oil pan.
All models (1.2) 1.5

(G) Intermediate Servo Assy., R&R or Renew
Includes: R&R oil pan and valve body.
350
All models (.8) 1.2
Recond servo add (.2) 2

(G) 1-2 Accumulator Piston and/or Spring, R&R or Renew
All models (.7) 1.1
Recond accumulator add (.1) 2

SERVICES REQUIRING R&R

250-250C

(G) Transmission Assembly, R&R or Renew
All models (2.1) 3.0

(G) Transmission Assembly, Reseal
Includes: R&R transmission and renew all seals and gaskets.
All models 6.0

(G) Transmission and Converter, R&R and Recondition
Includes: Drain and pressure test converter, recondition pump, clutch assemblies, shaft assemblies, carrier assembly, governor, servo's, and valve body. Adjust linkage.
All models (6.7) 10.5

(G) Torque Converter, Renew
All models (2.0) 2.9

(G) Flywheel (Flexplate), Renew
All models (2.2) 3.0

(G) Front Pump Oil Seal, Renew
All models (2.0) 3.0

(G) Front Oil Pump, Renew
Includes: Renew pump gasket and seal.
All models (2.2) 3.1
Recond pump add (.3) 3
Renew pump bushing add (.1) 1

(G) Intermediate Servo Assy., Renew
All models (2.9) 4.2
Recond servo add (.3) 3

(G) Direct and Forward Clutches, Intermediate Band, Renew
All models (3.7) 5.4
Recond valve body add (.4) 5
Recond oil pump add (.3) 4
Recond servo add (.3) 4
Recond direct clutch add (.4) 5
Recond forward clutch add (.4) 5
Renew bushing add-each (.1) 1

(G) Output Carrier, Sun Gear and Drive Shell, Renew
All models (3.9) 5.7
Recond valve body add (.4) 5
Recond oil pump add (.3) 4
Recond servo add (.3) 4
Recond sun gear and shell add (.2) 3
Recond bushings add-each (.1) 1

(G) Low and Reverse Clutch Housing and Output Shaft Assy., Renew
All models (4.0) 5.8
Recond valve body add (.4) 5
Recond oil pump add (.3) 4
Recond servo add (.3) 4
Recond direct clutch add (.4) 5
Recond forward clutch add (.4) 5

LABOR 23 AUTOMATIC TRANSMISSION 23 LABOR

	(Factory Time)	Chilton Time
Recond low and reverse clutch add	(.3)	.4
Renew bushings add-each	(.1)	.1

(G) Low and Reverse Clutch Piston Assy., Renew

All models	(4.4)	6.4
Drain and leak check converter add	(.2)	.3
Check converter end play add	(.2)	.3
Recond valve body add	(.4)	.5
Recond oil pump add	(.3)	.4
Recond direct clutch add	(.4)	.5
Recond forward clutch add	(.4)	.5
Recond sun gear and shell add	(.2)	.3
Recond reverse piston add	(.3)	.4
Recond gov or renew gear add	(.2)	.3
Renew gov bushing add	(.4)	.4
Renew bushings add-each	(.1)	.1

SERVICES REQUIRING R&R

350-350C

(G) Transmission Assembly, R&R or Renew

All models	(2.1)	3.0

(G) Transmission Assembly, Reseal

Includes: R&R transmission and renew all seals and gaskets.

All models		6.0

(G) Torque Converter, Renew

All models	(2.0)	2.9

(P) Transmission and Converter, R&R and Recondition

Includes: Drain and pressure test converter, recondition pump, clutch assemblies, shaft assemblies, carrier assembly, governor, servo's and valve body. Adjust linkage.

	(Factory Time)	Chilton Time
All models	(7.6)	11.0

(G) Flywheel (Flexplate), Renew

All models	(2.2)	3.0

(G) Front Pump Oil Seal, Renew

All models	(2.0)	3.0

(G) Front Oil Pump, Renew

Includes: Renew pump gasket and seal.

All models	(2.2)	3.1
Recond pump add	(.5)	.6
Renew pump bushing add	(.1)	.1

(G) Intermediate Clutch Assy., and/or Overrun Band, Renew

All models	(2.7)	3.9
Recond valve body add	(.6)	.7
Recond oil pump add	(.5)	.6
Clean pan and screen add	(.3)	.4
Renew bushings add-each	(.1)	.1

(G) Low and Reverse Roller Clutch, Support, Clutch Plates, Reaction Carrier and Output Shaft, Renew

All models	(3.7)	5.4
Recond valve body add	(.6)	.7
Recond oil pump add	(.5)	.6
Renew forward clutch drum and/or input shaft add	(.2)	.3
Recond low and reverse clutches add	(.1)	.2
Renew bushings add-each	(.1)	.1

(G) Direct and Forward Clutches, Intermediate Roller Clutch, Input Shaft and Ring Gear, Renew

	(Factory Time)	Chilton Time
All models	(3.3)	4.8
Recond valve body add	(.6)	.7
Recond oil pump and inter. clutch add	(.5)	.6
Recond direct and roller clutches add	(.4)	.5
Recond forward clutch add	(.4)	.5
Renew forward clutch drum and/or input shaft add	(.2)	.3
Renew sun gear and drive shell add	(.2)	.3
Renew bushings add-each	(.1)	.1

(G) Low and Reverse Clutch Piston Assy., Renew

All models	(3.8)	6.0
Drain and leak check converter add	(.2)	.3
Check converter end play add	(.2)	.3
Recond valve body add	(.6)	.7
Recond oil pump add	(.5)	.6
Recond direct and intermediate clutches add	(.4)	.5
Recond forward clutch add	(.4)	.5
Renew forward clutch drum and input shaft add	(.2)	.3
Recond sun gear and drive shell add	(.2)	.3
Recond low and reverse clutches add	(.1)	.2
Recond reverse piston add	(.3)	.4
Recond gov or renew gear add	(.2)	.3
Renew gov bore bushing add	(.4)	.5
Renew bushings add-each	(.1)	.1

PARTS 23 CONVERTER, PUMP & CLUTCH 23 PARTS

	Part No.	Price
(1) Converter Assy. (Rebuilt)		
Buick		
1983-84 (T.H. 250 trans.)		
exc. below	8641921	340.00
305, 307	8641925	340.00
1983 (T.H. 350 trans.)		
V-6	8641921	340.00
(350 Diesel)		
LeSabre-MX2	8641943	340.00
MV4	8641943	340.00
Regal-MX2	8641931	N.L.
MV4	8641942	N.L.
Chevrolet		
1983-84 (T.H. 250 trans.)		
exc. below	8641921	340.00
305, 307	8641925	340.00
1983-84 (T.H. 350 trans.)		
V-6	8641921	340.00
(305)		
exc. below	8641925	340.00
Malibu-4 dr. sedan	8641928	340.00
(350 Diesel)		
Impala, Caprice-MX2	8641943	340.00
MV4	8641943	340.00
Malibu, Monte Carlo-MX2	8641931	N.L.
MV4 (1983)	8641942	N.L.
MV4 (1984)	8641950	340.00
Oldsmobile		
1983-84 (T.H. 250 trans.)		
exc. below	8641921	340.00
305, 307	8641925	340.00
1983 (T.H. 350 trans)		
231	8641921	340.00
260	8641927	340.00

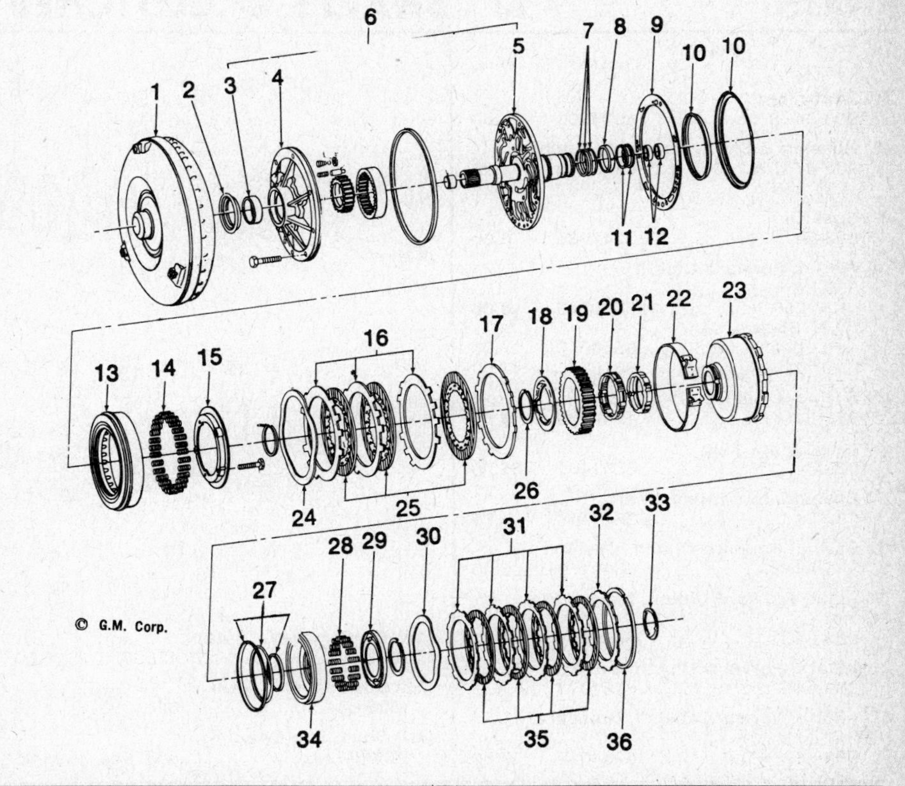

PARTS 23 CONVERTER, PUMP & CLUTCH 23 PARTS

	Part No.	Price
(350 Diesel)		
Delta 88, & 98-		
MX2	8641943	340.00
MV4	8641943	340.00
Cutlass-MX2	8641931	N.L.
MV4	8641942	N.L.
Pontiac		
1983-84 (T.H. 250 trans.)		
exc. below	8641921	340.00
305, 307	8641925	340.00
1983 (T.H. 350 trans.)		
V-6	8641921	340.00
305	8641925	340.00
(350 Diesel)		
Parisienne	8641943	340.00
Bonneville, Grand Prix	8641942	N.L.
(2) Seal, Oil Pump		
1983-84-exc. below	8641952	3.25
MX2 trans.	8641904	N.L.
(3) Bushing, Oil Pump		
1983-84	8623940	N.L.
(4) Body, Oil Pump		
1983-84	8641590	N.L.
(5) Cover, Oil Pump		
1983-84-exc. below	14033581	N.L.
T.H. 350 trans.	14022147	N.L.
(6) Pump Assy.		
Use component parts.		
(7) Ring, Clutch Drum		
1983-84	6261746	3.50
(8) Bushing, Clutch Drum		
1983-84	8640099	2.50
(9) Gasket, Pump Cover		
1983-84	8640671	.25
(10) Seal Kit, Inter. Clutch		
1983-84	3947088	6.50
(11) Ring, Forward Clutch		
1983-84	6261570	3.50
(12) Bushing, Stator Shaft-Rear		
1983-84	6261022	1.25
(13) Piston, Inter. Clutch		
1983-84-exc. below	1246318	14.25
V-8	1246319	18.00
(14) Spring, Inter. Clutch Piston		
1983-84	6261309	4.50
(15) Seat, Inter. Clutch Piston		
1983-84	1243126	4.75
(16) Plate, Inter. Clutch, Reaction		
1983-84	8640672	6.00
(17) Plate, Inter. Clutch–Pressure		
1983-84	8640943	7.50
(18) Retainer, Inter. Clutch		
1983-84	6261038	.50
(19) Race, Intermediate Clutch Outer		
1983-84	6261021	25.75
(20) Clutch, Inter. Overrun		
1983-84	356826	24.50
(21) Cam, Inter. Clutch		
1983-84	6260318	25.25
(22) Band, Inter. Clutch		
1983-84-exc. below	6261132	N.L.
T.H. 250C	8641196	23.50
(23) Drum, Direct Clutch		
1983-84-exc below	8640307	80.25
T.H. 250	14019950	80.25
(24) Spring, Inter. Clutch		
1983-84	6261309	4.50
(25) Plate, Inter. Clutch–Drive		
1983-84	8640943	7.50
(26) Retainer Ring, Inter. Clutch		
1983-84	6261038	.50
(27) Seal Kit, Direct Clutch Piston		
1983-84	3947087	5.00
(28) Spring, Direct Clutch Piston, (Return)		
1983-84	6261681	.25
(29) Seat, Direct Clutch Piston		
1983-84	8640323	5.00
(30) Spring, Direct Clutch Piston		
1983-84	8640176	5.00
(31) Plate, Direct Clutch–Drive		
1983-84 (steel)	6261071	N.L.
(32) Plate, Direct Clutch–Pressure		
1983-84	6261350	7.50
(33) Bearing, Direct Clutch Drum		
1983-84	9428864	6.75
(34) Piston, Direct Clutch		
1983-84 (T.H. 250 trans.)		
V-6	8641060	17.75
V-8	8640733	16.00
1983-84 (T.H. 350 trans.)		
V-6	6260196	18.25
V-8	6260197	19.00
(35) Plate, Direct Clutch–Drive		
1983-84 (faced)	6261071	N.L.
(36) Retainer Ring, Direct Clutch		
1983-84	6261048	.75

PARTS 23 SHAFTS & CLUTCHES 23 PARTS

	Part No.	Price
(1) Shaft, Input		
1983-84	14024301	75.50
(2) Housing & Shaft, Forward Clutch		
1983-84-T.H.250	8641939	71.75
T.H. 350	360943	N.L.
(3) Seal Kit		
1983-84	3947086	5.00
(4) Piston, Forward Clutch		
1983-84		
T.H. 250	8640723	16.00
(T.H. 350 trans.)		
exc. below	8640070	17.00
350 Diesel	8640071	17.00
(5) Spring & Seat, Forward Clutch		
1983-84	1242722	4.50
(6) Gear, Input Ring		
1983-84	6261401	65.50
(7) Bushing, Input Ring Gear		
1983-84	8641117	.75
(8) Spring, Forward Clutch, Cushion		
1983-84	8640176	5.00
(9) Plate, Forward Clutch, Drive (Line Plates)		
1983-84	6261071	N.L.
(10) Plate, Forward Clutch, Drive		
1983-84	6261071	N.L.
(11) Plate, Forward Clutch, Pressure (Steel)		
1983-84	6261072	7.50

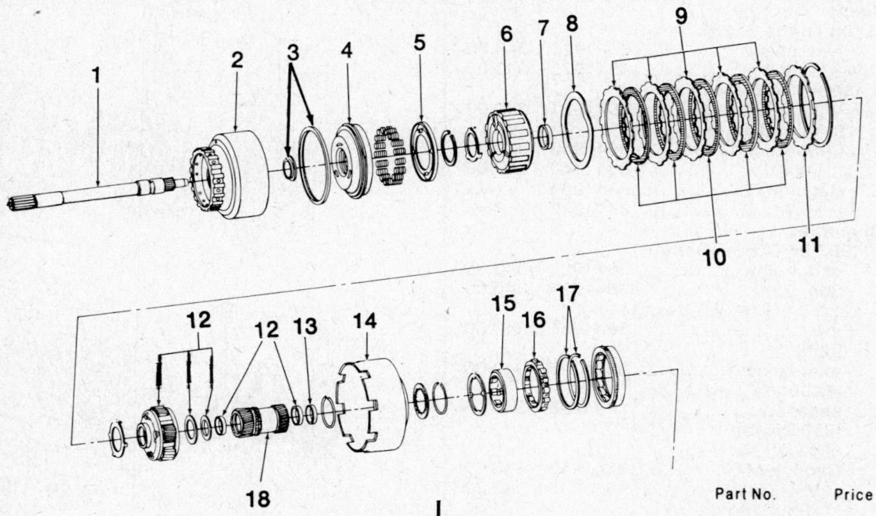

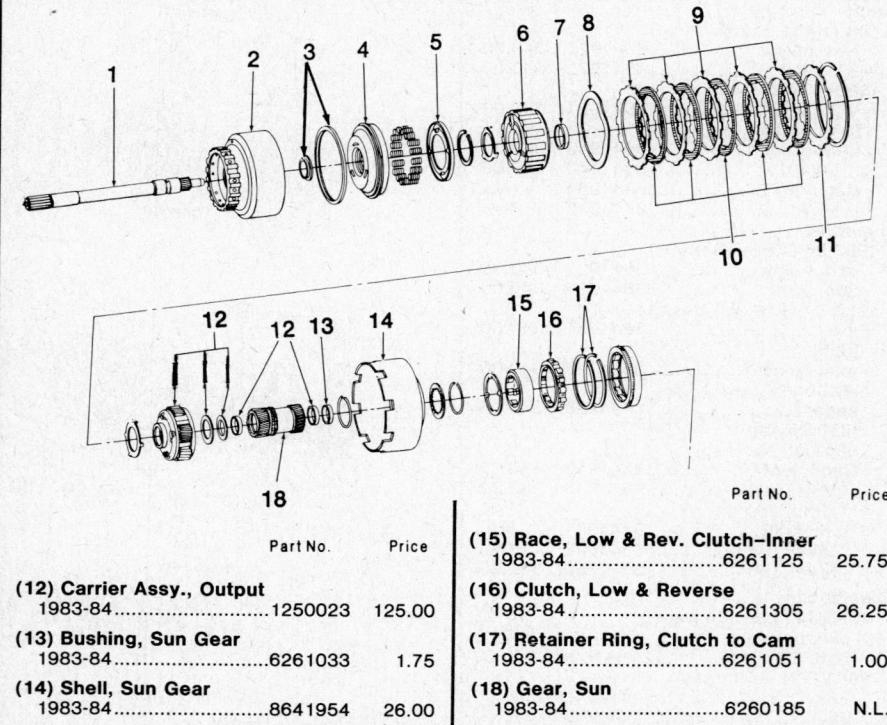

	Part No.	Price
(12) Carrier Assy., Output		
1983-84	1250023	125.00
(13) Bushing, Sun Gear		
1983-84	6261033	1.75
(14) Shell, Sun Gear		
1983-84	8641954	26.00
(15) Race, Low & Rev. Clutch–Inner		
1983-84	6261125	25.75
(16) Clutch, Low & Reverse		
1983-84	6261305	26.25
(17) Retainer Ring, Clutch to Cam		
1983-84	6261051	1.00
(18) Gear, Sun		
1983-84	6260185	N.L.

PARTS 23 SHAFTS & CLUTCHES 23 PARTS

	Part No.	Price
(19) Support, Low & Rev. Clutch (Inc. Cam)		
1983-84	8647411	57.00
(20) Plate, Rev. Clutch-Drive		
1983-84-T.H. 250	8641698	5.50
T.H. 350	8641511	N.L.
(21) Carrier, Reaction Planet		
1983-84	6261645	119.00
(22) Gear, Output Ring		
1983-84	8640707	N.L.
(23) Bushing, Case to Shaft		
1983-84	8641118	4.00
(24) Bearing, Output Rear Gear, Thrust		
1983-84	9427759	5.50
(25) Plate, Low & Rev. Clutch, Reaction		
1983-84	8641511	N.L.
(26) Seat, Reverse Clutch, w/Spring		
1983-84	6260382	4.75
(27) Piston, Low & Rev. Clutch		
1983-84-T.H. 250	8641011	16.00
T.H. 350	344212	17.00
(28) Seal Kit, Low & Rev. Clutch		
1983-84	3947089	1.25

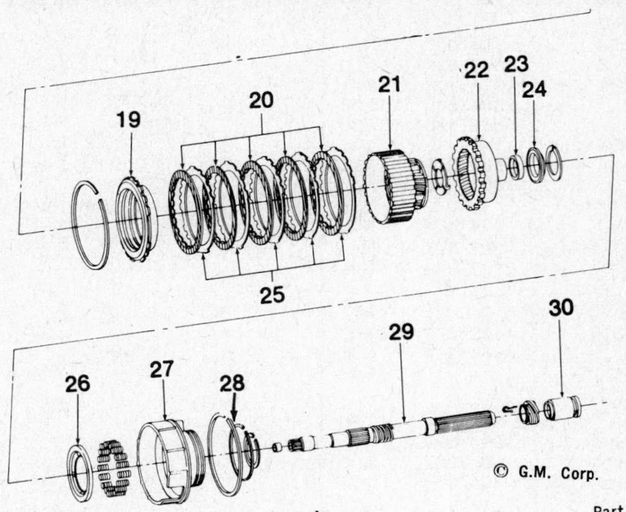

	Part No.	Price
(29) Shaft Assy., Output		
1983-84-T.H. 250	8640708	53.75
T.H. 350	8641076	56.75

	Part No.	Price
(30) Bushing Output Shaft		
1983-84	8641058	.50

PARTS 23 CONTROL VALVE BODY 23 PARTS

	Part No.	Price
Valve Body Assy.		
Buick		
1983-84 (T.H. 250 trans.)		
V-6	8647529	162.00
V-8	8647517	161.00
1983 (T.H. 350 trans.)		
231	8641827	160.00
(252)		
LeSabre	8641832	155.00
Regal	8641830	160.00
(350 Diesel)		
Electra,		
LeSabre (1983)	8641855	151.00
Regal	8641855	151.00
Chevrolet		
1983-84 (T.H. 250 trans.)		
229	8641596	160.00
231 (1983-84)	8647529	162.00
V-8	8641592	160.00
1983 (w/T.H. 350 trans. MX2)		
231	8641827	160.00
305	8641880	162.00
350 Diesel	8641855	151.00
1983-84 (T.H. 350 trans. MV4)		
(305)		
Caprice, Impala	8647564	160.00
Malibu, Monte		
Carlo	8647538	160.00
Oldsmobile		
1983-84 (T.H. 250 trans.)		
V-6	8647529	162.00
V-8	8647517	161.00
1983 (T.H. 350 trans. MX2)		
V-6	8641827	160.00
260	8641834	151.00
(350 Diesel)		
Cutlass	8641855	151.00
Delta 88		
(1983-84)	8641855	151.00
Pontiac		
1983-84 (T.H. 250 trans.)		
229	8641596	160.00
231	8647529	162.00
305	8641592	160.00
1983 (T.H. 350 trans.)		
231	8641827	160.00
252	8641830	160.00
305	8641880	162.00
(350 Diesel engine)		
MX2 trans.	8641855	151.00
MV4 trans.	8641821	155.00

PARTS 23 TURBO HYDRA-MATIC CASE & PARTS 23 PARTS

	Part No.	Price
Flywheel Flex Plate		
V-6-229		
1983-84	471591	55.75
V-6-231		
1983	25512346	70.50
1984-87	25512348	72.00
V-6-252		
1983	25512348	72.00
V-6-260 Diesel		
1983	22512002	75.25
V-8-267		
1983	471591	55.75
V-8-305		
1983-84	471591	55.75
V-8-307, 350R, & 403		
1983	22500807	85.50
V-8-350		
1983-84-Code L	471598	57.75
Code X	1262989	83.00
Diesel	22500808	85.50
Transmission Assembly (New)		
Buick		
1983 (T.H. 250 trans.)		
V-6	8647509	N.L.
V-8	8647506	1557.00
1984-84 (T.H. 250 trans.)		
231	8647545	1557.00
1983 (T.H. 350 trans.)		
231	8641879	N.L.
252		
Code KE	8641884	N.L.
Code KK	8647535	N.L.
350 Diesel		
Code LB	8641886	N.L.
Code LJ	8647505	N.L.
Chevrolet		
1983 (T.H. 250 trans.)		
229	8647531	1557.00
231	8647509	N.L.
305	8647530	1557.00
1984-84 (T.H. 250 trans.)		
229	8647531	1557.00
231	9647545	N.L.
305	8647530	1557.00
1983 (T.H. 350 trans.)		
V-6-231		
Code KA	8641879	N.L.
Code WD	8647503	N.L.
V-8-305		
Code WE	8641889	N.L.
Code WS	8647541	N.L.
V-8 350 Diesel		
Code LB	8641886	N.L.
Code LD	8647504	N.L.
Code LJ	8647505	N.L.
1984-84 (T.H. 350 trans.)		
exc. below	8647552	N.L.
305G	8647549	N.L.
Oldsmobile		
1983 (T.H. 250 trans.)		
V-6	8647509	N.L.
V-8	8647506	1557.00
1984-84 (T.H. 250 trans.)		
231	8647545	1557.00
1983 (T.H. 350 trans.)		
V-6	8641879	N.L.
(350 Diesel)		
Code LB	8641886	N.L.
Code LJ	8647505	N.L.
Pontiac		
Catalina & Bonneville		
1983 (T.H. 250 trans.)		
229	8647531	1557.00

	Part No.	Price
231	8647507	N.L.
305	8647530	1557.00
1984-84 (T.H. 250 trans.)		
231	8647545	1557.00
305	8647530	1557.00
1983 (T.H. 350 trans.)		
231	8641879	N.L.
305	8647503	N.L.
(350 Diesel)		
Code LB	8641886	N.L.
Code LD	8647504	N.L.
Code LJ	8647505	N.L.
Gasket Set		
1983-84-exc. below	14024372	29.00
MX2 trans.	8641914	N.L.
Seal Kits		
1983-84-inter clutch	3947088	6.50
reverse clutch	3947089	1.25
direct clutch	3947087	5.00
forward clutch	3947086	5.00
Ring Kit		
1983-84-T.H. 250	14024373	20.25
T.H. 350	338202	19.75
Overhaul Kit		
1983-84-w/T.H. 250	14024374	N.L.
(TH350 trans.)		
MX2	8641915	N.L.
MV4	14024375	101.00
Neutral Safety Switch		
1983-84	22509632	5.50
(1) Cover, Accum. Piston		
1983-84	1243476	2.25
(2) Seal, Accum. Piston Cover		
1983-84	338926	.75
(3) Spring, Accum. Piston		
Buick		
1983-84 (T.H. 250 trans.)		
V-6	6261333	2.50
V-8	344219	2.25
1983 (T.H. 350 trans.)		
MV4 trans.	6261140	2.25
(MX2 trans.)		
252	6261333	2.50
(350 Diesel)		
LeSabre	6261231	2.25
Regal	6261629	2.00
Chevrolet		
1983-84 (T.H. 250 trans.)		
229	6261629	2.00
231	6261333	2.50
267	8641290	2.25
305	344219	2.25
1983-84 (T.H. 350 trans.)		
exc. below	6261140	2.25
231	6261231	2.25
305	6261629	2.00
(350 Diesel)		
Caprice, Impala	6261231	2.25
Malibu, Monte Carlo	6261629	2.00
Oldsmobile		
(T.H. 250 trans.)		
1983-V-6	6261333	2.50
V-8	344219	2.25
1984-84	6261629	2.00
(T.H. 350 trans.)		
1983-exc. below	6261140	2.25
231	6261231	2.25
260	6261629	2.00
(350 Diesel)		
Cutlass	6261629	2.00
Delta 88	6261231	2.25

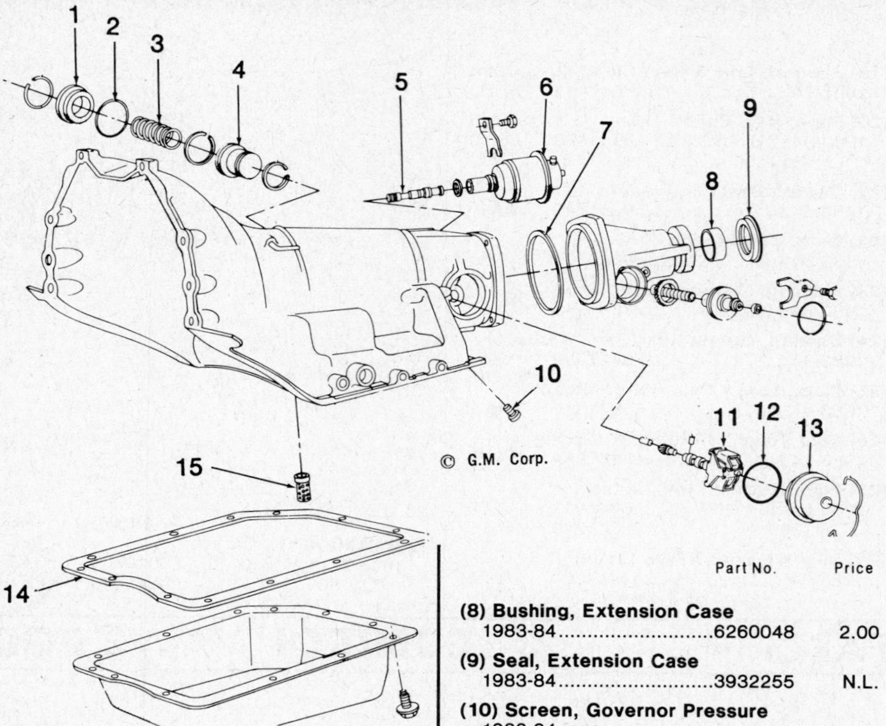

	Part No.	Price
Pontiac		
1983-84 (T.H. 250 trans.)		
231	6261629	2.00
305	344219	2.25
1983 (TH350 trans.)		
exc. below	6261140	2.25
252	6261333	2.50
350 Diesel	6261629	2.00
(4) Piston, Inter Clutch Accum.		
1983-84	1239836	6.25
(5) Valve, Modulator		
1983-84	6261516	6.25
(6) Modulator Assy.		
Buick		
1983-84-exc. below	3033639	N.L.
231	3049145	13.75
267, 350 Diesel	3035519	13.75
305	6259799	N.L.
Chevrolet		
1983-84-exc below	3035519	13.75
231A	3049145	13.75
Turbo 231	3033639	N.L.
305, 350	6259799	N.L.
Oldsmobile		
1983-84-exc. below	3035519	13.75
231	3049145	13.75
305	6259799	N.L.
307	3033639	N.L.
Pontiac		
1983-84-exc. below	3035519	13.75
231	3049145	13.75
305	6259799	N.L.
(7) Seal, Case Extension		
1983-84	1358899	1.25

	Part No.	Price
(8) Bushing, Extension Case		
1983-84	6260048	2.00
(9) Seal, Extension Case		
1983-84	3932255	N.L.
(10) Screen, Governor Pressure		
1983-84-exc. below	8643423	N.L.
MX2 trans.	6273269	.75
(11) Governor Assy.		
Buick		
1983-84-exc. below	8640234	N.L.
229, 267, 305	464200	N.L.
Chevrolet		
1983-84-exc. below	464200	N.L.
231, 350 Diesel	8640234	N.L.
Oldsmobile & Pontiac		
1983-84-exc. below	464200	N.L.
231, 350 Diesel	8640234	N.L.
(12) Seal, Governor		
1983-84	1241734	.75
(13) Cover, Governor		
1983-84	6261067	2.50
(14) Gasket, Oil Pan		
1983-84	25504700	N.L.
(15) Screen Pump Pressure		
1983-84	6261323	1.25

LOCKING TORQUE CONVERTER SYSTEM PARTS

	Part No.	Price
Converter Clutch Brake Switch		
1983-84-exc. below	25504682	N.L.
Cruise cont.	9794682	7.75
Vacuum Delay Valve		
1983	14020690	6.50
Clutch Solenoid Assy.		
1983-84 (M31, MV4 trans.)		
exc. below	1997585	18.00
350 Diesel	1997592	20.00
1983 (MX2 trans.)		
exc. below	1997583	23.00
350 Diesel	1997587	25.50

(Factory Time) Chilton Time

ON CAR SERVICES

(G) Drain and Refill Unit
All models.................................... .9

(G) Oil Pressure Check
All models.................................... .6

(M) Check Unit For Oil Leaks
Includes: Clean and dry outside of case and run to determine point of leak.
All models.................................... .9

(G) Neutral Safety Switch, Renew
All models (.3)................................ .4

(G) Shift Linkage, Adjust
All models
Neutral Safety Switch (.3).......... .4
Shift Indicator Needle (.2).......... .3
Shift Linkage (.4)......................... .5
T.V. Cable (.3).............................. .4

(G) Shift Linkage, Adjust (w/Diesel Eng)
All models
Fast idle speed (.2)..................... .3
Throttle rod/T.V. cable (.5).......... .6
Trans vacuum valve (.5)............. .6
Complete (.8)............................... 1.0

(G) Oil Pan Gasket, Renew
Buick Riviera
1983-85 (.6)................................ .9
Cadillac Eldorado & Seville
1983-85 (.6)................................ .9
Oldsmobile Toronado
1983-85 (.6)................................ .9

(G) Valve Body Assembly, Renew
Includes: R&R oil pan, screen and renew gasket.
Buick Riviera
1983-85 (.7)................................ 1.4
Cadillac Eldorado & Seville
1983-85 (.7)................................ 1.4
Oldsmobile Toronado
1983-85 (.7)................................ 1.4

(P) Valve Body Assy., R&R and Recondition
Includes: R&R oil pan and screen. Disassemble, clean, inspect, free all valves. Replace parts as required.
Buick Riviera
1983-85 (1.5).............................. 2.2
Cadillac Eldorado & Seville
1983-85 (1.5).............................. 2.2
Oldsmobile Toronado
1983-85 (1.5).............................. 2.2

(G) 1-2 Accumulator Spring and/or Piston, R&R or Renew
Includes: R&R oil pan, valve body, detent cable bracket. Check and add oil.
Buick Riviera
1983-85 (1.3).............................. 2.0
Cadillac Eldorado & Seville
1983-85 (1.3).............................. 2.0
Oldsmobile Toronado
1983-85 (1.3).............................. 2.0

(G) 1-2 Accumulator Piston, R&R and Recondition
Includes: R&R oil pan, valve body, detent cable bracket. Check and add oil.
Buick Riviera
1983-85 (1.5).............................. 2.3
Cadillac Eldorado & Seville
1983-85 (1.5).............................. 2.3
Oldsmobile Toronado
1983-85 (1.5).............................. 2.3

CHILTON'S AUTOMATIC TRANSMISSION TUNE-UP

1. Check engine performance
2. Check condition of transmission oil
3. Check transmission, oil cooler and oil cooler lines for external leaks
4. Remove oil pan, clean or renew screen or filter
5. Torque valve body
6. Adjust bands
7. Clean oil pan and install pan with new gasket
8. Check modulator and hose
9. Install new transmission oil to proper level
10. Adjust manual and throttle linkage
11. Road test

All models 1.5
Charge for parts used

(Factory Time) Chilton Time

(G) Pressure Regulator Valve, Renew
1983-85...................................... 1.0

(G) Manual Lever Shaft Seal, Detent Lever or Park Actuator Rod, Renew
Includes: R&R oil pan.
Buick Riviera
1983-85 (.7)................................ 1.4
Cadillac Eldorado & Seville
1983-85 (1.1).............................. 1.4
Oldsmobile Toronado
1983-85 (1.1).............................. 1.4

(G) Converter Clutch Solenoid, Renew
Includes: R&R oil pan.
1983-85 (.6)................................ 1.1

(G) 4-3 Pressure Switch, Renew
Includes: R&R oil pan.
1983-85 (.5)................................ 1.0

(G) 3-4 Accumulator Piston and/or Spring, R&R or Renew
Includes: R&R oil pan and valve body.
1983-85 (.9)................................ 1.4
Recond accumulator add' each (.2)........................... .2

(G) Throttle Valve Control Cable and/or 'O' Ring, Renew
Includes: Adjust cable.
Buick Riviera
1983-85 (.4)................................ .9
Cadillac Eldorado & Seville
1983-85-Gas (.4)......................... .9
Diesel (.7)................................ 1.0
Oldsmobile Toronado
1983-85 (.4)................................ .9

(G) Governor Assembly, Renew
Buick Riviera
1983-85 (.4)................................ .6
Cadillac Eldorado & Seville
1983-85 (.4)................................ .6
Oldsmobile Toronado
1983-85 (.4)................................ .6
Recond gov or renew gear add......... .2

(Factory Time) Chilton Time

(G) Intermediate Servo Assembly, R&R
Buick Riviera
1983-85 (.6)................................ 1.0
Cadillac Eldorado & Seville
1983-85 (.6)................................ 1.0
w/Diesel eng. (.6)...................... 1.0
Oldsmobile Toronado
1983-85 (.6)................................ 1.0
Recond servo add (.2)..................... .3

(G) Speedometer Driven Gear and/or Seal, Renew
Buick Riviera
1983-85 (.2)................................ .5
Cadillac Eldorado & Seville
1983-85 (.3)................................ .5
Oldsmobile Toronado
1983-85 (.2)................................ .5

(G) Transmission Mounts, Renew
V-6–1983-85
one (.5)...................................... .7
both (.8)..................................... 1.1
V-8–1983-85
one (.3)...................................... .5
both (.5)..................................... .8

(G) Speedometer Drive Gear, Renew
Includes: R&R governor cover and governor assy. R&R speedometer drive gear from governor.
Buick Riviera
1983-85 (.3)................................ .8
Cadillac Eldorado & Seville
1983-85 (.3)................................ .8
Oldsmobile Toronado
1983-85 (.3)................................ .8

SERVICES REQUIRING R&R

(G) Transmission Assembly, R&R or Renew
Includes: R&R starter, disconnect trans from final drive.
Buick Riviera
1983-85 (2.9).............................. 4.9
w/Turbocharger add (2.1)............. 2.1
Cadillac Eldorado & Seville
1983-85 (3.6).............................. 4.9
Oldsmobile Toronado
1983-85 (3.0).............................. 4.9
Renew trans add (.3)...................... .5
Leak check converter add (.2)........... .3
Flush oil cooler and lines add (.4)..... .6

(P) Transmission and Converter Assy., R&R and Recondition
Includes: R&R starter, disconnect trans from final drive. Disassemble trans, inspect and replace all parts, make all necessary adjustments. Road test.
Buick Riviera
1983-85 (7.5).............................. 11.3
w/Turbocharger add (2.6)............. 2.6
Cadillac Eldorado & Seville
1983-85 (8.1).............................. 11.3
Oldsmobile Toronado
1983-85 (7.5).............................. 11.3

(G) Transmission Assembly, Reseal
Includes: R&R trans and renew all seals and gaskets.
Buick Riviera
1983-85 (4.4).............................. 6.8
w/Turbocharger add (2.6)............. 2.6
Cadillac Eldorado & Seville
1983-85 (4.4).............................. 6.8
Oldsmobile Toronado
1983-85 (4.2).............................. 6.8

LABOR 23 AUTOMATIC TRANSMISSION 23 LABOR

(Factory Time) Chilton Time

(G) Torque Converter, Renew

Includes: R&R trans, check end play of converter.

Buick Riviera
1983-85 (2.8) 5.2
w/Turbocharger add (2.1) 2.1
Cadillac Eldorado & Seville
1983-85 (3.5) 5.2
Oldsmobile Toronado
1983-85 (2.8) 5.2

(G) Front Pump Oil Seal, Renew

Includes: R&R trans and converter.

Buick Riviera
1983-85 (2.9) 5.1
w/Turbocharger add (2.1) 2.1
Cadillac Eldorado & Seville
1983-85 (3.6) 5.1
Oldsmobile Toronado
1983-85 (2.9) 5.1

(G) Parking Pawl, Shaft, Rod or Spring, Renew

Buick Riviera
1983-85 (1.2) 5.4
Cadillac Eldorado & Seville
1983-85 (4.1) 5.4
Oldsmobile Toronado
1983-85 (1.2) 5.4

(G) Flywheel (Flex Plate), Renew

Includes: R&R trans and converter.

Buick Riviera
1983-85 (3.1) 5.4
w/Turbocharger add (2.1) 2.1
Cadillac Eldorado & Seville
1983-85 (3.7) 5.4
Oldsmobile Toronado
1983-85 (3.2) 5.4

(G) Front Oil Pump and/or Gasket, Renew

Includes: R&R trans and converter. R&R sprocket cover, snap rings and drive link assy.

Buick Riviera
1983-85 (3.4) 5.4
w/Turbocharger add (2.4) 2.4
Cadillac Eldorado & Seville
1983-85 (4.1) 5.4
Oldsmobile Toronado
1983-85 (3.4) 5.4

(G) Front Oil Pump, R&R and Recondition

Includes: R&R trans and converter. R&R sprocket cover, snap rings and drive link assy.

Buick Riviera
1983-85 (3.7) 5.9
w/Turbocharger add (2.4) 2.4
Cadillac Eldorado & Seville
1983-85 (4.4) 5.9
Oldsmobile Toronado
1983-85 (3.7) 5.9
Renew front pump bushing add (.1) 2

(G) Fourth Clutch Pack and Overdrive Unit, Renew

Includes: R&R trans and converter.

Buick Riviera
1983-85 (3.3) 5.4
Cadillac Eldorado & Seville
1983-85 (4.0) 5.4
Oldsmobile Toronado
1983-85 (3.3) 5.4
Recond O/Drive unit, add (.3) 5

(G) Forward and Direct Clutches and Intermediate Band, Renew

Includes: R&R trans and converter. R&R sprocket cover, drive link assy. and oil pump. Make all necessary adjustments.

Buick Riviera
1983-85 (5.2) 6.5
w/Turbocharger add (2.5) 2.5
Cadillac Eldorado & Seville
1983-85 (5.9) 6.5
Oldsmobile Toronado
1983-85 (5.2) 6.5

(G) Forward and Direct Clutches and Intermediate Band, R&R and Recondition

Includes: R&R trans and converter, R&R sprocket cover, drive link assy. and oil pump. Recondition forward and direct clutches. Make all necessary adjustments.

Buick Riviera
1983-85 (5.9) 8.0
w/Turbocharger add (2.5) 2.5
Cadillac Eldorado & Seville
1983-85 (6.6) 8.0
Oldsmobile Toronado
1983-85 (5.9) 8.0

(G) Output Carrier, Sun Gear and Drive Shell, Renew

Includes: R&R trans and converter, R&R direct clutch, foward clutch and intermediate band. Make all necessary adjustments.

Buick Riviera
1983-85 (5.5) 7.8
w/Turbocharger add (2.6) 2.6
Cadillac Eldorado & Seville
1983-85 (6.2) 7.8
Oldsmobile Toronado
1983-85 (5.5) 7.8
Recond sun gear add (.3) 6

(G) Low and Reverse Clutch Housing and Output Shaft Assembly, Renew

Includes: R&R trans and converter, R&R oil pan, valve body, servo, sprocket cover, drive link assy., case cover and clutch assemblies. Make all necessary adjustments.

Buick Rivera
1983-85 (5.8) 8.3
w/Turbocharger add (2.6) 2.6
Cadillac Eldorado & Seville
1983-85 (6.5) 8.3
Oldsmobile Toronado
1983-85 (5.8) 8.3

(G) Low and Reverse Clutch Housing and Output Shaft Assembly, R&R and Recondition

Includes: R&R trans and converter, R&R oil pan, valve body, servo, sprocket cover, drive link assy., case cover and clutch assemblies. Recondition low and reverse clutches. Make all necessary adjustments.

Buick Riviera
1983-85 (6.1) 8.8
w/Turbocharger add (2.6) 2.6
Cadillac Eldorado & Seville
1983-85 (6.8) 8.8
Oldsmobile Toronado
1983-85 (6.1) 8.8

(G) Sprocket Cover and/or Gasket, Renew

Includes: R&R transmission.

Buick Riviera
1983-85 (3.1) 5.0
w/Turbocharger add (2.5) 2.5
Cadillac Eldorado & Seville
1983-85 (3.8) 5.0
Oldsmobile Toronado
1983-85 (3.1) 5.0

(G) Drive Link Belt, Renew

Includes: R&R trans and sprocket cover.

Buick Riviera
1983-85 (3.2) 4.8
w/Turbocharger add (2.6) 2.6
Cadillac Eldorado & Seville
1983-85 (3.9) 4.8
Oldsmobile Toronado
1983-85 (3.2) 4.8
Renew case cover or sprocket supports add (.8) 1.2
Renew drive sprocket and/or bearing, add-one (.2) 4
both (.3) 5

PARTS 23 TURBO HYDRA-MATIC CASE & PARTS 23 PARTS

	Part No.	Price
Transmission Assembly		
1983 Transmission codes:		
AJ	8635720	2179.00
AL	8635721	2179.00
BE	8635726	2179.00
BJ	8635727	2179.00
OE	8635724	2179.00
OK	8635725	N.L.
1984 Transmission codes:		
AJ	8635875	2179.00
AL	8635876	2179.00
BE	8635880	2179.00
BJ	8635881	N.L.
OE	8635878	2179.00
OK	8635879	N.L.
1985 Transmission codes:		
AB	8639881	2179.00
AE	8639793	2179.00
BJ	8639797	2179.00
OQ	8639796	2179.00
OK	8639794	2179.00
OE	8639795	2179.00
Transmission Seal & Gasket Kit		
1983-85	8635906	68.25
Snap Ring Kit		
1983-85	8635912	5.50
Flywheel (Flex Plate)		
1983-85		
231 ('82-'83)	25512347	70.50
231 ('84-'85)	25512348	72.00
252	25512349	72.00
250	1623936	75.00
307, 305	22510188	1.00
350 Diesel	22500808	85.50
(1) Torque Converter (Rebuilt)		
1983-85-231	8635928	340.00
252	8633954	340.00
250	8635902	N.L.
307	8633955	340.00
350 Diesel	8638927	326.00
(2) Governor Assy.		
Buick Riviera		
1983-85		
V-6	8635480	60.00
V-8-exc. below	8635481	60.00
1985-307	8639888	60.50
Cadillac Eldorado		
1983-85-exc. below	8635481	60.00

PARTS 23 TURBO HYDRA-MATIC CASE & PARTS 23 PARTS

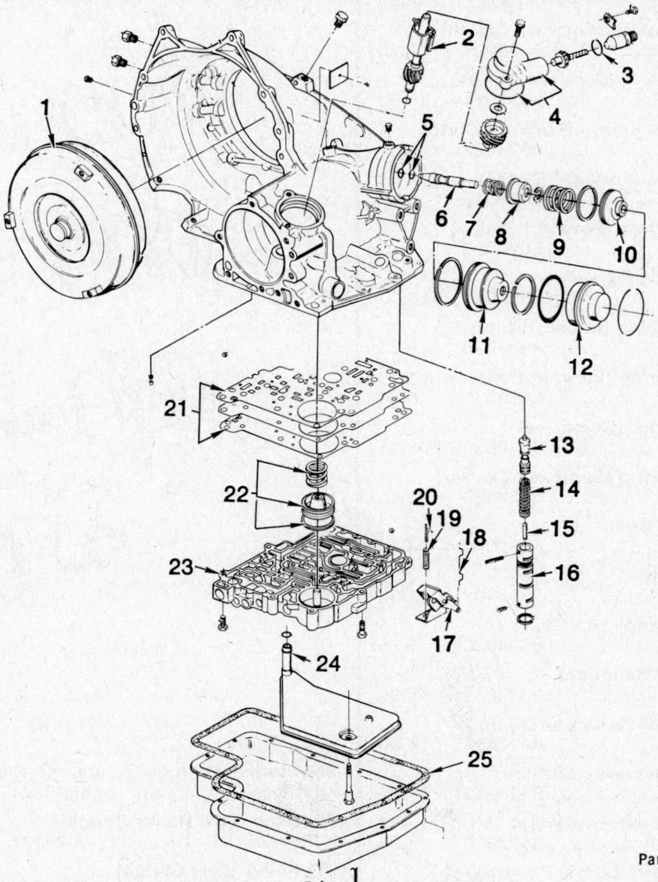

	Part No.	Price
250	8635480	60.00
Olds Toronado		
1983-85-exc.		
below	8635481	60.00
1985-307	8639888	60.50
(3) Seal		
1983-85	8622076	.50
(4) Governor Cover (w/Seal)		
1983	8632985	18.00
1984-85	8643984	22.50
(5) Seal (Interm. Band)		
1983-85	8630120	.25
(6) Pin and Seal (Interm. Band)		
1983-85		
1 groove	8632973	8.50
2 grooves	8632974	8.50
3 grooves	8632975	8.50
No grooves	8632976	8.50
(7) Interm. Servo Spring (Inner)		
1983-85	8632661	1.50
(8) Retainer		
1983-85	8632146	1.25
(9) Interm. Servo Spring (Cushion)		
Buick		
231		
1983-85	8630117	3.00
252		
1983-85	8630116	3.25
V-8 Gas		
1983-85	8628114	3.00
350 Diesel		
1983-85	8630117	3.00
Cadillac and Olds		
1983-85-exc.		
below	8630117	3.00
252	8630116	3.25
250	8628109	3.00
307	8628114	3.00
(10) Interm. Piston (Inner)		
1983-85	8632980	8.00
(11) Interm. Piston (Outer)		
1983-85	8638942	14.25
(12) Servo Cover (Interm.)		
1983-85	8632927	11.25
(13) Regulator Valve (Pressure)		
1983-85	8639718	12.75
(14) Spring (Regulator)		
1983-85-exc.		
below	8635210	2.50
252	8635142	2.75
(15) Guide Pin (Regulator)		
1983-85	117907	.50
(16) Bushing (Regulator)		
1983-85	8635063	10.50
(17) Throttle Lever		
1983-85	8635549	8.75
(18) Link (Lever to Cable)		
1983-85	8632681	N.L.
(19) Lifter Spring (T.V. Exh. Valve)		
1983-85	8628834	.75
(20) Lifter (T.V. Exh. Valve)		
1983-85	8628326	.75
(21) Gasket & Spacer Plate Kit		
1983-85	8635919	3.50
(22) Accumulator Piston		
1983-85	8635909	14.50
(23) Control Valve Assy.		
Buick & Oldsmobile		
1983-85-231	8635814	373.25
252	8639650	373.25
307 (1983)	8635953	373.25
307 (1984)	8639670	N.L.
2.73R	8639670	N.L.
3.15R	8639802	373.25
307 (1985)		
2.73R	8639675	373.50
3.15R	8639804	373.25
350 Diesel		
(1983)	8635777	N.L.
350 Diesel		
(1984)	8639680	393.50
350 Diesel		
(1985)	8639681	373.25
Cadillac		
1983-250	8639630	N.L.
350 Diesel	8635777	N.L.
1984-exc. below	8639640	373.25
350 Diesel	8639680	393.50
1985-exc. below	8639642	373.50
350 Diesel	8639681	373.25
(24) Oil Filter (w/Gaskets)		
1983-85	8635927	N.L.
(25) Oil Pan Gasket		
1983-85	8635884	N.L.

PARTS 23 GEAR TRAIN 23 PARTS

	Part No.	Price
(1) Band Assy. (Interm.)		
1983-85	8628098	N.L.
(2) Front Bushing (Direct Clutch)		
1983-85	8628918	6.50
(3) Retainer & Ball Assy. (Check Valve)		
1983-85	8628064	N.L.
(4) Housing & Drum Assy. (Direct Clutch)		
1983-85	8635926	130.00
(5) Rear Bushing (Direct Clutch)		
1983-85	8628917	6.75
(6) Seal Kit (Direct Clutch)		
1983-85	8628919	5.25
(7) Piston Kit (Direct Clutch)		
1983-85	8630913	22.00
(8) Retainer & Spring (Direct Clutch)		
1983-85-exc.		
below	8630096	9.00
V-6	8630211	9.00
(9) Steel Plate (Direct Clutch)		
1983-85	8628484	3.00
(10) Backing Plate (Direct Clutch)		
1983-85	8632570	10.50
(11) Seal (Turbine Shaft)		
1983-85	8628090	1.00
(12) Housing (Forward Clutch)		
1983-85	8632918	131.00
(13) Retainer & Ball Assy.		
1983-85	8628064	N.L.
(14) Plug (Turbine Shaft Cap)		
1983-85	8628145	.75

PARTS 23 GEAR TRAIN 23 PARTS

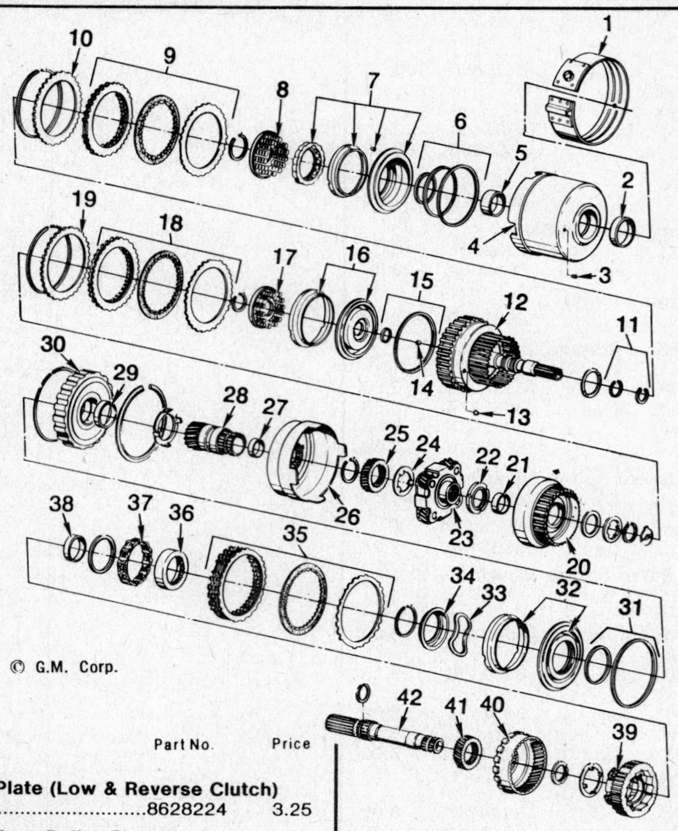

	Part No.	Price
(15) Piston Seal Kit (Forward Clutch)		
1983-85	8628924	3.25
(16) Piston & Ring (Forward Clutch)		
1983-85	8628971	15.00
(17) Retainer & Spring (Forward Clutch)		
1983-85	8628492	9.00
(18) Steel Plate (Forward Clutch)		
1983-85	8628086	3.00
(19) Backing Plate (Forward Clutch)		
1983-85	8628088	7.75
(20) Input Internal Gear		
1983-85	8632036	56.00
(21) Front Bushing (Internal Gear)		
1983-85	8630990	6.75
(22) Front Bearing (Internal Carrier)		
1983-85	8628202	5.50
(23) Input Carrier (Complete)		
1983-85	8632038	108.25
(24) Front Bearing (Sun Gear Carrier)		
1983-85	8628487	N.L.
(25) Input Sun Gear		
1983-85	8632040	24.25
(26) Input Drum		
1983-85	8628203	N.L.
(27) Rear Bushing (Sun Gear)		
1983-85	8628928	5.75
(28) Sun Gear (Reaction)		
1983-85	8632041	48.00
(29) Bushing (Reverse Clutch)		
1983-85	8628929	8.00
(30) Housing (Reverse Clutch)		
1983-85	8628212	51.00
(31) Seal Kit (Reverse Clutch)		
1983-85	8628930	4.25
(32) Piston Assy. (Low & Reverse)		
1983-85	8633934	20.00
(33) Release Spring (Reverse Clutch)		
1983-85 (Wave)	8628222	2.00
(34) Retainer (Reverse Clutch)		
1983-85	8628223	1.75

	Part No.	Price
(35) Steel Plate (Low & Reverse Clutch)		
1983-85	8628224	3.25
(36) Race (Low Roller Clutch)		
1983-85	8628184	16.50
(37) Roller (Low Clutch)		
1983-85	8628183	16.50
(38) Bushing (Rear Carrier)		
1983-85	8628947	6.25
(39) Reaction Carrier		
1983-85	8632044	149.00

	Part No.	Price
(40) Reaction Internal Gear		
1983-85	8632048	48.50
(41) Drive Gear (Governor)		
1983-85	8632051	26.50
(42) Output Shaft		
1983-85	8632540	63.25

PARTS 23 DRIVE LINK 23 PARTS

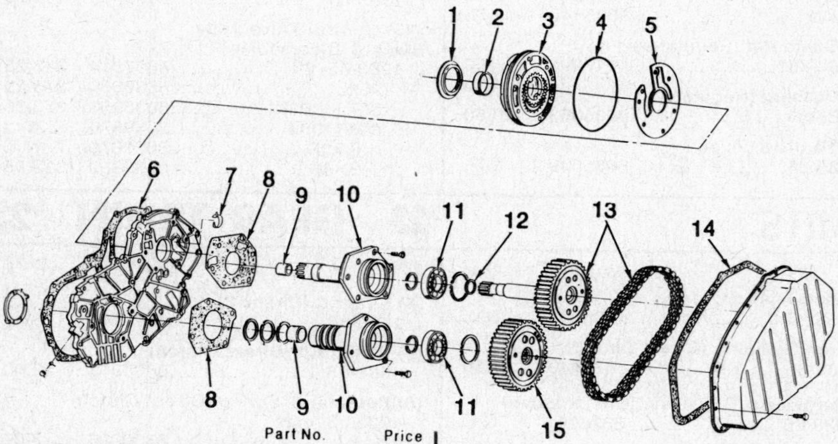

	Part No.	Price
(1) Seal (Oil Pump)		
1983-85	8630921	4.25
(2) Bushing (Oil Pump Body)		
1983-85	8628913	4.75
(3) Oil Pump Body (w/Gears)		
1983-85	8635022	132.00
(4) Seal (Pump to Case)		
1983-85	8625007	1.25
(6) Cover Gasket		
1983-85	8635013	4.00
(7) Out Check Valve (Converter)		
1983-85	8624076	1.50
(8) Support Gasket, Driven		
1983-85	8632018	1.50
(9) Bushing (Sprocket Support)		
1983-85-Serviced only with No. 10		
(10) Support (w/Stator)		
1983-85	8635040	113.00
(11) Bearing (Sprocket Shaft)		
1983-85-Order by model and description.		
(12) Oil Seal (Turbine Shaft)		
1983-85	8628090	1.00

	Part No.	Price
(13) Drive Sprocket Kit (w/Link)		
1983-85	8635087	143.00
(14) Cover Gasket		
1983-85-Use RTV sealant		

	Part No.	Price
(15) Driven Sprocket Assy.		
1983-85	8635089	118.50

 23 OVERDRIVE 23

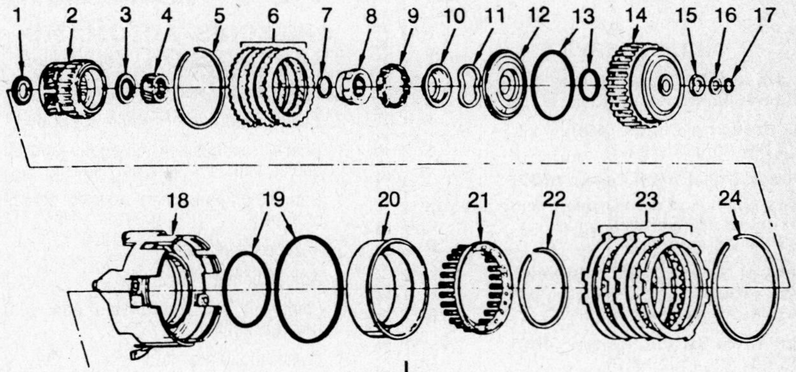

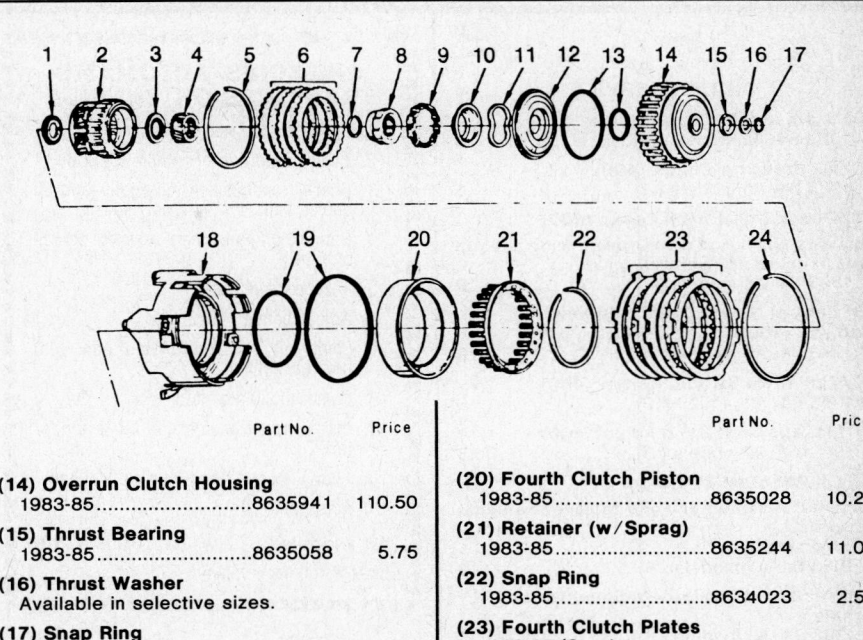

	Part No.	Price
(1) Thrust Bearing (Carrier to Drive Sprocket)		
1983-85	8634035	4.50
(2) Overdrive Carrier (Complete)		
1983-85	8635036	N.L.
(3) Thrust Bearing (Carrier to Sun Gear)		
1983-85	8634035	4.50
(4) Overdrive Sun Gear		
1983-85	8635033	38.00
(5) Snap Ring		
1983-85	8634056	1.50
(6) Overrun Clutch Plates		
1983-85 (Steel plate)	8634050	2.75
(Faced plate)	8634051	3.75
(Backing plate)	8634864	6.50
(7) Snap Ring		
1983-85	8634274	.75
(8) Cam (O.D. Clutch)		
1983-85	8635076	27.50
(9) Roller (O.D. Clutch)		
1983-85	930663	15.75
(10) Spring Retainer		
1983-85	8634061	1.50
(11) Overrun Clutch Spring (Waved)		
1983-85	8634116	2.50
(12) Piston (Overrun Clutch)		
1983-85	8634110	13.50
(13) Seal Kit (Overrun Clutch)		
1983-85	8634909	3.25
(14) Overrun Clutch Housing		
1983-85	8635941	110.50
(15) Thrust Bearing		
1983-85	8635058	5.75
(16) Thrust Washer		
Available in selective sizes.		
(17) Snap Ring		
1983-85	N.L.	
(18) Fourth Clutch Housing		
1983-85	8635735	75.50
(19) Seal Kit (Fourth Clutch)		
1983-85	8635924	6.50
(20) Fourth Clutch Piston		
1983-85	8635028	10.25
(21) Retainer (w/Sprag)		
1983-85	8635244	11.00
(22) Snap Ring		
1983-85	8634023	2.50
(23) Fourth Clutch Plates		
1983-85 (Steel plate)	8634026	3.50
(faced plate)	8634691	5.25
(backing plate)	8634866	6.75
(24) Snap Ring		
1983-85	8634158	2.25

LABOR 23 AUTOMATIC TRANSMISSION 23 LABOR

(Factory Time) Chilton Time

ON CAR SERVICE

(G) Drain and Refill Unit (400)
1983-84-All models (.6) 8

(G) Oil Pressure Check (400)
1983-84-All models (.3) 5

(M) Check Unit for Oil Leaks (400)
Includes: Clean and dry outside of case and run unit to determine point of leak.
1983-84-All models (.7) 9

(G) Neutral Safety Switch, Renew
Cadillac (400)
1983-84-All models (.4) 6

(G) Kickdown Switch, Renew (400)
1983-84-All models (.3) 5

(G) Linkage Check and Adjust (400)
1983-84-All models (.3) 5

(G) Oil Pan Gasket, Renew
Includes: Clean oil pan and replace strainer if necessary.
Cadillac (400)
1983-84-All models (.6) 9

(G) Vacuum Modulator Assembly, Renew
1983-84-All models (.3) 5

(G) Governor, Renew
Cadillac (400)
1983-84 (.4) 6

(G) Governor Assy., Recondition
Cadillac (400)
1983-84 (.9) 1.1

(G) Case Extension Rear Oil Seal, Renew
Includes: R&R propeller shaft.
Cadillac (400)
1983-84 (.5) 7

(G) Oil Control Valve Body, R&R or Renew
Includes: R&R oil pan.
Cadillac (400)
1983-84 (1.0) 1.2

(G) Oil Control Valve Body Assy., Disassemble and Clean
Includes: R&R oil pan and valve body.
Cadillac (400)
1983-84 (1.4) 2.0

(G) Speedometer Driven Gear, Renew
1983-84 (.3) 5

CHILTON'S AUTOMATIC TRANSMISSION TUNE-UP

1. Check engine performance
2. Check condition of transmission oil
3. Check transmission, oil cooler and oil cooler lines for external leaks
4. Remove oil pan, clean or renew screen or filter
5. Torque valve body
6. Adjust bands
7. Clean oil pan and install pan with new gasket
8. Check modulator and hose
9. Install new transmission oil to proper level
10. Adjust manual and throttle linkage
11. Road test

All models 1.5
Charge for parts used

(Factory Time) Chilton Time

(G) Servos, Renew or Recondition
Includes: R&R oil pan and valve body.
Cadillac (400)
1983-84 (1.0) 1.2

(G) Parking Pawl, Renew
Includes: R&R oil pan.
Cadillac (400)
1983-84 (1.2) 1.4

SERVICES REQUIRING R&R

(G) Transmission Assembly, R&R or Renew
Includes: Check oil pressure and adjust linkage.
Cadillac (400)
1983-84 (2.1) 3.3

(P) Transmission & Converter Assy., R&R and Recondition
Includes: Drain and pressure test converter. Recondition pump, clutch assemblies, gear unit, sprag clutch, planet carrier, governor, servos, valve body and adjust linkage.
Cadillac (400)
1983-84 (7.7) 10.9

(Factory Time) Chilton Time

(G) Torque Converter, Renew
Includes: R&R transmission, check pressure and end play of converter.
Cadillac (400)
1983-84 (2.3) 3.5

(G) Flywheel (Flex Plate), Renew
Includes: R&R transmission.
Cadillac (400)
1983-84 (2.2) 3.4

(G) Transmission Assy., Reseal
Includes: R&R trans and renew all external seals and gaskets.
Cadillac (400)
1983-84 (2.1) 5.0

(G) Front Oil Pump, Renew
Includes: R&R transmission, converter & pump seal.
Cadillac (400)
1983-84 (2.5) 3.7

(G) Front Oil Pump, Recondition
Includes: Recondition pressure regulator valve & R&R transmission.
Cadillac (400)
1983-84 (3.1) 4.5

(G) Front Oil Pump Seal, Renew
Includes: R&R transmission.
Cadillac (400)
1983-84 (2.2) 3.4

(G) Forward or Direct Clutch Drum, Recondition
Includes: R&R transmission.
Cadillac (400)
1983-84 (2.8) 4.8

(G) Intermediate Clutch Assy., Renew
Includes: R&R transmission.
Cadillac (400)
1983-84 (2.8) 4.8

(G) Low Sprag Unit, Renew
Includes: R&R transmission.
Cadillac (400)
1983-84 (4.2) 6.2

(G) Intermediate Sprag, Renew
Includes: R&R transmission.
Cadillac (400)
1983-84 (2.8) 5.2

PARTS 23 TURBO HYDRA-MATIC CASE & PARTS 23 PARTS

	Part No.	Price
Transmission Assembly		
Cadillac		
E.F.I.	8633974	340.00
G eng.	8642965	340.00
1983-exc. below	8633241	N.L.
Limo.	8633242	1494.00
1984-84-exc. below	8633294	1494.00
Comm. Chassis	8633295	1494.00
Transmission Gasket Set		
1983-87	8625905	N.L.
Transmission Snap Ring Kit		
1983-87	8623979	3.25
Transmission Overhaul Kit		
1983-87	8626984	N.L.
Flywheel (Flexplate)		
1983-87-exc. below	1616534	122.00
252	1623936	75.00
Neutral Safety/Backup Lamp Switch		
1983-87	1619499	26.00
(1) Retainer		
1983-84	8627650	.75
(2) Vacuum Modulator		
1983-84-Cadillac		
Limo.	3030843	29.75
Comm. Chassis	3027843	26.00
(3) Seal		
1983-84	1363951	.75
(4) Modulator Valve		
1983-84	8623983	8.50
(5) Cover		
1983-84	8623262	2.00
(6) Gasket		
1983-84	8623263	.50
(7) Governor Assy.		
1983-84-exc. below	8627882	49.50
Limo.	8629227	49.25
(8) Bushing		
1983-84	8623941	3.50
(9) Gasket		
1983-84	8624709	.75

PARTS 23 CASE & PLANET CARRIER 23 PARTS

	Part No.	Price
(10) Bushing		
1983-84	8626901	4.50
(11) Oil Seal		
1983-84-exc below	8625893	N.L.
(12) Sleeve Retainer		
1983-84	1254856	1.25
(13) Mainshaft		
1983-84	8625736	35.00
(14) Thrust Bearing (Kit)		
1983-84	8623921	4.50
(15) Rear Internal Gear		
1983-84	8623202	48.25
(16) Thrust Bearing (Kit)		
1983-84	8623922	4.25
(17) Output Shaft		
1983-84	8629221	113.50
(18) Thrust Bearing		
1983-84	8623920	4.00
(19) Bushing		
1983-84	8623944	4.50
(20) Sun Gear Shaft		
1983-84	8626809	15.25
(21) Bushing		
1983-84	8623944	4.50
(22) Sun Gear		
1983-84	8626807	31.50
(23) Reaction Carrier		
1983-84	8627893	168.00

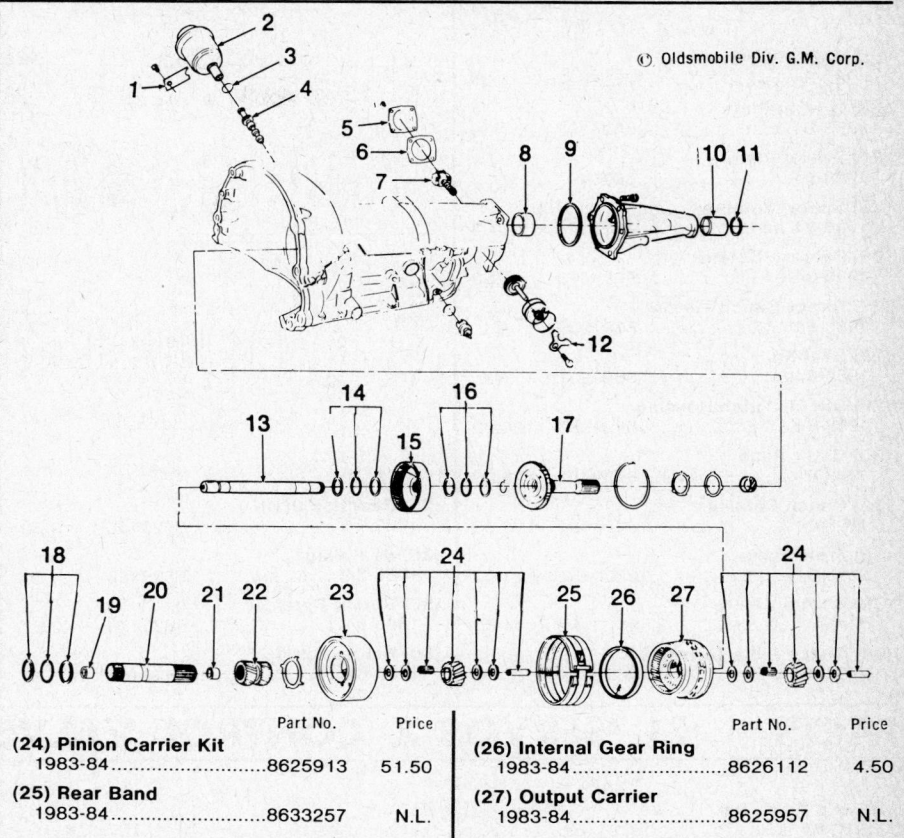

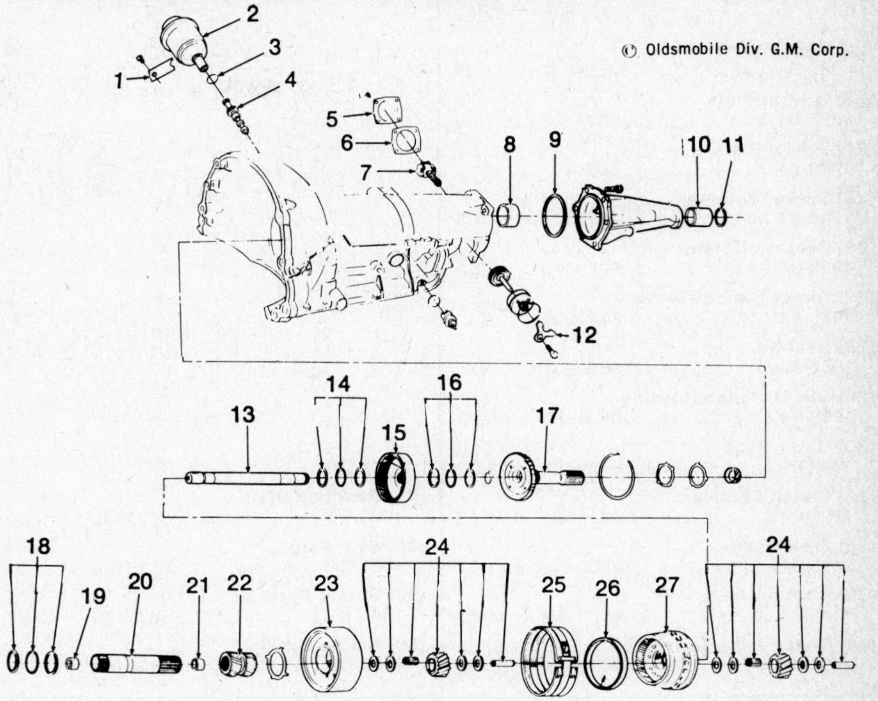

	Part No.	Price
(24) Pinion Carrier Kit		
1983-84	8625913	51.50
(25) Rear Band		
1983-84	8633257	N.L.
(26) Internal Gear Ring		
1983-84	8626112	4.50
(27) Output Carrier		
1983-84	8625957	N.L.

PARTS 23 PUMP, CLUTCH & CENTER SUPPORT 23 PARTS

	Part No.	Price
(1) Torque Converter		
1983-84-exc. below	8627946	N.L.
Limo	8627947	N.L.
252	8627945	169.00
(2) Oil Seal		
1983-84	8626916	N.L.
(3) Bushing		
1983-84	8623940	N.L.
(4) Bushing		
1983-84	8623944	4.50
(5) Front Oil Pump		
1983-84	8625954	N.L.
(6) Seal Ring		
1983-84	8626356	1.00
(7) Gasket		
1983-84	8623978	N.L.
(8) Seal		
1983-84	8626916	N.L.
(9) Turbine Shaft		
1983-84	8624772	38.50
(10) Pressure Regulator Valve		
1983-84	8623422	6.00
(11) Regulator Spring		
1983-84	8625648	3.25
(12) Forward Clutch Housing		
1983-84	8624908	56.00
(13) Seal Kit		
1983-84	8623917	N.L.

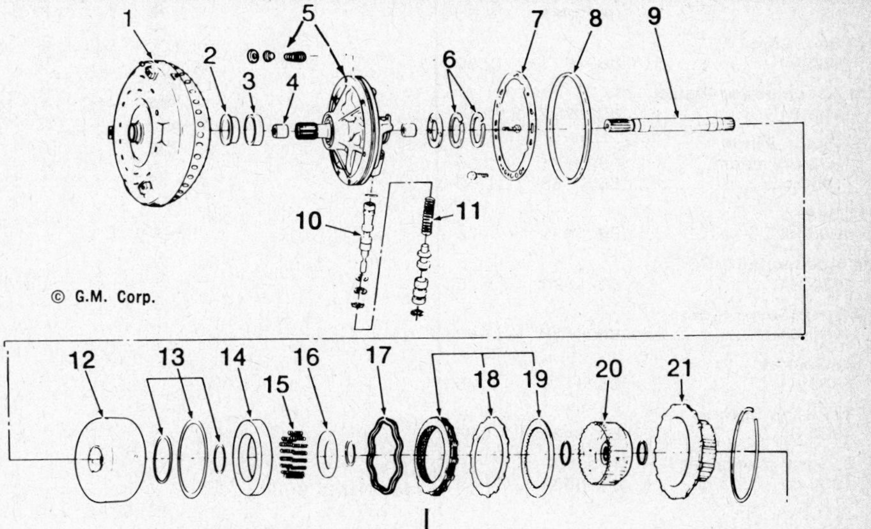

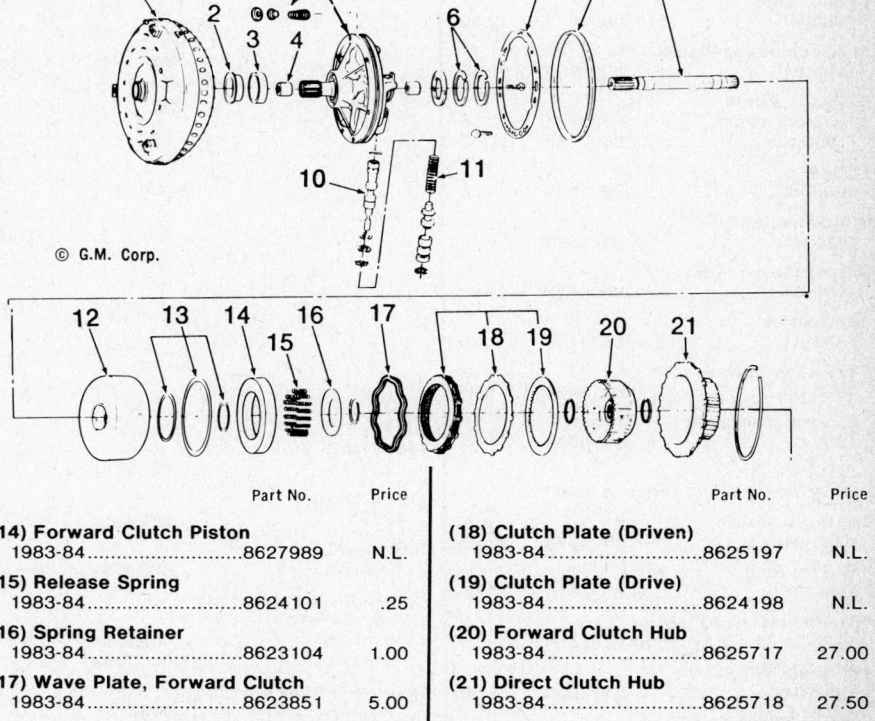

	Part No.	Price
(14) Forward Clutch Piston		
1983-84	8627989	N.L.
(15) Release Spring		
1983-84	8624101	.25
(16) Spring Retainer		
1983-84	8623104	1.00
(17) Wave Plate, Forward Clutch		
1983-84	8623851	5.00
(18) Clutch Plate (Driven)		
1983-84	8625197	N.L.
(19) Clutch Plate (Drive)		
1983-84	8624198	N.L.
(20) Forward Clutch Hub		
1983-84	8625717	27.00
(21) Direct Clutch Hub		
1983-84	8625718	27.50

PARTS 23 PUMP, CLUTCH & CENTER SUPPORT 23 PARTS

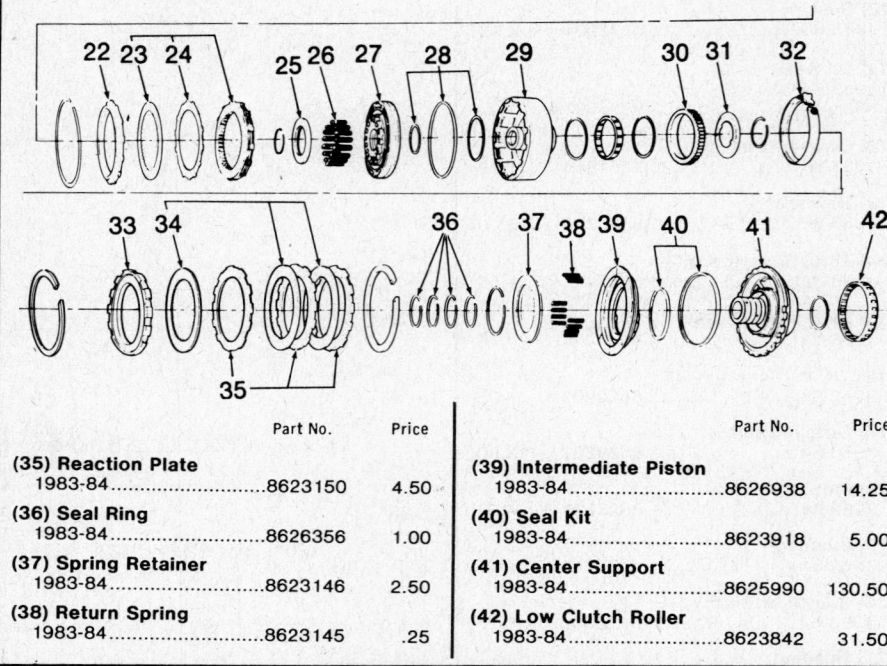

	Part No.	Price
(22) Backing Plate		
1983-84	8623122	11.25
(23) Driving Plate		
1983-84	8624198	N.L.
(24) Driven Plate		
1983-84	8625197	N.L.
(25) Spring Retainer		
1983-84	8623104	1.00
(26) Release Spring		
1983-84	8624073	.50
(27) Direct Clutch Piston		
1983-84	8627989	N.L.
(28) Seal Kit		
1983-84	8623917	N.L.
(29) Direct Clutch Housing		
1983-84	8627387	98.00
(30) Outer Race		
1983-84	8629487	45.00
(31) Clutch Retainer		
1983-84	8627334	2.00
(32) Front Band		
1983-84	12300852	21.00
(33) Backing Plate		
1983-84	8623152	14.50
(34) Clutch Plate (Driving)		
1983-84	8623151	4.75

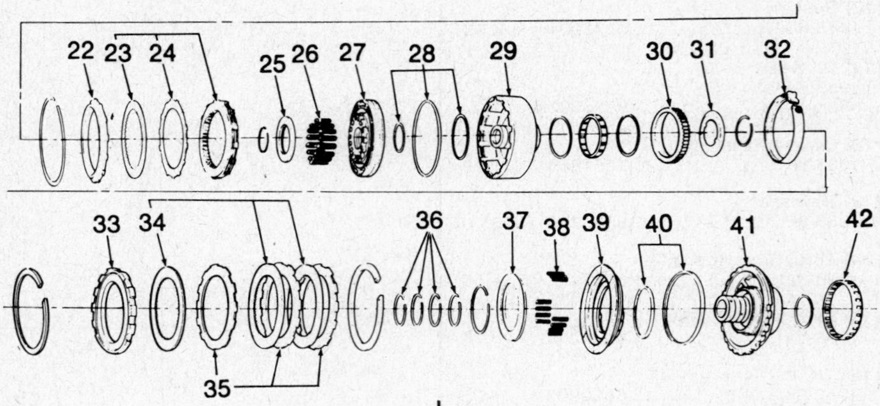

	Part No.	Price
(35) Reaction Plate		
1983-84	8623150	4.50
(36) Seal Ring		
1983-84	8626356	1.00
(37) Spring Retainer		
1983-84	8623146	2.50
(38) Return Spring		
1983-84	8623145	.25

	Part No.	Price
(39) Intermediate Piston		
1983-84	8626938	14.25
(40) Seal Kit		
1983-84	8623918	5.00
(41) Center Support		
1983-84	8625990	130.50
(42) Low Clutch Roller		
1983-84	8623842	31.50

PARTS 23 SERVOS & CONTROL VALVE BODY 23 PARTS

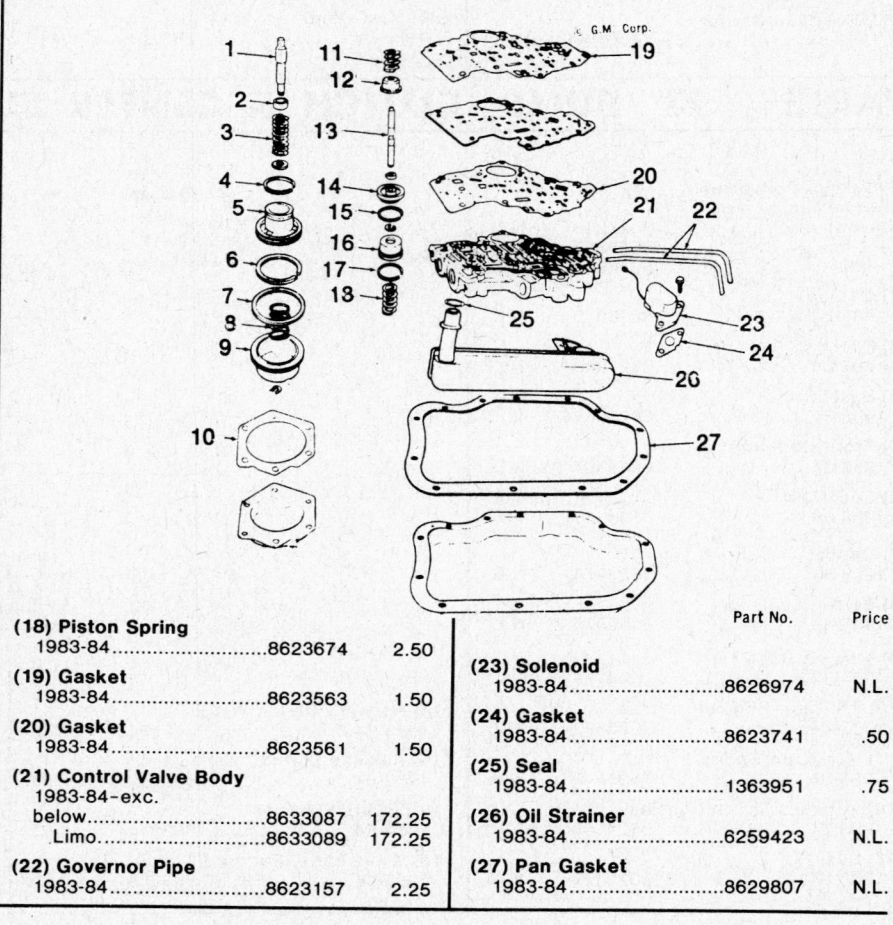

	Part No.	Price
(1) Band Apply Pin		
1983-84	8624139	5.25
(2) Spring Retainer		
1983-84	8623664	.75
(3) Piston Spring		
1983-84	8623666	1.50
(4) Seal Ring		
1983-84	8623671	2.50
(5) Accumulator Piston		
1983-84	8626902	15.50
(6) Piston Ring		
1983-84-inner	8623671	2.50
outer	8627153	1.50
(7) Seal		
1983-84	8623430	.75
(8) Accumulator Spring		
1983-84	8624391	1.75
(9) Rear Servo Piston		
1983-84	8624138	13.50
(10) Gasket		
1983-84	8623174	.75
(11) Piston Spring		
1983-84	8623489	1.50
(12) Spring Retainer		
1983-84	8626881	.75
(13) Piston Pin		
Order according to required length.		
(14) Front Piston		
1983-84	8626878	5.25
(15) Seal Ring		
1983-84	8623131	2.00
(16) Accumulator Piston		
1983-84-Order by model & description.		
(17) Seal Ring		
1983-84	8623653	1.00

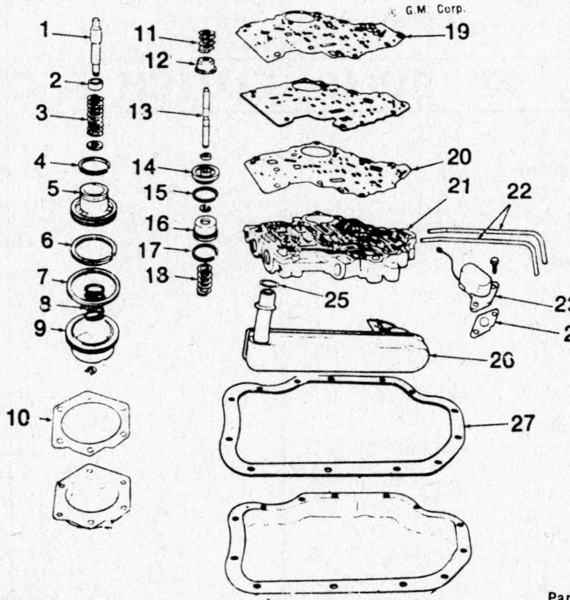

	Part No.	Price
(18) Piston Spring		
1983-84	8623674	2.50
(19) Gasket		
1983-84	8623563	1.50
(20) Gasket		
1983-84	8623561	1.50
(21) Control Valve Body		
1983-84-exc.		
below	8633087	172.25
Limo	8633089	172.25
(22) Governor Pipe		
1983-84	8623157	2.25

	Part No.	Price
(23) Solenoid		
1983-84	8626974	N.L.
(24) Gasket		
1983-84	8623741	.50
(25) Seal		
1983-84	1363951	.75
(26) Oil Strainer		
1983-84	6259423	N.L.
(27) Pan Gasket		
1983-84	8629807	N.L.

TURBO HYDRA-MATIC 440-T4
APPLICATION
1984-87
CHEVROLET CELEBRITY
BUICK CENTURY
OLDSMOBILE CIERA
PONTIAC 6000
CADILLAC DEVILLE-FLEETWOOD BROUGHAM (FWD)
CADILLAC ELDORADO-SEVILLE
BUICK ELECTRA (FWD)
BUICK LE SABRE (FWD)
BUICK RIVERA
OLDSMOBILE 88 (FWD)
OLDSMOBILE 98 REGENCY (FWD)
OLDSMOBILE TORONADO

(Factory Time) Chilton Time

ON CAR SERVICES

(G) Drain & Refill Unit
All models .9

(G) Oil Pressure Check
All models .5

(M) Check Unit For Oil Leaks
Includes: Clean and dry outside of case and run unit to determine point of leak.
All models .9

(G) Shift Linkage, Adjust
All models
Neutral Safety Switch (.3) .4
Shift Indicator Needle (.2) .3
Shift Linkage (.4) .5
T.V. Cable (.2) .4

(G) Modulator and/or Seal, Renew
All models (.4) .6

(G) Aspirator, R&R or Renew
All models (.3) .5

(G) Throttle Valve Control Cable and/or 'O' Ring, Renew
All models
Gas (.3) .5
Diesel (.4) .6

(G) Speedometer Driven Gear and/or Seal, Renew
All models (.3) .5

(G) Engine Metal Temperature Indicator Switch, Renew
All models (.2) .3

(G) Back-Up Lamp and Park/Neutral Switch, Renew
All models (.2) .3

(G) Governor Assy., R&R or Renew
Includes: Renew cover and 'O' ring.
All models (.5) .7
Recond gov or renew gear (.2) .3

(G) Oil Pan and/or Gasket, Renew
All models (.6) .9

(G) Valve Body Cover and/or Gasket, Renew
All models (2.0) 2.7

CHILTON'S AUTOMATIC TRANSMISSION TUNE-UP

1. Check engine performance
2. Check condition of transmission oil
3. Check transmission, oil cooler and oil cooler lines for external leaks
4. Remove oil pan, clean or renew screen or filter
5. Torque valve body
6. Adjust bands
7. Clean oil pan and install pan with new gasket
8. Check modulator and hose
9. Install new transmission oil to proper level
10. Adjust manual and throttle linkage
11. Road test

All models 1.5
Charge for parts used

(Factory Time) Chilton Time

(G) Valve Body and Oil Pump Assy., R&R or Renew
All models (2.3) 3.0
Recond valve body add (1.0) 1.0
Recond oil pump add (.4) .4

(G) Governor Pressure Switch and/or Electrical Connector, Renew
Includes: R&R trans oil pan, clean and inspect and renew gasket. R&R valve body cover. Renew 2-3 and/or 3-4 switches if required.
All models (2.1) 2.8

(G) Converter Clutch Solenoid Assy., Renew
All models (2.1) 2.8

(G) Auxiliary Valve Body, Renew
All models (2.4) 3.2

(G) Reverse Servo Assy., R&R or Renew
All models (.5) .7
Recond servo add (.2) .3

(G) 1-2 Servo Assy., R&R or Renew
All models (.5) .7
Recond servo add (.2) .3

(G) Accumulator Assy., R&R or Renew
All models (.8) 1.1

(G) Transmission Axle Shaft Oil Seals, Renew
All models
one side (.8) 1.1
both sides (1.4) 2.0

(G) Transmission Output Shaft, Renew
All models (1.1) 1.5

(G) Transmission Mounts, Renew
All models
front (.5) .7
rear (.5) .7
both (.9) 1.3

SERVICES REQUIRING R&R

(G) Transmission Assembly, Renew
1986-87
Eldorado-Seville (4.5) 6.0
Riviera (4.0) 6.0
Toronado (4.0) 6.0
1984-87
All other models (3.8) 5.1
w/Diesel eng add (.5) .5
w/Cruise control add (.2) .2

(G) Transmission and Converter Assy., R&R and Recondition
Includes: Drain and pressure test converter, recondition pump, clutch assemblies, servo's and accumulator. Recondition valve body, drive link, reaction carrier, sun gear and bands. Recondition differential and final drive.
1986-87
Eldorado-Seville (13.2) 17.8
Riviera (13.2) 17.8
Toronado (13.2) 17.8
1984-87
All other models (13.0) 17.5
w/Diesel eng add (.5) .5
w/Cruise control add (.2) .2
Leak check converter add .2

(G) Transmission Assembly, Reseal
Includes: R&R trans and renew all seals and gaskets.
1986-87
Eldorado-Seville 10.1
Riviera 10.1
Toronado 10.1
1984-87
All other models 9.2
w/Diesel eng add .5
w/Cruise control add (.2) .2

(G) Torque Converter, Renew
Includes: R&R transmission.
1986-87
Eldorado-Seville (4.3) 6.2
Riviera (4.0) 6.2
Toronado (4.0) 6.2
1984-87
All other models (3.8) 5.2
w/Diesel eng add (.5) .5
w/Cruise control add (.2) .2
Renew front seal add (.1) .1

(G) Flywheel (Flexplate), Renew
Includes: R&R transmission.
1986-87
Eldorado-Seville (4.5) 6.4
Riviera (4.2) 6.4
Toronado (4.2) 6.4
1984-87
All other models (4.0) 5.4
w/Diesel eng add (.5) .5
w/Cruise control add (.2) .2

(G) Converter Oil Seal, Renew
Includes: R&R transmission.
1986-87
Eldorado-Seville (4.3) 6.1
Riviera (4.1) 6.1
Toronado (4.1) 6.1
All other models (3.9) 5.2
w/Diesel eng add (.5) .5
w/Cruise control add (.2) .2
Renew bushing add (.1) .1

(G) Channel Plate and/or Gasket, Renew
Includes: R&R transmission.
1986-87
Eldorado-Seville (6.7) 9.0
Riviera (6.7) 9.0
Toronado (6.7) 9.0
1984-87
All other models (6.5) 8.7
w/Diesel eng add (.5) .5
w/Cruise control add (.2) .2
Recond valve body add (1.4) 1.4

LABOR 23 AUTOMATIC TRANSAXLE 23 LABOR

(Factory Time) — Chilton Time

Recond oil pump add (.4).................. .4
Recond servo's add, each (.2).......... .3
Recond accumulator add, each (.2)... .3

(G) Drive Link Assembly, Renew

Includes: R&R transmission.

1986-87
- Eldorado-Seville (7.0).................. 9.4
- Riviera (7.0) 9.4
- Toronado (7.0)............................ 9.4

1984-87
- All other models (6.8) 9.1

w/Diesel eng add (.5)........................ .5
w/Cruise control add (.2)................... .2
Recond valve body add (1.4)............ 1.4
Recond oil pump add (.4).................. .4
Recond servo's add, each (.2).......... .3
Recond accumulator add, each (.2)... .3

(G) Fourth Clutch Assy, and/or Driven Sprocket Support, R&R or Renew

Includes: R&R transmission.

1986-87
- Eldorado-Seville (7.2).................. 9.7
- Riviera (7.2) 9.7
- Toronado (7.2)............................ 9.7

1984-87
- All other models (7.0) 9.4

w/Diesel eng add (.5)........................ .5
w/Cruise control add (.2)................... .2
Recond valve body add (1.4)............ 1.4
Recond oil pump add (.4).................. .4
Recond servo's add, each (.2).......... .3
Recond accumulator add, each (.2)... .3
Renew turbine shaft seals
  add (.2).. .2
Recond fourth clutch and/or
  driven sprocket support add (.3) .4

(G) Second Clutch, Reverse Band, Input and Third Clutches, Renew

Includes: R&R transmission, renew input sprag, third roller clutch and reverse reaction drum.

1986-87
- Eldorado-Seville (7.5).................. 10.1
- Riviera (7.5) 10.1
- Toronado (7.5)............................ 10.1

1984-87
- All other models (7.3) 9.8

w/Diesel eng add (.5)........................ .5
w/Cruise control add (.2)................... .2
Recond valve body add (1.4)............ 1.4
Recond oil pump add (.4).................. .4
Recond servo's add, each (.2).......... .3
Recond accumulator add, each (.2)... .3
Renew turbine shaft seals
  add (.2).. .2
Recond fourth clutch and/or
  driven sprocket support add (.3) .4
Recond third roller clutch
  add (.3).. .4
Recond input & third clutches
  add (.4).. .5

(G) Differential and Final Drive Assy., Renew

Includes: R&R transmission.

1986-87
- Eldorado-Seville (8.1).................. 10.9
- Riviera (8.1) 10.9
- Toronado (8.1)............................ 10.9

1984-87
- All other models (7.9) 10.6

w/Diesel eng add (.5)........................ .5
w/Cruise control add (.2)................... .2
Recond valve body add (1.4)............ 1.4
Recond oil pump add (.4).................. .4
Recond servo's add, each (.2).......... .3
Recond accumulator add, each (.2)... .3
Renew turbine shaft seals add (.2).... .2
Recond fourth clutch and/or
  driven sprocket support add (.3) .4
Recond third roller clutch
  add (.3).. .4
Recond input & third clutches
  add (.4).. .5
Recond second clutch add (.3).......... .4
Recond accumulators add
  each (.2).. .3
Renew bushings add-each (.1).......... .1
Recond diff and final drive
  add (.8).. 1.0

PARTS 23 CASE AND PARTS 23 PARTS

Part No. — Price

(PART 1)

Transaxle Assy.

Part numbers shown are for pricing reference only. Order unit with complete year, model, engine and unit I.D. number.

1984-87
- Code AY 8656120 2678.00
- Code BA ....8656119 N.L.
- Code BN ....8656115 N.L.
- Code BS ....8656117 N.L.
- Code BU ....8656116 N.L.
- Code BX ....8658351 N.L.
- Code CP ....8656611 N.L.
- Code CW (1984-87)......................8656113 N.L.
- Code OB (1984-87)......................8656121 2678.00
- Code OV ....8649383 N.L.
- Code OY ....8656676 N.L.

Gasket Kit
- 1984 ....8644915 25.50
- 1985-86 ....8646942 62.25

Seal Kit (Turbine Shaft)
- 1984-87 ....8644920 4.50

(1) Torque Converter (Rebuilt)

V6-173
- 1984-87 ....8644932 340.00

V6-181

1984-87
- 3.06 axle......................8653939 340.00
- 3.33 axle......................8644936 340.00

V6-231

1984-87-Trans. Code
- BA......................8644936 340.00
- X......................8653959 340.00

V8-252
- 1985-87 ....8644935 340.00

V6-260 Diesel
- 1984-85 ....8644933 340.00

(2) Sleeve (Governor Shaft)
- 1984-87 ....8631328 2.75

(3) Governor

V-6-173
- 1984-87 ....8644955 N.L.

V-6-181
- 1984-87-3.06R......................8644954 52.00
- 3.33R......................8644958 35.50

V-6-231

1984-85-Code
- BA 8644953 52.00
- Code BC ....8644959 N.L.

1986-87
- 2.73, 2.84R......................8644966 52.00
- 2.97R......................8644968 46.00

V-8-252
- 1984-87 ....8644962 46.00

V-6-Diesel
- 1984-85-2.84R......................8644951 N.L.
- 3.06R......................8644956 52.00

(4) Drive Gear (Speedo.)
- 1984-87-10 teeth 8632646 2.00
- 35 teeth......................14047637 8.00

(5) Cover (Governor)
- 1984-87 ....8644924 21.00

(6) Driven Gear (Speedo.)

Order by year and model.

(7) Sleeve (Driven Gear)

Order by year and model.

(8) Transaxle Case (w/Bushing)
- 1984-87 ....8646909 475.00

(9) Electric Connector (w/Seal)

1984-87-exc.
- below......................8634383 13.00
- Diesel......................8635152 4.75

(10) Valve (Modulator)
- 1984-87 ....8656074 6.00

(11) Vacuum Modulator

1984-87-exc.
- below......................3057721 16.00
- Diesel......................8649099 13.50

(12) Channel Plate
- 1984-87 ....8644998 290.00

(13) Oil Filter
- 1984-87 ....8646902 14.50

(14) Oil Pan Gasket
- 1984-87 ....8656396 4.25

(15) Drive Shaft (Oil Pump)
- 1984-87 ....8656624 52.00

(16) Spacer Plate (Valve Body)

Part numbers for pricing reference only. Order by transmission I.D. code.
- 1984-87-173......................8658354 N.L.
- 181 ....8652494 N.L.
- 231 ....8646934 9.25
- 252 ....8658062 7.00
- Diesel-Ext. EGR 8658070 7.00
- Diesel wo/Ext. EGR ....8656032 N.L.

PARTS 23 CASE & PARTS 23 PARTS

	Part No.	Price
(17) Gasket Kit (Valve Body Spacer)		
1984-85 (1st design)	8646907	2.50
1985-87 (2nd des. 1985)	8646949	2.75
(18) Throttle Lever		
1984-87	8656090	23.25
(19) Link (Throttle Lever)		
1984-87	8649659	2.25
(20) Oil Pump Screen (Pressure)		
1984-87	8644494	1.50
(21) Bearing (Oil Pump Shaft)		
1984-87	8644516	4.25
(22) Screen (Clutch Solenoid)		
1984-87	8649474	2.50
(23) Control Valve		
Part numbers shown are for pricing reference only. Order with transmission I.D. code.		
V-6-173		
1984-87	8644975	385.00
V-6-181		
1984-87-3.06R	8644981	385.00
3.33R	8658496	385.00
V-6-231		
1984-87-exc. below	8644982	385.00
Code BC	8658476	N.L.
V-8-252		
1984-87	8644972	385.00
260 Diesel		
1984-87-exc. below	8644970	394.00
Ext. EGR	8644980	394.00
(24) Oil Pump (w/Gasket)		
1984-87-exc. below	8644990	375.00
252	8646900	230.00
(25) Harness (Pump Wiring)		
1984-87-exc. below	8658448	7.50
252	8649665	18.50
Diesel	8644799	18.50
(26) Pan (Case Side Cover)		
1984-87	8656398	30.00

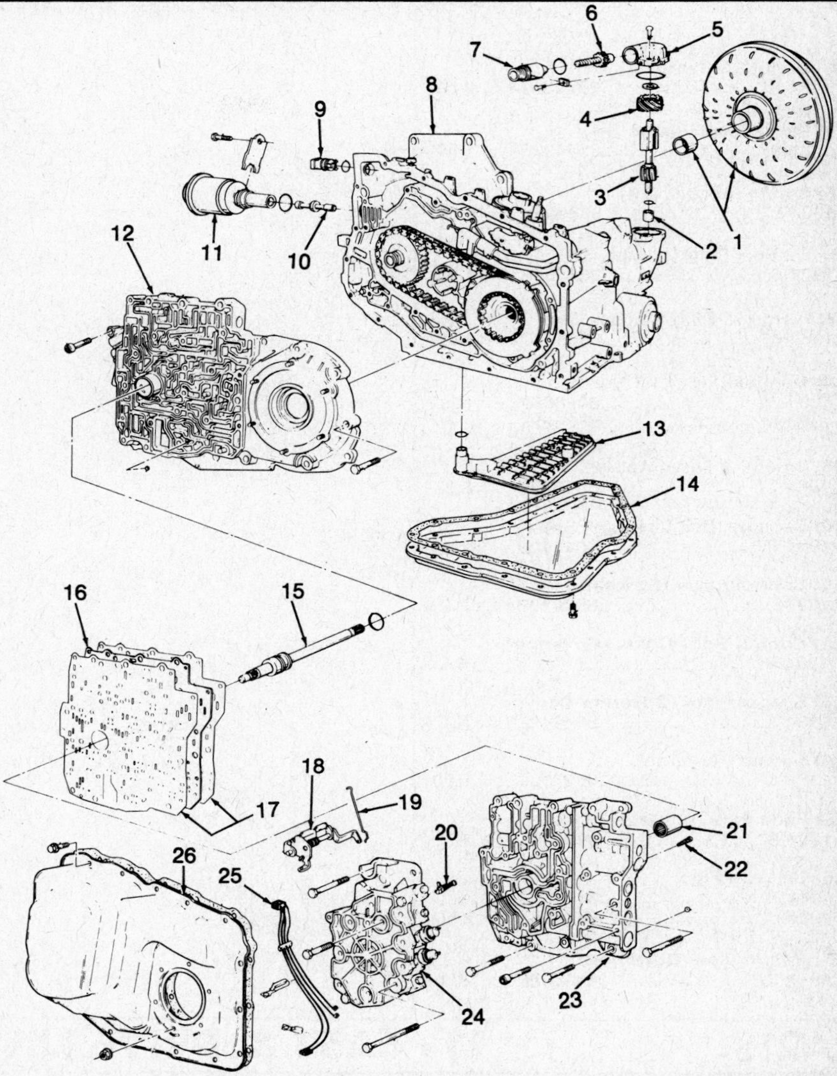

PARTS 23 CASE AND PARTS 23 PARTS

(PART 2)

	Part No.	Price
Gasket Kit (Channel Plate)		
1984-87	8646908	3.50
Element Kit (Thermo.)		
1984-87	8646904	2.50
Governor Retainer Kit (Oil Pressure)		
1984-87	8644929	N.L.
(1) Plate (Thermo. Element)		
1984-87	8646505	1.50
(2) Thermo Element		
1984-87	8646105	1.50
(3) Oil Scoop (Bottom Of Case)		
1984-87	8656242	4.25
(4) Return Spring (Oil Pipe)		
1984-87	8649375	1.00
(5) Retainer (Oil Pipe)		
1984-87	8656382	N.L.
(6) Oil Lube Pipe		
1984-87	8656346	2.00

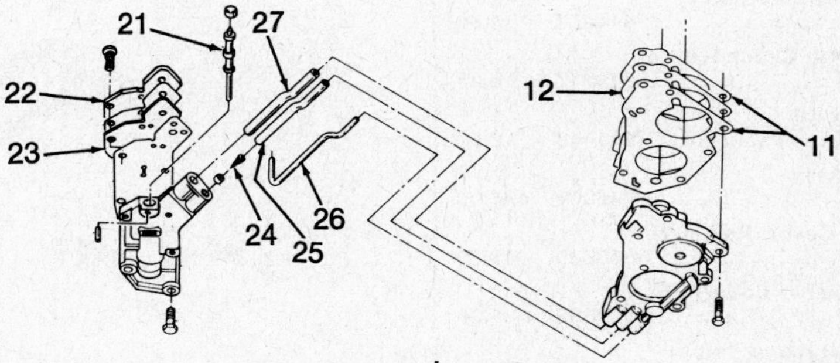

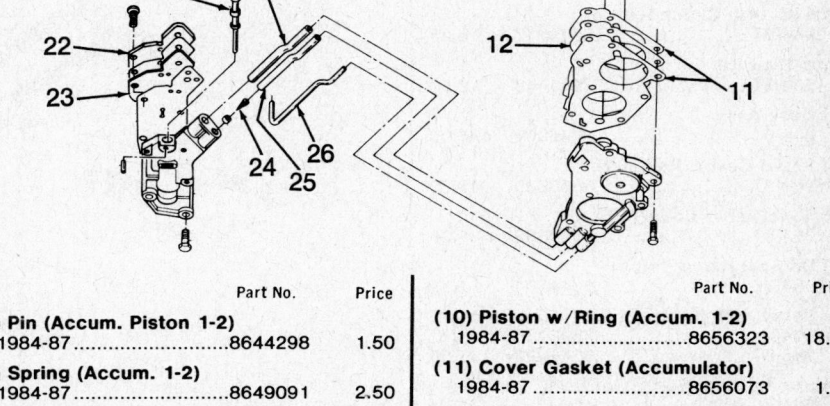

	Part No.	Price
(7) Pin (Accum. Piston 1-2)		
1984-87	8644298	1.50
(8) Spring (Accum. 1-2)		
1984-87	8649091	2.50
(9) Oil Seal Ring (Accum. 1-2)		
1984-87	8635568	1.50

	Part No.	Price
(10) Piston w/Ring (Accum. 1-2)		
1984-87	8656323	18.00
(11) Cover Gasket (Accumulator)		
1984-87	8656073	1.25
(12) Spacer Plate (Accumulator)		
1984-87	8649376	5.00

PARTS 23 CASE AND PARTS 23 PARTS

	Part No.	Price
(13) Stop (1-2 Band)		
1984-87	8649302	1.50
(14) Pin (Accum. Piston 3-4)		
1984-87	8644298	1.50
(15) Spring (Accum. 3-4)		
1984-87	8649092	2.50
(16) Oil Seal Ring (Accum. 3-4)		
1984-87	8635568	1.50
(17) Piston w/Ring (Accum. 3-4)		
1984-87	8656323	18.00
(18) Manifold Pipe (1-2 Servo)		
1984-85	8656632	N.L.
1986-87	8658225	12.25
(19) Pipe (1-2 Servo Apply)		
1984-87	8649695	3.25
(20) Capsule (Ball Check w/Spring.)		
1984-87	8646190	3.50
(21) Control Valve (Governor)		
1984	8649199	N.L.
(22) Control Body Cover (Governor)		
1984-87		N.L.
(23) Spacer Plate (Governor Body)		
1984	8649478	N.L.
(24) Screen (Governor)		
1984-87	8627509	1.00
(25) Feed Pipe (Governor)		
1984-87	8656381	2.75
(26) Oil Lube Pipe		
1984	8644313	N.L.
1985-87	8656651	2.50
(27) Return Pipe (Governor)		
1984-87	8656380	2.75

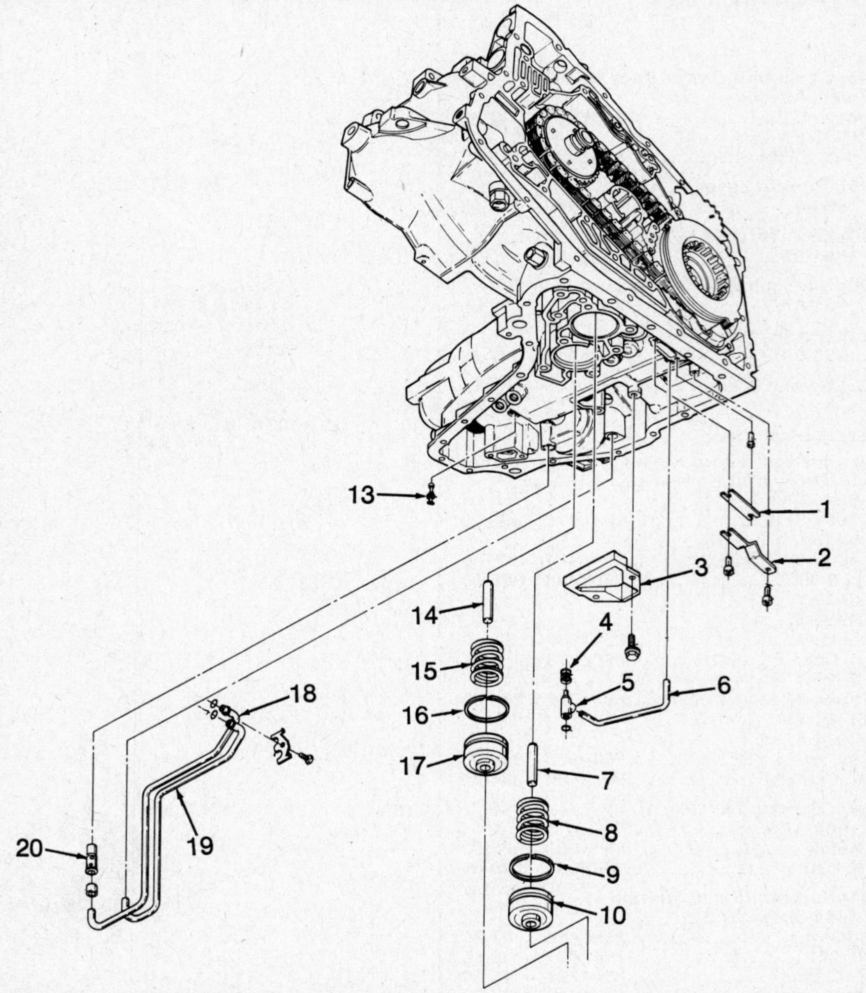

PARTS 23 CASE & DRIVE LINK 23 PARTS

	Part No.	Price
Overhaul & Repair Kit		
1984-87	8644916	124.00
Seal Kit (Turbine Shaft)		
1984-87	8644920	4.50
Seal Kit (4th Clutch Piston)		
1984-87	8644917	5.25
Snap Ring Kit		
1984-87	8631948	2.50
(1) Case Assy.		
1984-87	8646909	475.00
(2) Servo Cover (Rev. 1-2)		
1984-87	8656530	18.00
(3) Seal (Servo Cover)		
1984-87	8649832	1.00
(4) Oil Seal Ring (Piston)		
1984-87	8644081	N.L.
(5) Servo Piston (Rev. 1-2)		
1984	8649185	N.L.
1985-87	8646922	11.50
(6) Spring (Rev. Servo Cushion)		
1984-87-exc. below	8649095	2.50
Diesel	8649094	2.50

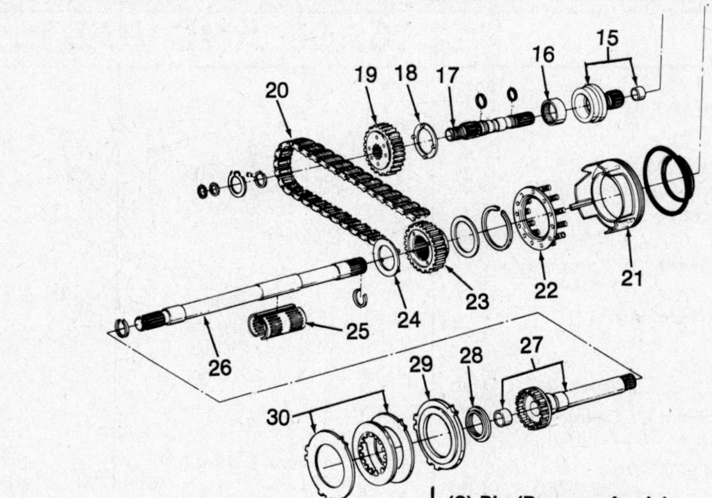

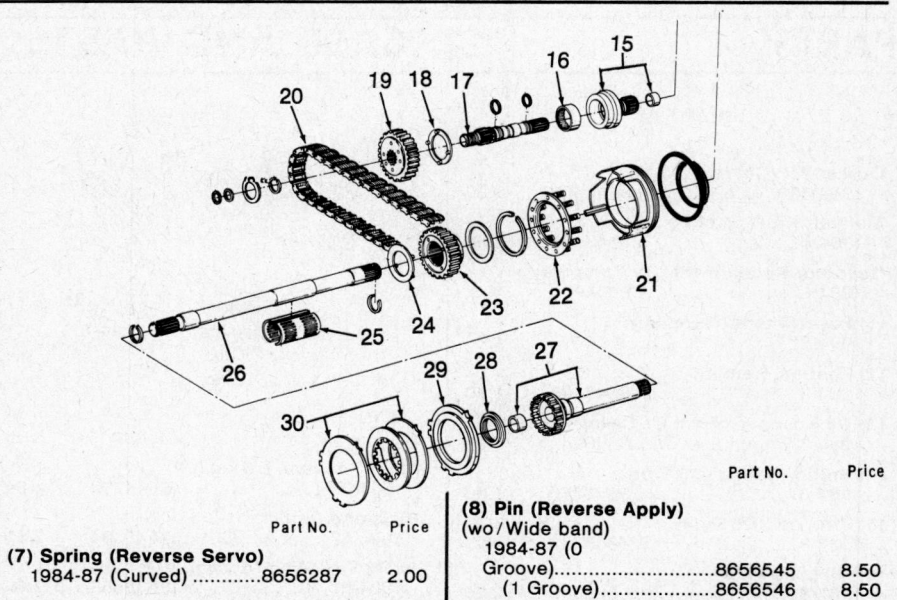

	Part No.	Price
(7) Spring (Reverse Servo)		
1984-87 (Curved)	8656287	2.00

	Part No.	Price
(8) Pin (Reverse Apply)		
(wo/Wide band)		
1984-87 (0 Groove)	8656545	8.50
(1 Groove)	8656546	8.50

PARTS 23 CASE & DRIVE LINK 23 PARTS

	Part No.	Price
(2 Groove)	8656547	8.50
(3 Groove)	8656548	8.50
(4 Groove)	8656544	8.50
(w/Wide band)		
1984-87 (1 Groove)	8656543	8.50
(9) Spring (Servo Return)		
1984-87	8649147	2.50
(10) Seal (Converter)		
1984-87	8637906	4.50
(11) Seal (Axle)		
1984-87	8631156	N.L.
(12) Bushing (Case)		
1984-87	8631119	1.75
(13) Pin (1-2 Band Apply)		
(wo/Wide band)		
1984-87 (1 ring)	8656539	8.50
(2 rings)	8656540	8.50
(3 rings)	8656541	8.50
(w/Wide band)		
1984-87 (0 rings)	8656542	8.50
(1 ring)	8656537	8.50
(2 rings)	8656538	8.50
(14) Spring (1-2 Servo Cushion)		
1984-87-exc. below	8646456	2.50
Diesel	8649098	2.50
(15) Support (Drive Sprocket)		
1984-87	8637185	70.00
(16) Bearing (Driven Sprocket)		
1984-87	8631186	8.25
(17) Turbine Shaft (w/Sleeve)		
1984-87	8644630	37.00
(18) Thrust Washer		
1984-87	8646125	N.L.
(19) Drive Sprocket		
1984-87-35 teeth	8644677	95.50
37 teeth	8644679	87.00
(20) Link (Drive Selective)		
1984-87	8652408	N.L.

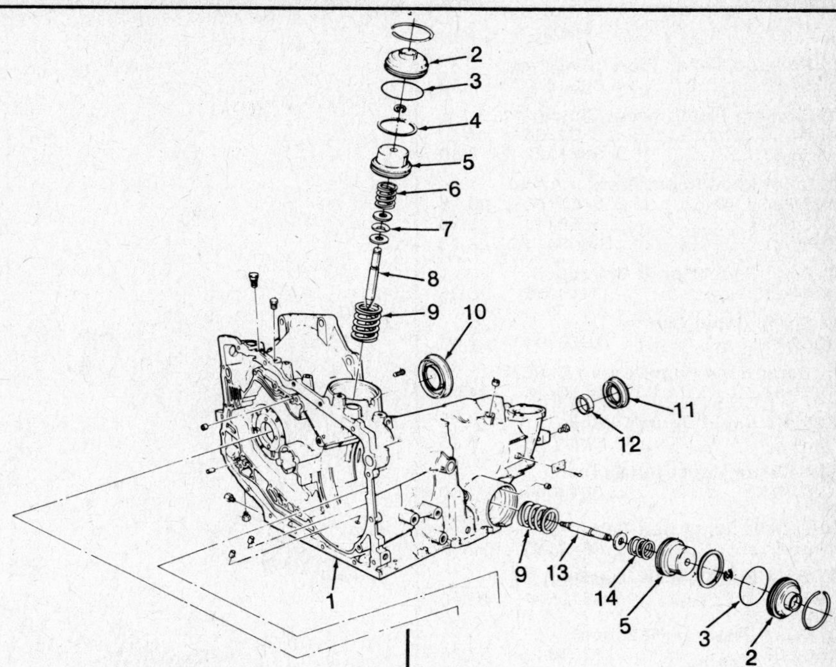

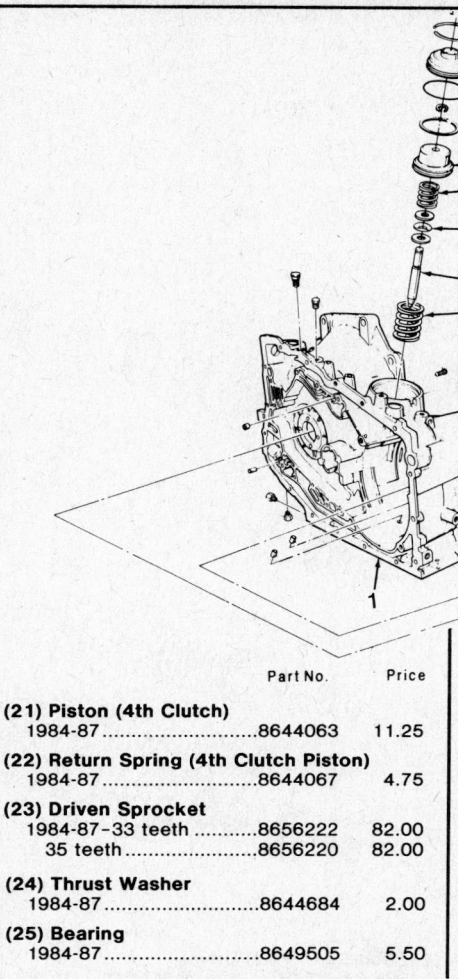

	Part No.	Price
(21) Piston (4th Clutch)		
1984-87	8644063	11.25
(22) Return Spring (4th Clutch Piston)		
1984-87	8644067	4.75
(23) Driven Sprocket		
1984-87-33 teeth	8656222	82.00
35 teeth	8656220	82.00
(24) Thrust Washer		
1984-87	8644684	2.00
(25) Bearing		
1984-87	8649505	5.50

	Part No.	Price
(26) Output Shaft		
1984-87	8649506	63.00
(27) Hub (4th Clutch)		
1984-87	8656355	58.25
(28) Thrust Bearing (4th Clutch)		
1984-87	8656393	6.25
(29) Plate (4th Clutch Apply)		
1984-87	8649831	4.75
(30) Reaction Plate (4th Clutch)		
1984-87	8644035	N.L.

PARTS 23 GEAR TRAIN 23 PARTS

	Part No.	Price
Piston Seal Kit (2nd Clutch)		
1984-87	8644918	5.25
Housing & Piston Seal Kit		
1984-87	8644919	5.25
(1) Bearing (Driven Sprocket)		
1984-87	8644054	17.00
(2) Support (Driven Sprocket)		
1984	8656390	N.L.
1985-87	8658097	185.00
(3) Scoop (Chain Scavenging)		
1984-87-exc. below	8656562	5.50
252	8656565	5.50
(4) Thrust Washer		
1984-87	8644069	1.00
(5) Oil Seal Ring		
1984-87	8656370	1.50
(6) Bushing		
Part of support No. 2.		
(7) Band (Reverse)		
1984-87	8649300	37.00
(8) Drum Kit w/Bushing (2nd Clutch)		
1984-87	8646929	58.00

	Part No.	Price
(9) Piston (2nd Clutch)		
1984-87	8656740	7.00
(10) Apply Ring (2nd Clutch)		
1984-87	8644109	16.00
(11) 2nd Clutch Plate (Flat)		
1984-87	8656642	3.75
(12) Backing Plate (2nd Clutch)		
1984-87	8656628	8.50
(13) Bushing (Input Shaft)		
Part of input shaft No. 16.		
(14) Bearing (Thrust Sprocket)		
1984-87	8649704	6.25
(15) Oil Seal Rings (Input Shaft)		
1984-87	8656342	1.50
(16) Input Shaft Kit		
1984	8646906	N.L.
1985-87	8646925	78.00
(17) Seal (Input Shaft)		
1984-87	8644919	5.25
(18) Thrust Washer (Input Shaft)		
1984	8649814	2.00
1985-87	8656369	2.25
(19) Piston (Input Clutch)		
1984-87	8644148	16.50

	Part No.	Price
(20) Input Spring (w/Retainer)		
1984-87	8644151	5.50
(21) Piston Housing (3rd Clutch)		
1984-87	8656310	15.00
(22) Piston Kit (3rd Clutch)		
1984-87	8646924	12.00
(23) Guide (3rd Clutch)		
1984	8644158	N.L.
1985-87	8658201	6.00
(24) 3rd Clutch Plate (Flat)		
1984-87-Steel	8656313	2.50
Faced	8646923	10.75
(25) Backing Plate (3rd Clutch)		
1984	8656752	N.L.
1985-87	8646923	10.75
(26) Roller Cam (3rd Clutch)		
1984-87	8644620	4.50
(27) Roller (3rd Clutch)		
1984-87	8646539	9.50
(28) Race (3rd Roller Clutch)		
1984-87	8646539	9.50
(29) Plate (Input Clutch Apply)		
1984-87	8644166	4.75

PARTS 23 GEAR TRAIN 23 PARTS

Part No. — Price

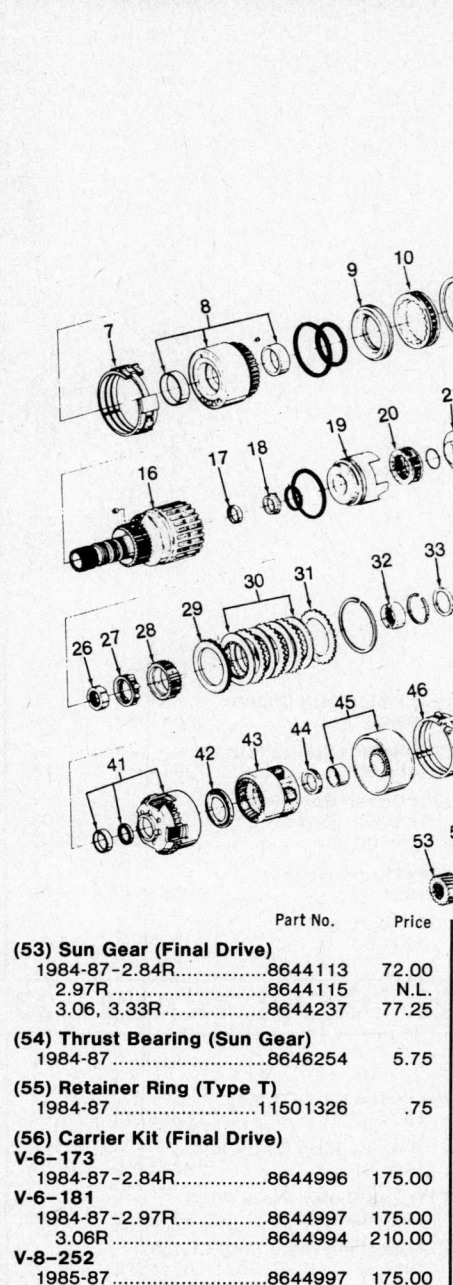

(30) Forward Clutch Plate (Flat Steel)
1984-87 .... 8631379 3.50

(31) Backing Plate (Direct Clutch)
1984 .... 8631764 N.L.
1985-87 .... 8631027 8.50

(32) Inner Race (Input Sprag Clutch)
1984-exc. below............ 8658450 28.75
C body 8658411 28.75
1985-87 .... 8658411 28.75

(33) Plate (Input Sprag Clutch)
1984-87 .... 8644016 5.25

(34) Sprag (Input Clutch)
1984-87 .... 8658501 22.00

(35) Outer Race (Input Sprag Clutch)
1984-87 .... 8656714 24.00

(36) Plate (Input Sprag Clutch)
1984-87 .... 8644016 5.25

(37) Retainer (Input Sprag Clutch)
1984-87 .... 8644044 1.00

(38) Spacer (Input Sun Gear)
1984-87 .... 8649545 2.00

(39) Input Sun Gear (w/Bushing)
1984-87 .... 8649504 27.25

(40) Drum (Reverse Reaction)
1984-87 .... 8656612 50.75

(41) Input Carrier (Complete)
1984-87 .... 8646500 108.00

(42) Bearing (Input Carrier)
1984-87 .... 8646504 5.50

(43) Reaction Carrier (Complete)
1984-87 .... 8649355 148.00

(44) Bearing
1984-87 .... 8649353 4.75

(45) Reaction Sun Gear (w/Drum & Bushing)
1984-87 .... 8649660 68.00

(46) Band (1 & 2)
1984-87 .... 8656647 47.50

(47) Sun Gear Shaft (Final Drive)
1984-87 .... 8649543 40.50

(48) Bushing (Final Drive)
Part of final drive gear No. 50.

(49) Bearing Assy.
1984-87 .... 8644206 4.75

(50) Gear (Final Drive)
1984-87 .... 8656372 68.00

(51) Thrust Bearing (Parking Gear)
1984-87 .... 8644240 5.20

(52) Gear (Parking)
1984-87 .... 8644238 12.00

Part No. — Price

(53) Sun Gear (Final Drive)
1984-87-2.84R.............. 8644113 72.00
2.97R .... 8644115 N.L.
3.06, 3.33R.................. 8644237 77.25

(54) Thrust Bearing (Sun Gear)
1984-87 .... 8646254 5.75

(55) Retainer Ring (Type T)
1984-87 .... 11501326 .75

(56) Carrier Kit (Final Drive)
V-6-173
1984-87-2.84R.............. 8644996 175.00
V-6-181
1984-87-2.97R.............. 8644997 175.00
3.06R 8644994 210.00
V-8-252
1985-87 .... 8644997 175.00
Diesel & V-6-231
1984-87 .... 8644994 210.00

(57) Drive Gear (Governor)
1984-87 .... 8631571 14.00

(58) Thrust Washer (1.65mm)
1984-87 .... 8631422 1.50
Smallest size listed other sizes available.

(59) Bearing (Diff. Carrier To Case)
1984-87 .... 8631362 6.50

(60) Side & Pinion Gear Kit
Part numbers for pricing reference only. Order with correct transmission I.D. code.
1984-87 .... 8646910 79.00
1985-87 .... 8637919 N.L.

PARTS 23 TRANSMISSION CASE COVER 23 PARTS

Part No. — Price

(1) Channel Plate (Complete)
1984-87 .... 8644998 290.00

(2) Oil Seal (Axle)
Order by model & year.
1984 .... 8631156 N.L.
1985-87 .... 8644637 3.25

(3) Sleeve (Cont. Body Align)
1984-87 .... 8656077 1.25

(4) Accumulator Piston (Conv. Clutch)
1984-87 .... 8646926 6.50

(5) Piston Seal (Accumulator Piston)
1984-87 .... 8658086 1.00

(6) Pin (Converter Clutch)
1984 .... 8649431 N.L.
1985-87 .... 8656730 1.00

(7) Accumulator Spring (Conv. Clutch)
1984 .... 8649430 N.L.
1985-87 .... 8656097 2.00

(8) Blow Off Plug (Conv. Clutch)
1984-87 .... 8656038 1.00

(9) Blow Off Spring (Conv. Clutch)
1984-87 .... 8658123 1.25

(10) Accumulator Piston (Input Clutch)
1984-87 .... 8646927 14.50

	Part No.	Price
(11) Ring (Input Clutch)		
1984	8644398	N.L.
1985-87	8649773	2.25
(12) Pin (Input Clutch)		
1984-87	8644399	N.L.
(13) Accumulator Spring (Input Shaft)		
1984-87-exc. below	8649089	4.75
Diesel	8649090	4.75
(14) Gasket Kit		
1984	8646908	3.50
1985-87	8644915	25.25
(15) Blow Off Spring (Low)		
1984-87	8644624	1.50
(16) Link (Manual Valve)		
1984-87	8649659	2.25
(17) Valve (Manual)		
1984-87-1st design	8649776	8.50
2nd design	8646933	8.50

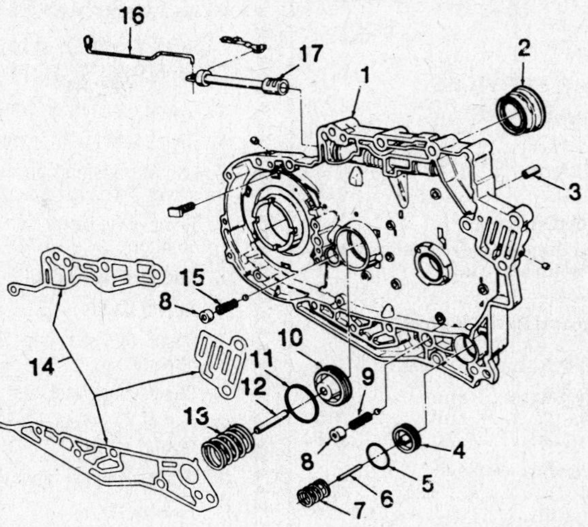

(Factory Time) Chilton Time

ON CAR SERVICES

(G) Drain & Refill Unit
All models 9

(G) Oil Pressure Check
All models (.5) 7

(M) Check Unit For Oil Leaks
Includes: Clean and dry outside of case and run unit to determine point of leak.
All models 9

(G) Back-Up Lamp and Park Neutral Switch, Renew
All models (.3) 5

(G) Neutral Safety Switch, Renew
Corvette (1.2) 1.5
All other models (.3) 5

(G) Shift Control Cable, Renew
Corvette (1.3) 1.7
All other models (.6) 1.0

(G) Shift Linkage, Adjust
All models
Neutral Safety Switch (.3) 4
Shift Indicator Needle (.2) 3
Shift Linkage (.4) 5
T.V. Cable (.3) 4

(G) Torque Converter Clutch Switch, Renew
All models
Brake (.2) 4
Thermal Vacuum (.3) 5
Coolant (.3) 5

(G) Detent Valve Control Cable and/or 'O' Ring, Renew
Includes: Adjust cable.
Corvette (.6) 1.4
All other models (.5) 9

(G) Speedometer Driven Gear and/or Seal, Renew
All models (.3) 5

(G) Extension Housing Rear Oil Seal, Renew
Includes: R&R driveshaft.
Corvette (1.8) 2.4
Camaro-Firebird (.9) 1.4
All other models (.6) 8

(G) Governor Cover and/or Seal, Renew
Corvette (1.0) 1.4
All other models (.3) 5

(G) Governor Assembly, R&R or Renew
Corvette (1.0) 1.4
All other models (.4) 7

(G) Governor Assy., R&R and Recondition
Corvette (1.2) 1.6
All other models (.6) 1.0

(G) Oil Pan and/or Gasket, Renew
All models (.5) 9

(G) Governor Pressure Switch, Renew
Includes: R&R oil pan.
All models (.6) 1.1

(G) Converter Clutch Solenoid, Renew
Includes: R&R oil pan.
All models (.6) 1.1

(G) Pressure Regulator Valve, Renew
All models (.7) 1.2

CHILTON'S AUTOMATIC TRANSMISSION TUNE-UP

1. Check engine performance
2. Check condition of transmission oil
3. Check transmission, oil cooler and oil cooler lines for external leaks
4. Remove oil pan, clean or renew screen or filter
5. Torque valve body
6. Adjust bands
7. Clean oil pan and install pan with new gasket
8. Check modulator and hose
9. Install new transmission oil to proper level
10. Adjust manual and throttle linkage
11. Road test

All models 1.5
Charge for parts used

(Factory Time) Chilton Time

(G) Valve Body Assembly, Renew
Includes: R&R oil pan and renew filter.
All models (.8) 1.5

(P) Valve Body Assy., R&R and Recondition
Includes: R&R oil pan and renew filter. Disassemble, clean, inspect and free all valves. Replace parts as required.
All models (1.7) 2.5
Renew selector shaft seal add 1
w/Converter clutch add (.1) 1

(G) 2-4 Servo Assy., R&R or Renew
Includes: R&R oil pan and valve body.
Corvette (1.4) 1.9
All other models (1.1) 1.6
Recond add (.2) 3

(G) Parking Pawl, Shaft, Rod or Spring, Renew
Includes: R&R oil pan.
All models (.6) 1.1
Renew pawl add (.5) 5

(G) 1-2 Accumulator Piston and/or Spring, Renew
Includes: R&R oil pan.
All models (.9) 1.5
Recond add (.1) 2

(G) Transmission Mount, Renew
1983-87
rear (.4) 6

SERVICES REQUIRING R&R

(G) Transmission Assy., R&R or Renew
Caprice-Impala-Parisienne
1983-87 (2.0) 2.9
Camaro-Firebird
1983-87 (1.8) 2.5
Corvette
1983-87 (2.8) 3.9

(P) Transmission and Converter, R&R and Recondition
Includes: Disassemble transmission completely, including valve body and overhaul unit. Clean and inspect all parts. Renew all parts as required. Make all necessary adjustments. Road test.

(Factory Time) Chilton Time

Caprice-Impala-Parisienne
1983-87 (7.1) 10.0
Camaro-Firebird
1983-87 (7.1) 10.0
Corvette
1983-87 (7.8) 10.9
Clean and leak check converter add (.2) 4
Check end play add (.2) 3

(G) Transmission Assy., R&R and Reseal
Includes: Install all new gaskets and seals.
Caprice-Impala-Parisienne
1983-87 .... 5.9
Camaro-Firebird
1983-87 .... 5.5
Corvette
1983-87 .... 6.9

(G) Flywheel (Flexplate), Renew
Includes: R&R transmission.
Caprice-Impala-Parisienne
1983-87 (2.2) 3.1
Camaro-Firebird
1983-87 (2.0) 2.8
Corvette
1983-87 (3.0) 4.2

(G) Torque Converter, Renew
Includes: R&R transmission.
Caprice-Impala-Parisienne
1983-87 (2.3) 3.2
Camaro-Firebird
1983-87 (1.9) 2.7
Corvette
1983-87 (3.0) 4.2

(G) Front Pump Oil Seal, Renew
Includes: R&R transmission.
Caprice-Impala-Parisienne
1983-87 (2.4) 3.3
Camaro-Firebird
1983-87 (1.9) 2.7
Corvette
1983-87 (3.0) 4.2

(G) Front Pump Assy., Renew or Recondition
Includes: R&R transmission.
Caprice-Impala-Parisienne
1983-87 (3.1) 4.3
Camaro-Firebird
1983-87 (2.7) 3.8
Corvette
1983-87 (3.8) 5.3
Recond front pump add (.5) 6
Renew bushing add (.1) 1

(G) Input Drum, Reverse and Input Clutch, Renew
Includes: R&R transmission.
Caprice-Impala-Parisienne
1983-87 (3.6) 5.0
Camaro-Firebird
1983-87 (3.5) 4.9
Corvette
1983-87 (4.2) 5.9
Recond valve body add (.4) 5
Recond front pump add (.5) 6
Renew bushings add-each (.1) 1

(G) 2-4 Band and Input Gear Set, Renew
Includes: R&R transmission.
Caprice-Impala-Parisienne
1983-87 (3.8) 5.3
Camaro-Firebird
1983-87 (3.7) 5.2
Corvette
1983-87 (4.4) 6.2
Recond valve body add (.4) 5
Recond front pump add (.5) 6

LABOR 23 AUTOMATIC TRANSMISSION 23 LABOR

(Factory Time)	Chilton Time
Recond reverse clutch add (.4)	.5
Recond input clutch add (.5)	.6
Renew input clutch drum add (.2)	.3
Renew bushings add-each (.1)	.1

(G) Reaction Gear Set, Renew

Includes: R&R transmission.

Caprice-Impala-Parisienne	
1983-87 (3.9)	5.4
Camaro-Firebird	
1983-87 (3.7)	5.2
Corvette	
1983-87 (4.5)	6.3

(Factory Time)	Chilton Time
Recond valve body add (.4)	.5
Recond front pump add (.5)	.6
Renew input clutch drum add (.2)	.3
Recond reaction gear set add (.2)	.2
Renew bushings add-each (.1)	.1

(G) Low and Reverse Clutch Piston Assy., Renew

Includes: R&R transmission.

Caprice-Impala-Parisienne	
1983-87 (4.1)	5.9
Camaro-Firebird	
1983-87 (4.0)	5.7

(Factory Time)	Chilton Time
Corvette	
1983-87 (4.7)	6.5
Recond valve body add (.4)	.5
Recond front pump add (.5)	.6
Recond reverse clutch add (.4)	.5
Recond input clutch add (.4)	.5
Renew input clutch drum add (.2)	.2
Recond reaction gear set add (.2)	.3
Recond low and reverse clutch add (.1)	.2
Recond reverse piston add (.3)	.4
Recond gov or renew gear add (.2)	.3
Renew gov bushing add (.4)	.5
Renew bushings add-each (.1)	.1

PARTS 23 CASE & PARTS 23 PARTS

	Part No.	Price
Transmission Assy.		
Chevrolet & Pontiac		
1983-305 eng.	8647115	1945.00
1984-305 eng.	8647391	1945.00
Canada	8649936	N.L.
1985-305 eng.	8654506	1945.00
Canada exc. below	8654540	1945.00
350 eng.	8654545	1945.00
4.3L eng.	8654505	1945.00
1986-87-305 eng. exc. below	8649934	N.L.
Canada	8649936	N.L.
350 eng.	8659905	N.L.
Camaro & Firebird		
2.5 engine		
1983	8647003	1945.00
1984	8647397	N.L.
1985	8654508	1945.00
2.8 engine		
1983-wo/Hi output	8642835	1945.00
Hi output	8647002	N.L.
1984-exc. below	8647395	1945.00
Canada	8659902	N.L.
1985	8654509	1945.00
1986-87	8659901	N.L.
305 engine		
1983-wo/EFI	8647243	1945.00
EFI	8642837	1945.00
1984-exc. below	8647393	1945.00
w/G eng.	8647394	1945.00
1984-87-Canada	8649942	N.L.
1985	8654510	1945.00
1986-87	8649940	N.L.
Corvette		
1984	8649906	N.L.
1985-exc. Canada	8654512	1945.00
Canada	8654546	1945.00
1986-87	8659906	N.L.
Transmission Overhaul Kit		
1983-85	8647980	109.00
1986-87	8649960	N.L.
Transmission Snap Ring Kit		
1983-87	8642910	9.25
(1) Converter		
Chevrolet & Pontiac		
1983-84-305 eng.	8642911	340.00
1985-87-4.3L eng.	8647902	340.00
305 eng.	8647901	340.00
Camaro & Firebird		
2.5 engine		
1983-85	8642972	324.00
2.8 engine		
1983	8642972	324.00

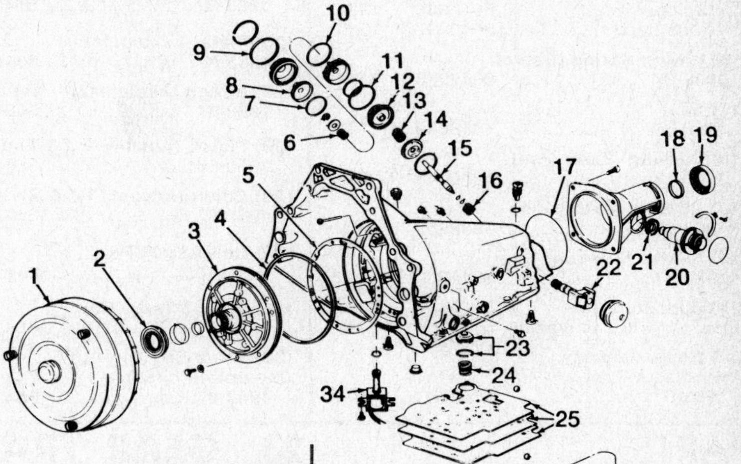

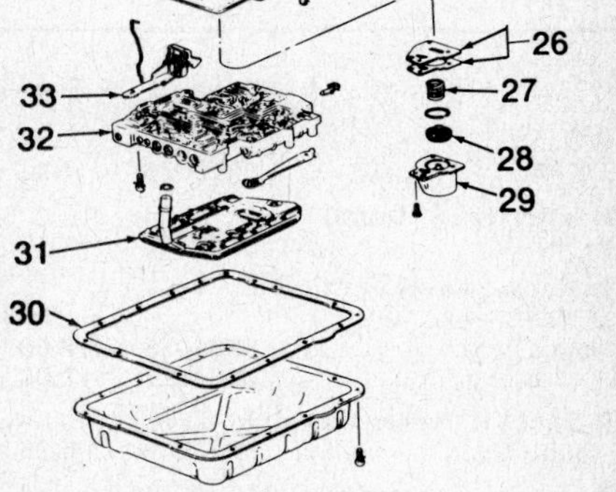

	Part No.	Price
1984	8642978	340.00
1985-87	8642968	340.00
305 engine		
1983	8642934	340.00
E.F.I.	8642965	340.00
1984-305H engine 1st design	8642934	340.00
1984-87-Canada	8647900	340.00
1985	8647902	340.00
1986-87	8647901	340.00
350 engine		
1986-87	8647904	340.00
Corvette		
1984-1st design	8642965	340.00
1984-2nd design	8647904	340.00
1985-87	8647904	340.00

2nd design has a letter T stamped on the pan rail, following the trans. I.D. number.

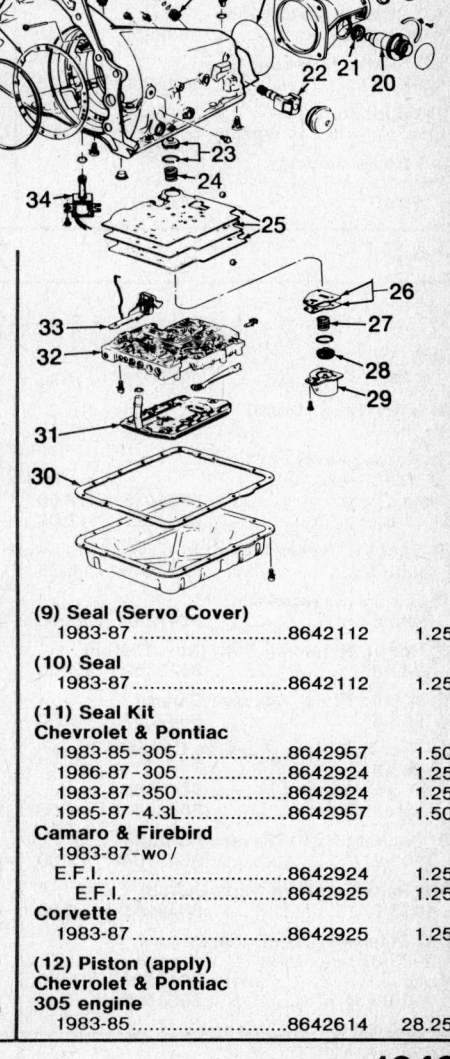

	Part No.	Price
(2) Seal (Front Pump)		
1983-87	8630921	4.25
(3) Front Pump Body		
1983-87	8642986	N.L.
(4) Front Seal (Pump to Case)		
1983-87	6261413	1.25
(5) Front Gasket (Pump to Case)		
1983-87	8642040	1.25
(6) Spring (Servo Apply Pin)		
1983-87	8642106	1.25
(7) Ring (Oil Seal)		
1983-87	8642480	1.25
(8) Piston (Apply)		
1983-87	8642478	13.00
(9) Seal (Servo Cover)		
1983-87	8642112	1.25
(10) Seal		
1983-87	8642112	1.25
(11) Seal Kit		
Chevrolet & Pontiac		
1983-85-305	8642957	1.50
1986-87-305	8642924	1.25
1983-87-350	8642924	1.25
1985-87-4.3L	8642957	1.50
Camaro & Firebird		
1983-87-wo/E.F.I.	8642924	1.25
E.F.I.	8642925	1.25
Corvette		
1983-87	8642925	1.25
(12) Piston (apply)		
Chevrolet & Pontiac		
305 engine		
1983-85	8642614	28.25

PARTS 23 CASE & PARTS 23 PARTS

	Part No.	Price
1986-87	8642613	13.00
350 engine		
1984-87	8642613	13.00
Camaro & Firebird		
1983-87-wo/ E.F.I.	8642613	13.00
E.F.I.	8642079	19.00
Corvette		
1983-87	8642079	19.00
(13) Spring (Servo)		
1983-87-exc. below	8642570	1.50
E.F.I. & Corvette	8642539	1.75
(14) Spring Retainer (Servo)		
1983-87	8642416	1.00
(15) Pin (Apply Piston)		
1983-87-1 ring	8642094	N.L.
2 rings	8642095	13.00
3 rings	8642096	13.00
wide band	8642097	13.50
(16) Return Spring (Servo)		
1983-87	8642273	1.00
(17) Seal		
1983-87	1358899	1.25
(18) Bushing (Extension)		
1983-87	6260048	2.00
(19) Oil Seal (Extension)		
1983-87	3932255	N.L.
(20) Sleeve (Speedo. Gear)		
1983-87	25512339	10.75
(21) Speedo. Gear		
Order by year and model.		
(22) Governor Assy.		
Chevrolet & Pontiac		
1983-87	8642731	N.L.

	Part No.	Price
Camaro & Firebird		
1983-85-2.5L eng.	8647038	45.50
1983-87-2.8L eng.	8647041	45.50
305 engine		
wo/E.F.I.	8642731	N.L.
E.F.I.	8642730	45.00
305F eng.	8647173	45.50
Corvette		
1984-87	8647173	45.50
(23) Piston (Accumulator 3rd & 4th)		
1983-87	8642946	8.25
(24) Spring (Accumulator 3rd & 4th)		
1983-87	8634162	N.L.
(25) Spacer Plate (Valve Body)		
1983-87	8647454	5.25
Gasket Kit (Spacer Plate)		
1983-87	8642974	1.50
(26) Plate (Accumulator)		
1983-87	8642987	13.00
(27) Spring (Accumulator 1st & 2nd)		
1983-87	8634163	1.75
(28) Piston (Accum. 1st & 2nd)		
1983-87	8642946	8.25
(29) Cover (Accum. 1st & 2nd)		
1983-87	8647347	13.00
(30) Gasket (Oil Pan)		
1983-87	8642360	N.L.
(31) Filter (Trans. Oil)		
1983-87	8642933	17.00
(32) Valve Body		
Chevrolet-Pontiac		
1983-87	8647299	379.00

	Part No.	Price
Camaro-Firebird		
2.5L engine		
1983	8647286	233.00
1984	8654011	233.00
1985	8654175	233.00
2.8L engine		
1983	8642579	233.00
1984-exc. below	8647437	233.00
Canada	8654003	233.00
1985	8654164	233.00
1986-87	8654470	233.00
305 engine		
1983-wo/E.F.I.	8647405	233.00
E.F.I.	8642577	233.00
1984-exc. below	8654013	233.00
G eng.	8654009	233.00
1985-exc. below	8654165	233.00
305F eng.	8654166	233.00
1986-87	8654471	233.00
Corvette		
1984	8654073	185.00
1985	8654167	233.00
1986-87	8654242	233.00
(33) Throttle Lever		
1983-87	8642351	N.L.
(34) Solenoid		
Chevrolet & Pontiac		
1983	8647311	16.00
1984-87	8644124	N.L.
Camaro & Firebird		
2.5L engine		
1983	8654129	18.00
1984	8654126	22.00
2.8L engine		
1983-87	8654129	18.00
305 engine		
1983	8647311	16.00
1984-87	8654124	16.50
Corvette		
1984-87	8654129	18.00

PARTS 23 GEAR TRAIN 23 PARTS

	Part No.	Price
(1) Band		
1983-87	8642076	N.L.
(2) Housing (w/Drum)		
1983-87	8642943	71.50
(3) Piston (Reverse Clutch)		
1983-87-exc. V-8 eng.	8654078	17.00
V-8 eng.	8654077	17.00
(4) Seal Kit (Reverse Clutch)		
1983-87	8642918	5.25
(5) Spring (Reverse Clutch)		
1983-87	8647284	5.00
(6) Spring Retaining Ring (Rev. Clutch)		
1983-87	8628059	1.00
(7) Waved Plate (Reverse Clutch)		
1983-87	8647067	5.00
(8) Grooved Plate (Reverse Clutch)		
1983-87		
Fiber (4 reqd)	8642062	N.L.
Steel (3 reqd)	8642061	7.50
(9) Backing Plate (Reverse Clutch)		
1983-87	8642064	7.50
(10) Retaining Ring (Rev. Clutch)		
1983-87	8642065	2.00
(11) Retainer (Check Valve)		
1983-87-exc. V-8 eng.	8647037	2.50
V-8 eng.	8634503	N.L.

	Part No.	Price
(12) Teflon Ring		
1983-87	8642420	1.25
(13) Housing (w/Shaft)		
1983-exc. V-8 eng.	8647965	185.00
V-8 eng.	8647127	N.L.
1984-w/2.5L, 2.8L eng.		
1st design	8647128	N.L.
2nd design	8654155	140.00
1984-V-8 eng.		
1st design	8647127	N.L.
2nd design	8654156	140.00
1985-87-exc. V-8 eng.	8654155	140.00
V-8 eng.	8654156	140.00
(14) Piston (3rd & 4th)		
1983-87	8642135	26.75
(15) Apply Ring (3rd & 4th)		
1983-87-1 bar	8642374	6.50
2 bars	8642375	6.50
(16) Spring		
1983-87	8642140	2.50
(17) Housing (Forward Clutch)		
1983-87	8642141	N.L.
(18) Piston (Forward Clutch)		
1983-87	8642144	26.75
(19) Piston (Overrun Clutch)		
1983-87	8642148	26.75

	Part No.	Price
(20) Spring (Overrun Clutch)		
1983-87	8642153	5.00
(21) Plate (Overrun Clutch)		
1983-87 (2 reqd.)		
Grooved	8642155	11.50
2.34mm	8642154	11.50
(22) Bearing (Sun Gear)		
1983-87	8642162	5.25
(23) Hub (Overrun Clutch)		
1983-87	8647082	18.25
(24) Sprag (Forward Clutch)		
1983-87	8647084	23.00
(25) Retainer (Forward Clutch)		
1983-87	8647085	35.00
(26) Race (Forward Clutch Outer)		
1983-87	8647090	32.75
(27) Plate (Forward Clutch Apply)		
1983-87-exc. V-8 eng.	8642711	7.50
V-8 eng.	8642163	11.50
(28) Spacer Plate		
1983-87	8642164	7.50
Not required w/V-8 engines.		
(29) Waved Plate (Forward Clutch)		
1983-87	8647058	5.00
(30) Plate (Forward Clutch)		
1983-87-Smooth type (5 reqd.)	8647350	7.50

PARTS 23 GEAR TRAIN 23 PARTS

	Part No.	Price
1983-87-1.97mm (4 reqd.)	8642167	7.50
(31) Backing Plate (Forward Clutch)		
1983-87	8642169	7.50
(32) Retaining Ring		
1983-87	8642170	5.00
(33) Ring Retain Plate (3rd & 4th)		
1983-87	8642171	7.50
(34) Apply Plate (3rd & 4th)		
1983-87	8642172	7.50
(35) Plate (3rd & 4th)		
1983-87-Smooth type (6 reqd.)	8642174	7.50
1983-87-1.97mm (5 reqd.)	8642173	N.L.
(36) Plate (3rd & 4th)		
1983-87 (400, 4.25)	8642624	7.50
Smallest size listed other sizes available for selective fit.		
(37) Retainer Ring		
1983-87	8642177	5.00
(38) Sun Gear		
1983-87	8647093	40.00
(39) Input Carrier		
1983-87-exc. Corvette	8654134	N.L.
1984-87 Corvette	8654329	60.00
(40) Thrust Bearing		
1983-87	8642191	6.00
(41) Gear (Input Internal)		
1983-87	8642866	64.00
(42) Shaft (Reaction Carrier)		
1983-87-exc. 305F eng.	8642196	N.L.
305F eng.	8654259	58.00
(43) Shell (Reaction Sun)		
1983-87	8642203	18.50
(44) Reaction Sun Gear		
1983-87	8642204	N.L.
(45) Race (Low & Rev. Overrun Clutch)		
1983-87	6261125	25.75
(46) Clutch (Low & Reverse)		
1983-87	6261305	26.25
(47) Support (Low & Rev. Clutch)		
1983-87	8647411	57.00
(48) Reaction Carrier		
1983	8647052	N.L.
1984-87-exc. V-8 eng.	8654132	94.50
V-8 eng.	8654200	94.50
(49) Reaction Plate (Low & Reverse)		
1983-87 (5 reqd.) .070	6261120	N.L.
.088	8641698	5.50

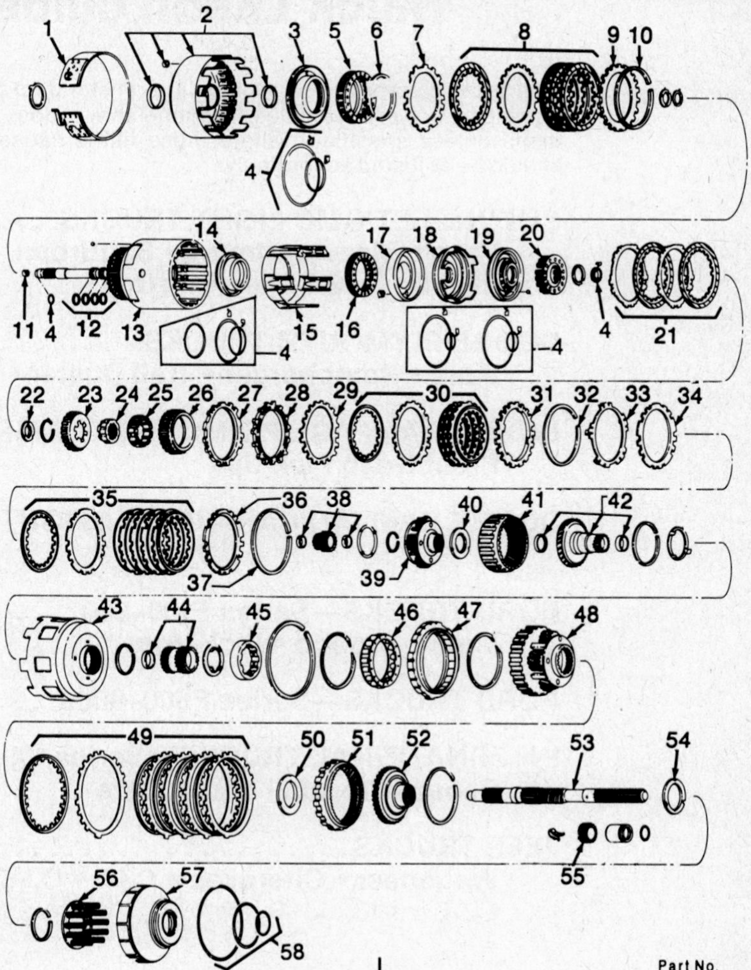

	Part No.	Price
(50) Thrust Bearing		
1983-87	8642215	5.00
(51) Internal Reaction Gear		
1983-87	8654161	26.00
(52) Support (Reaction Gear)		
1983-84	8642218	N.L.
1985-87	8654197	N.L.
(53) Output Shaft		
1983-84	8647236	N.L.
1985-87-exc. Corvette	8654060	80.00
1984 Corvette	8642650	79.50
1985-87 Corvette	8654061	79.50
(54) Bearing (Reaction Gear)		
1983-87	8642191	6.00
(55) Speedo. Gear (Drive)		
1983-87	8640188	2.00
(56) Spring (Low & Reverse)		
1983-87	8642227	5.00
(57) Piston (Low & Reverse)		
1983-87-exc. V-8 eng.	8642222	17.00
V-8 eng.	8642221	17.25
(58) Seal Kit (Low & Reverse)		
1983-87	8642916	1.50

PARTS 23 OIL PUMP 23 PARTS

	Part No.	Price
Pump Body		
1983-87	8649950	146.00
Seal (Front Pump)		
1983-87	8648394	4.50
Ring (Pump Vane)		
1983-87	8634086	3.00
Guide (Rotor)		
1983-87	8634271	1.25
Vane Kit		
1983-87	8634904	21.75
Valve (T.V. Boost)		
1983-87	8634941	6.25
Spring (Regulator Valve)		
1983-87	8642494	2.00
Valve (Pressure Regulator)		
1983-87	8637546	8.50
Screen (Pump Cover)		
1983-87	8642912	1.50
Spring (Pressure Relief)		
1983-87	8634106	1.25
Valve Spring (Inner)		
1983-87	8634378	1.00
Valve Spring (Outer)		
1983-87	8634399	1.00
Valve (Converter Clutch)		
1983-87	8634031	4.50

TRUCK LABOR GUIDE INDEX

This section covers Labor Guide data on standard production line, gasoline and diesel powered vehicles. The time shown does not include interference items unless specified. Where these items cause additional labor, times should be adjusted accordingly.

GROUP INDEX

ALPHABETICAL INDEX

LABOR 1 TUNE UP 1 LABOR

(Factory Time)	Chilton Time
Compression Test	
Four	
S-series	.6
Astro	.9
Six	.9
V-6	
Vans-Astro	.9
All other models	.7
V-8	1.4
Diesel	1.3

Engine Tune Up, (Electronic Ignition)

Includes: Test battery and clean connections. Tighten manifold and carburetor mounting bolts. Check engine compression, clean and adjust or renew spark plugs. Test resistance of spark plug cables. Inspect distributor cap and rotor. Adjust distributor air gap. Check vacuum advance operation. Reset ignition timing. Adjust idle mixture and idle speed. Service air cleaner. Inspect and adjust drive belts. Inspect choke operation and adjust or free up. Check operation of EGR valve.

(Factory Time)	Chilton Time
Four–1983-87	
S-series	1.5
Astro	1.8
Six–1983-87	
Vans	2.5
All other models	2.3
V-6–1983-87	
Vans-Astro	2.3
All other models	2.0
V-8–1983-87	
Vans	3.4
All other models	3.0
w/A.C. add	.5

LABOR 2 IGNITION SYSTEM 2 LABOR

GASOLINE ENGINES

(Factory Time)	Chilton Time
Spark Plugs, Clean and Reset or Renew	
Vans-Astro	
Four (.6)	.8
Six (.4)	*.8
V-6 (.6)	.8
V-8 (.9)	1.3
All Other Models	
Four (.3)	.5
Six (.3)	.6
V-6 (.4)	.6
V-8 (.6)	.9
*w/A.C. add (.5)	.5
Ignition Timing, Reset	
All models (.3)	.5

Distributor, Renew

Includes: Reset ignition timing.

(Factory Time)	Chilton Time
Vans-Astro	
Four (.6)	.9
Six (.3)	*.9
V-6 (.8)	1.1
V-8 (.6)	1.1
All Other Models	
Four	
eng code A (.3)	.5
eng code Y (.6)	.9
eng code E (.6)	.9
Six (.3)	.5
V-6 (.6)	1.0
V-8 (.4)	.6
*w/A.C. add (.5)	.5

Distributor, R&R and Recondition

Includes: Reset ignition timing.

(Factory Time)	Chilton Time
Vans-Astro	
Four (.9)	1.5
Six (.5)	*1.4
V-6 (1.1)	1.8
V-8 (.8)	1.6
All Other Models	
Four	
eng code A (.6)	1.0
eng code Y (.9)	1.5
eng code E (.9)	1.5
Six (.8)	1.0
V-6 (.9)	1.5
V-8 (.9)	1.1
*w/A.C. add (.5)	.5

Distributor Points and Condenser, Renew

Includes: Adjust dwell and timing.

(Factory Time)	Chilton Time
Vans	
Six (.6)	.8
V-8 (.7)	.9
All Other Models	
Six (.4)	.6
V-8 (.5)	.7
Distributor Cap and/or Rotor, Renew	
Vans-Astro	
Four (.3)	.5
Six (.3)	*.5
V-6 (.5)	.7
V-8 (.5)	.7
All Other Models	
All engs (.3)	.5
*w/A.C. add (.5)	.5

Ignition Coil, Renew

Includes: Test coil.

(Factory Time)	Chilton Time
Four	
eng code Y (2.0)	2.8
eng code E (.6)	.9
eng code A (.3)	.5
Six (.3)	*.5
V-6	
S-series (.7)	1.0
Vans-Astro (.5)	.8
All other models (.4)	.7
V-8 (.5)	.8
*w/A.C. add (.5)	.5

Vacuum Advance Assembly, Renew

Includes: Adjust dwell and timing.

(Factory Time)	Chilton Time
Vans	
Six (.3)	*.8
V-6 (.3)	.6
V-8 (.5)	1.0
All Other Models	
Four	
eng code A (.4)	.7
eng code Y (.6)	.9
eng code E (.6)	.9
Six (.3)	.6
V-6 (.6)	.9
V-8 (.4)	.8
*w/A.C. add (.5)	.5
Vacuum Advance Solenoid, Renew	
All models (.2)	.3

(Factory Time)	Chilton Time
Spark Plug Wires, Renew	
Vans	
Six (.3)	*.7
V-6 (.3)	.6
V-8 (.7)	1.2
All Other Models	
Four	
S-series (.3)	.5
Astro (.5)	.7
Six (.3)	.5
V-6 (.5)	.8
V-8 (.5)	.8
*w/A.C. add (.5)	.5
Ignition Switch, Renew	
All models (.5)	.9
Ignition Switch Lock Cylinder, Renew	
All models (.4)	.7
w/Tilt whl add (.1)	.1
Recode cyl add (.3)	.3
Vans, add	.2

ELECTRONIC IGNITION

(Factory Time)	Chilton Time
Distributor Module, Renew	
Vans	
Six (.3)	*.7
V-6 (.5)	.8
V-8 (.5)	.8
All Other Models	
Four (.3)	.6
Six (.3)	.6
V-6 (.6)	.9
V-8 (.3)	.6
*w/A.C. add (.5)	.5
Distributor Hall Effect Switch, Renew	
S-series-Astro (.5)	.8
ESC Detonation Sensor, Renew (Knock Sensor)	
All models (.4)	.6
ESC Module, Renew	
Vans-Astro (.9)	1.2
All other models (.4)	.4
Distributor Capacitor and/or Module Wiring Harness, Renew	
Vans	
Six (.4)	*.8
V-6 (.5)	.8
V-8 (.5)	.9

LABOR 2 IGNITION SYSTEM 2 LABOR

(Factory Time)	Chilton Time
All Other Models	
Four (.4)	.7
Six (.4)	.7
V-6 (.6)	.8
V-8 (.5)	.7
*w/A.C. add (.5)	.5

Distributor Pick-Up Coil and/or Pole Piece, Renew

Includes: R&R distributor and reset ignition timing.

(Factory Time)	Chilton Time
Vans	
Six (.5)	*1.1
V-6 (.8)	1.3
V-8 (.8)	1.3
All Other Models	
Four	
eng code A (.3)	.6
eng code Y (1.0)	1.5
Six (.5)	.7
V-6	
S-series (.7)	1.1
Astro (.9)	1.3
V-8 (.6)	.8
*w/A.C. add (.5)	.5

DIESEL IGNITION COMPONENTS

(Factory Time)	Chilton Time
Coolant Fast Idle Temperature Switch, Renew	
All models (.3)	.4
Glow Plug Relay, Renew	
Vans (.4)	.6
All other models (.2)	.3
Fast Idle Solenoid, Renew	
Vans (.5)	.7
All other models (.3)	.4
Glow Plugs, Renew	
All models	
Four (.5)	.7
V-8	
one	.4
one-each bank	.7
all-both banks	1.3
Glow Plug Module, Renew	
All models (.3)	.5
Glow Plug Control Switch, Renew	
Vans (.5)	.7
All other models (.3)	.4
Fast Idle Relay, Renew	
All models (.3)	.4
Starter Lockout Relay, Renew	
All models (.2)	.3

LABOR 3 FUEL SYSTEM 3 LABOR

GASOLINE ENGINES

Fuel Pump, Test

Includes: Disconnect line at carburetor, attach pressure gauge.

(Factory Time)	Chilton Time
All models	.3

Carburetor, Renew

Includes: Necessary adjustments.

(Factory Time)	Chilton Time
S-series	
Rochester (.6)	1.0
Isuzu (.8)	1.2
Astro (1.2)	1.7
Vans (.9)	1.4
All other models (.6)	1.0
To perform C.C.C. system test add (.5)	1.0

Carburetor, R&R and Clean or Recondition

Includes: Necessary adjustments.

(Factory Time)	Chilton Time
Vans	
1 bbl (2.5)	3.2
2 bbl (2.5)	3.2
4 bbl (2.7)	3.5
All Other Models	
1 bbl (2.3)	3.0
2 bbl (2.3)	3.0
4 bbl (2.5)	3.2
To perform C.C.C. system test add (.5)	1.0

Needle Valve and Seat, Renew

Includes: R&R carb air horn and floats. Adjust idle speed.

(Factory Time)	Chilton Time
Vans	
1 bbl (.7)	1.1
2 bbl (.8)	1.2
4 bbl (.9)	1.3
S-series	
Rochester (.9)	1.3
Isuzu (.8)	1.2
All Other Models	
1 bbl (.5)	.9
2 bbl (.7)	1.0
4 bbl (.8)	1.1
To perform C.C.C. system test add (.5)	1.0
Fuel Filter, Renew	
Vans (.4)	.5
All other models (.2)	.3
Anti-Dieseling or Idle Stop Solenoid, Renew	
S-series (.5)	.7
Vans (.4)	.5
All other models (.2)	.3
Automatic Choke Vacuum Diaphragm, Renew (One)	
S-series-Astro	
Rochester (.6)	.8
Isuzu (.9)	1.2
Vans (.6)	.8
All other models (.4)	.6
Carburetor Base Gasket EFE Heater, Renew	
S-series (.6)	1.0
Fuel Pump, Renew	
Four (.6)	*.9
Six (.5)	.7
V-6 (.6)	*.9
V-8 (1.0)	1.4
w/A.I.R. add (.3)	.3
*Astro, add	.4

Fuel Tank, Renew

Includes: Drain and refill tank.

(Factory Time)	Chilton Time
Cab Mount	
All models (.5)	1.0
Frame Mount	
side tank-each (1.2)	1.7
Pick-Ups (1.0)	1.8
Vans (.7)	1.2
Suburban & Blazer (.9)	1.4
Jimmy (.9)	1.4
S-series	
rear (1.2)	1.7
left-4X2 (1.0)	1.5
4X4 (1.5)	2.0
Astro (.9)	1.4
w/Fuel tank shield add (.3)	.4

Fuel Gauge (Tank), Renew

Includes: Drain and refill tank.

(Factory Time)	Chilton Time
Cab Mounted Tank	
All models (.5)	.9
Frame Mounted Tank	
side tank-each (1.0)	1.5
Pick-Ups (.9)	1.7
Vans (.7)	1.1
Suburban & Blazer (.9)	1.3
Jimmy (.9)	1.3
S-series	
rear (1.3)	1.8
left-4X2 (.9)	1.4
4X4 (1.5)	2.0
Astro (1.0)	1.5
w/Fuel tank shield add (.3)	.4
Fuel Gauge (Dash), Renew	
S-series (.3)	.5
Astro (.9)	1.4
All other models (.5)	.9
Intake Manifold, Renew	
Six	
Vans (1.8)	2.4
All other models (1.2)	1.8
w/P.S. add (.5)	.5
Intake and Exhaust Manifold Gaskets, Renew	
Six	
Vans (1.5)	2.1
All other models (1.4)	2.0
w/P.S. add (.5)	.5
Intake Manifold or Gasket, Renew	
Four	
eng code A (1.7)	2.5
eng code Y (1.9)	2.7
eng code E	
S-series (2.3)	3.2
Astro (2.2)	3.1
w/Cruise control add	.2
Six-All models (1.8)	2.6
V-6	
S-series (3.9)	5.5
Astro (2.6)	3.6
exc Vans (2.0)	2.8
Vans (2.3)	3.2
w/A.C. add (.2)	.2
w/C.C.C. add (.2)	.2
V-8-454 eng	
All models (2.0)	2.7
V-8-All other engs	
exc Vans (2.3)	3.3
Vans (2.4)	3.4
w/A.C. add (.7)	.7
Renew manif add (.3)	.5

FUEL INJECTION

(Factory Time)	Chilton Time
Throttle Body, R&R or Renew	
Astro (.9)	1.3
S-series (.7)	1.1
Renew throttle body kit add (.3)	.3
Renew fuel meter body add (.3)	.3
Throttle Body Fuel Meter Assy., and/or Gasket, Renew	
Astro (.6)	.8
S-series (.4)	.6

LABOR 3 FUEL SYSTEM 3 LABOR

(Factory Time) — Chilton Time

Idle Air Control Valve, Renew
Astro (.7) 1.0
S-series (.5) 8

Throttle Body Injector and/or Gasket, Renew
Astro-one (.9) 1.4
both (1.1) 1.7
S-series-one (.7) 1.2
both (.7) 1.3

Minimum Idle Speed, Adjust
Astro (.7) 1.0
S-series (.5) 8

Fuel Pressure Regulator and/or Gaskets, Renew
Astro (.9) 1.3
S-series (.7) 1.1

Fuel Pump, Renew (In Tank)
All models (1.3) 1.8

Fuel Pump Relay, Renew
Astro (.7) 9
S-series (.5) 7

DIESEL ENGINE

Air Cleaner, Service
All models (.2) 4

Air Intake Crossover, Renew
All models (.3) 5

Fuel Filter, Renew
All models (.2) 4

Idle Speed, Adjust
All models (.2) 4

Injection Timing, Check and Adjust
All models (.5) 9

Throttle Position Sensor, Renew
All models (.5) 7

Fuel Solenoid, Renew
Vans (2.0) *2.7
All other models (.5) 7
*w/A.C. add (.2) 2

Cold Advance Solenoid, Renew
Vans (2.1) *2.8
All other models (.6) 8
*w/A.C. add (.2) 2

Fuel Injection Head Seal, Renew
Includes: Renew head and drive shaft seals. Renew governor weight retaining ring.
All models
5.7L eng (3.3) 4.7
6.2L eng
Vans (4.0) 5.3
All other models (3.2) 4.1

Fuel Injection Pump, Renew
Includes: Pressure and electrical tests. Adjust timing.
All models
2.2L eng (1.9) 2.7
5.7L eng (2.6) 3.5
6.2L eng
Vans (3.8) *4.9
All other models (3.3) 4.4
*w/A.C. add (.2) 2

Fuel Return Lines (At Nozzles), Renew
All models-one side (.3) 5
both sides (.4) 7
return hose (.2) 3
w/A.C. add (.2) 2

High Pressure Fuel Lines, Renew
Includes: Flush lines.
Four-one (.4) 7
all (.5) 8
V-8-one (1.2) 1.5
one-each bank (1.4) 1.7
all-both banks (1.5) 2.5
w/A.C. add (.2) 2

Injector Nozzle and/or Seal, Renew
Four
one or all (.6) 1.0
V-8-one (.8) 1.2
one-each bank (1.0) 1.4
all-both banks (1.5) 3.0
w/A.C. add (.2) 2
Clean nozzles add-each 2

Fuel Supply Pump, Renew
All models (.5) 7
w/A.C. add (.2) 2

Fuel Injection Pump Throttle Shaft Seal, Renew
All models
5.7L eng (.9) 1.3
6.2L eng
Vans (2.0) *2.5
All other models (1.7) 2.3
*w/A.C. add (.2) 2

Injection Pump Adapter and/or Seal, Renew
All models
5.7L eng (1.9) 2.4
Locate new timing mark add (.1) 1

Vacuum Pump, Renew
Vans (1.2) 1.6
All other models (.3) 6

Intake Manifold or Gasket, Renew
All models
2.2L eng (.7) 1.2
5.7L eng (2.7) 3.5
6.2L eng (1.4) 2.0
Renew manif add (.2) 5

LABOR 3A EMISSION CONTROLS 3A LABOR

(Factory Time) — Chilton Time

GASOLINE ENGINES

Emission Control Check
Includes: Check and adjust engine idle speed, mixture and ignition timing.
All models 6

CRANKCASE EMISSION

Positive Crankcase Ventilation Valve, Renew
All models (.2) 3

Crankcase Vent Filter, Renew
All models (.2) 3

AIR INJECTION REACTOR TYPE

A.I.R. Air Pump Cleaner, Renew
All models (.2) 4

Air Pump, Renew
Four (.4) .... *.6
Six (.6) 8
V-6 (.4) .... *.7
V-8 (.8) 1.0
*Astro add 2

Air Pump Relief Valve, Renew
Six (.8) 1.0
V-8 (1.0) 1.2

Diverter or Gulp Valve, Renew
Vans-Astro (.4) 6
All other models (.2) 4

Check Valve, Renew (One)
Vans (.4) 6
All other models (.2) 4
each adtnl 1

Combustion Pipes and/or Extensions, Renew
Vans
Six (.6) 9
V-8-one (.6) 9
both (.8) 1.2
All Other Models
Four (.6) 1.0
Six (.5) 8
V-6-each (.3) 6
V-8-one (.3) 6
both (.5) 9

Vacuum Delay Valve, Renew
All models (.3) 4

Deceleration Valve, Renew
All models (.3) 4

CONTROLLED COMBUSTION TYPE

Air Cleaner Vacuum Motor, Renew
Vans-Astro (.6) 8
All other models (.3) 6

Air Cleaner Temperature Sensor, Renew
Vans-Astro (.4) 5
All other models (.3) 4

EGR/EFE Thermal Vacuum Switch, Renew
Vans-Astro (.4) 6
All other models (.3) 5

EVAPORATIVE EMISSION TYPE

Charcoal Canister, Renew
Vans (.7) 1.0
All other models (.2) 4

Canister Purge Thermal Vacuum Switch, Renew
exc Vans (.3) 4
Vans-Astro (.5) 6

TRANSMISSION CONTROLLED SPARK

Transmission Controlled Spark Solenoid, Renew
Vans (.4) 5
All other models (.2) 3

Thermostatic Vacuum Switch or Temperature Switch, Renew
Vans (.5) 6
All other models (.3) 4

Controlled Spark Relay, Renew (On Firewall)
All models (.2) 3

Thermal Vacuum Switch, Renew
All models (.3) 4

LABOR 3A EMISSION CONTROLS 3A LABOR

(Factory Time) Chilton Time

EXHAUST GAS RECIRCULATION SYSTEM

E.G.R. Valve, Renew
Four
eng code A (.8)........ 1.1
eng code Y (.3)........ .5
eng code E
Astro (.9)........ 1.2
S-series (.5)........ .8
Vans (.5)........ .8
Diesel
5.7L eng (.6)........ 1.0
6.2L eng (.2)........ .4
All other models (.3)........ .5

E.G.R. Vacuum Delay Valve, Renew
S-series (.2)........ .3

EARLY FUEL EVAPORATION SYSTEM

E.F.E. Valve, Renew
Six (.3)........ .6
V-6 & V-8 (.6)........ 1.0
dual exhaust (.5)........ .9

E.F.E. Actuator and Rod Assy., Renew
All models (.3)........ .6

E.F.E. Vacuum Check Valve, Renew
All models (.2)........ .3

COMPUTER COMMAND CONTROL SYSTEM (C.C.C.)

Computer Command Control System Performance Check
All models (.5)........ 1.0

Throttle Position Sensor, Adjust
Does not include system performance check.
All models (.4)........ .9

Manifold Absolute Pressure Sensor, Renew
Does not include system performance check.
S-series (.4)........ .6
All other models (.5)........ .7

Engine Speed Sensor, Renew
Does not include system performance check.
Vans (.7)........ .9
All other models (.5)........ .7

Calpak, Renew
Does not include system performance check.
All models (.5)........ .7

Electronic Control Module, Renew
Does not include system performance check.
All models (.5)........ .6

Mixture Control Solenoid, Renew
Does not include system performance check.
Vans-Astro (1.4)........ 1.8
All other models-2 bbl (1.1)........ 1.4
4 bbl (1.2)........ 1.5

Prom, Renew
Does not include system performance check.
All models (.5)........ .8

Coolant Temperature Sensor, Renew
Does not include system performance check.
Vans-Astro (.7)........ .9
All other models (.5)........ .6

Oxygen Sensor, Renew
Does not include system performance check.
All models (.5)........ .7

Barometric Sensor, Renew
Does not include system performance check.
All models (.5)........ .7

Manifold Differential Pressure Sensor, Renew
Does not include system performance check.
All models (.5)........ .7

Throttle Position Sensor, Renew
Does not include system performance check.
Vans-Astro (1.3)........ 1.7
All other models-2 bbl (1.1)........ 1.4
4 bbl (1.2)........ 1.5

Idle Speed Control Motor, Renew
Does not include system performance check.
All models (.5)........ .8

Air Control/Air Switching Valve, Renew
Does not include system performance check.
All models (.6)........ .8

E.G.R. Vacuum Control Solenoid, Renew
Does not include system performance check.
All models (.6)........ .8

Vehicle Speed Sensor, Renew
Does not include system performance check.
All models (1.0)........ 1.5

E.G.R. Bleed Control Solenoid, Renew
Does not include system performance check.
Vans-Astro (.5)........ .7
All other models (.4)........ .6

EFE/EGR Relay, Renew
Does not include system performance check.
All models (.3)........ .4

Tachometer Filter, Renew
Does not include system performance check.
All models (.3)........ .3

COASTING RICHER SYSTEM (C.R.S.)

Engine Speed Sensor, Renew
S-series (.3)........ .4

Accelerator Switch, Renew
S-series (.3)........ .4

Clutch Switch, Renew
S-series (.3)........ .4

Transmission Switch, Renew
S-series (.4)........ .7

Coasting Valve Solenoid, Renew
S-series (.3)........ .4

DIESEL ENGINE

Crankcase Depression Regulator Valve, Renew
Vans (.5)........ .7
All other models (.3)........ .4

Crankcase Ventilation Filter, Renew
All models (.3)........ .4

E.G.R. Valve and/or Gasket, Renew
All models
5.7L eng (.6)........ 1.0
6.2L eng (.2)........ .4

E.G.R. Control Valve Solenoid, Renew
Vans (.5)........ .7
All other models (.2)........ .3

E.P.R. Valve, Renew
Vans (.3)........ .4
All other models (.6)........ .8

E.P.R. Control Valve Switch, Renew
All models (.5)........ .7

E.P.R. Control Valve Solenoid, Renew
Vans (.7)........ 1.0
All other models (.5)........ .7

Vacuum Regulator Valve, Renew
Vans (.8)........ 1.1
All other models (.5)........ .7

LABOR 4 ALTERNATOR AND REGULATOR 4 LABOR

(Factory Time) Chilton Time

Delcotron Circuits, Test
Includes: Test battery, regulator and Delcotron output.
All models........ .6

Alternator Drive Belt, Renew
Four
eng code A (.2)........ .3
w/P.S. add (.2)........ .2
eng code E (.2)........ .3
eng code S (.2)........ .3
w/A.C. add (.1)........ .1
Six–exc Vans (.2)........ .3
Vans (.4)........ .5
w/AIR add (.2)........ .2
V-6 (.2)........ .3
w/AIR add (.1)........ .1
V-8–exc Vans (.2)........ .3
Vans (.3)........ .4
w/AIR add (.2)........ .2
Diesel (.2)........ .3

Delcotron, Renew
Includes: Transfer fan and pulley.
Four–
eng code A (.6)........ .8
eng code Y (.3)........ .5
eng code E (.3)........ .5
Six–exc Vans (.4)........ .6
Vans (.5)........ .7
V-6
Astro (.6)........ .9
All other models (.4)........ .6
V8–exc Vans (.6)........ .8
Vans (.8)........ 1.0
Diesel–exc Vans (.4)........ .6
Vans (.7)........ 1.0
Add circuit test if performed.

Delcotron, R&R and Recondition
Includes: Complete disassembly, replace parts as required, reassemble.

LABOR 4 ALTERNATOR AND REGULATOR 4 LABOR

(Factory Time)	Chilton Time
Four–	
eng code A (1.5)	2.2
eng code Y (1.3)	2.0
eng code E (1.1)	2.0
Six–exc Vans (1.2)	1.8
Vans (1.3)	1.9
V-6	
Astro (1.3)	2.2
All other models (1.1)	1.8
V-8–exc Vans (1.2)	2.0
Vans (1.4)	2.2
Diesel–exc Vans (1.3)	2.0
Vans (1.8)	2.7

Add circuit test if performed.

Delcotron Bearings, Renew (Both)

Includes: R&R Delcotron, separate end frames.

(Factory Time)	Chilton Time
Four–	
eng code A (.8)	1.1
eng code Y (.6)	1.0
eng code E (.6)	1.0
Six–exc Vans (.6)	.9
Vans (.7)	1.0
V-6	
Astro (.8)	1.1
All other models (.6)	1.0
V-8–exc Vans (.6)	.9
Vans (.8)	1.1
Diesel–exc Vans (.6)	.9
Vans (1.0)	1.4

Voltage Regulator, Test and Renew

Includes: Disassemble and reassemble Delcotron.

(Factory Time)	Chilton Time
Four–	
eng code A (.7)	1.0
eng code Y (.6)	1.1
eng code E (.6)	1.1
Six–exc Vans (.5)	.8
Vans (.6)	.9
V-6	
Astro (.8)	1.2
All other models (.6)	1.1
V-8–exc Vans (.6)	.9
Vans (.8)	1.1
Diesel–exc Vans (.6)	1.0
Vans (1.0)	1.4

Voltmeter, Renew

(Factory Time)	Chilton Time
S-series (.3)	.6
Astro (.9)	1.4
All other models (.6)	1.0

LABOR 5 STARTING SYSTEM 5 LABOR

Starter Draw Test (On Truck)

(Factory Time)	Chilton Time
All models	.3

Starter, Renew

(Factory Time)	Chilton Time
Four	
eng code A (.6)	1.0
eng code Y (.8)	1.2
eng code E	
4X2 (.7)	1.0
4X4 (1.6)	2.1
Six (.4)	.7
V-6	
4X2 (.6)	1.0
4X4 (1.1)	1.5
V-8 (.6)	.8
Diesel (.8)	1.1

Add draw test if performed.

Starter, R&R and Recondition

Includes: Turn down armature.

(Factory Time)	Chilton Time
Four	
eng code A (1.5)	2.3
eng code Y (2.0)	2.8
eng code E	
4X2 (1.5)	2.3
4X4 (2.4)	3.4
Six (1.2)	2.0
V-6	
4X2 (1.5)	2.3
4X4 (2.0)	2.8
V-8 (1.5)	2.1
Diesel (1.6)	2.2
Renew field coils add (.2)	.5

Add draw test if performed.

Starter Solenoid, Renew

Includes: R&R starter.

(Factory Time)	Chilton Time
Four	
eng code A (.6)	1.0
eng code Y (.9)	1.3
eng code E	
4X2 (.8)	1.1
4X4 (1.6)	2.2
Six (.5)	.8
V-6	
4X2 (.6)	1.0
4X4 (1.1)	1.5
V-8 (.7)	.9
Diesel (.8)	1.0

Starter Drive, Renew

Includes: R&R starter.

(Factory Time)	Chilton Time
Four	
eng code A (.8)	1.2
eng code Y (1.0)	1.4
eng code E	
4X2 (.9)	1.2
4X4 (1.8)	2.4
Six (.7)	1.0
V-6	
4X2 (.8)	1.2
4X4 (1.4)	1.8
V-8 (.8)	1.1
Diesel (1.0)	1.2

Battery Cables, Renew

(Factory Time)	Chilton Time
Positive-exc Vans (.3)	.4
Vans (.4)	.5
Negative (.2)	.3
batt to batt	
Vans (.7)	1.0
All other models (.3)	.4

LABOR 6 BRAKE SYSTEM 6 LABOR

Brakes, Adjust (Minor)

Includes: Adjust brake shoes, fill master cylinder.

(Factory Time)	Chilton Time
two wheels	.4

Bleed Brakes (Four Wheels)

Includes: Fill master cylinder.

(Factory Time)	Chilton Time
All models (.4)	.6

Brake Pedal Free Play, Adjust

(Factory Time)	Chilton Time
All models	.3

Brake Shoes and/or Pads, Renew

Includes: Install new or exchange shoes or pads, adjust service and hand brake. Bleed system.

(Factory Time)	Chilton Time
With Single Rear Wheels	
front-disc (.9)	1.2
rear-drum (1.0)	1.7
All four wheels	2.8
With Dual Rear Wheels	
front-disc (.9)	1.2
rear-drum (2.1)	3.0
All four wheels	4.0
Resurface brake rotor add, each	.9
Resurface brake drum add, each	.5

Brake Drum, Renew (One)

(Factory Time)	Chilton Time
w/Single rear wheels (.3)	.6
w/Dual rear wheels (1.0)	1.4

Free-Up or Renew Brake Self Adjusting Units (One)

(Factory Time)	Chilton Time
w/Single rear wheels (.4)	.7
w/Dual rear wheels (.7)	1.0

Brake Combination Valve and/or Switch, Renew

Includes: Bleed system.

(Factory Time)	Chilton Time
Vans (.8)	1.1
All other models	
w/2 wheel drive (.7)	1.0
w/4 wheel drive (.7)	1.0

BRAKE HYDRAULIC SYSTEM

Wheel Cylinder, Renew

Includes: Bleed system.

(Factory Time)	Chilton Time
With Single Rear Wheels	
one (.8)	1.3
both (1.1)	1.8
With Dual Rear Wheels	
one (1.0)	1.7
both (1.8)	2.6

Wheel Cylinder, R&R and Recondition

Includes: Home cylinder and bleed system.

(Factory Time)	Chilton Time
With Single Rear Wheels	
one (1.0)	1.6
both (1.5)	2.4
With Dual Rear Wheels	
one (1.2)	2.0
both (2.2)	3.2

Brake Hose, Renew

Includes: Bleed system.

(Factory Time)	Chilton Time
All models-front-one (.5)	.8
rear-one (.5)	.8

Master Cylinder, Renew

Includes: Bleed system.

LABOR 6 BRAKE SYSTEM 6 LABOR

(Factory Time) Chilton Time

All models (.6) 1.0

Master Cylinder, R&R and Recondition
All models (1.4) 1.8

POWER BRAKES

Power Brake Booster, Renew
S-series (1.2) 1.8
All other models (.6) 1.0

Power Brake Booster, R&R and Recondition
S-series
single (1.7) 2.5
tandem (1.8) 2.6
All other models (1.3) 1.8

Brake Booster Check Valve, Renew
All models (.3) 3

Hydra-Boost, Renew
Vans (1.2) 1.7
All other models (1.1) 1.6

Hydra-Boost, R&R and Recondition
Vans (1.8) 2.7
All other models (1.5) 2.4

Hydra-Boost Pump, Renew
All models (.7) 1.1
w/A.C. add (.2) 2

Hydra-Boost Pump, R&R and Recondition
All models (1.3) 1.9
w/A.C. add (.2) 2

Hydra-Boost Pump Line, Renew
All models-one (.5) 7

Hydra-Boost Pump Drive Belt, Renew
All models (.2) 3

Accumulator (Hydra-Boost), R&R or Renew
All models (.3) 7

DISC BRAKES

Brake Shoes and/or Pads, Renew

COMBINATIONS
Add to Brakes, Renew

See Machine Shop Operations

(Factory Time) Chilton Time

RENEW WHEEL CYLINDER
Each (.3) 4

REBUILD WHEEL CYLINDER
Each (.3) 6

REBUILD CALIPER ASSEMBLY
Each (.5) 6

RENEW BRAKE HOSE
Each 3

RENEW REAR WHEEL GREASE SEALS
Semi-floating axle
one (.2) 3
Full-floating axle
one (.3) 4

RENEW BRAKE DRUM (ONE)
With single rear whls (.4) 5
With dual rear whls (.5) 6

REPACK FRONT WHEEL BEARINGS (BOTH WHEELS)
All models (.6) 6

RENEW DISC BRAKE ROTOR
Each-w/2 whl drive (.3) 5
Each-w/4 whl drive (.6) 8

(Factory Time) Chilton Time

Includes: Install new or exchange shoes or pads, adjust service and hand brake. Bleed system.

With Single Rear Wheels
front-disc (.9) 1.2
rear-drum (1.0) 1.7
All four wheels 2.8

With Dual Rear Wheels
front-disc (.9) 1.2
rear-drum (2.1) 3.0
All four wheels 4.0

(Factory Time) Chilton Time

Resurface brake rotor add, each 9
Resurface brake drum add, each 6

Disc Brake Pads, Renew
Includes: Install new disc brake pads only.
All models (.9) 1.2

Disc Brake Rotor, Renew
With Two Wheel Drive
All models-one (.7) 1.0
both (1.2) 1.8
With Four Wheel Drive
All models-one (1.0) 1.2
both (1.8) 2.1

Caliper Assembly, Renew
Includes: Bleed system.
All models-one (.7) 1.1
both (1.1) 1.7

Caliper Assembly, R&R and Recondition
Includes: Bleed system.
All models-one (1.2) 1.6
both (2.1) 2.5

PARKING BRAKE

Parking Brake, Adjust
All models (.3) 4

Parking Brake Equalizer, Renew
All models (.3) 6

Parking Brake Control Assembly, Renew
S-series (1.2) 1.7
Vans (.9) 1.5
Astro (1.6) 2.3
All other models (.6) 9
w/Diesel eng add 4

Parking Brake Cables, Renew
Front
All models (.6) 1.0
Intermediate
All models (.3) 5
Rear-one
with single rear whls (.7) 1.0
with dual rear whls (.9) 1.2

LABOR 7 COOLING SYSTEM 7 LABOR

(Factory Time) Chilton Time

Winterize Cooling System
Includes: Run engine to check for leaks, tighten all hose connections. Test radiator and pressure cap, drain radiator and engine block. Add anti-freeze and refill coolant.
All models 8

Thermostat, Renew
All models
Gas engine (.4) 5
Diesel engine (.6) 8
Vans-w/A.C. add (.5) 5

Radiator Assembly, R&R or Renew
Gasoline Engines
All models-w/M.T. (.6) 1.0
w/A.T. (.8) 1.2
Diesel Engines
All models-w/M.T. (.8) 1.2
w/A.T. (1.0) 1.4
w/Eng oil cooler add (.2) 2
w/A.C. add (.3) 3
Renew side tank add
one side (.7) 1.0
both sides (1.2) 1.7

(Factory Time) Chilton Time

ADD THESE OPERATIONS TO RADIATOR R&R
Boil & Repair 1.5
Rod Clean 1.9
Repair Core 1.3
Renew Tank 1.6
Renew Trans. Oil Cooler 1.9
Recore Radiator 1.7

Radiator Hoses, Renew
Vans-Astro
upper (.4) 5
lower (.6) 6
both (.8) 1.0
All other models
upper (.3) 4
lower (.4) 5
both (.5) 7
by-pass (.3) .... *.5
*Vans-Astro add 3

Fan Blade or Clutch Assy., Renew
exc Vans (.3) 4
Vans (.6) 8

(Factory Time) Chilton Time

Fan Belt, Renew
All models-one (.2) 3
each adtnl (.2) 3
If necessary to R&R fan pulley
add (.2) 3

Water Pump, Renew
Four–
eng code A (.9) 1.3
eng code Y (.9) 1.5
eng code E
S-series (.9) 1.3
Astro (.9) 1.3
Six (.7) 1.3
V-6
S-series (1.2) 2.0
Astro (1.1) 1.9
V-8–exc Vans (.6) 1.5
Vans (.9) 1.7
Diesel
2.2L eng (1.1) 1.9
5.7L eng (1.0) 1.8
6.2L eng
exc Vans (1.6) 2.4
Vans (2.2) 3.0

LABOR 7 COOLING SYSTEM 7 LABOR

(Factory Time) Chilton Time

w/P.S. add (.2) 2
w/A.C. add (.5) 5
w/A.I.R. add (.3) 3

Water Jacket Expansion Plugs, Renew (Engine Block)
All models-each (.3) 5
Note: If necessary to R&R any component to gain access to plug, add appropriate time.

Temperature Gauge (Engine Unit), Renew
All models (.3) 4

Temperature Gauge (Dash Unit), Renew
exc Vans (.6) 1.0
Vans (.5) 1.0
S-series (.3) 6
Astro (.9) 1.4

Heater Hoses, Renew
Includes: Drain coolant at hose.
All models-each (.4) 5

Auxiliary Heater Hoses, Renew (One or All)
Includes: Drain coolant at hose.
All models (1.8) 2.4

Hot Water Shut Off Valve, Renew (Auxiliary Heater)
All models (.7) 1.1

Heater Core, R&R or Renew Without Air Conditioning
exc Vans (.8) *1.5
Vans-Astro (1.6) 3.0
S-series (.8) 1.5

With Air Conditioning
exc Vans (1.4) *2.5
Vans-Astro (2.7) 5.0
S-series (1.5) 3.5
*w/Diesel eng add 1.5

ADD THESE OPERATIONS TO HEATER CORE R&R
Boil & Repair 1.2
Repair Core 9
Recore 1.2

Heater Blower Motor, Renew
Astro (.6) 1.0
All other models (.3) 5
w/Diesel eng (1.0) 1.5

Heater Blower Motor Switch, Renew
All models (.4) 7

Heater Blower Motor Resistor, Renew
All models (.2) 4

Heater Control Assembly, Renew
All models (.5) 9

LABOR 8 EXHAUST SYSTEM 8 LABOR

(Factory Time) Chilton Time

Muffler, Renew
All models-each (.6) 1.0

Tail Pipe, Renew
All models-each (.5) 9

Catalytic Converter, Renew
S-series (.9) 1.3
All other models (.6) 1.0

Catalytic Converter Catalyst, Renew
All models (.5) 1.0

Front Exhaust Pipe, Renew
All models
right side (.7) 9
left side (.6) 9
crossover (.5) 1.1
to conv (.6) 9

Rear Exhaust Pipe, Renew
All models
right side (.4) 9
left side (1.0) 1.3
crossover (.7) 1.3

Intermediate Exhaust Pipe, Renew
All models (.4) 7

Resonator and Pipe Assy., Renew
All models (.4) 6

E.F.E. Valve (Heat Riser), Renew
Six (.3) 6
V-6 & V-8-single exh (.6) 1.0
dual exh (.5) 9

E.F.E. Actuator and Rod Assy., Renew
All models (.3) 6

Exhaust Manifold, Renew
Four–
eng codes A-Y (1.0) 1.5
w/A.C. add (.8) 8
w/P.S. add (.4) 4
eng code E
S-series (.7) 1.1
Astro (.9) 1.3
w/A.C. add (.4) 4
Six–exc Vans (1.1) 1.6
Vans (1.6) 2.1
w/P.S. add (.5) 5
w/A.I.R. add (.6) 6
V-6–
S-series
right side (.6) 1.0
left side (.9) 1.5
Astro
right side (1.1) 1.7
left side (.9) 1.5
exc Vans
right side (1.0) 1.5
left side (.8) 1.2
Vans
right side (.8) 1.2
left side (1.0) 1.5
w/A.C. add (.3) 3
w/P.S. add (.3) 3
w/C.C.C. add (.3) 3
V-8–454 eng
right side (1.0) 1.4
left side (.7) 1.1
V-8–All other engs
exc Vans-right side (1.0) 1.5
left side (.8) 1.2
Vans-right side (1.2) 1.8
left side (1.1) 1.5
w/P.S. add (.2) 2
w/A.C. add (.7) 7
w/A.I.R. add (.2) 2

Diesel
2.2L eng (.7) 1.2
5.7L eng
right side (.9) 1.3
left side (.7) 1.1
6.2L eng
right side (1.1) 1.6
left side (1.3) 1.8

COMBINATIONS

Muffler, Exhaust and Tail Pipe, Renew
Four (1.2) 1.7
Six (1.3) 1.9
V-6 (.7) 1.2
V-8-one side (1.1) 1.6

LABOR 9 FRONT SUSPENSION 9 LABOR

(Factory Time) Chilton Time

Note: On all front suspension operations alignment charges must be added if performed. Time given does not include alignment.

Check Alignment of Front End
All models 5
Note: Deduct if alignment is performed.

Toe-In, Adjust
All models (.4) 6

Align Front End
Includes: Adjust front wheel bearings.
S-series
4X2 (.7) 1.4
4X4 (1.1) 2.0
All other models (1.1) 2.0

Front Wheel Bearings, Clean and Repack
Two Wheel Drive
one wheel (.7) 8
both wheels (1.1) 1.4
Four Wheel Drive
one wheel (1.2) 1.4
both wheels (2.2) 2.5

Front Wheel Grease Seal, Renew
Two Wheel Drive
one wheel (.7) 7
both wheels (1.1) 1.2
Four Wheel Drive
one wheel (1.2) 1.3

(Factory Time) — Chilton Time

both wheels (2.2) — 2.4

Front Wheel Bearings and Cups, Renew
Two Wheel Drive
one wheel (.7) — .9
both wheels (1.1) — 1.5
Four Wheel Drive
one wheel (1.2) — 1.5
both wheels (2.2) — 2.6

Front Wheel Bearing and Hub Assy., Renew
S-series-4X4-Astro
one side (.8) — 1.1
both sides (1.4) — 2.0
Renew inner seal add
one (.4) — .4
both (.6) — .6

Front Shock Absorber, Renew
S-series 4X4
one (.5) — .7
both (.7) — 1.1
All other models-one (.3) — .5
both (.4) — .8

Steering Arm and Knuckle (Integral), Renew
Add alignment charges.
Two Wheel Drive
S-series-one (1.2) — 1.6
both (2.2) — 3.0
All other models-one (1.0) — 1.3
both (1.8) — 2.5

Steering Knuckle, Renew
Add alignment charges.
Four Wheel Drive
S-series
one (1.2) — 1.6
both (2.2) — 3.0
All other models-one (1.6) — 1.9
both (3.0) — 3.7

Lower Control Arm Assy., Renew
Add alignment charges.
S-series-4X2-one (1.1) — 1.6
both (2.1) — 3.1
4X4-one (1.5) — 2.0
both (2.8) — 3.8
All other models-one (.9) — 1.3
both (1.7) — 2.5

Lower Control Arm Bushings and Shaft, Renew
Add alignment charges.
S-series-4X2-one side (1.2) — 1.9
both sides (2.3) — 3.5
4X4-one side (1.4) — 2.1
both sides (2.5) — 4.0
Astro-one side (1.2) — 1.9
both sides (2.3) — 3.5
All other models-one side (.9) — 1.5
both sides (1.7) — 2.9

Upper Control Arm Assy., Renew
Add alignment charges.
S-series-4X2-one (.8) — 1.3
both (1.2) — 2.2
4X4-one (.9) — 1.4
both (1.7) — 2.7
All other models-one (.6) — 1.1
both (1.1) — 2.1

Upper Control Arm Bushings and Shaft, Renew
Add alignment charges.
S-series-one side (1.1) — 1.7
both sides (2.0) — 3.0
Astro-one side (1.0) — 1.6
both sides (1.8) — 2.8

(Factory Time) — Chilton Time

All other models-one side (.7) — 1.4
both sides (1.3) — 2.7

Upper Ball Joint, Renew
Add alignment charges.
S-series-4X4
one (.9) — 1.3
both (1.6) — 2.4
All other models-one (.7) — 1.1
both (1.2) — 2.1

Lower Ball Joint, Renew
Add alignment charges.
S-series-4X4
one (1.1) — 1.5
both (2.0) — 2.8
All models-one (.7) — 1.2
both (1.2) — 2.3

Ball Joints or King Pins (Upper and Lower), Renew
Four Wheel Drive
All models-one side (1.8) — 2.4
both sides (3.5) — 4.7

Front Spring, Renew
Coil
S-series-Astro-one (.8) — 1.3
both (1.5) — 2.5
All other models-one (.6) — 1.2
both (1.0) — 2.3
Leaf
All models-one (.7) — 1.4
both (1.1) — 2.7

Front Spring Shackle or Pin, Renew
All models-one (.4) — .7
both (.5) — 1.2

Front Spring Eye (Hanger End) Bushings, Renew
All models-one side (.8) — 1.5
both sides (1.4) — 2.9

Front Stabilizer Shaft, Renew
All models (.5) — .9

Front Stabilizer Shaft Bushings, Renew
All models-one (.4) — .7
both (.5) — .8

FOUR WHEEL DRIVE K-10-20-30 SERIES

Steering Knuckle Spindle Bearings, Renew
All models-one (1.1) — 1.4
both (2.1) — 2.7
Renew spindle add, each (.1) — .2
Renew knuckle add, each (.5) — .6

Front Wheel Hub, Renew
All models-one (.6) — .9
both (1.1) — 1.7

Free Wheeling Hub Control Mechanism, Recondition
All models-one (.3) — .5
both (.5) — .8
Recond add each (.5) — .6

Front Axle Shaft Oil Seals, Renew
All models-one (3.0) — 4.0
both (3.1) — 4.3

Front Differential Housing Assy., Renew
Includes: R&R drive shaft, transfer all parts as required. Bleed brakes and make all necessary adjustments.
All models (7.4) — 10.0

(Factory Time) — Chilton Time

Front Drive Axle Differential Case, R&R or Renew
All models
Corp axle (3.4) — 4.2
Dana axle (4.4) — 5.4

Ring Gear and Pinion Set, Renew
Includes: R&R differential case.
All models
Corp axle (4.3) — 5.4
Dana axle (5.5) — 6.9

Pinion Bearings, Renew
Includes: R&R differential case.
All models
Corp axle (4.0) — 5.5
Dana axle (5.2) — 6.6

Differenetial Side Bearings, Renew
Includes: R&R differential case.
All models
Corp axle (3.3) — 4.4
Dana axle (4.1) — 5.6

Front Axle Housing Cover and/or Gasket, Renew
All models (.4) — .7

Front Drive Shaft, R&R or Renew
All models (.4) — .9
w/Transfer case shield add (.1) — .1

Front U-Joints, Renew
All models
U-Joint (.6) — 1.0
C.V. Joint (1.2) — 1.7
w/Transfer case shield add (.1) — .1

Front Axle Shaft and/or Universal Joint, Renew (One Side)
Series 10-20 (1.2) — 1.7
Series 30 (1.2) — 1.7
Renew inner shaft add — .4
Renew outer shaft add — .4
Renew U-Joint add — .4
Renew spindle brg add — .1

S-SERIES

Front Torsion Bar, Adjust
S-Series (.3) — .5

Front Torsion Bar, Renew
S-Series-one side (.8) — 1.2
both sides (1.1) — 1.6
w/Skid plate add (.2) — .2

Torsion Bar Pivot Arm, Renew
S-Series-one side (.5) — .7
both sides (.7) — 1.1
w/Skid plate add (.2) — .2

Torsion Bar Support Crossmember, Renew
S-Series (1.0) — 1.5
w/Skid plate add (.2) — .2

Front Differential Vacuum Locking Actuator, Renew
S-series (.3) — .5

Front Differential Locking Cable, Renew
S-series (.4) — .6
w/Skid plate add (.1) — .1

Front Propeller Shaft U-Joints, Renew
S-series
front (.6) — .9
rear (1.1) — 1.5
both (1.3) — 2.0

Front Propeller Shaft Assy., Renew
S-series (.4) — .6

LABOR 9 FRONT SUSPENSION 9 LABOR

(Factory Time)	Chilton Time
Output Shaft, Renew	
S-Series	
right side (1.5)	2.1
left side (1.3)	1.8
both sides (2.7)	3.8
Renew shaft seal add each (.2)	.2
Drive Axle Assy., R&R or Renew	
S-Series	
one (1.1)	1.5
both (1.9)	2.6
Renew axle shaft, add each (1.0)	1.0
Renew C/V joint boot, add each (.2)	.2
Renew outer C/V joint, add each (.3)	.3
Renew D.O. joint, add each (.3)	.3
Repack or Recond joints, add-each (.4)	.4
Front Differential Cover or Gasket, Renew	
All models (.4)	.6
Differential Pinion Shaft Oil Seal and/or Flange, Renew	
All models (3.7)	5.2
Differential Output Shaft Tube Assy., R&R or Renew	
All models (1.4)	1.9
Renew output shaft seal add (.1)	.1
Renew pilot brg add (.1)	.1
Renew shaft assy add (.1)	.1
Recond tube assy add (.3)	.3
Differential Carrier Assy., Remove & Install	
All models (3.1)	4.3
Renew pinion shaft and/or side pinion gears add (.4)	.4
Renew side brgs add (1.0)	1.0
Renew pinion brgs add (1.7)	1.7
Renew ring and pinion assy, add (1.6)	1.6
Renew case add (1.2)	1.2
Renew carrier add (1.8)	1.8
Renew output shaft brgs add (.9)	.9
Renew mount bushs add (.2)	.2
Recond complete add (2.2)	3.0
Recond tube add (.3)	.3

LABOR 10 STEERING LINKAGE 10 LABOR

(Factory Time)	Chilton Time
Tie Rods or Tie Rod Ends, Renew	
Includes: Reset toe-in.	
Two Wheel Drive	
one (.8)	1.1
both (1.0)	1.6
Four Wheel Drive	
one (.7)	.9
both (.9)	1.4
Idler Arm, Renew	
All models (.7)	1.0
S-series 4X4 add	.2
Drag Link, Renew	
All models (.4)	.9
Intermediate Rod, Renew	
Includes: Reset toe-in.	
Vans (1.0)	1.4
All other models (.9)	1.3
S-series 4X4 add	.2
Pitman Arm, Renew	
All models (.5)	.8
S-series 4X4 add	.2
Steering Knuckle Arm, Renew	
Includes: Reset toe-in.	
All models-one (.9)	1.3
both (1.1)	1.7
Steering Damper, Renew	
All models (.3)	.6
S-series 4X4 add	.2
Idler Arm Bracket and Bushing, Renew	
All models (.4)	.8

LABOR 11 STEERING GEAR 11 LABOR

(Factory Time)	Chilton Time
STANDARD STEERING	
Steering Wheel, Renew	
All models (.3)	.4
Upper Mast Jacket Bearing, Renew	
All models-std column (.8)	1.4
tilt column (.9)	1.6
w/Cruise control add (.2)	.2
Tilt Column Bearing Housing, Renew	
All models (.9)	1.5
w/Cruise control add (.2)	.2
Steering Shaft Lower Coupling (Pot Joint), Renew	
Includes: R&R intermediate shaft.	
S-series (.4)	.7
w/P.S. add (.3)	.3
All other models (.7)	1.3
Flexible Coupling (Rag Joint), Renew	
All models (.6)	1.0
Steering Column Lock Actuator Parts, Renew	
All models	
std colm (.8)	1.4
tilt colm (.9)	1.6
w/Cruise control add (.2)	.2
Steering Gear, Adjust (On Truck)	
All models	1.0
Steering Gear, R&R or Renew	
All models (.6)	1.0
Steering Gear, R&R and Recondition	
Includes: Disassemble, renew necessary parts, reassemble and adjust.	
All models (1.5)	2.4
Pitman Shaft Seal, Renew	
Does not require gear R&R.	
All models (1.1)	1.4
POWER STEERING	
Trouble Shoot Power Steering	
Includes: Test pump and system pressure. Check pounds pull on steering wheel and check for leaks.	
All models	.5
Power Steering Belt, Renew	
All models (.2)	.4
Power Steering Gear, R&R or Renew	
S-series (.6)	1.1
All other models (.8)	1.3
Power Steering Gear, R&R and Recondition	
S-series (1.6)	2.5
All other models (1.8)	3.0
Valve Body, Recondition	
Includes: R&R gear assy.	
S-series (.9)	1.4
All other models (1.2)	1.8
Adjuster Plug, Recondition	
Includes: R&R gear assy.	
S-series (.8)	1.2
All other models (1.0)	1.5
Rack Piston Nut, Recondition	
Includes: R&R gear assy.	
S-series (1.0)	1.5
All other models (1.2)	1.8
Power Steering Pump, R&R or Renew	
All models (.8)	1.2
w/A.C. add (.2)	.2
Vans-w/Diesel eng add	.2
Power Steering Pump, R&R and Recondition	
All models (1.2)	1.8
w/A.C. add (.2)	.2
Vans-w/Diesel eng add	.2
Power Steering Reservoir and/or 'O' Ring Seal, Renew	
All models (1.0)	1.4
w/A.C. add (.2)	.2
Vans-w/Diesel eng add	.2
Pump Flow Control Valve, Renew	
S-series (.3)	.7
All other models (.6)	1.0
w/A.C. add (.2)	.2
Power Steering Hoses, Renew	
All models	
pressure (.4)	.6
return (.5)	.8
w/A.C. add (.2)	.2

(Factory Time) — Chilton Time

GASOLINE ENGINES

Compression Test

Four	.6
Six	.9
V-6	.9
V-8	1.4

Cylinder Head Gasket, Renew

Includes: Clean carbon and make all necessary adjustments.

Four	
eng code A (3.4)	4.7
eng code Y (3.7)	5.1
eng code E	
S-series (4.0)	5.6
Astro (4.4)	6.2
w/Cruise control add	.2
w/A.C. add (.8)	.8
w/P.S. add (.4)	.4
Six–exc Vans (3.0)	4.3
Vans (3.9)	5.6
w/P.S. add (.4)	.4
w/A.C. add (.5)	.5
w/A.I.R. add (.6)	.6
w/P.A.I.R. add	.6
V-6–	
S-series-Astro	
one (5.7)	8.1
both (7.6)	10.8
All other models	
one (4.2)	6.0
both (6.5)	9.2
w/A.C. add (.5)	.5
w/P.S. add (.5)	.5
w/C.C.C. add (.3)	.3
V-8–454 eng	
one (4.8)	6.2
both (6.7)	9.1
V-8–all other engs	
exc Vans–one (4.5)	6.2
both (6.4)	8.8
Vans–one (4.8)	6.6
both (7.0)	9.6
w/P.S. add (.2)	.2
w/A.C. add (.7)	.7
w/A.I.R. add (.2)	.2

Cylinder Head, Renew

Includes: Transfer all components, reface valves, clean carbon.

Four	
eng code A (5.7)	7.9
eng code Y (6.2)	8.7
eng code E	
S-series (5.5)	7.7
Astro (5.7)	8.0
w/Cruise control add	.2
w/A.C. add (.8)	.8
w/P.S. add (.4)	.4
Six–exc Vans (5.9)	8.5
Vans (6.0)	8.7
w/P.S. add (.4)	.4
w/A.C. add (.5)	.5
w/A.I.R. add (.6)	.6
w/P.A.I.R. add	.6
V-6–	
S-series-Astro	
one (6.5)	9.2
both (9.0)	12.8
All other models	
one (5.0)	7.1
both (7.6)	10.8
w/A.C. add (.5)	.5
w/P.S. add (.5)	.5
w/C.C.C. add (.3)	.3
V-8–454 eng	
one (5.8)	7.2
both (8.8)	11.2

COMBINATIONS

Add to Valve Job

See Machine Shop Operations

(Factory Time) — Chilton Time

GASOLINE ENGINES

DRAIN, EVACUATE & RECHARGE AIR CONDITIONING SYSTEM	
All models (.5)	1.0
ROCKER ARM STUD, RENEW	
Each (.3)	.3
HYDRAULIC VALVE LIFTERS, DISASSEMBLE AND CLEAN	
Each	.2
DISTRIBUTOR, RECONDITION	
All models (.5)	.9
CARBURETOR, RECONDITION	
1 BBL (1.0)	1.0
2 BBL (1.0)	1.2
4 BBL (.8)	1.5
VALVE GUIDES, REAM OVERSIZE	
Each (.1)	.1

(Factory Time) — Chilton Time

V-8–all other engs	
exc Vans–one (5.4)	7.4
both (8.1)	11.1
Vans–one (5.7)	7.8
both (8.7)	12.0
w/P.S. add (.2)	.2
w/A.C. add (.7)	.7
w/A.I.R. add (.2)	.2

Clean Carbon and Grind Valves

Includes: R&R cylinder heads, grind valves and seats. Minor tune up.

Four	
eng code A (5.2)	7.3
eng code Y (5.3)	7.4
eng code E	
S-series (5.6)	8.0
Astro (6.0)	8.5
w/Cruise control add	.2
w/A.C. add (.8)	.8
w/P.S. add (.4)	.4
Six–exc Vans (5.6)	8.1
Vans (5.7)	8.3
w/P.S. add (.4)	.4
w/A.C. add (.5)	.5
w/A.I.R. add (.6)	.6
w/P.A.I.R. add	.6
V-6–	
S-series-Astro	
one side (7.0)	9.9
both sides (9.4)	13.3
All other models	
one side (5.3)	7.5
both sides (7.8)	11.1
w/A.C. add (.5)	.5
w/P.S. add (.5)	.5
w/C.C.C add (.3)	.3
V-8–454 eng	
one bank (6.1)	7.7
both banks (9.1)	12.2
V-8–all other engs	
exc Vans–one bank (5.8)	8.0
both banks (8.8)	12.1
Vans–one bank (6.1)	8.4
both banks (9.4)	12.9
w/P.S. add (.2)	.2

(Factory Time) — Chilton Time

w/A.C. add (.7)	.7
w/A.I.R. add (.2)	.2

Valves, Adjust

Six (.5)	1.4
V-8 (.8)	1.9
w/A.C. add	.7
w/P.A.I.R. add	.6

Valve Cover Gasket, Renew

Four	
eng code A (.4)	.7
eng code Y (.6)	.9
eng code E	
S-series (.9)	1.3
Astro (1.4)	2.0
Six–exc Vans (.7)	.9
Vans (.8)	1.0
w/A.I.R. add (.3)	.3
w/P.A.I.R. add	.6
V-6–	
S-series-Astro	
one side (.9)	1.3
both sides (1.8)	2.6
exc Vans	
right side (.7)	1.0
left side (.3)	.5
both sides (.9)	1.4
Vans	
right side (.9)	1.3
left side (.5)	.8
both sides (1.1)	1.7
w/A.C. add (.3)	.3
w/C.C.C. add (.3)	.3
V-8–454 eng	
one (.6)	.8
both (1.1)	1.5
V-8–all other engs	
exc Vans–one (.6)	.8
both (1.0)	1.3
Vans–right (.8)	1.3
left (.6)	.8
both (1.2)	1.6
w/A.C. add (.7)	.7
w/A.I.R. add (.2)	.2

Push Rod Side Cover Gasket, Renew

Four	
eng code E	
S-series (1.6)	2.2
Astro (1.8)	2.5
Six–exc Vans	
front (.5)	.7
rear (.3)	.4
both (.7)	1.0
Vans	
front (.6)	.8
rear (.5)	.8
both (.7)	1.2

Valve Push Rods and/or Rocker Arms, Renew

Four	
eng code A-all (.9)	1.2
eng code Y-all (1.0)	1.4
eng code E	
S-series-all (1.4)	2.0
Astro-all (1.9)	2.7
Six–exc Vans	
one or two (.5)	*.8
three or more (.7)	*1.2
w/A.I.R. add (.3)	.3
w/P.A.I.R. add	.6
Vans	
one or two (.9)	1.2
three or more (1.1)	1.6
V-6–	
S-series-Astro	
one cyl (1.0)	1.5
one cyl-each side (1.8)	2.7

(Factory Time)	Chilton Time
exc Vans	
one cyl-right side (.9)	1.4
one cyl-left side (.5)	1.0
one cyl-both sides (1.2)	1.9
Vans	
one cyl-right side (1.1)	1.7
one cyl-left side (.7)	1.2
one cyl-each side (1.4)	2.2
each adtnl cyl	.1
w/A.C. add (.3)	.3
w/C.C.C. add (.3)	.3
V-8-454 eng	
one cyl (.8)	1.0
one cyl-each bank (1.4)	1.8
all-both banks (1.9)	2.4
V-8-all other engs	
exc Vans	
one cyl (.8)	1.1
one cyl-each bank (1.4)	1.9
all cyls-both banks (1.9)	2.6
Vans	
one cyl (1.0)	1.4
one cyl-each bank (1.5)	2.0
all cyls-both banks (2.1)	2.9
w/A.C. add (.7)	.7
w/A.I.R. add (.2)	.2

Valve Lifters, Renew

Includes: R&R intake manifold on V-6 & V-8 engs. Make all necessary adjustments.

(Factory Time)	Chilton Time
Four	
eng code E	
S-series-all (3.1)	4.3
Astro-all (3.3)	4.6
Six-exc Vans-one (1.0)	1.4
all (1.5)	2.0
Vans-one (1.3)	1.7
all (1.8)	2.3
w/A.I.R. add (.3)	.3
w/P.A.I.R. add	.6
V-6-	
S-series	
one cyl (4.1)	6.0
one cyl-each side (4.2)	6.2
all cyls-both sides (4.7)	6.9
Astro	
one cyl (3.0)	4.4
one cyl-each side (3.3)	4.8
all cyls-both sides (3.8)	5.5
All other models	
one cyl (2.6)	3.8
one cyl-each side (2.8)	4.1
all cyls-both sides (3.3)	4.8
w/A.C. add (.3)	.3
w/C.C.C. add (.3)	.3
V-8-454 eng	
one (2.5)	3.2
all (3.3)	4.2
V-8-all other engs	
exc Vans-one cyl (2.8)	3.8
all cyls (3.4)	4.6
Vans-one cyl (2.9)	4.0
all cyls (3.5)	4.8
w/A.C. add (.7)	.7
w/A.I.R. add (.2)	.2

Valve Springs or Valve Stem Oil Seals, Renew (Head on Truck)

(Factory Time)	Chilton Time
Four	
eng code A	
one cyl (.8)	1.3
all cyls (1.4)	2.2
eng code Y	
one cyl (1.1)	1.6
all cyls (2.0)	3.0
eng code E	
S-series	
one cyl (1.3)	1.9
all cyls (2.2)	3.1
Astro	
one cyl (1.8)	2.6
all cyls (2.7)	3.8
Six-exc Vans	
one cyl (.7)	1.1
all cyls (1.2)	2.1
Vans	
one cyl (1.1)	1.5
all cyls (1.2)	2.5
w/A.I.R. add (.3)	.3
w/P.A.I.R. add	.6
V-6	
S-series-Astro	
one cyl (1.3)	1.9
one cyl-each side (2.3)	3.4
all cyls-both sides (3.6)	5.3
All other models	
one cyl-right side (1.4)	2.0
one cyl-left side (1.0)	1.5
one cyl-each side (2.0)	2.9
all cyls-both sides (3.2)	4.7
V-8-454 eng	
one cyl (1.1)	1.5
all cyls (3.7)	5.3
V-8-all other engs	
exc Vans	
one cyl (1.1)	1.5
all cyls (3.6)	5.0
Vans	
one cyl (1.4)	1.9
all cyls (4.5)	6.2
w/A.C. add (.7)	.7
w/A.I.R. add (.2)	.2

Valve Rocker Arm Stud, Renew (One)

Includes: Drain and refill cooling system.

(Factory Time)	Chilton Time
Four	
eng code E	
S-series (1.0)	1.5
Astro (1.5)	2.2
Six-exc Vans (.7)	1.0
Vans (1.2)	1.5
w/P.A.I.R. add	.6
V-6	
S-series-Astro (1.3)	1.8
All other models	
right side (1.3)	1.8
left side (.9)	1.4
w/A.C. add (.3)	.3
w/C.C.C. add (.3)	.3
V-8-454 eng (.8)	1.1
V-8-all other engs	
exc Vans (1.1)	1.5
Vans (1.3)	1.8
each adtnl-all engs (.3)	.3
w/A.C. add (.7)	.7
w/A.I.R. add (.2)	.2

DIESEL ENGINE

Compression Test

(Factory Time)	Chilton Time
All models	1.3

Cylinder Head Gasket, Renew

Includes: R&R injector pump and lines. R&R intake manifold and disconnect exhaust manifolds. Clean gasket surfaces, bleed litters and adjust timing. Drain and refill cooling system.

(Factory Time)	Chilton Time
All models-5.7L eng	
right side (5.0)	6.1
left side (4.9)	6.0
both sides (7.2)	9.1
6.2L eng	
one side (5.8)	8.0
both sides (8.1)	11.2
2.2L eng (2.6)	3.8
w/A.C. add (.3)	.3
Vans-w/A.C. add (2.0)	2.0

Cylinder Head, Renew

Includes: R&R injector pump and lines. R&R intake manifold and disconnect exhaust manifolds. Clean gasket surfaces. Transfer parts, reface valves. Bleed lifters and adjust timing. Drain and refill cooling system.

(Factory Time)	Chilton Time
All models-5.7L eng	
right side (5.5)	6.9
left side (5.4)	6.8
both sides (8.1)	10.7
6.2L eng	
one side (6.8)	9.5
both sides (9.6)	13.3
2.2L eng (3.9)	5.7
w/A.C. add (.3)	.3
Vans-w/A.C. add (2.0)	2.0

Clean Carbon and Grind Valves

Includes: R&R injector pump and lines. R&R cylinder heads, clean carbon. Recondition valves and valve seats. Check and adjust valve stem length. Bleed lifters, drain and refill cooling system.

(Factory Time)	Chilton Time
All models-5.7L eng	
right side (5.4)	7.2
left side (5.3)	7.1
both sides (9.1)	12.6
6.2L eng	
one side (7.1)	9.8
both sides (10.4)	14.4
2.2L eng (3.9)	5.7
w/A.C. add (.3)	.3
Vans-w/A.C. add (2.0)	2.0

Rocker Arm Cover or Gasket, Renew

Includes: R&R injector pump and lines.

(Factory Time)	Chilton Time
All models-5.7L eng	
one side (2.0)	2.6
both sides (2.2)	2.9
6.2L eng	
one side (2.6)	3.6
both sides (3.1)	4.3
2.2L eng (.4)	.6
Vans-w/A.C. add (2.0)	2.0

Valve Spring or Valve Stem Oil Seals, Renew (Head on Truck)

Includes: R&R injector pump and lines.

(Factory Time)	Chilton Time
All models-5.7L eng	
one (2.2)	3.1
one-each bank (2.6)	3.7
each adtnl(.3)	.3
6.2L eng	
one cyl (3.0)	4.2
one cyl-each side (3.9)	5.4
each adtnl cyl (.4)	.4
2.2L eng	
one cyl (.8)	1.2
all cyls (1.3)	2.0
Vans-w/A.C. add (2.0)	2.0

Rocker Arm and/or Push Rod, Renew

Includes: R&R injector pump and lines.

(Factory Time)	Chilton Time
All models-5.7L eng	
one cyl (2.1)	3.0
one cyl-each side (2.5)	3.5
each adtnl cyl (.1)	.1
6.2L eng	
one cyl (2.7)	3.7
one cyl-each side (3.3)	4.6
each adtnl cyl (.1)	.1
2.2L eng	
one or all (.7)	1.2
Vans-w/A.C. add (2.0)	2.0

Valve Lifters, Renew

Includes: R&R fuel injection pump and lines.

All models-5.7L eng

LABOR 12 CYLINDER HEAD & VALVE SYSTEM 12 LABOR

(Factory Time)	Chilton Time
one cyl (3.2)	4.2
one cyl-each side (3.5)	4.5
each adtnl cyl (.1)	.2
6.2L eng-exc Vans	
one cyl (3.4)	4.7
one cyl-each side (4.6)	6.4
each adtnl cyl (.1)	.2
Vans	
one cyl (6.7)	9.3
one cyl-each side (8.8)	12.2
each adtnl cyl (.1)	.1
2.2L eng-all (6.9)	10.0
w/A.C. add (.8)	.8
w/P.S. add (.3)	.3
Vans-w/A.C. add (2.0)	2.0

Push Rod Side Cover Gasket, Renew

(Factory Time)	Chilton Time
All models	
2.2L eng (1.1)	1.5

Valve Clearance, Adjust

(Factory Time)	Chilton Time
All models	
2.2L eng (.6)	1.0

LABOR 13 ENGINE ASSEMBLY & MOUNTS 13 LABOR

GASOLINE ENGINES

Engine Assembly, R&R

Does not include transfer of any parts or equipment.

(Factory Time)	Chilton Time
Four	5.0
w/A.C. add	.9
w/P.S. add	.4
w/A.T. add	.3
Six-exc Vans	5.1
Vans	7.7
w/P.S. add	.5
w/A.C. add	.5
w/A.I.R. add	.5
w/P.A.I.R. add	.6
V-6	
S-series	
4X2	5.5
4X4	*6.7
*w/M.T. add	2.0
Astro	6.9
exc Vans	4.9
Vans	5.9
w/P.S. add	.3
w/C.C.C. add	.6
w/A.T. add	.4
w/A.C. add	
Vans	1.1
Astro	.9
All other models	.4
V-8–454 eng	6.2
V-8–all other engs	
exc Vans	6.2
Vans	8.6
w/A.C. add	1.5
w/P.S. add	.2
w/A.I.R. add	.4
Vans with Hydra-Boost add	1.1

Engine Assembly, Renew

Includes: R&R engine and transmission assy. Transfer all component parts not supplied with replacement engine. Minor tune up.

(Factory Time)	Chilton Time
Four	
eng code Y	
4X2 (5.4)	8.0
4X4 (8.4)	12.0
w/A.C. add	.4
w/P.S. add	.4
eng code E	
S-series	
4X2 (4.8)	7.0
4X4 (5.6)	8.1
Astro (6.6)	9.6
w/A.C. add	.9
w/P.S. add	.3
w/A.T. add	.3
Six-exc Vans (4.1)	8.2
Vans (5.5)	9.6
w/P.S. add (.4)	.5
w/A.C. add (.5)	.5
w/A.I.R. add (.4)	.5
w/P.A.I.R. add	.6
V-6	
S-series	
4X2 (6.2)	9.0
4X4 (7.1)	*10.2
*w/M.T. add	2.0
Astro (7.2)	10.4
exc Vans (5.8)	8.4
Vans (6.5)	9.4
w/P.S. add (.3)	.3
w/C.C.C. add (.6)	.6
w/A.T. add (.4)	.4
w/A.C. add	
Vans (1.1)	1.1
Astro (.9)	.9
All other models (.4)	.4
V-8–454 eng (6.9)	9.3
V-8–all other engs	
exc Vans (6.0)	8.2
Vans (7.6)	10.5
w/A.C. add (1.3)	1.5
w/P.S. add (.2)	.2
w/A.I.R. add (.4)	.4
Vans with Hydra-Boost add (1.1)	1.1

Cylinder Block, Renew (w/Internal Parts Less Head(s) and Oil Pan)

Includes: R&R engine and transmission assy. Transfer all components parts not supplied with replacement engine. Clean carbon, grind valves. Minor tune up.

(Factory Time)	Chilton Time
Four	
eng code A	
4X2 (8.0)	12.0
4X4 (8.9)	13.0
eng code Y	
4X2 (9.9)	14.5
4X4 (13.1)	19.0
w/A.C. add (.4)	.4
w/P.S. add (.4)	.4
eng code E	
S-series	
4X2 (9.0)	13.0
4X4 (9.9)	14.4
Astro (10.9)	15.8
w/A.C. add	.9
w/P.S. add	.3
w/A.T. add	.3
Six-exc Vans (9.1)	15.0
Vans (11.4)	17.3
w/P.S. add (.4)	.5
w/A.C. add (.5)	.5
w/A.I.R. add (.4)	.5
w/P.A.I.R. add	.6
V-6	
S-series	
4X2 (11.7)	16.9
4X4 (12.5)	*18.1
*w/M.T. add	2.0
Astro (13.1)	19.0
exc Vans (11.6)	16.8
Vans (12.4)	17.9
w/P.S. add (.3)	.3
w/C.C.C. add (.6)	.6
w/A.T. add (.4)	.4
w/A.C. add	
Vans (1.1)	1.1
Astro (.9)	.9
All other models (.4)	.4
V-8–454 eng (14.9)	20.1
V-8–all other engs	
exc Vans (14.2)	19.5
Vans (14.8)	20.8
w/A.C. add (1.3)	1.5
w/P.S. add (.2)	.2
w/A.I.R. add (.4)	.4
Vans with Hydra-Boost add (1.1)	1.1

Cylinder Block, Renew (w/Pistons, Rings and Bearings)

Includes: R&R engine and transmission assy. Transfer all component parts not supplied with replacement engine. Clean carbon, grind valves. Minor tune up.

(Factory Time)	Chilton Time
Four	
eng code E	
S-series	
4X2 (11.3)	16.4
4X4 (12.1)	17.5
Astro (13.1)	19.0
w/A.C. add	.9
w/P.S. add	.3
w/A.T. add	.3
Six-exc Vans (12.4)	17.0
Vans (15.0)	19.6
w/P.S. add (.4)	.5
w/A.C. add (.5)	.5
w/A.I.R. add (.4)	.5
w/P.A.I.R. add	.6
V-6	
S-series	
4X2 (14.1)	20.5
4X4 (14.9)	*21.6
*w/M.T. add	2.0
Astro (16.0)	23.2
exc Vans (14.5)	21.0
Vans (15.3)	22.2
w/P.S. add (.3)	.3
w/C.C.C. add (.6)	.6
w/A.T. add (.4)	.4
w/A.C. add	
Vans (1.1)	1.1
Astro (.9)	.9
All other models (.4)	.4
V-8–454 eng (17.7)	23.8
V-8–all other engs	
exc Vans (17.0)	23.4
Vans (17.6)	24.1
w/A.C. add (1.3)	1.5
w/P.S. add (.2)	.2
w/A.I.R. add (.4)	.4
Vans with Hydra-Boost add (1.1)	1.1

Engine Assy., R&R and Recondition

Includes: Rebore block, install new pistons, rings, rod and main bearings. Clean carbon, grind valves. Tune engine.

LABOR 13 ENGINE ASSEMBLY & MOUNTS 13 LABOR

(Factory Time)	Chilton Time
Four	
eng code A	
4X2 (13.2)	19.7
4X4 (14.1)	21.0
eng code Y	
4X2 (16.0)	23.8
4X4 (18.6)	27.7
w/A.C. add (.4)	.4
w/P.S. add (.4)	.4
eng code E	
S-series	
4X2 (13.5)	19.5
4X4 (14.4)	20.8
Astro (15.4)	22.3
w/A.C. add	.9
w/P.S. add	.3
w/A.T. add	.3
Six-exc Vans (25.0)	32.0
Vans (27.6)	34.6
w/P.S. add (.4)	.5
w/A.C. add (.5)	.5
w/A.I.R. add (.4)	.5
w/P.A.I.R. add	.6
V-6	
S-series	
4X2 (20.7)	28.4
4X4 (22.2)	*29.5
*w/M.T. add	2.0
Astro (23.4)	31.5
exc Vans (20.9)	28.8
Vans (21.7)	29.2
w/P.S. add (.3)	.3
w/C.C.C. add (.6)	.6
w/A.T. add (.4)	.4
w/A.C. add	
Vans (1.1)	1.1
Astro (.9)	.9
All other models (.4)	.4
V-8-454 eng (32.5)	41.9
V-8-all other engs	
exc Vans (30.7)	43.5
Vans (32.2)	45.0
w/A.C. add (1.3)	1.5
w/P.S. add (.2)	.2
w/A.I.R. add (.4)	.4
Vans with Hydra-Boost add (1.1)	1.1

Engine Mounts, Renew

(Factory Time)	Chilton Time
Front	
Four-one (.5)	.7
both (.7)	1.0
Six-exc Vans-one (.5)	1.1
both (.8)	1.4
Vans-one (.7)	1.3
both (1.0)	1.6
V-6	
S-series	
one (1.0)	1.4
both (1.4)	1.9
All other models	
one (.8)	1.1
both (1.2)	1.7
V-8-all engines	
one (.8)	1.3
both (1.2)	1.9
Rear	
All models (.4)	.9

DIESEL ENGINE

Engine Assembly, Remove & Install

Does not include transfer of any parts or equipment.

(Factory Time)	Chilton Time
All models	5.0
w/A.C. add	1.2
w/A.T. add	.8

Engine Assembly, Renew (Universal)

Includes: R&R engine assembly. Transfer all component parts not supplied with replacement engine. Make all necessary adjustments.

(Factory Time)	Chilton Time
All models	
5.7L eng	20.0
6.2L eng	22.0
w/A.C. add	1.2
w/A.T. add	.8

Cylinder Block, Renew (Partial)

Includes: Transfer all component parts not supplied with replacement block. Clean carbon, grind valves. Make all necessary adjustments.

(Factory Time)	Chilton Time
All models	
2.2L eng (11.1)	18.0
5.7L eng	21.3
6.2L eng	
Vans (17.4)	29.5
All other models (15.5)	27.6
w/A.C. add	1.2
w/A.T. add	.8

Engine Assembly, R&R and Recondition

Includes: Rebore block, install new pistons, rings, rod and main bearings. Clean carbon, grind valves. Make all necessary adjustments.

(Factory Time)	Chilton Time
All models	
2.2L eng	27.3
5.7L eng	37.2
6.2L eng	40.0
w/A.C. add	1.2
w/A.T. add	.8

Engine Assembly, Recondition (In Truck)

Includes: Expand or renew pistons, install new rings, pins, rod and main bearings. Clean carbon, grind valves. Make all necessary adjustments.

(Factory Time)	Chilton Time
All models	
2.2L eng	20.1
5.7L eng	28.5
6.2L eng	32.9
w/A.C. add (.3)	.3

Engine Mounts, Renew

(Factory Time)	Chilton Time
Front	
All models-5.7L eng	
one (.5)	.8
both (.6)	1.0
6.2L eng	
one (.7)	1.0
both (1.1)	1.5
2.2L eng	
one (1.0)	1.4
both (1.8)	2.6
Rear	
All models (.4)	.6

LABOR 14 PISTONS, RINGS & BEARINGS 14 LABOR

GASOLINE ENGINES

Rings, Renew (See Engine Combinations)

Includes: Remove cylinder top ridge, deglaze cylinder walls, replace rod bearings, clean carbon from cylinder heads. Clean piston and ring grooves. Minor tune up.

(Factory Time)	Chilton Time
Four	
eng code A	
one cyl (5.9)	8.5
each adtnl cyl	.7
4X4 add (.9)	.9
eng code Y	
one cyl (6.9)	10.0
each adtnl cyl	.7
4X4 add (.4)	.4
w/A.C. add (.4)	.4
w/P.S. add (.4)	.4
eng code E	
S-series	
4X2-one cyl (5.9)	8.5
4X4-one cyl (8.5)	12.3
Astro-one cyl (6.4)	9.3
each adtnl cyl	.7
w/A.C. add	.6
Six-exc Vans-one (4.7)	6.9
all (6.7)	10.3
Vans-one (4.8)	7.0
all (6.8)	10.4
w/P.S. add (.4)	.5
w/A.C. add (.5)	.5
w/A.I.R. add (.6)	.6
w/P.A.I.R. add	.6
V-6	
S-series-Astro	
one cyl (8.4)	12.2
one cyl-each side (10.2)	14.8
all cyls-both sides (12.1)	17.5
All other models	
one cyl (6.6)	9.5
one cyl-each side (8.8)	12.8
all cyls-both sides (10.7)	15.5
w/A.C. add (.5)	.5
w/P.S. add (.5)	.5
w/C.C.C. add (.3)	.3
V-8-454 eng-one (6.6)	9.1
all (10.9)	14.8
V-8-all other engs	
exc Vans-one (6.1)	8.4
all (10.8)	14.9
Vans-one (6.4)	8.8
all (11.4)	15.7
w/A.C. add (.7)	.7
w/P.S. add (.2)	.2
w/A.I.R. add (.2)	.2

Piston or Connecting Rod, Renew

Includes: Remove cylinder top ridge, deglaze cylinder walls, replace rod bearings, clean carbon from cylinder heads. Minor tune up.

(Factory Time)	Chilton Time
Four	
eng code A	
one cyl (6.3)	9.1
each adtnl cyl	.7
4X4 add (.9)	.9
eng code Y	
one cyl (7.3)	10.5
each adtnl cyl	.7
4X4 add (.4)	.4
w/A.C. add (.4)	.4
w/P.S. add (.4)	.4
eng code E	
S-series	
4X2-one cyl (6.6)	9.5
4X4-one cyl (9.2)	13.3
Astro-one cyl (7.1)	10.3
each adtnl cyl	.7

LABOR 14 PISTONS, RINGS & BEARINGS 14 LABOR

(Factory Time)	Chilton Time
w/A.C. add	.6
Six-exc Vans-one (4.7)	7.2
all (6.7)	11.8
Vans-one (4.8)	7.3
all (6.8)	11.9
w/P.S. add (.4)	.5
w/A.C. add (.5)	.5
w/A.I.R. add (.6)	.6
w/P.A.I.R. add	.6
V-6	
S-series-Astro	
one cyl (8.4)	12.5
one cyl-each side (10.2)	15.4
all cyls-both sides (12.8)	19.3
All other models	
one cyl (6.6)	9.8
one cyl-each side (8.8)	13.4
all cyls-both sides (13.3)	17.3
w/A.C. add (.5)	.5
w/P.S. add (.5)	.5
w/C.C.C. add (.3)	.3
V-8-454 eng-one (6.6)	9.4
all (10.9)	17.2
V-8-all other engs	
exc Vans-one (6.1)	8.7
all (10.8)	17.3
Vans-one (6.4)	9.1
all (11.4)	18.1
w/A.C. add (.7)	.7
w/P.S. add (.2)	.2
w/A.I.R. add (.2)	.2

Connecting Rod Bearings, Renew

(Factory Time)	Chilton Time
Four	
eng code A (4.8)	6.7
eng code Y	
4X2 (5.7)	8.0
4X4 (4.7)	6.5
w/A.C. add (.4)	.4
w/P.S. add (.4)	.4
eng code E	
4X2 (2.7)	4.0
4X4 (5.1)	7.4
Six-one (2.0)	2.8
all (3.5)	4.9
w/A.C. add (.7)	.7
V-6	
S-series	
4X2 (6.4)	9.4
4X4 (4.9)	7.3
All other models (3.4)	4.9
w/A.C. add (.2)	.2
w/P.S. add (.2)	.2
w/C.C.C. add (.2)	.2
w/A.T. add (.3)	.3
V-8-454 eng-one (1.8)	2.8
all (3.9)	5.4
V-8-all other engs	
All models-one (1.6)	2.4
all (3.7)	5.2
w/M.T. add (.2)	.2

COMBINATIONS

Add to Engine Work
See Machine Shop Operations

GASOLINE ENGINES

(Factory Time)	Chilton Time
DRAIN, EVACUATE AND RECHARGE AIR CONDITIONING SYSTEM	
All models (.5)	1.0
ROCKER ARM STUD, RENEW	
Each (.3)	.3
HYDRAULIC VALVE LIFTERS, DISASSEMBLE AND CLEAN	
Each	.2
DISTRIBUTOR, RECONDITION	
All models (.5)	.9
CARBURETOR, RECONDITION	
1 BBL (1.0)	1.0
2 BBL (1.0)	1.2
4 BBL (.8)	1.5
VALVE GUIDES, REAM OVERSIZE	
Each (.1)	.1
DEGLAZE CYLINDER WALLS	
Each (.1)	.1
REMOVE CYLINDER TOP RIDGE	
Each (.1)	.1
VALVES, RECONDITION	
Four (1.8)	2.5
Six (2.1)	3.0
V-6 (2.0)	3.0
V-8 (2.7)	3.5
PLASTIGAUGE BEARINGS	
Each (.1)	.1
OIL PUMP, RECONDITION	
All models	.6
w/P.S. add (.2)	.2
w/C.C.C. add (.2)	.2
OIL FILTER, RENEW	
Four (.3)	.4
Six (.2)	.3
V-6 (.3)	.4
V-8 (.3)	.4

DIESEL ENGINE

Rings, Renew (See Engine Combinations)

Includes: Remove cylinder to ridge, deglaze cylinder walls. Clean piston and ring grooves. Make all necessary adjustments.

(Factory Time)	Chilton Time
All models	
2.2L eng (10.0)	14.5
w/A.C. add (.8)	.8
w/P.S. add (.3)	.3
5.7L eng (10.6)	14.0
6.2L eng (15.4)	21.5
w/A.C. add (.3)	.3

Piston or Connecting Rod, Renew

Includes: Remove cylinder top ridge, deglaze cylinder walls. Make all necessary adjustments.

(Factory Time)	Chilton Time
All models	
2.2L eng (10.0)	16.3
w/A.C. add (.8)	.8
w/P.S. add (.3)	.3
5.7L eng (10.7)	16.8
6.2L eng (16.5)	23.9
w/A.C. add (.3)	.3

Connecting Rod Bearings, Renew

Includes: Raise engine and clean oil pump screen.

(Factory Time)	Chilton Time
All models	
2.2L eng (7.5)	10.8
w/A.C. add (.8)	.8
w/P.S. add (.3)	.3
5.7L eng (4.0)	5.6
6.2L eng	
Vans (5.6)	7.8
All other models (4.0)	5.8

LABOR 15 CRANKSHAFT & DAMPER 15 LABOR

GASOLINE ENGINES

Crankshaft and Main Bearings, Renew

Includes: R&R engine, plastigauge bearings.

(Factory Time)	Chilton Time
Four	
eng code A	
4X2 (7.8)	11.3
4X4 (8.9)	12.9
eng code Y	
4X2 (7.8)	11.5
4X4 (10.4)	15.0
w/A.C. add (.4)	.4
w/P.S. add (.4)	.4
eng code E	
S-series	
4X2 (6.4)	9.3
4X4 (7.3)	10.6
Astro (8.3)	12.0
w/A.C. add	.9
w/P.S. add	.3
w/A.T. add	.3
Six-exc Vans (6.5)	8.4
Vans (8.7)	11.8
w/P.S. add (.4)	.5
w/A.C. add (.5)	.5
w/A.I.R. add (.3)	.5
w/P.A.I.R. add	.6
V-6	
S-series	
4X2 (8.5)	12.3
4X4 (9.0)	*13.0
*w/M.T. add	2.0
Astro (10.2)	14.8
exc Vans (9.1)	13.2
Vans (9.7)	14.0
w/P.S. add (.3)	.3
w/C.C.C. add (.6)	.6
w/A.T. add (.4)	.4
w/A.C. add	
Vans (1.1)	1.1
Astro (.9)	.9
All other models (.4)	.4
V-8-454 eng (9.2)	12.4
V-8-all other engs	
exc Vans (8.8)	12.3
Vans (10.3)	14.8
w/A.C. add (1.3)	1.5
w/P.S. add (.2)	.2
w/A.I.R. add (.2)	.2
Vans with Hydra-Boost add (1.1)	1.1

LABOR 15 CRANKSHAFT & DAMPER 15 LABOR

Main Bearings, Renew

Includes: Plastigauge bearings.

(Factory Time)	Chilton Time
Four	
eng code A (5.2)	7.5
eng code Y	
4X2 (5.8)	8.4
4X4 (4.7)	6.8
w/A.C. add (.4)	.4
w/P.S. add (.4)	.4
eng code E	
4X2 (2.9)	4.2
4X4 (5.3)	7.7
Six–exc Vans (3.3)	4.9
Vans (3.5)	5.1
V-6	
S-series	
4X2 (6.1)	9.5
4X4 (4.9)	7.8
All other models (3.1)	4.5
w/A.C. add (.2)	.2
w/P.S. add (.2)	.2
w/C.C.C. add (.2)	.2
w/A.T. add (.3)	.3
V-8–454 eng (3.2)	5.0
V-8–all other engs	
All models (2.9)	4.5
w/M.T. add (.2)	.2

Rear Main Bearing Oil Seal, Renew

(Factory Time)	Chilton Time
Four	
eng code A (4.1)	*6.3
eng code Y	
4X2 (6.7)	*9.7
4X4 (9.2)	*13.3
w/A.C. add (.4)	.4
w/P.S. add (.4)	.4
eng code E	
4X2 (2.4)	3.5
4X4 (3.4)	5.0
w/A.T. add (.3)	.3
w/M.T. add (.4)	.4
Six–exc Vans (1.6)	2.7
Vans (1.8)	2.9
w/A.C. add (.7)	.7
V-6	
S-series	
Full Circle Type	
4X2 (7.3)	10.5
4X4 (7.8)	*11.3
w/A.C. add (.2)	.2
w/P.S. add (.2)	.2
w/C.C.C. add (.6)	.6
*w/M.T. add	2.0
Split Lip Type	
4X2 (3.0)	4.5
4X4 (3.6)	5.5
w/A.T. add (.4)	.4
All other models (2.2)	3.5
V-8–454 eng (2.0)	3.3
V-8–all other engs	
All models (1.6)	3.2
w/M.T. add (.2)	.2

*Includes R&R engine.

Harmonic Balancer (Vibration Damper), Renew

Includes: Renew timing cover oil seal.

(Factory Time)	Chilton Time
Four	
eng code A (.9)	1.5
eng code Y (.7)	1.4
eng code E (.5)	1.1
w/A.C. add (.2)	.2
w/P.S. add (.2)	.2
Six–exc Vans (.8)	1.2
Vans (.9)	1.6
w/P.S. add (.2)	.2
w/A.C. add (.2)	.2
w/A.I.R. add (.2)	.2
V-6	
All models (.8)	1.3
w/A.C. add (.2)	.2
w/P.S. add (.2)	.2
V-8–454 eng (1.2)	1.6
V-8–all other engs	
All models (1.0)	1.5
w/A.C. add (.2)	.2
w/P.S. add (.2)	.2
w/A.I.R. add (.2)	.2

DIESEL ENGINE

Crankshaft and Main Bearings, Renew

Includes: R&R engine, plastigauge bearings.

(Factory Time)	Chilton Time
All models	
2.2L eng (8.9)	13.0
w/A.C. add (.8)	.8
w/P.S. add (.3)	.3
5.7L eng (7.5)	10.9
6.2L eng	
Vans (13.4)	19.5
All other models (8.5)	12.3
w/A.C. add (.3)	.3
w/A.T. add	.8

Main Bearings, Renew

Includes: Plastigauge bearings.

(Factory Time)	Chilton Time
All models	
2.2L eng (7.9)	11.4
w/A.C. add (.8)	.8
w/P.S. add (.3)	.3
5.7L eng (3.5)	5.4
6.2L eng	
Vans (4.9)	7.0
All other models (3.5)	5.0

Main and Rod Bearings, Renew

Includes: Check all bearing clearance.

(Factory Time)	Chilton Time
All models	
2.2L eng (9.1)	12.6
w/A.C. add (.8)	.8
w/P.S. add (.3)	.3
5.7L eng (5.1)	7.8
6.2L eng	
Vans (7.3)	9.4
All other models (5.3)	7.4

Rear Main Bearing Oil Seals, Renew or Repack (Upper and Lower)

Includes: R&R oil pan and rear main bearing cap.

(Factory Time)	Chilton Time
All models	
2.2L eng (1.9)	2.8
5.7L eng (2.8)	4.0
6.2L eng	
Vans (3.7)	5.4
All other models (2.5)	3.6

Harmonic Balancer (Vibration Damper), Renew

(Factory Time)	Chilton Time
All models	
5.7L eng (.9)	1.3
6.2L eng	
Vans (1.2)	1.6
All other models (.8)	1.2
w/A.C. add (.4)	.4

Crankshaft Front Oil Seal, Renew

(Factory Time)	Chilton Time
All models	
5.7L eng (1.0)	1.5
6.2L eng	
Vans (1.2)	1.8
All other models (.8)	1.4
w/A.C. add (.4)	.4

LABOR 16 CAMSHAFT & TIMING GEARS 16 LABOR

GASOLINE ENGINES

Timing Cover Oil Seal, Renew

(Factory Time)	Chilton Time
Four	
eng code A (.9)	1.7
eng code Y (.7)	1.6
eng code E (.5)	1.2
w/A.C. add (.2)	.2
w/P.S. add (.2)	.2
Six–exc Vans (.8)	1.4
Vans (.9)	1.5
w/P.S. add (.2)	.2
w/A.C. add (.2)	.2
w/A.I.R. add (.2)	.2
V-6	
All models (.8)	1.4
w/A.C. add (.2)	.2
w/P.S. add (.2)	.2
V-8–454 eng (1.2)	1.6
V-8–all other engs	
All models (1.0)	1.6
w/A.C. add (.2)	.2
w/P.S. add (.2)	.2
w/A.I.R. add (.2)	.2

Timing Cover Gasket, Renew

Includes: Renew oil seal.

(Factory Time)	Chilton Time
Four	
eng code A (5.6)	8.0
eng code Y (1.7)	2.5
eng code E (1.3)	2.0
w/A.C. add (.4)	.4
w/P.S. add (.4)	.4
Six–all models (1.1)	1.8
w/P.S. add (.2)	.2
w/A.C. add (.2)	.2
w/A.I.R. add (.2)	.2
V-6	
S-series (2.0)	3.0
Astro (1.7)	2.5
exc Vans (1.8)	2.7
Vans (2.1)	3.1
w/A.C. add (.2)	.2
w/P.S. add (.3)	.3
V-8–454 eng (2.2)	2.8
V-8–all other engs	
all models (2.0)	*3.0
w/A.C. add (.5)	.5
w/P.S. add (.2)	.2
w/A.I.R. add (.2)	.2
*Vans w/A.C. add (1.2)	1.2

Timing Chain, Renew

Includes: R&R engine front cover.

(Factory Time)	Chilton Time
Four	
eng code A (5.7)	8.5
eng code Y (2.0)	3.0

LABOR 16 CAMSHAFT & TIMING GEARS 16 LABOR

(Factory Time) Chilton Time

w/A.C. add (.4) 4
w/P.S. add (.4) 4

V-6
S-series (2.3) 3.5
Astro (1.8) 3.0
exc Vans (1.9) 3.2
Vans (2.2) 3.6
w/A.C. add (.2) 2
w/P.S. add (.3) 3
V-8-454 eng (2.6) 3.3
V-8-all other engs
all models (2.2) *3.5
w/A.C. add (.5) 5
w/P.S. add (.2) 2
w/A.I.R. add (.2) 2
*Vans w/A.C. add (1.2) 1.2

Camshaft, Renew

Includes: R&R engine and front cover, where required.

Four
eng code A (1.0) 1.5
eng code Y (4.0) 6.0
eng code E
S-series (4.7) 6.8
Astro (6.0) 8.7
w/A.C. add 5
w/P.S. add 3
Six-exc Vans (3.9) 6.0
Vans (4.2) 8.3
w/P.S. add (.4) 5
w/A.C. add (.5) 5
w/A.I.R. add (.4) 5
w/P.A.I.R. add 6

V-6
S-series (5.1) 8.5
Astro (5.7) 8.8
All other models (6.0) 9.3
w/C.C.C. add (.3) 3
w/A.C. add (.3) 3
w/P.S. add (.3) 3
V-8-454 eng (6.2) 9.3
V-8-all other engs
exc Vans (5.8) 8.0
Vans (6.2) 9.5
w/A.C. add (1.4) 1.6
w/P.S. add (.2) 2
w/A.I.R. add (.4) 4
Vans with Hydra-Boost add (1.1) 1.1

Camshaft Timing Gear, Renew
Four
eng code A (.5) 9
eng code Y (2.0) 3.0

(Factory Time) Chilton Time

eng code E
S-series (4.7) 6.8
Astro (6.0) 8.7
w/A.C. add 5
w/P.S. add 3
V-6
S-series (2.3) 3.5
Astro (1.8) 3.0
exc Vans (1.9) 3.2
Vans (2.2) 3.6
w/A.C. add (.2) 2
w/P.S. add (.3) 3

DIESEL ENGINE

Timing Cover or Gasket, Renew

Includes: R&R fan blade, crankshaft pulley and balancer. Drain and refill oil and coolant.

All models
2.2L eng (2.5) 3.6
5.7L eng (2.3) 3.3
6.2L eng (4.3) 6.2
w/A.C. add (.4) 4

Timing Cover Oil Seal, Renew

Includes: R&R fan blade, crankshaft pulley and balancer. Drain and refill oil and coolant.

All models
2.2L eng (1.1) 2.0
5.7L eng (1.0) 1.6
6.2L eng
Vans (1.2) 2.0
All other models (.8) 1.5
w/A.C. add (.4) 4

Camshaft Gear and/or Timing Chain, Renew

Includes: R&R fan blades, crankshaft pulley and balancer. Drain and refill oil and coolant.

All models
5.7L eng (3.6) 4.8
6.2L eng (4.5) 6.7
w/A.C. add (.4) 4

Injector Pump Drive Gear, Renew

Includes: R&R timing gear and chain. R&R intake manifold and lifters. Drain and refill oil and coolant, where required.

All models
2.2L eng (.9) 1.5
5.7L eng (5.2) 7.2
6.2L eng (4.4) 6.6
w/A.C. add (.4) 4

(Factory Time) Chilton Time

Camshaft, Renew

Includes: R&R radiator, front cover, fuel pump, timing gear and chain. R&R injector pump, intake manifold and lifters. Disconnect exhaust system. Drain and refill oil and coolant. Make all necessary adjustments.

All models
2.2L eng (6.9) 10.0
w/A.C. add (.6) 6
w/P.S. add (.3) 3
5.7L eng (6.5) 10.8
6.2L eng (12.0) 17.4
w/A.C. add (2.0) 2.0
w/A.T. add (.3) 3

Camshaft Bearings, Renew

Includes: R&R radiator, front cover, fuel pump, timing gear and chain. R&R injector pump, intake manifold and lifters. Disconnect exhaust system. Drain and refill oil and coolant. Make all necessary adjustments.

All models
5.7L eng (9.5) 14.6
w/A.C. add (.2) 2

Camshaft Rear Bearing Plug, Renew

Note: Use appropriate labor operation for removal of necessary components to gain access to plug.

All models (.3) 6

Camshaft Timing Gear, Renew
All models
2.2L eng (.9) 1.6
w/A.C. add (.1) 1

Crankshaft Timing Gear, Renew
All models
2.2L eng (.9) 1.6
w/A.C. add (.1) 1

Camshaft Idler Pulley, Renew
All models
2.2L eng (.4) 6
w/A.C. add (.1) 1

Camshaft Drive Belt, Renew
All models
2.2L eng (.8) 1.5
w/A.C. add (.1) 1

Camshaft Drive Belt Covers and/or Gaskets, Renew
All models
2.2L eng
upper (.3) 5
lower or both (.6) 1.0
w/A.C. add (.1) 1

LABOR 17 ENGINE OILING SYSTEM 17 LABOR

(Factory Time) Chilton Time

GASOLINE ENGINE

Oil Pan and/or Gasket, Renew
Four
eng code A (3.7) 5.5
eng code Y
4X2 (4.3) 6.2
4X4 (3.2) 4.6
w/A.C. add (.4) 4
w/P.S. add (.4) 4
eng code E
4X2 (1.7) 2.5
4X4 (4.1) 6.0
Six-exc Vans (1.4) 2.4
Vans (1.6) 2.6
w/A.C. add (.7) 7

(Factory Time) Chilton Time

V-6
S-series
4X2 (4.9) 7.3
4X4 (3.4) 5.1
All other models (1.7) 2.5
w/A.C. add (.2) 2
w/P.S. add (.2) 2
w/C.C.C. add (.2) 2
w/A.T. add (.3) 3
V-8-454 eng (1.4) 2.5
V-8-all other engs (1.1) 2.0
w/M.T. add (.2) 2

Pressure Test Engine Bearings (Pan Off)
All models 1.0

(Factory Time) Chilton Time

Oil Pump, Renew
Four
eng code A (3.8) 5.7
eng code Y
4X2 (4.4) 6.4
4X4 (3.4) 4.8
w/A.C. add (.4) 4
w/P.S. add (.4) 4
eng code E
4X2 (1.9) 2.7
4X4 (4.2) 6.2
Six-exc Vans (1.5) 2.6
Vans (1.8) 2.8
w/A.C. add (.7) 7
V-6
S-series

LABOR 17 ENGINE OILING SYSTEM 17 LABOR

(Factory Time) Chilton Time

4X2 (4.9) 7.5
4X4 (3.4) 5.3
All other models (1.8) 2.7
w/A.C. add (.2) 2
w/P.S. add (.2) 2
w/C.C.C. add (.2) 2
w/A.T. add (.3) 3
V-8–454 eng (1.5) 2.7
V-8–all other engs (1.2) 2.2
w/M.T. add (.2) 2

Oil Pressure Gauge (Dash), Renew
S-series (.3) 5
Astro (.9) 1.4
All other models (.6) 1.0

Oil Pressure Gauge (Engine Unit), Renew
All models (.2) 5
w/A.C. add (.2) 2
w/Cruise control add (.4) 4

Oil Filter By-Pass Valve, Renew
Four-eng code Y (.3) 4
Six (.2) 3
V-6 (.3) 4
V-8 (.3) 4

Oil Filter Element, Renew
Four (.3) 4
Six (.2) 3
V-6 (.3) 4
V-8 (.3) 4

DIESEL ENGINE

Oil Pan and/or Gasket, Renew
Includes: Raise engine, R&R and clean oil pump screen.
All models
2.2L eng (.7) 1.2
5.7L eng (2.1) 3.0
6.2L eng
Vans (3.2) 4.6
All other models (2.0) 2.9
w/M.T. add (.3) 3

Pressure Test Engine Bearings (Pan Off)
All models 1.0

Oil Pump, Renew
Includes: Raise engine, R&R and clean oil pump screen.
All models
2.2L eng (5.9) 8.5
w/A.C. add (.6) 6
w/P.S. add (.3) 3
5.7L eng (2.2) 3.2
6.2L eng
Vans (3.2) 4.8
All other models (2.1) 3.1
w/M.T. add (.3) 3

Oil Pump, R&R and Recondition
Includes: Raise engine, R&R and clean oil pump screen.
All models
5.7L eng (2.4) 3.4

Oil Pressure Sending Unit, Renew
All models
5.7L eng (.3) 5
6.2L eng (1.4) 1.8

Oil Filter Element, Renew
All models (.3) 4

Crankcase and/or Gasket, Renew
All models
2.2L eng (5.8) 8.4
w/A.C. add (.6) 6
w/P.S. add (.3) 3

LABOR 18 CLUTCH & FLYWHEEL 18 LABOR

(Factory Time) Chilton Time

Clutch Pedal Free Play, Adjust
All models (.3) 4

Bleed Clutch Hydraulic System
All models (.5) 6

Clutch Master Cylinder, Renew
Includes: Bleed system.
All models (.8) 1.2
Recond cyl add (.4) 4

Clutch Slave (Actuator) Cylinder, Renew
Includes: Bleed system.
All models (.6) 1.0
Recond cyl add (.4) 4

Clutch Assembly, Renew
Includes: R&R trans and adjust clutch free play.
3 Speed
exc Vans
2 whl drive (2.2) 3.5
4 whl drive (4.0) 5.3
Vans (1.6) 3.0
4 Speed
exc below
2 whl drive (3.2) 4.5
4 whl drive (4.7) 6.0
Muncie
2 whl drive (2.2) 3.0
4 whl drive (3.0) 4.0
S-series
Isuzu
Four (2.7) 3.5
V-6 (2.2) 3.0
Warner (2.2) 2.7
Astro (1.9) 2.4
5 Speed
2 whl drive (2.2) 3.0
4 whl drive (3.5) 4.7
w/Skid plate add (.3) 3
w/Catalytic converter add (.4) 4
w/Power take off add (.3) 3
Renew pilot brg add (.2) 2

Clutch Release Bearing, Fork and/or Ball Stud, Renew
Includes: R&R trans, and adjust clutch free play.
3 Speed
exc Vans
2 whl drive (2.2) 3.3
4 whl drive (4.0) 5.1
Vans (1.6) 2.8
4 Speed
exc below
2 whl drive (3.2) 4.3
4 whl drive (4.7) 5.8
Muncie
2 whl drive (1.7) 2.3
4 whl drive (2.5) 3.4
S-series
Isuzu
Four (2.3) 3.1
V-6 (1.9) 2.4
Warner (1.9) 2.4
Astro (1.8) 2.3
5 Speed
2 whl drive (1.4) 1.9
4 whl drive (2.8) 3.8
w/Skid plate add (.3) 3
w/Catalytic converter add (.4) 4
w/Power take off add (.3) 3

Clutch Cross Shaft Assy., Renew
Includes: Raise vehicle and adjust linkage.
All models (.4) 9

Flywheel, Renew
Includes: R&R transmission.
3 Speed
exc Vans
2 whl drive (2.5) 3.9
4 whl drive (4.3) 5.7
Vans (1.7) 3.4
4 Speed
exc below
2 whl drive (3.4) 4.9
4 whl drive (5.0) 6.4
Muncie
2 whl drive (2.4) 3.2
4 whl drive (3.2) 4.3
S-series
Isuzu
Four (2.9) 3.8
V-6 (2.4) 3.3
Warner (2.4) 3.0
Astro (2.1) 2.7
5 Speed
2 whl drive (2.4) 3.2
4 whl drive (3.7) 4.9
w/Skid plate add (.3) 3
w/Catalytic converter add (.3) 4
w/Power take off add (.3) 3
Renew ring gear add 5

LABOR 19 STANDARD TRANSMISSION 19 LABOR

(Factory Time) Chilton Time

Transmission Assy., R&R or Renew
Includes: Raise vehicle and perform necessary adjustments. Transfer all attaching parts.
3 Speed
exc Vans
2 whl drive (1.7) 3.2
4 whl drive (3.6) 5.0
Vans (1.4) 2.7
4 Speed
exc below

LABOR 19 STANDARD TRANSMISSION 19 LABOR

(Factory Time)	Chilton Time
2 whl drive (2.6)	4.2
4 whl drive (4.3)	5.7
New Process (2.3)	3.0
Muncie	
2 whl drive (1.7)	2.3
4 whl drive (2.5)	3.4
New Process	
2 whl drive (1.5)	2.1
4 whl drive (2.4)	3.3
S-series	
Isuzu	
Four (2.3)	3.1
V-6 (1.9)	2.6
Warner	
2 whl drive (1.4)	1.9
4 whl drive (2.8)	3.8
Astro	
Muncie (1.4)	1.9
5 Speed	
2 whl drive (1.4)	1.9
4 whl drive (2.8)	3.8
w/Skid plate add (.3)	.3
w/Catalytic converter add (.4)	.4
w/Power take off add (.3)	.3

Transmission Assy., R&R and Recondition

Includes: Raise vehicle and perform all necessary adjustments.

(Factory Time)	Chilton Time
3 Speed	
exc Vans-w/2 whl drive	
Muncie (3.0)	4.9
Saginaw (3.0)	4.9
Tremec (3.8)	5.7
Vans-w/2 whl drive	
Muncie (2.7)	4.6
Saginaw (2.7)	4.6
4 Speed	
exc below	
2 whl drive (5.0)	6.9
4 whl drive (6.7)	8.6
New Process (4.2)	5.4
Muncie	
2 whl drive (4.2)	5.8
4 whl drive (5.0)	7.0
New Process	
2 whl drive (3.6)	5.0
4 whl drive (4.6)	6.4
S-series	
Isuzu	
Four (3.9)	5.3
V-6 (3.5)	4.7
Warner	
2 whl drive (3.2)	4.5
4 whl drive (4.6)	6.5
Astro	
Muncie (3.1)	4.5
5 Speed	
2 whl drive (3.4)	4.7
4 whl drive (4.8)	6.7
w/Skid plate add (.3)	.3
w/Catalytic converter add (.4)	.4
w/Power take off add (.3)	.3

Transmission Shift Cover, Renew or Recondition

Includes: Raise vehicle and adjust linkage.

(Factory Time)	Chilton Time
3 Speed	
exc Vans (.7)	1.3
Vans (.8)	1.4
4 Speed	
Saginaw (1.9)	2.6
New Process (.6)	1.0
Isuzu (.5)	.9
Warner (.8)	*1.4
Muncie	
10-30 Series (1.4)	2.0
Astro (.6)	.8
*Recond add (.6)	.8
5 Speed	
S-series (.8)	*1.4
Astro (1.8)	2.5
*Recond add (.6)	.8

Transmission Rear Oil Seal, Renew

Includes: Raise vehicle, R&R drive shaft.

(Factory Time)	Chilton Time
All models (.5)	.9

Speedometer Driven Gear, Renew

(Factory Time)	Chilton Time
All models (.3)	.6

Speedometer Drive Gear, Renew

(Factory Time)	Chilton Time
4 Speed	
All models (.9)	1.4
5 Speed	
Astro (1.8)	2.5

LABOR 20 TRANSFER CASE 20 LABOR

Transfer Case Assy., R&R or Renew

(Factory Time)	Chilton Time
Dana (3.1)	4.5
New Process Model 208 (1.3)	2.0
New Process Model 207 (1.4)	2.1
New Process Model 205 (1.4)	2.1
New Process Model 203 (2.5)	3.8
w/Power take off add (.3)	.3
w/Skid plate add (.3)	.3

Transfer Case Assy., R&R and Recondition

(Factory Time)	Chilton Time
Dana (5.2)	7.1
New Process Model 208 (3.5)	5.6
New Process Model 207 (3.4)	5.5
New Process Model 205 (3.9)	6.0
New Process Model 203 (6.8)	8.7
w/Power take off add (.3)	.3
w/Skid plate add (.3)	.3

Transfer Case Oil Seals, Renew

(Factory Time)	Chilton Time
Dana	
front (1.1)	1.7
rear (.6)	1.0
New Process Model 208	
front (.5)	.9
rear (.3)	.6
New Process Model 207	
front (.5)	.9
rear (.4)	.7
New Process Model 205	
front (1.1)	1.7
rear (.6)	1.0
New Process Model 203	
front (.8)	1.4
rear (.7)	1.3

Transfer Case Power Take Off Cover Gasket, Renew

(Factory Time)	Chilton Time
All models (.4)	.7

Transfer Case Rear Output Shaft Housing Gasket, Renew

(Factory Time)	Chilton Time
All models-New Process	
Model 208 (.5)	.8
Model 207 (.6)	1.0
Model 205 (.8)	1.2

Transfer Case Speedometer Drive Gear, Renew

(Factory Time)	Chilton Time
New Process Model 208 (.5)	.7
New Process Model 207 (.6)	1.0
New Process Model 205 (.8)	1.1
New Process Model 203 (.9)	1.2

Rear Output Shaft Housing, Renew

(Factory Time)	Chilton Time
All models-New Process	
Model 208 (.5)	.9
Model 207 (.6)	1.0
Model 205 (.8)	1.4

LABOR 21 SHIFT LINKAGE 21 LABOR

STANDARD

Shift Linkage, Adjust

(Factory Time)	Chilton Time
All models (.3)	.4

Gearshift Control Lever, Renew

(Factory Time)	Chilton Time
All models-column mount (.2)	.4
floor mount (.3)	.6

Transfer Case Gearshift Lever, Renew

(Factory Time)	Chilton Time
New Process Model 205 (.4)	.6
New Process Model 203 (.3)	.5

Transfer Case Shifter Assy., Renew

(Factory Time)	Chilton Time
New Process Model 203 (1.4)	2.1

Gearshift Control Rods, Renew

(Factory Time)	Chilton Time
All models-one (.4)	.6
two (.5)	.9

Gear Shift Tube and/or Levers, Renew

(Factory Time)	Chilton Time
exc Vans (1.7)	2.5
Vans (1.4)	2.2

AUTOMATIC

Linkage, Adjust

Includes: Adjust neutral safety switch, indicator needle and detent rod, cable or switch.

(Factory Time)	Chilton Time
All models (.4)	.7

Shift Linkage, Adjust (w/Diesel Eng)

(Factory Time)	Chilton Time
All models	
Fast idle speed (.2)	.3
Throttle rod/T.V.	

LABOR 21 SHIFT LINKAGE 21 LABOR

(Factory Time) Chilton Time

cable (.5).................... .6
Trans vacuum valve (.5).................... .6
Complete (.6).................... 1.0

Note: Does not apply to Vans with THM 400 trans.

Column Shift Selector Lever, Renew
All models (.2).................... .3

Shift Control Rods, Renew
Includes: Necessary adjustments.
All models-one (.3).................... .5

Cross Shaft Assembly, Renew
Includes: Necessary adjustments.
All models (.4).................... .6

Shift Indicator Needle, Renew
All models (.6).................... 1.0

LABOR 23 AUTOMATIC TRANSMISSION 23 LABOR

(Factory Time) Chilton Time

TURBO HYDRA-MATIC 200C

ON TRUCK SERVICES

Drain & Refill Unit
All models.................... .9

Oil Pressure Check
All models (.5).................... .7

Check Unit For Oil Leaks
Includes: Clean and dry outside of case and run unit to determine point of leak.
All models.................... .9

Neutral Safety Switch, Renew
All models (.3).................... .4

Throttle Valve Control Cable and/or 'O' Ring, Renew
Includes: Adjust cable.
All models (.5).................... .8

Speedometer Driven Gear and/or Seal, Renew
All models (.3).................... .5

Transmission Rear Oil Seal, Renew
Includes: R&R driveshaft.
All models (.4).................... .8

Torque Converter Clutch Switches, Renew
All models
Brake (.2).................... .4
Thermal Vacuum (.3).................... .5
Temp Indicator (.3).................... .5

Governor Assy., R&R or Renew
Includes: Renew governor seal.
All models (1.1).................... 1.7

Governor Assy., R&R and Recondition
Includes: Clean and inspect governor, renew seal and gear.
All models (1.3).................... 2.0

Oil Pan and/or Gasket, Renew
Includes: Clean pan and service screen.
All models (.6).................... .9

Manual Shaft Seal and/or Detent Lever, Renew
Includes: R&R oil pan.
All models (.7).................... 1.1

Valve Body Assembly, Renew
Includes: R&R oil pan and renew filter.
All models (.9).................... 1.5

Valve Body Assy., R&R and Recondition
Includes: R&R oil pan and renew filter. Disassemble, clean, inspect and free all valves. Replace parts as required.
All models (1.6).................... 2.8

Intermediate Servo Assy., R&R or Renew
All models (1.1).................... 1.7
Recond servo add (.2).................... .2

Parking Pawl, Shaft, Rod or Spring, Renew
Includes: R&R oil pan.
All models (1.3).................... 2.0

1-2 Accumulator Piston and/or Spring, R&R or Renew
Includes: R&R oil pan.
All models (.9).................... 1.4
Recond accumulator add (.2).................... .2

SERVICES REQUIRING R&R

Transmission Assembly, R&R or Renew
All models
4X2 (2.6).................... 3.7
4X4 (3.2).................... 4.6

Transmission and Converter, R&R and Recondition
Includes: Disassemble transmission completely, including valve body. Clean and inspect all parts. Renew all parts as required. Make all necessary adjustments. Road test.
All models
4X2 (6.2).................... 11.2
4X4 (6.8).................... 11.8

Transmission Assy., R&R and Reseal
Includes: Install all new gaskets and seals.
All models.................... 6.5
4X2.................... 6.5
4X4.................... 7.0

Flywheel (Flexplate), Renew
Includes: R&R transmission.
All models
4X2 (2.8).................... 3.9
4X4 (3.4).................... 4.8

Torque Converter, Renew
Includes: R&R transmission.
All models
4X2 (2.6).................... 3.8
4X4 (3.2).................... 4.7

Front Pump Oil Seal, Renew
Includes: R&R transmission.
All models
4X2 (2.6).................... 3.8
4X4 (3.2).................... 4.7

Front Pump Assy., Renew or Recondition
Includes: R&R transmission.
All models
4X2 (3.0).................... 4.3
4X4 (3.6).................... 5.2
Recond front pump add (.5).................... .8
Renew bushing add (.1).................... .1

Converter Clutch Solenoid Assy., Renew
Includes: R&R transmission, converter and oil pump.
All models
4X2 (2.6).................... 4.0
4X4 (3.2).................... 4.9

Apply and Actuator Valves and/or Bushing, Renew
Includes: R&R transmission, converter and oil pump.
All models
4X2 (2.6).................... 4.0
4X4 (3.2).................... 4.9

Direct, Forward Clutches and Intermediate Band, Renew
Includes: R&R transmission, converter, pump and seal, oil pan, valve body and servo.
All models
4X2 (3.4).................... 4.9
4X4 (4.0).................... 5.8
Recond valve body add (.7).................... 1.0
Recond oil pump add (.5).................... .8
Recond servo add (.2).................... .2
Recond direct clutch add (.3).................... .4
Recond forward clutch add (.4).................... .5
Renew bushings add-each (.1).................... .1

Output Carrier, Sun Gear and Drive Shell, R&R or Renew
Includes: R&R transmission, converter, pump and seal, oil pan, valve body, direct and forward clutches, intermediate band and servo.
All models
4X2 (3.5).................... 5.5
4X4 (4.1).................... 5.9
Recond valve body add (.7).................... 1.0
Recond oil pump add (.5).................... .8
Recond servo add (.2).................... .2
Recond direct clutch add (.3).................... .4
Recond forward clutch add (.4).................... .5
Recond sun gear and drum, add (.3).................... .4
Renew output shaft add (.7).................... 1.0
Renew bushings add-each (.1).................... .1

TURBO HYDRA-MATIC '350'

ON TRUCK SERVICE

Drain and Refill Unit
All models (.5).................... .7

Oil Pressure Check
All models (.5).................... .7

Check Unit for Leaks
Includes: Clean and dry outside of case and run unit to determine point of leak.
All models.................... .9

Vacuum Modulator, Renew
w/2 whl drive (.3).................... .4
w/4 whl drive (.5).................... .6

(Factory Time) Chilton Time

Detent Valve Control Cable or Seal, Renew
All models (.5) 9

Speedometer Drive Gear, Renew
Includes: R&R extension housing.
w/2 whl drive (.7) 1.2
w/4 whl drive (.6) 1.1

Speedometer Driven Gear, Renew
All models (.3) 5

Governor Assy., R&R or Renew
Includes: R&R cover and gasket.
All models (.3) 6

Governor Assy., R&R and Recondition
Includes: R&R cover and gasket.
All models (.6) 1.1

Extension Housing Rear Oil Seal, Renew
Includes: R&R drive shaft.
exc Vans (.5) 8
Vans (.4) 7

Torque Converter Clutch Brake Switch, Renew
All models (.2) 4

Torque Converter Clutch Thermal Vacuum Switch, Renew
All models (.3) 5

Torque Converter Clutch Vacuum Delay Valve, Renew
All models (.2) 3

Engine Low Vacuum Switch, Renew
All models (.2) 4

High Vacuum Switch, Renew
All models (.3) 5

Oil Pan and/or Gasket, Renew
Includes: Clean oil pan and service screen.
All models (.6) 1.0

Parking Pawl, Renew
Includes: R&R oil pan.
All models (1.4) 1.9

Intermediate Servo, Renew
Includes: R&R oil pan, valve body and adjust servo.
All models (.9) 1.4

Governor Pressure Switch and/or Electrical Connector, Renew
Includes: R&R oil pan.
All models (.6) 1.1

Auxiliary Valve Body and/or Apply Valve, Renew
Includes: R&R oil pan.
All models (.8) 1.4
Renew body gskt add (.2) 2

Converter Clutch Solenoid, Renew
Includes: R&R oil pan.
All models (.6) 1.1

Intermediate Clutch Accumulator, Renew
All models (.7) 1.2

Valve Body Assy., R&R or Renew
Includes: R&R oil pan and vacuum modulator, clean pan and strainer.
All models (1.0) 1.6

Valve Body, R&R and Recondition
Includes: R&R oil pan and vacuum modulator, clean pan and strainer. Disassemble, clean, inspect, free all valves. Replace parts as required.
All models (1.4) 2.4

SERVICES REQUIRING R&R

Transmission, R&R or Renew
2 whl drive (2.5) 4.6
4 whl drive (4.3) 6.1
w/Skid plate add (.3) 3
Pressure check converter add (.2) 2

Transmission and Converter, R&R and Recondition
Includes: Disassemble trans including valve body, clean, inspect and replace parts as required.
2 whl drive (6.5) 11.7
4 whl drive (8.3) 12.3
w/Skid plate add (.3) 3
Pressure check converter add (.2) 2

Transmission Assembly, Reseal
Includes: R&R transmission and renew all seals and gaskets.
2 whl drive (3.5) 6.8
4 whl drive (5.3) 8.1
w/Skid plate add (.3) 3

Front Pump Seal, Renew
Includes: R&R transmission.
2 whl drive (2.2) 4.9
4 whl drive (4.0) 6.4
w/Skid plate add (.3) 3

Flywheel (Flexplate), Renew
Includes: R&R transmission.
2 whl drive (2.2) 4.9
4 whl drive (4.0) 6.4
w/Skid plate add (.3) 3

Torque Converter, Renew
Includes: R&R transmission and check end play of converter.
2 whl drive (2.5) 5.2
4 whl drive (4.4) 6.7
w/Skid plate add (.3) 3

Forward, Direct or Intermediate Clutch, R&R or Renew
Includes: R&R transmission, converter and pump seal, intermediate, direct and forward clutches, oil pan, valve body and intermediate servo piston.
2 whl drive (3.4) 5.9
4 whl drive (5.2) 7.4
w/Skid plate add (.3) 3

Forward, Direct or Intermediate Clutch, R&R and Recondition
Includes: R&R transmission, converter and pump seal, intermediate, direct and forward clutches, oil pan, valve body and intermediate servo piston.
2 whl drive (4.3) 7.3
4 whl drive (6.1) 8.8
w/Skid plate add (.3) 3

Front Oil Pump, Renew
Includes: R&R transmission, converter and pump seal.
2 whl drive (2.7) 5.1
4 whl drive (4.5) 6.6
w/Skid plate add (.3) 3

Front Oil Pump, R&R and Recondition
Includes: R&R transmission, converter and pump seal.
2 whl drive (3.2) 5.8
4 whl drive (5.0) 7.3
w/Skid plate add (.3) 3

Low and Reverse Clutch Piston Assembly, R&R or Renew
Includes: R&R trans, converter, pump and seal, intermediate clutch, oil pan, valve body, intermediate servo piston, direct and forward clutches, intermediate band, output carrier, sungear and drive shell, extension housing, speedometer drive gears, governor, output ring gear, low and reverse roller clutch support, reaction carrier and output shell.
2 whl drive (3.9) 6.8
4 whl drive (5.7) 8.1
w/Skid plate add (.3) 3

Low and Reverse Clutch Piston Assembly, R&R and Recondition
Includes: R&R trans, converter, pump and seal, intermediate clutch, oil pan, valve body, intermediate servo piston, direct and forward clutches, intermediate band, output carrier, sungear and drive shell, extension housing, speedometer drive gears, governor, output ring gear, low and reverse roller clutch support, reaction carrier and output shell.
2 whl drive (4.4) 7.6
4 whl drive (6.2) 8.9
w/Skid plate add (.3) 3

Intermediate Band, Renew
Includes: R&R transmission, converter and pump seal, intermediate clutch, oil pan, valve body and intermediate servo piston.
2 whl drive (3.4) 6.1
4 whl drive (5.2) 7.6
w/Skid plate add (.3) 3

TURBO HYDRA-MATIC '400'

ON TRUCK SERVICES

Drain and Refill Unit
All models (.5) 7

Oil Pressure Check
All models (.5) 7

Check Unit for Leaks
Includes: Clean and dry outside of case and run unit to determine point of leak.
All models 9

Vacuum Modulator, Renew
w/2 whl drive (.3) 4
w/4 whl drive (.5) 6

Detent Solenoid, Renew or Adjust
Includes: R&R oil pan.
All models (.6) 1.1

Down Shift Control Switch, Renew
All models (.2) 4

Detent Solenoid Connector, Renew
Includes: R&R oil pan.
All models (.6) 1.1

Speedometer Drive Gear, Renew
Includes: R&R extension housing.
All models (1.0) 1.5

Speedometer Driven Gear, Renew
All models (.3) 5

Governor Assy., R&R or Renew
Includes: R&R cover and gasket.
w/2 whl drive (.3) 6
w/4 whl drive (1.4) 1.9

Governor Assy., R&R and Recondition
Includes: R&R cover and gasket.
w/2 whl drive (.6) 1.1
w/4 whl drive (1.7) 2.4

(Factory Time) Chilton Time

Extension Housing Rear Oil Seal, Renew

Includes: R&R drive shaft.

- All models (.7) ... 1.0

Oil Pan and/or Gasket, Renew

Includes: Clean oil pan and service screen.

- All models (.6) ... 1.0

Parking Pawl, Renew

Includes: R&R oil pan.

- All models (1.0) ... 1.5

Servos, Renew or Recondition

Includes: R&R oil pan, detent solenoid, servo cover and valve body. Adjust servo.

- All models-front (1.3) ... 1.8
- rear (1.5) ... 2.1

Pressure Regulator Valve, Renew

Includes: R&R oil pan.

- All models (.8) ... 1.4

Valve Body Assy., R&R or Renew

Includes: R&R oil pan and vacuum modulator, clean pan and strainer.

- All models (1.1) ... 1.6

Valve Body, R&R and Recondition

Includes: R&R oil pan and vacuum modulator, clean pan and strainer. Disassemble, clean, inspect, free all valves. Replace parts as required.

- All models (1.8) ... 2.6

SERVICES REQUIRING R&R

Transmission, R&R or Renew

- 2 whl drive (2.2) ... 3.0
- 4 whl drive (3.2) ... 4.3
- w/Skid plate add (.3) 3

Transmission and Converter, R&R and Recondition

Includes: Disassemble trans including valve body, clean, inspect and replace parts as required.

- 2 whl drive (8.3) ... 11.2
- 4 whl drive (9.3) ... 12.5
- w/Skid plate add (.3) 3
- Pressure check converter add (.2) 2

Transmission Assembly, Reseal

Includes: R&R transmission and renew all seals and gaskets.

- 2 whl drive (3.6) ... 6.9
- 4 whl drive (5.6) ... 8.2
- w/Skid plate add (.3) 3

Front Pump Seal, Renew

Includes: R&R transmission.

- 2 whl drive (2.2) ... 3.0
- 4 whl drive (3.1) ... 4.1
- w/Skid plate add (.3) 3

Flywheel (Flexplate), Renew

Includes: R&R transmission.

- 2 whl drive (2.4) ... 3.2
- 4 whl drive (3.4) ... 4.5
- w/Skid plate add (.3) 3

Torque Converter, Renew

Includes: R&R transmission and check end play of converter.

- 2 whl drive (2.3) ... 3.1
- 4 whl drive (3.2) ... 4.3
- w/Skid plate add (.3) 3

Front Oil Pump, Renew

Includes: R&R transmission and converter.

- 2 whl drive (2.4) ... 3.2
- 4 whl drive (3.2) ... 4.3
- w/Skid plate add (.3) 3

Front Oil Pump, R&R and Recondition

Includes: R&R transmission and converter.

- 2 whl drive (2.9) ... 3.9
- 4 whl drive (3.7) ... 5.0
- w/Skid plate add (.3) 3

Forward, Direct or Intermediate Clutch, R&R or Renew

Includes: R&R transmission, converter, oil pan, oil pump and seal.

- 2 whl drive (2.7) ... 3.6
- 4 whl drive (3.6) ... 4.8
- w/Skid plate add (.3) 3

Forward, Direct or Intermediate Clutch, R&R and Recondition

Includes: R&R transmission, converter, oil pan, oil pump and seal, forward clutch, sun gear shaft, front brake band and adjust end play.

- 2 whl drive (3.3) ... 4.4
- 4 whl drive (4.2) ... 5.6
- w/Skid plate add (.3) 3

Center Support and Gear Unit Assy., Renew

Includes: R&R transmission, converter, pump and seal, forward clutch, front brake band, valve body, case extension, speedometer driven gear. Check end play.

- 2 whl drive (3.7) ... 5.0
- 4 whl drive (4.6) ... 6.2
- w/Skid plate add (.3) 3

Center Support and Gear Unit Assy., R&R and Recondition

Includes: R&R transmission, converter, pump and seal, forward clutch, front brake band, valve body, case extension, speedometer driven gear. Check end play.

- 2 whl drive (4.3) ... 5.8
- 4 whl drive (5.2) ... 7.0
- w/Skid plate add (.3) 3

TURBO HYDRA-MATIC 700-R4

ON TRUCK SERVICES

Drain & Refill Unit

- All models 9

Oil Pressure Check

- All models (.5) 7

Check Unit For Oil Leaks

Includes: Clean and dry outside of case and run unit to determine point of leak.

- All models 9

Neutral Safety Switch, Renew

- All models (.3) 4

Shift Linkage, Adjust

- All models (.4) 6

Torque Converter Clutch Switches, Renew

- All models
  - Brake (.2) 4
  - Thermal Vacuum (.3) 5
  - Temp Indicator (.3) 5

Detent Valve Control Cable and/or 'O' Ring, Renew

Includes: Adjust cable.

- All models (.5) 9

Speedometer Driven Gear and/or Seal, Renew

- All models (.3) 5

Extension Housing Rear Oil Seal, Renew

Includes: R&R driveshaft.

- All models (.4) 8

Governor Cover and/or Seal, Renew

- S-series
  - 4 WD (1.0) ... 1.4
- All other models (.3) 5

Governor Assembly, R&R or Renew

- S-series
  - 4 WD (1.0) ... 1.4
- All other models (.4) 7

Governor Assy., R&R and Recondition

- S-series
  - 4 WD (1.2) ... 1.7
- All other models (.6) ... 1.0

Oil Pan and/or Gasket, Renew

- Vans (.8) ... 1.1
- All other models (.6) 9
- w/Skid plate add (.3) 3

Governor Pressure Switch, Renew

Includes: R&R oil pan.

- Vans (.8) ... 1.3
- All other models (.6) ... 1.1
- w/Skid plate add (.3) 3

Converter Clutch Solenoid, Renew

Includes: R&R oil pan.

- Vans (.8) ... 1.3
- All other models (.6) ... 1.1
- w/Skid plate add (.3) 3

Valve Body Assembly, Renew

Includes: R&R oil pan and renew filter.

- Vans-K-series (1.0) ... 1.7
- All other models (.8) ... 1.5
- w/Skid plate add (.3) 3

Valve Body Assy., R&R and Recondition

Includes: R&R oil pan and renew filter. Disassemble, clean, inspect and free all valves. Replace parts as required.

- Vans-K-series (1.9) ... 2.7
- All other models (1.7) ... 2.5
- w/Skid plate add (.3) 3

2-4 Servo Assy., R&R or Renew

- S-series (1.4) ... 1.9
- All other models (.5) ... 1.0
- w/Skid plate add (.3) 3
- Recond servo add (.2) 3

Parking Pawl, Shaft, Rod or Spring, Renew

Includes: R&R oil pan.

- All models (.6) ... 1.1
- Renew pawl add (.5) 5
- w/Skid plate add (.3) 3

1-2 Accumulator Piston and/or Spring, Renew

Includes: R&R oil pan.

- All models (.8) ... 1.5
- w/Skid plate add (.3) 3
- Recond add (.1) 2

SERVICES REQUIRING R&R

Transmission Assy., R&R or Renew

- 2 whl drive (2.2) ... 3.1
- 4 whl drive (4.0) ... 5.8
- w/Skid plate add (.3) 3

Transmission and Converter, R&R and Recondition

Includes: Disassemble transmission completely, including valve body and overhaul unit. Clean and inspect all parts. Renew all parts as required. Make all necessary adjustments. Road test.

- 2 whl drive (6.3) ... 12.0

LABOR 23 AUTOMATIC TRANSMISSION 23 LABOR

(Factory Time)	Chilton Time
4 whl drive (7.1)	15.0
w/Skid plate add (.3)	.3
Clean and leak check converter add (.2)	.4
Check end play add (.2)	.3

Transmission Assy., R&R and Reseal

Includes: Install all new gaskets and seals.

(Factory Time)	Chilton Time
2 whl drive	4.7
4 whl drive	7.4
w/Skid plate add	.3

Flywheel (Flexplate), Renew

Includes: R&R transmission.

(Factory Time)	Chilton Time
2 whl drive (2.4)	3.3
4 whl drive (4.2)	6.0
w/Skid plate add (.3)	.3

Torque Converter, Renew

Includes: R&R transmission.

(Factory Time)	Chilton Time
2 whl drive (2.1)	2.9
4 whl drive (3.9)	5.6
w/Skid plate add (.3)	.3

Front Pump Oil Seal, Renew

Includes: R&R transmission.

(Factory Time)	Chilton Time
2 whl drive (2.1)	3.0
4 whl drive (3.9)	5.6
w/Skid plate add (.3)	.3

Front Pump Assy., Renew or Recondition

Includes: R&R transmission.

(Factory Time)	Chilton Time
2 whl drive (2.7)	4.0
4 whl drive (4.5)	6.5
w/Skid plate add (.3)	.3
Recond front pump add (.5)	.6
Renew bushing add (.1)	.1

Input Drum, Reverse and Input Clutch, Renew

Includes: R&R transmission.

(Factory Time)	Chilton Time
2 whl drive (3.2)	4.6
4 whl drive (5.0)	7.2
w/Skid plate add (.3)	.3
Recond valve body add (.4)	.5
Recond front pump add (.5)	.6
Renew bushings add-each (.1)	.1

Reaction Gear Set, Renew

Includes: R&R transmission.

(Factory Time)	Chilton Time
2 whl drive (3.5)	5.2
4 whl drive (5.3)	7.6
w/Skid plate add (.3)	.3
Recond valve body add (.4)	.5
Recond front pump add (.5)	.6
Renew input clutch drum add (.2)	.3
Recond reaction gear set add (.2)	.2
Renew bushings add-each (.1)	.1

Low and Reverse Clutch Piston Assy., Renew

Includes: R&R transmission.

(Factory Time)	Chilton Time
2 whl drive (3.7)	5.7
4 whl drive (5.5)	7.9
w/Skid plate add (.3)	.3
Recond valve body add (.4)	.5
Recond front pump add (.5)	.6
Recond reverse clutch add (.4)	.5
Recond input clutch add (.4)	.5
Renew input clutch drum add (.2)	.2
Recond reaction gear set add (.2)	.3
Recond low and reverse clutch add (.1)	.2
Recond reverse piston add (.3)	.4
Recond gov or renew gear add (.2)	.3
Renew gov bushing add (.4)	.5
Renew bushings add-each (.1)	.1

LABOR 25 U-JOINTS & DRIVESHAFT 25 LABOR

Universal Joints, Renew

(Factory Time)	Chilton Time
All models-one (.6)	1.0
each adtnl (.3)	.4

Drive Shaft, R&R or Renew

One Piece Shaft

(Factory Time)	Chilton Time
All models (.3)	.5

Two Piece Shaft

(Factory Time)	Chilton Time
front shaft (.4)	.7
rear shaft (.3)	.5

Center Support Bearing, Renew

(Factory Time)	Chilton Time
All models (.5)	1.0

LABOR 26 REAR AXLE 26 LABOR

Rear Axle, Drain and Refill

(Factory Time)	Chilton Time
All models	.6

Rear Axle Housing Cover Gasket, Renew

(Factory Time)	Chilton Time
All models (.4)	.6

Rear Wheel Hub Assembly, Renew

(Factory Time)	Chilton Time
All models-one side (.8)	1.1
both sides (1.4)	1.8
w/Dual whls add-each side	.1

Rear Wheel Hub Oil Seal, Renew

(Factory Time)	Chilton Time
All models-one side (.6)	.9
both sides (1.0)	1.6
w/Dual whls add-each side	.1

Axle Shaft, Renew

Semi-Floating Axle

(Factory Time)	Chilton Time
one (.6)	.9
both (.7)	1.2

Full Floating Axle

(Factory Time)	Chilton Time
one (.3)	.6
both (.5)	.8

Axle Shaft Oil Seal, Renew

Semi-Floating Axle

(Factory Time)	Chilton Time
one (.6)	1.1
both (.8)	1.4

Full Floating Axle

(Factory Time)	Chilton Time
one (.7)	1.1
both (1.2)	1.6
w/Dual whls add, each side (.1)	.1

Axle Shaft Bearing, Renew

Semi-Floating Axle

(Factory Time)	Chilton Time
one (.7)	1.1
both (.9)	1.4

Full Floating Axle

(Factory Time)	Chilton Time
one (.9)	1.4
both (1.6)	2.7
w/Dual whls add-each side	.1

Pinion Shaft Oil Seal, Renew

Includes: Renew pinion flange if necessary.

(Factory Time)	Chilton Time
All models	
Semi-Floating (.5)	.8
Full Floating (.7)	1.1

Differential Case, Renew

Standard

(Factory Time)	Chilton Time
Semi-Floating (2.0)	3.1
Full Floating (2.2)	3.3

Limited Slip (Semi-Floating)

(Factory Time)	Chilton Time
Eaton Case (2.4)	3.5
exc Eaton Case (2.6)	3.7

Limited Slip (Full Floating)

(Factory Time)	Chilton Time
Eaton Case (2.4)	3.5
exc Eaton Case (2.1)	3.2

Ring and Pinion Gears, Renew

(Factory Time)	Chilton Time
Semi-Floating Axle (2.4)	4.1
Full Floating Axle (2.8)	4.6
Recond diff case add	
std (.3)	.5
limited slip (.7)	1.0

Pinion Shaft and/or Side and Pinion Gears, Renew

Note: Does not require case removal on semi-floating axles.

(Factory Time)	Chilton Time
Semi-Floating Axle (1.3)	2.1
Full Floating Axle (2.0)	3.4

Limited Slip Clutch Plates, Renew

Semi-Floating Axle

(Factory Time)	Chilton Time
Eaton Case (2.4)	3.5
exc Eaton Case (1.1)	2.0

Full Floating Axle

(Factory Time)	Chilton Time
Eaton Case (2.4)	3.5
exc Eaton Case (2.3)	3.4

Side and Pinion Gear Bearings, Renew

(Factory Time)	Chilton Time
Semi-Floating Axle (2.5)	4.1
Full Floating Axle (3.5)	5.1

Rear Axle Housing, Renew

(Factory Time)	Chilton Time
Semi-Floating Axle (4.5)	6.1
Full Floating Axle (5.1)	6.7
w/Dual whls add (.2)	.4

LABOR 27 REAR SUSPENSION 27 LABOR

(Factory Time) Chilton Time

Rear Spring, Renew
S-series-one (.7) 1.1
both (1.2) 2.0
All other models-one (.9) 1.3
both (1.5) 2.1
w/Aux fuel tank add (.6) 6
w/Dual whls add-each side 1
w/Skid plate add (.3) 3
Recond add-each side 5

Rear Spring Shackle, Renew
exc Vans-one (.5) 8
both (.8) 1.2
Vans-one (.6) 9
both (1.1) 1.7

Rear Spring Eye Bushing, Renew
Includes: R&R spring.
All models-one side (1.0) 1.4
both sides (1.8) 2.6
w/Dual whls add-each side 1
w/Skid plate add (.3) 3

Rear Shock Absorber, Renew
All models-one (.3) 5
both (.4) 8

LABOR 28 AIR CONDITIONING 28 LABOR

(Factory Time) Chilton Time

Note: If more than one item requires replacement where evacuation and discharging the system is already included in the operation, deduct 1.0 hour for each additional item to the times listed.

Drain, Evacuate and Recharge System
All models (.5) 1.0

Leak Test
Includes: Check all lines and connections.
All models 6

Refrigerant, Add Partial Charge
All models 6

Compressor Belt, Renew
All models (.2) 5
If necessary to R&R fan pulley, add (.3) 3
w/P.S. add (.2) 2
w/AIR add (.2) 2

COMPRESSOR - 6 CYLINDER AXIAL

Compressor Assembly, Renew
Includes: Transfer all necessary attaching parts. Evacuate and charge system.
Six (2.0) 3.1
V-8-exc Vans (1.9) 3.0
Vans (2.3) 3.4

Compressor Assy., R&R and Recondition
Includes: Complete disassembly and overhaul, making all checks and gauging operations. Evacuate and charge system.
Six (3.8) 6.3
V-8-exc Vans (3.8) 6.2
Vans (4.2) 6.8

Compressor Clutch Hub and Drive Plate, Renew
Includes: Check air gap. Does not include R&R compressor.
Six (.8) 1.1
V-8-exc Vans (.5) 8
Vans (.8) 1.1

Compressor Pulley and/or Bearing, Renew
Includes: R&R hub and drive plate.
Six (.9) 1.2
V-8-exc Vans (.6) 9
Vans (.9) 1.2

Compressor Clutch Holding Coil, Renew
Includes: R&R hub and drive plate, pulley and bearing.
Six (1.0) 1.4
V-8-exc Vans (.6) 1.1
Vans (1.0) 1.4

Compressor Shaft Seal Kit, Renew
Includes: R&R clutch hub and drive plate. Evacuate and charge system.
Six (1.7) 2.8
V-8-exc Vans (1.5) 2.6
Vans (1.7) 2.8

Compressor Rear Head, Oil Pump Gears and/or Rear Reed Assembly, Renew
Includes: R&R compressor. R&R rear head and rear reed plate assy. Clean and test parts. Add oil. Evacuate and charge system.
Six (2.0) 3.4
V-8-exc Vans (1.9) 3.3
Vans (2.4) 3.8

Compressor Front Head and/or Front Reed Assembly, Renew
Includes: R&R compressor. R&R rear head and reed plate assy. Disassemble shell to internal mechanism and front head assy. R&R front valve and reed plate and shaft seal assy. Clean and inspect parts. Add oil. Evacuate and charge system.
Six (2.7) 4.5
V-8-exc Vans (2.5) 4.3
Vans (3.1) 4.9

Internal Cylinder and Piston Assy., Renew
Includes: R&R compressor, disassemble, clean and inspect parts. Install new pre-assembled cylinder, pistons and wobble plate unit. Evacuate and charge system.
Six (2.7) 4.3
V-8-exc Vans (2.5) 4.2
Vans (3.1) 4.8

COMPRESSOR - 4 CYLINDER RADIAL

Compressor Assembly, Renew
Includes: Transfer all necessary attaching parts. Evacuate and charge system.
Astro-Vans (1.5) 2.5
All other models (1.0) 2.0

Compressor Clutch Hub and Drive Plate, Renew
Includes: Check air gap. Does not include R&R compressor.
All models (.5) 8

Compressor Rotor and/or Bearing, Renew
Astro-Vans (1.4) 2.3
All other models (.6) 1.0

Compressor Clutch Coil and/or Pulley Rim, Renew
Astro-Vans (1.4) 2.3
All other models (.6) 8

Compressor Shaft Seal Kit, Renew
Includes: R&R clutch hub and drive plate. Evacuate and charge system.
All models (1.3) 2.5

Compressor Front Bearing, Front Head and/or Seal, Renew
Includes: R&R clutch hub and drive plate, rotor, pulley and coil. Evacuate and charge system.
Astro-Vans (1.9) 3.0
All other models (1.5) 2.8

Compressor Outer Shell and/or 'O' Rings, Renew
Includes: R&R compressor. R&R clutch hub and drive plate, rotor, pulley and coil. Evacuate and charge system.
Astro-Vans (2.1) 3.2
All other models (1.7) 2.9

Compressor Discharge Valve Plate Assy., Renew
Includes: R&R compressor. R&R clutch hub and drive plate, rotor, pulley and coil. Evacuate and charge system.
Astro-Vans (2.2) 3.4
All other models (1.8) 2.9
Renew two or more valves add (.1) 2

Compressor Cylinder and Shaft Assy., Renew
Includes: R&R compressor. Transfer clutch hub, drive plate, rotor, pulley, and coil. Inspect front head. Add oil. Evacuate and charge system.
Astro-Vans (2.3) 3.5
All other models (1.9) 3.0

COMPRESSOR ASSEMBLY DA-6

Compressor Assembly, Renew
Includes: Transfer parts as required. Evacuate and charge system.
Vans-Astro (1.3) 2.4
All other models (1.0) 2.0

Compressor Clutch Plate and Hub Assy., Renew
Includes: R&R hub and drive plate assy. Check air gap.
Vans-Astro (.4) 7
All other models (.3) 6

Compressor Clutch Coil and/or Pulley Rim, Renew
Includes: R&R hub and drive plate assy.
Vans-Astro (1.0) 1.5
All other models (.8) 1.3

Compressor Rotor and/or Bearing, Renew
Includes: R&R hub and drive plate assy.
Vans-Astro (.9) 1.4
All other models (.7) 1.2

LABOR 28 AIR CONDITIONING 28 LABOR

(Factory Time)	Chilton Time
Compressor Shaft Seal Kit, Renew	
Includes: Evacuate and charge system.	
Vans-Astro (1.2)	2.6
All other models (1.1)	2.5
Compressor Front Head and/or Seal, Renew	
Includes: R&R compressor. R&R clutch and pulley assy. R&R shaft seal assy. Clean and inspect parts. Evacuate and charge system.	
Vans-Astro (1.6)	3.0
All other models (1.4)	2.8
Compressor Cylinder and Shaft Assy., Renew	
Includes: R&R compressor. R&R clutch and pulley assy. R&R shaft seal assy., remove and transfer front head assy. R&R compressor shell and 'O' rings. R&R compressor valve plates. Clean and inspect parts. Evacuate and charge system.	
Vans-Astro (2.1)	3.5
All other models (1.9)	3.3
Compressor Relief Valve, Renew	
Includes: Evacuate and charge system.	
exc Vans (.9)	2.0
Vans-Astro (1.1)	2.3
Condenser, Renew	
Includes: Evacuate and charge system.	
S-series (1.3)	2.8
exc Vans (1.5)	3.1
Vans-Astro (1.3)	2.8
w/Aux oil cooler add (.3)	.3
Evaporator Assembly, Renew	
Includes: Evacuate and charge system.	
Front Unit	
S-series (1.4)	2.8
exc Vans (1.3)	3.2
Vans-Astro (1.5)	3.5
All other models w/Diesel eng (2.9)	4.5

(Factory Time)	Chilton Time
Rear Unit	
exc Vans (1.7)	3.6
Vans (2.4)	4.3
Accumulator, Renew	
Includes: Evacuate and charge system.	
All models (.9)	1.5
Expansion Tube (Orifice), Renew	
Includes: Evacuate and charge system.	
All models (.7)	1.4
Pressure Cycling Switch, Renew	
All models (.2)	.3
Receiver - Dehydrator, Renew	
Includes: Evacuate and charge system.	
Vans (1.4)	2.2
Sight Glass and/or 'O' Ring, Renew	
Includes: Evacuate and charge system.	
Vans (.8)	2.0
Expansion Valve, Renew	
Includes: Evacuate and charge system.	
Series 10-20 rear valve (1.1)	2.2
Vans front valve (2.2)	3.3
Vans one or both rear valves (2.4)	3.5
Expansion Tube and Screen, Clean and Inspect or Renew	
Includes: Evacuate and charge system.	
All models (.9)	2.0
A.C. Blower Motor, Renew	
Front Unit	
Gas Engine	
S-series (.3)	.5
Astro (.6)	1.0
exc Vans (.2)	.5
Vans (.3)	.6
Diesel Eng	
Vans (.5)	.8
All other models (2.4)	4.0

(Factory Time)	Chilton Time
Rear Unit	
All models (1.1)	1.6
Blower Motor Switch, Renew	
Front unit (.5)	.9
Rear unit (.4)	.8
Temperature Control Assy., Renew	
All models (.5)	.9
Blower Motor Resistor, Renew	
Front unit (.2)	.4
Rear unit (.3)	*.5
*R&R seat add	.2
Blower Motor Relay, Renew	
All models (.3)	.5
Air Conditioning Hoses, Renew	
Includes: Evacuate and charge system.	
Condenser Outlet	
Astro (1.1)	2.2
Comp to Condenser	
exc Vans (1.1)	2.2
Vans (1.3)	2.4
Condenser to Receiver-Dehydrator	
Vans (1.4)	2.5
Receiver-Dehydrator to Exp Valve	
Vans (1.6)	2.7
Condenser to Evaporator	
S-series (.8)	1.7
w/Front A.C. (1.3)	2.4
w/Rear A.C. (1.5)	2.6
Hose, Muffler and Comp Manifold Assy.	
exc Suburban w/Rear A.C. (1.3)	2.4
Suburban-w/Rear A.C. (1.0)	2.1
Front to Rear Unit (Under Floor)	
exc Vans-one or both (1.4)	2.6
Vans-one or both (1.5)	2.7
Astro-one or both (1.5)	2.7
Hose and Plate Assy.–Pillar to Overhead	
Series 10-20-Rear Unit (1.3)	2.5
Chevy Van-Rear Unit (1.5)	2.7
Sport Van-Rear Unit (1.7)	2.9
Beauville-Rear Unit (2.9)	4.1

LABOR 30 HEAD AND PARKING LAMPS 30 LABOR

(Factory Time)	Chilton Time
Aim Headlamps	
two	.4
four	.6
Headlamp Sealed Beam Bulb, Renew	
All models-each (.2)	.3
Turn Signal or Parking Lamp Assy., Renew	
All models-each (.2)	.4
Side Marker Lamp Assy., Renew	
All models-each (.2)	.3
Tail and Stop Lamp Assy., Renew	
Includes: Back-up and/or marker lamp assy. on combination units.	
All models-each (.3)	.4
License Lamp Assy., Renew	
All models-each (.2)	.3
Roof Marker Lamp Assy., Renew	
All models-each (.2)	.3
Reflectors, Renew	
All models-each	.2

LABOR 31 WINDSHIELD WIPER & SPEEDOMETER 31 LABOR

(Factory Time)	Chilton Time
Windshield Wiper Motor, Renew	
S-series (.5)	.7
exc Vans (.3)	.6
Vans (.8)	1.2
w/A.C. add (.1)	.2
Recond motor add (.3)	.5
Wiper Transmission, Renew (One Side)	
All models (.6)	.8
w/A.C. add (.1)	.2
Wiper Switch, Renew	
std whl (1.2)	1.7
tilt whl (1.0)	1.5
Delay Wiper Controller Assy., Renew	
All models (.5)	.7
Windshield Washer Pump Assy., Renew	
All models (.3)	.4
Intermittant Wiper Controller Assy., Renew	
S-series (.3)	.5
All other models (.5)	.8
Pulse Wiper Control Module, Renew	
S-series (.6)	.8
All other models (.3)	.5

LABOR 31 WINDSHIELD WIPER & SPEEDOMETERS 31 LABOR

(Factory Time)	Chilton Time
Windshield Washer Pump Valve, Renew	
1983	
exc Vans (.3)	.4
Vans (1.1)	1.6
1984-87 (.2)	.4
Speedometer Head, R&R or Renew	
S-series (.4)	.8
exc Vans (.6)	1.0
Vans (.5)	.9
Astro (.7)	1.2
Reset odometer add	.2
Speedometer Cable and Casing, Renew	
1983	
Without Cruise Control	
upper cable (.4)	.7
lower cable (.3)	.6
one piece (.4)	.8
With Cruise Control	
upper cable (.4)	.6
intermediate cable (.4)	.6
lower cable (.5)	.7
1984-87	
upper cable (.4)	.6
lower cable (.3)	.5
one piece cable	
conv cab (.4)	.6
All other models (.7)	1.1

LABOR 32 LIGHT SWITCHES & WIRING 32 LABOR

(Factory Time)	Chilton Time
Headlamp Switch, Renew	
S-series (.6)	.8
exc Vans (.3)	.4
Vans-Astro (.5)	.6
w/A.C. add (.2)	.2
Headlamp Dimmer Switch, Renew	
S-series (.4)	.6
Vans-Astro (.5)	.7
All other models (.3)	.4
Turn Signal and Hazard Warning Switch, Renew	
All models (.7)	1.1
Back-Up Lamp and Park/Neutral Switch, Renew	
S-series (.4)	.6
All other models (.3)	.5
Starter Safety Switch, Renew	
w/A.T.-column mount (.3)	.5
w/M.T.-clutch mount (.2)	.4
Back-Up Lamp Switch, Renew	
w/A.T. (.3)	.5
w/M.T.-floor shift (.2)	.4
w/M.T.-column shift (.3)	.5
Stop Light Switch, Renew	
All models (.2)	.3
Parking Brake Lamp Switch, Renew	
S-series (.4)	.6
All other models (.2)	.4
Turn Signal or Hazard Warning Flasher, Renew	
S-series (.3)	.4
All other models (.2)	.3
Horn, Renew	
All models (.2)	.4

LABOR 34 CRUISE CONTROL 34 LABOR

(Factory Time)	Chilton Time
Regulator Assembly (Transducer), Renew	
Includes: Adjust.	
exc Vans (.4)	.8
Vans (.5)	.9
Engagement Switch, Renew	
All models (.4)	.6
Cruise Control Release Switch, Renew	
All models	
Brake (.4)	.5
Clutch (.4)	.5
Cruise Control Servo, Renew	
exc Vans (.3)	.5
Vans-Astro (.5)	.7
Renew bracket add (.1)	.2
Vacuum Hoses, Renew	
exc Vans (.2)	.3
Vans-Astro (.4)	.6
Cruise Control Cable or Chain, Renew	
Vans-Astro (.5)	.7
All other models (.3)	.5
Power Unit Solenoid, Renew	
All models (.2)	.3
Cruise Control Vacuum Regulator Valve, Renew	
(w/Diesel eng)	
All models (.2)	.3
Cruise Control Resume Solenoid, Renew	
All models (.2)	.3
Cruise Control Module, Renew	
All models (.3)	.5
Cruise Control Speed Sensor, Renew	
S-series-Vans-Astro (.6)	.9
All other models (.7)	1.0
Cruise Control Check Valve, Renew	
All models (.2)	.4

GROUP INDEX

ALPHABETICAL INDEX

MODEL IDENTIFICATION CHART

B 100 - DODGE TRADESMAN VAN

B 100 - DODGE SPORTSMAN WAGON

B 200 - DODGE TRADESMAN VAN

B 200 - DODGE SPORTSMAN WAGON

B 300 - DODGE TRADESMAN VAN

B 300 - DODGE SPORTSMAN WAGON

PB 100 - PLYMOUTH VOYAGER WAGON

PB 200 - PLYMOUTH VOYAGER WAGON

PB 300 - PLYMOUTH VOYAGER WAGON

CB 300 - FRONT SECTION - KARY VAN

CB 400 - FRONT SECTION - KARY VAN

AW 100 - RAMCHARGER - 4 WHEEL DRIVE

PW 100 - TRAILDUSTER - 4 WHEEL DRIVE

AD 100 - RAMCHARGER - 2 WHEEL DRIVE

AD 150 - SPORT UTILITY - 2 WHEEL DRIVE

PD 100 - TRAILDUSTER - 2 WHEEL DRIVE

D 100 - DODGE PICK-UP - 2 WHEEL DRIVE

D 150 - DODGE PICK-UP - 2 WHEEL DRIVE

D 200 - DODGE PICK-UP - 2 WHEEL DRIVE

RD 200 - DODGE RAIL-TRACK - 2 WHEEL DRIVE

D 300 - DODGE PICK-UP - 2 WHEEL DRIVE

W 100 - DODGE PICK-UP - 4 WHEEL DRIVE

AW 150 - SPORT UTILITY - 4 WHEEL DRIVE

W 200 - DODGE PICK-UP - 4 WHEEL DRIVE

W 300 - DODGE PICK-UP - 4 WHEEL DRIVE

W 400 - DODGE PICK-UP - 4 WHEEL DRIVE

LABOR 1 TUNE UP 1 LABOR

(Factory Time) Chilton Time

Compression Test

Six(.6)	.9
V-8–318-360 engs (.7)	1.0

Engine Tune Up, (Electronic Ignition)

Includes: Test battery and clean connections. Tighten manifold and carburetor mounting bolts. Check engine compression, clean and adjust or renew spark plugs. Test resistance of spark plug wires. Inspect distributor cap and rotor. Adjust distributor air gap. Check vacuum advance operation. Reset ignition timing. Adjust idle mixture and idle speed. Service carburetor air cleaner. Inspect crankcase ventilation system. Inspect and adjust drive belts. Inspect choke operation, adjust or free up as necessary. Check operation of E.G.R. valve.

Six	2.8
V-8–318-360 engs	3.2
w/A.C. add	.6

LABOR 2 IGNITION SYSTEM 2 LABOR

Spark Plugs, Clean and Reset or Renew

Six(.4)	.7
V-8–318-360 eng (.5)	.8

Ignition Timing, Reset

B-PB-CB Models (.5)	.7
All other models (.3)	.5

Distributor, Renew

Includes: Adjust ignition timing and renew oil seal if required.

Six–B-PB-CB Models (.7)	1.0
All other models (.6)	.9
V-8–318-360 engs	
B-PB-CB Models (.7)	1.0
All other models (.6)	.9

Distributor, R&R and Recondition

Includes: Adjust ignition timing and renew oil seal if required.

Six–B-PB-CB Models (1.4)	2.0
All other models (1.3)	1.9
V-8–318-360 engs	
B-PB-CB Models (1.4)	2.0
All other models (1.3)	1.9

Distributor Pick-Up Plate and Coil Assembly, Renew

Includes: R&R distributor, reset ignition timing.

Six–B-PB-CB Models (.9)	1.3
All other models (.8)	1.2
V-8–318-360 engs	
B-PB-CB Models (.9)	1.3
All other models (.8)	1.2

Electronic Distributor Reluctor, Renew

Includes: R&R distributor and reset ignition timing.

Six–B-PB-CB Models (.8)	1.2
All other models (.7)	1.1
V-8–318-360 engs	
B-PB-CB Models (.8)	1.2
All other models (.7)	1.1

Vacuum Control Unit, Renew

Includes: R&R distributor and reset ignition timing.

Six–B-PB-CB Models (.8)	1.2
All other models (.7)	1.1
V-8–318-360 engs	
B-PB-CB Models (.8)	1.2
All other models (.7)	1.1

Distributor Cap, Renew

B-PB-CB Models (.4)	.5
All other models (.3)	.4

Electronic Ignition Control Unit, Renew

B-PB-CB Models (.3)	.5
All other models (.2)	.4

Spark Control Computer, Renew

B-PB-CB models (.7)	1.1
All other models (.6)	1.0

Ignition Cables, Renew

Six(.5)	.8
V-8–318-360 engs (.6)	.9

Ignition Coil, Renew

B-PB-CB Models (.4)	.6
All other models (.3)	.5

Electronic Ignition Ballast Resistor, Renew

B-PB-CB Models (.3)	.5
All other models (.2)	.4

Ignition Switch, Renew

Includes: Renew lock cylinder if required.

1983-87	
std colm (.8)	1.2
tilt colm (.4)	.7

LABOR 3 FUEL SYSTEM 3 LABOR

(Factory Time) Chilton Time

Fuel Pump, Test
Includes: Disconnect line at carburetor, attach pressure gauge.
All models 3

Carburetor, Adjust (On Truck)
All models (.6) 8

Air Cleaner Vacuum Diaphragm, Renew
All models (.5) 8

Air Cleaner Vacuum Sensor, Renew
All models (.5) 8

Coolant Temperature Sensor/Switch, Renew
B-PB-CB models (.7) 1.1
All other models (.6) 1.0

Carburetor, Renew
Includes: All necessary adjustments.
1 bbl (.7) 1.1
2 bbl (.7) 1.1
4 bbl (.8) 1.2

Carburetor, R&R and Clean or Recondition
Includes: All necessary adjustments.
Holly-1 bbl (1.9) 2.5
Carter-2 bbl (2.3) 3.1
Holly-2 bbl (1.9) 2.5
Carter-4 bbl (2.6) 3.5

Fuel Pump, Renew
Six-B-PB-CB Models (.6) 9
All other models (.5) 8
V-8-318-360 engs (.5) 8
Add pump test if performed.

Fuel Tank, Renew
Includes: Drain and refill, test and renew tank gauge if necessary.
Main Tank
frame mount (1.0) 1.5
cab mount (.7) 1.2
plastic tank (1.0) 1.5
Auxiliary Tank
cab mount (1.2) 1.7
frame mount (1.0) 1.5
w/Skid plate add (.3) 3

Fuel Gauge (Tank), Renew
Main Tank
frame mount (.7) 1.2
cab mount (.5) 9
plastic tank (1.0) 1.4
Auxiliary Tank
cab mount (.5) 9
frame mount (.6) 1.0
w/Skid plate add (.3) 3

Fuel Gauge (Dash), Renew
1983-87
B-PB-CB Models (.6) 1.1
All other models (1.0) 1.5

Intake and Exhaust Manifold Gaskets, Renew
Six
B-PB-CB Models (2.0) 3.0
All other models (1.8) 2.8
w/A.C. add (.4) 4
Renew manif add 5

Intake Manifold Gasket, Renew
V-8
318-360 engs (2.5) 3.5
w/A.C. add (.4) 4
w/Air inj add 6
Renew manif add 5

LABOR 3A EMISSION CONTROLS 3A LABOR

(Factory Time) Chilton Time

CRANKCASE EMISSION

Positive Crankcase Ventilation Valve, Renew
All models (.2) 3

EVAPORATIVE EMISSION

Vapor Canister, Renew
All models (.3) 5

Vapor Canister Hoses, Renew
All models-one (.2) 3

Vapor Canister Filter, Renew
All models (.2) 3

Vapor Separator, Renew
All models (.9) 1.2

AIR INJECTION SYSTEM

Air Pump, Renew
Six (.9) 1.2
V-8 (.8) 1.1

Aspirator, Renew
All models (.3) 4

Diverter/Control Valve, Renew
Six (.3) 6
V-8 (.4) 7

Injection Tube and Check Valve Assy., Renew
Six (.4) 7
V-8 (.5) 8

Orifice Spark Advance Control Valve, Renew
All models (.2) 4

HEATED AIR SYSTEM

Air Cleaner Vacuum Diaphragm, Renew
1983-87 (.5) 8

Air Cleaner Vacuum Sensor, Renew
1983-87 (.5) 8

EXHAUST GAS RECIRCULATION SYSTEM

E.G.R. Valve, Renew
Six (.4) 6
V-8 (.5) 7

E.G.R. Coolant Control Valve, Renew
All models (.3) 5

E.G.R. Vacuum Amplifier, Renew
All models (.3) 5

E.G.R. Time Delay Timer, Renew
All models (.2) 4

E.G.R. Time Delay Solenoid, Renew
All models (.2) 4

Change Temperature Switch, Renew
All models (.2) 3

E.F.C. SYSTEM

Oxygen Sensor, Renew
All models (.3) 5

Emission Maintenance Reminder Module, Renew
All models (.2) 4

LABOR 4 ALTERNATOR AND REGULATOR 4 LABOR

(Factory Time) Chilton Time

Alternator Circuits, Test
Includes: Test battery, regulator and alternator output.
All models 6

Alternator, Renew
Six(.7) 1.2
V-8-318-360 engs
B-PB-CB Models (.9) 1.4
All other models (.7) 1.2
Add circuit test if performed.

Alternator, R&R and Recondition
Six(2.0) 3.1
V-8-318-360 engs
B-PB-CB Models (2.2) 3.3
All other models (2.0) 3.1
Add circuit test if performed.

Alternator Drive End Frame Bearing, Renew
Six(1.0) 1.5
V-8-318-360 engs
B-PB-CB Models (1.2) 1.7
All other models (1.0) 1.5
Renew rear brg add 2

Voltage Regulator, Test and Renew
All models (.2) 6

LABOR 5 STARTING SYSTEM 5 LABOR

(Factory Time) Chilton Time

Starter Draw Test (On Truck)
All models .3

Starter, Renew
Six(.6) 1.0
V-8-318-360 engs (.7) 1.2
Add draw test if performed.

Starter, R&R and Recondition
Six(1.8) 2.7
V-8-318-360 engs (1.9) 2.8

Renew field coils add .5
Add draw test if performed.

Starter Drive, Renew
Includes: R&R starter.
Six(1.1) 1.5
V-8-318-360 engs (1.2) 1.7

Starter Solenoid, Renew
Includes: R&R starter.
Six(1.1) 1.5
V-8-318-360 engs (1.2) 1.7

Starter Relay, Renew
All models (.3) .5

Battery Cables, Renew
All models-positive (.4) .6
ground (.2) .4
starter to relay (.3) .5

LABOR 6 BRAKE SYSTEM 6 LABOR

(Factory Time) Chilton Time

Brakes, Adjust (Minor)
Includes: Adjust brakes, fill master cylinder.
two wheels .5
four wheels .8

Brake Pedal Free Play, Adjust
All models .4

Bleed Brakes (Four Wheels)
Includes: Fill master cylinder.
All models (.4) .6

Brake Drum and Hub Assy., Renew
Includes: Repack and/or renew wheel bearings.
front-one (1.0) 1.6
rear-one (.8) 1.4
w/Dual rear whls add .3

Rear Brake Drum, Renew (One)
All models
semi-floating axle (.3) .6
full floating axle (1.8) 2.3
w/Dual rear whls add (.2) .3

Brake System Indicator Switch, Renew
All models (.3) .5

Brake Shoes and/or Pads, Renew
Includes: Install new or exchange shoes or pads. Service adjusters. Adjust service and hand brake. Bleed system.
front-disc (.6) 1.2
rear-drum
semi-floating axle (.7) 1.4
full floating axle (1.5) 2.5
All four wheels
semi-floating axle 2.5
full floating axle 4.4
Resurface brake rotor add, each 1.0
Resurface brake drum add, each .6

BRAKE HYDRAULIC SYSTEM

Wheel Cylinder, Renew (Standard Brakes)
Includes: Bleed brake system.
front-one (1.4) 1.8
both (2.1) 2.9
rear-one (1.4) 1.8
both (2.1) 2.9
All four wheels 5.0

Wheel Cylinder, R&R and Recondition (Standard Brakes)
Includes: Hone cylinder, bleed brake system.
front-one (1.7) 2.1
both (2.7) 3.3
rear-one (1.7) 2.1
both (2.7) 3.3
All four wheels 6.0

COMBINATIONS

Add to Brakes, Renew
See Machine Shop Operations

(Factory Time) Chilton Time

RENEW WHEEL CYLINDER
Each (.3) .4

REBUILD WHEEL CYLINDER
Each .6

RENEW BRAKE HOSE
Each (.4) .5

REBUILD CALIPER ASSEMBLY
Each (.4) .6

RENEW BRAKE DRUM
Front
Each .3
Rear
Full Floating Axle-each .3
Semi-FLoating Axle-each 1.0

RENEW DISC BRAKE ROTOR
Each (.3) .4

RENEW REAR WHEEL GREASE SEALS OR BEARINGS
Full Floating Axle-each .2
Semi-Floating Axle-each .8

RENEW FRONT WHEEL BEARINGS
(One Wheel) one or both
Drum Brakes .2
Disc Brakes .4

FRONT WHEEL BEARINGS, REPACK OR RENEW SEALS
(Both Wheels)
Drum Brakes .4
Disc Brakes .8

(Factory Time) Chilton Time

Wheel Cylinder, Renew (Disc Brakes)
rear-one (1.1) 1.5
both (2.1) 2.9
w/Dual rear whls add .3

Wheel Cylinder, R&R and Recondition (Disc Brakes)
Includes: Hone cylinder, bleed brake system.
rear-one (1.4) 1.8
both (2.7) 3.5
w/Dual rear whls add .3

Brake Hose, Renew (Flex)
Includes: Bleed brake system.
front-one (.4) .6
rear (.5) .7

Master Cylinder, Renew
Includes: Bleed brake system.
B-PB-CB Models (.8) 1.2
All other models (.5) 1.0

Master Cylinder, R&R and Recondition
Includes: Bleed brake system.
B-PB-CB Models 1.9
All other models 1.7

Brake Line Metering Valve, Renew
Includes: Bleed brake system.
All models (.5) .9

Brake System Combination Valve, Renew
Includes: Bleed brake system.

(Factory Time) Chilton Time

B-PB-CB models (.9) 1.3
All other models (.8) 1.2

POWER BRAKES

Power Brake Unit, Renew
All models
wo/Hydraboost (.5) 1.1
w/Hydraboost (.7) 1.3
w/A.C. add (.1) .3

Power Brake Check Valve, Renew
All models (.2) .4

Power Brake Vacuum Hose, Renew
All models (.3) .4

DISC BRAKES

Brake Shoes and/or Pads, Renew
Includes: Install new or exchange shoes or pads. Service adjusters. Adjust service and hand brake. Bleed system.
front-disc (.6) 1.2
rear-drum
semi-floating axle (.7) 1.4
full floating axle (1.5) 2.5
All four wheels
semi-floating axle 2.5
full floating axle 4.4
Resurface brake rotor add, each 1.0
Resurface brake drum add, each .6

Disc Brake Pads, Renew
Includes: Install new disc brake pads only.
All models (.6) 1.2

LABOR 6 BRAKE SYSTEM 6 LABOR

(Factory Time) Chilton Time

Disc Brake Rotor (w/Hub), Renew (One)
Includes: Repack and/or renew bearings.
2 WD
All models (.8) 1.4

4 WD
44 FBJ front axle (1.1) 2.0
60 F front axle (.9) 1.7

Disc Brake Caliper, Renew (One)
Includes: Bleed front brake lines only.
All models (.5) 1.0

Disc Brake Caliper, R&R and Recondition (One)
Includes: Renew parts as required, bleed front brake lines only.
All models (.8) 1.6

PARKING BRAKE

Parking Brake, Adjust
All models (.3) 5

Parking Brake Lever Assembly, Renew
All models (.6) 9

Parking Brake Cables, Renew
Front
All models (.6) 8
Intermediate
All models (.3) 5
Rear
2 wd-each (.6) 8
4 wd-each (1.0) 1.4
w/Dual rear whls add 3

LABOR 7 COOLING SYSTEM 7 LABOR

(Factory Time) Chilton Time

Winterize Cooling System
Includes: Run engine to check for leaks, tighten all hose connections. Test radiator and pressure cap, drain radiator and engine block. Add anti-freeze and refill coolant.
All models 5

Thermostat, Renew
All models (.5) 8
w/A.C. add (.3) 3

Radiator Assembly, R&R or Renew
B-PB-CB Models (1.0) 1.5
All other models (.7) 1.3
w/A.C. add (.4) 5
w/A.T. add (.1) 2

ADD THESE OPERATIONS TO RADIATOR R&R

Boil & Repair 1.5
Rod Clean 1.9
Repair Core 1.3
Renew Tank 1.6
Renew Trans. Oil Cooler 1.9
Recore Radiator 1.7

Radiator Hoses, Renew
All models-upper (.3) 5
lower (.4) 6
by-pass (.5) 7

Fan Belt, Renew
All models (.3) 5
w/Air inj add (.1) 1

Fluid Fan Drive Unit, Renew
B-PB-CB Models
w/225-318-360 engs (.8) 1.1
All other models
w/225-318-360 engs (.5) 7

Idler Pulley, Renew
All models (.3) 5

Fan Pulley, Renew
B-PB-CB Models
w/225-318-360 engs (.6) 8
All other models
w/225-318-360 engs (.4) 7

Coolant Reserve Tank, Renew
All models (.2) 3

Water Pump, Renew
Six-1983-87
B-PB-CB Models (.9) 1.4
D-AD-PD Models (.7) 1.3
AW-PW-W Models (1.0) 1.6
w/A.C. add (.3) 3
V-8-318-360 engs
B-PB-CB Models
1983-87
wo/A.C. (1.3) 1.8
w/A.C. (1.8) 2.6
w/P.S. add (.2) 2
w/100 Amp alt add (.6) 6
AD-PD-D-W Models
1983-87 (1.1) 1.5
w/A.C. add (.4) 6
w/P.S. add (.2) 2
w/Air inj add (.2) 2

Water Jacket Expansion Plugs, Renew
Engine Block
Six-All models
left side-one (1.9) 2.3
V-8-318-360 engs
All models
front-right or left-one (.6) 1.1
center-right or left-one (.6) 1.1
rear-right side (.5) 1.0
rear-left side (.8) 1.2

Water Jacket Expansion Plugs, Renew
Cylinder Head
V-8-318-360 engs
front-one-all models (.3) 6
Rear-one
B-PB-CB Models (.3) 6
All other models (3.1) 4.2

Temperature Gauge (Engine Unit), Renew
All models (.5) 7

Temperature Gauge (Dash Unit), Renew
B-PB-CB Models
1983-87 (.6) 1.2
All other models
1983-87 (.6) 1.2

Heater Core, R&R or Renew
Without Air Conditioning
Front
B-PB-CB Models
1983-87 (.7) 1.6
All other models
1983-87 (1.3) 2.2
Rear
1983-87-All models (.8) 1.5
With Air Conditioning
Front
B-PB-CB Models
1983-87 (2.7) *5.0
All other models
1983-87 (2.1) *4.0
Rear
1983-87-All models (.6) 1.2
w/Front and rear A.C. add (.3) 5
*Includes Recharge A.C. System.

ADD THESE OPERATIONS TO HEATER CORE R&R

Boil & Repair 1.2
Repair Core 9
Recore 1.2

Heater Water Valve, Renew
All models
w/Heater (.4) 7
w/A.C. (.5) 8

Heater Hoses, Renew
All models-one or both (.4) 6

Heater Blower Motor, Renew
Front
1983-87-All models (.5) 9
Rear
1983-87-All models (.4) 9

Heater Blower Motor Resistor, Renew
All models (.3) 5

Heater Blower Motor Switch, Renew
B-PB-CB Models
1983-87 (.4) 6
All other models
1983-87 (.4) 7

Heater Temperature Control Assembly, Renew
All models (.5) 8

LABOR 8 EXHAUST SYSTEM 8 LABOR

(Factory Time) Chilton Time

Muffler, Renew
All models (.7) 1.1

Tail Pipe, Renew
All models (.4) 7

Exhaust Pipe, Renew
Six(.6) 1.0

LABOR 8 EXHAUST SYSTEM 8 LABOR

(Factory Time) — Chilton Time

V-8–318-360 engs (.8) 1.2

Exhaust Pipe Extension, Renew
All models (.7) 1.1

Exhaust Pipe Flange Gasket, Renew
Six(.2) 5

Catalytic Converter, Renew
All models (.6) 1.1

Catalytic Converter Heat Shield, Renew
upper (.4) 9
lower (.2) 4
intermediate (.2) 5

Exhaust Manifold Heat Control

Valve, Recondition
Six(2.7) 3.4
w/A.C. add (.3) 3
V-8–318-360 engs (1.2) 1.9

Intake and Exhaust Manifold Gaskets, Renew
Six
B-PB-CB Models (2.0) 3.0
All other models (1.8) 2.8
w/A.C. add (.4) 4
Renew manif add 5

Exhaust Manifold or Gaskets, Renew
Six
B-PB-CB Models
1983-87 (2.1) 2.7
D-AD-PD Models
1983-87 (1.9) 2.5
W-AW-PW Models
1983-87 (1.9) 2.5
V-8–1983-87–318-360 engs
right side (.5) 1.1
left side (.7) 1.3

COMBINATIONS

Muffler, Exhaust and Tail Pipe, Renew
Six 1.6
V-8 .... 1.8

Muffler and Tail Pipe, Renew
All models 1.2

LABOR 9 FRONT SUSPENSION 9 LABOR

(Factory Time) — Chilton Time

Note: On all front suspension operations alignment charges must be added if performed. Time given does not include alignment.

Check Alignment of Front End
All models 8
Note: Deduct if alignment is performed.

Toe-In, Adjust
All models 7

Align Front End
Includes: Adjust front wheel bearings.
All models (1.4) 2.0

Wheels, Balance
one 5
each adtnl 3

Front Wheel Bearings, Clean and Repack (Both Wheels)
All models
w/Drum Brakes 1.0
w/Disc Brakes 1.5
w/4 wd 2.0

Front Wheel Bearings and Cups, Renew (One Wheel)
Drum Brakes (.6) 9
Disc Brakes
w/2 wd (.7) 1.1
w/4 wd (1.2) 1.7

Front Wheel Grease Seals, Renew (One Wheel)
All models
w/2 wd (.6) 8
w/4 wd (1.1) 1.5

Front Shock Absorbers, Renew
1983-87-one (.3) 6
both (.5) 9

Steering Knuckle, Renew (One)
w/2 WD
1983-87 (1.1) 1.7
w/4 WD
1983-87
w/44 FBJ Axle (1.5) 2.1
w/60 F Axle (1.2) 1.8

Lower Control Arm, Renew (One)
Add alignment charges.
1983-87 (1.3) 1.9

Lower Ball Joint, Renew (One)
Add alignment charges.
1983-87
w/2 wd (1.4) 2.0
w/4 wd (1.9) 2.7

Lower Control Arm Strut Bushings, Renew (One Side)
Add alignment charges.
1983-87 (.3) 6

Lower Control Arm Bushings, Renew (One Side)
Add alignment charges.
1983-87 (1.5) 2.3

Upper Control Arm, Renew (One)
Includes: Align front end.
1983-87 (1.9) 2.7

Upper Ball Joint, Renew (One)
Add alignment charges.
1983-87
w/2 wd (.9) 1.4
w/44 FBJ Axle (2.0) 3.2
w/60 F Axle (1.8) 3.0

Upper Control Arm Bushings, Renew (One Side)
Includes: Align front end.
1983-87 (1.8) 2.6

Front Sway Bar Bushings, Renew (One or All)
D-AD-PD 150
D-RD 250
D350-450 models (.6) 8
All other models (.4) 6

Front Sway Bar, Renew
All models (.4) 6

Front Spring, Renew (One)
Coil
1983-87 (1.2) 1.7
Leaf
1983-87 (.7) 1.1

Front Spring Shackle, Renew (One)
Includes: Renew bushings.
1983-87 (.8) 1.3

FOUR WHEEL DRIVE

Front Axle Shaft, R&R or Renew (One or Both–One Side)
1983-87
44 FBJ Axle (1.2) 1.8
60 F Axle (1.3) 1.9
Recond U-Joint add-each 2

Front Axle Inner Oil Seals, Renew (Both Sides)
1983-87
44 FBJ Axle (4.1) 6.0
60 F Axle (3.5) 5.0

Front Axle Shaft Spindle, Renew
All models
44 FBJ Axle (.9) 1.3
60F Axle (.8) 1.2

Locking Hub Assy., Renew or Recondition
All models
44 FBJ Axle
Spicer (.5) 9
Auto (.4) 8
60F Axle
Dualmatic (.2) 5

Drive Pinion Oil Seal, Renew
1983-87 (.5) 9

Front Axle Housing Cover and/or Gasket, Renew or Reseal
All models (.4) 8

Front Drive Shaft, Renew (Transfer Case To Front Axle)
1983-87 (.4) 7
w/Skid plate add (.3) 3

Front Drive Shaft Universal Joint, Renew
At Transfer Case
Dana-CV Type (.8) 1.3
Saginaw-CV Type (1.3) 2.0
At Front Axle(.6) 1.0

Front Axle Shaft Outer Oil Seal, Renew
All models-each (.9) 1.2

Front Axle Assy., R&R or Renew
Includes: Renew oil seals, transfer axle shafts and brake assemblies.
All models
44 FBJ Axle (3.8) 5.6
60 F Axle (3.7) 5.5
Renew axle shafts add-each 5

Differential Side Bearings, Renew
Includes: R&R ring and pinion, if necessary. Renew axle inner oil seals and adjust side bearing preload and backlash.
All models
44 FBJ Axle (5.5) 8.1
60 F Axle (4.9) 7.2

LABOR 9 FRONT SUSPENSION 9 LABOR

(Factory Time) Chilton Time

Differential Case, Renew

Includes: R&R ring and pinion, if necessary. Renew bearings and gears. Renew pinion seal and axle inner oil seals. Adjust backlash.

All models	
44 FBJ Axle (5.8)	8.5
60 F Axle (5.4)	7.9

Differential Side Gears, Renew

Includes: Renew axle inner oil seals if required.

All models	
44 FBJ Axle (4.5)	6.6
60 F Axle (3.8)	5.5

Ring Gear and Pinion Set, Renew

Includes: Renew pinion bearing, side bearings and all seals. Make all necessary adjustments.

All models	
44 FBJ Axle (6.5)	9.6
60 F Axle (5.8)	8.5
Renew diff case add (.3)	.5

LABOR 10 STEERING LINKAGE 10 LABOR

(Factory Time) Chilton Time

Tie Rods or Tie Rod Ends, Renew

Includes: Reset toe-in.

1983-87-each (.7)	1.0

Steering Knuckle Arm, Renew (One)

w/2 wd	
1983-87 (1.1)	1.5
w/4 wd	
1983-87 (.6)	.9

Center Link, Renew

B-PB-CB Models	
1983-87 (.6)	.8
All other models	
1983-87 (.4)	.6

Idler Arm, Renew

1983-87-one (.3)	.5
both (.5)	.7

Pitman Arm, Renew

B-PB-CB Models	
1983-87 (.4)	.7
All other models	
1983-87 (.5)	.8

Drag Link, Renew

B-PB-CB models (.3)	.6
All other models (.5)	.8

LABOR 11 STEERING GEAR 11 LABOR

(Factory Time) Chilton Time

STANDARD STEERING

Steering Gear, Adjust (On Truck)

All models (.9)	1.1

Steering Gear Assembly, Renew

B-PB-CB Models	
1983-87 (1.3)	1.9
D-AD-PD-RD Models	
1983-87 (.6)	1.2

Steering Gear Assy., R&R and Recondition

Includes: Disassemble, renew necessary parts, reassemble and adjust.

B-PB-CB Models	
1983-87 (1.9)	2.9
D-AD-PD-RD Models	
1983-87 (1.3)	2.2

Steering Column Mast Jacket, Renew

Does not include painting.

B-PB-CB Models	
1983-87	
column shift (1.4)	2.0
floor shift (1.1)	1.6
All other models	
1983-87	
column shift (1.6)	2.4
floor shift (1.1)	1.6
Tilt Column	
All models (2.3)	3.3

Upper Mast Jacket Bearing, Renew

All models	
w/Std column (.5)	1.0
w/Tilt column (1.1)	1.5

Steering Column Shift Housing, Renew

All models	
w/Std column (.9)	1.5
w/Tilt column (2.2)	3.3

Steering Gear Cross Shaft Oil Seal, Renew

All models (.8)	1.4

Steering Wheel, R&R or Renew

All models (.3)	.5

POWER STEERING

Trouble Shoot Power Steering

Includes: Test pump and system pressure. Check pounds pull on steering wheel and check for leaks.

All models	.5

Power Steering Belt, Renew

All models (.3)	.5
w/Air inj add (.1)	.1

Power Steering Gear Assy., Renew

B-PB-CB Models	
1983-87 (1.2)	1.7
All other models	
1983-87 (1.1)	1.6

Power Steering Gear, R&R and Recondition

B-PB-CB Models	
1983-87 (2.7)	3.9
All other models	
1983-87 (2.2)	3.2

Power Steering Gear Assy., Renew (w/Remanufactured Unit)

B-PB-CB Models	
1983-87 (1.2)	1.7

Steering Gear Cross Shaft Oil Seals, Renew (Inner and Outer)

B-PB-CB Models	
1983-87 (.9)	1.6
All other models	
1983-87 (1.2)	1.9

Gear Control Valve Assy., Renew

B-PB-CB Models	
1983-87 (.5)	.9
All other models	
1983-87 (1.5)	2.2

Pressure Control Valve, Renew

B-PB-CB Models	
1983-87 (.4)	.8

Power Steering Pump, Test and Renew

Includes: Transfer or renew pulley.

B-PB-CB Models	
1983-87 (1.1)	1.5
All other models	
1983-87 (.9)	1.4

Power Steering Pump, R&R and Recondition

B-PB-CB Models	
1983-87 (1.6)	2.5
All other models	
1983-87 (1.1)	2.3

Pump Flow Control Valve, Test and Clean or Renew

B-PB-CB models (1.1)	1.6
All other models (.9)	1.3
w/Air inj add (.2)	.2

Power Steering Pump Reservoir and/or Seals, Renew

B-PB-CB models (.8)	1.1
All other models (.7)	1.0
w/Air inj add (.2)	.2

Pump Drive Shaft Oil Seal, Renew

All models (.9)	1.3

Power Steering Hoses, Renew

All models	
pressure-each (.4)	.7
return-each (.3)	.6

LABOR 12 CYLINDER HEAD & VALVE SYSTEM 12 LABOR

(Factory Time)	Chilton Time
Compression Test	
Six(.6)	.9
V-8	
318-360 engs (.7)	1.0

Cylinder Head Gasket, Renew

Includes: Clean gasket surfaces, clean carbon, make all necessary adjustments.

(Factory Time)	Chilton Time
Six	
B-PB-CB Models	
1983-87 (3.6)	5.0
All other models	
1983-87 (2.5)	4.0
V-8–318-360 engs	
B-PB-CB Models	
1983-87-one (3.7)	4.5
both (4.9)	6.6
All other models	
1983-87-one (3.1)	4.3
both (4.2)	5.9
w/100 Amp alt add (.6)	.6
w/Air inj add (.6)	.6
w/A.C. add (.4)	.4

Cylinder Head, Renew

Includes: Transfer all parts, reface valves, make all necessary adjustments.

(Factory Time)	Chilton Time
Six	
B-PB-CB Models	
1983-87 (5.9)	8.2
All other models	
1983-87 (5.0)	7.0
V-8–318-360 engs	
B-PB-CB Models	
1983-87-one (5.0)	6.5
both (7.4)	9.6
All other models	
one (4.2)	6.3
both (6.7)	8.9
w/100 Amp alt add (.6)	.6
w/Air inj add (.6)	.6
w/A.C. add (.4)	.4

Clean Carbon and Grind Valves

Includes: R&R cylinder heads, clean gasket surfaces, clean carbon, reface valves and seats. Minor tune up.

(Factory Time)	Chilton Time
Six	
B-PB-CB Models	
1983-87 (5.4)	7.8
All other models	
1983-87 (4.9)	7.8
V-8–318-360 engs	
B-PB-CB Models	
1983-87 (7.0)	10.6
All other models	
1983-87 (6.2)	9.9

COMBINATIONS

Add to Valve Job

See Machine Shop Operations

GASOLINE ENGINES

(Factory Time)	Chilton Time
DRAIN, EVACUATE AND RECHARGE AIR CONDITIONING SYSTEM	
All Models	1.4
ROCKER ARMS & SHAFT ASSY., DISASSEMBLE AND CLEAN OR RECONDITION	
Six (.5)	.6
V-8-one side (.5)	.6
both sides (.9)	1.1
HYDRAULIC VALVE LIFTERS, DISASSEMBLE AND CLEAN	
Each	.2
DISTRIBUTOR, RECONDITION	
All Models (.7)	1.0
CARBURETOR, RECONDITION	
1 BBL (.9)	1.4
2 BBL (1.1)	1.6
4 BBL (1.6)	2.1
VALVE GUIDES, REAM OVERSIZE	
Each (.2)	.3
VALVES, RECONDITION (ALL)	
Cylinder Head Removed	
Six (2.2)	3.0
V-8 (2.7)	4.0

(Factory Time)	Chilton Time
w/100 Amp alt add (.6)	.6
w/Air inj add (.6)	.6
w/A.C. add (.4)	.4
Valves, Adjust	
Six	
B-PB-CB Models (.8)	1.2
All other models (.7)	1.1
Valve Cover Gasket, Renew	
Six	
B-PB-CB Models	
1983-87 (.9)	1.2
All other models	
1983-87 (.8)	1.1
V-8–318-360 engs	
B-PB-CB Models	
1983-87-one (.5)	.8
both (.8)	1.2
All other models	
1983-87-one (.5)	.8
both (.8)	1.2
w/Air inj add (.2)	.2
Valve Push Rod and/or Rocker Arm, Renew	
Six	
B-PB-CB Models	
1983-87-one or all (1.0)	1.7
All other models	
1983-87-one or all (.8)	1.5
V-8–318-360 engs	
B-PB-CB Models	
1983-87-one side (.6)	1.1
both sides (1.0)	2.1
All other models	
1983-87-one side (.5)	.9
both sides (.9)	1.6

Valve Tappets, Renew (SEE NOTE)

Includes: R&R cylinder head on 6 cyl engine, where required.

(Factory Time)	Chilton Time
Six	
B-PB-CB Models	
1983-87-one (1.6)	2.1
each adtnl (.1)	.1
All other models	
1983-87-one (1.5)	2.0
each adtnl (.1)	.1
V-8–318-360 engs-all models	
1983-87-one (1.0)	3.1
one-each bank (1.5)	3.6
all-both banks (2.4)	4.4
w/A.C. add (.2)	.2

NOTE: Factory time for V-8 engines is based on using magnetic tool through push rod opening to remove lifters. Chilton experience finds it better and safer to R&R intake manifold, since the lifters have a tendency to stick in the block and sometimes come apart.

(Factory Time)	Chilton Time
Valve Spring and/or Valve Stem Oil Seals, Renew (Head on Truck)	
Six–1983-87	
All models-one (1.0)	1.4
all (2.6)	3.6
V-8–318-360 engs-all models	
1983-87-one (1.1)	1.5
one-each bank (1.7)	2.4
all-both banks (4.4)	5.2

LABOR 13 ENGINE ASSEMBLY & MOUNTS 13 LABOR

Engine Assembly, R&R

Does not include transfer of any parts or equipment.

(Factory Time)	Chilton Time
Six	
B-PB-CB Models	
1983-87-w/M.T.	8.7
w/A.T.	7.8
All other models	
1983-87-w/M.T.	7.8
w/A.T.	6.6
V-8–318-360 engs	
B-PB-CB Models	
1983-87-w/M.T.	9.6
w/A.T.	9.2
All other models	
1983-87-w/M.T.	7.7
w/A.T.	6.5
w/P.S. add (.2)	.2
w/Skid plate add (.3)	.3
V-8–w/A.C. add (1.7)	*1.7

*Includes recharge A.C. system.

(G) Rebuilt Engine Assembly, Renew (w/Cyl. Head(s) and Oil Pan)

Includes: R&R engine assy. Transfer all component parts not supplied with replacement engine.

(Factory Time)	Chilton Time
Six	
B-PB-CB models	
1983-87-w/M.T.	11.7
w/A.T.	10.8
All other models	
1983-87-w/M.T.	10.8
w/A.T.	9.6
V-8	
318-360 engs	
B-PB-CB models	
1983-87-w/M.T.	12.6
w/A.T.	12.2
All other models	
1983-87-w/M.T.	10.7
w/A.T.	9.5
w/A.C. add	1.0
w/P.S. add	.2

LABOR 13 ENGINE ASSEMBLY & MOUNTS 13 LABOR

(Factory Time) Chilton Time

w/Air inj add 3
w/Skid plate add 3
V-8-w/A.C. add *1.7

*Includes: Recharge A.C. system.

Short Engine Assy., Renew (w/All Internal Parts Less Cylinder Head(s) and Oil Pan)

Includes: R&R engine, transfer all component parts not supplied with replacement engine. Clean carbon, grind valves. Tune engine.

Six
B-PB-CB Models
1983-87-w/M.T. (13.7).......... 18.5
w/A.T. (12.8).......... 17.6
All other models
1983-87-w/M.T. (11.0).......... 16.6
w/A.T. (10.1).......... 15.7
V-8-318-360 engs
B-PB-CB Models
1983-87-w/M.T. (15.2).......... 21.0
w/A.T. (14.3).......... 20.1
All other models
1983-87-w/M.T. (13.4).......... 19.2
w/A.T. (12.5).......... 18.3
w/P.S. add (.2) 2
w/Skid plate add (.3).......... .3
V-8-w/A.C. add (1.7).......... *1.7

*Includes recharge A.C. system.

Cylinder Block, Renew (w/Pistons and Rings)

Includes: R&R engine, transfer all component parts not supplied with replacement engine, clean carbon, grind valves. Tune engine.

Six
B-PB-CB Models
1983-87-w/M.T. (15.5).......... 22.7
w/A.T. (14.7).......... 21.8
All other models
1983-87-w/M.T. (14.6).......... 21.6
w/A.T. (13.7).......... 20.7

Engine Assembly, R&R and Recondition

Includes: Rebore block, install new pistons, rings, rod and main bearings. Clean carbon, grind valves. Tune engine.

Six
B-PB-CB Models
1983-87-w/M.T. (30.0).......... 35.2
w/A.T. (29.1).......... 34.3
All other models
1983-87-w/M.T. (28.6).......... 33.0
w/A.T. (27.4).......... 32.6
V-8-318-360 engs
B-PB-CB Models
1983-87-w/M.T. (36.3).......... 41.5
w/A.T. (35.9).......... 40.1
All other models
1983-87-w/M.T. (33.7).......... 38.9
w/A.T. (32.5).......... 37.7
w/P.S. add (.2).......... .2
w/Skid plate add (.3).......... .3
V-8-w/A.C. add (1.7).......... *1.7

*Includes recharge A.C. system.

Engine Mounts, Renew
Front
Six-all models
1983-87-one (.4).......... 1.0
V-8-318-360 engs
B-PB-CB Models
1983-87-one (.9).......... 1.2
All other models
1983-87-one (.4).......... .8
Rear
Six-1983-87 (.5).......... 1.0
V-8
B-PB-CB Models
1983-87 (.6).......... 1.0
All other models
1983-87 (1.0).......... 1.4

LABOR 14 PISTONS, RINGS & BEARINGS 14 LABOR

(Factory Time) Chilton Time

Rings, Renew (See Engine Combinations)

Includes: R&R pistons, remove cylinder top ridge, hone cylinder walls.

Six
B-PB-CB Models
1983-87 (6.8).......... 9.5
All other models
1983-87 (7.5).......... 10.1
V-8-318-360 engs
B-PB-CB Models
1983-87 (9.6).......... 13.4
All other models
1983-87 (9.7).......... 13.2
w/100 Amp alt add (.6).......... .6
w/Air inj add (.6).......... .6
w/A.C. add (.4).......... .4

Pistons (w/Pin), Renew

Includes: Remove cylinder top ridge, hone cylinder walls, renew connecting rod bearings if required.

Six
B-PB-CB Models
1983-87 (8.5).......... 11.3
All other models
1983-87 (8.8).......... 11.2
V-8-318-360 engs
B-PB-CB Models
1983-87 (12.1).......... 15.8
All other models
1983-87 (9.4).......... 12.9
w/100 Amp alt add (.6).......... .6
w/Air inj add (.6).......... .6
w/A.C. add (.4).......... .4

Connecting Rod Bearings, Renew
Six
B-PB-CB Models
1983-87-one (1.6).......... 2.3
all (3.1).......... 4.5
All other models
1983-87-one (2.3).......... 3.3
all (4.1).......... 5.9
V-8-318-360 engs
B-PB-CB Models
1983-87-one (2.5).......... 3.6
all (4.6).......... 6.6
All other models
1983-87-one (1.3).......... 2.4
all (3.4).......... 5.1

COMBINATIONS
Add to Engine Work

See Machine Shop Operations

GASOLINE ENGINES

(Factory Time) Chilton Time

DRAIN, EVACUATE AND RECHARGE AIR CONDITIONING SYSTEM
All models.......... 1.4

ROCKER ARMS & SHAFT ASSY., DISASSEMBLE AND CLEAN OR RECONDITION
Six (.5).......... .6
V-8-one side (.5).......... .6
both sides (.9).......... 1.1

HYDRAULIC VALVE LIFTERS, DISASSEMBLE AND CLEAN
Each.......... .2

DISTRIBUTOR, RECONDITION
All Models (.7).......... 1.0

CARBURETOR, RECONDITION
1 BBL (.9).......... 1.4
2 BBL (1.1).......... 1.6
4 BBL (1.6).......... 2.1

VALVE GUIDES, REAM OVERSIZE
Each (.2).......... .3

VALVE, RECONDITION (ALL)
Cylinder Head Removed
Six (2.2).......... 3.0
V-8 (2.7).......... 4.0

DEGLAZE CYLINDER WALLS
Each (.1).......... .2

REMOVE CYLINDER TOP RIDGE
Each (.1).......... .1

PLASTIGAUGE BEARINGS
Each (.1).......... .1

OIL PUMP, RECONDITION
Six (.2).......... .4
V-8 (.2).......... .4

OIL FILTER ELEMENT, RENEW
All Models (.2).......... .3

LABOR 15 CRANKSHAFT & DAMPER 15 LABOR

(Factory Time)	Chilton Time
Crankshaft and Main Bearings, Renew	
Includes: R&R engine assembly, plastigauge all bearings.	
Six	
B-PB-CB Models	
1983-87-w/M.T. (10.5)	13.6
w/A.T. (9.6)	12.7
All other models	
1983-87-w/M.T. (7.3)	10.4
w/A.T. (6.1)	9.6
V-8–318-360 engs	
B-PB-CB Models	
1983-87-w/M.T. (10.0)	14.7
w/A.T. (9.1)	14.2
All other models	
1983-87-w/M.T. (8.8)	12.2
w/A.T. (7.6)	11.0
w/P.S. add (.2)	.2
w/Skid plate add (.3)	.3
V-8–w/A.C. add (1.7)	*1.7
*Includes recharge A.C. system.	
Main Bearings, Renew	
Includes: Plastigauge bearings.	
Six	
B-PB-CB Models	
1983-87-one (2.7)	3.9
all (4.2)	6.0
All other models	
1983-87-one (1.6)	2.7
all (3.2)	5.2
V-8–318-360 engs	
B-PB-CB Models	
1983-87-one (2.6)	3.7
all (3.2)	4.6
All other models	
1983-87-one (1.8)	3.2
all (3.2)	5.4
Rod and Main Bearings, Renew	
Includes: Plastigauge bearings.	
Six	
B-PB-CB Models	
1983-87 (6.0)	8.7
All other models	
1983-87 (4.2)	6.4
V-8–318-360 engs	
B-PB-CB Models	
1983-87 (5.6)	8.1
All other models	
1983-87 (4.5)	7.2
Rear Main Bearing Oil Seals, Renew (Upper & Lower)	
Six	
B-PB-CB Models	
1983-87 (1.4)	2.0
All other models	
1983-87 (1.6)	2.8
V-8–318-360 engs	
B-PB-CB Models	
1983-87 (1.9)	2.7
All other models	
1983-87 (1.4)	3.1
NOTE: Upper seal removed with special tool. If necessary to R&R crankshaft, use Crankshaft and Main Bearings, Renew.	
Vibration Damper, Renew	
Six	
B-PB-CB Models	
1983-87 (.9)	1.4
D-AD-PD Models	
1983-87 (.8)	1.2
W-AW-PW Models	
1983-87 (.8)	1.4
V-8–318-360 engs	
B-PB-CB Models	
1983-87 (.7)	1.3
All other models	
1983-87 (.4)	.7
w/A.C. add (.4)	.4
Crankshaft Pulley, Renew	
All models	
1983-87 (.5)	.9

LABOR 16 CAMSHAFT & TIMING GEARS 16 LABOR

(Factory Time)	Chilton Time
Timing Chain Case Cover Gasket, Renew	
Six	
All models	
1983-87 (1.4)	2.5
V-8–318-360 engs	
B-PB-CB Models	
1983-87 (2.0)	2.9
All other models	
1983-87 (1.8)	2.6
w/P.S. add (.2)	.2
w/A.C. add (.2)	.2
w/100 Amp alt add (.5)	.5
w/Air inj add (.2)	.2
Timing Chain Case Cover Oil Seal, Renew	
Six	
B-PB-CB Models	
1983-87 (1.1)	1.7
D-AD-PD Models	
1983-87 (.9)	1.2
W-AW-PW Models	
1983-87 (.9)	1.2
V-8–318-360 engs	
All models	
1983-87 (.9)	1.3
w/P.S. add (.2)	.2
w/A.C. add (.4)	.4
Timing Chain or Gear, Renew	
Includes: Renew cover oil seal and crankshaft gear if necessary.	
Six	
1983-87 (2.2)	2.9
V-8–318-360 engs	
B-PB-CB Models	
1983-87 (2.4)	3.5
All other models	
1983-87 (2.3)	3.0
w/P.S. add (.2)	.2
w/A.C. add (.4)	.4
w/100 Amp alt add (.5)	.5
w/Air inj add (.2)	.2
Camshaft, Renew	
Includes: Renew valve tappets and adjust valve clearance when required.	
Six	
B-PB-CB Models	
1983-87 (4.4)	6.4
w/A.C. add (.8)	.8
V-8–318-360 engs	
B-PB-CB Models	
1983-87 (5.3)	7.6
All other models	
1983-87 (4.7)	7.1
w/A.C. add (.8)	.8
w/P.S. add (.2)	.2
w/A.T. add (.3)	.3
w/100 Amp alt add (.5)	.5
w/Air inj add (.8)	.8
Camshaft Bearings, Renew	
(Engine Removed and Disassembled)	
All models (2.0)	2.6

LABOR 17 ENGINE OILING SYSTEM 17 LABOR

(Factory Time)	Chilton Time
Oil Pan or Gasket, Renew	
Six	
B-PB-CB Models	
1983-87 (1.1)	1.7
All other models	
1983-87 (1.4)	2.0
V-8–318-360 engs	
B-PB-CB Models	
1983-87 (1.4)	2.0
All other models	
1983-87 (1.0)	1.6
Oil Pump, Renew	
Six	
B-PB-CB models	
1983-87 (.6)	1.2
All other models	
1983-87 (.9)	1.3
V-8–318-360 engs	
B-PB-CB Models	
1983-87 (1.7)	2.3
All other models	
1983-87 (1.1)	1.8
Oil Pump, R&R and Recondition	
Six	
B-PB-CB Models	
1983-87 (.8)	1.5
All other models	
1983-87 (1.4)	1.8
V-8–318-360 engs	
B-PB-CB Models	
1983-87 (2.1)	2.7
All other models	
1983-87 (1.6)	2.2
Pressure Test Engine Bearings (Pan Off)	
All models	1.2
Oil Pressure Gauge (Dash), Renew	
B-PB-CB Models	
1983-87 (.6)	1.1
All other models	
1983-87 (.6)	1.1
Oil Pressure Gauge (Engine), Renew	
All models (.4)	.6
Oil Filter Element, Renew	
All models (.2)	.3

LABOR 18 CLUTCH & FLYWHEEL 18 LABOR

(Factory Time)	Chilton Time
Clutch Pedal Free Play, Adjust	
All models (.3)	.5
Clutch Assembly, Renew	
4 Speed	
w/2 wheel drive (2.9)	4.1
w/4 wheel drive (3.9)	5.1
w/Skid plate add (.3)	.3
w/P.T.O. add (.3)	.5
Clutch Release Bearing, Renew	
4 Speed	
w/2 wheel drive (2.5)	3.9
w/4 wheel drive (3.5)	4.9
w/Skid plate add (.3)	.3
w/P.T.O. add (.3)	.5
Clutch Release Fork, Renew	
4 Speed	
B-PB-CB Models (.3)	.6
D-AD-PD-RD Models (.8)	1.2
W-AW-PW Models (.4)	.7
Clutch Torque Shaft, Renew	
Includes: Renew bearings.	
B-PB-CB Models (.3)	.6
All other models (.6)	.9
Flywheel Assembly, Renew	
4 Speed	
1983-87	
w/Overdrive (2.0)	3.7
w/NP-435-445 and 2/wd (3.2)	4.4
w/NP-435-445 and 4/wd (4.6)	5.8
Renew ring gear add (.6)	.9
w/Skid plate add (.3)	.3

LABOR 19 STANDARD TRANSMISSION 19 LABOR

(Factory Time)	Chilton Time
Transmission Assy., R&R or Renew	
4 Speed	
NP-A833 (2.0)	3.2
NP-435-445	
w/2 wheel drive (2.7)	3.9
w/4 wheel drive (3.7)	4.9
w/Skid plate add (.3)	.3
w/P.T.O. add (.3)	.5
Transmission Assy., R&R and Recondition	
4 Speed	
NP-A833 (4.9)	7.0
NP-435-445	
w/2 wheel drive (5.4)	7.5
w/4 wheel drive (6.4)	8.5
w/Skid plate add (.3)	.3
w/P.T.O. add (.3)	.5
Transmission, Recondition (Off Truck)	
NP-A833 (2.9)	3.9
NP-435-445 (2.7)	3.6
Transmission Front Oil Seal, Renew	
Includes: R&R transmission.	
4 Speed	
NP-A833 (2.5)	3.9
NP-435-445	
w/2 wheel drive (2.8)	4.2
w/4 wheel drive (3.8)	5.2
w/Skid plate add (.3)	.3
w/P.T.O. add (.3)	.5
Extension Housing Oil Seal, Renew	
All models (.5)	.7
Speedometer Drive Pinion, Renew	
All models (.3)	.6

LABOR 20 TRANSFER CASE 20 LABOR

(Factory Time)	Chilton Time
Transfer Case Assy., R&R or Renew	
All models (1.6)	2.5
w/Skid plate add (.3)	.3
Transfer Case Assy., R&R and Recondition	
All models (4.6)	6.7
w/Skid plate add (.3)	.3
Transfer Case Adapter, Renew	
All models (2.7)	3.6
w/Skid plate add (.3)	.3
Transfer Case Adapter Gasket, Renew	
All models (1.8)	2.4
w/Skid plate add (.3)	.3
Transfer Case Shift Lever, Renew	
All models (.4)	.7
Rear Output Shaft Seal, Renew	
All models (1.2)	1.6
Transfer Case Shift Rod, Renew	
All models-one (.3)	.5
both (.4)	.7
Transfer Case Front Yoke, Renew	
All models (.9)	1.2
Front Output Shaft Bearing and/or Gasket, Renew	
All models (1.2)	1.6
w/Skid plate add (.3)	.3
Speedometer Drive Pinion, Renew	
All models (.8)	1.1
Power Take Off Assy., R&R or Renew	
1983-87 (1.4)	2.5
Power Take Off Assy., R&R and Recondition	
1983-87 (3.1)	4.9
Power Take Off Mounting Gasket, Renew	
1983-87 (1.3)	2.4
Power Take Off Cover Gasket, Renew	
1983-87 (.4)	.7
Power Take Off Control Cable, Renew	
1983-87 (.6)	1.0

LABOR 21 SHIFT LINKAGE 21 LABOR

(Factory Time)	Chilton Time
STANDARD	
Shift Linkage, Adjust	
All models (.3)	.5
Gearshift Lever, Renew	
All models	
Overdrive (.2)	.4
NP435-445 (.5)	.7
Gearshift Control Rod and/or Swivels, Renew	
All models-one (.5)	.7
both (.7)	1.0
Gearshift Mechanism, Renew (4 Speed)	
All models-w/Overdrive (.6)	1.1
AUTOMATIC	
Throttle Linkage, Adjust	
All models (.3)	.5
Gearshift Lever, Renew	
All models (.4)	.6
Gearshift Control Rod, Renew	
All models (.4)	.6
Gear Selector Indicator, Renew	
All models	
inst panel mount (.7)	1.0
column mount (.2)	.4
Steering Column Shift Housing, Renew	
1983-87	
w/Std column (.9)	1.5
w/Tilt column (2.2)	3.3

(Factory Time) Chilton Time

ON TRUCK SERVICES

Drain and Refill Unit
All models 7

Oil Pressure Test
Note: Using 3 pressure test points.
All models 1.5

Check Unit For Oil Leaks
Includes: Clean and dry outside of case and run unit to determine point of leak.
All models 1.0

Neutral Safety Switch, Renew
All models (.3) 4

Oil Cooler Lines, Renew
Includes: Cut and form to size.
All models-one (.6) 1.0

Transmission Auxiliary Oil Cooler, Renew
All models (.7) 1.2

Throttle Linkage, Adjust
All models (.3) 5

Kickdown Band, Adjust
All models (.3) 5

Throttle Valve Lever Shaft Seal, Renew
All models (.3) 7

Valve Body Manual Lever Shaft Seal, Renew
All models (.4) 8

Extension Housing Oil Seal, Renew
All models (.5) 1.1

Extension Housing or Adapter Gasket, Renew
All models
w/2 wheel drive (1.3) 2.0
w/4 wheel drive (2.7) 3.4
w/Skid plate add (.3) 3

Governor Assy., R&R or Recondition
Includes: R&R extension housing.
All models
w/2 wheel drive (1.6) 2.5
w/4 wheel drive (3.0) 3.9
w/Skid plate add (.3) 3

Parking Lock Sprag, Renew
Includes: R&R extension housing.
All models
w/2 wheel drive (1.3) 2.2
w/4 wheel drive (2.7) 3.6
w/Skid plate add (.3) 3

Output Shaft Bearing and Oil Seal, Renew
Includes: R&R extension housing.
All models
w/2 wheel drive (1.4) 2.3
w/4 wheel drive (2.8) 3.7
w/Skid plate add (.3) 3

Oil Pan Gasket, Renew
All models (.5) 1.0

Oil Filter, Renew
All models (.6) 1.1

Parking Lock Sprag Control Rod, Renew
Includes: R&R oil pan and remove valve body.
All models (.9) 1.9

Accumulator Piston, Renew or Recondition
Includes: R&R oil pan and adjust band.
All models (.6) 1.7

Kickdown Servo, Renew or Recondition
Includes: R&R oil pan and adjust band.
All models (.9) 1.9

Reverse Servo, Renew or Recondition
Includes: R&R oil pan and adjust band.
All models (.8) 1.8

Valve Body Assembly, Renew
Includes: R&R oil pan and replace filter.
All models (.9) 1.7

Valve Body Assy., R&R and Recondition
Includes: R&R oil pan and replace filter. Disassemble, clean, inspect, free all valves. Replace parts as required.
All models (1.7) 2.4

Bands, Adjust
Includes: R&R oil pan.
All models
reverse (.6) 1.4

SERVICES REQUIRING R&R

Transmission Assembly, Remove and Reinstall
B-PB-CB Models
1983-87 (2.0) 4.7
D-AD-PD-RD Models
1983-87 (2.3) 5.0
W-AW-PW Models
1983-87 (4.1) 6.9
Renew trans add (.4) 5
Flush converter and lines add (.5) 7
w/Skid plate add (.3) 3

Transmission Assembly, Renew (w/Remanufactured Unit)
Includes: Remove and install all necessary interfering parts. Transfer all parts not supplied with replacement unit. Road test.
B-PB-CB Models
1983-87 (2.3) 5.2
D-AD-PD-RD Models
1983-87 (2.6) 5.5
W-AW-PW Models
1983-87 (4.5) 7.4
Pressure test governor add (.7) 1.1
w/Skid plate add (.3) 3

Transmission Assembly, Reseal
Includes: R&R trans and renew all seals and gaskets.
B-PB-CB Models
1983-87 (4.2) 6.8
D-AD-PD-RD Models
1983-87 (4.5) 7.1
W-AW-PW Models
1983-87 (6.3) 8.9
w/Skid plate add (.3) 3

Transmission and Converter, R&R and Recondition
Includes: Disassemble trans including valve body, clean, inspect and replace parts as required.
B-PB-CB Models
1983-87 (6.5) 11.8
D-AD-PD-RD Models
1983-87 (6.8) 12.1
W-AW-PW Models
1983-87 (8.6) 13.9
w/Skid plate add (.3) 3
Flush converter and lines add (.5) 7

Torque Converter, Renew
Includes: R&R transmission.
B-PB-CB Models
1983-87 (2.2) 5.1
D-AD-PD-RD Models
1983-87 (2.5) 5.4
W-AW-PW Models
1983-87 (4.3) 7.3
w/Skid plate add (.3) 3

Kickdown Band, Renew
Includes: R&R transmission.
B-PB-CB Models
1983-87 (2.7) 6.1
D-AD-PD-RD Models
1983-87 (3.0) 6.4
W-AW-PW Models
1983-87 (4.8) 8.3
w/Skid plate add (.3) 3

Reverse Band, Renew
Includes: R&R transmission.
B-PB-CB Models
1983-87 (3.1) 6.7
D-AD-PD-RD Models
1983-87 (3.4) 7.0
W-AW-PW Models
1983-87 (5.2) 8.9
w/Skid plate add (.3) 3

Transmission Case, Renew
Includes: R&R transmission.
B-PB-CB Models
1983-87 (3.9) 7.7
D-AD-PD-RD Models
1983-87 (4.2) 8.0
W-AW-PW Models
1983-87 (6.0) 9.9
w/Skid plate add (.3) 3

Front Pump Assembly, Renew or Recondition
Includes: R&R trans, replace reaction shaft if necessary.
B-PB-CB Models
1983-87 (2.6) 5.9
D-AD-PD-RD Models
1983-87 (2.9) 6.2
W-AW-PW Models
1983-87 (4.7) 8.1
w/Skid plate add (.3) 3

Front Pump Oil Seal, Renew
Includes: R&R transmission.
B-PB-CB Models
1983-87 (2.2) 5.1
D-AD-PD-RD Models
1983-87 (2.5) 5.4
W-AW-PW Models
1983-87 (4.3) 7.3
w/Skid plate add (.3) 3

LABOR 25 U-JOINTS & DRIVESHAFT 25 LABOR

(Factory Time) Chilton Time

Drive Shaft, R&R or Renew
All Models
trans to rear axle (.4) 7
transfer case bearing to rear axle (.4) 7
transfer case to front axle (.5) 8
transfer case to rear axle (.4) 7
trans to center brg (1.2) 1.7
w/Skid plate add (.3) 3

Universal Joints, Renew or Recondition
Includes: R&R drive shaft.
All Models

Single Piece Shaft
(without center bearing)
trans to rear axle (.8) 1.3
at rear axle (.6) 1.1
transfer case to rear axle (.9) 1.4
(transfer case to front axle)
Dana CV Type (.8) 1.3
Saginaw CV Type (1.5) 2.0
at front axle (.7) 1.3

Two Piece Shaft
(with center bearing)
any one (.8) 1.3
w/Skid plate add (.3) 3

Drive Shaft Center Bearing, Renew
Includes: Renew insulator if necessary.
All models (1.0) 1.7

LABOR 26 REAR AXLE 26 LABOR

(Factory Time) Chilton Time

Differential, Drain & Refill
All models 6

Rear Axle Housing Cover, Renew or Reseal
All models (.4) 6

Axle Shaft, Renew
Includes: Renew outer oil seal, bearing and gasket on 8³/₈- 9¹/₄axles.
8³/₈- 9¹/₄Axles
1983-87-one (1.1) 1.5
Spicer 60 - 70 Axle
1983-87-one (.5) 1.0

Axle Shaft Bearing, Renew
Includes: Renew oil seal.
8³/₈- 9¹/₄Axles
1983-87-one (1.0) 1.7

Axle Shaft Oil Seal, Renew
8³/₈- 9¹/₄Axles
1983-87-one (.9) 1.6

Pinion Shaft Oil Seal, Renew
All models (.6) 1.0

Rear Axle Housing, Renew
Includes: Renew pinion oil seal, inner and outer axle shaft or wheel bearing oil seals and gaskets.
8³/₈- 9¹/₄Axles
All models (4.2) 6.3
Spicer 60 - 70 Axles
All models (5.7) 8.5

Differential Carrier Assembly, Renew
Note: Assembly includes axle housing.
8³/₈- 9¹/₄Axles
All models (2.0) 3.1
Spicer 60 - 70 Axles
All models (3.0) 4.6

Differential Side Bearings, Renew
Includes: Renew pinion oil seal and adjust backlash.
8³/₈- 9¹/₄Axles
All models (2.4) 3.6
Spicer 60 - 70 Axles
All models (3.1) 4.6
Renew pinion bearings, add (.9) 1.4

Differential Case, Renew
Includes: Renew ring gear and pinion, bearings and side gears if necessary.
8³/₈- 9¹/₄Axles
Std & Sure Grip
All models (3.0) 4.5
Spicer 60 - 70 Axles
All models (3.6) 5.4

Differential Side Gears, Renew
Includes: Renew axle shaft oil seals.
8³/₈- 9¹/₄Axles
All models (1.1) 2.5
Spicer 60 - 70 Axles
All models (1.4) 3.0

Ring Gear and Pinion Set, Renew
Includes: Renew wheel bearing or inner axle shaft oil seals, pinion oil seal and gaskets.
8³/₈- 9¹/₄Axles
All models (3.7) 7.0
Spicer 60 - 70 Axles
All models (3.7) 7.0
Renew side bearings add (.3) 7

LABOR 27 REAR SUSPENSION 27 LABOR

(Factory Time) Chilton Time

Rear Spring, Renew
All models-one (.5) 9
both (1.0) 1.7

w/Aux. rear spring add, each (.5) 5
w/Skid plate add (.3) 3

Auxiliary Rear Spring, Renew
All models-one (.7) 1.5

Rear Spring Shackle, Renew
Includes: Renew bushings.
B-PB-CB Models
one (.3) 7
All other models
one (.6) 1.0
w/Skid plate add (.3) 3

Rear Shock Absorbers, Renew
All models-one (.2) 5
both (.4) 9

LABOR 28 AIR CONDITIONING 28 LABOR

(Factory Time) Chilton Time

Drain, Evacuate, Leak Test and Charge System
All models 1.7

Partial Charge
Includes: Leak test.
All models
w/Front unit (.6) 1.1
w/Front and rear unit (.9) 1.4

Performance Test
All models 8

Vacuum Leak Test
All models 9

ON TRUCK SERVICES

Compressor Belt, Renew
B-PB-CB Models (.4) 6
All other models (.3) 5
w/Air inj add (.1) 1

Compressor Clutch Field Coil, Renew
Includes: Renew pulley w/Hub, if necessary.
B-PB-CB Models
w/C-171 comp (.5) 9
All other models (.5) 9

Compressor Clutch Assembly, Renew
B-PB-CB Models
w/C-171 comp (.5) 8
All other models (.5) 8

C-171 COMP

Compressor Assembly, Renew
Includes: Transfer parts as required. Pressure test and charge system.
Six
All models (1.8) 3.2

LABOR 28 AIR CONDITIONING 28 LABOR

(Factory Time) — Chilton Time

V-8
B-PB-CB models (2.1) 3.5
All other models (1.7) 3.1
w/Rear A.C. add (.3) 3

Compressor Front Cover and/or Seal, Renew
Includes: Pressure test and charge system.
Six
All models (2.2) 3.5
V-8
B-PB-CB models (2.5) 3.8
All other models (2.1) 3.4

Compressor Rear Cover and/or Seal, Renew
Includes: Pressure test and charge system.
Six
All models (2.1) 3.4
V-8
B-PB-CB models (2.4) 3.7
All other models (2.0) 3.3

Compressor Center Seal, Renew
Includes: Pressure test and charge system.
Six
All models (2.3) 3.6
V-8
B-PB-CB models (2.6) 3.9
All other models (2.2) 3.5

Compressor Shaft Gas Seal, Renew
Includes: Pressure test and charge system.
Six
All models (2.2) 3.5
V-8
B-PB-CB models (2.5) 3.8
All other models (2.1) 3.4

Expansion Valve, Renew
Includes: Pressure test and charge system.
B-PB-CB Models
front unit (1.1) 2.0
rear unit (1.9) 2.8
All other models (1.0) 1.9

Receiver Drier, Renew
Includes: Add partial charge, leak test and charge system.
B-PB-CB Models
w/Front unit (1.1) 1.9
w/Front and rear unit (1.5) 2.3
All other models (1.1) 1.9

Low Pressure Cut Off Switch, Renew
Includes: Evacuate and charge system.
B-PB-CB Models
w/Front unit (1.0) 1.8
w/Front and rear unit (1.3) 2.1
All other models (1.0) 1.8

Clutch Cycling (Thermostatic Control) Switch, Renew
All models (.3) 5

Condenser Assembly, Renew
Includes: Add partial charge, leak test and charge system.
B-PB-CB Models
w/Front unit (1.6) 2.5
w/Front and rear unit (1.9) 3.0
All other models (1.2) 2.2

Evaporator Coil, Renew
Includes: Add partial charge, leak test and charge system.
B-PB-CB Models
Front Unit
1983-87 (2.9) 5.4
Front Unit-Front and Rear Unit Equipped
1983-87 (3.2) 6.0
Rear Unit (1.6) 2.8
All other models (2.3) 4.7

Blower Motor, Renew
B-PB-CB Models
1983-87
Front (.9) 1.5
Rear (.4) 9
All other models
1983-87 (.4) 9

Blower Motor Resistor, Renew
All models (.3) 4

Blower Motor Switch, Renew
All models
Front unit (.5) 9
Rear unit (.3) 6

Temperature Control Assembly, Renew
B-PB-CB Models
1983-87 (.6) 1.0
All other models
1983-87 (.5) 9

A.C. Push Button Vacuum Switch, Renew
All models (.6) 1.0

Air Conditioning Hoses, Renew
Includes: Evacuate and charge system.
SUCTION ASSY
B-PB Models (1.2) *2.0
All other models (1.1) 1.9
DISCHARGE ASSY
All models (1.1) *1.9
REAR UNIT TUBE ASSY
B-PB Models (3.7) 5.0
SUCTION HOSE
Rear unit to rear evap. (1.3) 2.1
DISCHARGE HOSE
Rear unit to rear evap. (1.3) 2.1
SUCTION HOSE
Rear unit to front tube (1.3) 2.1
DISCHARGE HOSE
Rear unit to front tube (1.3) 2.1
*w/Rear A.C. add (.3) 3

LABOR 30 HEAD AND PARKING LAMPS 30 LABOR

(Factory Time) — Chilton Time

Aim Headlamps
two 4
four 6

Headlamp Sealed Beam Bulb, Renew
Does not include aim headlamps.
All models-one (.3) 3

Parking Lamp or Turn Signal Lamp Lens or Bulb, Renew
All models-one (.2) 3

Tail and Stop Lamp Lens or Bulb, Renew
All models-one (.2) 3

Reflectors, Renew
All models-one (.2) 2

LABOR 31 WINDSHIELD WIPER & SPEEDOMETER 31 LABOR

(Factory Time) — Chilton Time

Windshield Wiper Motor, Renew
B-PB-CB Models
1983-87 (.8) 1.2
All other models
1983-87 (.6) 1.1

Windshield Wiper Pivot, Renew
All models-one (.5) 7

Wiper Link, Renew
All models-one (.5) 8

Wiper Switch, Renew
B-PB-CB Models
1983-87 (.3) 7
All other models
1983-87 (.4) 6

Wiper Delay Control Module, Renew
All models (.3) 5

Windshield Washer Pump, Renew
All models (.3) 5

Speedometer Head, R&R or Renew
B-PB-CB Models
1983-87 (.3) 6
All other models
1983-87 (.4) 7
Reset odometer add 2

Speedometer Cable and Casing, Renew
All models-each (.5) 7

LABOR 32 LIGHT SWITCHES & WIRING 32 LABOR

(Factory Time)	Chilton Time
Headlamp Switch, Renew	
B-PB-CB Models	
1983 (.7)	1.0
1984-87 (.4)	1.0
All other models	
1983-87 (.4)	.7
Headlamp Dimmer Switch, Renew	
All models (.3)	.5
Back-Up Lamp Switch, Renew	
(w/Manual Trans)	
All models (.3)	.4
Neutral Safety Switch, Renew	
All models (.3)	.4
Stop Light Switch, Renew	
All models (.3)	.4
Turn Signal Switch, Renew	
1983-87	
w/Std column (.5)	.9
w/Tilt column (.9)	1.4
Turn Signal or Hazard Warning Flasher, Renew	
All models (.2)	.3

LABOR 34 CRUISE CONTROL 34 LABOR

(Factory Time)	Chilton Time
Cruise Control Servo, Renew	
All models (.4)	.6
Cruise Control Cable, Renew	
All models (.3)	.5
Cruise Control Vacuum Hoses, Renew	
All models (.2)	.3
Cruise Control Switch (Turn Signal Lever), Renew	
1983-87	
w/Std column (.5)	.9
w/Tilt column (.9)	1.4
Cruise Control Cut-Off Safety Switch, Renew	
All models (.3)	.4

GROUP INDEX

ALPHABETICAL INDEX

LABOR SERVICE BAY OPERATIONS LABOR

(Factory Time) Chilton Time

COOLING

Winterize Cooling System
Includes: Run engine to check for leaks, tighten all hose connections. Test radiator and pressure cap, drain radiator and engine block. Add anti-freeze and refill system.
All models 5

Thermostat, Renew
All models (.4) 6

Radiator Hoses, Renew
All models-upper (.3) 4
lower (.5) 6

Drive Belt, Adjust
All models-one 3
each adtnl 1

FUEL

Carburetor Air Cleaner, Service
All models (.3) 3

Carburetor Float Level, Adjust
All models (.7) 1.1

Fuel Filter, Renew
All models
in line (.2) 3
in tank (.5) 8

BRAKES

Brakes, Adjust (Minor)
Includes: Adjust brakes, fill master cylinder.
two wheels 4

Bleed Brakes (Four Wheels)
Includes: Fill master cylinder.
All models (.4) 6

Parking Brake, Adjust
All models (.3) 4

LUBRICATION SERVICE

Lubricate Chassis, Change Oil & Filter
Includes: Inspect and correct all fluid levels.
All models 6
Install grease fittings add 1

Lubricate Chassis
Includes: Inspect and correct all fluid levels.
All models 4
Install grease fittings add 1

Engine Oil & Filter, Change
Includes: Inspect and correct all fluid levels.
All models 4

WHEELS

Wheel, Renew
one 5

Wheel, Balance
one 3
each adtnl 2

Wheels, Rotate (All)
All models 5

ELECTRICAL

Aim Headlamps
All models (.3) 4

Headlamp Sealed Beam Bulb, Renew
Does not include aim headlamps.
All models-each (.2) 3

Battery Cables, Renew
All models-ground (.2) 2
positive (.5) 6

Headlamp Switch, Renew
All models (.3) 4

Headlamp Dimmer Switch, Renew (Column Mounted)
All models (.3) 6

Stop Light Switch, Renew
All models (.3) 4
w/Cruise control add (.1) 1

Back-Up Lamp Switch, Renew (w/ Manual Trans)
All models (.2) 4

Neutral Safety Switch, Renew
All models (.3) 4

Turn Signal Switch, Renew
All models (.5) 1.0

License Lamp Lens, Renew
All models (.2) 2

Tail Lamp Lens, Renew
All models-one (.2) 3

Side Marker Lamp Assy., Renew
All models (.2) 3

License Lamp Assembly, Renew
All models (.2) 2

Turn Signal or Hazard Warning Flasher, Renew
All models (.2) 3

Horn Relay, Renew
All models (.2) 3

Horns, Renew
All models-one (.2) 4

LABOR 1 TUNE UP 1 LABOR

(Factory Time) Chilton Time

Compression Test
All models 6

Engine Tune Up, (Electronic Ignition)
Includes: Test battery and clean connections. Tighten manifold and carburetor mounting bolts. Check engine compression, clean and adjust or renew spark plugs. Test resistance of spark plug cables. Inspect distributor cap and rotor. Adjust air gap. Check vacuum advance operation. Reset ignition timing. Adjust idle mixture and idle speed. Service air cleaner. Inspect and adjust drive belts. Inspect choke operation and adjust or free up. Check operation of EGR valve.
All models 1.5

LABOR 2 IGNITION SYSTEM 2 LABOR

(Factory Time) Chilton Time

Spark Plugs, Clean and Reset or Renew
All models (.5) 6

Ignition Timing, Reset
All models (.3) 4

Spark Control Computer, Renew
All models (.3) 1.0

Distributor, Renew
Includes: Reset ignition timing.
All models (.4) 6

Distributor, R&R and Recondition
Includes: Reset ignition timing.
All models (.9) 1.5

Distributor Pick-Up Plate and Coil Assy., Renew
Includes: R&R distributor and reset ignition timing.
All models (.5) 8

Distributor Pick-Up Plate and Coil Assy., Renew (Hall Effect)
Does not require R&R of distributor.
All models (.3) 6

Vacuum Advance Unit, Renew
Includes: R&R distributor and reset ignition timing.
All models (.6) 9

Distributor Cap, Renew
All models (.2) 4

Ignition Coil, Renew
All models (.2) 4

Ignition Cables, Renew
All models (.2) 5

Ignition Switch, Renew
All models (.4) 8

Ignition Key Buzzer Switch, Renew
All models (.3) 5

Ignition Key Warning Buzzer, Renew
All models (.2) 3

Ignition Lock Housing, Renew
Does not include painting.
All models (.9) 1.6

LABOR 3 FUEL SYSTEM 3 LABOR

(Factory Time) Chilton Time

Fuel Pump, Test
Includes: Disconnect line at carburetor, attach pressure gauge.
All models 3

Carburetor Air Cleaner, Service
All models (.3) 3

Heated Air Door Sensor, Renew
All models (.2) 3

Automatic Choke, Renew
All models (.7) 1.0

Choke Vacuum Kick, Adjust
All models (.2) 3

Choke Vacuum Kick Diaphragm, Renew
All models (.2) 4

Accelerator Pump, Renew
All models (.4) 8

Needle Valve and Seat, Renew
Includes: Adjust float level and idle speed and mixture.
All models (.7) 1.1

Carburetor Assembly, Renew
Includes: All necessary adjustments.
All models (.8) 1.2

Carburetor, R&R and Clean or Recondition
Includes: All necessary adjustments.
All models (1.6) 2.4

Fuel Filter, Renew
All models
in line (.2) 3
in tank (.5) 8

Fuel Pump, Renew
All models (.5) 9
Add pump test if performed.

Fuel Tank, Renew
Includes: Drain and refill tank.
All models (.9) 1.5

Fuel Gauge (Dash), Renew
All models (.2) 5

Fuel Gauge (Tank), Renew
All models (.6) 1.0

Intake Manifold, Renew
All models (2.0) 3.7

Intake and Exhaust Manifold Gaskets, Renew
All models (1.9) 3.5

LABOR 3A EMISSION CONTROLS 3A LABOR

(Factory Time) Chilton Time

AIR INJECTION SYSTEM

Air Pump, Renew
All models (.5) 7

Injection Tube and Check Valve Assy., Renew
All models
ex manif mount (.5) 8
to conv
one or both (.4) 6

Air Pump Diverter/Switching Valve, Renew
All models (.4) 7

Aspirator, Renew
All models (.2) 4

Aspirator Tube, Renew
All models (.7) 1.0

Orifice Spark Advance Control Valve, Renew
All models (.3) 5

EVAPORATIVE EMISSION

Vapor Canister, Renew
All models (.4) 6

Vapor Canister Filter, Renew
All models (.2) 3

CRANKCASE EMISSION

Crankcase Vent Valve, Renew
All models (.2) 3

Crankcase Vent Hose, Renew
All models-one (.2) 2

E.G.R. SYSTEM

E.G.R. Valve, Renew
All models (.6) 8

E.G.R. Coolant Valve, Renew (CCEGR)
All models-one (.3) 5

Coolant Controlled Engine Vacuum Switch, Renew (CCEVS)
All models (.3) 5

HEATED INLET AIR SYSTEM

Carburetor Air Cleaner, Service
All models (.3) 3

Heated Air Door Sensor, Renew
All models-one (.2) 3

EFC SYSTEM

Oxygen Sensor, Renew
All models (.2) 4

LABOR 4 ALTERNATOR AND REGULATOR 4 LABOR

Alternator Circuits, Test
Includes: Test battery, regulator and alternator output.
All models 6

Alternator Assy., Renew
Includes: Transfer pulley if required.
All models (.8) 1.2
w/A.C. add (.5) 5
Add circuit test if performed.

Alternator, R&R and Recondition
Includes: Test and disassemble, renew parts as required.
All models (1.5) 2.1
w/A.C. add (.5) 5

Alternator Front Bearing or Retainer, Renew
Includes: R&R alternator.
All models (.8) 1.3
w/A.C. add (.5) 5
Renew rear brg. add 2

Alternator Regulator, Test and Renew
All models
External type (.2) 6

Alternator Gauge, Renew
All models (.2) 5

Instrument Cluster Voltage Limiter, Renew
All models (.2) 5

LABOR 5 STARTING SYSTEM 5 LABOR

Starter Draw Test (On Truck)
All models 3

Starter Assembly, Renew
Includes: Test starter relay, starter solenoid and amperage draw.
All models (1.0) 1.6

Starter, R&R and Recondition
Includes: Test relay, starter solenoid and amperage draw. Turn down armature.
All models (1.5) 2.5
Renew field coils add (.4) 5

Starter Drive, Renew
Includes: R&R starter.
All models (1.6) 2.0

Starter Solenoid, Renew
Includes: R&R starter.
All models (1.1) 1.8

Starter Relay, Renew
All models (.2) 3

Neutral Safety Switch, Renew
All models (.3) 4

Ignition Switch, Renew
All models (.4) 8

Battery Cables, Renew
All models-ground (.2) 2
positive (.5) 6

LABOR 6 BRAKE SYSTEM 6 LABOR

(Factory Time)	Chilton Time
Brake Pedal Free Play, Adjust	
All models	.3
Brakes, Adjust (Minor)	
Includes: Adjust brakes, fill master cylinder.	
two wheels	.4
Bleed Brakes (Four Wheels)	
Includes: Fill master cylinder.	
All models (.4)	.6
Brake Shoes and/or Pads, Renew	
Includes: Install new or exchange shoes or pads, adjust service and hand brake. Bleed system.	
All models	
Front-disc (.5)	.8
Rear-drum (.8)	1.5
All four wheels	2.2
Resurface rotor, add-each	.9
Resurface brake drum, add-each	.5
Rear Brake Drum, Renew	
All models-one (.5)	.6

BRAKE HYDRAULIC SYSTEM

(Factory Time)	Chilton Time
Wheel Cylinder, Renew	
Includes: Bleed system.	
All models-one (.7)	1.1
both (1.3)	2.1
Wheel Cylinder, R&R and Recondition	
Includes: Hone cylinder and bleed system.	
All models-one	1.2
both	2.3
Brake Hose, Renew (Flex)	
Includes: Bleed system.	
All models-front-one (.4)	.8
rear-one (.4)	.8
Master Cylinder, Renew	
Includes: Bleed complete system.	
All models (.5)	.9
Master Cylinder, R&R and Recondition	
Includes: Bleed complete system.	
All models	1.6
Master Cylinder Reservoir, Renew	
Includes: Bleed complete system.	
All models (.6)	1.0
Brake System Combination Valve, Renew	
Includes: Bleed complete system.	
All models (.7)	1.0
Load Sensing Proportioning Valve, Renew	
Includes: Adjust valve and bleed brakes.	
All models (.7)	1.1

COMBINATIONS

Add to Brakes, Renew

See Machine Shop Operations

(Factory Time)	Chilton Time
RENEW WHEEL CYLINDER	
Each (.3)	.3
REBUILD WHEEL CYLINDER	
Each	.4
REBUILD CALIPER ASSEMBLY	
Each	.5
RENEW MASTER CYLINDER	
All models (.5)	.6
REBUILD MASTER CYLINDER	
All models	.8
RENEW BRAKE HOSE	
Each (.3)	.3
RENEW REAR WHEEL GREASE SEALS	
One side (.2)	.3
RENEW BRAKE DRUM	
Each (.3)	.3
RENEW DISC BRAKE ROTOR	
Each (.2)	.2
DISC BRAKE ROTOR STUDS, RENEW	
Each	.1

POWER BRAKES

(Factory Time)	Chilton Time
Brake Booster Assembly, Renew	
All models (.8)	1.2
Brake Booster Check Valve, Renew	
All models (.2)	.2

DISC BRAKES

(Factory Time)	Chilton Time
Brake Shoes and/or Pads, Renew	
Includes: Install new or exchange shoes or pads, adjust service and hand brake. Bleed system.	
All models	
Front-disc (.5)	.8
Rear-drum (.8)	1.5
All four wheels	2.2
Resurface rotor, add-each	.9
Resurface brake drum, add-each	.5
Disc Brake Rotor w/Hub, Renew	
All models-each (1.0)	1.4
Disc Brake Rotor, Renew	
All models (.3)	.6
Caliper Assembly, Renew	
Includes: Bleed system.	
All models-each (.5)	.9
Caliper Assembly, R&R and Recondition	
Includes: Bleed system.	
All models-each (.8)	1.4

PARKING BRAKE

(Factory Time)	Chilton Time
Parking Brake, Adjust	
All models (.3)	.4
Parking Brake Warning Lamp Switch, Renew	
All models (.2)	.3
Parking Brake Lever, Renew	
All models (.4)	.7
Parking Brake Cables, Renew	
All models-front (.7)	1.0
rear-each (.4)	.6

LABOR 7 COOLING SYSTEM 7 LABOR

(Factory Time)	Chilton Time
Winterize Cooling System	
Includes: Run engine to check for leaks, tighten all hose connections. Test radiator and pressure cap, drain radiator and engine block. Add anti-freeze and refill system.	
All models	.5
Thermostat, Renew	
All models (.4)	.6
Radiator Assembly, R&R or Renew	
Includes: Drain and refill coolant.	
All models (.5)	.9
w/A.T. add (.1)	.1

ADD THESE OPERATIONS TO RADIATOR R&R

(Factory Time)	Chilton Time
Boil & Repair	1.5
Rod Clean	1.9
Repair Core	1.3
Renew Tank	1.6
Renew Trans. Oil Cooler	1.9
Recore Radiator	1.7
Coolant Reserve Tank, Renew	
All models (.5)	.7
Radiator Fan Motor, Renew	
All models (.4)	.5
Radiator Fan Motor Relay, Renew	
All models (.2)	.3
Radiator Fan Switch, Renew	
All models (.3)	.6
Radiator Hoses, Renew	
All models-upper (.3)	.4
lower (.5)	.6
Water Pump, Renew	
Includes: Drain and refill coolant.	
All models (1.1)	1.6
w/A.C. add (.5)	.7
Drive Belt, Adjust	
All models-one	.3
each adtnl	.1
Drive Belt, Renew	
All models	
A.C. (.2)	.3
Fan & Alter (.3)	.4
P/Str (.5)	.6
Transaxle Auxiliary Oil Cooler, Renew	
All models (.3)	.6
Temperature Gauge (Engine Unit), Renew	
All models (.3)	.4
Heater Hoses, Renew	
All models-one (.4)	.4
both (.5)	.6
Heater Core, R&R or Renew	
All models-wo/A.C. (1.0)	1.7
w/A.C. (2.5)	*4.2

*Includes recharge A.C. system.

LABOR 7 COOLING SYSTEM 7 LABOR

(Factory Time)	Chilton Time
ADD THESE OPERATIONS TO HEATER CORE R&R	
Boil & Repair	1.2
Repair Core	.9
Recore	1.2
Heater Control Assembly, Renew	
All models (.4)	.7
Heater Blower Motor, Renew	
All models (.4)	.6
Heater Blower Motor Resistor, Renew	
All models (.2)	.3
Heater Blower Motor Switch, Renew	
All models (.4)	.7
Water Valve, Renew (w/A.C.)	
All models (.3)	.5

LABOR 8 EXHAUST SYSTEM 8 LABOR

(Factory Time)	Chilton Time
Muffler, Renew	
All models (.4)	.8
Cut exhaust pipe add	.2
Catalytic Converter, Renew	
All models-one (.7)	.9
Exhaust Pipe Extension, Renew	
All models (.6)	1.0
Exhaust Pipe, Renew	
All models (.7)	1.1
Cut at muffler add	.2
Intake and Exhaust Manifold Gaskets, Renew	
All models (1.9)	3.5
Exhaust Manifold, Renew	
All models (2.7)	3.7
Exhaust Pipe Flange Gasket, Renew	
All models (.4)	.6
COMBINATIONS	
Muffler, Exhaust and Tail Pipe, Renew	
All models (1.0)	1.5

LABOR 9 FRONT SUSPENSION 9 LABOR

(Factory Time)	Chilton Time
Note: On all front suspension operations alignment charges must be added if performed. Time given does not include alignment.	
Wheel, Renew	
one (.3)	.5
Wheels, Rotate (All)	
All models	.5
Wheel, Balance	
one	.3
each adtnl	.2
Check Alignment of Front End	
All models	.5
Note: Deduct if alignment is performed.	
Toe-Out, Adjust	
All models	.6
Align Front End	
Includes: Adjust camber, toe-out and center steering wheel.	
All models (.8)	1.4
Steering Knuckle, Renew (One)	
Add alignment charges.	
All models (1.0)	1.6
Front Strut Assembly, R&R or Renew (One)	
Add alignment charges.	
All models (.8)	1.4
Lower Control Arm, Renew (One)	
Add alignment charges.	
All models (1.1)	1.6
Lower Ball Joint, Renew (One)	
Includes: Reset toe-in.	
All models (.8)	1.2
Front Coil Spring or Strut Bearing, Renew (One)	
Add alignment charges.	
All models (.8)	1.5
Steering Knuckle Bearing, Renew (One) (Wheel Bearing)	
All models (1.2)	1.6
Front Sway Bar, Renew	
All models (.4)	.7
Front Suspension Strut (Dual Path) Mount Assy., Renew	
Includes: Renew bearing.	
1984-87 (.8)	1.5
K-Frame Assembly, Renew	
Add alignment charges.	
All models (2.5)	4.0
Drive Shaft Boot, Renew	
Includes: Clean and lubricate C/V joint.	
All models	
one-inner or outer (.7)	1.0
both-one side (1.0)	1.4
Renew shaft seal, add	
right side (.1)	.1
left side (.3)	.3
Drive Shaft C/V Joint, Renew	
All models	
one-inner or outer (.7)	1.0
both-one side (1.0)	1.4
inter shaft U-joint (.6)	1.0
Renew shaft seal, add	
right side (.1)	.1
left side (.3)	.3
Front Wheel Drive Shaft Assy., Renew	
All models	
inter spline yoke (.6)	1.0
inter stub shaft (.6)	1.0
all others-each (1.0)	1.4
Renew shaft seal, add	
right side (.1)	.1
left side (.3)	.3
Intermediate Shaft Support Bearing, Renew	
All models-each (.6)	1.0
Drive Shaft Oil Seal, Renew	
All models	
right side (.5)	.8
left side (.7)	1.1

LABOR 11 STEERING GEAR 11 LABOR

(Factory Time)	Chilton Time
Tie Rod Ends, Renew	
Includes: Adjust toe, replace tie rod if necessary.	
All models	
outer-one (.9)	1.2
Inner and Outer	
w/P.S.-one (1.9)	2.5
STANDARD STEERING	
Horn Contact, Renew	
All models (.2)	.3
Steering Wheel, Renew	
All models (.2)	.3
Steering Column Jacket, Renew	
Does not include painting.	
All models (1.0)	1.9
Upper Mast Jacket Bearing, Renew	
Includes: Replace insulators if necessary.	
All models (.8)	1.7

LABOR 11 STEERING GEAR 11 LABOR

(Factory Time) Chilton Time

Steering Column Lower Shaft Bearing, Renew
Includes: Replace support if necessary.
All models (.4) 7

Steering Column Shaft, Renew
All models (.8) 2.0

Steering Column Flexible Coupling, Renew
All models (.5) 9

Steering Gear Assembly, Renew
All models (1.7) 3.0

POWER STEERING

Power Steering Pump Pressure Check
All models.... .5

Power Steering Pump Belt, Renew
All models (.5) 6
w/A.C. add (.1) 1

Power Steering Gear Assembly, Renew
All models (2.3) 3.1

Steering Gear Oil Seals, Renew
Includes: R&R gear assy. and reset toe-in.
All models (3.5) 5.1

Upper and Lower Valve Pinion Seals, Renew
All models (1.4) 2.0
Renew brgs add (.3).... .5

Power Steering Pump, Renew
Includes: Test pump and transfer pulley.
All models (1.2) 1.9

Power Steering Pump, R&R and Recondition
All models (1.5) 2.8

Pump Flow Control Valve, Test and Clean or Renew
All models (.6) 1.0

Power Steering Reservoir or Seals, Renew
All models (.9) 1.4

Pump Drive Shaft Oil Seal, Renew
All models (1.1) 1.9

Power Steering Hoses, Renew
All models-each (.4).... .5

LABOR 12 CYLINDER HEAD & VALVE SYSTEM 12 LABOR

(Factory Time) Chilton Time

Compression Test
All models.... .6

Cylinder Head Gasket, Renew
Includes: Clean carbon.
All models (3.4) 4.8
w/A.C. add (.1) 1
w/Air inj add (.2).... .2

Cylinder Head, Renew
Includes: Transfer all necessary parts. Clean carbon. Make all necessary adjustments.
All models (5.3) 8.0
w/A.C. add (.1).... .1
w/Air inj add (.2).... .2

Clean Carbon and Grind Valves
Includes: R&R cylinder head, adjust valve clearance when required. Minor engine tune up.
All models (4.8) 6.8
w/A.C. add (.1).... .1
w/Air inj add (.2).... .2

Cylinder Head Cover Gasket, Renew or Reseal
All models (.8) 1.1

Valve Rocker Arms or Shaft, Renew
All models (1.2) 1.6

Valve Springs and/or Valve Stem Oil Seals, Renew (Head on Car)
All models (1.9) 2.9

Valve Tappets, Renew
All models-one (1.0).... 1.5
all (1.9).... 2.9

LABOR 13 ENGINE ASSEMBLY & MOUNTS 13 LABOR

(Factory Time) Chilton Time

Engine Assembly, Remove and Install
Includes: R&R engine and transmission as a unit.
Does not include transfer of any parts or equipment.
All models.... 4.5
w/A.C. add (.5).... .5
w/Air inj add (.3).... .3

Short Engine Assembly, Renew (w/All Internal Parts Less Cyl. Head and Oil Pan)
Includes: R&R engine and transmission as a unit. Transfer all necessary parts not supplied with replacement engine. Clean carbon, grind valves. Minor tune up.
All models (9.1) 15.0
w/A.C. add (.5) 5
w/Air inj add (.3).... .3

Engine Assy., R&R and Recondition
Includes: Rebore block, install new pistons, rings, rod and main bearings. Clean carbon, grind valves, replace valve stem oil seals. Tune engine.
All models (17.8) 22.6
w/A.C. add (.5) 5
w/Air inj add (.3).... .3

Engine Support, Renew
All models
Engine-right side (.3) 5
left side (.3).... .5
center (.4) 6
Trans/Axle
Roll rod (.3).... .5

LABOR 14 PISTONS, RINGS & BEARINGS 14 LABOR

COMBINATIONS

Add to Engine Work

See Machine Shop Operations

DRAIN, EVACUATE & RECHARGE AIR CONDITIONING SYSTEM
All models 1.4

DISTRIBUTOR, RECONDITION
All models (.7).... .7

CARBURETOR, RECONDITION
All models 2.0

RECONDITION CYL. HEAD (HEAD REMOVED)
All models (1.4).... 2.0

CAMSHAFT, RENEW (HEAD DISASSEMBLED)
All models (.1).... .2

DEGLAZE CYLINDER WALLS
Each (.1) 1

REMOVE CYLINDER TOP RIDGE
Each (.1) 1

VALVES, RECONDITION (HEAD REMOVED)
All models (1.4).... 2.0

MAIN BEARINGS, RENEW (PAN REMOVED)
All models (.9).... 1.4

OIL PUMP, RENEW
All models (.2).... .3

OIL FILTER ELEMENT, RENEW
All models (.2).... .3

LABOR 14 PISTONS, RINGS & BEARINGS 14 LABOR

(Factory Time)	Chilton Time
Rings, Renew (See Engine Combinations)	
Includes: Replace connecting rod bearings, deglaze cylinder walls, clean carbon. Minor tune up.	
All models	
one cyl (4.6)	6.9
all cyls (5.9)	8.1
w/A.C. add (.2)	.2
w/Air inj add (.2)	.2
Pistons or Connecting Rods, Renew	
Includes: Replace rings and connecting rod bearings, deglaze cylinder walls, clean carbon. Minor tune up.	
All models	
one cyl (4.9)	7.2
all cyls (7.0)	9.3
w/A.C. add (.2)	.2
w/Air inj add (.2)	.2
Connecting Rod Bearings, Renew	
All models (2.1)	3.0

LABOR 15 CRANKSHAFT & DAMPER 15 LABOR

(Factory Time)	Chilton Time
Crankshaft and Main Bearings, Renew	
Includes: R&R engine assy.	
All models (6.7)	11.2
w/A.C. add (.2)	.2
w/P.S. add (.3)	.3
Main Bearings, Renew (All)	
Includes: R&R engine assy.	
All models (7.0)	11.0
w/A.C. add (.2)	.2
w/P.S. add (.3)	.3
Main and Rod Bearings, Renew (All)	
Includes: R&R engine assy.	
All models (7.7)	12.0
w/A.C. add (.2)	.2
w/P.S. add (.3)	.3
Rear Main Bearing Oil Seals, Renew (Complete)	
All models (3.5)	5.4
w/Cruise control add (.2)	.2
Crankshaft Rear Bearing Oil Seal Retainer, Renew	
Includes: Replace oil seal, complete.	
All models (4.1)	6.3
w/Cruise control add (.2)	.2
Crankshaft Front Oil Seal, Renew	
All models (1.3)	2.0
w/A.C. add (.2)	.2
w/P.S. add (.2)	.2
Crankshaft Pulley, Renew	
All models (.5)	.8
w/A.C. add (.1)	.1
w/P.S. add (.1)	.1

LABOR 16 CAMSHAFT & TIMING GEARS 16 LABOR

(Factory Time)	Chilton Time
Intermediate Shaft, Renew	
All models (1.3)	2.5
w/A.C. add (.2)	.2
w/P.S. add (.1)	.1
Intermediate Shaft Oil Seal, Renew	
All models (1.1)	1.8
w/A.C. add (.2)	.2
w/P.S. add (.2)	.2
Intermediate Shaft Sprocket, Renew	
All models (1.7)	2.7
w/A.C. add (.5)	.5
w/P.S. add (.2)	.2
w/Air inj add (.2)	.2
Camshaft, Renew	
All models (1.7)	2.8
Renew valve springs add (1.1)	1.1
Camshaft Sprocket, Renew	
Includes: Replace cover oil seal.	
All models (1.7)	2.4
w/A.C. add (.5)	.5
w/P.S. add (.2)	.2
w/Air inj add (.2)	.2
Timing Belt, Renew	
All models (1.6)	2.3
w/A.C. add (.5)	.5
w/P.S. add (.2)	.2
w/Air inj add (.1)	.1
Timing Belt Cover, Renew	
All models-upper (.2)	.4
lower (.6)	1.0
w/A.C. add (.2)	.2
w/P.S. add (.1)	.1
Timing Belt Tensioner, Renew	
All models (.9)	1.5
w/A.C. add (.2)	.2
w/P.S. add (.2)	.2
Camshaft Oil Seal, Renew	
All models-front (.7)	1.1
rear (.4)	.8

LABOR 17 ENGINE OILING SYSTEM 17 LABOR

(Factory Time)	Chilton Time
Oil Pan or Gasket, Renew	
All models (1.0)	1.4
Pressure Test Engine Bearings (Pan Off)	
All models	1.0
Oil Pump, Renew	
All models (1.3)	1.7
Oil Pump, R&R and Recondition	
All models (1.7)	2.2
Oil Pressure Gauge (Engine), Renew	
All models (.3)	.4
Oil Filter Element, Renew	
All models (.2)	.3

LABOR 18 CLUTCH & FLYWHEEL 18 LABOR

(Factory Time)	Chilton Time
Clutch Assembly, Renew	
All models (3.3)	4.6
Renew input seal add (.2)	.2
w/Cruise control add (.2)	.2
Clutch Release Bearing, Renew	
All models (3.2)	4.4
w/Cruise control add (.2)	.2
Clutch Self Adjusting Mechanism, Renew	
All models (.3)	.6
Clutch Release Cable, Renew	
All models (.3)	.5
Flywheel, Renew	
All models (3.4)	4.7
w/Cruise control add (.2)	.2
Renew ring gear add	.5

LABOR 19 STANDARD TRANSMISSION 19 LABOR

(Factory Time) Chilton Time

Front Wheel Drive Shaft Assy., Renew
All models-each (1.0)........ 1.5
Renew shaft seal, add
right side (.1)........ .1
left side (.3)........ .3

Drive Shaft Boot, Renew
Includes: Clean and lubricate C/V joint.
All models
one-inner or outer (.7)........ 1.0
both-one side (1.0)........ 1.4
Renew shaft seal, add
right side (.1)........ .1
left side (.3)........ .3

Drive Shaft C/V Joint, Renew
All models
one-inner or outer (.7)........ 1.0
both-one side (1.0)........ 1.4
Renew shaft seal, add
right side (.1)........ .1
left side (.3)........ .3

Drive Shaft Oil Seal, Renew
All models-right side (.5)........ .7
left side (.8)........ 1.1

Manual Trans/Axle, Remove & Install
Does not include transfer of any parts or equipment.
All models (3.1)........ 4.3

Manual Trans/Axle Assy., Renew
Includes: Transfer all necessary parts not supplied with replacement unit.
All models (3.5)........ 4.9

Manual Trans/Axle Assy., R&R and Recondition (Complete)
All models
w/A460 (5.6)........ 8.0
w/A465 (5.9)........ 8.5

LABOR 21 SHIFT LINKAGE 21 LABOR

(Factory Time) Chilton Time

MANUAL

Gearshift Control Rod and/or Swivel, Renew
All models (.3)........ .4

Crossover Rod, Renew
All models (.3)........ .4

Gearshift Lever, Renew
All models-floor shift (.4)........ .6

Gearshift Mechanism, Renew
All models (.6)........ .9
w/Console add (.1)........ .1

Gearshift Selector Tube Assy., Renew
All models (.4)........ .6

Selector Shaft Seal, Renew
All models (.8)........ 1.1

Trans/Axle Selector Shaft, Renew
All models (1.3)........ 1.7

AUTOMATIC

Throttle Linkage, Adjust
All models (.2)........ .4

Gearshift Lever, Renew
All models (.3)........ .5

Gearshift Mechanism, Renew
Includes: Replace knob and push button if necessary.
All models (.5)........ .8

Gearshift Control Cable, Renew
All models (.7)........ 1.0

Throttle Lever Control Cable, Renew
Includes: Adjust cable.
All models (.3)........ .6

LABOR 23 AUTOMATIC TRANSMISSION 23 LABOR

(Factory Time) Chilton Time

ON CAR SERVICES

Drain & Refill Unit
All models........ .6

Oil Pressure Check
All models........ .8

Check Unit For Oil Leaks
Includes: Clean and dry outside of case and run unit to determine point of leak.
All models........ .8

Neutral Safety Switch, Renew
All models (.3)........ .4

Oil Cooler Lines, Renew
Includes: Cut and form to size.
All models (.4)........ .6

Throttle Linkage, Adjust
All models (.2)........ .4

Kickdown Band, Adjust
All models (.2)........ .4

Throttle Valve Lever Shaft Seal, Renew
All models (.5)........ .8

Valve Body Manual Lever Shaft Seal, Renew
All models (.3)........ .6

Differential Gear Cover, Renew
All models (.8)........ 1.2

Drive Shaft Boot, Renew
Includes: Clean and lubricate C/V joint.
All models
one-inner or outer (.7)........ 1.0
both-one side (1.0)........ 1.4
Renew shaft seal, add
right side (.1)........ .1
left side (.3)........ .3

Drive Shaft C/V Joint, Renew
All models
one-inner or outer (.7)........ 1.0
both-one side (1.0)........ 1.4
inter shaft U-joint (.6)........ 1.0
Renew shaft seal, add
right side (.1)........ .1
left side (.3)........ .3

Front Wheel Drive Shaft Assy., Renew
All models
inter spline yoke (.6)........ 1.0
inter stub shaft (.6)........ 1.0
all others-each (1.0)........ 1.4
Renew shaft seal, add
right side (.1)........ .1
left side (.3)........ .3

Intermediate Shaft Support Bearing, Renew
All models-each (.6)........ 1.0

Drive Shaft Seal, Renew
All models-right side (.5)........ .8
left side (.8)........ 1.1

Transfer Gear Cover, Renew
All models (.5)........ .7

Governor Assy., Renew or Recondition
Includes: R&R oil pan.
All models (1.3)........ 2.4

Governor Support and Parking Gear, Renew
Includes: R&R oil pan.
All models (1.9)........ 2.9

Oil Pan and/or Gasket, Renew
All models (.6)........ 1.2

Oil Filter, Renew
Includes: R&R oil pan.
All models (.7)........ 1.4

Parking Lock Sprag, Renew
Includes: R&R oil pan.
All models (1.5)........ 2.6

Accumulator Piston, Renew or Recondition
Includes: R&R oil pan.
All models (1.1)........ 2.2

Kickdown Servo, Renew
Includes: R&R oil pan.
All models (1.4)........ 2.5

Reverse Servo, Renew
Includes: R&R oil pan.
All models (1.2)........ 2.2

Valve Body, Renew
Includes: R&R oil pan and renew filter.
All models (1.0)........ 2.1

LABOR 23 AUTOMATIC TRANSMISSION 23 LABOR

(Factory Time) Chilton Time

Valve Body, R&R and Recondition
Includes: R&R oil pan and renew filter.
All models (1.7) 3.2

SERVICES REQUIRING R&R

Trans/Axle Assy., Remove & Install
All models (3.1) 4.5

Trans/Axle Assembly, Reseal
Includes: R&R trans axle and renew all seals and gaskets.
All models (5.0) 7.0

Trans/Axle Assembly, Renew
Includes: Remove and install all necessary interfering parts. Transfer any parts not supplied with replacement unit. Road test.
All models (3.5) 4.9

Trans/Axle Assy., R&R and Recondition
Includes: Disassemble complete, clean, inspect and replace all parts as required.
All models (9.4) 12.7
Flush converter and cooler lines,
add (.5) 5

Kickdown Band, Renew
All models (4.0) 6.2

Reverse Band, Renew
All models (4.2) 6.5

Trans/Axle Case, Renew
All models (7.7) 10.0

Front and Rear Clutch Seals, Renew
All models (4.2) 6.5

Torque Converter, Renew
All models (3.3) 5.2

Torque Converter Drive Plate, Renew (With Ring Gear)
All models (3.3) 5.2

Front Oil Pump, Renew
All models (3.7) 6.0

Front Oil Pump Seal, Renew
All models (3.3) 5.2

Reaction Shaft and/or Bushing, Renew
Includes: Renew front pump if necessary.
All models (3.7) 6.0

LABOR 26 REAR AXLE AND SUSPENSION 26 LABOR

(Factory Time) Chilton Time

Rear Wheel Bearing, Renew or Repack
Includes: Replace bearing cups and grease seal.
All models-each (.6) 9

Rear Wheel Grease Seal, Renew
All models-each (.4) 7

Rear Spring, Renew
All models-one (.6) 9
both (1.1) 1.7

Rear Shock Absorbers, Renew
All models-one (.3) 4
both (.4) 6

Rear Spring Bushing and/or Shackle, Renew
All models-one (.4) 6

Stub Axle Spindle, Renew
All models-one (.5) 8

Rear Spring Hanger, Renew
All models-one (.7) 1.1

LABOR 28 AIR CONDITIONING 28 LABOR

(Factory Time) Chilton Time

Note: If more than one item requires replacement where evacuation and discharging the system is already included in the operation, deduct 1.0 hour for each additional item to the times listed.

Drain, Evacuate, Leak Test and Charge System
All models 1.4

Partial Charge
Includes: Leak test.
All models (.6) 8

Performance Test
All models 8

Vacuum Leak Test
All models 8

Compressor Drive Belt, Renew
All models (.2) 3

C-171 COMPRESSOR

Compressor Clutch Field Coil, Renew
Includes: Replace pulley w/hub if necessary.
All models (.6) 9

Compressor Clutch Pulley (W/Hub), Renew
All models (.4) 7

Compressor Clutch Assembly, Renew
All models (.6) 9

Compressor Assembly, Renew
Includes: Pressure test and charge system.
All models (1.4) 2.5

Compressor Front Cover or Seal, Renew
Includes: R&R compressor. Pressure test and charge system.
All models (2.1) 3.4

Compressor Rear Cover or Seal, Renew
Includes: R&R compressor. Pressure test and charge system.
All models (2.0) 3.3

Compressor Center Seal, Renew
Includes: R&R compressor. Pressure test and charge system.
All models (2.2) 3.5

Compressor Shaft Gas Seal, Renew
Includes: R&R compressor. Pressure test and charge system.
All models (2.1) 3.4

Expansion Valve, Renew
Includes: Pressure test and charge system.
All models (1.0) 1.7

Receiver Dryer, Renew
Includes: Add partial charge, leak test and charge system.
All models (.9) 1.6

Low Pressure Cut Off Switch, Renew
Includes: Charge system.
All models (.9) 1.4

Clutch Cycling (Thermostatic Control) Switch, Renew
All models (.3) 6

Condenser Assembly, Renew
Includes: Add partial charge, leak test and charge system.
All models (1.5) 2.2

Temperature Control Assembly, Renew
All models (.4) 7

Push Button Vacuum Switch, Renew
All models (.5) 9

Temperature Control Cable, Renew
All models (.6) 9

Vacuum Hose Control Assy., Renew
All models
main assy (2.0) 3.0

Evaporator Coil, Renew
Includes: Add partial charge, leak test and charge system.
All models (2.7) 3.9

Vacuum Actuator, Renew
All models
outside air door (.3) 6
heater/defroster door (.3) 6
A/C mode door (.6) 1.0

Blower Motor, Renew
All models (.6) 9

Blower Motor Resistor, Renew
All models (.3) 4

Blower Motor Switch, Renew
All models (.4) 8

Air Conditioning Hoses, Renew
Includes: Add partial charge, leak test and charge system.
All models-one (1.1) 1.5
each adtnl (.3) 5

LABOR 30 HEAD AND PARKING LAMPS 30 LABOR

(Factory Time) — Chilton Time

Aim Headlamps
All models (.3) 4

Headlamp Sealed Beam Bulb, Renew
Does not include aim headlamps.
All models-each (.2) 3

Side Marker Lamp Assy., Renew
All models (.2) 3

License Lamp Assembly, Renew
All models (.2) 2

License Lamp Lens, Renew
All models (.2) 2

Tail Lamp Lens, Renew
All models-one (.2) 3

LABOR 31 WINDSHIELD WIPER & SPEEDOMETERS 31 LABOR

(Factory Time) — Chilton Time

Windshield Wiper Motor, Renew
All models (.4) 7

Windshield Wiper Switch, Renew
All models (.4) 9

Wiper Pivot, Renew (One)
All models (.3) 5

Wiper Links, Renew
All models (.3) 6

Windshield Washer Pump, Renew
All models (.3) 4

Speedometer Head, R&R or Renew
Does not include reset odometer.
All models (.4) 7

Speedometer Cable and Casing, Renew
All models
speed control to trans (.2) 6
speed control to speedo (.3) 6
trans to speedo (.4) 9

Speedometer Cable (Inner), Renew or Lubricate
All models
speed control to trans (.2) 5
speed control to speedo (.3) 5
trans to speedo (.3) 7

Speedometer Drive Pinion, Renew
Includes: Replace oil seal.
All models (.2) 4

Radio, R&R
All models (.3) 7

LABOR 32 LIGHT SWITCHES & WIRING 32 LABOR

(Factory Time) — Chilton Time

Headlamp Switch, Renew
All models (.3) 4

Headlamp Dimmer Switch, Renew (Column Mounted)
All models (.3) 6

Stop Light Switch, Renew
All models (.3) 4
w/Cruise control add (.1) 1

Back-Up Lamp Switch, Renew (w/ Manual Trans)
All models (.2) 4

Neutral Safety Switch, Renew
All models (.3) 4

Turn Signal Switch, Renew
All models (.5) 1.0

Turn Signal or Hazard Warning Flasher, Renew
All models (.2) 3

Horn Relay, Renew
All models (.2) 3

Horns, Renew
All models-one (.2) 4

LABOR 34 CRUISE CONTROL 34 LABOR

(Factory Time) — Chilton Time

Speed Control Switch (Turn Signal Lever), Renew
All models (.3) 6

Speed Control Servo Assy., Renew
All models (.3) 5

Speed Control Cable, Renew
All models (.4) 7

Speed Control Vacuum Hose, Renew
All models (.2) 3

Cruise Control Clutch Safety Cut-Out Switch, Renew
All models (.3) 4

Dodge Ram Van • Caravan • Plymouth Voyager

GROUP INDEX

ALPHABETICAL INDEX

LABOR SERVICE BAY OPERATIONS LABOR

(Factory Time) Chilton Time

COOLING

Winterize Cooling System

Includes: Run engine to check for leaks, tighten all hose connections. Test radiator and pressure cap, drain radiator and engine block. Add anti-freeze and refill system.

All models 5

Thermostat, Renew

1984-87 (.4) 5

Drive Belts, Adjust

All models-one 2
each adtnl 1

Drive Belts, Renew

1984-87
Water Pump
2.6L eng (.3) 3
Fan & alter (.2) 3
Air pump (.3) 4
Pow str (.4) 6
w/A.C. add (.1) 1

Radiator Hoses, Renew

1984-87-upper (.3) 4
lower (.4) 6

FUEL

Carburetor Air Cleaner, Service

All models 3

Carburetor, Adjust (On Car)

Includes: Adjust idle mixture and idle speed. Check and reset ignition timing.

All models
Holly 2 bbl 6
All others 5

Automatic Choke, Renew

1984-87 (.7) 1.0

Carburetor Choke Vacuum Kick, Adjust

1984-87
Holly (.2) 4

BRAKES

Brake Pedal Free Play, Adjust

All models 3

Brakes, Adjust (Minor)

Includes: Adjust brake shoes, fill master cylinder.

two wheels 4

Bleed Brakes (Four Wheels)

Includes: Add fluid.

All models (.4) 6

Parking Brake, Adjust

All models 4

LUBRICATION SERVICE

Lubricate Chassis, Change Oil & Filter

Includes: Inspect and correct all fluid levels.

All models 6
Install grease fittings add 1

Engine Oil & Filter, Change

Includes: Inspect and correct all fluid levels.

All models 4

Lubricate Chassis

Includes: Inspect and correct all fluid levels.

All models 4
Install grease fittings add 1

WHEELS

Wheels, Balance

one 3
each adtnl 2

Wheel, Renew

one 5

Wheels, Rotate (All)

All models 5

ELECTRICAL

Aim Headlamps

two 4
four 6

Headlamp Sealed Beam Bulb, Renew

Does not include aim headlamps.

All models-each (.2) 3

License Lamp Lens, Renew

All models (.2) 2

License Lamp Assembly, Renew

All models (.2) 3

Turn Signal and Parking Lamp Assy., Renew

All models (.2) 4

Tail Lamp Assembly, Renew

All models (.5) 8

Side Marker Lamp Assy., Renew

All models-each (.2) 3

Turn Signal or Hazard Warning Flasher, Renew

All models (.2) 3

Horn Relay, Renew

All models (.2) 3

Horn, Renew

All models-one (.2) 4

Battery Cables, Renew

All models
positive (.5) 6
negative (.2) 2

LABOR 1 TUNE UP 1 LABOR

(Factory Time) Chilton Time

Compression Test

Four–1984-87 6

Engine Tune Up, (Electronic Ignition)

Includes: Test battery and clean connections. Tighten manifold and carburetor mounting bolts. Check engine compression, clean and adjust or renew spark plugs. Test resistance of spark plug cables. Inspect distributor cap and rotor, reluctor and pick up plate. Check vacuum advance operation. Reset ignition timing. Adjust idle mixture and idle speed. Service air cleaner. Inspect crankcase ventilation system. Inspect and adjust drive belts. Inspect choke operation and adjust or free up. Check operation of EGR valve.

Four–1984-87 .... 1.5

LABOR 2 IGNITION SYSTEM 2 LABOR

(Factory Time) Chilton Time

Spark plugs, Clean and Reset or Renew

1984-87 (.5) 6

Ignition Timing, Reset

1984-87 (.3) 4

Spark Control Computer, Renew (SCC)

1984-87 (.3) 1.0

Electronic Control Unit, Renew

1984-87
2.6L eng (.3) 5

Distributor Assembly, Renew

Includes: Reset ignition timing.

1984-87 (.4) 6

Distributor, R&R and Recondition

Includes: Reset ignition timing.

1984-87 (.9) 1.5

Distributor Pick-Up Plate and Coil Assy., Renew (Hall Effect)

Does not require R&R of distributor.

1984-87
2.2L & 2.5L engs (.3) 6

Distributor Pick-Up Set, Renew

Does not require R&R of distributor.

1984-87
2.6L eng (.5) 7

Distributor Ignitor Set, Renew

Does not require R&R of distributor.

1984-87
2.6L eng (.4) 6

Distributor Breaker Assy., Renew

Does not require R&R of distributor.

1984-87
2.6L eng (.4) 6

Distributor Reluctor and Governor Assy., Renew

Does not require R&R of distributor.

1984-87
2.6L eng (.3) 5

LABOR 2 IGNITION SYSTEM 2 LABOR

(Factory Time) Chilton Time

Distributor Vacuum Advance Control Unit, Renew
Does not require R&R of distributor.
1984-87
2.6L eng (.6)... .9

Distributor Cap and/or Rotor, Renew
1984-87 (.2)... .4

Ignition Coil, Renew
1984-87 (.2)... .4

Ignition Cables, Renew
1984-87 (.2)... .4

Ignition Switch, Renew
1984-87
std column (.4)... .8
tilt column (.4)... .9

Ignition Key Warning Buzzer, Renew
1984-87 (.2)... .3

Ignition Switch Time Delay Relay, Renew
1984-87 (.2)... .3

Ignition Key Buzzer/Chime Switch, Renew
1984-87
std column (.6)... 1.2
tilt column (.5)... 1.0

Ignition Lock Housing, Renew
1984-87-std colm (.8)... 1.3
Tilt Column
console shift (1.1)... 1.7
column shift (.8)... 1.3

LABOR 3 FUEL SYSTEM 3 LABOR

(Factory Time) Chilton Time

Fuel Pump, Test
All models... .3

Carburetor Air Cleaner, Service
All models... .3

Carburetor Idle Speed and Mixture, Adjust
Includes: Check and reset ignition timing.
All models
Holly-2 bbl... .6
All others... .5

Idle Solenoid, Renew
1984-87 (.4)... .6

Coolant Temperature Sensor/Switch, Renew
1984-87 (.2)... .4

Throttle Position Sensor (Potentometer), Renew
1984-87
2.6L eng (.2)... .3

Choke Vacuum Kick, Adjust
1984-87 (.2)... .3

Choke Vacuum Kick Diaphragm, Renew
1984-87 (.2)... .4

Accelerator Pump, Renew
1984-87
Holly (.4)... .8
All others (.8)... 1.1

Heated Air Door Sensor, Renew
1984-87 (.2)... .3

Carburetor Assembly, Renew
Includes: All necessary adjustments.
1984-87
Holly (.8)... 1.3
All others (.7)... 1.2

Carburetor, R&R and Clean or Recondition
Includes: All necessary adjustments.
1984-87
Holly (1.6)... 2.4
All others (2.5)... 3.5

Carburetor Needle and Seat, Renew
Includes: Adjust float level, idle speed and mixture.
1984-87
Holly (.7)... 1.1
All others (1.1)... 1.5

Fuel Filter, Renew
1984-87
in line (.2)... .3
in tank (.5)... .8

Fuel Pump, Renew
1984-87 (.4)... .7
Add pump test if performed.

Fuel Tank, Renew
1984-87 (.9)... 1.4

Fuel Gauge (Tank Unit), Renew
1984-87 (.6)... 1.0

Fuel Gauge (Dash Unit), Renew
1984-87 (.5)... .9

Intake Manifold or Gasket, Renew
1984-87
2.2L & 2.5L engs (2.0)... 3.7
2.6L eng (1.9)... 3.0
Renew manif add (.2)... .5

Intake and Exhaust Manifold Gaskets, Renew
1984-87
2.2L & 2.5L engs (1.9)... 3.5

LABOR 3A EMISSION CONTROLS 3A LABOR

(Factory Time) Chilton Time

CRANKCASE EMISSION

Crankcase Vent Valve, Renew
1984-87 (.2)... .3

AIR INJECTION SYSTEM

Air Pump, Renew
1984-87
2.2L & 2.5L engs (.4)... .7

Injection Tube and Check Valve Assy., Renew
1984-87-2.2L & 2.5L engs
ex manif mount (.5)... .8
to conv
one or both (.4)... .6

Aspirator Valve, Renew
1984-87 (.2)... .4

Air Pump Diverter/Switching Valve, Renew
1984-87
2.2L & 2.5L engs (.3)... .5

Enrichment Solenoid Valve, Renew
1984-87
2.6L eng (.3)... .4

Jet Air Control Valve, Renew
1984-87 (.5)... .7

Jet Mixture Solenoid Valve, Renew
1984-87
2.6L eng (.4)... .6

Deceleration Solenoid Valve, Renew
1984-87
2.6L eng (.3)... .6

Distributor/Air Switching Valve Solenoid Assy., Renew
1984-87 (.2)... .3

Intake Air Temperature Sensor, Renew
1984-87 (.2)... .3

EVAPORATIVE EMISSION

Vapor Canister, Renew
1984-87 (.3)... .4

Vapor Canister Filter, Renew
1984-87 (.2)... .3

Vapor Canister Valve, Renew
1985-87 (.2)... .3

E.G.R. SYSTEM

Coolant Vacuum Switch, Renew (CCEVS)
1984-87 (.3)... .4

Exhaust Gas Recirculation Control Valve, Renew
1984-87
2.2L & 2.5L engs (.6)... .7
2.6L eng (.3)... .5

E.G.R. and Purge Control Solenoid Bank, Renew
1984-87 (.2)... .3

Coolant Control Vacuum Valve, Renew (CCEGR)
1984-87-one (.3)... .5
both (.4)... .6

LABOR 3A EMISSION CONTROLS 3A LABOR

(Factory Time) — Chilton Time

EFE SYSTEM

Oxygen Sensor, Renew
1984-87
2.2L & 2.5L engs (.2) 4
2.6L eng (.5) 7

High Altitude Compensator, Renew
1984-87 (.3) 5

HEATED INLET AIR SYSTEM

Carburetor Air Cleaner, Service
1984-87 3

Air Cleaner Vacuum Sensor, Renew
1984-87-one (.2) 3

Heated Air Door Sensor, Renew
1984-87
2.6L eng (.2) 3

PULSE AIR SYSTEM

Pulse Air Feeder, Renew
1984-87 (.6) 9

Pulse Air Feeder Tube, Renew
1984-87 (.7) 1.1

LABOR 4 ALTERNATOR AND REGULATOR 4 LABOR

(Factory Time) — Chilton Time

Alternator Circuits, Test
Includes: Test battery, regulator and alternator output.
All models 6

Alternator Drive Belt, Renew
1984-87 (.2) 3
w/A.C. add (.1) 1

Alternator Assembly, Renew
Includes: Transfer pulley if required.
1984-87 (.8) 1.2
w/A.C. add (.3) 3
Add circuit test if performed.

Alternator, R&R and Recondition
Includes: Test and disassemble.
1984-87 (1.5) 2.1
w/A.C. add (.3) 3

Alternator Front Bearing or Retainer, Renew
1984-87 (.8) 1.1
w/A.C. add (.3) 3
Renew rear brg add 2

Voltage Regulator, Test and Renew
1984-87
external type (.2) 4
internal type (1.0) *1.6
*w/A.C. add (.3) 3

Alternator Gauge, Renew
1984-87 (.3) 6

Gauge Alert Module, Renew
1984-87 (.7) 1.1

LABOR 5 STARTING SYSTEM 5 LABOR

(Factory Time) — Chilton Time

Starter Draw Test (On Truck)
All models 3

Starter Assy., Renew
Includes: Test starter relay, starter solenoid and amperage draw.
1984-87
2.2L & 2.5L engs (1.0) 1.3
2.6L eng (.6) 1.0

Starter, R&R and Recondition
Includes: Turn down armature.
1984-87
2.2L & 2.5L engs 2.8
2.6L eng 2.5
Renew field coils add (.5) 5

Starter Drive, Renew
Includes: R&R starter.
1984-87
2.2L & 2.5L engs (1.4) 1.8
2.6L eng (.8) 1.1

Starter Solenoid or Switch, Renew
Includes: R&R starter.
1984-87
2.2L & 2.5L engs (1.0) 1.4
2.6L eng (1.0) 1.4

Starter Relay, Renew
1984-87 (.2) 3

Neutral Start and Back-Up Lamp Switch, Renew
1984-87 (.3) 4

Ignition Switch, Renew
1984-87
std column (.4) 8
tilt column (.4) 9

Battery Cables, Renew
1984-87
positive (.5) 6
negative (.2) 2

LABOR 6 BRAKE SYSTEM 6 LABOR

(Factory Time) — Chilton Time

Brake Pedal Free Play, Adjust
All models 3

Brakes, Adjust (Minor)
Includes: Adjust brake shoes, fill master cylinder.
two wheels 4

Bleed Brakes (Four Wheels)
Includes: Add fluid.
All models (.4) 6

Brake Shoes and/or Pads, Renew
Includes: Install new or exchange brake shoes or pads. Adjust service and hand brake. Bleed system.
1984-87-front-disc (.5) 8
rear-drum (.8) 1.5
all four wheels (1.3) 2.2
Resurface disc rotor, add-each 9
Resurface brake drum, add-each 5

Rear Brake Drum, Renew (One)
1984-87 (.5) 6

BRAKE HYDRAULIC SYSTEM

Wheel Cylinder, Renew
Includes: Bleed system.
1984-87-one (.7) 1.1
both (1.3) 2.1

Wheel Cylinder, R&R and Rebuild
Includes: Hone cylinder and bleed system.
1984-87-one 1.2
both 2.3

Brake Hose, Renew (Flex)
Includes: Bleed system.
1984-87-front-one (.4) 8
rear-one (.4) 8

Master Cylinder, Renew
Includes: Bleed complete system.
1984-87 (.5) 9

Master Cylinder, R&R and Rebuild
Includes: Bleed complete system.
1984-87 .... 1.6

Master Cylinder Reservoir, Renew
Includes: Bleed complete system.
1984-87 (.6) 1.0

Brake System, Flush and Refill
All models 1.2

POWER BRAKES

Brake Booster Assembly, Renew
1984-87 (.8) 1.2

LABOR 6 BRAKE SYSTEM 6 LABOR

(Factory Time) Chilton Time

Brake Booster Check Valve, Renew
1984-87 (.2) 2

DISC BRAKES

Disc Brake Pads, Renew
Includes: Install new disc brake pads only.
1984-87 (.5) 8

Disc Brake Rotor, Renew
1984-87-one (.3) 6

Disc Brake Rotor and Hub, Renew
1984-87-one (1.0) 1.4

Caliper Assembly, Renew
Includes: Bleed system.
1984-87-one (.5) 9
both 1.7

Caliper Assy., R&R and Recondition
Includes: Bleed system.
1984-87-one (.8) 1.4
both 2.7

Brake System Combination Valve, Renew
Includes: Bleed complete system.
1984-87 (1.2) 1.5

Load Sensing Proportioning Valve, Renew
Includes: Adjust valve and bleed brakes.
1984-87 (.7) 1.1

COMBINATIONS
Add to Brakes, Renew

See Machine Shop Operations

(Factory Time) Chilton Time

RENEW WHEEL CYLINDER
Each 3

REBUILD WHEEL CYLINDER
Each 4

REBUILD CALIPER ASSEMBLY
Each 5

RENEW MASTER CYLINDER
All models 6

REBUILD MASTER CYLINDER
All models 8

RENEW BRAKE HOSE
Each 3

RENEW REAR WHEEL GREASE SEALS
One side 3

RENEW DISC BRAKE ROTOR
Each 2

RENEW BRAKE DRUM
Each 3

DISC BRAKE ROTOR STUDS, RENEW
Each 1

(Factory Time) Chilton Time

PARKING BRAKE

Parking Brake, Adjust
1984-87 (.3) 4

Parking Brake Warning Lamp Switch, Renew
1984-87 (.8) 1.1

Parking Brake Control, Renew
1984-87 (.9) 1.4

Parking Brake Cables, Renew
Includes: Adjust parking brake.
1984-87-front (.5) 7
intermediate (.3) 5
rear-each (.6) 8

LABOR 7 COOLING SYSTEM 7 LABOR

(Factory Time) Chilton Time

Winterize Cooling System
Includes: Run engine to check for leaks, tighten all hose connections. Test radiator and pressure cap. Drain radiator and engine block. Add anti-freeze and refill system.
All models 5

Thermostat, Renew
1984-87 (.4) 6

Radiator Assembly, R&R or Renew
1984-87 (.5) 9
w/A.T. add (.1) 1

ADD THESE OPERATIONS TO RADIATOR R&R

Boil & Repair 1.5
Rod Clean 1.9
Repair Core 1.3
Renew Tank 1.6
Renew Trans. Oil Cooler 1.9
Recore Radiator 1.7

Fan Blades, Renew
1984-87 (.2) 5

Drive Belts, Renew
1984-87
Water Pump
2.6L eng (.3) 4
Fan & alter (.2) 3
Pow str (.4) 6
Air pump (.3) 4
w/A.C. add (.1) 1

Drive Belts, Adjust
All models-one 2
each adtnl 1

Radiator Hoses, Renew
1984-87-upper (.3) 4
lower (.4) 6

Water Pump, Renew
1984-87
2.2L & 2.5L engs (1.1) 1.6
2.6L eng (.7) 1.2
w/A.C. add 5

Coolant Temperature Sensor, Renew
1984-87 (.2) 3

Radiator Fan Coolant Sensor, Renew
1984-87 (.2) 3

Radiator Fan Motor, Renew
1984-87-wo/A.C. (.4) 5
w/A.C. (.4) 5

Radiator Fan Switch, Renew
1984-87 (.3) 6

Radiator Fan Motor Relay, Renew
1984-87 (.2) 3

Transaxle Auxiliary Oil Cooler, Renew
1984-87 (.5) 9

Water Jacket Expansion Plugs, Renew (Cylinder Block)
1984-87
2.6L eng
right side
front (.7) 1.0
center or rear (1.1) 1.5
left side
upper front or center (2.1) 3.0
lower front or center (.3) 5
rear (1.0) 1.4
2.2L & 2.5L engs
left side
front (.7) 1.0
rear (.4) 6
right side
front or center (.6) 9
rear (1.0) 1.4
w/P.S. add (.3) 3
w/Pulse air add (.6) 6

Water Jacket Expansion Plugs, Renew (Cylinder Head)
1984-87
2.2L & 2.5L engs
front (.6) 9
rear (.8) 1.1
2.6L eng
rear (.5) 7

Temperature Gauge (Dash Unit), Renew
1984-87 (.3) 6

Temperature Gauge (Engine Unit), Renew
1984-87
sending unit (.3) 4
light switch (.3) 4

Heater Hoses, Renew
1984-87-one (.4) 4
each adtnl (.1) 2

Heater Water Valve, Renew
1984-87-w/A.C. (.3) 5

Heater Control Assembly, Renew
1984-87-wo/A.C. (.4) 7
w/A.C. (.3) 6

LABOR 7 COOLING SYSTEM 7 LABOR

(Factory Time) Chilton Time

Vacuum Switch (Push Button), Renew
1984-87-w/A.C. (.4) .7

Blower Motor Switch, Renew
1984-87-wo/A.C. (.4) .8
w/A.C. (.4) .8

Heater Core, R&R or Renew
1984-87-wo/A.C. (1.8) 3.5
w/A.C. (2.4) *5.5
*Includes: Recharge A.C. system.

ADD THESE OPERATIONS TO HEATER CORE R&R
Boil & Repair 1.2
Repair Core .9
Recore 1.2

Heater Blower Motor, Renew
1984-87-wo/A.C. (.4) .6
w/A.C. (.6) 1.2

Blower Motor Resistor, Renew
1984-87-wo/A.C. (.2) .3
w/A.C. (.2) .4

LABOR 8 EXHAUST SYSTEM 8 LABOR

(Factory Time) Chilton Time

Muffler, Renew
1984-87 (.4) .7
Cut exhaust pipe add (.2) .2

Exhaust Pipe, Renew
1984-87 (.7) 1.1
Cut at muffler add (.2) .2

Exhaust Pipe Extension, Renew
1984-87 (.6) 1.0

Tail Pipe, Renew
1984-87 (.4) .6
Cut at muffler add (.2) .2

Catalytic Converter, Renew
1984-87
exh pipe mount (.7) .9
manif mount (.9) 1.3

Exhaust Manifold or Gasket, Renew
1984-87
2.2L & 2.5L engs (2.7) 3.7
2.6L eng (.7) 1.2

COMBINATIONS

Exhaust System, Renew (Complete)
1984-87 1.5

LABOR 9 FRONT SUSPENSION 9 LABOR

(Factory Time) Chilton Time

Note: On all front suspension operations alignment charges must be added if performed. Time given does not include alignment.

Wheel, Renew
one .5

Wheels, Rotate (All)
All models .5

Wheels, Balance
one .3
each adtnl .2

Check Alignment of Front End
All models .5
Note: Deduct if alignment is performed.

Toe-Out, Adjust
All models .6

Align Front End
Includes: Adjust camber, toe, car height and center steering wheel.
All models (.8) 1.4

Steering Knuckle Bearing, Renew (Wheel Bearing)
Add alignment charges.
1984-87-one (1.2) 1.6
both (2.3) 3.0

Steering Knuckle, Renew (One)
Add alignment charges.
1984-87 (1.0) 1.6

Front Strut Assy., R&R or Renew
Add alignment charges.
1984-87-one (.8) 1.4
both (1.5) 2.7

Lower Control Arm Assy., Renew
Includes: Reset toe-in.
1984-87-one (1.1) 1.6

Lower Ball Joint, Renew (One)
Add alignment charges.
1984-87 (.8) 1.2

Lower Control Arm Strut Bushings, Renew
Add alignment charges.
1984-87-one side (.6) .9

Front Coil Spring, Renew
Includes: R&R front strut.
Add alignment charges.
1984-87-one (.8) 1.5
both (1.5) 2.8

Front Sway Bar, Renew
1984-87 (.4) .7

Sway Bar Bracket and Bushings, Renew
1984-87-both (.5) .9

Front Suspension Strut (Dual Path) Mount Assy., Renew
Includes: Renew bearing.
1984-87 (.8) 1.5

K-Frame Assembly, Renew
Add alignment charges.
All models (2.5) 4.0

Drive Shaft Boot, Renew
Includes: Clean and lubricate C/V joint.
All models
1984-87
one-inner or outer (.7) 1.0
both-one side (1.0) 1.4
Renew shaft seal, add
right side (.1) .1
left side (.3) .3

Drive Shaft C/V Joint, Renew
All models
1984-87
one-inner or outer (.7) 1.0
both-one side (1.0) 1.4
inter shaft U-joint (.6) 1.0
Renew shaft seal, add
right side (.1) .1
left side (.3) .3

Front Wheel Drive Shaft Assy., Renew
All models
1984-87
inter spline yoke (.6) 1.0
inter stub shaft (.6) 1.0
all others-each (1.0) 1.4
Renew shaft seal, add
right side (.1) .1
left side (.3) .3

Intermediate Shaft Support Bearing, Renew
1984-87-each (.6) 1.0

LABOR 11 STEERING GEAR 11 LABOR

(Factory Time) Chilton Time

Tie Rods or Tie Rod Ends, Renew
Includes: Reset toe-out.
1984-87
outer-one (.9) 1.2
inner & outer-w/P.S.
one side (1.9) 2.5

STANDARD STEERING

Horn Contact Cable and Ring, Renew
1984-87 (.2) .4

Horn Switch, Renew
1984-87 (.2) .3

Steering Wheel, Renew
1984-87 (.2) .3

Steering Column Jacket, Renew
Does not include painting.

LABOR 11 STEERING GEAR 11 LABOR

(Factory Time)	Chilton Time
1984-87	
Std Column	
console shift (1.1)	1.8
column shift (1.5)	2.3
Tilt Column	
console shift (1.5)	2.6
column shift (1.6)	2.8

Upper Mast Jacket Bearing, Renew
Includes: Replace insulators if necessary.

1984-87	
std column (.4)	.9
tilt column (1.2)	2.0

Steering Column Gear Shift Tube, Renew

1984-87	
std column (1.3)	2.1
tilt column (1.8)	2.6

Steering Column Lower Shaft Bearing, Renew
Includes: Replace support if necessary.

1984-87	
Std Column	
console shift (.8)	1.6
column shift (.9)	1.7
Tilt Column	
console shift (.6)	1.0
column shift (.6)	1.0

Steering Gear Assy., R&R or Renew

1984-87 (1.6)	3.0

POWER STEERING

Power Steering Pump Pressure Check

All models	.5

Power Steering Pump Belt, Renew

1984-87 (.4)	.6
w/A.C. add (.1)	.1
w/Air inj add (.1)	.1

Power Steering Gear Assy., R&R or Renew
Includes: Reset toe-in.

1984-87 (1.1)	2.4
Renew gear add (.6)	1.0

Steering Gear Oil Seals, Renew (All)
Includes: R&R gear assy. and reset toe-in.

1984-87 (2.9)	5.1

Upper and Lower Valve Pinion Seals, Renew

1984-87 (1.4)	2.0
Renew brgs add (.3)	.5

Power Steering Pump, Renew
Includes: Test pump and transfer pulley.

1984-87	
2.2L & 2.5L engs (1.0)	1.4
2.6L eng (.8)	1.2

Power Steering Pump, R&R and Recondition

1984-87	
2.2L & 2.5L engs (1.5)	2.3
2.6L eng (1.3)	2.0

Pump Flow Control Valve, Test and Clean or Renew

1984-87	
2.2L & 2.5L engs (.6)	1.0
2.6L eng (.7)	1.1

Power Steering Reservoir or Seals, Renew

1984-87 (.7)	1.1

Pump Drive Shaft Oil Seal, Renew

1984-87	
2.2L & 2.5L engs (.9)	1.4
2.6L eng (.7)	1.1

Power Steering Hoses, Renew

1984-87-each (.4)	.5

LABOR 12 CYLINDER HEAD & VALVE SYSTEM 12 LABOR

Compression Test

(Factory Time)	Chilton Time
1984-87	.6

Cylinder Head Gasket, Renew
Includes: Clean carbon.

1984-87	
2.2L & 2.5L engs (3.4)	4.8
2.6L eng (2.8)	4.5
w/P.S. add (.2)	.2
w/Air inj add (.2)	.2

Cylinder Head, Renew
Includes: Transfer parts as required. Clean carbon, make all necessary adjustments.

1984-87	
2.2L & 2.5L engs (5.3)	8.0
2.6L eng (4.7)	7.4
w/P.S. add (.2)	.2
w/Air inj add (.2)	.2

Clean Carbon and Grind Valves
Includes: R&R cylinder head. Reface valves and seats. Minor tune up.

1984-87	
2.2L & 2.5L engs (4.8)	6.8
2.6L eng (5.4)	8.0
w/P.S. add (.2)	.2
w/Air inj add (.2)	.2

Cylinder Head Cover Gasket, Renew or Reseal

1984-87	
2.2L & 2.5L engs (.8)	1.1
2.6L eng (.4)	.6

Valve Rocker Arms or Shafts, Renew

1984-87	
2.2L & 2.5L engs	
all arms (1.2)	1.6
2.6L eng-one shaft (1.0)	1.4
both shafts (1.1)	1.7

COMBINATIONS
Add To Valve Job

See Machine Shop Operations

(Factory Time)	Chilton Time
DRAIN, EVACUATE & RECHARGE AIR CONDITIONING SYSTEM	
All models	1.0
CARBURETOR, RECONDITION	
Holly (.5)	.9
DISTRIBUTOR, RECONDITION	
All models (.7)	.7
RECONDITION CYL. HEAD (HEAD REMOVED)	
2.2L eng (1.4)	2.0
2.5L eng (1.4)	2.0
CAMSHAFT, RENEW (HEAD DISASSEMBLED)	
OHC engs (.1)	.2
REMOVE CYLINDER TOP RIDGE	
Each (.1)	.1
RENEW OIL PUMP	
All engs (.2)	.3
ROD BEARINGS, RENEW (PAN REMOVED)	
All engs (.7)	1.2
DEGLAZE CYLINDER WALLS	
Each (.1)	.1
PLASTIGAUGE BEARINGS	
Each (.1)	.1
OIL FILTER ELEMENT, RENEW	
All models (.3)	.3

Valve Tappets, Renew

(Factory Time)	Chilton Time
1984-87	
2.2L & 2.5L engs	
one (1.0)	1.4
each adtnl (.1)	.1

Valve Tappets, Adjust

1984-87	
2.6L eng (.9)	1.5

Jet Valves, Renew

1984-87	
2.6L eng-one or all (.9)	1.1

Valve Springs and/or Valve Stem Oil Seals, Renew

1984-87	
2.2L & 2.5L engs	
one (1.2)	1.5
all (1.9)	2.9
2.6L eng (4.7)	*6.0
*w/Head on car	3.5

LABOR 13 ENGINE ASSEMBLY & MOUNTS 13 LABOR

(Factory Time) Chilton Time

Engine Assembly, Remove & Install

Includes: R&R engine and transmission as a unit. Does not include transfer of any parts or equipment.

1984-87	
2.2L & 2.5L engs	6.0
2.6L eng	5.2
w/A.C. add	.5
w/P.S. add	.2

Short Engine Assembly, Renew (w/All Internal Parts Less Cyl. Head and Oil Pan)

Includes: R&R engine and transmission as a unit. Transfer all necessary parts not supplied with replacement engine. Clean carbon, grind valves. Minor tune up.

1984-87	
2.2L & 2.5L engs (9.1)	15.0
2.6L eng (9.4)	15.5
w/A.C. add (.5)	.5
w/P.S. add (.2)	.2

(P) Engine Assy., R&R and Recondition (Complete)

Includes: Rebore block, install new pistons, rings, rod and main bearings. Clean carbon, grind valves. Replace valve stem oil seals. Tune engine.

1984-87	
2.2L & 2.5L engs (17.8)	25.2
2.6L eng (17.0)	23.4
w/A.C. add (.5)	.5
w/P.S. add (.2)	.2

Engine Assembly, Recondition (In Car)

Includes: Expand or renew pistons, install rings, pins, rod and main bearings. Clean carbon, grind valves. Tune engine.

1984-87	
2.2L & 2.5L engs (15.2)	20.8
2.6L eng (14.4)	19.0
w/P.S. add (.2)	.2

Engine Support, Renew

1984-87-right side (.3)	.5
left side (.3)	.5
center (.4)	.6
Trans/Axle	
Roll rod (.2)	.5

LABOR 14 PISTONS, RINGS & BEARINGS 14 LABOR

(Factory Time) Chilton Time

Rings, Renew (See Engine Combinations)

Includes: Replace connecting rod bearings, deglaze cylinder walls, clean carbon. Minor tune up.

1984-87	
2.2L & 2.5L engs	
one cyl (4.6)	6.9
all cyls (5.9)	8.1
2.6L eng-one cyl (4.1)	6.3
all cyls (5.7)	8.0
w/P.S. add (.2)	.2
w/Air inj add (.2)	.2

Pistons or Connecting Rods, Renew

Includes: Replace connecting rod bearings and piston rings, deglaze cylinder walls. Clean carbon from cylinder head.

1984-87	
2.2L & 2.5L engs	
one cyl (4.9)	7.2
all cyls (6.1)	9.3
2.6L eng-one cyl (4.7)	6.6
all cyls (7.2)	9.2
w/P.S. add (.2)	.2
w/Air inj add (.2)	.2

Connecting Rod Bearings, Renew

1984-87	
2.2L & 2.5L engs (2.1)	3.0
2.6L eng (1.2)	2.2

COMBINATIONS

Add To Engine Work

See Machine Shop Operations

(Factory Time) Chilton Time

DRAIN, EVACUATE & RECHARGE AIR CONDITIONING SYSTEM

All models	1.0

CARBURETOR, RECONDITION

Holly (.5)	.9

DISTRIBUTOR, RECONDITION

All models (.7)	.7

R&R CYLINDER HEAD (ENGINE REMOVED)

All models	1.5

CONNECTING ROD, RENEW (ENGINE DISASSEMBLED)

Each	.4

REMOVE CYLINDER TOP RIDGE

Each (.1)	.1

RENEW OIL PUMP

All engs (.2)	.3

ROD BEARINGS, RENEW (PAN REMOVED)

All engs (.7)	1.2

DEGLAZE CYLINDER WALLS

Each (.1)	.1

PLASTIGAUGE BEARINGS

Each (.1)	.1

OIL FILTER ELEMENT, RENEW

All models (.3)	.3

LABOR 15 CRANKSHAFT & DAMPER 15 LABOR

(Factory Time) Chilton Time

Crankshaft and Main Bearings, Renew

Includes: R&R engine assembly.

1984-87	
2.2L & 2.5L engs (6.7)	11.2
2.6L eng (7.6)	12.1
w/A.C. add (.5)	.5
w/P.S. add (.2)	.2

Main Bearings, Renew

1984-87	
2.2L & 2.5L engs	
No 2-3 or 4 (1.8)	2.8
No 1 (3.0)	4.0
No 5 (5.6)	8.8
all (7.0)	11.0
2.6L eng (2.2)	3.0

Main and Rod Bearings, Renew

1984-87	
2.6L eng (2.9)	4.2

Rear Main Bearing Oil Seals, Renew (Complete)

1984-87	
2.2L & 2.5L engs (3.0)	5.4
2.6L eng-w/A.T. (3.2)	5.5

Crankshaft Pulley, Renew

1984-87	
2.2L & 2.5L engs (.5)	.7
2.6L eng (.4)	.6
w/A.C. add (.1)	.1
w/P.S. add (.1)	.1

Crankshaft Front Oil Seal, Renew

1984-87	
2.2L & 2.5L engs (1.3)	2.0
w/A.C. add (.2)	.2
w/P.S. add (.2)	.2

LABOR 16 CAMSHAFT & TIMING GEARS 16 LABOR

(Factory Time)	Chilton Time
Timing Chain or Belt Case/Cover, Renew	
Includes: Renew gasket.	
1984-87	
2.2L & 2.5L engs	
upper cover (.2)	.4
lower cover (.6)	1.0
2.6L eng (3.2)	4.5
w/A.C. add (.5)	.5
w/P.S. add (.1)	.1
Timing Belt, Renew	
1984-87	
2.2L & 2.5L engs (1.6)	2.2
w/A.C. add (.5)	.5
w/P.S. add (.2)	.2
Timing Chain, Renew	
Includes: Renew cover seal.	
1984-87	
2.6L eng	
cam drive (3.6)	5.0
shaft drive (3.4)	4.8
w/A.C. add (.2)	.2
w/P.S. add (.1)	.1
Timing Chain, Adjust	
1984-87	
2.6L eng (.4)	.8
Timing Chain Guide, Renew	
1984-87	
2.6L eng-cam drive	
right or left (3.2)	4.6
silent shaft-upper (3.2)	4.6
lower (3.2)	4.6
w/A.C. add (.2)	.2
w/P.S. add (.1)	.1
Timing Chain Tensioner, Renew	
1984-87	
2.6L eng (3.5)	4.9
w/A.C. add (.2)	.2
w/P.S. add (.1)	.1
Timing Belt Tensioner, Renew	
1984-87	
2.2L & 2.5L engs (.9)	1.5
w/A.C. add (.6)	.6
Timing Chain Cover Oil Seal, Renew	
1984-87	
2.6L eng (.5)	.9
w/P.S. add (.1)	.1
Camshaft Sprocket, Renew	
Includes: Renew cover oil seal, timing chain and crankshaft sprocket.	
1984-87	
2.2L & 2.5L engs (1.7)	2.4
2.6L eng (3.6)	5.0
w/A.C. add (.2)	.2
w/P.S. add (.2)	.2
Camshaft Oil Seal, Renew	
1984-87	
2.2L & 2.5L engs (.7)	1.1
2.2-2.6L eng-rear (.4)	.8
Camshaft, Renew	
1984-87	
2.2L & 2.5L engs (1.7)	*2.8
2.6L eng (1.6)	2.2
*Renew valve springs add (1.1)	1.1
Camshaft Distributor Drive Gear, Renew	
1984-87	
2.6L eng (.7)	1.1
Intermediate Shaft, Renew	
1984-87	
2.2L & 2.5L engs (1.3)	2.5
w/A.C. add (.2)	.2
Silent Shaft Sprocket, Renew	
1984-87	
2.6L eng-one or both (3.4)	4.7
w/A.C. add (.2)	.2
w/P.S. add (.1)	.1
Intermediate Shaft Sprocket, Renew	
1984-87	
2.2L & 2.5L engs (1.7)	2.7
w/A.C. add (.2)	.2
w/P.S. add (.2)	.2
Silent Shaft, Renew	
1984-87	
2.6L eng-right (4.0)	5.6
left (5.0)	7.0
both (5.3)	7.5
w/A.C. add (.4)	.4
w/P.S. add (.1)	.1

LABOR 17 ENGINE OILING SYSTEM 17 LABOR

(Factory Time)	Chilton Time
Oil Pan or Gasket, Renew or Reseal	
1984-87	
2.2L & 2.5L engs (1.0)	1.4
2.6L eng (.6)	1.0
Pressure Test Engine Bearings (Pan Off)	
All models	1.0
Oil Pump, Renew	
1984-87	
2.2L & 2.5L engs (1.3)	1.7
2.6L eng (3.8)	5.2
w/A.C. add (.2)	.2
w/P.S. add (.1)	.1
Oil Pump, R&R and Recondition	
1984-87	
2.2L eng (1.7)	2.2
Oil Pressure Relief Valve Spring, Renew	
1984-87	
2.2L & 2.5L engs (1.6)	2.2
2.6L eng (3.4)	4.7
Oil Pressure Gauge (Engine Unit), Renew	
1984-87 (.2)	.4
Oil Pressure Gauge (Dash), Renew	
1984-87 (.3)	.6
Oil Filter Element, Renew	
1984-87 (.2)	.3

LABOR 18 CLUTCH & FLYWHEEL 18 LABOR

(Factory Time)	Chilton Time
Clutch Self-Adjusting Mechanism, Renew	
1984-87 (.3)	.6
Clutch Release Cable, Renew	
1984-87 (.3)	.5
Clutch Release Lever and/or Seal, Renew	
1984-87 (.5)	.8
Clutch Release Bearing or Fork, Renew	
1984-87 (2.8)	3.8
Clutch Assembly, Renew	
1984-87 (2.9)	4.0
Renew input seal add (.2)	.2
Flywheel, Renew	
1984-87 (3.0)	4.2

LABOR 19 STANDARD TRANSMISSION 19 LABOR

(Factory Time)	Chilton Time
Drive Shaft Boot, Renew	
Includes: Clean and lubricate C/V joint.	
1984-87	
one-inner or outer (.7)	1.0
both-one side (1.0)	1.4
Renew shaft seal, add	
right side (.1)	.1
left side (.3)	.3
Drive Shaft C/V Joint, Renew	
1984-87	
one-inner or outer (.7)	1.0
both-one side (1.0)	1.4
Renew shaft seal, add	
right side (.1)	.1
left side (.3)	.3

LABOR 19 STANDARD TRANSMISSION 19 LABOR

(Factory Time) Chilton Time

Front Wheel Drive Shaft Assy., Renew
1984-87-each (1.0) 1.4
Renew shaft seal, add
right side (.1) 1
left side (.3) 3

Drive Shaft Oil Seal, Renew
1984-87-right (.5) 8
left (.7) 1.1

Manual Trans/Axle Assembly, Remove & Install
Does not include transfer of any parts.
1984-87 (2.7) 3.7
Renew assy add (.4) 6

Manual Trans/Axle Assy., R&R and Recondition (Complete)
1984-87 (5.5) 8.0
Renew ring gear and pinion add (.7) 1.5
Renew clutch assy add (.2) 2

Manual Trans/Axle Assy., Recondition (Off Car)
1984-87
A460 (2.5) 3.9
A465-A525 (2.8) 4.2

LABOR 21 SHIFT LINKAGE 21 LABOR

(Factory Time) Chilton Time

MANUAL

Gearshift Linkage, Adjust
1984-87 (.2) 4

Gearshift Lever, Renew
1984-87 (.4) 6

Gearshift Control Rod and/or Swivel, Renew
1984-87 (.3) 4

Gearshift Mechanism, Renew
1984-87
cable shift (.7) 1.1

Selector Shaft Seal, Renew
1984-87 (.8) 1.1

Trans/Axle Selector Shaft, Renew
1984-87 (1.3) 1.7

Gearshift Selector Cable, Renew
1984-87 (.9) 1.4

Gearshift Crossover Cable, Renew
1984-87 (.8) 1.3

AUTOMATIC

Throttle Linkage, Adjust
1984-87 (.2) 4

Selector Lever, Renew
1984-87 (.3) 4

Gearshift Mechanism, Renew
1984-87 (.4) 8

Gearshift Control Cable, Renew
1984-87 (.5) 8

Throttle Lever Control Cable, Renew
1984-87 (.3) 6

Gear Selector Dial, Renew
1984-87 (.7) 1.1

LABOR 23 AUTOMATIC TRANSMISSION 23 LABOR

(Factory Time) Chilton Time

ON CAR SERVICES

Drain & Refill Unit
All models 6

Oil Pressure Check
All models 8

Check Unit For Oil Leaks
Includes: Clean and dry outside of case and run unit to determine point of leak.
All models 9

Neutral Safety Switch, Renew
All models (.3) 4

Transmission Auxiliary Oil Cooler, Renew
1984-87 (.5) 9

Oil Cooler Lines, Renew
Includes: Cut and form to size.
1984-87 (.4) 6

Throttle Linkage, Adjust
1984-87 (.2) 4

Kickdown Band, Adjust
1984-87 (.2) 4

Throttle Valve Lever Shaft Seal, Renew
1984-87 (.5) 8

Valve Body Manual Lever Shaft Seal, Renew
1984-87 (.3) 6

Differential Gear Cover, Renew or Reseal
1984-87 (.8) 1.2

Drive Shaft Boot, Renew
Includes: Clean and lubricate C/V joint.
All models
1984-87
one-inner or outer (.7) 1.0
both-one side (1.0) 1.4
Renew shaft seal, add
right side (.1) 1
left side (.3) 3

Drive Shaft C/V Joint, Renew
All models
1984-87
one-inner or outer (.7) 1.0
both-one side (1.0) 1.4
inter shaft U-joint (.6) 1.0
Renew shaft seal, add
right side (.1) 1
left side (.3) 3

Front Wheel Drive Shaft Assy., Renew
All models
1984-87
inter spline yoke (.6) 1.0
inter stub shaft (.6) 1.0
all others-each (1.0) 1.4
Renew shaft seal, add
right side (.1) 1
left side (.3) 3

Intermediate Shaft Support Bearing, Renew
1984-87-each (.6) 1.0

Drive Shaft Seal, Renew
1984-87-right side (.5) 8
left side (.7) 1.1

Transfer Gear Cover, Renew or Reseal
1984-87 (.5) 7

Transfer Gear, Renew
Includes: R&R cover, renew bearing.
1984-87 (1.0) 1.3

Governor Assy., Renew or Recondition
Includes: R&R oil pan.
1984-87 (1.3) 2.4

Governor Support and Parking Gear, Renew
Includes: R&R oil pan.
1984-87 (1.9) 2.9

Oil Pan and/or Gasket, Renew
1984-87 (.6) 1.2

Oil Filter Element, Renew
Includes: R&R oil pan.
1984-87 (.7) 1.4

Parking Lock Sprag, Renew
Includes: R&R oil pan.
1984-87 (1.5) 2.6

Accumulator Piston, Renew or Recondition
Includes: R&R oil pan.
1984-87 (1.1) 2.2

Kickdown Servo, Renew
Includes: R&R oil pan.
1984-87 (1.4) 2.5

Reverse Servo, Renew
Includes: R&R oil pan.
1984-87 (1.2) 2.2

Valve Body, Renew
Includes: R&R oil pan.
1984-87 (1.0) 2.1

Valve Body, R&R and Recondition
Includes: R&R oil pan and renew filter.
1984-87 (1.7) 3.2

LABOR 23 AUTOMATIC TRANSMISSION 23 LABOR

(Factory Time) Chilton Time

SERVICES REQUIRING R&R

Trans/Axle Assy., Remove & Install
1984-87
2.2L & 2.5L engs (2.7) 3.7
2.6L eng (3.0) 4.1
Renew assy add (.4) 6

Trans/Axle Assembly, Reseal
Includes: R&R trans/axle and renew all seals and gaskets.
1984-87
2.2L & 2.5L engs (5.4) 7.0
2.6L eng (5.6) 7.4

Trans/Axle Assy., R&R and Recondition
Includes: Disassemble complete, clean, inspect and replace all parts as required.
1984-87
2.2L & 2.5L engs 12.5
2.6L eng 12.9
Flush conv and cooler lines add 5

Kickdown Band, Renew
1984-87
2.2L & 2.5L engs (4.0) 4.9
2.6L eng (4.3) 5.3

Reverse Band, Renew
1984-87
2.2L & 2.5L engs (4.2) 5.2
2.6L eng (4.5) 5.6

Trans/Axle Case, Renew
1984-87
2.2L & 2.5L engs (7.7) 10.0
2.6L eng (8.0) 10.4

Front and Rear Clutch Seals, Renew
1984-87
2.2L & 2.5L engs (4.2) 5.2
2.6L eng (4.5) 5.6

Torque Converter, Renew
1984-87
2.2L & 2.5L engs (3.3) 4.0
2.6L eng (3.6) 4.4

Torque Converter Drive Plate, Renew (w/Ring Gear)
1984-87
2.2L & 2.5L engs (3.3) 4.0
2.6L eng (3.6) 4.4

Front Oil Pump, Renew
1984-87
2.2L & 2.5L engs (3.7) 4.5
2.6L eng (4.0) 4.9

Front Pump Oil Seal, Renew
1984-87
2.2L & 2.5L engs (3.3) 4.0
2.6L eng (3.6) 4.4

Reaction Shaft and/or Bushing, Renew
Includes: Renew front pump if necessary.
1984-87
2.2L & 2.5L eng (3.7) 4.5
2.6L eng (4.0) 4.9

Trans/Axle Differential Assy., Recondition
Includes: R&R trans/axle, completely recondition differential assembly only.
1984-87
2.2L & 2.5L engs (6.6) 9.0
2.6L eng (6.9) 9.4

LABOR 26 REAR AXLE 26 LABOR

(Factory Time) Chilton Time

Rear Wheel Bearings, Renew or Repack
1984-87-one side (.6) 9
both sides (1.1) 1.7

Rear Wheel Grease Seal, Renew
1984-87-one side (.4) 7

Rear Shock Absorbers, Renew
1984-87-one (.3) 5
both (.4) 7

Rear Springs, Renew
1984-87-one (.9) 1.2
both (1.6) 2.2

Lower Control Arm Bushings, Renew
1984-87-one side (.6) 1.0

Stub Axle Spindle, Renew
1984-87-each (.5) 7

Rear Sway Bar, Renew
1984-87 (.4) 7

Rear Wheel Mounting Studs, Renew
1984-87-one (.5) 8
each adtnl 1

Rear Spring Shackle, Renew
1984-87-one (.4) 6

Rear Spring Bushing, Renew
1984-87-each (.4) 6

Rear Spring Front Hanger, Renew
1984-87-one (.7) 1.1

LABOR 28 AIR CONDITIONING 28 LABOR

(Factory Time) Chilton Time

Note: If more than one item requires replacement where evacuation and discharging the system is already included in the operation, deduct 1.0 hour for each additional item to the times listed.

Drain, Evacuate, Leak Test and Charge System
All models 1.0

Partial Charge
Includes: Leak test.
All models (.4) 6

Performance Test
All models 8

Vacuum Leak Test
All models 8

Compressor Drive Belt, Renew
1984-87 (.2) 3

C-171 COMPRESSOR

Compressor Assembly, Renew
Includes: Transfer parts as required. Pressure test and charge system.
1984-87
2.2L & 2.5L engs (1.4) 2.5
2.6L eng (1.9) 3.0

Compressor Clutch Field Coil, Renew
1984-87
2.2L & 2.5L engs (.6) 9
2.6L eng (.9) 1.4

Compressor Clutch Pulley (w/Hub), Renew
1984-87
2.2L & 2.5L engs (.4) 5
2.6L eng (.7) 1.0

Compressor Clutch Assembly, Renew
1984-87
2.2L & 2.5L engs (.6) 8
2.6L eng (.9) 1.3

Compressor Front Cover Seal, Renew
Includes: R&R compressor. Pressure test and charge system.
1984-87
2.2L & 2.5L engs (1.8) 3.1
2.6L eng (2.3) 3.6

Compressor Rear Cover Seal, Renew
Includes: R&R compressor. Pressure test and charge system.
1984-87
2.2L & 2.5L engs (1.7) 3.0
2.6L eng (2.2) 3.5

Compressor Center Seal, Renew
Includes: R&R compressor. Pressure test and charge system.
1984-87
2.2L & 2.5L engs (1.9) 3.2
2.6L eng (2.4) 3.7

Compressor Shaft Gas Seal, Renew
Includes: R&R compressor. Pressure test and charge system.
1984-87
2.2L & 2.5L engs (1.8) 3.1
2.6L eng (2.3) 3.6

Expansion Valve, Renew
Includes: Pressure test and charge system.
1984-87 (1.0) 1.7

LABOR 28 AIR CONDITIONING 28 LABOR

(Factory Time) Chilton Time

Receiver Drier, Renew
Includes: Add partial charge, leak test and charge system.
1984-87 (.9) ... 1.6

Low Pressure Cut Off Switch, Renew
Includes: Charge system.
1984-87 (.9) ... 1.4

High Pressure Cut Off Switch, Renew
1984-87 (.3) 5

Clutch Cycling (Thermostatic Control) Switch, Renew
1984-87 (.3) 6
pressure activated (.2) 4

Condenser Assembly, Renew
Includes: Add partial charge, leak test and charge system.
1984-87 (1.1) ... 2.0
Renew receiver drier add 2

Evaporator Coil, Renew
Includes: Add partial charge, leak test and charge system.
1984-87 (2.6) ... 4.5

Temperature Control Assembly, Renew
1984-87 (.3) 6

Push Button Vacuum Switch, Renew
1984-87 (.4) 8

Blower Motor Switch, Renew
1984-87 (.4) 8

Temperature Control Cable, Renew
1984-87 (1.2) ... 1.8

Blower Motor, Renew
1984-87 (.6) 9

Blower Motor Resistor, Renew
1984-87 (.2) 4

Vacuum Actuators, Renew
1984-87
outside air door (.2) 4
heater/defroster door (.3) 6
A/C mode door (.8) ... 1.5

Air Conditioning Hoses, Renew
Includes: Add partial charge, leak test and charge system.
1984-87
Suction Hose
2.2L & 2.5L engs (1.1) ... 1.5
2.6L eng (1.3) ... 1.7
Discharge Hose
2.2L eng (1.1) ... 1.5
2.6L eng (1.7) ... 2.1
Renew receiver drier add 2

LABOR 30 HEAD AND PARKING LAMPS 30 LABOR

(Factory Time) Chilton Time

Aim Headlamps
two 4
four 6

Headlamp Sealed Beam Bulb, Renew
Does not include aim headlamp.
All models-each (.2) 3

License Lamp Lens, Renew
All models (.2) 2

License Lamp Assembly, Renew
1984-87 (.2) 3

Turn Signal and Parking Lamp Assy., Renew
All models (.2) 3

Tail Lamp Assembly, Renew
All models (.5) 8

Side Marker Lamp Assy., Renew
All models-each (.2) 3

LABOR 31 WINDSHIELD WIPER & SPEEDOMETERS 31 LABOR

(Factory Time) Chilton Time

Windshield Wiper Motor, Renew
1984-87 (.4) 7

Wiper/Washer Switch Assy., Renew
1984-87
std column (.8) ... 1.2
tilt column (1.1) ... 1.5

Rear Window Wiper/Washer Switch, Renew
1984-87 (.5) 7

Rear Window Wiper Motor, Renew
1984-87 (.3) 5

Washer Pump, Renew
1984-87
front (.3) 4
rear (.7) ... 1.0

Wiper Link Assembly, Renew
1984-87 (.5) 7

Windshield Wiper Pivot, Renew
1984-87-one (.4) 6

Intermittent Wiper Control Module, Renew
1984-87 (.2) 4

Speedometer Head, R&R or Renew
Does not include reset odometer.
1984-87 (.6) ... 1.1
Reset odometer add 2

Speedometer Cable and Casing, Renew
1984-87
upper (.3) 6
lower (.5) 9
one piece (.6) ... 1.0

Speedometer Cable (Inner), Renew or Lubricate
1984-87
upper (.3) 5
lower (.4) 8
one piece (.4) 8
trans to speedo (.3) 5
Includes: Renew oil seal.
1984-87 (.3) 4

Radio, R&R
1984-87 (.3) 7

LABOR 32 LIGHT SWITCHES & WIRING 32 LABOR

Headlamp Switch, Renew
1984-87 (.5) 7

Headlamp Dimmer Switch, Renew
1984-87 (.3) 6

Back-Up Lamp Switch, Renew (w/Manual Trans)
1984-87 (.2) 4

Neutral Safety Switch, Renew
1984-87 (.3) 4

Stop Light Switch, Renew
1984-87 (.3) 4
w/Cruise control add (.1) 1

Parking Brake Warning Lamp Switch, Renew
1984-87 (.2) 3

Turn Signal Switch, Renew
1984-87
std column (.5) ... 1.0
tilt column (.8) ... 1.5

Turn Signal or Hazard Warning Flasher, Renew
1984-87 (.2) 3

Horn, Renew
1984-87-one (.2) 4

Horn Relay, Renew
1984-87 (.2) 3

Horn Switch, Renew
1984-87 (.2) 3

Wiring Harness, Renew
1984-87
Main harness to dash (1.2) ... 3.0
Body harness (1.3) ... 2.5

	(Factory Time)	Chilton Time
Speed Control Servo Assy., Renew		
1984-87	(.3)	.5
Speed Control Cable, Renew		
1984-87	(.4)	.7
Speed Control Turn Signal Lever Switch, Renew		
1984-87		
std column	(.5)	.9
tilt column	(1.0)	1.5
Speed Control Wiring Harness, Renew		
1984-87	(.3)	.6
Speed Control Safety (Cut-Out) Switch, Renew		
1984-87	(.3)	.4
(G) Electronic Speed Control Module, Renew		
1985-87	(.2)	.4

GROUP INDEX

ALPHABETICAL INDEX

LABOR 1 TUNE UP 1 LABOR

(Factory Time) Chilton Time

Compression Test

Four	.5
Six	.6
V-6	.7
V-8	.9

Engine Tune Up, (Electronic Ignition)

Includes: Test battery and clean connections. Tighten manifold and carburetor mounting bolts. Check engine compression, clean and adjust or renew spark plugs. Test resistance of spark plug cables. Inspect distributor cap and rotor. Adjust air gap. Reset ignition timing. Adjust idle mixture and idle speed. Service air cleaner. Inspect and adjust drive belts. Inspect choke operation and adjust or free up. Check operation of EGR valve.

Four	1.5
Six	2.1
V-6	2.0
V-8	2.7
w/A.C. add	.6

LABOR 2 IGNITION SYSTEM 2 LABOR

(Factory Time) Chilton Time

Spark Plugs, Clean and Reset or Renew

RANGER-BRONCO	
Four (.3)	.4
Six (.4)	.6
V-6 (.6)	.8
V-8 (.6)	.8
AEROSTAR	
Four (.5)	.7
V-6 (1.0)	1.4
ECONOLINE-Six (.5)	.7
V-8 (.6)	.8
F100-350-Six (.4)	.8
V-6 (.4)	.6
V-8 (.6)	.8

Ignition Timing, Reset

All models (.3)	.4

Distributor, R&R or Renew

Includes: Reset ignition timing.

RANGER (.8)	1.1
AEROSTAR	
Four (.6)	1.0
V-6 (.8)	1.3
BRONCO (.4)	.8
BRONCO II (.8)	1.1
ECONOLINE (.5)	.9
F100-350-Six (.5)	.9
V-6 (.5)	.9
V-8 (.6)	1.0

Distributor, R&R and Recondition

Includes: Reset ignition timing.

BRONCO-Six (1.2)	1.7
V-8 (1.5)	2.0
ECONOLINE-Six (1.4)	1.9
V-8 (1.6)	2.1
F100-350-Six (1.2)	1.7
V-6 (1.5)	2.0
V-8 (1.7)	2.2

Distributor Cap and/or Rotor, Renew

RANGER (.5)	.6
BRONCO (.3)	.5
ECONOLINE (.4)	.6
F100-350 (.3)	.5
AEROSTAR (.4)	.6

Distributor Points and Condenser, Renew

BRONCO (.4)	.7
ECONOLINE (.5)	.8
F100-350-Six (.4)	.7
V-8 (.5)	.8

Distributor Vacuum Control Valve, Renew

All models (.3)	.5

Vacuum Control Unit, Renew

Includes: R&R distributor and reset ignition timing.

BRONCO (.7)	1.2
ECONOLINE (.8)	1.2
F100-350-Six (.8)	1.2
V-8 (.9)	1.3

Ignition Coil, Renew

Includes: Test.

AEROSTAR (.3)	.5
RANGER (.4)	.5
BRONCO I & II (.4)	.5
ECONOLINE (.5)	.6
F100-350 (.4)	.5

Ignition Module Assembly, Renew

All models	
Dura-Spark II (.2)	.4
TFI (.5)	.7
Perform system test add (.3)	.3

Distributor Armature, Renew

All models (.3)	.6

Distributor Stator, Renew

Includes: R&R armature.

All models (.4)	.8

Ignition Cables, Renew

Includes: Test wiring.

AEROSTAR	
Four (.5)	.7
V-6 (.7)	1.0
RANGER (.6)	.8
BRONCO (.5)	.7
ECONOLINE (.5)	.8
F100-350 (.4)	.7

Ignition Switch, Renew

All models (.3)	.7

LABOR 3 FUEL SYSTEM 3 LABOR

(Factory Time) Chilton Time

GASOLINE ENGINES

Fuel Pump, Test

Includes: Disconnect line at carburetor, attach pressure gauge.

All models	
mechanical	.4
electric	.5

Fuel Filter, Renew

RANGER-BRONCO (.3)	.4
AEROSTAR	
Four (.7)	.9
V-6 (.3)	.4
ECONOLINE-Six (.4)	.5
V-8 (.3)	.4
F100-350	
Six (.4)	.5
V-8 (.3)	.4

Carburetor, Adjust (On Truck)

All models (.3)	.4

Carburetor, R&R or Renew

Includes: Necessary adjustments.

RANGER-BRONCO I & II	
Four (.4)	.7
Six (.5)	.9
V-6 (.6)	1.0
V-8 (.6)	1.0
AEROSTAR	
V-6 (.7)	1.1
ECONOLINE-Six (.8)	1.2
V-8 (.5)	.9
F100-350-Six (.5)	.9
V-6 (.5)	.9
V-8 (.8)	1.2

Carburetor, R&R and Clean or Recondition

Includes: Necessary adjustments.

RANGER-BRONCO I & II	
Four (1.7)	2.5
Six (1.1)	1.7
V-6 (2.2)	3.0
V-8 (1.6)	2.2
AEROSTAR	
V-6 (2.3)	3.1
ECONOLINE-Six (1.4)	2.0
V-8 (1.5)	2.1
F100-350-Six (1.1)	1.7
V-6 (1.3)	2.2
V-8-2 bbl	
w/Auto choke (1.8)	2.5
w/Manual choke (1.3)	1.9
4 bbl	
Motorcraft (1.8)	2.5
Holly (2.0)	2.7

LABOR 3 FUEL SYSTEM 3 LABOR

(Factory Time)	Chilton Time
Fuel Pump, R&R or Renew	
RANGER-Four (.3)	.5
V-6 (.5)	.8
AEROSTAR	
V-6 (.8)	1.1
BRONCO (.5)	.8
ECONOLINE (.4)	.7
F100-350 (.4)	.7
Add pump test if performed.	
Fuel Tank, Renew	
RANGER	
aft tank (.8)	1.4
mid tank (1.0)	1.8
AEROSTAR (1.1)	1.7
BRONCO (.7)	1.5
BRONCO II (2.1)	3.0
ECONOLINE (.9)	1.5
F100-350	
aft tank (.9)	1.5
mid tank (1.2)	2.0
Auxiliary Fuel Tank, R&R or Renew	
BRONCO (.7)	1.3
ECONOLINE (.9)	1.5
F100-350 (.9)	1.5
Fuel Gauge (Tank), Renew	
RANGER	
aft tank (.7)	1.1
mid tank (.8)	1.2
AEROSTAR (1.0)	1.5
BRONCO	
aft tank (.9)	1.3
mid tank (.7)	1.1
BRONCO II (2.1)	3.0
ECONOLINE	
rear mounted (.3)	.6
side mounted (1.1)	1.9
F100-350	
cab mounted (.3)	.6
rear mounted (1.1)	1.9
side mounted (.5)	.9
Fuel Gauge (Dash), Renew	
RANGER (.6)	1.0
AEROSTAR (.6)	1.0
BRONCO (.6)	1.0
BRONCO II (.6)	1.0
ECONOLINE (.5)	.9
F100-350 (.5)	.9
Intake Manifold or Gaskets, Renew	
RANGER-BRONCO I & II-AEROSTAR	
Four	
2.0 L eng (1.2)	2.0
w/P.S. add (.2)	.2
Six	
1983 & earlier (1.1)	1.6
1984 & later (3.4)	4.7
V-6 (2.8)	3.8
V-8 (1.9)	2.7
ECONOLINE-Six	
1983 & earlier (.9)	1.8
1984 & later (3.4)	4.9
V-8	
302-351 engs (1.6)	2.2
460 eng (2.3)	3.3
F100-350	
Six	
1983 & earlier (1.1)	1.6
1984 & later (3.4)	4.7
V-6 (2.3)	3.3
V-8	
255-302 351W engs (1.5)	2.2
351M-400 engs (1.9)	2.7
460 eng (2.0)	2.5
Renew manif add (.4)	.5

ELECTRONIC FUEL INJECTION (EFI)

(Factory Time)	Chilton Time
Fuel Injector Assy., Renew	
Four-one (.9)	1.3
all (1.0)	1.6
V-8-right side-all (1.4)	1.9
left side-all (.8)	1.1
both sides-all (1.7)	2.3
Air Intake Charge Throttle Body, Renew	
Four-All models (.6)	1.1
Fuel Charging Wiring Assy., Renew	
Four (.3)	.6
V-8 (1.2)	1.7
Fuel Charging Pressure Regulator Assy., Renew	
Four (1.0)	1.5
V-8 (.8)	1.3
Fuel Pump, Renew	
Four	
Ranger (.5)	.8
Aerostar (.6)	.9
w/P.S. add (.2)	.2
V-8 (.5)	.8
Fuel Injection Manifold, Renew	
Four	
Ranger (.8)	1.2
Aerostar (.9)	1.3
V-8-right side (1.3)	1.8
left side (.8)	1.3
both sides (1.7)	2.8
Intake Manifold and/or Gasket, Renew	
Four	
upper (1.1)	1.5
lower (2.2)	3.1
w/P.S. add (.2)	.2
V-8	
upper (1.1)	1.5
lower (3.0)	4.0

DIESEL ENGINE

(Factory Time)	Chilton Time
Glow Plugs, Renew	
Four-one (.2)	.4
all (.3)	.7
V-8-one (.4)	.6
all (.8)	1.2
Glow Plug Module, Renew	
Four (.3)	.4
Glow Plug Relay, Renew	
Econoline (.4)	.6
All other models (.3)	.4
Fuel/Water Separator, Renew	
V-8	
F series (.4)	.6
Econoline (.8)	1.0
Fuel Pump, Renew	
V-8	
All models (.5)	.7
Fuel Filter Element, Renew	
All models	
Four & V-8 (.3)	.4
Intake Manifold and or Gaskets, Renew	
Four	
2.2L eng (1.4)	2.2
2.3L eng (2.4)	3.3
V-8	
F series (2.4)	3.3
Econoline (2.6)	3.6
Renew manif add (.2)	.5
Fuel Injection Pump Nozzles, Renew	
Four-2.3L eng	
one (.8)	1.1
each adtnl (.2)	.2
all (1.2)	1.7
V-8	
one (.3)	.5
each adtnl (.5)	.6
all (1.5)	2.1
Fuel Injection Pump, Renew	
Four	
2.2L eng (1.6)	2.4
2.3L eng (1.4)	1.9
V-8	
F series (2.0)	2.7
Econoline (2.8)	3.8
Injection Pump Drive Gear, Renew	
Four (1.9)	2.9
2.2L eng (1.9)	2.9
2.3L eng (1.4)	2.0
V-8	
F series (1.8)	2.5
Econoline (3.4)	4.7

LABOR 3A EMISSION CONTROLS 3A LABOR

(Factory Time)	Chilton Time
Emission Control Check	
Includes: Check and adjust engine idle speed and mixture, reset ignition timing. Check PCV valve.	
All models (.4)	.6

CRANKCASE EMISSION

(Factory Time)	Chilton Time
Positive Crankcase Ventilation Valve, Clean or Renew	
All models-clean (.4)	.5
renew (.2)	.3

EVAPORATIVE EMISSION TYPE

(Factory Time)	Chilton Time
Canister, Renew	
Bronco (.2)	.4
Econoline (.2)	.4
F100-350 (.4)	.6
Vapor Separator, Renew	
Bronco (.2)	.4
Econoline (.2)	.4
F100-350	
cab mounted (.2)	.4
frame mounted (.3)	.5

CONTROLLED COMBUSTION TYPE

(Factory Time)	Chilton Time
Air Cleaner Motor, Renew	
All models (.2)	.3
Air Cleaner Sensor, Renew	
All models (.2)	.3

THERMACTOR TYPE

(Factory Time)	Chilton Time
Thermactor Air Pump, Renew	
Four (.3)	.5
V-6 (.5)	.7
Six (.3)	.5

(Factory Time) Chilton Time

V-8-302-351 W engs (.5) .7
351M, 400 engs (.7) 1.0
460 eng (.4) .7
•Aerostar add .2

Thermactor Drive Belt, Renew
All models (.3) .5

Anti-Backfire Valve, Renew
All models (.3) .4

Relief Valve, Renew
All models (.3) .4

Thermactor Air By-Pass Valve, Renew
All models (.4) .6

TRANSMISSION CONTROLLED SPARK

Controlled Spark Solenoid, Renew
All models (.2) .3

Thermostatic Vacuum Switch, Renew
All models (.2) .3

Temperature Switch, Renew
All models (.3) .5

Spark Relay, Renew
All models (.2) .3

Transmission Controlled Spark Switch, Renew
All models (.3) .5

E.G.R. TYPE

E.G.R. Valve, Renew
Four (.3) .5
Six (.4) .6
V-6 (.3) .5
V-8 (.5) .7
•Aerostar add .2

E.G.R. Switch, Renew
All models (.3) .4

Vacuum Switch, Renew
All models (.3) .4

Air Supply Pump, Renew
All models (.3) .4

Thermostatic Exhaust Control Valve, Renew
Econoline-Six (1.7) 2.4
F100-350-Six (1.5) 2.2

ELECTRONIC EMISSION CONTROL

EEC System, Test
BRONCO (.7) 1.0

EGR Cooler, Renew
Does not include system test.
BRONCO (.6) 1.0

Power Relay, Renew
Does not include system test.
BRONCO (.3) .4

Calibrator Assembly, Renew
Does not include system test.
BRONCO (.2) .4

Processor Assembly, Renew
Does not include system test.
BRONCO (.3) .6

Feedback Carburetor Actuator, Renew
Does not include system test.
BRONCO (.3) .4

Exhaust Gas Oxygen Sensor, Renew
Does not include system test.
BRONCO (.4) .7

(Factory Time) Chilton Time

Barometric Manifold Absolute Pressure Sensor, Renew
Does not include system test.
BRONCO (.3) .5

Thermactor Air Bypass and Air Diverter Solenoid, Renew
Does not include system test.
BRONCO (.3) .5

MCU SYSTEM

MCU System, Test
All models (.4) .6

Oxygen Sensor, Renew
Does not include system test.
All models (.3) .7

Thermactor Air Valve, Renew
Does not include system test.
All models (.5) .7

Ported Vacuum Switch, Renew
Does not include system test.
All models (.1) .2

Fuel Control Solenoid, Renew
Does not include system test.
All models (.1) .2

E.G.R. Valve, Renew
Does not include system test.
All models (.3) .4

TAB/TAD Solenoid, Renew
Does not include system test.
All models (.1) .2

Canister Purge Solenoid, Renew
Does not include system test.
All models (.1) .2

Vacuum Switch, Renew
Does not include system test.
All models (.3) .4

MCU/ECU Module, Renew
Does not include system test.
All models (.3) .5

Low Temperature Switch, Renew (Electric or Vacuum)
Does not include system test.
All models
2 port (.4) .5
3 port (.3) .4

Feedback Carburetor Actuator, Renew
Does not include system test.
All models (.4) .6

Solenoid, Renew
Does not include system test.
All models-one (.3) .4

Mid Temperature Switch, Renew (Electric or Vacuum)
Does not include system test.
All models (.3) .4

ELECTRONIC ENGINE CONTROL IV

E.E.C. System, Test
All models (.6) 1.0

Throttle Position Sensor, Renew
Does not include system test.
Four
All models (.6) .8
V-6
All models (.3) .5
Six
Econoline (.4) .6

(Factory Time) Chilton Time

All other models (.2) .4
V-8
Econoline (.4) .6
All other models (.3) .5

Idle Tracking Switch, Renew
Does not include system test.
All models (.2) .4

Air Change Temperature Sensor, Renew
Does not include system test.
All models (.1) .3

Exhaust Gas Oxygen Sensor, Renew
Does not include system test.
Four
All models (.2) .4
V-6
All models (.1) .3
Six
Econoline (.2) .4
All other models (.1) .3
V-8
All models (.2) .5

Knock Sensor, Renew
Does not include system test.
All models (.2) .4

Processor Assembly, Renew
Does not include system test.
All models (.2) .3

Electronic Control Power Relay, Renew
Does not include system test.
Four
All models (.1) .3
V-6
All models (.2) .4
Six & V-8
All models (.1) .3

Choke Cover, Renew
Does not include system test.
V-6
All models (.6) 1.0

E.G.R. Shut-Off Solenoid, Renew
Does not include system test.
Econoline (.2) .3
All other models (.1) .2

Fuel Pump Relay, Renew
Does not include system test.
Four
All models (.1) .2

Fuel Pump Inertia Switch Assy., Renew
Does not include system test.
Four
All models (.1) .2

Throttle Positioner Assembly, Renew
Does not include system test.
All models
Six (.5) .7
V-6 (.4) .6

Fuel Injector Assembly, Renew
Does not include system test.
Four
Ranger-one (.7) .9
all (.8) 1.3
Aerostar-one (1.1) 1.3
all (1.2) 1.7

LABOR 3A EMISSION CONTROLS 3A LABOR

(Factory Time) — Chilton Time

Knock Sensor, Renew
Does not include system test.
All models
- Four (.1) .3
- V-6 (.1) .3

Air Change Temperature Sensor, Renew
Does not include system test.
V-6
- All models (.1) .3

Canister Purge Valve, Renew
Does not include system test.
V-6
- All models (.1) .2

Six
- Econoline (.2) .3
- All other models (.1) .2

V-8
- All models (.2) .3

Engine Coolant Temperature Sensor, Renew
Does not include system test.
- All models (.2) .4

Feedback Control Solenoid, Renew
Does not include system test.
V-6
- All models (.3) .4

Six
- Econoline (.4) .6
- All other models (.2) .3

V-8
- Econoline (.3) .4
- All other models (.5) .7

Manifold Absolute Pressure Sensor, Renew
Does not include system test.
- All models (.1) .3

E.G.R. Valve Position Sensor, Renew
Does not include system test.
- All models (.2) .4

Thermactor Air Diverter Valve, Renew
Does not include system test.
- Econoline (.3) .5
- All other models (.2) .4

Thick Film Ignition Module, Renew
Does not include system test.
Four
- All models (.4) .6

V-6
- All models (.5) .7

Six & V-8
- Econoline (.4) .6
- All other models (.3) .4

Thermactor Air By-Pass Valve, Renew
Does not include system test.
- All models (.2) .3

E.G.R. Valve, Renew
Does not include system test.
Four
- Ranger (.3) .4
- Aerostar (.5) .7

V-6
- All models (.2) .4

V-8
- Econoline (.4) .6
- All other models (.3) .5

E.G.R. On-Off Solenoid, Renew
Does not include system test.
- All models (.2) .3

Throttle Kicker Actuator, Renew
Does not include system test.
- All models (.3) .4

Tab/Tad Solenoids, Renew
Does not include system test.
- All models (.2) .3

E.G.R. Control Solenoids, Renew
Does not include system test.
- All models (.2) .3

Throttle Kicker Solenoid, Renew
Does not include system test.
- All models (.2) .3

Profile Ignition Pick-Up Sensor, Renew
Does not include system test.
- Econoline (.6) .8
- All other models (.5) .7

LABOR 4 ALTERNATOR AND REGULATOR 4 LABOR

(Factory Time) — Chilton Time

Alternator Circuits, Test
Includes: Test battery, regulator and alternator output.
- All models (.4) .6

Alternator, R&R or Renew
- Four (.4) .7

Six
- Econoline (1.1) 1.5
- All other models (.4) .7

- V-6 (.5) .9

V-8
- Econoline-w/460 eng (1.2) *1.6
- All other models (.5) .9
- *w/Dual Therm. pumps add .5
- Renew brushes add .3
- Renew drive brg add .3
- Renew end brg add .2
- Renew rectifier assy add .4
- Renew stator assy add .4

Alternator Regulator, Renew
- All models (.3) .5

Add circuit test if performed.

Ammeter, Renew
- All models (.5) .9

Instrument Cluster Voltage Regulator, Renew
- All models (.5) .7

LABOR 5 STARTING SYSTEM 5 LABOR

(Factory Time) — Chilton Time

Starter Draw Test (On Truck)
- All models (.3) .3

Starter, R&R or Renew
Gas Engines
- All models (.4) .7

Diesel Engines
- Four (.8) 1.1
- V-8 (.5) .8

Renew brushes add
- TK .5
- Motorcraft .6
- Delco .2

Renew starter drive
- add .6

Recond complete add
- TK 1.5
- Motorcraft & Delco 1.0

- Renew field coils add .5

Add draw test if performed.

Starter Solenoid Relay, Renew
- All models (.3) .5

Battery Cables, Renew
- All models-each (.3) .4

LABOR 6 BRAKE SYSTEM 6 LABOR

(Factory Time) — Chilton Time

Brake Pedal Free Play, Adjust
- All models (.3) .4

Brakes, Adjust (Minor)
Includes: Adjust brakes, fill master cylinder.
- two wheels .4
- four wheels .7

Bleed Brakes (Four Wheels)
Includes: Fill master cylinder.
- All models (.3) .6

Brake Shoes, Renew
Includes: Install new or exchange shoes, service self adjustors. Adjust service and hand brake. Bleed system.
- BRONCO-front (1.5) 2.0

(Factory Time)	Chilton Time
rear (1.3)	1.8
All four wheels (2.2)	3.7
ECONOLINE-F100-350	
front (1.1)	1.5
rear (1.7)	2.2
All four wheels (2.3)	3.5
F100-250 4X4	
front (1.3)	1.8
rear (1.7)	2.2
All four wheels (2.5)	3.7
Resurface brake drum add, each	.5

Brake Shoes and/or Pads, Renew

Includes: Install new or exchange brake shoes or pads. Adjust service and hand brake. Bleed system.

All models	
front-disc (.7)	1.1
rear-drum (.9)	*1.8
All four wheels (1.3)	2.8
*w/Full floating axle aid	.6
Resurface brake rotor add, each	.9
Resurface brake drum add, each	.5

Front Brake Drum and Hub Assy., Renew

BRONCO-one (.7)	.9
both (1.2)	1.6
ECONOLINE-one (.5)	.8
both (.7)	1.1
F100-350-one (.5)	.8
both (.8)	1.2

Rear Brake Drum, Renew

All models	
Semi-Floating Axle	
one (.4)	.6
both (.6)	.9
Dana Axle (Full Floating)	
one (.7)	1.1
both (1.1)	1.9

Brake Pressure Warning Light Switch, Renew

All models (.3)	.5

BRAKE HYDRAULIC SYSTEM

Wheel Cylinder, Renew

Includes: Bleed system.

Front	
BRONCO-one (1.1)	1.5
both (2.1)	2.9
ECONOLINE, F100-350	
one (.9)	1.3
both (1.7)	2.5
F100-250 4X4	
one (1.0)	1.4
both (1.9)	2.7
Rear	
RANGER-AEROSTAR-one (.8)	1.4
both (1.5)	2.6
BRONCO-one (1.0)	1.5
both (1.9)	2.9
ECONOLINE, F100-350	
one (1.2)	1.6
both (2.3)	3.0
F100-250 4X4	
one (1.2)	1.6
both (2.3)	3.0

Wheel Cylinder, R&R and Recondition

Includes: Hone cylinder and bleed system.

Front	
BRONCO-one (1.1)	1.8
both (2.1)	3.5
ECONOLINE, F100-350	
one (.9)	1.6
both (1.7)	3.1
F100-250 4X4	
one (1.0)	1.7
both (1.9)	3.3
Rear	
RANGER-AEROSTAR-one (.8)	1.6
both (1.5)	3.0
BRONCO-one (1.0)	1.8
both (1.9)	3.5
ECONOLINE, F100-350	
one (1.2)	1.9
both (2.3)	3.7
F100-250 4X4	
one (1.2)	1.9
both (2.3)	3.7

COMBINATIONS

Add to Brakes, Renew

See Machine Shop Operations

(Factory Time)	Chilton Time
RENEW WHEEL CYLINDER	
Each (.3)	.4
REBUILD WHEEL CYLINDER	
Each (.3)	.6
REBUILD CALIPER ASSEMBLY	
Each (.5)	.8
RENEW MASTER CYLINDER	
All models (.4)	.7
REBUILD MASTER CYLINDER	
All models	1.3
RENEW BRAKE HOSE	
Each (.3)	.3
RENEW REAR WHEEL GREASE SEALS	
One side (.2)	.4
FRONT WHEEL BEARINGS, REPACK OR RENEW SEALS (BOTH WHEELS)	
Drum brakes (.3)	.6
Disc brakes (.4)	.7
4X4 (.6)	.8
RENEW BRAKE DRUM	
Each (.2)	.3
RENEW DISC BRAKE ROTOR	
Each (.3)	.5

Brake Hose, Renew

Includes: Bleed system.

Front	
RANGER-AEROSTAR-one (.5)	.8
both (.6)	1.0
BRONCO, F100-350, F100-250 4X4	
one (.5)	.8
both (.6)	1.0
ECONOLINE 100-350	
one (.6)	.9
both (.8)	1.1
Rear	
RANGER-AEROSTAR-one (.5)	.8
BRONCO, F100-250 4X4	
one (.5)	.8
ECONOLINE 100-350, F100-350	
one (.6)	.9

Master Cylinder, Renew

Includes: Bleed complete system.

Aerostar (.7)	1.1
All other models	
wo/Booster (.6)	1.0
w/Booster (.5)	.9

Master Cylinder, R&R and Recondition

Includes: Hone cylinder and bleed complete system.

Aerostar (1.0)	1.6
All other models	
wo/Booster (.8)	1.5
w/Booster (.7)	1.4

Vacuum Pump, Renew (w/Diesel Eng)

ECONOLINE-F-series (.6)	.9
All other models (.4)	.6

Brake Differential Valve, R&R or Renew

Includes: Bleed complete system and transfer switch.

All models (.7)	1.2

POWER BRAKES

Power Brake Booster, R&R or Renew

AEROSTAR (1.0)	1.5
BRONCO, F100-250 4X4 (.5)	.8
ECONOLINE (.4)	1.0
F100-350 (.5)	.8
w/Cruise control add (.2)	.2

DISC BRAKES

Brake Shoes and/or Pads, Renew

Includes: Install new or exchange brake shoes or pads. Adjust service and hand brake. Bleed system.

All models	
front-disc (.7)	1.1
rear-drum (.9)	*1.8
All four wheels (1.3)	2.8
*w/Full floating axle add	.6
Resurface brake rotor add, each	.9
Resurface brake drum add, each	.5

Disc Brake Rotor, Renew

Includes: Renew front wheel bearings and grease retainer and repack bearings.

4X2 models	
one (.6)	.9
both (1.0)	1.6
4X4 models	
one (.7)	1.0
both (1.1)	1.8
w/8 lug whl add	
each side	.1

Caliper Assembly, Renew

Includes: Bleed complete system.

All models	
one (.6)	1.0
both (.9)	1.4
w/8 lug whl add	
each side	.1

Caliper Assembly, R&R and Recondition

Includes: Bleed complete system.

All models	
Single Piston	
one (.8)	1.5
both (1.2)	2.4
Dual Piston	
one (.9)	1.6
both (1.3)	2.5
w/8 lug whl add	
each side	.1

PARKING BRAKE

Parking Brake, Adjust

All models (.3)	.5

LABOR 6 BRAKE SYSTEM 6 LABOR

(Factory Time)	Chilton Time
Parking Brake Control, Renew	
AEROSTAR (.4)	.7
RANGER (.5)	.8
ECONOLINE, F100-350 (.5)	.8
BRONCO, F100-250 4X4 (.6)	.9
BRONCO II (.5)	.8
Parking Brake Cable, Renew	
Front–All models (.6)	1.0
Rear	
Semi-Floating Axle	
one (.5)	.8
both (.8)	1.1
Full Floating Axle	
one (.8)	1.1
both (1.4)	2.0

LABOR 7 COOLING SYSTEM 7 LABOR

(Factory Time)	Chilton Time
Winterize Cooling System	
Includes: Run engine to check for leaks, tighten all hose connections. Test radiator and pressure cap, drain radiator and engine block. Add anti-freeze and refill system.	
All models	.5
Thermostat, Renew	
Gas Engines	
Four (.5)	.6
Six (.4)	.6
V-6 (.7)	.9
V-8 (.6)	.8
Diesel Engines	
Four (.5)	.6
V-8 (1.1)	1.4
Radiator Assembly, R&R or Renew	
Includes: Drain and refill cooling system.	
RANGER-AEROSTAR	
Gas (.6)	1.0
Diesel (.6)	1.0
BRONCO I & II	
Gas (.6)	1.0
ECONOLINE-Six (1.0)	1.5
V-8 (.6)	1.2
Diesel (.9)	1.5
F100-350	
Gas (.6)	1.0
Diesel (1.4)	2.0
ADD THESE OPERATIONS TO RADIATOR R&R	
Boil & Repair	1.5
Rod Clean	1.9
Repair Core	1.3
Renew Tank	1.6
Renew Trans. Oil Cooler	1.9
Renew Side Tank	.7
Recore Radiator	1.7
Radiator Hoses, Renew	
RANGER-upper (.3)	.4
lower (.4)	.5
both (.5)	.6
BRONCO, F100-250 4X4	
upper (.5)	.6
lower (.5)	.6
ECONOLINE	
upper (.4)	.5
lower (.6)	.7
F100-350	
upper (.5)	.6
lower (.6)	.7
Water Pump, Renew	
RANGER	
Four (1.2)	1.7
w/A.C. add (.3)	.3
w/P.S. add (.2)	.2
V-6 (1.4)	2.0
w/A.C. add (.4)	.4
Diesel	
2.2L eng (1.1)	1.7
2.3L eng (1.6)	2.3
AEROSTAR	
Four (1.1)	1.7
V-6 (1.3)	2.0
w/A.C. add (.3)	.3
w/P.S. add (.2)	.2
BRONCO-Six (.9)	1.5
V-6 (1.4)	2.0
w/A.C. add (.4)	.4
V-8 (1.1)	1.9
w/A.C. add (.2)	.2
ECONOLINE-Six (1.0)	1.6
V-8 (1.5)	2.1
Diesel (1.4)	2.0
F100-350-Six (1.0)	1.6
V-6 (1.1)	1.7
V-8	
302-351W engs (1.1)	1.7
351M-400 engs (1.3)	2.0
460 eng (1.5)	2.1
Diesel (1.9)	2.7
w/P.S. add	.3
w/A.C. add	.3
Fan Blade, Renew	
V-8-Diesel (.7)	1.0
All other engs	
wo/Viscous drive (.4)	.6
w/Viscous drive (.5)	.7
Drive Belt, Adjust	
All models-one (.3)	.4
each adtnl (.2)	.3
Temperature Gauge (Engine), Renew	
All models (.3)	.5
Temperature Gauge (Dash), Renew	
All models (.6)	1.0
Water Jacket Expansion Plugs, Renew (Side of Block)	
All models-each	.5
Add time to gain accessibility.	
Heater Core, R&R or Renew	
Without Air Conditioning	
AEROSTAR-Main (.6)	1.0
Auxiliary (.8)	1.4
RANGER (.5)	.9
BRONCO (.8)	1.6
BRONCO II (.5)	.9
ECONOLINE-Main (1.1)	1.0
Auxiliary (.8)	1.4
F100-350 (.8)	2.3
WITH AIR CONDITIONING	
1980 & later	
Econoline (1.1)	2.0
All other models (.5)	1.1
ADD THESE OPERATIONS TO HEATER CORE R&R	
Boil & Repair	1.2
Repair Core	.9
Recore	1.2
Heater Water Control Valve, Renew	
All models (.3)	.6
Heater Blower Motor, Renew	
AEROSTAR-Main (.5)	.9
Auxiliary (.4)	.7
RANGER (.3)	.7
BRONCO (.3)	.7
ECONOLINE-Main (.3)	.6
Auxiliary (.4)	.7
F100-350	
1980 & later (.3)	.6
Heater Control Assembly, Renew	
All models (.6)	1.1
Heater Blower Motor Switch, Renew	
AEROSTAR	
main (.6)	.9
front (.6)	.9
rear (.4)	.6
RANGER (.5)	.9
BRONCO (.4)	.7
BRONCO II (.5)	.9
ECONOLINE (.3)	.6
F100-350 (.5)	.9
Heater Blower Motor Resistor, Renew	
RANGER, BRONCO (.3)	.6
ECONOLINE (.3)	.6
F100-350 (.4)	.7
AEROSTAR-Main (.3)	.6
Auxiliary (.5)	.8

LABOR 8 EXHAUST SYSTEM 8 LABOR

(Factory Time)	Chilton Time
Catalytic Converter, Renew	
Four (.6)	.9
Six (.8)	1.2
V-6 (.8)	1.2
V-8 (.9)	1.6
Muffler, Renew	
RANGER-AEROSTAR	
Four (.4)	.7
V-6 (.6)	.9
Diesel (.5)	.8
BRONCO, F100-250 4X4 (.8)	1.4
BRONCO II (.6)	.9
ECONOLINE (.8)	1.4
F100-350	
Std W/B wo/Catalyst (.8)	1.4

LABOR 8 EXHAUST SYSTEM 8 LABOR

(Factory Time)	Chilton Time
w/Catalyst (.8)	1.4
Long W/B (.8)	1.4
V-6 (.7)	1.0
Intermediate Exhaust Pipe, Renew	
RANGER-AEROSTAR	
All models (.7)	1.2
BRONCO, F100-250 4X4	
Six (.5)	1.1
V-8 (.8)	1.4
BRONCO II (.7)	1.0
ECONOLINE-Six (.6)	1.2
V-8 (.9)	1.5
F100-350-Six (.6)	1.2
V-6 (.6)	.9
V-8-351M-400 engs	
Std W/B wo/Catalyst (1.6)	2.3
w/Catalyst (1.9)	2.6
Long W/B (.8)	1.4
460 eng-one (.7)	1.3
both (1.0)	1.9
Diesel (.6)	1.0
Tail Pipe, Renew	
BRONCO (.5)	.7
ECONOLINE (.5)	.7
F100-350 (.4)	.6
Exhaust Manifold, Renew	
Four	
Gas	
2.0L eng (.9)	1.5
2.3L eng (1.4)	2.0
Diesel	
2.2L eng (.9)	1.6
2.3L eng (2.4)	3.4
Six	
1983 & earlier (2.3)	3.0
1984 & later (3.1)	4.4
V-6	
right (1.5)	2.1
left (1.4)	*2.0
both (2.4)	*3.6
V-8	
302-351W engs	
one side (.7)	1.1
both sides (1.1)	1.9
351M-400 engs	
one side (.8)	1.3
both sides (1.2)	2.3
460 eng	
one side (.9)	1.6
both sides (1.3)	2.3
Diesel	
right side (1.7)	2.3
left side (1.6)	2.2
both sides (2.6)	3.8
* w/A.C. add (.3)	.3

COMBINATIONS

(Factory Time)	Chilton Time
Muffler, Exhaust and Tail Pipe, Renew	
RANGER	1.1
BRONCO	1.9
ECONOLINE	1.9
F100-350-one side	1.8
both sides	2.7

LABOR 9 FRONT SUSPENSION 9 LABOR

Note: On all front suspension operations alignment charges must be added if performed. Time given does not include alignment.

(Factory Time)	Chilton Time
Check Alignment of Front End	
All models (.5)	.6
Note: Deduct if alignment is performed.	
Toe-In, Adjust	
All models (.4)	.7
Align Front End	
Includes: Adjust front wheel bearings.	
Aerostar (1.2)	1.5
All other models (1.9)	2.5
Front Wheel Bearings, Clean and Repack (Both Wheels)	
drum brakes	1.0
disc brakes	1.4
4 wheel drive	2.5
Front Wheel Bearings and Cups, Renew (One Wheel)	
Drum Brakes	
Bronco, F100-250 4X4 (.8)	1.1
Econoline, F100-150 (.6)	.9
F250-350 (.7)	1.0
Disc Brakes	
Aerostar (.7)	1.1
Ranger (.8)	1.1
Bronco, F100-250 4X4 (.8)	1.1
Econoline 100-150, F100-150 (.7)	1.0
Econoline 250-350, F250-350 (.8)	1.1
Front Wheel Grease Seal, Renew (One Wheel)	
Drum Brakes	
Bronco (.6)	.8
Econoline (.4)	.6
F100-250 4X4 (.5)	.7
Disc Brakes	
Aerostar (.5)	.8
Ranger (.6)	.8
Bronco, F100-250 4X4 (.6)	.8
Econoline 100-150, F100-150 (.6)	.8
Econoline 250-350, F250-350 (.7)	.9
Front Shock Absorber or Bushings, Renew	
All models-one (.4)	.6
both (.5)	.8
Upper Control Arms, Renew	
Add alignment charges.	
Aerostar-one (1.0)	1.3
both (1.5)	2.0
Upper Control Arm Bushings, Renew	
Add alignment charges.	
Aerostar-one side (1.6)	2.2
both sides (2.5)	3.4
Lower Control Arms, Renew	
Add alignment charges.	
Aerostar-one side (1.5)	2.0
both sides (2.4)	3.2
Front Axle 'I' Beam, Renew	
Includes: R&R wheels and brake backing plates.	
Add alignment charges.	
STAMPED AXLE 4X2	
one side (2.3)	3.1
both sides (3.9)	5.3
FORGED AXLE 4X2	
one side (1.8)	2.4
both sides (2.7)	3.6
Renew ball joints	
add-each (.2)	.3
Renew pivot bushings	
add-each (.2)	.3
Front Spindle Assembly, Renew	
CONTROL ARM AXLE	
one side (1.4)	1.9
both sides (1.9)	2.9
STAMPED AXLE 4X2	
one side (1.6)	2.1
both sides (2.3)	3.1
FORGED AXLE 4X2	
one side (1.4)	1.9
both sides (1.9)	2.5
STAMPED AXLE 4X4	
one side (.6)	.9
both sides (.9)	1.3
FORGED AXLE 4X4	
one side (1.4)	1.9
both sides (1.9)	2.5
Rebush spindle, add	
each side (.4)	.5
Renew needle brgs, add	
each (.1)	.2
Steering Shock Absorber, Renew	
BRONCO, F100-250 4X4 (.3)	.6
Track Bar Assembly, Renew	
BRONCO, F100-250 4X4 (.6)	1.0
Radius Arm, Renew	
All models-one (1.4)	1.9
both (2.1)	2.8
Front Spring, Renew	
AEROSTAR	
one (.9)	1.2
both (1.6)	2.1
4X2	
All models	
one (.4)	.7
both (.7)	1.3
4X4	
Ranger-Bronco II	
one (.4)	.7
both (.7)	1.3
F series-Bronco	
one (.7)	1.1
both (1.1)	2.0
Renew tie bolt	
add-each (.5)	.5
Front Stabilizer Bushings, Renew	
All models (.5)	.7
Front Stabilizer Bar, Renew	
All models (.5)	.7

FRONT WHEEL DRIVE

(Factory Time)	Chilton Time
Front Axle Housing and Differential Assy., R&R (Complete)	
Includes: Drain and refill axle, R&R wheels, hubs and axle shafts. Road test.	
BRONCO (3.9)	5.4
F100 (3.7)	5.2
F250 (2.8)	4.2
Front Axle Housing, Renew (One Piece Assy)	
Includes: R&R housing and differential assy. Transfer all parts. Adjust ring gear and pinion.	

LABOR 9 FRONT SUSPENSION 9 LABOR

(Factory Time) Chilton Time

Does not include disassembly of differential case.
BRONCO (8.0) 9.6
F100 (7.4) 9.0
F250 (7.2) 9.0

Axle Housing Cover or Gasket, Renew
All models (.5) 7

Front Axle Arm (Beam), Renew (Independent Front Suspension)
w/coil springs
left side (3.8) 5.1
right side (2.9) 3.9
both sides (5.9) 7.9
w/leaf springs
left side (3.8) 5.1
right side (3.0) 4.0
both sides (6.1) 8.2
monobeam (4.8) 6.5
Renew ball joints
add-each (.2) 3
Renew pivot bushings
add-each (.2) 3

Front Axle Shaft, Renew
RANGER-BRONCO II
right side (1.2) 2.1
left side (.6) 8
both sides (1.6) 2.5
BRONCO-F150
one side (.9) 1.4
both sides (1.3) 1.9
F250-350
one side (.6) 1.1
both sides (1.2) 1.8
O/haul or renew U-Joints,
add-each (.3) 3

Front Axle Housing Oil Seals, Renew
RANGER-BRONCO II
right side (2.1) 2.7
left side (.7) 1.0
both sides (2.1) 2.8
BRONCO-F150
right side (2.2) 2.8
left side (.8) 1.1
both sides (2.3) 3.0
F250-350
right side (1.2) 1.5
left side (.6) 1.1
both sides (1.6) 2.2

Front Axle Pinion Oil Seal, Renew
All models (.6) 1.0

Front Axle Pivot Bushings, Renew
All models-one side (.5) 8
both sides (.7) 1.3

Front Drive Shaft, R&R
All models (.5) 7
Recond U-Joint, Add
one (.3) 4
all (.5) 6

Differential Carrier, R&R or Reseal
All models
w/coil springs (2.3) 3.2
w/leaf springs (2.4) 3.3
w/monobeam (3.0) 4.2

Ring Gear Backlash, Adjust
All models
w/coil springs (3.1) 4.3
w/leaf springs (3.2) 4.4
w/monobeam (3.8) 5.3

Ring Gear and Pinion Set, Renew
All models
w/coil springs (3.9) 5.4
w/leaf springs (4.0) 5.6
w/monobeam (4.6) 6.4
Renew pinion brgs add (.2) 4
Recond diff assy add (.2) 5

Differential Case, Renew
All models
w/coil springs
std (3.2) 4.5
locker (3.5) 4.9
w/leaf springs
std (3.3) 4.6
locker (3.6) 5.0
w/monobeam
std (3.9) 5.4
locker (4.2) 5.8
Renew diff brgs add (.2) 4

LABOR 10 STEERING LINKAGE 10 LABOR

(Factory Time) Chilton Time

Tie Rod Ends, Renew (One Side)
Includes: Reset toe-in.
All models (.8) 1.1

Tie Rod, Renew (One)
Includes: Reset toe-in.
All models (1.2) 1.5

Drag Link, Renew
Does not require toe-in adjustment.
All models (.5) 9

Pitman Arm, Renew
All models (.4) 9

Front Spindle Arm, Renew
Includes: R&R wheel hub and brake drum/rotor where required. Reset toe-in.
BRONCO-Part Time Hub
one (1.0) 1.4
both (1.9) 2.7
Full Time Hub
one (.9) 1.3
both (1.6) 2.4
ECONOLINE-one (.6) 1.0
both (1.0) 1.8
F100-350-one (1.1) 1.5
both (1.6) 2.2
F100-250 4X4
Part Time Hub-one (1.0) 1.4
both (1.9) 2.7
Full Time Hub-one (.9) 1.3
both (1.6) 2.4

LABOR 11 STEERING GEAR 11 LABOR

(Factory Time) Chilton Time

STANDARD

Steering Wheel, Renew
All models (.3) 5

Upper Mast Jacket Bearing, Renew
All models
std colm (.5) 9
tilt colm (.6) 1.0

Steering Column Lock Actuator, Renew
All models
std colm (1.0) 1.5
tilt colm (.9) 1.4

Steering Gear, Adjust (On Truck)
Includes: Bearing preload and gear mesh adjustments.
All models (.7) 1.0

Power Steering Pump, R&R and Recondition
Aerostar-Four (1.5) 2.3
V-6 (1.4) 2.2
All other models
Four
Gas (1.1) 1.8
Diesel
2.2L eng (1.2) 2.0
2.3L eng (1.6) 2.4
Six (1.1) 1.8
V-6 (1.3) 2.2
V-8
302-351W engs (1.1) 1.8
351M-400 engs (1.4) 2.0
460 eng (1.0) 1.8
Diesel (1.6) 2.2

Power Steering Pump Shaft Seal, Renew
Includes: R&R pump.
Aerostar-Four (1.2) 1.7
V-6 (1.1) 1.6
All other models
Four
Gas (.7) 1.2
Diesel
2.2L eng (.9) 1.4
2.3L eng (1.3) 1.8
Six (.7) 1.2
V-6 (.9) 1.4
V-8
302-351W engs (.6) 1.2
351M-400 engs (.9) 1.5
460 eng (.6) 1.2
Diesel (1.1) 1.6

LABOR 11 STEERING GEAR 11 LABOR

(Factory Time)	Chilton Time
Power Steering Control Valve, R&R or Renew	
ECONOLINE (2.0)	2.7
F250 4X4 (.9)	1.3
Power Steering Control Valve, R&R and Clean or Recondition	
ECONOLINE (2.8)	3.9
F250 4X4 (1.7)	2.4
Power Steering Hoses, Renew	
AEROSTAR	
pressure (.5)	.7
return (.4)	.6
BRONCO, F100-250 4X4	
pressure (.4)	.6
return (.5)	.7
ECONOLINE-Six (.7)	1.0
V-8 (.8)	1.1
RANGER, F100-350	
pressure (.4)	.6
return (.4)	.6
cooling (.3)	.5
V-8-Diesel	
cooling (.5)	.7
return (.7)	.9
pressure (.6)	.8

RACK AND PINION STEERING

(Factory Time)	Chilton Time
Steering Gear, R&R or Renew	
All models	
manual (.8)	1.3
power (1.0)	1.6
Purge system add (.3)	.3
Steering Gear, R&R and Recondition	
All models	
manual (2.4)	3.8
power (3.0)	4.8
Purge system add (.3)	.3

(Factory Time)	Chilton Time
Steering Gear, Adjust (On Truck)	
All models (.3)	.5
Tie Rod Ball Joint Sockets and Bellows, Renew	
All models	
manual (1.2)	1.9
power (1.5)	2.4
Purge system add (.3)	.3
Steering Gear, R&R or Renew	
All models (.7)	1.2
Steering Gear, R&R and Recondition	
Includes: Disassemble, renew necessary parts, reassemble and adjust.	
All models (1.4)	2.2

POWER STEERING

(Factory Time)	Chilton Time
Trouble Shoot Power Steering	
Includes: Test pump and system pressure. Check pounds pull on steering wheel and check for leaks.	
All models (.7)	1.0
Power Steering Belt, Renew	
Four	
Gas (.3)	.5
Diesel (.3)	.5
Six (.5)	.7
V-6 (.3)	.5
V-8	
302-351 engs (.4)	.6
460 eng (.8)	1.0
Diesel (.4)	.6
Power Steering Gear, R&R or Renew	
All models (.8)	1.4

(Factory Time)	Chilton Time
Power Steering Gear, R&R and Recondition	
Includes: Disassemble, renew necessary parts, reassemble and adjust.	
ECONOLINE	
Saginaw (2.5)	4.2
XR50 (2.2)	3.9
All other models (2.2)	3.8
Power Steering Cylinder Assembly, R&R or Renew	
ECONOLINE (1.6)	2.1
F250 4X4 (.7)	1.1
Power Steering Pump, R&R or Renew	
Includes: Transfer pulley where required.	
Aerostar-Four (1.1)	1.5
V-6 (1.0)	1.4
All other models	
Four	
Gas (.7)	1.0
Diesel	
2.2L eng (.8)	1.2
2.3L eng (1.2)	1.6
Six (.6)	1.0
V-6 (.8)	1.2
V-8	
302-351W engs (.6)	1.0
351M-400 engs (.8)	1.3
460 eng (.5)	1.0
Diesel (1.0)	1.4
Input Shaft and Valve Assy., Recondition	
All models	
manual (1.4)	2.2
power (1.6)	2.5
Purge system add (.3)	.3

LABOR 12 CYLINDER HEAD & VALVE SYSTEM 12 LABOR

GASOLINE ENGINES

(Factory Time)	Chilton Time
Compression Test	
Four	.5
Six	.6
V-6	.7
V-8	.9
Cylinder Head Gasket, Renew	
Includes: Check cylinder head and block flatness. Clean carbon and make all necessary adjustments.	
RANGER-BRONCO I & II	
Four	
2.0L eng (3.7)	5.2
2.3L eng (4.3)	6.0
w/A.C. add (.3)	.3
w/P.S. add (.2)	.2
Six (2.1)	3.8
V-6-one (4.3)	6.0
both (5.3)	7.4
V-8-302-351W engs	
one (3.0)	4.3
both (4.2)	6.6
351M-400 engs	
one (3.3)	4.6
both (4.5)	6.9
AEROSTAR	
Four (4.4)	6.1
V-6-one (4.4)	6.1
both (5.4)	7.5
w/A.C. add (.4)	.4
w/A.T. add (.1)	.1

COMBINATIONS

Add to Valve Job

(Factory Time)	Chilton Time
DRAIN, EVACUATE & RECHARGE AIR CONDITIONING SYSTEM	
All models (.7)	1.5
ROCKER ARMS OR SHAFT ASSY. DISASSEMBLE AND CLEAN OR RECONDITION	
Six (.6)	1.0
V-8-One side (.5)	.7
Both sides (1.0)	1.3
HYDRAULIC VALVE LIFTERS, DISASSEMBLE AND CLEAN	
Each (.2)	.2
ROCKER ARM STUD, RENEW	
Each (.3)	.3
DISTRIBUTOR, RECONDITION	
All models (.7)	1.0

(Factory Time)	Chilton Time
CARBURETOR, RECONDITION	
1 BBL (.9)	1.2
2 BBL (1.0)	1.3
4 BBL	
Ford (1.0)	1.5
Holly (1.3)	2.0
VALVE GUIDES, REAM OVERSIZE	
Each (.1)	.2
VALVE SEAT INSERT, RENEW	
DIESEL	
V-8-one (.2)	.3
each adtnl (.2)	.2
VALVE GUIDES, RENEW	
DIESEL	
V-8-one (.5)	.6
each adtnl (.5)	.5

(Factory Time)	Chilton Time
ECONOLINE-Six (3.4)	5.1
V-8-302-351W engs	
one (3.6)	4.8
both (5.4)	7.6

(Factory Time)	Chilton Time
351M-400 engs	
one (3.2)	4.4
both (4.4)	5.9
460 eng one (3.9)	5.0

(Factory Time)	Chilton Time
both (5.7)	7.9
w/P.S. add (.3)	.3
w/A.C. add (.7)	.7
F100-350	
Six (2.8)	3.9
V-6-one (4.7)	6.6
both (6.4)	8.8
V-8-255-302-351W engs	
one (3.0)	4.1
both (4.0)	6.2
351M-400 engs	
one (3.2)	4.3
both (4.4)	6.6
460 eng	
one (4.3)	5.4
both (6.1)	8.3
w/P.S. add (.3)	.3
w/A.C. add (2.0)	2.0

Cylinder Head, Renew

Includes: Transfer all components, clean carbon. Reface valves, check valve spring tension, assembled height and valve head runout.

(Factory Time)	Chilton Time
RANGER-BRONCO I & II	
Four	
2.0L eng (5.8)	8.1
w/A.C. add (.3)	.3
w/P.S. add (.2)	.2
Six (5.0)	6.7
V-6-one (4.5)	6.3
both (5.6)	7.8
V-8-302-351W engs	
one (4.2)	5.8
both (6.7)	9.6
351M-400 engs	
one (4.7)	6.1
both (7.3)	9.8
AEROSTAR	
V-6-one (4.8)	6.7
both (5.9)	8.2
w/A.C. add (.4)	.4
w/A.T. add (.1)	.1
ECONOLINE-Six (6.1)	8.6
V-8-302-351W engs	
one (4.8)	6.3
both (7.9)	10.6
351M-400 engs	
one (4.6)	5.9
both (7.2)	8.9
460 eng	
one (5.3)	7.0
both (8.5)	11.1
w/P.S. add (.3)	.3
w/A.C. add (.7)	.7
F100-350	
Six (5.4)	6.7
V-6-one (5.7)	8.0
both (8.3)	11.5
V-8-255-302-351W engs	
one (4.4)	5.7
both (6.8)	9.4
351M-400 engs	
one (4.6)	5.9
both (7.2)	9.8
460 eng	
one (5.7)	7.0
both (8.9)	11.5
w/P.S. add (.3)	.3
w/A.C. add (2.0)	2.0

Clean Carbon and Grind Valves

Includes: R&R cylinder heads, check valve spring tension, valve seat and head runout, stem to guide clearance and spring assembled height. Minor tune up.

(Factory Time)	Chilton Time
RANGER-BRONCO I & II	
Four	
2.0L eng (6.3)	8.9
w/A.C. add (.3)	.3
w/P.S. add (.2)	.2
Six (4.9)	7.5
V-6	
one side (6.7)	9.4
both sides (8.4)	11.7
V-8-302-351W engs	
one side (4.8)	6.3
both sides (7.8)	10.6
351M-400 engs	
one side (5.1)	6.6
both sides (8.1)	10.9
AEROSTAR	
V-6-one side (6.2)	9.6
both sides (8.5)	11.9
w/A.C. add (.4)	.4
w/A.T. add (.1)	.1
ECONOLINE-Six (6.1)	8.6
V-8-302-351W engs	
one side (5.4)	6.8
both sides (9.0)	11.6
351M-400 engs	
one side (5.0)	6.4
both sides (8.0)	9.9
460 eng (9.3)	11.9
w/P.S. add (.3)	.3
w/A.C. add (.7)	.7
F100-350	
Six (5.5)	8.1
V-6 (9.4)	12.9
V-8-255-302	
351W engs (7.6)	10.2
351M-400 engs (8.0)	10.6
460 eng (9.7)	12.3
w/P.S. add (.3)	.3
w/A.C. add (2.0)	2.0

Rocker Arm Cover or Gasket, Renew

(Factory Time)	Chilton Time
RANGER-BRONCO I & II	
Four	
2.0L eng (.7)	1.0
2.3L eng (1.3)	1.8
Six (.7)	1.0
V-6-one (.8)	1.2
both (1.2)	1.7
V-8-302-351W engs	
one (.4)	.6
both (.6)	1.0
351M-400 engs	
one (.6)	.8
both (.9)	1.3
AEROSTAR	
Four (1.2)	1.7
V-6-right (1.3)	1.8
left (1.5)	2.1
both (2.5)	3.5
ECONOLINE-Six (1.0)	1.3
V-8-302-351W engs	
right (.7)	.9
left (.5)	.7
both (.9)	1.3
351M-400 engs	
one (.6)	.8
both (.8)	1.2
460 eng	
one (.7)	.9
both (1.0)	1.3
F100-350	
Six (.6)	.8
V-6-one (.4)	.6
both (.6)	1.0
V-8-255-302-351W	
351M-400 engs	
one (.4)	.6
both (.6)	1.0
460 eng	
one (.5)	.7
both (.7)	1.1

Rocker Arm Shaft Assy., Recondition

Includes: R&R rocker arm cover.

(Factory Time)	Chilton Time
BRONCO-Six (1.1)	1.6

Valve Push Rod and/or Rocker Arm, Renew

Includes: R&R rocker arm cover.

(Factory Time)	Chilton Time
RANGER-BRONCO I & II	
Four	
2.0L eng	
one (.8)	1.2
all (1.1)	1.7
2.3L eng	
one (1.8)	2.5
all (2.3)	3.2
Six-one (.8)	1.1
all (1.1)	1.5
V-6-one (1.0)	1.4
all-one side (1.2)	1.7
all-both sides (2.1)	2.9
V-8-302-351W engs-one (.5)	.7
all (.9)	1.3
351M-400 engs	
one (.7)	.9
all (1.3)	1.7
AEROSTAR	
Four	
one (1.7)	2.4
all (2.2)	3.1
V-6	
one-right side (1.7)	2.4
one-left side (1.9)	2.7
all-both sides (3.4)	4.8
ECONOLINE-Six-one (1.1)	1.6
all (1.4)	1.9
V-8-302-351W engs	
right side-one (.8)	1.0
left side-one (.6)	.8
all-both sides (1.2)	1.6
351M-400 engs	
one (.7)	.9
all (1.2)	1.6
460 eng	
one (.8)	1.2
all-one side (.9)	1.4
all-both sides (1.4)	2.0
F100-350	
Six-one (.8)	1.1
all (1.1)	1.5
V-8-255-302-351W	
one (.5)	.9
all-one side (.7)	1.2
all-both sides (1.1)	1.9
351M-400 engs	
one (.5)	.9
all-one side (.6)	1.1
all-both sides (1.0)	1.7
460 eng	
one (.6)	1.0
all-one side (.8)	1.3
all-both sides (1.1)	1.9

Valve Tappets, Renew (All)

Includes: R&R intake manifold where required. Adjust carburetor and ignition timing.

(Factory Time)	Chilton Time
RANGER-BRONCO I & II	
Four	
2.0L eng (1.2)	1.7
2.3L eng (1.6)	2.2
Six (1.7)	3.0
V-6 (5.1)	7.1
V-8-302 eng (2.8)	4.5
w/A.C. add (.4)	.4
w/A.T. add (.2)	.2
AEROSTAR	
Four (5.0)	7.0
V-6 (6.1)	8.5
w/A.C. add (.3)	.3
ECONOLINE-Six (2.1)	3.5

LABOR 12 CYLINDER HEAD & VALVE SYSTEM 12 LABOR

(Factory Time)	Chilton Time
V-8-302-351W engs (2.8)	4.0
F100-350	
Six (1.7)	3.2
V-6 (2.6)	4.5
V-8-255-302	
351W engs (2.7)	4.4
460 eng (3.3)	5.0

Valve Tappets, Renew (Without Removing Intake Manifold)

(Factory Time)	Chilton Time
BRONCO-F100-350-V-8	
351M-400 engs	
one (.6)	1.1
one-each side (.9)	1.6
Each adtnl (4) tappets add (.2)	.4

Valve Spring or Valve Stem Oil Seals, Renew (Head on Truck)

Includes: R&R rocker arms or assy. and adjust valves, if adjustable.

(Factory Time)	Chilton Time
RANGER-BRONCO I & II	
Four	
2.0L eng	
one (.9)	1.4
all (1.7)	2.7
2.3L eng	
one (1.5)	2.1
all (3.1)	4.3
Six-one (.9)	1.3
all (2.1)	2.8
V-6-one (1.0)	1.5
each adtnl (.2)	.3
all (3.0)	4.2
V-8-302-351W engs-one (.6)	.9
each adtnl (.1)	.1
all-both sides (2.4)	3.5
AEROSTAR	
Four-one (1.4)	1.9
all (3.0)	4.2
V-6	
right side-one (1.5)	2.1
left side-one (1.7)	2.3
both sides-all (4.3)	6.0
ECONOLINE-Six-one (1.2)	1.6
all (2.4)	3.2
V-8-302-351W engs	
right side-one (.9)	1.2
left side-one(.7)	1.0
all-both sides (2.7)	3.6
351M-400 engs	
one (.8)	1.1
all (2.6)	3.5
460 eng	
one (.9)	1.3
one-each side (1.4)	1.8
all-both sides (2.8)	3.6
F100-350	
Six-one (.7)	1.0
all (2.0)	2.9
V-6-one (.6)	.9
all (2.0)	3.2
V-8-255-302-351W engs	
one (.6)	1.0
one-each side (.9)	1.3
all-both sides (2.2)	2.9
351M-400 engs	
one (.6)	1.0
one-each side (1.1)	1.5
all-both sides (2.6)	3.3
460 eng	
one (.7)	1.1
one-each side (1.1)	1.5
all-both sides (2.8)	3.5

Valve Clearance, Adjust

(Factory Time)	Chilton Time
FOUR	1.8
V-6	2.7

DIESEL ENGINE

Compression Test

(Factory Time)	Chilton Time
FOUR	1.0
V-8	1.8

Cylinder Head Gasket, Renew

(Factory Time)	Chilton Time
Four	
2.2L eng (2.8)	3.9
2.3L eng (6.2)	8.8
V-8	
F series	
right side (6.0)	8.4
left side (5.4)	7.5
both sides (8.5)	12.0
Econoline	
right side (7.3)	10.2
left side (6.3)	8.8
both sides (9.4)	13.1
w/A.C. add (.4)	.4
w/P.S. add (.5)	.5

Cylinder Head, Renew

Includes: Transfer all components. Clean, replace and lap valves. Make all necessary adjustments.

(Factory Time)	Chilton Time
Four	
2.2L eng (4.4)	6.1
2.3L eng (8.0)	11.3
V-8	
F series	
right side (6.2)	9.0
left side (5.6)	8.1
both sides (8.9)	12.9
Econoline	
right side (7.5)	10.8
left side (6.5)	9.4
both sides (9.8)	14.2
w/A.C. add (.4)	.4
w/P.S. add (.5)	.5

Clean Carbon and Grind Valves

Includes: R&R cylinder head. Reface valves and seats. Make all necessary adjustments.

(Factory Time)	Chilton Time
Four	
2.2L eng (5.9)	8.0
2.3L eng (8.7)	12.3
V-8	
F series	
right side (7.9)	11.4
left side (7.3)	10.5
both sides (12.2)	17.6
Econoline	
right side (9.2)	13.3
left side (8.2)	11.8
both sides (13.1)	18.9
w/A.C. add (.4)	.4
w/P.S. add (.5)	.5

Rocker Arm Cover and/or Gasket, Renew

(Factory Time)	Chilton Time
Four	
2.2L eng (.4)	.7
2.3L eng (.5)	.8
V-8	
F series	
right side (.7)	1.0
left side (.6)	.9
both sides (1.0)	1.6
Econoline	
right side (.9)	1.2
left side (.8)	1.1
both sides (1.3)	1.9

Valve Push Rods and/or Rocker Arms, Renew

(Factory Time)	Chilton Time
Four	
2.2L eng-one (.7)	1.2
all (.9)	1.6
2.3L eng-one (.7)	1.0
all (1.2)	1.7
V-8	
F series	
right side (1.0)	1.4
left side (.9)	1.3
both sides (1.5)	2.3
Econoline	
right side (1.2)	1.6
left side (1.1)	1.5
both sides (1.6)	2.6

Note: If necc to tilt eng to renew rods for # 3 & 5 cyls add&.2.0

Valve Springs and/or Valve Stem Oil Seals, Renew (Head on Truck)

(Factory Time)	Chilton Time
Four	
2.2L eng-one (.9)	1.6
all (1.4)	2.4
2.3L eng-one (.7)	1.1
all (1.7)	2.4
V-8	
F series	
one cyl (.9)	1.3
one cyl-each side (1.4)	2.2
all cyls-both sides (3.4)	4.9
Econoline	
one cyl (1.1)	1.5
one cyl-each side (1.7)	2.5
all cyls-both sides (3.7)	5.4

Valve Tappets, Renew

(Factory Time)	Chilton Time
Four	
2.2L eng	
all (6.1)	8.8
V-8	
F series	
one cyl (2.9)	4.2
all cyls-one side (3.2)	4.6
all cyls-both sides (4.0)	5.8
Econoline	
one cyl (4.0)	5.8
all cyls-one side (4.3)	6.2
all cyls-both sides (5.0)	7.2
w/A.C. add (.4)	.4
w/P.S. add (.5)	.5

LABOR 13 ENGINE ASSEMBLY & MOUNTS 13 LABOR

GASOLINE ENGINES

Engine Assembly, Remove & Install

Includes: R&R hood and radiator, adjust carburetor and linkage.

Does not include transfer of any parts or equipment.

(Factory Time)	Chilton Time
RANGER-BRONCO I & II	
Four 2.0L eng	
w/M.T. (3.1)	4.4
w/A.T. (3.4)	4.7
2.3L eng	
w/M.T. (4.5)	6.3
w/A.T. (3.4)	4.7
w/P.S. add (.2)	.2

(Factory Time)	Chilton Time
w/A.C. add (1.0)	1.0
Six (3.3)	4.8
V-6 (5.3)	7.2
V-8-302-351W engs	
w/M.T. (2.9)	4.2
w/A.T. (3.3)	4.8
351M-400 engs	
w/M.T. (2.6)	3.8
w/A.T. (3.3)	4.8
AEROSTAR	
Four (5.8)	8.1
V-6 (6.9)	9.6
w/A.C. add (.9)	.9
ECONOLINE	
Six-w/M.T. (6.3)	8.8
w/A.T. (5.8)	8.1
V-8-302-351W engs (3.9)	5.6
351M-400 engs (5.6)	7.8
460 eng (5.6)	7.1
F100-250-Six	
std trans (2.4)	3.9
auto trans (2.8)	4.3
V-6 (4.4)	6.2
V-8-255-302	
351W engs (2.9)	4.4
351M-400 engs (3.1)	4.6
460 eng (3.9)	5.4
F350	
w/Std trans (2.6)	4.1
351-400 engs	
auto trans (3.1)	4.6
w/P.S. add (.4)	.4
w/A.C. add (.6)	.6

Engine Assembly, Replace With New or Rebuilt Unit (With Cyl. Heads and Oil Pan)

Includes: R&R hood and radiator. R&R engine assembly, transfer all necessary parts, fuel and electrical units. Tune engine. Road test.

(Factory Time)	Chilton Time
BRONCO	
Six (5.0)	7.2
V-8-302-351W engs	
w/M.T. (6.2)	9.7
w/A.T. (6.6)	10.3
ECONOLINE	
Six-w/M.T. (8.0)	11.2
w/A.T. (7.5)	10.7
V-8-302-351W engs (6.2)	9.0
460 eng (8.9)	11.1
F100-250-Six	
std trans (5.1)	7.3
auto trans (5.5)	7.7
V-8-255-302	
351W engs (5.8)	8.0
351M-400 engs (6.0)	8.2
460 eng (7.2)	9.4
F350	
w/Std trans (5.5)	7.7
351-400 engs	
auto trans (6.0)	8.2
w/P.S. add (.4)	.4
w/A.C. add (.6)	.6

Cylinder Assembly, Renew (w/All Internal Parts Less Head(s) and Oil Pan)

Includes: R&R hood and radiator. R&R engine, transfer all component parts not supplied with replacement engine, clean carbon, grind valves, Minor tune up. Road test.

(Factory Time)	Chilton Time
RANGER-BRONCO I & II	
Four	
2.0L eng	
w/M.T. (9.7)	14.0
w/A.T. (10.0)	14.3
2.3L eng	
w/M.T. (11.4)	16.5
w/A.T. (10.3)	14.9
w/P.S. add (.2)	.2
w/A.C. add (1.0)	1.0
Six (10.7)	15.8
V-6 (13.2)	17.9
V-8-302-351W engs	
w/M.T. (10.8)	15.9
w/A.T. (11.2)	16.5
351M-400 engs	
w/M.T. (10.8)	15.9
w/A.T. (11.5)	16.9
AEROSTAR	
Four (12.7)	18.4
V-6 (14.5)	21.0
w/A.C. add (.9)	.9
ECONOLINE	
Six-w/M.T. (13.7)	20.2
w/A.T. (13.0)	19.5
V-8-302-351W engs (12.6)	18.6
351M-400 engs (14.6)	20.6
460 eng (15.5)	19.4
F100-250-Six	
std trans (14.8)	18.4
auto trans (15.2)	18.8
V-6 (11.3)	16.0
V-8-255-302	
351W engs (11.7)	15.4
351M-400 engs (12.2)	15.9
460 eng (13.8)	17.7
F350	
w/Std trans (12.1)	15.6
351-400 engs	
auto trans (12.2)	15.9
w/P.S. add (.4)	.4
w/A.C. add (.6)	.6

Engine Assembly, R&R and Recondition (Complete)

Includes: R&R hood and radiator. Rebore block, install new pistons, rings, rod and main bearings. Clean carbon, grind valves. Tune engine. Road test.

(Factory Time)	Chilton Time
RANGER-BRONCO I & II	
Four	
2.0L eng	
w/M.T. (16.4)	23.2
w/A.T. (16.7)	23.5
2.3L eng	
w/M.T. (16.9)	23.8
w/A.T. (15.8)	22.2
w/P.S. add (.2)	.2
w/A.C. add (1.0)	1.0
Six (19.1)	27.3
V-6 (19.5)	26.9
V-8-302-351W engs	
w/M.T. (24.5)	31.8
w/A.T. (24.9)	32.2
351M-400 engs	
w/M.T. (24.2)	31.5
w/A.T. (24.9)	32.2
AEROSTAR	
Four (17.1)	24.1
V-6 (20.4)	28.7
w/A.C. add (.9)	.9
ECONOLINE	
Six-w/M.T. (22.1)	29.3
w/A.T. (21.4)	29.6
V-8-302-351W engs (25.5)	31.8
351M-400 engs (27.2)	34.0
460 eng (34.7)	41.4
F100-250-Six	
std trans (23.9)	30.0
auto trans (24.3)	33.4
V-6 (23.8)	32.0
V-8-255-302	
351W engs (29.5)	37.3
351M-400 engs (29.7)	37.5
460 eng (31.2)	39.1
F350	
w/Std trans (29.2)	37.3
351-400 engs	
auto trans (29.7)	37.8
w/P.S. add (.4)	.4
w/A.C. add (.6)	.6

Engine Mounts, Renew

(Factory Time)	Chilton Time
Front	
RANGER-BRONCO-AEROSTAR	
Four	
2.0L eng-one (.4)	.6
both (.5)	.9
2.3L eng-one (1.4)	1.9
both (1.5)	2.0
Six-one (.4)	.7
both (.5)	1.1
V-6-right (.7)	1.0
left (.6)	.9
both (.9)	1.4
V-8-302-351W engs	
one (.4)	.6
both (.6)	1.0
351M-400 engs	
right (.7)	.9
left (.5)	.8
both (.8)	1.3
ECONOLINE	
Six-one (.4)	.7
both (.4)	1.0
V-8-302-351-400 engs	
right (.8)	1.1
left (.7)	1.0
both (1.0)	1.5
F100-350	
Six-one (.4)	.7
both (.5)	.9
V-6-right (.7)	1.0
left (.5)	.7
both (.9)	1.4
V-8-255-302-351W engs	
one (.4)	.7
both (.6)	1.0
351M-400 engs-one (.7)	1.2
both (.9)	1.5
460 eng-one (.6)	.8
both (.7)	1.1
Rear	
Ranger (.4)	.6
Bronco (.6)	.8
Aerostar (.5)	.7
Econoline (.4)	.7
F100-350	
one (.4)	.7
both (.5)	1.1

DIESEL ENGINE

Engine Assembly, Remove & Install

Includes: R&R hood and radiator. Does not include transfer of any parts or equipment.

(Factory Time)	Chilton Time
Four	
2.2L eng (3.7)	5.1
2.3L eng (4.6)	6.5
w/A.C. add (.4)	.4
w/P.S. add (.5)	.5
V-8	
F series (5.7)	7.9
w/A.T. add (.6)	.6
4X4 add (.2)	.2
Econoline (6.5)	9.1
w/A.C. add	
F series (.3)	.3
Econoline (1.0)	1.0

Cylinder Assembly, Renew (w/All Internal Parts Less Head(s) and Oil Pan)

Includes: R&R hood and radiator. R&R engine, transfer all component parts not supplied with replacement engine. Clean carbon, grind valves. Make all necessary adjustments.

(Factory Time)	Chilton Time
Four	
2.2L eng (12.6)	17.3
2.3L eng (11.6)	16.5

LABOR 13 ENGINE ASSEMBLY & MOUNTS 13 LABOR

(Factory Time)	Chilton Time
w/A.C. add (.4)	.4
w/P.S. add (.5)	.5
V-8	
F series (14.9)	20.8
w/A.T. add (.6)	.6
4X4 add (.2)	.2
Econoline (15.7)	21.9
w/A.C. add	
F series (.3)	.3
Econoline (1.0)	1.0

Engine Assembly, R&R and Recondition (Complete)

Includes: R&R hood and radiator. Install new cylinder sleeves, pistons, rings, rod and main bearings. Clean carbon, grind valves. Make all necessary adjustments.

(Factory Time)	Chilton Time
Four	
2.2L eng (17.7)	24.7
2.3L eng (16.6)	23.5
w/A.C. add (.4)	.4
w/P.S. add (.5)	.5
V-8	
F series (27.2)	38.0
w/A.T. add (.6)	.6
4X4 add (.2)	.2
Econoline (28.0)	39.2
w/A.C. add	
F series (.3)	.3
Econoline (1.0)	1.0

Engine Mounts, Renew

(Factory Time)	Chilton Time
Front	
Four-one (.6)	.8
both (.9)	1.2
V-8	
F series	
right (1.8)	2.4
left (1.6)	2.1
both (1.9)	2.6
Econoline	
right (1.9)	2.5
left (1.8)	2.3
both (2.1)	2.8
Rear	
Four (.4)	.6
V-8 (.4)	.6

LABOR 14 PISTONS, RINGS & BEARINGS 14 LABOR

GASOLINE ENGINES

Rings, Renew (All)

Includes: Remove cylinder top ridge, deglaze cylinder walls, replace rod bearings, clean carbon. Minor tune up.

(Factory Time)	Chilton Time
RANGER-BRONCO I & II	
Four	
2.0L eng (8.2)	12.8
2.3L eng (7.9)	12.5
w/A.C. & P.S. add (.6)	.6
Six (7.5)	11.1
V-6 (10.9)	15.2
V-8-302-351W engs (10.2)	15.0
351M-400 engs (10.3)	15.1
AEROSTAR	
Four (8.0)	11.9
V-6 (10.8)	15.2
w/A.C. add (.3)	.3
ECONOLINE-Six (8.5)	12.7
V-8-302-351W engs (14.5)	18.0
460 eng (17.3)	20.8
F100-350	
Six (8.5)	11.6
V-6 (10.1)	14.3
V-8-255-302	
351W engs (9.6)	13.1
351M-400 engs (11.1)	14.6
460 eng (13.6)	17.1

Piston or Connecting Rod, Renew (One)

Includes: Remove cylinder top ridge, deglaze cylinder walls, replace rod bearings, clean carbon. Minor tune up.

(Factory Time)	Chilton Time
RANGER-BRONCO I & II	
Four	
2.0L eng (7.2)	10.0
2.3L eng (7.2)	10.0
w/A.C. & P.S. add (.6)	.6
Six (5.2)	7.6
V-6 (7.8)	10.9
V-8-302-351W engs (5.6)	8.2
351M-400 engs (5.3)	7.8
AEROSTAR	
Four (7.3)	10.0
V-6 (7.9)	10.9
w/A.C. add (.3)	.3
ECONOLINE-Six (5.7)	7.4
V-8-302-351W engs (8.8)	10.7
460 eng (9.8)	11.7
F100-350	
Six (5.7)	7.4
V-6 (6.3)	8.9
V-8-255-302	
351W engs (4.6)	6.8
351M-400 engs (5.8)	7.5
460 eng (7.2)	9.0

COMBINATIONS

Add to Engine Work

(Factory Time)	Chilton Time
DRAIN, EVACUATE & RECHARGE AIR CONDITIONING SYSTEM	
All models (.7)	1.5
ROCKER ARMS OR SHAFT ASSY. DISASSEMBLE AND CLEAN OR RECONDITION	
Six (.6)	1.0
V-8-One side (.5)	.7
Both sides (1.0)	1.3
HYDRAULIC VALVE LIFTERS, DISASSEMBLE AND CLEAN	
Each (.2)	.2
ROCKER ARM STUD, RENEW	
Each (.3)	.3
DISTRIBUTOR, RECONDITION	
All models (.7)	1.0
CARBURETOR, RECONDITION	
1 BBL (.9)	1.2
2 BBL (1.0)	1.3
4 BBL	
Ford (1.0)	1.5
Holly (1.3)	2.0
TIMING CHAIN, RENEW (COVER REMOVED)	
All models (.3)	.5
VALVE GUIDES, REAM OVERSIZE	
Each (.1)	.2
DEGLAZE CYLINDER WALLS	
Each (.1)	.2
REMOVE CYLINDER TOP RIDGE	
Each (.1)	.1
MAIN BEARINGS, RENEW (PAN REMOVED)	
Four (1.9)	2.9
Six (1.6)	2.5
V-6 (1.5)	2.0
V-8 (1.9)	2.9
PLASTIGAUGE BEARINGS	
Each (.1)	.1
OIL PUMP, RECONDITION	
All models (.4)	.6
OIL FILTER ELEMENT, RENEW	
All models (.3)	.4

Connecting Rod Bearings, Renew

Includes: R&R oil pan, plastigauge and install new bearings. Clean oil pump pick up tube and screen. Renew oil filter.

(Factory Time)	Chilton Time
RANGER-BRONCO	
Four	
2.0L eng	
w/M.T. (3.1)	4.4
w/A.T. (3.5)	4.8
2.3L eng	
w/M.T. (3.9)	5.4
w/A.T. (3.3)	4.6
Six (3.5)	4.8
V-6	
4X2	
w/M.T. (3.3)	4.6
w/A.T. (3.4)	4.8
4X4	
w/M.T. (4.5)	6.3
w/A.T. (4.7)	6.5
V-8-302-351W engs (4.0)	5.7
351M-400 engs (4.2)	5.9
AEROSTAR	
Four (2.6)	3.6
V-6 (3.2)	4.4
ECONOLINE	
Six (3.9)	5.7
V-8-302-351W engs (6.3)	8.0
351M-400 engs (5.1)	6.9
460 eng (4.4)	5.4
F100-350 4X2	
Six (3.5)	4.5
V-6 (3.2)	4.6
V-8-255-302	
351W engs (3.1)	4.1
351M-400 engs	
std trans (3.4)	4.4
auto trans (3.7)	4.7
F100-250 4X4	
351-400 engs (3.6)	4.6
460 eng (4.0)	5.0

LABOR 14 PISTONS, RINGS & BEARINGS 14 LABOR

(Factory Time) Chilton Time

DIESEL ENGINE

Rings, Renew (All)

Includes: Remove cylinder top ridge, deglaze cylinder walls, replace rod bearings, clean carbon. Make all necessary adjustments.

Four
- 2.2L eng (8.8) ... 12.3
- 2.3L eng (8.8) ... 12.3

V-8
- F series (15.3) ... 22.1
- Econoline (15.8) ... 22.9

w/A.C. add
- F series (.3) 3
- Econoline (1.0) ... 1.0

Piston or Connecting Rod, Renew (One)

Includes: Remove cylinder top ridge, deglaze cylinder wall, replace rod bearing, clean carbon. Make all necessary adjustments.

Four
- 2.2L eng (7.9) ... 11.0
- 2.3L eng (7.7) ... 11.0

V-8
- F series (11.6) ... 16.8
- Econoline (12.1) ... 17.5

w/A.C. add
- F series (.3) 3
- Econoline (1.0) ... 1.0

Connecting Rod Bearings, Renew

Four
- 2.2L eng (4.2) ... 6.0
- 2.3L eng (3.7) ... 5.2

V-8
- F series
  - 4X2 (4.7) ... 6.8
  - 4X4 (5.2) ... 7.5
- Econoline (5.4) ... 7.8

LABOR 15 CRANKSHAFT & DAMPER 15 LABOR

(Factory Time) Chilton Time

GASOLINE ENGINES

Crankshaft and Main Bearings, Renew

Includes: R&R hood and radiator. R&R engine, check all bearing clearances.

RANGER-BRONCO I & II
- Four
  - 2.0L eng
    - w/M.T. (6.9) ... 9.7
    - w/A.T. (7.3) ... 10.3
  - 2.3L eng
    - w/M.T. (8.1) ... 11.4
    - w/A.T. (7.0) ... 10.3
- w/P.S. add (.2) 2
- w/A.C. add (1.0) ... 1.0
  - Six (7.9) ... 12.0
  - V-6 (8.9) ... 12.9
  - V-8-302-351W engs
    - w/M.T. (6.7) ... 10.2
    - w/A.T. (6.1) ... 9.2
  - 351M-400 engs
    - w/M.T. (6.8) ... 10.3
    - w/A.T. (7.5) ... 11.3

AEROSTAR
- Four (9.4) ... 13.6
- V-6 (10.5) ... 15.2
- w/A.C. add (.9) 9

ECONOLINE
- Six-w/M.T. (10.9) ... 16.5
  - w/A.T. (10.4) ... 15.7
- V-8-302-351W engs (7.7) ... 11.6
- 351M-400 engs (9.8) ... 14.8
- 460 eng (10.0) ... 13.4

F100-250-Six
- std trans (7.0) ... 10.4
- auto trans (7.4) ... 10.8
- V-6 (7.7) ... 10.8
- V-8-255-302
  - 351W engs (6.8) ... 11.3
  - 351M-400 engs (7.3) ... 11.8
- 460 eng (8.3) ... 12.8

F350
- w/Std trans (7.0) ... 11.0
- 351-400 engs
  - auto trans (7.3) ... 11.8

Main Bearings, Renew

Includes: R&R oil pan, plastigauge and install new main bearings. Recondition oil pump and renew oil filter.

RANGER-BRONCO I & II
- Four
  - 2.0L eng
    - w/M.T. (4.1) ... 5.9
    - w/A.T. (4.5) ... 6.3
  - 2.3L eng
    - w/M.T. (4.8) ... 6.9
    - w/A.T. (4.2) ... 6.0
  - Six (3.7) ... 5.5
  - V-6 (7.8) ... *11.3
- w/A.C. add (.4) 4
- w/A.T. add (.2) 2
  - V-8-302-351W engs (4.1) ... 6.2
  - 351M-400 engs (4.3) ... 6.4

AEROSTAR
- Four (3.5) ... 5.0

ECONOLINE
- Six (4.1) ... 6.4
- V-8-302-351W engs (6.4) ... 8.5
  - 351M-400 engs (5.2) ... 7.4
  - 460 eng (4.6) ... 5.8

F100-350 4X2
- Six-std trans (6.6) ... *10.0
  - auto trans (7.0) ... *10.4
- V-6 (3.3) ... 4.6
- V-8-255-302
  - 351W engs (3.3) ... 4.7
- 351M-400 engs
  - std trans (3.6) ... 5.1
  - auto trans (4.0) ... 5.5

F100-250 4X4
- 351-400 engs (3.8) ... 5.3
- 460 eng (4.2) ... 5.6

*Includes R&R engine.

Main and Rod Bearings, Renew

Includes: R&R oil pan, plastigauge and install new rod and main bearings. Recondition oil pump and renew oil filter.

RANGER-BRONCO I & II
- Four
  - 2.0L eng
    - w/M.T. (5.0) ... 7.1
    - w/A.T. (5.4) ... 7.5
  - 2.3L eng
    - w/M.T. (5.8) ... 8.1
    - w/A.T. (5.2) ... 7.2
  - Six (5.1) ... 7.3
  - V-6 (8.8) ... *12.5
- w/A.C. add (.4) 4
- w/A.T. add (.2) 2
  - V-8-302-351W engs (5.9) ... 8.6
  - 351M-400 engs (6.1) ... 8.8

AEROSTAR
- Four (4.5) ... 6.8

ECONOLINE
- Six (5.5) ... 8.2
- V-8-302-351W engs (8.2) ... 10.9
- 351M-400 engs (7.0) ... 9.8
  - 460 eng (6.3) ... 7.9

F100-350 4X2
- Six-std trans (8.2) ... *11.6
  - auto trans (8.6) ... *12.0
- V-6 (4.7) ... 6.4
- V-8-255-302
  - 351W engs (5.0) ... 6.8
- 351M-400 engs
  - std trans (5.3) ... 7.3
  - auto trans (5.7) ... 7.7

F100-250 4X4
- 351-400 engs (5.5) ... 7.4
- 460 eng (5.9) ... 7.7

*Includes R&R engine.

Rear Main Bearing Oil Seal, Renew (Upper & Lower) Split Lip Type

Includes: R&R transmission on all 6 cyl models. Includes R&R oil pan on all V-8 models.

RANGER-BRONCO-AEROSTAR
- Four
  - 2.0L eng
    - w/M.T. (3.0) ... 4.2
    - w/A.T. (3.4) ... 4.7
  - 2.3L eng
    - 4X2-w/M.T. (2.0) ... 2.8
      - w/A.T. (3.3) ... 4.6
    - 4X4-w/M.T. (3.4) ... 4.7
- V-6
  - 4X2-w/M.T. (3.3) ... 4.6
    - w/A.T. (3.6) ... 5.0
  - 4X4 (4.2) ... 5.9
- Six (4.4) ... 6.1
- V-8-302-351W engs (2.9) ... 4.3
- 351M-400 engs (3.1) ... 4.5

ECONOLINE
- Six-w/M.T. (1.6) ... 2.2
  - w/A.T. (2.7) ... 3.4
- V-8-302-351W engs (5.2) ... 6.6
- 351M-400 engs (4.0) ... 5.5
  - 460 eng (3.5) ... 4.2

F100-250-Six
- 3 spd (1.9) ... 2.5
- 4 spd (2.4) ... 3.1
- auto trans (2.3) ... 3.0
- V-6 (2.5) ... 3.5
- V-8-255-302
  - 351W engs (2.2) ... 2.9
- 351M-400 engs
  - std trans (2.5) ... 3.2
  - auto trans (2.8) ... 3.5
- F350
  - 351-400 engs (2.7) ... 3.4
  - 460 eng (3.1) ... 3.8

Crankshaft Front Oil Seal, Renew

Does not require R&R of front cover on V-6 & V-8 engines.

RANGER-BRONCO II-AEROSTAR
- Four-2.0L eng
  - Crank (1.7) ... 2.3
  - Cam (1.7) ... 2.3
  - Aux Shaft (1.8) ... 2.5
- w/A.C. add (.3) 3

LABOR 15 CRANKSHAFT & DAMPER 15 LABOR

(Factory Time)	Chilton Time
2.3L eng	
Crank (1.6)	2.2
Cam (1.5)	2.1
Aux shaft (1.5)	2.1
All (1.9)	2.7
V-6	
w/M.T. (1.0)	1.6
w/A.T. (1.1)	1.7
BRONCO-F150-350 4X4	
351M-400 engs (.8)	1.3
V-6 (1.0)	1.5
w/A.T. add (.1)	.1

DIESEL ENGINE

Crankshaft and Main Bearings, Renew

Includes: R&R engine assy., check all bearing clearances.

(Factory Time)	Chilton Time
Four	
2.2L eng (7.4)	10.7
2.3L eng (8.0)	11.6
V-8	
F series (11.8)	17.1
w/A.T. add (.6)	.6
4X4 add (.2)	.2
Econoline (12.6)	18.7
w/A.C. add	
F series (.3)	.3
Econoline (1.0)	1.0

Main Bearings, Renew

Includes: Check all bearing clearances.

(Factory Time)	Chilton Time
Four	
2.2L eng (5.0)	7.0
2.3L eng (4.6)	6.6
V-8	
F series	
4X2 (5.4)	7.8
4X4 (5.9)	8.5
Econoline (6.1)	8.8

Main and Rod Bearings, Renew

Includes: Check all bearing clearances.

(Factory Time)	Chilton Time
Four	
2.2L eng (6.0)	8.2
2.3L eng (5.6)	7.8
V-8	
F series	
4X2 (7.5)	10.2
4X4 (8.0)	10.9
Econoline (8.2)	11.2

Crankshaft Front Oil Seal, Renew

(Factory Time)	Chilton Time
Four	
2.2L eng (.9)	1.4
2.3L eng (1.7)	2.5
V-8	
F series (1.7)	2.5
Econoline (1.2)	1.8
w/A.C. add (.4)	.4
w/P.S. add (.5)	.5

Crankshaft Rear Oil Seal, Renew

(Factory Time)	Chilton Time
Four	
2.2L eng (1.9)	2.7
2.3L eng (3.4)	4.7
V-8	
F series	
4X2-w/M.T. (3.3)	4.8
w/A.T. (3.0)	4.3
4X4-w/M.T. (4.3)	6.2
w/A.T. (4.0)	6.0
Econoline (3.1)	4.5

Crankshaft and/or Camshaft Sprockets, Renew

(Factory Time)	Chilton Time
Four	
2.2L eng (1.9)	2.7
2.3L eng (1.1)	1.6
V-8	
F series (4.1)	5.9
Econoline (4.7)	6.8
w/A.C. add (.4)	.4
w/P.S. add (.5)	.5

Vibration Damper or Pulley, Renew

(Factory Time)	Chilton Time
Four	
2.2L eng (.8)	1.2
2.3L eng (.4)	.7
V-8	
F series (1.5)	2.1
Econoline (1.1)	1.5
w/A.C. add (.1)	.1

LABOR 16 CAMSHAFT & TIMING GEARS 16 LABOR

GASOLINE ENGINES

Timing Case Cover, Gasket or Oil Seal, Renew

Includes: R&R radiator. Does not require oil pan removal on 6 cyl (200) or 302 CID engines.

(Factory Time)	Chilton Time
RANGER-BRONCO-AEROSTAR	
Four	
2.0L eng (2.0)	2.9
2.3L eng (1.9)	2.7
w/P.S. add (.2)	.2
w/A.C. add (.3)	.3
Six (2.4)	3.4
V-6 (4.6)	6.4
V-8-302-351W engs (2.0)	2.8
351M-400 engs (3.8)	5.3
ECONOLINE	
Six (3.2)	4.9
V-8-302-351W engs (3.9)	5.5
351M-400 engs (3.9)	5.5
460 eng (3.0)	3.9
F100-350	
Six (2.4)	3.3
V-6 (3.7)	5.2
V-8-255-302	
351W engs (2.0)	2.9
351M-400 engs (3.4)	4.3
460 eng (2.3)	3.4

Timing Belt, Renew

(Factory Time)	Chilton Time
RANGER-AEROSTAR	
Four	
2.0L eng (1.6)	2.5
2.3L eng (1.3)	2.2
w/P.S. add (.2)	.2
w/A.C. add (.3)	.3

Timing Chain or Gears, Renew (SIX)

Includes: R&R timing case cover and radiator, renew gears or chain. Reset ignition timing.

(Factory Time)	Chilton Time
BRONCO-Six (2.7)	3.9
ECONOLINE-Six (3.5)	5.4
F100-350	
Six (2.7)	4.0

CRANKSHAFT GEAR ONLY. FOR CAMSHAFT FIBER GEAR USE CAMSHAFT, RENEW

Timing Chain or Gears, Renew (V-6 & V-8)

Includes: R&R timing case cover and radiator. Renew gears or chain. Reset ignition timing.

(Factory Time)	Chilton Time
RANGER-BRONCO-AEROSTAR	
V-6 (4.9)	6.9
V-8	
302-351W engs (2.3)	3.3
351M-400 engs (4.1)	5.8
ECONOLINE	
V-8	
302-351W engs (4.2)	5.8
351M-400 engs (4.2)	5.8
460 eng (3.3)	4.4
F100-350	
V-8	
255-302-351W engs (2.3)	3.4
351M-400 engs (3.6)	4.8
460 eng (2.7)	3.9

Camshaft or Camshaft Gear, Renew

Includes: R&R radiator, timing case cover. Adjust carburetor and ignition timing. Does not require oil pan removal on 302-360-390 CID engines.

(Factory Time)	Chilton Time
RANGER-BRONCO	
Four	
2.0L eng (2.2)	3.3
2.3L eng (4.2)	5.9
w/P.S. add (.2)	.2
w/A.C. add (.3)	.3
Six (5.5)	8.0
V-6 (8.9)	12.5
V-8-302-351W engs (5.0)	7.5
351M-400 engs (5.0)	7.5
AEROSTAR	
Four (5.4)	7.5
V-6 (9.6)	13.5
w/A.C. add (.2)	.2
w/P.S. add (.2)	.2
ECONOLINE	
Six (6.5)	9.6
V-8-302-351W engs (5.6)	8.3
351M-400 engs (6.7)	9.9
F100-350	
Six (5.5)	8.0
V-6 (6.9)	9.8
V-8-255-302	
351W engs (5.0)	7.5
351M-400 engs (5.0)	7.5
460 eng (5.6)	8.3

Camshaft Bearings, Renew

Includes: R&R hood, radiator and engine assembly where required. R&R camshaft and renew bearings. Adjust carburetor and ignition timing.

(Factory Time)	Chilton Time
RANGER-BRONCO	
Four	
2.0L eng (2.7)	4.1
w/P.S. add (.2)	.2
w/A.C. add (.3)	.3
Six (7.2)	10.8
V-6 (10.5)	14.7
V-8-302-351W engs	
w/M.T. (7.7)	11.5
w/A.T. (8.1)	12.1
351M-400 engs	
w/M.T. (7.8)	11.6
w/A.T. (8.5)	12.7
AEROSTAR	
V-6 (11.9)	17.2
w/A.C. add (.9)	.9
ECONOLINE	
Six-w/M.T. (10.2)	15.3
w/A.T. (9.7)	14.5
V-8-302-351W engs (8.7)	13.0

LABOR 16 CAMSHAFT & TIMING GEARS 16 LABOR

(Factory Time)	Chilton Time
351M-400 engs (10.8)	16.2
460 eng (11.4)	15.5
F100-250-Six	
std trans (6.2)	7.8
auto trans (6.6)	8.2
V-6 (11.4)	16.0
V-8-255-302	
351W engs (7.7)	9.3
351M-400 engs (8.3)	9.9
F350	
w/Std trans (7.8)	9.4
351-400 engs	
auto trans (8.3)	9.9

DIESEL ENGINE

Timing Cover Gasket, Renew

(Factory Time)	Chilton Time
Four	
2.2L eng (5.5)	7.9
2.3L eng (2.0)	3.0
V-8	
F series (3.9)	5.6
Econoline (4.5)	6.5
w/A.C. add (.4)	.4
w/P.S. add (.5)	.5

Camshaft, Renew

(Factory Time)	Chilton Time
Four	
2.2L eng (6.1)	8.8
2.3L eng (1.5)	2.2
V-8	
F series (8.5)	12.3
Econoline (9.5)	13.7
w/A.C. add	
F series (.3)	.3
Econoline (1.0)	1.0

Camshaft and/or Crankshaft Sprockets, Renew

(Factory Time)	Chilton Time
Four	
2.2L eng (1.9)	2.7
2.3L eng (1.1)	1.6
V-8	
F series (4.1)	5.9
Econoline (4.7)	6.8
w/A.C. add (.4)	.4
w/P.S. add (.5)	.5

Camshaft Idler Gear, Renew

(Factory Time)	Chilton Time
Four	
2.2L eng (2.0)	2.7
2.3L eng (1.0)	1.5
w/A.C. add (.4)	.4
w/P.S. add (.5)	.5

Timing Belt, Renew

(Factory Time)	Chilton Time
Four	
2.3L eng (1.0)	1.5

LABOR 17 ENGINE OILING SYSTEM 17 LABOR

GASOLINE ENGINES

Oil Pan or Gasket, Renew

Includes: Clean oil pick up tube and screen. Renew oil filter.

(Factory Time)	Chilton Time
RANGER-BRONCO	
Four	
2.0L eng	
w/M.T. (2.2)	3.0
w/A.T. (2.6)	3.6
2.3L eng	
4X2-w/M.T. (2.9)	4.0
w/A.T. (2.3)	3.2
4X4-w/M.T. (3.4)	4.7
w/A.T. (3.6)	5.0
Six (2.1)	3.0
V-6	
4X2	
w/M.T. (2.2)	3.0
w/A.T. (2.3)	3.2
4X4	
w/M.T. (3.4)	4.8
w/A.T. (3.6)	5.0
V-8-302-351W engs (2.2)	3.3
351M-400 engs (2.4)	3.5
AEROSTAR	
Four (1.6)	2.2
V-6 (2.2)	3.0
ECONOLINE	
Six (2.5)	3.9
V-8-302-351W engs (4.5)	5.6
351M-400 engs (3.3)	4.5
460 eng (2.7)	3.8
F100-350 4X2	
Six (1.9)	2.9
V-6 (1.8)	2.5
V-8-255-302	
351W engs (1.4)	2.4
351M-400 engs	
std trans (1.7)	2.8
auto trans (2.0)	3.1
F100-250 4X4	
351-400 engs (1.9)	2.9
460 eng (2.3)	3.4

Oil Pump, R&R or Renew

Includes: R&R oil pan, clean oil pump pick up tube and screen. Renew oil filter.

(Factory Time)	Chilton Time
RANGER-BRONCO	
Four	
2.0L eng	
w/M.T. (2.4)	3.2
w/A.T. (2.8)	3.8
2.3L eng	
4X2-w/M.T. (3.0)	4.2
w/A.T. (2.4)	3.4
4X4-w/M.T. (3.5)	4.9
w/A.T. (3.7)	5.2
Six (2.2)	3.2
V-6	
4X2	
w/M.T. (2.3)	3.2
w/A.T. (2.4)	3.4
4X4	
w/M.T. (3.5)	5.0
w/A.T. (3.7)	5.2
V-8-302-351W engs (2.3)	3.5
351M-400 engs (2.5)	3.7
AEROSTAR	
Four (1.7)	2.4
V-6 (2.3)	3.2
ECONOLINE	
Six (2.6)	4.1
V-8-302-351W engs (4.6)	5.8
351M-400 engs (3.4)	4.7
460 eng (2.7)	4.0
F100-350 4X2	
Six (2.1)	3.1
V-6 (.7)	1.1
V-8-255-302	
351W engs (1.5)	2.6
351M-400 engs	
std trans (1.9)	3.0
auto trans (2.1)	3.3
F100-250 4X4	
351-400 engs (2.0)	3.1
460 eng (2.4)	3.6
Recond pump add (.4)	.5

Pressure Test Engine Bearings (Pan Off)

(Factory Time)	Chilton Time
All models	1.0

Oil Pressure Gauge (Engine), Renew

(Factory Time)	Chilton Time
All models (.3)	.5

Oil Pressure Gauge (Dash), Renew

(Factory Time)	Chilton Time
RANGER (.6)	1.0
BRONCO (.4)	.7
BRONCO II (.6)	1.0
AEROSTAR (.6)	1.0
ECONOLINE (.5)	.8
F100-350 (.5)	1.0

Oil Filter Element, Renew

(Factory Time)	Chilton Time
All models (.3)	.4

DIESEL ENGINE

Oil Pan and/or Gasket, Renew

(Factory Time)	Chilton Time
Four	
2.2L eng (3.2)	4.5
2.3L eng (2.7)	3.7
V-8	
F series	3.6
4X2 (2.6)	3.6
4X4 (3.1)	4.3
Econoline (3.3)	4.7

Pressure Test Engine Bearings (Pan Off)

(Factory Time)	Chilton Time
All models	1.0

Oil Pump, Renew

(Factory Time)	Chilton Time
Four	
2.2L eng (3.4)	4.8
2.3L eng (1.4)	1.9
V-8	
F series	
4X2 (2.8)	3.9
4X4 (3.3)	4.6
Econoline (3.5)	5.0
Recond pump add	.5

Oil Cooler Assembly, Renew

(Factory Time)	Chilton Time
V-8 (1.6)	2.3

Oil Filter Element, Renew

(Factory Time)	Chilton Time
All models (.3)	.4

LABOR 18 CLUTCH & FLYWHEEL 18 LABOR

(Factory Time)	Chilton Time
Clutch Pedal Free Play, Adjust	
All models (.3)	.4
Clutch Master Cylinder Control Assy., Renew	
RANGER (.6)	1.0

Clutch Assembly, Renew

Includes: R&R trans and transfer case as a unit. Adjust clutch pedal free play.

(Factory Time)	Chilton Time
RANGER	
4 Speed	
4X2	
Four (2.0)	2.8
V-6 (2.5)	3.3
4X4	
Four (2.9)	3.9
V-6 (3.8)	5.2
5 Speed	
4X2	
Four (2.0)	2.8
V-6 (2.7)	3.6
4X4 (3.8)	5.2
AEROSTAR	
Four-TK-5 (2.0)	2.8
V-6-TK-5 (2.3)	3.1
BRONCO	
3 Speed (3.1)	4.1
4 Speed	
Warner T-18 (4.1)	5.4
SROD (3.3)	4.3
New Process 435 (4.2)	5.5
5 Speed	
TK-5 (3.8)	4.9
ECONOLINE	
3 Speed (1.4)	2.7
4 Speed (2.3)	3.5
4 Speed O.D. (1.6)	2.9
4 Speed	
New Process 435 (2.4)	3.6
F100-350 4X2	
3 Speed	
column shift (2.2)	3.3
floor shift (1.5)	2.4
4 Speed	
Overdrive (1.6)	2.5
SROD (1.6)	2.5
TOD (2.2)	3.0
Warner T-18 (2.4)	3.5
Warner T-19 (3.0)	4.0
New Process 435 (2.4)	3.5
F100-350 4X4	
4 Speed	
TOD (3.9)	5.3
Warner T-18 (4.1)	5.4
New Process 435 (4.2)	5.5
SROD (3.3)	4.3
Warner T-19 (3.9)	5.1
w/Skid plate add (.2)	.3
w/Full carpet add (.7)	1.0
w/P.T.O. add (.6)	.8
w/Coupling shaft add (.2)	.3

Clutch Release Bearing, Renew

Includes: R&R trans and transfer case as a unit. Adjust clutch pedal free play.

(Factory Time)	Chilton Time
RANGER	
4 Speed	
4X2	
Four (1.7)	2.5
V-6 (1.7)	3.0
4X4	
Four (3.4)	3.6
V-6 (3.4)	4.9
5 Speed	
4X2	
Four (1.7)	2.5
V-6 (1.7)	3.3
4X4 (3.4)	4.9
AEROSTAR	
Four-TK-5 (2.1)	2.7
V-6-TK-5 (2.1)	3.0
BRONCO	
3 Speed (2.4)	3.4
4 Speed	
Warner T-18 (3.4)	4.7
New Process 435 (3.5)	4.8
SROD (2.6)	3.6
5 Speed	
TK-5 (2.6)	4.8
ECONOLINE	
3 Speed (.8)	2.0
4 Speed (1.7)	2.6
4 Speed O.D. (1.0)	2.0
4 Speed	
New Process 435 (1.7)	2.8
F100-350 4X2	
3 Speed (.8)	1.7
4 Speed	
Overdrive (1.0)	1.8
SROD (.9)	1.8
TOD (1.6)	2.2
Warner T-18 (1.7)	2.8
Warner T-19 (2.2)	3.0
New Process 435 (1.7)	2.8
F100-350 4X4	
4 Speed	
TOD (3.3)	4.5
Warner T-18 (3.4)	4.7
New Process 435 (3.5)	4.8
SROD (2.6)	3.6
Warner T-19 (3.1)	4.5
w/Skid plate add (.2)	.3
w/Full carpet add (.7)	1.0
w/P.T.O. add (.6)	.8
w/Coupling shaft add (.2)	.3

Flywheel, Renew

Includes: R&R trans and transfer case as a unit. R&R clutch and adjust free play.

(Factory Time)	Chilton Time
RANGER	
4 Speed	
4X2	
Four (2.3)	3.1
V-6 (2.8)	3.6
4X4	
Four (3.2)	4.2
V-6 (4.1)	5.5
5 Speed	
4X2	
Four (2.3)	3.1
V-6 (3.0)	3.9
4X4 (4.1)	5.5
AEROSTAR	
Four-TK-5 (1.2)	3.1
V-6-TK-5 (2.8)	3.7
BRONCO	
3 Speed (3.2)	4.4
4 Speed	
Warner T-18 (4.2)	5.7
SROD (3.4)	4.6
New Process 435 (4.4)	5.8
5 Speed	
TK-5 (4.0)	5.2
ECONOLINE	
3 Speed (1.5)	3.0
4 Speed (2.4)	3.8
4 Speed O.D. (1.6)	3.2
4 Speed	
New Process 435 (2.5)	3.9
F100-350 4X2	
3 Speed	
column shift (2.3)	3.6
floor shift (1.7)	3.0
4 Speed	
Overdrive (1.8)	2.8
SROD (1.7)	2.8
TOD (2.4)	3.3
Warner T-18 (2.5)	3.8
Warner T-19 (4.0)	5.4
New Process 435 (2.5)	3.8
F100-350 4X4	
4 Speed	
TOD (4.1)	5.6
Warner T-18 (4.2)	5.7
New Process 435 (4.3)	5.8
SROD (3.4)	4.6
Warner T-19 (4.2)	5.4
w/Skid plate add (.2)	.3
w/Full carpet add (.7)	1.0
Renew ring gear add (.2)	.4
w/P.T.O. add (.6)	.8
w/Coupling shaft add (.2)	.3

LABOR 19 STANDARD TRANSMISSION 19 LABOR

Transmission Assy., Remove and Reinstall

Includes: R&R transmission and transfer case as a unit.

(Factory Time)	Chilton Time
RANGER	
4 Speed	
4X2	
Four (1.7)	2.5
V-6 (2.2)	3.0
4X4	
Four (2.6)	3.6
V-6 (3.5)	4.9
5 Speed	
4X2	
Four (1.7)	2.5
V-6 (2.4)	3.3
4X4 (3.5)	4.9
AEROSTAR	
Four-TK-5 (1.7)	2.5
V-6-TK-5 (2.0)	2.8
BRONCO	
3 Speed (2.4)	3.2
4 Speed	
Warner T-18 (3.4)	4.5
SROD (2.6)	3.4
New Process 435 (3.5)	4.6
5 Speed	
TK-5 (3.5)	4.6
ECONOLINE	
3 speed (.8)	1.8
4 speed (1.7)	2.6
4 speed O.D. (.9)	1.8
4 Speed	
New Process 435 (1.7)	2.6
F100-350 4X2	
3 Speed (.8)	1.5
4 Speed	
Overdrive (.9)	1.6
SROD (.9)	1.6
TOD (1.5)	2.1

LABOR 19 STANDARD TRANSMISSION 19 LABOR

(Factory Time)	Chilton Time
Warner T-18 (1.7)	2.6
Warner T-19 (2.2)	3.0
New Process 435 (1.7)	2.6
F100-350 4X4	
4 Speed	
TOD (3.2)	4.4
Warner T-18 (3.4)	4.5
New Process 435 (3.5)	4.6
SROD (2.6)	3.4
Warner T-19 (3.1)	4.3
w/Skid plate add (.2)	.3
w/Full carpet add (.7)	1.0
w/P.T.O. add (.6)	.8
w/Coupling shaft add (.2)	.3

Transmission Assy., R&R and Recondition

Includes: R&R trans and transfer case as a unit. Separate and overhaul transmission only.

(Factory Time)	Chilton Time
RANGER	
4 Speed	
4X2	
Four (3.9)	5.5
V-6 (4.4)	6.1
4X4	
Four (4.8)	6.7
V-6 (5.7)	8.0
5 Speed	
4X2	
Four (3.9)	5.5
V-6 (4.6)	6.4
4X4 (5.7)	8.0
AEROSTAR	
Four-TK-5 (6.0)	8.4
V-6-TK-5 (6.3)	8.8
BRONCO	
3 Speed (4.5)	6.1
4 Speed	
Warner T-18 (5.3)	7.3
SROD (4.4)	6.1
New Process 435 (5.5)	7.6
5 Speed	
TK-5 (7.8)	10.9
ECONOLINE	
3 Speed (2.9)	4.5
4 Speed O.D. (3.6)	5.0
4 Speed	
New Process 435 (3.9)	5.5
F100-350 4X2	
3 Speed (2.9)	4.0
4 Speed	
Overdrive (2.8)	3.9
SROD (2.7)	3.8
TOD (3.3)	4.6
Warner T-18 (3.6)	4.9
New Process 435 (3.7)	5.1
F100-350 4X4	
4 Speed	
TOD (5.0)	7.0
Warner T-18 (5.2)	7.2
New Process 435 (5.5)	7.6
SROD (4.4)	6.1
Warner T-19 (5.0)	7.0
w/Skid plate add (.2)	.3
w/Full carpet add (.7)	1.0
w/P.T.O. add (.6)	.8
w/Coupling shaft add (.2)	.3

Transmission, Recondition (Off Truck)

(Factory Time)	Chilton Time
3 Speed (2.1)	3.2
4 Speed	
TOD (1.8)	2.5
New Process (2.3)	3.4
Warner (1.9)	3.0
Overdrive (2.3)	3.4
SROD (1.9)	3.0
TK (2.2)	3.0
5 Speed	
TK-5 (4.3)	6.0
MMC5 (4.2)	5.9

Extension Housing, Bearing Retainer or Gasket, Renew

Includes: Renew oil seal.

(Factory Time)	Chilton Time
All models 4X2	
3 Speed (1.2)	1.7
4 Speed-O/D (1.3)	1.8
4 Speed-TOD (1.3)	1.8
4 Speed-SROD (1.4)	1.9
4 Speed-TK (1.2)	1.7
4 Speed-Warner T-19 (1.1)	1.7
4 Speed-Warner T-18 (2.4)	3.0
New Process 435 (1.3)	1.8
5 Speed-TK (1.2)	1.7
4X4	
TK (2.2)	2.8
TOD (2.2)	2.8
Warner T-18 (2.4)	3.0
New Process 435 (2.4)	3.0
Warner T-19 (2.0)	2.8
w/Coupling shaft add (.2)	.3

Transmission Rear Oil Seal and/or Bushing, Renew

(Factory Time)	Chilton Time
BRONCO (.7)	1.0
All other models (.5)	.8
w/Coupling shaft add (.2)	.3

LABOR 20 TRANSFER CASE 20 LABOR

Transfer Case Assembly, R&R or Renew

(Factory Time)	Chilton Time
All models (1.8)	2.5
Renew assy add	.5
w/P.T.O. add (.6)	.8
w/Coupling shaft add (.2)	.3

Transfer Case, R&R and Recondition

Includes: R&R trans and/or transfer case. Separate units and overhaul transfer case only.

(Factory Time)	Chilton Time
All models	
New Process 203	
Full Time (5.0)	8.3
New Process 205	
Part Time (4.3)	6.0
New Process 208	
Part Time (4.7)	6.4
Borg Warner 1345	
Part Time (3.8)	5.3
Borg Warner 1350	
Part Time (3.8)	5.3
w/P.T.O. add (.6)	.8
w/Coupling shaft add (.2)	.3

LABOR 21 SHIFT LINKAGE 21 LABOR

STANDARD

Shift Linkage, Adjust

(Factory Time)	Chilton Time
All models (.3)	.4

Gear Shift Tube Assy., Renew (3 SPEED)

(Factory Time)	Chilton Time
Bronco (.5)	1.1
ECONOLINE (.6)	1.1
F100-250 (1.1)	1.7

Gear Shift Rods, Renew

Includes: Adjust shift linkage.

(Factory Time)	Chilton Time
BRONCO (.4)	.7
ECONOLINE-3 spd (.5)	.7
F100-250-3 spd (.5)	.7

Transfer Case Control Lever, Renew

(Factory Time)	Chilton Time
All models (.5)	.7

AUTOMATIC

Manual Shift Linkage, Adjust

Includes: Adjust neutral safety switch.

(Factory Time)	Chilton Time
All models	
C-4 (.2)	.6
C-5 (.4)	.6
C-6 (.3)	.6
AOD (.3)	.6
A4LD (.3)	.6

Gear Shift Tube Assembly, Renew

(Factory Time)	Chilton Time
F100-350 (.7)	1.5

Gear Selector Lever, Renew

(Factory Time)	Chilton Time
All models (.3)	.5

(Factory Time) Chilton Time

ON TRUCK SERVICES

Drain and Refill Unit
All models (.7) 7

Oil Pressure Check
All models (.3) 5

Check Unit for Oil Leaks
Includes: Clean and dry outside of case, run unit to determine point of leak.
All models (.7) 9

Neutral Safety Switch, Renew
All models (.3) 4

Vacuum Modulator, Renew
All models (.4) 6

Vacuum Modulator, Adjust
Includes: Pressure check.
All models (.5) 9

Manual and Throttle Linkage, Adjust
Includes: Adjust dashpot, idle speed and accelerate pedal height if adjustable.
All models (.4) 7

Front Servo, Recondition
Includes: Adjust band.
RANGER-AEROSTAR
C-3 (.4) 7
C-5 (.6) 1.1
A4LD (.6) 1.1
BRONCO-C-4 (.7) 1.3
BRONCO II-C-5 (.6) 1.1
ECONOLINE, F100-350
C-4 (.6) 1.1
C-5 (.6) 1.1
C-6 (1.0) 1.9
AOD (1.0) 1.5

Rear Servo, Recondition
RANGER-C-5 (.5) 1.0
BRONCO-C-4 (.7) 1.3
ECONOLINE, F100-350
C-4 (.5) 1.0
AOD (1.0) 1.5

Extension Housing and/or Gasket, Renew
C-3 (.9) 1.5
C-5
4X2 (.9) 1.5
4X4 (1.0) 1.6
C-6
4X2 (1.0) 1.6
4X4 (2.2) 3.0
AOD (1.5) 2.3
A4LD (1.5) 2.3
w/Coupling shaft add (.2) 2

Extension Housing Rear Oil Seal, Renew
All models (.5) 8
w/Coupling shaft add (.2) 2

Front Band, Adjust
Includes: R&R oil pan and renew gasket on MX-FMX.
C-3 (.3) 7
C-4 (.3) 7
C-5 (.3) 7
C-6 (.2) 6
A4LD (.3) 7

Rear Band, Adjust
A4LD (.2) 6
C-4 (.2) 6
C-5 (.2) 6

Front and Rear Bands, Adjust
Includes: R&R oil pan and renew gasket on MX-FMX.
A4LD (.3) 9
C-4 (.3) 9
C-5 (.3) 9

Oil Pan or Gasket, Renew
A4LD (.9) 1.2
C-3 (.7) 1.2
C-5 (.7) 1.2
C-4 & C-6-exc below (.6) 1.1
C-6-w/460 eng (1.2) 1.7
AOD (.7) 1.2

Valve Body Assembly, Renew
Includes: R&R oil pan.
A4LD (1.2) 1.7
C-3 (1.0) 1.5
C-5 (.9) 1.5
C-4 & C-6-exc below (1.1) 1.5
C-6-w/460 eng (1.7) 2.2
AOD (1.3) 1.9

Valve Body Assy., R&R and Recondition
Includes: R&R oil pan and replace filter. Disassemble, clean, inspect, free all valves. Replace parts as required.
A4LD (1.7) 2.5
C-3 (1.5) 2.5
C-4 (1.7) 2.5
C-5 (1.4) 2.5
C-6-exc below (1.6) 2.4
C-6-w/460 eng (2.2) 3.0
AOD (1.7) 3.0

Parking Pawl, Renew
Includes: R&R oil pan or trans assy., as required.
A4LD
4X2 (1.0) 1.6
4X4 (2.4) 3.2
C-3 (1.0) 1.6
C-5
4X2 (3.4) 4.5
4X4 (5.0) 6.7
C-6
4X2 (3.9) 5.2
4X4 (5.3) 7.1
AOD (1.5) 2.4
w/Coupling shaft add (.2) 2

Governor and Counterweight Assy., Renew
Includes: Road test.
C-3 (1.0) 1.7
C-5
4X2 (3.4) 4.7
4X4 (5.0) 7.0
C-6
4X2 (3.9) 5.3
4X4 (5.3) 7.4
AOD (1.7) 2.6
w/Coupling shaft add (.2) 2

Governor (Less Counterweight), Renew
Includes: Road test.
C-4 (1.6) 2.4
C-3 (.9) 1.6
C-5
4X2 (1.3) 1.9
4X4 (2.3) 3.2
C-6
4X2 (1.2) 1.7
4X4 (2.2) 3.1
AOD (1.6) 2.5
A4LD
4X2 (1.0) 1.6
4X4 (1.8) 2.6
w/Coupling shaft add (.2) 2

SERVICES REQUIRING R&R

Transmission Assembly, R&R
Includes: R&R transmission and converter assembly. Drain and refill unit. Adjust linkage.
RANGER-AEROSTAR
C-3 (2.3) 4.0
C-5
4X2 (2.3) 4.0
4X4 (3.9) 5.4
A4LD
4X2 (2.2) 3.1
4X4 (3.9) 5.4
BRONCO (4.9) 6.9
BRONCO II 4X4 (3.9) 5.4
ECONOLINE (2.7) 4.8
F100-350 4X2
C-4 (2.9) 5.0
C-5 (2.4) 4.2
C-6-exc below (3.4) 5.5
C-6-w/460 eng (4.1) 6.2
AOD (2.9) 4.4
F100-150 4X4 (4.9) 6.9
F250-350 4X4 (4.2) 6.2
w/Skid plate add (.2) 3
w/P.T.O. add (.6) 8
w/Coupling shaft add (.2) 3

Transmission and Converter Assy., R&R and Recondition
Includes: Drain and refill unit. Disassemble trans including valve body, clean, inspect and replace parts as required. Adjust linkage. Road test.
RANGER-AEROSTAR
C-3 (6.3) 11.5
C-5
4X2 (6.4) 11.5
4X4 (8.0) 12.4
A4LD
4X2 (9.1) 12.3
4X4 (10.8) 14.5
BRONCO (9.1) 13.9
BRONCO II 4X4 (8.0) 12.4
ECONOLINE (6.9) 12.0
F100-350 4X2
C-4 (7.1) 12.3
C-5 (6.5) 11.3
C-6-exc below (7.6) 12.8
C-6-w/460 eng (8.3) 13.2
AOD (7.8) 12.5
F100-150 4X4 (9.1) 13.9
F250-350 4X4 (8.4) 13.4
Clean and check converter add (.5) 5
Flush oil cooler and lines add (.2) 2
w/Skid plate add (.2) 3
w/P.T.O. add (.6) 8
w/Coupling shaft add (.2) 3

Transmission Assembly, Renew
Includes: R&R transmission, transfer all necessary parts. Drain and refill unit. Adjust linkage. Road test.
RANGER-AEROSTAR
C-3 (2.5) 4.5
C-5
4X2 (2.8) 4.5
4X4 (4.4) 6.0
A4LD
4X2 (2.7) 3.7
4X4 (4.4) 6.0
BRONCO (5.4) 7.4
BRONCO II 4X4 (4.1) 6.0
ECONOLINE (3.2) 5.3
F100-350 4X2
C-4 (3.4) 5.5
C-5 (2.9) 5.0
C-6-exc below (3.9) 6.0
C-6-w/460 eng (4.6) 6.7
AOD (3.4) 5.5
F100-150 4X4 (5.4) 7.4

LABOR 23 AUTOMATIC TRANSMISSION 23 LABOR

(Factory Time)	Chilton Time
F250-350 4X4 (4.7)	6.7
w/Skid plate add (.2)	.3
w/P.T.O. add (.6)	.8
w/Coupling shaft add (.2)	.3

Transmission Assembly, Reseal

Includes: R&R transmission, drain and refill unit. Renew all seals and gaskets. Adjust linkage. Road test.

(Factory Time)	Chilton Time
RANGER-AEROSTAR	
C-3 (4.1)	6.0
C-5	
4X2 (4.1)	6.0
4X4 (5.7)	7.4
A4LD	
4X2 (4.0)	5.1
4X4 (5.7)	7.4
BRONCO (6.7)	8.2
BRONCO II 4X4	7.4
ECONOLINE (4.5)	6.5
F100-350 4X2	
C-4 (4.7)	6.8
C-5 (4.4)	6.5
C-6-exc below (5.2)	7.3
C-6-w/460 eng (5.9)	8.0
AOD	6.0
F100-150 4X4 (6.7)	8.2
F250-350 4X4 (6.0)	7.7
w/Skid plate add (.2)	.3
w/P.T.O. add (.6)	.8
w/Coupling shaft add (.2)	.3

Torque Converter, Renew

Includes: R&R transmission. Drain and refill unit. Adjust linkage. Road test.

(Factory Time)	Chilton Time
RANGER-AEROSTAR	
C-3 (2.8)	3.7
C-5	
4X2 (2.8)	3.7
4X4 (4.4)	5.9
A4LD	
4X2 (2.7)	3.6
4X4 (4.4)	5.9
BRONCO (5.0)	6.7
BRONCO II 4X4 (4.4)	5.9
ECONOLINE (2.8)	3.7
F100-350 4X2	
C-4 (3.0)	4.0
C-5 (2.9)	3.9
C-6-exc below (3.5)	4.7
C-6-w/460 eng (4.2)	5.6
AOD (3.0)	4.0
F100-150 4X4 (5.0)	6.7
F250-350 4X4 (4.3)	5.8
w/Skid plate add (.2)	.3
w/P.T.O. add (.6)	.8
w/Coupliong shaft add (.2)	.3

Bands, Renew (One or Both)

Includes: R&R transmission. Drain and refill unit. Renew gaskets and seals as necessary. Adjust linkage. Road test.

(Factory Time)	Chilton Time
RANGER	
C-3 (3.8)	5.5
C-5	
4X2 (3.6)	5.3
4X4 (5.2)	8.0
BRONCO	
C-4 (6.2)	8.3
C-6 (6.6)	8.7
BRONCO II 4X4 (5.2)	8.0
ECONOLINE	
C-4 (4.0)	6.5
C-6 (4.4)	6.9
F100-350 4X2	
C-4 (4.2)	6.3
C-5 (3.7)	6.4
C-6-exc below (5.1)	7.3
C-6-w/460 eng (5.8)	8.0
F100-150 4X4 (6.6)	8.7
F250-350 4X4 (5.9)	8.2
w/Skid plate add (.2)	.3
w/P.T.O. add (.6)	.8
w/Coupling shaft add (.2)	3

Front Oil Pump Seal, Renew

Includes: R&R transmission. Drain and refill unit. Adjust linkage. Road test.

(Factory Time)	Chilton Time
RANGER-AEROSTAR	
C-3 (2.4)	4.2
C-5	
4X2 (2.4)	4.2
4X4 (4.0)	6.2
A4LD	
4X2 (2.8)	3.8
4X4 (4.5)	6.1
BRONCO (5.0)	7.1
BRONCO II 4X4 (4.0)	6.2
ECONOLINE (2.8)	4.9
F100-350 4X2	
C-4 (3.0)	5.2
C-5 (2.5)	4.3
C-6-exc below (3.5)	5.7
C-6-w/460 eng (4.2)	6.4
AOD (3.0)	4.6
F100-150 4X4 (5.0)	7.1
F250-350 4X4 (4.3)	6.6
w/Skid plate add (.2)	.3
w/P.T.O. add (.6)	.8
w/Coupling shaft add (.2)	.3

Front Oil Pump, R&R and Recondition

Includes: R&R transmission. Drain and refill unit. Renew gaskets and seals as necessary. Adjust linkage. Road test.

(Factory Time)	Chilton Time
RANGER-AEROSTAR	
C-3 (2.9)	4.0
C-5	
4X2 (2.9)	4.0
4X4 (4.6)	6.4
A4LD	
4X2 (2.8)	3.9
4X4 (4.5)	6.3
BRONCO	
C-4 (5.6)	7.8
C-6 (6.1)	8.5
BRONCO II 4X4 (4.6)	6.4
ECONOLINE	
C-4 (3.4)	4.7
C-6 (3.9)	5.4
F100-350 4X2	
C-4 (3.6)	5.0
C-5 (3.1)	4.3
C-6-exc below (4.6)	6.4
C-6-w/460 eng (5.3)	7.4
AOD (3.5)	4.9
F100-150 4X4 (6.1)	8.5
F250-350 4X4 (5.4)	7.5
w/Skid plate add (.2)	.3
w/P.T.O. add (.6)	.6
w/Coupling shaft add (.2)	.3

Flywheel and Ring Gear Assy., Renew

Includes: R&R transmission. Drain and refill unit. Adjust linkage. Road test.

(Factory Time)	Chilton Time
RANGER-AEROSTAR	
C-3 (2.6)	4.3
C-5	
4X2 (2.6)	4.3
4X4 (4.2)	6.5
A4LD	
4X2 (2.5)	3.4
4X4 (4.2)	5.7
BRONCO (5.2)	7.4
BRONCO II 4X4 (4.2)	6.5
ECONOLINE (3.0)	5.3
F100-350 4X2	
C-4 (3.2)	5.5
C-5 (2.7)	4.7
C-6-exc below (3.7)	6.0
C-6-w/460 eng (4.4)	6.7
AOD (3.2)	4.8
F100-150 4X4 (5.2)	7.4
F250-350 4X4 (4.5)	6.7
w/Skid plate add (.2)	.3
w/P.T.O. add (.6)	.8
w/Coupling shaft add (.2)	.3

Parking Pawl, Renew

Includes: R&R transmission. Drain and refill unit. Renew gaskets and seals as necessary. Adjust linkage. Road test.

(Factory Time)	Chilton Time
BRONCO	
C-4 (6.3)	8.7
C-6 (6.6)	9.0
ECONOLINE	
C-4 (4.1)	6.3
C-6 (4.4)	6.6
F100-350 4X2	
C-4 (4.3)	6.8
C-5 (3.8)	6.6
C-6-exc below (5.1)	7.3
C-6-w/460 eng (5.8)	8.0
AOD (3.3)	4.9
F100-150 4X4 (6.6)	8.7
F250-350 4X4 (5.9)	8.0
w/Skid plate add (.2)	.3
w/P.T.O. add (.6)	.8
w/Coupling shaft add (.2)	.3

LABOR 25 U-JOINTS & DRIVESHAFT 25 LABOR

Drive Shaft, Renew

(Factory Time)	Chilton Time
RANGER-AEROSTAR (.4)	.6
BRONCO (.4)	.6
ECONOLINE, F100-350	
one piece shaft (.3)	.5
w/Coupling shaft (.6)	.9

Universal Joints, Recondition or Renew

Includes: R&R drive shaft.

(Factory Time)	Chilton Time
Without Coupling Shaft	
front (.8)	1.0
rear (.7)	.9
all (1.1)	1.4
With Coupling Shaft	
front (1.0)	1.4
center (1.0)	1.4
rear (.9)	1.3
all (1.6)	2.0

Drive Shaft Center Support Bearing, Renew

(Factory Time)	Chilton Time
All models (.8)	1.2

LABOR 26 REAR AXLE 26 LABOR

(Factory Time) Chilton Time

Ring Gear and Pinion, Adjust
Includes: Drain and refill axle. Adjust ring and pinion backlash. Road test.
All models
std axle (1.5) 2.2
limited slip/Trac-Lok (1.8) 2.6

Ring and Pinion Gear, Renew
Includes: Drain and refill axle. Adjust backlash. Road test.
All models
Ford axle (2.8) 4.0
Dana axle (2.4) 3.5
w/Limited slip add (.1) 2
Renew pinion brgs and cups add (.6) 8
Recond diff assy add
Ford 7.5 (.4) 6
Dana-std (.5) 7
Trac-Lok 2 pinion (.6) 8
Trac-Lok 4 pinion (.7) 1.0

REMOVABLE CARRIER

Differential Carrier, Remove & Install
Includes: Remove or renew axle shafts. Drain and refill axle. Renew oil seal and housing gasket.
All models
one piece shaft (1.7) 2.5
two piece shaft (1.8) 2.7
Adjust ring gear add (.2) 3
Check case run out add (.3) 4
Renew ring gear & pinion add
std (1.1) 1.5
limited slip/Trac-Lok (2.0) 2.9
Renew pinion brg cups add (.2) 3
Renew case add (1.0) 1.4
Renew diff brg add (.2) 3

LABOR 27 REAR SUSPENSION 27 LABOR

(Factory Time) Chilton Time

Rear Spring, Renew
4 lug wheel
Aerostar
one (.5) 8
both (.8) 1.4
All other models
one (.9) 1.3
both (1.6) 2.4
5 lug wheel
one (1.0) 1.5
both (1.8) 2.8
8 lug wheel
one (1.1) 1.6
both (1.9) 3.0
Renew spring bushings
add-each (.2) 2

Rear Spring Shackle and/or Bushing, Renew
RANGER-one (1.0) 1.5
both (1.6) 2.6
ALL OTHER MODELS
one (.8) 1.2
both (1.2) 2.1

Rear Shock Absorbers, Renew
All models-one (.3) 6
both (.4) 8

Rear Stabilizer Bar, Renew
All models (.5) 9

Upper Control Arm Bushings, Renew
Aerostar
one side (.7) 1.0
both sides (1.1) 1.7

LABOR 28 AIR CONDITIONING 28 LABOR

(Factory Time) Chilton Time

Note: If more than one item requires replacement where evacuation and discharging the system is already included in the operation, deduct 1.0 hour for each additional item to the times listed.

Drain, Evacuate and Recharge System
Includes: Check for leaks.
All models (.7) 1.5

Pressure Test System
All models 8

Compressor Belt, Renew
Four (.5) 7
All other engs (.3) 6

Compressor Assembly, Renew
Includes: Evacuate and charge system.
Four
Gas
2.0L eng (2.0) 3.0
2.3L eng
Ranger (2.1) 3.1
Aerostar (2.6) 3.7
Diesel
2.3L eng (1.3) 2.3
Six (1.6) 2.4
V-6 (1.5) 2.3
V-8
Gas (1.5) 2.3
Diesel (1.7) 2.5
Recond comp add (.7) 1.0

Compressor Shaft Seal Kit, Renew
Includes: Evacuate and charge system.
Four
Gas
2.0L eng (2.5) 3.5
2.3L eng
Ranger (2.4) 3.4
Aerostar (3.1) 4.2
Diesel (2.2) 3.0
Six (1.9) 2.6
V-6 (2.0) 2.8
V-8
Gas (1.8) 2.5
Diesel (2.1) 2.9

Condenser Assembly, Renew
Includes: Evacuate and charge system.
RANGER (1.0) 2.0
AEROSTAR (1.0) 2.0
BRONCO (1.1) 2.3
BRONCO II (1.0) 2.0
ECONOLINE (1.3) 2.7
F100-350 (1.1) 2.4

Expansion Valve, Renew
Includes: Evacuate and charge system.
All models (1.1) 2.4

Evaporator Core, Renew
Includes: Evacuate and charge system.
RANGER (1.4) 2.7
AEROSTAR (1.5) 2.9
BRONCO (1.9) 3.1
BRONCO II (1.4) 2.7
ECONOLINE (2.4) 3.6
F100-350
1980 & later (1.2) 2.4

Dehydrator Receiver Tank, Renew
Includes: Evacuate and charge system.
BRONCO (1.1) 2.2
ECONOLINE (1.4) 2.5
F100-350 (1.1) 2.2

Accumulator Assembly, Renew
Includes: Evacuate and charge system.
RANGER-BRONCO II (1.0) 1.5
AEROSTAR (1.3) 1.8
BRONCO-F100-350 (.9) 1.5

Orifice Valve, Renew
Includes: Evacuate and charge system.
RANGER-BRONCO II (1.1) 1.7
AEROSTAR
main (1.0) 1.5
auxiliary (1.3) 1.8
BRONCO-F100-350 (.9) 1.4

Blower Motor, Renew
RANGER (.4) 6
AEROSTAR
main (.4) 7
auxiliary (.4) 7
BRONCO
1980 & later (.3) 6
BRONCO II (.4) 6
ECONOLINE (.4) 1.0
F100-350
1980 & later (.3) 6

Blower Motor Switch, Renew
RANGER (.5) 7
AEROSTAR (.6) 9
BRONCO (.5) 7
ECONOLINE (.3) 6
F100-350 (.5) 7

Evaporator Thermostatic Switch, Renew
BRONCO (.6) 1.0
ECONOLINE (.3) 6
F100-350 (.7) 1.2

A/C Clutch Cycling Pressure Switch Assy., Renew
All models (.2) 4

LABOR 28 AIR CONDITIONING 28 LABOR

(Factory Time)	Chilton Time
Compressor Service Valve or Gasket, Renew	
Includes: Evacuate and charge system.	
All models (1.0)	1.9

(Factory Time)	Chilton Time
Air Conditioning Hoses, Renew	
Includes: Evacuate and charge system.	
All models-one (.8)	1.7
each adtnl (.3)	.5

LABOR 30 HEAD AND PARKING LAMPS 30 LABOR

(Factory Time)	Chilton Time
Aim Headlamps	
two	.4
four	.6
Headlamp Sealed Beam Bulb, Renew	
All models-each (.2)	.3

(Factory Time)	Chilton Time
Parking Lamp Assembly, Renew	
RANGER (.2)	.3
AEROSTAR (.3)	.4
BRONCO-ECONOLINE (.2)	.3
F100-350 (.4)	.5
Rear Lamp Assembly, Renew	
All models (.2)	.3

(Factory Time)	Chilton Time
License Lamp Assembly, Renew	
All models (.3)	.4
Reflector, Renew	
All models-each	.2

LABOR 31 WINDSHIELD WIPER & SPEEDOMETER 31 LABOR

(Factory Time)	Chilton Time
Wiper Motor, Renew	
RANGER-BRONCO II (.4)	.6
AEROSTAR	
front (.9)	1.4
rear (.7)	1.1
BRONCO (.9)	1.4
ECONOLINE (.9)	*1.4
F100-350 (.9)	1.4
*w/Cruise control add (.3)	.3
Wiper Switch, Renew	
All models	
front (.4)	.6
rear (.2)	.4
Wiper Pivot, Renew	
RANGER-BRONCO II-one (.4)	.7
both (.5)	.9
BRONCO-each (.8)	1.1
AEROSTAR-both (.4)	.7
ECONOLINE (.6)	.9
F100-350-each (.8)	1.1

(Factory Time)	Chilton Time
Washer Pump, Renew	
Aerostar	
front (.6)	.9
rear (.3)	.5
All other models-front (.3)	.4
rear (.8)	1.1
Windshield Wiper Governor Assy., Renew	
Aerostar (.5)	.7
All other models (.4)	.6
Speedometer Head, R&R or Renew	
All models	
Standard (.6)	1.2
Electronic (.7)	1.3
Reset odometer add	.2
Speedometer Cable and Casing, Renew	
RANGER-BRONCO II (.4)	.7
AEROSTAR (.4)	.7

(Factory Time)	Chilton Time
BRONCO	
one piece (.5)	.9
upper (.6)	1.1
lower (.4)	.7
ECONOLINE	
wo/Sensor (.4)	.7
w/Sensor-each (.3)	.5
one piece (.7)	1.3
upper or lower (.5)	.9
F100-350 (.5)	.9
Speedometer Cable (Inner), Renew or Lubricate	
RANGER-BRONCO II (.4)	.7
AEROSTAR (.4)	.7
BRONCO	
one piece (.4)	.8
upper (.6)	1.0
lower (.4)	.6
ECONOLINE	
one piece (.6)	1.1
upper (.6)	1.1
lower (.4)	.7
F100-350 (.5)	.8

LABOR 32 LIGHT SWITCHES & WIRING 32 LABOR

(Factory Time)	Chilton Time
Headlamp Switch, Renew	
All models (.4)	.6
Headlamp Dimmer Switch, Renew	
All models	
floor mount (.3)	.5
column mount (.5)	.9
Turn Signal Switch Assy., Renew	
RANGER (.4)	1.0
AEROSTAR (.5)	1.0
BRONCO-std whl (.5)	1.1
tilt whl (.6)	1.2
BRONCO II-std whl (.5)	1.1
tilt whl (.6)	1.2
ECONOLINE-std whl (.6)	1.2
tilt whl (.7)	1.3
F100-350-std whl (.5)	1.1
tilt whl (.6)	1.2
Turn Signal or Hazard Warning Flasher, Renew	
ECONOLINE (.4)	.6
All other models (.3)	.4

(Factory Time)	Chilton Time
Stop Light Switch, Renew	
All models (.3)	.5
Emergency Flasher Switch Assy., Renew	
BRONCO (.3)	.6
Parking Brake Indicator Lamp Switch, Renew	
All models (.3)	.4
Back-Up Lamp Switch, Renew (w/ Manual Trans)	
All models (.3)	.4
Neutral Safety Switch, Renew	
All models (.3)	.4
Horns, Renew	
All models-each (.2)	.3
Horn Relay, Renew	
All models (.3)	.4

(Factory Time)	Chilton Time
Cruise Control System Diagnosis	
All models (.4)	.6
Cruise Control Chain/Cable, Renew	
All models (.2)	.4
Speed Control Servo Assy., Renew	
All models (.4)	.6
Road test add (.3)	.3
Speed Control Relay, Renew	
All models (.3)	.5
Speed Control Sensor Assy., Renew	
All models (.3)	*.6
Road test add (.3)	.3
*Econoline w/V-8 Diesel add	.3
Speed Control Amplifier Assy., Renew	
All models (.3)	.6
Road test add (.3)	.3
Speed Control Actuator Switch Assy., Renew	
All models (.3)	.6
Road test add (.3)	.3
Speed Control Metering (Dump) Valve, Renew	
All models (.2)	.3
Speed Control Clutch Switch, Renew	
All models (.3)	.4
Road test add (.3)	.3

GROUP INDEX

ALPHABETICAL INDEX

LABOR 1 TUNE UP 1 LABOR

(Factory Time) Chilton Time

GASOLINE ENGINE

Compression Test

Six–exc below (.6)	.8
N series (.7)	.9
V-8–exc below (.9)	1.1
N series (1.1)	1.3

Engine Tune Up, Minor

Includes: Clean or renew spark plugs, renew ignition points and condenser, set ignition timing. Adjust carburetor idle speed and mixture. Service carburetor air cleaner. Clean or renew fuel filter.

Six–F series (1.4)	1.9
N series (1.8)	2.4
C series (1.5)	2.0
L series (1.5)	2.0
V-8–330, 361, 370, 389, 391, 429 engs	
F series (1.7)	2.3
N series (1.9)	2.5
C series (1.6)	1.9
L series (1.4)	1.9
V-8–401, 475, 477, 534 engs	
F series (1.7)	2.3
N series (1.9)	2.5
C series (1.4)	1.9
L series (1.4)	1.9

Engine Tune Up, Major

Includes: Clean or renew spark plugs. Check compression. Test battery and clean terminals. Renew or adjust distributor points and condenser. Check distributor cap and rotor. Adjust ignition timing and test coil. Free up manifold heat valve. Tighten manifold bolts. Adjust carburetor idle speed and mixture. Inspect and tighten all hose connections. Adjust fan belts. Service air cleaner and fuel filter. Clean or renew PCV valve (if equipped).

Six–F series (2.2)	3.2
N series (2.5)	3.5
C series (2.2)	3.2
L series (2.2)	3.2
V-8–330, 361, 370, 389, 391, 429 engs	
F series (2.7)	3.7
N series (2.9)	3.9
C series (2.5)	3.5
L series (2.5)	3.5
V-8–401, 475, 477, 534 engs	
F series (2.7)	3.7
N series (2.9)	3.9
C series (2.5)	3.5
L series (2.5)	3.5

DIESEL ENGINES

Compression Test

Includes: R&R injectors and other interfering parts, attach compression gauge and adjust injectors.

Caterpillar	
3208	
F & LN series (3.3)	4.0
C & L series (3.0)	3.7
3406	
All series (2.3)	3.0
Cummins	
Six (5.1)	6.1
V-8 (5.6)	7.3
Detroit	
6V-71-6V-92 (4.8)	6.0
6-71 (3.8)	4.8
8V-71-8V-92 (5.0)	6.3

Engine Tune Up, Minor

Includes: Test batteries and clean and tighten terminals. Check and adjust engine idle speed and throttle linkage. Change engine oil. Clean or renew oil, air, fuel and water filters. Tighten radiator hoses and manifold bolts. Check valve lash and adjust tappets. R&R and test injectors.
Does not include compression test or injector timing.

Caterpillar	
3208	
F & LN series (4.5)	5.3
C & L series (4.2)	5.0
3406	
All series (3.5)	4.3
Cummins	
NH743-855 (3.0)	3.8
NT855 (3.5)	4.5
V-VT555 (3.1)	4.0
V-VT903 (3.5)	4.5
KT(A)1150 (3.5)	4.5
Detroit	
6V-53-6V-92 (2.7)	3.5
6-71 (2.2)	3.0
8V-71-8V-92 (3.2)	4.0

Engine Tune Up, Major

Includes: Test batteries and clean and tighten terminals. Check and adjust engine idle speed and throttle linkage. Adjust injector timing and injectors. Steam clean engine. Change engine oil. Clean or renew air, oil, fuel and water filters. Check and lubricate shutters. Clean injectors and fuel connections. Inspect for oil, water and fuel leaks. Drain sediment from fuel tanks. Tighten intake manifold, exhaust manifold, turbocharger and engine mounting bolts. Clean turbocharger impeller and diffuser and fuel pump screen. Adjust crossheads and valves. Check crankshaft and clearance. Adjust and check fan belts. Road test.

Caterpillar	
3208	
F & LN series (9.4)	11.5
C & L series (9.1)	11.2
3406	
All series (8.4)	10.5
Cummins	
NH743, 855 (11.2)	14.3
NT855 (12.2)	15.3
V-VT555 (9.8)	12.9
V-VT903 (10.4)	13.5
KT(A)1150 (11.2)	14.3
Detroit	
6V-53-6V-92 (9.6)	11.7
6-71 (9.0)	11.1
8V-71-8V-92 (9.8)	11.9

LABOR 2 IGNITION SYSTEM 2 LABOR

(Factory Time) Chilton Time

Spark Plugs, Renew

Six (.5)	.7
V-8 (.6)	.8

Ignition Timing, Reset

All series (.4)	.6

Distributor, R&R or Renew

Includes: Reset ignition timing.

exc below (.6)	.8
C & L series (.5)	.7

Distributor, R&R and Recondition

Includes: Reset ignition timing.

Six–exc below (1.3)	1.7
C & L series (1.2)	1.6
V-8–exc below (1.7)	2.2
C & L series (1.6)	2.1

Distributor Cap and/or Rotor, Renew

All series (.4)	.6

Ignition Coil, Renew

All series (.5)	.7

Vacuum Control Unit, Renew

Includes: R&R distributor and reset ignition timing.

exc below (.9)	1.2
C & L series (.8)	1.0

Ignition Module, Renew

All series (.4)	.6

Distributor Armature, Renew

All series	.7

Ignition Cables, Renew

exc below (.5)	.7
401, 475, 477, 534 engs (.6)	.8

Ignition Switch, Renew

exc below (.4)	.6
F series (.6)	.8
CL series (.5)	.7

LABOR 3 FUEL SYSTEM 3 LABOR

(Factory Time) Chilton Time

GASOLINE ENGINES

Fuel Pump, Test
Includes: Disconnect line at carburetor, attach pressure gauge.
All series .3

Carburetor, Adjust (On Truck)
All series (.4) .6

Carburetor, R&R or Renew
Includes: All necessary adjustments.
Six–exc below (.7) .9
C series (.5) .7
L series (.6) .8
V-8–330, 361, 389, 391 engs
All series (.8) 1.0
V-8–370, 429 engs
All series (.7) 1.1
V-8–401, 475, 477, 534 engs
All series (.9) 1.2

Carburetor, R&R and Recondition
Includes: All necessary adjustments.
Six–exc below (1.3) 1.7
C series (1.1) 1.5
L series (1.2) 1.6
V-8–331, 361, 389, 391 engs
All series (1.3) 2.0
V-8–370-429 engs
All series
2 bbl (1.4) 2.0
4 bbl (1.9) 3.0
V-8–401, 475, 477, 534 engs
All series (1.4) 3.5

Fuel Pump, Renew
Pump on engine
Six–F series (.5) .7
C & L series (.4) .6
V-8–330, 361, 389, 391 engs
All series (.5) .7
V-8–370, 429 engs
All series (.6) .9
Pump in tank
Drum tank (1.0) 1.4
Frame tank (.5) .7
Rectangular tank
w/Batt,s (1.5) *2.0
All others (1.0) 1.4
*Includes: R&R batteries.

Fuel Tank, Renew
Includes: Transfer all necessary parts.
Rectangular-each (1.3) 1.7
Rectangular-w/Battery
each (2.0) 2.7
All other tanks (1.5) 2.0

Fuel Gauge (Tank), Renew
Rectangular
w & wo/Step
Gas (.9) 1.2
Diesel (1.0) 1.3
All other tanks (.4) .6

Fuel Gauge (Dash), Renew
F-L-LN series (.6) .9
C series (.5) .8
CL series (.4) .7
w/2 spd shift add (.1) .1

Intake Manifold Gasket, Renew
Six (1.1) 1.6
V-8–330, 361, 389, 391 engs
exc below (2.8) 3.3
L series (3.1) 3.6
V-8–370, 429 engs
All series (2.5) 3.4
V-8–401, 475, 477, 534 engs
exc below (2.7) 3.2
C series (2.1) 2.6
L series (2.6) 3.1
LN models (3.3) 3.9
Renew manif add (.4) .5

DIESEL ENGINES

Air Cleaner Assembly, R&R and Clean or Renew
All series (.4) .6

Engine Idle Speed, Adjust (Governor)
All series (.9) 1.3

Injectors, Adjust
Includes: R&R all normal interfering parts.
exc below (1.5) 2.2
Caterpillar (2.0) 2.6
Cummins
NT-743, 855 (2.8) 3.7
V-VT 785, V903 (4.4) 5.8

Injectors, Renew
Includes: R&R all normal interfering parts.
Caterpillar
3208
F & LN series-one (1.7) 2.5
all (2.8) 4.0
C & L series-one (1.0) 2.3
all (2.5) 3.7
3406
All series-one (1.1) 1.9
all (2.0) 3.2
Cummins
All engines
One (2.2) 3.0
Six (4.5) 5.5
Eight (4.8) 6.0
Detroit
All
6V-53-6V-92 (3.2) *4.3
6-71 (2.6) *3.7
8V-72-8V-92 (3.4) *4.6
*w/Jacobs brk add each (.1) .1
Recondition add
exc below-each (.5) .5
Cummins-each (.8) .8
Detroit
S inj-each (.5) .5
N inj-each (.8) .8

Injection Pump, Renew
Includes: R&R all normal interfering parts.
Caterpillar
All series
3208 (3.3) 4.4
3406 (2.2) 3.3
Cummins
NT-NH743, 855 (1.7) 2.4
V-VT555, 903 (2.6) 3.5
KT(A)1150 (1.6) 2.3
Detroit
6-71 (.7) .9
6V-53, 8V-71 (1.0) 1.9
6V-92, 8V-92 (1.0) 1.3

Injection Pump, R&R and Recondition
Includes: R&R all normal interfering parts.
Caterpillar
All series
3208 (5.6) 7.0
3406 (6.4) 7.9
Cummins
All series (3.4) 5.2
Detroit
6-71 (1.7) 2.2
6V-53, 8V-71 (2.0) 2.5
6V-92, 8V-92 (2.0) 2.5

Turbochargher, Renew
exc below-one (1.4) 2.1
both (2.1) 2.8
Caterpillar-3406 (1.3) 2.1
Cummins
NT855 (1.1) 2.6
VT555, 903 (2.3) 3.5
KT(A)1150 (1.4) 2.4

Supercharger, Renew
Cummins
NH743, 855 (4.8) 6.2

Shutdown Valve, Renew
exc below (.5) .8
Caterpillar (.2) .3
Cummins (1.0) 1.5

Aneroid Valve, Adjust
All series (1.1) 1.5

Fuel Filter, Renew
Cummins (.5) .7
Caterpillar (.2) .3
Detroit (.3) .4

Intake Manifold Gaskets, Renew
Caterpillar
All series
3208 (1.6) 2.2
3406 (1.4) 2.0
Cummins
NH743, 855 (1.6) 2.3
V-VT785, 903-one (2.3) 3.1
both (2.8) 4.0
V-555-one (1.9) 2.7
both (2.4) 3.6
KT(A)1150 (1.4) 1.9

LABOR 3A EMISSION CONTROLS 3A LABOR

(Factory Time) Chilton Time

Thermactor Air By-Pass Valve, Renew
All series (.4) .6

E.G.R. Vacuum Control Valve, Renew
All series (.3) .5

E.G.R. Valve, Renew
All series (.5) .7

Thermactor Air Pump, Renew
All series (.5) .9
Renew belt add (.2) .2

LABOR 4 ALTERNATOR & REGULATOR 4 LABOR

(Factory Time) Chilton Time

Alternator Circuits Test

Includes: Test battery, regulator and alternator output.

All models (.6) .6
Test each adtnl battery add (.2) .2

Alternator, R&R or Renew

GAS
All series
Motorcraft (.5) .8
Leece Neville (.6) .9
Delco (1.2) 1.5

DIESEL
All series (.6) 1.1
Recondition add
Ford (.6) .8
Leece Neville (1.8) 2.0
Delco (1.2) 1.4
Transfer pulley add (.1) .1

Alternator Regulator, Renew

exc below (.4) .7
Delco (1.0) 1.5

Add circuit test if performed.

Alternator Regulator, Adjust

Ford (.8) 1.1
Leece Neville (1.0) 1.3

Instrument Cluster Voltage Regulator, Renew

All series (.6) .9

LABOR 5 STARTING SYSTEM 5 LABOR

(Factory Time) Chilton Time

Starter Draw Test (On Truck)

All models (.3) 3

Starter, R&R or Renew

MOTORCRAFT
All series (.4) .6
PRESTOLITE
All series (.6) .8
DELCO
F series (1.3) 1.7
L-LN series (1.2) 1.6
CL series (1.9) 2.5
CUMMINS
L-LN series (1.0) 1.3
CL series (2.3) 3.0
CATERPILLAR
F-C series (1.1) 1.4
L series (1.5) 1.9
LN-CL series (1.8) 2.3
Renew starter drive
add (.3) .3
Renew brushes add (.6) .6
Renew armature add (.3) .3
Recond complete add (1.5) 2.0

Starter Solenoid Relay, Renew

GAS ENGINES
F-L series (.4) .8
CL series (.5) .9

Ammeter, Renew

F series (.6) .9
C series (.5) .8
CL series (.4) .7
L-LN series
Line Haul (.4) .7
City Deliv. (.6) .9

Battery Cables, Renew

GAS ENGINES
F series-each (.4) .5
C series-each (.5) .7
L series-each (.6) .8
CL series-each (.4) .5

LABOR 6 BRAKE SYSTEM 6 LABOR

(Factory Time) Chilton Time

Brakes, Adjust (Minor)

Includes: Adjust brake shoes at all wheels. Fill master cylinder. R&R one front drum.

single axle (.8) 1.0
tandem axle (1.0) 1.2

Bleed Brakes (Four Wheels)

single axle (.6) .8
tandem axle (.7) .9

Brake Pedal Free Play, Adjust

All models (.3) .4

Brake Drum or Hub, Renew

Includes: R&R wheel, renew bearings and adjust brakes.

FRONT
F600 4x4
one (1.1) 1.6
both (1.9) 2.7
500-9000 series
Disc-6 hole
one (1.1) 1.6
both (2.0) 2.8
Disc-10 hole
one (1.7) 2.1
both (3.2) 4.0
Cast wheel
one (1.3) 1.7
both (2.4) 3.2
REAR
500-9000
Disc-6 hole
one (1.6) 2.2
both (2.9) 3.8
Disc-10 hole
one (2.2) 2.8
both (4.0) 5.2
Cast wheel
one (1.7) 2.3
both (2.9) 3.8

Brake Shoes, Renew

Includes: R&R wheels, hubs and drums. Clean and inspect all parts. Install new or exchange shoes. Adjust brakes and road test.

F600 4WD-front (2.3) 2.9
rear (3.1) 4.0
all four wheels (5.0) 6.3
500-750 hydraulic
front (1.8) 2.3
rear
one axle (3.1) 4.0
both axles (5.7) 7.2
all wheels
one rear (4.5) 5.7
tandem rear (7.0) 8.8
Air brakes
front (2.3) 2.9
rear
one axle (3.1) 4.0
both axles (5.7) 7.2
all wheels
one rear (4.9) 6.2
tandem rear (7.5) 9.5
800-900 hydraulic
front (1.9) 2.5
rear
one axle (3.2) 4.2
both axles (5.9) 7.5
all wheels
one rear (4.6) 5.9
tandem rear (7.3) 9.2
Air brakes
front (2.3) 2.9
rear
one axle (3.1) 4.0
both axles (5.7) 7.2
all wheels
one rear (4.9) 6.2
tandem rear (7.5) 9.5
Bleed system add
single axle (.4) .6
tandem axle (.5) .7

BRAKE HYDRAULIC SYSTEM

Wheel Cylinder, Renew

Includes: R&R wheels, hubs and drums. Clean and inspect parts. Bleed lines, adjust brakes and road test.

F600 4WD
front-one (1.7) 2.2
both-one wheel (1.9) 2.5
all (3.5) 4.5
rear-one wheel (2.3) 2.9
both wheels (4.2) 5.3
500-750 hydraulic
front-one wheel (1.7) 2.2
both wheels (2.9) 3.7
rear
one axle-one wheel (2.3) 2.9
both wheels (4.2) 5.3
both axles (7.6) 9.5
800-900 hydraulic
front-one wheel (1.8) 2.3
both wheels (3.0) 3.8

	(Factory Time)	Chilton Time
rear		
one axle-one wheel	(2.4)	3.1
both wheels	(4.3)	5.4
both axles	(8.0)	10.0
Recondition, each add	(.2)	.5

Brake Hose, Renew

Includes: Bleed lines.

	(Factory Time)	Chilton Time
Front		
single axle-one	(.8)	1.3
both	(1.0)	1.5
tandem axle-one	(.9)	1.4
both	(1.1)	1.7
air hose-one	(.3)	.4
both	(.4)	.6
Rear		
single axle-one	(.9)	1.4
tandem axle-one	(1.0)	1.5
two	(1.1)	1.7
three	(1.3)	2.0
all	(1.5)	2.3

Master Cylinder, Renew

Includes: Bleed complete system, adjust pedal free play.

	(Factory Time)	Chilton Time
Standard Cylinder		
All series	(.8)	1.2
Hydra-Max		
C-series	(2.5)	3.5
All other series	(1.0)	1.4

Brake Differential Valve, Renew

Includes: Bleed system and transfer switch.

	(Factory Time)	Chilton Time
L series	(.6)	1.0

BRAKE BOOSTER

Brake Booster Assembly, Renew

	(Factory Time)	Chilton Time
Midland diaphragm		
dash mtg	(.7)	1.2
frame mtg	(.6)	1.1
Bendix		
diaphragm	(1.0)	1.5
piston	(1.0)	1.5
air hyd	(.8)	1.3
Hydra-Max		
F-series	(1.8)	2.5
All other series	(2.5)	3.5

Brake Booster, R&R and Recondition

	(Factory Time)	Chilton Time
Midland diaphragm		
dash mtg	(1.2)	2.7
frame mtg	(1.1)	2.6
Bendix		
diaphragm	(2.1)	3.6
piston	(3.1)	4.6
air hyd	(2.2)	3.7
Hydra-Max		
F-series	(2.9)	4.0

AIR BRAKES

Air Compressor Belts, Renew

	(Factory Time)	Chilton Time
All models	(.3)	.5

Air Pressure Gauge, Renew

	(Factory Time)	Chilton Time
exc below	(.8)	1.1
C & L series	(.6)	.9
CL series	(.4)	.7

Air Brake Pedal Control Valve, Adjust

	(Factory Time)	Chilton Time
All series	(.5)	.8

Air Brake Pedal Control Valve, Renew

	(Factory Time)	Chilton Time
exc below	(1.4)	2.0
CL series	(.8)	1.2

COMBINATIONS

Add To Brakes, Renew

	(Factory Time)	Chilton Time
RENEW WHEEL CYLINDER		
Each	(.3)	.4
RECONDITION WHEEL CYLINDERS Includes: Hone cylinder.		
Each	(.5)	.6
MASTER CYLINDER, RENEW		
All models	(.6)	.7
MASTER CYLINDER, RECONDITION		
All models		1.0
REAR WHEEL GREASE SEAL, RENEW		
One side	(.3)	.4
FRONT WHEEL BEARINGS, RENEW		
One wheel	(.7)	.8
FRONT WHEEL BEARINGS, REPACK		
All models	(.6)	.7
RELINE BRAKE SHOES		
Each axle set	(.7)	1.0
BRAKE DRUM OR ROTOR, RENEW		
Each	(.5)	.6
REBUILD CALIPER ASSEMBLY		
Each	(.6)	.6
AIR BRAKE ACTUATOR, RENEW		
Each	(.3)	.4
DISC BRAKE ROTOR, MACHINE		
Each	(1.0)	1.0

Slack Adjuster, Renew (One Wheel)

	(Factory Time)	Chilton Time
All series	(.6)	.8

Air Compressor, Renew

	(Factory Time)	Chilton Time
Gas		
6.1-7.0L engs		
All series	(1.5)	2.2
7.8-8.8L engs		
C-series	(2.4)	3.3
L-LN series	(1.8)	2.5
Diesel		
Caterpiller		
3208	(1.3)	1.8
3406	(1.2)	1.7
Detroit		
Six-L-series	(2.5)	3.5
LN series	(3.0)	4.2
6V-8V-92	(3.0)	4.2
8.2L	(1.7)	2.4
6V-8V-71	(1.5)	2.2
Cummins	(2.5)	3.2
Recondition add	(3.8)	5.0

Air Brake Chamber, R&R or Renew

Includes: Adjust slack adjuster.

	(Factory Time)	Chilton Time
one-front or rear	(.7)	1.0

Air Brake Chamber, R&R and Recondition

Includes: Adjust slack adjuster.

	(Factory Time)	Chilton Time
one-front or rear	(1.0)	1.5

DISC BRAKES

Disc Brake Rotor, Renew

Includes: Renew or transfer wheel bearings and repack.

	(Factory Time)	Chilton Time
All series-one	(1.2)	1.7
both	(2.3)	3.3

Caliper Assembly, Renew

Includes: Bleed system.

	(Factory Time)	Chilton Time
All series-one	(1.0)	1.5
both	(1.5)	2.5

Caliper Assy., R&R and Recondition

Includes: Bleed system.

	(Factory Time)	Chilton Time
All series-one	(1.6)	2.1
both	(2.7)	3.7

Disc Brake Pads, Renew

Includes: Install new disc brake pads only.

	(Factory Time)	Chilton Time
All series	(1.2)	1.5

AIR BRAKE ANTI-SKID SYSTEM

Skid Control Monitor Assy., Renew

	(Factory Time)	Chilton Time
All series		
Kelsey Hayes	(.4)	.7
Eaton	(.3)	.6

Skid Control Sensor Ring, R&R or Renew

	(Factory Time)	Chilton Time
All series	(.9)	1.3

Skid Control Wheel Sensor, R&R or Renew

	(Factory Time)	Chilton Time
All series	(1.1)	1.7

Skid Control Modulator Valve, R&R or Renew

	(Factory Time)	Chilton Time
All series		
Eaton-one	(1.1)	1.4
each adtnl	(1.0)	1.0
Kelsey-Hayes-one	(1.1)	1.4
each adtnl	(1.0)	1.0

Skid Control Modulator Controller, Renew

	(Factory Time)	Chilton Time
All series		
Kelsey Hayes-one	(.5)	.7
each adtnl	(.4)	.4
Eaton-one	(.7)	1.0
each adtnl	(.6)	.6

PARKING BRAKE

Parking Brake, Adjust

	(Factory Time)	Chilton Time
All models	(.4)	.5

Parking Brake Cable, Renew (To Equalizer)

	(Factory Time)	Chilton Time
F-series	(.5)	.8
C-series	(.8)	1.1
L-LN series	(.6)	.9

Parking Brake, Reline

	(Factory Time)	Chilton Time
band type	(1.1)	1.6
shoe type	(1.2)	1.7
w/Coupled shaft, add	(.2)	.2

Parking Brake Control, Renew

	(Factory Time)	Chilton Time
L series	(.4)	.7
C-series		
in cowl	(1.4)	1.8
All series-floor lever	(.6)	1.0

Parking Brake Drum, Renew

	(Factory Time)	Chilton Time
band type	(.7)	1.1
shoe type	(.7)	1.1
Transmatic	(1.8)	2.5
w/Coupled shaft, add	(.2)	.2

Thermostat, Renew

(Factory Time)	Chilton Time
GAS	
Six–F series (.4)	.6
C series (.6)	.9
L series (.5)	.8
V-8–330, 361, 389, 391 engs	
All series (.5)	.8
V-8–370, 429 engs	
All series (.5)	.8
V-8–401, 475, 477, 534 engs	
F-series	
Front (.8)	1.1
Rear (.7)	1.0
Both (.9)	1.2
All other series (.6)	.9
DIESEL	
Cummins	
KT1150-NH855 (1.4)	2.0
V-555 (.6)	1.0
VT903-one (1.4)	2.0
both (2.8)	3.8
Detroit	
Six (.8)	1.2
V-8 (.9)	1.3
Caterpillar	
3208 (1.0)	1.4
3406 (.7)	1.1

Radiator Shutter and Cylinder Assembly, Renew

(Factory Time)	Chilton Time
C series (.8)	1.2
F series	
w/Caterpillar V-8 (1.5)	2.2
CL series (.9)	1.3

Shutter Thermostat, Renew

(Factory Time)	Chilton Time
All series (.8)	1.1

Intercooler, Renew

(Factory Time)	Chilton Time
Detroit (1.0)	1.4
Cummins	
F series (3.3)	4.5
C-L series (2.9)	3.8

Radiator, R&R or Renew

(Factory Time)	Chilton Time
GAS	
SIX	
F-C series (1.3)	1.8
L series (.8)	1.2
V-8–330, 361, 389, 391 engs	
F series (1.4)	2.0
C series (1.6)	2.2
L series (1.0)	1.6
V-8–370, 429 engs	
F series (1.0)	1.6
C series (1.6)	2.2
L-LN series (1.4)	2.0
V-8–401, 475, 477, 534 engs	
C series (2.0)	2.8
L series (1.5)	2.3
DIESEL	
F series	
Cat V-8 (1.6)	2.6
C series	
Cat V-8 (1.3)	2.1
L-LN series	
Cat-Six (3.0)	4.3
V-8 (1.0)	1.5
Detroit (1.7)	2.7
Cummins (1.9)	2.9
CL series	
All engs (4.0)	5.5
w/Shutters add (.5)	.5
w/Rad mount A.C. condenser add (1.0)	1.0

Radiator Hose, Renew

(Factory Time)	Chilton Time
GAS	
Six–exc below-upper (.6)	.7
lower (.7)	.9
both (1.0)	1.3
L series-upper (.5)	.7
lower (.5)	.7
both (.6)	.9
V-8–330, 361, 389, 391 engs	
exc below-upper (.6)	.7
lower (.9)	1.1
both (1.1)	1.4
L series-upper (.5)	.7
lower (.6)	.8
both (.7)	1.1
V-8–370, 429 engs	
upper (.5)	.7
lower (.5)	.7
both (.7)	1.0
V-8–401, 475, 477, 534 engs	
exc below-upper (1.0)	1.3
lower (1.0)	1.4
both (1.2)	1.6
L series-upper (.7)	.9
lower (.8)	1.0
both (.9)	1.3
DIESEL	
F series	
exc below-upper (.6)	.8
lower (.7)	.9
both (.9)	1.2
F 8000-upper (.7)	.9
lower (.9)	1.2
both (1.0)	1.4
C series	
exc below-upper (.5)	.7
lower (.6)	.8
both (.8)	1.0
C 8000-upper (.5)	.7
lower (.6)	.8
both (.8)	1.0
L series-upper (.5)	.7
lower (.7)	.8
both (.8)	1.0
CL series	
upper (.7)	.9
lower (.7)	.9
both (.9)	1.3

Fan Blades, Renew

(Factory Time)	Chilton Time
GAS	
Six(.3)	.6
V-8–exc below (.8)	1.2
C series (1.1)	1.5
DIESEL	
F series (.6)	.9
C series	
exc below (.9)	1.3
C 8000 (1.6)	2.1
Caterpillar V-8 (.5)	.8
L series (.4)	.7
CL series (.8)	1.2

Fan Belts, Renew

(Factory Time)	Chilton Time
GAS	
F series-one (.3)	.5
each adtnl (.2)	.3
C series-one (.4)	.6
each adtnl (.2)	.3
L series-one (.3)	.5
each adtnl (.2)	.3
DIESEL	
F series	
exc below-one (.6)	.8
each adtnl (.3)	.5
F 8000-one (1.2)	1.5
each adtnl (.8)	1.0
C series-one (.5)	.7
each adtnl (.3)	.5
L series-one (.4)	.6
each adtnl (.2)	.3
V-8-one (.9)	1.2
each adtnl (.5)	.7
CL series-one (.9)	1.2
each adtnl (.5)	.7

Water Pump, Renew

(Factory Time)	Chilton Time
GAS	
Six(1.0)	1.5
V-8–330, 361, 389, 391 engs	
F series (1.9)	2.5
C series (1.3)	2.0
L series (1.4)	2.0
V-8–370, 429 engs	
F-C series (1.8)	2.5
V-8–401, 475, 477, 534 engs	
F series	
housing & pump (1.6)	2.2
pump only (1.2)	1.7
C series	
housing & pump (1.1)	1.9
pump only (.9)	1.4
L series	
housing & pump (1.7)	2.2
pump only (1.0)	1.7
DIESEL	
Cummins	
KT1150 (2.4)	2.9
V-903 (3.7)	4.7
NH855-V555 (2.5)	3.2
Detroit	
6-71 (1.0)	1.6
All V-8's (1.5)	2.1
Caterpillar	
3208	
F-series (1.9)	2.7
All other series (1.2)	2.0
3406	
All series (3.0)	4.0

Temperature Gauge (Engine), Renew

(Factory Time)	Chilton Time
All series (.4)	.6

Temperature Gauge (Dash), Renew

(Factory Time)	Chilton Time
F series	
exc below (.5)	.8
diesel w/A.C. (.8)	1.0
C series (.6)	1.0
L series	
city delivery (.6)	1.0
line haul (1.0)	1.3
CL series (.4)	.7

Heater Core, R&R or Renew

(Factory Time)	Chilton Time
F series	
wo/A.C. (.9)	1.5
w/A.C. (.6)	1.1
C series (1.0)	1.5
L series (.8)	1.2
CL series (.5)	1.0

Heater Blower Motor, Renew

(Factory Time)	Chilton Time
F-C series (.5)	.7
L series (.6)	.9
CL series (.5)	.9

Heater Switch, Renew

(Factory Time)	Chilton Time
F series (.6)	.9
C series (.3)	.5
L series (.5)	.7
CL series (.6)	.9

Heater Water Valve, Renew

(Factory Time)	Chilton Time
All series-Gas (.6)	.9
Diesel (1.1)	1.5

Blower Motor Resistor, Renew

(Factory Time)	Chilton Time
F-C series (.4)	.6
L series (.3)	.5
CL series (.3)	.5

LABOR 8 EXHAUST SYSTEM 8 LABOR

(Factory Time)	Chilton Time
Muffler, Renew	
Gas	
All series-one (1.0)	1.4
two (1.4)	1.9
Diesel	
Six (1.0)	1.4
V-6-V-8	
single (1.5)	1.9
dual (1.9)	2.4
Renew inlet pipe add (.3)	.3
Renew outlet pipe add (.3)	.3
Exhaust Pipe, Renew (Outlet)	
Gas	
6.1-7.0L engs	
right (.8)	1.1
left (.8)	1.1
both (1.3)	1.9
7.8-8.8L engs	
single (1.0)	1.4
dual (1.7)	2.2
Diesel	
Six	
single inlet (1.5)	2.0
connector (.6)	.9
extension (.6)	.9
dual inlet (1.0)	1.4
V-6-V-8	
inlet (.8)	1.1
connector (.8)	1.1
both (1.3)	1.9
dual inlet (1.5)	2.0
Outlet Pipe, Renew	
Gas	
single (.4)	.6
dual (.5)	.7
Diesel	
single (.4)	.6
dual (.6)	.8
Exhaust Manifold, R&R or Renew	
GAS	
Six–L series (1.3)	1.8
F-C series (1.5)	2.0
V-8–330, 361, 389, 391 engs	
F series-one (1.3)	1.8
both (2.4)	3.0
C series-one (.9)	1.4
both (1.7)	2.2
L series-right (.8)	1.3
left (.9)	1.4
both (1.5)	2.2
V-8–401, 475, 477, 534 engs	
F series-one (1.1)	1.6
both (1.9)	2.4
C series-one (.8)	1.3
both (1.5)	2.0
L series-one (.9)	1.4
both (1.5)	2.0
V-8–370, 429 engs	
C-LN series	
one (.9)	1.4
both (1.5)	2.0
DIESEL	
Caterpillar	
F series-one (1.0)	1.6
both (1.6)	2.8
C series-one (.7)	1.3
both (1.2)	2.4
L series-3208-one (.7)	1.3
both (1.2)	2.4
3406 (2.0)	2.9
LN series-one (1.0)	1.6
both (1.6)	2.8
CL series (2.0)	2.9
Cummins	
NH743, 855 (1.5)	2.7
NT855 (2.0)	3.2
V555-one (1.6)	2.4
both (2.5)	4.1
V-VT 903-one (2.4)	3.2
both (3.1)	4.7
KT (A) 1150 (1.8)	3.0
Detroit	
6V-53-6V-92-each (.6)	1.1
6-71 (1.0)	1.6
8V-71-8V-92-each (.8)	1.3

LABOR 9 FRONT SUSPENSION 9 LABOR

Note: On all front suspension operations alignment charges must be added if performed. Time given does not include alignment.

(Factory Time)	Chilton Time
Check Alignment of Front End	
All series	.8
Note: Deduct if alignment is performed.	
Toe-In, Adjust	
All series (.4)	.7
Front Wheel Grease Seal, Renew	
DRUM BRAKES	
Disc Wheel	
one side (1.0)	1.4
both sides (1.6)	2.2
Cast Spoke Wheel	
one side (.9)	1.3
both sides (1.4)	1.9
DISC BRAKES	
one side (1.1)	1.5
both sides (2.0)	2.8
Front Wheel Bearings and Cups, Clean and Repack or Renew	
DRUM BRAKES	
Disc Wheel	
one side (1.0)	1.5
both sides (1.8)	2.8
Cast Spoke Wheel	
one side (.9)	1.4
both sides (1.5)	2.5
DISC BRAKES	
one side (1.3)	1.7
both sides (2.3)	3.1
Front Axle, Renew	
Add alignment charges.	
5000, 5500 lb axles (4.2)	5.3
6000 lb axle (5.1)	6.5
7000-9000 lb (5.2)	6.6
12000-15000 lb (5.9)	*7.5
16000-22000 lb (6.1)	7.7
*w/Linkage type P.S. add (.3)	.3
Front Shock Absorbers, Renew	
All series-one (.4)	.5
both (.6)	.8
Steering Knuckle, Renew	
Add alignment charges.	
F600 4 x 4-one (1.3)	1.7
both (2.0)	2.5
6000 lb axle-right (2.1)	2.8
left (2.2)	2.9
both (3.5)	4.7
7000, 9500 lb axle	
right (2.1)	2.9
left (2.4)	3.2
both (3.9)	5.2
12000-15000 lb axle	
right (2.6)	3.5
left (2.7)	3.6
both (4.3)	5.8
16000-22000 lb axle	
right (2.6)	3.5
left (2.8)	3.7
both (4.6)	6.2
Steering Knuckle, Rebush	
Add alignment charges.	
6000 lb axle-right (2.5)	3.3
left (2.6)	3.5
both (4.3)	5.8
7000, 9500 lb axle	
right (2.6)	3.5
left (2.8)	3.7
both (4.7)	6.3
12000-15000 lb axle	
right (3.0)	4.0
left (3.1)	4.1
both (5.1)	6.8
16000-22000 lb axle	
right (3.0)	4.0
left (3.2)	4.3
both (5.4)	7.2
F600 4WD-one (1.5)	2.0
both (2.3)	3.1
King Pins and Bushings, Renew (Both Wheels)	
5000, 5500 lb axle (4.4)	5.9
7000-15000 lb (5.2)	7.0
16000-22000 lb (5.5)	7.4
F600 4WD (2.5)	3.3
Front Spring, Renew	
5000-7000 lb axle-one (1.2)	1.7
both (2.3)	3.2
9000-22000 lb axle	
one (1.5)	2.1
both (2.6)	3.9
CL series	
one (3.3)	4.6
both (6.5)	9.1
Ream spring bush add, each	.2
Spring Leaf or Tie Bolt, Renew	
5000-7000 lb axle-one (1.6)	2.2
both (3.1)	4.3
9000-22000 lb axle	
one (1.9)	2.6
both (3.4)	4.7
Spring Shackle and Bushing, Renew	
5000-7000 lb axle-one (2.1)	2.9
both (3.9)	5.4
9000-22000 lb axle	
one (2.4)	3.3
both (4.2)	5.8

LABOR 9 FRONT SUSPENSION 9 LABOR

(Factory Time) — Chilton Time

FRONT WHEEL DRIVE

Front Axle Shaft or Universal Joint, Renew

F600 4WD-one (1.3)	1.8
both (2.4)	3.0

Differential Carrier Assembly, R&R

Includes: R&R axle shafts, housing gasket. Drain and refill axle.

F600 4WD (3.0)	4.0

Differential Carrier Assembly, R&R and Recondition

Includes: R&R axle shafts, housing gasket. Drain and refill axle. Inspect, clean, renew or recondition all necessary parts.

F600 4WD (6.4)	8.0

Pinion Shaft Oil Seal, Renew

F600 4WD (1.0)	1.5

Front Drive Shaft, Renew

F600 4WD (.6)	1.0

Front Universal Joint, Renew (One)

F600 4WD (1.0)	1.5

LABOR 10 STEERING LINKAGE 10 LABOR

(Factory Time) — Chilton Time

Tie Rod or Tie Rod End, Renew

Includes: Toe-in adjustment.

exc below (1.1)	1.3
F600 4WD (.9)	1.2

Drag Link, Renew

Does not require resetting toe-in.

All series-one (.6)	.9

Drag Link, Adjust

All series (.4)	.5

Pitman Arm, Renew

exc below (.7)	1.0
CL series (.6)	1.0

Spindle Arm, Renew

Includes: Toe-in adjustment.

tapered arm-one (1.3)	1.7
both (1.7)	2.2
bolt on arm-one (1.5)	2.0
both (2.1)	2.7
F600 4WD-one (1.8)	2.3
both (3.1)	4.0

LABOR 11 STEERING GEAR 11 LABOR

(Factory Time) — Chilton Time

STANDARD STEERING

Steering Gear, Adjust (On Truck)

All series (1.1)	1.5

Steering Gear, R&R or Renew

F-C series (1.0)	1.8
L-LN series (.6)	1.4

Steering Gear, R&R and Recondition

Includes: Disassemble, inspect, clean, renew necessary parts, reassemble and adjust.

F-C series (1.9)	3.2
L-LN series (1.5)	2.7

Steering Mast Jacket Bearing, Renew

Includes: R&R steering column.

exc below (.9)	1.2
C series (.7)	.9
CL series (.8)	1.0

Steering Wheel, Renew

All series (.4)	.6

POWER STEERING

Trouble Shoot Power Steering

Includes: Check pounds pull on steering wheel, install checking gauges, test pump pressure and check for external leaks.

exc below (.8)	.8
C-CT series (.7)	.7

Power Steering Hoses, Renew

F500-900	
pressure (.7)	1.0
return (.9)	1.3
F series	
Cat V-8-each (.6)	.9
C series	
Cat V-8-each (.5)	.8
L series-each (.4)	.7
CL series-each (.5)	.8

Power Steering Control Valve Assy., Renew

F500-800 (.6)	1.0
C series (.9)	2.0
L-LN series (.8)	1.8
CL series (1.0)	2.0
Recond add (.8)	.8

Power Steering Cylinder, Renew

All series (.7)	1.5
Recond add (.8)	.8

Power Steering Gear, R&R or Renew

F series	
Gas (1.0)	1.5
Diesel (1.5)	2.0
C series (1.2)	1.7
L-LN series (1.5)	2.0
CL series (1.8)	2.3
Renew sector shaft seals add (.7)	1.0

Power Steering Gear, R&R and Recondition

Includes: Disassemble, inspect, clean, renew necessary parts, reassemble and adjust.

F series	
Gas (2.7)	3.6
Diesel (3.2)	4.4
C series (2.9)	3.9
L-LN series (3.2)	4.4
CL series (3.5)	4.8

Power Steering Pump, R&R or Renew

F series-Gas (.7)	1.1
F series-Detroit (1.3)	1.7
F7000-Cat-V-8 (.9)	1.4
C series-Gas (.7)	1.2
C series-Diesel (.7)	1.2
L series	
Gas (.8)	1.3
Detroit (1.1)	1.6
Caterpillar (.6)	1.1
Cummins (.7)	1.2
CL series	
Detroit (1.0)	1.5
Caterpillar (.7)	1.2
Cummins (2.4)	3.4

Power Steering Pump, R&R and Recondition

F series-Gas (1.3)	1.9
F series-Detroit (1.9)	2.5
F7000-Cat-V-8 (2.4)	3.3
C series-Gas (2.2)	3.1
C series-Diesel (2.2)	3.1
L series	
Gas (2.3)	3.2
Detroit (2.6)	3.5
Caterpillar (2.1)	3.0
Cummins (2.2)	3.1
CL series	
Detroit (1.6)	2.3
Caterpillar (1.3)	2.2
Cummins (3.0)	4.2

Pump Drive Belt, Renew

Gas (.4)	.7
Diesel	
Cummins (.4)	.7
Caterpillar (.5)	.9
Detroit	
CL series (.8)	1.2
All other series (.4)	.7

(Factory Time) — Chilton Time

GASOLINE ENGINES

Cylinder Head Gasket, Renew

Includes: R&R all normal interfering parts. Check cylinder head and block flatness. Adjust carburetor, valves (if adjustable) and ignition timing (when distributor is removed).

	Chilton Time
Six–C series (3.1)	4.2
F series (3.3)	4.5
L series (2.8)	3.8
V-8–330, 361, 389, 391 engs	
F series-one (3.5)	4.8
both (4.4)	6.0
C series-one (3.3)	4.5
both (4.0)	5.5
L series-one (4.5)	6.0
both (5.3)	7.0
V-8–370, 429 engs	
one (3.9)	5.4
both (5.7)	7.8
V-8–401, 475, 477, 534 engs	
F series-one (6.1)	7.5
both (8.4)	10.0
C series-one (5.6)	7.0
both (7.7)	9.5
L series-exc below	
one (6.7)	8.5
both (9.4)	11.5
LN models	
one (8.2)	10.3
both (11.5)	14.5

Cylinder Head, Renew

Includes: R&R all interfering parts. Check cylinder block flatness. Transfer all necessary components. Clean, reface and lap valves. Check valve spring tension, assembled height and valve head runout. Adjust carburetor, valves and distributor.

	Chilton Time
Six–C series (5.7)	7.2
F series (5.9)	7.5
L series (5.4)	6.8
V-8–330, 361, 389, 391 engs	
F series-one (4.9)	6.3
both (7.2)	9.0
C series-one (4.7)	6.0
both (6.8)	8.5
L series-one (5.9)	7.5
both (8.1)	10.0
V-8–370, 429 engs	
one (5.1)	7.0
both (8.2)	11.3
V-8–401, 475, 477, 534 engs	
F series-one (7.8)	9.3
both (11.2)	13.6
C series-one (7.0)	8.8
both (10.9)	13.1
L series-exc below	
one (8.1)	10.3
both (11.6)	15.1
LN models	
one (9.6)	12.0
both (14.7)	18.5

Clean Carbon and Grind Valves

Includes: R&R cylinder head and all interfering parts. Check cylinder head and block flatness. Clean, inspect and recondition or renew all necessary components. Check valve spring tension, assembled height and valve runout. Tune engine.

	Chilton Time
Six–C series (6.8)	8.7
F series (7.0)	9.0
L series (6.5)	8.3
V-8–330, 361, 389, 391 engs	
F series (9.0)	11.4
C series (8.6)	10.9
L series (9.9)	12.4
V-8–370, 429 engs (9.4)	12.9

COMBINATIONS

Add to Valve Job

(Factory Time)	Chilton Time
VALVE GUIDES, REAM FOR OVERSIZE STEMS	
One (.1)	.2
Twelve (.7)	.9
Sixteen (1.0)	1.2
ROCKER ARMS, RENEW OR DISASSEMBLE AND CLEAN	
Six (.8)	1.0
ROCKER ARM STUD, RENEW	
Each (.3)	.3
DISTRIBUTOR, RECONDITION	
Six (.9)	1.1
V-8 (1.0)	1.2
CARBURETOR, RECONDITION	
Six (.7)	1.2
V-8 (.9)	1.5

(Factory Time) — Chilton Time

	Chilton Time
V-8–401, 475, 477, 534 engs	
F series (13.7)	16.1
C series (13.0)	15.6
L series	
exc below (14.7)	17.6
LN models (16.8)	21.0

Valve Cover Gasket, Renew

	Chilton Time
Six–F-L series (.8)	1.0
C series (.7)	.9
V-8–330, 361, 389, 391 engs	
F series-one (.5)	.7
both (.7)	.9
C series-one (.4)	.6
both (.6)	.8
L series-one (.6)	.7
both (.9)	1.2
V-8–370, 429 engs	
right (.7)	.9
left (.5)	.7
both (1.0)	1.4
V-8–401, 475, 477, 534 engs	
F series-one (.6)	.8
both (.8)	1.0
C series-one (.4)	.6
both (.6)	.8
L series-exc below	
one (.9)	1.0
both (1.1)	1.5
LN models	
one (1.0)	1.3
both (1.3)	1.7

Push Rod Cover Gasket, Renew

	Chilton Time
Six(.6)	.9
V-8–401, 475, 477, 534 engs	
F series (2.9)	3.5
C series (2.3)	2.7
L series	
exc below (3.2)	4.0
LN models (3.8)	4.8

Push Rods, Renew

	Chilton Time
Six–F-L series-one (1.0)	1.3
all (1.3)	1.7
C series-one (.9)	1.2
all (1.2)	1.6
V-8–330, 361, 389, 391 engs	
F series-one (.6)	.8
all (1.0)	1.3
C series-one (.5)	.7
all (.9)	1.2
L series-one (.7)	.9
all (1.2)	1.6
V-8–370, 429 engs	
right side-one (.8)	1.1
left side-one (.6)	.8
all-both sides (1.4)	1.9
V-8–401, 475, 477, 534 eng	
F series-one (.9)	1.2
all (1.7)	2.2
C series-one (.7)	.9
all (1.5)	2.0
L series-exc below	
one (1.2)	1.6
all (2.0)	2.5
LN models	
one (1.3)	1.7
all (2.2)	2.8

Rocker Arm Assembly, R&R and Recondition

	Chilton Time
V-8–330, 361, 389, 391 engs	
F series-one (1.0)	1.5
both (1.7)	2.6
C series-one (.9)	1.4
both (1.6)	2.5
L series-one (1.1)	1.5
both (1.9)	2.6
V-8–401, 475, 477, 534 engs	
F series-one (5.9)	7.4
both (8.0)	9.9
C series-one (5.3)	6.7
both (7.5)	9.2
L series-exc below	
one (6.5)	8.3
both (9.3)	11.5
LN models	
one (8.0)	10.0
both (11.3)	14.2

Valve Lifters, Renew (All)

Includes: R&R intake manifold (V-8) and all interfering parts. Adjust valves, carburetor and ignition timing.

	Chilton Time
Six–F-L series (1.8)	3.4
C series (1.6)	3.2
V-8–330, 361, 389, 391 engs	
F series (2.8)	3.5
C series (3.2)	4.2
L series (3.2)	4.2
V-8–370, 429 engs (3.6)	5.0
V-8–401, 475, 477, 534 engs	
F series (4.3)	5.8
C series (3.7)	5.2
L series	
exc below (4.6)	6.0
LN models (5.6)	7.0

Valve Springs or Seals, Renew (All)

Includes: R&R valve covers and adjust valves.

	Chilton Time
Six–F-C series (2.0)	2.5
L series (2.3)	2.9
V-8–330, 361, 389, 391 engs	
F series (2.8)	3.5
C series (2.5)	*3.2
L series (2.7)	3.5
V-8–401, 475, 477, 534 engs	
F series (3.0)	3.8
C series (3.2)	*4.3
L series	
exc below (3.4)	4.5
LN models (3.5)	4.7
*R&R aux water tank add (.5)	.5

LABOR 12 CYLINDER HEAD & VALVE SYSTEM 12 LABOR

DIESEL ENGINES

Cylinder Head, R&R or Renew Gasket

Includes: R&R all normal interfering parts. Check cylinder head and block for flatness. Adjust valves and crossheads.

(Factory Time)	Chilton Time
Caterpillar	
F series-one (7.5)	10.8
both (11.4)	14.4
C series-one (6.4)	9.6
both (9.4)	12.8
L series 3208-one (6.4)	8.9
both (9.4)	11.6
3406 (11.8)	14.8
LN series-one (7.5)	10.8
both (11.4)	14.4
CL series (11.8)	14.8
Cummins	
NH & NT 743-855-one (7.3)	9.3
all (15.0)	19.2
V555-one (12.6)	16.1
all (20.5)	26.0
V & VT 785, 903	
one (14.1)	16.5
all (24.4)	30.8
KT(A)1150-one (6.8)	8.5
all (14.3)	17.0
Detroit	
6V-53-one (4.8)	6.4
both (8.0)	10.2
6V-92-one (5.0)	6.6
both (8.5)	10.7
6-71 (8.0)	10.0
8V-71-8V-92-one (5.5)	7.0
both (9.5)	12.0
w/Jacobs brk add (.5)	.5

Clean Carbon and Grind Valves

Includes: R&R head and all normal interfering parts. Check cylinder head and block flatness, magnaflux head. Clean, inspect and recondition all components as necessary. Pressure test head. Check spring tension, assembled height and valve runout. Adjust valves, crossheads and injectors. Road test.

(Factory Time)	Chilton Time
Caterpillar	
F series (15.4)	19.2
C series (13.4)	17.2
L series 3208 (13.4)	17.2
3406 (16.6)	20.4
LN series (15.4)	19.2
CL series (16.6)	20.4

COMBINATIONS

Add to Valve Job

(Factory Time)	Chilton Time
INJECTOR SLEEVES, RENEW	
One (.8)	1.0
Six (2.0)	2.5
Eight (2.8)	3.5
INJECTOR, RECONDITION	
One (.7)	1.0
each adtnl (.3)	.5

(Factory Time)	Chilton Time
Cummins	
NH & NT 743, 855 (23.0)	29.5
V555 (28.9)	37.0
V & VT 785, 903 (26.4)	32.9
KT(A)1150 (17.1)	21.2
Detroit	
6V-53 (23.0)	29.5
6V-92 (25.7)	31.2
6-71 (21.0)	25.6
8V-71-8V-92 (24.2)	31.0
w/Jacobs brk add (.5)	.5

Adjust Valves and Crossheads

Includes: R&R all normal interfering parts.

(Factory Time)	Chilton Time
Caterpillar	
F & LN series (1.7)	2.1
C & L series-3208 (1.4)	1.8
L & CL series-3406 (1.3)	1.7
Cummins	
NH & NT743, 855 (2.8)	3.5
V & VT785, 903 (4.4)	5.5
V-555 (3.0)	4.1
KT(A)1150 (2.3)	3.0
Detroit	
exc below (1.5)	2.0
6-71 (1.2)	1.6

Valve Cover Gasket, Renew

(Factory Time)	Chilton Time
Caterpillar	
All series-3208	
one (.3)	.5
both (.6)	.9
3406 (.9)	1.2

(Factory Time)	Chilton Time
CUMMINS	
KT(A)1150-one (.2)	.4
all (1.0)	1.5
NH & NT743, 855-one (1.1)	1.6
each adtnl (.9)	1.0
V & VT 555, 903-one (1.7)	2.2
each adtnl (1.5)	1.6
Detroit	
each (.3)	.5

Valve Push Rods, Renew (All)

Includes: R&R all normal interfering parts. All necessary adjustments.

(Factory Time)	Chilton Time
Caterpillar	
3208	
F & LN series (2.1)	2.7
C & L series (1.8)	2.4
3406	
All series (2.9)	3.6
CUMMINS	
KT(A)1150 (3.1)	3.8
NH & NT743, 855 (5.3)	6.0
V & VT555, 903 (5.7)	6.4
Detroit	
6V-53-6V-92 (2.9)	3.4
6-71 (2.8)	3.3
8V-71-8V-92 (3.6)	4.1

Valve Lifters, Renew (All)

Includes: R&R of all normal interfering parts. All necessary adjustments.

(Factory Time)	Chilton Time
Caterpillar	
F series (11.4)	14.5
C series (9.7)	13.2
L series-3208 (9.7)	13.2
3406 (3.5)	4.7
LN series (11.4)	14.5
CL series (3.5)	4.7
Cummins	
NH & NT743, 855 (10.0)	12.5
V-8 785, V903 (14.6)	18.3
KT(A)1150 (4.1)	6.4
V-VT555-903 (16.7)	20.4
Detroit	
6V-53-6V-92 (4.2)	5.3
6-71 (3.8)	4.8
8V-71-8V-92 (4.8)	6.0

LABOR 13 ENGINE ASSEMBLY & MOUNTS 13 LABOR

GASOLINE ENGINES

Engine Assembly, Remove and Reinstall

Includes: R&R of all normal interfering parts. Does not include transfer of any components.

(Factory Time)	Chilton Time
Six–F-C series (3.0)	4.0
L series (2.6)	3.7
V-8–330, 361, 389, 391 engs	
F series	
std trans (3.8)	5.0
auto trans (5.8)	7.5
C series (3.9)	5.2
L series	
exc below (3.2)	4.3
LN models (5.2)	6.8
V-8–370, 429 engs	
F series	
w/M.T. (8.0)	10.4
w/A.T. (9.8)	12.7
C-L series	
w/M.T. (5.5)	7.1
w/A.T. (7.0)	9.1
LN series	
w/M.T. (6.6)	8.5
w/A.T. (8.5)	11.0
V-8–401, 475, 477, 534 engs	
F series (9.9)	11.8
C series (7.8)	10.2
L series	
exc below (7.4)	9.5
LN models (8.8)	11.2
w/A.C. add (1.0)	1.0
w/P.S. add (.4)	.4
w/Air brks add	.6

Engine Assembly, Renew (Remanufactured Engine)

Includes: R&R engine and all normal interfering parts. Transfer all necessary components. Tune engine and road test.

(Factory Time)	Chilton Time
Six–F-C series (5.7)	7.5
L series (5.3)	7.0
V-8–330, 361, 389, 391 engs	
F series	
std trans (7.9)	10.0
auto trans (9.9)	12.0
C series (8.0)	10.0
L series	
exc below (7.3)	9.5
LN models (9.3)	11.5
V-8–370, 429 engs	
F series	
w/M.T. (11.5)	14.9
w/A.T. (13.3)	17.2

(Factory Time) Chilton Time

C-L series
w/M.T. (9.0) 11.7
w/A.T. (10.5) 13.6
LN series
w/M.T. (10.8) 13.1
w/A.T. (12.0) 15.6
V-8–401, 475, 477, 534 engs
F series (15.6) 19.0
C series (13.5) 15.5
L series
exc below (13.1) 17.9
LN models (14.5) 18.7
w/A.C. add (1.0) 1.0
w/P.S. add (.4) 4
w/Air brks add 6

Cylinder Assembly (Short Engine), Renew & Grind Valves

Includes: R&R engine and all normal interfering parts. Transfer all necessary parts and equipment. Check valve spring tension, valve seat and head runout, head flatness, stem to guide clearance, assembled height. Tune engine and road test.

Six–F-C series (11.4) 14.5
L series (11.0) 14.0
V-8–330, 361, 389, 391 engs
F series
std trans (13.8) 16.0
auto trans (15.8) 18.0
C series (13.4) 16.9
L series
exc below (13.6) 16.5
LN models (15.6) 18.5
V-8–370, 429 engs
F series
w/M.T. (13.7) 19.1
w/A.T. (15.5) 21.7
C-L series
w/M.T. (11.2) 15.6
w/A.T. (12.7) 17.7
LN series
w/M.T. (16.0) 22.4
w/A.T. (17.9) 25.0
V-8–401, 475, 477, 534 engs
F series (22.8) 26.0
C series (20.3) 23.4
L series
exc below (19.9) 24.9
LN models (21.3) 25.7
w/A.C. add (1.0) 1.0
w/P.S. add (.4) 4
w/Air brks add 6

Engine Assembly, R&R and Recondition (Complete)

Includes: R&R of all normal interfering parts. Disassemble and assemble complete engine. Inspect all components. Rebore block. Install new pistons, rings and pins. Align rods. Plastigauge and install new main, rod and camshaft bearings. Clean carbon and grind valves, test hydraulic tappets, renew if necessary. Renew all gaskets and seals as necessary. Tune engine and road test.

Six–F-C series (25.9) 31.0
L series (24.5) 29.4

(Factory Time) Chilton Time

V-8–330, 361, 389, 391 engs
F series
std trans (32.8) 38.2
auto trans (34.8) 40.2
C series (32.3) 37.7
L series
exc below (33.9) 40.5
LN models (35.9) 42.5
V-8–370, 429 engs
F series
w/M.T. (20.0) 27.0
w/A.T. (21.8) 29.4
C-L series
w/M.T. (17.5) 23.6
w/A.T. (19.0) 25.6
LN series
w/M.T. (18.6) 25.1
w/A.T. (20.5) 27.6

V-8–401, 475, 477, 534 engs
F series (45.6) 51.2
C series (42.8) 48.2
L series
exc below (44.9) 50.3
LN models (46.3) 53.0
w/A.C. add (1.0) 1.0
w/P.S. add (.4) 4
w/Air brks add 6

Engine Mounts, Renew

Front
Six–one (.4) 7
both (.5) 9
V-8–exc below–one (.5) 8
both (.8) 1.2
V-8–370, 429 engs (1.5) 2.2
Rear
All series (.5) 9

DIESEL ENGINES

Engine Assembly, Remove and Reinstall

Includes: R&R of all normal interfering parts. Does not include transfer of any components.

Caterpillar
F series (11.2) 13.4
C series (8.1) 10.4
L series-3208 (10.2) 12.4
3406 (20.4) 24.6
LN series (10.8) 13.1
CL series (12.7) 16.0

Cummins
NH & NT743, 855 (25.5) 31.6
V555 (24.4) 30.5
V & VT 785, 903 (24.0) 30.0
N927 (19.5) 24.5

Detroit
6V-53-6V-92 (22.2) 27.8
6-71 (24.6) 30.8
8V-71-8V-92 (23.4) 29.4

(Factory Time) Chilton Time

Cylinder Block, Renew

Includes: R&R engine and all normal interfering parts. Transfer all components without disassembly. Install new main and rod bearings. Renew all necessary seals and gaskets. Adjust timing and clearances. Road Test.
Does not include reconditioning of any component.

Caterpillar
F series (33.2) 44.5
C series (31.0) 38.6
L series-3208 (32.2) 40.2
3406 (53.9) 62.8
LN series (34.4) 43.3
CL series (46.2) 55.1
Cummins
NH & NT743, 855 (55.8) 64.3
V555 (55.7) 65.5
V & VT 785, 903 (54.8) 64.5
N927 (49.8) 59.5
Detroit
6V-53 (54.2) 62.8
6V-92 (56.2) 64.8
6-71 (58.6) 67.8
8V-71-8V-92 (60.4) 69.4

Engine Assembly, R&R and Recondition (Complete)

Includes: R&R of all normal interfering parts. Complete dissassembly and assembly of engine. Pressure test block and head. Plastigauge and renew main, rod and camshaft bearings. Install new pistons, rings, pins and liners. Rebore block. Recondition blower or turbocharger, water and injector pump, oil pump, injectors, governor and other sub-assemblies. Clean carbon and grind valves. Check and set all clearances. Tune engine and road test.

Caterpillar
F series (41.6) 55.9
C series (38.5) 49.9
L series-3208 (40.6) 53.7
3406 (50.8) 63.9
LN series (41.2) 54.3
CL series (43.1) 56.2
Cummins
NH & NT743, 855 (59.1) 74.1
V555 (62.4) 78.0
V & VT785, 903 (60.5) 75.7
N927 (57.0) 71.3
Detroit
6V-53 (82.2) 102.8
6V-92 (87.2) 107.8
6-71 (84.6) 105.9
8V-71-8V-92 (93.4) 117.0

Engine Mounts, Renew

Front
exc below-one (.6) 9
F series-Cat-V-8-one (.7) 1.0
C series-Cat-V-8 (1.7) 2.4
Rear
one (1.0) 1.5
both (2.0) 2.5

GASOLINE ENGINES

Rings, Pins, Rod and Main Bearings, Renew and Grind Valves

Includes: R&R of all normal interfering parts. Remove cylinder top ridge, hone cylinder walls, clean ring grooves, install new rings. Install new pins and align rods. Plastigauge and install new main and rod bearings. Renew gaskets and seals as necessary. Clean carbon and grind valves. Test valve spring tension, valve seat and head run-out, stem to guide clearance, head and block flatness and assembled height. Tune engine and road test.

(Factory Time)	Chilton Time
Six–F series (17.8)	*22.3
C series (18.1)	*22.7
L series (17.0)	*21.3
V-8–330, 361, 389, 391 engs	
F series (19.2)	24.6
C series (19.6)	23.9
L series (20.4)	25.0
V-8–370, 429 engs	
F-C-L-LN series (18.5)	25.7
V-8–401, 475, 477, 534 engs	
F series (26.6)	32.5
C series (25.2)	31.7
L series	
exc below (27.0)	33.9
LN models (28.9)	36.7
w/A.C. add (1.0)	1.0
w/P.S. add (.4)	.4

*Includes R&R engine.

Rings, Pins, Rod and Main Bearings, Renew

Includes: R&R of all normal interfering parts. Remove cylinder top ridge, hone cylinder walls, clean ring grooves, install new rings. Install new pins and align rods. Plastigauge and install new main and rod bearings. Renew gaskets and seals as necessary. Tune engine and road test.

(Factory Time)	Chilton Time
Six–F series (15.1)	*18.8
C series (15.4)	*19.2
L series (14.3)	*17.8
V-8–330, 361, 389, 391 engs	
F series (16.5)	20.1
C series (15.9)	19.4
L series (16.8)	20.5
V-8–370, 429 engs	
F-C-L-LN series (14.8)	20.4
V-8–401, 475, 477, 534 engs	
F series (22.3)	27.3
C series (21.6)	26.5
L series	
exc below (23.4)	28.7
LN models (25.3)	31.5
w/A.C. add (1.0)	1.0
w/P.S. add (.4)	.4

*Includes R&R engine.

Rings, Pins and Rod Bearings, Renew

Includes: R&R of all normal interfering parts. Remove cylinder top ridge, hone cylinder walls, clean ring grooves, install new rings. Install new pins and align rods. Plastigauge and install new rod bearings. Renew gaskets and seals as necessary. Tune engine and road test.

(Factory Time)	Chilton Time
Six–F series (11.5)	13.6
C series (11.8)	14.0
L series (10.7)	12.6
V-8–330, 361, 389, 391 engs	
F series (14.6)	17.2
C series (14.0)	16.5
L series (14.9)	17.6
V-8–370,429 engs	
F-C-L-LN series (13.9)	19.1

COMBINATIONS

(Factory Time)	Chilton Time
VALVE GUIDES, REAM FOR OVERSIZE STEMS	
One (.1)	.2
Twelve (.7)	.9
Sixteen (1.0)	1.2
ROCKER ARM STUD, RENEW	
Each (.3)	.3
ROCKER ARMS, RENEW OR DISASSEMBLE AND CLEAN	
Six (.8)	1.0
DISTRIBUTOR, RECONDITION	
Six (.9)	1.1
V-8 (1.0)	1.3
CARBURETOR, RECONDITION	
Six (.7)	1.2
V-8 (.9)	1.5
REMOVE CYLINDER TOP RIDGE	
Each (.1)	.1
DEGLAZE CYLINDER WALLS	
Six (1.2)	1.2
V-8 (1.5)	1.5
OIL PUMP, RECONDITION	
All (.4)	.6
MAIN BEARINGS, RENEW (PAN REMOVED)	
V-8 (2.0)	2.9
PLASTIGAUGE BEARINGS	
Each (.1)	.1

(Factory Time)	Chilton Time
V-8–401, 475, 477, 534 engs	
F series (20.3)	24.4
C series (19.6)	23.6
L series	
exc below (21.4)	25.8
LN models (23.3)	28.6
w/A.C. add (1.0)	1.0
w/P.S. add (.4)	.4

Rings, Renew

Includes: R&R all normal interfering parts. Remove cylinder top ridge, hone cylinder walls, clean ring grooves, install new rings. Renew gaskets and seals as necessary.

(Factory Time)	Chilton Time
Six–F series (8.1)	10.2
C series (8.4)	10.6
L series (7.3)	9.2
V-8–330, 361, 389, 391 engs	
F series (10.4)	13.0
C series (9.8)	12.3
L series (10.7)	13.4
V-8–370, 429 engs	
F-C-L-LN series (11.0)	15.6
V-8–401, 475, 477, 534 engs	
F series (16.1)	20.2
C series (15.4)	19.4
L series	
exc below (17.2)	21.6
LN models (19.1)	24.4
w/A.C. add (1.0)	1.0
w/P.S. add (.4)	.4

Piston, Renew (One)

Includes: R&R of all normal interfering parts. Remove cylinder top ridge, hone cylinder walls. Install new piston with rings.

(Factory Time)	Chilton Time
Six–F series (5.0)	6.1
C series (5.2)	6.6
L series (4.2)	5.4
V-8–370, 429 engs	
F-C-L-LN series (6.2)	8.8
V-8–330, 361, 389, 391 engs	
F series (5.3)	6.6
C series (5.1)	6.6
L series (5.6)	6.9
V-8–401, 475, 477, 534 engs	
F series (8.6)	10.6
C series (7.7)	9.1
L series	
exc below (8.9)	11.1
LN models (10.0)	12.4
w/A.C. add (1.0)	1.0
w/P.S. add (.4)	.4

Rod Bearings, Renew

Includes: R&R oil pan, recondition oil pump.

(Factory Time)	Chilton Time
Six–F series (3.4)	4.6
C series (3.7)	4.9
L series (3.1)	4.3
V-8–330, 361, 389, 391 engs	
exc below (3.6)	5.5
C series (3.3)	5.2
L series (3.3)	5.2
V-8–370, 429 engs	
F-LN series (3.2)	4.4
C-L series (2.9)	4.0
V-8–401, 475, 477, 534 engs	
All series (3.9)	5.8

DIESEL ENGINES

Rings, Pins, Rod and Main Bearings, Renew and Grind Valves

Includes: R&R of all normal interfering parts. Hone cylinder liner walls, clean ring grooves, install new rings. Install new pins and align rods. Plastigauge and install new main and rod bearings. Renew gaskets and seals as necessary. Clean carbon and grind valves. Clean oil pump. Set injection timing and valves and crossheads. Road test.
Does not include renew liners.

(Factory Time)	Chilton Time
Caterpillar	
F series (24.7)	31.6
C series (23.3)	30.2
L series-3208 (23.3)	30.2
3406 (26.5)	33.8
LN series (24.7)	31.6
CL series (26.5)	33.8
Cummins	
NH & NT743, 855 (37.8)	47.3
V555 (39.5)	49.0
V & VT785, 903 (38.9)	48.7
N927 (29.2)	36.6
KT(A)1150 (35.1)	44.6
Detroit	
6V-53 (40.4)	50.6
6V-92 (42.7)	52.9
6-71 (37.9)	47.5
8V-71-8V-92 (44.3)	55.4

Rings, Renew

Includes: R&R all normal interfering parts. Hone cylinder liner walls, clean ring grooves, install new rings. Renew gaskets and seals as necessary. Set injection timing and valves and crossheads. Road test.

(Factory Time)	Chilton Time
Caterpillar	
F series (17.1)	21.5
C series (15.7)	20.1
L series-3208 (15.7)	20.1
3406 (20.5)	24.9
LN series (17.1)	21.5
CL series (20.5)	24.9

LABOR 14 PISTONS, RINGS & BEARINGS 14 LABOR

(Factory Time)	Chilton Time
Cummins	
NH & NT743, 855 (21.2)	25.9
V555 (29.6)	34.3
V & VT785, 903 (36.4)	41.1
N927 (18.3)	22.9
Detroit	
6V-53 (18.2)	22.8
6V-92 (19.9)	24.5
6-71 (17.6)	22.1
8V-71-8V-92 (20.8)	26.0

Piston and Liner, Renew (One)

Includes: R&R all normal interfering parts. Hone block bore, check liner height, liner bore and O.D. for proper fit. Install new liner, piston with rings and pin. Renew gaskets and seals as necessary. Set injection timing and valves and crossheads.

(Factory Time)	Chilton Time
Caterpillar	
All series	
3406 (17.7)	22.0
Cummins	
NH & NT743, 855 (16.0)	20.6
V555 (18.6)	23.1
V & VT 785, 903 (21.5)	25.9
N927 (17.9)	22.6
KT(A)1150 (14.1)	18.5
each adtnl	2.0
Detroit	
6V-53 (8.0)	10.2
6V-92 (8.1)	10.4
6-71 (11.8)	15.7
8V-71-8V-92 (9.2)	11.8

COMBINATIONS

(Factory Time)	Chilton Time
INJECTOR SLEEVES, REAM	
One (.8)	1.0
Six (2.0)	2.5
Eight (2.8)	3.5
INJECTORS, RECONDITION	
One (.7)	1.0
each adtnl (.3)	.5
GRIND VALVES, HEAD REMOVED	
Caterpillar 3208-each (2.0)	2.7
3406 (4.8)	5.7
Cummins	
NH & NT-one (2.1)	2.9
all (6.2)	8.0
N927 (5.1)	6.7
V555 (8.2)	10.5
V & VT 785, 903	
One (4.3)	5.8
Both (8.5)	11.1
Detroit	
V-6-each (7.5)	9.9
Six (13.0)	17.0
V-8-each (9.0)	11.5
PRESSURE TEST HEAD	
Six (1.5)	2.0
V-6-each (1.0)	1.5
V-8-each (1.2)	1.8

Rod Bearings, Renew

Includes: R&R all normal interfering parts. Clean oil pump.

(Factory Time)	Chilton Time
Caterpillar	
All series	
3208 (3.7)	4.5
3406 (3.5)	4.3
Cummins	
NH & NT743, 855 (3.1)	4.2
V555 (6.7)	8.8
V & VT 785, 903 (5.7)	7.6
N927 (6.3)	8.3
KT(A)1150 (11.4)	13.8
Detroit	
6V-53 (4.3)	5.8
6V-92 (4.4)	5.9
6-71 (4.9)	6.6
8V-71-8V-92 (5.8)	7.7

LABOR 15 CRANKSHAFT & DAMPER 15 LABOR

GASOLINE ENGINES

Crankshaft and Main Bearings, Renew

Includes: R&R all normal interfering parts and engine. Plastigauge and install new bearings. Recondition oil pump.

(Factory Time)	Chilton Time
Six–F-C series (7.9)	10.4
L series (7.5)	10.3
V-8–330, 361, 389, 391 engs	
F series	
std trans (8.9)	11.6
auto trans (10.9)	14.1
C series (9.0)	11.8
L series	
exc below (8.3)	11.1
LN models (10.3)	13.6
V-8–370, 429 engs	
F series	
w/M.T. (12.7)	17.5
w/A.T. (14.5)	20.0
C-L series	
w/M.T. (10.2)	14.0
w/A.T. (11.7)	16.1
LN series	
w/M.T. (11.3)	15.5
w/A.T. (13.2)	18.2
V-8–401, 475, 477, 534 eng	
F series (15.4)	20.3
C series (13.3)	18.7
L series	
exc below (12.9)	18.0
LN models (14.3)	19.7
w/A.C. add (1.0)	1.0
w/P.S. add (.4)	.4
w/Air brks add	.6

Main and Rod Bearings, Renew

Includes: R&R all normal interfering parts. Plastigauge and install new main and rod bearings. Renew gaskets and seals as necessary. Recondition oil pump.

(Factory Time)	Chilton Time
Six–F-C series (9.2)	*11.8
L series (8.7)	*11.4
V-8–330, 361, 389, 391 engs	
exc below (5.5)	8.2
C series (5.2)	7.9
L series (5.2)	7.9
V-8–370, 429 engs	
F-LN series (5.1)	6.9
C-L series (4.8)	6.5
V-8–401, 475, 477, 534 engs	
All series (5.8)	8.2

*Includes: R&R engine.

Main Bearings, Renew

Includes: R&R all normal interfering parts. Plastigauge and install new main bearings. Renew gaskets and seals as necessary. Recondition oil pump.

(Factory Time)	Chilton Time
Six–F-C series (7.5)	*9.8
L series (7.4)	*9.4
V-8–330, 361, 389, 391 engs	
exc below (3.8)	6.0
C series (3.5)	5.7
V-8–370, 429 engs	
F-LN series (3.4)	4.5
C-L series (3.1)	4.1
V-8–401, 475, 477, 534 engs	
All series (3.8)	6.0

*Includes: R&R engine.

Rear Main Bearing Oil Seal, Renew

Includes: R&R all normal interfering parts.

(Factory Time)	Chilton Time
Six–F-C series	3.8
L series (2.2)	3.1
V-8–330, 361, 389, 391 engs	
exc below (2.3)	3.5
C series (2.0)	3.2
L series (2.0)	3.2
V-8–370, 429 engs	
F-LN series (2.3)	3.5
C-L series (2.0)	3.2
V-8–401, 475, 477, 534 engs	
F series (13.2)	*16.0
C series (10.7)	*13.0
L series	
exc below (10.3)	*12.6
LN models (11.7)	*14.0

*Includes: R&R engine.

Crankshaft Damper or Pulley, Renew

V-8–370, 429 engs (1.9)	2.5

Front Crankshaft Seal, Renew

Does not require R&R of front cover.

V-8–370, 429 engs (2.3)	3.2

DIESEL ENGINES

Crankshaft and Main Bearings, Renew

Includes: R&R all normal interfering parts and engine. Plastigauge and install new main bearings, recondition oil pump.

(Factory Time)	Chilton Time
Caterpillar	
F series (31.7)	40.7
C series (28.6)	36.7
L series-3208 (30.7)	38.1
3406 (47.3)	54.7
LN series (31.3)	40.7
CL series (39.6)	47.0
Cummins	
NH743, 855 (33.6)	42.1
NT855 (34.1)	42.7
V555 (48.0)	60.0

LABOR 15 CRANKSHAFT & DAMPER 15 LABOR

(Factory Time)	Chilton Time
N927 (31.1)	39.0
V & VT785, 903 (45.0)	56.3
KT(A)1150 (25.9)	34.0
Detroit	
6V-53 (29.7)	37.2
6V-92 (26.9)	34.4
6-71 (35.4)	44.4
8V-71-8V-92 (32.7)	40.9

Main and Rod Bearings, Renew

Includes: R&R all normal interfering parts. Plastiguage and install new main and rod bearings. Recondition oil pump.

(Factory Time)	Chilton Time
Caterpillar	
All series	
3208 (4.4)	6.5
3406 (6.8)	8.9
Cummins	
NH & NT743, 855 (8.1)	10.4
V555 (11.4)	15.3
V & VT785, 903 (10.4)	13.8
N927 (10.4)	13.8
KT(A)1150 (12.1)	16.0
Detroit	
6V-53 (6.4)	8.5
6V-92 (6.8)	8.9
6-71 (8.1)	10.4
8V-71-8V-92 (8.5)	11.1

Main Bearings, Renew

Includes: R&R all normal interfering parts. Plastigauge and install new main bearings. Recondition oil pump.

(Factory Time)	Chilton Time
Caterpillar	
All series	
3208 (2.5)	4.6
3406 (4.9)	7.0
Cummins	
NH & NT743, 855 (6.9)	9.1
V555 (9.6)	12.5
V & VT785, 903 (8.6)	11.2
N927 (9.2)	11.8
KT(A)1150 (10.3)	13.0
Detroit	
6V-53 (3.4)	4.8
6V-92 (3.8)	5.2
6-71 (5.1)	6.7
8V-71-8V-92 (4.5)	6.1

Rear Main Bearing Oil Seal, Renew

Includes: R&R all normal interfering parts.

(Factory Time)	Chilton Time
Caterpillar	
3208	
All series (5.3)	7.9
3406	
L series (7.7)	10.0
CL series (5.0)	7.4
Cummins	
NH & NT743, 855 (13.1)	16.9
V555 (10.3)	13.3
V & VT785, 903 (9.3)	11.9
N927 (9.1)	11.6
KT(A)1150 (8.5)	11.0
Detroit	
All series (6.8)	8.7

Crankshaft Damper, Renew

Includes: R&R all normal interfering parts.

(Factory Time)	Chilton Time
Caterpillar	
All series	
3208 (2.8)	3.7
3406 (3.5)	4.6
Cummins	
F series (3.3)	4.4
C, L, W series (.7)	1.0
Detroit	
All series (6.5)	8.4

LABOR 16 CAMSHAFT & TIMING GEARS 16 LABOR

GASOLINE ENGINES

Timing Case Cover, Gasket or Oil Seal, Renew

Includes: R&R all normal interfering parts.

(Factory Time)	Chilton Time
Six–F series (2.6)	3.5
C series (2.4)	3.3
L series (2.0)	2.9
V-8–330, 361, 389, 391 engs	
F series (4.1)	5.0
C series (4.2)	5.0
L series (3.4)	4.5
V-8–370, 429 engs (3.9)	5.4
V-8–401, 475, 477, 534 engs	
F series (5.0)	5.9
C series (3.6)	4.5
L series	
exc below (3.7)	5.0
LN models (4.1)	5.3
w/A.C. add (1.0)	1.0
w/P.S. add (.4)	.4

Timing Chain or Gears, Renew

Includes: R&R all normal interfering parts.

(Factory Time)	Chilton Time
Six–F series (3.1)	4.1
C series (2.9)	3.9
L series (2.5)	3.5
V-8–330, 361, 389, 391 engs	
F series (4.4)	5.6
C series (4.5)	5.6
L series (3.7)	5.1
V-8–370, 429 engs (4.2)	5.7
V-8–401, 475, 477, 534 engs	
F series (5.5)	6.6
C series (4.1)	5.2
L series	
exc below (4.2)	5.7
LN models (4.6)	6.0
w/A.C. add (1.0)	1.0
w/P.S. add (.4)	.4

Camshaft, Renew

Includes: R&R all normal interfering parts. Adjust timing and valves.

(Factory Time)	Chilton Time
Six–F-C series (5.5)	7.2
L series (5.1)	6.8
V-8–330, 361, 389, 391 engs	
F series (6.5)	8.2
C series (6.8)	8.2
L series (7.4)	9.0
V-8–370, 429 engs (7.4)	10.0
V-8–401, 475, 477, 534 engs	
F series (10.4)	12.6
C series (8.8)	10.2
L series	
exc below (9.4)	11.3
LN models (10.5)	12.6
w/A.C. add (1.0)	1.0
w/P.S. add (.4)	.4

Camshaft Bearings, Renew

Includes: R&R engine assembly and other parts for access. Install new camshaft bearings. Adjust valves, carburetor and ignition timing.

(Factory Time)	Chilton Time
Six–F-C series (6.8)	8.4
L series (6.4)	8.0
V-8–330, 361, 389, 391 engs	
F series	
std trans (9.8)	11.5
auto trans (11.8)	13.5
C series (9.9)	11.4
L series	
exc below (9.2)	11.0
LN models (11.2)	13.0
V-8–370, 429 engs	
F-LN series	
w/M.T. (13.9)	18.6
w/A.T. (15.7)	21.1
C-L series	
w/M.T. (11.4)	15.3
w/A.T. (12.9)	17.4
V-8–401, 475, 477, 534 engs	
F series (15.5)	18.5
C series (12.9)	14.8
L series	
exc below (13.0)	16.1
LN models (14.4)	17.8
w/A.C. add (1.0)	1.0
w/P.S. add (.4)	.4

DIESEL ENGINES

Cylinder Front Cover or Gasket, Renew

Includes: R&R all interfering parts.

(Factory Time)	Chilton Time
Caterpillar	
All series-3208 (10.3)	12.6
3406 (9.2)	11.5
Cummins	
NH-NT 743, 855 (8.7)	10.9
V & VT785, 903 (16.5)	19.7
V-555 (16.5)	19.7
KT(A)1150 (9.2)	11.4
Detroit	
exc below (8.7)	10.9
6V-53 (8.1)	10.2

Camshaft, Renew

Includes: R&R engine and all interfering parts. Adjust valves and injection timing.

(Factory Time)	Chilton Time
Caterpillar	
F seriess (19.8)	26.9
C series (18.4)	22.7
L series-3208 (18.4)	22.7
3406 (15.5)	19.8
LN series (19.8)	26.9
CL series (15.5)	19.8
Cummins	
NH & NT743, 855 (23.0)	29.5
V555	38.0
V & VT785, 903 (28.7)	36.7
N927	24.5
KT(A)1150 (19.9)	26.5
Detroit	
6V-53-one (8.5)	10.9
6V-92-one (9.5)	11.9
6-71-one (12.5)	16.2
8V-71-8V-92-one (10.3)	13.3

LABOR 17 ENGINE OILING SYSTEM 17 LABOR

(Factory Time)	Chilton Time
GASOLINE ENGINES	
Oil Pan or Gasket, Renew	
Six–F series (1.4)	2.3
C series (1.7)	2.6
L series (1.1)	2.0
V-8–330, 361, 389, 391 engs	
exc below (1.5)	2.5
C & L series (1.2)	2.2
V-8–370, 429 engs	
F-LN series (1.5)	2.1
C-L series (1.2)	1.8
V-8–401, 475, 477, 534 engs	
All series (1.5)	2.5
Oil Pump, Renew	
Six–F series (1.6)	2.6
C series (1.9)	2.9
L series (1.3)	2.3
V-8–330, 361, 389, 391 engs	
exc below (1.6)	2.7
C & L series (1.3)	2.4
V-8–370, 429 engs	
F-LN series (1.7)	2.3
C-L series (1.4)	2.0
V-8–401, 475, 477, 534 engs	
All series (1.6)	2.7
Oil Pump, R&R and Recondition	
Six–F series (1.8)	3.2
C series (2.1)	3.5
L series (1.5)	2.9
V-8–330, 361, 389, 391 engs	
exc below (1.9)	3.3
C & L series (1.6)	3.0
V-8–370, 429 engs	
F-LN series (2.1)	2.9
C-L series (1.8)	2.6
V-8–401, 475, 477, 534 engs	
All series (1.9)	3.3
Oil Cooler or Gasket, Renew	
V-8–401, 475, 477, 534 engs	
F series (1.5)	2.1
C series (1.2)	1.7
L series (1.1)	1.5
370, 429 engs	
All series (1.0)	1.4

(Factory Time)	Chilton Time
Oil Filter, Renew	
All series (.3)	.4
Pressure Test Engine Bearings (Pan Removed)	
All series	1.0
Oil Pressure Gauge (Dash), Renew	
exc below (.6)	1.0
CL series (.4)	.8
Oil Pressure Sending Unit, Renew	
All series (.3)	.5
DIESEL ENGINES	
Oil Pan or Gasket, Renew	
Caterpillar	
All series	
3208 (1.3)	1.9
3406 (1.7)	2.3
Cummins	
NH & NT743, 855 (3.1)	4.2
V555 (4.6)	6.2
V & VT785, 903 (3.0)	4.0
N927 (4.2)	5.5
KT (A) 1150 (9.6)	12.0
Detroit	
6V-53 (1.0)	1.5
6V-92 (1.4)	2.3
6-71 (1.6)	2.5
8V-71-8V-92 (1.5)	2.4
Oil Pump, Renew	
Caterpillar	
All series	
3208 (10.2)	13.0
3406 (2.3)	3.0
Cummins	
NH & NT743, 855 (1.6)	2.5
V555 (4.5)	6.3
V & VT 785, 903 (3.6)	4.8
N927	5.1
KT(A)1150 (9.7)	12.5
Detroit	
6V-53 (9.0)	11.5
6V-92 (9.6)	12.5
6-71 (5.8)	7.2
8V-71-8V-92 (9.6)	12.5

(Factory Time)	Chilton Time
Oil Pump, R&R and Recondition	
Caterpillar	
All series	
3208 (11.5)	14.5
3406 (3.1)	4.0
Cummins	
NH & NT743, 855 (2.7)	4.0
V555 (5.7)	7.8
V & VT 785, 903 (4.8)	6.3
N927	6.6
KT(A)1150 (11.8)	15.0
Detroit	
6V-53 (10.0)	13.0
6V-92 (10.6)	14.0
6-71 (7.8)	9.7
8V-71-8V-92 (10.6)	14.0
Oil Cooler, Renew	
Caterpillar	
All series	
3208 (1.7)	2.2
3406 (1.6)	2.1
Cummins	
NH & NT743, 855 (2.8)	3.9
V-VT 555, 903 (2.8)	3.9
KT(A)1150 (4.0)	5.4
Detroit	
6V-53 (2.6)	3.7
6V-92 (2.6)	3.7
6-71 (2.2)	3.0
8V-71-8V-92 (5.6)	7.5
Oil Filter, Renew	
Caterpillar	
All series	
3208 (.3)	.6
3406 (.4)	.7
Cummins (.9)	1.2
Detroit (.8)	1.0
Oil Pressure Gauge (Dash), Renew	
exc below (.8)	1.2
C series (.6)	1.0
Oil Pressure Sending Unit, Renew	
exc below (.4)	.6
Cummins (.6)	.8

LABOR 18 CLUTCH & FLYWHEEL 18 LABOR

(Factory Time)	Chilton Time
Clutch Pedal Free Play, Adjust	
All series (.4)	.5
Clutch Master Cylinder, Renew	
All series (.6)	.8
Clutch Master Cylinder, R&R and Recondition	
All series (.8)	1.2
Clutch Slave Cylinder, Renew	
All series (.6)	.9
Clutch Slave Cylinder, R&R and Recondition	
All series (.8)	1.2
Bleed Clutch Hydraulic System	
All series (.4)	.5
Clutch Assembly, Renew	
Includes: R&R transmission.	
4 Speed	
New Process 435 (2.6)	3.4
Borg Warner T-19 (2.7)	3.4

(Factory Time)	Chilton Time
5 Speed	
Clark	
280VO-282V-282VHD	
285V-285VHD-390/550	
397/557 (2.6)	3.4
Fuller	
T-905A-T-905B (3.5)	4.5
New Process	
542FD-542FL	
542FO (3.0)	3.9
Spicer	
5052A-5252A (3.0)	3.9
6052A-6052B-6052C	
C series (3.2)	4.2
L-LN series (4.2)	5.6
6 Speed	
Fuller	
RT-906 (3.7)	4.9
Spicer	
1062	
L-LN series (3.7)	4.9
CL series (5.3)	7.1

(Factory Time)	Chilton Time
9 Speed	
Fuller	
RT-9509A-RT-9509B-RT-12509	
L-LN series (4.2)	5.6
CL series (5.6)	7.5
10 Speed	
Fuller	
RT-610 (4.5)	5.9
RT-910-RTO-910	
RT-1110-RT-12510	
L-LN series (4.2)	5.6
CL series (5.6)	7.5
13 Speed	
Fuller	
RT-613 (4.2)	5.6
RT/RTO-9513-RT-12513	
L-LN series (4.2)	5.6
CL series (5.6)	7.5
16 Speed	
Spicer	
RP8516-3A	
w/Aux (5.4)	7.2
w/P.T.O. add (.6)	.6
w/Coupling shaft add (.2)	.2

LABOR 18 CLUTCH & FLYWHEEL 18 LABOR

(Factory Time)	Chilton Time
w/Detroit Diesel add (.5)	.5
w/Full carpet add (.7)	.7
w/Cat V-8 add	1.0
Clutch Release Bearing, Renew	
Includes: R&R transmission assembly.	
4 Speed	
New Process 435 (1.9)	2.7
Borg Warner T-19 (2.0)	2.7
5 Speed	
Clark	
280VO-282V-282VHD	
285V-285VHD-390/550	
397/557 (1.9)	2.7
Fuller	
T-905A-T-905B (2.8)	3.8
New Process	
542FD-542FL	
542FO (2.3)	3.2
Spicer	
5052A-5252A (2.3)	3.2
6052A-6052B-6052C	
C series (2.5)	3.5
L-LN series (3.5)	4.9
6 Speed	
Fuller	
RT-906 (3.0)	4.2
Spicer	
1062C	
L-LN series (3.0)	4.2
CL series (4.6)	6.4
9 Speed	
Fuller	
RT-9509A-RT-9509B-RT-12509	
L-LN series (3.5)	4.9
CL series (4.9)	6.8
10 Speed	
Fuller	
RT-610 (3.8)	5.2
RT-910-RTO-910	
RT-1110-RT-12510	
L-LN series (3.5)	4.9
CL series (4.9)	6.8
13 Speed	
Fuller	
RT-613 (3.5)	4.9
RT/RTO-9513-RT-12513	
L-LN series (3.5)	4.9
CL series (4.9)	6.8
16 Speed	
Spicer	
RP8516-3A	
w/Aux (4.7)	6.5
w/P.T.O. add (.6)	.6
w/Coupling shaft add (.2)	.2
w/Detroit Diesel add (.5)	.5
w/Full carpet add (.7)	.7
Flywheel, Renew	
Includes: R&R transmission.	
4 Speed	
New Process 435 (3.3)	4.2
Borg Warner T-19 (3.4)	4.2
5 Speed	
Clark	
280VO-282V-282VHD	
285V-285VHD-390/550	
397/557 (3.3)	4.2
Fuller	
T-905A-T-905B (4.2)	5.3
New Process	
542FD-542FL	
542FO (3.7)	4.7
Spicer	
5052A-5252A (3.7)	4.7
6052A-6052B-6052C	
C series (3.9)	5.0
L-LN series (4.9)	6.4
6 Speed	
Fuller	
RT-906 (4.4)	5.7
Spicer	
1062C	
L-LN series (4.4)	5.7
CL series (6.0)	7.9
9 Speed	
Fuller	
RT-9509A-RT-9509B-RT-12509	
L-LN series (4.9)	6.4
CL series (6.3)	8.3
10 Speed	
Fuller	
RT-610 (5.2)	6.6
RT-910-RTO-910	
RT-1110-RT-12510	
L-LN series (4.9)	6.4
CL series (6.3)	8.3
13 Speed	
Fuller	
RT-613 (4.9)	6.4
RT/RTO-9513-RT-12513	
L-LN series (4.9)	6.4
CL series (6.3)	8.3
16 Speed	
Spicer	
RP8516-3A	
w/Aux (6.1)	7.9
w/P.T.O. add (.6)	.6
w/Coupling shaft add (.2)	.2
w/Detroit Diesel add (.5)	.5
w/Full carpet add (.7)	.7
w/Cat V-8 add	1.0
Flywheel Ring Gear, Renew (Flywheel Removed)	
All series (.2)	.5

LABOR 19 STANDARD TRANSMISSION 19 LABOR

(Factory Time)	Chilton Time
Transmission Assembly, R&R	
4 Speed	
New Process 435 (1.9)	2.7
Borg Warner T-19 (2.0)	2.7
5 Speed	
Clark	
280VO-282V-282VHD	
285V-285VHD-390/550	
397/557 (1.9)	2.7
Fuller	
T-905A-T-905B (2.8)	3.8
New Process	
542FD-542FL	
542FO (2.3)	3.2
Spicer	
5052A-5252A (2.3)	3.2
6052A-6052B-6052C	
C series (2.5)	3.5
L-LN series (3.5)	4.9
6 Speed	
Fuller	
RT-906 (3.0)	4.2
Spicer	
1062C	
L-LN series (3.0)	4.2
CL series (4.6)	6.4
9 Speed	
Fuller	
RT-9509A-RT-9509B-RT-12509	
L-LN series (3.5)	4.9
CL series (4.9)	6.8
10 Speed	
Fuller	
RT-610 (3.8)	5.2
RT-910-RTO-910	
RT-1110-RT-12510	
L-LN series (3.5)	4.9
CL series (4.9)	6.8
13 Speed	
Fuller	
RT-613 (3.5)	4.9
RT/RTO-9513-RT-12513	
L-LN series (3.5)	4.9
CL series (4.9)	6.8
16 Speed	
Spicer	
RP8516-3A	
w/Aux (4.7)	6.5
w/P.T.O. add (.6)	.6
w/Coupling shaft add (.2)	.2
w/Detroit Diesel add (.5)	.5
w/Full carpet add (.7)	.7
Transmission Assembly, R&R and Recondition	
Includes: Complete disassembly and assembly of transmission. Inspect and clean all components. Renew parts, gaskets and seals as necessary. Make all normal adjustments. Road test.	
4 Speed	
New Process 435 (4.2)	5.8
Borg Warner T-19 (4.0)	5.8
5 Speed	
Clark	
280V-280VO-282VHD	
285V (4.3)	5.9
285HD-285VHD (4.6)	6.3
390V/550-397V/557 (4.9)	6.7
Fuller	
T-905A-T-905B (9.5)	13.1
New Process	
542FD-542FL	
542FO (7.1)	9.8
Spicer	
5052A-5252A (5.0)	6.9
6052A-6052B-6052C	
C series (7.4)	10.3
L-LN series (8.4)	11.6
6 Speed	
Fuller	
RT-906 (9.7)	14.5
Spicer	
1062C	
L-LN series (7.9)	11.0
CL series (9.5)	13.3
9 Speed	
Fuller	
RT-9509A-RT-9509B-RT-12509	
L-LN series (11.5)	16.1
CL series (12.9)	18.0
10 Speed	
Fuller	
RT-610 (15.3)	21.1

LABOR 19 STANDARD TRANSMISSION 19 LABOR

(Factory Time) Chilton Time

RT-910-RTO-910
L-LN series
complete (12.3).......... 16.5
front section (11.1).......... 14.9
rear section (7.1).......... 9.1
CL series
complete (13.7).......... 19.1
front section (12.5).......... 17.5
rear section (8.5).......... 11.9
RT-1110-RT-12510 (15.0).......... 20.7

13 Speed
Fuller
RT-613 (12.9).......... 17.8
RT/RTO-9513-RT-12513
L-LN series
complete (12.9).......... 17.8
front section (10.9).......... 15.0
rear section (6.9).......... 9.5
CL series
complete (13.8).......... 19.0
front section (11.8).......... 16.2
rear section (7.8).......... 10.7

16 Speed
Spicer
RP8516-3A
w/Aux (15.3).......... 23.4
w/P.T.O. add (.6).......... .6
w/Coupling shaft add (.2).......... .2
w/Detroit Diesel add (.5).......... .5
w/Full carpet add (.7).......... .7

Auxiliary Transmission, R&R
All series (1.5).......... 2.0

Auxiliary Transmission, Renew
Includes: R&R assembly, transfer all necessary components.
All series (3.1).......... 4.3

Auxiliary Transmission, R&R and Recondition
Includes: Assembly and disassembly. Cleaning and inspection of all parts. Renew or recondition all necessary components. Renew gaskets and seals as required. Road test.
All series
Spicer-7231 (5.1).......... 7.4
8341 (6.6).......... 8.8
7041 (6.5).......... 8.8

LABOR 23 AUTOMATIC TRANSMISSION 23 LABOR

(Factory Time) Chilton Time

ON TRUCK SERVICES

Oil Pressure Test
Allison-MT (1.2).......... 1.6
Ford-C6 (.9).......... 1.3

Check Unit for Oil Leaks
Includes: Clean and dry outside of case, run unit to determine point of leak.
All series.......... .9

Manual and Throttle Linkage, Adjust
Includes: Adjust dashpot, idle speed and accelerator pedal height (if adjustable).
Ford-C6 (.4).......... .7
Allison (.7).......... 1.0

Vacuum Modulator, Renew
Ford-C6 (.3).......... .6
Road test add (.3).......... .3

Transmission Rear Oil Seal or Bushing, Renew
Ford-C6 (.5).......... .9

Transmission Oil Filter Element, Renew
Allison-MT (.5).......... .8
AT (.2).......... .5

Front Servo, Recondition
Includes: Adjust band.
Ford-C6 (1.0).......... 1.7

Governor Assembly, Renew (Less Counterweight)
Ford-C6 (1.4).......... 2.1

Front Band, Adjust
Ford-C6 (.2).......... .6

Oil Pan or Gasket, Renew
Ford-C6 (.6).......... 1.0
Allison-MT (1.0).......... 1.4
Allison-AT (.6).......... 1.0

Valve Body Assembly, Renew
Includes: R&R oil pan.
Ford-C6 (1.1).......... 1.7
Allison-MT (1.6).......... 2.2
Allison-AT (1.6).......... 2.2

Valve Body Assy., R&R and Recondition
Includes: R&R oil pan and replace filter. Disassemble, clean, inspect, free all valves. Replace parts as required.
Ford-C6 (1.6).......... 2.6
Allison-MT (3.0).......... 4.0
Allison-AT (1.9).......... 2.9

Throttle and Manual Seals and/or Levers, Renew
Includes: R&R oil pan and valve body.
Ford-C6 (.9).......... 1.3
Allison-MT (1.4).......... 1.8

SERVICES REQUIRING R&R

Transmission Assembly, R&R
Includes: Drain and refill unit. Adjust linkage and road test.
Ford-C6 (4.1).......... 5.3
Allison-AT (5.2).......... 6.4
Allison-MT
C-F series (4.8).......... 6.0
L series (2.9).......... 3.7
w/P.T.O. add (.6).......... .6

Transmission Assembly, R&R and Recondition
Includes: Drain and refill unit, adjust all linkage. Disassemble and assemble complete transmission, inspect all parts. Clean, renew or recondition all components. Renew gaskets and seals as necessary. Road test.
Ford-C6 (8.3).......... 10.6
Allison-AT (14.9).......... 19.2
Allison-MT
C-F series (18.2).......... 24.0
L series (16.3).......... 22.2
w/P.T.O. add (.6).......... .6

Torque Converter, R&R and/or Recondition
Includes: R&R transmission assembly. Drain and refill unit. Adjust linkage and road test.
Ford-C6 (4.6).......... 6.0
Allison-MT
C-F series (6.0).......... 7.5
L series (4.1).......... 5.2
w/P.T.O. add (.6).......... .6

Front Oil Pump, R&R and/or Recondition
Includes: R&R transmission assembly. Drain and refill unit. Adjust linkage and road test.
Ford-C6 (5.3).......... 6.8
Allison-MT
C-F series (6.8).......... 8.5
L series (4.9).......... 6.2
w/P.T.O. add (.6).......... .6

Rear Oil Pump, R&R and Recondition
Includes: R&R transmission assembly. Drain and refill unit. Adjust linkage and road test.
Allison-MT
C-F series (6.9).......... 8.7
L series (5.0).......... 6.4
w/P.T.O. add (.6).......... .6

Front Pump Oil Seal, Renew
Includes: R&R transmission assembly. Drain and refill unit. Adjust linkage and road test.
Ford-C6 (4.2).......... 5.5
w/P.T.O. add (.6).......... .6

LABOR 25 U-JOINTS & DRIVESHAFT 25 LABOR

(Factory Time)	Chilton Time
Drive Shaft, R&R or Renew	
One piece shaft (.9)	1.1
Splined at coup shaft (.7)	1.0
Yoke at coup shaft (1.2)	1.5
Power divider to	
Rearward axle (.6)	1.0
Universal Joint, Recondition or Renew	
Does not include R&R drive shaft.	
exc below-front (.4)	.6
two (.3)	.5
three (.3)	.5
rear (.3)	.5
all (1.1)	1.9
Tandem	
500-700-front (.4)	.6
two (.3)	.5
rear (.3)	.5
all (.9)	1.5
750-900-front (.2)	.3
rear (.2)	.3
all (.4)	.6
w/Coupling shaft	
front (.2)	.3
two (.3)	.5
rear (.2)	.3
all (.6)	1.0
Inner-trans shaft	
front (.6)	.8
rear (.4)	.6
all (.9)	1.3
Main to aux trans shaft	
one (.7)	1.0
both (1.1)	1.5

(Factory Time)	Chilton Time
Center Support Coupling Shaft Bearing, Renew	
All series-one (.8)	1.2
each adtnl (.7)	.7
Center Support, Renew	
All series-one (.8)	1.0
each adtnl (.6)	.6
Coupling Shaft, Renew	
All series	
snap ring type (1.4)	1.8
each adtnl (1.2)	1.2
bolt end type (1.1)	1.5
each adtnl (.9)	.9

LABOR 26 REAR AXLE 26 LABOR

(Factory Time)	Chilton Time
Rear Axle Housing Cover Gasket, Renew or Reseal	
rear tandem (.8)	1.2
forward tandem (1.2)	1.5
Renew output shaft seal	
add (.2)	.2
Rear Axle Shaft Outer Oil Seal and/or Gasket, Renew	
6 hole wheel	.8
one (.5)	.8
each adtnl (.3)	.3
10 hole wheel	
one (.6)	.9
each adtnl (.5)	.5
cast wheel	
one (.5)	.8
each adtnl (.4)	.4
Axle Shaft, Renew	
All series-one (.5)	.8
two (.8)	1.3
Rear Wheel Bearings, Renew	
All series-one axle-one (1.3)	1.9
both (2.2)	3.1
all-both axles (3.9)	5.6
Rear Wheel Bearing Oil Seal, Renew	
All series-one axle-one (1.3)	1.8
both (2.2)	3.0
all-both axles (3.9)	5.5
Tandem Drive Line Alignment, Check	
Includes: Road test.	
All series (1.1)	1.5
Tandem Drive Line Alignment, Check and Adjust	
Includes: Alignment of engine, transmission, drive shafts and both axles. Road test.	
All series (4.5)	5.5
Pinion Shaft Oil Seal, Renew	
All series	
Rockwell-front (1.0)	1.5
Rockwell-rear (1.8)	2.7
Eaton-front (1.2)	1.8
Eaton-rear (1.8)	2.7

(Factory Time)	Chilton Time
Differential Carrier Assy., Remove and Install	
Includes: Drain and refill axle, renew gasket.	
Eaton	
single speed (3.3)	4.6
two speed (3.5)	4.9
Dana-Spicer	
two speed (3.5)	4.9
Rockwell	
single speed (3.0)	4.2
Tandem Eaton	
single speed-single reduction	
DS341	
forward (4.2)	5.9
rearward (3.8)	5.3
DS381-DS460P	
forward (5.0)	7.0
rearward (3.8)	5.3
Tandem Eaton	
single speed-double reduction	
DP381-DP460P	
forward (5.0)	7.0
rearward (3.8)	5.3
Tandem Eaton	
two speed-single reduction	
DT341	
forward (4.4)	6.1
rearward (4.0)	5.6
Tandem Rockwell	
single speed-single reduction	
SL-100	
forward (4.2)	5.9
rearward (3.8)	5.3
SQ-100-SSHD-SQHP	
forward (5.0)	7.0
rearward (3.8)	5.3
Differential Carrier Assembly, R&R and Recondition	
Includes: Drain and refill unit. R&R all normal interfering parts. Disassemble and assemble complete unit. Inspect, clean, renew or recondition all components. Road test.	
Eaton	
single speed (9.1)	12.8
two speed (9.7)	13.6
Dana-Spicer	
two speed (9.7)	13.6
Rockwell	
single speed (8.4)	11.8

(Factory Time)	Chilton Time
Tandem Eaton	
DS341	
forward (11.0)	15.5
rearward (9.6)	13.5
DS381-DS460P	
forward (11.8)	16.6
rearward (9.6)	13.5
Tandem Eaton	
single speed-double reduction	
DP381-DP460P	
forward (10.1)	14.2
rearward (8.4)	11.8
Tandem Eaton	
two speed-single reduction	
DT341	
forward (11.6)	16.3
rearward (10.2)	14.3
Tandem Rockwell	
single speed-single reduction	
SL-100	
forward (10.6)	14.9
rearward (8.9)	12.5
SQ-100-SSHD-SQHP	
forward (11.4)	16.0
rearward (8.9)	12.5
Renew wheel brgs add	
one side (.7)	.7
both sides (1.2)	1.2
Electric Shift Assembly, Renew	
Eaton-two spd (.4)	.6
Electric Shift Assembly, R&R and Recondition	
Eaton-two spd (1.1)	1.7
Two Speed Axle Switch, Renew	
All series (.4)	.6
Two Speed Axle Shift Motor, Renew	
All series (.7)	1.0
Power Divider Lockout Cylinder Assembly, Renew	
tandem (.6)	.9
Power Divider Lockout Cylinder Diaphragm, Renew	
tandem (.7)	1.1

LABOR 27 REAR SUSPENSION 27 LABOR

(Factory Time)	Chilton Time
Rear Spring, R&R or Renew	
SINGLE AXLE	
one (1.6)	2.2
both (2.9)	4.0
TANDEM AXLE	
Hendrickson	
one (2.3)	3.2
both (4.2)	5.8
Neway	
one (1.1)	1.5
both (1.9)	2.6
Reyco	
1 axle	
one (1.8)	2.5
both (3.2)	4.4
2 axles	
all (6.1)	8.5
Renew spring bushings add, each (.3)	.3
Renew aux spring leaf add (.6)	.6
Renew aux tie bolt add (.4)	.4
Renew spring leaf or tie bolt add-each side (.7)	7

(Factory Time)	Chilton Time
Rear Spring Shackle and/or Bushings, Renew	
All series	
one-one side (.9)	1.3
one-both sides (1.6)	2.4
Rear Spring Front Shackle Bolt and/or Bushing, Renew	
All series	
one (1.0)	1.5
two (1.7)	2.7
Auxiliary Spring, R&R or Renew	
All series (1.1)	1.5
Auxiliary Spring Leaf, Renew	
All series (1.8)	2.6
Tandem Suspension Support Beam, Renew	
Hendricson	
one (6.5)	8.2
both (10.7)	13.4
Reyco	
one (1.0)	1.4
both (1.7)	2.5

(Factory Time)	Chilton Time
Tandem Suspension Torque Arm Assembly, Renew	
All series-front (1.7)	2.4
rear (1.1)	1.6
both (2.6)	3.5
Center Support Beam Bushings and/or Bar, Renew	
Hendrickson	
tandem axle (3.2)	5.0
Tandem Support Beam Bushings, Renew	
Hendrickson	
tandem axle	
one side (3.5)	5.5
both sides (6.1)	10.0
Tandem Suspension Load Insulators, Renew	
Hendrickson	
one (2.6)	3.8
two (3.9)	5.8
Renew bushings or saddle, add-each (.4)	.5

LABOR 28 AIR CONDITIONING 28 LABOR

(Factory Time)	Chilton Time
Drain, Evacuate and Recharge System	
Includes: Check for leaks.	
All series (.7)	1.5
Note: Models equipped with 2 or more evaporators, require additional time to evacuate and charge the system. Labor charges for operations which require evacuation and recharging the system should be adjusted accordingly.	
Pressure Test System	
All series	.9
Compressor Assembly, Renew	
Includes: Evacuate and charge system.	
F series (1.5)	2.6
L series (1.5)	2.6
CL series (2.2)	3.3
Compressor Shaft Seal Kit, Renew	
Includes: Evacuate and charge system.	
F series (1.2)	2.3
L series (1.4)	2.5
CL series (1.6)	2.7
Compressor Valve Plate Kit, Renew	
Includes: Evacuate and charge system.	
F series (1.5)	2.6
L series (1.6)	2.7
CL series (2.2)	3.3

(Factory Time)	Chilton Time
Compressor Clutch Pulley Bearing, Renew	
CL series (1.0)	1.4
All other series (.6)	1.0
Compressor Clutch Brush Assy., Renew	
L series (.6)	1.0
A.C. Clutch Pressure Switch Assy., Renew	
F series (.2)	.3
Accumulator Assy., Renew	
Includes: Evacuate and charge system.	
F series (1.0)	1.5
Orifice Valve, Renew	
Includes: Evacuate and charge system.	
F series (.9)	1.5
Evaporator Thermostatic Switch, Renew	
All series (.5)	.9
Condenser Assembly, Renew	
Includes: Evacuate and charge system.	
F series (1.4)	2.5
L series (1.3)	2.5
CL series (1.2)	2.3

(Factory Time)	Chilton Time
Expansion Valve, Renew	
Includes: Evacuate and charge system.	
L series (1.4)	2.5
CL series (1.3)	2.4
Evaporator Core, Renew	
Includes: Evacuate and charge system.	
F series (1.4)	2.6
L-LN series (1.4)	2.6
CL series (1.6)	3.0
Dehydrator-Receiver Tank, Renew	
Includes: Evacuate and charge system.	
L series (1.1)	2.1
CL series (.9)	2.0
A.C. Blower Motor, Renew	
F series (.4)	.7
L-LN series (.6)	1.0
CL series (.5)	1.0
A.C. Blower Motor Switch, Renew	
CL series (.6)	1.0
City Deliv (.4)	.7
Line Haul (.5)	.8
Air Conditioning Hoses, Renew	
Includes: Evacuate and charge system.	
All series-one (1.2)	2.3
Fabricate hose add (.2)	.3

LABOR 30 HEAD & PARKING LAMPS 30 LABOR

(Factory Time)	Chilton Time
Aim Headlamps	
All series	.6
Headlamp Sealed Beam Bulb, Renew	
All series-each (.3)	.3

(Factory Time)	Chilton Time
Turn Signal Lamp Assy., Renew	
F series (.3)	.5
C series (.4)	.6
L series (.4)	.6
CL series (.3)	.5

(Factory Time)	Chilton Time
Exterior Bulb, Renew	
All series-each (.3)	4
Reflector, Renew	
All series-each	.2

LABOR 31 WINDSHIELD WIPER & SPEEDOMETER 31 LABOR

(Factory Time)	Chilton Time
Windshield Wiper Motor, Renew	
F series (.9)	1.2
C series-each (.6)	1.1
L series-elec (.6)	1.0
air (.6)	1.1
CL series (.5)	1.0
Windshield Wiper Switch, Renew	
F series (.4)	.7
C series (.4)	.9
L series (.3)	.7
CL series (.7)	1.0
Windshield Washer Pump, Renew	
All series (.3)	.5
Wiper Pivot, Renew	
F series-each (.9)	1.1
C series (.4)	1.0
L series-each (.6)	.9
Speedometer Head, R&R or Renew	
F series (.6)	1.0
C series (.7)	1.4
L-LN series (.6)	1.2
CL series (.4)	.9
Speedometer Cable and Casing, Renew	
F series	
one piece (.6)	1.1
upper (.4)	.7
lower (.4)	.7
C series	
one piece (.8)	1.5
upper (.4)	.7
lower (.3)	.6
mid cable (.3)	.3
L-LN series-upper (.5)	.9
lower (.4)	.7
CL series-upper (.4)	.7
lower (.7)	1.3
Tachometer, Renew	
F series (.6)	1.1
C series (.6)	1.1
L-LN series (.6)	1.1
CL series (.4)	.8
Tachometer Cable and Casing, Renew	
F series (.5)	1.0
C series (.7)	1.4
L-LN series-upper (.3)	.7
lower (.3)	.6
CL series-upper (.4)	.8
lower (.5)	1.0

LABOR 32 LIGHT SWITCHES & WIRING 32 LABOR

(Factory Time)	Chilton Time
Headlamp Switch, Renew	
F series (.4)	.6
C series (.5)	.8
L series (.4)	.6
CL series (.4)	.6
Headlamp Dimmer Switch, Renew	
All series (.3)	.6
Turn Signal Switch Assy., Renew	
F series (.4)	.8
C series (.4)	.8
L-LN series (.6)	1.1
CL series(.4)	.8
Turn Signal or Hazard Flasher, Renew	
All series (.3)	.5
Stop Light Switch, Renew	
F series-wo/Air (.4)	.7
w/Air (.3)	.6
C series-wo/Air (.5)	.7
w/Air (.3)	.6
L series (.3)	.6
CL series (.3)	.6
Back-Up Light Switch, Renew	
All series (.3)	.5
Marker Light or Blinker Emergency Flasher Switch Assy., Renew	
All series (.4)	.6
Horns, Renew	
All series-each (.3)	.5

GROUP INDEX

ALPHABETICAL INDEX

LABOR 1 TUNE UP 1 LABOR

(Factory Time) Chilton Time

Compression Test
- Four (.6) 8
- Six (.7) 1.0
- V-8 (.9) 1.2

Engine Tune Up, (Minor)

Includes: Clean or renew spark plugs, renew ignition points and condenser, set ignition timing, set carburetor idle speed and mixture. Service carburetor air cleaner. Clean or renew fuel filter.
- Four 1.8
- Six 2.0
- V-8 .... 2.3

Engine Tune Up, (Major)

Includes: Check engine compression, clean or renew spark plugs. Test battery, clean terminals. Renew or adjust distributor points and condenser, check distributor cap and rotor. Set ignition timing, test coil, free up manifold heat valve. Tighten manifold bolts. Adjust carburetor idle speed and mixture. Inspect and tighten all hose connections. Adjust fan belt. Service air cleaners (carburetor, vapor canister and air pump). Renew or clean PCV valve.
- Four 3.0
- Six 3.3
- V-8 .... 3.8

Engine Tune Up, (Electronic Ignition)

Includes: Test battery and clean connections. Tighten manifold and carburetor mounting bolts. Check engine compression, clean and adjust or renew spark plugs. Test resistance of spark plug cables. Inspect distributor cap and rotor. Adjust air gap. Check vacuum advance operation. Reset ignition timing. Adjust idle mixture and idle speed. Service air cleaner. Inspect crankcase ventilation system. Inspect and adjust drive belts. Inspect choke operation and adjust or free up. Check operation of EGR valve.
- Four 2.5
- Six 2.9
- V-8 .... 3.4

LABOR 2 IGNITION SYSTEM 2 LABOR

(Factory Time) Chilton Time

Spark Plugs, Clean and Reset or Renew
- Four (.4) 6
- Six (.6) 8
- V-8 (.7) 1.0

Ignition Timing, Reset
- All models (.3) 4

Distributor, R&R or Renew

Includes: Reset ignition timing.

Standard Ignition
- All models (.7) 1.0

Electronic Ignition
- All models (.6) 9
- w/Governor add (.1) 1

Distributor, R&R and Recondition

Includes: Reset ignition timing.

Standard Ignition
- Four (2.0) 2.5
- Six (1.7) 2.2
- V-8 (2.0) 2.5

Electronic Ignition
- All models (2.1) 2.6
- w/Governor add (.4) 5

Distributor Points and Condenser, Renew

Includes: R&R distributor, reset timing and dwell.
- All models (1.1) 1.4

Distributor Cap, Renew
- All models (.2) 4

Distributor Sensor Assembly, Renew (Electronic Ignition)

Includes: R&R distributor and reset ignition timing.
- All models (1.3) 1.9

Electronic Ignition Control, Renew

Includes: Test ignition system in chassis.
- All models (.8) 1.3

Ignition Coil, Renew

Includes: Test coil in chassis, transfer mounting bracket.
- All models (.6) 9

Vacuum Control Unit, Renew

Includes: R&R distributor and reset timing and dwell.
- All models 9

Spark Plug Cables, Renew
- Four (.2) 5
- Six (.3) 7
- V-8 (.4) 8

Ignition Switch, Renew
- SCOUT II (.9) 1.5
- 100-200-500 Series (.6) 1.0

LABOR 3 FUEL SYSTEM 3 LABOR

(Factory Time) Chilton Time

GASOLINE ENGINES

Fuel Pump, Test

Includes: Disconnect line at carburetor, attach pressure gauge.
- All models (.4) 4

Carburetor, Adjust (On Truck)
- All models (.2) 3

Governor R.P.M., Adjust (w/Tachometer)
- All models (.6) 8

Carburetor, Renew

Includes: All necessary adjustments.
- Four (.7) 1.0
- Six (.7) 1.0
- V-8 (.9) 1.2

Carburetor, R&R and Clean or Recondition

Includes: All necessary adjustments.
- Four (2.2) 3.2
- Six (2.2) 3.2
- V-8–2 bbl (2.4) 3.5
  - 4 bbl (2.7) 3.9

Fuel Pump, Renew
- Four (.4) 7
- Six (.5) 8
- V-8 (.6) 9

Add pump test if performed.

Fuel Tank, Renew

Includes: Drain and refill tank. Test evaporative loss system.
- SCOUT II (1.8) 2.6

Under Cab Mount
- 100-150-200 Series
- right side–front fill (1.3) 2.0
  - rear fill (1.1) 1.8
- left side–front fill (1.1) 1.8
- rear fender mount (1.0) 1.7

Fuel Gauge (Tank Unit), Renew

Includes: Drain and refill tank. R&R tank, test and renew gauge.
- SCOUT II (1.5) 2.3

Under Cab Mount
- 100-150-200 Series
- right side–front fill (1.2) 1.9
  - rear fill (1.1) 1.8
- left side–front fill (1.1) 1.8
- rear fender mount (.7) 1.4

Fuel Gauge (Dash Unit), Renew
- SCOUT II (.4) 7
- 100-150-200 Series (.6) 1.0

Intake Manifold or Gaskets, Renew
- Four (1.6) 2.0
- Six (1.4) 1.8
- V-8 (2.0) 2.6
- Renew manif add (.8) 8

DIESEL ENGINE

Fuel Injection Lines, R&R or Renew
- All models–one (.2) 3
  - each adtnl (.1) 2
  - all (.7) 1.2

Glow Plugs, Renew
- All models–one (.2) 3
  - all (.4) 7

Fuel Injection Nozzles, Renew
- All models–one (.5) 6
  - each adtnl (.3) 4
  - all (1.8) 2.4

LABOR 3 FUEL SYSTEM 3 LABOR

(Factory Time) Chilton Time

Fuel Injection Nozzles, Test
(Nozzles Removed)
All models-one (.4)........................ .6
each adtnl (.2)........................ .3
all (1.4)........................ 2.0

Fuel Injection Nozzles, Recondition
(Nozzles Removed)
All models-each (.6)........................ .8

Fuel Filter, Renew
All models-primary (.3)........................ .4

Fuel Injection Pump, Renew
All models (2.7)........................ 3.8

Fuel Injection Pump, R&R and Recondition
All models (11.3)........................ 15.0

Intake Manifold and/or Gasket, Renew
All models (.7)........................ 1.2

LABOR 3A EMISSION CONTROLS 3A LABOR

(Factory Time) Chilton Time

Emission Control Check
Includes: Check and adjust engine idle speed, mixture and ignition timing. Check PCV valve and air pump filter.
All models........................ 1.0

Positive Crankcase Ventilation Valve, Renew or Clean
All models
renew........................ .3
clean........................ .4

EVAPORATIVE LOSS CONTROL

Canister, Renew
All models........................ .5

Canister Filter, Renew
All models........................ .3

Liquid Vapor Separator, Renew
SCOUT II........................ 1.3

AIR INJECTION SYSTEM

Air Pump, Renew
All models........................ .6

Diverter Valve, Renew
All models........................ .8

EXHAUST GAS RECIRCULATION SYSTEM

Anti Back-Fire Valve, Renew
All models........................ .4

E.G.R. Valve, Renew
All models........................ .5

CONTROLLED COMBUSTION TYPE

Air Cleaner Element, Renew
All models........................ .2

Air Cleaner Sensor, Renew
All models........................ .4

Air Cleaner Vacuum Chamber, Renew
All models........................ .5

LABOR 4 ALTERNATOR AND REGULATOR 4 LABOR

(Factory Time) Chilton Time

Alternator Circuits, Test
Includes: Test battery, regulator and alternator output.
All models (.6)........................ .8

Alternator, Renew
Includes: Transfer pulley and fan.
All models (.9)........................ 1.2
w/A.C. add (.2)........................ .2

Alternator, R&R and Recondition
Includes: Disassemble, clean, inspect and test alternator parts. Renew parts as required, reassemble and test.
All models (2.2)........................ 3.0
w/A.C. add (.2)........................ .2

Alternator Drive End Frame Bearing, Renew
Includes: R&R alternator, separate end frames.
All models (1.1)........................ 1.4
w/A.C. add (.2)........................ .2

Voltage Regulator, Renew
All models
w/Integral reg (1.5)........................ 1.8
w/External reg (.6)........................ 1.0

LABOR 5 STARTING SYSTEM 5 LABOR

(Factory Time) Chilton Time

Starter Draw Test (On Truck)
All models (.3)........................ .3

Starter, Renew
Six (1.1)........................ 1.6
Four & V-8 (1.2)........................ 1.7
Diesel (1.0)........................ 1.5
Add draw test if performed.

Starter, R&R and Recondition
Includes: Turn down armature.
Six (2.2)........................ 2.6
Four & V-8 (2.4)........................ 2.8
Diesel (2.2)........................ 3.0
Renew field coils add (.5)........................ .5
Add draw test if performed.

Starter Drive, Renew
Includes: R&R starter.
Six (1.3)........................ 1.8
Four & V-8 (1.5)........................ 1.9
Diesel (1.3)........................ 1.8

Starter Solenoid, Renew
Includes: R&R starter.
Six (1.1)........................ 1.7
Four & V-8 (1.3)........................ 1.8
Diesel (1.1)........................ 1.6

Battery Cables, Renew
All models
positive (.4)........................ .6
negative (.3)........................ .4

LABOR 6 BRAKE SYSTEM 6 LABOR

(Factory Time) Chilton Time

Brakes, Adjust (Minor)
Includes: Adjust brakes, fill master cylinder.
All models
2 wheels........................ .5
4 wheels........................ .9

Bleed Brakes (Four Wheels)
Includes: Fill master cylinder.
All models (.8)........................ 1.0

Brake Pedal Free Play, Adjust
All models (.3)........................ .4

Brake Shoes, Renew
Includes: Install new or exchange brake shoes,

LABOR 6 BRAKE SYSTEM 6 LABOR

(Factory Time) Chilton Time

adjust service and hand brake. Bleed system.

Front–drum (2.0) 2.8
w/Locking hubs add (.3) .4
Rear–drum
semi-floating axle (1.5) 2.4
full floating axle (2.6) 3.4
All Four Wheels
semi-floating axle (3.0) 4.2
full floating axle (4.6) 5.8

Brake Shoes and/or Pads, Renew

Includes: Install new or exchange brake shoes or pads. Adjust service and hand brake. Bleed system.

Front–disc (1.0) 1.4
Rear–drum
semi-floating axle (1.5) 2.4
full floating axle (2.6) 3.4
All Four Wheels
semi-floating axle (2.2) 3.5
full floating axle (3.2) 4.4

Brake Drum, Renew (One)

Includes: Transfer hub to new drum, clean and repack front wheel bearings.

Front–4x2 (1.6) 1.8
4X4 (1.8) 2.0
Rear
Scout II (.5) .7
100-200-500 Series
semi-floating axle (.7) .9
full floating axle (1.7) 2.0

BRAKE HYDRAULIC SYSTEM

Wheel Cylinder, Renew (One)

Includes: Bleed lines.

Front
Scout II 4X2 (1.6) 2.2
4X4 (1.8) 2.4
100-200 Series
4x2 (1.8) 2.4
4X4 (1.9) 2.5
500 Series (2.1) 2.7
Rear
Scout II (1.4) 2.0
Semi-floating axle (1.5) 2.1
Full Floating Axle
100-200 Series (2.0) 2.6
500 Series (2.5) 3.1

Wheel Cylinder, Recondition (One)

Includes: Hone cylinder and bleed lines.

Front
Scout II 4X2 (2.0) 2.6
4X4 (2.2) 2.8
100-200 Series

COMBINATIONS

Add to Brakes, Renew

(Factory Time) Chilton Time

RENEW WHEEL CYLINDER
Each (.3) .4

REBUILD WHEEL CYLINDER
Each (.4) .6

RENEW BRAKE HOSE
Each (.4) .5

RENEW REAR AXLE GREASE SEALS
Semi-floating
Inner (1.1) 1.4
Outer (.4) .6
Full floating (.2) .4

RENEW FRONT WHEEL BEARINGS (ONE WHEEL)
w/Drum brakes .3
w/Disc brakes .4

FRONT WHEEL BEARING, REPACK OR RENEW SEAL (ONE WHEEL)
w/Drum brakes .2
w/Disc brakes .4

RENEW MASTER CYLINDER
All models (1.0) 1.4

REBUILD MASTER CYLINDER
All models (1.5) 2.0

REBUILD CALIPER ASSEMBLY
Each (.5) .8

RELINE BRAKE SHOES
Each axle set (.4) .6

(Factory Time) Chilton Time

4x2 (2.2) 2.8
4X4 (2.3) 2.9
500 Series (2.7) 3.3
Rear
Scout II (1.8) 2.4
Semi-floating axle (1.9) 2.5
Full Floating Axle
100-200 Series (2.4) 3.0
500 Series (3.2) 3.8

Master Cylinder, Renew

Includes: Bleed complete system.

(Factory Time) Chilton Time

All models
wo/Pwr brakes (1.2) 1.6
w/Pwr brakes (1.3) 1.7

Master Cylinder, R&R and Recondition

Includes: Hone cylinder and bleed system.

All models
wo/Pwr brakes (1.9) 2.4
w/Pwr brakes (2.0) 2.5

Brake Hose, Renew

Includes: Bleed line.

All models-one (.8) 1.1

POWER BRAKES

Power Brake Booster, Renew

Includes: Transfer mounting brackets. Bleed brake system and adjust linkage.

Scout II (1.5) 2.2
100-200 Series (1.6) 2.3
500 Series (1.8) 2.5

Power Brake Booster, R&R and Recondition (Diaphragm Type)

Includes: Bleed brake system and adjust linkage.

100-200 Series (2.0) 2.9
500 Series (2.2) 3.1

DISC BRAKES

Disc Brake Pads, Renew

Includes: Install new disc brake pads only.

All models (1.0) 1.4

Disc Brake Rotor, Renew (One)
two wheel drive (.7) 1.0
four wheel drive (.9) 1.2

Caliper Assembly, Renew (One)

Includes: Bleed lines.

All models (1.1) 1.5

Caliper Assy., R&R and Recondition (One)

Includes: Bleed lines.

All models (1.5) 2.0

PARKING BRAKE

Parking Brake, Adjust
All models (.2) .4

Parking Brake Lever Assy., Renew
Scout II (1.0) 1.4

Drive Line Brake Lining, Renew
open band type (1.0) 1.4
closed band type (1.3) 1.8

LABOR 7 COOLING SYSTEM 7 LABOR

(Factory Time) Chilton Time

Winterize Cooling System

Includes: Run engine to check for leaks, tighten all hose connections. Test radiator and pressure cap, drain radiator and engine block. Add anti-freeze and refill system.

All models .5

Thermostat, Renew
All models (.3) .5

Radiator Assembly, R&R or Renew
All models (.8) 1.2

ADD THESE OPERATIONS TO RADIATOR R&R

Boil & Repair 1.5
Rod Clean 1.9
Repair Core 1.3
Renew Tank 1.6
Renew Trans. Oil Cooler 1.9
Recore Radiator 1.7

Radiator Hoses, Renew
All models
upper (.3) .4
lower (.4) .5

Fan Belt, Renew
All models-one (.3) .5
each adtnl (.3) .3
w/P.S. add (.2) .2
w/A.C. add (.3) .3

Fan Belt, Adjust
All models (.2) .3

Water Pump, Renew
Four (1.0) 1.6
Six (1.1) 1.7
V-8
304-345-392 engs (1.1) 1.7
400 eng (1.3) 2.0
w/P.S. add (.2) .2
w/A.C. add (.3) .3
w/Modulated fan drive add (.4) .4

Fan Blade or Pulley, Renew
Four (.4) .6
Six (.5) .7
V-8 (.7) .9

LABOR 7 COOLING SYSTEM 7 LABOR

(Factory Time)	Chilton Time
Temperature Gauge (Engine Unit), Renew	
All models (.3)	.5
Temperature Gauge (Dash Unit), Renew	
Scout II (.4)	1.0
100-200-500 Series (.6)	1.1
Heater Core, R&R or Renew	
Without Air Conditioning	
Scout II (.5)	1.2
100-200-500 Series (.8)	1.7
With Air Conditioning	
100-200-500 Series (.7)	1.5

ADD THESE OPERATIONS TO HEATER CORE R&R

Boil & Repair	1.2
Repair Core	.9
Recore	1.2
Heater Temperature Control Valve, Renew	
All models (.3)	.6
Heater Blower Motor, Renew	
Includes: Transfer blower wheel.	
Scout II (.5)	1.0
100-200-500 Series (.6)	1.2
Heater Blower Motor Switch, Renew	
Scout II (.4)	.7
100-200-500 Series (.7)	1.1

LABOR 8 EXHAUST SYSTEM 8 LABOR

(Factory Time)	Chilton Time
Exhaust Pipes, Renew	
SCOUT II	
Four	
front exh pipe (1.0)	1.4
crossover pipe (.9)	1.3
Six(.8)	1.1
V-8	
front exh pipe-each (1.0)	1.4
crossover pipe (1.2)	1.7
100-200-500 Series	
Six	
front pipe (.9)	1.2
intermediate pipe (1.2)	1.7
rear pipe (1.2)	1.7
V-8–Single Exhaust	
left pipe (1.2)	1.6
crossover pipe (1.5)	2.1
rear pipe (1.6)	2.2
Dual Exhaust	
front pipe (1.0)	1.3
intermediate pipe (1.3)	1.8
Muffler, Renew	
All models-each (1.0)	1.4
Catalytic Converter, Renew	
All models (.7)	1.4
Tail Pipe, Renew	
All models (.8)	1.1
Exhaust Manifold or Gaskets, Renew	
Four (.9)	1.4
Six (1.3)	1.8
V-8-one side (1.0)	1.5
both sides (1.7)	2.7

COMBINATIONS

Muffler, Exhaust and Tail Pipes, Renew	
Four (1.5)	2.2
Six (1.3)	2.0
V-8-single exh (1.9)	2.6
dual exh-each side (1.2)	1.9
Diesel (.9)	1.4

LABOR 9 FRONT SUSPENSION 9 LABOR

Note: On all front suspension operations alignment charges must be added if performed. Time given does not include alignment.

(Factory Time)	Chilton Time
Check Alignment of Front End	
All models (.5)	.8
Note: Deduct if alignment is performed.	
Toe-In, Adjust	
SCOUT II (.8)	1.1
100-200-500 Series (.5)	.8
Align Front End	
Includes: Adjust front wheel bearings.	
Coil Spring Suspension	
All models (2.3)	3.0
Front Wheel Bearings, Clean and Repack (Both Wheels)	
SCOUT II	
w/Drum brakes (1.2)	1.6
w/Disc brakes (1.7)	2.1
100-200-500 Series	
Drum Brakes	
4X2 (1.1)	1.5
4X4 (1.3)	1.7
Disc Brakes	
4X2 (1.5)	1.9
4X4 (1.7)	2.1
w/Locking hubs add (.3)	.4
Front Wheel Bearings and Cups, Renew (One Wheel)	
SCOUT II	
w/Drum brakes (.9)	1.2
w/Disc brakes (1.1)	1.4
100-200-500 Series	
w/Drum brakes (1.2)	1.5
w/Disc brakes (1.3)	1.6
w/Locking hubs add (.1)	.2
Front Wheel Grease Seal, Renew (One Wheel)	
SCOUT II	
w/Drum brakes (.8)	1.0
w/Disc brakes (1.0)	1.2
100-200-500 Series	
w/Drum brakes (.9)	1.1
w/Disc brakes (1.1)	1.3
w/Locking hubs add (.1)	.2
Front Shock Absorber, Renew	
All models-one (.4)	.6
both (.5)	.8
Front Axle Assembly, R&R	
SCOUT II	
w/Drum brakes (2.9)	4.5
w/Disc brakes (2.6)	4.2
Front Axle Tube Assy., Renew	
SCOUT II	
w/Drum brakes (6.2)	9.1
w/Disc brakes (6.6)	9.5
Spindle Assembly, Renew (One)	
SCOUT II	
w/Drum brakes (1.3)	2.1
w/Disc brakes (1.5)	2.3
100-200-500 Series	
w/Drum brakes (1.4)	2.2
w/Disc brakes (1.7)	2.5
w/Locking hubs add (.2)	.2
Ball Sockets, Renew (One Side)	
SCOUT II	
w/Drum brakes (2.5)	3.9
w/Disc brakes (2.7)	4.1
100-200-500 Series	
w/Drum brakes (2.5)	3.9
w/Disc brakes (2.9)	4.3
w/Locking hubs add (.2)	.2
Steering Knuckle, Renew (One)	
SCOUT II	
w/Drum brakes (3.3)	5.1
w/Disc brakes (3.6)	5.4
100-200-500 Series	
w/Drum brakes (2.7)	4.5
w/Disc brakes (2.9)	4.7
w/Locking hubs add (.2)	.2
Front Spring Assembly, Renew (One)	
SCOUT II (.9)	1.5
100-200-500 Series (1.2)	1.7
Front Spring Shackle, Renew (One)	
Includes: Renew spring shackle only.	
SCOUT II (.4)	.8
100-200-500 Series (.7)	1.3

I BEAM SUSPENSION

Axle I Beam, Renew	
Add alignment charges.	
All models (3.1)	5.5
King Pins and Bushings, Renew (Both Sides)	
Add alignment charges.	
All models (3.2)	4.7
Steering Knuckle, Renew (One)	
Add alignment charges.	
All models (1.5)	2.7
Renew bushings add (.7)	1.0
Steering Arm, Renew (One)	
Add alignment charges.	

LABOR 9 FRONT SUSPENSION 9 LABOR

(Factory Time) Chilton Time

All models (1.3) 1.8

COIL SPRING SUSPENSION

Steering Knuckle, Renew (One)
Add alignment charges.
100-200-500 Series (1.9).... 2.7

Upper Control Arm, Renew (One)
Add alignment charges.
100-200-500 Series (.9).... 1.7

Ball Joints, Renew
Add alignment charges.
Series 100-200-500
one upper (1.0).... 1.8
one lower (2.4).... 3.2
upper & lower
one side (2.8).... 3.6

Lower Control Arm, Renew (One)
Add alignment charges.
100-200-500 Series (2.1).... 2.9

Lower Control Arm Bushings, Renew (One Side)
Add alignment charges.
100-200-500 Series (2.2).... 3.2

Upper Control Arm Bushings, Renew (One Side)
Add alignment charges.
100-200-500 Series (1.3).... 2.1

Coil Spring, Renew (One)
Add alignment charges.
100-200-500 Series (2.0).... 2.9

Lower Control Arm Rod Assy., Renew
100-200-500 Series (.6).... .9

Sway Bar, Renew
100-200-500 Series (.5).... 1.0

FOUR WHEEL DRIVE

Front Drive Axle Assy., R&R
SCOUT II
w/Drum brakes (3.5).... 6.1
w/Disc brakes (3.1).... 5.7
100-200 Series
w/Drum brakes (3.6).... 6.2
w/Disc brakes (3.2).... 5.8
w/Locking hubs add (.3).... .3

Front Drive Axle Assy., R&R and Recondition
SCOUT II
w/Drum brakes (13.1).... 16.6
w/Disc brakes (13.5).... 17.0

100-200 Series
w/Drum brakes (13.6).... 17.1
w/Disc brakes (13.4).... 16.9
w/Locking hubs add (.3).... .3

Front Axle Shaft U-Joint, Renew or Recondition

SCOUT II
w/Drum brakes (1.7).... 3.0
w/Disc brakes (1.9).... 3.2
100-200 Series
w/Drum brakes (1.9).... 3.2
w/Disc brakes (2.1).... 3.4

Front Axle Drive Shaft, Renew (One) (Inner or Outer)
SCOUT II
w/Drum brakes (1.5).... 2.6
w/Disc brakes (1.7).... 2.8
100-200 Series
w/Drum brakes (1.6).... 2.7
w/Disc brakes (1.9).... 3.0
w/Locking hubs add (.2).... .3

Front Differential Assy., R&R and Recondition
Includes: Renew ring gear and pinion.
SCOUT II
w/Drum brakes (9.9).... 13.4
w/Disc brakes (10.3).... 13.8
100-200 Series
w/Drum brakes (9.5).... 13.0
w/Disc brakes (9.3).... 12.8
w/Locking hubs add (.2).... .3

Front Drive Axle Housing, Renew
All models
w/Drum brakes (10.0).... 13.4
w/Disc brakes (10.4).... 13.7
w/Locking hubs add (.2).... .3

Front Drive Shaft, R&R or Renew
All models (.8).... 1.2

Front Universal Joint, Renew or Recondition
Includes: R&R drive shaft.
All models (.8).... 1.5

LABOR 10 STEERING LINKAGE 10 LABOR

(Factory Time) Chilton Time

Tie Rod, Renew
Includes: Transfer tie rod ends and reset toe-in.
SCOUT II (1.4).... 2.0
100-200-500 Series (1.0).... 1.5

Tie Rod Ends, Renew
Includes: Reset toe-in.
SCOUT II-one (1.2).... 1.7
both (1.4).... 1.9
100-200-500 Series-one (.8).... 1.0
both (1.0).... 1.4

Pitman Arm, Renew
SCOUT II (.5).... .9
100-200-500 Series (.6).... 1.0

Idler Arm, Renew
All models (.6).... .9
Renew bushing add (.1).... .2

Center Link Assembly, Renew
100-200-500 Series (.9).... 1.3

Drag Link, Renew
SCOUT II (.4).... .7
100-200-500 Series (.6).... 1.0

LABOR 11 STEERING GEAR 11 LABOR

STANDARD STEERING

Steering Wheel, Renew
SCOUT II (.4).... .6
100-200-500 Series
w/Std horn button (.5).... .7
Custom or Deluxe (.6).... .8

Energy Absorbing Steering Column, Renew
Includes: Disconnect battery, R&R column, transfer mounting bracket, lock cylinder, ignition switch and steering wheel.
SCOUT II (1.6).... 2.5

Energy Absorbing Steering Column, Recondition
Includes: Disconnect battery, R&R column, disassemble, clean, inspect and renew parts as required. Reassemble and align steering wheel.
SCOUT II (2.0).... 3.1

Steering Column Lock Cylinder, Renew
Includes: Disconnect battery. R&R steering wheel and turn signal switch.
SCOUT II (.7).... 1.3

Steering Gear, Adjust (On Truck)
All models (.4).... .8

Steering Gear, R&R or Renew
SCOUT II (.9).... 1.9
100-200-500 Series (1.0).... 2.0

Steering Gear, R&R and Recondition
Includes: Disassemble, renew necessary parts, reassemble and adjust.
SCOUT II (1.9).... 2.9
100-200-500 Series (2.3).... 3.3

POWER STEERING

Trouble Shoot Power Steering
Includes: Check pounds pull on steering wheel, install checking gauge. Test pump pressure and check for external leaks.
All models (.5).... .8

Power Steering Belt, Renew
All models (.3).... .5

Power Steering Hoses, Renew
Includes: Bleed system.
All models - each (.6).... .9

Power Steering Gear, R&R or Renew
SCOUT II (1.5).... 2.6
100-200-500 Series (1.4).... 2.5

Power Steering Gear, R&R and Recondition
Includes: Disassemble, renew necessary parts, reassemble and adjust.
SCOUT II (3.6).... 5.0
100-200-500 Series (3.7).... 5.1

Power Steering Pump, Renew
Includes: Transfer pulley and bleed system.
SCOUT II (.9).... 1.3
100-200-500 Series
Six (1.1).... 1.5
V-8-304-345-392 engs (1.0).... 1.4
400 eng (1.3).... 1.9

Power Steering Pump, R&R and Recondition
Includes: Bleed system.
SCOUT II (1.7).... 3.1
100-200-500 Series
V-8-304-345-392 engs (1.8).... 3.2
400 eng (2.1).... 3.5

LABOR 12 CYLINDER HEAD & VALVE SYSTEM 12 LABOR

(Factory Time)	Chilton Time
GASOLINE ENGINES	
Compression Test	
Four (.6)	.8
Six (.7)	1.0
V-8 (.9)	1.2
Cylinder Head Gasket, Renew	
Four (3.2)	4.6
Six (3.5)	4.9
V-8-one (3.2)	4.6
both (4.9)	7.7
w/P.S. add (.3)	.3
w/A.C. add (.6)	.6
w/Pwr brks add (.8)	.8
Cylinder Head (With Valves), Renew	
Four (4.7)	5.8
Six (4.9)	6.0
V-8-one (5.2)	6.7
both (7.0)	8.4
w/P.S. add (.3)	.3
w/A.C. add (.6)	.6
w/Pwr brks add (.8)	.8
Clean Carbon and Grind Valves	
Includes: R&R cylinder head(s), clean gasket surfaces, clean carbon, reface valves and seats. Minor tune up.	
Four (8.3)	10.5
Six (9.7)	12.0
V-8 (13.4)	16.3
w/P.S. add (.3)	.3
w/A.C. add (.6)	.6
w/Pwr brks add (.8)	.8
Rocker Arm Cover and/or Gasket, Renew	
Four (.3)	.5
Six (.7)	1.0
V-8-left (.5)	.8
right (.7)	1.0
w/P.S. add (.3)	.3
w/A.C. add (.6)	.6
w/Pwr brks add (.8)	.8
Valve Push Rod or Rocker Arm, Renew (One or All)	
Four (.8)	1.1
Six (1.0)	1.3
V-8-left bank (.8)	1.1
right bank (.9)	1.2
both banks (1.3)	1.9
Valve Lifters, Renew (One or All)	
Includes: R&R 6 cylinder head.	
Four (.9)	1.7

COMBINATIONS

Add To Valve Job

See Machine Shop Operations

(Factory Time)	Chilton Time
DRAIN, EVACUATE AND RECHARGE AIR CONDITIONING SYSTEM	
All models	1.8
HYDRAULIC VALVE LIFTERS, DISASSEMBLE AND CLEAN	
Each (.2)	.2
DISTRIBUTOR, RECONDITION	
All models (1.5)	1.9
CARBURETOR, RECONDITION	
1 BBL (1.3)	1.8
2 BBL (1.6)	2.1
4 BBL (1.9)	2.4
VALVE GUIDES, RENEW	
Each (.2)	.3
ROCKER ARMS, DISASSEMBLE AND CLEAN OR RENEW	
Four (.8)	1.0
Six (.6)	.8
V-8 (1.2)	1.4

(Factory Time)	Chilton Time
Six (4.9)	6.3
V-8-304-345-392 engs	
one cyl (.9)	1.7
one bank (1.3)	2.1
all-both banks (2.1)	3.0
400 eng	
one cyl (2.1)	3.0
one bank (2.5)	3.4
all-both banks (3.0)	4.3
w/P.S. add (.3)	.3
w/A.C. add (.6)	.6
w/Pwr brks add (.8)	.8
Valve Spring or Valve Stem Oil Seal, Renew (One) (Head on Truck)	
Four (.9)	1.2
Six (1.3)	1.6
V-8-left side (.8)	1.1
right side (.9)	1.2
each adtnl-all engs (.1)	.2
w/P.S. add (.3)	.3
w/A.C. add (.6)	.6

(Factory Time)	Chilton Time
w/Pwr brks add (.8)	.8
Rocker Arm Assy., R&R and Recondition	
Four (1.2)	1.8
Six (1.6)	2.2
V-8-both (2.2)	2.8
w/P.S. add (.3)	.3
w/A.C. add (.6)	.6
w/Pwr brks add (.8)	.8
Valve Push Rod Cover and/or Gasket, Renew	
Four (2.8)	3.5
V-8 (2.8)	3.5
DIESEL ENGINE	
Compression Test	
All models	2.0
Cylinder Head Gasket, Renew	
All models (4.4)	6.3
Cylinder Head (With Valves), Renew	
Does not include recondition fuel injectors.	
All models (6.5)	9.4
Cylinder Head (Less Valves), Renew	
Includes: Transfer parts as required. Does not include recondition fuel injectors.	
All models (7.9)	11.5
Clean Carbon and Grind Valves	
Includes: R&R cylinder head. Check valve guide and stem clearance. Reface valves, stems and seats.	
All models (9.9)	14.4
Rocker Arm Assembly, Recondition	
Includes: R&R, disassemble, clean. Renew required parts, reassemble.	
All models (1.9)	3.0
Valve Push Rods, Renew (One or All)	
All models (1.5)	2.1
Valve Tappets, Renew (All)	
Includes: Disassemble engine as required.	
All models (12.2)	21.0
Rocker Arm Cover and/or Gasket, Renew	
All models (.6)	1.0
Valve Clearance, Adjust	
All models (1.2)	1.8

LABOR 13 ENGINE ASSEMBLY & MOUNTS 13 LABOR

(Factory Time)	Chilton Time
GASOLINE ENGINES	
Engine Assembly, Remove & Install	
Does not include transfer of any parts or equipment.	
Four-w/M.T. (4.4)	5.8
w/A.T. (5.0)	6.5
Six-w/M.T. (4.9)	6.4
w/A.T. (5.5)	7.2
V-8-w/M.T. (5.0)	6.5
w/A.T. (5.6)	7.3
w/P.S. add (.3)	.3
w/A.C. add (.6)	.6
Engine Assembly, Renew	
Includes: R&R engine assembly, transfer all necessary parts, fuel and electrical units.	
Four-w/M.T. (10.4)	14.0
w/A.T. (10.7)	14.3
Six-w/M.T. (10.6)	14.2
w/A.T. (10.9)	14.5
V-8-w/M.T. (11.9)	15.5
w/A.T. (12.2)	15.8
w/P.S. add (.3)	.3
w/A.C. add (.6)	.6
Cylinder Assembly, Renew (w/All Internal Parts Less Cylinder Heads and Oil Pan)	
Includes: R&R engine assembly, transfer all component parts not supplied with replacement engine, clean carbon, grind valves. Tune engine.	
Four-w/M.T. (16.9)	21.9
w/A.T. (17.2)	22.2
Six-w/M.T. (18.6)	23.6
w/A.T. (18.8)	23.8
V-8-w/M.T. (22.7)	27.7
w/A.T. (23.0)	28.0
w/P.S. add (.3)	.3
w/A.C. add (.6)	.6
Engine Assy., R&R and Recondition	
Includes: Rebore block, install new pistons, rings, pins, rod and main bearings. Clean carbon, grind valves. Tune engine.	
Four-w/M.T. (27.7)	32.5
w/A.T. (27.9)	32.7

LABOR 13 ENGINE ASSEMBLY & MOUNTS 13 LABOR

	(Factory Time)	Chilton Time
Six-w/M.T.	(33.1)	39.7
w/A.T.	(33.4)	41.0
V-8-w/M.T.	(37.8)	47.5
w/A.T.	(38.1)	47.8
w/P.S. add	(.3)	.3
w/A.C. add	(.6)	.6

Engine Mounts, Renew

	(Factory Time)	Chilton Time
Front		
Four	(.6)	1.0
Six	(.7)	1.1
V-8	(.7)	1.2
Rear		
Four	(.6)	1.0
Six	(.7)	1.1
V-8	(.5)	.9

DIESEL ENGINE

Engine Assembly, Remove & Install

Does not include transfer of any parts or equipment.

	(Factory Time)	Chilton Time
All models-w/M.T.	(5.7)	8.5
w/A.T.	(6.3)	9.0

Engine Assembly, Renew (w/ Complete Engine)

Includes: R&R engine assembly, transfer all necessary parts, fuel and electrical units.

	(Factory Time)	Chilton Time
All models-w/M.T.	(8.6)	12.8
w/A.T.	(9.2)	13.3

Engine Assy., R&R and Recondition

Includes: Install new pistons, rings, pins, rod and main bearings. Clean carbon, grind valves. Recondition rocker arms. Make all necessary adjustments.

	(Factory Time)	Chilton Time
All models-w/M.T.	(31.6)	46.7
w/A.T.	(31.9)	47.2

Engine Mounts, Renew

	(Factory Time)	Chilton Time
All models-front	(.7)	1.1
rear	(.6)	1.0

LABOR 14 PISTONS, RINGS & BEARINGS 14 LABOR

GASOLINE ENGINES

Rings, Renew (See Engine Combinations)

Includes: Remove cylinder top ridge, deglaze cylinder walls. Minor tune up.

	(Factory Time)	Chilton Time
SCOUT II		
Four	(9.5)	12.5
Six	(11.7)	15.0
V-8	(14.4)	17.8
100-200-500 Series		
Six-w/M.T.	(15.1)	18.9
w/A.T.	(15.6)	19.4
V-8-304-345-392 engs	(15.8)	19.7
400 eng-w/M.T.	(18.2)	21.9
w/A.T.	(18.7)	22.4
w/P.S. add	(.3)	.3
w/A.C. add	(.6)	.6
w/Pwr brks add	(.8)	.8

Piston or Connecting Rod, Renew (One)

Includes: Remove cylinder top ridge, deglaze cylinder walls. Minor tune up.

	(Factory Time)	Chilton Time
SCOUT II		
Four	(8.2)	10.3
Six	(9.3)	11.8
V-8	(8.6)	11.1
100-200-500 Series		
Six-w/M.T.	(12.9)	15.5
w/A.T.	(13.4)	16.0
V-8-304-345-392 engs	(10.2)	12.8
400 eng-w/M.T.	(13.3)	16.0
w/A.T.	(13.8)	16.5

COMBINATIONS
Add to Engine Work

GASOLINE ENGINES

	(Factory Time)	Chilton Time
DRAIN, EVACUATE AND RECHARGE AIR CONDITIONING SYSTEM		
All models		1.8
HYDRAULIC VALVE LIFTERS, DISASSEMBLE AND CLEAN		
Each	(.2)	.2
DISTRIBUTOR, RECONDITION		
All models	(1.5)	1.9
CARBURETOR, RECONDITION		
1 BBL	(1.3)	1.8
2 BBL	(1.6)	2.1
4 BBL	(1.9)	2.4
VALVE GUIDES, RENEW		
Each	(.2)	.3
REMOVE CYLINDER TOP RIDGE		
Each	(.1)	.1
DEGLAZE CYLINDER WALLS		
Each	(.1)	.2
ROCKER ARMS, DISASSEMBLE AND CLEAN OR RENEW		
Four	(.8)	1.0
Six	(.6)	.8
V-8	(1.2)	1.4
MAIN BEARINGS, RENEW		
Four	(1.6)	2.5
Six	(1.9)	2.8
V-8	(1.6)	2.5
PLASTIGAUGE BEARINGS		
Each	(.1)	.1
OIL PUMP, RECONDITION		
All models	(.6)	.9
OIL FILTER ELEMENT, RENEW		
All models	(.3)	.4

DIESEL ENGINE

Rings, Renew (See Engine Combinations)

Includes: Remove cylinder top ridge, deglaze cylinder walls.

	(Factory Time)	Chilton Time
All models	(11.9)	17.7

Piston or Connecting Rod, Renew (One)

COMBINATIONS
Add To Engine Work

DIESEL ENGINE

	(Factory Time)	Chilton Time
DRAIN, EVACUATE AND RECHARGE AIR CONDITIONING SYSTEM		
All models		1.8
VALVE GUIDES, RENEW		
Each	(.2)	.3
ROCKER ARMS, DISASSEMBLE AND CLEAN OR RENEW		
All models	(.6)	.8
TIMING GEARS, RENEW (COVER REMOVED)		
All models	(1.1)	1.4
DEGLAZE CYLINDER WALLS		
Each	(.1)	.2
REMOVE CYLINDER TOP RIDGE		
Each	(.1)	.1
ROD BEARINGS, RENEW (PAN REMOVED)		
All models	(1.9)	2.5
MAIN BEARINGS, RENEW (PAN REMOVED)		
All models	(2.7)	3.5
PLASTIGAUGE BEARINGS		
Each	(.1)	.1
PISTON SLEEVES, RENEW		
One	(1.2)	1.5
Each adtnl	(.4)	.5
OIL PUMP, RECONDITION		
All models	(.6)	.8

LABOR 14 PISTONS, RINGS & BEARINGS 14 LABOR

(Factory Time) Chilton Time

Includes: Remove cylinder top ridge, hone cylinder as required. Install new piston rings and pin.

All models (9.1)	13.5

Connecting Rod Bearings, Renew

All models (3.4)	5.0
w/P.S. add (.3)	.3
w/A.C. add (.6)	.6
w/Pwr brks add (.8)	.8

Connecting Rod Bearings, Renew

Includes: Check bearing clearances.

SCOUT II	
Four (2.5)	3.4
Six (3.7)	4.9
V-8 (3.4)	4.6
100-200-500 Series	
Six–w/M.T. (7.8)	10.2
w/A.T. (8.2)	10.8
V-8–304-345-392 engs (5.0)	6.5
400 eng–w/M.T. (8.3)	10.9
w/A.T. (8.7)	11.3
w/P.S. add (.3)	.3
w/A.C. add (.6)	.6

LABOR 15 CRANKSHAFT & DAMPER 15 LABOR

(Factory Time) Chilton Time

GASOLINE ENGINES

Crankshaft and Main Bearings, Renew

Includes: R&R engine assembly and plastigauge bearings.

Four–w/M.T. (11.9)	16.0
w/A.T. (12.1)	16.3
Six–w/M.T. (13.0)	17.0
w/A.T. (13.2)	17.5
V-8–w/M.T. (13.9)	18.4
w/A.T. (14.1)	18.9
w/P.S. add (.3)	.3
w/A.C. add (.6)	.6
w/Pwr brks add (.8)	.8

Main Bearings, Renew

Includes: Plastigauge bearings.

SCOUT II	
Four (3.1)	4.5
Six (3.4)	4.8
V-8 (3.1)	4.5
100-200-500 Series	
Six–w/M.T. (8.4)	10.2
w/A.T. (8.9)	10.8
V-8–304-345-392 engs (4.7)	6.5
400 eng–w/M.T. (7.9)	9.8
w/A.T. (8.4)	10.3

Rear Main Bearing Oil Seal, Renew

Includes: R&R transmission and clutch or converter, except six cylinder.

SCOUT II–Manual trans	
Four & V-8	
4X2 (4.5)	5.9
4X4 (5.4)	6.8
Six (3.2)	4.3
Auto trans	
Four & V-8	
4X2 (5.4)	6.8
4X4 (5.9)	7.3
100-200-500 Series–Manual trans	
V-8 (5.3)	6.7
Auto trans	
V-8 (5.2)	6.6

Crankshaft Pulley, Renew

SCOUT II	
All engs (.4)	.8
100-200-500 Series	
All engs (1.4)	2.0
w/P.S. add (.2)	.2

DIESEL ENGINE

Crankshaft and Main Bearings, Renew

Includes: R&R engine assembly and plastigauge bearings.

All models–w/M.T. (14.2)	21.3
w/A.T. (14.4)	21.8

Main Bearings, Renew

Includes: Plastigauge bearings.

All models (4.1)	5.3

Main and Rod Bearings, Renew

Includes: Plastigauge bearings.

All models (6.0)	7.8

Rear Main Bearing Oil Seal, Renew (Lower Half Only)

All models (1.9)	2.8

Crankshaft Pulley, Renew

All models (1.6)	2.2

LABOR 16 CAMSHAFT & TIMING GEARS 16 LABOR

(Factory Time) Chilton Time

GASOLINE ENGINES

Timing Case Cover or Gasket, Renew

SCOUT II	
Four (3.3)	4.7
Six (3.7)	4.9
V-8 (3.6)	4.8
100-200-500 Series	
Six (5.1)	6.7
V-8 (5.4)	7.0
w/P.S. add (.2)	.2

Timing Case Cover Oil Seal, Renew

All engs–exc below (1.4)	1.9
400 eng (5.4)	7.0

Timing Gears and/or Chain, Renew

SCOUT II	
Four (3.9)	5.5
Six (4.3)	5.7
V-8 (4.2)	5.6
100-200-500 Series	
Six (5.7)	7.5
V-8 (5.9)	7.8
w/P.S. add (.2)	.2

Camshaft, Renew

SCOUT II	
Four (7.8)	9.7
Six (10.7)	12.6
V-8 (8.8)	10.7
100-200-500 Series	
Six (11.0)	13.0
V-8 (10.1)	12.4

Camshaft Bearings, Renew (Engine Removed and Disassembled)

All models (.5)	1.0

DIESEL ENGINE

Timing Case Cover Oil Seal, Renew

All models (1.7)	2.5

Timing Case Cover or Gasket, Renew

Includes: R&R oil pan and renew cover oil seal.

All models (4.0)	5.6

Timing Gears, Renew

All models (4.8)	6.6

Camshaft, Renew

Includes: Disassemble engine as required.

All models (12.0)	17.8

Camshaft Bearings, Renew (Engine Removed and Disassembled)

All models (.5)	1.0

LABOR 17 ENGINE OILING SYSTEM 17 LABOR

(Factory Time) Chilton Time

GASOLINE ENGINES

Oil Pan or Gasket, Renew

SCOUT II	
Four (1.4)	2.0
Six (2.4)	3.2
V-8 (1.4)	2.0
100-200-500 Series	
Six–w/M.T. (6.2)	8.0
w/A.T. (6.7)	8.5
V-8–304-345-392 engs (3.0)	3.9
400 eng–w/M.T. (6.4)	8.4
w/A.T. (6.9)	8.9

Oil Pump, Renew

Includes: Clean oil pan and pump screen.

SCOUT II	
Four (1.7)	2.3
Six (2.5)	3.4
V-8 (1.7)	2.3

LABOR 17 ENGINE OILING SYSTEM 17 LABOR

(Factory Time)	Chilton Time
100-200-500 Series	
Six–w/M.T. (6.5)	8.3
w/A.T. (6.9)	8.8
V-8–304-345-392 engs (3.2)	4.1
400 eng (1.0)	1.6
Pressure Test Engine Bearings (Pan Off)	
All models (1.0)	1.2
Oil Pressure Gauge (Dash), Renew	
All models (.6)	1.0
Oil Pressure Gauge (Engine), Renew	
All models (.2)	.5
Oil Filter Element, Renew	
All models (.3)	.4
DIESEL ENGINE	
Oil Pan and/or Gasket, Renew	
All models (1.6)	2.3
Pressure Test Engine Bearings (Pan Off)	
All models	1.2
Oil Pump, Renew	
All models (1.7)	2.7
Oil Pump, R&R and Recondition	
All models (2.2)	3.3
Oil Filter Element, Renew	
All models (.3)	.4

LABOR 18 CLUTCH & FLYWHEEL 18 LABOR

(Factory Time)	Chilton Time
Clutch Pedal Free Play, Adjust	
All models (.2)	.4
Clutch Assembly, Renew	
SCOUT II	
4X2 (4.0)	5.4
4X4 (5.0)	6.6
100-200-500 Series	
304-345-392 engs (4.4)	5.8
258-400 engs (4.7)	6.1
w/258 eng add (.3)	.3
Renew pilot brg add (.2)	.3
Clutch Release Bearing, Renew	
SCOUT II	
4X2 (2.9)	4.3
4X4 (3.9)	5.2
100-200-500 Series	
floor shift (3.7)	5.0
column shift (3.0)	4.3
Clutch Release Fork, Renew	
SCOUT II	
4X2 (3.5)	4.9
4X4 (4.5)	5.8
100-200-500 Series	
304-345-392 engs (4.3)	5.6
258-400 engs (4.5)	5.8
w/258 eng add (.3)	.3
Flywheel, Renew	
SCOUT II	
4X2 (4.4)	6.0
4X4 (5.3)	7.2
100-200-500 Series	
304-345-392 engs (5.2)	6.4
258-400 engs (5.5)	6.7
w/258 eng add (.3)	.3
Renew ring gear add (.5)	.6

LABOR 19 STANDARD TRANSMISSION 19 LABOR

(Factory Time)	Chilton Time
Transmission Assy., Remove & Reinstall	
Includes: R&R transmission and transfer case as a unit.	
SCOUT II	
4X2 (2.6)	4.0
4X4 (3.5)	4.9
100-200-500 Series	
3 speed (2.7)	4.1
4 & 5 speed (3.3)	4.7
Transmission Assembly, Renew	
Includes: R&R transmission and transfer case as a unit. Transfer drive gear or flange and transfer case where applicable.	
SCOUT II	
4X2 (3.2)	4.6
4X4 (4.5)	5.9
100-200-500 Series	
3 speed (3.2)	4.7
4 & 5 speed (3.9)	5.4
Transmission Assy., R&R and Recondition	
Includes: R&R transmission and transfer case as a unit. Separate units and overhaul transmission only.	
SCOUT II	
3 Speed	
4X2 (6.0)	8.1
4X4 (7.3)	9.4
4 Speed	
4X2 (7.1)	9.2
4X4 (8.4)	10.5
100-200-500 Series	
3 Speed	
column shift (7.0)	9.1
floor shift (7.7)	9.8
4 Speed (8.8)	10.5
5 Speed (8.7)	10.5
Transmission, Recondition (Off Truck)	
SCOUT II	
3 speed (3.2)	4.1
4 speed (4.5)	5.4
100-200-500 Series	
3 speed (4.2)	5.1
4 speed (5.3)	6.2
5 speed (5.1)	6.0
Transmission Rear Oil Seal, Renew	
All models (1.0)	1.6

LABOR 20 TRANSFER CASE 20 LABOR

(Factory Time)	Chilton Time
TRANSFER CASE	
Transfer Case Assy., Remove & Reinstall	
Includes: R&R transfer case only.	
SCOUT II	
w/M.T. (2.6)	4.0
w/A.T. (2.9)	4.3
100-200-500 Series	
N P Single Lever (2.6)	4.0
Chain Drive (2.1)	3.5
Travelalls add (.2)	.2
Transfer Case Assy., Renew	
Includes: R&R transfer case from transmission, install a new transfer case.	
SCOUT II	
w/M.T. (3.0)	4.4
w/A.T. (3.2)	4.7
100-200-500 Series	
N P Single Lever (3.9)	5.3
Chain Drive (2.6)	4.0
Travelalls add (.2)	.2
Transfer Case, Recondition (Off Truck)	
Chain Drive (3.0)	4.0
Spicer No. 20 (3.9)	4.9
N P Single Lever (5.4)	6.4
Transfer Case Assy., R&R and Recondition	
SCOUT II	
Chain Drive	
w/M.T. (5.7)	8.2
w/A.T. (6.0)	8.5
Spicer No. 20	
w/M.T. (6.7)	9.2
w/A.T. (6.9)	9.4
100-200-500 Series	
N P Single Lever (8.2)	10.7
Chain Drive (5.3)	7.8
Travelalls add (.2)	.2

LABOR 23 AUTOMATIC TRANSMISSION 23 LABOR

(Factory Time) — Chilton Time

Drain and Refill Unit
All models (.5) 7

Oil Pressure Check
All models (.5) 7

Check Unit For Oil Leaks
Includes: Clean and dry outside of case, run unit to determine point of leak.
All models (.8) 1.0

Adjust Transmission (Complete)
Includes: Drain and refill unit. R&R oil pan, gasket and screen. Adjust front and rear bands and vacuum control solenoid. Clean pan and screen.
All models (1.5) 2.3

Oil Pan and/or Gasket, Renew
All models (.6) 1.1

Transmission Assy., Remove & Reinstall
Includes: R&R transmission and transfer case as a unit.
SCOUT II
13039 - 13049
4X2 (2.6) 4.1
4X4 (3.5) 5.0
13407
4X2 (4.2) 5.7
4X4 (4.8) 6.3
100-200-500 Series
Six (4.3).......... 5.9
V-8 (4.0) 5.6

Transmission Assy., Renew
Includes: R&R transmission. Drain and refill unit. Transfer flange or drive gear and transfer case where applicable.
SCOUT II
13039-13049
4X2 (4.4) 5.9
4X4 (5.5) 7.0
13407
4X2 (5.1) 6.6
4X4 (6.1) 7.6
100-200-500 Series
Six (5.1).......... 6.7
V-8 (4.8) 6.4

Transmission Assy., R&R and Recondition
Includes: R&R transmission and transfer case as a unit. Separate units and overhaul transmission only.
SCOUT II
13039-13049
4X2 (12.1) 15.0
4X4 (13.2) 16.1
13407
4X2 (13.6) 16.5
4X4 (14.7) 17.6
100-200-500 Series
Six (13.8).......... 16.7
V-8 (13.5).......... 16.4

Converter Assembly, Renew
Includes: R&R transmission and transfer case as a unit. Drain and refill trans.
SCOUT II
13039-13049
4X2 (4.7) 6.2
4X4 (5.4) 6.9
13407
4X2 (4.6) 6.1
4X4 (5.2) 6.7
100-200-500 Series
Six (4.8).......... 6.4
V-8 (4.5).......... 6.1

LABOR 25 U-JOINTS & DRIVESHAFT 25 LABOR

(Factory Time) — Chilton Time

Drive Shaft, R&R or Renew
All models (.8) 1.1

Universal Joint, Renew (One)
All models (.8) 1.1

Universal Joint, Recondition (One)
All models (1.1) 1.4

Stub Shaft, Renew
All models (1.2) 1.6

Center Bearing, Renew or Recondition
All models (1.0) 1.4

Tighten Drive Shaft Flange (One)
All models (.5) 7

LABOR 26 REAR AXLE 26 LABOR

(Factory Time) — Chilton Time

Rear Axle, Drain and Refill
All models (.3) 6

Axle Housing Cover Gasket, Renew
All models (.6) 9

Axle Shaft, Renew
Includes: Renew axle shaft inner and outer seals. Transfer or renew wheel studs and bearing. Adjust axle shaft end play, where applicable.
SCOUT II
right side (1.5) 2.1
left side (1.7).......... 2.3
100-200-500 Series
Axle Codes
14015-14016-14017
14020-14025-14184
each (.3) 6
Axle Codes
14018-14028-14063
14083-14084
right side (1.5).......... 2.1
left side (1.7).......... 2.3

Axle Shaft Bearing and/or Seal, Renew

SCOUT II
right side (1.4) 2.0
left side (1.6).......... 2.2
100-200-500 Series
right side (1.5) 2.1
left side (1.7).......... 2.3

Inner and Outer Axle Shaft Oil Seals, Renew
All models
right side (1.4) 2.0
left side (1.6).......... 2.2

Pinion Shaft Oil Seal, Renew
SCOUT II (.9).......... 1.3
100-200-500 Series
Axle Codes
14015-14020-14025 (1.1) 1.5
14016-14017-14018
14028-14063-14083
14084 (.9) 1.3
14184 (1.0).......... 1.4

Rear Axle Assy., Remove & Reinstall
Includes: R&R wheels and brake drums. R&R brake lines at frame. R&R brake cable at backing plate. R&R rear spring pins. Bleed and adjust brakes.
SCOUT II (3.1).......... 4.6

100-200-500 Series
Axle Codes
14015-14016-14017
14020-14025 (3.7).......... 5.2
14018-14028-14063
14083-14084 (2.8).......... 4.3
14184 (4.3).......... 5.8

Rear Axle Assy., R&R and Recondition
Includes: Recondition differential and pinion assemblies. Renew ring gear and pinion set. Renew bearings and axle shaft oil seals. Make all necessary adjustments. Bleed and adjust brakes.
SCOUT II
Axle Codes
14018 (9.9).......... 12.0
14028 (10.3).......... 12.5
100-200-500 Series
Axle Codes
14016 (8.8).......... 11.0
14017 (9.4).......... 11.6
14018-14083 (9.2) 11.4
14028-14063, 14084 (10.0) 12.0

Differential Carrier Assy., R&R or Renew
Includes: R&R carrier assy. from axle housing. Drain and refill unit.
100-200-500 Series
Axle Codes
14015-14020-14025 (2.2) 3.0
14184 (3.0).......... 3.8

Differential Carrier Assy., R&R and Recondition
Includes: R&R carrier from axle housing. Overhaul differential as required, including ring gear and pinion set. Make all necessary adjustments. Drain and refill unit.

LABOR 26 REAR AXLE 26 LABOR

(Factory Time)	Chilton Time
100-200-500 Series	
Axle Codes	
14015-14020 (7.7)	9.3
14025 (7.8)	9.4
14184 (8.3)	10.1
Pinion Shaft Bearings, Renew	
Includes: Renew pinion bearings and cups. Make all necessary adjustments. Drain and refill unit.	
SCOUT II (7.0)	8.6
100-200-500 Series	
Axle Codes	
14015-14020-14025 (5.2)	6.8
14016-14017 (6.8)	8.4
14018-14028-14063 14083-14084 (6.6)	8.2
14184 (6.2)	7.8

LABOR 27 REAR SUSPENSION 27 LABOR

(Factory Time)	Chilton Time
Rear Spring, Renew (One)	
SCOUT II (.9)	1.5
100-200-500 Series (1.3)	1.9
Rear Spring, R&R and Recondition (One)	
SCOUT II (1.6)	2.5
100-200-500 Series (1.8)	2.7
Front and Rear Bushings, Renew (Rear Spring)	
Includes: R&R spring and shackles. Install new spring and shackle bushings.	
SCOUT II-one (1.5)	2.0
100-200-500 Series-one (1.7)	2.2
Rear Spring Shackle, Renew	
Includes: Renew shackle only, one spring.	
SCOUT II (.4)	.9
100-200-500 Series	
rubber mounted (.5)	.9
bushing mounted (.8)	1.4
Shackle Bushing, Renew (One Spring)	
Includes: Renew shackle bushing only.	
SCOUT II (.5)	1.0
100-200-500 Series	
rubber mounted (.6)	1.0
bushing mounted (.9)	1.5
Rear Shock Absorbers, Renew	
All models-one (.4)	.5
both (.5)	.8

LABOR 28 AIR CONDITIONING 28 LABOR

(Factory Time)	Chilton Time
Drain, Evacuate and Recharge System	
All models	1.8
Pressure Test System	
All models	.6
Add Partial Charge to System	
All models	1.0
Compressor Belt, Renew	
SCOUT II	
All engs (.6)	.8
100-200-500 Series	
Six (.5)	.7
V-8-304-345-392 engs (.6)	.8
400 eng (.3)	.5
Compressor Assembly, Renew	
Includes: Transfer all necessary attaching parts. Evacuate and charge system.	
SCOUT II (2.0)	3.1
100-200-500 Series (1.9)	3.0
Compressor Magnetic Clutch, Renew	
All models (.3)	.6
Electric Clutch Brush Assy., Renew	
Includes: R&R magnetic clutch.	
All models (.4)	.7
Dehydrator Filter, Renew	
Includes: Evacuate and charge system.	
SCOUT II (2.0)	2.8
100-200-500 Series (1.5)	2.3
Condenser Assembly, Renew	
Includes: Evacuate and charge system.	
SCOUT II (2.5)	3.7
100-200-500 Series (2.2)	3.4
Evaporator Core, Renew	
Includes: Evacuate and charge system.	
SCOUT II (3.0)	4.4
100-200-500 Series (2.9)	4.3
Expansion Valve Assembly, Renew	
Includes: Evacuate and charge system.	
SCOUT II (2.6)	3.9
100-200-500 Series (3.0)	4.4
Evaporator Core Freeze Control Switch, Renew	
SCOUT II (1.3)	2.1
Evaporator Relay, Renew	
100-200-500 Series (.3)	.5
Electric Clutch Override Switch, Renew	
100-200-500 Series (1.4)	2.2
Blower Motor, Renew	
SCOUT II (3.0)	4.2
100-200-500 Series (2.9)	4.1
Blower Motor Switch, Renew	
All models (.7)	1.0
Air Conditioner Relay Switch, Renew	
SCOUT II (.6)	.8
Air Conditioning Hoses, Renew	
Includes: Evacuate and charge system.	
Compressor to Evaporator	
All models (2.7)	3.5
Compressor to Condenser	
All models (2.5)	3.5
Hose with Sight Glass, to Evaporator	
All models (2.1)	3.2
Dehydrator Filter to Sight Glass	
All models (1.6)	2.7

LABOR 30 HEAD AND PARKING LAMPS 30 LABOR

(Factory Time)	Chilton Time
Aim Headlamps	
All models (.3)	.4
Headlamp Sealed Beam Bulb, Renew	
All models-each (.2)	.2
Parking Lamp Assy. or Lens, Renew	
All models (.2)	.3
Back-Up, Stop, Tail/Turn Signal Lamp or Lens, Renew	
All models-each (.2)	.3
License Lamp Assy. or Lens, Renew	
All models (.2)	.2
Reflector, Renew	
All models-each	.1

LABOR 31 WINDSHIELD WIPER & SPEEDOMETERS 31 LABOR

(Factory Time) — Chilton Time

Wiper Motor, Renew
SCOUT II
Early production (.7)........ 1.1
Lete Scout II- Terra-Traveler (.5)........ 1.0
100-200-500 Series (.7)........ 1.1

Wiper Switch, Renew
All models........ .6

Windshield Washer Pump, Renew
All models........ .4

Speedometer Head, R&R or Renew
All models........ 1.4

Speedometer Cable and Casing, Renew
wo/Cruise Control
All models (1.0)........ 1.6
w/Cruise Control
Trans to Speed Sensor
All models (.6)........ 1.1
Speed Sensor to Speedo
All models (.7)........ 1.3

Speedometer Cable (Inner), Renew or Lubricate
Does not include fabricate core from bulk stock.
wo/Cruise Control
All models (1.1)........ 1.7
w/Cruise Control
Trans to Speed Sensor
All models (.6)........ 1.0
Speed Sensor to Speedo
All models (.7)........ 1.2

LABOR 32 LIGHT SWITCHES & WIRING 32 LABOR

(Factory Time) — Chilton Time

Headlamp Switch, Renew
All models (.3)........ .5

Headlamp Dimmer Switch, Renew
All models (.2)........ .4

Ignition Switch, Renew
SCOUT II (.9)........ 1.5
100-200-500 Series (.6)........ 1.0

Stop Light Switch, Renew
All models (.3)........ .5

Back-Up Light Switch, Renew
All models
column mount (.2)........ .4
trans mount (.3)........ .5

Turn Signal Switch, Renew
SCOUT II (.9)........ 1.7
100-200-500 Series (1.0)........ 1.5

Turn Signal or Hazard Warning Flasher, Renew
All models (.2)........ .3

Horn, Renew
All models (.3)........ .4

BRAKE SYSTEM OPERATIONS

Resurface Disc Brake Rotor	each	.9
Resurface Brake Drums:		
Pass car and Lt. trucks	each	.5
Heavy Truck up to 16½" dia.	per in.	.2
Over 16½" dia.	per in.	.3
Remove Hub and Press into New Drum	each	.5
Press in New Hub and True-up Drum	each	.6
Reline Brake Shoes (Riveted):		
Pass cars & Light trucks	each	.1
Heavy trucks to 3¼" dia.	each	.2
over 3¼" dia.	each	.3
Cam Grind Brake Shoes	each	.2
Emergency Brake Bands Install:		
Light Trucks	each	.4
Med. & H.D. Trucks	each	.6

FRONT SUSPENSION OPERATIONS

Fit King Bolts and Install Bushings:		
Up to 1" dia.	pair	.6
Over 1" to 1⅛" dia.	pair	.8
Over 1⅛" dia.	pair	1.0
Fit King Bolts and Install Bushings:		
Volkswagen	pair	1.3
Fiat & M.G. (Stepped)	pair	1.3
Mercedes Benz	pair	1.8
Volvo	pair	1.8
Tapered Spindles	pair	2.0

CYLINDER HEAD & VALVE OPERATIONS

Resurface (Grind) Cylinder Head:		
Pass cars & trucks—4 cyl		1.0
6 cyl		1.5
V8—each		1.0
Diesel Engines		(Time Quote)
Grinding over .030 add	per cyl.	.2
Grinding to Specific Size Request, add	per cyl.	.2
Special Tool Cut Volkswagen Head—Per Cyl		.2

Overhaul Cylinder Head:

Includes: Disassemble, clean, reface valves, reseat head, grinding valves to seats, reassemble ready for installation.

Pass car engines. 4 cyl.		1.6
6 cyl		2.3
V8	each	1.6
F-heads	each	1.2
Volkswagen	each	1.2
H.D. truck engines, 6 cyl		2.8
V6	each	1.6
V8	each	1.8
All Diesel engines		(Time Quote)

NOTE: EXTRA CHARGE TO BE ADDED FOR RESEATING STELLITE VALVE SEATS OR REFACING STELLITE VALVES.

Cylinder Head Clean and Degrease		
Four cyl	each	.4
Six cyl	each	.5
V6	pair	.6
V8	pair	.8
Heli Coil, Install	one	1.0
Additional	each	.6

VALVE RESEATING

(Includes: Cleaning Valve Ports.)

Grind 1 or 2 Iron or Steel Seats:		
Up to 2$\frac{7}{16}$" ID.	each	.4
Grind 3 or More Seats, Add	each	.1
Grind 1 or 2 Iron or Steel Seats:		
Over 2$\frac{7}{16}$" ID.	each	.5
Grind 3 or More Seats, Add	each	.2
Grind One Stellite Seat	each	.6
Grind 2 or More Stellite Seats, Add	each	.3
Grind All Import Car Seats	each	.7
Note: Service charge to shop add		.7

VALVE GUIDE REAMING

Valve Guides, Ream for Oversize Stems		
Pass cars and Lt. trucks	One	.1
	Eight	.6
	Twelve	.8
	Sixteen	.9
Med. and H.D. Trucks	each	.2
Valve Guides, Knurl		
Each		.3
Valve Guides, Bronze Wall		
Each		.6

VALVE SEAT RINGS

Install Steel or Cast Iron Valve Seat Rings		
1 seat up to 2" ID	each	.8
Additional seats, add	each	.5
Complete sets	each	.4
Seats over 2" ID		(Special Quote)

NOTE: If Stellite seat rings are installed add charges for grinding.

VALVE ROCKER ARMS AND STUDS

Reface Valve Rocker Arms	each	.1
Remove and Replace One Stud (Drill)		.8
4 or more studs (drill) addtnl, add	each	.4
Remove and Replace One Stud (Pull)		.4
4 or more studs (pull) addtnl, add	each	.2

VALVE REFACING

(Includes: Cleaning Valves.)

Reface Valves up to ⅜" stem	each	.1
Over ⅜" stem	each	.2
Reface Stellite Valves	each	.3
Reface Valves over ½" Stem		(Special Quote)
Reface Valve Tappets	each	.1

ENGINE BLOCK OPERATIONS

RESURFACE ENGINE BLOCK

4 cyl	2.0
6 cyl	3.0
V8-each side	2.0

REBORING CYLINDERS:

Note: Boring blocks to customers specifications, or blocks with hard sleeves, add additional charges:

Passenger Car & Lt. Truck	one	2.0
Additional cylinders	each	1.0
Med. and H.D. Trucks up to 4½" Cyl	one	2.5
Additional cylinders	each	1.5
Over 5" Cylinder		(Special Quote)

HONING CYLINDERS

Hone or Deglaze Cylinders	per cyl	.2
Remove Cylinder Ridge	per cyl	.2

CYLINDER SLEEVES, INSTALL

(Includes Finishing to any oversize required.)

Pass Cars & Lt. Trucks	one	2.8
2 or 3 sleeves	per cyl	2.5
4 or more sleeves	per cyl	2.1
Angle Block	one	3.8
2 or 3 sleeves	per cyl	3.1
4 or more sleeves	per cyl	2.3
Trucks to 5″ Dia	One	3.2
2 or 3 sleeves	per cyl	3.1
4 or more sleeves	per cyl	2.3
Sleeves over 5″ Dia		(Special Quote)

Note: Engine in chassis and extra charge.

ENGINE BLOCK CLEAN & DEGREASE OR STEAM CLEAN

Small blocks	1.9
Large blocks	2.4

PISTONS, RINGS, PINS & BEARINGS OPERATIONS

Fit Pins

Includes: Disassembly, hone, fitting, assembly and align rod.

	per rod	.3
Align Rods	each	.1
Clean Piston & Install Rings	each	.2
Grind Piston:		
Pass cars & lt. trucks	each	.4
Med. & H.D. trucks	each	.5
Regroove Piston Top Ring Land		
Pass cars & lt. trucks	each	.3
Med. & H.D. trucks	each	.4
Expand or Knurl Pistons	each	.3

CRANKSHAFT OPERATIONS

(Shaft Removed)

Crankshaft Grind (Connecting Rod Throws)

1 con. rod throw		.8
2 con. rod throws	both	1.2
3. con. rod throws	All	1.6
4 con. rod throws	All	1.8
6 con. rod throws	All	2.0
8 con. rod throws	All	2.8

Crankshaft Grind (Main Bearing Throws)

2 main brg. throws	both	1.2
3 main brg. throws	All	1.8
4 main brg. throws	All	2.0
5 main brg. throws	All	2.2
6 main brg. throws	All	2.4
7 main brg. throws	All	2.6

Crankshaft Grind (Connecting Rod & Main Bearing Throws)

4 con. rod and 2 main brg. throws	2.5
4 con. rod and 3 main brg. throws	3.2
4 con. rod and 4 main brg. throws	3.4
4 con. rod and 5 main brg. throws	3.6
6 con. rod and 3 main brg. throws	3.2
6 con. rod and 4 main brg. throws	3.4
6 con. rod and 7 main brg. throws	4.4
8 con. rod and 4 main brg. throws	4.2
8 con. rod and 5 main brg. throws	4.9

(in Chassis)

Rod Journals Grind

Pass car & lt. truck	one	4.0
Additional journals	each	2.0
Med. & H.D. trucks	one	5.0
Additional journals	each	2.5
Throws over 2½″ dia.		(Special Quote)

Crankshaft Micro Finish

Pass car & lt. truck	1.2
Med. & H.D. trucks	2.0

CAMSHAFT AND GEAR OPERATIONS

Camshaft Gear, Press off and Renew	.5
Camshaft Bearings, Renew and Align Bore	
1 or 2 Bearings	2.0
3 Bearings	2.3
4 Bearings	2.7
5 Bearings	3.1
6 Bearings	3.8
7 Bearings	4.6

CLUTCH AND FLYWHEEL OPERATIONS

Adjust Clutch Pressure Plate Levers	(Finger Type)	.6
	(Diaphragm Type)	.7
Clutch Disc Facings, Install		.5
Recondition Clutch Pressure Plate	(Finger Type)	1.2
	(Diaphragm Type)	1.5
Resurface clutch pressure plate, add		.6
Flywheel, Reface (Grind)		
Flat up to 13″		1.2
14″		1.4
15″ to 17″		2.3
Concave-stepped up to 11″		1.4
12″ & 13″		2.0
14″		2.2
15″ to 17″		2.4
Flywheel Ring Gear, Renew		
Shrink		.7
Weld		1.1
Machine		2.0

REAR AXLE OPERATIONS

Rear Axle Bearings, Press off and Renew		
All exec below	each	.4
Chrysler products	each	.5
Pinion Shaft Rear Bearing Press off And Renew	each	.4

MAGNAFLUX OPERATIONS

Cylinder Heads		
Flat head - 4 cyl	each	1.5
6 cyl.	each	1.7
V8	each	1.5
O.H.V. - 4 cyl	each	1.8
6 cyl	each	2.0
V8	each	1.8
Engine Blocks		
4 cyl		2.0
6 cyl		2.5
V8		3.0
Camshaft caps add		1.0
Crankshafts		
4 cyl		1.5
6 cyl		1.7
V8		2.0

Chilton's LABOR CALCULATOR

For dollar rates ending with 50 cents or 1.00 add to the appropriate rate column.

TIME	.50 per hr.	$1.00 per hr.	$10.00 per hr.	$12.00 per hr.	$14.00 per hr.	$16.00 per hr.	$18.00 per hr.	$20.00 per hr.	$22.00 per hr.	$24.00 per hr.	$26.00 per hr.	$28.00 per hr.	$30.00 per hr.	$32.00 per hr.	$34.00 per hr.	$36.00 per hr.	$38.00 per hr.	$40.00 per hr.	$42.00 per hr.	$44.00 per hr.	$46.00 per hr.	$48.00 per hr.	$50.00 per hr.	$55.00 per hr.
.1	.05	.10	$1.00	$1.20	$1.40	$1.60	$1.80	$2.00	$2.20	$2.40	$2.60	$2.80	$3.00	$3.20	$3.40	$3.60	$3.80	$4.00	$4.20	$4.40	$4.60	$4.80	$5.00	$5.50
.2	.10	.20	2.00	2.40	2.80	3.20	3.60	4.00	4.40	4.80	5.20	5.60	6.00	6.40	6.80	7.20	7.60	8.00	8.40	8.80	9.20	9.60	10.00	11.00
.3	.15	.30	3.00	3.60	4.20	4.80	5.40	6.00	6.60	7.20	7.80	8.40	9.00	9.60	10.20	10.80	11.40	12.00	12.60	13.20	13.80	14.40	15.00	16.50
.4	.20	.40	4.00	4.80	5.60	6.40	7.20	8.00	8.80	9.60	10.40	11.20	12.00	12.80	13.60	14.40	15.20	16.00	16.80	17.60	18.40	19.20	20.00	22.00
.5	.25	.50	5.00	6.00	7.00	8.00	9.00	10.00	11.00	12.00	13.00	14.00	15.00	16.00	17.00	18.00	19.00	20.00	21.00	22.00	23.00	24.00	25.00	27.50
.6	.30	.60	6.00	7.20	8.40	9.60	10.80	12.00	13.20	14.40	15.60	16.80	18.00	19.20	20.40	21.60	22.80	24.00	25.20	26.40	27.60	28.80	30.00	33.00
.7	.35	.70	7.00	8.40	9.80	11.20	12.60	14.00	15.40	16.80	18.20	19.60	21.00	22.40	23.80	25.20	26.60	28.00	29.40	30.80	32.20	33.60	35.00	38.50
.8	.40	.80	8.00	9.60	11.20	12.80	14.40	16.00	17.60	19.20	20.80	22.40	24.00	25.60	27.20	28.80	30.40	32.00	33.60	35.20	36.80	38.40	40.00	44.00
.9	.45	.90	9.00	10.80	12.60	14.40	16.20	18.00	19.80	21.60	23.40	25.20	27.00	28.80	30.60	32.40	34.20	36.00	37.80	39.60	41.40	43.20	45.00	49.50
1.0	.50	1.00	10.00	12.00	14.00	16.00	18.00	20.00	22.00	24.00	26.00	28.00	30.00	32.00	34.00	36.00	38.00	40.00	42.00	44.00	46.00	48.00	50.00	55.00
1.1	.55	1.10	11.00	13.20	15.40	17.60	19.80	22.00	24.20	26.40	28.60	30.80	33.00	35.20	37.40	39.60	41.80	44.00	46.20	48.40	50.60	52.80	55.00	60.50
1.2	.60	1.20	12.00	14.40	16.80	19.20	21.60	24.00	26.40	28.80	31.20	33.60	36.00	38.40	40.80	43.20	45.60	48.00	50.40	52.80	55.20	57.60	60.00	66.00
1.3	.65	1.30	13.00	15.60	18.20	20.80	23.40	26.00	28.60	31.20	33.80	36.40	39.00	41.60	44.20	46.80	49.40	52.00	54.60	57.20	59.80	62.40	65.00	71.50
1.4	.70	1.40	14.00	16.80	19.60	22.40	25.20	28.00	30.80	33.60	36.40	39.20	42.00	44.80	47.60	50.40	53.20	56.00	58.80	61.60	64.40	67.20	70.00	77.00
1.5	.75	1.50	15.00	18.00	21.00	24.00	27.00	30.00	33.00	36.00	39.00	42.00	45.00	48.00	51.00	54.00	57.00	60.00	63.00	66.00	69.00	72.00	75.00	82.50
1.6	.80	1.60	16.00	19.20	22.40	25.60	28.80	32.00	35.20	38.40	41.60	44.80	48.00	51.20	54.40	57.60	60.80	64.00	67.20	70.40	73.60	76.80	80.00	88.00
1.7	.85	1.70	17.00	20.40	23.80	27.20	30.60	34.00	37.40	40.80	44.20	47.60	51.00	54.40	57.80	61.20	64.60	68.00	71.40	74.80	78.20	81.60	85.00	93.50
1.8	.90	1.80	18.00	21.60	25.20	28.80	32.40	36.00	39.60	43.20	46.80	50.40	54.00	57.60	61.20	64.80	68.40	72.00	75.60	79.20	82.80	86.40	90.00	99.00
1.9	.95	1.90	19.00	22.80	26.60	30.40	34.20	38.00	41.80	45.60	49.40	53.20	57.00	60.80	64.60	68.40	72.20	76.00	79.80	83.60	87.40	91.20	95.00	104.50
2.0	1.00	2.00	20.00	24.00	28.00	32.00	36.00	40.00	44.00	48.00	52.00	56.00	60.00	64.00	68.00	72.00	76.00	80.00	84.00	88.00	92.00	96.00	100.00	110.00
2.1	1.05	2.10	21.00	25.20	29.40	33.60	37.80	42.00	46.20	50.40	54.60	58.80	63.00	67.20	71.40	75.60	79.80	84.00	88.20	92.40	96.60	100.80	105.00	115.50
2.2	1.10	2.20	22.00	26.40	30.80	35.20	39.60	44.00	48.40	52.80	57.20	61.60	66.00	70.40	74.80	79.20	83.60	88.00	92.40	96.80	101.20	105.60	110.00	121.00
2.3	1.15	2.30	23.00	27.60	32.20	36.80	41.40	46.00	50.60	55.20	59.80	64.40	69.00	73.60	78.20	82.80	87.40	92.00	96.60	101.20	105.80	110.40	115.00	126.50
2.4	1.20	2.40	24.00	28.80	33.60	38.40	43.20	48.00	52.80	57.60	62.40	67.20	72.00	76.80	81.60	86.40	91.20	96.00	100.80	105.60	110.40	115.20	120.00	132.00
2.5	1.25	2.50	25.00	30.00	35.00	40.00	45.00	50.00	55.00	60.00	65.00	70.00	75.00	80.00	85.00	90.00	95.00	100.00	105.00	110.00	115.00	120.00	125.00	137.50
2.6	1.30	2.60	26.00	31.20	36.40	41.60	46.80	52.00	57.20	62.40	67.60	72.80	78.00	83.20	88.40	93.60	98.80	104.00	109.20	114.40	119.60	124.80	130.00	143.00
2.7	1.35	2.70	27.00	32.40	37.80	43.20	48.60	54.00	59.40	64.80	70.20	75.60	81.00	86.40	91.80	97.20	102.60	108.00	113.40	118.80	124.20	129.60	135.00	148.50
2.8	1.40	2.80	28.00	33.60	39.20	44.80	50.40	56.00	61.60	67.20	72.80	78.40	84.00	89.60	95.20	100.80	106.40	112.00	117.60	123.20	128.80	134.40	140.00	154.00
2.9	1.45	2.90	29.00	34.80	40.60	46.40	52.20	58.00	63.80	69.60	75.40	81.20	87.00	92.80	98.60	104.40	110.20	116.00	121.80	127.60	133.40	139.20	145.00	159.50
3.0	1.50	3.00	30.00	36.00	42.00	48.00	54.00	60.00	66.00	72.00	78.00	84.00	90.00	96.00	102.00	108.00	114.00	120.00	126.00	132.00	138.00	144.00	150.00	165.00
3.1	1.55	3.10	31.00	37.20	43.40	49.60	55.80	62.00	68.20	74.40	80.60	86.80	93.00	99.20	105.40	111.60	117.80	124.00	130.20	136.40	142.60	148.80	155.00	170.50
3.2	1.60	3.20	32.00	38.40	44.80	51.20	57.60	64.00	70.40	76.80	83.20	89.60	96.00	102.40	108.80	115.20	121.60	128.00	134.40	140.80	147.20	153.60	160.00	176.00
3.3	1.65	3.30	33.00	39.60	46.20	52.80	59.40	66.00	72.60	79.20	85.80	92.40	99.00	105.60	112.20	118.80	125.40	132.00	138.60	145.20	151.80	158.40	165.00	181.50
3.4	1.70	3.40	34.00	40.80	47.60	54.40	61.20	68.00	74.80	81.60	88.40	95.20	102.00	108.80	115.60	122.40	129.20	136.00	142.80	149.60	156.40	163.20	170.00	187.00
3.5	1.75	3.50	35.00	42.00	49.00	56.00	63.00	70.00	77.00	84.00	91.00	98.00	105.00	112.00	119.00	126.00	133.00	140.00	147.00	154.00	161.00	168.00	175.00	192.50
3.6	1.80	3.60	36.00	43.20	50.40	57.60	64.80	72.00	79.20	86.40	93.60	100.80	108.00	115.20	122.40	129.60	136.80	144.00	151.20	158.40	165.60	172.80	180.00	198.00
3.7	1.85	3.70	37.00	44.40	51.80	59.20	66.60	74.00	81.40	88.80	96.20	103.60	111.00	118.40	125.80	133.20	140.60	148.00	155.40	162.80	170.20	177.60	185.00	203.50
3.8	1.90	3.80	38.00	45.60	53.20	60.80	68.40	76.00	83.60	91.20	98.80	106.40	114.00	121.60	129.20	136.80	144.40	152.00	159.60	167.20	174.80	182.40	190.00	209.00
3.9	1.95	3.90	39.00	46.80	54.60	62.40	70.20	78.00	85.80	93.60	101.40	109.20	117.00	124.80	132.60	140.40	148.20	156.00	163.80	171.60	179.40	187.20	195.00	214.50
4.0	2.00	4.00	40.00	48.00	56.00	64.00	72.00	80.00	88.00	96.00	104.00	112.00	120.00	128.00	136.00	144.00	152.00	160.00	168.00	176.00	184.00	192.00	200.00	220.00
4.1	2.05	4.10	41.00	49.20	57.40	65.60	73.80	82.00	90.20	98.40	106.60	114.80	123.00	131.20	139.40	147.60	155.80	164.00	172.20	180.40	188.60	196.80	205.00	225.50
4.2	2.10	4.20	42.00	50.40	58.80	67.20	75.60	84.00	92.40	100.80	109.20	117.60	126.00	134.40	142.80	151.20	159.60	168.00	176.40	184.80	193.20	201.60	210.00	231.00
4.3	2.15	4.30	43.00	51.60	60.20	68.80	77.40	86.00	94.60	103.20	111.80	120.40	129.00	137.60	146.20	154.80	163.40	172.00	180.60	189.20	197.80	206.40	215.00	236.50
4.4	2.20	4.40	44.00	52.80	61.60	70.40	79.20	88.00	96.80	105.60	114.40	123.20	132.00	140.80	149.60	158.40	167.20	176.00	184.80	193.60	202.40	211.20	220.00	242.00
4.5	2.25	4.50	45.00	54.00	63.00	72.00	81.00	90.00	99.00	108.00	117.00	126.00	135.00	144.00	153.00	162.00	171.00	180.00	189.00	198.00	207.00	216.00	225.00	247.50
4.6	2.30	4.60	46.00	55.20	64.40	73.60	82.80	92.00	101.20	110.40	119.60	128.80	138.00	147.20	156.40	165.60	174.80	184.00	193.20	202.40	211.60	220.80	230.00	253.00
4.7	2.35	4.70	47.00	56.40	65.80	75.20	84.60	94.00	103.40	112.80	122.20	131.60	141.00	150.40	159.80	169.20	178.60	188.00	197.40	206.80	216.20	225.60	235.00	258.50
4.8	2.40	4.80	48.00	57.60	67.20	76.80	86.40	96.00	105.60	115.20	124.80	134.40	144.00	153.60	163.20	172.80	182.40	192.00	201.60	211.20	220.80	230.40	240.00	264.00
4.9	2.45	4.90	49.00	58.80	68.60	78.40	88.20	98.00	107.80	117.60	127.40	137.20	147.00	156.80	166.60	176.40	186.20	196.00	205.80	215.60	225.40	235.20	245.00	269.50
5.0	2.50	5.00	50.00	60.00	70.00	80.00	90.00	100.00	110.00	120.00	130.00	140.00	150.00	160.00	170.00	180.00	190.00	200.00	210.00	220.00	230.00	240.00	250.00	275.00
5.1	2.55	5.10	51.00	61.20	71.40	81.60	91.80	102.00	112.20	122.40	132.60	142.80	153.00	163.20	173.40	183.60	193.80	204.00	214.20	224.40	234.60	244.80	255.00	280.50
5.2	2.60	5.20	52.00	62.40	72.80	83.20	93.60	104.00	114.40	124.80	135.20	145.60	156.00	166.40	176.80	187.20	197.60	208.00	218.40	228.80	239.20	249.60	260.00	286.00
5.3	2.65	5.30	53.00	63.60	74.20	84.80	95.40	106.00	116.60	127.20	137.80	148.40	159.00	169.60	180.20	190.80	201.40	212.00	222.60	233.20	243.80	254.40	265.00	291.50
5.4	2.70	5.40	54.00	64.80	75.60	86.40	97.20	108.00	118.80	129.60	140.40	151.20	162.00	172.80	183.60	194.40	205.20	216.00	226.80	237.60	248.40	259.20	270.00	297.00
5.5	2.75	5.50	55.00	66.00	77.00	88.00	99.00	110.00	121.00	132.00	143.00	154.00	165.00	176.00	187.00	198.00	209.00	220.00	231.00	242.00	253.00	264.00	275.00	302.50

Chilton's LABOR CALCULATOR

For dollar rates ending with 50 cents or 1.00 add to the appropriate rate column.

TIME	.50 per hr.	$1.00 per hr.	$10.00 per hr.	$12.00 per hr.	$14.00 per hr.	$16.00 per hr.	$18.00 per hr.	$20.00 per hr.	$22.00 per hr.	$24.00 per hr.	$26.00 per hr.	$28.00 per hr.	$30.00 per hr.	$32.00 per hr.	$34.00 per hr.	$36.00 per hr.	$38.00 per hr.	$40.00 per hr.	$42.00 per hr.	$44.00 per hr.	$46.00 per hr.	$48.00 per hr.	$50.00 per hr.	$55.00 per hr.
5.6	2.80	5.60	56.00	67.20	78.40	89.60	100.80	112.00	123.20	134.40	145.60	156.80	168.00	179.20	190.40	201.60	212.80	224.00	235.20	246.40	257.60	268.80	280.00	308.00
5.7	2.85	5.70	57.00	68.40	79.80	91.20	102.60	114.00	125.40	136.80	148.20	159.60	171.00	182.40	193.80	205.20	216.60	228.00	239.40	250.80	262.20	273.60	285.00	313.50
5.8	2.90	5.80	58.00	69.60	81.20	92.80	104.40	116.00	127.60	139.20	150.80	162.40	174.00	185.60	197.20	208.80	220.40	232.00	243.60	255.20	266.80	278.40	290.00	319.00
5.9	2.95	5.90	59.00	70.80	82.60	94.40	106.20	118.00	129.80	141.60	153.40	165.20	177.00	188.80	200.60	212.40	244.20	236.00	247.80	259.60	271.40	283.20	295.00	324.50
6.0	3.00	6.00	60.00	72.00	84.00	96.00	108.00	120.00	132.00	144.00	156.00	168.00	180.00	192.00	204.00	216.00	228.00	240.00	252.00	264.00	276.00	288.00	300.00	330.00
6.1	3.05	6.10	61.00	73.20	85.40	97.60	109.80	122.00	134.20	146.40	158.60	170.80	183.00	195.20	207.40	219.60	231.80	244.00	256.20	268.40	280.60	292.80	305.00	335.50
6.2	3.10	6.20	62.00	74.40	86.80	99.20	111.60	124.00	136.40	148.80	161.20	173.60	186.00	198.40	210.80	223.20	235.60	248.00	260.40	272.80	285.20	297.60	310.00	341.00
6.3	3.15	6.30	63.00	75.60	88.20	100.80	113.40	126.00	138.60	151.20	163.80	176.40	189.00	201.60	214.20	226.80	239.40	252.00	264.60	277.20	289.80	302.40	315.00	346.50
6.4	3.20	6.40	64.00	76.80	89.60	102.40	115.20	128 00	140.80	153.60	166.40	179.20	192.00	204.80	217.60	230.40	243.20	256.00	268.80	281.60	294.40	307.20	320.00	352.00
6.5	3.25	6.50	65.00	78.00	91.00	104.00	117.00	130.00	143.00	156.00	169.00	182.00	195.00	208.00	221.00	234.00	247.00	260.00	273.00	286.00	299.00	312.00	325.00	357.50
6.6	3.30	6.60	66.00	79.20	92.40	105.60	118.80	132.00	145.20	158.40	171.60	184.80	198.00	211.20	224.40	237.60	250.80	264.00	277.20	290.40	303.60	316.80	330.00	363.00
6.7	3.35	6.70	67.00	80.40	93.80	107.20	120.60	134.00	147.40	160.80	174.20	187.60	201.00	214.40	227.80	241.20	254.60	268.00	281.40	294.80	308.20	321.60	335.00	368.50
6.8	3.40	6.80	68.00	81.60	95.20	108.80	122.40	136.00	149.60	163.20	176.80	190.40	204.00	217.60	231.20	244.80	258.40	272.00	285.60	299.20	312.80	326.40	340.00	374.00
6.9	3.45	6.90	69.00	82.80	96.60	110.40	124.20	138.00	151.80	165.60	179.40	193.20	207.00	220.80	234.60	248.40	262.20	276.00	289.80	303.60	317.40	331.20	345.00	379.50
7.0	3.50	7.00	70.00	84.00	98.00	112.00	126.00	140.00	154.00	168.00	182.00	196.00	210.00	224.00	238.00	252.00	266.00	280.00	294.00	308.00	322.00	336.00	350.00	385.00
7.1	3.55	7.10	71.00	85.20	99.40	113.60	127.80	142.00	156.20	170.40	184.60	198.80	213.00	227.20	241.40	255.60	269.80	284.00	298.20	312.40	326.60	340.80	355.00	390.50
7.2	3.60	7.20	72.00	86.40	100.80	115.20	129.60	144.00	158.40	172.80	187.20	201.60	216.00	230.40	244.80	259.20	273.60	288.00	302.40	316.80	331.20	345.60	360.00	396.00
7.3	3.65	7.30	73.00	87.60	102.20	116.80	131.40	146.00	160.60	175.20	189.80	204.40	219.00	233.60	248.20	262.80	277.40	292.00	306.60	321.20	335.80	350.40	365.00	401.50
7.4	3.70	7.40	74.00	88.80	103.60	118.40	133.20	148.00	162.80	177.60	192.40	207.20	222.00	236.80	251.60	266.40	281.20	296.00	310.80	325.60	340.40	355.20	370.00	407.00
7.5	3.75	7.50	75.00	90.00	105.00	120.00	135.00	150.00	165.00	180.00	195.00	210.00	225.00	240.00	255.00	270.00	285.00	300.00	315.00	330.00	345.00	360.00	375.00	412.50
7.6	3.80	7.60	76.00	91.20	106.40	121.60	136.80	152.00	167.20	182.40	197.60	212.80	228.00	243.20	258.40	273.60	288.80	304.00	319.20	334.40	349.60	364.80	380.00	418.00
7.7	3.85	7.70	77.00	92.40	107.80	123.20	138.60	154.00	169.40	184.80	200.20	215.60	231.00	246.40	261.80	277.20	292.60	308.00	323.40	338.80	354.20	369.60	385.00	423.50
7.8	3.90	7.80	78.00	93.60	109.20	124.80	140.40	156.00	171.60	187.20	202.80	218.40	234.00	249.60	265.20	280.80	296.40	312.00	327.60	343.20	358.80	374.40	390.00	429.00
7.9	3.95	7.90	79.00	94.80	110.60	126.40	142.20	158.00	173.80	189.60	205.40	221.20	237.00	252.80	268.60	284.40	300.20	316.00	331.80	347.60	363.40	379.20	395.00	434.50
8.0	4.00	8.00	80.00	96.00	112.00	128.00	144.00	160.00	176.00	192.00	208.00	224.00	240.00	256.00	272.00	288.00	304.00	320.00	336.00	352.00	368.00	384.00	400.00	440.00
8.1	4.05	8.10	81.00	97.20	113.40	129.60	145.80	162.00	178.20	194.40	210.60	226.80	243.00	259.20	275.40	291.60	307.80	324.00	340.20	356.40	372.60	388.80	405.00	445.50
8.2	4.10	8.20	82.00	98.40	114.80	131.20	147.60	164.00	180.40	196.80	213.20	229.60	246.00	262.40	278.80	295.20	311.60	328.00	344.40	360.80	377.20	393.60	410.00	451.00
8.3	4.15	8.30	83.00	99.60	116.20	132.80	149.40	166.00	182.60	199.20	215.80	232.40	249.00	265.60	282.20	298.80	315.80	332.00	348.60	365.20	381.80	398.40	415.00	456.50
8.4	4.20	8.40	84.00	100.80	117.60	134.40	151.20	168.00	184.80	201.60	218.40	235.20	252.00	268.80	285.60	302.40	319.20	336.00	352.80	369.60	386.40	403.20	420.00	462.00
8.5	4.25	8.50	85.00	102.00	119.00	136.00	153.00	170.00	187.00	204.00	221.00	238.00	255.00	272.00	289.00	306.00	323.00	340.00	357.00	374.00	391.00	408.00	425.00	467.50
8.6	4.30	8.60	86.00	103.20	120.40	137.60	154.80	172.00	189.20	206.40	223.60	240.80	258.00	275.20	292.40	309.60	326.80	344.00	361.20	378.40	395.60	412.80	430.00	473.00
8.7	4.35	8.70	87.00	104.40	121.80	139.20	156.60	174.00	191.40	208.80	226.20	243.60	261.00	278.40	295.80	313.20	330.60	348.00	365.40	382.80	400.20	417.60	435.00	478.50
8.8	4.40	8.80	88.00	105.60	123.20	140.80	158.40	176.00	193.60	211.20	228.80	246.40	264.00	281.60	299.20	316.80	334.40	352.00	369.60	387.20	404.80	422.40	440.00	484.00
8.9	4.45	8.90	89.00	106.80	124.60	142.40	160.20	178.00	195.80	213.60	231.40	249.20	267.00	284.80	302.60	320.40	338.20	356.00	373.80	391.60	409.40	427.20	445.00	489.50
9.0	4.50	9.00	90.00	108.00	126.00	144.00	162.00	180.00	198.00	216.00	234.00	252.00	270.00	288.00	306.00	324.00	342.00	360.00	378.00	396.00	414.00	432.00	450.00	495.00
9.1	4.55	9.10	91.00	109.20	127.40	145.60	163.80	182.00	200.20	218.40	236.60	254.80	273.00	291.20	309.40	327.60	345.80	364.00	382.20	400.40	418.60	436.80	455.00	500.50
9.2	4.60	9.20	92.00	110.40	128.80	147.20	165.60	184.00	202.40	220.80	239.20	257.60	276.00	294.40	312.80	331.20	349.60	368.00	386.40	404.80	423.20	441.60	460.00	506.00
9.3	4.65	9.30	93.00	111.60	130.20	148.80	167.40	186.00	204.60	223.20	241.80	260.40	279.00	297.60	316.20	334.80	353.40	372.00	390.60	409.20	427.80	446.40	465.00	511.50
9.4	4.70	9.40	94.00	112.80	131.60	150.40	169.20	188.00	206.80	225.60	244.40	263.20	282.00	300.80	319.60	338.40	357.20	376.00	394.80	413.60	432.40	451.20	470.00	517.00
9.5	4.75	9.50	95.00	114.00	133.00	152.00	171.00	190.00	209.00	228.00	247.00	266.00	285.00	304.00	323.00	342.00	361.00	380.00	399.00	418.00	437.00	456.00	475.00	522.50
9.6	4.80	9.60	96.00	115.20	134.40	153.60	172.80	192.00	211.20	230.40	249.60	268.80	288.00	307.20	326.40	345.60	364.80	384.00	403.20	422.40	441.60	460.80	480.00	528.00
9.7	4.85	9.70	97.00	116.40	135.80	155.20	174.60	194.00	213.40	232.80	252.20	271.60	291.00	310.40	329.80	349.20	368.60	388.00	407.40	426.80	446.20	465.60	485.00	533.50
9.8	4.90	9.80	98.00	117.60	137.20	156.80	176.40	196.00	215.60	235.20	254.80	274.40	294.00	313.60	333.20	352.80	372.40	392.00	411.60	431.20	450.80	470.40	490.00	539.00
9.9	4.95	9.90	99.00	118.80	138.60	158.40	178.20	198.00	217.80	237.60	257.40	277.20	297.00	316.80	336.60	356.40	376.20	396.00	415.80	435.60	455.40	475.20	495.00	544.50
10.0	5.00	10.00	100.00	120.00	140.00	160.00	180.00	200.00	220.00	240.00	260.00	280.00	300.00	320.00	340.00	360.00	380.00	400.00	420.00	440.00	460.00	480.00	500.00	550.00
11.0	5.50	11.00	110.00	132.00	154.00	176.00	198.00	220.00	242.00	264.00	286.00	308.00	330.00	352.00	374.00	396.00	418.00	440.00	462.00	484.00	506.00	528.00	550.00	605.00
12.0	6.00	12.00	120.00	144.00	168.00	192.00	216.00	240.00	264.00	288.00	312.00	336.00	360.00	384.00	408.00	432.00	456.00	480.00	504.00	528.00	552.00	576.00	600.00	660.00
13.0	6.50	13.00	130.00	156.00	182.00	208.00	234.00	260.00	286.00	312.00	338.00	364.00	390.00	416.00	442.00	468.00	494.00	520.00	546.00	572.00	598.00	624.00	650.00	715.00
14.0	7.00	14.00	140.00	168.00	196.00	224.00	252.00	280.00	308.00	336.00	364.00	392.00	420.00	448.00	476.00	504.00	532.00	560.00	588.00	616.00	644.00	672.00	700.00	770.00
15.0	7.50	15.00	150.00	180.00	210.00	240.00	270.00	300.00	330.00	360.00	390.00	420.00	450.00	480.00	510.00	540.00	570.00	600.00	630.00	660.00	690.00	720.00	750.00	825.00
16.0	8.00	16.00	160.00	192.00	224.00	256.00	288.00	320.00	352.00	384.00	416.00	448.00	480.00	512.00	544.00	576.00	608.00	640.00	672.00	704.00	736.00	768.00	800.00	880.00
17.0	8.50	17.00	170.00	204.00	238.00	272.00	306.00	340.00	374.00	408.00	442.00	476.00	510.00	544.00	578.00	612.00	646.00	680.00	714.00	748.00	782.00	816.00	850.00	935.00
18.0	9.00	18.00	180.00	216.00	252.00	288.00	324.00	360.00	396.00	432.00	468.00	504.00	540.00	576.00	612.00	648.00	684.00	720.00	756.00	792.00	828.00	864.00	900.00	990.00
19.0	9.50	19.00	190.00	228.00	266.00	304.00	342.00	380.00	418.00	456.00	494.00	532.00	570.00	608.00	646.00	684.00	722.00	760.00	798.00	836.00	874.00	912.00	950.00	1045.00
20.0	10.00	20.00	200.00	240.00	280.00	320.00	360.00	400.00	440.00	480.00	520.00	560.00	600.00	640.00	680.00	720.00	760.00	800.00	840.00	880.00	920.00	960.00	1000.00	1100.00

TOWING AND ROAD SERVICE

THE FOLLOWING CHARGES APPLY TO SERVICES PERFORMED ON OR NEAR PAVED HIGHWAYS UNDER CLEAR WEATHER CONDITIONS.

SERVICE CALLS

Charges Include One of the Following:

(1) Up to 15 minutes diagnosis or correction of fuel, ignition, or power train failures.

(2) Changing one wheel.

(3) 30 second battery "hot shot."

(4) Moving disabled vehicle to road shoulder.

TOWING

Charges Include:

(1) Secure steering wheel; rear lift.

(2) Attach hooks; front end lift.

DOLLY TOW

Charges Include:

(1) Lift front and rear of vehicle alternately.

(2) Use of auxiliary dollies to support vehicle to be moved.

CHART MILEAGE

Charges are based on one-way mileage coverage of the service vehicle.

ITEMS THAT JUSTIFY ADDITIONAL CHARGES

(1) Slippery road conditions.

(2) Changing more than one wheel.

(3) Disconnecting drive shaft.

(4) Use of cutting torch.

(5) Uprighting overturned vehicles.

(6) Moving vehicle to towing position.

(7) Opening locked vehicles (without keys).

(8) Securing or removing loose parts.

(9) Abnormal road conditions that consume extra time; such as detours and truck restrictions.

(10) Replacement parts removal and installation.

NOTE—Service Call charges are not contingent upon placing the disabled vehicle in operation.

SAFETY PRECAUTIONS

(1) Double park only when absolutely necessary.

(2) Use warning lights and approved flares when the service vehicle obstructs highway traffic.

(3) Check local highway regulations to determine if tow bar is permissible.

TOWING AND ROAD SERVICE CHARGES

Passenger car and light trucks up to 10,000 gross vehicle weight (GVW), single set rear wheels.

DISTANCE Up to	TOWING		Dolly Tow		TRUCKS 10,000 to 20,000 G.V.W. Dual Set Rear Wheels	
	Day	Night	Day	Night	Day	Night
1 mile	25.00	28.00	40.00	43.00	55.00	60.00
2 miles	27.00	30.00	42.00	45.00	58.00	63.00
3 miles	29.00	32.00	44.00	47.00	61.00	66.00
4 miles	31.00	34.00	46.00	49.00	64.00	69.00
5 miles	33.00	36.00	48.00	51.00	67.00	72.00
6 miles	35.00	38.00	50.00	53.00	70.00	75.00
7 miles	37.00	40.00	52.00	55.00	73.00	78.00
8 miles	39.00	42.00	54.00	57.00	76.00	81.00
9 miles	41.00	44.00	56.00	59.00	79.00	84.00
10 miles	43.00	46.00	58.00	61.00	82.00	87.00
11 miles	45.00	48.00	60.00	63.00	85.00	90.00
12 miles	47.00	50.00	62.00	65.00	88.00	93.00
13 miles	49.00	52.00	64.00	67.00	91.00	96.00
14 miles	51.00	54.00	66.00	69.00	94.00	99.00
15 miles	53.00	56.00	68.00	71.00	96.00	102.00

THIS CHART LISTS AVERAGE CHARGES WHICH MAY VARY ACCORDING TO INDIVIDUAL SITUATIONS

DAY RATES: 8 A.M. TO 6 P.M.

NIGHT RATES: 5 P.M. TO 8 A.M.

WAITING TIME OR EXTRA MAN; $15.00 PER HOUR ADDITIONAL

HOLIDAYS AND SUNDAYS, SAME AS NIGHT RATES

Use of tow-bar add $2.00 a mile.